McDougal Littell

CLASSZONE

Visit classzone.com and get connected.

ClassZone resources provide instruction, planning and assessment support for teachers.

California Resources

- Access your state-specific resources.

Animated Math

- Engaging activities with animated problem-solving graphics support each lesson.

Help with the Math

- @HomeTutor enables students to focus on the math and be more prepared for class, using animated examples and instruction.
- Hints and problem solving help offer assistance solving select homework exercises.

Practice, Practice, Practice

- eWorkbook includes interactive worksheets with additional practice problems.
- Problem of the Week features a new problem to solve every week.

Games and Activities

- Crossword puzzles, memory games, and other activities help students connect to essential math concepts.
- Math Vocabulary Flipcards are a fun way to learn math terminology.

You have immediate access to the the online version of the textbook and ClassZone resources at www.classzone.com

MCDTKASTMSMZ

Use this code to create your own user name and password.

McDougal Littell

Where Great Lessons Begin

GEOMETRY

Ron Larson
Laurie Boswell
Timothy D. Kanold
Lee Stiff

California Teacher's Edition

McDougal Littell
A DIVISION OF HOUGHTON MIFFLIN COMPANY
Evanston, Illinois • Boston • Dallas

TI-Navigator is a registered trademark of Texas Instruments Incorporated.

Pre-AP is a registered trademark of the College Entrance Examination Board, which was not involved in the production of and does not endorse this product.

Printed in Canada

ISBN-13: 978-0-618-81191-5
ISBN-10: 0-618-81191-5 3456789—TBQ—12 11 10 09 08

Internet Web Site: http://www.mcdougallittell.com

Contents

Using the California Teacher's Edition

The California Teacher's Edition includes correlations that show how *Geometry* meets the California Mathematics Content Standards for Geometry and the standards that are assessed on the California High School Exit Exam (CAHSEE). The full correlations appear at the front of the California Teacher's Edition, and lesson and chapter correlations appear at point of use throughout.

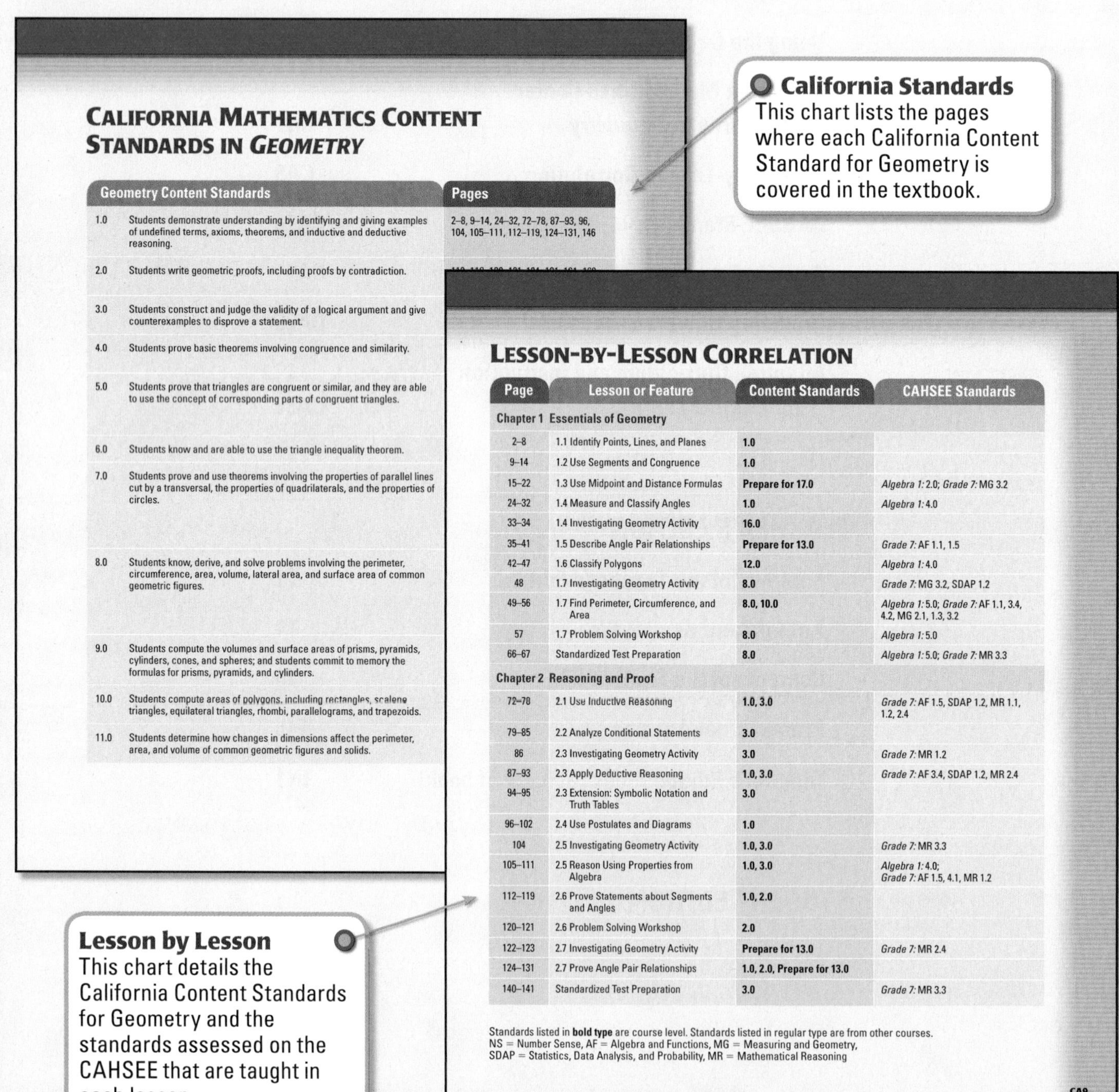

California Standards
This chart lists the pages where each California Content Standard for Geometry is covered in the textbook.

California Mathematics Content Standards in *Geometry*

Geometry Content Standards		Pages
1.0	Students demonstrate understanding by identifying and giving examples of undefined terms, axioms, theorems, and inductive and deductive reasoning.	2–8, 9–14, 24–32, 72–78, 87–93, 96, 104, 105–111, 112–119, 124–131, 146
2.0	Students write geometric proofs, including proofs by contradiction.	
3.0	Students construct and judge the validity of a logical argument and give counterexamples to disprove a statement.	
4.0	Students prove basic theorems involving congruence and similarity.	
5.0	Students prove that triangles are congruent or similar, and they are able to use the concept of corresponding parts of congruent triangles.	
6.0	Students know and are able to use the triangle inequality theorem.	
7.0	Students prove and use theorems involving the properties of parallel lines cut by a transversal, the properties of quadrilaterals, and the properties of circles.	
8.0	Students know, derive, and solve problems involving the perimeter, circumference, area, volume, lateral area, and surface area of common geometric figures.	
9.0	Students compute the volumes and surface areas of prisms, pyramids, cylinders, cones, and spheres; and students commit to memory the formulas for prisms, pyramids, and cylinders.	
10.0	Students compute areas of polygons, including rectangles, scalene triangles, equilateral triangles, rhombi, parallelograms, and trapezoids.	
11.0	Students determine how changes in dimensions affect the perimeter, area, and volume of common geometric figures and solids.	

Lesson-by-Lesson Correlation

Page	Lesson or Feature	Content Standards	CAHSEE Standards
Chapter 1	**Essentials of Geometry**		
2–8	1.1 Identify Points, Lines, and Planes	**1.0**	
9–14	1.2 Use Segments and Congruence	**1.0**	
15–22	1.3 Use Midpoint and Distance Formulas	**Prepare for 17.0**	*Algebra 1:* 2.0; *Grade 7:* MG 3.2
24–32	1.4 Measure and Classify Angles	**1.0**	*Algebra 1:* 4.0
33–34	1.4 Investigating Geometry Activity	**16.0**	
35–41	1.5 Describe Angle Pair Relationships	**Prepare for 13.0**	*Grade 7:* AF 1.1, 1.5
42–47	1.6 Classify Polygons	**12.0**	*Algebra 1:* 4.0
48	1.7 Investigating Geometry Activity	**8.0**	*Grade 7:* MG 3.2, SDAP 1.2
49–56	1.7 Find Perimeter, Circumference, and Area	**8.0, 10.0**	*Algebra 1:* 5.0; *Grade 7:* AF 1.1, 3.4, 4.2, MG 2.1, 1.3, 3.2
57	1.7 Problem Solving Workshop	**8.0**	*Algebra 1:* 5.0
66–67	Standardized Test Preparation	**8.0**	*Algebra 1:* 5.0; *Grade 7:* MR 3.3
Chapter 2	**Reasoning and Proof**		
72–78	2.1 Use Inductive Reasoning	**1.0, 3.0**	*Grade 7:* AF 1.5, SDAP 1.2, MR 1.1, 1.2, 2.4
79–85	2.2 Analyze Conditional Statements	**3.0**	
86	2.3 Investigating Geometry Activity	**3.0**	*Grade 7:* MR 1.2
87–93	2.3 Apply Deductive Reasoning	**1.0, 3.0**	*Grade 7:* AF 3.4, SDAP 1.2, MR 2.4
94–95	2.3 Extension: Symbolic Notation and Truth Tables	**3.0**	
96–102	2.4 Use Postulates and Diagrams	**1.0**	
104	2.5 Investigating Geometry Activity	**1.0, 3.0**	*Grade 7:* MR 3.3
105–111	2.5 Reason Using Properties from Algebra	**1.0, 3.0**	*Algebra 1:* 4.0; *Grade 7:* AF 1.5, 4.1, MR 1.2
112–119	2.6 Prove Statements about Segments and Angles	**1.0, 2.0**	
120–121	2.6 Problem Solving Workshop	**2.0**	
122–123	2.7 Investigating Geometry Activity	**Prepare for 13.0**	*Grade 7:* MR 2.4
124–131	2.7 Prove Angle Pair Relationships	**1.0, 2.0, Prepare for 13.0**	
140–141	Standardized Test Preparation	**3.0**	*Grade 7:* MR 3.3

Standards listed in **bold type** are course level. Standards listed in regular type are from other courses.
NS = Number Sense, AF = Algebra and Functions, MG = Measuring and Geometry,
SDAP = Statistics, Data Analysis, and Probability, MR = Mathematical Reasoning

CA9

Lesson by Lesson
This chart details the California Content Standards for Geometry and the standards assessed on the CAHSEE that are taught in each lesson.

CAHSEE STANDARDS IN GEOMETRY

This chart identifies locations in *Geometry* where you can find review and application of the California Content Standards from Grade 6, Grade 7, and Algebra 1 which are assessed on the California High School Exit Examination.

Content Standard		Pages
Number Sense Strand		
***Grade 7:* NS 1.0**	Students know the properties of, and compute with, rational numbers expressed in a variety of forms:	
***Grade 7:* NS 1.1**	Read, write, and compare rational numbers in scientific notation (positive and negative powers of 10), compare rational numbers in general.	871
***Grade 7:* NS 1.2**	Add, subtract, multiply, and divide rational numbers (integers, fractions, and terminating decimals) and take positive rational numbers to whole-number powers.	869, 870, 871, 885, 887
***Grade 7:* NS 1.3**	Convert fractions to decimals and percents and use these representations in estimations, computations, and applications.	885
***Grade 7:* NS 1.6**	Calculate the percentage of increases and decreases of a quantity.	349, 885
***Grade 7:* NS 1.7**	Solve problems that involve discounts, markups, commissions, and profit and compute simple and compound interest.	349, 885
***Grade 7:* NS 2.0**	Students use exponents, powers, and roots and use exponents in working with fractions:	
***Grade 7:* NS 2.1**	Understand negative whole-number exponents. Multiply and divide expressions involving exponents with a common base.	871
***Grade 7:* NS 2.2**	Add and subtract fractions by using factoring to find common denominators.	869
***Grade 7:* NS 2.3**	Multiply, divide, and simplify rational numbers by using exponent rules.	871
***Grade 7:* NS 2.4**	Use the inverse relationship between raising to a power and extracting the root of a perfect square integer; for an integer that is not square, determine without a calculator the two integers between which its square root lies and explain why.	874
***Grade 7:* NS 2.5**	Understand the meaning of the absolute value of a number; interpret the absolute value as the distance of the number from zero on a number line; and determine the absolute value of real numbers.	9–14, 287
Statistics, Data Analysis, and Probability Strand		
***Grade 6:* SDAP 1.0**	Students compute and analyze statistical measurements for d	
***Grade 6:* SDAP 1.1**	Compute the ~~range~~, mean, median, and mode of data sets.	84 (Ex. 3

Note: Strikethroughs within a standard indicate that this particular part of the standard is not to be assessed on the CAHSEE but is still part of the original standard.

State Assessment
This chart lists the pages where review and application of each standard assessed on the CAHSEE can be found.

4.6 Use Congruent Triangles

Before You used corresponding parts to prove triangles congruent.
Now You will use congruent triangles to prove corresponding parts congruent.
Why? So you can find the distance across a half pipe, as in Ex. 30.

Key Vocabulary
- **corresponding parts,** *p. 225*

By definition, congruent triangles have congruent corresponding parts. So, if you can prove that two triangles are congruent, you know that their corresponding parts must be congruent as well.

Standards

5.0 Students prove that triangles are congruent or similar, **and they are able to use the concept of corresponding parts of congruent triangles.**

16.0 Students perform basic constructions with a straightedge and compass, such as angle bisectors, perpendicular bisectors, and the line parallel to a given line through a point off the line.

EXAMPLE 1 Use congruent triangles

Explain how you can use the given information to prove that the hanglider parts are congruent.

GIVEN ▶ $\angle 1 \cong \angle 2$, $\angle RTQ \cong \angle RTS$

PROVE ▶ $\overline{QT} \cong \overline{ST}$

Solution

If you can show that $\triangle QRT \cong \triangle SRT$, you will know that $\overline{QT} \cong \overline{ST}$. First, copy the diagram and mark the given information. Then add the information that you can deduce. In this case, $\angle RQT$ and $\angle RST$ are supplementary to congruent angles, so $\angle RQT \cong \angle RST$. Also, $\overline{RT} \cong \overline{RT}$.

Mark given information. Add deduced information.

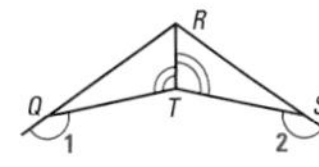

Two angle pairs and a non-included side are congruent, so by the AAS Congruence Theorem, $\triangle QRT \cong \triangle SRT$. Because corresponding parts of congruent triangles are congruent, $\overline{QT} \cong \overline{ST}$.

Animated Geometry at classzone.com

GUIDED PRACTICE for Example 1

1. *Explain* how you can prove that $\angle A \cong \angle C$.

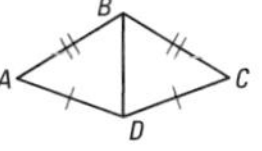

Lesson Content
Each lesson and activity is correlated to the California Mathematics Content Standards.

California Curriculum and Assessment

The material on pages CA7–CA20 will help you coordinate your teaching of *Geometry* with the California Mathematics Content Standards and with the standards assessed on the California High School Exit Examination (CAHSEE).

California Mathematics Content Standards in *Geometry*

The chart on pages CA7–CA8 contain a correlation of *Geometry* to the California Content Standards for Geometry. The first column of the charts lists the California Content Standards. The second column identifies the pages in the Student and Teacher's Editions that teach the material included in the Standards.

Lesson by Lesson Correlation

The chart on pages CA9–CA15 contain a correlation of the California Content Standards for Geometry and the CAHSEE standards to *Geometry.* The first two columns identify the page numbers and lesson or feature. The third column lists the Mathematics Content Standards covered in that lesson or feature. The fourth column lists CAHSEE standards that are applied or reviewed in that lesson or feature.

CAHSEE Standards in *Geometry*

The chart on pages CA16–CA20 contain a correlation of *Geometry* to the standards from Grade 6, Grade 7, and Algebra 1 that are assessed on the California High School Exit Examination. The first column lists the standards that are designated to be on the CAHSEE. The second column lists the pages where the content of those standards is either reviewed or applied to Geometry content.

California Mathematics Content Standards in *Geometry*

Geometry Content Standards		Pages
1.0	Students demonstrate understanding by identifying and giving examples of undefined terms, axioms, theorems, and inductive and deductive reasoning.	2–8, 9–14, 24–32, 72–78, 87–93, 96, 104, 105–111, 112–119, 124–131, 146
2.0	Students write geometric proofs, including proofs by contradiction.	112–119, 120–121, 124–131, 161–169, 208–209, 335–341
3.0	Students construct and judge the validity of a logical argument and give counterexamples to disprove a statement.	72–78, 79–85, 86, 87–93, 94–95, 104, 105–111, 140–141, 247
4.0	Students prove basic theorems involving congruence and similarity.	240–246, 249–255, 388–395, 396, 397–403, 449–456
5.0	Students prove that triangles are congruent or similar, and they are able to use the concept of corresponding parts of congruent triangles.	225–231, 232, 233, 234–239, 240–246, 249–255, 256–263, 264–270, 372–379, 381–387, 388–395, 409–415, 424–425, 448, 625, 696
6.0	Students know and are able to use the triangle inequality theorem.	328–334, 442–444
7.0	Students prove and use theorems involving the properties of parallel lines cut by a transversal, the properties of quadrilaterals, and the properties of circles.	147–152, 153, 154–160, 161–169, 190–197, 397–403, 404–405, 514, 515–521, 522–529, 530–531, 533–540, 541, 542–549, 552–557, 566–567, 651–658, 659–663, 664–670, 672–679, 680–686
8.0	Students know, derive, and solve problems involving the perimeter, circumference, area, volume, lateral area, and surface area of common geometric figures.	48, 49–56, 57, 66–67, 356–363, 372–379, 720–726, 729, 730–736, 737–743, 744, 746–752, 755–761, 762–768, 769, 770, 771–777, 786–787, 802, 803–809, 810–817, 819–825, 826–827, 828, 837, 838–845, 847–854
9.0	Students compute the volumes and surface areas of prisms, pyramids, cylinders, cones, and spheres; and students commit to memory the formulas for prisms, pyramids, and cylinders.	792–793, 794–801, 802, 803–809, 810–817, 819–825, 826–827, 829–836, 838–845
10.0	Students compute areas of polygons, including rectangles, scalene triangles, equilateral triangles, rhombi, parallelograms, and trapezoids.	49–56, 720–726, 729, 730–736, 762–768, 769
11.0	Students determine how changes in dimensions affect the perimeter, area, and volume of common geometric figures and solids.	372–379, 406–407, 409–415, 631, 737–743, 846, 847–854

Geometry Content Standards		Pages
12.0	Students find and use measures of sides and of interior and exterior angles of triangles and polygons to classify figures and solve problems.	42–47, 217–224, 265–270, 288–289, 303–309, 310–316, 318, 319–325, 328–334, 350–351, 364–370, 371, 381–387, 440, 441–447, 449–456, 483–489, 490–491, 506, 507–513, 552–557, 566–567
13.0	Students prove relationships between angles in polygons by using properties of complementary, supplementary, vertical, and exterior angles.	35–41, 124–131, 122–123, 216, 217–224
14.0	Students prove the Pythagorean theorem.	432, 433–439, 455, 736
15.0	Students use the Pythagorean theorem to determine distance and find missing lengths of sides of right triangles.	310–316, 433–439, 481–482, 500–501
16.0	Students perform basic constructions with a straightedge and compass, such as angle bisectors, perpendicular bisectors, and the line parallel to a given line through a point off the line.	33–34, 147–152, 169, 195, 234–239, 256–263, 307, 314, 323, 401, 408, 527, 594, 625, 626–632, 704, 767
17.0	Students prove theorems by using coordinate geometry, including the midpoint of a line segment, the distance formula, and various forms of equations of lines and circles.	15–22, 171–178, 179, 180–187, 208–209, 294, 295–301, 302, 319–325, 533–540, 572–579, 699–705;
18.0	Students know the definitions of the basic trigonometric functions defined by the angles of a right triangle. They also know and are able to use elementary relationships between them. For example, $\tan(x) = \frac{\sin(x)}{\cos(x)}$, $(\sin(x))^2 + (\cos(x))^2 = 1$.	466–472, 473–480, 481–482, 483–489, 490–491
19.0	Students use trigonometric functions to solve for an unknown length of a side of a right triangle, given an angle and a length of a side.	466–472, 473–480, 481–482, 483–489, 490–491, 764–768, 769
20.0	Students know and are able to use angle and side relationships in problems with special right triangles, such as 30°, 60°, and 90° triangles and 45°, 45°, and 90° triangles.	457–464, 466–472, 473–480, 500–501, 726
21.0	Students prove and solve problems regarding relationships among chords, secants, tangents, inscribed angles, and inscribed and circumscribed polygons of circles.	650, 651–658, 664–670, 672–679, 671, 680–686, 688, 689–695, 696, 714–715, 762–768, 769
22.0	Students know the effect of rigid motions on figures in the coordinate plane and space, including rotations, translations, and reflections.	271, 272–279, 572–579, 580–587, 588, 589–596, 598–605, 606, 607, 608–615, 616–618, 619–624, 642–643

LESSON-BY-LESSON CORRELATION

Page	Lesson or Feature	Content Standards	CAHSEE Standards
Chapter 1 Essentials of Geometry			
2–8	1.1 Identify Points, Lines, and Planes	**1.0**	
9–14	1.2 Use Segments and Congruence	**1.0**	
15–22	1.3 Use Midpoint and Distance Formulas	**Prepare for 17.0**	*Algebra 1:* 2.0; *Grade 7:* MG 3.2
24–32	1.4 Measure and Classify Angles	**1.0**	*Algebra 1:* 4.0
33–34	1.4 Investigating Geometry Activity	**16.0**	
35–41	1.5 Describe Angle Pair Relationships	**Prepare for 13.0**	*Grade 7:* AF 1.1, 1.5
42–47	1.6 Classify Polygons	**12.0**	*Algebra 1:* 4.0
48	1.7 Investigating Geometry Activity	**8.0**	*Grade 7:* MG 3.2, SDAP 1.2
49–56	1.7 Find Perimeter, Circumference, and Area	**8.0, 10.0**	*Algebra 1:* 5.0; *Grade 7:* AF 1.1, 3.4, 4.2, MG 2.1, 1.3, 3.2
57	1.7 Problem Solving Workshop	**8.0**	*Algebra 1:* 5.0
66–67	Standardized Test Preparation	**8.0**	*Algebra 1:* 5.0; *Grade 7:* MR 3.3
Chapter 2 Reasoning and Proof			
72–78	2.1 Use Inductive Reasoning	**1.0, 3.0**	*Grade 7:* AF 1.5, SDAP 1.2, MR 1.1, 1.2, 2.4
79–85	2.2 Analyze Conditional Statements	**3.0**	
86	2.3 Investigating Geometry Activity	**3.0**	*Grade 7:* MR 1.2
87–93	2.3 Apply Deductive Reasoning	**1.0, 3.0**	*Grade 7:* AF 3.4, SDAP 1.2, MR 2.4
94–95	2.3 Extension: Symbolic Notation and Truth Tables	**3.0**	
96–102	2.4 Use Postulates and Diagrams	**1.0**	
104	2.5 Investigating Geometry Activity	**1.0, 3.0**	*Grade 7:* MR 3.3
105–111	2.5 Reason Using Properties from Algebra	**1.0, 3.0**	*Algebra 1:* 4.0; *Grade 7:* AF 1.5, 4.1, MR 1.2
112–119	2.6 Prove Statements about Segments and Angles	**1.0, 2.0**	
120–121	2.6 Problem Solving Workshop	**2.0**	
122–123	2.7 Investigating Geometry Activity	**Prepare for 13.0**	*Grade 7:* MR 2.4
124–131	2.7 Prove Angle Pair Relationships	**1.0, 2.0, Prepare for 13.0**	
140–141	Standardized Test Preparation	**3.0**	*Grade 7:* MR 3.3

Standards listed in **bold type** are course level. Standards listed in regular type are from other courses.
NS = Number Sense, AF = Algebra and Functions, MG = Measuring and Geometry,
SDAP = Statistics, Data Analysis, and Probability, MR = Mathematical Reasoning

Page	Lesson or Feature	Content Standards	CAHSEE Standards
Chapter 3 Parallel and Perpendicular Lines			
146	3.1 Investigating Geometry Activity	**1.0**	
147–152	3.1 Identify Pairs of Lines and Angles	**16.0, Prepare for 7.0**	
153	3.2 Investigating Geometry Activity	**Prepare for 7.0**	*Algebra 1:* 8.0; *Grade 7:* MR 2.4
154–160	3.2 Use Parallel Lines and Transversals	**7.0**	*Algebra 1:* 4.0, 8.0, 10.0
161–169	3.3 Prove Lines are Parallel	**2.0, 7.0**	*Algebra 1:* 8.0
171–178	3.4 Find and Use Slopes of Lines	**Prepare for 17.0**	*Algebra 1:* 2.0, 8.0, 15.0; *Grade 7:* AF 1.5, 3.3, 3.4, 4.2, MG 1.3
179	3.4 Technology Activity	**Prepare for 17.0**	*Grade 7:* AF 3.3
180–187	3.5 Write and Graph Equations of Lines	**Prepare for 17.0**	*Algebra 1:* 5.0, 6.0, 7.0, 8.0, 9.0; *Grade 7:* AF 1.5, 3.3, 3.4
188–189	3.5 Problem Solving Workshop	**Enrichment**	
190–197	3.6 Prove Theorems about Perpendicular Lines	**7.0**	*Algebra 1:* 8.0
198–199	3.6 Extension: Taxicab Geometry	**Enrichment**	
208–209	Standardized Test Preparation	**Prepare for 2.0, 17.0**	*Grade 7:* MR 3.3
Chapter 4 Congruent Triangles			
216	4.1 Investigating Geometry Activity	**13.0**	
217–224	4.1 Apply Triangle Sum Properties	**12.0, 13.0**	*Grade 7:* AF 1.1
225–231	4.2 Apply Congruence and Triangles	**5.0**	*Grade 7:* MG 3.4
232	4.2 Problem Solving Workshop	**5.0**	
233	4.3 Investigating Geometry Activity	**Prepare for 5.0**	*Grade 7:* MG 3.4
234–239	4.3 Prove Triangles Congruent by SSS	**5.0, 16.0**	*Grade 7:* MG 3.4
240–246	4.4 Prove Triangles Congruent by SAS and HL	**4.0, 5.0**	*Grade 7:* MG 3.4
247	4.4 Technology Activity	**3.0**	*Grade 7:* MG 3.4
249–255	4.5 Prove Triangles Congruent by ASA and AAS	**4.0, 5.0**	*Grade 7:* MG 3.4
256–263	4.6 Use Congruent Triangles	**5.0, 16.0**	*Grade 7:* MG 3.4
264–270	4.7 Use Isosceles and Equilateral Triangles	**5.0, 12.0**	*Grade 7:* MG 3.4
271	4.8 Investigating Geometry Activity	**22.0**	*Grade 7:* MG 3.2
272–279	4.8 Perform Congruence Transformations	**22.0**	*Grade 7:* MG 3.2
288–289	Standardized Test Preparation	**12.0**	*Grade 7:* MG 3.2, MR 3.3

Page	Lesson or Feature	Content Standards	CAHSEE Standards
Chapter 5 Relationships within Triangles			
294	5.1 Investigating Geometry Activity	**Preparing for 17.0**	
295–301	5.1 Midsegment Theorem and Coordinate Proof	**17.0**	*Grade 7:* MG 3.2
302	5.1 Problem Solving Workshop	**17.0**	
303–309	5.2 Use Perpendicular Bisectors	**12.0**	*Grade 7:* MG 3.4
310–316	5.3 Use Angle Bisectors of Triangles	**12.0, 15.0**	*Grade 7:* MG 3.4
318	5.4 Investigating Geometry Activity	**Prepare for 12.0**	
319–325	5.4 Use Medians and Altitudes	**17.0, Prepare for 12.0**	*Grade 7:* MG 3.2
326–327	5.4 Technology Activity	**Enrichment**	
328–334	5.5 Use Inequalities in a Triangle	**6.0, 12.0**	*Algebra 1:* 5.0
335–341	5.6 Inequalities in Two Triangles and Indirect Proof	**2.0**	*Algebra 1:* 5.0; *Grade 7:* AF 4.2
350–351	Standardized Test Preparation	**12.0**	*Grade 7:* MR 3.3
Chapter 6 Similarity			
356–363	6.1 Ratios, Proportions, and the Geometric Mean	**Prepare for 8.0**	*Grade 7:* AF 1.1, 1.5, SDAP 1.2
364–370	6.2 Use Proportions to Solve Geometry Problems	**12.0**	*Algebra 1:* 2.0; *Grade 7:* AF 4.2, MG 1.2
371	6.3 Investigating Geometry Activity	**12.0**	*Grade 7:* MR 2.4
372–379	6.3 Use Similar Polygons	**5.0, 8.0, 11.0**	*Grade 7:* AF 1.5, 3.4
381–387	6.4 Prove Triangles Similar by AA	**5.0, 12.0**	
388–395	6.5 Prove Triangles Similar by SSS and SAS	**4.0, 5.0**	
396	6.6 Investigating Geometry Activity	**Prepare for 4.0**	*Algebra 1:* 8.0; *Grade 7:* MR 2.4
397–403	6.6 Use Proportionality Theorems	**4.0, 7.0**	*Algebra 1:* 8.0
404–405	6.6 Problem Solving Workshop	**7.0**	
406–407	6.6 Extension: Fractals	**11.0**	
408	6.7 Investigating Geometry Activity	**Enrichment**	
409–415	6.7 Perform Similarity Transformations	**5.0, 11.0**	*Grade 7:* MG 3.2
424–425	Standardized Test Preparation	**5.0**	*Grade 7:* MR 3.3

Standards listed in **bold type** are course level. Standards listed in regular type are from other courses.
NS = Number Sense, AF = Algebra and Functions, MG = Measuring and Geometry,
SDAP = Statistics, Data Analysis, and Probability, MR = Mathematical Reasoning

Page	Lesson or Feature	Content Standards	CAHSEE Standards
Chapter 7 Right Triangles and Trigonometry			
432	7.1 Investigating Geometry Activity	**14.0**	*Grade 7:* MG 3.3, MR 2.4
433–439	7.1 Apply the Pythagorean Theorem	**14.0, 15.0**	*Algebra 1:* 2.0; *Grade 7:* MG 3.3
440	7.2 Investigating Geometry Activity	**12.0**	*Grade 7:* MG 3.3, MR 2.4
441–447	7.2 Use the Converse of the Pythagorean Theorem	**12.0**	*Grade 7:* MG 3.3
448	7.3 Investigating Geometry Activity	**5.0**	*Grade 7:* MR 2.4
449–456	7.3 Use Similar Right Triangles	**4.0, 12.0**	
457–464	7.4 Special Right Triangles	**20.0**	*Grade 7:* MG 1.1
466–472	7.5 Apply the Tangent Ratio	**18.0, 19.0, 20.0**	*Grade 7:* MR 2.4
473–480	7.6 Apply the Sine and Cosine Ratios	**18.0, 19.0, 20.0**	
481–482	7.6 Problem Solving Workshop	**15.0, 19.0**	
483–489	7.7 Solve Right Triangles	**12.0, 19.0**	*Grade 7:* AF 1.1, SDAP 1.2
490–491	7.7 Extension: Law of Sines and Law of Cosines	**12.0, 19.0**	
500–501	Standardized Test Preparation	**15.0, 20.0**	*Grade 7:* MR 3.3
Chapter 8 Quadrilaterals			
506	8.1 Investigating Geometry Activity	**12.0**	*Grade 7:* AF 1.5
507–513	8.1 Find Angle Measures in Polygons	**12.0**	
514	8.2 Investigating Geometry Activity	**Prepare for 7.0**	*Grade 7:* MR 2.4
515–521	8.2 Use Properties of Parallelograms	**7.0**	*Algebra 1:* 10.0
522–529	8.3 Show that a Quadrilateral is a Parallelogram	**7.0**	
530–531	8.3 Problem Solving Workshop	**7.0**	
533–540	8.4 Properties of Rhombuses, Rectangles, and Squares	**7.0, 17.0**	
541	8.5 Investigating Geometry Activity	**Prepare for 7.0**	
542–549	8.5 Use Properties of Trapezoids and Kites	**7.0**	
550–551	8.5 Extension: Draw Three-Dimensional Figures	**Enrichment**	
552–557	8.6 Identify Special Quadrilaterals	**12.0**	
566–567	Standardized Test Preparation	**7.0**	*Grade 7:* MR 3.3

Page	Lesson or Feature	Content Standards	CAHSEE Standards
Chapter 9 Properties of Transformations			
572–579	9.1 Translate Figures and Use Vectors	**17.0, 22.0**	*Grade 7:* AF 4.2, MG 3.2
580–587	9.2 Use Properties of Matrices	**Prepare for 22.0**	*Grade 7:* MG 3.2
588	9.3 Investigating Geometry Activity	**22.0**	*Grade 7:* MG 3.2
589–596	9.3 Perform Reflections	**22.0**	*Grade 7:* MG 3.2
598–605	9.4 Perform Rotations	**22.0**	*Grade 7:* MG 3.2
606	9.4 Problem Solving Workshop	**22.0**	*Grade 7:* MG 3.2
607	9.5 Investigating Geometry Activity	**22.0**	*Grade 7:* MG 3.2
608–615	9.5 Apply Compositions of Transformations	**22.0**	*Grade 7:* MG 3.2
616–618	9.5 Extension: Tessellations	**22.0**	
619–624	9.6 Identify Symmetry	**22.0**	
625	9.7 Investigating Geometry Activity	**5.0, 16.0**	
626–632	9.7 Identify and Perform Dilations	**16.0**	*Grade 7:* MG 3.2
633	9.7 Technology Activity	**Enrichment**	
642–643	Standardized Test Preparation	**22.0**	*Grade 7:* MG 3.2, MR 3.3
Chapter 10 Properties of Circles			
650	10.1 Investigating Geometry Activity	**21.0**	*Grade 7:* MR 2.4
651–658	10.1 Use Properties of Tangents	**7.0, 21.0**	*Algebra 1:* 10.0
659–663	10.2 Find Arc Measures	**7.0**	
664–670	10.3 Apply Properties of Chords	**7.0, 21.0**	
671	10.4 Investigating Geometry Activity	**Prepare for 21.0**	*Grade 7:* MR 2.4
672–679	10.4 Use Inscribed Angles and Polygons	**7.0, 21.0**	
680–686	10.5 Apply Other Angle Relationships in Circles	**7.0, 21.0**	*Algebra 1:* 10.0
688	10.6 Investigating Geometry Activity	**Prepare for 21.0**	*Grade 7:* MR 2.4
689–695	10.6 Find Segment Lengths in Circles	**21.0**	
696	10.6 Problem Solving Workshop	**5.0, 21.0**	
697–698	10.6 Extension: Locus	**Enrichment**	
699–705	10.7 Write and Graph Equations of Circles	**17.0**	
714–715	Standardized Test Preparation	**21.0**	*Grade 7:* MR 3.3

Standards listed in **bold type** are course level. Standards listed in regular type are from other courses.
NS = Number Sense, AF = Algebra and Functions, MG = Measuring and Geometry,
SDAP = Statistics, Data Analysis, and Probability, MR = Mathematical Reasoning

Page	Lesson or Feature	Content Standards	CAHSEE Standards
Chapter 11	**Measuring Length and Area**		
720–726	11.1 Areas of Triangles and Parallelograms	**8.0, 10.0**	*Grade 7:* AF 4.2, MG 1.1, 1.3, 2.1, 2.2
727–728	11.1 Extension: Determine Precision and Accuracy	**Enrichment**	
729	11.2 Investigating Geometry Activity	**8.0**	*Grade 7:* MG 2.2
730–736	11.2 Areas of Trapezoids, Rhombuses, and Kites	**8.0, 10.0**	*Grade 7:* MG 2.1, 2.2
737–743	11.3 Perimeter and Area of Similar Figures	**8.0, 11.0**	*Grade 7:* AF 4.2, MG 1.2, 1.3, 2.1
744	11.3 Problem Solving Workshop	**8.0**	
746–752	11.4 Circumference and Arc Length	**8.0**	*Grade 7:* AF 1.1, MG 2.1
753–754	11.4 Extension: Geometry on a Sphere	**Enrichment**	
755–761	11.5 Areas of Circles and Sectors	**8.0**	*Grade 7:* MG 2.1, SDAP 1.1
762–769	11.6 Areas of Regular Polygons	**8.0, 10.0, 21.0**	*Grade 7:* AF 1.5, MG 2.1
769	11.6 Spreadsheet Activity	**8.0, 21.0**	
770	11.7 Investigating Geometry Activity	**8.0**	*Grade 6:* SDAP 3.3
771–777	11.7 Use Geometric Probability	**8.0**	*Grade 6:* SDAP 3.3
786–787	Standardized Test Preparation	**8.0**	*Grade 7:* MR 3.3
Chapter 12	**Surface Area and Volume of Solids**		
792–793	12.1 Investigating Geometry Activity	**Prepare for 9.0**	
794–801	12.1 Explore Solids	**Prepare for 9.0**	*Grade 7:* MG 2.3
802	12.2 Investigating Geometry Activity	**9.0, Prepare for 8.0**	*Grade 7:* MG 2.3, MR 2.4
803–809	12.2 Surface Area of Prisms and Cylinders	**8.0, 9.0**	*Grade 7:* MG 2.1, 2.3
810–817	12.3 Surface Area of Pyramids and Cones	**8.0, 9.0**	*Grade 7:* MG 2.1
819–825	12.4 Volume of Prisms and Cylinders	**8.0, 9.0**	*Grade 7:* MG 2.1, 2.3
826–827	12.4 Problem Solving Workshop	**8.0, 9.0**	
828	12.5 Investigating Geometry Activity	**Prepare for 8.0**	*Grade 7:* MR 2.4
829–836	12.5 Volume of Pyramids and Cones	**8.0, 9.0**	*Grade 7:* AF 1.5, 4.2, MG 1.3, 2.1
837	12.5 Spreadsheet Activity	**8.0**	
838–845	12.6 Surface Area and Volume of Spheres	**8.0, 9.0**	*Grade 7:* MG 2.1
846	12.7 Investigating Geometry Activity	**11.0**	*Grade 7:* MG 2.3, MR 2.4
847–854	12.7 Explore Similar Solids	**8.0, 11.0**	*Grade 7:* AF 1.5, MG 2.3, 2.4
862–863	Standardized Test Preparation	**8.0**	*Grade 7:* MR 3.3

Page	Lesson or Feature	Content Standards	CAHSEE Standards
Skills Review Handbook			
869	Operations with Rational Numbers		*Algebra 1:* 2.0; *Grade 7:* NS 1.2, 2.2
870	Simplifying and Evaluating Expressions		*Algebra 1:* 2.0; *Grade 7:* NS 1.2, 2.5, AF 1.2, 2.1
871	Properties of Exponents		*Grade 7:* NS 1.1, 1.2, 2.1, 2.3, AF 2.1, 2.2
872	Using the Distributive Property		*Grade 7:* AF 2.1
873	Binomial Products		*Grade 7:* AF 2.1
874	Radical Expressions		*Algebra 1:* 2.0; *Grade 7:* NS 2.4, AF 2.1
875	Solving Linear Equations		*Algebra 1:* 2.0, 4.0; *Grade 7:* AF 4.1
876	Solving and Graphing Linear Inequalities		*Grade 7:* AF 4.1
877	Solving Formulas		*Grade 7:* MG 2.1
878	Graphing Points and Lines		*Algebra 1:* 6.0
879	Slope and Intercepts of a Line		*Algebra 1:* 6.0; *Grade 7:* AF 3.3
880	Systems of Linear Equations		*Algebra 1:* 9.0
881	Linear Inequalities		*Algebra 1:* 9.0
882–883	Quadratic Equations and Functions		*Grade 7:* AF 1.2
884	Functions		*Grade 7:* AF 1.2
885	Problem Solving with Percents		*Grade 7:* NS 1.2, 1.3, 1.6, 1.7
886	Converting Measurements and Rates		*Algebra 1:* 15.0; *Grade 7:* MG 1.1, 2.4
887	Mean, Median, and Mode		*Grade 7:* NS 1.2; *Grade 6:* SDAP 1.1
888–889	Displaying Data		*Grade 6:* SDAP 1.1
890	Sampling and Surveys		*Grade 6:* SDAP 2.5
891–892	Counting Methods		*Grade 6:* SDAP 3.1
893	Probability		*Grade 6:* SDAP 3.1, 3.3, 3.5
894–895	Problem Solving Plan and Strategies		*Grade 7:* AF 1.1

Standards listed in **bold type** are course level. Standards listed in regular type are from other courses.
NS = Number Sense, AF = Algebra and Functions, MG = Measuring and Geometry,
SDAP = Statistics, Data Analysis, and Probability, MR = Mathematical Reasoning

CAHSEE STANDARDS IN *GEOMETRY*

This chart identifies locations in *Geometry* where you can find review and application of the California Content Standards from Grade 6, Grade 7, and Algebra 1 which are assessed on the California High School Exit Examination.

Content Standard		Pages
Number Sense Strand		
***Grade 7:* NS 1.0**	Students know the properties of, and compute with, rational numbers expressed in a variety of forms:	
***Grade 7:* NS 1.1**	Read, write, and compare rational numbers in scientific notation (positive and negative powers of 10), compare rational numbers in general.	871
***Grade 7:* NS 1.2**	Add, subtract, multiply, and divide rational numbers (integers, fractions, and terminating decimals) and take positive rational numbers to whole-number powers.	869, 870, 871, 885, 887
***Grade 7:* NS 1.3**	Convert fractions to decimals and percents and use these representations in estimations, computations, and applications.	885
***Grade 7:* NS 1.6**	Calculate the percentage of increases and decreases of a quantity.	349, 885
***Grade 7:* NS 1.7**	Solve problems that involve discounts, markups, commissions, and profit and compute simple and compound interest.	349, 885
***Grade 7:* NS 2.0**	Students use exponents, powers, and roots and use exponents in working with fractions:	
***Grade 7:* NS 2.1**	Understand negative whole-number exponents. Multiply and divide expressions involving exponents with a common base.	871
***Grade 7:* NS 2.2**	Add and subtract fractions by using factoring to find common denominators.	869
***Grade 7:* NS 2.3**	Multiply, divide, and simplify rational numbers by using exponent rules.	871
***Grade 7:* NS 2.4**	Use the inverse relationship between raising to a power and extracting the root of a perfect square integer; for an integer that is not square, determine without a calculator the two integers between which its square root lies and explain why.	874
***Grade 7:* NS 2.5**	Understand the meaning of the absolute value of a number; interpret the absolute value as the distance of the number from zero on a number line; and determine the absolute value of real numbers.	9–14, 287, 870
Statistics, Data Analysis, and Probability Strand		
***Grade 6:* SDAP 1.0**	Students compute and analyze statistical measurements for data sets:	
***Grade 6:* SDAP 1.1**	Compute the ~~range~~, mean, median, and mode of data sets.	84 (Ex. 34), 887, 888–889

Note: Strikethroughs within a standard indicate that this particular part of the standard is not to be assessed on the CAHSEE but is still part of the original standard.

Content Standard		Pages
***Grade 6:* SDAP 2.0** Students use data samples of a population and describe the characteristics and limitations of the samples:		
***Grade 6:* SDAP 2.5**	Identify claims based on statistical data and, in simple cases, evaluate the validity of the claims.	74, 78, 89, 92, 103, 890
***Grade 6:* SDAP 3.0** Students determine theoretical and experimental probabilities and use these to make predictions about events:		
***Grade 6:* SDAP 3.1**	Represent all possible outcomes for compound events in an organized way (e.g., tables, grids, tree diagrams) and express the theoretical probability of each outcome.	891–892, 893
***Grade 6:* SDAP 3.3**	Represent probabilities as ratios, proportions, decimals between 0 and 1, and percentages between 0 and 100 and verify that the probabilities computed are reasonable; know that if P is the probability of an event, $1 - P$ is the probability of an event not occurring.	770, 771–777, 893
***Grade 6:* SDAP 3.5**	Understand the difference between independent and dependent events.	893
***Grade 7:* SDAP 1.0** Students collect, organize, and represent data sets that have one or more variables and identify relationships among variables within a data set by hand and through the use of an electronic spreadsheet software program:		
***Grade 7:* SDAP 1.1**	Know various forms of display for data sets, ~~including a stem-and-leaf plot or box-and-whisker plot~~; use the forms to display a single set of data or to compare two sets of data.	760 (Ex. 39), 888–889
***Grade 7:* SDAP 1.2**	Represent two numerical variables on a scatterplot and informally describe how the data points are distributed and any apparent relationship that exists between the two variables (e.g., between time spent on homework and grade level).	48 , 74, 77 (Ex. 33), 89, 363 (Ex. 66), 488 (Ex. 39)
Algebra and Functions Strand		
***Grade 7:* AF 1.0** Students express quantitative relationships by using algebraic terminology, expressions, equations, inequalities, and graphs:		
***Grade 7:* AF 1.1**	Use variables and appropriate operations to write an expression, an equation, an inequality, or a system of equations or inequalities that represents a verbal description (e.g., three less than a number, half as large as area A).	37–41, 51–56, 58 (Ex. 4), 65, 69 (Ex. 10), 207, 220, 222 (Ex. 27), 359–363, 488 (Ex. 41), 747–752, 785, 895
***Grade 7:* AF 1.2**	Use the correct order of operations to evaluate algebraic expressions such as $3(2x + 5)^2$.	785, 870
***Grade 7:* AF 1.5**	Represent quantitative relationships graphically and interpret the meaning of a specific part of a graph in the situation represented by the graph.	41, 77, 111, 174 , 177 (Ex. 37), 182–187, 363 (Ex. 66), 378 (Ex. 33), 499 , 513 (Ex. 36), 565, 768 (Ex. 45), 835 (Ex. 39), 853 (Ex. 34), 882–883, 884
***Grade 7:* AF 2.0** Students interpret and evaluate expressions involving integer powers and simple roots:		
***Grade 7:* AF 2.1**	Interpret positive whole-number powers as repeated multiplication and negative whole-number powers as repeated division or multiplication by the multiplicative inverse. Simplify and evaluate expressions that include exponents.	139, 870, 871, 872, 873, 874

Note: Strikethroughs within a standard indicate that this particular part of the standard is not to be assessed on the CAHSEE but is still part of the original standard.

Content Standard		Pages
Grade 7: **AF 2.2**	Multiply and divide monomials; extend the process of taking powers and extracting roots to monomials when the latter results in a monomial with an integer exponent.	139, 871
Grade 7: **AF 3.0** Students graph and interpret linear and some nonlinear functions:		
Grade 7: **AF 3.1**	Graph functions of the form $y = nx^2$ and $y = nx^3$ and use in solving problems.	499, 882–883
Grade 7: **AF 3.3**	Graph linear functions, noting that the vertical change (change in *y*-value) per unit of horizontal change (change in *x*-value) is always the same and know that the ratio ("rise over run") is called the slope of a graph.	171–178, 179, 180–187, 879
Grade 7: **AF 3.4**	Plot the values of quantities whose ratios are always the same (e.g., cost to the number of an item, feet to inches, circumference to diameter of a circle). Fit a line to the plot and understand that the slope of a line equals the ratio of the quantities.	48, 89, 171–178, 180–187, 378 (Ex. 33)
Grade 7: **AF 4.0** Students solve simple linear equations and inequalities over the rational numbers:		
Grade 7: **AF 4.1**	Solve two-step linear equations and inequalities in one variable over the rational numbers, interpret the solution or solutions in the context from which they arose, and verify the reasonableness of the results.	24–32, 36, 65, 105–111, 875, 876
Grade 7: **AF 4.2**	Solve multistep problems involving rate, average speed, distance, and time or a direct variation.	51, 54 (Ex. 42), 65, 174, 177 (Exs. 36, 37, 39, 40), 336 (Example 2), 340 (Ex. 22), 366 (Example 5), 368 (Ex. 22), 575, 578 (Exs. 35–37), 722, 724 (Ex. 37), 739, 831 (Example 5), 834 (Ex. 29)
Measurement and Geometry Strand		
Grade 7: **MG 1.0** Students choose appropriate units of measure and use ratios to convert within and between measurement systems to solve problems:		
Grade 7: **MG 1.1**	Compare weights, capacities, geometric measures, times, and temperatures within and between measurement systems (e.g., miles per hour and feet per second, cubic inches to cubic centimeters).	49–56, 460, 722 (Example 3), 727, 886
Grade 7: **MG 1.2**	Construct and read drawings and models made to scale.	364–370, 371, 737–743, 745
Grade 7: **MG 1.3**	Use measures expressed as rates (e.g., speed, density) and measures expressed as products (e.g., person-days) to solve problems; check the units of the solutions; and use dimensional analysis to check the reasonableness of the answer.	51, 54 (Ex. 42), 65, 174, 177 (Exs. 36, 37, 39, 40), 722 (Example 3), 724 (Ex. 37), 739, 831 (Example 5), 834 (Ex. 29)
Grade 7: **MG 2.0** Students compute the perimeter, area, and volume of common geometric objects and use the results to find measures of less common objects. They know how perimeter, area, and volume are affected by changes of scale:		
Grade 7: **MG 2.1**	Use formulas routinely for finding the perimeter and area of basic two-dimensional figures and the surface area and volume of basic three-dimensional figures, including rectangles, parallelograms, trapezoids, squares, triangles, circles, prisms, and cylinders.	49–56, 110 (Exs. 31–32), 721–726, 730–736, 737–743, 746–752, 755–761, 762–768, 803–809, 810–817, 819–825, 829–836, 838–845, 877

Note: Strikethroughs within a standard indicate that this particular part of the standard is not to be assessed on the CAHSEE but is still part of the original standard.

Content Standard		Pages
Grade 7: **MG 2.2**	Estimate and compute the area of more complex or irregular two- and three-dimensional figures by breaking the figures down into more basic geometric objects.	722 (Example 3), 724 (Exs. 22–27), 729, 734–735 (Exs. 24–29, 37)
Grade 7: **MG 2.3**	Compute the length of the perimeter, the surface area of the faces, and the volume of a three-dimensional object built from rectangular solids. Understand that when the lengths of all dimensions are multiplied by a scale factor, the surface area is multiplied by the square of the scale factor and volume is multiplied by the cube of the scale factor.	794–801, 802, 803–809, 819–825, 846, 847–854
Grade 7: **MG 2.4**	Relate the changes in measurement with a change of scale to the units used (e.g., square inches, cubic feet) and to conversions between units (1 square foot = 144 square inches or [1 ft^2] = [144 in^2]; 1 cubic inch is approximately 16.38 cubic centimeters or [1 $in.^3$] = [16.38 cm^3]).	847–854, 886
Grade 7: **MG 3.0** Students know the Pythagorean theorem and deepen their understanding of plane and solid geometric shapes by constructing figures that meet given conditions and by identifying attributes of figures:		
Grade 7: **MG 3.2**	Understand and use coordinate graphs to plot simple figures, determine lengths and areas related to them, and determine their image under translations and reflections.	15–22, 48, 49–56, 271, 272, 279, 288–291, 295–301, 319–325, 572–579, 580–587, 588, 589–596, 597, 598–605, 606, 607, 608–615, 626–632, 633, 642–645, 732, 734, 878
Grade 7: **MG 3.3**	Know and understand the Pythagorean theorem and its converse and use it to find the length of the missing side of a right triangle and the lengths of other line segments and, in some situations, empirically verify the Pythagorean theorem by direct measurement.	432, 433–439, 440, 441–447
Grade 7: **MG 3.4**	Demonstrate an understanding of conditions that indicate two geometrical figures are congruent and what congruence means about the relationships between the sides and angles of the two figures.	225–231, 233, 234–239, 240–246, 247, 249–255, 256–263, 264–270, 303–309, 310–316
Algebra 1 Strand		
Algebra 1: **2.0**	Students understand and use such operations as taking the opposite, finding the reciprocal, and taking a root, ~~and raising to a fractional power.~~ They understand and use the rules of exponents.	17–22, 172–178, 364–370, 434–439, 869, 874, 875
Algebra 1: **3.0**	Students solve equations and inequalities involving absolute values.	287, 870
Algebra 1: **4.0**	Students simplify expressions before solving linear equations and inequalities in one variable, such as $3(2x - 5) + 4(x - 2) = 12$.	26–30, 45 (Exs. 28–30), 65, 105–111, 158 (Exs. 27–36), 875
Algebra 1: **5.0**	Students solve multistep problems, including word problems, involving linear equations and linear inequalities in one variable and provide justification for each step.	49–56, 57, 66–69, 171–178, 180–187, 188–189, 328–334, 335–341, 342, 515–521
Algebra 1: **6.0**	Students graph a linear equation and compute the *x*- and *y*-intercepts (e.g., graph $2x + 6y = 4$). ~~They are also able to sketch the region defined by linear inequalities (e.g., they sketch the region defined by $2x + 6y < 4$)~~.	171–178, 180–187, 188–189, 207, 878, 879

Note: Strikethroughs within a standard indicate that this particular part of the standard is not to be assessed on the CAHSEE but is still part of the original standard.

Content Standard		Pages
Algebra 1: **7.0**	Students verify that a point lies on a line, given an equation of the line. Students are able to derive linear equations. ~~by using the point-slope formula~~.	171–178, 180–187, 188–189
Algebra 1: **8.0**	Students understand the concepts of parallel lines ~~and perpendicular lines~~ and how their slopes are related. ~~Students are able to find the equation of a line perpendicular to a given line that passes through a given point.~~	153, 154–160, 161–169, 171–178, 180–187, 190–197, 396, 397–403
Algebra 1: **9.0**	Students solve a system of two linear equations in two variables algebraically and are able to interpret the answer graphically. Students are able to solve a system of two linear inequalities in two variables and to sketch the solution sets.	180–187, 188–189, 880, 881
Algebra 1: **10.0**	Students add, subtract, multiply, and divide monomials and polynomials. Students solve multistep problems, including word problems, by using these techniques.	154–160, 515–521, 641, 651–658, 680–686
Algebra 1: **15.0**	Students apply algebraic techniques to solve rate problems, work problems, and percent mixture problems.	177–178, 886
Mathematical Reasoning Strand		
***Grade 7:* MR 1.0** Students make decisions about how to approach problems:		
Grade 7: **MR 1.1**	Analyze problems by identifying relationships, distinguishing relevant from irrelevant information, identifying missing information, sequencing and prioritizing information, and observing patterns.	23, 58, 72–78, 103, 132, 170, 200, 248, 280, 317, 342, 380, 416, 465, 492, 532, 558, 597, 634, 687, 706, 745, 778, 818, 855
Grade 7: **MR 1.2**	Formulate and justify mathematical conjectures based on a general description of the mathematical question or problem posed.	72–78, 87–93, 99 (Exs. 11–13), 100 (Ex. 29), 105–111, 122–123, 140, 151, 153, 166, 169, 175, 269, 294, 371, 396, 407, 432, 440, 448, 466, 514, 650, 669, 671, 688, 735, 802, 828, 846
***Grade 7:* MR 2.0** Students use strategies, skills, and concepts in finding solutions:		
Grade 7: **MR 2.1**	Use estimation to verify the reasonableness of calculated results.	13, 32, 54, 178, 308, 315, 333, 366, 369, 378, 394, 468, 471, 472, 669, 682, 692, 722, 742, 751, 752, 760, 773, 774, 776, 816, 824, 844, 867, 885
Grade 7: **MR 2.3**	Estimate unknown quantities graphically and solve for them by using logical reasoning and arithmetic and algebraic techniques.	183, 200, 216
Grade 7: **MR 2.4**	Make and test conjectures by using both inductive and deductive reasoning.	72–78, 87–93; 99 (Exs. 11–13), 100 (Ex. 29), 122–123, 140, 151, 153, 166, 169, 175, 269, 294, 371, 396, 407, 432, 440, 448, 466, 514, 650, 669, 671, 688, 735, 802, 828, 846
***Grade 7:* MR 3.0** Students determine a solution is complete and move beyond a particular problem by generalizing to other situations:		
Grade 7: **MR 3.3**	Develop generalizations of the results obtained and the strategies used and apply them to new problem situations.	23, 58, 103, 132, 140–143, 170, 200, 208–301, 248, 280, 288–291, 317, 342, 350–353, 380, 416, 424–427, 465, 492, 500–503, 532, 558, 566–669,597, 634, 642–645, 66–69, 687, 706, 714–717, 745, 778, 786–789, 818, 855, 862–865

Note: Strikethroughs within a standard indicate that this particular part of the standard is not to be assessed on the CAHSEE but is still part of the original standard.

ACTIVITY GENERATOR RESOURCES

The McDougal Littell Activity Generator includes activities and geometry games involving concrete objects, patterns, data collection, and technology. These activities correspond to each lesson of *Geometry* and include extensive teacher notes and closure questions for classroom discussion.

Lesson	Lesson Title	Activity Title
1.1	Identify Points, Lines, and Planes	Representing Points, Lines, and Planes Geometry Game: Representing Points, Lines, and Rays
1.2	Use Segments and Congruence	Finding the Length of a Line Segment
1.3	Use Midpoint and Distance Formulas	Finding the Midpoint of a Segment Folding a Segment Bisector
1.4	Measure and Classify Angles	Constructing and Measuring Angles Folding an Angle Bisector
1.5	Describe Angle Pair Relationships	Geometry Game: Describe Angle Relationships
1.6	Classify Polygons	Investigating Concave and Convex Polygons Geometry Game: Using Geometric Language
1.7	Find Perimeter, Circumference, and Area	Investigate Perimeter and Area
2.1	Use Inductive Reasoning	Use Inductive Reasoning
2.2	Analyze Conditional Statements	Analyze Conditional Statements
2.3	Apply Deductive Reasoning	Logic Puzzles
2.3	Extension: Symbolic Notation and Truth Tables	Using Symbolic Notation and Truth Tables
2.4	Use Postulates and Diagrams	Modeling and Analyzing Planes
2.5	Reason Using Properties from Algebra	Justify a Number Trick
2.6	Prove Statements about Segments and Angles	Geometry Game: Completing Proofs
2.7	Prove Angle Pair Relationships	Angles and Intersecting Lines
3.1	Identify Pairs of Lines and Angles	Draw and Interpret Lines
3.2	Use Parallel Lines and Transversals	Parallel Lines and Angles Exploring Parallel Lines
3.3	Prove Lines are Parallel	Prove Lines are Parallel
3.4	Find and Use Slopes of Lines	TI-Navigator*: Calculating and Interpreting Slopes of Lines
3.5	Write and Graph Equations of Lines	Finding a Pattern and Writing a Rule TI-Navigator: Finding Equations of Lines
3.6	Prove Theorems about Perpendicular Lines	Investigating Properties of Perpendicular Lines Folding Perpendicular Lines
3.6	Extension: Taxicab Geometry	Determining the Number of Paths
4.1	Apply Triangle Sum Properties	Angle Sums in Triangles
4.2	Apply Congruence and Triangles	Exploring Congruent Triangles
4.3	Prove Triangles Congruent by SSS	Investigate Congruent Figures Copying a Triangle
4.4	Prove Triangles Congruent by SAS and HL	Drawing Triangles Using SAS and SSA

*TI-Navigator is a registered trademark of Texas Instruments Incorporated.

Lesson	Lesson Title	Activity Title
4.5	Prove Triangles Congruent by ASA and AAS	Drawing Triangles Using ASA and AAS
4.6	Use Congruent Triangles	Comparing Congruent Triangles
4.7	Use Isosceles and Equilateral Triangles	Investigating Isosceles and Equilateral Triangles
4.8	Perform Congruence Transformations	Investigate Slides and Flips
5.1	Midsegment Theorem and Coordinate Proof	Investigate Segments in Triangles
5.2	Use Perpendicular Bisectors	Exploring Properties of Perpendicular Bisectors Folding the Perpendicular Bisectors of a Triangle
5.3	Use Angle Bisectors of Triangles	Use Angle Bisectors of Triangles
5.4	Use Medians and Altitudes	Intersecting Medians
5.5	Use Inequalities in a Triangle	Use Inequalities in a Triangle
5.6	Inequalities in Two Triangles and Indirect Proof	Drawing and Comparing Triangles
6.1	Ratios, Proportions, and the Geometric Mean	Ratios, Proportions, and the Geometric Mean
6.2	Use Proportions to Solve Geometry Problems	Use Proportions to Solve Geometry Problems
6.3	Use Similar Polygons	Similar Polygons
6.4	Prove Triangles Similar by AA	Identifying Similar Triangles Exploring Angles and Similar Triangles
6.5	Prove Triangles Similar by SSS and SAS	TI-Navigator: Using Proportions to Prove Similarity
6.6	Use Proportionality Theorems	Investigate Proportionality
6.6	Extension: Fractals	Drawing and Analyzing Fractals
6.7	Perform Similarity Transformations	Dilations
7.1	Apply the Pythagorean Theorem	Pythagorean Theorem
7.2	Use the Converse of the Pythagorean Theorem	Converse of the Pythagorean Theorem
7.3	Use Similar Right Triangles	Similar Right Triangles
7.4	Special Right Triangles	TI-Navigator: Special Right Triangles
7.5	Apply the Tangent Ratio	Exploring the Tangent Ratio
7.6	Apply the Sine and Cosine Ratios	Apply the Sine and Cosine Ratios
7.7	Solve Right Triangles	TI-Navigator: Solving Real-World Problems Using Trigonometry
7.7	Extension: Law of Sines and Law of Cosines	Exploring the Law of Sines
8.1	Find Angle Measures in Polygons	Investigate Angle Sums in Polygons
8.2	Use Properties of Parallelograms	Investigate Parallelograms
8.3	Show that a Quadrilateral is a Parallelogram	Show that a Quadrilateral is a Parallelogram
8.4	Properties of Rhombuses, Rectangles, and Squares	Properties of Rhombuses, Rectangles, and Squares TI-Navigator: Exploring Properties of Rhombuses
8.5	Use Properties of Trapezoids and Kites	Midsegment of a Trapezoid
8.5	Extension: Draw Three-Dimensional Figures	Drawing Three-Dimensional Figures
8.6	Identify Special Quadrilaterals	Geometry Game: Identify Special Quadrilaterals

Lesson	Lesson Title	Activity Title
9.1	Translate Figures and Use Vectors	Comparing Translated Polygons
9.2	Use Properties of Matrices	Investigating Matrix Addition and Transformations
9.3	Perform Reflections	Reflections in the Plane
9.4	Perform Rotations	TI-Navigator: Performing Rotations
9.5	Apply Compositions of Transformations	Double Reflections
9.5	Extension: Tessellations	Tessellations
9.6	Identify Symmetry	Identify Symmetry
9.7	Identify and Perform Dilations	Investigate Dilations
10.1	Use Properties of Tangents	Explore Tangent Segments
10.2	Find Arc Measures	Geometry Game: Understanding Circle Vocabulary
10.3	Apply Properties of Chords	Exploring the Properties of Chords
10.4	Use Inscribed Angles and Polygons	Explore Inscribed Angles
10.5	Apply Other Angle Relationships in Circles	Investigating Angles Inside and Outside of a Circle
10.6	Find Segment Lengths in Circles	Investigate Segment Lengths
10.6	Extension: Draw a Locus	Locus
10.7	Write and Graph Equations of Circles	Determining Equations of Circles
11.1	Areas of Triangles and Parallelograms	TI-Navigator: Finding Areas of Triangles and Parallelograms
11.1	Extension: Determine Precision and Accuracy	Determine Precision and Accuracy
11.2	Areas of Trapezoids, Rhombuses, and Kites	Areas of Trapezoids and Kites
11.3	Perimeter and Area of Similar Figures	Perimeter and Area of Similar Figures
11.4	Circumference and Arc Length	Circumference and Arc Length
11.4	Extension: Geometry on a Sphere	Geometry on a Sphere
11.5	Areas of Circles and Sectors	Areas of Circles and Sectors
11.6	Areas of Regular Polygons	Finding the Area of Regular Polygons
11.7	Use Geometric Probability	Investigate Geometric Probability TI-Navigator: Making an Estimate Using Geometric Probability
12.1	Explore Solids	Investigate Solids
12.2	Surface Area of Prisms and Cylinders	Investigate Surface Area
12.3	Surface Area of Pyramids and Cones	Surface Areas of Pyramids and Cones
12.4	Volume of Prisms and Cylinders	Volumes of Prisms and Cylinders
12.5	Volume of Pyramids and Cones	Investigate the Volume of a Pyramid
12.6	Surface Area and Volume of Spheres	Geometry Game: Surface Area and Volume of Spheres
12.7	Explore Similar Solids	Investigate Similar Solids

Teaching Strategies

The articles on pages CA25–CA31 offer strategies for approaching the difficulties of teaching students with a wide variety of abilities in mathematics and varying mastery of English.

Providing Universal Access

The article on pages CA25–CA29 offers suggestions for teaching mathematics in a diverse classroom. Strategies are included for adapting curriculum and classroom instruction in a class that may include students who are ready to learn at an advanced level, at grade level, and below grade level.

Adapting Curriculum and Instruction for English Learners

The article on pages CA30 and CA31 offers suggestions for teaching mathematics to students who are learning English. Strategies are included for teaching students with either high or low achievement in mathematics and also with high or low achievement in reading.

Providing Universal Access

With careful planning, teachers can help all students reach a level of mathematical competence needed to continue their education in mathematics.

Diverse Students

In most classrooms, students present a variety of achievement levels, skills, and needs. The goal for all students is the same: We want them to develop sufficient computational, procedural, and problem solving skills to provide a solid foundation for further study in mathematics. However, all students do not arrive at these competencies at the same time or in the same way. In this article we suggest research-based strategies teachers can use to modify curriculum and instruction for special needs students. The basic instructional plan in *Geometry* is designed for students who are achieving at near grade level; but throughout each chapter we include specific suggestions for students who are achieving above and below grade level, and for students who are not fluent in English (see also the article titled "Adapting Curriculum and Instruction for English Learners", which may help native speakers as well).

Student Groups

Teachers may find it helpful to view students as members of four basic groups, as shown on the next page. (English learners can be found in all four groups.) Teachers do not need to place students in these groups; the categories are suggested so teachers can plan ahead to meet different needs of students. Note the use of the term *strategic learners* to emphasize the kind of instruction needed by students achieving below grade level. This term is not synonymous with special education. It may include some special education pupils but includes many more students whose low achievement levels are the result of inadequate prior schooling or attendance, high mobility rates, or a host of other reasons that have nothing to do with their abilities or disabilities. The term *strategic learner* was selected because it is a positive term that emphasizes what needs to happen in order for these students to be successful and implies what we believe: students achieving below grade level *can* be successful in mathematics given carefully designed instruction.

Setting the Right Tone

There are three key strategies recommended for teachers as they adapt any program to students' needs:

- Use frequent assessment as a way to determine what each student does or does not know, and use that assessment as the basis for planning.
- Plan modifications of curriculum and instruction ahead of time so that you are ready to differentiate as the need arises.
- Use a variety of grouping strategies to facilitate learning. A combination of whole class instruction and temporary groupings of students, with groups organized around students' needs, will facilitate management of the variety of achievement levels and learning needs in the classroom.

Assessment, planning, and flexible grouping are essential to ensuring that your students have the optimal chance for success. In addition to these three key strategies, general guidelines for establishing a classroom designed to meet students' needs are:

1. Establish an atmosphere where students feel comfortable asking questions and are rewarded for asking about things they don't understand.
2. Maintain the same goals for all students. Allow additional time and practice for students who need it, and provide challenging alternatives for those who are ready to move more quickly.
3. Clearly identify the skill, concept, or standards you are working on and measure progress towards those ends.
4. Have students show their work. It is much easier for teachers to understand where a student gets confused if they have evidence of the student's thought process.
5. Try small modifications in curriculum and instruction before more drastic ones.
6. Don't persist with a strategy that is not working. Try something else.
7. Encourage effort and persistence, and celebrate successes with your students.

Varying Curriculum and Instruction

Time Most students whose achievement is below grade level will need more time. Students who are not fluent in English will need more time. The contents of this book might be offered over a two-year period, or two periods a day. Perhaps the day can be extended through study hall, regular homework assignments, tutoring, or Saturday, summer, or "off track" catch-up sessions. Advanced students might "test out" of portions of the book and complete the material in half a year, or they may compact two courses into one.

FOUR BASIC STUDENT GROUPS

Advanced Group

Advanced students have already completed some of the grade-level material. They make rapid progress and become bored with repetition. They may have been formally identified as gifted or talented in the area of mathematics.

SUGGESTED PLAN

1. Assess what these students already know.
2. Allow these students to "test out" of chapters or assignments.
3. Substitute challenging assignments for easier ones.
4. Modify instruction so that it is more complex or more in-depth.

Grade Level Group

Students achieving at grade level may have minor, occasional difficulties but they can be assisted to maintain their progress with extra practice and individual or group assistance on an as-needed basis.

SUGGESTED PLAN

1. Assess what these students already know.
2. Progress through *Geometry* at the recommended pace and sequence.
3. On an ad hoc basis, review or provide additional practice as needed.

Strategic Group

Strategic learners are not achieving at expected grade level but can, with a program that provides targeted assistance. Systematic differentiation such as preteaching, reteaching, and additional instructional time should be planned.

SUGGESTED PLAN

1. Assess what these students already know.
2. Provide additional scaffolding and the instructional variations suggested in this book.
3. Focus on the key concepts and present material systematically.
4. Vary the kinds of instruction so that students have several opportunities to understand.
5. Provide additional practice homework.

Intensive Needs Group

Intensive needs students are those whose performance is two or more standard deviations below the mean on standardized measures. These students will probably already be eligible for special education services.

SUGGESTED PLAN

1. Assess what these students already know.
2. Determine if these students have an IEP.
3. Refer students for special education testing or child study team discussion; enlist the help of specialists.
4. Carefully consider each student's most appropriate placement in mathematics.
5. Use the specific suggestions for strategic learners.

Presentation Instructing in a variety of ways and taking a single concept and explaining it verbally and visually with concrete and abstract examples provide students multiple opportunities for understanding. Area, for example, is a key concept in geometry. In earlier grades students have found areas of simple objects, both by using tiles to cover an area, and by applying algorithms. Later, students divide unusual shapes into simpler ones. Finally, students tackle sophisticated examples like finding the shape with the maximum area given a fixed perimeter, using both trial and error and more abstract methods.

Task Parameters Multi-step problems can be especially difficult for students. These types of problems are just combinations of simpler problems and can be broken down into those simpler steps, with additional help and practice at each step. Confusing elements can be minimized and extraneous material can be eliminated. For advanced students, simpler problems can be eliminated and more challenging ones (as suggested in each chapter) may be substituted.

Methods of Assessment Students learning English may be able to demonstrate on paper what they cannot yet verbalize. Students with physical challenges may be unable to draw a graph but may be able to select the right graph from a series of options or verbally describe the graph so that someone else can draw it. Allow students to demonstrate their knowledge in a variety of ways while helping all students to master the skills and knowledge necessary to exhibit their understanding in standard ways.

Geometry is organized so that much of the differentiation for special needs students is built into the design of the program. Note that simpler concepts are introduced before more complex ones. Ample practice is provided. Challenge exercises are included throughout the pupil text. The program provides students with models for conceptual understanding of the mathematical reasoning behind each key concept. Mathematical reasoning is stressed throughout each chapter. Vocabulary words, examples, and Guided Practice exercises are standard features of each chapter. Each lesson includes Mixed Review exercises so that students recall and use skills and understandings from previous chapters. These features were designed to help you meet the needs of the students in your class.

Teaching Strategies

For Students who have Trouble Paying Attention

Some students in your classroom may be formally identified as having Attention Deficit Hyperactivity Disorder (ADHD) or Attention Deficit Disorder (ADD). Others may exhibit the same learning challenges but may not be formally identified.

Whether formally identified or not, students who have trouble paying attention generally share the following characteristics:

- Trouble paying attention is not just occasional. It occurs most or all of the time, across content areas, and is inappropriate for the age of the child.
- Forgetfulness, memory problems, losing things, disorganization
- Restlessness, fidgeting
- Socially inappropriate behavior such as excessive talking, interrupting others, and difficulty waiting their turn

These students may be very bright and capable in mathematics but have a hard time staying focused for long periods of time. They need to be taught strategies for organizing their work and keeping track of where they are. In general, students with attention problems need to be helped to develop coping strategies. The teacher should approach the student in a problem solving mode: "Let's find ways to help you concentrate and organize your work," rather than using one of the following strategies in a punitive way.

1. Present the work in smaller chunks, over smaller time periods, and then gradually increase expectations. If students have trouble completing long tests, for example, break the material into smaller quizzes and increase the length of the quizzes as the year progresses.
2. Use cumulative review and practice. Have students periodically review what they learned in previous chapters and provide additional practice if they have forgotten.

3. Make it more obvious what the student should focus on. For example, use the test generator to put only four problems on each page; use a large font; or use an index card or piece of cardboard with a hole cut out of the middle to place on the page so that the student can focus on one problem at a time. A pencil, finger, highlighter, or sticky paper can also be used by the student to keep track of which problem he or she is working on.
4. Have students race against the clock. For some students, racing against the clock to see how many problems can be completed accurately within a five-minute time period is more motivating than doing the same number of problems at their leisure. The time period can be extended gradually.
5. Help students develop simple strategies for bringing work to and from class. A two-pocket folder, where homework goes home in the left pocket and comes back in the right, is a simple way to keep track of assignments.
6. Allow movement and schedule breaks.
7. Minimize distractions by seating students who are easily distracted near the teacher and away from hallway noise. Tables with several students at a table are more distracting than rows of desks. When students are to work quietly, offer headphones to block out noise. Headphones can be set to play quiet music, "white noise," or can be used just as earplugs to help block out noise.
8. Graphic organizers such as Venn diagrams, tree diagrams, lists, outlines, tables, and charts can all provide structures for organizing and remembering information. Mental images, choral responses, or even hand signals can help students remember. Highlighters can be used to make sure that decimal points are lined up. Graph paper is excellent for keeping homework problems neat, even when a graph is not required.
9. Keep instructions simple and clear, especially at the beginning of the year. Establish routines (e.g., the week's homework is always due on Thursday; assignments are written in a specific place on the board; the last ten minutes of class is used to make sure everyone understands what homework is expected and how to do it). Students who know the routine find it easier to work independently.

For Students who have Trouble Understanding the Concepts

Success in mathematics, as in music, sports, or other areas, comes for most students only with hard work and persistent effort. Concepts may seem difficult at first, but with repeated teaching and practice virtually all students can master the mathematics they need to graduate from high school, access a variety of jobs, and lay the foundation for further study in mathematics or a related field.

With repeated teaching and practice virtually all students can master the mathematics they need.

Several strategies can help students make steady progress in mathematics. These include:

1. Focus on key mathematical concepts.
2. Review key concepts and skills from earlier lessons, chapters, or years.
3. Preteach key concepts and vocabulary.
4. Anticipate problem areas.
5. Provide scaffolding (guided practice) for students who need extra help.
6. Think out loud to show hidden steps.
7. Provide a sample problem to which students can return when they get stuck.
8. Break problems into simpler components.
9. Explicitly teach students a variety of problem solving strategies and help them select one that fits the situation.

10. Present concepts in a variety of ways: visually, verbally, concretely, abstractly, etc.

11. Encourage students to draw a picture or use a visual aid such as a number line, graph, or diagram.

12. Provide sufficient practice.

Finally, good teachers are perpetual students themselves. They are always looking for ways to deepen their understanding of mathematics and for good ways to explain and teach mathematics to others.

For Advanced Students

Occasionally students can demonstrate mastery of all the mathematics expected to be learned at a given grade level. Repeating previously learned material for a year is deadly to these students. It can make them dislike mathematics. For these students, moving them up a grade level for math is a simple and cost-effective solution.

Most advanced students, however, are advanced in some areas but not in others. They tend to learn quickly and need more instructional material, as well as more difficult material. The student edition, teacher's edition, and ancillaries for this program provide challenge exercises that can be used when students have demonstrated competence in a particular area. These challenge exercises should be substituted for the easier exercises in a homework assignment or lesson. When they have the time and interest, all students should be encouraged to work the challenge exercises.

General strategies for differentiating the curriculum for advanced learners include:

1. Vary the pacing. Allow advanced students some flexibility in how they progress through the course. Students who can demonstrate mastery of the objectives for a given lesson or chapter can be working on challenge exercises. Advanced students may become fascinated with a particular aspect of mathematics and want to spend *more* time on it.

2. Differentiate in terms of depth. Encourage advanced students to delve more in depth into mathematics. Looking at the details and the patterns; studying the language of the discipline; and looking at trends, themes, properties, theorems, proofs, and unanswered questions can enrich the curriculum for advanced students.

3. Differentiate in terms of complexity. Advanced students may be ready to connect ideas across disciplines in ways characteristic of older students or adults. Encourage them to investigate relationships between mathematics and art, history, science, and music, and to look at the development of mathematics over time.

Using Grouping to Benefit All Students

Grouping advanced learners together for investigations of challenge problems can provide you with time to work more closely with a group of students who need help in a particular area. Alternatively, while students who need more help are working on additional reinforcement activities or practice, you can work with a group of advanced students on a challenge project. Groups can be organized and revised daily, weekly, or by lesson according to how proficient students are with the concepts and skills targeted for that day, week, or lesson. At times you may have only one student who is ready for a challenge problem; at other times the whole class may be ready. Flexible grouping is the key to ensuring that students do not become "tracked." Asking advanced students to report to the whole class on their progress on challenge problems can provide the opportunity for the whole class to engage in more abstract and theoretical thinking.

TEACHING STRATEGIES

Adapting Curriculum and Instruction for English Learners

Assessing each student's competencies in mathematics and English will form a basis for program planning.

Introduction

English learners come to the classroom with all the variety of English speakers in regard to mathematics achievement. They may be at, behind, or ahead of grade expectations in mathematics. They may be gifted or eligible for special education services. They may have been born in the United States, or they may have arrived in this country very recently. They may speak one or more languages, and they may be literate in one or more languages other than English. They have in common one characteristic: They are all learning English.

With careful planning, teachers can maximize success for English learners in the mathematics classroom. Assessing each student's competencies in mathematics and English will form a basis for program planning.

Getting to know your students

Before school starts, check the cumulative folder on each student in your class to determine which ones are learning English. See if there is recent testing. Two types of testing are most useful: mathematics achievement and reading achievement levels. Use the chart on the following page as a guide to understanding student assessment data.

Suggestions for Mathematics Teachers of English Learners

1. Allocate additional time for mathematics. Many students will be translating from English to their primary language and back again. The meaning of many words will not be immediately clear. When you ask questions, allow extra time for students to respond. Reading mathematics textbooks and understanding what is asked for in a word problem will take more time.
2. Use students' background knowledge. Some English learners will have developed substantial background in mathematics; others will have very little. Find out what students know and then build on that knowledge.
3. Reduce the amount and sophistication of the English language used. This may be done by reordering the lessons in each chapter to begin with key vocabulary, followed by problems with a minimum of written English, followed by at least one word problem each day. Choose word problems that don't rely on assumed background knowledge. Monitor and simplify the speech you use. Speak more slowly, avoid idioms and slang, be precise and concise, and use short sentences and simple vocabulary. Using hand gestures and pictures as well as words aids communication.
4. Limit the number of concepts introduced per day. Keeping the focus of each day simple will aid students in understanding the point of the lesson. Focus on key concepts, and use mathematics instructional time well.
5. Use a variety of different methods for getting a point across. Presenting concepts verbally and visually, with concrete examples and in abstract mathematical symbols, and using

pictures, graphs, diagrams, and charts will enhance the chance that students will understand at least one of the presentations. As you introduce a new word, rule, or theorem, write it down.

6. Provide opportunities for English learners to interact with their English-speaking peers. Students who are learning a language need to hear native speakers using the language, and they need opportunities to use their new mathematics vocabulary in their speech and in their writing.
7. Provide opportunities for English learners to discuss their understandings with each other, confirm the homework assignments, or ask questions of each other in whatever language they may have in common.
8. Allow English learners to demonstrate what they know in a variety of ways. When students first learn a language, they are usually shy about speaking. They generally understand spoken language before they can produce it themselves. Students who have recently arrived from another country with good schooling may be able to read in English but not speak it. Allow students to point, nod, gesture, draw a picture, or work math problems without words as they learn English.
9. Extend mathematics instructional time through homework, an extra class period, summer school, or tutoring. Many of the language-related suggestions for English learners in this series can be carried out in collaboration with the language arts teacher.
10. Keep on hand picture dictionaries, foreign language dictionaries, multi-language glossaries, and drawing materials.

	Low Mathematics Achievement		High Mathematics Achievement	
	Who is the student?	**What to do?**	**Who is the student?**	**What to do?**
Low Reading Achievement	• Student may be new to the class, school, or country. • Student may have had inadequate schooling. • Student may have moved a lot. • Student may be unmotivated or have test anxiety. • Low reading achievement may be depressing mathematics scores. • Student may have gaps and holes in knowledge. • Student may need special education assistance.	• Examine cumulative folder for other testing, notes, etc. • Ask questions about language use and prior schooling. • Delay any testing for a week or two. Help student feel comfortable in the class during that period of time. • Administer mathematics achievement test and reading test, in an individual setting. • Assess this student at weekly intervals and monitor classroom work to determine if progress is being made. • Look at the English Learners suggestions in each chapter.	• Student has had good prior mathematics instruction. • Mathematics is an area where this student can excel. • Math achievement level may actually be higher than scores indicate. (Limited English reading skills affect math achievement as well.) • Word problems will be especially difficult.	• Mathematics instruction should proceed at normal or near normal pace. • Student should be involved in a systematic English language development program and intensive reading program outside of mathematics class. • Spend part of each class period on vocabulary study. • Provide student with a bilingual dictionary or math glossary and a mathematics text in the home language. • Look at the English Learners suggestions in each chapter for those that are most useful.
	Who is the student?	**What to do?**	**Who is the student?**	**What to do?**
High Reading Achievement	• Student may have been designated as an English learner because oral skills lag behind reading skills. • Student may not test well in mathematics. • Most students can make rapid progress in mathematics; a few may have learning difficulties that require the help of a specialist.	• Assess mathematics achievement in a variety of ways. • Concentrate on developing oral fluency. • Focus on vocabulary specific to mathematics. • Use a student's reading ability to improve his or her math scores.	• Student may be ready for designation as a fluent English speaker. • May need extra study in the specialized vocabulary of mathematics. Complex syntax may present obstacles to performance. • Given systematic instruction, this student should be able to achieve at or above grade level.	• Scan all of the suggestions for English learners in each chapter and progress through the ones the student needs as quickly as possible. • Monitor carefully to make sure this student continues to progress at a reasonable pace.

GEOMETRY

Ron Larson Laurie Boswell Timothy D. Kanold Lee Stiff

TEACHER'S EDITION

Contents

McDougal Littell
A DIVISION OF HOUGHTON MIFFLIN COMPANY
Evanston, Illinois • Boston • Dallas

Pre-AP is a registered trademark of the College Entrance Examination Board, which was not involved in the production of and does not endorse this product.

Printed in Canada

ISBN-13: 978-0-618-59557-0
ISBN-10: 0-618-59557-0 123456789—TBQ—12 11 10 09 08

Internet Web Site: http://www.mcdougallittell.com

About *Geometry*

In *Geometry*, students will develop reasoning and problem solving skills as they study topics such as congruence and similarity, and apply properties of lines, triangles, quadrilaterals, and circles. Students will also develop problem solving skills by using length, perimeter, area, circumference, surface area, and volume to solve real-world problems.

In addition to its geometry content, *Geometry* includes numerous examples and exercises involving algebra, data analysis, and probability. These math topics often appear on standardized tests, so maintaining students' familiarity with them is important. To help students prepare for standardized tests, *Geometry* provides instruction and practice on standardized test questions in a variety of formats—multiple choice, short response, extended response, and so on. Technology support for both learning geometry and preparing for standardized tests is available at classzone.com.

About the Authors

Ron Larson is a professor of mathematics at Penn State University at Erie, where he has taught since receiving his Ph.D. in mathematics from the University of Colorado. Dr. Larson is well known as the author of a comprehensive program for mathematics that spans middle school, high school, and college courses. Dr. Larson's numerous professional activities keep him in constant touch with the needs of teachers and supervisors. He closely follows developments in mathematics standards and assessment.

Laurie Boswell is a mathematics teacher at The Riverside School in Lyndonville, Vermont, and has taught mathematics at all levels, elementary through college. A recipient of the Presidential Award for Excellence in Mathematics Teaching, she was also a Tandy Technology Scholar. She served on the NCTM Board of Directors (2002–2005), and she speaks frequently at regional and national conferences on topics related to instructional strategies and course content.

Timothy D. Kanold is the superintendent of Adlai E. Stevenson High School District 125 in Lincolnshire, Illinois. Dr. Kanold served as a teacher and director of mathematics for 17 years prior to becoming superintendent. He is the recipient of the Presidential Award for Excellence in Mathematics and Science Teaching, and a past president of the Council for Presidential Awardees in Mathematics. Dr. Kanold is a frequent speaker at national and international mathematics meetings.

Lee Stiff is a professor of mathematics education in the College of Education and Psychology of North Carolina State University at Raleigh and has taught mathematics at the high school and middle school levels. He served on the NCTM Board of Directors and was elected President of NCTM for the years 2000–2002. He is a recipient of the W. W. Rankin Award for Excellence in Mathematics Education presented by the North Carolina Council of Teachers of Mathematics.

Advisers and Reviewers

California Program Advisers and Reviewers

Monette Bartel
Associate Adjunct Professor
College of the Canyons
Valencia, CA

Janice Beauchamp
Mathematics Teacher
Buchanan High School
Clovis, CA

Pauline Embree
Mathematics Department Chair
Rancho San Joaquin Middle School
Irvine, CA

Alberto Hernandez Galindo
Mathematics Department Chair
San Jose High Academy
San Jose, CA

Tom Griffith
Mathematics Department Chair
Scripps Ranch High School
San Diego, CA

Debra Konvalin
Mathematics Teacher
Hiram W. Johnson High School
Sacramento, CA

Alvin E. Nash, Jr.
Mathematics Teacher
Pasadena High School
Pasadena, CA

Jon Simon
Mathematics Teacher
Casa Grande High School
Petaluma, CA

Chapter 1 Summary

Chapter 1 introduces geometric concepts that students will use throughout the course. Students **identify and name** figures such as **points, lines, planes, and rays**. They **measure line segments**, comparing lengths and identifying **congruent segments**. Their work with measurement includes using the **Distance Formula** and the **Midpoint Formula**. Students **classify angles** and **polygons**. They measure angles and identify important angle pairs such as **complementary and supplementary angles**. The chapter concludes with a review of basic **perimeter** and **area** formulas. Throughout the chapter, students use **algebra** to solve geometric problems.

CHAPTER 1

Unit 1
Points, Lines, and Planes

Segment Addition Postulate, p. 14
$AC = AB + BC$

Essentials of Geometry

Chapter 1 Highlights

PROBLEM SOLVING

- **Mixed Review of Problem Solving,** 23, 58
- **Multiple Representations,** 41, 55, 57
- **Multi-Step Problems,** 8, 14, 23, 46, 54, 55, 58
- **Using Alternative Methods,** 57
- **Real-World Problem Solving Examples,** 10, 15, 27, 36, 44, 51, 65

★ ASSESSMENT

- **Standardized Test Practice Examples,** 18, 50
- **Multiple Choice,** 6, 13, 20, 29, 39, 44, 46, 53
- **Short Response/Extended Response,** 7, 12, 14, 20, 22, 23, 30, 32, 40, 47, 54, 55, 58, 66
- **Writing/Open-Ended,** 5, 12, 19, 23, 28, 38, 44, 52, 58

TECHNOLOGY

At classzone.com:

- **Animated Geometry,** 1, 3, 14, 21, 25, 43, 52
- **@Home Tutor,** xxii, 7, 13, 21, 31, 40, 46, 48, 54, 60
- **Online Quiz,** 8, 14, 22, 32, 41, 47, 56
- **Animated Algebra (Algebra Review),** 65
- **State Test Practice,** 23, 58, 69

CHAPTER 2

Unit 1
Points, Lines, and Planes

Properties of Congruence, p. 115
$\overline{AB} \cong \overline{CD}$

Reasoning and Proof

Chapter 2 Summary

Chapter 2 focuses on the role of **reasoning** in geometry. Students compare and contrast **inductive reasoning** and **deductive reasoning** and learn the importance of **counterexamples** in disproving statements. They analyze **conditional statements**, learning to identify the **hypothesis** and **conclusion** of a statement and write the **converse, inverse, and contrapositive**. Reasoning using properties from algebra serves as a starting point for reasoning using **postulates and theorems** from geometry. Students write **two-column proofs** about segments and angles, about angles formed by intersecting lines, and about important **angle pair** relationships.

Extension

2.3 **Symbolic Notation and Truth Tables** (pp. 94–95)

Chapter 2 Highlights

PROBLEM SOLVING

- **Mixed Review of Problem Solving,** 103, 132
- **Multiple Representations,** 77, 111, 120
- **Multi-Step Problems,** 85, 102, 103, 110, 119, 130, 132
- **Using Alternative Methods,** 120
- **Real-World Problem Solving Examples,** 74, 89, 106, 115

★ ASSESSMENT

- **Standardized Test Practice Examples,** 74, 127
- **Multiple Choice,** 75, 76, 83, 90, 99, 100, 109, 116, 128
- **Short Response/Extended Response,** 76, 78, 84, 92, 101, 102, 103, 110, 117, 119, 128, 130, 132, 140
- **Writing/Open-Ended,** 75, 82, 84, 90, 99, 100, 108, 109, 116, 127, 129, 132

TECHNOLOGY

At classzone.com:

- **Animated Geometry,** 71, 72, 81, 88, 97, 106, 119, 125
- **@Home Tutor,** 70, 77, 84, 91, 101, 110, 118, 123, 129, 134
- **Online Quiz,** 78, 85, 93, 102, 111, 119, 131
- **Animated Algebra,** 139
- **State Test Practice,** 103, 132, 143

Chapter 3 Summary

Chapter 3 focuses on reasoning about **parallel lines** and **perpendicular lines**. Students learn to identify **corresponding angles, consecutive interior angles, alternate interior angles, and alternate exterior angles**. They use postulates and theorems about these angle pairs when they are formed by **parallel lines intersected by a transversal**. In particular, students **prove lines are parallel**, using two-column proofs and **paragraph proofs**. A connection to **algebra** is made, as students **find slopes of parallel and perpendicular lines** and **write and graph equations of lines** that are parallel and perpendicular to given lines. Students also prove theorems about **perpendicular lines**.

Extension

3.6 **Taxicab Geometry** (pp. 198–199)

CHAPTER 3

Unit 1 Points, Lines, and Planes

Applying Slope, p. 174
Slope $= \frac{41}{80}$

Parallel and Perpendicular Lines

Chapter 3 Highlights

PROBLEM SOLVING

- **Mixed Review of Problem Solving,** 170, 200
- **Multiple Representations,** 174, 177, 188
- **Multi-Step Problems,** 166, 168, 170, 177, 186, 200
- **Using Alternative Methods,** 188
- **Real-World Problem Solving Examples,** 148, 156, 162, 164, 174, 182, 183, 193, 207

★ ASSESSMENT

- **Standardized Test Practice Example,** 173
- **Multiple Choice,** 151, 157, 158, 166, 176, 184, 185, 195, 208
- **Short Response/Extended Response,** 152, 158, 159, 166, 168, 169, 170, 176, 178, 187, 194, 196, 200
- **Writing/Open-Ended,** 150, 151, 157, 165, 170, 175, 184, 195, 200

TECHNOLOGY

At classzone.com:

- **Animated Geometry,** 145, 148, 155, 163, 174, 181
- **@Home Tutor,** 144, 151, 153, 159, 167, 176, 179, 186, 196, 202
- **Online Quiz,** 152, 160, 169, 178, 187, 197
- **Animated Algebra,** 207
- **State Test Practice,** 170, 200, 211

CHAPTER

4

Unit 2
Triangles

Indirect Measurement, p. 257
$\triangle MLK \cong \triangle MPN$

Congruent Triangles

Chapter 4 Highlights

PROBLEM SOLVING

- **Mixed Review of Problem Solving,** 248, 280
- **Multiple Representations,** 232
- **Multi-Step Problems,** 223, 231, 248, 269, 280
- **Using Alternative Methods,** 232
- **Real-World Problem Solving Examples,** 220, 226, 236, 242, 251, 257, 266, 274

★ ASSESSMENT

- **Standardized Test Practice Examples,** 235, 251
- **Multiple Choice,** 222, 223, 229, 237, 243, 246, 253, 260, 261, 268, 279, 288
- **Short Response/Extended Response,** 221, 224, 230, 231, 238, 248, 253, 254, 262, 267, 268, 270, 278, 280
- **Writing/Open-Ended,** 221, 228, 229, 230, 243, 244, 248, 252, 259, 267, 276, 277, 278, 280

TECHNOLOGY

At classzone.com:

- **Animated Geometry,** 215, 234, 242, 250, 256, 257, 274
- **@Home Tutor,** 214, 223, 230, 238, 245, 247, 254, 261, 269, 278, 282
- **Online Quiz,** 224, 231, 239, 246, 255, 263, 270, 279
- **Animated Algebra,** 287
- **State Test Practice,** 248, 280, 291

Chapter 4 Summary

Chapter 4 focuses on the topic of **congruence**, especially as it applies to **triangles**. Students write **congruence statements** for triangles and other geometric figures. They then continue to develop their understanding of **proof**, using key postulates and theorems to prove that triangles are congruent. Students use **corresponding parts of congruent triangles** to write proofs, including **flow proofs**. They also **classify triangles** and use theorems about **equilateral and isosceles triangles**. The chapter concludes with a lesson that relates congruence to **transformations** they will revisit in Chapter 9: **translations, reflections, and rotations**.

Chapter 5 Summary

Chapter 5 focuses on using **relationships within triangles** and developing skills in writing proofs, including **coordinate proofs**. Students first prove the **Midsegment Theorem** and use properties of midsegments to solve problems. In the lessons that follow, they learn properties of **perpendicular bisectors, angle bisectors, medians, and altitudes of triangles**, using these properties to justify statements and solve problems. Students also apply relationships among the angles and sides of a triangle or triangles, including the **Triangle Inequality Theorem**. The concluding lesson introduces **indirect proof** to prove properties and relationships by contradiction.

CHAPTER 5

Unit 2 Triangles

Inequalities in Triangles, p. 336
$150° > 135°$

Relationships within Triangles

Chapter 5 Highlights

PROBLEM SOLVING

- **Mixed Review of Problem Solving,** 317, 342
- **Multiple Representations,** 302
- **Multi-Step Problems,** 301, 317, 342
- **Using Alternative Methods,** 302
- **Real-World Problem Solving Examples,** 295, 305, 311, 329, 336, 349

★ ASSESSMENT

- **Standardized Test Practice Examples,** 320, 329
- **Multiple Choice,** 299, 307, 314, 322, 331, 332, 339
- **Short Response/Extended Response,** 300, 308, 315, 317, 323, 324, 332, 333, 334, 339, 340, 342, 350
- **Writing/Open-Ended,** 298, 306, 313, 317, 322, 331, 338, 342

TECHNOLOGY

At classzone.com:

- **Animated Geometry,** 293, 296, 304, 312, 321, 330, 336
- **@Home Tutor,** 292, 300, 308, 315, 324, 327, 333, 340, 344
- **Online Quiz,** 301, 309, 316, 325, 334, 341
- **Animated Algebra,** 349
- **State Test Practice,** 317, 342, 353

CHAPTER 6

Unit 2 Triangles

Applying Similar Triangles, p. 394

$\frac{66 \text{ in.}}{7 \text{ ft}} = \frac{x \text{ in.}}{102 \text{ ft}}$

Similarity

Chapter 6 Highlights

PROBLEM SOLVING

- **Mixed Review of Problem Solving,** 380, 416
- **Multiple Representations,** 363, 378, 404
- **Multi-Step Problems,** 362, 378, 380, 385, 394, 402, 414, 416
- **Using Alternative Methods,** 404
- **Real-World Problem Solving Examples,** 357, 359, 365, 366, 374, 390, 398, 410

★ ASSESSMENT

- **Standardized Test Practice Examples,** 383, 411
- **Multiple Choice,** 361, 368, 376, 377, 384, 385, 392, 400, 401, 412, 413
- **Short Response/Extended Response,** 361, 363, 377, 379, 380, 386, 387, 394, 402, 403, 413, 414, 415, 416, 424
- **Writing/Open-Ended,** 360, 367, 376, 380, 384, 385, 391, 394, 400, 412, 414, 416

TECHNOLOGY

At classzone.com:

- **Animated Geometry,** 355, 365, 375, 391, 394, 407, 414
- **@Home Tutor,** 354, 362, 368, 378, 386, 393, 396, 402, 414, 418
- **Online Quiz,** 363, 370, 379, 387, 395, 403, 415
- **Animated Algebra,** 423
- **State Test Practice,** 380, 416, 427

Chapter 6 Summary

Chapter 6 focuses on **ratio and proportion** as they apply to **similar figures**. Students first review **writing and solving proportions,** including solving problems involving the **geometric mean**. After solving problems involving **similar polygons**, students focus specifically on **similar triangles**. They write proofs and solve problems, including **indirect measurement problems**, using postulates and theorems about similar triangles. Students also use the Triangle Proportionality Theorem, its converse, and other **proportionality theorems** to justify their reasoning and solve problems. Finally, the chapter relates similarity to **dilations**, a topic students will revisit in Chapter 9.

Extension

6.6 **Fractals** (pp. 406–407)

Chapter 7 Summary

Chapter 7 focuses on **right triangles** and **trigonometry**. Students prove the **Pythagorean Theorem** and its converse, using both of these theorems to **solve problems**. The chapter includes a lesson on using **proportional reasoning** to solve problems involving **similar right triangles** and a lesson on solving problems involving **special right triangles**. The first part of the chapter serves as a basis for work with the **tangent, sine, and cosine ratios**. Students use these ratios to solve **indirect measurement** problems. Then, in the concluding lesson of the chapter, they **solve right triangles**, where a number of problems involve the application of **inverse trigonometric ratios**.

Extension

7.7 **Law of Sines and Law of Cosines** (pp. 490–491)

CHAPTER 7

Unit 3 Figures in the Plane

Angle of Elevation, p. 475
$\sin 21^\circ = \frac{\text{opp.}}{\text{hyp.}}$

Right Triangles and Trigonometry

Chapter 7 Highlights

PROBLEM SOLVING

- **Mixed Review of Problem Solving,** 465, 492
- **Multiple Representations,** 439, 480, 481, 488
- **Multi-Step Problems,** 438, 445, 456, 463, 465, 471, 479, 488, 492
- **Using Alternative Methods,** 481
- **Real-World Problem Solving Examples,** 434, 443, 450, 452, 459, 460, 468, 474, 475, 476, 485

★ ASSESSMENT

- **Standardized Test Practice Examples,** 434, 458
- **Multiple Choice,** 437, 438, 444, 454, 461, 462, 470, 478, 486, 487, 500
- **Short Response/Extended Response,** 438, 439, 446, 447, 455, 456, 463, 464, 465, 471, 472, 479, 487, 488, 492
- **Writing/Open-Ended,** 436, 444, 445, 453, 461, 462, 469, 477, 478, 485, 487, 488

TECHNOLOGY

At classzone.com:

- **Animated Geometry,** 431, 434, 442, 450, 460, 462, 475
- **@Home Tutor,** 430, 438, 440, 445, 455, 463, 471, 479, 487, 494
- **Online Quiz,** 439, 447, 456, 464, 472, 480, 489
- **Animated Algebra,** 499
- **State Test Practice,** 465, 492, 503

Unit 3
Figures in the Plane

Polygon Angle Sum, p. 512
$(n-2) \cdot 180°$

Quadrilaterals

Chapter 8 Summary

Chapter 8 focuses on properties of **special quadrilaterals** and on **angle measures in polygons**. In the first lesson, students develop and justify theorems about the **interior and exterior angle measures** of polygons, using these theorems to solve problems. In subsequent lessons, students **classify quadrilaterals** by their properties. They use properties of **parallelograms** to solve problems, and also prove that quadrilaterals are parallelograms. They move on to classifying **rectangles, rhombuses, squares, trapezoids, and kites**. In the concluding lesson of the chapter, students synthesize what they have learned about classifying special quadrilaterals.

Extension

8.5 **Draw Three-Dimensional Figures** (pp. 550–551)

Chapter 8 Highlights

PROBLEM SOLVING

- **Mixed Review of Problem Solving,** 532, 558
- **Multiple Representations,** 513, 530
- **Multi-Step Problems,** 512, 532, 539, 556, 558
- **Using Alternative Methods,** 530
- **Real-World Problem Solving Examples,** 510, 517, 523, 524, 536, 543, 545

★ ASSESSMENT

- **Standardized Test Practice Examples,** 509, 517, 553
- **Multiple Choice,** 511, 518, 519, 527, 538, 546, 547, 554, 566
- **Short Response/Extended Response,** 511, 513, 519, 526, 529, 532, 538, 540, 547, 548, 556, 558
- **Writing/Open-Ended,** 510, 518, 520, 526, 537, 546, 554, 558

TECHNOLOGY

At classzone.com:

- **Animated Geometry,** 505, 509, 519, 527, 535, 545, 551, 553
- **@Home Tutor,** 504, 512, 514, 520, 528, 539, 541, 548, 556, 560
- **Online Quiz,** 513, 521, 529, 540, 549, 557
- **Animated Algebra,** 565
- **State Test Practice,** 532, 558, 569

Chapter 9 Summary

Chapter 9 focuses on **transformations**. In the first lesson, the presentation of **transformations** introduces key vocabulary such as **image**, **preimage**, and **isometry**. Subsequent lessons cover **reflections**, **rotations**, **dilations**, and **compositions** of transformations. Students use **coordinate rules** for transformations and apply what they have learned to problem solving situations. A lesson on symmetry focuses on identifying **line symmetry and rotational symmetry**. In addition, the chapter introduces **matrix operations** and **vectors** as tools that students can use for transformations.

Extension

9.5 **Tessellations** (pp. 616–618)

CHAPTER 9

Unit 3 Figures in the Plane

Identifying Transformations, p. 595
$(a, b) \rightarrow (a, -b)$

Properties of Transformations

Chapter 9 Highlights

PROBLEM SOLVING

- **Mixed Review of Problem Solving,** 597, 634
- **Multiple Representations,** 606
- **Multi-Step Problems,** 577, 579, 586, 597, 605, 615, 624, 631, 634
- **Using Alternative Methods,** 606
- **Real-World Problem Solving Examples,** 575, 583, 591

★ ASSESSMENT

- **Standardized Test Practice Examples,** 601, 621
- **Multiple Choice,** 576, 584, 585, 593, 603, 613, 622, 630
- **Short Response/Extended Response,** 578, 586, 594, 596, 597, 603, 605, 614, 623, 630, 634, 642
- **Writing/Open-Ended,** 576, 584, 585, 593, 597, 602, 611, 613, 621, 623, 629, 630, 631, 634

TECHNOLOGY

At classzone.com:

- **Animated Geometry,** 571, 582, 590, 599, 602, 611, 617, 619, 626
- **@Home Tutor,** 570, 578, 586, 595, 604, 607, 613, 623, 631, 633, 636
- **Online Quiz,** 579, 587, 596, 605, 615, 624, 632
- **Animated Algebra,** 641
- **State Test Practice,** 597, 634, 645

CHAPTER 10

Unit 4 Circles and Measurement

Tangents and Secants, p. 692
$DC \cdot DB = AD^2$

Properties of Circles

Chapter 10 Highlights

PROBLEM SOLVING

- **Mixed Review of Problem Solving,** 687, 706
- **Multiple Representations,** 696
- **Multi-Step Problems,** 669, 687, 706
- **Using Alternative Methods,** 696
- **Real-World Problem Solving Examples,** 660, 665, 674, 682, 692, 701

★ ASSESSMENT

- **Standardized Test Practice Examples,** 673, 690
- **Multiple Choice,** 656, 662, 667, 677, 683, 693, 702, 703, 714
- **Short Response/Extended Response,** 657, 662, 663, 678, 684, 685, 687, 694, 695, 704, 706
- **Writing/Open-Ended,** 655, 661, 667, 668, 669, 676, 678, 683, 684, 687, 692, 702

TECHNOLOGY

At classzone.com:

- **Animated Geometry,** 649, 655, 661, 671, 682, 691, 701
- **@Home Tutor,** 648, 657, 663, 669, 677, 685, 688, 694, 703, 704, 708
- **Online Quiz,** 658, 663, 670, 679, 686, 695, 705
- **Animated Algebra,** 713
- **State Test Practice,** 687, 706, 717

Chapter 10 Summary

Chapter 10 focuses on using various properties of circles. Students identify **tangents, chords, and secants of circles and use them to solve problems**. Students also find **arc measures in circles** and use **properties of chords** to solve problems. Properties of **inscribed angles** and **inscribed polygons** are covered in the chapter, as are properties of other angles in circles and **lengths of segments** in circles. Throughout, students have the opportunity to justify the theorems that are presented and to apply them in problem solving situations. The chapter concludes with a lesson on **writing and graphing equations of circles**.

Extension

10.6 **Draw a Locus** (pp. 697–698)

Chapter 11 Summary

Chapter 11 focuses on measuring plane figures. Students **justify** the formulas for the **areas of triangles, parallelograms, rectangles, rhombuses,** and **kites,** using them to solve problems, including many that involve **rates**. Students also justify and apply formulas for finding the **area and circumference of a circle,** and for finding **arc lengths** and **areas of sectors**. The Pythagorean Theorem and trigonometry are applied as students find **areas and perimeters of regular polygons**. Problems involving **composite figures** are included throughout the chapter, and a lesson is devoted to perimeters and areas of **similar figures**. The chapter concludes with a lesson on **geometric probability**.

Extensions

11.1 **Determine Precision and Accuracy** (pp. 727–728)

11.4 **Geometry on a Sphere** (pp. 753–754)

CHAPTER 11

Unit 4 Circles and Measurement

Arc Length, p. 749

$2(84.39) + 2\left(\frac{1}{2} \cdot 2\pi \cdot 36.8\right)$

Measuring Length and Area

Chapter 11 Highlights

PROBLEM SOLVING

- **Mixed Review of Problem Solving,** 745, 778
- **Multiple Representations,** 744
- **Multi-Step Problems,** 726, 735, 742, 745, 778
- **Using Alternative Methods,** 744
- **Real-World Problem Solving Examples,** 722, 730, 738, 739, 747, 749, 763, 772, 773, 785

★ ASSESSMENT

- **Standardized Test Practice Examples,** 732, 738, 757
- **Multiple Choice,** 724, 733, 740, 742, 751, 759, 765, 775
- **Short Response/Extended Response,** 725, 726, 735, 736, 741, 743, 745, 751, 752, 760, 766, 768, 776, 778, 786
- **Writing/Open-Ended,** 723, 724, 733, 734, 740, 743, 745, 749, 758, 765, 774, 778

TECHNOLOGY

At classzone.com:

- **Animated Geometry,** 719, 720, 739, 749, 759, 765, 771
- **@Home Tutor,** 718, 725, 735, 742, 751, 760, 767, 769, 776, 780
- **Online Quiz,** 726, 736, 743, 752, 761, 768, 777
- **Animated Algebra,** 785
- **State Test Practice,** 745, 778, 789

CHAPTER

12

Unit 4

Circles and Measurement

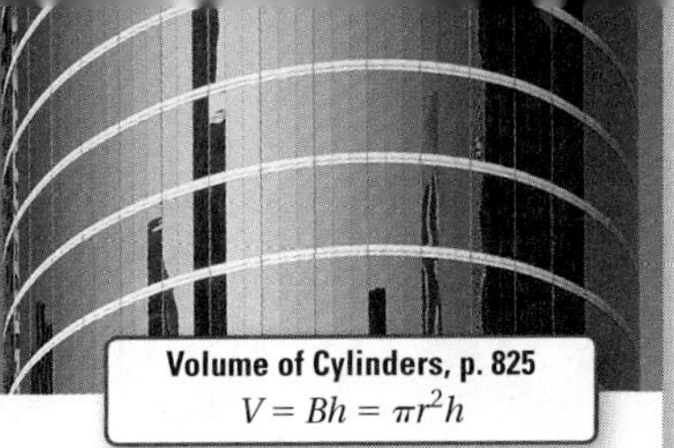

Surface Area and Volume of Solids

Chapter 12 Highlights

PROBLEM SOLVING

- **Mixed Review of Problem Solving,** 818, 855
- **Multiple Representations,** 826, 835, 853
- **Multi-Step Problems,** 800, 809, 816, 818, 824, 835, 844, 852, 855
- **Using Alternative Methods,** 826
- **Real-World Problem Solving Examples,** 796, 805, 813, 822, 831, 840, 848, 849

★ ASSESSMENT

- **Standardized Test Practice Examples,** 813, 839
- **Multiple Choice,** 799, 807, 808, 815, 822, 824, 832, 833, 842, 843, 850, 851, 862
- **Short Response/Extended Response,** 800, 808, 809, 816, 818, 825, 834, 844, 853, 855
- **Writing/Open-Ended,** 798, 806, 814, 818, 822, 832, 842, 850, 852

TECHNOLOGY

At classzone.com:

- **Animated Geometry,** 791, 795, 805, 821, 825, 833, 841, 852
- **@Home Tutor,** 790, 800, 808, 816, 824, 834, 837, 844, 852, 857
- **Online Quiz,** 801, 809, 817, 825, 836, 845, 854
- **State Test Practice,** 818, 855, 865

Chapter 12 Summary

Chapter 12 focuses on identifying, describing, and measuring solids. Students classify and sketch solids, describe **cross sections,** and apply **Euler's Theorem**. Work with **nets** reinforces ideas about **surface area,** so that students are able to justify and apply formulas. They also justify formulas for **volume** and have many opportunities for solving problems. Solids covered in the chapter include **prisms, cylinders, pyramids, cones,** and **spheres,** as well as **composite solids**. The chapter concludes with a lesson on surface area and volume of **similar solids.**

Contents of Student Resources

Using Your Textbook

Your textbook contains many resources that you can use for reference when you are studying or doing your homework.

IN EVERY CHAPTER

BIG IDEAS The second page of every chapter includes a list of important ideas developed in the chapter. More information about these ideas appears in the Chapter Summary page at the end of the chapter.

POSTULATES AND THEOREMS The Postulate and Theorem notebook displays present geometric properties you will use in reasoning about figures. You may want to copy these statements into your notes.

KEY CONCEPTS The Key Concept notebook displays present main ideas of the lesson. You may want to copy these ideas into your notes.

VOCABULARY New words and review words are listed in a column on the first page of every lesson. Vocabulary terms appear highlighted and in bold print within the lesson. A list of vocabulary appears in the Chapter Review at the end of each chapter.

MIXED REVIEW Every lesson ends with Mixed Review exercises. These exercises help you review earlier lessons and include exercises to prepare you for the next lesson. Page references with the exercises point you to the lessons being reviewed.

STUDENT RESOURCES AT THE BACK OF THE BOOK

- **SKILLS REVIEW HANDBOOK** Use the Skills Review Handbook topics on pages 869–895 to review material learned in previous courses.
- **EXTRA PRACTICE** Use the Extra Practice on pages 896–919 for more exercises or to review a chapter before a test.
- **TABLES** Refer to the tables on pages 920–925 for information about mathematical symbols, measures, formulas, squares, and trigonometric ratios.
- **POSTULATES AND THEOREMS** Refer to pages 926–931 for a complete list of all postulates and theorems presented in the book.
- **ADDITIONAL PROOFS** Refer to pages 932–938 for longer proofs of some of the theorems presented in the book.
- **GLOSSARY** Use the English-Spanish Glossary on pages 939–980 to see definitions in English and Spanish, as well as examples illustrating vocabulary.
- **INDEX** Look up items in the alphabetical Index on pages 981–1000 to find where a particular math topic is covered in the book.
- **WORKED-OUT SOLUTIONS** In each lesson, exercises identified by a red circle have complete worked-out solutions starting on page WS1. These provide a model for what a full solution should include.
- **SELECTED ANSWERS** Use the Selected Answers starting on page SA1 to check your work.

McDougal Littell

GEOMETRY

Where great lessons begin

- Engages students in active learning
- Adaptable to different teaching styles and student abilities
- Ongoing assessment integrated with instruction

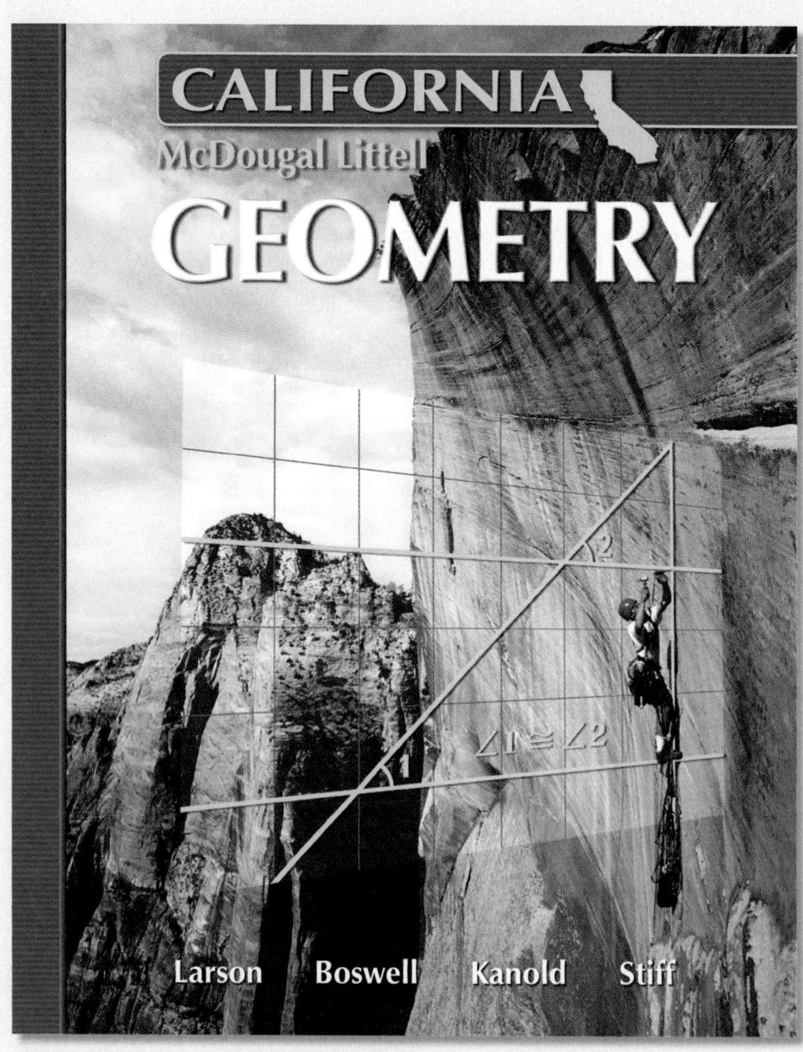

3 Parallel and Perpendicular Lines

Before

In previous chapters, you learned the following skills, which you'll use in Chapter 3: describing angle pairs, using properties and postulates, using angle pair relationships, and sketching a diagram.

Prerequisite Skills

VOCABULARY CHECK

Copy and complete the statement.

1. Adjacent angles share a common _?_.
2. Two angles are _?_ angles if the sum of their measures is 180°.

SKILLS AND ALGEBRA CHECK

The midpoint of $\overline{AB}$ is M. Find AB. *(Review p. 15 for 3.2.)*

3. $AM = 5x - 2$, $MB = 2x + 7$
4. $AM = 4z + 1$, $MB = 6z - 11$

Find the measure of each numbered angle. *(Review p. 124 for 3.2, 3.3.)*

5. 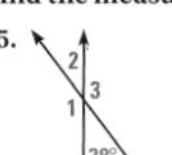

6. 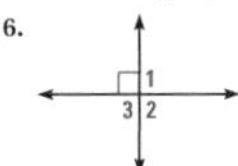

7. 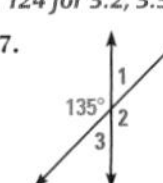

Sketch a diagram for each statement. *(Review pp. 2, 96 for 3.3.)*

8. $\overleftrightarrow{QR}$ is perpendicular to $\overleftrightarrow{WX}$.
9. Lines m and n intersect at point P.

@HomeTutor Prerequisite skills practice at classzone.com

Now

In Chapter 3, you will apply the big ideas listed below and reviewed in the Chapter Summary on page 201. You will also use the key vocabulary listed below.

Big Ideas

1. Using properties of parallel and perpendicular lines
2. Proving relationships using angle measures
3. Making connections to lines in algebra

KEY VOCABULARY

- parallel lines, *p. 147*
- skew lines, *p. 147*
- parallel planes, *p. 147*
- transversal, *p. 149*
- corresponding angles, *p. 149*
- alternate interior angles, *p. 149*
- alternate exterior angles, *p. 149*
- consecutive interior angles, *p. 149*
- paragraph proof, *p. 163*
- slope, *p. 171*
- slope-intercept form, *p. 180*
- standard form, *p. 182*
- distance from a point to a line, *p. 192*

Why?

You can use slopes of lines to determine steepness of lines. For example, you can compare the slopes of roller coasters to determine which is steeper.

Animated Geometry

The animation illustrated below for Example 5 on page 174 helps you answer this question: How steep is a roller coaster?

A roller coaster track rises a given distance over a given horizontal distance.

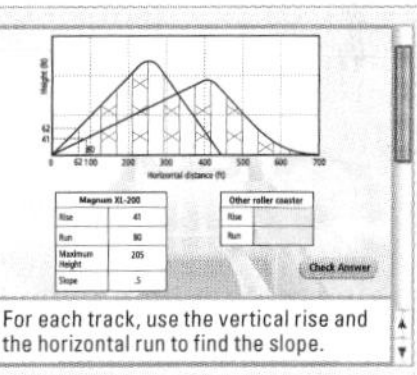

For each track, use the vertical rise and the horizontal run to find the slope.

Animated Geometry at classzone.com

Other animations for Chapter 3: pages 148, 155, 163, and 181

Animated Geometry

Animated Geometry includes interactive electronic activities that provide insights into both the how and the why of math.

- Each chapter opens with an animated activity related to a real-world problem in the chapter.
- Throughout the chapter, additional activities support and extend specific examples and exercises, providing opportunities to investigate geometric relationships and develop strong reasoning skills.

Meeting Student Needs

Clear Instruction

New concepts and methods are presented using clear, student-friendly language and visuals, and examples are carefully stepped out for easier understanding. Vocabulary and key ideas are highlighted.

Connect

New topics are related to what students have already studied and are applied to real-world problems.

Guide

Students are made aware of other solution methods, vocabulary connections, common errors, and so on.

11.2 Areas of Trapezoids, Rhombuses, and Kites

Before You found areas of triangles and parallelograms.
Now You will find areas of other types of quadrilaterals.
Why? So you can solve a problem in sports, as in Example 1.

Key Vocabulary
- **height of a trapezoid**
- **diagonal,** *p. 507*
- **bases of a trapezoid,** *p. 542*

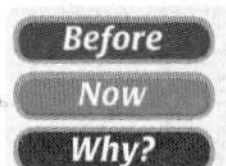
Standards

8.0 Students know, derive, and solve problems involving the perimeter, circumference, **area**, volume, lateral area, and surface area **of common geometric figures.**

10.0 Students compute areas of polygons, including rectangles, scalene triangles, equilateral triangles, **rhombi**, parallelograms, **and trapezoids.**

As you saw in the Activity on page 729, you can use the area formula for a parallelogram to develop area formulas for other special quadrilaterals. The areas of the figures below are related to the lengths of the marked segments.

The **height of a trapezoid** is the perpendicular distance between its bases.

Trapezoid

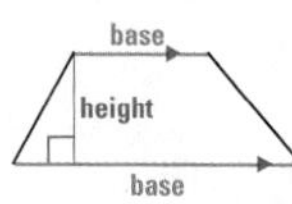

Kite

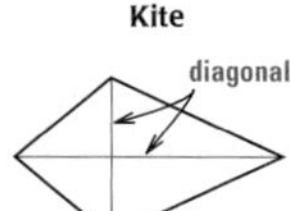

Rhombus

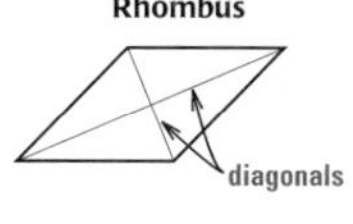

THEOREM *For Your Notebook*

THEOREM 11.4 Area of a Trapezoid

The area of a trapezoid is one half the product of the height and the sum of the lengths of the bases.

Proof: Ex. 40, p. 736

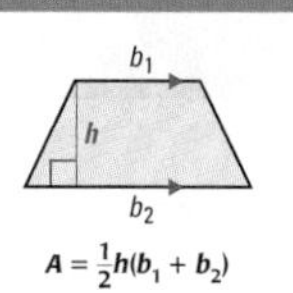

$A = \frac{1}{2}h(b_1 + b_2)$

EXAMPLE 1 Find the area of a trapezoid

BASKETBALL The free-throw lane on an international basketball court is shaped like a trapezoid. Find the area of the free-throw lane.

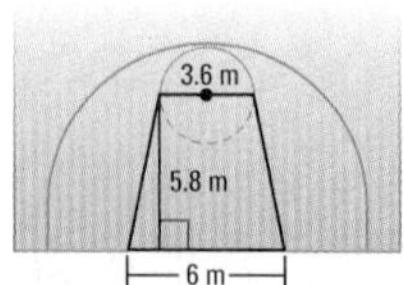

ANOTHER WAY
In a trapezoid, the average of the lengths of the bases is also the length of the midsegment. So, you can also find the area by multiplying the midsegment by the height.

Solution

The height of the trapezoid is 5.8 meters. The lengths of the bases are 3.6 meters and 6 meters.

$A = \frac{1}{2}h(b_1 + b_2)$ **Formula for area of a trapezoid**

$= \frac{1}{2}(5.8)(3.6 + 6)$ **Substitute 5.8 for h, 3.6 for b_1, and 6 for b_2.**

$= 27.84$ **Simplify.**

▸ The area of the free-throw lane is about 27.8 square meters.

730 Chapter 11 Measuring Length and Area

EXAMPLE 2 Find the length of the altitude to the hypotenuse

SWIMMING POOL The diagram below shows a cross-section of a swimming pool. What is the maximum depth of the pool?

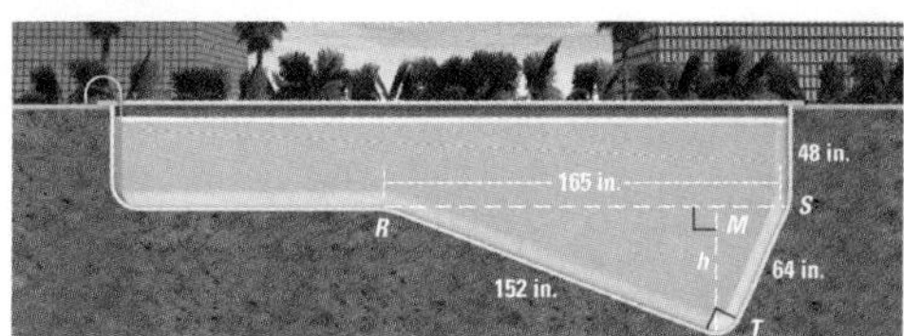

Solution

STEP 1 **Identify** the similar triangles and sketch them.

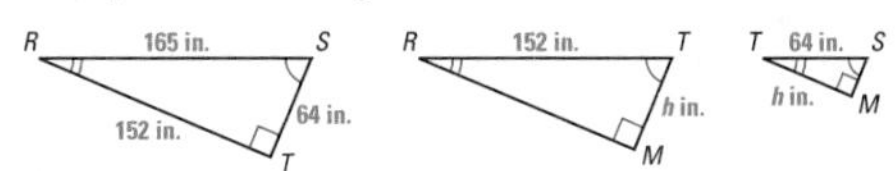

$\triangle RST \sim \triangle RTM \sim \triangle TSM$

AVOID ERRORS
Notice that if you tried to write a proportion using $\triangle RTM$ and $\triangle TSM$, there would be two unknowns, so you would not be able to solve for h.

STEP 2 **Find** the value of h. Use the fact that $\triangle RST \sim \triangle RTM$ to write a proportion.

$\frac{TM}{ST} = \frac{TR}{SR}$ Corresponding side lengths of similar triangles a...

$\frac{h}{64} = \frac{152}{165}$ Substitute.

$165h = 64(152)$ Cross Products Pr...

$h \approx 59$ Solve for h.

STEP 3 **Read** the diagram above. You can ... the pool is $h + 48$, which is about ...

▶ The maximum depth of the pool is about ...

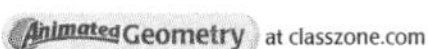
Animated Geometry at classzone.com

✓ GUIDED PRACTICE for Examples 1 and 2

Identify the similar triangles. Then find th...

1. $\triangle EGF$

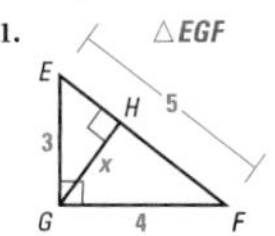

AUXILIARY LINES To prove certain theorems, you may need to add a line, a segment, or a ray to a given diagram. An *auxiliary* line is used in the proof of the Triangle Sum Theorem.

PROOF Triangle Sum Theorem

GIVEN ▶ $\triangle ABC$

PROVE ▶ $m\angle 1 + m\angle 2 + m\angle 3 = 180°$

Plan for Proof
a. Draw an auxiliary line through B and parallel to $\overline{AC}$.
b. Show that $m\angle 4 + m\angle 2 + m\angle 5 = 180°$, $\angle 1 \cong \angle 4$, and $\angle 3 \cong \angle 5$.
c. By substitution, $m\angle 1 + m\angle 2 + m\angle 3 = 180°$.

Plan in Action

	STATEMENTS	REASONS
a.	1. Draw $\overleftrightarrow{BD}$ parallel to $\overline{AC}$.	1. Parallel Postulate
b.	2. $m\angle 4 + m\angle 2 + m\angle 5 = 180°$	2. Angle Addition Postulate and definition of straight angle
	3. $\angle 1 \cong \angle 4$, $\angle 3 \cong \angle 5$	3. Alternate Interior Angles Theorem
	4. $m\angle 1 = m\angle 4$, $m\angle 3 = m\angle 5$	4. Definition of congruent angles
c.	5. $m\angle 1 + m\angle 2 + m\angle 3 = 180°$	5. Substitution Property of Equality

THEOREM *For Your Notebook*

THEOREM 4.2 Exterior Angle Theorem

The measure of an exterior angle of a triangle is equal to the sum of the measures of the two nonadjacent interior angles.

Proof: Ex. 50, p. 223

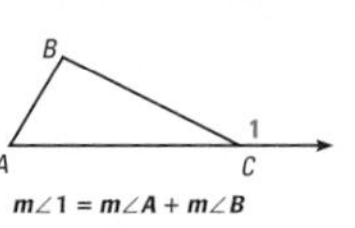

EXAMPLE 3 Find an angle measure

ALGEBRA Find $m\angle JKM$.

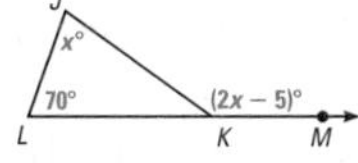

Solution

STEP 1 **Write** and solve an equation to find the value of x.

$(2x - 5)° = 70° + x°$ Apply the Exterior Angle Theorem.

$x = 75$ Solve for x.

STEP 2 **Substitute** 75 for x in $2x - 5$ to find $m\angle JKM$.

$2x - 5 = 2 \cdot 75 - 5 = 145$

▶ The measure of $\angle JKM$ is 145°.

Model
Stepped-out examples model how to interpret diagrams and solve word problems.

Reason
Building from experience with informal reasoning, students learn to plan and write formal proofs.

Varied, Leveled Practice

The wide variety of skill and problem solving exercises is carefully paced, ensuring that students build skills and feel confident about their work. The @Home Tutor and Animated Geometry features provide additional support.

Support
Exercises are correlated to examples, providing homework support and fostering independent student learning.

Analyze
Error analysis exercises give students the opportunity to analyze mathematical thinking.

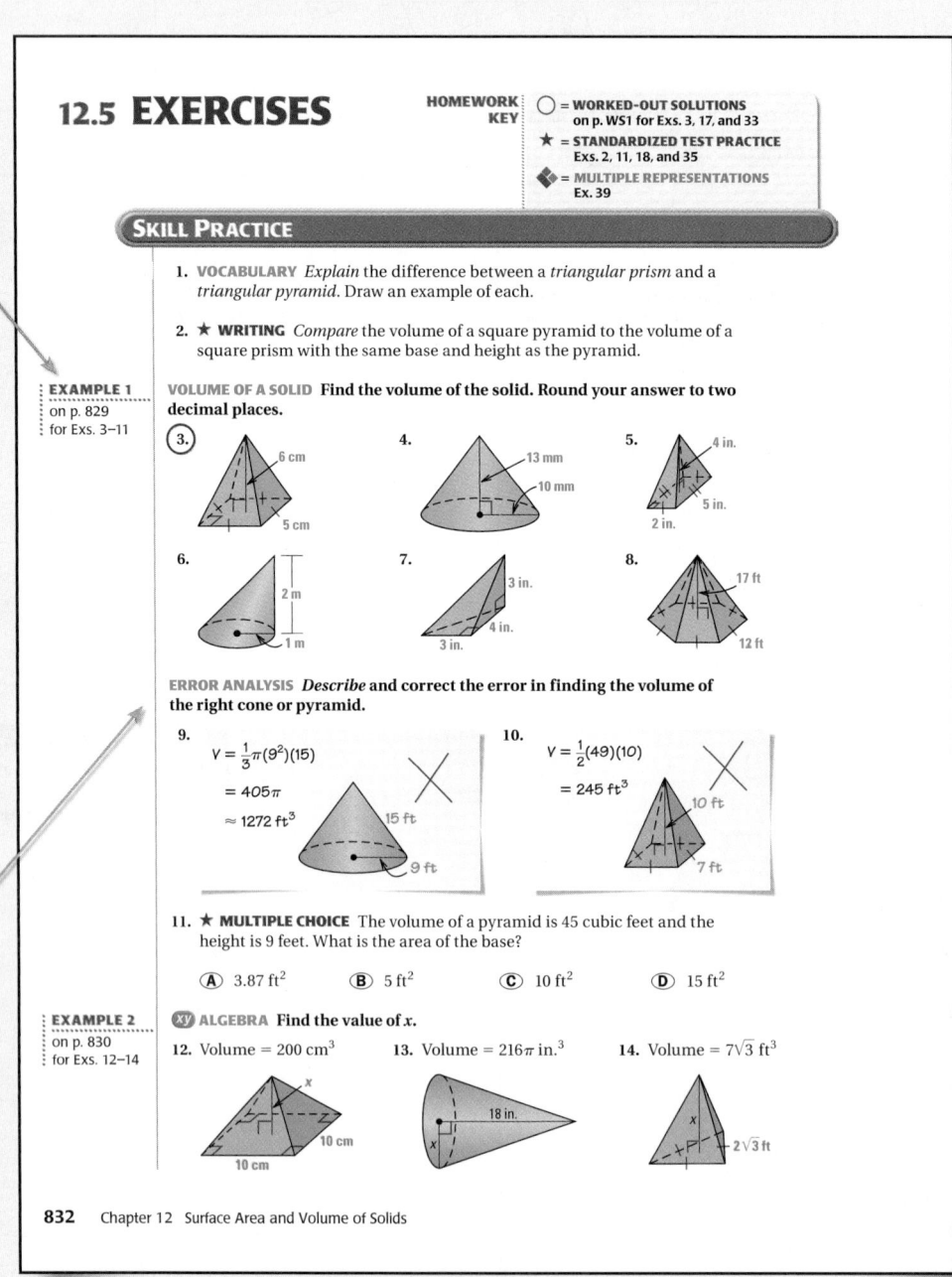

12.5 EXERCISES

HOMEWORK KEY
○ = WORKED-OUT SOLUTIONS on p. WS1 for Exs. 3, 17, and 33
★ = STANDARDIZED TEST PRACTICE Exs. 2, 11, 18, and 35
◆ = MULTIPLE REPRESENTATIONS Ex. 39

SKILL PRACTICE

1. VOCABULARY *Explain* the difference between a *triangular prism* and a *triangular pyramid*. Draw an example of each.

2. ★ WRITING *Compare* the volume of a square pyramid to the volume of a square prism with the same base and height as the pyramid.

EXAMPLE 1 on p. 829 for Exs. 3–11

VOLUME OF A SOLID **Find the volume of the solid. Round your answer to two decimal places.**

3. 6 cm; 5 cm
4. 13 mm; 10 mm
5. 4 in.; 5 in.; 2 in.
6. 2 m; 1 m
7. 3 in.; 4 in.; 3 in.
8. 17 ft; 12 ft

ERROR ANALYSIS *Describe* **and correct the error in finding the volume of the right cone or pyramid.**

9. $V = \frac{1}{3}\pi(9^2)(15)$
$= 405\pi$
$\approx 1272 \text{ ft}^3$
15 ft; 9 ft

10. $V = \frac{1}{2}(49)(10)$
$= 245 \text{ ft}^3$
10 ft; 7 ft

11. ★ MULTIPLE CHOICE The volume of a pyramid is 45 cubic feet and the height is 9 feet. What is the area of the base?

Ⓐ 3.87 ft^2 Ⓑ 5 ft^2 Ⓒ 10 ft^2 Ⓓ 15 ft^2

EXAMPLE 2 on p. 830 for Exs. 12–14

ALGEBRA **Find the value of x.**

12. Volume = 200 cm^3 — x; 10 cm; 10 cm
13. Volume = $216\pi \text{ in.}^3$ — 18 in.; x
14. Volume = $7\sqrt{3} \text{ ft}^3$ — x; $2\sqrt{3}$ ft

832 Chapter 12 Surface Area and Volume of Solids

24. CHALLENGE A plane parallel to the base of a cone divides the cone into two pieces with the dimensions shown. Find each ratio described.

a. The area of the top shaded circle to the area of the bottom shaded circle

b. The slant height of the top part of the cone to the slant height of the whole cone

c. The lateral area of the top part of the cone to the lateral area of the whole cone

d. The volume of the top part of the cone to the volume of the whole cone

e. The volume of the top part of the cone to the volume of the bottom part

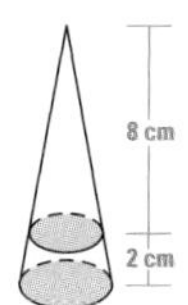

Challenge

Students with strong abilities find challenging skill and problem solving exercises in every lesson.

PROBLEM SOLVING

EXAMPLE 4 on p. 849 for Exs. 25–27

25. **COFFEE MUGS** The heights of two similar coffee mugs are 3.5 inches and 4 inches. The larger mug holds 12 fluid ounces. What is the capacity of the smaller mug?

@HomeTutor for problem solving help at classzone.com

26. **ARCHITECTURE** You have a pair of binoculars that is similar in shape to the structure on page 847. Your binoculars are 6 inches high, and the height of the structure is 45 feet. Find the ratio of the volume of your binoculars to the volume of the structure.

@HomeTutor for problem solving help at classzone.com

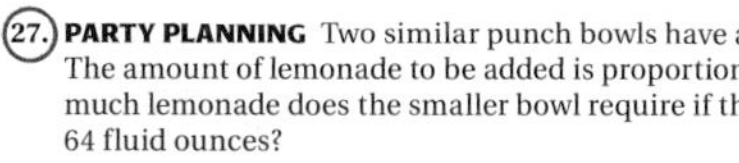

(27.) **PARTY PLANNING** Two similar punch bowls have a The amount of lemonade to be added is proportion much lemonade does the smaller bowl require if th 64 fluid ounces?

28. ★ **OPEN-ENDED MATH** Using the scale factor 2 : 5, s in the correct proportions. Label the dimensions of

29. MULTI-STEP PROBLEM Two oranges are both sphe 3.2 inches and 4 inches. The skin on both oranges h thickness of $\frac{1}{8}$ inch.

a. Find the volume of each unpeeled orange.

b. *Compare* the ratio of the diameters to the ratio o

c. Find the diameter of each orange after being pe

d. *Compare* the ratio of surface areas of the peeled the volumes of the peeled oranges.

Animated Geometry at classzone.com

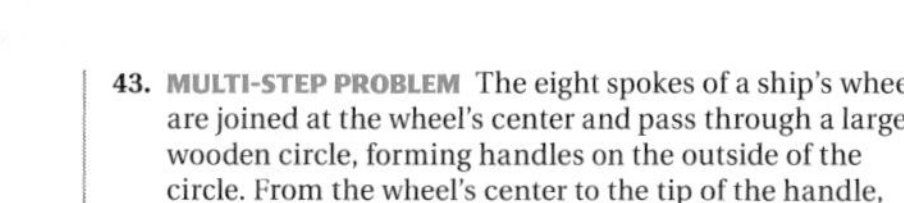

43. MULTI-STEP PROBLEM The eight spokes of a ship's wheel are joined at the wheel's center and pass through a large wooden circle, forming handles on the outside of the circle. From the wheel's center to the tip of the handle, each spoke is 21 inches long.

a. The circumference of the outer edge of the large wooden circle is 94 inches. Find the radius of the outer edge of the circle to the nearest inch.

b. Find the length x of a handle on the wheel. *Explain.*

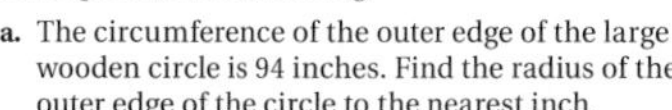

44. ◆ MULTIPLE REPRESENTATIONS Let x represent the length of a side of a square. Let y_1 and y_2 represent the perimeter and area of that square.

a. **Making a Table** Copy and complete the table.

Length, x	1	2	5	10	25
Perimeter, y_1	?	?	?	?	?
Area, y_2	?	?	?	?	?

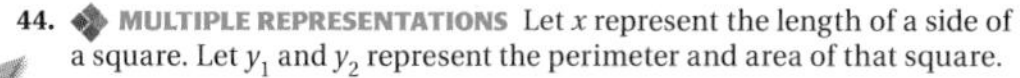

b. **Making a Graph** Use the completed table to write two sets of ordered pairs: (x, y_1) and (x, y_2). Graph each set of ordered pairs.

c. **Analyzing Data** *Describe* any patterns you see in the table from part (a) and in the graphs from part (b).

45. ★ **EXTENDED RESPONSE** The photograph at the right shows the Crown Fountain in Chicago, Illinois. At this fountain, images of faces appear on a large screen. The images are created by light-emitting diodes (LEDs) that are clustered in groups called modules. The LED modules are arranged in a rectangular grid.

a. The rectangular grid is approximately 7 meters wide and 15.2 meters high. Find the area of the grid.

b. Suppose an LED module is a square with a side length of 4 centimeters. How many rows and how many columns of LED modules would be needed to make the Crown Fountain screen? *Explain* your reasoning.

46. ASTRONOMY The diagram shows a gap in Saturn's circular rings. This gap is known as the *Cassini division*. In the diagram, the red circle represents the ring that borders the inside of the Cassini division. The yellow circle represents the ring that borders the outside of the division.

a. The radius of the red ring is 115,800 kilometers. The radius of the yellow ring is 120,600 kilometers. Find the circumference of the red ring and the circumference of the yellow ring. Round your answers to the nearest hundred kilometers.

b. Compare the circumferences of the two rings. About how many kilometers greater is the yellow ring's circumference than the red ring's circumference?

Represent

By representing problems in more than one way, students make important mathematical connections.

Explain

Concepts and writing skills are developed through exercises that ask students to explain their reasoning.

Focused Review

Throughout each chapter, carefully coordinated summaries and reviews focus on key concepts, vocabulary, and problem solving skills.

Synthesize
"Big ideas" introduced at the beginning of each chapter and reinforced in the chapter summary help students synthesize what they have learned.

Organize
Tables, charts, and visuals help students organize their thinking about mathematical concepts.

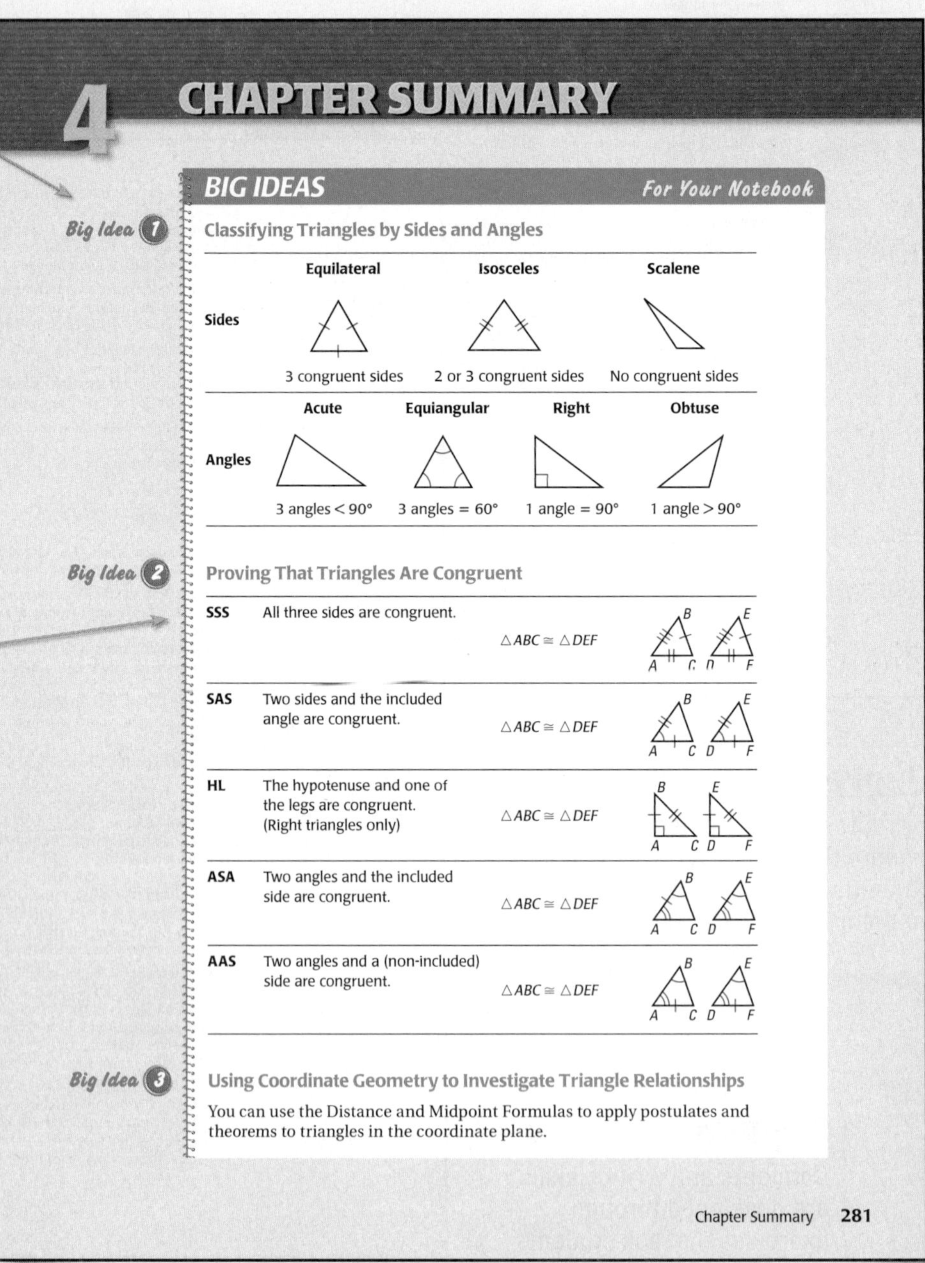
4 CHAPTER SUMMARY

BIG IDEAS — For Your Notebook

Big Idea 1
Classifying Triangles by Sides and Angles

	Equilateral	Isosceles	Scalene	
Sides	3 congruent sides	2 or 3 congruent sides	No congruent sides	
	Acute	**Equiangular**	**Right**	**Obtuse**
Angles	3 angles < 90°	3 angles = 60°	1 angle = 90°	1 angle > 90°

Big Idea 2
Proving That Triangles Are Congruent

SSS	All three sides are congruent.	$\triangle ABC \cong \triangle DEF$
SAS	Two sides and the included angle are congruent.	$\triangle ABC \cong \triangle DEF$
HL	The hypotenuse and one of the legs are congruent. (Right triangles only)	$\triangle ABC \cong \triangle DEF$
ASA	Two angles and the included side are congruent.	$\triangle ABC \cong \triangle DEF$
AAS	Two angles and a (non-included) side are congruent.	$\triangle ABC \cong \triangle DEF$

Big Idea 3
Using Coordinate Geometry to Investigate Triangle Relationships

You can use the Distance and Midpoint Formulas to apply postulates and theorems to triangles in the coordinate plane.

Chapter Summary 281

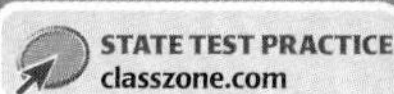

MIXED REVIEW of Problem Solving

STATE TEST PRACTICE classzone.com

Lessons 6.4–6.7

1. **OPEN-ENDED** The diagram shows the front of a house. What information would you need in order to show that $\triangle WXY \sim \triangle VXZ$ using the SAS Similarity Theorem?

2. **EXTENDED RESPONSE** You leave your house to go to the mall. You drive due north 8 miles, due east 7.5 miles, and due north again 2 miles.

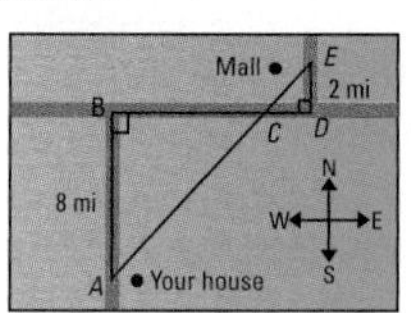

a. *Explain* how to prove that $\triangle ABC \sim \triangle EDC$.

b. Find CD.

c. Find AE, the distance between your house and the mall.

3. **SHORT RESPONSE** The Cardon cactus found in the Sonoran Desert in Mexico is the tallest type of cactus in the world. Marco stands 76 feet from the cactus so that his shadow coincides with the cactus' shadow. Marco is 6 feet tall and his shadow is 8 feet long. How tall is the Cardon cactus? *Explain.*

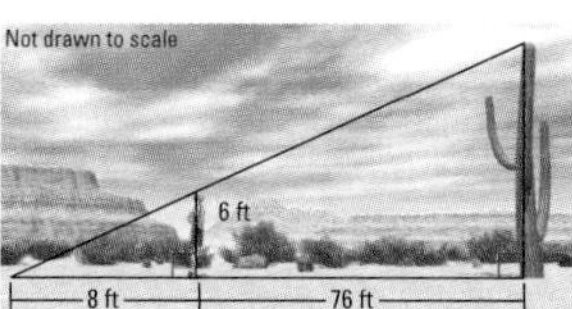

4. **SHORT RESPONSE** In the diagram, is it *always, sometimes,* or *never* true that $l_1 \parallel l_2 \parallel l_3$? *Explain.*

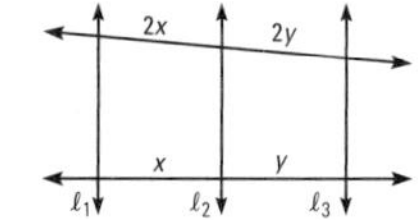

5. **GRIDDED ANSWER** In the diagram of the roof truss, $HK = 7$ meters, $KM = 8$ meters, $JL = 4.7$ meters, and $\angle 1 \cong \angle 2$. Find LM to the nearest tenth of a meter.

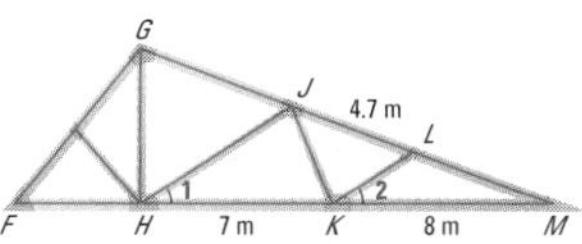

6. **GRIDDED ANSWER** You are designing a catalog for a greeting card company. The catalog features a $2\frac{4}{5}$ inch by

Reinforce

Mixed problem sets covering several lessons reinforce students' problem solving skills.

12 CHAPTER REVIEW

12.6 Surface Area and Volume of Spheres

pp. 838–845

EXAMPLE

Find the surface area of the sphere.

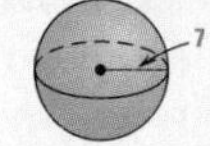

$S = 4\pi r^2$ **Write formula.**

$= 4\pi(7)^2$ **Substitute 7 for *r*.**

$= 196\pi$ **Simplify.**

▶ The surface area of the sphere is 196π, or about 615.75 square meters.

EXERCISES

EXAMPLES 1, 4, and 5 on pp. 839, 841 for Exs. 18–19

18. **ASTRONOMY** The shape of Pluto can be approximated as a sphere of diameter 2390 kilometers. Find the surface area and volume of Pluto. Round your answer to two decimal places.

19. A solid is composed of a cube with side length 6 meters and a hemisphere with diameter 6 meters. Find the volume of the solid. Round your answer to two decimal places.

12.7 Explore Similar Solids

pp. 847–854

EXAMPLE

The cones are similar with a scale factor of 1 : 2. Find the surface area and volume of Cone II given that the surface area of Cone I is 384π square inches and the volume of Cone I is 768π cubic inches.

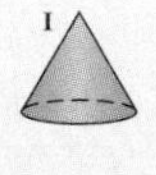

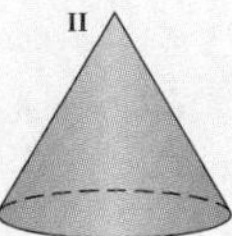

Use Theorem 12.13 to write and solve two proportions.

$\frac{\text{Surface area of I}}{\text{Surface area of II}} = \frac{a^2}{b^2}$ $\qquad$ $\frac{\text{Volume of I}}{\text{Volume of II}} = \frac{a^3}{b^3}$

$\frac{384\pi}{\text{Surface area of II}} = \frac{1^2}{2^2}$ $\qquad$ $\frac{768\pi}{\text{Volume of II}} = \frac{1^3}{2^3}$

Surface area of II $= 1536\pi$ in.^{2} $\qquad$ Volume of II $= 6144\pi$ in.^{3}

▶ The surface area of Cone II is 1536π, or about 4825.48 square inches, and the volume of Cone II is 6144π, or about 19,301.93 cubic inches.

EXERCISES

EXAMPLE 2 on p. 848 for Exs. 20–22

Solid A is similar to Solid B with the given scale factor of A to B. The surface area and volume of Solid A are given. Find the surface area and volume of Solid B.

20. Scale factor of 1 : 4
$S = 62$ cm^2
$V = 30$ cm^3

21. Scale factor of 1 : 3
$S = 112\pi$ m^2
$V = 160\pi$ m^3

22. Scale factor of 2 : 5
$S = 144\pi$ yd^2
$V = 288\pi$ yd^3

Interact

Interactive chapter reviews include examples and review exercises that are correlated to lesson examples.

Differentiating Instruction

Exercises are easily adapted to a range of abilities. For each lesson, both skill and problem solving exercises are labeled A-, B-, and C-level in the teacher's edition.

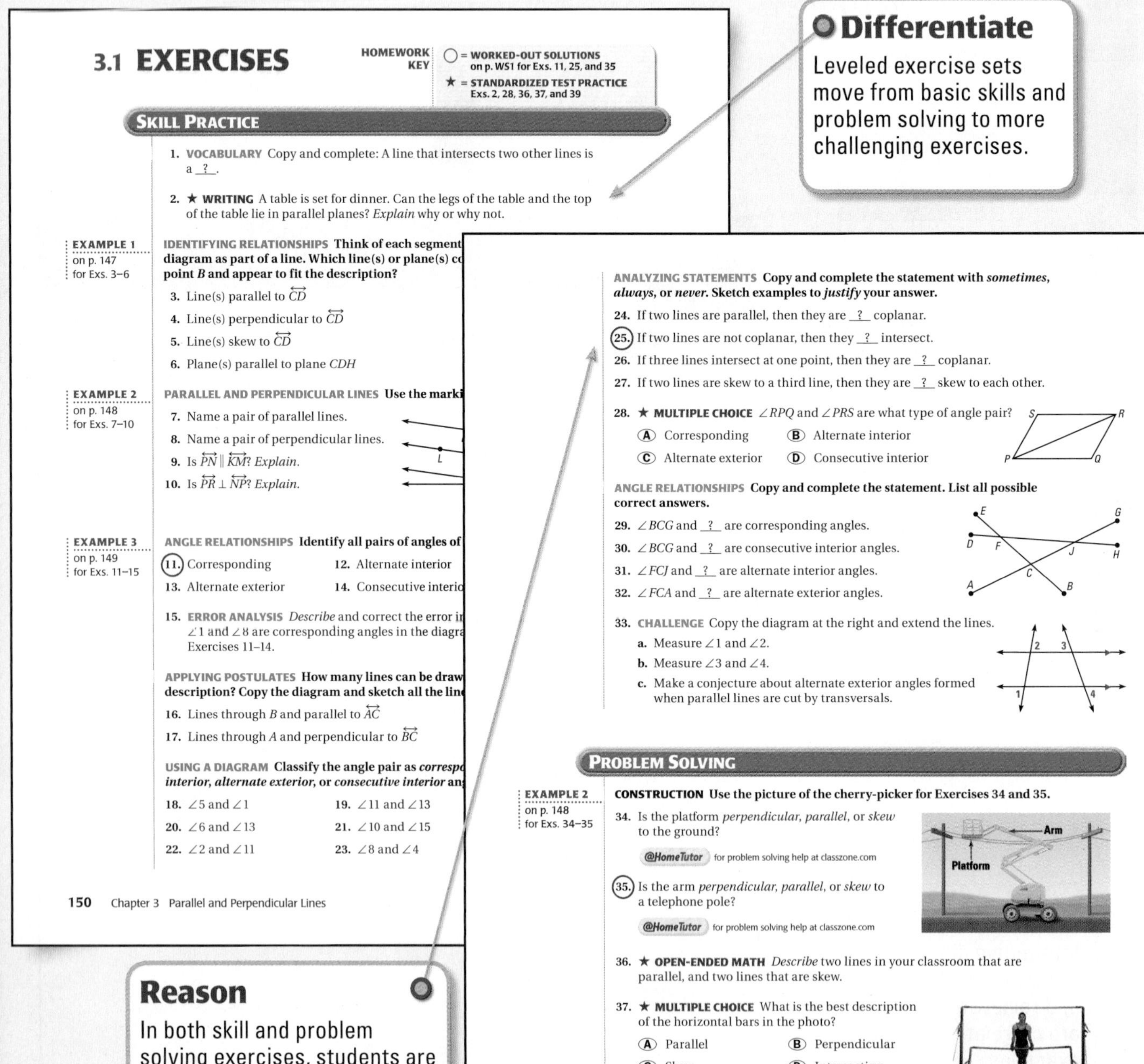

3.1 EXERCISES

HOMEWORK KEY ○ = WORKED-OUT SOLUTIONS on p. WS1 for Exs. 11, 25, and 35
★ = STANDARDIZED TEST PRACTICE Exs. 2, 28, 36, 37, and 39

SKILL PRACTICE

1. **VOCABULARY** Copy and complete: A line that intersects two other lines is a _?_.

2. ★ **WRITING** A table is set for dinner. Can the legs of the table and the top of the table lie in parallel planes? *Explain* why or why not.

EXAMPLE 1 on p. 147 for Exs. 3–6

IDENTIFYING RELATIONSHIPS Think of each segment diagram as part of a line. Which line(s) or plane(s) c point *B* and appear to fit the description?

3. Line(s) parallel to $\overleftrightarrow{CD}$
4. Line(s) perpendicular to $\overleftrightarrow{CD}$
5. Line(s) skew to $\overleftrightarrow{CD}$
6. Plane(s) parallel to plane *CDH*

EXAMPLE 2 on p. 148 for Exs. 7–10

PARALLEL AND PERPENDICULAR LINES Use the marki

7. Name a pair of parallel lines.
8. Name a pair of perpendicular lines.
9. Is $\overleftrightarrow{PN} \parallel \overleftrightarrow{KM}$? *Explain.*
10. Is $\overleftrightarrow{PR} \perp \overleftrightarrow{NP}$? *Explain.*

EXAMPLE 3 on p. 149 for Exs. 11–15

ANGLE RELATIONSHIPS Identify all pairs of angles of

11. Corresponding
12. Alternate interior
13. Alternate exterior
14. Consecutive interio

15. **ERROR ANALYSIS** *Describe* and correct the error i $\angle 1$ and $\angle 8$ are corresponding angles in the diagra Exercises 11–14.

APPLYING POSTULATES How many lines can be draw description? Copy the diagram and sketch all the lin

16. Lines through *B* and parallel to $\overleftrightarrow{AC}$
17. Lines through *A* and perpendicular to $\overleftrightarrow{BC}$

USING A DIAGRAM Classify the angle pair as *correspo interior, alternate exterior,* or *consecutive interior* an

18. $\angle 5$ and $\angle 1$
19. $\angle 11$ and $\angle 13$
20. $\angle 6$ and $\angle 13$
21. $\angle 10$ and $\angle 15$
22. $\angle 2$ and $\angle 11$
23. $\angle 8$ and $\angle 4$

150 Chapter 3 Parallel and Perpendicular Lines

ANALYZING STATEMENTS Copy and complete the statement with *sometimes, always,* or *never.* Sketch examples to *justify* your answer.

24. If two lines are parallel, then they are _?_ coplanar.
25. If two lines are not coplanar, then they _?_ intersect.
26. If three lines intersect at one point, then they are _?_ coplanar.
27. If two lines are skew to a third line, then they are _?_ skew to each other.

28. ★ **MULTIPLE CHOICE** $\angle RPQ$ and $\angle PRS$ are what type of angle pair?
Ⓐ Corresponding Ⓑ Alternate interior
Ⓒ Alternate exterior Ⓓ Consecutive interior

ANGLE RELATIONSHIPS Copy and complete the statement. List all possible correct answers.

29. $\angle BCG$ and _?_ are corresponding angles.
30. $\angle BCG$ and _?_ are consecutive interior angles.
31. $\angle FCJ$ and _?_ are alternate interior angles.
32. $\angle FCA$ and _?_ are alternate exterior angles.

33. **CHALLENGE** Copy the diagram at the right and extend the lines.
a. Measure $\angle 1$ and $\angle 2$.
b. Measure $\angle 3$ and $\angle 4$.
c. Make a conjecture about alternate exterior angles formed when parallel lines are cut by transversals.

PROBLEM SOLVING

EXAMPLE 2 on p. 148 for Exs. 34–35

CONSTRUCTION Use the picture of the cherry-picker for Exercises 34 and 35.

34. Is the platform *perpendicular, parallel,* or *skew* to the ground?

@HomeTutor for problem solving help at classzone.com

35. Is the arm *perpendicular, parallel,* or *skew* to a telephone pole?

@HomeTutor for problem solving help at classzone.com

36. ★ **OPEN-ENDED MATH** *Describe* two lines in your classroom that are parallel, and two lines that are skew.

37. ★ **MULTIPLE CHOICE** What is the best description of the horizontal bars in the photo?
Ⓐ Parallel Ⓑ Perpendicular
Ⓒ Skew Ⓓ Intersecting

3.1 Identify Pairs of Lines and Angles 151

Differentiate

Leveled exercise sets move from basic skills and problem solving to more challenging exercises.

Reason

In both skill and problem solving exercises, students are asked questions that promote conceptual thinking.

EXAMPLE 4 Solve a multi-step problem

SKATING RINK An ice-resurfacing machine is used to smooth the surface of the ice at a skating rink. The machine can resurface about 270 square yards of ice in one minute.

About how many minutes does it take the machine to resurface a rectangular skating rink that is 200 feet long and 90 feet wide?

ANOTHER WAY
For an alternative method for solving the problem in Example 4, turn to page 57 for the **Problem Solving Workshop**.

Solution

The machine can resurface the ice at a rate of 270 square yards per minute. So, the amount of time it takes to resurface the skating rink depends on its area.

STEP 1 **Find** the area of the rectangular skating rink.

Area = $\ell w = 200(90) = 18{,}000 \text{ ft}^2$

The resurfacing rate is in square yards per minute. Rewrite the area of the rink in square yards. There are 3 feet in 1 yard, and $3^2 = 9$ square feet in 1 square yard.

$18{,}000 \cancel{\text{ft}^2} \cdot \frac{1 \text{ yd}^2}{9 \cancel{\text{ft}^2}} = 2000 \text{ yd}^2$ **Use unit analysis.**

STEP 2 **Write** a verbal mode[...]
solve an equation b[...]

Let t represent the t[...]
the skating rink.

Area of rink (yd²) = R[...]

$2000 = 27$[...]

$7.4 \approx t$

▶ It takes the ice-resurfacing [...] the skating rink.

GUIDED PRACTICE for Exam[...]

4. Describe how to find the [...] to $\overline{EG}$ in the triangle at th[...]
5. Find the perimeter and t[...] triangle shown at the righ[...]
6. **WHAT IF?** In Example 4, [...] skating rink is twice as lo[...] as wide. Will it take an ic[...] machine twice as long to [...] skating rink? *Explain* you[...]

Interpret

Seeing alternative worked-out solutions helps students interpret problem solving situations.

PROBLEM SOLVING WORKSHOP LESSON 1.7

Using ALTERNATIVE METHODS

Another Way to Solve Example 4, page 51

MULTIPLE REPRESENTATIONS In Example 4 on page 51, you saw how to use an equation to solve a problem about a skating rink. *Looking for a pattern* can help you write an equation.

PROBLEM

SKATING RINK An ice-resurfacing machine is used to smooth the surface of the ice at a skating rink. The machine can resurface about 270 square yards of ice in one minute. About how many minutes does it take the machine to resurface a rectangular skating rink that is 200 feet long and 90 feet wide?

METHOD

Using a Pattern You can use a table to look for a pattern.

STEP 1 **Find** the area of the rink in square yards. In Example 4 on page 51, you found that the area was 2000 square yards.

STEP 2 **Make** a table that shows the relationship between the time spent resurfacing the ice and the area resurfaced. Look for a pattern.

Time (min)	Area resurfaced (yd²)
1	$1 \cdot 270 = 270$
2	$2 \cdot 270 = 540$
t	$t \cdot 270 = A$

Use the pattern to write an equation for the area A that has been resurfaced after t minutes.

STEP 3 **Use** the equation to find the time t (in minutes) that it takes the machine to resurface 2000 square yards of ice.

$270t = A$
$270t = 2000$
$t \approx 7.4$

▶ It takes about 7 minutes.

PRACTICE

1. **PLOWING** A square field is $\frac{1}{8}$ mile long on each side. A tractor can plow about 180,000 square feet per hour. To the nearest tenth of an hour, about how long does it take to plow the field? (1 mi = 5280 ft.)
2. **ERROR ANALYSIS** To solve Exercise 1 above, a student writes the equation $660 = 180{,}000t$, where t is the number of hours spent plowing. *Describe* and correct the error in the equation.
3. **PARKING LOT** A rectangular parking lot is 110 yards long and 45 yards wide. It costs about \$.60 to pave each square foot of the parking lot with asphalt. About how much will it cost to pave the parking lot?
4. **WALKING** A circular path has a diameter of 120 meters. Your average walking speed is 4 kilometers per hour. About how many minutes will it take you to walk around the path 3 times?

Varying Instruction

The textbook supports teaching in a variety of ways, including direct instruction, hands-on activities, geometry drawing software explorations, and visual examples.

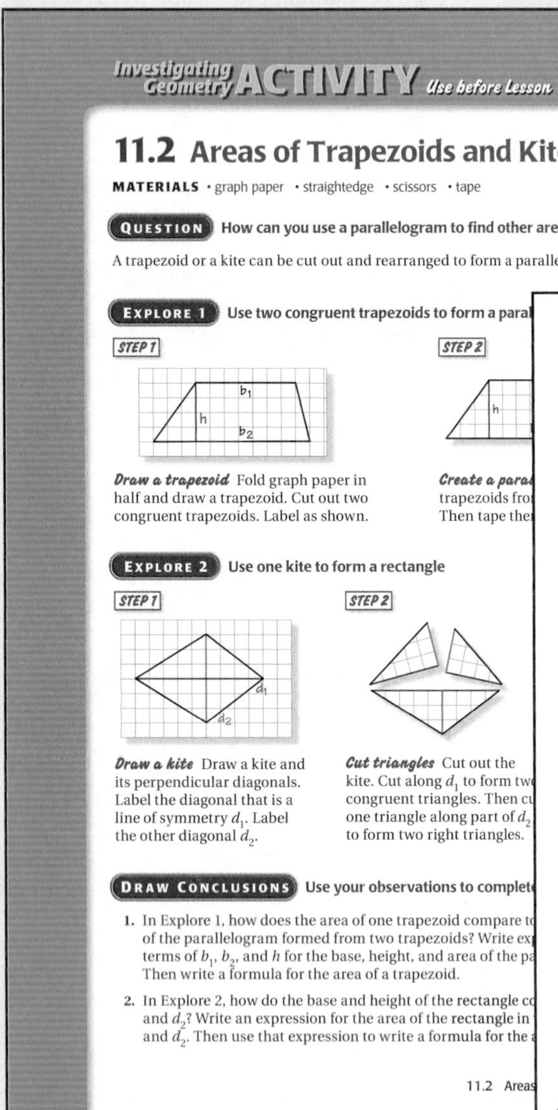

Investigating Geometry ACTIVITY *Use before Lesson 11.2*

11.2 Areas of Trapezoids and Kites

MATERIALS • graph paper • straightedge • scissors • tape

QUESTION How can you use a parallelogram to find other areas?

A trapezoid or a kite can be cut out and rearranged to form a parallelogram.

EXPLORE 1 Use two congruent trapezoids to form a paral

STEP 1 **Draw a trapezoid** Fold graph paper in half and draw a trapezoid. Cut out two congruent trapezoids. Label as shown.

STEP 2 **Create a paral** trapezoids fro Then tape the

EXPLORE 2 Use one kite to form a rectangle

STEP 1 **Draw a kite** Draw a kite and its perpendicular diagonals. Label the diagonal that is a line of symmetry d_1. Label the other diagonal d_2.

STEP 2 **Cut triangles** Cut out the kite. Cut along d_1 to form tw congruent triangles. Then cu one triangle along part of d_2 to form two right triangles.

DRAW CONCLUSIONS Use your observations to complet

1. In Explore 1, how does the area of one trapezoid compare to of the parallelogram formed from two trapezoids? Write ex terms of b_1, b_2, and h for the base, height, and area of the pa Then write a formula for the area of a trapezoid.
2. In Explore 2, how do the base and height of the rectangle co and d_2? Write an expression for the area of the rectangle in and d_2. Then use that expression to write a formula for the a

11.2 Areas

Explore

Hands-on explorations help students develop concepts and justify important formulas.

EXAMPLE 2 Find measures of a complement and a supplement

READ DIAGRAMS Angles are sometimes named with numbers. An angle measure in a diagram has a degree symbol. An angle name does not.

a. Given that ∠1 is a complement of ∠2 and $m\angle 1 = 68°$, find $m\angle 2$.

b. Given that ∠3 is a supplement of ∠4 and $m\angle 4 = 56°$, find $m\angle 3$.

Solution

a. You can draw a diagram with complementary adjacent angles to illustrate the relationship.

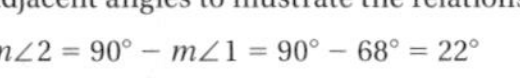

$m\angle 2 = 90° - m\angle 1 = 90° - 68° = 22°$

b. You can draw a diagram with supplementary adjacent angles to illustrate the relationship.

$m\angle 3 = 180° - m\angle 4 = 180° - 56° = 124°$

EXAMPLE 3 Find angle measures

READ DIAGRAMS In a diagram, you can assume that a line that looks straight *is* straight. In Example 3, *B*, *C*, and *D* lie on $\overleftrightarrow{BD}$. So, ∠*BCD* is a straight angle.

SPORTS When viewed from the side, the frame of a ball-return net forms a pair of supplementary angles with the ground. Find $m\angle BCE$ and $m\angle ECD$.

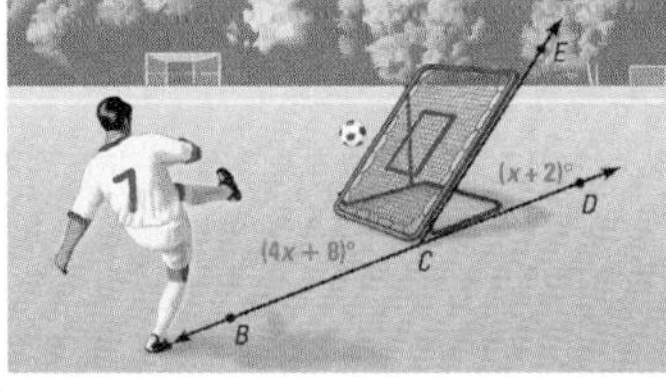

Solution

STEP 1 **Use** the fact that the sum of the measures of supplementary angles is 180°.

$m\angle BCE + m\angle ECD = 180°$ Write equation.

$(4x + 8)° + (x + 2)° = 180°$ Substitute.

$5x + 10 = 180$ Combine like terms.

$5x = 170$ Subtract 10 from each side.

$x = 34$ Divide each side by 5.

STEP 2 **Evaluate** the original expressions when $x = 34$.

$m\angle BCE = (4x + 8)° = (4 \cdot 34 + 8)° = 144°$

$m\angle ECD = (x + 2)° = (34 + 2)° = 36°$

▶ The angle measures are 144° and 36°.

✓ **GUIDED PRACTICE** for Examples 2 and 3

3. Given that ∠1 is a complement of ∠2 and $m\angle 2 = 8°$, find $m\angle 1$.
4. Given that ∠3 is a supplement of ∠4 and $m\angle 3 = 117°$, find $m\angle 4$.
5. ∠*LMN* and ∠*PQR* are complementary angles. Find the measures of the angles if $m\angle LMN = (4x - 2)°$ and $m\angle PQR = (9x + 1)°$.

36 Chapter 1 Essentials of Geometry

Model

Stepped-out examples, often applying algebra, offer clear instruction.

Investigating Geometry **ACTIVITY** *Use before Lesson 6.6*

@HomeTutor
classzone.com
Keystrokes

6.6 Investigate Proportionality

MATERIALS • graphing calculator or computer

QUESTION How can you use geometry drawing software to compare segment lengths in triangles?

EXPLORE 1 Construct a line parallel to a triangle's third side

STEP 1 *Draw a triangle* Draw a triangle. Label the vertices A, B, and C. Draw a point on $\overline{AB}$. Label the point D.

STEP 2 *Draw a parallel line* Draw a line through D that is parallel to $\overline{AC}$. Label the intersection of the line and $\overline{BC}$ as point E.

STEP 3 *Measure segments* Measure $\overline{BD}$, $\overline{DA}$, $\overline{BE}$, and $\overline{EC}$. Calculate the ratios $\frac{BD}{DA}$ and $\frac{BE}{EC}$.

STEP 4 *Compare ratios* Move one or more of the triangle's vertices to change its shape. *Compare* the ratios from Step 3 as the shape changes. Save as "EXPLORE1."

EXPLORE 2 Construct an angle bisector of a triangle

STEP 1 *Draw a triangle* Draw a triangle. Label the vertices P, Q, and R. Draw the angle bisector of $\angle QPR$. Label the intersection of the angle bisector and $\overline{QR}$ as point B.

STEP 2 *Measure segments* Measure $\overline{BR}$, $\overline{RP}$, $\overline{BQ}$, and $\overline{QP}$. Calculate the ratios $\frac{BR}{BQ}$ and $\frac{RP}{QP}$.

STEP 3 *Compare ratios* Move one or more of the triangle's vertices to change its shape. *Compare* the ratios from Step 3. Save as "EXPLORE2."

DRAW CONCLUSIONS Use your observations to complete the

1. Make a conjecture about the ratios of the lengths of the segment two sides of a triangle are cut by a line parallel to the triangle's t
2. Make a conjecture about how the ratio of the lengths of two side is related to the ratio of the lengths of the segments formed whe bisector is drawn to the third side.

396 Chapter 6 Similarity

Reason

Using geometry drawing software gives students opportunities to make and test conjectures.

CONCEPT SUMMARY *For Your Notebook*

Ways to Prove a Quadrilateral is a Parallelogram

1. Show both pairs of opposite sides are parallel. (DEFINITION)
2. Show both pairs of opposite sides are congruent. (THEOREM 8.7)
3. Show both pairs of opposite angles are congruent. (THEOREM 8.8)
4. Show one pair of opposite sides are congruent and parallel. (THEOREM 8.9)
5. Show the diagonals bisect each other. (THEOREM 8.10)

EXAMPLE 4 Use coordinate geometry

Show that quadrilateral *ABCD* is a parallelogram.

ANOTHER WAY
For alternative methods for solving the problem in Example 4, turn to page 530 for the **Problem Solving Workshop**.

Solution

One way is to show that a pair of sides are congruent and parallel. Then apply Theorem 8.9.

First use the Distance Formula to show that $\overline{AB}$ and $\overline{CD}$ are congruent.

$AB = \sqrt{[2-(-3)]^2 + (5-3)^2} = \sqrt{29}$ $CD = \sqrt{(5-0)^2 + (2-0)^2} = \sqrt{29}$

Because $AB = CD = \sqrt{29}$, $\overline{AB} \cong \overline{CD}$.

Then use the slope formula to show that $\overline{AB} \parallel \overline{CD}$.

Slope of $\overline{AB} = \frac{5-(3)}{2-(-3)} = \frac{2}{5}$ Slope of $\overline{CD} = \frac{2-0}{5-0} = \frac{2}{5}$

Because $\overline{AB}$ and $\overline{CD}$ have the same slope, they are parallel.

▸ $\overline{AB}$ and $\overline{CD}$ are congruent and parallel. So, $ABCD$ is a parallelogram by Theorem 8.9.

Graph

Frequent use of coordinate geometry adds depth to students' understanding.

✓ **GUIDED PRACTICE** for Example 4

6. Refer to the Concept Summary above. *Explain* how other methods can be used to show that quadrilateral $ABCD$ in Example 4 is a parallelogram.

8.3 Show that a Quadrilateral is a Parallelogram 525

Integrating Assessment

Ongoing assessment is embedded so that you can measure students' understanding and progress in each lesson and chapter.

Strategize

Standardized Test Practice examples develop math skills and suggest test-taking strategies.

★ **EXAMPLE 2** **Standardized Test Practice**

STAGE PROP You are constructing a stage prop that shows a large triangular mountain. The bottom edge of the mountain is about 27 feet long, the left slope is about 24 feet long, and the right slope is about 20 feet long. You are told that one of the angles is about 46° and one is about 59°. What is the angle measure of the peak of the mountain?

Ⓐ 46° Ⓑ 59° Ⓒ 75° Ⓓ 85°

ELIMINATE CHOICES
You can eliminate choice D because a triangle with a 46° angle and a 59° angle cannot have an 85° angle. The sum of the three angles in a triangle must be 180°, but the sum of 46, 59, and 85 is 190, not 180.

Solution

Draw a diagram and label the side lengths. The peak angle is opposite the longest side so, by Theorem 5.10, the peak angle is the largest angle.

largest angle, 75°, 24 ft, 20 ft, 46°, 59°, 27 ft longest side

The angle measures sum to 180°, so the third angle measure is $180° - (46° + 59°) = 75°$. You can now label the angle measures in your diagram.

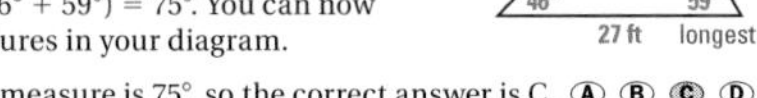

▸ The greatest angle measure is 75°, so the correct answer is C. Ⓐ Ⓑ Ⓒ Ⓓ

✓ **GUIDED PRACTICE** for Examples 1 and 2

1. List the sides of $\triangle RST$ in order from shortest to longest.

S, 121°, R, 29°, 30°, T

2. Another stage prop is a right triangle with sides that are 6, 8, and 10 feet long and angles of 90°, about 37°, and about 53°. Sketch and label a diagram with the shortest side on the bottom and the right angle at the left.

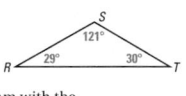

PROOF Theorem 5.10

GIVEN ▸ $BC > AB$
PROVE ▸ $m\angle BAC > m\angle C$

Locate a point D on $\overline{BC}$ such that $DB = BA$. Then draw $\overline{AD}$. In the isosceles triangle $\triangle ABD$, $\angle 1 \cong \angle 2$.

Because $m\angle BAC = m\angle 1 + m\angle 3$, it follows that $m\angle BAC > m\angle 1$. Substituting $m\angle 2$ for $m\angle 1$ produces $m\angle BAC > m\angle 2$.

By the Exterior Angle Theorem, $m\angle 2 = m\angle 3 + m\angle C$, so it follows that $m\angle 2 > m\angle C$ (see Exercise 27, page 332). Finally, because $m\angle BAC > m\angle 2$ and $m\angle 2 > m\angle C$, you can conclude that $m\angle BAC > m\angle C$.

5.5 Use Inequalities in a Triangle 329

SHUFFLEBOARD In the portion of the shuffleboard court

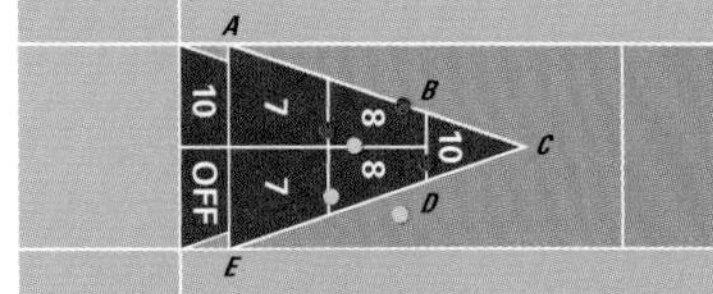

30. What additional piece of information do you need in
$\triangle BCD \sim \triangle ACE$ using the SSS Similarity Theorem?

31. What additional piece of information do you need in
$\triangle BCD \sim \triangle ACE$ using the SAS Similarity Theorem?

32. ★ **OPEN-ENDED MATH** Use a diagram to show why th
Similarity Postulate.

EXAMPLE 4 on p. 391 for Ex. 33

33. **MULTI-STEP PROBLEM** Ruby is standing in her back yard and she decides to estimate the height of a tree. She stands so that the tip of her shadow coincides with the tip of the tree's shadow, as shown. Ruby is 66 inches tall. The distance from the tree to Ruby is 95 feet and the distance between the tip of the shadows and Ruby is 7 feet.
   a. What postulate or theorem can you use to show th
   diagram are similar?
   b. About how tall is the tree, to the nearest foot?
   c. **What If?** Curtis is 75 inches tall. At a different time
   that the tip of his shadow and the tip of the tree's s
   described above. His shadow is 6 feet long. How fa

Animated Geometry at classzone.com

34. ★ **EXTENDED RESPONSE** Suppose you are given two
with one pair of corresponding legs and the pair of co
hypotenuses having the same length ratios.
   a. The lengths of the given pair of corresponding legs
   lengths of the hypotenuses are 10 and 30. Use the P
   to solve for the lengths of the other pair of corresponding legs. Draw a diagram.
   b. Write the ratio of the lengths of the second pair of corresponding legs.
   c. Are these triangles similar? Does this suggest a Hypotenuse-Leg Similarity Theorem for right triangles?

35. **PROOF** Given that $\triangle ABC$ is a right triangle and D, E, and F are midpoints, prove that $m\angle DEF = 90°$.

36. ★ **WRITING** Can two triangles have all pairs of corresponding angles in proportion? *Explain.*

394 ○ = WORKED-OUT SOLUTIONS on p. WS1 ★ = STANDARDIZED TEST PRACTICE

Prepare

Solving a variety of test-format questions prepares students for high-stakes tests.

12 ★ Standardized TEST PREPARATION

CONTEXT-BASED MULTIPLE CHOICE QUESTIONS

Some of the information you need to solve a context-based multiple choice question may appear in a table, a diagram, or a graph.

PROBLEM 1

One cubic foot of concrete weighs about 150 pounds. What is the approximate weight of the cylindrical section of concrete pipe shown?

Ⓐ 145 lb Ⓑ 686 lb

Ⓒ 2738 lb Ⓓ 5653 lb

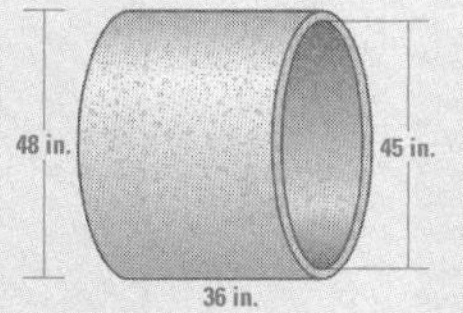

Plan

INTERPRET THE DIAGRAM The pipe is a cylinder with length 36 inches and diameter 48 inches. The hollow center is also a cylinder with length 36 inches and diameter 45 inches. Find the volume of concrete used (in cubic feet). Then multiply by 150 pounds per cubic foot to find the weight of the concrete.

Solution

STEP 1 Find the volume of concrete used in the pipe.

Find the volume of a cylinder with diameter 48 inches and height 36 inches.

$V = \pi r^2 h = \pi(24^2)(36) \approx 65{,}144 \text{ in.}^3$

Find the volume of a cylinder with diameter 45 inches and height 36 inches.

$V = \pi r^2 h = \pi(22.5^2)(36) \approx 57{,}256 \text{ in.}^3$

To find the volume of concrete used in the pipe, subtract the smaller volume from the larger volume.

Volume of concrete used in pipe $\approx 65{,}144 - 57{,}256 = 7889 \text{ in.}^3$

STEP 2 Convert the volume to cubic feet.

Use unit analysis to convert 7889 cubic inches to cubic feet. There are 12 inches in 1 foot, so there are $12^3 = 1728$ cubic inches in 1 cubic foot.

$7889 \text{ in.}^3 \cdot \frac{1 \text{ ft}^3}{1728 \text{ in.}^3} \approx 4.57 \text{ ft}^3$

STEP 3 Find the weight of the pipe.

To find the weight of the pipe, multiply the volume of the concrete used in the pipe by the weight of one cubic foot of concrete.

Weight of pipe $\approx 4.57 \text{ ft}^3 \cdot \frac{150 \text{ lb}}{1 \text{ ft}^3} = 685.5$ lb

The weight of the pipe is about 686 pounds.

The correct answer is B. Ⓐ Ⓑ Ⓒ Ⓓ

Interpret

Learning how to interpret information is a critical problem solving skill.

...dized TEST PRACTICE

...ram, which

...in.

...shape of the

...gle

...oid

...bin?

3. In the paperweight shown, a sphere with diameter 5 centimeters is embedded in a glass cube. What percent of the volume of the paperweight is taken up by the sphere?

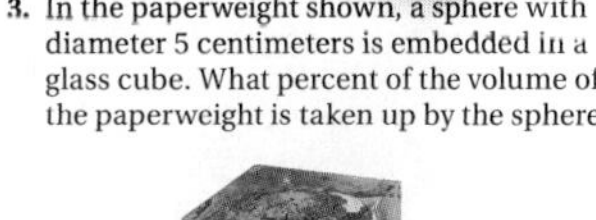

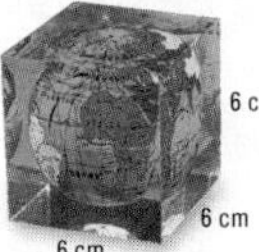

Ⓐ About 30% Ⓑ About 40%

Ⓒ About 50% Ⓓ About 60%

4. What is the volume of the solid formed when rectangle $JKLM$ is rotated 360° about $\overline{KL}$?

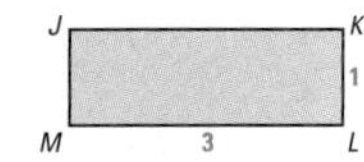

Ⓐ π Ⓑ 3π

Ⓒ 6π Ⓓ 9π

5. The skylight shown is made of four glass panes that are congruent isosceles triangles. One square foot of the glass used in the skylight weighs 3.25 pounds. What is the approximate total weight of the glass used in the four panes?

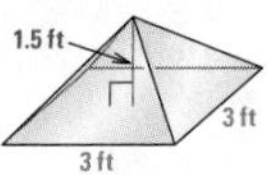

Ⓐ 10 lb Ⓑ 15 lb

Ⓒ 29 lb Ⓓ 41 lb

6. The volume of the right cone shown below is 16π cubic centimeters. What is the surface area of the cone?

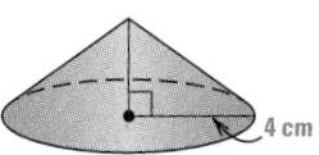

Ⓐ $12\pi \text{ cm}^2$ Ⓑ $18\pi \text{ cm}^2$

Ⓒ $36\pi \text{ cm}^2$ Ⓓ $72\pi \text{ cm}^2$

7. The shaded surface of the skateboard ramp shown is divided into a flat rectangular portion and a curved portion. The curved portion is one fourth of a cylinder with radius r feet and height h feet. Which equation can be used to find the area of the top surface of the ramp?

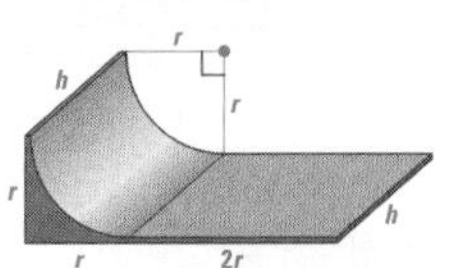

Ⓐ $2rh + 2\pi r^2$ Ⓑ $2rh + 2\pi rh$

Ⓒ $2rh + \frac{1}{4}\pi r^2$ Ⓓ $2rh + \frac{1}{2}\pi rh$

Practice

Thorough practice builds students' confidence and skills.

PROGRAM OVERVIEW

Geometry provides a complete set of resources organized for ease of use.

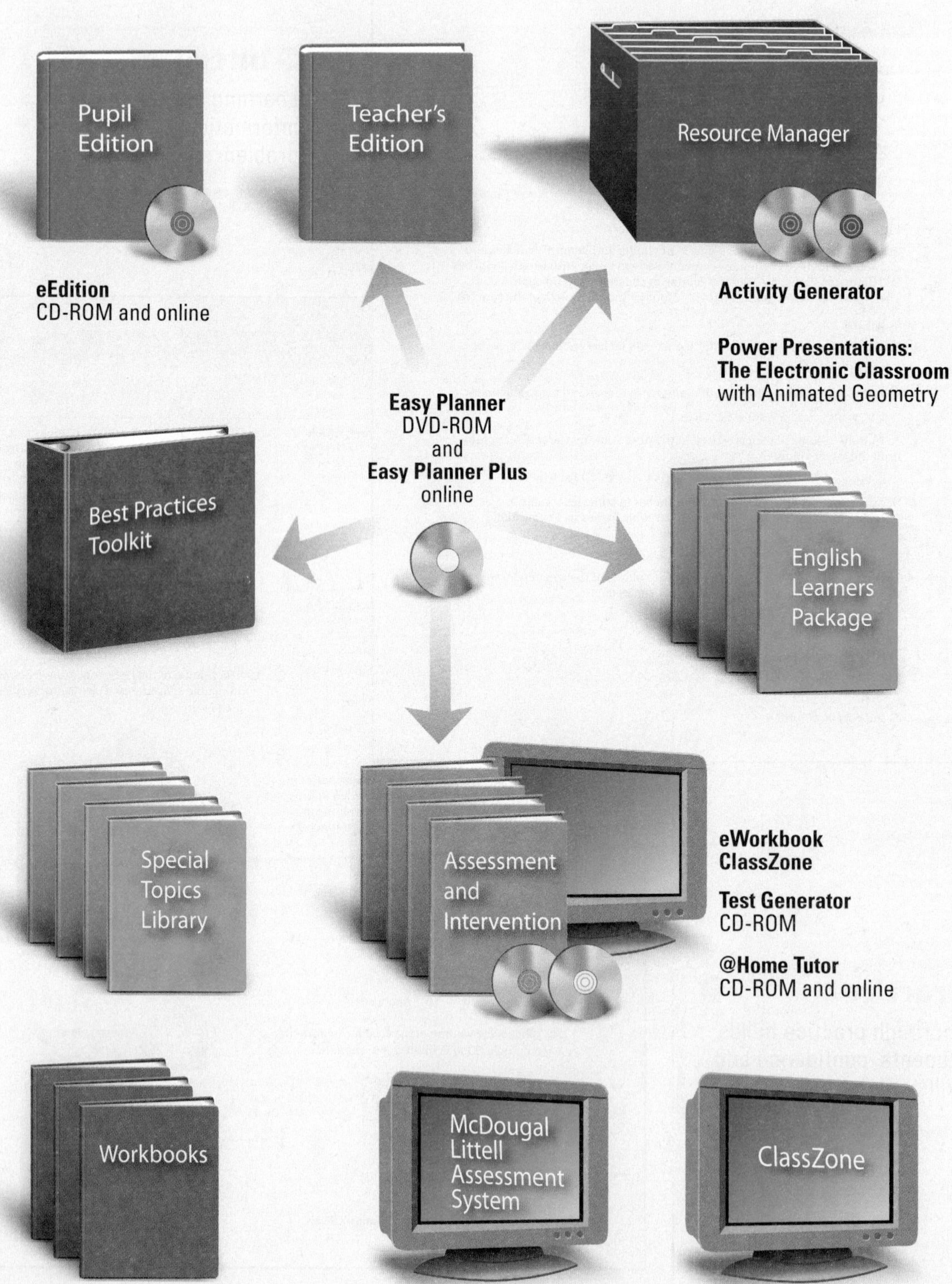

RESOURCE MANAGER

The Resource Manager contains Chapter Resource Books and Transparency Books to help you adapt the program to your teaching style and to the needs of your students.

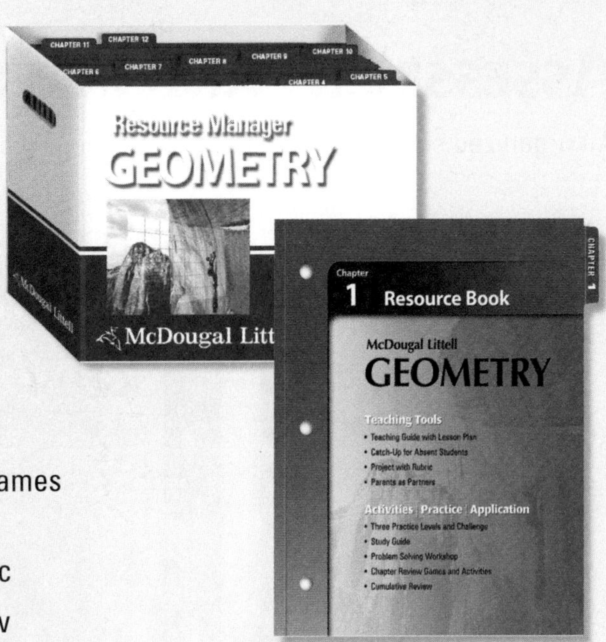

Note: There is one resource book for each chapter in the book.

CHAPTER RESOURCE BOOKS

- Parents as Partners
- Teaching Guide with Lesson Plan (regular/block)
- Practice (Levels A, B, and C)
- Study Guide
- Problem Solving Workshop
- Challenge
- Catch-Up for Absent Students
- Activities
- Applications
- Chapter Review Games and Activities
- Project with Rubric
- Cumulative Review
- Answers

WORKED-OUT SOLUTION KEY

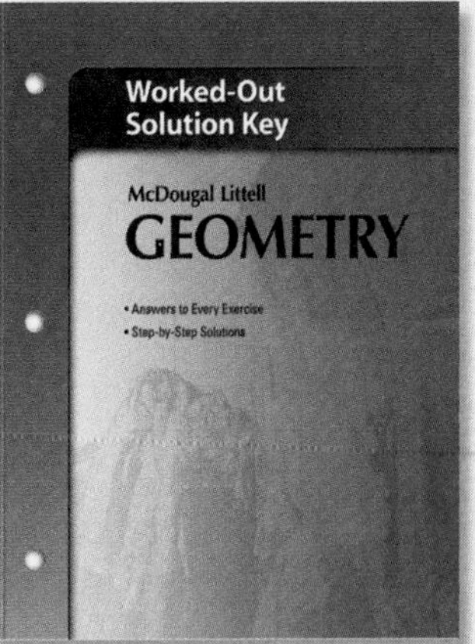

CHAPTER TRANSPARENCY BOOKS

- Warm-Up and Daily Homework Quiz
- Notetaking Guide (transparencies)
- Answers (evens and odds)

Note: There is one transparency book for each chapter in the book.

WORKBOOKS

- Practice Workbook
- Notetaking Guide (PE and TE)

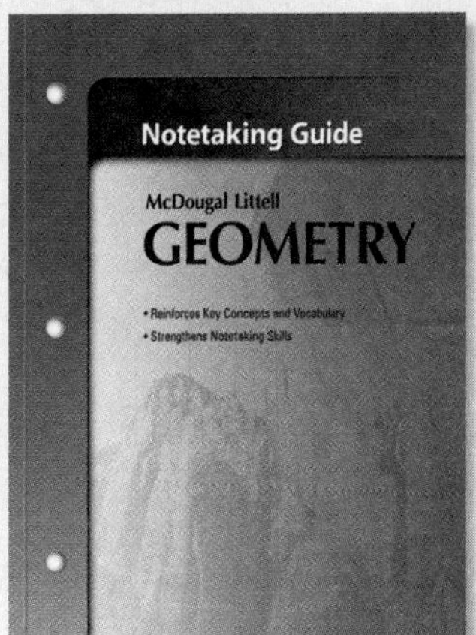

Assessment and Intervention System

An organized set of resources helps you keep track of ongoing progress.

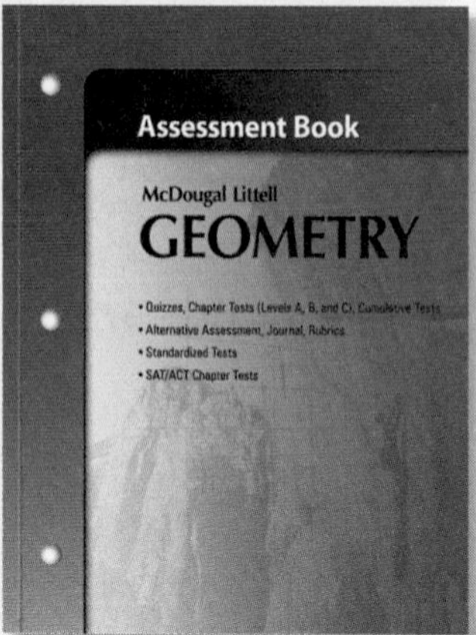

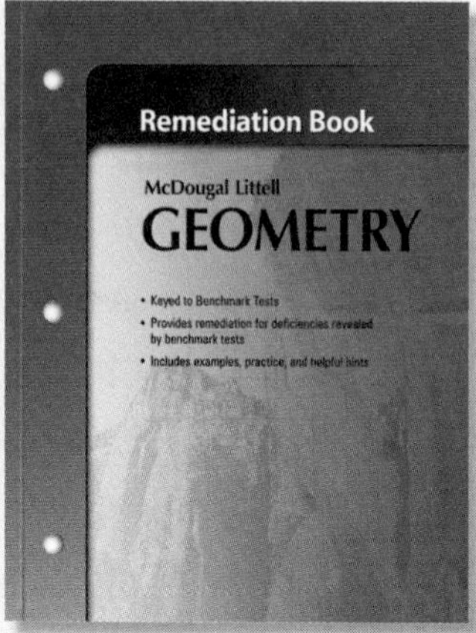

Best Practices Toolkit

This teaching resource contains professional materials such as suggestions for in-service workshops, professional articles on various aspects of teaching, and tips for new teachers.

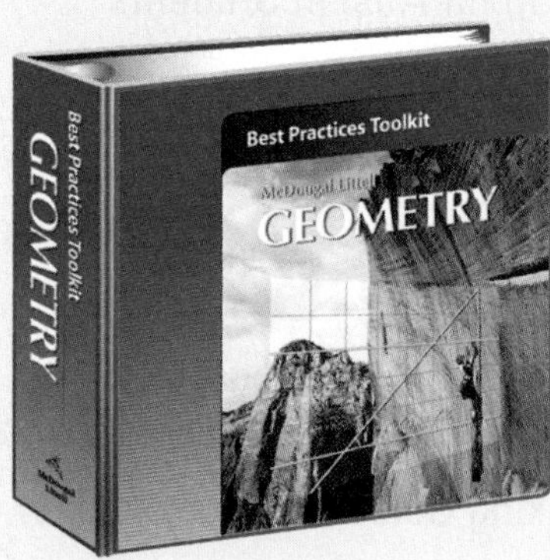

Strategies For Effective Teaching

- The Bigger Picture of Mathematics
- Research-Based Solutions for Your Classroom
- Reading, Writing, Notetaking
- Differentiated Instruction
- English Learners
- Inclusion
- Strategies for Success with Sample Worksheets
- Using Technology in the Classroom
- Tips for New Teachers
- Math Background Notes
- Assessment Strategies and Rubrics with Samples

Pre-AP Resources

- Pre-AP* Overview
- Pre-AP Pacing and Assignment Guide
- Pre-AP Best Practices
- Pre-AP Copymasters

Teacher Survival Activities

- Start-of-School Activities
- Before-Vacation Activities
- Substitute Teachers' Activities
- Quick Change-of-Pace Activities
- Bulletin Board Ideas

Teacher Tool Transparencies

- Includes graphic organizers and tools such as graph paper, rulers, protractor, and coordinate grids.

Answers

- Includes Answers to Activities and Worksheets

*Pre-AP is a registered trademark of the College Entrance Examination Board, which was not involved in the production of and does not endorse this product.

ENGLISH LEARNERS PACKAGE

A variety of resources are available to help you address the needs of English learners.

Student Resources in Spanish (PE)
Textbook exercises, chapter reviews and tests, and chapter standardized test preparation and practice pages are translated into Spanish.

Spanish Study Guide
Provides examples and extra practice in Spanish.

Assessment Book
English Assessment Book in Spanish

Multi-Language Visual Glossary
A visual math glossary is translated into nine languages.

Quick Reference: English Learner Strategies for Math
This quick reference guide offers strategies for helping English learners in your math classroom.

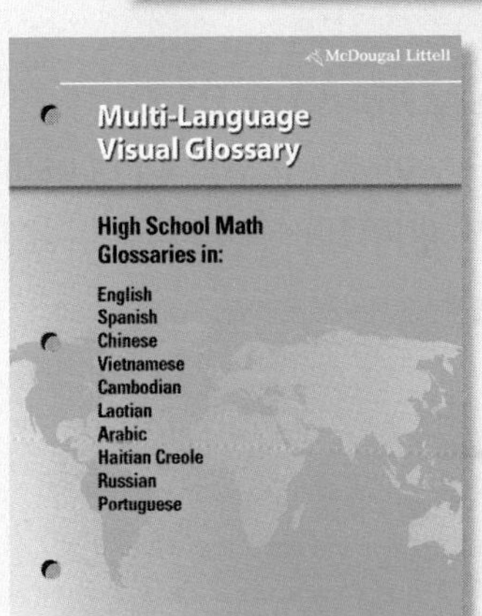

SPECIAL TOPICS LIBRARY

These student materials focus on topics of high interest. New materials are added to the library on an ongoing basis.

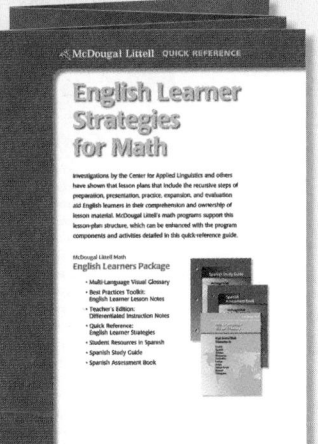

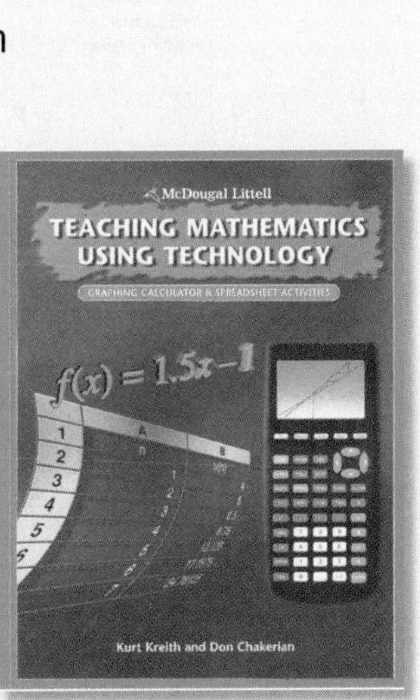

TECHNOLOGY RESOURCES

McDougal Littell offers flexible, easy-to-navigate resources online and on CD-ROM for planning, motivation, instruction, and assessment.

Power Presentations: The Electronic Classroom CD-ROM

- All the classroom resources you need to teach an interactive lesson

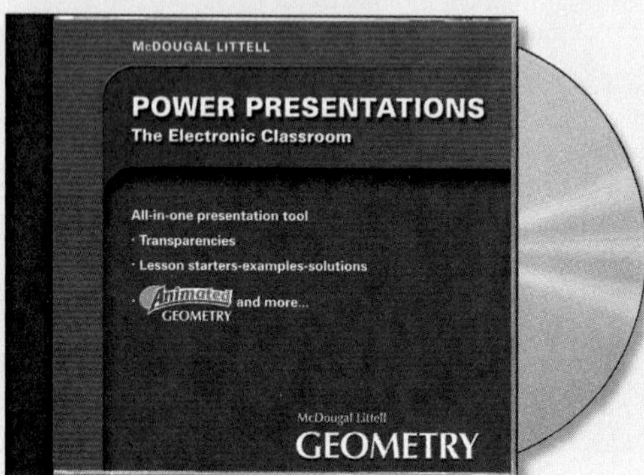

Activity Generator CD-ROM

- Leveled activities (A, B, C) for each lesson
- Teaching commentary to guide students from concrete to abstract

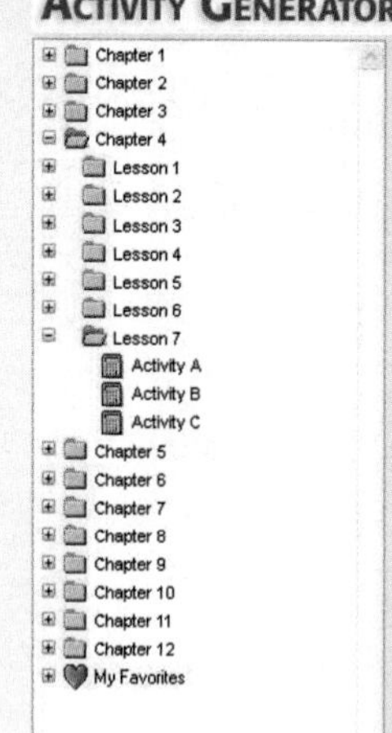

Activity B

4.7 Use Isosceles and Equilateral Triangles

MATERIALS • geometry drawing software

QUESTION If two sides of a triangle are congruent, what is true about the angles in the triangle?

EXPLORE Investigate properties of isosceles and equilateral triangles

STEP 1 ***Draw a triangle***

Draw and label $\triangle ABC$.

STEP 2 ***Measure*** $\triangle ABC$

Measure the three sides and three angles of $\triangle ABC$. Record their measurements on the screen.

STEP 3 ***Drag point B***

Drag point B until AB and BC are equal. Record the new measurements of $\triangle ABC$ in the table below.

	AB	BC	AC	$m\angle ABC$	$m\angle ACB$	$m\angle BAC$
Measurement						

STEP 4 ***Drag point C***

Move B so that the lengths are all different. Drag point C until BC and AC are equal. Record the new measurements of $\triangle ABC$ in the table below.

Easy Planner DVD

- Lesson plans you can customize
- All print teaching resources

classzone.com

McDougal Littell's companion website provides full support for the student at home.

- Extra examples
- Animations
- Quizzes
- Vocabulary support
- eWorkbook

CD-Rom and Online Formats

Animated Geometry

- Engaging, interactive activities that support textbook lessons and exercises

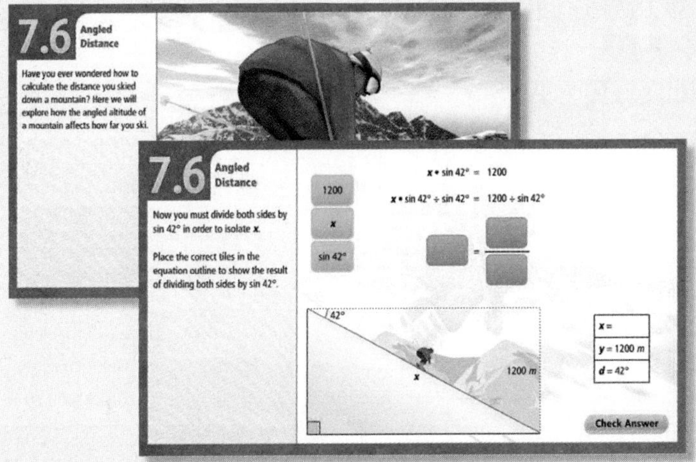

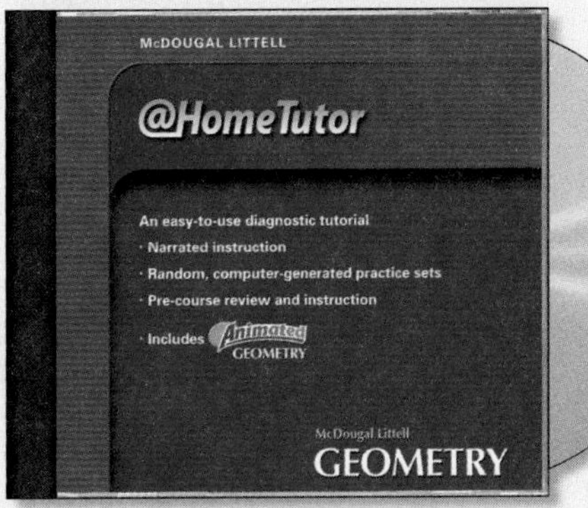

@HomeTutor

- Animated examples and instruction
- Self-scoring exercises
- Customized student progress reports

Now available 

Larson Learning courseware provides multi-sensory learning to enhance core instruction in McDougal Littell textbooks. For more information about Larson Learning products, visit **mcdougallittell.com**

ASSESSMENT

McDougal Littell Assessment System

- Innovative standards-based system
- Helps you test, score, report, reteach
- Tests and answer sheets can be printed on plain paper

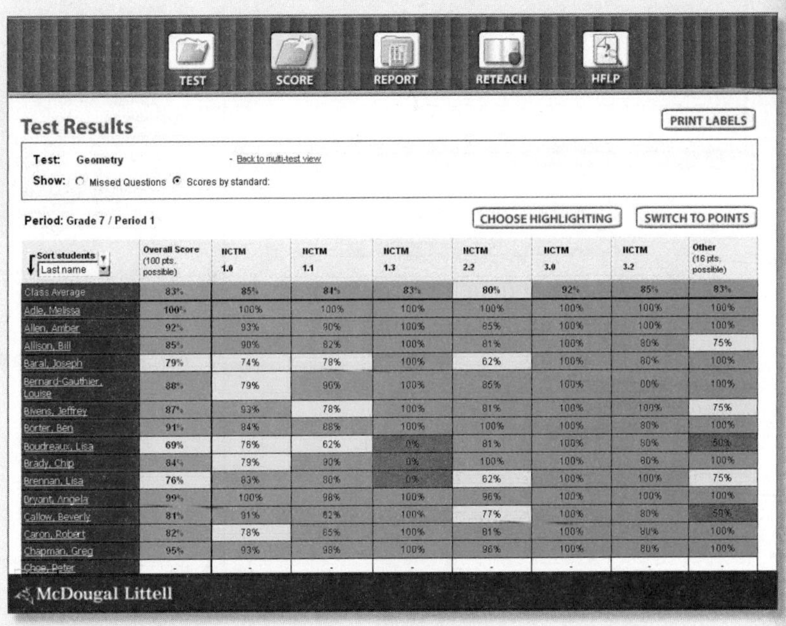

Sort students Last name	Overall Score (100 pts. possible)	NCTM 1.0	NCTM 1.1	NCTM 1.3	NCTM 2.2	NCTM 3.0	NCTM 3.2	Other (16 pts. possible)
Class Average	83%	85%	84%	83%	80%	92%	85%	83%
Adle, Melissa	100%	100%	100%	100%	100%	100%	100%	100%
Allen, Amber	92%	93%	90%	100%	85%	100%	100%	100%
Allison, Bill	85%	90%	82%	100%	81%	100%	80%	75%
Baral, Joseph	79%	74%	78%	100%	62%	100%	80%	100%
Bernard-Gauthier, Louise	88%	79%	90%	100%	85%	100%	80%	100%
Bivens, Jeffrey	87%	93%	78%	100%	81%	100%	100%	75%
Borter, Ben	91%	84%	88%	100%	100%	100%	80%	100%
Boudreaux, Lisa	69%	76%	62%	0%	81%	100%	80%	50%
Brady, Chip	84%	79%	90%	0%	100%	100%	80%	100%
Brennan, Lisa	76%	83%	80%	0%	62%	100%	100%	75%
Bryant, Angela	99%	100%	98%	100%	96%	100%	100%	100%
Callow, Beverly	81%	91%	82%	100%	77%	100%	80%	50%
Caron, Robert	82%	78%	85%	100%	81%	100%	80%	100%
Chapman, Greg	95%	93%	98%	100%	96%	100%	80%	100%
Choe, Peter	-	-	-	-	-	-	-	-

Test Generator

Planning the Chapter

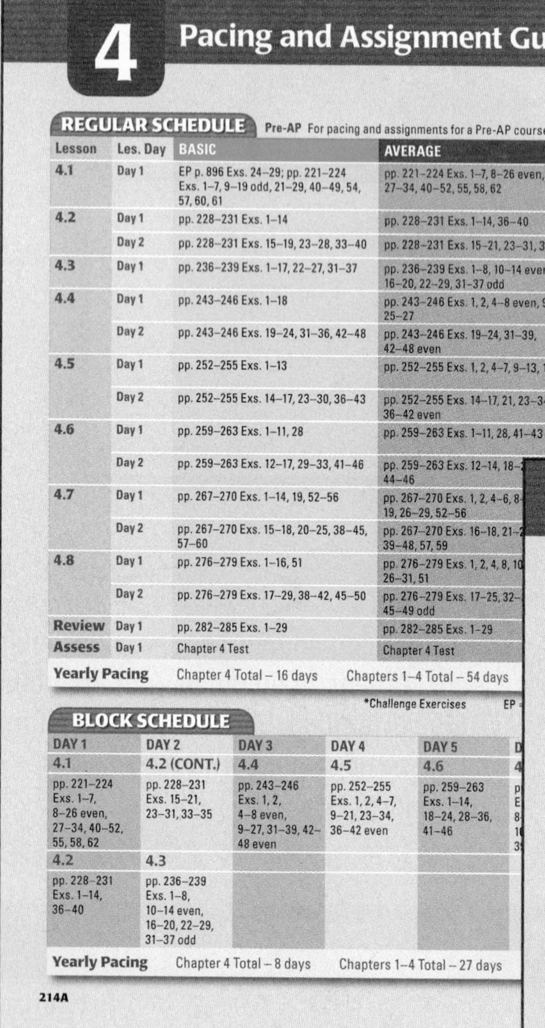

4 Pacing and Assignment Guide

REGULAR SCHEDULE Pre-AP For pacing and assignments for a Pre-AP course, see the *Geometry Toolkit*.

Lesson	Les. Day	BASIC	AVERAGE	ADVANCED
4.1	Day 1	EP p. 896 Exs. 24–29; pp. 221–224 Exs. 1–7, 9–19 odd, 21–29, 40–49, 54, 57, 60, 61	pp. 221–224 Exs. 1–7, 8–26 even, 27–34, 40–52, 55, 58, 62	pp. 221–224 Exs. 1–7, 10, 13, 16, 19, 20, 27, 28, 31–40*, 42–53*, 56, 59, 63
4.2	Day 1	pp. 228–231 Exs. 1–14	pp. 228–231 Exs. 1–14, 36–40	pp. 228–231 Exs. 1–4, 7–14, 22*, 36–40
	Day 2	pp. 228–231 Exs. 15–19, 23–28, 33–40	pp. 228–231 Exs. 15–21, 23–31, 33–35	pp. 228–231 Exs. 15–21, 24–35*
4.3	Day 1	pp. 236–239 Exs. 1–17, 22–27, 31–37	pp. 236–239 Exs. 1–8, 10–14 even, 16–20, 22–29, 31–37 odd	pp. 236–239 Exs. 1–4, 7, 8, 11, 12, 14–30*, 33, 36, 37
4.4	Day 1	pp. 243–246 Exs. 1–18	pp. 243–246 Exs. 1, 2, 4–8 even, 9–18, 25–27	pp. 243–246 Exs. 1, 2, 6–8, 12–18, 25–30*
	Day 2	pp. 243–246 Exs. 19–24, 31–36, 42–48	pp. 243–246 Exs. 19–24, 31–39, 42–48 even	pp. 243–246 Exs. 19–24, 31–41*, 43–47 odd
4.5	Day 1	pp. 252–255 Exs. 1–13	pp. 252–255 Exs. 1, 2, 4–7, 9–13, 18–20	pp. 252–255 Exs. 1, 2, 5–7, 9–13, 18–20, 22*
	Day 2	pp. 252–255 Exs. 14–17, 23–30, 36–43	pp. 252–255 Exs. 14–17, 21, 23–34, 36–42 even	pp. 252–255 Exs. 14–17, 23–35*, 37–43 odd
4.6	Day 1	pp. 259–263 Exs. 1–11, 28	pp. 259–263 Exs. 1–11, 28, 41–43	pp. 259–263 Exs. 1, 2, 4–11, 27*, 28, 41–43
	Day 2	pp. 259–263 Exs. 12–17, 29–33, 41–46	pp. 259–263 Exs. 12–14, 18– 44–46	
4.7	Day 1	pp. 267–270 Exs. 1–14, 19, 52–56	pp. 267–270 Exs. 1, 2, 4–6, 8– 19, 26–29, 52–56	
	Day 2	pp. 267–270 Exs. 15–18, 20–25, 38–45, 57–60	pp. 267–270 Exs. 16–18, 21– 39–48, 57, 59	
4.8	Day 1	pp. 276–279 Exs. 1–16, 51	pp. 276–279 Exs. 1, 2, 4, 8, 10 26–31, 51	
	Day 2	pp. 276–279 Exs. 17–29, 38–42, 45–50	pp. 276–279 Exs. 17–25, 32– 45–49 odd	
Review	Day 1	pp. 282–285 Exs. 1–29	pp. 282–285 Exs. 1–29	
Assess	Day 1	Chapter 4 Test	Chapter 4 Test	

Yearly Pacing Chapter 4 Total – 16 days Chapters 1–4 Total – 54 days

*Challenge Exercises EP =

BLOCK SCHEDULE

DAY 1	DAY 2	DAY 3	DAY 4	DAY 5
4.1	4.2 (CONT.)	4.4	4.5	4.6
pp. 221–224 Exs. 1–7, 8–26 even, 27–34, 40–52, 55, 58, 62	pp. 228–231 Exs. 15–21, 23–31, 33–35	pp. 243–246 Exs. 1, 2, 4–8 even, 9–27, 31–39, 42–48 even	pp. 252–255 Exs. 1, 2, 4–7, 9–21, 23–34, 36–42 even	pp. 259–263 Exs. 1–14, 18–24, 28–36, 41–46
4.2	4.3			
pp. 228–231 Exs. 1–14, 36–40	pp. 236–239 Exs. 1–8, 10–14 even, 16–20, 22–29, 31–37 odd			

Yearly Pacing Chapter 4 Total – 8 days Chapters 1–4 Total – 27 days

214A

Regular and Block schedules for pacing the course

A handy guide for integrating resource materials into your lessons

Chapter Resource Guide 4

RESOURCE MANAGER

Chapter Resource Book								
CHAPTER SUPPORT								
Parents as Partners (Chapter Overview with home involvement exercises and activity)							p. 1	
LESSON SUPPORT	**4.1**	**4.2**	**4.3**	**4.4**	**4.5**	**4.6**	**4.7**	**4.8**
Teaching Guide/Lesson Plan	p. 3	p. 18	p. 32	p. 45	p. 60	p. 74	p. 87	p. 101
Activity Masters	p. 5	p. 20			p. 62		p. 89	p. 103
Technology Activities & Keystrokes				p. 47				
Activity Support Masters								
Practice (3 levels)	p. 7	p. 21	p. 34	p. 48	p. 63	p. 76	p. 90	p. 105
Study Guide	p. 13	p. 27	p. 40	p. 54	p. 69	p. 82	p. 96	p. 111
Catch-Up for Absent Students	p. 15	p. 29	p. 42	p. 56	p. 71	p. 84	p. 98	p. 113
Problem Solving/Application	p. 16	p. 30	p. 43	p. 57	p. 72	p. 85	p. 99	p. 114
Challenge Practice	p. 17	p. 31	p. 44	p. 59	p. 73	p. 86	p. 100	p. 115
REVIEW								
Chapter Review Games and Activities		p. 116		Cumulative Practice			p. 119	
Project with Rubric		p. 117		Resource Book Answers			A1	

Transparencies	4.1	4.2	4.3	4.4	4.5	4.6	4.7	4.8
Warm-Up/Daily Homework Quiz	✔	✔	✔	✔	✔	✔	✔	✔
Notetaking Guide	✔	✔	✔	✔	✔	✔	✔	✔
Teacher Support	✔		✔		✔			✔
Answer Transparencies	✔	✔	✔	✔	✔	✔	✔	✔

ASSESSMENT BOOK

Quizzes	p. 46	SAT/ACT Chapter Test	p. 57
Chapter Tests (3 levels)	p. 49	Alternative Assessment with Rubric	p. 59
Standardized Chapter Test	p. 55		

TECHNOLOGY

- Easy Planner
- Test and Practice Generator
- Power Presentations
- @HomeTutor
- Activity Generator
- Animated Geometry
- Classzone.com
- eEdition Plus Online
- eWorkbook Plus Online
- ML Assessment System

ADDITIONAL RESOURCES

- Worked-Out Solution Key
- Notetaking Guide
- Practice Wookbook
- Geometry Toolkit
- Benchmark Tests
- Remediation Book
- Spanish Study Guide
- Spanish Assessment Book
- Student Resources in Spanish
- Multi-Language Visual Glossary

214B

For each chapter, reduced facsimiles of the Practice B pages and the quizzes, Chapter Test B, Standardized Test, and Alternative Assessment are provided. These facsimiles with answers help you check students' papers quickly.

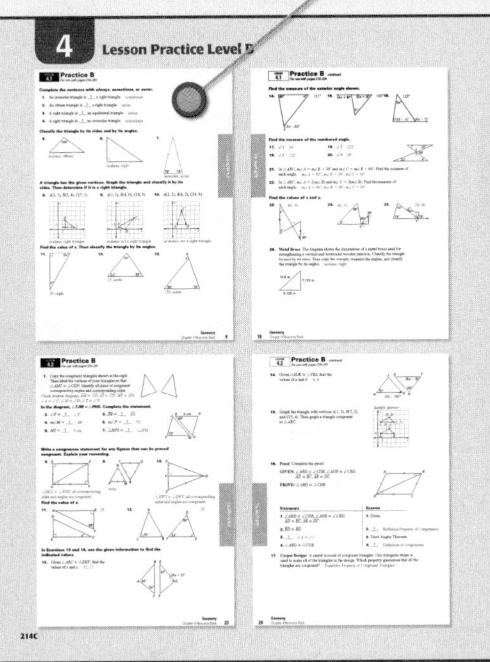

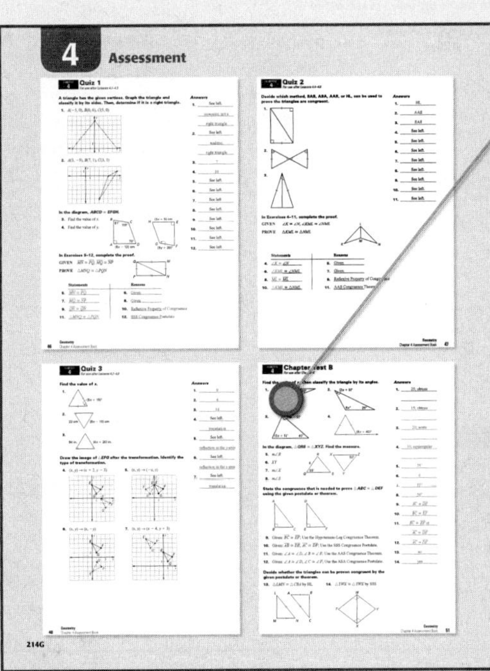

LESSON 4.1

Practice B

For use with pages 216–224

Complete the sentence with *always, sometimes,* or *never.*

1. An isosceles triangle is __?__ a right triangle. sometimes
2. An obtuse triangle is __?__ a right triangle. never
3. A right triangle is __?__ an equilateral triangle. never
4. A right triangle is __?__ an isosceles triangle. sometimes

Classify the triangle by its sides and by its angles.

5. 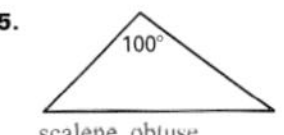

scalene, obtuse

6. 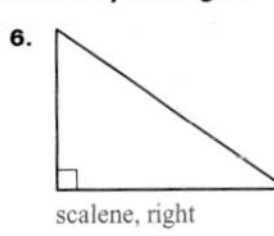
scalene, right

7. 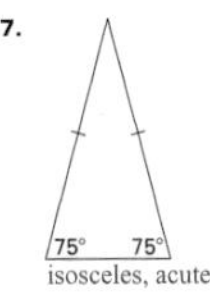

isosceles, acute

A triangle has the given vertices. Graph the triangle and classify it by its sides. Then determine if it is a right triangle.

8. $A(3, 1), B(3, 4), C(7, 1)$
9. $A(1, 1), B(4, 0), C(8, 5)$
10. $A(2, 2), B(6, 2), C(4, 8)$

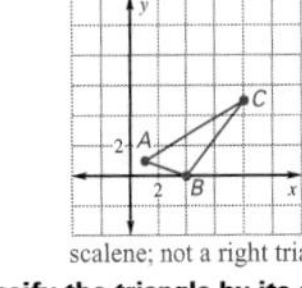
scalene; right triangle

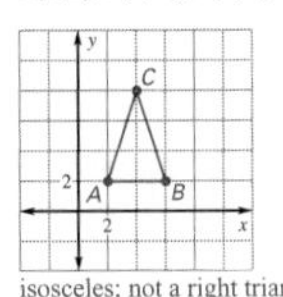
scalene; not a right triangle

isosceles; not a right triangle

Find the value of x. Then classify the triangle by its angles.

11. 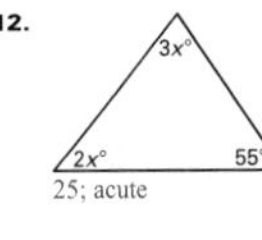

30; right

12. 

25; acute

13. 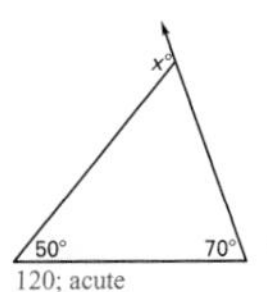

120; acute

LESSON 4.1

CHAPTER 4

Chapter Test B

For use after Chapter 4

Find the value of x. Then classify the triangle by its angles.

1. 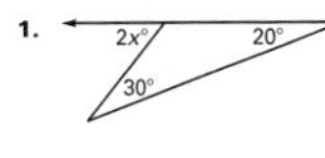

2. 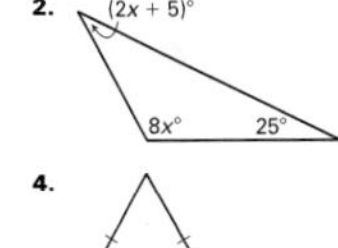

3. 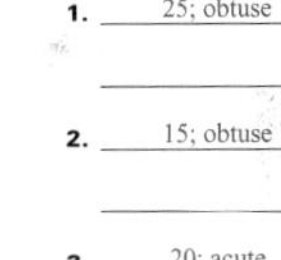

4.

In the diagram, $\triangle QRS \cong \triangle XYZ$. Find the measure.

5. $m\angle R$
6. XY
7. $m\angle X$
8. $m\angle S$

State the congruence that is needed to prove $\triangle ABC \cong \triangle DEF$ using the given postulate or theorem.

9. Given: $\overline{BC} \cong \overline{EF}$; Use the Hypotenuse-Leg Congruence Theorem.
10. Given: $\overline{AB} \cong \overline{DE}$, $\overline{AC} \cong \overline{DF}$; Use the SSS Congruence Postulate.
11. Given: $\angle A \cong \angle D$, $\angle B \cong \angle E$; Use the AAS Congruence Theorem.
12. Given: $\angle A \cong \angle D$, $\angle C \cong \angle F$; Use the ASA Congruence Postulate.

Decide whether the triangles can be proven congruent by the given postulate or theorem.

13. $\triangle LMN \cong \triangle CBA$ by HL
14. $\triangle TWX \cong \triangle YWX$ by SSS

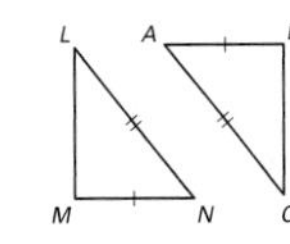

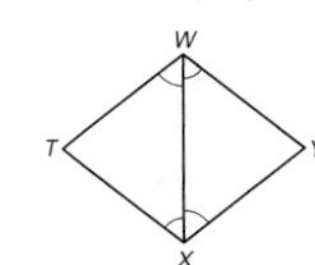

Answers

1. 25; obtuse
2. 15; obtuse
3. 20; acute
4. 10; equiangular
5. 75°
6. 6
7. 55°
8. 50°
9. $\overline{AC} \cong \overline{DF}$
10. $\overline{BC} \cong \overline{EF}$
11. $\overline{BC} \cong \overline{EF}$ or $\overline{AC} \cong \overline{DF}$
12. $\overline{AC} \cong \overline{DF}$
13. no
14. yes

Planning the Lesson

Plan and Prepare

- Warm-Up Exercises
- Notetaking Guide
- Pacing summary

Focus and Motivate

- Essential Question
- Motivating the Lesson

Teach

- Extra Example for each example in the book
- Key Questions to Ask for examples in the book
- Closing the Lesson summary and Essential Question at the end of each lesson
- Differentiated Instruction notes . . . AND MORE

---

1 PLAN AND PREPARE

Warm-Up Exercises

Transparency Available

Suppose that $\triangle XYZ \cong \triangle RST$. Complete each statement.

1. $\overline{XY} \cong$? $\overline{RS}$
2. $\angle Z \cong$? $\angle T$
3. $m\angle S = m\angle$? Y
4. If $\angle A \cong \angle B$, $m\angle A = (2x + 40)°$, and $m\angle B = (3x - 10)°$, find x. 50

Notetaking Guide

Transparency Available

Promotes interactive learning and notetaking skills, pp. 104–107.

Pacing

Basic: 2 days
Average: 2 days
Advanced: 2 days
Block: 1 block
• See *Teaching Guide/Lesson Plan.*

2 FOCUS AND MOTIVATE

Essential Question

Big Idea 2, p. 215

How can you use congruent triangles to prove angles or sides congruent? **Tell students they will learn how to answer this question by using corresponding parts of congruent triangles.**

4.6 Use Congruent Triangles

Before You used corresponding parts to prove triangles congruent.
Now You will use congruent triangles to prove corresponding parts congruent.
Why? So you can find the distance across a half pipe, as in Ex. 30.

Key Vocabulary
• corresponding parts, *p. 225*

By definition, congruent triangles have congruent corresponding parts. So, if you can prove that two triangles are congruent, you know that their corresponding parts must be congruent as well.

Standards

5.0 Students prove that triangles are congruent or similar, **and they are able to use the concept of corresponding parts of congruent triangles.**

16.0 Students perform basic constructions with a straightedge and compass, such as angle bisectors, perpendicular bisectors, and the line parallel to a given line through a point off the line.

EXAMPLE 1 Use congruent triangles

Explain how you can use the given information to prove that the hanglider parts are congruent.

GIVEN ▶ $\angle 1 \cong \angle 2$, $\angle RTQ \cong \angle RTS$
PROVE ▶ $\overline{QT} \cong \overline{ST}$

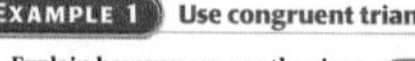

Solution

If you can show that $\triangle QRT \cong \triangle SRT$, you will know that $\overline{QT} \cong \overline{ST}$. First, copy the diagram and mark the given information. Then add the information that you can deduce. In this case, $\angle RQT$ and $\angle RST$ are supplementary to congruent angles, so $\angle RQT \cong \angle RST$. Also, $\overline{RT} \cong \overline{RT}$.

Mark given information. Add deduced information.

Two angle pai... AAS Congrue... parts of congr...

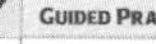

GUIDED PRACT...

1. *Explain* h... Since $\overline{BD} \cong$ B... are congruent... correspondin...

Resource Planning Guide

Chapter Resource Book
• Teaching Guide/Lesson Plan (pp. 74–75)
• Practice levels A, B, C (pp. 76–81)
• Study Guide (pp. 82–83)
• Catch-up for Absent Students (p. 84)
• Application (p. 85)
• Challenge (p. 86)

Workbooks
• Notetaking Guide (pp. 104–107)
• Practice Workbook (pp. 76–78)

Teaching Options
• **Power Presentations CD-ROM** provides dynamic electronic teaching resources for the classroom.
• **Activity Generator CD-ROM** provides editable activities for all ability levels.

Inter... • Eas... • Pow... • Acti... • Ani... • Test... • Onli... • eWo... • eEd... • @H...

EXAMPLE 2 Use congruent triangles for measurement

INDIRECT MEASUREMENT
When you cannot easily measure a length directly, you can make conclusions about the length *indirectly*, usually by calculations based on known lengths.

SURVEYING Use the following method to find the distance across a river, from point N to point P.

• Place a stake at K on the near side so that $\overline{NK} \perp \overline{NP}$.
• Find M, the midpoint of $\overline{NK}$.
• Locate the point L so that $\overline{NK} \perp \overline{KL}$ and L, P, and M are collinear.
• Explain how this plan allows you to find the distance.

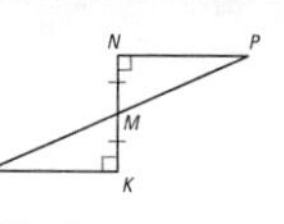

Solution

Because $\overline{NK} \perp \overline{NP}$ and $\overline{NK} \perp \overline{KL}$, $\angle N$ and $\angle K$ are congruent right angles. Because M is the midpoint of $\overline{NK}$, $\overline{NM} \cong \overline{KM}$. The vertical angles $\angle KML$ and $\angle NMP$ are congruent. So, $\triangle MLK \cong \triangle MPN$ by the ASA Congruence Postulate. Then, because corresponding parts of congruent triangles are congruent, $\overline{KL} \cong \overline{NP}$. So, you can find the distance NP across the river by measuring $\overline{KL}$.

EXAMPLE 3 Plan a proof involving pairs of triangles

Use the given information to write a plan for proof.

GIVEN ▶ $\angle 1 \cong \angle 2$, $\angle 3 \cong \angle 4$
PROVE ▶ $\triangle BCE \cong \triangle DCE$

Solution

In $\triangle BCE$ and $\triangle DCE$, you know $\angle 1 \cong \angle 2$ and $\overline{CE} \cong \overline{CE}$. If you can show that $\overline{CB} \cong \overline{CD}$, you can use the SAS Congruence Postulate.

To prove that $\overline{CB} \cong \overline{CD}$, you can first prove that $\triangle CBA \cong \triangle CDA$. You are given $\angle 1 \cong \angle 2$ and $\angle 3 \cong \angle 4$. $\overline{CA} \cong \overline{CA}$ by the Reflexive Property. You can use the ASA Congruence Postulate to prove that $\triangle CBA \cong \triangle CDA$.

▶ **Plan for Proof** Use the ASA Congruence Postulate to prove that $\triangle CBA \cong \triangle CDA$. Then state that $\overline{CB} \cong \overline{CD}$. Use the SAS Congruence Postulate to prove that $\triangle BCE \cong \triangle DCE$.

Animated Geometry at classzone.com

GUIDED PRACTICE for Examples 2 and 3

2. In Example 2, does it matter how far from point N you place a stake at point K? *Explain.* **See margin.**
3. Using the information in the diagram at the right, write a plan to prove that $\triangle PTU \cong \triangle UQP$. **See margin.**

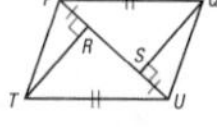

2. No; since M is the midpoint of $\overline{NK}$, $\overline{NM} \cong \overline{MK}$. No matter how far apart the stakes at K and M are placed, the triangles will be congruent by ASA.

3. Since you already know that $\overline{TU} \cong \overline{QP}$ and $\overline{UP} \cong \overline{PU}$ you need only show $\overline{PT} \cong \overline{UQ}$ to prove the triangles are congruent by SSS. This can be done by showing right triangles QSP and TRU are congruent by LL leading to right triangles USQ and PRT being congruent by LL which gives you $\overline{PT} \cong \overline{UQ}$.

Motivating the Lesson

Tell students that congruent triangles can be used to find distances that are difficult to measure directly. Tell them that in this lesson they will see some examples of how to do this.

3 TEACH

Extra Example 1

Use the given information to prove the parts of the kite are congruent.
Given: $\overline{GK}$ bisects $\angle FGH$ and $\angle FKH$.
Prove: $\overline{FK} \cong \overline{HK}$

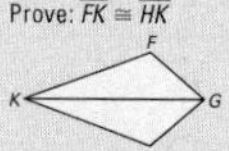

$\angle FGK \cong \angle HGK$ and $\angle FKG \cong \angle HKG$ by the def. of $\angle$ bisector. $\overline{GK} \cong \overline{GK}$ by the Refl. Prop. of $\cong$ Segs. Therefore $\triangle FGK \cong \triangle HGK$ by the ASA Cong. Post. So $\overline{FK} \cong \overline{HK}$ since Corr. Parts of $\cong$ $\triangle$s are $\cong$.

An **Animated Geometry** activity is available on-line for **Example 1.** This activity is also available on the **Power Presentations CD-ROM.**

Extra Example 2

If P is the midpoint of $\overline{MS}$, how wide is the bull's pasture? 40 ft

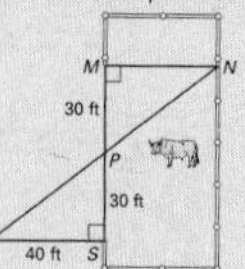

Differentiated Instruction

Kinesthetic Learners Take students outside to construct and solve a problem similar to **Example 2.** Find a distance that may be difficult to measure directly with a measuring tape and use congruent triangles to find the distance. Direct students to draw a diagram of the problem, make measurements, write distance measurements on the diagram, and use these measurements and the appropriate postulate to find the distance. See also the *Geometry Toolkit* for more strategies.

Practice and Apply

- Assignment Guide
- Differentiated Instruction
- Homework Check exercises
- Extra Practice references

4.6 EXERCISES

HOMEWORK KEY
○ = WORKED-OUT SOLUTIONS on p. WS1 for Exs. 19, 23, and 31
★ = STANDARDIZED TEST PRACTICE Exs. 2, 14, 31, and 36

SKILL PRACTICE

A

1. **VOCABULARY** Copy and complete: Corresponding parts of congruent triangles are _?_. congruent

2. ★ **WRITING** *Explain* why you might choose to use congruent triangles to measure the distance across a river. Give another example where it may be easier to measure with congruent triangles rather than directly.
Sample answer: You are unable to cross the river; measuring the distance across a lake.

EXAMPLES 1 and 2 on p. 256–257 for Exs. 3–11

CONGRUENT TRIANGLES **Tell which triangles you can show are congruent in order to prove the statement. What postulate or theorem would you use?**

3. $\angle A \cong \angle D$
$\triangle CBA$, $\triangle CBD$; SSS

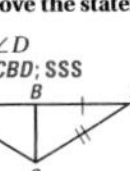

4. $\angle Q \cong \angle T$
$\triangle QPR$, $\triangle TPS$; SAS

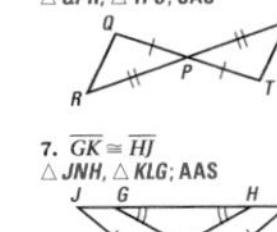

5. $\overline{JM} \cong \overline{LM}$
$\triangle JKM$, $\triangle LKM$; HL

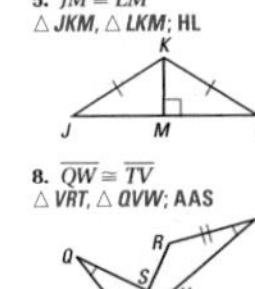

6. $\overline{AC} \cong \overline{BD}$
$\triangle CAD$, $\triangle BDA$; AAS

7. $\overline{GK} \cong \overline{HJ}$
$\triangle JNH$, $\triangle KLG$; AAS

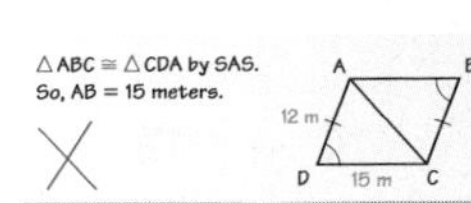

8. $\overline{QW} \cong \overline{TV}$
$\triangle VRT$, $\triangle QVW$; AAS

9. **ERROR ANALYSIS** *Describe* the error in the statement.
The angle is not the included angle; the triangles cannot be said to be congruent.

$\triangle ABC \cong \triangle CDA$ by SAS.
So, AB = 15 meters.

10. Show $\triangle VST \cong \triangle TUV$ by SSS since $\overline{VT} \cong \overline{TV}$ by the Reflexive Property of Congruence. Then use the Corresponding Parts of Congruent Triangles Theorem.

11. Show

PLANNING FOR PROOF **Use the diagram to write a plan for proof.**

10. **PROVE** ▶ $\angle S \cong \angle U$

11. **PROVE** ▶ $\overline{LM} \cong \overline{LQ}$

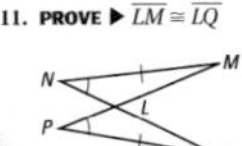

...nnecting any pair of ...entagons are congruent. Make a ...
diagonals are corresponding sides ...nt triangles; see margin for art.
...DEF, $m\angle A = 70°$, $m\angle B = 60°$, ...$= \left(\frac{y}{3} + 20\right)°$, and $m\angle F = (z^2 + 14)°$,

4.6 Use Congruent Triangles 259

4 PRACTICE AND APPLY

Assignment Guide

Answer Transparencies available for all exercises

Basic:
Day 1: pp. 259–263
Exs. 1–11, 28
Day 2: pp. 259–263
Exs. 12–17, 29–33, 41–46

Average:
Day 1: pp. 259–263
Exs. 1–11, 28, 41–43
Day 2: pp. 259–263
Exs. 12–14, 18–24, 29–36, 44–46

Advanced:
Day 1: pp. 259–263
Exs. 1, 2, 4–11, 27*, 28, 41–43
Day 2: pp. 259–263
Exs. 12–14, 19–26, 31–40*, 44–46

Block:
pp. 259–263
Exs. 1–14, 18–24, 28–36, 41–46

Differentiated Instruction

See *Geometry Best Practices Toolkit* for suggestions on addressing the needs of a diverse classroom.

Homework Check

For a quick check of student understanding of key concepts, go over the following exercises:
Basic: 4, 10, 16, 28, 32
Average: 6, 10, 18, 28, 32
Advanced: 8, 11, 20, 28, 32

Extra Practice

- Student Edition, p. 903
- Chapter 4 Resource Book: Practice levels A, B, C, pp. 76–81

Practice Worksheet

An easily-readable reduced practice page (with answers) for this lesson can be found on p. 214C.

259

40. **CHALLENGE** In the diagram of pentagon *ABCDE*, $\overline{AB} \parallel \overline{EC}$, $\overline{AC} \parallel \overline{ED}$, $\overline{AB} \cong \overline{ED}$, and $\overline{AC} \cong \overline{EC}$. Write a proof that shows $\overline{AD} \cong \overline{EB}$. See margin.

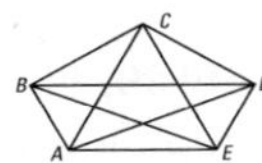

MIXED REVIEW

How many lines can be drawn that fit each description? Copy the diagram and sketch all the lines. *(p. 147)* 41–43. See margin for art.

41. Line(s) through *B* and parallel to $\overleftrightarrow{AC}$ one
42. Line(s) through *A* and perpendicular to $\overleftrightarrow{BC}$ one
43. Line(s) through *D* and *C* one

PREVIEW
Prepare for Lesson 4.7 in Exs. 44–46.

The variable expressions represent the angle measures of a triangle. Find the measure of each angle. Then classify the triangle by its angles. *(p. 217)*

44. $m\angle A = x°$
$m\angle B = (4x)°$
$m\angle C = (5x)°$
18°, 72°, 90°; right triangle

45. $m\angle A = x°$
$m\angle B = (5x)°$
$m\angle C = (x + 19)°$
23°, 115°, 42°; obtuse triangle

46. $m\angle A = (x - 22)°$
$m\angle B = (x + 16)°$
$m\angle C = (2x - 14)°$
28°, 66°, 86°; acute triangle

QUIZ for Lessons 4.4–4.6

Decide which method, SAS, ASA, AAS, or HL, can be used to prove that the triangles are congruent. *(pp. 240, 249)*

1. 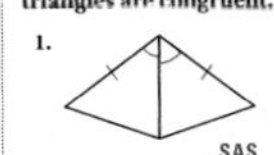
SAS

2. 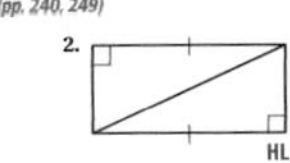
HL

3. 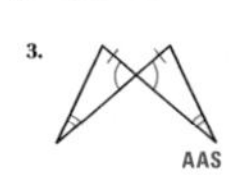
AAS

Use the given information to write a proof. 4–6. See margin.

4. **GIVEN** ▶ $\angle BAC \cong \angle DCA$, $\overline{AB} \cong \overline{CD}$
PROVE ▶ $\triangle ABC \cong \triangle CDA$ *(p. 240)*

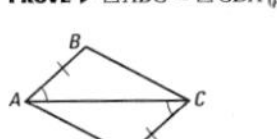

5. **GIVEN** ▶ $\angle W \cong \angle Z$, $\overline{VW} \cong \overline{YZ}$
PROVE ▶ $\triangle VWX \cong \triangle YZX$ *(p. 249)*

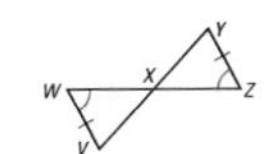

6. Write a plan for a proof. *(p. 256)*
GIVEN ▶ $\overline{PQ} \cong \overline{MN}$, $m\angle P = m\angle M = 90°$
PROVE ▶ $\overline{QL} \cong \overline{NL}$

EXTRA PRACTICE for Lesson 4.6, p. 903 **ONLINE QUIZ** at classzone.com 263

41.

42.

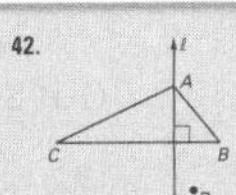

43.

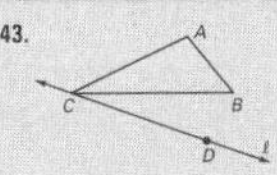

5 ASSESS AND RETEACH

Daily Homework Quiz

Transparency Available

1. Tell which triangles you can show are congruent in order to prove $AE = DE$. What postulate or theorem would you use?
$\triangle AEC \cong \triangle DEB$ by the AAS Cong. Thm. or by the ASA Cong. Post.

2. Write a plan to prove $\angle 1 \cong \angle 2$.
Show $\overline{LM} \cong \overline{LM}$ by the Refl. Prop. of $\cong$ Segs. Hence $\triangle OLM \cong \triangle NML$ by the SAS Cong. Post. This gives $\angle NLM \cong \angle OML$, since Corr. Parts of $\cong$ ▵ are $\cong$. So $\angle 1 \cong \angle 2$ by the Vert. ∠ Thm. and properties of $\cong$ ∠.

Online Quiz
Available at **classzone.com**

Diagnosis/Remediation

- Practice A, B, C in Chapter 4 Resource Book, pp. 76–81
- Study Guide in Chapter 4 Resource Book, pp. 82–83
- Practice Workbook, pp. 76–78
- @HomeTutor

Challenge

Additional challenge is available in the Chapter 4 Resource Book, p. 86.

Quiz

An easily-readable reduced copy of the quiz (with answers) on Lessons 4.4–4.6 from the Assessment Book can be found on p. 214G.

40, Quiz 4–6. See Additional Answers beginning on p. AA1.

263

Assess and Reteach

- Daily Homework Quiz
- Online Quiz for each lesson
- Diagnosis/Remediation
- Challenge

Pacing the Course

The Pacing Chart below shows the number of days allotted for each chapter. The Regular Schedule requires 160 days. The Block Schedule requires 80 days. These time frames include days for review and assessment: 2 days per chapter for the Regular Schedule and 1 day per chapter for the Block Schedule. Semester and trimester divisions are indicated by blue and green rules, respectively.

	SEMESTER 1						SEMESTER 2					
CHAPTER	1	2	3	4	5	6	7	8	9	10	11	12
Regular Schedule	12	14	12	16	12	14	14	12	14	12	14	14
Block Schedule	6	7	6	8	6	7	7	6	7	6	7	7
	Trimester 1				Trimester 2				Trimester 3			

Assignments are provided with each lesson for a basic course, an average course, an advanced course, and a block-schedule course. Each of the four courses covers all twelve chapters.

Basic Course

The basic course is intended for students who enter with below-average mathematical and problem solving skills. Assignments include:

- spiral review of pre-course and on-level topics through Skills Review Handbook and Extra Practice references
- substantial work with the skills and concepts presented in the lesson
- straightforward applications of these skills and concepts
- test preparation and mixed review exercises

Average Course

The average course is intended for students who enter with typical mathematical and problem-solving skills. Assignments include:

- substantial work with the skills and concepts presented in the lesson
- applications of these skills and concepts
- test preparation and mixed review exercises

Advanced Course

The advanced course is intended for students who enter with above-average mathematical and problem-solving skills. Assignments include:

- substantial work with the skills and concepts presented in the lesson
- more complex applications and challenge exercises
- test preparation and mixed review exercises
- optional extra challenge exercises provided in the Chapter Resource Books

Block-Schedule Course

The block-schedule course is intended for schools that use a block schedule. It covers the same content as the regular-schedule course. The exercises assigned are comparable to the exercises for the average course.

The Pacing and Assignment Guide for each chapter is located on the interleaved pages preceding the chapter. Part of the Pacing Chart for Chapter 4 is shown here.

Regular-Schedule Chart

This chart provides pacing for the basic, average, and advanced courses.

REGULAR SCHEDULE

Lesson	Les. Day	BASIC	AVERAGE	ADVANCED
4.1	Day 1	EP p. 896 Exs. 24–29; pp. 221–224 Exs. 1–7, 9–19 odd, 21–29, 40–49, 54, 57, 60, 61	pp. 221–224 Exs. 1–7, 8–26 even, 27–34, 40–52, 55, 58, 62	pp. 221–224 Exs. 1–7, 10, 13, 16, 19, 20, 27, 28, 31–40*, 42–53*, 56, 59, 63
4.2	Day 1	pp. 228–231 Exs. 1–14	pp. 228–231 Exs. 1–14, 36–40	pp. 228–231 Exs. 1–4, 7–14, 22*, 36–40
	Day 2	pp. 228–231 Exs. 15–19, 23–28, 33–40	pp. 228–231 Exs. 15–21, 23–31, 33–35	pp. 228–231 Exs. 15–21, 24–35*
4.3	Day 1	pp. 236–239 Exs. 1–17, 22–27, 31–37	pp. 236–239 Exs. 1–8, 10–14 even, 16–20, 22–29, 31–37 odd	pp. 236–239 Exs. 1–4, 7, 8, 11, 12, 14–30*, 33, 36, 37

Block-Schedule Chart

This chart provides pacing for the block-schedule course.

BLOCK SCHEDULE

DAY 1	DAY 2	DAY 3	DAY 4	DAY 5	DAY 6	DAY 7	DAY 8
4.1	**4.2 (CONT.)**	**4.4**	**4.5**	**4.6**	**4.7**	**4.8**	**REVIEW**
pp. 221–224 Exs. 1–7, 8–26 even, 27–34, 40–52, 55, 58, 62	pp. 228–231 Exs. 15–21, 23–31, 33–35	pp. 243–246 Exs. 1, 2, 4–8 even, 9–27, 31–39, 42–48 even	pp. 252–255 Exs. 1, 2, 4–7, 9–21, 23–34, 36–42 even	pp. 259–263 Exs. 1–14, 18–24, 28–36, 41–46	pp. 267–270 Exs. 1, 2, 4–6, 8–10, 12–14, 16–19, 21–31, 39–48, 52–57, 59	pp. 276–279 Exs. 1, 2, 4, 8, 10–16 even, 17–36, 38–43, 45–49 odd, 51	pp. 282–285 Exs. 1–29
4.2	**4.3**						**ASSESS**
pp. 228–231 Exs. 1–14, 36–40	pp. 236–239 Exs. 1–8, 10–14 even, 16–20, 22–29, 31–37 odd						Chapter 4 Test

Assignment Guide

An assignment guide for each lesson is provided at the beginning of the exercise set. Assignments are given for basic, average, advanced, and block-schedule courses.

Assignment Guide

Basic

Day 1: EP p. 896 Exs. 24–29; pp. 221–224 Exs. 1–7, 9–19 odd, 21–29, 40–49, 54, 57, 60, 61

Average

Day 1: pp. 221–224 Exs. 1–7, 8–26 even, 27–34, 40–52, 55, 58, 62

Advanced

Day 1: pp. 221–224 Exs. 1–7, 10, 13, 16, 19, 20, 27, 28, 31–40*, 42–53*, 56, 59, 63

Block

pp. 221–224 Exs. 1–7, 8–26 even, 27–34, 40–52, 55, 58, 62

Meeting your planning and teaching needs

Contents

The following pages include information about the *Geometry* program and explain how it reflects current research in mathematics instruction.

A letter from the authors

Dear Colleagues,

We wanted to create a program that would help your students succeed in mathematics and make your teaching job easier. To achieve these objectives, we reviewed and addressed the curriculum and assessment guidelines of many states. We also developed an extensive collection of teacher resources to assist you in the classroom. Our overall goal was to prepare your students both for important assessments and for future mathematics courses.

Our commitment has always been to writing books that contain accurate mathematics, sound pedagogy, and student-friendly presentations. We believe that a balance of teaching approaches is generally most effective. Therefore, we combine clear, straightforward instruction in concepts and skills with thought-provoking student activities, relevant real-life applications, and powerful strategies for problem solving and communication. We have also incorporated feedback from many teachers and students nationwide who have used earlier editions or pilot materials in the classroom.

During more than 16 years of working together as an author team, we have remained dedicated to helping students at all levels achieve high mathematics standards. Our textbooks provide differentiated instruction for struggling students, carefully constructed examples and practice for the majority of students, and demanding challenge exercises for more advanced students.

We wish you success as you strive to give every student in your classroom a quality mathematics education.

Ron Larson

Laurie Boswell

Tim Kanold

Lee Stiff

A Program You Can Trust

A program you can count on to help students gain understanding and achieve success

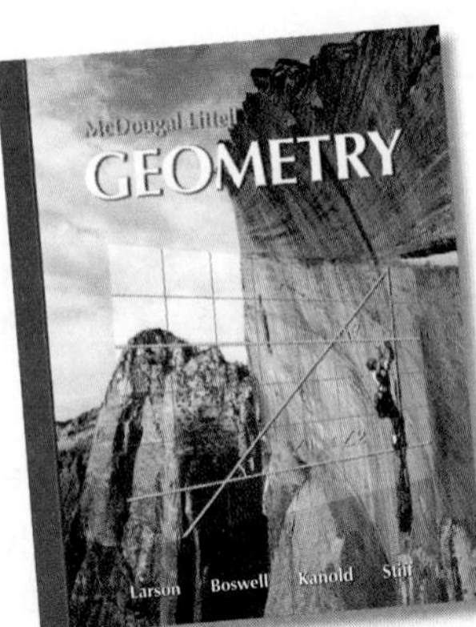

McDougal Littell Geometry is a program you can count on to teach the mathematical concepts and methods your students need to know to meet high curriculum standards and succeed on high-stakes tests. Including the appropriate content, however, is not enough. The math must be presented in a way that students can understand and that will motivate them to learn. The distinguished author team of *McDougal Littell Geometry* and the thorough, research-based planning and development process ensure that students gain conceptual understanding and achieve success on important assessments.

Distinguished Author Team

The experienced, expert author team of Ron Larson, Laurie Boswell, Timothy Kanold, and Lee Stiff brings a wealth of mathematical expertise, writing talent, and classroom teaching and curriculum planning experience from middle school through college to the creation of this program. Lead author Ron Larson has been writing highly-respected and widely-used textbooks for more than 20 years, and each new book benefits from the comments of the many teachers and students who used earlier editions.

Standards-Based Instruction and Assessment

In planning the outline and writing the textbook, the authors paid careful attention to state curriculum standards and state assessment objectives from all states to make sure that the important mathematical concepts and skills were included and given appropriate emphasis. The authors also made sure that the outline and course content fully addressed the standards of national organizations such as the National Assessment of Educational Progress (see page T59).

... validated by research

Supporting Best Practices from Research

Recent research studies have confirmed strategies for increasing student achievement. These strategies, which reflect the best practices of successful teachers, can help all students learn more effectively. The authors kept this research in mind as they planned and wrote *Geometry*, so that the content, organization, and instructional strategies in the program would make it easy for you to implement best-practice instruction in your classroom.

Comprehensive Research and Review

Several years prior to publication, the authors and teams of editors, consultants, graphic designers, professional researchers, and experts in content, instruction, and technology began gathering and analyzing the extensive data on which this program is based. Data were gathered in the following ways:

- **Classroom Visits** Discussions and classroom observations took place in schools throughout the country to determine the key needs of teachers and students, the obstacles that they face in achieving their goals, and the types of materials that can help them achieve success.
- **Nationwide Research Surveys** Comprehensive mail surveys on Geometry curriculum needs, instructional practices, student achievement levels, and teacher preferences regarding instructional materials were conducted early in the development process to guide the planning of the program.
- **Teacher Panels** Panels of expert teachers from different areas of the country participated in the development of the program by identifying instructional and curriculum needs, reviewing prototype outlines and sample materials for both print and electronic materials, and providing suggestions for teaching-support publications.
- **Student Discussion Groups** Discussion groups were held with Geometry students to determine the textbook characteristics that make it easy or hard for them to learn and the extent to which they have access to and feel comfortable using electronic products.
- **Focus Tests** Focus tests in which teachers discussed their instructional goals and evaluated sample student and teacher materials were held in different areas of the country. The teachers were chosen to represent the wide range of types of schools, philosophies of instruction, and teacher characteristics (like number of years of teaching) in the teaching population. The feedback from these diverse groups was used to revise and refine the project plans.
- **Curriculum Advisers and Reviewers** The Curriculum Advisers and Reviewers listed on page T4 participated in planning the program and read all the proof for the student edition in detail with regard to clarity, accuracy, and appropriateness for classroom use. Other teacher reviewers read selected chapters for these characteristics.
- **Learner Verification** The *Algebra 1, Geometry, Algebra 2 Research-Based Framework and Learner Verification* book provides information about the instructional research on which the program was based as well as classroom research demonstrating the effectiveness of the program.

Professional Articles

What is mathematics?

The Bigger Picture of Mathematics

by Dr. Ron Larson,
Lead Author of the
Larson Mathematics Series

What is Mathematics? You would think that this is an easy question to answer. But, it isn't.

Was mathematics discovered or was it invented? Is mathematics a logical system that exists devoid of applications or is mathematics a problem solving language whose very essence is solving real-life problems? Is correct calculation an important part of mathematics or is it only important to be able to "set the problem up" correctly? Is mathematics a system of rules or is mathematics a way of thinking?

As mathematics teachers, it is important for us to realize that mathematics is all of these things. We need to be careful to pass this understanding on to our students so that they will not have a narrow answer to the question "What is Mathematics?" We need to show them the bigger picture of mathematics.

Mathematics as Calculation

Most people equate mathematics with calculation. While this view of mathematics is too limited, it is still true that calculation plays a critical role in mathematics.

I worry when I hear educators dismissing calculation as "something best left to calculators" or even worse, as "drill and kill." I prefer to think about other phrases that describe the importance of calculation, such as "practice makes perfect."

... in our world

When I drive across a bridge, I am thankful that the teacher of the civil engineer who designed the bridge believed in the importance of correct calculation.

The point is that part of our job as mathematics teachers is to help prepare skilled professionals who can fly planes, prescribe medicines, and do any of thousands of other technically difficult jobs.

But, there may be a stronger reason for teaching students to calculate correctly. It is simply the way that students learn best. They learn specific examples first. Generalization comes later.

After a career in mathematics, it is clear to me that we derive important insights into a mathematical theory when we see how it relates to actual calculations.

Mathematics as a Field of Study

Mathematics, of course, is not simply a collection of techniques for calculating sums, products, slopes, and so on. Mathematics has content. It has a vocabulary of defined and undefined terms. It has a collection of axioms and theorems.

The vocabulary and rules of mathematics comprise much of the curriculum we teach from grade school through high school.

Like it or not, the vocabulary of mathematics is formal. It has to be in order to provide for clear communication. It is important that students know the difference between an expression and an equation. We *evaluate* an expression. We *solve* an equation.

The rules of mathematics are also formal—they are rigid and unforgiving. We don't do students favors when we allow them to approach mathematics in a sloppy manner. Mathematics must be approached carefully, with the confidence that comes from knowing its rules.

Mathematics as a Modeling Language

It is difficult to know which of the many faces of mathematics was the first to show itself on our planet. Surely, one of the first was the use of symbols and calculations to model and solve real-life problems.

To me, the perennial debate about the virtues of applied versus pure mathematics isn't productive. From a historical point of view, it seems clear that both must be taught—hand-in-hand—from grade school through high school.

To be good at mathematics, students must understand the various types of models we use: linear, quadratic, cubic, radical, rational, exponential, logarithmic, and trigonometric. They must learn to translate real-life situations to mathematical models, obtain mathematical solutions, and then translate those solutions back into the context of the real-life application.

Mathematics as Logical Thought

Perhaps the most difficult task we face as mathematics teachers is to teach our students to think logically.

The real world is filled with logical fallacy—such as some advertisements and political slogans that contain illogical arguments. As mathematics teachers, we can improve our nation and our world by teaching careful logical thought to our students.

In light of all these things, I hope that this text helps your students get a view of the bigger picture of mathematics.

Continued

The Bigger Picture in *Geometry*

The following chart shows how the various ways of looking at mathematics described in the article on pages T50–T51 are developed across the *Geometry* book.

Because these strands of thought are integrated throughout the book, the lesson references here are selected examples in each category, not a comprehensive listing.

Mathematics as Calculation

Performing calculations	Using midpoint and distance formulas (1.3), finding angle measures (1.4, 1.5, 8.1), finding area (1.7, 11.1–11.3, 11.5–11.6), using ratios and proportions (6.1, 6.2), using the Pythagorean Theorem (7.1–7.4), using trigonometry (7.5–7.7), finding surface area (12.2, 12.3, 12.6, 12.7), finding volume (12.4, 12.5, 12.7)

Mathematics as a Field of Study

Using mathematical vocabulary	Points, lines, planes, rays, and angles (1.1–1.5), polygons (1.6, 4.1, 8.6), inductive and deductive reasoning (2.1, 2.3), space figures (11.1), transformations (4.7, 4.8, 6.7, 9.1, 9.3–9.7)
Knowing mathematical principles	Using postulates (2.4), using properties of equality and congruence (2.5, 2.6), writing proofs (2.6, 3.3, 5.1, 5.6)

Mathematics as a Modeling Language

Using mathematical models	Notation for translations (4.8), coordinate proof (5.1), composition of transformations (9.5), indirect measurement (6.4, 7.5), vectors (9.1), matrices as models for transformations (9.2), geometric probability (11.7), algebraic models (throughout; see also Algebra Reviews and Skills Review Handbook)
Translating real-life situations to mathematical models, obtaining solutions, then translating solutions back into real-life contexts	Skating rink (1.7), shopping mall (2.6), roller coaster (3.4), sculpture (4.1), sightseeing (5.5), city travel (6.6), swimming pool (7.3), carpentry (8.4), softball (9.2), gardening (10.4), commuter trains (10.7), track (11.4), transportation (11.7), compact disks (12.2), consumer economics (12.7)

Mathematics as Logical Thought

Thinking logically	Inductive and deductive reasoning (2.1, 2.3), counterexamples (2.1), conditional statements (2.2), using properties (2.5, 2.6), writing proofs (2.6, 3.3, 5.1, 5.6), analysis and reasoning exercises (throughout)

Professional Articles

Providing Universal Access

Approaching students with different needs

We want *all* students to develop computational, procedural, and problem solving skills to provide a solid foundation for further study in mathematics. In most classrooms, however, students present a variety of achievement levels, skills, and needs, and they do not arrive at competencies at the same time or in the same way.

Geometry is organized so that much of the differentiation for special needs students is built into the program. Simpler concepts are introduced before more complex ones. Activities provide students with models for conceptual understanding of the mathematical reasoning behind each key concept. Ample practice is provided, and each lesson includes exercises that recall and use skills and understandings from previous chapters. Mathematical reasoning is emphasized and challenge exercises are included throughout each chapter.

You can use the table below to help plan your approach to students with various needs. See also the *Geometry Best Practices Toolkit* for more suggestions.

FOUR BASIC STUDENT GROUPS

Advanced Group	Grade Level Group	Underachieving Group	Intensive Needs Group
Advanced students have already completed some of the grade-level material. They make rapid progress and become bored with repetition. They may have been formally identified as gifted or talented in the area of mathematics.	Students achieving at grade level may have minor, occasional difficulties but they can be assisted to maintain their progress with extra practice and individual or group assistance on an as-needed basis.	These learners are not achieving at expected grade level but can, with a program that provides targeted assistance. Systematic differentiation such as preteaching, reteaching, and additional instructional time should be planned.	Intensive needs students are those whose performance is two or more standard deviations below the mean on standardized measures. These students will probably already be eligible for special education services.
SUGGESTED PLAN **1.** Assess what these students already know. **2.** Allow these students to "test out" of chapters or assignments. **3.** Substitute challenging assignments for easier ones. **4.** Modify instruction so that it is more complex or more in-depth.	**SUGGESTED PLAN** **1.** Assess what these students already know. **2.** Progress through *Geometry* at the recommended pace and sequence. **3.** On an ad hoc basis, review or provide additional practice as needed.	**SUGGESTED PLAN** **1.** Assess what these students already know. **2.** Provide additional scaffolding and the instructional variations suggested in this book. **3.** Focus on the key concepts and present material systematically. **4.** Vary the kinds of instruction so that students have several opportunities to understand. **5.** Provide additional practice homework.	**SUGGESTED PLAN** **1.** Assess what these students already know. **2.** Determine if these students have an IEP. **3.** Refer students for special education testing or child study team discussion; enlist the help of specialists. **4.** Carefully consider each student's most appropriate placement in mathematics. **5.** Use the specific suggestions for underachieving learners.

Professional Articles

Maximizing Success for English Learners

Accommodating various levels of reading and math achievement

English learners in your classroom may be at, behind, or ahead of grade expectations in mathematics. You can maximize success for English learners by assessing each student's competencies in mathematics and English to form a basis for program planning. The table below summarizes the attributes of various English learners and how you can help accommodate their needs.

In the *Geometry Best Practices Toolkit*, you will find suggestions to help you modify curriculum and instruction so the content is accessible to English learners. The suggestions and activities are designed to teach mathematical vocabulary, explain mathematical concepts in a variety of ways, and dissect the structure of word problems.

	Low Mathematics Achievement		High Mathematics Achievement	
	Who is the student?	**What to do?**	**Who is the student?**	**What to do?**
Low Reading Achievement	• Student may be new to the class, school, or country. • Student may have had inadequate schooling. • Student may have moved a lot. • Student may be unmotivated or have test anxiety. • Low reading achievement may be depressing mathematics scores. • Student may have gaps and holes in knowledge. • Student may need special education assistance.	• Examine cumulative folder for other testing, notes, etc. • Ask questions about language use and prior schooling. • Delay any testing for a week or two. Help student feel comfortable in the class during that period of time. • Administer mathematics achievement test and reading test, in an individual setting. • Assess this student at weekly intervals and monitor classroom work to determine if progress is being made. • Look at the English Learners suggestions in each chapter.	• Student has had good prior mathematics instruction. • Mathematics is an area where this student can excel. • Math achievement level may actually be higher than scores indicate. (Limited English reading skills affect math achievement as well.) • Word problems will be especially difficult.	• Mathematics instruction should proceed at normal or near normal pace. • Student should be involved in a systematic English language development program and intensive reading program outside of mathematics class. • Spend part of each class period on vocabulary study. • Provide student with a bilingual dictionary or math glossary and a mathematics text in the home language. • Look at the English Learners suggestions in each chapter for those that are most useful.
	Who is the student?	**What to do?**	**Who is the student?**	**What to do?**
High Reading Achievement	• Student may have been designated as an English learner because oral skills lag behind reading skills. • Student may not test well in mathematics. • Most students can make rapid progress in mathematics; a few may have learning difficulties that require the help of a specialist.	• Assess mathematics achievement in a variety of ways. • Concentrate on developing oral fluency. • Focus on vocabulary specific to mathematics. • Use a student's reading ability to improve his or her math scores.	• Student may be ready for designation as a fluent English speaker. • May need extra study in the specialized vocabulary of mathematics. Complex syntax may present obstacles to performance. • Given systematic instruction, this student should be able to achieve at or above grade level.	• Scan all of the suggestions for English learners in each chapter and progress through the ones the student needs as quickly as possible. • Monitor carefully to make sure this student continues to progress at a reasonable pace.

Differentiating Instruction

Providing material to reach all students

All students, whether they are struggling, average, or advanced learners, must have opportunities to make continuing progress in developing the skills they need to become successful adults. To develop these skills, students need to participate in courses that are based on challenging curriculum standards and assessment objectives. *McDougal Littell Geometry* has been designed around sound, challenging curriculum standards. Through ongoing assessment and practice with test-taking skills and standardized test formats, this program prepares students for high-stakes tests.

The *McDougal Littell Geometry* program provides you with helpful materials for differentiating instruction to reach all students, for assessing student progress throughout the course, and for diagnosing student understanding in order to provide appropriate prescription and remediation. The charts below illustrate some of the ways in which this program helps you differentiate for the diverse classroom.

PLANNING AND MOTIVATING THE LESSON

Feature	Description
Student Edition: Chapter Prerequisite Skills	Exercises at the beginning of each chapter that review pre-chapter vocabulary and skills
Student Edition: Investigating Geometry Activities	Pre-lesson activities where students explore concepts and discover mathematical results
Teacher's Edition: Pacing and Assignment Guides	Schedules for teaching the lessons of each chapter, along with three levels of exercise assignments for every lesson (basic, average, and advanced)
Teacher's Edition: Warm-Up Exercises	Exercises that review skills needed for the upcoming lesson; also available on transparencies
Teaching Guides with Lesson Plans (in Chapter Resource Books)	Tips for getting students ready for each lesson, teaching the lesson, assigning homework, and assessing students' knowledge
Best Practices Toolkit	A collection of effective teaching strategies, pre-AP resources, "teacher survival" activities (for use at the start of the school year, before vacation, etc.), and teacher tool transparencies
Easy Planner	Software that provides customizable lesson plans as well as all print teaching resources in an electronic format
Activity Generator	Software that offers leveled activities for each lesson and teaching commentary to guide students from the concrete to the abstract
Animated Geometry	Interactive electronic activities that support textbook lessons and exercises

Continued

... in the diverse classroom

TEACHING THE LESSON

Feature	Description
Student Edition: Guided Practice	Problems for each example that help you monitor how well students are grasping concepts and skills as you present the lesson
Student Edition: Leveled Exercise Sets	Exercise sets for each lesson that are divided into three difficulty levels (A, B, and C); levels are labeled in the Teacher's Edition
Student Edition: Problem Solving Workshops	Features that present alternative methods for solving an example from the preceding lesson
Teacher's Edition: Extra Examples	Additional examples modeled after each example in the textbook
Teacher's Edition: Differentiated Instruction Notes	Tips for tailoring instruction to students of different abilities and learning styles
Chapter Resource Books	Booklets for every chapter that include a chapter study guide, a project, catch-up for absent students, and additional activities, applications, cumulative review, and challenge exercises
Notetaking Guide	A workbook that gives students a framework for recording the key concepts of every lesson
@HomeTutor	Software that provides animated examples and instruction, self-scoring exercises, and customized student progress reports
Power Presentations: The Electronic Classroom	All the classroom resources needed to teach an interactive lesson using Microsoft PowerPoint

REVIEWING AND ASSESSING

Feature	Description
Student Edition: Skills Review Handbook	Examples and practice for reviewing essential prerequisite skills from earlier courses
Student Edition: Extra Practice	Exercises for each chapter that can be used by students who need more practice or who want to review for chapter tests
Benchmark Tests	Tests for measuring student progress, including a Pre-Course Test and End-of-Course Tests
Remediation Book	A guide containing examples, practice, and helpful hints for remediating deficiencies revealed by benchmark tests
Assessment Book (English and Spanish)	A resource that provides quizzes, three levels of chapter tests, SAT/ACT chapter tests, cumulative tests, and alternative assessment
Spanish Study Guide	Extra examples and practice in Spanish
Student Resources in Spanish	Chapter reviews, chapter tests, and standardized test preparation and practice in Spanish
Test Generator	Software that creates customized, editable tests and practice worksheets based on topics you select
McDougal Littell Assessment System	Innovative standards-based assessment software that helps you test, score, report, and reteach

Professional Articles

Teaching vital skills for today and the future

Reading, Writing, Notetaking

Vital Skills Today more than ever, students need strong skills in reading, writing, and notetaking in mathematics in order to understand course content, be successful on important state and national assessments, and develop the ability to become independent learners. Acquiring these skills in a Geometry course will build an important foundation for more advanced courses and for adult life. *McDougal Littell Geometry* provides many opportunities in the textbook and in the teacher's materials to help students develop their reading, writing, and notetaking skills.

Recent Research Recent brain research and classroom research in reading and writing have provided new insights into learning and also confirmed the value of well-known practices of successful teachers. Although the focus of this research is often on reading in language arts and social studies, many of the strategies also help those reading mathematical material. Two important aspects of reading addressed by research are vocabulary development and reading comprehension. *Geometry* offers substantial learning support in these core areas.

Vocabulary Development

The textbook provides strong support to students in learning, practicing, and reviewing vocabulary. In the Prerequisite Skills box on the opening page of each chapter, key review words are practiced in the Vocabulary exercises. In the Big Ideas box on the facing page, the key vocabulary words for the chapter are listed. Then, at the beginning of each lesson, the key vocabulary for the lesson appears under the Vocabulary list, and new vocabulary in the lesson is emphasized by boldface type with yellow highlighting. Reading notes in the margin serve as a built-in vocabulary, reading, and problem solving tutor. In the Teacher's Edition, Reading Strategy, Vocabulary, and other notes suggest ways teachers can help students read and learn new vocabulary words. See SE pp. 70, 145, 217, 296, 305; TE pp. 265, 312, 407, 485, 516.

Vocabulary

Discuss with students whether each side of an equilateral triangle can be called a leg of the triangle. Call attention to how the legs of an isosceles triangle are defined. Have students note that the word is applied only to isosceles triangles that have exactly two congruent sides.

In the Exercises, the Skill Practice exercises include vocabulary as well as writing exercises. The Chapter Reviews provide a list of key vocabulary and include vocabulary exercises. See SE pp. 19, 82, 344.

Various sections throughout the *Best Practices Toolkit* give specific suggestions for helping students understand and remember vocabulary. The Strategies for Reading Mathematics on pp. 9–32 contain visual glossaries for some of the key vocabulary in each chapter. Also see, the Strategies for Effective Teaching, pp. 145–156.

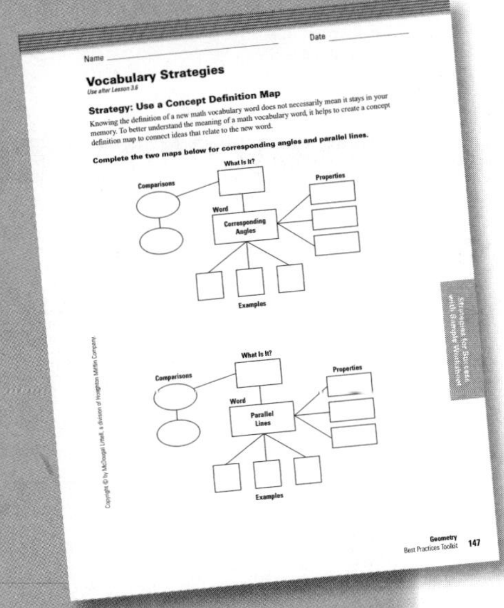

Name ______________ Date ______________

Vocabulary Strategies

Use after Lesson 3.6

Strategy: Use a Concept Definition Map

Knowing the definition of a new math vocabulary word does not necessarily mean it stays in your memory. To better understand the meaning of a math vocabulary word, it helps to create a concept definition map to connect ideas that relate to the new word.

Complete the two maps below for corresponding angles and parallel lines.

Geometry Best Practices Toolkit 147

PROFESSIONAL DEVELOPMENT

Reading Comprehension

The student textbook and teacher's materials provide strategies to help students to identify the main idea of a lesson or feature, understand the vocabulary, know what's important in the lesson, and be active readers.

Establishing a Context A useful comprehension strategy supported by both brain and classroom research is connecting new learning to prior knowledge. This strategy is incorporated throughout *Geometry* in the Before/Now/Why sections at the beginning of chapters and Before/Now/Why lists at the beginnings of lessons. In the Teacher's Edition, a Motivating the Lesson note in each lesson helps teachers give students a real-life context to help them anticipate the math facts covered in the lesson. See SE pp. 292–293, 354–355, 473; TE pp. 3, 235, 398, 543, 660.

Facilitating Understanding In order to create a student-friendly book, the authors kept these principles in mind as they wrote: Students can learn new concepts more easily when they are presented in short sentences that use simple syntax and are accompanied by appropriate proofs, tables, charts, and diagrams. Clear definitions that enable students to determine easily whether a particular mathematical object fits the definition or not are essential for comprehension. Students need special help in understanding the symbols of mathematics and knowing how to use them in writing mathematical expressions. See SE pp. 11, 43, 217.

Reflecting on Learning An effective strategy for increasing both reading comprehension and thinking skills is reflection on what has been read or learned and how it was learned (metacognition). The Chapter Review pages in each chapter review what students learned in the chapter. Throughout the book, students explain their reasoning in Short Response, Extended Response, and Reasoning exercises. In the Teacher's Edition, Essential Questions, Key Questions to Ask, and Activity Assessments all suggest questions to ask to test understanding and promote classroom discussions. See SE pp. 282–285, 377, 387; TE pp. 161, 234, 373, 475, 514, 588.

Using Graphic Organizers Graphic organizers such as charts, flow proofs, Venn diagrams, or concept maps can be especially helpful for classifying mathematical objects such as types of numbers or types of geometric figures. These organizers are used throughout the textbook. See SE pp. 40, 47, 244, 367, 688.

Writing Opportunities

In order to become good writers, students need frequent opportunities to practice their writing skills. These opportunities occur throughout the textbook in the Short Response, Extended Response, Reasoning, and Writing exercises, as well as in the Investigating Geometry Activities. See SE pp. 40, 47, 244, 367, 688.

Effective Notetaking

The authors identified the goal of helping students develop their notetaking skills as an important objective of the program, and they have incorporated many notetaking aids into the program. See, especially, the Key Concept, Concept Summary, and Theorem and Postulate boxes in many lessons in the textbook which carry the subhead For Your Notebook, and the Notetaking Guide workbooks and overhead visuals in the teacher's materials. See SE pp. 16, 114, 381, 397.

KEY CONCEPT *For Your Notebook*

The Midpoint Formula

The coordinates of the midpoint of a segment are the averages of the x-coordinates and of the y-coordinates of the endpoints.

If $A(x_1, y_1)$ and $B(x_2, y_2)$ are points in a coordinate plane, then the midpoint M of $\overline{AB}$ has coordinates

$$\left(\frac{x_1 + x_2}{2}, \frac{y_1 + y_2}{2}\right).$$

National Assessment of Educational Progress

The NAEP is used to assess student understanding of math across the nation. The chart below lists the topics assessed by the NAEP, and lessons and features from *McDougal Littell Geometry* that address them.

Number Properties and Operations

1. Number sense	1.7, 6.1–6.3, 7.5, 7.6, 11.4, 11.5, Algebra Reviews (Chs. 2, 4, 6), Skills Review Handbook
2. Estimation	1.4 (Exs. 56–61), 5.2 (Ex. 28), 5.3 (Ex. 33), 6.3 (Ex. 34), 11.4 (Ex. 39), 11.5 (Ex. 41), 11.7, Skills Review Handbook
3. Number operations	1.7, 3.4, 11.4, 11.5, 12.2–12.6, Skills Review Handbook
4. Ratios and proportional reasoning	6.1, 6.2, 6.6, 7.5, 7.6, Algebra Review (Ch. 5), Skills Review Handbook
5. Properties of number and operations	2.1, 2.5, 6.2, Skills Review Handbook

Measurement

1. Measuring physical attributes	1.3, 1.4, 1.7, 3.2, 4.4–4.6, 5.3, 7.4–7.7, 8.1, 11.1–11.6, 12.2–12.6, Skills Review Handbook
2. Systems of measurement	6.1–6.7, 12.2–12.7, Skills Review Handbook

Geometry

1. Dimension and shape	1.6, 4.7, 7.4, 7.7, Ch. 8, 10.7, 12.1
2. Transformation of shapes and preservation of properties	4.8, 6.7, Ch. 9, 12.7
3. Relationships between geometric figures	3.1–3.3, 4.6, 5.2–5.4, 7.1, 7.2, 7.7, 8.2–8.6, Ch. 10
4. Position and direction	1.1, 1.2, 3.4, 3.5, 3.6 Ext., 5.1, 9.1, 9.3, 9.5
5. Mathematical reasoning	Ch. 2, 3.3, 3.6, 4.3–4.5, 5.6, 6.4, 6.5, 8.3, 11.7

Data Analysis and Probability

1. Data representation	8.4, 9.2, 9.7, Skills Review Handbook
2. Characteristics of data sets	Skills Review Handbook
3. Experiments and samples	6.1, 6.2, Act. 11.7, Skills Review Handbook
4. Probability	11.7, 11.7 Act., Skills Review Handbook

Algebra

1. Patterns, relations, and functions	1.7, 2.1, 3.5, Ext. 6.6, 8.1 (Ex. 36), 9.5 Ext., Skills Review Handbook
2. Algebraic representations	1.7, 3.4, 3.5, 9.1, 10.7, Algebra Reviews (Chs. 3, 7, 8, 11), Skills Review Handbook
3. Variables, expressions, and operations	7.3–7.7, 11.1–11.6, Algebra Reviews (Chs. 1–7, 9–11), Skills Review Handbook
4. Equations and inequalities	1.2–1.7, 2.5, 3.3–3.5, 5.1, 6.1, 6.2, 6.4, 6.6, 11.1–11.6, 12.2–12.6, Algebra Reviews (Chs. 1, 3, 4, 6, 7, 9, 11), Skills Review Handbook

1 Pacing and Assignment Guide

REGULAR SCHEDULE

Pre-AP For pacing and assignments for a Pre-AP course, see the *Geometry Toolkit*.

Lesson	Les. Day	BASIC	AVERAGE	ADVANCED
1.1	Day 1	SRH p. 876 Exs. 1–6; pp. 5–8 Exs. 1–16, 17–27 odd, 40–44, 47, 50, 53, 56	pp. 5–8 Exs. 1, 2, 3–11 odd, 12–16, 20–26, 27–37 odd, 40–45, 48, 51, 54, 57	pp. 5–8 Exs. 1, 5–7, 10, 11, 13–16, 20–38 even, 39–46*, 49, 52, 55, 58
1.2	Day 1	SRH p. 878 Exs. 7–12; pp. 12–14 Exs. 1–8, 12–23, 32–34, 37–45	pp. 12–14 Exs. 1–5, 7–10, 12–20 even, 21–30, 32–35, 37–45 odd	pp. 12–14 Exs. 1–5, 9–11, 15–19 odd, 20–36*, 39, 42, 44
1.3	Day 1	SRH p. 870 Exs. 13–20; pp. 19–22 Exs. 1–16, 48, 55, 56, 60–64	pp. 19–22 Exs. 1–6, 9, 10, 12–15, 35–40, 48, 60–64	pp. 19–22 Exs. 1, 5–10, 14–16, 35–40, 47*, 48, 60–64
	Day 2	pp. 19–22 Exs. 17–27, 31–37, 41, 42, 49–52, 57–59	pp. 19–22 Exs. 19–24, 28–34, 41–46, 49–53, 55–59	pp. 19–22 Exs. 20–23, 27–34, 41–46, 49–59*
1.4	Day 1	pp. 28–32 Exs. 1–21, 65–73	pp. 28–32 Exs. 1, 2, 4–6, 9–18, 21, 44–48, 65–73 odd	pp. 28–32 Exs. 1, 2, 4–6, 8–10, 12–14, 18–21, 44–48, 66–72 even
	Day 2	pp. 28–32 Exs. 22–39, 51–58, 64	pp. 28–32 Exs. 22–32, 33–43 odd, 51–62, 64	pp. 28–32 Exs. 24, 26–28, 30–32, 34–42 even, 43, 49–64*
1.5	Day 1	pp. 38–41 Exs. 1–7, 9–15 odd, 16, 17–27 odd, 28–35, 46–54, 57, 61	pp. 38–41 Exs. 1, 2, 4–7, 8–28 even, 29, 30–44 even, 46–55, 59, 62	pp. 38–41 Exs. 1, 2, 5, 7, 11, 15, 16, 19, 25–30, 33–45* odd, 48–56*, 60, 63
1.6	Day 1	pp. 44–47 Exs. 1–10, 14–21, 24, 25, 32–40, 43–53 odd	pp. 44–47 Exs. 1, 2, 4–7, 9–11, 14–17, 21–30, 32–41, 44, 50, 52	pp. 44–47 Exs. 1, 2, 5–7, 12, 13, 15–17, 22–32*, 35–42*, 45, 48, 54
1.7	Day 1	SRH p. 886 Exs. 1–15 odd; pp. 52–56 Exs. 1–19, 40, 41, 51, 52	pp. 52–56 Exs. 1–19, 40, 41, 51, 52	pp. 52–56 Exs. 1, 2, 4–10, 12–19, 40, 41, 49–52
	Day 2	pp. 52–56 Exs. 20–32, 42–44, 49, 50	pp. 52–56 Exs. 23–38, 42–45, 49, 50	pp. 52–56 Exs. 24–39*, 42–48*
Review	Day 1	pp. 60–63 Exs. 1–40	pp. 60–63 Exs. 1–40	pp. 60–63 Exs. 1–40
Assess	Day 1	Chapter 1 Test	Chapter 1 Test	Chapter 1 Test
Yearly Pacing		Chapter 1 Total – 12 days	Chapter 1 Total – 12 days	Remaining – 148 days

*Challenge Exercises EP = Extra Practice SRH = Skills Review Handbook

BLOCK SCHEDULE

DAY 1	DAY 2	DAY 3	DAY 4	DAY 5	DAY 6
1.1	1.3	1.4	1.5	1.7	REVIEW
pp. 5–8 Exs. 1, 2, 3–11 odd, 12–16, 20–26, 27–37 odd, 40–45, 48, 51, 54, 57	pp. 19–22 Exs. 1–6, 9, 10, 12–15, 19–24, 28–46, 48–53, 55–64	pp. 28–32 Exs. 1, 2, 4–6, 9–18, 21–32, 33–43 odd, 44–48, 51–62, 64, 65–73 odd	pp. 38–41 Exs. 1, 2, 4–7, 8–28 even, 29, 30–44 even, 46–55, 59, 62	pp. 52–56 Exs. 1–19, 23–38, 40–45, 49–52	pp. 60–63 Exs. 1–40
1.2			1.6		ASSESS
pp. 12–14 Exs. 1–5, 7–10, 12–20 even, 21–30, 32–35, 37–45 odd			pp. 44–47 Exs. 1, 2, 4–7, 9–11, 14–17, 21–30, 32–41, 44, 50, 52		Chapter 1 Test
Yearly Pacing	Chapter 1 Total – 6 days	Chapter 1 Total – 6 days	Remaining – 74 days		

Chapter Resource Guide 1

RESOURCE MANAGER

Chapter Resource Book

CHAPTER SUPPORT							
Parents as Partners (Chapter Overview with home involvement exercises and activity)						p. 1	
LESSON SUPPORT	**1.1**	**1.2**	**1.3**	**1.4**	**1.5**	**1.6**	**1.7**
Teaching Guide/Lesson Plan	p. 3	p. 17	p. 31	p. 47	p. 61	p. 74	p. 89
Activity Masters	p. 5	p. 19		p. 49			
Technology Activities & Keystrokes			p. 33			p. 76	p. 91
Activity Support Masters							
Practice (3 levels)	p. 6	p. 20	p. 35	p. 50	p. 63	p. 78	p. 92
Study Guide	p. 12	p. 26	p. 41	p. 56	p. 69	p. 84	p. 98
Catch-Up for Absent Students	p. 14	p. 28	p. 43	p. 58	p. 71	p. 86	p. 100
Problem Solving/Application	p. 15	p. 29	p. 44	p. 59	p. 72	p. 87	p. 101
Challenge Practice	p. 16	p. 30	p. 46	p. 60	p. 73	p. 88	p. 102

REVIEW			
Chapter Review Games and Activities	p. 103	Cumulative Practice	p. 106
Project with Rubric	p. 104	Resource Book Answers	A1

Transparencies	1.1	1.2	1.3	1.4	1.5	1.6	1.7
Warm-Up/Daily Homework Quiz	✔	✔	✔	✔	✔	✔	✔
Notetaking Guide	✔	✔	✔	✔	✔	✔	✔
Teacher Support		✔	✔	✔			✔
Answer Transparencies	✔	✔	✔	✔	✔	✔	✔

ASSESSMENT BOOK

Quizzes	p. 1	SAT/ACT Chapter Test	p. 12
Chapter Tests (3 levels)	p. 4	Alternative Assessment with Rubric	p. 14
Standardized Chapter Test	p. 10		

TECHNOLOGY

- Easy Planner
- Test and Practice Generator
- Power Presentations
- @HomeTutor
- Activity Generator
- Animated Geometry
- Classzone.com
- eEdition Plus Online
- eWorkbook Plus Online
- ML Assessment System

ADDITIONAL RESOURCES

- Worked-Out Solution Key
- Notetaking Guide
- Practice Wookbook
- Geometry Toolkit
- Benchmark Tests
- Remediation Book
- Spanish Study Guide
- Spanish Assessment Book
- Student Resources in Spanish
- Multi-Language Visual Glossary

1 Lesson Practice Level B

LESSON 1.1

Practice B

For use with pages 2–8

Use the diagram to decide whether the given statement is *true* or *false*.

1. Points H, I, and G are collinear. true
2. Points H, I, and J are coplanar. true
3. $\overrightarrow{EG}$ and $\overrightarrow{FG}$ are opposite rays. false
4. All points on $\overleftrightarrow{GI}$ and $\overleftrightarrow{GF}$ are coplanar. true
5. The intersection of $\overleftrightarrow{EF}$ and plane JKH is $\overleftrightarrow{HI}$. false
6. The intersection of $\overleftrightarrow{EF}$, $\overleftrightarrow{HI}$, and $\overleftrightarrow{JG}$ is point G. true
7. The intersection of plane EGH and plane JGI is point G. false
8. The intersection of plane EFI and plane JKG is $\overleftrightarrow{HG}$. true

10. *Sample answer:*

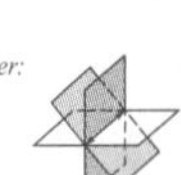

Sketch the figure described.

9. Two rays that do not intersect.
Sample answer:

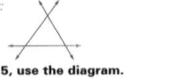

10. Three planes that intersect in one line.

11. Three lines that intersect in three points.
Sample answer:

12. A ray that intersects a plane in one point.
Sample answer:

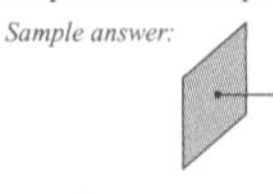

In Exercises 13–15, use the diagram.

13. Name 12 different rays.
14. Name 2 pairs of opposite rays.
15. Name 3 lines that intersect at point C.

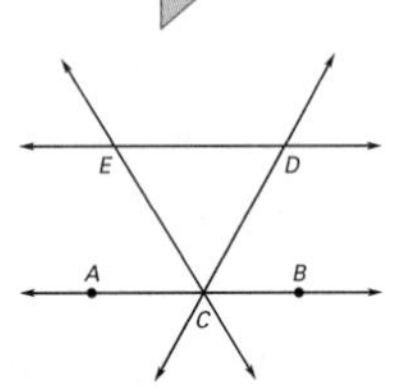

13. $\overrightarrow{AB}$, $\overrightarrow{BA}$, $\overrightarrow{AC}$, $\overrightarrow{CA}$, $\overrightarrow{BC}$, $\overrightarrow{CB}$, $\overrightarrow{CD}$, $\overrightarrow{DC}$, $\overrightarrow{EC}$, $\overrightarrow{CE}$, $\overrightarrow{ED}$, $\overrightarrow{DE}$
14. *Sample answer:* $\overrightarrow{AB}$, $\overrightarrow{BA}$, and $\overrightarrow{CA}$, $\overrightarrow{CB}$
15. $\overleftrightarrow{EC}$, $\overleftrightarrow{CD}$, $\overleftrightarrow{AB}$

16. Draw four noncollinear points A, B, C, and D. Then sketch $\overline{AB}$, $\overrightarrow{BC}$, and $\overleftrightarrow{AD}$. See below.
17. Sketch plane M intersecting plane N. Then sketch plane O so that it intersects plane N, but not plane M.

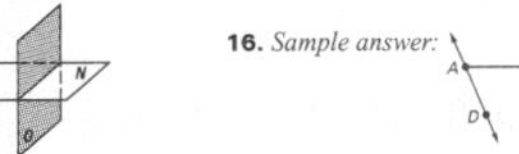
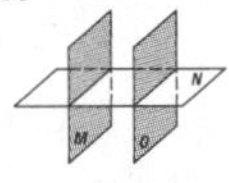

16. *Sample answer:*

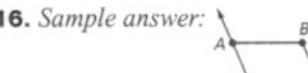

LESSON 1.1

Practice B *continued*

For use with pages 2–8

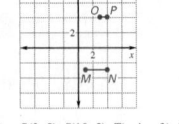

You are given an equation of a line and a point. Use substitution to determine whether the point is on the line.

18. $y = 5x + 3$; $A(1, 8)$ yes
19. $y = -x + 3$; $A(6, 3)$ no
20. $y = -3x - 6$; $A(2, 0)$ no
21. $2x - y = 7$; $A(3, -1)$ yes
22. $x + 6y = 40$; $A(-10, 5)$ no
23. $-x - 4y = -14$; $A(-6, 2)$ no

Graph the inequality on a number line. Tell whether the graph is a *segment*, *a ray or rays*, *a point*, or *a line*.

24. $x \ge 2$ ray

0 1 2 3 4 5 6 7 8

25. $2 \le x \le 5$ segment

0 1 2 3 4 5 6 7 8

26. $x \le 0$ and $x \ge 8$ rays

27. $|x| \le 0$ point

−2 0 2 4 6

28. **Counter Stools** Two different types of stools are shown below.
   a. One stool rocks slightly from side to side on your kitchen floor. Which of the two stools could this possibly be? *Explain* why this might occur.
   b. Suppose that each stool is placed on a flat surface that is slightly sloped. Do you expect either of the stools to rock from side to side? *Explain* why or why not.

28. a. four-legged stool; Possible explanation: The tips of the 4 legs are not coplanar.

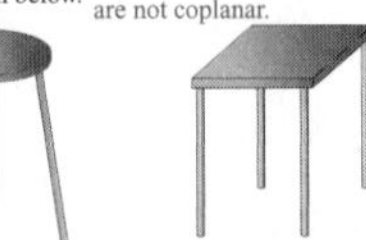

Three-legged stool   Four-legged stool

Possible explanation: The three-legged stool will not rock because the tips of its legs will always be coplanar. The four-legged stool may rock if the tips of its legs are not coplanar.

29. **Perspective Drawings** Recall from the text, that a perspective drawing is drawn using vanishing points. Yes, it has one vanishing point.
   a. Does the drawing at the right represent a perspective drawing? *Explain* why or why not.
   b. Using heavy dashed lines, draw the hidden lines of the prism.
   c. Redraw the prism so that it uses two vanishing points.

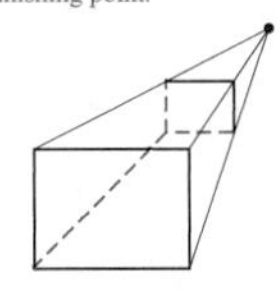

LESSON 1.2

Practice B

For use with pages 9–14

Measure the length of the segment to the nearest tenth of a centimeter.

1. A ——— B 3.4 cm
2. M ——— N 1.8 cm
3. E ——— F 2.1 cm

Use the Segment Addition Postulate to find the indicated length.

4. Find RT. 25.5

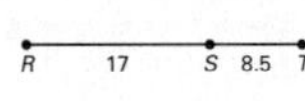

5. Find BC. 29

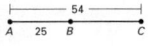

54
A 25 B C

6. Find MN. 6

32
M N 26 P

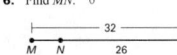

Plot the given points in a coordinate plane. Then determine whether the line segments named are congruent.

7. $A(2, 2)$, $B(4, 2)$, $C(-1, -1)$, $D(-1, 1)$;
$\overline{AB}$ and $\overline{CD}$ congruent
8. $M(1, -3)$, $N(4, -3)$, $O(3, 4)$, $P(4, 4)$;
$\overline{MN}$ and $\overline{OP}$ not congruent
9. $E(-3, 4)$, $F(-1, 4)$, $G(2, 4)$, $H(-1, 1)$;
$\overline{EG}$ and $\overline{FH}$ not congruent

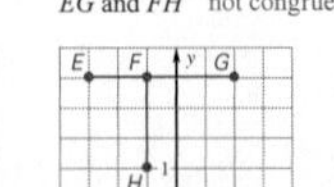

10. $R(3, 5)$, $S(10, 5)$, $T(-4, -3)$, $U(-11, -3)$;
$\overline{RS}$ and $\overline{TU}$ congruent

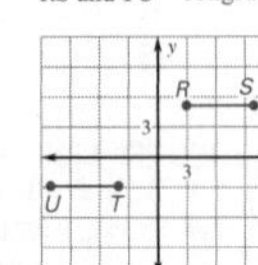

Use the number line to find the indicated distance.

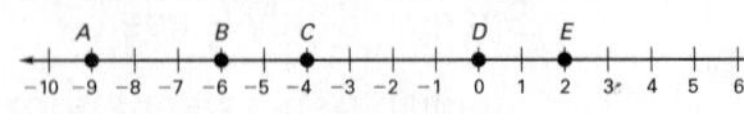

11. AB 3
12. AD 9
13. CD 4
14. BD 6
15. CE 6
16. AE 11
17. BE 8
18. DE 2

LESSON 1.2

Practice B *continued*

For use with pages 2–8

In the diagram, points *A*, *B*, *C*, and *D* are collinear, points *C*, *X*, *Y*, and *Z* are collinear, *AB* = *BC* = *CX* = *YZ*, *AD* = 54, *XY* = 22, and *XZ* = 33. Find the indicated length.

19. AB 11
20. BD 43
21. CY 33
22. CD 32
23. XC 11
24. CZ 44

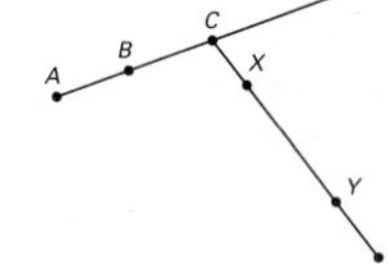

Find the indicated length. (Segments are not drawn to scale.)

25. Find ST. 24

32
R 4x S 12x T

26. Find AC. 28

4x + 4
A 14 B 3x − 4 C

27. Find NP. 32

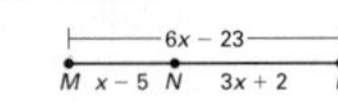

Point *J* is between *H* and *K* on $\overline{HK}$. Use the given information to write an equation in terms of *x*. Solve the equation. Then find *HJ* and *JK*.

28. $HJ = 2x$ $2x + 3x = 25$; $HJ = 10$; $JK = 15$
$JK = 3x$
$KH = 25$
29. $HJ = \frac{x}{4}$ $\frac{x}{4} + 3x - 4 = 22$; $HJ = 2$; $JK = 20$
$JK = 3x - 4$
$KH = 22$
30. $HJ = 5x - 4$ $5x - 4 + 8x - 10 = 38$; $HJ = 16$; $JK = 22$
$JK = 8x - 10$
$KH = 38$
31. $HJ = 5x - 3$ $5x - 3 + x - 9 = 5x$; $HJ = 57$; $JK = 3$
$JK = x - 9$
$KH = 5x$

32. **Hiking** On the map, $\overline{AB}$ represents a trail that you are hiking. You start from the beginning of the trail and hike for 90 minutes at a rate of 1.4 miles per hour. How much farther do you need to hike to reach the end of the trail? 3.1 mi

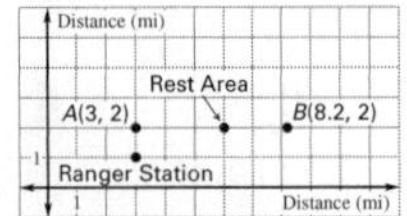

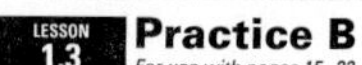

LESSON 1.3 Practice B
For use with pages 15–22

1. Line RS bisects $\overline{PQ}$ at point R. Find RQ if $PQ = 14$ centimeters. 7 cm
2. Line JK bisects $\overline{MN}$ at point J. Find MN if $JM = 6\frac{3}{4}$ feet. 13.5 ft
3. Point T bisects $\overline{UV}$. Find UV if $UT = 4\frac{1}{2}$ yards. 9 yd
4. Point C bisects $\overline{AB}$. Find CB if $AB = 14.8$ meters. 7.4 m

In the diagram, *M* is the midpoint of the segment. Find the indicated length.

5. Find LN. 24
6. Find AM. 26
7. Find MR. 10

$x + 9$, $4x$ (L, M, N) $x + 20$, $5x - 4$ (A, M, C) $4x - 12$, $-2x + 21$ (P, M, R)

Find the coordinates of the midpoint of the segment with the given endpoints.

8. $S(4, -1)$ and $T(6, 0)$ $\left(5, -\frac{1}{2}\right)$
9. $L(4, 2)$ and $P(0, 2)$ $(2, 2)$
10. $H(-5, 5)$ and $I(7, 3)$ $(1, 4)$
11. $G(-2, -8)$ and $H(-3, -12)$ $\left(-2\frac{1}{2}, -10\right)$

Use the given endpoint *R* and midpoint *M* of $\overline{RS}$ to find the coordinates of the other endpoint.

12. $R(6, 0), M(0, 2)$ $(-6, 4)$
13. $R(3, 4), M(3, -2)$ $(3, -8)$
14. $R(-3, -2), M(-1, -8)$ $(1, -14)$
15. $R(11, -5), M(-4, -4)$ $(-19, -3)$

Find the length of the segment. Round to the nearest tenth of a unit.

16. 3.2

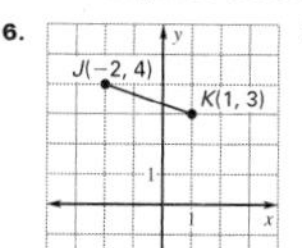

17. 5.4

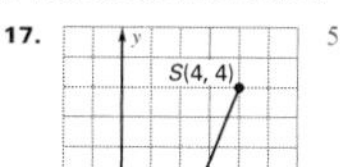

18. 4.5

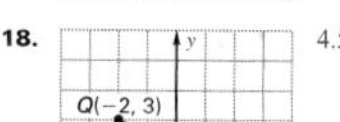

19. 11.3

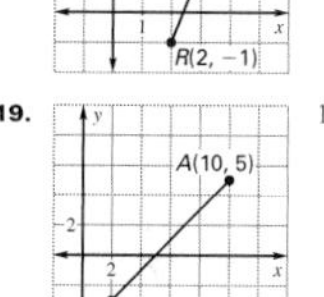

LESSON 1.3

LESSON 1.3 Practice B *continued*
For use with pages 15–22

Find the length of the segment. Then find the coordinates of the midpoint of the segment.

20.

9; 1.5

21.

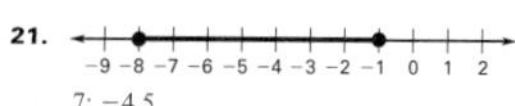

7; −4.5

The endpoints of two segments are given. Find each segment length. Tell whether the segments are congruent.

22. $\overline{AB}$: $A(2, 6), B(0, 3)$; $\overline{CD}$: $C(-1, 0), D(1, 3)$ $AB = \sqrt{13}$; $CD = \sqrt{13}$; congruent
23. $\overline{RS}$: $R(5, 4), S(0, 4)$; $\overline{TU}$: $T(-4, -3), U(-1, 1)$ $RS = 5$; $TU = 5$; congruent
24. $\overline{KL}$: $K(-4, 13), L(-10, 6)$; $\overline{MN}$: $M(-1, -2), N(-1, -11)$ $KL = \sqrt{85}$; $MN = 9$; not congruent
25. $\overline{OP}$: $O(6, -2), P(3, -2)$; $\overline{QR}$: $Q(5, 2), R(1, 5)$ $OP = 9$; $QR = 5$; not congruent
26. **Distances** Your house and the mall are 9.6 miles apart on the same straight road. The movie theater is halfway between your house and the mall, on the same road.
    a. Draw and label a sketch to represent this situation. How far is your house from the movie theater? House Movie Theater Mall 4.8 mi
    b. You walk at an average speed of 3.2 miles per hour. About how long would it take you to walk to the movie theater? 1.5 h

In Exercises 27–29, use the map. The locations of the towns on the map are: Dunkirk (0, 0), Clearfield (10, 2), Lake City (5, 7), and Allentown (1, 4). The coordinates are given in miles.

27. Find the distance between each pair of towns. Round to the nearest tenth of a mile. See below.
28. Which two towns are closest together? Which two towns are farthest apart? See below.
29. The map is being used to plan a 26-mile marathon. Which of the following plans is the best route for the marathon? *Explain.*
    A. Dunkirk to Clearfield to Allentown to Dunkirk
    B. Dunkirk to Clearfield to Lake City to Allentown to Dunkirk
    C. Dunkirk to Lake City to Clearfield to Dunkirk
    D. Dunkirk to Lake City to Allentown to Dunkirk
    Choice C because the total distance of the path is closest to 26 miles.

Distance (mi) Lake City (5,7) Allentown (1, 4) Clearfield (10, 2) Dunkirk (0, 0)

27. Dunkirk to Clearfield = 10.2 mi; Dunkirk to Lake City = 8.6 mi; Dunkirk to Allentown = 4.1 mi; Clearfield to Lake City = 7.1 mi; Clearfield to Allentown = 9.2 mi; Lake City to Allentown = 5 mi
28. Dunkirk and Allentown; Dunkirk and Clearfield

LESSON 1.3

LESSON 1.4 Practice B
For use with pages 24–34

1. 60°; ∠ABC, ∠CBA, or ∠B; B, $\overrightarrow{BA}$, $\overrightarrow{BC}$
2. 38°; ∠MOP, ∠POM, or ∠O; O, $\overrightarrow{OM}$, $\overrightarrow{OP}$
3. 112°; ∠EFG, ∠GFE, or ∠F; F, $\overrightarrow{FE}$, $\overrightarrow{FG}$

Use a protractor to measure the angle to the nearest degree. Write two names for the angle. Then name the vertex and the sides of the angle. See above.

1.

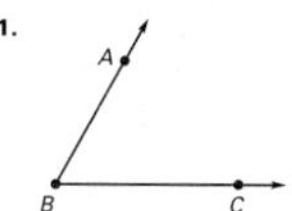

2.

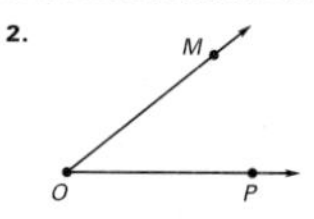

3.

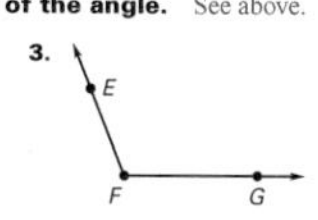

Give another name for the angle in the diagram. Tell whether the angle appears to be *acute, obtuse, right,* or *straight.*

4. ∠JKN
5. ∠KMN
6. ∠PQM
7. ∠JML
8. ∠QPN
9. ∠PLK

4. *Sample answer:* ∠K; right 5. *Sample answer:* ∠KLM; straight
6. *Sample answer:* ∠MQP; acute 7. *Sample answer:* ∠JMK; acute
8. *Sample answer:* ∠P; acute 9. *Sample answer:* ∠KLP; obtuse

Use the given information to find the indicated angle measure.

10. Given $m\angle ABC = 94°$, find $m\angle CBD$. 25°

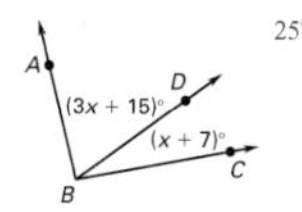

11. Given $m\angle QST = 135°$, find $m\angle QSR$. 85°

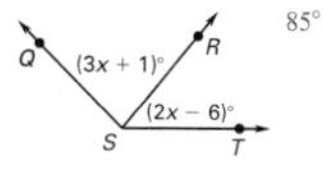

Find the indicated angle measure.

12. $a°$ 20°
13. $b°$ 160°
14. $c°$ 15°
15. $d°$ 75°

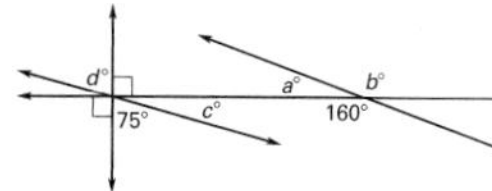

In the diagram, $\overrightarrow{BD}$ bisects ∠ABC. Find $m\angle ABC$.

16. 48°

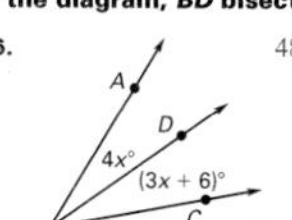

17. 98°

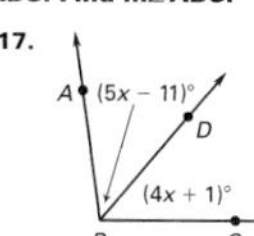

18. 112°

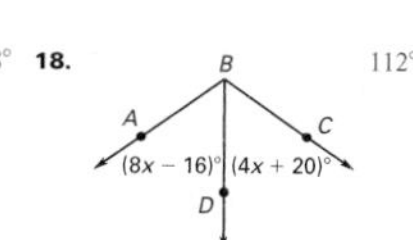

LESSON 1.4

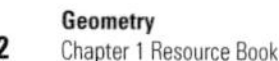

LESSON 1.4 Practice B *continued*
For use with pages 24–34

Plot the points in a coordinate plane and draw ∠ABC. Classify the angle. Then give the coordinates of a point that lies in the interior of the angle.

19. $A(2, 3), B(3, 0), C(2, 6)$ acute; *Sample answer:* (2, 5)
20. $A(6, 2), B(-1, -2), C(2, 3)$ acute; *Sample answer:* (2, 1)

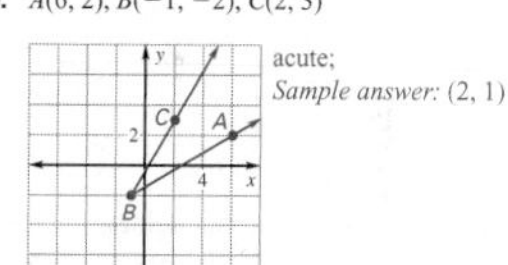

21. $A(-4, -3), B(-1, 3), C(4, 4)$ obtuse; *Sample answer:* (2, −8)
22. $A(-2, -4), B(-2, -1), C(3, -1)$ right; *Sample answer:* (0, −3)

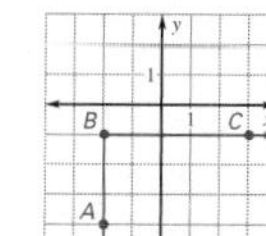

23. Let $(3x + 24)°$ represent the measure of an obtuse angle. What are the possible values of x? $22 < x < 52$
24. **Streets** The diagram shows the intersection of four streets. In the diagram, $m\angle AEB = 60°$, $m\angle BEC = m\angle CED$, and ∠AED is a right angle. What is the measure of ∠CED? 15°

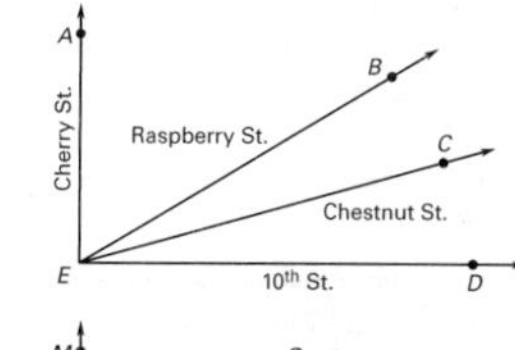

25. **Flags** In the flag shown, ∠MNP is a straight angle and $\overrightarrow{NR}$ bisects ∠MNP and ∠QNS.
    a. Which angles are acute? obtuse? right?
    b. Identify the congruent angles.
    c. If $m\angle QNR = 30°$, find $m\angle MNR$, $m\angle RNS$, $m\angle QNS$, and $m\angle QNP$.

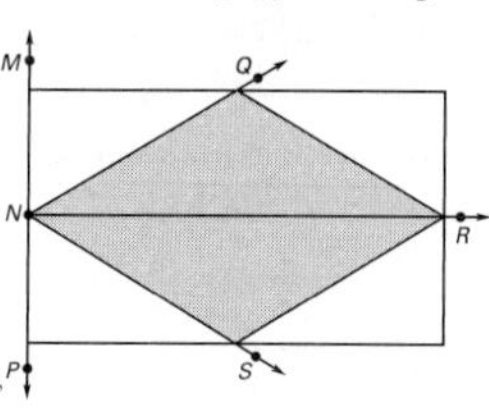

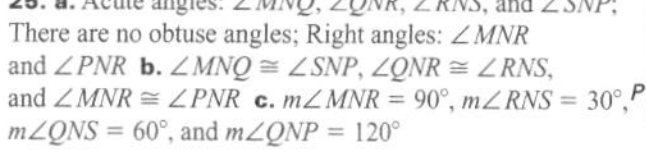

25. a. Acute angles: ∠MNQ, ∠QNR, ∠RNS, and ∠SNP; There are no obtuse angles; Right angles: ∠MNR and ∠PNR b. ∠MNQ ≅ ∠SNP, ∠QNR ≅ ∠RNS, and ∠MNR ≅ ∠PNR c. $m\angle MNR = 90°$, $m\angle RNS = 30°$, $m\angle QNS = 60°$, and $m\angle QNP = 120°$

LESSON 1.4

1 Lesson Practice Level B

LESSON 1.5 Practice B
For use with pages 35–41

$\angle 1$ and $\angle 2$ are complementary angles and $\angle 2$ and $\angle 3$ are supplementary angles. Given the measure of $\angle 1$, find $m\angle 2$ and $m\angle 3$.

1. $m\angle 1 = 80°$ 10°; 170° **2.** $m\angle 1 = 33°$ 57°; 123° **3.** $m\angle 1 = 72°$ 18°; 162° **4.** $m\angle 1 = 7°$ 83°; 97°

Find $m\angle ABC$ and $m\angle CBD$.

5.

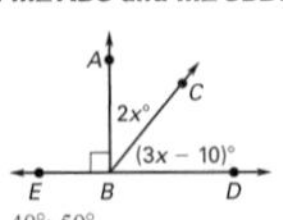

40°; 50°

6. (5x − 22)° (8x + 46)° C A B D 38°; 142°

7.

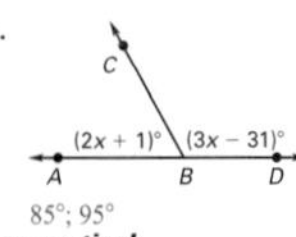

85°; 95°

In Exercises 8–12, use the diagram. Tell whether the angles are *vertical angles*, *a linear pair*, or *neither*.

8. $\angle 1$ and $\angle 3$ neither

9. $\angle 2$ and $\angle 3$ neither

10. $\angle 4$ and $\angle 5$ linear pair

11. $\angle 5$ and $\angle 8$ vertical angles

12. $\angle 4$ and $\angle 9$ vertical angles

13. The measure of one angle is three times the measure of its complement. Find the measure of each angle. 22.5°; 67.5°

14. Two angles form a linear pair. The measure of one angle is 8 times the measure of the other angle. Find the measure of each angle. 20°; 160°

15. The measure of one angle is 38° less than the measure of its supplement. Find the measure of each angle. 71°; 109°

Find the values of x and y.

16.

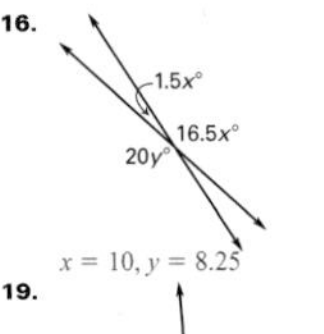

$x = 10, y = 8.25$

17.

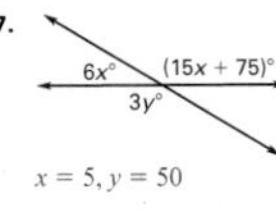

$x = 5, y = 50$

18.

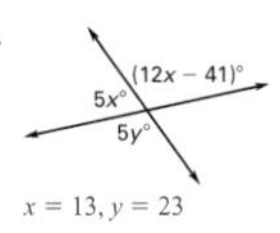

$x = 13, y = 23$

19.

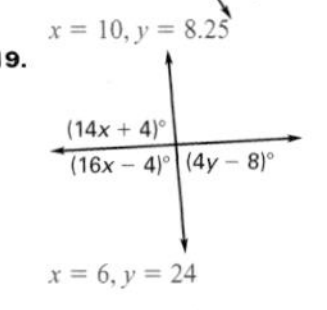

$x = 6, y = 24$

20.

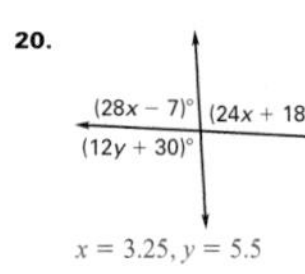

$x = 3.25, y = 5.5$

21.

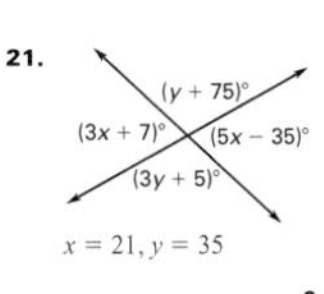

$x = 21, y = 35$

LESSON 1.5 Practice B *continued*
For use with pages 35–41

33. *Sample answer:* $\angle AIB$ and $\angle AIH$, $\angle AJB$ and $\angle AJG$
34. *Sample answer:* $\angle HBG$ and $\angle GBC$, $\angle BCF$ and $\angle FCE$
35. *Sample answer:* $\angle AIB$ and $\angle HIJ$, $\angle BIJ$ and $\angle AIH$

Tell whether the statement is *always*, *sometimes*, or *never* true.

22. Two complementary angles form a linear pair. never

23. The supplement of an obtuse angle is an acute angle. always

24. An angle that has a supplement also has a complement. sometimes

$\angle A$ and $\angle B$ are complementary angles. Find $m\angle A$ and $m\angle B$.

25. $m\angle A = x°$ 55°; 35°
$m\angle B = (2x - 75)°$

26. $m\angle A = (4x + 34)°$ 50°; 40°
$m\angle B = (x + 36)°$

27. $m\angle A = (4x - 18)°$ 32.4°; 57.6°
$m\angle B = (6x - 18)°$

28. $m\angle A = (2x + 10)°$ 60°; 30°
$m\angle B = (-x + 55)°$

$\angle A$ and $\angle B$ are supplementary angles. Find $m\angle A$ and $m\angle B$.

29. $m\angle A = (x + 50)°$ 65°; 115°
$m\angle B = (x + 100)°$

30. $m\angle A = 6x°$ 150°; 30°
$m\angle B = (x + 5)°$

31. $m\angle A = (2x + 3)°$ 163°; 17°
$m\angle B = (3x - 223)°$

32. $m\angle A = (-4x + 40)°$ 160°; 20°
$m\angle B = (x + 50)°$

Roof trusses can have several different layouts. The diagram below shows one type of roof truss made out of beams of wood. Use the diagram to identify two different examples of the indicated type of angle pair. In the diagram, $\angle HBC$ and $\angle BCE$ are right angles.

33. Supplementary angles See above.

34. Complementary angles See above.

35. Vertical angles See above.

36. Linear pair angles See below.

37. Adjacent angles See below.

B C I J L K A H G F E D

38. Angle of elevation An *angle of elevation* is the angle between the horizontal line and the line of site of an object above the horizontal. In the diagram, a plane is flying horizontally across the sky and $\angle RST$ represents the angle of elevation. How is the angle of elevation affected as the plane flies closer to the person? *Explain.*

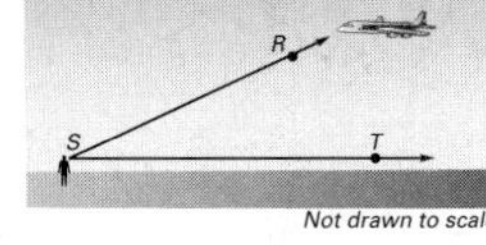

The angle of elevation is increasing. The closer the plane gets, the higher up you have to look.

36. *Sample answer:* $\angle AIB$ and $\angle AIH$, $\angle AJB$ and $\angle AJG$
37. *Sample answer:* $\angle AIB$ and $\angle AIH$, $\angle AJB$ and $\angle AJG$

LESSON 1.6 Practice B
For use with pages 42–47

Tell whether the figure is a polygon. If it is not, explain why. If it is a polygon, tell whether it is *convex* or *concave*.

1.

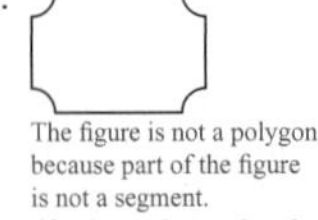

The figure is not a polygon because part of the figure is not a segment.

2.

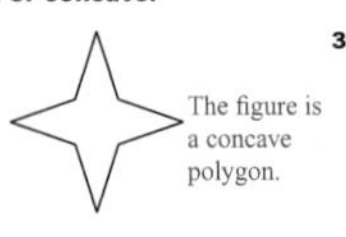

The figure is a concave polygon.

3.

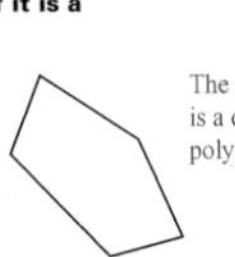

The figure is a convex polygon.

Classify the polygon by the number of sides. Tell whether the polygon is *equilateral*, *equiangular*, or *regular*. Explain your reasoning.

4. 3 m 3 m 3 m 3 m 3 m regular pentagon; It has 5 sides, and it is both equilateral and equiangular.

5.

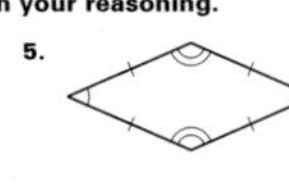

equilateral quadrilateral; It has 4 sides. It is equilateral, but not equiangular.

6.

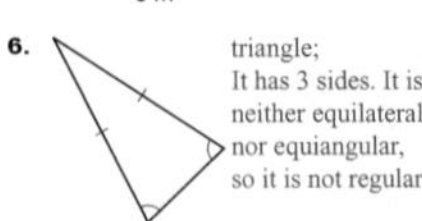

triangle; It has 3 sides. It is neither equilateral nor equiangular, so it is not regular.

7.

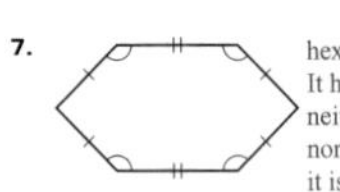

hexagon; It has 6 sides. It is neither equilateral nor equiangular, so it is not regular.

8. The lengths (in feet) of two sides of a regular quadrilateral are represented by the expressions $8x - 6$ and $4x + 22$. Find the length of a side of the quadrilateral. 50 ft

9. The expressions $(3x + 63)°$ and $(7x - 45)°$ represent the measures of two angles of a regular decagon. Find the measure of an angle of the decagon. 144°

10. The expressions $-2x + 41$ and $7x - 40$ represent the lengths (in kilometers) of two sides of an equilateral pentagon. Find the length of a side of the pentagon. 23 km

Tell whether the statement is *always*, *sometimes*, or *never* true.

11. A quadrilateral is convex. sometimes

12. An octagon is regular. sometimes

13. A triangle is concave. never

14. A regular polygon is equilateral. always

Draw a figure that fits the description.

15. A quadrilateral that is not regular
Sample answer:

16. A convex heptagon
Sample answer:

17. A concave pentagon
Sample answer:

18. An equiangular hexagon that is not equilateral
Sample answer:

LESSON 1.6 Practice B *continued*
For use with pages 42–47

Each figure is a regular polygon. Find the value of x.

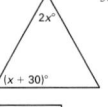

19. 30

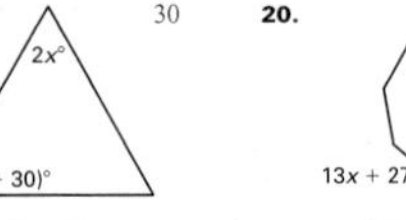

20. $3\frac{1}{2}$

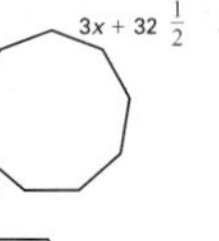

21. ±7

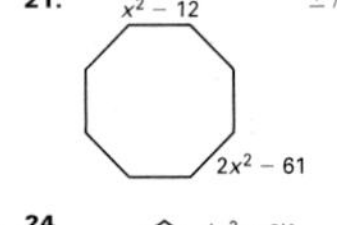

22. ±1

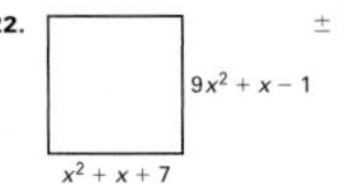

23. 6

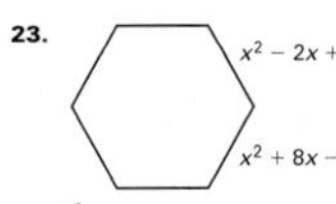

24. 5

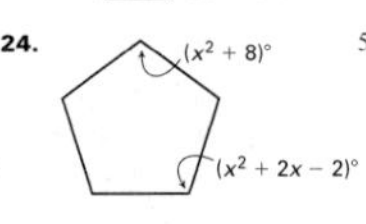

25. The vertices of a figure are given below. Plot and connect the points so that they form a convex polygon. Classify the figure. Then show that the figure is equilateral using algebra.

$A(3, 0), B(3, 6), C(2, 3), D(4, 3)$

B(3, 6) C(2, 3) D(4, 3) A(3, 0)

quadrilateral;
$AC = \sqrt{(3-2)^2 + (0-3)^2} = \sqrt{10}$,
$AD = \sqrt{(3-4)^2 + (0-3)^2} = \sqrt{10}$,
$BC = \sqrt{(3-2)^2 + (6-3)^2} = \sqrt{10}$,
$BD = \sqrt{(3-4)^2 + (6-3)^2} = \sqrt{10}$;
$AC = AD = BC = BD$

26. Picture frames A picture frame with a wooden border is a regular triangle, as shown. You want to decorate the frame by wrapping a ribbon around it. How many feet of ribbon are needed to wrap the ribbon around the border one time?

(7x + 8) in. (3x + 16) in.

5.5 ft; The sides of the triangle are congruent because the triangle is regular. Using this fact, write and solve an equation to find x. Then determine the perimeter of the triangle in feet.

27. Parachutes The canopy of a parachute is shown in the diagram.

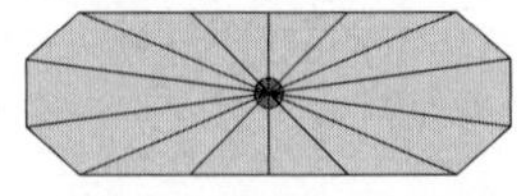

a. Is the shape of the canopy a *convex* or *concave* polygon? convex

b. Classify the polygon by the number of sides. Then use a ruler and a protractor to determine whether the figure is equilateral, equiangular, or regular. equiangular octagon

c. Determine the number of lines of symmetry in the canopy. How does this differ from a regular octagon? 2; This octagon has only 2 lines of symmetry while a regular octagon has 8.

LESSON 1.7
Practice B
For use with pages 48–56

Find the perimeter and area of the figure.

1.
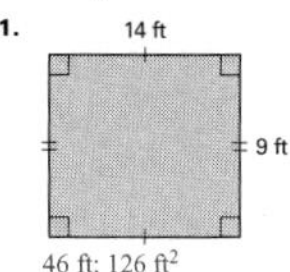

46 ft; 126 ft^2

2.
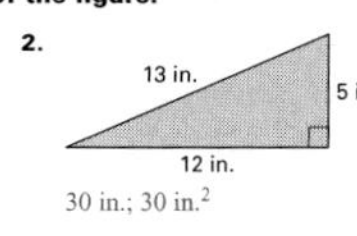

30 in.; 30 in.^{2}

3.
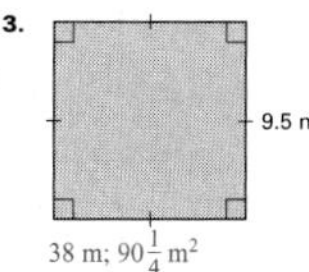

38 m; $90\frac{1}{4}$ m^2

Find the circumference and area of the circle. Round to the nearest tenth.

4.
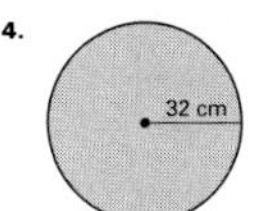

201.0 cm; 3215.4 cm^2

5.
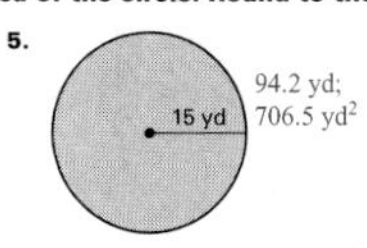

94.2 yd; 706.5 yd^2

6.
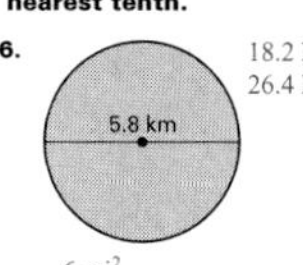

18.2 km; 26.4 km^2

7. A triangle has a base of 6 miles and a height of 2 miles. Sketch the triangle and find its area.

8. A circle has a radius of 25 inches. Sketch the circle and find its area. Round your answer to the nearest tenth.

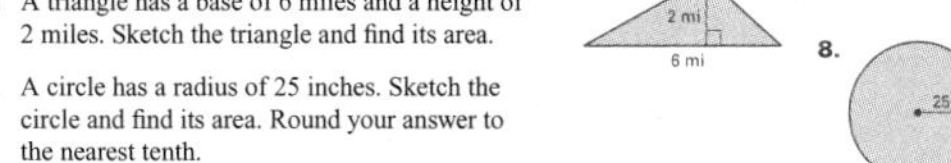

7. 6 mi^2
8. 1962.5 in.^{2}

Find the perimeter of the figure. Round to the nearest tenth of a unit.

9.
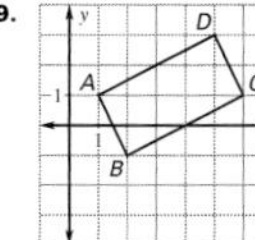

13.4 units

10.
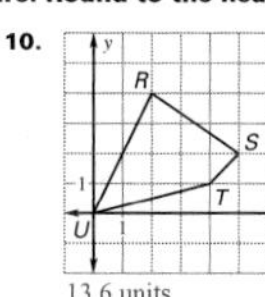

13.6 units

11.
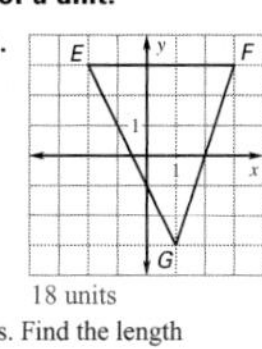

18 units

12. The area of a triangle is 48 square inches, and its height is 16 inches. Find the length of its base. 6 in.

13. The area of a rectangle is 365.2 square meters, and its length is 22 meters. Find the length of its width. 16.6 m

Copy and complete the statement.

14. 72 cm^2 = _?_ m^2 0.0072
15. 22 m^2 = _?_ km^2 0.000022
16. 18 in.^{2} = _?_ ft^2 0.125
17. 14 yd^2 = _?_ ft^2 126
18. 13 cm^2 = _?_ mm^2 1300
19. 1.5 km^2 = _?_ m^2 1,500,000
20. 585 ft^2 = _?_ yd^2 65
21. 12 ft^2 = _?_ in.^{2} 1728
22. 100 mm^2 = _?_ cm^2 1

LESSON 1.7

LESSON 1.7
Practice B *continued*
For use with pages 48–56

Use the information about the figure to find the indicated measure.

23. Area = 504 in.^{2} 24 in.

Find the height h.

24. Area = 55.5 m^2 12 m

Find the base b.

25. Perimeter = 112.5 m $43\frac{3}{4}$ m

Find the length ℓ.

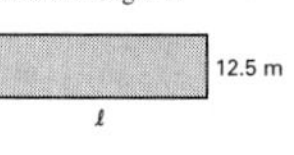

26. The perimeter of a rectangle 28.8 centimeters. The length of the rectangle is twice as long as its width. Find the length and width of the rectangle. length = 9.6 m, width = 4.8 m

27. The area of a triangle is 338 square yards. The height of the triangle is four times its base. Find the height and base of the triangle. height = 52 yd, base = 13 yd

28. In the figure, the radius of the large circle is three times the radius of the small circle. About what percent of the large circle is covered by the small circle? $\frac{1}{9} \approx 0.11$

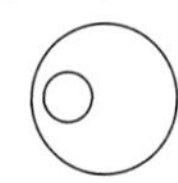

29. **Land** You are planting grass on a square plot of land. You are also building a fence around the edge of the plot. The side length of the plot is 54 yards. How much area do you need to cover with grass seed? How many feet of fencing do you need? 2916 yd^2; 648 ft

30. **Windows** You make a window out of a rectangular pane of glass by surrounding it with a wooden frame that is x inches wide. The pane of glass is 20 inches long and 24 inches wide. The perimeter of the window is $8\frac{2}{3}$ feet. What is the value of x? 2

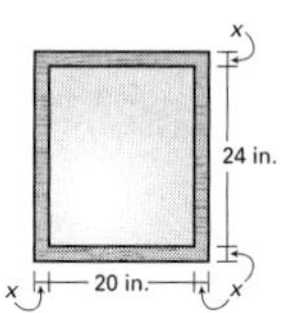

31. **Looms** A triangular loom used for knitting covers an area of 12.25 square feet. It has a base that is twice as long as its height.

a. Sketch and label a diagram for the situation.

b. Find the base and the height of the loom. base = 7 ft, height = 3.5 ft

c. Suppose the base of the loom was increased by 6 inches while the height remained the same. The area that the loom covers increased by how many square inches? square feet? 126 in.^{2}; 0.875 ft^2

a.
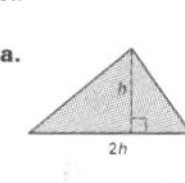

LESSON 1.7

1 Assessment

CHAPTER 1 Quiz 1
For use after Lessons 1.1–1.3

1. Sketch a plane and a line that intersects the plane at a point.

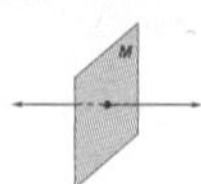

Find the indicated length.

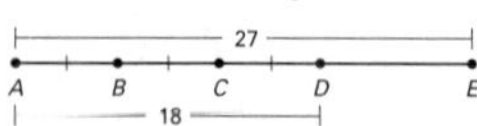

2. DE 3. AB
4. AC 5. BD
6. CE 7. BE

8. The endpoints of $\overline{ST}$ are $S(-3, 2)$ and $T(5, 8)$. Find the coordinates of the midpoint of $\overline{ST}$. Then find ST.

Answers
1. See left.
2. 9
3. 6
4. 12
5. 12
6. 15
7. 21
8. midpoint: (1, 5); $ST = 10$

CHAPTER 1 Quiz 2
For use after Lessons 1.4–1.5

In the diagram, $\overrightarrow{BD}$ bisects $\angle ABC$. Find $m\angle ABD$ and $m\angle DBC$.

1.
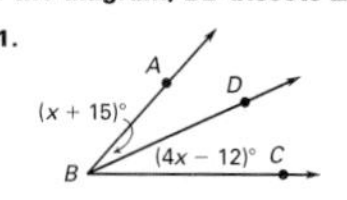

2.
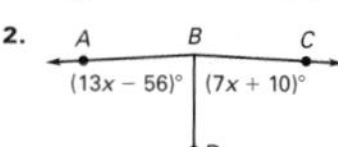

3.
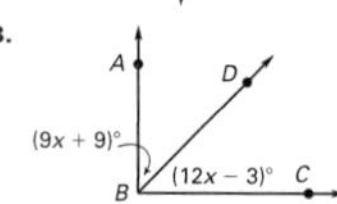

Find the measure of the complement of $\angle 1$ and the measure of the supplement of $\angle 1$.

4. $m\angle 1 = 51°$ 5. $m\angle 1 = 17°$
6. $m\angle 1 = 80°$ 7. $m\angle 1 = 3°$

Answers
1. 24°; 24°
2. 87°; 87°
3. 45°; 45°
4. 39°; 129°
5. 73°; 163°
6. 10°; 100°
7. 87°; 177°

CHAPTER 1 Quiz 3
For use after Lessons 1.6–1.7

Tell whether the figure is a polygon. If it is not, *explain* why. If it is a polygon, tell whether it is *convex* or *concave*.

1.

2.

3.

Find the perimeter and area of the shaded figure.

4.
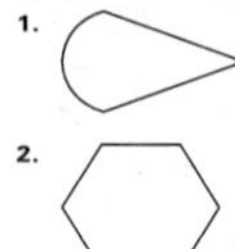

5.
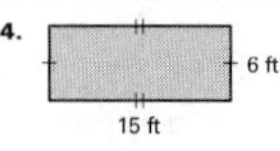

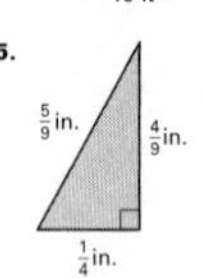

6.
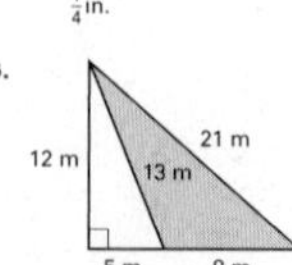

7. You are spreading grass seed on a rectangular area that is $4\frac{1}{2}$ yards long and $3\frac{1}{2}$ yards wide. One bag of grass seed covers 100 square feet. How many bags of grass seed do you need?

Answers
1. Part of the figure is not a segment, therefore it is not a polygon.
2. convex polygon
3. concave polygon
4. 42 ft; 90 ft²
5. $1\frac{1}{4}$ in.; $\frac{1}{18}$ in.²
6. 43 m; 54 m²
7. 2 bags

CHAPTER 1 Chapter Test B
For use after Chapter 1

In Exercises 1–3, use the diagram to decide whether the statement is *true* or *false*.

1. Point R lies on line g.
2. Points A, M, R, and Z are coplanar.
3. Points A and Q are collinear.

4. The diagram shows three houses on a street. Find the distance from House A to House C.

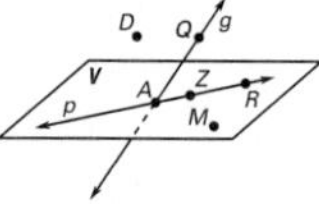

In each diagram, M is the midpoint of the segment. Find the indicated length.

5. XM 6. CG

Find the exact distance between the points.

7. A and B
8. C and F
9. D and E

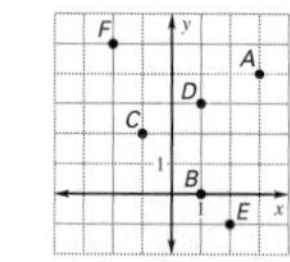

Use the given information to find the value of x.

10. $\angle ABD \cong \angle DBC$ 11. $\angle WXZ \cong \angle ZXY$

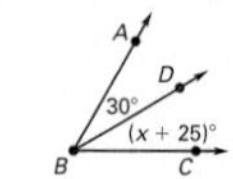

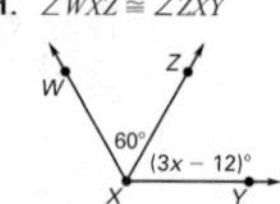

12. Given that $\angle 1$ is a complement of $\angle 2$ and $m\angle 2 = 17°$, find $m\angle 1$.
13. Given that $\angle 3$ is a supplement of $\angle 4$ and $m\angle 3 = 46°$, find $m\angle 4$.

Answers
1. false
2. true
3. true
4. 150 ft
5. 7
6. 38
7. $\sqrt{20}$
8. $\sqrt{10}$
9. $\sqrt{17}$
10. 5
11. 24
12. 73°
13. 134°

CHAPTER 1

Chapter Test B *continued*

For use after Chapter 1

14. Two angles form a linear pair. The measure of one angle is four times greater than the measure of the other angle. Find the measure of each angle.

15. Two angles form a linear pair. The measure of one angle is six more than twice the measure of the other angle. Find the measure of each angle.

Tell whether the statement is *always, sometimes,* or *never* true.

16. A pentagon is a plane figure.

17. A triangle is concave.

18. A hexagon has six congruent sides.

19. A quadrilateral is equiangular but not equilateral.

Use the given information to find the value of x. Use 3.14 for π.

20. $C = 56.52$ feet

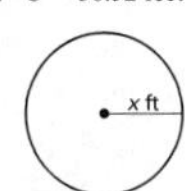

21. $P = 25$ inches

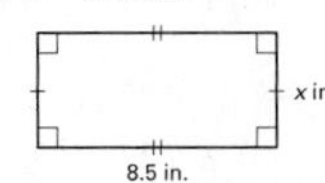

22. $A = 24$ square inches

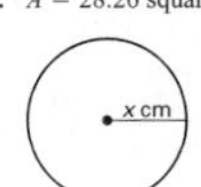

23. $A = 28.26$ square centimeters

24. A table is 6 feet long and 4 feet wide. A table cloth covers the entire table and there is 1 foot of extra cloth hanging over each edge of the table. What is the area of the table cloth?

25. Joe ran from Point A to Point C and Mike ran from Point B to Point C. About how much farther did Joe run than Mike? Round your answer to the nearest tenth. The distance between consecutive grid lines represents 1 yard.

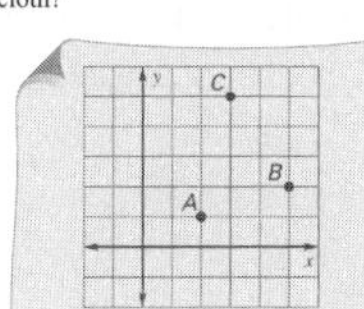

Answers

14. 36°; 144°

15. 58°; 122°

16. always

17. never

18. sometimes

19. sometimes

20. 9

21. 4

22. 4

23. 3

24. 48 ft^2

25. 0.5 yd

CHAPTER 1

Standardized Test

For use after Chapter 1

Multiple Choice

1. Which statement about the figure is true? C

Ⓐ Lines x and y intersect at point A.

Ⓑ Points A, B, and C are collinear.

Ⓒ $\overrightarrow{EC}$ and $\overrightarrow{ED}$ are opposite rays.

Ⓓ Another name for $\overline{AE}$ is $\overline{AB}$.

2. Name three points that are collinear. A

Ⓐ G, H, and I Ⓑ H, G, and J

Ⓒ F, G, and I Ⓓ G, J, and I

3. What is the intersection of plane HGY and plane HFX? B

Ⓐ $\overrightarrow{HZ}$

Ⓑ $\overleftrightarrow{HZ}$

Ⓒ Point H

Ⓓ Plane EFH

4. What is the length of $\overline{ST}$? D

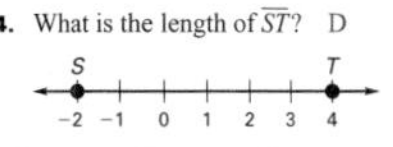

Ⓐ 2 Ⓑ 4 Ⓒ −2 Ⓓ 6

5. If $\overline{WX} \cong \overline{XY}$, what is the length of $\overline{WZ}$? B

Ⓐ 7 Ⓑ 10 Ⓒ 3 Ⓓ 4

6. The endpoints of $\overline{CD}$ are $C(6, 1)$ and $D(-4, -1)$. Find the midpoint M of $\overline{CD}$. D

Ⓐ $M(10, 2)$ Ⓑ $M(-10, -2)$

Ⓒ $M(2, 0)$ Ⓓ $M(1, 0)$

7. $\overline{JK}$ has a length of 4.5 units. If $\overline{LM}$ has endpoints $L(3, 1)$ and $M(-1, 4)$, how much longer than $\overline{JK}$ is $\overline{LM}$? A

Ⓐ 0.5 unit Ⓑ 2 units

Ⓒ 2.5 units Ⓓ $\overline{JK}$ is longer.

8. Name the acute angles in the given figure. A

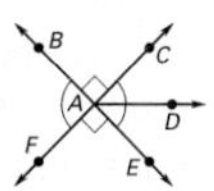

Ⓐ $\angle CAD$ and $\angle DAE$

Ⓑ $\angle BAC$ and $\angle FAE$

Ⓒ $\angle BAF$ and $\angle CAE$

Ⓓ $\angle BAD$ and $\angle FAD$

9. If the measure of $\angle RST$ is 134°, find the measure of $\angle QST$. B

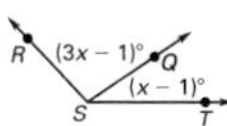

Ⓐ 67° Ⓑ 33° Ⓒ 34° Ⓓ 98°

10. $m\angle A$ is 42° greater than $m\angle B$. If $\angle A$ and $\angle B$ are supplementary, find $m\angle A$ and $m\angle B$. A

Ⓐ $m\angle A = 111°$, $m\angle B = 69°$

Ⓑ $m\angle A = 42°$, $m\angle B = 48°$

Ⓒ $m\angle A = 42°$, $m\angle B = 138°$

Ⓓ $m\angle A = 66°$, $m\angle B = 24°$

CHAPTER 1

Standardized Test *continued*

For use after Chapter 1

11. Name a pair of vertical angles in the figure shown. B

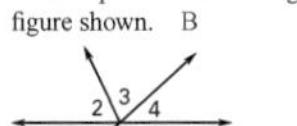

Ⓐ $\angle 2$ and $\angle 4$ Ⓑ $\angle 1$ and $\angle 4$

Ⓒ $\angle 3$ and $\angle 5$ Ⓓ there are none

12. Which describes the following polygon? A

Ⓐ equilateral

Ⓑ equiangular

Ⓒ regular

Ⓓ none of these

13. Which of the following is a convex polygon? C

Ⓐ  Ⓑ

Ⓒ 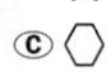 Ⓓ

14. Find the area of a circle with a radius of 4 feet. Use 3.14 for π. D

Ⓐ 25.12 ft^2 Ⓑ 8 ft^2

Ⓒ 16 ft^2 Ⓓ 50.24 ft^2

15. Find CD. C

Ⓐ 5

Ⓑ 28

Ⓒ 56

Ⓓ 96

16. Find the perimeter of the polygon. B

Ⓐ 12 units

Ⓑ 16.97 units

Ⓒ 28 units

Ⓓ 11.31 units

Gridded Answer

17. Find the area, in square inches, of a triangle with vertices $X(-7, 2)$, $Y(8, 2)$, and $Z(6, 7)$.

37.5

Short Response

18. A swimmer stands somewhere in a circular pool. The distance to the farthest side (through the center of the pool) is 3 times the distance to the nearest side. If the circumference of the pool is 100 feet:

a. How close is the swimmer to the nearest side? $\frac{25}{\pi}$ ft

b. How far must he swim to get to the center? $\frac{75}{\pi}$ ft

Extended Response

19. You are a surveyor. You take your first measurement facing due north. You turn to the right to take your second measurement and then right again, 4 times as far, to take your third measurement. You are now facing due west.

a. How many degrees did you turn to take your second measurement? 54°

b. How many degrees should you have turned after your second measurement if you wanted to take your third measurement facing south? 126°

c. How many degrees must you turn to the left in order to take a fourth measurement in the opposite direction of your second measurement? 36°

CHAPTER 1

Alternative Assessment and Math Journal

For use after Chapter 1

Journal

1. a. If three points are collinear, are the three points necessarily coplanar? *Explain.* Use examples to support your reasoning.

b. Are all equiangular polygons equilateral polygons? Are all equilateral polygons equiangular polygons? *Explain.* Use examples to support your reasoning.

Multi-Step Problem

2. A company that makes craft supplies is designing a metal tag that is used in crafting projects such as making scrapbooks. The tag is shown below.

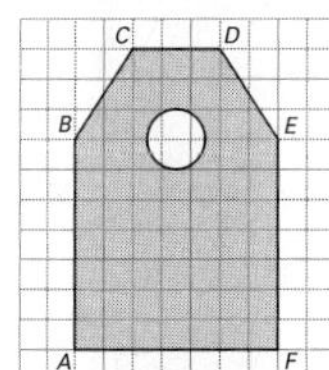

a. The tag is a polygon. Classify the polygon by the number of sides. Tell whether it appears to be *equilateral, equiangular,* or *regular.*

b. Draw axes on the figure above and find the coordinates of the vertices of the tag.

c. The center of the tag's hole is located midway between point B and point E. What are the coordinates of the center of the hole?

d. Find the perimeter of the tag.

e. Identify any congruent line segments formed by the tag.

f. Find the area and circumference of the tag's hole.

g. Given that $m\angle EBA = 90°$ and $m\angle CBA = 150°$, find $m\angle CBE$.

h. How could you use what you know about the areas of triangles, rectangles, and circles to find the shaded area of the tag?

1. a. an explanation that three collinear points must be coplanar; example of three collinear points that are coplanar **b.** explanations that all equiangular polygons are not equilateral and all equilateral polygons are not equiangular; examples of an equiangular polygon that is not equilateral (e.g. rectangle) and an equilateral polygon that is not equiangular (e.g. rhombus)

2. a. hexagon; not equilateral, equiangular, or regular

b. *Sample answer:*

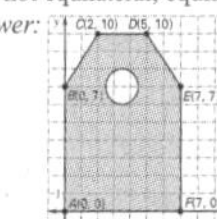

c. *Sample answer:* (3.5, 7) **d.** about 31.21 units **e.** $\overline{AB}$, $\overline{AF}$, and $\overline{EF}$; $\overline{CB}$ and $\overline{DE}$ **f.** Area: about 3.14 square units; Circumference: about 6.28 units **g.** $m\angle CBE = 60°$ **h.** *Sample answer:* Divide the tag into two rectangles and two triangles. Then find the areas of these figures and add the areas together. Then subtract the area of the circle to get the area of the tag.

PLAN AND PREPARE

Main Ideas

In this chapter students will name and sketch geometric figures, use postulates to identify congruent segments, find lengths of segments in the coordinate plane, and find the midpoint of a segment. Students also will name, measure and classify angles, identify complementary and supplementary angles, and classify polygons. Finally, they will find circumference and area of circles, and area and perimeter of rectangles.

Prerequisite Skills

- Simplifying numerical expressions
- Evaluating variable expressions
- Solving equations
- Finding lengths and areas

Additional resources for reviewing prerequisite skills are:

- Skills Review Handbook, pp. 869–895
- @HomeTutor

1 Essentials of Geometry

Before

In previous courses, you learned the following skills, which you'll use in Chapter 1: finding measures, evaluating expressions, and solving equations.

Prerequisite Skills

VOCABULARY CHECK

Copy and complete the statement.

1. The distance around a rectangle is called its _?_, and the distance around a circle is called its _?_. **perimeter, circumference**
2. The number of square units covered by a figure is called its _?_. **area**

SKILLS AND ALGEBRA CHECK

Evaluate the expression. *(Review p. 870 for 1.2, 1.3, 1.7.)*

3. $|4 - 6|$ **2**
4. $|3 - 11|$ **8**
5. $|-4 + 5|$ **1**
6. $|-8 - 10|$ **18**

Evaluate the expression when $x = 2$. *(Review p. 870 for 1.3–1.6.)*

7. $5x$ **10**
8. $20 - 8x$ **4**
9. $-18 + 3x$ **−12**
10. $-5x - 4 + 2x$ **−10**

Solve the equation. *(Review p. 875 for 1.2–1.7.)*

11. $274 = -2z$ **−137**
12. $8x + 12 = 60$ **6**
13. $2y - 5 + 7y = -32$ **−3**
14. $6p + 11 + 3p = -7$ **−2**
15. $8m - 5 = 25 - 2m$ **3**
16. $-2n + 18 = 5n - 24$ **6**

@HomeTutor Prerequisite skills practice at classzone.com

Chapter Planning Guide

Chapter 1 Resource Book
- Teaching Guide/Lesson Plan (pp. 3, 17, 31, 47, 61, 74, 89)
- Project with Rubric (p. 104)

Assessment and Intervention
- Assessment Book (pp. 1–15)
- Benchmark Tests
- Remediation Book

Interactive Technology
- Easy Planner
- Power Presentations CD-ROM
- Activity Generator CD-ROM
- Animated Geometry
- Test Generator CD-ROM
- Online Quizzes
- eWorkbook
- eEdition
- @HomeTutor

Resources for English Learners
- Quick Reference for English Learners
- Spanish Study Guide
- Multi-Language Visual Glossary
- Student Resources in Spanish

California Standards for Chapter 1

Geometry: 1.0, 16.0, 12.0, 8.0, 10.0

Now

In Chapter 1, you will apply the big ideas listed below and reviewed in the Chapter Summary on page 59. You will also use the key vocabulary listed below.

Big Ideas

1. **Describing geometric figures**
2. **Measuring geometric figures**
3. **Understanding equality and congruence**

KEY VOCABULARY

- undefined terms, *p. 2* point, line, plane
- defined terms, *p. 3*
- line segment, endpoints, *p. 3*
- ray, opposite rays, *p. 3*
- postulate, axiom, *p. 9*
- congruent segments, *p. 11*
- midpoint, *p. 15*
- segment bisector, *p. 15*
- acute, right, obtuse, straight angles, *p. 25*
- congruent angles, *p. 26*
- angle bisector, *p. 28*
- linear pair, *p. 37*
- vertical angles, *p. 37*
- polygon, *p. 42*
- convex, concave, *p. 42*
- *n*-gon, *p. 43*
- equilateral, equiangular, regular, *p. 43*

Why?

Geometric figures can be used to represent real-world situations. For example, you can show a climber's position along a stretched rope by a point on a line segment.

Animated Geometry

The animation illustrated below for Exercise 35 on page 14 helps you answer this question: How far must a climber descend to reach the bottom of a cliff?

Start
Your goal is to find the distance from a climber's position to the bottom of a cliff.

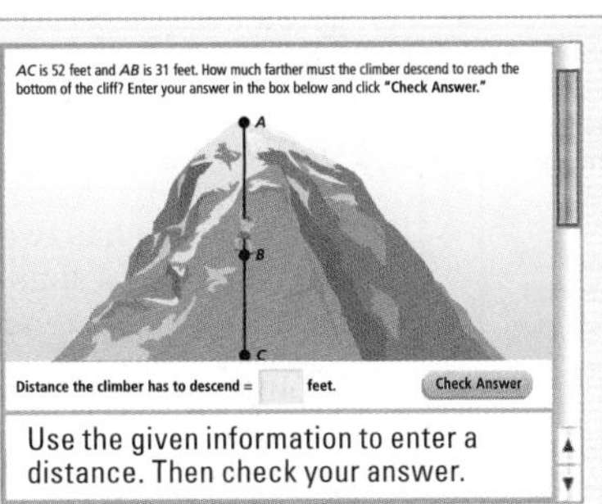

AC is 52 feet and AB is 31 feet. How much farther must the climber descend to reach the bottom of the cliff? Enter your answer in the box below and click "Check Answer."
A
B
C
Distance the climber has to descend = feet.
Check Answer
Use the given information to enter a distance. Then check your answer.

Animated Geometry at classzone.com

Other animations for Chapter 1: pages 3, 21, 25, 43, and 52

1

Geometry Toolkit

- Reading Strategies for Chapter 1, pp. 9–10
- Differentiated Instruction Notes, pp. 39–42
- English Learners Notes, pp. 91–92
- Inclusion Notes, pp. 121–122
- Teaching Strategies with Sample Worksheets, pp. 145–168
- Using Technology in the Classroom, pp. 169–174
- Tips for New Teachers, pp. 175–176
- Math Background Notes, pp. 199–201
- Pre-AP Strategies and Copymasters, pp. 283–284, 307–318
- Teacher Survival Activities, pp. 421–422, 445–446
- Bulletin Board Idea, p. 469
- Teacher Tool Transparencies, following p. 480

1 PLAN AND PREPARE

Warm-Up Exercises

Transparency Available

Graph each inequality.

1. $x \leq 1$

2. $-2 \leq x \leq 3$

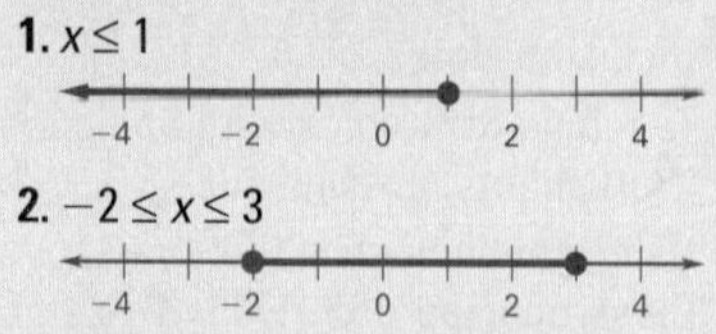

3. Juan has more than 5 but fewer than 11 fish in his aquarium. Write an inequality to express the number of fish f Juan has. **$5 < f < 11$**

Notetaking Guide

Transparency Available

Promotes interactive learning and notetaking skills, pp. 1–4.

Pacing

Basic: 1 day
Average: 1 day
Advanced: 1 day
Block: 0.5 block with 1.2

• See *Teaching Guide/Lesson Plan.*

2 FOCUS AND MOTIVATE

Essential Question

Big Idea 1, p. 1

How do you name geometric figures? **Tell students they will learn how to answer this question by learning about labeling points, lines, segments, rays, and planes.**

1.1 Identify Points, Lines, and Planes

Before You studied basic concepts of geometry.
Now You will name and sketch geometric figures.
Why So you can use geometry terms in the real world, as in Ex. 13.

Key Vocabulary
- **undefined terms** point, line, plane
- **collinear points**
- **coplanar points**
- **defined terms**
- **line segment**
- **endpoints**
- **ray**
- **opposite rays**
- **intersection**

In the diagram of a football field, the positions of players are represented by *points*. The yard lines suggest *lines*, and the flat surface of the playing field can be thought of as a *plane*.

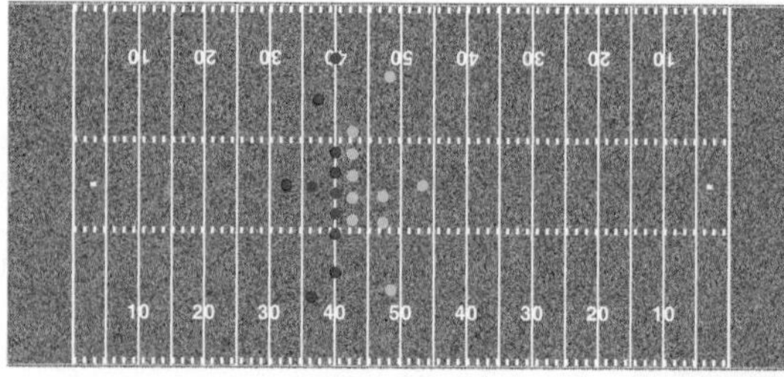

In geometry, the words *point, line,* and *plane* are **undefined terms**. These words do not have formal definitions, but there is agreement about what they mean.

TAKE NOTES
When you write new concepts and yellow-highlighted vocabulary in your notebook, be sure to copy all associated diagrams.

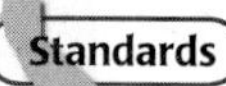

Standards
1.0 Students demonstrate understanding by identifying and giving examples of undefined terms, axioms, theorems, and inductive and deductive reasoning.

KEY CONCEPT *For Your Notebook*

Undefined Terms

Point A **point** has no dimension. It is represented by a dot.

point A

Line A **line** has one dimension. It is represented by a line with two arrowheads, but it extends without end.

Through any two points, there is exactly one line. You can use any two points on a line to name it.

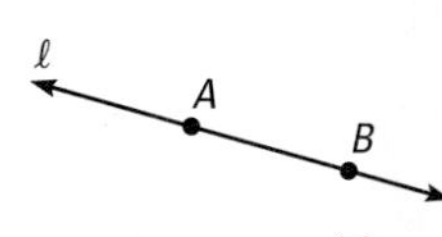

line ℓ, line AB ($\overleftrightarrow{AB}$), or line BA ($\overleftrightarrow{BA}$)

Plane A **plane** has two dimensions. It is represented by a shape that looks like a floor or a wall, but it extends without end.

Through any three points not on the same line, there is exactly one plane. You can use three points that are not all on the same line to name a plane.

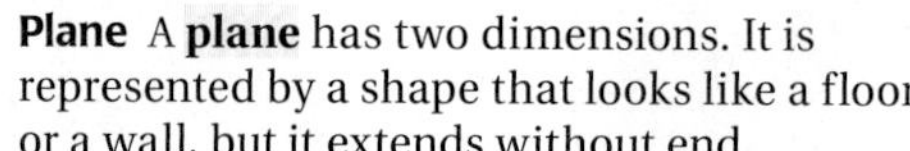

plane M or plane ABC

Collinear points are points that lie on the same line. **Coplanar points** are points that lie in the same plane.

Resource Planning Guide

Chapter Resource Book
- Teaching Guide/Lesson Plan (pp. 3–4)
- Activity Master (p. 5)
- Practice levels A, B, C (pp. 6–11)
- Study Guide (pp. 12–13)
- Catch-up for Absent Students (p. 14)
- Application (p. 15)
- Challenge (p. 16)

Workbooks
- Notetaking Guide (pp. 1–4)
- Practice Workbook (pp. 1–3)

Teaching Options
- **Power Presentations CD-ROM** provides dynamic electronic teaching resources for the classroom.
- **Activity Generator CD-ROM** provides editable activities for all ability levels.

Interactive Technology
- Easy Planner
- Power Presentations CD-ROM
- Activity Generator CD-ROM
- Animated Geometry
- Test Generator CD-ROM
- Online Quiz
- eWorkbook
- eEdition
- @HomeTutor

Resources for English Learners
- Quick Reference for English Learners
- Spanish Study Guide
- Multi-Language Visual Glossary
- Student Resources in Spanish

See also the *Geometry Toolkit* for more strategies for meeting individual needs.

EXAMPLE 1 Name points, lines, and planes

VISUAL REASONING

There is a line through points S and Q that is not shown in the diagram. Try to imagine what plane SPQ would look like if it were shown.

a. Give two other names for $\overleftrightarrow{PQ}$ and for plane R.

b. Name three points that are collinear. Name four points that are coplanar.

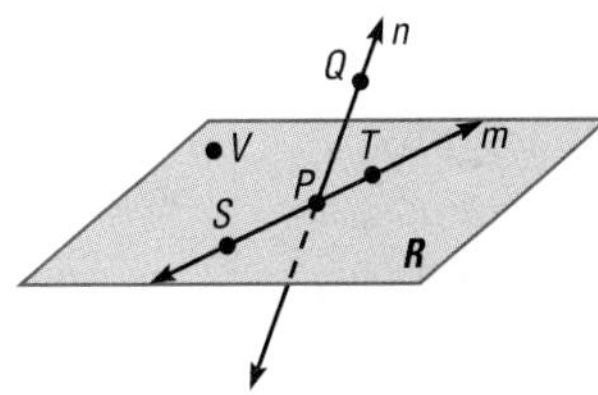

Solution

a. Other names for $\overleftrightarrow{PQ}$ are $\overleftrightarrow{QP}$ and line n. Other names for plane R are plane SVT and plane PTV.

b. Points S, P, and T lie on the same line, so they are collinear. Points S, P, T, and V lie in the same plane, so they are coplanar.

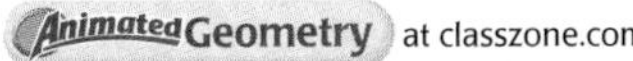

at classzone.com

GUIDED PRACTICE for Example 1

1. Use the diagram in Example 1. Give two other names for $\overleftrightarrow{ST}$. Name a point that is *not* coplanar with points Q, S, and T. ***Sample answer:*** $\overleftrightarrow{TS}$, $\overleftrightarrow{PT}$; **point *V***

DEFINED TERMS In geometry, terms that can be described using known words such as *point* or *line* are called **defined terms**.

KEY CONCEPT *For Your Notebook*

Defined Terms: Segments and Rays

Line AB (written as $\overleftrightarrow{AB}$) and points A and B are used here to define the terms below.

line
A B

Segment The **line segment** AB, or **segment** AB, (written as $\overline{AB}$) consists of the **endpoints** A and B and all points on $\overleftrightarrow{AB}$ that are between A and B. Note that $\overline{AB}$ can also be named $\overline{BA}$.

segment
endpoint endpoint
A B

Ray The **ray** AB (written as $\overrightarrow{AB}$) consists of the endpoint A and all points on $\overleftrightarrow{AB}$ that lie on the same side of A as B.

Note that $\overrightarrow{AB}$ and $\overrightarrow{BA}$ are different rays.

ray
endpoint
A B

endpoint
A B

If point C lies on $\overleftrightarrow{AB}$ between A and B, then $\overrightarrow{CA}$ and $\overrightarrow{CB}$ are **opposite rays**.

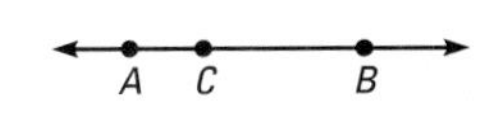

Segments and rays are collinear if they lie on the same line. So, opposite rays are collinear. Lines, segments, and rays are coplanar if they lie in the same plane.

Motivating the Lesson

Ask students to identify a point, line, segment, and flat surface in the classroom. Help them describe the intersection of one wall with the ceiling as a segment, and the intersection of two walls and the ceiling as a point.

Teaching Strategy

Students can benefit from a discussion of some real world examples of the ideas in the Key Concepts box on page 2. The ideas that two points determine a line and that three noncollinear points determine a plane will be revisited and formally presented as postulates in Chapter 2.

Extra Example 1

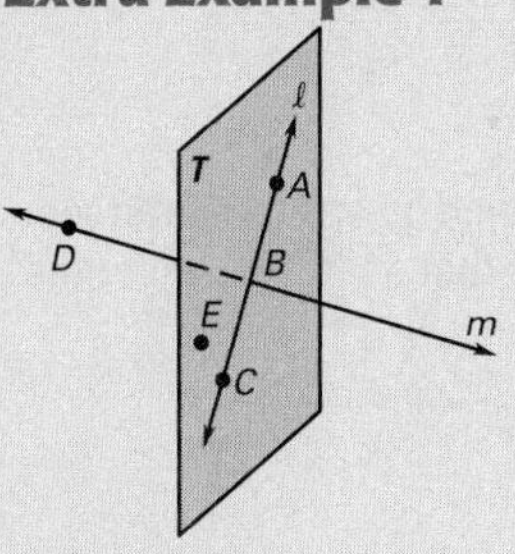

a. Give two other names for $\overleftrightarrow{BD}$. $\overleftrightarrow{DB}$, ***m***

b. Give another name for plane T. ***Sample answer:*** **plane *ABE***

c. Name three points that are collinear. ***A, B, C***

d. Name four points that are coplanar. ***A, B, C, E***

An **Animated Geometry** activity is available on-line for **Example 1**. This activity is also available on the **Power Presentations CD-ROM**.

Extra Example 2

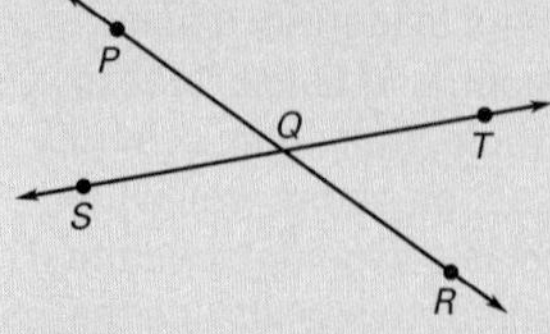

a. Give another name for $\overline{PR}$. **$\overline{RP}$**

b. Name all rays with endpoint Q. Which of these rays are opposite rays? **$\overrightarrow{QP}$, $\overrightarrow{QR}$, $\overrightarrow{QT}$, $\overrightarrow{QS}$; $\overrightarrow{QT}$ and $\overrightarrow{QS}$ are opposite rays, as are $\overrightarrow{QP}$ and $\overrightarrow{QR}$.**

Extra Example 3

a. Sketch a plane and two intersecting lines that intersect the plane at separate points.

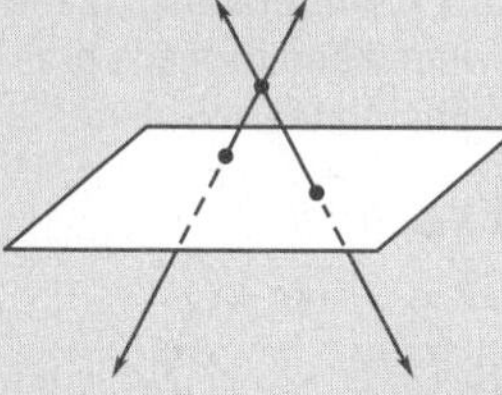

b. Sketch a plane and two intersecting lines that do not intersect the plane.

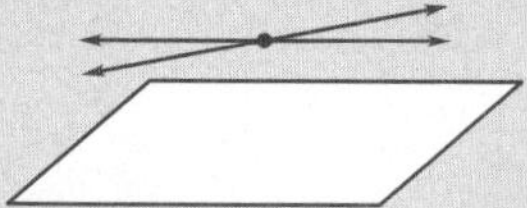

c. Sketch a plane and two intersecting lines that lie in the plane.

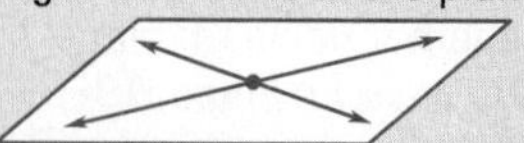

Key Question to Ask for Example 3

- Can a line intersect a plane in only two points? Explain. **No; a line can intersect a plane in one point if it does not lie in the plane or in an infinite number of points if it does lie in the plane, but never in only two points.**

Avoiding Common Errors

Students may forget to include the line, segment, or ray symbol above letters. Remind them to be sure to include the correct symbol so they can determine whether the named figure is a line, segment, or ray.

EXAMPLE 2 Name segments, rays, and opposite rays

a. Give another name for $\overline{GH}$.

b. Name all rays with endpoint J. Which of these rays are opposite rays?

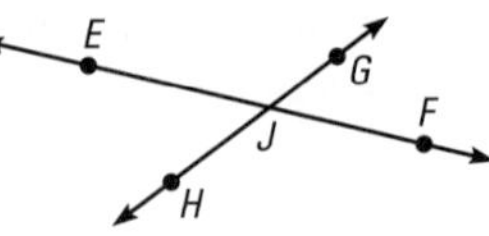

AVOID ERRORS

In Example 2, $\overrightarrow{JG}$ and $\overrightarrow{JF}$ have a common endpoint, but are not collinear. So they are *not* opposite rays.

Solution

a. Another name for $\overline{GH}$ is $\overline{HG}$.

b. The rays with endpoint J are $\overrightarrow{JE}$, $\overrightarrow{JG}$, $\overrightarrow{JF}$, and $\overrightarrow{JH}$. The pairs of opposite rays with endpoint J are $\overrightarrow{JE}$ and $\overrightarrow{JF}$, and $\overrightarrow{JG}$ and $\overrightarrow{JH}$.

✓ **GUIDED PRACTICE** for Example 2

Use the diagram in Example 2.

2. Give another name for $\overline{EF}$. **$\overline{FE}$**

3. Are $\overrightarrow{HJ}$ and $\overrightarrow{JH}$ the same ray? Are $\overrightarrow{HJ}$ and $\overrightarrow{HG}$ the same ray? *Explain.*
No; the rays have different endpoints; yes; points J and G lie on the same side of H.

INTERSECTIONS Two or more geometric figures *intersect* if they have one or more points in common. The **intersection** of the figures is the set of points the figures have in common. Some examples of intersections are shown below.

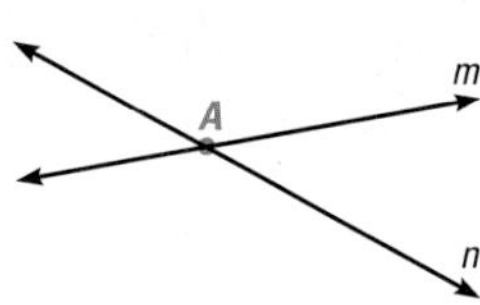

The intersection of two different lines is a point.

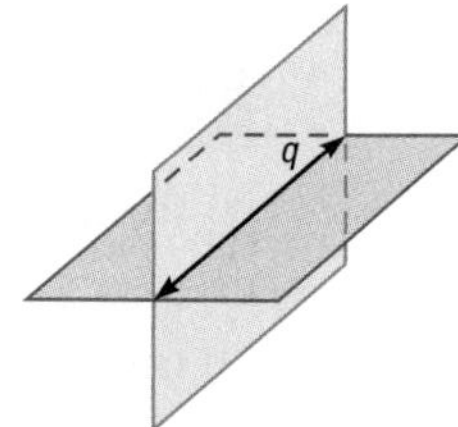

The intersection of two different planes is a line.

EXAMPLE 3 Sketch intersections of lines and planes

a. Sketch a plane and a line that is in the plane.

b. Sketch a plane and a line that does not intersect the plane.

c. Sketch a plane and a line that intersects the plane at a point.

Solution

a.

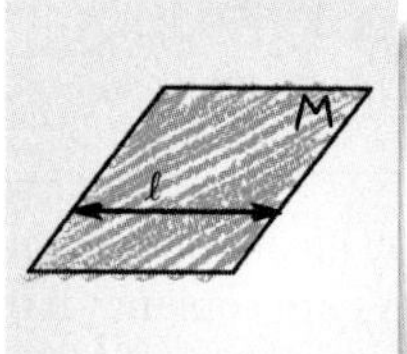

b.

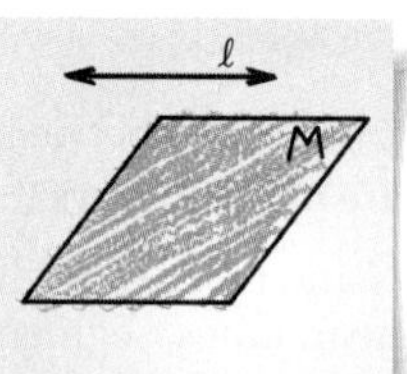

c.

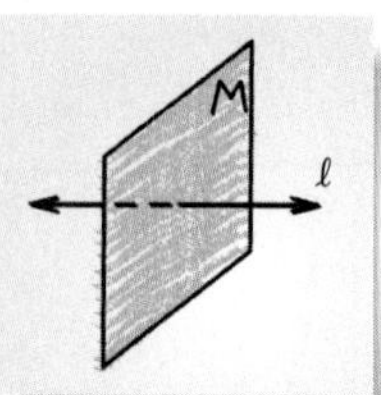

Differentiated Instruction

Kinesthetic Learners While discussing **Example 3**, have students simulate the three cases by using a sheet of paper to represent the plane and a pen or pencil to represent the line. Then have students experiment to see that these are the only three possibilities involving a plane and a line.

See also the *Geometry Toolkit* for more strategies.

EXAMPLE 4 Sketch intersections of planes

Sketch two planes that intersect in a line.

Solution

STEP 1 **Draw** a vertical plane. Shade the plane.

STEP 2 **Draw** a second plane that is horizontal. Shade this plane a different color. Use dashed lines to show where one plane is hidden.

STEP 3 **Draw** the line of intersection.

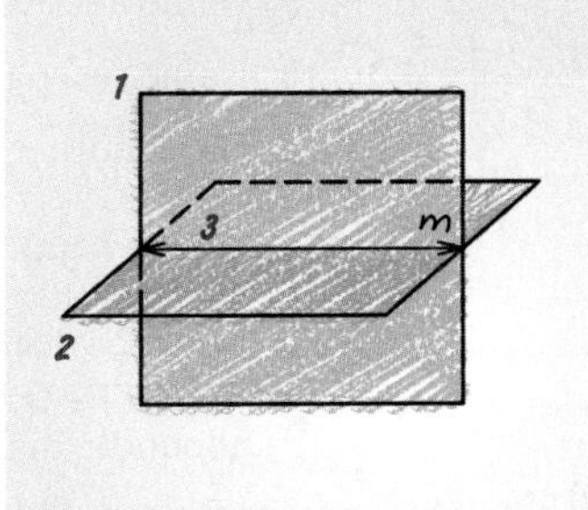

GUIDED PRACTICE for Examples 3 and 4

4. Sketch two different lines that intersect a plane at the same point. **See margin.**

Use the diagram at the right.

5. Name the intersection of $\overleftrightarrow{PQ}$ and line k. **point *M***
6. Name the intersection of plane A and plane B. **line *k***
7. Name the intersection of line k and plane A. **line *k***

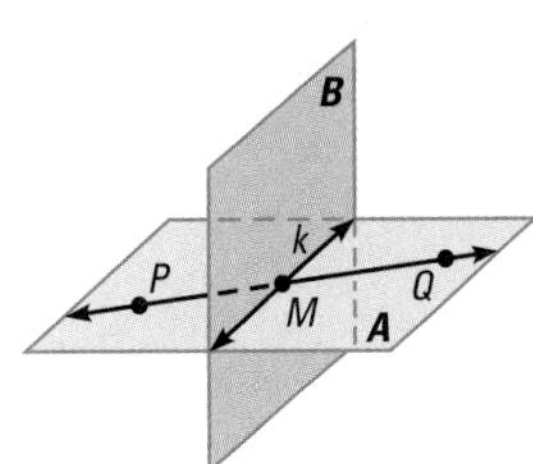

1.1 EXERCISES

HOMEWORK KEY

○ = **WORKED-OUT SOLUTIONS** on p. WS1 for Exs. 15, 19, and 43

★ = **STANDARDIZED TEST PRACTICE** Exs. 2, 7, 13, 16, and 43

SKILL PRACTICE

A

1. **VOCABULARY** Write in words what each of the following symbols means.

   a. Q **point *Q*** b. $\overline{MN}$ **line segment *MN*** c. $\overrightarrow{ST}$ **ray *ST*** d. $\overleftrightarrow{FG}$ **line *FG***

2. ★ **WRITING** *Compare* collinear points and coplanar points. Are collinear points also coplanar? Are coplanar points also collinear? *Explain.* **See margin.**

EXAMPLE 1 on p. 3 for Exs. 3–7

NAMING POINTS, LINES, AND PLANES In Exercises 3–7, use the diagram.

3. Give two other names for $\overleftrightarrow{WQ}$. **$\overleftrightarrow{QW}$, line *g***
4. Give another name for plane V. ***Sample answer:* plane *RTS***
5. Name three points that are collinear. Then name a fourth point that is *not* collinear with these three points. ***Sample answer:* points *R, Q, S*; point *T***
6. Name a point that is *not* coplanar with R, S, and T. **point *W***

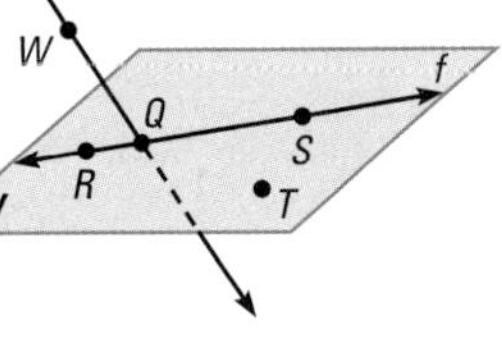

7. ★ **WRITING** Is point W coplanar with points Q and R? *Explain.*
Yes; through any three points not on the same line, there is exactly one plane.

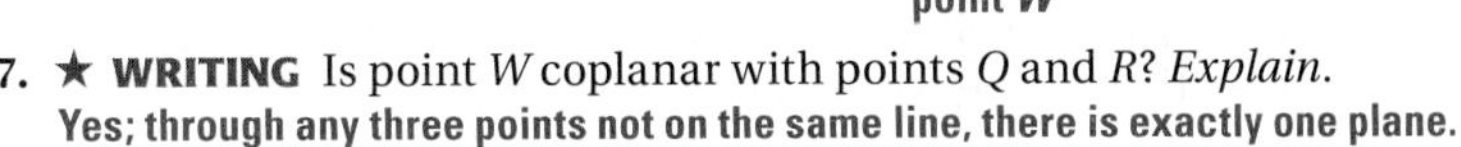

Extra Example 4

Sketch two planes that do not intersect in a line.

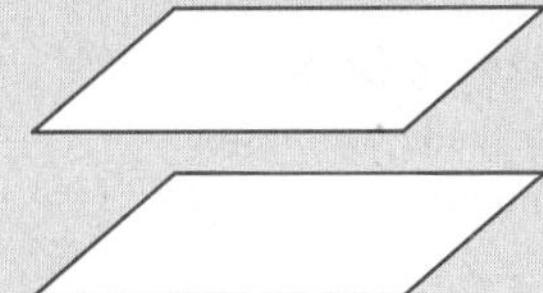

Key Question to Ask for Example 4

- Can two planes intersect in a segment? Explain. **No; since the intersecting planes extend without end, their intersection must be a line.**

Closing the Lesson

Have students summarize the major points of the lesson and answer the Essential Question: How do you name geometric figures?

- **You can sketch and name points, lines, planes, segments, and rays.**
- **A line may intersect a plane in one point or lie in the plane.**
- **The intersection of two planes is a line.**

Use one letter to name a point, two letters to name the endpoints of a segment, two letters to name the endpoint and one other point of a ray, and two letters to name any two points of a line. Use three letters for three noncollinear points in a plane to name the plane.

Guided Practice

4. *Sample:*

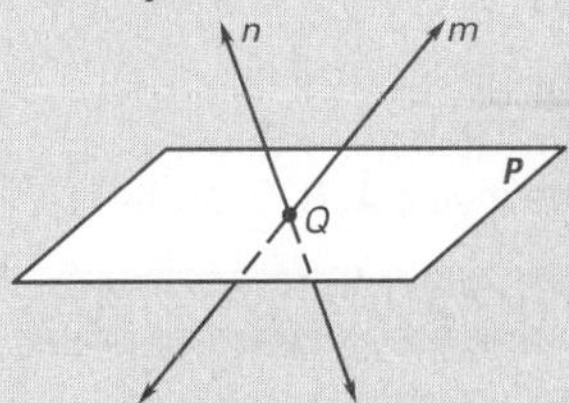

Skill Practice

2. Yes; no; collinear points are points that lie on the same line and therefore in the same plane, while coplanar points lie in the same plane but not necessarily on the same line.

4 PRACTICE AND APPLY

Assignment Guide

Answer Transparencies available for all exercises

Basic:
Day 1: SRH p. 876 Exs. 1–6
pp. 5–8
Exs. 1–16, 17–27 odd, 40–44, 47, 50, 53, 56

Average:
Day 1: pp. 5–8
Exs. 1, 2, 3–11 odd, 12–16, 20–26, 27–37 odd, 40–45, 48, 51, 54, 57

Advanced:
Day 1: pp. 5–8
Exs. 1, 5–7, 10, 11, 13–16, 20–38 even, 39–46*, 49, 52, 55, 58

Block:
pp. 5–8
Exs. 1, 2, 3–11 odd, 12–16, 20–26, 27–37 odd, 40–45, 48, 51, 54, 57 (with 1.2)

Differentiated Instruction

See *Geometry Best Practices Toolkit* for suggestions on addressing the needs of a diverse classroom.

Homework Check

For a quick check of student understanding of key concepts, go over the following exercises:

Basic: 4, 8, 14, 21, 40
Average: 5, 9, 14, 20, 41
Advanced: 6, 13, 22, 26, 42

Extra Practice

- Student Edition, p. 896
- Chapter 1 Resource Book: Practice levels A, B, C, pp. 6–11

Practice Worksheet

An easily-readable reduced practice page (with answers) for this lesson can be found on p. 1C.

EXAMPLE 2 on p. 4 for Exs. 8–13

NAMING SEGMENTS AND RAYS **In Exercises 8–12, use the diagram.**

8. What is another name for $\overline{ZY}$? $\overline{YZ}$
9. Name all rays with endpoint V. $\overrightarrow{VY}$, $\overrightarrow{VX}$, $\overrightarrow{VZ}$, $\overrightarrow{VW}$
10. Name two pairs of opposite rays.
11. Give another name for $\overrightarrow{WV}$. $\overrightarrow{WX}$

10. $\overrightarrow{VX}$ and $\overrightarrow{VW}$, $\overrightarrow{VY}$ and $\overrightarrow{VZ}$

12. **ERROR ANALYSIS** A student says that $\overrightarrow{VW}$ and $\overrightarrow{VZ}$ are opposite rays because they have the same endpoint. *Describe* the error. **Point V must lie between points W and Z, which means the three points must be collinear.**

13. ★ **MULTIPLE CHOICE** Which statement about the diagram at the right is true? **B**

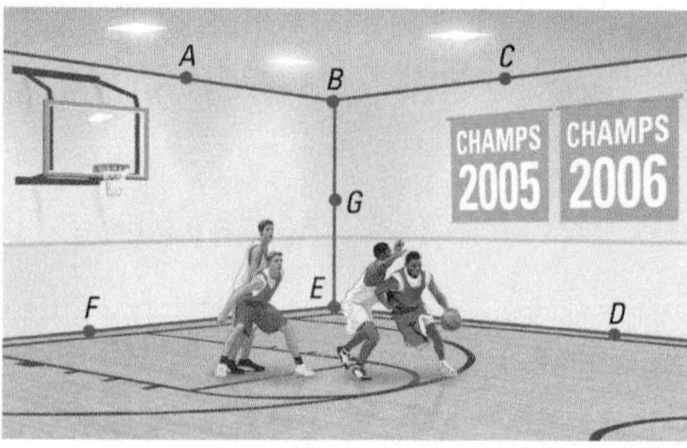

Ⓐ A, B, and C are collinear.
Ⓑ C, D, E, and G are coplanar.
Ⓒ B lies on $\overrightarrow{GE}$.
Ⓓ $\overrightarrow{EF}$ and $\overrightarrow{ED}$ are opposite rays.

EXAMPLES 3 and 4 on pp. 4–5 for Exs. 14–23

SKETCHING INTERSECTIONS **Sketch the figure described.** **14, 15. See margin.**

14. Three lines that lie in a plane and intersect at one point
15. One line that lies in a plane, and one line that does not lie in the plane

16. ★ **MULTIPLE CHOICE** Line AB and line CD intersect at point E. Which of the following are opposite rays? **A**

Ⓐ $\overrightarrow{EC}$ and $\overrightarrow{ED}$ Ⓑ $\overrightarrow{CE}$ and $\overrightarrow{DE}$ Ⓒ $\overrightarrow{AB}$ and $\overrightarrow{BA}$ Ⓓ $\overrightarrow{AE}$ and $\overrightarrow{BE}$

READING DIAGRAMS **In Exercises 17–22, use the diagram at the right.**

17. Name the intersection of $\overleftrightarrow{PR}$ and $\overleftrightarrow{HR}$. **point R**
18. Name the intersection of plane EFG and plane FGS. $\overleftrightarrow{FG}$
19. Name the intersection of plane PQS and plane HGS. $\overleftrightarrow{RS}$
20. Are points P, Q, and F collinear? Are they coplanar? **no; yes**
21. Are points P and G collinear? Are they coplanar? **yes; yes**
22. Name three planes that intersect at point E. ***Sample answer:* plane PEF, plane PEH, plane HEF**
23. **SKETCHING PLANES** Sketch plane J intersecting plane K. Then draw a line ℓ in plane J that intersects plane K at a single point. **See margin.**
24. **NAMING RAYS** Name 10 different rays in the diagram at the right. Then name 2 pairs of opposite rays.
25. **SKETCHING** Draw three noncollinear points J, K, and L. Sketch $\overline{JK}$ and add a point M on $\overline{JK}$. Then sketch $\overrightarrow{ML}$. **See margin.**
26. **SKETCHING** Draw two points P and Q. Then sketch $\overrightarrow{PQ}$. Add a point R on the ray so that Q is between P and R. **See margin.**

24. Sample answer: $\overrightarrow{AC}$ (or $\overrightarrow{AD}$), $\overrightarrow{AB}$ (or $\overrightarrow{AE}$), $\overrightarrow{DC}$ (or $\overrightarrow{DA}$), $\overrightarrow{EB}$ (or $\overrightarrow{EA}$), $\overrightarrow{CB}$, $\overrightarrow{BC}$, $\overrightarrow{CD}$, $\overrightarrow{CA}$; $\overrightarrow{CD}$, and $\overrightarrow{CA}$, $\overrightarrow{BA}$ and $\overrightarrow{BE}$

◯ = **WORKED-OUT SOLUTIONS** on p. WS1 ★ = **STANDARDIZED TEST PRACTICE**

---

14. ***Sample:***

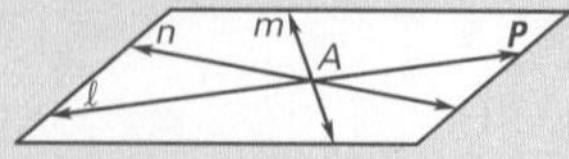

15. ***Sample:***

23. ***Sample:***

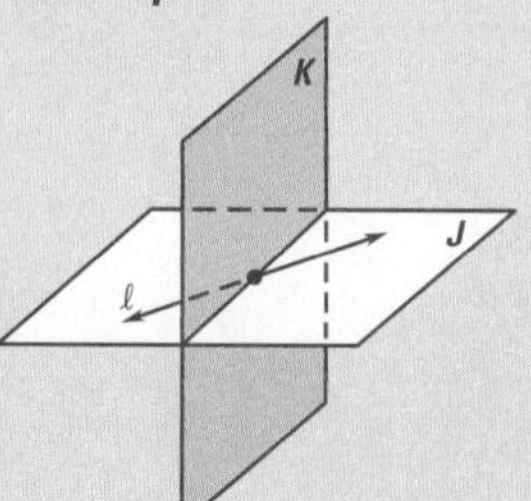

25. ***Sample:***

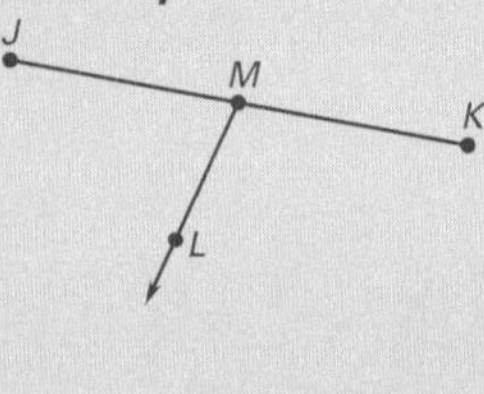

REVIEW ALGEBRA
For help with equations of lines, see p. 878.

ALGEBRA In Exercises 27–32, you are given an equation of a line and a point. Use substitution to determine whether the point is on the line.

27. $y = x - 4$; $A(5, 1)$ **on the line**
28. $y = x + 1$; $A(1, 0)$ **not on the line**
29. $y = 3x + 4$; $A(7, 1)$ **not on the line**
30. $y = 4x + 2$; $A(1, 6)$ **on the line**
31. $y = 3x - 2$; $A(-1, -5)$ **on the line**
32. $y = -2x + 8$; $A(-4, 0)$ **not on the line**

GRAPHING Graph the inequality on a number line. Tell whether the graph is a *segment*, a *ray* or *rays*, a *point*, or a *line*. **33–38. See margin for art.**

33. $x \le 3$ **ray**
34. $x \ge -4$ **ray**
35. $-7 \le x \le 4$ **segment**
36. $x \ge 5$ or $x \le -2$ **rays**
37. $x \ge -1$ or $x \le 5$ **line**
38. $|x| \le 0$ **point**

C 39. **CHALLENGE** Tell whether each of the following situations involving three planes is possible. If a situation is possible, make a sketch. **See margin for art.**

a. None of the three planes intersect. **possible**
b. The three planes intersect in one line. **possible**
c. The three planes intersect in one point. **possible**
d. Two planes do not intersect. The third plane intersects the other two. **possible**
e. Exactly two planes intersect. The third plane does not intersect the other two. **not possible**

PROBLEM SOLVING

EXAMPLE 3 A on p. 4 for Exs. 40–42

EVERYDAY INTERSECTIONS What kind of geometric intersection does the photograph suggest?

40.

intersecting lines

41. **intersection of a line and a plane**

42.
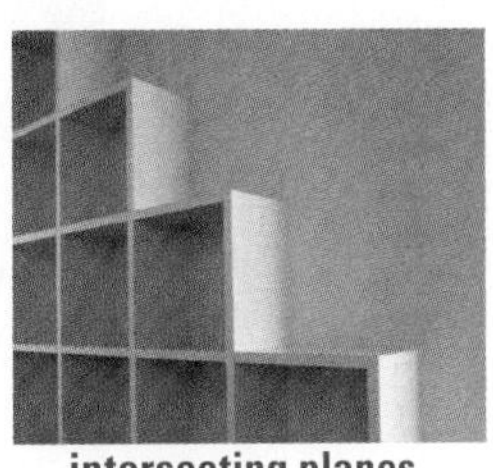
intersecting planes

43. Four points are not necessarily coplanar; no; three points determine a unique plane.

43. ★ **SHORT RESPONSE** *Explain* why a four-legged table may rock from side to side even if the floor is level. Would a three-legged table on the same level floor rock from side to side? Why or why not?

for problem solving help at classzone.com

B 44. **SURVEYING** A surveying instrument is placed on a tripod. The tripod has three legs whose lengths can be adjusted.

a. When the tripod is sitting on a level surface, are the tips of the legs coplanar? **yes**
b. Suppose the tripod is used on a sloping surface. The length of each leg is adjusted so that the base of the surveying instrument is level with the horizon. Are the tips of the legs coplanar? *Explain.*

44b. Yes; three points determine a unique plane.

for problem solving help at classzone.com

Vocabulary

Exercise 13 To help students remember the meaning of the terms collinear and coplanar, discuss other words that use the prefix *co-*, which means *together*.

Reading Strategy

Exercises 17–22 Point out to students that in the figure different planes are shaded lighter or darker blue to help them visualize the shape.

Teaching Strategy

Exercises 17–22 To help students better understand the diagram, you may wish to have them work in groups and provide each group with a three-dimensional model; a tissue box would work well. Students could label the corner points with a marker.

39a.
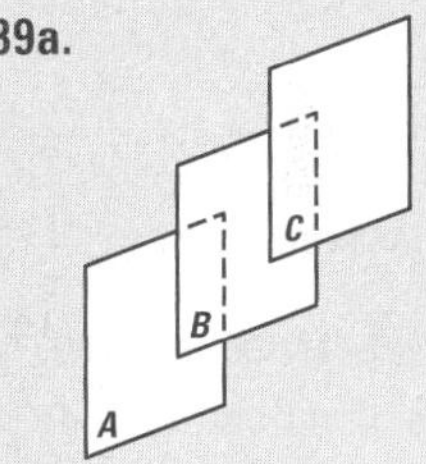

39b.
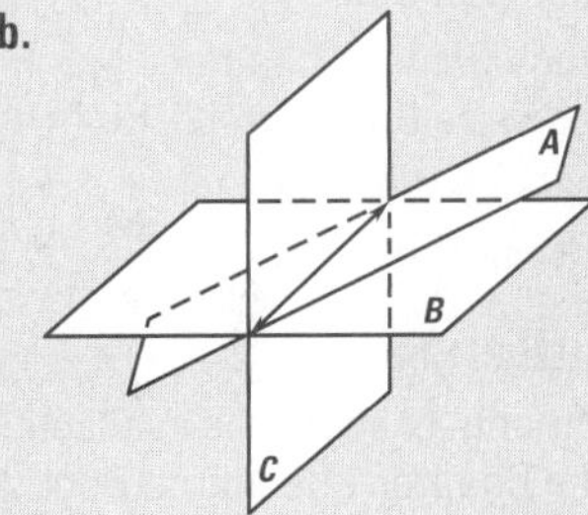

39c.

39d.
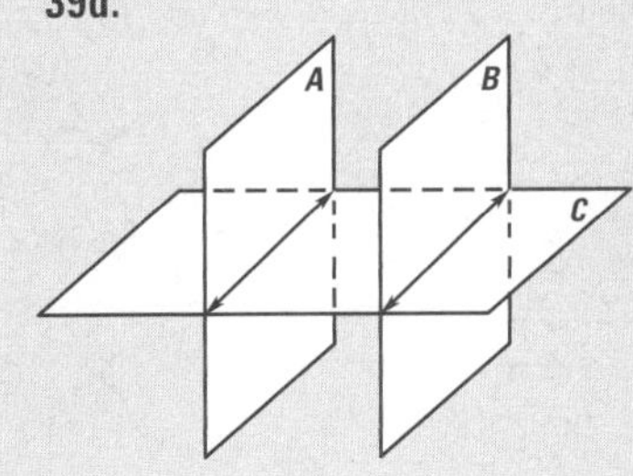

26. *Sample:*
P Q R

33. **34.** **35.**
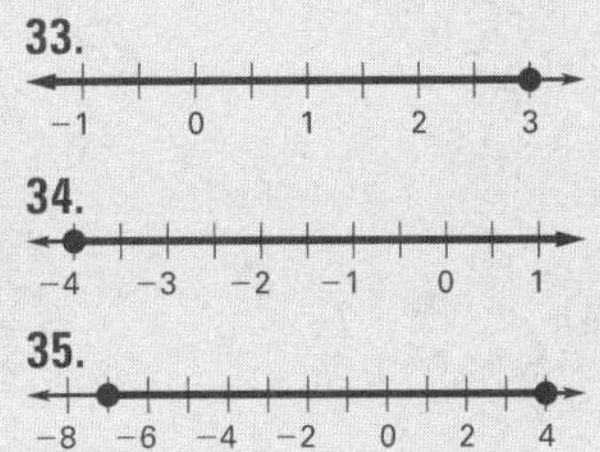

36. **37.** **38.**
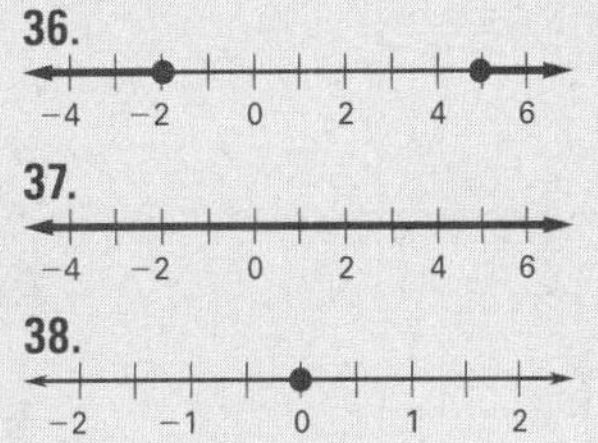

5 ASSESS AND RETEACH

Daily Homework Quiz

Transparency Available

Use this figure for Exercises 1–4.

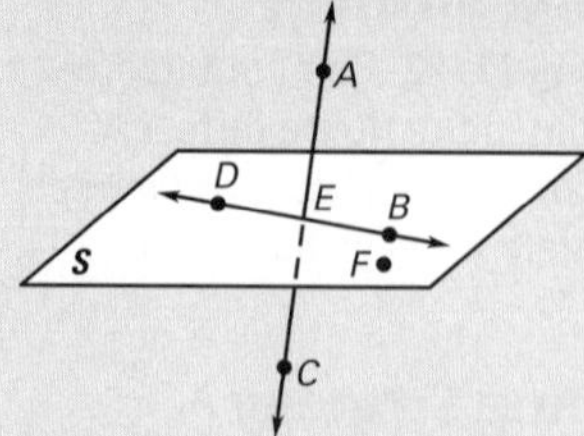

1. Give two other names for $\overleftrightarrow{AE}$. **$\overleftrightarrow{EC}$, $\overleftrightarrow{AC}$**
2. Give another name for plane S. ***Sample answer:* plane *DEF***
3. Name three collinear points. ***Sample answer: A, E, C***
4. Name the intersection of $\overleftrightarrow{AC}$ and plane S. ***E***

Available at **classzone.com**

Diagnosis/Remediation

- Practice A, B, C in Chapter 1 Resource Book, pp. 6–11
- Study Guide in Chapter 1 Resource Book, pp. 12–13
- Practice Workbook, pp. 1–3
- @HomeTutor

Challenge

Additional challenge is available in the Chapter 1 Resource Book, p. 16.

45a–c. See Additional Answers beginning on p. AA1.

45. MULTI-STEP PROBLEM In a *perspective drawing*, lines that do not intersect in real life are represented by lines that appear to intersect at a point far away on the horizon. This point is called a *vanishing point*. The diagram shows a drawing of a house with two vanishing points. **45a–c. See margin.**

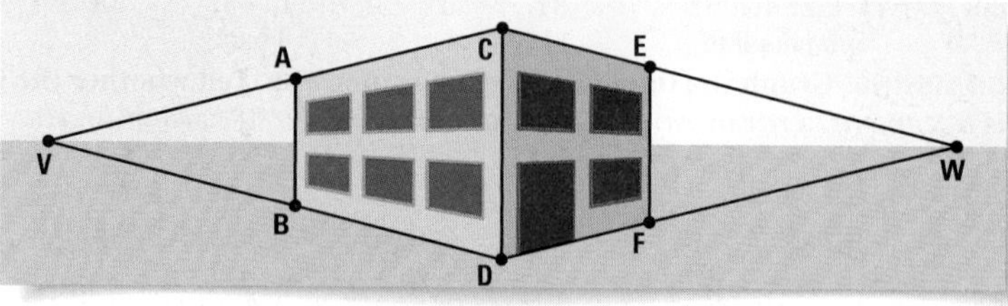

a. Trace the black line segments in the drawing. Using lightly dashed lines, join points A and B to the vanishing point W. Join points E and F to the vanishing point V.

b. Label the intersection of $\overleftrightarrow{EV}$ and $\overleftrightarrow{AW}$ as G. Label the intersection of $\overleftrightarrow{FV}$ and $\overleftrightarrow{BW}$ as H.

c. Using heavy dashed lines, draw the hidden edges of the house: $\overline{AG}$, $\overline{EG}$, $\overline{BH}$, $\overline{FH}$, and $\overline{GH}$.

C **46. CHALLENGE** Each street in a particular town intersects every existing street exactly one time. Only two streets pass through each intersection.

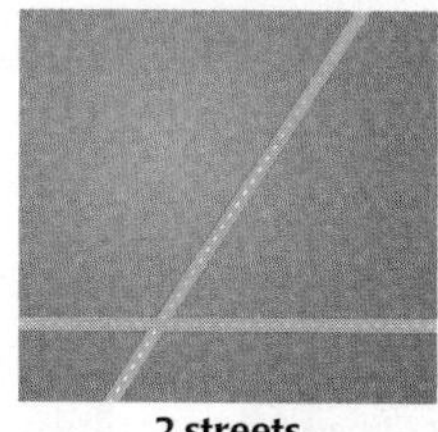
2 streets

3 streets

4 streets

a. A traffic light is needed at each intersection. How many traffic lights are needed if there are 5 streets in the town? 6 streets? **10 traffic lights; 15 traffic lights**

b. *Describe* a pattern you can use to find the number of additional traffic lights that are needed each time a street is added to the town. **Let *n* represent the number of streets. To find the additional number of traffic lights needed, find $n - 1$.**

MIXED REVIEW

Find the difference. *(p. 869)*

47. $-15 - 9$ **−24**	**48.** $6 - 10$ **−4**	**49.** $-25 - (-12)$ **−13**
50. $13 - 20$ **−7**	**51.** $16 - (-4)$ **20**	**52.** $-5 - 15$ **−20**

PREVIEW Prepare for Lesson 1.2 in Exs. 53–58.

Evaluate the expression. *(p. 870)*

53. $5 \cdot \lvert -2 + 1 \rvert$ **5**	**54.** $\lvert -8 + 7 \rvert - 6$ **−5**	**55.** $-7 \cdot \lvert 8 - 10 \rvert$ **−14**

Plot the point in a coordinate plane. *(p. 878)* **56–58. See margin.**

56. $A(2, 4)$	**57.** $B(-3, 6)$	**58.** $E(6, 7.5)$

56–58.

y
E(6, 7.5)
B(−3, 6)
A(2, 4)
1
−1
x

1.2 Use Segments and Congruence

Before You learned about points, lines, and planes.

Now You will use segment postulates to identify congruent segments.

Why? So you can calculate flight distances, as in Ex. 33.

Key Vocabulary
- **postulate, axiom**
- **coordinate**
- **distance**
- **between**
- **congruent segments**

Standards

1.0 Students demonstrate understanding by identifying and giving examples of undefined terms, **axioms,** theorems, and inductive and deductive reasoning.

In Geometry, a rule that is accepted without proof is called a **postulate** or **axiom**. A rule that can be proved is called a *theorem*, as you will see later. Postulate 1 shows how to find the distance between two points on a line.

POSTULATE *For Your Notebook*

POSTULATE 1 Ruler Postulate

The points on a line can be matched one to one with the real numbers. The real number that corresponds to a point is the **coordinate** of the point.

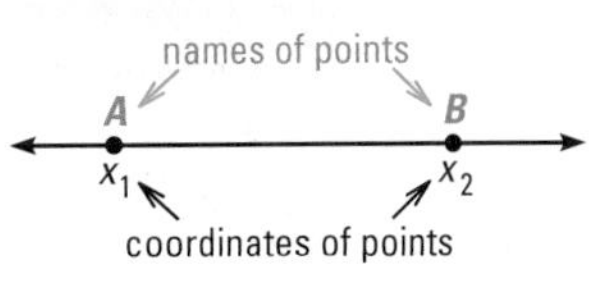

The **distance** between points A and B, written as AB, is the absolute value of the difference of the coordinates of A and B.

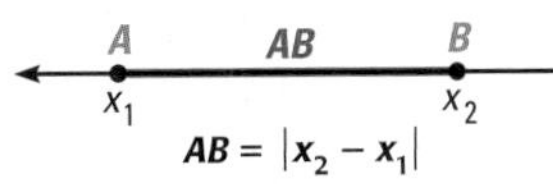

In the diagrams above, the small numbers in the coordinates x_1 and x_2 are called *subscripts*. The coordinates are read as "x sub one" and "x sub two."

The distance between points A and B, or AB, is also called the *length* of $\overline{AB}$.

EXAMPLE 1 Apply the Ruler Postulate

Measure the length of $\overline{ST}$ to the nearest tenth of a centimeter.

Solution

Align one mark of a metric ruler with S. Then estimate the coordinate of T. For example, if you align S with 2, T appears to align with 5.4.

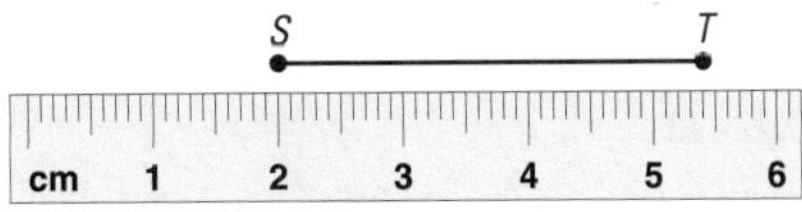

$ST = |5.4 - 2| = 3.4$ **Use Ruler Postulate.**

▶ The length of $\overline{ST}$ is about 3.4 centimeters.

1 PLAN AND PREPARE

Warm-Up Exercises

Transparency Available

1. Solve $3x + 5 + 2x - 4 = 36$. **7**

2. Find three cities on this map that appear to be collinear. **Chicago, Bloomington, Springfield**

Notetaking Guide

Transparency Available

Promotes interactive learning and notetaking skills, pp. 5–7.

Pacing

Basic: 1 day

Average: 1 day

Advanced: 1 day

Block: 0.5 block with 1.1

- See *Teaching Guide/Lesson Plan.*

2 FOCUS AND MOTIVATE

Essential Question

Big Idea 3, p. 1

What are congruent segments? **Tell students they will learn how to answer this question by finding lengths of segments.**

Resource Planning Guide

Chapter Resource Book
- Teaching Guide/Lesson Plan (pp. 17–18)
- Activity Master (p. 19)
- Practice levels A, B, C (pp. 20–25)
- Study Guide (pp. 26–27)
- Catch-up for Absent Students (p. 28)
- Application (p. 29)
- Challenge (p. 30)

Workbooks
- Notetaking Guide (pp. 5–7)
- Practice Workbook (pp. 4–6)

Teaching Options
- **Power Presentations CD-ROM** provides dynamic electronic teaching resources for the classroom.
- **Activity Generator CD-ROM** provides editable activities for all ability levels.

Interactive Technology
- Easy Planner
- Power Presentations CD-ROM
- Activity Generator CD-ROM
- Animated Geometry
- Test Generator CD-ROM
- Online Quiz
- eWorkbook
- eEdition
- @HomeTutor

Resources for English Learners
- Quick Reference for English Learners
- Spanish Study Guide
- Multi-Language Visual Glossary
- Student Resources in Spanish

See also the *Geometry Toolkit* for more strategies for meeting individual needs.

Motivating the Lesson

Ask students to think of three places they go that are in a straight line, perhaps their house, a friend's house, and school. Tell them that in this lesson they will learn how to find the third distance between these places when they are given the other two.

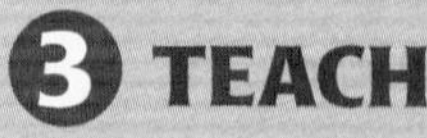

Extra Example 1

Measure the length of $\overline{PQ}$ to the nearest tenth of a centimeter. **3.2 cm**

Key Question to Ask for Example 1

- What if you had aligned S with 1 instead of 2? **The distance is still 3.4, but this time found by using $|4.4 - 1|$.**

Extra Example 2

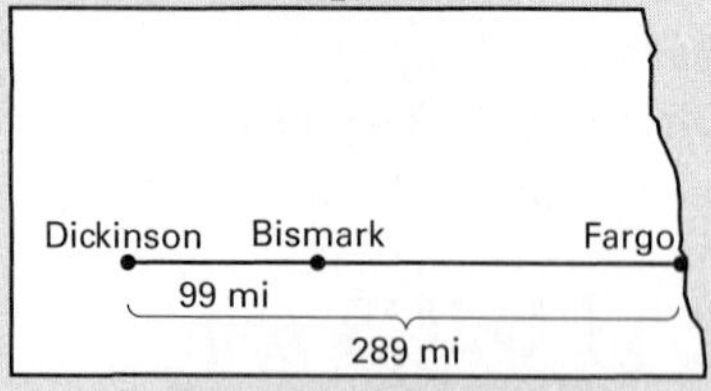

The cities shown on the map lie approximately in a straight line. Use the given distances to find the distance from Bismarck to Fargo. **190 mi**

Key Question to Ask for Example 2

- Could you have found the distance if the points were not in a straight line? Explain. **No, because the Segment Addition Postulate would no longer apply.**

ADDING SEGMENT LENGTHS When three points are collinear, you can say that one point is **between** the other two.

Point *B* is between points *A* and *C*.

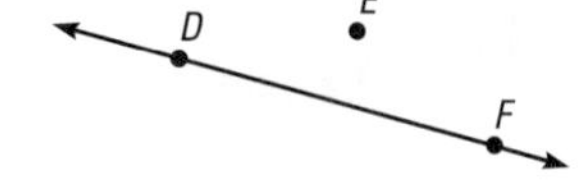

Point *E* is not between points *D* and *F*.

POSTULATE — *For Your Notebook*

POSTULATE 2 Segment Addition Postulate

If B is between A and C, then $AB + BC = AC$.

If $AB + BC = AC$, then B is between A and C.

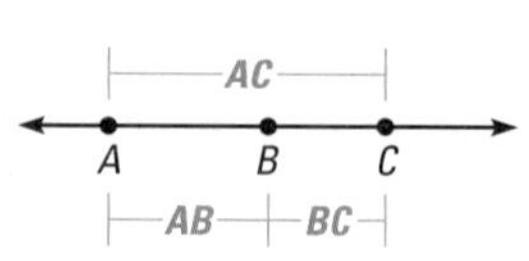

EXAMPLE 2 Apply the Segment Addition Postulate

MAPS The cities shown on the map lie approximately in a straight line. Use the given distances to find the distance from Lubbock, Texas, to St. Louis, Missouri.

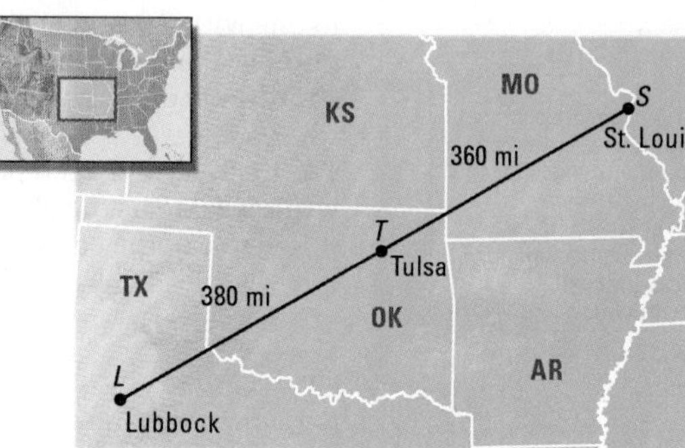

Solution

Because Tulsa, Oklahoma, lies between Lubbock and St. Louis, you can apply the Segment Addition Postulate.

$$LS = LT + TS = 380 + 360 = 740$$

▶ The distance from Lubbock to St. Louis is about 740 miles.

✓ GUIDED PRACTICE for Examples 1 and 2

Use a ruler to measure the length of the segment to the nearest $\frac{1}{8}$ inch.

1. M ——— N $1\frac{5}{8}$ **in.**
2. P ——— Q $1\frac{3}{8}$ **in.**

In Exercises 3 and 4, use the diagram shown.

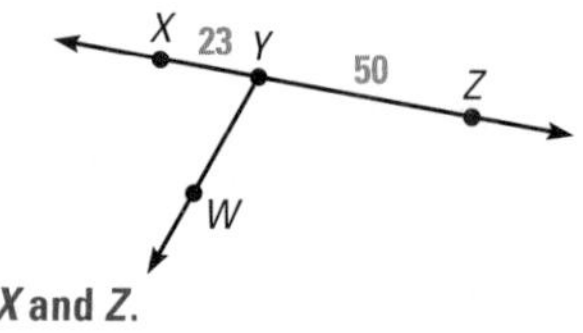

3. Use the Segment Addition Postulate to find XZ. **73**
4. In the diagram, $WY = 30$. Can you use the Segment Addition Postulate to find the distance between points W and Z? *Explain* your reasoning. **No; *W* is not between *X* and *Z*.**

Differentiated Instruction

English Learners Have students work problems similar to **Example 2** using maps of other countries. In particular, find locations where English learners or their family members have come from.

See also the *Geometry Toolkit* for more strategies.

EXAMPLE 3 Find a length

Use the diagram to find GH.

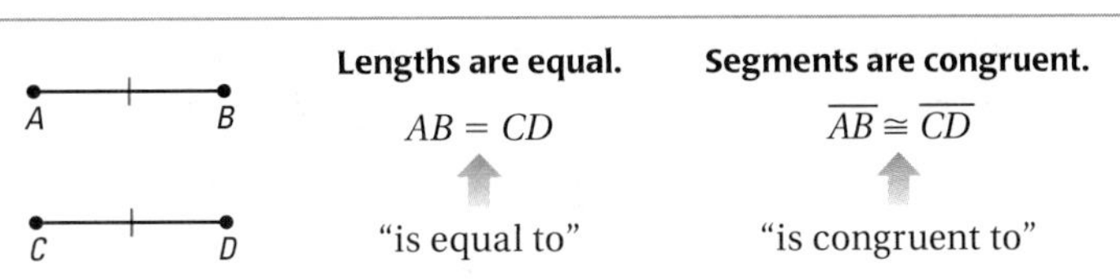

Solution

Use the Segment Addition Postulate to write an equation. Then solve the equation to find GH.

$FH = FG + GH$ **Segment Addition Postulate**

$36 = 21 + GH$ **Substitute 36 for FH and 21 for FG.**

$15 = GH$ **Subtract 21 from each side.**

CONGRUENT SEGMENTS Line segments that have the same length are called **congruent segments**. In the diagram below, you can say "the length of $\overline{AB}$ is equal to the length of $\overline{CD}$," or you can say "$\overline{AB}$ *is congruent to* $\overline{CD}$." The symbol $\cong$ means "is congruent to."

	Lengths are equal.	Segments are congruent.
A———B C———D	$AB = CD$ ↑ "is equal to"	$\overline{AB} \cong \overline{CD}$ ↑ "is congruent to"

READ DIAGRAMS
In the diagram, the red tick marks indicate that $\overline{AB} \cong \overline{CD}$.

EXAMPLE 4 Compare segments for congruence

Plot $J(-3, 4)$, $K(2, 4)$, $L(1, 3)$, and $M(1, -2)$ in a coordinate plane. Then determine whether $\overline{JK}$ and $\overline{LM}$ are congruent.

Solution

To find the length of a horizontal segment, find the absolute value of the difference of the x-coordinates of the endpoints.

$JK = |2 - (-3)| = 5$ **Use Ruler Postulate.**

To find the length of a vertical segment, find the absolute value of the difference of the y-coordinates of the endpoints.

$LM = |-2 - 3| = 5$ **Use Ruler Postulate.**

▶ $\overline{JK}$ and $\overline{LM}$ have the same length. So, $\overline{JK} \cong \overline{LM}$.

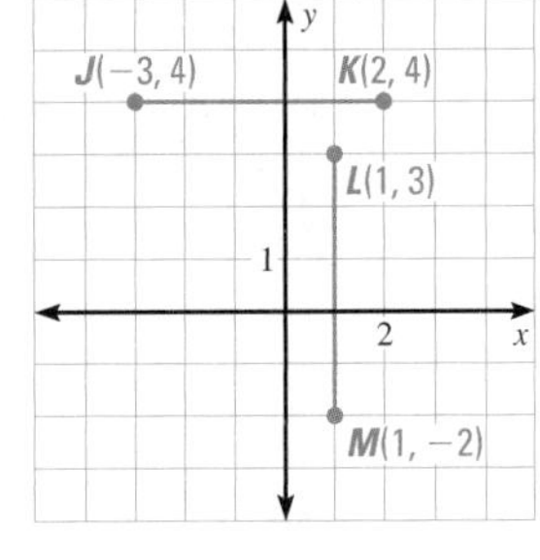

REVIEW USING A COORDINATE PLANE
For help with using a coordinate plane, see p. 878.

✓ GUIDED PRACTICE for Examples 3 and 4

5. Use the diagram at the right to find WX. **107**

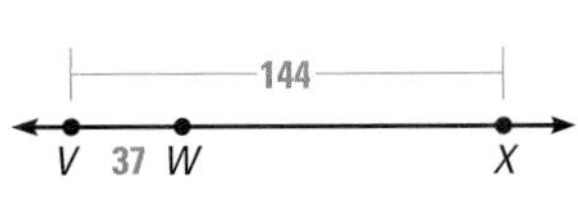

6. Plot the points $A(-2, 4)$, $B(3, 4)$, $C(0, 2)$, and $D(0, -2)$ in a coordinate plane. Then determine whether $\overline{AB}$ and $\overline{CD}$ are congruent. **no**

Extra Example 3

Find CD. **25**

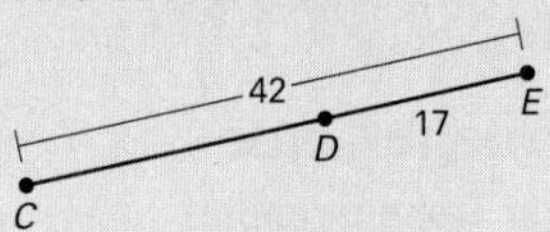

Extra Example 4

Graph the points $X(-2, -5)$, $Y(-2, 3)$, $W(-4, 3)$, and $Z(4, 3)$ in a coordinate plane. Are $\overline{XY}$ and $\overline{WZ}$ congruent? **Yes, both equal 8.**

Key Question to Ask for Example 4

- How can you determine which coordinates to subtract? **You subtract the coordinates that are not equal.**

Avoiding Common Errors

Students tend to be lax when using equal and congruent. Stress the concept in the box above Example 4 to point out that lengths, which are numbers, are equal and that segments, which are figures, are congruent.

Closing the Lesson

Have students summarize the major points of the lesson and answer the Essential Question: What are congruent segments?

- **To find the distance between two points on a number line, subtract their coordinates, and find the absolute value of the difference.**
- **The length of a segment is the sum of the lengths of its nonoverlapping parts.**

Congruent segments are segments that have the same length.

Differentiated Instruction

Below Level To stress the difference between equal and congruent, show students two identical one foot rulers. Ask students what the length of each ruler is and have them write the relationship 12 in. = 12 in. (or 1 ft = 1 ft). Turn the rulers over, label one as A–B and the other as C–D. Tell students to write the relationship between $\overline{AB}$ and $\overline{CD}$. Students should write $\overline{AB} \cong \overline{CD}$.

See also the *Geometry Toolkit* for more strategies.

4 PRACTICE AND APPLY

Assignment Guide

Answer Transparencies available for all exercises

Basic:
Day 1: SRH p. 878 Exs. 7–12
pp. 12–14
Exs. 1–8, 12–23, 32–34, 37–45

Average:
Day 1: pp. 12–14
Exs. 1–5, 7–10, 12–20 even, 21–30, 32–35, 37–45 odd

Advanced:
Day 1: pp. 12–14
Exs. 1–5, 9–11, 15–19 odd, 20–36*, 39, 42, 44

Block:
pp. 12–14
Exs. 1–5, 7–10, 12–20 even, 21–30, 32–35, 37–45 odd (with 1.1)

Differentiated Instruction

See *Geometry Best Practices Toolkit* for suggestions on addressing the needs of a diverse classroom.

Homework Check

For a quick check of student understanding of key concepts, go over the following exercises:

Basic: 3, 6, 14, 22, 33
Average: 4, 8, 16, 24, 33
Advanced: 5, 10, 19, 26, 33

Extra Practice

- Student Edition, p. 896
- Chapter 1 Resource Book: Practice levels A, B, C, pp. 20–25

Practice Worksheet

An easily-readable reduced practice page (with answers) for this lesson can be found on p. 1C.

1.2 EXERCISES

HOMEWORK KEY
○ = **WORKED-OUT SOLUTIONS** on p. WS1 for Exs. 13, 17, and 33
★ = **STANDARDIZED TEST PRACTICE** Exs. 2, 20, 27, and 34

SKILL PRACTICE

A

In Exercises 1 and 2, use the diagram at the right.

M P Q N

1. VOCABULARY *Explain* what $\overline{MN}$ means and what MN means.
$\overline{MN}$ means segment MN while MN is the length of $\overline{MN}$.

2. ★ **WRITING** *Explain* how you can find PN if you know PQ and QN. How can you find PN if you know MP and MN?
Find the sum $PQ + QN$; find the difference $MN - MP$.

EXAMPLE 1 on p. 9 for Exs. 3–5

MEASUREMENT Measure the length of the segment to the nearest tenth of a centimeter.

3. 

2.1 cm

4. 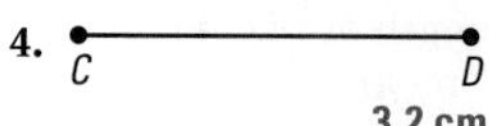

3.2 cm

5. E F **3.5 cm**

EXAMPLES 2 and 3 on pp. 10–11 for Exs. 6–12

SEGMENT ADDITION POSTULATE Find the indicated length.

6. Find MP. **23**
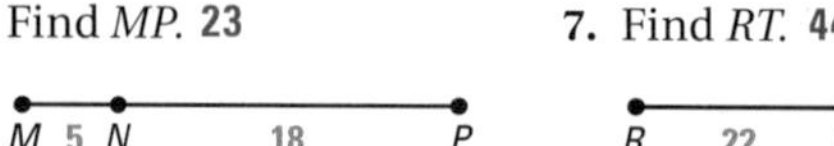

7. Find RT. **44**
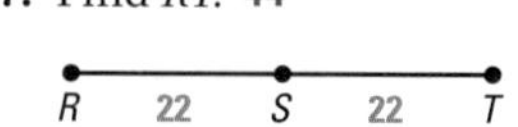

8. Find UW. **65**
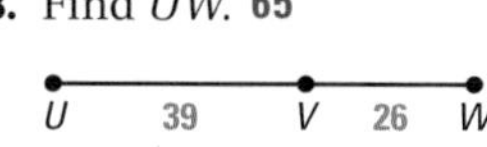

9. Find XY. **23**
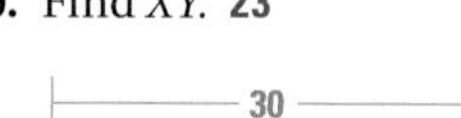

10. Find BC. **15**
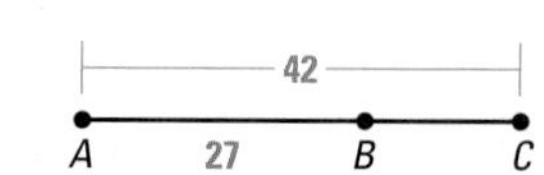

11. Find DE. **13**
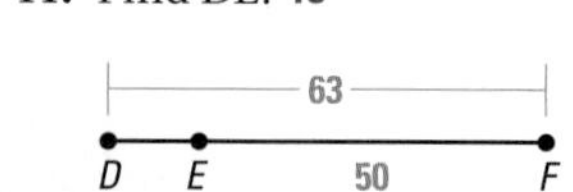

12. ERROR ANALYSIS In the figure at the right, $AC = 14$ and $AB = 9$. *Describe* and correct the error made in finding BC.
9 should be subtracted from 14, not added; $BC = 14 - 9 = 5$.

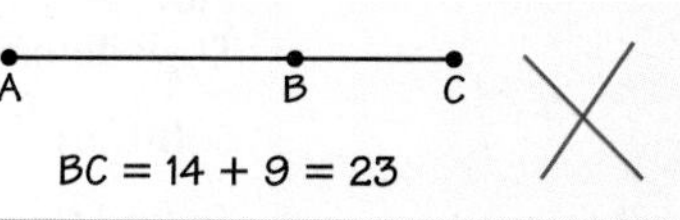

EXAMPLE 4 on p. 11 for Exs. 13–19

CONGRUENCE In Exercises 13–15, plot the given points in a coordinate plane. Then determine whether the line segments named are congruent.

13. $A(0, 1)$, $B(4, 1)$, $C(1, 2)$, $D(1, 6)$; $\overline{AB}$ and $\overline{CD}$ **congruent**

14. $J(-6, -8)$, $K(-6, 2)$, $L(-2, -4)$, $M(-6, -4)$; $\overline{JK}$ and $\overline{LM}$ **not congruent**

15. $R(-200, 300)$, $S(200, 300)$, $T(300, -200)$, $U(300, 100)$; $\overline{RS}$ and $\overline{TU}$ **not congruent**

ALGEBRA Use the number line to find the indicated distance.

16. JK **3**
17. JL **7**
18. JM **12**
19. KM **9**

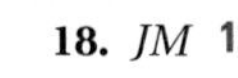
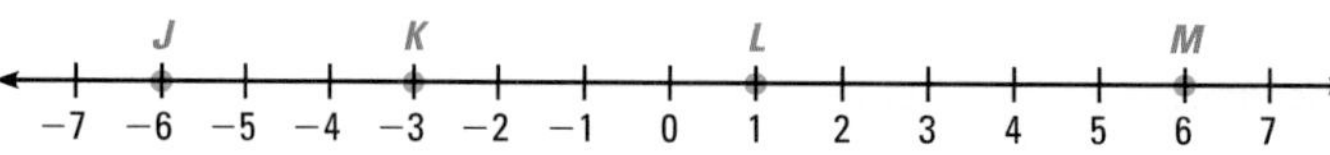

B

20. ★ **SHORT RESPONSE** Use the diagram. Is it possible to use the Segment Addition Postulate to show that $FB > CB$ or that $AC > DB$? *Explain.*

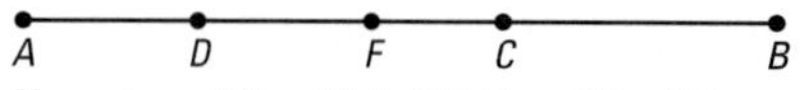

Yes, since $FB = FC + CB$, then $FB > CB$; no, the relationship between AD and BC is not known.

FINDING LENGTHS In the diagram, points V, W, X, Y, and Z are collinear, $VZ = 52$, $XZ = 20$, and $WX = XY = YZ$. Find the indicated length.

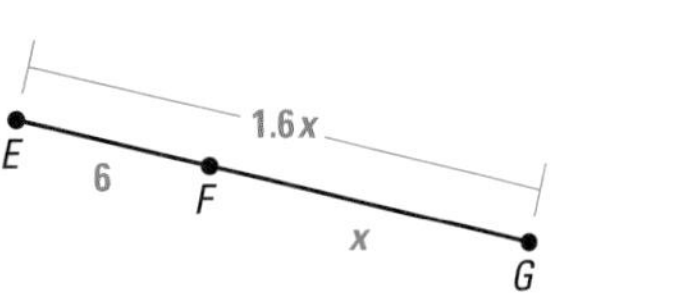

21. WX **10**
22. VW **22**
23. WY **20**
24. VX **32**
25. WZ **30**
26. VY **42**

27. ★ **MULTIPLE CHOICE** Use the diagram. What is the length of $\overline{EG}$? **D**

Ⓐ 1 Ⓑ 4.4 Ⓒ 10 Ⓓ 16

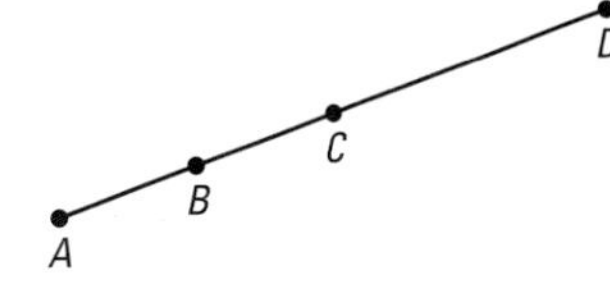

ALGEBRA Point S is between R and T on $\overline{RT}$. Use the given information to write an equation in terms of x. Solve the equation. Then find RS and ST.

28. **(2x + 10) + (x − 4) = 21; 5; 20, 1**
29. **(3x − 16) + (4x − 8) = 60; 12; 20, 40**
30. **(2x − 8) + (3x − 10) = 17; 7; 6, 11**

28. $RS = 2x + 10$, $ST = x - 4$, $RT = 21$
29. $RS = 3x - 16$, $ST = 4x - 8$, $RT = 60$
30. $RS = 2x - 8$, $ST = 3x - 10$, $RT = 17$

C 31. **CHALLENGE** In the diagram, $\overline{AB} \cong \overline{BC}$, $\overline{AC} \cong \overline{CD}$, and $AD = 12$. Find the lengths of all the segments in the diagram. Suppose you choose one of the segments at random. What is the probability that the measure of the segment is greater than 3? *Explain.*
$AC = 6$, $CD = 6$, $AB = 3$, $BC = 3$, $BD = 9$, $AD = 12$; $\frac{2}{3}$; four of the six segment lengths are greater than 3.

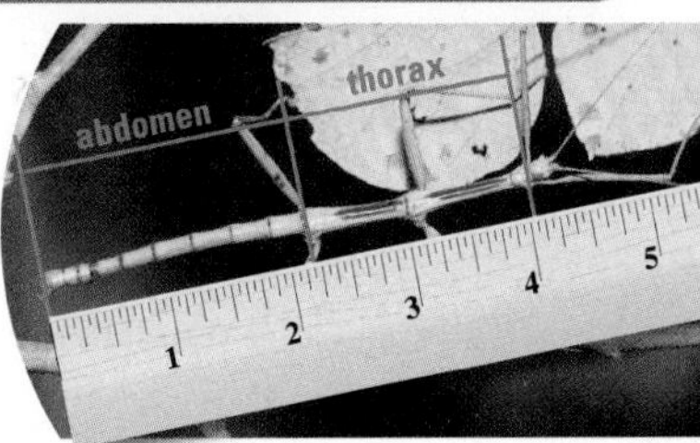

PROBLEM SOLVING

32. $2\frac{1}{4}$ in., $1\frac{3}{4}$ in.; $\frac{1}{2}$ in.

A 32. **SCIENCE** The photograph shows an insect called a walkingstick. Use the ruler to estimate the length of the abdomen and the length of the thorax to the nearest $\frac{1}{4}$ inch. About how much longer is the walkingstick's abdomen than its thorax?

@HomeTutor for problem solving help at classzone.com

EXAMPLE 2 on p. 10 for Ex. 33

33. **MODEL AIRPLANE** In 2003, a remote-controlled model airplane became the first ever to fly nonstop across the Atlantic Ocean. The map shows the airplane's position at three different points during its flight.

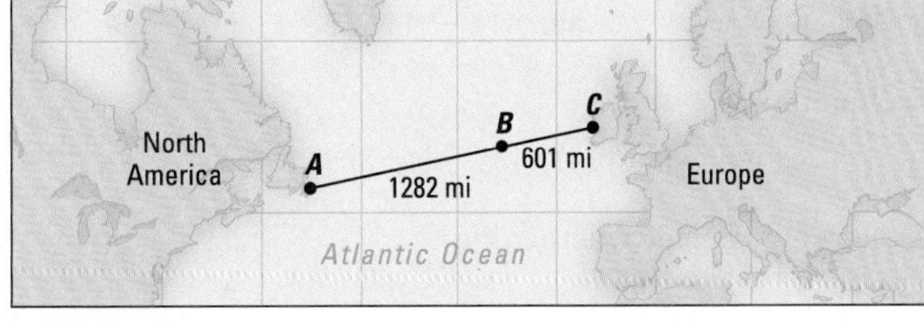

A	Leave Cape Spear, Newfoundland
B	Approximate position after about 1 day
C	Land at Mannin Bay, Ireland, after nearly 38 hours

a. Find the total distance the model airplane flew. **1883 mi**

b. The model airplane's flight lasted nearly 38 hours. Estimate the airplane's average speed in miles per hour. **about 50 mi/h**

@HomeTutor for problem solving help at classzone.com

Avoiding Common Errors

Exercises 21–26 Students may assume that W is the midpoint of $\overline{VZ}$. Have them first write all the given measures on the diagram and figure out how long each part is before starting the exercises.

Study Strategy

Exercises 28–30 Have students sketch a diagram and label it with the given lengths. This should help them write an equation.

Exercise 32 More information about walkingsticks can be found at www.zoo.org/educate/fact_sheets/walking/vtwalking.htm

An **Animated Geometry** activity is available on-line for **Exercise 35**. This activity is also available on the **Power Presentations CD-ROM**.

5 ASSESS AND RETEACH

Daily Homework Quiz

Transparency Available

1. Measure $\overline{AB}$ to the nearest $\frac{1}{8}$ inch. $1\frac{3}{8}$ in.

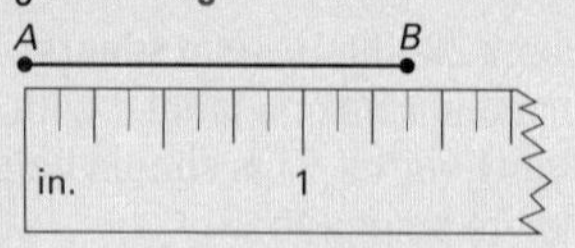

2. Find CE. 22

3. Plot the points $F(-3, 5)$, $G(2, 5)$, $H(3, 1)$, and $J(3, -3)$ in a coordinate plane. Are $\overline{FG}$ and $\overline{HJ}$ congruent? Explain. **No, $FG = 5$ and $HJ = 4$.**

4. Find KL. 7

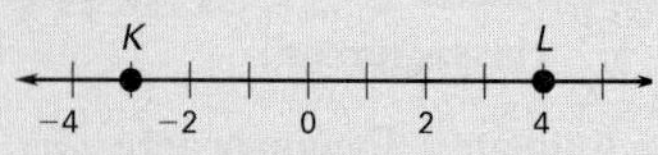

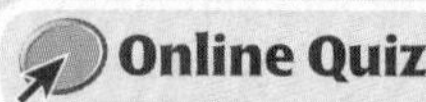

Available at **classzone.com**

Diagnosis/Remediation

- Practice A, B, C in Chapter 1 Resource Book, pp. 20–25
- Study Guide in Chapter 1 Resource Book, pp. 26–27
- Practice Workbook, pp. 4–6
- @HomeTutor

Challenge

Additional challenge is available in the Chapter 1 Resource Book, p. 30.

35a. *Sample:*

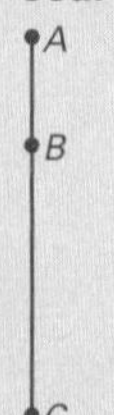

36. See Additional Answers beginning on p. AA1.

34a. 5, 5, 5; games lost

34b. about 45%, about 42%, about 38%

B 34. ★ **SHORT RESPONSE** The bar graph shows the win-loss record for a lacrosse team over a period of three years.

a. Use the scale to find the length of the yellow bar for each year. What does the length represent?

b. For each year, find the percent of games lost by the team.

c. *Explain* how you are applying the Segment Addition Postulate when you find information from a stacked bar graph like the one shown. ***Sample answer:* The sum of the lengths of the bars for wins and losses represents the total number of games played.**

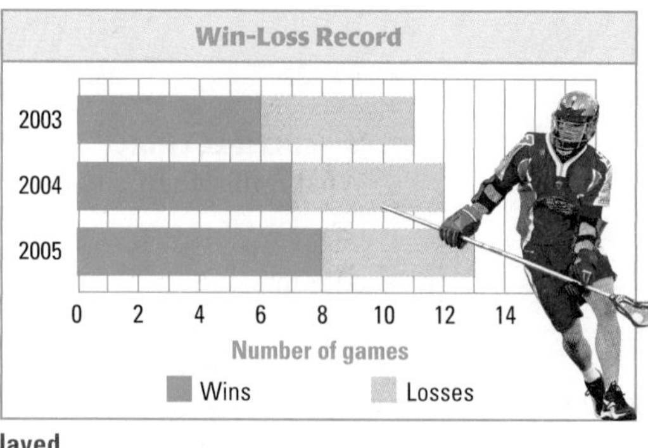

35. **MULTI-STEP PROBLEM** A climber uses a rope to descend a vertical cliff. Let A represent the point where the rope is secured at the top of the cliff, let B represent the climber's position, and let C represent the point where the rope is secured at the bottom of the cliff.

a. **Model** Draw and label a line segment that represents the situation. **See margin.**

b. **Calculate** If AC is 52 feet and AB is 31 feet, how much farther must the climber descend to reach the bottom of the cliff? **21 ft**

Animated Geometry at classzone.com

C 36. **CHALLENGE** Four cities lie along a straight highway in this order: City A, City B, City C, and City D. The distance from City A to City B is 5 times the distance from City B to City C. The distance from City A to City D is 2 times the distance from City A to City B. Copy and complete the mileage chart. **See margin.**

	City A	City B	City C	City D
City A		?	?	?
City B	?		?	?
City C	?	?		10 mi
City D	?	?	?	

MIXED REVIEW

PREVIEW Prepare for Lesson 1.3 in Exs. 37–42.

Simplify the expression. Write your answer in simplest radical form. *(p. 874)*

37. $\sqrt{45 + 99}$ **12**

38. $\sqrt{14 + 36}$ **$5\sqrt{2}$**

39. $\sqrt{42 + (-2)^2}$ **$\sqrt{46}$**

Solve the equation. *(p. 875)*

40. $4m + 5 = 7 + 6m$ **−1**

41. $13 - 4h = 3h - 8$ **3**

42. $17 + 3x = 18x - 28$ **3**

Use the diagram to decide whether the statement is *true* or *false*. *(p. 2)*

43. Points A, C, E, and G are coplanar. **true**

44. $\overleftrightarrow{DF}$ and $\overleftrightarrow{AG}$ intersect at point E. **true**

45. $\overrightarrow{AE}$ and $\overrightarrow{EG}$ are opposite rays. **false**

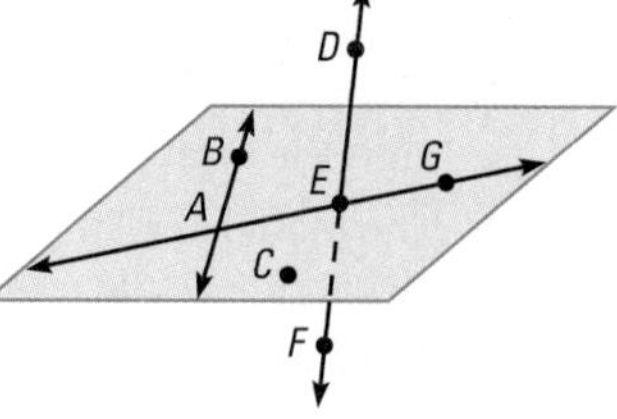

1.3 Use Midpoint and Distance Formulas

Before	You found lengths of segments.
Now	You will find lengths of segments in the coordinate plane.
Why?	So you can find an unknown length, as in Example 1.

Key Vocabulary
- midpoint
- segment bisector

Standards

Prepare for 7.0
Students prove theorems by using coordinate geometry, including the midpoint of a line segment, the distance formula, and various forms of equations of lines and circles.

ACTIVITY FOLD A SEGMENT BISECTOR

STEP 1

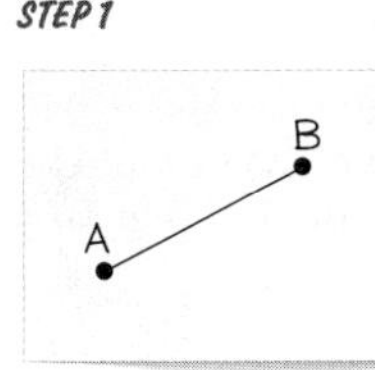

Draw $\overline{AB}$ on a piece of paper.

STEP 2

Fold the paper so that B is on top of A.

STEP 3

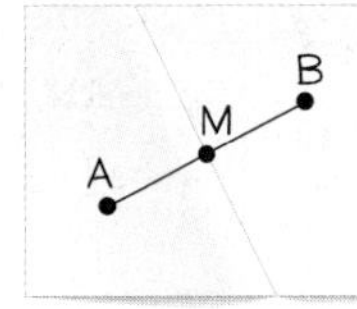

$AM = MB = \frac{1}{2}AB$

Label point M. Compare AM, MB, and AB.

MIDPOINTS AND BISECTORS The **midpoint** of a segment is the point that divides the segment into two congruent segments. A **segment bisector** is a point, ray, line, line segment, or plane that intersects the segment at its midpoint. A midpoint or a segment bisector *bisects* a segment.

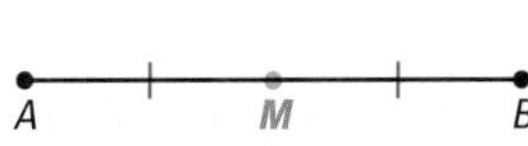

M is the midpoint of $\overline{AB}$.
So, $\overline{AM} \cong \overline{MB}$ and $AM = MB$.

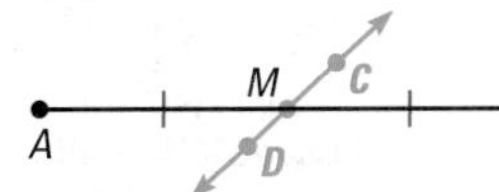

$\overleftrightarrow{CD}$ is a segment bisector of $\overline{AB}$.
So, $\overline{AM} \cong \overline{MB}$ and $AM = MB$.

EXAMPLE 1 Find segment lengths

SKATEBOARD In the skateboard design, $\overline{VW}$ bisects $\overline{XY}$ at point T, and $XT = 39.9$ cm. Find XY.

Solution

Point T is the midpoint of $\overline{XY}$. So, $XT = TY = 39.9$ cm.

$XY = XT + TY$	**Segment Addition Postulate**
$= 39.9 + 39.9$	**Substitute.**
$= 79.8$ cm	**Add.**

1 PLAN AND PREPARE

Warm-Up Exercises

Transparency Available

1. Find a point between $A(-3, 5)$ and $B(7, 5)$. ***Sample:* (2, 5)**
2. Find the average of -11 and 5. **-3**
3. Solve $\frac{x + 7}{2} = 5$. **3**
4. Find $\sqrt{30}$ to the nearest hundredth. **5.48**
5. Find $\sqrt{5} + \sqrt{20}$ to the nearest hundredth. **6.71**

Notetaking Guide

Transparency Available

Promotes interactive learning and notetaking skills, pp. 8–11.

Pacing

Basic: 2 days
Average: 2 days
Advanced: 2 days
Block: 1 block
- See *Teaching Guide/Lesson Plan.*

2 FOCUS AND MOTIVATE

Essential Question

Big Idea 2, p. 1

How do you find the distance and the midpoint between two points in the coordinate plane? **Tell students they will learn how to answer this question by using the distance and midpoint formulas.**

Resource Planning Guide

Chapter Resource Book
- Teaching Guide/Lesson Plan (pp. 31–32)
- Activity Master (p. 33)
- Practice levels A, B, C (pp. 35–40)
- Study Guide (pp. 41–42)
- Catch-up for Absent Students (p. 43)
- Problem Solving Workshop (p. 44)
- Challenge (p. 46)

Workbooks
- Notetaking Guide (pp. 8–11)
- Practice Workbook (pp. 7–9)

Teaching Options
- **Power Presentations CD-ROM** provides dynamic electronic teaching resources for the classroom.
- **Activity Generator CD-ROM** provides editable activities for all ability levels.

Interactive Technology
- Easy Planner
- Power Presentations CD-ROM
- Activity Generator CD-ROM
- Animated Geometry
- Test Generator CD-ROM
- Online Quiz
- eWorkbook
- eEdition
- @HomeTutor

Resources for English Learners
- Quick Reference for English Learners
- Spanish Study Guide
- Multi-Language Visual Glossary
- Student Resources in Spanish

See also the *Geometry Toolkit* for more strategies for meeting individual needs.

Motivating the Lesson

Sue is late for her piano class so she runs diagonally across a rectangular park instead of around it. Tell students that in this lesson they will learn how to find the distance Sue runs and how much shorter the diagonal route is than a route along the outer rim.

3 TEACH

Activity Note

The purpose of this paper folding activity is to have the students locate the midpoint of a segment. They will see that the midpoint is on the fold of the paper. Ask students to measure the distances from the midpoint to each endpoint. Ask what is true of these distances. **They are equal.**

Extra Example 1

The figure shows a gate with diagonal braces. $\overline{MO}$ bisects $\overline{NP}$ at Q. If $PQ = 22.6$ in., find PN. **45.2 in.**

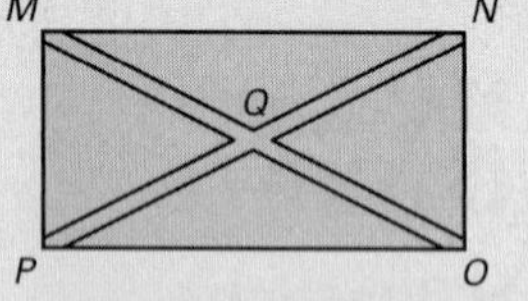

Key Question to Ask for Example 1

- How is XT related to XY? **It is half of XY.**

Extra Example 2

Point S is the midpoint of $\overline{RT}$. Find ST. **23**

5x − 2 3x + 8

R S T

Key Question to Ask for Example 2

- How do you know that $VM = MW$? **M is a midpoint.**

EXAMPLE 2 Use algebra with segment lengths

ALGEBRA Point M is the midpoint of $\overline{VW}$. Find the length of $\overline{VM}$.

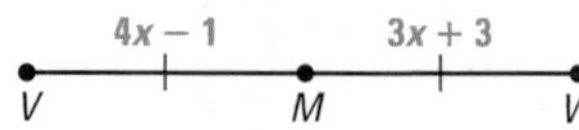

REVIEW ALGEBRA
For help with solving equations, see p. 875.

Solution

STEP 1 **Write** and solve an equation. Use the fact that $VM = MW$.

$VM = MW$	Write equation.
$4x - 1 = 3x + 3$	Substitute.
$x - 1 = 3$	Subtract $3x$ from each side.
$x = 4$	Add 1 to each side.

STEP 2 **Evaluate** the expression for VM when $x = 4$.

$VM = 4x - 1 = 4(4) - 1 = 15$

▶ So, the length of $\overline{VM}$ is 15.

CHECK Because $VM = MW$, the length of $\overline{MW}$ should be 15. If you evaluate the expression for MW, you should find that $MW = 15$.

$MW = 3x + 3 = 3(4) + 3 = 15$ ✓

✓ GUIDED PRACTICE for Examples 1 and 2

READ DIRECTIONS
Always read direction lines carefully. Notice that this direction line has two parts.

In Exercises 1 and 2, identify the segment bisector of $\overline{PQ}$. Then find PQ.

1.

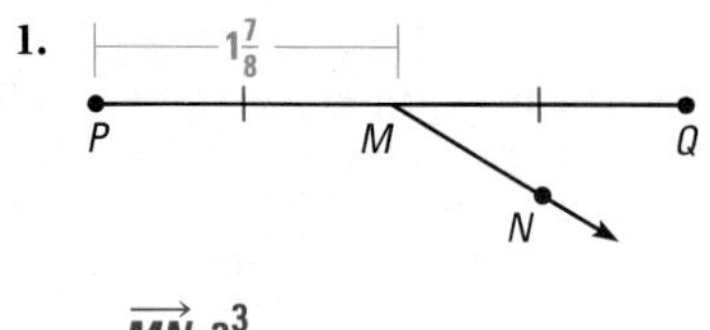

$\overrightarrow{MN}$; $3\frac{3}{4}$

2.

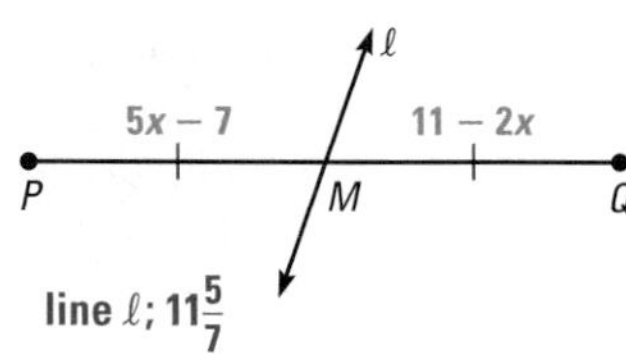

line ℓ; $11\frac{5}{7}$

COORDINATE PLANE You can use the coordinates of the endpoints of a segment to find the coordinates of the midpoint.

KEY CONCEPT *For Your Notebook*

The Midpoint Formula

The coordinates of the midpoint of a segment are the averages of the x-coordinates and of the y-coordinates of the endpoints.

If $A(x_1, y_1)$ and $B(x_2, y_2)$ are points in a coordinate plane, then the midpoint M of $\overline{AB}$ has coordinates

$$\left(\frac{x_1 + x_2}{2}, \frac{y_1 + y_2}{2}\right).$$

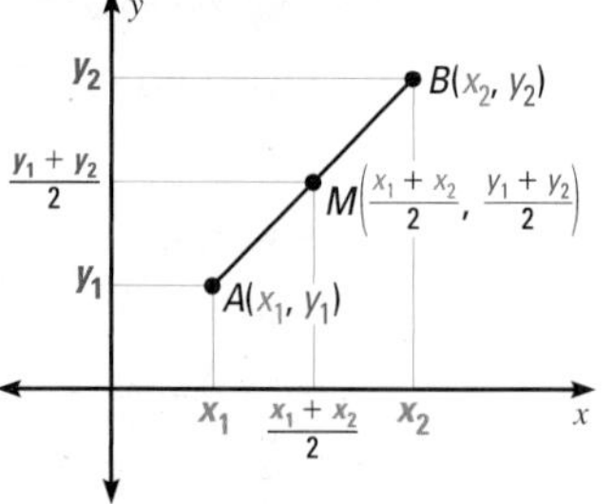

EXAMPLE 3 Use the Midpoint Formula

a. FIND MIDPOINT The endpoints of $\overline{RS}$ are $R(1, -3)$ and $S(4, 2)$. Find the coordinates of the midpoint M.

b. FIND ENDPOINT The midpoint of $\overline{JK}$ is $M(2, 1)$. One endpoint is $J(1, 4)$. Find the coordinates of endpoint K.

Solution

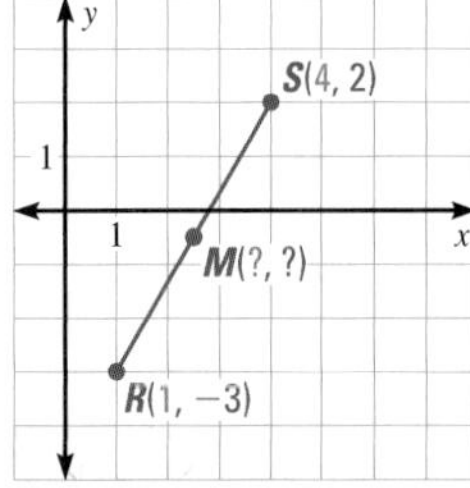

a. FIND MIDPOINT Use the Midpoint Formula.

$$M\left(\frac{1+4}{2}, \frac{-3+2}{2}\right) = M\left(\frac{5}{2}, -\frac{1}{2}\right)$$

▶ The coordinates of the midpoint M are $\left(\frac{5}{2}, -\frac{1}{2}\right)$.

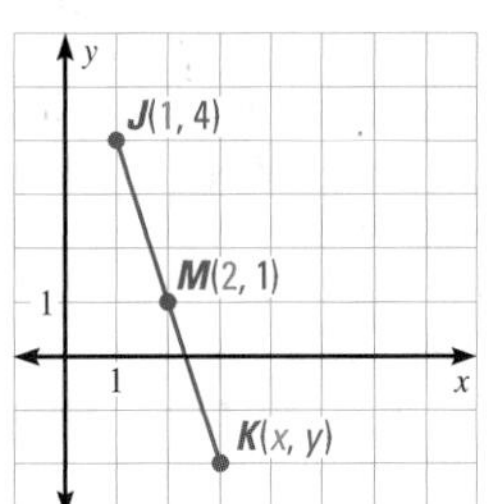

b. FIND ENDPOINT Let (x, y) be the coordinates of endpoint K. Use the Midpoint Formula.

CLEAR FRACTIONS
Multiply each side of the equation by the denominator to clear the fraction.

STEP 1 Find x.	*STEP 2* Find y.
$\frac{1+x}{2} = 2$	$\frac{4+y}{2} = 1$
$1 + x = 4$	$4 + y = 2$
$x = 3$	$y = -2$

▶ The coordinates of endpoint K are $(3, -2)$.

✓ **GUIDED PRACTICE** for Example 3

3. The endpoints of $\overline{AB}$ are $A(1, 2)$ and $B(7, 8)$. Find the coordinates of the midpoint M. **(4, 5)**

4. The midpoint of $\overline{VW}$ is $M(-1, -2)$. One endpoint is $W(4, 4)$. Find the coordinates of endpoint V. **(−6, −8)**

DISTANCE FORMULA The Distance Formula is a formula for computing the distance between two points in a coordinate plane.

KEY CONCEPT *For Your Notebook*

The Distance Formula

If $A(x_1, y_1)$ and $B(x_2, y_2)$ are points in a coordinate plane, then the distance between A and B is

$$AB = \sqrt{(x_2 - x_1)^2 + (y_2 - y_1)^2}.$$

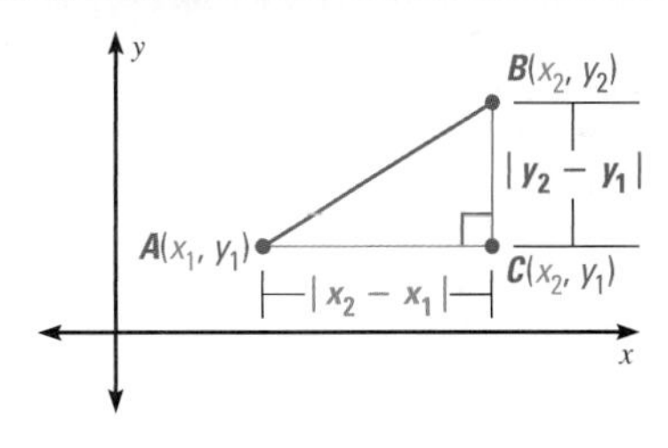

READ DIAGRAMS
The red mark at one corner of the triangle shown indicates a right triangle.

Extra Example 3

a. The endpoints of $\overline{GH}$ are $G(7, -2)$ and $H(-5, -6)$. Find the coordinates of the midpoint P. **(1, −4)**

b. The midpoint of $\overline{AB}$ is $M(5, 8)$. One endpoint is $A(2, -3)$. Find the coordinates of endpoint B. **(8, 19)**

Key Question to Ask for Example 3

- In part a, which point was used for (x_1, y_1) in the midpoint formula? Could you have used the other point? **R(1, −3); yes, S(4, 2) would work just as well.**

Mathematical Reasoning

In Example 3b, have students note that as you go from $J(1, 4)$ to $M(2, 1)$, the x-coordinate increases by 1 and the y-coordinate decreases by 3. If you follow this pattern to get from M to K, you again get $x = 3$ and $y = -2$.

Differentiated Instruction

Inclusion The subscripts sometimes cause students to make errors in substitution with the Midpoint Formula and the Distance Formula. Remind students that the x-coordinate in the midpoint formula is the average of the two x-values, and the y-coordinate of the midpoint formula is the average of the two y-values. Similarly, the square of the distance in the distance formula is just the square of the difference in the x-values plus the square of the difference in the y-values.

See also the *Geometry Toolkit* for more strategies.

Extra Example 4

What is the approximate length of $\overline{PQ}$ with endpoints $P(2, 5)$ and $Q(-4, 8)$? **B**

Ⓐ 3.61 Ⓑ 6.71 Ⓒ 9.0 Ⓓ 13.15

Key Question to Ask for Example 4

- To use the Pythagorean Theorem instead of the distance formula, where would the right angle be located? **(2, −1) or (4, 3)**

Reading Strategy

The symbol $\approx$ is introduced in Example 4. Ask students to differentiate among the symbols $=$, $\cong$, and $\approx$.

Closing the Lesson

Have students summarize the major points of the lesson and answer the Essential Question: how do you find the distance and the midpoint between two points in the coordinate plane?

- **The midpoint of a segment is the point that divides the segment into two congruent parts.**
- **The length of a segment in the coordinate plane is the distance between its endpoints.**

To find the distance between the points (x_1, y_1) and (x_2, y_2), use the distance formula, $d = \sqrt{(x_2 - x_1)^2 + (y_2 - y_1)^2}$. To find the midpoint, use the midpoint formula, $\left(\frac{x_1 + x_2}{2}, \frac{y_1 + y_2}{2}\right)$.

The Distance Formula is based on the *Pythagorean Theorem,* which you will see again when you work with right triangles in Chapter 7.

Distance Formula

$(AB)^2 = (x_2 - x_1)^2 + (y_2 - y_1)^2$

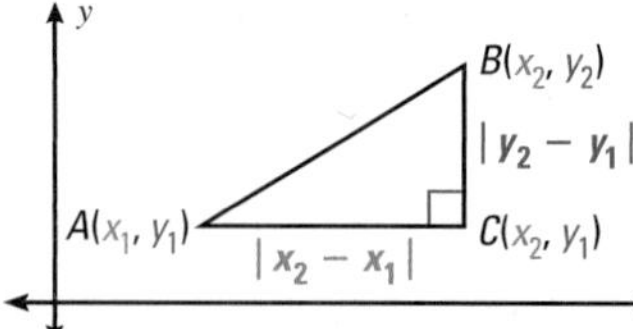

Pythagorean Theorem

$c^2 = a^2 + b^2$

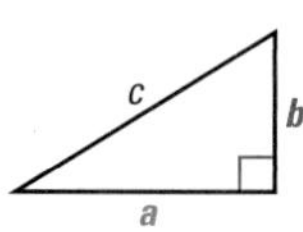

★ **EXAMPLE 4** **Standardized Test Practice**

ELIMINATE CHOICES
Drawing a diagram can help you eliminate choices. You can see that choice A is not large enough to be *RS*.

What is the approximate length of $\overline{RS}$ with endpoints $R(2, 3)$ and $S(4, -1)$?

Ⓐ 1.4 units Ⓑ 4.0 units Ⓒ 4.5 units Ⓓ 6 units

Solution

Use the Distance Formula. You may find it helpful to draw a diagram.

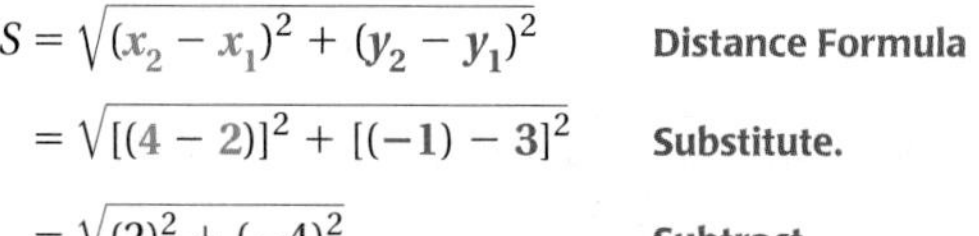

$RS = \sqrt{(x_2 - x_1)^2 + (y_2 - y_1)^2}$ **Distance Formula**

$= \sqrt{[(4 - 2)]^2 + [(-1) - 3]^2}$ **Substitute.**

$= \sqrt{(2)^2 + (-4)^2}$ **Subtract.**

$= \sqrt{4 + 16}$ **Evaluate powers.**

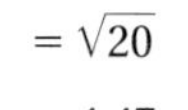

$= \sqrt{20}$ **Add.**

≈ 4.47 **Use a calculator to approximate the square root.**

READ SYMBOLS
The symbol $\approx$ means "is approximately equal to."

y
R(2, 3)
1
1
x
S(4, −1)

▸ The correct answer is C. Ⓐ Ⓑ Ⓒ Ⓓ

✓ **GUIDED PRACTICE** for Example 4

5. In Example 4, does it matter which ordered pair you choose to substitute for (x_1, y_1) and which ordered pair you choose to substitute for (x_2, y_2)? *Explain.*

5. No. *Sample answer:* When squaring the differences in the coordinates, you get the same answer as long as you choose the *x* and *y* values from the same point.

6. What is the approximate length of $\overline{AB}$, with endpoints $A(-3, 2)$ and $B(1, -4)$? **B**

Ⓐ 6.1 units Ⓑ 7.2 units Ⓒ 8.5 units Ⓓ 10.0 units

1.3 EXERCISES

HOMEWORK KEY
○ = **WORKED-OUT SOLUTIONS** on p. WS1 for Exs. 15, 35, and 49
★ = **STANDARDIZED TEST PRACTICE** Exs. 2, 23, 34, 41, 42, and 53

SKILL PRACTICE

A

1. **VOCABULARY** Copy and complete: To find the length of $\overline{AB}$, with endpoints $A(-7, 5)$ and $B(4, -6)$, you can use the _?_. **Distance Formula**

2. ★ **WRITING** *Explain* what it means to bisect a segment. Why is it impossible to bisect a line? **Divide a segment into two congruent segments; a line has infinite length.**

EXAMPLE 1 on p. 15 for Exs. 3–10

FINDING LENGTHS Line ℓ bisects the segment. Find the indicated length.

3. Find RT if $RS = 5\frac{1}{8}$ in. **$10\frac{1}{4}$ in.**

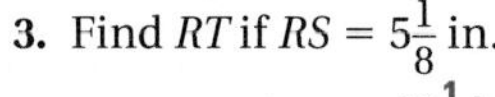
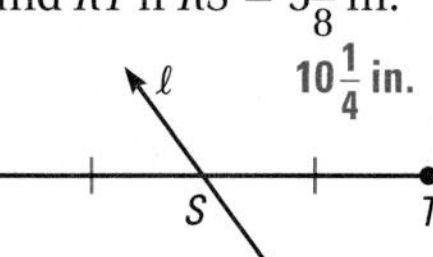

4. Find UW if $VW = \frac{5}{8}$ in. **$1\frac{1}{4}$ in.**

ℓ
U V W

5. Find EG if $EF = 13$ cm. **26 cm**

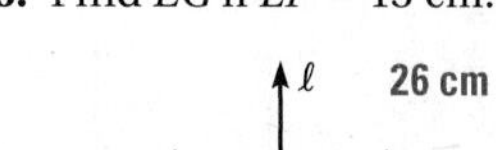

6. Find BC if $AC = 19$ cm. **9.5 cm**

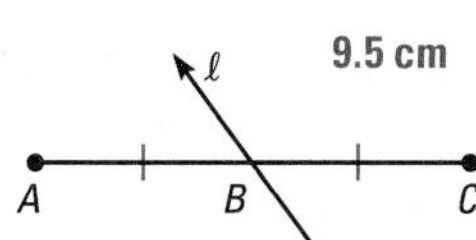

7. Find QR if $PR = 9\frac{1}{2}$ in. **$4\frac{3}{4}$ in.**

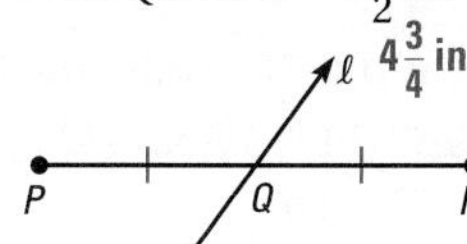

8. Find LM if $LN = 137$ mm. **68.5 mm**

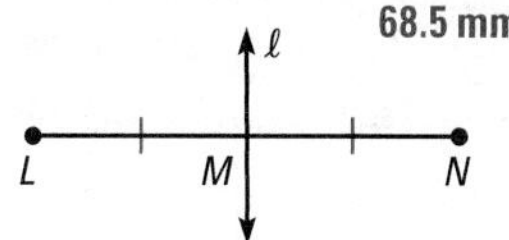

9. **SEGMENT BISECTOR** Line RS bisects $\overline{PQ}$ at point R. Find RQ if $PQ = 4\frac{3}{4}$ inches. **$2\frac{3}{8}$ in.**

10. **SEGMENT BISECTOR** Point T bisects $\overline{UV}$. Find UV if $UT = 2\frac{7}{8}$ inches. **$5\frac{3}{4}$ in.**

EXAMPLE 2 on p. 16 for Exs. 11–16

ALGEBRA In each diagram, M is the midpoint of the segment. Find the indicated length.

11. Find AM. **10**

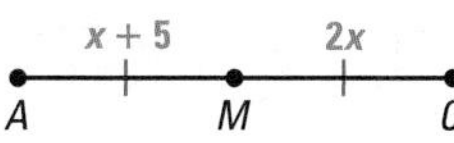

12. Find EM. **42**

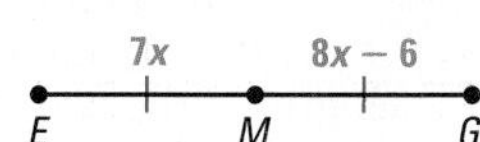

13. Find JM. **1**

$6x + 7$, $4x + 5$; J M L

14. Find PR. **98**

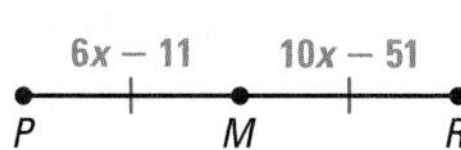

15. Find SU. **70**

$x + 15$, $4x - 45$; S M U

16. Find XZ. **146**

$2x + 35$, $5x - 22$; X M Z

EXAMPLE 3 on p. 17 for Exs. 17–30

FINDING MIDPOINTS Find the coordinates of the midpoint of the segment with the given endpoints.

17. $C(3, 5)$ and $D(7, 5)$ **(5, 5)**
18. $E(0, 4)$ and $F(4, 3)$ **$\left(2, 3\frac{1}{2}\right)$**
19. $G(-4, 4)$ and $H(6, 4)$ **(1, 4)**
20. $J(-7, -5)$ and $K(-3, 7)$ **(−5, 1)**
21. $P(-8, -7)$ and $Q(11, 5)$ **$\left(1\frac{1}{2}, -1\right)$**
22. $S(-3, 3)$ and $T(-8, 6)$ **$\left(-5\frac{1}{2}, 4\frac{1}{2}\right)$**

23. ★ **WRITING** Develop a formula for finding the midpoint of a segment with endpoints $A(0, 0)$ and $B(m, n)$. *Explain* your thinking. **$\left(\frac{m}{2}, \frac{n}{2}\right)$; when x_2 and y_2 are replaced by zero in the Midpoint Formula and x_1 and y_1 are replaced by m and n the result is $\left(\frac{m}{2}, \frac{n}{2}\right)$.**

4 PRACTICE AND APPLY

Assignment Guide

Answer Transparencies available for all exercises

Basic:
Day 1: SRH p. 870 Exs. 13–20
pp. 19–22
Exs. 1–16, 48, 55, 56, 60–64
Day 2: pp. 19–22
Exs. 17–27, 31–37, 41, 42, 49–52, 57–59

Average:
Day 1: pp. 19–22
Exs. 1–6, 9, 10, 12–15, 35–40, 48, 60–64
Day 2: pp. 19–22
Exs. 19–24, 28–34, 41–46, 49–53, 55–59

Advanced:
Day 1: pp. 19–22
Exs. 1, 5–10, 14–16, 35–40, 47*, 48, 60–64
Day 2: pp. 19–22
Exs. 20–23, 27–34, 41–46, 49–59*

Block:
pp. 19–22
Exs. 1–6, 9, 10, 12–15, 19–24, 28–46, 48–53, 55–64

Differentiated Instruction

See *Geometry Best Practices Toolkit* for suggestions on addressing the needs of a diverse classroom.

Homework Check

For a quick check of student understanding of key concepts, go over the following exercises:
Basic: 4, 12, 18, 31, 48
Average: 6, 14, 28, 32, 48
Advanced: 8, 16, 30, 33, 48

Extra Practice

- Student Edition, p. 896
- Chapter 1 Resource Book: Practice levels A, B, C, pp. 35–40

Practice Worksheet

An easily-readable reduced practice page (with answers) for this lesson can be found on p. 1D.

Study Strategy

Exercises 25–30 Point out that in each exercise, the letter M is used for the midpoint of the segment. Discuss how students can check their answers by using the midpoint formula with the coordinates of the point they find and the coordinates of the given endpoint to verify that they get the given coordinates of M.

Avoiding Common Errors

Exercises 31–33 To minimize substitution errors, suggest that students write the distance formula in full before they make any substitutions. Then have them write (x_1, y_1) and (x_2, y_2) below the specific pairs of numbers that they plan to use for the substitutions.

Graphing Calculator

Exercise 41 Suggest that students do paper and pencil calculations to find that $LF = \sqrt{26}$ and $JR = \sqrt{5}$. They can then use the calculator to find the approximate value of $\sqrt{26} - \sqrt{5}$.

24. 8 should be added to 2 and 3 should be added to −1; $\left(\frac{8+2}{2}, \frac{3+(-1)}{2}\right)$, (5, 1).

24. ERROR ANALYSIS *Describe* the error made in finding the coordinates of the midpoint of a segment with endpoints $S(8, 3)$ and $T(2, -1)$.

$\left(\frac{8-2}{2}, \frac{3-(-1)}{2}\right) = (3, 2)$ ✗

FINDING ENDPOINTS **Use the given endpoint R and midpoint M of $\overline{RS}$ to find the coordinates of the other endpoint S.**

25. $R(3, 0)$, $M(0, 5)$ **(−3, 10)**
26. $R(5, 1)$, $M(1, 4)$ **(−3, 7)**
27. $R(6, -2)$, $M(5, 3)$ **(4, 8)**
28. $R(-7, 11)$, $M(2, 1)$ **(11, −9)**
29. $R(4, -6)$, $M(-7, 8)$ **(−18, 22)**
30. $R(-4, -6)$, $M(3, -4)$ **(10, −2)**

EXAMPLE 4 on p. 18 for Exs. 31–34

DISTANCE FORMULA **Find the length of the segment. Round to the nearest tenth of a unit.**

31. **4.5**

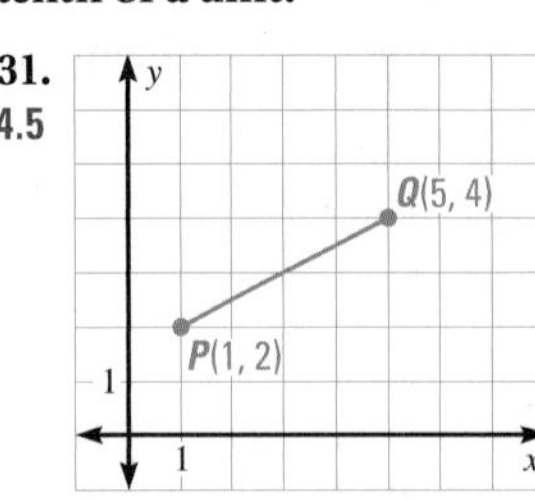

32. **5.4**

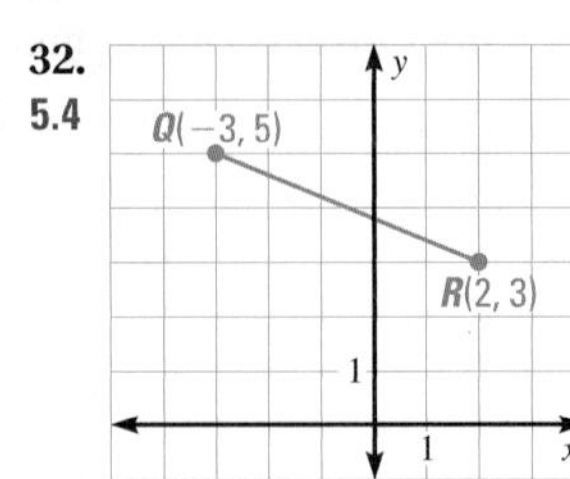

33. **5.7**

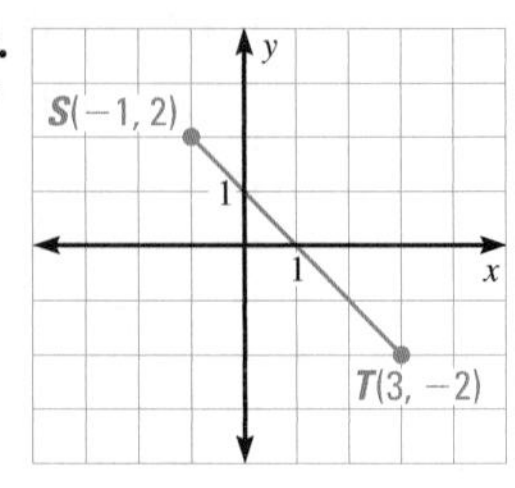

B

34. ★ **MULTIPLE CHOICE** The endpoints of $\overline{MN}$ are $M(-3, -9)$ and $N(4, 8)$. What is the approximate length of $\overline{MN}$? **D**

Ⓐ 1.4 units Ⓑ 7.2 units Ⓒ 13 units Ⓓ 18.4 units

NUMBER LINE **Find the length of the segment. Then find the coordinate of the midpoint of the segment.**

(35.)

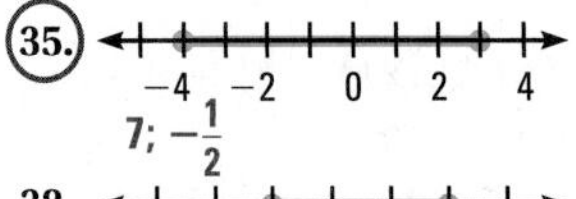

7; $-\frac{1}{2}$

36.

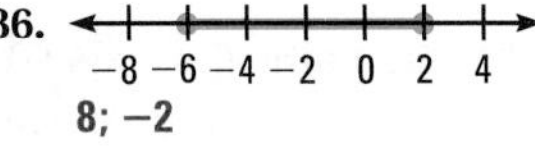

8; −2

37.

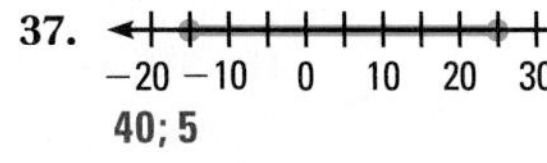

40; 5

38.

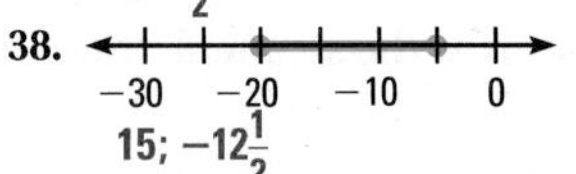

15; $-12\frac{1}{2}$

39.

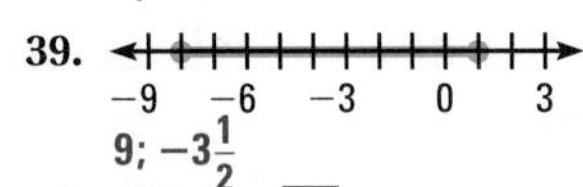

9; $-3\frac{1}{2}$

40.

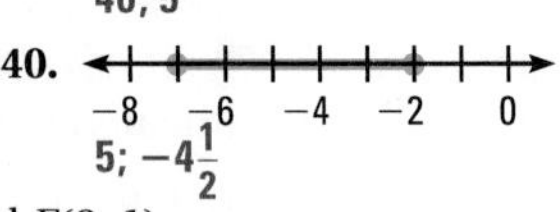

5; $-4\frac{1}{2}$

41. ★ **MULTIPLE CHOICE** The endpoints of $\overline{LF}$ are $L(-2, 2)$ and $F(3, 1)$. The endpoints of $\overline{JR}$ are $J(1, -1)$ and $R(2, -3)$. What is the approximate difference in the lengths of the two segments? **B**

Ⓐ 2.24 Ⓑ 2.86 Ⓒ 5.10 Ⓓ 7.96

42. *Sample answer:* Use the Distance Formula to find *PM*, then multiply *PM* by 2 to find *PQ* (*PQ* = 5, *PM* = 10).

42. ★ **SHORT RESPONSE** One endpoint of $\overline{PQ}$ is $P(-2, 4)$. The midpoint of $\overline{PQ}$ is $M(1, 0)$. *Explain* how to find PQ.

43. $AB = 3\sqrt{5}$, $CD = 2\sqrt{10}$; not congruent

44. $EF = 5$, $GH = \sqrt{41}$; not congruent

45. $JK = 8\sqrt{2}$, $LM = \sqrt{130}$; not congruent

COMPARING LENGTHS **The endpoints of two segments are given. Find each segment length. Tell whether the segments are congruent.**

43. $\overline{AB}$: $A(0, 2)$, $B(-3, 8)$
$\overline{CD}$: $C(-2, 2)$, $D(0, -4)$

44. $\overline{EF}$: $E(1, 4)$, $F(5, 1)$
$\overline{GH}$: $G(-3, 1)$, $H(1, 6)$

45. $\overline{JK}$: $J(-4, 0)$, $K(4, 8)$
$\overline{LM}$: $L(-4, 2)$, $M(3, -7)$

46. **ALGEBRA** Points S, T, and P lie on a number line. Their coordinates are 0, 1, and x, respectively. Given $SP = PT$, what is the value of x? $\frac{1}{2}$

C

47. **CHALLENGE** M is the midpoint of $\overline{JK}$, $JM = \frac{x}{8}$, and $JK = \frac{3x}{4} - 6$. Find MK. $1\frac{1}{2}$

◯ = WORKED-OUT SOLUTIONS on p. WS1 ★ = STANDARDIZED TEST PRACTICE

PROBLEM SOLVING

EXAMPLE 1 [A] on p. 15 for Ex. 48

48. **WINDMILL** In the photograph of a windmill, $\overline{ST}$ bisects $\overline{QR}$ at point M. The length of $\overline{QM}$ is $18\frac{1}{2}$ feet. Find QR and MR. **$QR = 37$ ft, $MR = 18\frac{1}{2}$ ft**

@HomeTutor for problem solving help at classzone.com

49. **DISTANCES** A house and a school are 5.7 kilometers apart on the same straight road. The library is on the same road, halfway between the house and the school. Draw a sketch to represent this situation. Mark the locations of the house, school, and library. How far is the library from the house? **See margin for art; 2.85 km**

@HomeTutor for problem solving help at classzone.com

ARCHAEOLOGY The points on the diagram show the positions of objects at an underwater archaeological site. Use the diagram for Exercises 50 and 51.

50. Find the distance between each pair of objects. Round to the nearest tenth of a meter if necessary.

a. A and B **3.2 m** b. B and C **4.5 m** c. C and D **3.6 m**

d. A and D **5 m** e. B and D **2.2 m** f. A and C **5.1 m**

51. Which two objects are closest to each other? Which two are farthest apart?

51. objects B and D; objects A and C

Animated Geometry at classzone.com

[B] 52. **WATER POLO** The diagram shows the positions of three players during part of a water polo match. Player A throws the ball to Player B, who then throws it to Player C. How far did Player A throw the ball? How far did Player B throw the ball? How far would Player A have thrown the ball if he had thrown it directly to Player C? Round all answers to the nearest tenth of a meter. **10.4 m; 9.2 m; 18.9 m**

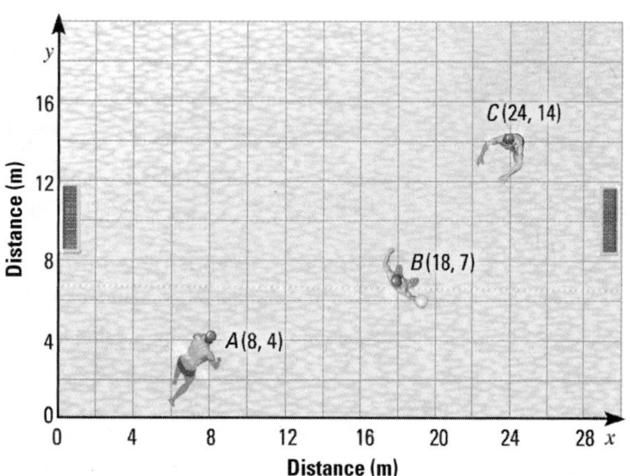

Internet Reference

Exercise 50 Additional information about underwater archaeology studies in the United States can be found at www.cr.nps.gov/seac/underh2o.htm

Mathematical Reasoning

Exercise 50 Have students write down the coordinates of each point from the graph before they begin to calculate distances. This will prevent them from having to recalculate the coordinates each time.

Animated Geometry classzone.com

An **Animated Geometry** activity is available on-line for **Exercise 51**. This activity is also available on the **Power Presentations CD-ROM**.

49.

5 ASSESS AND RETEACH

Daily Homework Quiz

Transparency Available

1. $\overline{AB}$ bisects $\overline{CD}$ at E. If $CE = 2\frac{1}{4}$ in., find CD. $4\frac{1}{2}$ in.
2. Point M is the midpoint of $\overline{XY}$. Find XM. **17**

   $2x + 7$ $8x - 23$ — X, M, Y

3. Point M is the midpoint of $\overline{PQ}$ with endpoints $P(2, -6)$ and $Q(-8, 0)$. Find the coordinates of M. $(-3, -3)$
4. The midpoint of $\overline{GH}$ is $M(4, -1)$. One endpoint is $G(5, 3)$. Find the coordinates of H. $(3, -5)$
5. To find the distance between the swing and the sandbox in his backyard, Darren made a graph and found the coordinates of the swing to be (7, 2) and the coordinates of the sandbox to be (−3, 8). Find the distance between the swing and the sandbox to the nearest tenth of a unit. **11.7**

Online Quiz

Available at **classzone.com**

Diagnosis/Remediation

- Practice A, B, C in Chapter 1 Resource Book, pp. 35–40
- Study Guide in Chapter 1 Resource Book, pp. 41–42
- Practice Workbook, pp. 7–9
- @HomeTutor

Challenge

Additional challenge is available in the Chapter 1 Resource Book, p. 46.

Quiz

An easily-readable reduced copy of the quiz (with answers) on Lessons 1.1–1.3 from the Assessment Book can be found on p. 1G.

---

53. ★ **EXTENDED RESPONSE** As shown, a path goes around a triangular park.

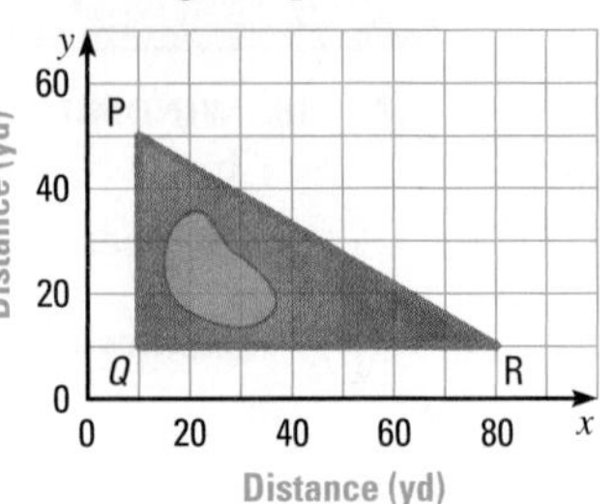

a. Find the distance around the park to the nearest yard. **191 yd**

b. A new path and a bridge are constructed from point Q to the midpoint M of $\overline{PR}$. Find QM to the nearest yard. **40 yd**

c. A man jogs from P to Q to M to R to Q and back to P at an average speed of 150 yards per minute. About how many minutes does it take? *Explain.* **About 1.5 min; find the total distance, about 230 yards, and divide by 150 yards per minute.**

C **54.** **CHALLENGE** $\overline{AB}$ bisects $\overline{CD}$ at point M, $\overline{CD}$ bisects $\overline{AB}$ at point M, and $AB = 4 \cdot CM$. *Describe* the relationship between AM and CD. **They are equal lengths.**

MIXED REVIEW

The graph shows data about the number of children in the families of students in a math class. *(p. 888)*

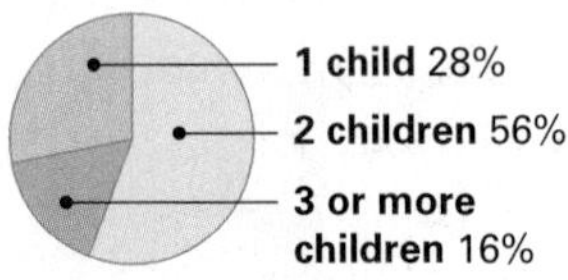

55. What percent of the students in the class belong to families with two or more children? **72%**

56. If there are 25 students in the class, how many students belong to families with two children? **14 students**

PREVIEW Prepare for Lesson 1.4 in Exs. 57–59.

Solve the equation. *(p. 875)*

57. $3x + 12 + x = 20$ **2**   **58.** $9x + 2x + 6 - x = 10$ $\frac{2}{5}$ **59.** $5x - 22 - 7x + 2 = 40$ **−30**

In Exercises 60–64, use the diagram at the right. *(p. 2)*

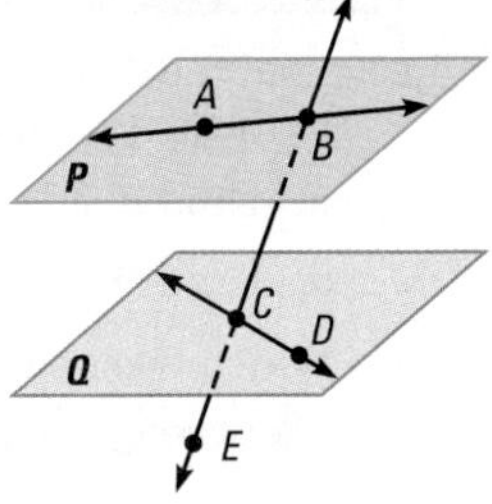

60. Name all rays with endpoint B. $\overrightarrow{BA}$, $\overrightarrow{BC}$ (or $\overrightarrow{BE}$)

61. Name all the rays that contain point C. $\overrightarrow{CD}$, $\overrightarrow{CB}$, $\overrightarrow{CE}$, $\overrightarrow{DC}$, $\overrightarrow{BC}$ (or $\overrightarrow{BE}$), $\overrightarrow{EC}$ (or $\overrightarrow{EB}$)

62. Name a pair of opposite rays. $\overrightarrow{CB}$ **and** $\overrightarrow{CE}$

63. Name the intersection of $\overleftrightarrow{AB}$ and $\overleftrightarrow{BC}$. **point B**

64. Name the intersection of $\overleftrightarrow{BC}$ and plane P. **point B**

QUIZ for Lessons 1.1–1.3

1. Sketch two lines that intersect the same plane at two different points. The lines intersect each other at a point not in the plane. *(p. 2)* **See margin.**

In the diagram of collinear points, $AE = 26$, $AD = 15$, and $AB = BC = CD$. Find the indicated length. *(p. 9)*

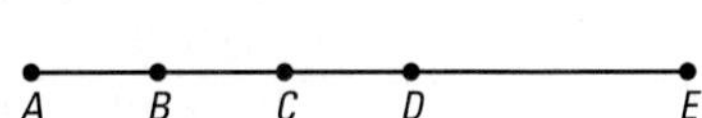

2. DE **11**   **3.** AB **5**   **4.** AC **10**

5. BD **10**   **6.** CE **16**   **7.** BE **21**

8. The endpoints of $\overline{RS}$ are $R(-2, -1)$ and $S(2, 3)$. Find the coordinates of the midpoint of $\overline{RS}$. Then find the distance between R and S. *(p. 15)* **(0, 1); about 5.7**

MIXED REVIEW of Problem Solving

Lessons 1.1–1.3

1. **MULTI-STEP PROBLEM** The diagram shows existing roads ($\overleftrightarrow{BD}$ and $\overleftrightarrow{DE}$) and a new road ($\overline{CE}$) under construction.

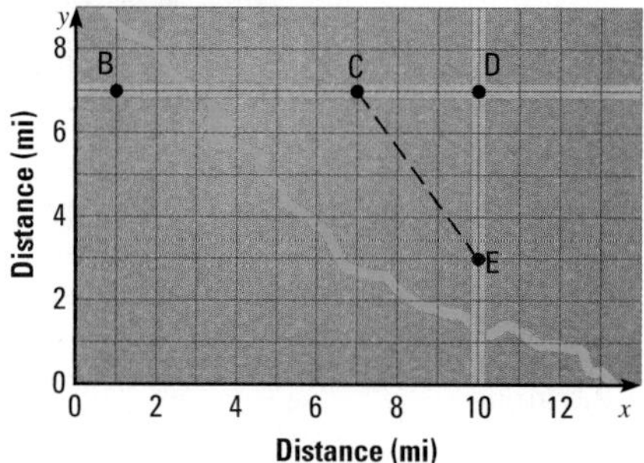

   a. If you drive from point B to point E on existing roads, how far do you travel? **13 mi**

   b. If you use the new road as you drive from B to E, about how far do you travel? Round to the nearest tenth of a mile if necessary. **11 mi**

   c. About how much shorter is the trip from B to E if you use the new road? **2 mi**

2. **GRIDDED ANSWER** Point M is the midpoint of $\overline{PQ}$. If $PM = 23x + 5$ and $MQ = 25x - 4$, find the length of $\overline{PQ}$. **217**

3. **GRIDDED ANSWER** You are hiking on a trail that lies along a straight railroad track. The total length of the trail is 5.4 kilometers. You have been hiking for 45 minutes at an average speed of 2.4 kilometers per hour. How much farther (in kilometers) do you need to hike to reach the end of the trail? **3.6 km**

4. **SHORT RESPONSE** The diagram below shows the frame for a wall. $\overline{FH}$ represents a vertical board, and $\overline{EG}$ represents a brace. If $FG = 143$ cm, does the brace bisect $\overline{FH}$? If not, how long should $\overline{FG}$ be so that the brace does bisect $\overline{FH}$? *Explain.* **No; 1.4 m; half of 2.8 meters is 1.4 meters.**

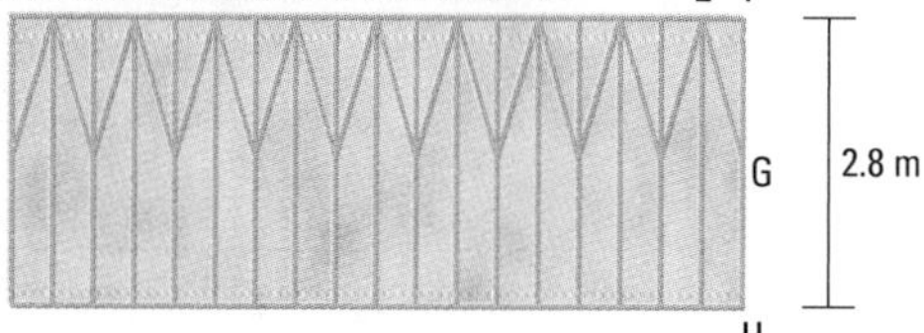

5. **SHORT RESPONSE** Point E is the midpoint of $\overline{AB}$ and the midpoint of $\overline{CD}$. The endpoints of $\overline{AB}$ are $A(-4, 5)$ and $B(6, -5)$. The coordinates of point C are $(2, 8)$. Find the coordinates of point D. *Explain* how you got your answer. **See margin.**

6. **OPEN-ENDED** The distance around a figure is its *perimeter*. Choose four points in a coordinate plane that can be connected to form a rectangle with a perimeter of 16 units. Then choose four other points and draw a different rectangle that has a perimeter of 16 units. Show how you determined that each rectangle has a perimeter of 16 units. **See margin.**

7. **SHORT RESPONSE** Use the diagram of a box. What are all the names that can be used to describe the plane that contains points B, F, and C? Name the intersection of planes ABC and BFE. *Explain.* **See margin.**

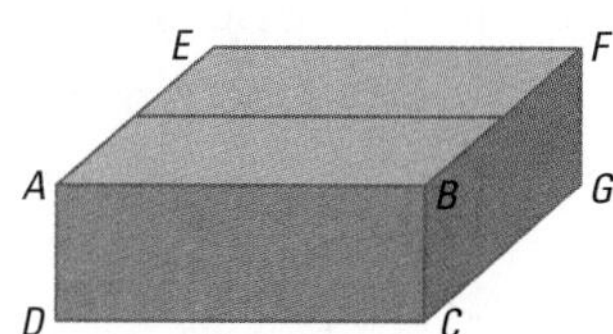

8. **EXTENDED RESPONSE** Jill is a salesperson who needs to visit towns A, B, and C. On the map below, $AB = 18.7$ km and $BC = 2AB$. Assume Jill travels along the road shown.

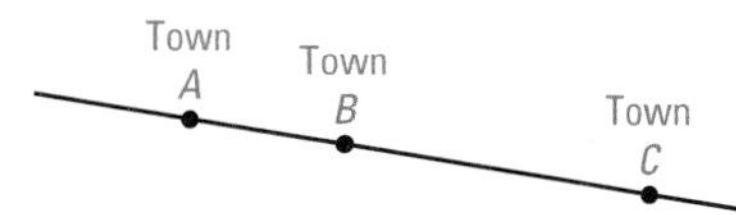

   a. Find the distance Jill travels if she starts at Town A, visits Towns B and C, and then returns to Town A. **112.2 km**

   b. About how much time does Jill spend driving if her average driving speed is 70 kilometers per hour? **about 1.6 h**

   c. Jill needs to spend 2.5 hours in each town. Can she visit all three towns and return to Town A in an 8 hour workday? *Explain.* **No; *Sample answer:* $3(2.5) + 1.6 > 8$**

5. $(0, -8)$; use the coordinates of points A and B and the midpoint formula to find the coordinates of point E, then use the coordinates of points C and E and the midpoint formula to find the coordinates of point D.

6. Check students' work. *Sample answer:* For each rectangle, find the length of each of the four sides and add them.

7. Plane BFC, plane BFG, plane FGC, plane GCB; $\overleftrightarrow{AB}$; $\overline{AB}$ is the edge of the box where plane ABC intersects plane BFE.

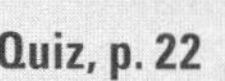

Quiz, p. 22

1.

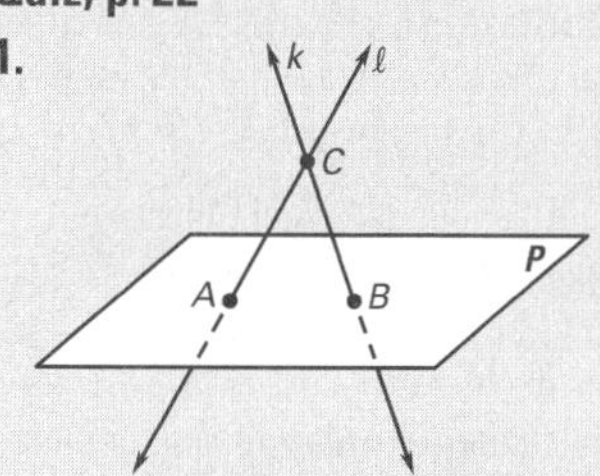

1 PLAN AND PREPARE

Warm-Up Exercises

Transparency Available

Solve each equation.

1. $5x + 6 + 2x - 14 = 90$ **14**

2. $4x - 30 + x + 25 = 180$ **37**

3. $\frac{x}{3} + 2 = x - 5$ **10.5**

Notetaking Guide

Transparency Available

Promotes interactive learning and notetaking skills, pp. 12–15.

Pacing

Basic: 2 days

Average: 2 days

Advanced: 2 days

Block: 1 block

- See *Teaching Guide/Lesson Plan.*

2 FOCUS AND MOTIVATE

Essential Question

Big Idea 1, p. 1

How do you identify whether an angle is acute, right, obtuse, or straight? **Tell students they will learn how to answer this question by learning the definitions of these types of angles and how to find angle measures.**

1.4 Measure and Classify Angles

Before You named and measured line segments.

Now You will name, measure, and classify angles.

Why? So you can identify congruent angles, as in Example 4.

Key Vocabulary
- **angle**
  acute, right, obtuse, straight
- **sides, vertex of an angle**
- **measure of an angle**
- **congruent angles**
- **angle bisector**

Standards

1.0 Students demonstrate understanding by identifying and giving examples of undefined terms, **axioms,** theorems, and inductive and deductive reasoning.

An **angle** consists of two different rays with the same endpoint. The rays are the **sides** of the angle. The endpoint is the **vertex** of the angle.

The angle with sides $\overrightarrow{AB}$ and $\overrightarrow{AC}$ can be named $\angle BAC$, $\angle CAB$, or $\angle A$. Point A is the vertex of the angle.

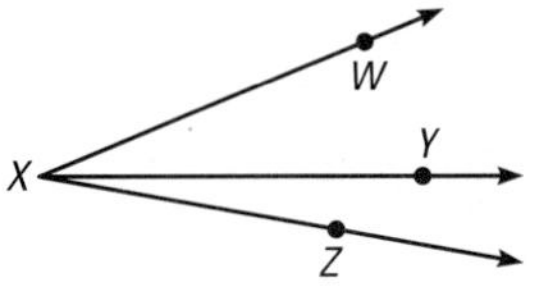

EXAMPLE 1 Name angles

Name the three angles in the diagram.

$\angle WXY$, or $\angle YXW$

$\angle YXZ$, or $\angle ZXY$

$\angle WXZ$, or $\angle ZXW$

You should not name any of these angles $\angle X$ because all three angles have X as their vertex.

MEASURING ANGLES A protractor can be used to approximate the *measure* of an angle. An angle is measured in units called *degrees* (°). For instance, the measure of $\angle WXZ$ in Example 1 above is 32°. You can write this statement in two ways.

Words The measure of $\angle WXZ$ is 32°.

Symbols $m\angle WXZ = 32°$

POSTULATE *For Your Notebook*

POSTULATE 3 Protractor Postulate

Consider $\overleftrightarrow{OB}$ and a point A on one side of $\overleftrightarrow{OB}$. The rays of the form $\overrightarrow{OA}$ can be matched one to one with the real numbers from 0 to 180.

The **measure** of $\angle AOB$ is equal to the absolute value of the difference between the real numbers for $\overrightarrow{OA}$ and $\overrightarrow{OB}$.

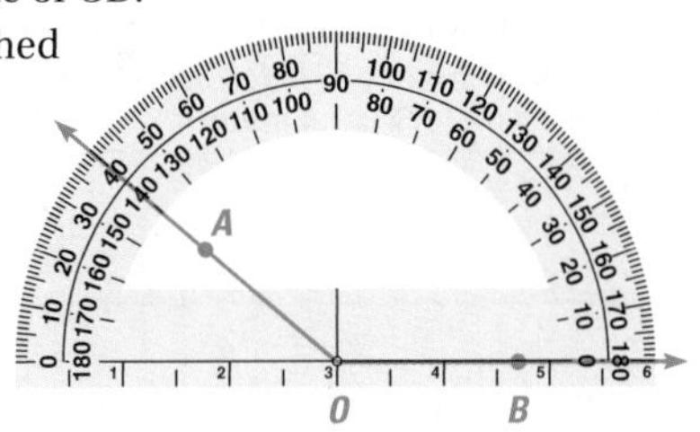

Resource Planning Guide

Chapter Resource Book
- Teaching Guide/Lesson Plan (pp. 47–48)
- Activity Master (p. 49)
- Practice levels A, B, C (pp. 50–55)
- Study Guide (pp. 56–57)
- Catch-up for Absent Students (p. 58)
- Problem Solving Workshop (p. 59)
- Challenge (p. 60)

Workbooks
- Notetaking Guide (pp. 12–15)
- Practice Workbook (pp. 10–12)

Teaching Options
- **Power Presentations CD-ROM** provides dynamic electronic teaching resources for the classroom.
- **Activity Generator CD-ROM** provides editable activities for all ability levels.

Interactive Technology
- Easy Planner
- Power Presentations CD-ROM
- Activity Generator CD-ROM
- Animated Geometry
- Test Generator CD-ROM
- Online Quiz
- eWorkbook
- eEdition
- @HomeTutor

Resources for English Learners
- Quick Reference for English Learners
- Spanish Study Guide
- Multi-Language Visual Glossary
- Student Resources in Spanish

See also the *Geometry Toolkit* for more strategies for meeting individual needs.

CLASSIFYING ANGLES Angles can be classified as **acute**, **right**, **obtuse**, and **straight**, as shown below.

READ DIAGRAMS
A red square inside an angle indicates that the angle is a right angle.

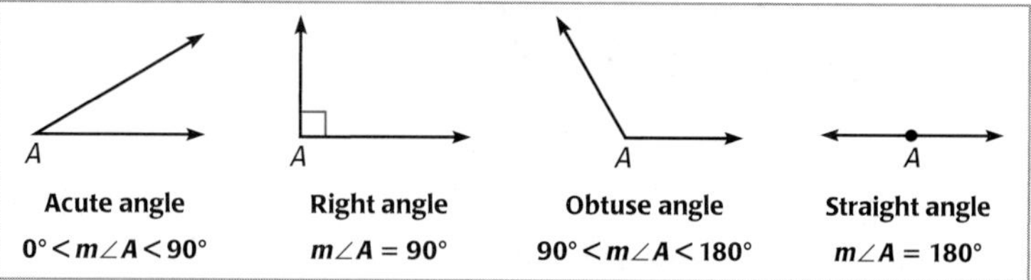

Acute angle	Right angle	Obtuse angle	Straight angle
$0° < m\angle A < 90°$	$m\angle A = 90°$	$90° < m\angle A < 180°$	$m\angle A = 180°$

EXAMPLE 2 Measure and classify angles

Use the diagram to find the measure of the indicated angle. Then classify the angle.

a. $\angle KHJ$ **b.** $\angle GHK$ **c.** $\angle GHJ$ **d.** $\angle GHL$

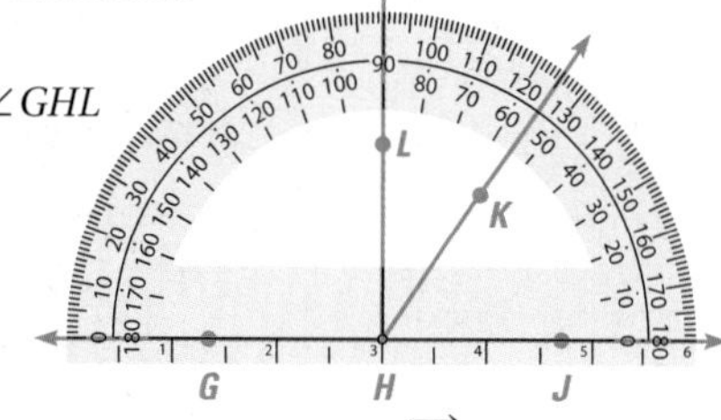

Solution

A protractor has an inner and an outer scale. When you measure an angle, check to see which scale to use.

a. $\overrightarrow{HJ}$ is lined up with the 0° on the inner scale of the protractor. $\overrightarrow{HK}$ passes through 55° on the inner scale. So, $m\angle KHJ = 55°$. It is an acute angle.

b. $\overrightarrow{HG}$ is lined up with the 0° on the outer scale, and $\overrightarrow{HK}$ passes through 125° on the outer scale. So, $m\angle GHK = 125°$. It is an obtuse angle.

c. $m\angle GHJ = 180°$. It is a straight angle.

d. $m\angle GHL = 90°$. It is a right angle.

 at classzone.com

GUIDED PRACTICE for Examples 1 and 2

1. Name all the angles in the diagram at the right. Which angle is a right angle? **$\angle PQR$, $\angle PQS$, $\angle RQS$; $\angle PQS$**
2. Draw a pair of opposite rays. What type of angle do the rays form? **See margin for art; straight angle.**

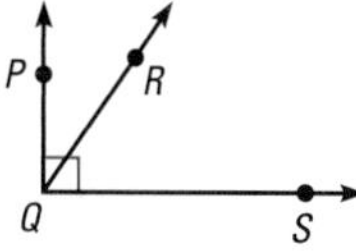

READ DIAGRAMS
A point is in the *interior* of an angle if it is between points that lie on each side of the angle.

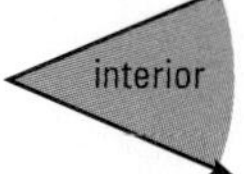

POSTULATE *For Your Notebook*

POSTULATE 4 Angle Addition Postulate

Words If P is in the interior of $\angle RST$, then the measure of $\angle RST$ is equal to the sum of the measures of $\angle RSP$ and $\angle PST$.

Symbols If P is in the interior of $\angle RST$, then $m\angle RST = m\angle RSP + m\angle PST$.

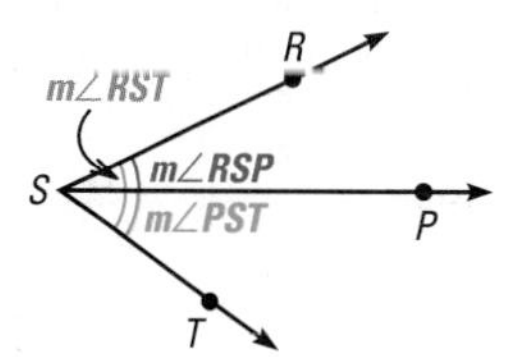

Motivating the Lesson

A piece of glass must be cut to fit the top of a table that has four sides of different lengths. Tell students that in this lesson they will learn how to use angle measures to ensure that the glass will fit perfectly.

3 TEACH

Extra Example 1

Name the three angles in the diagram. ***Sample answer:* $\angle MNO$, $\angle ONP$, $\angle MNP$**

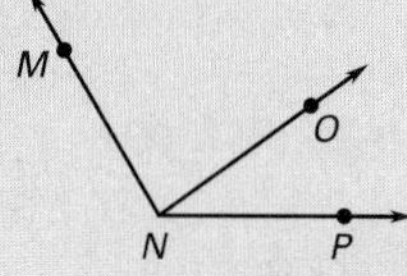

Extra Example 2

Use the diagram to find the measure of each angle and classify the angle.

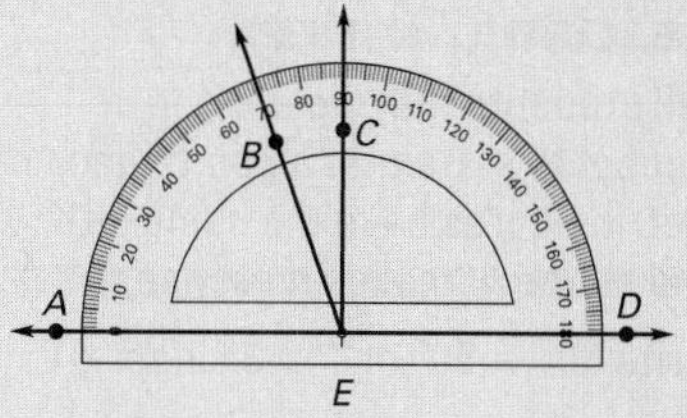

a. $\angle DEC$ **90°, right**
b. $\angle DEA$ **180°, straight**
c. $\angle CEB$ **20°, acute**
d. $\angle DEB$ **110°, obtuse**

***Animated* Geometry**
classzone.com

An **Animated Geometry** activity is available on-line for **Example 2**. This activity is also available on the **Power Presentations CD-ROM**.

2. 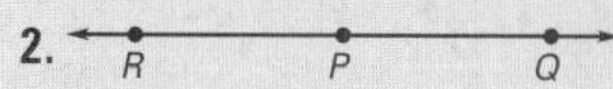

Differentiated Instruction

Inclusion Students may have difficulty remembering which angles are acute and which are obtuse. Have students remember that "acute" means "sharp," and relate this to the fact that the sides of an acute angle form a sharp point.

See also the *Geometry Toolkit* for more strategies.

Study Strategy

Have students make up a phrase for remembering AROS, which lists acute, right, obtuse, and straight angles in order of size. One possibility is "All Rain Or Snow."

Extra Example 3

If $m\angle XYZ = 72°$, find $m\angle XYW$ and $m\angle ZYW$. **51°, 21°**

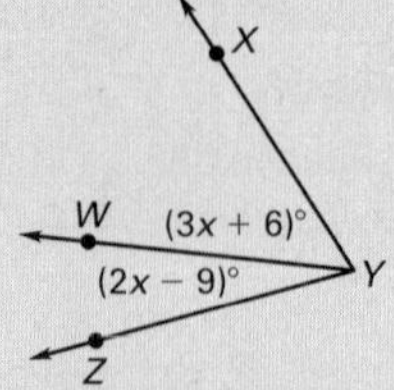

Key Question to Ask for Example 3

- How can you check that the answer of 56° and 89° is correct? **See if the angle measures add up to 145°.**

Teaching Strategy

Tell students that we use the ≅ symbol to state that a pair of geometric figures have the same size and shape. It makes no sense to write $50° \cong 50°$ or $\frac{6}{2} \cong 3$ since measures and numbers are not geometric figures.

EXAMPLE 3 Find angle measures

ALGEBRA Given that $m\angle LKN = 145°$, find $m\angle LKM$ and $m\angle MKN$.

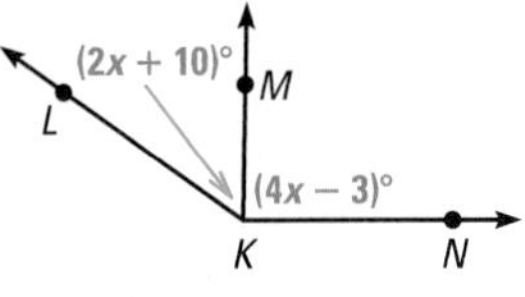

Solution

STEP 1 **Write** and solve an equation to find the value of x.

$m\angle LKN = m\angle LKM + m\angle MKN$	**Angle Addition Postulate**
$145° = (2x + 10)° + (4x - 3)°$	**Substitute angle measures.**
$145 = 6x + 7$	**Combine like terms.**
$138 = 6x$	**Subtract 7 from each side.**
$23 = x$	**Divide each side by 6.**

STEP 2 **Evaluate** the given expressions when $x = 23$.

$m\angle LKM = (2x + 10)° = (2 \cdot 23 + 10)° = 56°$

$m\angle MKN = (4x - 3)° = (4 \cdot 23 - 3)° = 89°$

▸ So, $m\angle LKM = 56°$ and $m\angle MKN = 89°$.

✓ **GUIDED PRACTICE** for Example 3

Find the indicated angle measures.

3. Given that $\angle KLM$ is a straight angle, find $m\angle KLN$ and $m\angle NLM$. **125°, 55°**

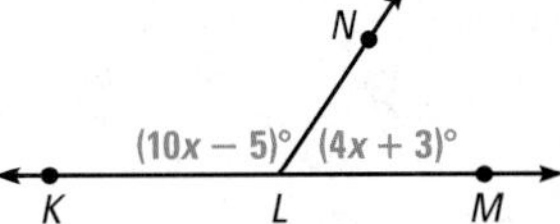

4. Given that $\angle EFG$ is a right angle, find $m\angle EFH$ and $m\angle HFG$. **60°, 30°**

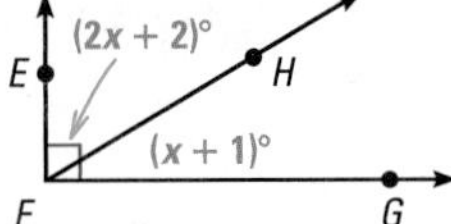

CONGRUENT ANGLES Two angles are **congruent angles** if they have the same measure. In the diagram below, you can say that "the measure of angle A is equal to the measure of angle B," or you can say "angle A *is congruent to* angle B."

READ DIAGRAMS
Matching arcs are used to show that angles are congruent. If more than one pair of angles are congruent, double arcs are used, as in Example 4 on page 27.

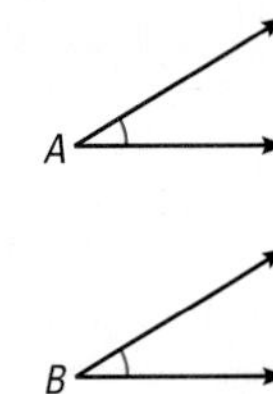

Angle measures are equal.	**Angles are congruent.**
$m\angle A = m\angle B$	$\angle A \cong \angle B$
⬆	⬆
"is equal to"	"is congruent to"

Differentiated Instruction

Advanced Students have learned what it means for segments to be congruent and for angles to be congruent. Ask students to conjecture what it would mean for two triangles to be congruent, and then for two rectangles. Have students extend their conjectures to include any kind of polygon.

See also the *Geometry Toolkit* for more strategies.

EXAMPLE 4 Identify congruent angles

TRAPEZE The photograph shows some of the angles formed by the ropes in a trapeze apparatus. Identify the congruent angles. If $m\angle DEG = 157°$, what is $m\angle GKL$?

Solution

There are two pairs of congruent angles:

$\angle DEF \cong \angle JKL$ and $\angle DEG \cong \angle GKL$.

Because $\angle DEG \cong \angle GKL$, $m\angle DEG = m\angle GKL$. So, $m\angle GKL = 157°$.

GUIDED PRACTICE for Example 4

Use the diagram shown at the right.

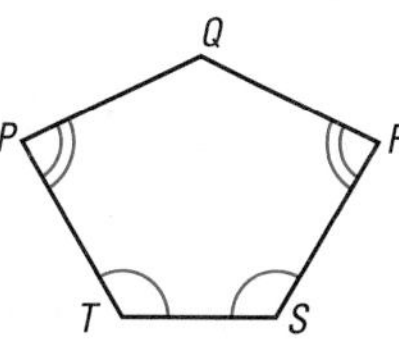

5. Identify all pairs of congruent angles in the diagram. **$\angle T$ and $\angle S$, $\angle P$ and $\angle R$**

6. In the diagram, $m\angle PQR = 130°$, $m\angle QRS = 84°$, and $m\angle TSR = 121°$. Find the other angle measures in the diagram. **$m\angle PTS = 121°$, $m\angle QPT = 84°$**

ACTIVITY FOLD AN ANGLE BISECTOR

STEP 1

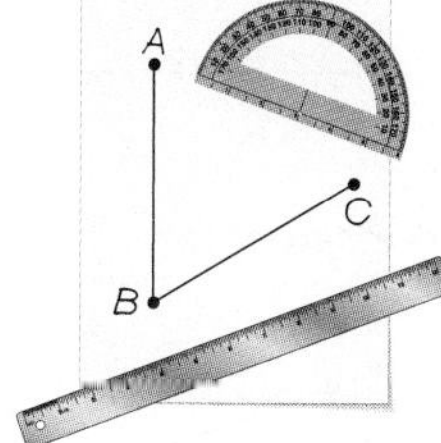

Use a straightedge to draw and label an acute angle, $\angle ABC$.

STEP 2

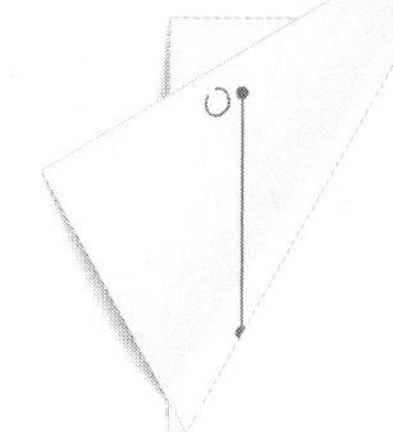

Fold the paper so that $\overrightarrow{BC}$ is on top of $\overrightarrow{BA}$.

STEP 3

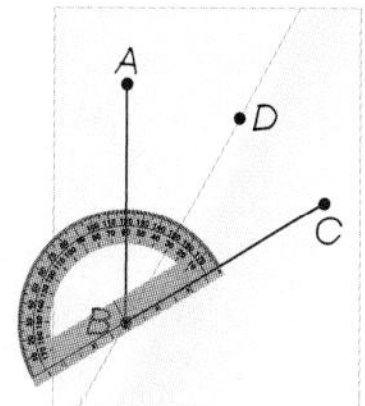

Draw a point *D* on the fold inside $\angle ABC$. Then measure $\angle ABD$, $\angle DBC$, and $\angle ABC$. What do you observe?

Extra Example 4

The figure shows angles formed by the legs of an ironing board. Identify the congruent angles. If $m\angle HGI = 40°$, what is $m\angle GJK$?

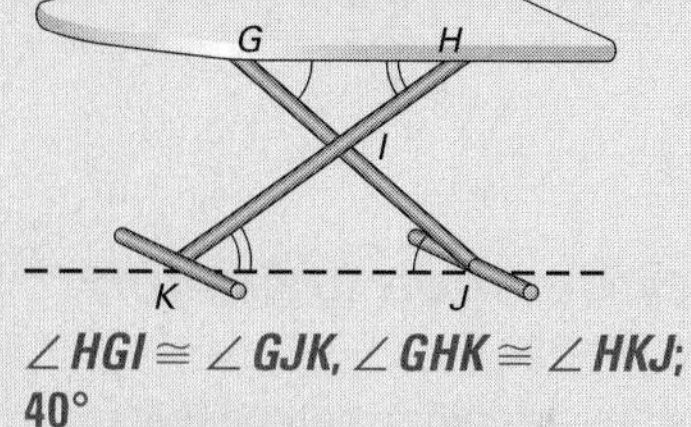

$\angle HGI \cong \angle GJK$, $\angle GHK \cong \angle HKJ$; 40°

Key Question to Ask for Example 4

- What is true about the measures of congruent angles? **They are equal.**

Activity Note

The purpose of this folding activity is to show students that an angle bisector divides an angle into two congruent angles. Ask students what the fold represents. **the angle bisector**

Extra Example 5

In the diagram, $\overrightarrow{MN}$ bisects $\angle PMQ$, and $m\angle PMQ = 122°$. Find $m\angle PMN$. **61°**

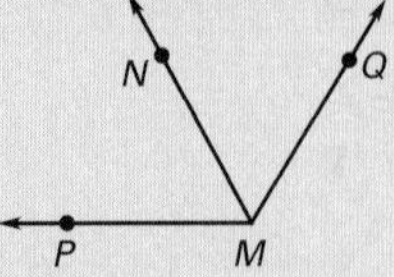

Key Question to Ask for Example 5

- Is there another method that could be used to find $m\angle XYZ$? **Yes; by the definition of angle bisector $m\angle XYW = \frac{1}{2}m\angle XYZ$. Thus $m\angle XYZ = 2m\angle XYW$ or $m\angle XYZ = 2 \cdot 18 = 36°$.**

Closing the Lesson

Have students summarize the major points of the lesson and answer the Essential Question: How do you identify whether an angle is acute, right, obtuse, or straight?

- **An angle is formed by two rays that have the same endpoint.**
- **Angles are classified as acute, right, obtuse, or straight.**
- **An angle bisector divides an angle into two congruent angles.**

Acute angles have measure between 0° and 90°, right angles have measure 90°, obtuse angles have measures between 90° and 180°, and straight angles have measure 180°.

Guided Practice

7.

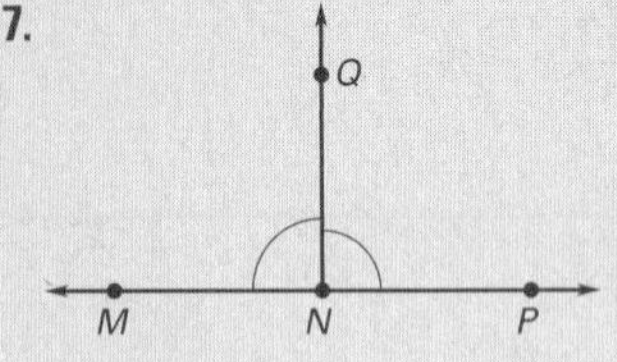

An **angle bisector** is a ray that divides an angle into two angles that are congruent. In the activity on page 27, $\overrightarrow{BD}$ bisects $\angle ABC$. So, $\angle ABD \cong \angle DBC$ and $m\angle ABD = m\angle DBC$.

EXAMPLE 5 Double an angle measure

In the diagram at the right, $\overrightarrow{YW}$ bisects $\angle XYZ$, and $m\angle XYW = 18°$. Find $m\angle XYZ$.

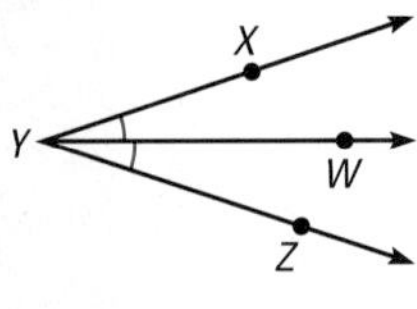

Solution

By the Angle Addition Postulate, $m\angle XYZ = m\angle XYW + m\angle WYZ$. Because $\overrightarrow{YW}$ bisects $\angle XYZ$, you know that $\angle XYW \cong \angle WYZ$.

So, $m\angle XYW = m\angle WYZ$, and you can write

$$m\angle XYZ = m\angle XYW + m\angle WYZ = 18° + 18° = 36°.$$

GUIDED PRACTICE for Example 5

7. Angle MNP is a straight angle, and $\overrightarrow{NQ}$ bisects $\angle MNP$. Draw $\angle MNP$ and $\overrightarrow{NQ}$. Use arcs to mark the congruent angles in your diagram, and give the angle measures of these congruent angles. **See margin for art; 90°.**

1.4 EXERCISES

HOMEWORK KEY
○ = **WORKED-OUT SOLUTIONS** on p. WS1 for Exs. 15, 23, and 53
★ = **STANDARDIZED TEST PRACTICE** Exs. 2, 21, 27, 43, and 62

SKILL PRACTICE

A

1. **VOCABULARY** Sketch an example of each of the following types of angles: acute, obtuse, right, and straight. **See margin.**

2. ★ **WRITING** *Explain* how to find the measure of $\angle PQR$, shown at the right. **The measure of $\angle PQR$ is equal to the absolute value of the difference between the degree measures for $\overrightarrow{QP}$ and $\overrightarrow{QR}$.**

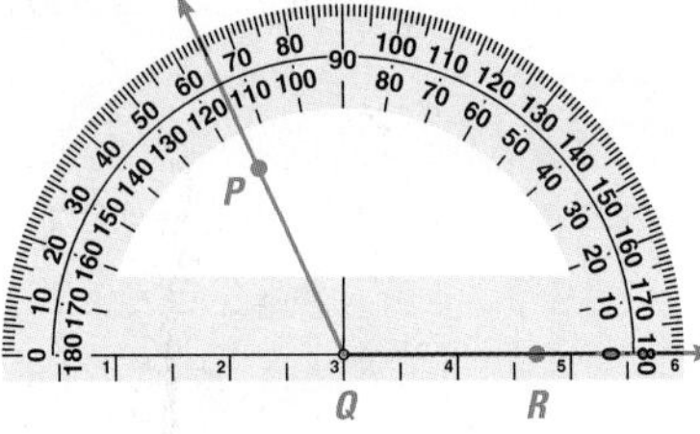

EXAMPLE 1 on p. 24 for Exs. 3–6

NAMING ANGLES AND ANGLE PARTS **In Exercises 3–5, write three names for the angle shown. Then name the vertex and sides of the angle.**

3. 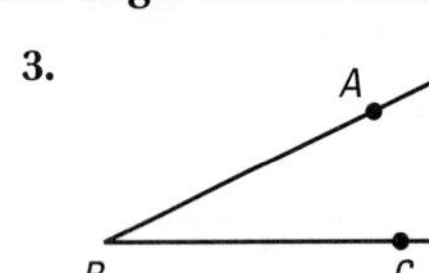

$\angle ABC$, $\angle B$, $\angle CBA$; B, $\overrightarrow{BA}$, $\overrightarrow{BC}$

4. **$\angle NQT$, $\angle Q$, $\angle TQN$; Q, $\overrightarrow{QN}$, $\overrightarrow{QT}$**

5. 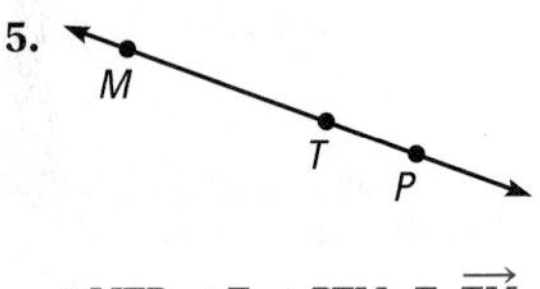

$\angle MTP$, $\angle T$, $\angle PTM$; T, $\overrightarrow{TM}$, $\overrightarrow{TP}$

Skill Practice

1. ***Sample:***

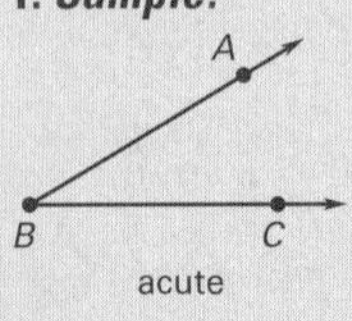

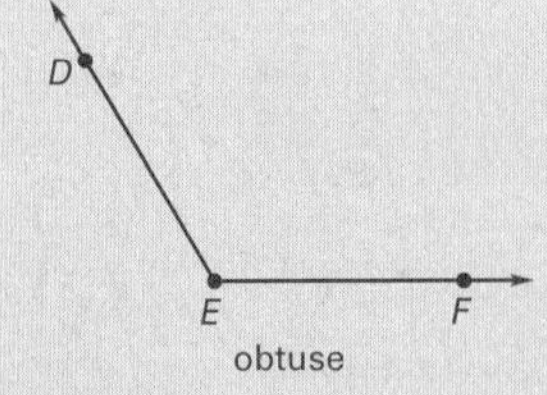

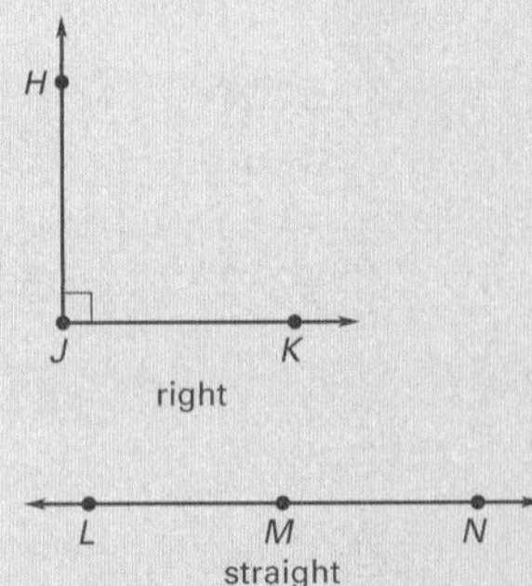

6. **NAMING ANGLES** Name three different angles in the diagram at the right. **∠*QRT*, ∠*QRS*, ∠*SRT***

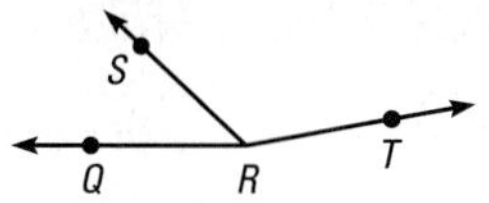

EXAMPLE 2
on p. 25
for Exs. 7–21

CLASSIFYING ANGLES Classify the angle with the given measure as *acute, obtuse, right,* or *straight.*

7. $m\angle W = 180°$ **straight**
8. $m\angle X = 30°$ **acute**
9. $m\angle Y = 90°$ **right**
10. $m\angle Z = 95°$ **obtuse**

MEASURING ANGLES Trace the diagram and extend the rays. Use a protractor to find the measure of the given angle. Then classify the angle as *acute, obtuse, right,* or *straight.*

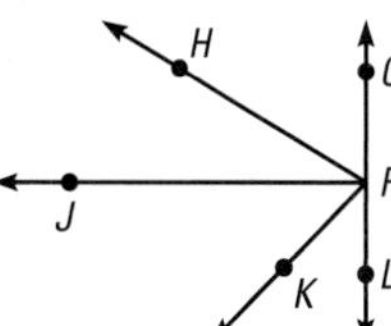

11. $\angle JFL$ **90°; right**
12. $\angle GFH$ **60°; acute**

13. $\angle GFK$ **135°; obtuse**
14. $\angle GFL$ **180°; straight**

15–20. Sample answers are given.

15. ∠*BCA*; right

16. ∠*CBA*; acute

17. ∠*DFB*; straight

18. ∠*CEA*; obtuse

19. ∠*CDB*; acute

20. ∠*CEB*; acute

NAMING AND CLASSIFYING Give another name for the angle in the diagram below. Tell whether the angle appears to be *acute, obtuse, right,* or *straight.*

15. $\angle ACB$
16. $\angle ABC$
17. $\angle BFD$
18. $\angle AEC$
19. $\angle BDC$
20. $\angle BEC$

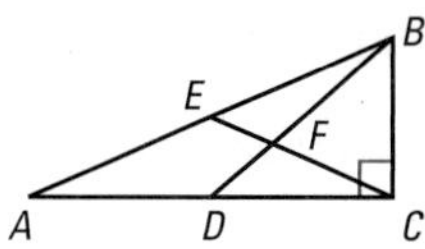

21. ★ **MULTIPLE CHOICE** Which is a correct name for the obtuse angle in the diagram? **B**

Ⓐ $\angle ACB$ Ⓑ $\angle ACD$

Ⓒ $\angle BCD$ Ⓓ $\angle C$

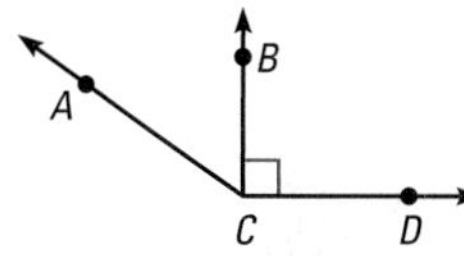

EXAMPLE 3
on p. 26
for Exs. 22–27

ANGLE ADDITION POSTULATE Find the indicated angle measure.

22. $m\angle QST = \underline{?}$ **99°**

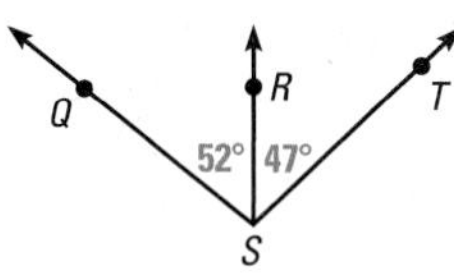

23. $m\angle ADC = \underline{?}$ **65°**

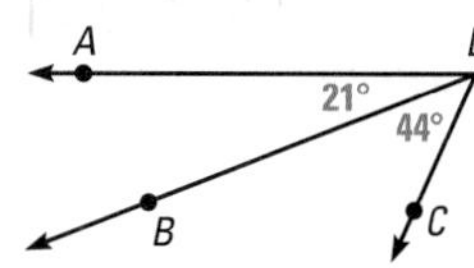

24. $m\angle NPM = \underline{?}$ **101°**

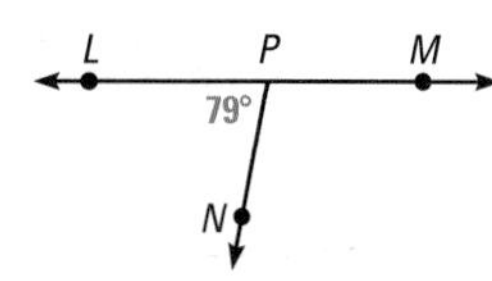

xy **ALGEBRA Use the given information to find the indicated angle measure.**

25. Given $m\angle WXZ = 80°$, find $m\angle YXZ$. **55°**

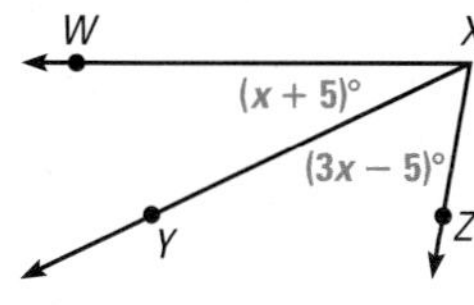

26. Given $m\angle FJH = 168°$, find $m\angle FJG$. **135°**

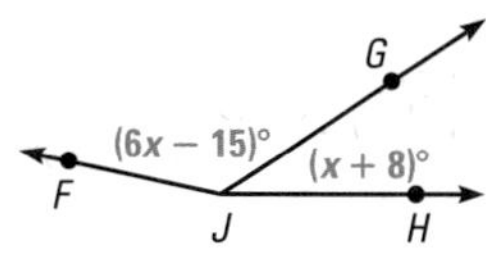

27. ★ **MULTIPLE CHOICE** In the diagram, the measure of $\angle XYZ$ is 140°. What is the value of x? **A**

Ⓐ 27 Ⓑ 33

Ⓒ 67 Ⓓ 73

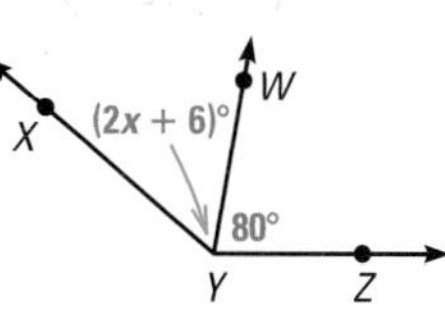

4 PRACTICE AND APPLY

Assignment Guide

Answer Transparencies available for all exercises

Basic:
Day 1: pp. 28–32
Exs. 1–21, 65–73
Day 2: pp. 28–32
Exs. 22–39, 51–58, 64

Average:
Day 1: pp. 28–32
Exs. 1, 2, 4–6, 9–18, 21, 44–48, 65–73 odd
Day 2: pp. 28–32
Exs. 22–32, 33–43 odd, 51–62, 64

Advanced:
Day 1: pp. 28–32
Exs. 1, 2, 4–6, 8–10, 12–14, 18–21, 44–48, 66–72 even
Day 2: pp. 28–32
Exs. 24, 26–28, 30–32, 34–42 even, 43, 49–64*

Block:
pp. 28–32
Exs. 1, 2, 4–6, 9–18, 21–32, 33–43 odd, 44–48, 51–62, 64, 65–73 odd

Differentiated Instruction

See *Geometry Best Practices Toolkit* for suggestions on addressing the needs of a diverse classroom.

Homework Check

For a quick check of student understanding of key concepts, go over the following exercises:

Basic: 3, 12, 22, 28, 53
Average: 4, 18, 24, 30, 54
Advanced: 5, 20, 26, 31, 55

Extra Practice

- Student Edition, p. 896
- Chapter 1 Resource Book: Practice levels A, B, C, pp. 50–55

Practice Worksheet

An easily-readable reduced practice page (with answers) for this lesson can be found on p. 1D.

Avoiding Common Errors

Exercise 21 Some students may answer hastily and select choice D. Point out that one-letter notation cannot give the correct answer since all three of the angles have vertex *C*.

32.

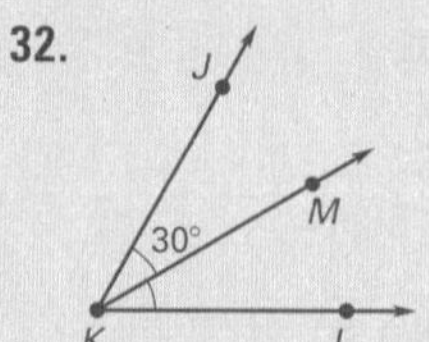

39. ***Sample:***

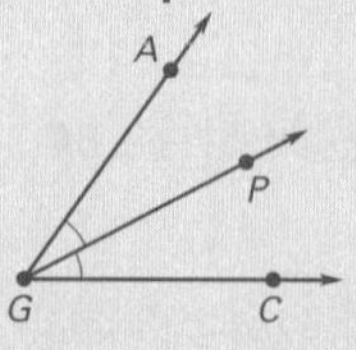

44.

45.

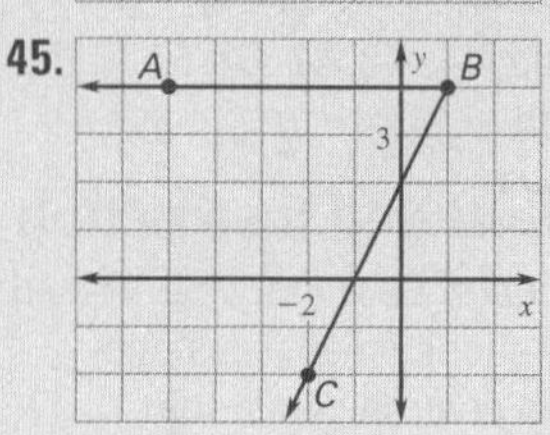

46.

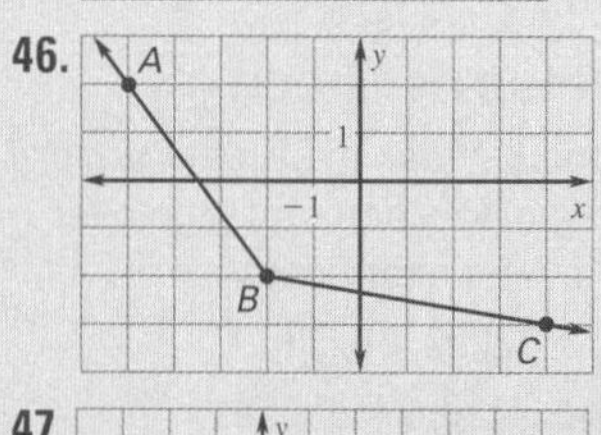

47.

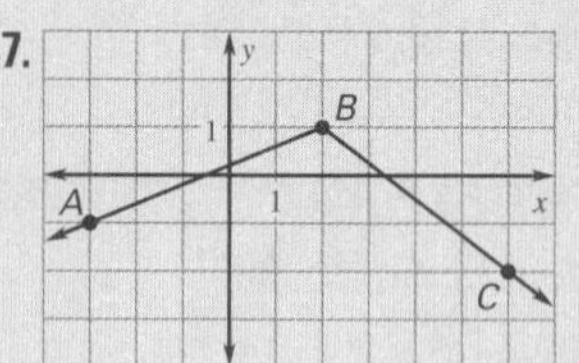

EXAMPLE 4
on p. 27
for Ex. 28

28. $\angle AED \cong \angle ADE \cong \angle ABD \cong \angle DAB \cong \angle BDC \cong \angle BCD \cong$, and $\angle EAD \cong \angle ADB \cong \angle DBC$; 34°, 112°

EXAMPLE 5
on p. 28
for Exs. 29–32

28. CONGRUENT ANGLES In the photograph below, $m\angle AED = 34°$ and $m\angle EAD = 112°$. Identify the congruent angles in the diagram. Then find $m\angle BDC$ and $m\angle ADB$.

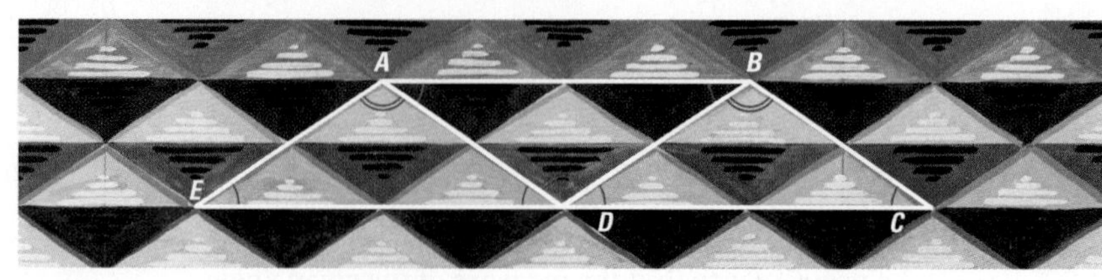

ANGLE BISECTORS Given that $\overrightarrow{WZ}$ bisects $\angle XWY$, find the two angle measures not given in the diagram.

29. (52°) $m\angle XWY = 104°$, $m\angle ZWY = 52°$

30. (68°) $m\angle XWY = 136°$, $m\angle XWZ = 68°$

31. (71°) $m\angle XWZ = 35.5°$, $m\angle YWZ = 35.5°$

32. ERROR ANALYSIS $\overrightarrow{KM}$ bisects $\angle JKL$ and $m\angle JKM = 30°$. *Describe* and correct the error made in stating that $m\angle JKL = 15°$. Draw a sketch to support your answer. **To find $m\angle JKL$, $m\angle JKM$ should be doubled, not halved; $m\angle JKL = 60°$; see margin for art.**

B **FINDING ANGLE MEASURES Find the indicated angle measure.**

33. $a°$ **38°** **34.** $b°$ **38°**

35. $c°$ **142°** **36.** $d°$ **37°**

37. $e°$ **53°** **38.** $f°$ **37°**

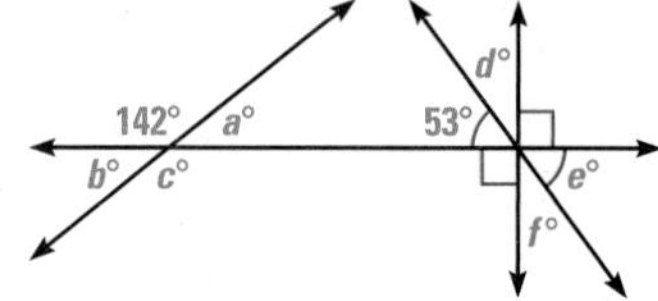

39. ERROR ANALYSIS A student states that $\overrightarrow{AD}$ can bisect $\angle AGC$. *Describe* and correct the student's error. Draw a sketch to support your answer. **If a ray bisects $\angle AGC$, then its endpoint must be point *G*; see margin for art.**

ALGEBRA In each diagram, $\overrightarrow{BD}$ bisects $\angle ABC$. Find $m\angle ABC$.

40. 156° $(4x - 2)°$, $(3x + 18)°$

41. 80° $4x°$, $(2x + 20)°$

42. 134°

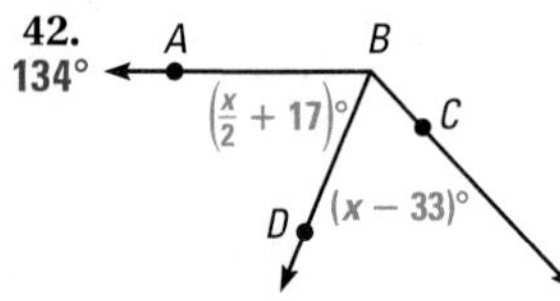

43. ★ **SHORT RESPONSE** You are measuring $\angle PQR$ with a protractor. When you line up $\overrightarrow{QR}$ with the 20° mark, $\overrightarrow{QP}$ lines up with the 80° mark. Then you move the protractor so that $\overrightarrow{QR}$ lines up with the 15° mark. What mark does $\overrightarrow{QP}$ line up with? *Explain.* **75°; both angle measures are 5° less.**

ALGEBRA Plot the points in a coordinate plane and draw $\angle ABC$. Classify the angle. Then give the coordinates of a point that lies in the interior of the angle. **44–47. See margin for art.**

44. $A(3, 3)$, $B(0, 0)$, $C(3, 0)$ **Acute. *Sample answer:* (3, 1)**

45. $A(-5, 4)$, $B(1, 4)$, $C(-2, -2)$ **Acute. *Sample answer:* (−2, 0)**

46. $A(-5, 2)$, $B(-2, -2)$, $C(4, -3)$ **Obtuse. *Sample answer:* (0, 0)**

47. $A(-3, -1)$, $B(2, 1)$, $C(6, -2)$ **Obtuse. *Sample answer:* (2, 0)**

49. 68°. *Sample answer:* Since $m\angle VSP = 17°$, the $m\angle RSP = 34°$. Since $m\angle RSP = 34°$, $m\angle RSQ = 68°$ which is equal to $m\angle TSQ$, so $m\angle TSQ = 68°$.

48. **ALGEBRA** Let $(2x - 12)°$ represent the measure of an acute angle. What are the possible values of x? **$6 < x < 51$**

C 49. **CHALLENGE** $\overrightarrow{SQ}$ bisects $\angle RST$, $\overrightarrow{SP}$ bisects $\angle RSQ$, and $\overrightarrow{SV}$ bisects $\angle RSP$. The measure of $\angle VSP$ is 17°. Find $m\angle TSQ$. *Explain.*

50. **FINDING MEASURES** In the diagram, $m\angle AEB = \frac{1}{2} \cdot m\angle CED$, and $\angle AED$ is a straight angle. Find $m\angle AEB$ and $m\angle CED$. **30°, 60°**

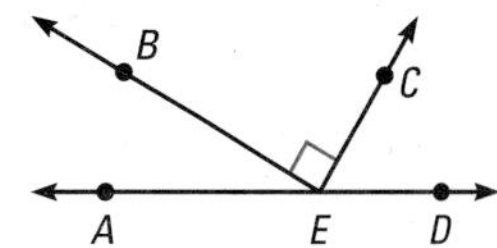

Avoiding Common Errors

Exercise 48 Students may write $2x - 12 < 90$ but forget $2x - 12 > 0$. Remind them that they need both inequalities to comply with the definition of an acute angle.

Mathematical Reasoning

Exercise 50 Have students use x to represent $m\angle CED$. Then they can write an equation to find x.

Reading Strategy

Exercise 53 Tell the students that reading and understanding a geometry exercise often requires reading not only the words but also a diagram. The diagram for this exercise contains several segments that are not used in answering the exercise. Students may want to make a separate sketch to show only the parts of the truss that are needed for coming up with the answer.

PROBLEM SOLVING

A 51. **SCULPTURE** In the sculpture shown in the photograph, suppose the measure of $\angle LMN$ is 79° and the measure of $\angle PMN$ is 47°. What is the measure of $\angle LMP$? **32°**

@HomeTutor for problem solving help at classzone.com

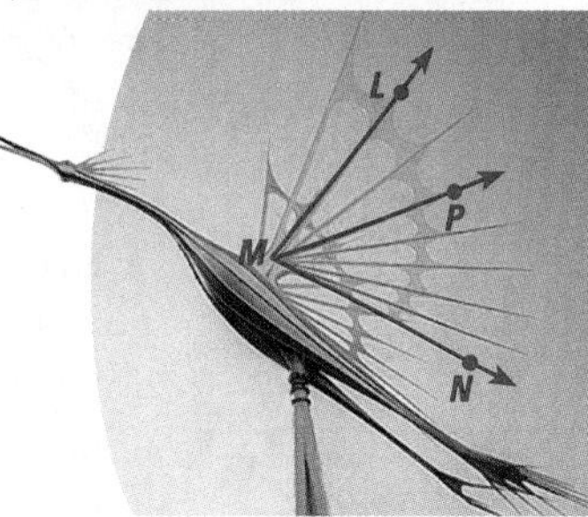

52. **MAP** The map shows the intersection of three roads. Malcom Way intersects Sydney Street at an angle of 162°. Park Road intersects Sydney Street at an angle of 87°. Find the angle at which Malcom Way intersects Park Road. **75°**

@HomeTutor for problem solving help at classzone.com

EXAMPLES 4 and 5 on pp. 27–28 for Exs. 53–55

CONSTRUCTION In Exercises 53–55, use the photograph of a roof truss.

53. In the roof truss, $\overrightarrow{BG}$ bisects $\angle ABC$ and $\angle DEF$, $m\angle ABC = 112°$, and $\angle ABC \cong \angle DEF$. Find the measure of the following angles.

a. $m\angle DEF$ **112°** b. $m\angle ABG$ **56°**

c. $m\angle CBG$ **56°** d. $m\angle DEG$ **56°**

54. In the roof truss, $\overrightarrow{GB}$ bisects $\angle DGF$. Find $m\angle DGE$ and $m\angle FGE$. **90°, 90°**

55. Name an example of each of the following types of angles: *acute, obtuse, right,* and *straight.*

55. *Sample answer:* acute: $\angle ABG$, obtuse: $\angle ABC$, right: $\angle DGE$, straight: $\angle DGF$

5 ASSESS AND RETEACH

Daily Homework Quiz

Transparency Available

Classify each angle as acute, obtuse, right, or straight.

1. $m\angle A = 90°$ **right**
2. $m\angle B = 62°$ **acute**
3. $m\angle C = 119°$ **obtuse**
4. If $m\angle DEG = 84°$, find $m\angle FEG$. **14°**

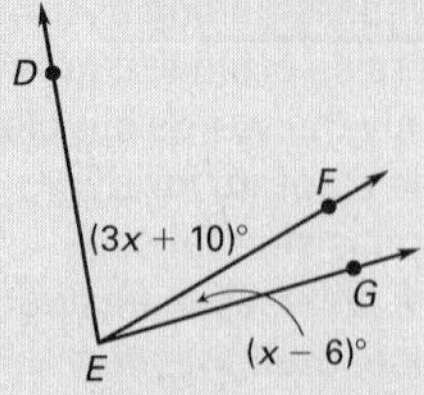

5. If $\overrightarrow{XY}$ bisects $\angle ZXW$ and $m\angle ZXY = 36°$, find $m\angle ZXW$. **72°**

Online Quiz

Available at **classzone.com**

Diagnosis/Remediation

- Practice A, B, C in Chapter 1 Resource Book, pp. 50–55
- Study Guide in Chapter 1 Resource Book, pp. 56–57
- Practice Workbook, pp. 10–12
- @HomeTutor

Challenge

Additional challenge is available in the Chapter 1 Resource Book, p. 60.

62c. $m\angle DFE = 26°$, $\angle DFE \cong \angle AFB$; $m\angle BFC = 64°$, it is complementary to $\angle AFB$; $m\angle CFD = 64°$, $\angle CFD \cong \angle BFC$; $m\angle AFC = 90°$, it is a right angle ($\angle AFE$ is a straight angle bisected by $\overrightarrow{FC}$); $m\angle AFD = 154°$, $m\angle AFD = m\angle AFC + m\angle CFD$; $m\angle BFD = 128°$, $m\angle BFD = m\angle BFC + m\angle CFD$.

B **GEOGRAPHY** **For the given location on the map, estimate the measure of $\angle PSL$, where P is on the Prime Meridian (0° longitude), S is the South Pole, and L is the location of the indicated research station.**

56. Macquarie Island **about 158°**	**57.** Dumont d'Urville **about 140°**	**58.** McMurdo **about 167°**
59. Mawson **about 62°**	**60.** Syowa **about 39°**	**61.** Vostok **about 107°**

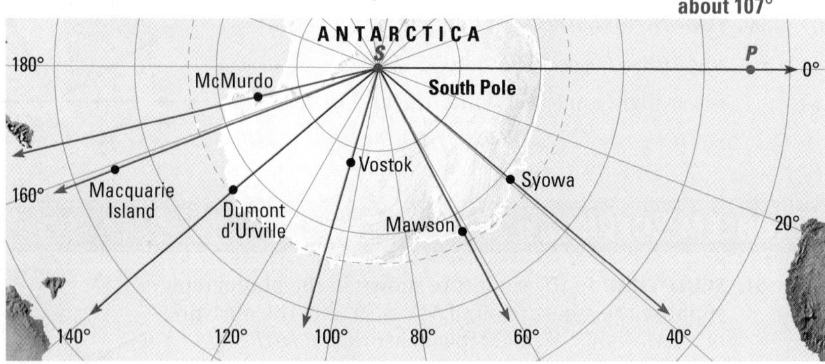

62. ★ **EXTENDED RESPONSE** In the flag shown, $\angle AFE$ is a straight angle and $\overrightarrow{FC}$ bisects $\angle AFE$ and $\angle BFD$.

a. Which angles are acute? obtuse? right?

b. Identify the congruent angles.

c. If $m\angle AFB = 26°$, find $m\angle DFE$, $m\angle BFC$, $m\angle CFD$, $m\angle AFC$, $m\angle AFD$, and $m\angle BFD$. *Explain.* **See margin.**

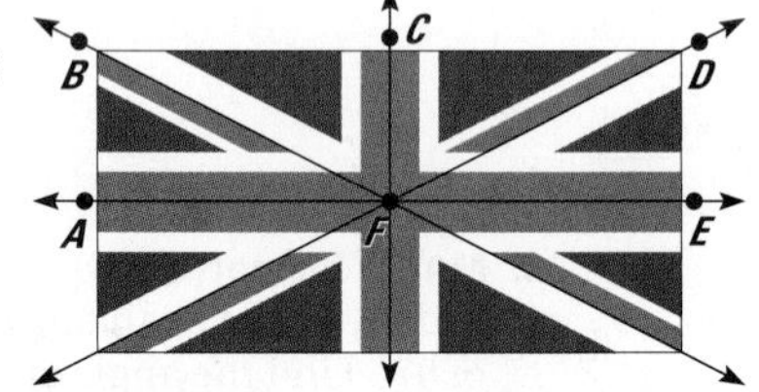

62a. $\angle AFB$, $\angle BFC$, $\angle CFD$, $\angle DFE$; $\angle AFD$, $\angle BFE$; $\angle AFC$, $\angle CFE$

62b. $\angle AFB \cong \angle EFD$, $\angle AFC \cong \angle EFC$, $\angle BFC \cong \angle DFC$

C **63.** **CHALLENGE** Create a set of data that could be represented by the circle graph at the right. *Explain* your reasoning. ***Sample answer:*** **In your pocket you have 4 pennies, 4 nickels, 4 dimes, 6 quarters, 6 dollar bills; nickels, dimes, pennies each represent $\frac{1}{6}$, and quarters and dollar bills each represent $\frac{1}{4}$.**

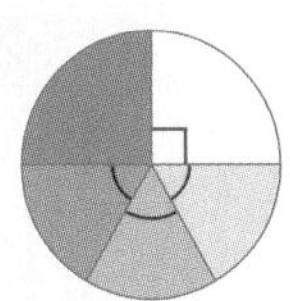

MIXED REVIEW

PREVIEW Prepare for Lesson 1.5 in Ex. 64.

64. You and a friend go out to dinner and each pay for your own meal. The total cost of the two meals is $25. Your meal cost $4 more than your friend's meal. How much does each meal cost? *(p. 894)* **your meal: $14.50, friend's meal: $10.50**

Graph the inequality on a number line. Tell whether the graph is a *segment*, a *ray* or *rays*, a *point*, or a *line*. *(p. 2)* **65–70. See margin for art.**

65. $x \le -8$ **ray**	**66.** $x \ge 6$ **ray**	**67.** $-3 \le x \le 5$ **segment**
68. $x \ge -7$ and $x \le -1$ **segment**	**69.** $x \ge -2$ or $x \le 4$ **line**	**70.** $\lvert x \rvert \ge 0$ **line**

Find the coordinate of the midpoint of the segment. *(p. 15)*

71. 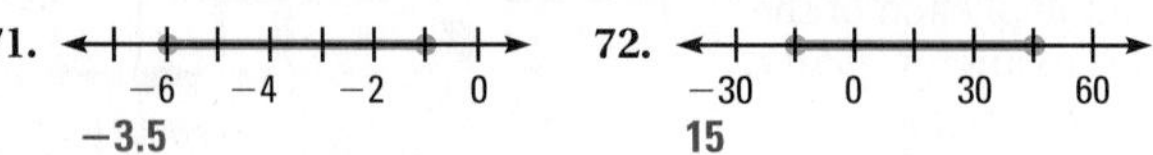

−3.5

72. **15**

73. 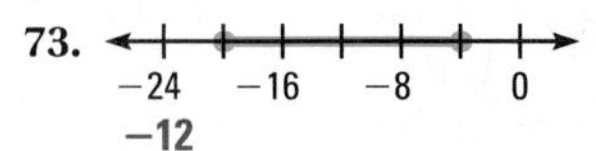

−12

 EXTRA PRACTICE for Lesson 1.4, p. 896 **ONLINE QUIZ** at classzone.com

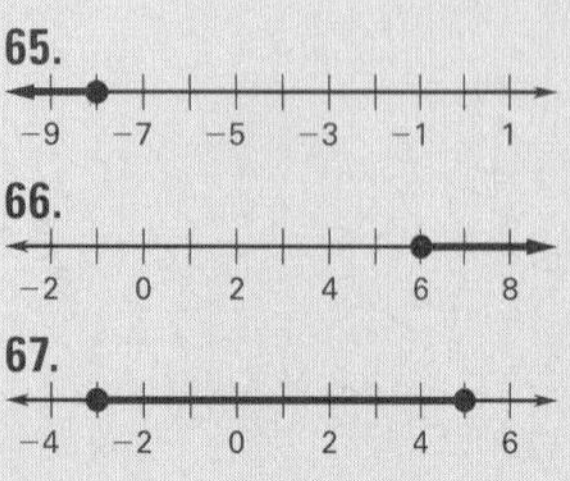

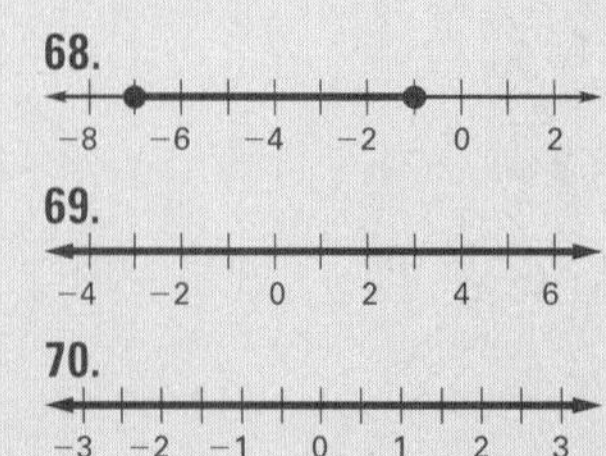

1.4 Copy and Bisect Segments and Angles

MATERIALS • compass • straightedge

QUESTION **How can you copy and bisect segments and angles?**

A **construction** is a geometric drawing that uses a limited set of tools, usually a *compass* and *straightedge*. You can use a compass and straightedge (a ruler without marks) to construct a segment that is congruent to a given segment, and an angle that is congruent to a given angle.

Standards

16.0 Students perform basic constructions with a straightedge and compass, such as angle bisectors, perpendicular bisectors, and the line parallel to a given line through a point off the line.

EXPLORE 1 **Copy a segment**

Use the following steps to construct a segment that is congruent to $\overline{AB}$.

STEP 1

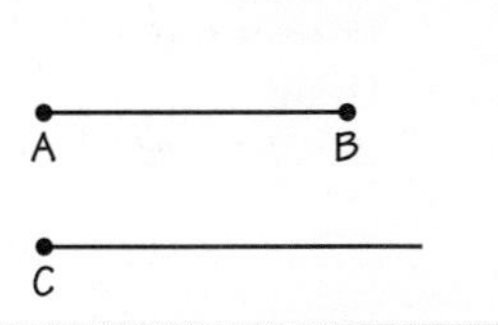

Draw a segment Use a straightedge to draw a segment longer than $\overline{AB}$. Label point C on the new segment.

STEP 2

Measure length Set your compass at the length of $\overline{AB}$.

STEP 3

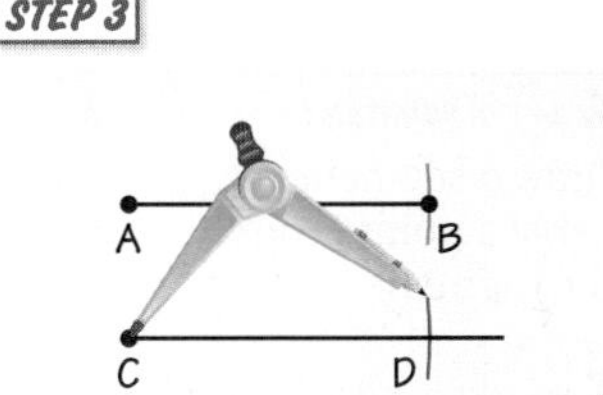

Copy length Place the compass at C. Mark point D on the new segment. $\overline{CD} \cong \overline{AB}$.

EXPLORE 2 **Bisect a segment**

Use the following steps to construct a bisector of $\overline{AB}$ and to find the midpoint M of $\overline{AB}$.

STEP 1

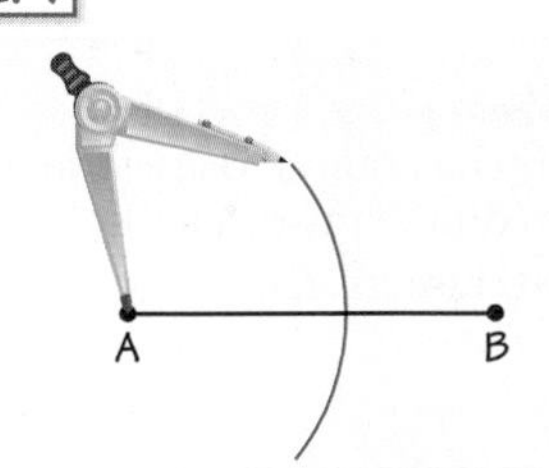

Draw an arc Place the compass at A. Use a compass setting that is greater than half the length of $\overline{AB}$. Draw an arc.

STEP 2

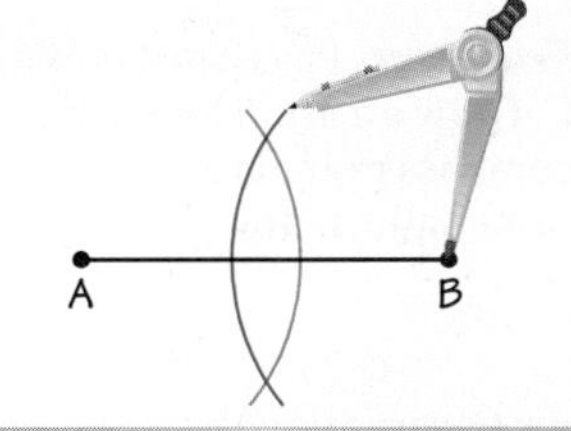

Draw a second arc Keep the same compass setting. Place the compass at B. Draw an arc. It should intersect the other arc at two points.

STEP 3

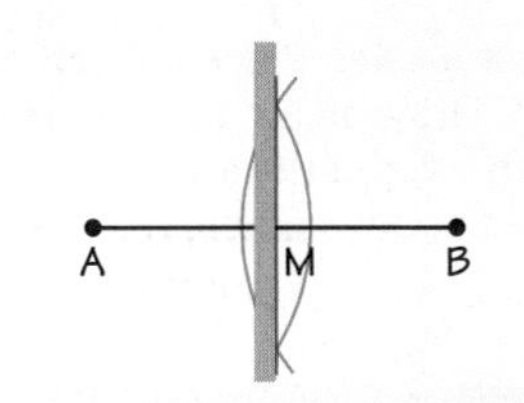

Bisect segment Draw a segment through the two points of intersection. This segment bisects $\overline{AB}$ at M, the midpoint of $\overline{AB}$.

1 PLAN AND PREPARE

Explore the Concept

- Students will copy and bisect a segment and an angle.
- This activity supplements the study of congruent segments and angles, and segment and angle bisectors in Lessons 1.3 and 1.4.

Materials

Each student will need:

- compass
- straightedge

Recommended Time

Work activity: 15 min

Discuss results: 5 min

Grouping

Students should work individually.

2 TEACH

Tips for Success

In Explore 2, point out to students that it is important not to change the compass setting after they draw the first arc.

In Explore 4, students should note that the figure for Step 2 used a different compass setting from that used in Step 1. The same compass setting for all three arcs will also work.

Alternative Strategy

Demonstrate these constructions on the chalkboard or with a figure on the overhead projector.

Key Discovery

There are infinitely many bisectors of a segment but the one that is constructed in this activity is perpendicular to the segment. There is only one bisector of an angle.

3 ASSESS AND RETEACH

1. How many compass settings would you need to construct a segment that is three times as long as a given segment? **one**
2. When you construct an angle bisector, are there any restrictions on the radius of the two small arcs you draw in Step 2? Explain. **Yes, the radius should be noticeably greater than half the length of $\overline{CB}$. Otherwise, you cannot see clearly where the arcs intersect. The arcs will not even intersect if the radius is less than half of CB.**

2. Step 1

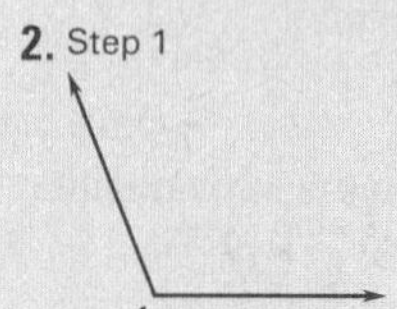

Step 2

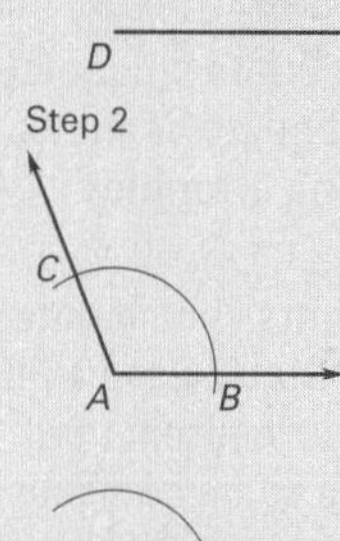

Step 3

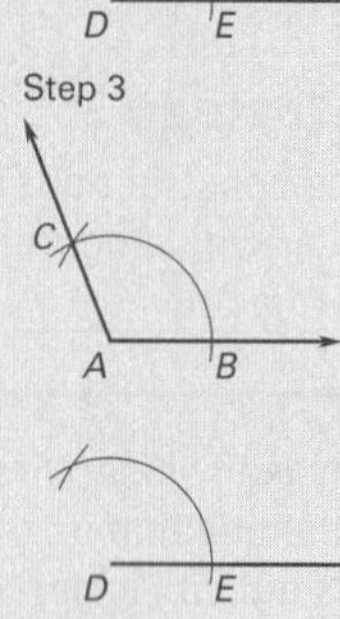

Step 4

F
D E

EXPLORE 3 Copy an angle

Use the following steps to construct an angle that is congruent to $\angle A$. In this construction, the *radius* of an arc is the distance from the point where the compass point rests (the *center* of the arc) to a point on the arc drawn by the compass.

STEP 1

A
D

Draw a segment Draw a segment. Label a point D on the segment.

STEP 2

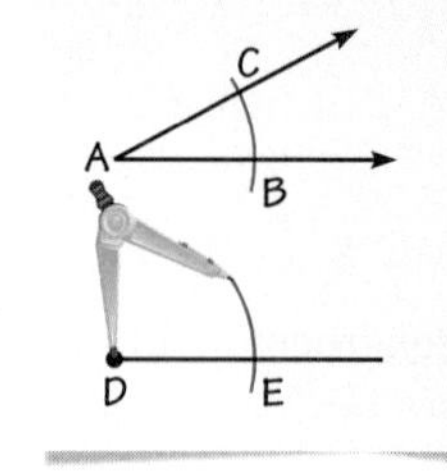

Draw arcs Draw an arc with center A. Using the same radius, draw an arc with center D.

STEP 3

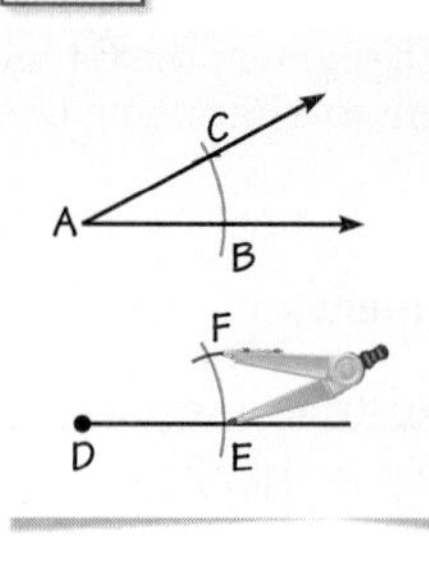

Draw arcs Label B, C, and E. Draw an arc with radius BC and center E. Label the intersection F.

STEP 4

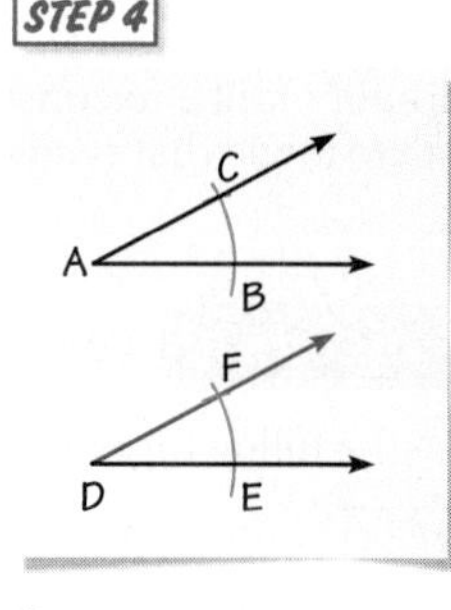

Draw a ray Draw $\overrightarrow{DF}$. $\angle EDF \cong \angle BAC$.

EXPLORE 4 Bisect an angle

Use the following steps to construct an angle bisector of $\angle A$.

STEP 1

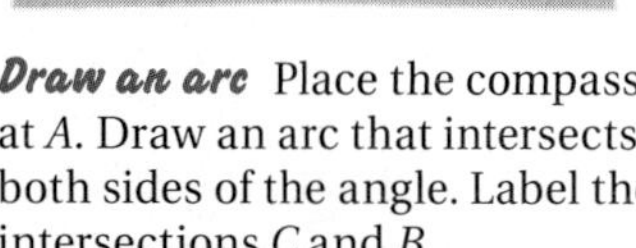

Draw an arc Place the compass at A. Draw an arc that intersects both sides of the angle. Label the intersections C and B.

STEP 2

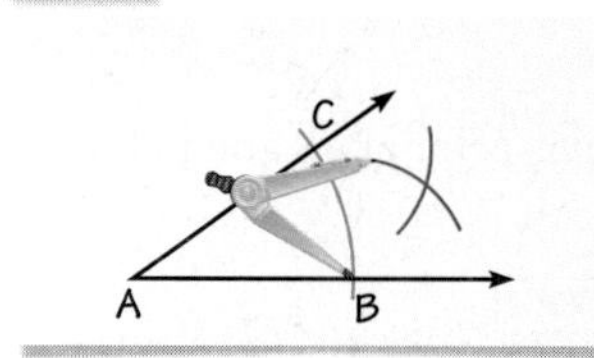

Draw arcs Place the compass at C. Draw an arc. Then place the compass point at B. Using the same radius, draw another arc.

STEP 3

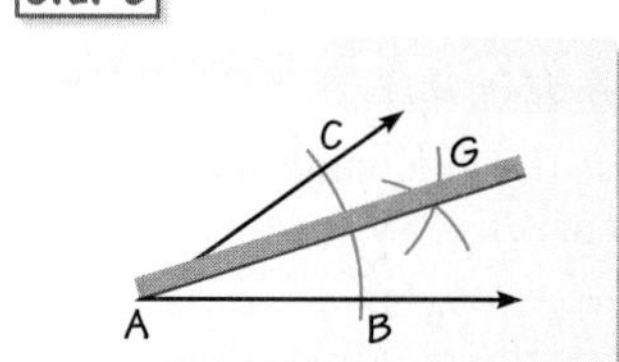

Draw a ray Label the intersection G. Use a straightedge to draw a ray through A and G. $\overrightarrow{AG}$ bisects $\angle A$.

DRAW CONCLUSIONS Use your observations to complete these exercises

1. *Describe* how you could use a compass and a straightedge to draw a segment that is twice as long as a given segment.
   Sample answer: **Copy the shorter line segment twice end-to-end.**
2. Draw an obtuse angle. Copy the angle using a compass and a straightedge. Then bisect the angle using a compass and straightedge. **See margin.**

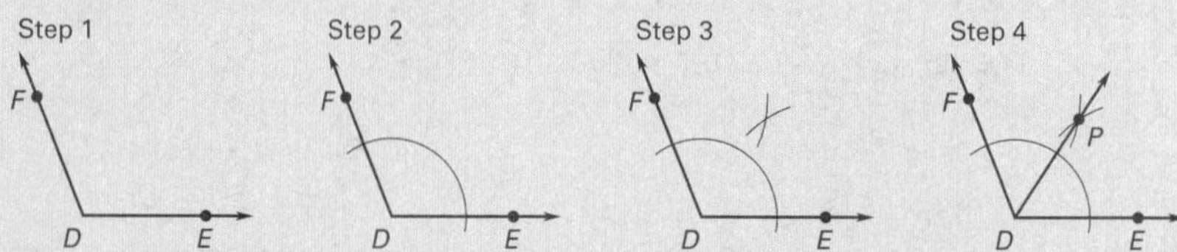

1.5 Describe Angle Pair Relationships

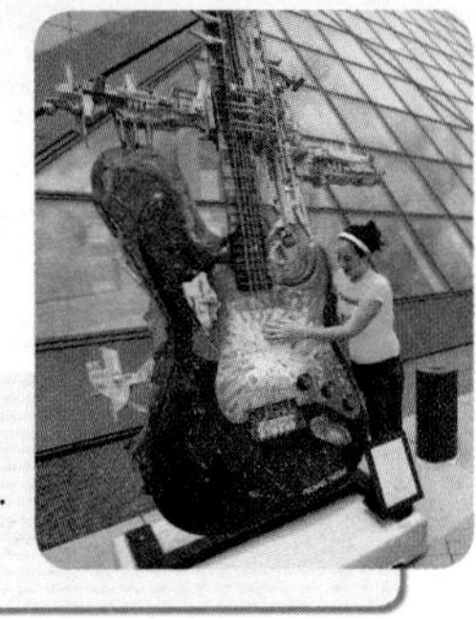

Before You used angle postulates to measure and classify angles.
Now You will use special angle relationships to find angle measures.
Why? So you can find measures in a building, as in Ex. 53.

Key Vocabulary
- **complementary angles**
- **supplementary angles**
- **adjacent angles**
- **linear pair**
- **vertical angles**

Standards

Prepare for 13.0 Students prove relationships between angles in polygons by *using properties of complementary, supplementary,* vertical, and exterior *angles.*

Two angles are **complementary angles** if the sum of their measures is 90°. Each angle is the *complement* of the other. Two angles are **supplementary angles** if the sum of their measures is 180°. Each angle is the *supplement* of the other.

Complementary angles and supplementary angles can be *adjacent angles* or *nonadjacent angles.* **Adjacent angles** are two angles that share a common vertex and side, but have no common interior points.

Complementary angles

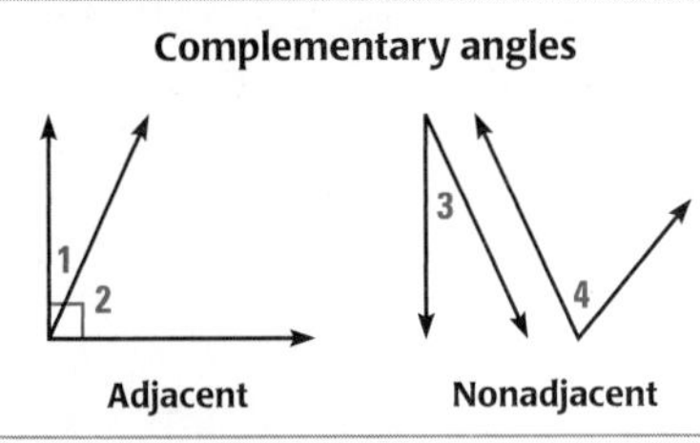

Supplementary angles

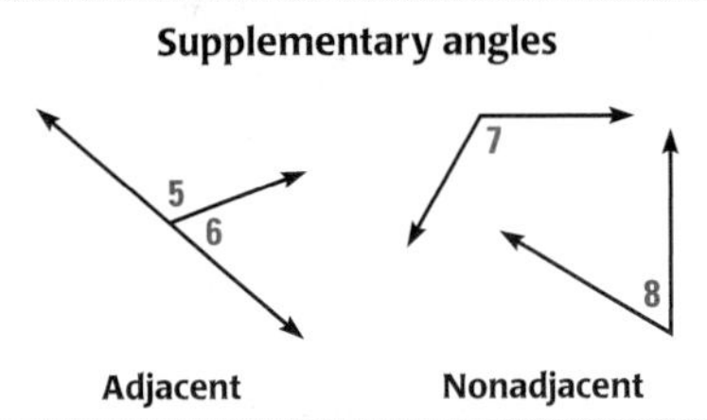

EXAMPLE 1 Identify complements and supplements

AVOID ERRORS

In Example 1, $\angle DAC$ and $\angle DAB$ share a common vertex. But they share common interior points, so they are *not* adjacent angles.

In the figure, name a pair of complementary angles, a pair of supplementary angles, and a pair of adjacent angles.

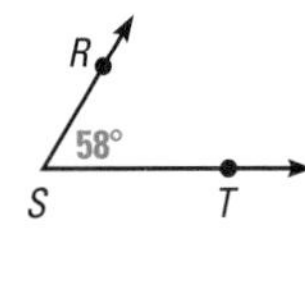

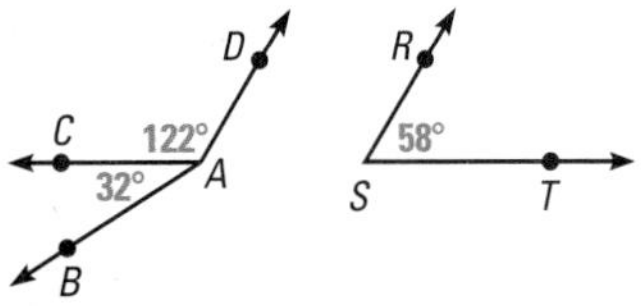

Solution

Because $32° + 58° = 90°$, $\angle BAC$ and $\angle RST$ are complementary angles.

Because $122° + 58° = 180°$, $\angle CAD$ and $\angle RST$ are supplementary angles.

Because $\angle BAC$ and $\angle CAD$ share a common vertex and side, they are adjacent.

GUIDED PRACTICE for Example 1

1. In the figure, name a pair of complementary angles, a pair of supplementary angles, and a pair of adjacent angles. **$\angle FGK$ and $\angle GKL$, $\angle HGK$ and $\angle GKL$, $\angle FGK$ and $\angle HGK$**
2. Are $\angle KGH$ and $\angle LKG$ adjacent angles? Are $\angle FGK$ and $\angle FGH$ adjacent angles? *Explain.*

2. No, they do not share a common vertex; no, they have common interior points.

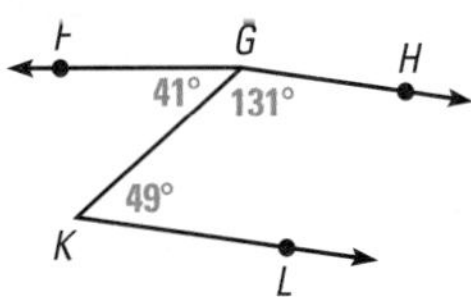

1 PLAN AND PREPARE

Warm-Up Exercises

Transparency Available

1. The sum of two numbers is 90 and one number is 4 times the other. Write an equation and solve to find the numbers. **$x + 4x = 90$; 18, 72**
2. Find $m\angle ABD$. What kind of angle is it? **180°, straight**

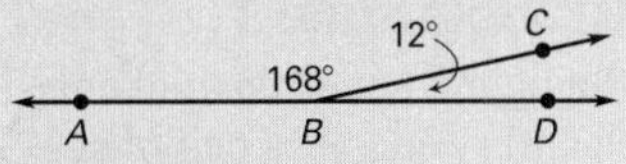

(Figure: A, B, D on a line; ray BC; 168°, 12°)

Notetaking Guide

Transparency Available

Promotes interactive learning and notetaking skills, pp. 16–20.

Pacing

Basic: 1 day
Average: 1 day
Advanced: 1 day
Block: 0.5 block with 1.6
- See *Teaching Guide/Lesson Plan.*

2 FOCUS AND MOTIVATE

Essential Question

Big Idea 2, p. 1

How do you identify complementary and supplementary angles? **Tell students they will learn how to answer this question by finding the sum of the measures of two given angles.**

Resource Planning Guide

Chapter Resource Book
- Teaching Guide/Lesson Plan (pp. 61–62)
- Practice levels A, B, C (pp. 63–68)
- Study Guide (pp. 69–70)
- Catch-up for Absent Students (p. 71)
- Application (p. 72)
- Challenge (p. 73)

Workbooks
- Notetaking Guide (pp. 16–20)
- Practice Workbook (pp. 13–15)

Teaching Options
- **Power Presentations CD-ROM** provides dynamic electronic teaching resources for the classroom.
- **Activity Generator CD-ROM** provides editable activities for all ability levels.

Interactive Technology
- Easy Planner
- Power Presentations CD-ROM
- Activity Generator CD-ROM
- Animated Geometry
- Test Generator CD-ROM
- Online Quiz
- eWorkbook
- eEdition
- @HomeTutor

Resources for English Learners
- Quick Reference for English Learners
- Spanish Study Guide
- Multi-Language Visual Glossary
- Student Resources in Spanish

See also the *Geometry Toolkit* for more strategies for meeting individual needs.

Motivating the Lesson

Parts for furniture that you assemble yourself often include parts that must fit together to form right angles or straight edges. Tell students that in this lesson they will learn terms that are useful in understanding how the angles for such parts are related.

3 TEACH

Extra Example 1

In the figure, name a pair of complementary angles, a pair of supplementary angles, and a pair of adjacent angles.

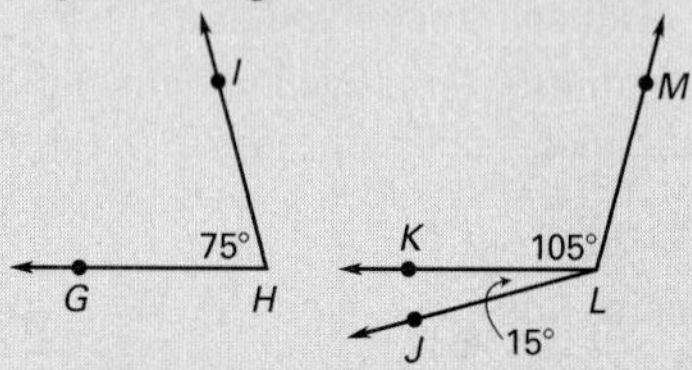

$\angle GHI$, $\angle JLK$; $\angle GHI$, $\angle KLM$; $\angle JLK$, $\angle KLM$

Extra Example 2

a. Given that $\angle 1$ is a complement of $\angle 2$ and $m\angle 1 = 17°$, find $m\angle 2$. **73°**

b. Given that $\angle 3$ is a supplement of $\angle 4$ and $m\angle 3 = 119°$, find $m\angle 4$. **61°**

Extra Example 3

Two roads intersect to form supplementary angles, $\angle XYW$ and $\angle WYZ$. Find $m\angle XYW$ and $m\angle WYZ$. **76°, 104°**

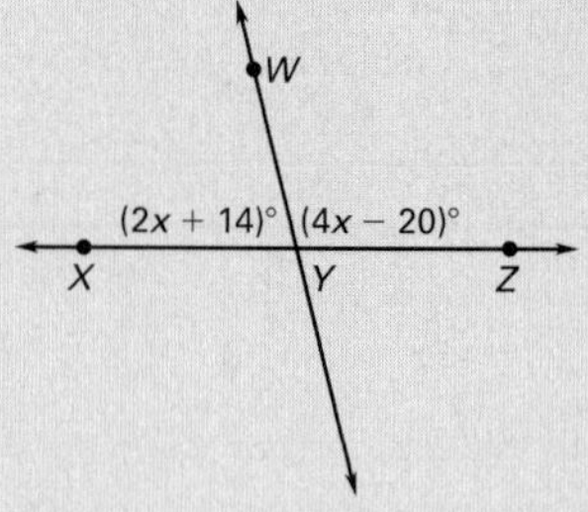

EXAMPLE 2 Find measures of a complement and a supplement

READ DIAGRAMS
Angles are sometimes named with numbers. An angle measure in a diagram has a degree symbol. An angle name does not.

a. Given that $\angle 1$ is a complement of $\angle 2$ and $m\angle 1 = 68°$, find $m\angle 2$.

b. Given that $\angle 3$ is a supplement of $\angle 4$ and $m\angle 4 = 56°$, find $m\angle 3$.

Solution

a. You can draw a diagram with complementary adjacent angles to illustrate the relationship.

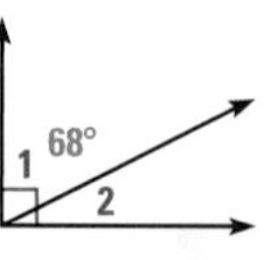

$m\angle 2 = 90° - m\angle 1 = 90° - 68° = 22°$

b. You can draw a diagram with supplementary adjacent angles to illustrate the relationship.

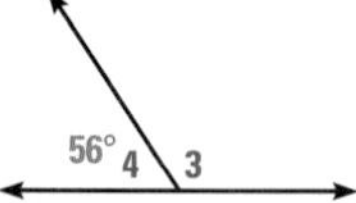

$m\angle 3 = 180° - m\angle 4 = 180° - 56° = 124°$

EXAMPLE 3 Find angle measures

READ DIAGRAMS
In a diagram, you can assume that a line that looks straight *is* straight. In Example 3, *B*, *C*, and *D* lie on $\overleftrightarrow{BD}$. So, $\angle BCD$ is a straight angle.

SPORTS When viewed from the side, the frame of a ball-return net forms a pair of supplementary angles with the ground. Find $m\angle BCE$ and $m\angle ECD$.

Solution

STEP 1 **Use** the fact that the sum of the measures of supplementary angles is 180°.

$m\angle BCE + m\angle ECD = 180°$	**Write equation.**
$(4x + 8)° + (x + 2)° = 180°$	**Substitute.**
$5x + 10 = 180$	**Combine like terms.**
$5x = 170$	**Subtract 10 from each side.**
$x = 34$	**Divide each side by 5.**

STEP 2 **Evaluate** the original expressions when $x = 34$.

$m\angle BCE = (4x + 8)° = (4 \cdot 34 + 8)° = 144°$

$m\angle ECD = (x + 2)° = (34 + 2)° = 36°$

▶ The angle measures are 144° and 36°.

GUIDED PRACTICE for Examples 2 and 3

3. Given that $\angle 1$ is a complement of $\angle 2$ and $m\angle 2 = 8°$, find $m\angle 1$. **82°**

4. Given that $\angle 3$ is a supplement of $\angle 4$ and $m\angle 3 = 117°$, find $m\angle 4$. **63°**

5. $\angle LMN$ and $\angle PQR$ are complementary angles. Find the measures of the angles if $m\angle LMN = (4x - 2)°$ and $m\angle PQR = (9x + 1)°$. **26°, 64°**

Differentiated Instruction

Inclusion Students may confuse the definitions of *complementary angles* and *supplementary angles*. One memory device is to notice that both of the sets {complementary, supplementary} and {90°, 180°} are in alphabetical order and ascending order, respectively.

See also the *Geometry Toolkit* for more strategies.

ANGLE PAIRS Two adjacent angles are a **linear pair** if their noncommon sides are opposite rays. The angles in a linear pair are supplementary angles.

Two angles are **vertical angles** if their sides form two pairs of opposite rays.

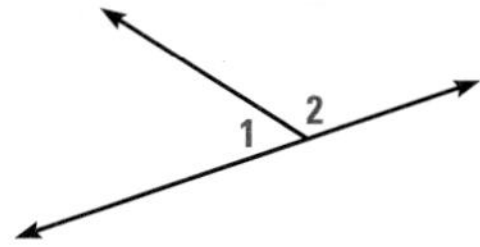

$\angle 1$ and $\angle 2$ are a linear pair.

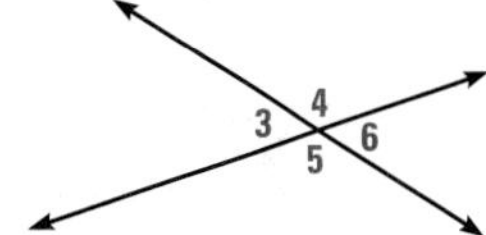

$\angle 3$ and $\angle 6$ are vertical angles.
$\angle 4$ and $\angle 5$ are vertical angles.

EXAMPLE 4 Identify angle pairs

AVOID ERRORS
In the diagram, one side of $\angle 1$ and one side of $\angle 3$ are opposite rays. But the angles are not a linear pair because they are not adjacent.

Identify all of the linear pairs and all of the vertical angles in the figure at the right.

Solution

To find vertical angles, look for angles formed by intersecting lines.

▶ $\angle 1$ and $\angle 5$ are vertical angles.

To find linear pairs, look for adjacent angles whose noncommon sides are opposite rays.

▶ $\angle 1$ and $\angle 4$ are a linear pair. $\angle 4$ and $\angle 5$ are also a linear pair.

EXAMPLE 5 Find angle measures in a linear pair

DRAW DIAGRAMS
You may find it useful to draw a diagram to represent a word problem like the one in Example 5.

ALGEBRA **Two angles form a linear pair. The measure of one angle is 5 times the measure of the other. Find the measure of each angle.**

Solution

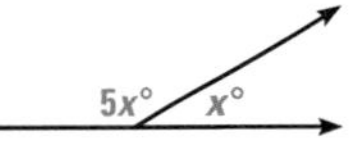

Let $x°$ be the measure of one angle. The measure of the other angle is $5x°$. Then use the fact that the angles of a linear pair are supplementary to write an equation.

$x° + 5x° = 180°$ Write an equation.

$6x = 180$ Combine like terms.

$x = 30$ Divide each side by 6.

▶ The measures of the angles are 30° and $5(30°) = 150°$.

GUIDED PRACTICE for Examples 4 and 5

6. Do any of the numbered angles in the diagram at the right form a linear pair? Which angles are vertical angles? *Explain.*

7. The measure of an angle is twice the measure of its complement. Find the measure of each angle. **60°, 30°**

6. No, no adjacent angles have their noncommon sides as opposite rays; $\angle 1$ and $\angle 4$, $\angle 2$ and $\angle 5$, $\angle 3$ and $\angle 6$, these pairs of angles have sides that form two pairs of opposite rays.

Extra Example 4

Identify all of the linear pairs and all of the vertical angles in the figure.

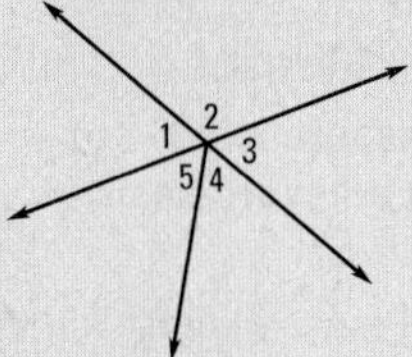

$\angle 2$ and $\angle 3$, $\angle 1$ and $\angle 2$; $\angle 1$ and $\angle 3$

Key Question to Ask for Example 4

- The noncommon sides of $\angle 2$ and $\angle 3$ form an angle. What kind of angle pair will this angle form with $\angle 4$? **vertical**

Extra Example 5

Two angles form a linear pair. The measure of one angle is 3 times the measure of the other angle. Find the measure of each angle. **45°, 135°**

Key Question to Ask for Example 5

- How would your equation change if one angle was 5° more than the other? **It would be $x° + (x + 5)° = 180°$.**

Closing the Lesson

Have students summarize the major points of the lesson and answer the Essential Question: How do you identify complementary and supplementary angles?

- **Complementary angles have a sum of 90°.**
- **Supplementary angles have a sum of 180°.**
- **Adjacent angles share a vertex but no common interior points, while a linear pair are adjacent angles whose noncommon sides are opposite rays.**
- **Vertical angles are angles whose sides form two pairs of opposite rays.**

Add the measures of the angles. If the sum is 90°, the angles are complementary. If the sum is 180°, the angles are supplementary.

4 PRACTICE AND APPLY

Assignment Guide

Answer Transparencies available for all exercises

Basic:
Day 1: pp. 38–41
Exs. 1–7, 9–15 odd, 16, 17–27 odd, 28–35, 46–54, 57, 61

Average:
Day 1: pp. 38–41
Exs. 1, 2, 4–7, 8–28 even, 29, 30–44 even, 46–55, 59, 62

Advanced:
Day 1: pp. 38–41
Exs. 1, 2, 5, 7, 11, 15, 16, 19, 25–30, 33–45* odd, 48–56*, 60, 63

Block:
pp. 38–41
Exs. 1, 2, 4–7, 8–28 even, 29, 30–44 even, 46–55, 59, 62 (with 1.6)

Differentiated Instruction

See *Geometry Best Practices Toolkit* for suggestions on addressing the needs of a diverse classroom.

Homework Check

For a quick check of student understanding of key concepts, go over the following exercises:

Basic: 4, 9, 17, 23, 46
Average: 6, 12, 18, 24, 50
Advanced: 7, 15, 19, 28, 53

Extra Practice

- Student Edition, p. 897
- Chapter 1 Resource Book: Practice levels A, B, C, pp. 63–68

Practice Worksheet

An easily-readable reduced practice page (with answers) for this lesson can be found on p. 1E.

CONCEPT SUMMARY *For Your Notebook*

Interpreting a Diagram

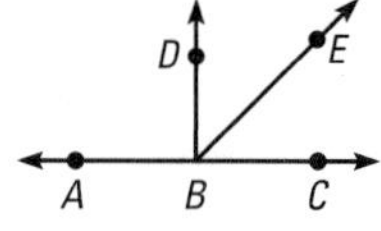

There are some things you can conclude from a diagram, and some you cannot. For example, here are some things that you ***can* conclude** from the diagram at the right:

- All points shown are coplanar.
- Points *A*, *B*, and *C* are collinear, and *B* is between *A* and *C*.
- $\overleftrightarrow{AC}$, $\overrightarrow{BD}$, and $\overrightarrow{BE}$ intersect at point *B*.
- $\angle DBE$ and $\angle EBC$ are adjacent angles, and $\angle ABC$ is a straight angle.
- Point *E* lies in the interior of $\angle DBC$.

In the diagram above, you ***cannot* conclude** that $\overline{AB} \cong \overline{BC}$, that $\angle DBE \cong \angle EBC$, or that $\angle ABD$ is a right angle. This information must be indicated, as shown at the right.

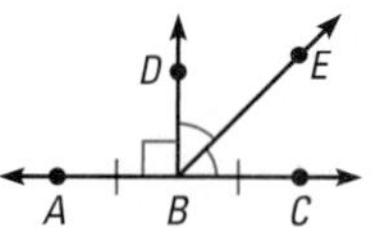

1.5 EXERCISES

HOMEWORK KEY

○ = **WORKED-OUT SOLUTIONS** on p. WS1 for Exs. 9, 21, and 47

★ = **STANDARDIZED TEST PRACTICE** Exs. 2, 16, 30, and 53

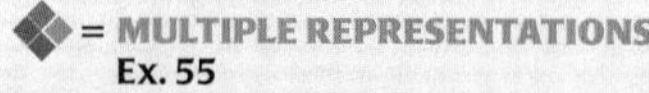

◆ = **MULTIPLE REPRESENTATIONS** Ex. 55

SKILL PRACTICE

A

1. **VOCABULARY** Sketch an example of adjacent angles that are complementary. Are all complementary angles adjacent angles? *Explain.* **See margin.**

2. ★ **WRITING** Are all linear pairs supplementary angles? Are all supplementary angles linear pairs? *Explain.* **See margin.**

EXAMPLE 1 on p. 35 for Exs. 3–7

IDENTIFYING ANGLES Tell whether the indicated angles are adjacent.

3. $\angle ABD$ and $\angle DBC$ **adjacent**

4. $\angle WXY$ and $\angle XYZ$ **not adjacent**

5. $\angle LQM$ and $\angle NQM$ **adjacent**

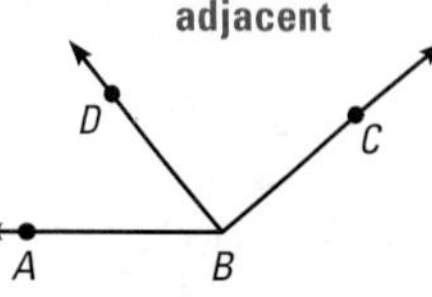

IDENTIFYING ANGLES Name a pair of complementary angles and a pair of supplementary angles.

6. **6. $\angle RTS$ and $\angle UWV$, $\angle QTS$ and $\angle UWV$**

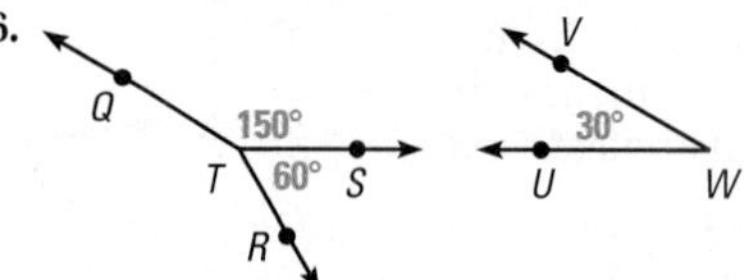

7. **$\angle GLH$ and $\angle HLJ$, $\angle GLJ$ and $\angle JLK$**

1.

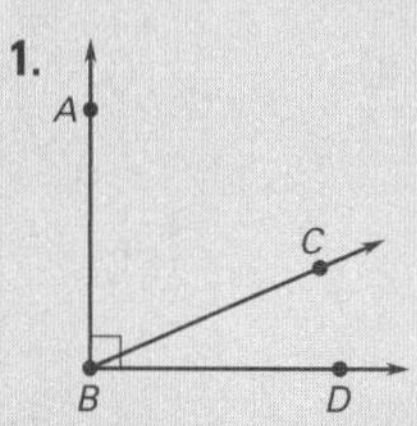

No. *Sample answer:* Any two angles whose angle measures add up to 90° are complementary, but they do not have to have a common vertex and side.

2. Yes; no. *Sample answer:* To be a linear pair, the noncommon sides of two adjacent angles must be opposite rays, which make a straight angle; supplementary angles need not be linear pairs because they can be nonadjacent.

EXAMPLE 2
on p. 36
for Exs. 8–16

COMPLEMENTARY ANGLES **$\angle 1$ and $\angle 2$ are complementary angles. Given the measure of $\angle 1$, find $m\angle 2$.**

8. $m\angle 1 = 43°$ **47°**
9. $m\angle 1 = 21°$ **69°**
10. $m\angle 1 = 89°$ **1°**
11. $m\angle 1 = 5°$ **85°**

SUPPLEMENTARY ANGLES **$\angle 1$ and $\angle 2$ are supplementary angles. Given the measure of $\angle 1$, find $m\angle 2$.**

12. $m\angle 1 = 60°$ **120°**
13. $m\angle 1 = 155°$ **25°**
14. $m\angle 1 = 130°$ **50°**
15. $m\angle 1 = 27°$ **153°**

16. ★ **MULTIPLE CHOICE** The arm of a crossing gate moves 37° from vertical. How many more degrees does the arm have to move so that it is horizontal? **B**

Ⓐ 37°
Ⓑ 53°
Ⓒ 90°
Ⓓ 143°

EXAMPLE 3
on p. 36
for Exs. 17–19

 **ALGEBRA** **Find $m\angle DEG$ and $m\angle GEF$.**

17. **135°, 45°**

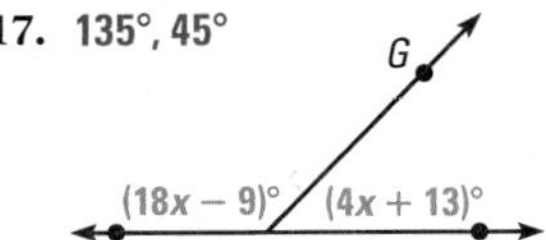

18. **67°, 113°**

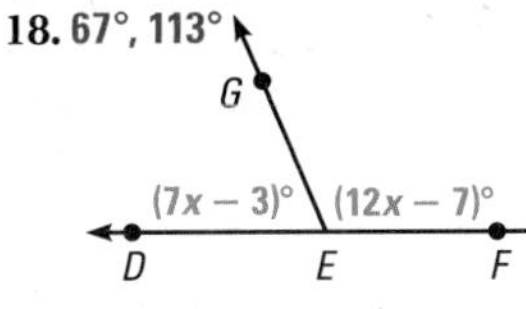

19. **54°, 36°**

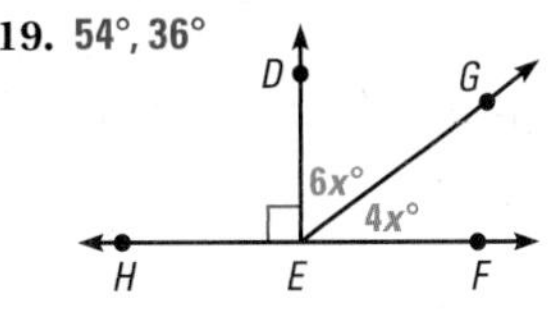

EXAMPLE 4
on p. 37
for Exs. 20–27

IDENTIFYING ANGLE PAIRS **Use the diagram below. Tell whether the angles are *vertical angles*, a *linear pair*, or *neither*.**

20. $\angle 1$ and $\angle 4$ **vertical angles**
21. $\angle 1$ and $\angle 2$ **linear pair**
22. $\angle 3$ and $\angle 5$ **neither**
23. $\angle 2$ and $\angle 3$ **vertical angles**
24. $\angle 7$, $\angle 8$, and $\angle 9$ **neither**
25. $\angle 5$ and $\angle 6$ **linear pair**
26. $\angle 6$ and $\angle 7$ **neither**
27. $\angle 5$ and $\angle 9$ **neither**

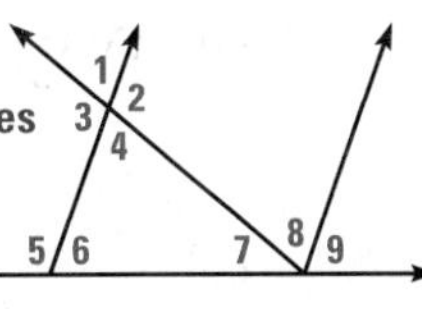

EXAMPLE 5
on p. 37
for Exs. 28–30

28.  **ALGEBRA** Two angles form a linear pair. The measure of one angle is 4 times the measure of the other angle. Find the measure of each angle. **36° and 144°**

29. **ERROR ANALYSIS** *Describe* and correct the error made in finding the value of x. **The angles are complementary so they should be equal to 90°; $x + 3x = 90°$, $4x = 90$, $x = 22.5$.**

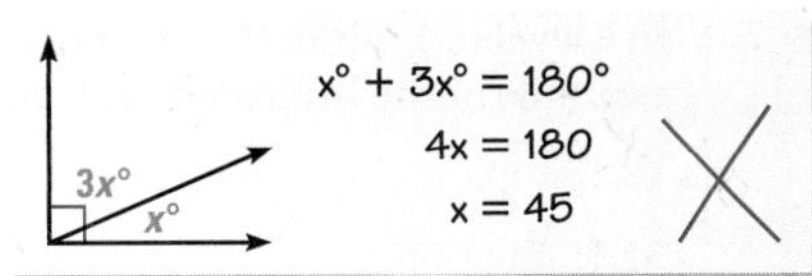

30. ★ **MULTIPLE CHOICE** The measure of one angle is 24° greater than the measure of its complement. What are the measures of the angles? **C**

Ⓐ 24° and 66°
Ⓑ 24° and 156°
Ⓒ 33° and 57°
Ⓓ 78° and 102°

B **ALGEBRA** **Find the values of x and y.**

31. **10, 35**

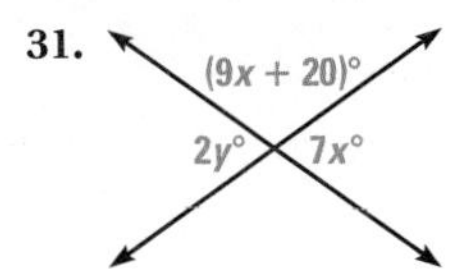

32. **14, 20**

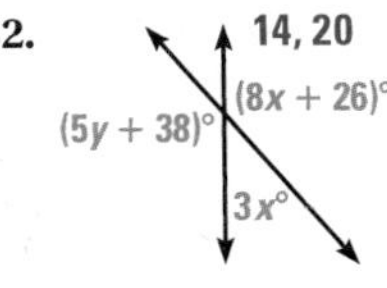

33. **55, 30**

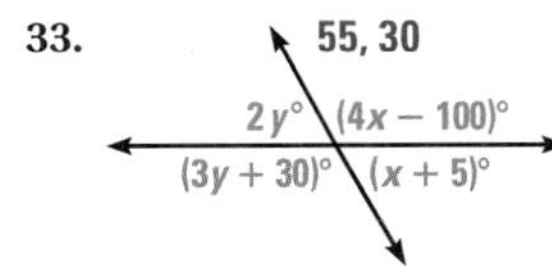

Teaching Strategy

Exercises 8–15 To help students remember that measures of complementary angles add up to 90° and those of supplementary angles add up to 180°, observe that C comes before S in the alphabet and 90 is smaller than 180.

Avoiding Common Errors

Exercises 24 Some students may say that these angles form a linear pair. Point out that here we have three angles, not a pair of angles.

Study Strategy

Exercise 30 Check each choice to see if one angle measure is 24° greater than the other and whether the measures add up to 90°. Have students explain why choices B and D can be eliminated without any arithmetic.

Mathematical Reasoning

Exercises 35 and 36 Have students compare the wording in these two exercises. Have them describe in their own words how the answer to one of these exercises implies the answer to the other.

Exercises 46–48 Ask students to explain how they arrived at their answers. Some students may say that they simply looked at the clocks to decide. Ask how they would respond if someone challenged one of their answers.

Exercises 49–52 More information about the Rock and Roll Hall of Fame can be found at www.rockhall.com/museum

34. Never; an obtuse angle is larger than 90°, and it is not possible to have a complement of an angle that is greater than 90°.

35. Never; a straight angle is 180°, and it is not possible to have a complement of an angle that is 180°.

36. Sometimes; a straight angle does not have a supplement.

37. Always; the sum of complementary angles is 90°, so each angle must be less than 90°, making them acute.

38. Always; an acute angle is less than 90°, since the sum of supplementary angles is 180° and one of the angles is less than 90°, the other angle must be larger than 90°, which makes it obtuse.

45. $(x + 90)°$. *Sample answer:* Since $m\angle GHJ = x°$ and $\angle RST$ is its complement, $m\angle RST = (90 - x)°$. $\angle ABC$ is a supplement of $\angle RST$ so $m\angle ABC = 180° - (90 - x)°$, $m\angle ABC = (x + 90)°$.

REASONING **Tell whether the statement is *always, sometimes,* or *never* true. *Explain* your reasoning.** **34–38. See margin.**

34. An obtuse angle has a complement.

35. A straight angle has a complement.

36. An angle has a supplement.

37. The complement of an acute angle is an acute angle.

38. The supplement of an acute angle is an obtuse angle.

FINDING ANGLES **$\angle A$ and $\angle B$ are complementary. Find $m\angle A$ and $m\angle B$.**

39. $m\angle A = (3x + 2)°$, $m\angle B = (x - 4)°$ **71°, 19°**

40. $m\angle A = (15x + 3)°$, $m\angle B = (5x - 13)°$ **78°, 12°**

41. $m\angle A = (11x + 24)°$, $m\angle B = (x + 18)°$ **68°, 22°**

FINDING ANGLES **$\angle A$ and $\angle B$ are supplementary. Find $m\angle A$ and $m\angle B$.**

42. $m\angle A = (8x + 100)°$, $m\angle B = (2x + 50)°$ **124°, 56°**

43. $m\angle A = (2x - 20)°$, $m\angle B = (3x + 5)°$ **58°, 122°**

44. $m\angle A = (6x + 72)°$, $m\angle B = (2x + 28)°$ **132°, 48°**

C **45. CHALLENGE** You are given that $\angle GHJ$ is a complement of $\angle RST$ and $\angle RST$ is a supplement of $\angle ABC$. Let $m\angle GHJ$ be $x°$. What is the measure of $\angle ABC$? *Explain* your reasoning. **See margin.**

PROBLEM SOLVING

A **IDENTIFYING ANGLES** **Tell whether the two angles shown are *complementary, supplementary,* or *neither.***

46. **complementary**

47. **neither**

48. **supplementary**

@HomeTutor for problem solving help at classzone.com

49–52. Sample answers are given.

49. $\angle FGB$, $\angle BGC$

50. $\angle FGE$, $\angle BGC$

51. $\angle AGE$, $\angle EGD$

52. $\angle AGB$, $\angle BGC$

ARCHITECTURE **The photograph shows the Rock and Roll Hall of Fame in Cleveland, Ohio. Use the photograph to identify an example of the indicated type of angle pair.**

49. Supplementary angles

50. Vertical angles

51. Linear pair

52. Adjacent angles

@HomeTutor for problem solving help at classzone.com

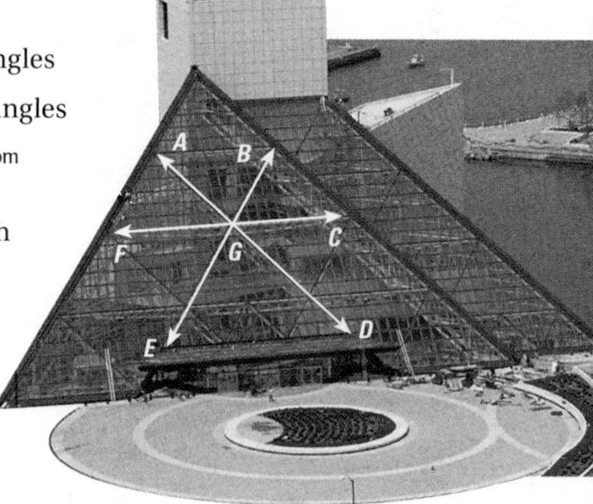

53. ★ **SHORT RESPONSE** Use the photograph shown at the right. Given that $\angle FGB$ and $\angle BGC$ are supplementary angles, and $m\angle FGB = 120°$, *explain* how to find the measure of the complement of $\angle BGC$. ***Sample answer:* Subtract 90° from $m\angle FGB$.**

○ = WORKED-OUT SOLUTIONS on p. WS1 ★ = STANDARDIZED TEST PRACTICE

55b.

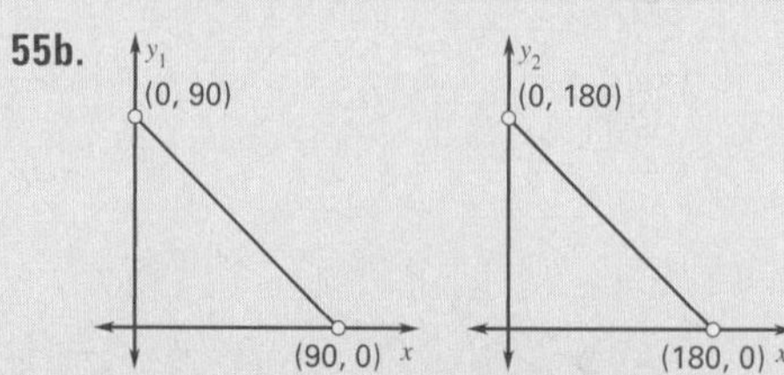

54. The shadow gets shorter and the angle measure increases.

B

54. **SHADOWS** The length of a shadow changes as the sun rises. In the diagram below, the length of $\overline{CB}$ is the length of a shadow. The end of the shadow is the vertex of $\angle ABC$, which is formed by the ground and the sun's rays. *Describe* how the shadow and angle change as the sun rises.

55a. $y_1 = 90 - x$, $0 < x < 90$; $y_2 = 180 - x$, $0 < x < 180$; the measure of a complement must be less than 90° and the measure of its supplement must be less than 180°.

55. ◆ **MULTIPLE REPRESENTATIONS** Let $x°$ be an angle measure. Let $y_1°$ be the measure of a complement of the angle and let $y_2°$ be the measure of a supplement of the angle.

a. **Writing an Equation** Write equations for y_1 as a function of x, and for y_2 as a function of x. What is the domain of each function? *Explain.*

b. **Drawing a Graph** Graph each function and *describe* its range.
See margin for art; $0 < y_1 < 90$, $0 < y_2 < 180$.

C

56. **CHALLENGE** The sum of the measures of two complementary angles exceeds the difference of their measures by 86°. Find the measure of each angle. *Explain* how you found the angle measures.
47°, 43°. *Sample answer:* Solve the system: $x + y = 90$, $x + y - 86 = x - y$.

MIXED REVIEW

Make a table of values and graph the function. *(p. 884)* **57–60. See margin.**

57. $y = 5 - x$ 58. $y = 3x$ 59. $y = x^2 - 1$ 60. $y = -2x^2$

PREVIEW
Prepare for Lesson 1.6 in Exs. 61–63.

In each figure, name the congruent sides and congruent angles. *(pp. 9, 24)*

61.

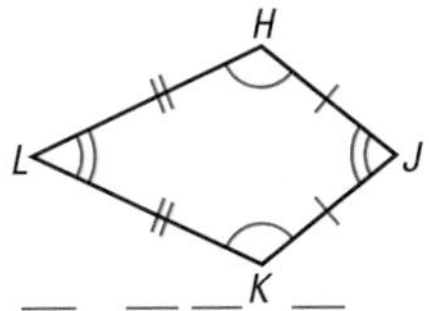

$\overline{HJ} \cong \overline{JK}$, $\overline{KL} \cong \overline{LH}$; $\angle J \cong \angle L$, $\angle K \cong \angle H$

62.

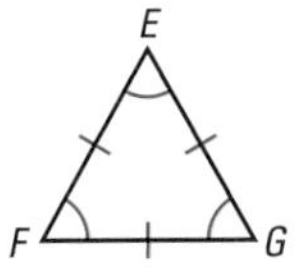

$\overline{EG} \cong \overline{GF} \cong \overline{FE}$; $\angle E \cong \angle G \cong \angle F$

63.

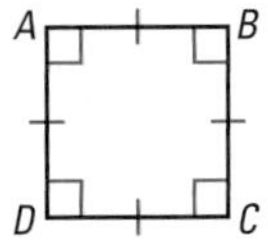

$\overline{AB} \cong \overline{BC} \cong \overline{CD} \cong \overline{DA}$; $\angle A \cong \angle B \cong \angle C \cong \angle D$

QUIZ for Lessons 1.4–1.5

In each diagram, $\overrightarrow{BD}$ bisects $\angle ABC$. Find $m\angle ABD$ and $m\angle DBC$. *(p. 24)*

1.

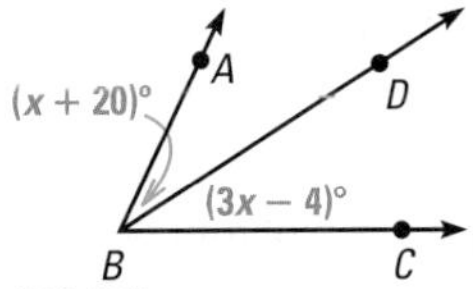

32°, 32°

2.

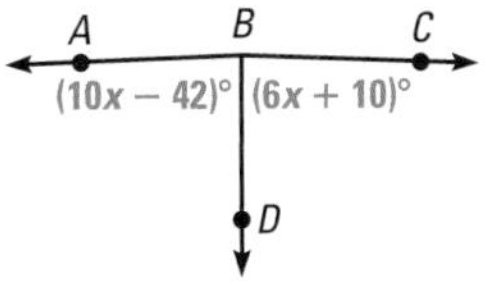

88°, 88°

3.

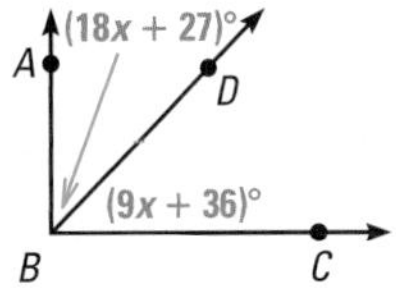

45°, 45°

Find the measure of (a) the complement and (b) the supplement of $\angle 1$. *(p. 35)* **4–7. See margin.**

4. $m\angle 1 = 47°$ 5. $m\angle 1 = 19°$ 6. $m\angle 1 = 75°$ 7. $m\angle 1 = 2°$

4a. 43°
4b. 133°
5a. 71°
5b. 161°
6a. 15°
6b. 105°
7a. 88°
7b. 178°

57–60. See Additional Answers beginning on p. AA1.

5 ASSESS AND RETEACH

Daily Homework Quiz

Transparency Available

1. $\angle 1$ and $\angle 2$ are supplementary. If $m\angle 1 = 97°$, find $m\angle 2$. **83°**
2. $\angle 3$ and $\angle 4$ are complementary angles. If $m\angle 3 = 74°$, find $m\angle 4$. **16°**
3. Find $m\angle EFH$. **96°**

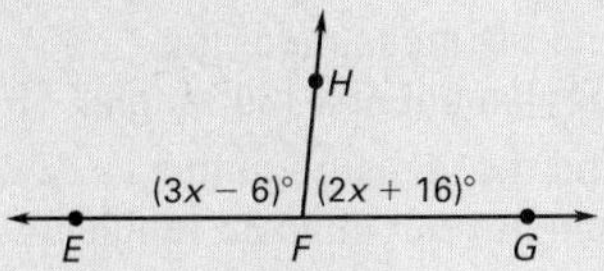

4. Find $m\angle ABC$. **36°**

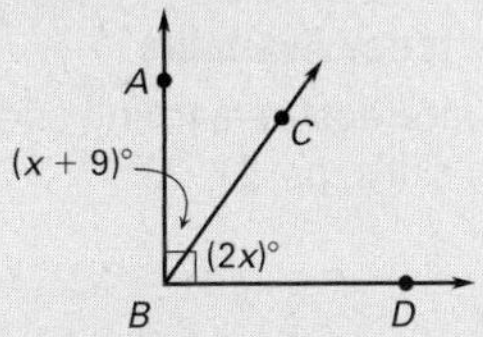

5. Is it possible to draw a figure that contains exactly one pair of vertical angles? Explain. **No; once you have drawn a pair of vertical angles, you have drawn two pairs of opposite rays. This automatically gives another pair of vertical angles.**

Online Quiz
Available at **classzone.com**

Diagnosis/Remediation

- Practice A, B, C in Chapter 1 Resource Book, pp. 63–68
- Study Guide in Chapter 1 Resource Book, pp. 69–70
- Practice Workbook, pp. 13–15
- @HomeTutor

Challenge

Additional challenge is available in the Chapter 1 Resource Book, p. 73.

Quiz

An easily-readable reduced copy of the quiz (with answers) on Lessons 1.4–1.5 from the Assessment Book can be found on p. 1G.

1.6 Classify Polygons

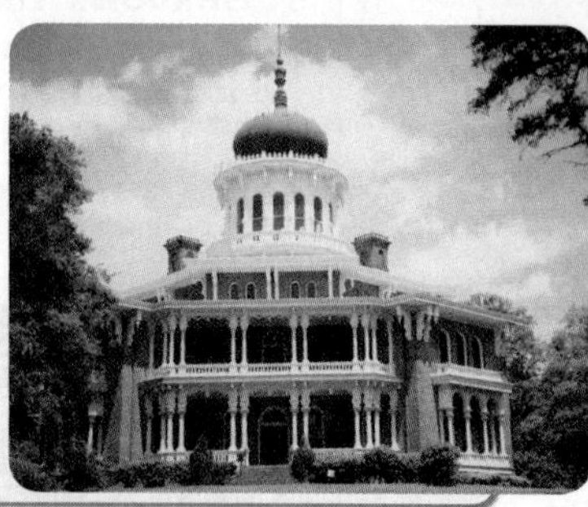

Before You classified angles.
Now You will classify polygons.
Why? So you can find lengths in a floor plan, as in Ex. 32.

1 PLAN AND PREPARE

Warm-Up Exercises

Transparency Available

1. Draw an acute angle and shade the interior.

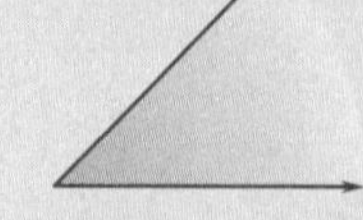

2. Find the measure of the supplement of a 130° angle. **50°**
3. Find the measure of the complement of an 86° angle. **4°**

Notetaking Guide

Transparency Available

Promotes interactive learning and notetaking skills, pp. 21–23.

Pacing

Basic: 1 day
Average: 1 day
Advanced: 1 day
Block: 0.5 block with 1.5
• See *Teaching Guide/Lesson Plan.*

2 FOCUS AND MOTIVATE

Essential Question

Big Idea 1, p. 1

How do you classify polygons? **Tell students they will learn how to answer this question by learning the names of the most common polygons.**

Key Vocabulary
- **polygon** side, vertex
- **convex**
- **concave**
- ***n*-gon**
- **equilateral**
- **equiangular**
- **regular**

Standards

12.0 Students find and use measures of sides and of interior and exterior angles **of** triangles and **polygons to classify figures and solve problems.**

KEY CONCEPT *For Your Notebook*

Identifying Polygons

In geometry, a figure that lies in a plane is called a *plane figure*. A **polygon** is a closed plane figure with the following properties.

1. It is formed by three or more line segments called **sides**.
2. Each side intersects exactly two sides, one at each endpoint, so that no two sides with a common endpoint are collinear.

Each endpoint of a side is a **vertex** of the polygon. The plural of vertex is *vertices*. A polygon can be named by listing the vertices in consecutive order. For example, *ABCDE* and *CDEAB* are both correct names for the polygon at the right.

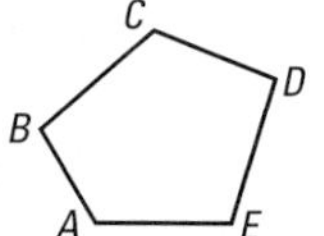

A polygon is **convex** if no line that contains a side of the polygon contains a point in the interior of the polygon. A polygon that is not convex is called *nonconvex* or **concave**.

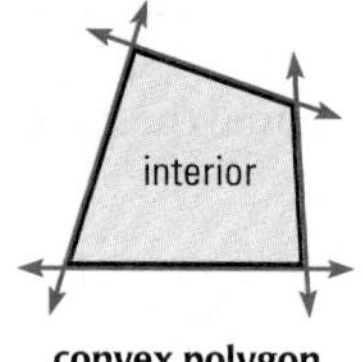

convex polygon

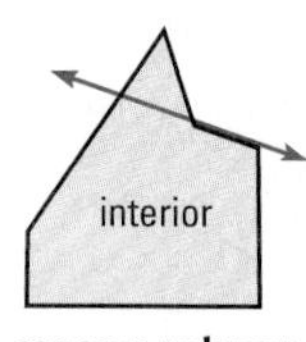

concave polygon

EXAMPLE 1 Identify polygons

READ VOCABULARY
A *plane figure* is two-dimensional. Later, you will study three-dimensional *space figures* such as prisms and cylinders.

Tell whether the figure is a polygon and whether it is *convex* or *concave*.

a. 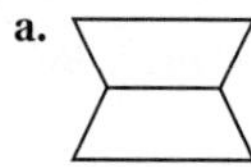 **b.**  **c.** 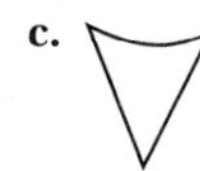 **d.** 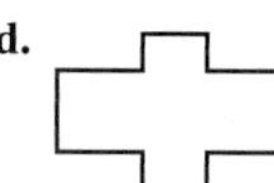

Solution

a. Some segments intersect more than two segments, so it is not a polygon.
b. The figure is a convex polygon.
c. Part of the figure is not a segment, so it is not a polygon.
d. The figure is a concave polygon.

Resource Planning Guide

Chapter Resource Book
- Teaching Guide/Lesson Plan (pp. 74–75)
- Activity Master (p. 76)
- Practice levels A, B, C (pp. 78–83)
- Study Guide (pp. 84–85)
- Catch-up for Absent Students (p. 86)
- Application (p. 87)
- Challenge (p. 88)

Workbooks
- Notetaking Guide (pp. 21–23)
- Practice Workbook (pp. 16–18)

Teaching Options
- **Power Presentations CD-ROM** provides dynamic electronic teaching resources for the classroom.
- **Activity Generator CD-ROM** provides editable activities for all ability levels.

Interactive Technology
- Easy Planner
- Power Presentations CD-ROM
- Activity Generator CD-ROM
- Animated Geometry
- Test Generator CD-ROM
- Online Quiz
- eWorkbook
- eEdition
- @HomeTutor

Resources for English Learners
- Quick Reference for English Learners
- Spanish Study Guide
- Multi-Language Visual Glossary
- Student Resources in Spanish

See also the *Geometry Toolkit* for more strategies for meeting individual needs.

CLASSIFYING POLYGONS A polygon is named by the number of its sides.

Number of sides	Type of polygon	Number of sides	Type of polygon
3	Triangle	8	Octagon
4	Quadrilateral	9	Nonagon
5	Pentagon	10	Decagon
6	Hexagon	12	Dodecagon
7	Heptagon	n	n-gon

The term ***n*-gon**, where n is the number of a polygon's sides, can also be used to name a polygon. For example, a polygon with 14 sides is a 14-gon.

In an **equilateral** polygon, all sides are congruent. In an **equiangular** polygon, all angles in the interior of the polygon are congruent. A **regular** polygon is a convex polygon that is both equilateral and equiangular.

regular pentagon

EXAMPLE 2 Classify polygons

READ DIAGRAMS
Double marks are used in part (b) of Example 2 to show that more than one pair of sides are congruent and more than one pair of angles are congruent.

Classify the polygon by the number of sides. Tell whether the polygon is equilateral, equiangular, or regular. Explain your reasoning.

a. 

b. 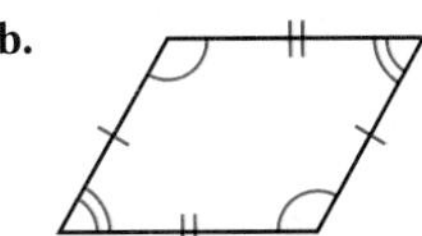

c. 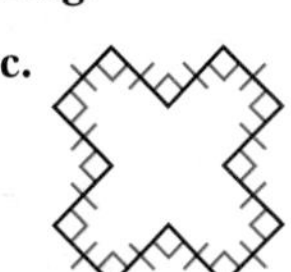

Solution

a. The polygon has 6 sides. It is equilateral and equiangular, so it is a regular hexagon.

b. The polygon has 4 sides, so it is a quadrilateral. It is not equilateral or equiangular, so it is not regular.

c. The polygon has 12 sides, so it is a dodecagon. The sides are congruent, so it is equilateral. The polygon is not convex, so it is not regular.

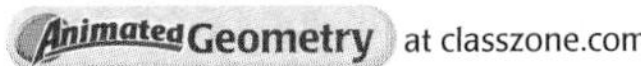

at classzone.com

✓ GUIDED PRACTICE for Examples 1 and 2

1. Sketch an example of a convex heptagon and an example of a concave heptagon. **See margin.**

2. Classify the polygon shown at the right by the number of sides. *Explain* how you know that the sides of the polygon are congruent and that the angles of the polygon are congruent.
Quadrilateral; they all have the same length; they are all right angles.

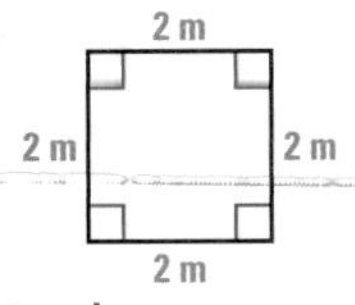

Motivating the Lesson

Ask students to give examples of triangles, squares, rectangles, and other figures in the real world.

3 TEACH

Extra Example 1

Tell whether each figure is a polygon. If it is, tell whether it is convex or concave.

a. 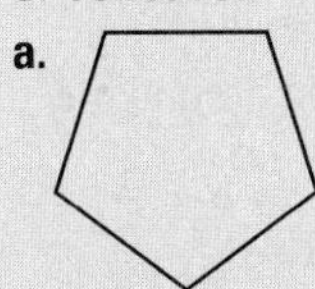

b. 

yes; convex **yes; concave**

Extra Example 2

Classify the polygon by the number of sides. Tell whether the polygon is equilateral, equiangular, or regular. Explain your reasoning.

a. 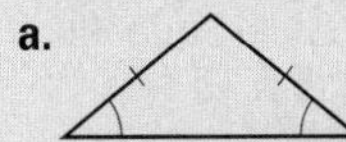

triangle; only 2 sides ≅, only 2 angles ≅, so not equilateral, not equiangular, not regular

b. 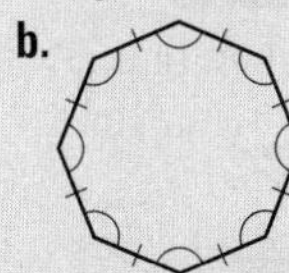

octagon; equilateral, equiangular, regular

c. 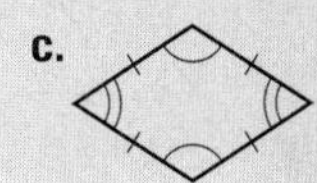

quadrilateral; equilateral, not equiangular, so not regular

An **Animated Geometry** activity is available on-line for **Example 2**. This activity is also available on the **Power Presentations CD-ROM**.

1. See Additional Answers beginning on p. AA1.

Differentiated Instruction

Below Level Tell the students that a polygon is concave if it is dented inward at one or more of its vertices. To help them remember this term, you may want to suggest that they make a mental connection with the words *cavity* and *cave*.

See also the *Geometry Toolkit* for more strategies.

Extra Example 3

A rack for billiard balls is shaped like an equilateral triangle. Find the length of a side. **14 in.**

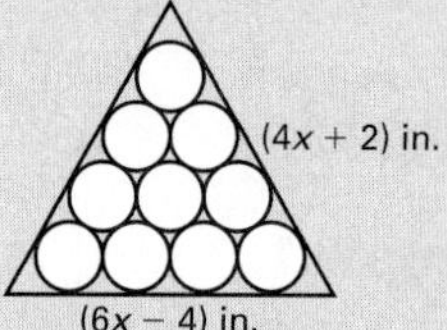

Key Question to Ask for Example 3

- What is the distance around the table? **180 in.**

Closing the Lesson

Have students summarize the major points of the lesson and answer the Essential Question: How do you classify polygons?

- **A polygon is a plane figure formed by three or more line segments. Each side intersects exactly two other sides, one at each endpoint, so that no two sides with a common endpoint are collinear.**
- **A polygon is convex if no line that contains a side of the polygon contains a point in the interior. Otherwise, the polygon is concave.**
- **A polygon is regular if all sides are congruent and all angles in the interior are congruent.**

The most basic way of classifying a polygon is by the number of sides. You can also tell whether the polygon is convex or concave, or indicate whether all the sides or angles are congruent. If all the sides of a convex polygon are congruent and all the angles are congruent, the polygon is a regular polygon.

2. Yes, the string will match the sides of a convex polygon, so it will be the perimeter of the polygon; no, the length of the string will be less than the perimeter of the polygon.

3. polygon; concave

4. Not a polygon; part of the figure is not a segment.

5. polygon; convex

6. Not a polygon; some segments intersect more than two segments.

EXAMPLE 3 Find side lengths

READ VOCABULARY
Hexagonal means "shaped like a hexagon."

 **ALGEBRA A table is shaped like a regular hexagon. The expressions shown represent side lengths of the hexagonal table. Find the length of a side.**

(3x + 6) in.
(4x − 2) in.

Solution

First, write and solve an equation to find the value of x. Use the fact that the sides of a regular hexagon are congruent.

$3x + 6 = 4x - 2$	**Write equation.**
$6 = x - 2$	**Subtract $3x$ from each side.**
$8 = x$	**Add 2 to each side.**

Then find a side length. Evaluate one of the expressions when $x = 8$.

$3x + 6 = 3(8) + 6 = 30$

▶ The length of a side of the table is 30 inches.

✓ **GUIDED PRACTICE** for Example 3

3. The expressions $8y°$ and $(9y - 15)°$ represent the measures of two of the angles in the table in Example 3. Find the measure of an angle. **120°**

1.6 EXERCISES

HOMEWORK KEY
○ = **WORKED-OUT SOLUTIONS on p. WS1 for Exs. 13, 19, and 33**
★ = **STANDARDIZED TEST PRACTICE Exs. 2, 7, 37, 39, and 40**

SKILL PRACTICE

A

1. **VOCABULARY** *Explain* what is meant by the term n-gon. **An n-gon is a polygon with n sides.**
2. ★ **WRITING** Imagine that you can tie a string tightly around a polygon. If the polygon is convex, will the length of the string be equal to the distance around the polygon? What if the polygon is concave? *Explain.* **See margin.**

EXAMPLE 1 on p. 42 for Exs. 3–7

IDENTIFYING POLYGONS Tell whether the figure is a polygon. If it is not, *explain* why. If it is a polygon, tell whether it is *convex* or *concave*. **3–6. See margin.**

3. 
4. 
5. 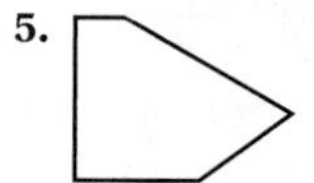
6. 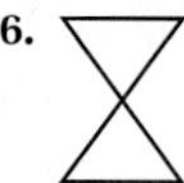

7. ★ **MULTIPLE CHOICE** Which of the figures is a concave polygon? **C**

Ⓐ 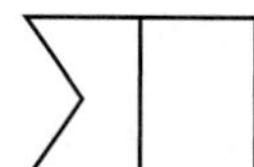
Ⓑ 
Ⓒ 
Ⓓ 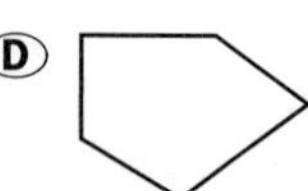

EXAMPLE 2 on p. 43 for Exs. 8–14

CLASSIFYING Classify the polygon by the number of sides. Tell whether the polygon is equilateral, equiangular, or regular. *Explain* your reasoning. 8–13. See margin.

8. 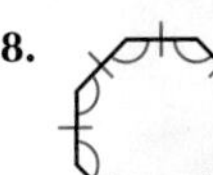

9. 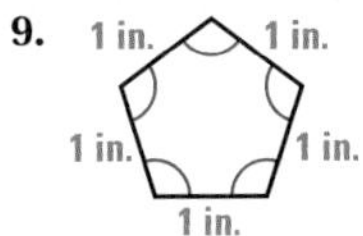

10. 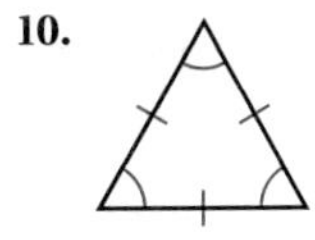

11. 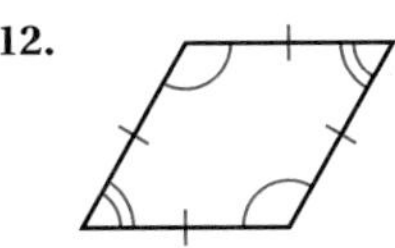

12.

(13.) 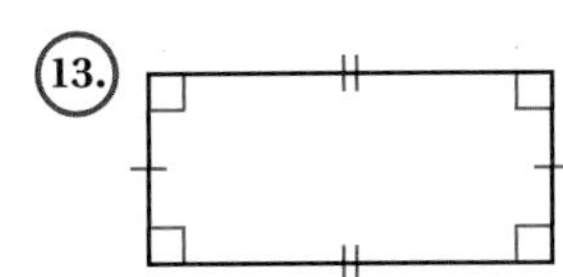

14. ERROR ANALYSIS Two students were asked to draw a regular hexagon, as shown below. *Describe* the error made by each student.
Student A: the hexagon is concave, Student B: the hexagon does not have congruent sides.

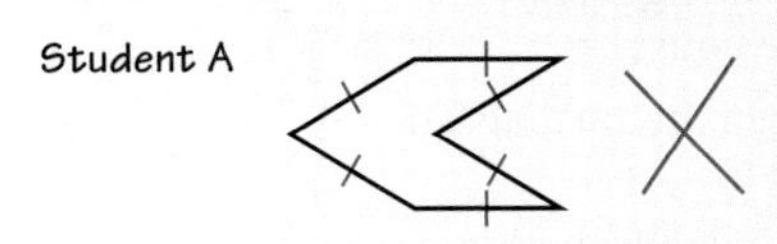

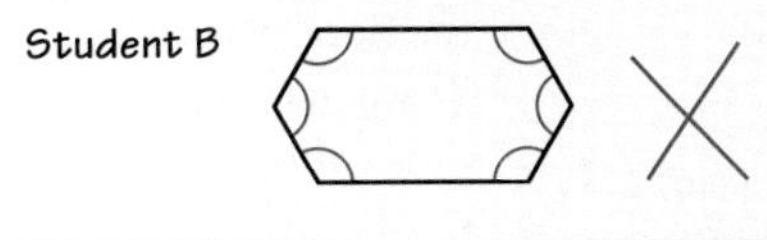

EXAMPLE 3 on p. 44 for Exs. 15–17

15. ALGEBRA The lengths (in inches) of two sides of a regular pentagon are represented by the expressions $5x - 27$ and $2x - 6$. Find the length of a side of the pentagon. 8 in.

16. ALGEBRA The expressions $(9x + 5)^\circ$ and $(11x - 25)^\circ$ represent the measures of two angles of a regular nonagon. Find the measure of an angle of the nonagon. 140°

17. ALGEBRA The expressions $3x - 9$ and $23 - 5x$ represent the lengths (in feet) of two sides of an equilateral triangle. Find the length of a side. 3 ft

B

USING PROPERTIES Tell whether the statement is *always, sometimes,* or *never* true.

18. A triangle is convex. always

(19.) A decagon is regular. sometimes

20. A regular polygon is equiangular. always

21. A circle is a polygon. never

22. A polygon is a plane figure. always

23. A concave polygon is regular. never

DRAWING Draw a figure that fits the description. 24–27. See margin.

24. A triangle that is not regular

25. A concave quadrilateral

26. A pentagon that is equilateral but not equiangular

27. An octagon that is equiangular but not equilateral

ALGEBRA Each figure is a regular polygon. Expressions are given for two side lengths. Find the value of x.

28. 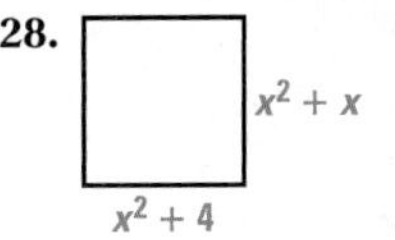

4

29. 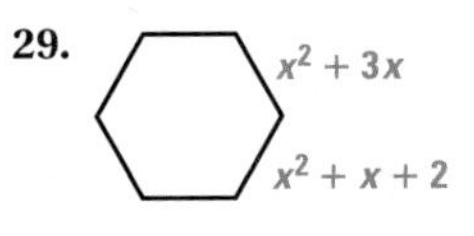

1

30. 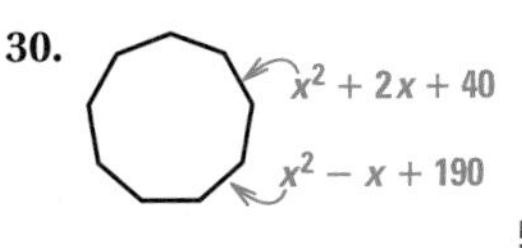

50

4 PRACTICE AND APPLY

Assignment Guide

Answer Transparencies available for all exercises

Basic:
Day 1: pp. 44–47
Exs. 1–10, 14–21, 24, 25, 32–40, 43–53 odd

Average:
Day 1: pp. 44–47
Exs. 1, 2, 4–7, 9–11, 14–17, 21–30, 32–41, 44, 50, 52

Advanced:
Day 1: pp. 44–47
Exs. 1, 2, 5–7, 12, 13, 15–17, 22–32*, 35–42*, 45, 48, 54

Block:
pp. 44–47
Exs. 1, 2, 4–7, 9–11, 14–17, 21–30, 32–41, 44, 50, 52 (with 1.5)

Differentiated Instruction

See *Geometry Best Practices Toolkit* for suggestions on addressing the needs of a diverse classroom.

Homework Check

For a quick check of student understanding of key concepts, go over the following exercises:

Basic: 4, 8, 15, 34, 39

Average: 5, 10, 16, 35, 39

Advanced: 6, 12, 17, 36, 39

Extra Practice

- Student Edition, p. 897
- Chapter 1 Resource Book: Practice levels A, B, C, pp. 78–83

Practice Worksheet

An easily-readable reduced practice page (with answers) for this lesson can be found on p. 1E.

8. Octagon; regular; it has 8 congruent sides and angles.
9. Pentagon; regular; it has 5 congruent sides and angles.
10. Triangle; regular; it has 3 congruent sides and angles.
11. Triangle; none of these; the sides and/or the angles are not all congruent.
12. Quadrilateral; equilateral; it has 4 congruent sides.
13. Quadrilateral; equiangular; it has 4 congruent angles.

24–27. Sample answers are given.

24.

25.

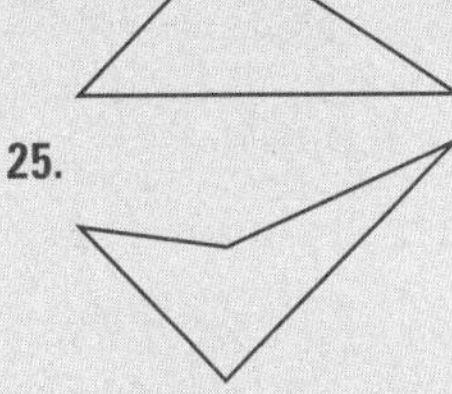

26. 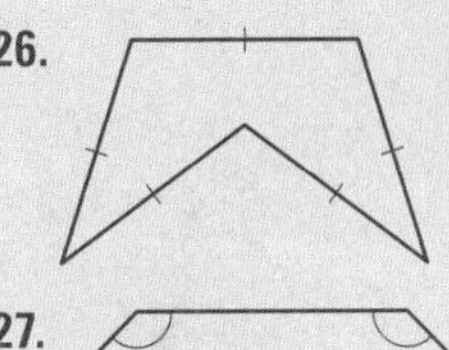

27. 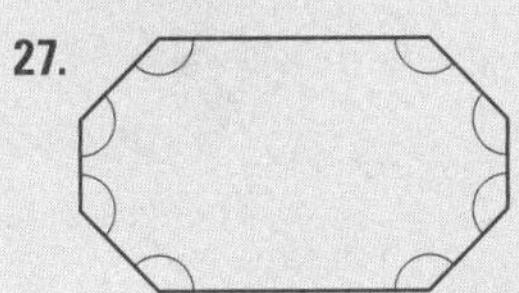

Avoiding Common Errors

Exercise 11 Some students may classify the triangle as equilateral or equiangular because two sides or two angles are congruent, respectively. Remind students that *all* the sides or *all* the angles must be congruent for a figure to be equilateral or equiangular.

Teaching Strategy

Exercise 37 Have the students graph the given ordered pairs and use reasoning to determine the possible locations of the other two vertices.

31. 72°, 72°, 36°. *Sample answer:* To find the measure of the angles of the pentagon, solve $20x + 48 = 33x + 9$ to get $x = 3$. This will get the measures of the angles of the pentagon equal to 108°. $\angle ABC$ and $\angle ACB$ form a linear pair with an angle of a pentagon so they are both equal to $180° - 108° = 72°$. $\angle BAC$, $\angle CAD$, and $\angle DAE$ must have a sum of 180°. Since $\angle CAB \cong \angle DAE$, $2y + 108 = 180$, $y = 36$, so $m\angle CAB = 36°$.

C **31. CHALLENGE** Regular pentagonal tiles and triangular tiles are arranged in the pattern shown. The pentagonal tiles are all the same size and shape and the triangular tiles are all the same size and shape. Find the angle measures of the triangular tiles. *Explain* your reasoning. **See margin.**

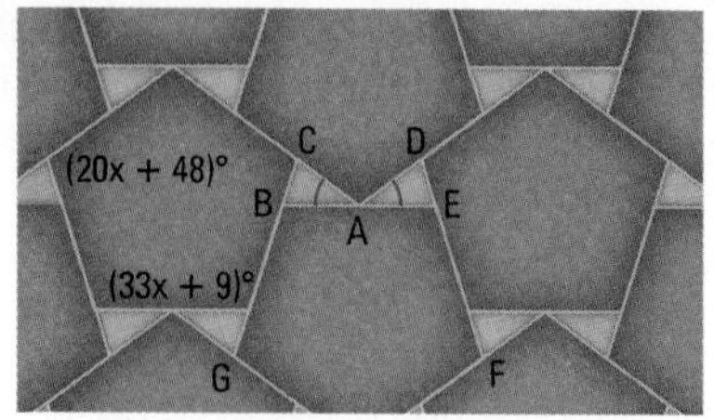

PROBLEM SOLVING

A **32. ARCHITECTURE** Longwood House, shown in the photograph on page 42, is located in Natchez, Mississippi. The diagram at the right shows the floor plan of a part of the house.

a. Tell whether the red polygon in the diagram is *convex* or *concave*. **convex**

b. Classify the red polygon and tell whether it appears to be regular.

32b. Octagon, it appears to be regular.

@HomeTutor for problem solving help at classzone.com

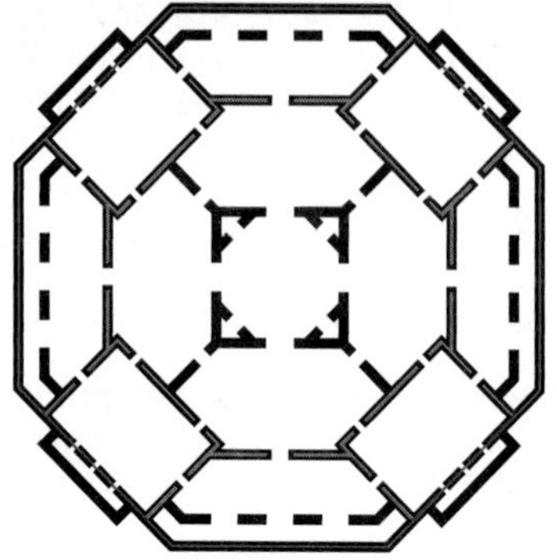

EXAMPLE 2 on p. 43 for Exs. 33–36

SIGNS Each sign suggests a polygon. Classify the polygon by the number of sides. Tell whether it appears to be *equilateral, equiangular,* or *regular.*

33. 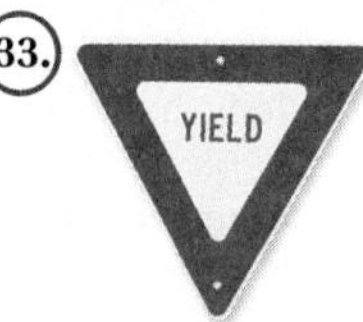

34. 

35. 

36. 

33. triangle; regular

34. quadrilateral; equiangular

35. octagon; regular

36. dodecagon; none of these

@HomeTutor for problem solving help at classzone.com

37. ★ MULTIPLE CHOICE Two vertices of a regular quadrilateral are $A(0, 4)$ and $B(0, -4)$. Which of the following could be the other two vertices? **C**

Ⓐ $C(4, 4)$ and $D(4, -4)$ Ⓑ $C(-4, 4)$ and $D(-4, -4)$

Ⓒ $C(8, -4)$ and $D(8, 4)$ Ⓓ $C(0, 8)$ and $D(0, -8)$

38. MULTI-STEP PROBLEM The diagram shows the design of a lattice made in China in 1850.

38a–b. See margin.

a. Sketch five different polygons you see in the diagram. Classify each polygon by the number of sides.

b. Tell whether each polygon you sketched is concave or convex, and whether the polygon appears to be equilateral, equiangular, or regular.

○ = WORKED-OUT SOLUTIONS on p. WS1 ★ = STANDARDIZED TEST PRACTICE

38a–b. *Sample:*

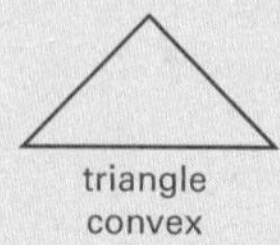
triangle
convex
none

quadrilateral
convex
regular

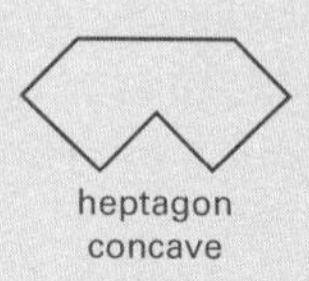
pentagon
convex
none

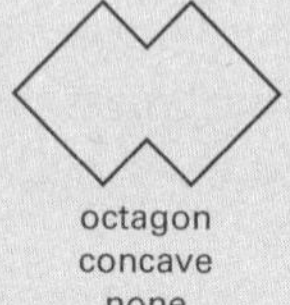
heptagon
concave
none

octagon
concave
none

EXAMPLE 3 on p. 44 for Ex. 39

39. 105 mm; each side of the button is 15 millimeters long, so the perimeter of the button is 15(7) = 105 millimeters.

39. ★ **SHORT RESPONSE** The shape of the button shown is a regular polygon. The button has a border made of silver wire. How many millimeters of silver wire are needed for this border? *Explain.*

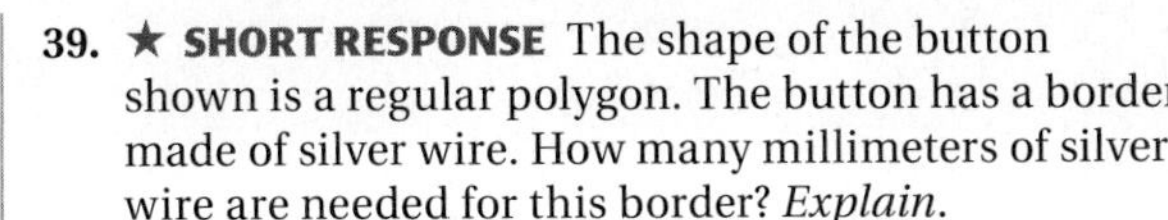

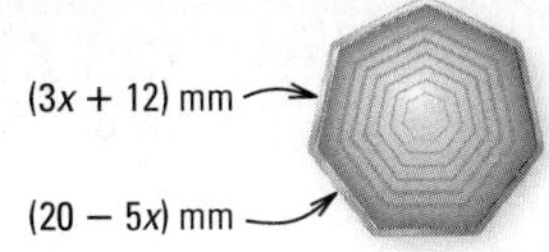

B 40. ★ **EXTENDED RESPONSE** A segment that joins two nonconsecutive vertices of a polygon is called a *diagonal*. For example, a quadrilateral has two diagonals, as shown below.

Type of polygon	Diagram	Number of sides	Number of diagonals
Quadrilateral		4	2
Pentagon	?	? **5**	? **5**
Hexagon	?	? **6**	? **9**
Heptagon	?	? **7**	? **14**

40a. See margin for art. *Sample answer:* The difference between successive number of diagonals is increasing by one.

a. Copy and complete the table. *Describe* any patterns you see.

b. How many diagonals does an octagon have? a nonagon? *Explain.* **20 diagonals; 27 diagonals. *Sample answer:* The pattern described continues.**

c. The expression $\frac{n(n-3)}{2}$ can be used to find the number of diagonals in an n-gon. Find the number of diagonals in a 60-gon. **1710 diagonals**

41. **LINE SYMMETRY** A figure has *line symmetry* if it can be folded over exactly onto itself. The fold line is called the *line of symmetry.* A regular quadrilateral has four lines of symmetry, as shown. Find the number of lines of symmetry in each polygon.

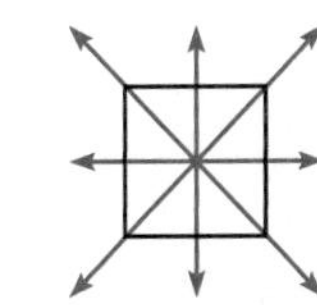

regular quadrilateral
4 lines of symmetry

a. A regular triangle **3**
b. A regular pentagon **5**
c. A regular hexagon **6**
d. A regular octagon **8**

C 42. **CHALLENGE** The diagram shows four identical squares lying edge-to-edge. Sketch all the different ways you can arrange four squares edge-to-edge. Sketch all the different ways you can arrange five identical squares edge-to-edge. **See margin.**

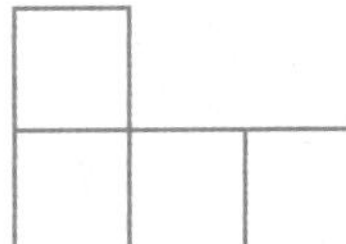

MIXED REVIEW

PREVIEW Prepare for Lesson 1.7 in Exs. 43–51.

Solve the equation.

43. $\frac{1}{2}(35)b = 140$ *(p. 875)* **8**
44. $x^2 = 144$ *(p. 882)* **±12**
45. $3.14r^2 = 314$ *(p. 882)* **±10**

Copy and complete the statement. *(p. 886)*

46. 500 m = __?__ cm **50,000**
47. 12 mi = __?__ ft **63,360**
48. 672 in. = __?__ yd **$18\frac{2}{3}$**
49. 1200 km = __?__ m **1,200,000**
50. $4\frac{1}{2}$ ft = __?__ yd **$1\frac{1}{2}$**
51. 3800 m = __?__ km **3.8**

Find the distance between the two points. *(p. 15)*

52. $D(-13, 13)$, $E(0, -12)$ **about 28.2**
53. $F(-9, -8)$, $G(-9, 7)$ **15**
54. $H(10, 5)$, $J(-2, -2)$ **about 13.9**

5 ASSESS AND RETEACH

Daily Homework Quiz

Transparency Available

1. Draw a convex hexagon.

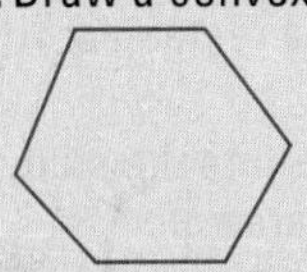

2. This figure shows the tiles on a kitchen floor. What type of polygon are the tiles? Are they regular polygons? **quadrilaterals; not regular**

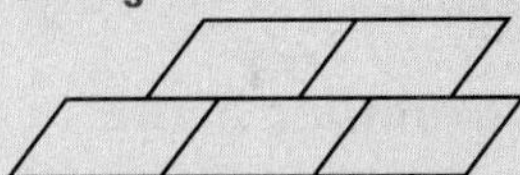

3. This figure is a regular polygon. Find the length of each side. **16 cm**

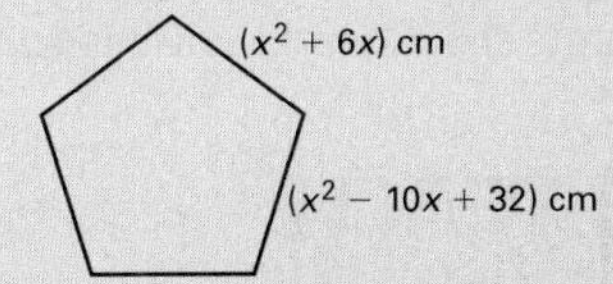

Available at **classzone.com**

Diagnosis/Remediation

- Practice A, B, C in Chapter 1 Resource Book, pp. 78–83
- Study Guide in Chapter 1 Resource Book, pp. 84–85
- Practice Workbook, pp. 16–18
- @HomeTutor

Challenge

Additional challenge is available in the Chapter 1 Resource Book, p. 88.

40a.

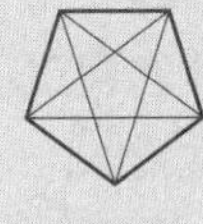

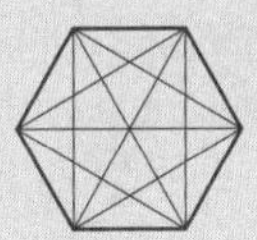

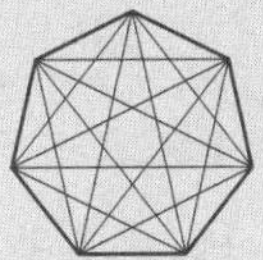

42. See Additional Answers beginning on p. AA1.

@HomeTutor
classzone.com
Keystrokes

1.7 Investigate Perimeter and Area

MATERIALS • graph paper • graphing calculator

QUESTION **How can you use a graphing calculator to find the smallest possible perimeter for a rectangle with a given area?**

You can use the formulas below to find the perimeter P and the area A of a rectangle with length ℓ and width w.

$$P = 2\ell + 2w \qquad A = \ell w$$

Standards

8.0 Students know, derive, and **solve problems involving the** perimeter, circumference, **area**, volume, lateral area, and surface area **of common geometric figures.**

EXPLORE **Find perimeters of rectangles with fixed areas**

STEP 1 ***Draw rectangles*** Draw different rectangles, each with an area of 36 square units. Use lengths of 2, 4, 6, 8, 10, 12, 14, 16, and 18 units.

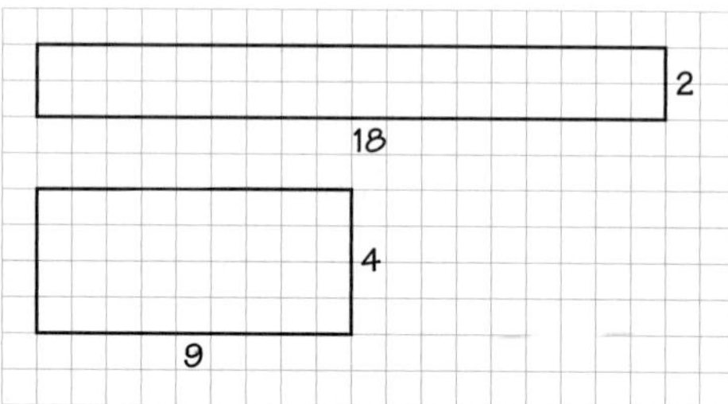

STEP 2 ***Enter data*** Use the STATISTICS menu on a graphing calculator. Enter the rectangle lengths in List 1. Use the keystrokes below to calculate and enter the rectangle widths and perimeters in Lists 2 and 3.

L1	L2	L3
2	18	
4	9	
6	6	
8	4.5	
10	3.6	

L3=2*L1+2*L2

Keystrokes for entering widths in List 2:

36 [÷] [2nd] [L1] [ENTER]

Keystrokes for entering perimeters in List 3:

2 [×] [2nd] [L1] [+] 2 [×] [2nd] [L2] [ENTER]

STEP 3 ***Make a scatter plot*** Make a scatter plot using the lengths from List 1 as the x-values and the perimeters from List 3 as the y-values. Choose an appropriate viewing window. Then use the *trace* feature to see the coordinates of each point.

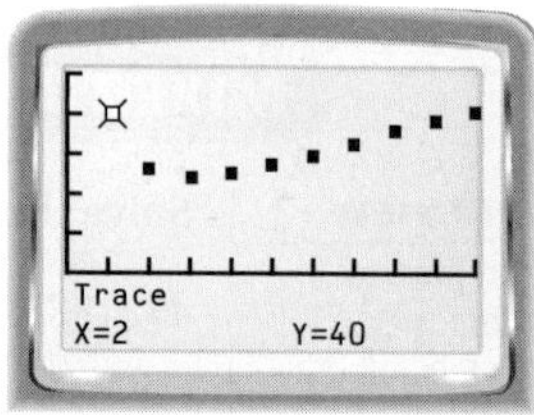

How does the graph show which of your rectangles from Step 1 has the smallest perimeter? **The rectangle with the point associated with the lowest y-value.**

DRAW CONCLUSIONS **Use your observations to complete these exercises**

1. Repeat the steps above for rectangles with areas of 64 square units. **See margin.**
2. Based on the Explore and your results from Exercise 1, what do you notice about the shape of the rectangle with the smallest perimeter? ***Sample answer:*** **It is a square.**

1 PLAN AND PREPARE

Explore the Concept

- Students will use a graphing calculator to find the smallest possible perimeter for a rectangle with a given area.
- This activity leads into the study of perimeter and area of a rectangle in Lesson 1.7.

Materials

Each student will need:

- graph paper
- graphing calculator

Recommended Time

Work activity: 10 min
Discuss results: 5 min

Grouping

Students should work individually.

2 TEACH

Tips for Success

Demonstrate Steps 2 and 3 on the overhead with a calculator so students can see how to enter the data into their calculators. Review how to create a scatter plot, set the window, and use the trace feature.

Key Question

What would be a reasonable viewing window? **possible answer: Xmin = 0, Xmax = 20, Ymin = 0, Ymax = 50**

Key Discovery

The perimeter of a rectangle with a given area will be smallest when the rectangle is a square.

3 ASSESS AND RETEACH

1. What is the smallest possible perimeter of a rectangle with area 100 square units? **40 units**

1. Step 1: Check students' sketches. These rectangles are possible: 2 × 32, 4 × 16, 6 × 10.67, 8 × 8, 10 × 6.4, 12 × 5.33, 14 × 4.56, 18 × 3.56.

Step 2:

L1	L2	L3
2	32	68
4	16	40
6	10.66	33.33
8	8	32
10	6.4	32.8
12	5.33	24.67
14	4.67	37.14

Step 3:

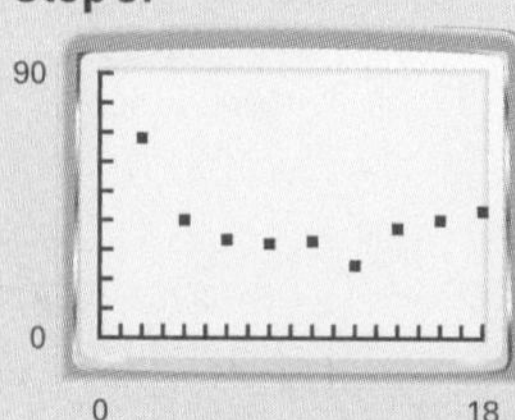

1.7 Find Perimeter, Circumference, and Area

Before You classified polygons.
Now You will find dimensions of polygons.
Why? So you can use measures in science, as in Ex. 46.

Key Vocabulary
- **perimeter,** *p. 923*
- **circumference,** *p. 923*
- **area,** *p. 923*
- **diameter,** *p. 923*
- **radius,** *p. 923*

Standards

8.0 Students know, derive, and **solve problems involving the perimeter, circumference, area,** volume, lateral area, and surface area **of common geometric figures.**

10.0 Students compute areas of polygons, including rectangles, scalene triangles, equilateral triangles, rhombi, parallelograms, and trapezoids.

Recall that *perimeter* is the distance around a figure, *circumference* is the distance around a circle, and *area* is the amount of surface covered by a figure. Perimeter and circumference are measured in units of length, such as meters (m) and feet (ft). Area is measured in square units, such as square meters (m^2) and square feet (ft^2).

KEY CONCEPT *For Your Notebook*

Formulas for Perimeter *P*, Area *A*, and Circumference *C*

Square
side length s
$P = 4s$
$A = s^2$

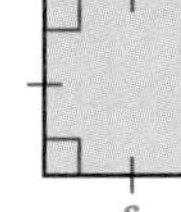

Rectangle
length ℓ and width w
$P = 2\ell + 2w$
$A = \ell w$

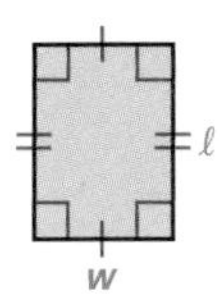

Triangle
side lengths a, b, and c, base b, and height h
$P = a + b + c$
$A = \frac{1}{2}bh$

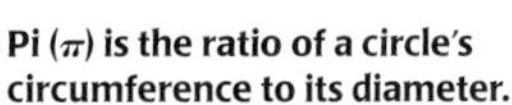

Circle
diameter d and radius r
$C = \pi d = 2\pi r$
$A = \pi r^2$

Pi (π) is the ratio of a circle's circumference to its diameter.

EXAMPLE 1 Find the perimeter and area of a rectangle

BASKETBALL Find the perimeter and area of the rectangular basketball court shown.

Perimeter	**Area**
$P = 2\ell + 2w$	$A = \ell w$
$= 2(84) + 2(50)$	$= 84(50)$
$= 268$	$= 4200$

▶ The perimeter is 268 feet and the area is 4200 square feet.

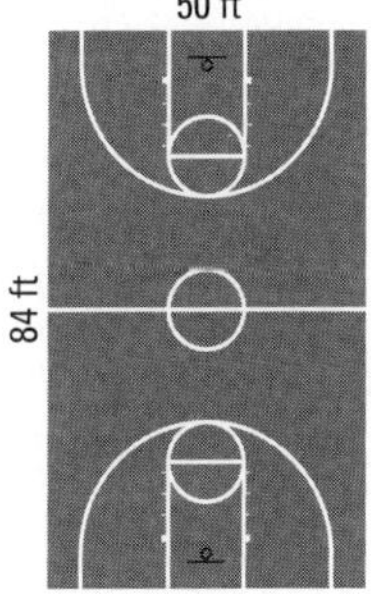

1 PLAN AND PREPARE

Warm-Up Exercises

Transparency Available

1. Find the approximate distance between (2, 3) and (−1, 4). Round to the nearest tenth. **3.2**
2. Change 72 inches to feet. **6 ft**
3. Solve $\frac{1}{2}(5x) = 30$. **12**
4. Michelle will put braid around the edges of a rug. She calculates that she needs 14 yards. How many feet of braid does she need? **42 ft**

Notetaking Guide

Transparency Available

Promotes interactive learning and notetaking skills, pp. 24–27.

Pacing

Basic: 2 days
Average: 2 days
Advanced: 2 days
Block: 1 block
- See *Teaching Guide/Lesson Plan.*

2 FOCUS AND MOTIVATE

Essential Question

Big Idea 2, p. 1

How do you find the area and perimeter of a figure? **Tell students they will learn how to answer this question by using formulas for the area and perimeter of different figures.**

Resource Planning Guide

Chapter Resource Book
- Teaching Guide/Lesson Plan (pp. 89–90)
- Practice levels A, B, C (pp. 92–97)
- Study Guide (pp. 98–99)
- Catch-up for Absent Students (p. 100)
- Problem Solving Workshop (p. 101)
- Challenge (p. 102)

Workbooks
- Notetaking Guide (pp. 24–27)
- Practice Workbook (pp. 19–21)

Teaching Options
- **Power Presentations CD-ROM** provides dynamic electronic teaching resources for the classroom.
- **Activity Generator CD-ROM** provides editable activities for all ability levels.

Interactive Technology
- Easy Planner
- Power Presentations CD-ROM
- Activity Generator CD-ROM
- Animated Geometry
- Test Generator CD-ROM
- Online Quiz
- eWorkbook
- eEdition
- @HomeTutor

Resources for English Learners
- Quick Reference for English Learners
- Spanish Study Guide
- Multi-Language Visual Glossary
- Student Resources in Spanish

See also the *Geometry Toolkit* for more strategies for meeting individual needs.

Motivating the Lesson

Antonio is making a tablecloth for a round table with diameter 5 feet. He wants it to hang 8 inches over the edge. To find out how much fabric he needs, he can use the formula for the area of a circle, one of the formulas in this lesson.

3 TEACH

Extra Example 1

Find the perimeter and area of the dining room shown. **42 ft, 108 ft^2**

Extra Example 2

Find the approximate circumference and area of the circular window shown. **56.5 in.; 254.3 in.^{2}**

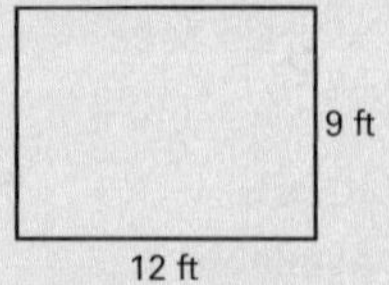

Key Question to Ask for Example 2

- How could you write the circumference formula in terms of the diameter instead of the radius? ***$C = \pi d$***

Extra Example 3

Triangle *ABC* has vertices *A*(2, 5), *B*(4, 1), and *C*(8, 3). What is the approximate perimeter of $\triangle ABC$? **B**

Ⓐ 8.9 Ⓑ 15.3
Ⓒ 16.0 Ⓓ 17.3

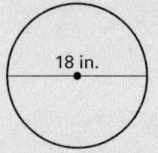

EXAMPLE 2 Find the circumference and area of a circle

TEAM PATCH You are ordering circular cloth patches for your soccer team's uniforms. Find the approximate circumference and area of the patch shown.

APPROXIMATE π
The approximations 3.14 and $\frac{22}{7}$ are commonly used as approximations for the irrational number π. Unless told otherwise, use 3.14 for π.

Solution

First find the radius. The diameter is 9 centimeters, so the radius is $\frac{1}{2}(9) = 4.5$ centimeters.

Then find the circumference and area. Use 3.14 to approximate the value of π.

$C = 2\pi r \approx 2(3.14)(4.5) = 28.26$

$A = \pi r^2 \approx 3.14(4.5)^2 = 63.585$

▶ The circumference is about 28.3 cm. The area is about 63.6 cm^2.

GUIDED PRACTICE for Examples 1 and 2

Find the area and perimeter (or circumference) of the figure. If necessary, round to the nearest tenth.

1.
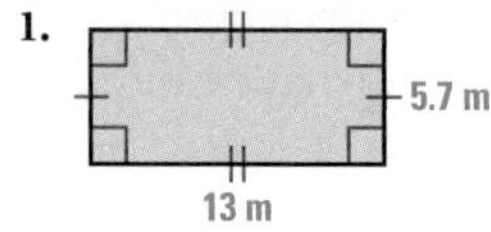

74.1 m^2, 37.4 m

2.
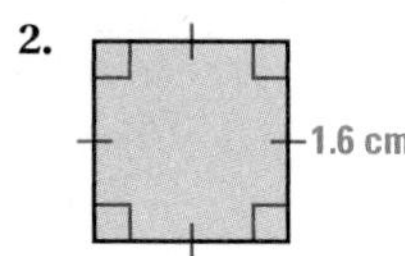

2.6 cm^2, 6.4 cm

3.
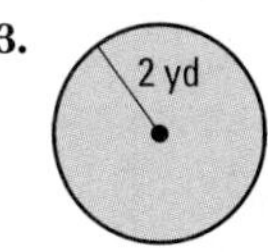

12.6 yd^2, 12.6 yd

★ EXAMPLE 3 Standardized Test Practice

Triangle *QRS* has vertices *Q*(1, 2), *R*(4, 6), and *S*(5, 2). What is the approximate perimeter of triangle *QRS*?

Ⓐ 8 units Ⓑ 8.3 units Ⓒ 13.1 units Ⓓ 25.4 units

Solution

AVOID ERRORS
Write down your calculations to make sure you do not make a mistake substituting values in the Distance Formula.

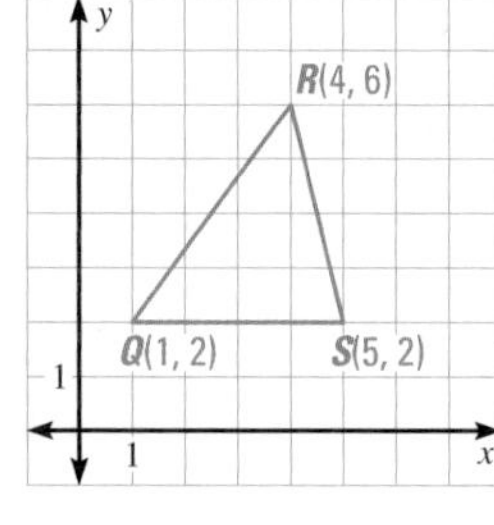

First draw triangle *QRS* in a coordinate plane. Find the side lengths. Use the Distance Formula to find *QR* and *RS*.

$QS = |5 - 1| = 4$ units

$QR = \sqrt{(4 - 1)^2 + (6 - 2)^2} = \sqrt{25} = 5$ units

$RS = \sqrt{(5 - 4)^2 + (2 - 6)^2} = \sqrt{17} \approx 4.1$ units

Then find the perimeter.

$P = QS + QR + RS \approx 4 + 5 + 4.1 = 13.1$ units

▶ The correct answer is C. Ⓐ Ⓑ Ⓒ Ⓓ

Differentiated Instruction

Kinesthetic Learners When discussing **Example 3**, reinforce the calculations made using the Distance Formula by having students measure the length of each side of the triangle. Have students create a paper ruler on which 1 unit is equal to a grid length in the given coordinate plane.

See also the *Geometry Toolkit* for more strategies.

EXAMPLE 4 Solve a multi-step problem

SKATING RINK An ice-resurfacing machine is used to smooth the surface of the ice at a skating rink. The machine can resurface about 270 square yards of ice in one minute.

About how many minutes does it take the machine to resurface a rectangular skating rink that is 200 feet long and 90 feet wide?

ANOTHER WAY
For an alternative method for solving the problem in Example 4, turn to page 57 for the **Problem Solving Workshop**.

Solution

The machine can resurface the ice at a rate of 270 square yards per minute. So, the amount of time it takes to resurface the skating rink depends on its area.

STEP 1 **Find** the area of the rectangular skating rink.

Area $= \ell w = 200(90) = 18{,}000 \text{ ft}^2$

The resurfacing rate is in square yards per minute. Rewrite the area of the rink in square yards. There are 3 feet in 1 yard, and $3^2 = 9$ square feet in 1 square yard.

$18{,}000 \cancel{\text{ft}^2} \cdot \frac{1 \text{ yd}^2}{9 \cancel{\text{ft}^2}} = 2000 \text{ yd}^2$ **Use unit analysis.**

STEP 2 **Write** a verbal model to represent the situation. Then write and solve an equation based on the verbal model.

Let t represent the total time (in minutes) needed to resurface the skating rink.

Area of rink (yd^2)	=	Resurfacing rate (yd^2 per min)	×	Total time (min)

$2000 = 270 \cdot t$ **Substitute.**

$7.4 \approx t$ **Divide each side by 270.**

▶ It takes the ice-resurfacing machine about 7 minutes to resurface the skating rink.

Extra Example 4

Wilhelmena can mow 600 square feet of grass in 10 minutes. About how long will it take her to mow the grass on a rectangular field that is 60 feet wide and 80 feet long?
80 min

Key Question to Ask for Example 4

- How could you solve the problem directly using yards? **You could convert 200 feet and 90 feet to yards before solving the problem. Then $A = \ell w$ would become $A = \left(66\frac{2}{3}\right)(30) = 2000 \text{ yd}^2$.**

An **Animated Geometry** activity is available on-line for **Example 4**. This activity is also available on the **Power Presentations CD-ROM**.

✓ GUIDED PRACTICE for Examples 3 and 4

4. Describe how to find the height from F to $\overline{EG}$ in the triangle at the right.

4. The height is the length of the segment from point F to $\overline{EG}$ at the point (1, 3). Using the coordinate grid to count units, the height is 6.

5. Find the perimeter and the area of the triangle shown at the right. **about 16.8, 12**

6. **WHAT IF?** In Example 4, suppose the skating rink is twice as long and twice as wide. Will it take an ice-resurfacing machine twice as long to resurface the skating rink? *Explain* your reasoning.
No; the new area is more than twice as big.

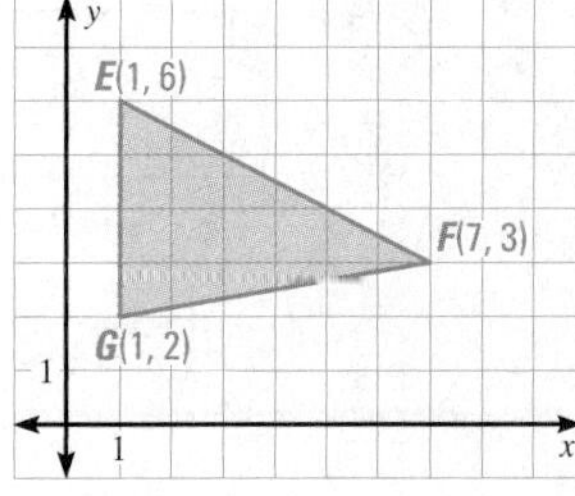

Extra Example 5

The base of a triangle is 14 cm. Its area is 42 cm^2. Find the height of the triangle. **6 cm**

Key Questions to Ask for Example 5

- How could you check the answer? **Multiply $\frac{1}{2}$ by 22 by 28 to see if the result is 308.**
- To solve the equation, could you first multiply by 2? **yes**

Closing the Lesson

Have students summarize the major points of the lesson and answer the Essential Question: How do you find the area and perimeter of a figure?

- **Perimeter is the distance around a polygon. Circumference is the distance around a circle.**
- **Area is the amount of surface covered by the figure.**
- **The formula for the area of a triangle is $\frac{1}{2}bh$, the area of a square is s^2, the area of a rectangle is ℓw, and the area of a circle is πr^2.**

To find the area and perimeter of a figure, you choose the correct formulas, substitute the given values, and calculate the area or perimeter.

EXAMPLE 5 Find unknown length

The base of a triangle is 28 meters. Its area is 308 square meters. Find the height of the triangle.

Solution

$A = \frac{1}{2}bh$ — Write formula for the area of a triangle.

$308 = \frac{1}{2}(28)h$ — Substitute 308 for A and 28 for b.

$22 = h$ — Solve for h.

▶ The height is 22 meters.

✓ GUIDED PRACTICE for Example 5

7. The area of a triangle is 64 square meters, and its height is 16 meters. Find the length of its base. **8 m**

1.7 EXERCISES

HOMEWORK KEY

○ = **WORKED-OUT SOLUTIONS** on p. WS2 for Exs. 7, 21, and 41

★ = **STANDARDIZED TEST PRACTICE** Exs. 2, 19, 26, 38, and 45

= **MULTIPLE REPRESENTATIONS** Ex. 44

SKILL PRACTICE

A

1. **VOCABULARY** How are the diameter and radius of a circle related? ***Sample answer:*** **The diameter is twice the radius.**

2. ★ **WRITING** *Describe* a real-world situation in which you would need to find a perimeter, and a situation in which you would need to find an area. What measurement units would you use in each situation? ***Sample answer:*** **Find the perimeter of the yard to fence it in; find the area of the yard to fertilize it; ft; ft^2.**

3. (52)(9) must be divided by 2; $\frac{52(9)}{2} = 234$ ft^2.

EXAMPLE 1 on p. 49 for Exs. 3–10

3. **ERROR ANALYSIS** *Describe* and correct the error made in finding the area of a triangle with a height of 9 feet and a base of 52 feet.

$A = 52(9) = 468$ ft^2

PERIMETER AND AREA Find the perimeter and area of the shaded figure.

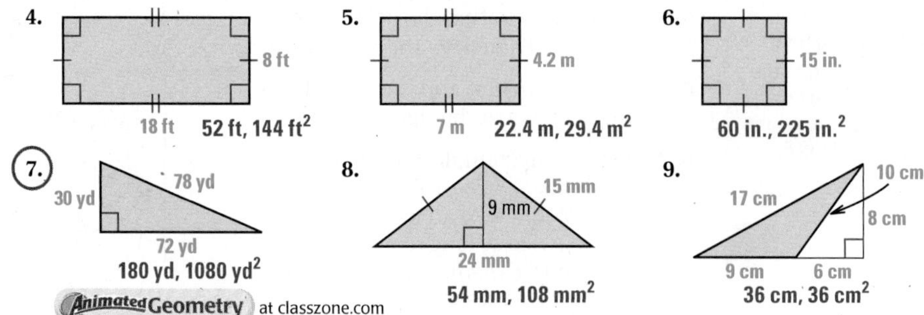

4. **52 ft, 144 ft^2**
5. **22.4 m, 29.4 m^2**
6. **60 in., 225 in.^{2}**
7. **180 yd, 1080 yd^2**
8. **54 mm, 108 mm^2**
9. **36 cm, 36 cm^2**

AnimatedGeometry at classzone.com

10. **DRAWING A DIAGRAM** The base of a triangle is 32 feet. Its height is $16\frac{1}{2}$ feet. Sketch the triangle and find its area. **See margin for art; 264 ft².**

EXAMPLE 2 on p. 50 for Exs. 11–15

CIRCUMFERENCE AND AREA Use the given diameter d or radius r to find the circumference and area of the circle. Round to the nearest tenth.

11. $d = 27$ cm 12. $d = 5$ in. 13. $r = 12.1$ cm 14. $r = 3.9$ cm **24.5 cm, 47.8 cm²**

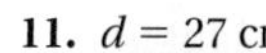
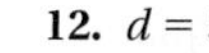
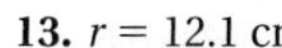

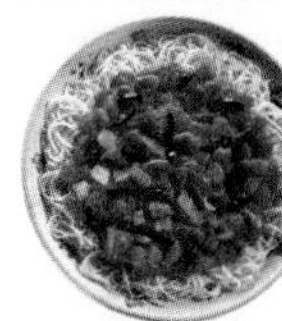
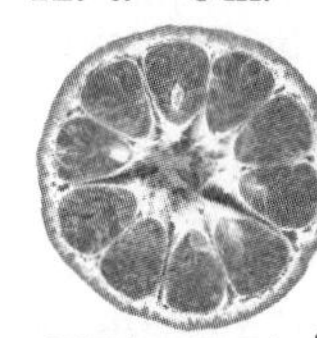

84.8 cm, 572.3 cm² **15.7 in., 19.6 in.²** **76.0 cm, 459.7 cm²**

15. **DRAWING A DIAGRAM** The diameter of a circle is 18.9 centimeters. Sketch the circle and find its circumference and area. Round your answers to the nearest tenth. **See margin for art; 59.3 cm, 280.4 cm².**

EXAMPLE 3 on p. 50 for Exs. 16–19

DISTANCE FORMULA Find the perimeter of the figure. Round to the nearest tenth of a unit.

16.
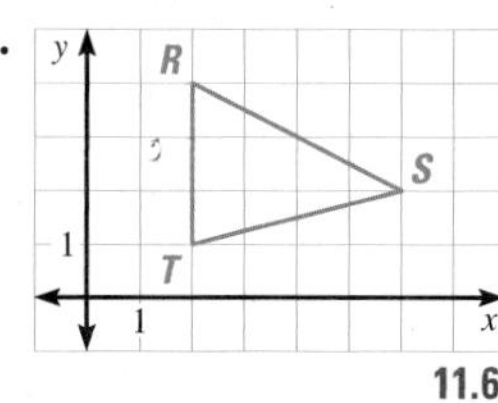

11.6

17.
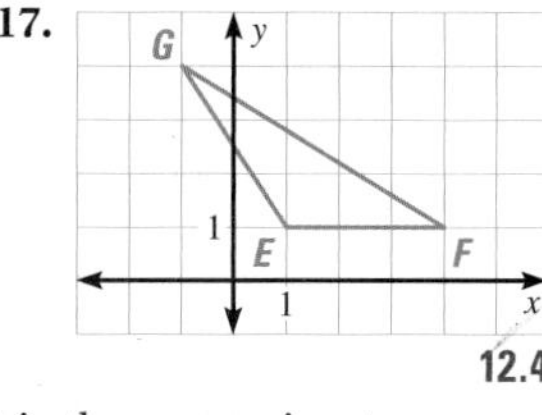

12.4

18.
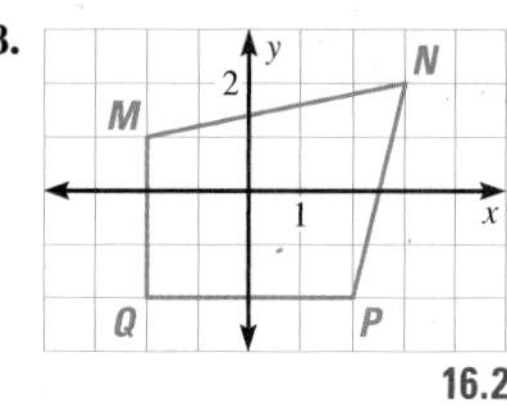

16.2

19. ★ **MULTIPLE CHOICE** What is the approximate area (in square units) of the rectangle shown at the right? **D**

Ⓐ 6.7 Ⓑ 8.0
Ⓒ 9.0 Ⓓ 10.0

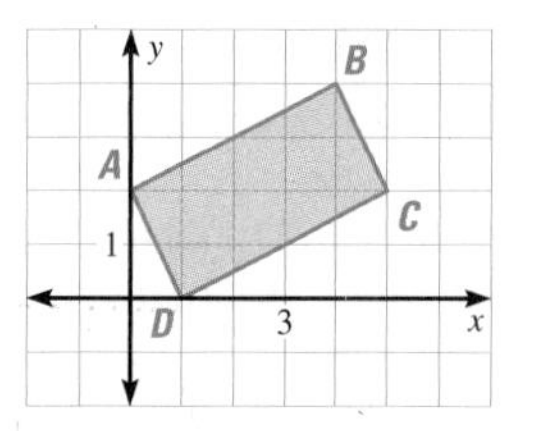

EXAMPLE 4 on p. 51 for Exs. 20–26

CONVERTING UNITS Copy and complete the statement.

20. 187 cm² = ? m² **0.0187** 21. 13 ft² = ? yd² **1.44** 22. 18 in.² = ? ft² **0.125**

23. 8 km² = ? m² **8,000,000** 24. 12 yd² = ? ft² **108** 25. 24 ft² = ? in.² **3,456**

26. ★ **MULTIPLE CHOICE** A triangle has an area of 2.25 square feet. What is the area of the triangle in square inches? **D**

Ⓐ 27 in.² Ⓑ 54 in.² Ⓒ 144 in.² Ⓓ 324 in.²

EXAMPLE 5 on p. 52 for Exs. 27–30

UNKNOWN MEASURES Use the information about the figure to find the indicated measure.

27. Area = 261 m²
Find the height h. **14.5 m**

h
36 m

28. Area = 66 in.²
Find the base b. **16 in.**

$8\frac{1}{4}$ in.
b

29. Perimeter = 25 in.
Find the width w. **4.5 in.**

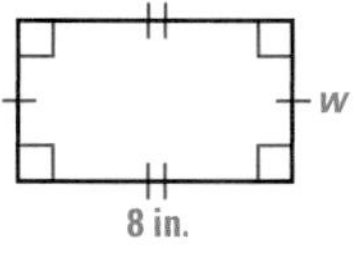

4 PRACTICE AND APPLY

Assignment Guide

Answer Transparencies available for all exercises

Basic:
Day 1: SRH p. 886 Exs. 1–15 odd
pp. 52–56
Exs. 1–19, 40, 41, 51, 52
Day 2: pp. 52–56
Exs. 20–32, 42–44, 49, 50

Average:
Day 1: pp. 52–56
Exs. 1–19, 40, 41, 51, 52
Day 2: pp. 52–56
Exs. 23–38, 42–45, 49, 50

Advanced:
Day 1: pp. 52–56
Exs. 1, 2, 4–10, 12–19, 40, 41, 49–52
Day 2: pp. 52–56
Exs. 24–39*, 42–48*

Block:
pp. 52–56
Exs. 1–19, 23–38, 40–45, 49–52

Differentiated Instruction

See *Geometry Best Practices Toolkit* for suggestions on addressing the needs of a diverse classroom.

Homework Check

For a quick check of student understanding of key concepts, go over the following exercises:

Basic: 6, 12, 16, 27, 40
Average: 8, 14, 17, 24, 41
Advanced: 10, 18, 24, 28, 42

Extra Practice

- Student Edition, p. 897
- Chapter 1 Resource Book: Practice levels A, B, C, pp. 92–97

Practice Worksheet

An easily-readable reduced practice page (with answers) for this lesson can be found on p. 1F.

10. *Sample:*

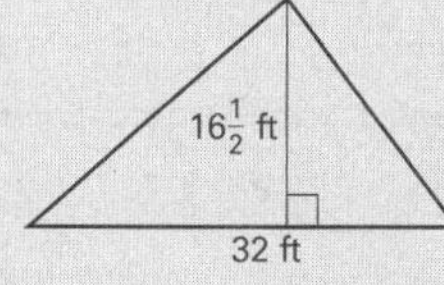

15.

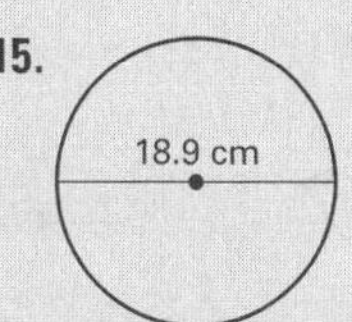

Avoiding Common Errors

Exercise 9 Students may use 15 as the base of the triangle instead of 9. Remind them that the base must be the length of a side of the triangle.

Internet Reference

Exercise 40 For more information about the giant Amazon water lily, visit www.livingrainforest.org/about/plants/giantwaterlily

Reading Strategy

Exercises 41, 42 Students should pay close attention to the units used in these exercises as some answers require different units than those given in the problems.

30. UNKNOWN MEASURE The width of a rectangle is 17 inches. Its perimeter is 102 inches. Find the length of the rectangle. **34 in.**

B

31. xy ALGEBRA The area of a rectangle is 18 square inches. The length of the rectangle is twice its width. Find the length and width of the rectangle. **6 in., 3 in.**

32. xy ALGEBRA The area of a triangle is 27 square feet. Its height is three times the length of its base. Find the height and base of the triangle. **$9\sqrt{2}$ ft, $3\sqrt{2}$ ft**

33. xy ALGEBRA Let x represent the side length of a square. Find a regular polygon with side length x whose perimeter is twice the perimeter of the square. Find a regular polygon with side length x whose perimeter is three times the length of the square. *Explain* your thinking.

33. Octagon; dodecagon; the square has 4 sides, so a polygon with the same side length and twice the perimeter would have to have 2(4) = 8 sides, an octagon; a polygon with the same side length and three times the perimeter would have to have 4(3) = 12 sides, a dodecagon.

FINDING SIDE LENGTHS **Find the side length of the square with the given area. Write your answer as a radical in simplest form.**

34. $A = 184\text{ cm}^2$ **$2\sqrt{46}$ cm**

35. $A = 346\text{ in.}^2$ **$\sqrt{346}$ in.**

36. $A = 1008\text{ mi}^2$ **$12\sqrt{7}$ mi**

37. $A = 1050\text{ km}^2$ **$5\sqrt{42}$ km**

38. ★ **SHORT RESPONSE** In the diagram, the diameter of the yellow circle is half the diameter of the red circle. What fraction of the area of the red circle is *not* covered by the yellow circle? *Explain.* **$\frac{3}{4}$; the area of the yellow circle is $\frac{1}{4}$ the area of the red one.**

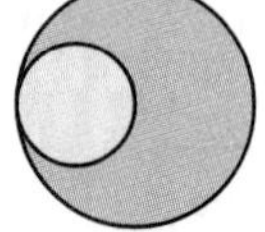

C

39. CHALLENGE The area of a rectangle is 30 cm^2 and its perimeter is 26 cm. Find the length and width of the rectangle. **10 cm and 3 cm**

PROBLEM SOLVING

EXAMPLES 1 and 2 on pp. 49–50 for Exs. 40–41

A

40. **WATER LILIES** The giant Amazon water lily has a lily pad that is shaped like a circle. Find the circumference and area of a lily pad with a diameter of 60 inches. Round your answers to the nearest tenth. **188.4 in., 2826 in.^{2}**

@HomeTutor for problem solving help at classzone.com

41. **LAND** You are planting grass on a rectangular plot of land. You are also building a fence around the edge of the plot. The plot is 45 yards long and 30 yards wide. How much area do you need to cover with grass seed? How many feet of fencing do you need? **1350 yd^2; 450 ft**

@HomeTutor for problem solving help at classzone.com

EXAMPLE 4 on p. 51 for Ex. 42

42. MULTI-STEP PROBLEM Chris is installing a solar panel. The maximum amount of power the solar panel can generate in a day depends in part on its area. On a sunny day in the city where Chris lives, each square meter of the panel can generate up to 125 watts of power. The flat rectangular panel is 84 centimeters long and 54 centimeters wide.

a. Find the area of the solar panel in square meters. **0.4536 m^2**

b. What is the maximum amount of power (in watts) that the panel could generate if its area was 1 square meter? 2 square meters? *Explain.* **125 watts, 250 watts; twice the area generates twice the watts.**

c. Estimate the maximum amount of power Chris's solar panel can generate. *Explain* your reasoning.

42c. 56.7 watts; Chris' solar panel is 0.4536 square meters so it can generate at most 125(0.4536) = 56.7 watts.

○ = WORKED-OUT SOLUTIONS on p. WS1 ★ = STANDARDIZED TEST PRACTICE  = MULTIPLE REPRESENTATIONS

43b. 6 in.; the spoke is 21 inches long from the center to the tip, and it is 15 inches from the center to the outer edge, so 21 − 15 = 6 inches is the length of the handle.

43. **MULTI-STEP PROBLEM** The eight spokes of a ship's wheel are joined at the wheel's center and pass through a large wooden circle, forming handles on the outside of the circle. From the wheel's center to the tip of the handle, each spoke is 21 inches long.

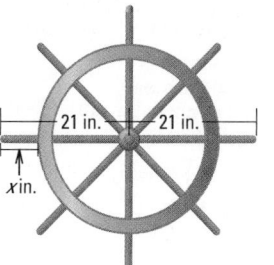

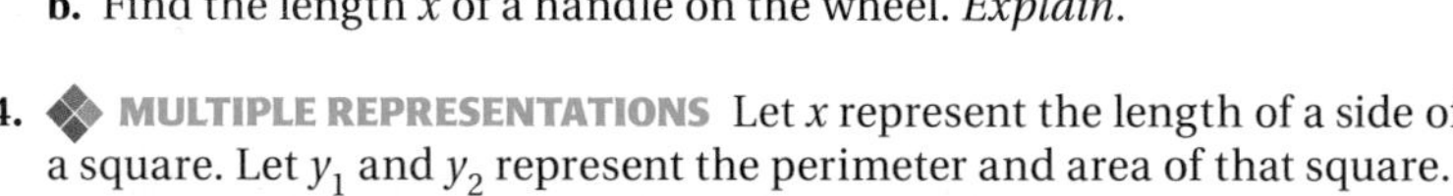

a. The circumference of the outer edge of the large wooden circle is 94 inches. Find the radius of the outer edge of the circle to the nearest inch. **15 in.**

b. Find the length x of a handle on the wheel. *Explain.*

B 44. **MULTIPLE REPRESENTATIONS** Let x represent the length of a side of a square. Let y_1 and y_2 represent the perimeter and area of that square.

a. **Making a Table** Copy and complete the table.

Length, x	1	2	5	10	25
Perimeter, y_1	? 4	? 8	? 20	? 40	? 100
Area, y_2	? 1	? 4	? 25	? 100	? 625

b. **Making a Graph** Use the completed table to write two sets of ordered pairs: (x, y_1) and (x, y_2). Graph each set of ordered pairs. **See margin.**

c. **Analyzing Data** *Describe* any patterns you see in the table from part (a) and in the graphs from part (b). **See margin.**

45b. 380 rows, 175 columns. *Sample answer:* The panel is 1520 centimeters high and each module is 4 centimeters so there are 1520 ÷ 4 = 380 rows; the panel is 700 centimeters wide and each module is 4 centimeters therefore there are 700 ÷ 4 = 175 columns.

45. ★ **EXTENDED RESPONSE** The photograph at the right shows the Crown Fountain in Chicago, Illinois. At this fountain, images of faces appear on a large screen. The images are created by light-emitting diodes (LEDs) that are clustered in groups called modules. The LED modules are arranged in a rectangular grid.

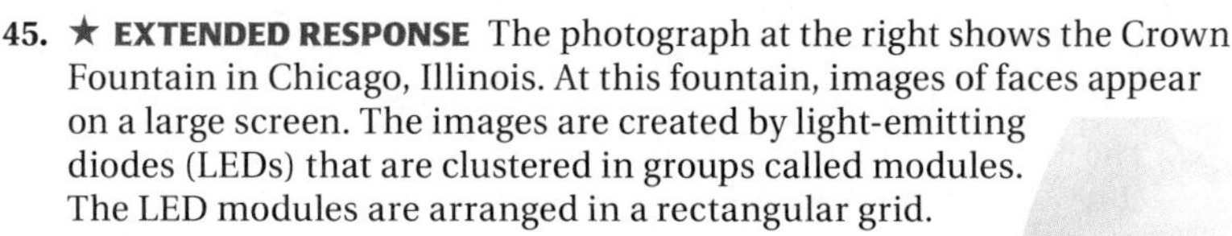

a. The rectangular grid is approximately 7 meters wide and 15.2 meters high. Find the area of the grid. **106.4 m²**

b. Suppose an LED module is a square with a side length of 4 centimeters. How many rows and how many columns of LED modules would be needed to make the Crown Fountain screen? *Explain* your reasoning.

C 46. **ASTRONOMY** The diagram shows a gap in Saturn's circular rings. This gap is known as the *Cassini division*. In the diagram, the red circle represents the ring that borders the inside of the Cassini division. The yellow circle represents the ring that borders the outside of the division.

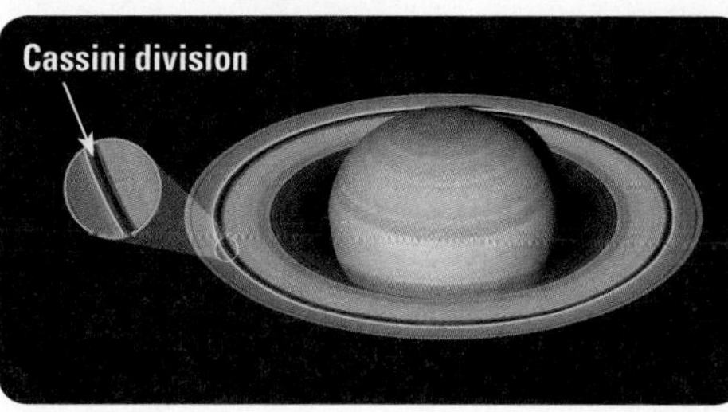

a. The radius of the red ring is 115,800 kilometers. The radius of the yellow ring is 120,600 kilometers. Find the circumference of the red ring and the circumference of the yellow ring. Round your answers to the nearest hundred kilometers. **727,200 km, 757,400 km**

b. Compare the circumferences of the two rings. About how many kilometers greater is the yellow ring's circumference than the red ring's circumference? **about 30,200 km**

Teaching Strategy

Exercise 44 You may want to have students work in pairs. One student in each pair could do one of the graphs and then they can discuss the results to describe any patterns they observe. Students often do better looking for generalizations if they are working with another another student.

44b.

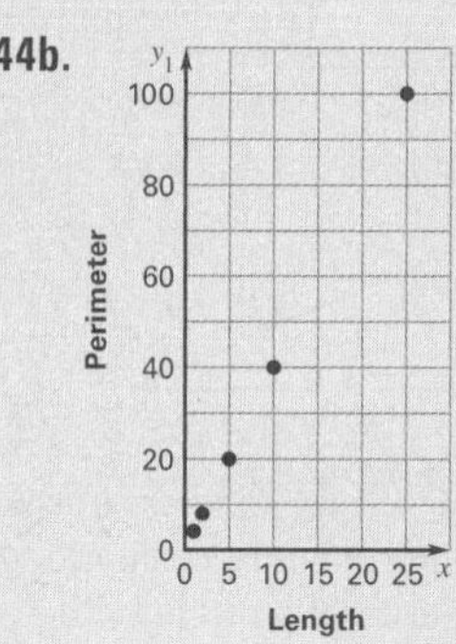

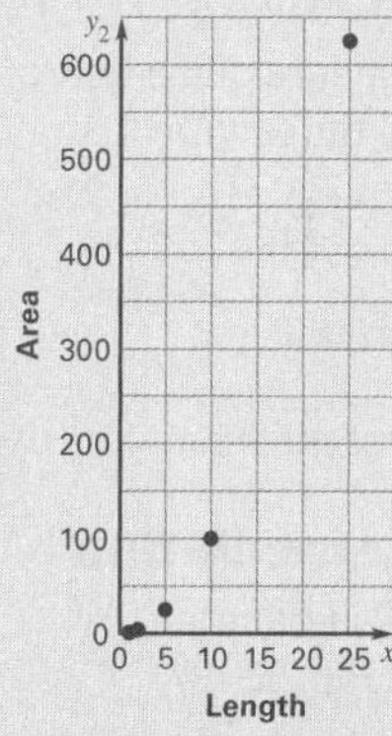

44c. *Sample answer:* As the length of the side increases, the perimeter increases linearly and the area increases exponentially.

5 ASSESS AND RETEACH

Daily Homework Quiz

Transparency Available

Find the perimeter and area of each figure.

1.
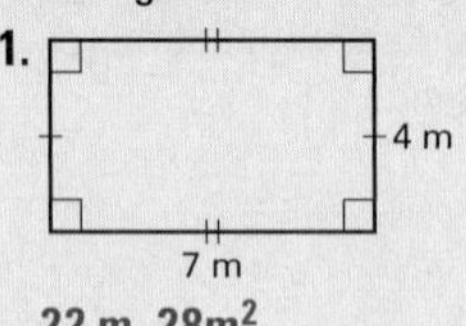

22 m, 28m²

2.
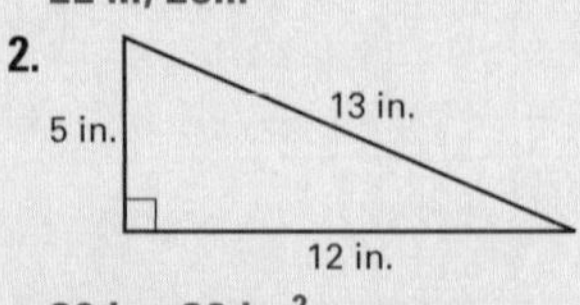

30 in., 30 in.²

3. Find the approximate circumference and area of a circle with radius 5 cm. **31.4 cm, 78.5 cm²**

4. The area of a square game board is 144 in.². Find the length of a side. **12 in.**

Available at **classzone.com**

Diagnosis/Remediation

- Practice A, B, C in Chapter 1 Resource Book, pp. 92–97
- Study Guide in Chapter 1 Resource Book, pp. 98–99
- Practice Workbook, pp. 19–21
- @HomeTutor

Challenge

Additional challenge is available in the Chapter 1 Resource Book, p. 102.

Quiz

An easily-readable reduced copy of the quiz (with answers) on Lessons 1.6–1.7 from the Assessment Book can be found on p. 1G.

---

47. $\frac{\pi}{2}$; **the area of the square is $2r^2$ and the area of the circle is πr^2, so the circle is $\frac{\pi r^2}{2r^2} = \frac{\pi}{2}$ times greater than the area of the square.**

47. **CHALLENGE** In the diagram at the right, how many times as great is the area of the circle as the area of the square? *Explain* your reasoning.

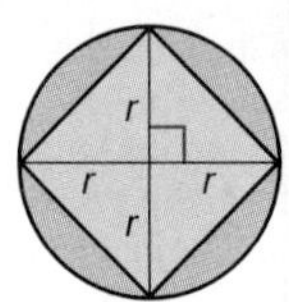

48. **ALGEBRA** You have 30 yards of fencing with which to make a rectangular pen. Let x be the length of the pen.

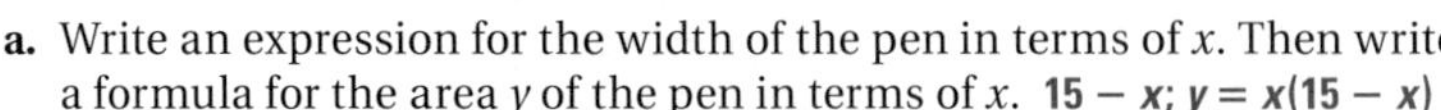

a. Write an expression for the width of the pen in terms of x. Then write a formula for the area y of the pen in terms of x. **$15 - x$; $y = x(15 - x)$**

b. You want the pen to have the greatest possible area. What length and width should you use? *Explain* your reasoning. **7.5 yd, 7.5 yd; a square maximizes area.**

MIXED REVIEW

PREVIEW Prepare for Lesson 2.1 in Exs. 49–50.

49. Use the equation $y = 2x + 1$ to copy and complete the table of values. *(p. 884)*

x	1	2	3	4	5
y	? **3**	? **5**	? **7**	? **9**	? **11**

50. Each number in a pattern is 6 less than the previous number. The first number in the pattern is 100. Write the next three numbers. *(p. 894)* **94, 88, 82**

In Exercises 51 and 52, draw a diagram to represent the problem. Then find the indicated measure. *(p. 42)* **51–52. See margin for art.**

51. The lengths (in inches) of two sides of a regular triangle are given by the expressions $5x + 40$ and $8x - 13$. Find the length of a side of the triangle. **$128\frac{1}{3}$ in.**

52. The measures of two angles of an equiangular hexagon are $12x°$ and $(10x + 20)°$. Find the measure of an angle of the hexagon. **120°**

QUIZ for Lessons 1.6–1.7

Tell whether the figure is a polygon. If it is not, *explain* why. If it is a polygon, tell whether it is *convex* or *concave*. *(p. 42)*

1.
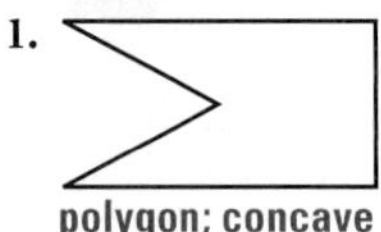

polygon; concave

2.
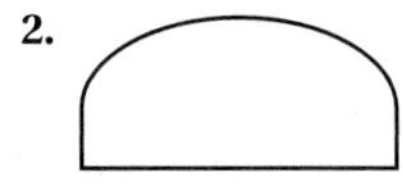

2. Not a polygon; part of the figure is not a segment.

3.
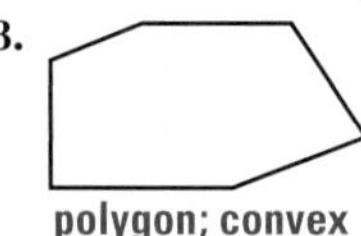

polygon; convex

Find the perimeter and area of the shaded figure. *(p. 49)*

4.
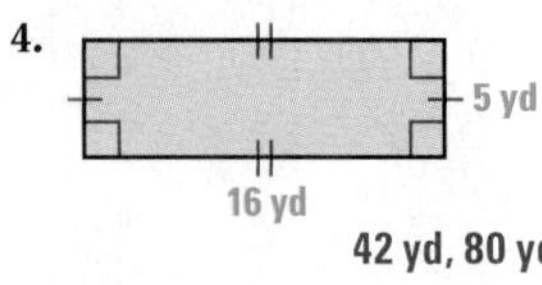

42 yd, 80 yd²

5.
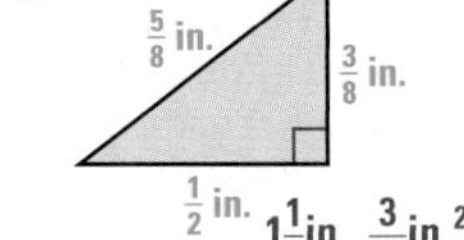

$1\frac{1}{2}$ in., $\frac{3}{32}$ in.²

6.
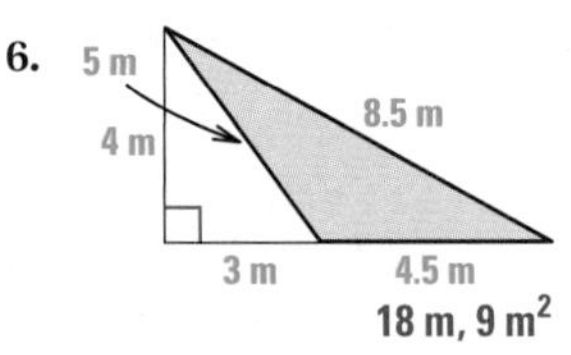

18 m, 9 m²

7. **GARDENING** You are spreading wood chips on a rectangular garden. The garden is $3\frac{1}{2}$ yards long and $2\frac{1}{2}$ yards wide. One bag of wood chips covers 10 square feet. How many bags of wood chips do you need? *(p. 49)* **8 bags**

EXTRA PRACTICE for Lesson 1.7, p. 897

51.
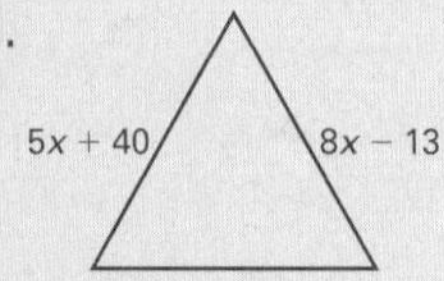

52. *Sample:*
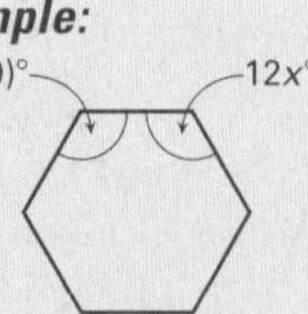

Using ALTERNATIVE METHODS

Another Way to Solve Example 4, page 51

MULTIPLE REPRESENTATIONS In Example 4 on page 51, you saw how to use an equation to solve a problem about a skating rink. *Looking for a pattern* can help you write an equation.

PROBLEM

SKATING RINK An ice-resurfacing machine is used to smooth the surface of the ice at a skating rink. The machine can resurface about 270 square yards of ice in one minute. About how many minutes does it take the machine to resurface a rectangular skating rink that is 200 feet long and 90 feet wide?

METHOD

Standards

8.0 Students know, derive, and **solve problems involving the** perimeter, circumference, **area,** volume, lateral area, and surface area **of common geometric figures.**

Using a Pattern You can use a table to look for a pattern.

STEP 1 **Find** the area of the rink in square yards. In Example 4 on page 51, you found that the area was 2000 square yards.

STEP 2 **Make** a table that shows the relationship between the time spent resurfacing the ice and the area resurfaced. Look for a pattern.

Time (min)	Area resurfaced (yd²)
1	$1 \cdot 270 = 270$
2	$2 \cdot 270 = 540$
t	$t \cdot 270 = A$

Use the pattern to write an equation for the area A that has been resurfaced after t minutes.

STEP 3 **Use** the equation to find the time t (in minutes) that it takes the machine to resurface 2000 square yards of ice.

$$270t = A$$
$$270t = 2000$$
$$t \approx 7.4$$

▶ It takes about 7 minutes.

PRACTICE

1. **PLOWING** A square field is $\frac{1}{8}$ mile long on each side. A tractor can plow about 180,000 square feet per hour. To the nearest tenth of an hour, about how long does it take to plow the field? (1 mi = 5280 ft.) **2.4 h**

2. **ERROR ANALYSIS** To solve Exercise 1 above, a student writes the equation $660 = 180{,}000t$, where t is the number of hours spent plowing. *Describe* and correct the error in the equation. **660 is the length of the field, not the area; $435{,}600 = 180{,}000t$.**

3. **PARKING LOT** A rectangular parking lot is 110 yards long and 45 yards wide. It costs about $.60 to pave each square foot of the parking lot with asphalt. About how much will it cost to pave the parking lot? **$26,730**

4. **WALKING** A circular path has a diameter of 120 meters. Your average walking speed is 4 kilometers per hour. About how many minutes will it take you to walk around the path 3 times? **about 17 min**

Alternative Strategy

Example 4 on page 51 can also be solved by using a pattern to write an equation. This method allows students to visualize the relationship between the area resurfaced and the time and will help them understand functions in later mathematics classes.

Avoiding Common Errors

Remind students that the machine can resurface 270 square yards per minute but the dimensions of the rink are given in feet. They may forget to change the units of measure in the problem.

Graphing Calculator

Students can enter the equation $y = 270x$ on the Y= list and use the TABLE feature to display a table of values. Discuss how using an appropriate value for △Tbl can help them solve the problem.

Teaching Strategy

Put students in pairs to work on these problems. Often they will learn from discussing these problems with each other. Try to pair a more competent student with a weaker student.

STATE TEST PRACTICE classzone.com

3a. *Sample answer:* ∠*DGB* and ∠*BGH*, ∠*HGC* and ∠*CGF*; ∠*DBG* and ∠*HBG*, ∠*HCG* and ∠*FCG*, ∠*DBG* and ∠*HCG*, ∠*HBG* and ∠*FCG*, ∠*HGD* and ∠*HGF*

3b. 21°, ∠*FGC* ≅ ∠*DGB*; 69°, ∠*BGH* is complementary to ∠*DGB*; 69°, ∠*HGC* is complementary to ∠*FGC*.

3c. 55°, ∠*HCG* ≅ ∠*HBG*; 125°, ∠*DBG* is supplementary to ∠*HBG*; 125°, ∠*FCG* is supplementary to ∠*HCG*.

5a. 108 bricks, about 98 bricks; convert total perimeter to inches and then divide by 10.

Lessons 1.4–1.7

1. **MULTI-STEP PROBLEM** You are covering the rectangular roof of a shed with shingles. The roof is a rectangle that is 4 yards long and 3 yards wide. Asphalt shingles cost \$.75 per square foot and wood shingles cost \$1.15 per square foot.
   a. Find the area of the roof in square feet. **108 ft²**
   b. Find the cost of using asphalt shingles and the cost of using wood shingles. **\$81, \$124.20**
   c. About how much more will you pay to use wood shingles for the roof? **\$43.20**

2. **OPEN-ENDED** In the window below, name a convex polygon and a concave polygon. Classify each of your polygons by the number of sides. ***Sample answer: GBC, GBCDEFA*; triangle, heptagon**

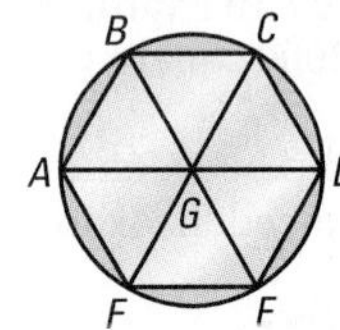

3. **EXTENDED RESPONSE** The diagram shows a decoration on a house. In the diagram, ∠*HGD* and ∠*HGF* are right angles, $m\angle DGB = 21°$, $m\angle HBG = 55°$, $\angle DGB \cong \angle FGC$, and $\angle HBG \cong \angle HCG$.

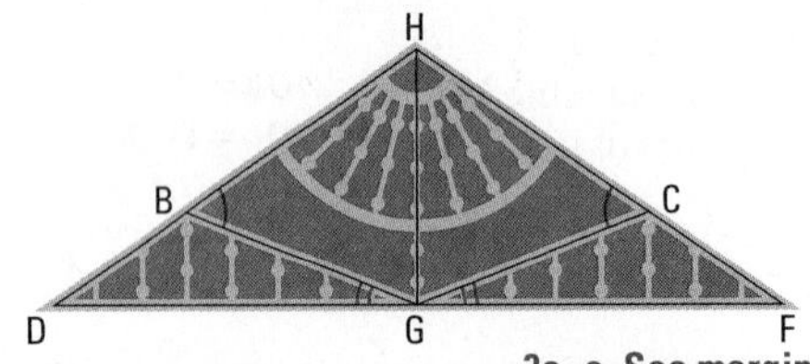

3a–c. See margin.

   a. List two pairs of complementary angles and five pairs of supplementary angles.
   b. Find $m\angle FGC$, $m\angle BGH$, and $m\angle HGC$. *Explain* your reasoning.
   c. Find $m\angle HCG$, $m\angle DBG$, and $m\angle FCG$. *Explain* your reasoning.

4. **GRIDDED ANSWER** ∠1 and ∠2 are supplementary angles, and ∠1 and ∠3 are complementary angles. Given $m\angle 1$ is 28° less than $m\angle 2$, find $m\angle 3$ in degrees. **14°**

5. **EXTENDED RESPONSE** You use bricks to outline the borders of the two gardens shown below. Each brick is 10 inches long.

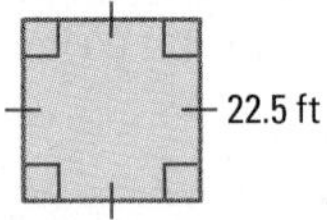

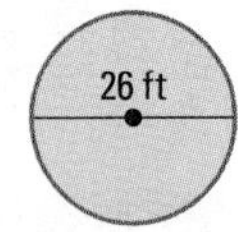

   a. You lay the bricks end-to-end around the border of each garden. How many bricks do you need for each garden? *Explain.* **See margin.**
   b. The bricks are sold in bundles of 100. How many bundles should you buy? *Explain.* **3 bundles; 206 bricks are needed, thus 3 bundles.**

6. **SHORT RESPONSE** The frame of a mirror is a regular pentagon made from pieces of bamboo. Use the diagram to find how many feet of bamboo are used in the frame. **7.5 ft of bamboo**

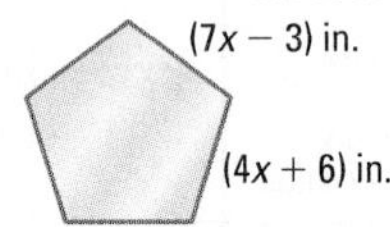

7. **GRIDDED ANSWER** As shown in the diagram, a skateboarder tilts one end of a skateboard. Find $m\angle ZWX$ in degrees. **37°**

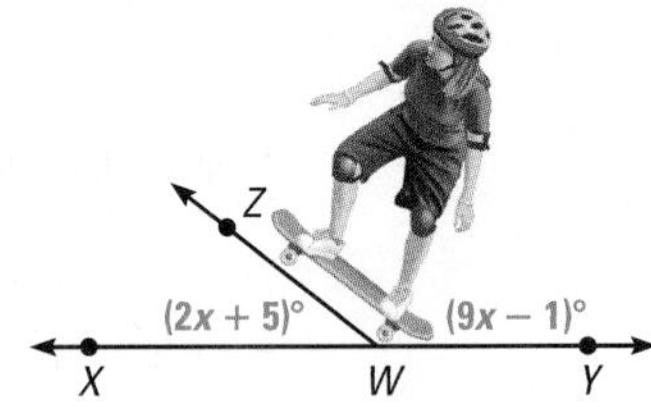

8. **SHORT RESPONSE** Use the diagram below.

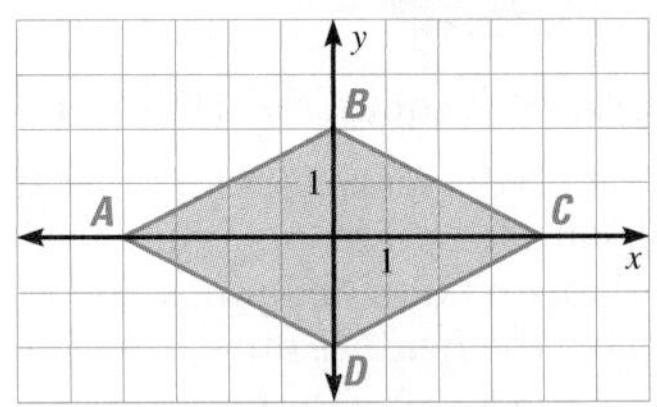

   a. Find the perimeter of quadrilateral *ABCD*. **$8\sqrt{5}$ units**
   b. Find the area of triangle *ABC* and the area of triangle *ADC*. What is the area of quadrilateral *ABCD*? *Explain.* **8 square units, 8 square units; 16 square units; the area of the quadrilateral is the sum of the areas of the two triangles.**

1 CHAPTER SUMMARY

BIG IDEAS *For Your Notebook*

Big Idea 1

Describing Geometric Figures

You learned to identify and classify geometric figures.

Point *A*	Line *AB* ($\overleftrightarrow{AB}$)	Plane *M*	Segment *AB* ($\overline{AB}$)
A	A B	M	A B

Ray *AB* ($\overrightarrow{AB}$) **Angle *A* ($\angle A$, $\angle BAC$, or $\angle CAB$)** **Polygon**

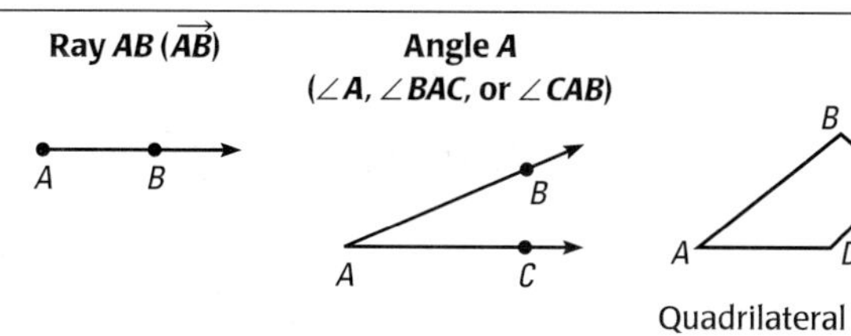

A B C D — Quadrilateral *ABCD*

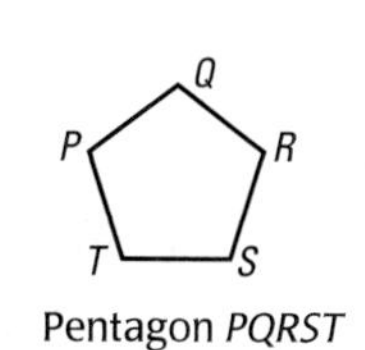

Pentagon *PQRST*

Big Idea 2

Measuring Geometric Figures

SEGMENTS You measured segments in the coordinate plane.

Distance Formula

Distance between $A(x_1, y_1)$ and $B(x_2, y_2)$:

$$AB = \sqrt{(x_1 - x_2)^2 + (y_1 - y_2)^2}$$

Midpoint Formula

Coordinates of midpoint M of $\overline{AB}$, with endpoints $A(x_1, y_1)$ and $B(x_2, y_2)$:

$$M\left(\frac{x_1 + x_2}{2}, \frac{y_1 + y_2}{2}\right)$$

ANGLES You classified angles and found their measures.

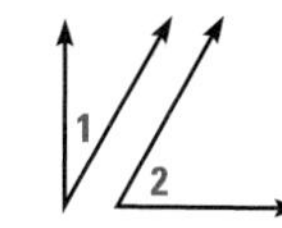

Complementary angles

$m\angle 1 + m\angle 2 = 90°$

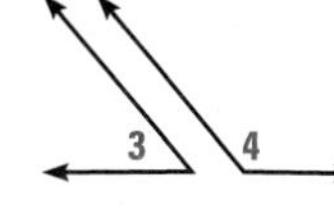

Supplementary angles

$m\angle 3 + m\angle 4 = 180°$

FORMULAS Perimeter and area formulas are reviewed on page 49.

Understanding Equality and Congruence

Congruent segments have equal lengths. Congruent angles have equal measures.

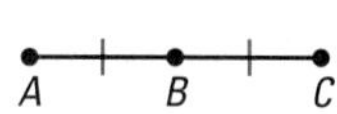

$\overline{AB} \cong \overline{BC}$ and $AB = BC$

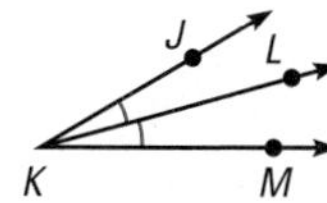

$\angle JKL \cong \angle LKM$ and $m\angle JKL = m\angle LKM$

Additional Resources

The following resources are available to help review the materials in this chapter.

Chapter 1 Resource Book

- Chapter Review Games and Activities, p. 103
- Cumulative Practice, Ch. 1, pp. 106–107

Student Resources in Spanish

eWorkbook

@HomeTutor

Vocabulary Practice

Vocabulary practice is available at **classzone.com**

Extra Example 1.1

Use the diagram shown.

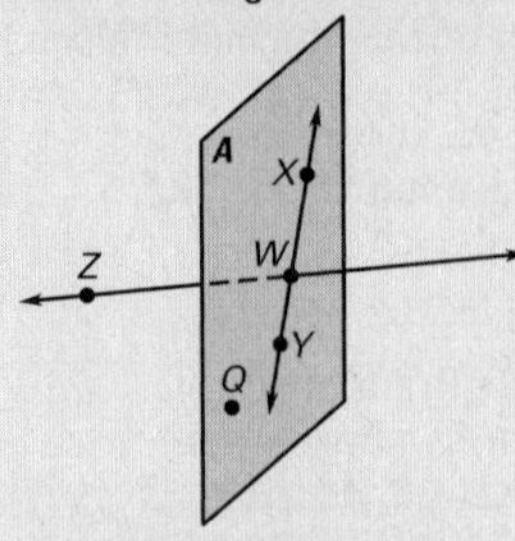

a. Give another name for $\overleftrightarrow{XY}$. **$\overleftrightarrow{XW}$, $\overleftrightarrow{YW}$, $\overleftrightarrow{WX}$, $\overleftrightarrow{WY}$, or $\overleftrightarrow{YX}$**

b. Name three points that are collinear. ***X, W, Y***

c. Name four points that are coplanar. ***X, W, Y, Q***

2. *Sample:*

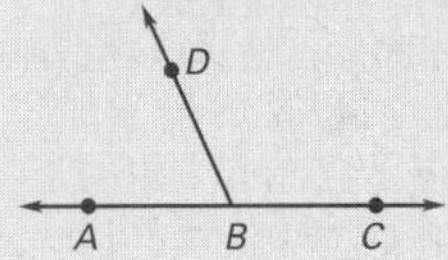

1 CHAPTER REVIEW

@HomeTutor
classzone.com
- Multi-Language Glossary
- Vocabulary Practice

REVIEW KEY VOCABULARY

For a list of postulates and theorems, see pp. 926–931.

- undefined terms, *p. 2*
  point, line, plane
- collinear, coplanar points, *p. 2*
- defined terms, *p. 3*
- line segment, endpoints, *p. 3*
- ray, opposite rays, *p. 3*
- intersection, *p. 4*
- postulate, axiom, *p. 9*
- coordinate, *p. 9*
- distance, *p. 9*
- between, *p. 10*
- congruent segments, *p. 11*
- midpoint, *p. 15*
- segment bisector, *p. 15*
- angle, *p. 24*
  sides, vertex, measure
- acute, right, obtuse, straight, *p. 25*
- congruent angles, *p. 26*
- angle bisector, *p. 28*
- construction, *p. 33*
- complementary angles, *p. 35*
- supplementary angles, *p. 35*
- adjacent angles, *p. 35*
- linear pair, *p. 37*
- vertical angles, *p. 37*
- polygon, *p. 42*
  side, vertex
- convex, concave, *p. 42*
- *n*-gon, *p. 43*
- equilateral, equiangular, regular, *p. 43*

VOCABULARY EXERCISES

1. Copy and complete: Points *A* and *B* are the __?__ of $\overline{AB}$. **endpoints**
2. Draw an example of a *linear pair.* **See margin.**
3. If *Q* is between points *P* and *R* on $\overleftrightarrow{PR}$, and $PQ = QR$, then *Q* is the __?__ of $\overline{PR}$. **midpoint**

REVIEW EXAMPLES AND EXERCISES

Use the review examples and exercises below to check your understanding of the concepts you have learned in each lesson of Chapter 1.

1.1 Identify Points, Lines, and Planes *pp. 2–8*

EXAMPLE

Use the diagram shown at the right.

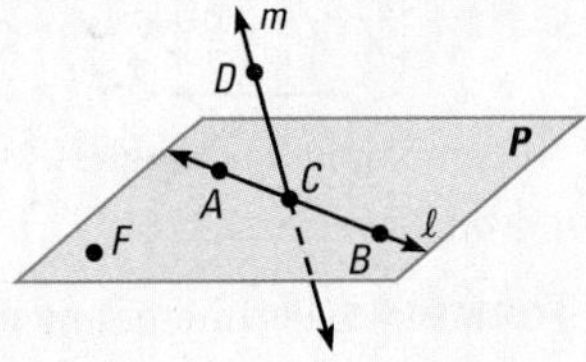

Another name for $\overleftrightarrow{CD}$ is line *m*.

Points *A*, *B*, and *C* are collinear.

Points *A*, *B*, *C*, and *F* are coplanar.

EXERCISES

EXAMPLES 1, 2, and 3 on pp. 3–4 for Exs. 4–8

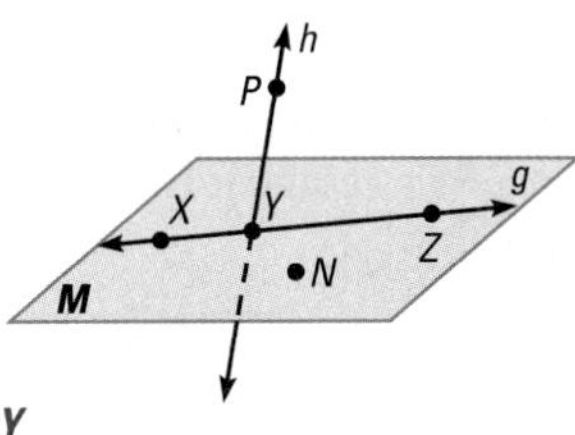

4. Give another name for line *g*. ***Sample answer:*** **$\overleftrightarrow{YZ}$**
5. Name three points that are *not* collinear. ***Sample answer:*** **points *P, Y, Z***
6. Name four points that are coplanar. ***Sample answer: N, X, Y, Z***
7. Name a pair of opposite rays. **$\overrightarrow{YZ}$, $\overrightarrow{YX}$**
8. Name the intersection of line *h* and plane *M*. **point *Y***

@HomeTutor
classzone.com
Chapter Review Practice

1.2 Use Segments and Congruence

pp. 9–14

EXAMPLE

Find the length of $\overline{HJ}$.

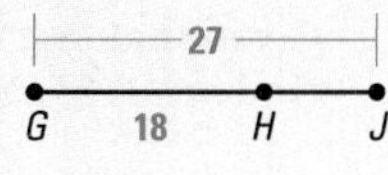

$GJ = GH + HJ$ **Segment Addition Postulate**

$27 = 18 + HJ$ **Substitute 27 for *GJ* and 18 for *GH*.**

$9 = HJ$ **Subtract 18 from each side.**

EXERCISES

EXAMPLES 2, 3, and 4 on pp. 10–11 for Exs. 9–12

Find the indicated length.

9. Find *AB*. **1.2**

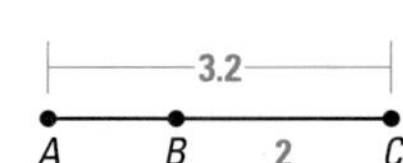

10. Find *NP*. **30**

11. Find *XY*. **7**

12. The endpoints of $\overline{DE}$ are $D(-4, 11)$ and $E(-4, -13)$. The endpoints of $\overline{GH}$ are $G(-14, 5)$ and $H(-9, 5)$. Are $\overline{DE}$ and $\overline{GH}$ congruent? *Explain.* **no; $DE = 24$, $GH = 5$**

1.3 Use Midpoint and Distance Formulas

pp. 15–22

EXAMPLE

$\overline{EF}$ has endpoints $E(1, 4)$ and $F(3, 2)$. Find (a) the length of $\overline{EF}$ rounded to the nearest tenth of a unit, and (b) the coordinates of the midpoint *M* of $\overline{EF}$.

a. Use the Distance Formula.

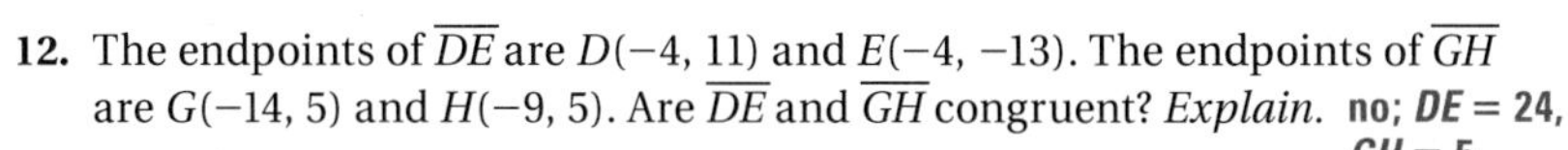

$$EF = \sqrt{(3-1)^2 + (2-4)^2} = \sqrt{2^2 + (-2)^2} = \sqrt{8} \approx 2.8 \text{ units}$$

b. Use the Midpoint Formula.

$$M\left(\frac{1+3}{2}, \frac{4+2}{2}\right) = M(2, 3)$$

EXERCISES

EXAMPLES 2, 3, and 4 on pp. 16–18 for Exs. 13–19

13. Point *M* is the midpoint of $\overline{JK}$. Find *JK* when $JM = 6x - 7$ and $MK = 2x + 3$. **16**

In Exercises 14–17, the endpoints of a segment are given. Find the length of the segment rounded to the nearest tenth. Then find the coordinates of the midpoint of the segment.

14. $A(2, 5)$ and $B(4, 3)$ **2.8; (3, 4)**

15. $F(1, 7)$ and $G(6, 0)$ **8.6; (3.5, 3.5)**

16. $H(-3, 9)$ and $J(5, 4)$ **9.4; (1, 6.5)**

17. $K(10, 6)$ and $L(0, -7)$ **16.4; (5, −0.5)**

18. Point $C(3, 8)$ is the midpoint of $\overline{AB}$. One endpoint is $A(-1, 5)$. Find the coordinates of endpoint *B*. **(7, 11)**

19. The endpoints of $\overline{EF}$ are $E(2, 3)$ and $F(8, 11)$. The midpoint of $\overline{EF}$ is *M*. Find the length of $\overline{EM}$. **5**

Extra Example 1.2

Find the length of $\overline{NP}$. **20**

Extra Example 1.3

$\overline{PQ}$ has endpoints $P(-4, -2)$ and $Q(-6, 8)$. Find

a. the length of $\overline{PQ}$ to the nearest tenth of a unit. **10.2 units**

b. the midpoint *M* of $\overline{PQ}$. **(−5, 3)**

Extra Example 1.4

Given that $m\angle KLM$ is 84°, find $m\angle KLN$ and $m\angle NLM$. **57°, 27°**

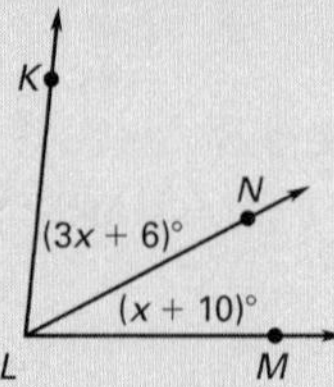

Extra Example 1.5

a. $\angle 1$ and $\angle 2$ are complementary angles. Given that $m\angle 1 = 59°$, find $m\angle 2$. **31°**

b. $\angle 3$ and $\angle 4$ are supplementary angles. Given that $m\angle 3 = 84°$, find $m\angle 4$. **96°**

1.4 Measure and Classify Angles — pp. 24–32

EXAMPLE

Given that $m\angle YXV$ is 60°, find $m\angle YXZ$ and $m\angle ZXV$.

STEP 1 **Find** the value of x.

$m\angle YXV = m\angle YXZ + m\angle ZXV$ — **Angle Addition Postulate**

$60° = (2x + 11)° + (x + 13)°$ — **Substitute angle measures.**

$x = 12$ — **Solve for x.**

STEP 2 **Evaluate** the given expressions when $x = 12$.

$m\angle YXZ = (2x + 11)° = (2 \cdot 12 + 11)° = 35°$

$m\angle ZXV = (x + 13)° = (12 + 13)° = 25°$

EXERCISES

EXAMPLES 3 and 5 on pp. 26, 28 for Exs. 20–21

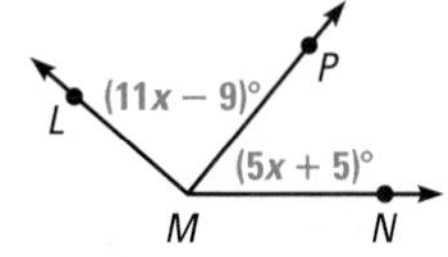

20. In the diagram shown at the right, $m\angle LMN = 140°$. Find $m\angle PMN$. **50°**

21. $\overrightarrow{VZ}$ bisects $\angle UVW$, and $m\angle UVZ = 81°$. Find $m\angle UVW$. Then classify $\angle UVW$ by its angle measure. **162°; obtuse**

1.5 Describe Angle Pair Relationships — pp. 35–41

EXAMPLE

a. $\angle 1$ and $\angle 2$ are complementary angles. Given that $m\angle 1 = 37°$, find $m\angle 2$.

$m\angle 2 = 90° - m\angle 1 = 90° - 37° = 53°$

b. $\angle 3$ and $\angle 4$ are supplementary angles. Given that $m\angle 3 = 106°$, find $m\angle 4$.

$m\angle 4 = 180° - m\angle 3 = 180° - 106° = 74°$

EXERCISES

EXAMPLES 2 and 3 on p. 36 for Exs. 22–31

$\angle 1$ and $\angle 2$ are complementary angles. Given the measure of $\angle 1$, find $m\angle 2$.

22. $m\angle 1 = 12°$ **78°** **23.** $m\angle 1 = 83°$ **7°** **24.** $m\angle 1 = 46°$ **44°** **25.** $m\angle 1 = 2°$ **88°**

$\angle 3$ and $\angle 4$ are supplementary angles. Given the measure of $\angle 3$, find $m\angle 4$.

26. $m\angle 3 = 116°$ **64°** **27.** $m\angle 3 = 56°$ **124°** **28.** $m\angle 3 = 89°$ **91°** **29.** $m\angle 3 = 12°$ **168°**

30. $\angle 1$ and $\angle 2$ are complementary angles. Find the measures of the angles when $m\angle 1 = (x - 10)°$ and $m\angle 2 = (2x + 40)°$. **10°, 80°**

31. $\angle 1$ and $\angle 2$ are supplementary angles. Find the measures of the angles when $m\angle 1 = (3x + 50)°$ and $m\angle 2 = (4x + 32)°$. Then classify $\angle 1$ by its angle measure. **92°, 88°; obtuse**

@HomeTutor
classzone.com
Chapter Review Practice

1.6 Classify Polygons *pp. 42–47*

EXAMPLE

Classify the polygon by the number of sides. Tell whether it is equilateral, equiangular, or regular. *Explain.*

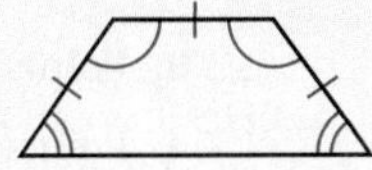

The polygon has four sides, so it is a quadrilateral. It is not equiangular or equilateral, so it is not regular.

EXERCISES

EXAMPLES 2 and 3 on pp. 43–44 for Exs. 32–35

Classify the polygon by the number of sides. Tell whether it is equilateral, equiangular, or regular. *Explain.* **32–34. See margin.**

32.

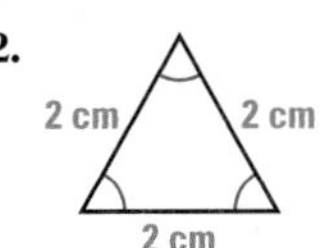

33.

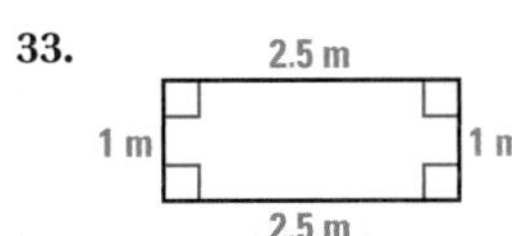

34.

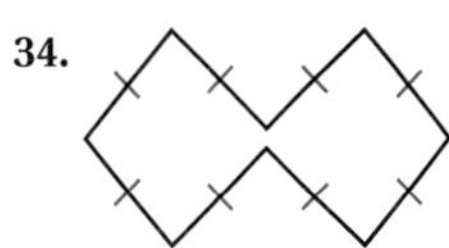

35. Pentagon *ABCDE* is a regular polygon. The length of $\overline{BC}$ is represented by the expression $5x - 4$. The length of $\overline{DE}$ is represented by the expression $2x + 11$. Find the length of $\overline{AB}$. **21**

1.7 Find Perimeter, Circumference, and Area *pp. 49–56*

EXAMPLE

The diameter of a circle is 10 feet. Find the circumference and area of the circle. Round to the nearest tenth.

The radius is half of the diameter, so $r = \frac{1}{2}(10) = 5$ ft.

Circumference

$C = 2\pi r \approx 2(3.14)(5) = 31.4$ ft

Area

$A = \pi r^2 \approx 3.14(5^2) = 78.5\ \text{ft}^2$

EXERCISES

EXAMPLES 1, 2, and 3 on pp. 49–50 for Exs. 36–40

In Exercises 36–38, find the perimeter (or circumference) and area of the figure described. If necessary, round to the nearest tenth.

36. Circle with diameter 15.6 meters **49.0 m, 191.0 m²**

37. Rectangle with length $4\frac{1}{2}$ inches and width $2\frac{1}{2}$ inches **14 in., 11.3 in.²**

38. Triangle with vertices $U(1, 2)$, $V(-8, 2)$, and $W(-4, 6)$ **21.1 units, 18 square units**

39. The height of a triangle is 18.6 meters. Its area is 46.5 square meters. Find the length of the triangle's base. **5 m**

40. The area of a circle is 320 square meters. Find the radius of the circle. Then find the circumference. Round your answers to the nearest tenth. **10.1 m; 63.4 m**

Extra Example 1.6

Classify the polygon shown by the number of sides and decide whether it is a regular polygon.

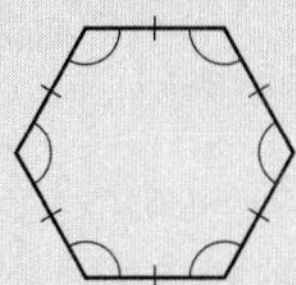

hexagon, regular

Extra Example 1.7

The diameter of a circle is 22 inches. Find the following. Round to the nearest tenth.

a. circumference **69.1 in.**

b. area **379.9 in.²**

32. Triangle; regular; it has three congruent sides and three congruent angles.

33. Quadrilateral; equiangular; it has four congruent angles but its four sides are not all congruent.

34. Octagon; equilateral; it has eight congruent sides but its eight angles are not all congruent.

1 CHAPTER TEST

Additional Resources

Assessment Book

- Chapter Test, Levels A, B, C, pp. 4–9
- Standardized Chapter Test, pp. 10–11
- SAT/ACT Chapter Test, pp. 12–13
- Alternative Assessment, pp. 14–15

Test Generator CD-ROM

Chapter Test

Easily-readable reduced copies (with answers) of Chapter Test B, the Standardized Chapter Test, and the Alternative Assessment from the Assessment Book can be found on pp. 1G–1H.

20. *Sample:*

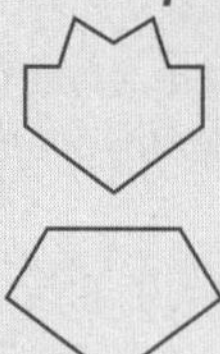

Use the diagram to decide whether the statement is *true* or *false*.

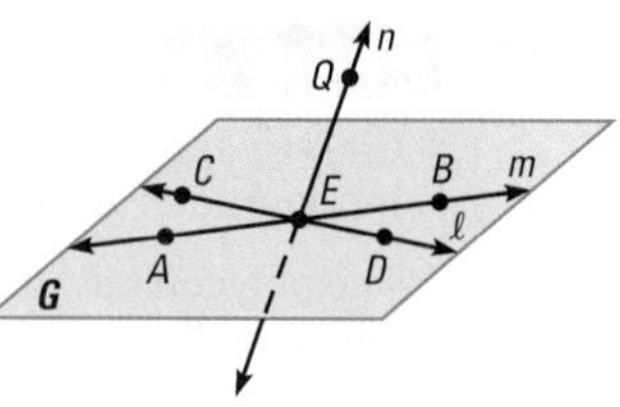

1. Point A lies on line m. **true**
2. Point D lies on line n. **false**
3. Points B, C, E, and Q are coplanar. **false**
4. Points C, E, and B are collinear. **false**
5. Another name for plane G is plane QEC. **false**

Find the indicated length.

6. Find HJ. **22**

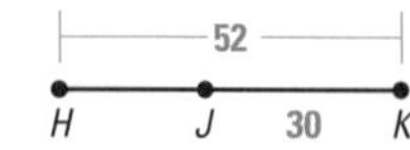

7. Find BC. **11**

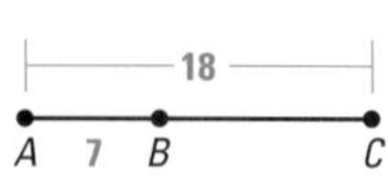

8. Find XZ. **71**

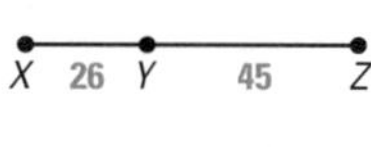

In Exercises 9–11, find the distance between the two points.

9. $T(3, 4)$ and $W(2, 7)$ **$\sqrt{10} \approx 3.2$**
10. $C(5, 10)$ and $D(6, -1)$ **$\sqrt{122} \approx 11.0$**
11. $M(-8, 0)$ and $N(-1, 3)$ **$\sqrt{58} \approx 7.6$**
12. The midpoint of $\overline{AB}$ is $M(9, 7)$. One endpoint is $A(3, 9)$. Find the coordinates of endpoint B. **(15, 5)**
13. Line t bisects $\overline{CD}$ at point M, $CM = 3x$, and $MD = 27$. Find CD. **54**

In Exercises 14 and 15, use the diagram.

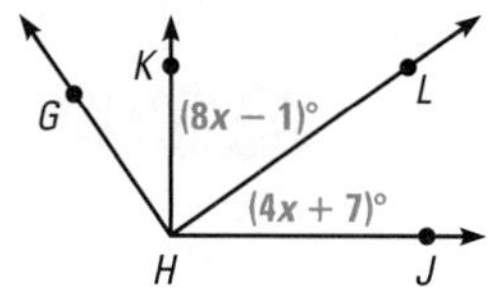

14. Trace the diagram and extend the rays. Use a protractor to measure $\angle GHJ$. Classify it as *acute*, *obtuse*, *right*, or *straight*. **125°; obtuse**
15. Given $m\angle KHJ = 90°$, find $m\angle LHJ$. **35°**
16. The measure of $\angle QRT$ is 154°, and $\overrightarrow{RS}$ bisects $\angle QRT$. What are the measures of $\angle QRS$ and $\angle SRT$? **77°, 77°**

In Exercises 17 and 18, use the diagram at the right.

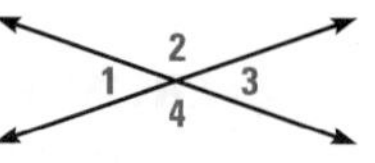

17. Name four linear pairs.

17. $\angle 1$ and $\angle 2$, $\angle 2$ and $\angle 3$, $\angle 3$ and $\angle 4$, $\angle 4$ and $\angle 1$

18. Name two pairs of vertical angles. **$\angle 1$ and $\angle 3$, $\angle 2$ and $\angle 4$**
19. The measure of an angle is 64°. What is the measure of its complement? What is the measure of its supplement? **26°, 116°**
20. A convex polygon has half as many sides as a concave 10-gon. Draw the concave polygon and the convex polygon. Classify the convex polygon by the number of sides it has. **See margin for art; pentagon.**
21. Find the perimeter of the regular pentagon shown at the right. **120**

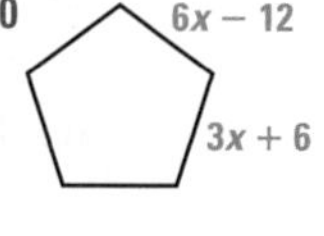

22. **CARPET** You can afford to spend \$300 to carpet a room that is 5.5 yards long and 4.5 yards wide. The cost to purchase and install the carpet you like is \$1.50 per square foot. Can you afford to buy this carpet? *Explain.* **No; it would cost \$334.13 to carpet the room.**

xy ALGEBRA REVIEW

Animated Algebra classzone.com

SOLVE LINEAR EQUATIONS AND WORD PROBLEMS

EXAMPLE 1 Solve linear equations

Solve the equation $-3(x + 5) + 4x = 25$.

$-3(x + 5) + 4x = 25$ **Write original equation.**

$-3x - 15 + 4x = 25$ **Use the Distributive Property.**

$x - 15 = 25$ **Group and combine like terms.**

$x = 40$ **Add 15 to each side.**

EXAMPLE 2 Solve a real-world problem

MEMBERSHIP COSTS A health club charges an initiation fee of $50. Members then pay $45 per month. You have $400 to spend on a health club membership. For how many months can you afford to be a member?

Let n represent the number of months you can pay for a membership.

$400 = Initiation fee + (Monthly Rate × Number of Months)

$400 = 50 + 45n$ **Substitute.**

$350 = 45n$ **Subtract 50 from each side.**

$7.8 = n$ **Divide each side by 45.**

▶ You can afford to be a member at the health club for 7 months.

EXERCISES

EXAMPLE 1 for Exs. 1–9

Solve the equation.

1. $9y + 1 - y = 49$ **6**
2. $5z + 7 + z = -8$ **$-2\frac{1}{2}$**
3. $-4(2 - t) = -16$ **-2**
4. $7a - 2(a - 1) = 17$ **3**
5. $\frac{4x}{3} + 2(3 - x) = 5$ **$1\frac{1}{2}$**
6. $\frac{2x - 5}{7} = 4$ **$16\frac{1}{2}$**
7. $9c - 11 = -c + 29$ **4**
8. $2(0.3r + 1) = 23 - 0.1r$ **30**
9. $5(k + 2) = 3(k - 4)$ **-11**

EXAMPLE 2 for Exs. 10–12

10. **GIFT CERTIFICATE** You have a $50 gift certificate at a store. You want to buy a book that costs $8.99 and boxes of stationery for your friends. Each box costs $4.59. How many boxes can you buy with your gift certificate? **8 boxes**

11. **CATERING** It costs $350 to rent a room for a party. You also want to hire a caterer. The caterer charges $8.75 per person. How many people can come to the party if you have $500 to spend on the room and the caterer? **17 people**

12. **JEWELRY** You are making a necklace out of glass beads. You use one bead that is $1\frac{1}{2}$ inches long and smaller beads that are each $\frac{3}{4}$ inch long. The necklace is 18 inches long. How many smaller beads do you need? **22 smaller beads**

Extra Example 1

Solve the equation $4(x - 2) + 5x = 19$. **3**

Extra Example 2

Mrs. Clarett ordered business cards. The company charged $25 for the design and $20 for each box of cards. If the total charge was $145, how many boxes of cards did Mrs. Clarett order? **6 boxes**

Using Rubrics

The rubric given on the pupil page is a sample of a three-level rubric. Other rubrics may contain four, five, or six levels. For more information on rubrics, see the *Geometry Toolkit*.

Test-Taking Strategy

Read the question carefully. Watch for different units in the problem. Here the cost is per square foot but the dimensions are in yards. Draw and label a diagram of the dance floor and convert the dimensions to feet. This will prevent conversion errors later in the solution.

Avoiding Common Errors

Students may change square yards to square feet by multiplying by 3. Remind them that there are 9 square feet in one square yard.

Scoring Rubric

Full Credit
- solution is complete and correct

Partial Credit
- solution is complete but has errors, *or*
- solution is without error but incomplete

No Credit
- no solution is given, *or*
- solution makes no sense

Standards

8.0 Students know, derive, and **solve problems involving the** perimeter, circumference, **area,** volume, lateral area, and surface area **of common geometric figures.**

SHORT RESPONSE QUESTIONS

PROBLEM

You want to rent portable flooring to set up a dance floor for a party. The table below shows the cost of renting portable flooring from a local company. You want to have a rectangular dance floor that is 5 yards long and 4 yards wide. How much will it cost to rent flooring? *Explain* your reasoning.

If the floor area is ...	Then the cost is ...
less than 100 square feet	\$6.50 per square foot
between 100 and 200 square feet	\$6.25 per square foot

Below are sample solutions to the problem. Read each solution and the comments in blue to see why the sample represents full credit, partial credit, or no credit.

SAMPLE 1: Full credit solution

Find the area of the dance floor. Area $= \ell w = 5(4) = 20 \text{ yd}^2$.

Then convert this area to square feet. There are $3^2 = 9 \text{ ft}^2$ in 1 yd^2.

The reasoning is correct, and the computations are accurate.

$$20 \text{ yd}^2 \cdot \frac{9 \text{ ft}^2}{1 \text{ yd}^2} = 180 \text{ ft}^2$$

Because 180 ft^2 is between 100 ft^2 and 200 ft^2, the price of flooring is \$6.25 per square foot. Multiply the price per square foot by the area.

$$\text{Total cost} = \frac{\$6.25}{1 \text{ ft}^2} \cdot 180 \text{ ft}^2 = \$1125$$

It will cost \$1125 to rent flooring.

The answer is correct.

SAMPLE 2: Partial credit solution

The area of the dance floor is $5(4) = 20$ square yards. Convert this area to square feet. There are 3 feet in 1 yard.

$$20 \text{ yd}^2 \cdot \frac{3 \text{ ft}^2}{1 \text{ yd}^2} = 60 \text{ ft}^2$$

The reasoning is correct, but an incorrect conversion leads to an incorrect answer.

The flooring will cost \$6.50 per square foot because 60 ft^2 is less than 100 ft^2. To find the total cost, multiply the area by the cost per square foot.

$$60 \text{ ft}^2 \cdot \frac{\$6.50}{1 \text{ ft}^2} = \$390$$

It will cost \$390 to rent flooring.

SAMPLE 3: Partial credit solution

The computations and the answer are correct, but the reasoning is incomplete.

> The area of the room is 180 ft^2, so the flooring price is \$6.25. The total cost is $180 \cdot 6.25 = \$1125$.
>
> It will cost \$1125 to rent flooring.

SAMPLE 4: No credit solution

The student's reasoning is incorrect, and the answer is incorrect.

> Floor area $= 4 \times 5 = 20$.
>
> Cost $= 20 \times \$650 = \$13{,}000$.
>
> It will cost \$13,000 to rent flooring.

PRACTICE Apply the Scoring Rubric

Use the rubric on page 66 to score the solution to the problem below as *full credit, partial credit,* or *no credit. Explain* your reasoning. 1–4. See margin.

> **PROBLEM** You have 450 daffodil bulbs. You divide a 5 yard by 2 yard rectangular garden into 1 foot by 1 foot squares. You want to plant the same number of bulbs in each square. How many bulbs should you plant in each square? *Explain* your reasoning.

1. First find the area of the plot in square feet. There are 3 feet in 1 yard, so the length is $5(3) = 15$ feet, and the width is $2(3) = 6$ feet. The area is $15(6) = 90$ square feet. The garden plot can be divided into 90 squares with side length 1 foot. Divide 450 by 90 to get 5 bulbs in each square.

2. The area of the garden plot is $5(2) = 10$ square yards. There are 3 feet in 1 yard, so you can multiply 10 square yards by 3 to get an area of 30 square feet. You can divide the garden plot into 30 squares. To find how many bulbs per square, divide 450 bulbs by 30 to get 15 bulbs.

3. Divide 450 by the area of the plot: 450 bulbs $\div$ 10 yards $=$ 45 bulbs. You should plant 45 bulbs in each square.

4. Multiply the length and width by 3 feet to convert yards to feet. The area is 15 ft $\times$ 6 ft $=$ 90 ft^2. Divide the garden into 90 squares.

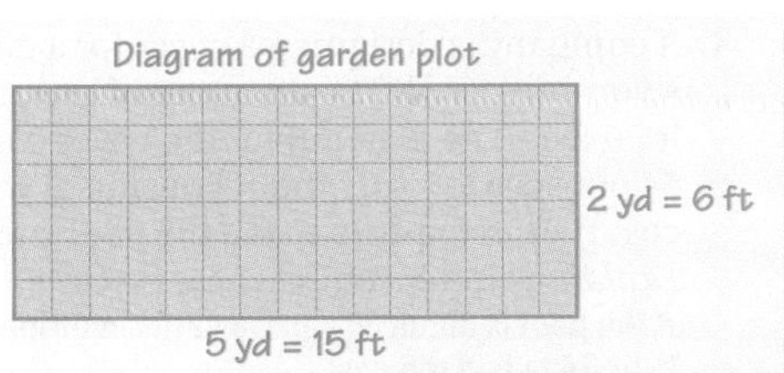

Study Strategy

Have students make a detailed list of the steps they would use to solve the problem in Practice. This will help them identify errors and things overlooked in each of the proposed solutions.

1. Full Credit; the reasoning is correct and the computations are accurate.

2. Partial Credit; the reasoning is correct, but an incorrect conversion leads to an incorrect solution.

3. No Credit; the reasoning is incorrect and the solution is incorrect.

4. Partial Credit; the reasoning is correct, but incomplete.

2. (−0.5, −1.5); 2.9 km; use the Midpoint Formula to find the coordinates of *H* and then the Distance Formula to find the distance between your house and the library.

3. 4158 gal; the surface area of the pool is 236.25 square feet, multiply 236.25 by 17.6 to find the number of gallons evaporated.

5. About \$1.88; $x + 5 = 4x - 7$, so $x = 4$. Then the pentagon has 9 in. sides and perimeter = 45 in.; $\frac{\$1.50}{1 \text{ yd}} \cdot 45 \text{ in.} \cdot \frac{1 \text{ yd}}{36 \text{ in.}} \approx \$1.88$.

6. 120°; find the measure of angle *B* to be 60°, then subtract the measure of angle *B* from 180°.

7. About 2.2 km; the distance when driving through Baxton is 8 kilometers; the direct distance is about 5.8 kilometers, so their difference is about 2.2 kilometers.

8. 12 pairs; using the same unit, divide the length of wire by the circumference of one earring to find the number of earrings that can be made. Divide that by 2 to find the number of pairs that can be made.

SHORT RESPONSE

1. It costs \$2 per square foot to refinish a hardwood floor if the area is less than 300 square feet, and \$1.75 per square foot if the area is greater than or equal to 300 square feet. How much does it cost to refinish a rectangular floor that is 6 yards long and 4.5 yards wide? *Explain* your reasoning. **\$486; the area is 243 square feet, so 243 must be multiplied by \$2.**

2. As shown below, the library (point *L*) and the Town Hall (point *T*) are on the same straight road. Your house is on the same road, halfway between the library and the Town Hall. Let point *H* mark the location of your house. Find the coordinates of *H* and the approximate distance between the library and your house. *Explain* your reasoning. **See margin.**

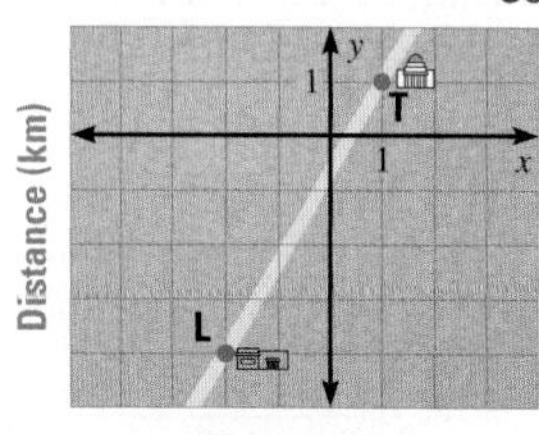

3. The water in a swimming pool evaporates over time if the pool is not covered. In one year, a swimming pool can lose about 17.6 gallons of water for every square foot of water that is exposed to air. About how much water would evaporate in one year from the surface of the water in the pool shown? *Explain* your reasoning. **See margin.**

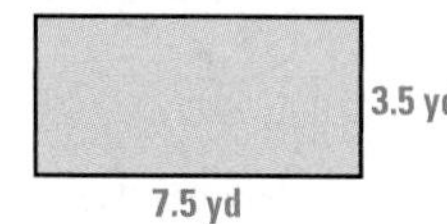

4. A company is designing a cover for a circular swimming pool. The diameter of the pool is 20 feet. The material for the cover costs \$4 per square yard. About how much will it cost the company to make the pool cover? *Explain* your reasoning. **About \$140; the area of the pool is about 35 square yards, multiply 35 by \$4 to find the cost.**

5. You are making a mat with a fringed border. The mat is shaped like a regular pentagon, as shown below. Fringe costs \$1.50 per yard. How much will the fringe for the mat cost? *Explain* your reasoning. **See margin.**

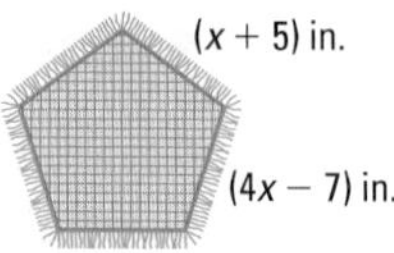

6. Angles *A* and *B* are complementary angles, $m\angle A = (2x - 4)^\circ$, and $m\angle B = (4x - 8)^\circ$. Find the measure of the supplement of $\angle B$. *Explain* your reasoning. **See margin.**

7. As shown on the map, you have two ways to drive from Atkins to Canton. You can either drive through Baxton, or you can drive directly from Atkins to Canton. About how much shorter is the trip from Atkins to Canton if you do not go through Baxton? *Explain* your reasoning. **See margin.**

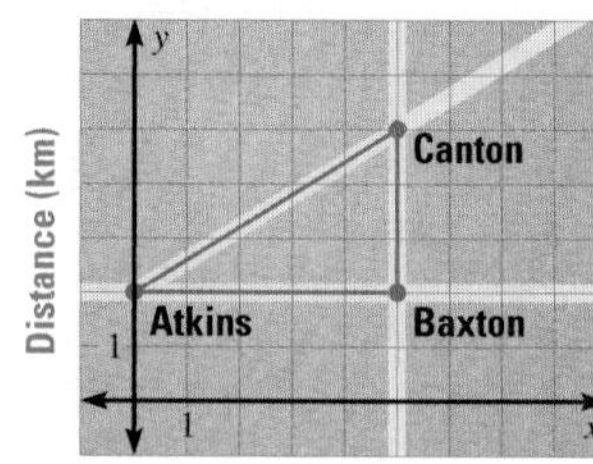

8. A jeweler is making pairs of gold earrings. For each earring, the jeweler will make a circular hoop like the one shown below. The jeweler has 2 meters of gold wire. How many pairs of gold hoops can the jeweler make? *Justify* your reasoning. **See margin.**

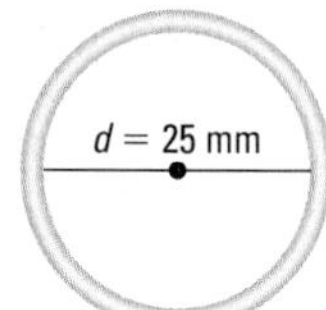

MULTIPLE CHOICE

9. The midpoint of $\overline{AB}$ is $M(4, -2)$. One endpoint is $A(-2, 6)$. What is the length of $\overline{AB}$? **C**

   Ⓐ 5 units

   Ⓑ 10 units

   Ⓒ 20 units

   Ⓓ 28 units

10. The perimeter of a rectangle is 85 feet. The length of the rectangle is 4 feet more than its width. Which equation can be used to find the width w of the rectangle? **C**

    Ⓐ $85 = 2(w + 4)$

    Ⓑ $85 = 2w + 2(w - 4)$

    Ⓒ $85 = 2(2w + 4)$

    Ⓓ $85 = w(w + 4)$

GRIDDED ANSWER

11. In the diagram, $\overrightarrow{YW}$ bisects $\angle XYZ$. Find $m\angle XYZ$ in degrees. **114°**

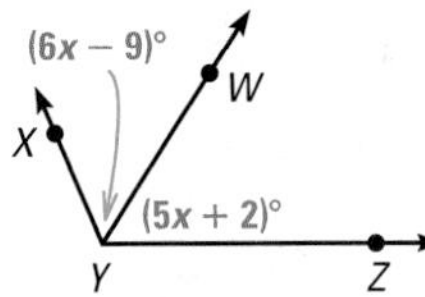

12. Angles A and B are complements, and the measure of $\angle A$ is 8 times the measure of $\angle B$. Find the measure (in degrees) of the supplement of $\angle A$. **100°**

13. The perimeter of the triangle shown is 400 feet. Find its area in square feet. **6000 ft²**

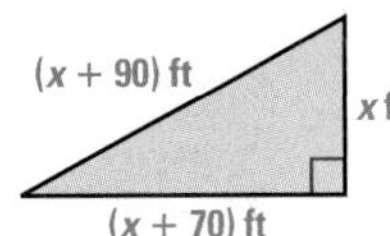

EXTENDED RESPONSE

14. The athletic director at a college wants to build an indoor playing field. The playing field will be twice as long as it is wide. Artificial turf costs $4 per square foot. The director has $50,000 to spend on artificial turf.

    a. What is the largest area that the director can afford to cover with artificial turf? *Explain.* **12,500 ft²; divide 50,000 by 4.**

    b. Find the approximate length and width of the field to the nearest foot. **158 ft, 79 ft**

15. An artist uses black ink to draw the outlines of 30 circles and 25 squares, and red ink to fill in the area of each circle and square. The diameter of each circle is 1 inch, and the side length of each square is 1 inch. Which group of drawings uses more black ink, the *circles* or the *squares*? Which group of drawings uses more red ink? *Explain.* **See margin.**

16. Points A and C represent the positions of two boats in a large lake. Point B represents the position of a fixed buoy.

    a. Find the distance from each boat to the buoy. **See margin.**

    b. The boat at point A travels toward the buoy in a straight line at a rate of 5 kilometers per hour. The boat at point C travels to the buoy at a rate of 5.2 kilometers per hour. Which boat reaches the buoy first? *Explain.* **Boat *C*; boat *A* takes about 1.3 hours to get to the buoy, and boat *C* takes about 1.1 hours to get to the buoy.**

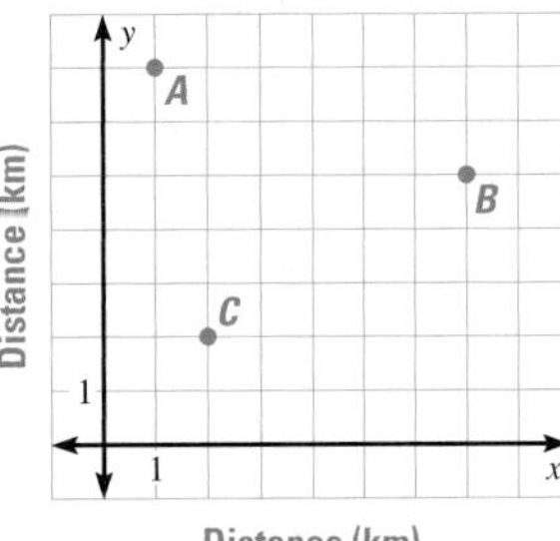

15. Square; square; the perimeter of 1 square is 4 inches and there are 25 squares, so there are 100 inches for the squares. The circumference of 1 circle is about 3.14 inches and there are 30 circles, so there are about 94.2 inches for the circles; the area of 1 square is 1 square inch and there are 25 squares, so there are 25 square inches for the squares. The area of 1 circle is about 0.785 square inch and there are 30 circles, so there are about 23.6 square inches for the circles.

16a. boat at point A: $2\sqrt{10} \approx 6.3$ km, boat at point C: $\sqrt{34} \approx 5.8$ km

2 Pacing and Assignment Guide

REGULAR SCHEDULE

Pre-AP For pacing and assignments for a Pre-AP course, see the *Geometry Toolkit.*

Lesson	Les. Day	BASIC	AVERAGE	ADVANCED
2.1	Day 1	pp. 75–78 Exs. 1–8, 12–22, 32–34, 39–49 odd	pp. 75–78 Exs. 1–5, 8–20, 22–28 even, 32–36, 40–48 even	pp. 75–78 Exs. 1, 2, 4, 5, 10–13, 16, 17–21 odd, 22, 23–27 odd, 29–38*, 42, 46, 49
2.2	Day 1	pp. 82–85 Exs. 1–15, 31, 32	pp. 82–85 Exs. 1, 2, 4–10, 13–15, 26–29, 31, 32	pp. 82–85 Exs. 1, 2, 4, 5, 9, 10, 14, 15, 26–32*
	Day 2	pp. 82–85 Exs. 16–25, 33, 34, 40–55	pp. 82–85 Exs. 16–25, 33–36, 40–55	pp. 82–85 Exs. 16–25, 33–39*, 42, 45, 47, 49, 52, 55
2.3	Day 1	pp. 90–93 Exs. 1–10, 16, 17, 34–38	pp. 90–93 Exs. 1–6, 8–10, 14, 16, 17, 34–38	pp. 90–93 Exs. 1–6, 9, 10, 14–17*, 34–38
	Day 2	pp. 90–93 Exs. 11–13, 18–24, 30–33	pp. 90–93 Exs. 11–13, 18–28, 30–33	pp. 90–93 Exs. 11–13, 18–30*, 32
2.4	Day 1	pp. 99–102 Exs. 1–18, 30–41, 46–56 even	pp. 99–102 Exs. 1, 2, 4, 5, 8–10, 15–23 odd, 24–28, 30–44, 47, 50, 53	pp. 99–102 Exs. 1, 2, 5, 8–12 even, 19–29*, 32–45*, 48, 51, 55
2.5	Day 1	SRH p. 872 Exs. 1–6; pp. 108–111 Exs. 1–20	pp. 108–111 Exs. 1–20	pp. 108–111 Exs. 1–20
	Day 2	pp. 108–111 Exs. 21–27, 31–35, 39–42	pp. 108–111 Exs. 21–29, 31–36, 39–42	pp. 108–111 Exs. 21–30*, 32–38*, 40, 42
2.6	Day 1	pp. 116–119 Exs. 1–12, 34–36	pp. 116–119 Exs. 1–12, 34–36	pp. 116–119 Exs. 1–12, 34–36
	Day 2	pp. 116–119 Exs. 13–17, 21–28, 31–33	pp. 116–119 Exs. 13–19, 21–29, 31, 33	pp. 116–119 Exs. 15–20*, 22–30*, 32
2.7	Day 1	pp. 127–131 Exs. 1–7, 36–39, 49–53	pp. 127–131 Exs. 1–7, 36–39, 49–53	pp. 127–131 Exs. 1–7, 36–39, 43, 44, 49–53
	Day 2	pp. 127–131 Exs. 8–26, 40	pp. 127–131 Exs. 9–15 odd, 16, 17–29 odd, 30, 40–45	pp. 127–131 Exs. 10, 11, 14–30 even, 31–35*, 40–42, 45–48*
Review	Day 1	pp. 134–137 Exs. 1–24	pp. 134–137 Exs. 1–24	pp. 134–137 Exs. 1–24
Assess	Day 1	Chapter 2 Test	Chapter 2 Test	Chapter 2 Test
Yearly Pacing		Chapter 2 Total – 14 days	Chapters 1–2 Total – 26 days	Remaining – 134 days

*Challenge Exercises EP = Extra Practice SRH = Skills Review Handbook

BLOCK SCHEDULE

DAY 1	DAY 2	DAY 3	DAY 4	DAY 5	DAY 6	DAY 7
2.1	2.2 (CONT.)	2.3 (CONT.)	2.5	2.6	2.7	REVIEW
pp. 75–78 Exs. 1–5, 8–20, 22–28 even, 32–36, 40–48 even	pp. 82–85 Exs. 16–25, 33–36, 40–55	pp. 90–93 Exs. 11–13, 18–28, 30–33	pp. 108–111 Exs. 1–29, 31–36, 39–42	pp. 116–119 Exs. 1–19, 21–29, 31, 33–36	pp. 127–131 Exs. 1–7, 9–15 odd, 16, 17–29 odd, 30, 36–45, 49–53	pp. 134–137 Exs. 1–24
2.2	2.3	2.4				ASSESS
pp. 82–85 Exs. 1, 2, 4–10, 13–15, 26–29, 31, 32	pp. 90–93 Exs. 1–6, 8–10, 14, 16, 17, 34–38	pp. 99–102 Exs. 1, 2, 4, 5, 8–10, 15–23 odd, 24–28, 30–44, 47, 50, 53				Chapter 2 Test
Yearly Pacing	Chapter 2 Total – 7 days		Chapters 1–2 Total – 13 days		Remaining – 67 days	

Chapter Resource Guide 2

RESOURCE MANAGER

Chapter Resource Book							
CHAPTER SUPPORT							
Parents as Partners (Chapter Overview with home involvement exercises and activity)						p. 1	
LESSON SUPPORT	**2.1**	**2.2**	**2.3**	**2.4**	**2.5**	**2.6**	**2.7**
Teaching Guide/Lesson Plan	p. 3	p. 18	p. 31	p. 45	p. 60	p. 73	p. 87
Activity Masters	p. 5			p. 47		p. 75	
Technology Activities & Keystrokes							p. 89
Activity Support Masters			p. 33				
Practice (3 levels)	p. 7	p. 20	p. 34	p. 48	p. 62	p. 76	p. 90
Study Guide	p. 13	p. 26	p. 40	p. 54	p. 68	p. 82	p. 96
Catch-Up for Absent Students	p. 15	p. 28	p. 42	p. 56	p. 70	p. 84	p. 98
Problem Solving/Application	p. 16	p. 29	p. 43	p. 57	p. 71	p. 85	p. 99
Challenge Practice	p. 17	p. 30	p. 44	p. 59	p. 72	p. 86	p. 100
REVIEW							
Chapter Review Games and Activities		p. 101		Cumulative Practice		p. 104	
Project with Rubric		p. 102		Resource Book Answers		A1	

Transparencies	2.1	2.2	2.3	2.4	2.5	2.6	2.7
Warm-Up/Daily Homework Quiz	✔	✔	✔	✔	✔	✔	✔
Notetaking Guide	✔	✔	✔	✔	✔	✔	✔
Teacher Support							
Answer Transparencies	✔	✔	✔	✔	✔	✔	✔

ASSESSMENT BOOK

Quizzes	p. 16	SAT/ACT Chapter Test	p. 27
Chapter Tests (3 levels)	p. 19	Alternative Assessment with Rubric	p. 29
Standardized Chapter Test	p. 25		

TECHNOLOGY

- Easy Planner
- Test and Practice Generator
- Power Presentations
- @HomeTutor
- Activity Generator
- Animated Geometry
- Classzone.com
- eEdition Plus Online
- eWorkbook Plus Online
- ML Assessment System

ADDITIONAL RESOURCES

- Worked-Out Solution Key
- Notetaking Guide
- Practice Wookbook
- Geometry Toolkit
- Benchmark Tests
- Remediation Book
- Spanish Study Guide
- Spanish Assessment Book
- Student Resources in Spanish
- Multi-Language Visual Glossary

2 Lesson Practice Level B

LESSON 2.1 Practice B
For use with pages 72–78

Sketch the next figure in the pattern.

1. 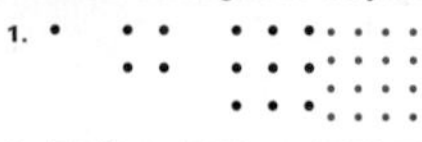 

2.  

3.  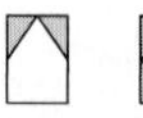

4.  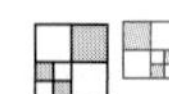

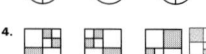

Describe a pattern in the numbers. Write the next number in the pattern. Graph the pattern on a number line.

5. 113, 224, 335, 446, . . .

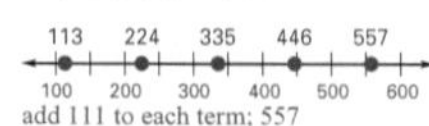

add 111 to each term; 557

6. 4, 6, 9, 13, 18, . . . add consecutive integers to each term, starting with 2; 24

7. $\frac{1}{3}, \frac{3}{4}, \frac{5}{5}, \frac{7}{6}, \ldots$ add 2 to the numerator and 1 to the denominator; $\frac{9}{7}$

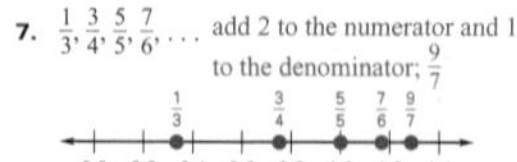
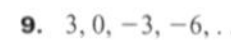

8. $\frac{7}{8}, \frac{6}{7}, \frac{5}{6}, \frac{4}{5}, \ldots$ subtract 1 from the numerator and 1 from the denominator; $\frac{3}{4}$

9. 3, 0, −3, −6, . . .

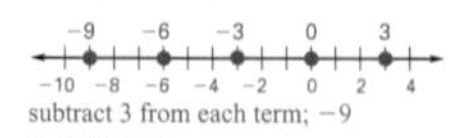

subtract 3 from each term; −9

10. 1, 4, 9, 16, . . . square numbers; 25

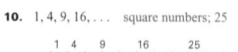

11. 2, 5, 11, 23, . . .

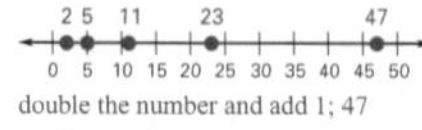

double the number and add 1; 47

12. 2, 3, 5, 7, 11, . . . prime numbers; 13

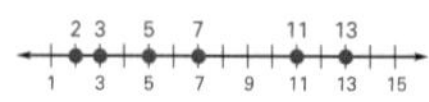

The first three objects in a pattern are shown. How many squares are in the next object?

13.  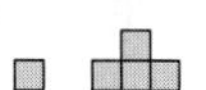 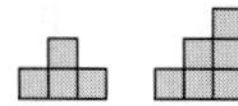 16

14.  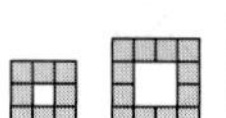 20

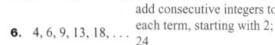

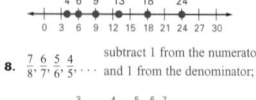

LESSON 2.1 Practice B *continued*
For use with pages 72–78

Show the conjecture is false by finding a counterexample.

15. The quotient of two whole numbers is a whole number. *Sample answer:* $\frac{2}{4} = 0.5$

16. The difference of the absolute value of two numbers is positive, meaning $|a| - |b| > 0$. *Sample answer:* $|5| - |7| = -2$

17. If $m \neq -1$, then $\frac{m}{m+1} < 1$. *Sample answer:* $\frac{-2}{-2+1} = 2$

18. The square root of a number x is always less than x. *Sample answer:* $\sqrt{\frac{1}{4}} = \frac{1}{2}; \frac{1}{2} > \frac{1}{4}$

Write a function rule relating *x* and *y*.

19.

x	1	2	3
y	1	8	27

$y = x^3$

20.

x	1	2	3
y	−5	−3	−1

$y = 2x - 7$

21.

x	1	2	3
y	4	3	2

$y = -x + 5$

22.

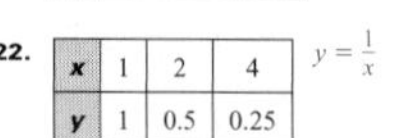

x	1	2	4
y	1	0.5	0.25

$y = \frac{1}{x}$

23. **Bacteria Growth** Suppose you are studying bacteria in biology class. The table shows the number of bacteria after *n* doubling periods. Your teacher asks you to predict the number of bacteria after 7 doubling periods. What would your prediction be? 512 billion bacteria

n (periods)	0	1	2	3	4	5
billions of bacteria	4	8	16	32	64	128

24. **Chemistry** The half-life of an isotope is the amount of time it takes for half of the isotope to decay. Suppose you begin with 25 grams of Platinum-191, which has a half-life of 3 days. How many days will it take before there is less than 1 gram of the isotope? 15 days

LESSON 2.2 Practice B
For use with pages 79–85

Rewrite the conditional statement in if-then form.

1. It is time for dinner if it is 6 P.M. If it is 6 P.M., then it is time for dinner.
2. There are 12 eggs if the carton is full. If the carton is full, then there are 12 eggs
3. An obtuse angle is an angle that measures more than 90° and less than 180°. If an angle is obtuse, then it measures more than 90° and less than 180°.
4. The car runs when there is gas in the tank. If there is gas in the tank, then the car will run.

Write the converse, inverse, and contrapositive of each statement.

5. If you like hockey, then you go to the hockey game.
   converse: If you go to the hockey game, then you like hockey; inverse: If you do not like hockey, then you do not go to the hockey game; contrapositive: If you do not go to the hockey game, then you do not like hockey.
6. If x is odd, then $3x$ is odd.
   converse: If $3x$ is odd, then x is odd; inverse: If x is not odd, then $3x$ is not odd; contrapositive: If $3x$ is not odd, then x is not odd.

Decide whether the statement is *true* or *false*. If false, provide a counterexample.

7. The equation $4x - 3 = 12 + 2x$ has exactly one solution. true
8. If $x^2 = 36$, then x must equal 18 or −18. false; $x = \pm 6$
9. If $m\angle A = 122°$, then the measure of the supplement of $\angle A$ is 58°. true
10. Two lines intersect in at most one point. true

Write the converse of each true statement. If the converse is also true, combine the statements to write a true biconditional statement.

11. If an angle measures 30°, then it is acute.
    If an angle is acute, then it measures 30°.
12. If two angles are supplementary, then their sum is 180°.
    converse: If the sum of two angles is 180°, then they are supplementary; biconditional: Two angles are supplementary if and only if their sum is 180°.
13. If two circles have the same diameter, then they have the same circumference.
    converse: If two circles have the same circumference, then they have the same diameter; biconditional: Two circles have the same circumference if and only if they have the same diameter.
14. If an animal is a panther, then it lives in the forest.
    If an animal lives in the forest, then it is a panther.

LESSON 2.2 Practice B *continued*
For use with pages 79–85

Rewrite the biconditional statement as a conditional statement and its converse.

15. Two lines are perpendicular if and only if they intersect to form right angles.
    conditional statement: If two lines are perpendicular, then they intersect to form right angles; converse: If two lines intersect to form right angles, then the two lines are perpendicular.
16. A point is a midpoint of a segment if and only if it divides the segment into two congruent segments.
    conditional statement: If a point is a midpoint of a segment, then it divides the segment into two congruent segments; converse: If a point divides a segment into two congruent segments, then the point is the midpoint of the segment.

Decide whether the statement is a valid definition.

17. If a number is divisible by 2 and 3, then it is divisible by 6. yes
18. If two angles have the same measure, then they are congruent. yes
19. If two angles are not adjacent, then they are vertical angles. No; the angles could be in a triangle.

In Exercises 20–24, use the information in the table to write a definition for each type of saxophone.

Instrument	Frequency (cycles per second) Lower limit (Hz)	Upper limit (Hz)
E-flat baritone saxophone	69	415
B-flat tenor saxophone	103	622
E-flat alto saxophone	138	830

20. E-flat baritone saxophone
21. B-flat tenor saxophone
22. E-flat alto saxophone
23. If the frequency of a saxophone was 95 Hz, what could you conclude?
24. If the frequency of a saxophone was 210 Hz, what could you conclude?

20. A saxophone that has a frequency of 69 cycles per second to 415 cycles per second is called an E-flat baritone saxophone.
21. A saxophone that has a frequency of 103 cycles per second to 622 cycles per second is called a B-flat tenor saxophone.
22. A saxophone that has a frequency of 138 cycles per second to 830 cycles per second is called an E-flat alto saxophone.
23. The saxophone is an E-flat baritone saxophone.
24. nothing; It could be any of the three saxophones.

LESSON 2.3 Practice B

For use with pages 86–93

Determine if statement (3) follows from statements (1) and (2) by either the Law of Detachment or the Law of Syllogism. If it does, state which law was used. If it does not, write invalid.

1. (1) If an angle measures more than 90°, then it is not acute. Law of Detachment

(2) $m\angle ABC = 120°$

(3) $\angle ABC$ is not acute.

2. (1) All 45° angles are congruent. invalid

(2) $\angle A \cong \angle B$

(3) $\angle A$ and $\angle B$ are 45° angles.

3. (1) If you order the apple pie, then it will be served with ice cream. Law of Detachment

(2) Matthew ordered the apple pie.

(3) Matthew was served ice cream.

4. (1) If you wear the school colors, then you have school spirit. Law of Syllogism

(2) If you have school spirit, then the team feels great.

(3) If you wear the school colors, then the team will feel great.

5. (1) If you eat too much turkey, then you will get sick. invalid

(2) Kinsley got sick.

(3) Kinsley ate too much turkey.

6. (1) If $\angle 2$ is acute, then $\angle 3$ is obtuse. Law of Syllogism

(2) If $\angle 3$ is obtuse, then $\angle 4$ is acute.

(3) If $\angle 2$ is acute, then $\angle 4$ is acute.

7. deductive reasoning; Deductive reasoning is based on logic and order. If Walt is taller than Peter and Peter is taller than Natalie, then Walt is taller than Natalie.

8. inductive reasoning; Inductive reasoning depends on previous examples and patterns to form a conjecture. If Brand Y costs more than Brand X and Brand X costs more than any other brand, then Brand Y costs more than all other brands.

9. inductive reasoning; Inductive reasoning depends on previous examples and patterns to form a conjecture. Dana came to her conclusion based on previous examples.

In Exercises 7–10, decide whether *inductive* or *deductive* reasoning is used to reach the conclusion. *Explain* your reasoning. See above.

7. Angela knows that Walt is taller than Peter. She also knows that Peter is taller than Natalie. Angela reasons that Walt is taller than Natalie.

8. Josh knows that Brand X computers cost less than Brand Y computers. All other brands that Josh knows of cost less than Brand X. Josh reasons that Brand Y costs more than all other brands.

9. For the past three Wednesdays, the cafeteria has served macaroni and cheese for lunch. Dana concludes that the cafeteria will serve macaroni and cheese for lunch this Wednesday.

LESSON 2.3 Practice B *continued*

For use with pages 86–93

10. If you live in Nevada and are between the ages of 16 and 18, then you must take driver's education to get your license. Anthony lives in Nevada, is 16 years old, and has his driver's license. Therefore, Anthony took driver's education.

10. deductive reasoning; Deductive reasoning is based on logic and order. If Anthony is a 16–18 year old with a license in Nevada, then Anthony must have taken the required driver education.

In Exercises 11 and 12, state whether the argument is valid. *Explain* your reasoning.

11. Jeff knows that if he does not do his chores in the morning, he will not be allowed to play video games later the same day. Jeff does not play video games on Saturday afternoon. So Jeff did not do his chores on Saturday morning.

not valid; It does not say that Jeff is not allowed to play video games on Saturday afternoon, it says that he does not play video games on Saturday afternoon.

12. Katie knows that all sophomores take driver education in her school. Brandon takes driver education. So Brandon is a sophomore.

not valid; Katie knows that all sophomores take driver education. It does not say that only sophomores take driver education. You do not know if Brandon is a sophomore.

In Exercises 13–16, use the true statements below to determine whether you know the conclusion is *true* or *false*. *Explain* your reasoning.

If Dan goes shopping, then he will buy a pretzel.

If the mall is open, then Jodi and Dan will go shopping.

If Jodi goes shopping, then she will buy a pizza.

The mall is open.

13. false; The mall is open, therefore Jodi and Dan went shopping, and therefore Dan bought a pretzel. You cannot conclude that Dan also bought a pizza.

13. Dan bought a pizza.

14. Jodi and Dan went shopping.
true; The mall is open, therefore Jodi and Dan went shopping.

15. Jodi bought a pizza. See below.

16. Jodi had some of Dan's pretzel. See below.

17. Robotics Because robots can withstand higher temperatures than humans, a fire-fighting robot is under development. Write the following statements about the robot in order. Then use the Law of Syllogism to complete the statement, "If there is a fire, then __?__."

A. If the robot sets off the fire alarm, then it concludes there is a fire.

B. If the robot senses high levels of smoke and heat, then it sets off a fire alarm.

C. If the robot locates the fire, then the robot extinguishes the fire.

D. If there is a fire, then the robot senses high levels of smoke and heat.

E. If the robot concludes there is a fire, then it locates the fire.

D, B, A, E, C; the robot extinguishes the fire

15. true; The mall is open, therefore Jodi and Dan went shopping, and therefore Jodi bought a pizza.

16. false; The mall is open, therefore Jodi and Dan went shopping, and therefore Dan bought a pretzel and Jodi bought a pizza. You cannot conclude whether or not Jodi had some of Dan's pretzel.

LESSON 2.4 Practice B

For use with pages 96–102

Draw a sketch to illustrate each postulate.

1. If two lines intersect, then their intersection is exactly one point.

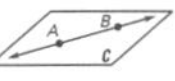

2. If two points lie in a plane, then the line containing them lies in the plane.

3. If two planes intersect, then their intersection is a line.

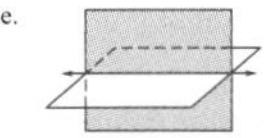

Use the diagram to state and write out the postulate that verifies the truth of the statement.

4. The points E, F, and H lie in a plane (labeled R). Postulate 8: Through any three noncollinear points there exists exactly one plane.

5. The points E and F lie on a line (labeled m).
Postulate 5: Through any two points there exists exactly one line.

6. The planes Q and R intersect in a line (labeled n).
Postulate 11: If two planes intersect, then their intersection is a line.

7. The points E and F lie in a plane R. Therefore, line m lies in plane R.
Postulate 10: If two points lie in a plane, then the line containing them lies in the plane.

In Exercises 8–11, think of the intersection of the ceiling and the front wall of your classroom as line *k*. Think of the center of the floor as point *A* and the center of the ceiling as point *B*.

8. Is there more than one line that contains both points A and B?
No. Through any two points there exists exactly one line.

9. Is there more than one plane that contains both points A and B?
Yes. Points A and B could lie on the line intersecting two planes.

10. Is there a plane that contains line k and point A?
Yes. Take point A and any two points on line k and you can form a plane through those three points that contains all of line k.

11. Is there a plane that contains points A, B, and a point on the front wall?
Yes. The plane that runs from the front of the room to the back of the room through points A and B contains both points and a point on the front wall.

LESSON 2.4 Practice B *continued*

For use with pages 96–102

In Exercises 12–19, use the diagram to determine if the statement is *true* or *false*.

12. Points A, B, D, and J are coplanar. true

13. $\angle EBA$ is a right angle. false

14. Points E, G, and A are collinear. false

15. $\overleftrightarrow{FG} \perp$ plane H. false

16. $\angle ABD$ and $\angle EBC$ are vertical angles. true

17. Planes H and K intersect at $\overleftrightarrow{AB}$. true

18. $\overleftrightarrow{FG}$ and $\overleftrightarrow{DE}$ intersect. false

19. $\angle GCA$ and $\angle CBD$ are congruent angles. false

20. Neighborhood Map A friend e-mailed you the following statements about a neighborhood. Use the statements to complete parts (a)–(e).

Building B is due south of Building A.

Buildings A and B are on Street 1.

Building C is due east of Building B.

Buildings B and C are on Street 2.

Building D is southeast of Building B.

Buildings B and D are on Street 3.

Building E is due west of Building C.

$\angle DBE$ formed by Streets 2 and 3 is acute.

a. Draw a diagram of the neighborhood.

b. Where do Streets 1 and 2 intersect? building B

c. Classify the angle formed by Streets 1 and 2. right

d. What street is building E on? 2

e. Is building E between Buildings B and C? *Explain.*
Yes, because $\angle DBE$ is acute and Building E is due west of Building C.

a.

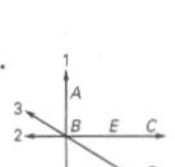

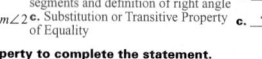

LESSON 2.5 **Practice B** *For use with pages 104–111*

4. a. Reflexive Property of Equality b. Addition Property of Equality c. Angle Addition Postulate d. Angle Addition Postulate e. Substitution Property of Equality

Complete the logical argument by giving a reason for each step.

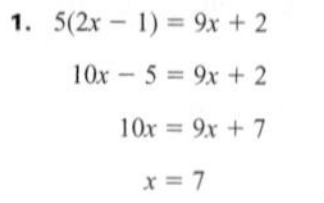

1. $5(2x - 1) = 9x + 2$ Given
   $10x - 5 = 9x + 2$ a. ___?___ Distributive Property
   $10x = 9x + 7$ b. ___?___ Addition Property of Equality
   $x = 7$ c. ___?___ Subtraction Property of Equality
2. $8x - 5 = -2x - 15$ Given
   $10x - 5 = -15$ a. ___?___ Addition Property of Equality
   $10x = -10$ b. ___?___ Addition Property of Equality
   $x = -1$ c. ___?___ Division Property of Equality
3. $AB = BC$ Given
   $AC = AB + BC$ a. ___?___ Segment Addition Postulate
   $AC = AB + AB$ b. ___?___ Substitution Property of Equality
   $AC = 2(AB)$ c. ___?___ Distributive Property
4. $m\angle AEB = m\angle CED$ See above. Given
   $m\angle BEC = m\angle BEC$ a. ___?___
   $m\angle AEB + m\angle BEC = m\angle CED + m\angle BEC$ b. ___?___
   $m\angle AEC = m\angle AEB + m\angle BEC$ c. ___?___
   $m\angle BED = m\angle CED + m\angle BEC$ d. ___?___
   $m\angle AEC = m\angle BED$ e. ___?___

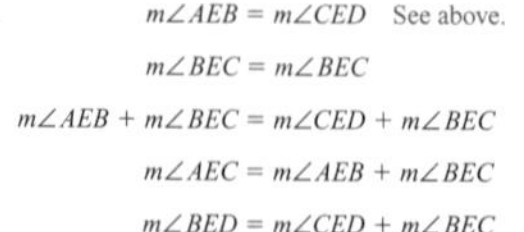

5. $\overleftrightarrow{AB} \perp \overleftrightarrow{EF}$, $\overleftrightarrow{CD} \perp \overleftrightarrow{EF}$ Given
   $m\angle 1 = 90°$ a. ___?___ a. Definition of perpendicular segments and definition of right angle
   $m\angle 2 = 90°$ b. ___?___ b. Definition of perpendicular segments and definition of right angle
   $m\angle 1 = m\angle 2$ c. ___?___ c. Substitution or Transitive Property of Equality

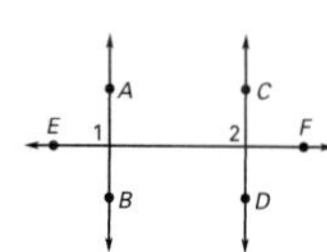

Use the property to complete the statement.

6. Reflexive Property of Angle Measure: $m\angle B =$ ___?___. $m\angle B$
7. Transitive Property of Equality: If $CD = GH$ and ___?___ $= RS$, then ___?___. GH, $CD = RS$
8. Addition Property of Equality: If $x = 3$, then $14 + x =$ ___?___. 17
9. Symmetric Property of Equality: If $BC = RL$, then ___?___. $RL = BC$
10. Substitution Property of Equality: If $m\angle A = 45°$, then $3(m\angle A) =$ ___?___. 3(45)

LESSON 2.5 **Practice B** *continued* *For use with pages 104–111*

11. Multiplication Property of Equality: If $m\angle A = 45°$, then ___?___ $(m\angle A) = 15°$. $\frac{1}{3}$
12. **Distance** You are given the following information about the diagram at the right: $AB = CD$, $CD = OE$. Find the coordinates of points C and E. *Explain* your reasoning.
    $C(-3, 6)$, $E(5, 0)$; AB is 5 units long. Because $AB = CD$, then CD is 5 units long. So the coordinates of C are $(-3, 6)$. Because $CD = OE$, then OE is 5 units long. So the coordinates of E are $(5, 0)$.

In Exercises 13–15, use the following information.

Treadmill Mark works out for 45 minutes on a treadmill. He spends t minutes walking and the rest of the time running. He walks 0.06 mi/min and runs 0.11 mi/min. The total distance (in miles) he travels is given by the function $D = 0.06t + 0.11(45 - t)$.

13. Solve the formula for t and write a reason for each step. See below.
14. Make a table that shows the time spent walking for the following distances traveled: 2.7, 3, 3.7, 4.3, and 4.5. See below.
15. Use the table from Exercise 14 to graph the time spent walking as a function of the distance traveled. What happens to the time spent walking as distance increases?

13. $D = 0.06t + 0.11(45 - t)$ Given
    $D = 0.06t + 4.95 - 0.11t$ Distributive Property
    $D = 0.06t - 0.11t + 4.95$ Group like terms.
    $D = -0.05t + 4.95$ Simplify.
    $0.05t + D = 4.95$ Addition Property of Equality
    $0.05t = -D + 4.95$ Subtraction Property of Equality
    $t = -20D + 99$ Division Property of Equality

In Exercises 16–18, use the following information.

Statistics The students at a school vote for one of four candidates for class president. The circle graph below shows the results of the election. Each sector on the graph represents the percent of the total votes that each candidate received. You know the following about the circle graph.

$m\angle 1 + m\angle 2 + m\angle 3 + m\angle 4 = 360°$
$m\angle 2 + m\angle 3 = 200°$
$m\angle 1 = m\angle 4$
$m\angle 2 = m\angle 4$

14.

D	2.7	3	3.7	4.3	4.5
t	45	39	25	13	9

16. Find the angle measure for each sector. $m\angle 1 = 80°$, $m\angle 2 = 80°$, $m\angle 3 = 120°$, $m\angle 4 = 80°$
17. What percent of the vote did each candidate receive? Candidate 1: 22.2%, Candidate 2: 22.2%, Candidate 3: 33.3%, Candidate 4: 22.2%
18. How many votes did each candidate receive if there were a total of 315 votes? Candidate 1: 70, Candidate 2: 70, Candidate 3: 105, Candidate 4: 70

LESSON 2.6 **Practice B** *For use with pages 112–119*

In Exercises 1–4, complete the proof.

1. **GIVEN:** $HI = 9$, $IJ = 9$, $\overline{IJ} \cong \overline{JH}$
   PROVE: $\overline{HI} \cong \overline{JH}$

Statements	Reasons
1. $HI = 9$	1. ___?___ 1. Given
2. $IJ = 9$	2. ___?___ 2. Given
3. $HI = IJ$	3. ___?___ 3. Substitution Property of Equality
4. ___?___ 4. $\overline{HI} \cong \overline{IJ}$	4. Definition of congruent segments
5. $\overline{IJ} \cong \overline{JH}$	5. ___?___ 5. Given
6. $\overline{HI} \cong \overline{JH}$	6. ___?___ 6. Transitive Property of Congruence

2. **GIVEN:** $\angle 3$ and $\angle 2$ are complementary, $m\angle 1 + m\angle 2 = 90°$
   PROVE: $\angle 3 \cong \angle 1$

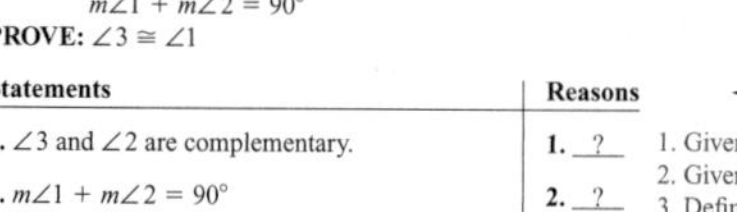

Statements	Reasons
1. $\angle 3$ and $\angle 2$ are complementary.	1. ___?___ 1. Given
2. $m\angle 1 + m\angle 2 = 90°$	2. ___?___ 2. Given
3. $m\angle 3 + m\angle 2 = 90°$	3. ___?___ 3. Definition of complementary angles
4. $m\angle 1 + m\angle 2 = m\angle 3 + m\angle 2$	4. ___?___ 4. Transitive Property of Equality
5. $m\angle 1 = m\angle 3$	5. ___?___ 5. Subtraction Property of Equality
6. $\angle 1 \cong \angle 3$	6. ___?___ 6. Definition of congruent angles

3. **GIVEN:** $AL = SK$
   PROVE: $AS = LK$

Statements	Reasons
1. $AL = SK$	1. ___?___ 1. Given
2. $LS = LS$	2. ___?___ 2. Reflexive Property of Equality
3. $AL + LS = SK + LS$	3. ___?___ 3. Addition Property of Equality
4. $AL + LS = AS$	4. ___?___ 4. Segment Addition Postulate
5. $SK + LS = LK$	5. ___?___ 5. Segment Addition Postulate
6. $AS = LK$	6. ___?___ 6. Substitution Property of Equality

LESSON 2.6 **Practice B** *continued* *For use with pages 112–119*

5. $x = 6$; Because the angles are congruent, the measures of the angles are congruent by the definition of congruent angles. Set the measure of the angles equal to each other to find x.

4. **GIVEN:** $m\angle 4 = 120°$, $\angle 2 \cong \angle 5$, $\angle 4 \cong \angle 5$
   PROVE: $m\angle 2 = 120°$

Statements	Reasons
1. $m\angle 4 = 120°$, $\angle 2 \cong \angle 5$, $\angle 4 \cong \angle 5$	1. ___?___ 1. Given
2. $\angle 2 \cong \angle 4$	2. ___?___ 2. Transitive Property of Angle Congruence
3. ___?___ 3. $m\angle 2 = m\angle 4$	3. Definition of $\cong$ angles
4. $m\angle 2 = 120°$	4. ___?___ 4. Substitution Property of Equality

Solve for x using the given information. *Explain* your steps.

5. $\angle W \cong \angle Z$ See above.

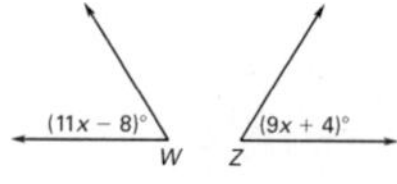

6. $\overline{FG} \cong \overline{FJ}$, $\overline{FJ} \cong \overline{JH}$ $x = 3$; By the transitive property, $\overline{FG} \cong \overline{JH}$. Set the lengths of the segments equal to each other to find x.

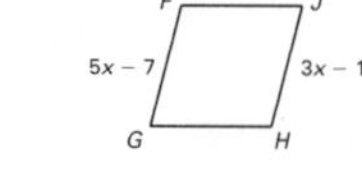

7. $\angle ABD \cong \angle DBE$, $\angle EBC \cong \angle DBE$ $x = 5$; By the transitive property, $\angle ABD \cong \angle EBC$. Because the angles are congruent, the measures of the angles are congruent by the definition of congruent angles. Set the measures of the angles equal to each other to find x.
8. $\overline{KP} \cong \overline{PN}$, $KP = 18$ See below.
9. **Optical Illusion** To create the illusion at the right, a special grid was used. In the grid, corresponding row heights are the same measure. For instance, $\overline{UV}$ and $\overline{ZY}$ are congruent. You decide to make this design yourself. You draw the grid, but you need to make sure that the row heights are the same. You measure $\overline{UV}$, $\overline{UW}$, $\overline{ZY}$, and $\overline{ZX}$. You find that $\overline{UV} \cong \overline{ZY}$ and $\overline{UW} \cong \overline{ZX}$. Write an argument that allows you to conclude that $\overline{VW} \cong \overline{YX}$.

   $\overline{UV} \cong \overline{ZY}$, $\overline{UW} \cong \overline{ZX}$ (Given)
   $UV = ZY$, $UW = ZX$ (Def. of $\cong$)
   $VW = UW - UV$ (Segment Addition Postulate)
   $YX = ZX - ZY$ (Segment Addition Postulate)
   $YX = UW - UV$ (Substitution Property of Equality)
   $VW = YX$ (Transitive Property of Segment Congruence)
   $\overline{VW} \cong \overline{YX}$ (Def. of $\cong$)

8. $x = 4$; Because the segments are congruent, the lengths of the segments are congruent by the definition of congruent segments. Set the lengths of the segments equal to each other to find x.

LESSON 2.7 Practice B

For use with pages 122–131

Use the diagram to decide whether the statement is *true* or *false*.

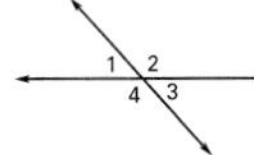

1. If $m\angle 1 = 47°$, then $m\angle 2 = 43°$. false
2. If $m\angle 1 = 47°$, then $m\angle 3 = 47°$. true
3. $m\angle 1 + m\angle 3 = m\angle 2 + m\angle 4$. false
4. $m\angle 1 + m\angle 4 = m\angle 2 + m\angle 3$. true

Make a sketch of the given information. Label all angles which can be determined.

5. Adjacent complementary angles where one angle measures 42°
   See below.
6. Nonadjacent supplementary angles where one angle measures 42°

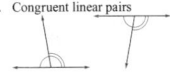

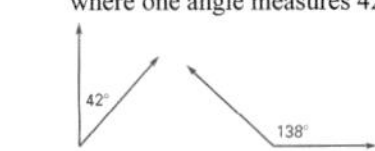

7. Congruent linear pairs
8. Vertical angles which measure 42°
   See below.
9. $\angle ABC$ and $\angle CBD$ are adjacent, complementary angles. $\angle CBD$ and $\angle DBF$ are adjacent, complementary angles.

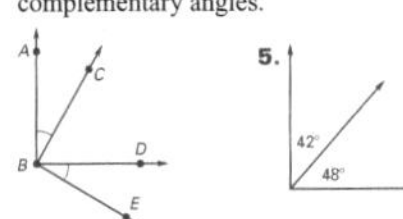

10. $\angle 1$ and $\angle 2$ are complementary. $\angle 3$ and $\angle 4$ are complementary. $\angle 1$ and $\angle 3$ are vertical angles.

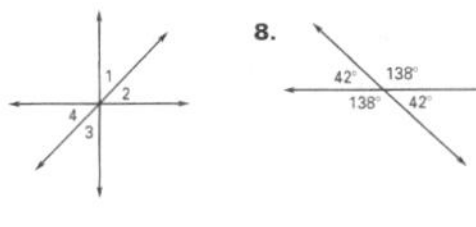

5. 42° 48°

8. 42° 138° 138° 42°

Find the value of the variables and the measure of each angle in the diagram.

11. 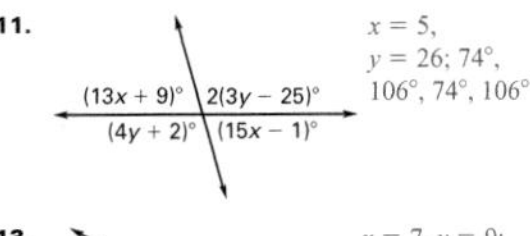

$x = 5$, $y = 26$; 74°, 106°, 74°, 106°

12. 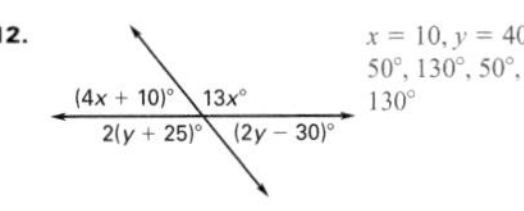

$x = 10, y = 40$; 50°, 130°, 50°, 130°

13. 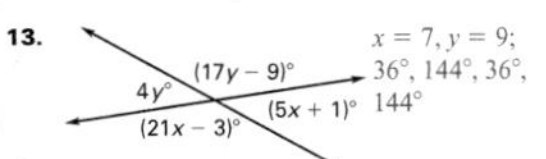

$x = 7, y = 9$; 36°, 144°, 36°, 144°

14. 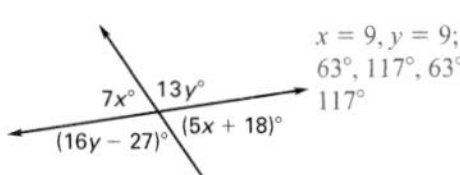

$x = 9, y = 9$; 63°, 117°, 63°, 117°

LESSON 2.7 Practice B *continued*

For use with pages 122–131

Give a reason for each step of the proof.

15. GIVEN: $\angle 2 \cong \angle 3$
    PROVE: $\angle 1 \cong \angle 4$

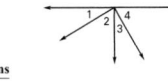

Statements	Reasons
1. $\angle 2 \cong \angle 3$	1. ?
2. $\angle 3 \cong \angle 4$	2. ?
3. $\angle 2 \cong \angle 4$	3. ?
4. $\angle 1 \cong \angle 2$	4. ?
5. $\angle 1 \cong \angle 4$	5. ?

1. Given
2. Vertical angles are congruent
3. Transitive Property of Congruence
4. Vertical angles are congruent
5. Transitive Property of Congruence

16. GIVEN: $\angle 1$ and $\angle 2$ are complementary.
    $\angle 1 \cong \angle 3$, $\angle 2 \cong \angle 4$
    PROVE: $\angle 3$ and $\angle 4$ are complementary.

Statements	Reasons
1. $\angle 1$ and $\angle 2$ are complementary.	1. ?
2. $m\angle 1 + m\angle 2 = 90°$	2. ?
3. $\angle 1 \cong \angle 3$, $\angle 2 \cong \angle 4$	3. ?
4. $m\angle 1 \cong m\angle 3$, $m\angle 2 \cong m\angle 4$	4. ?
5. $m\angle 3 + m\angle 2 = 90°$	5. ?
6. $m\angle 3 + m\angle 4 = 90°$	6. ?
7. $\angle 3$ and $\angle 4$ are complementary.	7. ?

1. Given
2. Definition of complementary angles
3. Given
4. Definition of congruent angles
5. Substitution Property of Equality
6. Substitution Property of Equality
7. Definition of complementary angles

In the diagram, $\angle 1$ is a right angle and $m\angle 6 = 36°$. Complete the statement with <, >, or =.

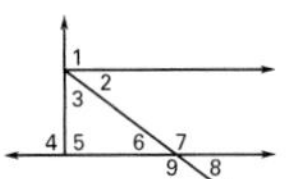

17. $m\angle 6 + m\angle 7$? $m\angle 4 + m\angle 5$ =
18. $m\angle 6 + m\angle 8$? $m\angle 2 + m\angle 3$ <
19. $m\angle 9$? $3(m\angle 6)$ >
20. $m\angle 2 + m\angle 3$? $m\angle 1$ =

2 Assessment

CHAPTER 2 Quiz 1
For use after Lessons 2.1–2.3

Show the conjecture is false by finding a counterexample.

1. If the product of two numbers is positive, then the two numbers must be positive.
2. The sum of any two prime numbers is always even.

For the given statement, write the if-then form, the converse, the inverse, and the contrapositive.

3. The measure of a straight angle is 180°.

   If-then form: If an angle is a straight angle, then its measure is 180°. Converse: If the measure of an angle is 180°, then the angle is a straight angle. Inverse: If an angle is not a straight angle, then its measure is not 180°. Contrapositive: If the measure of an angle is not 180°, then it is not a straight angle.

4. A quadrilateral has four sides.

   If-then form: If a polygon is a quadrilateral, then it has 4 sides. Converse: If a polygon has 4 sides, then it is a quadrilateral. Inverse: If a polygon is not a quadrilateral, then it does not have 4 sides. Contrapositive: If a polygon does not have 4 sides, then it is not a quadrilateral.

Make a valid conclusion in the situation.

5. If $x > 5$, then $x + 7 > 11$. The value of x is 8.
6. If you save \$150, then you can purchase a bicycle on sale. You have saved \$135.

Answers

1. $(-2)(-5) = 10$
2. $2 + 3 = 5$
3. See left.
4. See left.
5. $8 + 7 > 11$
6. You cannot buy a bicycle on sale.

CHAPTER 2 Quiz 2
For use after Lessons 2.4–2.5

Use the diagram to determine if the statement is *true* or *false*.

1. Points A, C, and D are coplanar.
2. Point D is on line m.
3. Points B, C, and D are collinear.

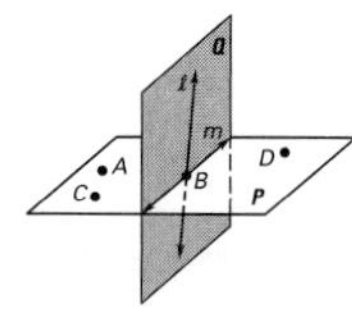

Solve the equation. Write a reason for each step.

4. $x + 25 = 45$ — Original equation
   $x = 20$ — Subtraction Property of Equality
5. $6x - 15 = 17 - 2x$ — Original equation
   $6x - 15 + 2x = 17 - 2x + 2x$ — Addition Property of Equality
   $8x - 15 = 17$ — Simplify
   $8x - 15 + 15 = 17 + 15$ — Addition Property of Equality
   $8x = 32$ — Simplify
   $x = 4$ — Division Property of Equality

Use the property to copy and complete the statement.

6. Addition Property of Equality:
   If $AB = CD$, then __?__ $+ EF =$ __?__ $+ EF$.
7. Symmetric Property of Equality:
   For any real numbers a and b, if $a = b$, then __?__ = __?__.

Answers

1. true
2. false
3. false
4. See left.
5. See left.
6. If $AB = CD$, then $AB + EF = CD + EF$.
7. For any real numbers a and b, if $a = b$, then $b = a$.

CHAPTER 2 Quiz 3
For use after Lessons 2.6–2.7

In Exercises 1–3, match the statement with the property that it illustrates.

1. If $\angle 1 \cong \angle 2$ and $\angle 2 \cong \angle 3$, then $\angle 1 \cong \angle 3$.
2. If $\angle ABC \cong \angle DEF$, then $\angle DEF \cong \angle ABC$.
3. $\angle HJK \cong \angle HJK$

A. Reflexive Property of Congruence
B. Symmetric Property of Congruence
C. Transitive Property of Congruence

In Exercises 4–11, complete the proof.

GIVEN $\angle 1 \cong \angle 2$
PROVE $\angle 3 \cong \angle 4$

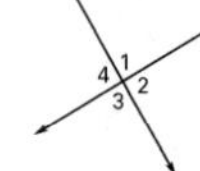

Statements	Reasons
4. $\angle 1 \cong \angle 2$	5. Given
6. $\angle 3 \cong \angle 1$, $\angle 2 \cong \angle 4$	7. Vertical Angles Congruence Theorem
8. $\angle 1 \cong \angle 4$	9. Transitive Property of Congruent Angles
10. $\angle 3 \cong \angle 4$	11. Transitive Property of Congruent Angles

Answers

1. C
2. B
3. A
4. See left.
5. See left.
6. See left.
7. See left.
8. See left.
9. See left.
10. See left.
11. See left.

CHAPTER 2 Chapter Test B
For use after Chapter 2

1. Sketch the fourth figure in the pattern below.

2. Write the next three numbers in the pattern.
   0, 1, 3, 6, . . .

Find a counterexample to disprove the conjecture.

3. All intersecting planes form right angles.
4. The value of x^3 is always greater than the value of x.
5. Regular polygons always have an even number of sides.

For the statement "Band members are musicians.", determine if each statement is *true* or *false*.

6. If you are not a musician, then you are not a band member.
7. If you are a musician, then you are a band member.
8. If you are not a band member, then you are not a musician.
9. If you are a band member, then you are a musician.
10. Rewrite the statements as a biconditional.
    If Chris is elected class president, then he has the most votes.
    If Chris has the most votes, then he will be elected class president.

Label the following planes and points appropriately on the diagram.

11. Label the vertical plane as A and the horizontal plane as B.
12. Draw two points X and Y on the diagram so they lie in plane A, but not in plane B.
13. Draw point Z on the diagram so it lies in both plane A and plane B.
14. Plot points Q and R on the diagram so that $\overleftrightarrow{QR}$ is the intersection of plane A and plane B.

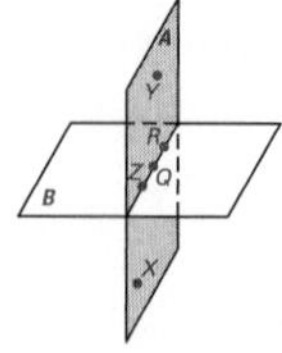

Answers

1. See left.
2. 10, 15, 21
3. See left.
4. $x = -2$
5. regular pentagon
6. true
7. false
8. false
9. true
10. Chris will be elected class president if and only if he has the most votes.
11. See left.
12. See left.
13. See left.
14. See left.

3.

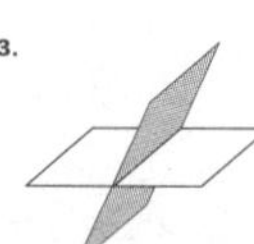

CHAPTER 2 **Chapter Test B** *continued*

For use after Chapter 2

What conclusions can you make using the true statement?

15. If the light is on, then someone is home. The light is on.

16. The Liberty Bell is located in Philadelphia, Pennsylvania. Rob has never been in Pennsylvania.

Solve the equation and write a reason for each step.

17. $6(x + 4) = 60$	Original equation
$6x + 24 = 60$	Distributive Property
$6x = 36$	Subtraction Property of Equality
$x = 6$	Division Property of Equality
18. $\frac{1}{4}(-x - 8) = 45$	Original equation
$-\frac{1}{4}x - 2 = 45$	Distributive Property
$-\frac{1}{4}x = 47$	Addition Property of Equality
$x = -188$	Multiplication Property of Equality

Complete the proof.

GIVEN: $\overline{AB} \cong \overline{FG}$

$\overline{AC} \cong \overline{EG}$

PROVE: $EF = 3$

Statements	Reasons
$AC = 13, BC = 3$	**19.** Given
$AC = AB + BC$	**20.** Segment Addition Postulate
$13 = AB + 3$	**21.** Substitution Property of Equality
$AB = 10$	**22.** Subtraction Property of Equality
$\overline{AB} \cong \overline{FG}, \overline{AC} \cong \overline{EG}$	**23.** Given
$AB = FG, AC = EG$	**24.** Definition of Congruent Segments
$FG = 10, EG = 13$	**25.** Substitution Property of Equality
$EG = EF + FG$	**26.** Segment Addition Postulate
$13 = EF + 10$	**27.** Substitution Property of Equality
$EF = 3$	**28.** Subtraction Property of Equality

Answers

15. Someone is home.

16. Rob has never seen the Liberty Bell.

17. See left.

18. See left.

19. See left.

20. See left.

21. See left.

22. See left.

23. See left.

24. See left.

25. See left.

26. See left.

27. See left.

28. See left.

CHAPTER 2 **Standardized Test**

For use after Chapter 2

Multiple Choice

1. What is the next letter in the sequence? A, B, D, G, K, . . . C

Ⓐ N Ⓑ O
Ⓒ P Ⓓ Q

2. What conjecture can be made if John is older than Mark, Sue is older than John, and Betty is younger than Sue? B

Ⓐ John is younger than Betty.
Ⓑ Sue is the oldest.
Ⓒ Mark is the youngest.
Ⓓ none of these

3. What is the converse of the given statement? D

GIVEN: If $m\angle B = 90°$, then $\angle B$ is a right angle.

Ⓐ If $m\angle B \neq 90°$, then $\angle B$ is not a right angle.
Ⓑ If $m\angle B = 90°$, then $\angle B$ is not a right angle.
Ⓒ If $\angle B$ is not a right angle, then $m\angle B \neq 90°$.
Ⓓ If $\angle B$ is a right angle, then $m\angle B = 90°$.

4. Which statement's inverse is true? A

Ⓐ If two lines intersect to form a right angle, then they are perpendicular lines.
Ⓑ If $m\angle W$ is less than 45°, then $\angle W$ is acute.
Ⓒ If point K is the midpoint of $\overleftrightarrow{JL}$, then points J, K, and L are collinear.
Ⓓ If two rays are opposite rays, then they have a common endpoint.

5. If all sides of a polygon are congruent, the polygon is equilateral. All sides of polygon A are 5 inches. Using the Law of Detachment, which conclusion can be made? B

Ⓐ Polygon A is congruent.
Ⓑ Polygon A is equilateral.
Ⓒ All polygon sides are 5 inches.
Ⓓ All polygons are equilateral.

6. If point B is the midpoint of $\overline{AC}$, then point B bisects $\overline{AC}$. If point B bisects $\overline{AC}$, then $\overline{AB} \cong \overline{BC}$. Using the Law of Syllogism, what conclusion can be drawn? A

Ⓐ If point B is the midpoint of $\overline{AC}$, then $\overline{AB} \cong \overline{BC}$.
Ⓑ If $\overline{AB} \cong \overline{BC}$, then point B bisects $\overline{AC}$.
Ⓒ If $\overline{AB} \cong \overline{BC}$, then point B is the midpoint of $\overline{AC}$.
Ⓓ Points A, B, and C are collinear.

7. Which statement is *not* a point, line, or plane postulate? D

Ⓐ A plane contains at least 3 noncollinear points.
Ⓑ If 2 lines intersect, then their intersection is exactly 1 point.
Ⓒ A line contains at least 2 points.
Ⓓ Coplanar points are points that lie on the same plane.

8. Which of the following statements can be determined from the figure? C

Ⓐ $\angle ABL \cong \angle JBK$
Ⓑ Points A, B, and J are collinear.
Ⓒ $\overline{JM}$ bisects $\overline{LK}$.
Ⓓ $\overleftrightarrow{CK} \perp \overleftrightarrow{AC}$

CHAPTER 2 **Standardized Test** *continued*

For use after Chapter 2

9. Which property of equality does the statement represent?

GIVEN: For any angles $\angle A$ and $\angle B$, if $m\angle A = m\angle B$, then $m\angle B = m\angle A$. C

Ⓐ distributive Ⓑ transitive
Ⓒ symmetric Ⓓ reflexive

10. The formula for the area of a circle is $A = \pi r^2$. Use the properties of equality to find the radius of a circle with an area of 100 square inches. B

Ⓐ $\frac{100}{\pi}$ Ⓑ $\frac{10}{\sqrt{\pi}}$
Ⓒ $\frac{10}{\pi}$ Ⓓ $\frac{100}{\sqrt{\pi}}$

11. Using the Transitive Property of Angle Congruence, if $\angle A \cong \angle B$ and $\angle B \cong \angle C$, then: A

Ⓐ $\angle A \cong \angle C$.
Ⓑ $\angle A$, $\angle B$, and $\angle C$ are right angles.
Ⓒ $\angle A$ and $\angle C$ are supplementary.
Ⓓ $\angle A$ and $\angle C$ are complementary.

12. The statement $\overline{XY} \cong \overline{XY}$ illustrates which property? B

Ⓐ Transitive Property of Equality
Ⓑ Reflexive Property of Segment Congruence
Ⓒ Substitution Property of Equality
Ⓓ Symmetric Property of Segment Congruence

13. $\angle P$ and $\angle Q$ are supplementary. If $m\angle P$ is double $m\angle Q$, find $m\angle P$ and $m\angle Q$. D

Ⓐ $m\angle P = 30°, m\angle Q = 60°$
Ⓑ $m\angle P = 60°, m\angle Q = 30°$
Ⓒ $m\angle P = 60°, m\angle Q = 120°$
Ⓓ $m\angle P = 120°, m\angle Q = 60°$

Gridded Answer

14. At 1:00 P.M. a thermometer reads 76°. A cold front moves in and drops the temperature 1.5° every half hour for the next 3.5 hours. What is the temperature at 4:30 P.M.?

6 5 . 5

Short Response

15. What is the next number in the sequence: 3, 9, 21, 45, 93, . . .? Write an equation that represents the sequence. 189; $n = 2x + 3$

Extended Response

16. A full 20-gallon gas tank has a gauge as shown.

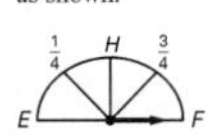

You travel until you have a $\frac{1}{4}$ tank of fuel remaining.

a. How many degrees did the gauge turn? 135°

b. How many gallons of gas are left in the tank? 5

c. You continue traveling until the tank is empty. You fill up the tank to $\frac{7}{8}$ full. How many degrees did the gauge turn while filling up? 157.5°

d. How many gallons did you get? 12.5

CHAPTER 2 **Alternative Assessment and Math Journal**

For use after Chapter 2

Journal **1.** Use the given information and the diagram to prove the statement.

GIVEN: $\angle 1$ and $\angle 3$ are supplementary.

PROVE: $\angle 2 \cong \angle 3$

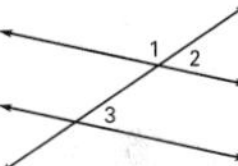

Multi-Step Problem **2.** You and your friend, who lives in a different city, are comparing the malls in your respective cities. Your friend describes the locations of some of the mall stores in the following way.

The music store (M) is due north of the bookstore (B) along hallway 1. The shoe store (S) is due east of the music store along hallway 1. The clothing store (C) is northeast of the music store along hallway 2 so that $\angle MSC$ is obtuse. The shoe store and clothing store are on hallway 2. The arcade (A) is southeast of the bookstore along hallway 3 so that $\angle CSA$ is acute. The shoe store and arcade are on hallway 3. The food court (F) is due east of the shoe store on hallway 1.

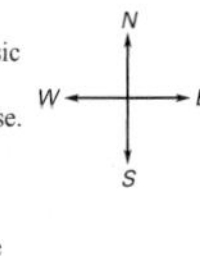

a. Draw a diagram of the mall.

b. Where do the hallways intersect?

c. You and your friend go to the bookstore and see two signs. One sign reads "Only paperback books are on sale." Another sign reads "The sale price is 20% off of the original price." Write each sign's statement in if-then form.

d. If possible, use the Law of Syllogism to write a new conditional statement from the statements in part (c).

e. Write the converse, the inverse, and the contrapositive of the statement from part (d).

f. Is $\angle FSA$ acute or obtuse? *Explain* your reasoning.

1. Statements: 1. $\angle 1$ and $\angle 3$ are supplements. 2. $\angle 1$ and $\angle 2$ are a linear pair. 3. $\angle 1$ and $\angle 2$ are supplements. 4. $m\angle 1 + m\angle 3 = 180°$ and $m\angle 1 + m\angle 2 = 180°$ 5. $m\angle 1 + m\angle 3 = m\angle 1 + m\angle 2$ 6. $m\angle 3 = m\angle 2$ 7. $\angle 3 \cong \angle 2$ **Reasons:** 1. Given 2. Definition of linear pair, as shown in the diagram. 3. Lincar Pair Postulate 4. Definition of supplementary angles 5. Transitive Property of Equality 6. Subtraction Property of Equality 7. Definition of congruent angles

2. a.

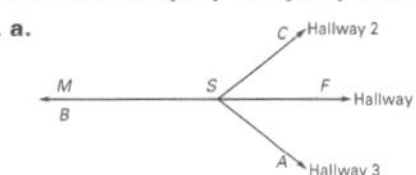

b. the shoe store **c.** If a book is a paperback, then it is on sale. If a book is on sale, then its sale price is 20% off of the original price. **d.** If a book is a paperback, then its sale price is 20% off of the original price.

e. Converse: If the sale price of a book is 20% off of the original price, then the book is a paperback. Inverse: If a book is not a paperback, then its sale price is not 20% off of the original price. Contrapositive: If the sale price is not 20% off of the original price, then the book is not a paperback. **f.** acute; Because $m\angle CSA = m\angle CSF + m\angle FSA$, $m\angle FSA < m\angle CSA$. Because $\angle CSA$ is acute, $m\angle CSA < 90°$ which means $m\angle FSA < 90°$. So $\angle FSA$ is acute.

PLAN AND PREPARE

Main Ideas

In this chapter, students will describe patterns, including visual and number patterns, and use inductive reasoning to make and test conjectures. They will analyze conditional statements and write the converse, inverse, and contrapositive of a conditional statement. They will explore how conditional and biconditional statements are used to state definitions. Students will use deductive reasoning, the Law of Detachment, and the Law of Syllogism to develop simple logical arguments. Students will learn what can and cannot be assumed from a diagram. Finally, they will use properties of equality and the laws of logic to prove basic theorems about congruence, supplementary angles, complementary angles, and vertical angles.

Prerequisite Skills

- Using a diagram to name types of angles
- Describing notation used for segments, lines, distance and rays
- Solving an equation
- Naming a postulate to justify a statement

Additional resources for reviewing prerequisite skills are:

- Skills Review Handbook, pp. 869–895
- @HomeTutor

2 Reasoning and Proof

Before

In previous courses and in Chapter 1, you learned the following skills, which you'll use in Chapter 2: naming figures, using notations, drawing diagrams, solving equations, and using postulates.

Prerequisite Skills

VOCABULARY CHECK

Use the diagram to name an example of the described figure. **1–4. Sample answers are given.**

1. A right angle **$\angle AGC$**
2. A pair of vertical angles **$\angle BGC$, $\angle EGF$**
3. A pair of supplementary angles **$\angle BGC$, $\angle CGE$**
4. A pair of complementary angles **$\angle AGB$, $\angle BGC$**

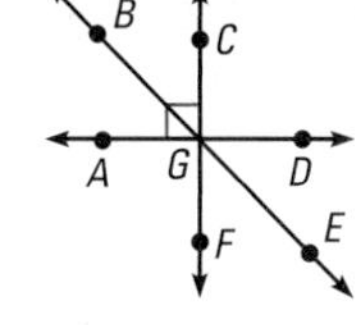

SKILLS AND ALGEBRA CHECK

Describe **what the notation means. Draw the figure.** *(Review p. 2 for 2.4.)* **5–8. See margin for art.**

5. $\overline{AB}$ **segment *AB***   6. $\overleftrightarrow{CD}$ **line *CD***   7. EF **length of segment *EF***   8. $\overrightarrow{GH}$ **ray *GH***

Solve the equation. *(Review p. 875 for 2.5.)*

9. $3x + 5 = 20$ **5**   10. $4(x - 7) = -12$ **4**   11. $5(x + 8) = 4x$ **−40**

Name the postulate used. Draw the figure. *(Review pp. 9, 24 for 2.5.)* **12–13. See margin.**

12. $m\angle ABD + m\angle DBC = m\angle ABC$ 13. $ST + TU = SU$

@HomeTutor Prerequisite skills practice at classzone.com

Chapter Planning Guide

Chapter 2 Resource Book
- Teaching Guide/Lesson Plan (pp. 3, 18, 31, 45, 60, 73, 87)
- Project with Rubric (p. 102)

Assessment and Intervention
- Assessment Book (pp. 16–30)
- Benchmark Tests
- Remediation Book

Interactive Technology
- Easy Planner
- Power Presentations CD-ROM
- Activity Generator CD-ROM
- Animated Geometry
- Test Generator CD-ROM
- Online Quizzes
- eWorkbook
- eEdition
- @HomeTutor

Resources for English Learners
- Quick Reference for English Learners
- Spanish Study Guide
- Multi-Language Visual Glossary
- Student Resources in Spanish

California Standards for Chapter 2

Geometry: 1.0, 2.0, 3.0

Now

In Chapter 2, you will apply the big ideas listed below and reviewed in the Chapter Summary on page 133. You will also use the key vocabulary listed below.

Big Ideas

1. **Use inductive and deductive reasoning**
2. **Understanding geometric relationships in diagrams**
3. **Writing proofs of geometric relationships**

KEY VOCABULARY

- conjecture, *p. 73*
- inductive reasoning, *p. 73*
- counterexample, *p. 74*
- conditional statement, *p. 79* converse, inverse, contrapositive
- if-then form, *p. 79* hypothesis, conclusion
- negation, *p. 79*
- equivalent statements, *p. 80*
- perpendicular lines, *p. 81*
- biconditional statement, *p. 82*
- deductive reasoning, *p. 87*
- proof, *p. 112*
- two-column proof, *p. 112*
- theorem, *p. 113*

Why?

You can use reasoning to draw conclusions. For example, by making logical conclusions from organized information, you can make a layout of a city street.

Animated Geometry

The animation illustrated below for Exercise 29 on page 119 helps you answer this question: Is the distance from the restaurant to the movie theater the same as the distance from the cafe to the dry cleaners?

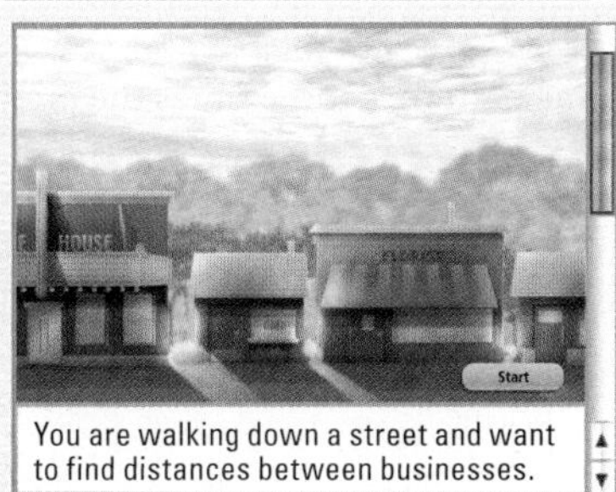

You are walking down a street and want to find distances between businesses.

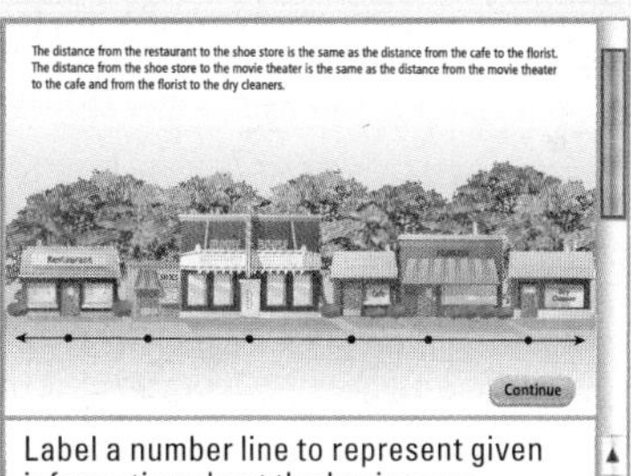

Label a number line to represent given information about the businesses.

Animated Geometry at classzone.com

Other animations for Chapter 2: pages 72, 81, 88, 97, 106, and 125

Geometry Toolkit

- Reading Strategies for Chapter 2, pp. 11–12
- Differentiated Instruction Notes, pp. 43–46
- English Learners Notes, pp. 93–94
- Inclusion Notes, pp. 123–124
- Teaching Strategies with Sample Worksheets, pp. 145–168
- Using Technology in the Classroom, pp. 169–174
- Tips for New Teachers, pp. 177–178
- Math Background Notes, pp. 202–205
- Pre-AP Strategies and Copymasters, pp. 285–286, 319–324
- Teacher Survival Activities, pp. 423–424, 447–448
- Bulletin Board Idea, p. 470
- Teacher Tool Transparencies, following p. 480

5–8. Sample answers are given.

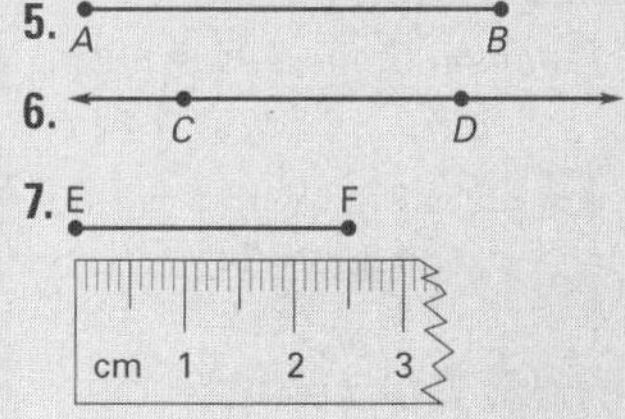

12. Angle Addition Postulate. ***Sample:***

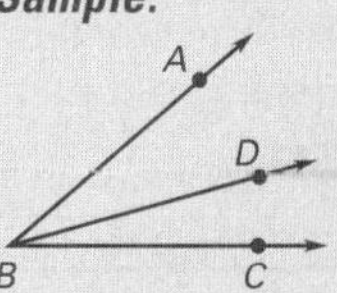

13. Segment Addition Postulate. ***Sample:***

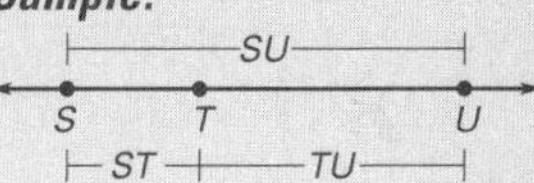

1 PLAN AND PREPARE

Warm-Up Exercises

Transparency Available

1. Find the length of a segment with endpoints $A(1, -3)$ and $B(-2, -7)$. **5**
2. If $M(4, -3)$ is the midpoint of $\overline{RS}$, and the coordinates of R are $(8, -2)$, find the coordinates of S. **(0, −4)**
3. $\angle A$ and $\angle B$ are supplementary. If the measure of $\angle A$ is three times the measure of $\angle B$, find the measure of $\angle B$. **45°**

Notetaking Guide

Transparency Available

Promotes interactive learning and notetaking skills, pp. 31–34.

Pacing

Basic: 1 day
Average: 1 day
Advanced: 1 day
Block: 0.5 block with 2.2

• See *Teaching Guide/Lesson Plan.*

2 FOCUS AND MOTIVATE

Essential Question

Big Idea 1, p. 71

How do you use inductive reasoning in mathematics? **Tell students they will learn how to answer this question by describing patterns suggested by geometric figures and numbers.**

2.1 Use Inductive Reasoning

Before You classified polygons by the number of sides.
Now You will describe patterns and use inductive reasoning.
Why? So you can make predictions about baseball, as in Ex. 32.

Key Vocabulary
• **conjecture**
• **inductive reasoning**
• **counterexample**

Standards

1.0 Students demonstrate understanding by identifying and giving examples of undefined terms, axioms, theorems, and **inductive** and deductive **reasoning.**

3.0 Students construct and judge the validity of a logical argument and **give counterexamples to disprove a statement.**

Geometry, like much of science and mathematics, was developed partly as a result of people recognizing and describing patterns. In this lesson, you will discover patterns yourself and use them to make predictions.

EXAMPLE 1 Describe a visual pattern

Describe how to sketch the fourth figure in the pattern. Then sketch the fourth figure.

Figure 1 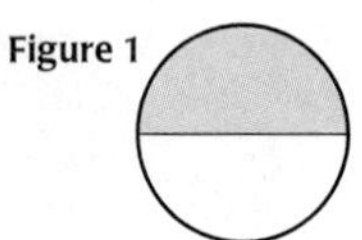 Figure 2 Figure 3 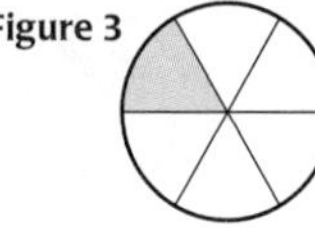

Solution

Each circle is divided into twice as many equal regions as the figure number. Sketch the fourth figure by dividing a circle into eighths. Shade the section just above the horizontal segment at the left.

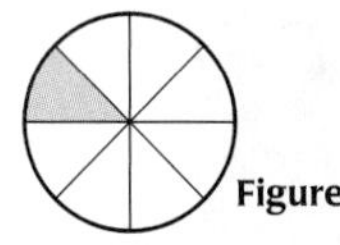
Figure 4

EXAMPLE 2 Describe a number pattern

READ SYMBOLS
The three dots (. . .) tell you that the pattern continues.

Describe the pattern in the numbers −7, −21, −63, −189, . . . and write the next three numbers in the pattern.

Notice that each number in the pattern is three times the previous number.

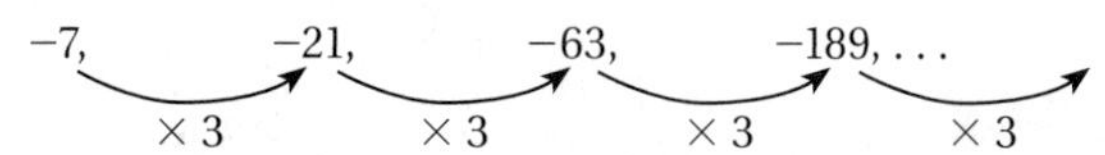

▶ Continue the pattern. The next three numbers are −567, −1701, and −5103.

Animated Geometry at classzone.com

✓ GUIDED PRACTICE for Examples 1 and 2

1. Sketch the fifth figure in the pattern in Example 1. **See margin.**
2. *Describe* the pattern in the numbers 5.01, 5.03, 5.05, 5.07, ... Write the next three numbers in the pattern. **The numbers are increasing by 0.02; 5.09, 5.11, 5.13.**

Resource Planning Guide

Chapter Resource Book
• Teaching Guide/Lesson Plan (pp. 3–4)
• Activity Master (p. 5)
• Practice levels A, B, C (pp. 7–12)
• Study Guide (pp. 13–14)
• Catch-up for Absent Students (p. 15)
• Application (p. 16)
• Challenge (p. 17)

Workbooks
• Notetaking Guide (pp. 31–34)
• Practice Workbook (pp. 22–24)

Teaching Options
• **Power Presentations CD-ROM** provides dynamic electronic teaching resources for the classroom.
• **Activity Generator CD-ROM** provides editable activities for all ability levels.

Interactive Technology
• Easy Planner
• Power Presentations CD-ROM
• Activity Generator CD-ROM
• Animated Geometry
• Test Generator CD-ROM
• Online Quiz
• eWorkbook
• eEdition
• @HomeTutor

Resources for English Learners
• Quick Reference for English Learners
• Spanish Study Guide
• Multi-Language Visual Glossary
• Student Resources in Spanish

See also the *Geometry Toolkit* for more strategies for meeting individual needs.

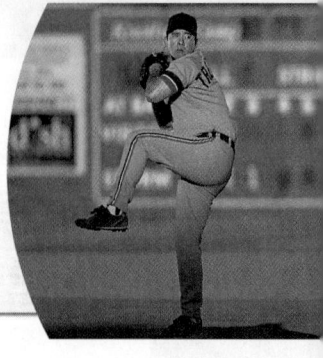

INDUCTIVE REASONING A **conjecture** is an unproven statement that is based on observations. You use **inductive reasoning** when you find a pattern in specific cases and then write a conjecture for the general case.

EXAMPLE 3 Make a conjecture

Given five collinear points, make a conjecture about the number of ways to connect different pairs of the points.

Solution

Make a table and look for a pattern. Notice the pattern in how the number of connections increases. You can use the pattern to make a conjecture.

Number of points	1	2	3	4	5
Picture					
Number of connections	0	1	3	6	?

+ 1 + 2 + 3 + ?

▶ **Conjecture** You can connect five collinear points 6 + 4, or 10 different ways.

EXAMPLE 4 Make and test a conjecture

Numbers such as 3, 4, and 5 are called *consecutive integers.* Make and test a conjecture about the sum of any three consecutive integers.

Solution

STEP 1 **Find** a pattern using a few groups of small numbers.

$3 + 4 + 5 = 12 = 4 \cdot 3$ $\quad$ $7 + 8 + 9 = 24 = 8 \cdot 3$

$10 + 11 + 12 = 33 = 11 \cdot 3$ $\quad$ $16 + 17 + 18 = 51 = 17 \cdot 3$

▶ **Conjecture** The sum of any three consecutive integers is three times the second number.

STEP 2 **Test** your conjecture using other numbers. For example, test that it works with the groups −1, 0, 1 and 100, 101, 102.

$-1 + 0 + 1 = 0 = 0 \cdot 3$ ✓ $\quad$ $100 + 101 + 102 = 303 = 101 \cdot 3$ ✓

GUIDED PRACTICE for Examples 3 and 4

3. Suppose you are given seven collinear points. Make a conjecture about the number of ways to connect different pairs of the points. **You can connect seven collinear points 15 + 6 or 21 different ways.**
4. Make and test a conjecture about the sign of the product of any three negative integers.

4. The product of three negative integers is a negative integer. ***Sample answer:*** **$-2 \cdot (-5) \cdot (-4) = -40$.**

Motivating the Lesson

Your favorite sports team has won 6 consecutive games. Do you think the team will win or lose the 7th game? If you answered, "win", you used inductive reasoning.

3 TEACH

Extra Example 1

Describe how to sketch the fourth figure in the pattern.

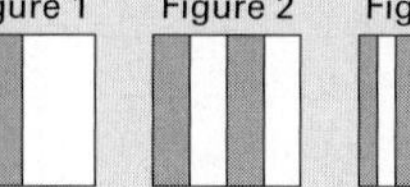
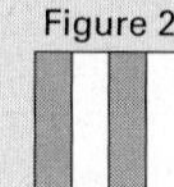
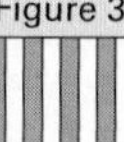

Each large region has twice as many equal regions as the previous figure. Sketch the fourth figure by dividing a square into 16 equal-sized vertical rectangles. Shade alternate regions.

Extra Example 2

Describe the pattern in the numbers 1000, 500, 250, 125, . . . and write the next three numbers in the pattern. **Each number in the pattern is one-half of the previous number; 62.5, 31.25, 15.625**

An **Animated Geometry** activity is available on-line for **Example 2.** This activity is also available on the **Power Presentations CD-ROM.**

Extra Example 3

Given the pattern of triangles below, make a conjecture about the number of segments in a similar diagram with 5 triangles.

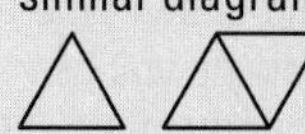

7 + 2 + 2 = 11 segments

1. See Additional Answers beginning on p. AA1.

Differentiated Instruction

Below Level If students have difficulty with **Example 2,** encourage them to concentrate on successive pairs of numbers. Ask students whether they can add the same number each time to get from one number to the next or whether they can multiply by the same number each time to get from one number to the next.

See also the *Geometry Toolkit* for more strategies.

Extra Example 4

Numbers such as 3, 11, 15, and 29 are odd numbers. Make and test a conjecture about the product of any two odd numbers **The product of any two odd numbers is odd.**

Extra Example 5

Find a counterexample to disprove the conjecture:

Supplementary angles are always adjacent.

Sample:

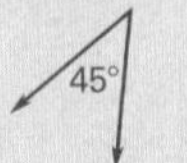

Extra Example 6

Which conjecture could you make based on the graph? **D**

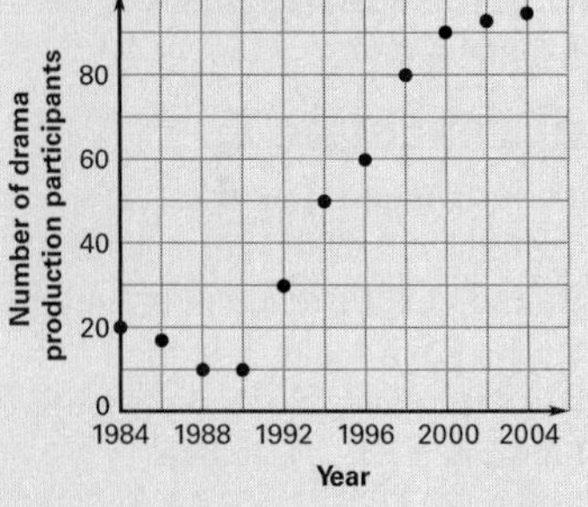

Ⓐ Participants have remained steady since 1984.

Ⓑ The number of girls participating in a drama production exceeds the number of boys.

Ⓒ The number of participants for *West Side Story* is over 50.

Ⓓ Participants have increased steadily since 1990.

Closing the Lesson

Have students summarize the major points of the lesson and answer the Essential Question: How do you use inductive reasoning in mathematics?

- **A conjecture is an unproven statement based on observations.**
- **You use inductive reasoning to find patterns and make conjectures.**
- **A counterexample disproves a conjecture.**

You use inductive reasoning to discover patterns. You conjecture that the pattern will continue to hold unless you find a counterexample.

DISPROVING CONJECTURES To show that a conjecture is true, you must show that it is true for all cases. You can show that a conjecture is false, however, by simply finding one *counterexample*. A **counterexample** is a specific case for which the conjecture is false.

EXAMPLE 5 Find a counterexample

A student makes the following conjecture about the sum of two numbers. Find a counterexample to disprove the student's conjecture.

Conjecture The sum of two numbers is always greater than the larger number.

Solution

To find a counterexample, you need to find a sum that is less than the larger number.

$-2 + -3 = -5$

$-5 \ngtr -2$

▶ Because a counterexample exists, the conjecture is false.

EXAMPLE 6 Standardized Test Practice

ELIMINATE CHOICES
Because the graph does not show data about boys or the World Cup games, you can eliminate choices A and C.

Which conjecture could a high school athletic director make based on the graph at the right?

Ⓐ More boys play soccer than girls.

Ⓑ More girls are playing soccer today than in 1995.

Ⓒ More people are playing soccer today than in the past because the 1994 World Cup games were held in the United States.

Ⓓ The number of girls playing soccer was more in 1995 than in 2001.

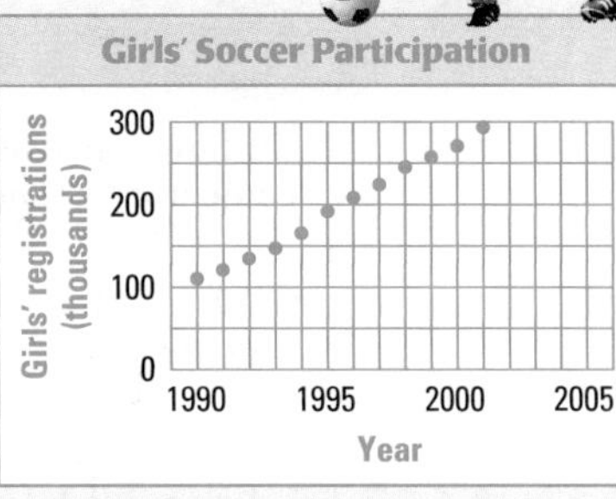

Solution

Choices A and C can be eliminated because they refer to facts not presented by the graph. Choice B is a reasonable conjecture because the graph shows an increase from 1990–2001, but does not give any reasons for that increase.

▶ The correct answer is B. Ⓐ Ⓑ Ⓒ Ⓓ

✓ **GUIDED PRACTICE** for Examples 5 and 6

5. Find a counterexample to show that the following conjecture is false.
   Conjecture The value of x^2 is always greater than the value of x. ***Sample answer:*** $x = \frac{1}{2}, x^2 = \frac{1}{4}$

6. Use the graph in Example 6 to make a conjecture that *could* be true. Give an explanation that supports your reasoning.

6. The number of girls playing soccer in the year 2002 will increase over previous years; the number of girls participating in soccer has increased for the past 11 years.

Differentiated Instruction

Below Level In Example 4, students can systematically examine the possible sums $0 + 1 + 2, 1 + 2 + 3, 2 + 3 + 4$, and so on. The sums are the successive multiples of 3. Students can factor 3 out of each sum and note that each time, the other factor is the middle number in the expression.

Advanced Ask students to use algebra to examine the conjecture for **Example 4**. Ask them to describe what they observe when they simplify $n + (n + 1) + (n + 2)$ and factor the result.

See also the *Geometry Toolkit* for more strategies.

2.1 EXERCISES

HOMEWORK KEY

○ = **WORKED-OUT SOLUTIONS** on p. WS2 for Exs. 7, 15, and 33

★ = **STANDARDIZED TEST PRACTICE** Exs. 2, 5, 19, 22, and 36

◆ = **MULTIPLE REPRESENTATIONS** Ex. 35

SKILL PRACTICE

A

1. **VOCABULARY** Write a definition of *conjecture* in your own words. ***Sample answer:* A guess based on observation**

2. ★ **WRITING** The word *counter* has several meanings. Look up the word in a dictionary. Identify which meaning helps you understand the definition of *counterexample*. ***Sample answer:* Contrary, opposite, opposing**

EXAMPLE 1 on p. 72 for Exs. 3–5

SKETCHING VISUAL PATTERNS **Sketch the next figure in the pattern.** **3, 4. See margin.**

3.  

4. 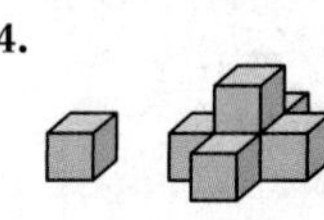 

5. ★ **MULTIPLE CHOICE** What is the next figure in the pattern? **C**

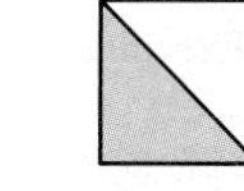 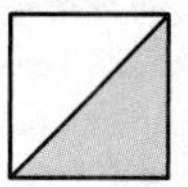 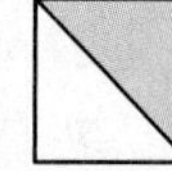

Ⓐ Ⓑ Ⓒ Ⓓ

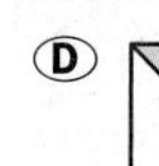

7. The numbers are 4 times the previous number; 768.

8. The numbers are $\frac{1}{2}$ of the previous number; 0.625.

EXAMPLE 2 on p. 72 for Exs. 6–11

DESCRIBING NUMBER PATTERNS ***Describe*** **the pattern in the numbers. Write the next number in the pattern.**

6. 1, 5, 9, 13, . . . **The numbers are increasing by 4; 17.**

7. 3, 12, 48, 192, . . .

8. 10, 5, 2.5, 1.25, . . .

9. 4, 3, 1, −2, . . . **The rate of decrease is increasing by 1; −6.**

10. $1, \frac{2}{3}, \frac{1}{3}, 0, \ldots$ **The numbers are decreasing by $\frac{1}{3}$; $-\frac{1}{3}$**

11. −5, −2, 4, 13, . . .

11. The numbers are increasing by successive multiples of 3; 25.

MAKING CONJECTURES **In Exercises 12 and 13, copy and complete the conjecture based on the pattern you observe in the specific cases.**

EXAMPLE 3 on p. 73 for Ex. 12

12. Given seven noncollinear points, make a conjecture about the number of ways to connect different pairs of the points.

Number of points	3	4	5	6	7
Picture					?
Number of connections	3	6	10	15	?

Conjecture You can connect seven noncollinear points __?__ different ways. **21**

EXAMPLE 4 on p. 73 for Ex. 13

13. Use these sums of odd integers: 3 + 7 = 10, 1 + 7 = 8, 17 + 21 = 38

Conjecture The sum of any two odd integers is __?__. **even**

4 PRACTICE AND APPLY

Assignment Guide

Answer Transparencies available for all exercises

Basic:
Day 1: pp. 75–78
Exs. 1–8, 12–22, 32–34, 39–49 odd

Average:
Day 1: pp. 75–78
Exs. 1–5, 8–20, 22–28 even, 32–36, 40–48 even

Advanced:
Day 1: pp. 75–78
Exs. 1, 2, 4, 5, 10–13, 16, 17–21 odd, 22, 23–27 odd, 29–38*, 42, 46, 49

Block:
pp. 75–78
Exs. 1–5, 8–20, 22–28 even, 32–36, 40–48 even (with 2.2)

Differentiated Instruction

See *Geometry Best Practices Toolkit* for suggestions on addressing the needs of a diverse classroom.

Homework Check

For a quick check of student understanding of key concepts, go over the following exercises:

Basic: 3, 6, 12, 14, 33
Average: 4, 8, 13, 16, 33
Advanced: 5, 10, 13, 17, 33

Extra Practice

- Student Edition, p. 898
- Chapter 2 Resource Book: Practice levels A, B, C, pp. 7–12

Practice Worksheet

An easily-readable reduced practice page (with answers) for this lesson can be found on p. 70C.

Differentiated Instruction

Visual Learners Before assigning **Exercises 6–12**, remind students that they should always write a list of the differences or ratios of consecutive numbers in each list of numbers in order to see if there is a pattern.

See also the *Geometry Toolkit* for more strategies.

3.

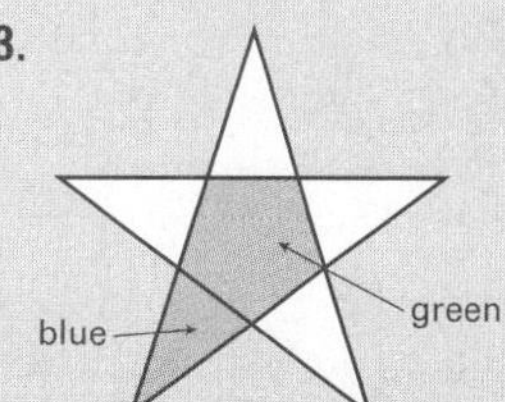

4.

Teaching Strategy

Exercises 6–11 If students have difficulty describing the pattern in the numbers, ask them to write a separate phrase for each number and the next and then generalize from the phrases. For example, the phrases for Exercise 9 might be: subtract 1, subtract 2, subtract 3, and so on.

Mathematical Reasoning

Exercise 12 Ask students if it is possible to write a rule for the number of connections by using n for the number of number of points. They may discover that the number of connections is $\frac{n(n-1)}{2}$.

Avoiding Common Errors

Exercise 16 Students may overlook the one exception to the statement. Suggest that they list the first 12 counting numbers and put a check mark above those that have exactly two divisors.

Mathematical Reasoning

Exercises 20–21 Remind students that a function rule will express the value of y, the dependent variable, in terms of the value of x, the independent variable. To discover the function rule, students can find the differences in successive y-values and then use *guess-and-check* to write y in terms of x. Stress that it is wise to check that the rule works for every pair of values in the table.

EXAMPLE 5 on p. 74 for Exs. 14–17

23. Previous numerator becomes the next denominator while the numerator is one more than the denominator; $\frac{6}{5}$.

24. Successive natural numbers are cubed; 216.

25. 0.25 is being added to each number; 1.45.

26. The rate of increase is increasing by 1; 21.

27. Multiply the first number by 10 to get the second number, take half of the second number to get the third number, and repeat the pattern; 500.

28. The numbers are 6 times the previous number; $0.4(6)^4$.

29. $r > 1$; $0 < r < 1$; raising numbers greater than one by successive natural number powers increases the result while raising a number between 0 and 1 by successive natural number powers decreases the result.

31a. Successive powers of $\frac{1}{2}$ are being added to each number; $1\frac{15}{16}$, $1\frac{31}{32}$, $1\frac{63}{64}$.

FINDING COUNTEREXAMPLES In Exercises 14–17, show the conjecture is false by finding a counterexample. **14–17. Sample answers are given.**

14. If the product of two numbers is positive, then the two numbers must both be positive. **$-4 \cdot -7 = 28$**

15. The product $(a + b)^2$ is equal to $a^2 + b^2$, for $a \neq 0$ and $b \neq 0$. **$(3 + 4)^2 = 7^2 = 49 \neq 3^2 + 4^2 = 9 + 16 = 25$**

16. All prime numbers are odd. **2**

17. If the product of two numbers is even, then the two numbers must both be even. **$3 \cdot 6 = 18$**

18. ERROR ANALYSIS *Describe* and correct the error in the student's reasoning. **All angles are not acute; some angles are obtuse angles, some angles are acute, and some angles are right.**

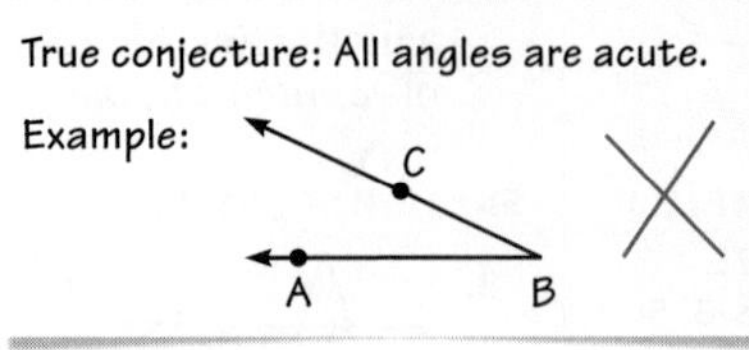

19. ★ SHORT RESPONSE *Explain* why only one counterexample is necessary to show that a conjecture is false. **To be true, a conjecture must be true for all cases.**

ALGEBRA In Exercises 20 and 21, write a function rule relating x and y.

20.

x	1	2	3
y	−3	−2	−1

$y = x - 4$

21.

x	1	2	3
y	2	4	6

$y = 2x$

22. ★ MULTIPLE CHOICE What is the first number in the pattern? **B**

_?_, _?_, _?_, 81, 243, 729

Ⓐ 1 Ⓑ 3 Ⓒ 9 Ⓓ 27

MAKING PREDICTIONS ***Describe*** **a pattern in the numbers. Write the next number in the pattern. Graph the pattern on a number line.** **23–28. See margin for art.**

23. $2, \frac{3}{2}, \frac{4}{3}, \frac{5}{4}, \ldots$

24. 1, 8, 27, 64, 125, . . .

25. 0.45, 0.7, 0.95, 1.2, . . .

26. 1, 3, 6, 10, 15, . . .

27. 2, 20, 10, 100, 50, . . .

28. $0.4(6), 0.4(6)^2, 0.4(6)^3, \ldots$

29. ALGEBRA Consider the pattern $5, 5r, 5r^2, 5r^3, \ldots$. For what values of r will the values of the numbers in the pattern be increasing? For what values of r will the values of the numbers be decreasing? *Explain.*

30. REASONING A student claims that the next number in the pattern 1, 2, 4, . . . is 8, because each number shown is two times the previous number. Is there another description of the pattern that will give the same first three numbers but will lead to a different pattern? *Explain.* **Yes; the rate of increase is increasing by 1, which would make the next number 7.**

31. CHALLENGE Consider the pattern $1, 1\frac{1}{2}, 1\frac{3}{4}, 1\frac{7}{8}, \ldots$.

a. *Describe* the pattern. Write the next three numbers in the pattern.

b. What is happening to the values of the numbers? **They are getting larger.**

c. Make a conjecture about later numbers. *Explain* your reasoning. **They are getting closer and closer to the number 2; the difference between 2 and each new term is getting smaller.**

○ = WORKED-OUT SOLUTIONS on p. WS1

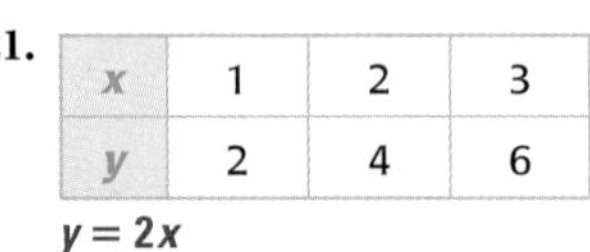

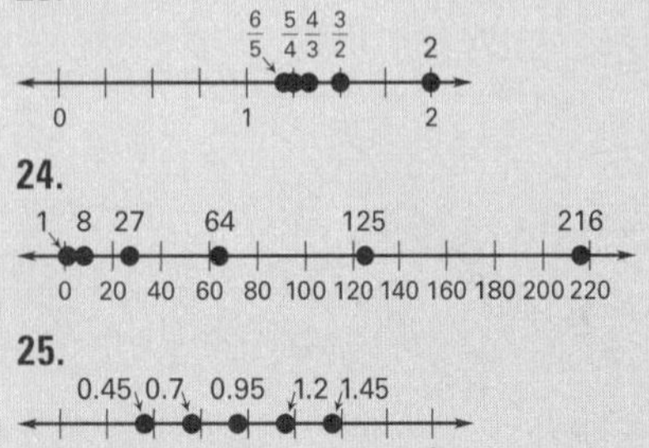

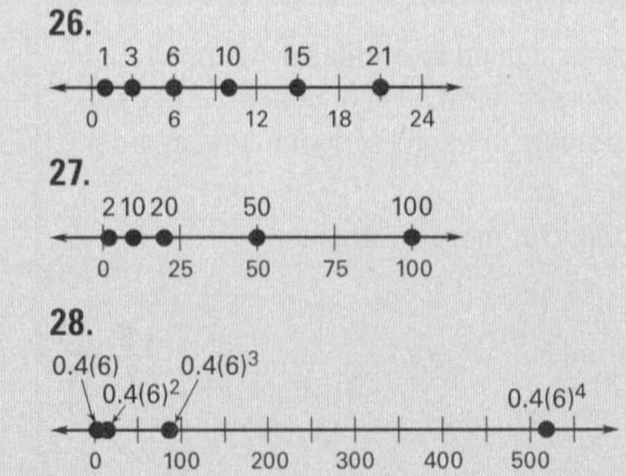

PROBLEM SOLVING

A **32. BASEBALL** You are watching a pitcher who throws two types of pitches, a fastball (F, in white below) and a curveball (C, in red below). You notice that the order of pitches was F, C, F, F, C, C, F, F, F. Assuming that this pattern continues, predict the next five pitches. **C, C, C, F, F**

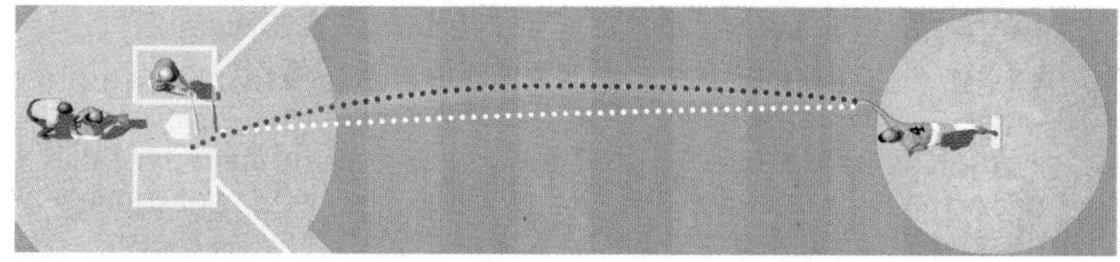

@HomeTutor for problem solving help at classzone.com

EXAMPLE 6 on p. 74 for Ex. 33

33. STATISTICS The scatter plot shows the number of person-to-person e-mail messages sent each year. Make a conjecture that *could* be true. Give an explanation that supports your reasoning. ***Sample answer:* The number of e-mail messages will increase in 2004; the number of e-mail messages has increased for the past 7 years.**

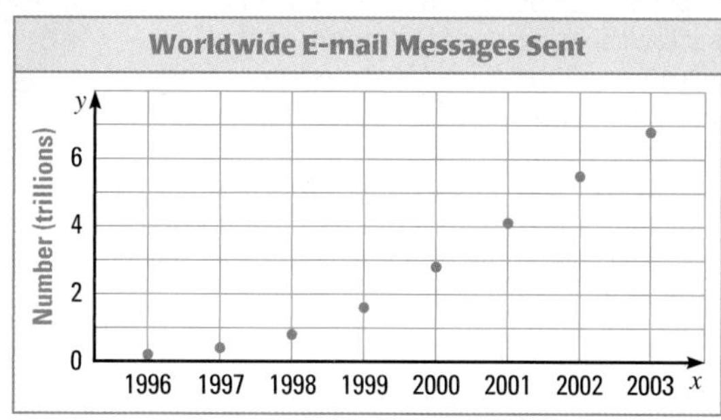

@HomeTutor for problem solving help at classzone.com

B **34. VISUAL REASONING** Use the pattern below. Each figure is made of squares that are 1 unit by 1 unit.

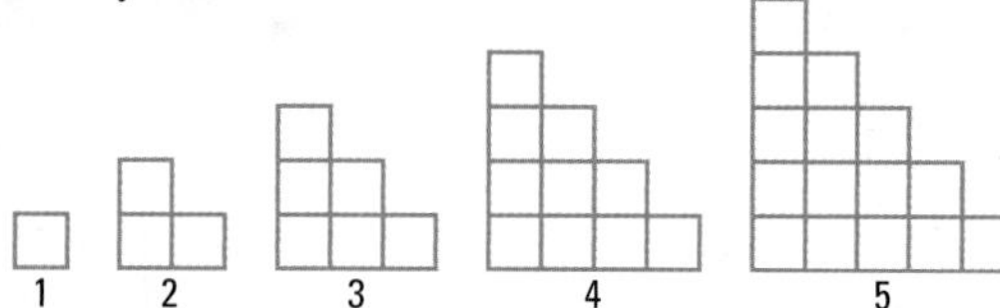

a. Find the distance around each figure. Organize your results in a table. **See margin.**

b. Use your table to *describe* a pattern in the distances. **The distances are increasing each time by 4 units.**

c. Predict the distance around the 20th figure in this pattern. **80 units**

35. MULTIPLE REPRESENTATIONS Use the given function table relating x and y.

a. **Making a Table** Copy and complete the table.

b. **Drawing a Graph** Graph the table of values. **See margin.**

c. **Writing an Equation** *Describe* the pattern in words and then write an equation relating x and y. **Double the value of x and add 1 to the result, $y = 2x + 1$.**

x	y
−3	−5
? **0**	1
5	11
? **7**	15
12	? **25**
15	31

34a.

Figure number	1	2	3	4	5
Distance around (units)	4	8	12	16	20

35b.

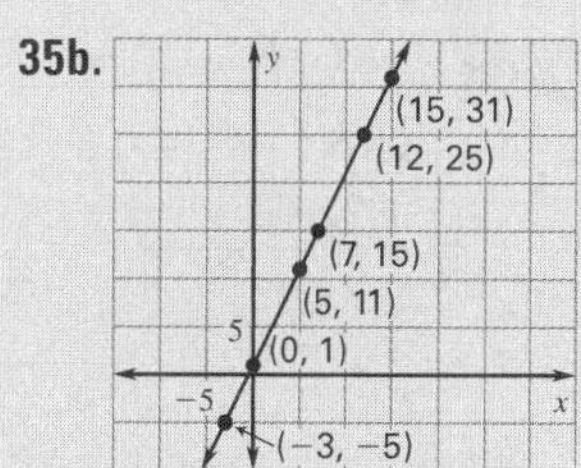

5 ASSESS AND RETEACH

Daily Homework Quiz

Transparency Available

1. Describe a pattern in the numbers. Write the next number in the pattern. 20, 22, 25, 29, 34, ... **Start by adding 2 to 22, then add numbers that successively increase by 1; 40.**
2. Find a counterexample for the following conjecture: If the sum of two numbers is positive, then the two numbers must be positive. ***Sample:* 20 + (−10)**
3. The scatter plot shows the average number of hours of homework done per week by a student during the first 10 weeks of a school term. Make a conjecture that could be true. Explain your reasoning.

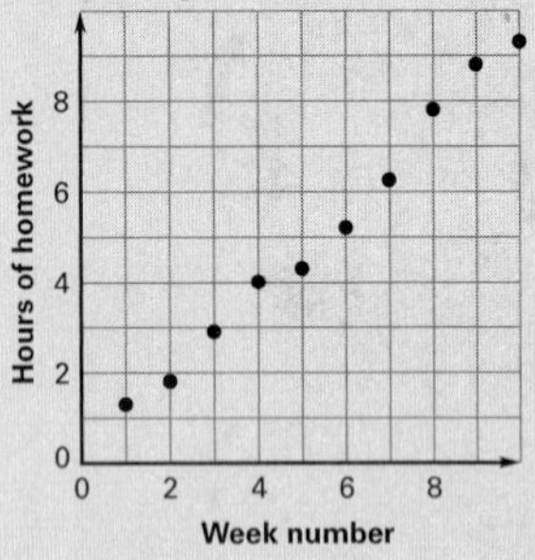

***Sample answer:* The student will do about 11 hours of homework in week 11. The number of hours of homework per week increased steadily during the first 10 weeks.**

Available at **classzone.com**

Diagnosis/Remediation

- Practice A, B, C in Chapter 2 Resource Book, pp. 7–12
- Study Guide in Chapter 2 Resource Book, pp. 13–14
- Practice Workbook, pp. 22–24
- @HomeTutor

Challenge

Additional challenge is available in the Chapter 2 Resource Book, p. 17.

36a–b. See Additional Answers beginning on p. AA1.

36d. 57 tickets; substitute 14 into the inequality $y < 0.25x$ for y; $14 < 0.25x$, $56 < x$, $x > 56$.

36. ★ **EXTENDED RESPONSE** Your class is selling raffle tickets for $.25 each.
    - a. Make a table showing your income if you sold 0, 1, 2, 3, 4, 5, 10, or 20 raffle tickets. **See margin.**
    - b. Graph your results. *Describe* any pattern you see. **See margin.**
    - c. Write an equation for your income y if you sold x tickets. $y = 0.25x$
    - d. If your class paid $14 for the raffle prize, at least how many tickets does your class need to sell to make a profit? *Explain.*
    - e. How many tickets does your class need to sell to make a profit of $50? **256 tickets**

C

37. **FIBONACCI NUMBERS** The *Fibonacci numbers* are shown below. Use the Fibonacci numbers to answer the following questions.

    1, 1, 2, 3, 5, 8, 13, 21, 34, 55, 89, . . .

    - a. Copy and complete: After the first two numbers, each number is the _?_ of the _?_ previous numbers. **sum, two**
    - b. Write the next three numbers in the pattern. **144, 233, 377**
    - c. **Research** This pattern has been used to describe the growth of the *nautilus shell.* Use an encyclopedia or the Internet to find another real-world example of this pattern. ***Sample answer:* spiral patterns on the head of a sunflower**

38. **CHALLENGE** Set A consists of all multiples of 5 greater than 10 and less than 100. Set B consists of all multiples of 8 greater than 16 and less than 100. Show that each conjecture is false by finding a counterexample. **Sample answers are given.**
    - a. Any number in set A is also in set B. **15**
    - b. Any number less than 100 is either in set A or in set B. **16**
    - c. No number is in both set A and set B. **40**

MIXED REVIEW

Use the Distributive Property to write the expression without parentheses. *(p. 872)*

39. $4(x - 5)$ $\mathbf{4x - 20}$ 40. $-2(x - 7)$ $\mathbf{-2x + 14}$ 41. $(-2n + 5)4$ $\mathbf{-8n + 20}$ 42. $x(x + 8)$ $\mathbf{x^2 + 8x}$

PREVIEW
Prepare for Lesson 2.2 in Exs. 43–46.

You ask your friends how many pets they have. The results are: 1, 5, 1, 0, 3, 6, 4, 2, 10, and 1. Use these data in Exercises 43–46. *(p. 887)*

43. Find the mean. **3.3 pets** 44. Find the median. **2.5 pets** 45. Find the mode(s). **1 pet**

46. Tell whether the *mean, median,* or *mode(s)* best represent(s) the data. **median**

Find the perimeter and area of the figure. *(p. 49)*

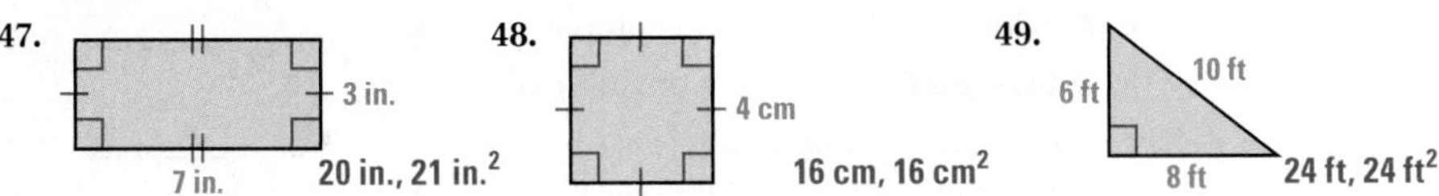

47. **20 in., 21 in.²** 48. **16 cm, 16 cm²** 49. **24 ft, 24 ft²**

2.2 Analyze Conditional Statements

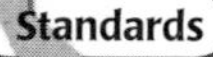

Before You used definitions.

Now You will write definitions as conditional statements.

Why? So you can verify statements, as in Example 2.

Key Vocabulary
- **conditional statement** converse, inverse, contrapositive
- **if-then form** hypothesis, conclusion
- **negation**
- **equivalent statements**
- **perpendicular lines**
- **biconditional statement**

Standards

3.0 Students construct and judge the validity of a logical argument and give counterexamples to disprove a statement.

A **conditional statement** is a logical statement that has two parts, a *hypothesis* and a *conclusion*. When a conditional statement is written in **if-then form**, the "if" part contains the **hypothesis** and the "then" part contains the **conclusion**. Here is an example:

If **it is raining**, then **there are clouds in the sky**.

Hypothesis — Conclusion

EXAMPLE 1 Rewrite a statement in if-then form

Rewrite the conditional statement in if-then form.

a. All birds have feathers.

b. Two angles are supplementary if they are a linear pair.

Solution

First, identify the **hypothesis** and the **conclusion**. When you rewrite the statement in if-then form, you may need to reword the hypothesis or conclusion.

a. **All birds** have **feathers**.

If **an animal is a bird**, then **it has feathers**.

b. **Two angles are supplementary** if **they are a linear pair**.

If **two angles are a linear pair**, then **they are supplementary**.

✓ **GUIDED PRACTICE** for Example 1

Rewrite the conditional statement in if-then form.

1. All 90° angles are right angles.

1. If the measure of an angle is 90°, then it is a right angle.

2. $2x + 7 = 1$, because $x = -3$.
If $x = -3$, then $2x + 7 = 1$.

3. When $n = 9$, $n^2 = 81$.
If $n = 9$, then $n^2 = 81$.

4. Tourists at the Alamo are in Texas.
If tourists are at the Alamo, then they are in Texas.

NEGATION The **negation** of a statement is the *opposite* of the original statement. Notice that Statement 2 is already negative, so its negation is positive.

Statement 1 The ball is red.

Negation 1 The ball is *not* red.

Statement 2 The cat is *not* black.

Negation 2 The cat is black.

1 PLAN AND PREPARE

Warm-Up Exercises

Transparency Available

Classify each of the following angles as acute, right, or obtuse.

1. 102° **obtuse** **2.** 37° **acute**

3. Find the complement and supplement of $\angle XYZ$ if $m\angle XYZ = 80°$. **10°; 100°**

4. If $XY = YZ$, is Y the midpoint of $\overline{XZ}$? If not, give a counterexample. **No; X, Y, and Z are collinear.**

Notetaking Guide

Transparency Available

Promotes interactive learning and notetaking skills, pp. 35–38.

Pacing

Basic: 2 days

Average: 2 days

Advanced: 2 days

Block: 0.5 block with 2.1
0.5 block with 2.3

- See *Teaching Guide/Lesson Plan.*

2 FOCUS AND MOTIVATE

Essential Question

Big Idea 1, p. 71

How do you rewrite a biconditional statement? **Tell students they will learn how to answer this question by rewriting a statement and its converse.**

Resource Planning Guide

Chapter Resource Book
- Teaching Guide/Lesson Plan (pp. 18–19)
- Practice levels A, B, C (pp. 20–25)
- Study Guide (pp. 26–27)
- Catch-up for Absent Students (p. 28)
- Application (p. 29)
- Challenge (p. 30)

Workbooks
- Notetaking Guide (pp. 35–38)
- Practice Workbook (pp. 25–27)

Teaching Options
- **Power Presentations CD-ROM** provides dynamic electronic teaching resources for the classroom.
- **Activity Generator CD-ROM** provides editable activities for all ability levels.

Interactive Technology
- Easy Planner
- Power Presentations CD-ROM
- Activity Generator CD-ROM
- Animated Geometry
- Test Generator CD-ROM
- Online Quiz
- eWorkbook
- eEdition
- @HomeTutor

Resources for English Learners
- Quick Reference for English Learners
- Spanish Study Guide
- Multi-Language Visual Glossary
- Student Resources in Spanish

See also the *Geometry Toolkit* for more strategies for meeting individual needs.

Motivating the Lesson

Students have encountered many situations in which one event leads to another. For example, if they do their homework, then they can watch TV. Ask them about other real-world situations that can be described in if-then form.

3 TEACH

Extra Example 1

Rewrite the conditional statement in if-then form.

a. All whales are mammals. **If an animal is a whale, then it is a mammal.**

b. Three points are collinear if there is a line containing them. **If there is a line containing three points, then the points are collinear.**

Key Question to Ask for Example 1

- How can you tell which statement is the hypothesis in part (b). **The hypothesis follows the word "if."**

Extra Example 2

Write the if-then form, the converse, the inverse, and the contrapositive of the statement "Soccer players are athletes." Decide whether each statement is true or false.

If-then form: If you are a soccer player, then you are an athlete; true.
Converse: If you are an athlete, then you are a soccer player; false.

Inverse: If you are not a soccer player, then you are not an athlete; false.

Contrapositive: If you are not an athlete, then you are not a soccer player; true.

VERIFYING STATEMENTS Conditional statements can be true or false. To show that a conditional statement is true, you must prove that the conclusion is true every time the hypothesis is true. To show that a conditional statement is false, you need to give *only one* counterexample.

RELATED CONDITIONALS To write the **converse** of a conditional statement, exchange the **hypothesis** and **conclusion**.

READ VOCABULARY
To *negate* part of a conditional statement, you write its negation.

To write the **inverse** of a conditional statement, negate both the hypothesis and the conclusion. To write the **contrapositive**, first write the converse and then negate both the hypothesis and the conclusion.

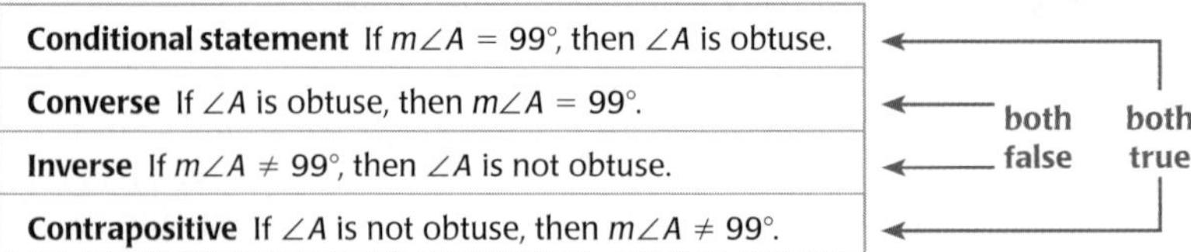

Statement	
Conditional statement If $m\angle A = 99°$, then $\angle A$ is obtuse.	both true
Converse If $\angle A$ is obtuse, then $m\angle A = 99°$.	both false
Inverse If $m\angle A \neq 99°$, then $\angle A$ is not obtuse.	both false
Contrapositive If $\angle A$ is not obtuse, then $m\angle A \neq 99°$.	both true

EXAMPLE 2 Write four related conditional statements

Write the if-then form, the converse, the inverse, and the contrapositive of the conditional statement "Guitar players are musicians." Decide whether each statement is *true* or *false*.

Solution

If-then form If you are a guitar player, then you are a musician. *True*, guitars players are musicians.

Converse If you are a musician, then you are a guitar player. *False*, not all musicians play the guitar.

Inverse If you are not a guitar player, then you are not a musician. *False*, even if you don't play a guitar, you can still be a musician.

Contrapositive If you are not a musician, then you are not a guitar player. *True*, a person who is not a musician cannot be a guitar player.

GUIDED PRACTICE for Example 2

Write the converse, the inverse, and the contrapositive of the conditional statement. Tell whether each statement is *true* or *false*.

5. If a dog is a Great Dane, then it is large.

6. If a polygon is equilateral, then the polygon is regular.

5. If a dog is large, then it is a Great Dane, false; if a dog is not a Great Dane, then it is not large, false; if a dog is not large, then it is not a Great Dane, true.

6. If a polygon is regular, then it is equilateral, true; if a polygon is not equilateral, then it is not regular, true; if a polygon is not regular, then it is not equilateral, false.

EQUIVALENT STATEMENTS A conditional statement and its contrapositive are either both true or both false. Similarly, the converse and inverse of a conditional statement are either both true or both false. Pairs of statements such as these are called *equivalent statements*. In general, when two statements are both true or both false, they are called **equivalent statements**.

Differentiated Instruction

Inclusion One way for students to remember the four types of statements discussed in this lesson is to study the following:

Conditional (If x, then y.) *Contrapositive* (If not y, then not x.)
Converse (If y, then x.) *Inverse* (If not x, then not y.)

Stress that the form of each of the last three types is based on the conditional statement.

See also the *Geometry Toolkit* for more strategies.

DEFINITIONS You can write a definition as a conditional statement in if-then form or as its converse. Both the conditional statement and its converse are true. For example, consider the definition of *perpendicular lines*.

KEY CONCEPT *For Your Notebook*

Perpendicular Lines

Definition If two lines intersect to form a right angle, then they are **perpendicular lines**.

The definition can also be written using the converse: If two lines are perpendicular lines, then they intersect to form a right angle.

You can write "line ℓ is perpendicular to line m" as $\ell \perp m$.

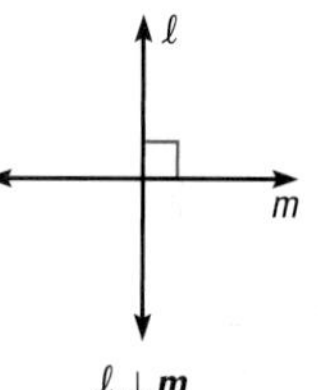

$\ell \perp m$

READ DIAGRAMS
In a diagram, a red square may be used to indicate a right angle or that two intersecting lines are perpendicular.

EXAMPLE 3 Use definitions

Decide whether each statement about the diagram is true. Explain your answer using the definitions you have learned.

a. $\overleftrightarrow{AC} \perp \overleftrightarrow{BD}$

b. $\angle AEB$ and $\angle CEB$ are a linear pair.

c. $\overrightarrow{EA}$ and $\overrightarrow{EB}$ are opposite rays.

Solution

a. This statement is *true*. The right angle symbol in the diagram indicates that the lines intersect to form a right angle. So you can say the lines are perpendicular.

b. This statement is *true*. By definition, if the noncommon sides of adjacent angles are opposite rays, then the angles are a linear pair. Because $\overrightarrow{EA}$ and $\overrightarrow{EC}$ are opposite rays, $\angle AEB$ and $\angle CEB$ are a linear pair.

c. This statement is *false*. Point E does not lie on the same line as A and B, so the rays are not opposite rays.

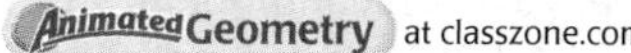

at classzone.com

GUIDED PRACTICE for Example 3

Use the diagram shown. Decide whether each statement is true. *Explain* your answer using the definitions you have learned.

7. $\angle JMF$ and $\angle FMG$ are supplementary.

8. Point M is the midpoint of $\overline{FH}$.

9. $\angle JMF$ and $\angle HMG$ are vertical angles.

10. $\overleftrightarrow{FH} \perp \overleftrightarrow{JG}$

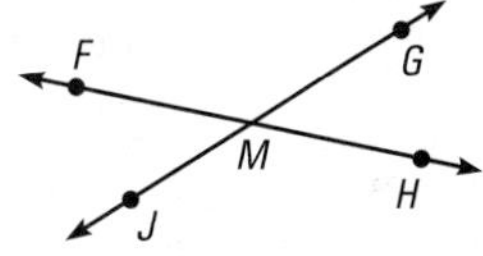

7. True; linear pairs of angles are supplementary.

8. False; it is not known that $\overline{FM} \cong \overline{MH}$.

9. True; two intersecting lines form 2 pairs of vertical angles.

10. False; it is not known that the lines intersect to form right angles.

Extra Example 3

Decide whether each statement about the diagram is true. Explain your answer using the definitions you have learned.

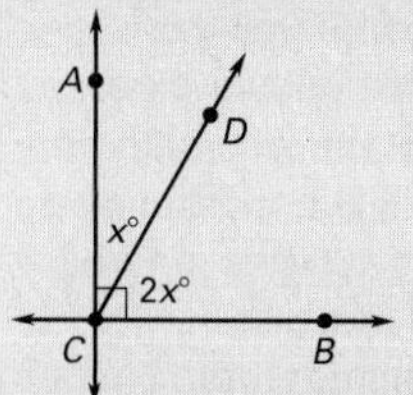

a. $\overleftrightarrow{AC} \perp \overleftrightarrow{BC}$ **True; the right angle symbol indicates that the lines intersect to form a right angle. So you can say the lines are perpendicular.**

b. $\angle ACD$ and $\angle DCB$ are complementary. **True; by the Angle Addition Postulate, $m\angle ACD + m\angle DCB = 90°$, so the angles are complementary by definition.**

c. $\overrightarrow{CD}$ bisects $\angle ACB$. **False; since x is positive, $x°$ and $2x°$ cannot be equal.**

An **Animated Geometry** activity is available on-line for **Example 3**. This activity is also available on the **Power Presentations CD-ROM**.

Extra Example 4

Write the definition of supplementary angles as a biconditional. **Definition: If the sum of the measures of two angles is 180°, then the angles are supplementary. Converse: If two angles are supplementary, then the sum of their measures is 180°. Biconditional: The sum of the measures of two angles is 180° if and only if the angles are supplementary.**

Key Questions to Ask for Example 4

- What are the key words that let you identify a statement as a biconditional? **if and only if**

Closing the Lesson

Have students summarize the major points of the lesson and answer the Essential Question How do you rewrite a biconditional statement?

- **A conditional statement can be written in if-then form. The if part is the hypothesis. The then part is the conclusion. The statement can be true or false.**
- **You can write the converse, inverse, and contrapositive of a conditional.**
- **A biconditional statement can be written when a conditional statement and its converse are both true.**

Write or rewrite the statement in if-then form. Write its converse in if-then form. Determine if both are true. If so, rewrite them together using if and only if.

READ DEFINITIONS
All definitions can be interpreted forward and backward in this way.

BICONDITIONAL STATEMENTS When a conditional statement and its converse are both true, you can write them as a single *biconditional statement.* A **biconditional statement** is a statement that contains the phrase "if and only if."

Any valid definition can be written as a biconditional statement.

EXAMPLE 4 Write a biconditional

Write the definition of perpendicular lines as a biconditional.

Solution

Definition	If two lines intersect to form a right angle, then **they are perpendicular**.
Converse	If **two lines are perpendicular**, then they intersect to form a right angle.
Biconditional	**Two lines are perpendicular** if and only if they intersect to form a right angle.

GUIDED PRACTICE for Example 4

11. Rewrite the definition of *right angle* as a biconditional statement.
12. Rewrite the statements as a biconditional.
    If Mary is in theater class, she will be in the fall play. If Mary is in the fall play, she must be taking theater class.

11. An angle is a right angle if and only if the measure of the angle is 90°.

12. Mary is in the theater class if and only if she will be in the fall play.

2.2 EXERCISES

HOMEWORK KEY
 = **WORKED-OUT SOLUTIONS on p. WS2 for Exs. 11, 17, and 33**
★ = **STANDARDIZED TEST PRACTICE Exs. 2, 25, 29, 33, 34, and 35**

SKILL PRACTICE

A

1. **VOCABULARY** Copy and complete: The __?__ of a conditional statement is found by switching the hypothesis and the conclusion. **converse**

2. ★ **WRITING** Write a definition for the term *collinear points,* and show how the definition can be interpreted as a biconditional. **Points are collinear if one line contains them; points are collinear if and only if one line contains the points.**

EXAMPLE 1 on p. 79 for Exs. 3–6

REWRITING STATEMENTS Rewrite the conditional statement in if-then form.

3. When $x = 6$, $x^2 = 36$. **If $x = 6$, then $x^2 = 36$.**
4. The measure of a straight angle is 180°.
   If an angle is a straight angle, then its measure is 180°.
5. Only people who are registered are allowed to vote.
   If a person is registered to vote, then they are allowed to vote.
6. **ERROR ANALYSIS** *Describe* and correct the error in writing the if-then statement.

   Given statement: All high school students take four English courses.

   If-then statement: If a high school student takes four courses, then all four are English courses.

6. The hypothesis and conclusion are not written correctly; if a student is a high school student, then the student takes four English courses.

7. If two angles are complementary, then they add to 90°; if two angles add to 90°, then they are complementary; if two angles are not complementary, then they do not add to 90°; if two angles do not add to 90°, then they are not complementary.

8. If it is an ant, then it is an insect; if it is an insect, then it is an ant; if it is not an ant, then it is not an insect; if it is not an insect, then it is not an ant.

9. If $x = 2$, then $3x + 10 = 16$; if $3x + 10 = 16$, then $x = 2$; if $x \neq 2$, then $3x + 10 \neq 16$; if $3x + 10 \neq 16$, then $x \neq 2$.

EXAMPLE 2
on p. 80
for Exs. 7–15

WRITING RELATED STATEMENTS For the given statement, write the if-then form, the converse, the inverse, and the contrapositive. **7–10. See margin.**

7. The complementary angles add to 90°. **8.** Ants are insects.

9. $3x + 10 = 16$, because $x = 2$. **10.** A midpoint bisects a segment.

ANALYZING STATEMENTS Decide whether the statement is *true* or *false*. If false, provide a counterexample.

11. If a polygon has five sides, then it is a regular pentagon. **False; see margin for art.**

12. If $m\angle A$ is 85°, then the measure of the complement of $\angle A$ is 5°. **true**

13. Supplementary angles are always linear pairs. **False. *Sample answer:* $m\angle ABC = 60°$, $m\angle GEF = 120°$**

14. If a number is an integer, then it is rational. **true**

15. If a number is a real number, then it is irrational. **False. *Sample answer:* 2**

EXAMPLE 3
on p. 81
for Exs. 16–18

USING DEFINITIONS Decide whether each statement about the diagram is true. *Explain* your answer using the definitions you have learned.

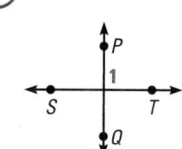

16. $m\angle ABC = 90°$ 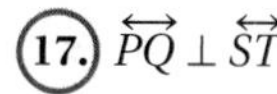 **17.** $\overleftrightarrow{PQ} \perp \overleftrightarrow{ST}$ **18.** $m\angle 2 + m\angle 3 = 180°$

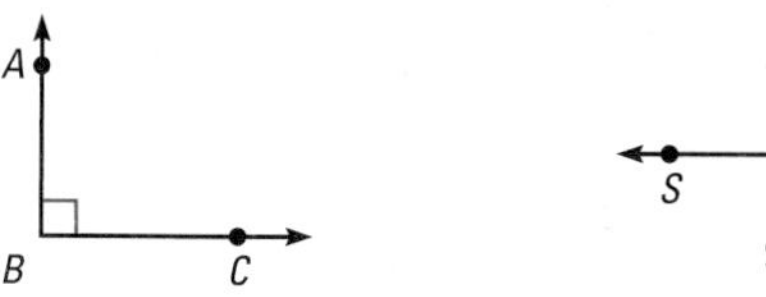

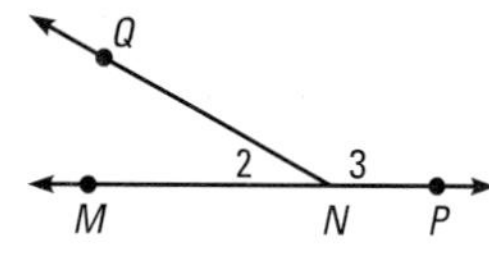

16. True; the diagram indicates that $\angle ABC$ is a right angle and the measure of a right angle is 90°.

17. False; there is no indication of a right angle in the diagram.

18. True; $\angle MNP$ is a straight angle and the measure of a straight angle is 180°. B

EXAMPLE 4
on p. 82
for Exs. 19–21

REWRITING STATEMENTS In Exercises 19–21, rewrite the definition as a biconditional statement.

19. An angle with a measure between 90° and 180° is called *obtuse*. **An angle is obtuse if and only if its measure is between 90° and 180°.**

20. Two angles are a *linear pair* if they are adjacent angles whose noncommon sides are opposite rays. **Two angles are a linear pair if and only if they are adjacent angles whose noncommon sides are opposite rays.**

21. *Coplanar points* are points that lie in the same plane. **Points are coplanar if and only if they lie in the same plane.**

DEFINITIONS Determine whether the statement is a valid definition.

22. If two rays are *opposite rays*, then they have a common endpoint. **not a good definition**

23. If the sides of a triangle are all the same length, then the triangle is *equilateral*. **good definition**

24. If an angle is a *right angle*, then its measure is greater than that of an acute angle. **not a good definition**

25. ★ **MULTIPLE CHOICE** Which statement has the same meaning as the given statement? **A**

GIVEN ▶ You can go to the movie after you do your homework.

(A) If you do your homework, then you can go to the movie afterwards.

(B) If you do not do your homework, then you can go to the movie afterwards.

(C) If you cannot go to the movie afterwards, then do your homework.

(D) If you are going to the movie afterwards, then do not do your homework.

4 PRACTICE AND APPLY

Assignment Guide

Answer Transparencies available for all exercises

Basic:
Day 1: pp. 82–85
Exs. 1–15, 31, 32
Day 2: pp. 82–85
Exs. 16–25, 33, 34, 40–55

Average:
Day 1: pp. 82–85
Exs. 1, 2, 4–10, 13–15, 26–29, 31, 32
Day 2: pp. 82–85
Exs. 16–25, 33–36, 40–55

Advanced:
Day 1: pp. 82–85
Exs. 1, 2, 4, 5, 9, 10, 14, 15, 26–32*
Day 2: pp. 82–85
Exs. 16–25, 33–39*, 42, 45, 47, 49, 52, 55

Block:
pp. 82–85
Exs. 1, 2, 4–10, 13–15, 26–29, 31, 32 (with 2.1)
pp. 82–85
Exs. 16–25, 33–36, 40–55 (with 2.3)

Differentiated Instruction

See *Geometry Best Practices Toolkit* for suggestions on addressing the needs of a diverse classroom.

Homework Check

For a quick check of student understanding of key concepts, go over the following exercises:

Basic: 3, 8, 16, 19, 31
Average: 4, 13, 17, 20, 31
Advanced: 5, 14, 18, 21, 32

Extra Practice

- Student Edition, p. 898
- Chapter 2 Resource Book: Practice levels A, B, C, pp. 20–25

Practice Worksheet

An easily-readable reduced practice page (with answers) for this lesson can be found on p. 70C.

10. If a point is the midpoint of a segment, then the point bisects the segment; if a point bisects a segment, then it is the midpoint of the segment; if a point is not the midpoint of a segment, then the point does not bisect the segment; if a point does not bisect a segment, then it is not the midpoint of the segment.

11. *Sample:*

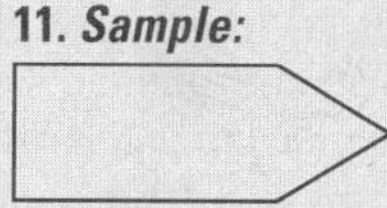

Avoiding Common Errors

Exercises 6–10 Students often make errors in deciding which part of the statement is the hypothesis and which part is the conclusion. Suggest that they think of the phrase before the verb as corresponding to the hypothesis and the phrase after the verb as corresponding to the conclusion.

Study Strategy

Exercises 22–24 Ask students to think of counterexamples when trying to decide if a definition is a good definition.

Exercises 31–32 For more information about volcanoes, visit www.geology.sdsu.edu/how_volcanoes_work/Home.html

34b. If the mean of the data is between x and y, then x and y are the least and greatest values in the data set; false; the mean can lie between two numbers in the data set neither of which is the smallest and/or largest.

34c. Mode. *Sample answer:* The mode is the number that occurs most often and has to be an element of the set. The mean and median can both be a number that is not in the set.

36a. If igneous rock is formed, then molten rock was cooled; if sedimentary rock is formed, then the rock was formed from pieces of other rocks; if metamorphic rock is formed, then there were changes in temperature, pressure, or chemistry.

ALGEBRA Write the converse of each true statement. Tell whether the converse is true. If false, *explain* why.

26. If $x > 4$, then $x > 0$.

26. If $x > 0$, then $x > 4$; false. *Sample answer:* 2 is greater than zero but not greater than 4.

27. If $x < 6$, then $-x > -6$. **If $-x > -6$, then $x < 6$; true.**

28. If $x \le -x$, then $x \le 0$. **If $x \le 0$, then $x \le -x$; true.**

29. ★ **OPEN-ENDED MATH** Write a statement that is true but whose converse is false. ***Sample answer:* If the dog sits, she gets a treat.**

C

30. CHALLENGE Write a series of if-then statements that allow you to find the measure of each angle, given that $m\angle 1 = 90°$. Use the definition of linear pairs.
If $\angle 1$ and $\angle 2$ are linear pairs, then $m\angle 2$ is 90°; if $\angle 1$ and $\angle 4$ are linear pairs, then the $m\angle 4$ is 90°; if $\angle 4$ and $\angle 3$ are linear pairs, then the $m\angle 3$ is 90°.

PROBLEM SOLVING

EXAMPLE 4 A on p. 82 for Exs. 31–32

In Exercises 31 and 32, use the information about volcanoes to determine whether the biconditional statement is *true* or *false*. If false, provide a counterexample.

VOLCANOES Solid fragments are sometimes ejected from volcanoes during an eruption. The fragments are classified by size, as shown in the table.

Type of fragment	Diameter d (millimeters)
Ash	$d < 2$
Lapilli	$2 \le d \le 64$
Block or bomb	$d > 64$

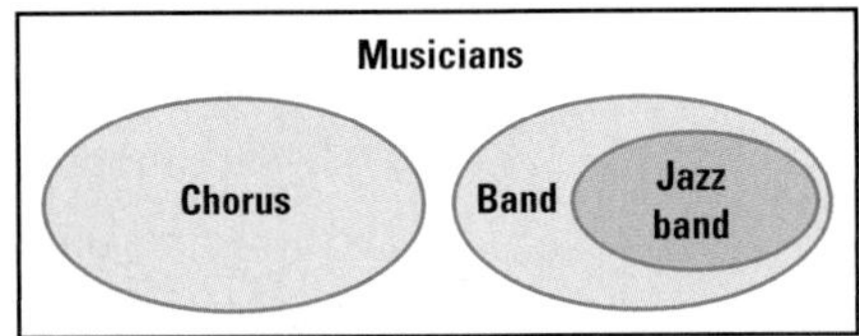

31. A fragment is called a *block* or *bomb* if and only if its diameter is greater than 64 millimeters. **true**

@HomeTutor for problem solving help at classzone.com

32. A fragment is called a *lapilli* if and only if its diameter is less than 64 millimeters.

32. False; $d = 1$ mm (ash).

@HomeTutor for problem solving help at classzone.com

33. ★ **SHORT RESPONSE** How can you show that the statement, "If you play a sport, then you wear a helmet." is false? *Explain.*
Find a counterexample. *Sample answer:* Tennis is a sport, but the participants do not wear helmets.

B

34. ★ **EXTENDED RESPONSE** You measure the heights of your classmates to get a data set.

a. Tell whether this statement is true: If x and y are the least and greatest values in your data set, then the mean of the data is between x and y. *Explain* your reasoning.

34a. True, the mean is the average which lies between the smallest value and the largest value unless all heights are the same.

b. Write the converse of the statement in part (a). Is the converse true? *Explain.* **See margin.**

c. Copy and complete the statement using *mean, median,* or *mode* to make a conditional that is true for any data set. *Explain* your reasoning. **See margin.**

Statement If a data set has a mean, a median, and a mode, then the _?_ of the data set will always be one of the measurements.

35. ★ **OPEN-ENDED MATH** The Venn diagram at the right represents all of the musicians at a high school. Write an if-then statement that describes a relationship between the various groups of musicians.

Musicians: Chorus; Band; Jazz band

35. *Sample answer:* If a student is a member of the jazz band, then the student is a member of the band but not the chorus.

○ = WORKED-OUT SOLUTIONS on p. WS1 ★ = STANDARDIZED TEST PRACTICE

36b. If molten rock is cooled, then igneous rock is formed; if the rock was formed from pieces of other rocks, then it is sedimentary; if a rock was formed by changes in temperature, pressure, or chemistry, then it is metamorphic; true, true, true; each hypothesis is the definition of the conclusion.

36c. *Sample answer:* If it is a rock, then it could have been formed in different ways; false; if something can be formed in different ways, it doesn't necessarily mean it has to be a rock. It could be soil for example.

38. No; if the contrapositive is true, then the conditional must also be true, but the converse can be true or false. You can write a biconditional only when both the conditional and its converse are true.

39. It is Tuesday, I have art class, I don't have study hall, I have music class; since it is Tuesday I have art class, since I have art class I don't have study hall, and since I don't have study hall I have music class.

36. **MULTI-STEP PROBLEM** The statements below describe three ways that rocks are formed. Use these statements in parts (a)–(c). **a–c. See margin.**

Igneous rock is formed from the cooling of molten rock.

Sedimentary rock is formed from pieces of other rocks.

Metamorphic rock is formed by changing temperature, pressure, or chemistry.

a. Write each statement in if-then form.

b. Write the converse of each of the statements in part (a). Is the converse of each statement true? *Explain* your reasoning.

c. Write a true if-then statement about rocks. Is the converse of your statement *true* or *false*? *Explain* your reasoning.

C 37. **ALGEBRA** Can the statement, "If $x^2 - 10 = x + 2$, then $x = 4$," be combined with its converse to form a true biconditional? **no**

38. **REASONING** You are given that the contrapositive of a statement is true. Will that help you determine whether the statement can be written as a true biconditional? *Explain.*

39. **CHALLENGE** Suppose each of the following statements is true. What can you conclude? *Explain* your answer.

If it is Tuesday, then I have art class.

It is Tuesday.

Each school day, I have either an art class or study hall.

If it is Friday, then I have gym class.

Today, I have either music class or study hall.

MIXED REVIEW

PREVIEW Prepare for Lesson 2.3 in Exs. 40–45.

Find the product of the integers. *(p. 869)*

40. $(-2)(10)$ **−20**
41. $(15)(-3)$ **−45**
42. $(-12)(-4)$ **48**
43. $(-5)(-4)(10)$ **200**
44. $(-3)(6)(-2)$ **36**
45. $(-4)(-2)(-5)$ **−40**

Sketch the figure described. *(p. 2)* **46–49. See margin.**

46. $\overleftrightarrow{AB}$ intersects $\overleftrightarrow{CD}$ at point E.
47. $\overleftrightarrow{XY}$ intersects plane P at point Z.
48. $\overleftrightarrow{GH}$ is parallel to $\overleftrightarrow{JK}$.
49. Planes X and Y intersect in $\overleftrightarrow{MN}$.

Find the coordinates of the midpoint of the segment with the given endpoints. *(p. 15)*

50. $A(10, 5)$ and $B(4, 5)$ **(7, 5)**
51. $P(4, -1)$ and $Q(-2, 3)$ **(1, 1)**
52. $L(2, 2)$ and $N(1, -2)$ $\left(\frac{3}{2}, 0\right)$

Tell whether the figure is a polygon. If it is not, *explain* why. If it is a polygon, tell whether it is *convex* or *concave*. *(p. 42)*

53. 
polygon; convex

54. 
Not a polygon; part of the figure is not a segment.

55. 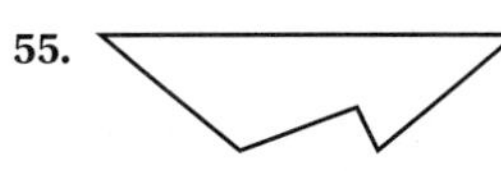
polygon; concave

46–49. Sample answers are given.

46. 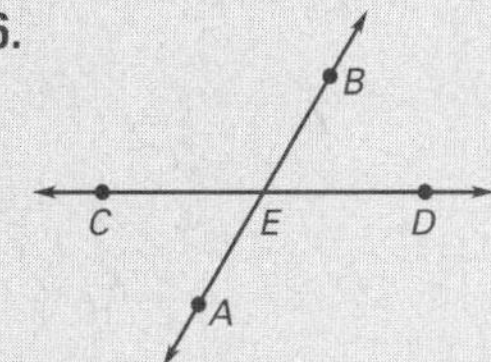

47.

48. 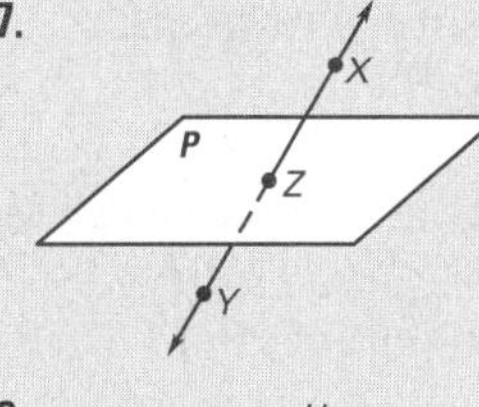

49. 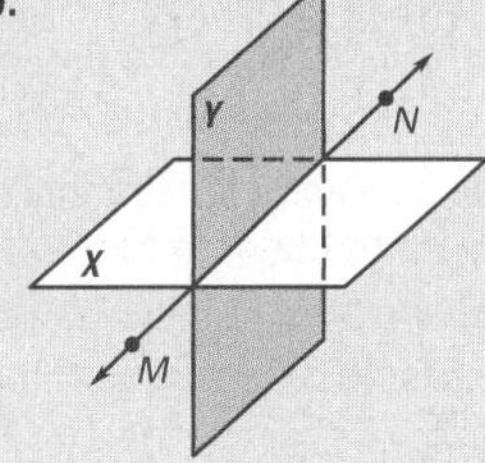

5 ASSESS AND RETEACH

Daily Homework Quiz

Transparency Available

1. For the given statement, write the if-then form, the converse, the inverse, and the contrapositive.
Sophomores take driving lessons. **If-then: If you are a sophomore, then you take driving lessons. Converse: If you take driving lessons, then you are a sophomore. Inverse: If you are not a sophomore, then you do not take driving lessons. Contrapositive: If you do not take driving lessons, then you are not a sophomore.**

2. Decide if the statement about the diagram is true. Explain.
$\overrightarrow{BD}$ *bisects* $\angle ABC$.

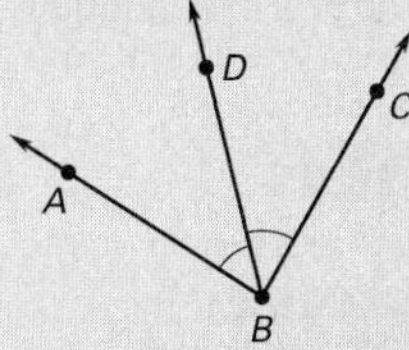

Yes; point D is in the interior of $\angle ABC$ and $m\angle ABD = m\angle CBD$, so $\overrightarrow{BD}$ bisects $\angle ABC$.

Determine whether the statements are good definitions.

3. If two angles are supplementary, then the sum of their measures is 180°. **yes**

4. If an angle is obtuse, then its measure is greater than that of an acute angle. **no**

Online Quiz

Available at **classzone.com**

Diagnosis/Remediation

- Practice A, B, C in Chapter 2 Resource Book, pp. 20–25
- Study Guide in Chapter 2 Resource Book, pp. 26–27
- Practice Workbook, pp. 25–27
- @HomeTutor

Challenge

Additional challenge is available in the Chapter 2 Resource Book, p. 30.

1 PLAN AND PREPARE

Explore the Concept

- Students will use deductive reasoning to solve a logic problem.
- This activity leads into the study of the Law of Detachment and the Law of Syllogism in Examples 1 and 2 of Lesson 2.3.

Materials

Each student will need:

- graph paper
- Activity Support Master (*Chapter 2 Resource Book*, p. 33)

Recommended Time

Work activity: 10 min

Discuss results: 5 min

Grouping

Students should work individually.

2 TEACH

Tips for Success

Ask students to rewrite the clues as conditional statements before they begin to draw conclusions from them and mark the grid.

Key Discovery

If-then statements, deductive reasoning, and a chart can be used to solve a logic puzzle.

3 ASSESS AND RETEACH

If statement A is true, then statement B is true. If statement B is true, then statement C is true. Suppose statement A is true, can you conclude that statement C is true? yes

2.3 Logic Puzzles

MATERIALS • graph paper • pencils

Standards

3.0 Students construct **and judge the validity of a logical argument and give counterexamples to disprove a statement.**

QUESTION **How can reasoning be used to solve a logic puzzle?**

EXPLORE **Solve a logic puzzle**

Using the clues below, you can determine an important mathematical contribution and interesting fact about each of five mathematicians.

Copy the chart onto your graph paper. Use the chart to keep track of the information given in Clues 1–7. Place an X in a box to indicate a definite "no." Place an O in a box to indicate a definite "yes."

Clue 1 Pythagoras had his contribution named after him. He was known to avoid eating beans.

Clue 2 Albert Einstein considered Emmy Noether to be one of the greatest mathematicians and used her work to show the theory of relativity.

Clue 3 Anaxagoras was the first to theorize that the moon's light is actually the sun's light being reflected.

Clue 4 Julio Rey Pastor wrote a book at age 17.

Clue 5 The mathematician who is fluent in Latin contributed to the study of differential calculus.

Clue 6 The mathematician who did work with n-dimensional geometry was not the piano player.

Clue 7 The person who first used perspective drawing to make scenery for plays was not Maria Agnesi or Julio Rey Pastor.

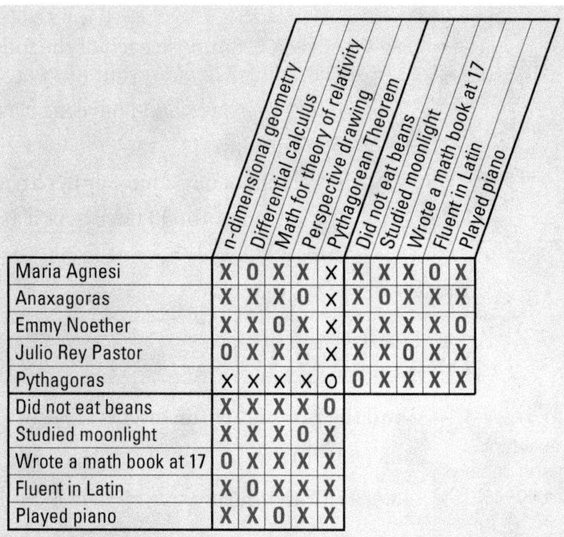

	n-dimensional geometry	Differential calculus	Math for theory of relativity	Perspective drawing	Pythagorean Theorem	Did not eat beans	Studied moonlight	Wrote a math book at 17	Fluent in Latin	Played piano
Maria Agnesi	X	O	X	X	X	X	X	X	O	X
Anaxagoras	X	X	X	O	X	X	O	X	X	X
Emmy Noether	X	X	O	X	X	X	X	X	X	O
Julio Rey Pastor	O	X	X	X	X	X	X	O	X	X
Pythagoras	X	X	X	X	O	O	X	X	X	X
Did not eat beans	X	X	X	X	O					
Studied moonlight	X	X	X	O	X					
Wrote a math book at 17	O	X	X	X	X					
Fluent in Latin	X	O	X	X	X					
Played piano	X	X	O	X	X					

DRAW CONCLUSIONS **Use your observations to complete these exercises** 1–3. See margin.

1. Write Clue 4 as a conditional statement in if-then form. Then write the contrapositive of the statement. *Explain* why the contrapositive of this statement is a helpful clue.
2. *Explain* how you can use Clue 6 to figure out who played the piano.
3. *Explain* how you can use Clue 7 to figure out who worked with perspective drawing.

1. If it is Julio Rey Pastor, then he wrote a book at age 17; if he did not write a book at age 17, then it is not Julio Rey Pastor; no other mathematician in the list wrote a book at age 17.
2. *Sample answer:* Find the individual who worked with n-dimensional geometry and eliminate him/her from the possible piano players.
3. *Sample answer:* Eliminate both Maria Agnesi and Julio Rey Pastor from the possibilities for perspective drawing.

2.3 Apply Deductive Reasoning

Before You used inductive reasoning to form a conjecture.
Now You will use deductive reasoning to form a logical argument.
Why So you can reach logical conclusions about locations, as in Ex. 18.

Key Vocabulary
- **deductive reasoning**

Deductive reasoning uses facts, definitions, accepted properties, and the laws of logic to form a logical argument. This is different from *inductive reasoning*, which uses specific examples and patterns to form a conjecture.

READ VOCABULARY
The Law of Detachment is also called a *direct argument*. The Law of Syllogism is sometimes called the *chain rule*.

Standards

1.0 Students demonstrate understanding by identifying and giving examples of undefined terms, axioms, theorems, and **inductive and deductive reasoning.**

3.0 Students construct and judge the validity of a logical argument and give counterexamples to disprove a statement.

KEY CONCEPT *For Your Notebook*

Laws of Logic

Law of Detachment

If the hypothesis of a true conditional statement is true, then the conclusion is also true.

Law of Syllogism

If **hypothesis** p, then **conclusion** q. ⟩ If these statements are true,
If **hypothesis** q, then **conclusion** r.
If **hypothesis** p, then **conclusion** r. ← then this statement is true.

EXAMPLE 1 Use the Law of Detachment

Use the Law of Detachment to make a valid conclusion in the true situation.

a. If two segments have the same length, then they are congruent. You know that $BC = XY$.

b. Mary goes to the movies every Friday and Saturday night. Today is Friday.

Solution

a. Because $BC = XY$ satisfies the hypothesis of a true conditional statement, the conclusion is also true. So, $\overline{BC} \cong \overline{XY}$.

b. First, identify the hypothesis and the conclusion of the first statement. The hypothesis is "If it is Friday or Saturday night," and the conclusion is "then Mary goes to the movies."

"Today is Friday" satisfies the hypothesis of the conditional statement, so you can conclude that Mary will go to the movies tonight.

1 PLAN AND PREPARE

Warm-Up Exercises

Transparency Available

1. Write the converse, inverse, and contrapositive of "If the measure of an angle is less than 90°, then the angle is acute." **Converse: If an angle is acute, then the measure is less than 90°. Inverse: If the measure of an angle is not less than 90°, then the angle is not acute. Contrapositive: If an angle is not acute, then its measure is not less than 90°.**

Notetaking Guide

Transparency Available

Promotes interactive learning and notetaking skills, pp. 39–42.

Pacing

Basic: 2 days
Average: 2 days
Advanced: 2 days
Block: 0.5 block with 2.2
0.5 block with 2.4
- See *Teaching Guide/Lesson Plan*.

2 FOCUS AND MOTIVATE

Essential Question

Big Idea 1, p. 71

How do you construct a logical argument? **Tell students they will learn how to answer this question by using the Laws of Detachment and Syllogism.**

Resource Planning Guide

Chapter Resource Book
- Teaching Guide/Lesson Plan (pp. 31–32)
- Practice levels A, B, C (pp. 34–39)
- Study Guide (pp. 40–41)
- Catch-up for Absent Students (p. 42)
- Application (p. 43)
- Challenge (p. 44)

Workbooks
- Notetaking Guide (pp. 39–42)
- Practice Workbook (pp. 28–30)

Teaching Options
- **Power Presentations CD-ROM** provides dynamic electronic teaching resources for the classroom.
- **Activity Generator CD-ROM** provides editable activities for all ability levels.

Interactive Technology
- Easy Planner
- Power Presentations CD-ROM
- Activity Generator CD-ROM
- Animated Geometry
- Test Generator CD-ROM
- Online Quiz
- eWorkbook
- eEdition
- @HomeTutor

Resources for English Learners
- Quick Reference for English Learners
- Spanish Study Guide
- Multi-Language Visual Glossary
- Student Resources in Spanish

See also the *Geometry Toolkit* for more strategies for meeting individual needs.

Motivating the Lesson

Your coach has told you that if you miss more than one practice during the week, you will not be allowed to play on Saturday. You missed practice yesterday and today. What do you think will happen?

3 TEACH

Extra Example 1

Use the Law of Detachment to make a valid conclusion in the true situation.

a. If two angles are right angles, then they are congruent. $\angle C$ and $\angle D$ are right angles. $\angle C \cong \angle D$

b. If Nathan is enrolled at Metro High School, then Nathan has an ID number. Nathan is enrolled at Metro High School. **Nathan has an ID number.**

Extra Example 2

If possible, use the Law of Syllogism to write a new conditional statement that follows from the pair of true statements.

a. If the radius of a circle is 4 ft, then the diameter is 8 ft. If the radius of a circle is 4 ft, then its area is 16π ft^2. **not possible**

b. If Joe takes Geometry this year, then he will take Algebra 2 next year. If Joe takes Algebra 2 next year, then he will graduate. **If Joe takes Geometry this year, then he will graduate.**

c. If $y^3 = 8$, then $y = 2$. If $y = 2$, then $3y + 4 = 10$. **If $y^3 = 8$, then $3y + 4 = 10$.**

An **Animated Geometry** activity is available on-line for **Example 2**. This activity is also available on the **Power Presentations CD-ROM**.

EXAMPLE 2 Use the Law of Syllogism

If possible, use the Law of Syllogism to write a new conditional statement that follows from the pair of true statements.

a. If Rick takes chemistry this year, then Jesse will be Rick's lab partner.

If Jesse is Rick's lab partner, then Rick will get an A in chemistry.

b. If $x^2 > 25$, then $x^2 > 20$.

If $x > 5$, then $x^2 > 25$.

c. If a polygon is regular, then all angles in the interior of the polygon are congruent.

If a polygon is regular, then all of its sides are congruent.

Solution

a. The conclusion of the first statement is the hypothesis of the second statement, so you can write the following new statement.

If Rick takes chemistry this year, then Rick will get an A in chemistry.

AVOID ERRORS
The order in which the statements are given does not affect whether you can use the Law of Syllogism.

b. Notice that the conclusion of the second statement is the hypothesis of the first statement, so you can write the following new statement.

If $x > 5$, then $x^2 > 20$.

c. Neither statement's conclusion is the same as the other statement's hypothesis. You cannot use the Law of Syllogism to write a new conditional statement.

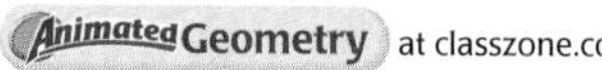

✓ GUIDED PRACTICE for Examples 1 and 2

1. If $90° < m\angle R < 180°$, then $\angle R$ is obtuse. The measure of $\angle R$ is 155°. Using the Law of Detachment, what statement can you make? **$\angle R$ is obtuse.**

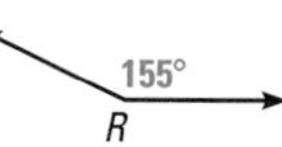

2. If Jenelle gets a job, then she can afford a car. If Jenelle can afford a car, then she will drive to school. Using the Law of Syllogism, what statement can you make? **If Jenelle gets a job, then she will drive to school.**

State the law of logic that is illustrated.

3. If you get an A or better on your math test, then you can go to the movies. If you go to the movies, then you can watch your favorite actor.

   If you get an A or better on your math test, then you can watch your favorite actor. **Law of Syllogism**

4. If $x > 12$, then $x + 9 > 20$. The value of x is 14.

   Therefore, $x + 9 > 20$. **Law of Detachment**

ANALYZING REASONING In Geometry, you will frequently use inductive reasoning to make conjectures. You will also be using deductive reasoning to show that conjectures are true or false. You will need to know which type of reasoning is being used.

EXAMPLE 3 Use inductive and deductive reasoning

ALGEBRA What conclusion can you make about the product of an even integer and any other integer?

Solution

STEP 1 **Look** for a pattern in several examples. Use inductive reasoning to make a conjecture.

$(-2)(2) = -4$, $(-1)(2) = -2$, $2(2) = 4$, $3(2) = 6$,

$(-2)(-4) = 8$, $(-1)(-4) = 4$, $2(-4) = -8$, $3(-4) = -12$

Conjecture Even integer • Any integer = Even integer

STEP 2 **Let** n and m each be any integer. Use deductive reasoning to show the conjecture is true.

$2n$ is an even integer because any integer multiplied by 2 is even.

$2nm$ represents the product of an even integer and any integer m.

$2nm$ is the product of 2 and an integer nm. So, $2nm$ is an even integer.

▶ The product of an even integer and any integer is an even integer.

EXAMPLE 4 Reasoning from a graph

Tell whether the statement is the result of *inductive reasoning* or *deductive reasoning*. Explain your choice.

a. The northern elephant seal requires more strokes to surface the deeper it dives.

b. The northern elephant seal uses more strokes to surface from 250 meters than from 60 meters.

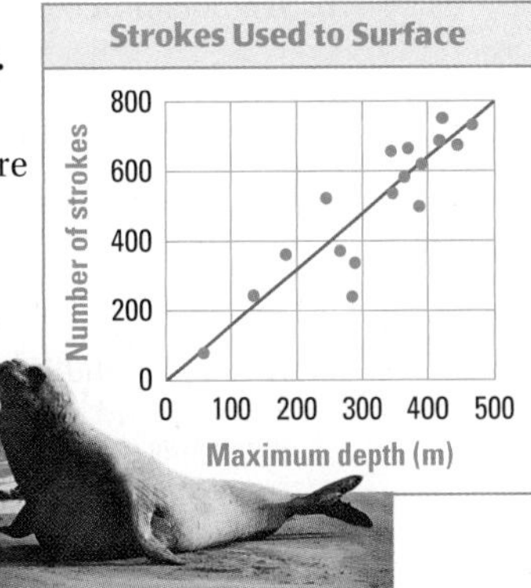

Solution

a. Inductive reasoning, because it is based on a pattern in the data

b. Deductive reasoning, because you are comparing values that are given on the graph

5. The sum of a number and itself is twice the number; $n + n = 2n$.

6. *Sample answer;* The more strokes it takes for the northern elephant to surface, the deeper it dove; the northern elephant seal uses fewer strokes to surface from 190 meters than from 410 meters.

GUIDED PRACTICE for Examples 3 and 4

5. Use inductive reasoning to make a conjecture about the sum of a number and itself. Then use deductive reasoning to show the conjecture is true. **See margin.**

6. Use inductive reasoning to write another statement about the graph in Example 4. Then use deductive reasoning to write another statement. **See margin.**

Differentiated Instruction

English Learners *Inductive reasoning* uses patterns in specific examples to lead *into* the general case. Point out that **Example 4a** uses some points on the graph to make a conclusion about the general behavior of the graph. *Deductive reasoning* leads from the general case to a specific instance. Show students that **Example 4b** uses the general behavior of the graph to make a conclusion about specific values.

See also the *Geometry Toolkit* for more strategies.

Extra Example 3

What conclusion can you make about the product of two odd numbers? **odd number • odd number = odd number**

Key Question to Ask for Example 3

- How does this example use both inductive and deductive reasoning? **Inductive reasoning is used to discover a pattern, and deductive reasoning is used to prove that the pattern always holds.**

Extra Example 4

Tell whether the statement is a result of inductive reasoning or deductive reasoning. Explain your choice.

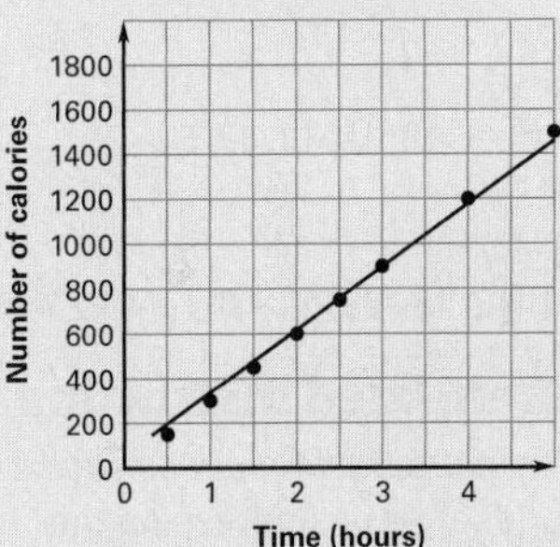

a. A 120 pound person uses twice as many calories when cycling 4 hours than when cycling 2 hours. **Deductive reasoning, because you are comparing values given on the graph.**

b. The 120 pound person uses more calories per hour the longer he or she cycles. **Inductive reasoning, because it is based on a pattern in the data.**

Closing the Lesson

Have students summarize the major points of the lesson and answer the Essential Question: How do you construct a logical argument?

- **The Law of Detachment allows you to make a valid conclusion in a true situation.**
- **The Law of Syllogism allows you to write a new conditional statement that follows from a pair of true statements.**

You construct a logical argument by applying the Law of Detachment and the Law of Syllogism along with known facts and definitions.

4 PRACTICE AND APPLY

Assignment Guide

Answer Transparencies available for all exercises

Basic:
Day 1: pp. 90–93
Exs. 1–10, 16, 17, 34–38
Day 2: pp. 90–93
Exs. 11–13, 18–24, 30–33

Average:
Day 1: pp. 90–93
Exs. 1–6, 8–10, 14, 16, 17, 34–38
Day 2: pp. 90–93
Exs. 11–13, 18–28, 30–33

Advanced:
Day 1: pp. 90–93
Exs. 1–6, 9, 10, 14–17*, 34–38
Day 2: pp. 90–93
Exs. 11–13, 18–30*, 32

Block:
pp. 90–93
Exs. 1–6, 8–10, 14, 16, 17, 34–38 (with 2.2)
pp. 90–93
Exs. 11–13, 18–28, 30–33 (with 2.4)

Differentiated Instruction

See *Geometry Best Practices Toolkit* for suggestions on addressing the needs of a diverse classroom.

Homework Check

For a quick check of student understanding of key concepts, go over the following exercises:

Basic: 4, 8, 11, 16, 20
Average: 5, 9, 11, 16, 20
Advanced: 6, 10, 11, 17, 20

Extra Practice

- Student Edition, p. 898
- Chapter 2 Resource Book: Practice levels A, B, C, pp. 34–39

Practice Worksheet

An easily-readable reduced practice page (with answers) for this lesson can be found on p. 70D.

2.3 EXERCISES

HOMEWORK KEY
○ = **WORKED-OUT SOLUTIONS on p. WS2 for Exs. 7, 17, and 21**
★ = **STANDARDIZED TEST PRACTICE Exs. 2, 3, 12, 20, and 23**

SKILL PRACTICE

A

1. **VOCABULARY** Copy and complete: If the hypothesis of a true if-then statement is true, then the conclusion is also true by the Law of ___?___. **Detachment**

★ **WRITING Use deductive reasoning to make a statement about the picture.**

2. 

3. 

2. ***Sample answer:*** **The person in the center of the photo is wearing jeans.**
3. ***Sample answer:*** **The door to this room is closed.**

EXAMPLE 1 on p. 87 for Exs. 4–6

LAW OF DETACHMENT Make a valid conclusion in the situation.

4. If the measure of an angle is 90°, then it is a right angle. The measure of $\angle A$ is 90°. **$\angle A$ is a right angle.**

5. If $x > 12$, then $-x < -12$. The value of x is 15. **$-15 < -12$**

6. If a book is a biography, then it is nonfiction. You are reading a biography. **It is nonfiction.**

EXAMPLE 2 on p. 88 for Exs. 7–10

LAW OF SYLLOGISM In Exercises 7–10, write the statement that follows from the pair of statements that are given.

7. If a rectangle has four equal side lengths, then it is a square. If a polygon is a square, then it is a regular polygon.

7. If a rectangle has four equal side lengths, then it is a regular polygon.

8. If $y > 0$, then $2y > 0$. If $2y > 0$, then $2y - 5 \neq -5$. **If $y > 0$, then $2y - 5 \neq -5$.**

9. If you play the clarinet, then you play a woodwind instrument. If you play a woodwind instrument, then you are a musician. **If you play the clarinet, then you are a musician.**

10. If $a = 3$, then $5a = 15$. If $\frac{1}{2}a = 1\frac{1}{2}$, then $a = 3$. **If $\frac{1}{2}a = 1\frac{1}{2}$, then $5a = 15$.**

EXAMPLE 3 on p. 89 for Ex. 11

11. **REASONING** What can you say about the sum of an even integer and an even integer? Use inductive reasoning to form a conjecture. Then use deductive reasoning to show that the conjecture is true.

11. Sum is even; the sum of two even integers is even; $2n$ and $2m$ are even, $2n + 2m = 2(n + m)$, $2(n + m)$ is even.

B

12. ★ **MULTIPLE CHOICE** If two angles are vertical angles, then they have the same measure. You know that $\angle 1$ and $\angle 2$ are vertical angles. Using the Law of Detachment, which conclusion could you make? **B**

Ⓐ $m\angle 1 > m\angle 2$ Ⓑ $m\angle 1 = m\angle 2$
Ⓒ $m\angle 1 + m\angle 2 = 90°$ Ⓓ $m\angle 1 + m\angle 2 = 180°$

13. **ERROR ANALYSIS** *Describe* and correct the error in the argument: "If two angles are a linear pair, then they are supplementary. Angles C and D are supplementary, so the angles are a linear pair." **See margin.**

13. Linear pairs are not the only pairs of angles that are supplementary. *Sample answer:* Angles C and D are supplementary, so the sum of their measures is 180°.

14b. If one endpoint is 2 units to the right and 3 units above the other endpoint, then the segment is congruent to the given segments; let $J(1, 1)$ and $K(3, 4)$ then $JK = \sqrt{13}$, use the Distance Formula.

14c. One endpoint is (x, y) and the second is $(x + 2, y + 3)$. Using the Distance Formula the distance between the two points is $\sqrt{13}$.

14. **ALGEBRA** Use the segments in the coordinate plane.

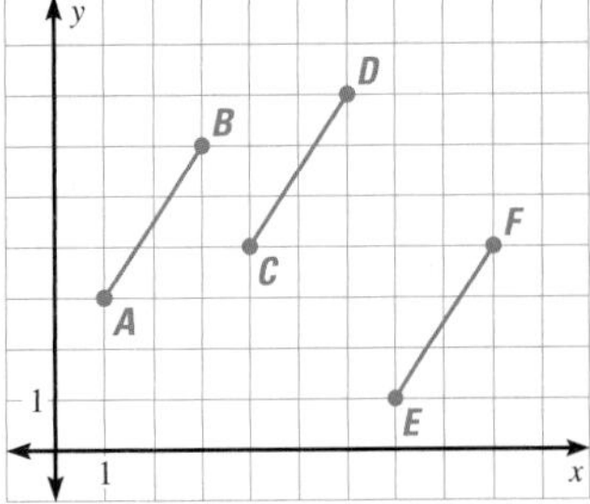

a. Use the distance formula to show that the segments are congruent. **$AB = CD = EF = \sqrt{13}$.**

b. Make a conjecture about some segments in the coordinate plane that are congruent to the given segments. Test your conjecture, and *explain* your reasoning.

c. Let one endpoint of a segment be (x, y). Use algebra to show that segments drawn using your conjecture will always be congruent.

d. A student states that the segments described below will each be congruent to the ones shown above. Determine whether the student is correct. *Explain* your reasoning.

$\overline{MN}$, with endpoints $M(3, 5)$ and $N(5, 2)$ **$\overline{MN}$, correct, by the Distance Formula;**

$\overline{PQ}$, with endpoints $P(1, -1)$ and $Q(4, -3)$ **$\overline{PQ}$, correct, by the Distance Formula;**

$\overline{RS}$, with endpoints $R(-2, 2)$ and $S(1, 4)$ **$\overline{RS}$, correct, by the Distance Formula.**

C 15. **CHALLENGE** Make a conjecture about whether the Law of Syllogism works when used with the contrapositives of a pair of statements. Use this pair of statements to *justify* your conjecture. **See margin.**

If a creature is a wombat, then it is a marsupial.

If a creature is a marsupial, then it has a pouch.

PROBLEM SOLVING

EXAMPLES 1 and 2 on pp. 87–88 for Exs. 16–17

A **USING THE LAWS OF LOGIC In Exercises 16 and 17, what conclusions can you make using the true statement?**

16. **CAR COSTS** If you save \$2000, then you can buy a car. You have saved \$1200. **You can't buy a car.**

@HomeTutor for problem solving help at classzone.com

17. **PROFIT** The bakery makes a profit if its revenue is greater than its costs. You will get a raise if the bakery makes a profit.

@HomeTutor for problem solving help at classzone.com

17. You will get a raise if the revenue is greater than its costs.

USING DEDUCTIVE REASONING Select the word(s) that make(s) the conclusion true.

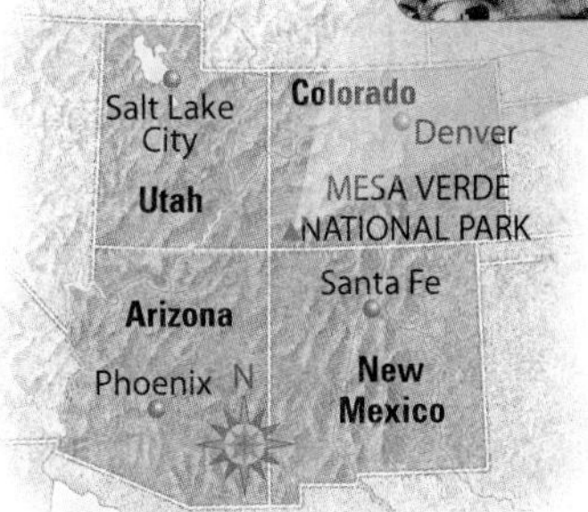

18. Mesa Verde National Park is in Colorado. Simone vacationed in Colorado. So, Simone (*must have, may have,* or *never*) visited Mesa Verde National Park. **may have**

19. The cliff dwellings in Mesa Verde National Park are accessible to visitors only when accompanied by a park ranger. Billy is at a cliff dwelling in Mesa Verde National Park. So, Billy *(is, may be, is not)* with a park ranger. **is**

Mathematical Reasoning

Exercise 14 Students should notice that each segment can be thought of as a diagonal of a 2 by 3 rectangle. Using the distance formula gives a length of $\sqrt{13}$. The segments do not have to be parallel.

Internet Reference

Exercises 18–19 For more information on Mesa Verde National Park, go to the National Park Service's website at www.nps.gov/meve

15. Law of Syllogism does apply; the contrapositive of the statements are: if the creature is not a marsupial, then it is not a wombat; if the creature does not have a pouch, then it is not a marsupial; using the Law of Syllogism it can be stated that if the creature does not have a pouch, then it is not a wombat.

Exercise 20 More information about the Mohs scale of hardness, including a complete listing of the scale, can be found at www.kgs.ku.edu/Extension/KGSrocks/hardness.html

Mathematical Reasoning

Exercises 25–28 Ask students to apply the laws of logic very carefully in these exercises. Point out that the given information implies that Mia will buy popcorn. But we cannot be certain that she will not also buy a hot dog.

20a. ***Sample answer:*** **If Gypsum is scratched against Calcite, then a scratch mark is left on the Gypsum; if Talc is scratched against Calcite, then a scratch mark is left on the Talc; if Calcite is scratched against Fluorite, then a scratch mark is left on the Calcite.**

EXAMPLE 4 B on p. 89 for Ex. 20

20b. Mineral *A* cannot be Fluorite since Mineral *B* can scratch it; Mineral *C* must be Talc since it is the softest of the minerals.

20c. ***Sample answer:*** **If Mineral *D* scratches Mineral *B* then *D* is the Fluorite otherwise *B* is the Fluorite; if Mineral *B* is Fluroite, take Mineral *A* and Mineral *D* and do one scratch test to identify them.**

21. Deductive; laws of logic were used to reach the conclusion.

24. For want of a nail the rider is lost; the hypothesis and conclusion are directly linked by the Law of Syllogism.

25. True; since the game is not sold out, Arlo goes and buys a hot dog.

26. True; Arlo and Mia go to the game since it is not sold out.

20. ★ **EXTENDED RESPONSE** Geologists use the Mohs scale to determine a mineral's hardness. Using the scale, a mineral with a higher rating will leave a scratch on a mineral with a lower rating. Geologists use scratch tests to help identify an unknown mineral.

Mineral	Talc	Gypsum	Calcite	Fluorite
Mohs rating	1	2	3	4

a. Use the table to write three if-then statements such as "If talc is scratched against gypsum, then a scratch mark is left on the talc." **See margin.**

b. You must identify four minerals labeled *A*, *B*, *C*, and *D*. You know that the minerals are the ones shown in the table. The results of your scratch tests are shown below. What can you conclude? *Explain* your reasoning.

Mineral *A* is scratched by Mineral *B*.

Mineral *C* is scratched by all three of the other minerals.

c. What additional test(s) can you use to identify *all* the minerals in part (b)?

REASONING In Exercises 21 and 22, decide whether *inductive* or *deductive* reasoning is used to reach the conclusion. *Explain* your reasoning.

21. The rule at your school is that you must attend all of your classes in order to participate in sports after school. You played in a soccer game after school on Monday. Therefore, you went to all of your classes on Monday.

22. For the past 5 years, your neighbor goes on vacation every July 4th and asks you to feed her hamster. You conclude that you will be asked to feed her hamster on the next July 4th. **Inductive; a pattern leads to the conclusion.**

23. ★ **SHORT RESPONSE** Let an even integer be $2n$ and an odd integer be $2n + 1$. *Explain* why the sum of an even integer and an odd integer is an odd integer. **$2n + (2n + 1) = (2n + 2n) + 1 = 4n + 1$, which is odd.**

24. **LITERATURE** George Herbert wrote a poem, *Jacula Prudentum*, that includes the statements shown. Use the Law of Syllogism to write a new conditional statement. *Explain* your reasoning.

For want of a nail the shoe is lost,
for want of a shoe the horse is lost,
for want of a horse the rider is lost.

REASONING In Exercises 25–28, use the true statements below to determine whether you know the conclusion is *true* or *false*. *Explain* your reasoning.

If Arlo goes to the baseball game, then he will buy a hot dog.

If the baseball game is not sold out, then Arlo and Mia will go to the game.

If Mia goes to the baseball game, then she will buy popcorn.

The baseball game is not sold out.

25. Arlo bought a hot dog.

26. Arlo and Mia went to the game.

27. Mia bought a hot dog. **False; Mia will buy popcorn.**

28. Arlo had some of Mia's popcorn. **False; Arlo buys a hotdog.**

○ = WORKED-OUT SOLUTIONS on p. WS1 ★ = STANDARDIZED TEST PRACTICE

29b. Since Bob lies, Charlie must be telling the truth but he isn't because Adam doesn't lie.

29c. Bob; Adam, Charlie; there is no contradiction if Bob is telling the truth.

29. CHALLENGE Use these statements to answer parts (a)–(c).

Adam says Bob lies.

Bob says Charlie lies.

Charlie says Adam and Bob both lie.

a. If Adam is telling the truth, then Bob is lying. What can you conclude about Charlie's statement? **It is true.**

b. Assume Adam is telling the truth. *Explain* how this leads to a contradiction.

c. Who is telling the truth? Who is lying? How do you know?

MIXED REVIEW

PREVIEW
Prepare for Lesson 2.4 in Exs. 30–33.

In Exercises 30–33, use the diagram. *(p. 2)* **30–33. Sample answers are given.**

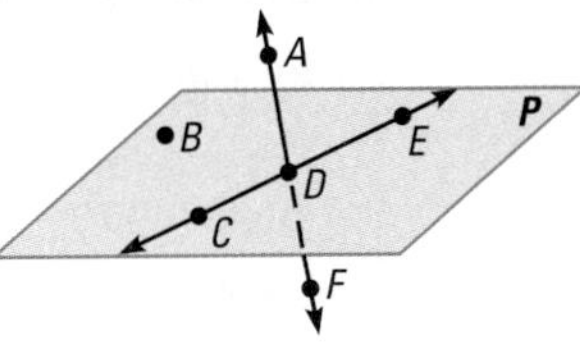

30. Name two lines. $\overleftrightarrow{CE}$, $\overleftrightarrow{AF}$

31. Name four rays. $\overrightarrow{DF}$, $\overrightarrow{AF}$, $\overrightarrow{DC}$, $\overrightarrow{EC}$

32. Name three collinear points. **C, D, E**

33. Name four coplanar points. **B, C, D, E**

Plot the given points in a coordinate plane. Then determine whether $\overline{AB}$ and $\overline{CD}$ are congruent. *(p. 9)* **34, 35. See margin for art.**

34. $A(1, 4)$, $B(5, 4)$, $C(3, -4)$, $D(3, 0)$ **congruent**

35. $A(-1, 0)$, $B(-1, -5)$, $C(1, 2)$, $D(-5, 2)$ **not congruent**

Rewrite the conditional statement in if-then form. *(p. 79)*

36. When $x = -2$, $x^2 = 4$. **If $x = -2$, then $x^2 = 4$.**

37. The measure of an acute angle is less than 90°. **If an angle is acute, then its measure is less than 90°.**

38. Only people who are members can access the website. **If a person is a member, then he/she can access the website.**

QUIZ *for Lessons 2.1–2.3*

3. If points lie on the same line, then they are called collinear points; if points are not collinear, then the points do not lie on the same line.

6. A multiple of 3 is, by definition, divisible by 3; thus if a number is divisible by a multiple of 3 it is divisible by 3.

Show the conjecture is false by finding a counterexample. *(p. 72)*

1. If the product of two numbers is positive, then the two numbers must be negative. ***Sample answer:*** **$2 \cdot 3 = 6$**

2. The sum of two numbers is always greater than the larger number. ***Sample answer:*** **$8 + -7 = 1$**

In Exercises 3 and 4, write the if-then form and the contrapositive of the statement. *(p. 79)*

3. Points that lie on the same line are called collinear points.

4. $2x - 8 - 2$, because $x = 5$. **If $x = 5$, then $2x - 8 = 2$; if $2x - 8 \neq 2$, then $x \neq 5$.**

5. Make a valid conclusion about the following statements:
If it is above 90°F outside, then I will wear shorts. It is 98°F. *(p. 87)* **I will wear shorts.**

6. *Explain* why a number that is divisible by a multiple of 3 is also divisible by 3. *(p. 87)*

34.

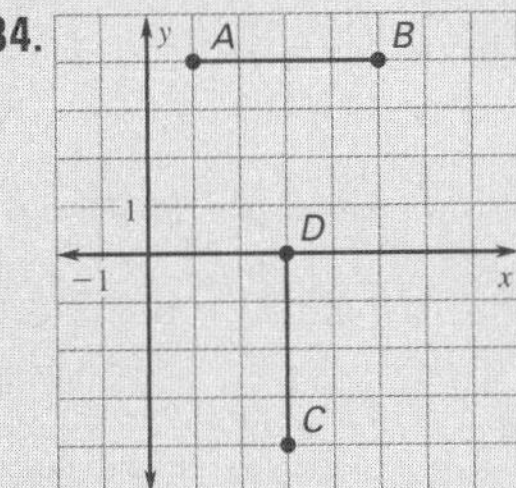

35.

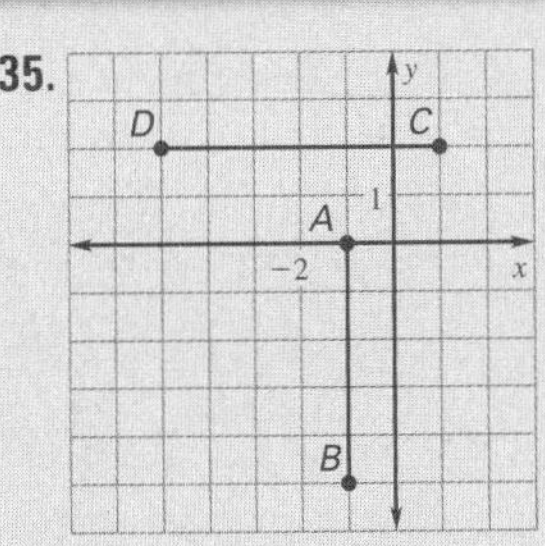

5 ASSESS AND RETEACH

Daily Homework Quiz

Transparency Available

1. Use the Law of Detachment to make a valid conclusion in the true situation. If two angles are complementary, then the sum of their measures is 90°. $\angle C$ and $\angle D$ are complementary. **$m\angle C + m\angle D = 90°$**

2. Use the Law of Syllogism to make a valid conclusion in the true situation. If water is at room temperature, then it is a liquid. If water is a liquid, then it is not frozen. **If water is at room temperature, then it is not frozen.**

Use the true statements below to determine whether the conclusion is true or false. Explain your reasoning. If Jeanine does her homework, then she goes to the movies. If Joaquin goes to the movies, then he buys popcorn. If Jeanine goes to the movies, then she buys popcorn. Jeanine does her homework.

3. Jeanine buys popcorn. **true; the Law of Syllogism**

4. If Jeanine goes to the movies, Joaquin goes to the movies. **False; no laws of logic apply.**

Available at **classzone.com**

Diagnosis/Remediation

- Practice A, B, C in Chapter 2 Resource Book, pp. 34–39
- Study Guide in Chapter 2 Resource Book, pp. 40–41
- Practice Workbook, pp. 28–30
- @HomeTutor

Challenge

Additional challenge is available in the Chapter 2 Resource Book, p. 44.

Quiz

An easily-readable reduced copy of the quiz (with answers) on Lessons 2.1–2.3 from the Assessment Book can be found on p. 70G.

1 PLAN AND PREPARE

Warm-Up Exercises

1. Name the hypothesis and conclusion of the statement, "If an animal flies, then it is a bird." **hypothesis: an animal flies conclusion: it is a bird**
2. Write the converse, inverse, and contrapositive of the conditional, "If a polygon is regular, then it has congruent sides." **Converse: If a polygon has congruent sides, then it is regular. Inverse: If a polygon is not regular, then it does not have congruent sides. Contrapositive: If a polygon does not have congruent sides, then it is not regular.**

2 FOCUS AND MOTIVATE

Essential Question

Big Idea 1, p. 71

How can you represent a logical statement symbolically? **Tell students they will learn how to answer this question by using variables to represent statements in conditionals.**

Extension

Use after Lesson 2.3

Symbolic Notation and Truth Tables

GOAL Use symbolic notation to represent logical statements.

Key Vocabulary
- **truth value**
- **truth table**

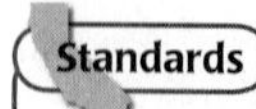

Standards

3.0 Students construct and judge the validity of a logical argument and give counterexamples to disprove a statement.

Conditional statements can be written using *symbolic notation*, where letters are used to represent statements. An arrow ($\rightarrow$), read "implies," connects the hypothesis and conclusion. To write the negation of a statement p you write the symbol for negation ($\sim$) before the letter. So, "not p" is written $\sim p$.

KEY CONCEPT *For Your Notebook*

Symbolic Notation

Let p be "the angle is a right angle" and let q be "the measure of the angle is 90°."

Conditional If p, then q. $p \rightarrow q$

Example: If an angle is a right angle, then its measure is 90°.

Converse If q, then p. $q \rightarrow p$

Example: If the measure of an angle is 90°, then the angle is a right angle.

Inverse If not p, then not q. $\sim p \rightarrow \sim q$

Example: If an angle is not a right angle, then its measure is not 90°.

Contrapositive If not q, then not p. $\sim q \rightarrow \sim p$

If the measure of an angle is not 90°, then the angle is not a right angle.

Biconditional p if and only if q $p \leftrightarrow q$

Example: An angle is a right angle if and only if its measure is 90°.

EXAMPLE 1 **Use symbolic notation**

Let p be "the car is running" and let q be "the key is in the ignition."

a. Write the conditional statement $p \rightarrow q$ in words.

b. Write the converse $q \rightarrow p$ in words.

c. Write the inverse $\sim p \rightarrow \sim q$ in words.

d. Write the contrapositive $\sim q \rightarrow \sim p$ in words.

Solution

a. Conditional: If the car is running, then the key is in the ignition.

b. Converse: If the key is in the ignition, then the car is running.

c. Inverse: If the car is not running, then the key is not in the ignition.

d. Contrapositive: If the key is not in the ignition, then the car is not running.

2. If polygon *ABCDE* is equiangular and equilateral, then it is a regular polygon.

3. Polygon *ABCDE* is not both equiangular and equilateral.

4. If polygon *ABCDE* is not a regular polygon, then it is not both equiangular and equilateral.

5. Polygon *ABCDE* is equiangular and equilateral if and only if it is a regular polygon.

TRUTH TABLES The **truth value** of a statement is either true (T) or false (F). You can determine the conditions under which a conditional statement is true by using a **truth table**. The truth table at the right shows the truth values for hypothesis p and conclusion q. The conditional $p \to q$ is only false when a true hypothesis produces a false conclusion.

Conditional		
p	q	$p \to q$
T	T	T
T	F	F
F	T	T
F	F	T

EXAMPLE 2 Make a truth table

Use the truth table above to make truth tables for the converse, inverse, and contrapositive of a conditional statement $p \to q$.

Solution

Converse		
p	q	$q \to p$
T	T	T
T	F	T
F	T	F
F	F	T

Inverse				
p	q	$\sim p$	$\sim q$	$\sim p \to \sim q$
T	T	F	F	T
T	F	F	T	T
F	T	T	F	F
F	F	T	T	T

Contrapositive				
p	q	$\sim q$	$\sim p$	$\sim q \to \sim p$
T	T	F	F	T
T	F	T	F	F
F	T	F	T	T
F	F	T	T	T

READ TRUTH TABLES

A conditional statement and its contrapositive are *equivalent statements* because they have the same truth table. The same is true of the converse and the inverse.

PRACTICE

EXAMPLE 1 on p. 94 for Exs. 1–6

1. **WRITING** *Describe* how to use symbolic notation to represent the contrapositive of a conditional statement. $\sim q \to \sim p$

WRITING STATEMENTS **Use p and q to write the symbolic statement in words.** **2–5. See margin.**

p: Polygon *ABCDE* is equiangular and equilateral.

q: Polygon *ABCDE* is a regular polygon.

2. $p \to q$
3. $\sim p$
4. $\sim q \to \sim p$
5. $p \leftrightarrow q$

6. **LAW OF SYLLOGISM** Use the statements p, q, and r below to write a series of conditionals that would satisfy the Law of Syllogism. How could you write your reasoning using symbolic notation?

$p: x + 5 = 12$ $q: x = 7$ $r: 3x = 21$

6. ***Sample answer:*** **If $x + 5 = 12$, then $x = 7$; if $x = 7$, then $3x = 21$; if $x + 5 = 12$, then $3x = 21$; $p \to q$ and $q \to r$, so $p \to r$.**

EXAMPLE 2 on p. 95 for Exs. 7–8

7. **WRITING** Is the truth value of a statement always true (T)? *Explain.*

7. **No; it is false when the hypothesis is true while the conclusion is false.**

8. **TRUTH TABLE** Use the statement "If an animal is a poodle, then it is a dog."
   a. Identify the hypothesis p and the conclusion q in the conditional. **p: animal is a poodle; q: animal is a dog.**
   b. Make a truth table for the converse. *Explain* what each row in the table means in terms of the original statement. **See margin.**

8b.

Converse			
p	q	$q \to p$	Statement
T	T	F	If an animal is a dog, then it is a poodle, which is false.
T	F	F	If an animal is not a dog, then it is a poodle, which is false.
F	T	F	If an animal is a dog, then it is not a poodle, which is false.
F	F	T	If an animal is not a dog, then it is not a poodle, which is true.

3 TEACH

Extra Example 1

Let p be "snow is falling" and let q be "it is winter".

a. Write the conditional statement $p \to q$ in words. **If snow is falling, then it is winter.**

b. Write the converse $q \to p$ in words. **If it is winter, then snow is falling.**

c. Write the inverse $\sim p \to \sim q$ in words. **If snow is not falling, then it is not winter.**

d. Write the contrapositve $\sim q \to \sim p$ in words. **If it is not winter, then snow is not falling.**

Extra Example 2

Use the truth tables on page 95 to make a truth table for the biconditional $p \leftrightarrow q$.

p	q	$p \to q$	$p \to q$	$p \leftrightarrow q$
T	T	T	T	T
T	F	F	T	F
F	T	T	F	F
F	F	T	T	T

Closing the Lesson

Have students summarize the major points of the lesson and answer the Essential Question: How can you represent a logical statement symbolically?

- **Use different variables to represent the hypothesis and conclusion of a statement. Use ~ to represent "not".**
- **Rewrite the conditional using variables, ~, and an arrow to represent "if-then".**

You can represent a logical statement symbolically by using variables to represent phrases and arrows to represent "if-then".

4 PRACTICE AND APPLY

Mathematical Reasoning

Exercise 6 The Law of Syllogism can be stated symbolically as $(p \to q \text{ and } q \to r) \to (p \to r)$.

2.4 Use Postulates and Diagrams

Before You used postulates involving angle and segment measures.

Now You will use postulates involving points, lines, and planes.

Why? So you can draw the layout of a neighborhood, as in Ex. 39.

1 PLAN AND PREPARE

Warm-Up Exercises

Transparency Available

State which postulate justifies each statement.

1. If D is in the interior of $\angle ABC$, then $m\angle ABD + m\angle DBC = m\angle ABC$. **Angle Addition Postulate**
2. If M is between X and Y, then $XM + MY = XY$. **Segment Addition Postulate**
3. Find the measure of MN if N is between M and P, $MP = 6x - 2$, $MN = 4x$, and $MP = 16$. **12**

Notetaking Guide

Transparency Available

Promotes interactive learning and notetaking skills, pp. 43–45.

Pacing

Basic: 1 day

Average: 1 day

Advanced: 1 day

Block: 0.5 block with 2.3

- See *Teaching Guide/Lesson Plan.*

2 FOCUS AND MOTIVATE

Essential Question

Big Idea 2, p. 71

How can you identify postulates illustrated by a diagram? **Tell students they will learn how to answer this question by interpreting diagrams.**

Key Vocabulary
- **line perpendicular to a plane**
- **postulate,** *p. 8*

Standards

1.0 Students demonstrate understanding by identifying and giving examples of undefined terms, axioms, theorems, and inductive and deductive reasoning.

In geometry, rules that are accepted without proof are called *postulates* or *axioms.* Rules that are proved are called *theorems.* Postulates and theorems are often written in conditional form. Unlike the converse of a definition, the converse of a postulate or theorem cannot be assumed to be true.

You learned four postulates in Chapter 1.

POSTULATE 1	Ruler Postulate	page 9
POSTULATE 2	Segment Addition Postulate	page 10
POSTULATE 3	Protractor Postulate	page 24
POSTULATE 4	Angle Addition Postulate	page 25

Here are seven new postulates involving points, lines, and planes.

POSTULATES *For Your Notebook*

Point, Line, and Plane Postulates

POSTULATE 5 Through any two points there exists exactly one line.

POSTULATE 6 A line contains at least two points.

POSTULATE 7 If two lines intersect, then their intersection is exactly one point.

POSTULATE 8 Through any three noncollinear points there exists exactly one plane.

POSTULATE 9 A plane contains at least three noncollinear points.

POSTULATE 10 If two points lie in a plane, then the line containing them lies in the plane.

POSTULATE 11 If two planes intersect, then their intersection is a line.

ALGEBRA CONNECTION You have been using many of Postulates 5–11 in previous courses.

One way to graph a linear equation is to plot two points whose coordinates satisfy the equation and then connect them with a line. Postulate 5 guarantees that there is exactly one such line. A familiar way to find a common solution of two linear equations is to graph the lines and find the coordinates of their intersection. This process is guaranteed to work by Postulate 7.

Resource Planning Guide

Chapter Resource Book
- Teaching Guide/Lesson Plan (pp. 45–46)
- Activity Master (p. 47)
- Practice levels A, B, C (pp. 48–53)
- Study Guide (pp. 54–55)
- Catch-up for Absent Students (p. 56)
- Problem Solving Workshop (p. 57)
- Challenge (p. 59)

Workbooks
- Notetaking Guide (pp. 43–45)
- Practice Workbook (pp. 31–33)

Teaching Options
- **Power Presentations CD-ROM** provides dynamic electronic teaching resources for the classroom.
- **Activity Generator CD-ROM** provides editable activities for all ability levels.

Interactive Technology
- Easy Planner
- Power Presentations CD-ROM
- Activity Generator CD-ROM
- Animated Geometry
- Test Generator CD-ROM
- Online Quiz
- eWorkbook
- eEdition
- @HomeTutor

Resources for English Learners
- Quick Reference for English Learners
- Spanish Study Guide
- Multi-Language Visual Glossary
- Student Resources in Spanish

See also the *Geometry Toolkit* for more strategies for meeting individual needs.

EXAMPLE 1 Identify a postulate illustrated by a diagram

State the postulate illustrated by the diagram.

a. 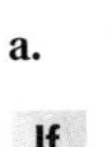 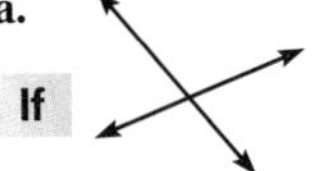

b. 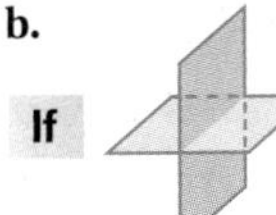 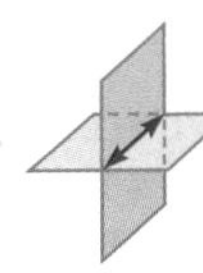

Solution

a. Postulate 7 If two lines intersect, then their intersection is exactly one point.

b. Postulate 11 If two planes intersect, then their intersection is a line.

EXAMPLE 2 Identify postulates from a diagram

Use the diagram to write examples of Postulates 9 and 10.

Postulate 9 Plane *P* contains at least three noncollinear points, *A*, *B*, and *C*.

Postulate 10 Point *A* and point *B* lie in plane *P*, so line *n* containing *A* and *B* also lies in plane *P*.

at classzone.com

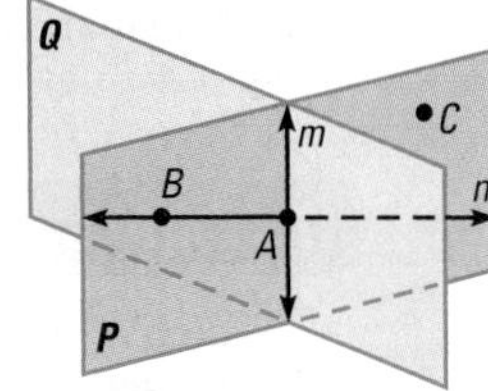

GUIDED PRACTICE for Examples 1 and 2

1. Use the diagram in Example 2. Which postulate allows you to say that the intersection of plane *P* and plane *Q* is a line? **Postulate 11**

2. Use the diagram in Example 2 to write examples of Postulates 5, 6, and 7. **Line *n* passes through points *A* and *B*, line *n* contains points *A* and *B*, line *m* and line *n* intersect at point *A*.**

CONCEPT SUMMARY — *For Your Notebook*

Interpreting a Diagram

When you interpret a diagram, you can assume information about size or measure only if it is marked.

YOU CAN ASSUME	YOU CANNOT ASSUME
All points shown are coplanar.	*G*, *F*, and *E* are collinear.
$\angle AHB$ and $\angle BHD$ are a linear pair.	$\overleftrightarrow{BF}$ and $\overleftrightarrow{CE}$ intersect.
$\angle AHF$ and $\angle BHD$ are vertical angles.	$\overleftrightarrow{BF}$ and $\overleftrightarrow{CE}$ do not intersect.
A, *H*, *J*, and *D* are collinear.	$\angle BHA \cong \angle CJA$
$\overleftrightarrow{AD}$ and $\overleftrightarrow{BF}$ intersect at *H*.	$\overleftrightarrow{AD} \perp \overleftrightarrow{BF}$ or $m\angle AHB = 90°$

Differentiated Instruction

Kinesthetic Learners Some students find it difficult to visualize three-dimensional situations in a sketch. Students may need to build models of some of the figures in this book, or you can create them and bring them to class.

See also the *Geometry Toolkit* for more strategies.

Motivating the Lesson

There are four buildings on the school campus. How many paths need to be constructed to connect all four buildings? To answer this question, it helps to use a postulate of geometry that tells you how many lines pass through two points.

3 TEACH

Extra Example 1

State the postulate illustrated by the diagram.

a.

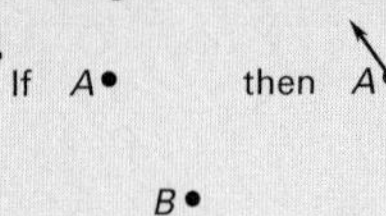

Postulate 5: Through any two points there exists exactly one line.

b.

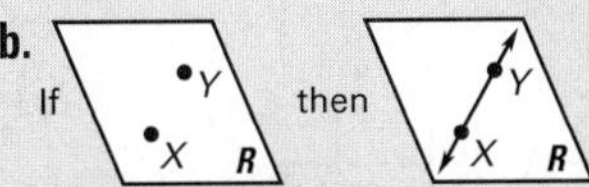

Postulate 10: If two points lie in a plane, then the line containing them lies in the plane.

Extra Example 2

Use the diagram to write examples of Postulates 6 and 8.

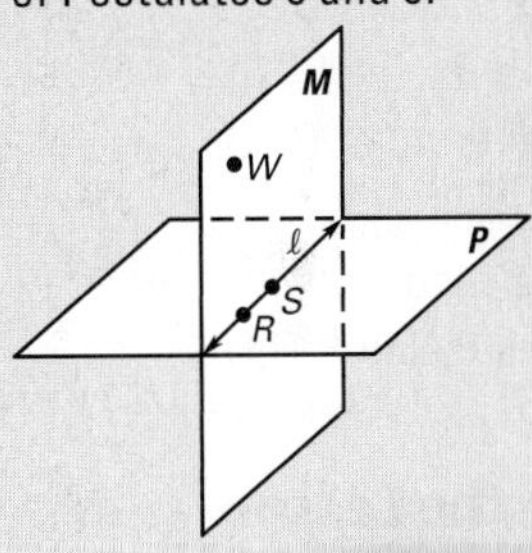

Postulate 6: Line ℓ contains at least two points *R* and *S*.

Postulate 8: Through noncollinear points *R*, *S*, and *W*, there exists exactly one plane *M*.

Animated Geometry
classzone.com

An **Animated Geometry** activity is available on-line for **Example 2**. This activity is also available on the **Power Presentations CD-ROM**.

Extra Example 3

Sketch a diagram showing $\overrightarrow{FH} \perp \overline{EG}$ at its midpoint M.

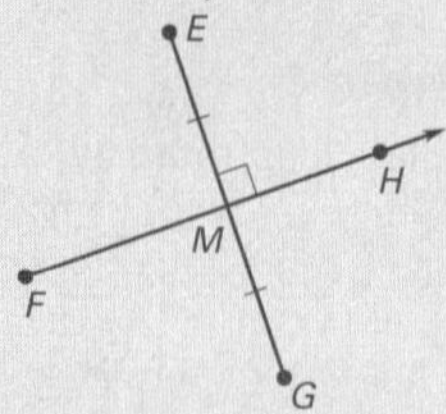

Extra Example 4

Which of the following cannot be assumed from the diagram?

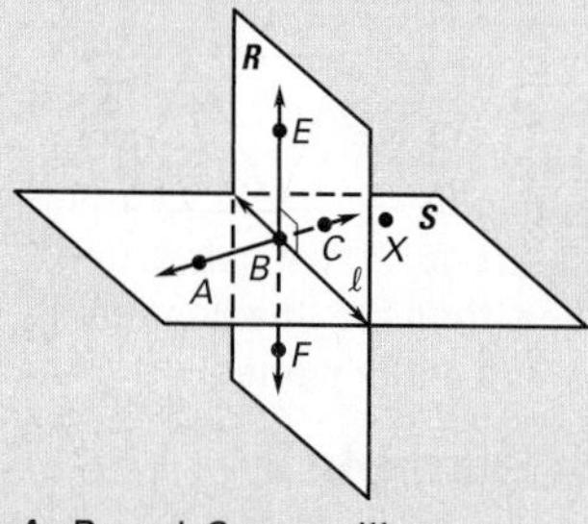

A, B, and C are collinear.
$\overleftrightarrow{EF} \perp$ line ℓ
$\overleftrightarrow{BC} \perp$ plane R
$\overleftrightarrow{EF}$ intersects $\overleftrightarrow{AC}$ at B.
line $\ell \perp \overleftrightarrow{AB}$
Points B, C, and X are collinear.
$\overleftrightarrow{BC} \perp$ plane R, line $\ell \perp \overleftrightarrow{AB}$, Points B, C, and X are collinear.

Closing the Lesson

Have students summarize the major points of the lesson and answer the Essential Question: How can you identify postulates from a diagram?

- **Analyze a diagram to determine what you can assume.**
- **Verify what you can assume by determining which postulates apply.**

You can identify postulates from a diagram by determining which information you can assume. Do not assume congruence, perpendicularity, collinearity, midpoints, and bisectors. Determine which postulate applies.

EXAMPLE 3 Use given information to sketch a diagram

Sketch a diagram showing $\overleftrightarrow{TV}$ intersecting $\overline{PQ}$ at point W, so that $\overline{TW} \cong \overline{WV}$.

Solution

AVOID ERRORS
Notice that the picture was drawn so that W does not look like a midpoint of $\overline{PQ}$. Also, it was drawn so that $\overline{PQ}$ is not perpendicular to $\overleftrightarrow{TV}$.

STEP 1 **Draw** $\overleftrightarrow{TV}$ and label points T and V.

STEP 2 **Draw** point W at the midpoint of $\overline{TV}$. Mark the congruent segments.

STEP 3 **Draw** $\overline{PQ}$ through W.

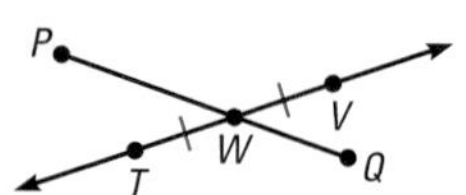

PERPENDICULAR FIGURES A line is a **line perpendicular to a plane** if and only if the line intersects the plane in a point and is perpendicular to every line in the plane that intersects it at that point.

In a diagram, a line perpendicular to a plane must be marked with a right angle symbol.

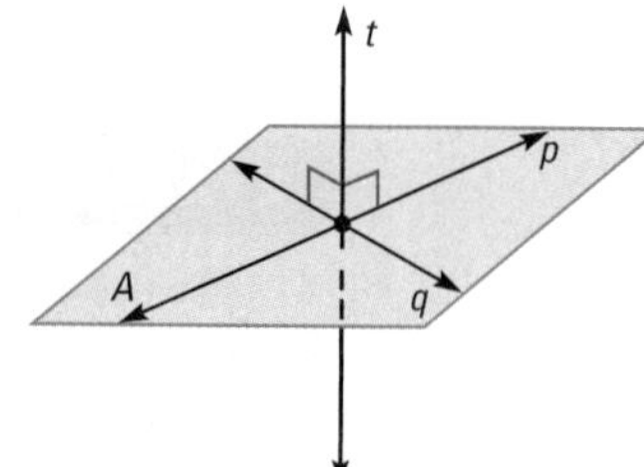

EXAMPLE 4 Interpret a diagram in three dimensions

Which of the following statements *cannot* be assumed from the diagram?

A, B, and F are collinear.
E, B, and D are collinear.
$\overline{AB} \perp$ plane S
$\overline{CD} \perp$ plane T
$\overleftrightarrow{AF}$ intersects $\overleftrightarrow{BC}$ at point B.

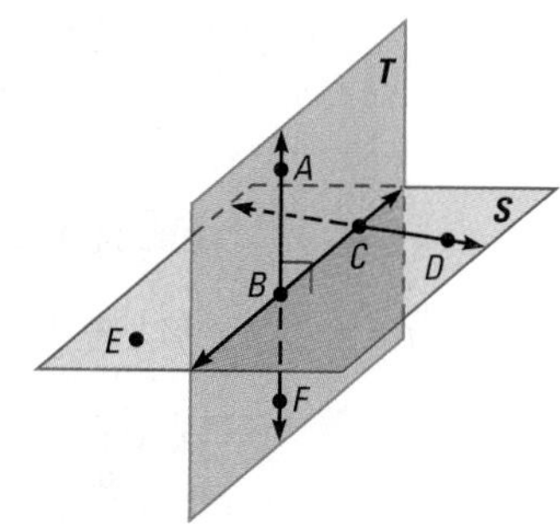

Solution

No drawn line connects E, B, and D, so you cannot assume they are collinear. With no right angle marked, you cannot assume $\overline{CD} \perp$ plane T.

✓ GUIDED PRACTICE for Examples 3 and 4

In Exercises 3 and 4, refer back to Example 3.

3. If the given information stated $\overline{PW}$ and $\overline{QW}$ are congruent, how would you indicate that in the diagram? **See margin.**
4. Name a pair of supplementary angles in the diagram. *Explain.* ***Sample answer:*** **$\angle TWP$, $\angle VWP$; they form a linear pair.**
5. In the diagram for Example 4, can you assume plane S intersects plane T at $\overleftrightarrow{BC}$? **yes**
6. *Explain* how you know that $\overleftrightarrow{AB} \perp \overleftrightarrow{BC}$ in Example 4.

6. It is given that line *AB* is perpendicular to plane *S*, therefore line *AB* is perpendicular to every line in the plane that intersects it at point *B*.

3.
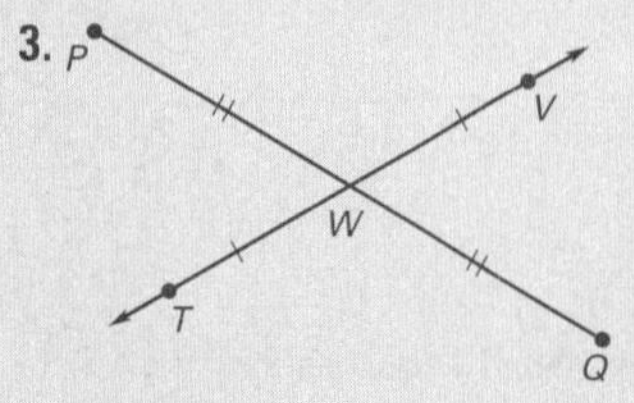

Differentiated Instruction

Below Level Before beginning a discussion of **Example 4**, have students make a two-column list of statements that can and cannot be assumed from the diagram.

See also the *Geometry Toolkit* for more strategies.

2.4 EXERCISES

HOMEWORK KEY
○ = **WORKED-OUT SOLUTIONS** on p. WS2 for Exs. 7, 13, and 31
★ = **STANDARDIZED TEST PRACTICE** Exs. 2, 10, 24, 25, 33, 39, and 41

SKILL PRACTICE

A

1. **VOCABULARY** Copy and complete: A __?__ is a line that intersects the plane in a point and is perpendicular to every line in the plane that intersects it. **line perpendicular to a plane**

2. ★ **WRITING** *Explain* why you cannot assume $\angle BHA \cong \angle CJA$ in the Concept Summary on page 97. **We don't know that they have the same measure.**

EXAMPLE 1 on p. 97 for Exs. 3–5

IDENTIFYING POSTULATES **State the postulate illustrated by the diagram.**

3. 4.

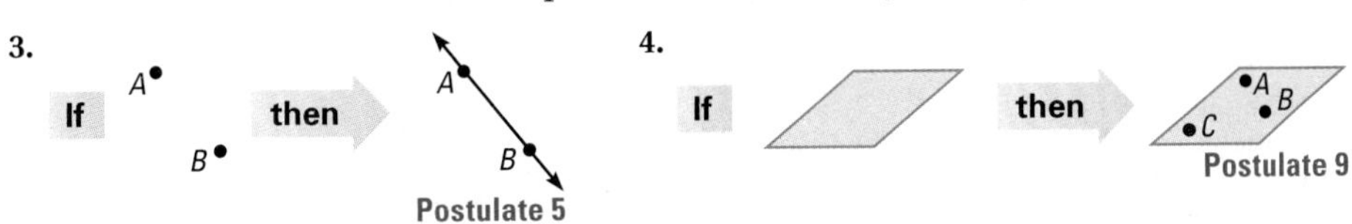

5a. If three points are not collinear, then there exists exactly one plane that contains all three points.

5. **CONDITIONAL STATEMENTS** Postulate 8 states that through any three noncollinear points there exists exactly one plane.
   a. Rewrite Postulate 8 in if-then form.
   b. Write the converse, inverse, and contrapositive of Postulate 8. **See margin.**
   c. Which statements in part (b) are true? **all of them**

EXAMPLE 2 on p. 97 for Exs. 6–8

USING A DIAGRAM **Use the diagram to write an example of each postulate.**
6–8. Sample answers are given.

6. Postulate 6
   line q containing points K and H
7. Postulate 7
   lines p and q intersecting in point H
8. Postulate 8
   points G, K, L contained in plane M

EXAMPLES 3 and 4 on p. 98 for Exs. 9–10

9. **SKETCHING** Sketch a diagram showing $\overleftrightarrow{XY}$ intersecting $\overleftrightarrow{WV}$ at point T, so $\overleftrightarrow{XY} \perp \overleftrightarrow{WV}$. In your diagram, does $\overline{WT}$ have to be congruent to $\overline{TV}$? *Explain* your reasoning. **See margin for art; no; $\overleftrightarrow{XY}$ does not necessarily bisect $\overline{WV}$.**

10. ★ **MULTIPLE CHOICE** Which of the following statements *cannot* be assumed from the diagram? **B**
   Ⓐ Points A, B, C, and E are coplanar.
   Ⓑ Points F, B, and G are collinear.
   Ⓒ $\overleftrightarrow{HC} \perp \overleftrightarrow{GE}$
   Ⓓ $\overleftrightarrow{EC}$ intersects plane M at point C.

B

ANALYZING STATEMENTS **Decide whether the statement is true or false. If it is false, give a real-world counterexample.**

11. Through any three points, there exists exactly one line.

11. False. *Sample answer:* Consider a highway with two houses on the right side and one house on the left.

12. A point can be in more than one plane. **true**
13. Any two planes intersect.
   False. *Sample answer:* Consider any pair of opposite sides of a rectangular prism.

5b. If there exists exactly one plane that contains three points, then the three points are noncollinear; if three points are collinear, then there does not exist exactly one plane that contains all three; if there is not exactly one plane containing three points, then the three points are collinear.

4 PRACTICE AND APPLY

Assignment Guide

Answer Transparencies available for all exercises

Basic:
Day 1: pp. 99–102
Exs. 1–18, 30–41, 46–56 even

Average:
Day 1: pp. 99–102
Exs. 1, 2, 4, 5, 8–10, 15–23 odd, 24–28, 30–44, 47, 50, 53

Advanced:
Day 1: pp. 99–102
Exs. 1, 2, 5, 8–12 even, 19–29*, 32–45*, 48, 51, 55

Block:
pp. 99–102
Exs. 1, 2, 4, 5, 8–10, 15–23 odd, 24–28, 30–44, 47, 50, 53 (with 2.3)

Differentiated Instruction

See *Geometry Best Practices Toolkit* for suggestions on addressing the needs of a diverse classroom.

Homework Check

For a quick check of student understanding of key concepts, go over the following exercises:
Basic: 3, 6, 9, 14, 35
Average: 4, 7, 10, 19, 36
Advanced: 5, 8, 10, 22, 37

Extra Practice

- Student Edition, p. 898
- Chapter 2 Resource Book: Practice levels A, B, C, pp. 48–53

Practice Worksheet

An easily-readable reduced practice page (with answers) for this lesson can be found on p. 70D.

9. *Sample:*

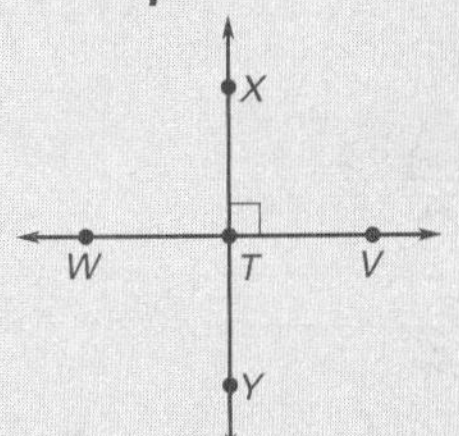

Avoiding Common Errors

Exercise 10 Some students may say that choice B can be assumed. Point out that while the points do appear to line up, the diagram does not show a line that passes through them.

Teaching Strategy

Exercises 14–23 If students chose "false", ask them to explain why. You may want to have students approach this group of problems by drawing the intersecting planes first, then individually trying to add/justify each of the statements as they compose the figure.

Mathematical Reasoning

Exercise 27 Have students think about the order in which Postulates 5 and 9 must be applied. Also, ask students to show that a plane must contain at least three lines.

25. *Sample:*

Postulate 5

Sample:

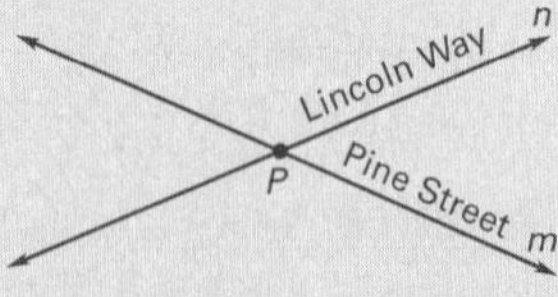

Postulate 7

Sample:

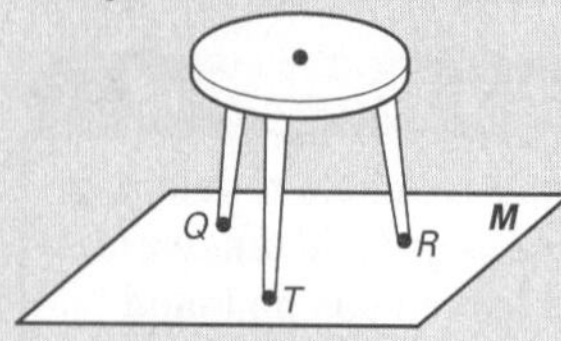

Postulate 8

26. *Sample answer:* **A line contains at least two points; three points are sometimes contained in a line.**

27. *Sample answer:* **Postulate 9 guarantees three noncollinear points in a plane while Postulate 5 guarantees that through any two there exists exactly one line; therefore there exists at least one line in the plane.**

28. *Sample answer:* **Postulate 9 guarantees three noncollinear points in the plane, one of them being *X*. If *A* and *B* are the other two then Postulate 5 guarantees $\overleftrightarrow{XA}$ and $\overleftrightarrow{XB}$ exist on plane *M*.**

29. See margin for art; 1 plane. *Sample answer:* **Postulate 6 guarantees the existence of two points on line *m* and Postulate 8 guarantees the existence of one plane containing those two points and point *C*.**

USING A DIAGRAM **Use the diagram to determine if the statement is *true* or *false*.**

14. Planes W and X intersect at $\overleftrightarrow{KL}$. **true**
15. Points Q, J, and M are collinear. **false**
16. Points K, L, M, and R are coplanar. **false**
17. $\overleftrightarrow{MN}$ and $\overleftrightarrow{RP}$ intersect. **false**
18. $\overleftrightarrow{RP} \perp$ plane W **false**
19. $\overleftrightarrow{JK}$ lies in plane X. **true**
20. $\angle PLK$ is a right angle. **false**
21. $\angle NKL$ and $\angle JKM$ are vertical angles. **true**
22. $\angle NKJ$ and $\angle JKM$ are supplementary angles. **true**
23. $\angle JKM$ and $\angle KLP$ are congruent angles. **false**

24. ★ **MULTIPLE CHOICE** Choose the diagram showing $\overleftrightarrow{LN}$, $\overleftrightarrow{AB}$, and $\overleftrightarrow{DC}$ intersecting at point M, $\overleftrightarrow{AB}$ bisecting $\overline{LN}$, and $\overleftrightarrow{DC} \perp \overleftrightarrow{LN}$. **C**

Ⓐ
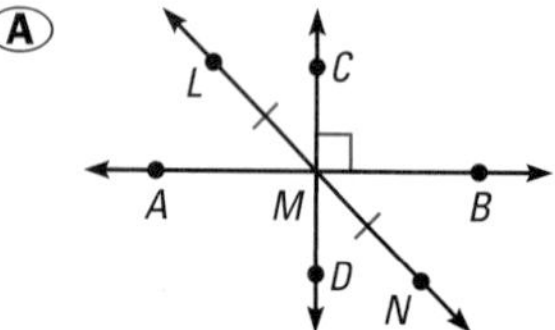

Ⓑ
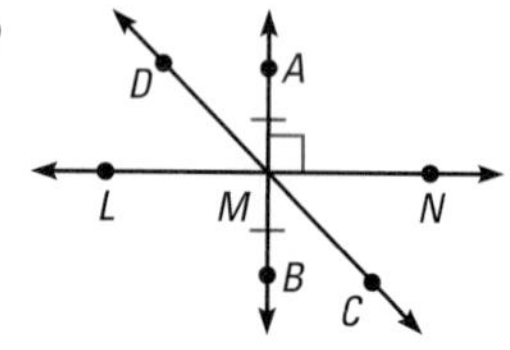

Ⓒ
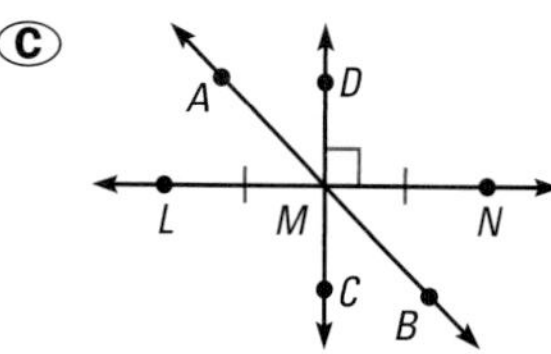

Ⓓ
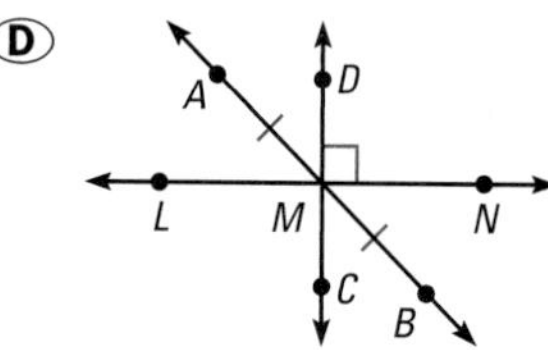

25. ★ **OPEN-ENDED MATH** Sketch a diagram of a real-world object illustrating three of the postulates about points, lines, and planes. List the postulates used. **See margin.**

26. **ERROR ANALYSIS** A student made the false statement shown. Change the statement in two different ways to make it true. **See margin.**

Three points are always contained in a line.

27. **REASONING** Use Postulates 5 and 9 to *explain* why every plane contains at least one line. **See margin.**

28. **REASONING** Point X lies in plane M. Use Postulates 5 and 9 to *explain* why there are at least two lines in plane M that contain point X. **See margin.**

29. **CHALLENGE** Sketch a line m and a point C not on line m. Make a conjecture about how many planes can be drawn so that line m and point C lie in the plane. Use postulates to justify your conjecture.

○ = WORKED-OUT SOLUTIONS on p. WS1

★ = STANDARDIZED TEST PRACTICE

29.

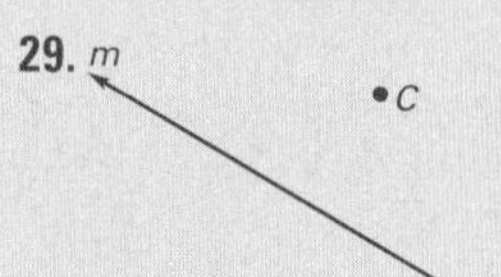

PROBLEM SOLVING

A **REAL-WORLD SITUATIONS Which postulate is suggested by the photo?**

30. 
Postulate 5

(31.) 
Postulate 7

32. EARTH
Postulate 11

33. Sample answer: A stoplight with a red, yellow, and green light.

33. ★ **SHORT RESPONSE** Give a real-world example of Postulate 6, which states that a line contains at least two points.

@HomeTutor for problem solving help at classzone.com

34. **DRAW A DIAGRAM** Sketch two lines that intersect, and another line that does not intersect either one. **See margin.**

@HomeTutor for problem solving help at classzone.com

35. The line ZU exists through points Z and U.

36. $\overleftrightarrow{SZ}$ and $\overleftrightarrow{ZU}$ intersect at point U.

37. The floor is a plane containing points W, X, and Y.

USING A DIAGRAM Use the pyramid to write examples of the postulate indicated. 35–38. Sample answers are given.

35. Postulate 5

36. Postulate 7

37. Postulate 9

38. Postulate 10 **Points X and Y lie in the plane that is the floor, so $\overleftrightarrow{XY}$ also lies in the plane of the floor.**

B 39. ★ **EXTENDED RESPONSE** A friend e-mailed you the following statements about a neighborhood. Use the statements to complete parts (a)–(e).

Subject Neighborhood

Building B is due west of Building A.
Buildings A and B are on Street 1.
Building D is due north of Building A.
Buildings A and D are on Street 2.
Building C is southwest of Building A.
Buildings A and C are on Street 3.
Building E is due east of Building B.
∠CAE formed by Streets 1 and 3 is obtuse.

a. Draw a diagram of the neighborhood. **See margin.**

b. Where do Streets 1 and 2 intersect? **Building A**

c. Classify the angle formed by Streets 1 and 2. **right angle**

d. Is Building E between Buildings A and B? *Explain.*

e. What street is Building E on? **Street 1**

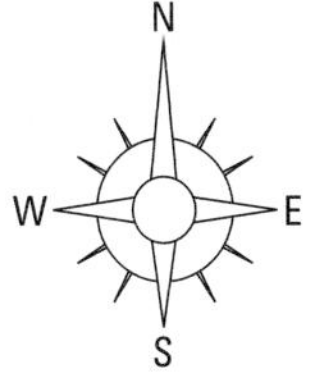

39d. No; since $\angle CAE$ is obtuse, Building E must be on the east side of Building A.

Teaching Strategy

Exercises 40–41 You may want to pair advanced students with other students who are struggling with these exercises, which have multiple steps. This will give the struggling students assistance as well as help the advanced students review what they know.

34. *Sample:*

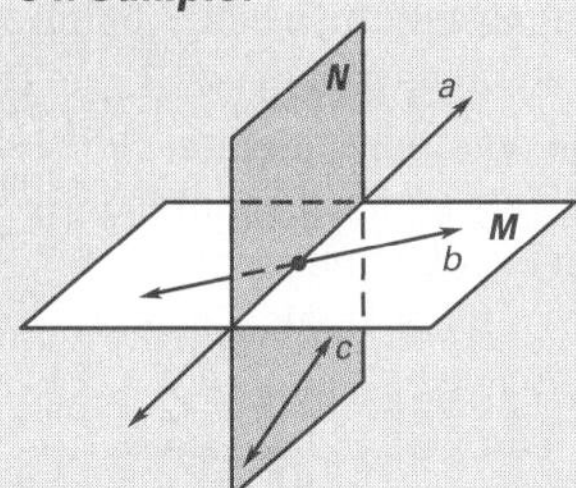

39a. *Sample:*

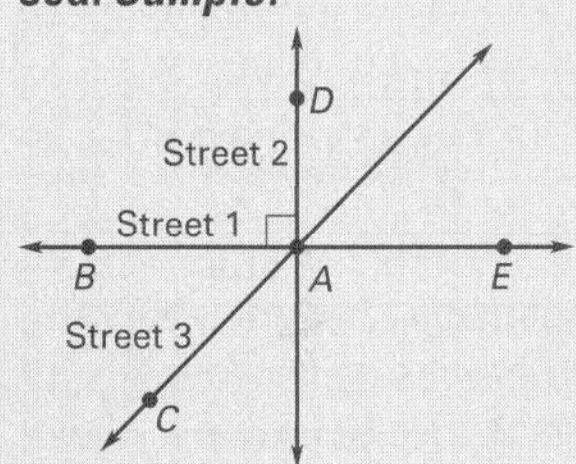

5 ASSESS AND RETEACH

Daily Homework Quiz

Transparency Available

1. Use the diagram to write an example of Postulate 7.

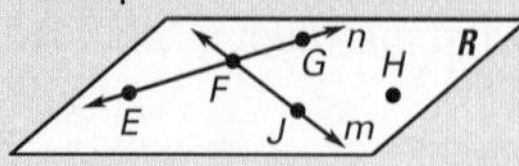

Line *m* intersects line *n* in point *F* and no other point.

2. Decide whether the statement "Two planes can intersect in exactly one point *R*" is true or false. If false, give a reason. **False; Postulate 11 says that if two planes intersect, their intersection is a line.**

Use the diagram to determine if the statement is true or false.

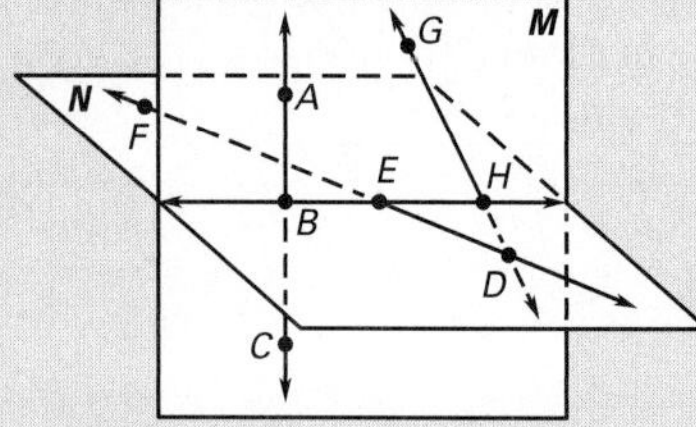

3. The intersection of planes *M* and *N* is points *B*, *E*, and *H*. **false**
4. $\overleftrightarrow{GH}$ lies in plane *M*. **true**
5. ∠*ABE* and ∠*HED* are vertical angles. **false**

Available at **classzone.com**

Diagnosis/Remediation

- Practice A, B, C in Chapter 2 Resource Book, pp. 48–53
- Study Guide in Chapter 2 Resource Book, pp. 54–55
- Practice Workbook, pp. 31–33
- @HomeTutor

Challenge

Additional challenge is available in the Chapter 2 Resource Book, p. 59.

40a–e, 41–44. See Additional Answers beginning on p. AA1.

40d. On the intersection of planes *X* and *Y*.

41. They must be collinear; they must be noncollinear; see margin for art.

45. 4 planes; 2 planes; when the legs are all different lengths there are 4 different combinations of 3 of the 4 leg ends; when 3 of the legs are the same length, there are 2 different combinations of the leg ends.

40. **MULTI-STEP PROBLEM** Copy the figure and label the following points, lines, and planes appropriately. **a–e. See margin for art.**
    a. Label the horizontal plane as *X* and the vertical plane as *Y*.
    b. Draw two points *A* and *B* on your diagram so they lie in plane *Y*, but not in plane *X*.
    c. Illustrate Postulate 5 on your diagram.
    d. If point *C* lies in both plane *X* and plane *Y*, where would it lie? Draw point *C* on your diagram.
    e. Illustrate Postulate 9 for plane *X* on your diagram.

41. ★ **SHORT RESPONSE** Points *E*, *F*, and *G* all lie in plane *P* and in plane *Q*. What must be true about points *E*, *F*, and *G* if *P* and *Q* are different planes? What must be true about points *E*, *F*, and *G* to force *P* and *Q* to be the same plane? Make sketches to support your answers.

DRAWING DIAGRAMS **$\overleftrightarrow{AC}$ and $\overleftrightarrow{DB}$ intersect at point *E*. Draw one diagram that meets the additional condition(s) and another diagram that does not.** **42–44. See margin.**

42. ∠*AED* and ∠*AEB* are right angles.
43. Point *E* is the midpoint of $\overline{AC}$.
44. $\overrightarrow{EA}$ and $\overrightarrow{EC}$ are opposite rays. $\overrightarrow{EB}$ and $\overrightarrow{ED}$ are not opposite rays.

C 45. **CHALLENGE** Suppose none of the four legs of a chair are the same length. What is the maximum number of planes determined by the lower ends of the legs? Suppose exactly three of the legs of a second chair have the same length. What is the maximum number of planes determined by the lower ends of the legs of the second chair? *Explain* your reasoning.

MIXED REVIEW

PREVIEW
Prepare for Lesson 2.5 in Exs. 46–48.

Find the indicated length. *(p. 9)*

46. Find *MP*. **27**

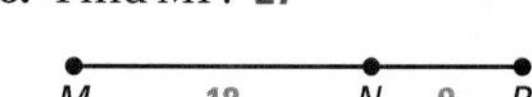

47. Find *AC*. **32**

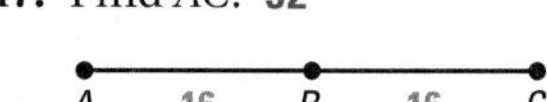

48. Find *RS*. **18**

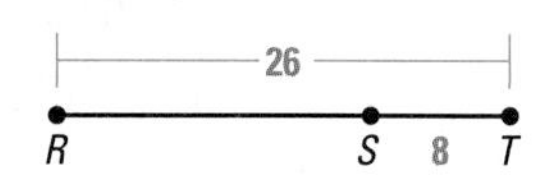

Line ℓ bisects the segment. Find the indicated length. *(p. 15)*

49. Find *JK*. **23**

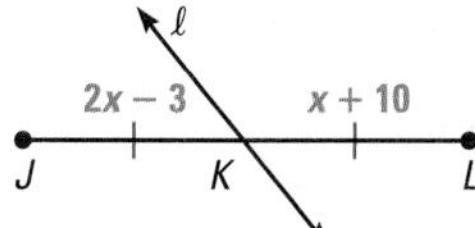

50. Find *XZ*. **74**

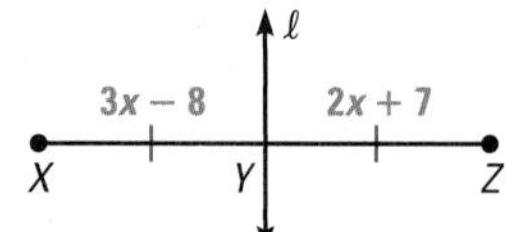

51. Find *BC*. **4**

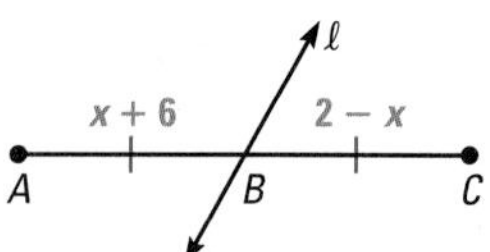

Draw an example of the type of angle described. *(p. 24)* **52–55. See margin.**

52. Right angle
53. Acute angle
54. Obtuse angle
55. Straight angle
56. Two angles form a linear pair. The measure of one angle is 9 times the measure of the other angle. Find the measure of each angle. *(p. 35)* **18°, 162°**

52–55. Sample answers are given.

52.

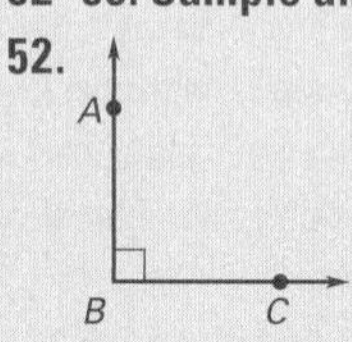

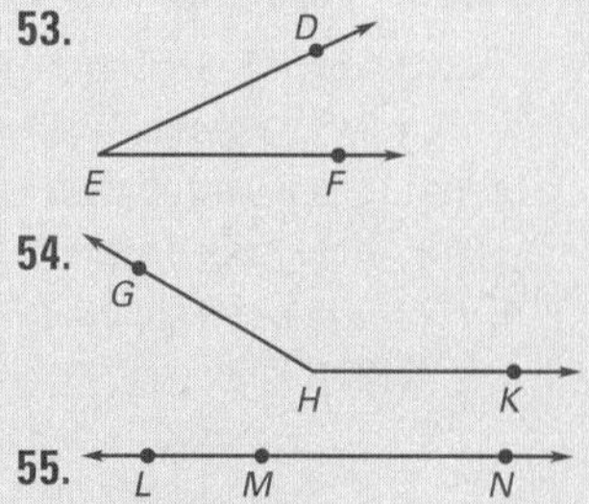

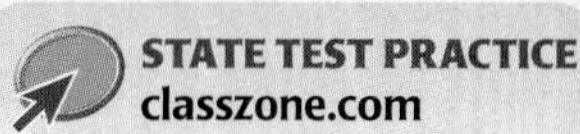

Lessons 2.1–2.4

1. **MULTI-STEP PROBLEM** The table below shows the time of the sunrise on different days in Galveston, Texas.

Date in 2006	Time of sunrise (Central Standard Time)
Jan. 1	7:14 A.M.
Feb. 1	7:08 A.M.
Mar. 1	6:45 A.M.
Apr. 1	6:09 A.M.
May 1	5:37 A.M.
June 1	5:20 A.M.
July 1	5:23 A.M.
Aug. 1	5:40 A.M.

   a. *Describe* the pattern, if any, in the times shown in the table. **See margin.**

   b. Use the times in the table to make a reasonable prediction about the time of the sunrise on September 1, 2006. ***Sample answer:* 6:12 A.M.**

2. **SHORT RESPONSE** As shown in the table below, hurricanes are categorized by the speed of the wind in the storm. Use the table to determine whether the statement is *true* or *false*. If false, provide a counterexample.

Hurricane category	Wind speed w (mi/h)
1	$74 \le w \le 95$
2	$96 \le w \le 110$
3	$111 \le w \le 130$
4	$131 \le w \le 155$
5	$w > 155$

   a. A hurricane is a category 5 hurricane if and only if its wind speed is greater than 155 miles per hour. **true**

   b. A hurricane is a category 3 hurricane if and only if its wind speed is less than 130 miles per hour. **See margin.**

3. **GRIDDED ANSWER** Write the next number in the pattern.

   1, 2, 5, 10, 17, 26, . . . **37**

4. **EXTENDED RESPONSE** The graph shows concession sales at six high school football games. Tell whether each statement is the result of *inductive reasoning* or *deductive reasoning*. *Explain* your thinking.

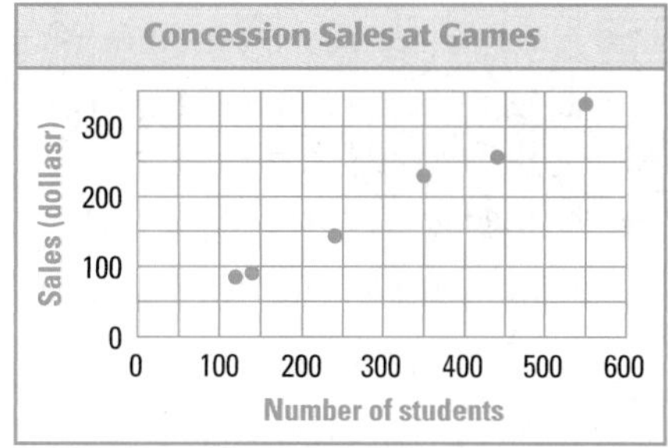

   a. If 500 students attend a football game, the high school can expect concession sales to reach $300. **Inductive reasoning; conclusion is based on an observation.**

   b. Concession sales were highest at the game attended by 550 students. **Deductive reasoning; it's a fact.**

   c. The average number of students who come to a game is about 300. **Inductive reasoning; conclusion is based on an observation.**

5. **SHORT RESPONSE** Select the phrase that makes the conclusion true. *Explain* your reasoning.

   a. A person needs a library card to check out books at the public library. You checked out a book at the public library. You (*must have, may have,* or *do not have*) a library card. **Must have; you can't check out a book unless you have a library card.**

   b. The islands of Hawaii are volcanoes. Bob has never been to the Hawaiian Islands. Bob (*has visited, may have visited,* or *has never visited*) volcanoes. **See margin.**

6. **SHORT RESPONSE** Sketch a diagram showing $\overleftrightarrow{PQ}$ intersecting $\overleftrightarrow{RS}$ at point N. In your diagram, $\angle PNS$ should be an obtuse angle. Identify two acute angles in your diagram. *Explain* how you know that these angles are acute. **See margin.**

1a. ***Sample answer:*** **The sun rises earlier each month until July.**

2b. False. ***Sample answer:*** **100 miles per hour is less than 130 miles per hour but this hurricane is a category 2.**

5b. May have visited; just because Bob has not been to the Hawaiian Islands doesn't mean he has not visited a volcano elsewhere.

6. ***Sample:***

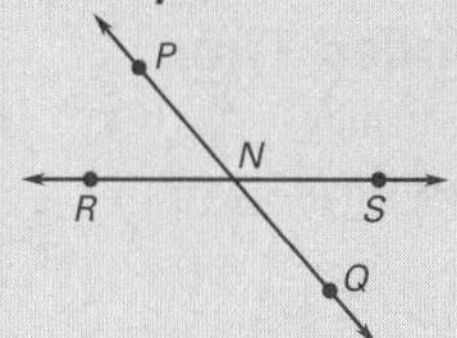

$\angle RNP$, $\angle SNQ$; they each form a linear pair with an obtuse angle.

1 PLAN AND PREPARE

Explore the Concept

- Students will use algebra to verify the steps of a number trick.
- This activity leads into the study of solving equations by using algebraic properties in Example 1 in Lesson 2.5.

Recommended Time

Work activity: 10 min
Discuss results: 5 min

Grouping

Students should work individually.

2 TEACH

Tips for Success

Students may want to use a calculator for this activity.

Alternative Strategy

Ask students to write their own number trick, describe the pattern, and verify that the number trick works. Then have them switch with a classmate.

Key Discovery

Number tricks work because algebra justifies the steps.

3 ASSESS AND RETEACH

Let x represent the number for a number trick. If you want the answer to be 12 more than the original number, express the answer in terms of x. **$x + 12$**

1. x, $2x$, $2x + 4$, $5(2x + 4)$, $5(2x + 4) + 12$, $10[5(2x + 4) + 12]$, $10[5(2x + 4) + 12] - 320$, $[10[5(2x + 4) + 12] - 320] \div 100 = x$

2. x is chosen, $2x$ doubles x, $2x + 4$ is four more than $2x$, $5(2x + 4)$ is five times the previous number, $5(2x + 4) + 12$ is 12 more than the previous number, $10[5(2x + 4) + 12]$ multiplies the previous number by 10, $10[5(2x + 4) + 12] - 320$ reduces the previous number by 320, crossing out the zeros (dividing by 100) leaves x.

2.5 Justify a Number Trick

MATERIALS • paper • pencil

Standards

1.0 Students demonstrate understanding by identifying and giving examples of undefined terms, axioms, theorems, and inductive and **deductive reasoning.**

3.0 Students construct and judge the validity of a logical argument and give counterexamples to disprove a statement.

QUESTION **How can you use algebra to justify a number trick?**

Number tricks can allow you to guess the result of a series of calculations.

EXPLORE **Play the number trick**

STEP 1 ***Pick a number*** Follow the directions below.

a. Pick any number between 11 and 98 that does not end in a zero.	23
b. Double the number.	$23 \cdot 2$
c. Add 4 to your answer.	$46 + 4$
d. Multiply your answer by 5.	$50 \cdot 5$
e. Add 12 to your answer.	$250 + 12$
f. Multiply your answer by 10.	$262 \cdot 10$
g. Subtract 320 from your answer.	$2620 - 320$
h. Cross out the zeros in your answer.	23~~00~~

STEP 2 ***Repeat the trick*** Repeat the trick three times using three different numbers. What do you notice? **The result is the same as the number you start with.**

DRAW CONCLUSIONS **Use your observations to complete these exercises** **1–4. See margin.**

1. Let x represent the number you chose in the Explore. Write algebraic expressions for each step. Remember to use the Order of Operations.
2. *Justify* each expression you wrote in Exercise 1.
3. Another number trick is as follows:

   Pick any number.
   Multiply your number by 2.
   Add 18 to your answer.
   Divide your answer by 2.
   Subtract your original number from your answer.

   What is your answer? Does your answer depend on the number you chose? How can you change the trick so your answer is always 15? *Explain.*

4. **REASONING** Write your own number trick.

3. 9; no; change the third step to add 30 to your answer, instead of 18, the algebraic expression would then be $\frac{2x + 30}{2} - x$, which simplifies to $x + 15 - x$, which will always be 15.

4. ***Sample answer:*** Pick any number, triple your number, add 10 to your answer, then subtract twice the original number from your answer.

2.5 Reason Using Properties from Algebra

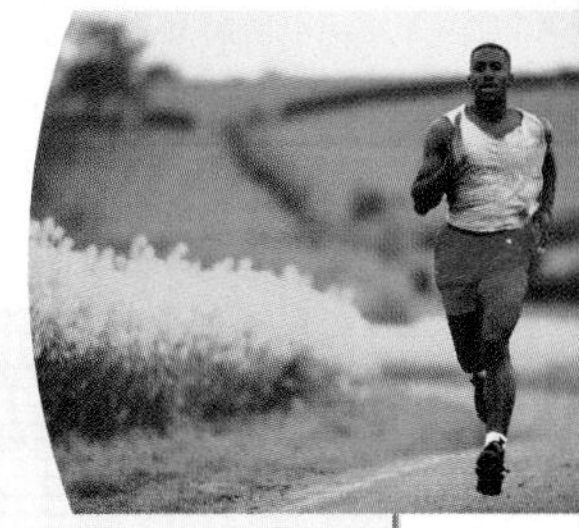

Before You used deductive reasoning to form logical arguments.
Now You will use algebraic properties in logical arguments too.
Why So you can apply a heart rate formula, as in Example 3.

Key Vocabulary
- **equation,** *p. 875*
- **solve an equation,** *p. 875*

Standards

1.0 Students demonstrate understanding by identifying and giving examples of undefined terms, **axioms,** theorems, and inductive **and deductive reasoning.**

3.0 Students construct and judge the validity of a logical argument and give counterexamples to disprove a statement.

When you *solve an equation,* you use properties of real numbers. Segment lengths and angle measures are real numbers, so you can also use these properties to write logical arguments about geometric figures.

KEY CONCEPT *For Your Notebook*

Algebraic Properties of Equality

Let a, b, and c be real numbers.

Addition Property	If $a = b$, then $a + c = b + c$.
Subtraction Property	If $a = b$, then $a - c = b - c$.
Multiplication Property	If $a = b$, then $ac = bc$.
Division Property	If $a = b$ and $c \neq 0$, then $\frac{a}{c} = \frac{b}{c}$.
Substitution Property	If $a = b$, then a can be substituted for b in any equation or expression.

EXAMPLE 1 Write reasons for each step

Solve $2x + 5 = 20 - 3x$. Write a reason for each step.

Equation	Explanation	Reason
$2x + 5 = 20 - 3x$	Write original equation.	Given
$2x + 5 + 3x = 20 - 3x + 3x$	Add $3x$ to each side.	Addition Property of Equality
$5x + 5 = 20$	Combine like terms.	Simplify.
$5x = 15$	Subtract 5 from each side.	Subtraction Property of Equality
$x = 3$	Divide each side by 5.	Division Property of Equality

▶ The value of x is 3.

1 PLAN AND PREPARE

Warm-Up Exercises

Transparency Available

Solve each equation.

1. $6x + 2 = -3x - 16$ **−2**
2. $-4(x - 8) = -16$ **12**
3. Solve $P = 2\ell + 2w$ for w. $w = \frac{P - 2\ell}{2}$
4. $\angle S$ is the complement of $\angle R$. If $m\angle R = 38°$, find $m\angle S$. If $\angle T$ is also the complement of $\angle R$, what is true about $m\angle S$ and $m\angle T$? **52°; $m\angle S = m\angle T$**

Notetaking Guide

Transparency Available

Promotes interactive learning and notetaking skills, pp. 46–49.

Pacing

Basic: 2 days
Average: 2 days
Advanced: 2 days
Block: 1 block
- See *Teaching Guide/Lesson Plan.*

2 FOCUS AND MOTIVATE

Essential Question

Big Idea 1, p. 71

How do you solve an equation? **Tell students they will learn how to answer this question by using algebraic properties to justify the steps in finding the solution.**

Resource Planning Guide

Chapter Resource Book
- Teaching Guide/Lesson Plan (pp. 60–61)
- Practice levels A, B, C (pp. 62–67)
- Study Guide (pp. 68–69)
- Catch-up for Absent Students (p. 70)
- Problem Solving Workshop (p. 71)
- Challenge (p. 72)

Workbooks
- Notetaking Guide (pp. 46–49)
- Practice Workbook (pp. 34–36)

Teaching Options
- **Power Presentations CD-ROM** provides dynamic electronic teaching resources for the classroom.
- **Activity Generator CD-ROM** provides editable activities for all ability levels.

Interactive Technology
- Easy Planner
- Power Presentations CD-ROM
- Activity Generator CD-ROM
- Animated Geometry
- Test Generator CD-ROM
- Online Quiz
- eWorkbook
- eEdition
- @HomeTutor

Resources for English Learners
- Quick Reference for English Learners
- Spanish Study Guide
- Multi-Language Visual Glossary
- Student Resources in Spanish

See also the *Geometry Toolkit* for more strategies for meeting individual needs.

Motivating the Lesson

The performance of athletes has improved over the years as formulas for optimum heart rate and other components of sports have been developed. Tell students that they will learn how to use algebra to work with formulas in this lesson.

3 TEACH

Extra Example 1

Solve $3x + 8 = -4x - 34$. Write a reason for each step.

Equation (Reason)

$3x + 8 = -4x - 34$ (Given)

$3x + 8 + 4x = -4x - 34 + 4x$ (Addition Property of Equality)

$7x + 8 = -34$ (Simplify.)

$7x + 8 - 8 = -34 - 8$ (Subtraction Property of Equality)

$7x = -42$ (Simplify.)

$x = -6$ (Division Property of Equality)

The value of x is -6.

Extra Example 2

Solve $60 = -3(8x - 4)$. Write a reason for each step.

Equation (Reason)

$60 = -3(8x - 4)$ (Given)

$60 = -24x + 12$ (Distributive Property)

$48 = -24x$ (Subtraction Property of Equality)

$-2 = x$ (Division Property of Equality)

The value of x is -2.

An **Animated Geometry** activity is available on-line for **Example 2**. This activity is also available on the **Power Presentations CD-ROM**.

KEY CONCEPT *For Your Notebook*

Distributive Property

$a(b + c) = ab + ac$, where a, b, and c are real numbers.

EXAMPLE 2 Use the Distributive Property

Solve $-4(11x + 2) = 80$. Write a reason for each step.

Solution

Equation	Explanation	Reason
$-4(11x + 2) = 80$	Write original equation.	Given
$-44x - 8 = 80$	Multiply.	Distributive Property
$-44x = 88$	Add 8 to each side.	Addition Property of Equality
$x = -2$	Divide each side by -44.	Division Property of Equality

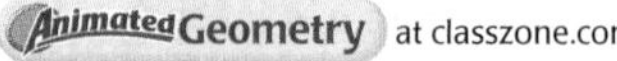

EXAMPLE 3 Use properties in the real world

HEART RATE When you exercise, your target heart rate should be between 50% to 70% of your maximum heart rate. Your target heart rate r at 70% can be determined by the formula $r = 0.70(220 - a)$ where a represents your age in years. Solve the formula for a.

Solution

Equation	Explanation	Reason
$r = 0.70(220 - a)$	Write original equation.	Given
$r = 154 - 0.70a$	Multiply.	Distributive Property
$r - 154 = -0.70a$	Subtract 154 from each side.	Subtraction Property of Equality
$\frac{r - 154}{-0.70} = a$	Divide each side by -0.70.	Division Property of Equality

GUIDED PRACTICE for Examples 1, 2, and 3

In Exercises 1 and 2, solve the equation and write a reason for each step. 1, 2. See margin.

1. $4x + 9 = -3x + 2$
2. $14x + 3(7 - x) = -1$
3. Solve the formula $A = \frac{1}{2}bh$ for b. $b = \frac{2A}{h}$

Differentiated Instruction

Below Level While discussing **Example 1**, remind students that the goal is to isolate the variable on one side of the equation and to make the coefficient equal to 1. Have students consider whether the steps in the solution could be done in a different order.

See also the *Geometry Toolkit* for more strategies.

PROPERTIES The following properties of equality are true for all real numbers. Segment lengths and angle measures are real numbers, so these properties of equality are true for segment lengths and angle measures.

KEY CONCEPT *For Your Notebook*

Reflexive Property of Equality

Real Numbers	For any real number a, $a = a$.
Segment Length	For any segment AB, $AB = AB$.
Angle Measure	For any angle A, $m\angle A = m\angle A$.

Symmetric Property of Equality

Real Numbers	For any real numbers a and b, if $a = b$, then $b = a$.
Segment Length	For any segments AB and CD, if $AB = CD$, then $CD = AB$.
Angle Measure	For any angles A and B, if $m\angle A = m\angle B$, then $m\angle B = m\angle A$.

Transitive Property of Equality

Real Numbers	For any real numbers a, b, and c, if $a = b$ and $b = c$, then $a = c$.
Segment Length	For any segments AB, CD, and EF, if $AB = CD$ and $CD = EF$, then $AB = EF$.
Angle Measure	For any angles A, B, and C, if $m\angle A = m\angle B$ and $m\angle B = m\angle C$, then $m\angle A = m\angle C$.

EXAMPLE 4 Use properties of equality

LOGO You are designing a logo to sell daffodils. Use the information given. Determine whether $m\angle EBA = m\angle DBC$.

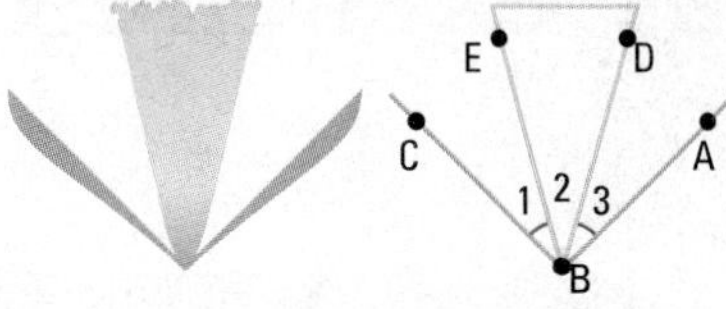

Solution

Equation	Explanation	Reason
$m\angle 1 = m\angle 3$	Marked in diagram.	Given
$m\angle EBA = m\angle 3 + m\angle 2$	Add measures of adjacent angles.	Angle Addition Postulate
$m\angle EBA = m\angle 1 + m\angle 2$	Substitute $m\angle 1$ for $m\angle 3$.	Substitution Property of Equality
$m\angle 1 + m\angle 2 = m\angle DBC$	Add measures of adjacent angles.	Angle Addition Postulate
$m\angle EBA = m\angle DBC$	Both measures are equal to the sum of $m\angle 1 + m\angle 2$.	Transitive Property of Equality

1. Equation (Reason)
$4x + 9 = -3x + 2$ (Given)
$7x + 9 = 2$ (Addition Property of Equality)
$7x = -7$ (Subtraction Property of Equality)
$x = -1$ (Division Property of Equality)

2. Equation (Reason)
$14x + 3(7 - x) = -1$ (Given)
$14x + 21 - 3x = -1$ (Distributive Property)
$11x + 21 = -1$ (Simplify.)
$11x = -22$ (Subtraction Property of Equality)
$x = -2$ (Division Property of Equality)

Extra Example 3

The cost C of using a certain cell phone can be modeled by the plan rate formula $C = 0.30(m - 300) + 39.99$, where m represents the number of minutes over 300. Solve the formula for m.

Equation (Reason)
$C = 0.30(m - 300) + 39.99$ (Given)
$C = 0.30m - 90 + 39.99$ (Distributive Property)
$C = 0.3m - 50.01$ (Simplify.)
$C + 50.01 = 0.3m$ (Addition Property of Equality)
$\frac{C + 50.01}{0.3} = m$ (Division Property of Equality)

Key Question to Ask for Example 3

- When would you use the new form of the formula? **when you want to find the age that corresponds to a known heart rate**

Avoiding Common Errors

Students may have difficulty interpreting the properties of equality for geometric quantities. Remind them that the properties of equality can be used for the measures of segments and angles.

Extra Example 4

The city is planning to add two stations between the beginning and end of a commuter train line. Use the information given. Determine whether $RS = TU$.

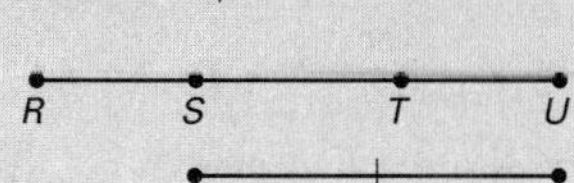

Equation (Reason)
$RT = SU$ (Given)
$ST = ST$ (Reflexive Property)
$RT - ST = SU - ST$ (Subtraction Property of Equality)
$RT - ST = RS$ (Segment Addition Postulate)
$SU - ST = TU$ (Segment Addition Postulate)
$RS = TU$ (Substitution Property of Equality)

Extra Example 5

In the diagram $m\angle ABD = m\angle CBE$. Show that $m\angle 1 = m\angle 3$.

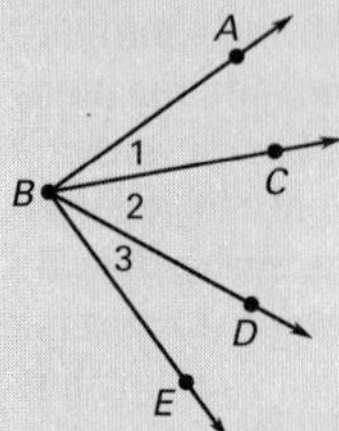

Equation (Reason)

$m\angle ABD = m\angle CBE$ (Given)

$m\angle ABD - m\angle 2 = m\angle 1$ (Angle Addition Postulate)

$m\angle CBE - m\angle 2 = m\angle 3$ (Angle Addition Postulate)

$m\angle ABD - m\angle 2 = m\angle CBE - m\angle 2$ (Substitution Property of Equality)

$m\angle 1 = m\angle 3$ (Substitution Property of Equality)

Closing the Lesson

Have students summarize the major points of the lesson and answer the Essential Question: How do you solve an equation?

- The algebraic properties of equality can be used to justify each step of solving an equation.
- The algebraic properties of equality and the reflexive, symmetric, and transitive properties of equality can be used to justify steps in solving geometric problems.

You solve an equation by applying the properties of algebra to justify the reason for each step.

3. Subtraction Property of Equality, Addition Property of Equality, Division Property of Equality

4. Distributive Property, Subtraction Property of Equality, Addition Property of Equality

6–20. See Additional Answers beginning on p. AA1.

EXAMPLE 5 Use properties of equality

In the diagram, $AB = CD$. Show that $AC = BD$.

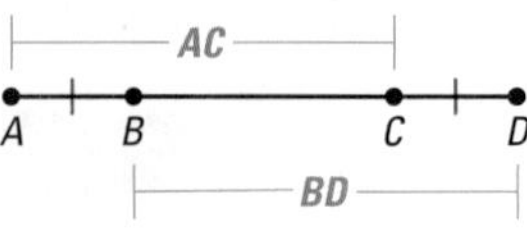

Solution

Equation	Explanation	Reason
$AB = CD$	Marked in diagram.	Given
$AC = AB + BC$	Add lengths of adjacent segments.	Segment Addition Postulate
$BD = BC + CD$	Add lengths of adjacent segments.	Segment Addition Postulate
$AB + BC = CD + BC$	Add BC to each side of $AB = CD$.	Addition Property of Equality
$AC = BD$	Substitute AC for $AB + BC$ and BD for $BC + CD$.	Substitution Property of Equality

GUIDED PRACTICE for Examples 4 and 5

Name the property of equality the statement illustrates.

4. If $m\angle 6 = m\angle 7$, then $m\angle 7 = m\angle 6$. **Symmetric Property of Equality**
5. If $JK = KL$ and $KL = 12$, then $JK = 12$. **Transitive Property of Equality**
6. $m\angle W = m\angle W$ **Reflexive Property of Equality**

2.5 EXERCISES

HOMEWORK KEY
○ = WORKED-OUT SOLUTIONS on p. WS2 for Exs. 9, 21, and 31
★ = STANDARDIZED TEST PRACTICE Exs. 2, 5, 27, and 35
◆ = MULTIPLE REPRESENTATIONS Ex. 36

SKILL PRACTICE

A

1. **VOCABULARY** The following statement is true because of what property? The measure of an angle is equal to itself. **Reflexive Property of Equality for Angle Measure**

2. ★ **WRITING** *Explain* how to check the answer to Example 3 on page 106. **Substitute the value of *a* into the original equation to see if it is a solution.**

EXAMPLES 1 and 2 on pp. 105–106 for Exs. 3–14

WRITING REASONS **Copy the logical argument. Write a reason for each step.** 3, 4. See margin.

3. $3x - 12 = 7x + 8$ Given
   $-4x - 12 = 8$?
   $-4x = 20$?
   $x = -5$?

4. $5(x - 1) = 4x + 13$ Given
   $5x - 5 = 4x + 13$?
   $x - 5 = 13$?
   $x = 18$?

26. x should be subtracted from each side, not added.

Equation (Reason)

$7x = x + 24$ (Given)

$6x = 24$ (Subtraction Property of Equality)

$x = 4$ (Division Property of Equality)

Differentiated Instruction

Below Level Students may have difficulty with **Example 5** because they find the notation confusing. Suggest that they use specific numbers for the lengths of the segments to help them follow the reasoning in the argument.

See also the *Geometry Toolkit* for more strategies.

5. ★ **MULTIPLE CHOICE** Name the property of equality the statement illustrates: If $XY = AB$ and $AB = GH$, then $XY = GH$. **D**

Ⓐ Substitution Ⓑ Reflexive Ⓒ Symmetric Ⓓ Transitive

WRITING REASONS **Solve the equation. Write a reason for each step.** **6–14. See margin.**

6. $5x - 10 = -40$
7. $4x + 9 = 16 - 3x$
8. $5(3x - 20) = -10$
9. $3(2x + 11) = 9$
10. $2(-x - 5) = 12$
11. $44 - 2(3x + 4) = -18x$
12. $4(5x - 9) = -2(x + 7)$
13. $2x - 15 - x = 21 + 10x$
14. $3(7x - 9) - 19x = -15$

EXAMPLE 3 on p. 106 for Exs. 15–20

ALGEBRA **Solve the equation for *y*. Write a reason for each step.** **15–20. See margin.**

15. $5x + y = 18$
16. $-4x + 2y = 8$
17. $12 - 3y = 30x$
18. $3x + 9y = -7$
19. $2y + 0.5x = 16$
20. $\frac{1}{2}x - \frac{3}{4}y = -2$

EXAMPLES 4 and 5 on pp. 107–108 for Exs. 21–25

COMPLETING STATEMENTS **In Exercises 21–25, use the property to copy and complete the statement.**

21. Substitution Property of Equality: If $AB = 20$, then $AB + CD = \underline{?}$. **20 + *CD***
22. Symmetric Property of Equality: If $m\angle 1 = m\angle 2$, then $\underline{?}$. **$m\angle 2 = m\angle 1$**
23. Addition Property of Equality: If $AB = CD$, then $\underline{?} + EF = \underline{?} + EF$. ***AB, CD***
24. Distributive Property: If $5(x + 8) = 2$, then $\underline{?}\,x + \underline{?} = 2$. **5, 40**
25. Transitive Property of Equality: If $m\angle 1 = m\angle 2$ and $m\angle 2 = m\angle 3$, then $\underline{?}$. **$m\angle 1 = m\angle 3$**

26. **ERROR ANALYSIS** *Describe* and correct the error in solving the equation for x. **See margin.**

$7x = x + 24$	Given
$8x = 24$	Addition Property of Equality
$x = 3$	Division Property of Equality

27. *Sample answer:* Look in the mirror and see your reflection; 12 in. = 1 ft, so 1 ft = 12 in.; 10 pennies = 1 dime and 1 dime = 2 nickels, so 10 pennies = 2 nickels.

B 27. ★ **OPEN-ENDED MATH** Write examples from your everyday life that could help you remember the *Reflexive*, *Symmetric*, and *Transitive* Properties of Equality.

PERIMETER **In Exercises 28 and 29, show that the perimeter of triangle *ABC* is equal to the perimeter of triangle *ADC*.** **28–29. See margin.**

28.

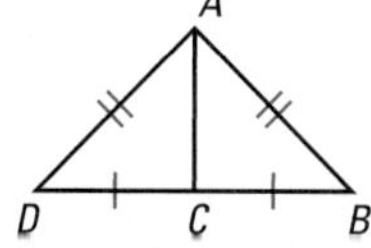

29.

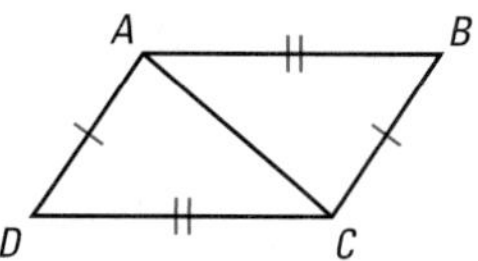

C 30. **CHALLENGE** In the figure at the right, $\overline{ZY} \cong \overline{XW}$, $ZX = 5x + 17$, $YW = 10 - 2x$, and $YX = 3$. Find ZY and XW. **9, 9**

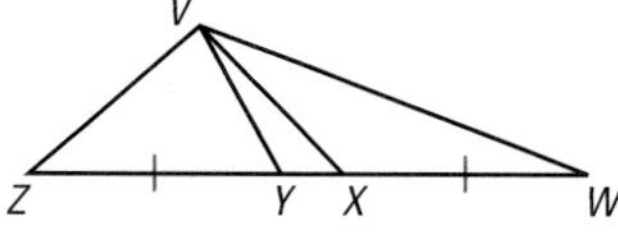

4 PRACTICE AND APPLY

Assignment Guide

Answer Transparencies available for all exercises

Basic:
Day 1: SRH p. 872 Exs. 1–6
pp. 108–111
Exs. 1–20
Day 2: pp. 108–111
Exs. 21–27, 31–35, 39–42

Average:
Day 1: pp. 108–111
Exs. 1–20
Day 2: pp. 108–111
Exs. 21–29, 31–36, 39–42

Advanced:
Day 1: pp. 108–111
Exs. 1–20
Day 2: pp. 108–111
Exs. 21–30*, 32–38*, 40, 42

Block:
pp. 108–111
Exs. 1–29, 31–36, 39–42

Differentiated Instruction

See *Geometry Best Practices Toolkit* for suggestions on addressing the needs of a diverse classroom.

Homework Check

For a quick check of student understanding of key concepts, go over the following exercises:

Basic: 3, 16, 22, 31, 35
Average: 4, 18, 24, 31, 35
Advanced: 4, 20, 25, 32, 35

Extra Practice

- Student Edition, p. 899
- Chapter 2 Resource Book: Practice levels A, B, C, pp. 62–67

Practice Worksheet

An easily-readable reduced practice page (with answers) for this lesson can be found on p. 70E.

28. Equation (Reason)

$AD = AB$, $DC = BC$ (Given)
$AC = AC$ (Reflexive Property of Equality)
$AD + DC = AB + DC$ (Addition Property of Equality)
$AD + DC = AB + BC$ (Substitution)
$AD + DC + AC = AB + BC + AC$ (Addition Property of Equality)

29. Equation (Reason)

$AD = CB$, $DC = BA$ (Given)
$AC = AC$ (Reflexive Property of Equality)
$AD + DC = CB + DC$ (Addition Property of Equality)
$AD + DC = CB + BA$ (Substitution)
$AD + DC + AC = CB + BA + AC$ (Addition Property of Equality)

Avoiding Common Errors

Exercises 6–14 Students who are proficient in algebra may have errors in the reasons they give. If this seems due to their combining steps to arrive at the solution quickly, urge them not to combine steps and explain why this is important for these exercises.

Reading Strategy

Exercises 21–25 If students have difficulty getting started with these exercises, suggest that they compare each statement they are to complete with the appropriate algebraic property on page 105.

Avoiding Common Errors

Exercises 28–29 Some students may fail to include the shared side of triangle ABC and triangle ADC. Help students see that all three sides of each triangle must be included.

31. Equation (Reason)

$P = 2\ell + 2w$ (Given)

$P - 2w = 2\ell$ (Subtraction Property of Equality)

$\frac{P - 2w}{2} = \ell$ (Division Property of Equality)

16.5 m

32. Equation (Reason)

$A = \frac{1}{2}bh$ (Given)

$2A = bh$ (Multiplication Property of Equality)

$\frac{2A}{b} = h$ (Division Property of Equality)

68 in.

33. Row 1: Marked in diagram; Row 2: Substitute $m\angle GHF$ for 90°; Row 3: Angle Addition Postulate; Row 4: Substitution Property of Equality; Row 5: $m\angle 1 + m\angle 2 = m\angle 3 + m\angle 1$; Substitution Property of Equality; Row 6: Subtract $m\angle 1$ from both sides.

PROBLEM SOLVING

EXAMPLE 3 A on p. 106 for Exs. 31–32

31. **PERIMETER** The formula for the perimeter P of a rectangle is $P = 2\ell + 2w$ where ℓ is the length and w is the width. Solve the formula for ℓ and write a reason for each step. Then find the length of a rectangular lawn whose perimeter is 55 meters and whose width is 11 meters. **See margin.**

@HomeTutor for problem solving help at classzone.com

32. **AREA** The formula for the area A of a triangle is $A = \frac{1}{2}bh$ where b is the base and h is the height. Solve the formula for h and write a reason for each step. Then find the height of a triangle whose area is 1768 square inches and whose base is 52 inches. **See margin.**

@HomeTutor for problem solving help at classzone.com

33. **PROPERTIES OF EQUALITY** Copy and complete the table to show $m\angle 2 = m\angle 3$. **See margin.**

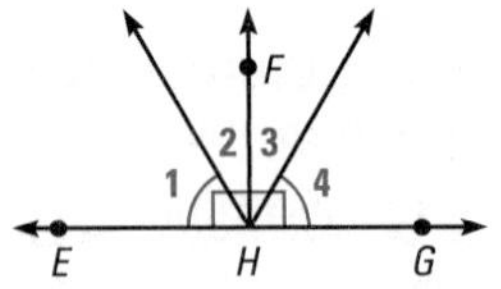

Equation	Explanation	Reason
$m\angle 1 = m\angle 4$, $m\angle EHF = 90°$, $m\angle GHF = 90°$	?	Given
$m\angle EHF = m\angle GHF$	?	Substitution Property of Equality
$m\angle EHF = m\angle 1 + m\angle 2$ $m\angle GHF = m\angle 3 + m\angle 4$	Add measures of adjacent angles.	?
$m\angle 1 + m\angle 2 = m\angle 3 + m\angle 4$	Write expressions equal to the angle measures.	?
?	Substitute $m\angle 1$ for $m\angle 4$.	?
$m\angle 2 = m\angle 3$	?	Subtraction Property of Equality

34. **MULTI-STEP PROBLEM** Points A, B, C, and D represent stops, in order, along a subway route. The distance between Stops A and C is the same as the distance between Stops B and D. **a–c. See margin.**
    a. Draw a diagram to represent the situation.
    b. Use the Segment Addition Postulate to show that the distance between Stops A and B is the same as the distance between Stops C and D.
    c. *Justify* part (b) using the Properties of Equality.

EXAMPLE 4 on p. 107 for Ex. 35

35. ★ **SHORT RESPONSE** A flashlight beam is reflected off a mirror lying flat on the ground. Use the information given below to find $m\angle 2$. **116°**

$m\angle 1 + m\angle 2 + m\angle 3 = 180°$

$m\angle 1 + m\angle 2 = 148°$

$m\angle 1 = m\angle 3$

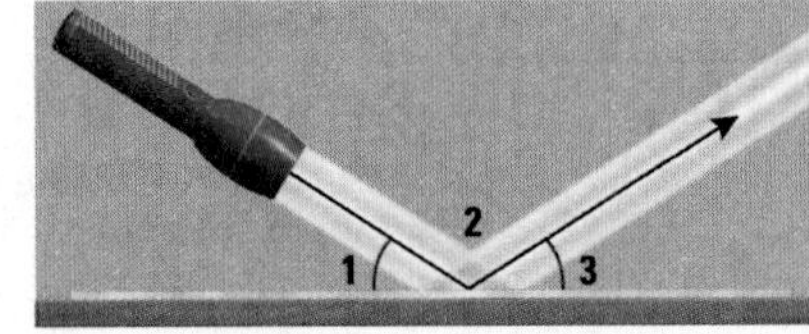

○ = WORKED-OUT SOLUTIONS on p. WS1 ★ = STANDARDIZED TEST PRACTICE 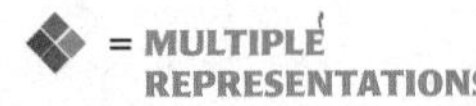 = MULTIPLE REPRESENTATIONS

34a. ***Sample:***

A B C D

34b. $AC = BD$

$AB + BC = AC$, $BC + CD = BD$

$AB + BC = BC + CD$

$AB = CD$

34c. Equation (Reason)

$AC = BD$ (Given)

$AB + BC = AC$, $BC + CD = BD$ (Segment Addition Postulate)

$AB + BC = BC + CD$ (Substitution)

$AB = CD$ (Subtraction Property of Equality)

B 36. ◆ **MULTIPLE REPRESENTATIONS** The formula to convert a temperature in degrees Fahrenheit (°F) to degrees Celsius (°C) is $C = \frac{5}{9}(F - 32)$. **a–c. See margin.**

a. **Writing an Equation** Solve the formula for F. Write a reason for each step.

b. **Making a Table** Make a table that shows the conversion to Fahrenheit for each temperature: 0°C, 20°C, 32°C, and 41°C.

c. **Drawing a Graph** Use your table to graph the temperature in degrees Fahrenheit (°F) as a function of the temperature in degrees Celsius (°C). Is this a linear function?

C **CHALLENGE In Exercises 37 and 38, decide whether the relationship is *reflexive, symmetric,* or *transitive.***

37. **Group:** two employees in a grocery store
Relationship: "worked the same hours as"
Example: Yen worked the same hours as Jim. **symmetric**

38. **Group:** negative numbers on a number line
Relationship: "is less than"
Example: −4 is less than −1. **transitive**

MIXED REVIEW

PREVIEW
Prepare for Lesson 2.6 in Exs. 39–40.

In the diagram, $m\angle ADC = 124°$. *(p. 24)*

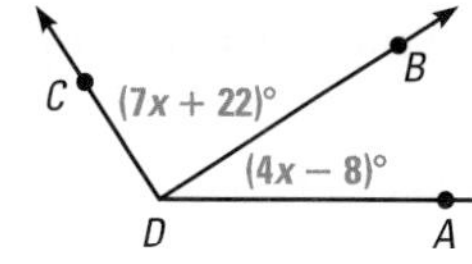

39. Find $m\angle ADB$. **32°**

40. Find $m\angle BDC$. **92°**

41. Find a counterexample to show the conjecture is false.

Conjecture All polygons have five sides. *(p. 72)* ***Sample answer:* square**

42. Select the word(s) that make(s) the conclusion true. If $m\angle X = m\angle Y$ and $m\angle Y = m\angle Z$, then $m\angle X$ (*is, may be,* or *is not*) equal to $m\angle Z$. *(p. 87)* **is**

QUIZ for Lessons 2.4–2.5

Use the diagram to determine if the statement is *true* or *false*. *(p. 96)*

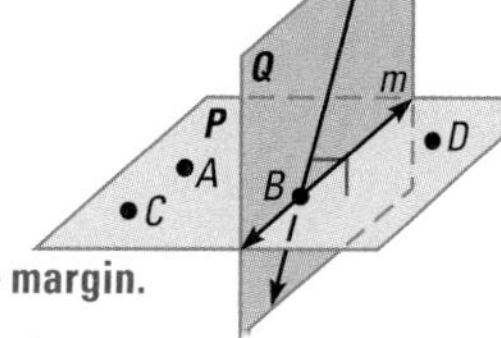

1. Points B, C, and D are coplanar. **true**

2. Point A is on line ℓ. **false**

3. Plane P and plane Q are perpendicular. **true**

Solve the equation. Write a reason for each step. *(p. 105)* **4, 5. See margin.**

4. $x + 20 = 35$

5. $5x - 14 = 16 + 3x$

Use the property to copy and complete the statement. *(p. 105)*

6. Subtraction Property of Equality: If $AB = CD$, then $\underline{?} - EF = \underline{?} - EF$. ***AB, CD***

7. Transitive Property of Equality: If $a = b$ and $b = c$, then $\underline{?} = \underline{?}$. ***a, c***

5 ASSESS AND RETEACH

Daily Homework Quiz

Transparency Available

Solve. Give a reason for each step.

1. $-5x + 18 = 3x - 38$

Equation (Reason)

$-5x + 18 = 3x - 38$ **(Given)**

$-8x + 18 = -38$ **(Subtr. Prop. of Eq.)**

$-8x = -56$ **(Subtr. Prop. of Eq.)**

$x = 7$ **(Division Prop. of Eq.)**

2. $-3(x - 5) = 2(x + 10)$

Equation (Reason)

$-3(x - 5) = 2(x + 10)$ **(Given)**

$-3x + 15 = 2x + 20$ **(Distributive Prop.)**

$15 = 5x + 20$ **(Addition Prop. of Eq.)**

$-5 = 5x$ **(Subtr. Prop. of Eq.)**

$-1 = x$ **(Division Prop. of Eq.)**

Identify the property of equality.

3. If $m\angle 3 = m\angle 5$ and $m\angle 5 = m\angle 8$, then $m\angle 3 = m\angle 8$ **Transitive Prop. of Eq.**

4. If $CD = EF$, then $EF = CD$. **Symmetric Prop. of Eq.**

Available at **classzone.com**

Diagnosis/Remediation

- Practice A, B, C in Chapter 2 Resource Book, pp. 62–67
- Study Guide in Chapter 2 Resource Book, pp. 68–69
- Practice Workbook, pp. 34–36
- @HomeTutor

Challenge

Additional challenge is available in the Chapter 2 Resource Book, p. 72.

Quiz

An easily-readable reduced copy of the quiz (with answers) on Lessons 2.4–2.5 from the Assessment Book can be found on p. 70G.

36a–c, Quiz 4, 5. See Additional Answers beginning on p. AA1.

2.6 Prove Statements about Segments and Angles

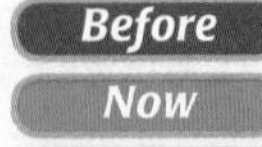

Before You used deductive reasoning.

Now You will write proofs using geometric theorems.

Why? So you can prove angles are congruent, as in Ex. 21.

1 PLAN AND PREPARE

Warm-Up Exercises

Transparency Available

Use a property of equality to complete the statement.

1. If $m\angle 1 = m\angle 3$, then $m\angle 3 = \underline{?}$. **$m\angle 1$**
2. If $AB = CD$ and $CD = TU$, then $\underline{?}$. **$AB = TU$**
3. If $RS = WX$, then $\underline{?} + AB = \underline{?} + AB$. **$RS$; WX**
4. If $m\angle EFG = 28°$ and $m\angle GFH = 62°$, then $\underline{?} + 62° = m\angle EFG + m\angle GFH$. **28°**

Notetaking Guide

Transparency Available

Promotes interactive learning and notetaking skills, pp. 50–53.

Pacing

Basic: 2 days
Average: 2 days
Advanced: 2 days
Block: 1 block
- See *Teaching Guide/Lesson Plan.*

2 FOCUS AND MOTIVATE

Essential Question

Big Idea 3, p. 71

How do you write a geometric proof? **Tell students they will learn how to answer this question using geometric theorems and algebraic properties to do proofs.**

Key Vocabulary
- **proof**
- **two-column proof**
- **theorem**

A **proof** is a logical argument that shows a statement is true. There are several formats for proofs. A **two-column proof** has numbered statements and corresponding reasons that show an argument in a logical order.

In a two-column proof, each statement in the left-hand column is either given information or the result of applying a known property or fact to statements already made. Each reason in the right-hand column is the explanation for the corresponding statement.

EXAMPLE 1 Write a two-column proof

WRITE PROOFS
Writing a two-column proof is a formal way of organizing your reasons to show a statement is true.

Write a two-column proof for the situation in Example 4 on page 107.

GIVEN ▶ $m\angle 1 = m\angle 3$

PROVE ▶ $m\angle EBA = m\angle DBC$

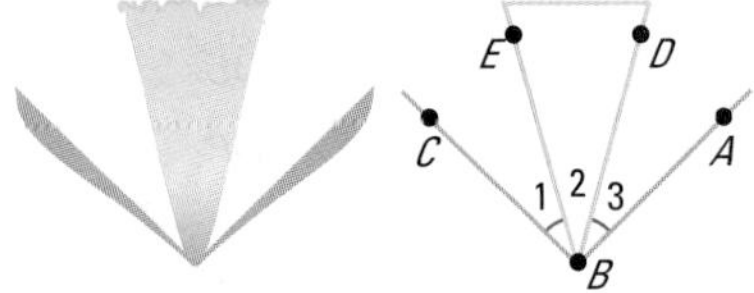

STATEMENTS	REASONS
1. $m\angle 1 = m\angle 3$	1. Given
2. $m\angle EBA = m\angle 3 + m\angle 2$	2. Angle Addition Postulate
3. $m\angle EBA = m\angle 1 + m\angle 2$	3. Substitution Property of Equality
4. $m\angle 1 + m\angle 2 = m\angle DBC$	4. Angle Addition Postulate
5. $m\angle EBA = m\angle DBC$	5. Transitive Property of Equality

✓ GUIDED PRACTICE for Example 1

1. Four steps of a proof are shown. Give the reasons for the last two steps.

GIVEN ▶ $AC = AB + AB$

PROVE ▶ $AB = BC$

A B C

STATEMENTS	REASONS
1. $AC = AB + AB$	1. Given
2. $AB + BC = AC$	2. Segment Addition Postulate
3. $AB + AB = AB + BC$	3. $\underline{?}$ **Transitive Property of Equality**
4. $AB = BC$	4. $\underline{?}$ **Subtraction Property of Equality**

Resource Planning Guide

Chapter Resource Book
- Teaching Guide/Lesson Plan (pp. 73–74)
- Activity Master (p. 75)
- Practice levels A, B, C (pp. 76–81)
- Study Guide (pp. 82–83)
- Catch-up for Absent Students (p. 84)
- Application (p. 85)
- Challenge (p. 86)

Workbooks
- Notetaking Guide (pp. 50–53)
- Practice Workbook (pp. 37–39)

Teaching Options
- **Power Presentations CD-ROM** provides dynamic electronic teaching resources for the classroom.
- **Activity Generator CD-ROM** provides editable activities for all ability levels.

Interactive Technology
- Easy Planner
- Power Presentations CD-ROM
- Activity Generator CD-ROM
- Animated Geometry
- Test Generator CD-ROM
- Online Quiz
- eWorkbook
- eEdition
- @HomeTutor

Resources for English Learners
- Quick Reference for English Learners
- Spanish Study Guide
- Multi-Language Visual Glossary
- Student Resources in Spanish

See also the *Geometry Toolkit* for more strategies for meeting individual needs.

THEOREMS The reasons used in a proof can include definitions, properties, postulates, and *theorems*. A **theorem** is a statement that can be proven. Once you have proven a theorem, you can use the theorem as a reason in other proofs.

TAKE NOTES
Be sure to copy all new theorems in your notebook. Notice that the theorem box tells you where to find the proof(s).

Standards

1.0 Students demonstrate understanding by identifying and giving examples of undefined terms, **axioms, theorems,** and inductive **and deductive reasoning.**

2.0 Students write geometric proofs, including proofs by contradiction.

THEOREMS *For Your Notebook*

THEOREM 2.1 Congruence of Segments

Segment congruence is reflexive, symmetric, and transitive.

Reflexive For any segment AB, $\overline{AB} \cong \overline{AB}$.

Symmetric If $\overline{AB} \cong \overline{CD}$, then $\overline{CD} \cong \overline{AB}$.

Transitive If $\overline{AB} \cong \overline{CD}$ and $\overline{CD} \cong \overline{EF}$, then $\overline{AB} \cong \overline{EF}$.

Proofs: p. 137; Ex. 5, p. 121; Ex. 26, p. 118

THEOREM 2.2 Congruence of Angles

Angle congruence is reflexive, symmetric, and transitive.

Reflexive For any angle A, $\angle A \cong \angle A$.

Symmetric If $\angle A \cong \angle B$, then $\angle B \cong \angle A$.

Transitive If $\angle A \cong \angle B$ and $\angle B \cong \angle C$, then $\angle A \cong \angle C$.

Proofs: Ex. 25, p. 118; Concept Summary, p. 114; Ex. 21, p. 137

EXAMPLE 2 Name the property shown

Name the property illustrated by the statement.

a. If $\angle R \cong \angle T$ and $\angle T \cong \angle P$, then $\angle R \cong \angle P$.

b. If $\overline{NK} \cong \overline{BD}$, then $\overline{BD} \cong \overline{NK}$.

Solution

a. Transitive Property of Angle Congruence

b. Symmetric Property of Segment Congruence

✓ **GUIDED PRACTICE** for Example 2

Name the property illustrated by the statement.

2. $\overline{CD} \cong \overline{CD}$ **Reflexive Property of Congruence**

3. If $\angle Q \cong \angle V$, then $\angle V \cong \angle Q$. **Symmetric Property of Congruence**

In this lesson, most of the proofs involve showing that congruence and equality are equivalent. You may find that what you are asked to prove seems to be obviously true. It is important to practice writing these proofs so that you will be prepared to write more complicated proofs in later chapters.

Motivating the Lesson

Much of science was developed because scientists had a "theory" about how things work, and they tried to prove the theory. Have students give examples from science that they know.

3 TEACH

Extra Example 1

Write a two-column proof for Extra Example 4 on page 107.

Given: $RT = SU$

Prove: $RS = TU$

Statements (Reasons)

1. $RT = SU$ (Given)
2. $ST = ST$ (Reflexive Prop.)
3. $RT - ST = SU - ST$ (Subtraction Prop. of Eq.)
4. $RT - ST = RS$ (Segment Addition Post.)
5. $SU - ST = TU$ (Segment Addition Post.)
6. $RS = TU$ (Substitution Prop. of Eq.)

Extra Example 2

Name the property illustrated by each statement.

a. If $\angle RST \cong \angle MNP$, then $\angle MNP \cong \angle RST$. **Symmetric Prop. of Angle Congruence**

b. If $\overline{AB} \cong \overline{FG}$ and $\overline{FG} \cong \overline{MN}$, then $\overline{AB} \cong \overline{MN}$. **Transitive Prop. of Segment Congruence**

Key Question to Ask for Example 2

- Why is the reason for part a the Transitive Property of Angle Congruence and not the Transitive Property of Equality? **Congruence is a relation between geometric figures rather than numbers.**

Differentiated Instruction

Below Level In the discussion of **Example 2**, remind students of the Reflexive, Symmetric, and Transitive Properties of Equality from algebra. Point out similarities to the corresponding properties of congruence for segments and for angles.

See also the *Geometry Toolkit* for more strategies.

Extra Example 3

If you know that M is the midpoint of $\overline{AB}$, N is the midpoint of $\overline{CD}$, and $AB = CD$, prove that $AM = CN$.

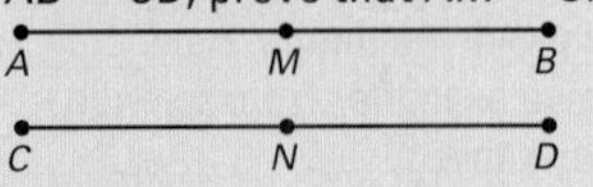

Given: M is the midpoint of $\overline{AB}$; N is the midpoint of $\overline{CD}$; $AB = CD$.

Prove: $AM = CN$

Statements (Reasons)

1. **M is the midpoint of $\overline{AB}$; N is the midpoint of $\overline{CD}$; $AB = CD$. (Given)**
2. **$\overline{AM} \cong \overline{MB}$; $\overline{CN} \cong \overline{ND}$ (Definition of midpoint)**
3. **$AM = MB$; $CN = ND$ (Definition of congruent segments)**
4. **$AM + MB = AB$; $CN + ND = CD$ (Segment Addition Post.)**
5. **$AM + AM = AB$; $CN + CN = CD$ (Substitution Prop. of Eq.)**
6. **$2AM = AB$; $2CN = CD$ (Distributive Prop.)**
7. **$2AM = 2CN$ (Substitution Prop. of Eq.)**
8. **$AM = CN$ (Division Prop. of Eq.)**

Key Question to Ask for Example 3

- Why can't you go from step 1 to step 3 in the proof? **The definition of midpoint is given in terms of congruence, not equality.**

Teaching Strategy

Have students analyze the Concept Summary Box carefully. If possible, photocopy the box onto a transparency, then cut out each section of the summary. Mix up the sections, then rearrange them correctly as a demonstration as you discuss them.

EXAMPLE 3 Use properties of equality

Prove this property of midpoints: If you know that M is the midpoint of $\overline{AB}$, prove that AB is two times AM and AM is one half of AB.

WRITE PROOFS Before writing a proof, organize your reasoning by copying or drawing a diagram for the situation described. Then identify the GIVEN and PROVE statements.

GIVEN ▶ M is the midpoint of $\overline{AB}$.

PROVE ▶ **a.** $AB = 2 \cdot AM$

b. $AM = \frac{1}{2}AB$

A M B

STATEMENTS	REASONS
1. M is the midpoint of $\overline{AB}$.	1. Given
2. $\overline{AM} \cong \overline{MB}$	2. Definition of midpoint
3. $AM = MB$	3. Definition of congruent segments
4. $AM + MB = AB$	4. Segment Addition Postulate
5. $AM + AM = AB$	5. Substitution Property of Equality
a. 6. $2AM = AB$	6. Distributive Property
b. 7. $AM = \frac{1}{2}AB$	7. Division Property of Equality

GUIDED PRACTICE for Example 3

4. **WHAT IF?** Look back at Example 3. What would be different if you were proving that $AB = 2 \cdot MB$ and that $MB = \frac{1}{2}AB$ instead? **In steps 5, 6, and 7, AM would be replaced by MB.**

CONCEPT SUMMARY *For Your Notebook*

Writing a Two-Column Proof

In a proof, you make one statement at a time, until you reach the conclusion. Because you make statements based on facts, you are using deductive reasoning. Usually the first statement-and-reason pair you write is given information.

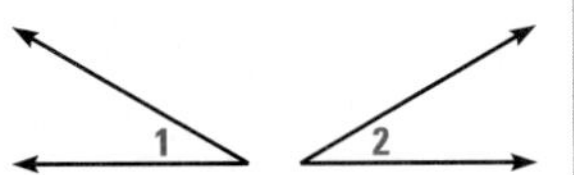

Copy or draw diagrams and label given information to help develop proofs.

Proof of the Symmetric Property of Angle Congruence

GIVEN ▶ $\angle 1 \cong \angle 2$

PROVE ▶ $\angle 2 \cong \angle 1$

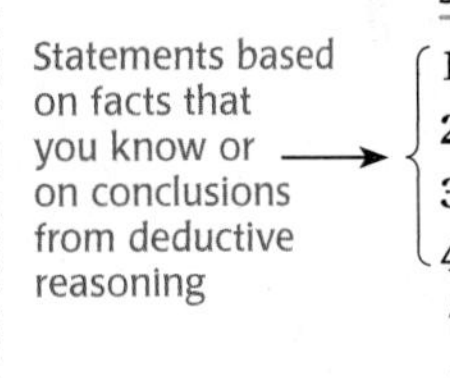

Statements based on facts that you know or on conclusions from deductive reasoning →

STATEMENTS	REASONS
1. $\angle 1 \cong \angle 2$	1. Given
2. $m\angle 1 = m\angle 2$	2. Definition of congruent angles
3. $m\angle 2 = m\angle 1$	3. Symmetric Property of Equality
4. $\angle 2 \cong \angle 1$	4. Definition of congruent angles

← Definitions, postulates, or proven theorems that allow you to state the corresponding statement

↑ The number of statements will vary.

↑ Remember to give a reason for the last statement.

Differentiated Instruction

Inclusion For many students, proofs are the most difficult part of geometry. Suggest that students write all the postulates and theorems on index cards as well as in a notebook. When they are given a problem, they can try to arrange some of the index cards as a method of completing the proof.

See also the *Geometry Toolkit* for more strategies.

EXAMPLE 4 Solve a multi-step problem

SHOPPING MALL Walking down a hallway at the mall, you notice the music store is halfway between the food court and the shoe store. The shoe store is halfway between the music store and the bookstore. Prove that the distance between the entrances of the food court and music store is the same as the distance between the entrances of the shoe store and bookstore.

ANOTHER WAY

For an alternative method for solving the problem in Example 4, turn to page 120 for the **Problem Solving Workshop**.

Solution

STEP 1 **Draw** and label a diagram.

food court — music store — shoe store — bookstore
A — B — C — D

STEP 2 **Draw** separate diagrams to show mathematical relationships.

A B C D A B C D

STEP 3 **State** what is given and what is to be proved for the situation. Then write a proof.

GIVEN ▶ B is the midpoint of $\overline{AC}$.
C is the midpoint of $\overline{BD}$.

PROVE ▶ $AB = CD$

STATEMENTS	REASONS
1. B is the midpoint of $\overline{AC}$. C is the midpoint of $\overline{BD}$.	1. Given
2. $\overline{AB} \cong \overline{BC}$	2. Definition of midpoint
3. $\overline{BC} \cong \overline{CD}$	3. Definition of midpoint
4. $\overline{AB} \cong \overline{CD}$	4. Transitive Property of Congruence
5. $AB = CD$	5. Definition of congruent segments

✓ **GUIDED PRACTICE** for Example 4

5. In Example 4, does it matter what the actual distances are in order to prove the relationship between AB and CD? *Explain.* **No; the critical factor is the midpoint.**

6. In Example 4, there is a clothing store halfway between the music store and the shoe store. What other two store entrances are the same distance from the entrance of the clothing store? **food court, bookstore**

Extra Example 4

The distance from the park to the pool is the same as the distance from your house to the school. The school is between the pool and the house. Prove that the distance from the park to the school is the same as the distance from the pool to your house.

Step 1: A (Park), B (Pool), C (School), D (House)

Step 2:

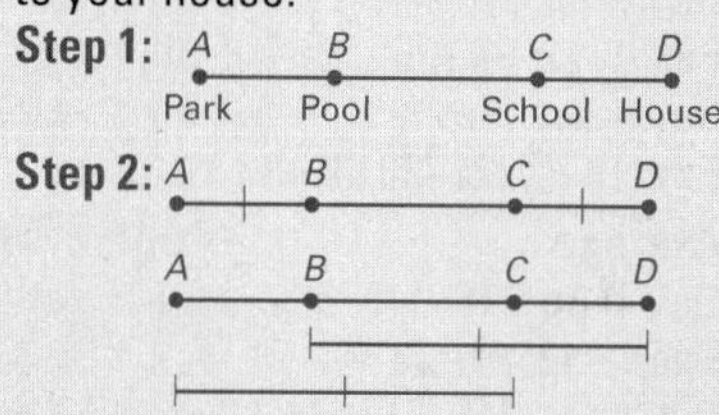

Given: $AB = CD$

Prove: $AC = BD$

Statements (Reasons)

1. $AB = CD$ (Given)
2. $BC = BC$ (Reflexive Prop. of Eq.)
3. $AB + BC = BC + CD$ (Addition Prop. of Eq.)
4. $AB + BC = AC$; $BC + CD = BD$ (Segment Addition Post.)
5. $AC = BD$ (Substitution Prop. of Eq.)

Closing the Lesson

Have students summarize the major points of the lesson and answer the Essential Question: How do you write a geometric proof?

- **A two-column proof has numbered statements and corresponding reasons in a logical order.**
- **A theorem is a statement that can be proved. Proved theorems can be used as reasons in proofs.**

You write a geometric proof by organizing the steps as described below.

- **Draw and label a diagram.**
- **Show mathematical relationships in the diagram.**
- **State what is given and what is to be proved for the situation.**
- **Write the proof using given information, definitions, theorems, and postulates.**

2.6 EXERCISES

HOMEWORK KEY ○ = **WORKED-OUT SOLUTIONS** on p. WS2 for Exs. 7, 15, and 21
★ = **STANDARDIZED TEST PRACTICE** Exs. 2, 4, 12, 19, 27, and 28

4 PRACTICE AND APPLY

Assignment Guide

Answer Transparencies available for all exercises

Basic:
Day 1: pp. 116–119
Exs. 1–12, 34–36
Day 2: pp. 116–119
Exs. 13–17, 21–28, 31–33

Average:
Day 1: pp. 116–119
Exs. 1–12, 34–36
Day 2: pp. 116–119
Exs. 13–19, 21–29, 31, 33

Advanced:
Day 1: pp. 116–119
Exs. 1–12, 34–36
Day 2: pp. 116–119
Exs. 15–20*, 22–30*, 32

Block:
pp. 116–119
Exs. 1–19, 21–29, 31, 33–36

Differentiated Instruction

See *Geometry Best Practices Toolkit* for suggestions on addressing the needs of a diverse classroom.

Homework Check

For a quick check of student understanding of key concepts, go over the following exercises:
Basic: 3, 6, 14, 22, 23
Average: 3, 6, 14, 22, 24
Advanced: 4, 10, 15, 22, 25

Extra Practice

- Student Edition, p. 899
- Chapter 2 Resource Book: Practice levels A, B, C, pp. 76–81

Practice Worksheet

An easily-readable reduced practice page (with answers) for this lesson can be found on p. 70E.

SKILL PRACTICE

A

1. **VOCABULARY** What is a *theorem*? How is it different from a *postulate*? **A theorem is a statement that can be proven; a postulate is a rule that is accepted without proof.**
2. ★ **WRITING** You can use theorems as reasons in a two-column proof. What other types of statements can you use as reasons in a two-column proof? Give examples. ***Sample answer:* Definitions, properties, postulates; Definition of a Right Angle, Transitive Property, Angle Addition Postulate**

EXAMPLE 1 on p. 112 for Exs. 3–4

3. **DEVELOPING PROOF** Copy and complete the proof.

GIVEN ▶ $AB = 5, BC = 6$
PROVE ▶ $AC = 11$

A 5 B 6 C

STATEMENTS	REASONS
1. $AB = 5, BC = 6$	1. Given
2. $AC = AB + BC$	2. Segment Addition Postulate
3. $AC = 5 + 6$	3. _?_ **Substitution Property of Equality**
4. _?_ **$AC = 11$**	4. Simplify.

4. ★ **MULTIPLE CHOICE** Which property listed is the reason for the last step in the proof? **A**

GIVEN ▶ $m\angle 1 = 59°, m\angle 2 = 59°$
PROVE ▶ $m\angle 1 = m\angle 2$

STATEMENTS	REASONS
1. $m\angle 1 = 59°, m\angle 2 = 59°$	1. Given
2. $59° = m\angle 2$	2. Symmetric Property of Equality
3. $m\angle 1 = m\angle 2$	3. _?_

Ⓐ Transitive Property of Equality Ⓑ Reflexive Property of Equality
Ⓒ Symmetric Property of Equality Ⓓ Distributive Property

EXAMPLES 2 and 3 on pp. 113–114 for Exs. 5–13

USING PROPERTIES **Use the property to copy and complete the statement.**

5. Reflexive Property of Congruence: _?_ $\cong \overline{SE}$ **$\overline{SE}$**
6. Symmetric Property of Congruence: If _?_ $\cong$ _?_, then $\angle RST \cong \angle JKL$. **$\angle JKL$, $\angle RST$**
7. Transitive Property of Congruence: If $\angle F \cong \angle J$ and _?_ $\cong$ _?_, then $\angle F \cong \angle L$. **$\angle J$, $\angle L$**

NAMING PROPERTIES **Name the property illustrated by the statement.**

8. If $\overline{DG} \cong \overline{CT}$, then $\overline{CT} \cong \overline{DG}$.
9. $\angle VWX \cong \angle VWX$
10. If $\overline{JK} \cong \overline{MN}$ and $\overline{MN} \cong \overline{XY}$, then $\overline{JK} \cong \overline{XY}$. **Transitive Property of Congruence**
11. $YZ = ZY$ **Reflexive Property of Equality**
12. ★ **MULTIPLE CHOICE** Name the property illustrated by the statement "If $\overline{CD} \cong \overline{MN}$, then $\overline{MN} \cong \overline{CD}$." **C**

Ⓐ Reflexive Property of Equality Ⓑ Symmetric Property of Equality
Ⓒ Symmetric Property of Congruence Ⓓ Transitive Property of Congruence

8. Symmetric Property of Congruence
9. Reflexive Property of Congruence

17.

Equation	Explanation	Reason
$\overline{QR} \cong \overline{PQ}, \overline{RS} \cong \overline{PQ}$	Write original statement.	Given
$\overline{QR} \cong \overline{RS}$	Both segments are congruent to $\overline{PQ}$.	Transitive Property of Congruent Segments
$2x + 5 = 10 - 3x$	Write an equation using the equal segment lengths.	Definition of congruent segments
$5x + 5 = 10$	Add $3x$ to each side.	Addition Property of Equality
$5x = 5$	Subtract 5 from each side.	Subtraction Property of Equality
$x = 1$	Divide each side by 5.	Division Property of Equality

13. **ERROR ANALYSIS** In the diagram below, $\overline{MN} \cong \overline{LQ}$ and $\overline{LQ} \cong \overline{PN}$. *Describe* and correct the error in the reasoning. **The reason is the Transitive Property of Congruence, not the Reflexive Property of Congruence.**

> Because $\overline{MN} \cong \overline{LQ}$ and $\overline{LQ} \cong \overline{PN}$, then $\overline{MN} \cong \overline{PN}$ by the Reflexive Property of Segment Congruence.

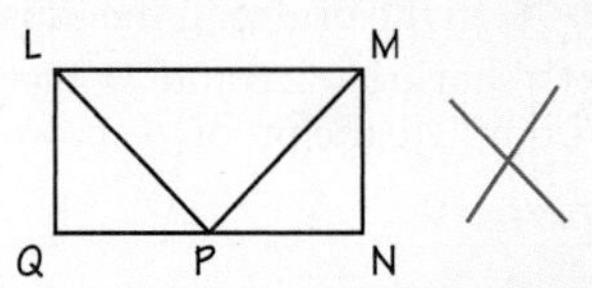

EXAMPLE 4 on p. 115 for Exs. 14–15

MAKING A SKETCH In Exercises 14 and 15, sketch a diagram that represents the given information. **14, 15. See margin.**

14. **CRYSTALS** The shape of a crystal can be represented by intersecting lines and planes. Suppose a crystal is *cubic*, which means it can be represented by six planes that intersect at right angles.

15. **BEACH VACATION** You are on vacation at the beach. Along the boardwalk, the bike rentals are halfway between your cottage and the kite shop. The snack shop is halfway between your cottage and the bike rentals. The arcade is halfway between the bike rentals and the kite shop.

16. **DEVELOPING PROOF** Copy and complete the proof.

GIVEN ▶ $RT = 5$, $RS = 5$, $\overline{RT} \cong \overline{TS}$

PROVE ▶ $\overline{RS} \cong \overline{TS}$

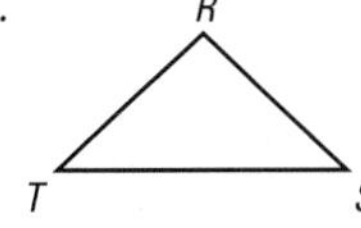

STATEMENTS	REASONS
1. $RT = 5$, $RS = 5$, $\overline{RT} \cong \overline{TS}$	1. _?_ **Given**
2. $RS = RT$	2. Transitive Property of Equality
3. $RT = TS$	3. Definition of congruent segments
4. $RS = TS$	4. Transitive Property of Equality
5. $\overline{RS} \cong \overline{TS}$	5. _?_ **Definition of congruent segments**

B **ALGEBRA** **Solve for x using the given information. *Explain* your steps.** **17, 18. See margin.**

17. **GIVEN** ▶ $\overline{QR} \cong \overline{PQ}$, $\overline{RS} \cong \overline{PQ}$

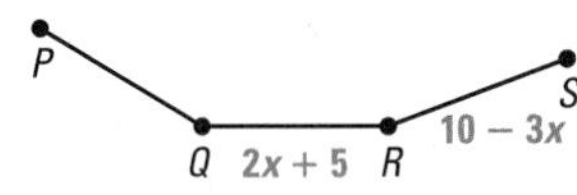

18. **GIVEN** ▶ $m\angle ABC = 90°$

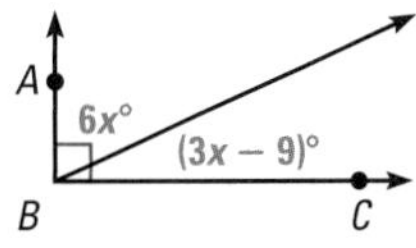

19. ★ **SHORT RESPONSE** *Explain* why writing a proof is an example of deductive reasoning, not inductive reasoning. **A proof is deductive reasoning because it uses facts, definitions, accepted properties, and laws of logic.**

C 20. **CHALLENGE** Point P is the midpoint of $\overline{MN}$ and point Q is the midpoint of $\overline{MP}$. Suppose $\overline{AB}$ is congruent to $\overline{MP}$, and $\overline{PN}$ has length x. Write the length of the segments in terms of x. *Explain*.

a. $\overline{AB}$ b. $\overline{MN}$ c. $\overline{MQ}$ d. $\overline{NQ}$

20a. ***x*. *Sample answer:*** $AB = MP$, and $MP = PN$, so $AB = PN$, by the Transitive Property of Equality. $PN = x$, therefore $AB = x$.

20b. **$2x$. Sample answer:** $MP = PN = x$, $MP + PN = MN$, therefore $MN = 2x$.

20c. **$\frac{x}{2}$. *Sample answer:*** $MQ = QP$, $MQ + QP = x$, $MQ + MQ = x$, $2MQ = x$, therefore $MQ = \frac{x}{2}$.

20d. **$\frac{3x}{2}$. *Sample answer:*** $NP = x$, $PQ = \frac{x}{2}$, $NP + PQ = NQ$, $x + \frac{x}{2} = NQ$, therefore $\frac{3x}{2} = NQ$.

Avoiding Common Errors

Exercises 8–12 Naming the property illustrated by the statement may be difficult for some students because they confuse the properties. Encourage them to use note cards with each property listed, then check the note cards as they do these exercises. They can also add these exercises as examples to their note cards.

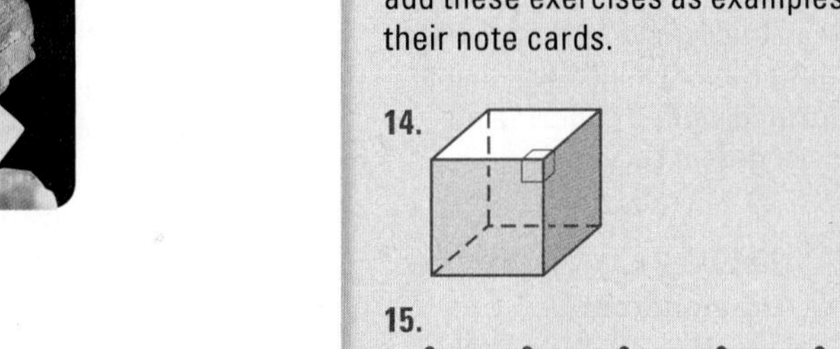

17. See p. 116.

18. See below.

18.

Equation	Explanation	Reason
$m\angle ABC = 90°$	Write original statement.	Given
$m\angle ABC = 6x° + (3x - 9)°$	Marked in diagram.	Angle Addition Postulate
$6x° + (3x - 9)° = 90°$	Replace $m\angle ABC$ with $6x° + (3x - 9)°$.	Substitution
$9x - 9 = 90$	Add $6x$ to $3x$.	Combine like terms.
$9x = 99$	Add 9 to each side.	Addition Property of Equality
$x = 11$	Divide each side by 9.	Division Property of Equality

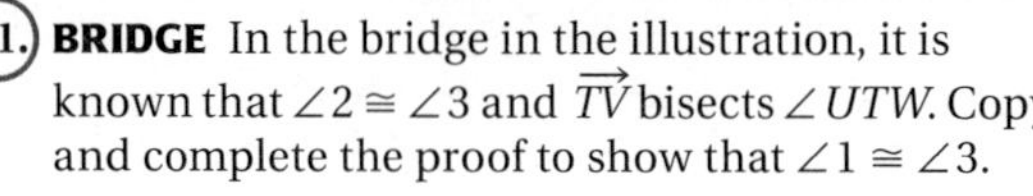

Problem Solving

Teaching Strategy

Exercises 22–26 Have students work with a partner to write the proofs and verify the correctness of each reason. Encourage students to think of alternate ways to prove the statements.

Mathematical Reasoning

Exercise 23 Students may want to include the definition of midpoint to do this proof. Remind them that a midpoint divides a segment into two congruent segments.

An **Animated Geometry** activity is available on-line for **Exercise 29**. This activity is also available on the **Power Presentations CD-ROM**.

23. Statements (Reasons)
1. $2AB = AC$ (Given)
2. $AC = AB + BC$ (Segment Addition Postulate)
3. $2AB = AB + BC$ (Transitive Property of Segment Equality)
4. $AB = BC$ (Subtraction Property of Equality)

24. Statements (Reasons)
1. $m\angle 1 + m\angle 2 = 180°$, $m\angle 1 = 62°$ (Given)
2. $62° + m\angle 2 = 180°$ (Substitution)
3. $m\angle 2 = 118°$ (Subtraction Property of Equality)

25. Statements (Reasons)
1. A is an angle. (Given)
2. $m\angle A = m\angle A$ (Reflexive Property of Equality)
3. $\angle A \cong \angle A$ (Definition of congruent angles)

26. Statements (Reasons)
1. $\overline{WX} \cong \overline{XY}$ and $\overline{XY} \cong \overline{YZ}$ (Given)
2. $WX = XY$ and $XY = YZ$ (Definition of congruent segments)
3. $WX = YZ$ (Transitive Property of Equality)
4. $\overline{WX} \cong \overline{YZ}$ (Definition of congruent segments)

21. Definition of angle bisector; Transitive Property of Congruence

21. **BRIDGE** In the bridge in the illustration, it is known that $\angle 2 \cong \angle 3$ and $\overrightarrow{TV}$ bisects $\angle UTW$. Copy and complete the proof to show that $\angle 1 \cong \angle 3$.

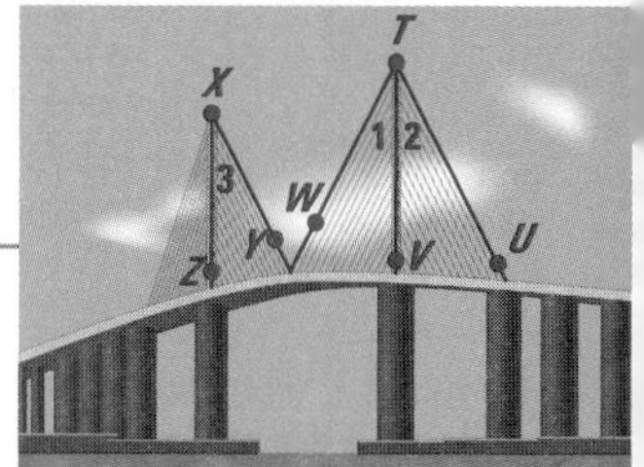

STATEMENTS	REASONS
1. $\overrightarrow{TV}$ bisects $\angle UTW$.	1. Given
2. $\angle 1 \cong \angle 2$	2. ?
3. $\angle 2 \cong \angle 3$	3. Given
4. $\angle 1 \cong \angle 3$	4. ?

@HomeTutor for problem solving help at classzone.com

EXAMPLE 3 on p. 114 for Ex. 22

22. **DEVELOPING PROOF** Write a complete proof by matching each statement with its corresponding reason.

GIVEN ▶ $\overrightarrow{QS}$ is an angle bisector of $\angle PQR$.

PROVE ▶ $m\angle PQS = \frac{1}{2} m\angle PQR$

STATEMENTS	REASONS
1. $\overrightarrow{QS}$ is an angle bisector of $\angle PQR$. D	A. Definition of angle bisector
2. $\angle PQS \cong \angle SQR$ A	B. Distributive Property
3. $m\angle PQS = m\angle SQR$ F	C. Angle Addition Postulate
4. $m\angle PQS + m\angle SQR = m\angle PQR$ C	D. Given
5. $m\angle PQS + m\angle PQS = m\angle PQR$ G	E. Division Property of Equality
6. $2 \cdot m\angle PQS = m\angle PQR$ B	F. Definition of congruent angles
7. $m\angle PQS = \frac{1}{2} m\angle PQR$ E	G. Substitution Property of Equality

@HomeTutor for problem solving help at classzone.com

PROOF **Use the given information and the diagram to prove the statement.** 23, 24. See margin.

23. **GIVEN** ▶ $2AB = AC$
PROVE ▶ $AB = BC$

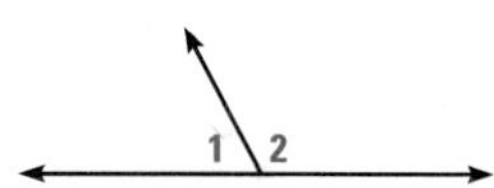

24. **GIVEN** ▶ $m\angle 1 + m\angle 2 = 180°$
$m\angle 1 = 62°$
PROVE ▶ $m\angle 2 = 118°$

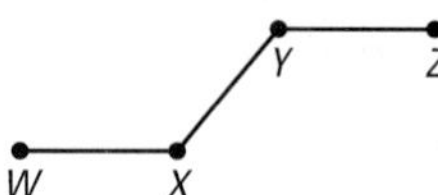

PROVING PROPERTIES **Prove the indicated property of congruence.** 25, 26. See margin.

25. Reflexive Property of Angle Congruence
GIVEN ▶ A is an angle.
PROVE ▶ $\angle A \cong \angle A$

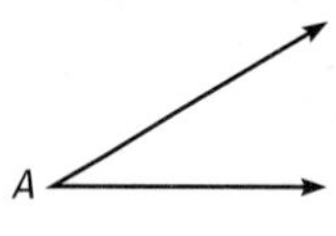

26. Transitive Property of Segment Congruence
GIVEN ▶ $\overline{WX} \cong \overline{XY}$ and $\overline{XY} \cong \overline{YZ}$
PROVE ▶ $\overline{WX} \cong \overline{YZ}$

W X Y Z

○ = WORKED-OUT SOLUTIONS on p. WS1 ★ = STANDARDIZED TEST PRACTICE

29a. R S M C F D — Restaurant Shoe Movie Cafe Florist Dry

29c. Statements (Reasons)
1. $RS = CF$, $SM = MC = FD$ (Given)
2. $RS + SM = RM$ (Segment Addition Postulate)
3. $CF + FD = CD$ (Segment Addition Postulate)
4. $CF + FD = RM$ (Substitution)
5. $RM = CD$ (Transitive Property of Equality)

27. Equiangular; Transitive Property of Congruent Angles implies $\angle 1 \cong \angle 3$, so all angle measures are the same.

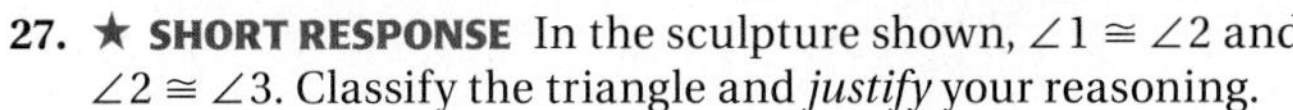

27. ★ **SHORT RESPONSE** In the sculpture shown, $\angle 1 \cong \angle 2$ and $\angle 2 \cong \angle 3$. Classify the triangle and *justify* your reasoning.

B

28. ★ **SHORT RESPONSE** You use a computer drawing program to create a line segment. You copy the segment and paste it. You copy the pasted segment and then paste it, and so on. How do you know all the line segments are congruent? **See margin.**

EXAMPLE 4 on p. 115 for Ex. 29

29. **MULTI-STEP PROBLEM** The distance from the restaurant to the shoe store is the same as the distance from the cafe to the florist. The distance from the shoe store to the movie theater is the same as the distance from the movie theater to the cafe, and from the florist to the dry cleaners.

28. ***Sample answer:*** The length of each segment is the same, therefore the segments are congruent.

Use the steps below to prove that the distance from the restaurant to the movie theater is the same as the distance from the cafe to the dry cleaners.

a. Draw and label a diagram to show the mathematical relationships. **See margin.**

b. State what is given and what is to be proved for the situation.

c. Write a two-column proof. **See margin.**

29b. Given: $RS = CF$, $SM = MC = FD$; Prove: $RM = CD$

Animated Geometry at classzone.com

C

30. **CHALLENGE** The distance from Springfield to Lakewood City is equal to the distance from Springfield to Bettsville. Janisburg is 50 miles farther from Springfield than Bettsville is. Moon Valley is 50 miles farther from Springfield than Lakewood City is.

a. Assume all five cities lie in a straight line. Draw a diagram that represents this situation. **See margin.**

b. Suppose you do not know that all five cities lie in a straight line. Draw a diagram that is different from the one in part (a) to represent the situation. **See margin.**

c. *Explain* the differences in the two diagrams. ***Sample answer:*** **In the second diagram Bettsville and Lakewood City are not in opposite directions from Springfield.**

MIXED REVIEW

PREVIEW Prepare for Lesson 2.7 in Exs. 31–33.

Given $m\angle 1$, find the measure of an angle that is complementary to $\angle 1$ and the measure of an angle that is supplementary to $\angle 1$. *(p. 35)*

31. $m\angle 1 = 47°$ **43°, 133°**

32. $m\angle 1 = 29°$ **61°, 151°**

33. $m\angle 1 = 89°$ **1°, 91°**

Solve the equation. Write a reason for each step. *(p. 105)* **34–36. See margin.**

34. $5x + 14 = -16$

35. $2x - 9 = 15 - 4x$

36. $x + 28 = -11 - 3x - 17$

34. Equation (Reason)

$5x + 14 = -16$ (Given)

$5x = -30$ (Subtraction Property of Equality)

$x = -6$ (Division Property of Equality)

35. Equation (Reason)

$2x - 9 = 15 - 4x$ (Given)

$6x - 9 = 15$ (Addition Property of Equality)

$6x = 24$ (Addition Property of Equality)

$x = 4$ (Division Property of Equality)

36. Equation (Reason)

$x + 28 = -11 - 3x - 17$ (Given)

$x + 28 = -3x - 28$ (Simplify.)

$4x + 28 = -28$ (Addition Property of Equality)

$4x = -56$ (Subtraction Property of Equality)

$x = -14$ (Division Property of Equality)

5 ASSESS AND RETEACH

Daily Homework Quiz

Transparency Available

1. Copy and complete the proof.

M A T H

Given: $MA = TH$

Prove: $MT = AH$

Statements (Reasons)

1. $MA = TH$ (?) **Given**
2. ? (Reflexive Prop. of Eq.) **$AT = AT$**
3. $MA + AT = AT + TH$ (?) **Addition Prop. of Eq.**
4. $MA + AT = MT$; $AT + TH = AH$ (?) **Segment Add. Post.**
5. ? (Substitution Prop. of Eq.) **$MT = AH$**

2. Use the given information to prove the statement.

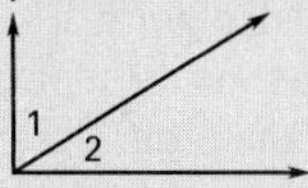

Given: $m\angle 1 + m\angle 2 = 90°$; $m\angle 1 = 59°$

Prove: $m\angle 2 = 31°$

Statements (Reasons)

1. $m\angle 1 + m\angle 2 = 90°$; $m\angle 1 = 59°$ (Given)

2. $m\angle 2 = 90° - m\angle 1$ (Subtraction Prop. of Eq.)

3. $m\angle 2 = 90° - 59°$ (Substitution Prop. of Eq.)

4. $m\angle 2 = 31°$ (Simplify.)

Available at **classzone.com**

Diagnosis/Remediation

- Practice A, B, C in Chapter 2 Resource Book, pp. 76–81
- Study Guide in Chapter 2 Resource Book, pp. 82–83
- Practice Workbook, pp. 37–39
- @HomeTutor

Challenge

Additional challenge is available in the Chapter 2 Resource Book, p. 86.

30a–b. See Additional Answers beginning on p. AA1.

Alternative Strategy

Example 4 on page 115 was solved by writing a two-column proof. The method shown on this page allows students to visualize a plan for the proof using a visual organizer or diagram, then write a proof using the verbal statements from the organizer.

Teaching Strategy

Emphasize that the deductions flow from the given information as sentences, and then the sentences are translated into mathematical language. The proofs may not appear the same as previous two-column proofs.

Mathematical Reasoning

Multiple Representations

Encourage students to use the method in this workshop to help them organize and write their proofs. They could also write statements and reasons on separate slips of paper and organize them like a flowchart with arrows connecting them.

Using ALTERNATIVE METHODS

Another Way to Solve Example 4, page 115

MULTIPLE REPRESENTATIONS The first step in writing any proof is to make a plan. A diagram or *visual organizer* can help you plan your proof. The steps of a proof must be in a logical order, but there may be more than one correct order.

PROBLEM

Standards

2.0 Students write geometric proofs, including proofs by contradiction.

SHOPPING MALL Walking down a hallway at the mall, you notice the music store is halfway between the food court and the shoe store. The shoe store is halfway between the music store and the bookstore. Prove that the distance between the entrances of the food court and music store is the same as the distance between the entrances of the shoe store and bookstore.

METHOD

Using a Visual Organizer

STEP 1 **Use** a visual organizer to map out your proof.

The music store is halfway between the food court and the shoe store. The shoe store is halfway between the music store and the bookstore.

Given information	M is halfway between F and S. ↓	S is halfway between M and B. ↓
Deductions from given information	M is the midpoint of $\overline{FS}$. So, $FM = MS$. ↘	S is the midpoint of $\overline{MB}$. So, $MS = SB$. ↙
Statement to prove	$FM = SB$	

STEP 2 **Write** a proof using the lengths of the segments.

GIVEN ▶ M is halfway between F and S.
S is halfway between M and B.

PROVE ▶ $FM = SB$

STATEMENTS	REASONS
1. M is halfway between F and S.	**1.** Given
2. S is halfway between M and B.	**2.** Given
3. M is the midpoint of $\overline{FS}$.	**3.** Definition of midpoint
4. S is the midpoint of $\overline{MB}$.	**4.** Definition of midpoint
5. $FM = MS$ and $MS = SB$	**5.** Definition of midpoint
6. $MS = MS$	**6.** Reflexive Property of Equality
7. $FM = SB$	**7.** Substitution Property of Equality

PRACTICE

1. **COMPARE PROOFS** *Compare* the proof on the previous page and the proof in Example 4 on page 115.
   a. How are the proofs the same? How are they different? **See margin.**
   b. Which proof is easier for you to understand? *Explain.* ***Sample answer:*** **Both the same; the logic is similar.**
2. **REASONING** Below is a proof of the Transitive Property of Angle Congruence. What is another reason you could give for Statement 3? *Explain.* **substitution; replace $m\angle B$ with $m\angle C$.**

GIVEN ▶ $\angle A \cong \angle B$ and $\angle B \cong \angle C$

PROVE ▶ $\angle A \cong \angle C$

STATEMENTS	REASONS
1. $\angle A \cong \angle B$, $\angle B \cong \angle C$	1. Given
2. $m\angle A = m\angle B$, $m\angle B = m\angle C$	2. Definition of congruent angles
3. $m\angle A = m\angle C$	3. Transitive Property of Equality
4. $\angle A \cong \angle C$	4. Definition of congruent angles

3. **SHOPPING MALL** You are at the same mall as on page 120 and you notice that the bookstore is halfway between the shoe store and the toy store. Draw a diagram or make a visual organizer, then write a proof to show that the distance from the entrances of the food court and music store is the same as the distance from the entrances of the book store and toy store. **See margin.**

4. **WINDOW DESIGN** The entrance to the mall has a decorative window above the main doors as shown. The colored dividers form congruent angles. Draw a diagram or make a visual organizer, then write a proof to show that the angle measure between the red dividers is half the measure of the angle between the blue dividers. **See margin.**

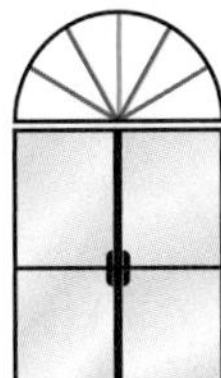

5. **COMPARE PROOFS** Below is a proof of the Symmetric Property of Segment Congruence.

GIVEN ▶ $\overline{DE} \cong \overline{FG}$

PROVE ▶ $\overline{FG} \cong \overline{DE}$

D •———• E
F •———• G

STATEMENTS	REASONS
1. $\overline{DE} \cong \overline{FG}$	1. Given
2. $DE = FG$	2. Definition of congruent segments
3. $FG = DE$	3. Symmetric Property of Equality
4. $\overline{FG} \cong \overline{DE}$	4. Definition of congruent segments

   a. *Compare* this proof to the proof of the Symmetric Property of Angle Congruence in the Concept Summary on page 114. What makes the proofs different? *Explain.* **See margin.**
   b. *Explain* why Statement 2 above cannot be $\overline{FG} \cong \overline{DE}$. ***Sample answer:*** **If $\overline{FG} \cong \overline{DE}$ is the second statement, the reason would have to be Symmetric Property of Segment Congruence and you cannot use a property that you are proving as a reason in the proof.**

Avoiding Common Errors

Doing Exercise 1 carefully can help students understand the proof process better and help avoid some common errors in how one step flows from the next.

Reading Strategy

For Exercise 3, have students who draw diagrams or make visual organizers point to corresponding parts of verbal information in the exercise and in the diagram or organizer.

1a. *Sample answer:* The logic used is similar; one uses segment length and the other uses segment congruence.

3, 4. See Additional Answers beginning on p. AA1.

5a. *Sample answer:* The proof on page 114 involves angle congruence while this one involves segment congruence.

1 PLAN AND PREPARE

Explore the Concept

- Students will use a graphing calculator or computer to discover the relationship between vertical angles.
- This activity leads into the study of congruent vertical angles in Example 3 in Lesson 2.7.

Materials

Each student or group of students will need a graphing calculator or computer.

Recommended Time

Work activity: 15 min

Discuss results: 5 min

Grouping

Students can work individually or in groups of 2–4. If students work in groups, they can alternate doing the explorations.

2 TEACH

Alternative Strategy

If software is not available, ask students to draw two intersecting lines for each exploration and then use protractors to measure the angles.

Key Discovery

Vertical angles are congruent.

2.7 Angles and Intersecting Lines

MATERIALS • graphing calculator or computer

Standards

Prepare for 13.0 Students prove relationships between angles in polygons by *using properties of complementary, supplementary, vertical,* and exterior angles.

QUESTION **What is the relationship between the measures of the angles formed by intersecting lines?**

You can use geometry drawing software to investigate the measures of angles formed when lines intersect.

EXPLORE 1 **Measure linear pairs formed by intersecting lines**

STEP 1 ***Draw two intersecting lines*** Draw and label $\overleftrightarrow{AB}$. Draw and label $\overleftrightarrow{CD}$ so that it intersects $\overleftrightarrow{AB}$. Draw and label the point of intersection E.

STEP 2

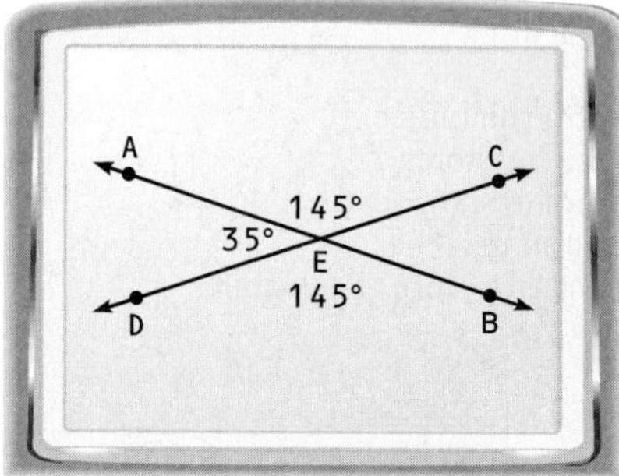

Measure angles Measure $\angle AEC$, $\angle AED$, and $\angle DEB$. Move point C to change the angles.

STEP 3

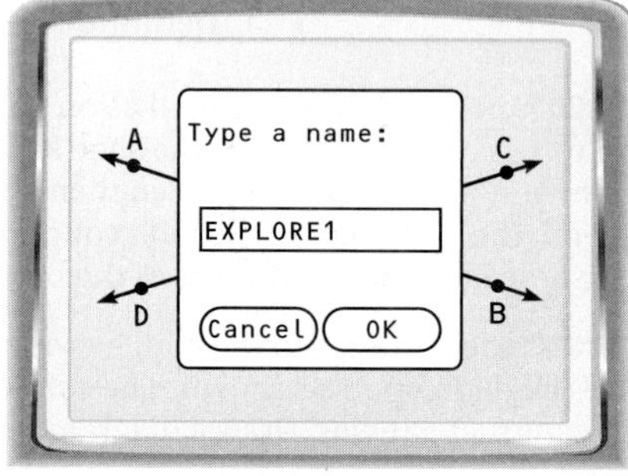

Save Save as "EXPLORE1" by choosing Save from the F1 menu and typing the name.

DRAW CONCLUSIONS **Use your observations to complete these exercises**

1. *Describe* the relationship between $\angle AEC$ and $\angle AED$. **linear pair, supplementary angles**
2. *Describe* the relationship between $\angle AED$ and $\angle DEB$. **linear pair, supplementary angles**
3. What do you notice about $\angle AEC$ and $\angle DEB$? $m\angle AEC = m\angle DEB$
4. In Explore 1, what happens when you move C to a different position? Do the angle relationships stay the same? Make a conjecture about two angles supplementary to the same angle. **Angle measures change; yes; two angles supplementary to the same angle are congruent.**
5. Do you think your conjecture will be true for supplementary angles that are not adjacent? *Explain.* **No. *Sample answer:* When supplementary angles are not adjacent, only one angle can change as point *C* changes.**

@HomeTutor
classzone.com
Keystrokes

EXPLORE 2 Measure complementary angles

STEP 1 ***Draw two perpendicular lines*** Draw and label $\overleftrightarrow{AB}$. Draw point E on $\overleftrightarrow{AB}$. Draw and label $\overleftrightarrow{EC} \perp \overleftrightarrow{AB}$. Draw and label point D on $\overleftrightarrow{EC}$ so that E is between C and D as shown in Step 2.

STEP 2

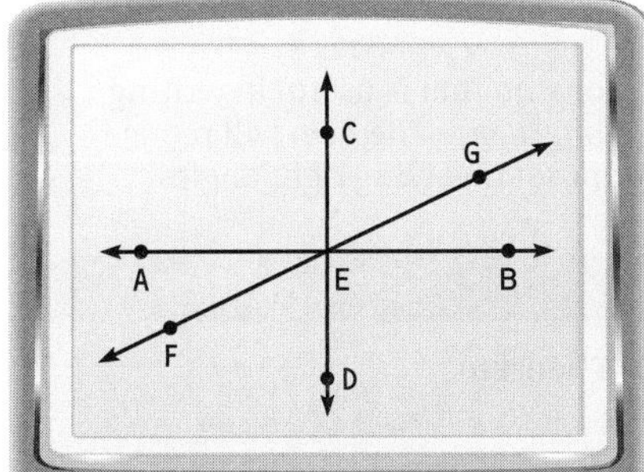

Draw another line Draw and label $\overleftrightarrow{EG}$ so that G is in the interior of $\angle CEB$. Draw point F on $\overleftrightarrow{EG}$ as shown. Save as "EXPLORE2".

STEP 3

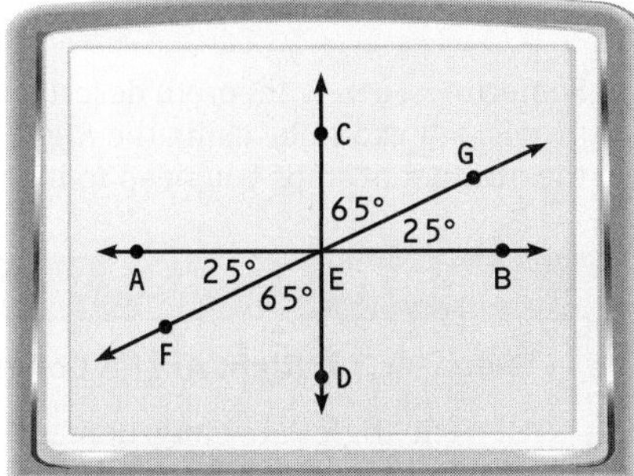

Measure angles Measure $\angle AEF$, $\angle FED$, $\angle CEG$, and $\angle GEB$. Move point G to change the angles.

EXPLORE 3 Measure vertical angles formed by intersecting lines

STEP 1 ***Draw two intersecting lines*** Draw and label $\overleftrightarrow{AB}$. Draw and label $\overleftrightarrow{CD}$ so that it intersects $\overleftrightarrow{AB}$. Draw and label the point of intersection E.

STEP 2 ***Measure angles*** Measure $\angle AEC$, $\angle AED$, $\angle BEC$, and $\angle DEB$. Move point C to change the angles. Save as "EXPLORE3".

DRAW CONCLUSIONS Use your observations to complete these exercises

6. In Explore 2, does the angle relationship stay the same as you move G? **yes**
7. In Explore 2, make a conjecture about the relationship between $\angle CEG$ and $\angle GEB$. Write your conjecture in if-then form. **They are complementary; if $\angle CEB$ is a right angle, then $\angle CEG$ and $\angle GEB$ are complementary.**
8. In Explore 3, the intersecting lines form two pairs of vertical angles. Make a conjecture about the relationship between any two vertical angles. Write your conjecture in if-then form. **The vertical angles are congruent; if two lines intersect, then the vertical angles formed are congruent.**
9. Name the pairs of vertical angles in Explore 2. Use this drawing to test your conjecture from Exercise 8. **$\angle AEC$ and $\angle BED$, $\angle AEF$ and $\angle BEG$, $\angle DEF$ and $\angle CEG$, $\angle CEB$ and $\angle DEA$, $\angle AEG$ and $\angle FEB$, $\angle GED$ and $\angle CEF$**

3 ASSESS AND RETEACH

1. Given that lines m and n intersect to form an angle of 82°, find the measures of the other three angles formed by the lines. **82°, 98°, 98°**
2. If all four angles formed by two intersecting lines are congruent, what can be said about the lines? **They are perpendicular.**

1 PLAN AND PREPARE

Warm-Up Exercises

Transparency Available

Give a reason for each statement.

1. If $m\angle 1 = 90°$ and $m\angle 2 = 90°$, then $m\angle 1 = m\angle 2$ **(Transitive Prop. of Eq.)**
2. If $\overline{AB} \perp \overline{BC}$, then $\angle ABC$ is a right angle. **(Def. of perpendicular)**
3. If $\overline{FG} \cong \overline{RS}$, then $FG = RS$. **(Def. of segment congruence)**

Notetaking Guide

Transparency Available

Promotes interactive learning and notetaking skills, pp. 54–57.

Pacing

Basic: 2 days
Average: 2 days
Advanced: 2 days
Block: 1 block
- See *Teaching Guide/Lesson Plan.*

2 FOCUS AND MOTIVATE

Essential Question

Big Idea 3, p. 71

What is the relationship between vertical angles, between two angles that are supplementary to the same angle, and between two angles that are complementary to the same angle? **Tell students they will learn how to answer this question by proving theorems about special pairs of angles.**

2.7 Prove Angle Pair Relationships

Before You identified relationships between pairs of angles.
Now You will use properties of special pairs of angles.
Why? So you can describe angles found in a home, as in Ex. 44.

Key Vocabulary
- **complementary angles,** *p. 35*
- **supplementary angles,** *p. 35*
- **linear pair,** *p. 37*
- **vertical angles,** *p. 37*

Sometimes, a new theorem describes a relationship that is useful in writing proofs. For example, using the *Right Angles Congruence Theorem* will reduce the number of steps you need to include in a proof involving right angles.

THEOREM *For Your Notebook*

THEOREM 2.3 Right Angles Congruence Theorem

All right angles are congruent.

Proof: below

PROOF Right Angles Congruence Theorem

WRITE PROOFS
When you prove a theorem, write the hypothesis of the theorem as the GIVEN statement. The conclusion is what you must PROVE.

GIVEN ▶ $\angle 1$ and $\angle 2$ are right angles.
PROVE ▶ $\angle 1 \cong \angle 2$

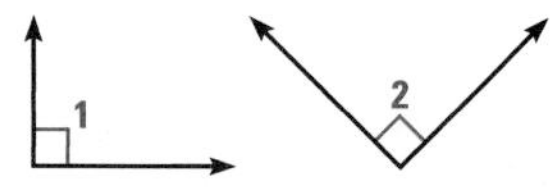

STATEMENTS	REASONS
1. $\angle 1$ and $\angle 2$ are right angles.	1. Given
2. $m\angle 1 = 90°$, $m\angle 2 = 90°$	2. Definition of right angle
3. $m\angle 1 = m\angle 2$	3. Transitive Property of Equality
4. $\angle 1 \cong \angle 2$	4. Definition of congruent angles

EXAMPLE 1 Use right angle congruence

Write a proof.

AVOID ERRORS
The given information in Example 1 is about perpendicular lines. You must then use deductive reasoning to show the angles are right angles.

GIVEN ▶ $\overline{AB} \perp \overline{BC}$, $\overline{DC} \perp \overline{BC}$
PROVE ▶ $\angle B \cong \angle C$

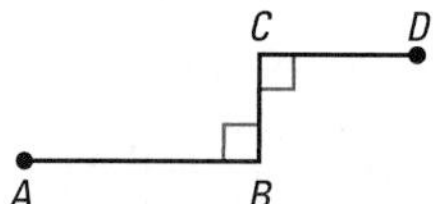

STATEMENTS	REASONS
1. $\overline{AB} \perp \overline{BC}$, $\overline{DC} \perp \overline{BC}$	1. Given
2. $\angle B$ and $\angle C$ are right angles.	2. Definition of perpendicular lines
3. $\angle B \cong \angle C$	3. Right Angles Congruence Theorem

Resource Planning Guide

Chapter Resource Book
- Teaching Guide/Lesson Plan (pp. 87–88)
- Practice levels A, B, C (pp. 90–95)
- Study Guide (pp. 96–97)
- Catch-up for Absent Students (p. 98)
- Problem Solving Workshop (p. 99)
- Challenge (p. 100)

Workbooks
- Notetaking Guide (pp. 54–57)
- Practice Workbook (pp. 40–42)

Teaching Options
- **Power Presentations CD-ROM** provides dynamic electronic teaching resources for the classroom.
- **Activity Generator CD-ROM** provides editable activities for all ability levels.

Interactive Technology
- Easy Planner
- Power Presentations CD-ROM
- Activity Generator CD-ROM
- Animated Geometry
- Test Generator CD-ROM
- Online Quiz
- eWorkbook
- eEdition
- @HomeTutor

Resources for English Learners
- Quick Reference for English Learners
- Spanish Study Guide
- Multi-Language Visual Glossary
- Student Resources in Spanish

See also the *Geometry Toolkit* for more strategies for meeting individual needs.

Standards

1.0 Students demonstrate understanding by identifying and giving examples of undefined terms, **axioms, theorems,** and inductive **and deductive reasoning.**

2.0 Students write geometric proofs, including proofs by contradiction.

Prepare for 13.0 Students prove relationships between angles in polygons by *using properties of complementary, supplementary, vertical,* and exterior angles.

THEOREMS *For Your Notebook*

THEOREM 2.4 Congruent Supplements Theorem

If two angles are supplementary to the same angle (or to congruent angles), then they are congruent.

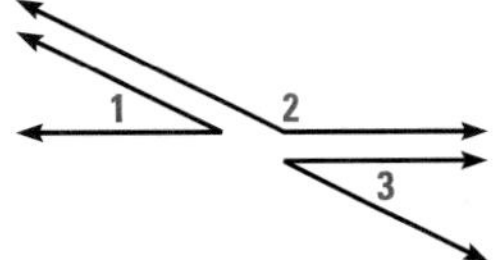

If $\angle 1$ and $\angle 2$ are supplementary and $\angle 3$ and $\angle 2$ are supplementary, then $\angle 1 \cong \angle 3$.

Proof: Example 2, below; Ex. 36, p. 129

THEOREM 2.5 Congruent Complements Theorem

If two angles are complementary to the same angle (or to congruent angles), then they are congruent.

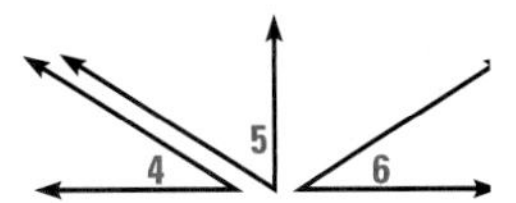

If $\angle 4$ and $\angle 5$ are complementary and $\angle 6$ and $\angle 5$ are complementary, then $\angle 4 \cong \angle 6$.

Proof: Ex. 37, p. 129; Ex. 41, p. 130

To prove Theorem 2.4, you must prove two cases: one with angles supplementary to the same angle and one with angles supplementary to congruent angles. The proof of Theorem 2.5 also requires two cases.

EXAMPLE 2 Prove a case of Congruent Supplements Theorem

Prove that two angles supplementary to the same angle are congruent.

GIVEN ▶ $\angle 1$ and $\angle 2$ are supplements.
$\angle 3$ and $\angle 2$ are supplements.

PROVE ▶ $\angle 1 \cong \angle 3$

STATEMENTS	REASONS
1. $\angle 1$ and $\angle 2$ are supplements. $\angle 3$ and $\angle 2$ are supplements.	**1.** Given
2. $m\angle 1 + m\angle 2 = 180°$ $m\angle 3 + m\angle 2 = 180°$	**2.** Definition of supplementary angles
3. $m\angle 1 + m\angle 2 = m\angle 3 + m\angle 2$	**3.** Transitive Property of Equality
4. $m\angle 1 = m\angle 3$	**4.** Subtraction Property of Equality
5. $\angle 1 \cong \angle 3$	**5.** Definition of congruent angles

Animated Geometry at classzone.com

✓ GUIDED PRACTICE for Examples 1 and 2

1. How many steps do you save in the proof in Example 1 by using the *Right Angles Congruence Theorem*? **2 steps**
2. Draw a diagram and write GIVEN and PROVE statements for a proof of each case of the *Congruent Complements Theorem*. **See margin.**

Motivating the Lesson

Are there pairs of angles in architectural structures that you can be sure are congruent without making measurements? The theorems in this lesson will help you answer this question.

3 TEACH

Extra Example 1

Write a proof.

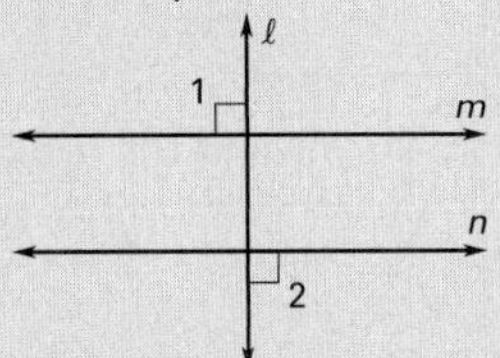

Given: $\ell \perp m, \ell \perp n$

Prove: $\angle 1 \cong \angle 2$

Statements (Reasons)

1. $\ell \perp m; \ell \perp n$ **(Given)**

2. $\angle 1$ **and** $\angle 2$ **are right angles. (Def. of perpendicular)**

3. $\angle 1 \cong \angle 2$ **(Right Angles Congruence Thm.)**

Extra Example 2

Write a proof.

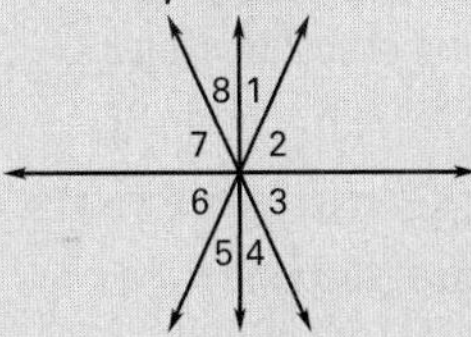

Given: $\angle 1$ and $\angle 3$ are complements; $\angle 3$ and $\angle 5$ are complements.

Prove: $\angle 1 \cong \angle 5$

Statements (Reasons)

1. $\angle 1$ **and** $\angle 3$ **are complements;** $\angle 3$ **and** $\angle 5$ **are complements. (Given)**

2. $\angle 1 \cong \angle 5$ **(Congruent Complements Thm.)**

2. See Additional Answers beginning on p. AA1.

Differentiated Instruction

Below Level Use cardboard models of angles to illustrate the Congruent Supplements Theorem. Do the same for the Congruent Complements Theorem.

See also the *Geometry Toolkit* for more strategies.

INTERSECTING LINES When two lines intersect, pairs of vertical angles and linear pairs are formed. The relationship that you used in Lesson 1.5 for linear pairs is formally stated below as the *Linear Pair Postulate*. This postulate is used in the proof of the *Vertical Angles Congruence Theorem*.

POSTULATE *For Your Notebook*

POSTULATE 12 Linear Pair Postulate

If two angles form a linear pair, then they are supplementary.

$\angle 1$ and $\angle 2$ form a linear pair, so $\angle 1$ and $\angle 2$ are supplementary and $m\angle 1 + m\angle 2 = 180°$.

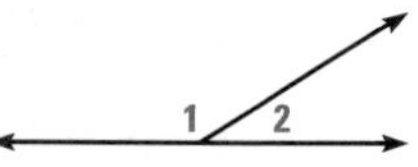

THEOREM *For Your Notebook*

THEOREM 2.6 Vertical Angles Congruence Theorem

Vertical angles are congruent.

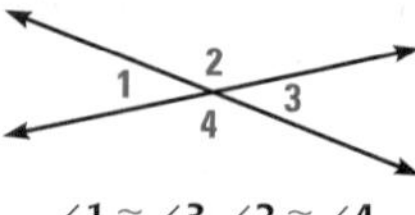

$\angle 1 \cong \angle 3$, $\angle 2 \cong \angle 4$

Proof: Example 3, below

EXAMPLE 3 Prove the Vertical Angles Congruence Theorem

Prove vertical angles are congruent.

GIVEN ▶ $\angle 5$ and $\angle 7$ are vertical angles.

PROVE ▶ $\angle 5 \cong \angle 7$

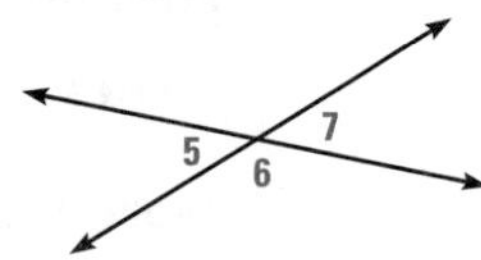

STATEMENTS	REASONS
1. $\angle 5$ and $\angle 7$ are vertical angles.	1. Given
2. $\angle 5$ and $\angle 6$ are a linear pair. $\angle 6$ and $\angle 7$ are a linear pair.	2. Definition of linear pair, as shown in the diagram
3. $\angle 5$ and $\angle 6$ are supplementary. $\angle 6$ and $\angle 7$ are supplementary.	3. Linear Pair Postulate
4. $\angle 5 \cong \angle 7$	4. Congruent Supplements Theorem

USE A DIAGRAM
You can use information labeled in a diagram in your proof.

GUIDED PRACTICE for Example 3

In Exercises 3–5, use the diagram.

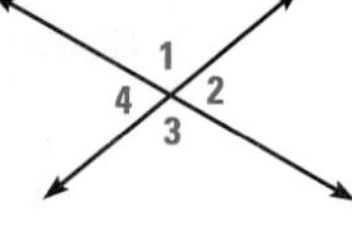

3. If $m\angle 1 = 112°$, find $m\angle 2$, $m\angle 3$, and $m\angle 4$. **68°, 112°, 68°**
4. If $m\angle 2 = 67°$, find $m\angle 1$, $m\angle 3$, and $m\angle 4$. **113°, 113°, 67°**
5. If $m\angle 4 = 71°$, find $m\angle 1$, $m\angle 2$, and $m\angle 3$. **109°, 71°, 109°**
6. Which previously proven theorem is used in Example 3 as a reason? **Congruent Supplements Theorem**

An **Animated Geometry** activity is available on-line for **Example 2**. This activity is also available on the **Power Presentations CD-ROM**.

Extra Example 3

Write a proof.

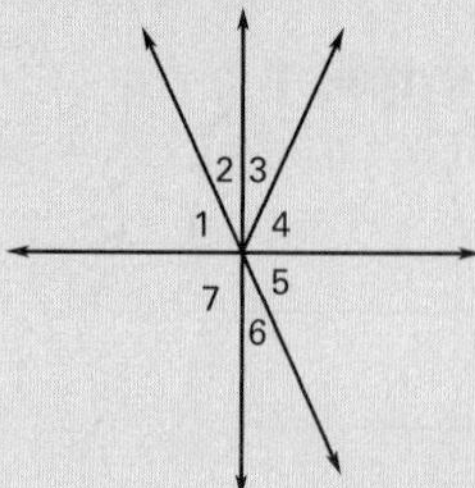

Given: $\angle 2 \cong \angle 3$

Prove: $\angle 3 \cong \angle 6$

Statements (Reasons)

1. **$\angle 2 \cong \angle 3$ (Given)**
2. **$\angle 2 \cong \angle 6$ (Vertical Angles Congruence Thm.)**
3. **$\angle 3 \cong \angle 6$ (Transitive Prop. of Congruence)**

Key Question to Ask for Example 3

- What law of logic is used to proceed from step 2 to step 3? **Law of Detachment**

Avoiding Common Errors

The converse of the Linear Pair Postulate is not true, although sometimes students make this error. Ask students to demonstrate this fact.

Mathematical Reasoning

Some students may think that the proof of the Vertical Angles Congruence Theorem is incomplete because we did not go on to prove that the other set of vertical angles are congruent. Discuss why it is not necessary to consider this as a separate case.

Differentiated Instruction

Auditory Learners Have students work with a partner to answer **Guided Practice Exercises 3–6**. In addition to finding the angle measures, have students tell their partner which theorem or postulate they applied when finding each angle measure.

See also the *Geometry Toolkit* for more strategies.

★ **EXAMPLE 4** **Standardized Test Practice**

ELIMINATE CHOICES
Look for angle pair relationships in the diagram. The angles in the diagram are supplementary, not complementary or congruent, so eliminate choices A and C.

Which equation can be used to find x?

Ⓐ $32 + (3x + 1) = 90$

Ⓑ $32 + (3x + 1) = 180$

Ⓒ $32 = 3x + 1$

Ⓓ $3x + 1 = 212$

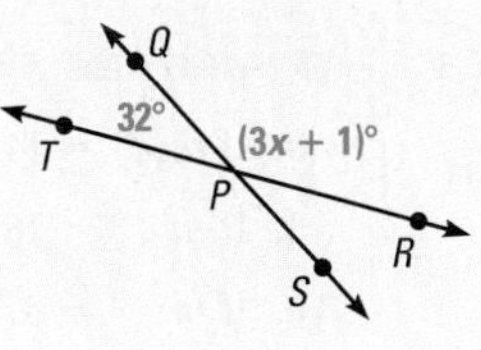

Solution

Because $\angle TPQ$ and $\angle QPR$ form a linear pair, the sum of their measures is 180°.

▸ The correct answer is B. Ⓐ Ⓑ Ⓒ Ⓓ

GUIDED PRACTICE for Example 4

Use the diagram in Example 4.

7. Solve for x. **49**

8. Find $m\angle TPS$. **148°**

2.7 EXERCISES

HOMEWORK KEY
○ = **WORKED-OUT SOLUTIONS** on p. WS3 for Exs. 5, 13, and 39
★ = **STANDARDIZED TEST PRACTICE** Exs. 2, 7, 16, 30, and 45

SKILL PRACTICE

A

1. **VOCABULARY** Copy and complete: If two lines intersect at a point, then the _?_ angles formed by the intersecting lines are congruent. **vertical**

2. ★ **WRITING** *Describe* the relationship between the angle measures of complementary angles, supplementary angles, vertical angles, and linear pairs. **The sum is 90°, the sum is 180°, same, the sum is 180°.**

EXAMPLES 1 and 2 on pp. 124–125 for Exs. 3–7

IDENTIFY ANGLES **Identify the pair(s) of congruent angles in the figures below. *Explain* how you know they are congruent.**

3. (N, P, Q, M, S, R; 50°, 50°)
$\angle MSN$ and $\angle PSQ$, $\angle NSP$ and $\angle QSR$, $\angle MSP$ and $\angle PSR$; indicated in diagram, Congruent Complements Theorem, Right Angles Congruence Theorem

4. $\angle ABC$ is supplementary to $\angle CBD$. $\angle CBD$ is supplementary to $\angle DEF$.

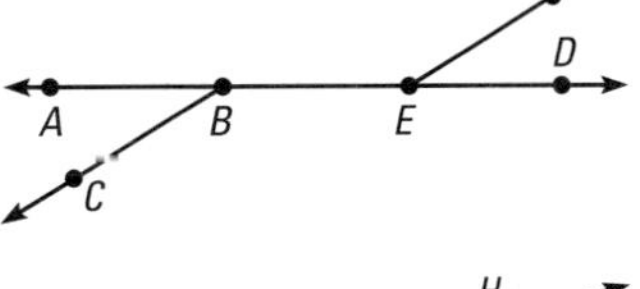

4. $\angle ABC$ and $\angle DEF$, $\angle CBD$ and $\angle FEB$; Congruent Supplements Theorem

5.

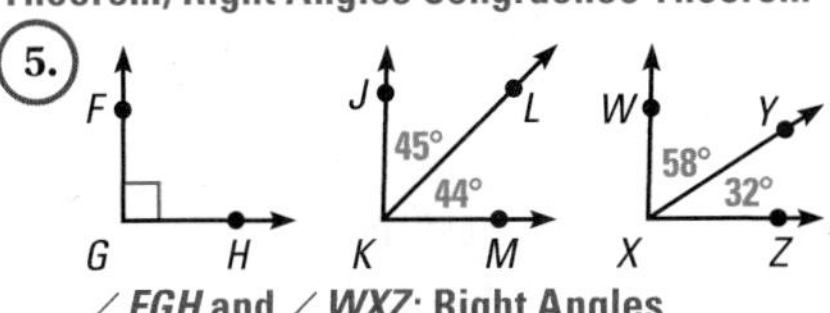

$\angle FGH$ and $\angle WXZ$; Right Angles Congruence Theorem

6.

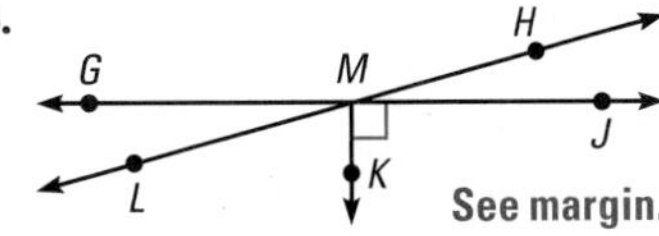

See margin.

Extra Example 4

Which equation can be used to find x? **A**

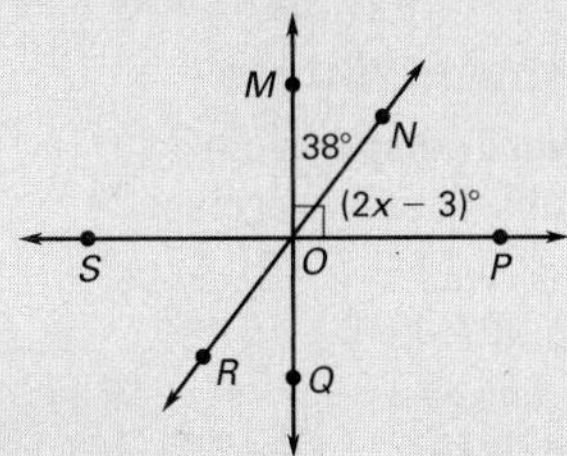

Ⓐ $38 + (2x - 3) = 90$

Ⓑ $38 + (2x - 3) = 180$

Ⓒ $38 = (2x - 3)$

Ⓓ $(2x - 3) = 128$

Key Question to Ask for Example 4

- What is the relationship between $\angle TPQ$ and $\angle QPR$? **They are supplementary.**

Closing the Lesson

Have students summarize the major points of the lesson and answer the Essential Question: What is the relationship between vertical angles, between two angles that are supplementary to the same angle, and between two angles that are complementary to the same angle?

- **All right angles are congruent.**
- **Supplements of congruent angles or the same angle are congruent.**
- **Complements of congruent angles or the same angle are congruent.**
- **Vertical angles are congruent.**

Vertical angles are congruent. Supplements of the same angle or of congruent angles are congruent, and complements of the same angle or of congruent angles are congruent.

6. $\angle GML$ and $\angle HMJ$, $\angle GMH$ and $\angle LMJ$, $\angle JMK$ and $\angle GMK$; Vertical Angles Congruence Theorem, Vertical Angles Congruence Theorem, Right Angles Congruence Theorem

4 PRACTICE AND APPLY

Assignment Guide

Answer Transparencies available for all exercises

Basic:
Day 1: pp. 127–131
Exs. 1–7, 36–39, 49–53
Day 2: pp. 127–131
Exs. 8–26, 40

Average:
Day 1: pp. 127–131
Exs. 1–7, 36–39, 49–53
Day 2: pp. 127–131
Exs. 9–15 odd, 16, 17–29 odd, 30, 40–45

Advanced:
Day 1: pp. 127–131
Exs. 1–7, 36–39, 43, 44, 49–53
Day 2: pp. 127–131
Exs. 10, 11, 14–30 even, 31–35*, 40–42, 45–48*

Block:
pp. 127–131
Exs. 1–7, 9–15 odd, 16, 17–29 odd, 30, 36–45, 49–53

Differentiated Instruction

See *Geometry Best Practices Toolkit* for suggestions on addressing the needs of a diverse classroom.

Homework Check

For a quick check of student understanding of key concepts, go over the following exercises:

Basic: 3, 8, 12, 18, 36
Average: 4, 10, 13, 20, 38
Advanced: 6, 11, 14, 22, 40

Extra Practice

- Student Edition, p. 899
- Chapter 2 Resource Book: Practice levels A, B, C, pp. 90–95

Practice Worksheet

An easily-readable reduced practice page (with answers) for this lesson can be found on p. 70F.

---

7. ★ **SHORT RESPONSE** The x-axis and y-axis in a coordinate plane are perpendicular to each other. The axes form four angles. Are the four angles congruent right angles? *Explain.* **Yes; perpendicular lines form right angles, and all right angles are congruent.**

EXAMPLE 3 on p. 126 for Exs. 8–11

FINDING ANGLE MEASURES **In Exercises 8–11, use the diagram at the right.**

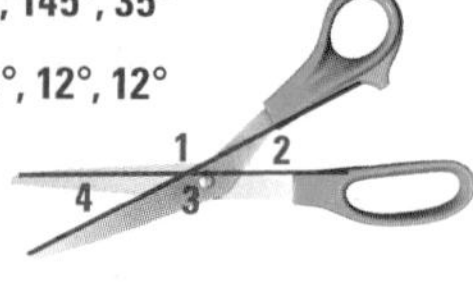

8. If $m\angle 1 = 145°$, find $m\angle 2$, $m\angle 3$, and $m\angle 4$. **35°, 145°, 35°**
9. If $m\angle 3 = 168°$, find $m\angle 1$, $m\angle 2$, and $m\angle 4$. **168°, 12°, 12°**
10. If $m\angle 4 = 37°$, find $m\angle 1$, $m\angle 2$, and $m\angle 3$. **143°, 37°, 143°**
11. If $m\angle 2 = 62°$, find $m\angle 1$, $m\angle 3$, and $m\angle 4$. **118°, 118°, 62°**

EXAMPLE 4 on p. 127 for Exs. 12–14

ALGEBRA **Find the values of x and y.**

12. 13.

12. **$x = 11$, $y = 17$**
13. **$x = 13$, $y = 20$**
14. $(10x - 4)°$, $16y°$, $(18y - 18)°$, $6(x + 2)°$ **$x = 4$, $y = 9$**

15. **ERROR ANALYSIS** *Describe* the error in stating that $\angle 1 \cong \angle 4$ and $\angle 2 \cong \angle 3$.
Sample answer: **It was assumed that $\angle 1$ and $\angle 3$, and $\angle 2$ and $\angle 4$ are linear pairs, but they are not; $\angle 1$ and $\angle 4$, and $\angle 2$ and $\angle 3$ are not vertical angles and are not congruent.**

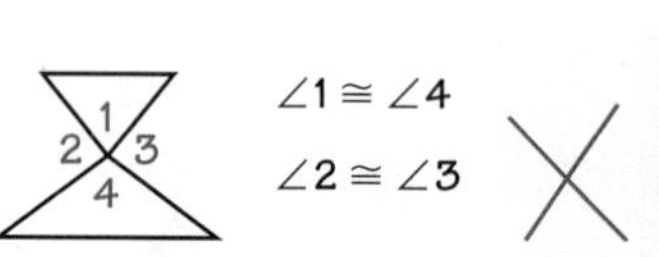

16. ★ **MULTIPLE CHOICE** In a figure, $\angle A$ and $\angle D$ are complementary angles and $m\angle A = 4x°$. Which expression can be used to find $m\angle D$? **D**

Ⓐ $(4x + 90)°$ Ⓑ $(180 - 4x)°$ Ⓒ $(180 + 4x)°$ Ⓓ $(90 - 4x)°$

FINDING ANGLE MEASURES **In Exercises 17–21, copy and complete the statement given that $m\angle FHE = m\angle BHG = m\angle AHF = 90°$.**

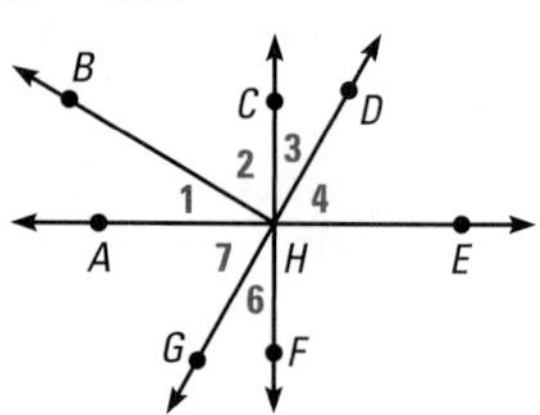

17. If $m\angle 3 = 30°$, then $m\angle 6 =$ _?_. **30°**
18. If $m\angle BHF = 115°$, then $m\angle 3 =$ _?_. **25°**
19. If $m\angle 6 = 27°$, then $m\angle 1 =$ _?_. **27°**
20. If $m\angle DHF = 133°$, then $m\angle CHG =$ _?_. **133°**
21. If $m\angle 3 = 32°$, then $m\angle 2 =$ _?_. **58°**

B **ANALYZING STATEMENTS** **Two lines that are not perpendicular intersect such that $\angle 1$ and $\angle 2$ are a linear pair, $\angle 1$ and $\angle 4$ are a linear pair, and $\angle 1$ and $\angle 3$ are vertical angles. Tell whether the statement is true or false.**

22. $\angle 1 \cong \angle 2$ **false**
23. $\angle 1 \cong \angle 3$ **true**
24. $\angle 1 \cong \angle 4$ **false**
25. $\angle 3 \cong \angle 2$ **false**
26. $\angle 2 \cong \angle 4$ **true**
27. $m\angle 3 + m\angle 4 = 180°$ **true**

ALGEBRA **Find the measure of each angle in the diagram.**

28.

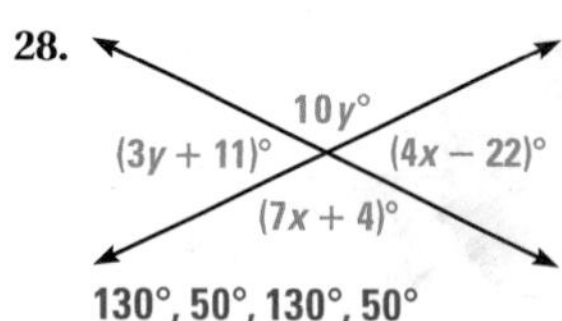

130°, 50°, 130°, 50°

29.

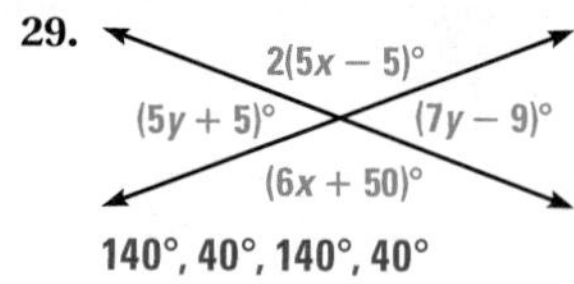

140°, 40°, 140°, 40°

◯ = WORKED-OUT SOLUTIONS on p. WS1   ★ = STANDARDIZED TEST PRACTICE

30. ★ **OPEN-ENDED MATH** In the diagram, $m\angle CBY = 80°$ and $\overleftrightarrow{XY}$ bisects $\angle ABC$. Give two more true statements about the diagram.
Sample answer: $m\angle CBX = 100°$, $m\angle ABX = 100°$

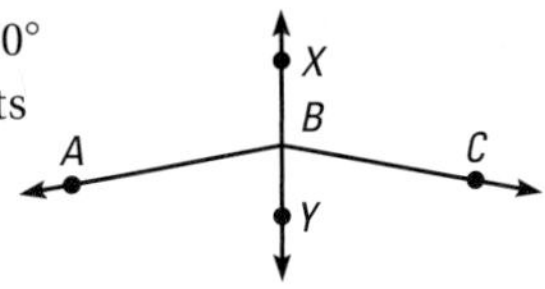

32. $\angle 1$ and $\angle 9$; Congruent Supplements Theorem

33. *Sample answer:* $\angle CEB$ and $\angle DEB$; Right Angles Congruence Theorem

34. $\angle 5$ and $\angle 1$; Congruent Complements Theorem

C **DRAWING CONCLUSIONS In Exercises 31–34, use the given statement to name two congruent angles. Then give a reason that justifies your conclusion.**

31. In triangle GFE, $\overrightarrow{GH}$ bisects $\angle EGF$. **$\angle FGH$ and $\angle EGH$; Definition of angle bisector**

32. $\angle 1$ is a supplement of $\angle 6$, and $\angle 9$ is a supplement of $\angle 6$.

33. $\overline{AB}$ is perpendicular to $\overline{CD}$, and $\overline{AB}$ and $\overline{CD}$ intersect at E.

34. $\angle 5$ is complementary to $\angle 12$, and $\angle 1$ is complementary to $\angle 12$.

35. **CHALLENGE** Sketch two intersecting lines j and k. Sketch another pair of lines ℓ and m that intersect at the same point as j and k and that bisect the angles formed by j and k. Line ℓ is perpendicular to line m. *Explain* why this is true.
See margin for art. *Sample answer:* ℓ and m bisect supplementary angles.

PROBLEM SOLVING

EXAMPLE 2 A
on p. 125 for Ex. 36

36. **PROVING THEOREM 2.4** Prove the second case of the Congruent Supplements Theorem where two angles are supplementary to congruent angles. **See margin.**

GIVEN ▶ $\angle 1$ and $\angle 2$ are supplements.
$\angle 3$ and $\angle 4$ are supplements.
$\angle 1 \cong \angle 4$

PROVE ▶ $\angle 2 \cong \angle 3$

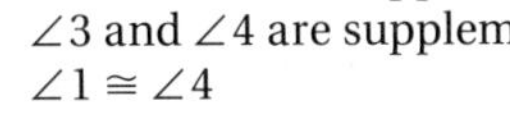

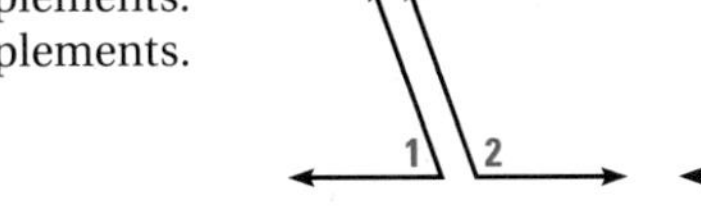

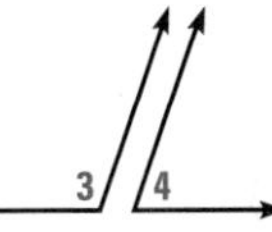

@HomeTutor for problem solving help at classzone.com

37. **PROVING THEOREM 2.5** Copy and complete the proof of the first case of the Congruent Complements Theorem where two angles are complementary to the same angle.

GIVEN ▶ $\angle 1$ and $\angle 2$ are complements.
$\angle 1$ and $\angle 3$ are complements.

PROVE ▶ $\angle 2 \cong \angle 3$

STATEMENTS	REASONS
1. $\angle 1$ and $\angle 2$ are complements. $\angle 1$ and $\angle 3$ are complements.	1. ? **Given**
2. $m\angle 1 + m\angle 2 = 90°$ $m\angle 1 + m\angle 3 = 90°$	2. ? **Definition of complementary angles**
3. ? $m\angle 1 + m\angle 2 = m\angle 1 + m\angle 3$	3. Transitive Property of Equality
4. ? $m\angle 2 = m\angle 3$	4. Subtraction Property of Equality
5. $\angle 2 \cong \angle 3$	5. ? **Definition of congruent angles**

@HomeTutor for problem solving help at classzone.com

Teaching Strategy

Exercises 12–14 These exercises can be done by solving two equations in one variable or by solving a system of two equations in two variables. Discuss both approaches and ask which theorem is being applied to justify each approach.

Mathematical Reasoning

Exercises 22–27 Ask students to draw a diagram that reflects the information given in the directions for the exercises. Discuss whether there is more than one way to draw the diagram.

35. ***Sample:***

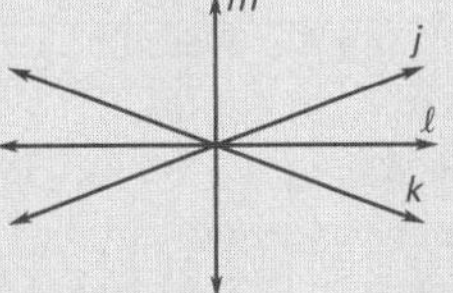

36. Statements (Reasons)

1. $\angle 1$ and $\angle 2$ are supplements; $\angle 3$ and $\angle 4$ are supplements; $\angle 1 \cong \angle 4$. (Given)

2. $m\angle 1 + m\angle 2 = 180°$; $m\angle 3 + m\angle 4 = 180°$ (Definition of supplementary angles)

3. $m\angle 1 = m\angle 4$ (Definition of congruent angles)

4. $m\angle 1 + m\angle 2 = m\angle 3 + m\angle 4$ (Transitive Property of Equality)

5. $m\angle 1 + m\angle 2 = m\angle 3 + m\angle 1$ (Substitution)

6. $m\angle 2 = m\angle 3$ (Subtraction Property of Equality)

7. $\angle 2 \cong \angle 3$ (Definition of congruent angles)

B **PROOF** **Use the given information and the diagram to prove the statement.** **38, 39. See margin.**

38. **GIVEN ▶** $\angle ABD$ is a right angle. $\angle CBE$ is a right angle.

PROVE ▶ $\angle ABC \cong \angle DBE$

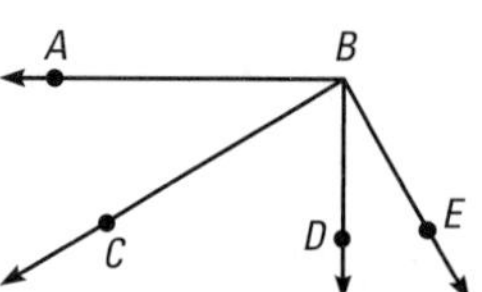

(39.) **GIVEN ▶** $\overline{JK} \perp \overline{JM}$, $\overline{KL} \perp \overline{ML}$, $\angle J \cong \angle M$, $\angle K \cong \angle L$

PROVE ▶ $\overline{JM} \perp \overline{ML}$ and $\overline{JK} \perp \overline{KL}$

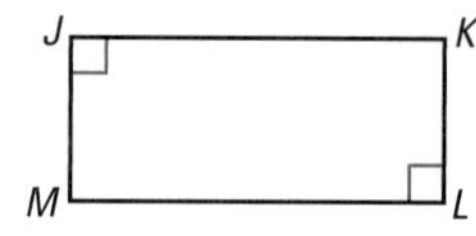

40. **MULTI-STEP PROBLEM** Use the photo of the folding table.

a. If $m\angle 1 = x°$, write expressions for the other three angle measures.

b. Estimate the value of x. What are the measures of the other angles?

c. As the table is folded up, $\angle 4$ gets smaller. What happens to the other three angles? *Explain* your reasoning.

40a. $m\angle 2 = (180 - x)°$, $m\angle 3 = x°$, $m\angle 4 = (180 - x)°$

40b. *Sample answer:* $x \approx 110$, $m\angle 2 \approx 70°$, $m\angle 3 \approx 110°$, $m\angle 4 \approx 70°$

40c. $\angle 2$ gets smaller, while $\angle 1$ and $\angle 3$ will get larger. *Sample answer:* $\angle 3$ and $\angle 4$, and $\angle 1$ and $\angle 2$ form linear pairs. Since the sum of the angles in a linear pair is always 180°, as one angle in a linear pair gets smaller the other angle of the linear pair will get larger.

41. **PROVING THEOREM 2.5** Write a two-column proof for the second case of Theorem 2.5 where two angles are complementary to congruent angles. **See margin.**

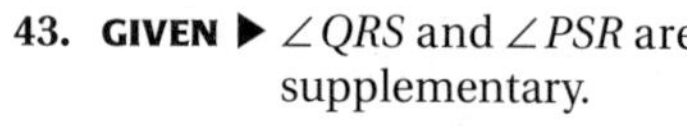

WRITING PROOFS **Write a two-column proof.** **42, 43. See margin.**

42. **GIVEN ▶** $\angle 1 \cong \angle 3$

PROVE ▶ $\angle 2 \cong \angle 4$

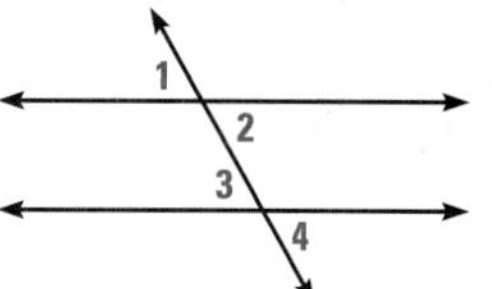

43. **GIVEN ▶** $\angle QRS$ and $\angle PSR$ are supplementary.

PROVE ▶ $\angle QRL \cong \angle PSR$

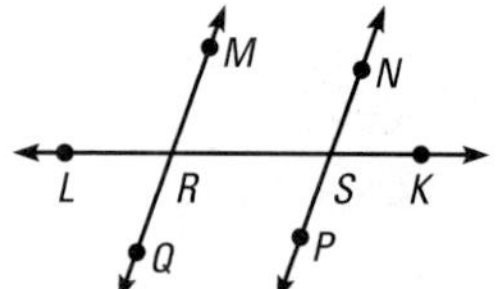

44. **STAIRCASE** Use the photo and the given information to prove the statement. **See margin.**

GIVEN ▶ $\angle 1$ is complementary to $\angle 3$. $\angle 2$ is complementary to $\angle 4$.

PROVE ▶ $\angle 1 \cong \angle 4$

45. ★ **EXTENDED RESPONSE** $\angle STV$ is bisected by $\overrightarrow{TW}$, and $\overrightarrow{TX}$ and $\overrightarrow{TW}$ are opposite rays. You want to show $\angle STX \cong \angle VTX$. **a–c. See margin.**

a. Draw a diagram.

b. Identify the GIVEN and PROVE statements for the situation.

c. Write a two-column proof.

○ = **WORKED-OUT SOLUTIONS on p. WS1** ★ = **STANDARDIZED TEST PRACTICE**

38. Statements (Reasons)

1. $\angle ABD$ is a right angle; $\angle CBE$ is a right angle. (Given)
2. $\angle ABC$ and $\angle CBD$ are complementary. (Definition of complementary angles)
3. $\angle DBE$ and $\angle CBD$ are complementary. (Definition of complementary angles)
4. $\angle ABC \cong \angle DBE$ (Congruent Complements Theorem)

39. Statements (Reasons)

1. $\overline{JK} \perp \overline{JM}$, $\overline{KL} \perp \overline{ML}$, $\angle J \cong \angle M$, $\angle K \cong \angle L$ (Given)
2. $\angle J$ and $\angle L$ are right angles. (Definition of perpendicular lines)
3. $m\angle J = 90°$ and $m\angle L = 90°$ (Definition of right angles)
4. $m\angle J = m\angle M$ and $m\angle L = m\angle K$ (Definition of congruent angles)
5. $m\angle M = 90°$ and $m\angle K = 90°$ (Transitive Property of Equality)
6. $\angle M$ and $\angle K$ are right angles. (Definition of right angles)
7. $\overline{JM} \perp \overline{ML}$, $\overline{JK} \perp \overline{KL}$ (Definition of perpendicular lines)

41. Statements (Reasons)

1. $\angle 1$ and $\angle 2$ are complementary; $\angle 3$ and $\angle 4$ are complementary; $\angle 1 \cong \angle 4$. (Given)
2. $m\angle 1 + m\angle 2 = 90°$; $m\angle 3 + m\angle 4 = 90°$ (Definition of complementary)
3. $m\angle 1 = m\angle 4$ (Definition of congruent angles)
4. $m\angle 1 + m\angle 2 = m\angle 3 + m\angle 4$ (Transitive Property of Equality)
5. $m\angle 1 + m\angle 2 = m\angle 3 + m\angle 1$ (Substitution)
6. $m\angle 2 = m\angle 3$ (Subtraction Property of Equality)
7. $\angle 2 \cong \angle 3$ (Definition of congruent angles)

42. Statements (Reasons)

1. $\angle 1 \cong \angle 3$ (Given)
2. $\angle 1 \cong \angle 2$; $\angle 3 \cong \angle 4$ (Vertical Angles Theorem)
3. $\angle 2 \cong \angle 3$ (Transitive Property of Angle Congruence)
4. $\angle 2 \cong \angle 4$ (Transitive Property of Angle Congruence)

43. Statements (Reasons)

1. $\angle QRS$ and $\angle PSR$ are supplementary. (Given)
2. $\angle QRS$ and $\angle QRL$ are a linear pair. (Definition of linear pair)
3. $\angle QRS$ and $\angle QRL$ are supplementary. (Definition of linear pair)
4. $\angle QRL \cong \angle PSR$ (Congruent Supplements Theorem)

44, 45a–c. See Additional Answers beginning on p. AA1.

C **46. USING DIAGRAMS** Copy and complete the statement with <, >, or =.

a. $m\angle 3$ _?_ $m\angle 7$ =

b. $m\angle 4$ _?_ $m\angle 6$ =

c. $m\angle 8 + m\angle 6$ _?_ $150°$ <

d. If $m\angle 4 = 30°$, then $m\angle 5$ _?_ $m\angle 4$ >

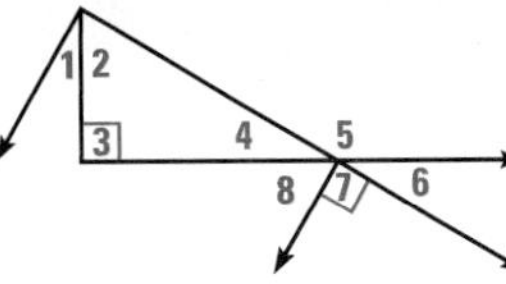

CHALLENGE In Exercises 47 and 48, write a two-column proof. **47, 48. See margin.**

47. GIVEN ▶ $m\angle WYZ = m\angle TWZ = 45°$
PROVE ▶ $\angle SWZ \cong \angle XYW$

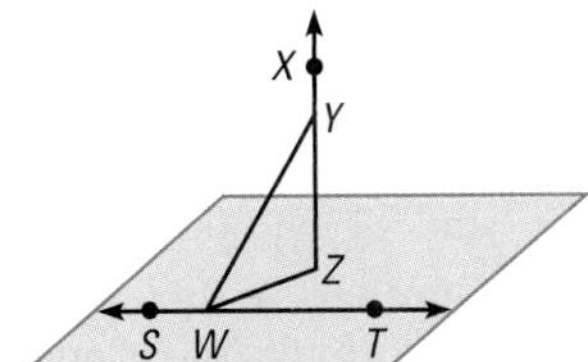

48. GIVEN ▶ The hexagon is regular.
PROVE ▶ $m\angle 1 + m\angle 2 = 180°$

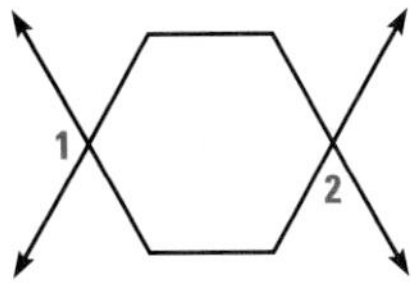

MIXED REVIEW

PREVIEW
Prepare for Lesson 3.1 in Exs. 49–52.

In Exercises 49–52, sketch a plane. Then sketch the described situation. *(p. 2)* **49–53. See margin.**

49. Three noncollinear points that lie in the plane

50. A line that intersects the plane at one point

51. Two perpendicular lines that lie in the plane

52. A plane perpendicular to the given plane

53. Sketch the next figure in the pattern. *(p. 72)*

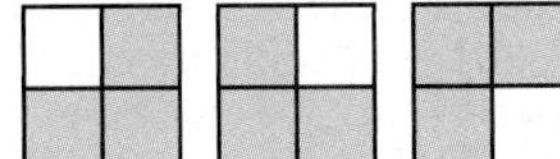

QUIZ *for Lessons 2.6–2.7*

Match the statement with the property that it illustrates. *(p. 112)*

1. If $\overline{HJ} \cong \overline{LM}$, then $\overline{LM} \cong \overline{HJ}$. **B**

2. If $\angle 1 \cong \angle 2$ and $\angle 2 \cong \angle 4$, then $\angle 1 \cong \angle 4$. **C**

3. $\angle XYZ \cong \angle XYZ$ **A**

A. Reflexive Property of Congruence

B. Symmetric Property of Congruence

C. Transitive Property of Congruence

4. Write a two-column proof. *(p. 124)* **See margin.**

GIVEN ▶ $\angle XWY$ is a straight angle.
$\angle ZWV$ is a straight angle.
PROVE ▶ $\angle XWV \cong \angle ZWY$

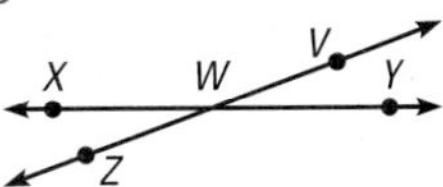

49–52. See Additional Answers beginning on p. AA1.

53.

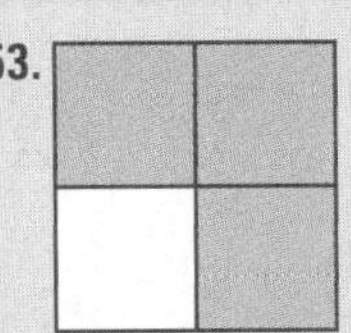

5 ASSESS AND RETEACH

Daily Homework Quiz

Transparency Available

1. Give the reason for each step.

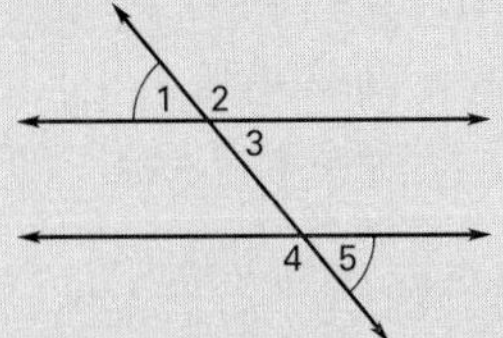

Given: $\angle 1 \cong \angle 5$
Prove: $\angle 1$ is supplementary to $\angle 4$.

Statements (Reasons)

1. $\angle 1 \cong \angle 5$ **(Given)**
2. $m\angle 1 = m\angle 5$ **(Def. of ≅)**
3. $\angle 4$ and $\angle 5$ are a linear pair. **(Def. of linear pair)**
4. $\angle 4$ and $\angle 5$ are supplementary. **(Linear Pair Post.)**
5. $m\angle 4 + m\angle 5 = 180$ **(Def. of supplementary)**
6. $m\angle 4 + m\angle 1 = 180$ **(Substitution Prop. of Eq.)**
7. $\angle 1$ is supplementary to $\angle 4$. **(Def. of supplementary)**

Online Quiz

Available at **classzone.com**

Diagnosis/Remediation

- Practice A, B, C in Chapter 2 Resource Book, pp. 90–95
- Study Guide in Chapter 2 Resource Book, pp. 96–97
- Practice Workbook, pp. 40–42
- @HomeTutor

Challenge

Additional challenge is available in the Chapter 2 Resource Book, p. 100.

Quiz

An easily-readable reduced copy of the quiz (with answers) on Lessons 2.6–2.7 from the Assessment Book can be found on p. 70G.

47, 48, Quiz 4. See Additional Answers beginning on p. AA1.

STATE TEST PRACTICE
classzone.com

1a. Statements (Reasons)

1. $\overrightarrow{BD}$ bisects $\angle ABC$; $\overrightarrow{BC}$ bisects $\angle DBE$. (Given)
2. $m\angle ABD = m\angle DBC$; $m\angle DBC = m\angle CBE$ (Definition of angle bisector)
3. $m\angle ABD = m\angle CBE$ (Transitive Property of Equality)

1b. 33°; $m\angle DBC = \frac{1}{3} m\angle ABE$

2. Yes; each piece is $\frac{1}{4}$ the original width.

4. *Sample answer:* Congruent Supplements Theorem states exactly what is to be explained while the Transitive Property of Angle Congruence requires $\angle 1 \cong \angle 2$ and $\angle 2 \cong \angle 3$ to be able to state $\angle 1 \cong \angle 3$.

5a. Equation (Reason)

$T = c(1 + s)$ (Given)

$\frac{T}{c} = 1 + s$ (Division Property of Equality)

$\frac{T}{c} - 1 = s$ (Subtraction Property of Equality)

5c. Yes; distribute the c, then subtract c from both sides, followed by dividing both sides by c.

6. *Sample answer:* Either $m\angle BAC$ or $m\angle CAD$; since $\angle GAD$ is a straight angle, if two of the three angles are known, the third angle can be found.

7. $m\angle 1 = m\angle 2 = 45°$, $m\angle 3 = m\angle 4 = 135°$; $m\angle 1 + m\angle 3 = m\angle 1 + 3m\angle 1 = 4m\angle 1 = 180°$

8. $\angle EAF$ and $\angle BAC$ are complementary. *Sample answer:* $m\angle BAC + m\angle CAD + m\angle DAE + m\angle EAF = m\angle BAF$ by the Angle Addition Postulate; $m\angle BAF = 180°$ and $m\angle CAD + m\angle DAE = 90°$, so $m\angle BAC + m\angle EAF = 90°$.

Lessons 2.5–2.7

1. **MULTI-STEP PROBLEM** In the diagram below, $\overrightarrow{BD}$ bisects $\angle ABC$ and $\overrightarrow{BC}$ bisects $\angle DBE$. **1a, b. See margin.**

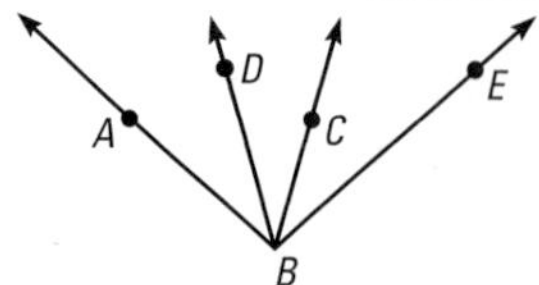

   a. Prove $m\angle ABD = m\angle CBE$.

   b. If $m\angle ABE = 99°$, what is $m\angle DBC$? *Explain.*

2. **SHORT RESPONSE** You are cutting a rectangular piece of fabric into strips that you will weave together to make a placemat. As shown, you cut the fabric in half lengthwise to create two congruent pieces. You then cut each of these pieces in half lengthwise. Do all of the strips have the same width? *Explain* your reasoning. **See margin.**

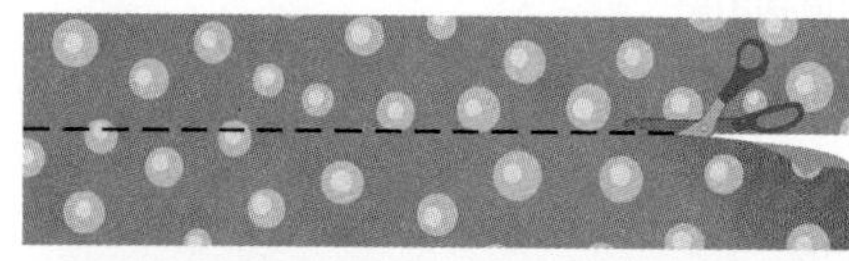

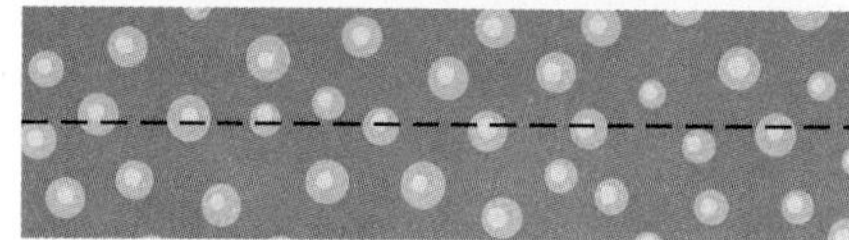

3. **GRIDDED ANSWER** The cross section of a concrete retaining wall is shown below. Use the given information to find the measure of $\angle 1$ in degrees. **100°**

$m\angle 1 = m\angle 2$

$m\angle 3 = m\angle 4$

$m\angle 3 = 80°$

$m\angle 1 + m\angle 2 + m\angle 3 + m\angle 4 = 360°$

4. **EXTENDED RESPONSE** *Explain* how the Congruent Supplements Theorem and the Transitive Property of Angle Congruence can both be used to show how angles that are supplementary to the same angle are congruent. **See margin.**

5. **EXTENDED RESPONSE** A formula you can use to calculate the total cost of an item including sales tax is $T = c(1 + s)$, where T is the total cost including sales tax, c is the cost not including sales tax, and s is the sales tax rate written as a decimal.

   a. Solve the formula for s. Give a reason for each step. **See margin.**

   b. Use your formula to find the sales tax rate on a purchase that was \$26.75 with tax and \$25 without tax. **0.07, or 7%**

   c. Look back at the steps you used to solve the formula for s. Could you have solved for s in a different way? *Explain.* **See margin.**

6. **OPEN-ENDED** In the diagram below, $m\angle GAB = 36°$. What additional information do you need to find $m\angle BAC$ and $m\angle CAD$? *Explain* your reasoning. **See margin.**

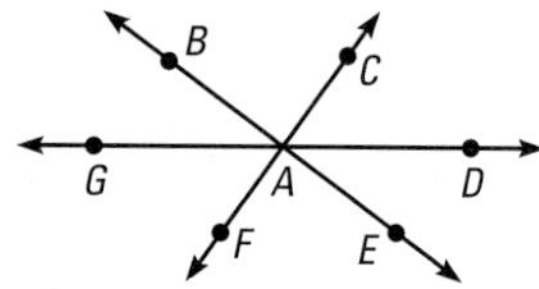

7. **SHORT RESPONSE** Two lines intersect to form $\angle 1$, $\angle 2$, $\angle 3$, and $\angle 4$. The measure of $\angle 3$ is three times the measure of $\angle 1$ and $m\angle 1 = m\angle 2$. Find all four angle measures. *Explain* your reasoning. **See margin.**

8. **SHORT RESPONSE** Part of a spider web is shown below. If you know that $\angle CAD$ and $\angle DAE$ are complements and that $\overrightarrow{AB}$ and $\overrightarrow{AF}$ are opposite rays, what can you conclude about $\angle BAC$ and $\angle EAF$? *Explain* your reasoning. **See margin.**

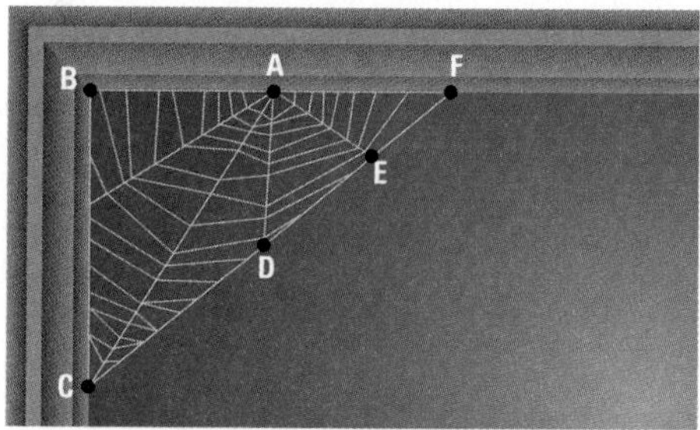

2 CHAPTER SUMMARY

BIG IDEAS — For Your Notebook

Big Idea 1

Using Inductive and Deductive Reasoning

When you make a conjecture based on a pattern, you use inductive reasoning. You use deductive reasoning to show whether the conjecture is true or false by using facts, definitions, postulates, properties, or proven theorems. If you can find one counterexample to the conjecture, then you know the conjecture is false.

Big Idea 2

Understanding Geometric Relationships in Diagrams

The following can be assumed from the diagram:

A, B, and C are coplanar.

$\angle ABH$ and $\angle HBF$ are a linear pair.

Plane T and plane S intersect in $\overleftrightarrow{BC}$.

$\overleftrightarrow{CD}$ lies in plane S.

$\angle ABC$ and $\angle HBF$ are vertical angles.

$\overleftrightarrow{AB} \perp$ plane S.

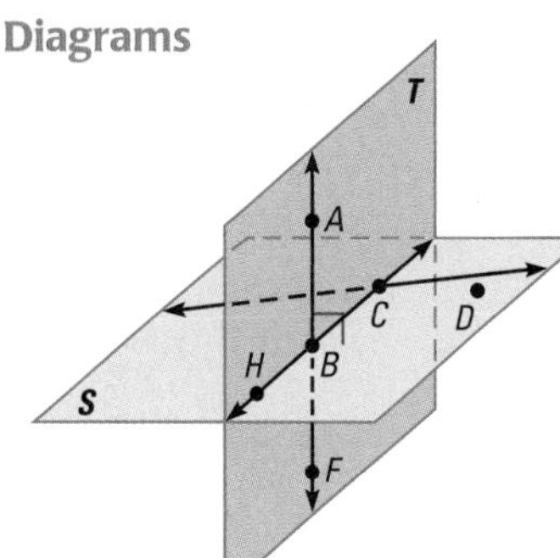

Diagram assumptions are reviewed on page 97.

Big Idea 3

Writing Proofs of Geometric Relationships

You can write a logical argument to show a geometric relationship is true. In a two-column proof, you use deductive reasoning to work from GIVEN information to reach a conjecture you want to PROVE.

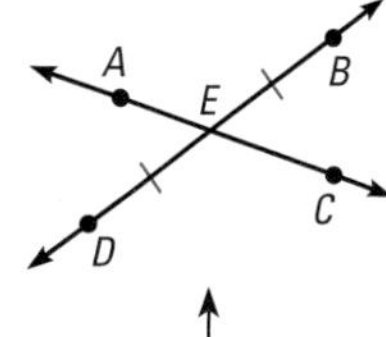

Diagram of geometric relationship with given information labeled to help you write the proof

GIVEN ▶ The hypothesis of an if-then statement

PROVE ▶ The conclusion of an if-then statement

STATEMENTS	REASONS
1. Hypothesis	1. Given
______	______
______	______
______	______
n. Conclusion	*n.* ______

Statements based on facts that you know or conclusions from deductive reasoning

Use postulates, proven theorems, definitions, and properties of numbers and congruence as reasons.

Proof summary is on page 114.

Additional Resources

The following resources are available to help review the materials in this chapter.

Chapter 2 Resource Book

- Chapter Review Games and Activities, p. 101
- Cumulative Practice, Chs. 1–2, pp. 104–105

Student Resources in Spanish

eWorkbook

@HomeTutor

Vocabulary Practice

Vocabulary practice is available at **classzone.com**

Extra Example 2.1

Describe the pattern in the numbers 6, 24, 96, 384, . . . , and write the next three numbers in the pattern. **Each number is 4 times the previous number; 1536, 6144, 24,576**

2 CHAPTER REVIEW

@HomeTutor
classzone.com
• Multi-Language Glossary
• Vocabulary practice

REVIEW KEY VOCABULARY

See pp. 926–931 for a list of postulates and theorems.

- conjecture, *p. 73*
- inductive reasoning, *p. 73*
- counterexample, *p. 74*
- conditional statement, *p. 79* converse, inverse, contrapositive
- if-then form, *p. 79* hypothesis, conclusion
- negation, *p. 79*
- equivalent statements, *p. 80*
- perpendicular lines, *p. 81*
- biconditional statement, *p. 82*
- deductive reasoning, *p. 87*
- line perpendicular to a plane, *p. 98*
- proof, *p. 112*
- two-column proof, *p. 112*
- theorem, *p. 113*

VOCABULARY EXERCISES

2. In the inverse the hypothesis and conclusion are negated while in the converse the hypothesis and conclusion are switched.

1. Copy and complete: A statement that can be proven is called a(n) __?__. **theorem**
2. WRITING *Compare* the inverse of a conditional statement to the converse of the conditional statement.
3. You know $m\angle A = m\angle B$ and $m\angle B = m\angle C$. What does the Transitive Property of Equality tell you about the measures of the angles? $m\angle A = m\angle C$

REVIEW EXAMPLES AND EXERCISES

Use the review examples and exercises below to check your understanding of the concepts you have learned in each lesson of Chapter 2.

2.1 Use Inductive Reasoning *pp. 72–78*

EXAMPLE

Describe the pattern in the numbers 3, 21, 147, 1029, ..., and write the next three numbers in the pattern.

Each number is seven times the previous number.

So, the next three numbers are 7203, 50,421, and 352,947.

EXERCISES

4. Each number is $\frac{1}{4}$ of the previous number; −80, −20, −5.

EXAMPLES 2 and 5 on pp. 72–74 for Exs. 4–5

4. *Describe* the pattern in the numbers −20,480, −5120, −1280, −320, ... Write the next three numbers.
5. Find a counterexample to disprove the conjecture:

   If the quotient of two numbers is positive, then the two numbers must both be positive. ***Sample answer:*** $\frac{-10}{-2} = 5$

@HomeTutor
classzone.com
Chapter Review Practice

2.2 Analyze Conditional Statements

pp. 79–85

EXAMPLE

Write the if-then form, the converse, the inverse, and the contrapositive of the statement "Black bears live in North America."

a. If-then form: If a bear is a black bear, then it lives in North America.

b. Converse: If a bear lives in North America, then it is a black bear.

c. Inverse: If a bear is not a black bear, then it does not live in North America.

d. Contrapositive: If a bear does not live in North America, then it is not a black bear.

EXERCISES

EXAMPLES 2, 3, and 4 on pp. 80–82 for Exs. 6–8

6. Write the if-then form, the converse, the inverse, and the contrapositive of the statement "An angle whose measure is 34° is an acute angle." **See margin.**

7. Is this a valid definition? *Explain* why or why not.

"If the sum of the measures of two angles is 90°, then the angles are complementary."

Yes. *Sample answer:* This is the definition for complementary angles.

8. Write the definition of an *equiangular polygon* as a biconditional statement.

The interior angles of a polygon are congruent if and only if the polygon is equiangular.

2.3 Apply Deductive Reasoning

pp. 87–93

EXAMPLE

Use the Law of Detachment to make a valid conclusion in the true situation.

If two angles have the same measure, then they are congruent. You know that $m\angle A = m\angle B$.

▸ Because $m\angle A = m\angle B$ satisfies the hypothesis of a true conditional statement, the conclusion is also true. So, $\angle A \cong \angle B$.

EXERCISES

EXAMPLES 1, 2, and 4 on pp. 87–89 for Exs. 9–11

9. Use the Law of Detachment to make a valid conclusion.

If an angle is a right angle, then the angle measures 90°. $\angle B$ is a right angle.

$\angle B$ measures 90°.

10. Use the Law of Syllogism to write the statement that follows from the pair of true statements. **If $4x = 12$, then $2x = 6$.**

If $x = 3$, then $2x = 6$.

If $4x = 12$, then $x = 3$.

11. What can you say about the sum of any two odd integers? Use inductive reasoning to form a conjecture. Then use deductive reasoning to show that the conjecture is true.

The sum of two odd integers is even. *Sample answer:* $7 + 1 = 8$; $2n + 1$ and $2m + 1$ are odd, but their sum $(2n + 1) + (2m + 1) = 2m + 2n + 2 = 2(m + n + 1)$ is even.

Extra Example 2.2

Write the if-then form, the converse, the inverse, and the contrapositive of the statement "The heart of a mouse beats at least 600 times a minute." **If-then: If an animal is a mouse, then its heart beats at least 600 times a minute. Converse: If an animal's heart beats at least 600 times a minute, then the animal is a mouse. Inverse: If an animal is not a mouse, then its heart does not beat at least 600 times a minute. Contrapositive: If an animal's heart does not beat at least 600 times a minute, then the animal is not a mouse.**

Extra Example 2.3

Use the Law of Detachment to make a valid conclusion. If two segments have the same length, then they are congruent. The length of $\overline{MP}$ is the same as the length of $\overline{WU}$. $\overline{MP} \cong \overline{WU}$

6. If an angle measures 34°, then the angle is an acute angle; if an angle is an acute angle, then it measures 34°; if an angle does not measure 34°, then the angle is not an acute angle; if an angle is not an acute angle, then it does not measure 34°.

2 CHAPTER REVIEW

Extra Example 2.4

$\overleftrightarrow{MN}$ intersects $\overline{RS}$ at its midpoint T so that $\overleftrightarrow{MN} \perp \overline{RS}$. Sketch a diagram that represents the given information.

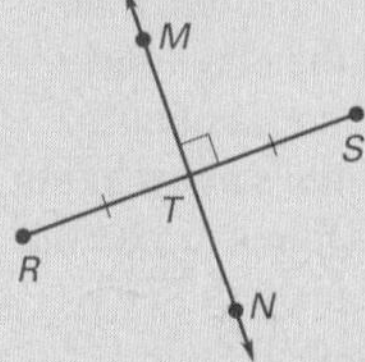

Extra Example 2.5

Solve $-4x + 2(3x + 8) = -(x + 8)$ and write a reason for each step.

Equation (Reason)

$-4x + 2(3x + 8) = -(x + 8)$ (Write the original equation.)

$-4x + 6x + 16 = -x - 8$ (Distributive Prop.)

$2x + 16 = -x - 8$ (Simplify)

$3x = -24$ (Addition Prop. of Eq.)

$x = -8$ (Division Prop. of Eq.)

12. *Sample:*

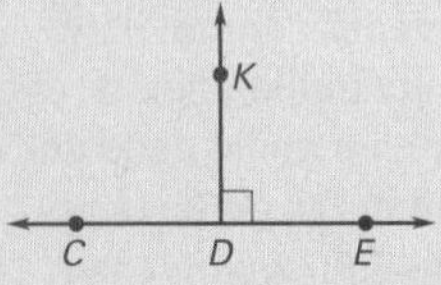

14. Equation (Reason)

$-9x - 21 = -20x - 87$ (Given)

$11x - 21 = -87$ (Addition Property of Equality)

$11x = -66$ (Addition Property of Equality)

$x = -6$ (Division Property of Equality)

15. Equation (Reason)

$15x + 22 = 7x + 62$ (Given)

$8x + 22 = 62$ (Subtraction Property of Equality)

$8x = 40$ (Subtraction Property of Equality)

$x = 5$ (Division Property of Equality)

16. Equation (Reason)

$3(2x + 9) = 30$ (Given)

$2x + 9 = 10$ (Division Property of Equality)

$2x = 1$ (Subtraction Property of Equality)

$x = \frac{1}{2}$ (Division Property of Equality)

2.4 Use Postulates and Diagrams

pp. 96–102

EXAMPLE

$\angle ABC$, an acute angle, is bisected by $\overrightarrow{BE}$. Sketch a diagram that represents the given information.

1. Draw $\angle ABC$, an acute angle, and label points A, B, and C.
2. Draw angle bisector $\overrightarrow{BE}$. Mark congruent angles.

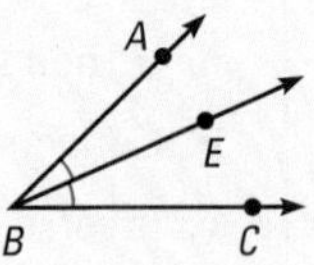

EXERCISES

EXAMPLES 3 and 4 on p. 98 for Exs. 12–13

12. Straight angle CDE is bisected by $\overrightarrow{DK}$. Sketch a diagram that represents the given information. **See margin.**

13. Which of the following statements *cannot* be assumed from the diagram? **B**

   (A) A, B, and C are coplanar.

   (B) $\overleftrightarrow{CD} \perp$ plane P

   (C) A, F, and B are collinear.

   (D) Plane M intersects plane P in $\overleftrightarrow{FH}$.

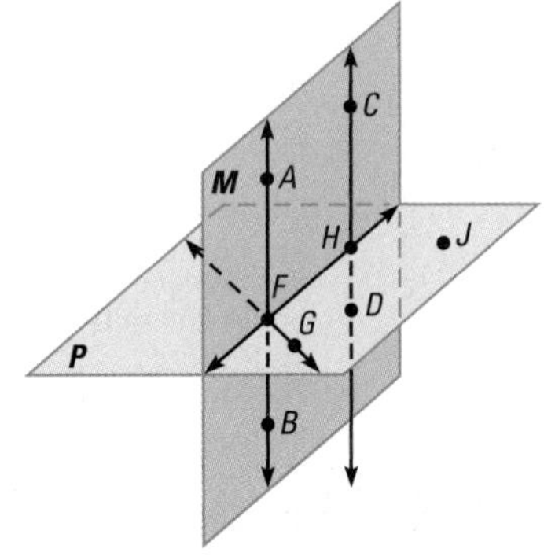

2.5 Reason Using Properties from Algebra

pp. 105–111

EXAMPLE

Solve $3x + 2(2x + 9) = -10$. Write a reason for each step.

$3x + 2(2x + 9) = -10$	Write original equation.
$3x + 4x + 18 = -10$	Distributive Property
$7x + 18 = -10$	Simplify.
$7x = -28$	Subtraction Property of Equality
$x = -4$	Division Property of Equality

EXERCISES

EXAMPLES 1 and 2 on pp. 105–106 for Exs. 14–17

Solve the equation. Write a reason for each step. **14–17. See margin.**

14. $-9x - 21 = -20x - 87$
15. $15x + 22 = 7x + 62$
16. $3(2x + 9) = 30$
17. $5x + 2(2x - 23) = -154$

17. Equation (Reason)

$5x + 2(2x - 23) = -154$ (Given)

$5x + 4x - 46 = -154$ (Distributive Property)

$9x - 46 = -154$ (Simplify.)

$9x = -108$ (Addition Property of Equality)

$x = -12$ (Division Property of Equality)

@HomeTutor
classzone.com
Chapter Review Practice

2.6 Prove Statements about Segments and Angles pp. 112–119

EXAMPLE

Prove the Reflexive Property of Segment Congruence.

GIVEN ▶ $\overline{AB}$ is a line segment.

PROVE ▶ $\overline{AB} \cong \overline{AB}$

STATEMENTS	REASONS
1. $\overline{AB}$ is a line segment.	1. Given
2. AB is the length of $\overline{AB}$.	2. Ruler Postulate
3. $AB = AB$	3. Reflexive Property of Equality
4. $\overline{AB} \cong \overline{AB}$	4. Definition of congruent segments

EXERCISES

EXAMPLES 2 and 3 on pp. 113–114 for Exs. 18–21

Name the property illustrated by the statement.

18. If $\angle DEF \cong \angle JKL$, then $\angle JKL \cong \angle DEF$. **See margin.**

19. $\angle C \cong \angle C$ **Reflexive Property of Congruence**

20. If $MN = PQ$ and $PQ = RS$, then $MN = RS$. **Transitive Property of Equality**

21. Prove the Transitive Property of Angle Congruence. **See margin.**

18. Symmetric Property of Congruence

2.7 Prove Angle Pair Relationships pp. 124–131

EXAMPLE

GIVEN ▶ $\angle 5 \cong \angle 6$

PROVE ▶ $\angle 4 \cong \angle 7$

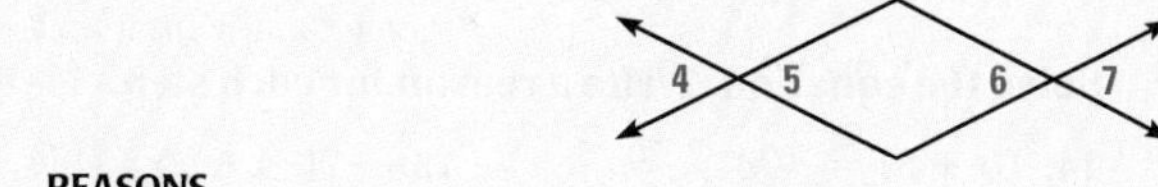

STATEMENTS	REASONS
1. $\angle 5 \cong \angle 6$	1. Given
2. $\angle 4 \cong \angle 5$	2. Vertical Angles Congruence Theorem
3. $\angle 4 \cong \angle 6$	3. Transitive Property of Congruence
4. $\angle 6 \cong \angle 7$	4. Vertical Angles Congruence Theorem
5. $\angle 4 \cong \angle 7$	5. Transitive Property of Congruence

EXERCISES

EXAMPLES 2 and 3 on pp. 125–126 for Exs. 22–24

In Exercises 22 and 23, use the diagram at the right.

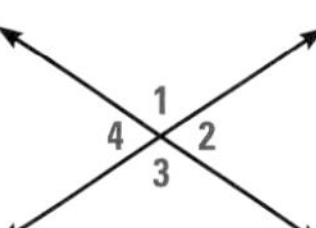

22. If $m\angle 1 = 114°$, find $m\angle 2$, $m\angle 3$, and $m\angle 4$. **66°, 114°, 66°**

23. If $m\angle 4 = 57°$, find $m\angle 1$, $m\angle 2$, and $m\angle 3$. **123°, 57°, 123°**

24. Write a two-column proof. **See margin.**

GIVEN ▶ $\angle 12$ and $\angle 11$ are complementary. $m\angle 10 + m\angle 11 = 90°$

PROVE ▶ $\angle 12 \cong \angle 10$

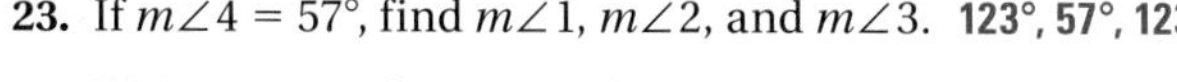

21. Statements (Reasons)

1. $\angle A \cong \angle B$, $\angle B \cong \angle C$ (Given)
2. $m\angle A = m\angle B$, $m\angle B = m\angle C$ (Definition of angle congruence)
3. $m\angle A = m\angle C$ (Transitive Property of Equality)
4. $\angle A \cong \angle C$ (Definition of angle congruence)

Extra Example 2.6

Prove the Transitive Property of Angle Congruence.

Given: $\angle A \cong \angle B$, $\angle B \cong \angle C$

Prove: $\angle A \cong \angle C$

Statements (Reasons)

1. $\angle A \cong \angle B$, $\angle B \cong \angle C$ (Given)
2. $m\angle A = m\angle B$, $m\angle B = m\angle C$ (Def. of congruent angles)
3. $m\angle A = m\angle C$ (Transitive Prop. of Eq.)
4. $\angle A \cong \angle C$ (Def. of congruent angles)

Extra Example 2.7

Given: $\angle 1 \cong \angle 3$, $\angle 2 \cong \angle 4$

Prove: $\angle RST \cong \angle STU$

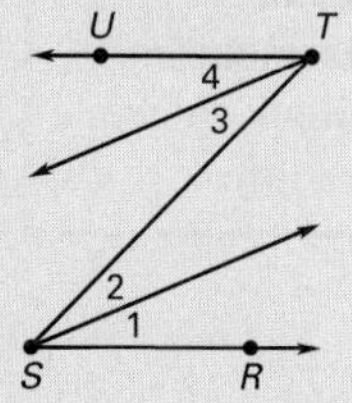

Statements (Reasons)

1. $\angle 1 \cong \angle 3$, $\angle 2 \cong \angle 4$ (Given)
2. $m\angle 1 = m\angle 3$, $m\angle 2 = m\angle 4$ (Def. of congruent angles)
3. $m\angle 1 + m\angle 2 = m\angle 3 + m\angle 4$ (Addition Prop. of Eq.)
4. $m\angle 1 + m\angle 2 = m\angle RST$, $m\angle 3 + m\angle 4 = m\angle STU$ (Angle Addition Post.)
5. $m\angle RST = m\angle STU$ (Substitution Prop. of Eq.)
6. $\angle RST \cong \angle STU$ (Def. of congruent angles)

24. Statements (Reasons)

1. $\angle 3$ and $\angle 2$ are complementary angles; $m\angle 1 + m\angle 2 = 90°$. (Given)
2. $m\angle 2 + m\angle 3 = 90°$ (Definition of complementary angles)
3. $m\angle 2 + m\angle 3 = m\angle 1 + m\angle 2$ (Transitive Property of Equality)
4. $m\angle 3 = m\angle 1$ (Subtraction Property of Equality)
5. $\angle 1 \cong \angle 3$ (Definition of angle congruence)

Additional Resources

Assessment Book

- Chapter Test, Levels A, B, C, pp. 19–24
- Standardized Chapter Test, pp. 25–26
- SAT/ACT Chapter Test, pp. 27–28
- Alternative Assessment, pp. 29–30

Test Generator CD-ROM

Chapter Test

Easily-readable reduced copies (with answers) of Chapter Test B, the Standardized Chapter Test, and the Alternative Assessment from the Assessment Book can be found on pp. 70G–70H.

1. 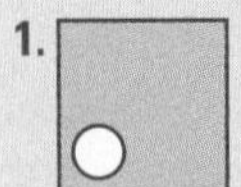

2. 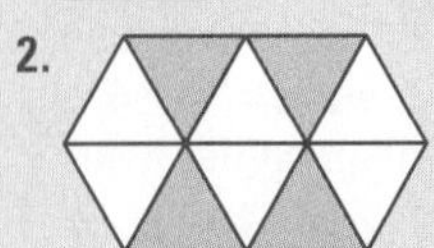

14. Equation (Reason)
$9x + 31 = -23$ (Given)
$9x = -54$ (Subtraction Property of Equality)
$x = -6$ (Division Property of Equality)

15. Equation (Reason)
$-7(-x + 2) = 42$ (Given)
$-x + 2 = -6$ (Division Property of Equality)
$-x = -8$ (Subtraction Property of Equality)
$x = 8$ (Division Property of Equality)

16. Equation (Reason)
$26 + 2(3x + 11) = -18x$ (Given)
$26 + 6x + 22 = -18x$ (Distributive Property)
$48 + 6x = -18x$ (Simplify.)
$48 = -24x$ (Subtraction Property of Equality)
$-2 = x$ (Division Property of Equality)

2 CHAPTER TEST

4. $-\frac{1}{2}$ of the previous number; 6.25

5. If the angles are right angles, then they are congruent; if the angles are congruent, then they are right angles; if the angles are not right angles, then they are not congruent; if the angles are not congruent, then they are not right angles.

6. If the creature is a frog, then it is an amphibian; if the creature is an amphibian, then it is a frog; if the creature is not a frog, then it is not an amphibian; if the creature is not an amphibian, then it is not a frog.

7. If $x = -2$, then $5x + 4 = -6$; if $5x + 4 = -6$, then $x = -2$; if $x \neq -2$, then $5x + 4 \neq -6$; if $5x + 4 \neq -6$, then $x \neq -2$.

8. If a polygon is regular, then it is equilateral; if a polygon is equilateral, then it is regular; if a polygon is not regular, then it is not equilateral; if a polygon is not equilateral, then it is not regular.

Sketch the next figure in the pattern. 1, 2. See margin.

1. 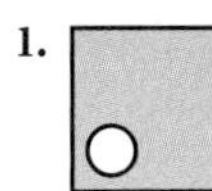  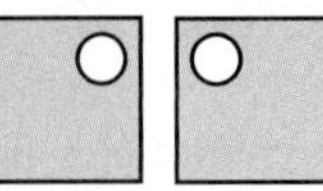

2.  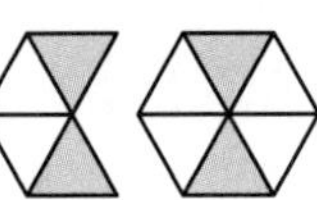 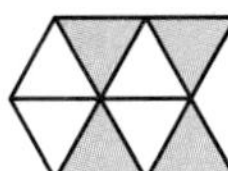

Describe **the pattern in the numbers. Write the next number.**

3. $-6, -1, 4, 9, \ldots$ increasing by 5; 14
4. $100, -50, 25, -12.5, \ldots$

In Exercises 5–8, write the if-then form, the converse, the inverse, and the contrapositive for the given statement.

5. All right angles are congruent.
6. Frogs are amphibians.
7. $5x + 4 = -6$, because $x = -2$.
8. A regular polygon is equilateral.
9. If you decide to go to the football game, then you will miss band practice. Tonight, you are going the football game. Using the Law of Detachment, what statement can you make? You will miss band practice.
10. If Margot goes to college, then she will major in Chemistry. If Margot majors in Chemistry, then she will need to buy a lab manual. Using the Law of Syllogism, what statement can you make? If Margot goes to college, then she will need to buy a lab manual.

Use the diagram to write examples of the stated postulate.

11. A line contains at least two points. *Sample answer:* $\overleftrightarrow{MP}$ contains points M and P.
12. A plane contains at least three noncollinear points. *Sample answer:* Plane X contains points M, Q, and P.
13. If two planes intersect, then their intersection is a line. Planes X and Y intersect at $\overleftrightarrow{NQ}$.

Solve the equation. Write a reason for each step. 14–16. See margin.

14. $9x + 31 = -23$
15. $-7(-x + 2) = 42$
16. $26 + 2(3x + 11) = -18x$

In Exercises 17–19, match the statement with the property that it illustrates.

17. If $\angle RST \cong \angle XYZ$, then $\angle XYZ \cong \angle RST$. B
18. $\overline{PQ} \cong \overline{PQ}$ A
19. If $\overline{FG} \cong \overline{JK}$ and $\overline{JK} \cong \overline{LM}$, then $\overline{FG} \cong \overline{LM}$. C

A. Reflexive Property of Congruence
B. Symmetric Property of Congruence
C. Transitive Property of Congruence

20. Use the Vertical Angles Congruence Theorem to find the measure of each angle in the diagram at the right. 54°, 54°, 126°, 126°

21. Write a two-column proof. See margin.

GIVEN ▶ $\overline{AX} \cong \overline{DX}$, $\overline{XB} \cong \overline{XC}$

PROVE ▶ $\overline{AC} \cong \overline{BD}$

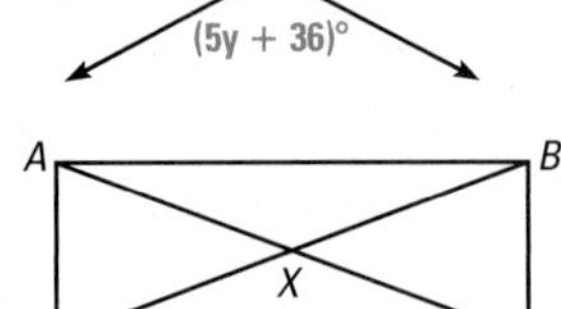

21. Statements (Reasons)
1. $\overline{AX} \cong \overline{DX}$, $\overline{XB} \cong \overline{XC}$ (Given)
2. $AX = DX$, $XB = XC$ (Definition of congruent segments)
3. $AX + XC = AC$, $BX + XD = BD$ (Segment Addition Postulate)
4. $DX + XC = AC$, $XC + XD = BD$ (Substitution)
5. $AC = BD$ (Transitive Property of Equality)
6. $\overline{AC} \cong \overline{BD}$ (Definition of congruent segments)

xy ALGEBRA REVIEW

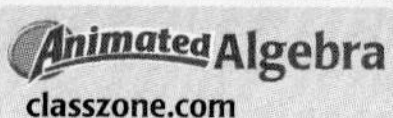

SIMPLIFY RATIONAL AND RADICAL EXPRESSIONS

EXAMPLE 1 Simplify rational expressions

a. $\frac{2x^2}{4xy}$ b. $\frac{3x^2 + 2x}{9x + 6}$

Solution

To simplify a rational expression, factor the numerator and denominator. Then divide out any common factors.

a. $\frac{2x^2}{4xy} = \frac{\cancel{2} \cdot \cancel{x} \cdot x}{\cancel{2} \cdot 2 \cdot \cancel{x} \cdot y} = \frac{x}{2y}$ b. $\frac{3x^2 + 2x}{9x + 6} = \frac{x\cancel{(3x + 2)}}{3\cancel{(3x + 2)}} = \frac{x}{3}$

EXAMPLE 2 Simplify radical expressions

a. $\sqrt{54}$ b. $2\sqrt{5} - 5\sqrt{2} - 3\sqrt{5}$ c. $(3\sqrt{2})(-6\sqrt{6})$

Solution

a. $\sqrt{54} = \sqrt{9} \cdot \sqrt{6}$ **Use product property of radicals.**

$= 3\sqrt{6}$ **Simplify.**

b. $2\sqrt{5} - 5\sqrt{2} - 3\sqrt{5} = -\sqrt{5} - 5\sqrt{2}$ **Combine like terms.**

c. $(3\sqrt{2})(-6\sqrt{6}) = -18\sqrt{12}$ **Use product property and associative property.**

$= -18 \cdot 2\sqrt{3}$ **Simplify $\sqrt{12}$.**

$= -36\sqrt{3}$ **Simplify.**

EXERCISES

EXAMPLE 1 for Exs. 1–9

Simplify the expression, if possible.

1. $\frac{5x^4}{20x^2}$ $\mathbf{\frac{x^2}{4}}$
2. $\frac{-12ab^3}{9a^2b}$ $\mathbf{\frac{-4b^2}{3a}}$
3. $\frac{5m + 35}{5}$ $\mathbf{m + 7}$
4. $\frac{36m - 48m}{6m}$ $\mathbf{-2}$
5. $\frac{k + 3}{-2k + 3}$ $\mathbf{\frac{k + 3}{-2k + 3}}$
6. $\frac{m + 4}{m^2 + 4m}$ $\mathbf{\frac{1}{m}}$
7. $\frac{12x + 16}{8 + 6x}$ $\mathbf{2}$
8. $\frac{3x^3}{5x + 8x^2}$ $\mathbf{\frac{3x^2}{5 + 8x}}$
9. $\frac{3x^2 - 6x}{6x^2 - 3x}$ $\mathbf{\frac{x - 2}{2x - 1}}$

EXAMPLE 2 for Exs. 10–24

Simplify the expression, if possible. All variables are positive.

10. $\sqrt{75}$ $\mathbf{5\sqrt{3}}$
11. $-\sqrt{180}$ $\mathbf{-6\sqrt{5}}$
12. $\pm\sqrt{128}$ $\mathbf{\pm 8\sqrt{2}}$
13. $\sqrt{2} - \sqrt{18} + \sqrt{6}$
14. $\sqrt{28} - \sqrt{63} - \sqrt{35}$
15. $4\sqrt{8} + 3\sqrt{32}$ $\mathbf{20\sqrt{2}}$
16. $(6\sqrt{5})(2\sqrt{2})$ $\mathbf{12\sqrt{10}}$
17. $(-4\sqrt{10})(-5\sqrt{5})$ $\mathbf{100\sqrt{2}}$
18. $(2\sqrt{6})^2$ $\mathbf{24}$
19. $\sqrt{(25)^2}$ $\mathbf{25}$
20. $\sqrt{x^2}$ $\mathbf{x}$
21. $\sqrt{(-a)^2}$ $\mathbf{a}$
22. $\sqrt{(3y)^2}$ $\mathbf{3y}$
23. $\sqrt{3^2 + 2^2}$ $\mathbf{\sqrt{13}}$
24. $\sqrt{h^2 + k^2}$ $\mathbf{\sqrt{h^2 + k^2}}$

13. $\mathbf{-2\sqrt{2} + \sqrt{6}}$

14. $\mathbf{-\sqrt{7} - \sqrt{35}}$

Extra Example 1

Simplify the rational expressions.

a. $\frac{6x^4}{3xy^2}$ $\mathbf{\frac{2x^3}{y^2}}$

b. $\frac{4x^2 + 6x}{8x + 12}$ $\mathbf{\frac{x}{2}}$

Extra Example 2

Simplify the radical expressions.

a. $\sqrt{72}$ $\mathbf{6\sqrt{2}}$

b. $4\sqrt{3} - 6\sqrt{3} + \sqrt{3}$ $\mathbf{-\sqrt{3}}$

c. $(5\sqrt{3})(-2\sqrt{3})$ $\mathbf{-30}$

Using Rubrics

The rubric given on the pupil page is a sample of a three-level rubric. Other rubrics may contain four, five, or six levels. For more information on rubrics, see the *Geometry Toolkit*.

Test-Taking Strategy

Many (but not all) multi-step problems are sequential problems. That is, each successive part of the problem depends on the answer to the previous step. Students should be encouraged to read all the steps of the problem before starting their calculations so they can determine if this is true. If so, they will know they must work on the steps in the given order. If not, they may bypass a step they cannot solve in order to maximize their score by completing the remaining steps.

Scoring Rubric

Full Credit
- solution is complete and correct

Partial Credit
- solution is complete but has errors,
or
- solution is without error but incomplete

No Credit
- no solution is given,
or
- solution makes no sense

Standards

3.0 Students construct and judge the validity of a logical argument and give counterexamples to disprove a statement.

EXTENDED RESPONSE QUESTIONS

PROBLEM

Seven members of the student government (Frank, Gina, Henry, Isabelle, Jack, Katie, and Leah) are posing for a picture for the school yearbook. For the picture, the photographer will arrange the students in a row according to the following restrictions:

Henry must stand in the middle spot.

Katie must stand in the right-most spot.

There must be exactly two spots between Gina and Frank.

Isabelle cannot stand next to Henry.

Frank must stand next to Katie.

a. *Describe* one possible ordering of the students.

b. Which student(s) can stand in the second spot from the left?

c. If the condition that Leah must stand in the left-most spot is added, will there be exactly one ordering of the students? *Justify* your answer.

Below are sample solutions to the problem. Read each solution and the comments in blue to see why the sample represents full credit, partial credit, or no credit.

SAMPLE 1: Full credit solution

The method of representation is clearly explained.

a. Using the first letters of the students' names, here is one possible ordering of the students:

I L G H J F K

The conclusion is correct and shows understanding of the problem.

b. The only students without fixed positions are Isabelle, Leah, and Jack. There are no restrictions on placement in the second spot from the left, so any of these three students can occupy that location.

c. Henry, Frank, Katie, and Gina have fixed positions according to the restrictions. If Leah must stand in the left-most spot, the ordering looks like:

L _ G H _ F K

The reasoning behind the answer is explained clearly.

Because Isabelle cannot stand next to Henry, she must occupy the spot next to Leah. Therefore, Jack stands next to Henry and the only possible order would have to be:

L I G H J F K.

Yes, there would be exactly one ordering of the students.

SAMPLE 2: Partial credit solution

The answer to part (a) is correct.

Part (b) is correct but not explained.

The student did not recall that Isabelle cannot stand next to Henry; therefore, the conclusion is incorrect.

a. One possible ordering of the students is:
Jack, Isabelle, Gina, Henry, Leah, Frank, and Katie.

b. There are three students who could stand in the second spot from the left. They are Isabelle, Leah, and Jack.

c. No, there would be two possible orderings of the students. With Leah in the left-most spot, the ordering looks like:

Leah, ____, Gina, Henry, ____, Frank, and Katie

Therefore, the two possible orderings are
Leah, Isabelle, Gina, Henry, Jack, Frank, and Katie
or
Leah, Jack, Gina, Henry, Isabelle, Frank, and Katie.

SAMPLE 3: No credit solution

The answer to part (a) is incorrect because Isabelle is next to Henry.

Parts (b) and (c) are based on the incorrect conclusion in part (a).

a. One possible ordering of the students is **L G J H I F K**.

b. There are four students who can stand in the second spot from the left. Those students are Leah, Gina, Isabelle, and Jack.

c. The two possible orderings are **L G J H I F K** and **L J G H I F K**.

PRACTICE Apply the Scoring Rubric

1. Full Credit; each part has a correct answer and both parts (b) and (c) are explained clearly.

1. A student's solution to the problem on the previous page is given below. Score the solution as *full credit, partial credit,* or *no credit. Explain* your reasoning. If you choose *partial credit* or *no credit,* explain how you would change the solution so that it earns a score of full credit.

a. A possible ordering of the students is I - J - G - H - L - F - K.

b. There are no restrictions on the second spot from the left. Leah, Isabelle, and Jack could all potentially stand in this location.

c. The positions of Gina, Henry, Frank, and Katie are fixed.

_ - _ - G - H - _ - F - K.

Because Isabelle cannot stand next to Henry, she must occupy the left-most spot or the second spot from the left. There are no restrictions on Leah or Jack. That leaves four possible orderings:

I - J - G - H - L - F - K   I - L - G - H - J - F - K
L - I - G - H - J - F - K   J - I - G - H - L - F - K.

If the restriction is added that Leah must occupy the left-most spot, there is exactly one ordering that would satisfy all conditions:

L - I - G - H - J - F - K.

1a. Equation (Reason)

$H = \frac{4}{5}(200 - A)$ (Given)

$\frac{5}{4}H = 200 - A$ (Multiplication Property of Equality)

$\frac{5}{4}H - 200 = -A$ (Subtraction Property of Equality)

$-\frac{5H}{4} + 200 = A$ (Division Property of Equality)

2a. No; if you add the number of students who use each type of transportation you get 1200, which is not very close to 1500.

2b. Yes; $\frac{1}{3}$ of 1200 is 400, and 400 students take public transportation to school.

3a. See below.

3b. *Sample answer:* The junior class president is seated in seat 2 and the junior class treasurer must be seated in seat 4. After all of the clues have been used the only unoccupied seat for the senior class secretary is seat 3.

3c. No. *Sample answer:* Since the junior class president is in the second seat and the sophomore class president is in seat 9 and the two sophomores are next to each other, seat 8 must be the sophomore class vice president, therefore seat 8 cannot be the senior class vice president.

EXTENDED RESPONSE

1. In some bowling leagues, the handicap H of a bowler with an average score A is found using the formula $H = \frac{4}{5}(200 - A)$. The handicap is then added to the bowler's score.
   a. Solve the formula for A. Write a reason for each step. **See margin.**
   b. Use your formula to find a bowler's average score with a handicap of 12. **185**
   c. Using this formula, is it possible to calculate a handicap for a bowler with an average score above 200? *Explain* your reasoning. **No; if the average score is above 200, the handicap would be negative.**

2. A survey was conducted at Porter High School asking students what form of transportation they use to go to school. All students in the high school were surveyed. The results are shown in the bar graph.

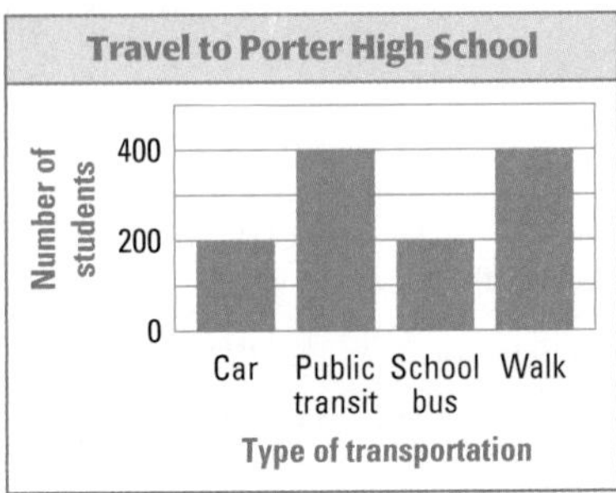

   a. Does the statement "About 1500 students attend Porter High School" follow from the data? *Explain.* **See margin.**
   b. Does the statement "About one third of all students at Porter take public transit to school" follow from the data? *Explain.* **See margin.**
   c. John makes the conclusion that Porter High School is located in a city or a city suburb. *Explain* his reasoning and tell if his conclusion is the result of *inductive reasoning* or *deductive reasoning.* **Since some students use public transportation, the school must be in a city or suburb; inductive.**
   d. Betty makes the conclusion that there are twice as many students who walk as take a car to school. *Explain* her reasoning and tell if her conclusion is the result of *inductive reasoning* or *deductive reasoning.* **About 400 students walk, which is twice as many as the 200 students who take a car; deductive.**

3. The senior class officers are planning a meeting with the principal and some class officers from the other grades. The senior class president, vice president, treasurer, and secretary will all be present. The junior class president and treasurer will attend. The sophomore class president and vice president, and freshmen treasurer will attend. The secretary makes a seating chart for the meeting using the following conditions.

   The principal will sit in chair 10. The senior class treasurer will sit at the other end.

   The senior class president will sit to the left of the principal, next to the junior class president, and across from the sophomore class president.

   All three treasurers will sit together. The two sophomores will sit next to each other.

   The two vice presidents and the freshman treasurer will sit on the same side of the table. **a–c. See margin.**

   a. Draw a diagram to show where everyone will sit.
   b. *Explain* why the senior class secretary must sit between the junior class president and junior class treasurer.
   c. Can the senior class vice-president sit across from the junior class president? *Justify* your answer.

3a.

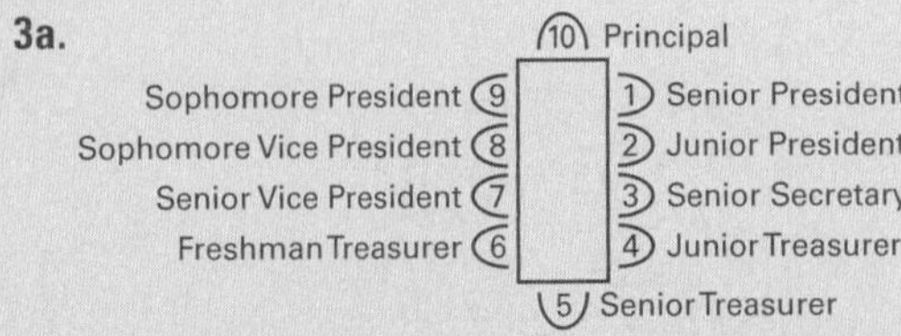

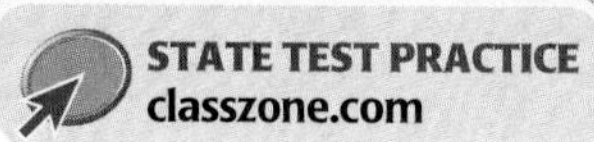

MULTIPLE CHOICE

4. If d represents an odd integer, which of the expressions represents an even integer? **C**

   Ⓐ $d + 2$

   Ⓑ $2d - 1$

   Ⓒ $3d + 1$

   Ⓓ $3d + 2$

5. In the repeating decimal 0.23142314. . . , where the digits 2314 repeat, which digit is in the 300th place to the right of the decimal point? **D**

   Ⓐ 1

   Ⓑ 2

   Ⓒ 3

   Ⓓ 4

GRIDDED ANSWER

6. Use the diagram to find the value of x. **3**

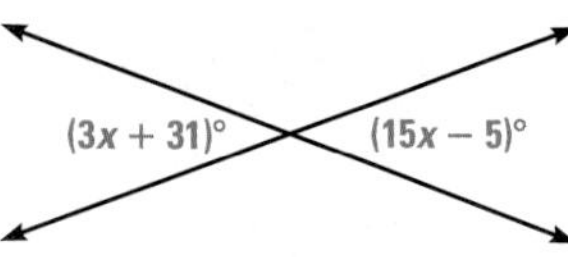

7. Three lines intersect in the figure shown. What is the value of $x + y$? **160**

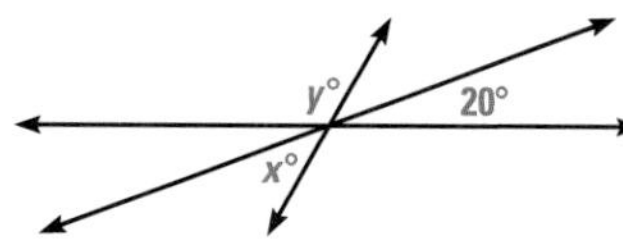

8. R is the midpoint of $\overline{PQ}$, and S and T are the midpoints of $\overline{PR}$ and $\overline{RQ}$, respectively. If $ST = 20$, what is PT? **30**

SHORT RESPONSE

9. Is this a correct conclusion from the given information? If so, *explain* why. If not, *explain* the error in the reasoning.
   No; the conclusion was true but that does not imply the hypothesis is true.

   If you are a soccer player, then you wear shin guards. Your friend is wearing shin guards. Therefore, she is a soccer player.

10. *Describe* the pattern in the numbers. Write the next number in the pattern.

    192, −48, 12, −3, . . . **$-\frac{1}{4}$ of the previous number; $\frac{3}{4}$.**

11. Points A, B, C, D, E, and F are coplanar. Points A, B, and F are collinear. The line through A and B is perpendicular to the line through C and D, and the line through C and D is perpendicular to the line through E and F. Which four points must lie on the same line? *Justify* your answer. **See margin.**

12. Westville High School offers after-school tutoring with five student volunteer tutors for this program: Jen, Kim, Lou, Mike, and Nina. On any given weekday, three tutors are scheduled to work. Due to the students' other commitments after school, the tutoring work schedule must meet the following conditions.

    Jen can work any day except every other Monday and Wednesday.

    Kim can only work on Thursdays and Fridays.

    Lou can work on Tuesdays and Wednesdays.

    Mike cannot work on Fridays.

    Nina cannot work on Tuesdays.

    Name three tutors who can work on *any* Wednesday. *Justify* your answer. **Lou, Mike, and Nina; Lou can work Wednesdays, Mike's only restriction is that he cannot work on Fridays, Nina's only restriction is that she cannot work on Tuesdays.**

11. Points A, B, E, and F; since the line containing C and D is perpendicular to the line containing A and B, it is perpendicular to the line containing E and F, therefore E must lie on the line containing A, B, and F.

3 Pacing and Assignment Guide

REGULAR SCHEDULE

Pre-AP For pacing and assignments for a Pre-AP course, see the *Geometry Toolkit.*

Lesson	Les. Day	BASIC	AVERAGE	ADVANCED
3.1	Day 1	pp. 150–152 Exs. 1–15, 17–23 odd, 34–39, 45–49	pp. 150–152 Exs. 1, 2, 4–6, 8–10, 12–15, 16–22 even, 24–28, 34–42, 45–49 odd	pp. 150–152 Exs. 1, 2, 5, 6, 9, 10, 13, 14, 16–28 even, 29–44*, 46, 48
3.2	Day 1	pp. 157–160 Exs. 1–8, 9–15 odd, 17–24, 37–40, 44–52 even	pp. 157–160 Exs. 1–3, 4–20 even, 21–34, 37–42, 44, 45, 49, 51	pp. 157–160 Exs. 1–3, 7, 8, 13, 15, 18, 19, 21–37*, 39–43*, 47, 50, 52
3.3	Day 1	pp. 165–169 Exs. 1–17, 29, 30	pp. 165–169 Exs. 1, 2, 5–9, 12–17, 27, 29, 30, 46–51	pp. 165–169 Exs. 1, 2, 4–8, 11–17, 29, 30
	Day 2	pp. 165–169 Exs. 18–23, 31–38, 46–54	pp. 165–169 Exs. 18–26, 31–44, 52–54	pp. 165–169 Exs. 18, 21–28*, 31–45*, 52–54
3.4	Day 1	SRH p. 869 Exs. 1, 8, 11, 16; pp. 175–178 Exs. 1–18	pp. 175–178 Exs. 1, 2, 4–6, 8–12, 14–18 even, 23–25, 43–49	pp. 175–178 Exs. 1, 2, 4–10 even, 14–18 even, 23–26, 43–49
	Day 2	pp. 175–178 Exs. 19–22, 33–38, 43–49	pp. 175–178 Exs. 19–22, 26–31*, 33–41	pp. 175–178 Exs. 19–22, 27–42*
3.5	Day 1	SRH p. 879 Exs. 5–12; pp. 184–187 Exs. 1–6, 9–13, 16–19, 22–25, 29, 70–75	pp. 184–187 Exs. 1, 2, 4–6, 9, 11–13, 17–19, 22, 24–26, 29, 49–52, 70–75	pp. 184–187 Exs. 1, 2, 6–9, 13–15, 19–22, 26–29, 49–52, 70–75
	Day 2	pp. 184–187 Exs. 30–33, 36–39, 45–49, 60–63, 67–69	pp. 184–187 Exs. 31–33, 40–42, 45–48, 53–57, 60–65, 67–69	pp. 184–187 Exs. 33–35, 42–44, 46–48, 53–69*
3.6	Day 1	pp. 194–197 Exs. 1–7, 31, 32, 42–47	pp. 194–197 Exs. 1, 3–7, 22–25, 31, 32, 42–47	pp. 194–197 Exs. 1, 4, 6, 7, 22–28*, 31, 32, 42–46 even
	Day 2	pp. 194–197 Exs. 8–17, 29, 30, 39–41	pp. 194–197 Exs. 9–14, 17–21, 29, 30, 33, 34, 40	pp. 194–197 Exs. 10–12, 17–21, 29, 30, 33–38*, 41
Review	Day 1	pp. 202–205 Exs. 1–28	pp. 202–205 Exs. 1–28	pp. 202–205 Exs. 1–28
Assess	Day 1	Chapter 3 Test	Chapter 3 Test	Chapter 3 Test
Yearly Pacing		Chapter 3 Total – 12 days	Chapters 1–3 Total – 38 days	Remaining – 122 days

*Challenge Exercises   EP = Extra Practice   SRH = Skills Review Handbook

BLOCK SCHEDULE

DAY 1	DAY 2	DAY 3	DAY 4	DAY 5	DAY 6
3.1	**3.3**	**3.4**	**3.5**	**3.6**	**REVIEW**
pp. 150–152 Exs. 1, 2, 4–6, 8–10, 12–15, 16–22 even, 24–28, 34–42, 45–49 odd	pp. 165–169 Exs. 1, 2, 5–9, 12–27, 29–44, 46–54	pp. 175–178 Exs. 1, 2, 4–6, 8–12, 14–18 even, 19–31*, 33–41, 43–49	pp. 184–187 Exs. 1, 2, 4–6, 9, 11–13, 17–19, 22, 24–26, 29, 31–33, 40–42, 45–57, 60–65, 67–75	pp. 194–197 Exs. 1, 3–7, 9–14, 17–25, 29–34, 40, 42–47	pp. 202–205 Exs. 1–28
3.2					**ASSESS**
pp. 157–160 Exs. 1–3, 4–20 even, 21–34, 37–42, 44, 45, 49, 51					Chapter 3 Test
Yearly Pacing	Chapter 3 Total – 6 days	Chapters 1–3 Total – 19 days	Remaining – 61 days		

RESOURCE MANAGER

Chapter Resource Book

CHAPTER SUPPORT						
Parents as Partners (Chapter Overview with home involvement exercises and activity)					p. 1	
LESSON SUPPORT	**3.1**	**3.2**	**3.3**	**3.4**	**3.5**	**3.6**
Teaching Guide/Lesson Plan	p. 3	p. 16	p. 30	p. 45	p. 59	p. 74
Activity Masters			p. 32		p. 61	p. 76
Technology Activities & Keystrokes		p. 18		p. 47		
Activity Support Masters						
Practice (3 levels)	p. 5	p. 19	p. 33	p. 48	p. 63	p. 77
Study Guide	p. 11	p. 25	p. 39	p. 54	p. 69	p. 83
Catch-Up for Absent Students	p. 13	p. 27	p. 41	p. 56	p. 71	p. 85
Problem Solving/Application	p. 14	p. 28	p. 42	p. 57	p. 72	p. 86
Challenge Practice	p. 15	p. 29	p. 44	p. 58	p. 73	p. 87

REVIEW			
Chapter Review Games and Activities	p. 88	Cumulative Practice	p. 91
Project with Rubric	p. 89	Resource Book Answers	A1

Transparencies	3.1	3.2	3.3	3.4	3.5	3.6
Warm-Up/Daily Homework Quiz	✔	✔	✔	✔	✔	✔
Notetaking Guide	✔	✔	✔	✔	✔	✔
Teacher Support				✔	✔	✔
Answer Transparencies	✔	✔	✔	✔	✔	✔

ASSESSMENT BOOK

Quizzes	p. 31	SAT/ACT Chapter Test	p. 42
Chapter Tests (3 levels)	p. 34	Alternative Assessment with Rubric	p. 44
Standardized Chapter Test	p. 40		

TECHNOLOGY

- Easy Planner
- Test and Practice Generator
- Power Presentations
- @HomeTutor
- Activity Generator
- Animated Geometry
- Classzone.com
- eEdition Plus Online
- eWorkbook Plus Online
- ML Assessment System

ADDITIONAL RESOURCES

- Worked-Out Solution Key
- Notetaking Guide
- Practice Wookbook
- Geometry Toolkit
- Benchmark Tests
- Remediation Book
- Spanish Study Guide
- Spanish Assessment Book
- Student Resources in Spanish
- Multi-Language Visual Glossary

LESSON 3.1 Practice B
For use with pages 146–152

Think of each segment in the diagram as part of a line. Complete the statement with *parallel*, *skew*, or *perpendicular*.

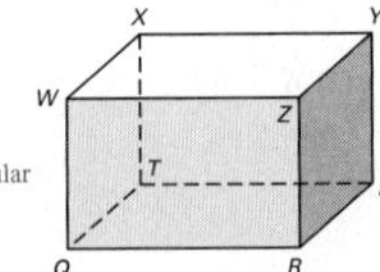

1. $\overleftrightarrow{WZ}$ and $\overleftrightarrow{ZR}$ are __?__. perpendicular
2. $\overleftrightarrow{WZ}$ and $\overleftrightarrow{ST}$ are __?__. parallel
3. $\overleftrightarrow{QT}$ and $\overleftrightarrow{YS}$ are __?__. skew
4. Plane *WZR* and plane *SYZ* are __?__. perpendicular
5. Plane *RQT* and plane *YXW* are __?__. parallel

Think of each segment in the diagram as part of a line. Which line(s) or plane(s) appear to fit the description?

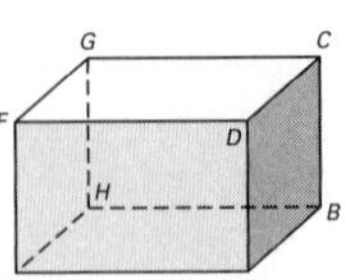

6. Line(s) parallel to $\overleftrightarrow{EH}$ $\overleftrightarrow{FG}, \overleftrightarrow{DC}, \overleftrightarrow{AB}$
7. Line(s) perpendicular to $\overleftrightarrow{EH}$ $\overleftrightarrow{AE}, \overleftrightarrow{BH}, \overleftrightarrow{EF}, \overleftrightarrow{HG}$
8. Line(s) skew to $\overleftrightarrow{CD}$ and containing point *F* $\overleftrightarrow{EF}$
9. Plane(s) perpendicular to plane *AEH*
10. Plane(s) parallel to plane *FGC* plane *EHB*

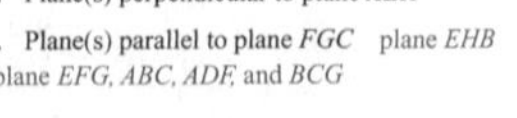

9. plane *EFG*, *ABC*, *ADF*, and *BCG*

Classify the angle pair as *corresponding*, *alternate interior*, *alternate exterior*, or *consecutive interior* angles.

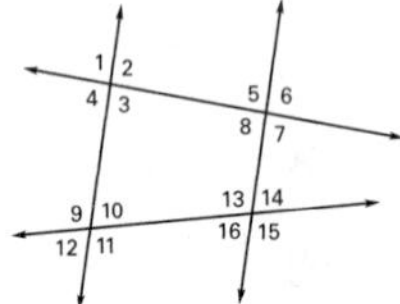

11. ∠1 and ∠9 corresponding
12. ∠8 and ∠13 consecutive interior
13. ∠6 and ∠16 alternate exterior
14. ∠4 and ∠10 alternate interior
15. ∠8 and ∠16 corresponding
16. ∠10 and ∠13 consecutive interior

In Exercises 17–20, use the markings in the diagram.

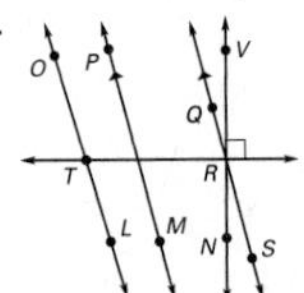

17. Name a pair of parallel lines. $\overleftrightarrow{PM} \parallel \overleftrightarrow{QS}$
18. Name a pair of perpendicular lines. $\overleftrightarrow{VN} \perp \overleftrightarrow{RT}$
19. Is $\overleftrightarrow{OL} \parallel \overleftrightarrow{TR}$? Explain. No; the lines intersect at *T*.
20. Is $\overleftrightarrow{OL} \perp \overleftrightarrow{TR}$? Explain. No; there is no right angle symbol shown.

LESSON 3.1

LESSON 3.1 Practice B *continued*
For use with pages 146–152

Copy and complete the statement with *sometimes*, *always*, or *never*.

21. If two lines are parallel, then they __?__ intersect. never
22. If one line is skew to another, then they are __?__ coplanar. never
23. If two lines intersect, then they are __?__ perpendicular. sometimes
24. If two lines are coplanar, then they are __?__ parallel. sometimes

Copy the diagram and sketch the line. See below.

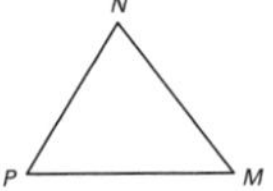

25. Line through *M* and parallel to $\overleftrightarrow{NP}$.
26. Line through *N* and perpendicular to $\overleftrightarrow{MP}$.
27. Line through *M* and perpendicular to $\overleftrightarrow{MP}$.
28. Line through *P* and parallel to $\overleftrightarrow{MN}$.

Use construction tools to construct a line through point *P* that is parallel to line *m*. 29–30. Check students' drawings.

29. • *P*

30. • *P*

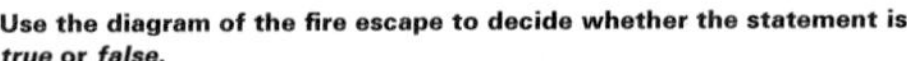

Use the diagram of the fire escape to decide whether the statement is *true* or *false*.

31. The planes containing the platforms outside of each pair of windows are parallel to the ground. true
32. The planes containing the stairs are parallel to each other. true
33. The planes containing the platforms outside of each pair of windows are perpendicular to the planes containing the stairs. false
34. The planes containing the platform outside of each pair of windows are perpendicular to the plane containing the side of the building. true

25. 26. 27. 28.

LESSON 3.1

LESSON 3.2 Practice B
For use with pages 153–160

1. 50°; Corresponding Angles Postulate
2. 135°; Consecutive Interior Angles Theorem

Find the angle measure. Tell which postulate or theorem you use.

1. If $m\angle 1 = 50°$, then $m\angle 5 =$ __?__.
2. If $m\angle 4 = 45°$, then $m\angle 6 =$ __?__.
3. If $m\angle 2 = 130°$, then $m\angle 7 =$ __?__.
4. If $m\angle 6 = 123°$, then $m\angle 3 =$ __?__.

3. 130°; Alternate Exterior Angles Theorem
4. 123°; Alternate Interior Angles Theorem

Find $m\angle 1$ and $m\angle 2$.

5. 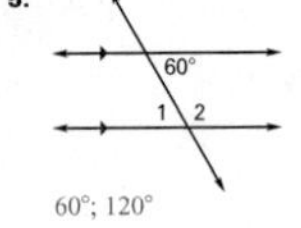

60°; 120°

6. 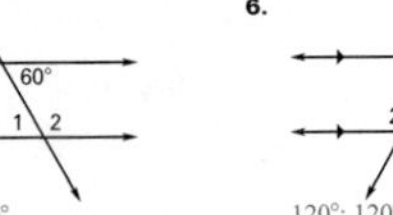

120°; 120°

7. 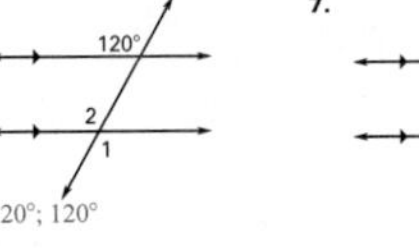
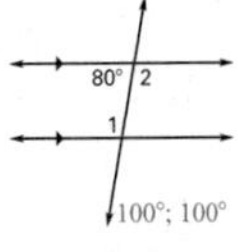

100°; 100°

8. 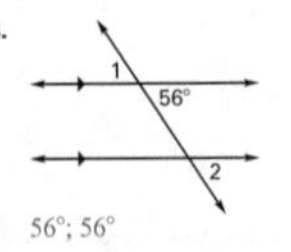

56°; 56°

9. 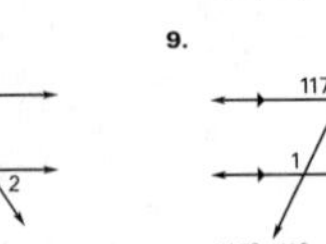

117°; 63°

10. 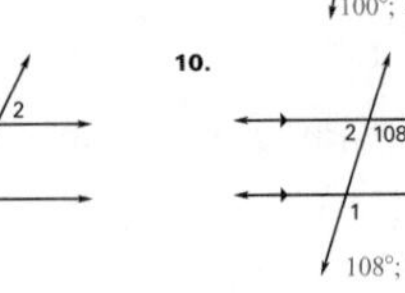

108°; 72°

Find the values of *x* and *y*.

11. 110; 110

12. 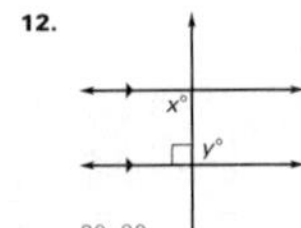

90; 90

13. 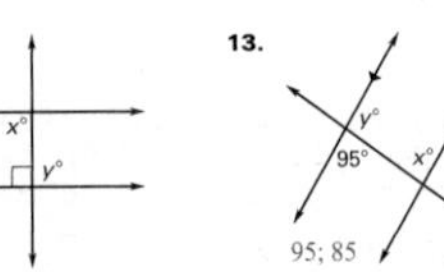

95; 85

14. 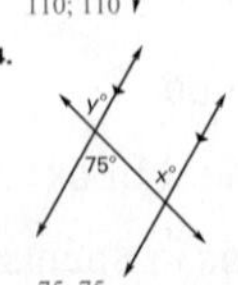

75; 75

15. 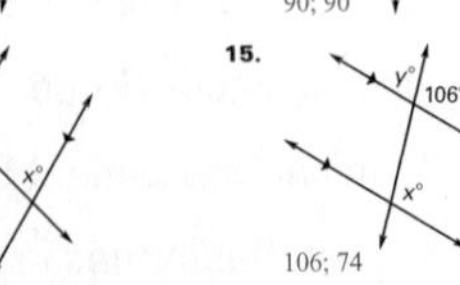

106; 74

16. 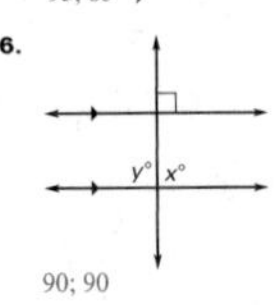

90; 90

LESSON 3.2

LESSON 3.2 Practice B *continued*
For use with pages 153–160

Find the value of *x*.

17. 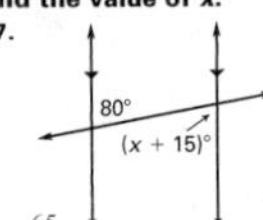

65

18. 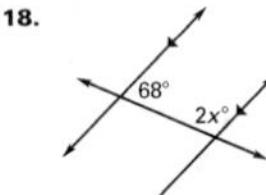

56

19. 48

20. 23

21. 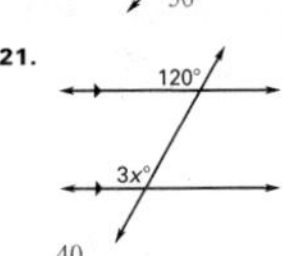

40

22. 77

In Exercises 23–31, complete the two-column proof.

GIVEN: $p \perp q$, $q \parallel r$

PROVE: $p \perp r$

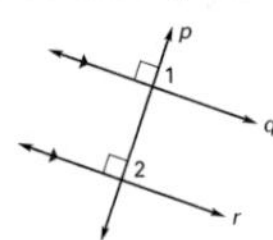

Statements	Reasons	
$p \perp q$	23. __?__	Given
∠1 is a right angle	24. __?__	Perpendicular lines form right angles
$m\angle 1 = 90°$	25. __?__	Definition of right angle
$q \parallel r$	26. __?__	Given
$\angle 1 \cong \angle 2$	27. __?__	Corresponding Angles Postulate
$m\angle 1 = m\angle 2$	28. __?__	Definition of congruent angles
$m\angle 2 = 90°$	29. __?__	Substitution Property of Equality
∠2 is a right angle	30. __?__	Definition of right angle
$p \perp r$	31. __?__	Perpendicular lines form right angles

LESSON 3.2

LESSON 3.3 Practice B
For use with pages 161–169

Is it possible to prove that lines *p* and *q* are parallel? If so, state the postulate or theorem you would use.

1. 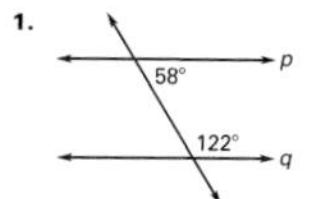

yes; Consecutive Interior Angles Converse

2. 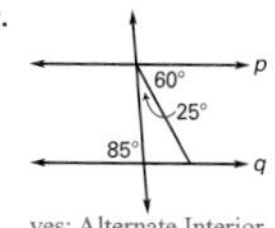

yes; Alternate Interior Angles Converse

3. 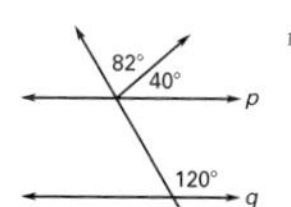

no

Find the value of *x* that makes *m* ∥ *n*.

4. 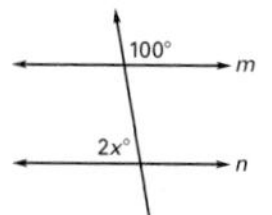

40

5. 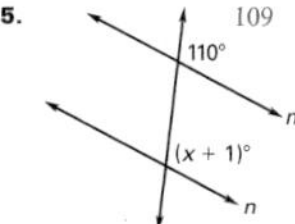

109

6. 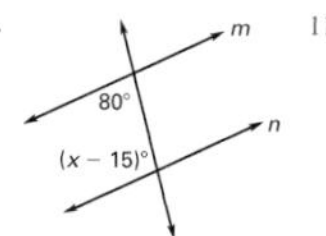

115

7. 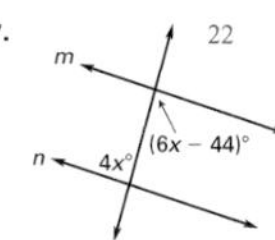

22

8. 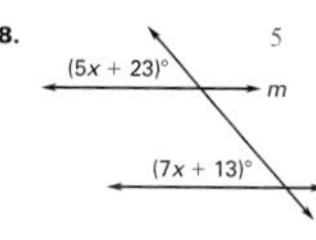

5

9. 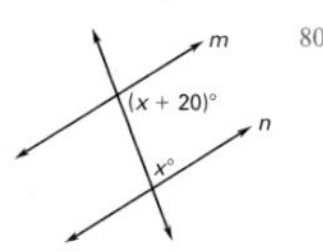

80

In Exercises 10–12, choose the word that best completes the statement.

10. If two lines are cut by a transversal so the alternate interior angles are (*congruent, supplementary, complementary*), then the lines are parallel. congruent

11. If two lines are cut by a transversal so the consecutive interior angles are (*congruent, supplementary, complementary*), then the lines are parallel. supplementary

12. If two lines are cut by a transversal so the corresponding angles are (*congruent, supplementary, complementary*), then the lines are parallel. congruent

13. Gardens A garden has five rows of vegetables. Each row is parallel to the row immediately next to it. *Explain* why the first row is parallel to the last row.
Each row is parallel to the one next to it, so $r_1 \parallel r_2$, $r_2 \parallel r_3$, and so on. Then $r_1 \parallel r_3$ by the Transitive Property of Parallel Lines. By continuing this reasoning, $r_1 \parallel r_5$. So, the first row is parallel to the last row.

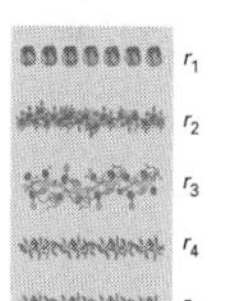

LESSON 3.3

LESSON 3.3 Practice B *continued*
For use with pages 161–169

In Exercises 14–18, complete the two-column proof.

GIVEN: $g \parallel h$, $\angle 1 \cong \angle 2$

PROVE: $p \parallel r$

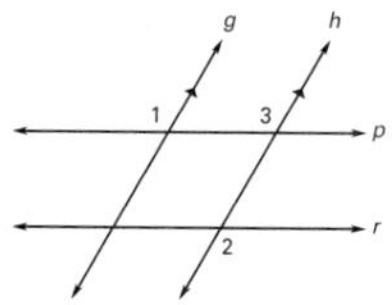

Statements	Reasons	
$g \parallel h$	**14.** ?	Given
$\angle 1 \cong \angle 3$	**15.** ?	Corresponding Angles Postulate
$\angle 1 \cong \angle 2$	**16.** ?	Given
$\angle 2 \cong \angle 3$	**17.** ?	Transitive Property of Equality
$p \parallel r$	**18.** ?	Alternate Exterior Angles Converse

In Exercises 19–23, complete the two-column proof.

GIVEN: $n \parallel m$, $\angle 1 \cong \angle 2$

PROVE: $p \parallel r$

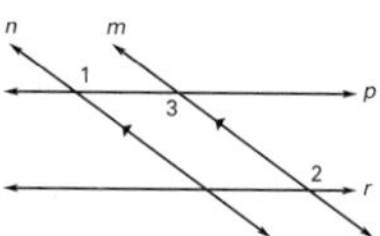

Statements	Reasons	
$n \parallel m$	**19.** ?	Given
$\angle 1 \cong \angle 3$	**20.** ?	Alternate Interior Angles Theorem
$\angle 1 \cong \angle 2$	**21.** ?	Given
$\angle 2 \cong \angle 3$	**22.** ?	Transitive Property of Equality
$p \parallel r$	**23.** ?	Alternate Interior Angles Converse

24. Railroad Tracks Two sets of railroad tracks intersect as shown. How do you know that line *n* is parallel to line *m*?
Corresponding Angles Converse

LESSON 3.3

LESSON 3.4 Practice B
For use with pages 171–179

LESSON 3.4

Find the slope of the line that passes through the points.

1. 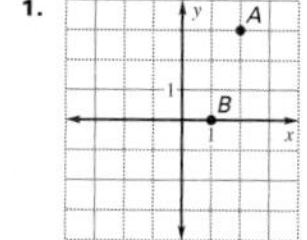
3

2. 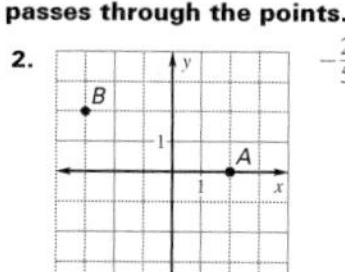
$-\frac{2}{5}$

3. 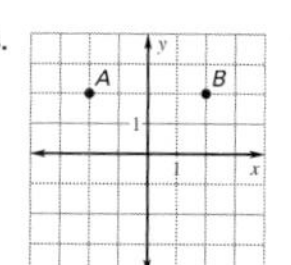
1

Find the slope of each line. Are the lines parallel? See below.

4. 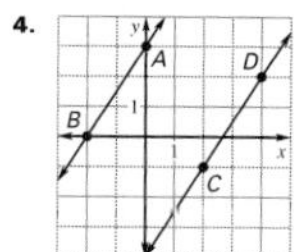

5. 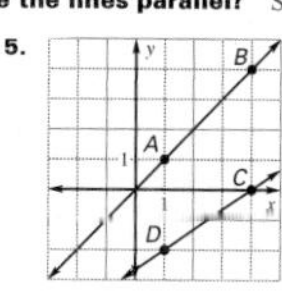

6. 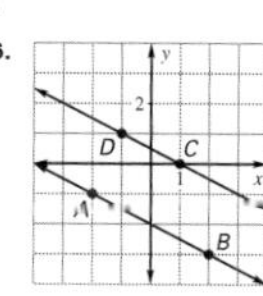

Find the slope of each line. Are the lines perpendicular? See below.

7. 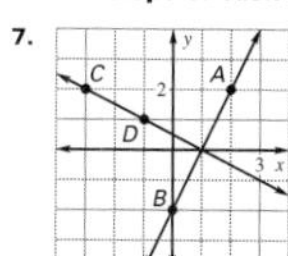

8. 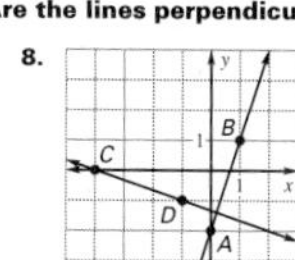

9. 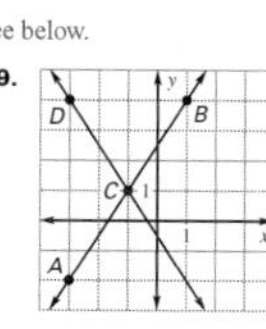

Tell whether the lines through the given points are *parallel, perpendicular,* or *neither*.

10. Line 1: (−1, 2), (2, 3)
Line 2: (0, 0), (3, 1)
parallel

11. Line 1: (0, 1), (1, 3)
Line 2: (4, −1), (5, 2)
neither

12. Line 1: (−5, 0), (−3, −2)
Line 2: (−2, 2), (0, 4)
perpendicular

13. Line 1: (−3, 4), (−3, 1)
Line 2: (2, 1), (5, 5)
neither

14. Line 1: (−5, 2), (−2, 2)
Line 2: (2, 1), (4, 1)
parallel

15. Line 1: (−2, 5), (1, 4)
Line 2: (4, 0), (5, 3)
perpendicular

Tell whether the intersection of $\overleftrightarrow{AB}$ and $\overleftrightarrow{CD}$ forms a right angle.

16. $A(-8, 3), B(1, 2), C(0, 9), D(-1, 0)$ yes

17. $A(3, 2), B(5, 10), C(7, -4), D(3, -3)$ yes

18. $A(5, 4), B(-3, 20), C(9, -2), D(6, 4)$ no

19. $A(7, 12), B(1, 5), C(10, -7), D(3, -1)$ yes

20. $A(-8, 17), B(-5, 18), C(6, 11), D(5, 8)$ no

21. $A(-7, 3), B(-10, 15), C(-1, 5), D(4, 35)$ no

4. $m_{\overleftrightarrow{AB}} = \frac{3}{2}, m_{\overleftrightarrow{CD}} = \frac{3}{2}$; yes **5.** $m_{\overleftrightarrow{AB}} = 1, m_{\overleftrightarrow{CD}} = \frac{2}{3}$; no **6.** $m_{\overleftrightarrow{AB}} = -\frac{1}{2}, m_{\overleftrightarrow{CD}} = -\frac{1}{2}$; yes

7. $m_{\overleftrightarrow{AB}} = 2, m_{\overleftrightarrow{CD}} = -\frac{1}{2}$; yes **8.** $m_{\overleftrightarrow{AB}} = 3, m_{\overleftrightarrow{CD}} = -\frac{1}{3}$; yes **9.** $m_{\overleftrightarrow{AB}} = \frac{3}{2}, m_{\overleftrightarrow{CD}} = -\frac{3}{2}$; no

LESSON 3.4 Practice B *continued*
For use with pages 171–179

LESSON 3.4

Graph the line parallel to line *AB* that passes through point *P*.

22. 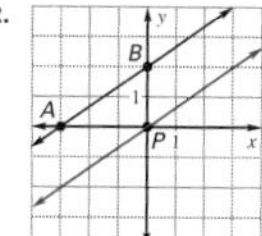

23. 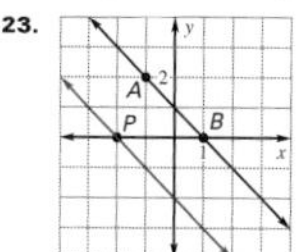

24. 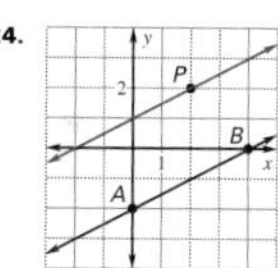

Graph the line perpendicular to line *AB* that passes through point *P*.

25.

26. 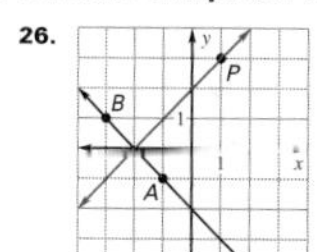

27. 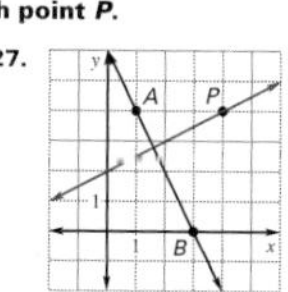

In Exercises 28 and 29, consider the three given lines.

Line *a*: through the point (2, 0) with a *y*-intercept of (0, 1)
Line *b*: through the point (2, 0) with a *y*-intercept of (0, 5)
Line *c*: through the point (2, 0) with a *y*-intercept of (0, 3)

28. Which line is most steep? line *b*

29. Which line is least steep? line *a*

30. Parallelograms A parallelogram is a four-sided figure whose opposite sides are parallel. *Explain* why the figure shown is a parallelogram.
$m_{\overleftrightarrow{AB}} = \frac{3}{2}, m_{\overleftrightarrow{CD}} = \frac{3}{2}, m_{\overleftrightarrow{BC}} = 0, m_{\overleftrightarrow{AD}} = 0$;
The opposite sides of the figure are parallel because they have the same slope.

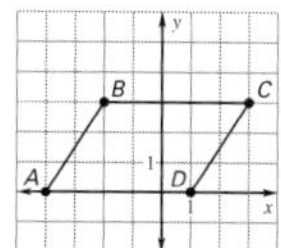

31. Escalators On an escalator, you move 2 feet vertically for every 3 feet you move horizontally. When you reach the top of the escalator, you have moved a horizontal distance of 90 feet. Find the height *h* of the escalator. 60 feet

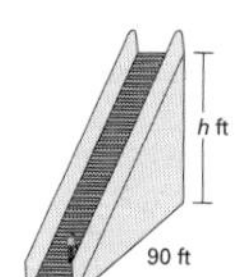

3 Lesson Practice Level B

LESSON 3.5 Practice B
For use with pages 180–187

Write an equation of line *AB* in slope-intercept form. See below.

1. 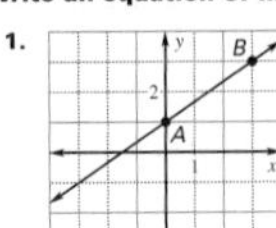 **2.** 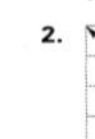 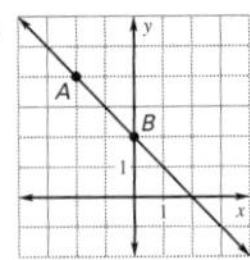 **3.** 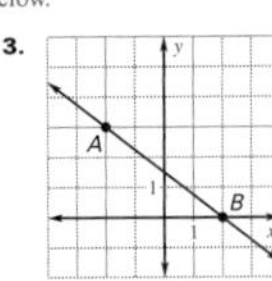

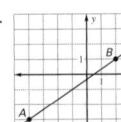

4. **5.** **6.** 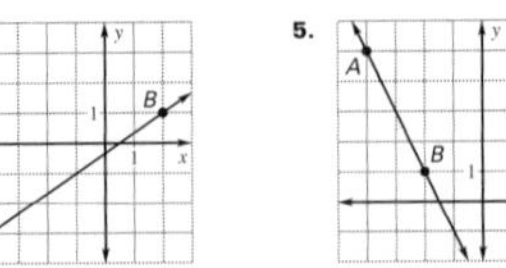

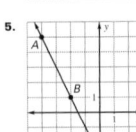

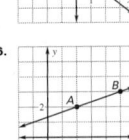

Write an equation of the line that passes through point *P* and is parallel to the line with the given equation. See below.

7. $P(-2, 0); y = -\frac{1}{2}x + 6$ **8.** $P(3, 9); y = 4x - 8$ **9.** $P(-5, -4); y = -2x - 10$

Write an equation of the line that passes through point *P* and is perpendicular to the line with the given equation. See below.

10. $P(5, 20); y = \frac{1}{2}x + 8$ **11.** $P(4, 5); y = -\frac{1}{3}x - 6$ **12.** $P(3, 5); y = 4$

Write an equation of the line that passes through point *P* and is parallel to line *AB*.

13. 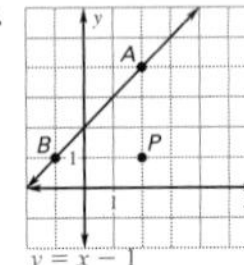
$y = x - 1$

14. 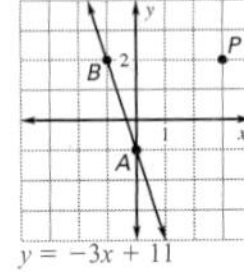
$y = -3x + 11$

15. 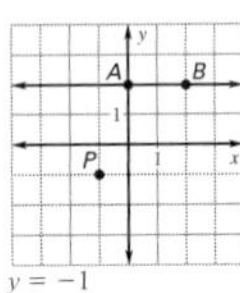
$y = -1$

1. $y = \frac{2}{3}x + 1$ **2.** $y = -x + 2$ **3.** $y = -\frac{3}{4}x + \frac{3}{2}$ **4.** $y = \frac{2}{3}x - \frac{1}{3}$
5. $y = -2x - 3$ **6.** $y = \frac{1}{3}x + \frac{4}{3}$ **7.** $y = -\frac{1}{2}x - 1$ **8.** $y = 4x - 3$
9. $y = -2x - 14$ **10.** $y = -2x + 30$ **11.** $y = 3x - 7$ **12.** $x = 3$

LESSON 3.5

LESSON 3.5 Practice B *continued*
For use with pages 180–187

Write an equation of the line that passes through point *P* and is perpendicular to line *AB*.

16. 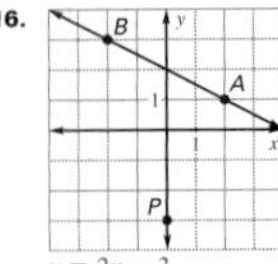
$y = 2x - 3$

17. 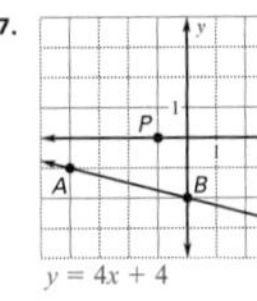
$y = 4x + 4$

18. 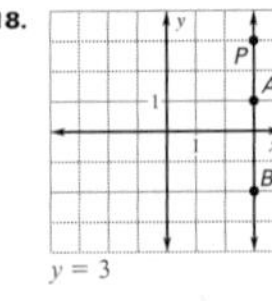
$y = 3$

Graph the equation.

19. $-2x + y = -1$ 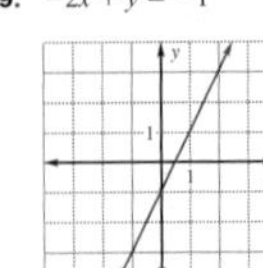

20. $y - 3 = -3x + 2$ 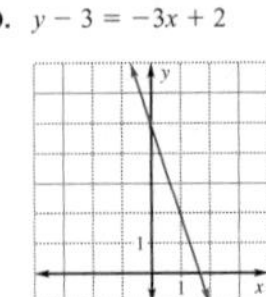 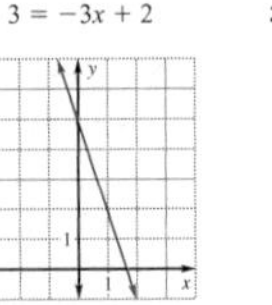

21. $y + 6 = 3$

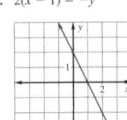

22. $2(x - 1) = -y$ 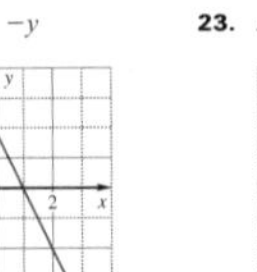

23. $x - 4 = 0$ 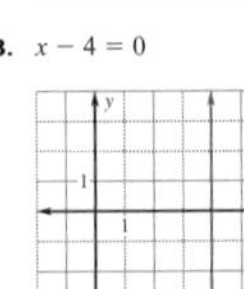

24. $2y - 4 = 2x$ 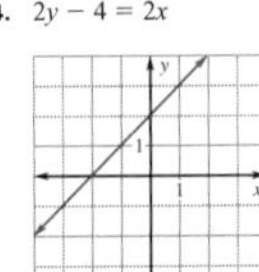

25. Country Club The graph models the total cost of joining a country club. Write an equation of the line. *Explain* the meaning of the slope and the *y*-intercept of the line.

$y = 500x + 5000$; The slope is the monthly fee, \$500, and the *y*-intercept is the initial cost to join the club, \$5000.

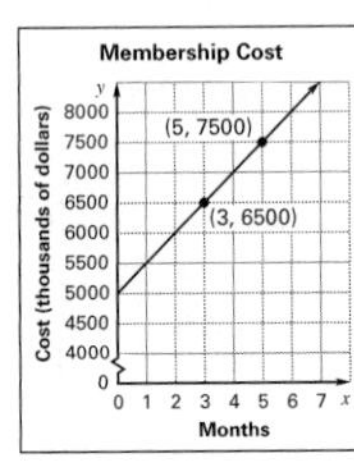

LESSON 3.5

LESSON 3.6 Practice B
For use with pages 190–197

What can you conclude from the given information? State the reason for your conclusion.

1. $\angle 1 \cong \angle 2$ 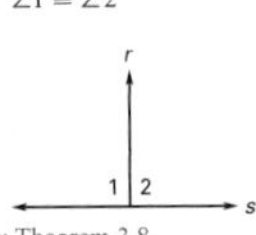
$r \perp s$; Theorem 3.8

2. $n \perp m$ 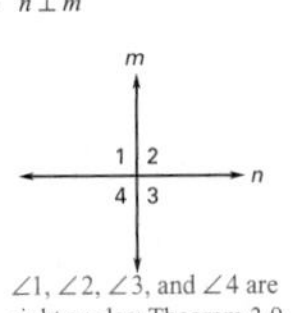
$\angle 1, \angle 2, \angle 3$, and $\angle 4$ are right angles; Theorem 3.9

3. $\overrightarrow{BA} \perp \overrightarrow{BC}$ 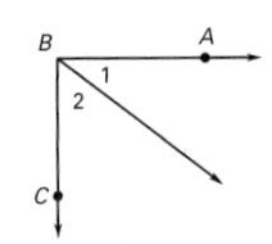
$\angle 1$ and $\angle 2$ are complementary; Theorem 3.10

Find the value of *x*.

4. 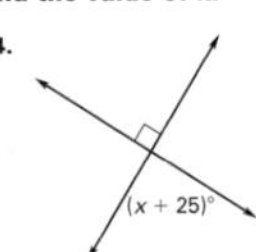 65

5. 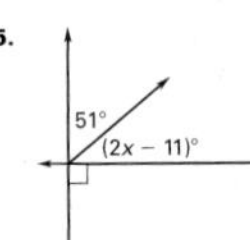 25

6. 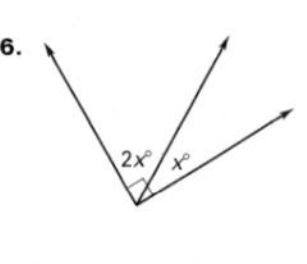 30

7. 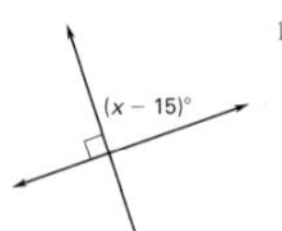 105

8. 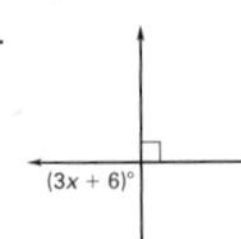 28

9. 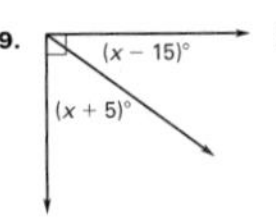 50

Find the measure of the indicated angle.

10. $\angle 1$ 90° **11.** $\angle 2$ 30°
12. $\angle 3$ 60° **13.** $\angle 4$ 30°
14. $\angle 5$ 30° **15.** $\angle 6$ 60°

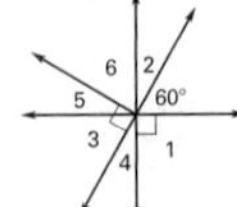

In Exercises 16–18, use the diagram.

16. Is $r \parallel s$? no
17. Is $m \parallel n$? yes
18. Is $s \parallel t$? yes

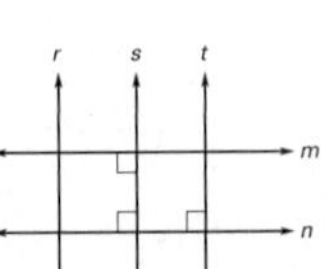

LESSON 3.6

LESSON 3.6 Practice B *continued*
For use with pages 190–197

Find the distance from point *A* to line *c*. Round your answers to the nearest tenth.

19. 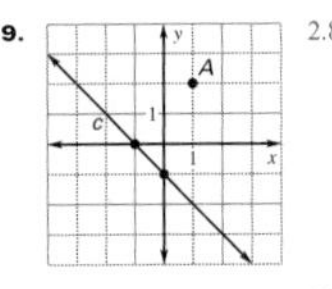 2.8 **20.** 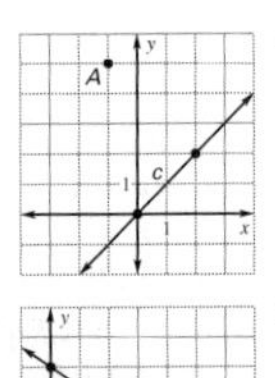 4.2 **21.** 4.5

22. 3.2 **23.** 3.6 **24.** 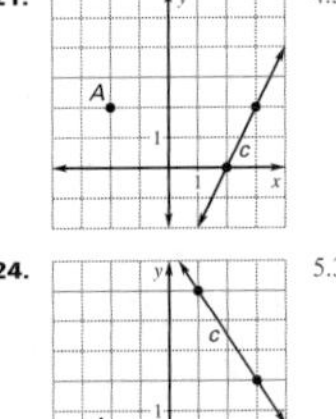 5.3

25. Maps A map of a neighborhood is drawn on a graph where units are measured in feet.

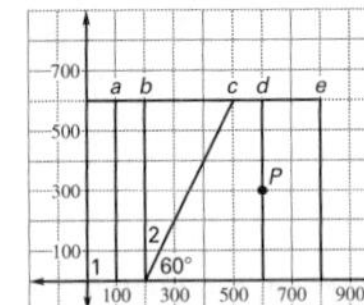

a. Find $m\angle 1$. 90°
b. Find $m\angle 2$. 30°
c. Find the distance from point *P* to line *a*. 500 ft
d. Find the distance from point *P* to line *c*. Round your answer to the nearest foot. 224 ft

LESSON 3.6

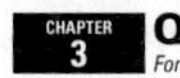

Quiz 1
For use after Lessons 3.1–3.2

Complete the statement.

1. ∠1 and __?__ are corresponding angles.
2. ∠4 and __?__ are consecutive interior angles.
3. ∠3 and __?__ are alternate interior angles.
4. ∠1 and __?__ are alternate exterior angles.

Find the value of *x*.

5.
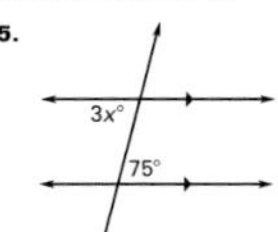

6.
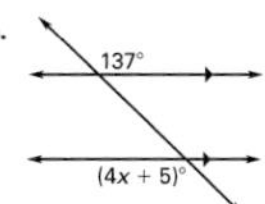

7.
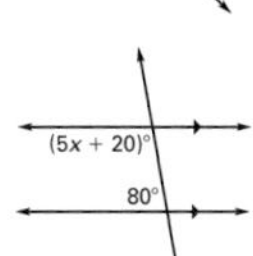

Answers

1. ∠5
2. ∠6
3. ∠6
4. ∠8
5. 25
6. 33
7. 16

Quiz 2
For use after Lessons 3.3–3.4

Find the value of *x* that makes $m \parallel n$.

1. 4x°, 84°
2. (2x + 5)°, 135°
3. 70°, (3x − 8)°

Find the slope of the line that passes through the given points.

4. (2, −2), (6, 6)
5. (3, 4), (5, 6)
6. (−4, 3), (−9, 7)

Answers

1. 24
2. 65
3. 26
4. 2
5. 1
6. $-\frac{4}{5}$

Quiz 3
For use after Lessons 3.5–3.6

Write an equation of the line that passes through point *P* and is parallel to the line with the given equation.

1. $P(1, 1), y = -2x + 4$
2. $P(-7, -8), y - 6 = 3x + 6$
3. $P(5, 3), x = -2$

Write an equation of the line that passes through point *P* and is perpendicular to the line with the given equation.

4. $P(8, 9), y = 4x - 2$
5. $P(3, 6), y = -5$
6. $P(2, 0), 36x + 6y = 18$

Determine which lines, if any, must be parallel. Explain.

7.

8.
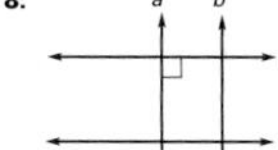

Answers

1. $y = -2x + 3$
2. $y = 3x + 13$
3. $x = 5$
4. $y = -\frac{1}{4}x + 11$
5. $x = 3$
6. $y = \frac{1}{6}x - \frac{1}{3}$
7. ℓ and *n*; Lines Perpendicular to a Transversal Theorem
8. None. *Sample answer:* It is not known whether *b* is perpendicular to *c*.

3 Assessment

Chapter Test B
CHAPTER 3 *For use after Chapter 3*

Identify the pairs of angles as *corresponding, alternate interior, alternate exterior, consecutive interior,* or *vertical* angles.

1. $\angle 1$ and $\angle 8$
2. $\angle 4$ and $\angle 5$
3. $\angle 4$ and $\angle 6$
4. $\angle 2$ and $\angle 3$
5. $\angle 3$ and $\angle 7$
6. $\angle 2$ and $\angle 7$

Find the value of *x*.

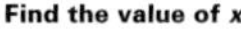

7.

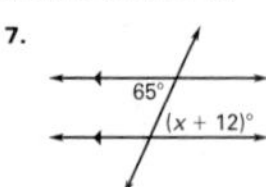

8.

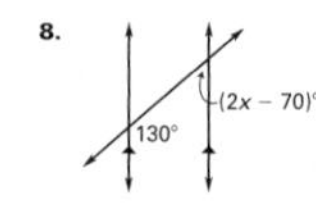

9.

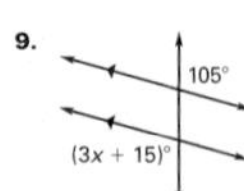

10.

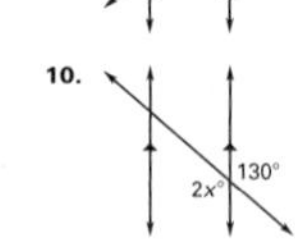

Find the value of *x* that makes $m \parallel n$.

11.

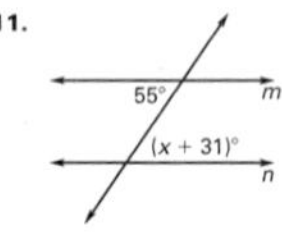

12.

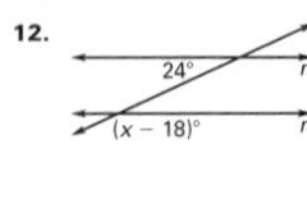

Tell whether the lines through the given points are *parallel, perpendicular,* or *neither.*

13. Line 1: (1, 2), (2, 0)
    Line 2: (0, −1), (−2, −2)
14. Line 1: (−2, 1), (1, −1)
    Line 2: (1, 3), (4, 1)
15. Line 1: (0, 1), (1, 4)
    Line 2: (3, 2), (6, 3)
16. Line 1: (−1, 1), (1, 3)
    Line 2: (2, −1), (4, 1)

Answers

1. alternate exterior
2. alternate interior
3. consecutive interior
4. vertical
5. corresponding
6. alternate exterior
7. 53
8. 60
9. 30
10. 65
11. 24
12. 174
13. perpendicular
14. parallel
15. neither
16. parallel

Chapter Test B *continued*
CHAPTER 3 *For use after Chapter 3*

Graph the equation.

17. $y = -\frac{1}{4}x - 1$

18. $y = \frac{3}{2}x + \frac{1}{2}$

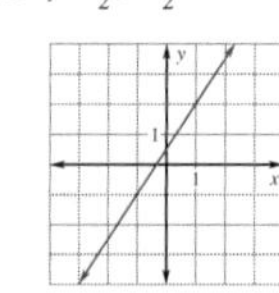

Write an equation of the line that passes through point *P* and is parallel to the line with the given equation.

19. $P(-1, 3), y = 4x - 2$
20. $P(2, 4), y = -3x$

Write an equation of the line that passes through point *P* and is perpendicular to the line with the given equation.

21. $P(0, 2), y = \frac{1}{2}x + 1$
22. $P(4, 3), y = -x$

23. The graph models the total cost of renting a bike. Write an equation of the line. Explain the meaning of the slope and the *y*-intercept of the line.

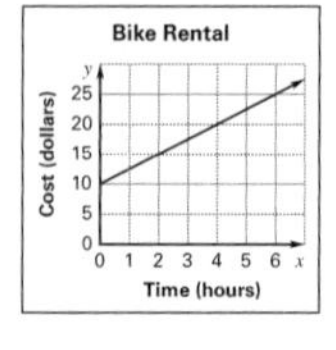

In the diagram, $\overleftrightarrow{AB} \perp \overleftrightarrow{BC}$. Find the value of *x*.

24.

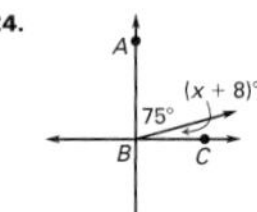

25.

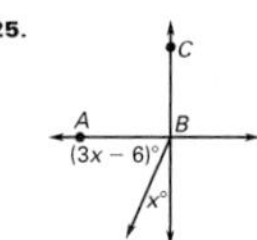

Answers

17. See left.
18. See left.
19. $y = 4x + 7$
20. $y = -3x + 10$
21. $y = -2x + 2$
22. $y = x - 1$
23. $y = 2.5x + 10$; slope is the cost per hour; *y*-intercept is the initial cost to rent a bike
24. 7
25. 24

Standardized Test
CHAPTER 3 *For use after Chapter 3*

Multiple Choice

1. Which pair of angles are corresponding angles? B

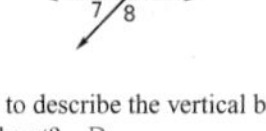

Ⓐ $\angle 1$ and $\angle 8$
Ⓑ $\angle 3$ and $\angle 7$
Ⓒ $\angle 3$ and $\angle 5$
Ⓓ $\angle 2$ and $\angle 7$

2. What is one way to describe the vertical bars of a football goalpost? D

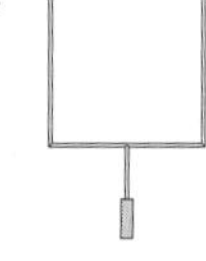

Ⓐ perpendicular
Ⓑ intersecting
Ⓒ skew
Ⓓ parallel

3. If two angles lie between two lines and on opposite sides of a transversal, then the angles are: B

Ⓐ consecutive interior angles.
Ⓑ alternate interior angles.
Ⓒ alternate exterior angles.
Ⓓ corresponding angles.

4. Find $m\angle 1$. D

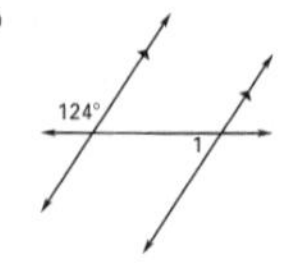

Ⓐ 34° Ⓑ 45° Ⓒ 124° Ⓓ 56°

5. Based on the diagram, which theorem would you use to support the statement $m\angle A + m\angle B = 180°$? C

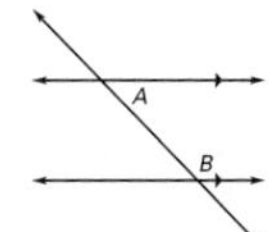

Ⓐ Alternate Interior Angles Theorem
Ⓑ Alternate Exterior Angles Theorem
Ⓒ Consecutive Interior Angles Theorem
Ⓓ Parallel Lines Theorem

6. Find *x* and *y*. C

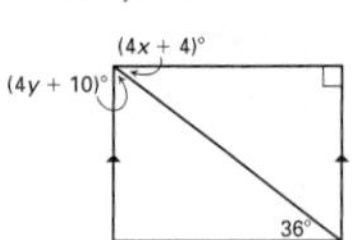

Ⓐ $x = 11, y = 8$ Ⓑ $x = 12, y = 8$
Ⓒ $x = 8, y = 11$ Ⓓ $x = 11, y = 12$

7. If two lines are cut by a transversal so the alternate exterior angles are congruent, then the lines are: B

Ⓐ intersecting. Ⓑ parallel.
Ⓒ congruent. Ⓓ perpendicular.

8. What value must *x* be in order to conclude $Q \parallel R$? A

Ⓐ 36
Ⓑ 45
Ⓒ 60
Ⓓ 72

Standardized Test
CHAPTER 3 *For use after Chapter 3*

9. Describe the slope of the line passing through points $A(-2, 3)$ and $B(4, -3)$. B

Ⓐ positive Ⓑ negative
Ⓒ zero Ⓓ undefined

10. Find the slope of a ladder placed 4 feet from the wall and touching the wall at a height of 12 feet. A

Ⓐ 3 Ⓑ −3 Ⓒ $\frac{1}{3}$ Ⓓ $-\frac{1}{3}$

11. What is the equation of the line through point (2, 1) and perpendicular to the line through (−4, 1) and (3, −2)? D

Ⓐ $y = \frac{7}{3}x + \frac{11}{3}$ Ⓑ $y = \frac{3}{7}x + \frac{11}{3}$
Ⓒ $y = -\frac{3}{7}x - \frac{11}{3}$ Ⓓ $y = \frac{7}{3}x - \frac{11}{3}$

12. Write an equation of the line with slope = −2 and *y*-intercept = 5. D

Ⓐ $y = -5x + 2$ Ⓑ $y = 2x - 5$
Ⓒ $y = 5x - 2$ Ⓓ $y = -2x + 5$

13. What best describes the relationship between line $6x - 2y = 1$ and line $x + 3y = 12$? B

Ⓐ parallel Ⓑ perpendicular
Ⓒ skew Ⓓ equivalent

14. Find *x* if $\overline{CD} \perp \overline{FG}$. C

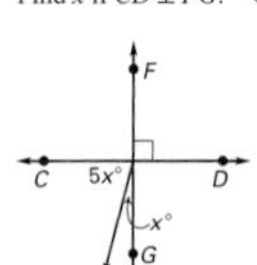

Ⓐ 18 Ⓑ 30 Ⓒ 15 Ⓓ 90

Gridded Answer

15. Find the distance between points (−5, 4) and (10, 12). 17

17. a.

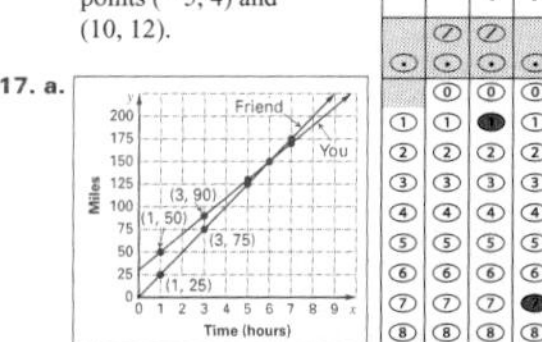

Short Response

16. Persons A and B stand directly across the street from each other. Person A crosses the street to get to a restaurant while person B crosses the street to get to a music store. If they both walk the same distance, what can be said about the distance between person A and the music store and the distance between person B and the restaurant? Will this always be the case? *Explain.*
They are equal; yes; SAS

Extended Response

17. You race your bike at a speed of 20 miles per hour. Your friend races at a speed of 25 miles per hour. Suppose your friend decides to give you a 30-mile head start.
    a. Draw a graph plotting the progress of both bikers in a 7-hour race. See above.
    b. Write an equation for each of the two lines.
    c. Is there a relationship between the slope of each line and the race? the *y*-intercept and the race? *Explain.*
    d. Who would win a 5-hour race? a 6-hour race? a 7-hour race? if the slopes were equal?

b. your line: $y = 20x + 30$; friend's line: $y = 25x$ **c.** slope is the miles per hour; *y*-intercept is the head start **d.** 5-hour race: you; 6-hour race: tie; 7-hour race: friend; equal slopes: you; because speed would be equal and you had a head start.

CHAPTER 3

Alternative Assessment and Math Journal

For use after Chapter 3

Journal

1. **a.** *Explain* how to show that the given lines are parallel by using angles. Then show that the lines are parallel by using this method.

   b. *Explain* how to show that the given lines are parallel by using the equations of the two lines. Then show that the lines are parallel by using this method.

   c. *Explain* how to find the distance between the given lines.

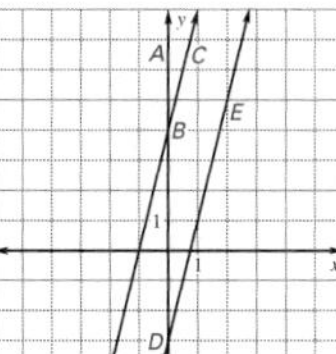

Multi-Step Problem

2. The figure at the right shows the front view of a cellular phone tower's structure.

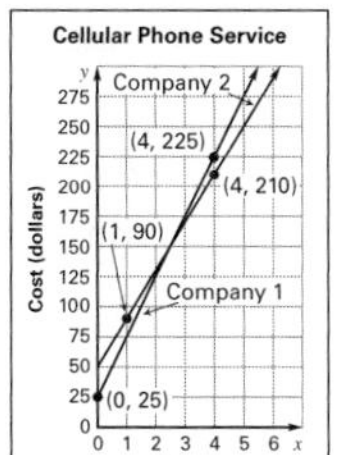

   a. Identify all pairs of corresponding angles, alternate interior angles, alternate exterior angles, and consecutive interior angles formed by lines m, n, and p.

   b. Suppose that lines m and n are parallel. Identify all congruent angles formed by lines m, n, and p.

   c. Suppose that lines m and n are parallel and that $m\angle 1 = 46^\circ$ and $m\angle 6 = (2x)^\circ$. Find the value of x.

   d. Suppose that $m\angle 3 = 112^\circ$ and $m\angle 7 = (4x)^\circ$. Find the value of x that makes $m \parallel n$.

   e. The graph models the total cost of cellular phone service from two companies for several months. Write an equation of each line. Tell what the slope and y-intercept mean in this situation.

   f. Which company would you use for your cellular phone service? What other factors might you consider when you are choosing a company? *Explain.*

Cellular Phone Service

Company 2 · (4, 225) · (4, 210) · (1, 90) · Company 1 · (0, 25) · Cost (dollars) · Months

1. a. *Sample answer:* Let the y-axis be the transversal that cuts the lines in the graph. The lines are parallel by the Corresponding Angles Converse because $m\angle ABC = m\angle BDE = 14^\circ$. **b.** Find the slopes of the lines. If they are the same, then the lines are parallel. The slopes of the given lines are both 4, so the lines are parallel. **c.** Use the distance formula to find the length of a perpendicular segment that connects the two lines.
2. a. corresponding angles: $\angle 1$ and $\angle 5$, $\angle 2$ and $\angle 6$, $\angle 3$ and $\angle 7$, $\angle 4$ and $\angle 8$; alternate interior angles: $\angle 3$ and $\angle 6$, $\angle 4$ and $\angle 5$; alternate exterior angles: $\angle 1$ and $\angle 8$, $\angle 2$ and $\angle 7$; consecutive interior angles: $\angle 3$ and $\angle 5$, $\angle 4$ and $\angle 6$
b. $\angle 1$, $\angle 4$, $\angle 5$, and $\angle 8$; $\angle 2$, $\angle 3$, $\angle 6$, and $\angle 7$ **c.** 67 **d.** 28
e. $y = 50x + 25$; $y = 40x + 50$; The slope is the amount of money paid each month and the y-intercept is the initial cost of the service.
f. *Sample answer:* Company 2, because it appears to cost less as time goes on. Other factors might include how many free minutes the plan includes and whether the plan includes a free phone or not.

CHAPTER 3

Alternative Assessment Rubric *continued*

For use after Chapter 3

Journal Solution

1. Complete answers should include:

   a. an explanation that a transversal should be drawn on the graph and that one of the following postulates or theorems should be used along with measuring the appropriate angles to determine whether the lines are parallel: Corresponding Angles Converse, Alternate Interior Angles Converse, Alternate Exterior Angles Converse, Consecutive Interior Angles Converse; a solution that shows a transversal drawn on the graph, the measures of the appropriate angles, a statement of the theorem or postulate that was used in the conclusion.

   b. an explanation that the slopes of the lines should be determined and compared; a solution that shows the slopes of both lines as 4, and the conclusion that because the slopes are equal, the lines are parallel.

   c. an explanation that the length of a perpendicular segment from one line to the other should be found by using the distance formula.

Multi-Step Problem Solution

2. **a.** corresponding angles: $\angle 1$ and $\angle 5$, $\angle 2$ and $\angle 6$, $\angle 3$ and $\angle 7$, $\angle 4$ and $\angle 8$; alternate interior angles: $\angle 3$ and $\angle 6$, $\angle 4$ and $\angle 5$; alternate exterior angles: $\angle 1$ and $\angle 8$, $\angle 2$ and $\angle 7$; consecutive interior angles: $\angle 3$ and $\angle 5$, $\angle 4$ and $\angle 6$

   b. $\angle 1$, $\angle 4$, $\angle 5$, and $\angle 8$; $\angle 2$, $\angle 3$, $\angle 6$, and $\angle 7$

   c. 67

   d. 28

   e. $y = 50x + 25$; $y = 40x + 50$; The slope is the amount of money paid each month and the y-intercept is the initial cost of the service.

   f. *Sample answer:* Company 2, because it appears to cost less as time goes on. Other factors might include how many free minutes the plan includes and whether the plan includes a free phone or not.

Multi-Step Problem Rubric

4 The student answers all parts of the problem correctly and completely. The student shows all work. The student's work is neat.

3 The student answers all parts of the problem. The student's work may have one or two errors in the identification of pair of angles, the calculation of angle measures, or in the calculation of the equations of the lines. The student shows most work. The student's work is neat.

2 The student answers all parts of the problem. The student's work contains multiple errors, but the student shows most work. The student's work is sloppy.

1 The student does not complete all parts of the problem. The work contains many errors in logic. The student's work is sloppy, or no work is shown.

PLAN AND PREPARE

Main Ideas

In this chapter students will classify angle pairs formed by three intersecting lines, study angle pairs formed by a line that intersects two parallel lines, and use angle relationships to prove lines parallel. They will investigate slopes of lines and study the relationship between slopes of parallel and perpendicular lines. Students will find equations of lines. Finally, they will prove theorems about perpendicular lines and find the distance between parallel lines in the coordinate plane.

Prerequisite Skills

- Describing angle pairs
- Using properties and postulates
- Sketching a diagram
- Using angle pair relationships

Additional resources for reviewing prerequisite skills are:

- Skills Review Handbook, pp. 869–895
- @HomeTutor

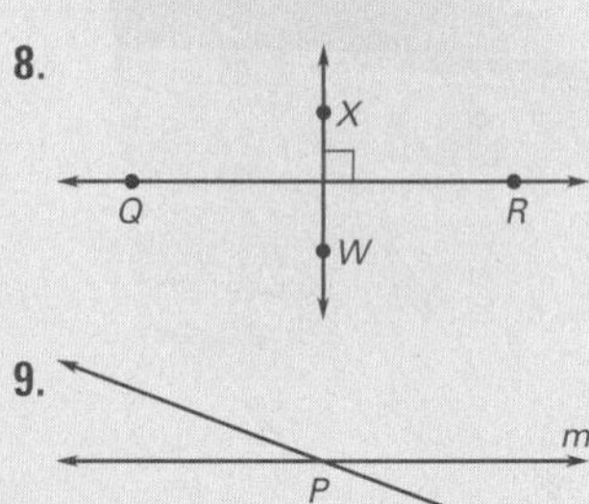

3 Parallel and Perpendicular Lines

Before

In previous chapters, you learned the following skills, which you'll use in Chapter 3: describing angle pairs, using properties and postulates, using angle pair relationships, and sketching a diagram.

Prerequisite Skills

VOCABULARY CHECK

Copy and complete the statement.

1. Adjacent angles share a common _?_ and _?_. **vertex, side**
2. Two angles are _?_ angles if the sum of their measures is 180°. **supplementary**

SKILLS AND ALGEBRA CHECK

The midpoint of $\overline{AB}$ is M. Find AB. *(Review p. 15 for 3.2.)*

3. $AM = 5x - 2$, $MB = 2x + 7$ **26**
4. $AM = 4z + 1$, $MB = 6z - 11$ **50**

Find the measure of each numbered angle. *(Review p. 124 for 3.2, 3.3.)*

5. 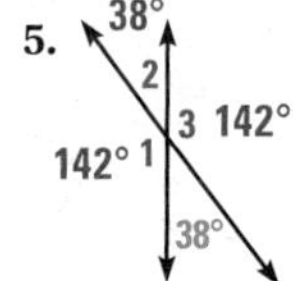

6. 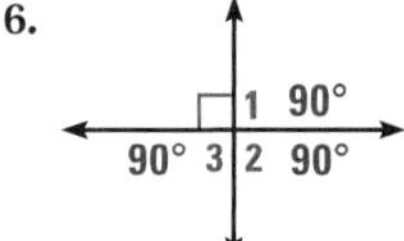

7. 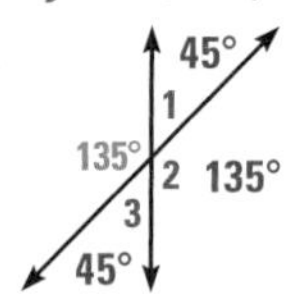

Sketch a diagram for each statement. *(Review pp. 2, 96 for 3.3.)* **8, 9. See margin.**

8. $\overleftrightarrow{QR}$ is perpendicular to $\overleftrightarrow{WX}$.
9. Lines m and n intersect at point P.

@HomeTutor Prerequisite skills practice at classzone.com

Chapter Planning Guide

Chapter 3 Resource Book
- Teaching Guide/Lesson Plan (pp. 3, 16, 30, 45, 59, 74)
- Project with Rubric (p. 89)

Assessment and Intervention
- Assessment Book (pp. 31–45)
- Benchmark Tests
- Remediation Book

Interactive Technology
- Easy Planner
- Power Presentations CD-ROM
- Activity Generator CD-ROM
- Animated Geometry
- Test Generator CD-ROM
- Online Quizzes
- eWorkbook
- eEdition
- @HomeTutor

Resources for English Learners
- Quick Reference for English Learners
- Spanish Study Guide
- Multi-Language Visual Glossary
- Student Resources in Spanish

California Standards for Chapter 3

Geometry: 1.0, 2.0, 7.0, 16.0

Now

In Chapter 3, you will apply the big ideas listed below and reviewed in the Chapter Summary on page 201. You will also use the key vocabulary listed below.

Big Ideas

1. **Using properties of parallel and perpendicular lines**
2. **Proving relationships using angle measures**
3. **Making connections to lines in algebra**

KEY VOCABULARY

- parallel lines, *p. 147*
- skew lines, *p. 147*
- parallel planes, *p. 147*
- transversal, *p. 149*
- corresponding angles, *p. 149*
- alternate interior angles, *p. 149*
- alternate exterior angles, *p. 149*
- consecutive interior angles, *p. 149*
- paragraph proof, *p. 163*
- slope, *p. 171*
- slope-intercept form, *p. 180*
- standard form, *p. 182*
- distance from a point to a line, *p. 192*

Why?

You can use slopes of lines to determine steepness of lines. For example, you can compare the slopes of roller coasters to determine which is steeper.

Animated Geometry

The animation illustrated below for Example 5 on page 174 helps you answer this question: How steep is a roller coaster?

A roller coaster track rises a given distance over a given horizontal distance.

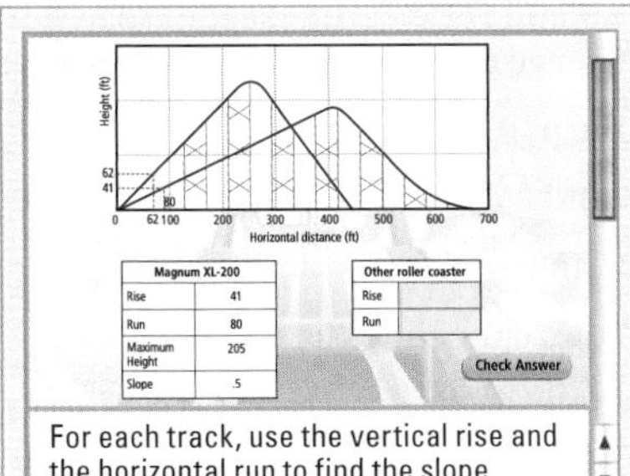

For each track, use the vertical rise and the horizontal run to find the slope.

Animated Geometry at classzone.com

Other animations for Chapter 3: pages 148, 155, 163, and 181

Geometry Toolkit

- Reading Strategies for Chapter 3, pp. 13–14
- Differentiated Instruction Notes, pp. 47–50
- English Learners Notes, pp. 95–96
- Inclusion Notes, pp. 125–126
- Teaching Strategies with Sample Worksheets, pp. 145–168
- Using Technology in the Classroom, pp. 169–174
- Tips for New Teachers, pp. 179–180
- Math Background Notes, pp. 206–208
- Pre-AP Strategies and Copymasters, pp. 287–288, 325–330
- Teacher Survival Activities, pp. 425–426, 449–450
- Bulletin Board Idea, p. 471
- Teacher Tool Transparencies, following p. 480

1 PLAN AND PREPARE

Explore the Concept

- Students will draw a representation of a three-dimensional figure.
- This activity leads into the study of the relationships of lines in space in Example 1 of Lesson 3.1.

Materials

Each student will need:

- straightedge
- lined paper

Recommended Time

Work activity: 10 min

Discuss results: 5 min

Grouping

Students should work individually.

2 TEACH

Tips for Success

Remind students that in drawings of three-dimensional figures, lines may appear to intersect that in fact do not. Urge students to keep this in mind as they draw their figures.

Alternative Strategy

Use a rectangular box as a model to demonstrate the relationships between the lines in the figure.

Key Discovery

Lines in space may or may not intersect. A pair of lines that intersect lie in the same plane.

3 ASSESS AND RETEACH

If two lines do not intersect, must they lie in different planes? Explain. **No, it is possible for two lines to lie in the same plane and not intersect. For example, see $\overleftrightarrow{JM}$ and $\overleftrightarrow{NR}$ in the diagram.**

3.1 Draw and Interpret Lines

MATERIALS • pencil • straightedge • lined paper

Standards

1.0 Students demonstrate understanding by identifying and giving examples of undefined terms, axioms, theorems, and inductive and **deductive reasoning.**

QUESTION How are lines related in space?

You can use a straightedge to draw a representation of a three-dimensional figure to explore lines in space.

EXPLORE Draw lines in space

STEP 1 ***Draw rectangles***

Use a straightedge to draw two identical rectangles.

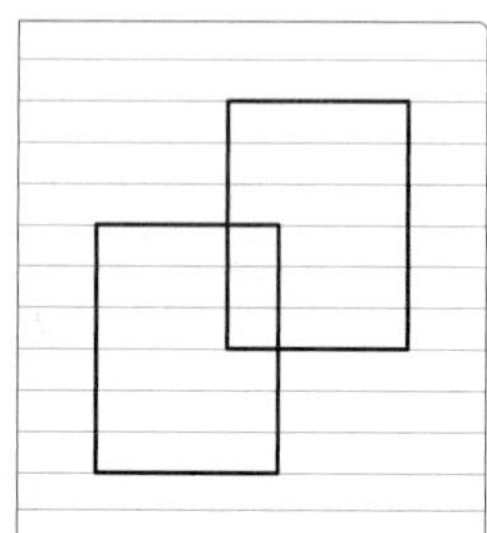

STEP 2 ***Connect corners***

Connect the corresponding corners of the rectangles.

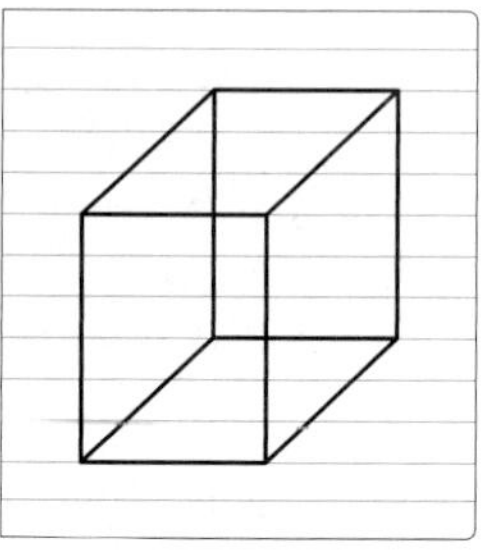

STEP 3 ***Erase parts***

Erase parts of "hidden" lines to form dashed lines.

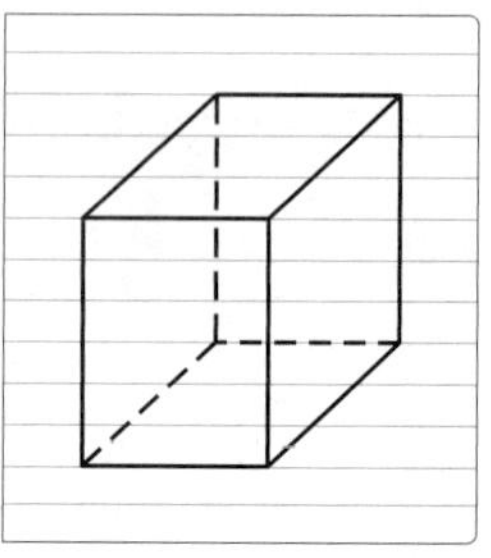

DRAW CONCLUSIONS Use your observations to complete these exercises

Using your sketch from the steps above, label the corners as shown at the right. Then extend $\overline{JM}$ and $\overline{LQ}$. Add lines to the diagram if necessary.

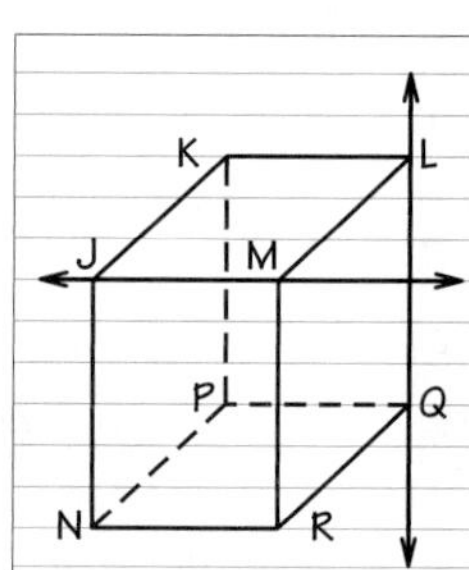

1. Will $\overleftrightarrow{JM}$ and $\overleftrightarrow{LQ}$ ever intersect in space? (Lines that intersect on the page do not necessarily intersect in space.) **no**
2. Will the pair of lines intersect in space?
   a. $\overleftrightarrow{JK}$ and $\overleftrightarrow{NR}$ **no** **b.** $\overleftrightarrow{QR}$ and $\overleftrightarrow{MR}$ **yes**
   c. $\overleftrightarrow{LM}$ and $\overleftrightarrow{MR}$ **yes** **d.** $\overleftrightarrow{KL}$ and $\overleftrightarrow{NQ}$ **no**
3. Does the pair of lines lie in one plane?
   a. $\overleftrightarrow{JK}$ and $\overleftrightarrow{QR}$ **yes** **b.** $\overleftrightarrow{QR}$ and $\overleftrightarrow{MR}$ **yes**
   c. $\overleftrightarrow{JN}$ and $\overleftrightarrow{LR}$ **no** **d.** $\overleftrightarrow{JL}$ and $\overleftrightarrow{NQ}$ **yes**

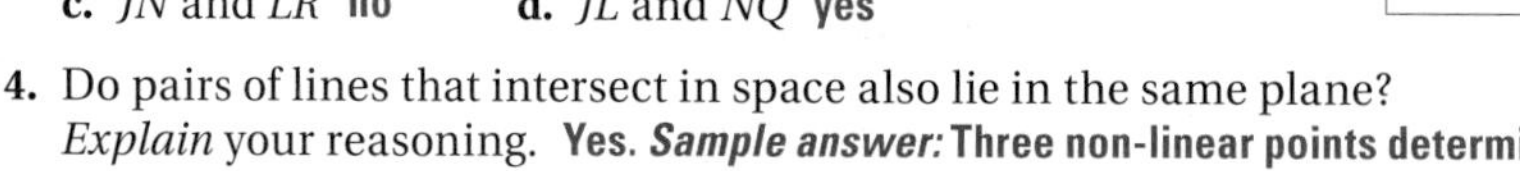

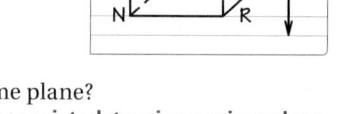

4. Do pairs of lines that intersect in space also lie in the same plane? *Explain* your reasoning. **Yes. *Sample answer:* Three non-linear points determine a unique plane.**
5. Draw a rectangle that is not the same as the one you used in the Explore. Repeat the three steps of the Explore. Will any of your answers to Exercises 1–3 change? **Check students' work; no.**

3.1 Identify Pairs of Lines and Angles

Before You identified angle pairs formed by two intersecting lines.

Now You will identify angle pairs formed by three intersecting lines.

Why? So you can classify lines in a real-world situation, as in Exs. 40–42.

Key Vocabulary
- parallel lines
- skew lines
- parallel planes
- transversal
- corresponding angles
- alternate interior angles
- alternate exterior angles
- consecutive interior angles

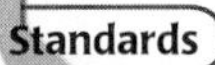

Standards

Prepare for 7.0 Students prove and use theorems involving the *properties of parallel lines cut by a transversal,* the properties of quadrilaterals, and the properties of circles.

16.0 Students perform basic constructions with a straightedge and compass, such as angle bisectors, perpendicular bisectors, and **the line parallel to a given line through a point off the line.**

Two lines that do not intersect are either *parallel lines* or *skew lines*. Two lines are **parallel lines** if they do not intersect and are coplanar. Two lines are **skew lines** if they do not intersect and are not coplanar. Also, two planes that do not intersect are **parallel planes**.

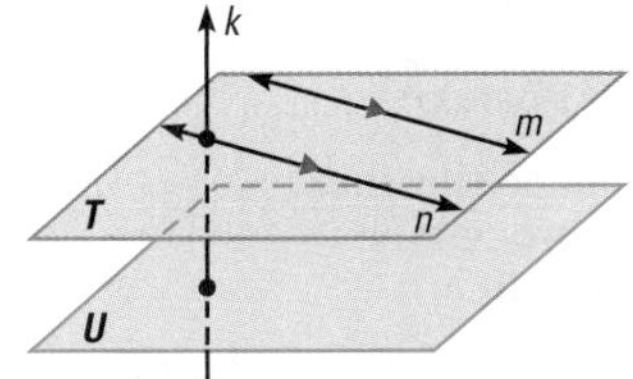

Lines m and n are parallel lines ($m \parallel n$).

Lines m and k are skew lines.

Planes T and U are parallel planes ($T \parallel U$).

Lines k and n are intersecting lines, and there is a plane (not shown) containing them.

Small directed triangles, as shown on lines m and n above, are used to show that lines are parallel. The symbol $\parallel$ means "is parallel to," as in $m \parallel n$.

Segments and rays are parallel if they lie in parallel lines. A line is parallel to a plane if the line is in a plane parallel to the given plane. In the diagram above, line n is parallel to plane U.

EXAMPLE 1 Identify relationships in space

Think of each segment in the figure as part of a line. Which line(s) or plane(s) in the figure appear to fit the description?

a. Line(s) parallel to $\overleftrightarrow{CD}$ and containing point A

b. Line(s) skew to $\overleftrightarrow{CD}$ and containing point A

c. Line(s) perpendicular to $\overleftrightarrow{CD}$ and containing point A

d. Plane(s) parallel to plane EFG and containing point A

Solution

a. $\overleftrightarrow{AB}$, $\overleftrightarrow{HG}$, and $\overleftrightarrow{EF}$ all appear parallel to $\overleftrightarrow{CD}$, but only $\overleftrightarrow{AB}$ contains point A.

b. Both $\overleftrightarrow{AG}$ and $\overleftrightarrow{AH}$ appear skew to $\overleftrightarrow{CD}$ and contain point A.

c. $\overleftrightarrow{BC}$, $\overleftrightarrow{AD}$, $\overleftrightarrow{DE}$, and $\overleftrightarrow{FC}$ all appear perpendicular to $\overleftrightarrow{CD}$, but only $\overleftrightarrow{AD}$ contains point A.

d. Plane ABC appears parallel to plane EFG and contains point A.

1 PLAN AND PREPARE

Warm-Up Exercises

Transparency Available

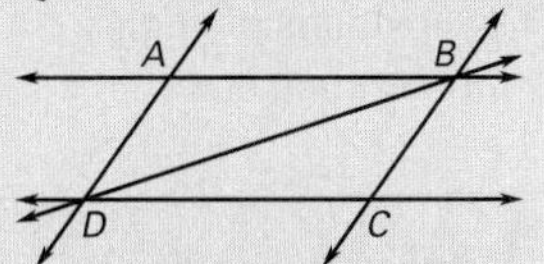

1. Name a line that does not intersect $\overleftrightarrow{AD}$. $\overleftrightarrow{BC}$
2. What is the intersection of $\overleftrightarrow{AD}$ and $\overleftrightarrow{DB}$? D

Notetaking Guide

Transparency Available

Promotes interactive learning and notetaking skills, pp. 60–63.

Pacing

Basic: 1 day
Average: 1 day
Advanced: 1 day
Block: 0.5 block with 3.2
- See *Teaching Guide/Lesson Plan.*

2 FOCUS AND MOTIVATE

Essential Question

Big Idea 1, p. 145

What angle pairs are formed by transversals? **Tell students they will learn how to answer this question by studying three intersecting lines and the relative positions of the angles they determine.**

Resource Planning Guide

Chapter Resource Book
- Teaching Guide/Lesson Plan (pp. 3–4)
- Practice levels A, B, C (pp. 5–10)
- Study Guide (pp. 11–12)
- Catch-up for Absent Students (p. 13)
- Application (p. 14)
- Challenge (p. 15)

Workbooks
- Notetaking Guide (pp. 60–63)
- Practice Workbook (pp. 43–45)

Teaching Options
- **Power Presentations CD-ROM** provides dynamic electronic teaching resources for the classroom.
- **Activity Generator CD-ROM** provides editable activities for all ability levels.

Interactive Technology
- Easy Planner
- Power Presentations CD-ROM
- Activity Generator CD-ROM
- Animated Geometry
- Test Generator CD-ROM
- Online Quiz
- eWorkbook
- eEdition
- @HomeTutor

Resources for English Learners
- Quick Reference for English Learners
- Spanish Study Guide
- Multi-Language Visual Glossary
- Student Resources in Spanish

See also the *Geometry Toolkit* for more strategies for meeting individual needs.

Motivating the Lesson

Tell students that artists and architects need to understand lines in two and three dimensions that do and do not intersect. Tell them that in this lesson, they will study these lines and the positions of angles formed by intersecting lines.

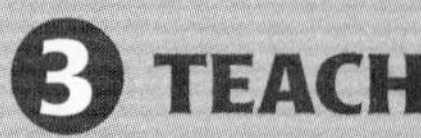

Extra Example 1

Think of each segment in the figure as part of a line. Which line(s) or plane(s) appear to fit the description?

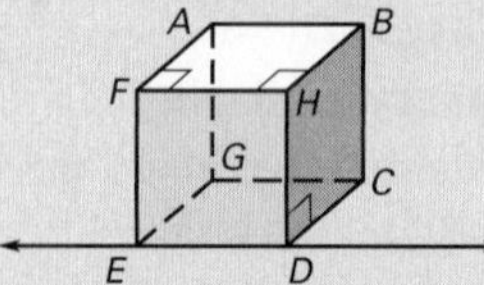

a. Line(s) parallel to $\overleftrightarrow{ED}$ and containing point C ***$\overleftrightarrow{GC}$***

b. Line(s) skew to $\overleftrightarrow{ED}$ ***$\overleftrightarrow{BC}$, $\overleftrightarrow{AG}$, $\overleftrightarrow{AF}$, $\overleftrightarrow{BH}$***

c. Line(s) perpendicular to $\overleftrightarrow{ED}$ ***$\overleftrightarrow{CD}$, $\overleftrightarrow{GE}$, $\overleftrightarrow{FE}$, $\overleftrightarrow{HD}$***

d. Plane(s) parallel to plane *ABH* ***plane CDE***

Extra Example 2

The figure shows a swing set on a playground.

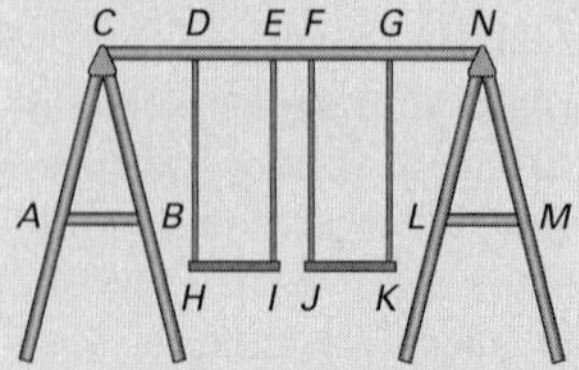

a. Name a pair of perpendicular lines. ***Sample answer: $\overleftrightarrow{DH} \perp \overleftrightarrow{HI}$***

b. Name a pair of parallel lines. ***Sample answer: $\overleftrightarrow{AB} \parallel \overleftrightarrow{LM}$***

c. Is $\overleftrightarrow{DH}$ perpendicular to $\overleftrightarrow{LM}$? Explain. **No, the lines are skew.**

PARALLEL AND PERPENDICULAR LINES Two lines in the same plane are either parallel or intersect in a point.

Through a point not on a line, there are infinitely many lines. Exactly one of these lines is parallel to the given line, and exactly one of them is perpendicular to the given line.

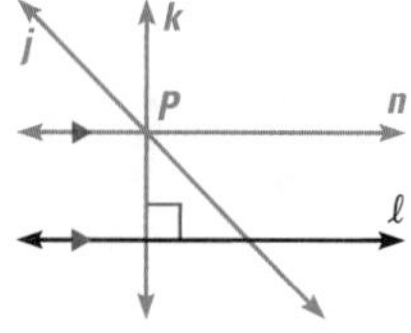

Animated Geometry at classzone.com

POSTULATES — *For Your Notebook*

POSTULATE 13 Parallel Postulate

If there is a line and a point not on the line, then there is exactly one line through the point parallel to the given line.

There is exactly one line through P parallel to ℓ.

POSTULATE 14 Perpendicular Postulate

If there is a line and a point not on the line, then there is exactly one line through the point perpendicular to the given line.

There is exactly one line through P perpendicular to ℓ.

EXAMPLE 2 Identify parallel and perpendicular lines

PHOTOGRAPHY The given line markings show how the roads are related to one another.

a. Name a pair of parallel lines.

b. Name a pair of perpendicular lines.

c. Is $\overleftrightarrow{FE} \parallel \overleftrightarrow{AC}$? Explain.

Niagara Falls, New York

Solution

a. $\overleftrightarrow{MD} \parallel \overleftrightarrow{FE}$ **b.** $\overleftrightarrow{MD} \perp \overleftrightarrow{BF}$

c. $\overleftrightarrow{FE}$ is not parallel to $\overleftrightarrow{AC}$, because $\overleftrightarrow{MD}$ is parallel to $\overleftrightarrow{FE}$ and by the Parallel Postulate there is exactly one line parallel to $\overleftrightarrow{FE}$ through M.

✓ **GUIDED PRACTICE** for Examples 1 and 2

1. Look at the diagram in Example 1. Name the lines through point H that appear skew to $\overleftrightarrow{CD}$. **$\overleftrightarrow{AH}$, $\overleftrightarrow{EH}$**

2. In Example 2, can you use the Perpendicular Postulate to show that $\overleftrightarrow{AC}$ is *not* perpendicular to $\overleftrightarrow{BF}$? *Explain* why or why not.

2. Yes; since A is not on $\overleftrightarrow{MD}$ and $\overleftrightarrow{MD}$ is $\perp$ to $\overleftrightarrow{BF}$, the Perpendicular Postulate guarantees that there is exactly one line through a point perpendicular to a line, so $\overleftrightarrow{AC}$ can not be perpendicular to $\overleftrightarrow{BF}$ also.

Differentiated Instruction

English Learners Students learning English may confuse *parallel* and *perpendicular*. Tell them to think of the two *l*'s in *parallel* as two lines that do not intersect. Point out that the two *l*'s resemble the symbol for parallel lines, ∥. There is only one *l* in perpendicular. Have them relate this *l* to the symbol for perpendicular, ⊥, which tells them that two lines meet at a 90° angle.

See also the *Geometry Toolkit* for more strategies.

ANGLES AND TRANSVERSALS A **transversal** is a line that intersects two or more coplanar lines at different points.

KEY CONCEPT *For Your Notebook*

Angles Formed by Transversals

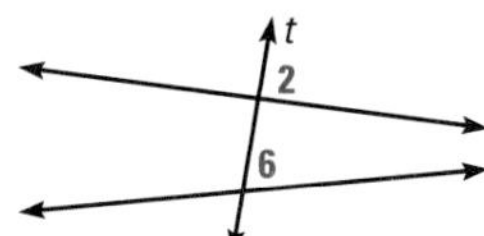

Two angles are **corresponding angles** if they have corresponding positions. For example, $\angle 2$ and $\angle 6$ are above the lines and to the right of the transversal *t*.

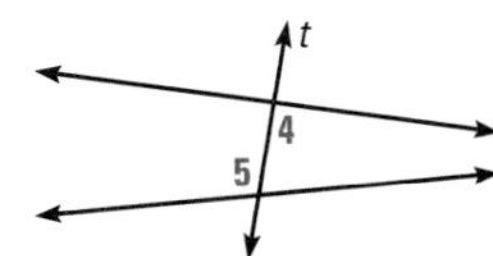

Two angles are **alternate interior angles** if they lie between the two lines and on opposite sides of the transversal.

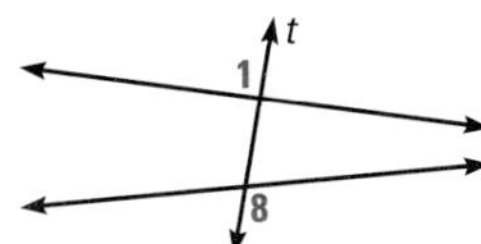

Two angles are **alternate exterior angles** if they lie outside the two lines and on opposite sides of the transversal.

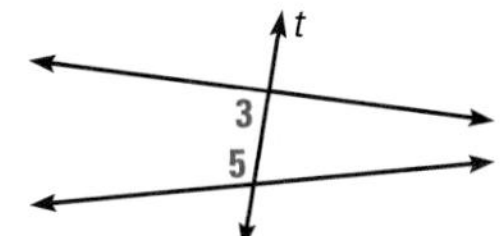

Two angles are **consecutive interior angles** if they lie between the two lines and on the same side of the transversal.

READ VOCABULARY
Another name for consecutive interior angles is **same-side interior angles**.

EXAMPLE 3 Identify angle relationships

Identify all pairs of angles of the given type.

a. Corresponding **b.** Alternate interior
c. Alternate exterior **d.** Consecutive interior

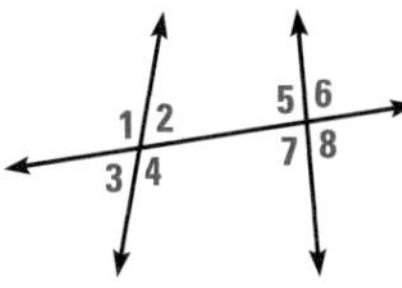

Solution

a. $\angle 1$ and $\angle 5$
$\angle 2$ and $\angle 6$
$\angle 3$ and $\angle 7$
$\angle 4$ and $\angle 8$

b. $\angle 2$ and $\angle 7$
$\angle 4$ and $\angle 5$

c. $\angle 1$ and $\angle 8$
$\angle 3$ and $\angle 6$

d. $\angle 2$ and $\angle 5$
$\angle 4$ and $\angle 7$

✓ GUIDED PRACTICE for Example 3

Classify the pair of numbered angles.

3.

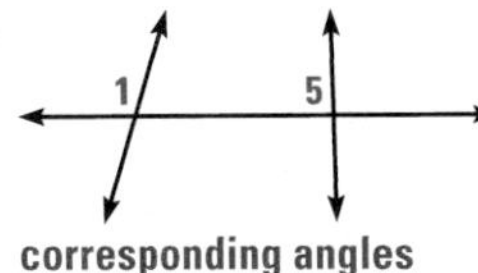

corresponding angles

4.

alternate exterior angles

5. (4, 5)

alternate interior angles

Differentiated Instruction

Below level Draw two lines and a transversal. Show students how they can draw an F to identify corresponding angles. Also show them that by drawing a Z they can identify alternate interior angles. Have them use these techniques while doing the exercises.

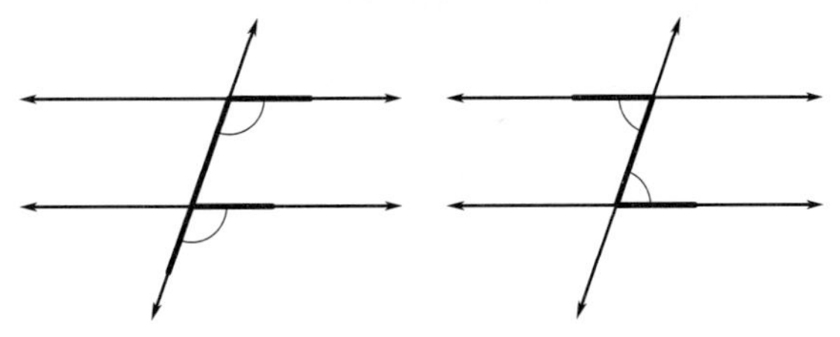

See also the *Geometry Toolkit* for more strategies.

Extra Example 3

Identify all pairs of angles of the given type.

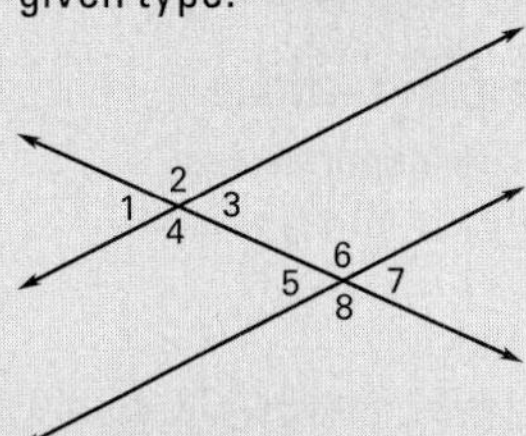

a. Corresponding **$\angle 1$ and $\angle 5$; $\angle 3$ and $\angle 7$; $\angle 2$ and $\angle 6$; $\angle 4$ and $\angle 8$**

b. Alternate interior **$\angle 3$ and $\angle 5$; $\angle 4$ and $\angle 6$**

c. Alternate exterior **$\angle 1$ and $\angle 7$; $\angle 2$ and $\angle 8$**

d. Consecutive interior **$\angle 3$ and $\angle 6$; $\angle 4$ and $\angle 5$**

Key Question to Ask for Example 3

- Explain the difference between alternate interior angles and consecutive interior angles. **Alternate interior angles are on different sides of the transversal. Consecutive interior angles are on the same side of the transversal.**

Closing the Lesson

Have students summarize the major points of the lesson and answer the Essential Question: What angle pairs are formed by transversals?

- **Parallel lines do not intersect and are coplanar.**
- **Skew lines do not intersect and are not coplanar.**
- **Corresponding angles have corresponding positions.**
- **Alternate interior angles lie between the two lines and on opposite sides of the transversal.**

Angle pairs formed by three intersecting lines include corresponding, alternate interior, consecutive interior, and alternate exterior angles.

4 PRACTICE AND APPLY

Assignment Guide

Answer Transparencies available for all exercises

Basic:
Day 1: pp. 150–152
Exs. 1–15, 17–23 odd, 34–39, 45–49

Average:
Day 1: pp. 150–152
Exs. 1, 2, 4–6, 8–10, 12–15, 16–22 even, 24–28, 34–42, 45–49 odd

Advanced:
Day 1: pp. 150–152
Exs. 1, 2, 5, 6, 9, 10, 13, 14, 16–28 even, 29–44*, 46, 48

Block:
pp. 150–152
Exs. 1, 2, 4–6, 8–10, 12–15, 16–22 even, 24–28, 34–42, 45–49 odd (with 3.2)

Differentiated Instruction

See *Geometry Best Practices Toolkit* for suggestions on addressing the needs of a diverse classroom.

Homework Check

For a quick check of student understanding of key concepts, go over the following exercises:

Basic: 4, 7, 12, 23, 34
Average: 5, 8, 13, 20, 34
Advanced: 6, 10, 14, 22, 35

Extra Practice

- Student Edition, p. 900
- Chapter 3 Resource Book: Practice levels A, B, C, pp. 5–10

Practice Worksheet

An easily-readable reduced practice page (with answers) for this lesson can be found on p. 144C.

3.1 EXERCISES

HOMEWORK KEY
○ = **WORKED-OUT SOLUTIONS** on p. WS3 for Exs. 11, 25, and 35
★ = **STANDARDIZED TEST PRACTICE** Exs. 2, 28, 36, 37, and 39

SKILL PRACTICE

A

1. **VOCABULARY** Copy and complete: A line that intersects two other lines is a _?_. **transversal**

2. ★ **WRITING** A table is set for dinner. Can the legs of the table and the top of the table lie in parallel planes? *Explain* why or why not. **No; the legs intersect the tabletop.**

EXAMPLE 1 on p. 147 for Exs. 3–6

IDENTIFYING RELATIONSHIPS **Think of each segment in the diagram as part of a line. Which line(s) or plane(s) contain point *B* and appear to fit the description?**

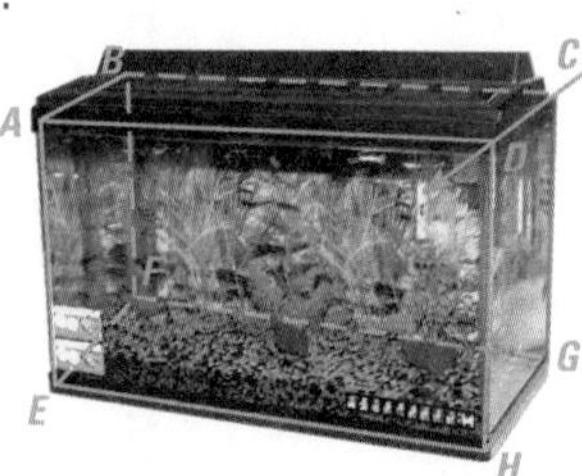

3. Line(s) parallel to $\overleftrightarrow{CD}$ **$\overleftrightarrow{AB}$**
4. Line(s) perpendicular to $\overleftrightarrow{CD}$ **$\overleftrightarrow{BC}$**
5. Line(s) skew to $\overleftrightarrow{CD}$ **$\overleftrightarrow{BF}$**
6. Plane(s) parallel to plane *CDH* **plane *ABF***

EXAMPLE 2 on p. 148 for Exs. 7–10

PARALLEL AND PERPENDICULAR LINES **Use the markings in the diagram.**

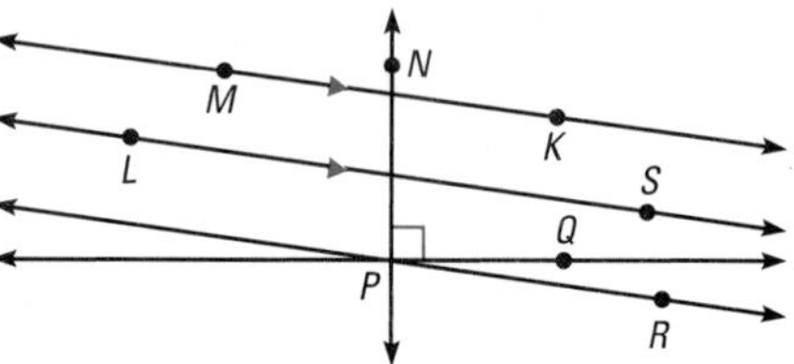

7. Name a pair of parallel lines. **$\overleftrightarrow{MK}$, $\overleftrightarrow{LS}$**
8. Name a pair of perpendicular lines. **$\overleftrightarrow{PQ}$, $\overleftrightarrow{PN}$**
9. Is $\overleftrightarrow{PN} \parallel \overleftrightarrow{KM}$? *Explain.*
10. Is $\overleftrightarrow{PR} \perp \overleftrightarrow{NP}$? *Explain.* **No. *Sample answer:* There is no right angle symbol indicating they are perpendicular.**

9. No. *Sample answer:* The lines intersect.

EXAMPLE 3 on p. 149 for Exs. 11–15

ANGLE RELATIONSHIPS **Identify all pairs of angles of the given type.**

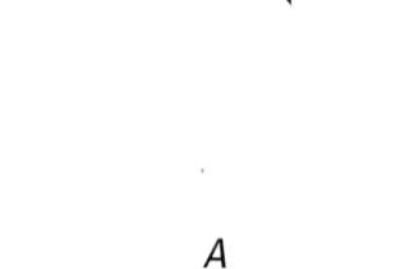

11. Corresponding
12. Alternate interior **∠3 and ∠6, ∠4 and ∠5**
13. Alternate exterior **∠1 and ∠8, ∠2 and ∠7**
14. Consecutive interior **∠3 and ∠5, ∠4 and ∠6**
15. **ERROR ANALYSIS** *Describe* and correct the error in saying that ∠1 and ∠8 are corresponding angles in the diagram for Exercises 11–14. **∠1 and ∠8 are not in corresponding positions. ∠1 and ∠8 are alternate exterior angles.**

11. ∠1 and ∠5, ∠3 and ∠7, ∠2 and ∠6, ∠4 and ∠8

B

APPLYING POSTULATES **How many lines can be drawn that fit each description? Copy the diagram and sketch all the lines.**

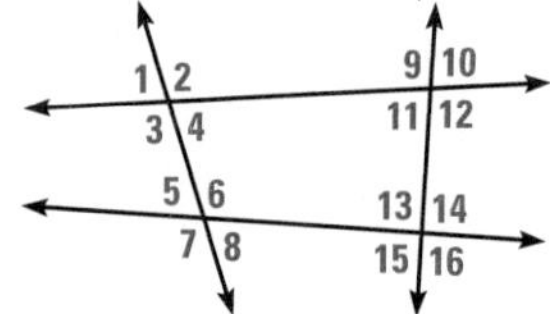

16. Lines through *B* and parallel to $\overleftrightarrow{AC}$ **1 line; see margin for art.**
17. Lines through *A* and perpendicular to $\overleftrightarrow{BC}$ **1 line; see margin for art.**

USING A DIAGRAM **Classify the angle pair as *corresponding, alternate interior, alternate exterior,* or *consecutive interior* angles.**

18. ∠5 and ∠1 **corresponding**
19. ∠11 and ∠13 **consecutive interior**
20. ∠6 and ∠13 **consecutive interior**
21. ∠10 and ∠15 **alternate exterior**
22. ∠2 and ∠11 **alternate interior**
23. ∠8 and ∠4 **corresponding**

16.
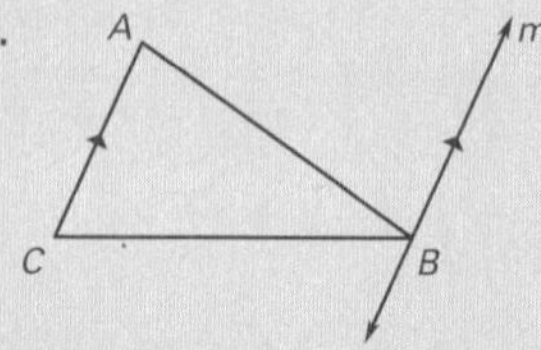

17.
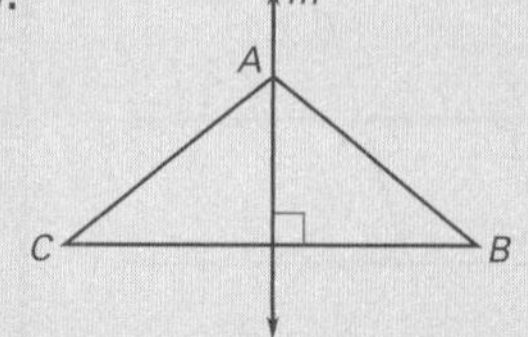

24.
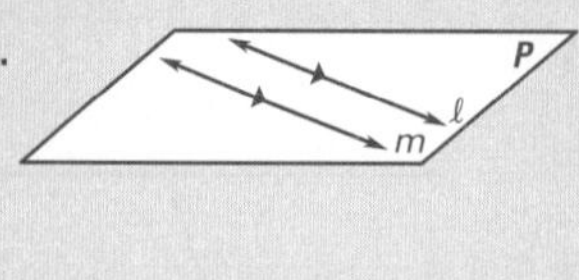

25.
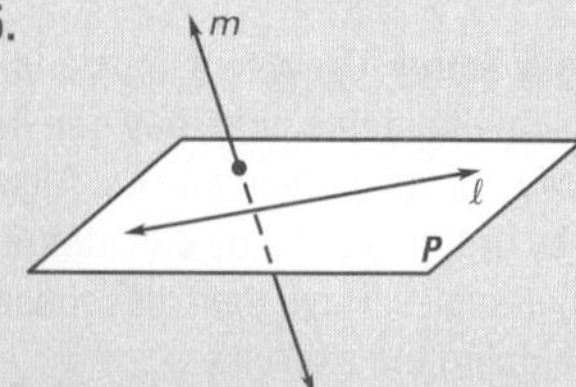

ANALYZING STATEMENTS **Copy and complete the statement with *sometimes, always,* or *never.* Sketch examples to *justify* your answer.** **24–27. See margin for art.**

24. If two lines are parallel, then they are ___?___ coplanar. **always**

25. If two lines are not coplanar, then they ___?___ intersect. **never**

26. If three lines intersect at one point, then they are ___?___ coplanar. **sometimes**

27. If two lines are skew to a third line, then they are ___?___ skew to each other. **sometimes**

28. ★ **MULTIPLE CHOICE** $\angle RPQ$ and $\angle PRS$ are what type of angle pair? **B**

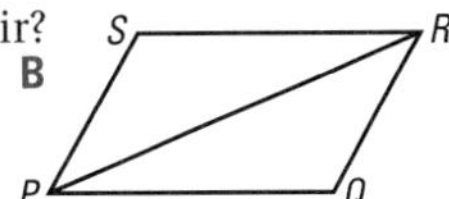

Ⓐ Corresponding Ⓑ Alternate interior

Ⓒ Alternate exterior Ⓓ Consecutive interior

C **ANGLE RELATIONSHIPS** **Copy and complete the statement. List all possible correct answers.**

29. $\angle BCG$ and ___?___ are corresponding angles. $\angle$ **CFJ**, $\angle$ **HJG**

30. $\angle BCG$ and ___?___ are consecutive interior angles. $\angle$ **CJH**

31. $\angle FCJ$ and ___?___ are alternate interior angles. $\angle$ **DFC**, $\angle$ **CJH**

32. $\angle FCA$ and ___?___ are alternate exterior angles. $\angle$ **GJH**

33. **CHALLENGE** Copy the diagram at the right and extend the lines.

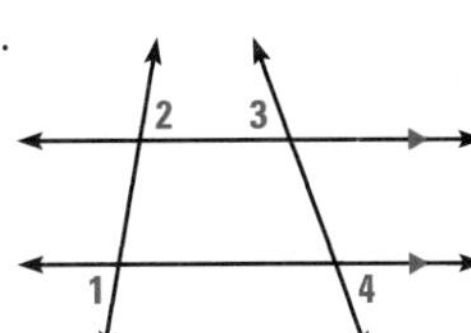

a. Measure $\angle 1$ and $\angle 2$. **80°, 80°**

b. Measure $\angle 3$ and $\angle 4$. **70°, 70°**

c. Make a conjecture about alternate exterior angles formed when parallel lines are cut by transversals.
If parallel lines are cut by a transversal then alternate exterior angles are congruent.

PROBLEM SOLVING

EXAMPLE 2 A on p. 148 for Exs. 34–35

CONSTRUCTION **Use the picture of the cherry-picker for Exercises 34 and 35.**

34. Is the platform *perpendicular, parallel,* or *skew* to the ground? **parallel**

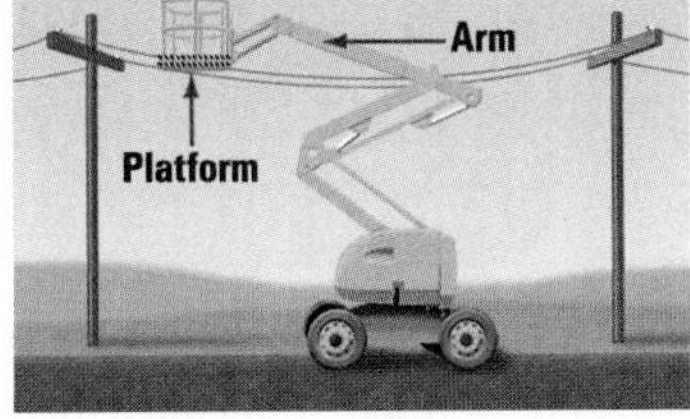

@HomeTutor for problem solving help at classzone.com

35. Is the arm *perpendicular, parallel,* or *skew* to a telephone pole? **skew**

@HomeTutor for problem solving help at classzone.com

36. ★ **OPEN-ENDED MATH** *Describe* two lines in your classroom that are parallel, and two lines that are skew. **Check students' work.**

37. ★ **MULTIPLE CHOICE** What is the best description of the horizontal bars in the photo? **A**

Ⓐ Parallel Ⓑ Perpendicular

Ⓒ Skew Ⓓ Intersecting

Avoiding Common Errors

Exercises 18–23 Students may make errors because they are not focusing on a single transversal and the two lines it intersects. Point out that for each exercise, the transversal is the line through the vertices of the two angles. It may help students to use a finger to cover up the eight angles whose vertices are not on the transversal for a particular exercise.

Teaching Strategy

Exercise 28 Have students extend all the segments so they can see the appropriate lines and transversal more clearly.

Study Strategy

Exercises 29–32 It is important in these exercises to be clear about which line is to be considered as the transversal of the other two. Each of the given angles has vertex *C*. Have students sketch copies of the figure. In one copy, have them show $\overline{AG}$ with a heavy line. In the other, have them show $\overline{EB}$ with a heavy line. The heavy lines are the possible transversals.

26. or

27. or

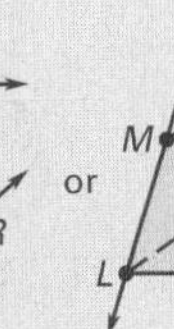

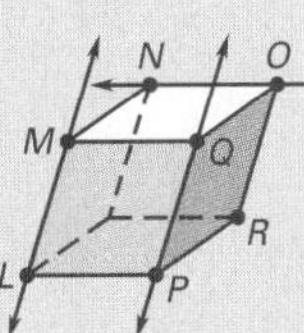

5 ASSESS AND RETEACH

Daily Homework Quiz

Transparency Available

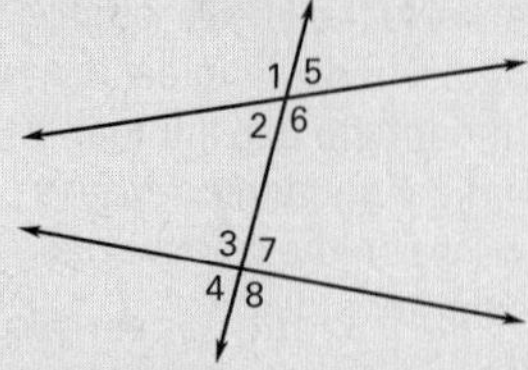

1. Name the pairs of corresponding angles. **∠1 and ∠3; ∠5 and ∠7; ∠2 and ∠4; ∠6 and ∠8**
2. Name the pairs of alternate interior angles. **∠2 and ∠7; ∠3 and ∠6**
3. Name the pairs of consecutive interior angles. **∠2 and ∠3; ∠6 and ∠7**
4. The figure shows a painting easel.

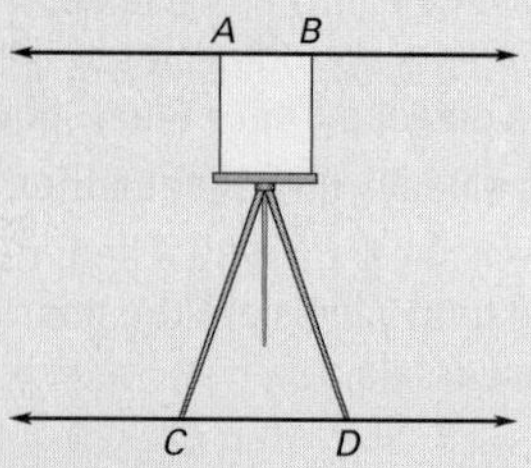

Does $\overleftrightarrow{AB}$ appear to be parallel, perpendicular, or skew to $\overleftrightarrow{CD}$? **parallel**

Available at **classzone.com**

Diagnosis/Remediation

- Practice A, B, C in Chapter 3 Resource Book, pp. 5–10
- Study Guide in Chapter 3 Resource Book, pp. 11–12
- Practice Workbook, pp. 43–45
- @HomeTutor

Challenge

Additional challenge is available in the Chapter 3 Resource Book, p. 15.

B **38. CONSTRUCTION** Use these steps to construct a line through a given point P that is parallel to a given line m. **Check students' work.**

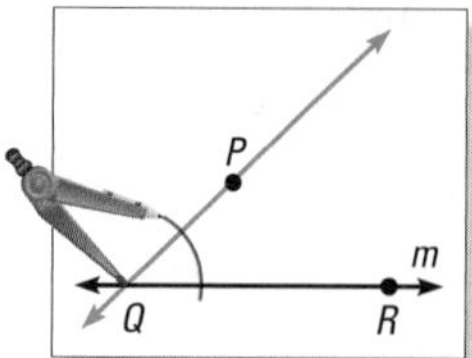

STEP 1 Draw points Q and R on m. Draw $\overleftrightarrow{PQ}$. Draw an arc with the compass point at Q so it crosses $\overleftrightarrow{QP}$ and $\overleftrightarrow{QR}$.

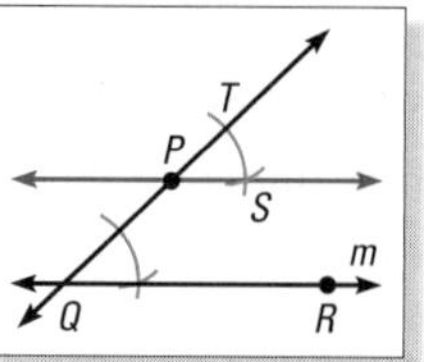

STEP 2 Copy $\angle PQR$ on $\overleftrightarrow{QP}$. Be sure the two angles are corresponding. Label the new angle $\angle TPS$. Draw $\overleftrightarrow{PS}$. $\overleftrightarrow{PS} \parallel \overleftrightarrow{QR}$.

39. ★ SHORT RESPONSE Two lines are cut by a transversal. Suppose the measure of a pair of alternate interior angles is 90°. *Explain* why the measure of all four interior angles must be 90°.

39. The adjacent interior angles are supplementary thus the measure of the other two angles must be 90°.

TREE HOUSE In Exercises 40–42, use the photo to decide whether the statement is *true* or *false*.

40. The plane containing the floor of the tree house is parallel to the ground. **true**

41. All of the lines containing the railings of the staircase, such as $\overleftrightarrow{AB}$, are skew to the ground. **false**

42. All of the lines containing the *balusters*, such as $\overleftrightarrow{CD}$, are perpendicular to the plane containing the floor of the tree house. **true**

C **CHALLENGE Draw the figure described.** **43, 44. See margin.**

43. Lines ℓ and m are skew, lines ℓ and n are skew, and lines m and n are parallel.

44. Line ℓ is parallel to plane A, plane A is parallel to plane B, and line ℓ is not parallel to plane B.

MIXED REVIEW

Use the Law of Detachment to make a valid conclusion. *(p. 87)*

45. If the measure of an angle is less than 90°, then the angle is acute. The measure of $\angle A$ is 46°. **∠A is an acute angle.**

46. If a food has less than 140 milligrams of sodium per serving, then it is low sodium. A serving of soup has 90 milligrams of sodium per serving. **A serving of soup is low sodium.**

PREVIEW Prepare for Lesson 3.2 in Exs. 47–49.

Find the measure of each numbered angle. *(p. 124)*

47. 120°, 1, 2, 3 — **$m\angle 1 = 60°$, $m\angle 2 = 120°$, $m\angle 3 = 60°$**

48. 110°, 1, 2, 3 — **$m\angle 1 = 70°$, $m\angle 2 = 110°$, $m\angle 3 = 70°$**

49. 50°, 1, 2, 3 — **$m\angle 1 = 130°$, $m\angle 2 = 50°$, $m\angle 3 = 130°$**

Investigating Geometry ACTIVITY Use before Lesson 3.2

@HomeTutor classzone.com Keystrokes

3.2 Parallel Lines and Angles

MATERIALS • graphing calculator or computer

QUESTION **What are the relationships among the angles formed by two parallel lines and a transversal?**

You can use geometry drawing software to explore parallel lines.

Standards

Prepare for 7.0 Students prove and use theorems involving the *properties of parallel lines cut by a transversal,* the properties of quadrilaterals, and the properties of circles.

EXPLORE **Draw parallel lines and a transversal**

STEP 1 ***Draw line*** Draw and label two points *A* and *B*. Draw $\overleftrightarrow{AB}$.

STEP 2 ***Draw parallel line*** Draw a point not on $\overleftrightarrow{AB}$. Label it *C*. Choose Parallel from the F3 menu and select $\overleftrightarrow{AB}$. Then select *C* to draw a line through *C* parallel to $\overleftrightarrow{AB}$. Draw a point on the parallel line you constructed. Label it *D*.

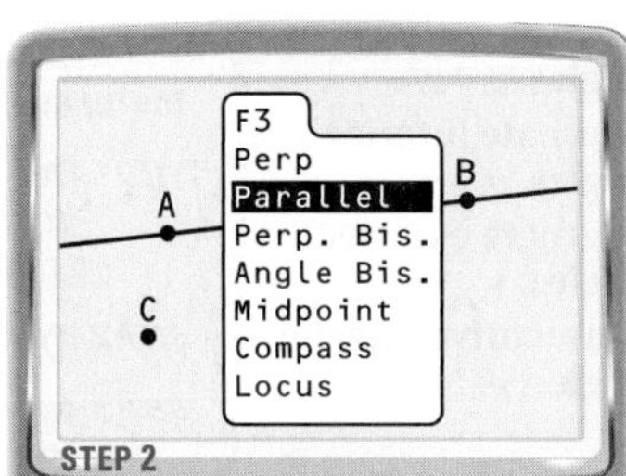

STEP 3 ***Draw transversal*** Draw two points *E* and *F* outside the parallel lines. Draw transversal $\overleftrightarrow{EF}$. Find the intersection of $\overleftrightarrow{AB}$ and $\overleftrightarrow{EF}$ by choosing Point from the F2 menu. Then choose Intersection. Label the intersection *G*. Find and label the intersection *H* of $\overleftrightarrow{CD}$ and $\overleftrightarrow{EF}$.

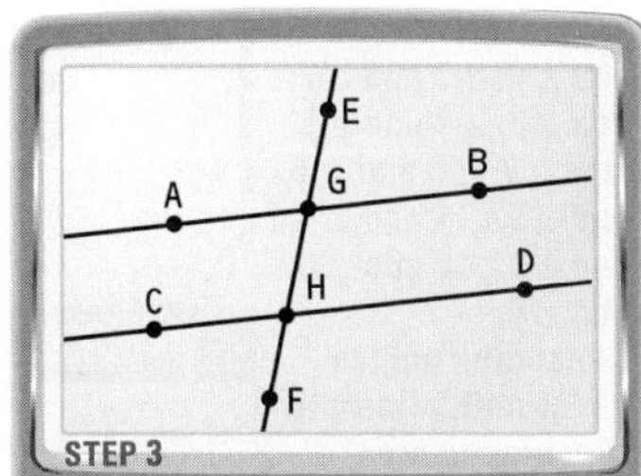

STEP 4 ***Measure angle*** Measure all eight angles formed by the three lines by choosing Measure from the F5 menu, then choosing Angle.

DRAW CONCLUSIONS **Use your observations to complete these exercises**

1. Record the angle measures from Step 4 in a table like the one shown. Which angles are congruent? **Check students' work; $\angle AGE \cong \angle BGH \cong \angle CHG \cong \angle DHF$, $\angle EGB \cong \angle AGH \cong \angle GHD \cong \angle CHF$.**

Angle	∠AGE	∠EGB	∠AGH	∠BGH	∠CHG	∠GHD	∠CHF	∠DHF
Measure 1	?	?	?	?	?	?	?	?

2. Drag point *E* or *F* to change the angle the transversal makes with the parallel lines. Be sure *E* and *F* stay outside the parallel lines. Record the new angle measures as row "Measure 2" in your table. **Check students' work.**

3. Make a conjecture about the measures of the given angles when two parallel lines are cut by a transversal.

   a. Corresponding angles **Corresponding angles are congruent.**

   b. Alternate interior angles **Alternate interior angles are congruent.**

4. **REASONING** Make and test a conjecture about the sum of the measures of two consecutive interior angles when two parallel lines are cut by a transversal. **Consecutive interior angles are supplementary.**

1 PLAN AND PREPARE

Explore the Concept

- Students will use geometric software to find relationships among the angles formed by two parallel lines and a transversal.
- This activity leads into the study of finding angle measures in Example 1 in Lesson 3.2.

Materials

Each student will need a graphing calculator or computer with geometry software.

Recommended Time

Work activity: 10 min
Discuss results: 5 min

Grouping

Students should work individually.

2 TEACH

Tips for Success

Remind students that when they measure an angle, they need to click on three points of the angle. The second point should always be the vertex of the angle.

Alternative Strategy

Have students construct parallel lines and a transversal with compass and straightedge and measure all the angles with a protractor. Then answer the same questions.

Key Discovery

For two parallel lines and a transversal, corresponding angles and alternate interior angles are congruent.

3 ASSESS AND RETEACH

Make a conjecture about alternate exterior angles when two parallel lines are cut by a transversal. **They are congruent.**

p. 152

43.

44.

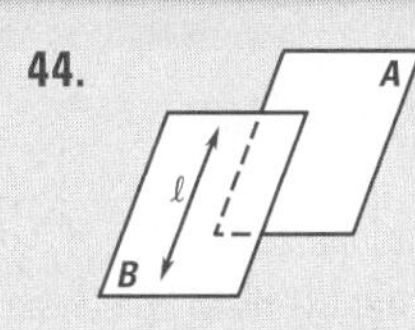

1 PLAN AND PREPARE

Warm-Up Exercises

Transparency Available

Identify the type of angles.

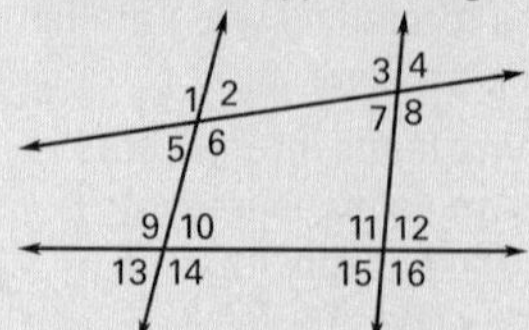

1. ∠5, ∠7 **corresponding**
2. ∠3, ∠6 **alternate interior**
3. ∠1, ∠8 **alternate exterior**

Notetaking Guide

Transparency Available

Promotes interactive learning and notetaking skills, pp. 64–66.

Pacing

Basic: 1 day
Average: 1 day
Advanced: 1 day
Block: 0.5 block with 3.1

- See *Teaching Guide/Lesson Plan.*

2 FOCUS AND MOTIVATE

Essential Question

Big Idea 1, p. 145

How are corresponding angles and alternate interior angles related for two parallel lines and a transversal? **Tell students they will learn how to answer this question by studying the postulate and theorems in this lesson.**

3.2 Use Parallel Lines and Transversals

Before You identified angle pairs formed by a transversal.
Now You will use angles formed by parallel lines and transversals.
Why? So you can understand angles formed by light, as in Example 4.

Key Vocabulary
- **corresponding angles,** *p. 149*
- **alternate interior angles,** *p. 149*
- **alternate exterior angles,** *p. 149*
- **consecutive interior angles,** *p. 149*

ACTIVITY EXPLORE PARALLEL LINES

Materials: lined paper, tracing paper, straightedge

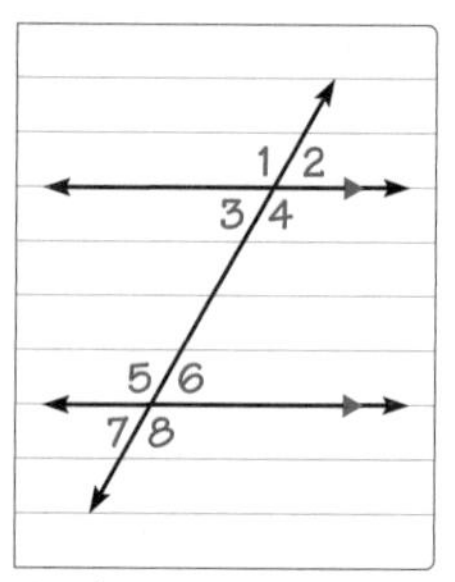

STEP 1 **Draw** a pair of parallel lines cut by a nonperpendicular transversal on lined paper. Label the angles as shown.

STEP 2 **Trace** your drawing onto tracing paper.

STEP 3 **Move** the tracing paper to position ∠1 of the traced figure over ∠5 of the original figure. Compare the angles. Are they congruent? **Yes**

STEP 4 **Compare** the eight angles and list all the congruent pairs. What do you notice about the special angle pairs formed by the transversal? **See margin.**

Step 4. ∠1 and ∠5, ∠2 and ∠6, ∠3 and ∠7, ∠4 and ∠8, ∠1 and ∠8, ∠2 and ∠7, ∠3 and ∠6, ∠4 and ∠5, ∠1 and ∠4, ∠2 and ∠3, ∠5 and ∠8, ∠7 and ∠6; corresponding angles are congruent, alternate exterior angles are congruent, and alternate interior angles are congruent.

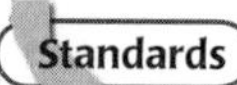

Standards

7.0 Students prove and use theorems involving the properties of parallel lines cut by a transversal, the properties of quadrilaterals, and the properties of circles.

POSTULATE *For Your Notebook*

POSTULATE 15 Corresponding Angles Postulate

If two parallel lines are cut by a transversal, then the pairs of corresponding angles are congruent.

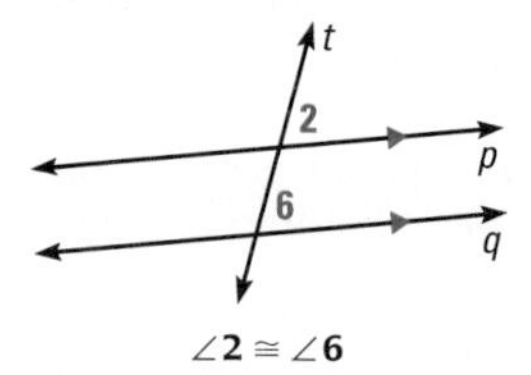

EXAMPLE 1 Identify congruent angles

The measure of three of the numbered angles is 120°. Identify the angles. Explain your reasoning.

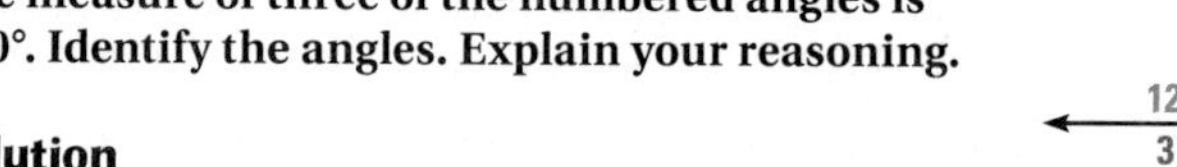

Solution

By the Corresponding Angles Postulate, $m\angle 5 = 120°$.
Using the Vertical Angles Congruence Theorem, $m\angle 4 = 120°$.
Because ∠4 and ∠8 are corresponding angles, by the Corresponding Angles Postulate, you know that $m\angle 8 = 120°$.

Resource Planning Guide

Chapter Resource Book
- Teaching Guide/Lesson Plan (pp. 16–17)
- Practice levels A, B, C (pp. 19–24)
- Study Guide (pp. 25–26)
- Catch-up for Absent Students (p. 27)
- Problem Solving Workshop (p. 28)
- Challenge (p. 29)

Workbooks
- Notetaking Guide (pp. 64–66)
- Practice Workbook (pp. 46–48)

Teaching Options
- **Power Presentations CD-ROM** provides dynamic electronic teaching resources for the classroom.
- **Activity Generator CD-ROM** provides editable activities for all ability levels.

Interactive Technology
- Easy Planner
- Power Presentations CD-ROM
- Activity Generator CD-ROM
- Animated Geometry
- Test Generator CD-ROM
- Online Quiz
- eWorkbook
- eEdition
- @HomeTutor

Resources for English Learners
- Quick Reference for English Learners
- Spanish Study Guide
- Multi-Language Visual Glossary
- Student Resources in Spanish

See also the *Geometry Toolkit* for more strategies for meeting individual needs.

THEOREMS — *For Your Notebook*

THEOREM 3.1 Alternate Interior Angles Theorem

If two parallel lines are cut by a transversal, then the pairs of alternate interior angles are congruent.

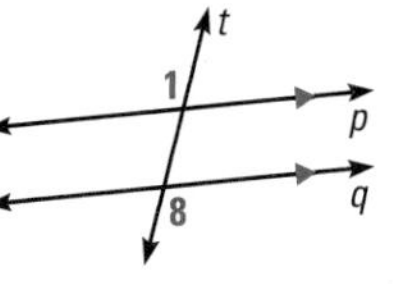

$\angle 4 \cong \angle 5$

Proof: Example 3, p. 156

THEOREM 3.2 Alternate Exterior Angles Theorem

If two parallel lines are cut by a transversal, then the pairs of alternate exterior angles are congruent.

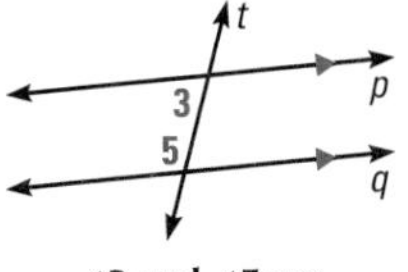

$\angle 1 \cong \angle 8$

Proof: Ex. 37, p. 159

THEOREM 3.3 Consecutive Interior Angles Theorem

If two parallel lines are cut by a transversal, then the pairs of consecutive interior angles are supplementary.

$\angle 3$ and $\angle 5$ are supplementary.

Proof: Ex. 41, p. 159

EXAMPLE 2 Use properties of parallel lines

ALGEBRA Find the value of x.

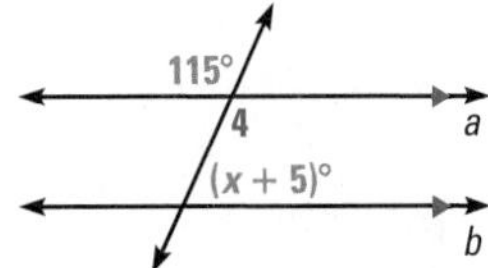

Solution

By the Vertical Angles Congruence Theorem, $m\angle 4 = 115°$. Lines a and b are parallel, so you can use the theorems about parallel lines.

$m\angle 4 + (x + 5)° = 180°$	**Consecutive Interior Angles Theorem**
$115° + (x + 5)° = 180°$	**Substitute 115° for $m\angle 4$.**
$x + 120 = 180$	**Combine like terms.**
$x = 60$	**Subtract 120 from each side.**

Animated Geometry at classzone.com

GUIDED PRACTICE for Examples 1 and 2

Use the diagram at the right.

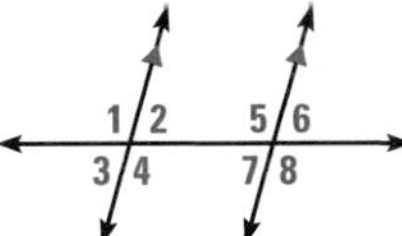

1. If $m\angle 1 = 105°$, find $m\angle 4$, $m\angle 5$, and $m\angle 8$. Tell which postulate or theorem you use in each case.

2. If $m\angle 3 = 68°$ and $m\angle 8 = (2x + 4)°$, what is the value of x? Show your steps. **54; $m\angle 7 + m\angle 8 = 180°$, $m\angle 3 = m\angle 7$, $68 + 2x + 4 = 180$, $2x + 72 = 180$, $2x = 108$, $x = 54$**

1. $m\angle 4 = 105°$, Vertical Angles Congruence Theorem; $m\angle 5 = 105°$, Corresponding Angles Postulate; $m\angle 8 = 105°$, Alternate Exterior Angles Theorem

Motivating the Lesson

Have students visualize a slanting line that crosses all the parallel lines on a sheet of notebook paper. Tell them that in this lesson, they will learn how to find the measures of all the angles formed by measuring just one of the angles.

3 TEACH

Activity Note

The purpose of this activity is to show students that corresponding angles formed by parallel lines and a transversal are congruent.

Extra Example 1

The measure of three of the numbered angles is 55°. Identify the angles. Explain your reasoning.

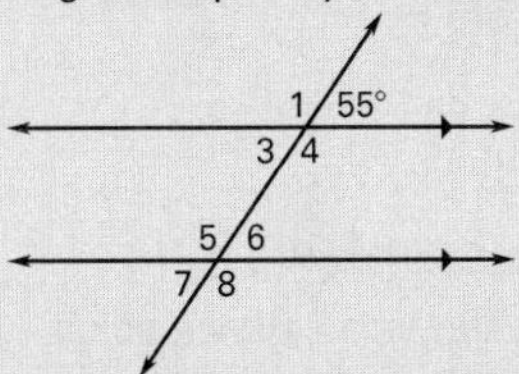

$\angle 6$, $\angle 3$, $\angle 7$; $m\angle 6 = 55°$ by the Corresponding Angles Postulate. $m\angle 3 = 55°$ and $m\angle 7 = 55°$ by the Vertical Angles Congruence Theorem.

Key Question to Ask for Example 1

- What is the measure of the other four angles in the figure? **60°**

Extra Example 2

Find the value of x. **165**

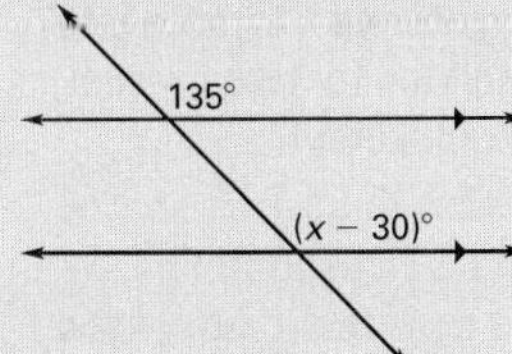

Differentiated Instruction

Kinesthetic Learners Have students draw a pair of parallel lines cut by a transversal. Then have them identify two alternate interior angles, two alternate exterior angles, and two consecutive interior angles. Have them measure each angle to support their understanding of the theorems.

See also the *Geometry Toolkit* for more strategies.

EXAMPLE 3 Prove the Alternate Interior Angles Theorem

Prove that if two parallel lines are cut by a transversal, then the pairs of alternate interior angles are congruent.

Solution

WRITE PROOFS You can use the information from the diagram in your proof. Find any special angle pairs. Then decide what you know about those pairs.

Draw a diagram. Label a pair of alternate interior angles as $\angle 1$ and $\angle 2$. You are looking for an angle that is related to both $\angle 1$ and $\angle 2$. Notice that one angle is a vertical angle with $\angle 2$ and a corresponding angle with $\angle 1$. Label it $\angle 3$.

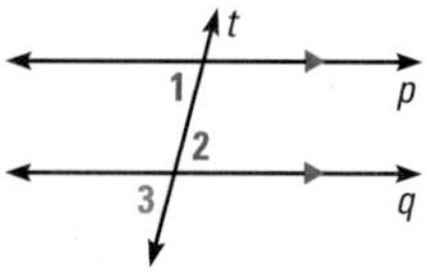

GIVEN ▶ $p \parallel q$

PROVE ▶ $\angle 1 \cong \angle 2$

STATEMENTS	REASONS
1. $p \parallel q$	1. Given
2. $\angle 1 \cong \angle 3$	2. Corresponding Angles Postulate
3. $\angle 3 \cong \angle 2$	3. Vertical Angles Congruence Theorem
4. $\angle 1 \cong \angle 2$	4. Transitive Property of Congruence

EXAMPLE 4 Solve a real-world problem

SCIENCE When sunlight enters a drop of rain, different colors of light leave the drop at different angles. This process is what makes a rainbow. For violet light, $m\angle 2 = 40°$. What is $m\angle 1$? How do you know?

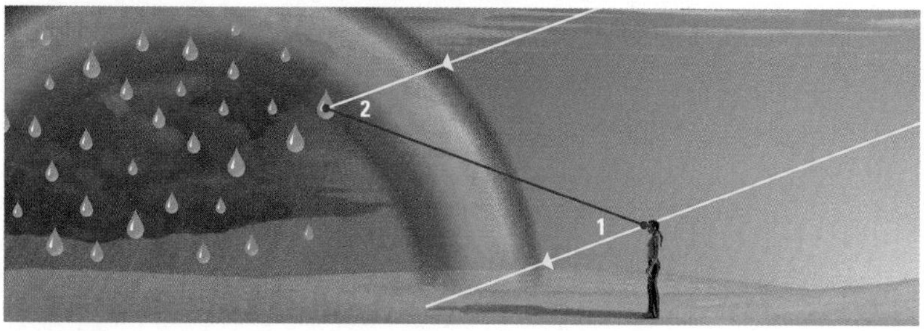

Solution

Because the sun's rays are parallel, $\angle 1$ and $\angle 2$ are alternate interior angles. By the Alternate Interior Angles Theorem, $\angle 1 \cong \angle 2$. By the definition of congruent angles, $m\angle 1 = m\angle 2 = 40°$.

✓ **GUIDED PRACTICE** for Examples 3 and 4

3. In the proof in Example 3, if you use the third statement before the second statement, could you still prove the theorem? *Explain.* **Yes. *Sample answer:* $\angle 3$ and $\angle 2$ congruence is not dependent on the congruence of $\angle 1$ and $\angle 3$.**
4. **WHAT IF?** Suppose the diagram in Example 4 shows yellow light leaving a drop of rain. Yellow light leaves the drop at an angle of 41°. What is $m\angle 1$ in this case? How do you know?

4. 41°; $\angle 1$ and $\angle 2$ are alternate interior angles. By the Alternate Interior Angles Theorem $\angle 1 \cong \angle 2$, and by the definition of congruent angles $m\angle 1 = m\angle 2 = 41°$.

Extra Example 3

Prove that if two parallel lines are cut by a transversal, then the exterior angles on the same side of the transversal are supplementary.

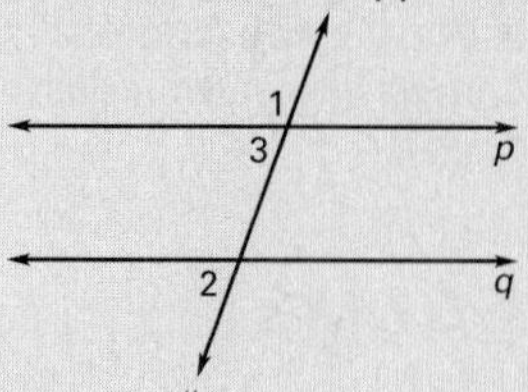

Given: $p \parallel q$

Prove: $\angle 1$ and $\angle 2$ are supp.

Statements (Reasons)

1. **$p \parallel q$ (Given)**
2. **$m\angle 1 + m\angle 3 = 180°$ (Linear Pair Post.)**
3. **$\angle 2 \cong \angle 3$ (Corr. ∠s Post.)**
4. **$m\angle 2 = m\angle 3$ (Def. of ≅ ∠s)**
5. **$m\angle 1 + m\angle 2 = 180°$ (Substitution)**
6. **$\angle 1$ and $\angle 2$ are supp. (Def. of supp. ∠s)**

Extra Example 4

The figure shows a balance scale. If $m\angle 1 = 70°$, what is $m\angle 2$? How do you know?

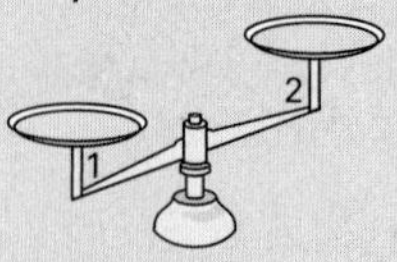

110°; Consecutive Interior Angles Theorem

Closing the Lesson

Have students summarize the major points of the lesson and answer the Essential Question: How are corresponding angles and alternate interior angles related for two parallel lines and a transversal?

- **If two parallel lines are cut by a transversal, corresponding angles are congruent, alternate interior angles are congruent, alternate exterior angles are congruent, and consecutive interior angles are supplementary.**

Corresponding angles are congruent, and alternate interior angles are congruent.

3.2 EXERCISES

HOMEWORK KEY ○ = **WORKED-OUT SOLUTIONS** on p. WS3 for Exs. 5, 9, and 39
★ = **STANDARDIZED TEST PRACTICE** Exs. 2, 3, 21, 33, 39, and 40

SKILL PRACTICE

A

1. **VOCABULARY** Draw a pair of parallel lines and a transversal. Label a pair of *corresponding angles.* **See margin.**

2. ★ **WRITING** Two parallel lines are cut by a transversal. Which pairs of angles are congruent? Which pairs of angles are supplementary? **See margin.**

EXAMPLES 1 and 2 on pp. 154–155 for Exs. 3–16

3. ★ **MULTIPLE CHOICE** In the figure at the right, which angle has the same measure as $\angle 1$? **C**

Ⓐ $\angle 2$ Ⓑ $\angle 3$
Ⓒ $\angle 4$ Ⓓ $\angle 5$

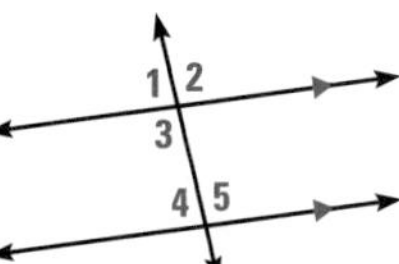

2. congruent: alternate interior angles, alternate exterior angles, corresponding angles, vertical angles; supplementary: adjacent angles, consecutive interior angles, exterior angles on the same side of the

USING PARALLEL LINES **Find the angle measure. Tell which postulate or theorem you use.**

4. If $m\angle 4 = 65°$, then $m\angle 1 =$ _?_.
65°; Vertical Angles Congruence Theorem
5. If $m\angle 7 = 110°$, then $m\angle 2 =$ _?_.
110°; Alternate Exterior Angles Theorem
6. If $m\angle 5 = 71°$, then $m\angle 4 =$ _?_.
71°; Alternate Interior Angles Theorem
7. If $m\angle 3 = 117°$, then $m\angle 5 =$ _?_.
63°; Consecutive Interior Angles Theorem
8. If $m\angle 8 = 54°$, then $m\angle 1 =$ _?_.
54°; Alternate Exterior Angles Theorem

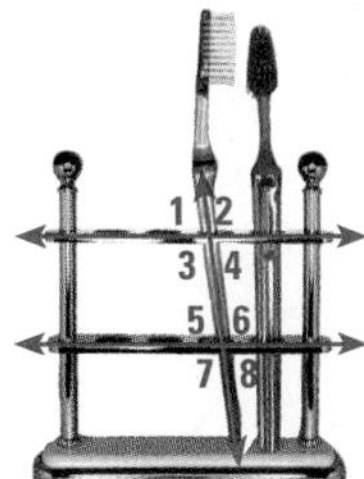

USING POSTULATES AND THEOREMS **What postulate or theorem justifies the statement about the diagram?**

9. $\angle 1 \cong \angle 5$
10. $\angle 4 \cong \angle 5$ **Alternate Interior Angles Theorem**
11. $\angle 2 \cong \angle 7$
12. $\angle 2$ and $\angle 5$ are supplementary. **Consecutive Interior Angles Theorem**
13. $\angle 3 \cong \angle 6$
14. $\angle 3 \cong \angle 7$ **Corresponding Angles Postulate**
15. $\angle 1 \cong \angle 8$ **Alternate Exterior Angles Theorem**
16. $\angle 4$ and $\angle 7$ are supplementary. **Consecutive Interior Angles Theorem**

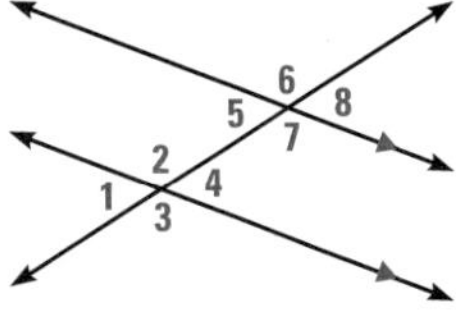

9. Corresponding Angles Postulate

11. Alternate Interior Angles Theorem

13. Alternate Exterior Angles Theorem

B

USING PARALLEL LINES Find $m\angle 1$ and $m\angle 2$. *Explain* your reasoning. **18, 19. See margin**

17.
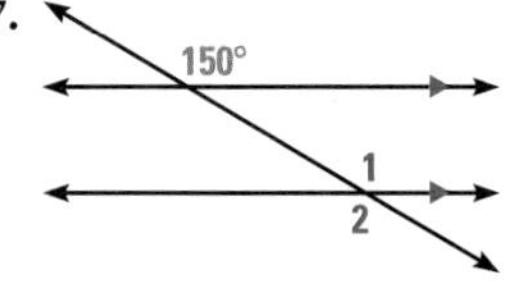

18.
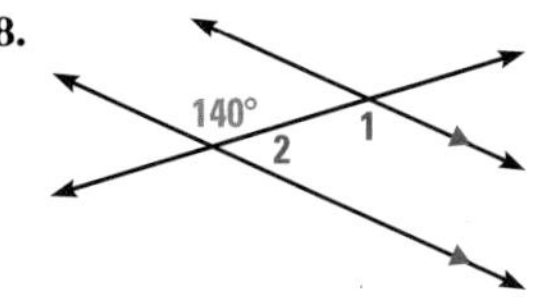

19.
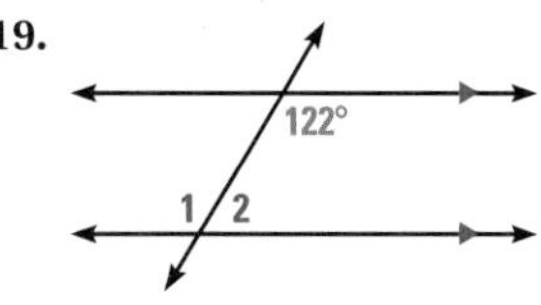

17. $m\angle 1 = 150°$, $m\angle 2 = 150°$; Corresponding Angles Postulate, Vertical Angles Congruence Theorem

20. **ERROR ANALYSIS** A student concludes that $\angle 9 \cong \angle 10$ by the Corresponding Angles Postulate. Describe and correct the error in this reasoning.
The lines are not known to be parallel, therefore $\angle 9$ and $\angle 10$ are not necessarily congruent.

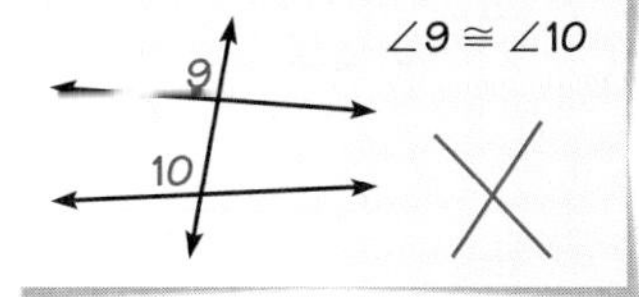

4 PRACTICE AND APPLY

Assignment Guide

Answer Transparencies available for all exercises

Basic:
Day 1: pp. 157–160
Exs. 1–8, 9–15 odd, 17–24, 37–40, 44–52 even

Average:
Day 1: pp. 157–160
Exs. 1–3, 4–20 even, 21–34, 37–42, 44, 45, 49, 51

Advanced:
Day 1: pp. 157–160
Exs. 1–3, 7, 8, 13, 15, 18, 19, 21–37*, 39–43*, 47, 50, 52

Block:
pp. 157–160
Exs. 1–3, 4–20 even, 21–34, 37–42, 44, 45, 49, 51 (with 3.1)

Differentiated Instruction

See *Geometry Best Practices Toolkit* for suggestions on addressing the needs of a diverse classroom.

Homework Check

For a quick check of student understanding of key concepts, go over the following exercises:

Basic: 4, 11, 17, 37, 38
Average: 6, 14, 18, 37, 39
Advanced: 8, 13, 19, 37, 40

Extra Practice

- Student Edition, p. 900
- Chapter 3 Resource Book: Practice levels A, B, C, pp. 19–24

Practice Worksheet

An easily-readable reduced practice page (with answers) for this lesson can be found on p. 144C.

1. *Sample:*

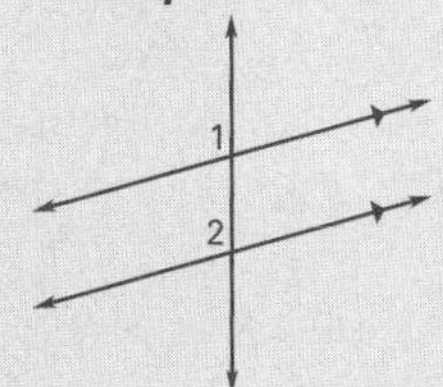

18. $m\angle 1 = 140°$, $m\angle 2 = 40°$; Alternate Interior Angles Theorem, Consecutive Interior Angles Theorem

19. $m\angle 1 = 122°$, $m\angle 2 = 58°$; Alternate Interior Angles Theorem, Consecutive Interior Angles Theorem

Avoiding Common Errors

Exercises 25–26 Students may immediately assume that both pairs of opposite sides of *ABCD* are parallel. Redraw the figure for Exercise 25 with only $\overline{AB}$ and $\overline{CD}$ parallel so they can see that $m\angle ADB$ is not equal to $m\angle DBC$ and $m\angle DAC$ is not equal to $m\angle BCA$. Redraw the figure for Exercise 26 so only $\overline{AD}$ and $\overline{BC}$ are parallel and discuss which angle measures are equal.

Reading Strategy

Exercise 34 Students will have errors if they label the sides of the figure with the letters in the wrong order. Urge students to check their sketches carefully against the wording in the exercise to make sure each condition in the exercise is met.

Mathematical Reasoning

Exercise 43 Some students may say that the answer is simply $m\angle 5$. Point out that a specific number would be more desirable. A clue that a specific number can be obtained is that the answer $m\angle 5$ could easily be obtained by using only part of the given information.

23. $m\angle 1 = 90°$, **supplementary to the right angle by the Consecutive Interior Angles Theorem;** $m\angle 3 = 65°$, **it forms a linear pair with the angle measuring 115°;** $m\angle 2 = 115°$, **supplementary to $\angle 3$ by the Consecutive Interior Angles Theorem**

24. $m\angle 3 = 47°$, **supplementary to the angle measuring 133° by the Consecutive Interior Angles Theorem;** $m\angle 2 = 133°$, **it forms a linear pair with $\angle 3$;** $m\angle 1 = 47°$, $m\angle 1 = m\angle 3$ **by the Alternate Interior Angles Theorem**

22. $m\angle 1 = 100°$, **Consecutive Interior Angles Theorem;** $m\angle 2 = 80°$, **Consecutive Interior Angles Theorem;** $m\angle 3 = 100°$, **Consecutive Interior Angles Theorem**

25. ***Sample answer:*** $\angle BAC$ **and** $\angle DCA$, $\angle ABD$ **and** $\angle CDB$

21. ★ **SHORT RESPONSE** Given $p \parallel q$, *describe* two methods you can use to show that $\angle 1 \cong \angle 4$.
Sample answer: $\angle 1 \cong \angle 4$ **by the Alternate Exterior Angles Theorem;** $\angle 1 \cong \angle 2 \cong \angle 3 \cong \angle 4$ **by Vertical Angles Congruence Theorem, Alternate Interior Angles Theorem, and the Transitive Property of Angle Congruence.**

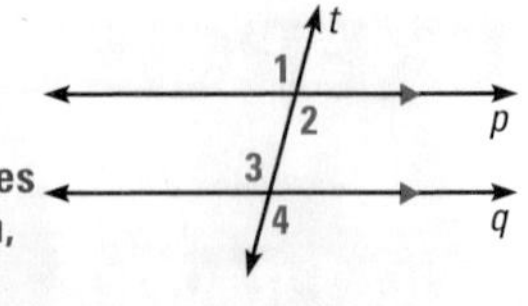

USING PARALLEL LINES Find $m\angle 1$, $m\angle 2$, and $m\angle 3$. *Explain* your reasoning. **23, 24. See margin.**

22. 23. 24.

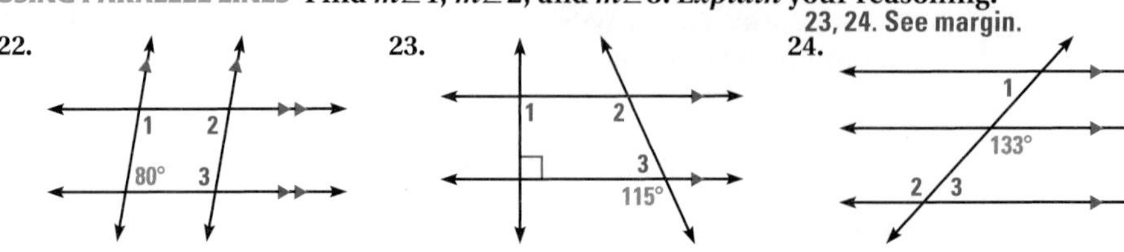

ANGLES Use the diagram at the right.

25. Name two pairs of congruent angles if $\overleftrightarrow{AB}$ and $\overleftrightarrow{DC}$ are parallel.

26. Name two pairs of supplementary angles if $\overleftrightarrow{AD}$ and $\overleftrightarrow{BC}$ are parallel. ***Sample answer:*** $\angle BAD$ **and** $\angle ABC$, $\angle CDA$ **and** $\angle DCB$

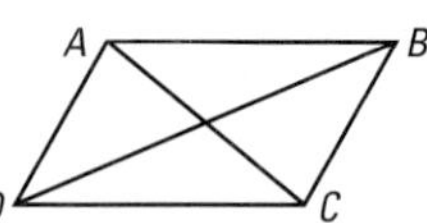

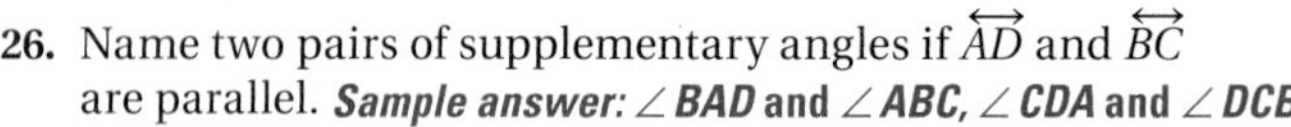

ALGEBRA Find the values of *x* and *y*.

27. **45, 85**

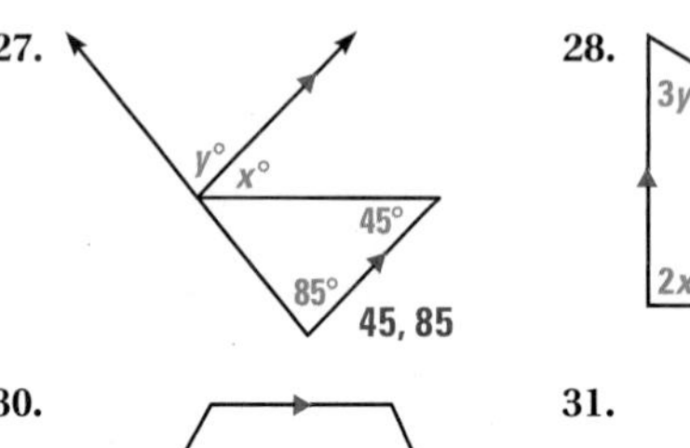

28. **45, 20**

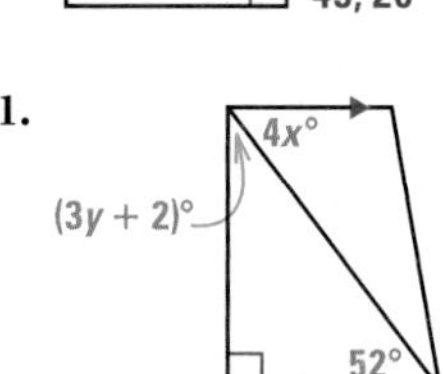

29. **65, 60**

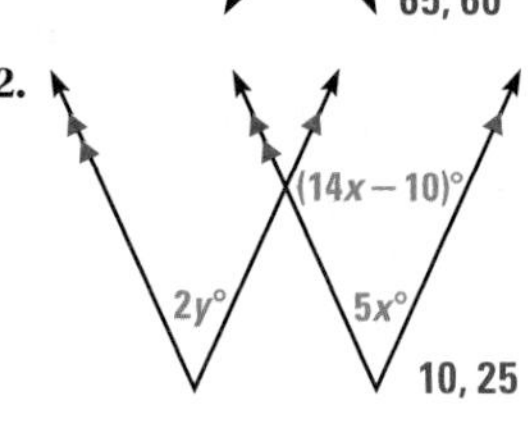

30. **20, 10**

31. **13, 12**

32. **10, 25**

33. ★ **MULTIPLE CHOICE** What is the value of *y* in the diagram? **B**

Ⓐ 70 Ⓑ 75

Ⓒ 110 Ⓓ 115

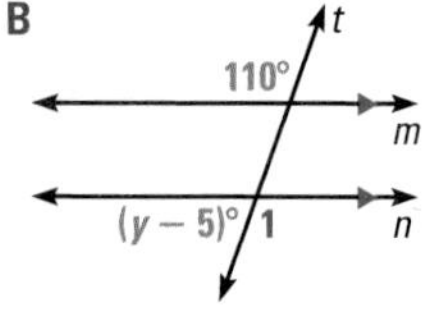

34. **DRAWING** Draw a four-sided figure with sides $\overline{MN}$ and $\overline{PQ}$, such that $\overline{MN} \parallel \overline{PQ}$, $\overline{MP} \parallel \overline{NQ}$, and $\angle MNQ$ is an acute angle. Which angle pairs formed are congruent? *Explain* your reasoning. **See margin.**

C **CHALLENGE** Find the values of *x* and *y*.

35. **65, 10**

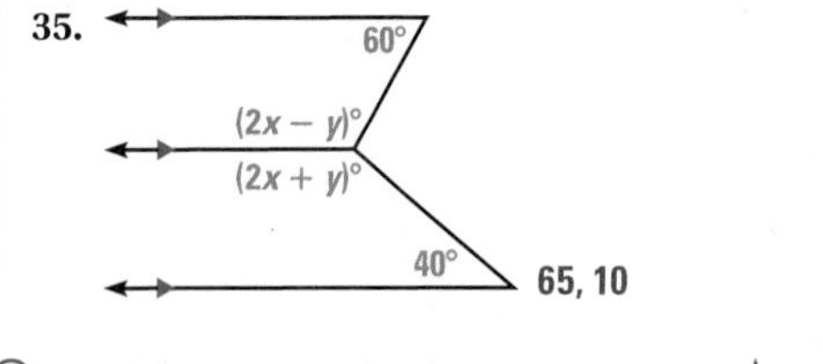

36. **8, 10**

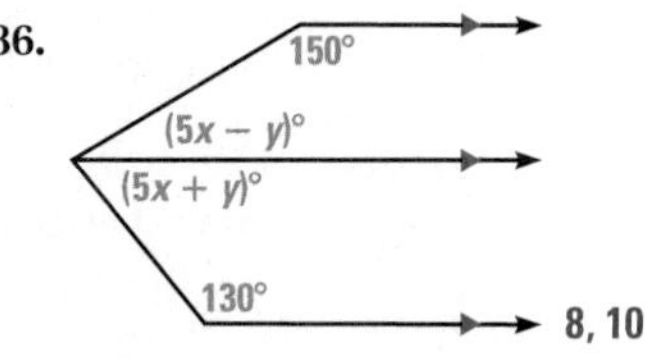

○ = WORKED-OUT SOLUTIONS on p. WS1 ★ = STANDARDIZED TEST PRACTICE

34.

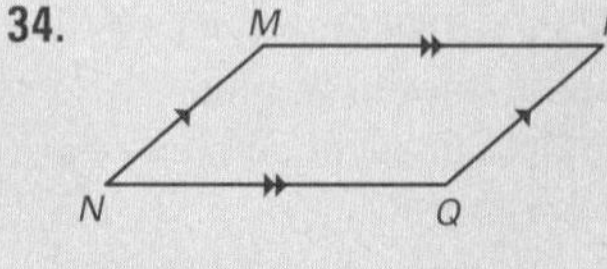

$\angle M$ **and** $\angle Q$, $\angle P$ **and** $\angle N$. ***Sample answer:*** $\angle P$ **is supplementary to** $\angle M$ **and** $\angle Q$, **therefore by the Congruent Supplements Theorem they are congruent;** $\angle Q$ **is supplementary to** $\angle P$ **and** $\angle N$, **therefore by the Congruent Supplements Theorem they are congruent.**

PROBLEM SOLVING

EXAMPLE 3 A
on p. 156
for Ex. 37

37. **PROVING THEOREM 3.2** If two parallel lines are cut by a transversal, then the pairs of alternate exterior angles are congruent. Use the steps below to write a proof of the Alternate Exterior Angles Theorem. **See margin.**

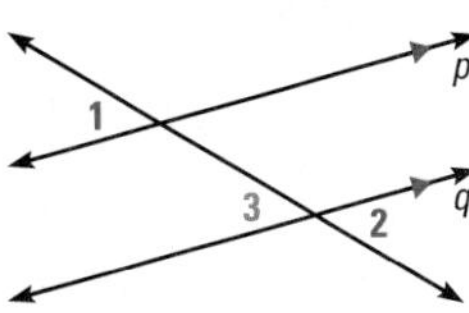

GIVEN ▶ $p \parallel q$

PROVE ▶ $\angle 1 \cong \angle 2$

a. Show that $\angle 1 \cong \angle 3$.

b. Then show that $\angle 1 \cong \angle 2$.

@HomeTutor for problem solving help at classzone.com

EXAMPLE 4
on p. 156
for Exs. 38–40

38. **PARKING LOT** In the diagram, the lines dividing parking spaces are parallel. The measure of $\angle 1$ is $110°$.

a. Identify the angle(s) congruent to $\angle 1$. **$\angle 4, \angle 5, \angle 8$**

b. Find $m\angle 6$. **70°**

@HomeTutor for problem solving help at classzone.com

B

39. ★ **SHORT RESPONSE** The *Toddler*™ is a walking robot. Each leg of the robot has two parallel bars and a foot. When the robot walks, the leg bars remain parallel as the foot slides along the surface.

a. As the legs move, are there pairs of angles that are always congruent? always supplementary? If so, which angles?

39a. yes; $\angle 1$ and $\angle 5$, $\angle 2$ and $\angle 6$; yes; $\angle 1$ and $\angle 2$, $\angle 1$ and $\angle 6$, $\angle 2$ and $\angle 5$, $\angle 5$ and $\angle 6$

b. *Explain* how having parallel leg bars allows the robot's foot to stay flat on the floor as it moves.
Sample answer: **The transversal stays parallel to the floor.**

40. ★ **EXTENDED RESPONSE** You are designing a box like the one below.

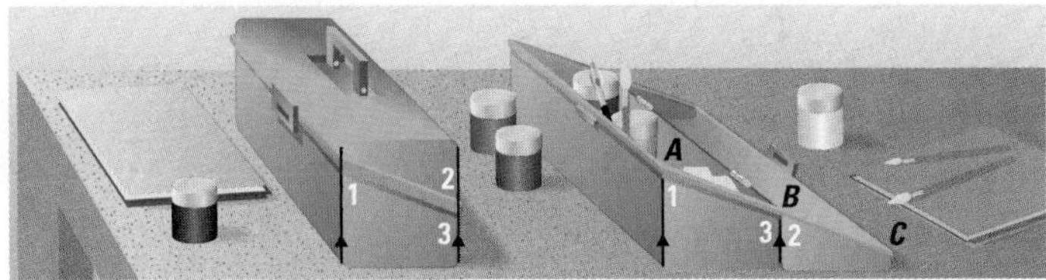

a. The measure of $\angle 1$ is $70°$. What is $m\angle 2$? What is $m\angle 3$? **70°, 110°**

b. *Explain* why $\angle ABC$ is a straight angle. **See margin.**

c. **What If?** If $m\angle 1$ is $60°$, will $\angle ABC$ still be a straight angle? Will the opening of the box be *more steep* or *less steep*? *Explain.* **Yes; steeper. *Sample answer:* The points are collinear, if $m\angle 1$ is 60°, the angle is smaller and the line becomes steeper.**

41. **PROVING THEOREM 3.3** If two parallel lines are cut by a transversal, then the pairs of consecutive interior angles are supplementary. Write a proof of the Consecutive Interior Angles Theorem. **See margin.**

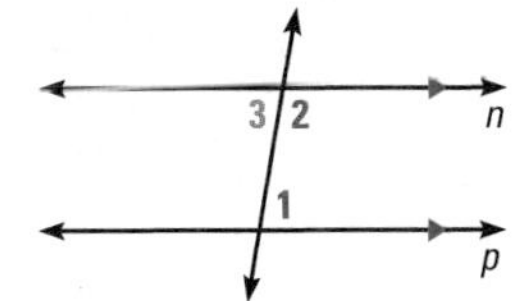

GIVEN ▶ $n \parallel p$

PROVE ▶ $\angle 1$ and $\angle 2$ are supplementary.

Internet Reference

Exercise 39 To learn more about walking robots, visit www.news.cornell.edu/releases/Feb05/AAAS.Ruina.bipedal.ws.html

37. Statements (Reasons)

1. $p \parallel q$ (Given)

2. $\angle 1 \cong \angle 3$ (Corresponding Angles Postulate)

3. $\angle 3 \cong \angle 2$ (Vertical Angles Congruence Theorem)

4. $\angle 1 \cong \angle 2$ (Transitive Property of Angle Congruence)

40b. *Sample answer:* $\angle 1$ and $\angle 2$ are corresponding angles and therefore congruent. $\angle 1$ and $\angle 3$ are supplementary so by substitution $\angle 2$ and $\angle 3$ are supplementary, so $\angle ABC$ is a straight angle.

41. Statements (Reasons)

1. $n \parallel p$ (Given)

2. $\angle 1 \cong \angle 3$ (Alternate Interior Angles Theorem)

3. $m\angle 1 = m\angle 3$ (Definition of congruent angles)

4. $m\angle 2 + m\angle 3 = 180°$ (Definition of supplementary angles)

5. $m\angle 2 + m\angle 1 = 180°$ (Substitution)

6. $\angle 1$ and $\angle 2$ are supplementary. (Definition of supplementary angles)

5 ASSESS AND RETEACH

Daily Homework Quiz

Transparency Available

What theorem justifies each statement?

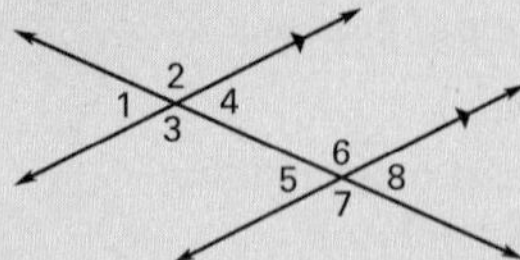

1. $\angle 3 \cong \angle 6$ **Alt. Interior ⦣s Thm.**
2. $\angle 4$ and $\angle 6$ are supplementary. **Consec. Interior ⦣s Thm.**
3. If $m\angle 2 = 115°$, find $m\angle 7$. **115°**
4. Find the values of x and y. **17.5, 35**

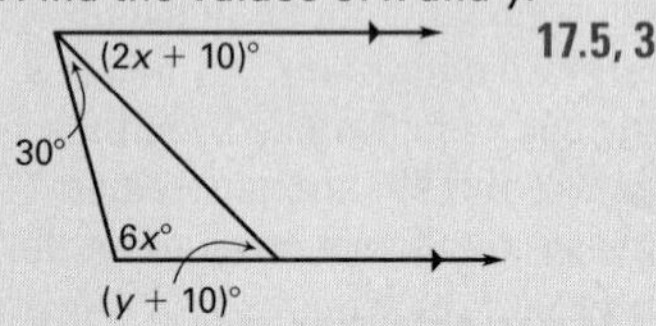

5. The figure shows a plant trellis. If $m\angle 1 = 82°$, find $m\angle 2$. **82°**

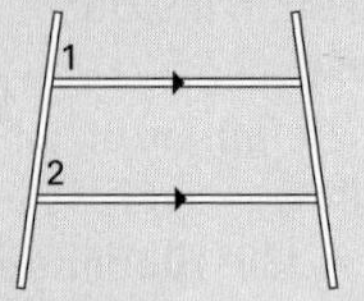

Online Quiz

Available at **classzone.com**

Diagnosis/Remediation

- Practice A, B, C in Chapter 3 Resource Book, pp. 19–24
- Study Guide in Chapter 3 Resource Book, pp. 25–26
- Practice Workbook, pp. 46–48
- @HomeTutor

Challenge

Additional challenge is available in the Chapter 3 Resource Book, p. 29.

Quiz

An easily-readable reduced copy of the quiz (with answers) on Lessons 3.1–3.2 from the Assessment Book can be found on p. 144F.

42. See Additional Answers beginning on p. AA1.

42. **PROOF** The Perpendicular Transversal Theorem (page 192) states that if a transversal is perpendicular to one of two parallel lines, then it is perpendicular to the other. Write a proof of the Perpendicular Transversal Theorem. **See margin.**

GIVEN ▶ $t \perp r$, $r \parallel s$

PROVE ▶ $t \perp s$

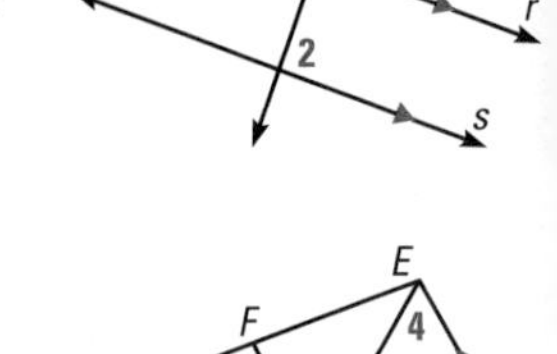

C 43. **CHALLENGE** In the diagram, $\angle 4 \cong \angle 5$. $\overline{SE}$ bisects $\angle RSF$. Find $m\angle 1$. *Explain* your reasoning. **60°. *Sample answer:* $\angle 4 \cong \angle 2$ by the Alternate Interior Angles Theorem, $\angle 2 \cong \angle 3$ by Definition of angle bisector, $\angle 5 \cong \angle 1$ by Corresponding Angles Postulate, $\angle 4 \cong \angle 5$ is given, so $\angle 1 \cong \angle 2 \cong \angle 3 \cong \angle 4 \cong \angle 5$. Since $m\angle 1 + m\angle 2 + m\angle 3 = 180°$, they must each be 60°.**

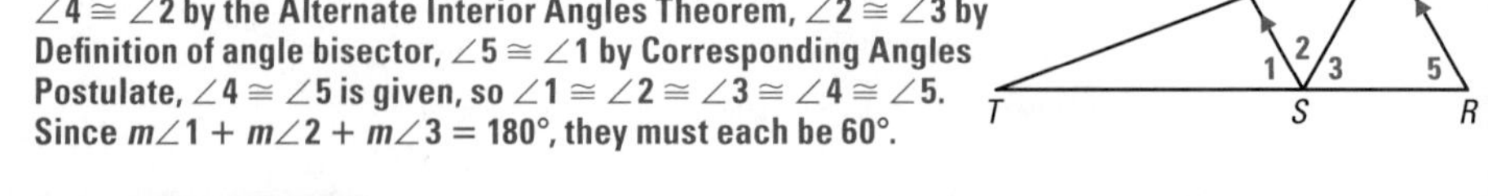

MIXED REVIEW

44. Find the length of each segment in the coordinate plane at the right. Which segments are congruent? *(p. 15)*
$OA = 2\sqrt{2}$, $OB = 3\sqrt{2}$, $OC = 3$, $OD = 3$; $\overline{OC}$ and $\overline{OD}$

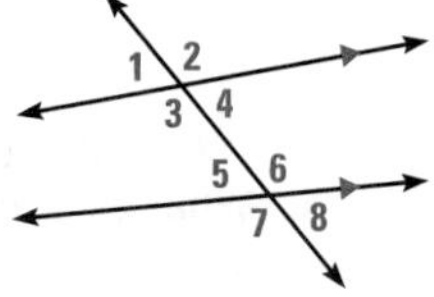

Are angles with the given measures *complementary*, *supplementary*, or *neither*? *(p. 35)*

45. $m\angle 1 = 62°$, $m\angle 2 = 128°$ **neither**
46. $m\angle 3 = 130°$, $m\angle 4 = 70°$ **neither**
47. $m\angle 5 = 44°$, $m\angle 6 = 46°$ **complementary**

Find the perimeter of the equilateral figure with the given side length. *(pp. 42, 49)*

48. Pentagon, 20 cm **100 cm**
49. Octagon, 2.5 ft **20 ft**
50. Decagon, 33 in. **330 in.**

PREVIEW Prepare for Lesson 3.3 in Exs. 51–52.

Write the converse of the statement. Is the converse true? *(p. 79)*

51. Three points are collinear if they lie on the same line. **If three points are collinear, then they lie on the same line; yes.**
52. If the measure of an angle is 119°, then the angle is obtuse. **If an angle is obtuse, then the measure of the angle is 119°; no.**

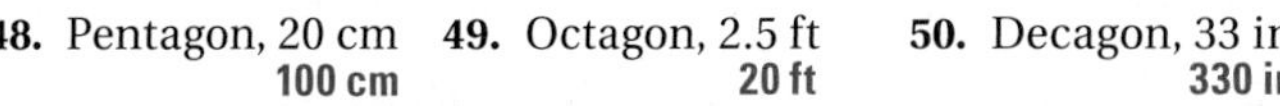

QUIZ for Lessons 3.1–3.2

Copy and complete the statement. *(p. 147)*

1. $\angle 2$ and __?__ are corresponding angles. **$\angle 6$**
2. $\angle 3$ and __?__ are consecutive interior angles. **$\angle 5$**
3. $\angle 3$ and __?__ are alternate interior angles. **$\angle 6$**
4. $\angle 2$ and __?__ are alternate exterior angles. **$\angle 7$**

Find the value of x. *(p. 154)*

5. 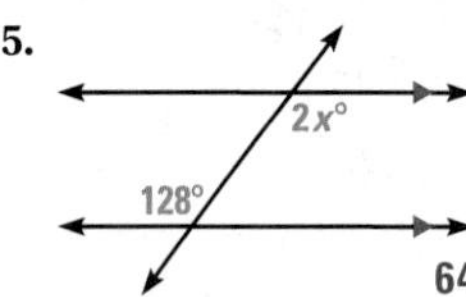 **64**

6. 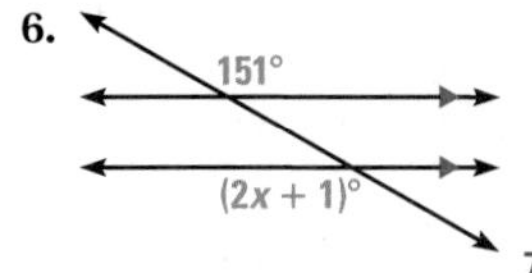 **75**

7. 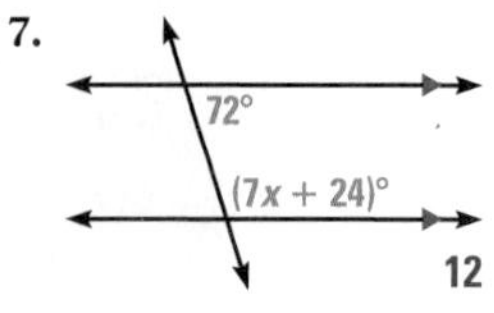 **12**

3.3 Prove Lines are Parallel

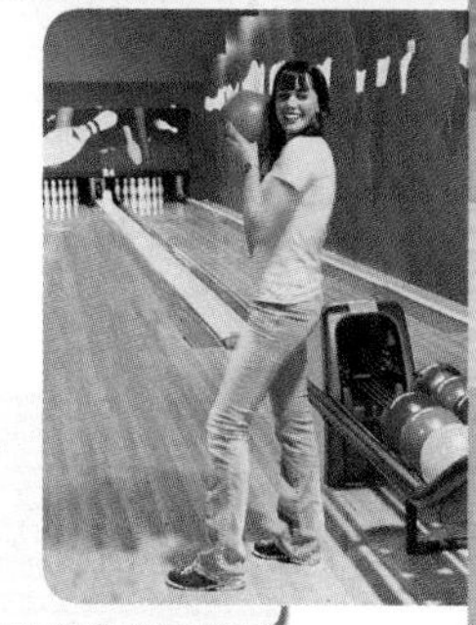

Before You used properties of parallel lines to determine angle relationships.
Now You will use angle relationships to prove that lines are parallel.
Why? So you can describe how sports equipment is arranged, as in Ex. 32.

Key Vocabulary
- **paragraph proof**
- **converse,** *p. 80*
- **two-column proof,** *p. 112*

Standards

7.0 Students prove and use theorems involving the properties of parallel lines cut by a transversal, the properties of quadrilaterals, and the properties of circles.

2.0 Students write geometric proofs, including proofs by contradiction.

Postulate 16 below is the converse of Postulate 15 in Lesson 3.2. Similarly, the theorems in Lesson 3.2 have true converses. Remember that the converse of a true conditional statement is not necessarily true, so each converse of a theorem must be proved, as in Example 3.

POSTULATE *For Your Notebook*

POSTULATE 16 Corresponding Angles Converse

If two lines are cut by a transversal so the corresponding angles are congruent, then the lines are parallel.

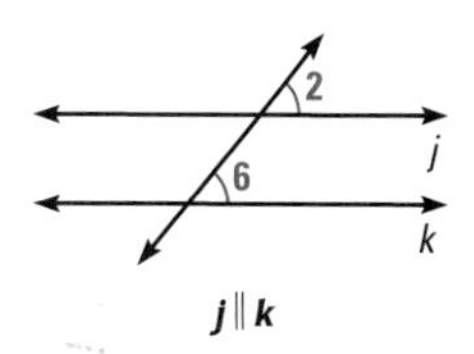

EXAMPLE 1 Apply the Corresponding Angles Converse

ALGEBRA Find the value of x that makes $m \parallel n$.

Solution

Lines m and n are parallel if the marked corresponding angles are congruent.

$(3x + 5)° = 65°$ **Use Postulate 16 to write an equation.**

$3x = 60$ **Subtract 5 from each side.**

$x = 20$ **Divide each side by 3.**

▶ The lines m and n are parallel when $x = 20$.

GUIDED PRACTICE for Example 1

1. Is there enough information in the diagram to conclude that $m \parallel n$? *Explain.*
2. *Explain* why Postulate 16 is the converse of Postulate 15. **Postulate 16 switches the hypothesis and conclusion of Postulate 15.**

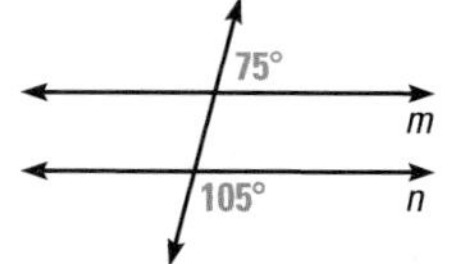

1. Yes. ***Sample answer:*** ***m*** **∥ *n* because the angle corresponding to the angle measuring 75° also measures 75° since it forms a linear pair with the 105° angle. So, corresponding angles are congruent.**

1 PLAN AND PREPARE

Warm-Up Exercises

Transparency Available

1. Find the value of x. **32**

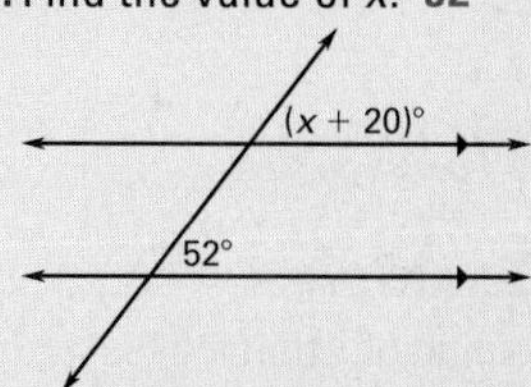

2. Write the converse of the following statement. If it is raining, then Josh needs an umbrella. **If Josh needs an umbrella, then it is raining.**

Notetaking Guide

Transparency Available

Promotes interactive learning and notetaking skills, pp. 67–70.

Pacing

Basic: 2 days
Average: 2 days
Advanced: 2 days
Block: 1 block
- See *Teaching Guide/Lesson Plan.*

2 FOCUS AND MOTIVATE

Essential Question

Big Idea 2, p. 145

How do you prove lines parallel? **Tell students they will learn how to answer this question by studying the postulate and theorems in this lesson.**

Resource Planning Guide

Chapter Resource Book
- Teaching Guide/Lesson Plan (pp. 30–31)
- Activity Master (p. 32)
- Practice levels A, B, C (pp. 33–38)
- Study Guide (pp. 39–40)
- Catch-up for Absent Students (p. 41)
- Problem Solving Workshop (p. 42)
- Challenge (p. 44)

Workbooks
- Notetaking Guide (pp. 67–70)
- Practice Workbook (pp. 49–51)

Teaching Options
- **Power Presentations CD-ROM** provides dynamic electronic teaching resources for the classroom.
- **Activity Generator CD-ROM** provides editable activities for all ability levels.

Interactive Technology
- Easy Planner
- Power Presentations CD-ROM
- Activity Generator CD-ROM
- Animated Geometry
- Test Generator CD-ROM
- Online Quiz
- eWorkbook
- eEdition
- @HomeTutor

Resources for English Learners
- Quick Reference for English Learners
- Spanish Study Guide
- Multi-Language Visual Glossary
- Student Resources in Spanish

See also the *Geometry Toolkit* for more strategies for meeting individual needs.

Motivating the Lesson

Tell students that building plans usually include many examples of lines that need to be parallel. Tell them that in this lesson they will learn how to use angle measures to ensure that lines are parallel.

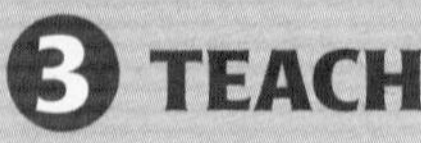

3 TEACH

Extra Example 1

Find the value of y that makes $a \parallel b$. **23**

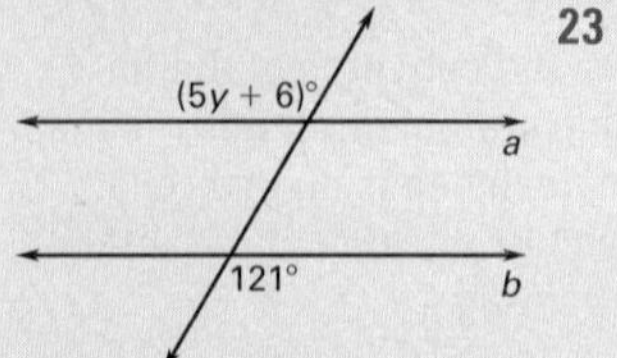

Key Question to Ask for Example 1

- What is the difference between what you can prove with the Corresponding Angles Converse and the Corresponding Angles Postulate? **The converse is for proving that lines are parallel. The postulate is for proving that angles are congruent.**

Extra Example 2

Marie was stenciling this design on her kitchen walls. How can she tell if the top and bottom lines of the design are parallel?

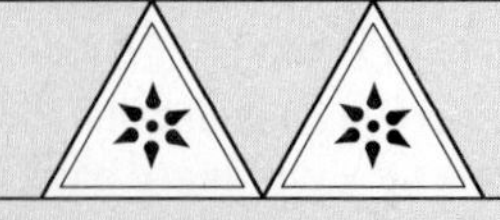

She can measure alternate interior angles and see if they are congruent.

Key Question to Ask for Example 2

- What other angles could you measure? **corresponding angles**

THEOREMS *For Your Notebook*

THEOREM 3.4 Alternate Interior Angles Converse

If two lines are cut by a transversal so the alternate interior angles are congruent, then the lines are parallel.

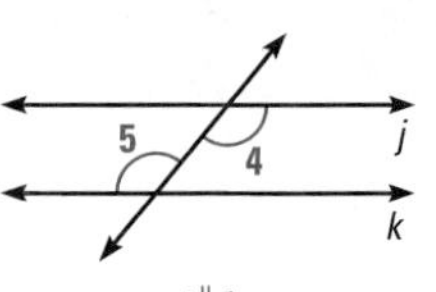

Proof: Example 3, p. 163

THEOREM 3.5 Alternate Exterior Angles Converse

If two lines are cut by a transversal so the alternate exterior angles are congruent, then the lines are parallel.

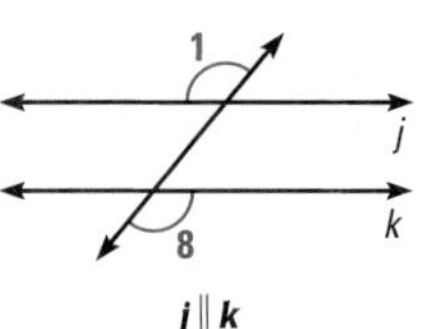

Proof: Ex. 36, p. 168

THEOREM 3.6 Consecutive Interior Angles Converse

If two lines are cut by a transversal so the consecutive interior angles are supplementary, then the lines are parallel.

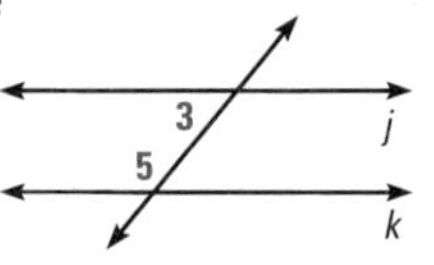

If $\angle 3$ and $\angle 5$ are supplementary, then $j \parallel k$.

Proof: Ex. 37, p. 168

EXAMPLE 2 Solve a real-world problem

SNAKE PATTERNS How can you tell whether the sides of the pattern are parallel in the photo of a diamond-back snake?

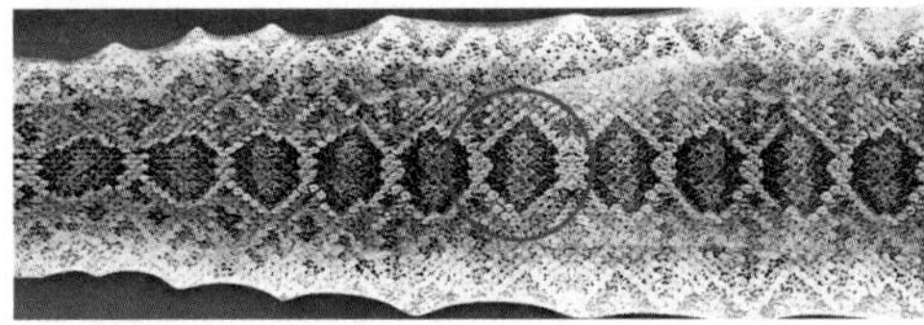

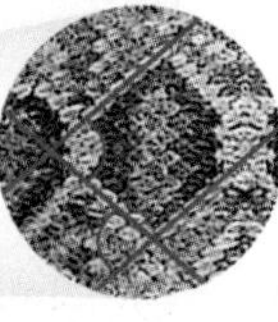

Solution

Because the alternate interior angles are congruent, you know that the sides of the pattern are parallel.

GUIDED PRACTICE for Example 2

Can you prove that lines *a* and *b* are parallel? *Explain* why or why not.

3.

4.

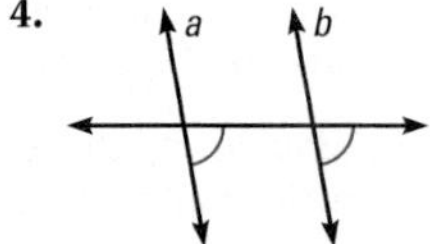

5. $m\angle 1 + m\angle 2 = 180°$

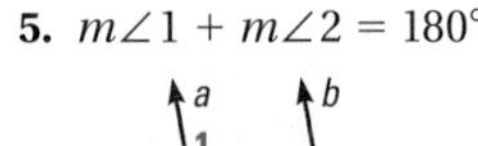

3. yes; Alternate Exterior Angles Converse

4. yes; Corresponding Angles Converse

5. No. *Sample answer:* Supplementary angles do not have to be congruent.

EXAMPLE 3 Prove the Alternate Interior Angles Converse

Prove that if two lines are cut by a transversal so the alternate interior angles are congruent, then the lines are parallel.

AVOID ERRORS
Before you write a proof, identify the GIVEN and PROVE statements for the situation described or for any diagram you draw.

Solution

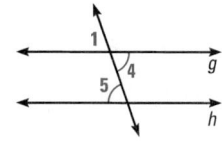

GIVEN ▶ $\angle 4 \cong \angle 5$

PROVE ▶ $g \parallel h$

STATEMENTS	REASONS
1. $\angle 4 \cong \angle 5$	1. Given
2. $\angle 1 \cong \angle 4$	2. Vertical Angles Congruence Theorem
3. $\angle 1 \cong \angle 5$	3. Transitive Property of Congruence
4. $g \parallel h$	4. Corresponding Angles Converse

Animated Geometry at classzone.com

PARAGRAPH PROOFS A proof can also be written in paragraph form, called a **paragraph proof**. The statements and reasons in a paragraph proof are written in sentences, using words to explain the logical flow of the argument.

EXAMPLE 4 Write a paragraph proof

In the figure, $r \parallel s$ and $\angle 1$ is congruent to $\angle 3$. Prove $p \parallel q$.

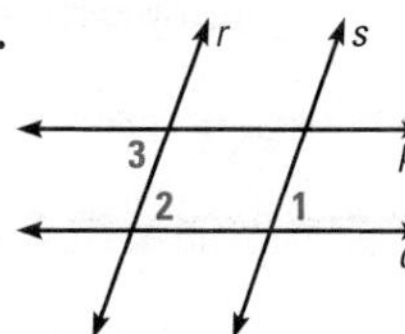

Solution

Look at the diagram to make a plan. The diagram suggests that you look at angles 1, 2, and 3. Also, you may find it helpful to focus on one pair of lines and one transversal at a time.

Plan for Proof

a. Look at $\angle 1$ and $\angle 2$.

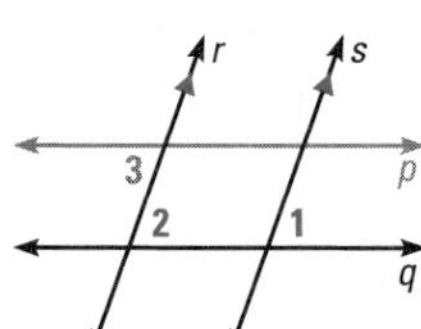

$\angle 1 \cong \angle 2$ because $r \parallel s$.

b. Look at $\angle 2$ and $\angle 3$.

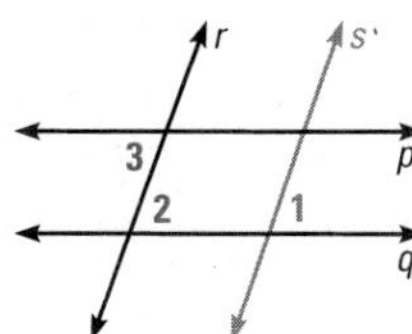

If $\angle 2 \cong \angle 3$, then $p \parallel q$.

TRANSITIONAL WORDS
In paragraph proofs, **transitional words** such as *so, then,* and *therefore* help to make the logic clear.

Plan in Action

a. It is given that $r \parallel s$, so by the Corresponding Angles Postulate, $\angle 1 \cong \angle 2$.

b. It is also given that $\angle 1 \cong \angle 3$. Then $\angle 2 \cong \angle 3$ by the Transitive Property of Congruence for angles. Therefore, by the Alternate Interior Angles Converse, $p \parallel q$.

Extra Example 3

Prove that if $\angle 1$ and $\angle 4$ are supplementary, then $a \parallel b$.

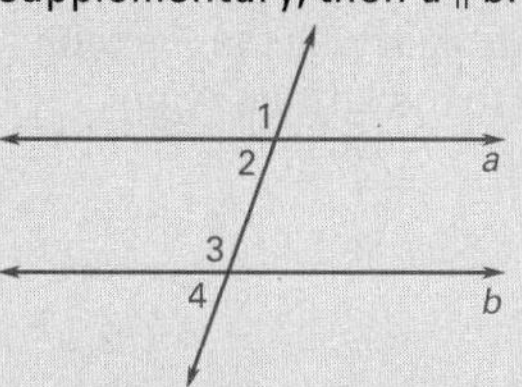

Given: $\angle 1$ and $\angle 4$ are supp.
Prove: $a \parallel b$
Statements (Reasons)

1. **$\angle 1$ and $\angle 4$ are supp. (Given)**
2. **$m\angle 1 + m\angle 4 = 180°$ (Def. of supp. ∡)**
3. **$m\angle 1 + m\angle 2 = 180°$, $m\angle 3 + m\angle 4 = 180°$ (Linear Pair Post.)**
4. **$m\angle 1 + m\angle 2 + m\angle 3 + m\angle 4 = 360°$ (Prop. of =)**
5. **$m\angle 1 + m\angle 4 + m\angle 2 + m\angle 3 = 360°$ (Prop. of Addn. and =)**
6. **$180° + m\angle 2 + m\angle 3 = 360°$ (Substitution)**
7. **$m\angle 2 + m\angle 3 = 180°$ (Subtr. Prop. of =)**
8. **$a \parallel b$ (Consec. Int. ∡ Conv.)**

Extra Example 4

In the figure, $a \parallel b$ and $\angle 1$ is congruent to $\angle 3$. Prove $c \parallel d$. Use a paragraph proof.

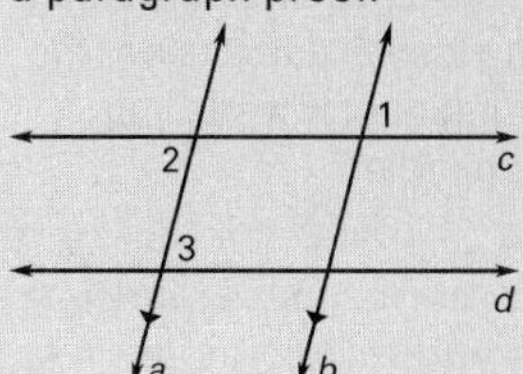

It is given that $a \parallel b$, so $\angle 1 \cong \angle 2$ by Alt. Ext. Ang. Thm. Since $\angle 1 \cong \angle 3$, it follows that $\angle 2 \cong \angle 3$ by Trans. Prop. of ≅. Therefore, $c \parallel d$ by the Alt. Int. ∡ Conv.

Key Question to Ask for Examples 3 and 4

- Could Example 3 have been done in a paragraph proof and Example 4 in a two-column proof? Explain. **Yes, any proof could be done in either format.**

Differentiated Instruction

Inclusion Some students may have difficulty understanding how to write a proof in paragraph form. After completing **Example 4**, have students go back to **Example 3** and work with a partner to rewrite that proof in paragraph form. Guide students by encouraging them to write each step as a sentence which connects their thoughts, using words such as *so, then,* and *therefore*.

See also the *Geometry Toolkit* for more strategies.

Extra Example 5

In the figure each rung of the ladder is parallel to the rung directly above it. Explain why the top rung is parallel to the bottom rung.

Rung 1 is parallel to rung 2, rung 2 parallel to rung 3, therefore rung 1 parallel to rung 3. By continuing this reasoning, you see that the top rung is parallel to the bottom rung.

Key Question to Ask for Example 5

- Suppose the flag is being repaired. Stripes s_1 through s_9 are flat on the top of a rectangular work table. Stripe s_{10} is lined up with an edge of the table, and stripes s_{11} through s_{13} are hanging down from the edge of the table. Are the first and last stripes still parallel? Explain. **Yes. In Theorem 3.7, the three lines do not have to lie in the same plane.**

Closing the Lesson

Have students summarize the major points of the lesson and answer the Essential Question: How do you prove lines parallel?

- **Lines can be proved parallel by congruent corresponding angles, alternate interior angles, or alternate exterior angles. They can also be proved parallel if consecutive interior angles are supplementary.**
- **If two lines are parallel to the same line, then they are parallel to each other.**

You prove lines parallel by showing that corresponding angles, alternate interior angles, or alternate exterior angles are congruent, or by showing that consecutive interior angles are supplementary.

THEOREM *For Your Notebook*

THEOREM 3.7 Transitive Property of Parallel Lines

If two lines are parallel to the same line, then they are parallel to each other.

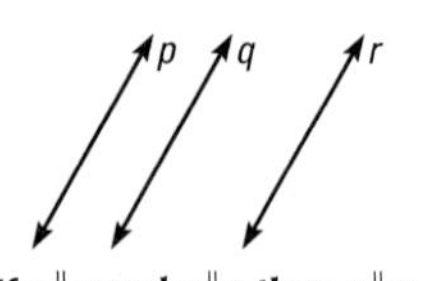

Proofs: Ex. 38, p. 168; Ex. 38, p. 177

If $p \parallel q$ and $q \parallel r$, then $p \parallel r$.

EXAMPLE 5 Use the Transitive Property of Parallel Lines

U.S. FLAG The flag of the United States has 13 alternating red and white stripes. Each stripe is parallel to the stripe immediately below it. Explain why the top stripe is parallel to the bottom stripe.

Solution

USE SUBSCRIPTS
When you name several similar items, you can use one variable with subscripts to keep track of the items.

The stripes from top to bottom can be named $s_1, s_2, s_3, \ldots, s_{13}$. Each stripe is parallel to the one below it, so $s_1 \parallel s_2$, $s_2 \parallel s_3$, and so on. Then $s_1 \parallel s_3$ by the Transitive Property of Parallel Lines. Similarly, because $s_3 \parallel s_4$, it follows that $s_1 \parallel s_4$. By continuing this reasoning, $s_1 \parallel s_{13}$. So, the top stripe is parallel to the bottom stripe.

✓ **GUIDED PRACTICE** for Examples 3, 4, and 5

6. If you use the diagram at the right to prove the Alternate Exterior Angles Converse, what GIVEN and PROVE statements would you use? **Given: $\angle 1 \cong \angle 8$, Prove: $j \parallel k$**

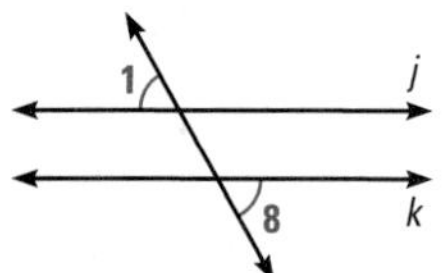

7. Copy and complete the following paragraph proof of the Alternate Interior Angles Converse using the diagram in Example 3.

   It is given that $\angle 4 \cong \angle 5$. By the __?__, $\angle 1 \cong \angle 4$. Then by the Transitive Property of Congruence, __?__. So, by the __?__, $g \parallel h$.

7. Vertical Angles Congruence Theorem; $\angle 1 \cong \angle 5$; Corresponding Angles Converse

8. Each step is parallel to the step immediately above it. The bottom step is parallel to the ground. *Explain* why the top step is parallel to the ground.

8. All of the steps are parallel. Since the bottom step is parallel to the ground, the Transitive Property of Parallel Lines applies, and the top step is parallel to the ground.

3.3 EXERCISES

HOMEWORK KEY
○ = **WORKED-OUT SOLUTIONS** on p. WS3 for Exs. 11, 29, and 37
★ = **STANDARDIZED TEST PRACTICE** Exs. 2, 16, 23, 24, 33, and 39

SKILL PRACTICE

A

1. **VOCABULARY** Draw a pair of parallel lines with a transversal. Identify all pairs of *alternate exterior angles*. **See margin.**

2. ★ **WRITING** Use the theorems from the previous lesson and the converses of those theorems in this lesson. Write three biconditionals about parallel lines and transversals. **See margin.**

EXAMPLE 1 on p. 161 for Exs. 3–9

ALGEBRA **Find the value of x that makes $m \parallel n$.**

3. 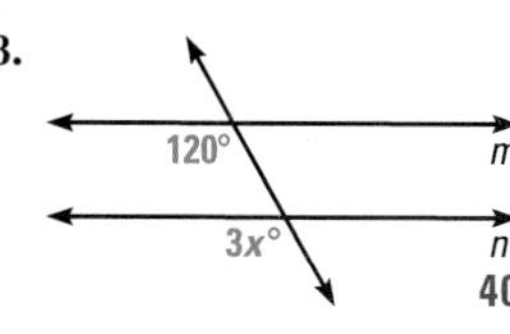

40

4. 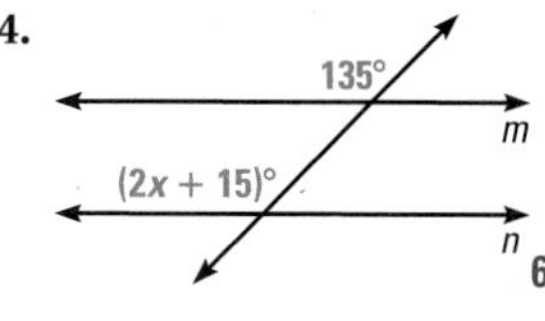

60

5. 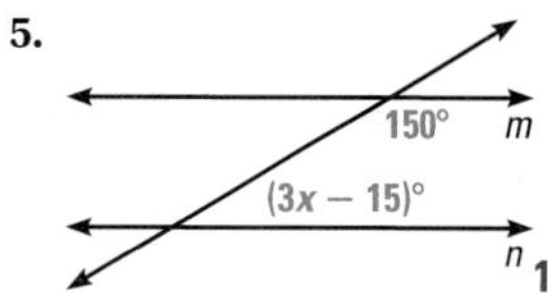

15

6. 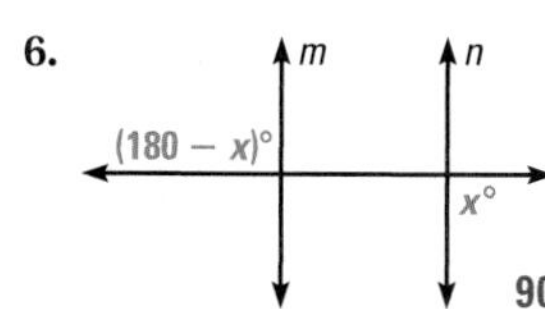

90

7. 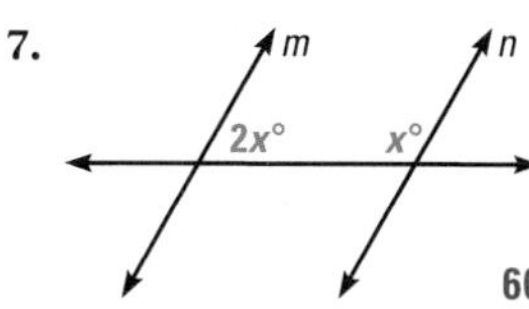

60

8. 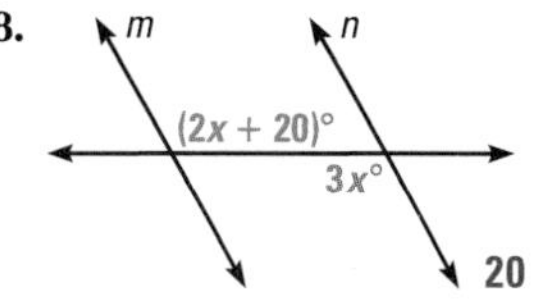

20

9. **ERROR ANALYSIS** A student concluded that lines a and b are parallel. *Describe* and correct the student's error.
The student believes that $x = y$ but there is no indication that they are equal.

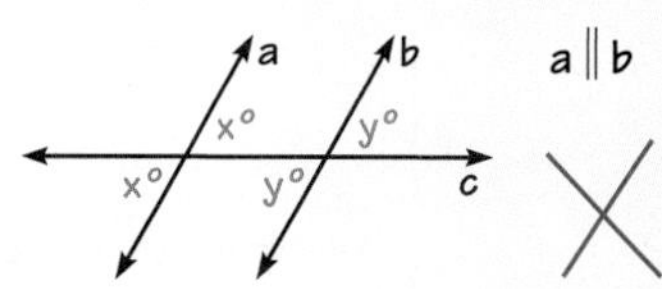

EXAMPLE 2 on p. 162 for Exs. 10–17

IDENTIFYING PARALLEL LINES **Is there enough information to prove $m \parallel n$? If so, state the postulate or theorem you would use.**

10. 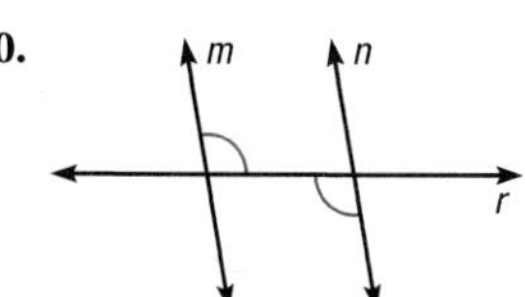

11. 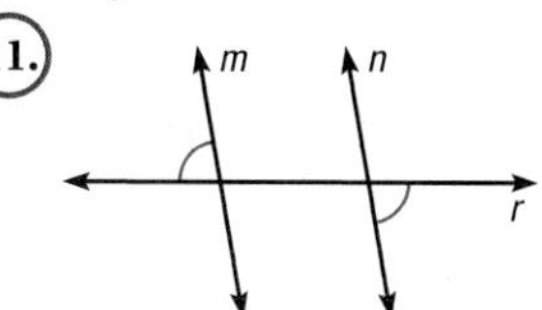

12. 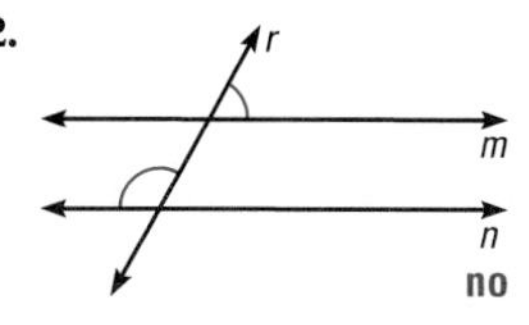

no

13. 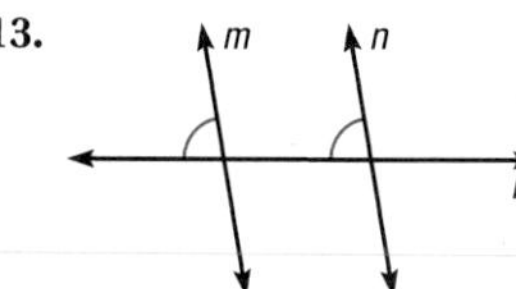

14. 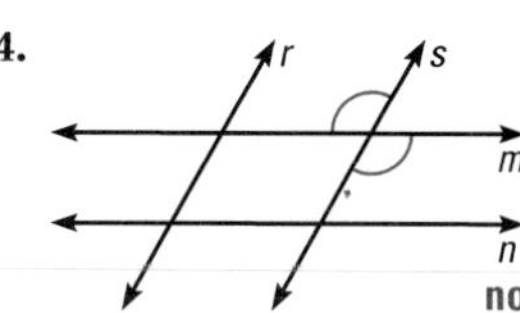

no

15. 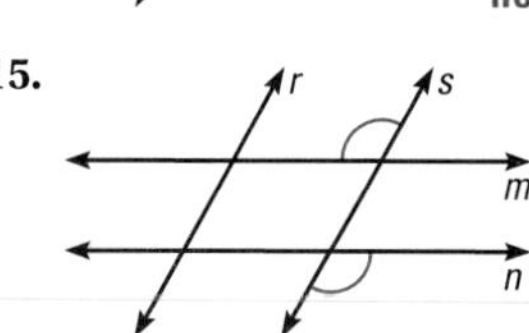

10. yes; Alternate Interior Angles Converse

11. yes; Alternate Exterior Angles Converse

13. yes; Corresponding Angles Converse

15. yes; Alternate Exterior Angles Converse

16. ★ **OPEN-ENDED MATH** Use lined paper to draw two parallel lines cut by a transversal. Use a protractor to measure one angle. Find the measures of the other seven angles without using the protractor. Give a theorem or postulate you use to find each angle measure. **See margin.**

4 PRACTICE AND APPLY

Assignment Guide

Answer Transparencies available for all exercises

Basic:
Day 1: pp. 165–169
Exs. 1–17, 29, 30
Day 2: pp. 165–169
Exs. 18–23, 31–38, 46–54

Average:
Day 1: pp. 165–169
Exs. 1, 2, 5–9, 12–17, 27, 29, 30, 46–51
Day 2: pp. 165–169
Exs. 18–26, 31–44, 52–54

Advanced:
Day 1: pp. 165–169
Exs. 1, 2, 4–8, 11–17, 29, 30
Day 2: pp. 165–169
Exs. 18, 21–28*, 31–45*, 52–54

Block:
pp. 165–169
Exs. 1, 2, 5–9, 12–27, 29–44, 46–54

Differentiated Instruction

See *Geometry Best Practices Toolkit* for suggestions on addressing the needs of a diverse classroom.

Homework Check

For a quick check of student understanding of key concepts, go over the following exercises:
Basic: 4, 12, 18, 33, 36
Average: 6, 14, 33, 34, 36
Advanced: 8, 16, 33, 35, 37

Extra Practice

- Student Edition, p. 900
- Chapter 3 Resource Book: Practice levels A, B, C, pp. 33–38

Practice Worksheet

An easily-readable reduced practice page (with answers) for this lesson can be found on p. 144D.

1. *Sample:*

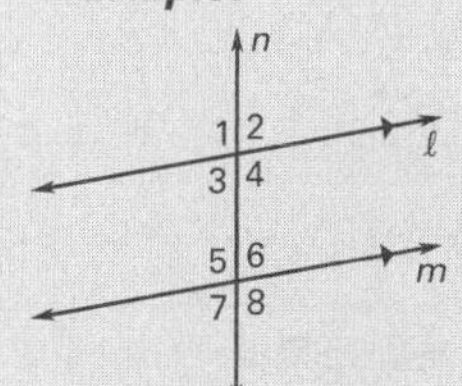

∠1 and ∠8, ∠2 and ∠7

2. Given two lines cut by a transversal, alternate interior angles are congruent if and only if the lines are parallel; given two lines cut by a transversal, alternate exterior angles are congruent if and only if the lines are parallel; given two lines cut by a transversal, consecutive interior angles are supplementary if and only if the lines are parallel.

16. See Additional Answers beginning on p. AA1.

18a. ***Sample:***

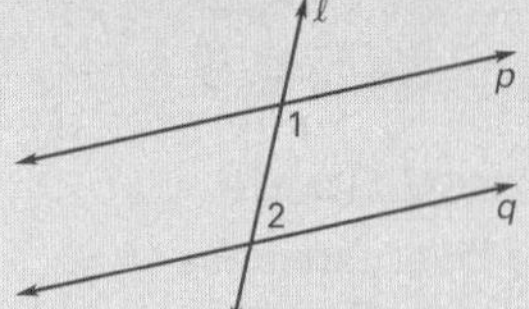

17. **MULTI-STEP PROBLEM** Complete the steps below to determine whether $\overleftrightarrow{DB}$ and $\overleftrightarrow{HF}$ are parallel.

a. Find $m\angle DCG$ and $m\angle CGH$. $m\angle DCG = 115°$, $m\angle CGH = 65°$

b. *Describe* the relationship between $\angle DCG$ and $\angle CGH$.

17b. They are consecutive interior angles and they are supplementary.

c. Are $\overleftrightarrow{DB}$ and $\overleftrightarrow{HF}$ parallel? *Explain* your reasoning.
yes; Consecutive Interior Angles Converse

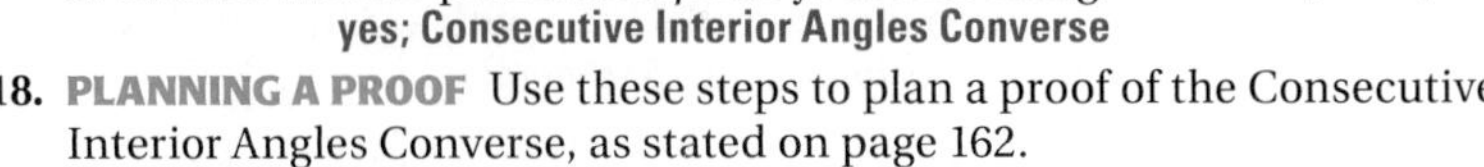

EXAMPLE 3 on p. 163 for Ex. 18

18. **PLANNING A PROOF** Use these steps to plan a proof of the Consecutive Interior Angles Converse, as stated on page 162.

a. Draw a diagram you can use in a proof of the theorem. **See margin.**

b. Write the GIVEN and PROVE statements.
Given: $\angle 1$ and $\angle 2$ are supplementary, Prove: $p \parallel q$

B **REASONING** **Can you prove that lines *a* and *b* are parallel? If so, *explain* how.**

19.

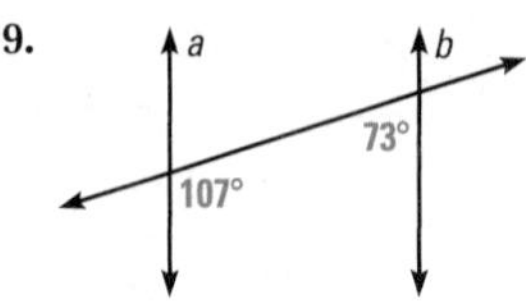

20.

21.

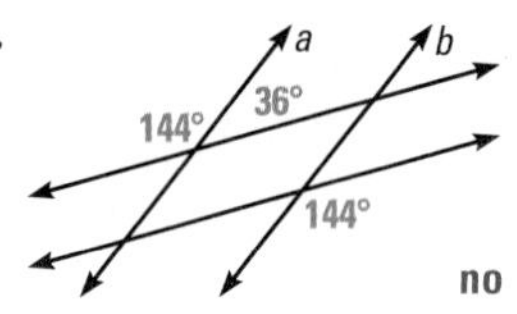

no

19. yes; Consecutive Interior Angles Converse

20. yes; Alternate Exterior Angles Converse

22. **ERROR ANALYSIS** A student decided that $\overleftrightarrow{AD} \parallel \overleftrightarrow{BC}$ based on the diagram below. *Describe* and correct the student's error.

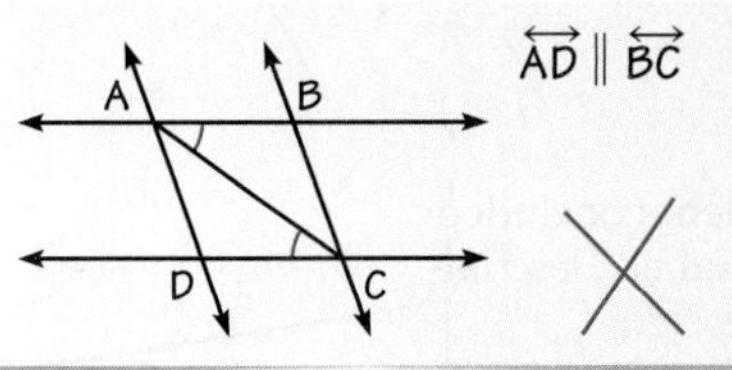

The student assumed the congruent angles were alternate interior angles between $\overleftrightarrow{AB}$ and $\overleftrightarrow{BC}$. By the Alternate Interior Angles Converse, $\overleftrightarrow{AB} \parallel \overleftrightarrow{DC}$.

23. ★ **MULTIPLE CHOICE** Use the diagram at the right. You know that $\angle 1 \cong \angle 4$. What can you conclude? **D**

Ⓐ $p \parallel q$ Ⓑ $r \parallel s$

Ⓒ $\angle 2 \cong \angle 3$ Ⓓ None of the above

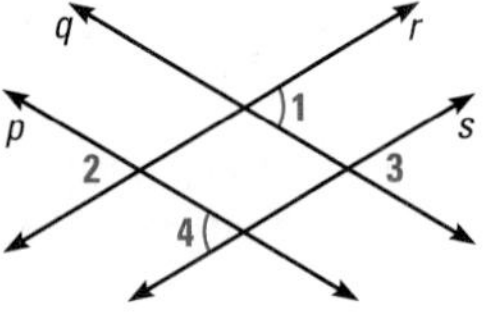

REASONING **Use the diagram at the right for Exercises 24 and 25.**

24. ★ **SHORT RESPONSE** In the diagram, assume $j \parallel k$. How many angle measures must be given in order to find the measure of every angle? *Explain* your reasoning.

24. 1 angle. ***Sample answer:*** Using the Vertical Angles Congruence Theorem, the Linear Pair Postulate, and the Alternate Interior Angles Theorem the other angle measures can be found.

25. **PLANNING A PROOF** In the diagram, assume $\angle 1$ and $\angle 7$ are supplementary. Write a plan for a proof showing that lines *j* and *k* are parallel. ***Sample answer:*** **$\angle 1 \cong \angle 4$ therefore $\angle 4$ and $\angle 7$ are supplementary. Lines *j* and *k* are parallel by the Consecutive Interior Angles Converse.**

26. **REASONING** Use the diagram at the right. Which rays are parallel? Which rays are not parallel? *Justify* your conclusions.
$\overrightarrow{EA} \parallel \overrightarrow{HC}$; $\overrightarrow{EB}$ is not parallel to $\overrightarrow{HD}$, $\angle GHC \cong \angle HEA$, $\angle GHD$ is not congruent to $\angle HEB$.

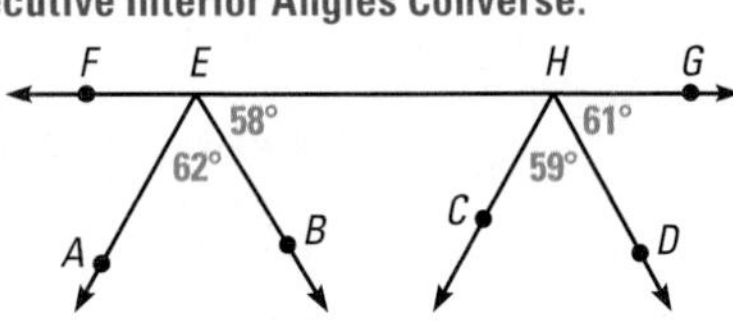

○ = WORKED-OUT SOLUTIONS on p. WS1 ★ = STANDARDIZED TEST PRACTICE

C **27. VISUAL REASONING** A point R is not in plane ABC.

a. How many lines through R are perpendicular to plane ABC? **1 line**

b. How many lines through R are parallel to plane ABC? **an infinite number of lines**

c. How many planes through R are parallel to plane ABC? **1 plane**

28. CHALLENGE Use the diagram.

a. Find x so that $p \parallel q$. **54**

b. Find y so that $r \parallel s$. **47.5**

c. Can r be parallel to s and p be parallel to q at the same time? *Explain.*

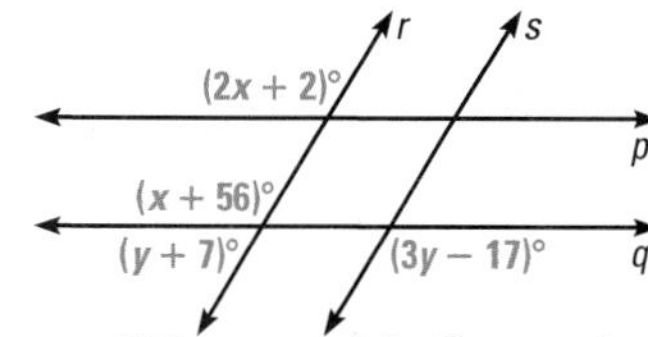

No. *Sample answer:* For p to be parallel to q, $x = 54$, then $y = 63$ because of the linear pair formed, but in order for r and s to be parallel, y must equal 47.5.

PROBLEM SOLVING

EXAMPLE 2 A on p. 162 for Exs. 29–30

29. PICNIC TABLE How do you know that the top of the picnic table is parallel to the ground?

 for problem solving help at classzone.com

Alternate Interior Angles Converse Theorem

30. KITEBOARDING The diagram of the control bar of the kite shows the angles formed between the control bar and the kite lines. How do you know that n is parallel to m? **Corresponding Angles Converse**

@HomeTutor for problem solving help at classzone.com

31. DEVELOPING PROOF Copy and complete the proof.

GIVEN ▶ $m\angle 1 = 115°, m\angle 2 = 65°$

PROVE ▶ $m \parallel n$

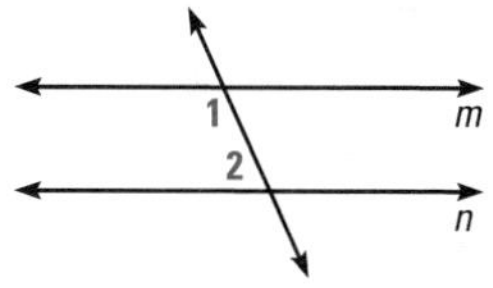

STATEMENTS	REASONS
1. $m\angle 1 = 115°$ and $m\angle 2 = 65°$	1. Given
2. $115° + 65° = 180°$	2. Addition
3. $m\angle 1 + m\angle 2 = 180°$	3. _?_ **Substitution**
4. $\angle 1$ and $\angle 2$ are supplementary.	4. _?_ **Definition of supplementary angles**
5. $m \parallel n$	5. _?_ **Consecutive Interior Angles Converse**

Reading Strategy

Exercise 27 For students who have difficulty visualizing a situation described in words, a sketch or physical model will be a great help. You might suggest that they think of the floor of the classroom as plane *ABC* and a corner point at the ceiling as point *R*.

Avoiding Common Errors

Exercise 28 For part b, students may set $3y - 17$ equal to $y + 7$. Point out that these angles are not corresponding angles. Ask students if they can identify the angle that corresponds to the angle labeled $(y + 7)°$ when the transversal is line q. Ask if they can write an expression that involves y for the measure of the angle.

Study Strategy

Exercises 34–35 If students are having difficulty getting started, suggest that they sketch a copy of the figure and mark the angles that are given congruent.

33. Yes. ***Sample answer:*** **E 20th is parallel to E 19th by the Corresponding Angles Converse. E 19th is parallel to E 18th by the Alternate Exterior Angles Converse. E 18th is parallel to E 17th by the Alternate Interior Angles Converse. They are all parallel by the Transitive Property of Parallel Lines.**

34. Statements (Reasons)

1. $\angle 1 \cong \angle 2, \angle 3 \cong \angle 4$ (Given)

2. $\angle 2 \cong \angle 3$ (Vertical Angles Congruence Theorem)

3. $\angle 1 \cong \angle 4$ (Transitive Property of Angle Congruence)

4. $\overline{AB} \parallel \overline{CD}$ (Alternate Interior Angles Converse)

35. Statements (Reasons)

1. $a \parallel b, \angle 2 \cong \angle 3$ (Given)

2. $\angle 2$ and $\angle 4$ are supplementary. (Consecutive Interior Angles Theorem)

3. $\angle 3$ and $\angle 4$ are supplementary. (Substitution)

4. $c \parallel d$ (Consecutive Interior Angles Converse)

36. Statements (Reasons)

1. $\angle 2 \cong \angle 7$ (Given)

2. $\angle 7 \cong \angle 6$ (Vertical Angles Congruence Theorem)

3. $\angle 2 \cong \angle 6$ (Transitive Property of Congruence)

4. $m \parallel n$ (Corresponding Angles Converse)

37. You are given that $\angle 3$ and $\angle 5$ are supplementary. By the Linear Pair Postulate, $\angle 5$ and $\angle 6$ are also supplementary. So $\angle 3 \cong \angle 6$ by the Congruent Supplements Theorem. By the Alternate Interior Angles Converse, $m \parallel n$.

32. BOWLING PINS How do you know that the bowling pins are set up in parallel lines? **Alternate Exterior Angles Converse Theorem**

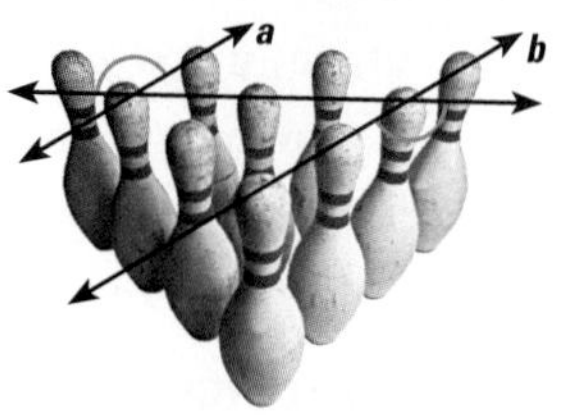

EXAMPLE 5 on p. 164 for Ex. 33

33. ★ SHORT RESPONSE The map shows part of Denver, Colorado. Use the markings on the map. Are the numbered streets parallel to one another? *Explain* how you can tell. **See margin.**

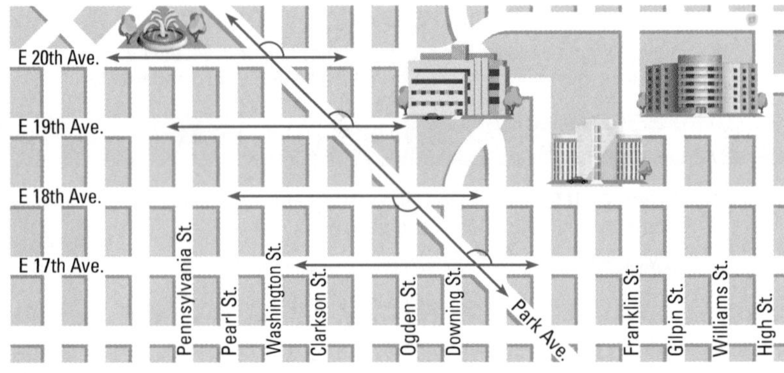

EXAMPLE 3 B on p. 163 for Exs. 34–35

PROOF Use the diagram and the given information to write a two-column or paragraph proof. **34, 35. See margin.**

34. GIVEN ▶ $\angle 1 \cong \angle 2, \angle 3 \cong \angle 4$

PROVE ▶ $\overline{AB} \parallel \overline{CD}$

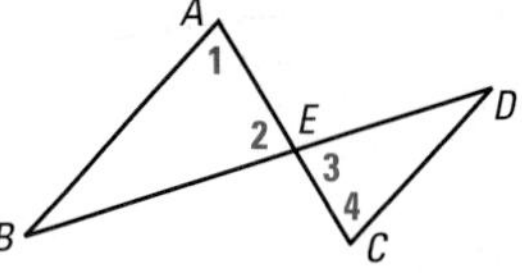

35. GIVEN ▶ $a \parallel b, \angle 2 \cong \angle 3$

PROVE ▶ $c \parallel d$

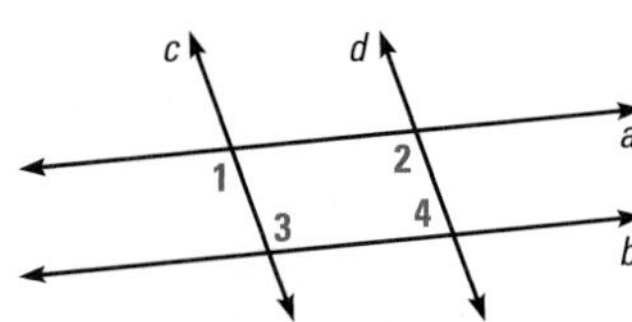

EXAMPLE 4 on p. 163 for Exs. 36–37

PROOF In Exercises 36 and 37, use the diagram to write a paragraph proof. **36, 37. See margin.**

36. PROVING THEOREM 3.5 Prove the Alternate Exterior Angles Converse.

(37.) PROVING THEOREM 3.6 Prove the Consecutive Interior Angles Converse.

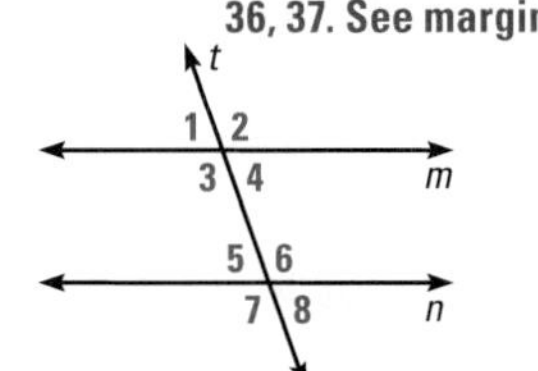

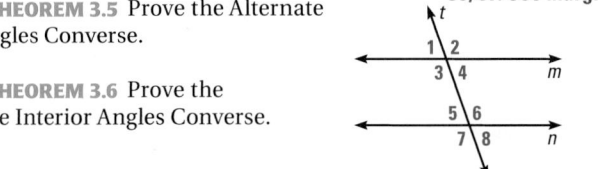

38. MULTI-STEP PROBLEM Use these steps to prove Theorem 3.7, the Transitive Property of Parallel Lines.

a. Copy the diagram in the Theorem box on page 164. Draw a transversal through all three lines. **See margin.**

b. Write the GIVEN and PROVE statements. **Given: $p \parallel q$ and $q \parallel r$, Prove: $p \parallel r$**

c. Use the properties of angles formed by parallel lines and transversals to prove the theorem. **See margin.**

○ = **WORKED-OUT SOLUTIONS on p. WS1** ★ = **STANDARDIZED TEST PRACTICE**

38a.

38c. Statements (Reasons)

1. $p \parallel q$ and $q \parallel r$ (Given)

2. $\angle 1 \cong \angle 2$ (Alternate Interior Angles Theorem)

3. $\angle 2 \cong \angle 3$ (Vertical Angles Congruence Theorem)

4. $\angle 3 \cong \angle 4$ (Alternate Interior Angles Theorem)

5. $\angle 1 \cong \angle 4$ (Transitive Property of Angle Congruence)

6. $p \parallel r$ (Alternate Interior Angles Converse)

39. ★ **EXTENDED RESPONSE** Architects and engineers make drawings using a plastic triangle with angle measures 30°, 60°, and 90°. The triangle slides along a fixed horizontal edge.

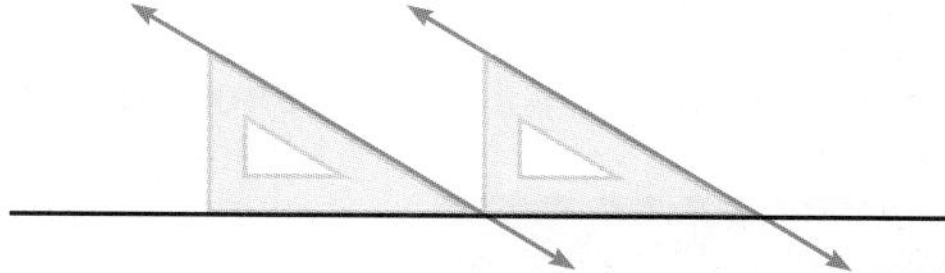

a. *Explain* why the blue lines shown are parallel. ***Sample answer:* Corresponding Angles Converse Theorem**

b. *Explain* how the triangle can be used to draw vertical parallel lines.

39b. Slide the triangle along a fixed horizontal line and use the edge that forms the 90° angle to draw vertical lines.

REASONING **Use the diagram below in Exercises 40–44. How would you show that the given lines are parallel? 40–44. See margin.**

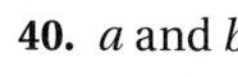

40. a and b

41. b and c

42. d and f

43. e and g

44. a and c

C 45. CHALLENGE Use these steps to investigate the angle bisectors of corresponding angles. **a–b. See margin.**

a. **Construction** Use a compass and straightedge or geometry drawing software to construct line ℓ, point P not on ℓ, and line n through P parallel to ℓ. Construct point Q on ℓ and construct $\overline{PQ}$. Choose a pair of alternate interior angles and construct their angle bisectors.

b. **Write a Proof** Are the angle bisectors parallel? Make a conjecture. Write a proof of your conjecture.

MIXED REVIEW

Solve the equation. *(p. 875)*

46. $\frac{3}{4}x = -1$ $\mathbf{-\frac{4}{3}}$

47. $\frac{-2}{3}x = -1$ $\mathbf{\frac{3}{2}}$

48. $\frac{1}{5}x = -1$ **−5**

49. $-6x = -1$ $\mathbf{\frac{1}{6}}$

50. You can choose one of eight sandwich fillings and one of four kinds of bread. How many different sandwiches are possible? *(p. 891)* **32 sandwiches**

51. Find the value of x if $\overline{AB} \cong \overline{AD}$ and $\overline{CD} \cong \overline{AD}$. *Explain* your steps. *(p. 112)*
4; by the Transitive Property of Congruence, $\overline{AB} \cong \overline{CD}$, so $9x - 11 = 6x + 1$, $3x = 12$, $x = 4$.

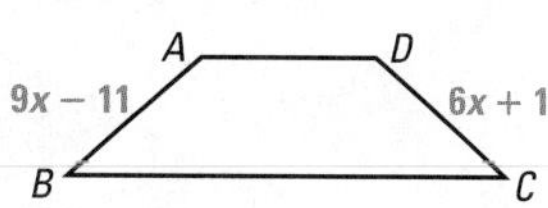

PREVIEW
Prepare for Lesson 3.4 in Exs. 52–54.

Simplify the expression.

52. $\frac{-7-2}{8-(-4)}$ *(p. 870)* $\mathbf{-\frac{3}{4}}$

53. $\frac{0-(-3)}{1-6}$ *(p. 870)* $\mathbf{-\frac{3}{5}}$

54. $\frac{3x-x}{-4x+2x}$ *(p. 139)* **−1**

5 ASSESS AND RETEACH

Daily Homework Quiz

Transparency Available

1. Find the value of x that makes $p \parallel q$. **43**

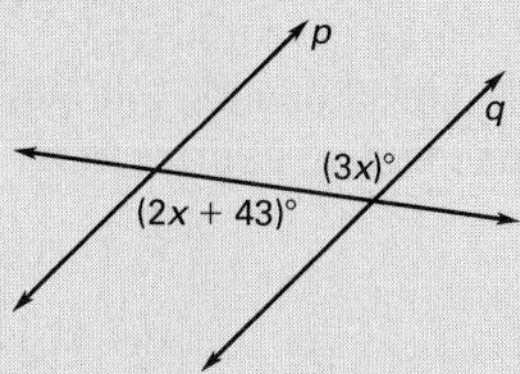

2. Can you prove $a \parallel b$? If so, what theorem would you use?

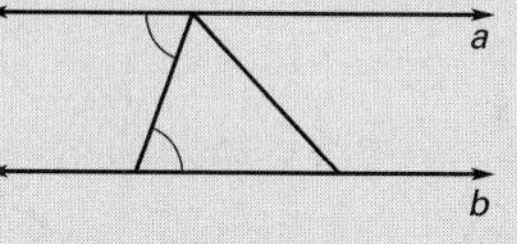

Yes; Alternate Interior Angles Converse

3. Which lines are parallel? $\overleftrightarrow{EF} \parallel \overleftrightarrow{DG}$

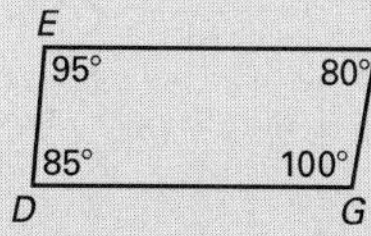

4. In the figure, if $\overline{HJ} \parallel \overline{KL}$ and $\overline{KL} \parallel \overline{MN}$, what can you conclude? What theorem justifies your conclusion?

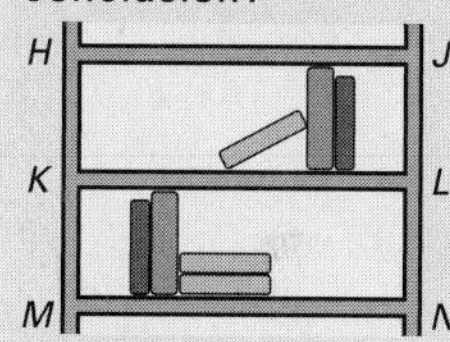

$\overline{HJ} \parallel \overline{MN}$ by Transitive Property of Parallel Lines

Available at **classzone.com**

Diagnosis/Remediation

- Practice A, B, C in Chapter 3 Resource Book, pp. 33–38
- Study Guide in Chapter 3 Resource Book, pp. 39–40
- Practice Workbook, pp. 49–51
- @HomeTutor

Challenge

Additional challenge is available in the Chapter 3 Resource Book, p. 44.

40–44, 45a–b. See Additional Answers beginning on p. AA1.

STATE TEST PRACTICE classzone.com

2a. ∠2: supplementary, ∠3: supplementary, ∠4: vertical, ∠5: corresponding, ∠6: supplementary, ∠7: alternate exterior, ∠8: supplementary

4. yes; Alternate Interior Angles Converse

7. $x = 92$, supplementary to 88°; $y = 116$, $c \parallel d$ by the Alternate Interior Angles Converse followed by the Consecutive Interior Angles Theorem

Lessons 3.1–3.3

1. **MULTI-STEP PROBLEM** Use the diagram of the tennis court below.

   a. Identify two pairs of parallel lines so each pair is on a different plane. ***Sample answer; q and p, k and m***
   b. Identify a pair of skew lines. ***Sample answer; q and m***
   c. Identify two pairs of perpendicular lines. ***Sample answer; n and m, n and k***

2. **MULTI-STEP PROBLEM** Use the picture of the tile floor below.

   a. Name the kind of angle pair each angle forms with ∠1. **See margin.**
   b. Lines *r* and *s* are parallel. Name the angles that are congruent to ∠3. **∠2, ∠6, ∠8**

3. **OPEN-ENDED** The flag of Jamaica is shown. Given that $n \parallel p$ and $m\angle 1 = 53°$, determine the measure of ∠2. *Justify* each step in your argument, labeling any angles needed for your justification.
   53°; Alternate Exterior Angles Theorem

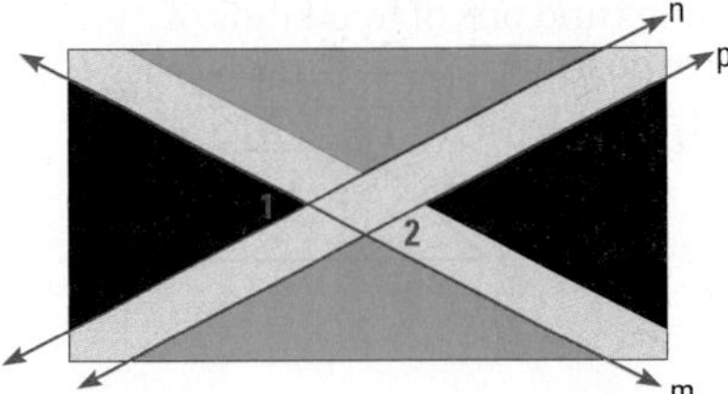

5b. 23°; Transitive Property of Parallel Lines and Alternate Interior Angles Theorem

4. **SHORT RESPONSE** A neon sign is shown below. Are the top and the bottom of the Z parallel? *Explain* how you know. **See margin.**

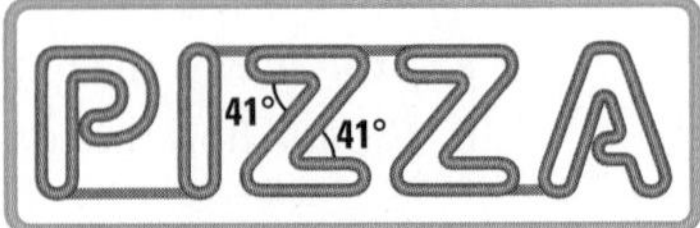

5. **EXTENDED RESPONSE** Use the diagram of the bridge below.

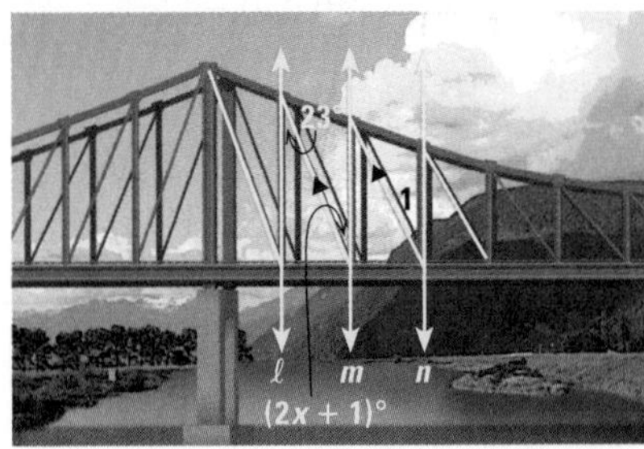

   a. Find the value of *x* that makes lines ℓ and *m* parallel. **11**
   b. Suppose that $\ell \parallel m$ and $\ell \parallel n$. Find $m\angle 1$. *Explain* how you found your answer. Copy the diagram and label any angles you need for your explanation. **See below.**

6. **GRIDDED ANSWER** In the photo of the picket fence, $m \parallel n$. What is $m\angle 1$ in degrees? **150°**

7. **SHORT RESPONSE** Find the values of *x* and *y*. *Explain* your steps. **See margin.**

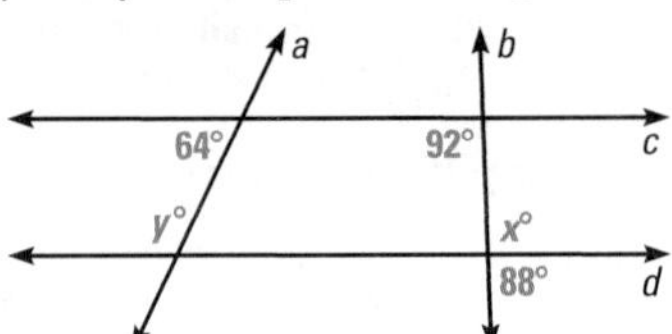

3.4 Find and Use Slopes of Lines

Before You used properties of parallel lines to find angle measures.
Now You will find and compare slopes of lines.
Why So you can compare rates of speed, as in Example 4.

Key Vocabulary
- **slope,** *p. 879*
- **rise,** *p. 879*
- **run,** *p. 879*

Standards
Prepare for 17.0 Students prove theorems by *using coordinate geometry,* including the midpoint of a line segment, the distance formula, and various forms of equations of lines and circles.

The **slope** of a nonvertical line is the ratio of vertical change (*rise*) to horizontal change (*run*) between any two points on the line.

If a line in the coordinate plane passes through points (x_1, y_1) and (x_2, y_2) then the slope m is

$$m = \frac{\text{rise}}{\text{run}} = \frac{\text{change in } y}{\text{change in } x} = \frac{y_2 - y_1}{x_2 - x_1}.$$

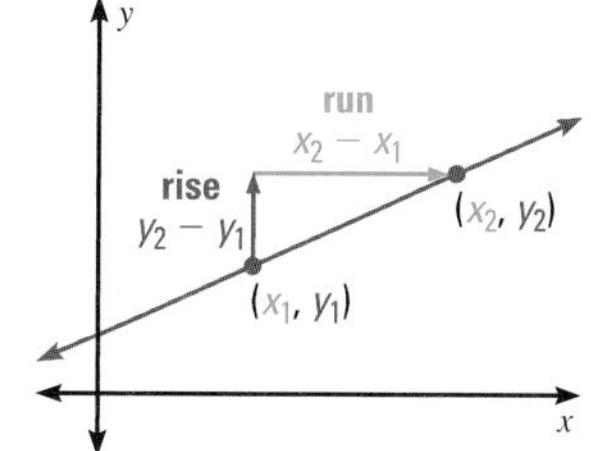
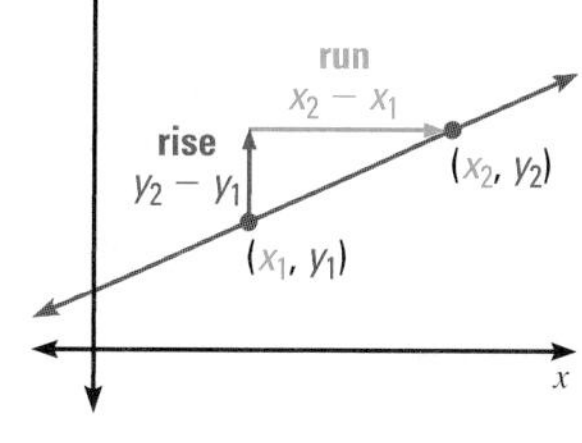

KEY CONCEPT *For Your Notebook*

Slope of Lines in the Coordinate Plane

Negative slope: falls from left to right, as in line j

Positive slope: rises from left to right, as in line k

Zero slope (slope of 0): horizontal, as in line ℓ

Undefined slope: vertical, as in line n

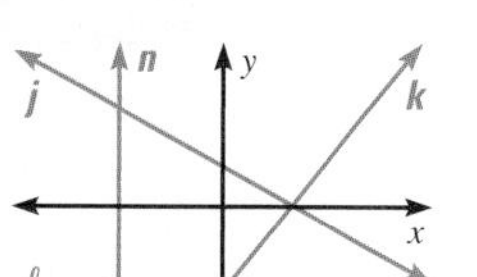

EXAMPLE 1 **Find slopes of lines in a coordinate plane**

REVIEW SLOPE
For more help with slope, see p. 879.

Find the slopes of line a and line d.

Solution

Slope of line a: $m = \frac{y_2 - y_1}{x_2 - x_1} = \frac{4 - 2}{6 - 8} = \frac{2}{-2} = -1$

Slope of line d: $m = \frac{y_2 - y_1}{x_2 - x_1} = \frac{4 - 0}{6 - 6} = \frac{4}{0}$, which is undefined.

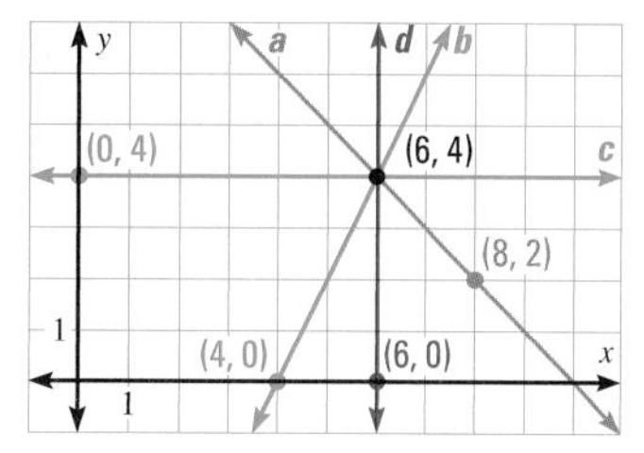

GUIDED PRACTICE for Example 1

Use the graph in Example 1. Find the slope of the line.

1. Line b **2**
2. Line c **0**

1 PLAN AND PREPARE

Warm-Up Exercises
Transparency Available

1. Evaluate $\frac{a - b}{c - d}$ if $a = 5$, $b = 2$, $c = 1$, and $d = 7$. $-\frac{1}{2}$
2. Solve $\frac{x - 3}{3 - 4} = \frac{1}{5}$. $\frac{14}{5}$
3. What is the reciprocal of $\frac{2}{3}$? $\frac{3}{2}$
4. Julie was thinking of a number. The product of her number and 6 is −1. What was Julie's number? $-\frac{1}{6}$

Notetaking Guide
Transparency Available

Promotes interactive learning and notetaking skills, pp. 71–73.

Pacing
Basic: 2 days
Average: 2 days
Advanced: 2 days
Block: 1 block
- See *Teaching Guide/Lesson Plan.*

2 FOCUS AND MOTIVATE

Essential Question
Big Idea 3, p. 145
How do you find the slope of a line given the coordinates of two points on the line? **Tell students they will learn how to answer this question by using the slope formula.**

Resource Planning Guide

Chapter Resource Book
- Teaching Guide/Lesson Plan (pp. 45–46)
- Practice levels A, B, C (pp. 48–53)
- Study Guide (pp. 54–55)
- Catch-up for Absent Students (p. 56)
- Application (p. 57)
- Challenge (p. 58)

Workbooks
- Notetaking Guide (pp. 71–73)
- Practice Workbook (pp. 52–54)

Teaching Options
- **Power Presentations CD-ROM** provides dynamic electronic teaching resources for the classroom.
- **Activity Generator CD-ROM** provides editable activities for all ability levels.

Interactive Technology
- Easy Planner
- Power Presentations CD-ROM
- Activity Generator CD-ROM
- Animated Geometry
- Test Generator CD-ROM
- Online Quiz
- eWorkbook
- eEdition
- @HomeTutor

Resources for English Learners
- Quick Reference for English Learners
- Spanish Study Guide
- Multi-Language Visual Glossary
- Student Resources in Spanish

See also the *Geometry Toolkit* for more strategies for meeting individual needs.

Motivating the Lesson

Sergio is making a skateboard ramp. When he uses it, he wants to rise 1 foot for every 5 feet he travels horizontally. Tell students that in this lesson, they will learn to describe the steepness of the ramp by using the ratio that compares change in height to horizontal distance traveled.

3 TEACH

Extra Example 1

Find the slope of line b and line c.

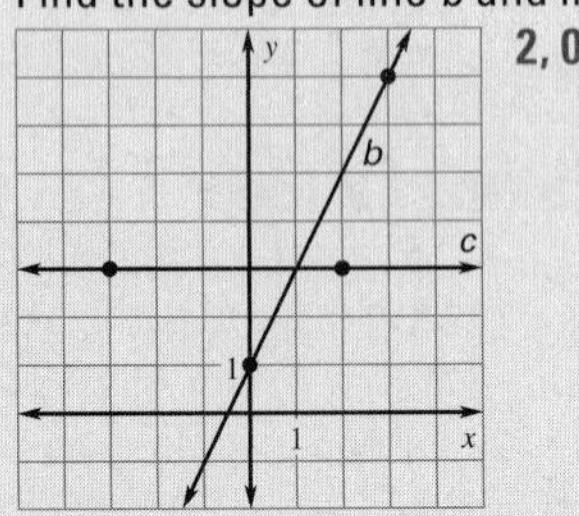

2, 0

Extra Example 2

Find the slope of each line. Which lines are parallel?

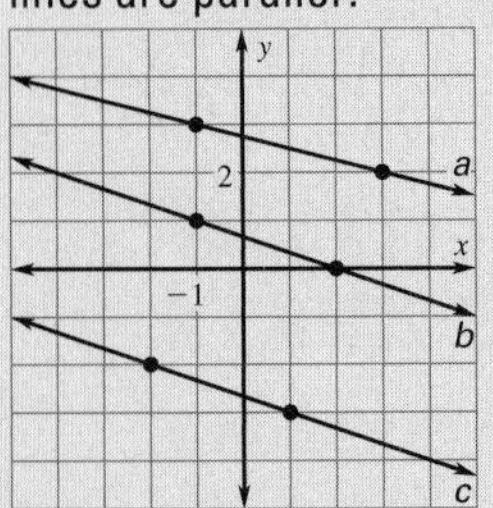

line a: $-\frac{1}{4}$; line b: $-\frac{1}{3}$; line c: $-\frac{1}{3}$; $b \parallel c$

Key Question to Ask for Example 2

- To find the slope of k_1, could you have used $\frac{4-0}{-2-(-3)}$ instead? Explain. **Yes, as long as you subtract the x-coordinates in the same order as the y-coordinates, the order does not matter.**

COMPARING SLOPES When two lines intersect in a coordinate plane, the steeper line has the slope with greater absolute value. You can also compare slopes to tell whether two lines are parallel or perpendicular.

READ VOCABULARY
If the product of two numbers is −1, then the numbers are called *negative reciprocals.*

POSTULATES *For Your Notebook*

POSTULATE 17 Slopes of Parallel Lines

In a coordinate plane, two nonvertical lines are parallel if and only if they have the same slope.

Any two vertical lines are parallel.

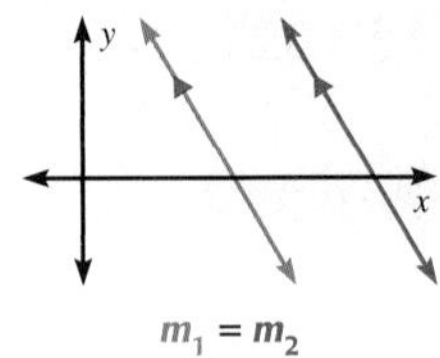

$m_1 = m_2$

POSTULATE 18 Slopes of Perpendicular Lines

In a coordinate plane, two nonvertical lines are perpendicular if and only if the product of their slopes is −1.

Horizontal lines are perpendicular to vertical lines.

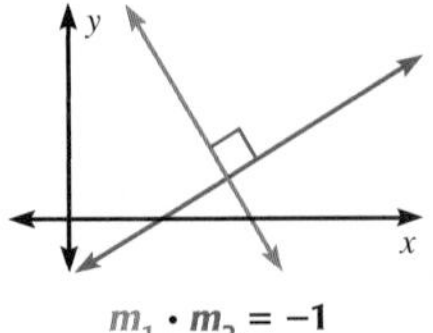

$m_1 \cdot m_2 = -1$

EXAMPLE 2 Identify parallel lines

Find the slope of each line. Which lines are parallel?

Solution

Find the slope of k_1 through (−2, 4) and (−3, 0).

$$m_1 = \frac{0-4}{-3-(-2)} = \frac{-4}{-1} = 4$$

Find the slope of k_2 through (4, 5) and (3, 1).

$$m_2 = \frac{1-5}{3-4} = \frac{-4}{-1} = 4$$

Find the slope of k_3 through (6, 3) and (5, −2).

$$m_3 = \frac{-2-3}{5-6} = \frac{-5}{-1} = 5$$

▶ Compare the slopes. Because k_1 and k_2 have the same slope, they are parallel. The slope of k_3 is different, so k_3 is not parallel to the other lines.

GUIDED PRACTICE for Example 2

3. Line m passes through (−1, 3) and (4, 1). Line t passes through (−2, −1) and (3, −3). Are the two lines parallel? *Explain* how you know.
Yes; they have the same slope.

Differentiated Instruction

English Learners Students learning English may not understand the phrase "if and only if" in Postulates 17 and 18. Explain that Postulate 17, for example, could be rewritten as: "Two nonvertical lines are parallel *if* they have the same slope *and* two nonvertical lines are parallel *only if* they have the same slope." Further explain that the *only if* part means "If two nonvertical lines are parallel, then they have the same slope."

See also the *Geometry Toolkit* for more strategies.

EXAMPLE 3 Draw a perpendicular line

Line h passes through (3, 0) and (7, 6). Graph the line perpendicular to h that passes through the point (2, 5).

Solution

STEP 1 **Find** the slope m_1 of line h through (3, 0) and (7, 6).

$$m_1 = \frac{6 - 0}{7 - 3} = \frac{6}{4} = \frac{3}{2}$$

STEP 2 **Find** the slope m_2 of a line perpendicular to h. Use the fact that the product of the slopes of two perpendicular lines is -1.

$\frac{3}{2} \cdot m_2 = -1$ **Slopes of perpendicular lines**

$m_2 = \frac{-2}{3}$ **Multiply each side by $\frac{2}{3}$.**

STEP 3 **Use** the rise and run to graph the line.

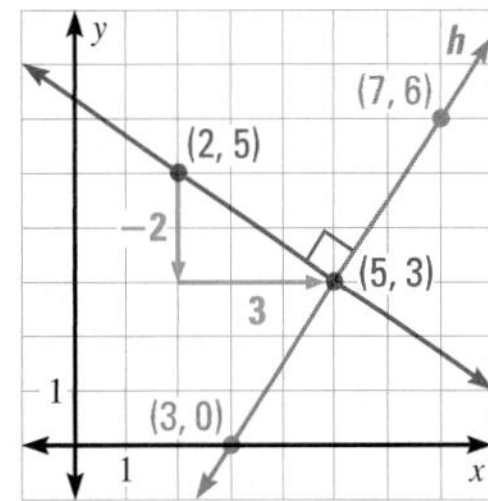

REVIEW GRAPHING
Given a point on a line and the line's slope, you can use the rise and run to find a second point and draw the line.

★ EXAMPLE 4 Standardized Test Practice

A skydiver made jumps with three parachutes. The graph shows the height of the skydiver from the time the parachute opened to the time of the landing for each jump. Which statement is true?

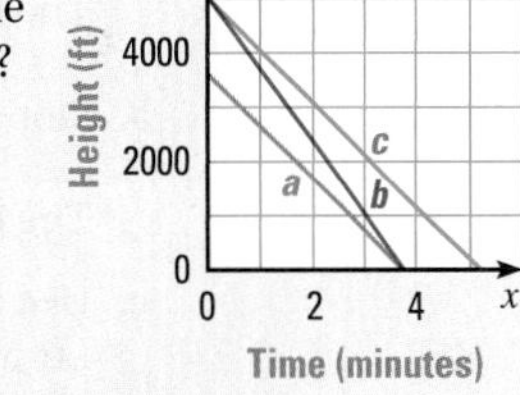

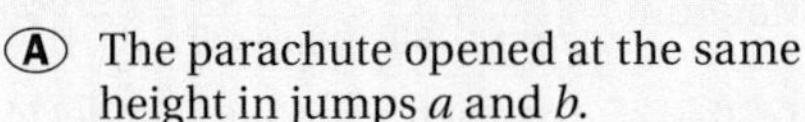
Ⓐ The parachute opened at the same height in jumps a and b.

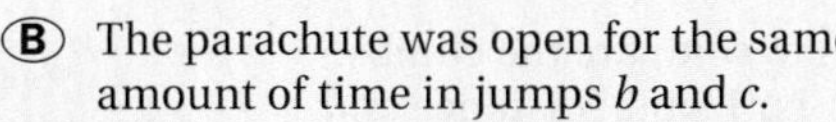
Ⓑ The parachute was open for the same amount of time in jumps b and c.

Ⓒ The skydiver descended at the same rate in jumps a and b.

Ⓓ The skydiver descended at the same rate in jumps a and c.

ELIMINATE CHOICES
The y-intercept represents the height when the parachute opened, so the heights in jumps a and b were not the same. So you can eliminate choice A.

Solution

The rate at which the skydiver descended is represented by the slope of the segments. The segments that have the same slope are a and c.

▶ The correct answer is D. Ⓐ Ⓑ Ⓒ Ⓓ

GUIDED PRACTICE for Examples 3 and 4

4. Line n passes through (0, 2) and (6, 5). Line m passes through (2, 4) and (4, 0). Is $n \perp m$? *Explain.* **Yes; the product of their slopes is −1.**

5. In Example 4, which parachute is in the air for the longest time? *Explain.*

6. In Example 4, what do the x-intercepts represent in the situation? How can you use this to eliminate one of the choices? **Time of the landing. *Sample answer:* *b* and *c* are in the air different amounts of time, so you can eliminate choice *B*.**

5. Parachute *c*. *Sample answer:* It was in the air approximately 1.25 minutes longer than either *a* or *b*.

Extra Example 3

Line k passes through (0, 3) and (5, 2). Graph the line perpendicular to k that passes through the point (1, 2).

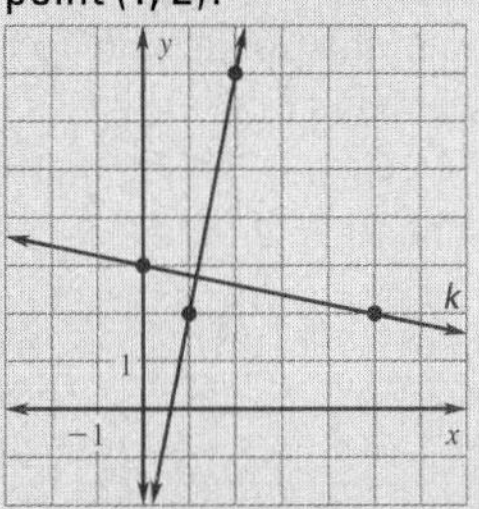

Key Question to Ask for Example 3

- How could you have found the slope of m_1 from the graph without using the formula? **Count spaces to find the rise and run from (3, 0) to (7, 6).**

Extra Example 4

Rodney drained the water from the old tanks at three farms before installing new tanks. The graph shows the amount of water in each tank from the time the water began to drain until the tank was empty. Which statement is true? **C**

Draining Tanks

Ⓐ The tanks all began draining at the same time.

Ⓑ Tank b was empty 4 minutes before tank c.

Ⓒ Tank c drained at the fastest rate.

Ⓓ Tank a was larger than tank b.

Key Question to Ask for Example 4

- For which jump did the skydiver descend the fastest? **jump b**

Extra Example 5

A candle is lit at the center of the table at the beginning of a dinner party. Its height decreases by 1.75 inches every 25 minutes. At the beginning of the dinner, the candle was 8 inches tall.

a. Make a table showing the height of the candle at 25 minute intervals.

Time (min)	0	25	50	75
Height (in.)	8	6.25	4.5	2.75

b. Write a fraction that represents the decrease in height for each minute the candle burns. What does the numerator represent? $-\frac{0.07}{1}$; **the slope in decimal form**

c. The stick candle is replaced with a thinner candle when dessert is served. It burns with a slope of −0.5, starting at a height of 5 inches. Use a graph to compare the way the candles burn. Which graph is steeper?

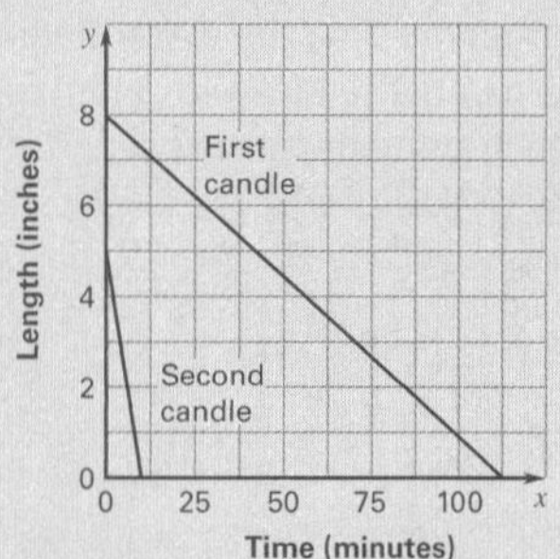

The graph for the second candle is steeper.

Closing the Lesson

Have students summarize the major points of the lesson and answer the Essential Question: How do you find the slope of a line given the coordinates of two points on the line?

- **The slope of a line is the rise over the run.**
- **Two nonvertical lines are parallel if and only if the lines have the same slope.**
- **Two nonvertical lines are perpendicular if and only if the product of their slopes is −1.**

To find the slope of a line, use the slope formula: $m = \frac{y_2 - y_1}{x_2 - x_1}$.

EXAMPLE 5 Solve a real-world problem

ROLLER COASTERS During the climb on the Magnum XL-200 roller coaster, you move 41 feet upward for every 80 feet you move horizontally. At the crest of the hill, you have moved 400 feet forward.

a. Making a Table Make a table showing the height of the Magnum at every 80 feet it moves horizontally. How high is the roller coaster at the top of its climb?

b. Calculating Write a fraction that represents the height the Magnum climbs for each foot it moves horizontally. What does the numerator represent?

c. Using a Graph Another roller coaster, the Millenium Force, climbs at a slope of 1. At its crest, the horizontal distance from the starting point is 310 feet. Compare this climb to that of the Magnum. Which climb is steeper?

Solution

a.

Horizontal distance (ft)	80	160	240	320	400
Height (ft)	41	82	123	164	205

The Magnum XL-200 is 205 feet high at the top of its climb.

b. Slope of the Magnum $= \frac{\text{rise}}{\text{run}} = \frac{41}{80} = \frac{41 \div 80}{80 \div 80} = \frac{0.5125}{1}$

The numerator, 0.5125, represents the slope in decimal form.

c. Use a graph to compare the climbs. Let x be the horizontal distance and let y be the height. Because the slope of the Millenium Force is 1, the rise is equal to the run. So the highest point must be at (310, 310).

▶ The graph shows that the Millenium Force has a steeper climb, because the slope of its line is greater (1 > 0.5125).

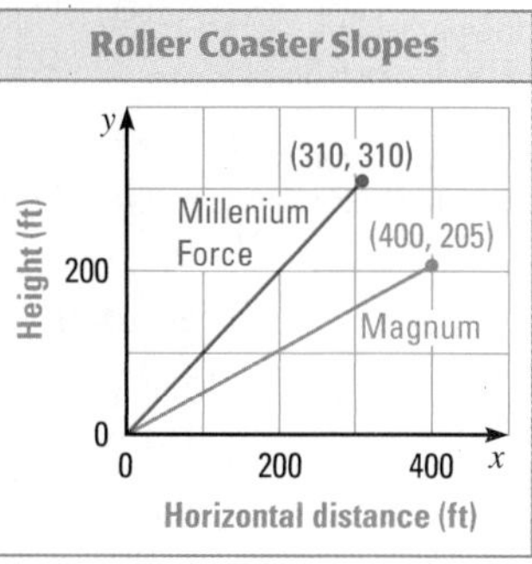

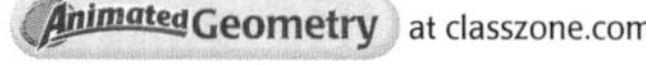

✓ GUIDED PRACTICE for Example 5

7. Line q passes through the points (0, 0) and (−4, 5). Line t passes through the points (0, 0) and (−10, 7). Which line is steeper, q or t? **line q**

8. **WHAT IF?** Suppose a roller coaster climbed 300 feet upward for every 350 feet it moved horizontally. Is it *more steep* or *less steep* than the Magnum? than the Millenium Force? **more steep; less steep**

13. Perpendicular; the product of their slopes is −1.

14. Neither; the slopes are not equal and their product is not −1.

15. Perpendicular; the product of their slopes is −1.

3.4 EXERCISES

HOMEWORK KEY

○ = **WORKED-OUT SOLUTIONS** on p. WS3 for Exs. 7, 13, and 35

★ = **STANDARDIZED TEST PRACTICE** Exs. 2, 34, 35, and 41

◆ = **MULTIPLE REPRESENTATIONS** Ex. 37

SKILL PRACTICE

A

1. **VOCABULARY** *Describe* what is meant by the slope of a nonvertical line. **See margin.**

2. ★ **WRITING** What happens when you apply the slope formula to a horizontal line? What happens when you apply it to a vertical line? **Slope is 0; slope is undefined.**

EXAMPLE 1 on p. 171 for Exs. 3–12

1. The slope of a nonvertical line is the ratio of vertical change (rise) to horizontal change (run) between any two points on the line.

MATCHING Match the description of the slope of a line with its graph.

3. m is positive. **D**　4. m is negative. **A**　5. m is zero. **B**　6. m is undefined. **C**

A.　B.　C.　D.

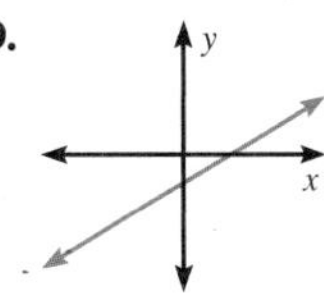

FINDING SLOPE Find the slope of the line that passes through the points.

7. (3, 5), (5, 6) $\frac{1}{2}$　8. (−2, 2), (2, −6) **−2**　9. (−5, −1), (3, −1) **0**　10. (2, 1), (0, 6) $-\frac{5}{2}$

ERROR ANALYSIS ***Describe*** **and correct the error in finding the slope of the line.**

11. Slope was computed using $\frac{run}{rise}$, it should be $\frac{rise}{run}$; $m = \frac{3}{4}$.

11.

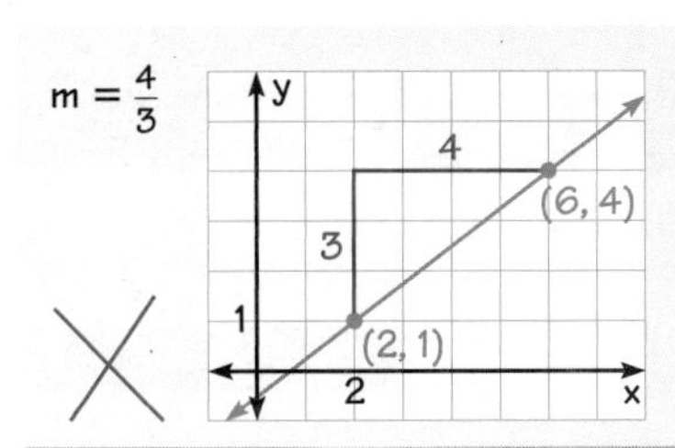

12.

Slope of the line through (2, 7) and (4, 5)

$m = \frac{y_2 - y_1}{x_2 - x_1} = \frac{7-5}{4-2} = \frac{2}{2} = 1$

x_2 and x_1 were interchanged; $\frac{7-5}{2-4} = \frac{2}{-2} = -1$.

EXAMPLES 2 and 3 on pp. 172–173 for Exs. 13–18

TYPES OF LINES Tell whether the lines through the given points are *parallel*, *perpendicular*, or *neither*. *Justify* your answer. **13–15. See margin.**

13. **Line 1:** (1, 0), (7, 4)
Line 2: (7, 0), (3, 6)

14. **Line 1:** (−3, 1), (−7, −2)
Line 2: (2, −1), (8, 4)

15. **Line 1:** (−9, 3), (−5, 7)
Line 2: (−11, 6), (−7, 2)

GRAPHING Graph the line through the given point with the given slope. **16–18. See margin.**

16. $P(3, -2)$, slope $-\frac{1}{6}$　17. $P(-4, 0)$, slope $\frac{5}{2}$　18. $P(0, 5)$, slope $\frac{2}{3}$

EXAMPLES 4 and 5 on pp. 173–174 for Exs. 19–22　B

STEEPNESS OF A LINE Tell which line through the given points is steeper.

19. **Line 1:** (−2, 3), (3, 5)
Line 2: (3, 1), (6, 5)
line 2

20. **Line 1:** (−2, −1), (1, −2)
Line 2: (−5, −3), (−1, −4)
line 1

21. **Line 1:** (−4, 2), (−3, 6)
Line 2: (1, 6), (3, 8)
line 1

22. **REASONING** Use your results from Exercises 19–21. *Describe* a way to determine which of two lines is steeper without graphing them. **Find the slopes and compare them. The one that has a larger absolute value is steeper.**

16. (3, −2), (9, −3)

17.

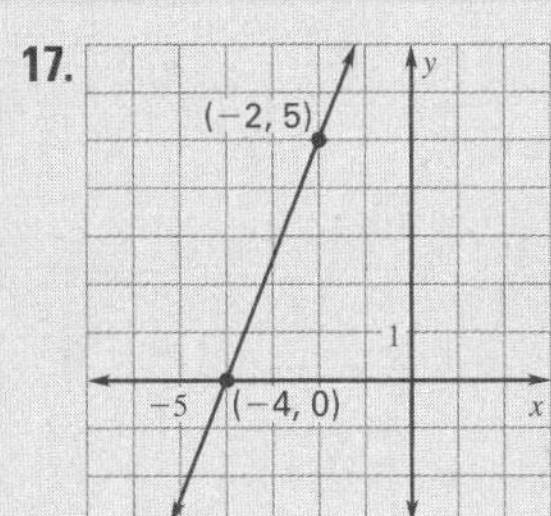

18.

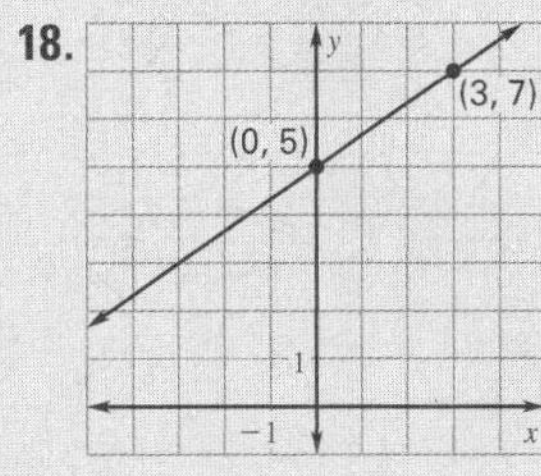

4 PRACTICE AND APPLY

Assignment Guide

Answer Transparencies available for all exercises

Basic:
Day 1: SRH p. 869 Exs. 1, 8, 11, 16
pp. 175–178
Exs. 1–18
Day 2: pp. 175–178
Exs. 19–22, 33–38, 43–49

Average:
Day 1: pp. 175–178
Exs. 1, 2, 4–6, 8–12, 14–18 even, 23–25, 43–49
Day 2: pp. 175–178
Exs. 19–22, 26–31*, 33–41

Advanced:
Day 1: pp. 175–178
Exs. 1, 2, 4–10 even, 14–18 even, 23–26, 43–49
Day 2: pp. 175–178
Exs. 19–22, 27–42*

Block:
pp. 175–178
Exs. 1, 2, 4–6, 8–12, 14–18 even, 19–31*, 33–41, 43–49

Differentiated Instruction

See *Geometry Best Practices Toolkit* for suggestions on addressing the needs of a diverse classroom.

Homework Check

For a quick check of student understanding of key concepts, go over the following exercises:

Basic: 6, 14, 16, 19, 34
Average: 8, 14, 18, 20, 36
Advanced: 10, 18, 21, 24, 37

Extra Practice

- Student Edition, p. 901
- Chapter 3 Resource Book: Practice levels A, B, C, pp. 48–53

Practice Worksheet

An easily-readable reduced practice page (with answers) for this lesson can be found on p. 144D.

Avoiding Common Errors

Exercises 7–10 Students may substitute incorrectly when they use the slope formula. Remind them that the numerator is the difference of the y-coordinates and the denominator is the difference of the corresponding x-coordinates. Suggest that they write the formula before they substitute. It may also help if they write (x_1, y_1) and (x_2, y_2) on the same line of their notebook paper and then, directly below, the specific ordered pairs of numbers that they will use for the substitution.

Mathematical Reasoning

Exercise 26 If students have difficulty with the exercise, ask them to find the slope of the line they would travel to go straight from (−3, 3) to (1, −2). Then have them do the same for the line from (−3, 3) to (4, 0). Ask what they can conclude from their results.

23. −2;

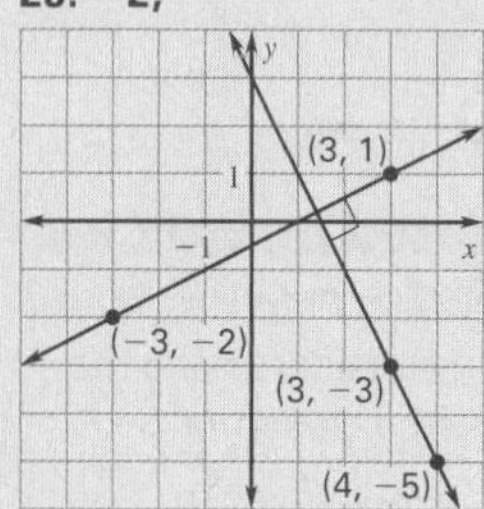

24. $\frac{1}{3}$;

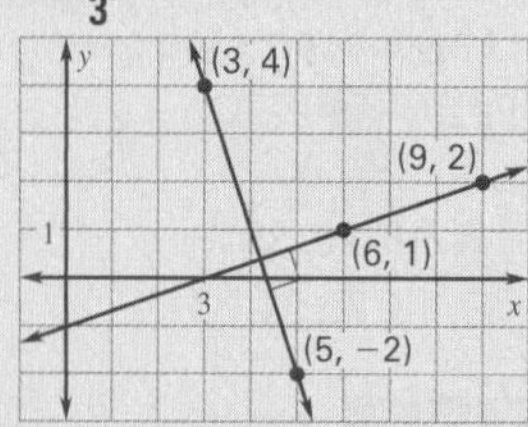

25. 7;

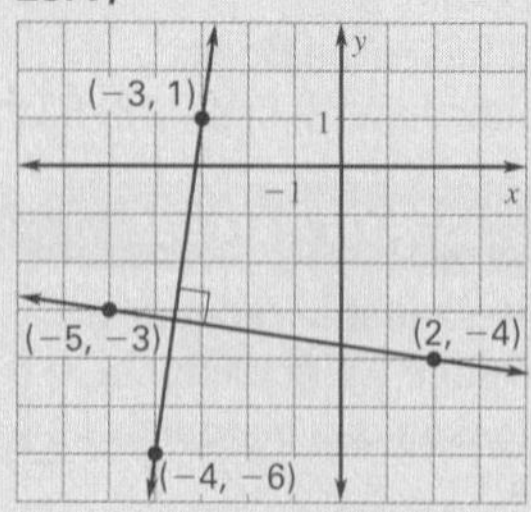

26.

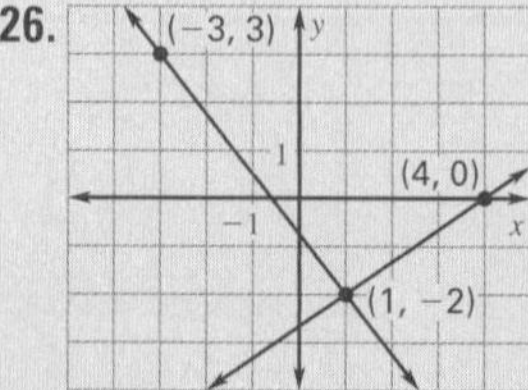

PERPENDICULAR LINES **Find the slope of line n perpendicular to line h and passing through point P. Then copy the graph and graph line n.** **23–25. See margin.**

23. 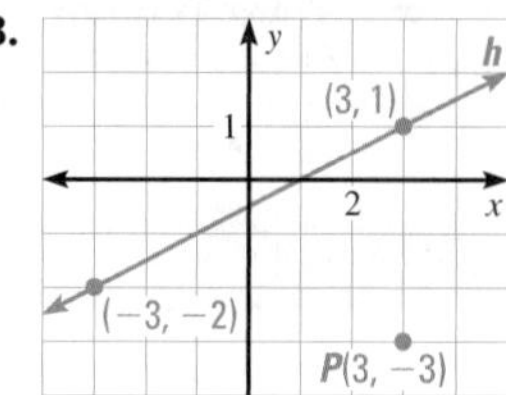

24. 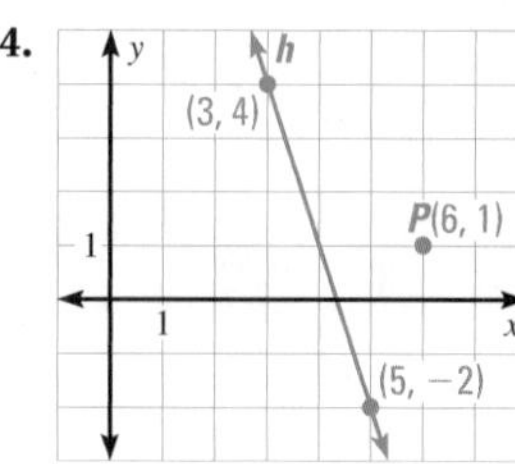

25. 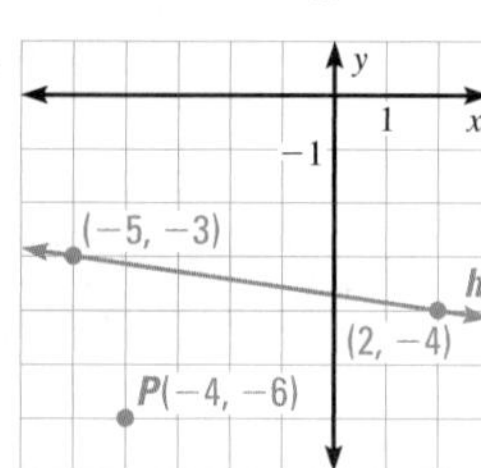

26. No; the slope between points (−3, 3) and (1, −2) is $\frac{-5}{4}$ while the slope between points (1, −2) and (4, 0) is $\frac{2}{3}$; see margin for art.

26. **REASONING** Use the concept of slope to decide whether the points (−3, 3), (1, −2), and (4, 0) lie on the same line. *Explain* your reasoning and include a diagram.

GRAPHING **Graph a line with the given description.** **27–29. See margin.**

27. Through (0, 2) and parallel to the line through (−2, 4) and (−5, 1)

28. Through (1, 3) and perpendicular to the line through (−1, −1) and (2, 0)

29. Through (−2, 1) and parallel to the line through (3, 1) and $(4, -\frac{1}{2})$

C **CHALLENGE** **Find the unknown coordinate so the line through the points has the given slope.**

30. (−3, 2), (0, y); slope −2 **−4**
31. (−7, −4), (x, 0); slope $\frac{1}{3}$ **5**
32. (4, −3), (x, 1); slope −4 **3**

PROBLEM SOLVING

A 33. **WATER SLIDE** The water slide is 6 feet tall, and the end of the slide is 9 feet from the base of the ladder. About what slope does the slide have? **$\frac{2}{3}$**

@HomeTutor for problem solving help at classzone.com

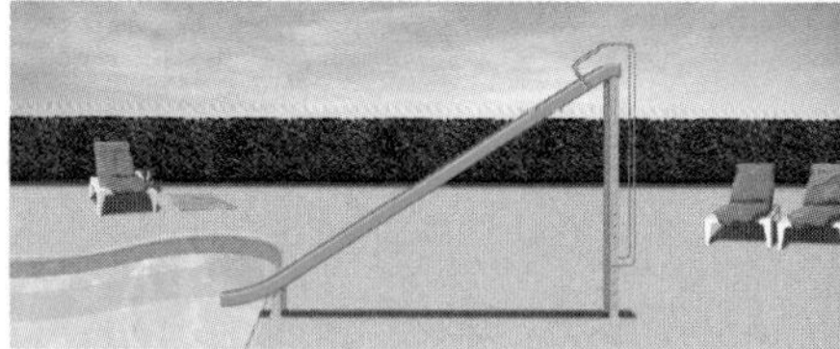

EXAMPLE 5 on p. 174 for Exs. 34–37

34. ★ **MULTIPLE CHOICE** Which car has better gas mileage? **B**

Ⓐ A Ⓑ B
Ⓒ Same rate Ⓓ Cannot be determined

@HomeTutor for problem solving help at classzone.com

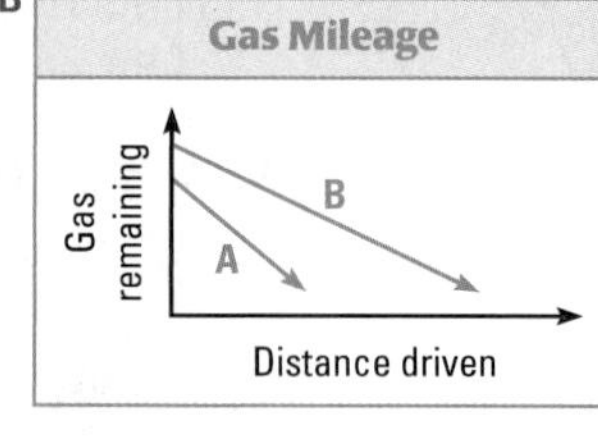

35. ★ **SHORT RESPONSE** *Compare* the graphs of the three lines described below. Which is most steep? Which is the least steep? Include a sketch in your answer. **Line b; line c; see margin for art.**

Line a: through the point (3, 0) with a y-intercept of 4
Line b: through the point (3, 0) with a y-intercept greater than 4
Line c: through the point (3, 0) with a y-intercept between 0 and 4

○ = WORKED-OUT SOLUTIONS on p. WS1 ★ = STANDARDIZED TEST PRACTICE

= MULTIPLE REPRESENTATIONS

27. 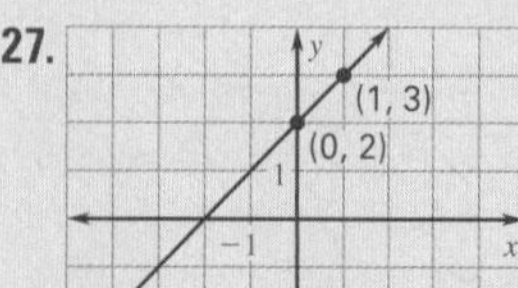

28. 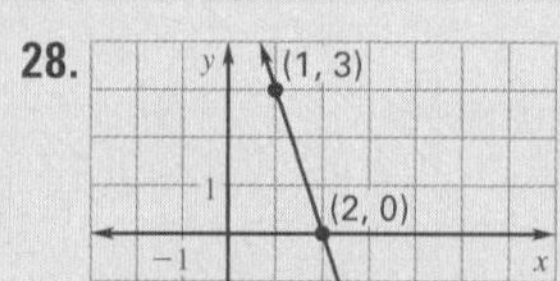

29. 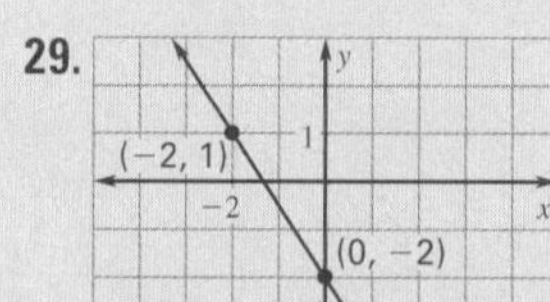

36. **MULTI-STEP PROBLEM** Ladder safety guidelines include the following recommendation about ladder placement. The horizontal distance h between the base of the ladder and the object the ladder is resting against should be about one quarter of the vertical distance v between the ground and where the ladder rests against the object.

Make sure to place the ladder on a level place. If the ladder is not steady, it is not safe to climb.

Place the base so the distance h to the building is about one quarter of the height v to where the ladder hits the building.

a. Find the recommended slope for a ladder. **4**

b. Suppose the base of a ladder is 6 feet away from a building. The ladder has the recommended slope. Find v. **24 ft**

c. Suppose a ladder is 34 feet from the ground where it touches a building. The ladder has the recommended slope. Find h. **8.5 ft**

B 37. **MULTIPLE REPRESENTATIONS** The Duquesne (pronounced "du-KAYN") Incline was built in 1888 in Pittsburgh, Pennsylvania, to move people up and down a mountain there. On the incline, you move about 29 feet vertically for every 50 feet you move horizontally. When you reach the top of the hill, you have moved a horizontal distance of about 700 feet.

a. **Making a Table** Make a table showing the vertical distance that the incline moves for each 50 feet of horizontal distance during its climb. How high is the incline at the top? **See margin for table; 406 ft.**

b. **Drawing a Graph** Write a fraction that represents the slope of the incline's climb path. Draw a graph to show the climb path. **$\frac{29}{50}$; see margin for art.**

c. **Comparing Slopes** The Burgenstock Incline in Switzerland moves about 144 vertical feet for every 271 horizontal feet. Write a fraction to represent the slope of this incline's path. Which incline is steeper, the *Burgenstock* or the *Duquesne*? **$\frac{144}{271}$; Duquesne**

38. **PROVING THEOREM 3.7** Use slopes of lines to write a paragraph proof of the Transitive Property of Parallel Lines on page 164.

38. *Sample answer:* Given $p \parallel q$ and $q \parallel r$, prove $p \parallel r$. Since $p \parallel q$, lines p and q have the same slope, by the Slopes of Parallel Lines Postulate. Similarly, since $q \parallel r$, lines q and r have the same slope. So lines p, q, and r all have the same slope. Therefore, lines p and r have the same slope, and $p \parallel r$ by the Slopes of Parallel Lines Postulates.

AVERAGE RATE OF CHANGE In Exercises 39 and 40, slope can be used to describe an *average rate of change.* To write an average rate of change, rewrite the slope fraction so the denominator is one.

39. **BUSINESS** In 2000, a business made a profit of \$8500. In 2006, the business made a profit of \$15,400. Find the average rate of change in dollars per year from 2000 to 2006. **\$1150 per year**

40. **ROCK CLIMBING** A rock climber begins climbing at a point 400 feet above sea level. It takes the climber 45 minutes to climb to the destination, which is 706 feet above sea level. Find the average rate of change in feet per minute for the climber from start to finish. **6.8 ft/min**

Study Strategy

Exercise 37 Suggest that students compare this exercise to Example 5.

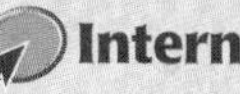

Internet Reference

Exercise 37 Additional information about the Duquesne Incline can be found at incline.pghfree.net/historyfacts.htm

35. *Sample:*

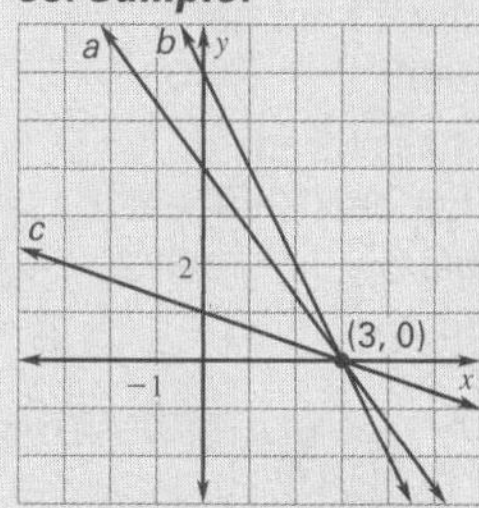

37a. See below.

37b.

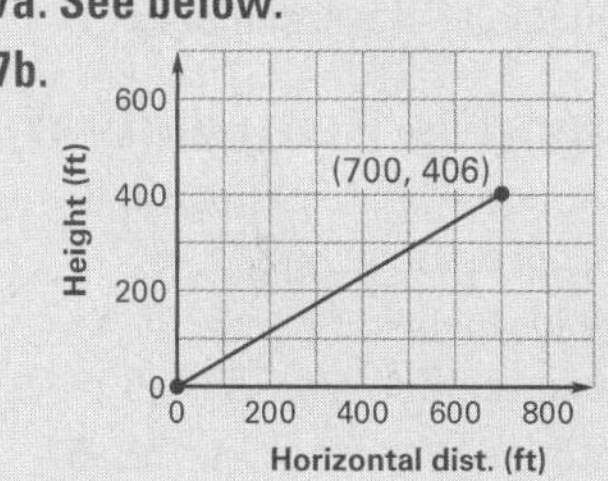

37a.

Horizontal distance (ft)	50	100	150	200	250	300	350	400	450	500	550	600	650	700
Height (ft)	29	58	87	116	145	174	203	232	261	290	319	348	377	406

5 ASSESS AND RETEACH

Daily Homework Quiz

Transparency Available

1. Find the slope of the line containing the points (4, −3) and (5, 2). **5**
2. Line *k* passes through the points (−1, 2) and (3, 5). Line *n* passes through the points (3, 7) and (6, 3). Are lines *k* and *n* parallel, perpendicular, or neither? **perpendicular**
3. A highway has a grade of 7 percent. For each 200 feet it goes horizontally, how many feet does it rise? **14 ft**

Available at **classzone.com**

Diagnosis/Remediation

- Practice A, B, C in Chapter 3 Resource Book, pp. 48–53
- Study Guide in Chapter 3 Resource Book, pp. 54–55
- Practice Workbook, pp. 52–54
- @HomeTutor

Challenge

Additional challenge is available in the Chapter 3 Resource Book, p. 58.

Quiz

An easily-readable reduced copy of the quiz (with answers) on Lessons 3.3–3.4 from the Assessment Book can be found on p. 144F.

41a. 1985 to 1990. *Sample answer:* about 2 million people per year

41b. 1995 to 2000. *Sample answer:* about 3 million people per year

41c. *Sample answer:* There was moderate but steady increase in attendance for the NFL over the time period of 1985–2000.

41. ★ **EXTENDED RESPONSE** The line graph shows the regular season attendance (in millions) for three professional sports organizations from 1985 to 2000.

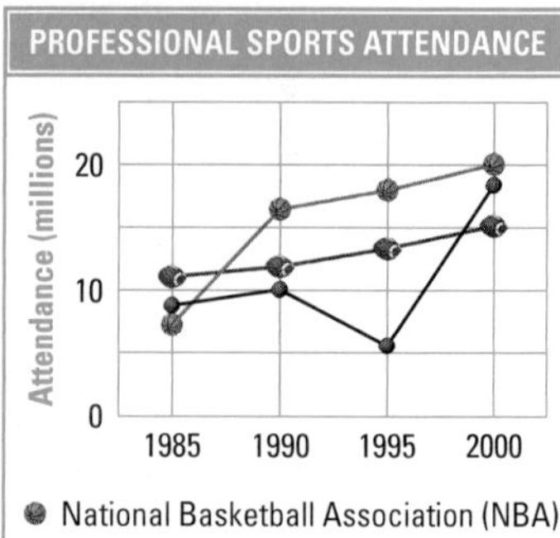

a. During which five-year period did the NBA attendance increase the most? Estimate the rate of change for this five-year period in people per year.

b. During which five-year period did the NHL attendance increase the most? Estimate the rate of change for this five-year period in people per year.

c. **Interpret** The line graph for the NFL seems to be almost linear between 1985 and 2000. Write a sentence about what this means in terms of the real-world situation.

42. [C] CHALLENGE Find two values of k such that the points $(-3, 1)$, $(0, k)$, and $(k, 5)$ are collinear. *Explain* your reasoning.
3, −5. *Sample answer:* Set $\frac{k-1}{3} = \frac{k-5}{-k}$ and solve for k.

MIXED REVIEW

43. Yes. *Sample answer:* Substitute (−1, −7) into the equation $y = 2x - 5$, $-7 = 2(-1) - 5$.

45. *Sample answer:* $\overleftrightarrow{CD}$, $\overleftrightarrow{FD}$

PREVIEW Prepare for Lesson 3.5 in Exs. 47–49.

43. Is the point $(-1, -7)$ on the line $y = 2x - 5$? *Explain.* *(p. 878)*

44. Find the intercepts of the graph of $y = -3x + 9$. *(p. 879)* **See margin.**

Use the diagram to write two examples of each postulate. *(p. 96)*

45. Through any two points there exists exactly one line.

46. Through any three noncollinear points there exists exactly one plane. ***Sample answer:* A, D, F in plane Q; C, D, F in plane P**

Solve the equation for *y*. Write a reason for each step. *(p. 105)* **47–49. See margin.**

47. $6x + 4y = 40$ **48.** $\frac{1}{2}x - \frac{5}{4}y = -10$ **49.** $16 - 3y = 24x$

QUIZ for Lessons 3.3–3.4

Find the value of *x* that makes $m \parallel n$. *(p. 161)*

1.
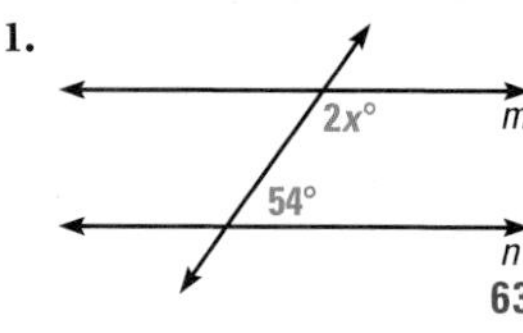

63

2.
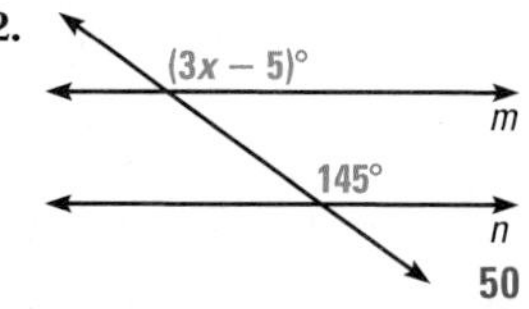

50

3.
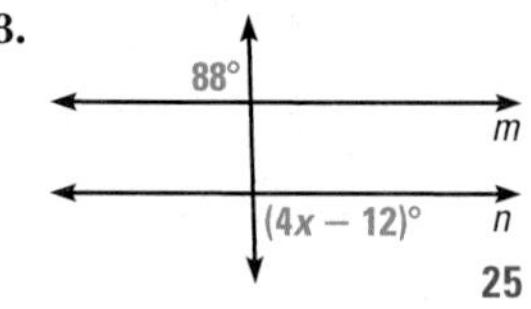

25

Find the slope of the line that passes through the given points. *(p. 171)*

4. (1, −1), (3, 3) **2** **5.** (1, 2), (4, 5) **1** **6.** (−3, −2), (−7, −6) **1**

44. *x*-intercept: 3, *y*-intercept: 9
47–49. See Additional Answers beginning on p. AA1.

@HomeTutor
classzone.com
Keystrokes

3.4 Investigate Slopes

MATERIALS • graphing calculator or computer

Standards

Prepare for
17.0 Students prove theorems by *using coordinate geometry,* including the midpoint of a line segment, the distance formula, and various forms of equations of lines and circles.

QUESTION How can you verify the Slopes of Parallel Lines Postulate?

You can verify the postulates you learned in Lesson 3.4 using geometry drawing software.

EXAMPLE Verify the Slopes of Parallel Lines Postulate

STEP 1 ***Show axes*** Show the x-axis and the y-axis by choosing Hide/Show Axes from the F5 menu.

STEP 2 ***Draw line*** Draw a line by choosing Line from the F2 menu. Do not use one of the axes as your line. Choose a point on the line and label it A.

STEP 3 ***Graph point*** Graph a point not on the line by choosing Point from the F2 menu.

STEP 4 ***Draw parallel line*** Choose Parallel from the F3 menu and select the line. Then select the point not on the line.

STEP 5 ***Measure slopes*** Select one line and choose Measure Slope from the F5 menu. Repeat this step for the second line.

STEP 6 ***Move line*** Drag point A to move the line. What do you expect to happen?

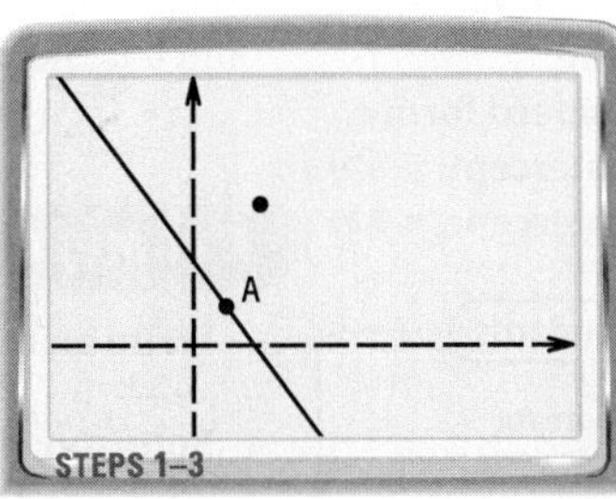

STEPS 1–3

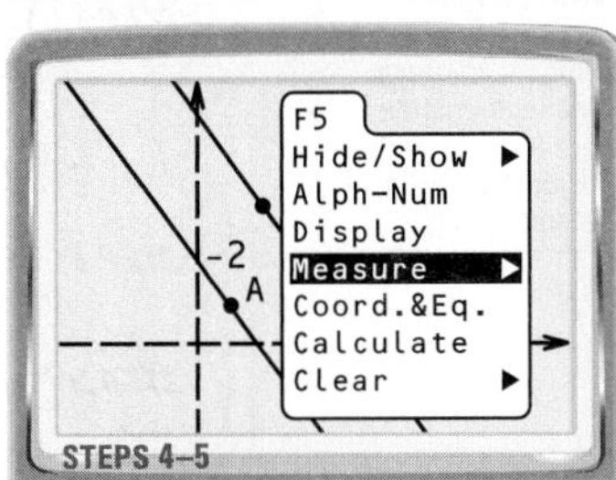

STEPS 4–5

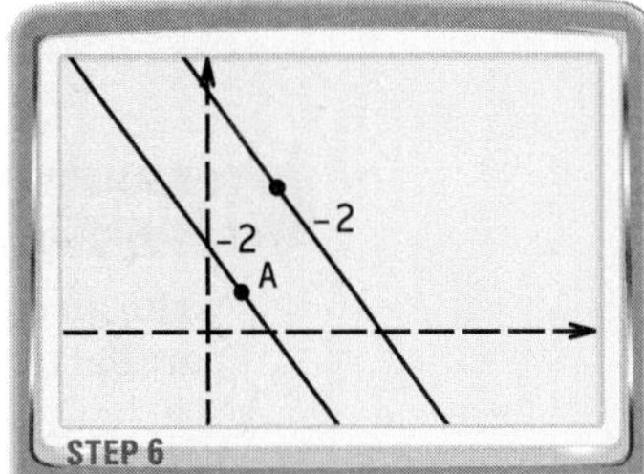

STEP 6

PRACTICE

1. Use geometry drawing software to verify the Slopes of Perpendicular Lines Postulate.
   a. Construct a line and a point not on that line. Use Steps 1–3 from the Example above. **Check students' work.**
   b. Construct a line that is perpendicular to your original line and passes through the given point. **Check students' work.**
   c. Measure the slopes of the two lines. Multiply the slopes. What do you expect the product of the slopes to be? **–1**

2. **WRITING** Use the arrow keys to move your line from Exercise 1. *Describe* what happens to the product of the slopes when one of the lines is vertical. *Explain* why this happens.
The result will be undefined. The vertical line has an undefined slope.

1 PLAN AND PREPARE

Learn the Method

• Students will verify that parallel lines have the same slope.

Keystroke Help

Keystrokes for several models of calculators are available in blackline format in the *Chapter 3 Resource Book.*

2 TEACH

Tips for Success

Be sure to construct the parallel line with the software instead of just drawing it so it looks parallel.

Alternative Strategy

Do the construction as a demonstration with a computer and an overhead projector. Ask students to conjecture about the slopes and then calculate them. Have students move the line and watch the slope values.

Extra Example 1

Construct a different line and choose a point on the line. Label the point B. Graph a point not on the line and construct a line through the point, parallel to the first line. Measure the slopes of both lines. How do they compare? **They are equal.**

3 ASSESS AND RETEACH

1. If a line has a slope of m, what will be the slope of any line parallel to it? m

1 PLAN AND PREPARE

Warm-Up Exercises

Transparency Available

1. If $2x + 5y = -20$ and $x = 0$, what is y? **−4**
2. What is the slope of the line containing the points (2, 7) and (3, −10)? **−17**
3. Orphelia bought x apples. If each apple cost $.59, write an equation for y, the total cost of x apples. **$y = 0.59x$**

Notetaking Guide

Transparency Available

Promotes interactive learning and notetaking skills, pp. 74–78.

Pacing

Basic: 2 days
Average: 2 days
Advanced: 2 days
Block: 1 block
- See *Teaching Guide/Lesson Plan.*

2 FOCUS AND MOTIVATE

Essential Question

Big Idea 3, p. 145

How do you write an equation of a line? **Tell students they will learn how to answer this question by using the slope, the y-intercept and the slope-intercept form for a line.**

3.5 Write and Graph Equations of Lines

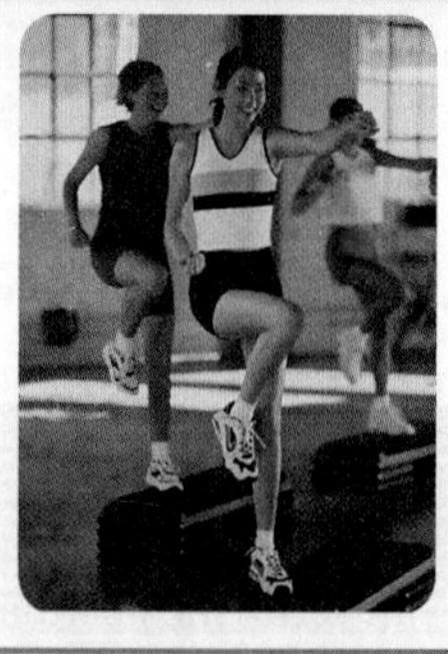

Before You found slopes of lines.
Now You will find equations of lines.
Why? So you can find monthly gym costs, as in Example 4.

Key Vocabulary
- **slope-intercept form**
- **standard form**
- ***x*-intercept,** *p. 879*
- ***y*-intercept,** *p. 879*

Standards
Prepare for 17.0 Students prove theorems by *using coordinate geometry,* including the midpoint of a line segment, the distance formula, and *various forms of equations of lines* and circles.

Linear equations may be written in different forms. The general form of a linear equation in **slope-intercept form** is $y = mx + b$, where m is the slope and b is the y-intercept.

EXAMPLE 1 Write an equation of a line from a graph

Write an equation of the line in slope-intercept form.

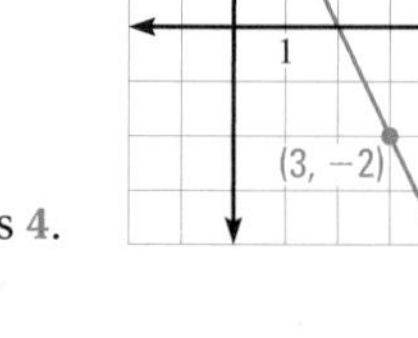

Solution

STEP 1 **Find** the slope. Choose two points on the graph of the line, (0, 4) and (3, −2).

$$m = \frac{4 - (-2)}{0 - 3} = \frac{6}{-3} = -2$$

STEP 2 **Find** the y-intercept. The line intersects the y-axis at the point (0, 4), so the y-intercept is 4.

STEP 3 **Write** the equation.

$y = mx + b$ — Use slope-intercept form.

$y = -2x + 4$ — Substitute −2 for m and 4 for b.

EXAMPLE 2 Write an equation of a parallel line

Write an equation of the line passing through the point (−1, 1) that is parallel to the line with the equation $y = 2x - 3$.

Solution

STEP 1 **Find** the slope m. The slope of a line parallel to $y = 2x - 3$ is the same as the given line, so the slope is 2.

LINEAR EQUATIONS
The graph of a linear equation represents all the solutions of the equation. So, the given point must be a solution of the equation.

STEP 2 **Find** the y-intercept b by using $m = 2$ and $(x, y) = (-1, 1)$.

$y = mx + b$ — Use slope-intercept form.

$1 = 2(-1) + b$ — Substitute for x, y, and m.

$3 = b$ — Solve for b.

▶ Because $m = 2$ and $b = 3$, an equation of the line is $y = 2x + 3$.

Resource Planning Guide

Chapter Resource Book
- Teaching Guide/Lesson Plan (pp. 59–60)
- Activity Master (p. 61)
- Practice levels A, B, C (pp. 63–68)
- Study Guide (pp. 69–70)
- Catch-up for Absent Students (p. 71)
- Problem Solving Workshop (p. 72)
- Challenge (p. 73)

Workbooks
- Notetaking Guide (pp. 74–78)
- Practice Workbook (pp. 55–57)

Teaching Options
- **Power Presentations CD-ROM** provides dynamic electronic teaching resources for the classroom.
- **Activity Generator CD-ROM** provides editable activities for all ability levels.

Interactive Technology
- Easy Planner
- Power Presentations CD-ROM
- Activity Generator CD-ROM
- Animated Geometry
- Test Generator CD-ROM
- Online Quiz
- eWorkbook
- eEdition
- @HomeTutor

Resources for English Learners
- Quick Reference for English Learners
- Spanish Study Guide
- Multi-Language Visual Glossary
- Student Resources in Spanish

See also the *Geometry Toolkit* for more strategies for meeting individual needs.

CHECKING BY GRAPHING You can check that equations are correct by graphing. In Example 2, you can use a graph to check that $y = 2x - 3$ is parallel to $y = 2x + 3$.

Animated Geometry at classzone.com

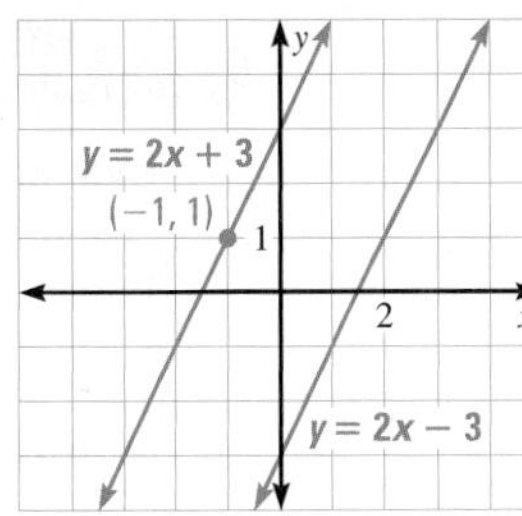

EXAMPLE 3 Write an equation of a perpendicular line

Write an equation of the line *j* passing through the point (2, 3) that is perpendicular to the line *k* with the equation $y = -2x + 2$.

Solution

STEP 1 **Find** the slope m of line j. Line k has a slope of -2.

$-2 \cdot m = -1$ The product of the slopes of ⊥ lines is −1.

$m = \frac{1}{2}$ Divide each side by −2.

STEP 2 **Find** the y-intercept b by using $m = \frac{1}{2}$ and $(x, y) = (2, 3)$.

$y = mx + b$ Use slope-intercept form.

$3 = \frac{1}{2}(2) + b$ Substitute for x, y, and m.

$2 = b$ Solve for b.

▶ Because $m = \frac{1}{2}$ and $b = 2$, an equation of line j is $y = \frac{1}{2}x + 2$. You can check that the lines j and k are perpendicular by graphing, then using a protractor to measure one of the angles formed by the lines.

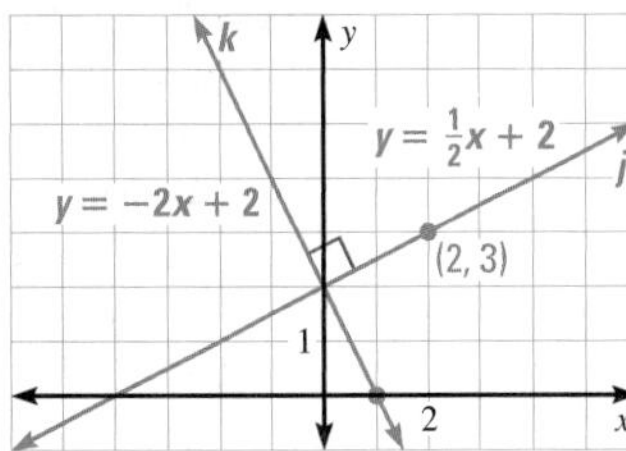

GUIDED PRACTICE for Examples 1, 2, and 3

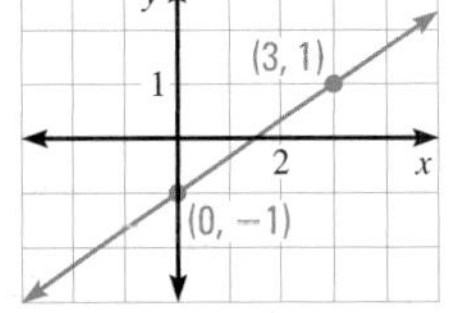

1. Write an equation of the line in the graph at the right. $y = \frac{2}{3}x - 1$
2. Write an equation of the line that passes through $(-2, 5)$ and $(1, 2)$. $y = -x + 3$
3. Write an equation of the line that passes through the point $(1, 5)$ and is parallel to the line with the equation $y = 3x - 5$. Graph the lines to check that they are parallel. **$y = 3x + 2$; see margin for art.**
4. How do you know the lines $x = 4$ and $y = 2$ are perpendicular? ***Sample answer:*** **$x = 4$ is a vertical line while $y = 2$ is a horizontal line.**

Motivating the Lesson

Sandra signed up for high-speed Internet service on her home computer for $79 plus the monthly fee of $19.99. In this lesson students will learn to write an equation for the cost of the Internet access and use the equation to find the cost after any number of months.

Extra Example 1

Write an equation of the line in slope-intercept form. **$y = 4x - 3$**

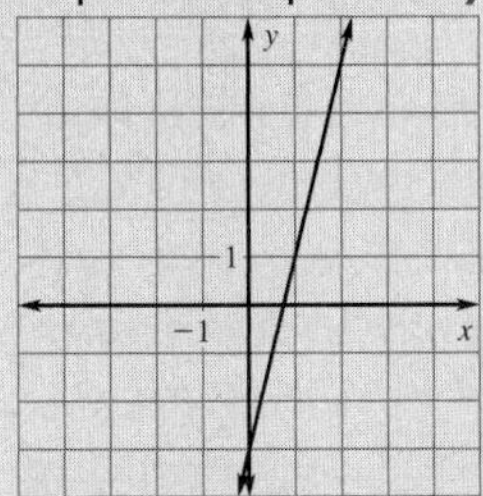

Key Question to Ask for Example 1

- Could you have used two different points to compute the slope? Explain. **Yes, any two points on the line will give the same slope.**

Extra Example 2

Write an equation of the line passing through the point $(2, -3)$ that is parallel to the line with the equation $y = 6x + 4$. **$y = 6x - 15$**

Extra Example 3

Write an equation of the line a passing through the point $(3, -4)$ that is perpendicular to the line b with the equation $y = -\frac{1}{2}x - 1$. **$y = 2x - 10$**

3. See Additional Answers beginning on p. AA1.

Differentiated Instruction

Advanced Provide a brief discussion of *set-builder notation*, pointing out that it can be used to represent linear equations like the ones found in **Examples 1–3**. Remind students that a line is formed by an infinite number of collinear points. Point out that this set of points can be written using set-builder notation. For instance, the line found in Example 1 can be written as $\{(x, y) \mid y = -2x + 4\}$, which is read "the set of all ordered pairs (x, y) such that y equals $-2x + 4$." Ask students to suggest the set-builder notations that would represent the lines found in Examples 2 and 3.

See also the *Geometry Toolkit* for more strategies.

Extra Example 4

The graph shows the cost of having cable television installed in your home. Write an equation of the line. Explain the meaning of the slope and the y-intercept of the line.

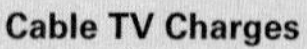

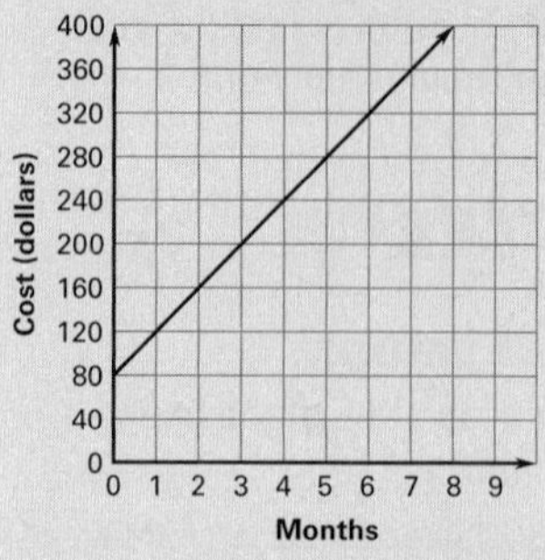

$y = 40x + 80$; the slope is the cost per month, and the y-intercept is the initial charge.

Key Question to Ask for Example 4

- What other values could you have substituted for x and y to find b? **5 and 363**

Extra Example 5

Graph $2x - 3y = -12$.

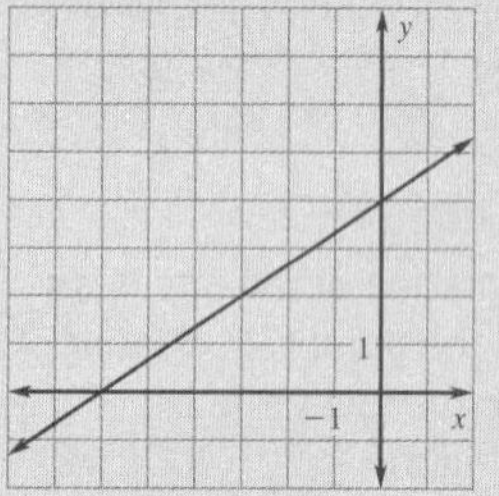

Key Question to Ask for Example 5

- How else could you graph this line? **Rewrite the equation in slope-intercept form, graph the y-intercept, and use the slope to find another point on the line. Then draw the line.**

Vocabulary

Point out that we say that equations such as $3x = 6$ and $-2y = 5$ are in standard form even though they contain only one variable.

EXAMPLE 4 Write an equation of a line from a graph

GYM MEMBERSHIP The graph models the total cost of joining a gym. Write an equation of the line. Explain the meaning of the slope and the y-intercept of the line.

Solution

STEP 1 **Find** the slope.

$$m = \frac{363 - 231}{5 - 2} = \frac{132}{3} = 44$$

STEP 2 **Find** the y-intercept. Use the slope and one of the points on the graph.

$y = mx + b$	**Use slope-intercept form.**
$231 = 44 \cdot 2 + b$	**Substitute for x, y, and m.**
$143 = b$	**Simplify.**

STEP 3 **Write** the equation. Because $m = 44$ and $b = 143$, an equation of the line is $y = 44x + 143$.

▶ The equation $y = 44x + 143$ models the cost. The slope is the monthly fee, \$44, and the y-intercept is the initial cost to join the gym, \$143.

STANDARD FORM Another form of a linear equation is *standard form*. In **standard form**, the equation is written as $Ax + By = C$, where A and B are not both zero.

EXAMPLE 5 Graph a line with equation in standard form

Graph $3x + 4y = 12$.

Solution

> **CHOOSE A METHOD**
> Another way you could graph the equation is to solve the equation for y. Then the equation will be in slope-intercept form. Use rise and run from the point where the line crosses the y-axis to find a second point. Then graph the line.

The equation is in standard form, so you can use the intercepts.

STEP 1 **Find** the intercepts.

To find the x-intercept, let $y = 0$.	To find the y-intercept, let $x = 0$.
$3x + 4y = 12$	$3x + 4y = 12$
$3x + 4(0) = 12$	$3(0) + 4y = 12$
$x = 4$	$y = 3$

STEP 2 **Graph** the line.

The line intersects the axes at (4, 0) and (0, 3). Graph these points, then draw a line through the points.

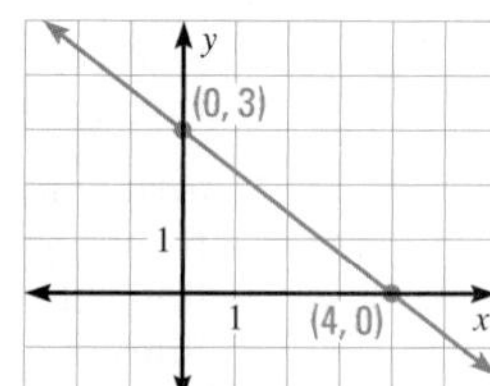

✓ GUIDED PRACTICE for Examples 4 and 5

5. The equation $y = 50x + 125$ models the total cost of joining a climbing gym. What are the meaning of the slope and the y-intercept of the line?
Slope: monthly fee, y-intercept: initial cost to join gym

Graph the equation. **6–8. See margin.**

6. $2x - 3y = 6$ 7. $y = 4$ 8. $x = -3$

WRITING EQUATIONS You can write linear equations to model real-world situations, such as comparing costs to find a better buy.

EXAMPLE 6 Solve a real-world problem

DVD RENTAL You can rent DVDs at a local store for $4.00 each. An Internet company offers a flat fee of $15.00 per month for as many rentals as you want. How many DVDs do you need to rent to make the online rental a better buy?

ANOTHER WAY
For alternative methods for solving the problem in Example 6, turn to page 188 for the **Problem Solving Workshop**.

Solution

STEP 1 **Model** each rental with an equation.

Cost of one month's rental online: $y = 15$

Cost of one month's rental locally: $y = 4x$, where x represents the number of DVDs rented

STEP 2 **Graph** each equation.

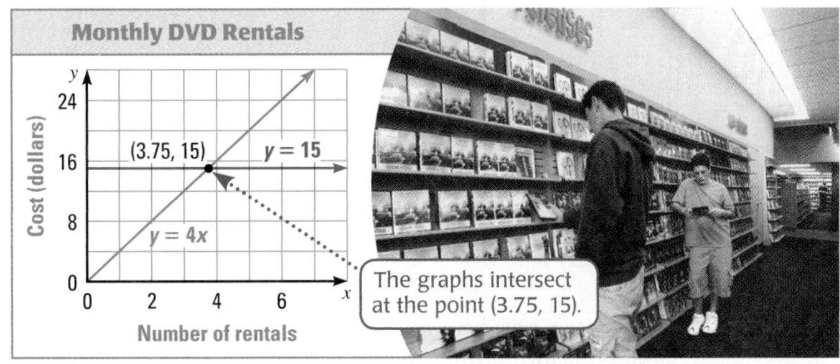

READ VOCABULARY
The point at which the costs are the same is sometimes called the *break-even point*.

▶ The point of intersection is (3.75, 15). Using the graph, you can see that it is cheaper to rent locally if you rent 3 or fewer DVDs per month. If you rent 4 or more DVDs per month, it is cheaper to rent online.

✓ GUIDED PRACTICE for Example 6

9. **WHAT IF?** In Example 6, suppose the online rental is $16.50 per month and the local rental is $4 each. How many DVDs do you need to rent to make the online rental a better buy? **5 DVDs**

10. How would your answer to Exercise 9 change if you had a 2-for-1 coupon that you could use once at the local store?

10. Online rental would have to increase to 6 DVDs to be a better buy.

Extra Example 6

One bank charges $1.50 for each use of its debit card. Another bank charges $10 per month for an unlimited number of debit card uses. How many times per month would you need to use your debit card to make the bank that charges a flat rate the better choice?
7 times or more

Closing the Lesson

Have students summarize the major points of the lesson and answer the Essential Question: How do you write an equation of a line?

- **The general form of a linear equation in slope-intercept form is $y = mx + b$, where m is the slope and b is the y-intercept.**
- **A linear equation in standard form can be graphed if you use its intercepts.**

Use the coordinates of two points on the line to find the slope m. Substitute the coordinates of one of the points and the value of m in the slope-intercept equation $y = mx + b$. Solve the resulting equation for b. Then substitute the values of m and b in $y = mx + b$ to get the slope-intercept form of the equation of the line.

6.
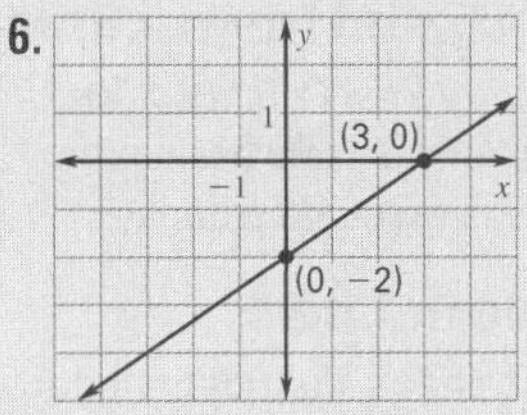

7.
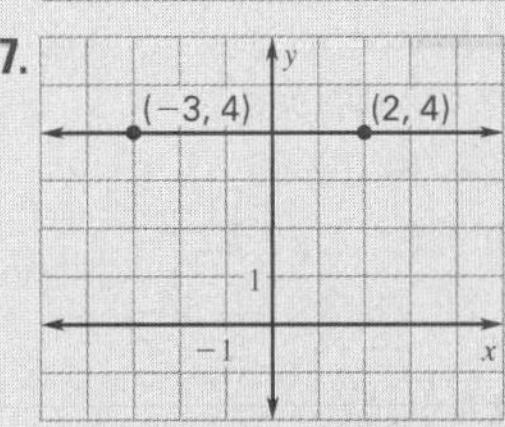

8.
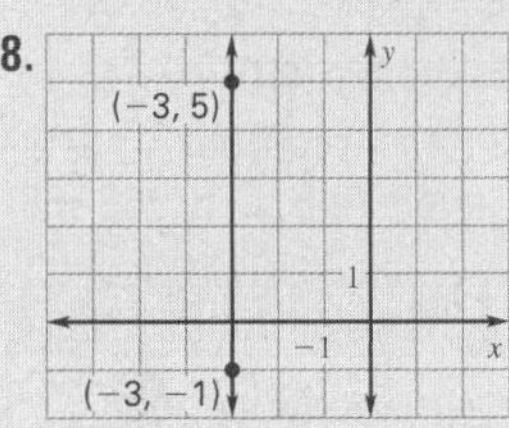

4 PRACTICE AND APPLY

Assignment Guide

Answer Transparencies available for all exercises

Basic:

Day 1: SRH p. 879 Exs. 5–12
pp. 184–187
Exs. 1–6, 9–13, 16–19, 22–25, 29, 70–75

Day 2: pp. 184–187
Exs. 30–33, 36–39, 45–49, 60–63, 67–69

Average:

Day 1: pp. 184–187
Exs. 1, 2, 4–6, 9, 11–13, 17–19, 22, 24–26, 29, 49–52, 70–75

Day 2: pp. 184–187
Exs. 31–33, 40–42, 45–48, 53–57, 60–65, 67–69

Advanced:

Day 1: pp. 184–187
Exs. 1, 2, 6–9, 13–15, 19–22, 26–29, 49–52, 70–75

Day 2: pp. 184–187
Exs. 33–35, 42–44, 46–48, 53–69*

Block:

pp. 184–187
Exs. 1, 2, 4–6, 9, 11–13, 17–19, 22, 24–26, 29, 31–33, 40–42, 45–57, 60–65, 67–75

Differentiated Instruction

See *Geometry Best Practices Toolkit* for suggestions on addressing the needs of a diverse classroom.

Homework Check

For a quick check of student understanding of key concepts, go over the following exercises:

Basic: 12, 24, 30, 36, 60

Average: 16, 26, 32, 40, 62

Advanced: 20, 28, 34, 44, 64

Extra Practice

- Student Edition, p. 901
- Chapter 3 Resource Book: Practice levels A, B, C, pp. 63–68

Practice Worksheet

An easily-readable reduced practice page (with answers) for this lesson can be found on p. 144E.

3.5 EXERCISES

HOMEWORK KEY

○ = **WORKED-OUT SOLUTIONS** on p. WS4 for Exs. 17, 23, and 61

★ = **STANDARDIZED TEST PRACTICE** Exs. 2, 9, 29, 64, and 65

SKILL PRACTICE

A

1. **VOCABULARY** What does *intercept* mean in the expression *slope-intercept form*? **The point of intersection on the y-axis when graphing a line.**

2. ★ **WRITING** Explain how you can use the standard form of a linear equation to find the intercepts of a line. **See margin.**

EXAMPLE 1 on p. 180 for Exs. 3–22

2. ***Sample answer:*** **To find the x-intercept let $y = 0$ and solve for x. To find the y-intercept let $x = 0$ and solve for y.**

3. $y = \frac{4}{3}x - 4$

4. $y = \frac{1}{5}x - 2$

5. $y = -\frac{3}{2}x - \frac{1}{2}$

6. $y = -\frac{6}{5}x - \frac{3}{5}$

7. $y = \frac{3}{2}x - \frac{3}{2}$

8. $y = -\frac{1}{3}x - \frac{8}{3}$

WRITING EQUATIONS Write an equation of the line shown.

3. 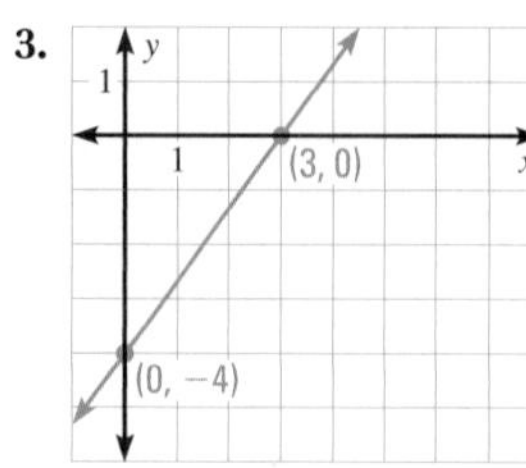

4. 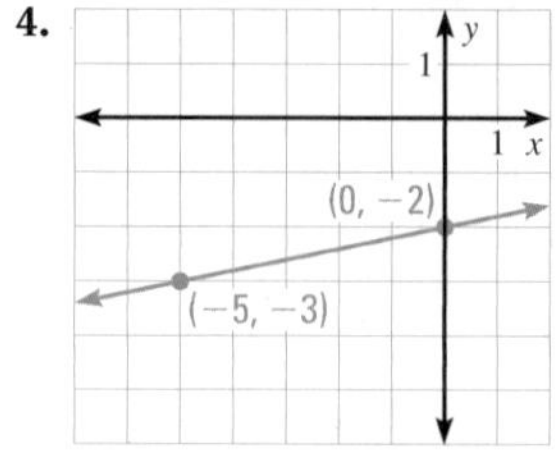

5. 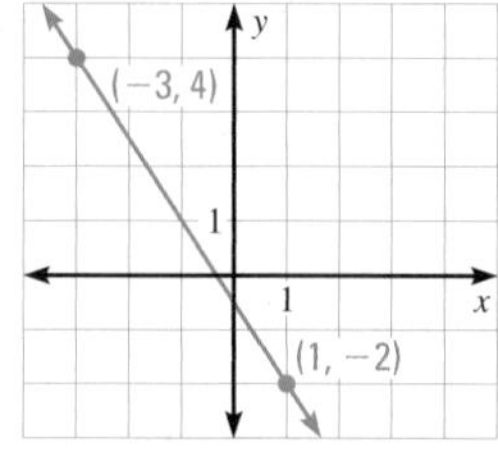

6. 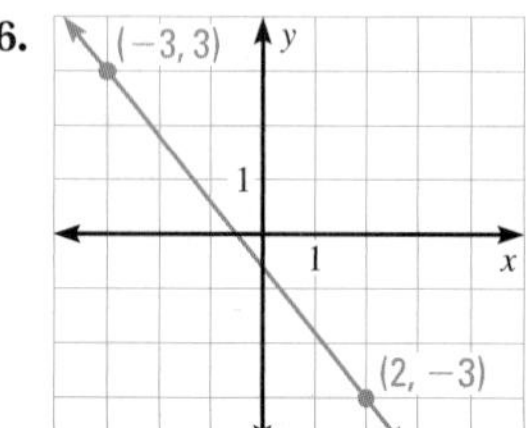

7. 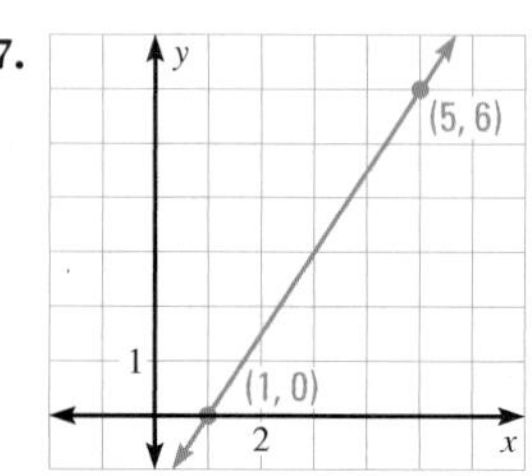

8. 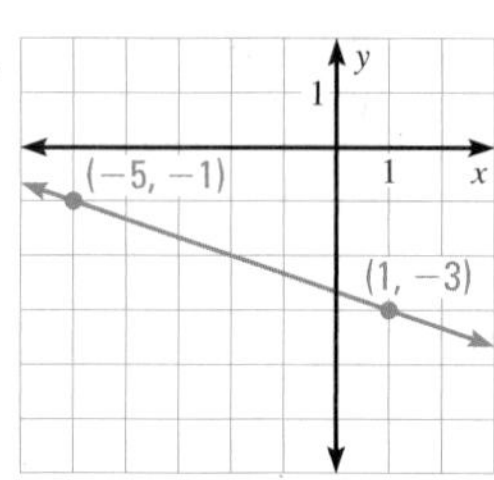

9. ★ **MULTIPLE CHOICE** Which equation is an equation of the line in the graph? **B**

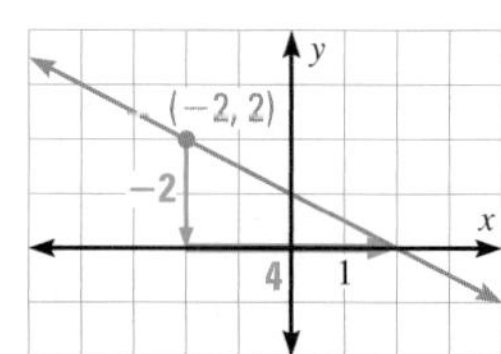

Ⓐ $y = -\frac{1}{2}x$ Ⓑ $y = -\frac{1}{2}x + 1$

Ⓒ $y = -2x$ Ⓓ $y = -2x + 1$

WRITING EQUATIONS Write an equation of the line with the given slope m and y-intercept b.

10. $m = -5, b = -12$ **$y = -5x - 12$**

11. $m = 3, b = 2$ **$y = 3x + 2$**

12. $m = 4, b = -6$ **$y = 4x - 6$**

13. $m = -\frac{5}{2}, b = 0$ **$y = -\frac{5}{2}x$**

14. $m = \frac{4}{9}, b = -\frac{2}{9}$ **$y = \frac{4}{9}x - \frac{2}{9}$**

15. $m = -\frac{11}{5}, b = -12$ **$y = -\frac{11}{5}x - 12$**

WRITING EQUATIONS Write an equation of the line that passes through the given point P and has the given slope m.

16. $P(-1, 0), m = -1$ **$y = -x - 1$**

17. $P(5, 4), m = 4$ **$y = 4x - 16$**

18. $P(6, -2), m = 3$ **$y = 3x - 20$**

19. $P(-8, -2), m = -\frac{2}{3}$ **$y = -\frac{2}{3}x - \frac{22}{3}$**

20. $P(0, -3), m = -\frac{1}{6}$ **$y = -\frac{1}{6}x - 3$**

21. $P(-13, 7), m = 0$ **$y = 7$**

22. **WRITING EQUATIONS** Write an equation of a line with undefined slope that passes through the point $(3, -2)$. **$x = 3$**

36. 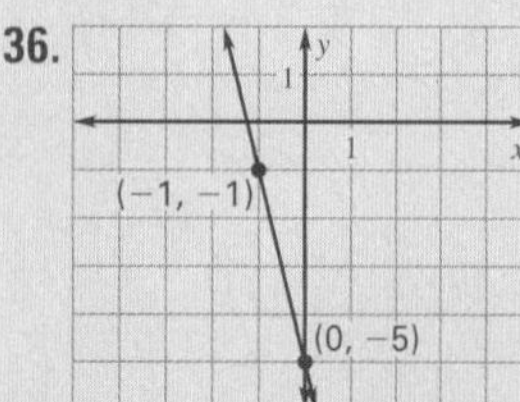

37. 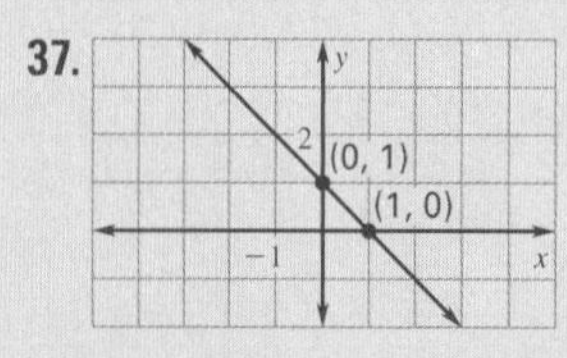

38. 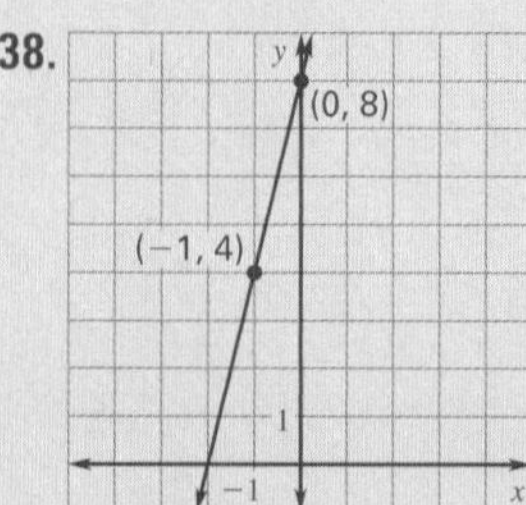

EXAMPLE 2
on p. 180
for Exs. 23–29

25. $y = \frac{1}{5}x + \frac{37}{5}$

27. $y = -\frac{5}{2}x - 4$

28. $y = \frac{1}{2}x - 2$

30. $y = \frac{1}{9}x$

EXAMPLE 3
on p. 181
for Exs. 30–35

31. $y = -\frac{3}{7}x + \frac{4}{7}$

33. $y = \frac{1}{2}x + 2$

EXAMPLE 5
on p. 182
for Exs. 36–45

35. $y = -\frac{5}{3}x - \frac{40}{3}$

45. *Sample:* The student replaced the wrong variable with 0 to find each intercept. To find the x-intercept, let $y = 0$, $5x - 3(0) = -15$, $x = -3$, $(-3, 0)$. To find the y-intercept, let $x = 0$, $5(0) - 3y = -15$, $y = 5$, $(0, 5)$.

46. $y = 3x - 4$ and $3(x + 1) = y - 2$

47. $y = 0.5x + 7$ and $-x + 2y = -5$

48. no parallel lines

49. 4, 4; $y = -x + 4$

50. −2, −5 $y = \ \frac{5}{2}x \ \ 5$

51. −20, 10 $y = \frac{1}{2}x + 10$

52. $(2, 0)$; $\left(0, -\frac{1}{2}\right)$

PARALLEL LINES **Write an equation of the line that passes through point P and is parallel to the line with the given equation.**

23. $P(0, -1)$, $y = -2x + 3$ $\quad y = -2x - 1$

24. $P(-7, -4)$, $y = 16$ $\quad y = -4$

25. $P(3, 8)$, $y - 1 = \frac{1}{5}(x + 4)$

26. $P(-2, 6)$, $x = -5$ $\quad x = -2$

27. $P(-2, 1)$, $10x + 4y = -8$

28. $P(4, 0)$, $-x + 2y = 12$

29. ★ **MULTIPLE CHOICE** Line a passes through points $(-2, 1)$ and $(2, 9)$. Which equation is an equation of a line parallel to line a? **D**

Ⓐ $y = -2x + 5$ Ⓑ $y = -\frac{1}{2}x + 5$ Ⓒ $y = \frac{1}{2}x - 5$ Ⓓ $y = 2x - 5$

PERPENDICULAR LINES **Write an equation of the line that passes through point P and is perpendicular to the line with the given equation.**

30. $P(0, 0)$, $y = -9x - 1$

31. $P(-1, 1)$, $y = \frac{7}{3}x + 10$

32. $P(4, -6)$, $y = -3$ $\quad x = 4$

33. $P(2, 3)$, $y - 4 = -2(x + 3)$

34. $P(0, -5)$, $x = 20$ $\quad y = -5$

35. $P(-8, 0)$, $3x - 5y = 6$

GRAPHING EQUATIONS **Graph the equation.** 36–44. See margin.

36. $8x + 2y = -10$

37. $x + y = 1$

38. $4x - y = -8$

39. $-x + 3y = -9$

40. $y - 2 = -1$

41. $y + 2 = x - 1$

42. $x + 3 = -4$

43. $2y - 4 = -x + 1$

44. $3(x - 2) = -y - 4$

45. **ERROR ANALYSIS** *Describe* and correct the error in finding the x- and y-intercepts of the graph of $5x - 3y = -15$.

To find the x-intercept, let x = 0:	To find the y-intercept, let y = 0:
$5x - 3y = -15$	$5x - 3y = -15$
$5(0) - 3y = -15$	$5x - 3(0) = -15$
$y = 5$	$x = -3$

B

IDENTIFYING PARALLEL LINES **Which lines are parallel, if any?**

46. $y = 3x - 4$
$x + 3y = 6$
$3(x + 1) = y - 2$

47. $x + 2y = 9$
$y = 0.5x + 7$
$-x + 2y = -5$

48. $x - 6y = 10$
$6x - y = 11$
$x + 6y = 12$

USING INTERCEPTS **Identify the x- and y-intercepts of the line. Use the intercepts to write an equation of the line.**

49.
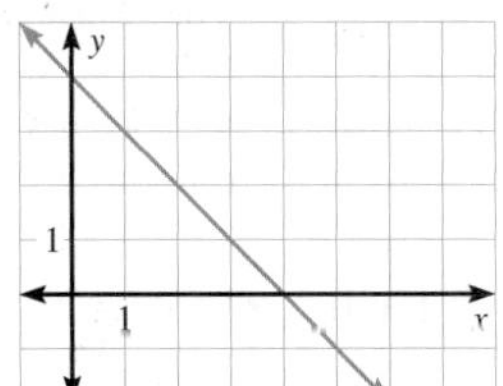

50.
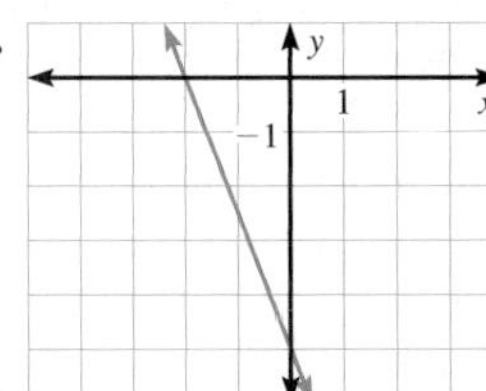

51.
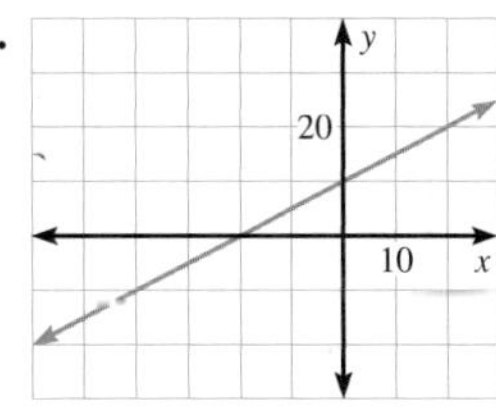

52. **INTERCEPTS** A line passes through the points $(-10, -3)$ and $(6, 1)$. Where does the line intersect the x-axis? Where does the line intersect the y-axis?

Avoiding Common Errors

Exercises 3–8 Be sure students use the y-intercept for b in the equation and not the x-intercept. Review with them which is which.

Study Strategy

Exercises 3–8 Suggest that students check their equations by substituting the coordinates of each of the given points to see if the result is a true equation.

Teaching Strategy

Exercises 33 and 35 If students are not sure how to get started, suggest that they write each equation in slope-intercept form.

Mathematical Reasoning

Exercises 36–44 Ask students how they can tell simply by looking at an equation whether its graph will have one or two intercepts.

42.
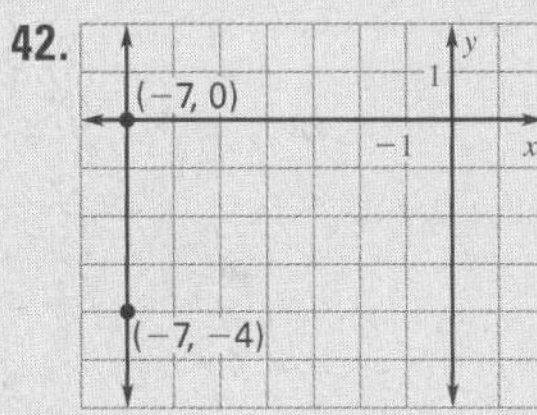

43.
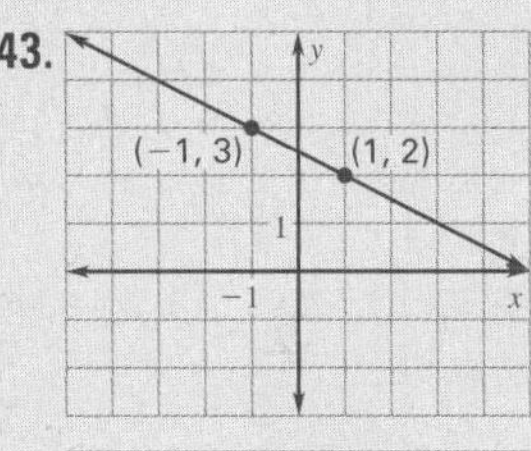

44.
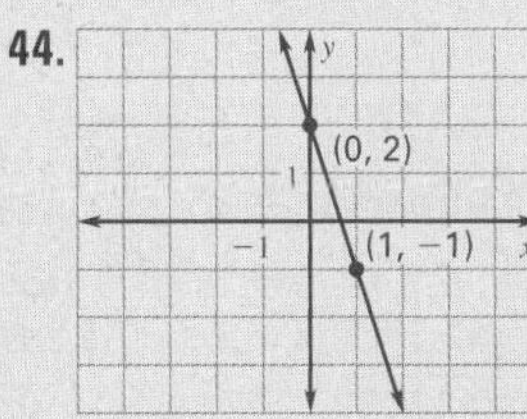

39.
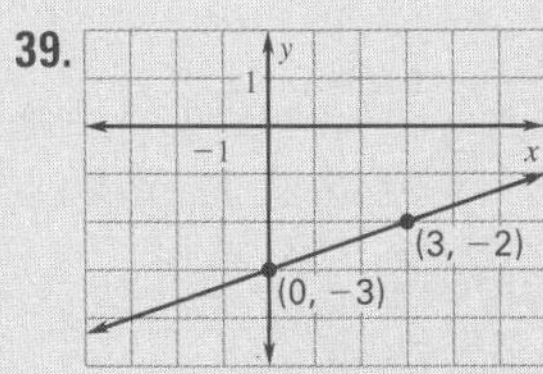

40.
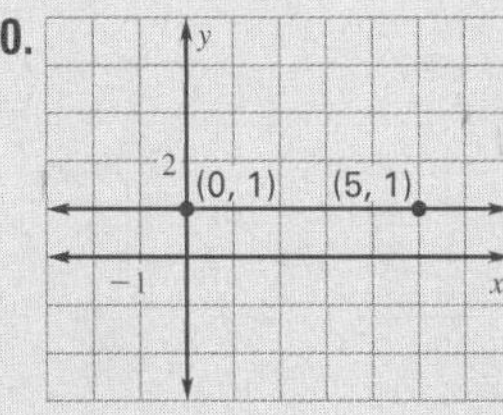

41.
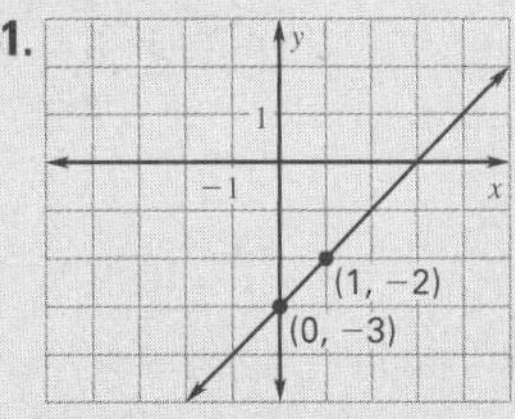

Graphing Calculator

Exercises 53–55 If students graph the equations by hand, suggest that they check their graphs by using a graphing calculator.

Internet Reference

Exercise 61 For more information about the Tyrannosaurus Rex at the Field Museum, visit www.fieldmuseum.org/sue/

53.

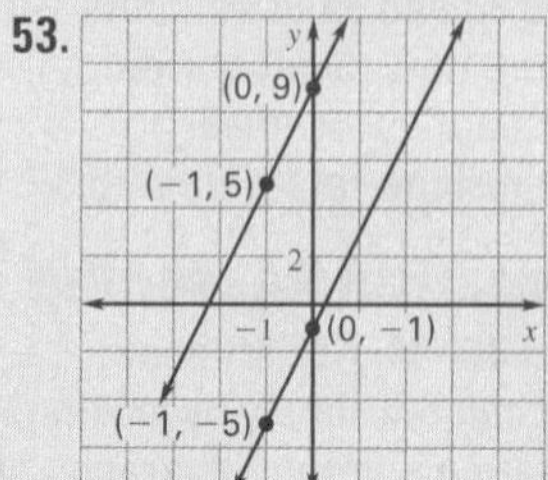

no solutions

54.

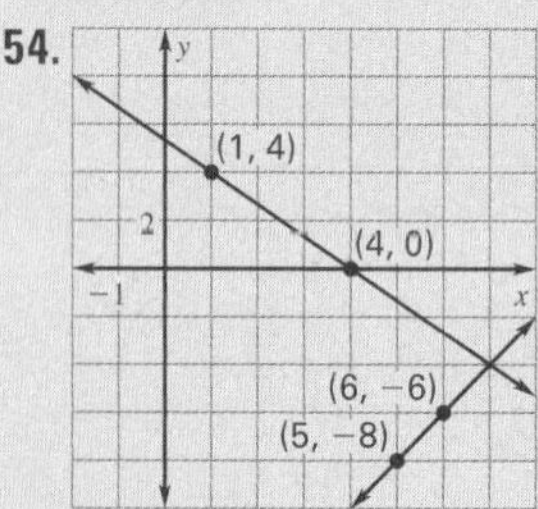

one solution

55.

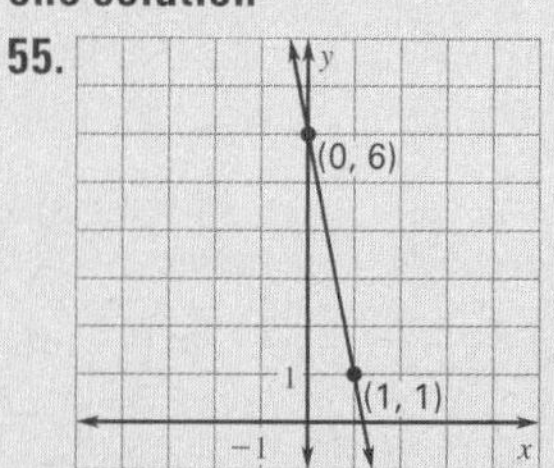

infinitely many solutions

59.

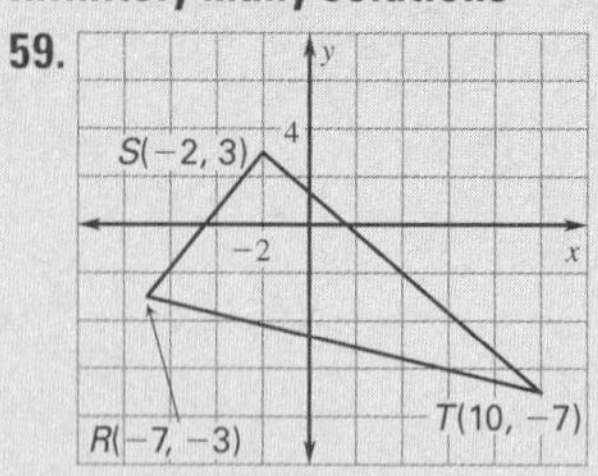

RS: $y = \frac{6}{5}x + \frac{27}{5}$

ST: $y = -\frac{5}{6}x + \frac{4}{3}$

RS: $y = -\frac{4}{17}x - \frac{72}{17}$

---

56. Check students' work. ***Sample answer:*** **If a false equation occurs the lines are parallel. If the variables drop out, a true equation occurs and the lines are the same line. If a point is found the lines intersect at that point.**

SOLUTIONS TO EQUATIONS **Graph the linear equations. Then use the graph to estimate how many solutions the equations share.** **53–55. See margin.**

53. $y = 4x + 9$
$4x - y = 1$

54. $3y + 4x = 16$
$2x - y = 18$

55. $y = -5x + 6$
$10x + 2y = 12$

56. **ALGEBRA** Solve Exercises 53–55 algebraically. (For help, see Skills Review Handbook, p. 880.) Make a conjecture about how the solution(s) can tell you whether the lines intersect, are parallel, or are the same line.

C **57.** **ALGEBRA** Find a value for k so that the line through $(-1, k)$ and $(-7, -2)$ is parallel to the line with equation $y = x + 1$. **4**

58. **ALGEBRA** Find a value for k so that the line through $(k, 2)$ and $(7, 0)$ is perpendicular to the line with equation $y = x - \frac{28}{5}$. **5**

59. **CHALLENGE** Graph the points $R(-7, -3)$, $S(-2, 3)$, and $T(10, -7)$. Connect them to make $\triangle RST$. Write an equation of the line containing each side. *Explain* how you can use slopes to show that $\triangle RST$ has one right angle. **See margin.**

PROBLEM SOLVING

EXAMPLE 4 A
on p. 182
for Exs. 60–61

59. See margin for art; check the slopes of each line segment. If two of the slopes are negative reciprocals of one another the lines are perpendicular and form a right angle.

60. $y =$ **$23x + 50$; slope: the monthly charge, y-intercept: initial one-time charge; $326**

60. WEB HOSTING The graph models the total cost of using a web hosting service for several months. Write an equation of the line. Tell what the slope and y-intercept mean in this situation. Then find the total cost of using the web hosting service for one year. **See margin.**

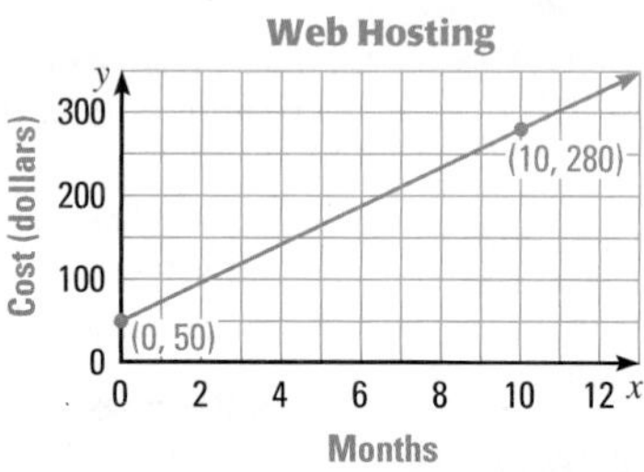

@HomeTutor for problem solving help at classzone.com

61. **SCIENCE** Scientists believe that a Tyrannosaurus Rex weighed about 2000 kilograms by age 14. It then had a growth spurt for four years, gaining 2.1 kilograms per day. Write an equation to model this situation. What are the slope and y-intercept? Tell what the slope and y-intercept mean in this situation.

Field Museum, Chicago, Illinois

@HomeTutor for problem solving help at classzone.com

$y = 2.1x + 2000$; slope: gain in weight per day, y-intercept: starting weight before the growth spurt

EXAMPLE 6 B
on p. 183
for Exs. 62–65

62. **MULTI-STEP PROBLEM** A national park has two options: a \$50 pass for all admissions during the year, or a \$4 entrance fee each time you enter.

a. Model Write an equation to model the cost of going to the park for a year using a pass and another equation for paying a fee each time. **$y = 50$, $y = 4x$**

b. Graph Graph both equations you wrote in part (a). **See margin.**

c. Interpret How many visits do you need to make for the pass to be cheaper? *Explain.* **13 visits**

○ = **WORKED-OUT SOLUTIONS on p. WS1** ★ = **STANDARDIZED TEST PRACTICE**

62b.

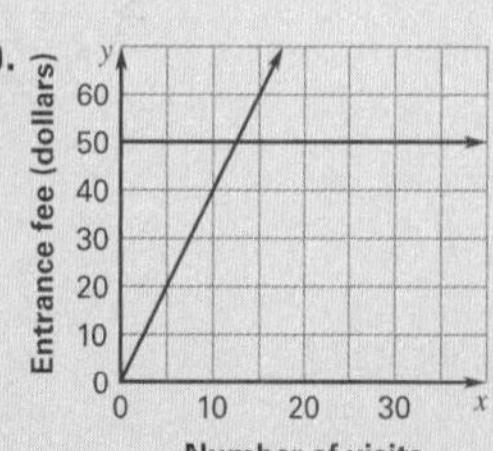

64.

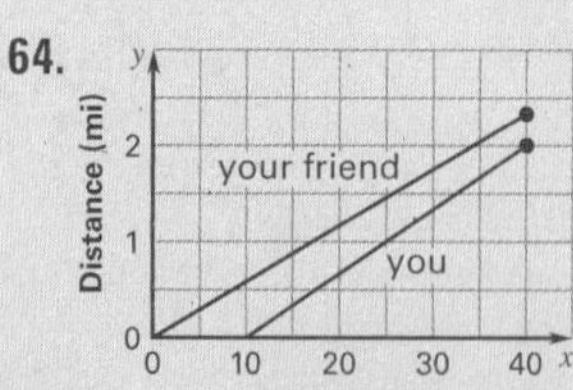

65b.

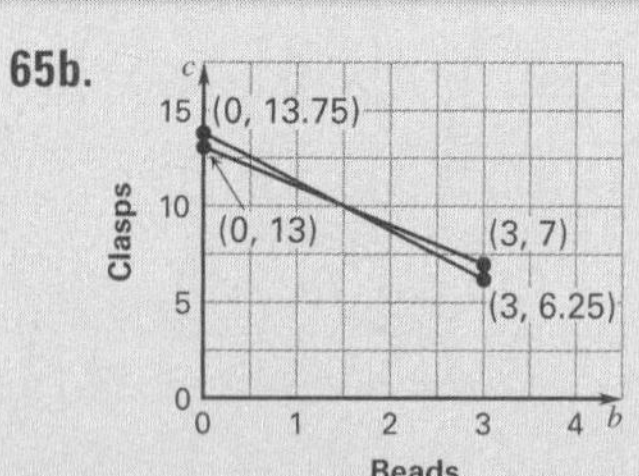

63. $2x + 3y = 24$; A: cost of a small slice, B: cost of a large slice, C: amount of money you can spend.

63. **PIZZA COSTS** You are buying slices of pizza for you and your friends. A small slice costs \$2 and a large slice costs \$3. You have \$24 to spend. Write an equation in standard form $Ax + By = C$ that models this situation. What do the values of A, B, and C mean in this situation?

64. ★ **SHORT RESPONSE** You run at a rate of 4 miles per hour and your friend runs at a rate of 3.5 miles per hour. Your friend starts running 10 minutes before you, and you run for a half hour on the same path. Will you catch up to your friend? Use a graph to support your answer. **No; see margin for art.**

65. ★ **EXTENDED RESPONSE** Audrey and Sara are making jewelry. Audrey buys 2 bags of beads and 1 package of clasps for a total of \$13. Sara buys 5 bags of beads and 2 packages of clasps for a total of \$27.50.

a. Let b be the price of one bag of beads and let c be the price of one package of clasps. Write equations to represent the total cost for Audrey and the total cost for Sara. $2b + c = 13, 5b + 2c = 27.50$

b. Graph the equations from part (a). **See margin.**

c. *Explain* the meaning of the intersection of the two lines in terms of the real-world situation.

65c. *Sample answer:* It's where the number of packages of beads and the number of packages of clasps would be the same for both girls.

C 66. **CHALLENGE** Michael is deciding which gym membership to buy. Points (2, 112) and (4, 174) give the cost of gym membership at one gym after two and four months. Points (1, 62) and (3, 102) give the cost of gym membership at a second gym after one and three months. Write equations to model the cost of each gym membership. At what point do the graphs intersect, if they intersect? Which gym is cheaper? *Explain.*
First gym: $y = 31x + 50$, second gym: $y = 20x + 42$; $\left(-\frac{8}{11}, \frac{302}{11}\right)$; second gym: it has a lower initial cost and a lower monthly cost.

MIXED REVIEW

PREVIEW Prepare for Lesson 3.6 in Exs. 67–69.

Find the length of each segment. Round to the nearest tenth of a unit. *(p. 15)*

67. 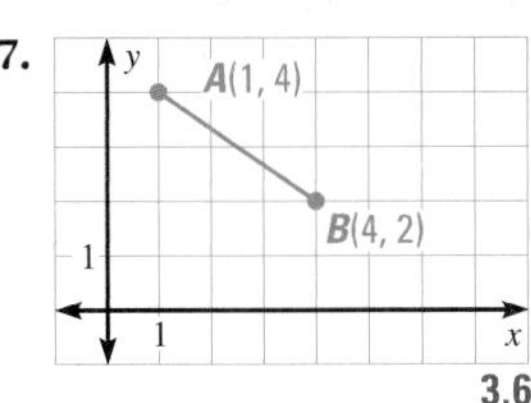

3.6

68. 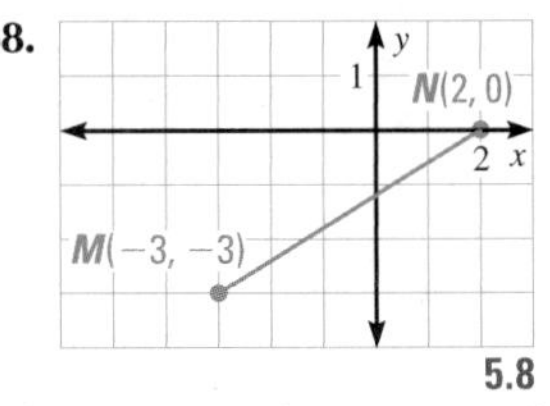

5.8

69. 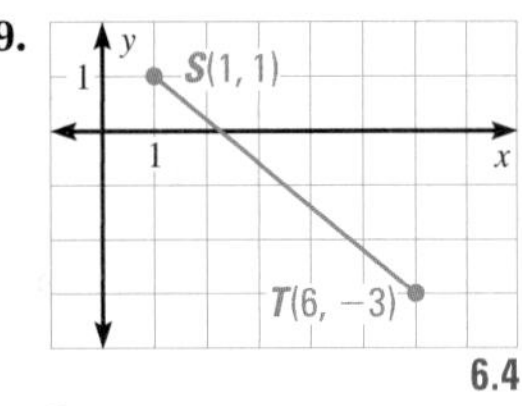

6.4

Describe the pattern in the numbers. Write the next number in the pattern. *(p. 72)*

70. −2, −7, −12, −17, . . .
71. 4, 8, 16, 32, . . .
72. 101, 98, 95, 92, . . .

70. Each number is decreasing by 5; −22.
71. Each number is twice the previous number; 64.
72. Each number is decreasing by 3; 89.

Find $m\angle 1$ and $m\angle 2$. *Explain* your reasoning. *(p. 154)* **73–75. See margin.**

73. 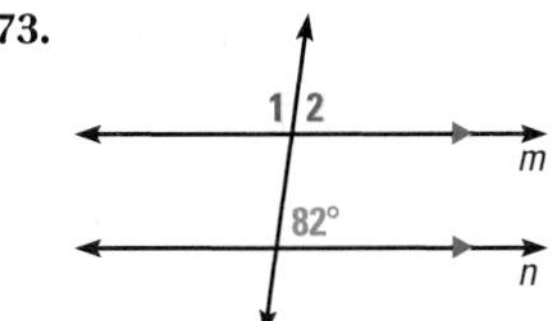

74. 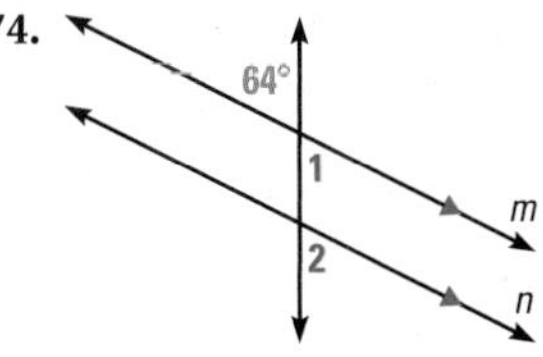

75. 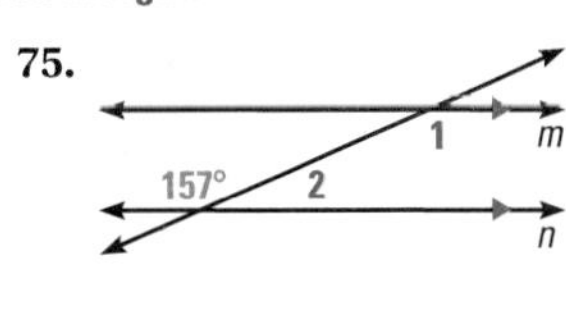

5 ASSESS AND RETEACH

Daily Homework Quiz

Transparency Available

1. Write an equation of the line that has slope $\frac{3}{4}$ and y-intercept −1. $y = \frac{3}{4}x - 1$
2. Write an equation of the line that passes through the point (4, −2) and has slope 3. $y = 3x - 14$
3. Write an equation of the line that passes through the point (7, 1) and is parallel to the line with equation $x = 4$. $x = 7$
4. Write an equation of the line that passes through the point (7, 1) and is perpendicular to the line with equation $6x - 3y = 8$. $y = -\frac{1}{2}x + \frac{9}{2}$
5. Toni's puppy weighed 10 pounds when it was 2 months old. It gained 2 pounds a month for 6 months. Write an equation for the puppy's weight w after m months during this time. $w = 2m + 6$

Online Quiz

Available at **classzone.com**

Diagnosis/Remediation

- Practice A, B, C in Chapter 3 Resource Book, pp. 63–68
- Study Guide in Chapter 3 Resource Book, pp. 69–70
- Practice Workbook, pp. 55–57
- @HomeTutor

Challenge

Additional challenge is available in the Chapter 3 Resource Book, p. 73.

73. 98°, 82°. *Sample answer:* ∠2 corresponds to the angle measuring 82° and ∠1 is supplementary to ∠2.

74. 64°, 64°. *Sample answer:* ∠1 and the angle measuring 64° are vertical angles and ∠1 and ∠2 are corresponding angles.

75. 157°, 23°. *Sample answer:* ∠2 and the angle measuring 157° are supplementary and ∠1 and ∠2 are consecutive interior angles.

Using ALTERNATIVE METHODS

Alternative Strategy

Example 6 on page 183 can be solved by using a table or equation. These methods allow students to visualize the situation by seeing a pattern in the table. They can see when the local renting cost becomes greater than the online renting cost. Some students may understand the process better by writing equations for each rental option and using algebra to solve the system to find when the costs are the same.

Another Way to Solve Example 6, page 183

MULTIPLE REPRESENTATIONS In Example 6 on page 183, you saw how to graph equations to solve a problem about renting DVDs. Another way you can solve the problem is *using a table.* Alternatively, you can use the equations to solve the problem *algebraically.*

PROBLEM

DVD RENTAL You can rent DVDs at a local store for $4.00 each. An Internet company offers a flat fee of $15.00 per month for as many rentals as you want. How many DVDs do you need to rent to make the online rental a better buy?

METHOD 1

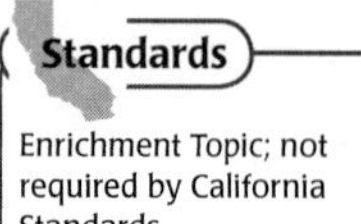

Standards

Enrichment Topic; not required by California Standards.

Using a Table You can make a table to answer the question.

STEP 1 **Make** a table representing each rental option.

DVDs rented	Renting locally	Renting online
1	$4	$15
2	$8	$15

STEP 2 **Add** rows to your table until you see a pattern.

DVDs rented	Renting locally	Renting online
1	$4	$15
2	$8	$15
3	$12	$15
4	$16	$15
5	$20	$15
6	$24	$15

STEP 3 **Analyze** the table. Notice that the values in the second column (the cost of renting locally) are less than the values in the third column (the cost of renting online) for three or fewer DVDs. However, the values in the second column are greater than those in the third column for four or more DVDs.

▶ It is cheaper to rent locally if you rent 3 or fewer DVDs per month. If you rent 4 or more DVDs per month, it is cheaper to rent online.

METHOD 2

Using Algebra You can solve one of the equations for one of its variables. Then substitute that expression for the variable in the other equation.

STEP 1 **Write** an equation for each rental option.

Cost of one month's rental online: $y = 15$

Cost of one month's rental locally: $y = 4x$, where x represents the number of DVDs rented

STEP 2 **Substitute** the value of y from one equation into the other equation.

$y = 4x$

$15 = 4x$ Substitute 15 for y.

$3.75 = x$ Divide each side by 4.

STEP 3 **Analyze** the solution of the equation. If you could rent 3.75 DVDs, your cost for local and online rentals would be the same. However, you can only rent a whole number of DVDs. Look at what happens when you rent 3 DVDs and when you rent 4 DVDs, the whole numbers just less than and just greater than 3.75.

▶ It is cheaper to rent locally if you rent 3 or fewer DVDs per month. If you rent 4 or more DVDs per month, it is cheaper to rent online.

PRACTICE

1. **IN-LINE SKATES** You can rent in-line skates for \$5 per hour, or buy a pair of skates for \$130. How many hours do you need to skate for the cost of buying skates to be cheaper than renting them? **27 h**

2. **WHAT IF?** Suppose the in-line skates in Exercise 1 also rent for \$12 per day. How many days do you need to skate for the cost of buying skates to be cheaper than renting them? **11 days**

3. **BUTTONS** You buy a button machine for \$200 and supplies to make one hundred fifty buttons for \$30. Suppose you charge \$2 for a button. How many buttons do you need to sell to earn back what you spent? **115 buttons**

4. **MANUFACTURING** A company buys a new widget machine for \$1200. It costs \$5 to make each widget. The company sells each widget for \$15. How many widgets do they need to sell to earn back the money they spent on the machine? **120 widgets**

5. **WRITING** Which method(s) did you use to solve Exercises 1–4? *Explain* your choice(s). **See margin.**

6. **MONEY** You saved \$1000. If you put this money in a savings account, it will earn 1.5% annual interest. If you put the \$1000 in a certificate of deposit (CD), it will earn 3% annual interest. To earn the most money, does it ever make sense to put your money in the savings account? *Explain.* **no**

Graphing Calculator

Students could also solve the system of equations for Method 2 by graphing both equations on a graphing calculator. They can use the *intersect* feature to get the coordinates of the point where the graphs intersect.

Reading Strategy

For Exercises 3 and 4, ask students to compare and contrast the kinds of information they are given about the situations.

5. ***Sample answer:*** **In each case an equation modeling the situation was solved.**

1 PLAN AND PREPARE

Warm-Up Exercises

Transparency Available

1. What is the distance between the points (2, 3) and (5, 7)? **5**
2. 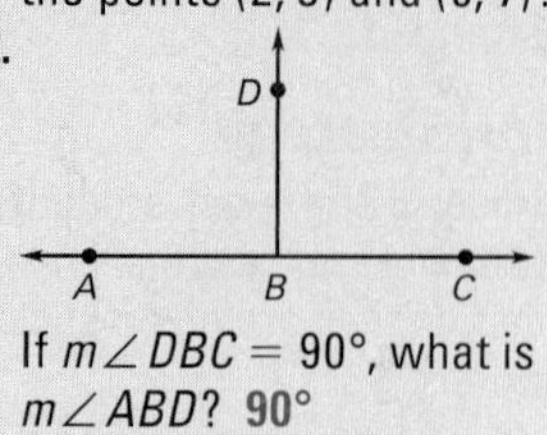

If $m\angle DBC = 90°$, what is $m\angle ABD$? **90°**

Notetaking Guide

Transparency Available

Promotes interactive learning and notetaking skills, pp. 79–82.

Pacing

Basic: 2 days
Average: 2 days
Advanced: 2 days
Block: 1 block
• See *Teaching Guide/Lesson Plan.*

2 FOCUS AND MOTIVATE

Essential Question

Big Idea 3, p. 145

How do you find the distance between a point and a line? **Tell students they will learn how to answer this question by using the equation of another line perpendicular to the given line.**

3.6 Prove Theorems About Perpendicular Lines

Before You found the distance between points in the coordinate plane.
Now You will find the distance between a point and a line.
Why? So you can determine lengths in art, as in Example 4.

Key Vocabulary
• **distance from a point to a line**

Standards

7.0 Students prove and use theorems involving the properties of parallel lines cut by a transversal, the properties of quadrilaterals, and the properties of circles.

2. 90°, 90°, 90°, 90°; all the angles are congruent; all the angles are right angles.

ACTIVITY FOLD PERPENDICULAR LINES

Materials: paper, protractor

STEP 1

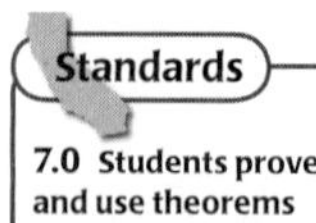

Fold a piece of paper.

STEP 2

Fold the paper again, so that the original fold lines up on itself.

STEP 3

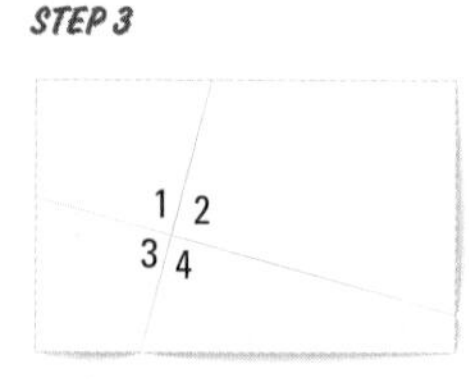

Unfold the paper.

DRAW CONCLUSIONS

1. What type of angles appear to be formed where the fold lines intersect? **right angles**
2. Measure the angles with a protractor. Which angles are congruent? Which angles are right angles? **See margin.**

The activity above suggests several properties of perpendicular lines.

THEOREMS — *For Your Notebook*

THEOREM 3.8

If two lines intersect to form a linear pair of congruent angles, then the lines are perpendicular.

If $\angle 1 \cong \angle 2$, then $g \perp h$.

Proof: Ex. 31, p. 196

THEOREM 3.9

If two lines are perpendicular, then they intersect to form four right angles.

If $a \perp b$, then $\angle 1$, $\angle 2$, $\angle 3$, and $\angle 4$ are right angles.

Proof: Ex. 32, p. 196

Resource Planning Guide

Chapter Resource Book
• Teaching Guide/Lesson Plan (pp. 74–75)
• Activity Master (p. 76)
• Practice levels A, B, C (pp. 77–82)
• Study Guide (pp. 83–84)
• Catch-up for Absent Students (p. 85)
• Problem Solving Workshop (p. 86)
• Challenge (p. 87)

Workbooks
• Notetaking Guide (pp. 79–82)
• Practice Workbook (pp. 58–60)

Teaching Options
• **Power Presentations CD-ROM** provides dynamic electronic teaching resources for the classroom.
• **Activity Generator CD-ROM** provides editable activities for all ability levels.

Interactive Technology
• Easy Planner
• Power Presentations CD-ROM
• Activity Generator CD-ROM
• Animated Geometry
• Test Generator CD-ROM
• Online Quiz
• eWorkbook
• eEdition
• @HomeTutor

Resources for English Learners
• Quick Reference for English Learners
• Spanish Study Guide
• Multi-Language Visual Glossary
• Student Resources in Spanish

See also the *Geometry Toolkit* for more strategies for meeting individual needs.

EXAMPLE 1 Draw conclusions

In the diagram at the right, $\overleftrightarrow{AB} \perp \overleftrightarrow{BC}$. What can you conclude about $\angle 1$ and $\angle 2$?

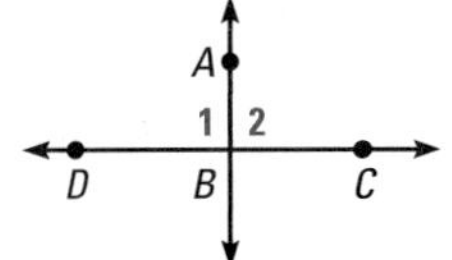

Solution

$\overleftrightarrow{AB}$ and $\overleftrightarrow{BC}$ are perpendicular, so by Theorem 3.9, they form four right angles. You can conclude that $\angle 1$ and $\angle 2$ are right angles, so $\angle 1 \cong \angle 2$.

THEOREM *For Your Notebook*

THEOREM 3.10

If two sides of two adjacent acute angles are perpendicular, then the angles are complementary.

If $\overrightarrow{BA} \perp \overrightarrow{BC}$, then $\angle 1$ and $\angle 2$ are complementary.

Proof: Example 2, below

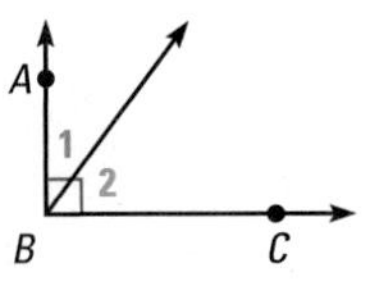

EXAMPLE 2 Prove Theorem 3.10

Prove that if two sides of two adjacent acute angles are perpendicular, then the angles are complementary.

GIVEN ▶ $\overrightarrow{ED} \perp \overrightarrow{EF}$

PROVE ▶ $\angle 7$ and $\angle 8$ are complementary.

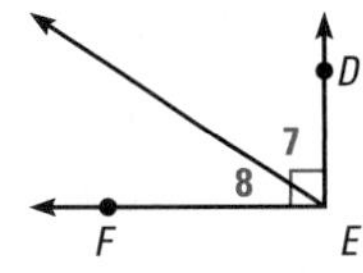

STATEMENTS	REASONS
1. $\overrightarrow{ED} \perp \overrightarrow{EF}$	1. Given
2. $\angle DEF$ is a right angle.	2. $\perp$ lines intersect to form 4 rt. $\angle$s. (Theorem 3.9)
3. $m\angle DEF = 90°$	3. Definition of a right angle
4. $m\angle 7 + m\angle 8 = m\angle DEF$	4. Angle Addition Postulate
5. $m\angle 7 + m\angle 8 = 90°$	5. Substitution Property of Equality
6. $\angle 7$ and $\angle 8$ are complementary.	6. Definition of complementary angles

GUIDED PRACTICE for Examples 1 and 2

1. Given that $\angle ABC \cong \angle ABD$, what can you conclude about $\angle 3$ and $\angle 4$? *Explain* how you know.

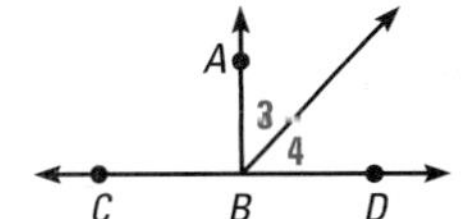

2. Write a plan for proof for Theorem 3.9, that if two lines are perpendicular, then they intersect to form four right angles. ***Sample answer:*** **The definition of perpendicular lines implies that angles formed by the intersecting lines are right angles.**

1. They are complementary. *Sample answer:* $\angle ABD$ is a right angle since 2 lines intersect to form a linear pair of congruent angles (Theorem 3.8), so $\overrightarrow{BA} \perp \overleftrightarrow{CD}$. Then $\angle 3$ and $\angle 4$ are complementary by Theorem 3.10.

Motivating the Lesson

If you needed to build a service road to connect two parallel highways, how would you do it to keep the cost of building materials as low as possible? Tell students that in this lesson, they will learn how geometry can help answer such questions.

3 TEACH

Activity Note

This activity is to show students that perpendicular lines form four right angles.

Extra Example 1

In the figure, $\angle 1$ and $\angle 2$ are congruent. What can you conclude about $m\angle 2$? $m\angle 2 = 90°$

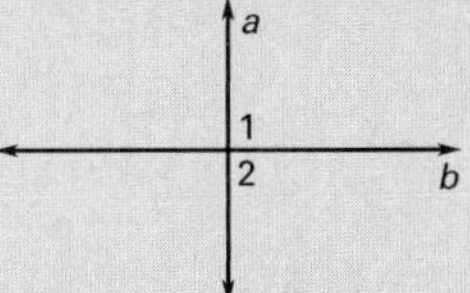

Extra Example 2

Prove that if $\angle 1$ and $\angle 2$ are complementary, then $\overleftrightarrow{BA} \perp \overleftrightarrow{BC}$.

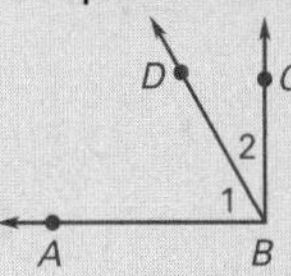

Given: $\angle 1$ and $\angle 2$ are comp.

Prove: $\overleftrightarrow{BA} \perp \overleftrightarrow{BC}$

Statements (Reasons)

1. $\angle 1$ and $\angle 2$ are comp. (Given)
2. $m\angle 1 + m\angle 2 = 90°$ (Def. of comp. $\angle$s)
3. $m\angle ABC = m\angle 1 + m\angle 2$ ($\angle$ Add. Post.)
4. $m\angle ABC = 90°$ (Subst. Prop. of =)
5. $\angle ABC$ is a rt. $\angle$ (Def. of rt. $\angle$)
6. $\overleftrightarrow{BA} \perp \overleftrightarrow{BC}$ (Def. of $\perp$ lines)

Extra Example 3

Determine which other lines, if any, must be perpendicular. Explain your reasoning.

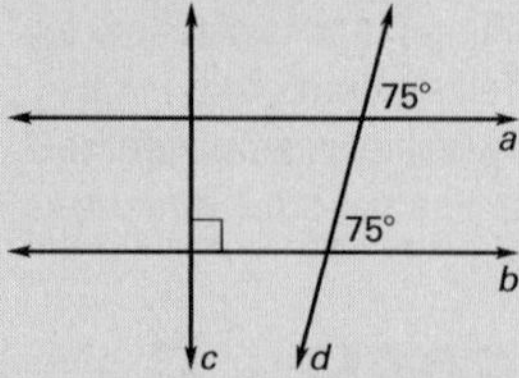

b and *c* are ⊥; By the Corr. ∠s Conv. Post., $a \parallel b$. So $a \perp c$ by Perpendicular Transversal Theorem

Key Question to Ask for Example 3

- Is $u \perp p$? Explain. There is no way to know, since we have no information that lets us tell what kinds of angles line *u* forms with any of the other lines.

THEOREMS *For Your Notebook*

THEOREM 3.11 Perpendicular Transversal Theorem

If a transversal is perpendicular to one of two parallel lines, then it is perpendicular to the other.

If $h \parallel k$ and $j \perp h$, then $j \perp k$.

Proof: Ex. 42, p. 160; Ex. 33, p. 196

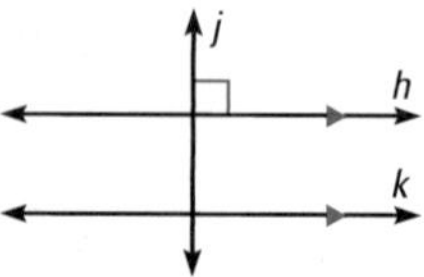

THEOREM 3.12 Lines Perpendicular to a Transversal Theorem

In a plane, if two lines are perpendicular to the same line, then they are parallel to each other.

If $m \perp p$ and $n \perp p$, then $m \parallel n$.

Proof: Ex. 34, p. 196

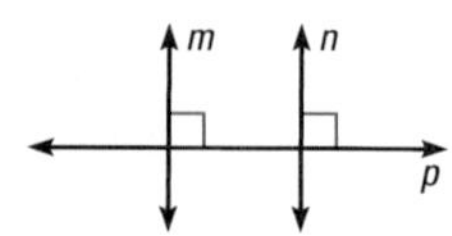

EXAMPLE 3 Draw conclusions

Determine which lines, if any, must be parallel in the diagram. Explain your reasoning.

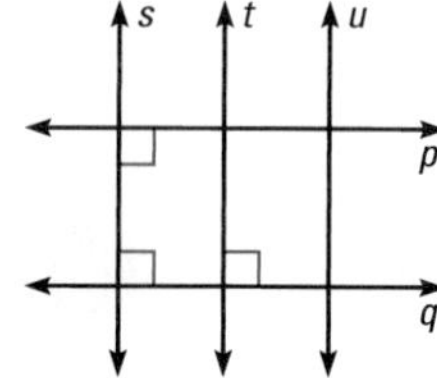

Solution

Lines *p* and *q* are both perpendicular to *s*, so by Theorem 3.12, $p \parallel q$. Also, lines *s* and *t* are both perpendicular to *q*, so by Theorem 3.12, $s \parallel t$.

✓ **GUIDED PRACTICE for Example 3**

Use the diagram at the right.

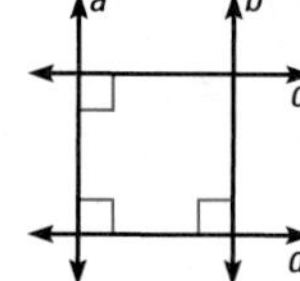

3. Is $b \parallel a$? *Explain* your reasoning.
4. Is $b \perp c$? *Explain* your reasoning.

3. yes; Lines Perpendicular to a Transversal Theorem

4. yes; $c \parallel d$ by the Lines Perpendicular to a Transversal Theorem, therefore $b \perp c$ by the Perpendicular Transversal Theorem

DISTANCE FROM A LINE The **distance from a point to a line** is the length of the perpendicular segment from the point to the line. This perpendicular segment is the shortest distance between the point and the line. For example, the distance between point *A* and line *k* is *AB*. You will prove this in Chapter 5.

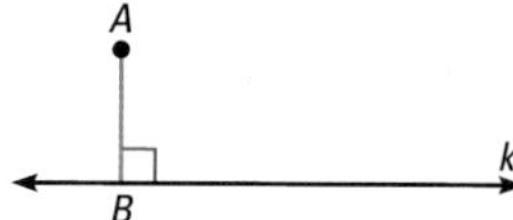

Distance from a point to a line

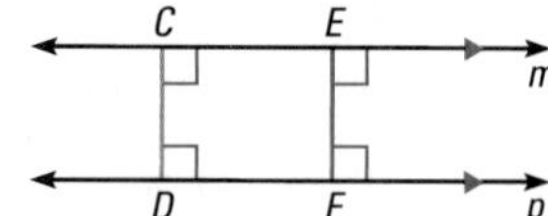

Distance between two parallel lines

The *distance between two parallel lines* is the length of any perpendicular segment joining the two lines. For example, the distance between line *p* and line *m* above is *CD* or *EF*.

Differentiated Instruction

Kinesthetic Learners Give pairs of students a piece of string that is about 3 feet long. Ask them to find a line in the classroom and then choose a point near the line. Direct them to hold one end of the string on the point and stretch the string to the line. Have them compare the distance from the point to several different points on the line with the distance to the line along a perpendicular segment from the point to the line.

See also the *Geometry Toolkit* for more strategies.

EXAMPLE 4 Find the distance between two parallel lines

SCULPTURE The sculpture below is drawn on a graph where units are measured in inches. What is the approximate length of $\overline{SR}$, the depth of a seat?

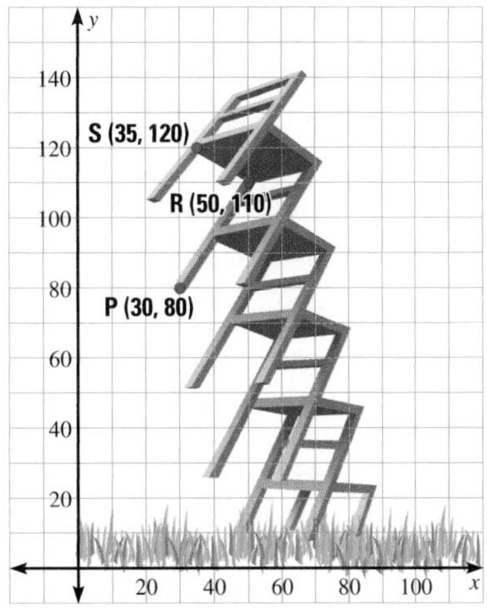

Solution

You need to find the length of a perpendicular segment from a back leg to a front leg on one side of the chair.

Using the points $P(30, 80)$ and $R(50, 110)$, the slope of each leg is

$$\frac{110 - 80}{50 - 30} = \frac{30}{20} = \frac{3}{2}.$$

The segment SR has a slope of

$$\frac{120 - 110}{35 - 50} = -\frac{10}{15} = -\frac{2}{3}.$$

The segment $\overline{SR}$ is perpendicular to the leg so the distance SR is

$$d = \sqrt{(35 - 50)^2 + (120 - 110)^2} \approx 18.0 \text{ inches.}$$

▶ The length of $\overline{SR}$ is about 18.0 inches.

GUIDED PRACTICE for Example 4

Use the graph at the right for Exercises 5 and 6.

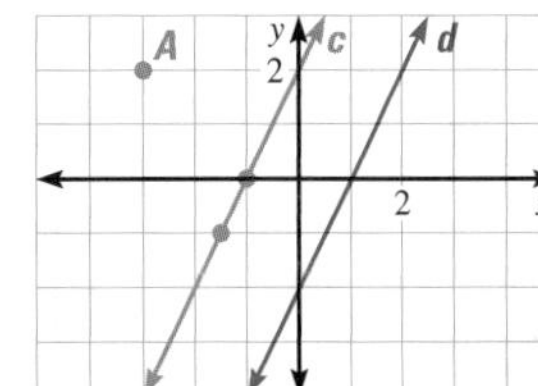

5. What is the distance from point A to line c? **about 2.7**
6. What is the distance from line c to line d? **about 1.8**
7. Graph the line $y = x + 1$. What point on the line is the shortest distance from the point (4, 1)? What is the distance? Round to the nearest tenth. **(2, 3); 2.8**

Extra Example 4

What is the distance between the two parallel sides of this table top? **5**

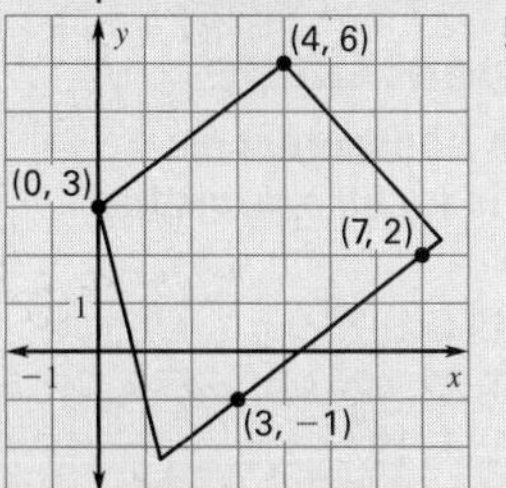

Key Question to Ask for Example 4

- Could you use a point on the other side of the sculpture? Explain. **No, it must be on a segment perpendicular to the line.**

Avoiding Common Errors

For Guided Practice Exercise 6, some students may count spaces between the y-intercepts. Ask students to think of c and d as parallel streets. What is the shortest path from one street to the other?

Closing the Lesson

Have students summarize the major points of the lesson and answer the Essential Question: How do you find the distance between a point and a line?

- **The distance from a point to a line is the length of the perpendicular segment from the point to the line.**
- **Perpendicular lines form four right angles.**
- **Two lines perpendicular to the same line are parallel.**

For the coordinate plane, write an equation for the line through the given point and perpendicular to the given line. Find the point of intersection. Then use the distance formula to calculate the distance from the point of intersection to the given point.

Differentiated Instruction

Advanced Ask students if they can find ways to simplify the algebra and arithmetic when they find the distance between two parallel lines. One possibility is to use a line through the origin that is perpendicular to both lines.

See also the *Geometry Toolkit* for more strategies.

4 PRACTICE AND APPLY

Assignment Guide

Answer Transparencies available for all exercises

Basic:
Day 1: pp. 194–197
Exs. 1–7, 31, 32, 42–47
Day 2: pp. 194–197
Exs. 8–17, 29, 30, 39–41

Average:
Day 1: pp. 194–197
Exs. 1, 3–7, 22–25, 31, 32, 42–47
Day 2: pp. 194–197
Exs. 9–14, 17–21, 29, 30, 33, 34, 40

Advanced:
Day 1: pp. 194–197
Exs. 1, 4, 6, 7, 22–28*, 31, 32, 42–46 even
Day 2: pp. 194–197
Exs. 10–12, 17–21, 29, 30, 33–38*, 41

Block:
pp. 194–197
Exs. 1, 3–7, 9–14, 17–25, 29–34, 40, 42–47

Differentiated Instruction

See *Geometry Best Practices Toolkit* for suggestions on addressing the needs of a diverse classroom.

Homework Check

For a quick check of student understanding of key concepts, go over the following exercises:

Basic: 2, 8, 14, 16, 31
Average: 4, 10, 18, 23, 32
Advanced: 6, 12, 20, 24, 33

Extra Practice

- Student Edition, p. 901
- Chapter 3 Resource Book: Practice levels A, B, C, pp. 77–82

Practice Worksheet

An easily-readable reduced practice page (with answers) for this lesson can be found on p. 144E.

3.6 EXERCISES

HOMEWORK KEY
○ = **WORKED-OUT SOLUTIONS** on p. WS4 for Exs. 19, 23, and 29
★ = **STANDARDIZED TEST PRACTICE** Exs. 11, 12, 21, 22, and 30

SKILL PRACTICE

A

1. **VOCABULARY** The length of which segment shown is called the distance between the two parallel lines? *Explain.*
$\overline{AB}$; it's ⊥ to the parallel lines.

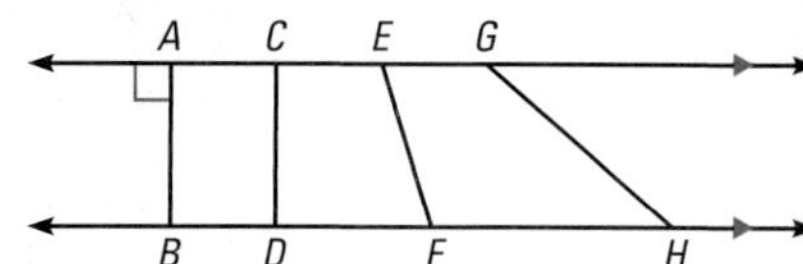

EXAMPLES 1 and 2 on p. 191 for Exs. 2–7

JUSTIFYING STATEMENTS **Write the theorem that justifies the statement.**

2. $j \perp k$

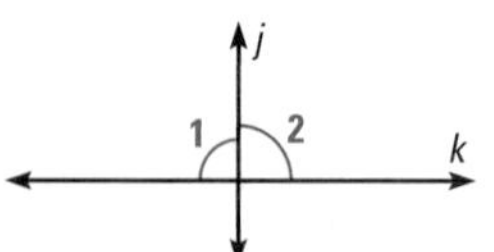

2. If two lines intersect to form a linear pair of congruent angles, then the lines are perpendicular.

3. $\angle 4$ and $\angle 5$ are complementary.

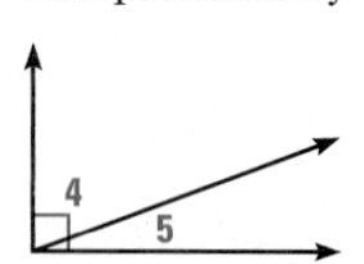

3. If two sides of two adjacent acute angles are perpendicular, then the angles are complementary.

4. $\angle 1$ and $\angle 2$ are right angles.

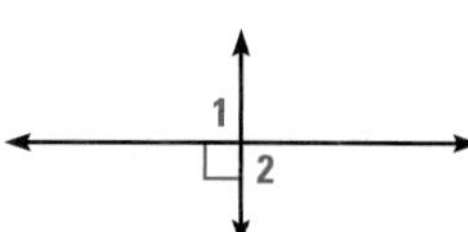

4. If two lines are perpendicular, then they intersect to form four right angles.

APPLYING THEOREMS **Find $m\angle 1$.**

5. 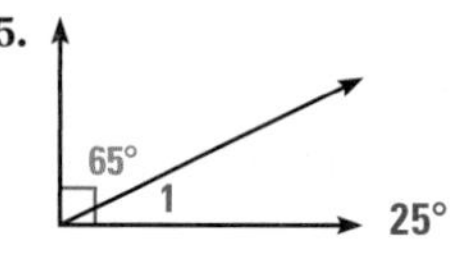

25°

6. **90°**

7. 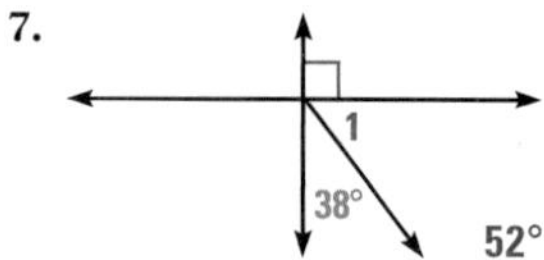

52°

EXAMPLE 3 on p. 192 for Exs. 8–12

SHOWING LINES PARALLEL ***Explain*** **how you would show that $m \parallel n$.** **8–10. See margin.**

8. 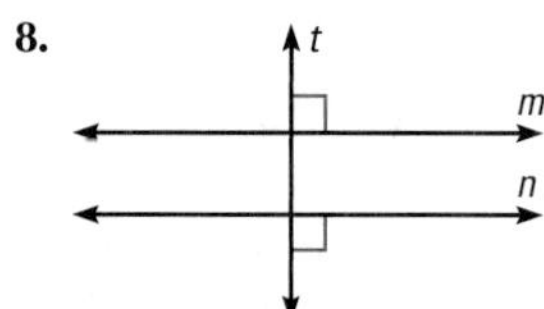

9.

10. 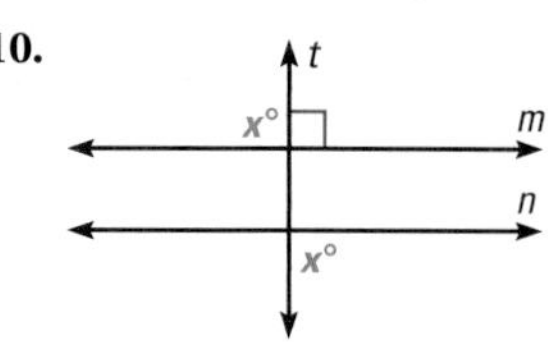

11. ★ **SHORT RESPONSE** *Explain* how to draw two parallel lines using only a straightedge and a protractor. ***Sample answer:*** **Draw a line. Construct a second line perpendicular to the first line. Construct a third line perpendicular to the second line.**

12. ★ **SHORT RESPONSE** *Describe* how you can fold a sheet of paper to create two parallel lines that are perpendicular to the same line. **See margin.**

EXAMPLES 3 and 4 on pp. 192–193 for Exs. 13–14

ERROR ANALYSIS ***Explain*** **why the statement about the figure is incorrect.**

13. 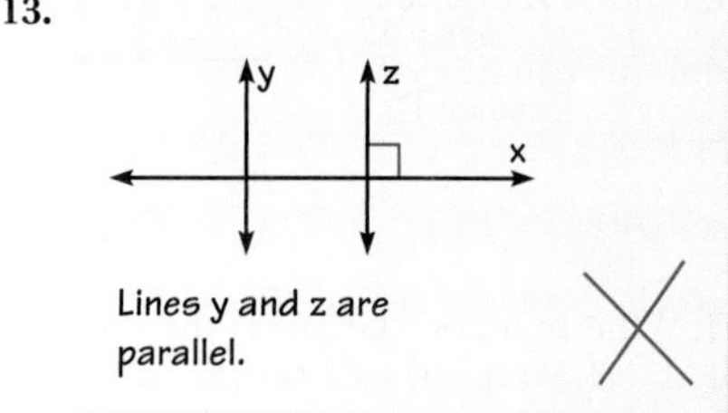

Lines y and z are parallel.

13. There is no information to indicate that $y \parallel z$ or $y \perp x$.

14. The distance from $\overleftrightarrow{AB}$ to point C is 12 cm.

$\overline{AC}$ is not ⊥ to $\overleftrightarrow{AB}$.

8. Lines Perpendicular to a Transversal Theorem

9. Since the two angles labeled $x°$ form a linear pair of congruent angles, $t \perp n$; since the two lines are perpendicular to the same line, they are parallel to each other.

10. Alternate Exterior Angles Converse

12. Fold the paper into thirds lengthwise and then in half across its width.

18. Lines n and p; they are perpendicular to line k.

19. Lines f and g; they are perpendicular to line d.

20. Lines z and y; they are perpendicular to line w. Lines v, w, and x; lines v and w are perpendicular to line y, and lines w and x are perpendicular to line z.

B FINDING ANGLE MEASURES **In the diagram, $\overleftrightarrow{FG} \perp \overleftrightarrow{GH}$. Find the value of x.**

15. 13

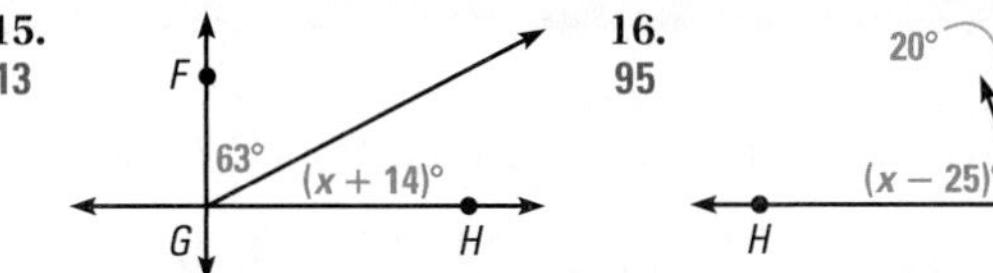

16. 95

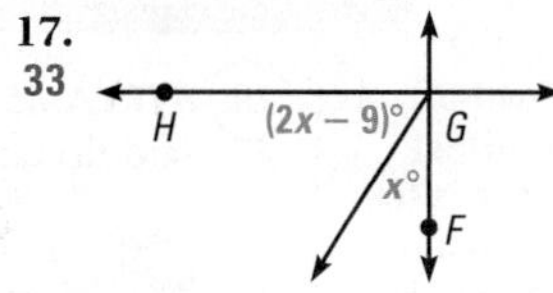

17. 33

DRAWING CONCLUSIONS **Determine which lines, if any, must be parallel. *Explain* your reasoning.**

18.

19.

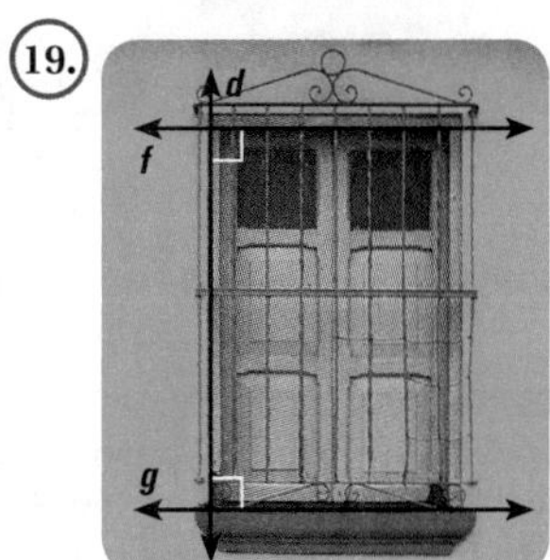

20.

21. ★ **MULTIPLE CHOICE** Which statement must be true if $c \perp d$? **A**

Ⓐ $m\angle 1 + m\angle 2 = 90°$ Ⓑ $m\angle 1 + m\angle 2 < 90°$

Ⓒ $m\angle 1 + m\angle 2 > 90°$ Ⓓ Cannot be determined

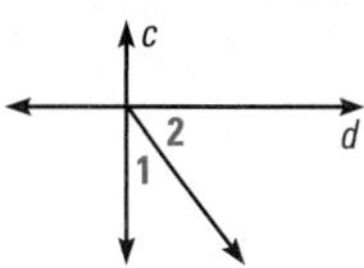

22. ★ **WRITING** *Explain* why the distance between two lines is only defined for parallel lines.
The distance between nonparallel lines is not constant.

EXAMPLE 4 on p. 193 for Exs. 23–24

FINDING DISTANCES **Use the Distance Formula to find the distance between the two parallel lines. Round to the nearest tenth, if necessary.**

23.

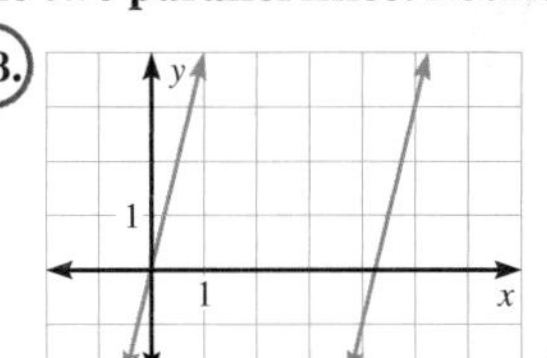

4.1

24.

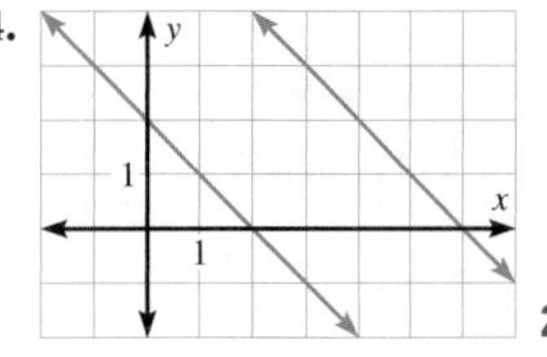

2.8

25. CONSTRUCTION You are given a line n and a point P not on n. Use a compass to find two points on n equidistant from P. Then use the steps for the construction of a segment bisector (page 33) to construct a line perpendicular to n through P. **Check students' work.**

C **26.** FINDING ANGLES Find all the unknown angle measures in the diagram at the right. *Justify* your reasoning for each angle measure.

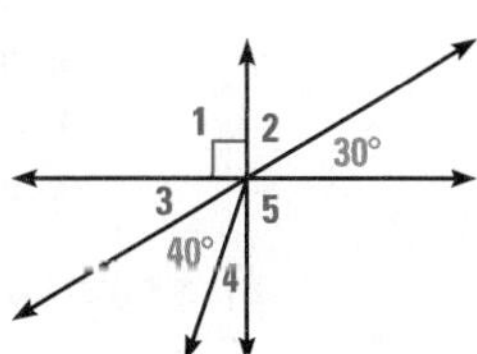

26. *Sample answer:* $m\angle 1 = 90°$ since it is a right angle; $m\angle 2 + 30° = 90°$, therefore $m\angle 2 = 60°$; $m\angle 5 = 90°$ since it is vertical to $\angle 1$; $m\angle 3 = 30°$ since it is vertical to the angle measuring 30°; $m\angle 4 = 20°$; since $m\angle 3 + m\angle 4 + 40° = 90°$.

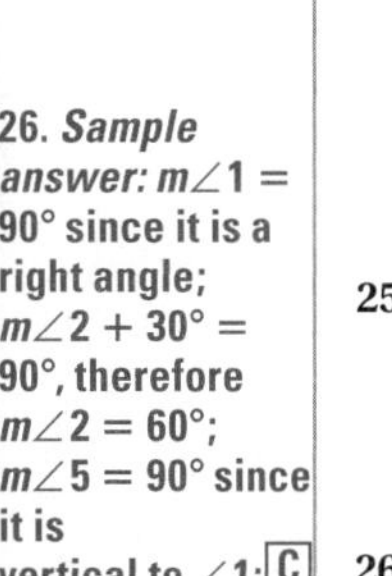

27. FINDING DISTANCES Find the distance between the lines with the equations $y = \frac{3}{2}x + 4$ and $-3x + 2y = -1$. **2.5**

28. CHALLENGE *Describe* how you would find the distance from a point to a plane. Can you find the distance from a line to a plane? *Explain.*
Construct a perpendicular line to the plane passing through the point. Find the length of the perpendicular segment from the point to the point where the segment intersects the plane; if and only if the line is parallel to the plane.

Avoiding Common Errors

Exercise 1 If there are students who say that either $\overline{CD}$ or $\overline{AB}$ would work, review what we are and are not allowed to assume from a diagram. We know from markings that $\overline{AB}$ is perpendicular to the parallel lines. We have no way to be sure that this is so for $\overline{CD}$.

Mathematical Reasoning

Exercises 15–17 Have students tell what theorem from this lesson they are using in these exercises.

Mathematical Reasoning

Exercise 31 Ask students why the angles in the figure are marked with arcs instead of right angle symbols. If they do not have a ready answer, use questioning to help them understand that the figure we use when we start a proof should show only *given* information, not what we are trying to prove.

32. Given: $a \perp b$

Prove: $\angle 1$, $\angle 2$, $\angle 3$, and $\angle 4$ are right angles.

Because $a \perp b$, $\angle 1$ is a right angle by the definition of perpendicular lines, and $m\angle 1 = 90°$. By the Vertical Angles Congruence Theorem, $\angle 1 \cong \angle 4$ so $m\angle 4 = 90°$ and $\angle 4$ is a right angle. Because $\angle 1$ and $\angle 2$ form a linear pair, they are supplementary angles, so $m\angle 1 + m\angle 2 = 180°$. So $m\angle 2 = 90°$, and $\angle 2$ is a right angle. Similarly, $\angle 1$ and $\angle 3$ form a linear pair, so $m\angle 3 = 90°$ and $\angle 3$ is a right angle.

33. See Additional Answers beginning on p. AA1.

PROBLEM SOLVING

29. Point *C*; the shortest distance is the length of the perpendicular segment.

A

(29.) **STREAMS** You are trying to cross a stream from point *A*. Which point should you jump to in order to jump the shortest distance? *Explain.*

@HomeTutor for problem solving help at classzone.com

30. Check students sketches; perpendicular segments; shortest distance between 2 parallel lines is a perpendicular line, so the perpendicular lines would require less paint than the diagonal ones.

30. ★ **SHORT RESPONSE** The segments that form the path of a crosswalk are usually perpendicular to the crosswalk. Sketch what the segments would look like if they were perpendicular to the crosswalk. Which method requires less paint? *Explain.*

@HomeTutor for problem solving help at classzone.com

EXAMPLE 2 on p. 191 for Exs. 31–34

31. **PROVING THEOREM 3.8** Copy and complete the proof that if two lines intersect to form a linear pair of congruent angles, then the lines are perpendicular.

GIVEN ▶ $\angle 1$ and $\angle 2$ are a linear pair.
$\angle 1 \cong \angle 2$

PROVE ▶ $g \perp h$

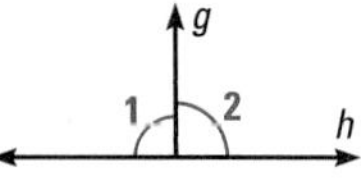

STATEMENTS	REASONS
1. $\angle 1$ and $\angle 2$ are a linear pair.	1. Given
2. $\angle 1$ and $\angle 2$ are supplementary.	2. _?_ **Linear Pair Postulate**
3. _?_ **$m\angle 1 + m\angle 2 = 180°$**	3. Definition of supplementary angles
4. $\angle 1 \cong \angle 2$	4. Given
5. $m\angle 1 = m\angle 2$	5. _?_ **Definition of congruent angles**
6. $m\angle 1 + m\angle 1 = 180°$	6. Substitution Property of Equality
7. $2(m\angle 1) = 180°$	7. Combine like terms.
8. $m\angle 1 = 90°$ **$\angle 1$ is a right angle.**	8. _?_ **Division Property of Equality**
9. _?_	9. Definition of a right angle
10. $g \perp h$	10. _?_ **Definition of perpendicular lines**

B

PROVING THEOREMS **Write a proof of the given theorem.** **32–34. See margin.**

32. Theorem 3.9

33. Theorem 3.11, Perpendicular Transversal Theorem

34. Theorem 3.12, Lines Perpendicular to a Transversal Theorem

◯ = WORKED-OUT SOLUTIONS on p. WS1 ★ = STANDARDIZED TEST PRACTICE

34. Given: $m \perp p$, $n \perp p$

Prove: $m \parallel n$

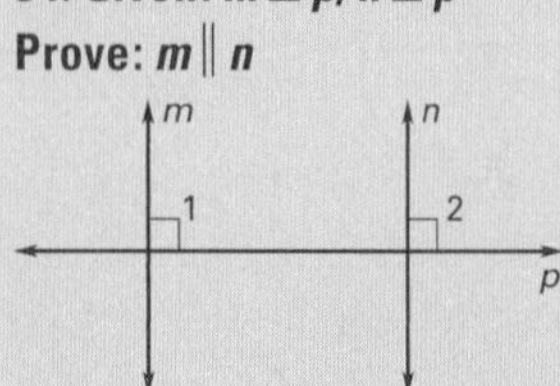

Statements (Reasons)

1. $m \perp p$, $n \perp p$ (Given)

2. $\angle 1$ and $\angle 2$ are right angles. (Perpendicular lines intersect to form four right angles.)

3. $\angle 1 \cong \angle 2$ (Right Angles Congruence Theorem)

4. $m \parallel n$ (Corresponding Angles Converse)

C **CHALLENGE** **Suppose the given statement is true. Determine whether $\overrightarrow{AB} \perp \overrightarrow{AC}$.**

35. $\angle 1$ and $\angle 2$ are congruent. **no**

36. $\angle 3$ and $\angle 4$ are complementary. **no**

37. $m\angle 1 = m\angle 3$ and $m\angle 2 = m\angle 4$ **yes**

38. $m\angle 1 = 40°$ and $m\angle 4 = 50°$ **yes**

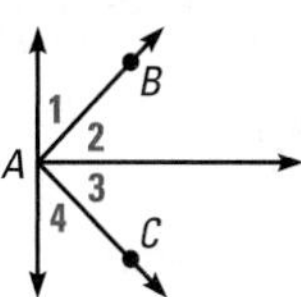

MIXED REVIEW

PREVIEW Prepare for Lesson 4.1 in Exs. 39–41.

Find the value of x. *(p. 24)*

39.
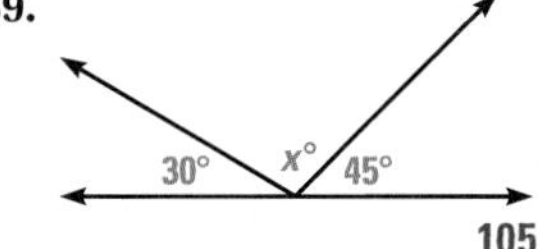

105

40.
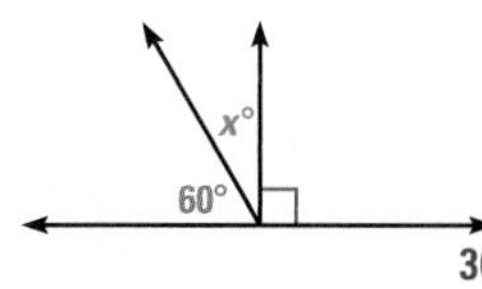

30

41.
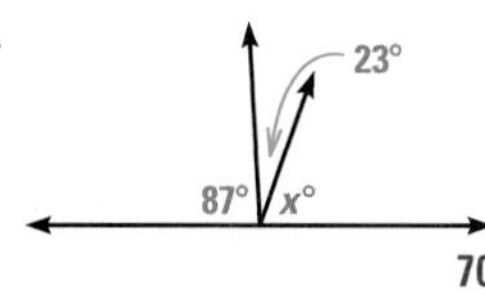

70

Find the circumference and area of the circle. Round to the nearest tenth. *(p. 49)*

42.
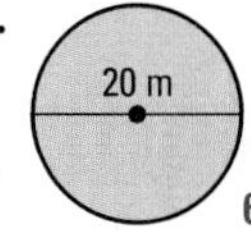

62.8 m, 314 m²

43.
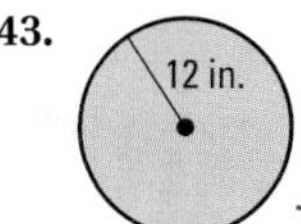

75.4 in., 452.2 in.²

44.
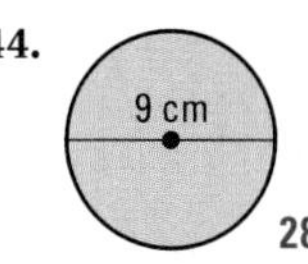

28.3 cm, 63.6 cm²

Find the value of x that makes $m \parallel n$. *(p. 161)*

45.
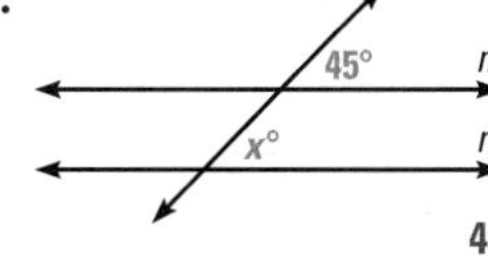

45

46.
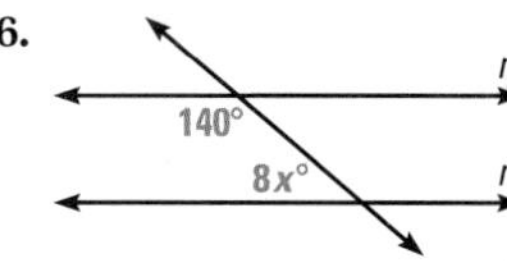

5

47.
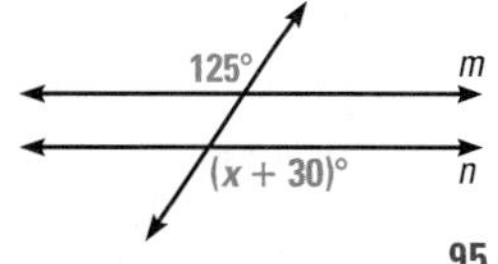

95

QUIZ for Lessons 3.5–3.6

Write an equation of the line that passes through point P and is parallel to the line with the given equation. *(p. 180)*

1. $P(0, 0)$, $y = -3x + 1$ **$y = -3x$**

2. $P(-5, -6)$, $y - 8 = 2x + 10$ **$y = 2x + 4$**

3. $P(1, -2)$, $x = 15$ **$x = 1$**

Write an equation of the line that passes through point P and is perpendicular to the line with the given equation. *(p. 180)*

4. $P(3, 4)$, $y = 2x - 1$ **$y = -\frac{1}{2}x + \frac{11}{2}$**

5. $P(2, 5)$, $y = -6$ **$x = 2$**

6. $P(4, 0)$, $12x + 3y = 9$ **$y = \frac{1}{4}x - 1$**

Determine which lines, if any, must be parallel. *Explain.* *(p. 190)*

7.
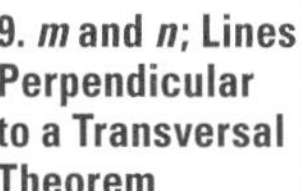

8.
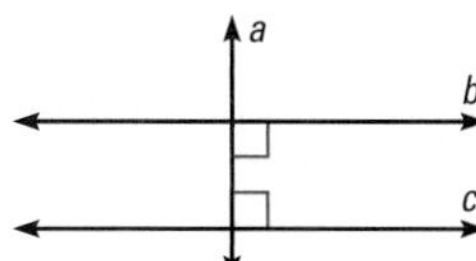

9.
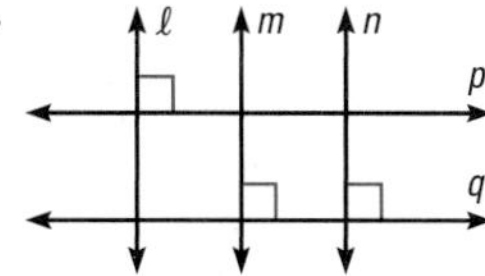

7. None. ***Sample answer:*** **It is not known whether w is perpendicular to y.**

8. b and c; Lines Perpendicular to a Transversal Theorem

9. m and n; Lines Perpendicular to a Transversal Theorem

5 ASSESS AND RETEACH

Daily Homework Quiz

Transparency Available

1. Find $m\angle 3$. **18°**

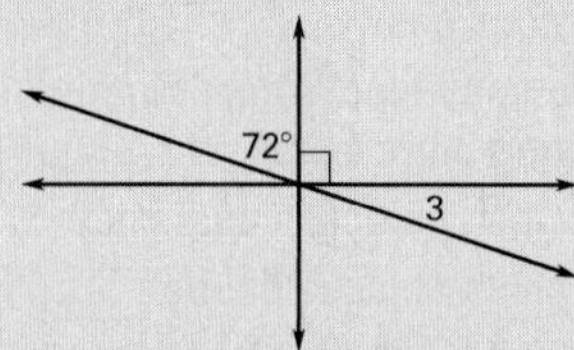

2. How do you know that a and b are parallel? **Both are perpendicular to c.**

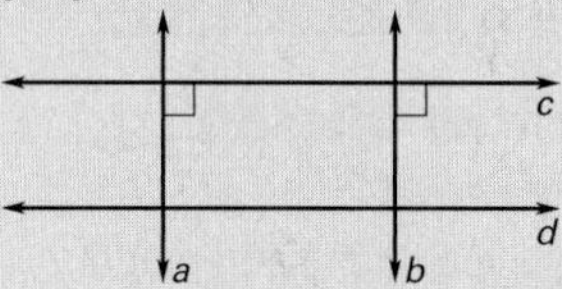

3. Find the distance between the two parallel lines. Round to the nearest tenth. **6.4**

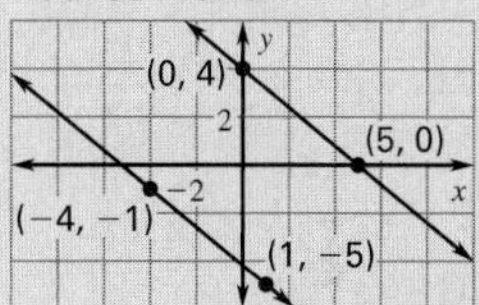

Available at **classzone.com**

Diagnosis/Remediation

- Practice A, B, C in Chapter 3 Resource Book, pp. 77–82
- Study Guide in Chapter 3 Resource Book, pp. 83–84
- Practice Workbook, pp. 58–60
- @HomeTutor

Challenge

Additional challenge is available in the Chapter 3 Resource Book, p. 87.

Quiz

An easily-readable reduced copy of the quiz (with answers) on Lessons 3.5–3.6 from the Assessment Book can be found on p. 144F.

1 PLAN AND PREPARE

Warm-Up Exercises

John walks 5 blocks north, 4 blocks east, 2 more blocks north and 1 more block east.

1. How many blocks north of his starting point is he? **7**
2. How many blocks east is he? **5**
3. How many blocks did he walk? **12**

2 FOCUS AND MOTIVATE

Essential Question

Big Idea 3, p. 145

How do you find the distance between two points on a coordinate plane when you can only move horizontally or vertically? **Tell students they will learn how to answer this question by studying the taxicab distance formula.**

3 TEACH

Extra Example 1

Find the taxicab distance from $C(3, 2)$ to $D(-2, -1)$. Draw two different shortest paths from C to D.
8; *Sample:*

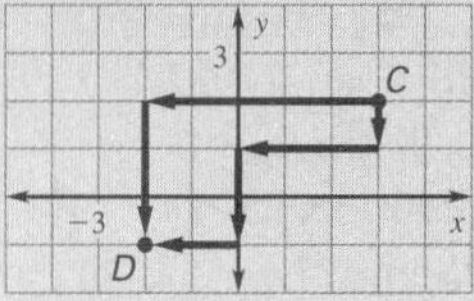

Extension Taxicab Geometry

Use after Lesson 3.6

GOAL Find distances in a non-Euclidean geometry.

Key Vocabulary
- **taxicab geometry**

HISTORY NOTE

Euclidean geometry is named after a Greek mathematician. Euclid (circa third century B.C.) used postulates and deductive reasoning to prove the theorems you are studying in this book. **Non-Euclidean geometries** start by assuming different postulates, so they result in different theorems.

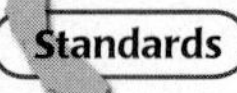

Enrichment Topic; not required by California Standards.

You have learned that the shortest distance between two points is the length of the straight line segment between them. This is true in the *Euclidean* geometry that you are studying. But think about what happens when you are in a city and want to get from point A to point B. You cannot walk through the buildings, so you have to go along the streets.

Taxicab geometry is the non-Euclidean geometry that a taxicab or a pedestrian must obey.

In taxicab geometry, you can travel either horizontally or vertically parallel to the axes. In this geometry, the distance between two points is the shortest number of *blocks* between them.

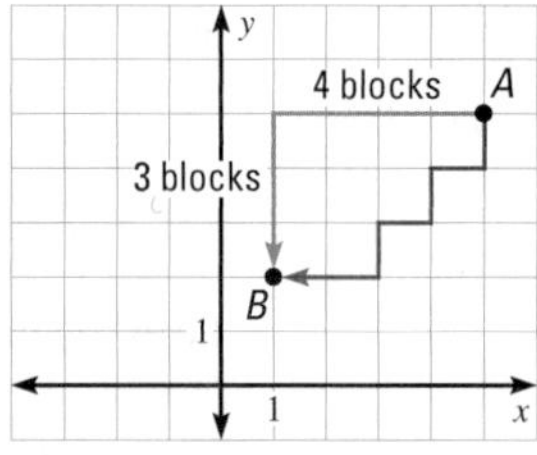

KEY CONCEPT — *For Your Notebook*

Taxicab Distance

The distance between two points is the sum of the differences in their coordinates.

$AB = |x_2 - x_1| + |y_2 - y_1|$

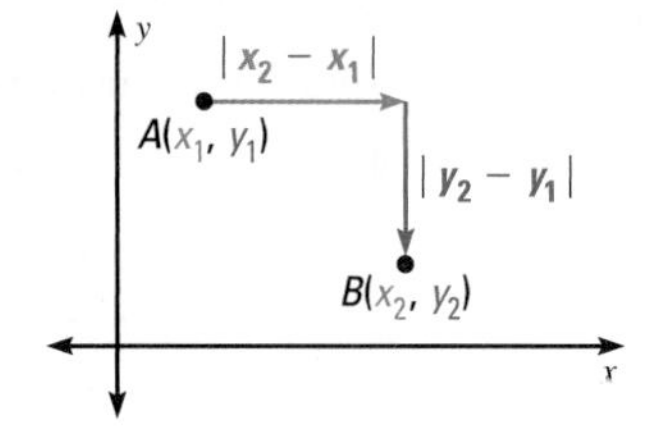

EXAMPLE 1 Find a taxicab distance

Find the taxicab distance from $A(-1, 5)$ to $B(4, 2)$. Draw two different shortest paths from A to B.

Solution

$$AB = |x_2 - x_1| + |y_2 - y_1|$$
$$= |4 - (-1)| + |2 - 5|$$
$$= |5| + |-3|$$
$$= 8$$

▶ The shortest path is 8 blocks. Two possible paths are shown.

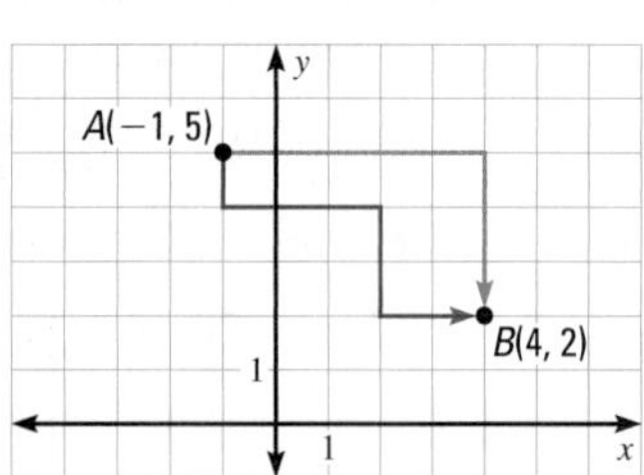

REVIEW ABSOLUTE VALUE

For help with absolute value, see p. 870.

CIRCLES In Euclidean geometry, a *circle* is all points that are the same distance from a fixed point, called the *center.* That distance is the *radius.* Taxicab geometry uses the same definition for a circle, but taxicab circles are not round.

EXAMPLE 2 Draw a taxicab circle

Draw the taxicab circle with the given radius r and center C.

a. $r = 2$, $C(1, 3)$

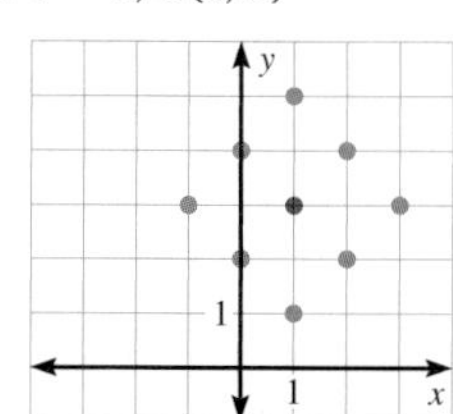

b. $r = 1$, $C(-2, -4)$

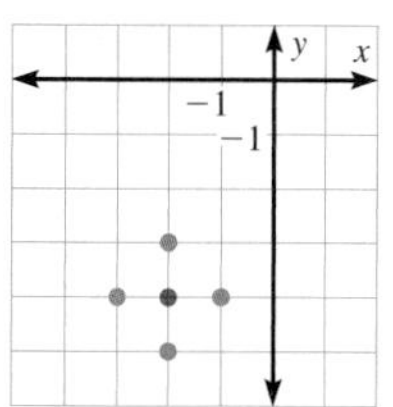

Extra Example 2

Draw a taxicab circle with the given radius r and center C.

a. $r = 3$, $C(1, 1)$

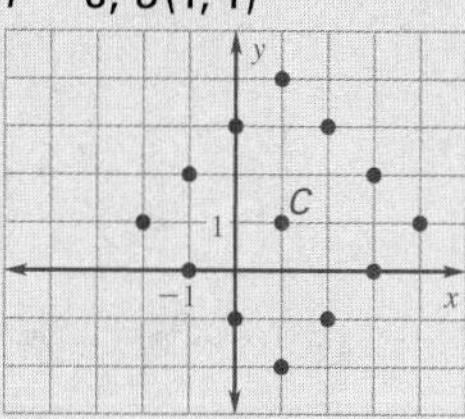

b. $r = 2$, $C(4, -2)$

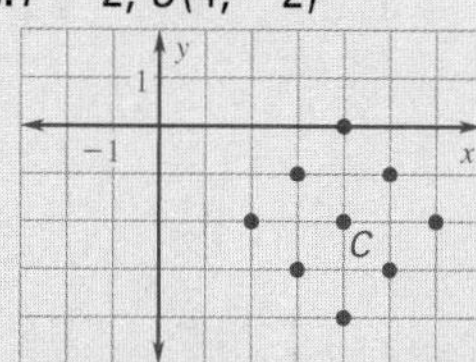

Closing the Lesson

Have students summarize the major points of the lesson and answer the Essential Question: How do you find the distance between two points on a coordinate plane when you can only move horizontally or vertically?

- **In taxicab geometry the distance between two points is the sum of the differences in their coordinates.**

You find the distance between two points by using the taxicab distance formula: find the sum of the differences of the coordinates of the two points.

PRACTICE

EXAMPLE 1 on p. 198 for Exs. 1–6

FINDING DISTANCE Find the taxicab distance between the points.

1. (4, 2), (0, 0) **6**
2. (3, 5), (6, 2) **6**
3. (−6, 3), (8, 5) **16**
4. (−1, −3), (5, −2) **7**
5. (−3, 5), (−1, 5) **2**
6. (−7, 3), (−7, −4) **7**

EXAMPLE 2 on p. 199 for Exs. 7–9

DRAWING CIRCLES Draw the taxicab circle with radius r and center C. **7–9. See margin.**

7. $r = 2$, $C(3, 4)$
8. $r = 4$, $C(0, 0)$
9. $r = 5$, $C(-1, 3)$

FINDING MIDPOINTS A *midpoint* in taxicab geometry is a point where the distances to the endpoints are equal. Find all the midpoints of $\overline{AB}$.

10. $A(2, 4)$, $B(-2, -2)$ **(2, −1), (1, 0), (0, 1), (−1, 2), (−2, 3)**
11. $A(1, -3)$, $B(1, 3)$ **(1, 0)**
12. $A(2, 2)$, $B(-3, 0)$ **(0.5, 0), (0, 0.5), (−0.5, 1), (−1, 1.5), (−1.5, 2)**
13. **TRAVEL PLANNING** A hotel's website claims that the hotel is an easy walk to a number of sites of interest. What are the coordinates of the hotel? **(10, 4)**

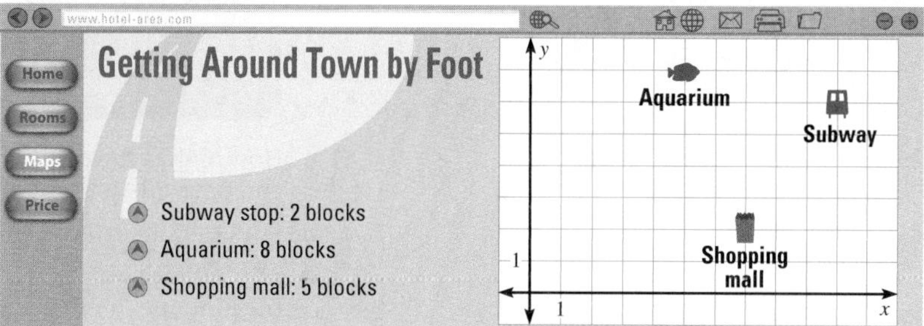

14. **REASONING** The taxicab distance between two points is always greater than or equal to the Euclidean distance between the two points. *Explain* what must be true about the points for both distances to be equal.

14. Both points must be on the same vertical or horizontal line.

4 PRACTICE AND APPLY

Study Strategy

Exercises 1–6 Graph the points and count squares or "blocks" between them to find the distance. The Euclidean distance formula will not work in taxicab geometry.

Mathematical Reasoning

Exercises 10–12 Where do the midpoints between two points A and B lie? **on one of the shortest paths from A to B**

7.

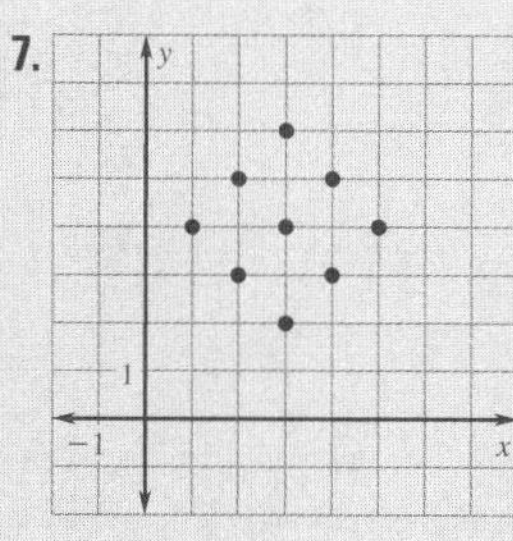

8.

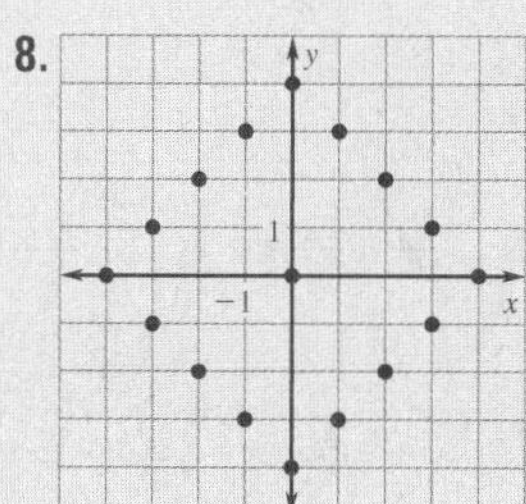

9.

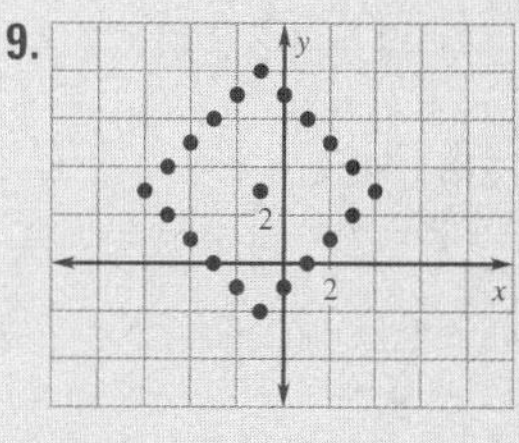

1a. $y = 35x$, $y = 20x$

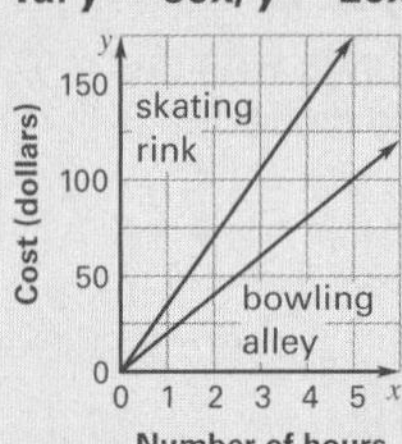

1b. No; they don't have the same slope.

1c. cost per hour of renting each facility

1d. $y = 20x + 25$;

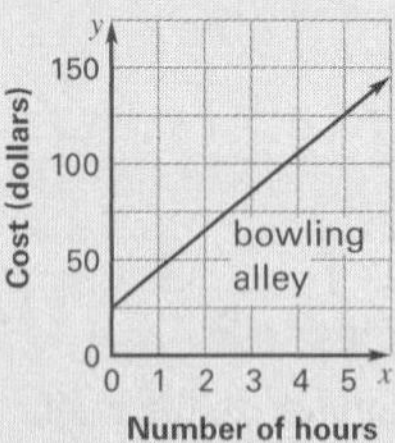

Yes; $y = 20x$ and $y = 20x + 25$ have the same slope.

3. *Sample answer:* $4x + 6y = 8$; *Sample answer:* $2y - 3x = -2$

4. 96.6. *Sample answer:* It's the perpendicular distance to the line.

5c. Monongahela Incline. *Sample answer:* $0.7 > 0.68$

STATE TEST PRACTICE classzone.com

Lessons 3.4–3.6

1. **MULTI-STEP PROBLEM** You are planning a party. You would like to have the party at a roller skating rink or bowling alley. The table shows the total cost to rent the facilities by number of hours.

Hours	Roller skating rink cost ($)	Bowling alley cost ($)
1	35	20
2	70	40
3	105	60
4	140	80
5	175	100

a–d. See margin.

a. Use the data in the table. Write and graph two equations to represent the total cost y to rent the facilities, where x is the number of hours you rent the facility.

b. Are the lines from part (a) parallel? *Explain* why or why not.

c. What is the meaning of the slope in each equation from part (a)?

d. Suppose the bowling alley charges an extra $25 set-up fee. Write and graph an equation to represent this situation. Is this line parallel to either of the lines from part (a)? *Explain* why or why not.

2. **GRIDDED ANSWER** The graph models the accumulated cost of buying a used guitar and taking lessons over the first several months. Find the slope of the line. **15**

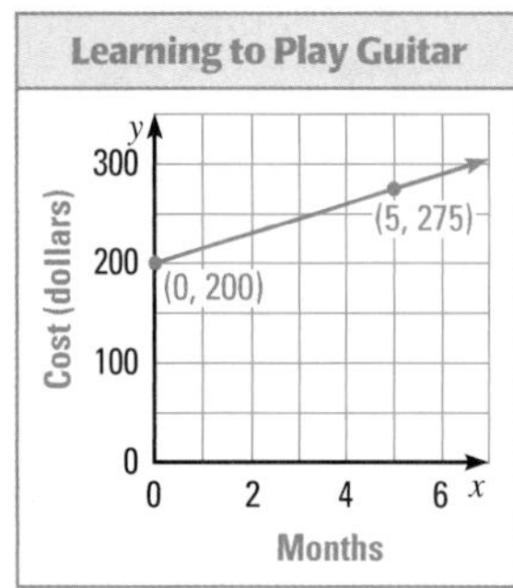

3. **OPEN-ENDED** Write an equation of a line parallel to $2x + 3y = 6$. Then write an equation of a line perpendicular to your line. **See margin.**

4. **SHORT RESPONSE** You are walking across a field to get to a hiking path. Use the graph below to find the shortest distance you can walk to reach the path. *Explain* how you know you have the shortest distance. **See margin.**

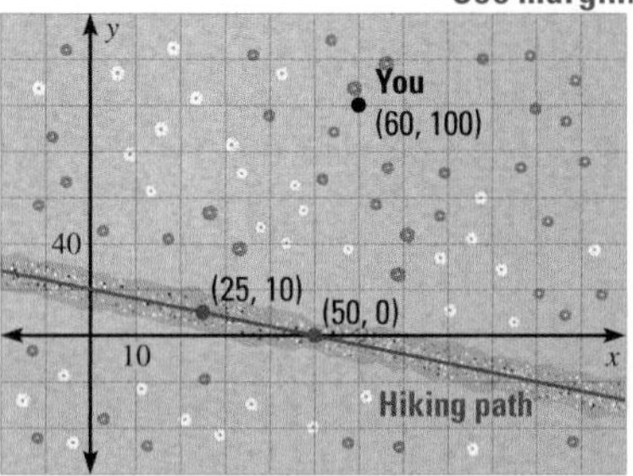

5. **EXTENDED RESPONSE** The Johnstown Inclined Plane in Johnstown, Pennsylvania, is a cable car that transports people up and down the side of a hill. During the cable car's climb, you move about 17 feet upward for every 25 feet you move forward. At the top of the incline, the horizontal distance from where you started is about 500 feet.

a. How high is the car at the top of its climb compared to its starting height? **340 ft**

b. Find the slope of the climb. $\frac{17}{25}$

c. Another cable car incline in Pennsylvania, the Monongahela Incline, climbs at a slope of about 0.7 for a horizontal distance of about 517 feet. *Compare* this climb to that of the Johnstown Inclined Plane. Which is steeper? *Justify* your answer. **See margin.**

3 CHAPTER SUMMARY

BIG IDEAS *For Your Notebook*

Big Idea 1

Using Properties of Parallel and Perpendicular Lines

When parallel lines are cut by a transversal, angle pairs are formed. Perpendicular lines form congruent right angles.

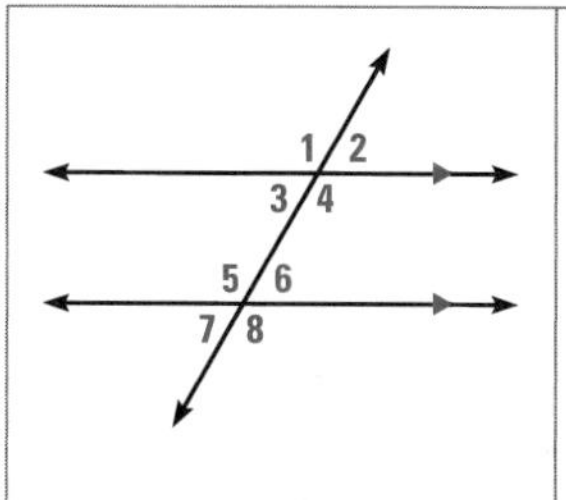	$\angle 2$ and $\angle 6$ are corresponding angles, and they are congruent. $\angle 3$ and $\angle 6$ are alternate interior angles, and they are congruent. $\angle 1$ and $\angle 8$ are alternate exterior angles, and they are congruent. $\angle 3$ and $\angle 5$ are consecutive interior angles, and they are supplementary.
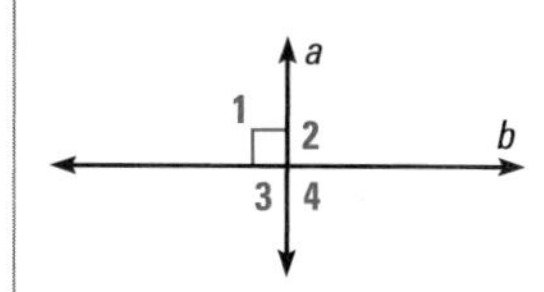	If $a \perp b$, then $\angle 1$, $\angle 2$, $\angle 3$, and $\angle 4$ are all right angles.

Big Idea 2

Proving Relationships Using Angle Measures

You can use the angle pairs formed by lines and a transversal to show that the lines are parallel. Also, if lines intersect to form a right angle, you know that the lines are perpendicular.

Through point A not on line q, there is only one line r parallel to q and one line s perpendicular to q.

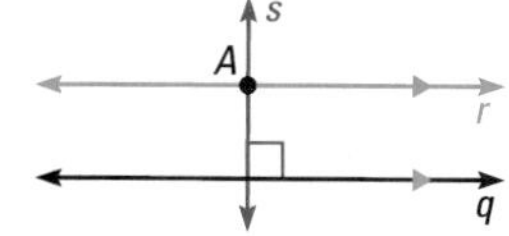

Big Idea 3

Making Connections to Lines in Algebra

In Algebra 1, you studied slope as a rate of change and linear equations as a way of modeling situations.

Slope and equations of lines are also a useful way to represent the lines and segments that you study in Geometry. For example, the slopes of parallel lines are the same ($a \parallel b$), and the product of the slopes of perpendicular lines is -1 ($a \perp c$, and $b \perp c$).

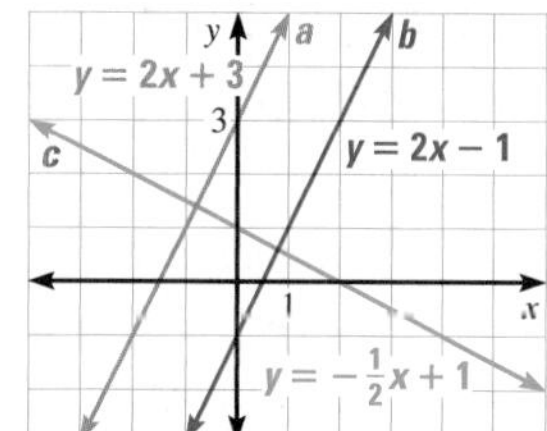

Additional Resources

The following resources are available to help review the materials in this chapter.

Chapter 3 Resource Book

- Chapter Review Games and Activities, p. 88
- Cumulative Practice, Chs. 1–3, pp. 91–92

Student Resources in Spanish

eWorkbook

@HomeTutor

Vocabulary Practice

Vocabulary practice is available at **classzone.com**

Extra Example 3.1

Think of each segment in the rectangular box as part of a line.

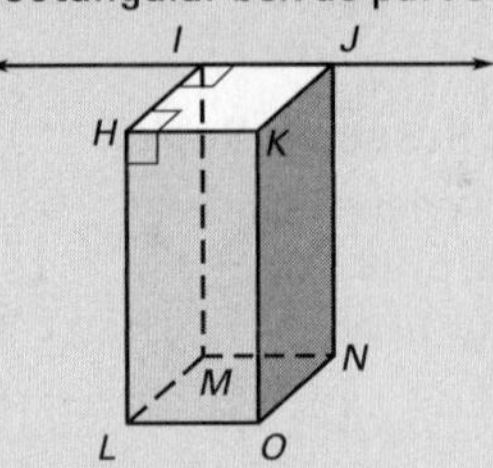

a. $\overleftrightarrow{HI}$, $\overleftrightarrow{KJ}$, $\overleftrightarrow{IM}$, and $\overleftrightarrow{JN}$ are perpendicular to $\overleftrightarrow{IJ}$.

b. $\overleftrightarrow{HK}$, $\overleftrightarrow{MN}$, and $\overleftrightarrow{LO}$ are parallel to $\overleftrightarrow{IJ}$.

c. $\overleftrightarrow{NO}$ and $\overleftrightarrow{ML}$ are skew to $\overleftrightarrow{IJ}$.

d. Plane *HIM* is parallel to plane *KJN*.

3 CHAPTER REVIEW

@HomeTutor
classzone.com
- Multi-Language Glossary
- Vocabulary practice

REVIEW KEY VOCABULARY

For a list of postulates and theorems, see pp. 926–931.

- parallel lines, *p. 147*
- skew lines, *p. 147*
- parallel planes, *p. 147*
- transversal, *p. 149*
- corresponding angles, *p. 149*
- alternate interior angles, *p. 149*
- alternate exterior angles, *p. 149*
- consecutive interior angles, *p. 149*
- paragraph proof, *p. 163*
- slope, *p. 171*
- slope-intercept form, *p. 180*
- standard form, *p. 182*
- distance from a point to a line, *p. 192*

VOCABULARY EXERCISES

1. Copy and complete: Two lines that do not intersect and are not coplanar are called __?__. **skew lines**

2. WRITING *Compare* alternate interior angle pairs and consecutive interior angle pairs.

2. Alternate interior angle pairs lie between the two lines and on opposite sides of the transversal while consecutive interior angle pairs lie between the two lines and on the same side of the transversal.

Copy and complete the statement using the figure at the right.

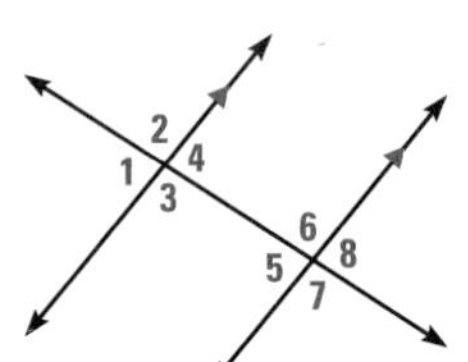

3. $\angle 1$ and __?__ are corresponding angles. **$\angle 5$**

4. $\angle 3$ and __?__ are alternate interior angles. **$\angle 6$**

5. $\angle 4$ and __?__ are consecutive interior angles. **$\angle 6$**

6. $\angle 7$ and __?__ are alternate exterior angles. **$\angle 2$**

Identify the form of the equation as *slope-intercept form* or *standard form*.

7. $14x - 2y = 26$ **standard form**

8. $y = 7x - 13$ **slope-intercept form**

REVIEW EXAMPLES AND EXERCISES

Use the review examples and exercises below to check your understanding of the concepts you have learned in each lesson of Chapter 3.

3.1 Identify Pairs of Lines and Angles

pp. 147–152

EXAMPLE

Think of each segment in the rectangular box at the right as part of a line.

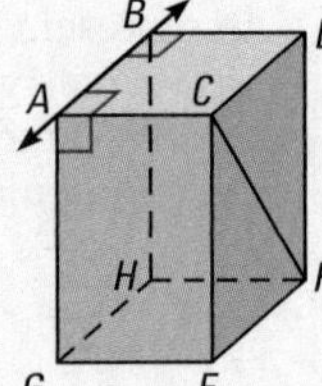

a. $\overleftrightarrow{BD}$, $\overleftrightarrow{AC}$, $\overleftrightarrow{BH}$, and $\overleftrightarrow{AG}$ appear perpendicular to $\overleftrightarrow{AB}$.

b. $\overleftrightarrow{CD}$, $\overleftrightarrow{GH}$, and $\overleftrightarrow{EF}$ appear parallel to $\overleftrightarrow{AB}$.

c. $\overleftrightarrow{CF}$ and $\overleftrightarrow{EG}$ appear skew to $\overleftrightarrow{AB}$.

d. Plane *EFG* appears parallel to plane *ABC*.

EXERCISES

EXAMPLE 1 on p. 147 for Exs. 9–12

Think of each segment in the diagram of a rectangular box as part of a line. Which line(s) or plane(s) contain point *N* and appear to fit the description?

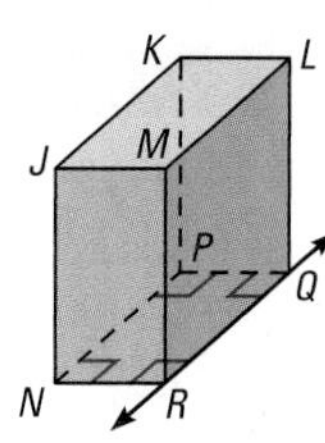

9. Line(s) perpendicular to $\overleftrightarrow{QR}$ **$\overleftrightarrow{NR}$**
10. Line(s) parallel to $\overleftrightarrow{QR}$ **$\overleftrightarrow{NP}$**
11. Line(s) skew to $\overleftrightarrow{QR}$ **$\overleftrightarrow{JN}$**
12. Plane(s) parallel to plane *LMQ* **plane *KJN***

Extra Example 3.2

Use properties of parallel lines to find the value of *x*. **62**

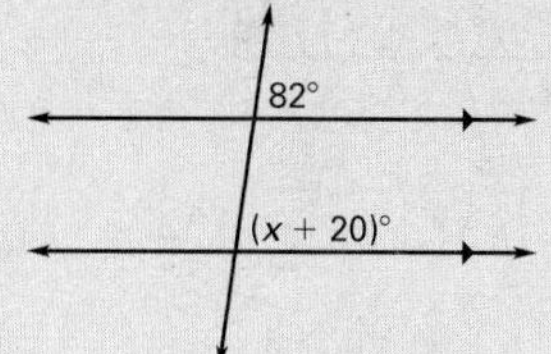

3.2 Use Parallel Lines and Transversals *pp. 154–160*

EXAMPLE

Use properties of parallel lines to find the value of *x*.

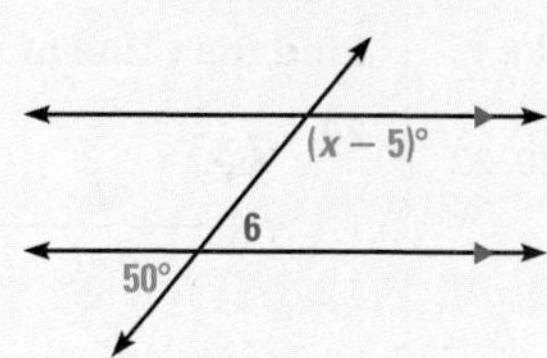

By the Vertical Angles Congruence Theorem, $m\angle 6 = 50°$.

$(x - 5)° + m\angle 6 = 180°$	**Consecutive Interior Angles Theorem**
$(x - 5)° + 50° = 180°$	**Substitute 50° for $m\angle 6$.**
$x = 135$	**Solve for *x*.**

EXERCISES

EXAMPLES 1 and 2 on pp. 154–155 for Exs. 13–19

Find $m\angle 1$ and $m\angle 2$. *Explain* your reasoning.

13.

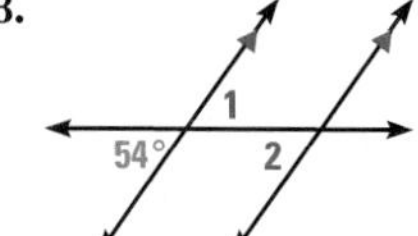

14.

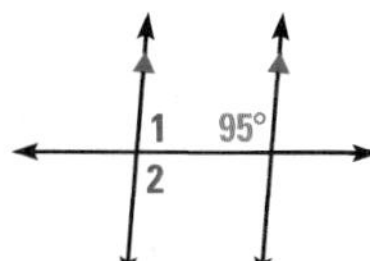

15.

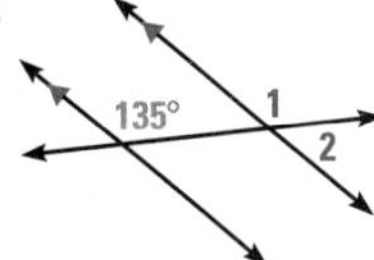

13. $m\angle 1 = 54°$, **vertical angles;** $m\angle 2 = 54°$, **corresponding angles**

14. $m\angle 1 = 85°$, **consecutive interior angles;** $m\angle 2 = 95°$, **alternate interior angles**

15. $m\angle 1 = 135°$, **corresponding angles;** $m\angle 2 = 45°$, **supplementary angles**

Find the values of *x* and *y*.

16. **145, 35**

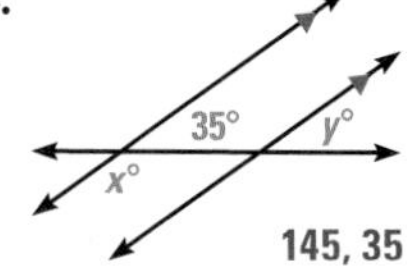

17. **13, 132**

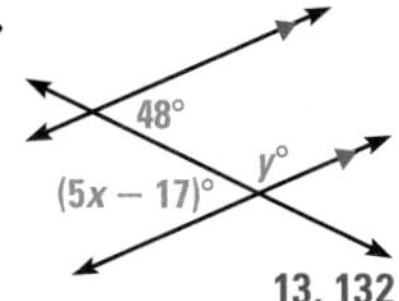

18. **61, 29**

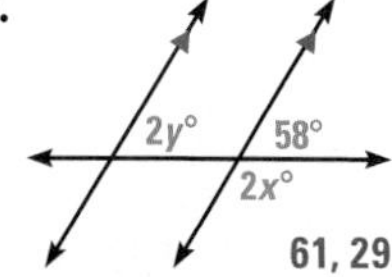

19. **FLAG OF PUERTO RICO** Sketch the rectangular flag of Puerto Rico as shown at the right. Find the measure of $\angle 1$ if $m\angle 3 = 55°$. *Justify* each step in your argument. **35°. *Sample answer:* $\angle 2$ and $\angle 3$ are complementary, so $m\angle 2 = 90° - 55° = 35°$. $m\angle 1 = m\angle 2$ because $\angle 1$ and $\angle 2$ are corresponding angles for two parallel lines cut by a transversal.**

3 CHAPTER REVIEW

Extra Example 3.3

Find the value of x that makes $m \parallel n$. **41**

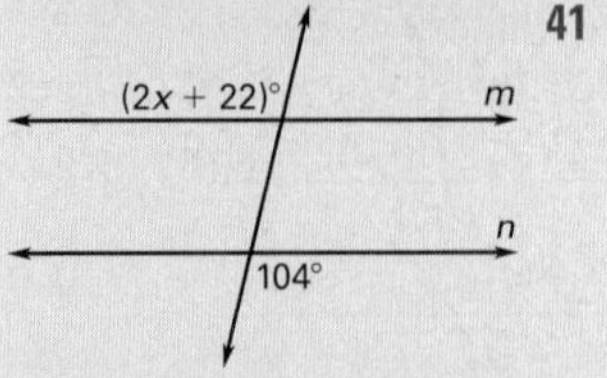

Extra Example 3.4

Find the slope of each line. Which lines are parallel?

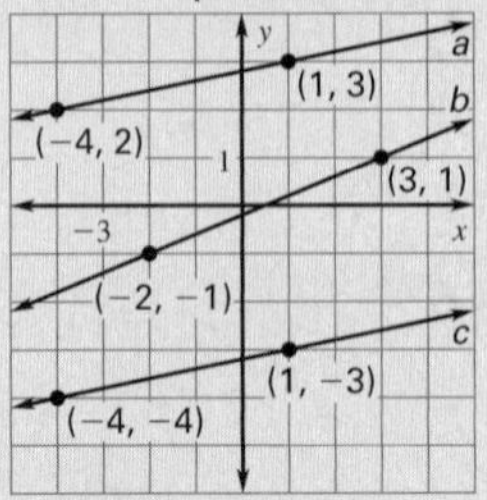

line a: $\frac{1}{5}$; line b: $\frac{2}{5}$; line c: $\frac{1}{5}$; $a \parallel c$

3.3 Prove Lines are Parallel
pp. 161–169

EXAMPLE

Find the value of x that makes $m \parallel n$.

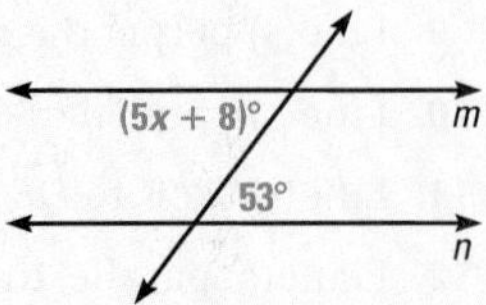

Lines m and n are parallel when the marked corresponding angles are congruent.

$$(5x + 8)° = 53°$$

$$5x = 45$$

$$x = 9$$

▶ The lines m and n are parallel when $x = 9$.

EXERCISES

EXAMPLE 1 on p. 161 for Exs. 20–22

Find the value of x that makes $m \parallel n$.

20.

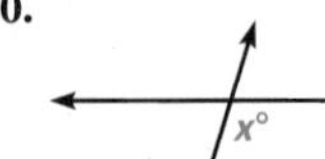

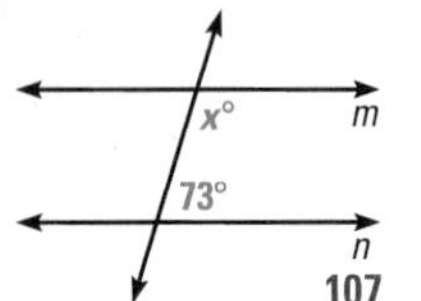

107

21.

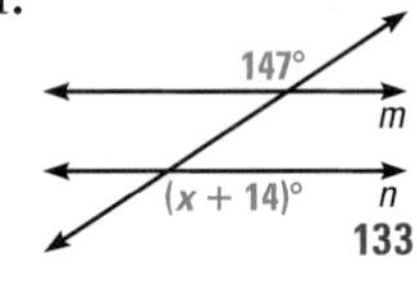

133

22.

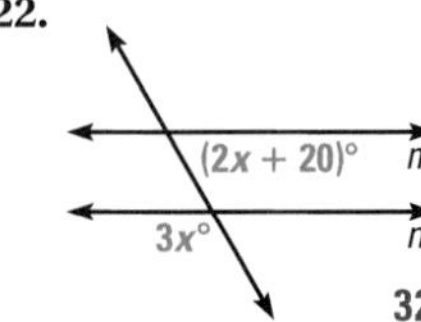

32

3.4 Find and Use Slopes of Lines
pp. 171–178

EXAMPLE

Find the slope of each line. Which lines are parallel?

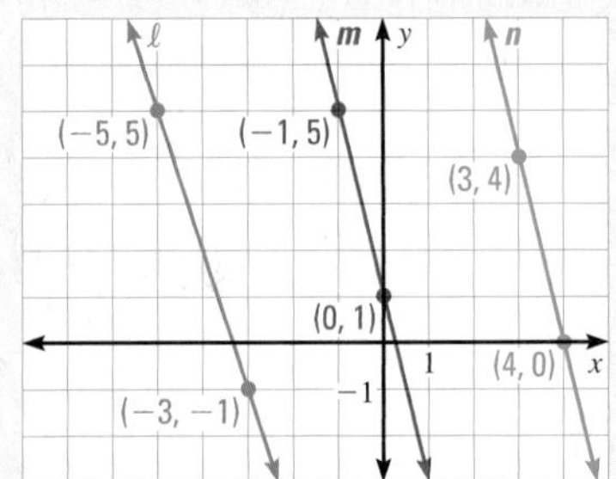

$$\text{Slope of } \ell = \frac{-1-5}{-3-(-5)} = \frac{-6}{2} = -3$$

$$\text{Slope of } m = \frac{1-5}{0-(-1)} = \frac{-4}{1} = -4$$

$$\text{Slope of } n = \frac{0-4}{4-3} = \frac{-4}{1} = -4$$

▶ Because m and n have the same slope, they are parallel. The slope of ℓ is different, so ℓ is not parallel to the other lines.

EXERCISES

EXAMPLES 2 and 3 on pp. 172–173 for Exs. 23–24

Tell whether the lines through the given points are *parallel, perpendicular,* or *neither.*

23. Line 1: (8, 12), (7, −5)
Line 2: (−9, 3), (8, 2) **perpendicular**

24. Line 1: (3, −4), (−1, 4)
Line 2: (2, 7), (5, 1) **parallel**

3.5 Write and Graph Equations of Lines

pp. 180–187

EXAMPLE

Write an equation of the line k passing through the point (−4, 1) that is perpendicular to the line n with the equation $y = 2x - 3$.

First, find the slope of line k. Line n has a slope of 2.

$$2 \cdot m = -1$$

$$m = -\frac{1}{2}$$

Then, use the given point and the slope in the slope-intercept form to find the y-intercept.

$$y = mx + b$$

$$1 = -\frac{1}{2}(-4) + b$$

$$-1 = b$$

▶ An equation of line k is $y = -\frac{1}{2}x - 1$.

EXERCISES

EXAMPLES 2 and 3 on pp. 180–181 for Exs. 25–26

Write equations of the lines that pass through point P and are (a) parallel and (b) perpendicular to the line with the given equation.

25. $P(3, -1)$, $y = 6x - 4$ **a.** $y = 6x - 19$ **b.** $y = -\frac{1}{6}x - \frac{1}{2}$

26. $P(-6, 5)$, $7y + 4x = 2$ **a.** $y = -\frac{4}{7}x + \frac{11}{7}$ **b.** $y = \frac{7}{4}x + \frac{31}{2}$

3.6 Prove Theorems About Perpendicular Lines

pp. 190–197

EXAMPLE

Find the distance between $y = 2x + 3$ and $y = 2x + 8$.

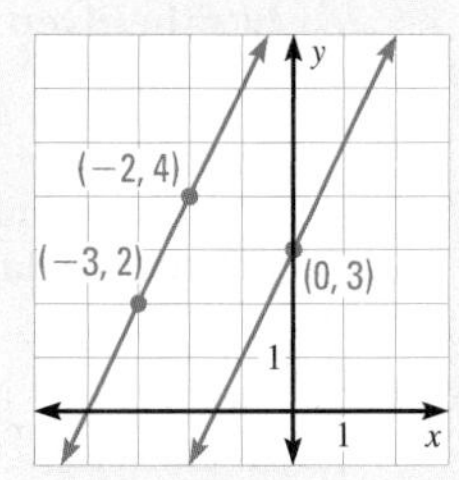

Find the length of a perpendicular segment from one line to the other. Both lines have a slope of 2, so the slope of a perpendicular segment to each line is $-\frac{1}{2}$.

The segment from (0, 3) to (−2, 4) has a slope of $\frac{4-3}{-2-0} = -\frac{1}{2}$. So, the distance between the lines is $d = \sqrt{(-2-0)^2 + (4-3)^2} = \sqrt{5} \approx 2.2$ units.

EXERCISES

EXAMPLE 4 on p. 193 for Exs. 27–28

Use the Distance Formula to find the distance between the two parallel lines. Round to the nearest tenth, if necessary.

27.

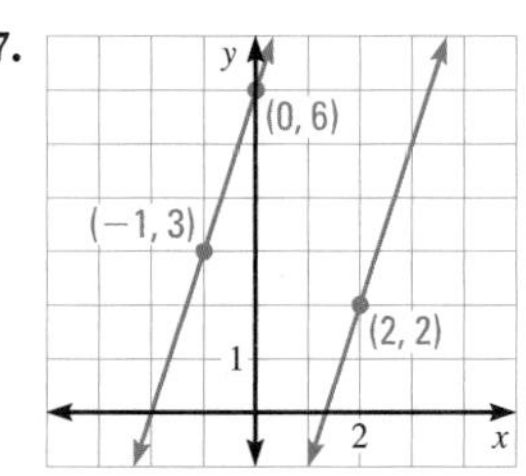

3.2

28.

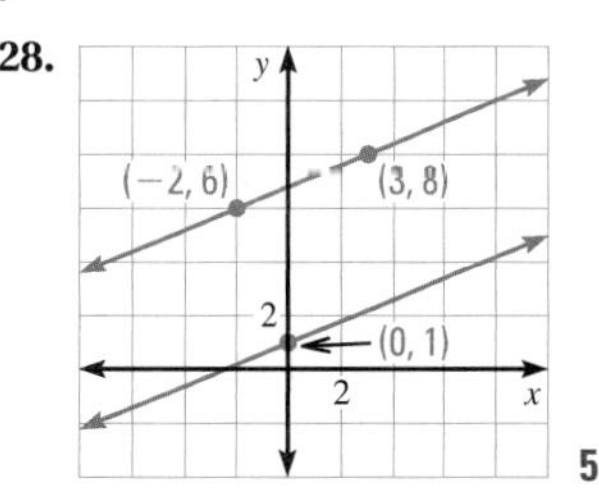

5.4

Extra Example 3.5

Write an equation of the line ℓ passing through the point (6, −4) that is perpendicular to the line m with the equation $y = 3x - 5$.

$y = -\frac{1}{3}x - 2$

Extra Example 3.6

Find the distance between $y = 4x - 1$ and $y = 4x + 3$.

$\frac{4\sqrt{17}}{17} \approx 0.97$ units

Additional Resources

Assessment Book

- Chapter Test, Levels A, B, C, pp. 34–39
- Standardized Chapter Test, pp. 40–41
- SAT/ACT Chapter Test, pp. 42–43
- Alternative Assessment, pp. 44–45

Test Generator CD-ROM

Chapter Test

Easily-readable reduced copies (with answers) of Chapter Test B, the Standardized Chapter Test, and the Alternative Assessment from the Assessment Book can be found on pp. 144G–144H.

3 CHAPTER TEST

Classify the pairs of angles as *corresponding, alternate interior, alternate exterior,* or *consecutive interior.*

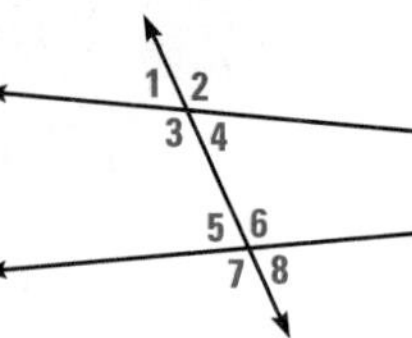

1. $\angle 1$ and $\angle 8$ alternate exterior
2. $\angle 2$ and $\angle 6$ corresponding
3. $\angle 3$ and $\angle 5$ consecutive interior
4. $\angle 4$ and $\angle 5$ alternate interior
5. $\angle 3$ and $\angle 7$ corresponding
6. $\angle 3$ and $\angle 6$ alternate interior

Find the value of x.

7. 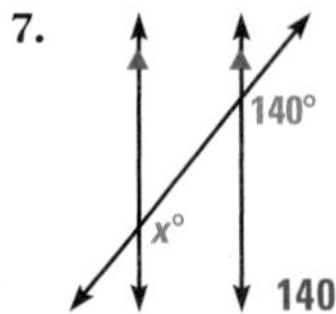

140

8. 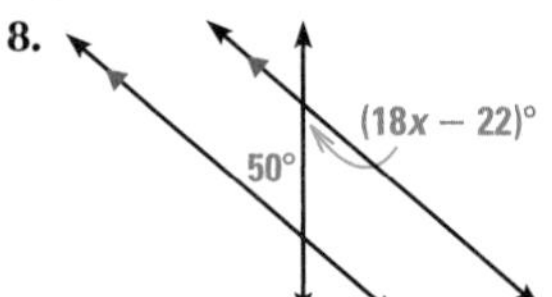

4

9. 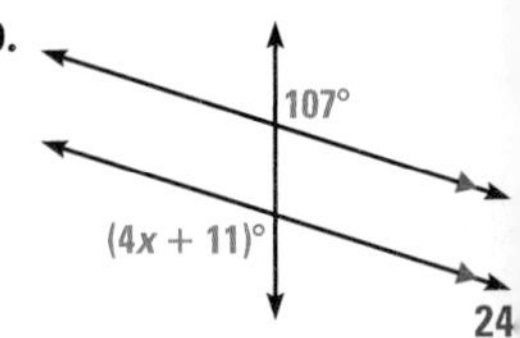

24

Find the value of x that makes $m \parallel n$.

10. 

43

11. 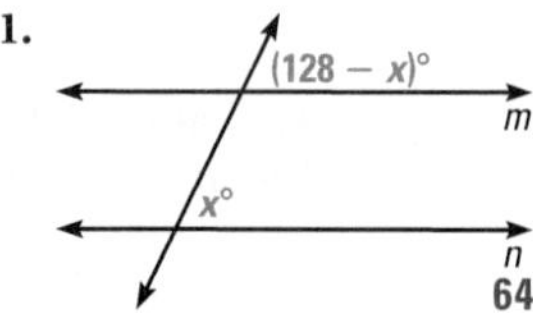

64

12. 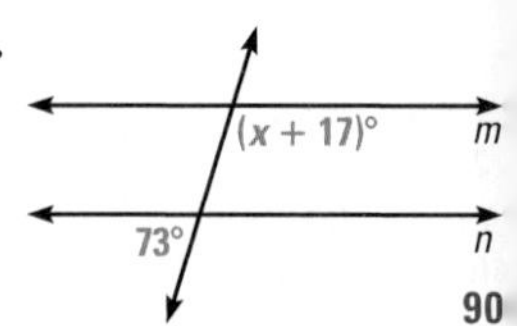

90

Find the slope of the line that passes through the points.

13. $(3, -1), (3, 4)$ undefined slope
14. $(2, 7), (-1, -3)$ $\frac{10}{3}$
15. $(0, 5), (-6, 12)$ $-\frac{7}{6}$

Write an equation of the line that passes through the given point P and has the given slope m.

16. $P(-2, 4), m = 3$ $y = 3x + 10$
17. $P(7, 12), m = -0.2$ $y = -0.2x + 13.4$
18. $P(3, 5), m = -8$ $y = -8x + 29$

Write an equation of the line that passes through point P and is perpendicular to the line with the given equation.

19. $y = -\frac{1}{2}x + \frac{7}{2}$

19. $P(1, 3), y = 2x - 1$
20. $P(0, 2), y = -x + 3$ $y = x + 2$
21. $P(2, -3), x - y = 4$ $y = -x - 1$

In Exercises 22–24, $\overline{AB} \perp \overline{BC}$. Find the value of x.

22. 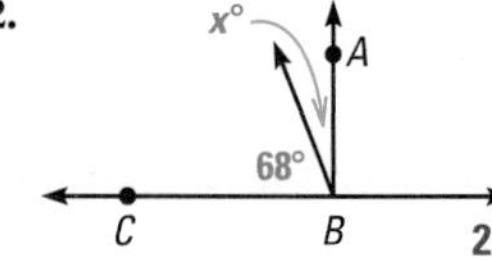

22

23. 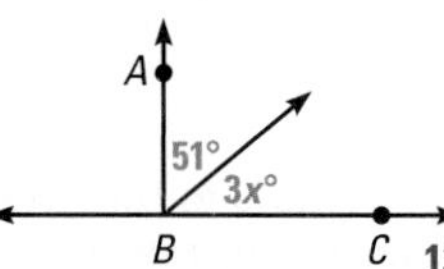

13

24. 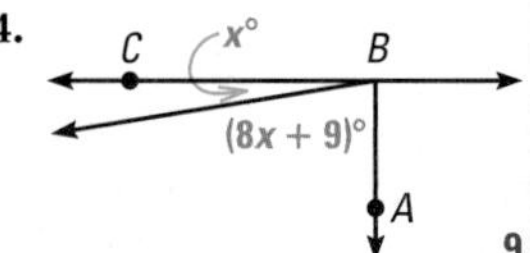

9

25. **RENTAL COSTS** The graph at the right models the cost of renting a moving van. Write an equation of the line. Then find the cost of renting the van for a 100 mile trip.
$y = \frac{3}{5}x + 30$; \$90

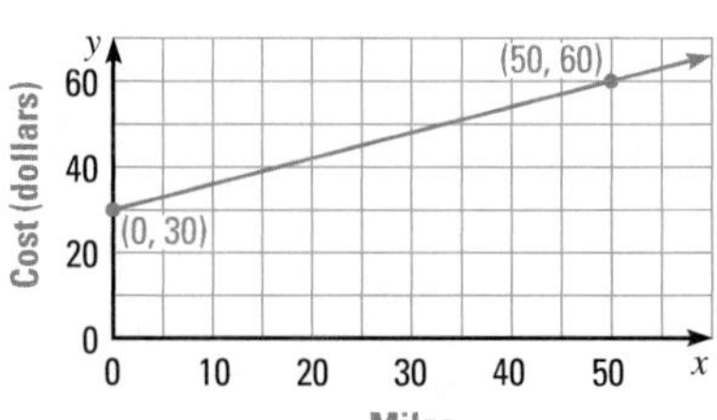

3 xy ALGEBRA REVIEW

Animated Algebra classzone.com

GRAPH AND SOLVE LINEAR INEQUALITIES

EXAMPLE 1 Graph a linear inequality in two variables

Graph the inequality $0 > 2x - 3 - y$.

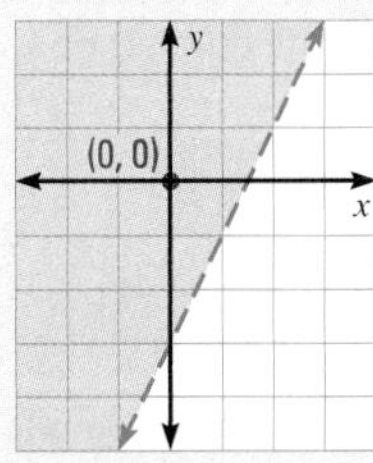

Solution

Rewrite the inequality in slope-intercept form, $y > 2x - 3$.

The boundary line $y = 2x - 3$ is not part of the solution, so use a dashed line.

To decide where to shade, use a point not on the line, such as (0, 0), as a test point. Because $0 > 2 \cdot 0 - 3$, (0, 0) is a solution. Shade the half-plane that includes (0, 0).

EXAMPLE 2 Use an inequality to solve a real-world problem

SAVINGS Lily has saved \$49. She plans to save \$12 per week to buy a camera that costs \$124. In how many weeks will she be able to buy the camera?

Solution

Let w represent the number of weeks needed.

$49 + 12w \geq 124$	**Write an algebraic model.**
$12w \geq 75$	**Subtract 49 from each side.**
$w \geq 6.25$	**Divide each side by 12.**

▶ She must save for 7 weeks to be able to buy the camera.

EXERCISES

EXAMPLE 1 for Exs. 1–8

Graph the linear inequality. **1–8. See margin.**

1. $y > -2x + 3$
2. $y \leq 0.5x - 4$
3. $-2.5x + y \geq 1.5$
4. $x < 3$
5. $y < -2$
6. $5x - y > -5$
7. $2x + 3y \geq -18$
8. $3x - 4y \leq 6$

EXAMPLE 2 for Exs. 9–11

Solve.

9. **LOANS** Eric borrowed \$46 from his mother. He will pay her back at least \$8 each month. At most, how many months will it take him? **6 mo**

10. **GRADES** Manuel's quiz scores in history are 76, 81, and 77. What score must he get on his fourth quiz to have an average of at least 80? **at least 86**

11. **PHONE CALLS** Company A charges a monthly fee of \$5 and \$.07 per minute for phone calls. Company B charges no monthly fee, but charges \$.12 per minute. After how many minutes of calls is the cost of using Company A less than the cost of using Company B? **after 100 min**

Extra Example 1

Graph the inequality $3x - 4 + y \leq 0$.

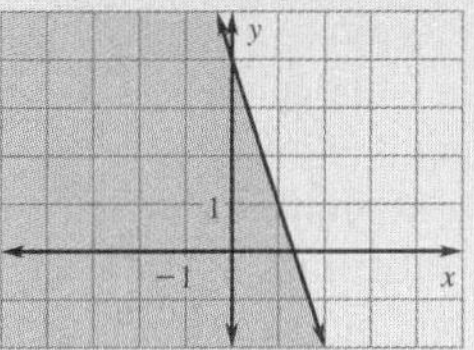

Extra Example 2

Maurice needs to save 30 cereal box tops to get a free watch. If he saves 4 box tops each week, in how many weeks will he be able to send for the watch? **8**

4.

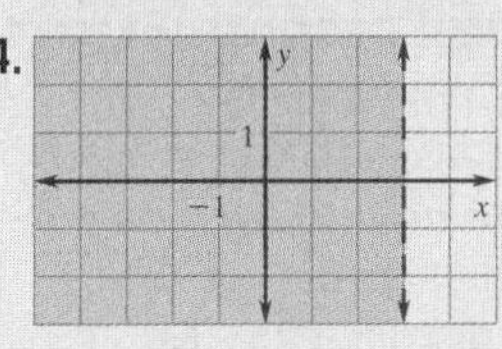

5.

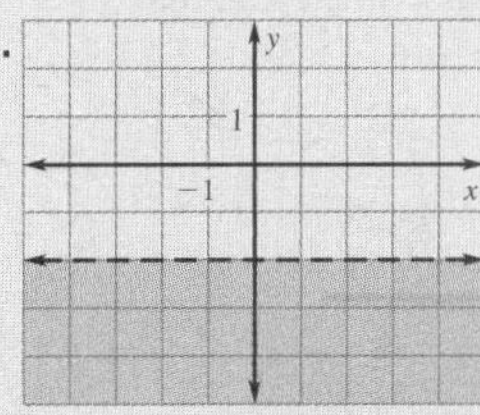

6.

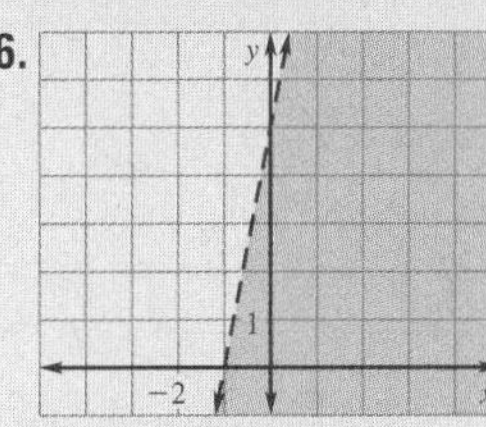

7.

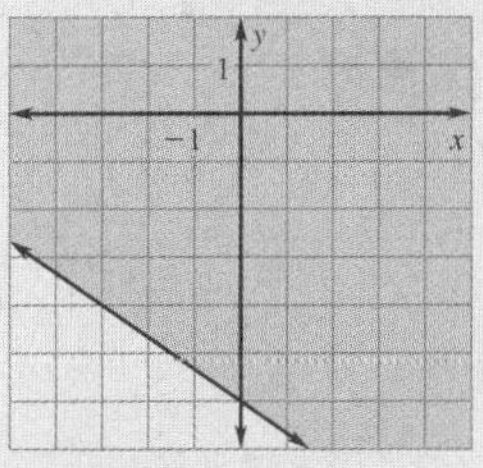

8.

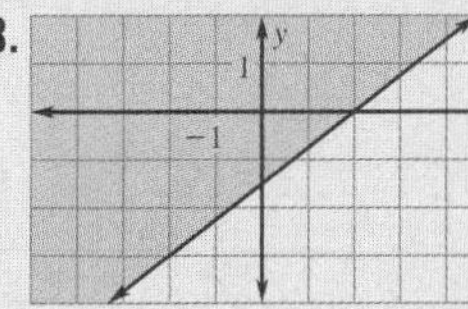

1.

2.

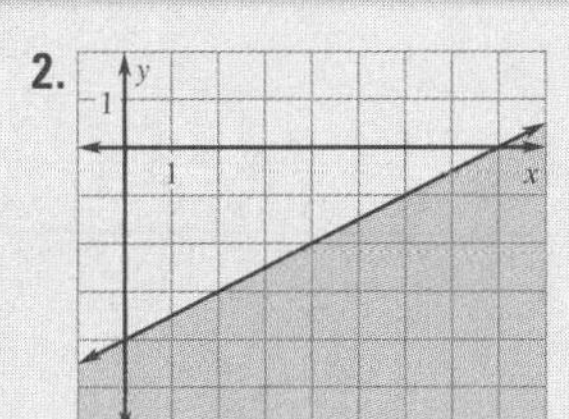

3.

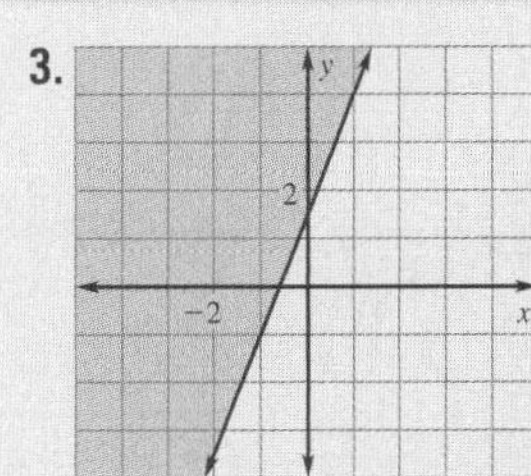

Test-Taking Strategy

For Problem 1, students could graph both lines on a graphing calculator to see which choice is a reasonable point of intersection. Alternatively, students could use Method 2 to substitute the coordinates of each choice into each equation. They do not need to test a point in the second equation if it does not work in the first equation. For Problem 2, students can calculate the slope of the given line, find the negative reciprocal, and use the result to eliminate choices.

Avoiding Common Errors

In Method 1 of Problem 1, students may forget to multiply by 3 when they substitute $2x - 5$ for y in the second equation. Remind them that they must distribute the 3 after they substitute.

MULTIPLE CHOICE QUESTIONS

If you have difficulty solving a multiple choice problem directly, you may be able to use another approach to eliminate incorrect answer choices and obtain the correct answer.

Standards

Prepare for
17.0 Students prove theorems by using coordinate geometry, including the midpoint of a line segment, the distance formula, and *various forms of equations of lines* and circles.

Prepare for
2.0 Students write geometric proofs, including *proofs by contradiction.*

PROBLEM 1

Which ordered pair is a solution of the equations $y = 2x - 5$ and $4x + 3y = 45$?

Ⓐ (3, 11) Ⓑ (5, 5) Ⓒ (6, 7) Ⓓ (7, 6)

METHOD 1

SOLVE DIRECTLY Find the ordered pair that is the solution by using substitution.

Because the first equation is solved for y, substitute $y = 2x - 5$ into $4x + 3y = 45$.

$$4x + 3y = 45$$
$$4x + 3(2x - 5) = 45$$
$$4x + 6x - 15 = 45$$
$$10x - 15 = 45$$
$$10x = 60$$
$$x = 6$$

Solve for y by substituting 6 for x in the first equation.

$$y = 2x - 5$$
$$y = 2(6) - 5$$
$$y = 12 - 5$$
$$y = 7$$

So, the solution of the linear system is (6, 7), which is choice C. Ⓐ Ⓑ Ⓒ Ⓓ

METHOD 2

ELIMINATE CHOICES Another method is to eliminate incorrect answer choices.

Substitute choice A into the equations.

$$y = 2x - 5$$
$$11 \stackrel{?}{=} 2(3) - 5$$
$$11 \stackrel{?}{=} 6 - 5$$
$$11 \neq 1 \text{ ✗}$$

The point is not a solution of $y = 2x - 5$, so there is no need to check the other equation. You can eliminate choice A.

Substitute choice B into the equations.

$y = 2x - 5$	$4x + 3y = 45$
$5 \stackrel{?}{=} 2(5) - 5$	$4(5) + 3(5) \stackrel{?}{=} 45$
$5 \stackrel{?}{=} 10 - 5$	$20 + 15 \stackrel{?}{=} 45$
$5 = 5$ ✓	$35 \neq 45$ ✗

You can eliminate choice B.

Substitute choice C into the equations.

$y = 2x - 5$	$4x + 3y = 45$
$7 \stackrel{?}{=} 2(6) - 5$	$4(6) + 3(7) \stackrel{?}{=} 45$
$7 \stackrel{?}{=} 12 - 5$	$24 + 21 \stackrel{?}{=} 45$
$7 = 7$ ✓	$45 = 45$ ✓

Choice C makes both equations true, so the answer is choice C. Ⓐ Ⓑ Ⓒ Ⓓ

PROBLEM 2

Which equation is an equation of the line through the point (−1, 1) and perpendicular to the line through the points (2, 4) and (−4, 6)?

Ⓐ $y = -\frac{1}{3}x + \frac{2}{3}$ Ⓑ $y = 3x + 4$

Ⓒ $y = \frac{1}{3}x + \frac{4}{3}$ Ⓓ $y = 3x - 2$

METHOD 1

SOLVE DIRECTLY Find the slope of the line through the points (2, 4) and (−4, 6).

$$m = \frac{6 - 4}{-4 - 2} = \frac{2}{-6} = -\frac{1}{3}$$

The slope of the line perpendicular to this line is 3, because $3 \cdot \left(-\frac{1}{3}\right) = -1$. Use $y = 3x + b$ and the point (−1, 1) to find b.

$1 = 3(-1) + b$, so $b = 4$.

The equation of the line is $y = 3x + 4$. The correct answer is B. Ⓐ Ⓑ Ⓒ Ⓓ

METHOD 2

ELIMINATE CHOICES Another method to consider is to eliminate choices based on the slope, then substitute the point to find the correct equation.

$$m = \frac{6 - 4}{-4 - 2} = -\frac{1}{3}$$

The slope of the line perpendicular to this line is 3. Choices A and C do not have a slope of 3, so you can eliminate these choices. Next, try substituting the point (−1, 1) into answer choice B.

$1 \stackrel{?}{=} 3(-1) + 4$ ✓

This is a true statement.

The correct answer is B. Ⓐ Ⓑ Ⓒ Ⓓ

PRACTICE

Explain **why you can eliminate the highlighted answer choice.**

1. Use the diagram below. Which pair of angles are alternate exterior angles?

   Ⓐ 4 and 5 Ⓑ 2 and 6

   Ⓒ 1 and 8 Ⓓ ✗ 1 and 10

   Choice D can be eliminated because ∠1 and ∠10 are not formed by the same transversal.

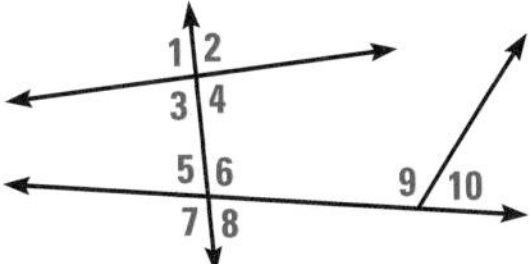

2. Which equation is an equation of the line parallel to the line through the points (−1, 4) and (1, 1)?

   Ⓐ $y = -\frac{3}{2}x - 3$ Ⓑ $y = \frac{3}{2}x - 3$

   Ⓒ ✗ $y = \frac{2}{3}x - 3$ Ⓓ $y = 3x - 3$

   Choice C can be eliminated because its slope $\frac{2}{3}$ is not the same as the slope through the points (−1, 4) and (1, 1) which is $\frac{3}{2}$.

Graphing Calculator

Another method of solving a system of linear equations is to graph both equations on a graphing calculator and then use *intersect* on the *calculate* menu.

3 ★ Standardized TEST PRACTICE

MULTIPLE CHOICE

1. A line is to be drawn through point P in the graph so that it never crosses the y-axis. Through which point does it pass? **C**

   Ⓐ $(-2, 3)$
   Ⓑ $(-3, -2)$
   Ⓒ $(3, 2)$
   Ⓓ $(-3, 2)$

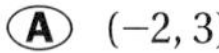

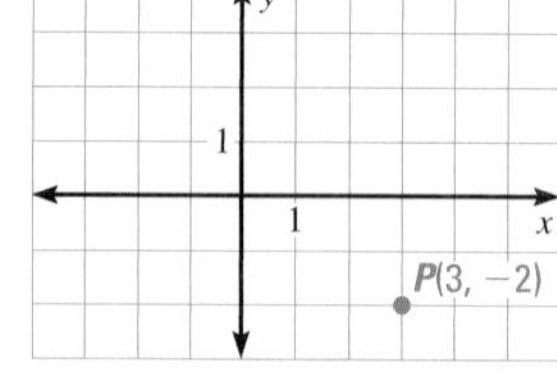

2. Which equation is an equation of a line parallel to $-2x + 3y = 15$? **B**

   Ⓐ $y = -\frac{2}{3}x + 7$ Ⓑ $y = \frac{2}{3}x + 7$
   Ⓒ $y = -\frac{3}{2}x + 7$ Ⓓ $y = -6x + 7$

3. Two trains, E and F, travel along parallel tracks. Each track is 110 miles long. They begin their trips at the same time. Train E travels at a rate of 55 miles per hour and train F travels at a rate of 22 miles per hour. How many miles will train F have left to travel after train E completes its trip? **D**

   Ⓐ 5 miles Ⓑ 33 miles
   Ⓒ 60 miles Ⓓ 66 miles

4. A line segment is parallel to the y-axis and is 9 units long. The two endpoints are $(3, 6)$ and (a, b). What is a value of b? **B**

   Ⓐ -6 Ⓑ -3
   Ⓒ 3 Ⓓ 6

5. Which equation is an equation of a line perpendicular to $y = 5x + 7$? **D**

   Ⓐ $y = -5x + 9$
   Ⓑ $y = 5x + 16$
   Ⓒ $y = \frac{1}{5}x + 7$
   Ⓓ $y = -\frac{1}{5}x + 7$

6. According to the graph, which is the closest approximation of the decrease in sales between week 4 and week 5? **B**

   Ⓐ 24 DVD players
   Ⓑ 20 DVD players
   Ⓒ 18 DVD players
   Ⓓ 15 DVD players

7. In the diagram, $m \parallel n$. Which pair of angles have equal measures? **C**

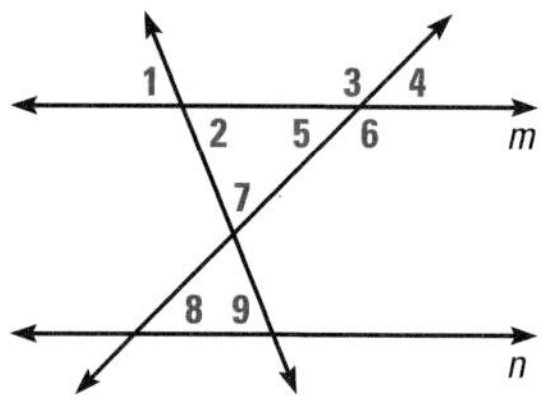

   Ⓐ $\angle 3$ and $\angle 5$ Ⓑ $\angle 4$ and $\angle 7$
   Ⓒ $\angle 1$ and $\angle 9$ Ⓓ $\angle 2$ and $\angle 6$

8. Five lines intersect as shown in the diagram. Lines a, b, and c are parallel. What is the value of $x + y$? **B**

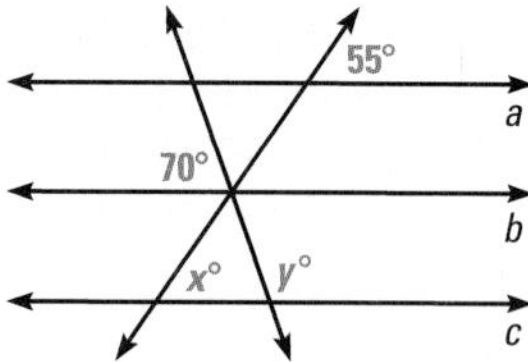

   Ⓐ 125 Ⓑ 165
   Ⓒ 195 Ⓓ 235

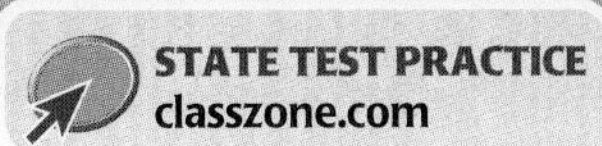

GRIDDED ANSWER

9. What is the slope of a line perpendicular to $5x - 3y = 9$? **−0.6**

10. What is the slope of the line passing through the points (1, 1) and (−2, −2)? **1**

11. What is the *y*-intercept of the line that is parallel to the line $2x - y = 3$ and passes through the point (−3, 4)? **10**

12. What is the value of *a* if line *j* is parallel to line *k*? **55**

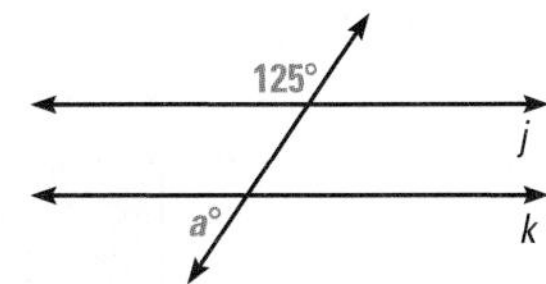

SHORT RESPONSE

13. *Explain* how you know that lines *m* and *n* are parallel to each other. **See margin.**

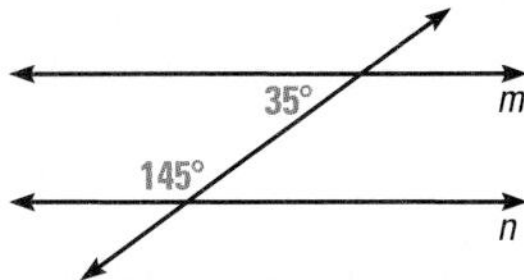

14. What is one possible value for the slope of a line passing through the point (1, 1) and passing *between* the points (−2, −2) and (−2, −3) but not containing either one of them? ***Sample answer:*** $\frac{7}{6}$

EXTENDED RESPONSE

15. Mrs. Smith needs a babysitter. Lauren who lives next door charges \$5 per hour for her services. Zachary who lives across town charges \$4 per hour plus \$3 for bus fare.

a. Using this information, write equations to represent Lauren and Zachary's babysitting fees. Let *F* represent their fees and *h* represent the number of hours. **Lauren: $F = 5h$, Zachary: $F = 4h + 3$**

b. Graph the equations you wrote in part (a). **See margin.**

c. Based on their fees, which babysitter would be a better choice for Mrs. Smith if she is going out for two hours? *Explain* your answer. **Lauren; for 2 hours, it would cost \$10 for Lauren and \$11 for Zachary.**

d. Mrs. Smith needs to go out for four hours. Which babysitter would be the less expensive option for her? *Justify* your response. **Zachary; for 4 hours, it would cost \$20 for Lauren and \$19 for Zachary.**

16. In a game of pool, a cue ball is hit from point *A* and follows the path of arrows as shown on the pool table at the right. In the diagram, $\overline{AB} \parallel \overline{DC}$ and $\overline{BC} \parallel \overline{ED}$.

a. *Compare* the slopes of $\overline{AB}$ and $\overline{BC}$. What can you conclude about $\angle ABC$? **The product of the slopes is −1; $\angle ABC$ is a right angle.**

b. If $m\angle BCG = 45°$, what is $m\angle DCH$? *Explain* your reasoning. **See margin.**

c. If the cue ball is hit harder, will it fall into Pocket F? *Justify* your answer. **No. *Sample answer:* Following the same path, even if the cue ball is hit harder it will not fall into Pocket *F*, it will hit to the right of the pocket.**

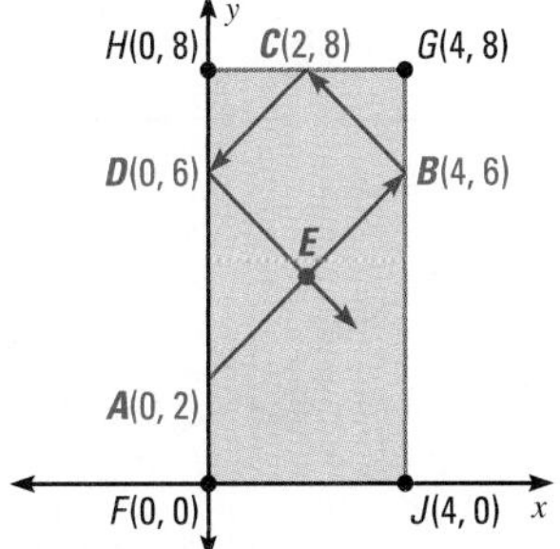

13. If two lines are cut by a transversal so the consecutive interior angles are supplementary, then the lines are parallel.

15b.

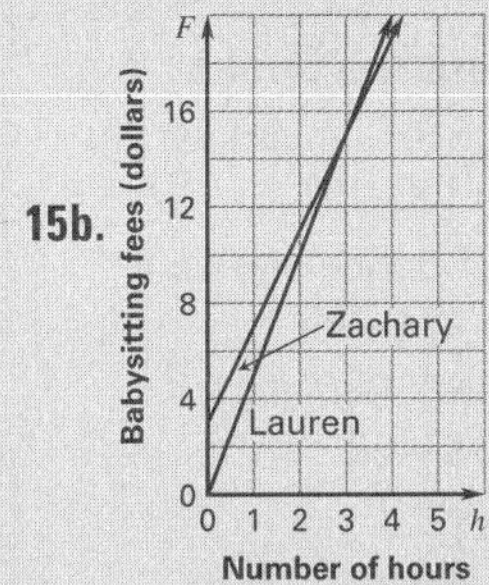

16b. 45°. *Sample answer:* Since $m\angle ABC = 90°$, $m\angle BCD = 90°$. Since $m\angle DCH + m\angle BCD + m\angle BCG = 180°$, $m\angle DCH + 90° + 45° = 180°$, and $m\angle DCH = 45°$.

Additional Resources

The following resources are available to help review the materials in Chapters 1–3.

Chapter Resource Books

- Chapter 1 CRB, Cumulative Review, pp. 106–107
- Chapter 2 CRB, Cumulative Review, pp. 104–105
- Chapter 3 CRB, Cumulative Review, pp. 91–92

16. Equation (Reason)

$3x - 14 = 34$ (Given)

$3x = 48$ (Addition Property of Equality)

$x = 16$ (Division Property of Equality)

17. Equation (Reason)

$-4(x + 3) = -28$ (Given)

$x + 3 = 7$ (Division Property of Equality)

$x = 4$ (Subtraction Property of Equality)

18. Equation (Reason)

$43 - 9(x - 7) = -x - 6$ (Given)

$-9(x - 7) = -x - 49$ (Subtraction Property of Equality)

$-9x + 63 = -x - 49$ (Distributive Property)

$-8x + 63 = -49$ (Addition Property of Equality)

$-8x = -112$ (Subtraction Property of Equality)

$x = 14$ (Division Property of Equality)

Line ℓ bisects the segment. Find the indicated lengths. *(p. 15)*

1. GH and FH **28, 56**

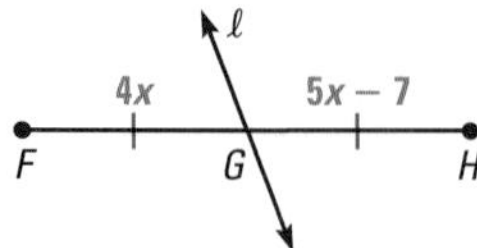

2. XY and XZ **7, 14**

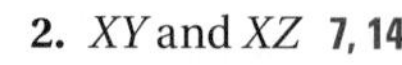

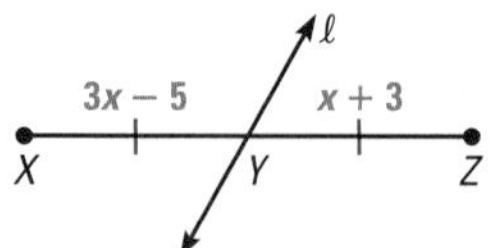

Classify the angle with the given measure as *acute, obtuse, right,* or *straight.* *(p. 24)*

3. $m\angle A = 28°$ **acute**

4. $m\angle A = 113°$ **obtuse**

5. $m\angle A = 79°$ **acute**

6. $m\angle A = 90°$ **right**

Find the perimeter and area of the figure. *(p. 49)*

7.

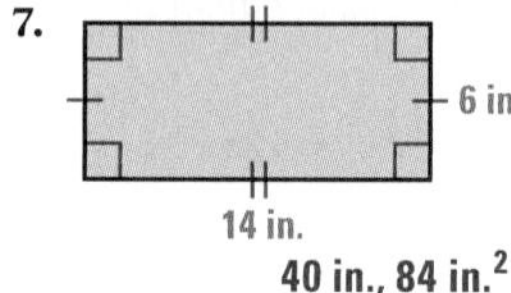

40 in., 84 in.^{2}

8.

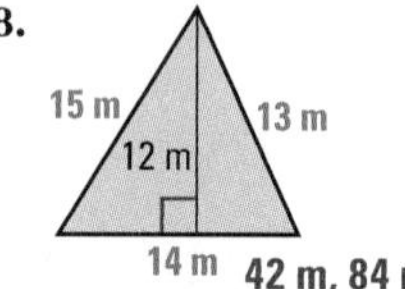

42 m, 84 m^2

9.

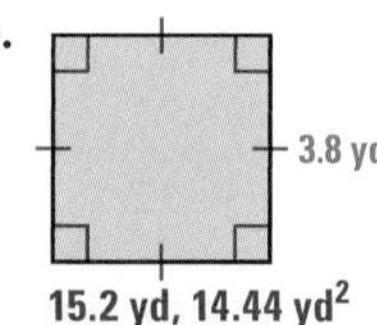

15.2 yd, 14.44 yd^2

Describe **the pattern in the numbers. Write the next number in the pattern.** *(p. 72)*

10. 1, 8, 27, 64, . . .

11. 128, 32, 8, 2, . . .

12. 2, −6, 18, −54, . . . **Each number is being multiplied by −3; 162.**

10. The natural numbers are being cubed; 125.

11. Each number is being multiplied by $\frac{1}{4}$; $\frac{1}{2}$.

Use the Law of Detachment to make a valid conclusion. *(p. 87)*

13. If $6x < 42$, then $x < 7$. The value of $6x$ is 24. **$x < 7$**

14. If an angle measure is greater than 90°, then it is an obtuse angle. The measure of $\angle A$ is 103°. **$\angle A$ is an obtuse angle.**

15. If a musician plays a violin, then the musician plays a stringed instrument. The musician is playing a violin. **The musician is playing a stringed instrument.**

Solve the equation. Write a reason for each step. *(p. 105)* **16–18. See margin.**

16. $3x - 14 = 34$

17. $-4(x + 3) = -28$

18. $43 - 9(x - 7) = -x - 6$

Find the value of the variable(s). *(pp. 124, 154)*

19. 34° (4x + 30)° **29**

20.

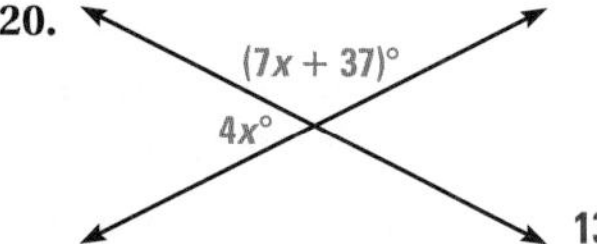

13

21.

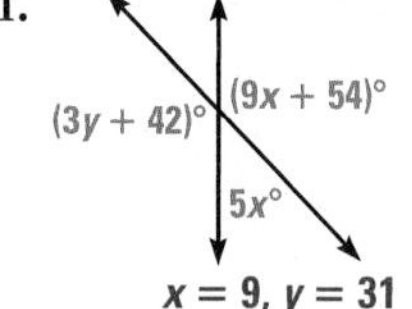

x = 9, y = 31

22.

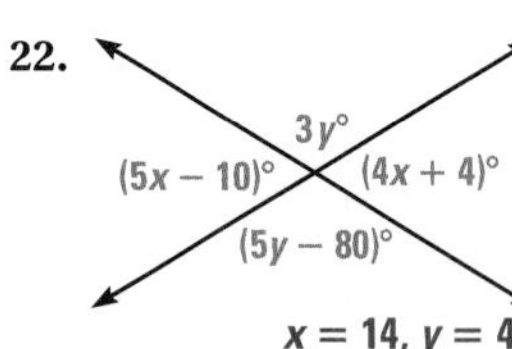

x = 14, y = 40

23.

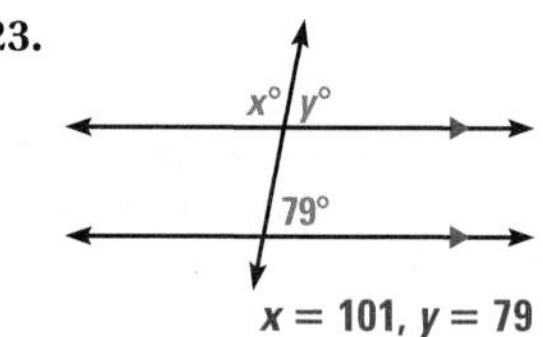

x = 101, y = 79

24.

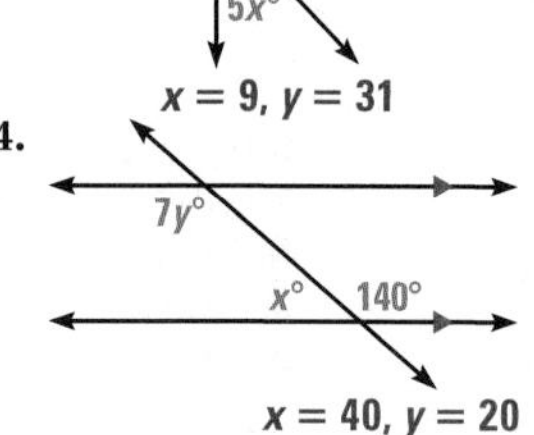

x = 40, y = 20

28a. $y = 6x - 20$

28b. $y = -\frac{1}{6}x - \frac{3}{2}$

29a. $y = -x + 10$

29b. $y = x + 14$

30a. $y = -\frac{1}{3}x + \frac{4}{3}$

30b. $y = 3x - 22$

32. *Sample answer:* a line perpendicular to a plane

33. *Sample answer:* parallel and perpendicular lines

34. parallel and perpendicular planes

37. If you want the lowest television prices, then come see Matt's TV Warehouse; if you want the lowest television prices; come see Matt's TV Warehouse.

38. If you see Matt's TV Warehouse, then you see the lowest television prices; if you do not want the lowest television prices, then don't come see Matt's TV Warehouse; if you don't come see Matt's TV Warehouse, then you don't want the lowest television prices.

Find the slope of the line through the given points. *(p. 171)*

25. $(5, -2), (7, -2)$ **0**

26. $(8, 3), (3, 14)$ $-\frac{11}{5}$

27. $(-1, 2), (0, 4)$ **2**

Write equations of the lines that pass through point P and are (a) parallel and (b) perpendicular to the line with the given equation. *(p. 180)*

28. $P(3, -2), y = 6x + 7$

29. $P(-2, 12), y = -x - 3$

30. $P(7, -1), 6y + 2x = 18$

31. Use the diagram at the right. If $\angle AEB \cong \angle AED$, is $\overleftrightarrow{AC} \perp \overleftrightarrow{DB}$? *Explain* how you know. *(p. 190)* **Yes; if two lines intersect to form a linear pair of congruent angles, then the lines are perpendicular.**

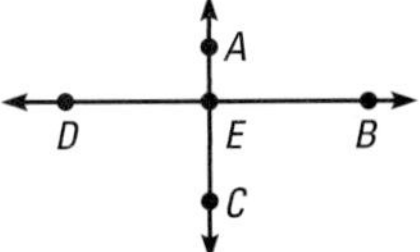

EVERYDAY INTERSECTIONS **In Exercises 32–34, what kind of geometric intersection does the photograph suggest?** *(p. 2)*

32. 

33. 

34. 

35. MAPS The distance between Westville and Easton is 37 miles. The distance between Reading and Easton is 52 miles. How far is Westville from Reading? *(p. 9)* **89 mi**

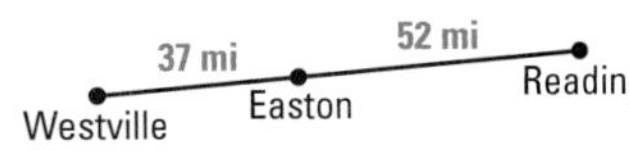

36. GARDENING A rectangular garden is 40 feet long and 25 feet wide. What is the area of the garden? *(p. 49)* **1000 ft^2**

ADVERTISING **In Exercises 37 and 38, use the following advertising slogan: "Do you want the lowest prices on new televisions? Then come and see Matt's TV Warehouse."** *(p. 79)*

37. Write the slogan in if-then form. What are the hypothesis and conclusion of the conditional statement?

38. Write the converse, inverse, and contrapositive of the conditional statement you wrote in Exercise 37.

39. CARPENTRY You need to cut eight wood planks that are the same size. You measure and cut the first plank. You cut the second piece using the first plank as a guide, as shown at the right. You use the second plank to cut the third plank. You continue this pattern. Is the last plank you cut the same length as the first? *Explain* your reasoning. *(p. 112)* **Yes. *Sample answer:* Transitive Property of Congruence of Segments**

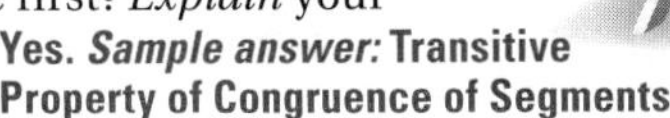

4 Pacing and Assignment Guide

REGULAR SCHEDULE

Pre-AP For pacing and assignments for a Pre-AP course, see the *Geometry Toolkit.*

Lesson	Les. Day	BASIC	AVERAGE	ADVANCED
4.1	Day 1	EP p. 896 Exs. 24–29; pp. 221–224 Exs. 1–7, 9–19 odd, 21–29, 40–49, 54, 57, 60, 61	pp. 221–224 Exs. 1–7, 8–26 even, 27–34, 40–52, 55, 58, 62	pp. 221–224 Exs. 1–7, 10, 13, 16, 19, 20, 27, 28, 31–40*, 42–53*, 56, 59, 63
4.2	Day 1	pp. 228–231 Exs. 1–14	pp. 228–231 Exs. 1–14, 36–40	pp. 228–231 Exs. 1–4, 7–14, 22*, 36–40
	Day 2	pp. 228–231 Exs. 15–19, 23–28, 33–40	pp. 228–231 Exs. 15–21, 23–31, 33–35	pp. 228–231 Exs. 15–21, 24–35*
4.3	Day 1	pp. 236–239 Exs. 1–17, 22–27, 31–37	pp. 236–239 Exs. 1–8, 10–14 even, 16–20, 22–29, 31–37 odd	pp. 236–239 Exs. 1–4, 7, 8, 11, 12, 14–30*, 33, 36, 37
4.4	Day 1	pp. 243–246 Exs. 1–18	pp. 243–246 Exs. 1, 2, 4–8 even, 9–18, 25–27	pp. 243–246 Exs. 1, 2, 6–8, 12–18, 25–30*
	Day 2	pp. 243–246 Exs. 19–24, 31–36, 42–48	pp. 243–246 Exs. 19–24, 31–39, 42–48 even	pp. 243–246 Exs. 19–24, 31–41*, 43–47 odd
4.5	Day 1	pp. 252–255 Exs. 1–13	pp. 252–255 Exs. 1, 2, 4–7, 9–13, 18–20	pp. 252–255 Exs. 1, 2, 5–7, 9–13, 18–20, 22*
	Day 2	pp. 252–255 Exs. 14–17, 23–30, 36–43	pp. 252–255 Exs. 14–17, 21, 23–34, 36–42 even	pp. 252–255 Exs. 14–17, 23–35*, 37–43 odd
4.6	Day 1	pp. 259–263 Exs. 1–11, 28	pp. 259–263 Exs. 1–11, 28, 41–43	pp. 259–263 Exs. 1, 2, 4–11, 27*, 28, 41–43
	Day 2	pp. 259–263 Exs. 12–17, 29–33, 41–46	pp. 259–263 Exs. 12–14, 18–24, 29–36, 44–46	pp. 259–263 Exs. 12–14, 19–26, 31–40*, 44–46
4.7	Day 1	pp. 267–270 Exs. 1–14, 19, 52–56	pp. 267–270 Exs. 1, 2, 4–6, 8–10, 12–14, 19, 26–29, 52–56	pp. 267–270 Exs. 1, 2, 4–6, 8–10, 12–14, 19, 26–29, 35, 36, 52–56 even
	Day 2	pp. 267–270 Exs. 15–18, 20–25, 38–45, 57–60	pp. 267–270 Exs. 16–18, 21–25, 30, 31, 39–48, 57, 59	pp. 267–270 Exs. 16–18, 22, 24, 30–34, 37*, 40–51*, 58, 60
4.8	Day 1	pp. 276–279 Exs. 1–16, 51	pp. 276–279 Exs. 1, 2, 4, 8, 10–16 even, 26–31, 51	pp. 276–279 Exs. 1, 2, 4–16 even, 26–31, 37*, 51
	Day 2	pp. 276–279 Exs. 17–29, 38–42, 45–50	pp. 276–279 Exs. 17–25, 32–36, 38–43, 45–49 odd	pp. 276–279 Exs. 17–25, 32–36, 38–44*, 46, 50
Review	Day 1	pp. 282–285 Exs. 1–29	pp. 282–285 Exs. 1–29	pp. 282–285 Exs. 1–29
Assess	Day 1	Chapter 4 Test	Chapter 4 Test	Chapter 4 Test

Yearly Pacing Chapter 4 Total – 16 days Chapters 1–4 Total – 54 days Remaining – 106 days

*Challenge Exercises EP = Extra Practice SRH = Skills Review Handbook

BLOCK SCHEDULE

DAY 1	DAY 2	DAY 3	DAY 4	DAY 5	DAY 6	DAY 7	DAY 8
4.1	**4.2 (CONT.)**	**4.4**	**4.5**	**4.6**	**4.7**	**4.8**	**REVIEW**
pp. 221–224 Exs. 1–7, 8–26 even, 27–34, 40–52, 55, 58, 62	pp. 228–231 Exs. 15–21, 23–31, 33–35	pp. 243–246 Exs. 1, 2, 4–8 even, 9–27, 31–39, 42–48 even	pp. 252–255 Exs. 1, 2, 4–7, 9–21, 23–34, 36–42 even	pp. 259–263 Exs. 1–14, 18–24, 28–36, 41–46	pp. 267–270 Exs. 1, 2, 4–6, 8–10, 12–14, 16–19, 21–31, 39–48, 52–57, 59	pp. 276–279 Exs. 1, 2, 4, 8, 10–16 even, 17–36, 38–43, 45–49 odd, 51	pp. 282–285 Exs. 1–29
4.2	**4.3**						**ASSESS**
pp. 228–231 Exs. 1–14, 36–40	pp. 236–239 Exs. 1–8, 10–14 even, 16–20, 22–29, 31–37 odd						Chapter 4 Test

Yearly Pacing Chapter 4 Total – 8 days Chapters 1–4 Total – 27 days Remaining – 53 days

Chapter Resource Guide 4

RESOURCE MANAGER

Chapter Resource Book								
CHAPTER SUPPORT								
Parents as Partners (Chapter Overview with home involvement exercises and activity)							p. 1	
LESSON SUPPORT	**4.1**	**4.2**	**4.3**	**4.4**	**4.5**	**4.6**	**4.7**	**4.8**
Teaching Guide/Lesson Plan	p. 3	p. 18	p. 32	p. 45	p. 60	p. 74	p. 87	p. 101
Activity Masters	p. 5	p. 20			p. 62		p. 89	p. 103
Technology Activities & Keystrokes				p. 47				
Activity Support Masters								
Practice (3 levels)	p. 7	p. 21	p. 34	p. 48	p. 63	p. 76	p. 90	p. 105
Study Guide	p. 13	p. 27	p. 40	p. 54	p. 69	p. 82	p. 96	p. 111
Catch-Up for Absent Students	p. 15	p. 29	p. 42	p. 56	p. 71	p. 84	p. 98	p. 113
Problem Solving/Application	p. 16	p. 30	p. 43	p. 57	p. 72	p. 85	p. 99	p. 114
Challenge Practice	p. 17	p. 31	p. 44	p. 59	p. 73	p. 86	p. 100	p. 115

REVIEW			
Chapter Review Games and Activities	p. 116	Cumulative Practice	p. 119
Project with Rubric	p. 117	Resource Book Answers	A1

Transparencies	*4.1*	*4.2*	*4.3*	*4.4*	*4.5*	*4.6*	*4.7*	*4.8*
Warm-Up/Daily Homework Quiz	✔	✔	✔	✔	✔	✔	✔	✔
Notetaking Guide	✔	✔	✔	✔	✔	✔	✔	✔
Teacher Support	✔		✔		✔			✔
Answer Transparencies	✔	✔	✔	✔	✔	✔	✔	✔

ASSESSMENT BOOK

Quizzes	p. 46	SAT/ACT Chapter Test	p. 57
Chapter Tests (3 levels)	p. 49	Alternative Assessment with Rubric	p. 59
Standardized Chapter Test	p. 55		

TECHNOLOGY

- Easy Planner
- Test and Practice Generator
- Power Presentations
- @HomeTutor
- Activity Generator
- Animated Geometry
- Classzone.com
- eEdition Plus Online
- eWorkbook Plus Online
- ML Assessment System

ADDITIONAL RESOURCES

- Worked-Out Solution Key
- Notetaking Guide
- Practice Wookbook
- Geometry Toolkit
- Benchmark Tests
- Remediation Book
- Spanish Study Guide
- Spanish Assessment Book
- Student Resources in Spanish
- Multi-Language Visual Glossary

Lesson Practice Level B

LESSON 4.1 Practice B

For use with pages 216–224

Complete the sentence with *always, sometimes,* or *never.*

1. An isosceles triangle is __?__ a right triangle. sometimes
2. An obtuse triangle is __?__ a right triangle. never
3. A right triangle is __?__ an equilateral triangle. never
4. A right triangle is __?__ an isosceles triangle. sometimes

Classify the triangle by its sides and by its angles.

5. 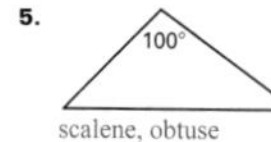

scalene, obtuse

6. 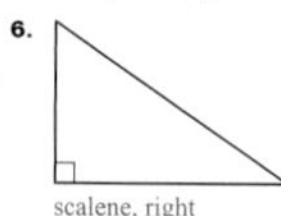
scalene, right

7. 

isosceles, acute

A triangle has the given vertices. Graph the triangle and classify it by its sides. Then determine if it is a right triangle.

8. $A(3, 1), B(3, 4), C(7, 1)$
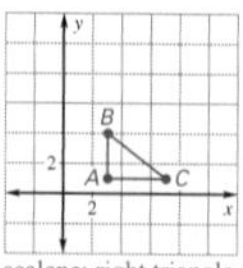
scalene; right triangle

9. $A(1, 1), B(4, 0), C(8, 5)$
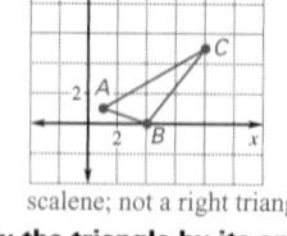
scalene; not a right triangle

10. $A(2, 2), B(6, 2), C(4, 8)$
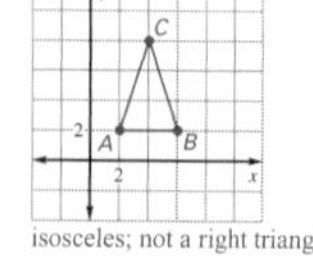
isosceles; not a right triangle

Find the value of *x*. Then classify the triangle by its angles.

11. 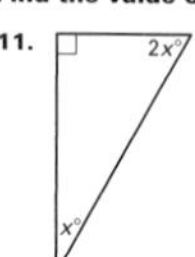

30; right

12. 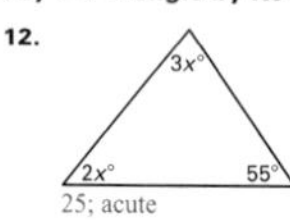

25; acute

13. 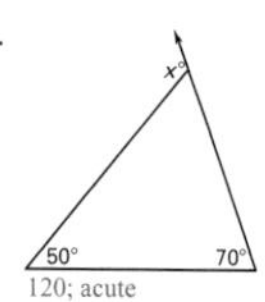

120; acute

LESSON 4.1 Practice B *continued*

For use with pages 216–224

Find the measure of the exterior angle shown.

14. 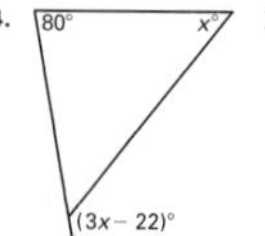

131°

15. 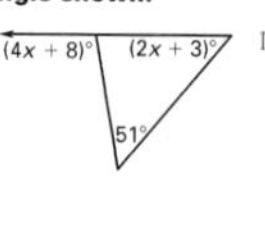

100°

16. 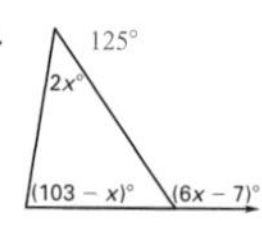

125°

Find the measure of the numbered angle.

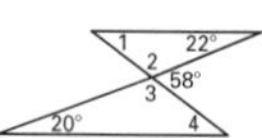

17. $\angle 1$ 36°
18. $\angle 2$ 122°
19. $\angle 3$ 122°
20. $\angle 4$ 38°

21. In $\triangle ABC$, $m\angle A = m\angle B + 30°$ and $m\angle C = m\angle B + 60°$. Find the measure of each angle. $m\angle A = 60°$, $m\angle B = 30°$, $m\angle C = 90°$

22. In $\triangle ABC$, $m\angle A = 2(m\angle B)$ and $m\angle C = 3(m\angle B)$. Find the measure of each angle. $m\angle A = 60°$, $m\angle B = 30°$, $m\angle C = 90°$

Find the values of *x* and *y*.

23. 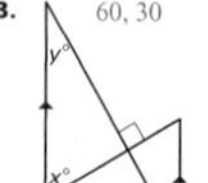

60, 30

24. 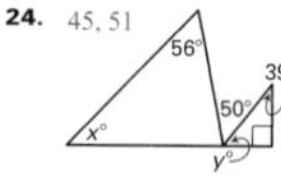

45, 51

25. 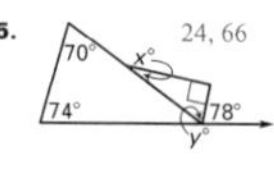

24, 66

26. **Metal Brace** The diagram shows the dimensions of a metal brace used for strengthening a vertical and horizontal wooden junction. Classify the triangle formed by its sides. Then copy the triangle, measure the angles, and classify the triangle by its angles. scalene; right

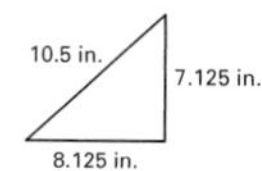

LESSON 4.2 Practice B

For use with pages 225–231

1. Copy the congruent triangles shown at the right. Then label the vertices of your triangles so that $\triangle AMT \cong \triangle CDN$. Identify all pairs of congruent corresponding angles and corresponding sides.
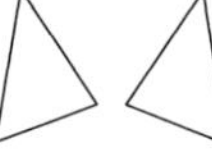
Check student diagram; $\overline{AM} \cong \overline{CD}$; $\overline{AT} \cong \overline{CN}$; $\overline{MT} \cong \overline{DN}$; $\angle A \cong \angle C$; $\angle M \cong \angle D$; $\angle T \cong \angle N$

In the diagram, $\triangle TJM \cong \triangle PHS$. Complete the statement.

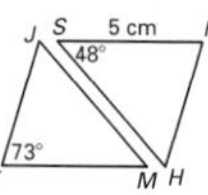

2. $\angle P \cong$ __?__ $\angle T$
3. $\overline{JM} \cong$ __?__ $\overline{HS}$
4. $m\angle M =$ __?__ 48°
5. $m\angle P =$ __?__ 73°
6. $MT =$ __?__ 5 cm
7. $\triangle HPS \cong$ __?__ $\triangle JTM$

Write a congruence statement for any figures that can be proved congruent. *Explain* your reasoning.

8. 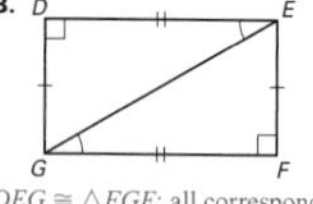

$\triangle DEG \cong \triangle FGE$; all corresponding sides and angles are congruent.

9. 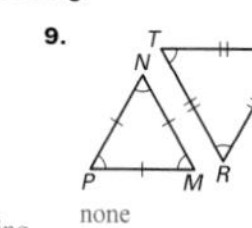

none

10. 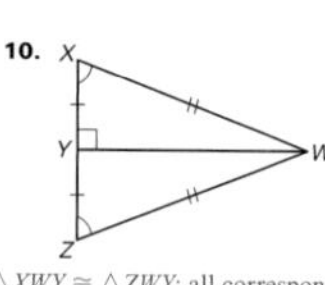

$\triangle XWY \cong \triangle ZWY$; all corresponding sides and angles are congruent.

Find the value of *x*.

11. 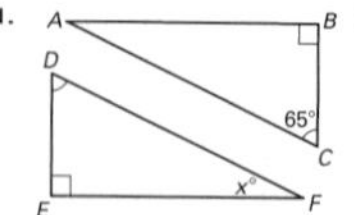

25

12. 
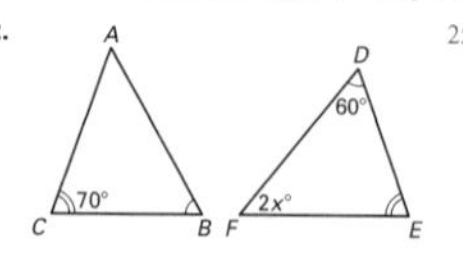

25

In Exercises 13 and 14, use the given information to find the indicated values.

13. Given $\triangle ABC \cong \triangle DEF$, find the values of x and y. 17, 17
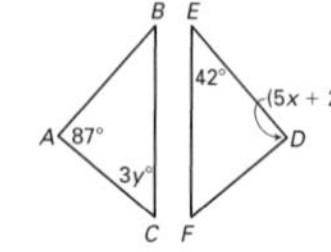

LESSON 4.2 Practice B *continued*

For use with pages 225–231

14. Given $\triangle HJK \cong \triangle TRS$, find the values of a and b. 9, 8
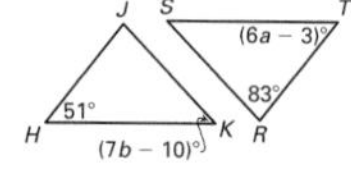

15. Graph the triangle with vertices $A(1, 2)$, $B(7, 2)$, and $C(5, 4)$. Then graph a triangle congruent to $\triangle ABC$.
Sample answer:
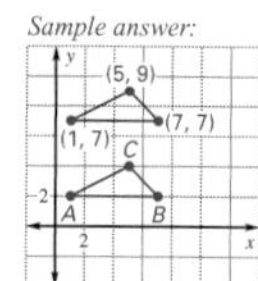

16. **Proof** Complete the proof.

GIVEN: $\angle ABD \cong \angle CDB$, $\angle ADB \cong \angle CBD$, $\overline{AD} \cong \overline{BC}$, $\overline{AB} \cong \overline{DC}$

PROVE: $\triangle ABD \cong \triangle CDB$

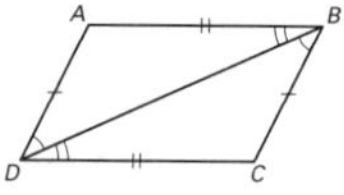

Statements	Reasons
1. $\angle ABD \cong \angle CDB$, $\angle ADB \cong \angle CBD$, $\overline{AD} \cong \overline{BC}$, $\overline{AB} \cong \overline{DC}$	1. Given
2. $\overline{BD} \cong \overline{BD}$	2. __?__ Reflexive Property of Congruence
3. __?__ $\angle A \cong \angle C$	3. Third Angles Theorem
4. $\triangle ABD \cong \triangle CDB$	4. __?__ Definition of congruence

17. **Carpet Designs** A carpet is made of congruent triangles. One triangular shape is used to make all of the triangles in the design. Which property guarantees that all the triangles are congruent? Transitive Property of Congruent Triangles

LESSON 4.3

Practice B

For use with pages 233–239

Decide whether the congruence statement is true. *Explain* your reasoning.

1. $\triangle ABD \cong \triangle CDB$ **2.** $\triangle RST \cong \triangle RQT$ **3.** $\triangle ABC \cong \triangle DEF$

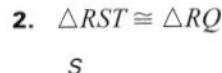

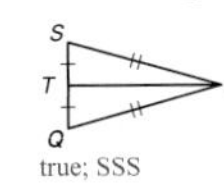

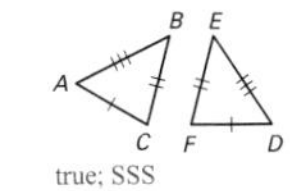

true; SSS true; SSS true; SSS

Use the given coordinates to determine if $\triangle ABC \cong \triangle DEF$.

4. $A(1, 2), B(4, -3), C(2, 5), D(4, 7), E(7, 2), F(5, 10)$ congruent

5. $A(1, 1), B(4, 0), C(7, 5), D(4, -5), E(6, -6), F(9, -1)$ not congruent

6. $A(2, -2), B(5, 1), C(4, 8), D(7, 5), E(10, 8), F(9, 13)$ not congruent

7. $A(-3, 0), B(6, 2), C(-1, 9), D(4, -10), E(13, -8), F(6, -1)$ congruent

Decide whether the figure is stable. *Explain* your reasoning. See below.

8.

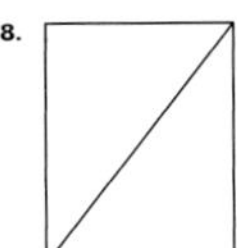

9.

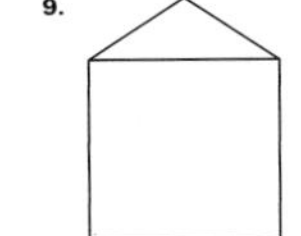

10.

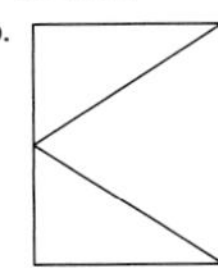

Determine whether $\triangle ABC \cong \triangle DEF$. *Explain* your reasoning.

11.

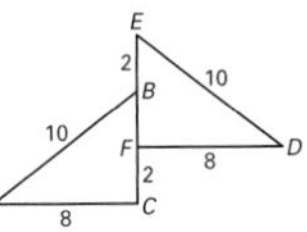

Yes; the corresponding sides are congruent.

12.

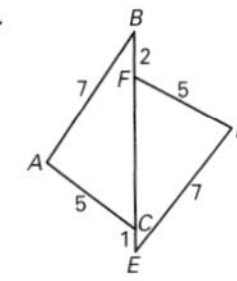

No; the corresponding sides are not congruent.

8. Stable; the figure forms triangles of fixed side lengths which cannot change shape by the SSS Congruence Postulate.

9. Not stable; there are many possible shapes for a four-sided figure with the given side lengths.

10. Stable; the figure forms triangles of fixed side lengths which cannot change shape by the SSS Congruence Postulate.

LESSON 4.3

Practice B *continued*

For use with pages 233–239

13. Proof Complete the proof.

GIVEN: $\overline{AB} \cong \overline{CD}, \overline{BC} \cong \overline{AD}$

PROVE: $\triangle ABC \cong \triangle CDA$

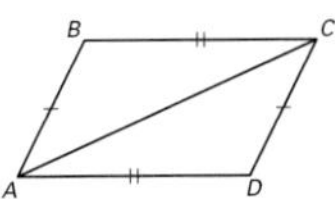

Statements	Reasons
1. $\overline{AB} \cong \overline{CD}$	**1.** ? Given
2. $\overline{BC} \cong \overline{AD}$	**2.** ? Given
3. $\overline{AC} \cong \overline{AC}$	**3.** ? Reflexive Property of Congruence
4. $\triangle ABC \cong \triangle CDA$	**4.** ? SSS Congruence Postulate

14. Proof Complete the proof.

GIVEN: $\overline{AB} \cong \overline{CB}$, D is the midpoint of $\overline{AC}$

PROVE: $\triangle ABD \cong \triangle CBD$

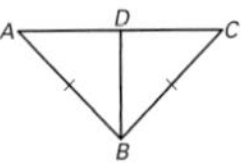

Statements	Reasons
1. $\overline{AB} \cong \overline{CB}$	**1.** ? Given
2. D is the midpoint of $\overline{AC}$	**2.** ? Given
3. $\overline{AD} \cong \overline{CD}$	**3.** ? Definition of midpoint
4. $\overline{BD} \cong \overline{BD}$	**4.** ? Reflexive Property of Congruence
5. $\triangle ABD \cong \triangle CBD$	**5.** ? SSS Congruence Postulate

15. Picture Frame The backs of two different picture frames are shown below. Which picture frame is stable? *Explain* your reasoning.

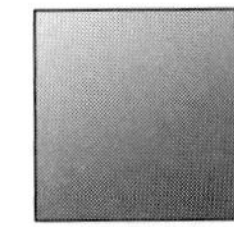

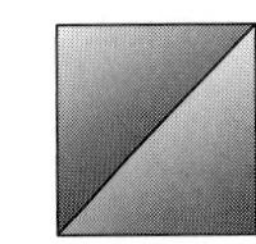

The second picture frame is stable because the brace and the sides form triangles of fixed side lengths which cannot change shape by the SSS Congruence Postulate.

LESSON 4.4

Practice B

For use with pages 240–246

Use the diagram to name the included angle between the given pair of sides.

1. $\overline{AB}$ and $\overline{BC}$ $\angle ABC$ **2.** $\overline{BC}$ and $\overline{CD}$ $\angle BCD$

3. $\overline{AB}$ and $\overline{BD}$ $\angle ABD$ **4.** $\overline{BD}$ and $\overline{DA}$ $\angle BDA$

5. $\overline{DA}$ and $\overline{AB}$ $\angle DAB$ **6.** $\overline{CD}$ and $\overline{DB}$ $\angle CDB$

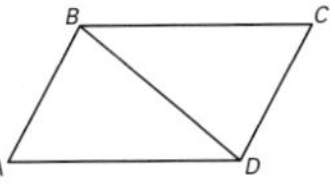

Decide whether enough information is given to prove that the triangles are congruent using the SAS Congruence Postulate.

7. $\triangle MAE, \triangle TAE$ not enough **8.** $\triangle DKA, \triangle TKS$ enough **9.** $\triangle JRM, \triangle JTM$ not enough

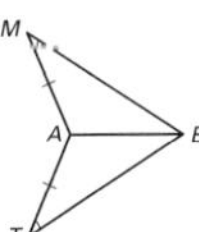

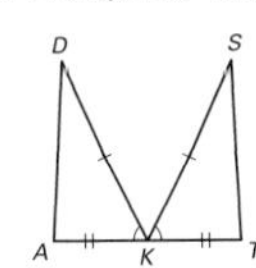

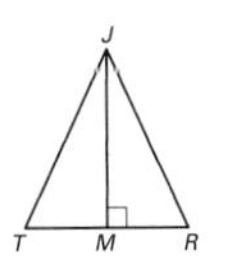

Decide whether enough information is given to prove that the triangles are congruent. If there is enough information, state the congruence postulate or theorem you would use.

10. $\triangle ABC, \triangle DEF$ **11.** $\triangle MNO, \triangle RON$ **12.** $\triangle ABC, \triangle ADC$

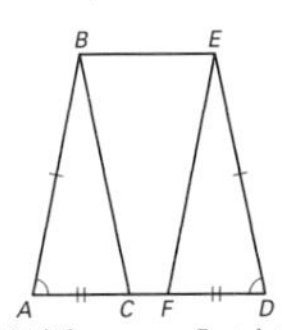

Yes, SAS Congruence Postulate

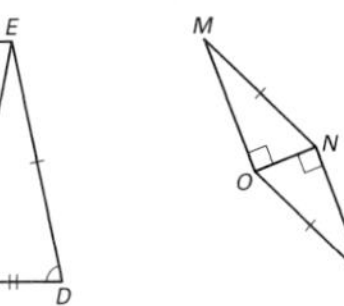

Yes, HL Congruence Theorem

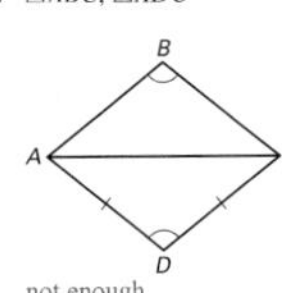

not enough

State the third congruence that must be given to prove that $\triangle JRM \cong \triangle DFB$ using the indicated postulate.

13. GIVEN: $\overline{JR} \cong \overline{DF}, \overline{JM} \cong \overline{DB}$, ? $\cong$?
Use the SSS Congruence Postulate. $\overline{RM} \cong \overline{FB}$

14. GIVEN: $\overline{JR} \cong \overline{DF}, \overline{JM} \cong \overline{DB}$, ? $\cong$?
Use the SAS Congruence Postulate. $\angle J \cong \angle D$

15. GIVEN: $\overline{RM} \cong \overline{FB}$, $\angle J$ is a right angle and $\angle J \cong \angle D$, ? $\cong$?
Use the HL Congruence Theorem. $\overline{JM} \cong \overline{DB}$ or $\overline{JR} \cong \overline{DF}$

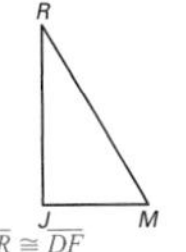

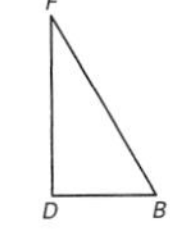

LESSON 4.4

Practice B *continued*

For use with pages 240–246

16. Proof Complete the proof.

GIVEN: B is the midpoint of $\overline{AE}$.
B is the midpoint of $\overline{CD}$.

PROVE: $\triangle ABD \cong \triangle EBC$

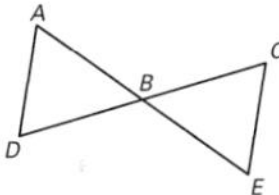

Statements	Reasons
1. B is the midpoint of $\overline{AE}$.	**1.** ? Given
2. ? $\overline{AB} \cong \overline{BE}$	**2.** Definition of midpoint
3. B is the midpoint of $\overline{CD}$.	**3.** ? Given
4. ? $\overline{CB} \cong \overline{BD}$	**4.** Definition of midpoint
5. $\angle ABD \cong \angle EBC$	**5.** ? Vertical Angles Theorem
6. $\triangle ABD \cong \triangle EBC$	**6.** ? SAS Congruence Postulate

17. Proof Complete the proof.

GIVEN: $\overline{AB} \parallel \overline{CD}, \overline{AB} \cong \overline{CD}$

PROVE: $\triangle ABC \cong \triangle DCB$

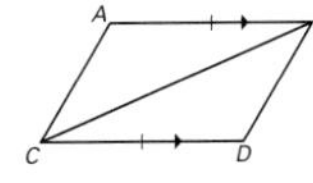

Statements	Reasons
1. $\overline{AB} \parallel \overline{CD}$	**1.** ? Given
2. $\angle ABC \cong \angle DCB$	**2.** ? Alternate Interior Angles Theorem
3. $\overline{AB} \cong \overline{CD}$	**3.** ? Given
4. $\overline{CB} \cong \overline{CB}$	**4.** ? Reflexive Property of Congruence
5. $\triangle ABC \cong \triangle DCB$	**5.** ? SAS Congruence Postulate

4 Lesson Practice Level B

LESSON 4.5 Practice B
For use with pages 249–255

State the third congruence that is needed to prove that $\triangle DEF \cong \triangle MNO$ using the given postulate or theorem.

1. GIVEN: $\overline{DE} \cong \overline{MN}$, $\angle M \cong \angle D$, _?_ $\cong$ _?_
   Use the SAS Congruence Postulate. $\overline{DF} \cong \overline{MO}$
2. GIVEN: $\overline{FE} \cong \overline{ON}$, $\angle F \cong \angle O$, _?_ $\cong$ _?_
   Use the AAS Congruence Theorem. $\angle D \cong \angle M$
3. GIVEN: $\overline{DF} \cong \overline{MO}$, $\angle F \cong \angle O$, _?_ $\cong$ _?_
   Use the ASA Congruence Postulate. $\angle D \cong \angle M$

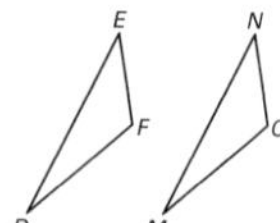

State the third congruence that is needed to prove that $\triangle ABC \cong \triangle XYZ$ using the given postulate or theorem.

4. GIVEN: $\angle A \cong \angle X$, $\angle B \cong \angle Y$, _?_ $\cong$ _?_ $\overline{BC} \cong \overline{YZ}$ or
   Use the AAS Congruence Theorem. $\overline{AC} \cong \overline{XZ}$
5. GIVEN: $\angle A \cong \angle X$, $\overline{AB} \cong \overline{XY}$, _?_ $\cong$ _?_
   Use the ASA Congruence Postulate. $\angle B \cong \angle Y$
6. GIVEN: $\overline{BC} \cong \overline{YZ}$, $\angle C \cong \angle Z$, _?_ $\cong$ _?_
   Use the AAS Congruence Theorem. $\angle A \cong \angle X$

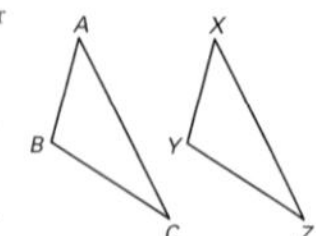

Is it possible to prove that the triangles are congruent? If so, state the postulate(s) or theorem(s) you would use.

7.
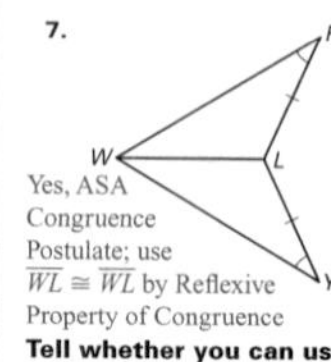

Yes, ASA Congruence Postulate; use $\overline{WL} \cong \overline{WL}$ by Reflexive Property of Congruence

8.
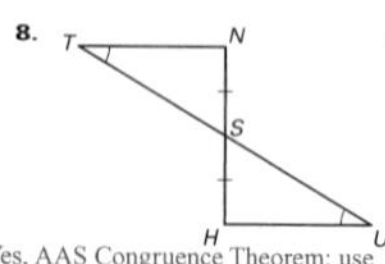

Yes, AAS Congruence Theorem; use $\angle TSN \cong \angle USH$ by Vertical Angles Theorem

9.
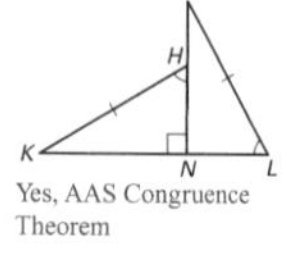

Yes, AAS Congruence Theorem

Tell whether you can use the given information to determine whether $\triangle JRM \cong \triangle XYZ$. *Explain* your reasoning. See below.

10. $\overline{JM} \cong \overline{XZ}$, $\angle M \cong \angle Z$, $\angle R \cong \angle Y$
11. $\overline{JM} \cong \overline{XZ}$, $\overline{JR} \cong \overline{XY}$, $\angle J \cong \angle X$
12. $\angle J \cong \angle X$, $\angle M \cong \angle Z$, $\angle R \cong \angle Y$
13. $\angle M \cong \angle Z$, $\angle R \cong \angle Y$, $\overline{JM} \cong \overline{XY}$

10. Yes, AAS Congruence Theorem

11. Yes, SAS Congruence Postulate

12. No; three pairs of congruent angles is insufficient to prove triangle congruence.

13. No; two angles and a non-included side are congruent, but the non-included sides are not corresponding parts.

LESSON 4.5

LESSON 4.5 Practice B *continued*
For use with pages 249–255

Explain how you can prove that the indicated triangles are congruent using the given postulate or theorem. See below.

14. $\triangle BEF \cong \triangle BED$ by SAS
15. $\triangle ADB \cong \triangle CFB$ by ASA
16. $\triangle AFB \cong \triangle CDB$ by AAS

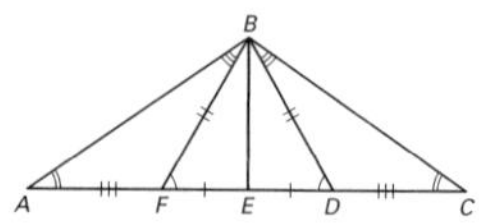

17. **Proof** Complete the proof.
    GIVEN: $\overline{WU} \parallel \overline{YV}$, $\overline{XU} \parallel \overline{ZV}$, $\overline{WX} \cong \overline{YZ}$
    PROVE: $\triangle WXU \cong \triangle YZV$

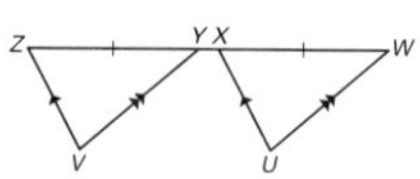

Statements	Reasons
1. $\overline{WU} \parallel \overline{YV}$	1. _?_ Given
2. $\angle UWX \cong \angle VYZ$	2. _?_ Corresponding Angles Postulate
3. $\overline{XU} \parallel \overline{ZV}$	3. _?_ Given
4. $\angle UXW \cong \angle VZY$	4. _?_ Corresponding Angles Postulate
5. $\overline{WX} \cong \overline{YZ}$	5. _?_ Given
6. $\triangle WXU \cong \triangle YZV$	6. _?_ ASA Congruence Postulate

18. **Proof** Write a proof.
    GIVEN: $\angle B \cong \angle D$, $\angle DAE \cong \angle BEA$
    PROVE: $\triangle ABC \cong \triangle EDC$

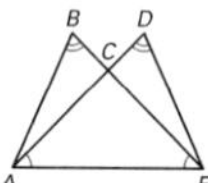

It is given that $\angle B \cong \angle D$. By the Converse of Base Angles Theorem, $\overline{AC} \cong \overline{EC}$. By the Vertical Angles Theorem, $\angle BCA \cong \angle DCE$. $\triangle ABC \cong \triangle EDC$ by the AAS Congruence Theorem.

14. Two pairs of corresponding sides ($\overline{BF} \cong \overline{BD}$, $\overline{EF} \cong \overline{ED}$) and the corresponding included angles ($\angle BFE \cong \angle BDE$) are congruent.

15. Two pairs of corresponding angles ($\angle ADB \cong \angle CFB$, $\angle BAD \cong \angle BCF$) and the corresponding included sides ($\overline{AD} \cong \overline{CF}$) are congruent.

16. Two pairs of corresponding angles ($\angle ABF \cong \angle CBD$, $\angle BAF \cong \angle BCD$) and the corresponding non-included sides ($\overline{AF} \cong \overline{CD}$) are congruent.

LESSON 4.5

LESSON 4.6 Practice B
For use with pages 256–263

Tell which triangles you can show are congruent in order to prove the statement. What postulate or theorem would you use?

1. $\overline{BC} \cong \overline{AD}$
   $\triangle ABC \cong \triangle CDA$; SAS

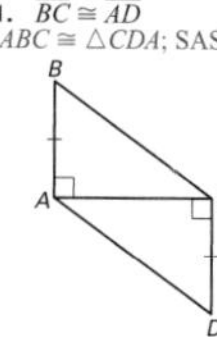

2. $\angle TSU \cong \angle VSU$
   $\triangle TSU \cong \triangle VSU$; AAS

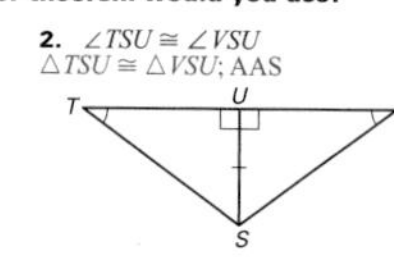

3. $\angle ADB \cong \angle CBD$
   $\triangle ABD \cong \triangle CDB$; SSS

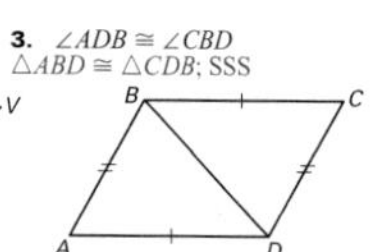

4. $\angle KHN \cong \angle MGT$
   $\triangle NKH \cong \triangle TMG$; AAS

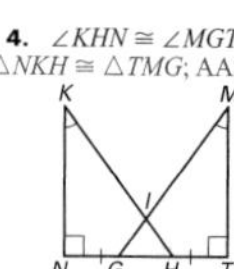

5. $\overline{BD} \cong \overline{BE}$
   $\triangle ABD \cong \triangle CBE$; ASA

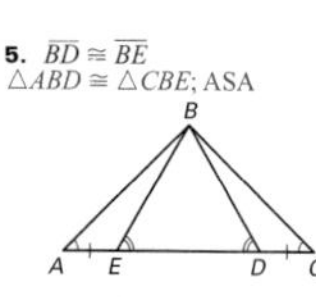

6. $\overline{BC} \cong \overline{AT}$
   $\triangle ABC \cong \triangle STA$; AAS

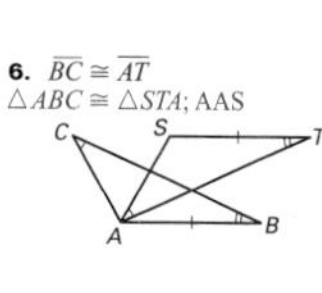

Use the diagram to write a plan for a proof.

7. PROVE: $\angle DAB \cong \angle BCD$

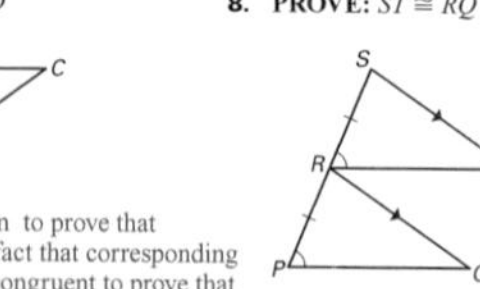

Use the HL Congruence Theorem to prove that $\triangle DAB \cong \triangle BCD$. Then use the fact that corresponding parts of congruent triangles are congruent to prove that $\angle DAB \cong \angle BCD$.

8. PROVE: $\overline{ST} \cong \overline{RQ}$

Because $\overline{ST} \parallel \overline{RQ}$, $\angle PRQ \cong \angle RST$ by the Corresponding Angles Postulate. Use the ASA Congruence Postulate to prove that $\triangle PRQ \cong \triangle RST$. Then use the fact that corresponding parts of congruent triangles are congruent to prove that $\overline{ST} \cong \overline{RQ}$.

Use the vertices of $\triangle ABC$ and $\triangle DEF$ to show that $\angle A \cong \angle D$. *Explain* your reasoning.

9. $A(1, 2)$, $B(4, -3)$, $C(2, 5)$, $D(4, 7)$, $E(7, 2)$, $F(5, 10)$

10. $A(2, 3)$, $B(2, 9)$, $C(6, 6)$, $D(8, 5)$, $E(8, 11)$, $F(12, 8)$

9. Use the Distance Formula to find the side lengths of the triangles. Use the SSS Congruence Postulate to show that $\triangle ABC \cong \triangle DEF$. Then use the fact that corresponding parts of congruent triangles are congruent to prove that $\angle A \cong \angle D$.

10. Use the Distance Formula to find the side lengths of the triangles. Use the SSS Congruence Postulate to show that $\triangle ABC \cong \triangle DEF$. Then use the fact that corresponding parts of congruent triangles are congruent to prove that $\angle A \cong \angle D$.

LESSON 4.6

LESSON 4.6 Practice B *continued*
For use with pages 256–263

11. **Proof** Complete the proof.
    GIVEN: $\overline{YX} \cong \overline{WX}$
    $\overline{ZX}$ bisects $\angle YXW$.
    PROVE: $\overline{YZ} \cong \overline{WZ}$

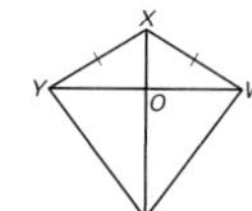

Statements	Reasons
1. $\overline{YX} \cong \overline{WX}$	1. _?_ Given
2. $\overline{ZX}$ bisects $\angle YXW$.	2. _?_ Given
3. $\angle YXZ \cong \angle WXZ$	3. _?_ Definition of angle bisector
4. $\overline{XZ} \cong \overline{XZ}$	4. _?_ Reflexive Property of Congruence
5. $\triangle YXZ \cong \triangle WXZ$	5. _?_ SAS Congruence Postulate
6. $\overline{YZ} \cong \overline{WZ}$	6. _?_ Corresponding parts of congruent triangles are congruent.

Use the information given in the diagram to write a proof.

12. PROVE: $\overline{MN} \cong \overline{TQ}$

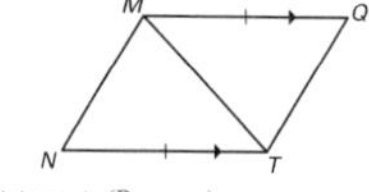

Statements (Reasons)
1. $\overline{MQ} \cong \overline{NT}$ (Given)
2. $\overline{MQ} \parallel \overline{NT}$ (Given)
3. $\angle NTM \cong \angle QMT$ (Alternate Interior Angles Theorem)
4. $\overline{MT} \cong \overline{MT}$ (Reflexive Property of Congruence)
5. $\triangle NTM \cong \triangle QMT$ (SAS Congruence Postulate)
6. $\overline{MN} \cong \overline{TQ}$ (Corresponding parts of congruent triangles are congruent.)

13. PROVE: $\overline{DB} \cong \overline{CB}$

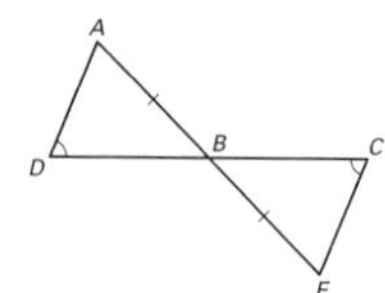

Statements (Reasons)
1. $\overline{AB} \cong \overline{BE}$ (Given)
2. $\angle ADB \cong \angle ECB$ (Given)
3. $\angle ABD \cong \angle EBC$ (Vertical Angles Theorem)
4. $\triangle ABD \cong \triangle EBC$ (AAS Congruence Theorem)
5. $\overline{DB} \cong \overline{CB}$ (Corresponding parts of congruent triangles are congruent.)

LESSON 4.6

LESSON 4.7 Practice B
For use with pages 264–270

Find the values of x and y.

1. 22, 35
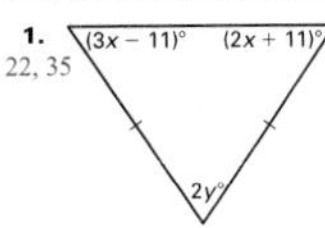

2. 15, 38
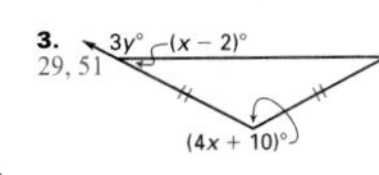

3. 29, 51
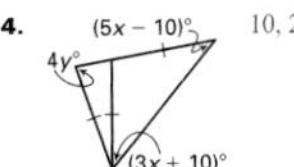

4. 10, 20
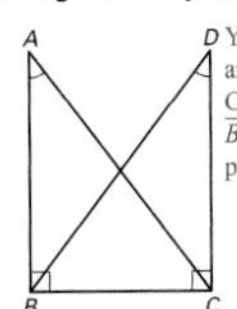

5. 32, 19
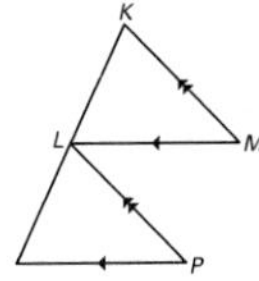

6. 30, 13
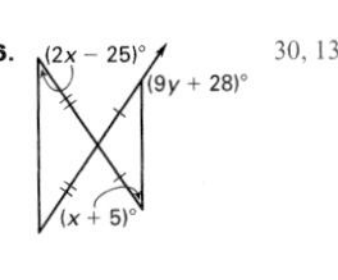

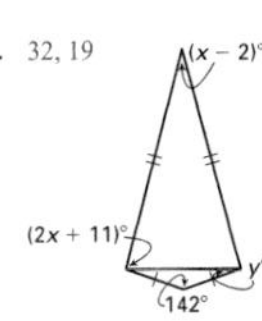

Decide whether enough information is given to prove that the triangles are congruent. *Explain* your answer.

7. You can prove the triangles are congruent by AAS Congruence Theorem. Use $\overline{BC} \cong \overline{BC}$ by the reflexive property of congruence.

8. There is not enough information. You only know that $\angle M \cong \angle P$, because two sets of lines are parallel. You do not know the lengths of any of the sides.

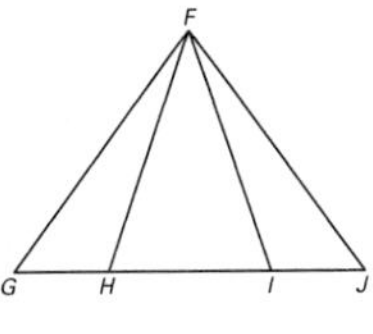

In Exercises 9 and 10, complete the proof.

9. GIVEN: $\overline{FG} \cong \overline{FJ}, \overline{HG} \cong \overline{IJ}$

PROVE: $\overline{HF} \cong \overline{IF}$

Statements	Reasons
1. $\overline{FG} \cong \overline{FJ}$	1. _?_ Given
2. _?_ $\angle G \cong \angle J$	2. Base Angles Theorem
3. $\overline{HG} \cong \overline{IJ}$	3. _?_ Given
4. _?_ $\triangle FGH \cong \triangle FJI$	4. SAS Congruence Postulate
5. $\overline{HF} \cong \overline{IF}$	5. _?_ Corresponding parts of congruent triangles are congruent.

LESSON 4.7 Practice B *continued*
For use with pages 264–270

10. GIVEN: $\angle 1 \cong \angle 2, \overline{AC} \cong \overline{BD}$

PROVE: $\angle 3 \cong \angle 4$

Statements	Reasons
1. $\angle 1 \cong \angle 2$	1. _?_ Given
2. $\overline{AC} \cong \overline{BD}$	2. _?_ Given
3. $\angle AEC \cong \angle BED$	3. _?_ Vertical Angles Theorem
4. _?_ $\triangle AEC \cong \triangle BED$	4. AAS Congruence Theorem
5. $\overline{AE} \cong \overline{BE}$	5. _?_ Corresponding parts of congruent triangles are congruent.
6. $\angle 3 \cong \angle 4$	6. _?_ Base Angles Theorem

In Exercises 11–16, use the diagram. Complete the statement. Tell what theorem you used.

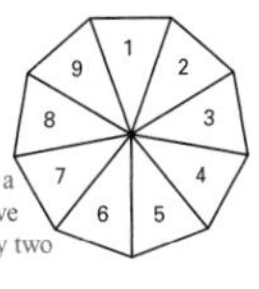

11. If $\overline{PQ} \cong \overline{PT}$, then $\angle$ _?_ $\cong \angle$ _?_. Q, T; Base Angles Theorem

12. If $\angle PQV \cong \angle PVQ$, then _?_ $\cong$ _?_. $\overline{PQ}, \overline{PV}$; Converse of Base Angles Theorem

13. If $\overline{RP} \cong \overline{SP}$, then $\angle$ _?_ $\cong \angle$ _?_. PRS, PSR; Base Angles Theorem

14. If $\overline{TP} \cong \overline{TR}$, then $\angle$ _?_ $\cong \angle$ _?_. PRT, RPT; Base Angles Theorem

15. If $\angle PSQ \cong \angle SPQ$, then _?_ $\cong$ _?_. $\overline{QS}, \overline{QP}$; Converse of Base Angles Theorem

16. If $\angle PUV \cong \angle PVU$, then _?_ $\cong$ _?_. $\overline{PU}, \overline{PV}$; Converse of Base Angles Theorem

In Exercises 17–19, use the following information.

Prize Wheel A radio station sets up a prize wheel when they are out promoting their station. People spin the wheel and receive the prize that corresponds to the number the wheel stops on. The 9 triangles in the diagram are isosceles triangles with congruent vertex angles.

17. The measure of the vertex angle of triangle 1 is 40°. Find the measures of the base angles. 70°

18. Explain how you know that triangle 1 is congruent to triangle 6.
Each of the triangles is isosceles and every pair of adjacent triangles have a common side, so the legs of all the triangles are congruent by the Transitive Property of Congruence. The common vertex angles are congruent, so any two of the triangles are congruent by the SAS Congruence Postulate.

19. Trace the prize wheel. Then form a triangle whose vertices are the midpoints of the bases of the triangles 1, 4, and 7. What type of triangle is this? equilateral

LESSON 4.8 Practice B
For use with pages 271–279

Name the type of transformation shown.

1. reflection
2. translation
3. rotation

4. Figure *ABCD* has vertices $A(1, 2)$, $B(4, -3)$, $C(5, 5)$, and $D(4, 7)$. Sketch *ABCD* and draw its image after the translation $(x, y) \rightarrow (x + 5, y + 3)$.

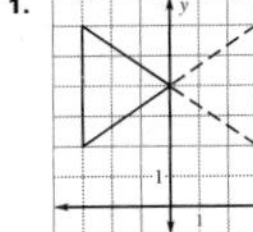

5. Figure *ABCD* has vertices $A(-2, 3)$, $B(1, 7)$, $C(6, 2)$, and $D(-1, -2)$. Sketch *ABCD* and draw its image after the translation $(x, y) \rightarrow (x - 2, y - 4)$.

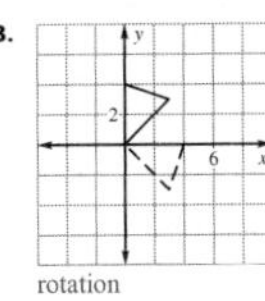

6. Figure *ABCD* has vertices $A(3, -1)$, $B(6, -2)$, $C(5, 3)$, and $D(0, 4)$. Sketch *ABCD* and draw its image after the translation $(x, y) \rightarrow (x - 3, y + 2)$.

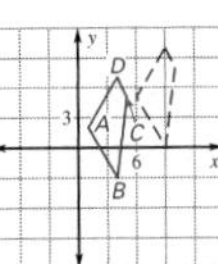

7. Figure *ABCD* has vertices $A(-1, 3)$, $B(4, -1)$, $C(6, 4)$, and $D(1, 5)$. Sketch *ABCD* and draw its image after the translation $(x, y) \rightarrow (x + 4, y - 5)$.

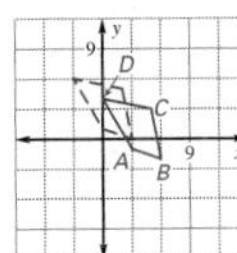

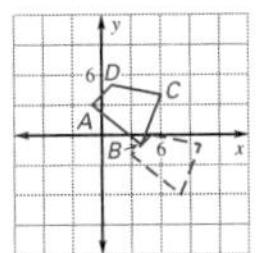

Use coordinate notation to describe the translation.

8. 3 units to the right, 5 units down $(x, y) \rightarrow (x + 3, y - 5)$

9. 7 units to the left, 2 units down $(x, y) \rightarrow (x - 7, y - 2)$

10. 4 units to the left, 6 units up $(x, y) \rightarrow (x - 4, y + 6)$

11. 1 unit to the right, 8 units up $(x, y) \rightarrow (x + 1, y + 8)$

LESSON 4.8 Practice B *continued*
For use with pages 271–279

Use a reflection in the y-axis to draw the other half of the figure.

12.
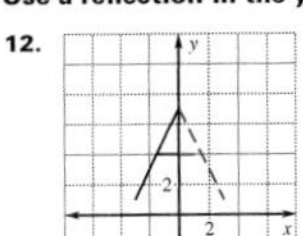

13.
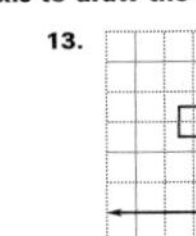

14.
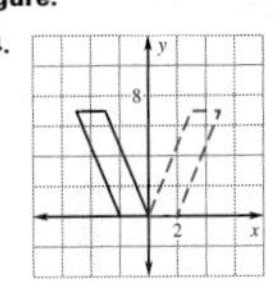

Use the coordinates to graph $\overline{AB}$ and $\overline{CD}$. Tell whether $\overline{CD}$ is a rotation of $\overline{AB}$ about the origin. If so, give the angle and direction of rotation.

15. $A(-2, 5)$, $B(-2, 0)$, $C(0, 1)$, $D(3, 1)$ not a rotation

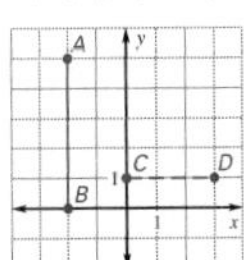

16. $A(1, 4)$, $B(4, 1)$, $C(1, -4)$, $D(4, -1)$ rotation; 90° clockwise

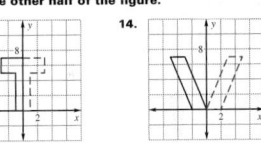

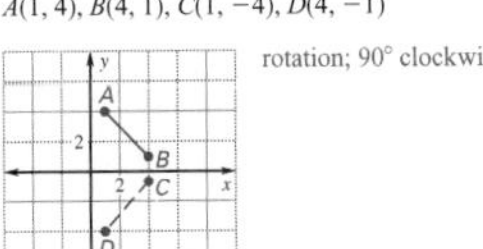

Complete the statement using the description of the translation. In the description, points (2, 0) and (3, 4) are two vertices of a triangle.

17. If (2, 0) translates to (4, 1), then (3, 4) translates to _?_. (5, 5)

18. If (2, 0) translates to (−2, −1), then (3, 4) translates to _?_. (−1, 3)

A point on an image and the translation are given. Find the corresponding point on the original figure.

19. Point on image: (2, −4); translation: $(x, y) \rightarrow (x - 4, y + 3)$ (6, −7)

20. Point on image: (−5, −7); translation: $(x, y) \rightarrow (x, -y)$ (−5, 7)

21. **Verifying Congruence** Verify that $\triangle DEF$ is a congruence transformation of $\triangle ABC$. Explain your reasoning.
Use the Distance Formula to show that corresponding sides are congruent. $\triangle ABC \cong \triangle DEF$ by SSS Congruence Postulate.

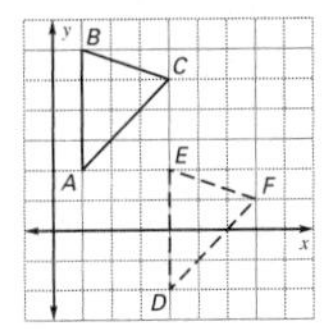

4 Assessment

CHAPTER 4 Quiz 1
For use after Lessons 4.1–4.3

A triangle has the given vertices. Graph the triangle and classify it by its sides. Then, determine if it is a right triangle.

1. $A(-5, 0)$, $B(0, 6)$, $C(5, 0)$

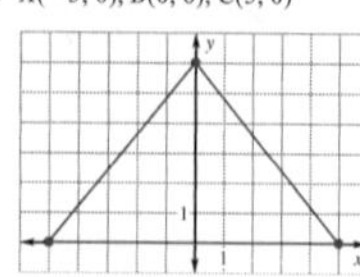

2. $A(3, -5)$, $B(7, 1)$, $C(3, 1)$

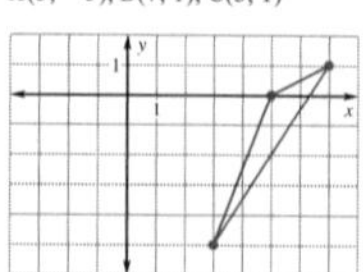

In the diagram, $ABCD \cong EFGH$.

3. Find the value of x.
4. Find the value of y.

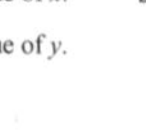

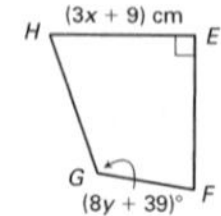

In Exercises 5–12, complete the proof.

GIVEN $\overline{MN} \cong \overline{PQ}$, $\overline{MQ} \cong \overline{NP}$

PROVE $\triangle MNQ \cong \triangle PQN$

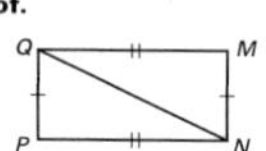

Statements	Reasons
5. $\overline{MN} \cong \overline{PQ}$	6. Given
7. $\overline{MQ} \cong \overline{NP}$	8. Given
9. $\overline{QN} \cong \overline{QN}$	10. Reflexive Property of Congruence
11. $\triangle MNQ \cong \triangle PQN$	12. SSS Congruence Postulate

Answers

1. See left.
   isosceles; not a right triangle
2. See left.
   scalene; right triangle
3. 7
4. 10
5. See left.
6. See left.
7. See left.
8. See left.
9. See left.
10. See left.
11. See left.
12. See left.

CHAPTER 4 Quiz 2
For use after Lessons 4.4–4.6

Decide which method, SAS, ASA, AAS, or HL, can be used to prove the triangles are congruent.

1.

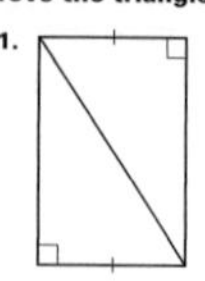

2.

3.

In Exercises 4–11, complete the proof.

GIVEN $\angle K \cong \angle N$, $\angle KML \cong \angle NML$

PROVE $\triangle KML \cong \triangle NML$

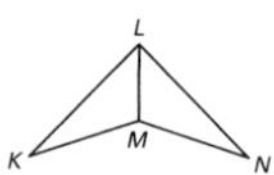

Statements	Reasons
4. $\angle K \cong \angle N$	5. Given
6. $\angle KML \cong \angle NML$	7. Given
8. $\overline{ML} \cong \overline{ML}$	9. Reflexive Property of Congruence
10. $\triangle KML \cong \triangle NML$	11. AAS Congruence Theorem

Answers

1. HL
2. AAS
3. SAS
4. See left.
5. See left.
6. See left.
7. See left.
8. See left.
9. See left.
10. See left.
11. See left.

CHAPTER 4 Quiz 3
For use after Lessons 4.7–4.8

Find the value of x.

1.

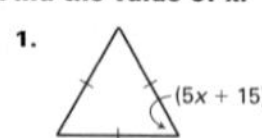

2.

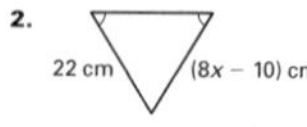

3.

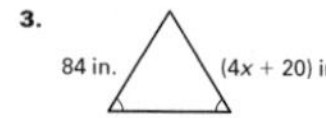

Draw the image of $\triangle EFG$ after the transformation. Identify the type of transformation.

4. $(x, y) \rightarrow (x + 2, y - 3)$

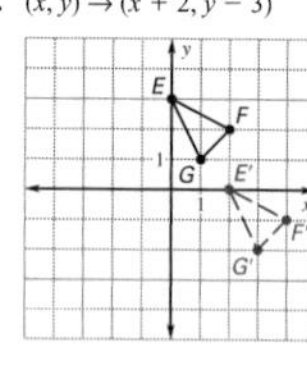

5. $(x, y) \rightarrow (-x, y)$

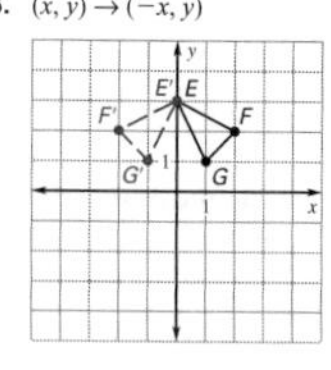

6. $(x, y) \rightarrow (x, -y)$

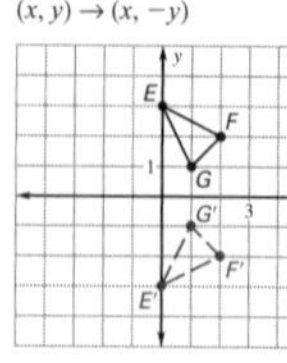

7. $(x, y) \rightarrow (x - 4, y + 3)$

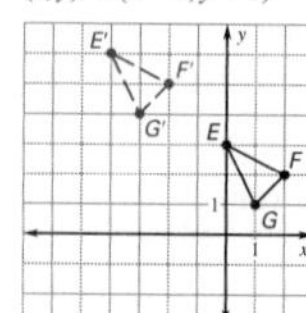

Answers

1. 9
2. 4
3. 16
4. See left.
   translation
5. See left.
   reflection in the y-axis
6. See left.
   reflection in the x-axis
7. See left.
   translation

CHAPTER 4 Chapter Test B
For use after Chapter 4

Find the value of x. Then classify the triangle by its angles.

1. 2. 3. 4.

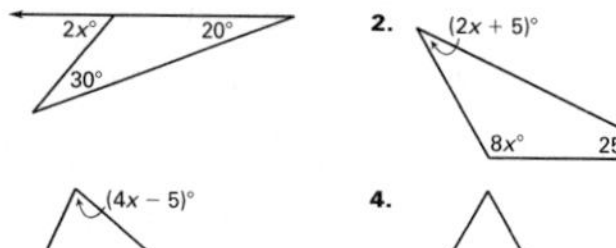

In the diagram, $\triangle QRS \cong \triangle XYZ$. Find the measure.

5. $m\angle R$
6. XY
7. $m\angle X$
8. $m\angle S$

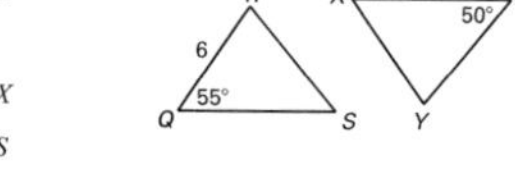

State the congruence that is needed to prove $\triangle ABC \cong \triangle DEF$ using the given postulate or theorem.

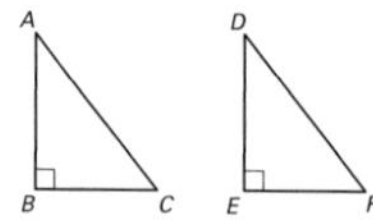

9. Given: $\overline{BC} \cong \overline{EF}$; Use the Hypotenuse-Leg Congruence Theorem.
10. Given: $\overline{AB} \cong \overline{DE}$, $\overline{AC} \cong \overline{DF}$; Use the SSS Congruence Postulate.
11. Given: $\angle A \cong \angle D$, $\angle B \cong \angle E$; Use the AAS Congruence Theorem.
12. Given: $\angle A \cong \angle D$, $\angle C \cong \angle F$; Use the ASA Congruence Postulate.

Decide whether the triangles can be proven congruent by the given postulate or theorem.

13. $\triangle LMN \cong \triangle CBA$ by HL
14. $\triangle TWX \cong \triangle YWX$ by SSS

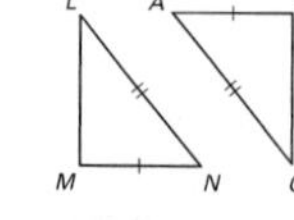

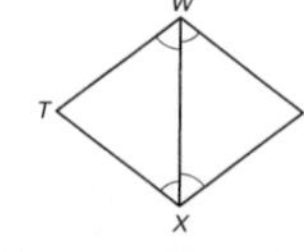

Answers

1. 25; obtuse
2. 15; obtuse
3. 20; acute
4. 10; equiangular
5. 75°
6. 6
7. 55°
8. 50°
9. $\overline{AC} \cong \overline{DF}$
10. $\overline{BC} \cong \overline{EF}$
11. $\overline{BC} \cong \overline{EF}$ or $\overline{AC} \cong \overline{DF}$
12. $\overline{AC} \cong \overline{DF}$
13. no
14. yes

CHAPTER 4 Chapter Test B *continued*
For use after Chapter 4

Find the value of x.

15.
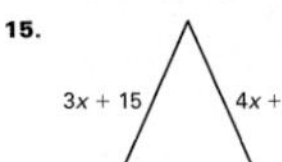

16.
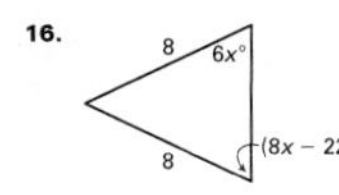

17.
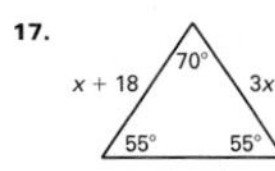

18.
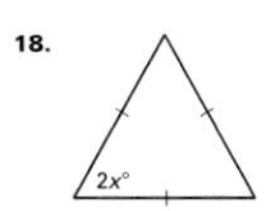

Sketch the image of the figure after the translation.

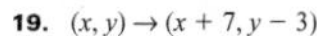

19. $(x, y) \to (x + 7, y - 3)$

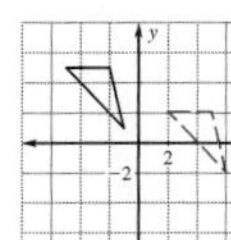

20. $(x, y) \to (x - 6, y + 4)$

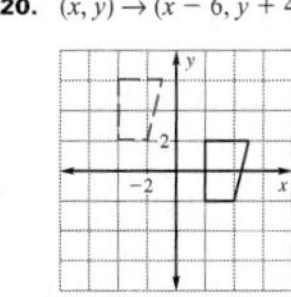

21. The endpoints of $\overline{CD}$ are $C(1, 1)$ and $D(2, 4)$. A reflection of $\overline{CD}$ results in the image $\overline{MN}$, with coordinates $M(-1, 1)$ and $N(-2, 4)$. Which axis was $\overline{CD}$ reflected in? Write the coordinate rule for the reflection.

In Exercises 22–25, use the diagram. What number does the hour hand point to when it is transformed in the following way?

22. Reflection in the x-axis

23. Reflection in the y-axis

24. Rotated 90° clockwise

25. Rotated 120° counterclockwise

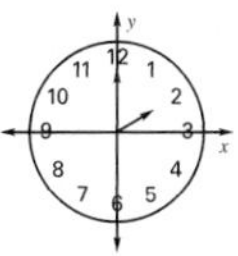

Answers

15. 3
16. 11
17. 9
18. 30
19. See left.
20. See left.
21. y-axis; $(x, y) \to (-x, y)$
22. 4
23. 10
24. 5
25. 10

CHAPTER 4 Standardized Test
For use after Chapter 4

Multiple Choice

In Exercises 1 and 2, use the figure.

1. Which triangle is obtuse? C

Ⓐ $\triangle ABC$ Ⓑ $\triangle ABD$
Ⓒ $\triangle ADE$ Ⓓ $\triangle BCE$

2. Which triangle is acute? B

Ⓐ $\triangle AFC$ Ⓑ $\triangle BFD$
Ⓒ $\triangle ABF$ Ⓓ $\triangle ABE$

3. Given $\triangle EFG \cong \triangle XYZ$, find $m\angle X$. D

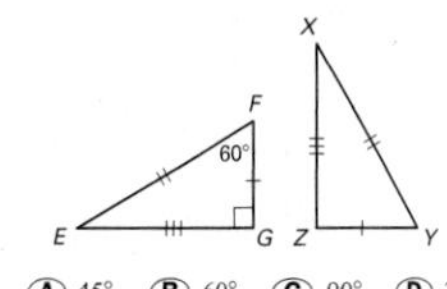

Ⓐ 45° Ⓑ 60° Ⓒ 90° Ⓓ 30°

4. If three sides of one triangle are congruent to three sides of a second triangle, then the two triangles are: B

Ⓐ equilateral. Ⓑ congruent.
Ⓒ acute. Ⓓ scalene.

5. The sum of the measures of the interior angles of a triangle is: A

Ⓐ 180°. Ⓑ 360°. Ⓒ 90°. Ⓓ 270°.

6. Which statement can you *not* conclude from the diagram? C

Ⓐ $\triangle QPS \cong \triangle SPR$
Ⓑ $\triangle PQR \cong \triangle QRS$
Ⓒ $\triangle QPT \cong \triangle PTR$
Ⓓ $\overline{PQ} \cong \overline{RS}$

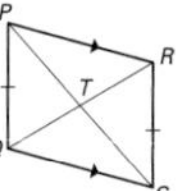

7. In a right triangle, the sides adjacent to the right angle are called the legs. The side opposite the right angle is called the: C

Ⓐ transversal. Ⓑ diagonal.
Ⓒ hypotenuse. Ⓓ diameter.

8. To prove $\triangle KLM \cong \triangle KLN$, which triangle congruence postulate could you use? D

Ⓐ AAS
Ⓑ SSS
Ⓒ SAS
Ⓓ ASA

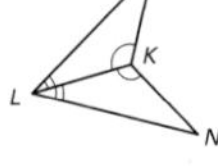

9. Given $\triangle DEF \cong \triangle WXY$, use the Hypotenuse-Leg Congruence Theorem to find x. A

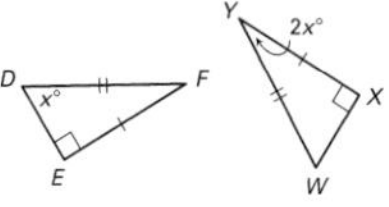

Ⓐ 30 Ⓑ 45 Ⓒ 60 Ⓓ 90

CHAPTER 4 Standardized Test *continued*
For use after Chapter 4

10. Use the diagram to determine which statement is true. B

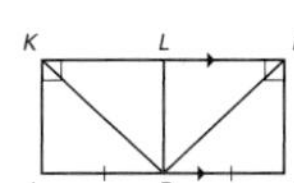

Ⓐ $\overline{KJ} \cong \overline{KL}$ Ⓑ $\angle KJP \cong \angle MNP$
Ⓒ $\angle KLP \cong \angle MLP$ Ⓓ $\overline{LP} \perp \overline{JN}$

11. The angle formed by the legs of an isosceles triangle is called the: A

Ⓐ vertex angle. Ⓑ base angle.
Ⓒ isosceles angle. Ⓓ leg angle.

12. How many isosceles triangles can be found? D

Ⓐ 2
Ⓑ 0
Ⓒ 6
Ⓓ 4

13. Which of the following is *not* a type of congruence transformation? C

Ⓐ translation Ⓑ rotation
Ⓒ refraction Ⓓ reflection

14. Given a triangle with vertices $A(4, -1)$, $B(-3, 0)$, and $C(7, 2)$, which points represent a reflection of $\triangle ABC$ in the y-axis? A

Ⓐ $A(-4, -1), B(3, 0), C(-7, 2)$
Ⓑ $A(4, 1), B(-3, 0), C(7, -2)$
Ⓒ $A(-4, 1), B(3, 0), C(-7, -2)$
Ⓓ $A(-1, 4), B(0, -3), C(2, 7)$

Gridded Answer

15. Find the value of x.

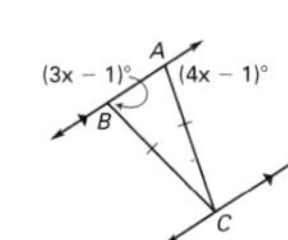

Gridded answer: 26

Short Response

16. Match the theorem with the correct pair of congruent triangles. a–4; b–2; c–5; d–1; e–3

a. ASA
b. SAS
c. HL
d. SSS
e. AAS

Extended Response

17. Use the diagram to find the following.

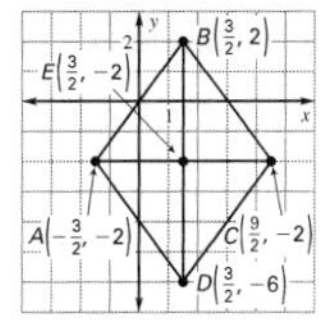

a. All segments congruent to $\overline{AB}$. *Explain.* See left.

b. All triangles congruent to $\triangle ABC$. *Explain.* See left.

c. All angles congruent to $\angle BEC$. *Explain.* See left.

d. All right triangles. *Explain.* See left.

17. a. Using the distance formula, $\overline{AB} \cong \overline{BC} \cong \overline{CD} \cong \overline{DA}$. **b.** Using the distance formula and SSS, or HL, $\triangle ABC \cong \triangle ADC$. **c.** Using the distance formula and SSS, $\triangle BEC \cong \triangle BEA \cong \triangle AED \cong \triangle CED$. **d.** Using the distance formula and HL, $\triangle AEB$, $\triangle CEB$, $\triangle CED$, and $\triangle AED$ are right triangles.

CHAPTER 4 Alternative Assessment and Math Journal
For use after Chapter 4

Journal **1.** Identify three methods for proving that triangles are congruent and explain when to use each method. Write example triangle pairs that illustrate when to use each method.

Multi-Step Problem **2.** The figure at the right shows a cabin at a campground. Use the figure to answer the questions below.

a. Identify each triangle in the figure by its angles and by its sides.

b. Prove that $\triangle ABD$ is congruent to $\triangle CBD$.

c. Identify all pairs of congruent corresponding parts in $\triangle ABD$ and $\triangle CBD$.

d. Suppose that $m\angle BAD = 33°$. Find $m\angle ABC$.

e. A design of two triangles will be put on the side of the cabin as a decorative element. One triangle that will be used is shown in the figure. Draw the other triangle in the design by using the transformation $(x, y) \to (-x, y)$.

f. What kind of transformation did you perform in part (e)?

g. *Explain* how you can show that the two triangles are congruent to verify that the transformation is a congruence transformation.

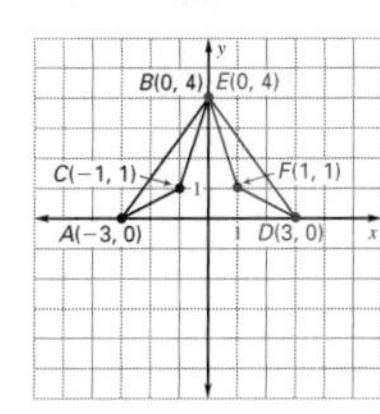

1. Complete answers should include: a list of three of the five methods presented in Chapter 4 (SSS, ASA, HL, SAS, AAS); an explanation of when to use each of the three chosen methods (see the Concept Summary in Lesson 4.5); an example triangle pair for each chosen method that illustrates the student's explanation of when to use the method.

2. a. $\triangle ABD$ and $\triangle CBD$ are scalene right triangles; $\triangle ABC$ is an acute isosceles triangle; $\triangle EFG$ is an obtuse scalene triangle **b.** It is given that $\triangle ABD$ and $\triangle CBD$ are right triangles and $\overline{AB} \cong \overline{CB}$. By the Reflexive Property, $\overline{BD} \cong \overline{BD}$. So, by the HL Congruence Theorem, $\triangle ABD \cong \triangle CBD$. **c.** $\angle BAD \cong \angle BCD$; $\angle ABD \cong \angle CBD$; $\angle ADB \cong \angle CDB$; $\overline{AB} \cong \overline{CB}$; $\overline{BD} \cong \overline{BD}$; $\overline{AD} \cong \overline{CD}$ **d.** 114° **f.** reflection in y-axis **g.** *Sample answer:* Use the Distance Formula to find the side lengths of all three triangles. Then use the SSS Congruence Postulate.

4 Congruent Triangles

Before

In previous chapters, you learned the following skills, which you'll use in Chapter 4: classifying angles, solving linear equations, finding midpoints, and using angle relationships.

Prerequisite Skills

VOCABULARY CHECK

Classify the angle as *acute, obtuse, right,* or *straight*.

1. $m\angle A = 115°$ **obtuse**
2. $m\angle B = 90°$ **right**
3. $m\angle C = 35°$ **acute**
4. $m\angle D = 95°$ **obtuse**

SKILLS AND ALGEBRA CHECK

Solve the equation. *(Review p. 65 for 4.1, 4.2.)*

5. $70 + 2y = 180$ **55**
6. $2x = 5x - 54$ **18**
7. $40 + x + 65 = 180$ **75**

Find the coordinates of the midpoint of $\overline{PQ}$. *(Review p. 15 for 4.3.)* **8–10. See margin.**

8. $P(2, -5), Q(-1, -2)$
9. $P(-4, 7), Q(1, -5)$
10. $P(h, k), Q(h, 0)$

Name the theorem or postulate that justifies the statement about the diagram. *(Review p. 154 for 4.3–4.5.)* **11–14. See margin.**

11. $\angle 2 \cong \angle 3$
12. $\angle 1 \cong \angle 4$
13. $\angle 2 \cong \angle 6$
14. $\angle 3 \cong \angle 5$

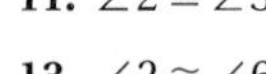

@HomeTutor Prerequisite skills practice at classzone.com

PLAN AND PREPARE

Main Ideas

In this chapter the students will classify triangles, find measures of angles of triangles, identify congruent figures, and prove triangles congruent. They will also use theorems about isosceles and equilateral triangles and perform transformations.

Prerequisite Skills

- Measuring and classifying angles
- Solving linear equations
- Applying distance and midpoint formulas
- Using angle relationships

Additional resources for reviewing prerequisite skills are:

- Skills Review Handbook, pp. 869–895
- @HomeTutor

8. $\left(\frac{1}{2}, -\frac{7}{2}\right)$
9. $\left(-\frac{3}{2}, 1\right)$
10. $\left(h, \frac{k}{2}\right)$
11. **Vertical Angles Congruence Theorem**
12. **Corresponding Angles Postulate**
13. **Alternate Interior Angles Theorem**
14. **Alternate Exterior Angles Theorem**

Chapter Planning Guide

Chapter 4 Resource Book
- Teaching Guide/Lesson Plan (pp. 3, 18, 32, 45, 60, 74, 87, 101)
- Project with Rubric (p. 117)

Assessment and Intervention
- Assessment Book (pp. 46–60)
- Benchmark Tests
- Remediation Book

Interactive Technology
- Easy Planner
- Power Presentations CD-ROM
- Activity Generator CD-ROM
- Animated Geometry
- Test Generator CD-ROM
- Online Quizzes
- eWorkbook
- eEdition
- @HomeTutor

Resources for English Learners
- Quick Reference for English Learners
- Spanish Study Guide
- Multi-Language Visual Glossary
- Student Resources in Spanish

California Standards for Chapter 4

Geometry: 3.0, 4.0, 5.0, 12.0, 13.0, 16.0, 22.0

Now

In Chapter 4, you will apply the big ideas listed below and reviewed in the Chapter Summary on page 281. You will also use the key vocabulary listed below.

Big Ideas

1. **Classifying triangles by sides and angles**
2. **Proving that triangles are congruent**
3. **Using coordinate geometry to investigate triangle relationships**

KEY VOCABULARY

- triangle, *p. 217*
  scalene, isosceles, equilateral, acute, right, obtuse, equiangular
- interior angles, *p. 218*
- exterior angles, *p. 218*
- corollary, *p. 220*
- congruent figures, *p. 225*
- corresponding parts, *p. 225*
- right triangle, *p. 241*
  legs, hypotenuse
- flow proof, *p. 250*
- isosceles triangle, *p. 264*
  legs, vertex angle, base, base angles
- transformation, *p. 272*
  translation, reflection, rotation

Why?

Triangles are used to add strength to structures in real-world situations. For example, the frame of a hang glider involves several triangles.

Animated Geometry

The animation illustrated below for Example 1 on page 256 helps you answer this question: What must be true about $\overline{QT}$ and $\overline{ST}$ for the hang glider to fly straight?

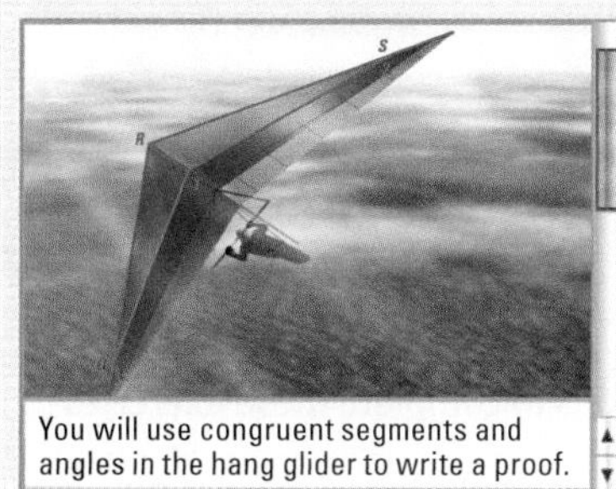

You will use congruent segments and angles in the hang glider to write a proof.

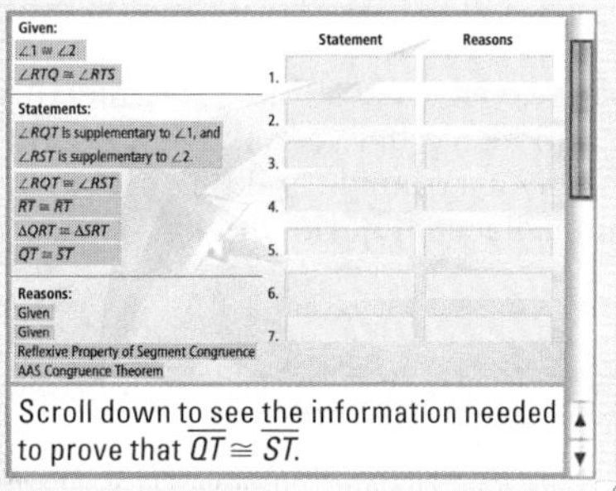

Scroll down to see the information needed to prove that $\overline{QT} \cong \overline{ST}$.

Animated Geometry at classzone.com

Other animations for Chapter 4: pages 234, 242, 250, 257, and 274

215

Geometry Toolkit

- Reading Strategies for Chapter 4, pp. 15–16
- Differentiated Instruction Notes, pp. 51–54
- English Learners Notes, pp. 97–98
- Inclusion Notes, pp. 127–128
- Teaching Strategies with Sample Worksheets, pp. 145–168
- Using Technology in the Classroom, pp. 169–174
- Tips for New Teachers, pp. 181–182
- Math Background Notes, pp. 209–211
- Pre-AP Strategies and Copymasters, pp. 289–290, 331–342
- Teacher Survival Activities, pp. 427–428, 451–452
- Bulletin Board Idea, p. 472
- Teacher Tool Transparencies, following p. 480

1 PLAN AND PREPARE

Explore the Concept

- Students will find the sum of the measures of three angles of a triangle.
- This activity leads into the study of the Triangle Sum Theorem in Lesson 4.1.

Materials

Each student will need:

- scissors
- ruler

Recommended Time

Work activity: 10 min
Discuss results: 5 min

Grouping

Students should work individually.

2 TEACH

Tips for Success

Be sure students arrange the corners with the vertices at the same point. Have them place them on a line on lined paper so the relationship is easy to see.

Key Question

- Does it matter what kind of triangle you use? **no**

Alternative Strategy

Demonstrate on an overhead projector with triangles drawn on transparencies.

Key Discovery

The sum of the measures of the angles of a triangle is 180°.

3 ASSESS AND RETEACH

1. Given the measures of three angles, how can you tell whether they could be the measures of the angles of a triangle? **Check to see whether their sum is 180°.**

4.1 Angle Sums in Triangles

MATERIALS • paper • pencil • scissors • ruler

Standards

13.0 Students prove relationships between angles in polygons by using properties of complementary, **supplementary,** vertical, and exterior **angles.**

QUESTION What are some relationships among the *interior angles* of a triangle and *exterior angles* of a triangle?

EXPLORE 1 Find the sum of the measures of interior angles

STEP 1 ***Draw triangles*** Draw and cut out several different triangles.

STEP 2 ***Tear off corners*** For each triangle, tear off the three corners and place them next to each other, as shown in the diagram.

STEP 3 ***Make a conjecture*** Make a conjecture about the sum of the measures of the interior angles of a triangle.

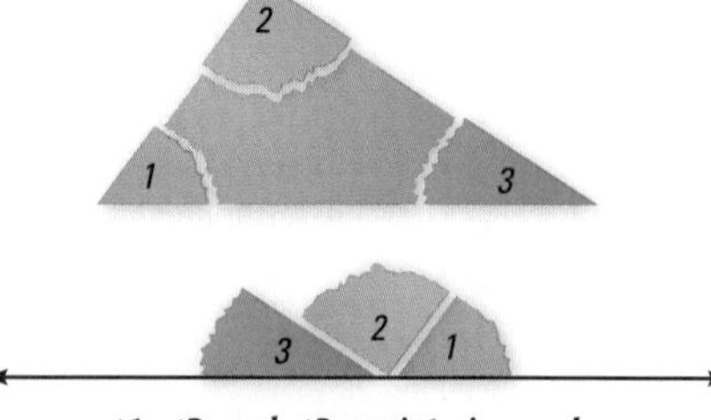

∠1, ∠2, and ∠3 are *interior angles.*

EXPLORE 2 Find the measure of an exterior angle of a triangle

STEP 1 ***Draw exterior angle*** Draw and cut out several different triangles. Place each triangle on a piece of paper and extend one side to form an *exterior angle*, as shown in the diagram.

STEP 2 ***Tear off corners*** For each triangle, tear off the corners that are not next to the exterior angle. Use them to fill the exterior angle, as shown.

STEP 3 ***Make a conjecture*** Make a conjecture about the relationship between the measure of an exterior angle of a triangle and the measures of the nonadjacent interior angles.

In the top figure, ∠*BCD* is an *exterior angle.*

DRAW CONCLUSIONS Use your observations to complete these exercises

1. Given the measures of two interior angles of a triangle, how can you find the measure of the third angle? **Subtract the sum of the given measures from 180°.**
2. Draw several different triangles that each have one right angle. Show that the two acute angles of a right triangle are complementary.
Check students' work. The sum of the measures of the acute angles for each triangle should be 90°, so the angles are complementary.

4.1 Apply Triangle Sum Properties

Before You classified angles and found their measures.
Now You will classify triangles and find measures of their angles.
Why? So you can place actors on stage, as in Ex. 40.

Key Vocabulary
- **triangle**
  scalene, isosceles, equilateral, acute, right, obtuse, equiangular
- **interior angles**
- **exterior angles**
- **corollary to a theorem**

A **triangle** is a polygon with three sides. A triangle with vertices A, B, and C is called "triangle ABC" or "$\triangle ABC$."

KEY CONCEPT *For Your Notebook*

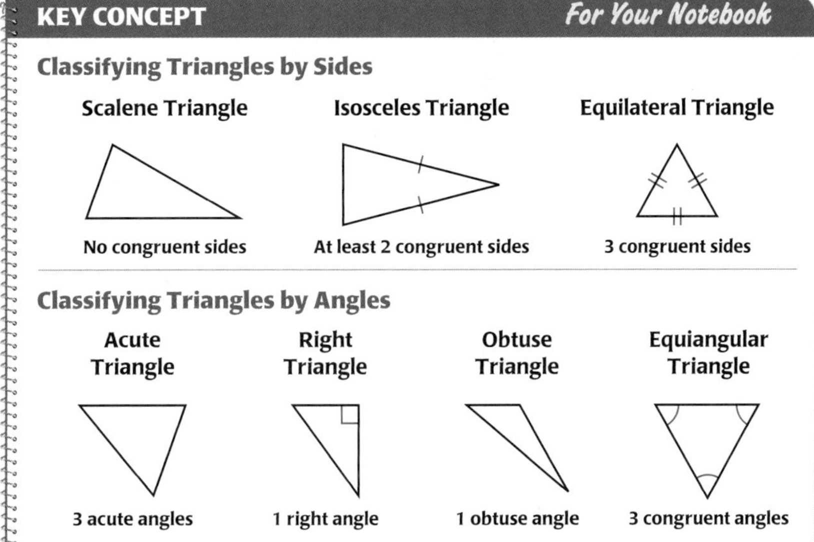

Classifying Triangles by Sides
Scalene Triangle
Isosceles Triangle
Equilateral Triangle
No congruent sides
At least 2 congruent sides
3 congruent sides
Classifying Triangles by Angles
Acute Triangle
Right Triangle
Obtuse Triangle
Equiangular Triangle
3 acute angles
1 right angle
1 obtuse angle
3 congruent angles

READ VOCABULARY
Notice that an equilateral triangle is also isosceles. An equiangular triangle is also acute.

EXAMPLE 1 Classify triangles by sides and by angles

SUPPORT BEAMS Classify the triangular shape of the support beams in the diagram by its sides and by measuring its angles.

Solution

The triangle has a pair of congruent sides, so it is isosceles. By measuring, the angles are 55°, 55°, and 70°. It is an acute isosceles triangle.

Standards

12.0 Students find and use measures of sides and of interior and exterior angles of triangles and polygons **to classify figures and solve problems.**

13.0 Students prove relationships between angles in polygons by using properties of complementary, **supplementary**, vertical, and **exterior angles.**

1 PLAN AND PREPARE

Warm-Up Exercises

Transparency Available

Classify each angle as acute, obtuse, or right.

1. 90° **right** **2.** 72° **acute**
3. 116° **obtuse**

4. How do you know that $\angle 1 \cong \angle 2$?

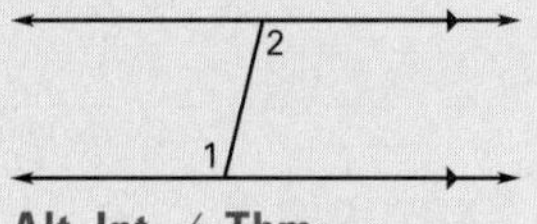

Alt. Int. ∠s Thm.

Notetaking Guide

Transparency Available

Promotes interactive learning and notetaking skills, pp. 85–88.

Pacing

Basic: 1 day
Average: 1 day
Advanced: 1 day
Block: 0.5 block with 4.2
- See *Teaching Guide/Lesson Plan.*

2 FOCUS AND MOTIVATE

Essential Question

Big Idea 1, p. 215

How can you find the measure of the third angle of a triangle if you know the measure of the other two angles? **Tell students they will learn how to answer this question by studying the Triangle Sum Theorem and its Corollary.**

Resource Planning Guide

Chapter Resource Book
- Teaching Guide/Lesson Plan (pp. 3–4)
- Activity Master (p. 5)
- Practice levels A, B, C (pp. 7–12)
- Study Guide (pp. 13–14)
- Catch-up for Absent Students (p. 15)
- Problem Solving Workshop (p. 16)
- Challenge (p. 17)

Workbooks
- Notetaking Guide (pp. 85–88)
- Practice Workbook (pp. 61–63)

Teaching Options
- **Power Presentations CD-ROM** provides dynamic electronic teaching resources for the classroom.
- **Activity Generator CD-ROM** provides editable activities for all ability levels.

Interactive Technology
- Easy Planner
- Power Presentations CD-ROM
- Activity Generator CD-ROM
- Animated Geometry
- Test Generator CD-ROM
- Online Quiz
- eWorkbook
- eEdition
- @HomeTutor

Resources for English Learners
- Quick Reference for English Learners
- Spanish Study Guide
- Multi-Language Visual Glossary
- Student Resources in Spanish

See also the *Geometry Toolkit* for more strategies for meeting individual needs.

Motivating the Lesson

Ask students to think of pictures they have seen of the pyramids in Egypt. Ask them to imagine that they need to find the measure of the angle at the top of one of the triangular sides of a pyramid. Tell them that in this lesson, they will learn how to find the measure of the top angle by measuring the two angles at the bottom.

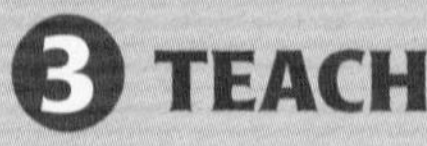

3 TEACH

Extra Example 1

Classify the triangle in the gate shown in the diagram by measuring its sides and angles.

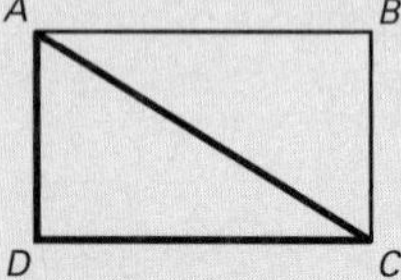

scalene triangle, right triangle

Key Question to Ask for Example 1

- Are there other kinds of triangles in the diagram? If so, classify them. **scalene right triangle, obtuse isosceles triangle**

Extra Example 2

Classify $\triangle ABC$ by its sides and by its angles. **right isosceles triangle**

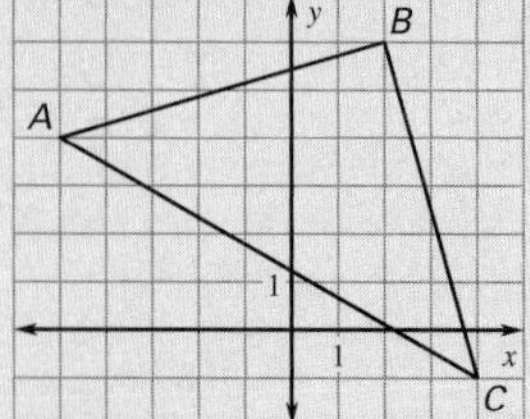

Key Question to Ask for Example 2

- How would you show $\triangle PQO$ is a right triangle using the lengths of the sides? **Note that $(\sqrt{5})^2 + (\sqrt{45})^2 = (\sqrt{50})^2$.**

EXAMPLE 2 Classify a triangle in a coordinate plane

Classify $\triangle PQO$ by its sides. Then determine if the triangle is a right triangle.

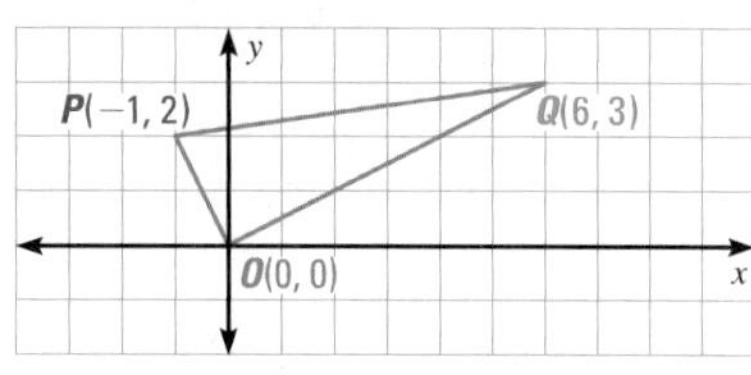

Solution

STEP 1 **Use** the distance formula to find the side lengths.

$$OP = \sqrt{(x_2 - x_1)^2 + (y_2 - y_1)^2} = \sqrt{((-1) - 0)^2 + (2 - 0)^2} = \sqrt{5} \approx 2.2$$

$$OQ = \sqrt{(x_2 - x_1)^2 + (y_2 - y_1)^2} = \sqrt{(6 - 0)^2 + (3 - 0)^2} = \sqrt{45} \approx 6.7$$

$$PQ = \sqrt{(x_2 - x_1)^2 + (y_2 - y_1)^2} = \sqrt{(6 - (-1))^2 + (3 - 2)^2} = \sqrt{50} \approx 7.1$$

STEP 2 **Check** for right angles. The slope of $\overline{OP}$ is $\frac{2 - 0}{-1 - 0} = -2$. The slope of $\overline{OQ}$ is $\frac{3 - 0}{6 - 0} = \frac{1}{2}$. The product of the slopes is $-2\left(\frac{1}{2}\right) = -1$, so $\overline{OP} \perp \overline{OQ}$ and $\angle POQ$ is a right angle.

▶ Therefore, $\triangle PQO$ is a right scalene triangle.

✓ GUIDED PRACTICE for Examples 1 and 2

1. Draw an obtuse isosceles triangle and an acute scalene triangle. **See margin.**
2. Triangle ABC has the vertices $A(0, 0)$, $B(3, 3)$, and $C(-3, 3)$. Classify it by its sides. Then determine if it is a right triangle. **isosceles; right triangle**

ANGLES When the sides of a polygon are extended, other angles are formed. The original angles are the **interior angles**. The angles that form linear pairs with the interior angles are the **exterior angles**.

READ DIAGRAMS
Each vertex has a *pair* of congruent exterior angles. However, it is common to show only *one* exterior angle at each vertex.

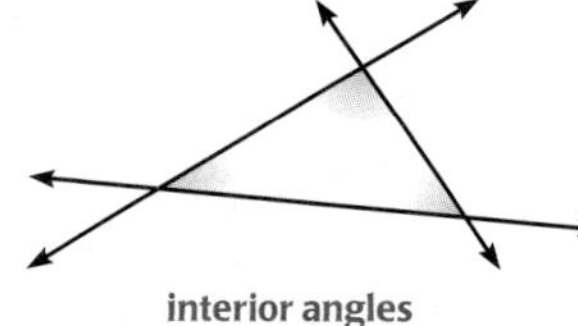

interior angles

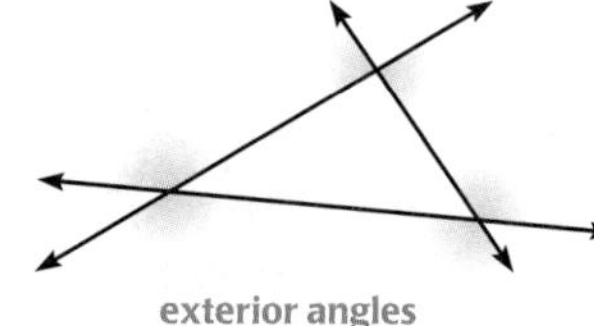

exterior angles

THEOREM *For Your Notebook*

THEOREM 4.1 Triangle Sum Theorem

The sum of the measures of the interior angles of a triangle is 180°.

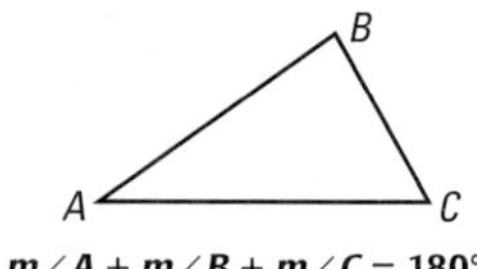

$m\angle A + m\angle B + m\angle C = 180°$

Proof: p. 219; Ex. 53, p. 224

1. *Sample:*

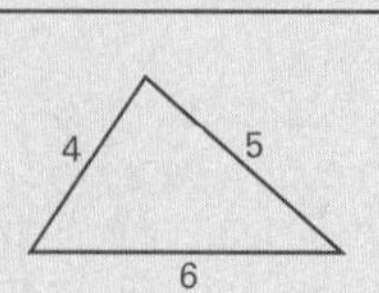

AUXILIARY LINES To prove certain theorems, you may need to add a line, a segment, or a ray to a given diagram. An *auxiliary* line is used in the proof of the Triangle Sum Theorem.

PROOF Triangle Sum Theorem

GIVEN ▶ $\triangle ABC$

PROVE ▶ $m\angle 1 + m\angle 2 + m\angle 3 = 180°$

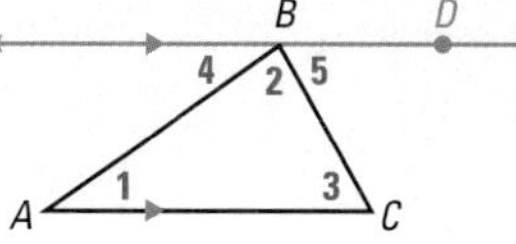

Plan for Proof

a. Draw an auxiliary line through B and parallel to $\overline{AC}$.

b. Show that $m\angle 4 + m\angle 2 + m\angle 5 = 180°$, $\angle 1 \cong \angle 4$, and $\angle 3 \cong \angle 5$.

c. By substitution, $m\angle 1 + m\angle 2 + m\angle 3 = 180°$.

Plan in Action

	STATEMENTS	REASONS
a.	**1.** Draw $\overleftrightarrow{BD}$ parallel to $\overline{AC}$.	**1.** Parallel Postulate
b.	**2.** $m\angle 4 + m\angle 2 + m\angle 5 = 180°$	**2.** Angle Addition Postulate and definition of straight angle
	3. $\angle 1 \cong \angle 4$, $\angle 3 \cong \angle 5$	**3.** Alternate Interior Angles Theorem
	4. $m\angle 1 = m\angle 4$, $m\angle 3 = m\angle 5$	**4.** Definition of congruent angles
c.	**5.** $m\angle 1 + m\angle 2 + m\angle 3 = 180°$	**5.** Substitution Property of Equality

THEOREM *For Your Notebook*

THEOREM 4.2 Exterior Angle Theorem

The measure of an exterior angle of a triangle is equal to the sum of the measures of the two nonadjacent interior angles.

Proof: Ex. 50, p. 223

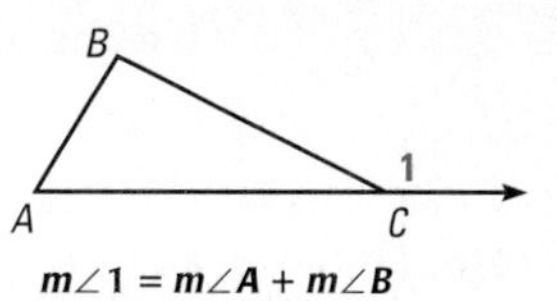

$m\angle 1 = m\angle A + m\angle B$

EXAMPLE 3 Find an angle measure

ALGEBRA Find $m\angle JKM$.

Solution

STEP 1 **Write** and solve an equation to find the value of x.

$(2x - 5)° = 70° + x°$ **Apply the Exterior Angle Theorem.**

$x = 75$ **Solve for x.**

STEP 2 **Substitute** 75 for x in $2x - 5$ to find $m\angle JKM$.

$2x - 5 = 2 \cdot 75 - 5 = 145$

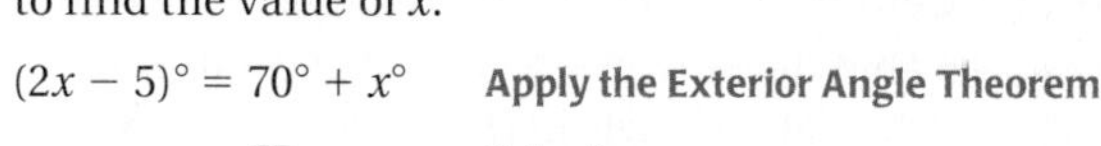

▶ The measure of $\angle JKM$ is 145°.

Teaching Strategy

Review the distance formula and slope formula. Remind students that they can use the distance formula to determine whether or not sides are congruent. To decide whether an angle is a right angle, they can use slopes. Slopes must be negative reciprocals for two nonvertical sides to be perpendicular.

Avoiding Common Errors

Example 3 Students may find x but forget to substitute to find $m\angle JKM$. Tell them to look back at the original problem to be sure they have found what was asked for.

Extra Example 3

Find $m\angle DEF$. **117°**

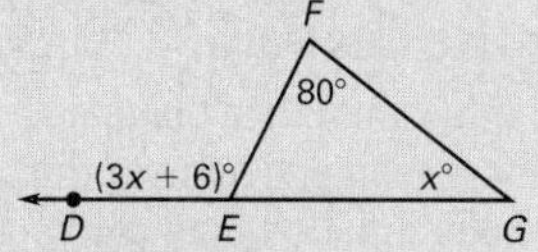

Key Questions to Ask for Example 3

- How can you use the fact that $m\angle JKM = (2x - 5)°$ to write an expression for $m\angle JKL$? **$\angle JKM$ and $\angle JKL$ are supplementary, so $m\angle JKL = 180° - (2x - 5)°$.**
- What expression do you get for $m\angle JKL$ if you use the Triangle Sum Theorem? **$180° - (x° + 70°)$**
- How can you use these expressions to find x? **Solve $180 - (2x - 5) = 180 - (x + 70)$.**

Differentiated Instruction

Inclusion To help students think about why the Exterior Angle Theorem is true in **Example 3**, have them review the Angle Addition Postulate and the definition of a straight angle. Have students write an equation to find the value of the third interior angle of the triangle. The appropriate equation is $180° - (2x - 5)° = m\angle 3$. Then have them use the Triangle Sum Theorem to write another equation to find the value of the third interior angle; $180° - (70 + x)° = m\angle 3$. When comparing the two equations, students should notice that $(2x - 5)° = (70 + x)°$.

See also the *Geometry Toolkit* for more strategies.

Extra Example 4

The support for the skateboard ramp shown forms a right triangle. The measure of one acute angle in the triangle is five times the measure of the other. Find the measure of each acute angle. **15°, 75°**

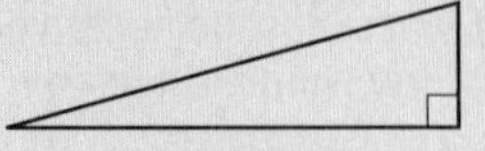

Key Question to Ask for Example 4

- If you use the Triangle Sum Theorem to solve this problem, what equation would you write? What can you do to this equation to get the equation obtained from the corollary? $x + 2x + 90 = 180$; **Subtract 90 from both sides.**

Closing the Lesson

Have students summarize the major points of the lesson and answer the Essential Question: How can you find the measure of the third angle of a triangle if you know the measures of the other two angles?

- **Equilateral triangles have three congruent sides, isosceles triangles have at least two congruent sides, and scalene triangles have no congruent sides.**
- **Equiangular triangles have three congruent angles, acute triangles have three acute angles, obtuse triangles have one obtuse angle, and right triangles have one right angle.**
- **The sum of the measures of the interior angles of a triangle is 180°.**

Add the two known angle measures and subtract the result from 180°.

A **corollary to a theorem** is a statement that can be proved easily using the theorem. The corollary below follows from the Triangle Sum Theorem.

COROLLARY *For Your Notebook*

Corollary to the Triangle Sum Theorem

The acute angles of a right triangle are complementary.

Proof: Ex. 48, p. 223

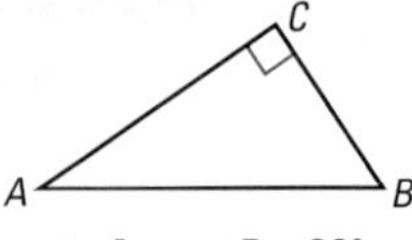

$m\angle A + m\angle B = 90°$

EXAMPLE 4 Find angle measures from a verbal description

ARCHITECTURE The tiled staircase shown forms a right triangle. The measure of one acute angle in the triangle is twice the measure of the other. Find the measure of each acute angle.

Solution

First, sketch a diagram of the situation. Let the measure of the smaller acute angle be $x°$. Then the measure of the larger acute angle is $2x°$. The Corollary to the Triangle Sum Theorem states that the acute angles of a right triangle are complementary.

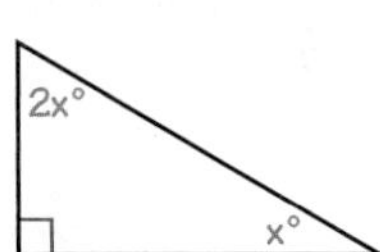

Use the corollary to set up and solve an equation.

$x° + 2x° = 90°$ **Corollary to the Triangle Sum Theorem**

$x = 30$ **Solve for *x*.**

▶ So, the measures of the acute angles are 30° and $2(30°) = 60°$.

✓ **GUIDED PRACTICE** for Examples 3 and 4

3. Find the measure of $\angle 1$ in the diagram shown. **65°**

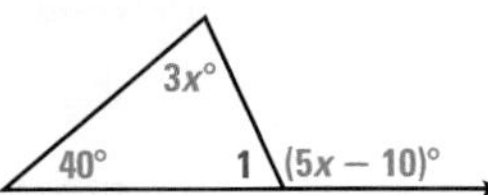

4. Find the measure of each interior angle of $\triangle ABC$, where $m\angle A = x°$, $m\angle B = 2x°$, and $m\angle C = 3x°$. $m\angle A = 30°$, $m\angle B = 60°$, $m\angle C = 90°$

5. Find the measures of the acute angles of the right triangle in the diagram shown. **26°, 64°**

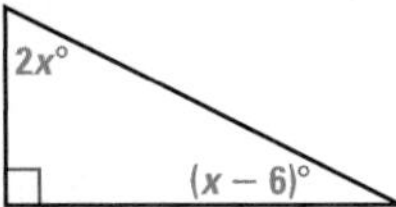

6. In Example 4, what is the measure of the obtuse angle formed between the staircase and a segment extending from the horizontal leg? **150°**

4.1 EXERCISES

HOMEWORK KEY
◯ = **WORKED-OUT SOLUTIONS** on p. WS4 for Exs. 9, 15, and 41
★ = **STANDARDIZED TEST PRACTICE** Exs. 7, 20, 31, 43, and 51

SKILL PRACTICE

A **VOCABULARY** **Match the triangle description with the most specific name.**

1. Angle measures: 30°, 60°, 90° **C**
2. Side lengths: 2 cm, 2 cm, 2 cm **E**
3. Angle measures: 60°, 60°, 60° **F**
4. Side lengths: 6 m, 3 m, 6 m **A**
5. Side lengths: 5 ft, 7 ft, 9 ft **B**
6. Angle measures: 20°, 125°, 35° **D**

A. Isosceles
B. Scalene
C. Right
D. Obtuse
E. Equilateral
F. Equiangular

7. ★ **WRITING** Can a right triangle also be obtuse? *Explain* why or why not.
No; in a right triangle, the other two angles are complementary so they are both less than 90°.

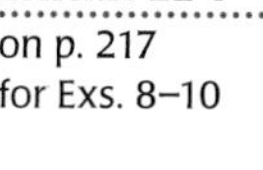

EXAMPLE 1 on p. 217 for Exs. 8–10

CLASSIFYING TRIANGLES **Copy the triangle and measure its angles. Classify the triangle by its sides and by its angles.**

8. 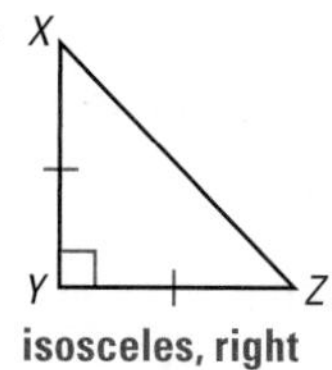

isosceles, right

9. 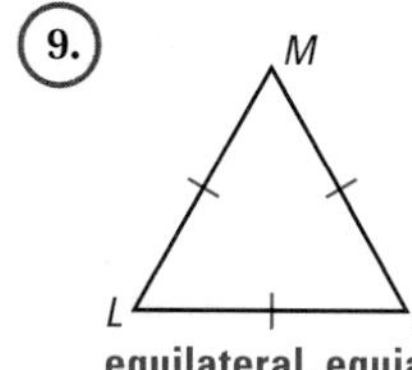

equilateral, equiangular

10. 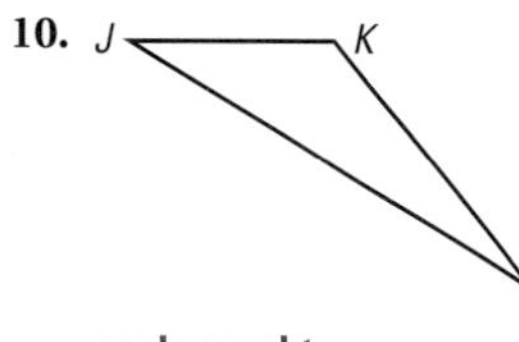

scalene, obtuse

EXAMPLE 2 on p. 218 for Exs. 11–13

COORDINATE PLANE **A triangle has the given vertices. Graph the triangle and classify it by its sides. Then determine if it is a right triangle.** **11–13. See margin for art.**

11. $A(2, 3)$, $B(6, 3)$, $C(2, 7)$ **isosceles; right triangle**
12. $A(3, 3)$, $B(6, 9)$, $C(6, -3)$ **isosceles; not a right triangle**
13. $A(1, 9)$, $B(4, 8)$, $C(2, 5)$ **scalene; not a right triangle**

EXAMPLE 3 on p. 219 for Exs. 14–19

FINDING ANGLE MEASURES **Find the value of x. Then classify the triangle by its angles.**

14. 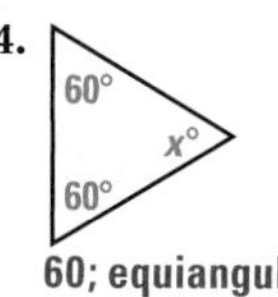

60; equiangular

15. 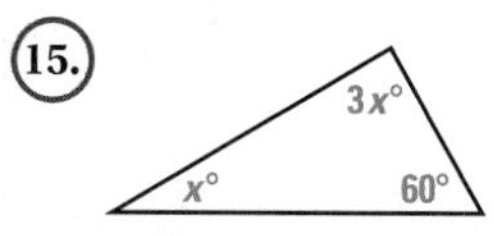

30; right

16. 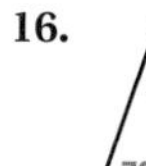

134; acute

ALGEBRA **Find the measure of the exterior angle shown.**

17. 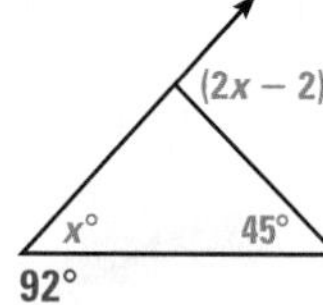

92°

18. 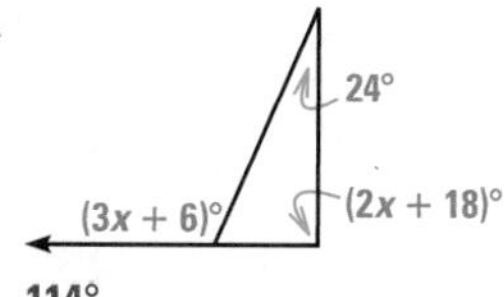

114°

19. 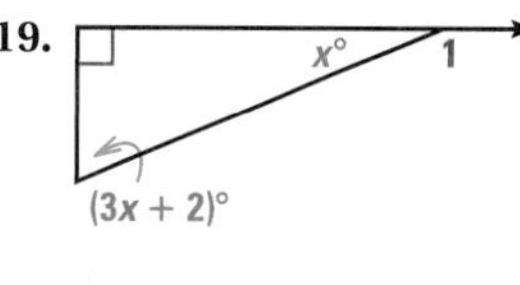

158°

EXAMPLE 4 on p. 220 for Ex. 20

20. ★ **SHORT RESPONSE** *Explain* how to use the Corollary to the Triangle Sum Theorem to find the measure of each angle.
Set $3x + 2x = 90$ and solve for x. Then find the values of $3x$ and $2x$.

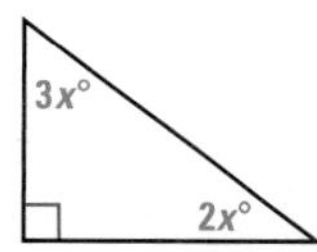

4 PRACTICE AND APPLY

Assignment Guide

Answer Transparencies available for all exercises

Basic:
Day 1: EP p. 896 Exs. 24–29
pp. 221–224
Exs. 1–7, 9–19 odd, 21–29, 40–49, 54, 57, 60, 61

Average:
Day 1: pp. 221–224
Exs. 1–7, 8–26 even, 27–34, 40–52, 55, 58, 62

Advanced:
Day 1: pp. 221–224
Exs. 1–7, 10, 13, 16, 19, 20, 27, 28, 31–40*, 42–53*, 56, 59, 63

Block:
pp. 221–224
Exs. 1–7, 8–26 even, 27–34, 40–52, 55, 58, 62 (with 4.2)

Differentiated Instruction

See *Geometry Best Practices Toolkit* for suggestions on addressing the needs of a diverse classroom.

Homework Check

For a quick check of student understanding of key concepts, go over the following exercises:
Basic: 9, 11, 17, 19, 40
Average: 8, 12, 18, 20, 40
Advanced: 10, 13, 19, 20, 40

Extra Practice

- Student Edition, p. 902
- Chapter 4 Resource Book: Practice levels A, B, C, pp. 7–12

Practice Worksheet

An easily-readable reduced practice page (with answers) for this lesson can be found on p. 214C.

11. 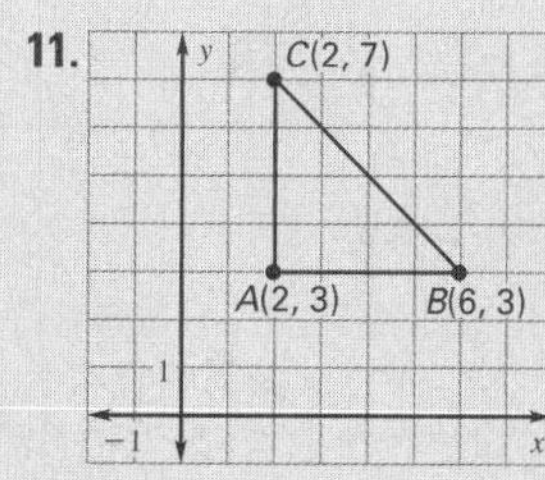

12. 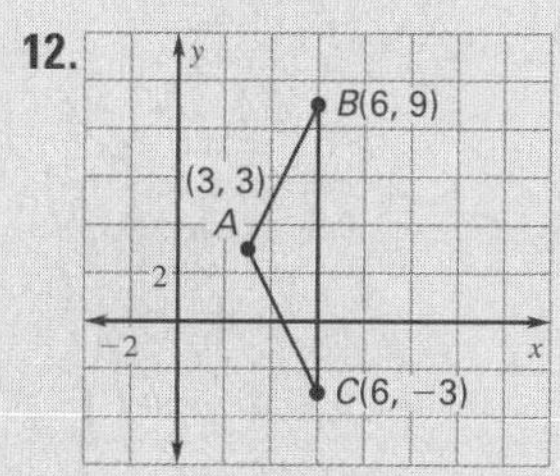

13. 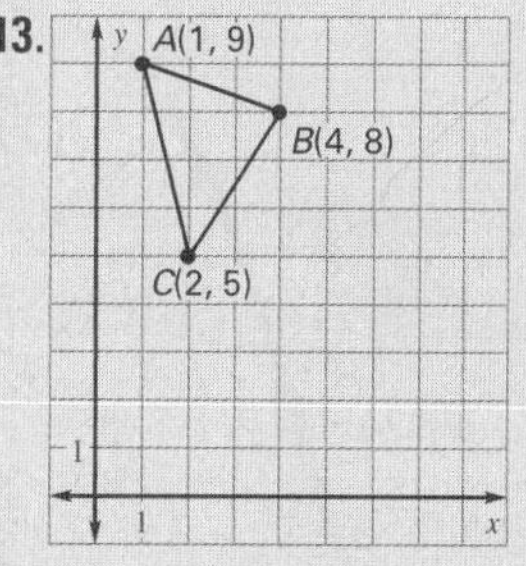

Avoiding Common Errors

Exercises 17–18 Students may add the measure of the exterior angle and the measures of the two nonadjacent interior angles and set the sum equal to 180°. Discuss the difference between the Triangle Sum Theorem and the Exterior Angle Theorem to help them understand why that is not a correct procedure.

Study Strategy

Exercises 32–33, 35 If students have difficulty with these exercises, call attention to the fact that each diagram is marked to show a pair of parallel segments.

39c.

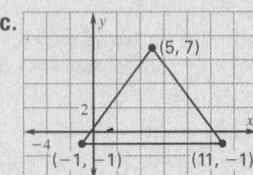

29. Isosceles does not guarantee the third side is congruent to the two congruent sides; so if $\triangle ABC$ is equilateral, then it is isosceles as well.

30. The measure of the exterior angle is equal to the sum of the measures of the two nonadjacent interior angles; $m\angle 1 = 80° + 50° = 130°$.

38. No. *Sample answer:* In a right triangle, the two acute angles are complementary. So, one of the acute angle measures can be as small as desired, while the other angle measure is less than 90°. The largest angle is the right angle, which measures 90°, so the triangle does not need to be obtuse.

39a. *Sample answer:* They will always form a triangle unless they intersect in one point, or unless at least two lines are parallel.

B **ANGLE RELATIONSHIPS** **Find the measure of the numbered angle.**

21. $\angle 1$ **50°** **22.** $\angle 2$ **130°**

23. $\angle 3$ **50°** **24.** $\angle 4$ **130°**

25. $\angle 5$ **40°** **26.** $\angle 6$ **30°**

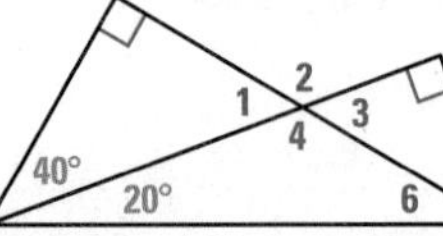

27. **ALGEBRA** In $\triangle PQR$, $\angle P \cong \angle R$ and the measure of $\angle Q$ is twice the measure of $\angle R$. Find the measure of each angle. **$m\angle P = 45°$, $m\angle Q = 90°$, $m\angle R = 45°$**

28. **ALGEBRA** In $\triangle EFG$, $m\angle F = 3(m\angle G)$, and $m\angle E = m\angle F - 30°$. Find the measure of each angle. **$m\angle 60°$, $m\angle 90°$, $m\angle 30°$**

ERROR ANALYSIS **In Exercises 29 and 30, *describe* and correct the error.**

29.

All equilateral triangles are also isosceles. So, if $\triangle$ ABC is isosceles, then it is equilateral as well.

30.

$m\angle 1 + 80° + 50° = 180°$

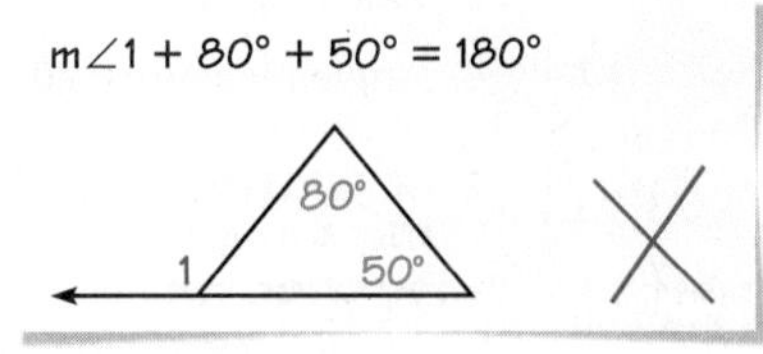

31. ★ **MULTIPLE CHOICE** Which of the following is not possible? **B**

(A) An acute scalene triangle (B) A triangle with two acute exterior angles

(C) An obtuse isosceles triangle (D) An equiangular acute triangle

ALGEBRA **In Exercises 32–37, find the values of *x* and *y*.**

32.

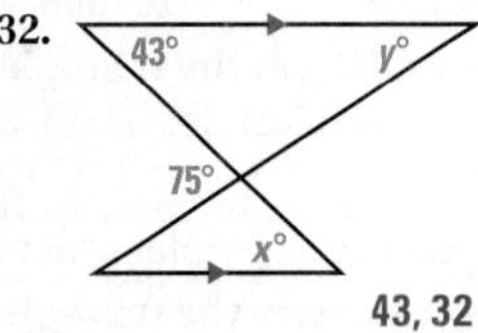

43, 32

33.

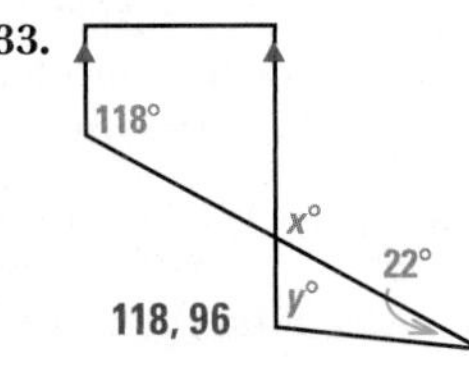

118, 96

34.

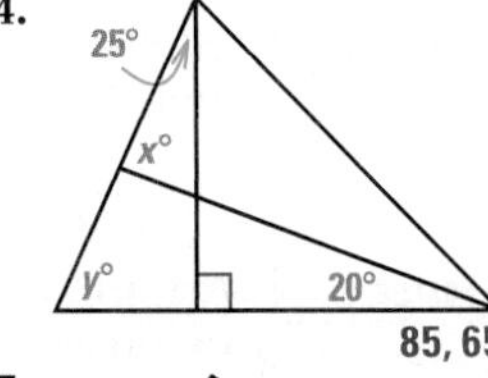

85, 65

35.

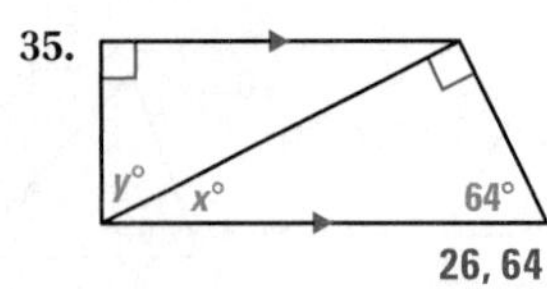

26, 64

36.

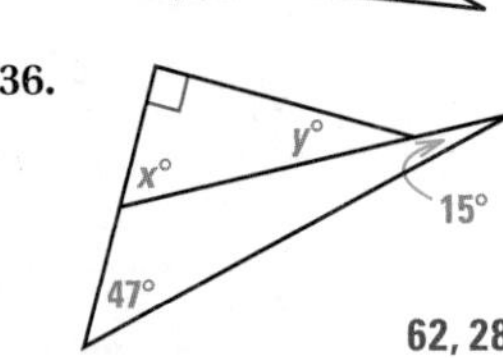

62, 28

37.

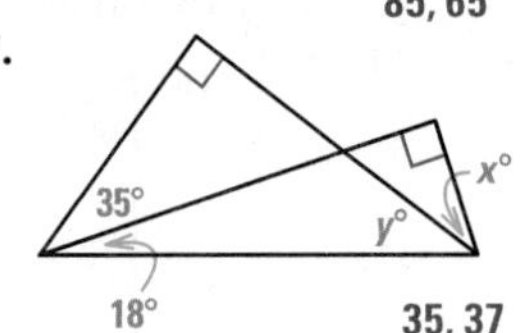

35, 37

C **38.** **VISUALIZATION** Is there an angle measure that is so small that any triangle with that angle measure will be an obtuse triangle? *Explain.*

39. **CHALLENGE** Suppose you have the equations $y = ax + b$, $y = cx + d$, and $y = ex + f$.

a. When will these three lines form a triangle?

b. Let $c = 1$, $d = 2$, $e = 4$, and $f = -7$. Find values of a and b so that no triangle is formed by the three equations. ***Sample answer:* 0, 5**

c. Draw the triangle formed when $a = \frac{4}{3}$, $b = \frac{1}{3}$, $c = -\frac{4}{3}$, $d = \frac{41}{3}$, $e = 0$, and $f = -1$. Then classify the triangle by its sides. **See margin for art; isosceles.**

PROBLEM SOLVING

EXAMPLE 1 on p. 217 for Ex. 40

A **40. THEATER** Three people are standing on a stage. The distances between the three people are shown in the diagram. Classify the triangle formed by its sides. Then copy the triangle, measure the angles, and classify the triangle by its angles. **scalene; acute**

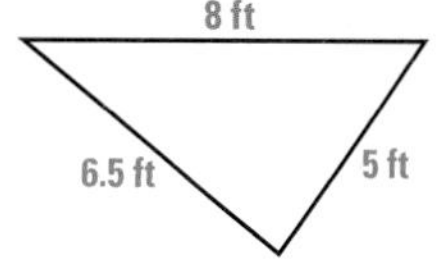

@HomeTutor for problem solving help at classzone.com

41. 2 in.; 60°; in an equilateral triangle all sides have the same length $\left(\frac{6}{3}\right)$. In an equiangular triangle the angles always measure 60°.

41. KALEIDOSCOPES You are making a kaleidoscope. The directions state that you are to arrange three pieces of reflective mylar in an equilateral and equiangular triangle. You must cut three strips from a piece of mylar 6 inches wide. What are the side lengths of the triangle used to form the kaleidoscope? What are the measures of the angles? *Explain.*

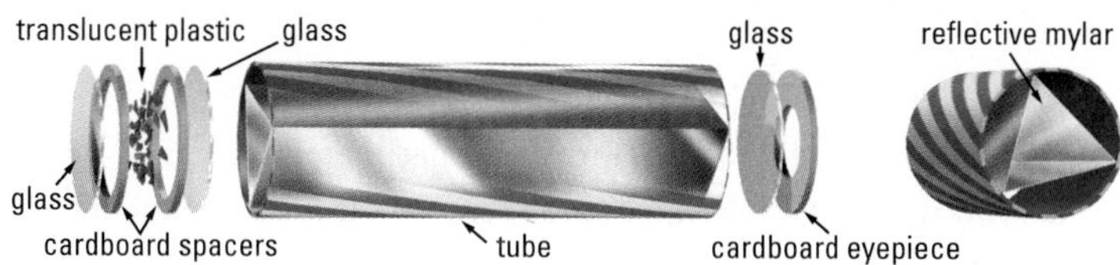

@HomeTutor for problem solving help at classzone.com

42. SCULPTURE You are bending a strip of metal into an isosceles triangle for a sculpture. The strip of metal is 20 inches long. The first bend is made 6 inches from one end. *Describe* two ways you could complete the triangle. **Bend the strip again at 7 inches or bend the strip again at 8 inches.**

43. ★ MULTIPLE CHOICE Which inequality describes the possible measures of an angle of a triangle? **C**

Ⓐ $0° \le x° \le 180°$  Ⓑ $0° \le x° < 180°$  Ⓒ $0° < x° < 180°$ 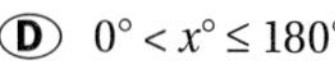 Ⓓ $0° < x° \le 180°$

SLING CHAIRS The brace of a sling chair forms a triangle with the seat and legs of the chair. Suppose $m\angle 2 = 50°$ and $m\angle 3 = 65°$.

44. Find $m\angle 6$. **115°**

45. Find $m\angle 5$. **115°**

46. Find $m\angle 1$. **130°**

47. Find $m\angle 4$. **65°**

B **48. PROOF** Prove the Corollary to the Triangle Sum Theorem on page 220. **See margin.**

49. MULTI-STEP PROBLEM The measures of the angles of a triangle are $(2\sqrt{2x})°$, $(5\sqrt{2x})°$, and $(2\sqrt{2x})°$.

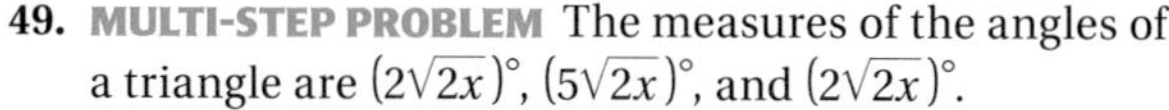

a. Write an equation to show the relationship of the angles. $2\sqrt{2x} + 5\sqrt{2x} + 2\sqrt{2x} = 180$

b. Find the measure of each angle. **40°, 100°, 40°**

c. Classify the triangle by its angles. **obtuse**

50. PROVING THEOREM 4.2 Prove the Exterior Angle Theorem. (*Hint:* Find two equations involving $m\angle ACB$.) **See margin.**

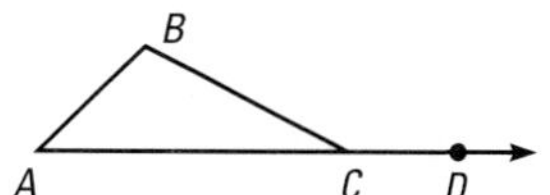

Mathematical Reasoning

Exercise 42 Have students relate the two ways of completing the triangle to the definition of an isosceles triangle.

48. Statements (Reasons)

1. $\triangle ABC$ is a right triangle. (Given)
2. $m\angle C = 90°$ (Definition of right angle)
3. $m\angle A + m\angle B + m\angle C = 180°$ (Triangle Sum Theorem)
4. $m\angle A + m\angle B + 90° = 180°$ (Substitution Property of Equality)
5. $m\angle A + m\angle B = 90°$ (Subtraction Property of Equality)
6. $\angle A$ and $\angle B$ are complementary. (Definition of complementary angles)

50. Statements (Reasons)

1. $m\angle ACB + m\angle BCD = 180°$ (Linear Pair Postulate and definition of supplementary angles)
2. $m\angle A + m\angle B + m\angle ACB = 180°$ (Triangle Sum Theorem)
3. $m\angle ACB + m\angle BCD = m\angle A + m\angle B + m\angle ACB$ (Transitive Property of Equality)
4. $m\angle BCD = m\angle A + m\angle B$ (Subtraction Property of Equality)

5 ASSESS AND RETEACH

Daily Homework Quiz

Transparency Available

1. Graph $\triangle ABC$ with vertices $A(0, 6)$, $B(-4, -1)$, and $C(4, -1)$. Classify it by its sides. Then determine if it is a right triangle. **isosceles; not a right triangle**

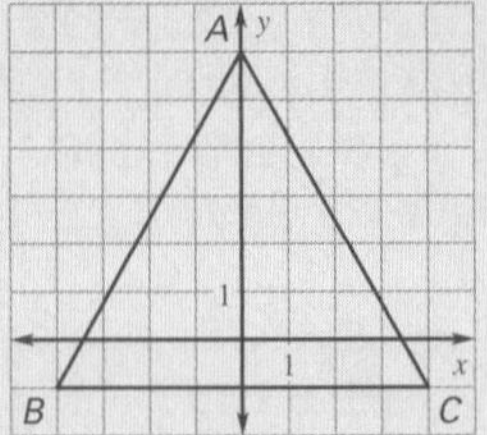

2. Find x. Then classify the triangle by its angles. **22; acute**

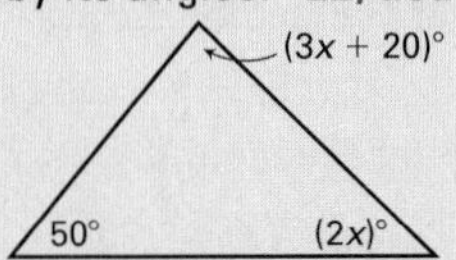

3. Find the measure of the exterior angle shown. **104°**

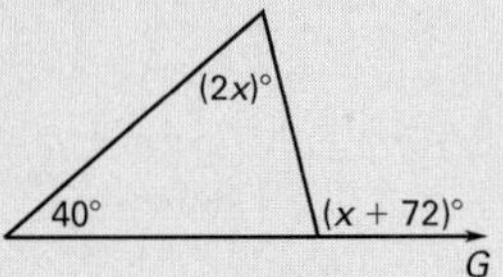

4. Find x and y. **82, 58**

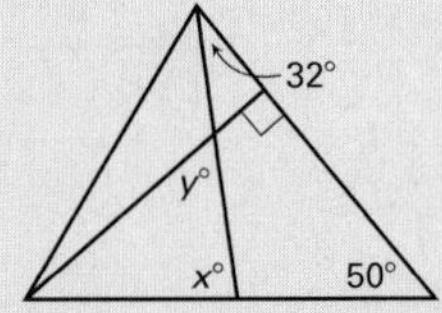

Online Quiz

Available at **classzone.com**

Diagnosis/Remediation

- Practice A, B, C in Chapter 4 Resource Book, pp. 7–12
- Study Guide in Chapter 4 Resource Book, pp. 13–14
- Practice Workbook, pp. 61–63
- @HomeTutor

Challenge

Additional challenge is available in the Chapter 4 Resource Book, p. 17.

53. See Additional Answers beginning on p. AA1.

51. *Sample answer:* They both reasoned correctly but their initial plan was incorrect. The measure of the exterior angle should be 150°.

51. ★ **EXTENDED RESPONSE** The figure below shows an initial plan for a triangular flower bed that Mary and Tom plan to build along a fence. They are discussing what the measure of $\angle 1$ should be.

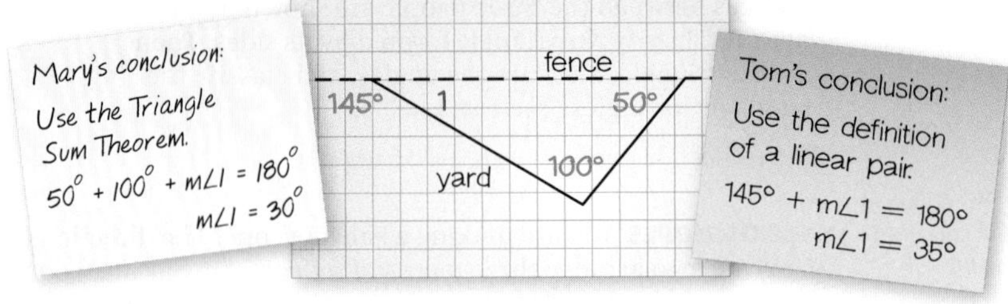

Did Mary and Tom both reason correctly? If not, who made a mistake and what mistake was made? If they did both reason correctly, what can you conclude about their initial plan? *Explain.*

52. **ALGEBRA** $\triangle ABC$ is isosceles. $AB = x$ and $BC = 2x - 4$.

a. Find two possible values for x if the perimeter of $\triangle ABC$ is 32. **8, 9**

b. How many possible values are there for x if the perimeter of $\triangle ABC$ is 12? **one value**

C 53. **CHALLENGE** Use the diagram to write a proof of the Triangle Sum Theorem. Your proof should be different than the proof of the Triangle Sum Theorem on page 219. **See margin.**

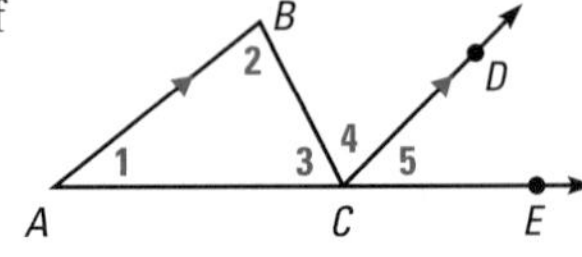

MIXED REVIEW

$\angle A$ and $\angle B$ are complementary. Find $m\angle A$ and $m\angle B$. *(p. 35)*

54. $m\angle A = (3x + 16)°$, $m\angle B = (4x - 3)°$ **49°, 41°**

55. $m\angle A = (4x - 2)°$, $m\angle B = (7x + 4)°$ **30°, 60°**

56. $m\angle A = (3x + 4)°$, $m\angle B = (2x + 6)°$ **52°, 38°**

PREVIEW Prepare for Lesson 4.2 in Exs. 57–59.

Each figure is a regular polygon. Find the value of x. *(p. 42)*

57. 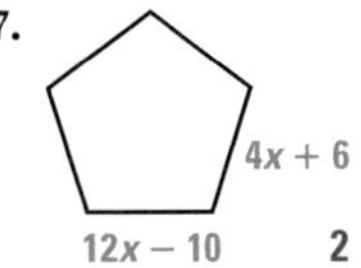

2

58. 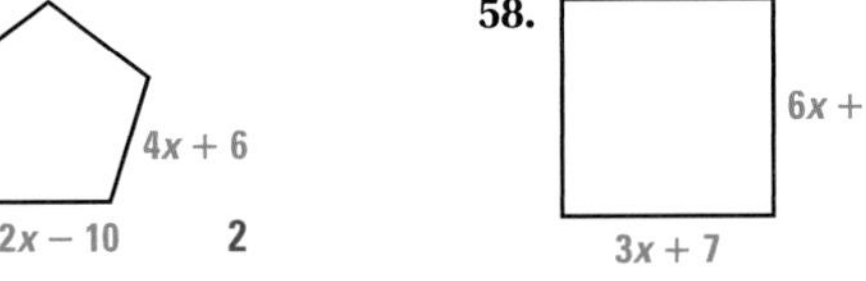

2

59. 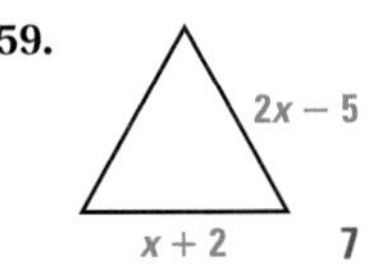

7

60. Use the Symmetric Property of Congruence to complete the statement: If __?__ ≅ __?__, then $\angle DEF \cong \angle PQR$. *(p. 112)* **$\angle PQR$, $\angle DEF$**

Use the diagram at the right. *(p. 124)*

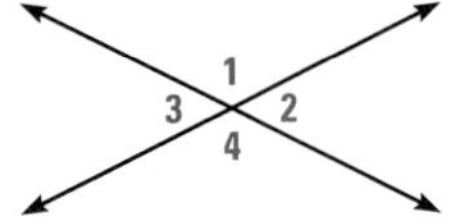

61. If $m\angle 1 = 127°$, find $m\angle 2$, $m\angle 3$, and $m\angle 4$. **53°, 53°, 127°**

62. If $m\angle 4 = 170°$, find $m\angle 1$, $m\angle 2$, and $m\angle 3$. **170°, 10°, 10°**

63. If $m\angle 3 = 54°$, find $m\angle 1$, $m\angle 2$, and $m\angle 4$. **126°, 54°, 126°**

4.2 Apply Congruence and Triangles

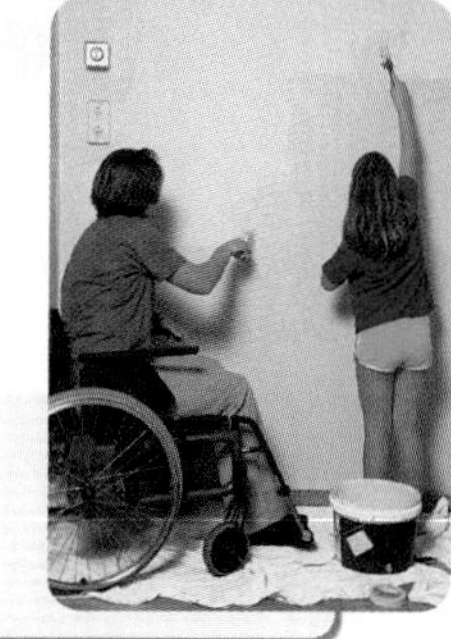

Before You identified congruent angles.

Now You will identify congruent figures.

Why? So you can determine if shapes are identical, as in Example 3.

Key Vocabulary
- **congruent figures**
- **corresponding parts**

Standards

5.0 Students prove that triangles are congruent or similar, **and they are able to use the concept of corresponding parts of congruent triangles.**

Two geometric figures are *congruent* if they have exactly the same size and shape. Imagine cutting out one of the congruent figures. You could then position the cut-out figure so that it fits perfectly onto the other figure.

Congruent

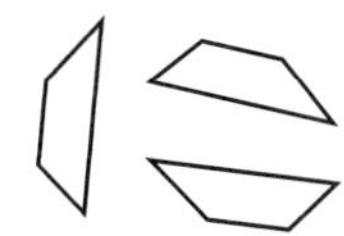

Same size and shape

Not congruent

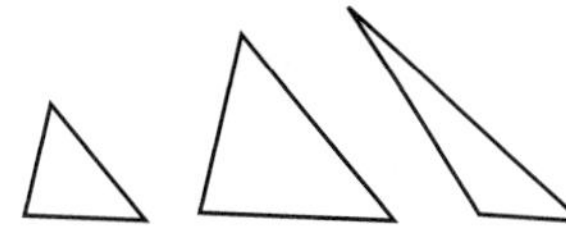

Different sizes or shapes

In two **congruent figures**, all the parts of one figure are congruent to the **corresponding parts** of the other figure. In congruent polygons, this means that the *corresponding sides* and the *corresponding angles* are congruent.

CONGRUENCE STATEMENTS When you write a congruence statement for two polygons, always list the corresponding vertices in the same order. You can write congruence statements in more than one way. Two possible congruence statements for the triangles at the right are $\triangle ABC \cong \triangle FED$ or $\triangle BCA \cong \triangle EDF$.

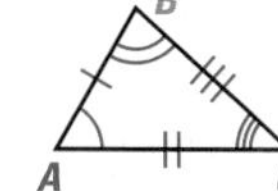

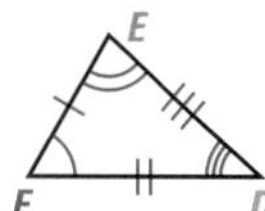

Corresponding angles	$\angle A \cong \angle F$	$\angle B \cong \angle E$	$\angle C \cong \angle D$
Corresponding sides	$\overline{AB} \cong \overline{FE}$	$\overline{BC} \cong \overline{ED}$	$\overline{AC} \cong \overline{FD}$

EXAMPLE 1 Identify congruent parts

VISUAL REASONING
To help you identify corresponding parts, turn $\triangle RST$.

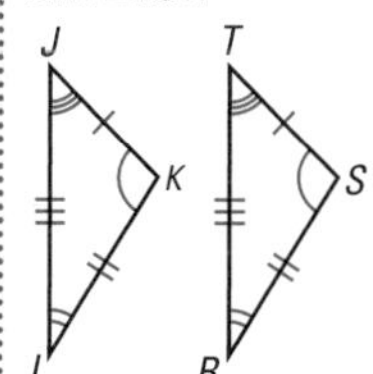

Write a congruence statement for the triangles. Identify all pairs of congruent corresponding parts.

J K L R S T

Solution

The diagram indicates that $\triangle JKL \cong \triangle TSR$.

Corresponding angles $\angle J \cong \angle T, \angle K \cong \angle S, \angle L \cong \angle R$

Corresponding sides $\overline{JK} \cong \overline{TS}, \overline{KL} \cong \overline{SR}, \overline{LJ} \cong \overline{RT}$

1 PLAN AND PREPARE

Warm-Up Exercises

Transparency Available

1. When are two angles congruent? **when they have the same measure**
2. In $\triangle ABC$, if $m\angle A = 64°$ and $m\angle B = 71°$, what is $m\angle C$? **45°**
3. What property of angle congruence is illustrated by this statement? If $\angle A \cong \angle B$ and $\angle B \cong \angle C$, then $\angle A \cong \angle C$. **Transitive Property**

Notetaking Guide

Transparency Available

Promotes interactive learning and notetaking skills, pp. 89–92.

Pacing

Basic: 2 days
Average: 2 days
Advanced: 2 days
Block: 0.5 block with 4.1
0.5 block with 4.3

- See *Teaching Guide/Lesson Plan.*

2 FOCUS AND MOTIVATE

Essential Question

Big Idea 2, p. 215

What are congruent figures? **Tell students they will learn how to answer this question by studying the definition of congruent figures.**

Resource Planning Guide

Chapter Resource Book
- Teaching Guide/Lesson Plan (pp. 18–19)
- Activity Master (p. 20)
- Practice levels A, B, C (pp. 21–26)
- Study Guide (pp. 27–28)
- Catch-up for Absent Students (p. 29)
- Application (p. 30)
- Challenge (p. 31)

Workbooks
- Notetaking Guide (pp. 89–92)
- Practice Workbook (pp. 64–66)

Teaching Options
- **Power Presentations CD-ROM** provides dynamic electronic teaching resources for the classroom.
- **Activity Generator CD-ROM** provides editable activities for all ability levels.

Interactive Technology
- Easy Planner
- Power Presentations CD-ROM
- Activity Generator CD-ROM
- Animated Geometry
- Test Generator CD-ROM
- Online Quiz
- eWorkbook
- eEdition
- @HomeTutor

Resources for English Learners
- Quick Reference for English Learners
- Spanish Study Guide
- Multi-Language Visual Glossary
- Student Resources in Spanish

See also the *Geometry Toolkit* for more strategies for meeting individual needs.

Motivating the Lesson

To replace missing or damaged tiles in old houses, it is often necessary to supply information to get tiles made to order. Tell students that in this lesson, they will learn what kinds of information they might need to supply to ensure they get tiles that are just the size and shape required.

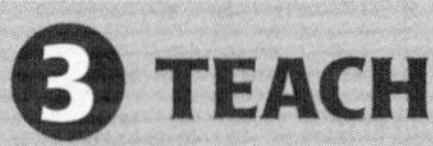

3 TEACH

Extra Example 1

Write a congruence statement for the triangles shown. Identify all pairs of congruent corresponding parts.

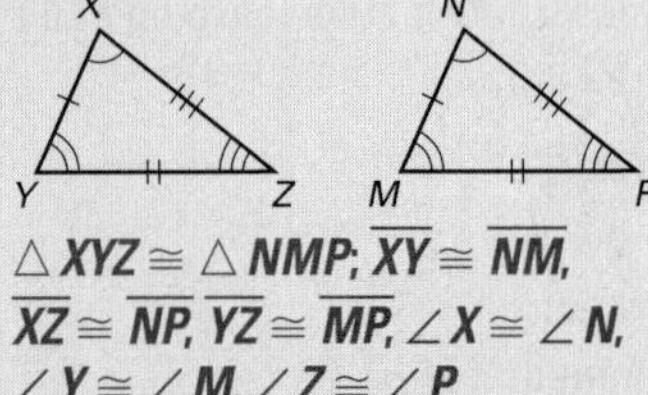

$\triangle XYZ \cong \triangle NMP$; $\overline{XY} \cong \overline{NM}$, $\overline{XZ} \cong \overline{NP}$, $\overline{YZ} \cong \overline{MP}$, $\angle X \cong \angle N$, $\angle Y \cong \angle M$, $\angle Z \cong \angle P$

Key Question to Ask for Example 1

- Is there any other way you could have written the congruence statement? Explain. **Yes; another statement is $\triangle KLJ \cong \triangle SRT$.**

Extra Example 2

In the diagram, $ABCD \cong FGHK$.

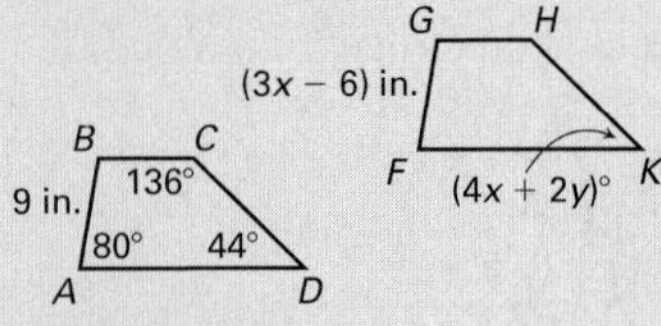

a. Find the value of x. **5**

b. Find the value of y. **12**

Key Question to Ask for Example 2

- What are the measures of $\angle S$ and $\angle R$? **102°, 84°**

EXAMPLE 2 Use properties of congruent figures

In the diagram, $DEFG \cong SPQR$.

a. Find the value of x.

b. Find the value of y.

Solution

a. You know that $\overline{FG} \cong \overline{QR}$.

$FG = QR$

$12 = 2x - 4$

$16 = 2x$

$8 = x$

b. You know that $\angle F \cong \angle Q$.

$m\angle F = m\angle Q$

$68° = (6y + x)°$

$68 = 6y + 8$

$10 = y$

EXAMPLE 3 Show that figures are congruent

PAINTING If you divide the wall into orange and blue sections along $\overline{JK}$, will the sections of the wall be the same size and shape? *Explain.*

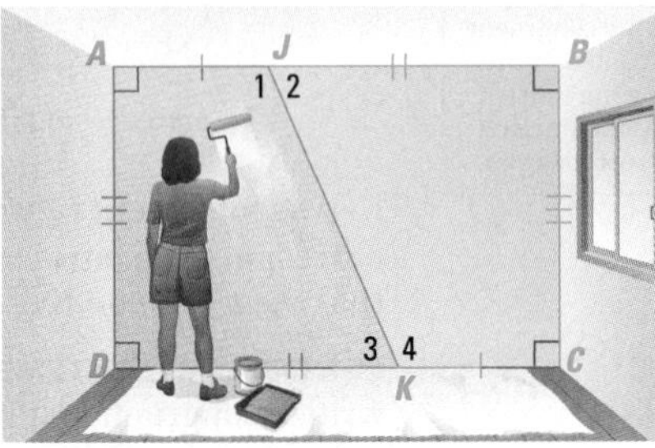

Solution

From the diagram, $\angle A \cong \angle C$ and $\angle D \cong \angle B$ because all right angles are congruent. Also, by the Lines Perpendicular to a Transversal Theorem, $\overline{AB} \parallel \overline{DC}$. Then, $\angle 1 \cong \angle 4$ and $\angle 2 \cong \angle 3$ by the Alternate Interior Angles Theorem. So, all pairs of corresponding angles are congruent.

The diagram shows $\overline{AJ} \cong \overline{CK}$, $\overline{KD} \cong \overline{JB}$, and $\overline{DA} \cong \overline{BC}$. By the Reflexive Property, $\overline{JK} \cong \overline{KJ}$. All corresponding parts are congruent, so $AJKD \cong CKJB$.

▶ Yes, the two sections will be the same size and shape.

GUIDED PRACTICE for Examples 1, 2, and 3

1. $\overline{AB} \cong \overline{CD}$, $\overline{BG} \cong \overline{DE}$, $\overline{GH} \cong \overline{EF}$, $\overline{HA} \cong \overline{FC}$, $\angle A \cong \angle C$, $\angle B \cong \angle D$, $\angle G \cong \angle E$, $\angle H \cong \angle F$

In the diagram at the right, $ABGH \cong CDEF$.

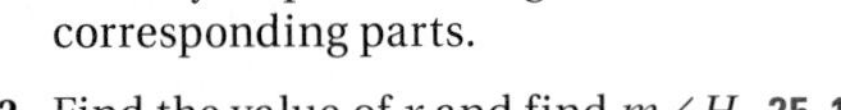

1. Identify all pairs of congruent corresponding parts.
2. Find the value of x and find $m\angle H$. **25, 105°**
3. Show that $\triangle PTS \cong \triangle RTQ$. **All of the corresponding parts of $\triangle PTS$ are congruent to those of $\triangle RTQ$ by the indicated markings, the Vertical Angles Theorem, and the Alternate Interior Angles Theorem.**

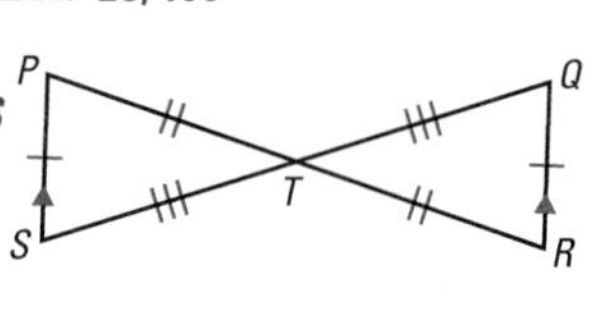

THEOREM *For Your Notebook*

THEOREM 4.3 Third Angles Theorem

If two angles of one triangle are congruent to two angles of another triangle, then the third angles are also congruent.

Proof: Ex. 28, p. 230

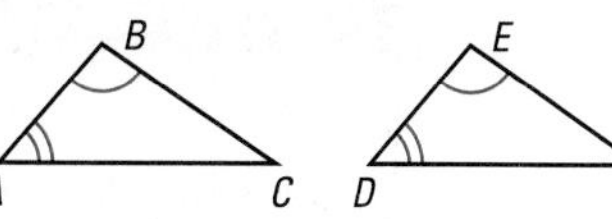

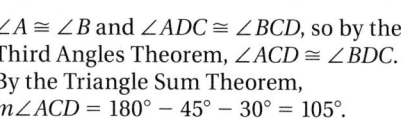

If $\angle A \cong \angle D$, and $\angle B \cong \angle E$, then $\angle C \cong \angle F$.

EXAMPLE 4 Use the Third Angles Theorem

Find $m\angle BDC$.

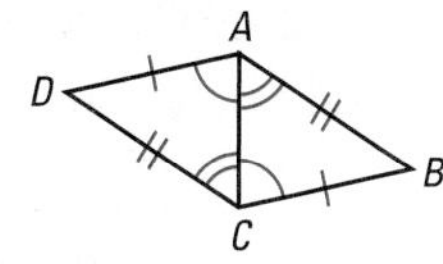

Solution

$\angle A \cong \angle B$ and $\angle ADC \cong \angle BCD$, so by the Third Angles Theorem, $\angle ACD \cong \angle BDC$. By the Triangle Sum Theorem, $m\angle ACD = 180° - 45° - 30° = 105°$.

▶ So, $m\angle ACD = m\angle BDC = 105°$ by the definition of congruent angles.

ANOTHER WAY

For an alternative method for solving the problem in Example 4, turn to page 232 for the **Problem Solving Workshop**.

EXAMPLE 5 Prove that triangles are congruent

Write a proof.

GIVEN ▶ $\overline{AD} \cong \overline{CB}$, $\overline{DC} \cong \overline{BA}$, $\angle ACD \cong \angle CAB$, $\angle CAD \cong \angle ACB$

PROVE ▶ $\triangle ACD \cong \triangle CAB$

Plan for Proof
a. Use the Reflexive Property to show that $\overline{AC} \cong \overline{AC}$.
b. Use the Third Angles Theorem to show that $\angle B \cong \angle D$.

Plan in Action

	STATEMENTS	REASONS
	1. $\overline{AD} \cong \overline{CB}$, $\overline{DC} \cong \overline{BA}$	1. Given
a.	2. $\overline{AC} \cong \overline{AC}$	2. Reflexive Property of Congruence
	3. $\angle ACD \cong \angle CAB$, $\angle CAD \cong \angle ACB$	3. Given
b.	4. $\angle B \cong \angle D$	4. Third Angles Theorem
	5. $\triangle ACD \cong \triangle CAB$	5. Definition of $\cong$ figures

✓ GUIDED PRACTICE for Examples 4 and 5

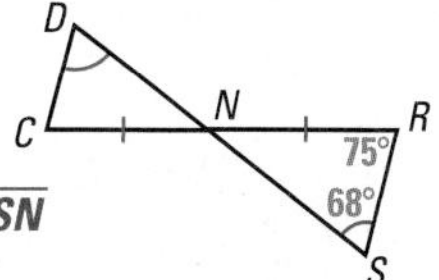

4. In the diagram, what is $m\angle DCN$? **75°**
5. By the definition of congruence, what additional information is needed to know that $\triangle NDC \cong \triangle NSR$? **$\overline{DC} \cong \overline{SR}$ and $\overline{DN} \cong \overline{SN}$**

Differentiated Instruction

Kinesthetic Learners Some students may find it challenging to visualize that two triangles in different orientations are congruent. Have these students trace the triangles in **Example 5** onto tracing paper, cut them out, and arrange them so one triangle fits exactly on top of the other.

See also the *Geometry Toolkit* for more strategies.

Extra Example 3

Maggie took the piece of fabric *STUV* shown in the diagram and cut it on the diagonal to make a scarf for her and a friend. Are the two pieces the same size and shape? Explain.

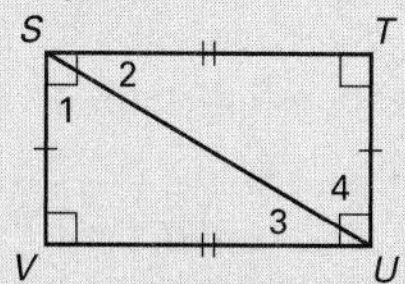

Yes; $\angle V \cong \angle T$ since both are right angles. $\overline{ST} \parallel \overline{VU}$ and $\overline{SV} \parallel \overline{TU}$ by the Lines Perpendicular to a Transversal Theorem. It is given that $\overline{SV} \cong \overline{UT}$ and $\overline{VU} \cong \overline{TS}$, and $\overline{SU} \cong \overline{SU}$ by the Refl. Prop. of $\cong$. All corresponding parts are $\cong$, so $\triangle UVS \cong \triangle STU$.

Extra Example 4

Find $m\angle YXW$. **105°**

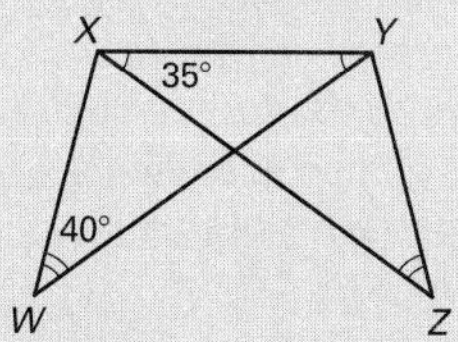

Extra Example 5

Given: $\overline{SV} \cong \overline{RV}$, $\overline{TV} \cong \overline{WV}$, $\overline{ST} \cong \overline{RW}$, $\angle T \cong \angle W$

Prove: $\triangle STV \cong \triangle RWV$

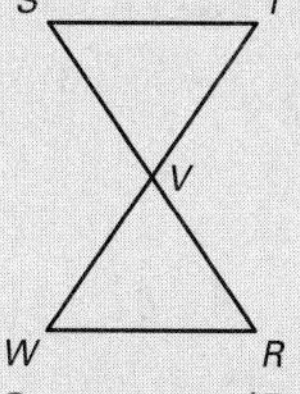

Statements (Reasons)

1. **$\overline{SV} \cong \overline{RV}$, $\overline{TV} \cong \overline{WV}$, $\overline{ST} \cong \overline{RW}$ (Given)**
2. **$\angle T \cong \angle W$ (Given)**
3. **$\angle SVT \cong \angle RVW$ (Vert. $\angle$s Thm.)**
4. **$\angle S \cong \angle R$ (Third $\angle$s Thm.)**
5. **$\triangle STV \cong \triangle RWV$ (Def. of $\cong$ $\triangle$s)**

Key Question to Ask for Example 5

- How many pairs of sides and pairs of angles must you show are congruent when you use the definition of congruent triangles to show that two triangles are congruent? **three pairs of sides, three pairs of angles**

Closing the Lesson

Have students summarize the major points of the lesson and answer the Essential Question: What are congruent figures?

- **Triangles can be proved congruent by showing that all 3 pairs of corresponding sides and all 3 pairs of corresponding angles are congruent.**
- **If two angles of one triangle are congruent to two angles of another, then the third angles are congruent.**

Congruent figures are figures that have exactly the same size and shape.

1.

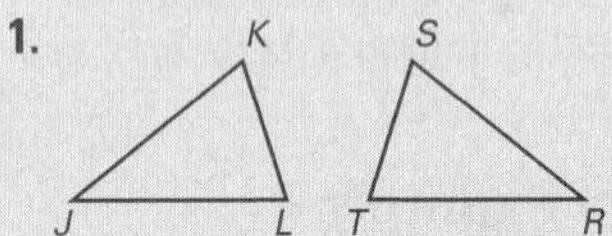

2. 3 pairs of congruent sides and 3 pairs of congruent angles; to prove two figures congruent it must be shown that all corresponding sides and angles are congruent.

3. $\angle A$ and $\angle D$, $\angle C$ and $\angle F$, $\angle B$ and $\angle E$, $\overline{AB}$ and $\overline{DE}$, $\overline{AC}$ and $\overline{DF}$, $\overline{BC}$ and $\overline{EF}$. *Sample answer:* $\triangle CAB \cong \triangle FDE$

4. $\angle G$ and $\angle Q$, $\angle H$ and $\angle R$, $\angle K$ and $\angle T$, $\angle J$ and $\angle S$, $\overline{GH}$ and $\overline{QR}$, $\overline{HJ}$ and $\overline{RS}$, $\overline{JK}$ and $\overline{ST}$, $\overline{KG}$ and $\overline{TQ}$. *Sample answer:* $HJKG \cong RSTQ$

PROPERTIES OF CONGRUENT TRIANGLES The properties of congruence that are true for segments and angles are also true for triangles.

THEOREM *For Your Notebook*

THEOREM 4.4 Properties of Congruent Triangles

Reflexive Property of Congruent Triangles

For any triangle ABC, $\triangle ABC \cong \triangle ABC$.

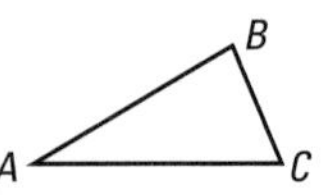

Symmetric Property of Congruent Triangles

If $\triangle ABC \cong \triangle DEF$, then $\triangle DEF \cong \triangle ABC$.

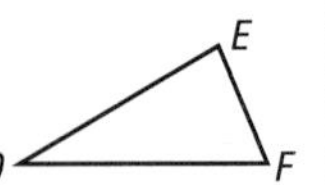

Transitive Property of Congruent Triangles

If $\triangle ABC \cong \triangle DEF$ and $\triangle DEF \cong \triangle JKL$, then $\triangle ABC \cong \triangle JKL$.

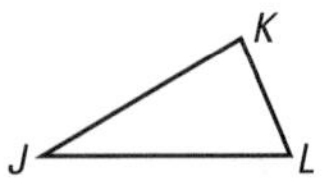

4.2 EXERCISES

HOMEWORK KEY

○ = **WORKED-OUT SOLUTIONS** on p. WS4 for Exs. 9, 15, and 25

★ = **STANDARDIZED TEST PRACTICE** Exs. 2, 18, 21, 24, 27, and 30

SKILL PRACTICE

A

1. **VOCABULARY** Copy the congruent triangles shown. Then label the vertices of the triangles so that $\triangle JKL \cong \triangle RST$. Identify all pairs of congruent *corresponding angles* and *corresponding sides*.

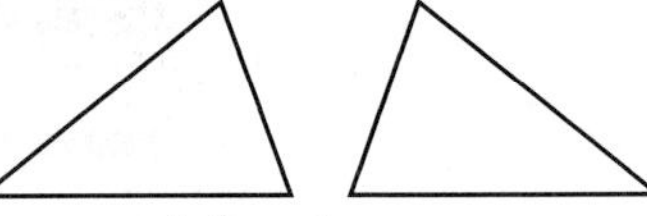

$\overline{JK} \cong \overline{RS}$, $\overline{KL} \cong \overline{ST}$, $\overline{JL} \cong \overline{RT}$, $\angle J \cong \angle R$, $\angle K \cong \angle S$, $\angle L \cong \angle T$; see margin for art.

2. ★ **WRITING** Based on this lesson, what information do you need to prove that two triangles are congruent? *Explain.* **See margin.**

EXAMPLE 1 on p. 225 for Exs. 3–4

USING CONGRUENCE Identify all pairs of congruent corresponding parts. Then write another congruence statement for the figures. **3, 4. See margin.**

3. $\triangle ABC \cong \triangle DEF$

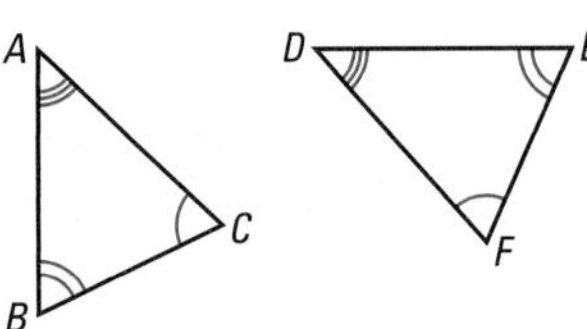

4. $GHJK \cong QRST$

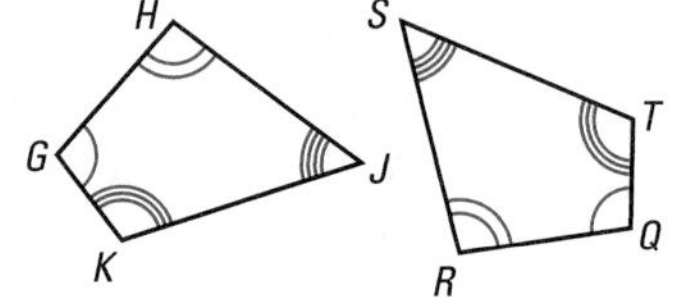

EXAMPLE 2 on p. 226 for Exs. 5–10

READING A DIAGRAM In the diagram, $\triangle XYZ \cong \triangle MNL$. Copy and complete the statement.

5. $m\angle Y =$ __?__ **124°**
6. $m\angle M =$ __?__ **33°**
7. $YX =$ __?__ **8**
8. $\overline{YZ} \cong$ __?__ **$\overline{NL}$**
9. $\triangle LNM \cong$ __?__ **$\triangle ZYX$**
10. $\triangle YXZ \cong$ __?__ **$\triangle NML$**

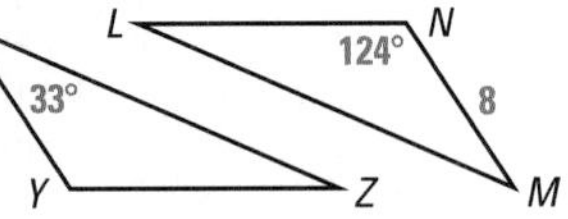

EXAMPLE 3
on p. 226 for Exs. 11–14

NAMING CONGRUENT FIGURES **Write a congruence statement for any figures that can be proved congruent. *Explain* your reasoning.**

11. 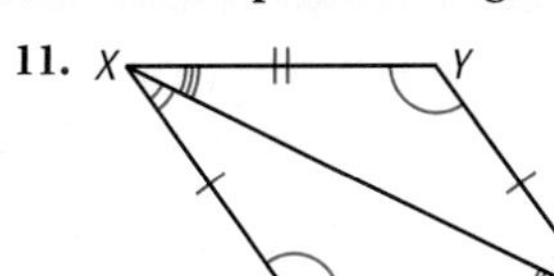

$\triangle XYZ \cong \triangle ZWX$; all corresponding sides and angles are congruent.

12. 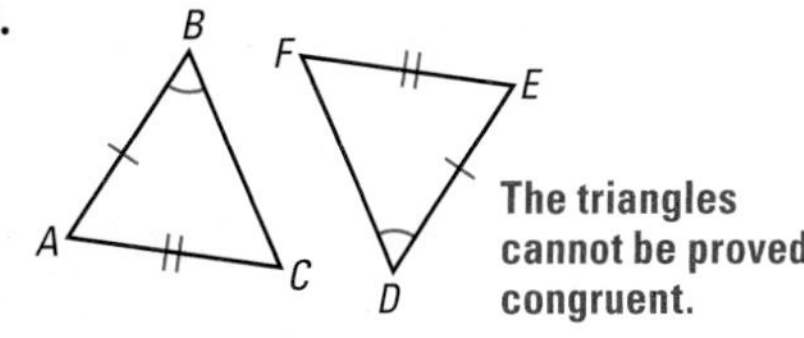

The triangles cannot be proved congruent.

13. 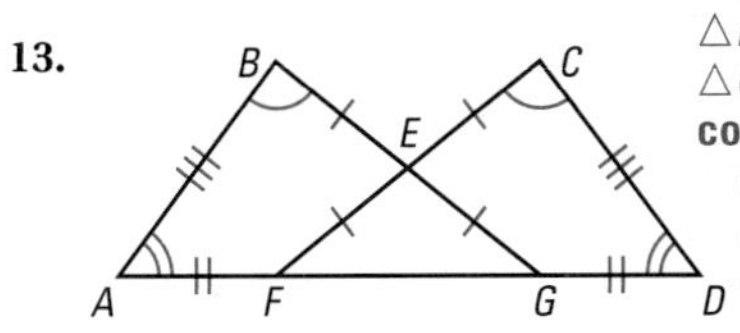

$\triangle BAG \cong \triangle CDF$; all corresponding sides and angles are congruent.

14. 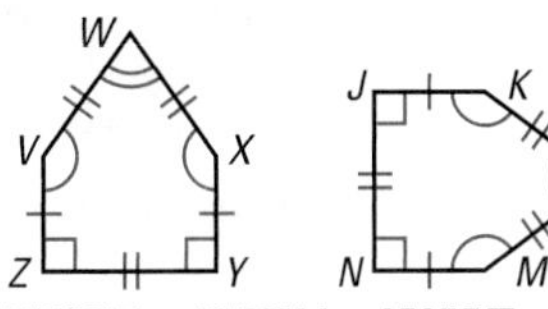

***VWXYZ* ≅ *KLMNJ* or *VWXYZ* ≅ *MLKJN*; all corresponding sides and angles are congruent.**

EXAMPLE 4
on p. 227 for Exs. 15–16

THIRD ANGLES THEOREM **Find the value of *x*.**

15. 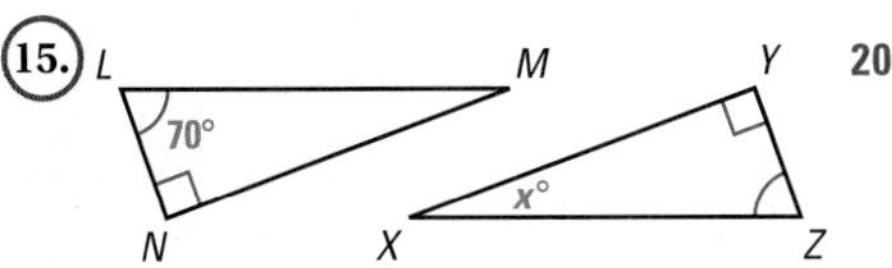

20

16. 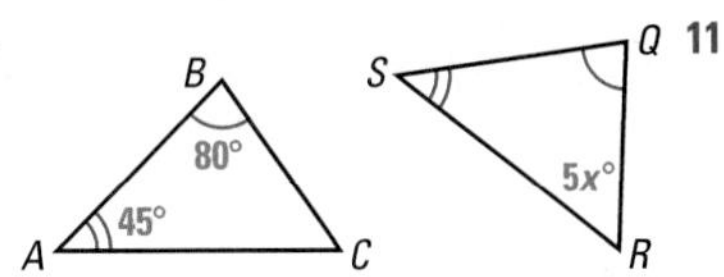

11

B

17. **ERROR ANALYSIS** A student says that $\triangle MNP \cong \triangle RSP$ because the corresponding angles of the triangles are congruent. *Describe* the error in this statement. **Student still needs to show that corresponding sides are congruent.**

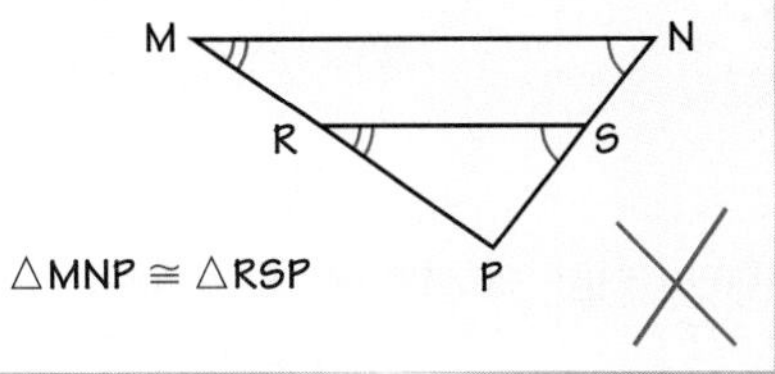

18. ★ **OPEN-ENDED MATH** Graph the triangle with vertices $L(3, 1)$, $M(8, 1)$, and $N(8, 8)$. Then graph a triangle congruent to $\triangle LMN$. **See margin.**

ALGEBRA **Find the values of *x* and *y*.**

19. 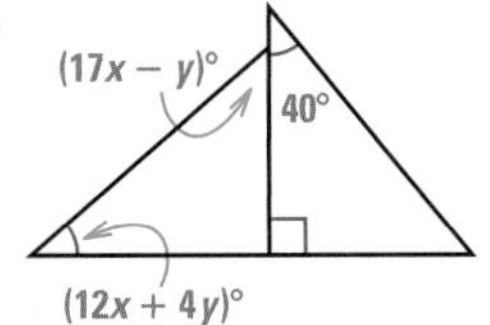

3, 1

20. 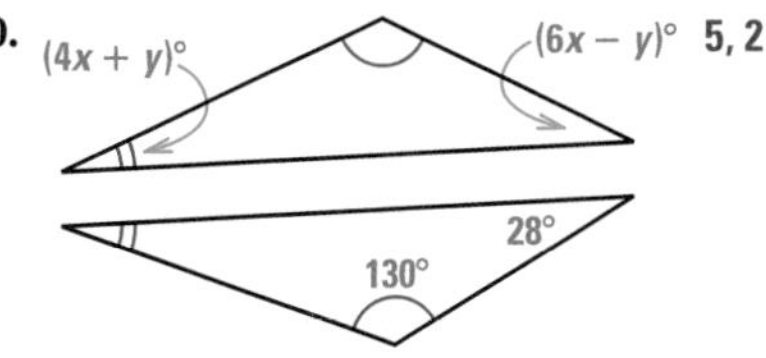

5, 2

21. ★ **MULTIPLE CHOICE** Suppose $\triangle ABC \cong \triangle EFD$, $\triangle EFD \cong \triangle GIH$, $m\angle A = 90°$, and $m\angle F = 20°$. What is $m\angle H$? **B**

Ⓐ 20° Ⓑ 70° Ⓒ 90° Ⓓ Cannot be determined

C

22. **CHALLENGE** A hexagon is contained in a cube, as shown. Each vertex of the hexagon lies on the midpoint of an edge of the cube. This hexagon is equiangular. *Explain* why it is also regular. **It is regular because all angles are congruent and all sides will be congruent because they are all connecting the midpoints of edges.**

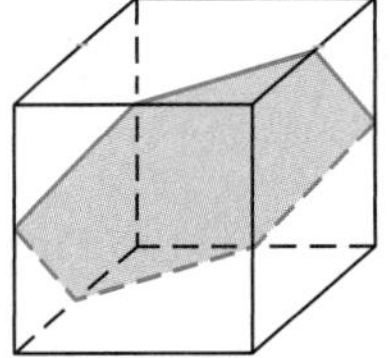

18. *Sample:*

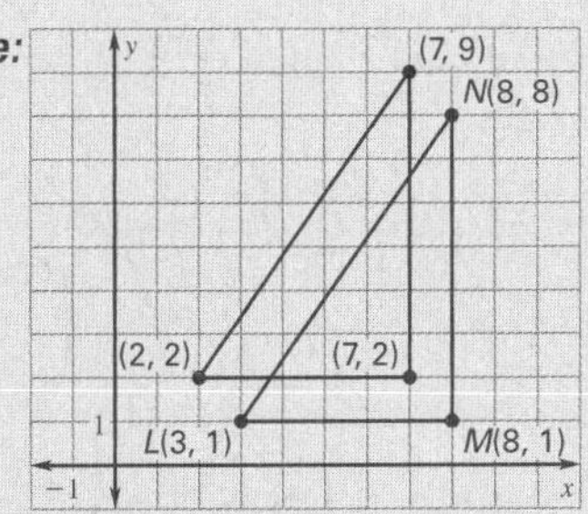

4 PRACTICE AND APPLY

Assignment Guide

Answer Transparencies available for all exercises

Basic:
Day 1: pp. 228–231
Exs. 1–14
Day 2: pp. 228–231
Exs. 15–19, 23–28, 33–40

Average:
Day 1: pp. 228–231
Exs. 1–14, 36–40
Day 2: pp. 228–231
Exs. 15–21, 23–31, 33–35

Advanced:
Day 1: pp. 228–231
Exs. 1–4, 7–14, 22*, 36–40
Day 2: pp. 228–231
Exs. 15–21, 24–35*

Block:
pp. 228–231
Exs. 1–14, 36–40 (with 4.1)
pp. 228–231
Exs. 15–21, 23–31, 33–35 (with 4.3)

Differentiated Instruction

See *Geometry Best Practices Toolkit* for suggestions on addressing the needs of a diverse classroom.

Homework Check

For a quick check of student understanding of key concepts, go over the following exercises:

Basic: 3, 6, 12, 16, 26
Average: 3, 8, 13, 16, 26
Advanced: 4, 10, 14, 16, 26

Extra Practice

- Student Edition, p. 902
- Chapter 4 Resource Book: Practice levels A, B, C, pp. 21–26

Practice Worksheet

An easily-readable reduced practice page (with answers) for this lesson can be found on p. 214C.

Mathematical Reasoning

Exercise 1 Discuss the number of ways the letters *J*, *K*, and *L* can be used to label the vertices of the triangle on the left. Assuming it has been decided how to label the vertices of that triangle, ask students if there is more than one correct way to label the vertices of the triangle on the right. Stress that only one correct labeling is possible.

Avoiding Common Errors

Exercises 11–14 Students may write the letters in the wrong order in the congruence statement. Review how the order of the letters in a congruence statement tells which sides and angles correspond to one another.

Mathematical Reasoning

Exercises 19–20 Ask students whether the triangles in each exercise are or are not congruent. Help them understand that despite the diagram, it is not possible to say whether the triangles are or are not congruent, since we have no definite information about the sides of the triangles.

Teaching Strategy

Exercise 27 If students have trouble drawing an appropriate figure, it may help them to first draw and label $\triangle ABC$. They can put tracing paper over the triangle, trace it, and label the vertices of the copy. They can then change the position of the copy so that points *B* and *C* of the copy fall on top of points *C* and *B* of the original triangle. This will enable them to determine an appropriate location for point *D*.

Avoiding Common Errors

Exercise 28 Remind students that since they are proving the Third Angle Theorem, they may not use the Third Angle Theorem as a reason in their proof. They should follow the Plan for the Proof that is given in the exercise.

PROBLEM SOLVING

A

23. RUG DESIGNS The rug design is made of congruent triangles. One triangular shape is used to make all of the triangles in the design. Which property guarantees that all the triangles are congruent? **Transitive Property of Congruent Triangles**

 for problem solving help at classzone.com

24. ★ OPEN-ENDED MATH Create a design for a rug made with congruent triangles that is different from the one in the photo above. **See margin.**

(25.) CAR STEREO A car stereo fits into a space in your dashboard. You want to buy a new car stereo, and it must fit in the existing space. What measurements need to be the same in order for the new stereo to be congruent to the old one? **length, width, and depth**

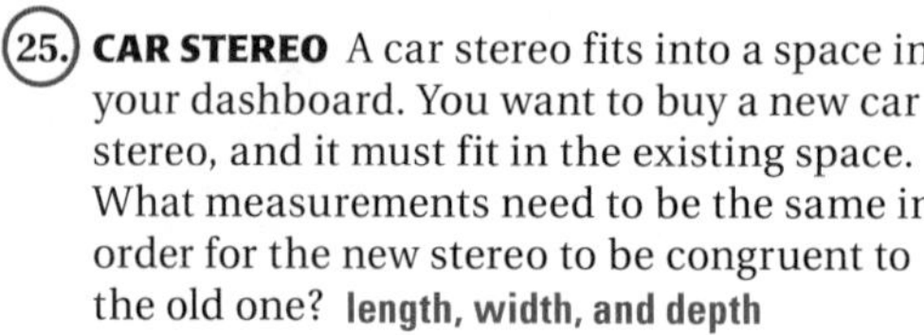

@HomeTutor for problem solving help at classzone.com

EXAMPLE 5 on p. 227 for Ex. 26

B

26. PROOF Copy and complete the proof.

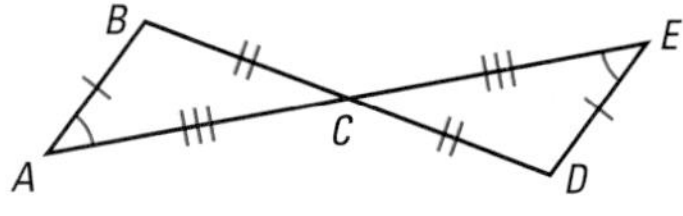

GIVEN ▶ $\overline{AB} \cong \overline{ED}$, $\overline{BC} \cong \overline{DC}$, $\overline{CA} \cong \overline{CE}$, $\angle BAC \cong \angle DEC$

PROVE ▶ $\triangle ABC \cong \triangle EDC$

STATEMENTS	REASONS
1. $\overline{AB} \cong \overline{ED}$, $\overline{BC} \cong \overline{DC}$, $\overline{CA} \cong \overline{CE}$, $\angle BAC \cong \angle DEC$	1. Given
2. $\angle BCA \cong \angle DCE$	2. ? **Vertical Angles Congruence Theorem**
3. ? **$\angle ABC \cong \angle EDC$**	3. Third Angles Theorem
4. $\triangle ABC \cong \triangle EDC$	4. ? **Definition of congruent figures**

27. ★ SHORT RESPONSE Suppose $\triangle ABC \cong \triangle DCB$, and the triangles share vertices at points *B* and *C*. Draw a figure that illustrates this situation. Is $\overline{AC} \parallel \overline{BD}$? *Explain.* **Yes; alternate interior angles are congruent; see margin for art.**

28. PROVING THEOREM 4.3 Use the plan to prove the Third Angles Theorem. **See margin.**

GIVEN ▶ $\angle A \cong \angle D$, $\angle B \cong \angle E$

PROVE ▶ $\angle C \cong \angle F$

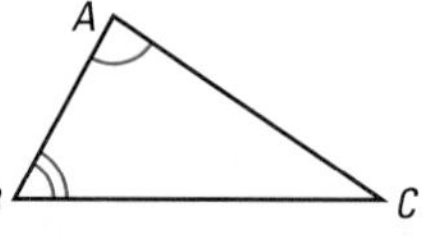

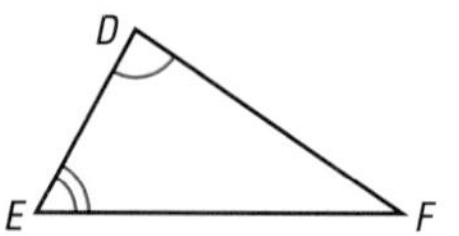

Plan for Proof Use the Triangle Sum Theorem to show that the sums of the angle measures are equal. Then use substitution to show $\angle C \cong \angle F$.

○ = WORKED-OUT SOLUTIONS on p. WS1 ★ = STANDARDIZED TEST PRACTICE

24. *Sample:*

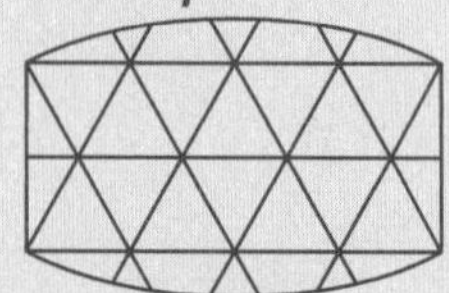

27.

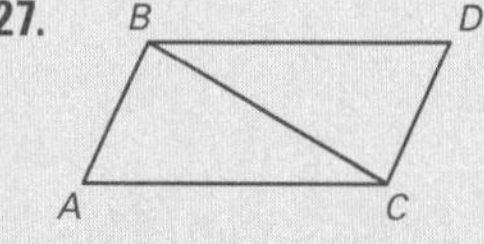

28. See Additional Answers beginning on p. AA1.

29.

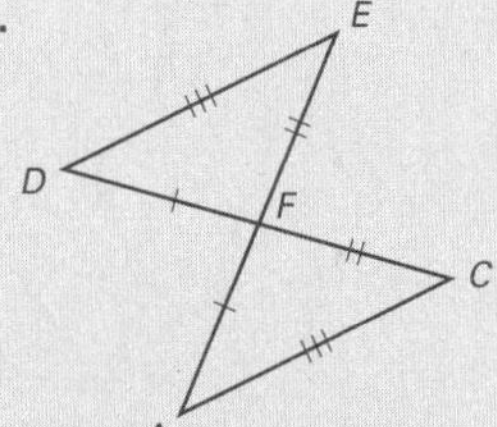

29. **REASONING** Given that $\triangle AFC \cong \triangle DFE$, must F be the midpoint of $\overline{AD}$ and $\overline{EC}$? Include a drawing with your answer. **No; see margin for art.**

30. ★ **SHORT RESPONSE** You have a set of tiles that come in two different shapes, as shown. You can put two of the triangular tiles together to make a quadrilateral that is the same size and shape as the quadrilateral tile.

Explain how you can find all of the angle measures of each tile by measuring only two angles. **Measure two angles of the triangle and use the Triangle Sum Theorem to find the third angle. The angles in the quadrilateral can be found using the angle measures of the triangle.**

31a. Corresponding parts of congruent figures are congruent.

31b. They are supplementary to two congruent angles and therefore are congruent.

31. **MULTI-STEP PROBLEM** In the diagram, quadrilateral $ABEF \cong$ quadrilateral $CDEF$.

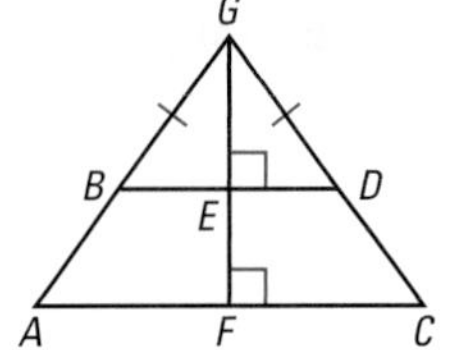

a. *Explain* how you know that $\overline{BE} \cong \overline{DE}$ and $\angle ABE \cong \angle CDE$.

b. *Explain* how you know that $\angle GBE \cong \angle GDE$.

c. *Explain* how you know that $\angle GEB \cong \angle GED$. ***Sample answer:* All right angles are congruent.**

d. Do you have enough information to prove that $\triangle BEG \cong \triangle DEG$? *Explain*. **Yes; all corresponding parts of both triangles are congruent.**

C 32. **CHALLENGE** Use the diagram to write a proof.

GIVEN ▶ $\overline{WX} \perp \overrightarrow{VZ}$ at Y, Y is the midpoint of $\overline{WX}$, $\overline{VW} \cong \overline{VX}$, and $\overrightarrow{VZ}$ bisects $\angle WVX$.

PROVE ▶ $\triangle VWY \cong \triangle VXY$ **See margin.**

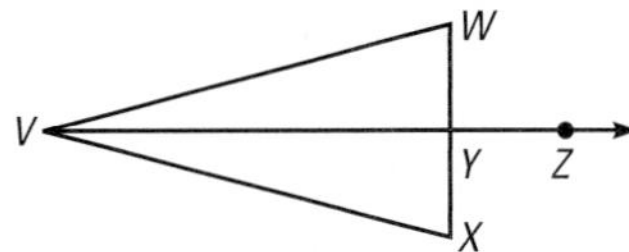

MIXED REVIEW

PREVIEW
Prepare for Lesson 4.3 in Exs. 33–35.

Use the Distance Formula to find the length of the segment. Round your answer to the nearest tenth of a unit. *(p. 15)*

33.

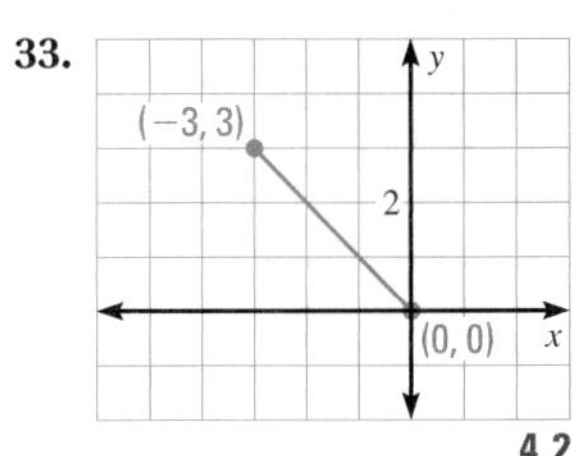

4.2

34. (−2, −1), (3, 2) **5.8**

35.

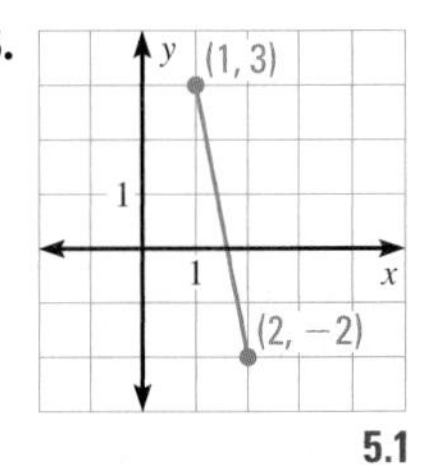

5.1

Line ℓ bisects the segment. Write a congruence statement. *(p. 15)*

36. **$\overline{AB} \cong \overline{CB}$**

37. **$\overline{LM} \cong \overline{NM}$**

38. **$\overline{RS} \cong \overline{TS}$**

Write the converse of the statement. *(p. 79)*

39. If three points are coplanar, then they lie in the same plane. **If three points lie in the same plane, then the three points are coplanar.**

40. If the sky is cloudy, then it is raining outside. **If it is raining outside, then the sky is cloudy.**

5 ASSESS AND RETEACH

Daily Homework Quiz

Transparency Available

In the diagram, $\triangle ABC \cong \triangle DEF$. Complete each statement.

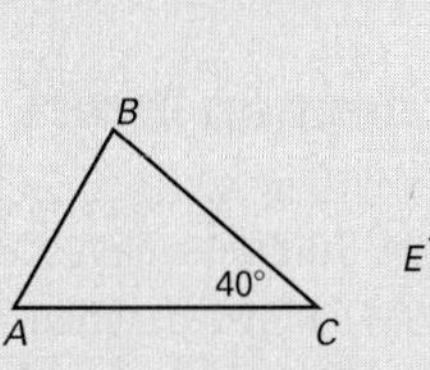

1. $m\angle A = \underline{?}$ **60°**

2. $\overline{FD} \cong \underline{?}$ **$\overline{CA}$**

3. $\triangle EDF \cong \underline{?}$ **$\triangle BAC$**

4. Write a congruence statement for the two small triangles. Explain your reasoning.

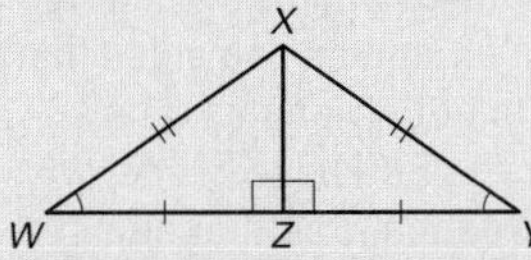

$\triangle WXZ \cong \triangle YXZ$; The diagram tells us that $\angle W \cong \angle Y$ and $\angle WZX \cong \angle YZX$. $\angle WXZ \cong \angle YXZ$ by the Third ∆s Thm. From the diagram $\overline{WX} \cong \overline{YX}$ and $\overline{WZ} \cong \overline{YZ}$, and $\overline{XZ} \cong \overline{XZ}$ by Refl. Prop. of $\cong$.

Online Quiz

Available at **classzone.com**

Diagnosis/Remediation

- Practice A, B, C in Chapter 4 Resource Book, pp. 21–26
- Study Guide in Chapter 4 Resource Book, pp. 27–28
- Practice Workbook, pp. 64–66
- @HomeTutor

Challenge

Additional challenge is available in the Chapter 4 Resource Book, p. 31.

32. See Additional Answers beginning on p. AA1.

Using ALTERNATIVE METHODS

Alternative Strategy

In Example 4 on page 227 students proved overlapping triangles congruent. Overlapping triangles can be redrawn so they are next to each other. This makes it easier to see and mark the congruent sides and angles to determine why the triangles are congruent.

Avoiding Common Errors

In Practice 1, $\overline{JM}$ is marked congruent to $\overline{LM}$. Students may mark $\overline{HM}$ and $\overline{GM}$ congruent when they draw the triangles apart from each other. Remind them that it is just the small parts of these sides that are congruent.

Study Strategy

Have students look back at the overlapping triangles in the original diagram for angles and sides that belong to both triangles. They can use the Reflexive Property of Congruence for either sides or angles.

1a.

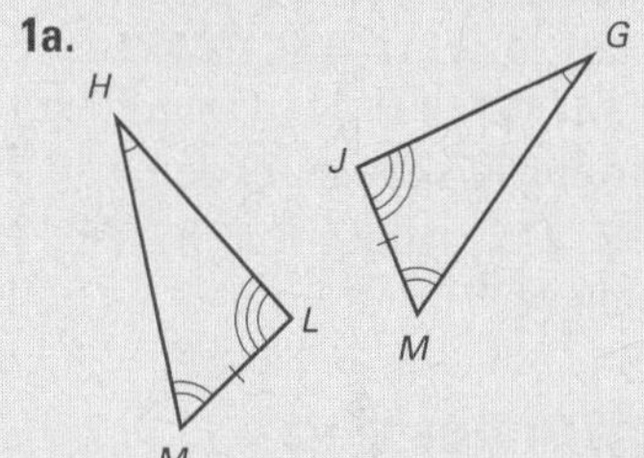

1b.

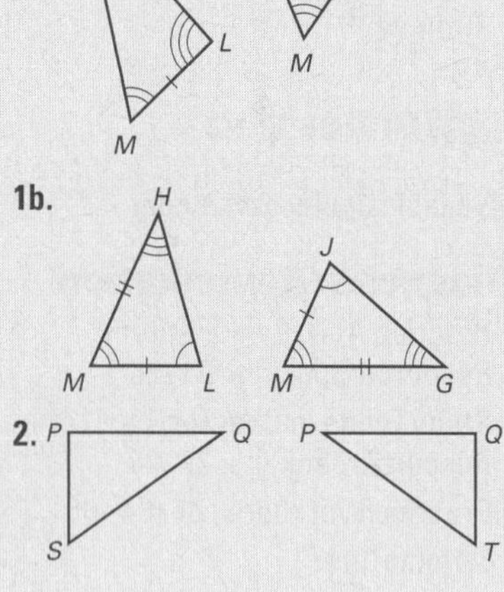

Another Way to Solve Example 4, page 227

MULTIPLE REPRESENTATIONS In Example 4 on page 227, you used congruencies in triangles that overlapped. When you solve problems like this, it may be helpful to redraw the art so that the triangles do not overlap.

PROBLEM

Find $m\angle BDC$.

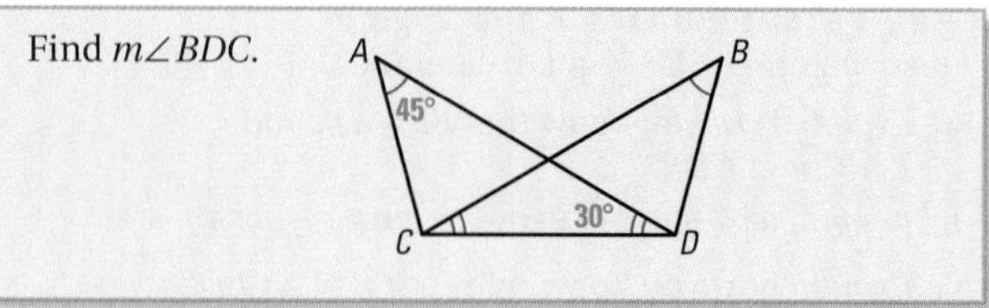

METHOD

Drawing A Diagram

Standards

5.0 Students prove that triangles are congruent or similar, **and they are able to use the concept of corresponding parts of congruent triangles.**

STEP 1 **Identify** the triangles that overlap. Then redraw them so that they are separate. Copy all labels and markings.

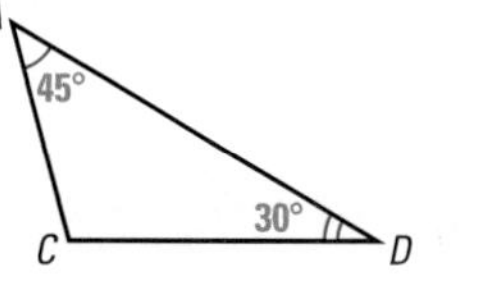

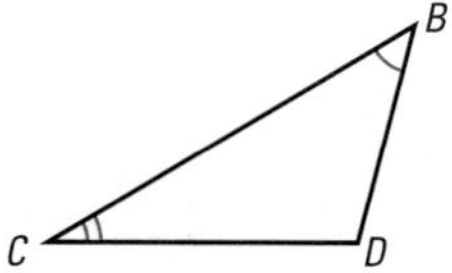

STEP 2 **Analyze** the situation. By the Triangle Sum Theorem, $m\angle ACD = 180° - 45° - 30° = 105°$.

Also, because $\angle A \cong \angle B$ and $\angle ADC \cong \angle BCD$, by the Third Angles Theorem, $\angle ACD \cong \angle BDC$, and $m\angle ACD = m\angle BDC = 105°$.

PRACTICE

1. **DRAWING FIGURES** Draw $\triangle HLM$ and $\triangle GJM$ so they do not overlap. Copy all labels and mark any known congruences. **a, b. See margin.**

a.

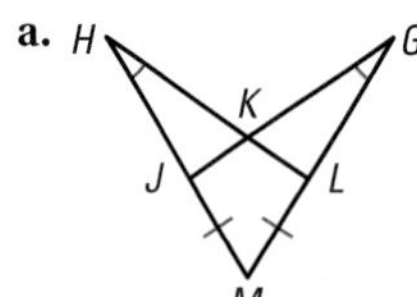

b. H J M L G

2. **ENVELOPE** Draw $\triangle PQS$ and $\triangle QPT$ so that they do not overlap. Find $m\angle PTS$. **35°; see margin for art.**

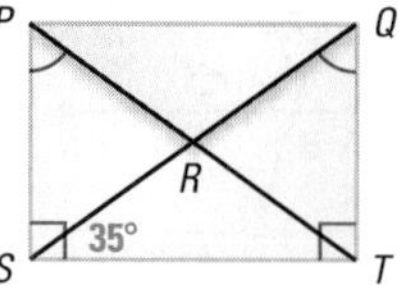

4.3 Investigate Congruent Figures

MATERIALS • straws • string • ruler • protractor

Standards

Prepare for 5.0
Students prove that triangles are congruent or similar, and they are able to use *the concept of corresponding parts of congruent triangles.*

QUESTION **How much information is needed to tell whether two figures are congruent?**

EXPLORE 1 **Compare triangles with congruent sides**

STEP 1

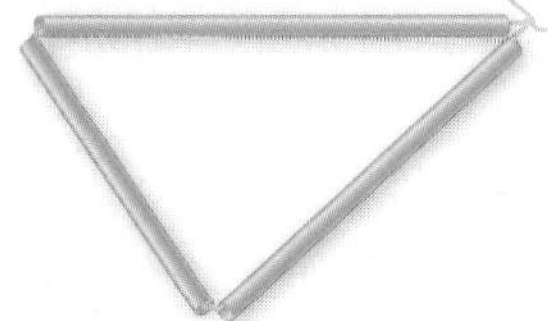

Make a triangle Cut straws to make side lengths of 8 cm, 10 cm, and 12 cm. Thread the string through the straws. Make a triangle by connecting the ends of the string.

STEP 2

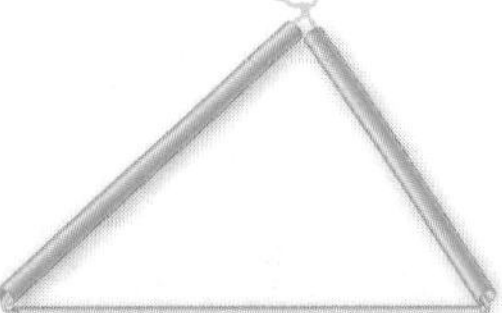

Make another triangle Use the same length straws to make another triangle. If possible, make it different from the first. Compare the triangles. What do you notice?

EXPLORE 2 **Compare quadrilaterals with congruent sides**

STEP 1

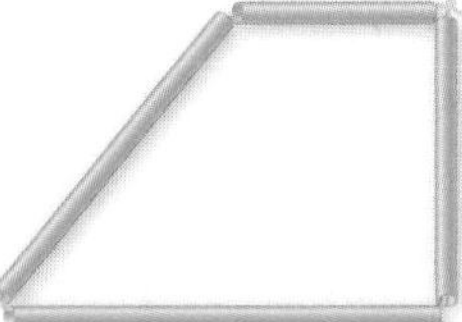

Make a quadrilateral Cut straws to make side lengths of 5 cm, 7 cm, 9 cm, and 11 cm. Thread the string through the straws. Make a quadrilateral by connecting the string.

STEP 2

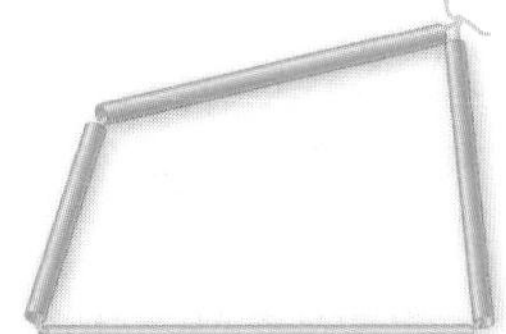

Make another quadrilateral Make a second quadrilateral using the same length straws. If possible, make it different from the first. Compare the quadrilaterals. What do you notice?

DRAW CONCLUSIONS **Use your observations to complete these exercises**

1. Can you make two triangles with the same side lengths that are different shapes? *Justify* your answer. **No. *Sample answer:* In the activity once the triangle lengths were established it was impossible to create two different triangles.**
2. If you know that three sides of a triangle are congruent to three sides of another triangle, can you say the triangles are congruent? *Explain.* **Yes. *Sample answer:* The activity indicates that this is true.**
3. Can you make two quadrilaterals with the same side lengths that are different shapes? *Justify* your answer. **Yes. *Sample answer:* In the activity it was possible to change the angles in the quadrilateral thus allowing for more than one figure.**
4. If four sides of a quadrilateral are congruent to four sides of another quadrilateral, can you say the quadrilaterals are congruent? *Explain.* **No. *Sample answer:* The activity established that this would not be sufficient to prove congruence.**

1 PLAN AND PREPARE

Explore the Concept

- Students will investigate how many congruent sides are needed for two triangles to be congruent.
- This activity leads into proving triangles congruent by SSS in Lesson 4.3.

Materials

Each student or group of students will need:

- straws
- string
- ruler, protractor, scissors

Recommended Time

Work activity: 15 min
Discuss results: 5 min

Grouping

Students can work individually or in groups of two. If students work in groups, one can cut the straws and the other can thread the string.

2 TEACH

Tips for Success

Use straws that are big enough so that students do not have trouble threading the string through them.

Key Question

- Are triangles congruent if one can be turned or flipped over to match the other? **yes**

Alternative Strategy

Demonstrate with straws on the overhead projector.

Key Discovery

Three pairs of congruent sides make triangles congruent.

3 ASSESS AND RETEACH

1. If you have only information about sides, how much information is necessary to prove two triangles congruent? **three pairs of congruent sides**

1 PLAN AND PREPARE

Warm-Up Exercises

Transparency Available

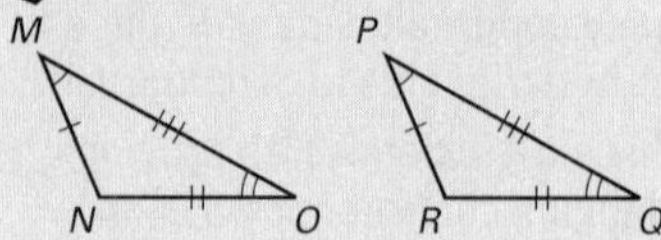

1. Write a congruence statement. **$\triangle MNO \cong \triangle PRQ$**

2. How do you know that $\angle N \cong \angle R$? **Third ∆ Thm.**

3. Find x. **30**

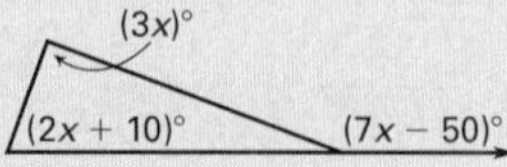

Notetaking Guide

Transparency Available

Promotes interactive learning and notetaking skills, pp. 93–95.

Pacing

Basic: 1 day

Average: 1 day

Advanced: 1 day

Block: 0.5 block with 4.2

- See *Teaching Guide/Lesson Plan.*

2 FOCUS AND MOTIVATE

Essential Question

Big Idea 2, p. 215

How can you use side lengths to prove triangles congruent? **Tell students they will see how to answer this question by learning the SSS Congruence Postulate.**

4.3 Prove Triangles Congruent by SSS

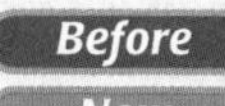

Before You used the definition of congruent figures.

Now You will use the side lengths to prove triangles are congruent.

Why So you can determine if triangles in a tile floor are congruent, as in Ex. 22.

Key Vocabulary
- **congruent figures,** *p. 225*
- **corresponding parts,** *p. 225*

Standards

5.0 Students prove that triangles are congruent or similar, and they are able to use the concept of corresponding parts of congruent triangles.

16.0 Students perform basic constructions with a straightedge and compass, such as angle bisectors, perpendicular bisectors, and the line parallel to a given line through a point off the line.

In the Activity on page 233, you saw that there is only one way to form a triangle given three side lengths. In general, any two triangles with the same three side lengths must be congruent.

POSTULATE *For Your Notebook*

POSTULATE 19 Side-Side-Side (SSS) Congruence Postulate

If three sides of one triangle are congruent to three sides of a second triangle, then the two triangles are congruent.

If Side $\overline{AB} \cong \overline{RS}$,
Side $\overline{BC} \cong \overline{ST}$, and
Side $\overline{CA} \cong \overline{TR}$,
then $\triangle ABC \cong \triangle RST$.

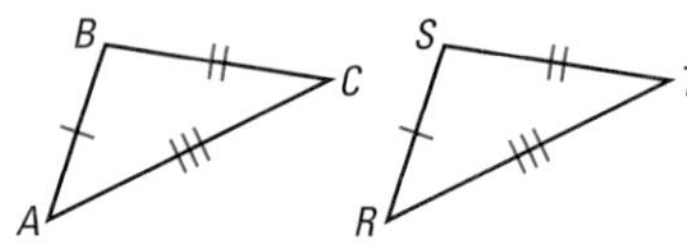

EXAMPLE 1 Use the SSS Congruence Postulate

Write a proof.

GIVEN ▶ $\overline{KL} \cong \overline{NL}$, $\overline{KM} \cong \overline{NM}$

PROVE ▶ $\triangle KLM \cong \triangle NLM$

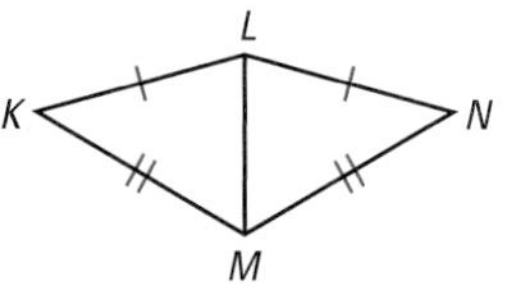

Proof It is given that $\overline{KL} \cong \overline{NL}$ and $\overline{KM} \cong \overline{NM}$. By the Reflexive Property, $\overline{LM} \cong \overline{LM}$. So, by the SSS Congruence Postulate, $\triangle KLM \cong \triangle NLM$.

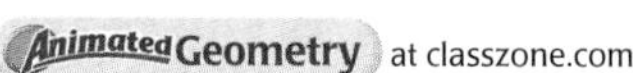

at classzone.com

GUIDED PRACTICE for Example 1

Decide whether the congruence statement is true. *Explain* your reasoning.

1. $\triangle DFG \cong \triangle HJK$

F J D G H K

yes; SSS

2. $\triangle ACB \cong \triangle CAD$

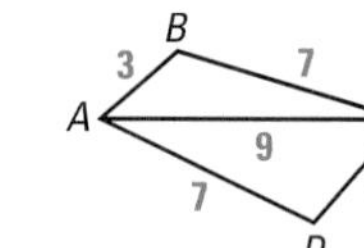

2. No; corresponding sides $\overline{AB}$ and $\overline{CD}$ are not congruent.

3. $\triangle QPT \cong \triangle RST$

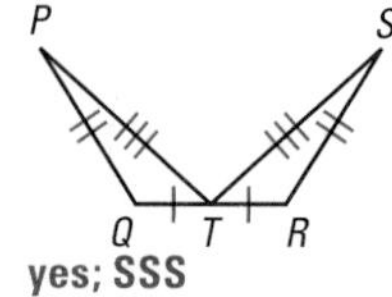

yes; SSS

Resource Planning Guide

Chapter Resource Book
- Teaching Guide/Lesson Plan (pp. 32–33)
- Practice levels A, B, C (pp. 34–39)
- Study Guide (pp. 40–41)
- Catch-up for Absent Students (p. 42)
- Application (p. 43)
- Challenge (p. 44)

Workbooks
- Notetaking Guide (pp. 93–95)
- Practice Workbook (pp. 67–69)

Teaching Options
- **Power Presentations CD-ROM** provides dynamic electronic teaching resources for the classroom.
- **Activity Generator CD-ROM** provides editable activities for all ability levels.

Interactive Technology
- Easy Planner
- Power Presentations CD-ROM
- Activity Generator CD-ROM
- Animated Geometry
- Test Generator CD-ROM
- Online Quiz
- eWorkbook
- eEdition
- @HomeTutor

Resources for English Learners
- Quick Reference for English Learners
- Spanish Study Guide
- Multi-Language Visual Glossary
- Student Resources in Spanish

See also the *Geometry Toolkit* for more strategies for meeting individual needs.

EXAMPLE 2 Standardized Test Practice

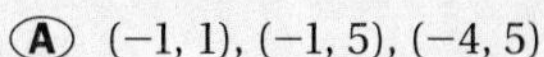

Which are the coordinates of the vertices of a triangle congruent to $\triangle PQR$?

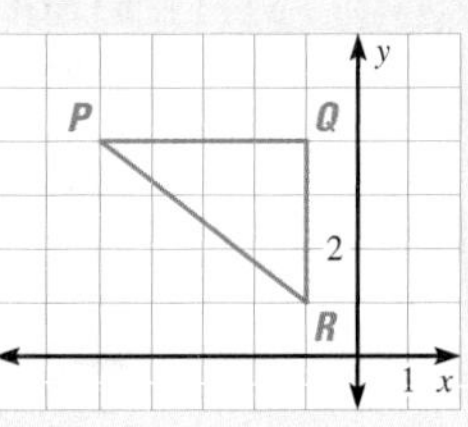

Ⓐ (−1, 1), (−1, 5), (−4, 5)

Ⓑ (−2, 4), (−7, 4), (−4, 6)

Ⓒ (−3, 2), (−1, 3), (−3, 1)

Ⓓ (−7, 7), (−7, 9), (−3, 7)

Solution

By counting, $PQ = 4$ and $QR = 3$. Use the Distance Formula to find PR.

$$d = \sqrt{(x_2 - x_1)^2 + (y_2 - y_1)^2}$$

$$PR = \sqrt{(-1 - (-5))^2 + (1 - 4)^2} = \sqrt{4^2 + (-3)^2} = \sqrt{25} = 5$$

By the SSS Congruence Postulate, any triangle with side lengths 3, 4, and 5 will be congruent to $\triangle PQR$. The distance from (−1, 1) to (−1, 5) is 4. The distance from (−1, 5) to (−4, 5) is 3. The distance from (−1, 1) to (−4, 5) is $\sqrt{(5-1)^2 + ((-4) - (-1))^2} = \sqrt{4^2 + (-3)^2} = \sqrt{25} = 5$.

▶ The correct answer is A. Ⓐ Ⓑ Ⓒ Ⓓ

ELIMINATE CHOICES

Once you know the side lengths of $\triangle PQR$, look for pairs of coordinates with the same x-coordinates or the same y-coordinates. In Choice C, (−3, 2) and (−3, 1) are only 1 unit apart. You can eliminate D in the same way.

GUIDED PRACTICE for Example 2

4. $\triangle JKL$ has vertices $J(-3, -2)$, $K(0, -2)$, and $L(-3, -8)$. $\triangle RST$ has vertices $R(10, 0)$, $S(10, -3)$, and $T(4, 0)$. Graph the triangles in the same coordinate plane and show that they are congruent. **$KJ = SR = 3$, $JL = RT = 6$, $LK = TS = 3\sqrt{5}$; see margin for art.**

ACTIVITY COPY A TRIANGLE

Follow the steps below to construct a triangle that is congruent to $\triangle ABC$.

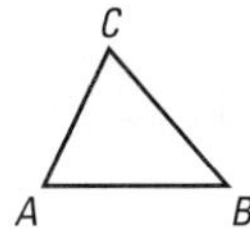

STEP 1

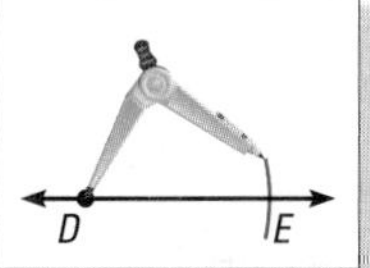

Construct $\overline{DE}$ so that it is congruent to $\overline{AB}$.

STEP 2

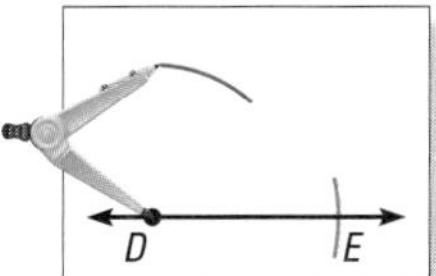

Open your compass to the length AC. Use this length to draw an arc with the compass point at D.

STEP 3

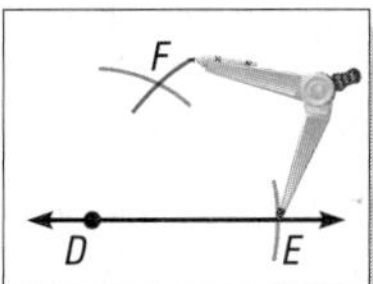

Draw an arc with radius BC and center E that intersects the arc from Step 2. Label the intersection point F.

STEP 4

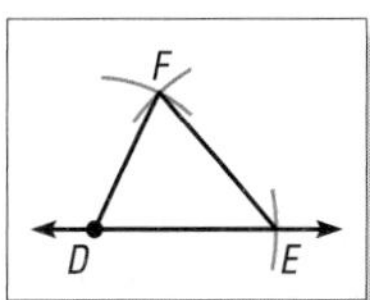

Draw $\triangle DEF$. By the SSS Congruence Postulate, $\triangle ABC \cong \triangle DEF$.

Motivating the Lesson

Tell students that a builder needs to order a triangular slab of marble for a section of museum wall. The builder knows the side lengths for the slab but does not have the angle measures. Tell students that in this lesson, they will learn whether the builder has enough information to order the slab she needs.

3 TEACH

Extra Example 1

Prove $\triangle ABD \cong \triangle CDB$.

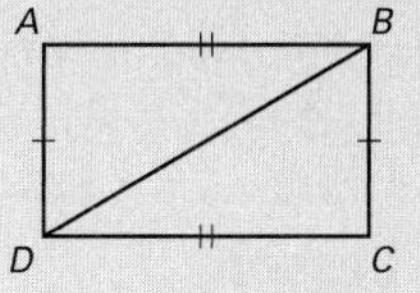

It is given that $\overline{AB} \cong \overline{CD}$ and $\overline{AD} \cong \overline{CB}$. By the Refl. Prop. of $\cong$ Segments, $\overline{BD} \cong \overline{BD}$. So, by the SSS $\cong$ Post., $\triangle ABD \cong \triangle CDB$.

Animated Geometry classzone.com

An **Animated Geometry** activity is available on-line for **Example 1**. This activity is also available on the **Power Presentations CD-ROM**.

Extra Example 2

Which are the coordinates of the vertices of a triangle congruent to $\triangle XYZ$? **B**

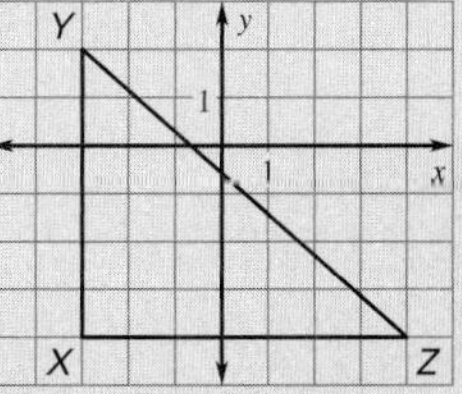

Ⓐ (6, 2), (0, −6), (6, −5)

Ⓑ (5, 1), (−1, −6), (5, −6)

Ⓒ (4, 0), (−1, −7), (4, −7)

Ⓓ (3, −1), (−3, −7), (3, −8)

4.

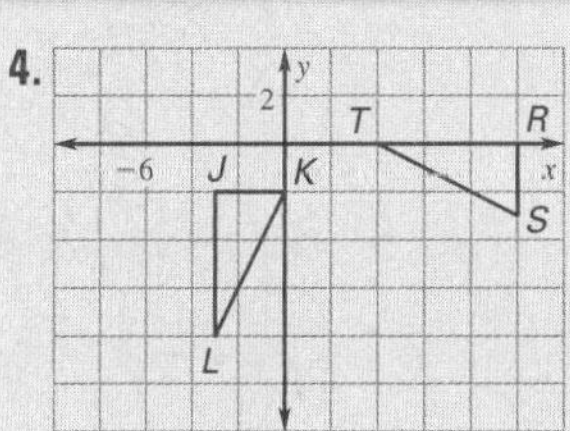

Activity Note

This activity reinforces the idea that the size and shape of a triangle are completely determined by the side lengths.

Extra Example 3

The opposite sides of the gate are the same length. How would you put a brace on the gate to be sure that the gate keeps its shape? Explain.

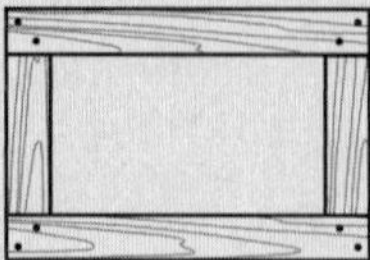

Diagonally, since the triangles will be rigid and, by the SSS ≅ Post., cannot change shape.

Closing the Lesson

Have students summarize the major points of the lesson and answer the Essential Question: How can you use side lengths to prove triangles congruent?

- **Two triangles with the same side lengths are congruent by the SSS Congruence Postulate.**

Show that the sides can be matched so that all three pairs of corresponding sides are congruent.

EXAMPLE 3 Solve a real-world problem

STRUCTURAL SUPPORT Explain why the bench with the diagonal support is stable, while the one without the support can collapse.

Solution

The bench with a diagonal support forms triangles with fixed side lengths. By the SSS Congruence Postulate, these triangles cannot change shape, so the bench is stable. The bench without a diagonal support is not stable because there are many possible quadrilaterals with the given side lengths.

GUIDED PRACTICE for Example 3

Determine whether the figure is stable. *Explain* your reasoning.

5. 

Not stable; a figure without diagonal support is not stable.

6. 

Stable; the figure has diagonal support with fixed side lengths.

7. 

Not stable; the lower half of the figure does not have diagonal support.

4.3 EXERCISES

HOMEWORK KEY

○ = **WORKED-OUT SOLUTIONS** on p. WS4 for Exs. 7, 9, and 25

★ = **STANDARDIZED TEST PRACTICE** Exs. 16, 17, and 28

SKILL PRACTICE

A **VOCABULARY** **Tell whether the angles or sides are *corresponding angles, corresponding sides*, or *neither*.**

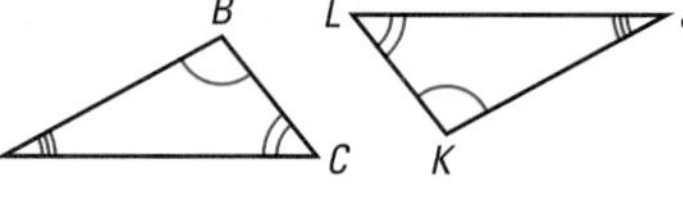

1. $\angle C$ and $\angle L$ **corresponding angles**
2. $\overline{AC}$ and $\overline{JK}$ **neither**
3. $\overline{BC}$ and $\overline{KL}$ **corresponding sides**
4. $\angle B$ and $\angle L$ **neither**

EXAMPLE 1 on p. 234 for Exs. 5–7

DETERMINING CONGRUENCE **Decide whether the congruence statement is true. *Explain* your reasoning.**

5. $\triangle RST \cong \triangle TQP$ **not true; $\triangle RST \cong \triangle PQT$**

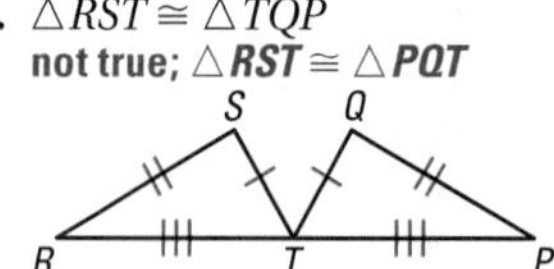

6. $\triangle ABD \cong \triangle CDB$ **true; SSS**

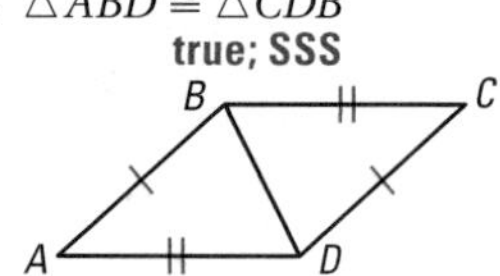

7. $\triangle DEF \cong \triangle DGF$ **true; SSS**

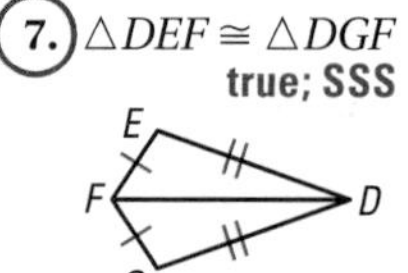

EXAMPLE 2 on p. 235 for Exs. 8–12

8. **ERROR ANALYSIS** *Describe* and correct the error in writing a congruence statement for the triangles in the coordinate plane. **The triangle vertices do not correspond. *Sample answer:* $\triangle WXZ \cong \triangle YZX$.**

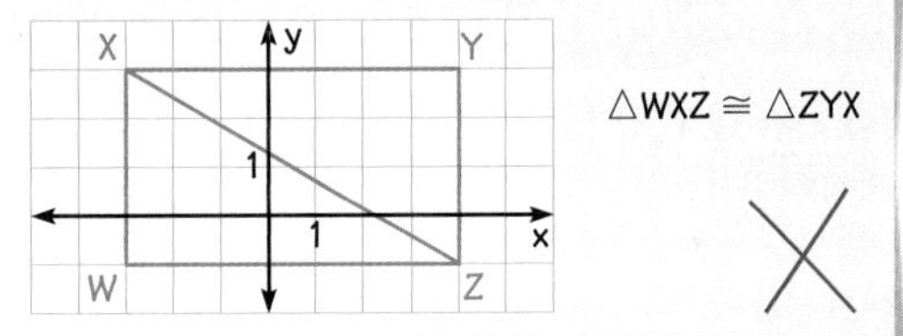

ALGEBRA **Use the given coordinates to determine if $\triangle ABC \cong \triangle DEF$.**

9. $A(-2, -2)$, $B(4, -2)$, $C(4, 6)$, $D(5, 7)$, $E(5, 1)$, $F(13, 1)$ **congruent**

10. $A(-2, 1)$, $B(3, -3)$, $C(7, 5)$, $D(3, 6)$, $E(8, 2)$, $F(10, 11)$ **not congruent**

11. $A(0, 0)$, $B(6, 5)$, $C(9, 0)$, $D(0, -1)$, $E(6, -6)$, $F(9, -1)$ **congruent**

12. $A(-5, 7)$, $B(-5, 2)$, $C(0, 2)$, $D(0, 6)$, $E(0, 1)$, $F(4, 1)$ **not congruent**

EXAMPLE 3 on p. 236 for Exs. 13–15

USING DIAGRAMS **Decide whether the figure is stable. *Explain.***

13. 

14. 

15. 

13. Stable; the figure has diagonal support with fixed side lengths. B

14. Not stable; a figure without diagonal support is not stable.

15. Stable; the figure has diagonal support with fixed side lengths.

16. ★ **MULTIPLE CHOICE** Let $\triangle FGH$ be an equilateral triangle with point J as the midpoint of $\overline{FG}$. Which of the statements below is *not* true? **B**

Ⓐ $\overline{FH} \cong \overline{GH}$ Ⓑ $\overline{FJ} \cong \overline{FH}$ Ⓒ $\overline{FJ} \cong \overline{GJ}$ Ⓓ $\triangle FHJ \cong \triangle GHJ$

17. ★ **MULTIPLE CHOICE** Let $ABCD$ be a rectangle separated into two triangles by $\overline{DB}$. Which of the statements below is *not* true? **B**

Ⓐ $\overline{AD} \cong \overline{CB}$ Ⓑ $\overline{AB} \cong \overline{AD}$ Ⓒ $\overline{AB} \cong \overline{CD}$ Ⓓ $\triangle DAB \cong \triangle BCD$

APPLYING SEGMENT ADDITION **Determine whether $\triangle ABC \cong \triangle DEF$. If they are congruent, write a congruence statement. *Explain* your reasoning.**

18. **not congruent; $CA \neq FD$**

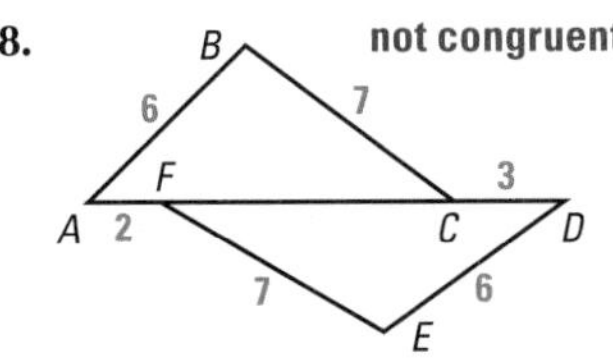

19. **Not congruent; the congruence statement should read $\triangle ABC \cong \triangle FED$.**

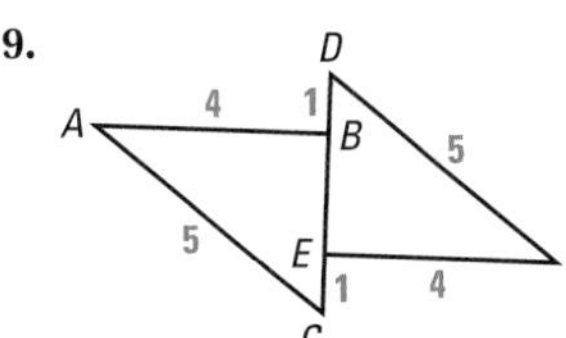

20. **3-D FIGURES** In the diagram, $\overline{PK} \cong \overline{PL}$ and $\overline{JK} \cong \overline{JL}$. Show that $\triangle JPK \cong \triangle JPL$. **Since $\overline{JP} \cong \overline{JP}$ the triangles are congruent by SSS.**

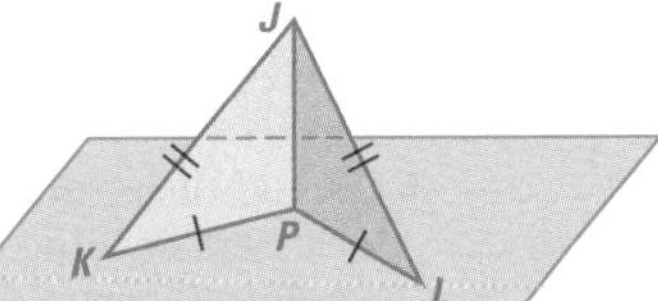

21. **CHALLENGE** Find all values of x that make the triangles congruent. *Explain.*

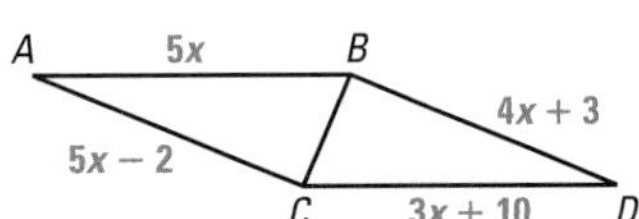

21. 5; setting $5x = 4x + 3$ and $5x - 2 = 3x + 10$ yields $x = 3$ and $x = 6$ which is inconsistent. Setting $5x = 3x + 10$ and $5x - 2 = 4x + 3$ yields $x = 5$ in both equations and is the answer. C

4 PRACTICE AND APPLY

Assignment Guide

Answer Transparencies available for all exercises

Basic:
Day 1: pp. 236–239
Exs. 1–17, 22–27, 31–37

Average:
Day 1: pp. 236–239
Exs. 1–8, 10–14 even, 16–20, 22–29, 31–37 odd

Advanced:
Day 1: pp. 236–239
Exs. 1–4, 7, 8, 11, 12, 14–30*, 33, 36, 37

Block:
pp. 236–239
Exs. 1–8, 10–14 even, 16–20, 22–29, 31–37 odd (with 4.2)

Differentiated Instruction

See *Geometry Best Practices Toolkit* for suggestions on addressing the needs of a diverse classroom.

Homework Check

For a quick check of student understanding of key concepts, go over the following exercises:

Basic: 5, 10, 13, 22, 23
Average: 6, 10, 14, 22, 23
Advanced: 7, 12, 15, 22, 23

Extra Practice

- Student Edition, p. 902
- Chapter 4 Resource Book: Practice levels A, B, C, pp. 34–39

Practice Worksheet

An easily-readable reduced practice page (with answers) for this lesson can be found on p. 214C.

Study Strategy

Exercises 25, 27 These exercises involve proving overlapping triangles congruent. Draw and label the triangles apart from each other. It may be easier to see the corresponding sides.

Mathematical Reasoning

Exercise 26 Students should ask themselves what conclusion follows from the given information that E is the midpoint of $\overline{BD}$. They should mark the diagram accordingly and be sure to include the statement $\overline{BE} \cong \overline{DE}$ as one step in the proof.

Exercise 29 Addition information about the construction and layout of a baseball field can be found at edis.ifas.ufl.edu/EP092

24. Statements (Reasons)

1. $\overline{GH} \cong \overline{JK}$, $\overline{HJ} \cong \overline{KG}$ (Given)
2. $\overline{JG} \cong \overline{GJ}$ (Reflexive Property of Congruence)
3. $\triangle GHJ \cong \triangle JKG$ (SSS)

25. Statements (Reasons)

1. $\overline{WX} \cong \overline{VZ}$, $\overline{WY} \cong \overline{VY}$, $\overline{YZ} \cong \overline{YX}$ (Given)
2. $\overline{WV} \cong \overline{VW}$ (Reflexive Property of Congruence)
3. $WY = VY$, $YZ = YX$ (Definition of segment congruence)
4. $WY + YZ = VY + YZ$ (Addition Property of Equality)
5. $WY + YZ = VY + YX$ (Substitution Property of Equality)
6. $WZ = VX$ (Segment Addition Postulate)
7. $\overline{WZ} \cong \overline{VX}$ (Definition of segment congruence)
8. $\triangle VWX \cong \triangle WVZ$ (SSS)

26. Statements (Reasons)

1. $\overline{AE} \cong \overline{CE}$, $\overline{AB} \cong \overline{CD}$, E is the midpoint of $\overline{BD}$. (Given)
2. $\overline{BE} \cong \overline{DE}$ (Definition of midpoint)
3. $\triangle EAB \cong \triangle ECD$ (SSS)

PROBLEM SOLVING

EXAMPLE 1 [A] on p. 234 for Ex. 22

22. TILE FLOORS You notice two triangles in the tile floor of a hotel lobby. You want to determine if the triangles are congruent, but you only have a piece of string. Can you determine if the triangles are congruent? *Explain.* **Yes; use the string to measure each side of one triangle and then measure the sides of the second triangle to see if they are congruent to the corresponding sides of the first triangle.**

@HomeTutor for problem solving help at classzone.com

EXAMPLE 3 on p. 236 for Ex. 23

23. GATES Which gate is stable? *Explain* your reasoning. **See margin.**

@HomeTutor for problem solving help at classzone.com

23. Gate 1. *Sample Answer:* **Gate 1 has a diagonal support that forms two triangles with fixed side lengths, and these triangles cannot change shape. Gate 2 is not stable because the gate is a quadrilateral which can take many different shapes.**

PROOF Write a proof. **24–27. See margin.**

24. GIVEN ▶ $\overline{GH} \cong \overline{JK}$, $\overline{HJ} \cong \overline{KG}$
PROVE ▶ $\triangle GHJ \cong \triangle JKG$

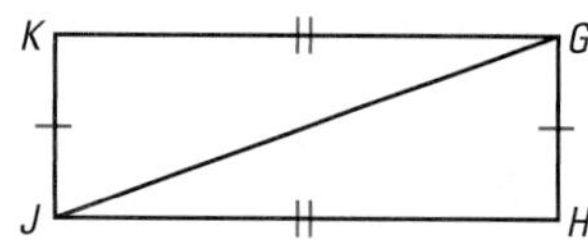

25. GIVEN ▶ $\overline{WX} \cong \overline{VZ}$, $\overline{WY} \cong \overline{VY}$, $\overline{YZ} \cong \overline{YX}$
PROVE ▶ $\triangle VWX \cong \triangle WVZ$

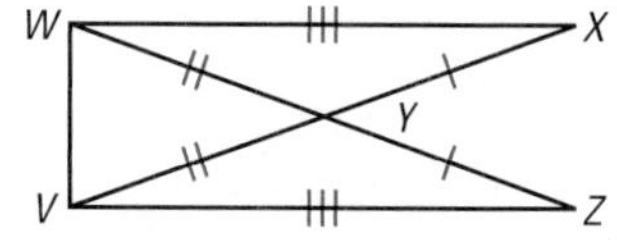

[B]

26. GIVEN ▶ $\overline{AE} \cong \overline{CE}$, $\overline{AB} \cong \overline{CD}$, E is the midpoint of $\overline{BD}$.
PROVE ▶ $\triangle EAB \cong \triangle ECD$

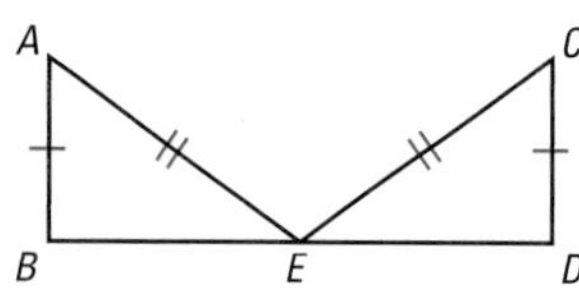

27. GIVEN ▶ $\overline{FM} \cong \overline{FN}$, $\overline{DM} \cong \overline{HN}$, $\overline{EF} \cong \overline{GF}$, $\overline{DE} \cong \overline{HG}$
PROVE ▶ $\triangle DEN \cong \triangle HGM$

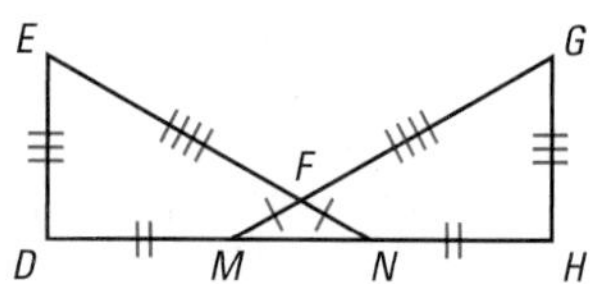

28. ★ EXTENDED RESPONSE When rescuers enter a partially collapsed building they often have to reinforce damaged doors for safety.

a. Diagonal braces are added to Door 1 as shown below. *Explain* why the door is more stable with the braces.

28a. A figure with diagonal support and fixed side lengths is stable.

b. Would these braces be a good choice for rescuers needing to enter and exit the building through this doorway? **no**

c. In the diagram, Door 2 has only a corner brace. Does this solve the problem from part (b)? **yes**

d. *Explain* why the corner brace makes the door more stable. **It is more stable because there is one diagonal support.**

1 2

○ = WORKED-OUT SOLUTIONS on p. WS1 ★ = STANDARDIZED TEST PRACTICE

27. Statements (Reasons)

1. $\overline{FM} \cong \overline{FN}$, $\overline{DM} \cong \overline{HN}$, $\overline{EF} \cong \overline{GF}$, $\overline{DE} \cong \overline{HG}$ (Given)
2. $MN = NM$ (Reflexive Property of Equality)
3. $FM = FN$, $DM = HN$, $EF = GF$ (Definition of segment congruence)
4. $EF + FN = GF + FN$, $DM + MN = HN + MN$ (Addition Property of Equality)
5. $EF + FN = GF + FM$, $DM + MN = HN + NM$ (Substitution Property of Equality)
6. $EN = GM$, $DN = HM$ (Segment Addition Postulate)
7. $\overline{EN} \cong \overline{GM}$, $\overline{DN} \cong \overline{HM}$ (Definition of segment congruence)
8. $\triangle DEN \cong \triangle HGM$ (SSS)

29. **BASEBALL FIELD** To create a baseball field, start by placing home plate. Then, place second base 127 feet $3\frac{3}{8}$ inches from home plate. Then, you can find first base using two tape measures. Stretch one from second base toward first base and the other from home plate toward first base. The point where the two tape measures cross at the 90 foot mark is first base. You can find third base in a similar manner. *Explain* how and why this process will always work.
Only one triangle can be created from three fixed sides.

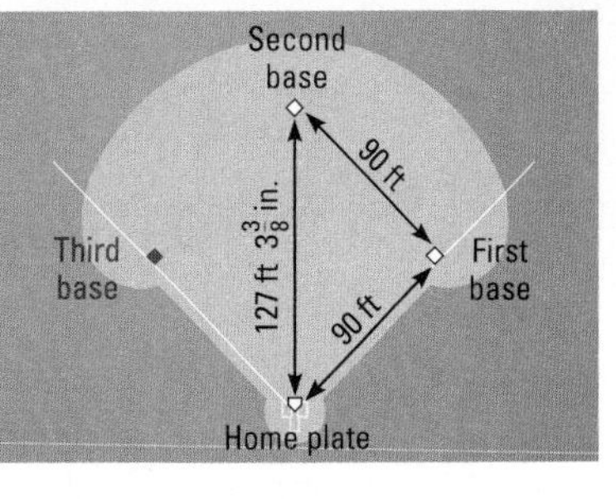

C 30. **CHALLENGE** Draw and label the figure described below. Then, identify what is given and write a two-column proof.

In an isosceles triangle, if a segment is added from the vertex between the congruent sides to the midpoint of the third side, then two congruent triangles are formed. **See margin.**

MIXED REVIEW

PREVIEW Prepare for Lesson 4.4 in Exs. 31–33.

Find the slope of the line that passes through the points. *(p. 171)*

31. $A(3, 0), B(7, 4)$ **1**

32. $F(1, 8), G(-9, 2)$ $\mathbf{\frac{3}{5}}$

33. $M(-4, -10), N(6, 2)$ $\mathbf{\frac{6}{5}}$

Use the x- and y-intercepts to write an equation of the line. *(p. 180)*

34.

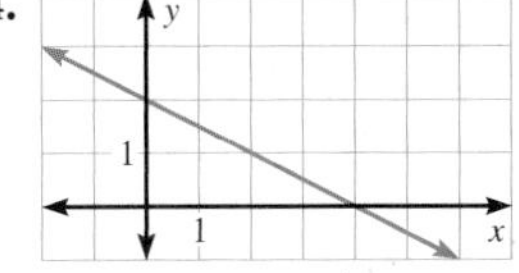

35.

36.

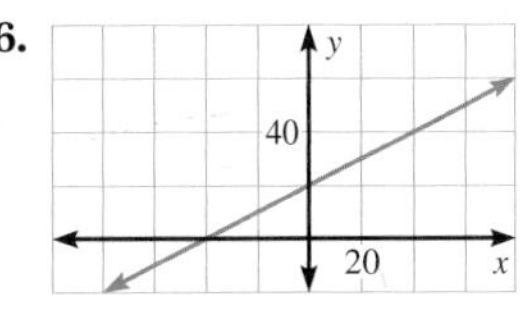

34. $y = -\frac{1}{2}x + 2$

35. $y = -x - 6$

36. $y = \frac{1}{2}x + 20$

37. Write an equation of a line that passes through $(-3, -1)$ and is parallel to $y = 3x + 2$. *(p. 180)* $\mathbf{y = 3x + 8}$

QUIZ *for Lessons 4.1–4.3*

A triangle has the given vertices. Graph the triangle and classify it by its sides. Then determine if it is a right triangle. *(p. 217)* **1–3. See margin for art.**

1. $A(-3, 0), B(0, 4), C(3, 0)$ **isosceles; not a right triangle**

2. $A(2, -4), B(5, -1), C(2, -1)$ **isosceles; right triangle**

3. $A(-7, 0), B(1, 6), C(-3, 4)$ **scalene; not a right triangle**

In the diagram, $HJKL \cong NPQM$. *(p. 225)*

4. Find the value of x. **9**

5. Find the value of y. **5**

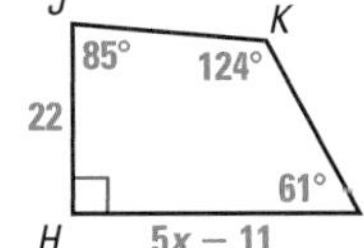

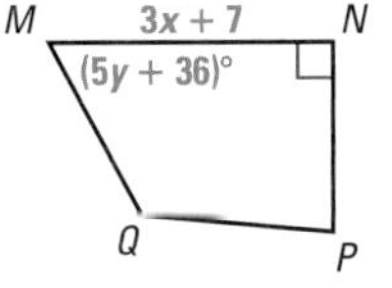

6. Write a proof. *(p. 234)* **See margin.**

GIVEN ▶ $\overline{AB} \cong \overline{AC}$, $\overline{AD}$ bisects $\overline{BC}$.

PROVE ▶ $\triangle ABD \cong \triangle ACD$

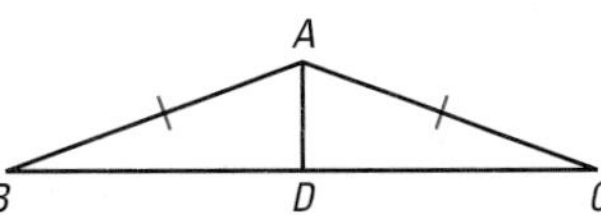

5 ASSESS AND RETEACH

Daily Homework Quiz

Transparency Available

1. The vertices of $\triangle GHI$ and $\triangle RST$ are $G(-2, 5)$, $H(2, 5)$, $I(-2, 2)$, $R(-9, 8)$, $S(-5, 8)$, and $T(-9, 5)$. Is $\triangle GHI \cong \triangle RST$? Explain. **Yes. $GH = RS = 4$, $HI = ST = 5$, and $IG = TR = 3$. By the SSS $\cong$ Post., it follows that $\triangle GHI \cong \triangle RST$.**

2. Is $\triangle ABC \cong \triangle XYZ$? Explain.

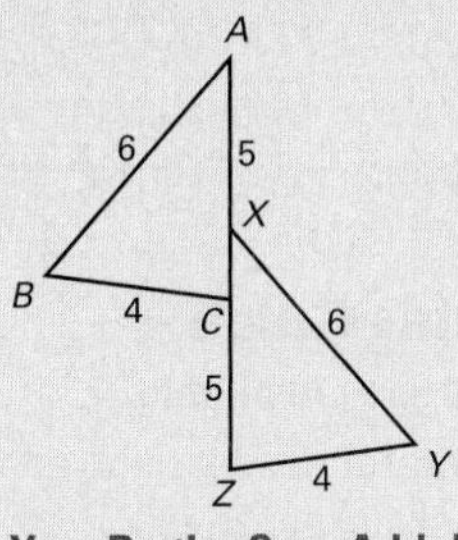

Yes. By the Seg. Add. Post., $\overline{AC} \cong \overline{XZ}$. Also, $\overline{AB} \cong \overline{XY}$ and $\overline{BC} \cong \overline{YZ}$. So $\triangle ABC \cong \triangle XYZ$ by the SSS $\cong$ Post.

Online Quiz

Available at **classzone.com**

Diagnosis/Remediation

- Practice A, B, C in Chapter 4 Resource Book, pp. 34–39
- Study Guide in Chapter 4 Resource Book, pp. 40–41
- Practice Workbook, pp. 67–69
- @HomeTutor

Challenge

Additional challenge is available in the Chapter 4 Resource Book, p. 44.

Quiz

An easily-readable reduced copy of the quiz (with answers) on Lessons 4.1–4.3 from the Assessment Book can be found on p. 214G.

30, Quiz 1–3, 6. See Additional Answers beginning on p. AA1.

1 PLAN AND PREPARE

Warm-Up Exercises

Transparency Available

Given: $\overline{DF}$ bisects $\overline{CE}$, $\overline{DC} \cong \overline{DE}$

Prove: $\triangle CDF \cong \triangle EDF$

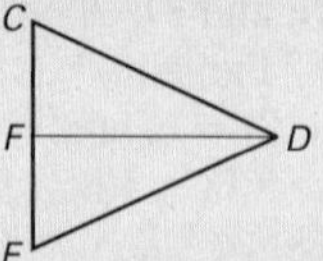

It is given that $\overline{DC} \cong \overline{DE}$ and $\overline{DF}$ bisects $\overline{CE}$. $\overline{CF} \cong \overline{EF}$ by the def. of bisector. $\overline{DF} \cong \overline{DF}$ by the Refl. Prop. of $\cong$ Segs. So $\triangle CDF \cong \triangle EDF$ by the SSS $\cong$ Post.

Notetaking Guide

Transparency Available

Promotes interactive learning and notetaking skills, pp. 96–99.

Pacing

Basic: 2 days

Average: 2 days

Advanced: 2 days

Block: 1 block

- See *Teaching Guide/Lesson Plan.*

2 FOCUS AND MOTIVATE

Essential Question

Big Idea 2, p. 215

How can you use two sides and an angle to prove triangles congruent? **Tell students they will learn how to answer this question by using the SAS Post. and the HL Thm.**

4.4 Prove Triangles Congruent by SAS and HL

Before You used the SSS Congruence Postulate.

Now You will use sides and angles to prove congruence.

Why? So you can show triangles are congruent, as in Ex. 33.

Key Vocabulary
- **leg of a right triangle**
- **hypotenuse**

Standards

5.0 Students prove that triangles are congruent or similar, and they are able to use the concept of corresponding parts of congruent triangles.

4.0 Students prove basic theorems involving congruence and similarity.

Consider a relationship involving two sides and the angle they form, their *included* angle. To picture the relationship, form an angle using two pencils.

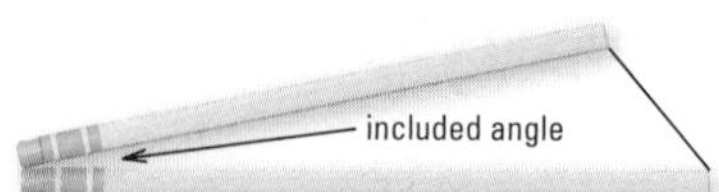

Any time you form an angle of the same measure with the pencils, the side formed by connecting the pencil points will have the same length. In fact, any two triangles formed in this way are congruent.

POSTULATE *For Your Notebook*

POSTULATE 20 Side-Angle-Side (SAS) Congruence Postulate

If two sides and the included angle of one triangle are congruent to two sides and the included angle of a second triangle, then the two triangles are congruent.

If Side $\overline{RS} \cong \overline{UV}$,
Angle $\angle R \cong \angle U$, and
Side $\overline{RT} \cong \overline{UW}$,
then $\triangle RST \cong \triangle UVW$.

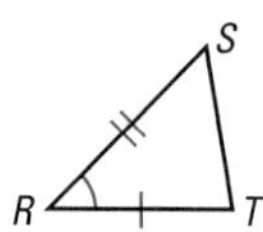

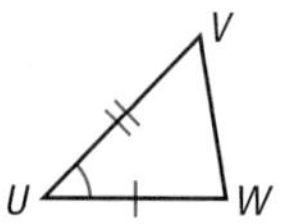

EXAMPLE 1 Use the SAS Congruence Postulate

Write a proof.

GIVEN ▶ $\overline{BC} \cong \overline{DA}$, $\overline{BC} \parallel \overline{AD}$

PROVE ▶ $\triangle ABC \cong \triangle CDA$

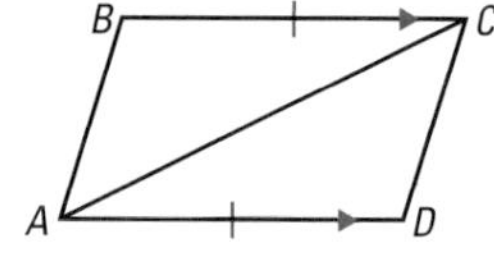

WRITE PROOFS
Make your proof easier to read by identifying the steps where you show congruent sides (S) and angles (A).

	STATEMENTS	REASONS
S	1. $\overline{BC} \cong \overline{DA}$	1. Given
	2. $\overline{BC} \parallel \overline{AD}$	2. Given
A	3. $\angle BCA \cong \angle DAC$	3. Alternate Interior Angles Theorem
S	4. $\overline{AC} \cong \overline{CA}$	4. Reflexive Property of Congruence
	5. $\triangle ABC \cong \triangle CDA$	5. SAS Congruence Postulate

Resource Planning Guide

Chapter Resource Book
- Teaching Guide/Lesson Plan (pp. 45–46)
- Practice levels A, B, C (pp. 48–53)
- Study Guide (pp. 54–55)
- Catch-up for Absent Students (p. 56)
- Problem Solving Workshop (p. 57)
- Challenge (p. 59)

Workbooks
- Notetaking Guide (pp. 96–99)
- Practice Workbook (pp. 70–72)

Teaching Options
- **Power Presentations CD-ROM** provides dynamic electronic teaching resources for the classroom.
- **Activity Generator CD-ROM** provides editable activities for all ability levels.

Interactive Technology
- Easy Planner
- Power Presentations CD-ROM
- Activity Generator CD-ROM
- Animated Geometry
- Test Generator CD-ROM
- Online Quiz
- eWorkbook
- eEdition
- @HomeTutor

Resources for English Learners
- Quick Reference for English Learners
- Spanish Study Guide
- Multi-Language Visual Glossary
- Student Resources in Spanish

See also the *Geometry Toolkit* for more strategies for meeting individual needs.

EXAMPLE 2 Use SAS and properties of shapes

In the diagram, $\overline{QS}$ and $\overline{RP}$ pass through the center *M* of the circle. What can you conclude about $\triangle MRS$ and $\triangle MPQ$?

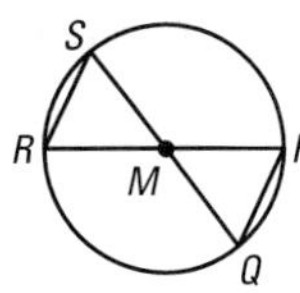

Solution

Because they are vertical angles, $\angle PMQ \cong \angle RMS$. All points on a circle are the same distance from the center, so *MP*, *MQ*, *MR*, and *MS* are all equal.

▶ $\triangle MRS$ and $\triangle MPQ$ are congruent by the SAS Congruence Postulate.

GUIDED PRACTICE for Examples 1 and 2

In the diagram, *ABCD* is a square with four congruent sides and four right angles. *R, S, T,* and *U* are the midpoints of the sides of *ABCD*. Also, $\overline{RT} \perp \overline{SU}$ and $\overline{SV} \cong \overline{VU}$.

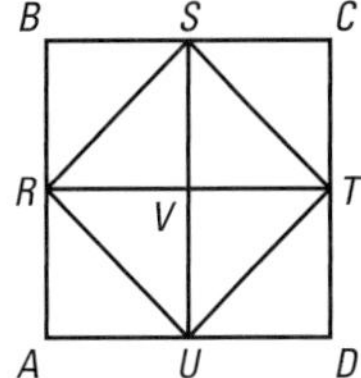

1. Prove that $\triangle SVR \cong \triangle UVR$. **See margin.**
2. Prove that $\triangle BSR \cong \triangle DUT$. **See margin.**

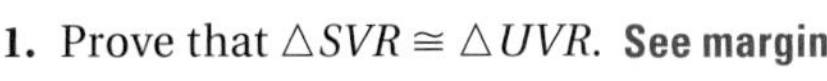

In general, if you know the lengths of two sides and the measure of an angle that is *not included* between them, you can create two different triangles.

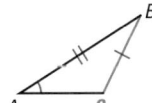

READ VOCABULARY
The two sides of a triangle that form an angle are *adjacent* to the angle. The side not adjacent to the angle is *opposite* the angle.

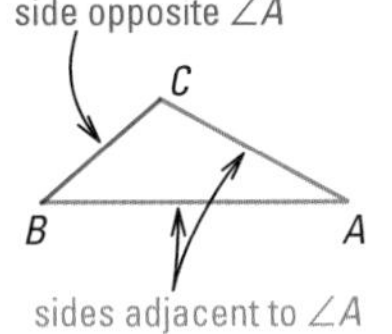

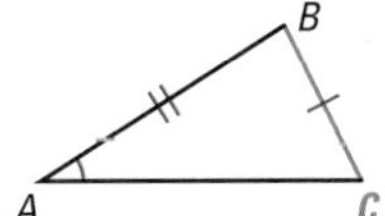

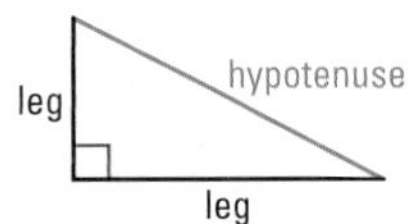

Therefore, SSA is *not* a valid method for proving that triangles are congruent, although there is a special case for right triangles.

RIGHT TRIANGLES In a right triangle, the sides adjacent to the right angle are called the **legs**. The side opposite the right angle is called the **hypotenuse** of the right triangle.

THEOREM *For Your Notebook*

THEOREM 4.5 Hypotenuse-Leg (HL) Congruence Theorem

If the hypotenuse and a leg of a right triangle are congruent to the hypotenuse and a leg of a second right triangle, then the two triangles are congruent.

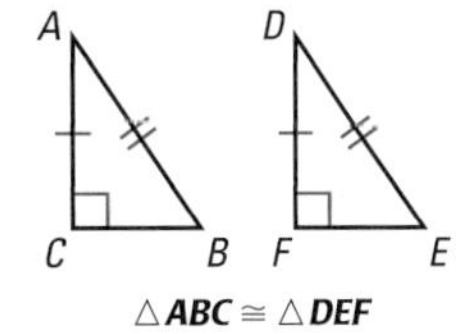

$\triangle ABC \cong \triangle DEF$

Proofs: Ex. 37, p. 439; p. 932

Differentiated Instruction

Below Level Put students in pairs so that a weaker student is paired with a better student. Give them fill-in-the-blank proofs to work on. As they complete the proofs, increase the number of blanks that must be filled in. Working in pairs will help the weaker students get the idea of proof and the better students will learn more by explaining the material to their partners. After they have done the fill-in-the-blank proofs, have them move on to completing entire proofs on their own.

See also the *Geometry Toolkit* for more strategies.

Motivating the Lesson

Tell students that in this lesson they will learn what information about angles is need to prove two triangles congruent if it is given that two sides of one triangle are congruent to two sides of another.

3 TEACH

Extra Example 1

Given: $\overline{MP} \cong \overline{NP}$, $\overline{OP}$ bisects $\angle MPN$.

Prove: $\triangle MOP \cong \triangle NOP$

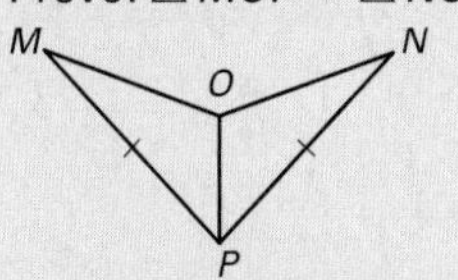

Statements (Reasons)

1. $\overline{MP} \cong \overline{NP}$ (Given)
2. $\overline{OP}$ bisects $\angle MPN$. (Given)
3. $\angle MPO \cong \angle NPO$ (Def. $\angle$ Bis.)
4. $\overline{OP} \cong \overline{OP}$ (Refl. Prop. of $\cong$)
5. $\triangle MOP \cong \triangle NOP$ (SAS $\cong$ Post.)

Extra Example 2

In the diagram *R* is the center of the circle. If $\angle SRT \cong \angle URT$, what can you conclude about $\triangle SRT$ and $\triangle URT$? **They are $\cong$ by SAS $\cong$ Post.**

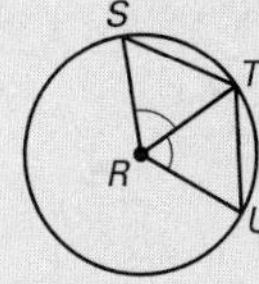

Key Question to Ask for Example 2

- Is there only one way to match the vertices to get a true congruence statement? Explain. **No; since the triangles are isosceles, both $\triangle MRS \cong \triangle MQP$ and $\triangle MRS \cong \triangle MPQ$ are true.**

1, 2. See Additional Answers beginning on p. AA1.

Extra Example 3

Given: $\overline{YW} \perp \overline{XZ}$, $\overline{XY} \cong \overline{ZY}$

Prove: $\triangle XYW \cong \triangle ZYW$

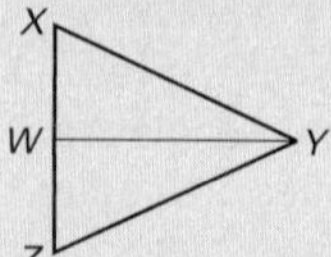

Statements (Reasons)

1. $\overline{YW} \perp \overline{XZ}$ (Given)
2. $\overline{XY} \cong \overline{ZY}$ (Given)
3. $\angle XWY$ and $\angle ZWY$ are rt. $\angle$s. ($\perp$ lines form 4 rt. $\angle$s)
4. $\triangle XYW$ and $\triangle ZYW$ are rt. $\triangle$s. (Def. of rt. $\triangle$)
5. $\overline{YW} \cong \overline{YW}$ (Refl. Prop. of $\cong$)
6. $\triangle XYW \cong \triangle ZYW$ (HL $\cong$ Thm.)

An **Animated Geometry** activity is available on-line for **Exercise 3**. This activity is also available on the **Power Presentations CD-ROM**.

Extra Example 4

If you know that $\overline{AB} \cong \overline{CB}$ and $\angle ABD \cong \angle CBD$, what postulate or theorem can you use to conclude that $\triangle ABD$ and $\triangle CBD$, are congruent? **SAS $\cong$ Post.**

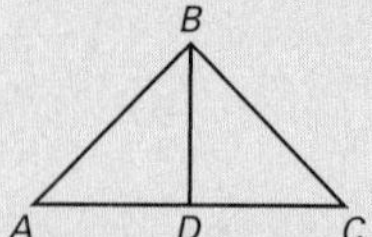

Closing the Lesson

Have students summarize the major points of the lesson and answer the Essential Question: How can you use two sides and an angle to prove triangles congruent?

- **Triangles are congruent by the SAS Congruence Postulate.**
- **Right triangles are congruent by the HL Congruence Theorem.**

You can prove triangles congruent if you know that two sides and the included angle of one triangle are congruent to two sides and the included angle of the other. If the triangles are right triangles, you can prove them congruent if they have congruent hypotenuses and a pair of congruent legs.

3, 4. See Additional Answers beginning on p. AA1.

EXAMPLE 3 Use the Hypotenuse-Leg Congruence Theorem

USE DIAGRAMS
If you have trouble matching vertices to letters when you separate the overlapping triangles, leave the triangles in their original orientations.

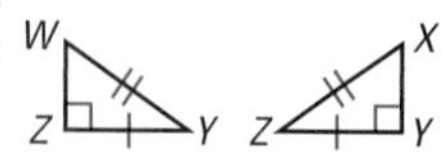

Write a proof.

GIVEN ▶ $\overline{WY} \cong \overline{XZ}$, $\overline{WZ} \perp \overline{ZY}$, $\overline{XY} \perp \overline{ZY}$

PROVE ▶ $\triangle WYZ \cong \triangle XZY$

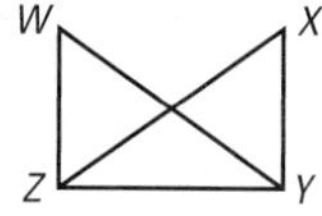

Solution

Redraw the triangles so they are side by side with corresponding parts in the same position. Mark the given information in the diagram.

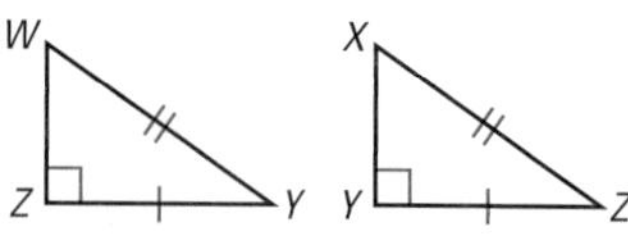

	STATEMENTS	REASONS
H	1. $\overline{WY} \cong \overline{XZ}$	1. Given
	2. $\overline{WZ} \perp \overline{ZY}$, $\overline{XY} \perp \overline{ZY}$	2. Given
	3. $\angle Z$ and $\angle Y$ are right angles.	3. Definition of $\perp$ lines
	4. $\triangle WYZ$ and $\triangle XZY$ are right triangles.	4. Definition of a right triangle
L	5. $\overline{ZY} \cong \overline{YZ}$	5. Reflexive Property of Congruence
	6. $\triangle WYZ \cong \triangle XZY$	6. HL Congruence Theorem

Animated Geometry at classzone.com

EXAMPLE 4 Choose a postulate or theorem

SIGN MAKING You are making a canvas sign to hang on the triangular wall over the door to the barn shown in the picture. You think you can use two identical triangular sheets of canvas. You know that $\overline{RP} \perp \overline{QS}$ and $\overline{PQ} \cong \overline{PS}$. What postulate or theorem can you use to conclude that $\triangle PQR \cong \triangle PSR$?

Solution

You are given that $\overline{PQ} \cong \overline{PS}$. By the Reflexive Property, $\overline{RP} \cong \overline{RP}$. By the definition of perpendicular lines, both $\angle RPQ$ and $\angle RPS$ are right angles, so they are congruent. So, two sides and their included angle are congruent.

▶ You can use the SAS Congruence Postulate to conclude that $\triangle PQR \cong \triangle PSR$.

GUIDED PRACTICE for Examples 3 and 4

Use the diagram at the right.

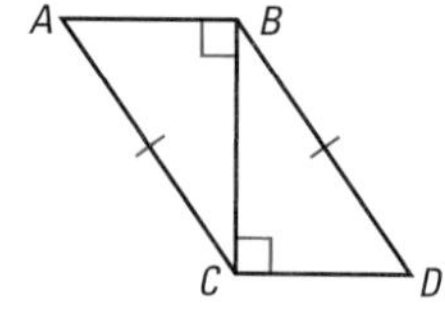

3. Redraw $\triangle ACB$ and $\triangle DBC$ side by side with corresponding parts in the same position. **See margin.**
4. Use the information in the diagram to prove that $\triangle ACB \cong \triangle DBC$. **See margin.**

Differentiated Instruction

Visual Learners Before students begin **Guided Practice Exercises 1 and 2** on page 241, have them trace the diagram. As they work through the problem, have them mark congruent angles and sides on the diagram in corresponding colors. Stress that several sides and angles are congruent to one another.

See also the *Geometry Toolkit* for more strategies.

4.4 EXERCISES

HOMEWORK KEY
○ = **WORKED-OUT SOLUTIONS** on p. WS4 for Exs. 13, 19, and 31
★ = **STANDARDIZED TEST PRACTICE** Exs. 2, 15, 23, and 39

SKILL PRACTICE

A

1. **VOCABULARY** Copy and complete: The angle between two sides of a triangle is called the _?_ angle. **included**

2. ★ **WRITING** *Explain* the difference between proving triangles congruent using the SAS and SSS Congruence Postulates. **See margin.**

EXAMPLE 1 on p. 240 for Exs. 3–15

2. SAS requires two sides and the included angle of one triangle to be congruent to the corresponding two sides and the included angle of a second triangle. *SSS* requires that three sides of one triangle be congruent to the corresponding sides of a second triangle.

NAMING INCLUDED ANGLES Use the diagram to name the included angle between the given pair of sides.

3. $\overline{XY}$ and $\overline{YW}$ $\angle XYW$
4. $\overline{WZ}$ and $\overline{ZY}$ $\angle WZY$
5. $\overline{ZW}$ and $\overline{YW}$ $\angle ZWY$
6. $\overline{WX}$ and $\overline{YX}$ $\angle WXY$
7. $\overline{XY}$ and $\overline{YZ}$ $\angle XYZ$
8. $\overline{WX}$ and $\overline{WZ}$ $\angle XWZ$

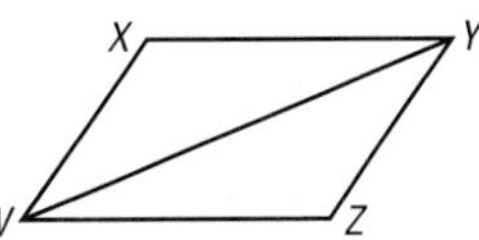

REASONING Decide whether enough information is given to prove that the triangles are congruent using the SAS Congruence Postulate.

9. $\triangle ABD, \triangle CDB$ **not enough**
10. $\triangle LMN, \triangle NQP$ **enough**
11. $\triangle YXZ, \triangle WXZ$ **not enough**

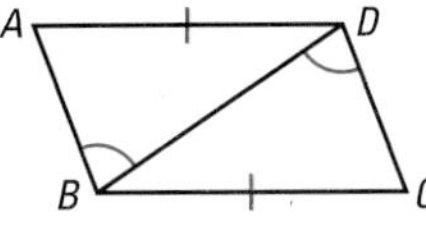

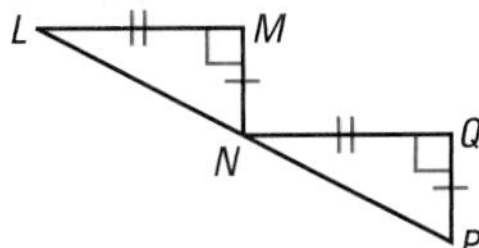

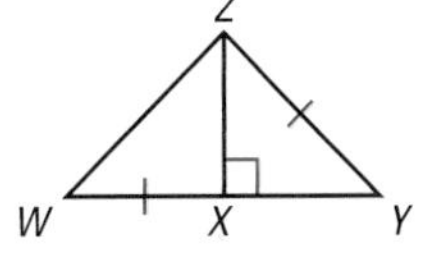

12. $\triangle QRV, \triangle TSU$ **not enough**
13. $\triangle EFH, \triangle GHF$ **enough**
14. $\triangle KLM, \triangle MNK$ **not enough**

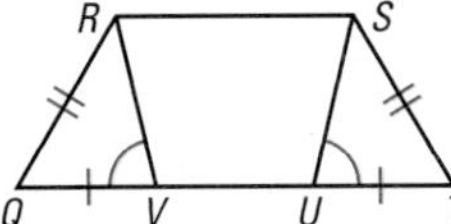

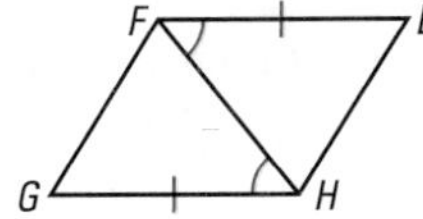

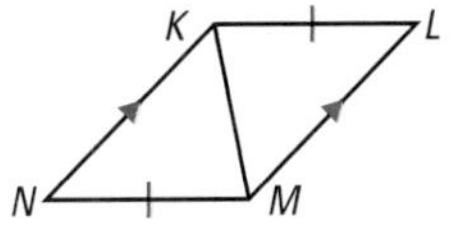

15. ★ **MULTIPLE CHOICE** Which of the following sets of information does not allow you to conclude that $\triangle ABC \cong \triangle DEF$? **B**

Ⓐ $\overline{AB} \cong \overline{DE}, \overline{BC} \cong \overline{EF}, \angle B \cong \angle E$
Ⓑ $\overline{AB} \cong \overline{DF}, \overline{AC} \cong \overline{DE}, \angle C \cong \angle E$
Ⓒ $\overline{AC} \cong \overline{DF}, \overline{BC} \cong \overline{EF}, \overline{BA} \cong \overline{DE}$
Ⓓ $\overline{AB} \cong \overline{DE}, \overline{AC} \cong \overline{DF}, \angle A \cong \angle D$

EXAMPLE 2 on p. 241 for Exs. 16–18

APPLYING SAS In Exercises 16–18, use the given information to name two triangles that are congruent. *Explain* your reasoning. **16–18. See margin.**

16. *ABCD* is a square with four congruent sides and four congruent angles.

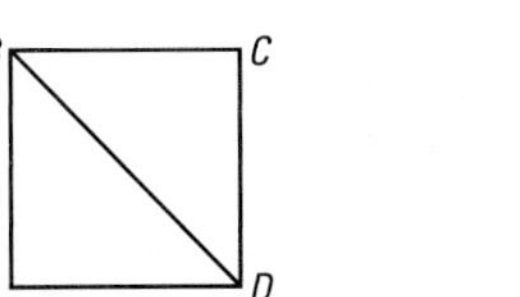

17. *RSTUV* is a regular pentagon.

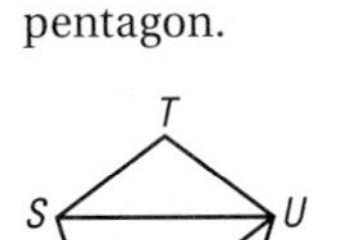
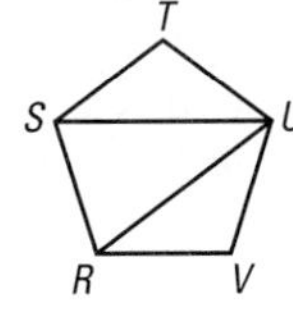

18. $\overline{MK} \perp \overline{MN}$ and $\overline{KL} \perp \overline{NL}$.

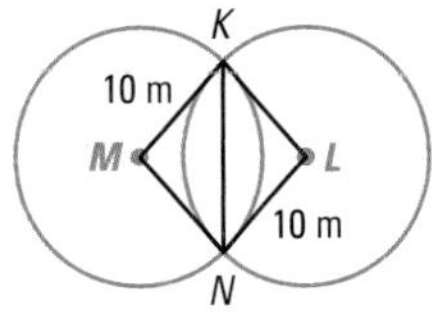

16. $\triangle BAD, \triangle DCB$. *Sample answer:* $\angle A \cong \angle C$ because they are both right angles, $\overline{AB} \cong \overline{CD}$ and $\overline{AD} \cong \overline{CB}$ because the sides of a square are congruent, therefore $\triangle BAD \cong \triangle DCB$ by SAS.

17. $\triangle STU, \triangle RVU$; $\overline{ST} \cong \overline{TU} \cong \overline{UV} \cong \overline{VR}$ and $\angle T \cong \angle V$ because it is a regular pentagon, therefore $\triangle STU \cong \triangle RVU$ by SAS.

18. $\triangle KMN, \triangle KLN$. *Sample answer:* $\overline{MK} \cong \overline{MN} \cong \overline{LN} \cong \overline{LK}$ since they are all radii of the same size circle. It is given that $\overline{MK} \perp \overline{MN}$ and $\overline{LK} \perp \overline{LN}$. $\angle KMN$ and $\angle KLN$ are right angles and since all right angles are congruent, $\angle KMN \cong \angle KLN$. Therefore $\triangle KMN \cong \triangle KLN$ by SAS.

4 PRACTICE AND APPLY

Assignment Guide

Answer Transparencies available for all exercises

Basic:
Day 1: pp. 243–246
Exs. 1–18
Day 2: pp. 243–246
Exs. 19–24, 31–36, 42–48

Average:
Day 1: pp. 243–246
Exs. 1, 2, 4–8 even, 9–18, 25–27
Day 2: pp. 243–246
Exs. 19–24, 31–39, 42–48 even

Advanced:
Day 1: pp. 243–246
Exs. 1, 2, 6–8, 12–18, 25–30*
Day 2: pp. 243–246
Exs. 19–24, 31–41*, 43–47 odd

Block:
pp. 243–246
Exs. 1, 2, 4–8 even, 9–27, 31–39, 42–48 even

Differentiated Instruction

See *Geometry Best Practices Toolkit* for suggestions on addressing the needs of a diverse classroom.

Homework Check

For a quick check of student understanding of key concepts, go over the following exercises:
Basic: 6, 16, 19, 20, 34
Average: 10, 17, 19, 21, 34
Advanced: 12, 18, 19, 22, 34

Extra Practice

- Student Edition, p. 902
- Chapter 4 Resource Book: Practice levels A, B, C, pp. 48–53

Practice Worksheet

An easily-readable reduced practice page (with answers) for this lesson can be found on p. 214C.

Avoiding Common Errors

Exercise 12 Students may think that this is an example of the SAS Congruence Postulate. Remind students that SAS requires two sides and the *included* angle.

Study Strategy

Exercises 20–21 For each exercise, have students list two sides in one triangle that are congruent to two sides of the other triangle. Then have them ask whether the angles that they know are congruent are the included angles for these sides.

19.

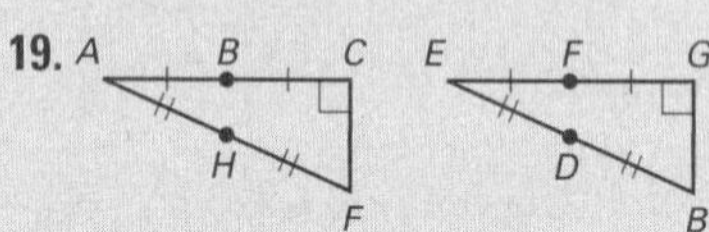

EXAMPLE 3 on p. 242 for Ex. 19

19. OVERLAPPING TRIANGLES Redraw $\triangle ACF$ and $\triangle EGB$ so they are side by side with corresponding parts in the same position. *Explain* how you know that $\triangle ACF \cong \triangle EGB$. **HL; see margin for art.**

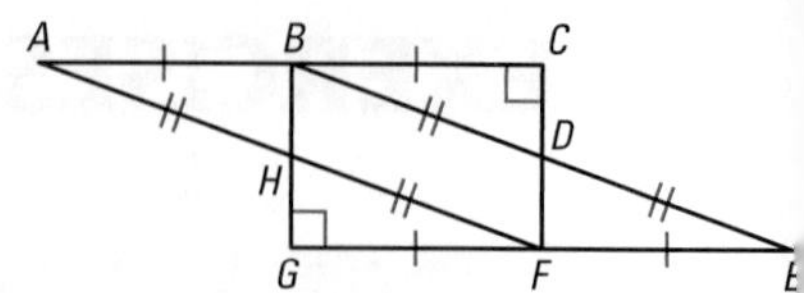

EXAMPLE 4 on p. 242 for Exs. 20–22

REASONING **Decide whether enough information is given to prove that the triangles are congruent. If there is enough information, state the congruence postulate or theorem you would use.**

20.

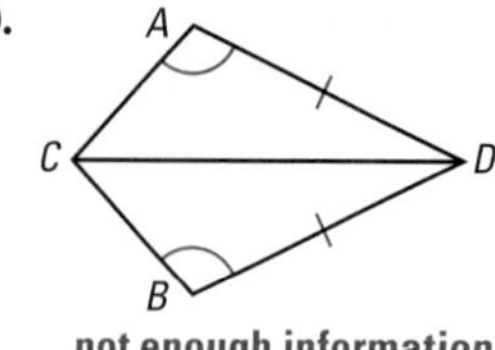

not enough information

21. Z is the midpoint of $\overline{PY}$ and $\overline{XQ}$. **SAS**

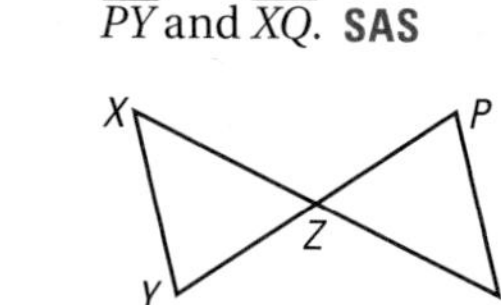

22.

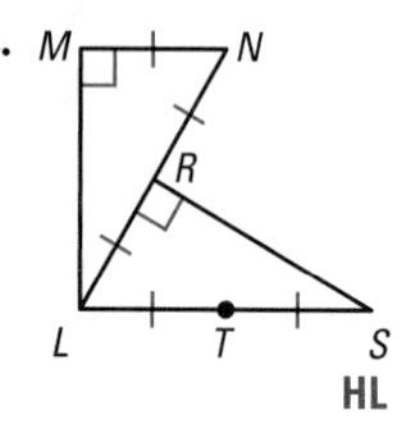

HL

B

23. ★ **WRITING** Suppose both pairs of corresponding legs of two right triangles are congruent. Are the triangles congruent? *Explain.*
Yes; they are congruent by the SAS Congruence Postulate.

24. ERROR ANALYSIS *Describe* and correct the error in finding the value of x.
$\overline{YX}$ and $\overline{YW}$ should have the same length since it can be shown that $\triangle XZY \cong \triangle WZY$; $4x + 6 = 5x - 1$, $-x = -7$, $x = 7$.

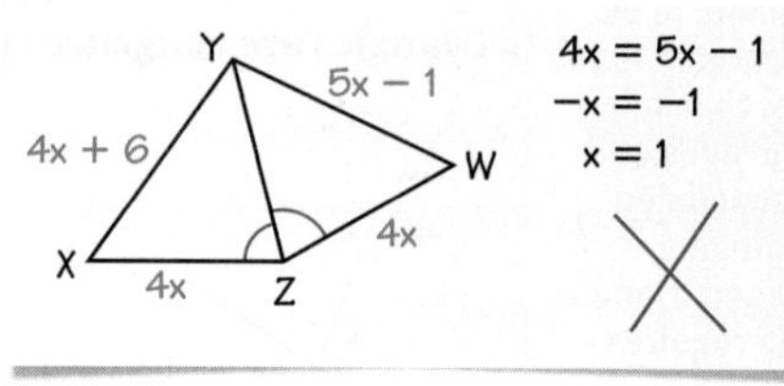

USING DIAGRAMS **In Exercises 25–27, state the third congruence that must be given to prove that $\triangle ABC \cong \triangle DEF$ using the indicated postulate.**

25. GIVEN ▶ $\overline{AB} \cong \overline{DE}$, $\overline{CB} \cong \overline{FE}$, _?_ $\cong$ _?_
Use the SSS Congruence Postulate. **$\overline{AC} \cong \overline{DF}$**

26. GIVEN ▶ $\angle A \cong \angle D$, $\overline{CA} \cong \overline{FD}$, _?_ $\cong$ _?_
Use the SAS Congruence Postulate. **$\overline{BA} \cong \overline{ED}$**

27. GIVEN ▶ $\angle B \cong \angle E$, $\overline{AB} \cong \overline{DE}$, _?_ $\cong$ _?_ **$\overline{BC} \cong \overline{EF}$**
Use the SAS Congruence Postulate.

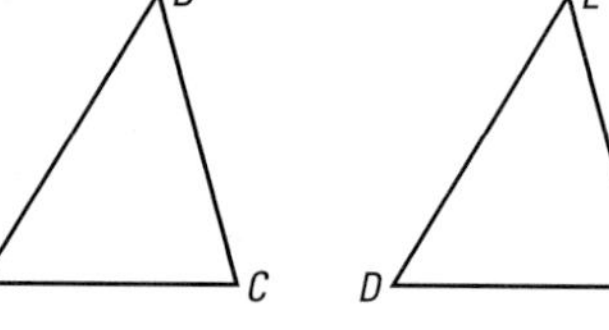

C

28. USING ISOSCELES TRIANGLES Suppose $\triangle KLN$ and $\triangle MLN$ are isosceles triangles with $\overline{KL} \cong \overline{LN}$ and $\overline{ML} \cong \overline{LN}$, and $\overline{NL}$ bisects $\angle KLM$. Is there enough information to prove that $\triangle KLN \cong \triangle MLN$? *Explain.*
Yes; they are congruent by SAS.

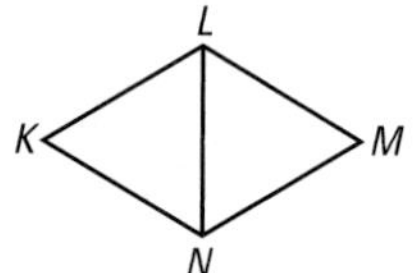

29. REASONING Suppose M is the midpoint of $\overline{PQ}$ in $\triangle PQR$. If $\overline{RM} \perp \overline{PQ}$, *explain* why $\triangle RMP \cong \triangle RMQ$. **Because $\overline{RM} \perp \overline{PQ}$, $\angle RMQ$ and $\angle RMP$ are right angles and thus are congruent. $\overline{QM} \cong \overline{MP}$ and $\overline{MR} \cong \overline{MR}$. So, $\triangle RMP \cong \triangle RMQ$ by SAS.**

30. CHALLENGE Suppose $\overline{AB} \cong \overline{AC}$, $\overline{AD} \cong \overline{AF}$, $\overline{AD} \perp \overline{AB}$, and $\overline{AF} \perp \overline{AC}$. *Explain* why you can conclude that $\triangle ACD \cong \triangle ABF$. **Since $\angle DAC \cong \angle FAB$ the triangles are congruent by SAS.**

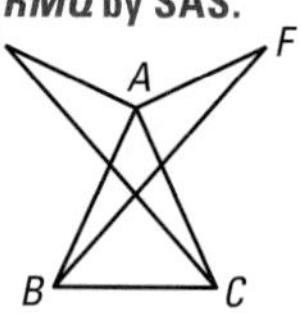

○ = WORKED-OUT SOLUTIONS on p. WS1

★ = STANDARDIZED TEST PRACTICE

Problem Solving

A **CONGRUENT TRIANGLES In Exercises 31 and 32, identify the theorem or postulate you would use to prove the triangles congruent.**

31. 

SAS

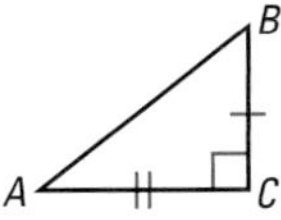

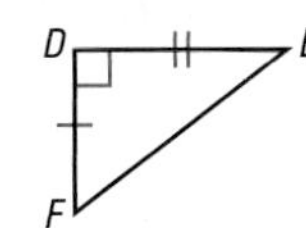

32. 

SAS

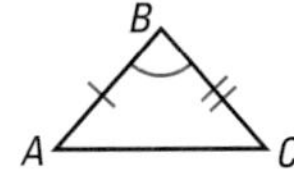

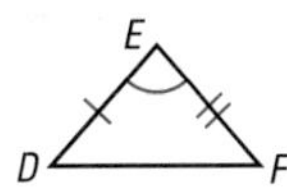

33. Two sides and the included angle of one sail need to be congruent to two sides and the included angle of the second sail; the two sails need to be right triangles with congruent hypotenuses and one pair of congruent legs.

33. **SAILBOATS** Suppose you have two sailboats. What information do you need to know to prove that the triangular sails are congruent using SAS? using HL?

@HomeTutor for problem solving help at classzone.com

EXAMPLE 3
on p. 242
for Ex. 34

34. **DEVELOPING PROOF** Copy and complete the proof.

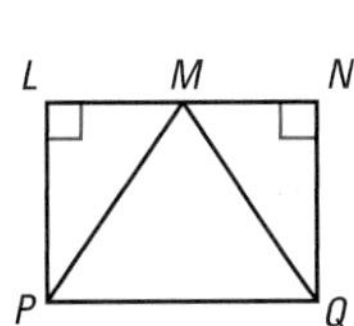

GIVEN ▶ Point M is the midpoint of $\overline{LN}$.
$\triangle PMQ$ is an isosceles triangle with $\overline{MP} \cong \overline{MQ}$.
$\angle L$ and $\angle N$ are right angles.

PROVE ▶ $\triangle LMP \cong \triangle NMQ$

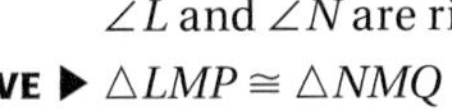

STATEMENTS	REASONS
1. $\angle L$ and $\angle N$ are right angles.	1. Given
2. $\triangle LMP$ and $\triangle NMQ$ are right triangles.	2. ? **Definition of a right triangle**
3. Point M is the midpoint of $\overline{LN}$.	3. ? **Given**
4. ? $\overline{LM} \cong \overline{NM}$	4. Definition of midpoint
5. $\overline{MP} \cong \overline{MQ}$	5. Given
6. $\triangle LMP \cong \triangle NMQ$	6. ? **HL**

@HomeTutor for problem solving help at classzone.com

B **PROOF In Exercises 35 and 36, write a proof.** **35, 36. See margin.**

35. **GIVEN ▶** $\overline{PQ}$ bisects $\angle SPT$, $\overline{SP} \cong \overline{TP}$
PROVE ▶ $\triangle SPQ \cong \triangle TPQ$

36. **GIVEN ▶** $\overline{VX} \cong \overline{XY}$, $\overline{XW} \cong \overline{YZ}$, $\overline{XW} \parallel \overline{YZ}$
PROVE ▶ $\triangle VXW \cong \triangle XYZ$

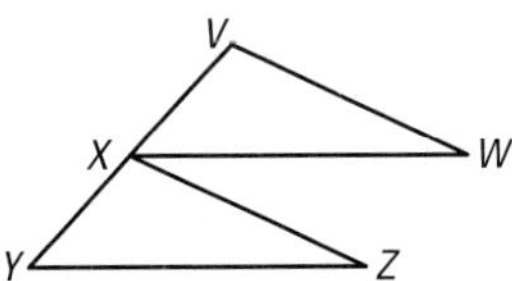

Reading Strategy

Exercise 34 As students read the given information, have them mark a copy of the diagram to show congruent segments. Students should be able to justify all the marks they make by referring to a piece of given information.

35. Statements (Reasons)
1. $\overline{PQ}$ bisects $\angle SPT$, $\overline{SP} \cong \overline{TP}$. (Given)
2. $\angle SPQ \cong \angle TPQ$ (Definition of angle bisector)
3. $\overline{PQ} \cong \overline{PQ}$ (Reflexive Property of Congruence)
4. $\triangle SPQ \cong \triangle TPQ$ (SAS)

36. Statements (Reasons)
1. $\overline{VX} \cong \overline{XY}$, $\overline{XW} \cong \overline{YZ}$, $\overline{XW} \parallel \overline{YZ}$ (Given)
2. $\angle VXW \cong \angle XYZ$ (Corresponding Angles Postulate)
3. $\triangle VXW \cong \triangle XYZ$ (SAS)

5 ASSESS AND RETEACH

Daily Homework Quiz

Transparency Available

Is there enough given information to prove the triangles congruent? If there is, state the postulate or theorem.

1. $\triangle ABE$, $\triangle CBD$ **SAS ≅ Post.**

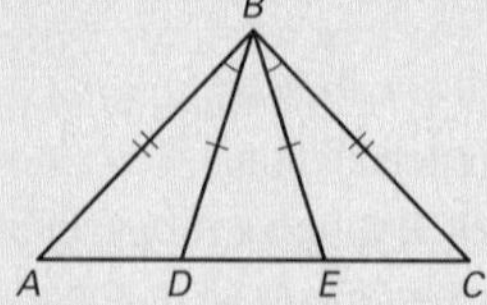

2. $\triangle FGH$, $\triangle HJK$ **HL ≅ Thm.**

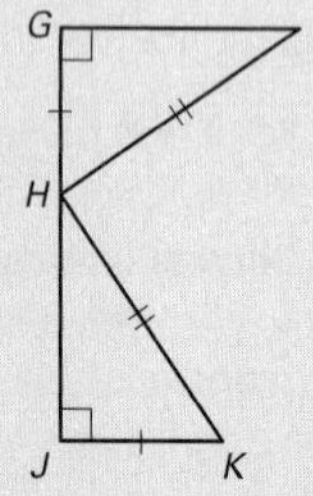

State a third congruence that would allow you to prove $\triangle RST \cong \triangle XYZ$ by the SAS Congruence Postulate.

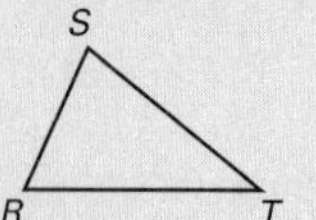

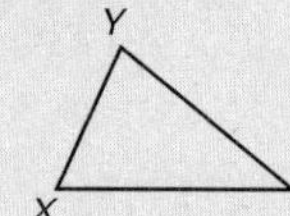

3. $\overline{ST} \cong \overline{YZ}$, $\overline{RS} \cong \overline{XY}$ **$\angle S \cong \angle Y$**

4. $\angle T \cong \angle Z$, $\overline{RT} \cong \overline{XZ}$ **$\overline{ST} \cong \overline{YZ}$**

Online Quiz

Available at **classzone.com**

Diagnosis/Remediation

- Practice A, B, C in Chapter 4 Resource Book, pp. 48–53
- Study Guide in Chapter 4 Resource Book, pp. 54–55
- Practice Workbook, pp. 70–72
- @HomeTutor

Challenge

Additional challenge is available in the Chapter 4 Resource Book, p. 59.

37, 38, 40, 41. See Additional Answers beginning on p. AA1.

PROOF In Exercises 37 and 38, write a proof. **37, 38. See margin.**

37. **GIVEN** ▶ $\overline{JM} \cong \overline{LM}$
PROVE ▶ $\triangle JKM \cong \triangle LKM$

38. **GIVEN** ▶ D is the midpoint of $\overline{AC}$.
PROVE ▶ $\triangle ABD \cong \triangle CBD$

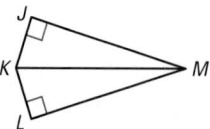

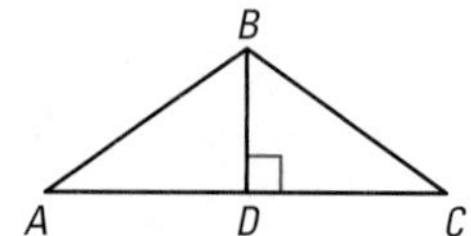

39. ★ **MULTIPLE CHOICE** Which triangle congruence can you prove, then use to prove that $\angle FED \cong \angle ABF$? **D**

Ⓐ $\triangle ABE \cong \triangle ABF$ Ⓑ $\triangle AED \cong \triangle ABD$

Ⓒ $\triangle ACD \cong \triangle ADF$ Ⓓ $\triangle AEC \cong \triangle ABD$

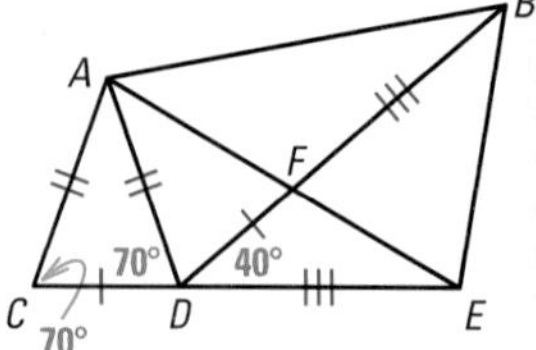

C **40.** **PROOF** Write a two-column proof. **See margin.**

GIVEN ▶ $\overline{CR} \cong \overline{CS}$, $\overline{QC} \perp \overline{CR}$, $\overline{QC} \perp \overline{CS}$
PROVE ▶ $\triangle QCR \cong \triangle QCS$

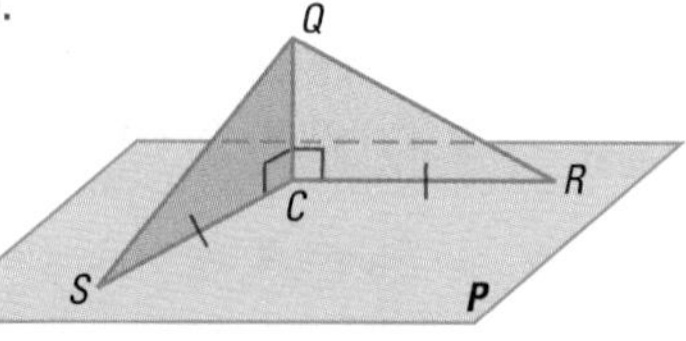

41. **CHALLENGE** *Describe* how to show that $\triangle PMO \cong \triangle PMN$ using the SSS Congruence Postulate. Then show that the triangles are congruent using the SAS Congruence Postulate without measuring any angles. *Compare* the two methods. **See margin.**

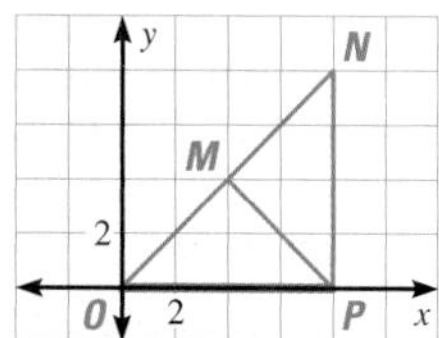

MIXED REVIEW

Draw a figure that fits the description. *(p. 42)* **42, 43. See margin.**

42. A pentagon that is not regular.

43. A quadrilateral that is equilateral but not equiangular.

Write an equation of the line that passes through point *P* and is perpendicular to the line with the given equation. *(p. 180)*

44. $P(3, -1)$, $y = -x + 2$ **$y = x - 4$**

45. $P(3, 3)$, $y = \frac{1}{3}x + 2$ **$y = -3x + 12$**

46. $P(-4, -7)$, $y = -5$ **$x = -4$**

PREVIEW Prepare for Lesson 4.5 in Exs. 47–48.

Find the value of *x*. *(p. 225)*

47. **5**

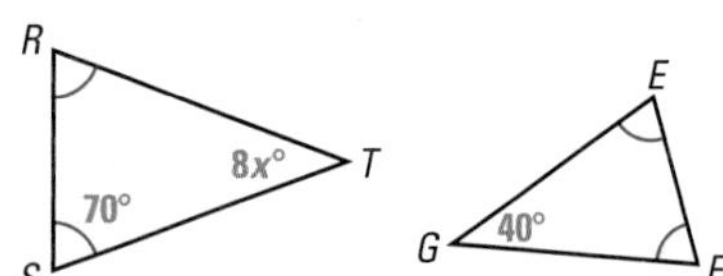

48. **19**

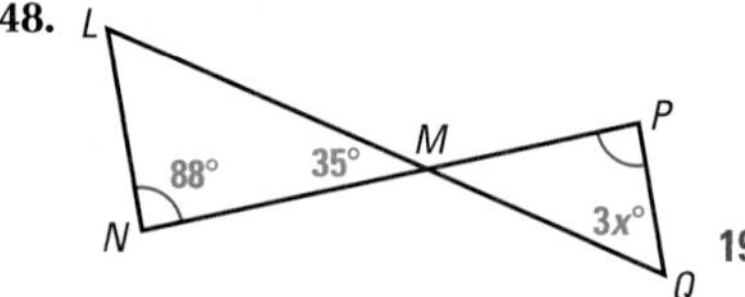

42. *Sample:*

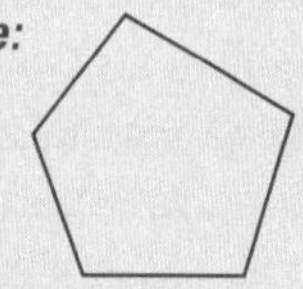

43. *Sample:*

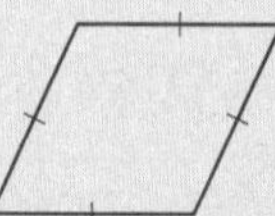

@HomeTutor
classzone.com
Keystrokes

4.4 Investigate Triangles and Congruence

MATERIALS • graphing calculator or computer

QUESTION **Can you prove triangles are congruent by SSA?**

You can use geometry drawing software to show that if two sides and a nonincluded angle of one triangle are congruent to two sides and a nonincluded angle of another triangle, the triangles are not necessarily congruent.

Standards
3.0 Students construct and judge the validity of a logical argument and **give counterexamples to disprove a statement.**

EXAMPLE **Draw two triangles**

STEP 1

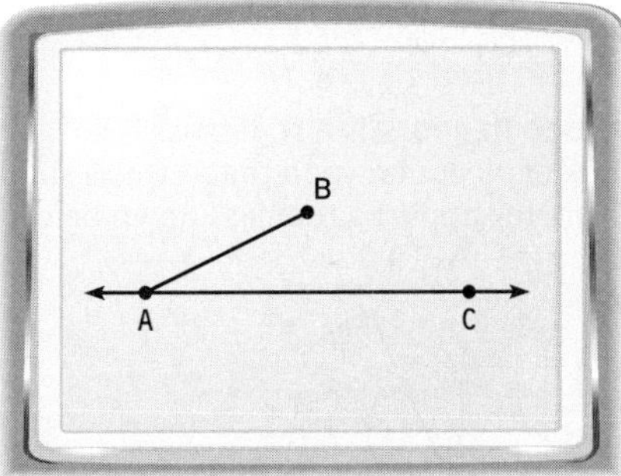

Draw a line Draw points A and C. Draw line $\overleftrightarrow{AC}$. Then choose point B so that $\angle BAC$ is acute. Draw $\overline{AB}$.

STEP 2

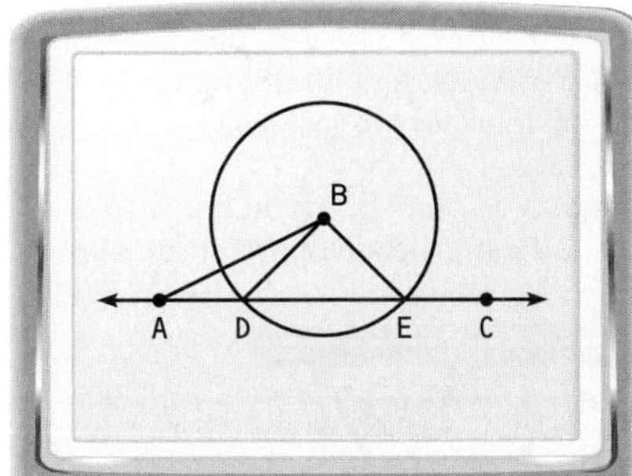

Draw a circle Draw a circle with center at B so that the circle intersects $\overleftrightarrow{AC}$ at two points. Label the points D and E. Draw $\overline{BD}$ and $\overline{BE}$. Save as "EXAMPLE".

STEP 3 ***Use your drawing***
Explain why $\overline{BD} \cong \overline{BE}$. In $\triangle ABD$ and $\triangle ABE$, what other sides are congruent? What angles are congruent? **They are radii of the same circle; $\overline{AB} \cong \overline{AB}$; $\angle BAD \cong \angle BAE$.**

PRACTICE

1. *Explain* how your drawing shows that $\triangle ABD \ncong \triangle ABE$. **$\overline{DA}$ is not congruent to $\overline{EA}$.**
2. Change the diameter of your circle so that it intersects $\overleftrightarrow{AC}$ in only one point. Measure $\angle BDA$. *Explain* why there is exactly one triangle you can draw with the measures AB, BD, and a 90° angle at $\angle BDA$.
3. *Explain* why your results show that SSA cannot be used to show that two triangles are congruent but that HL can. **The activity shows that SSA can yield two non-congruent triangles but that HL results in only one triangle.**

2. Since $\triangle ABD$ is a right triangle, the Hypotenuse-Leg Congruence Theorem guarantees that any triangle with these dimensions will also be congruent to $\triangle ABD$.

1 PLAN AND PREPARE

Learn the Method

- Students will use geometry software to show that SSA does not necessarily prove triangles congruent.

Keystroke Help

Keystrokes for several models of calculators are available in blackline format in the *Chapter 4 Resource Book*.

2 TEACH

Tips for Success

Be sure students make $\angle BAC$ acute and draw the circle with a small enough radius so it intersects $\overleftrightarrow{AC}$ in two points on the same side of point A. Have students hide point C so they do not use it as a vertex of their triangle.

Extra Example

Draw a line, label points A and C on the line, and construct an obtuse $\angle CAB$. Hide point C. Construct a circle with center B that intersects $\overline{AC}$. How many triangles are formed with vertices A, B, and the intersecton of the circle with $\overleftrightarrow{AC}$? Are they congruent? **2; no**

3 ASSESS AND RETEACH

1. Suppose two sides and an angle of one triangle are congruent to two sides and the corresponding angle of another triangle. What do you need to know about the angles to be sure that the triangles are congruent? **The angles must be the included angles for the congruent sides or the given congruent angles must be right angles.**

STATE TEST PRACTICE classzone.com

1a. $\triangle ACE$ and $\triangle DCF$ are obtuse triangles, and $\triangle ECB$, $\triangle FCG$, $\triangle ABC$, and $\triangle DGC$ are acute triangles.

2. *Sample answer:* Using the distance formula it can be shown that $\triangle PQR \cong \triangle STR$ by SSS.

4. Yes; Because $\overline{AC} \cong \overline{GE}$ and $\overline{AB} \cong \overline{FE}$, $\overline{BC} \cong \overline{GF}$. Also, since $\overline{AG} \cong \overline{CE}$ and $\overline{AH} \cong \overline{DE}$, $\overline{HG} \cong \overline{CD}$. $\angle G$ and $\angle C$ are right angles, so they are congruent. Therefore, $\triangle BCD \cong \triangle FGH$ by SAS.

5a. Statements (Reasons)

1. $\overline{BG} \perp \overline{FH}$, $\overline{GF} \cong \overline{GH}$ (Given)
2. $\angle BGF$ and $\angle BGH$ are right angles. (Definition of perpendicular lines)
3. $\angle BGF \cong \angle BGH$ (Right Angles Congruence Theorem)
4. $\overline{BG} \cong \overline{BG}$ (Reflexive Property of Congruence)
5. $\triangle FGB \cong \triangle HGB$ (SAS)

5b. yes;

Statements (Reasons)

1. $\overline{DF} \cong \overline{EH}$, $m\angle EHB = 25°$, $m\angle BFG = 65°$, $\overline{DF} \perp \overline{AG}$ at point F (Given)
2. $\triangle FGB \cong \triangle HGB$ (Problem 5a)
3. $\overline{FB} \cong \overline{HB}$ (Corr. parts of $\cong$ $\triangle$s are $\cong$.)
4. $\angle DFG$ is a right angle. (Definition of perpendicular lines)
5. $m\angle DFG = 90°$ (Definition of right angle)
6. $m\angle DFB + m\angle BFG = m\angle DFC$ (Angle Addition Postulate)
7. $m\angle DFB + 65° = 90°$ (Substitution Property of Equality)
8. $m\angle DFB = 25°$ (Subtraction Property of Equality)
9. $m\angle DFB = m\angle EHB$ (Transitive Property of Equality)
10. $\angle DFB \cong \angle EHB$ (Definition of congruent angles)
11. $\triangle BDF \cong \triangle BEH$ (SAS)

Lessons 4.1–4.4

1. **MULTI-STEP PROBLEM** In the diagram, $\overline{AC} \cong \overline{CD}$, $\overline{BC} \cong \overline{CG}$, $\overline{EC} \cong \overline{CF}$, and $\angle ACE \cong \angle DCF$.

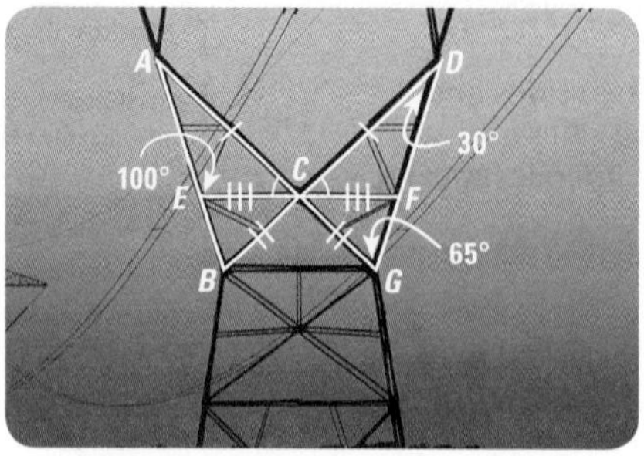

   a. Classify each triangle in the figure by angles. **See margin.**

   b. Classify each triangle in the figure by sides. **All triangles are scalene.**

2. **OPEN-ENDED** *Explain* how you know that $\triangle PQR \cong \triangle STR$ in the keyboard stand shown. **See margin.**

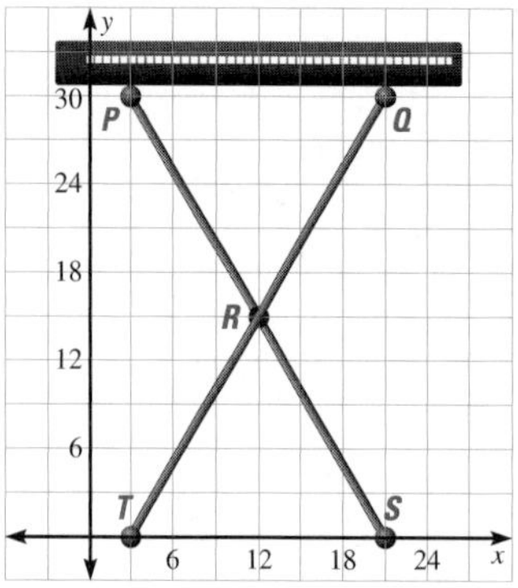

3. **GRIDDED ANSWER** In the diagram below, find the measure of $\angle 1$ in degrees. **70°**

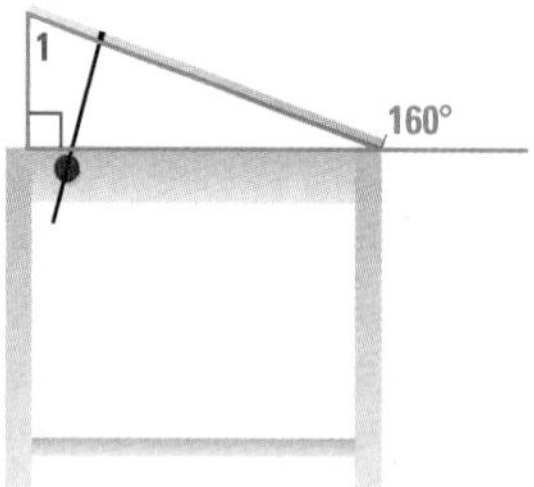

4. **SHORT RESPONSE** A rectangular "diver down" flag is used to indicate that scuba divers are in the water. On the flag, $\overline{AB} \cong \overline{FE}$, $\overline{AH} \cong \overline{DE}$, $\overline{CE} \cong \overline{AG}$, and $\overline{EG} \cong \overline{AC}$. Also, $\angle A$, $\angle C$, $\angle E$, and $\angle G$ are right angles. Is $\triangle BCD \cong \triangle FGH$? *Explain.* **See margin.**

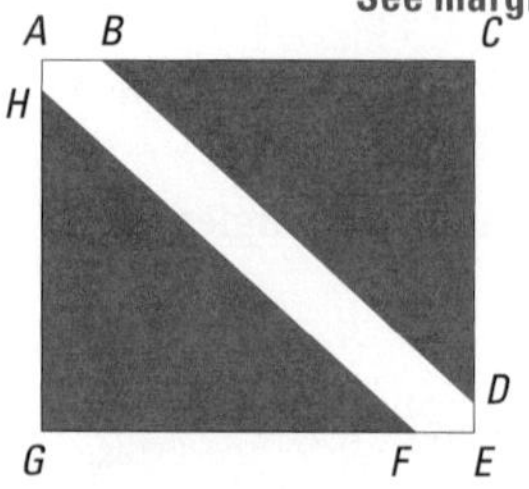

5. **EXTENDED RESPONSE** A roof truss is a network of pieces of wood that forms a stable structure to support a roof, as shown below.

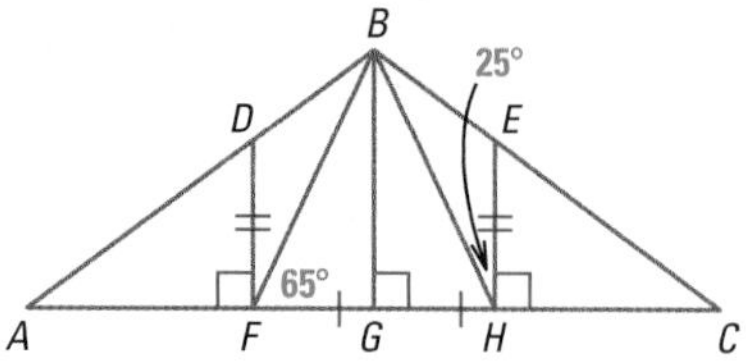

   a. Prove that $\triangle FGB \cong \triangle HGB$. **a, b. See margin.**

   b. Is $\triangle BDF \cong \triangle BEH$? If so, prove it.

6. **GRIDDED ANSWER** In the diagram below, $BAFC \cong DEFC$. Find the value of x. **23**

4.5 Prove Triangles Congruent by ASA and AAS

Before You used the SSS, SAS, and HL congruence methods.

Now You will use two more methods to prove congruences.

Why? So you can recognize congruent triangles in bikes, as in Exs. 23–24.

Key Vocabulary
- flow proof

Standards

5.0 Students prove that triangles are congruent or similar, and they are able to use the concept of corresponding parts of congruent triangles.

4.0 Students prove basic theorems involving congruence and similarity.

Suppose you tear two angles out of a piece of paper and place them at a fixed distance on a ruler. Can you form more than one triangle with a given length and two given angle measures as shown below?

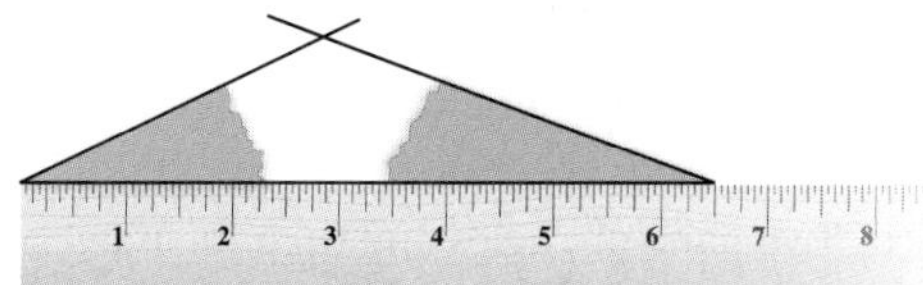

In a polygon, the side connecting the vertices of two angles is the *included* side. Given two angle measures and the length of the included side, you can make only one triangle. So, all triangles with those measurements are congruent.

THEOREMS — *For Your Notebook*

POSTULATE 21 Angle-Side-Angle (ASA) Congruence Postulate

If two angles and the included side of one triangle are congruent to two angles and the included side of a second triangle, then the two triangles are congruent.

If Angle $\angle A \cong \angle D$,
Side $\overline{AC} \cong \overline{DF}$, and
Angle $\angle C \cong \angle F$,
then $\triangle ABC \cong \triangle DEF$.

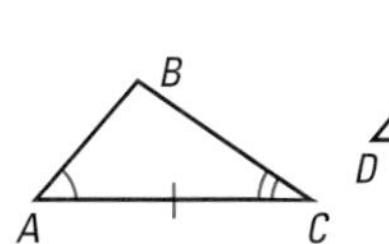

THEOREM 4.6 Angle-Angle-Side (AAS) Congruence Theorem

If two angles and a non-included side of one triangle are congruent to two angles and the corresponding non-included side of a second triangle, then the two triangles are congruent.

If Angle $\angle A \cong \angle D$,
Angle $\angle C \cong \angle F$, and
Side $\overline{BC} \cong \overline{EF}$,
then $\triangle ABC \cong \triangle DEF$.

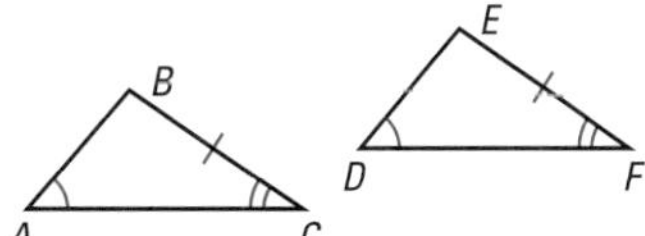

Proof: Example 2, p. 250

1 PLAN AND PREPARE

Warm-Up Exercises

Transparency Available

Tell whether the pair of triangles is congruent or not and why.

Yes; HL ≅ Thm.

Notetaking Guide

Transparency Available

Promotes interactive learning and notetaking skills, pp. 100–103.

Pacing

Basic: 2 days
Average: 2 days
Advanced: 2 days
Block: 1 block
- See *Teaching Guide/Lesson Plan.*

2 FOCUS AND MOTIVATE

Essential Question

Big Idea 2, p. 215

If a side of one triangle is congruent to a side of another triangle, what information about the angles would allow you to prove the triangles are congruent? **Tell students they will learn how to answer this question by learning about the ASA Postulate and the AAS Theorem.**

Resource Planning Guide

Chapter Resource Book
- Teaching Guide/Lesson Plan (pp. 60–61)
- Activity Master (p. 62)
- Practice levels A, B, C (pp. 63–68)
- Study Guide (pp. 69–70)
- Catch-up for Absent Students (p. 71)
- Application (p. 72)
- Challenge (p. 73)

Workbooks
- Notetaking Guide (pp. 100–103)
- Practice Workbook (pp. 73–75)

Teaching Options
- **Power Presentations CD-ROM** provides dynamic electronic teaching resources for the classroom.
- **Activity Generator CD-ROM** provides editable activities for all ability levels.

Interactive Technology
- Easy Planner
- Power Presentations CD-ROM
- Activity Generator CD-ROM
- Animated Geometry
- Test Generator CD-ROM
- Online Quiz
- eWorkbook
- eEdition
- @HomeTutor

Resources for English Learners
- Quick Reference for English Learners
- Spanish Study Guide
- Multi-Language Visual Glossary
- Student Resources in Spanish

See also the *Geometry Toolkit* for more strategies for meeting individual needs.

Motivating the Lesson

Tell students that in this lesson they will learn how a surveyor can decide whether two triangular plots of land are the same size and shape by measuring the length of one side and two angles of each triangle.

3 TEACH

Extra Example 1

Can the triangles be proven congruent with the information given in the diagram? If so, state the postulate or theorem you would use.

a.

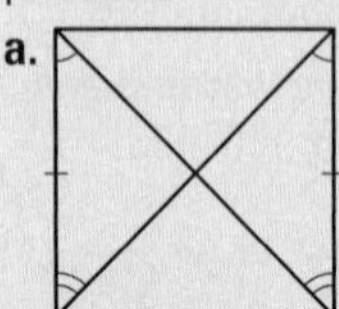

ASA Congruence Postulate

b.

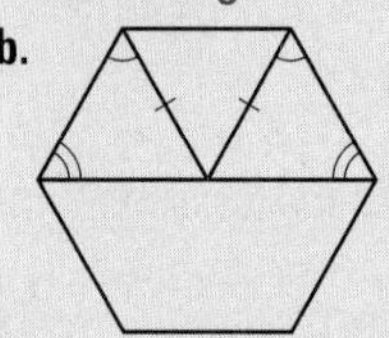

AAS Congruence Theorem

c.

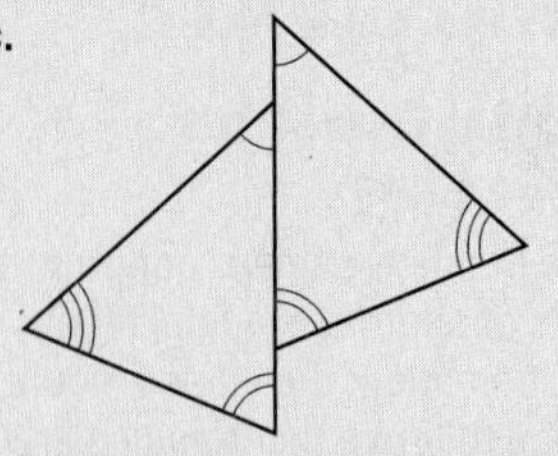

cannot be proven congruent

2. See Additional Answers beginning on p. AA1.

EXAMPLE 1 Identify congruent triangles

Can the triangles be proven congruent with the information given in the diagram? If so, state the postulate or theorem you would use.

a. 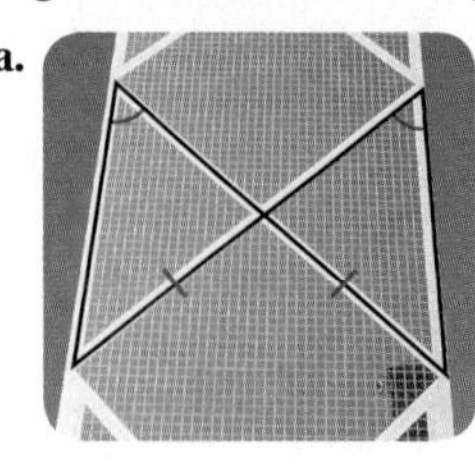

b. 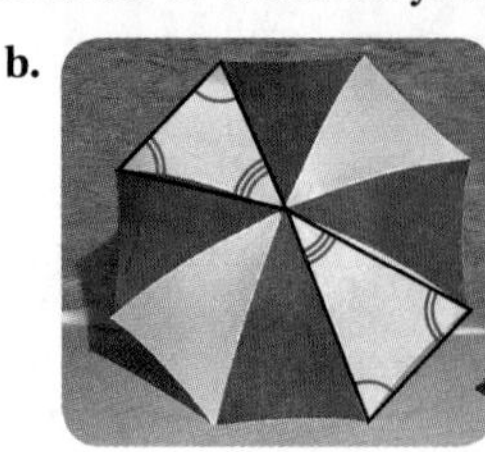

c. 

Solution

a. The vertical angles are congruent, so two pairs of angles and a pair of non-included sides are congruent. The triangles are congruent by the AAS Congruence Theorem.

AVOID ERRORS
You need at least one pair of congruent corresponding sides to prove two triangles congruent.

b. There is not enough information to prove the triangles are congruent, because no sides are known to be congruent.

c. Two pairs of angles and their included sides are congruent. The triangles are congruent by the ASA Congruence Postulate.

FLOW PROOFS You have written two-column proofs and paragraph proofs. A **flow proof** uses arrows to show the flow of a logical argument. Each reason is written below the statement it justifies.

EXAMPLE 2 Prove the AAS Congruence Theorem

Prove the Angle-Angle-Side Congruence Theorem.

GIVEN ▶ $\angle A \cong \angle D$, $\angle C \cong \angle F$, $\overline{BC} \cong \overline{EF}$

PROVE ▶ $\triangle ABC \cong \triangle DEF$

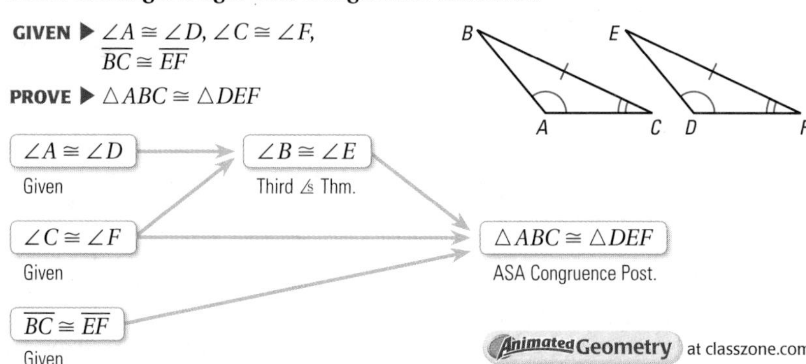

 Animated Geometry at classzone.com

✓ **GUIDED PRACTICE** for Examples 1 and 2

1. In the diagram at the right, what postulate or theorem can you use to prove that $\triangle RST \cong \triangle VUT$? *Explain.* **AAS; $\angle RTS$ and $\angle VTU$ are congruent.**

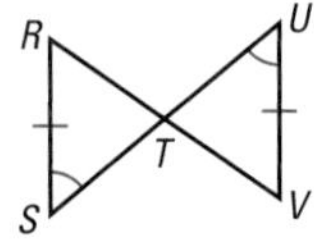

2. Rewrite the proof of the Triangle Sum Theorem on page 219 as a flow proof. **See margin.**

Differentiated Instruction

Inclusion It may be challenging for some students to remember the triangle congruence postulates. Point out that the order in which the letters in the abbreviations appear is the same order in which the corresponding parts must exist in the two triangles. Write SSS, SAS, HL, ASA, and AAS on the board and have students describe what corresponding parts must be congruent for each postulate.

See also the *Geometry Toolkit* for more strategies.

EXAMPLE 3 Write a flow proof

In the diagram, $\overline{CE} \perp \overline{BD}$ and $\angle CAB \cong \angle CAD$. Write a flow proof to show $\triangle ABE \cong \triangle ADE$.

Solution

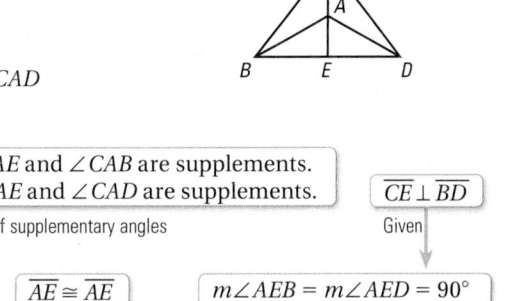

GIVEN ▶ $\overline{CE} \perp \overline{BD}$, $\angle CAB \cong \angle CAD$

PROVE ▶ $\triangle ABE \cong \triangle ADE$

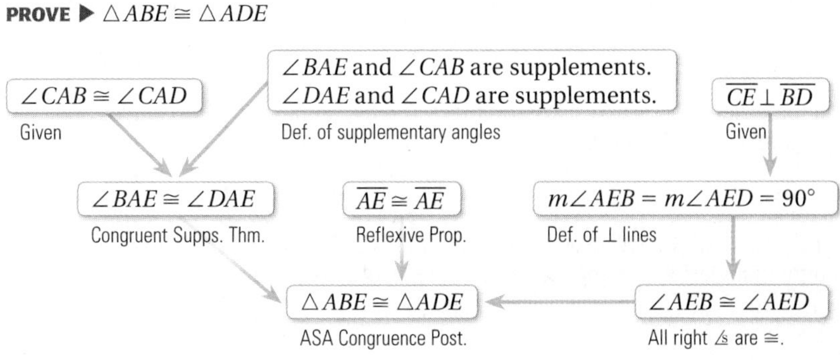

EXAMPLE 4 Standardized Test Practice

FIRE TOWERS The forestry service uses fire tower lookouts to watch for forest fires. When the lookouts spot a fire, they measure the angle of their view and radio a dispatcher. The dispatcher then uses the angles to locate the fire. How many lookouts are needed to locate a fire?

Ⓐ 1 Ⓑ 2 Ⓒ 3 Ⓓ Not enough information

The locations of tower A, tower B, and the fire form a triangle. The dispatcher knows the distance from tower A to tower B and the measures of $\angle A$ and $\angle B$. So, the measures of two angles and an included side of the triangle are known.

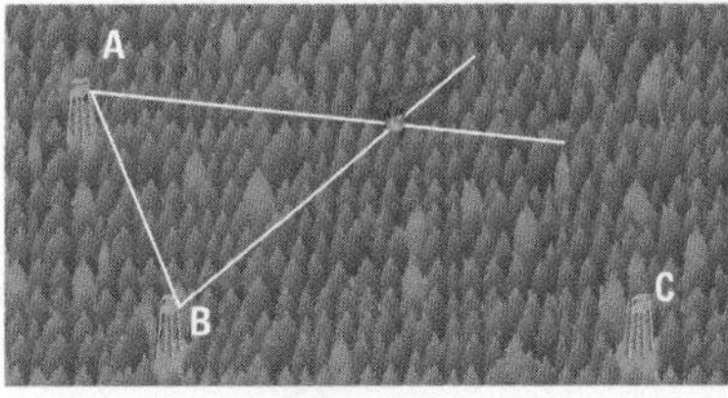

By the ASA Congruence Postulate, all triangles with these measures are congruent. So, the triangle formed is unique and the fire location is given by the third vertex. Two lookouts are needed to locate the fire.

▶ The correct answer is B. Ⓐ Ⓑ Ⓒ Ⓓ

GUIDED PRACTICE for Examples 3 and 4

3. In Example 3, suppose $\angle ABE \cong \angle ADE$ is also given. What theorem or postulate besides ASA can you use to prove that $\triangle ABE \cong \triangle ADE$? **AAS Congruence Theorem**

4. **WHAT IF?** In Example 4, suppose a fire occurs directly between tower B and tower C. Could towers B and C be used to locate the fire? *Explain.* **No; no triangle is formed by the location of the fire and the towers, so the fire could be anywhere between towers *B* and *C*.**

Extra Example 2

In the diagram, $\overline{AB} \perp \overline{BC}$, $\overline{DE} \perp \overline{EF}$, $\overline{AC} \cong \overline{DF}$, and $\angle C \cong \angle F$. Prove that $\triangle ABC \cong \triangle DEF$.

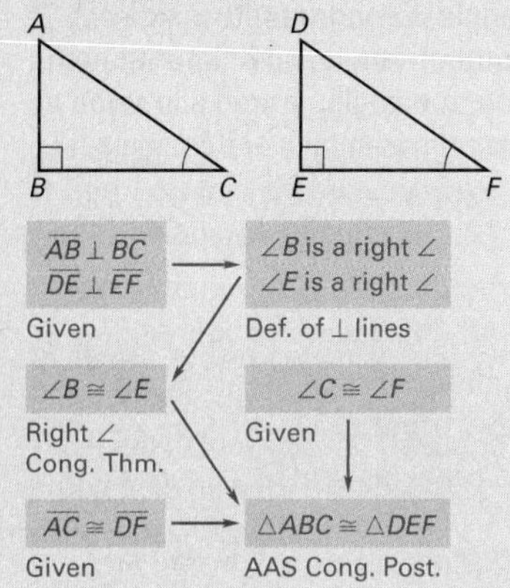

Extra Example 3

In the diagram, $\angle CBF \cong \angle CDF$ and $\overline{BF} \cong \overline{FD}$. Write a flow proof to show that $\triangle ABF \cong \triangle EDF$.

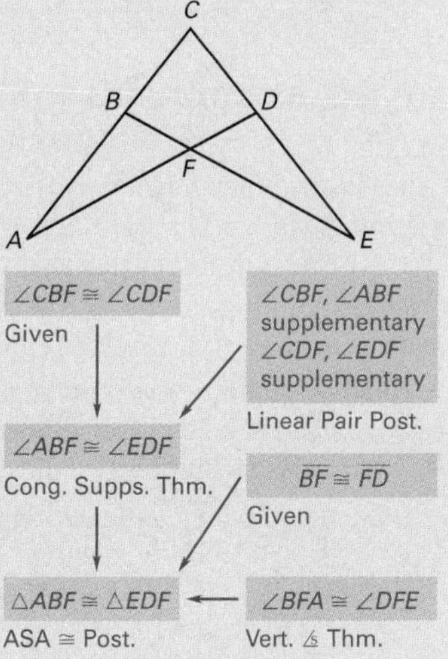

Extra Example 4

Several observers along a straight shoreline measure the angle between the shoreline and the parachute of a space capsule that has just returned to Earth. If the distance between each pair of observers is known, how many of the angle measures are needed to locate the capsule parachute? **two**

Differentiated Instruction

Advanced Have the students construct a triangle given two side lengths and the measure of the included angle. Also have them construct a triangle given the measures of two angles and the length of the included side. Challenge them to construct a triangle given the measures of two angles and the length of a non-included side and then the lengths of two sides and measure of a non-included acute angle.

See also the *Geometry Toolkit* for more strategies.

Closing the Lesson

Have students summarize the major points of the lesson and answer the Essential Question: If a side of one triangle is congruent to a side of another triangle, what information about the angles would allow you to prove the triangles are congruent?

- **Triangles are congruent by the ASA Congruence Postulate.**
- **Triangles are congruent by the AAS Congruence Theorem.**
- **Another format for proofs is the flow proof.**

The triangles will be congruent if the conditions of the ASA Congruence Postulate or of the AAS Congruence Theorem are met.

CONCEPT SUMMARY *For Your Notebook*

Triangle Congruence Postulates and Theorems

You have learned five methods for proving that triangles are congruent.

SSS	SAS	HL (right △s only)	ASA	AAS
All three sides are congruent.	Two sides and the included angle are congruent.	The hypotenuse and one of the legs are congruent.	Two angles and the included side are congruent.	Two angles and a (non-included) side are congruent.

In the Exercises, you will prove three additional theorems about the congruence of right triangles: **A**ngle-**L**eg, **L**eg-**L**eg, and **H**ypotenuse-**A**ngle.

4.5 EXERCISES

HOMEWORK KEY
○ = **WORKED-OUT SOLUTIONS** on p. WS5 for Exs. 5, 9, and 27
★ = **STANDARDIZED TEST PRACTICE** Exs. 2, 7, 21, and 26

SKILL PRACTICE

A

1. **VOCABULARY** Name one advantage of using a flow proof rather than a two-column proof. ***Sample answer:*** **A flow proof shows the flow of a logical argument.**

2. ★ **WRITING** You know that a pair of triangles has two pairs of congruent corresponding angles. What other information do you need to show that the triangles are congruent? **a pair of congruent sides that are either both included or both not included**

EXAMPLE 1 on p. 250 for Exs. 3–7

IDENTIFY CONGRUENT TRIANGLES **Is it possible to prove that the triangles are congruent? If so, state the postulate or theorem you would use.**

3. $\triangle ABC$, $\triangle QRS$ **yes; AAS**

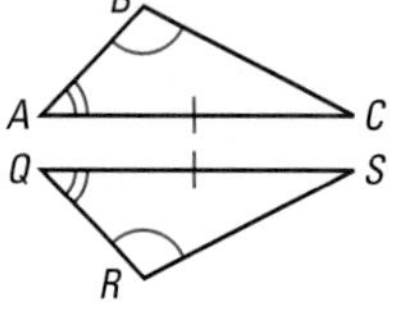

4. $\triangle XYZ$, $\triangle JKL$ **no**

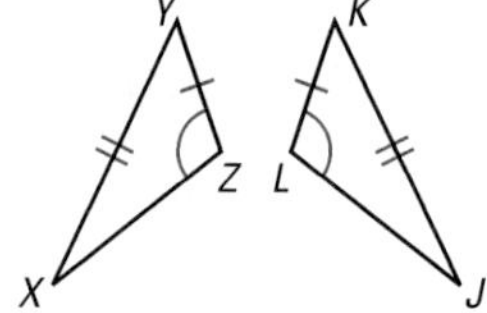

5. $\triangle PQR$, $\triangle RSP$ **yes; ASA**

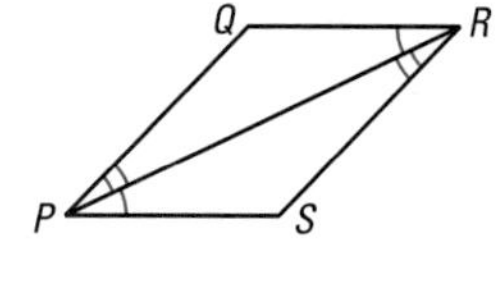

6. **ERROR ANALYSIS** *Describe* the error in concluding that $\triangle ABC \cong \triangle XYZ$. **There is no AAA postulate or theorem.**

By AAA,
$\triangle ABC \cong \triangle XYZ$.

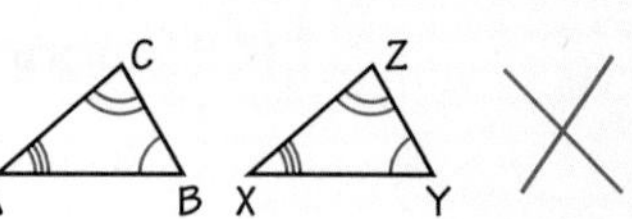

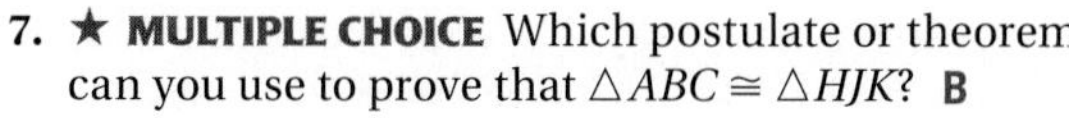

7. ★ **MULTIPLE CHOICE** Which postulate or theorem can you use to prove that $\triangle ABC \cong \triangle HJK$? **B**

Ⓐ HL　　Ⓑ AAS

Ⓒ SAS　　Ⓓ Not enough information

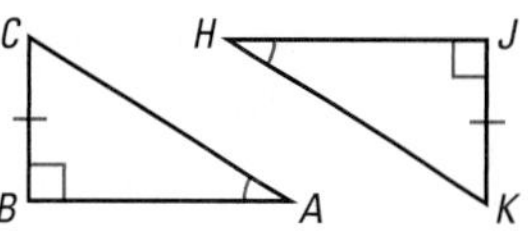

EXAMPLE 2 on p. 250 for Exs. 8–13

DEVELOPING PROOF **State the third congruence that is needed to prove that $\triangle FGH \cong \triangle LMN$ using the given postulate or theorem.**

8. **GIVEN ▶** $\overline{GH} \cong \overline{MN}$, $\angle G \cong \angle M$, _?_ $\cong$ _?_
Use the AAS Congruence Theorem. **$\angle F$, $\angle L$**

9. **GIVEN ▶** $\overline{FG} \cong \overline{LM}$, $\angle G \cong \angle M$, _?_ $\cong$ _?_
Use the ASA Congruence Postulate. **$\angle F$, $\angle L$**

10. **GIVEN ▶** $\overline{FH} \cong \overline{LN}$, $\angle H \cong \angle N$, _?_ $\cong$ _?_
Use the SAS Congruence Postulate. **$\overline{HG}$, $\overline{NM}$**

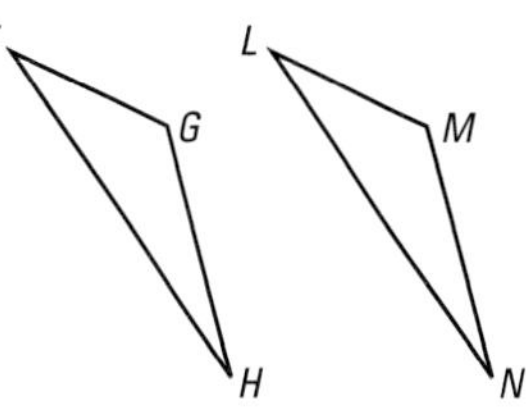

OVERLAPPING TRIANGLES ***Explain*** **how you can prove that the indicated triangles are congruent using the given postulate or theorem.** **11, 12. See margin**

11. $\triangle AFE \cong \triangle DFB$ by SAS
12. $\triangle AED \cong \triangle BDE$ by AAS
13. $\triangle AED \cong \triangle BDC$ by ASA
$\angle EDA \cong \angle DCB$ by the Corresponding Angles Postulate.

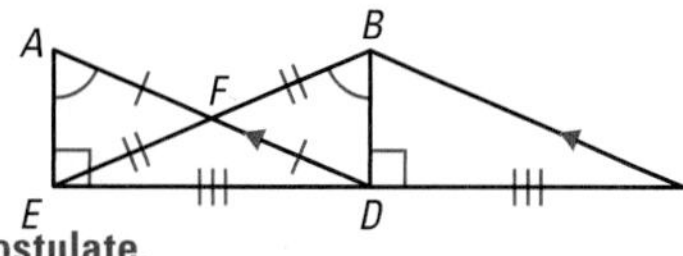

11. **$\angle AFE \cong \angle DFB$ by the Vertical Angles Theorem.**

12. $\overline{ED} \cong \overline{ED}$ by the Reflexive Property of Segment Congruence.

B

DETERMINING CONGRUENCE **Tell whether you can use the given information to determine whether $\triangle ABC \cong \triangle DEF$.** ***Explain*** **your reasoning.**

14. $\angle A \cong \angle D$, $\overline{AB} \cong \overline{DE}$, $\overline{AC} \cong \overline{DF}$ **yes; SAS**

15. $\angle A \cong \angle D$, $\angle B \cong \angle E$, $\angle C \cong \angle F$

16. $\angle B \cong \angle E$, $\angle C \cong \angle F$, $\overline{AC} \cong \overline{DE}$
No; $\overline{AC}$ and $\overline{DE}$ are not corresponding sides.

17. $\overline{AB} \cong \overline{EF}$, $\overline{BC} \cong \overline{FD}$, $\overline{AC} \cong \overline{DE}$

15. No; there is no AAA postulate or theorem.

17. No; the segments that are congruent are not corresponding sides.

IDENTIFY CONGRUENT TRIANGLES **Is it possible to prove that the triangles are congruent? If so, state the postulate(s) or theorem(s) you would use.**

18. $\triangle ABC$, $\triangle DEC$ **no**

19. $\triangle TUV$, $\triangle TWV$ **yes; the SAS Congruence Postulate**

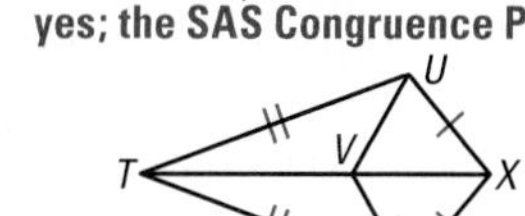

20. $\triangle QML$, $\triangle LPN$ **no**

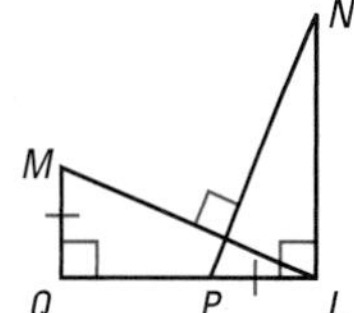

21. ★ **EXTENDED RESPONSE** Use the graph at the right. **a–c. See margin.**
   a. Show that $\angle CAD \cong \angle ACB$. *Explain* your reasoning.
   b. Show that $\angle ACD \cong \angle CAB$. *Explain* your reasoning.
   c. Show that $\triangle ABC \cong \triangle CDA$. *Explain* your reasoning.

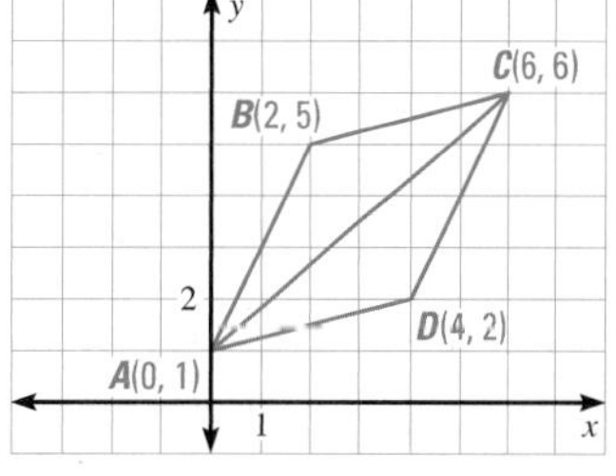

C

22. **CHALLENGE** Use a coordinate plane.
   a. Graph the lines $y = 2x + 5$, $y = 2x - 3$, and $x = 0$ in the same coordinate plane. **See margin.**
   b. Consider the equation $y = mx + 1$. For what values of m will the graph of the equation form two triangles if added to your graph? For what values of m will those triangles be congruent? *Explain.*

22b. Any real value except 2; $-\frac{1}{2}$ or 0; the resulting triangles are right triangles with one pair of acute angles forming a linear pair and both hypotenuses 4 units long, so they are congruent by AAS.

4 PRACTICE AND APPLY

Assignment Guide

Answer Transparencies available for all exercises

Basic:
Day 1: pp. 252–255
Exs. 1–13
Day 2: pp. 252–255
Exs. 14–17, 23–30, 36–43

Average:
Day 1: pp. 252–255
Exs. 1, 2, 4–7, 9–13, 18–20
Day 2: pp. 252–255
Exs. 14–17, 21, 23–34, 36–42 even

Advanced:
Day 1: pp. 252–255
Exs. 1, 2, 5–7, 9–13, 18–20, 22*
Day 2: pp. 252–255
Exs. 14–17, 23–35*, 37–43 odd

Block:
pp. 252–255
Exs. 1, 2, 4–7, 9–21, 23–34, 36–42 even

Differentiated Instruction

See *Geometry Best Practices Toolkit* for suggestions on addressing the needs of a diverse classroom.

Homework Check

For a quick check of student understanding of key concepts, go over the following exercises:

Basic: 3, 8, 14, 25, 26
Average: 4, 10, 15, 25, 26
Advanced: 5, 12, 16, 25, 26

Extra Practice

- Student Edition, p. 903
- Chapter 4 Resource Book: Practice levels A, B, C, pp. 63–68

Practice Worksheet

An easily-readable reduced practice page (with answers) for this lesson can be found on p. 214C.

21a. $\overline{BC}$ and $\overline{AD}$ are parallel, because their slopes are equal, with $\overline{AC}$ being a transversal. The Alternate Interior Angles Theorem applies.

21b. $\overline{AB}$ and $\overline{CD}$ are parallel, because their slopes are equal, with $\overline{AC}$ being a transversal. The Alternate Interior Angles Theorem applies.

21c. Using parts 21a, 21b, and the fact that $\overline{AC} \cong \overline{CA}$, they are congruent by ASA.

22a.

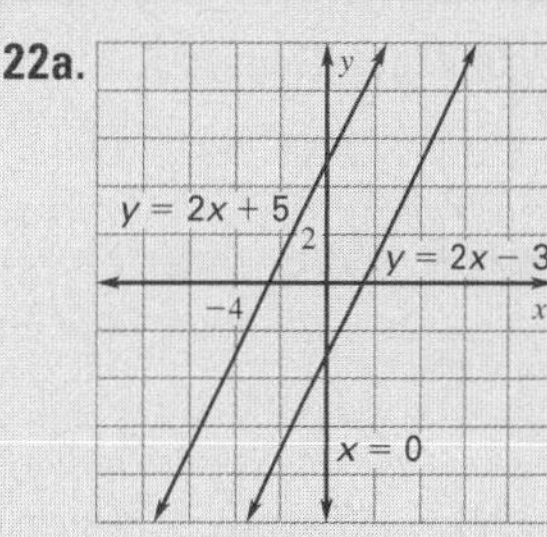

Avoiding Common Errors

Exercise 7 Some students may think that they must find some way to use the HL Congruence Theorem, since the triangles are right triangles. Point out that that the problem gives two pairs of congruent angles but only one pair of congruent sides. This suggests that it might be necessary to use the ASA Congruence Postulate or the AAS Congruence Theorem.

Study Strategy

Exercise 19 Students may notice that there is more than one way to conclude that $\triangle TUV \cong \triangle TWV$. Students may want to write a brief explanation of why they chose a particular postulate or theorem.

Mathematical Reasoning

Exercise 25 Ask students how else the triangles could be proved congruent.

Internet Reference

Exercise 26 For more information about orienteering, visit the International Orienteering Federation's site at www.orienteering.org and click on the "Orienteering" link.

26.

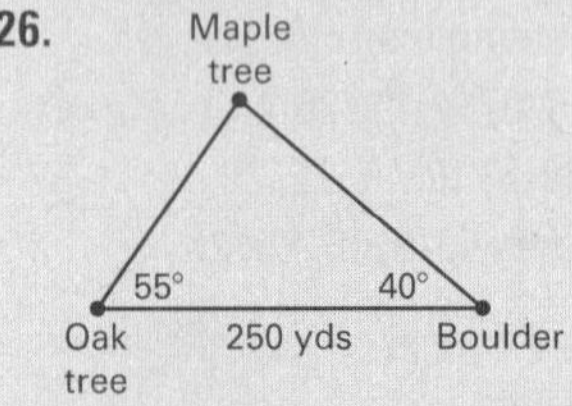

Yes. *Sample answer:* The triangle formed with these measures is unique and the third vertex gives the location of the maple tree.

PROBLEM SOLVING

23. Two pairs of angles and an included pair of sides are congruent. The triangles are congruent by ASA.

A **CONGRUENCE IN BICYCLES** *Explain* why the triangles are congruent. **23, 24. See margin.**

23. 24.

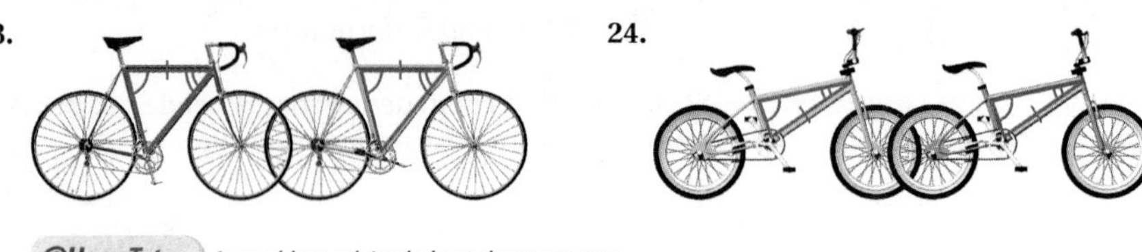

@HomeTutor for problem solving help at classzone.com

EXAMPLE 3 on p. 251 for Ex. 25

24. Two pairs of angles and a nonincluded pair of sides are congruent. The triangles are congruent by AAS.

25. **FLOW PROOF** Copy and complete the flow proof.

GIVEN ▶ $\overline{AD} \parallel \overline{CE}$, $\overline{BD} \cong \overline{BC}$

PROVE ▶ $\triangle ABD \cong \triangle EBC$

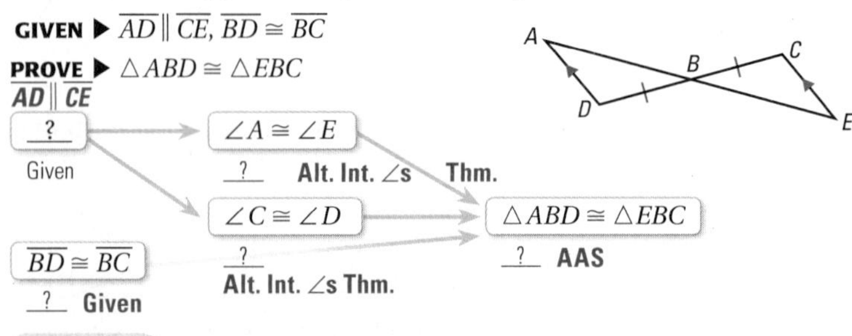

@HomeTutor for problem solving help at classzone.com

EXAMPLE 4 on p. 251 for Ex. 26

26. ★ **SHORT RESPONSE** You are making a map for an orienteering race. Participants start at a large oak tree, find a boulder 250 yards due east of the oak tree, and then find a maple tree that is 50° west of north of the boulder and 35° east of north of the oak tree. Sketch a map. Can you locate the maple tree? *Explain.* **See margin.**

27. **AIRPLANE** In the airplane at the right, $\angle C$ and $\angle F$ are right angles, $\overline{BC} \cong \overline{EF}$, and $\angle A \cong \angle D$. What postulate or theorem allows you to conclude that $\triangle ABC \cong \triangle DEF$? **AAS**

28. Since all right angles are congruent and the right angles are the included angles of the congruent legs in the triangles, the triangles are congruent by SAS.

29. Since all right angles are congruent, the two triangles are congruent by either AAS, if the side is not included, or ASA, if it is the included side.

B **RIGHT TRIANGLES** **In Lesson 4.4, you learned the Hypotenuse-Leg Theorem for right triangles. In Exercises 28–30, write a paragraph proof for these other theorems about right triangles.**

28. **Leg-Leg (LL) Theorem** If the legs of two right triangles are congruent, then the triangles are congruent.

29. **Angle-Leg (AL) Theorem** If an angle and a leg of a right triangle are congruent to an angle and a leg of a second right triangle, then the triangles are congruent.

30. **Hypotenuse-Angle (HA) Theorem** If an angle and the hypotenuse of a right triangle are congruent to an angle and the hypotenuse of a second right triangle, then the triangles are congruent. **Since all right angles are congruent, the two triangles are congruent by AAS.**

○ = WORKED-OUT SOLUTIONS on p. WS1 ★ = STANDARDIZED TEST PRACTICE

31. Statements (Reasons)

1. $\overline{AK} \cong \overline{CJ}$, $\angle BJK \cong \angle BKJ$, $\angle A \cong \angle C$ (Given)

2. $\triangle ABK \cong \triangle CBJ$ (ASA)

32.

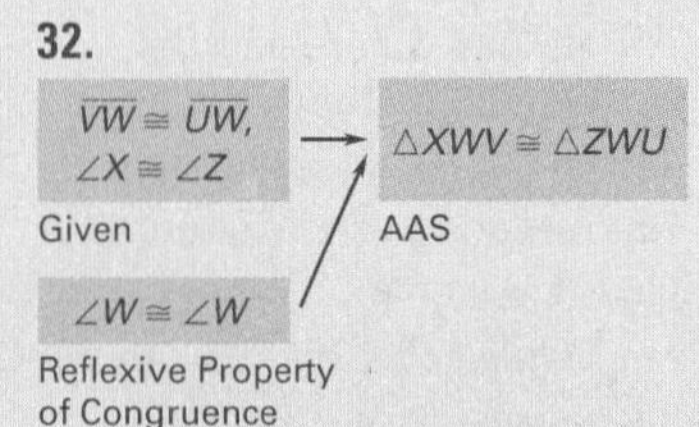

33.

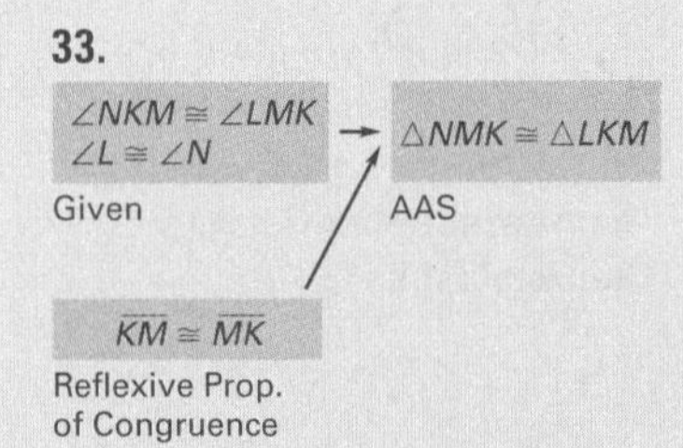

31. PROOF Write a two-column proof.

GIVEN ▶ $\overline{AK} \cong \overline{CJ}$, $\angle BJK \cong \angle BKJ$, $\angle A \cong \angle C$

PROVE ▶ $\triangle ABK \cong \triangle CBJ$

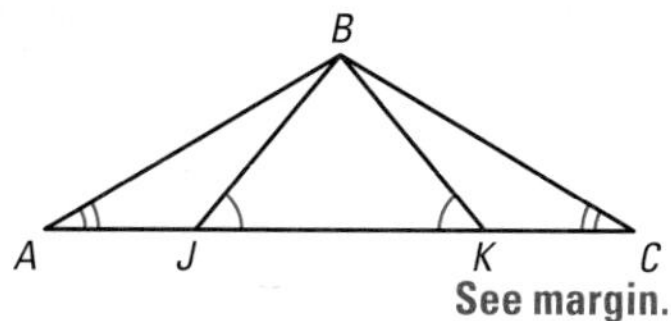

See margin.

32. PROOF Write a flow proof.

GIVEN ▶ $\overline{VW} \cong \overline{UW}$, $\angle X \cong \angle Z$

PROVE ▶ $\triangle XWV \cong \triangle ZWU$

See margin.

33. PROOF Write a proof.

GIVEN ▶ $\angle NKM \cong \angle LMK$, $\angle L \cong \angle N$

PROVE ▶ $\triangle NMK \cong \triangle LKM$ **See margin.**

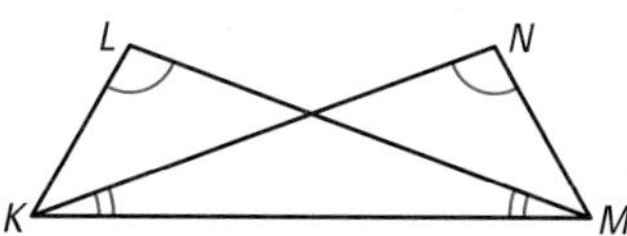

34. PROOF Write a proof.

GIVEN ▶ X is the midpoint of $\overline{VY}$ and $\overline{WZ}$.

PROVE ▶ $\triangle VWX \cong \triangle YZX$ **See margin.**

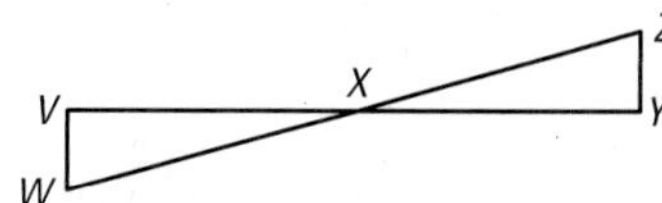

C **35. CHALLENGE** Write a proof.

GIVEN ▶ $\triangle ABF \cong \triangle DFB$, F is the midpoint of $\overline{AE}$, B is the midpoint of $\overline{AC}$.

PROVE ▶ $\triangle FDE \cong \triangle BCD \cong \triangle ABF$ **See margin.**

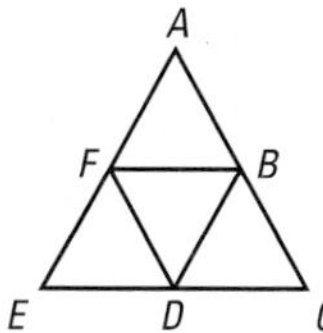

MIXED REVIEW

Find the value of x that makes $m \parallel n$. *(p. 161)*

36.

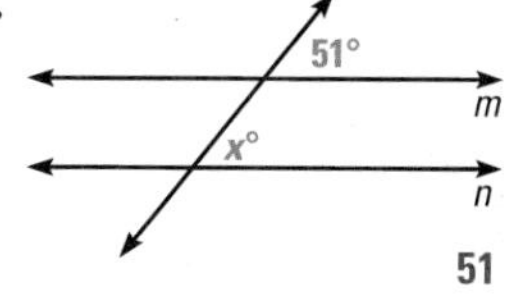

51

37.

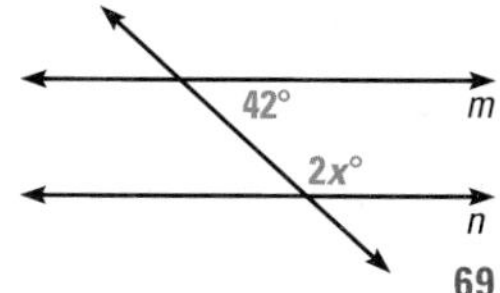

69

38.

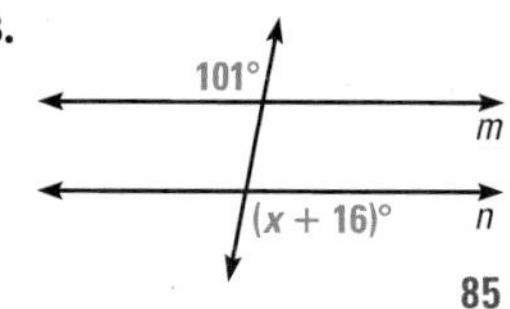

85

Write an equation of the line that passes through point P and is parallel to the line with the given equation. *(p. 180)*

39. $P(0, 3)$, $y = x - 8$ $\mathbf{y = x + 3}$

40. $P(-2, 4)$, $y = -2x + 3$ $\mathbf{y = -2x}$

PREVIEW
Prepare for Lesson 4.6 in Exs. 41–43.

Decide which method, SSS, SAS, or HL, can be used to prove that the triangles are congruent. *(pp. 234, 240)*

41. $\triangle HJK \cong \triangle LKJ$ **SSS**

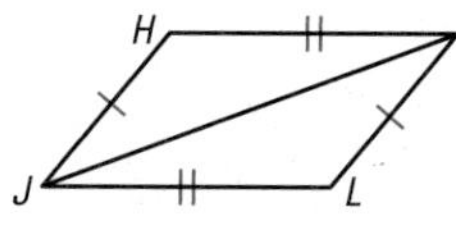

42. $\triangle UTV \cong \triangle WVT$ **HL**

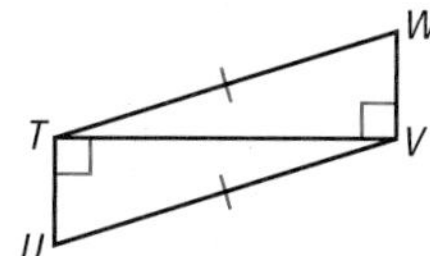

43. $\triangle XYZ \cong \triangle RQZ$ **SAS**

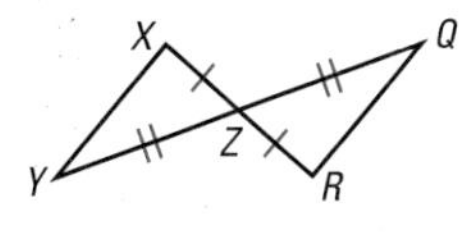

5 ASSESS AND RETEACH

Daily Homework Quiz

Transparency Available

Tell whether each pair of triangles is congruent by SAS, ASA, SSS, AAS, or HL. If it is not possible to prove the triangles congruent, write *not necessarily congruent.*

1. 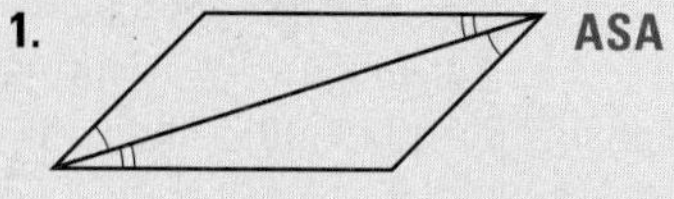 **ASA**

2. 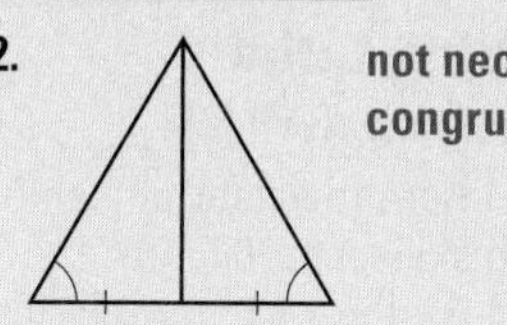 **not necessarily congruent**

3. Write a flow proof.
Given: $\overline{BD}$ bisects $\angle ABC$, $\angle A \cong \angle C$
Prove: $\triangle ABD \cong \triangle CBD$

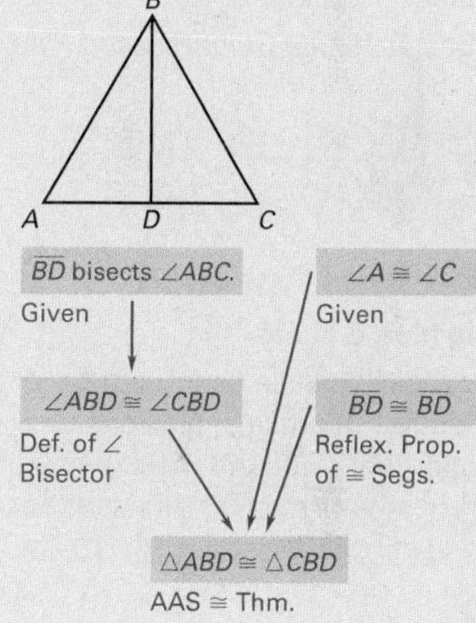

Online Quiz

Available at **classzone.com**

Diagnosis/Remediation

- Practice A, B, C in Chapter 4 Resource Book, pp. 63–68
- Study Guide in Chapter 4 Resource Book, pp. 69–70
- Practice Workbook, pp. 73–75
- @HomeTutor

Challenge

Additional challenge is available in the Chapter 4 Resource Book, p. 73.

34, 35. See Additional Answers beginning on p. AA1.

1 PLAN AND PREPARE

Warm-Up Exercises

Transparency Available

Suppose that $\triangle XYZ \cong \triangle RST$. Complete each statement.

1. $\overline{XY} \cong$? $\overline{RS}$
2. $\angle Z \cong$? $\angle T$
3. $m\angle S = m\angle$? Y
4. If $\angle A \cong \angle B$, $m\angle A = (2x + 40)°$, and $m\angle B = (3x - 10)°$, find x. **50**

Notetaking Guide

Transparency Available

Promotes interactive learning and notetaking skills, pp. 104–107.

Pacing

Basic: 2 days

Average: 2 days

Advanced: 2 days

Block: 1 block

- See *Teaching Guide/Lesson Plan.*

2 FOCUS AND MOTIVATE

Essential Question

Big Idea 2, p. 215

How can you use congruent triangles to prove angles or sides congruent? **Tell students they will learn how to answer this question by using corresponding parts of congruent triangles.**

4.6 Use Congruent Triangles

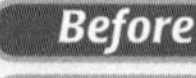

Before You used corresponding parts to prove triangles congruent.

Now You will use congruent triangles to prove corresponding parts congruent.

Why? So you can find the distance across a half pipe, as in Ex. 30.

Key Vocabulary
- **corresponding parts,** *p. 225*

Standards

5.0 Students prove that triangles are congruent or similar, **and they are able to use the concept of corresponding parts of congruent triangles.**

16.0 Students perform basic constructions with a straightedge and compass, such as angle bisectors, perpendicular bisectors, and the line parallel to a given line through a point off the line.

By definition, congruent triangles have congruent corresponding parts. So, if you can prove that two triangles are congruent, you know that their corresponding parts must be congruent as well.

EXAMPLE 1 Use congruent triangles

Explain how you can use the given information to prove that the hanglider parts are congruent.

GIVEN ▶ $\angle 1 \cong \angle 2$, $\angle RTQ \cong \angle RTS$

PROVE ▶ $\overline{QT} \cong \overline{ST}$

Solution

If you can show that $\triangle QRT \cong \triangle SRT$, you will know that $\overline{QT} \cong \overline{ST}$. First, copy the diagram and mark the given information. Then add the information that you can deduce. In this case, $\angle RQT$ and $\angle RST$ are supplementary to congruent angles, so $\angle RQT \cong \angle RST$. Also, $\overline{RT} \cong \overline{RT}$.

Mark given information.

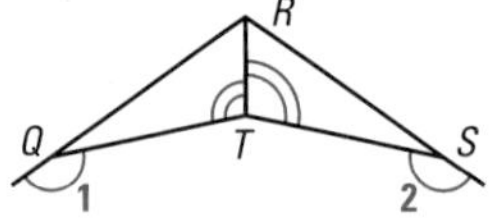

Add deduced information.

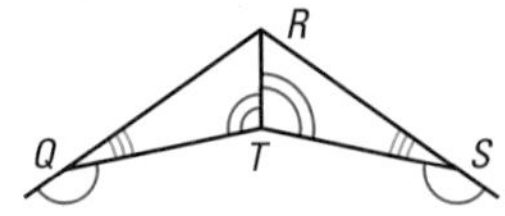

Two angle pairs and a non-included side are congruent, so by the AAS Congruence Theorem, $\triangle QRT \cong \triangle SRT$. Because corresponding parts of congruent triangles are congruent, $\overline{QT} \cong \overline{ST}$.

Animated Geometry at classzone.com

GUIDED PRACTICE for Example 1

1. *Explain* how you can prove that $\angle A \cong \angle C$.
Since $\overline{BD} \cong \overline{BD}$ by the Reflexive Property, the triangles are congruent by SSS. So, $\angle A \cong \angle C$ because they are corresponding parts of congruent triangles

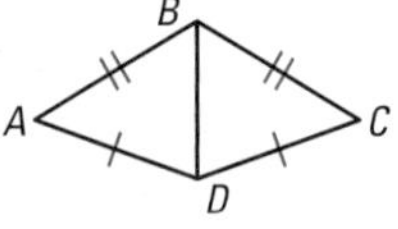

Resource Planning Guide

Chapter Resource Book
- Teaching Guide/Lesson Plan (pp. 74–75)
- Practice levels A, B, C (pp. 76–81)
- Study Guide (pp. 82–83)
- Catch-up for Absent Students (p. 84)
- Application (p. 85)
- Challenge (p. 86)

Workbooks
- Notetaking Guide (pp. 104–107)
- Practice Workbook (pp. 76–78)

Teaching Options
- **Power Presentations CD-ROM** provides dynamic electronic teaching resources for the classroom.
- **Activity Generator CD-ROM** provides editable activities for all ability levels.

Interactive Technology
- Easy Planner
- Power Presentations CD-ROM
- Activity Generator CD-ROM
- Animated Geometry
- Test Generator CD-ROM
- Online Quiz
- eWorkbook
- eEdition
- @HomeTutor

Resources for English Learners
- Quick Reference for English Learners
- Spanish Study Guide
- Multi-Language Visual Glossary
- Student Resources in Spanish

See also the *Geometry Toolkit* for more strategies for meeting individual needs.

EXAMPLE 2 Use congruent triangles for measurement

INDIRECT MEASUREMENT
When you cannot easily measure a length directly, you can make conclusions about the length *indirectly*, usually by calculations based on known lengths.

SURVEYING Use the following method to find the distance across a river, from point N to point P.

- Place a stake at K on the near side so that $\overline{NK} \perp \overline{NP}$.
- Find M, the midpoint of $\overline{NK}$.
- Locate the point L so that $\overline{NK} \perp \overline{KL}$ and L, P, and M are collinear.
- Explain how this plan allows you to find the distance.

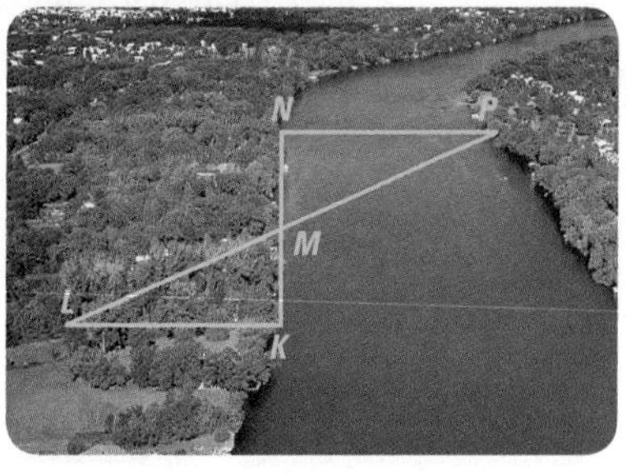

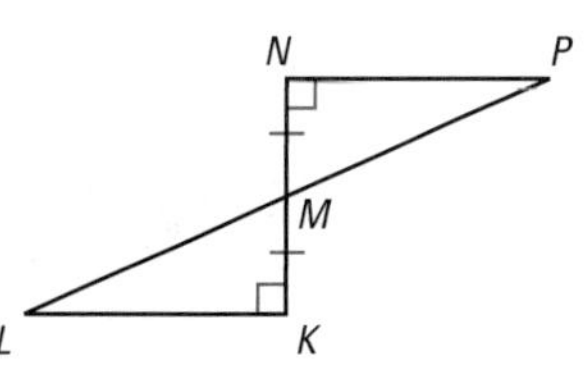

Solution

Because $\overline{NK} \perp \overline{NP}$ and $\overline{NK} \perp \overline{KL}$, $\angle N$ and $\angle K$ are congruent right angles. Because M is the midpoint of $\overline{NK}$, $\overline{NM} \cong \overline{KM}$. The vertical angles $\angle KML$ and $\angle NMP$ are congruent. So, $\triangle MLK \cong \triangle MPN$ by the ASA Congruence Postulate. Then, because corresponding parts of congruent triangles are congruent, $\overline{KL} \cong \overline{NP}$. So, you can find the distance NP across the river by measuring $\overline{KL}$.

EXAMPLE 3 Plan a proof involving pairs of triangles

Use the given information to write a plan for proof.

GIVEN ▶ $\angle 1 \cong \angle 2$, $\angle 3 \cong \angle 4$

PROVE ▶ $\triangle BCE \cong \triangle DCE$

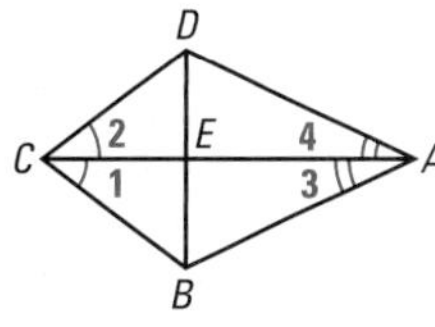

Solution

In $\triangle BCE$ and $\triangle DCE$, you know $\angle 1 \cong \angle 2$ and $\overline{CE} \cong \overline{CE}$. If you can show that $\overline{CB} \cong \overline{CD}$, you can use the SAS Congruence Postulate.

To prove that $\overline{CB} \cong \overline{CD}$, you can first prove that $\triangle CBA \cong \triangle CDA$. You are given $\angle 1 \cong \angle 2$ and $\angle 3 \cong \angle 4$. $\overline{CA} \cong \overline{CA}$ by the Reflexive Property. You can use the ASA Congruence Postulate to prove that $\triangle CBA \cong \triangle CDA$.

▶ **Plan for Proof** Use the ASA Congruence Postulate to prove that $\triangle CBA \cong \triangle CDA$. Then state that $\overline{CB} \cong \overline{CD}$. Use the SAS Congruence Postulate to prove that $\triangle BCE \cong \triangle DCE$.

Animated Geometry at classzone.com

✓ **GUIDED PRACTICE** for Examples 2 and 3

2. In Example 2, does it matter how far from point N you place a stake at point K? *Explain.* **See margin.**
3. Using the information in the diagram at the right, write a plan to prove that $\triangle PTU \cong \triangle UQP$. **See margin.**

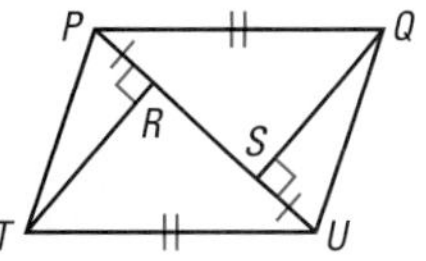

2. No; since M is the midpoint of $\overline{NK}$, $\overline{NM} \cong \overline{MK}$. No matter how far apart the stakes at K and M are placed, the triangles will be congruent by ASA.

3. Since you already know that $\overline{TU} \cong \overline{QP}$ and $\overline{UP} \cong \overline{PU}$ you need only show $\overline{PT} \cong \overline{UQ}$ to prove the triangles are congruent by SSS. This can be done by showing right triangles QSP and TRU are congruent by HL leading to right triangles USQ and PRT being congruent by HL which gives you $\overline{PT} \cong \overline{UQ}$.

Motivating the Lesson

Tell students that congruent triangles can be used to find distances that are difficult to measure directly. Tell them that in this lesson they will see some examples of how to do this.

3 TEACH

Extra Example 1

Use the given information to prove the parts of the kite are congruent.
Given: $\overline{GK}$ bisects $\angle FGH$ and $\angle FKH$.
Prove: $\overline{FK} \cong \overline{HK}$

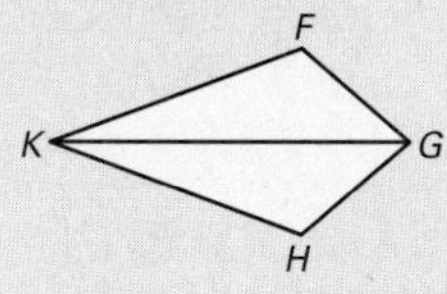

$\angle FGK \cong \angle HGK$ and $\angle FKG \cong \angle HKG$ by the def. of $\angle$ bisector. $\overline{GK} \cong \overline{GK}$ by the Refl. Prop. of $\cong$ Segs. Therefore $\triangle FGK \cong \triangle HGK$ by the ASA Cong. Post. So $\overline{FK} \cong \overline{HK}$ since Corr. Parts of $\cong$ $\triangle$s are $\cong$.

An **Animated Geometry** activity is available on-line for **Example 1**. This activity is also available on the **Power Presentations CD-ROM**.

Extra Example 2

If P is the midpoint of $\overline{MS}$, how wide is the bull's pasture? **40 ft**

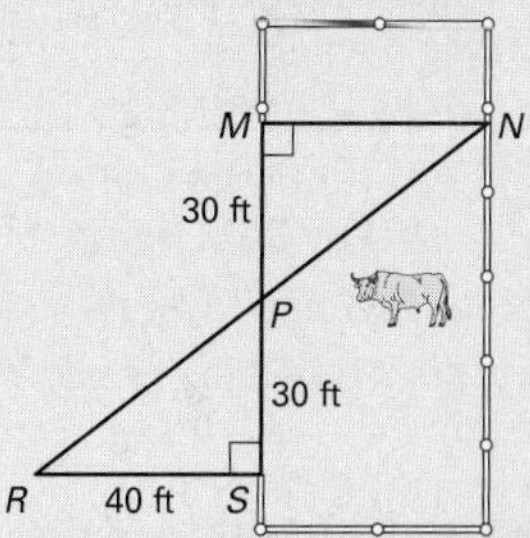

Differentiated Instruction

Kinesthetic Learners Take students outside to construct and solve a problem similar to **Example 2**. Find a distance that may be difficult to measure directly with a measuring tape and use congruent triangles to find the distance. Direct students to draw a diagram of the problem, make measurements, write distance measurements on the diagram, and use these measurements and the appropriate postulate to find the distance. See also the *Geometry Toolkit* for more strategies.

Extra Example 3

Write a plan for a proof.

Given: $\angle 1 \cong \angle 2$, $\angle 3 \cong \angle 4$

Prove: $\triangle MNR \cong \triangle QPR$

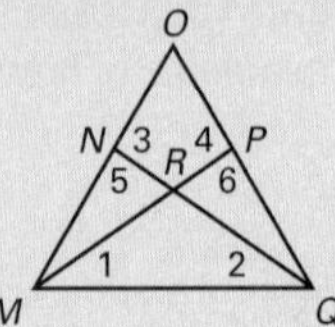

By the Cong. Supplements Thm. $\angle 5 \cong \angle 6$. By the Refl. Prop. of $\cong$ Segs. $\overline{MQ} \cong \overline{MQ}$. By the AAS Cong. Thm. $\triangle MNQ \cong \triangle QPM$. Since corr. parts of $\cong$ △ are $\cong$, $\overline{MN} \cong \overline{PQ}$. By the Vert. △ Thm. $\angle MRN \cong \angle QRP$. By the AAS Cong. Thm. $\triangle MNR \cong \triangle QPR$.

An **Animated Geometry** activity is available on-line for **Example 3**. This activity is also available on the **Power Presentations CD-ROM**.

Extra Example 4

Prove that the construction for bisecting a segment is valid.

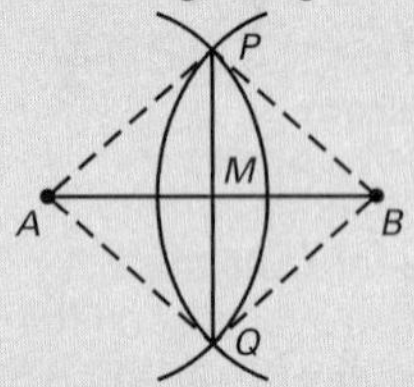

Since the compass setting is the same, $\overline{AP} \cong \overline{BP}$ and $\overline{AQ} \cong \overline{BQ}$. By the Refl. Prop. of $\cong$, $\overline{PQ} \cong \overline{PQ}$. So $\triangle APQ \cong \triangle BPQ$ by SSS. Corresponding parts of $\cong$ △ are $\cong$, so $\angle APM \cong \angle BPM$. Since $\overline{PM} \cong \overline{PM}$ (Refl. Prop. of $\cong$), $\triangle APM \cong \triangle BPM$ by SAS. Hence the corr. sides $\overline{AM}$ and $\overline{BM}$ are $\cong$ and $\overline{PQ}$ bisects $\overline{AB}$ by the def. of bisector.

Closing the Lesson

Have students summarize the major points of the lesson and answer the Essential Question: How can you use congruent triangles to prove angles or sides congruent?

- **If triangles are congruent, their corresponding parts are congruent.**

Use the fact that Corr. Parts of $\cong$ △ are $\cong$.

PROVING CONSTRUCTIONS On page 34, you learned how to use a compass and a straightedge to copy an angle. The construction is shown below. You can use congruent triangles to prove that this construction is valid.

STEP 1

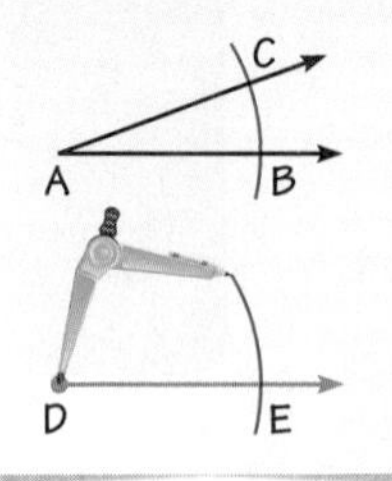

To copy $\angle A$, draw a segment with initial point *D*. Draw an arc with center *A*. Using the same radius, draw an arc with center *D*. Label points *B*, *C*, and *E*.

STEP 2

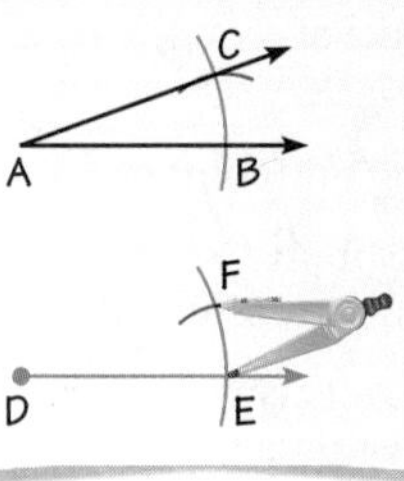

Draw an arc with radius *BC* and center *E*. Label the intersection *F*.

STEP 3

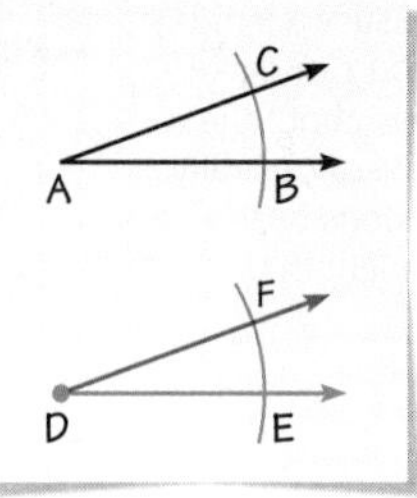

Draw $\overrightarrow{DF}$. In Example 4, you will prove that $\angle D \cong \angle A$.

EXAMPLE 4 Prove a construction

Write a proof to verify that the construction for copying an angle is valid.

Solution

Add $\overline{BC}$ and $\overline{EF}$ to the diagram. In the construction, $\overline{AB}$, $\overline{DE}$, $\overline{AC}$, and $\overline{DF}$ are all determined by the same compass setting, as are $\overline{BC}$ and $\overline{EF}$. So, you can assume the following as given statements.

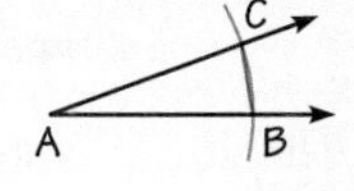

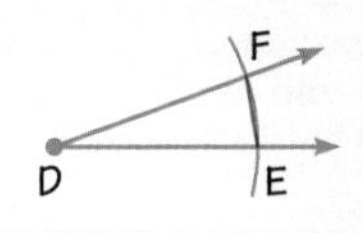

GIVEN ▶ $\overline{AB} \cong \overline{DE}$, $\overline{AC} \cong \overline{DF}$, $\overline{BC} \cong \overline{EF}$

PROVE ▶ $\angle D \cong \angle A$

Plan for Proof Show that $\triangle CAB \cong \triangle FDE$, so you can conclude that the corresponding parts $\angle A$ and $\angle D$ are congruent.

Plan in Action

STATEMENTS	REASONS
1. $\overline{AB} \cong \overline{DE}$, $\overline{AC} \cong \overline{DF}$, $\overline{BC} \cong \overline{EF}$	1. Given
2. $\triangle FDE \cong \triangle CAB$	2. SSS Congruence Postulate
3. $\angle D \cong \angle A$	3. Corresp. parts of $\cong$ △ are $\cong$.

✓ GUIDED PRACTICE for Example 4

4. Look back at the construction of an angle bisector in Explore 4 on page 34. What segments can you assume are congruent? **$\overline{AC}$ and $\overline{AB}$**

4.6 EXERCISES

HOMEWORK KEY
○ = **WORKED-OUT SOLUTIONS** on p. WS5 for Exs. 19, 23, and 31
★ = **STANDARDIZED TEST PRACTICE** Exs. 2, 14, 31, and 36

SKILL PRACTICE

A

1. **VOCABULARY** Copy and complete: Corresponding parts of congruent triangles are __?__. **congruent**

2. ★ **WRITING** *Explain* why you might choose to use congruent triangles to measure the distance across a river. Give another example where it may be easier to measure with congruent triangles rather than directly.
Sample answer: You are unable to cross the river; measuring the distance across a lake.

EXAMPLES 1 and 2 on p. 256–257 for Exs. 3–11

CONGRUENT TRIANGLES **Tell which triangles you can show are congruent in order to prove the statement. What postulate or theorem would you use?**

3. $\angle A \cong \angle D$
△ *CBA*, △ *CBD*; SSS

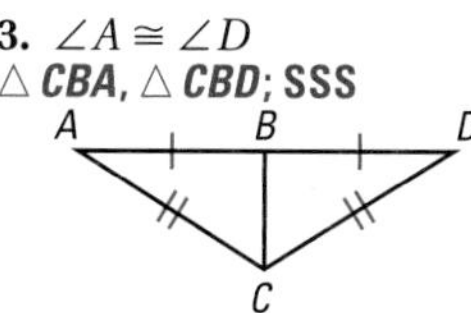

4. $\angle Q \cong \angle T$
△ *QPR*, △ *TPS*; SAS

5. $\overline{JM} \cong \overline{LM}$
△ *JKM*, △ *LKM*; HL

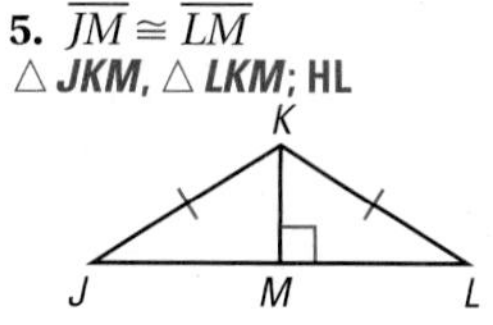

6. $\overline{AC} \cong \overline{BD}$
△ *CAD*, △ *BDA*; AAS

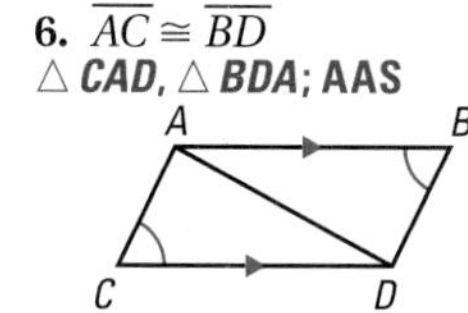

7. $\overline{GK} \cong \overline{HJ}$
△ *JNH*, △ *KLG*; AAS

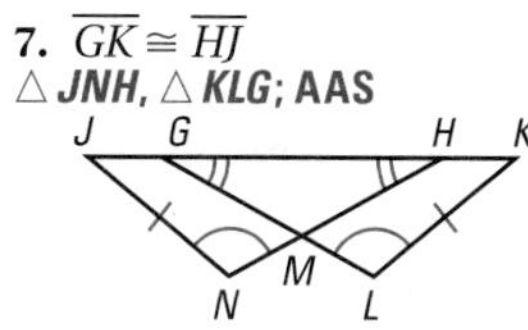

8. $\overline{QW} \cong \overline{TV}$
△ *VRT*, △ *QVW*; AAS

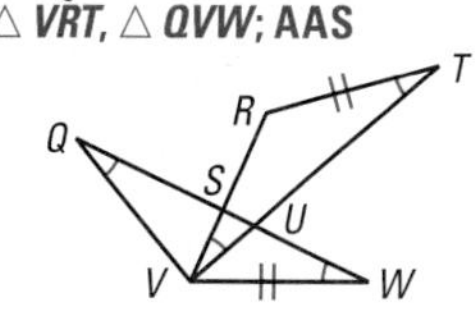

9. **ERROR ANALYSIS** *Describe* the error in the statement. **The angle is not the included angle; the triangles cannot be said to be congruent.**

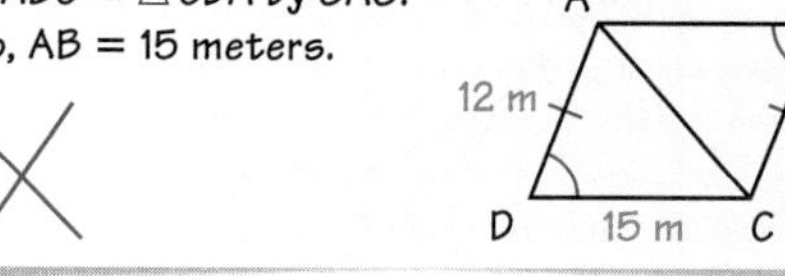

PLANNING FOR PROOF **Use the diagram to write a plan for proof.**

10. **PROVE ▶** $\angle S \cong \angle U$

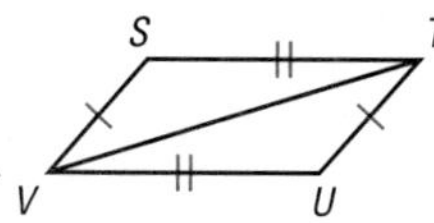

11. **PROVE ▶** $\overline{LM} \cong \overline{LQ}$

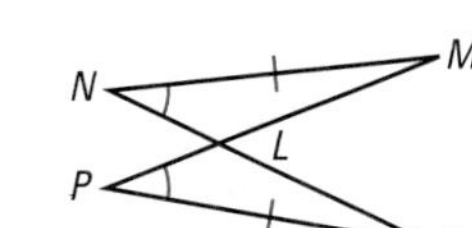

10. Show △ *VST* ≅ △ *TUV* by SSS since $\overline{VT} \cong \overline{TV}$ by the Reflexive Property of Congruence. Then ∠*S* ≅ ∠*U* because corresponding parts of congruent triangles are congruent.

11. Show △ *NML* ≅ △ *PQL* by AAS since ∠*NLM* ≅ ∠*PLQ* by the Vertical Angles Congruence Theorem. Then $\overline{LM} \cong \overline{LQ}$ because corresponding parts of congruent triangles are congruent.

B

12. **PENTAGONS** *Explain* why segments connecting any pair of corresponding vertices of congruent pentagons are congruent. Make a sketch to support your answer. **Corresponding diagonals are corresponding sides of two congruent triangles; see margin for art.**

13. **ALGEBRA** Given that $\triangle ABC \cong \triangle DEF$, $m\angle A = 70°$, $m\angle B = 60°$, $m\angle C = 50°$, $m\angle D = (3x + 10)°$, $m\angle E = \left(\frac{y}{3} + 20\right)°$, and $m\angle F = (z^2 + 14)°$, find the values of x, y, and z. **20, 120, ±6**

4 PRACTICE AND APPLY

Assignment Guide

Answer Transparencies available for all exercises

Basic:
Day 1: pp. 259–263
Exs. 1–11, 28
Day 2: pp. 259–263
Exs. 12–17, 29–33, 41–46

Average:
Day 1: pp. 259–263
Exs. 1–11, 28, 41–43
Day 2: pp. 259–263
Exs. 12–14, 18–24, 29–36, 44–46

Advanced:
Day 1: pp. 259–263
Exs. 1, 2, 4–11, 27*, 28, 41–43
Day 2: pp. 259–263
Exs. 12–14, 19–26, 31–40*, 44–46

Block:
pp. 259–263
Exs. 1–14, 18–24, 28–36, 41–46

Differentiated Instruction

See *Geometry Best Practices Toolkit* for suggestions on addressing the needs of a diverse classroom.

Homework Check

For a quick check of student understanding of key concepts, go over the following exercises:
Basic: 4, 10, 16, 28, 32
Average: 6, 10, 18, 28, 32
Advanced: 8, 11, 20, 28, 32

Extra Practice

- Student Edition, p. 903
- Chapter 4 Resource Book: Practice levels A, B, C, pp. 76–81

Practice Worksheet

An easily-readable reduced practice page (with answers) for this lesson can be found on p. 214C.

12. *Sample:*

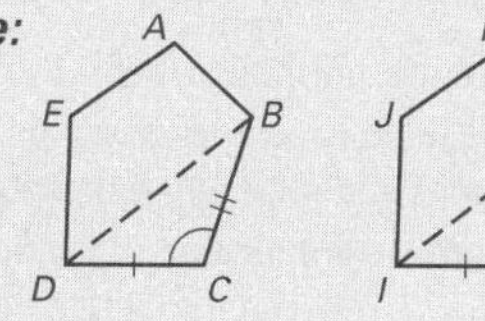

Avoiding Common Errors

Exercise 6 Students may say that $\triangle ACD \cong \triangle DBC$ because $\angle CAD \cong \angle BDA$ are congruent alternate interior angles. These angles are congruent, but point out that we do not know this until after we have proved that the triangles are congruent.

Study Strategy

Exercise 13 Tell students to draw and label a diagram before they try to write and solve the equations.

Reading Strategy

Exercise 15 Students should be careful reading the labels on the figure. $\angle 1$ is $\angle KFJ$ not the entire right angle. Likewise $\angle 2$ is $\angle HGJ$.

15. Show $\triangle KFG \cong \triangle HGF$ by AAS, which gives you $\overline{HG} \cong \overline{KF}$. This along with $\angle FJK \cong \angle GJH$ by vertical angles gives you $\triangle FJK \cong \triangle GJH$, therefore $\angle 1 \cong \angle 2$.

16. $\triangle AEB \cong \triangle DEC$ by AAS which makes $\angle ABE \cong \angle DCE$. Then by the Congruent Supplements Theorem, $\angle 1 \cong \angle 2$.

17. Show $\triangle STR \cong \triangle QTP$ by ASA using the givens and vertical angles STR and QTP. Since $\overline{PT} \cong \overline{RT}$ and using vertical angles PTS and RTQ, $\triangle PTS \cong \triangle RTQ$ by SAS, which gives you $\angle 1 \cong \angle 2$.

18. Show $\triangle ABC \cong \triangle CBE$ by ASA, which gives you $\overline{AE} \cong \overline{CE}$. Use the Angle Addition Postulate and congruent angles to show $\angle FAE \cong \angle DCE$. Then $\triangle AEF \cong \triangle CED$ by SAS, and $\angle 1 \cong \angle 2$.

19. Show $\triangle KNP \cong \triangle MNP$ by SSS. Now $\angle KPL \cong \angle MPL$ and $\overline{PL} \cong \overline{PL}$ leads to $\triangle LKP \cong \triangle LMP$ by SAS, which gives you $\angle 1 \cong \angle 2$.

14. ★ **MULTIPLE CHOICE** Which set of given information does *not* allow you to conclude that $\overline{AD} \cong \overline{CD}$? **B**

Ⓐ $\overline{AE} \cong \overline{CE}$, $m\angle BEA = 90°$

Ⓑ $\overline{BA} \cong \overline{BC}$, $\angle BDC \cong \angle BDA$

Ⓒ $\overline{AB} \cong \overline{CB}$, $\angle ABE \cong \angle CBE$

Ⓓ $\overline{AE} \cong \overline{CE}$, $\overline{AB} \cong \overline{CB}$

EXAMPLE 3 on p. 257 for Exs. 15–20

PLANNING FOR PROOF **Use the information given in the diagram to write a plan for proving that $\angle 1 \cong \angle 2$.** **15–20. See margin.**

15. 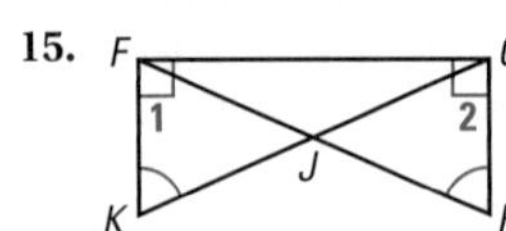

16. 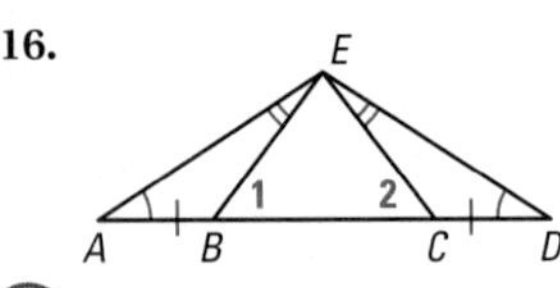

17. 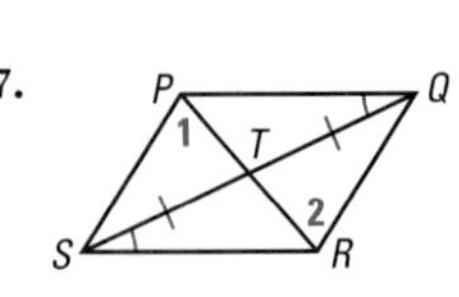

18. 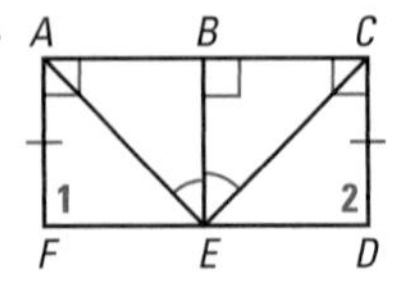

19. 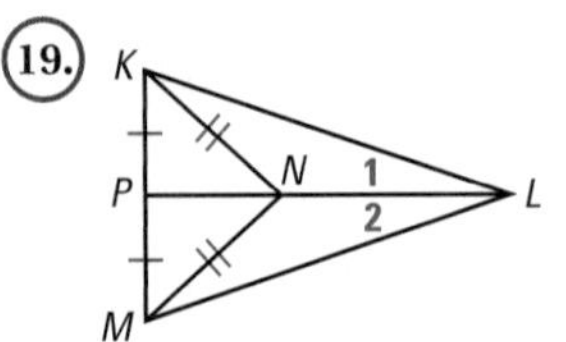

20. 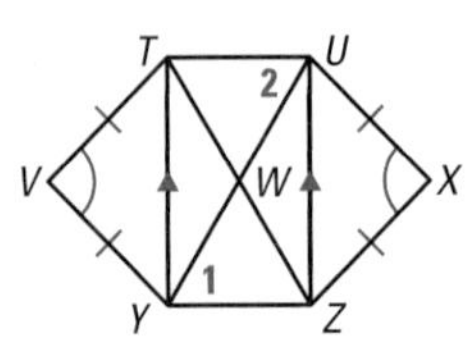

USING COORDINATES **Use the vertices of $\triangle ABC$ and $\triangle DEF$ to show that $\angle A \cong \angle D$. *Explain* your reasoning.**

21. $A(3, 7)$, $B(6, 11)$, $C(11, 13)$, $D(2, -4)$, $E(5, -8)$, $F(10, -10)$ **The triangles are congruent by SSS.**

22. $A(3, 8)$, $B(3, 2)$, $C(11, 2)$, $D(-1, 5)$, $E(5, 5)$, $F(5, 13)$ **The triangles are congruent by SSS.**

PROOF **Use the information given in the diagram to write a proof.** **23–26. See margin.**

23. **PROVE** ▶ $\angle VYX \cong \angle WYZ$

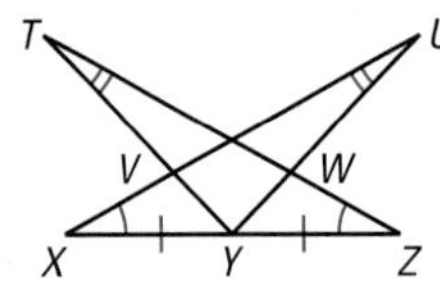

24. **PROVE** ▶ $\overline{FL} \cong \overline{HN}$

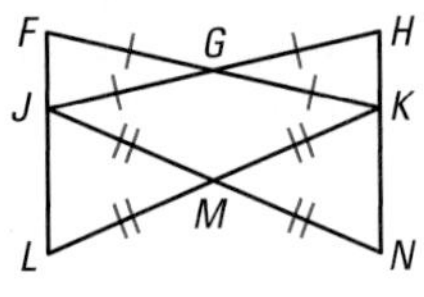

C 25. **PROVE** ▶ $\triangle PUX \cong \triangle QSY$

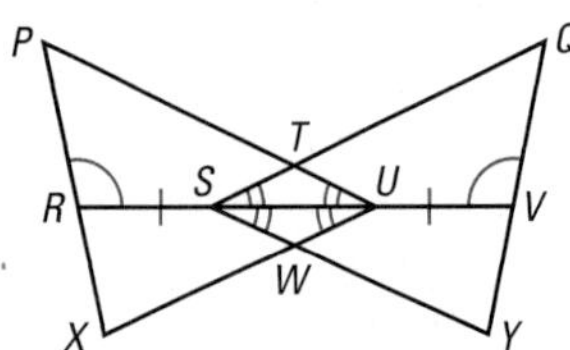

26. **PROVE** ▶ $\overline{AC} \cong \overline{GE}$

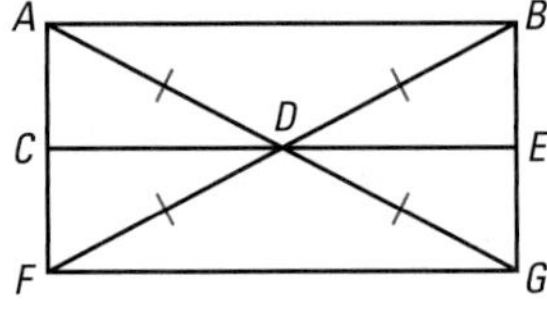

27. **CHALLENGE** Which of the triangles below are congruent? **$\triangle ABC$, $\triangle NPQ$, $\triangle DEF$, and $\triangle GHJ$**

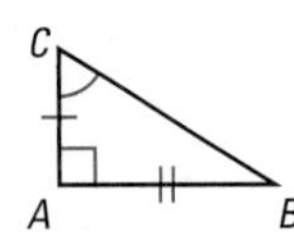 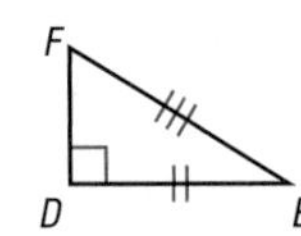 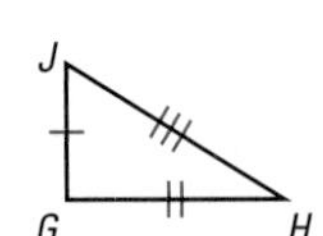 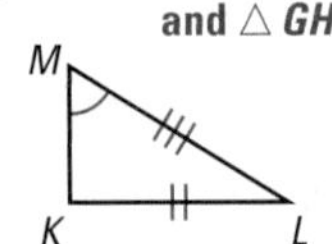 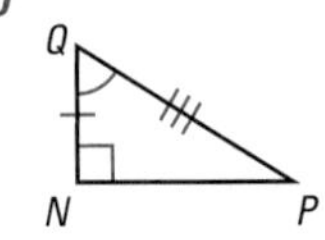

○ = **WORKED-OUT SOLUTIONS on p. WS1**   ★ = **STANDARDIZED TEST PRACTICE**

20. Since $\triangle TVY \cong \triangle UXZ$ by SAS you have $\overline{YT} \cong \overline{ZU}$. Since $\overline{YT} \parallel \overline{ZU}$, you have $\angle YTW \cong \angle UZW$ and $\angle TYW \cong \angle ZUW$ by the Alternate Interior Angles Theorem, making $\triangle TYW \cong \triangle ZUW$ by ASA. Using corresponding parts and vertical angles, you have $\triangle TWU \cong \triangle ZWY$ by SAS, making $\angle 1 \cong \angle 2$.

23–26. See Additional Answers beginning on p. AA1.

PROBLEM SOLVING

EXAMPLE 2 A
on p. 257
for Ex. 28

28. Because $\overline{BD} \perp \overline{DE}$ and $\overline{BD} \perp \overline{AC}$, $\angle D$ and $\angle C$ are congruent right angles. The vertical angles, $\angle DBE$ and $\angle CBA$, are congruent. So, $\triangle DBE \cong \triangle CBA$ by ASA. Then because corresponding parts of congruent triangles are congruent, $\overline{AC} \cong \overline{DE}$. So, you can find the distance AC across the canyon by measuring DE.

28. CANYON *Explain* how you can find the distance across the canyon.

@HomeTutor for problem solving help at classzone.com

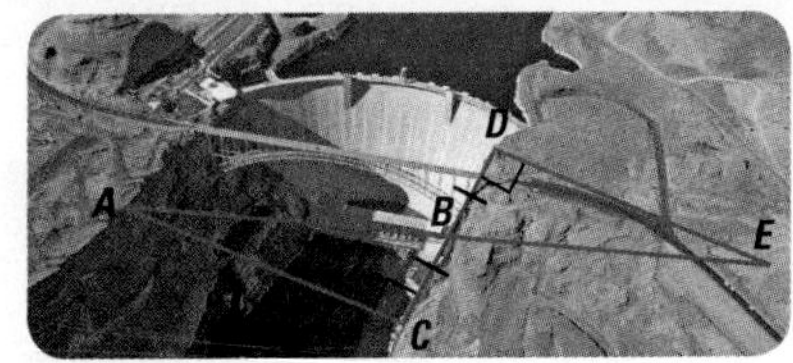

29. PROOF Use the given information and the diagram to write a two-column proof.

GIVEN ▶ $\overline{PQ} \parallel \overline{VS}$, $\overline{QU} \parallel \overline{ST}$, $\overline{PQ} \cong \overline{VS}$

PROVE ▶ $\angle Q \cong \angle S$ **See margin.**

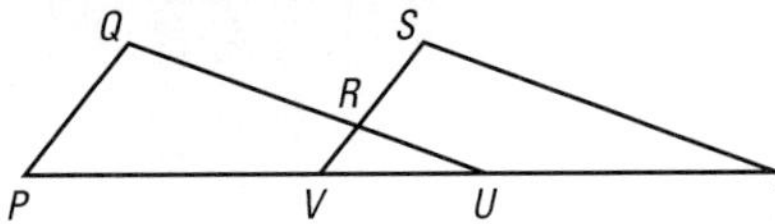

@HomeTutor for problem solving help at classzone.com

30. SNOWBOARDING In the diagram of the half pipe below, C is the midpoint of $\overline{BD}$. If $EC \approx 11.5$ m, and $CD \approx 2.5$ m, find the approximate distance across the half pipe. *Explain* your reasoning.

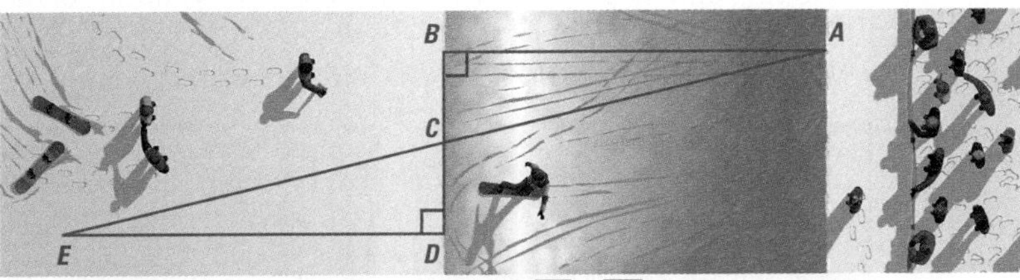

11.2 m. ***Sample answer:*** $\triangle ABC \cong \triangle EDC$ **thus** $\overline{ED} \cong \overline{AB}$**. Since** $ED \approx 11.2$ **then** $AB = 11.2$**.**

31. ★ MULTIPLE CHOICE Using the information in the diagram, you can prove that $\overline{WY} \cong \overline{ZX}$. Which reason would *not* appear in the proof? **A**

(A) SAS Congruence Postulate

(B) AAS Congruence Theorem

(C) Alternate Interior Angles Theorem

(D) Right Angles Congruence Theorem

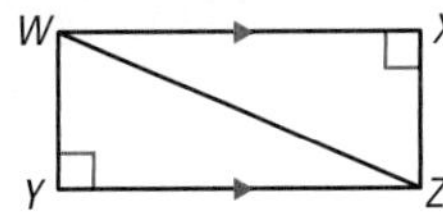

EXAMPLE 4 B
on p. 258
for Ex. 32

32. PROVING A CONSTRUCTION The diagrams below show the construction on page 34 used to bisect $\angle A$. By construction, you can assume that $\overline{AB} \cong \overline{AC}$ and $\overline{BG} \cong \overline{CG}$. Write a proof to verify that $\overrightarrow{AG}$ bisects $\angle A$. **See margin.**

STEP 1

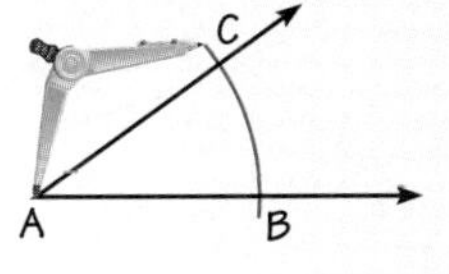

First draw an arc with center A. Label the points where the arc intersects the sides of the angle points B and C.

STEP 2

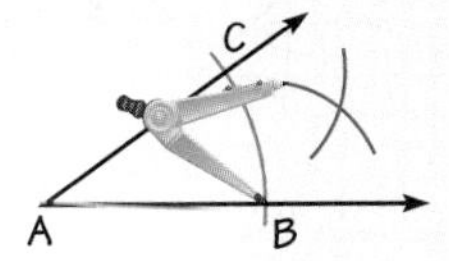

Draw an arc with center C. Using the same radius, draw an arc with center B. Label the intersection point G.

STEP 3

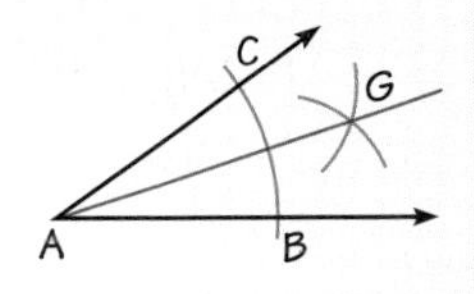

Draw $\overrightarrow{AG}$. It follows that $\angle BAG \cong \angle CAG$.

29. Statements (Reasons)

1. $\overline{PQ} \parallel \overline{VS}$, $\overline{QU} \parallel \overline{ST}$, $\overline{PQ} \cong \overline{VS}$ (Given)
2. $\angle QPU \cong \angle SVT$, $\angle QUP \cong \angle STV$ (Corresponding Angles Postulate)
3. $\triangle PQU \cong \triangle VST$ (AAS)
4. $\angle Q \cong \angle S$ (Corr. parts of $\cong$ △s are $\cong$.)

32. Statements (Reasons)

1. $\overline{AB} \cong \overline{AC}$, $\overline{BG} \cong \overline{CG}$ (Given)
2. $\overline{AG} \cong \overline{AG}$ (Reflexive Property of Segment Congruence)
3. $\triangle ACG \cong \triangle ABG$ (SSS)
4. $\angle CAG \cong \angle BAG$ (Corr. parts of $\cong$ △s are $\cong$.)
5. $\overrightarrow{AG}$ bisects $\angle A$. (Definition of angle bisector)

Study Strategy

Exercises 38–39 Draw the overlapping triangles apart from each other. Mark the parts congruent for the first pair of triangles you are planning to prove congruent in a different color than the parts you are going to use for the second pair of triangles.

37. Statements (Reasons)

1. $\overline{MN} \cong \overline{KN}$, $\angle PMN \cong \angle NKL$ (Given)
2. $\angle MNP \cong \angle KNL$ (Vertical Angles Congruence Theorem)
3. $\triangle PMN \cong \triangle LKN$ (ASA)
4. $\overline{MP} \cong \overline{KL}$, $\angle MPJ \cong \angle KLQ$ (Corr. parts of $\cong$ $\triangle$s are $\cong$.)
5. $\overline{MJ} \perp \overline{PN}$, $\overline{KQ} \perp \overline{LN}$ (Given in diagram)
6. $\angle KQL$ and $\angle MJP$ are right angles. (Perpendicular lines intersect to form four right angles.)
7. $\angle KQL \cong \angle MJP$ (Right Angles Congruence Theorem)
8. $\triangle MJP \cong \triangle KQL$ (AAS)
9. $\angle 1 \cong \angle 2$ (Corr. parts of $\cong$ $\triangle$s are $\cong$.)

38. Statements (Reasons)

1. $\overline{TS} \cong \overline{TV}$, $\overline{SR} \cong \overline{VW}$ (Given)
2. $TS = TV$, $SR = VW$ (Definition of congruent segments)
3. $TS + SR = TR$, $TV + VW = TW$ (Segment Addition Postulate)
4. $TV + SR = TR$, $TV + SR = TW$ (Substitution Property of Equality)
5. $TR = TW$ (Transitive Property of Equality)
6. $\overline{TR} \cong \overline{TW}$ (Definition of congruent segments)
7. $\angle RTV \cong \angle WTS$ (Reflexive Property of Congruence)
8. $\triangle RTV \cong \triangle WTS$ (SAS)
9. $\overline{RV} \cong \overline{WS}$ (Corr. parts of $\cong$ $\triangle$s are $\cong$.)
10. $\overline{SV} \cong \overline{VS}$ (Reflexive Property of Congruence)
11. $\triangle RSV \cong \triangle WVS$ (SSS)
12. $\angle RSV \cong \angle WVS$ (Corr. parts of $\cong$ $\triangle$s are $\cong$.)
13. $\angle RSV \cong \angle 1$ are supplementary; $\angle WVS$ and $\angle 2$ are supplementary. (Definition of supplementary angles)
14. $\angle 1 \cong \angle 2$ (Congruent Supplements Theorem)

33. No; the given angle is not an included angle.

34. Yes; $\overline{AE} \cong \overline{CE}$ by Corr. parts of $\cong$ $\triangle$s are $\cong$, $\angle CEB \cong \angle AEB$ by the Right Angle Congruence Theorem and $\overline{BE} \cong \overline{BE}$ so $\triangle BAE \cong \triangle BCE$. By Corr. parts of $\cong$ $\triangle$s are $\cong$, $\overline{AB} \cong \overline{BC}$.

35. Yes; $\angle BDA \cong \angle BDC$, $\overline{AD} \cong \overline{CD}$ and $\overline{BD} \cong \overline{BD}$. By SAS, $\triangle ABD \cong \triangle CBD$. By Corr. parts of $\cong$ $\triangle$s are $\cong$, $\overline{AB} \cong \overline{BC}$.

ARCHITECTURE **Can you use the given information to determine that $\overline{AB} \cong \overline{BC}$? *Justify* your answer.** 33–35. See margin.

33. $\angle ABD \cong \angle CBD$, $AD = CD$

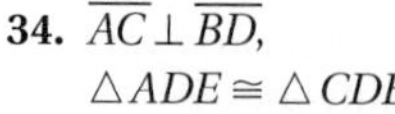

34. $\overline{AC} \perp \overline{BD}$, $\triangle ADE \cong \triangle CDE$

35. $\overline{BD}$ bisects $\overline{AC}$, $\overline{AD} \perp \overline{BD}$

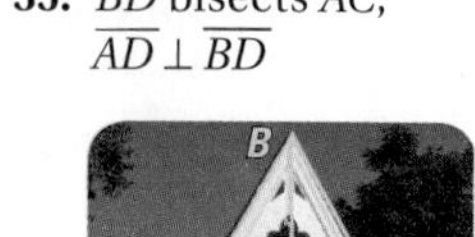

36. ★ **EXTENDED RESPONSE** You can use the method described below to find the distance across a river. You will need a cap with a visor.

- Stand on one side of the river and look straight across to a point on the other side. Align the visor of your cap with that point.
- Without changing the inclination of your neck and head, turn sideways until the visor is in line with a point on your side of the stream.
- Measure the distance BD between your feet and that point.

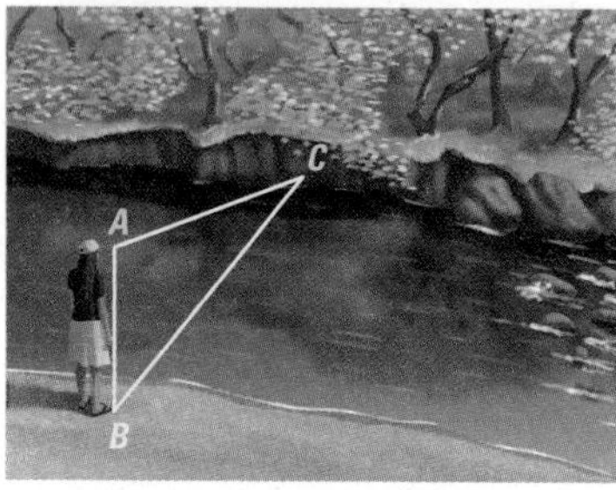

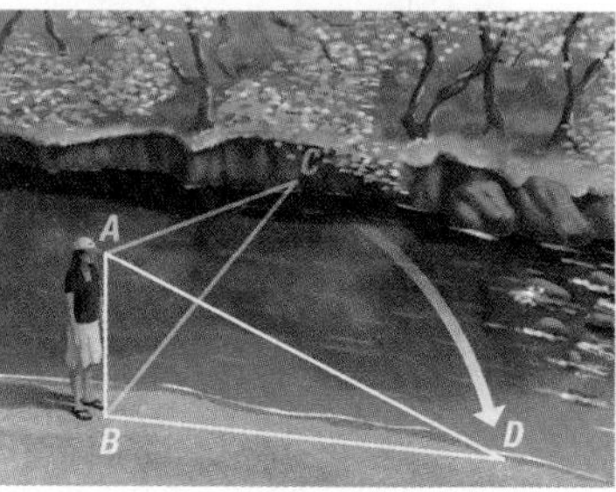

a. What corresponding parts of the two triangles can you assume are congruent? What postulate or theorem can you use to show that the two triangles are congruent?

36a. *Sample answer:* $\overline{AB} \cong \overline{AB}$, $\angle BAC \cong \angle BAD$, $\angle ACB \cong \angle ADB$; AAS

b. *Explain* why BD is also the distance across the stream.
Sample answer: $\triangle BAC \cong \triangle BAD$ therefore $\overline{BC} \cong \overline{BD}$.

C **PROOF** **Use the given information and the diagram to prove that $\angle 1 \cong \angle 2$.** 37–39. See margin.

37. **GIVEN** ▶ $\overline{MN} \cong \overline{KN}$, $\angle PMN \cong \angle NKL$

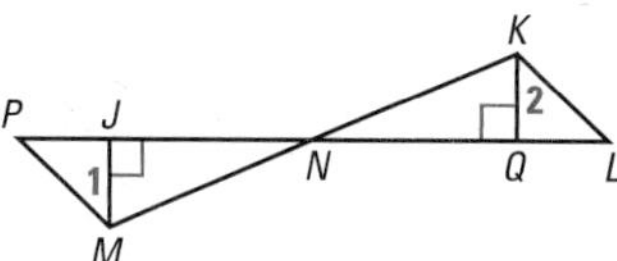

38. **GIVEN** ▶ $\overline{TS} \cong \overline{TV}$, $\overline{SR} \cong \overline{VW}$

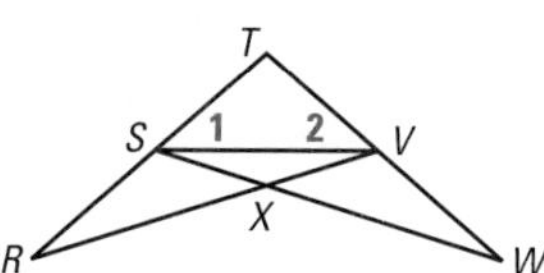

39. **PROOF** Write a proof.

GIVEN ▶ $\overline{BA} \cong \overline{BC}$, D and E are midpoints, $\angle A \cong \angle C$, $\overline{DF} \cong \overline{EF}$

PROVE ▶ $\overline{FG} \cong \overline{FH}$

○ = **WORKED-OUT SOLUTIONS** on p. WS1   ★ = **STANDARDIZED TEST PRACTICE**

39. See Additional Answers beginning on p. AA1.

40. **CHALLENGE** In the diagram of pentagon $ABCDE$, $\overline{AB} \parallel \overline{EC}$, $\overline{AC} \parallel \overline{ED}$, $\overline{AB} \cong \overline{ED}$, and $\overline{AC} \cong \overline{EC}$. Write a proof that shows $\overline{AD} \cong \overline{EB}$. **See margin.**

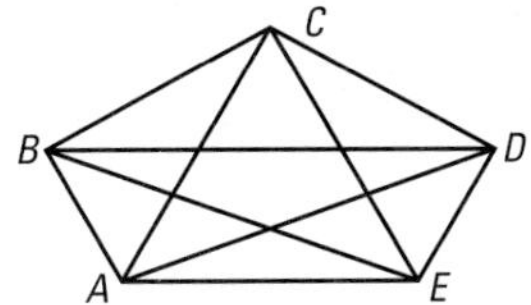

MIXED REVIEW

How many lines can be drawn that fit each description? Copy the diagram and sketch all the lines. *(p. 147)* **41–43. See margin for art.**

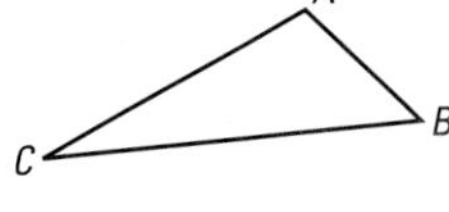

41. Line(s) through B and parallel to $\overleftrightarrow{AC}$ **one**
42. Line(s) through A and perpendicular to $\overleftrightarrow{BC}$ **one**
43. Line(s) through D and C **one**

PREVIEW Prepare for Lesson 4.7 in Exs. 44–46.

The variable expressions represent the angle measures of a triangle. Find the measure of each angle. Then classify the triangle by its angles. *(p. 217)*

44. $m\angle A = x°$, $m\angle B = (4x)°$, $m\angle C = (5x)°$ **18°, 72°, 90°; right triangle**
45. $m\angle A = x°$, $m\angle B = (5x)°$, $m\angle C = (x + 19)°$ **23°, 115°, 42°; obtuse triangle**
46. $m\angle A = (x - 22)°$, $m\angle B = (x + 16)°$, $m\angle C = (2x - 14)°$ **28°, 66°, 86°; acute triangle**

QUIZ for Lessons 4.4–4.6

Decide which method, SAS, ASA, AAS, or HL, can be used to prove that the triangles are congruent. *(pp. 240, 249)*

1. 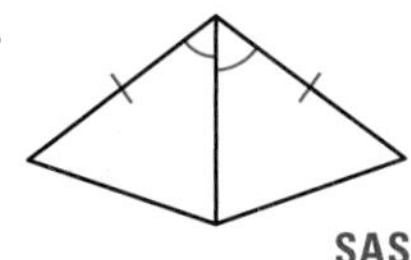 **SAS**
2. 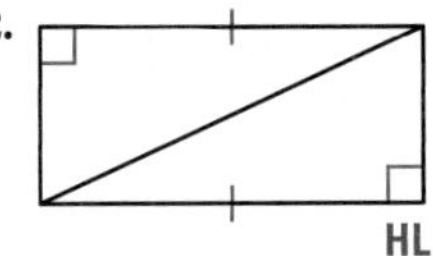 **HL**
3. 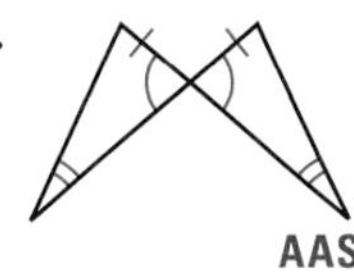 **AAS**

Use the given information to write a proof. **4–6. See margin.**

4. **GIVEN** ▶ $\angle BAC \cong \angle DCA$, $\overline{AB} \cong \overline{CD}$
   PROVE ▶ $\triangle ABC \cong \triangle CDA$ *(p. 240)*

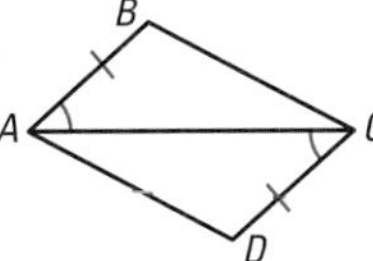

5. **GIVEN** ▶ $\angle W \cong \angle Z$, $\overline{VW} \cong \overline{YZ}$
   PROVE ▶ $\triangle VWX \cong \triangle YZX$ *(p. 249)*

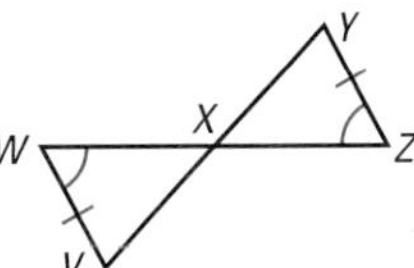

6. Write a plan for a proof. *(p. 256)*
   GIVEN ▶ $\overline{PQ} \cong \overline{MN}$, $m\angle P = m\angle M = 90°$
   PROVE ▶ $\overline{QL} \cong \overline{NL}$

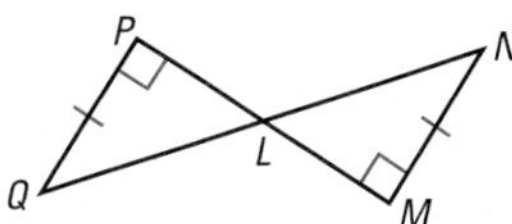

41. 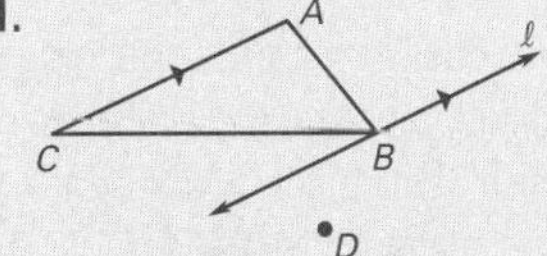

42. 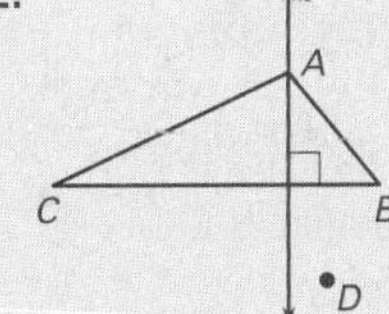

43. 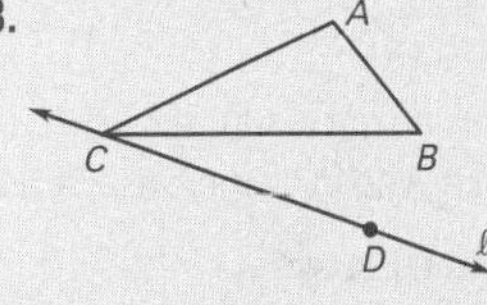

5 ASSESS AND RETEACH

Daily Homework Quiz

Transparency Available

1. Tell which triangles you can show are congruent in order to prove $AE = DE$. What postulate or theorem would you use?

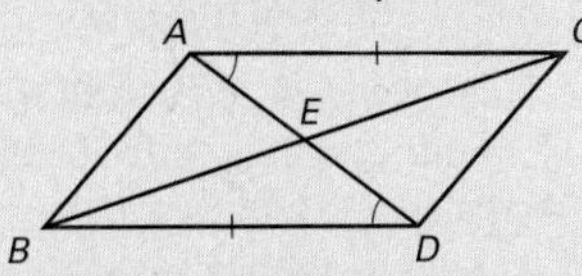

$\triangle AEC \cong \triangle DEB$ by the AAS Cong. Thm. or by the ASA Cong. Post.

2. Write a plan to prove $\angle 1 \cong \angle 2$.

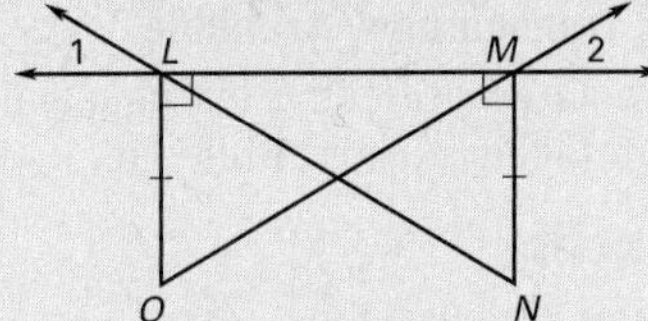

Show $\overline{LM} \cong \overline{LM}$ by the Refl. Prop. of ≅ Segs. Hence $\triangle OLM \cong \triangle NML$ by the SAS Cong. Post. This gives $\angle NLM \cong \angle OML$, since Corr. Parts of ≅ △ are ≅. So $\angle 1 \cong \angle 2$ by the Vert. ∠ Thm. and properties of ≅ ∠.

 **Online Quiz**

Available at **classzone.com**

Diagnosis/Remediation

- Practice A, B, C in Chapter 4 Resource Book, pp. 76–81
- Study Guide in Chapter 4 Resource Book, pp. 82–83
- Practice Workbook, pp. 76–78
- @HomeTutor

Challenge

Additional challenge is available in the Chapter 4 Resource Book, p. 86.

Quiz

An easily-readable reduced copy of the quiz (with answers) on Lessons 4.4–4.6 from the Assessment Book can be found on p. 214G.

40, Quiz 4–6. See Additional Answers beginning on p. AA1.

1 PLAN AND PREPARE

Warm-Up Exercises

Transparency Available

Classify each triangle by its sides.

1. 2 cm, 2 cm, 2 cm **equilateral**
2. 7 ft, 11 ft, 7 ft **isosceles**
3. 9 m, 8 m, 10 m **scalene**
4. In $\triangle ABC$, if $m\angle A = 70°$ and $m\angle B = 50°$, what is $m\angle C$? **60°**
5. In $\triangle DEF$, if $m\angle D = m\angle E$ and $m\angle F = 26°$, what are the measures of $\angle D$ and $\angle E$? **77°, 77°**

Notetaking Guide

Transparency Available

Promotes interactive learning and notetaking skills, pp. 108–110.

Pacing

Basic: 2 days
Average: 2 days
Advanced: 2 days
Block: 1 block

- See *Teaching Guide/Lesson Plan.*

2 FOCUS AND MOTIVATE

Essential Question

Big Idea 2, p. 215

How are the sides and angles of a triangle related if there are two or more congruent sides or angles? **Tell students they will learn how to answer this question by learning the Base Angles Theorem and its converse.**

4.7 Use Isosceles and Equilateral Triangles

Before You learned about isosceles and equilateral triangles.
Now You will use theorems about isosceles and equilateral triangles.
Why? So you can solve a problem about architecture, as in Ex. 40.

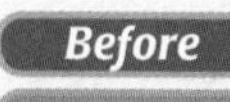

Key Vocabulary
- legs
- vertex angle
- base
- base angles

In Lesson 4.1, you learned that a triangle is isosceles if it has at least two congruent sides. When an isosceles triangle has exactly two congruent sides, these two sides are the **legs**. The angle formed by the legs is the **vertex angle**. The third side is the **base** of the isosceles triangle. The two angles adjacent to the base are called **base angles**.

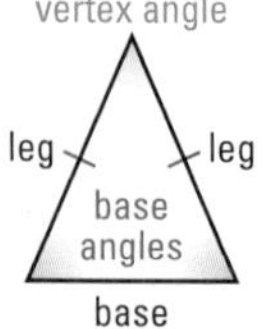

Standards

12.0 Students find and use measures of sides and of interior and exterior angles of triangles and polygons **to classify figures and solve problems.**

5.0 Students prove that triangles are congruent or similar, **and they are able to use the concept of corresponding parts of congruent triangles.**

THEOREMS — For Your Notebook

THEOREM 4.7 Base Angles Theorem

If two sides of a triangle are congruent, then the angles opposite them are congruent.

If $\overline{AB} \cong \overline{AC}$, then $\angle B \cong \angle C$.

Proof: p. 265

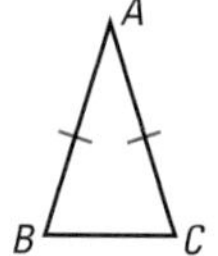

THEOREM 4.8 Converse of Base Angles Theorem

If two angles of a triangle are congruent, then the sides opposite them are congruent.

If $\angle B \cong \angle C$, then $\overline{AB} \cong \overline{AC}$.

Proof: Ex. 45, p. 269

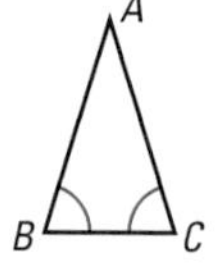

EXAMPLE 1 Apply the Base Angles Theorem

In $\triangle DEF$, $\overline{DE} \cong \overline{DF}$. Name two congruent angles.

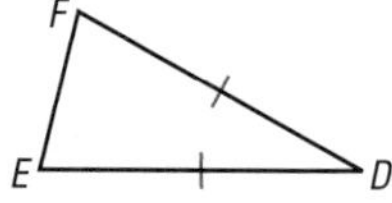

Solution

▶ $\overline{DE} \cong \overline{DF}$, so by the Base Angles Theorem, $\angle E \cong \angle F$.

GUIDED PRACTICE for Example 1

Copy and complete the statement.

1. If $\overline{HG} \cong \overline{HK}$, then $\angle$ _?_ $\cong \angle$ _?_. ***HGK, HKG***
2. If $\angle KHJ \cong \angle KJH$, then _?_ $\cong$ _?_. ***KH, KJ***

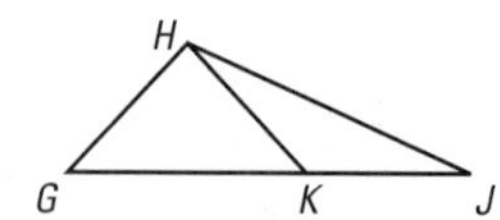

Resource Planning Guide

Chapter Resource Book
- Teaching Guide/Lesson Plan (pp. 87–88)
- Activity Master (p. 89)
- Practice levels A, B, C (pp. 90–95)
- Study Guide (pp. 96–97)
- Catch-up for Absent Students (p. 98)
- Application (p. 99)
- Challenge (p. 100)

Workbooks
- Notetaking Guide (pp. 108–110)
- Practice Workbook (pp. 79–81)

Teaching Options
- **Power Presentations CD-ROM** provides dynamic electronic teaching resources for the classroom.
- **Activity Generator CD-ROM** provides editable activities for all ability levels.

Interactive Technology
- Easy Planner
- Power Presentations CD-ROM
- Activity Generator CD-ROM
- Animated Geometry
- Test Generator CD-ROM
- Online Quiz
- eWorkbook
- eEdition
- @HomeTutor

Resources for English Learners
- Quick Reference for English Learners
- Spanish Study Guide
- Multi-Language Visual Glossary
- Student Resources in Spanish

See also the *Geometry Toolkit* for more strategies for meeting individual needs.

PROOF Base Angles Theorem

GIVEN ▶ $\overline{JK} \cong \overline{JL}$

PROVE ▶ $\angle K \cong \angle L$

Plan for Proof
a. Draw $\overline{JM}$ so that it bisects $\overline{KL}$.
b. Use SSS to show that $\triangle JMK \cong \triangle JML$.
c. Use properties of congruent triangles to show that $\angle K \cong \angle L$.

Plan in Action

	STATEMENTS	REASONS
	1. M is the midpoint of $\overline{KL}$.	1. Definition of midpoint
a.	2. Draw $\overline{JM}$.	2. Two points determine a line.
	3. $\overline{MK} \cong \overline{ML}$	3. Definition of midpoint
	4. $\overline{JK} \cong \overline{JL}$	4. Given
	5. $\overline{JM} \cong \overline{JM}$	5. Reflexive Property of Congruence
b.	6. $\triangle JMK \cong \triangle JML$	6. SSS Congruence Postulate
c.	7. $\angle K \cong \angle L$	7. Corresp. parts of $\cong$ ▲ are $\cong$.

Recall that an equilateral triangle has three congruent sides.

COROLLARIES *For Your Notebook*

WRITE A BICONDITIONAL
The corollaries state that a triangle is *equilateral* if and only if it is *equiangular.*

Corollary to the Base Angles Theorem

If a triangle is equilateral, then it is equiangular.

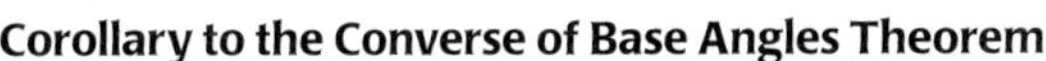

Corollary to the Converse of Base Angles Theorem

If a triangle is equiangular, then it is equilateral.

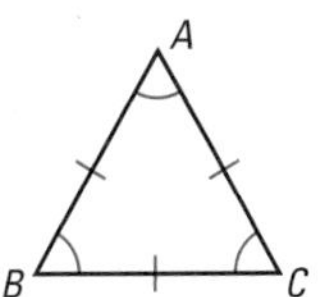

EXAMPLE 2 Find measures in a triangle

Find the measures of $\angle P$, $\angle Q$, and $\angle R$.

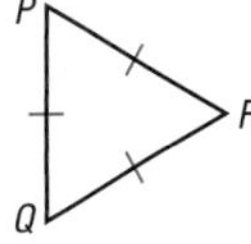

The diagram shows that $\triangle PQR$ is equilateral. Therefore, by the Corollary to the Base Angles Theorem, $\triangle PQR$ is equiangular. So, $m\angle P = m\angle Q = m\angle R$.

$3(m\angle P) = 180°$ **Triangle Sum Theorem**

$m\angle P = 60°$ **Divide each side by 3.**

▶ The measures of $\angle P$, $\angle Q$, and $\angle R$ are all 60°.

✓ GUIDED PRACTICE for Example 2

3. Find ST in the triangle at the right. **5**

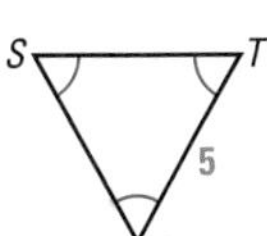

4. Is it possible for an equilateral triangle to have an angle measure other than 60°? *Explain.*
No. *Sample answer:* The Triangle Sum Theorem and the fact that the triangle is equilateral guarantees the angles measure 60° because all pairs of angles could be considered base angles of an isosceles triangle.

Motivating the Lesson

Isosceles and equilateral triangles appear in many figures that students will study in art and architecture. Tell students that in this lesson, they will learn properties of triangles that have two or more congruent sides or angles.

Extra Example 1

In $\triangle PQR$, $\overline{PQ} \cong \overline{QR}$. Name two congruent angles. **$\angle P \cong \angle R$**

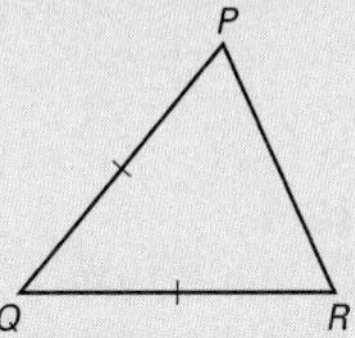

Extra Example 2

Find the measures of $\angle X$ and $\angle Z$. **65°, 65°**

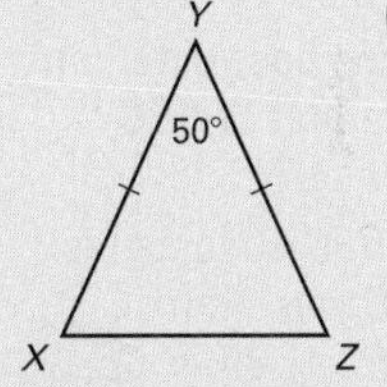

Key Question to Ask for Example 2

- Can an equilateral triangle have an angle of 61°? Explain. **No; each angle must have a measure of 60°.**

Vocabulary

Discuss with students whether each side of an equilateral triangle can be called a leg of the triangle. Call attention to how the legs of an isosceles triangle are defined on page 264. Have students note that the word is applied only to isosceles triangles that have exactly two congruent sides.

Extra Example 3

Find the values of x and y in the diagram. **7, 3**

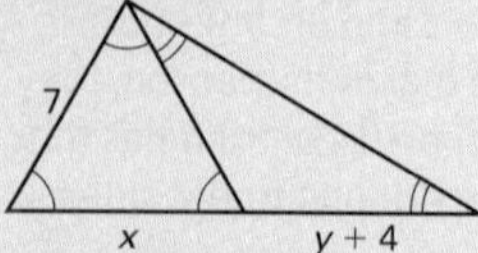

Key Question to Ask for Example 3

- Explain how you could find $m\angle M$. **$m\angle KLN = 60°$ because the triangle is equilateral. So $m\angle MLN = 120°$. That leaves 60° for $m\angle M + m\angle MNL$, and since $m\angle M$ and $m\angle MNL$ are equal, each must be 30°.**

Extra Example 4

Diagonal braces $\overline{AC}$ and $\overline{BD}$ are used to reinforce a signboard that advertises fresh eggs and produce at a roadside stand. Each brace is 14 feet long.

a. What congruence postulate can you use to prove that $\triangle ABC \cong \triangle DCB$? **SSS Cong. Post.**

b. Explain why $\triangle BEC$ is isosceles. **$\angle DBC \cong \angle ACB$ since corr. parts of $\cong$ ▲ are $\cong$. $\overline{BE} \cong \overline{CE}$ by the Conv. of the Base Angles Thm., and this implies that $\triangle BEC$ is isosceles.**

c. What triangles would you use to show that $\triangle AED$ is isosceles?

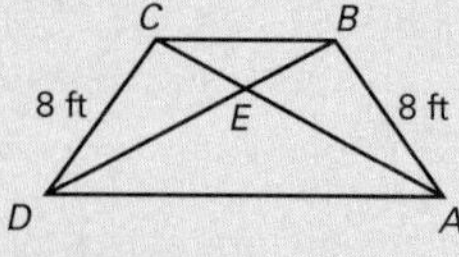

$\triangle ABD$ and $\triangle DCA$

Closing the Lesson

Have students summarize the major points of the lesson and answer the Essential Question: How are the sides and angles of a triangle related if there are two or more congruent sides or angles?

- **Angles opposite congruent sides of a triangle are congruent and conversely.**
- **If a triangle is equilateral, then it is equiangular and conversely.**

If two sides of a triangle are congruent, then the angles opposite them are congruent. The converse is also true.

EXAMPLE 3 Use isosceles and equilateral triangles

ALGEBRA Find the values of x and y in the diagram.

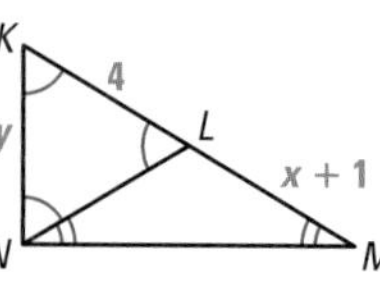

Solution

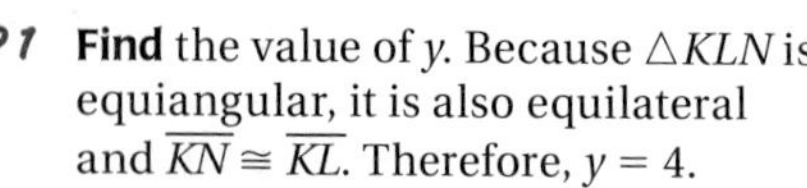

STEP 1 **Find** the value of y. Because $\triangle KLN$ is equiangular, it is also equilateral and $\overline{KN} \cong \overline{KL}$. Therefore, $y = 4$.

AVOID ERRORS
You cannot use $\angle N$ to refer to $\angle LNM$ because three angles have N as their vertex.

STEP 2 **Find** the value of x. Because $\angle LNM \cong \angle LMN$, $\overline{LN} \cong \overline{LM}$ and $\triangle LMN$ is isosceles. You also know that $LN = 4$ because $\triangle KLN$ is equilateral.

$LN = LM$	Definition of congruent segments
$4 = x + 1$	Substitute 4 for LN and $x + 1$ for LM.
$3 = x$	Subtract 1 from each side.

EXAMPLE 4 Solve a multi-step problem

LIFEGUARD TOWER In the lifeguard tower, $\overline{PS} \cong \overline{QR}$ and $\angle QPS \cong \angle PQR$.

a. What congruence postulate can you use to prove that $\triangle QPS \cong \triangle PQR$?

b. Explain why $\triangle PQT$ is isosceles.

c. Show that $\triangle PTS \cong \triangle QTR$.

Solution

AVOID ERRORS
When you redraw the triangles so that they do not overlap, be careful to copy all given information and labels correctly.

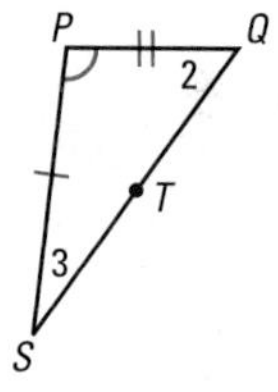

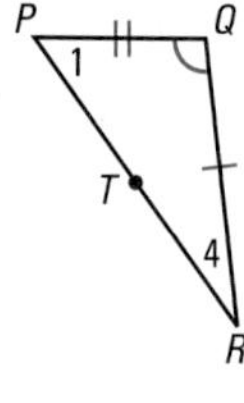

a. Draw and label $\triangle QPS$ and $\triangle PQR$ so that they do not overlap. You can see that $\overline{PQ} \cong \overline{QP}$, $\overline{PS} \cong \overline{QR}$, and $\angle QPS \cong \angle PQR$. So, by the SAS Congruence Postulate, $\triangle QPS \cong \triangle PQR$.

b. From part (a), you know that $\angle 1 \cong \angle 2$ because corresp. parts of $\cong$ ▲ are $\cong$. By the Converse of the Base Angles Theorem, $\overline{PT} \cong \overline{QT}$, and $\triangle PQT$ is isosceles.

c. You know that $\overline{PS} \cong \overline{QR}$, and $\angle 3 \cong \angle 4$ because corresp. parts of $\cong$ ▲ are $\cong$. Also, $\angle PTS \cong \angle QTR$ by the Vertical Angles Congruence Theorem. So, $\triangle PTS \cong \triangle QTR$ by the AAS Congruence Theorem.

✓ GUIDED PRACTICE for Examples 3 and 4

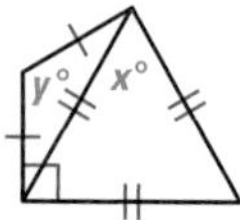

5. Find the values of x and y in the diagram. **60, 120**

6. **REASONING** Use parts (b) and (c) in Example 4 and the SSS Congruence Postulate to give a different proof that $\triangle QPS \cong \triangle PQR$. **See margin.**

6. By the Segment Addition Postulate $QT + TS = QS$ and $PT + TR = PR$. Since $\overline{PT} \cong \overline{QT}$ from part (b) and $\overline{TS} \cong \overline{TR}$ from part (c), then $\overline{QS} \cong \overline{PR}$. $\overline{PQ} \cong \overline{PQ}$ by the Reflexive Property and it is given that $\overline{PS} \cong \overline{QR}$, therefore $\triangle QPS \cong \triangle PQR$ by the SSS Congruence Postulate.

Differentiated Instruction

Inclusion Some students may not understand where to begin to find the values of x and y in **Guided Practice Exercise 5**. Guide them by asking the following questions: "What can you say about the angles of a triangle with three congruent sides? What is the measure of each angle in an equilateral triangle? How can you find the measures of the two angles that make up the 90° angle using information about the angles in an equilateral triangle?"

See also the *Geometry Toolkit* for more strategies.

4.7 EXERCISES

HOMEWORK KEY
○ = WORKED-OUT SOLUTIONS on p. WS5 for Exs. 5, 17, and 41
★ = STANDARDIZED TEST PRACTICE Exs. 2, 18, 19, 30, 31, and 46

SKILL PRACTICE

A

1. VOCABULARY Define the *vertex angle* of an isosceles triangle.
The angle formed by the legs is the vertex angle.
2. ★ WRITING What is the relationship between the base angles of an isosceles triangle? *Explain.* **They are congruent.**

EXAMPLE 1 on p. 264 for Exs. 3–6

USING DIAGRAMS **In Exercises 3–6, use the diagram. Copy and complete the statement. Tell what theorem you used.**

3. If $\overline{AE} \cong \overline{DE}$, then $\angle$ _?_ $\cong \angle$ _?_. ***A, D*; Base Angles Theorem**
4. If $\overline{AB} \cong \overline{EB}$, then $\angle$ _?_ $\cong \angle$ _?_. ***A, BEA*; Base Angles Theorem**
5. If $\angle D \cong \angle CED$, then _?_ $\cong$ _?_. **$\overline{CD}$, $\overline{CE}$; Converse of Base Angles Theorem**
6. If $\angle EBC \cong \angle ECB$, then _?_ $\cong$ _?_.
$\overline{EB}$, $\overline{EC}$; Converse of Base Angles Theorem

EXAMPLE 2 on p. 265 for Exs. 7–14

REASONING **Find the unknown measure.**

7.
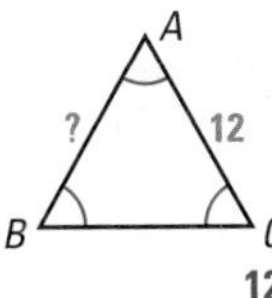

12

8.
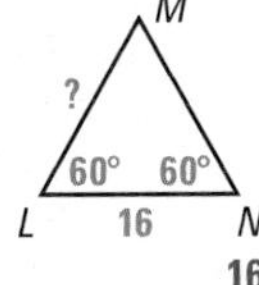

16

9.
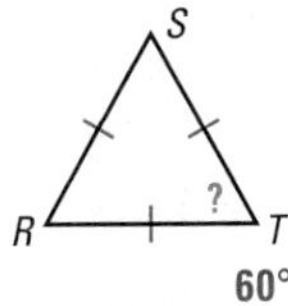

60°

10. DRAWING DIAGRAMS A base angle in an isosceles triangle measures 37°. Draw and label the triangle. What is the measure of the vertex angle?
106°; see margin for art.

ALGEBRA **Find the value of *x*.**

11.
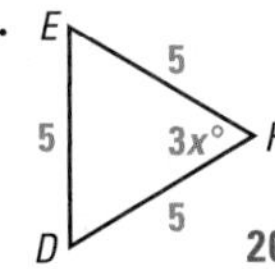

20

12.
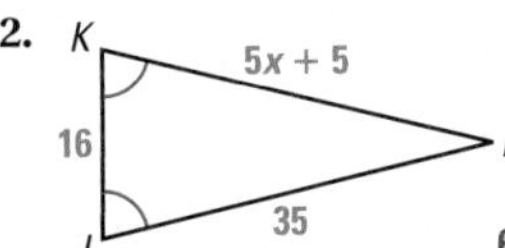

6

13.
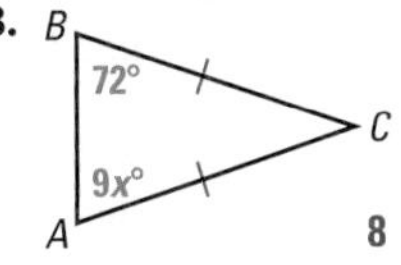

8

14. ERROR ANALYSIS *Describe* and correct the error made in finding *BC* in the diagram shown.
$\overline{AC}$ is not congruent to $\overline{BC}$. $\overline{AB} \cong \overline{BC}$, which makes $BC = 5$.

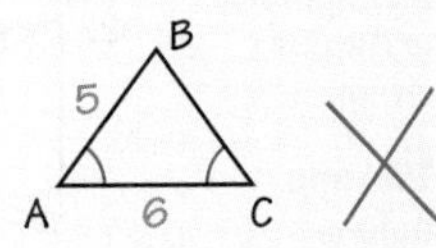

EXAMPLE 3 on p. 266 for Exs. 15–17

ALGEBRA **Find the values of *x* and *y*.**

15.
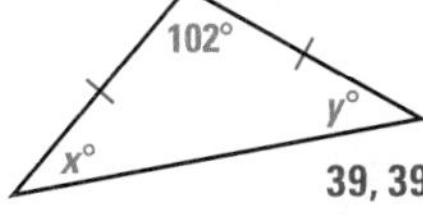

39, 39

16.
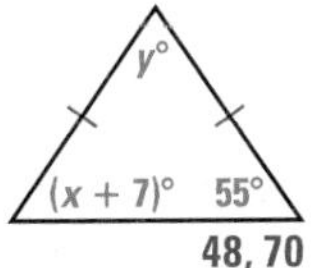

48, 70

17. x°, 9y°
45, 5

18. ★ SHORT RESPONSE Are isosceles triangles always acute triangles? *Explain* your reasoning. **No; an isosceles triangle can have an obtuse or a right vertex angle, which would make it an obtuse or a right triangle.**

10.
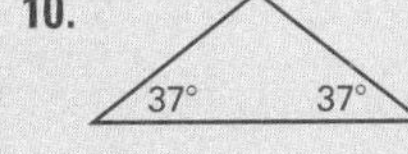

4 PRACTICE AND APPLY

Assignment Guide

Answer Transparencies available for all exercises

Basic:
Day 1: pp. 267–270
Exs. 1–14, 19, 52–56
Day 2: pp. 267–270
Exs. 15–18, 20–25, 38–45, 57–60

Average:
Day 1: pp. 267–270
Exs. 1, 2, 4–6, 8–10, 12–14, 19, 26–29, 52–56
Day 2: pp. 267–270
Exs. 16–18, 21–25, 30, 31, 39–48, 57, 59

Advanced:
Day 1: pp. 267–270
Exs. 1, 2, 4–6, 8–10, 12–14, 19, 26–29, 35, 36, 52–56 even
Day 2: pp. 267–270
Exs. 16–18, 22, 24, 30–34, 37*, 40–51*, 58, 60

Block:
pp. 267–270
Exs. 1, 2, 4–6, 8–10, 12–14, 16–19, 21–31, 39–48, 52–57, 59

Differentiated Instruction

See *Geometry Best Practices Toolkit* for suggestions on addressing the needs of a diverse classroom.

Homework Check

For a quick check of student understanding of key concepts, go over the following exercises:
Basic: 3, 8, 15, 38, 42
Average: 4, 10, 16, 39, 42
Advanced: 6, 12, 16, 40, 42

Extra Practice

- Student Edition, p. 903
- Chapter 4 Resource Book: Practice levels A, B, C, pp. 90–95

Practice Worksheet

An easily-readable reduced practice page (with answers) for this lesson can be found on p. 214C.

Graphing Calculator

Exercise 17 After the students write the system of equations $x = 9y$ and $x + 9y = 90$, have them solve each for y and enter it on the Y= list of their graphing calculator. Graph the lines and find the intersection point, which is the solution of the system.

Teaching Strategy

Exercise 21 You may wish to have students model the figure by using new, unsharpened pencils for the congruent segments. Have students note that while specific numerical values for x and y are not determined by the figure, y can be expressed in terms of x.

Avoiding Common Errors

Exercise 22 Some students may not include -4 as a possible value of x, reasoning that the side lengths of a triangle must be positive. Point out that $3x^2 - 32$ is the expression that is used for a length, not x.

34. 90, about 8.66; one triangle is equiangular, one is isosceles, and the third one is a right triangle. Use the equiangular and isosceles triangles to establish the right triangle and then use the Pythagorean Theorem.

35. 50°, 50°, 80°; 65°, 65°, 50°; there are two distinct exterior angles. If the angle is supplementary to the base angle, the base angles measure 50°. If the angle is supplementary to the vertex angle, then the base angles measure 65°.

36. Since $\angle A$ is the vertex angle of isosceles $\triangle ABC$, $\angle B$ must be congruent to $\angle C$. Since 2 times any angle measure will always be an even number, an even number will be subtracted from 180 to find $m\angle A$. 180 minus an even number will always be an even number, therefore $m\angle A$ must be even.

20. 50, $\frac{1}{2}$; first find y by using the Triangle Sum Theorem followed by the Base Angles Theorem. Next find x by using the Definition of linear pair followed by the Base Angles Theorem. B

21. There is not enough information to find x or y. We need to know the measure of one of the vertex angles.

22. ± 4, 4; since $y + 12 = 3x^2 - 32$ and $3x^2 - 32 = 5y - 4$, use the Transitive Property of Equality and set $y + 12 = 5y - 4$ to solve for y and use the value of y to solve for x.

30. Isosceles; two of the angles have the same measure, so two of the sides have the same length by the Converse of the Base Angles Theorem. C

32. 150; one triangle is equiangular and the other two triangles are congruent making $x°$ the measure of the third angle in the center. $x + x + 60 = 360$.

19. ★ **MULTIPLE CHOICE** What is the value of x in the diagram? **B**

Ⓐ 5 Ⓑ 6

Ⓒ 7 Ⓓ 9

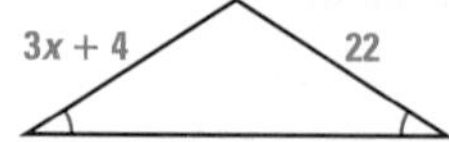

ALGEBRA **Find the values of x and y, if possible. *Explain* your reasoning.** **20–22. See margin.**

20.

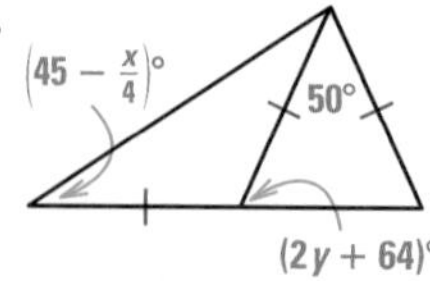

21.

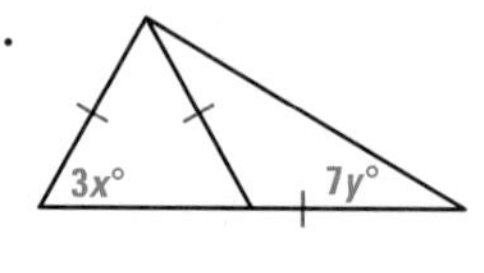

22.

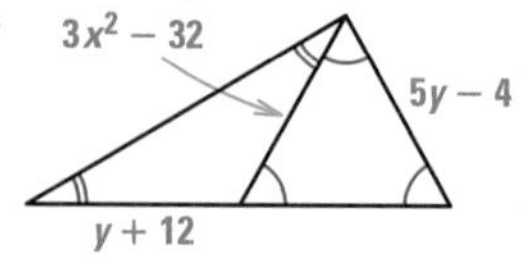

ALGEBRA **Find the perimeter of the triangle.**

23.

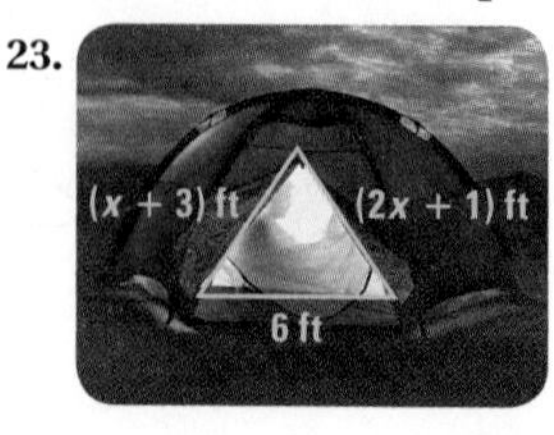

16 ft

24.

17 in.

25. (21 − x) in., (2x − 3) in., (x + 5) in. **39 in.**

REASONING **In Exercises 26–29, use the diagram. State whether the given values for x, y, and z are possible or not. If not, *explain*.**

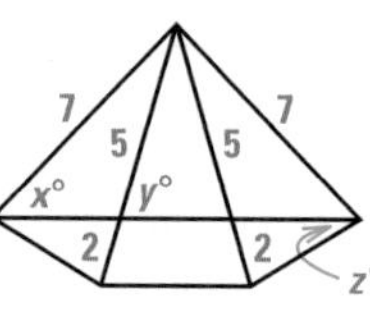

26. $x = 90, y = 68, z = 42$

27. $x = 40, y = 72, z = 36$ **possible**

28. $x = 25, y = 25, z = 15$

29. $x = 42, y = 72, z = 33$ **possible**

26. Not possible; the isosceles triangle with legs of length 7 cannot contain two 90° angles.

28. Not possible; $x = y$ forms parallel segments, which cannot be two sides of a triangle.

30. ★ **SHORT RESPONSE** In $\triangle DEF$, $m\angle D = (4x + 2)°$, $m\angle E = (6x - 30)°$, and $m\angle F = 3x°$. What type of triangle is $\triangle DEF$? *Explain* your reasoning. **See margin.**

31. ★ **SHORT RESPONSE** In $\triangle ABC$, D is the midpoint of $\overline{AC}$, and $\overline{BD}$ is perpendicular to $\overline{AC}$. *Explain* why $\triangle ABC$ is isosceles. **$\triangle ABD \cong \triangle CBD$ by SAS making $\overline{BA} \cong \overline{BC}$ because corresponding parts of congruent triangles are congruent.**

ALGEBRA **Find the value(s) of the variable(s). *Explain* your reasoning.**

32.

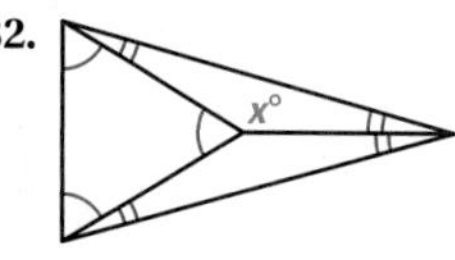

33. x°, y° **60, 120; solve the system $x + y = 180$ and $180 + 2x - y = 180$.**

34. 40, 40, x°, 30°, 8y **See margin.**

35. **REASONING** The measure of an exterior angle of an isosceles triangle is 130°. What are the possible angle measures of the triangle? *Explain*. **See margin.**

36. **PROOF** Let $\triangle ABC$ be isosceles with vertex angle $\angle A$. Suppose $\angle A$, $\angle B$, and $\angle C$ have integer measures. Prove that $m\angle A$ must be even. **See margin.**

37. **CHALLENGE** The measure of an exterior angle of an isosceles triangle is $x°$. What are the possible angle measures of the triangle in terms of x? *Describe* all the possible values of x. **$180 - x, 180 - x, 2x - 180$; $\frac{x}{2}, \frac{x}{2}, 180 - x$; $0 < x < 180$**

○ = WORKED-OUT SOLUTIONS on p. WS1 ★ = STANDARDIZED TEST PRACTICE

PROBLEM SOLVING

A

38. SPORTS The dimensions of a sports pennant are given in the diagram. Find the values of x and y. **79, 22**

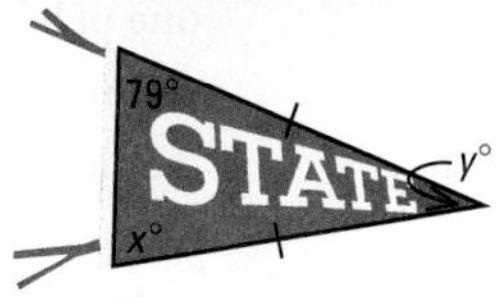

@HomeTutor for problem solving help at classzone.com

39. ADVERTISING A logo in an advertisement is an equilateral triangle with a side length of 5 centimeters. Sketch the logo and give the measure of each side and angle. **See margin.**

@HomeTutor for problem solving help at classzone.com

40. ARCHITECTURE The Transamerica Pyramid building shown in the photograph has four faces shaped like isosceles triangles. The measure of a base angle of one of these triangles is about 85°. What is the approximate measure of the vertex angle of the triangle? **10°**

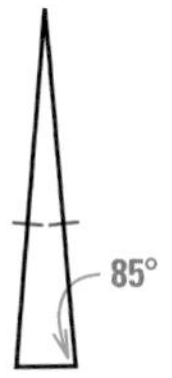

(41.) MULTI-STEP PROBLEM To make a zig-zag pattern, a graphic designer sketches two parallel line segments. Then the designer draws blue and green triangles as shown below. **41a–c. See margin.**

a. Prove that $\triangle ABC \cong \triangle BCD$.

b. Name all the isosceles triangles in the diagram.

c. Name four angles that are congruent to $\angle ABC$.

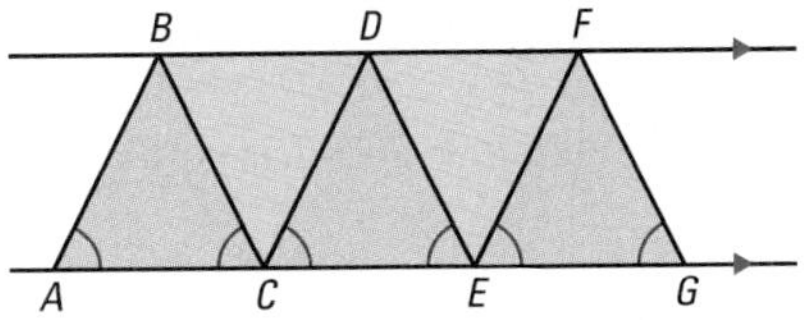

42. ★ VISUAL REASONING In the pattern below, each small triangle is an equilateral triangle with an area of 1 square unit.

Triangle			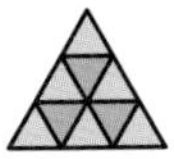	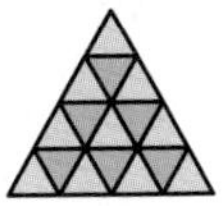
Area	1 square unit	?	?	?

a. **Reasoning** *Explain* how you know that any triangle made out of equilateral triangles will be an equilateral triangle.

b. **Area** Find the areas of the first four triangles in the pattern.

c. **Make a Conjecture** *Describe* any patterns in the areas. Predict the area of the seventh triangle in the pattern. *Explain* your reasoning.

B

43. REASONING Let $\triangle PQR$ be an isosceles right triangle with hypotenuse $\overline{QR}$. Find $m\angle P$, $m\angle Q$, and $m\angle R$. **90°, 45°, 45°**

44. REASONING *Explain* how the Corollary to the Base Angles Theorem follows from the Base Angles Theorem. **If a triangle is equilateral it is also isosceles, using these two facts it can be shown that the triangle is equiangular.**

45. PROVING THEOREM 4.8 Write a proof of the Converse of the Base Angles Theorem. **See margin.**

1a. $\angle A$, $\angle ACB$, $\angle CBD$, and $\angle CDB$ are congruent and $\overline{BC} \cong \overline{CB}$ making $\triangle ABC \cong \triangle BCD$ by AAS.

1b. $\triangle ABC$, $\triangle BCD$, $\triangle CDE$, $\triangle DEF$, $\triangle EFG$

1c. $\angle BCD$, $\angle CDE$, $\angle DEF$, $\angle EFG$

EXAMPLE 4 on p. 266 for Exs. 41–42

42a. The sides of each new triangle are the sum of the same number of congruent segments.

42b. 1 square unit, 4 square units, 9 square units, 16 square units

42c. $1^2, 2^2, 3^2 \ldots$; 49 square units; the numbers representing the areas are the sequence of perfect squares.

Mathematical Reasoning

Exercise 37 Suggest that students sketch an isosceles triangle and indicate congruent sides with hash marks. Have them draw an exterior angle at each vertex. Then have them consider which exterior angle to label $x°$. This should help them see that there is more than one possibility.

39.

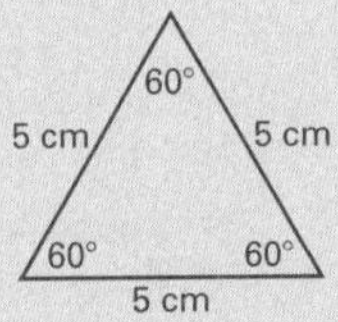

45. Statements (Reasons)

1. $\triangle ABC$ with $\angle B \cong \angle C$ (Given)
2. Draw the altitude from A to $\overline{BC}$ and label its intersection with $\overline{BC}$ as D. (Perpendicular Postulate)
3. $\angle ADB$ and $\angle ADC$ are right angles. (If two lines are $\perp$, then they form 4 right angles.)
4. $\angle ADB \cong \angle ADC$ (Right Angles Congruence Theorem)
5. $\overline{AD} \cong \overline{AD}$ (Reflexive Property of Congruence)
6. $\triangle ADB \cong \triangle ADC$ (AAS)
7. $\overline{AB} \cong \overline{AC}$ (Corr. parts of $\cong$ △s are $\cong$.)

5 ASSESS AND RETEACH

Daily Homework Quiz

Transparency Available

Find the value of x.

1. 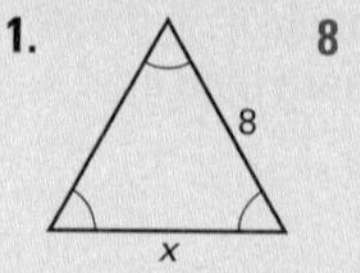

8

2. 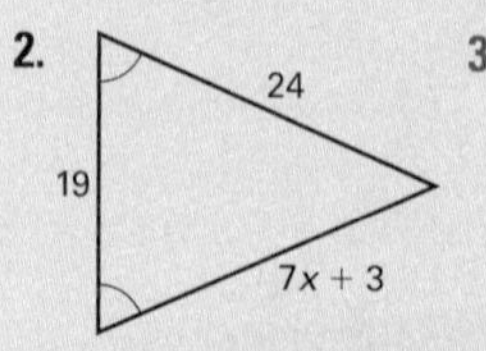

3

3. If the measure of the vertex angle of an isosceles triangle is 112°, what are the measures of the base angles? **34°, 34°**

4. Find the perimeter of the triangle.

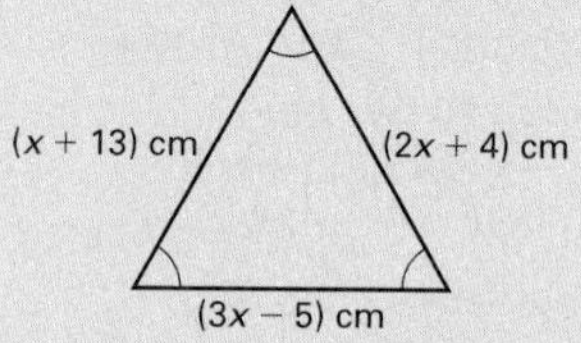

66 cm

Available at **classzone.com**

Diagnosis/Remediation

- Practice A, B, C in Chapter 4 Resource Book, pp. 90–95
- Study Guide in Chapter 4 Resource Book, pp. 96–97
- Practice Workbook, pp. 79–81
- @HomeTutor

Challenge

Additional challenge is available in the Chapter 4 Resource Book, p. 100.

46a. Statements (Reasons)

1. $\overline{AB} \cong \overline{CD}$, $\overline{AE} \cong \overline{DE}$, $\angle BAE \cong \angle CDB$ (Given)
2. $\triangle ABE \cong \triangle DCE$ (SAS)

46b. $\triangle AED$, $\triangle BEC$

46c. $\angle EDA$, $\angle EBC$, $\angle ECB$

49, 50. See Additional Answers beginning on p. AA1.

46. ★ **EXTENDED RESPONSE** Sue is designing fabric purses that she will sell at the school fair. Use the diagram of one of her purses. **a–c. See margin.**

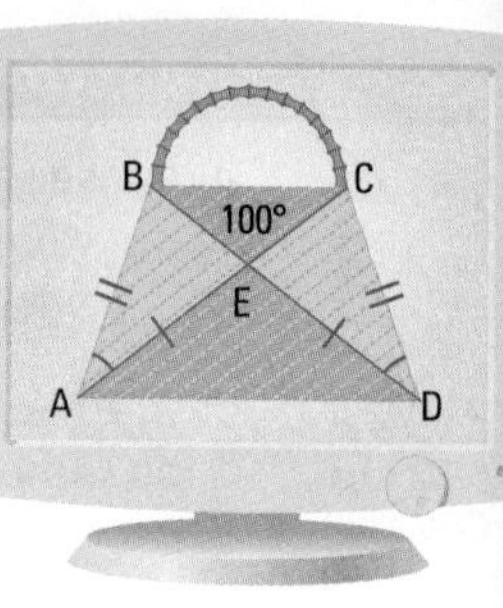

a. Prove that $\triangle ABE \cong \triangle DCE$.

b. Name the isosceles triangles in the purse.

c. Name three angles that are congruent to $\angle EAD$.

d. What If? If the measure of $\angle BEC$ changes, does your answer to part (c) change? *Explain.* **No; $\triangle AED$ and $\triangle BEC$ remain isosceles triangles with $\angle BEC \cong \angle AED$.**

REASONING FROM DIAGRAMS **Use the information in the diagram to answer the question.** ***Explain*** **your reasoning.**

47. Is $p \parallel q$?

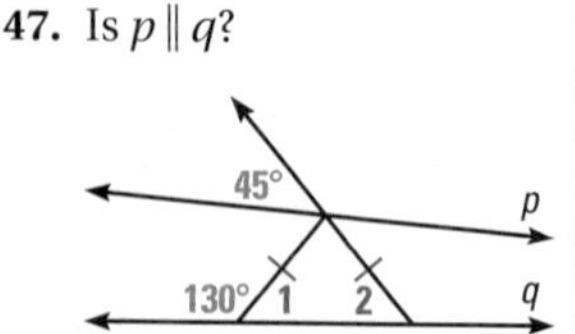

No; $m\angle 1 = 50°$, so $m\angle 2 = 50°$ and corresponds to the angle measuring 45°, therefore p is not parallel to q.

48. Is $\triangle ABC$ isosceles?

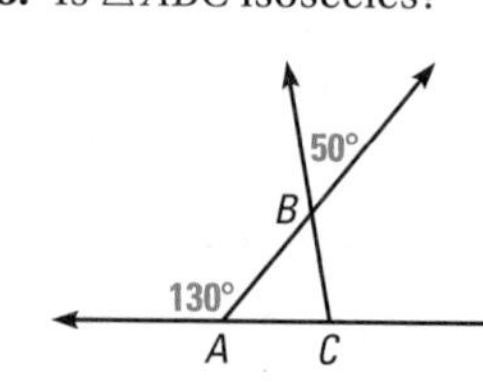

Yes; $m\angle ABC = 50$ and $m\angle BAC = 50°$ The Converse of Base Angles Theorem guarantees that $\overline{AC} \cong \overline{BC}$ making $\triangle ABC$ isosceles.

C **49. PROOF** Write a proof. **See margin.**

GIVEN ▶ $\triangle ABC$ is equilateral, $\angle CAD \cong \angle ABE \cong \angle BCF$.

PROVE ▶ $\triangle DEF$ is equilateral.

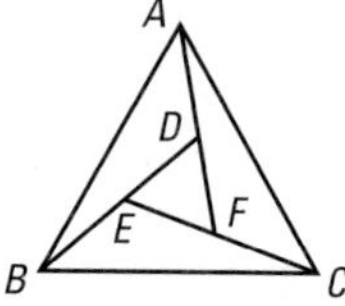

50. COORDINATE GEOMETRY The coordinates of two vertices of $\triangle TUV$ are $T(0, 4)$ and $U(4, 0)$. *Explain* why the triangle will always be an isosceles triangle if V is any point on the line $y = x$ except (2, 2). **See margin.**

51. CHALLENGE The lengths of the sides of a triangle are $3t$, $5t - 12$, and $t + 20$. Find the values of t that make the triangle isosceles. *Explain.* **6, 8, 10; set $3t = 5t - 12$, $3t = t + 20$, $5t - 12 = t + 20$ and solve for t.**

MIXED REVIEW

What quadrant contains the point? *(p. 878)*

52. (−1, −3) **III** **53.** (−2, 4) **II** **54.** (5, −2) **IV**

Copy and complete the given function table. *(p. 884)*

55.

x	−7	0	5
$y = x - 4$	?	?	?

−11, −4, 1

56.

?	−2	0	1
?	−6	0	3

x, $y = 3x$

PREVIEW Prepare for Lesson 4.8 in Exs. 57–60.

Use the Distance Formula to decide whether $\overline{AB} \cong \overline{AC}$. *(p. 15)*

57. $A(0, 0)$, $B(-5, -6)$, $C(6, 5)$ **congruent**

58. $A(3, -3)$, $B(0, 1)$, $C(-1, 0)$ **congruent**

59. $A(0, 1)$, $B(4, 7)$, $C(-6, 3)$ **not congruent**

60. $A(-3, 0)$, $B(2, 2)$, $C(2, -2)$ **congruent**

4.8 Investigate Slides and Flips

MATERIALS • graph paper • pencil

Standards

22.0 Students know the effect of rigid motions on figures in the coordinate plane and space, **including** rotations, **translations, and reflections.**

QUESTION What happens when you slide or flip a triangle?

EXPLORE 1 Slide a triangle

STEP 1 ***Draw a triangle*** Draw a scalene right triangle with legs of length 3 units and 4 units on a piece of graph paper. Cut out the triangle.

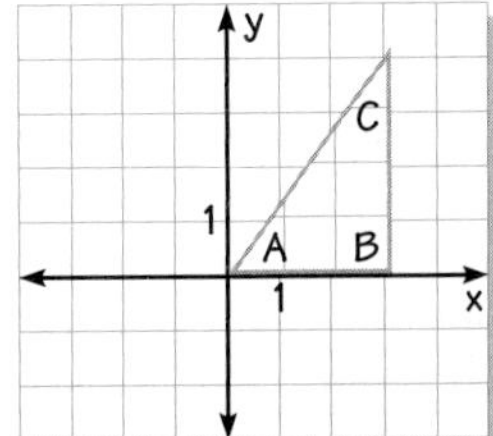

STEP 2 ***Draw coordinate plane*** Draw axes on the graph paper. Place the cut-out triangle so that the coordinates of the vertices are integers. Trace around the triangle and label the vertices.

STEP 3 ***Slide triangle*** Slide the cut-out triangle so it moves left and down. Write a description of the *transformation* and record ordered pairs in a table like the one shown. Repeat this step three times, sliding the triangle left or right *and* up or down to various places in the coordinate plane.

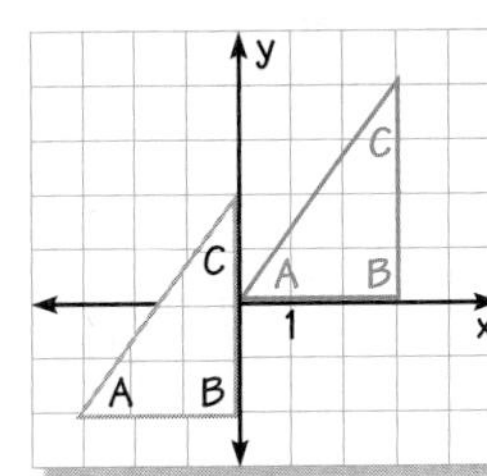

Slide 3 units left and 2 units down.		
Vertex	Original position	New position
A	(0, 0)	(−3, −2)
B	(3, 0)	(0, −2)
C	(3, 4)	(0, 2)

EXPLORE 2 Flip a triangle

STEP 1 ***Draw a coordinate plane*** Draw and label a second coordinate plane. Place the cut-out triangle so that one vertex is at the origin and one side is along the *y*-axis, as shown.

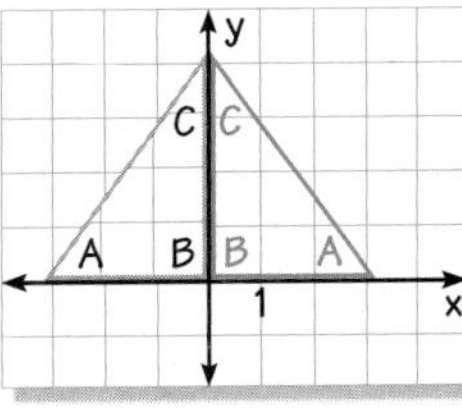

STEP 2 ***Flip triangle*** Flip the cut-out triangle over the *y*-axis. Record a description of the *transformation* and record the ordered pairs in a table. Repeat this step, flipping the triangle over the *x*-axis.

DRAW CONCLUSIONS Use your observations to complete these exercises

1. How are the coordinates of the original position of the triangle related to the new position in a slide? in a flip? **See margin.**
2. Is the original triangle congruent to the new triangle in a slide? in a flip? *Explain* your reasoning. **Yes; yes; they remain the same size and shape.**

1. The *x*-coordinate has been increased or decreased by the direction and magnitude of the horizontal movement while the *y*-coordinate has been increased or decreased by the direction and magnitude of the vertical movement; the coordinates of *B*, *C*, and the *y*-coordinate of *A* remain the same. The *x*-coordinate of *A* is the opposite of the original *x*-coordinate.

1 PLAN AND PREPARE

Explore the Concept

- Students will slide and flip a triangle.
- This activity leads into the study of transformations in Lesson 4.8.

Materials

Each student will need:

- graph paper
- scissors

Recommended Time

Work activity: 10 min

Discuss results: 5 min

Grouping

Students should work individually.

2 TEACH

Tips for Success

For the activity, students can cut the triangle they are going to move from colored card stock.

Key Questions

- How can you obtain algebraically the coordinates of the image after a slide? **Add or subtract from *x*- and *y*-coordinates as indicated.**
- Reflect the triangle over the *y*-axis without putting one side on the *y*-axis. How are the coordinates of the new triangle related to those of the original? ***x*-coordinates are opposites, *y*-coordinates are equal.**

Key Discovery

A triangle obtained by a slide or a flip is congruent to the original triangle.

3 ASSESS AND RETEACH

1. Explain how you can obtain the coordinates of the new triangle after a flip over the *x*-axis or *y*-axis. **Take the opposite of the *y*- or *x*-coordinates.**

1 PLAN AND PREPARE

Warm-Up Exercises

Transparency Available

1. Find the length of $\overline{AB}$ for $A(2, 7)$ and $B(7, -5)$. **13**
2. What point is 6 units to the right of $(3, 5)$? **(9, 5)**
3. Are these triangles congruent?

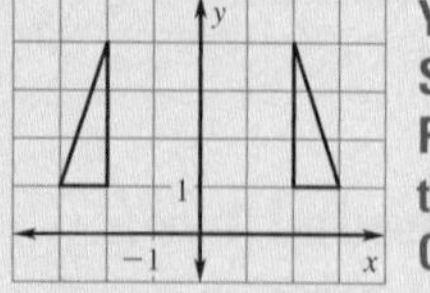

Yes, by the SSS Cong. Post. or by the SAS Cong. Post.

Notetaking Guide

Transparency Available

Promotes interactive learning and notetaking skills, pp. 111–115.

Pacing

Basic: 2 days
Average: 2 days
Advanced: 2 days
Block: 1 block

- See *Teaching Guide/Lesson Plan.*

2 FOCUS AND MOTIVATE

Essential Question

Big Idea 3, p. 215

What transformations create an image congruent to the original figure? **Tell students they will learn how to answer this question by learning about reflections, rotations, and translations.**

4.8 Perform Congruence Transformations

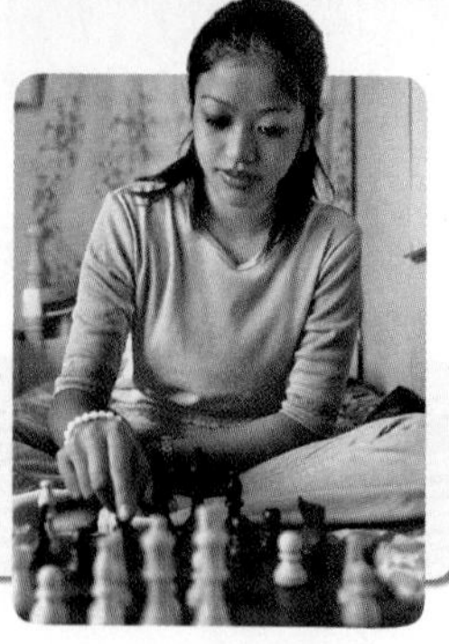

Before You determined whether two triangles are congruent.
Now You will create an image congruent to a given triangle.
Why So you can describe chess moves, as in Ex. 41.

Key Vocabulary
- transformation
- image
- translation
- reflection
- rotation
- congruence transformation

A **transformation** is an operation that moves or changes a geometric figure in some way to produce a new figure. The new figure is called the **image.** A transformation can be shown using an arrow.

The order of the vertices in the transformation statement tells you that P is the image of A, Q is the image of B, and R is the image of C.

$\triangle ABC \rightarrow \triangle PQR$
Original figure — Image

There are three main types of transformations. A **translation** moves every point of a figure the same distance in the same direction. A **reflection** uses a *line of reflection* to create a mirror image of the original figure. A **rotation** turns a figure about a fixed point, called the *center of rotation.*

TRANSFORMATIONS You will learn more about transformations in Lesson 6.7 and in Chapter 9.

EXAMPLE 1 Identify transformations

Name the type of transformation demonstrated in each picture.

a.

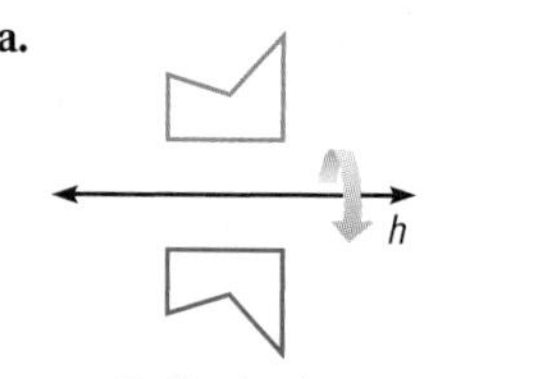

Reflection in a horizontal line

b.

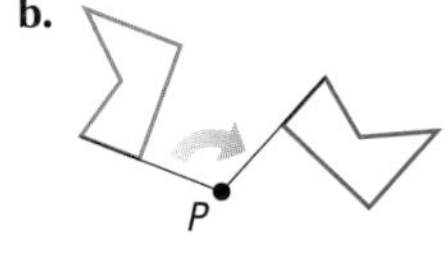

Rotation about a point

c.

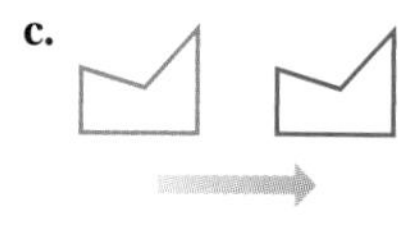

Translation in a straight path

GUIDED PRACTICE for Example 1

1. Name the type of transformation shown. **reflection**

Standards

22.0 Students know the effect of rigid motions on figures in the coordinate plane and space, including rotations, translations, and reflections.

CONGRUENCE Translations, reflections, and rotations are three types of *congruence transformations.* A **congruence transformation** changes the position of the figure without changing its size or shape.

Resource Planning Guide

Chapter Resource Book
- Teaching Guide/Lesson Plan (pp. 101–102)
- Activity Master (p. 103)
- Practice levels A, B, C (pp. 105–110)
- Study Guide (pp. 111–112)
- Catch-up for Absent Students (p. 113)
- Problem Solving Workshop (p. 114)
- Challenge (p. 115)

Workbooks
- Notetaking Guide (pp. 111–115)
- Practice Workbook (pp. 82–84)

Teaching Options
- **Power Presentations CD-ROM** provides dynamic electronic teaching resources for the classroom.
- **Activity Generator CD-ROM** provides editable activities for all ability levels.

Interactive Technology
- Easy Planner
- Power Presentations CD-ROM
- Activity Generator CD-ROM
- Animated Geometry
- Test Generator CD-ROM
- Online Quiz
- eWorkbook
- eEdition
- @HomeTutor

Resources for English Learners
- Quick Reference for English Learners
- Spanish Study Guide
- Multi-Language Visual Glossary
- Student Resources in Spanish

See also the *Geometry Toolkit* for more strategies for meeting individual needs.

TRANSLATIONS In a coordinate plane, a translation moves an object a given distance right or left and up or down. You can use coordinate notation to describe a translation.

READ DIAGRAMS
In this book, the original figure is blue and the transformation of the figure is red, unless otherwise stated.

KEY CONCEPT *For Your Notebook*

Coordinate Notation for a Translation

You can describe a translation by the notation

$(x, y) \rightarrow (x + a, y + b)$

which shows that each point (x, y) of the blue figure is translated horizontally a units and vertically b units.

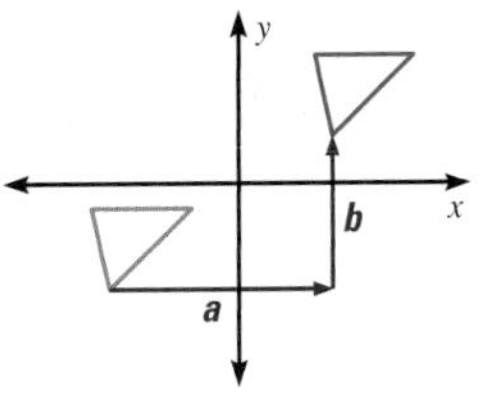

EXAMPLE 2 **Translate a figure in the coordinate plane**

Figure $ABCD$ has the vertices $A(-4, 3)$, $B(-2, 4)$, $C(-1, 1)$, and $D(-3, 1)$. Sketch $ABCD$ and its image after the translation $(x, y) \rightarrow (x + 5, y - 2)$.

Solution

First draw $ABCD$. Find the translation of each vertex by adding 5 to its x-coordinate and subtracting 2 from its y-coordinate. Then draw $ABCD$ and its image.

$(x, y) \rightarrow (x + 5, y - 2)$

$A(-4, 3) \rightarrow (1, 1)$

$B(-2, 4) \rightarrow (3, 2)$

$C(-1, 1) \rightarrow (4, -1)$

$D(-3, 1) \rightarrow (2, -1)$

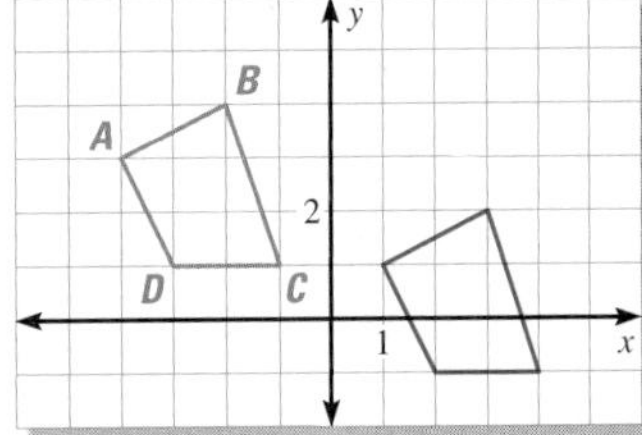

REFLECTIONS In this lesson, when a reflection is shown in a coordinate plane, the line of reflection is always the x-axis or the y-axis.

KEY CONCEPT *For Your Notebook*

Coordinate Notation for a Reflection

Reflection in the x-axis

Multiply the y-coordinate by -1.

$(x, y) \rightarrow (x, -y)$

Reflection in the y-axis

Multiply the x-coordinate by -1.

$(x, y) \rightarrow (-x, y)$

Motivating the Lesson

Have students consider drawing a pattern that is symmetric about a vertical line. They could draw one side of the pattern and then reflect it over the line to get the other half. Tell students they will study several transformations that keep figures the same size and shape. These are used in many fields including art.

3 TEACH

Extra Example 1

Name the type of transformation demonstrated in each picture.

a.

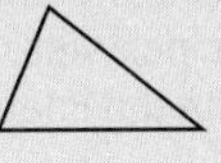

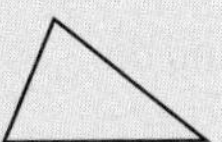

translation in a straight path

b.

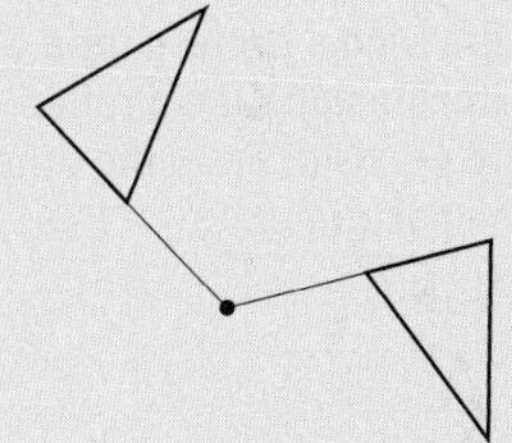

rotation about a point

c.

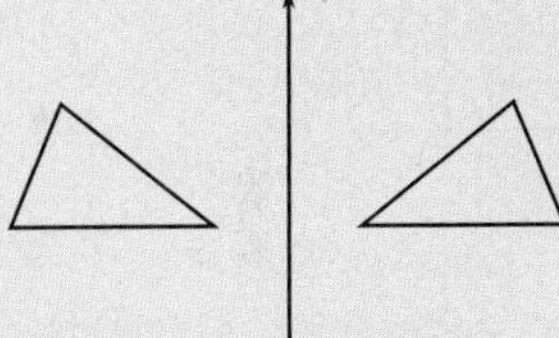

reflection in a vertical line

Key Question to Ask for Example 1

- Is the image figure in each case congruent to the original figure? Explain. **Yes, they have the same size and shape.**

Extra Example 2

Figure $WXYZ$ has the vertices $W(-1, 2)$, $X(2, 3)$, $Y(5, 0)$, and $Z(1, -1)$. Sketch $WXYZ$ and its image after the translation $(x, y) \rightarrow (x - 1, y + 3)$.

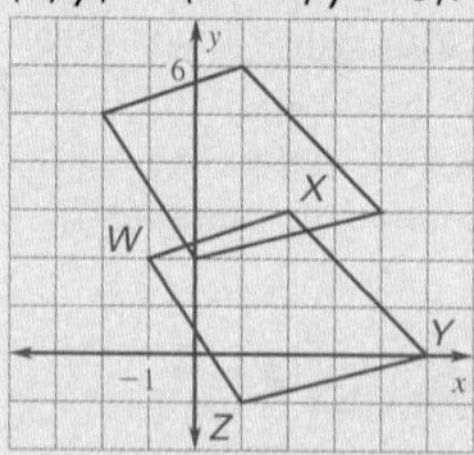

Key Questions to Ask for Example 2

- In the example, the orientation of $ABCD$ is clockwise. What is the orientation of the image? **clockwise**
- Does a translation keep the orientation the same? **yes**

Extra Example 3

You are drawing a pattern for a cross stitch design. Use a reflection in the y-axis to draw the other half of the pattern.

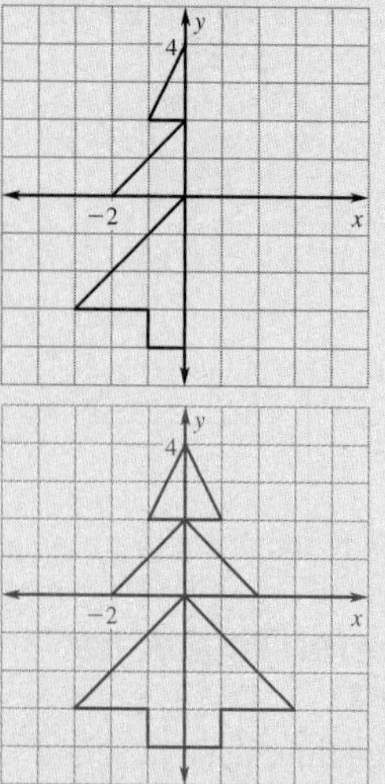

Key Question to Ask for Example 3

- Does a reflection preserve orientation? **No, it reverses it.**

An **Animated Geometry** activity is available on-line for **Example 3**. This activity is also available on the **Power Presentations CD-ROM**.

274

EXAMPLE 3 Reflect a figure in the x-axis

WOODWORK You are drawing a pattern for a wooden sign. Use a reflection in the x-axis to draw the other half of the pattern.

Solution

Multiply the y-coordinate of each vertex by -1 to find the corresponding vertex in the image.

$$(x, y) \rightarrow (x, -y)$$

$(-1, 0) \rightarrow (-1, 0)$ $\quad$ $(-1, 2) \rightarrow (-1, -2)$

$(1, 2) \rightarrow (1, -2)$ $\quad$ $(1, 4) \rightarrow (1, -4)$

$(5, 0) \rightarrow (5, 0)$

Use the vertices to draw the image. You can check your results by looking to see if each original point and its image are the same distance from the x-axis.

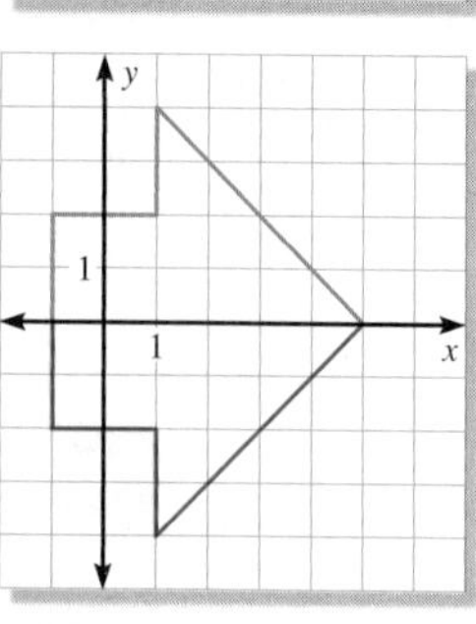

Animated Geometry at classzone.com

GUIDED PRACTICE for Examples 2 and 3

2. The vertices of $\triangle ABC$ are $A(1, 2)$, $B(0, 0)$, and $C(4, 0)$. A translation of $\triangle ABC$ results in the image $\triangle DEF$ with vertices $D(2, 1)$, $E(1, -1)$, and $F(5, -1)$. *Describe* the translation in words and in coordinate notation.

   2. Add one to each x-coordinate and subtract one from each y-coordinate, $(x, y) \rightarrow (x + 1, y - 1)$.

3. The endpoints of $\overline{RS}$ are $R(4, 5)$ and $S(1, -3)$. A reflection of $\overline{RS}$ results in the image $\overline{TU}$, with coordinates $T(4, -5)$ and $U(1, 3)$. Tell which axis $\overline{RS}$ was reflected in and write the coordinate rule for the reflection. **x-axis, $(x, y) \rightarrow (x, -y)$**

ROTATIONS In this lesson, if a rotation is shown in a coordinate plane, the center of rotation is the origin.

The direction of rotation can be either *clockwise* or *counterclockwise*. The *angle of rotation* is formed by rays drawn from the center of rotation through corresponding points on the original figure and its image.

90° clockwise rotation

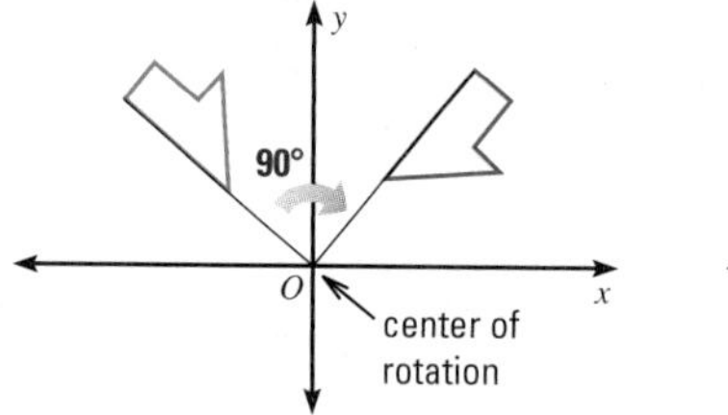

60° counterclockwise rotation

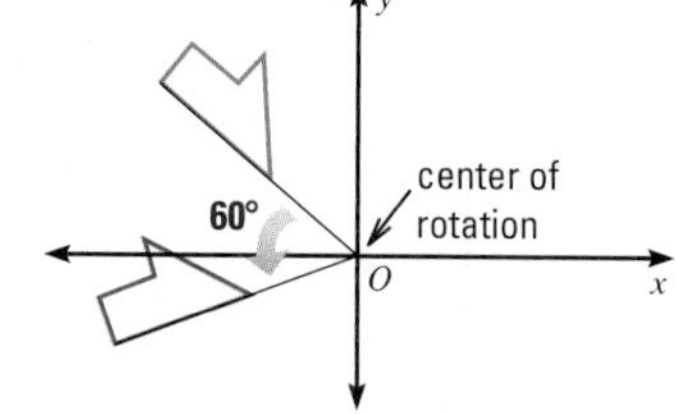

Notice that rotations preserve distances from the center of rotation. So, segments drawn from the center of rotation to corresponding points on the figures are congruent.

Differentiated Instruction

English Learners Students learning English may confuse the words *transformation*, *translation*, *reflection*, and *rotation*. Explain that a transformation refers to a translation, reflection, or rotation. *Transform* means "to change." Help students remember each transformation by thinking about these definitions: *translate* means "to move something," *reflect* means "to show a mirror image," and *rotate* means "to turn around a point."

See also the *Geometry Toolkit* for more strategies.

EXAMPLE 4 Identify a rotation

Graph $\overline{AB}$ and $\overline{CD}$. Tell whether $\overline{CD}$ is a rotation of $\overline{AB}$ about the origin. If so, give the angle and direction of rotation.

a. $A(-3, 1), B(-1, 3), C(1, 3), D(3, 1)$

b. $A(0, 1), B(1, 3), C(-1, 1), D(-3, 2)$

Solution

a.

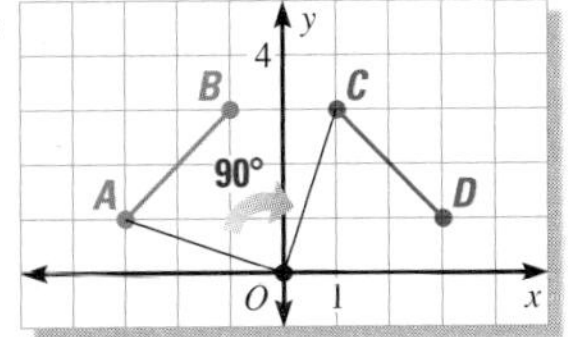

$m\angle AOC = m\angle BOD = 90°$
This is a 90° clockwise rotation.

b.

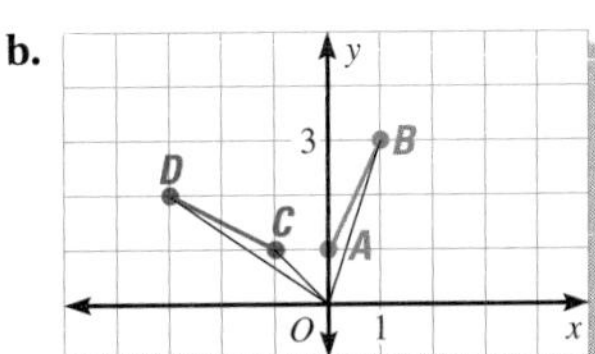

$m\angle AOC < m\angle BOD$
This is not a rotation.

EXAMPLE 5 Verify congruence

The vertices of $\triangle ABC$ are $A(4, 4)$, $B(6, 6)$, and $C(7, 4)$. The notation $(x, y) \to (x + 1, y - 3)$ describes the translation of $\triangle ABC$ to $\triangle DEF$. Show that $\triangle ABC \cong \triangle DEF$ to verify that the translation is a congruence transformation.

Solution

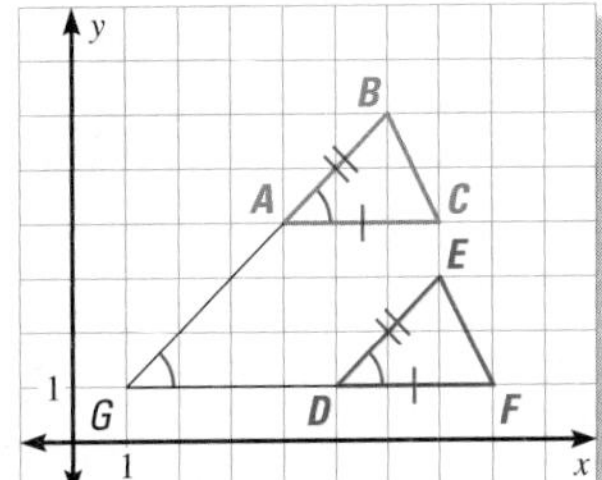

S You can see that $AC = DF = 3$, so $\overline{AC} \cong \overline{DF}$.

A Using the slopes, $\overline{AB} \parallel \overline{DE}$ and $\overline{AC} \parallel \overline{DF}$. If you extend $\overline{AB}$ and $\overline{DF}$ to form $\angle G$, the Corresponding Angles Postulate gives you $\angle BAC \cong \angle G$ and $\angle G \cong \angle EDF$. Then, $\angle BAC \cong \angle EDF$ by the Transitive Property of Congruence.

S Using the Distance Formula, $AB = DE = 2\sqrt{2}$ so $\overline{AB} \cong \overline{DE}$. So, $\triangle ABC \cong \triangle DEF$ by the SAS Congruence Postulate.

▶ Because $\triangle ABC \cong \triangle DEF$, the translation is a congruence transformation.

✓ GUIDED PRACTICE for Examples 4 and 5

4. Tell whether $\triangle PQR$ is a rotation of $\triangle STR$. If so, give the angle and direction of rotation.
yes; 180° counterclockwise
5. Show that $\triangle PQR \cong \triangle STR$ to verify that the transformation is a congruence transformation.
$\overline{PQ} \cong \overline{ST}$, $\overline{PR} \cong \overline{SR}$, by HL, $\triangle PQR \cong \triangle STR$ so it is a congruence transformation.

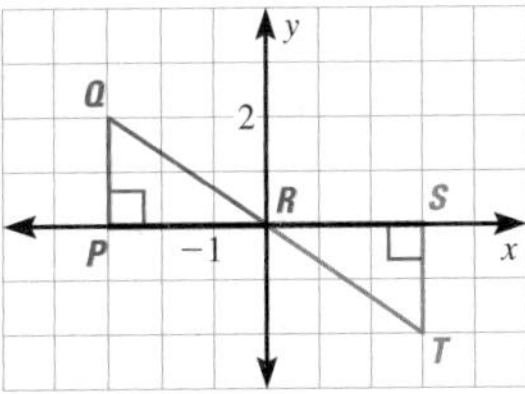

Vocabulary

Have students develop a method to remember what a reflection, rotation, and translation are. For example, it might help to observe that the words "flip" and "reflection" both contain the letter combination "fl". The words "translation" and "slide" both contain the letter combination "sl".

Extra Example 4

Graph $\overline{PQ}$ and $\overline{RS}$. Tell whether $\overline{RS}$ is a rotation of $\overline{PQ}$ about the origin. If so, give the angle and direction of rotation.

a. $P(2, 6), Q(5, 1), R(6, -1), S(1, -2)$
not rotation

b. $P(4, 2), Q(3, 3), R(-2, 4), S(-3, 3)$
rotation 90° counterclockwise

Extra Example 5

The vertices of $\triangle DEF$ are $D(-1, 3)$, $E(4, 2)$, and $F(1, -2)$. The rule $(x, y) \to (x - 2, y + 4)$ was used to translate $\triangle DEF$ to $\triangle XYZ$. Show that $\triangle DEF \cong \triangle XYZ$ to verify that the translation is a congruence transformation. **$DE = XY = \sqrt{26}$; $DF = XZ = \sqrt{29}$; $EF = YZ = 5$. $\triangle DEF \cong \triangle XYZ$ by the SSS Congruence Postulate.**

Key Question to Ask for Example 5

- How else could you have proved the triangles congruent? **Find the lengths of all three sides of both triangles and use SSS.**

Closing the Lesson

Have students summarize the major points of the lesson and answer the Essential Question: What transformations create an image congruent to the original figure?

- **A translation is a transformation that moves every point of a figure the same distance in the same direction.**
- **A reflection is a transformation that uses a line of reflection to create a mirror image of the original figure.**
- **A rotation is a transformation in which a figure is turned about a fixed point.**

Translations, reflections, and rotations create an image congruent to the original figure.

4 PRACTICE AND APPLY

Assignment Guide

Answer Transparencies available for all exercises

Basic:
Day 1: pp. 276–279
Exs. 1–16, 51
Day 2: pp. 276–279
Exs. 17–29, 38–42, 45–50

Average:
Day 1: pp. 276–279
Exs. 1, 2, 4, 8, 10–16 even, 26–31, 51
Day 2: pp. 276–279
Exs. 17–25, 32–36, 38–43, 45–49 odd

Advanced:
Day 1: pp. 276–279
Exs. 1, 2, 4–16 even, 26–31, 37*, 51
Day 2: pp. 276–279
Exs. 17–25, 32–36, 38–44*, 46, 50

Block:
pp. 276–279
Exs. 1, 2, 4, 8, 10–16 even, 17–36, 38–43, 45–49 odd, 51

Differentiated Instruction

See *Geometry Best Practices Toolkit* for suggestions on addressing the needs of a diverse classroom.

Homework Check

For a quick check of student understanding of key concepts, go over the following exercises:

Basic: 4, 10, 17, 20, 38
Average: 8, 12, 18, 21, 38
Advanced: 8, 14, 19, 22, 42

Extra Practice

- Student Edition, p. 903
- Chapter 4 Resource Book: Practice levels A, B, C, pp. 105–110

Practice Worksheet

An easily-readable reduced practice page (with answers) for this lesson can be found on p. 214C.

4.8 EXERCISES

HOMEWORK KEY ○ = WORKED-OUT SOLUTIONS on p. WS5 for Exs. 11, 23, and 39
★ = STANDARDIZED TEST PRACTICE Exs. 2, 25, 40, 41, and 43

SKILL PRACTICE

A

1. **VOCABULARY** *Describe* the translation $(x, y) \rightarrow (x - 1, y + 4)$ in words.
Subtract one from each x-coordinate and add 4 to each y-coordinate.
2. ★ **WRITING** *Explain* why the term *congruence transformation* is used in describing translations, reflections, and rotations.
The image is congruent to the original figure.

EXAMPLE 1 on p. 272 for Exs. 3–8

IDENTIFYING TRANSFORMATIONS **Name the type of transformation shown.**

3. 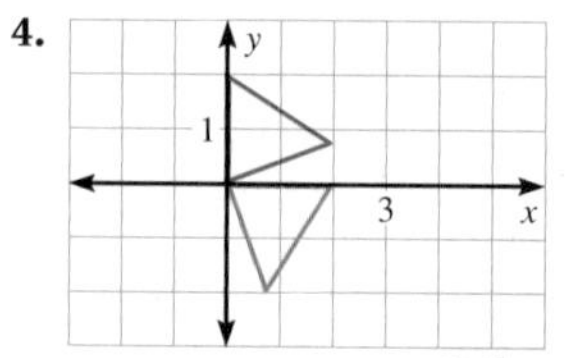 **translation**

4. **rotation**

5. 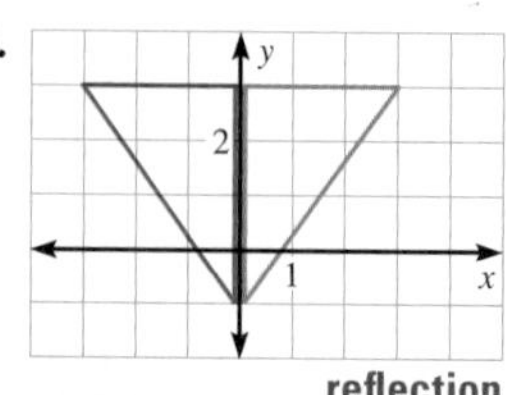 **reflection**

WINDOWS **Decide whether the moving part of the window is a translation.**

6. Double hung **yes**

7. Casement **no**

8. Sliding **yes**

EXAMPLE 2 on p. 273 for Exs. 9–16

DRAWING A TRANSLATION **Copy figure *ABCD* and draw its image after the translation.** **9–12. See margin.**

9. $(x, y) \rightarrow (x + 2, y - 3)$
10. $(x, y) \rightarrow (x - 1, y - 5)$
11. $(x, y) \rightarrow (x + 4, y + 1)$
12. $(x, y) \rightarrow (x - 2, y + 3)$

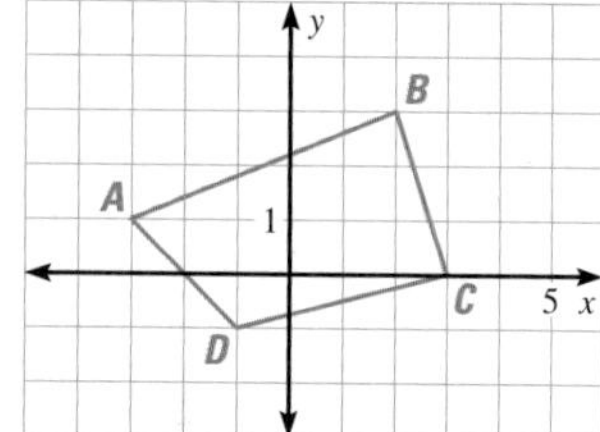

COORDINATE NOTATION **Use coordinate notation to *describe* the translation.**

13. 4 units to the left, 2 units down **$(x, y) \rightarrow (x - 4, y - 2)$**
14. 6 units to the right, 3 units up **$(x, y) \rightarrow (x + 6, y + 3)$**
15. 2 units to the right, 1 unit down **$(x, y) \rightarrow (x + 2, y - 1)$**
16. 7 units to the left, 9 units up **$(x, y) \rightarrow (x - 7, y + 9)$**

EXAMPLE 3 on p. 274 for Exs. 17–19

DRAWING **Use a reflection in the x-axis to draw the other half of the figure.** **17–19. See margin.**

17. 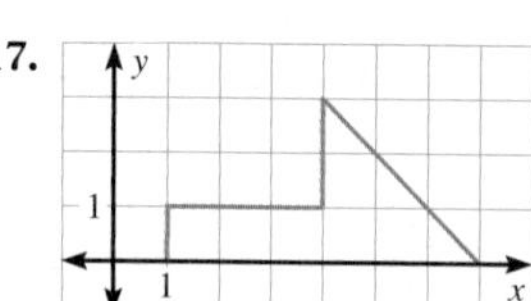

18. 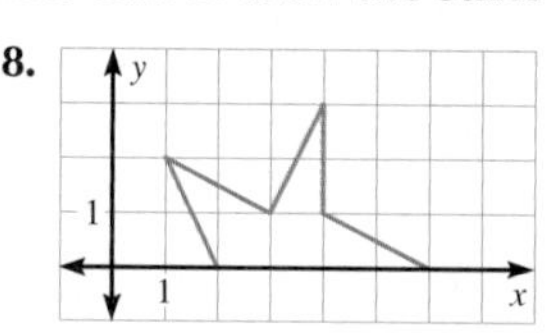

19. 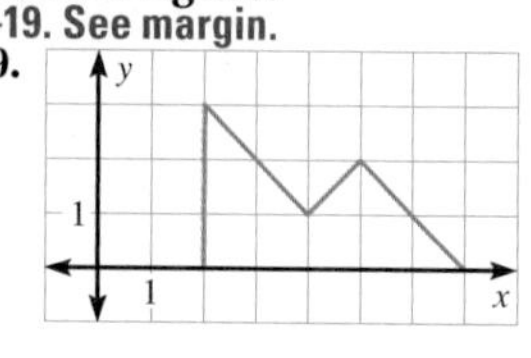

9. 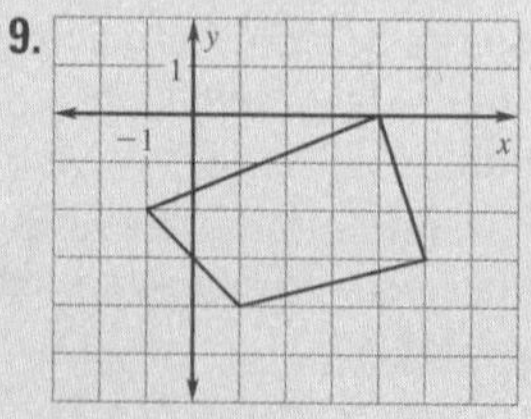

10. 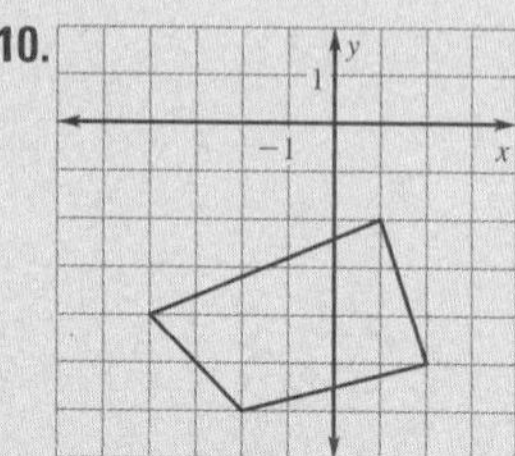

11. 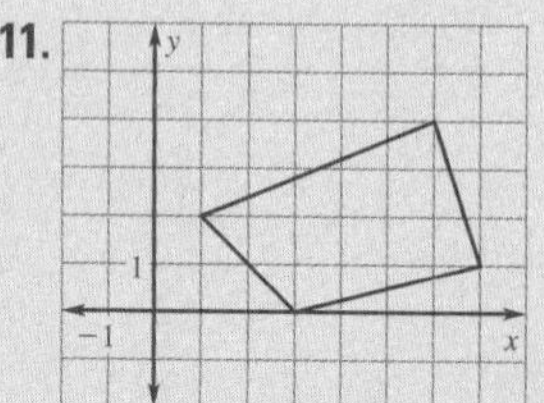

12. 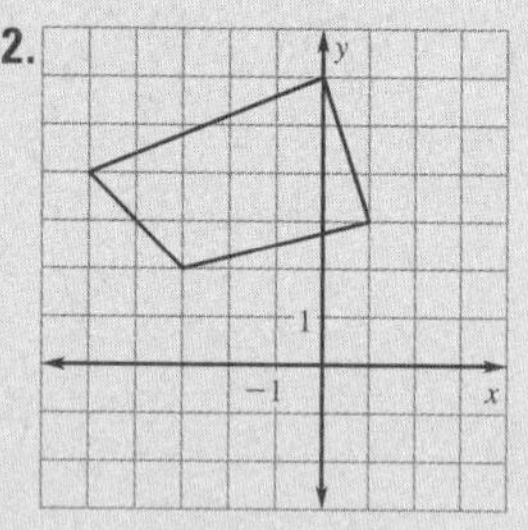

EXAMPLE 4
on p. 275
for Exs. 20–23

ROTATIONS Use the coordinates to graph $\overline{AB}$ and $\overline{CD}$. Tell whether $\overline{CD}$ is a rotation of $\overline{AB}$ about the origin. If so, give the angle and direction of rotation. 20–23. See margin for art.

20. $A(1, 2), B(3, 4), C(2, -1), D(4, -3)$ rotation; 90° clockwise
21. $A(-2, -4), B(-1, -2), C(4, 3), D(2, 1)$ not a rotation
22. $A(-4, 0), B(-4, -4), C(4, 4), D(0, 4)$ not a rotation
23. $A(1, 2), B(3, 0), C(2, -1), D(2, -3)$ not a rotation

24. **ERROR ANALYSIS** A student says that the red triangle is a 120° clockwise rotation of the blue triangle about the origin. *Describe* and correct the error.
The red triangle rotation segment should connect corresponding angles of the triangle; the red triangle is rotated 90° clockwise.

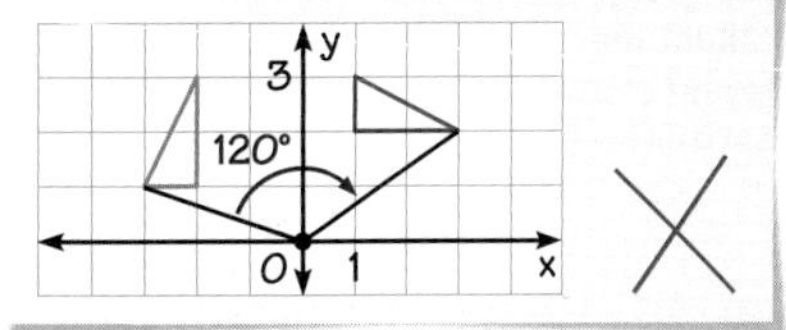

B

25. ★ **WRITING** Can a point or a line segment be its own image under a transformation? *Explain* and illustrate your answer.
Yes; take any point or any line segment and rotate 360°; see margin for art.

APPLYING TRANSLATIONS Complete the statement using the description of the translation. In the description, points (0, 3) and (2, 5) are two vertices of a hexagon.

26. If (0, 3) translates to (0, 0), then (2, 5) translates to _?_. (2, 2)
27. If (0, 3) translates to (1, 2), then (2, 5) translates to _?_. (3, 4)
28. If (0, 3) translates to (−3, −2), then (2, 5) translates to _?_. (−1, 0)

xy ALGEBRA A point on an image and the translation are given. Find the corresponding point on the original figure.

29. Point on image: (4, 0); translation: $(x, y) \to (x + 2, y - 3)$ (2, 3)
30. Point on image: (−3, 5); translation: $(x, y) \to (-x, y)$ (3, 5)
31. Point on image: (6, −9); translation: $(x, y) \to (x - 7, y - 4)$ (13, −5)

32. **CONGRUENCE** Show that the transformation in Exercise 3 is a congruence transformation.
The corresponding sides of each triangle are congruent therefore the triangles are congruent.

DESCRIBING AN IMAGE State the segment or triangle that represents the image. You can use tracing paper to help you see the rotation.

33. 90° clockwise rotation of $\overline{ST}$ about E $\overline{UV}$
34. 90° counterclockwise rotation of $\overline{BX}$ about E $\overline{AV}$
35. 180° rotation of $\triangle BWX$ about E $\triangle DST$
36. 180° rotation of $\triangle TUA$ about E $\triangle XYC$

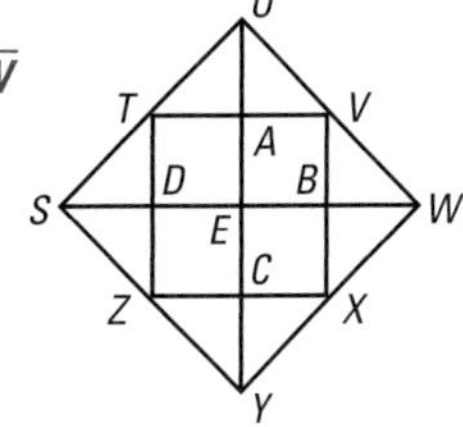

C

37. **CHALLENGE** Solve for the variables in the transformation of $\overline{AB}$ to $\overline{CD}$ and then to $\overline{EF}$. $m = 3, n = 11, a = 2, g = 2, h = \frac{1}{4}$

$A(2, 3)$, $B(4, 2a)$ → Translation: $(x, y) \to (x - 2, y + 1)$ → $C(m - 3, 4)$, $D(n - 9, 5)$ → Reflection: in x-axis → $E(0, g - 6)$, $F(8h, -5)$

Avoiding Common Errors

Exercises 9–12 Students may reverse the effects on x and y in the rule. For instance, in Exercise 9 they may move up 2 and left 3. Review the idea that a change in the x-coordinate corresponds to a change in horizontal position and a change in the y-coordinate corresponds to a change in vertical position.

Study Strategy

Exercises 29–31 Suggest that students graph the point they are given and work backwards. Since the translation in Exercise 29 moves points 2 units to the right and 3 units down, start with the final point and move 2 units to the left and up 3 units to find the original point.

20.
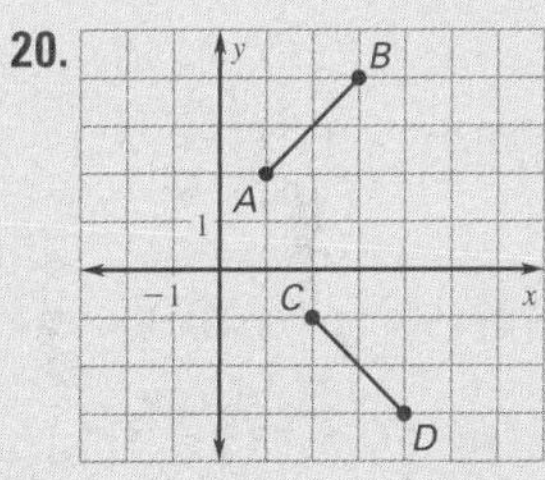

21.
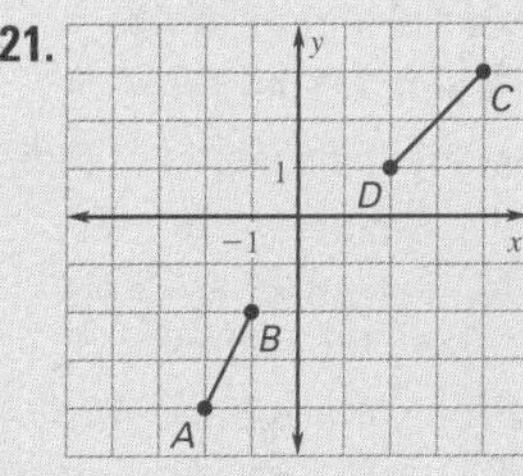

22.
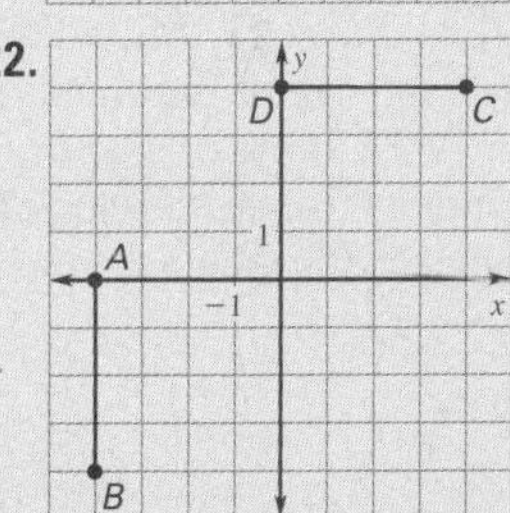

23.
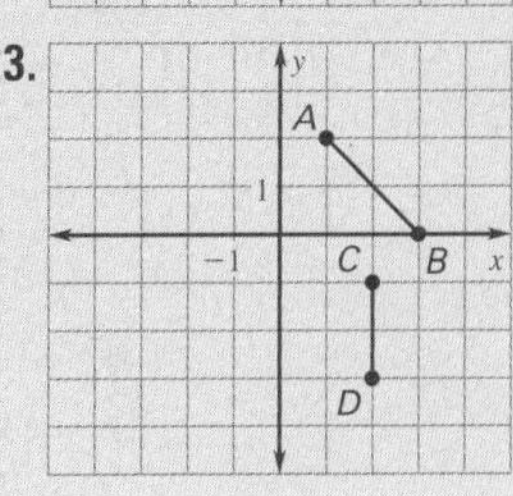

25.
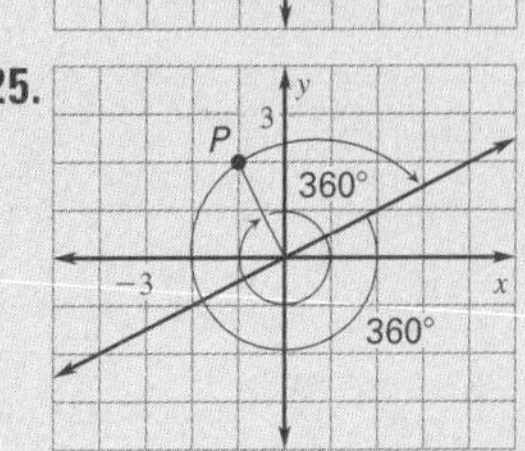

17.
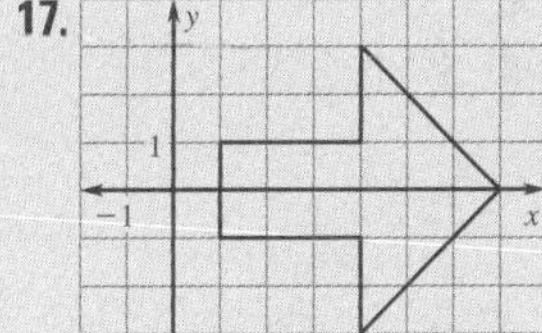

18.
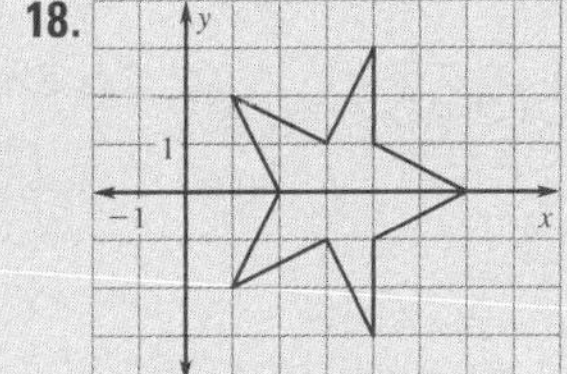

19.
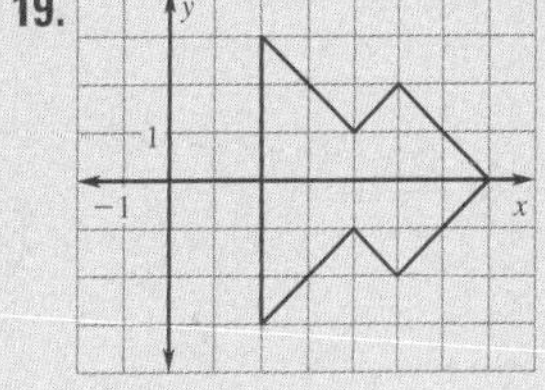

Mathematical Reasoning

Exercise 39 Ask students how they could use reflections instead of rotations to move the stencil from *A* to *B* and from *A* to *C*. **Reflect in the *y*-axis and then reflect in the *x*-axis.**

Internet Reference

Exercise 41 Additional information about playing the game of chess can be found at www.uschess.org/beginners/letsplay.php

Teaching Strategy

Exercise 43 If students have difficulty visualizing the resulting figure, let them use a piece of paper and scissors, do the cuts and compare the result to the choices.

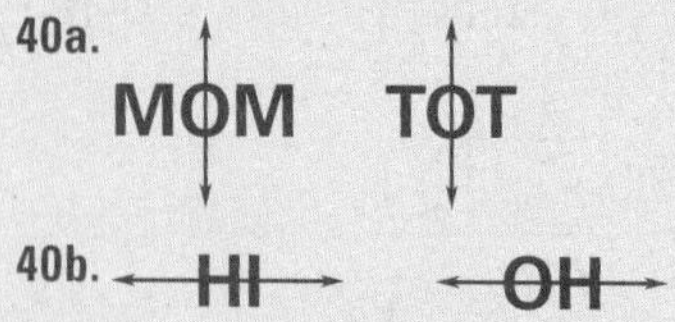

42. The slopes of $\overline{BC}$ and $\overline{EF}$ are both −1 and the slopes of $\overline{AB}$ and $\overline{DE}$ are both 1. Therefore, $\overline{AB} \perp \overline{BC}$ since the product of their slopes is −1. Similarly, $\overline{DE} \perp \overline{EF}$. Thus $\triangle ABC$ and $\triangle DEF$ are right triangles. Using the distance formula, $BC = EF = \sqrt{2}$ and $AC = DF = \sqrt{10}$. So, $\overline{BC} \cong \overline{EF}$, $\overline{AC} \cong \overline{DF}$. By the HL Congruence Theorem, $\triangle ABC \cong \triangle DEF$. Therefore, $\triangle DEF$ is a congruence transformation of $\triangle ABC$, described by the notation $(x, y) \to (x - 5, y + 1)$.

PROBLEM SOLVING

EXAMPLE 3 A
on p. 274
for Ex. 38

38a. The designer can reflect the layout over the horizontal line.

38. KITES The design for a kite shows the layout and dimensions for only half of the kite.

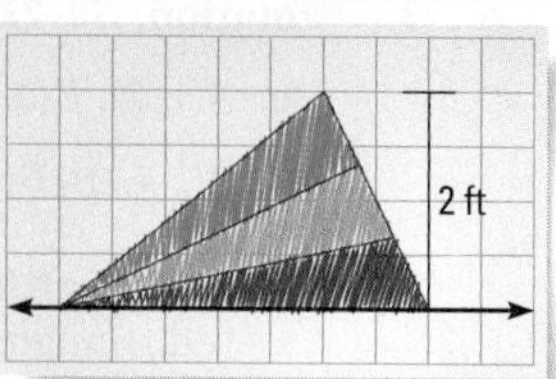

a. What type of transformation can a designer use to create plans for the entire kite?

b. What is the maximum width of the entire kite? **4 ft**

@HomeTutor for problem solving help at classzone.com

39. STENCILING You are stenciling a room in your home. You want to use the stencil pattern below on the left to create the design shown. Give the angles and directions of rotation you will use to move the stencil from *A* to *B* and from *A* to *C*. **90° clockwise, 90° counterclockwise**

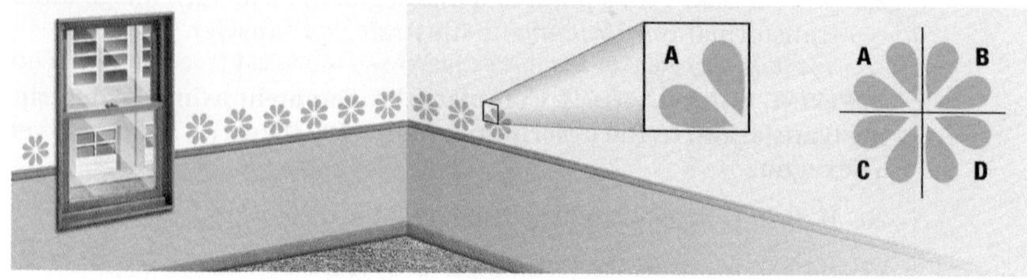

@HomeTutor for problem solving help at classzone.com

40. ★ OPEN-ENDED MATH Some words reflect onto themselves through a vertical line of reflection. An example is shown. **40a, b. See margin for art.**

a. Find two other words with vertical lines of reflection. Draw the line of reflection for each word. ***Sample answer:* MOM, TOT**

b. Find two words with horizontal lines of reflection. Draw the line of reflection for each word. ***Sample answer:* HI, OH**

B

41. ★ SHORT RESPONSE In chess, six different kinds of pieces are moved according to individual rules. The Knight (shaped like a horse) moves in an "L" shape. It moves two squares horizontally or vertically and then one additional square perpendicular to its original direction. When a knight lands on a square with another piece, it *captures* that piece.

a. *Describe* the translation used by the Black Knight to capture the White Pawn. $(x, y) \to (x - 1, y + 2)$

b. *Describe* the translation used by the White Knight to capture the Black Pawn. $(x, y) \to (x + 2, y - 1)$

c. After both pawns are captured, can the Black Knight capture the White Knight? *Explain.* **No; the translation needed does not match a knight's move.**

EXAMPLE 5
on p. 275
for Ex. 42

42. VERIFYING CONGRUENCE Show that $\triangle ABC$ and $\triangle DEF$ are right triangles and use the HL Congruence Theorem to verify that $\triangle DEF$ is a congruence transformation of $\triangle ABC$. **See margin.**

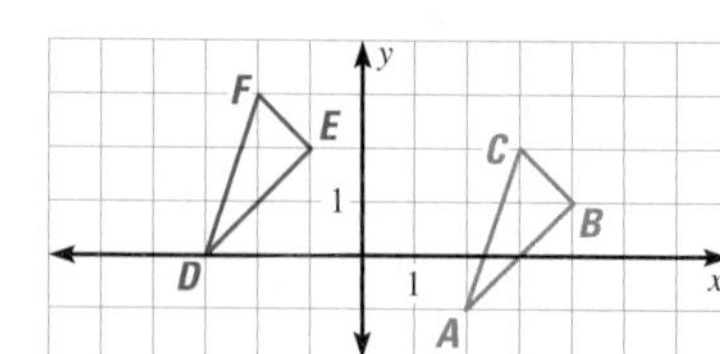

○ = WORKED-OUT SOLUTIONS on p. WS1

★ = STANDARDIZED TEST PRACTICE

Quiz, p. 279

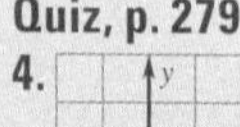

4.
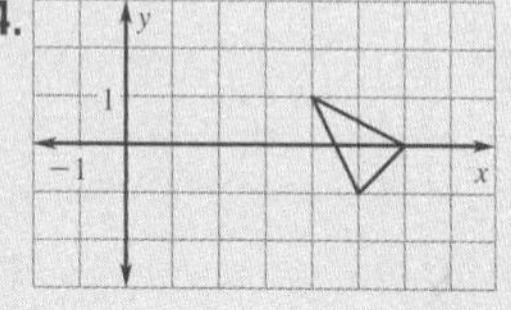

5.
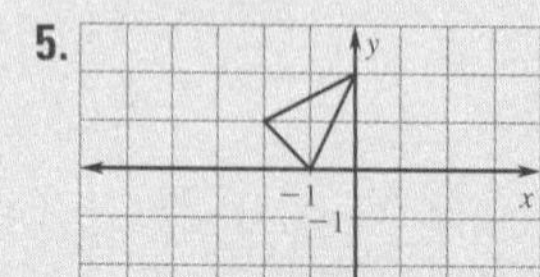

6.
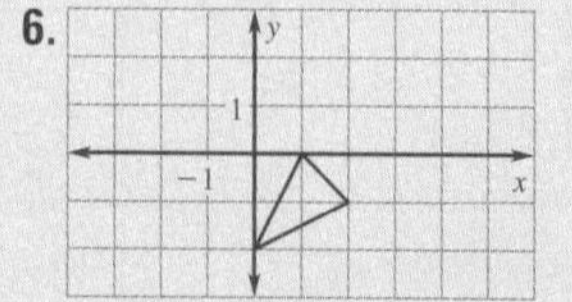

7.
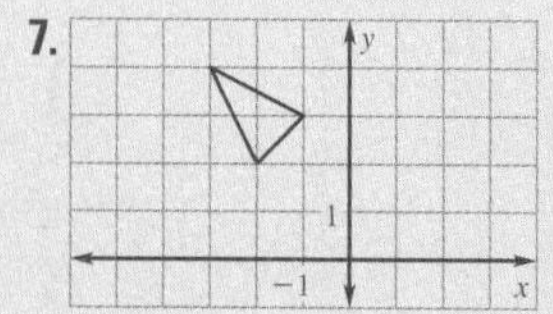

43. ★ **MULTIPLE CHOICE** A piece of paper is folded in half and some cuts are made, as shown. Which figure represents the unfolded piece of paper? **B**

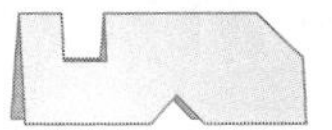

Ⓐ 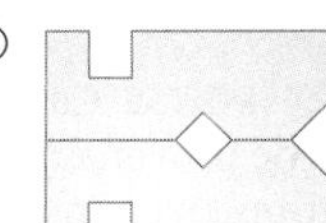 Ⓑ 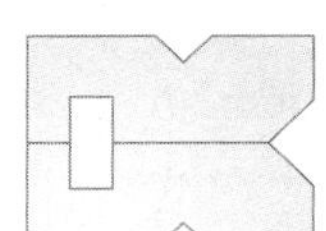 Ⓒ 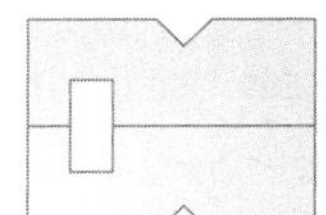 Ⓓ 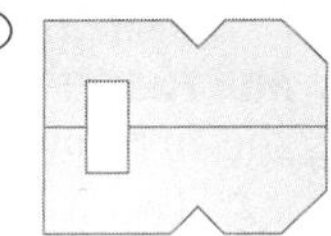

C 44. **CHALLENGE** A triangle is rotated 90° counterclockwise and then translated three units up. The vertices of the final image are $A(-4, 4)$, $B(-1, 6)$, and $C(-1, 4)$. Find the vertices of the original triangle. Would the final image be the same if the original triangle was translated 3 units up and then rotated 90° counterclockwise? *Explain* your reasoning.
(1, 4), (1, 1), (3, 1); no; the final image would have a different rotation segment.

MIXED REVIEW

PREVIEW
Prepare for Lesson 5.1 in Exs. 45–50.

Simplify the expression. Variables *a* and *b* are positive.

45. $\dfrac{-a-0}{0-(-b)}$ *(p. 870)* $-\dfrac{a}{b}$ 46. $|(a+b)-a|$ *(p. 870)* b 47. $\dfrac{2a+2b}{2}$ *(p. 139)* $a+b$

Simplify the expression. Variables *a* and *b* are positive. *(p. 139)*

48. $\sqrt{(-b)^2}$ b 49. $\sqrt{(2a)^2}$ $2a$ 50. $\sqrt{(2a-a)^2+(0-b)^2}$ $\sqrt{a^2+b^2}$

51. Use the SSS Congruence Postulate to show $\triangle RST \cong \triangle UVW$. *(p. 234)*

$R(1, -4), S(1, -1), T(6, -1)$ $U(1, 4), V(1, 1), W(6, 1)$
Sample answer: $\overline{RS} \cong \overline{UV}$, $\overline{ST} \cong \overline{VW}$, $\overline{TR} \cong \overline{WU}$

QUIZ *for Lessons 4.7–4.8*

Find the value of *x*. *(p. 264)*

1. 

2

2. 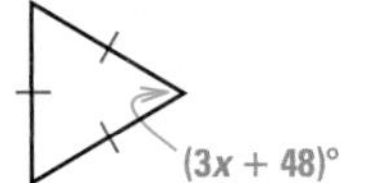

4

3. 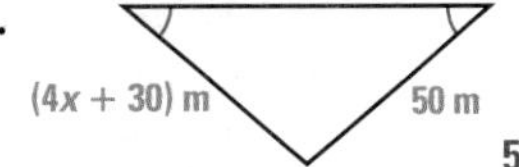

5

Copy $\triangle EFG$ and draw its image after the transformation. Identify the type of transformation. *(p. 272)* **4–7. See margin for art.**

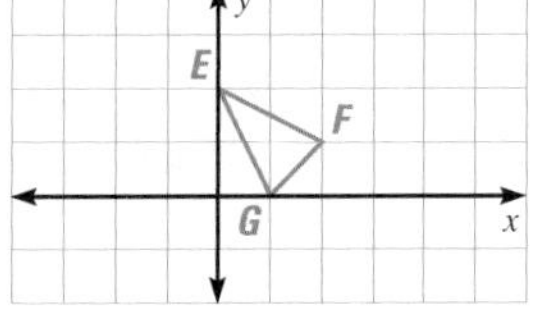

4. $(x, y) \to (x + 4, y - 1)$ **translation**
5. $(x, y) \to (-x, y)$ **reflection in the y-axis**
6. $(x, y) \to (x, -y)$ **reflcotion in the x-axis**
7. $(x, y) \to (x - 3, y + 2)$ **translation**

8. Is Figure B a rotation of Figure A about the origin? If so, give the angle and direction of rotation. *(p. 272)* **no**

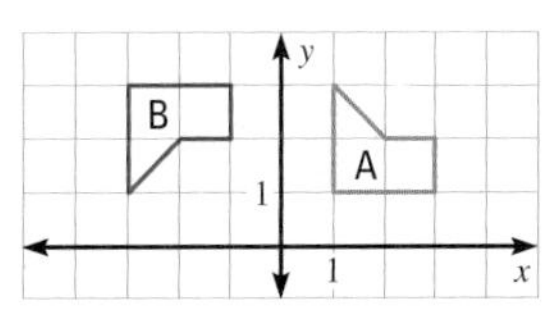

5 ASSESS AND RETEACH

Daily Homework Quiz

Transparency Available

1. Use coordinate notation to describe the translation 3 units to the left and 1 unit up.
$(x, y) \to (x - 3, y + 1)$
2. Use a reflection in the x-axis to draw the other half of the figure.

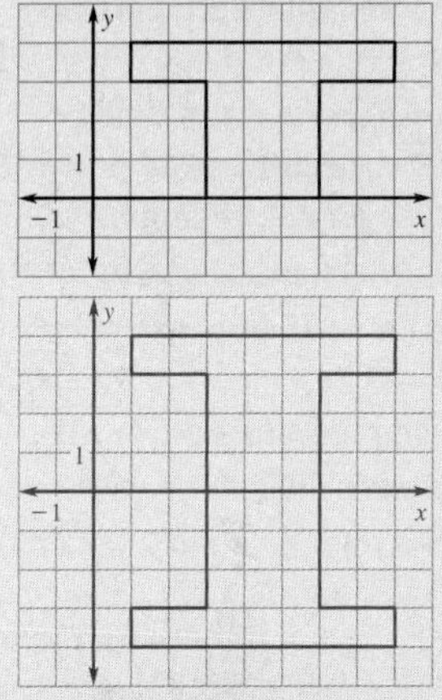

3. Tell whether $\overline{XY}$ is a rotation of $\overline{GH}$ about the origin if the points are $X(-6, 2)$, $Y(-4, 3)$, $G(6, -2)$, and $H(4, -3)$. If so, give the angle and direction of rotation. **Yes; 180° clockwise or counterclockwise**

 **Online Quiz**

Available at **classzone.com**

Diagnosis/Remediation

- Practice A, B, C in Chapter 4 Resource Book, pp. 105–110
- Study Guide in Chapter 4 Resource Book, pp. 111–112
- Practice Workbook, pp. 82–84
- @HomeTutor

Challenge

Additional challenge is available in the Chapter 4 Resource Book, p. 115.

Quiz

An easily-readable reduced copy of the quiz (with answers) on Lessons 4.7–4.8 from the Assessment Book can be found on p. 214G.

3. the length of the side forming the 34° angle with side measuring 8 centimeters, the angle the third side makes with the side measuring 8 centimeters, or the angle the third side makes with the side forming the 34° angle with the side measuring 8 centimeters

4. Yes; yes; $\angle ACD$ and $\angle BCE$ are vertical angles so they are congruent which makes $\triangle ACD \cong \triangle BCE$ by SAS. Since $\triangle ACD \cong \triangle BCE$, $\overline{AD} \cong \overline{BE}$ because corr. parts of $\cong$ ▲s are $\cong$.

5a. In $\triangle ABC$, it is given that $\overline{AB} \cong \overline{CB}$, therefore $\angle BCE \cong \angle BAE$ by the Base Angles Theorem.

5b. *Sample answer:* $\triangle ABE \cong \triangle CBE$ by AAS. $\overline{CE} \cong \overline{AE}$ because corr. parts of $\cong$ ▲s are $\cong$. $\triangle FAE \cong \triangle DCE$ by ASA and therefore $\overline{AF} \cong \overline{CD}$ because corr. parts of $\cong$ ▲s are $\cong$.

MIXED REVIEW *of Problem Solving*

STATE TEST PRACTICE
classzone.com

Lessons 4.5–4.8

1. **MULTI-STEP PROBLEM** Use the quilt pattern shown below.

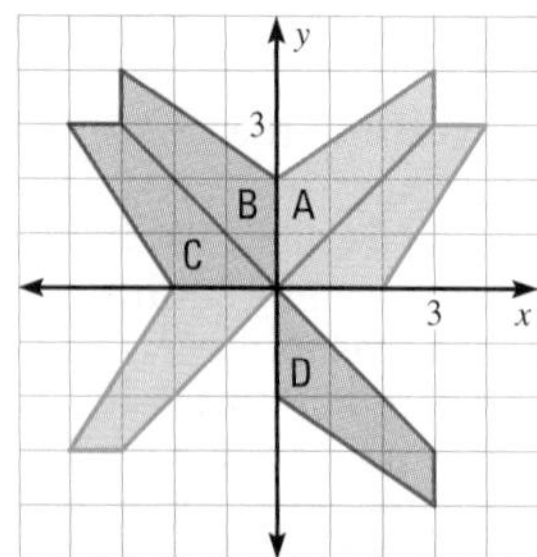

   a. Figure B is the image of Figure A. Name and *describe* the transformation. **reflection in the *y*-axis**
   b. Figure C is the image of Figure A. Name and *describe* the transformation. **rotation of 90° counterclockwise**
   c. Figure D is the image of Figure A. Name and *describe* the transformation. **reflection in the *x*-axis**
   d. *Explain* how you could complete the quilt pattern using transformations of Figure A. **Rotate Figure A 90° clockwise and 180°.**

2. **SHORT RESPONSE** You are told that a triangle has sides that are 5 centimeters and 3 centimeters long. You are also told that the side that is 5 centimeters long forms an angle with the third side that measures 28°. Is there only one triangle that has these given dimensions? *Explain* why or why not. **No; the given angle is not the included angle.**

3. **OPEN-ENDED** A friend has drawn a triangle on a piece of paper and she is describing the triangle so that you can draw one that is congruent to hers. So far, she has told you that the length of one side is 8 centimeters and one of the angles formed with this side is 34°. *Describe* three pieces of additional information you could use to construct the triangle. **See margin.**

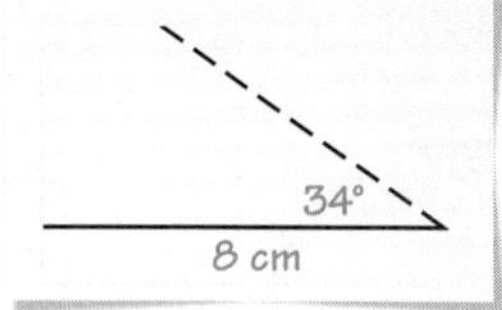

4. **SHORT RESPONSE** Can the triangles *ACD* and *BCE* be proven congruent using the information given in the diagram? Can you show that $\overline{AD} \cong \overline{BE}$? *Explain.* **See margin.**

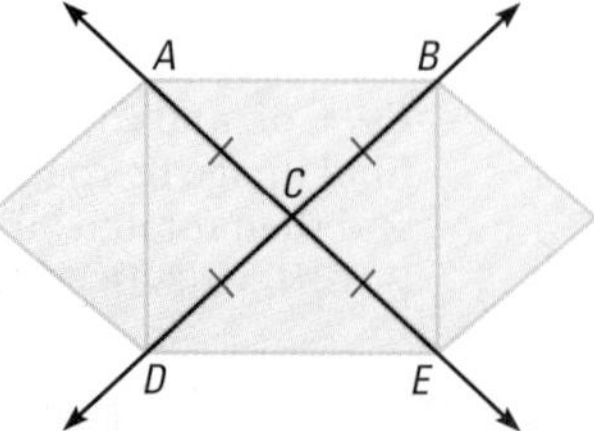

5. **EXTENDED RESPONSE** Use the information given in the diagram to prove the statements below. **a, b. See margin.**

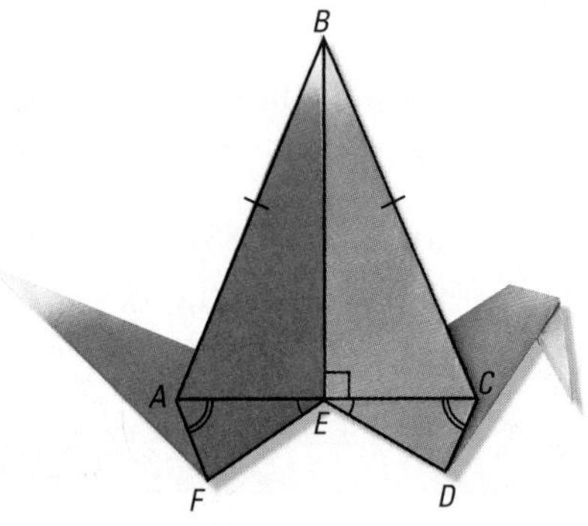

   a. Prove that $\angle BCE \cong \angle BAE$.
   b. Prove that $\overline{AF} \cong \overline{CD}$.

6. **GRIDDED ANSWER** Find the value of *x* in the diagram. **7**

CHAPTER SUMMARY

BIG IDEAS *For Your Notebook*

Big Idea 1

Classifying Triangles by Sides and Angles

	Equilateral	Isosceles	Scalene
Sides	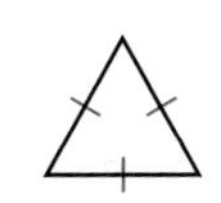	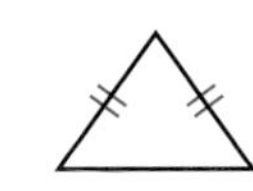	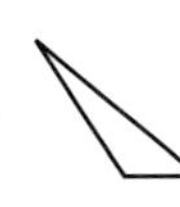
	3 congruent sides	2 or 3 congruent sides	No congruent sides

	Acute	Equiangular	Right	Obtuse
Angles	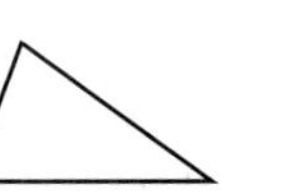		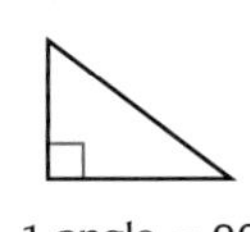	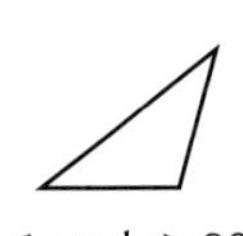
	3 angles $< 90°$	3 angles $= 60°$	1 angle $= 90°$	1 angle $> 90°$

Big Idea 2

Proving That Triangles Are Congruent

SSS	All three sides are congruent.	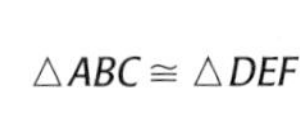 $\triangle ABC \cong \triangle DEF$	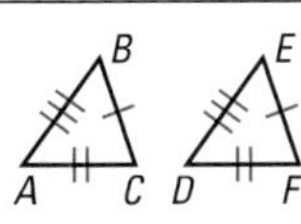
SAS	Two sides and the included angle are congruent.	$\triangle ABC \cong \triangle DEF$	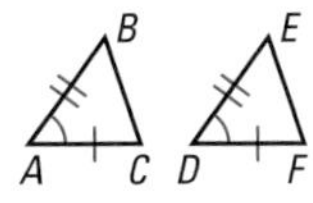
HL	The hypotenuse and one of the legs are congruent. (Right triangles only)	$\triangle ABC \cong \triangle DEF$	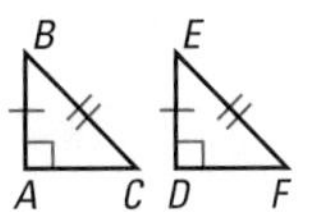
ASA	Two angles and the included side are congruent.	$\triangle ABC \cong \triangle DEF$	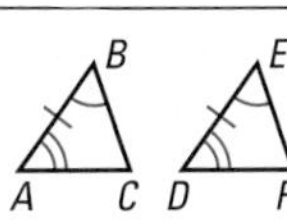
AAS	Two angles and a (non-included) side are congruent.	$\triangle ABC \cong \triangle DEF$	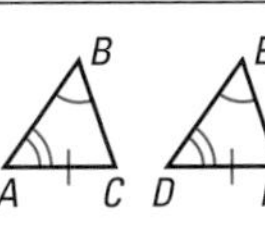

Big Idea 3

Using Coordinate Geometry to Investigate Triangle Relationships

You can use the Distance and Midpoint Formulas to apply postulates and theorems to triangles in the coordinate plane.

Additional Resources

The following resources are available to help review the materials in this chapter.

Chapter 4 Resource Book

- Chapter Review Games and Activities, p. 116
- Cumulative Practice, Chs. 1–4, pp. 119–120

Student Resources in Spanish

eWorkbook

@HomeTutor

Vocabulary Practice

Vocabulary practice is available at **classzone.com**

Extra Example 4.1

Find the measure of the exterior angle shown. **110°**

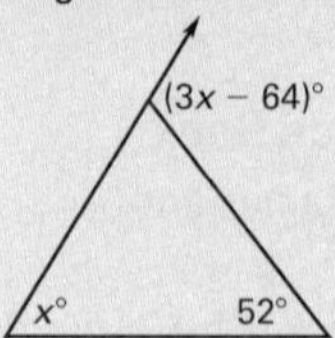

3. An isosceles triangle has at least two congruent sides while a scalene triangle has no congruent sides.

4.

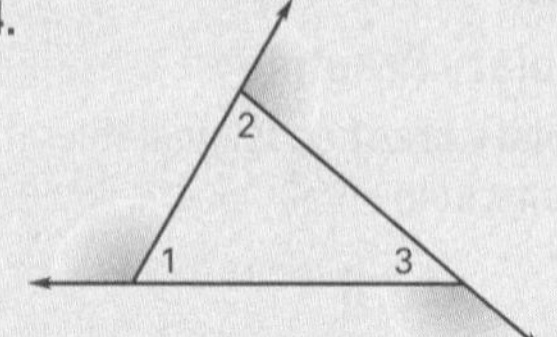

4 CHAPTER REVIEW

@HomeTutor
classzone.com
- Multi-Language Glossary
- Vocabulary practice

REVIEW KEY VOCABULARY

For a list of postulates and theorems, see pp. 926–931.

- triangle, *p. 217* scalene, isosceles, equilateral, acute, right, obtuse, equiangular
- interior angles, *p. 218*
- exterior angles, *p. 218*
- corollary to a theorem, *p. 220*
- congruent figures, *p. 225*
- corresponding parts, *p. 225*
- right triangle, *p. 241* legs, hypotenuse
- flow proof, *p. 250*
- isosceles triangle, *p. 264* legs, vertex angle, base, base angles
- transformation, *p. 272*
- image, *p. 272*
- congruence transformation, *p. 272* translation, reflection, rotation

3. An isosceles triangle has at least two congruent sides while a scalene triangle has no congruent sides.

VOCABULARY EXERCISES

1. Copy and complete: A triangle with three congruent angles is called __?__. **equiangular**
2. WRITING *Compare* vertex angles and base angles. **In an isosceles triangle, base angles are opposite the congruent sides while the congruent sides form the vertex angle.**
3. WRITING *Describe* the difference between isosceles and scalene triangles. **See margin.**
4. Sketch an acute scalene triangle. Label its interior angles 1, 2, and 3. Then draw and shade its exterior angles. **See margin.**
5. If $\triangle PQR \cong \triangle LMN$, which angles are corresponding angles? Which sides are corresponding sides? **$\angle P$ and $\angle L$, $\angle Q$ and $\angle M$, $\angle R$ and $\angle N$; $\overline{PQ}$ and $\overline{LM}$, $\overline{QR}$ and $\overline{MN}$, $\overline{RP}$ and $\overline{NL}$**

REVIEW EXAMPLES AND EXERCISES

Use the review examples and exercises below to check your understanding of the concepts you have learned in each lesson of Chapter 4.

4.1 Apply Triangle Sum Properties *pp. 217–224*

EXAMPLE

Find the measure of the exterior angle shown.

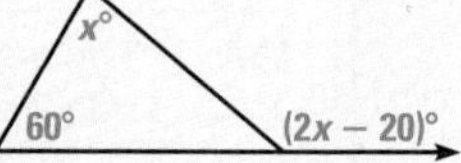

Use the Exterior Angle Theorem to write and solve an equation to find the value of x.

$(2x - 20)° = 60° + x°$ **Apply the Exterior Angle Theorem.**

$x = 80$ **Solve for x.**

The measure of the exterior angle is $(2 \cdot 80 - 20)°$, or $140°$.

EXERCISES

EXAMPLE 3 on p. 219 for Exs. 6–8

Find the measure of the exterior angle shown.

6. **65°**

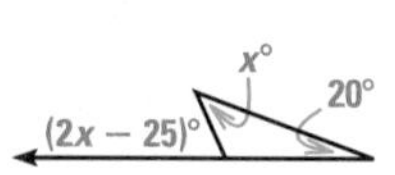

7. **120°**

8. **90°**

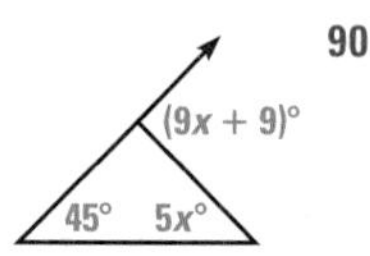

@HomeTutor
classzone.com
Chapter Review Practice

4.2 Apply Congruence and Triangles

pp. 225–231

EXAMPLE

Use the Third Angles Theorem to find $m\angle X$.

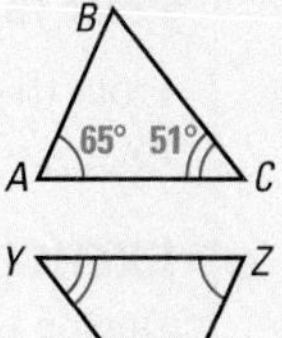

In the diagram, $\angle A \cong \angle Z$ and $\angle C \cong \angle Y$. By the Third Angles Theorem, $\angle B \cong \angle X$. Then by the Triangle Sum Theorem, $m\angle B = 180° - 65° - 51° = 64°$.

So, $m\angle X = m\angle B = 64°$ by the definition of congruent angles.

EXERCISES

EXAMPLES 2 and 4 on pp. 226–227 for Exs. 9–14

In the diagram, $\triangle ABC \cong \triangle VTU$. Find the indicated measure.

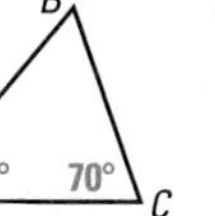

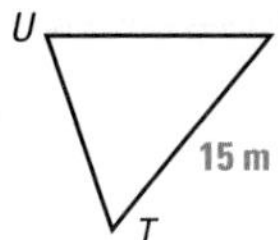

9. $m\angle B$ **60°**
10. AB **15 m**
11. $m\angle T$ **60°**
12. $m\angle V$ **50°**

Find the value of x.

13.

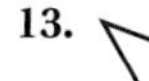

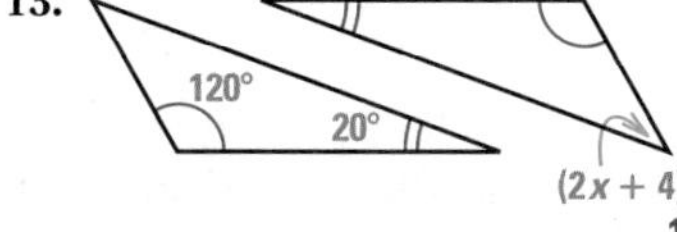

18

14.

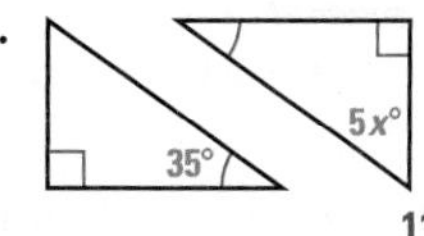

11

4.3 Prove Triangles Congruent by SSS

pp. 234–239

EXAMPLE

Prove that $\triangle LMN \cong \triangle PMN$.

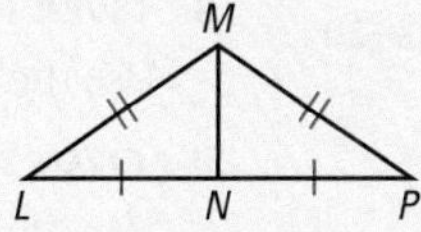

The marks on the diagram show that $\overline{LM} \cong \overline{PM}$ and $\overline{LN} \cong \overline{PN}$. By the Reflexive Property, $\overline{MN} \cong \overline{MN}$.

So, by the SSS Congruence Postulate, $\triangle LMN \cong \triangle PMN$.

EXERCISES

EXAMPLE 1 on p. 234 for Exs. 15–16

Decide whether the congruence statement is true. *Explain* your reasoning.

15. $\triangle XYZ \cong \triangle RST$

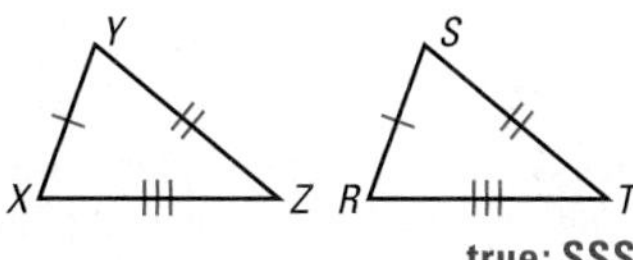

true; SSS

16. $\triangle ABC \cong \triangle DCB$

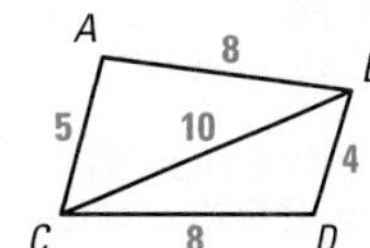

not true; $BD \neq CA$

Extra Example 4.2

Use the Third Angle Theorem to find $m\angle P$. **18°**

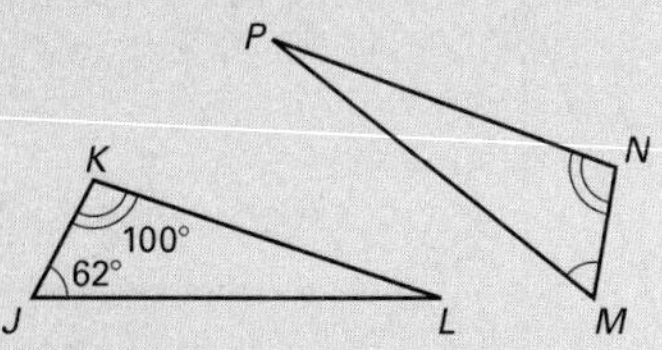

Extra Example 4.3

Prove that $\triangle RST \cong \triangle TUR$.

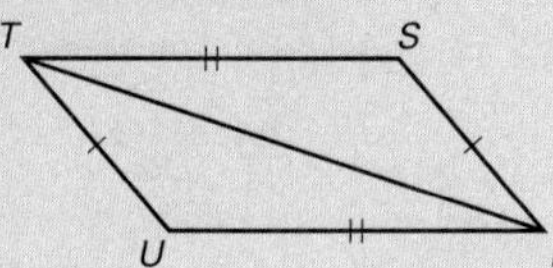

The marks show that $\overline{RS} \cong \overline{UT}$ and $\overline{ST} \cong \overline{UR}$. By the Refl. Prop. of Cong. Segs., $\overline{RT} \cong \overline{RT}$. So $\triangle RST \cong \triangle TUR$ by the SSS Cong. Post.

Extra Example 4.4

Prove that $\triangle ABC \cong \triangle DBC$.

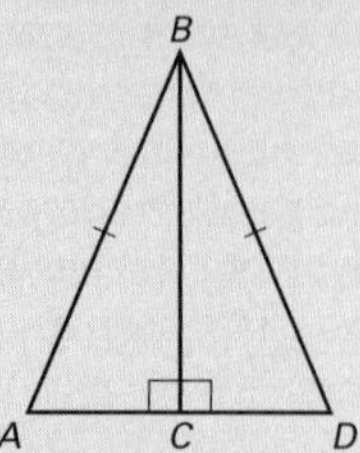

From the diagram, $\angle ACB$ and $\angle DCB$ are right angles and $\overline{AB} \cong \overline{DB}$. By the Refl. Prop. of $\cong$ Segs., $\overline{BC} \cong \overline{BC}$. Therefore, $\triangle ABC \cong \triangle DBC$ by the HL Cong. Thm.

Extra Example 4.5

Prove that $\triangle EFG \cong \triangle HJG$.

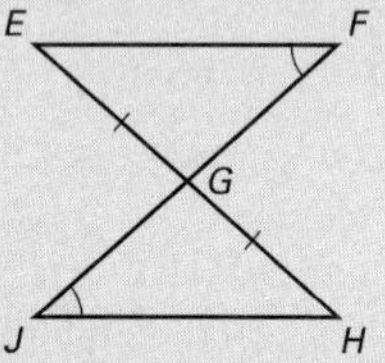

From the diagram, $\overline{EG} \cong \overline{HG}$ and $\angle F \cong \angle J$. $\angle EGF \cong \angle HGJ$ by the Vertical Angles Thm. Therefore, $\triangle EFG \cong \triangle HJG$ by the AAS Cong. Thm.

Extra Example 4.6

Given: $\overline{KL} \cong \overline{KN}$, $\overline{LM} \cong \overline{NM}$

Prove: $\angle LKM \cong \angle NKM$.

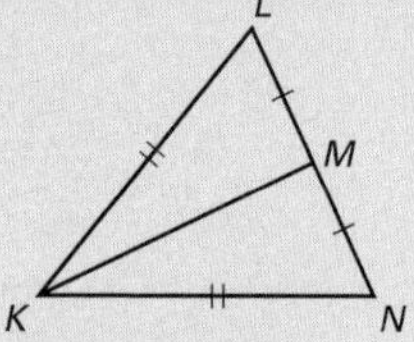

It is given that $\overline{KL} \cong \overline{KN}$ and $\overline{LM} \cong \overline{NM}$. By the Refl. Prop. of $\cong$ Segs., $\overline{KM} \cong \overline{KM}$. So, $\triangle KLM \cong \triangle KNM$ by the SSS Cong. Post. Corresponding parts of $\cong$ ≜ are $\cong$, so $\angle LKM \cong \angle NKM$.

4 CHAPTER REVIEW

4.4 Prove Triangles Congruent by SAS and HL

pp. 240–246

EXAMPLE

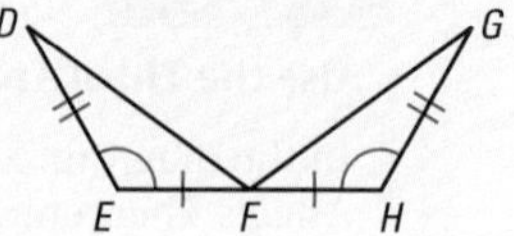

Prove that $\triangle DEF \cong \triangle GHF$.

From the diagram, $\overline{DE} \cong \overline{GH}$, $\angle E \cong \angle H$, and $\overline{EF} \cong \overline{HF}$. By the SAS Congruence Postulate, $\triangle DEF \cong \triangle GHF$.

EXERCISES

EXAMPLES 1 and 3 on pp. 240, 242 for Exs. 17–18

Decide whether the congruence statement is true. *Explain* your reasoning.

17. $\triangle QRS \cong \triangle TUS$ **true; SAS**

18. $\triangle DEF \cong \triangle GHF$ **false; $\triangle DEF \cong \triangle HGF$ by HL**

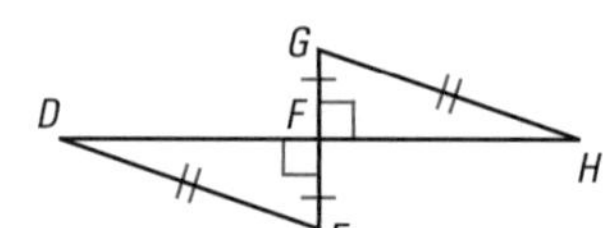

4.5 Prove Triangles Congruent by ASA and AAS

pp. 249–255

EXAMPLE

Prove that $\triangle DAC \cong \triangle BCA$.

By the Reflexive Property, $\overline{AC} \cong \overline{AC}$. Because $\overline{AD} \parallel \overline{BC}$ and $\overline{AB} \parallel \overline{DC}$, $\angle DAC \cong \angle BCA$ and $\angle DCA \cong \angle BAC$ by the Alternate Interior Angles Theorem. So, by the ASA Congruence Postulate, $\triangle ADC \cong \triangle CBA$.

EXERCISES

EXAMPLES 1 and 2 on p. 250 for Exs. 19–20

State the third congruence that is needed to prove that $\triangle DEF \cong \triangle GHJ$ using the given postulate or theorem.

19. GIVEN ▶ $\overline{DE} \cong \overline{GH}$, $\angle D \cong \angle G$, __?__ $\cong$ __?__
Use the AAS Congruence Theorem. **$\angle F$, $\angle J$**

20. GIVEN ▶ $\overline{DF} \cong \overline{GJ}$, $\angle F \cong \angle J$, __?__ $\cong$ __?__
Use the ASA Congruence Postulate. **$\angle D$, $\angle G$**

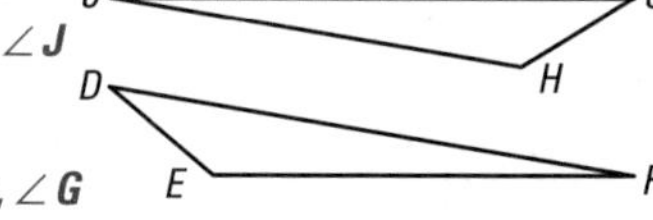

4.6 Use Congruent Triangles

pp. 256–263

EXAMPLE

GIVEN ▶ $\overline{FG} \cong \overline{JG}$, $\overline{EG} \cong \overline{HG}$
PROVE ▶ $\overline{EF} \cong \overline{HJ}$

You are given that $\overline{FG} \cong \overline{JG}$ and $\overline{EG} \cong \overline{HG}$. By the Vertical Angles Congruence Theorem, $\angle FGE \cong \angle JGH$. So, $\triangle FGE \cong \triangle JGH$ by the SAS Congruence Postulate. Corresponding parts of $\cong$ ≜ are $\cong$, so $\overline{EF} \cong \overline{HJ}$.

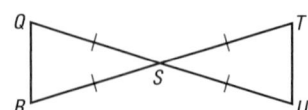

@HomeTutor
classzone.com
Chapter Review Practice

EXERCISES

EXAMPLE 3 on p. 257 for Exs. 21–23

Write a plan for proving that ∠1 ≅ ∠2. 21–23. See margin.

21.

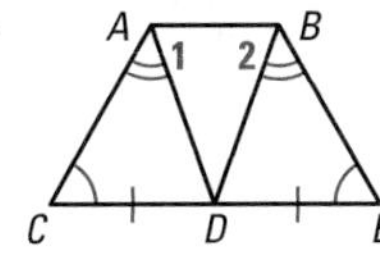

22.

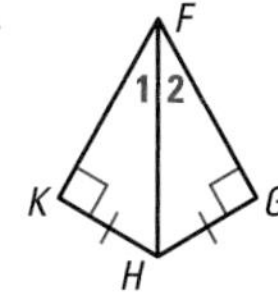

23.

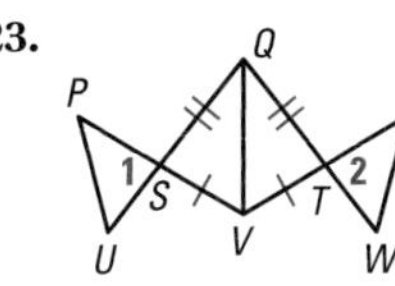

4.7 Use Isosceles and Equilateral Triangles *pp. 264–270*

EXAMPLE

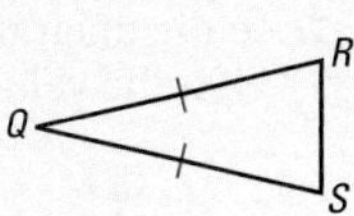

△QRS is isosceles. Name two congruent angles.

$\overline{QR} \cong \overline{QS}$, so by the Base Angles Theorem, ∠R ≅ ∠S.

EXERCISES

EXAMPLE 3 on p. 266 for Exs. 24–26

Find the value of x.

24.

65

25.

20

26.

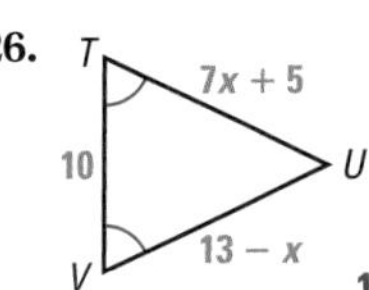

1

4.8 Perform Congruence Transformations *pp. 272–279*

EXAMPLE

Triangle ABC has vertices A(−5, 1), B(−4, 4), and C(−2, 3). Sketch △ABC and its image after the translation (x, y) → (x + 5, y + 1).

(x, y) → (x + 5, y + 1)

A(−5, 1) → (0, 2)

B(−4, 4) → (1, 5)

C(−2, 3) → (3, 4)

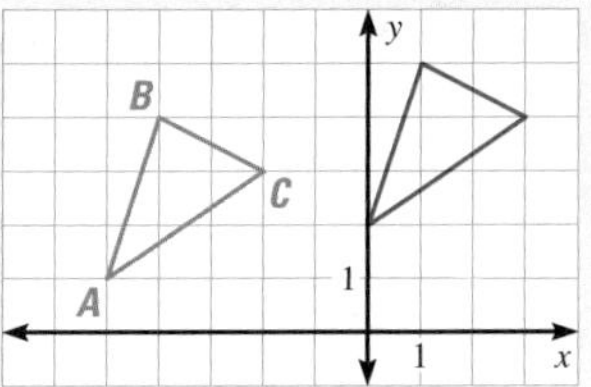

EXERCISES

EXAMPLES 2 and 3 on pp. 273–274 for Exs. 27–29

Triangle QRS has vertices Q(2, −1), R(5, −2), and S(2, −3). Sketch △QRS and its image after the transformation. 27–29. See margin.

27. (x, y) → (x − 1, y + 5)

28. (x, y) → (x, −y)

29. (x, y) → (−x, −y)

Extra Example 4.7

△XYZ is isosceles. Name two congruent angles. ∠X ≅ ∠Z

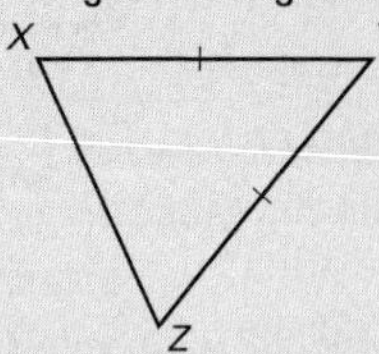

Extra Example 4.8

Triangle RST has vertices R(−1, −5), S(4, 1), and T(5, −3). Sketch △RST and its image after the translation (x, y) → (x − 2, y + 4).

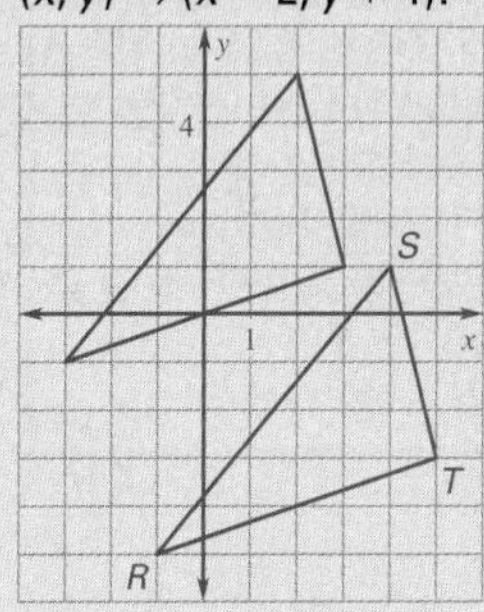

27.

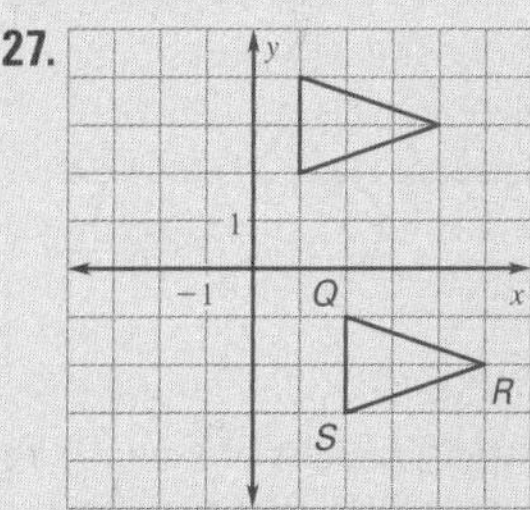

28.

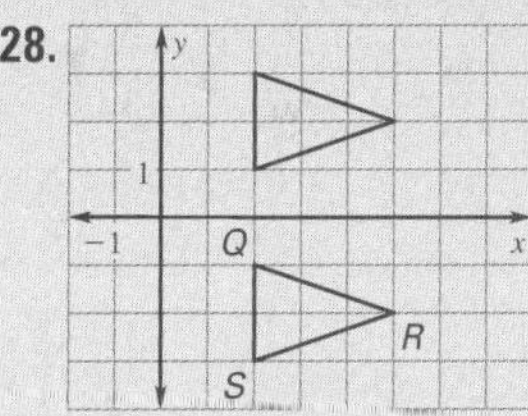

29.

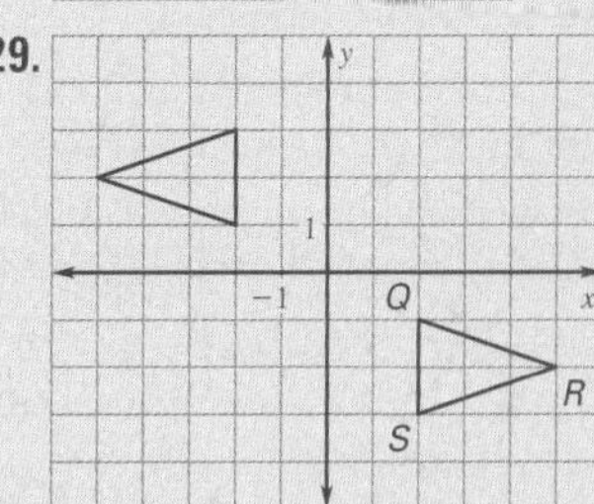

21. Show △ACD and △BED are congruent by AAS, which makes $\overline{AD}$ congruent to $\overline{BD}$. △ABD is then an isosceles triangle, which makes ∠1 and ∠2 congruent.

22. Show △FHK and △FHG are congruent using HL. ∠1 and ∠2 will be congruent because corr. parts of ≅ ≙ are ≅.

23. Show △QVS congruent to △QVT by SSS, which gives ∠QSV congruent to ∠QTV. Using vertical angles and the Transitive Property, you get ∠1 congruent to ∠2.

4 CHAPTER TEST

Additional Resources

Assessment Book

- Chapter Test, Levels A, B, C, pp. 49–54
- Standardized Chapter Test, pp. 55–56
- SAT/ACT Chapter Test, pp. 57–58
- Alternative Assessment, pp. 59–60

Test Generator CD-ROM

Chapter Test

Easily-readable reduced copies (with answers) of Chapter Test B, the Standardized Chapter Test, and the Alternative Assessment from the Assessment Book can be found on pp. 214G–214H.

11. Statements (Reasons)

1. $\triangle ABC$ is isosceles with base $\overline{AC}$, $\overline{BD}$ bisects $\angle B$. (Given)
2. $\overline{AB} \cong \overline{BC}$ (Definition of isosceles triangle)
3. $\angle ABD \cong \angle CBD$ (Definition of angle bisector)
4. $\overline{BD} \cong \overline{BD}$ (Reflexive Property of Segment Congruence)
5. $\triangle ABD \cong \triangle CBD$ (SAS)

Classify the triangle by its sides and by its angles.

1. 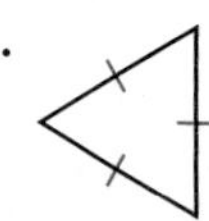 equilateral, acute (or equiangular)
2. 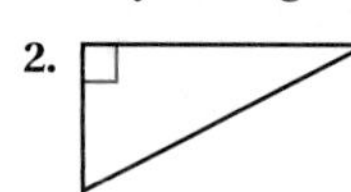 scalene, right
3. 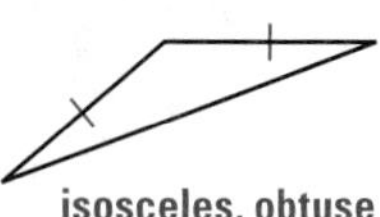 isosceles, obtuse

In Exercises 4–6, find the value of x.

4. 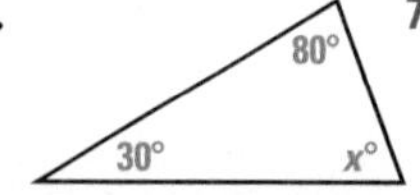

70
5. 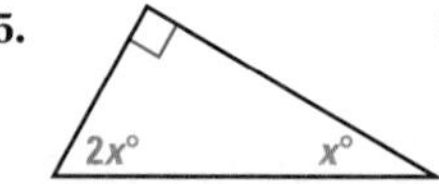

30
6. 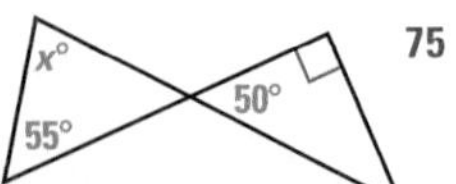

75

7. In the diagram, $DEFG \cong WXFG$. Find the values of x and y. 5, 15

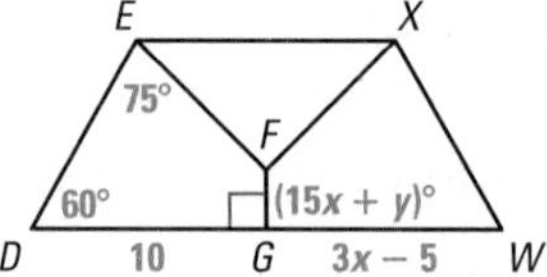

In Exercises 8–10, decide whether the triangles can be proven congruent by the given postulate.

8. $\triangle ABC \cong \triangle EDC$ by SAS proven

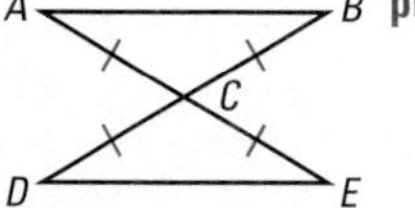

9. $\triangle FGH \cong \triangle JKL$ by ASA proven

10. $\triangle MNP \cong \triangle PQM$ by SSS proven

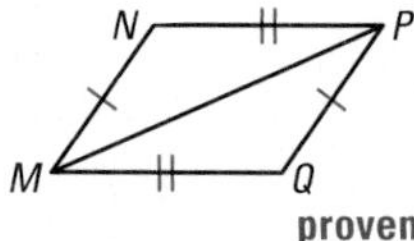

11. Write a proof. See margin.

GIVEN ▶ $\triangle ABC$ is isosceles with base $\overline{AC}$, $\overline{BD}$ bisects $\angle B$.

PROVE ▶ $\triangle ABD \cong \triangle CBD$

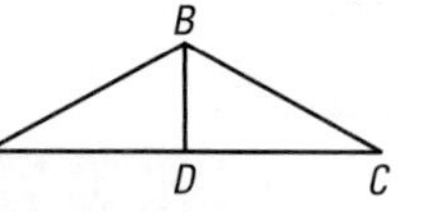

12. What is the third congruence needed to prove that $\triangle PQR \cong \triangle STU$ using the indicated theorem?

a. HL $\overline{QP} \cong \overline{TS}$ or $\overline{QR} \cong \overline{TU}$ **b.** AAS $\angle P \cong \angle S$ or $\angle R \cong \angle U$

Decide whether the transformation is a *translation, reflection,* or *rotation.*

13. 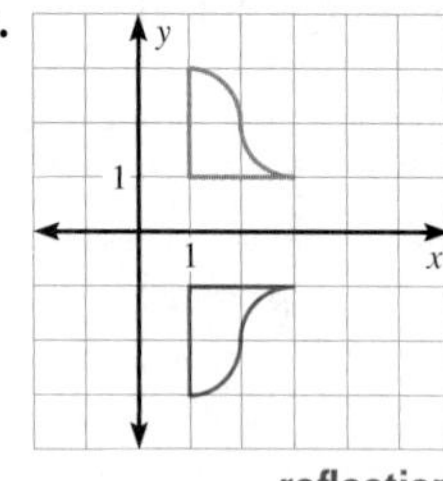 reflection
14. 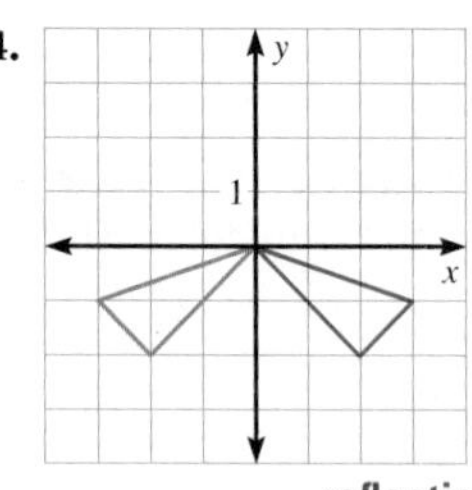 reflection
15. 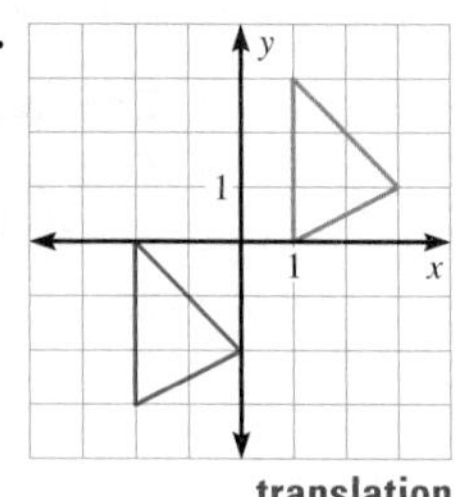 translation

ALGEBRA REVIEW

Animated Algebra
classzone.com

SOLVE INEQUALITIES AND ABSOLUTE VALUE EQUATIONS

EXAMPLE 1 Solve inequalities

Solve $-3x + 7 \le 28$. Then graph the solution.

When you multiply or divide each side of an inequality by a *negative* number, you must reverse the inequality symbol to obtain an equivalent inequality.

$-3x + 7 \le 28$ **Write original inequality.**

$-3x \le 21$ **Subtract 7 from both sides.**

$x \ge -7$ **Divide each side by −3. Reverse the inequality symbol.**

▶ The solutions are all real numbers greater than or equal to −7. The graph is shown at the right.

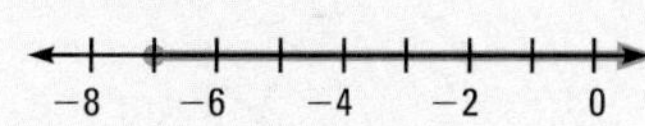

EXAMPLE 2 Solve absolute value equations

Solve $|2x + 1| = 5$.

The expression inside the absolute value bars can represent 5 or −5.

STEP 1 Assume $2x + 1$ represents 5.

$2x + 1 = 5$

$2x = 4$

$x = 2$

STEP 2 Assume $2x + 1$ represents −5.

$2x + 1 = -5$

$2x = -6$

$x = -3$

▶ The solutions are 2 and −3.

EXERCISES

EXAMPLE 1 for Exs. 1–12

Solve the inequality. Then graph the solution. **1–12. See margin for art.**

1. $x - 6 > -4$ $x > 2$
2. $7 - c \le -1$ $c \ge 8$
3. $-54 \ge 6x$ $x \le -9$
4. $\frac{5}{2}t + 8 \le 33$ $t \le 10$
5. $3(y + 2) < 3$ $y < -1$
6. $\frac{1}{4}z < 2$ $z < 8$
7. $5k + 1 \ge -11$ $k \ge -\frac{12}{5}$
8. $13.6 > -0.8 - 7.2r$ $r > -2$
9. $6x + 7 < 2x - 3$ $x < -\frac{5}{2}$
10. $-v + 12 \le 9 - 2v$ $v \le -3$
11. $4(n + 5) \ge 5 - n$ $n \ge -3$
12. $5y + 3 \ge 2(y - 9)$ $y \ge -7$

EXAMPLE 2 for Exs. 13–27

Solve the equation.

13. $|x - 5| = 3$ **2, 8**
14. $|x + 6| = 2$ **−8, −4**
15. $|4 - x| = 4$ **0, 8**
16. $|2 - x| = 0.5$ **1.5, 2.5**
17. $|3x - 1| = 8$ $-\frac{7}{3}, 3$
18. $|4x + 5| = 7$ $-3, \frac{1}{2}$
19. $|x - 1.3| = 2.1$ **−0.8, 3.4**
20. $|3x - 15| = 0$ **5**
21. $|6x - 2| = 4$ $-\frac{1}{3}, 1$
22. $|8x + 1| = 17$ $-\frac{9}{4}, 2$
23. $|9 - 2x| = 19$ **−5, 14**
24. $|0.5x - 4| = 2$ **4, 12**
25. $|5x - 2| = 8$ $-\frac{6}{5}, 2$
26. $|7x + 4| = 11$ $-\frac{15}{7}, 1$
27. $|3x - 11| = 4$ $\frac{7}{3}, 5$

Extra Example 1

Solve $4x - 7 > 29$. Then graph the solution. $x > 9$

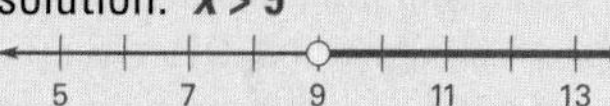

Extra Example 2

Solve $|5x - 6| = 9$. $3, -\frac{3}{5}$

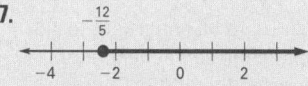

1. −1 0 1 2
2. −2 0 2 4 6 8 10 12 14
3. −9; −12 −8 −4 0
4. −2 0 2 4 6 8 10 12 14
5. −4 −2 0 2
6. −2 0 2 4 6 8 10
7. $-\frac{12}{5}$; −4 −2 0 2
8. −4 −2 0 2 4 6 8
9. $-\frac{5}{2}$; −4 −2 0 2
10. −5 −4 −3 −2 −1 0 1
11. −4 −2 0 2
12. −10 −8 −6 −4 −2 0 2

Test-Taking Strategy

Students should read and interpret any graph or diagram that is provided with the question. Often they will need additional information from the graph or diagram to answer the question. As they begin to solve the problem, have them refer to the graph or diagram to see what additional information they can find that will be helpful.

Avoiding Common Errors

In Problem 1 students may overlook the 5's on the axis and just count by 1's. Stress the importance of examining the graph to see what the scale is.

Teaching Strategy

For Problem 1, instead of computing all the distances, show students that for $\overline{JL}$ to be congruent to $\overline{AC}$ it must be the same number of gridlines on the graph. Count the gridlines between *A* and *C* and move to the right that same number from *J*. Then find the coordinates of this new point *L*.

Standards

12.0 Students find and use measures of sides and of interior and exterior angles of triangles and polygons **to** classify figures and **solve problems.**

CONTEXT-BASED MULTIPLE CHOICE QUESTIONS

Some of the information you need to solve a context-based multiple choice question may appear in a table, a diagram, or a graph.

PROBLEM 1

Five of six players on a lacrosse team are set up in a 2-3-1 formation. In this formation, the players form two congruent triangles. Three **attackmen** form one triangle. Three **midfielders** form the second triangle. In the diagram, where should player *L* stand so that $\triangle ABC \cong \triangle JKL$?

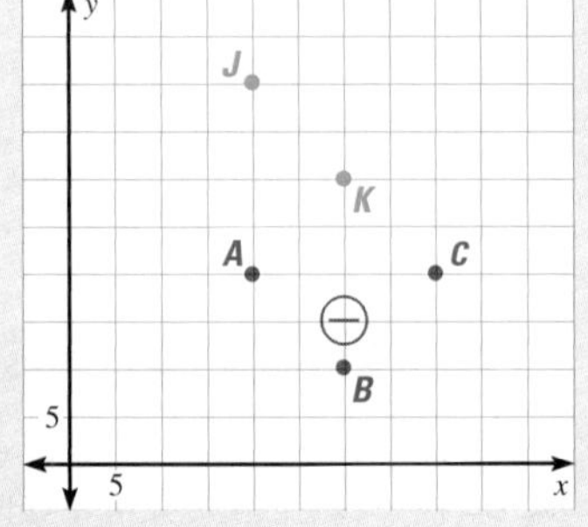

Ⓐ (8, 8) Ⓑ (20, 60)

Ⓒ (40, 40) Ⓓ (30, 15)

Plan

INTERPRET THE GRAPH Use the graph to determine the coordinates of each player. Use the Distance Formula to check the coordinates in the choices.

Solution

STEP 1 Find the coordinates of each vertex.

For $\triangle ABC$, the coordinates are $A(20, 20)$, $B(30, 10)$, and $C(40, 20)$. For $\triangle JKL$, the coordinates are $J(20, 40)$, $K(30, 30)$, and $L(\underline{\ ?\ }, \underline{\ ?\ })$.

STEP 2 Calculate *BC* and *CA*.

Because $\triangle ABC \cong \triangle JKL$, $BC = KL$ and $CA = LJ$. Find *BC* and *CA*.

By the Distance Formula, $BC = \sqrt{(40-30)^2 + (20-10)^2} = \sqrt{200} = 10\sqrt{2}$ yards.

Also, $CA = \sqrt{(20-40)^2 + (20-20)^2} = \sqrt{400} = 20$ yards.

STEP 3 Check the choices to find the coordinates that produce the congruent corresponding sides.

Check the coordinates given in the choices to see whether $LJ = CA = 20$ yards and $KL = BC = 10\sqrt{2}$ yards. As soon as one set of coordinates does not work for the first side length, you can move to the next set.

Choice A: $L(8, 8)$, so $LJ = \sqrt{(20-8)^2 + (40-8)^2} = 4\sqrt{73} \neq 20$ ✗

Choice B: $L(20, 60)$, so $LJ = \sqrt{(20-20)^2 + (40-60)^2} = \sqrt{400} = 20$ ✓

and $KL = \sqrt{(20-30)^2 + (60-30)^2} = \sqrt{1000} \neq 10\sqrt{2}$ ✗

Choice C: $L(40, 40)$, so $LJ = \sqrt{(20-40)^2 + (40-40)^2} = \sqrt{400} = 20$ ✓

and $KL = \sqrt{(40-30)^2 + (40-30)^2} = \sqrt{200} = 10\sqrt{2}$ ✓

Player *L* should stand at (40, 40). The correct answer is C. Ⓐ Ⓑ Ⓒ Ⓓ

PROBLEM 2

Use the diagram to find the value of y.

Ⓐ 15.5　　Ⓑ 27.5

Ⓒ 43　　Ⓓ 82

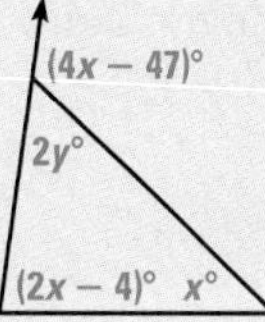

Plan

INTERPRET THE DIAGRAM All of the angle measures in the diagram are labeled with algebraic expressions. Use what you know about the angles in a triangle to find the value of y.

Solution

STEP 1 Find the value of x.

Use the Exterior Angle Theorem to find the value of x.

$(4x - 47)° = (2x - 4)° + x°$	**Exterior Angle Theorem**
$4x - 47 = 3x - 4$	**Combine like terms.**
$x = 43$	**Solve for x.**

STEP 2 Find the value of y.

Use the Linear Pair Postulate to find the value of y.

$(4x - 47)° + 2y° = 180°$	**Linear Pair Postulate**
$[4(43) - 47] + 2y = 180$	**Substitute 43 for x.**
$125 + 2y = 180$	**Simplify.**
$y = 27.5$	**Solve for y.**

The correct answer is B.  Ⓐ Ⓑ Ⓒ Ⓓ

PRACTICE

1. In Problem 2, what are the measures of the interior angles of the triangle? **D**

   Ⓐ 27.5°, 43°, 109.5°　　Ⓑ 27.5°, 51°, 86°

   Ⓒ 40°, 60°, 80°　　Ⓓ 43°, 55°, 82°

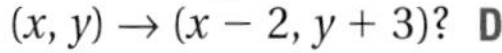

2. What are the coordinates of the vertices of the image of $\triangle FGH$ after the translation $(x, y) \to (x - 2, y + 3)$? **D**

   Ⓐ (3, 4), (−4, 4), (−1, 6)

   Ⓑ (−2, −1), (1, 3), (5, 1)

   Ⓒ (4, 1), (7, −1), (1, −3)

   Ⓓ (−4, 2), (−1, 6), (3, 4)

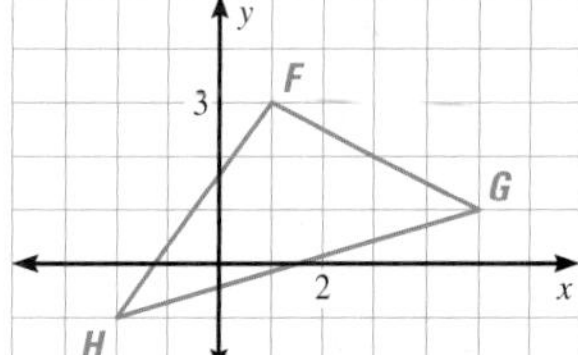

Mathematical Reasoning

For Problem 2, suggest that students write another system of two equations they could use to solve the problem. Ask which system is easier to solve and why? **$2y + 3x - 4 = 180$, $4x - 47 + 2y = 180$; The system in the given solution is easier, because one of the equations has only one variable.**

Graphing Calculator

For Exercise 1 students can put the ordered pairs they are given into L_1 and L_2 in the Stat menu of their graphing calculators. Then they can assign $L_3 = L_1 - 2$ and $L_4 = L_2 + 3$. The image coordinates will be in L_3 and L_4.

4 ★ Standardized TEST PRACTICE

MULTIPLE CHOICE

1. A teacher has the pennants shown below. Which pennants can you prove are congruent? **B**

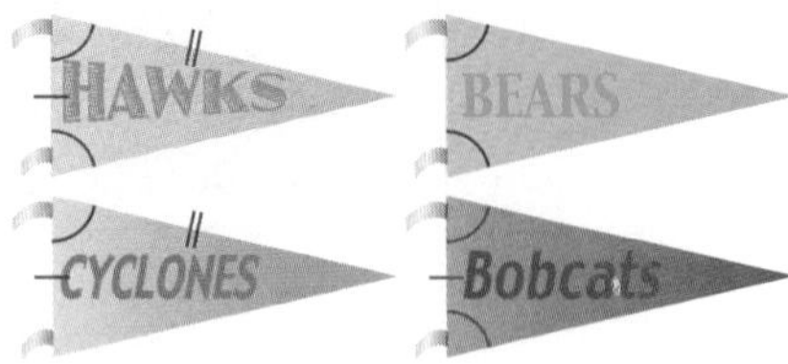

Ⓐ All of the pennants can be proven congruent.

Ⓑ The Hawks, Cyclones, and Bobcats pennants can be proven congruent.

Ⓒ The Bobcats and Bears pennants can be proven congruent.

Ⓓ None of the pennants can be proven congruent.

In Exercises 2 and 3, use the graph below.

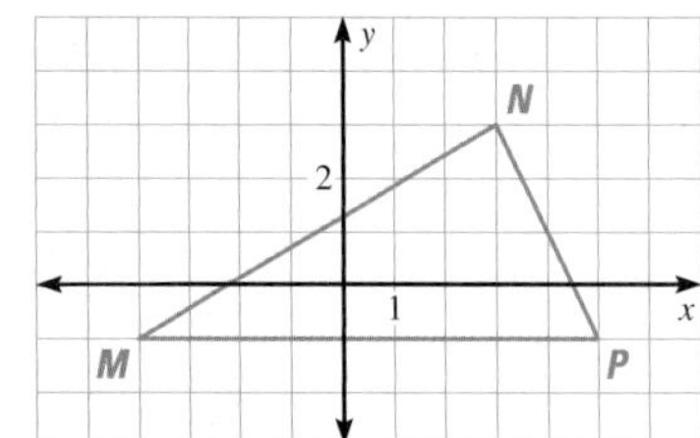

2. What type of triangle is $\triangle MNP$? **A**

Ⓐ Scalene

Ⓑ Isosceles

Ⓒ Right

Ⓓ Not enough information

3. Which are the coordinates of point Q such that $\triangle MNP \cong \triangle QPN$? **C**

Ⓐ $(0, -3)$

Ⓑ $(-6, 3)$

Ⓒ $(12, 3)$

Ⓓ $(3, -5)$

4. The diagram shows the final step in folding an origami butterfly. Use the congruent quadrilaterals, outlined in red, to find the value of $x + y$. **C**

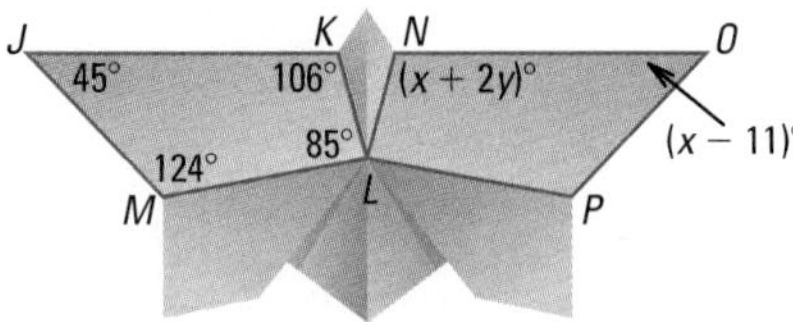

Ⓐ 25 Ⓑ 56

Ⓒ 81 Ⓓ 106

5. Which reason cannot be used to prove that $\angle A \cong \angle D$? **C**

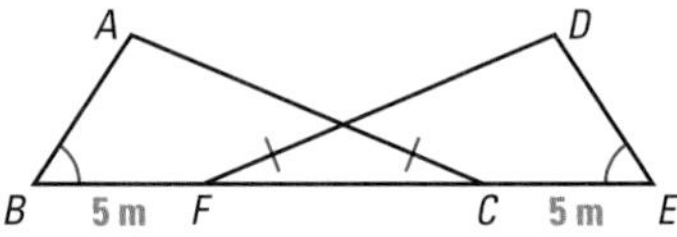

Ⓐ Base Angles Theorem

Ⓑ Segment Addition Postulate

Ⓒ SSS Congruence Postulate

Ⓓ Corresponding parts of congruent triangles are congruent.

6. Which coordinates are the vertices of a triangle congruent to $\triangle JKL$? **C**

Ⓐ $(-5, 0), (-5, 6), (-1, 6)$

Ⓑ $(-1, -5), (-1, -1), (1, -5)$

Ⓒ $(2, 1), (2, 3), (5, 1)$

Ⓓ $(4, 6), (6, 6), (6, 4)$

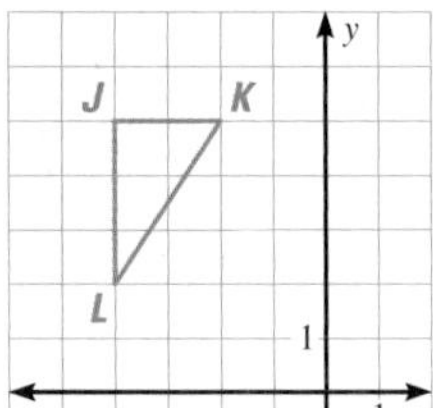

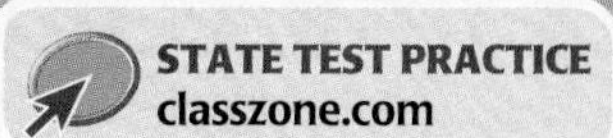

GRIDDED ANSWER

7. What is the perimeter of the triangle? **51**

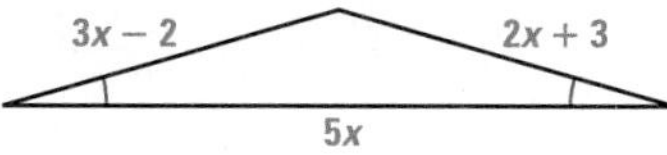

8. Figure $ABCD$ has vertices $A(0, 2)$, $B(-2, -4)$, $C(2, 7)$, and $D(5, 0)$. What is the y-coordinate of the image of vertex B after the translation $(x, y) \to (x + 8, y - 0.5)$? **−4.5**

9. What is the value of x? **14**

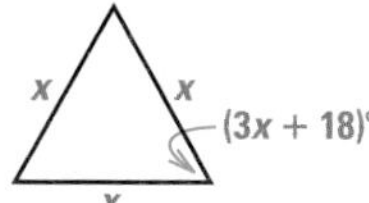

SHORT RESPONSE

10. If $\triangle ABE \cong \triangle EDC$, show that $\triangle EFA \cong \triangle CBE$. **See margin.**

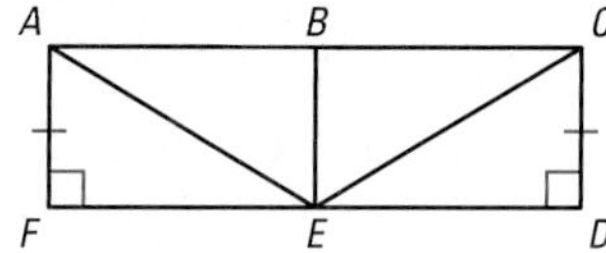

11. Two triangles have the same base and height. Are the triangles congruent? *Justify* your answer using an example. **No; see margin for art.**

12. If two people construct wooden frames for a triangular weaving loom using the instructions below, will the frames be congruent triangles? *Explain* your reasoning. **yes; ASA**

> Construct the frame so that the loom has a 90° angle at the bottom and 45° angles at the two upper corners. The piece of wood at the top should measure 72 inches.

EXTENDED RESPONSE

13. Use the diagram at the right.

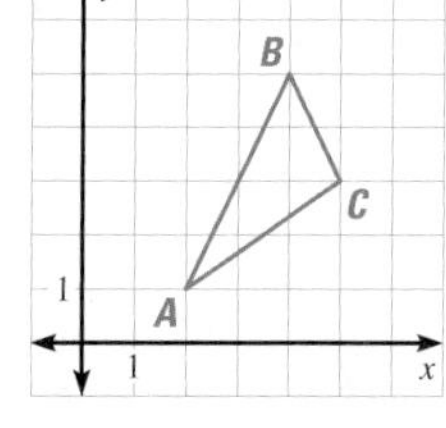

a. Copy the diagram onto a piece of graph paper. Reflect $\triangle ABC$ in the x-axis. **See margin.**

b. Copy and complete the table. *Describe* what you notice about the coordinates of the image compared to the coordinates of $\triangle ABC$.

	A	B	C
Coordinates of $\triangle ABC$	? (2, 1)	? (4, 5)	? (5, 3)
Coordinates of image	?	?	?
	(2, −1)	(4, −5)	(5, −3)

The x-coordinates are the same but the y-coordinates are opposites of one another.

14. Kylie is designing a quilting pattern using two different fabrics. The diagram shows her progress so far.

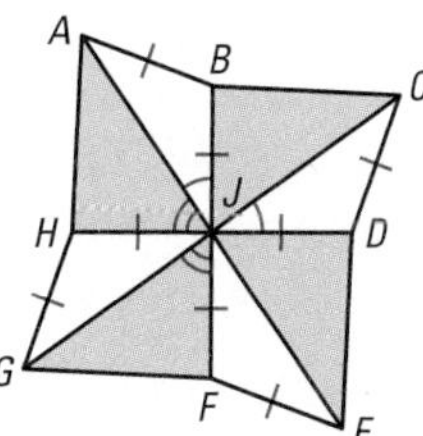

a. Use the markings on the diagram to prove that all of the white triangles are congruent. **a, b. See margin.**

b. Prove that all of the blue triangles are congruent.

c. Can you prove that the blue triangles are right triangles? *Explain.* **No; there is not enough information to establish a right angle.**

10. Statements (Reasons)

1. $\triangle ABE \cong \triangle EDC$, $\overline{FA} \cong \overline{DC}$, $\angle F$ and $\angle D$ are right angles. (Given)

2. $\angle ABE \cong \angle D$, $\overline{BE} \cong \overline{DC}$, $\overline{CE} \cong \overline{EA}$ (Corr. parts of $\cong$ △s are $\cong$.)

3. $m\angle ABE = m\angle D$ (Definition of congruent angles)

4. $m\angle ABE = 90°$ (Definition of right angle)

5. $m\angle CBE = 90°$ (Definition of linear pair)

6. $\angle CBE$ is a right angle (Definition of right angle)

7. $\triangle CBE$ is a right triangle. (Definition of right triangle)

8. $\overline{FA} \cong \overline{BE}$ (Transitive Property of Congruence)

9. $\triangle EFA \cong \triangle CBE$ (HL)

11.

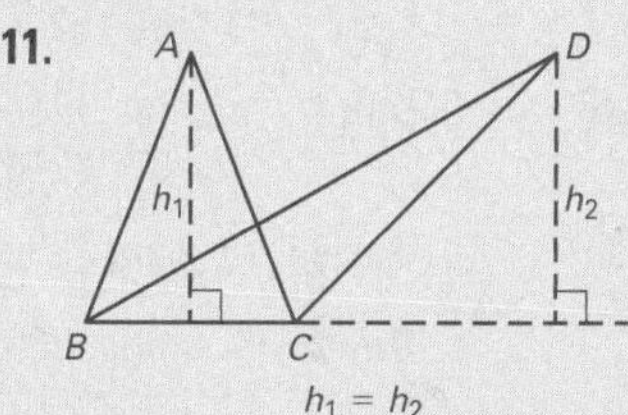

13a.

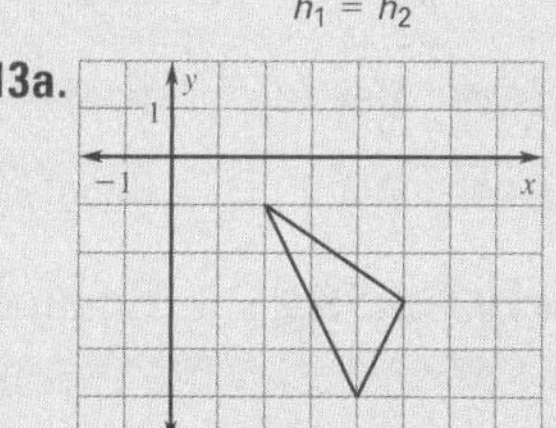

14a. The triangles are isosceles, so the base angles are congruent, and the triangles are congruent by AAS.

14b. Because corr. parts of $\cong$ △s are $\cong$, the triangles are congruent by SAS.

Pacing and Assignment Guide

REGULAR SCHEDULE

Pre-AP For pacing and assignments for a Pre-AP course, see the *Geometry Toolkit*.

Lesson	Les. Day	BASIC	AVERAGE	ADVANCED
5.1	Day 1	EP p. 896 Exs. 18–23; pp. 298–301 Exs. 1–11, 47–52	pp. 298–301 Exs. 1–11, 47–52	pp. 298–301 Exs. 1–11, 47–52
	Day 2	pp. 298–301 Exs. 12–25, 35–41	pp. 298–301 Exs. 13–19 odd, 20, 21–27 odd, 28–32, 35–44	pp. 298–301 Exs. 16–28 even, 29–46*
5.2	Day 1	pp. 306–309 Exs. 1–15	pp. 306–309 Exs. 1–10, 13–15, 18, 19	pp. 306–309 Exs. 1–9, 13–15, 18, 19
	Day 2	pp. 306–309 Exs. 16–19, 24–28, 34–41	pp. 306–309 Exs. 16, 17, 20–22, 24–30, 34–41	pp. 306–309 Exs. 16, 17, 20–33*, 34–40 even
5.3	Day 1	pp. 313–316 Exs. 1–17 odd, 18–24, 28–33, 39–47 odd	pp. 313–316 Exs. 1, 2–22 even, 23–26, 28–36, 40–46 even	pp. 313–316 Exs. 1, 2, 5, 8, 11, 14, 17–38*, 41, 44, 47
5.4	Day 1	pp. 322–325 Exs. 1–11, 25–27, 46–49, 53–55	pp. 322–325 Exs. 1, 2, 4, 5, 7–11, 25–27, 33–35, 46–49, 53–55	pp. 322–325 Exs. 1, 2, 5–11, 25–27, 33–35, 46–49, 53–55
	Day 2	pp. 322–325 Exs. 12–24, 28, 37–41, 50–52	pp. 322–325 Exs. 12–22 even, 23, 24, 28–32, 37–44, 50–52	pp. 322–325 Exs. 12, 14, 15, 21–24, 28–32, 36*, 39–45*, 50–52
5.5	Day 1	pp. 331–334 Exs. 1–9, 12–17, 20–28, 37–42, 49–53 odd	pp. 331–334 Exs. 1–5, 7–9, 12–15, 17, 18, 20–26 even, 27–34, 38–45, 50, 52	pp. 331–334 Exs. 1, 2, 5, 10–12, 15, 18–20, 25–36*, 39–48*, 50, 54
5.6	Day 1	pp. 338–341 Exs. 1–10, 22	pp. 338–341 Exs. 1–10, 16–18, 22	pp. 338–341 Exs. 1–10, 16–18, 22
	Day 2	pp. 338–341 Exs. 11–14, 23–25, 29–35	pp. 338–341 Exs. 11–15, 19, 23–26, 29–35	pp. 338–341 Exs. 11–15, 19–21*, 23–28*, 30, 34, 35
Review	Day 1	pp. 344–347 Exs. 1–27	pp. 344–347 Exs. 1–27	pp. 344–347 Exs. 1–27
Assess	Day 1	Chapter 5 Test	Chapter 5 Test	Chapter 5 Test
Yearly Pacing		Chapter 5 Total – 12 days	Chapters 1–5 Total – 66 days	Remaining – 94 days

*Challenge Exercises EP = Extra Practice SRH = Skills Review Handbook

BLOCK SCHEDULE

DAY 1	DAY 2	DAY 3	DAY 4	DAY 5	DAY 6
5.1	**5.2**	**5.3**	**5.4 (CONT.)**	**5.6**	**REVIEW**
pp. 298–301 Exs. 1–11, 13–19 odd, 20, 21–27 odd, 28–32, 35–44, 47–52	pp. 306–309 Exs. 1–10, 13–22, 24–30, 34–41	pp. 313–316 Exs. 1, 2–22 even, 23–26, 28–36, 40–46 even	pp. 322–325 Exs. 12–22 even, 23, 24, 28–32, 37–44, 50–52	pp. 338–341 Exs. 1–19, 22–26, 29–35	pp. 344–347 Exs. 1–27
		5.4	**5.5**		**ASSESS**
		pp. 322–325 Exs. 1, 2, 4, 5, 7–11, 25–27, 33–35, 46–49, 53–55	pp. 331–334 Exs. 1–5, 7–9, 12–15, 17, 18, 20–26 even, 27–34, 38–45, 50, 52		Chapter 5 Test
Yearly Pacing	Chapter 5 Total – 6 days	Chapters 1–5 Total – 33 days	Remaining – 47 days		

Chapter Resource Guide 5

RESOURCE MANAGER

Chapter Resource Book						
CHAPTER SUPPORT						
Parents as Partners (Chapter Overview with home involvement exercises and activity)					p. 1	
LESSON SUPPORT	**5.1**	**5.2**	**5.3**	**5.4**	**5.5**	**5.6**
Teaching Guide/Lesson Plan	p. 3	p. 17	p. 31	p. 46	p. 62	p. 77
Activity Masters		p. 19	p. 33			p. 79
Technology Activities & Keystrokes				p. 48	p. 64	
Activity Support Masters	p. 5					
Practice (3 levels)	p. 6	p. 20	p. 34	p. 52	p. 66	p. 80
Study Guide	p. 12	p. 26	p. 40	p. 57	p. 72	p. 86
Catch-Up for Absent Students	p. 14	p. 28	p. 42	p. 59	p. 74	p. 88
Problem Solving/Application	p. 15	p. 29	p. 43	p. 60	p. 75	p. 89
Challenge Practice	p. 16	p. 30	p. 45	p. 61	p. 76	p. 90
REVIEW						
Chapter Review Games and Activities		p. 91	Cumulative Practice			p. 94
Project with Rubric		p. 92	Resource Book Answers			A1

Transparencies	*5.1*	*5.2*	*5.3*	*5.4*	*5.5*	*5.6*
Warm-Up/Daily Homework Quiz	✔	✔	✔	✔	✔	✔
Notetaking Guide	✔	✔	✔	✔	✔	✔
Teacher Support	✔			✔		
Answer Transparencies	✔	✔	✔	✔	✔	✔

ASSESSMENT BOOK

Quizzes	p. 61	SAT/ACT Chapter Test	p. 72
Chapter Tests (3 levels)	p. 64	Alternative Assessment with Rubric	p. 74
Standardized Chapter Test	p. 70		

TECHNOLOGY

- Easy Planner
- Test and Practice Generator
- Power Presentations
- @HomeTutor
- Activity Generator
- Animated Geometry
- Classzone.com
- eEdition Plus Online
- eWorkbook Plus Online
- ML Assessment System

ADDITIONAL RESOURCES

- Worked-Out Solution Key
- Notetaking Guide
- Practice Wookbook
- Geometry Toolkit
- Benchmark Tests
- Remediation Book
- Spanish Study Guide
- Spanish Assessment Book
- Student Resources in Spanish
- Multi-Language Visual Glossary

5 Lesson Practice Level B

LESSON 5.1 **Practice B**
For use with pages 294–301

$\overline{DE}$ is a midsegment of $\triangle ABC$. Find the value of x.

1. 14 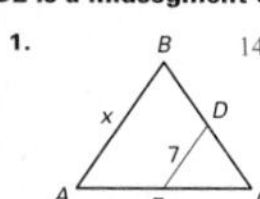

2. 8

3. 17 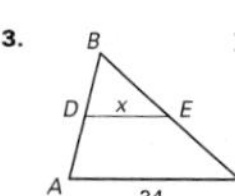

In $\triangle JKL$, $\overline{JR} \cong \overline{RK}$, $\overline{KS} \cong \overline{SL}$, and $\overline{JT} \cong \overline{TL}$. Copy and complete the statement.

4. $\overline{RS} \parallel$ __?__ $\overline{JL}$

5. $\overline{ST} \parallel$ __?__ $\overline{JK}$

6. $\overline{KL} \parallel$ __?__ $\overline{RT}$

7. $\overline{SL} \cong$ __?__ $\cong$ __?__ $\overline{KS}, \overline{RT}$

8. $\overline{JR} \cong$ __?__ $\cong$ __?__ $\overline{KR}, \overline{ST}$

9. $\overline{JT} \cong$ __?__ $\cong$ __?__ $\overline{LT}, \overline{RS}$

Place the figure in a coordinate plane in a convenient way. Assign coordinates to each vertex.

10. Right triangle: leg lengths are 5 units and 3 units *Sample answer:* (0, 0), (5, 0), (0, 3)

11. Rectangle: length is 7 units and width is 4 units *Sample answer:* (0, 0), (7, 0), (7, 4), (0, 4)

12. Square: side length is 6 units (0, 0), (6, 0), (6, 6), (0, 6)

13. Isosceles right triangle: leg length is 12 units (0, 0), (12, 0), (0, 12)

Use $\triangle GHJ$, where D, E, and F are midpoints of the sides.

14. If $DE = 4x + 5$ and $GJ = 3x + 25$, what is DE? 17

15. If $EF = 2x + 7$ and $GH = 5x - 1$, what is EF? 37

16. If $HJ = 8x - 2$ and $DF = 2x + 11$, what is HJ? 46

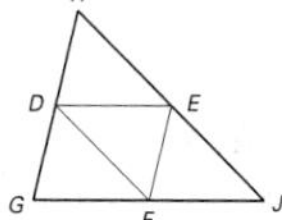

LESSON 5.1 **Practice B** *continued*
For use with pages 294–301

Find the unknown coordinates of the point(s) in the figure. Then show that the given statement is true.

17. $\triangle ABC \cong \triangle DEC$ $B(-h, k)$; Proof

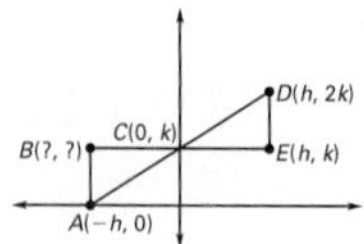

18. $\overline{PT} \cong \overline{SR}$ $S\left(\frac{h}{2}, \frac{k}{2}\right), T\left(\frac{3h}{2}, \frac{k}{2}\right)$; Proof

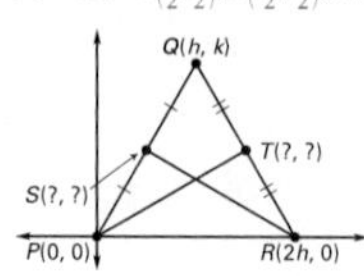

19. The coordinates of $\triangle ABC$ are $A(0, 5)$, $B(8, 20)$, and $C(0, 26)$. Find the length of each side and the perimeter of $\triangle ABC$. Then find the perimeter of the triangle formed by connecting the three midsegments of $\triangle ABC$. $AB = 17$, $BC = 10$, $AC = 21$; 48; 24

20. Swing Set You are assembling the frame for a swing set. The horizontal crossbars in the kit you purchased are each 36 inches long. You attach the crossbars at the midpoints of the legs. At each end of the frame, how far apart will the bottoms of the legs be when the frame is assembled? *Explain.*
72 in.; The crossbar is the midsegment of the legs.

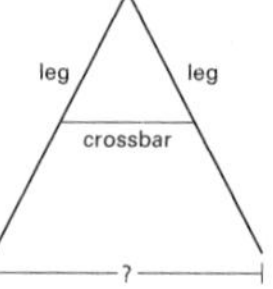

21. A-Frame House In an A-frame house, the floor of the second level, labeled $\overline{LM}$, is closer to the first floor, $\overline{NP}$, than midsegment $\overline{JK}$. If $\overline{JK}$ is 14 feet long, can $\overline{LM}$ be 12 feet long? 14 feet long? 20 feet long? 24 feet long? 30 feet long? *Explain.* no; no; yes; yes; no; $14 < LM < 28$

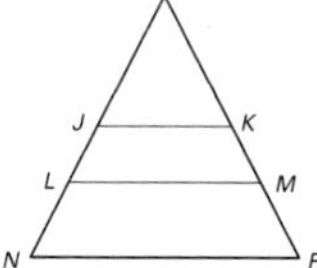

LESSON 5.2 **Practice B**
For use with pages 303–309

Find the length of $\overline{AB}$.

1. 4

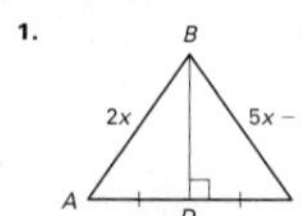

2. 26

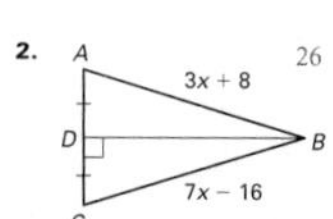

3. 35

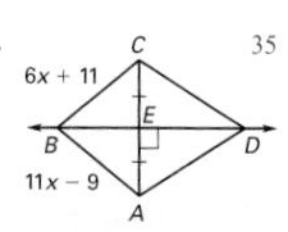

Tell whether the information in the diagram allows you to conclude that C is on the perpendicular bisector of $\overline{AB}$.

4. yes

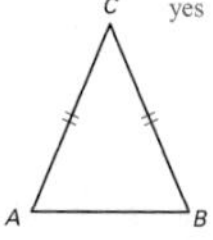

5. no

6. yes

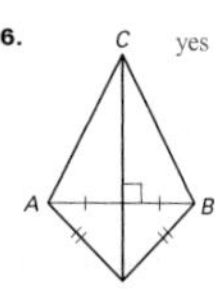

Use the diagram. $\overleftrightarrow{EH}$ is the perpendicular bisector of $\overline{DF}$. Find the indicated measure.

7. Find EF. 44 **8.** Find DE. 44

9. Find FG. 36 **10.** Find DG. 36

11. Find FH. 31 **12.** Find DF. 62

In the diagram, the perpendicular bisectors of $\triangle ABC$ meet at point G and are shown dashed. Find the indicated measure.

13. Find AG. 25 **14.** Find BD. 20

15. Find CF. 24 **16.** Find BG. 25

17. Find CE. 15 **18.** Find AC. 48

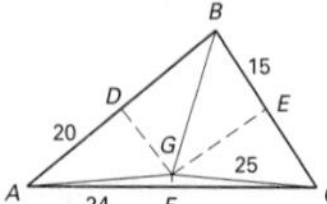

LESSON 5.2 **Practice B** *continued*
For use with pages 303–309

Draw $\overline{AB}$ with the given length. Construct the perpendicular bisector and choose point C on the perpendicular bisector so that the distance between C and $\overline{AB}$ is 1 inch. Measure $\overline{AC}$ and $\overline{BC}$. See below.

19. $AB = 0.5$ inch **20.** $AB = 1$ inch **21.** $AB = 2$ inches

Write a two-column or a paragraph proof. See below.

22. GIVEN: C is on the perpendicular bisector of $\overline{AB}$.
PROVE: $\triangle ACD \cong \triangle BCD$

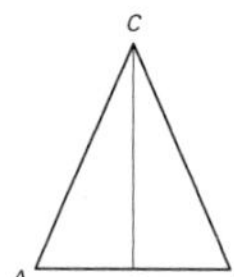

23. GIVEN: $\triangle GHJ \cong \triangle FHJ$
PROVE: $\overline{EF} \cong \overline{EG}$

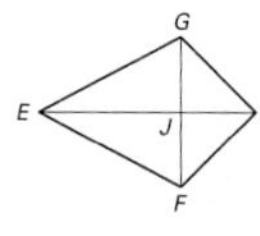

24. Early Aircraft Set On many of the earliest airplanes, wires connected vertical posts to the edges of the wings, which were wooden frames covered with cloth. The lengths of the wires from the top of a post to the edges of the frame are the same and distances from the bottom of the post to the ends of the two wires are the same. What does that tell you about the post and the section of frame between the ends of the wires? The post is the ⊥ bisector of the segment between the ends of the wires.

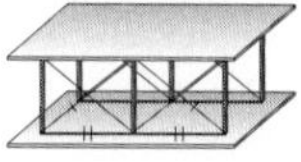

19. Check student's drawing; $AC = BC = 1$ in.

20. Check student's drawing; $AC = BC = 1.125$ in.

21. Check student's drawing; $AC = BC = 1.4375$ in.

22. Because a point on the ⊥ bisector is equidistant to the endpoints, $\overline{AC} \cong \overline{BC}$. By the Reflexive Property of $\cong$, $\overline{CD} \cong \overline{CD}$. By the definition of bisector, $\overline{AD} \cong \overline{BD}$. By the SSS Congruence Postulate, $\triangle ACD \cong \triangle BCD$.

23. Because corresponding parts of $\cong$ $\triangle$s are $\cong$, $\overline{GJ} \cong \overline{FG}$ and $\angle GJH \cong \angle FJH$. By the Vertical $\angle$s Theorem, $\angle GJH \cong \angle EJF$ and $\angle FJH \cong \angle EJG$. By the Transitive Property, $\angle EJF \cong \angle EJG$. By the Reflexive Property, $\overline{EJ} \cong \overline{EJ}$. By the SAS $\cong$ Postulate, $\triangle EJG \cong \triangle EJF$. Because corresponding parts of $\cong$ $\triangle$s are $\cong$, $\overline{EF} \cong \overline{EG}$.

LESSON 5.3

Practice B

For use with pages 310–316

Use the information in the diagram to find the measure.

1. Find AD. 19

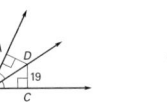

2. Find $m\angle EFH$. 28°

3. Find $m\angle JKL$. 86°

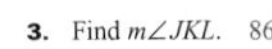

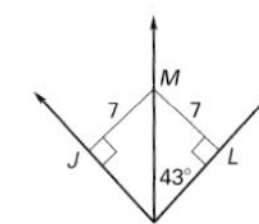

Can you conclude that $\overrightarrow{BD}$ bisects $\angle ABC$? Explain.

4. No; you don't know that D is equidistant to rays.

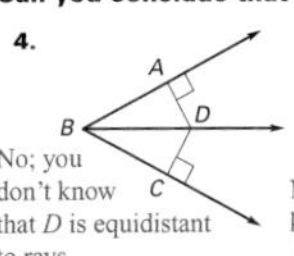

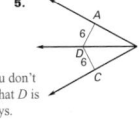

5. No; you don't know that D is $\perp$ to rays.

6. Yes; Converse of Angle Bisector Theorem

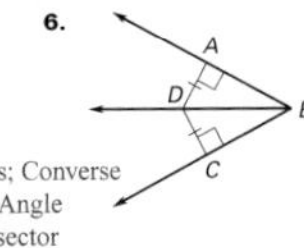

Find the value of x.

7. 7

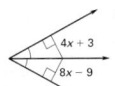

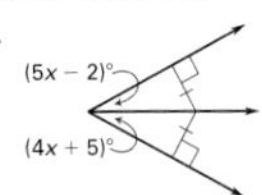

8. 3

9. 8

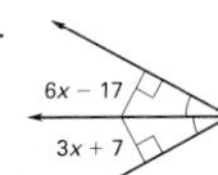

Can you find the value of x? Explain.

10. Yes; $x = 9$ by Angle Bisector Theorem.

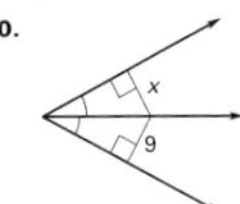

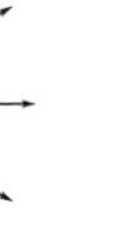

11. No; you need to know that congruent segments are $\perp$ to rays.

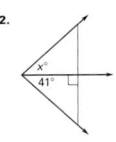

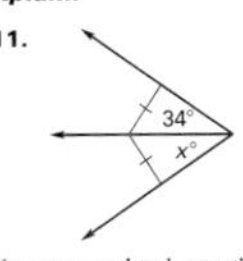

12. No; you need to know that the two segments are equal.

LESSON 5.3

LESSON 5.3

Practice B *continued*

For use with pages 310–316

Find the indicated measure.

13. Point G is the incenter of $\triangle ACE$. Find BG. 16

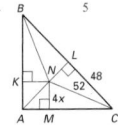

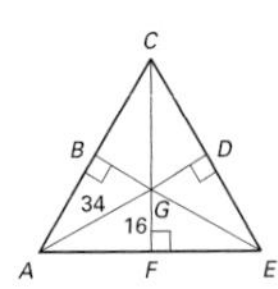

14. Point P is the incenter of $\triangle HKM$. Find JP. 7

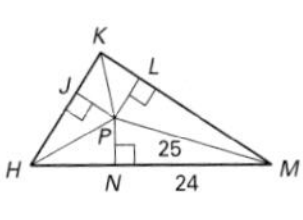

Find the value of x that makes N the incenter of the triangle.

15. 5

16. 8

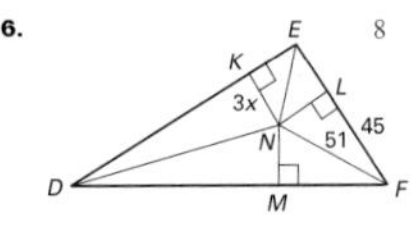

17. **Hockey** You and a friend are playing hockey in your driveway. You are the goalie, and your friend is going to shoot the puck from point S. The goal extends from left goalpost L to right goalpost R. Where should you position yourself (point G) to have the best chance to prevent your friend from scoring a goal? *Explain.*

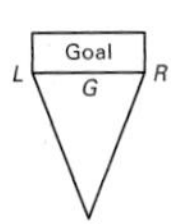

Directly between points L and R so that $\overline{SG}$ bisects $\angle LSR$; the distance between you and each goalpost is equal which minimizes the amount you have to move in either direction.

18. **Monument** You are building a monument in a triangular park. You want the monument to be the same distance from each edge of the park. Use the figure with incenter G to determine how far from point D you should build the monument. 35 ft

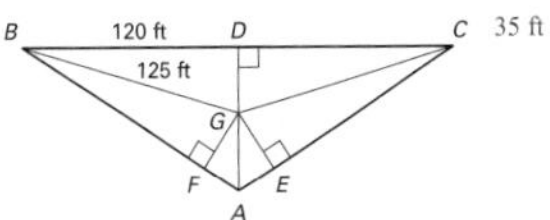

LESSON 5.3

LESSON 5.4

Practice B

For use with pages 318–327

G is the centroid of $\triangle ABC$, $AD = 8$, $AG = 10$, and $CD = 18$. Find the length of the segment.

1. $\overline{BD}$ 8

2. $\overline{AB}$ 16

3. $\overline{EG}$ 5

4. $\overline{AE}$ 15

5. $\overline{CG}$ 12

6. $\overline{DG}$ 6

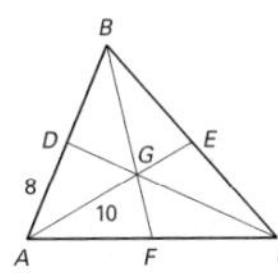

7. Use the graph shown.

a. Find the coordinates of M, the midpoint of $\overline{JK}$. Use the median $\overline{LM}$ to find the coordinates of the centroid P. $M(2, 4)$; $P(2, 1)$

b. Find the coordinates of N, the midpoint of $\overline{JL}$. Verify that $KP = \frac{2}{3}KN$.

$N(0, 1)$; $KP = 4$ and $KN = 6$ therefore $KP = \frac{2}{3}KN$.

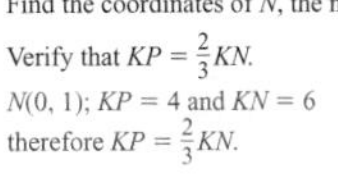

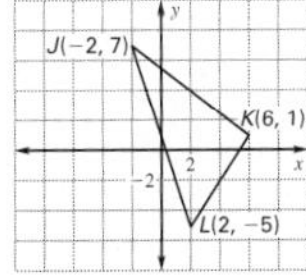

Find the coordinates of the centroid P of $\triangle ABC$.

8. $A(-7, -4)$, $B(-3, 5)$, $C(1, -4)$ $(-3, -1)$

9. $A(0, -2)$, $B(6, 1)$, $C(9, -5)$ $(5, -2)$

Is $\overline{BD}$ a *perpendicular bisector* of $\triangle ABC$? Is $\overline{BD}$ a *median*? an *altitude*?

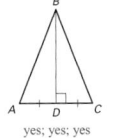

10. yes; yes; yes

11. no; no; no

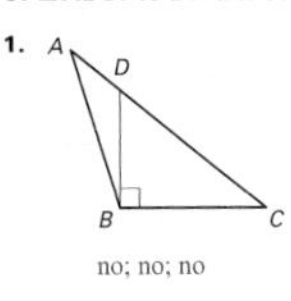

12. no; yes; no

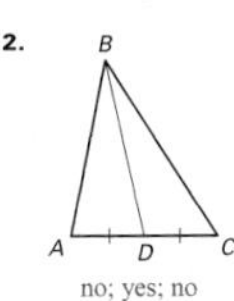

Find the measurements.

13. Given that $AB = BC$, find AD and $m\angle ABC$. 12; 78°

14. Given that G is the centroid of $\triangle ABC$, find FG and BD. 6.5; 15

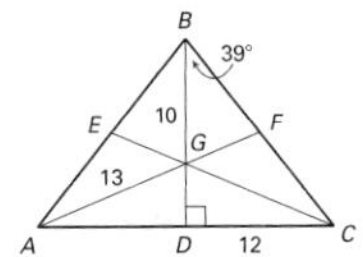

LESSON 5.4

LESSON 5.4

Practice B *continued*

For use with pages 318–327

Copy and complete the statement for $\triangle HJK$ with medians $\overline{HN}$, $\overline{JL}$, and $\overline{KM}$, and centroid P.

15. $PN =$? HN $\frac{1}{3}$

16. $PL =$? JP $\frac{1}{2}$

17. $KP =$? KM $\frac{2}{3}$

Point G is the centroid of $\triangle ABC$. Use the given information to find the value of x.

18. $CG = 3x + 7$ and $CE = 6x$ 7

19. $FG = x + 8$ and $AF = 9x - 6$ 5

20. $BG = 5x - 1$ and $DG = 4x - 5$ 3

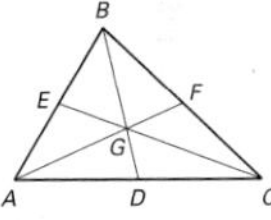

Complete the sentence with *always*, *sometimes*, or *never*.

21. The median of a triangle is ? the perpendicular bisector. sometimes

22. The altitude of a triangle is ? the perpendicular bisector. sometimes

23. The medians of a triangle ? intersect inside the triangle. always

24. The altitudes of a triangle ? intersect inside the triangle. sometimes

25. **House Decoration** You are going to put a decoration on your house in the triangular area above the front door. You want to place the decoration on the centroid of the triangle. You measure the distance from point A to point B (see figure). How far down from point A should you place the decoration? *Explain.* See below.

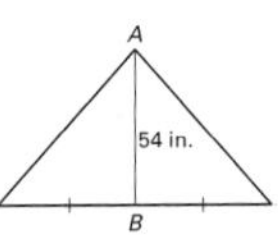

26. **Art Project** You are making an art piece which consists of different items of all shapes and sizes. You want to insert an isosceles triangle with the dimensions shown. In order for the triangle to fit, the height (altitude) must be less than 8.5 millimeters. Find the altitude. Will the triangle fit in your art piece? 8 mm; yes

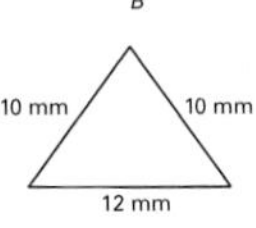

25. 36 in.; By Theorem 5.8, the distance from the vertex to the centroid is $\frac{2}{3}$ times the median ($\overline{AB}$).

5 Lesson Practice Level B

LESSON 5.5 Practice B
For use with pages 328–334

Use a ruler and protractor to draw the given type of triangle. Mark the largest angle and longest side in red and the smallest angle and shortest side in blue. What do you notice?

1. Obtuse scalene **2.** Acute isosceles **3.** Right isosceles

1–3. Check student's drawings. Longest side and largest angle are opposite each other, shortest side and smallest angle are opposite each other.

List the sides and the angles in order from smallest to largest.

4. 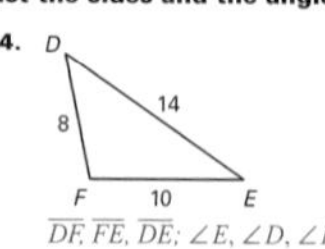

$\overline{DF}, \overline{FE}, \overline{DE}$; $\angle E, \angle D, \angle F$

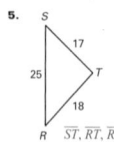

5. S, 17, 25, T, 18, R
$\overline{ST}, \overline{RT}, \overline{RS}$; $\angle R, \angle S, \angle T$

6. 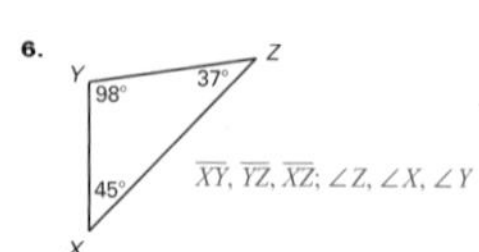

$\overline{XY}, \overline{YZ}, \overline{XZ}$; $\angle Z, \angle X, \angle Y$

7. 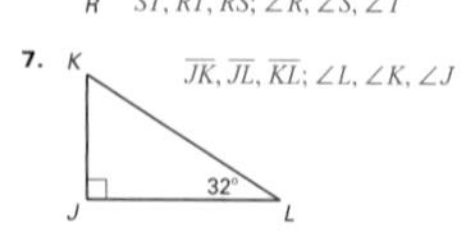

$\overline{JK}, \overline{JL}, \overline{KL}$; $\angle L, \angle K, \angle J$

8. 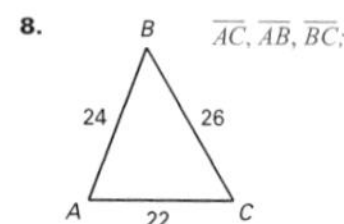

$\overline{AC}, \overline{AB}, \overline{BC}$; $\angle B, \angle C, \angle A$

9. 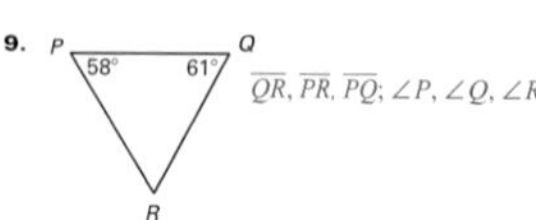

$\overline{QR}, \overline{PR}, \overline{PQ}$; $\angle P, \angle Q, \angle R$

Sketch and label the triangle described.

10. Side lengths: 14, 17, and 19, with longest side on the bottom
Angle measures: 45°, 60°, and 75°, with smallest angle at the right

11. Side lengths: 11, 18, and 24, with shortest side on the bottom
Angle measures: 25°, 44°, and 111°, with largest angle at the left

12. Side lengths: 32, 34, and 48, with shortest side arranged vertically at the right.
Angle measures: 42°, 45°, and 93°, with largest angle at the top.

Is it possible to construct a triangle with the given side lengths? If not, *explain* why not.

13. 3, 4, 5 yes **14.** 1, 4, 6 No; 1 + 4 < 6. **15.** 17, 17, 33 yes

16. 22, 26, 65 No; 22 + 26 < 65. **17.** 6, 43, 39 yes **18.** 7, 54, 45 No; 7 + 45 < 54.

LESSON 5.5 Practice B *continued*
For use with pages 328–334

***Describe* the possible lengths of the third side of the triangle given the lengths of the other two sides.**

19. 6 in., 9 in. 3 in. $< x <$ 15 in. **20.** 4 ft, 12 ft 8 ft $< x <$ 16 ft **21.** 9 m, 18 m 9 m $< x <$ 27 m

22. 21 yd, 16 yd 5 yd $< x <$ 37 yd **23.** 22 in., 2 ft 2 in. $< x <$ 46 in. **24.** 24 in., 1 yd 12 in. $< x <$ 60 in.

Is it possible to build a triangle using the given side lengths? If so, order the angle measures of the triangle from least to greatest.

25. $RS = \sqrt{46}, ST = 3\sqrt{5}, RT = 5$ yes; $\angle S, \angle R, \angle T$ **26.** $AB = \sqrt{26}, BC = 4\sqrt{5}, AC = 2\sqrt{2}$ no

***Describe* the possible values of *x*.**

27. 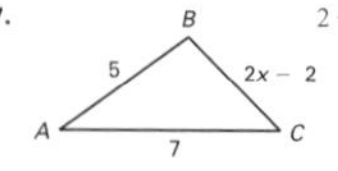

$2 < x < 7$

28. 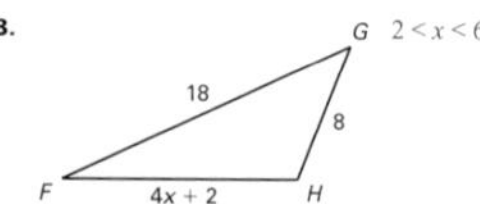

$2 < x < 6$

29. Building You are standing 200 feet from a tall building. The angle of elevation from your feet to the top of the building is 51° (as shown in the figure). What can you say about the height of the building? The building is taller than 200 feet.

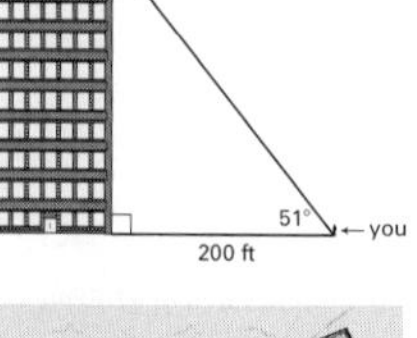

32. Think of the 60- and 24-foot distances as two sides of a triangle. Then the unknown distance d is 36 ft $< d <$ 84 ft. This doesn't account for the cases when the ball lands straight forward (d = 36 ft) or straight backward (d = 84 ft).

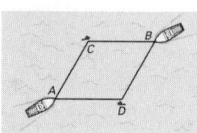

30. Sea Rescue The figure shows the relative positions of two rescue boats and two people in the water. Talking by radio, the captains use certain angle relationships to conclude that boat A is the closest to person C and boat B is the closest to person D. *Describe* the angle relationships that would lead to this conclusion. $m\angle ABC < m\angle BAC$ and $m\angle BAD < m\angle ABD$

31. Airplanes Two airplanes leave the same airport heading in different directions. After 2 hours, one airplane has traveled 710 miles and the other has traveled 640 miles. *Describe* the range of distances that represents how far apart the two airplanes can be at this time. 70 mi $< d <$ 1350 mi

32. Baseball A pitcher throws a baseball 60 feet from the pitcher's mound to home plate. A batter pops the ball up and it comes down just 24 feet from home plate. What can you determine about how far the ball lands from pitcher's mound? Explain why the Triangle Inequality Theorem can be used to describe all but the shortest and longest possible distances. See above.

LESSON 5.6 Practice B
For use with pages 335–341

Copy and complete with <, >, or =. *Explain*.

1. ST __?__ VW

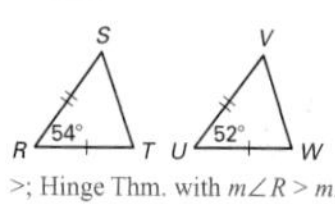

>; Hinge Thm. with $m\angle R > m\angle U$

2. DE __?__ EF

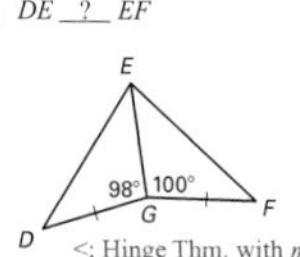

<; Hinge Thm. with $m\angle DGE < m\angle EGF$

3. JK __?__ LM

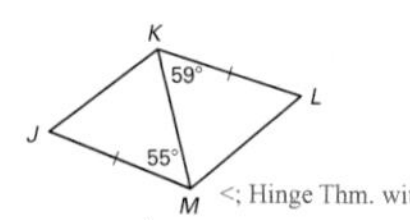

<; Hinge Thm. with $m\angle JMK < m\angle LKM$

4. $m\angle 1$ __?__ $m\angle 2$

61, 60, 1, 2

>; Converse of Hinge Thm. with the side opposite $\angle 1$ longer than the side opposite $\angle 2$.

5. $m\angle 1$ __?__ $m\angle 2$

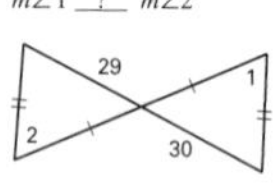

>; Converse of Hinge Thm. with the side opposite $\angle 1$ longer than the side opposite $\angle 2$.

6. $m\angle 1$ __?__ $m\angle 2$

29, 31, 1, 2

<; Converse of Hinge Thm. with the side opposite $\angle 1$ shorter than the side opposite $\angle 2$.

7. $m\angle 1$ __?__ $m\angle 2$

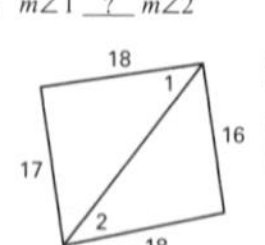

>; Converse of Hinge Thm. with the side opposite $\angle 1$ longer than the side opposite $\angle 2$.

8. AB __?__ CD

B, C, 9, 9, E, A, D

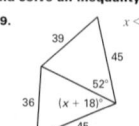

=; The triangles are ≅ by SAS.

Use the Hinge Theorem or its converse and properties of triangles to write and solve an inequality to describe a restriction on the value of *x*.

9. 39, 45, 52°, 36, $(x + 18)°$, 45 $x < 34$

10. 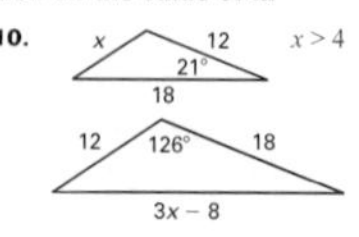

$x > 4$

LESSON 5.6 Practice B *continued*
For use with pages 335–341

Write a temporary assumption you could make to prove the conclusion indirectly.

11. If two lines in a plane are parallel, then the two lines do not contain two sides of a triangle. Assume temporarily that the two parallel lines contain two sides of a triangle.

12. If two parallel lines are cut by a transversal so that a pair of consecutive interior angles is congruent, then the transversal is perpendicular to the parallel lines. Assume temporarily that the transversal is not perpendicular to the parallel lines.

13. Table Making All four legs of the table shown have identical measurements, but they are attached to the table top so that $\angle 3$ is smaller than $\angle 1$.

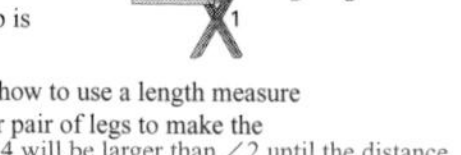

a. Use the Hinge Theorem to *explain* why the table top is not level. See below.

b. Use the Converse of the Hinge Theorem to *explain* how to use a length measure to determine when $\angle 4 \cong \angle 2$ in reattaching the rear pair of legs to make the table level. By the Converse of the Hinge Thm., $\angle 4$ will be larger than $\angle 2$ until the distance between the tops of each pair of legs is the same.

14. Fishing Contest One contestant in a catch-and-release fishing contest spends the morning at a location 1.8 miles due north of the starting point, then goes 1.2 miles due east for the rest of the day. A second contestant starts out 1.2 miles due east of the starting point, then goes another 1.8 miles in a direction 84° south of due east to spend the rest of the day. Which angler is farther from the starting point at the end of the day? *Explain* how you know. the second angler; The included ∠ for the second angler is 96° and for the first angler is 90°.

15. Indirect Proof Arrange statements A–F in order to write an indirect proof of Case 1. F, E, B, A, D, C

GIVEN: $\overline{AD}$ is a median of $\triangle ABC$; $\angle ADB \cong \angle ADC$

PROVE: $AB = AC$

Case 1:

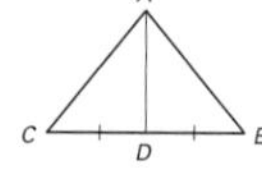

A. Then $m\angle ADB < m\angle ADC$ by the converse of the Hinge Theorem.

B. Then $\overline{BD} \cong \overline{CD}$ by the definition of midpoint. Also, $\overline{AD} \cong \overline{AD}$ by the reflexive property.

C. This contradiction shows that the temporary assumption that $AB < AC$ is false.

D. But this contradicts the given statement that $\angle ADB \cong \angle ADC$.

E. Because $\overline{AD}$ is a median of $\triangle ABC$, D is the midpoint of $\overline{BC}$.

F. Temporarily assume that $AB < AC$.

16. Indirect Proof There are two cases to consider for the proof in Exercise 15. Write an indirect proof for Case 2. Temporarily assume that $AB > AC$. The steps of the proof correspond to the steps of the proof in Ex. 15.

13. a. Because $m\angle 3 < m\angle 1$, by the Hinge Thm, the far side of the table is lower than the near side.

CHAPTER 5 Quiz 1

For use after Lessons 5.1–5.2

$\overline{DE}$ **is a midsegment of $\triangle ABC$. Find the value of x.**

1.

2. 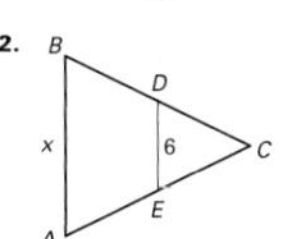

3. 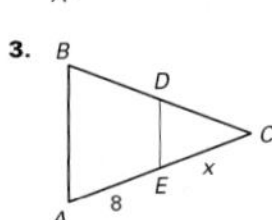

Find the value of x. Identify the theorem used to find the answer.

4. 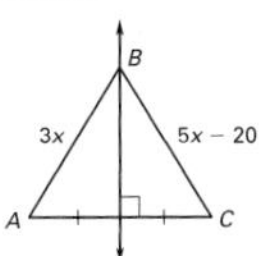

5. 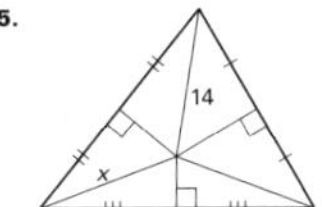

Answers

1. 19
2. 12
3. 8
4. 10; Perpendicular Bisector Theorem
5. 14; Concurrency of Perpendicular Bisectors Theorem

CHAPTER 5 Quiz 2

For use after Lessons 5.3–5.4

Find the value of x.

1.

2.

3.

In the figure, P is the centroid of $\triangle ABC$ and $BP = 8$.

4. Find the length of $\overline{BF}$.
5. Find the length of $\overline{FP}$.

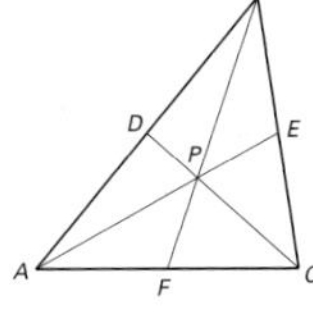

Answers

1. 7
2. 7
3. 6
4. 12
5. 4

CHAPTER 5 Quiz 3

For use after Lessons 5.5–5.6

Is it possible to construct a triangle with the given side lengths? If not, *explain* why.

1. 8, 9, 15
2. 4, 7, 13

Describe the possible lengths of the third side of the triangle given the lengths of the other two sides.

3. 5 inches, 6 inches
4. 14 feet, 21 feet

List the sides and angles in order from smallest to largest.

5.

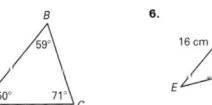

6. 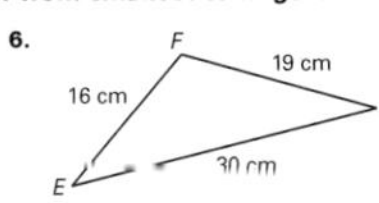

Copy and complete with <, >, or =.

7. PR __?__ VT
8. $m\angle 1$ __?__ $m\angle 2$

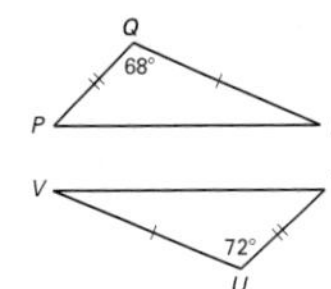

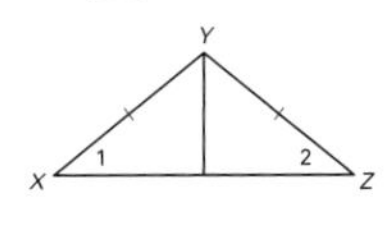

Answers

1. yes
2. No, 4 + 7 < 13.
3. $1 < x < 11$
4. $7 < x < 35$
5. $\overline{BC}, \overline{AC}, \overline{AB}$
6. $\angle D, \angle E, \angle F$
7. <
8. =

CHAPTER 5 Chapter Test B
For use after Chapter 5

$\overline{WY}$ is the midsegment of $\triangle QRS$. Find the value of x.

1. 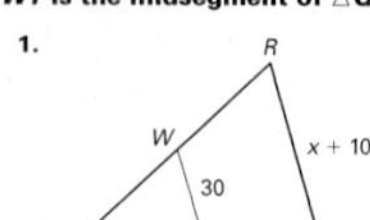

2. 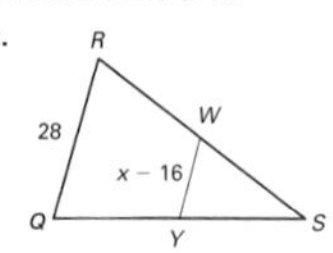

3. 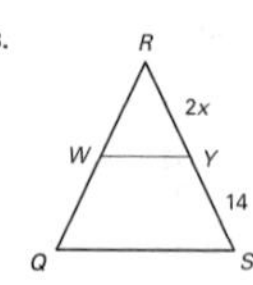

4. 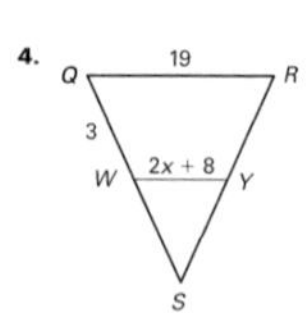

Place the figure in a coordinate plane in a convenient way. Give the coordinates of each vertex.

5. Isosceles right triangle: leg length is 3

6. Rectangle: length is 3 and width is 2

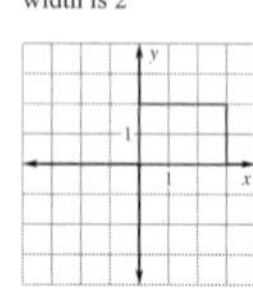

In the diagram, the perpendicular bisectors of $\triangle WXY$ meet at point Z. Find the indicated measure.

7. WZ

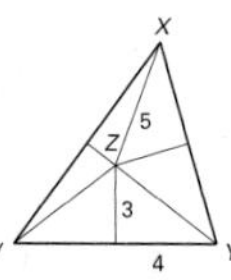

8. ZY

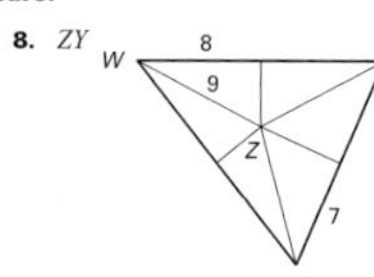

Answers

1. 50
2. 30
3. 7
4. $\frac{3}{4}$
5. See left. (0, 0), (0, 3), (3, 0)
6. See left. (0, 0), (0, 2), (3, 2), (3, 0)
7. 5
8. 9

CHAPTER 5 Chapter Test B *continued*
For use after Chapter 5

Use the information in the diagram to find x.

9. 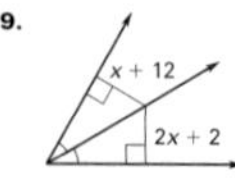

10. 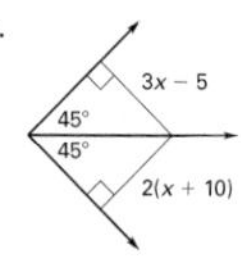

In $\triangle ABC$, Q is the centroid. Find the indicated length.

11. $QC = 12$. Find QM.

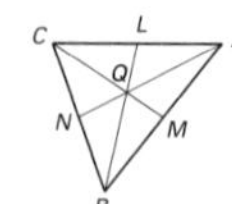

12. $QC = 6$. Find QL.

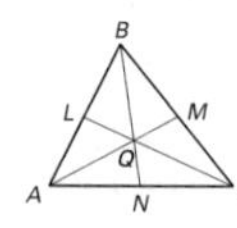

List the unknown sides in order from smallest to largest.

13. 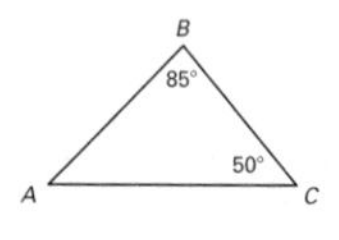

14. 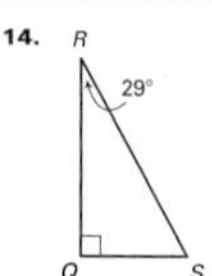

15. A triangle has one side of length 10 and another of length 6. Describe the possible lengths of the third side.

Copy and complete with <, >, or =.

16. AB _?_ BC

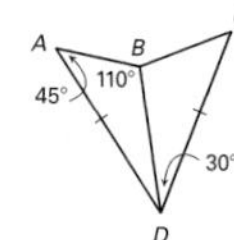

17. RS _?_ VU

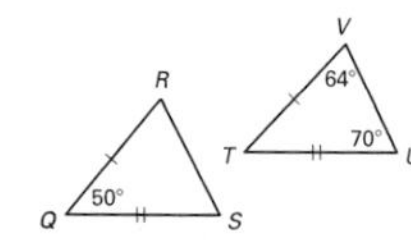

18. Suppose you wanted to prove the statement "If $x + y > 20$ and $y = 5$, then $x > 15$." What temporary assumption could you make to prove the conclusion indirectly?

Answers

9. 10
10. 25
11. 6
12. 3
13. $\overline{BC}, \overline{AB}, \overline{AC}$
14. $\overline{QS}, \overline{QR}, \overline{RS}$
15. $4 < x < 16$
16. <
17. >
18. $x \le 15$

CHAPTER 5 Standardized Test
For use after Chapter 5

Multiple Choice

1. The segment connecting the midpoints of two sides of a triangle is parallel to the third side and is _?_. B

Ⓐ twice as long Ⓑ half as long
Ⓒ one third as long Ⓓ the same length

2. If $\overline{RS}$, $\overline{RT}$, $\overline{ST}$, $\overline{WY}$, $\overline{WZ}$, and $\overline{YZ}$ are all midsegments, find x. D

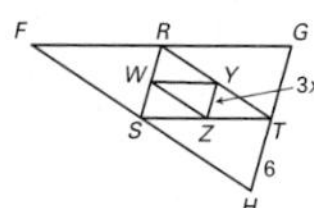

Ⓐ $\frac{1}{2}$ Ⓑ 2 Ⓒ 3 Ⓓ 1

3. If $\overline{QS}$ is the perpendicular bisector of $\overline{PR}$, find RS. B

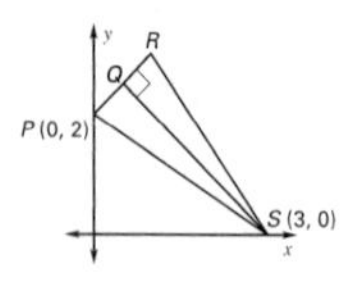

Ⓐ $\frac{3}{2}$ Ⓑ $\sqrt{13}$ Ⓒ $\sqrt{5}$ Ⓓ $\frac{5}{2}$

4. By the Concurrency of Perpendicular Bisectors Theorem, if $\overline{QJ}$, $\overline{QK}$, and $\overline{QL}$ are perpendicular bisectors, then _?_. C

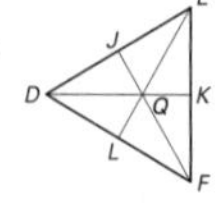

Ⓐ $\angle JQK \cong \angle KQL \cong \angle LQJ$
Ⓑ $DE = EF = FD$
Ⓒ $QD = QE = QF$
Ⓓ $\angle EQK \cong \angle FQL \cong \angle DQJ$

5. Point A is the incenter of $\triangle FGH$. Find AS. A

Ⓐ 3
Ⓑ 2
Ⓒ 4
Ⓓ 5

6. Given the inscribed circle with center K, which statement can you *not* conclude? A

Ⓐ $XK = YK$ Ⓑ $\angle NZK \cong \angle OZK$
Ⓒ $\overline{NK} \perp \overline{YZ}$ Ⓓ $MK = OK$

7. The point of concurrency of the three medians of a triangle is called the _?_ of the triangle. D

Ⓐ tri-sector point Ⓑ centrino
Ⓒ median point Ⓓ centroid

8. If point P is the centroid of $\triangle ABC$, find CP. B

Ⓐ 5 Ⓑ $\frac{10}{3}$ Ⓒ $\frac{5}{3}$ Ⓓ $\frac{7}{3}$

9. Which is the longest side of $\triangle DEF$? A

Ⓐ $\overline{DE}$
Ⓑ $\overline{DF}$
Ⓒ $\overline{EF}$
Ⓓ cannot be determined

CHAPTER 5 Standardized Test *continued*
For use after Chapter 5

10. Which is a possible value of x? B

Ⓐ 2
Ⓑ 4
Ⓒ 14
Ⓓ 17

11. Using the Hinge Theorem and the diagram, you can conclude: C

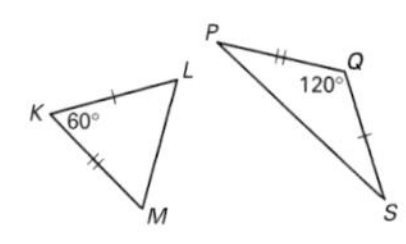

Ⓐ $m\angle KLM < m\angle QSR$
Ⓑ $QS = LM$
Ⓒ $PS > LM$
Ⓓ none of these

12. Based on the diagram, which is a true statement? A

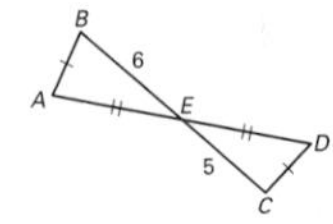

Ⓐ $m\angle A > m\angle D$
Ⓑ $m\angle A < m\angle D$
Ⓒ $m\angle A = m\angle D$
Ⓓ E is the midpoint of $\overline{BC}$.

Gridded Answer

13. G is the centroid of $\triangle MNP$ and $JP = 21$. Find the perimeter of $\triangle MJR$. 43

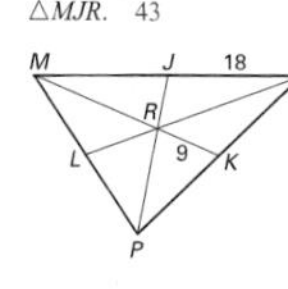

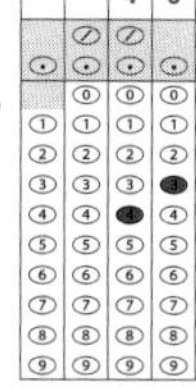

Short Response

14. In $\triangle PQR$, $PQ = 20$ and $PR = 9$. Write an inequality to show all possible values for QR. $11 < QR < 29$

Extended Response

15. A campground has a convenience store located 100 yards due south of the shower facilities. There is a game room 100 yards due east of the convenience store.

a. Camper A leaves the game room for the shower. What is the shortest travel distance possible? 141.4 yd

b. Camper B is doing laundry half way between the game room and the convenience store. Find the shortest distance Camper B can travel to get to the pool located half way between the store and the shower? See below.

c. Camper C is lost, standing at the convenience store facing west. If his tent is equidistant from the store, the shower, and the game room, provide two-step instructions to get Camper C back to the tent. See below.

b. By the Pythagorean Theorem, $a^2 + b^2 = c^2$, so $50^2 + 50^2 = c^2$ and $c = 70.7$. By the Midsegment Theorem, because the pool and laundry room are midpoints, the distance from the laundry room to the pool is half the distance from the game room to the shower. **c.** Turn clockwise 135° and walk forward 70.7 yards.

CHAPTER 5

Alternative Assessment and Math Journal

For use after Chapter 5

Journal 1. Describe the important elements of a coordinate proof and an indirect proof. Give examples of each kind of proof.

Multi-Step Problem 2. A landscape planner is working on a blueprint for a new garden park in a city. A diagram of the plan is shown.

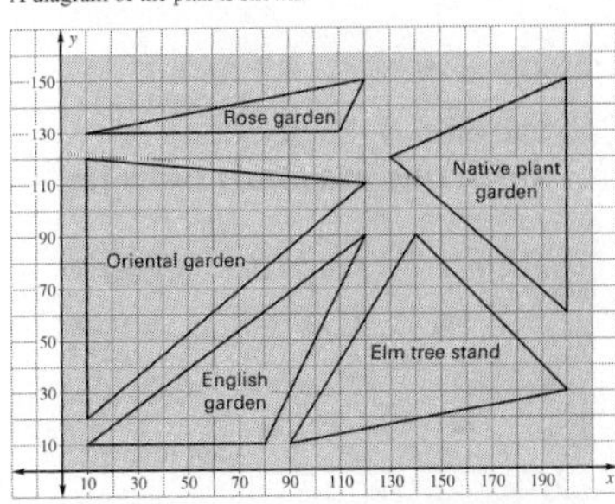

a. A path will cut through the English garden so that it is the midsegment of the side of the garden that is parallel to the horizontal axis. Find the coordinates of the endpoints of the midsegment.

b. Find the length of the path that cuts through the English garden.

c. The planner wants to place a bench at the circumcenter of the rose garden. Is this possible? *Explain* your reasoning.

d. A statue will be placed at the incenter of the English garden. Approximate the coordinates of this point.

e. A water fountain will be placed at the orthocenter of the oriental garden. Approximate the coordinates of this point.

f. A triangular trellis will be placed at the centroid of the native plant garden. Approximate the coordinates of this point.

g. If two of the lengths of the sides of the base of the triangular trellis are 4 feet and 3 feet, describe the possible lengths for the third side of the trellis.

1. Complete answers should include: an explanation that a coordinate proof involves placing geometric figures in a coordinate plane; an explanation that when variables are used to represent the coordinates of a figure in a coordinate proof, the results are true for all figures of the given type; an example of a coordinate proof; an explanation that an indirect proof involves the assumption that the desired conclusion is false and that this original assumption must be shown to be impossible; an example of an indirect proof.
2. a. (65, 50) and (100, 50) **b.** 35 units **c.** No. Because the triangle is obtuse, the circumcenter will lie outside of the rose garden. **d.** about (70, 30) **e.** about (20, 110) **f.** about (173, 110) **g.** The length of the third side must be less than 7 feet and greater than 1 foot.

CHAPTER 5

Alternative Assessment Rubric *continued*

For use after Chapter 5

Journal Solution

1. Complete answers should include:
   - an explanation that a coordinate proof involves placing geometric figures in a coordinate plane; an explanation that when variables are used to represent the coordinates of a figure in a coordinate proof, the results are true for all figures of the given type; an example of a coordinate proof.
   - an explanation that an indirect proof involves the assumption that the desired conclusion is false and that this original assumption must be shown to be impossible; an example of an indirect proof.

Multi-Step Problem Solution

2. a. (65, 50) and (100, 50)
   b. 35 units
   c. No. Because the triangle is obtuse, the circumcenter will lie outside of the rose garden.
   d. about (70, 30)
   e. about (20, 110)
   f. about (173, 110)
   g. The length of the third side must be less than 7 feet and greater than 1 foot.

Multi-Step Problem Rubric

4 The student answers all parts of the problem correctly and completely. The student shows all work. The student's work is neat.

3 The student answers all parts of the problem. The student's work may have one or two errors in finding the coordinates of the points. The student shows most work. The student's work is neat.

2 The student answers all parts of the problem. The student's work contains multiple errors, but the student shows most work. The student's work is sloppy.

1 The student does not complete all parts of the problem. The work contains many errors in logic. The student's work is sloppy, or no work is shown.

PLAN AND PREPARE

Main Ideas

In this chapter students use properties of midsegments to find lengths of segments in triangles. They then learn to write a coordinate proof. They explore perpendicular bisectors and use the concurrency of perpendicular bisectors of a triangle to solve problems. They use angle bisectors to find distance relationships and explore the concurrency of angle bisectors of a triangle. Students use medians of a triangle to find the centroid and to find segment lengths, and they use altitudes of a triangle to find and explore the orthocenter. Students relate side length and angle measures of a triangle, find possible side lengths for the third side of a triangle, use inequalities to make comparisons in two triangles, and use the Hinge Theorem and its converse to solve multi-step problems. Finally, students learn to write indirect proofs.

Prerequisite Skills

- Reviewing the definition of distance from a point to a line
- Simplifying algebraic expressions
- Graphing a triangle in the coordinate plane and classifying it
- Finding the measure of angles related to angle bisectors and segments related to midpoints
- Solving an equation or inequality

Additional resources for reviewing prerequisite skills are:

- Skills Review Handbook, pp. 869–895
- @HomeTutor

5 Relationships within Triangles

Before

In previous courses and in Chapters 1–4, you learned the following skills, which you'll use in Chapter 5: simplifying expressions, finding distances and slopes, using properties of triangles, and solving equations and inequalities.

Prerequisite Skills

VOCABULARY CHECK

1. Is the *distance from point P to line AB* equal to the length of $\overline{PQ}$? *Explain* why or why not. **No; $\overline{PQ}$ is not perpendicular to $\overleftrightarrow{AB}$.**

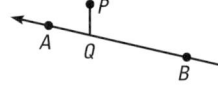

SKILLS AND ALGEBRA CHECK

Simplify the expression. All variables are positive. *(Review pp. 139, 870 for 5.1.)*

2. $\sqrt{(0-h)^2}$ **h**
3. $\frac{2m+2n}{2}$ **$m+n$**
4. $|(x+a)-a|$ **x**
5. $\sqrt{r^2+r^2}$ **$r\sqrt{2}$**

$\triangle PQR$ has the given vertices. Graph the triangle and classify it by its sides. Then determine if it is a right triangle. *(Review p. 217 for 5.1, 5.4.)* **6, 7. See margin for art.**

6. $P(2, 0)$, $Q(6, 6)$, and $R(12, 2)$ **isosceles; right triangle**
7. $P(2, 3)$, $Q(4, 7)$, and $R(11, 3)$ **scalene; not a right triangle**

Ray AD bisects $\angle BAC$ and point E bisects $\overline{CB}$. Find the measurement. *(Review pp. 15, 24, 217 for 5.2, 5.3, 5.5.)*

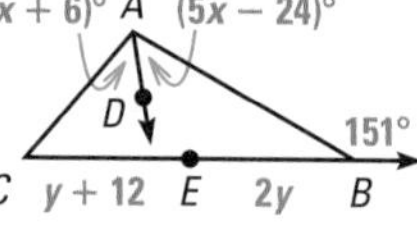

8. CE **24**
9. $m\angle BAC$ **102°**
10. $m\angle ACB$ **49°**

Solve. *(Review pp. 287, 882 for 5.3, 5.5.)*

11. $x^2 + 24^2 = 26^2$ **± 10**
12. $48 + x^2 = 60$ **$\pm 2\sqrt{3}$**
13. $43 > x + 35$ **$x < 8$**

@HomeTutor Prerequisite skills practice at classzone.com

Chapter Planning Guide

Chapter 5 Resource Book
- Teaching Guide/Lesson Plan (pp. 3, 17, 31, 46, 62, 77)
- Project with Rubric (p. 92)

Assessment and Intervention
- Assessment Book (pp. 61–75)
- Benchmark Tests
- Remediation Book

Interactive Technology
- Easy Planner
- Power Presentations CD-ROM
- Activity Generator CD-ROM
- Animated Geometry
- Test Generator CD-ROM
- Online Quizzes
- eWorkbook
- eEdition
- @HomeTutor

Resources for English Learners
- Quick Reference for English Learners
- Spanish Study Guide
- Multi-Language Visual Glossary
- Student Resources in Spanish

California Standards for Chapter 5

Geometry: 2.0, 6.0, 12.0, 15.0, 17.0

Now

In Chapter 5, you will apply the big ideas listed below and reviewed in the Chapter Summary on page 343. You will also use the key vocabulary listed below.

Big Ideas

1. **Using properties of special segments in triangles**
2. **Using triangle inequalities to determine what triangles are possible**
3. **Extending methods for justifying and proving relationships**

KEY VOCABULARY

- midsegment of a triangle, *p. 295*
- coordinate proof, *p. 296*
- perpendicular bisector, *p. 303*
- equidistant, *p. 303*
- point of concurrency, *p. 305*
- circumcenter, *p. 306*
- incenter, *p. 312*
- median of a triangle, *p. 319*
- centroid, *p. 319*
- altitude of a triangle, *p. 320*
- orthocenter, *p. 321*
- indirect proof, *p. 337*

Why?

You can use triangle relationships to find and compare angle measures and distances. For example, if two sides of a triangle represent travel along two roads, then the third side represents the distance back to the starting point.

Animated Geometry

The animation illustrated below for Example 2 on page 336 helps you answer this question: After taking different routes, which group of bikers is farther from the camp?

Two groups of bikers head out from the same point and use different routes.

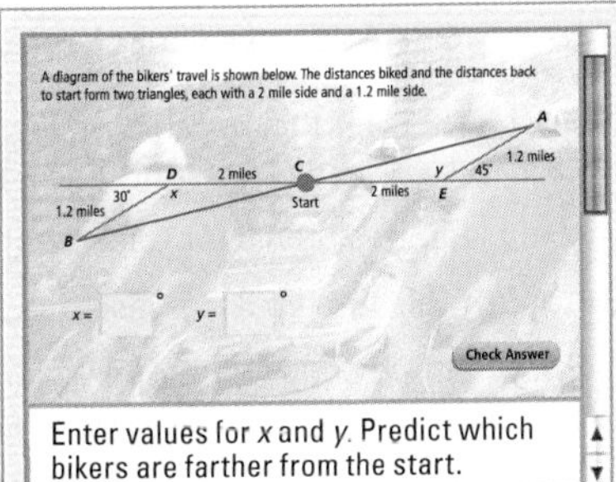

Enter values for x and y. Predict which bikers are farther from the start.

Animated Geometry at classzone.com

Other animations for Chapter 5: pages 296, 304, 312, 321, and 330

Geometry Toolkit

- Reading Strategies for Chapter 5, pp. 17–18
- Differentiated Instruction Notes, pp. 55–58
- English Learners Notes, pp. 99–100
- Inclusion Notes, pp. 129–130
- Teaching Strategies with Sample Worksheets, pp. 145–168
- Using Technology in the Classroom, pp. 169–174
- Tips for New Teachers, pp. 183–184
- Math Background Notes, pp. 212–214
- Pre-AP Strategies and Copymasters, pp. 291–292, 343–348
- Teacher Survival Activities, pp. 429–430, 453–454
- Bulletin Board Idea, p. 473
- Teacher Tool Transparencies, following p. 480

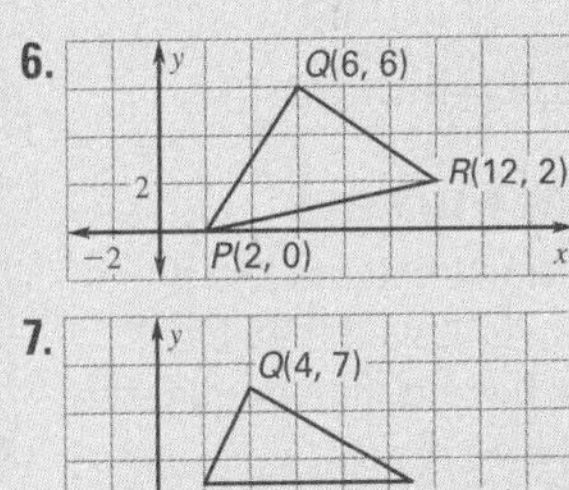

1 PLAN AND PREPARE

Explore the Concept

- Students will draw a midsegment of a triangle and compare it to the third side of the triangle.
- This activity leads into the study of midsegments in Lesson 5.1, Example 1.

Materials

Each student will need:

- graph paper
- ruler
- Activity Support Master (*Chapter 5 Resource Book*, p. 5)

Recommended Time

Work activity: 10 min

Discuss results: 5 min

Grouping

Students should work individually.

2 TEACH

Tips for Success

Suggest that students use the Midpoint Formula if they have difficulty finding the coordinates of *D* and *E*.

Key Questions

- How does $\overline{DE}$ compare to $\overline{AB}$? **It is half as long.**
- Is the midsegment relationship true in any triangle? **yes**

Alternative Strategy

Demonstrate how to do this activity on the overhead projector, record the results in a table, and ask students to make conjectures from the table.

Key Discovery

The segment connecting the midpoints of two sides of a triangle is parallel to the third side and half as long.

3 ASSESS AND RETEACH

1. If one side of a triangle is 16 units long, how long is the midsegment of the other two sides? **8 units**

Investigating Geometry ACTIVITY *Use before Lesson 5.1*

5.1 Investigate Segments in Triangles

MATERIALS • graph paper • ruler • pencil

Standards

Prepare for 17.0 *Students prove theorems by using coordinate geometry,* including the midpoint of a line segment, the distance formula, and various forms of equations of lines and circles.

QUESTION **How are the midsegments of a triangle related to the sides of the triangle?**

A *midsegment* of a triangle connects the midpoints of two sides of a triangle.

EXPLORE **Draw and find a midsegment**

STEP 1 ***Draw a right triangle***

Draw a right triangle with legs on the x-axis and the y-axis. Use vertices $A(0, 8)$, $B(6, 0)$, and $O(0, 0)$ as Case 1.

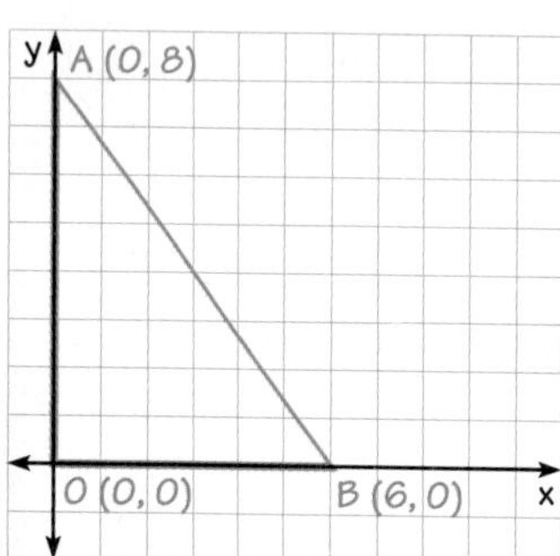

STEP 2 ***Draw the midsegment***

Find the midpoints of $\overline{OA}$ and $\overline{OB}$. Plot the midpoints and label them D and E. Connect them to create the midsegment $\overline{DE}$.

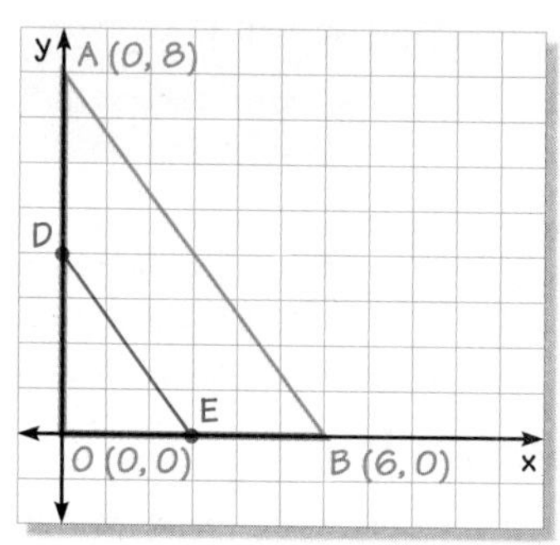

STEP 3 ***Make a table***

Draw the Case 2 triangle below. Copy and complete the table. **See margin.**

	Case 1	Case 2
O	(0, 0)	(0, 0)
A	(0, 8)	(0, 11)
B	(6, 0)	(5, 0)
D	?	?
E	?	?
Slope of $\overline{AB}$	?	?
Slope of $\overline{DE}$	?	?
Length of $\overline{AB}$	?	?
Length of $\overline{DE}$	?	?

DRAW CONCLUSIONS **Use your observations to complete these exercises**

1. Choose two other right triangles with legs on the axes. Add these triangles as Cases 3 and 4 to your table. **See margin.**
2. Expand your table in Step 3 for Case 5 with $A(0, n)$, $B(k, 0)$, and $O(0, 0)$. **See margin.**
3. Expand your table in Step 3 for Case 6 with $A(0, 2n)$, $B(2k, 0)$, and $O(0, 0)$. **See margin.**
4. What do you notice about the slopes of $\overline{AB}$ and $\overline{DE}$? What do you notice about the lengths of $\overline{AB}$ and $\overline{DE}$? **They are the same; $\overline{DE}$ is half the length of $\overline{AB}$.**
5. In each case, is the midsegment $\overline{DE}$ parallel to $\overline{AB}$? *Explain.* **Yes; they have the same slope.**
6. Are your observations true for the midsegment created by connecting the midpoints of $\overline{OA}$ and $\overline{AB}$? What about the midsegment connecting the midpoints of $\overline{AB}$ and $\overline{OB}$? **yes; yes**
7. Make a conjecture about the relationship between a midsegment and a side of the triangle. Test your conjecture using an acute triangle. **A midsegment of a triangle and the third side of the triangle are parallel and the midsegment is half the length of the third side.**

Step 3, 1–3. See Additional Answers beginning on p. AA1.

p. 295

1.

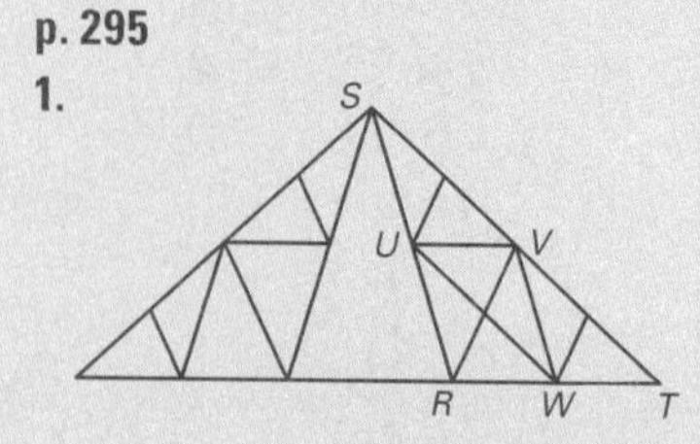

5.1 Midsegment Theorem and Coordinate Proof

Before You used coordinates to show properties of figures.

Now You will use properties of midsegments and write coordinate proofs.

Why? So you can use indirect measure to find a height, as in Ex. 35.

Key Vocabulary
- **midsegment of a triangle**
- **coordinate proof**

Standards

17.0 **Students prove theorems by using coordinate geometry, including the midpoint of a line segment,** the distance formula, and various forms of equations of lines and circles.

A **midsegment of a triangle** is a segment that connects the midpoints of two sides of the triangle. Every triangle has three midsegments.

The midsegments of $\triangle ABC$ at the right are $\overline{MP}$, $\overline{MN}$, and $\overline{NP}$.

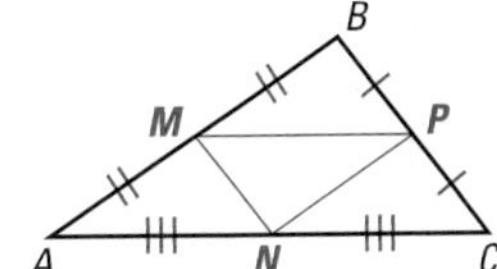

THEOREM *For Your Notebook*

THEOREM 5.1 Midsegment Theorem

The segment connecting the midpoints of two sides of a triangle is parallel to the third side and is half as long as that side.

Proof: Example 5, p. 297; Ex. 41, p. 300

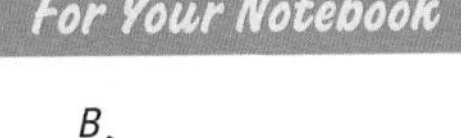

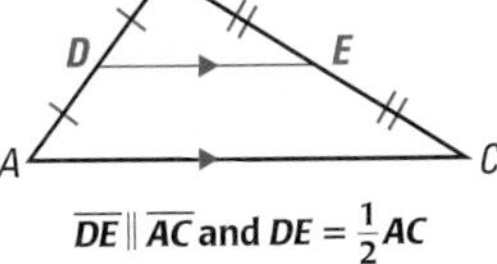

$\overline{DE} \parallel \overline{AC}$ and $DE = \frac{1}{2}AC$

EXAMPLE 1 **Use the Midsegment Theorem to find lengths**

READ DIAGRAMS
In the diagram for Example 1, midsegment $\overline{UV}$ can be called "the midsegment opposite $\overline{RT}$."

CONSTRUCTION Triangles are used for strength in roof trusses. In the diagram, $\overline{UV}$ and $\overline{VW}$ are midsegments of $\triangle RST$. Find UV and RS.

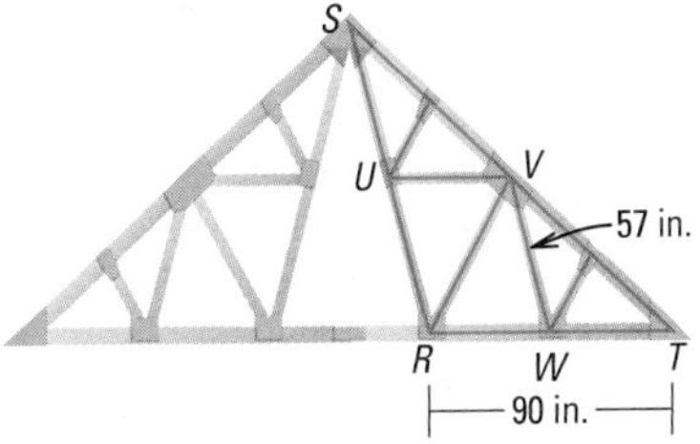

Solution

$$UV = \frac{1}{2} \cdot RT = \frac{1}{2}(90 \text{ in.}) = 45 \text{ in.}$$

$$RS = 2 \cdot VW = 2(57 \text{ in.}) = 114 \text{ in.}$$

✓ **GUIDED PRACTICE** for Example 1

1. Copy the diagram in Example 1. Draw and name the third midsegment.

2. In Example 1, suppose the distance UW is 81 inches. Find VS. **81 in.**

1. $\overline{UW}$; see margin on p. 294 for art.

1 PLAN AND PREPARE

Warm-Up Exercises

Transparency Available

For Exercises 1–4, use $A(0, 10)$, $B(24, 0)$, and $C(0, 0)$.

1. Find AB. **26**
2. Find the midpoint of $\overline{CA}$. **(0, 5)**
3. Find the midpoint of $\overline{AB}$. **(12, 5)**
4. Find the slope of $\overline{AB}$. $-\frac{5}{12}$

Notetaking Guide

Transparency Available

Promotes interactive learning and notetaking skills, pp. 119–121.

Pacing

Basic: 2 days
Average: 2 days
Advanced: 2 days
Block: 1 block
- See *Teaching Guide/Lesson Plan.*

2 FOCUS AND MOTIVATE

Essential Question

Big Idea 3, p. 293

How do you write a coordinate proof? **Tell students they will learn how to answer this question by placing a figure in the coordinate plane, asssigning coordinates to the vertices, and then using the midpoint, distance, and/or slope formulas.**

Resource Planning Guide

Chapter Resource Book
- Teaching Guide/Lesson Plan (pp. 3–4)
- Practice levels A, B, C (pp. 6–11)
- Study Guide (pp. 12–13)
- Catch-up for Absent Students (p. 14)
- Application (p. 15)
- Challenge (p. 16)

Workbooks
- Notetaking Guide (pp. 119–121)
- Practice Workbook (pp. 85–87)

Teaching Options
- **Power Presentations CD-ROM** provides dynamic electronic teaching resources for the classroom.
- **Activity Generator CD-ROM** provides editable activities for all ability levels.

Interactive Technology
- Easy Planner
- Power Presentations CD-ROM
- Activity Generator CD-ROM
- Animated Geometry
- Test Generator CD-ROM
- Online Quiz
- eWorkbook
- eEdition
- @HomeTutor

Resources for English Learners
- Quick Reference for English Learners
- Spanish Study Guide
- Multi-Language Visual Glossary
- Student Resources in Spanish

See also the *Geometry Toolkit* for more strategies for meeting individual needs.

Motivating the Lesson

The sides of a playground swing set are inverted "A" frames, with a horizontal bar joining the supports at their midpoints. Tell students that this lesson investigates the segment that joins the midpoints of two sides of a triangle.

3 TEACH

Extra Example 1

In the diagram of an A-frame house, $\overline{DG}$ and $\overline{DH}$ are midsegments of $\triangle ABF$. Find DG and BF.

$DG = 6$ ft; $BF = 20$ ft

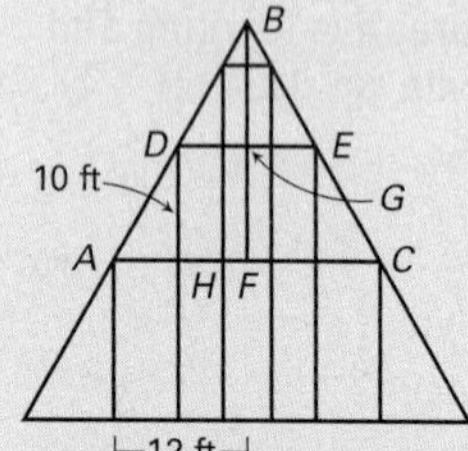

Extra Example 2

In the diagram, $\overline{RS} \cong \overline{TS}$ and $\overline{RW} \cong \overline{VW}$. Show that $\overline{VT} \parallel \overline{WS}$.

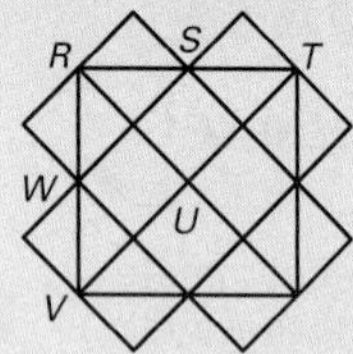

$\overline{RS} \cong \overline{TS}$ and $\overline{RW} \cong \overline{VW}$, so S and W are the midpoints of $\overline{RT}$ and $\overline{RV}$, respectively. $\overline{VT} \parallel \overline{WS}$ by the Midsegment Theorem.

Extra Example 3

Place a square and a right triangle in a coordinate plane in a way that is convenient for finding side lengths. Assign coordinates to each vertex.

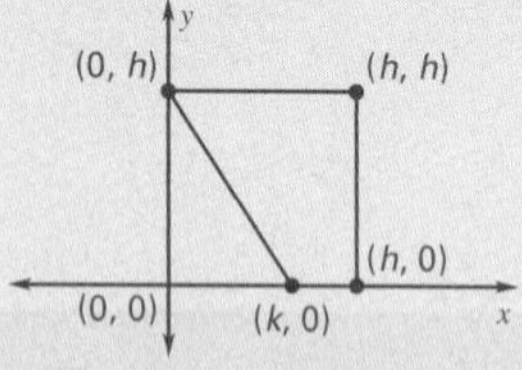

EXAMPLE 2 Use the Midsegment Theorem

In the kaleidoscope image, $\overline{AE} \cong \overline{BE}$ and $\overline{AD} \cong \overline{CD}$. Show that $\overline{CB} \parallel \overline{DE}$.

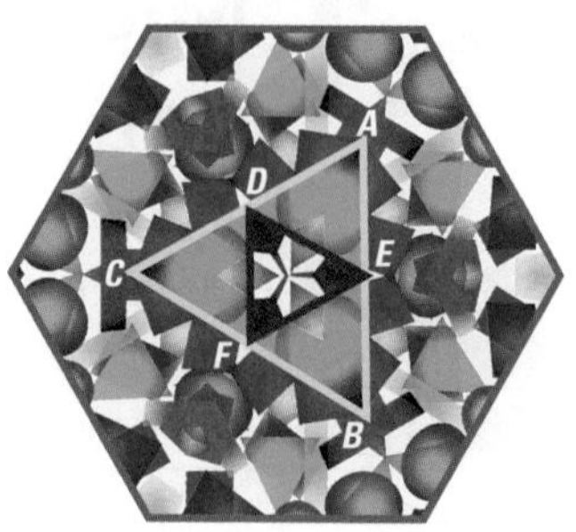

Solution

Because $\overline{AE} \cong \overline{BE}$ and $\overline{AD} \cong \overline{CD}$, E is the midpoint of $\overline{AB}$ and D is the midpoint of $\overline{AC}$ by definition. Then $\overline{DE}$ is a midsegment of $\triangle ABC$ by definition and $\overline{CB} \parallel \overline{DE}$ by the Midsegment Theorem.

COORDINATE PROOF A **coordinate proof** involves placing geometric figures in a coordinate plane. When you use variables to represent the coordinates of a figure in a coordinate proof, the results are true for all figures of that type.

EXAMPLE 3 Place a figure in a coordinate plane

Place each figure in a coordinate plane in a way that is convenient for finding side lengths. Assign coordinates to each vertex.

a. A rectangle **b.** A scalene triangle

Solution

It is easy to find lengths of horizontal and vertical segments and distances from (0, 0), so place one vertex at the origin and one or more sides on an axis.

USE VARIABLES
The rectangle shown represents a general rectangle because the choice of coordinates is based only on the definition of a rectangle. If you use this rectangle to prove a result, the result will be true for all rectangles.

a. Let h represent the length and k represent the width.

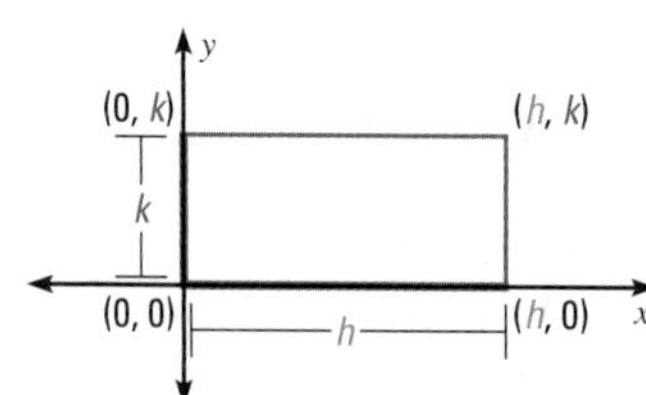

b. Notice that you need to use three different variables.

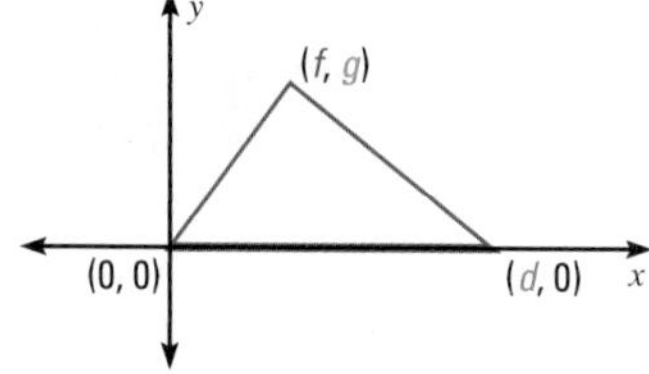

AnimatedGeometry at classzone.com

✓ GUIDED PRACTICE for Examples 2 and 3

3. In Example 2, if F is the midpoint of $\overline{CB}$, what do you know about $\overline{DF}$?

3. $\overline{DF}$ is a midsegment of $\triangle ABC$, $\overline{DF} \parallel \overline{AB}$, and DF is half the length of AB.

4. Show another way to place the rectangle in part (a) of Example 3 that is convenient for finding side lengths. Assign new coordinates. **See margin.**

5. Is it possible to find any of the side lengths in part (b) of Example 3 without using the Distance Formula? *Explain.* **Yes; the length of one side is d.**

6. A square has vertices (0, 0), (m, 0), and (0, m). Find the fourth vertex. **(m, m)**

Differentiated Instruction

Below Level Students who need more practice with midsegments should be instructed to draw examples of scalene, right, and obtuse triangles. Ask them to use a ruler to locate the midpoints, to draw the midsegments, and to verify that the midsegment is one half the third side. Then ask them to use a protractor to verify that the midsegment is parallel to the third side.

See also the *Geometry Toolkit* for more strategies.

EXAMPLE 4 Apply variable coordinates

Place an isosceles right triangle in a coordinate plane. Then find the length of the hypotenuse and the coordinates of its midpoint M.

ANOTHER WAY

For an alternative method for solving the problem in Example 4, turn to page 302 for the **Problem Solving Workshop**.

Solution

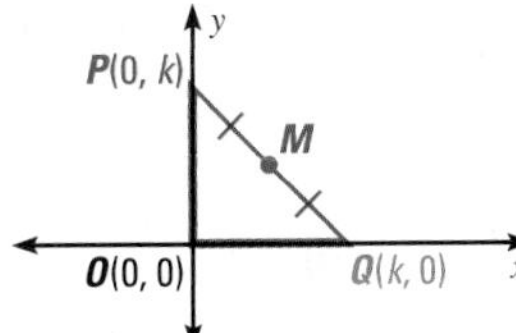

Place $\triangle PQO$ with the right angle at the origin. Let the length of the legs be k. Then the vertices are located at $P(0, k)$, $Q(k, 0)$, and $O(0, 0)$.

Use the Distance Formula to find PQ.

$$PQ = \sqrt{(k-0)^2 + (0-k)^2} = \sqrt{k^2 + (-k)^2} = \sqrt{k^2 + k^2} = \sqrt{2k^2} = k\sqrt{2}$$

Use the Midpoint Formula to find the midpoint M of the hypotenuse.

$$M\left(\frac{0+k}{2}, \frac{k+0}{2}\right) = M\left(\frac{k}{2}, \frac{k}{2}\right)$$

EXAMPLE 5 Prove the Midsegment Theorem

Write a coordinate proof of the Midsegment Theorem for one midsegment.

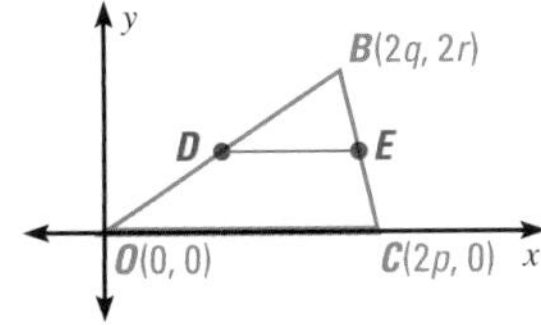

GIVEN ▶ $\overline{DE}$ is a midsegment of $\triangle OBC$.

PROVE ▶ $\overline{DE} \parallel \overline{OC}$ and $DE = \frac{1}{2}OC$

Solution

WRITE PROOFS

You can often assign coordinates in several ways, so choose a way that makes computation easier. In Example 5, you can avoid fractions by using $2p$, $2q$, and $2r$.

STEP 1 **Place** $\triangle OBC$ and assign coordinates. Because you are finding midpoints, use $2p$, $2q$, and $2r$. Then find the coordinates of D and E.

$$D\left(\frac{2q+0}{2}, \frac{2r+0}{2}\right) = D(q, r) \qquad E\left(\frac{2q+2p}{2}, \frac{2r+0}{2}\right) = E(q+p, r)$$

STEP 2 **Prove** $\overline{DE} \parallel \overline{OC}$. The y-coordinates of D and E are the same, so $\overline{DE}$ has a slope of 0. $\overline{OC}$ is on the x-axis, so its slope is 0.

▶ Because their slopes are the same, $\overline{DE} \parallel \overline{OC}$.

STEP 3 **Prove** $DE = \frac{1}{2}OC$. Use the Ruler Postulate to find $\overline{DE}$ and $\overline{OC}$.

$$DE = |(q+p) - q| = p \qquad OC = |2p - 0| = 2p$$

▶ So, the length of $\overline{DE}$ is half the length of $\overline{OC}$.

✓ GUIDED PRACTICE for Examples 4 and 5

7. In Example 5, find the coordinates of F, the midpoint of $\overline{OC}$. Then show that $\overline{EF} \parallel \overline{OB}$. **See margin.**

8. Graph the points $O(0, 0)$, $H(m, n)$, and $J(m, 0)$. Is $\triangle OHJ$ a right triangle? Find the side lengths and the coordinates of the midpoint of each side. **See margin.**

Animated Geometry
classzone.com

An **Animated Geometry** activity is available on-line for **Example 3**. This activity is also available on the **Power Presentations CD-ROM**.

Extra Example 4

Place a rectangle in a coordinate plane. Then find the length of a diagonal and the coordinates of the midpoint M of the diagonal.

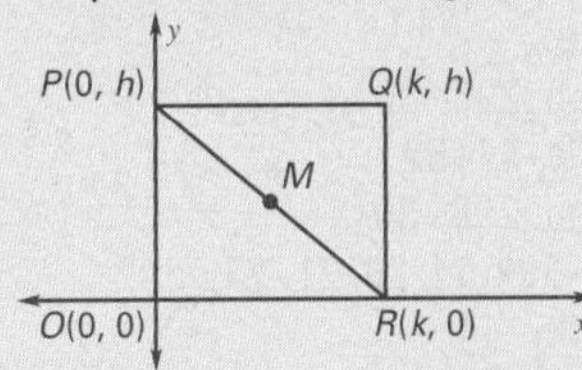

$PR = \sqrt{k^2 + h^2}$; $M\left(\frac{k}{2}, \frac{h}{2}\right)$

Extra Example 5

Write a coordinate proof of the Midsegment Theorem for the midsegment parallel to $\overline{OB}$.

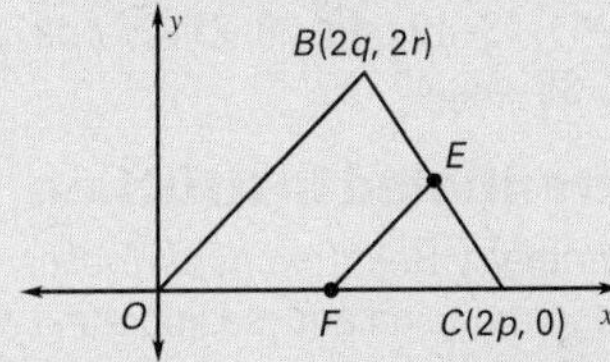

Given: $\overline{FE}$ is a midsegment.

Prove: $\overline{FE} \parallel \overline{OB}$ and $FE = \frac{1}{2}OB$

The midpoints are $E(q+p, r)$ and $F = F(p, 0)$. The slope of both $\overline{FE}$ and $\overline{OB}$ is $\frac{r}{q}$ so $\overline{FE} \parallel \overline{OB}$. Also, $FE = \sqrt{q^2 + r^2}$ and $OB = 2\sqrt{q^2 + r^2}$, so $FE = \frac{1}{2}OB$.

Closing the Lesson

Have students summarize the major points of the lesson and answer the Essential Question: How do you write a coordinate proof?

- **Assign coordinates to vertices that are convenient for finding lengths.**
- **Use coordinates to find midpoints, distances, and slopes.**

Assign convenient coordinates to vertices and use the midpoint, distance, and slope formulas to generate the proof.

Differentiated Instruction

Inclusion Some students may have difficulty grasping the idea that when variables are used to represent the coordinates of a figure, the results are true for all figures of that type. To demonstrate that this is true, have students replace the variables in **Example 5** with reasonable numbers and show that $\overline{DE}$ is half thelength of $\overline{OC}$. Have them repeat this work with other numbers to see that $\overline{DE}$ will always be half the length of $\overline{OC}$ in this type of triangle.

See also the *Geometry Toolkit* for more strategies.

4.

y
(−h, k) (h, k)
O x
(−h, −k) (h, −k)

7, 8. See Additional Answers beginning on p. AA1.

4 PRACTICE AND APPLY

Assignment Guide

Answer Transparencies available for all exercises

Basic:
Day 1: EP p. 896 Exs. 18–23
pp. 298–301
Exs. 1–11, 47–52
Day 2: pp. 298–301
Exs. 12–25, 35–41

Average:
Day 1: pp. 298–301
Exs. 1–11, 47–52
Day 2: pp. 298–301
Exs. 13–19 odd, 20, 21–27 odd, 28–32, 35–44

Advanced:
Day 1: pp. 298–301
Exs. 1–11, 47–52
Day 2: pp. 298–301
Exs. 16–28 even, 29–46*

Block:
pp. 298–301
Exs. 1–11, 13–19 odd, 20, 21–27 odd, 28–32, 35–44, 47–52

Differentiated Instruction

See *Geometry Best Practices Toolkit* for suggestions on addressing the needs of a diverse classroom.

Homework Check

For a quick check of student understanding of key concepts, go over the following exercises:

Basic: 3, 6, 14, 20, 36
Average: 4, 8, 17, 23, 36
Advanced: 5, 10, 18, 22, 37

Extra Practice

- Student Edition, p. 904
- Chapter 5 Resource Book: Practice levels A, B, C, pp. 6–11

Practice Worksheet

An easily-readable reduced practice page (with answers) for this lesson can be found on p. 292C.

5.1 EXERCISES

HOMEWORK KEY ○ = **WORKED-OUT SOLUTIONS** on p. WS6 for Exs. 9, 21, and 37
★ = **STANDARDIZED TEST PRACTICE** Exs. 2, 31, and 39

SKILL PRACTICE

A

1. **VOCABULARY** Copy and complete: In $\triangle ABC$, D is the midpoint of $\overline{AB}$ and E is the midpoint of $\overline{AC}$. $\overline{DE}$ is a _?_ of $\triangle ABC$. **midsegment**

2. ★ **WRITING** *Explain* why it is convenient to place a right triangle on the grid as shown when writing a coordinate proof. How might you want to relabel the coordinates of the vertices if the proof involves midpoints? ***Sample answer:*** **The vertex of the right triangle is located at the origin and the other two vertices are located on the x-axis and y-axis which limits the number of variables need to label them; label the vertex on the x-axis $(2a, 0)$ and the vertex on the y-axis $(0, 2b)$.**

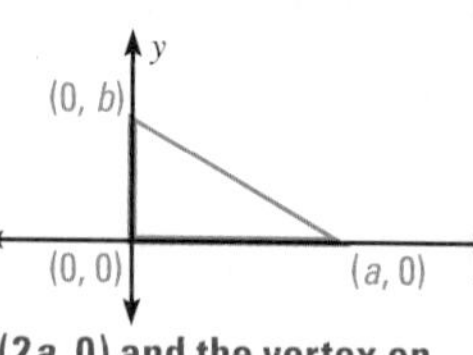

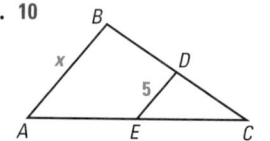

EXAMPLES 1 and 2 on pp. 295–296 for Exs. 3–11

FINDING LENGTHS $\overline{DE}$ **is a midsegment of** $\triangle ABC$. **Find the value of** x.

3. **13**

4. **10**

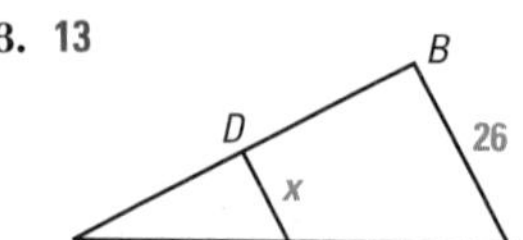

5. **6**

USING THE MIDSEGMENT THEOREM In $\triangle XYZ$, $\overline{XJ} \cong \overline{JY}$, $\overline{YL} \cong \overline{LZ}$, and $\overline{XK} \cong \overline{KZ}$. Copy and complete the statement.

6. $\overline{JK} \parallel$ _?_ $\overline{YZ}$
7. $\overline{JL} \parallel$ _?_ $\overline{XZ}$
8. $\overline{XY} \parallel$ _?_ $\overline{KL}$
9. $\overline{YJ} \cong$ _?_ $\cong$ _?_ $\overline{JX}, \overline{KL}$
10. $\overline{JL} \cong$ _?_ $\cong$ _?_ $\overline{XK}, \overline{KZ}$
11. $\overline{JK} \cong$ _?_ $\cong$ _?_ $\overline{YL}, \overline{LZ}$

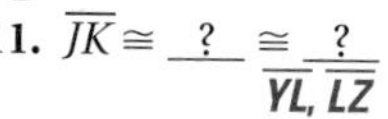

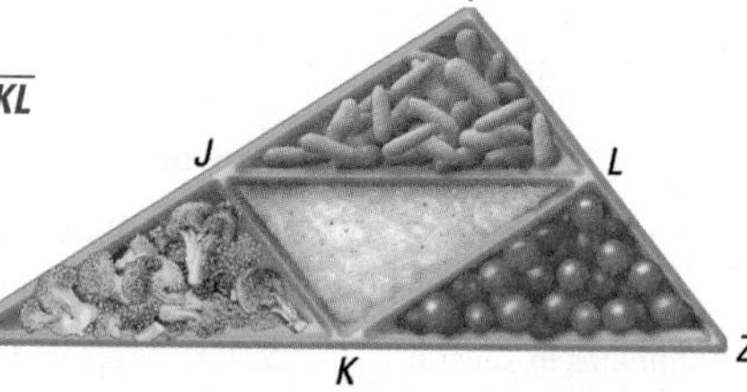

EXAMPLE 3 on p. 296 for Exs. 12–19

PLACING FIGURES Place the figure in a coordinate plane in a convenient way. Assign coordinates to each vertex. **Sample answers are given.**

12. Right triangle: leg lengths are 3 units and 2 units **(0, 0), (3, 0), (0, 2)**
13. Isosceles right triangle: leg length is 7 units **(0, 0), (7, 0), (0, 7)**
14. Square: side length is 3 units **(0, 0), (3, 0), (3, 3), (0, 3)**
15. Scalene triangle: one side length is $2m$ **(0, 0), (2m, 0), (a, b)**
16. Rectangle: length is a and width is b **(0, 0), (a, 0), (a, b), (0, b)**
17. Square: side length is s **(0, 0), (s, 0), (s, s), (0, s)**
18. Isosceles right triangle: leg length is p **(0, 0), (p, 0), (0, p)**
19. Right triangle: leg lengths are r and s **(0, 0), (r, 0), (0, s)**

EXAMPLES 4 and 5 on p. 297 for Exs. 20–23

20. **COMPARING METHODS** Find the length of the hypotenuse in Exercise 19. Then place the triangle another way and use the new coordinates to find the length of the hypotenuse. Do you get the same result? $\sqrt{r^2 + s^2}$; **yes**

B

APPLYING VARIABLE COORDINATES Sketch $\triangle ABC$. Find the length and the slope of each side. Then find the coordinates of each midpoint. Is $\triangle ABC$ a right triangle? Is it isosceles? *Explain.* (Assume all variables are positive, $p \neq q$, and $m \neq n$.) **21–23. See margin.**

21. $A(0, 0)$, $B(p, q)$, $C(2p, 0)$
22. $A(0, 0)$, $B(h, h)$, $C(2h, 0)$
23. $A(0, n)$, $B(m, n)$, $C(m, 0)$

21.

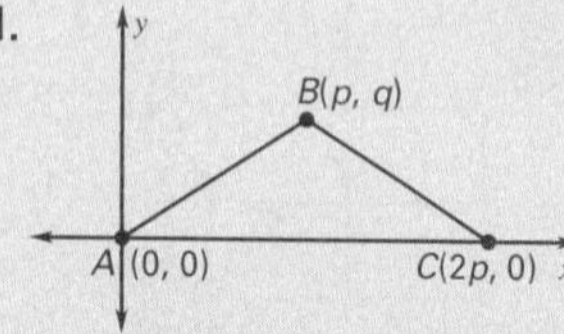

$AB = \sqrt{p^2 + q^2}, \frac{q}{p}, \left(\frac{p}{2}, \frac{q}{2}\right)$; $BC = \sqrt{p^2 + q^2}, -\frac{q}{p}, \left(\frac{3p}{2}, \frac{q}{2}\right)$; $CA = 2p, 0, (p, 0)$; **no; yes; it's not a right triangle because none of the slopes are negative reciprocals, and it is isosceles because two of the sides are the same length.**

ALGEBRA **Use $\triangle GHJ$, where A, B, and C are midpoints of the sides.**

24. If $AB = 3x + 8$ and $GJ = 2x + 24$, what is AB? **14**

25. If $AC = 3y - 5$ and $HJ = 4y + 2$, what is HB? **13**

26. If $GH = 7z - 1$ and $BC = 4z - 3$, what is GH? **34**

27. **ERROR ANALYSIS** *Explain* why the conclusion is incorrect.

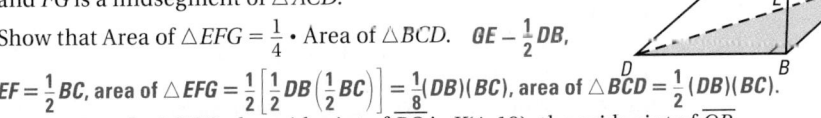

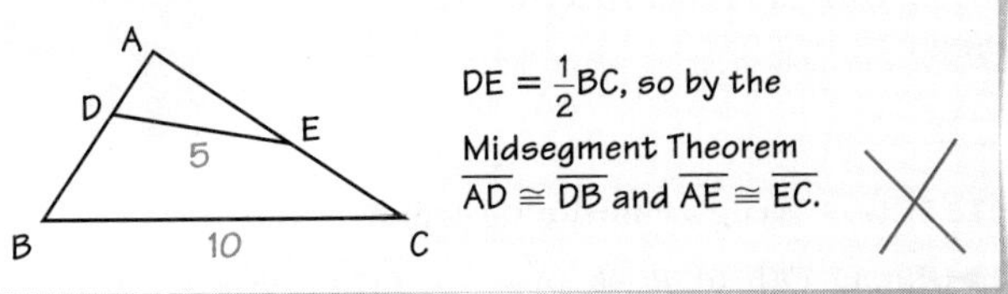

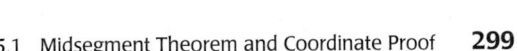

You don't know that $\overline{DE}$ and $\overline{BC}$ are parallel.

28. **FINDING PERIMETER** The midpoints of the three sides of a triangle are $P(2, 0)$, $Q(7, 12)$, and $R(16, 0)$. Find the length of each midsegment and the perimeter of $\triangle PQR$. Then find the perimeter of the original triangle. **$PQ = 13$, $PR = 14$, $QR = 15$, perimeter $= 42$; 84**

APPLYING VARIABLE COORDINATES **Find the coordinates of the red point(s) in the figure. Then show that the given statement is true.** **29, 30. See margin.**

29. $\triangle OPQ \cong \triangle RSQ$

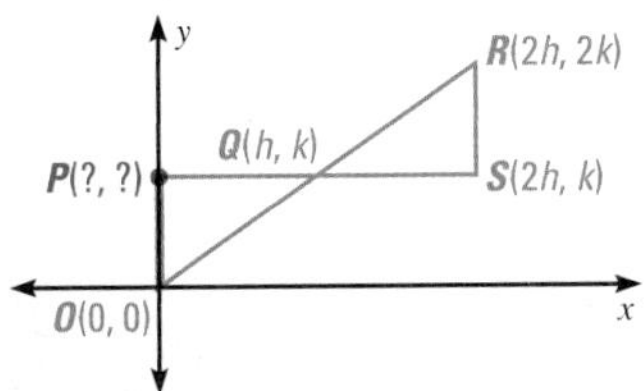

30. slope of $\overline{HE} = -$(slope of $\overline{DG}$)

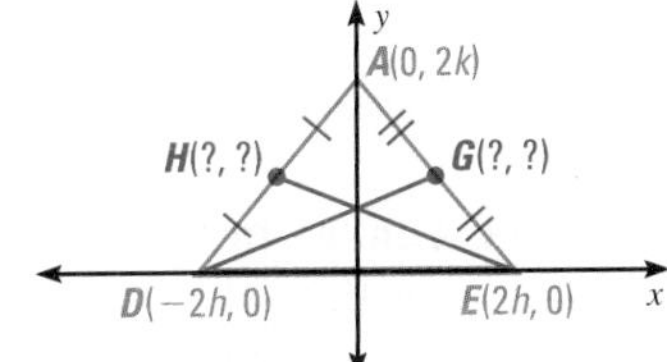

31. ★ **MULTIPLE CHOICE** A rectangle with side lengths $3h$ and k has a vertex at $(-h, k)$. Which point *cannot* be a vertex of the rectangle? **A**

Ⓐ (h, k) Ⓑ $(-h, 0)$ Ⓒ $(2h, 0)$ Ⓓ $(2h, k)$

32. **RECONSTRUCTING A TRIANGLE** The points $T(2, 1)$, $U(4, 5)$, and $V(7, 4)$ are the midpoints of the sides of a triangle. Graph the three midsegments. Then show how to use your graph and the properties of midsegments to draw the original triangle. Give the coordinates of each vertex. **See margin for art; $(-1, 2)$, $(5, 0)$, $(9, 8)$.**

C **33.** **3-D FIGURES** Points A, B, C, and D are the vertices of a *tetrahedron* (a solid bounded by four triangles). $\overline{EF}$ is a midsegment of $\triangle ABC$, $\overline{GE}$ is a midsegment of $\triangle ABD$, and $\overline{FG}$ is a midsegment of $\triangle ACD$.

Show that Area of $\triangle EFG = \frac{1}{4} \cdot$ Area of $\triangle BCD$. **$GE = \frac{1}{2}DB$, $EF = \frac{1}{2}BC$, area of $\triangle EFG = \frac{1}{2}\left[\frac{1}{2}DB\left(\frac{1}{2}BC\right)\right] = \frac{1}{8}(DB)(BC)$, area of $\triangle BCD = \frac{1}{2}(DB)(BC)$.**

34. **CHALLENGE** In $\triangle PQR$, the midpoint of $\overline{PQ}$ is $K(4, 12)$, the midpoint of $\overline{QR}$ is $L(5, 15)$, and the midpoint of $\overline{PR}$ is $M(6.4, 10.8)$. Show how to find the vertices of $\triangle PQR$. *Compare* your work for this exercise with your work for Exercise 32. How were your methods different? **See margin.**

29. $(0, k)$. ***Sample answer:*** **Since $\triangle OPQ$ and $\triangle RSQ$ are right triangles with $\overline{OP} \cong \overline{RS}$ and $\overline{PQ} \cong \overline{SQ}$, the triangles are congruent by SAS.**

30. **$H(-h, k)$, $G(h, k)$; slope of $\overline{HE} = -\frac{k}{3h}$ and the slope of $\overline{DG} = \frac{k}{3h}$.**

34. **Find the slope of each midsegment which gives you the slope of each side of the triangles. Use the slope and the known point on each side to find the equation of the line containing each side. Solve the three systems to find the vertices of the triangle; in Exercise 32, the vertices were found graphically and in this exercise, the vertices were found algebraically.**

Study Strategy

Exercises 21–23 Students may attempt to do these exercises haphazardly. Suggest that they use a system to keep all the information organized. For example, they could first find all the lengths, then find all the slopes, and then find all the midpoints.

Teaching Strategy

Exercise 32 To reconstruct a triangle from the midpoints, suggest that students use the fact that midsegments are parallel to the third sides of the triangle. Have students draw lines parallel to each midsegment through the third vertex, and use the intersections of pairs of lines to find the vertices of the original triangle.

Vocabulary

Exercise 33 A tetrahedron is a solid figure with four faces, each of which is a triangle.

23.

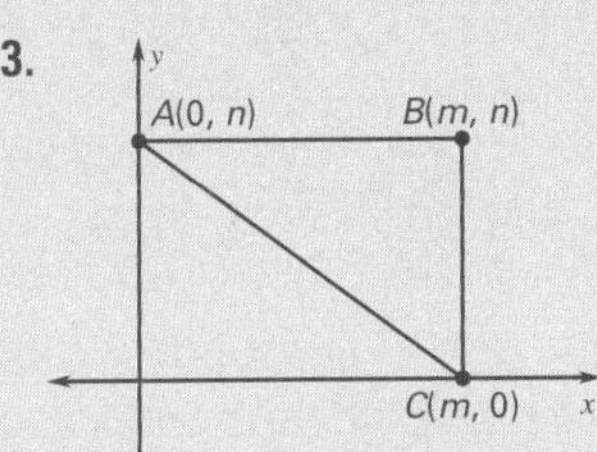

$AB = m$, 0, $\left(\frac{m}{2}, n\right)$; $BC = n$, undefined, $\left(m, \frac{n}{2}\right)$; $CA = \sqrt{m^2 + n^2}$, $-\frac{n}{m}$, $\left(\frac{m}{2}, \frac{n}{2}\right)$; yes; no; one side is vertical and one side is horizontal thus the triangle is a right triangle. It is not isosceles since none of the sides are the same length.

32.

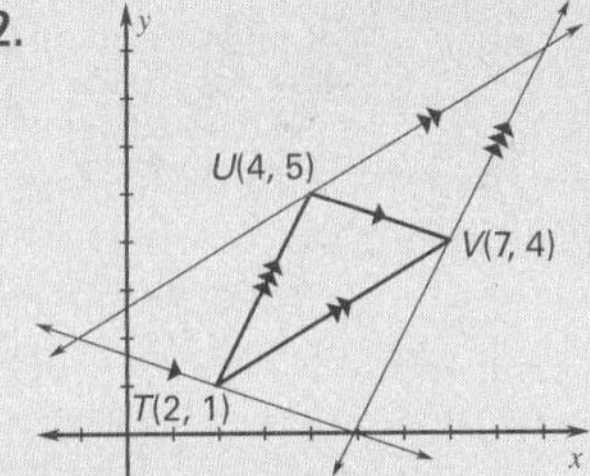

22.

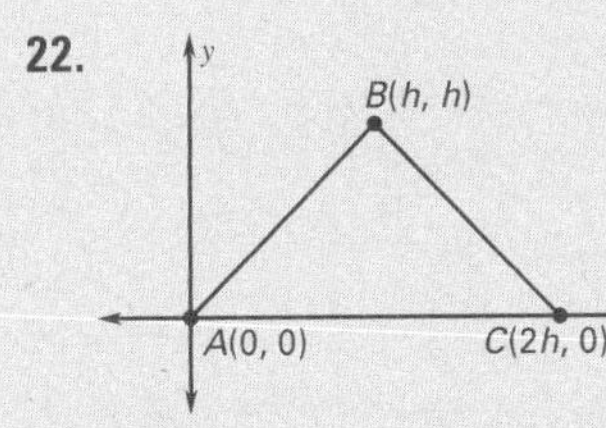

$AB = h\sqrt{2}$, 1, $\left(\frac{h}{2}, \frac{h}{2}\right)$; $BC = h\sqrt{2}$, -1, $\left(\frac{3h}{2}, \frac{h}{2}\right)$; $CA = 2h$, 0, $(h, 0)$; yes; yes; it is a right triangle and an isosceles triangle since two sides are both congruent and perpendicular.

Teaching Strategy

Exercise 42 Use this exercise to point out how using coordinates may make a proof easier. Ask students to try to plan the proof without coordinates. They should see that while it is easy to show that $CB = CD$, it is not easy to show both are equal to CA.

Mathematical Reasoning

Exercise 43 This design consists of self-similar triangles, or triangles that are similar to those in previous stages of the design. Students will study self-similarity and fractals in Chapter 6.

41. ***Sample answer:*** **The coordinates of D are (q, r) and the coordinates of F are $(p, 0)$ since $\left(\frac{2p+0}{2}, \frac{0+0}{2}\right) = (p, 0)$. The slope of $\overline{DF}$ is $\frac{r-0}{q-p} = \frac{r}{q-p}$ and the slope of $\overline{BC}$ is $\frac{2r-0}{2q-2p} = \frac{r}{q-p}$, so $\overline{DF} \parallel \overline{BC}$. $DF = \sqrt{(p-q)^2 + r^2}$ and $BC = \sqrt{(2q-2p)^2 + (2r)^2} = 2\sqrt{(p-q)^2 + r^2}$ making $DF = \frac{1}{2}BC$.**

42. ***Sample answer:*** **Let $A(0, 0)$, $B(0, p)$, and $D(q, 0)$ be the vertices of $\triangle ABD$. Since C is the midpoint of $\overline{BD}$, its coordinates are $\left(\frac{q}{2}, \frac{p}{2}\right)$. $AC = \sqrt{\left(\frac{q}{2}\right)^2 + \left(\frac{p}{2}\right)^2} = \frac{\sqrt{p^2+q^2}}{2}$, $BC = \sqrt{\left(\frac{q}{2} - 0\right)^2 + \left(p - \frac{p}{2}\right)^2} = \frac{\sqrt{p^2+q^2}}{2}$, and $DC = \sqrt{\left(\frac{q}{2} - q\right)^2 + \left(\frac{p}{2} - 0\right)^2} = \frac{\sqrt{p^2+q^2}}{2}$, so $AC = BC = DC$.**

PROBLEM SOLVING

A

35. FLOODLIGHTS A floodlight on the edge of the stage shines upward onto the backdrop as shown. Constance is 5 feet tall. She stands halfway between the light and the backdrop, and the top of her head is at the midpoint of $\overline{AC}$. The edge of the light just reaches the top of her head. How tall is her shadow? **10 ft**

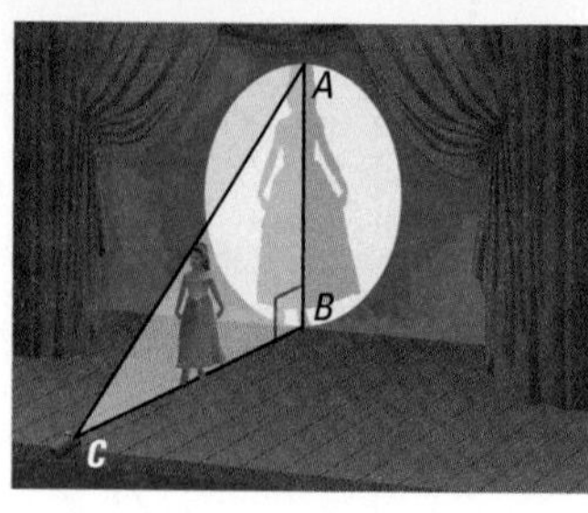

@HomeTutor for problem solving help at classzone.com

EXAMPLE 5 on p. 297 for Exs. 36–37

COORDINATE PROOF **Write a coordinate proof.**

36. GIVEN ▶ $P(0, k)$, $Q(h, 0)$, $R(-h, 0)$

PROVE ▶ $\triangle PQR$ is isosceles.

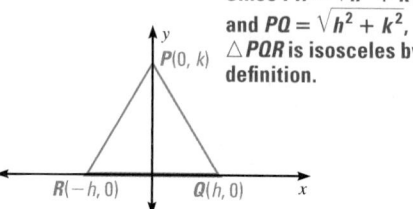

Since $PR = \sqrt{h^2 + k^2}$ and $PQ = \sqrt{h^2 + k^2}$, $\triangle PQR$ is isosceles by definition.

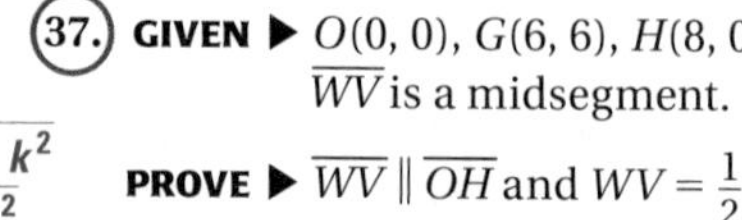

(37.) GIVEN ▶ $O(0, 0)$, $G(6, 6)$, $H(8, 0)$, $\overline{WV}$ is a midsegment.

PROVE ▶ $\overline{WV} \parallel \overline{OH}$ and $WV = \frac{1}{2}OH$

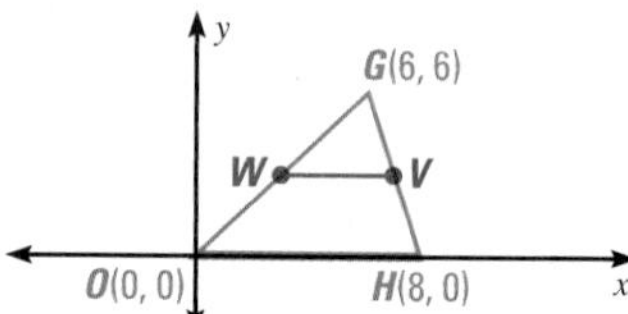

37. The coordinates of W are (3, 3) and the coordinates of V are (7, 3). The slope of $\overline{WV}$ is 0 and the slope of $\overline{OH}$ is 0 making $\overline{WV} \parallel \overline{OH}$. $WV = 4$ and $OH = 8$ thus $WV = \frac{1}{2}OH$.

@HomeTutor for problem solving help at classzone.com

38. CARPENTRY In the set of shelves shown, the third shelf, labeled $\overline{CD}$, is closer to the bottom shelf, $\overline{EF}$, than midsegment $\overline{AB}$ is. If $\overline{EF}$ is 8 feet long, is it possible for $\overline{CD}$ to be 3 feet long? 4 feet long? 6 feet long? 8 feet long? *Explain.* **No, no, yes, no; $AB = 4$ feet since it is half the length of $\overline{EF}$. The length of $\overline{CD}$ must be greater than 4 feet but less than 8 feet.**

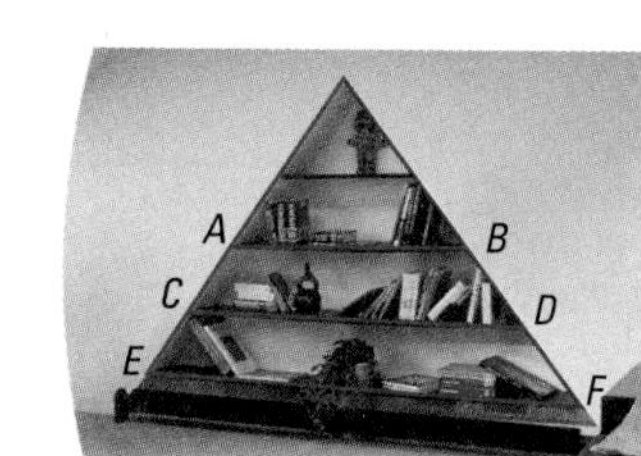

B

39. ★ SHORT RESPONSE Use the information in the diagram at the right. What is the length of side $\overline{AC}$ of $\triangle ABC$? *Explain* your reasoning. **16. *Sample answer:* DE is half the length of $\overline{FG}$ which makes $FG = 8$. FG is half the length of $\overline{AC}$ which makes $AC = 16$.**

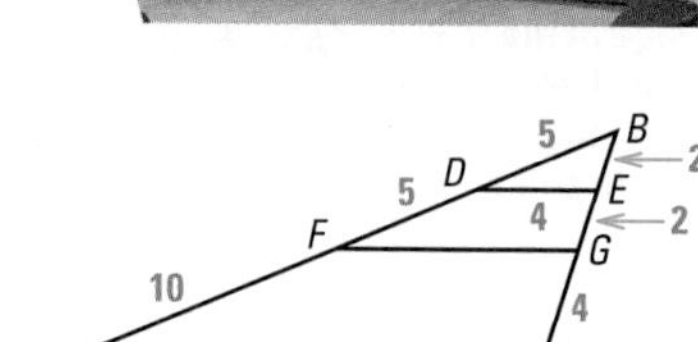

40. PLANNING FOR PROOF Copy and complete the plan for proof.

GIVEN ▶ $\overline{ST}$, $\overline{TU}$, and $\overline{SU}$ are midsegments of $\triangle PQR$.

PROVE ▶ $\triangle PST \cong \triangle SQU$

Use _?_ to show that $\overline{PS} \cong \overline{SQ}$. Use _?_ to show that $\angle QSU \cong \angle SPT$. Use _?_ to show that $\angle$ _?_ $\cong \angle$ _?_. Use _?_ to show that $\triangle PST \cong \triangle SQU$. **Definition of midsegment, Midsegment Theorem and Corresponding Angles Postulate, Midsegment Theorem and Corresponding Angles Postulate, PST, SQU, ASA**

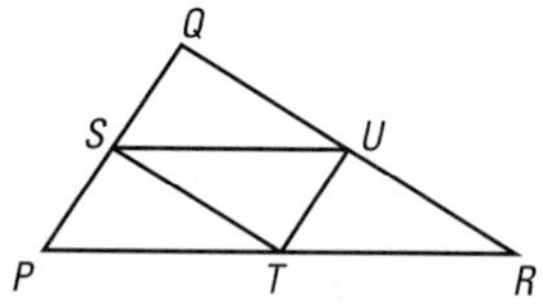

41. PROVING THEOREM 5.1 Use the figure in Example 5. Draw the midpoint F of $\overline{OC}$. Prove that $\overline{DF}$ is parallel to $\overline{BC}$ and $DF = \frac{1}{2}BC$. **See margin.**

○ = **WORKED-OUT SOLUTIONS** on p. WS1

★ = **STANDARDIZED TEST PRACTICE**

42. COORDINATE PROOF Write a coordinate proof. **See margin.**

GIVEN ▶ $\triangle ABD$ is a right triangle, with the right angle at vertex A. Point C is the midpoint of hypotenuse BD.

PROVE ▶ Point C is the same distance from each vertex of $\triangle ABD$.

43. MULTI-STEP PROBLEM To create the design below, shade the triangle formed by the three midsegments of a triangle. Then repeat the process for each unshaded triangle. Let the perimeter of the original triangle be 1.

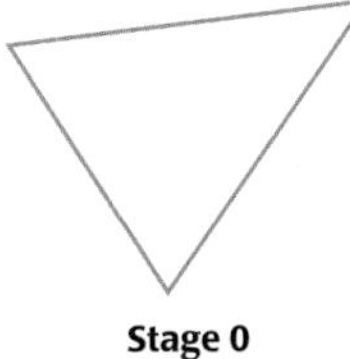
Stage 0

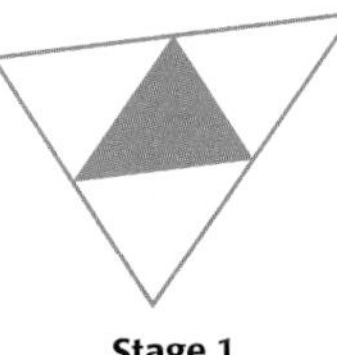
Stage 1

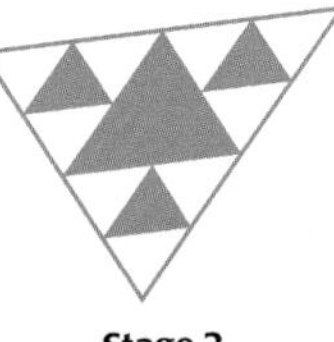
Stage 2

Stage 3

a. What is the perimeter of the triangle that is shaded in Stage 1? $\frac{1}{2}$

b. What is the total perimeter of all the shaded triangles in Stage 2? $\frac{5}{4}$

c. What is the total perimeter of all the shaded triangles in Stage 3? $\frac{19}{8}$

RIGHT ISOSCELES TRIANGLES **In Exercises 44 and 45, write a coordinate proof.** **44–46. See margin.**

44. Any right isosceles triangle can be subdivided into a pair of congruent right isosceles triangles. (*Hint:* Draw the segment from the right angle to the midpoint of the hypotenuse.)

C **45.** Any two congruent right isosceles triangles can be combined to form a single right isosceles triangle.

46. CHALLENGE XY is a midsegment of $\triangle LMN$. Suppose $\overline{DE}$ is called a "quarter-segment" of $\triangle LMN$. What do you think an "eighth-segment" would be? Make a conjecture about the properties of a quarter-segment and of an eighth-segment. Use variable coordinates to verify your conjectures.

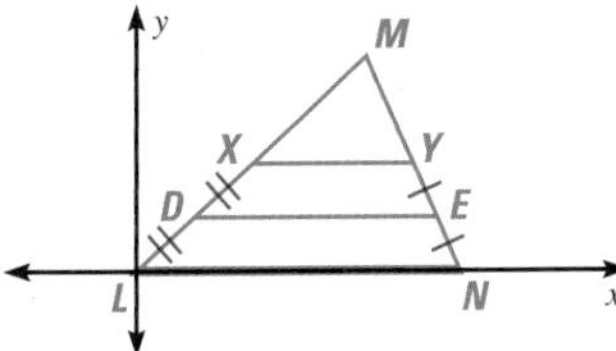

MIXED REVIEW

PREVIEW
Prepare for Lesson 5.2 in Exs. 47–49.

Line ℓ bisects the segment. Find LN. *(p. 15)*

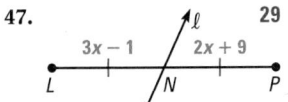

47. 29

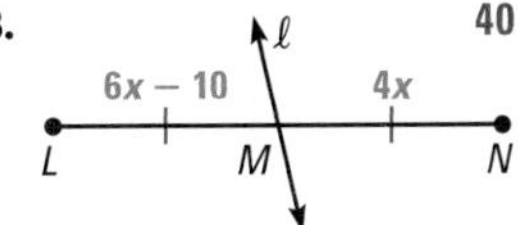

48. 40

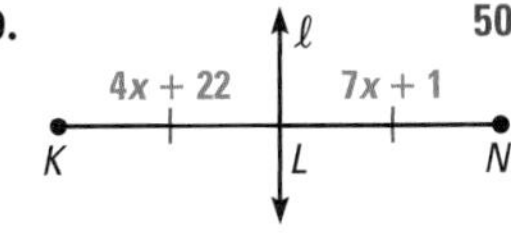

49. 50

State which postulate or theorem you can use to prove that the triangles are congruent. Then write a congruence statement. *(pp. 225, 249)*

50.

SSS; *Sample answer:* $\triangle WXY \cong \triangle WZY$

51.

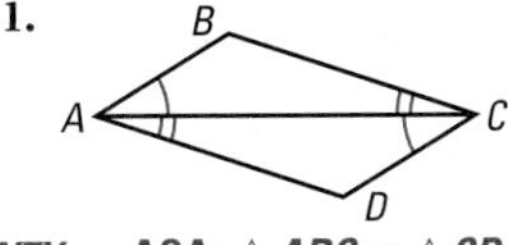

ASA; $\triangle ABC \cong \triangle CDA$

52.

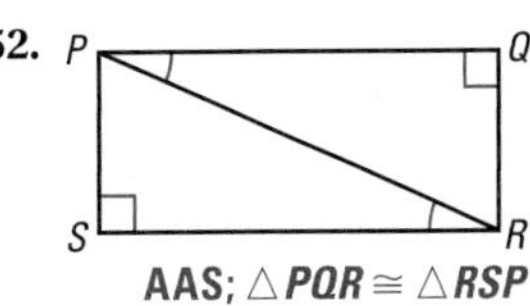

AAS; $\triangle PQR \cong \triangle RSP$

5 ASSESS AND RETEACH

Daily Homework Quiz

Transparency Available

Use the figure below for Exercises 1–4.

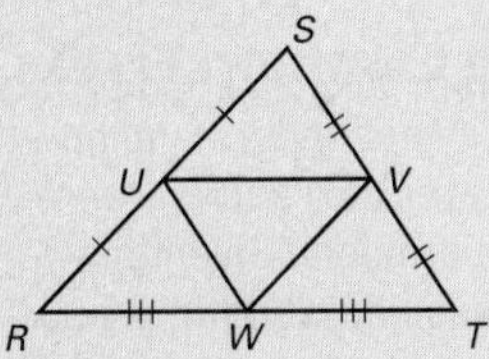

1. If $UV = 13$, find RT. **26**
2. If $ST = 20$, find UW. **10**
3. If the perimeter of $\triangle RST = 68$ inches, find the perimeter of $\triangle UVW$. **34 in.**
4. If $VW = 2x - 4$ and $RS = 3x - 3$, what is VW? **6**
5. Place a rectangle in a coordinate plane so its vertical side has length a and its horizontal side has width $2a$. Label the coordinates of each vertex.

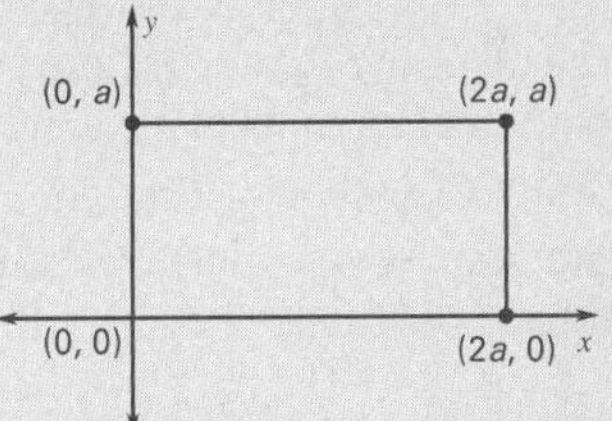

Online Quiz

Available at **classzone.com**

Diagnosis/Remediation

- Practice A, B, C in Chapter 5 Resource Book, pp. 6–11
- Study Guide in Chapter 5 Resource Book, pp. 12–13
- Practice Workbook, pp. 85–87
- @HomeTutor

Challenge

Additional challenge is available in the Chapter 5 Resource Book, p. 16.

44–46. See Additional Answers beginning on p. AA1.

PROBLEM SOLVING WORKSHOP LESSON 5.1 Using ALTERNATIVE METHODS

Alternative Strategy

Example 4 on page 297 can be solving by placing the isosceles right triangle so that the hypotenuse is on the x-axis and the right-angle vertex is on the y-axis. This is useful because the length of the hypotenuse can be found easily.

Avoiding Common Errors

Students may not understand how the coordinates of A and B are found in the problem. Given that the hypotenuse has length $2h$ and the midpoint of the hypotenuse is $(0, 0)$, you can conclude that the coordinates of A and B are labeled correctly.

Mathematical Reasoning

Students can use this reasoning to show that the third vertex is $C(0, h)$: In isosceles right triangle ABC, the y-axis is perpendicular to $\overline{AB}$ and $m\angle A = 45°$, so $\triangle AOC$ is an isosceles right triangle. Since $OA = h$, then $OC = h$.

1. The slopes of $\overline{AC}$ and $\overline{BC}$ are negative reciprocals of each other, so $\overline{AC} \perp \overline{BC}$ making $\angle C$ a right angle; $AC = h\sqrt{2}$ and $BC = h\sqrt{2}$ making $\triangle ABC$ isosceles.

3a.

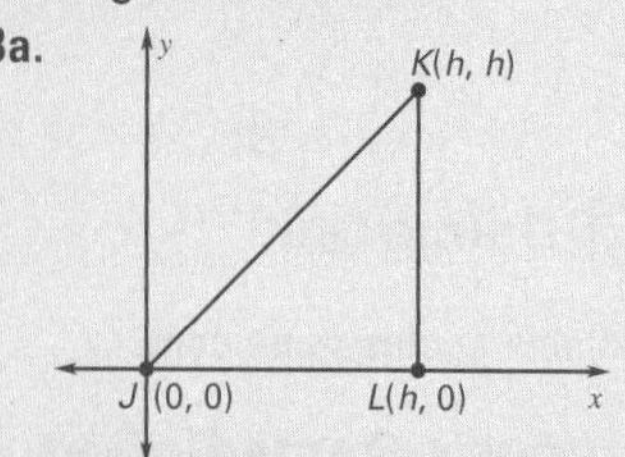

$JL = LK = h$ and $\overline{JL}$ is a horizontal line and $\overline{LK}$ is a vertical line, so $\overline{JL} \perp \overline{LK}$; $h\sqrt{2}$, $\left(\frac{h}{2}, \frac{h}{2}\right)$.

3b.

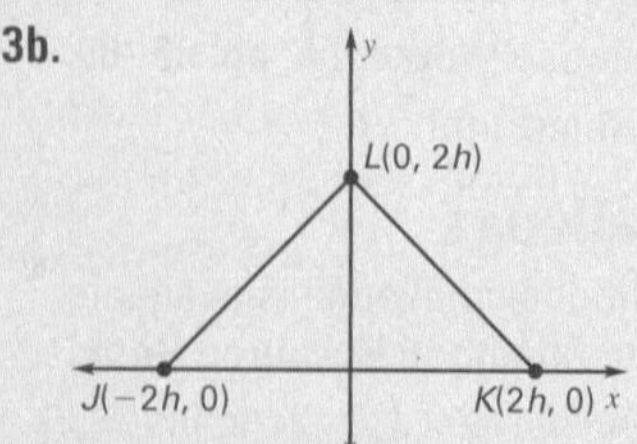

$JL = LK = 2h\sqrt{2}$ and the slope of $\overline{JL} = 1$ and the slope of $\overline{LK} = -1$, so $\overline{JL} \perp \overline{LK}$; $4h$, $(0, 0)$.

Another Way to Solve Example 4, page 297

MULTIPLE REPRESENTATIONS When you write a coordinate proof, you often have several options for how to place the figure in the coordinate plane and how to assign variables.

PROBLEM

Place an isosceles right triangle in a coordinate plane. Then find the length of the hypotenuse and the coordinates of its midpoint M.

METHOD

Standards

17.0 Students prove theorems by using coordinate geometry, including the midpoint of a line segment, the distance formula, and various forms of equations of lines and circles.

Placing Hypotenuse on an Axis Place the triangle with point C at $(0, h)$ on the y-axis and the hypotenuse $\overline{AB}$ on the x-axis. To make $\angle ACB$ be a right angle, position A and B so that legs $\overline{CA}$ and $\overline{CB}$ have slopes of 1 and −1.

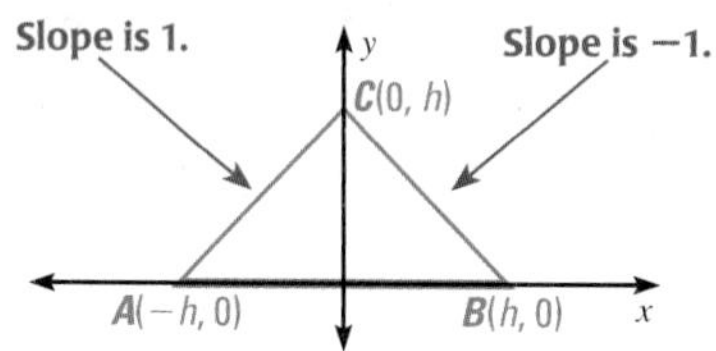

Length of hypotenuse $= 2h$

$$M = \left(\frac{-h + h}{2}, \frac{0 + 0}{2}\right) = (0, 0)$$

PRACTICE

1. **VERIFYING TRIANGLE PROPERTIES** Verify that $\angle C$ above is a right angle. Verify that $\triangle ABC$ is isosceles by showing $AC = BC$. **See margin.**

2. **MULTIPLES OF 2** Find the midpoint and length of each side using the placement below. What is the advantage of using $2h$ instead of h for the leg lengths? **$\overline{OD}$: $(0, h)$, $2h$, $\overline{DE}$: (h, h), $2h\sqrt{2}$, $\overline{OE}$: $(h, 0)$, $2h$; the midpoint formula requires division by 2 which results in midpoints without fractions.**

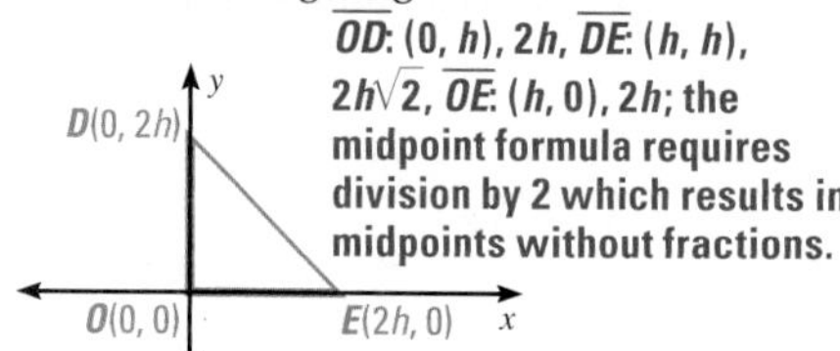

3. **OTHER ALTERNATIVES** Graph $\triangle JKL$ and verify that it is an isosceles right triangle. Then find the length and midpoint of $\overline{JK}$. **a, b. See margin.**
   a. $J(0, 0)$, $K(h, h)$, $L(h, 0)$
   b. $J(-2h, 0)$, $K(2h, 0)$, $L(0, 2h)$

4. **CHOOSE** Suppose you need to place a right isosceles triangle on a coordinate grid and assign variable coordinates. You know you will need to find all three side lengths and all three midpoints. How would you place the triangle? *Explain* your reasoning. **See margin.**

5. **RECTANGLES** Place rectangle $PQRS$ with length m and width n in the coordinate plane. Draw $\overline{PR}$ and $\overline{QS}$ connecting opposite corners of the rectangle. Then use coordinates to show that $\overline{PR} \cong \overline{QS}$. **See margin.**

6. **PARK** A square park has paths as shown. Use coordinates to determine whether a snack cart at point N is the same distance from each corner. ***Sample answer:* Square $ABCD$ with vertices at $A(0, 0)$, $B(0, 2s)$, $C(2s, 2s)$, $D(2s, 0)$, and center $N(s, s)$. $AN = BN = CN = DN = s\sqrt{2}$.**

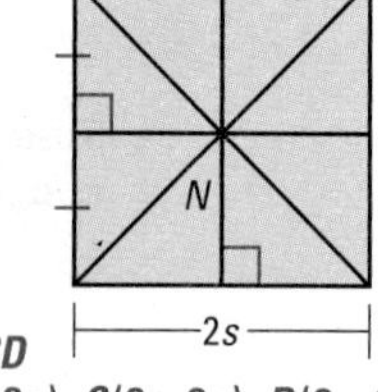

4. *Sample answer:* Place the coordinates of the vertices at $(-2a, 0)$, $(0, 2a)$, and $(2a, 0)$ with the right angle at $(0, 2a)$; since the midpoint formula requires division by 2 the resulting points will be $(-a, a)$, (a, a), and $(0, 0)$.

5. *Sample answer:* $PQRS$ with $P(0, 0)$, $Q(0, m)$, $R(n, m)$, and $S(n, 0)$; $PR = QS = \sqrt{m^2 + n^2}$ making $\overline{PR} \cong \overline{QS}$.

5.2 Use Perpendicular Bisectors

Before You used segment bisectors and perpendicular lines.

Now You will use perpendicular bisectors to solve problems.

Why? So you can solve a problem in archaeology, as in Ex. 28.

Key Vocabulary
- **perpendicular bisector**
- **equidistant**
- **concurrent**
- **point of concurrency**
- **circumcenter**

In Lesson 1.3, you learned that a segment bisector intersects a segment at its midpoint. A segment, ray, line, or plane that is perpendicular to a segment at its midpoint is called a **perpendicular bisector**.

A point is **equidistant** from two figures if the point is the *same distance* from each figure. Points on the perpendicular bisector of a segment are equidistant from the segment's endpoints.

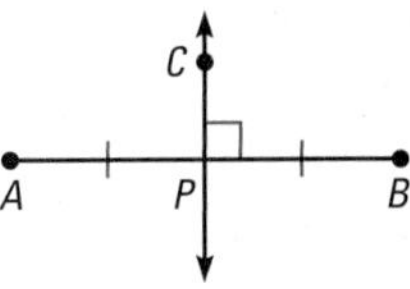

$\overleftrightarrow{CP}$ is a $\perp$ bisector of $\overline{AB}$.

Standards

12.0 Students find and use measures of sides and of interior and exterior angles **of triangles** and polygons **to** classify figures and **solve problems.**

THEOREMS *For Your Notebook*

THEOREM 5.2 Perpendicular Bisector Theorem

In a plane, if a point is on the perpendicular bisector of a segment, then it is equidistant from the endpoints of the segment.

If $\overleftrightarrow{CP}$ is the $\perp$ bisector of $\overline{AB}$, then $CA = CB$.

Proof: Ex. 26, p. 308

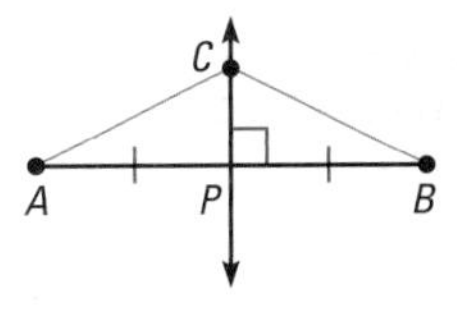

THEOREM 5.3 Converse of the Perpendicular Bisector Theorem

In a plane, if a point is equidistant from the endpoints of a segment, then it is on the perpendicular bisector of the segment.

If $DA = DB$, then D lies on the $\perp$ bisector of $\overline{AB}$.

Proof: Ex. 27, p. 308

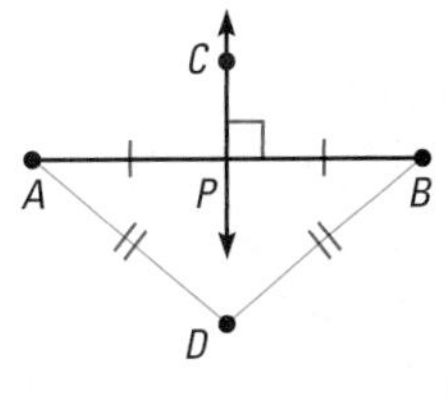

EXAMPLE 1 Use the Perpendicular Bisector Theorem

ALGEBRA $\overleftrightarrow{BD}$ **is the perpendicular bisector of** $\overline{AC}$. **Find** AD.

$AD = CD$	**Perpendicular Bisector Theorem**
$5x = 3x + 14$	**Substitute.**
$x = 7$	**Solve for x.**

▶ $AD = 5x = 5(7) = 35$.

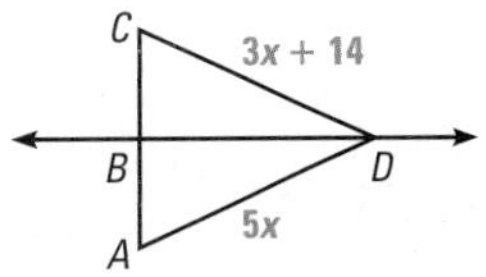

1 PLAN AND PREPARE

Warm-Up Exercises

Transparency Available

1. Solve $3x = 8x - 15$. **3**
2. Solve $6x + 3 = 8x - 14$. **8.5**
3. If M is the midpoint of $\overline{AB}$, $AM = 5x - 2$, and $BM = 3x + 6$, find AB. **36**

Notetaking Guide

Transparency Available

Promotes interactive learning and notetaking skills, pp. 122–124.

Pacing

Basic: 2 days
Average: 2 days
Advanced: 2 days
Block: 1 block
- See *Teaching Guide/Lesson Plan*.

2 FOCUS AND MOTIVATE

Essential Question

Big Idea 1, p. 293

How do you find the point of concurrency of the perpendicular bisectors of the sides of a triangle? **Tell students they will learn how to answer this question by drawing the three perpendicular bisectors and finding their common point of intersection.**

Resource Planning Guide

Chapter Resource Book
- Teaching Guide/Lesson Plan (pp. 17–18)
- Activity Master (p. 19)
- Practice levels A, B, C (pp. 20–25)
- Study Guide (pp. 26–27)
- Catch-up for Absent Students (p. 28)
- Problem Solving Workshop (p. 29)
- Challenge (p. 30)

Workbooks
- Notetaking Guide (pp. 122–124)
- Practice Workbook (pp. 88–90)

Teaching Options
- **Power Presentations CD-ROM** provides dynamic electronic teaching resources for the classroom.
- **Activity Generator CD-ROM** provides editable activities for all ability levels.

Interactive Technology
- Easy Planner
- Power Presentations CD-ROM
- Activity Generator CD-ROM
- Animated Geometry
- Test Generator CD-ROM
- Online Quiz
- eWorkbook
- eEdition
- @HomeTutor

Resources for English Learners
- Quick Reference for English Learners
- Spanish Study Guide
- Multi-Language Visual Glossary
- Student Resources in Spanish

See also the *Geometry Toolkit* for more strategies for meeting individual needs.

Motivating the Lesson

Have each student draw a kite and then list the features of their kite. Ask students whether, in their drawing, there is a segment that is the perpendicular bisector of another segment. Tell students that in this lesson they will explore perpendicular bisectors of segments.

3 TEACH

Extra Example 1

In the diagram, $\overleftrightarrow{RS}$ is the perpendicular bisector of $\overline{PQ}$. Find PR. **27**

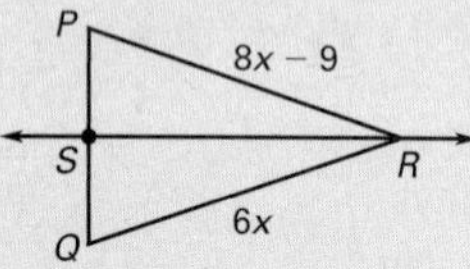

Extra Example 2

In the diagram, $\overleftrightarrow{JM}$ is the perpendicular bisector of $\overline{HK}$.

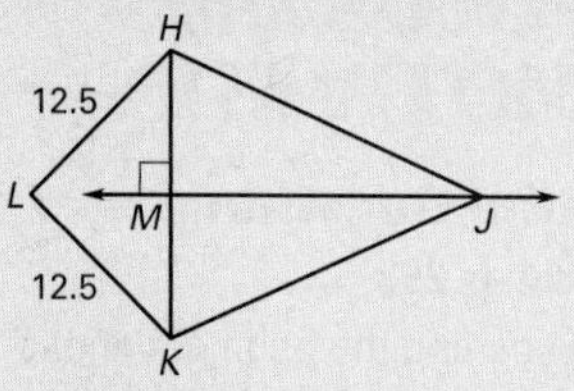

a. Which lengths in the diagram are equal? ***HM* = *KM*; *HJ* = *KJ*; *HL* = *KL***

b. Is L on $\overleftrightarrow{JM}$? **yes**

Key Question to Ask for Example 2

- If T is another point on $\overleftrightarrow{WX}$, is $YT = ZT$? **yes**

An **Animated Geometry** activity is available on-line for **Example 2**. This activity is also available on the **Power Presentations CD-ROM**.

EXAMPLE 2 Use perpendicular bisectors

In the diagram, $\overleftrightarrow{WX}$ is the perpendicular bisector of $\overline{YZ}$.

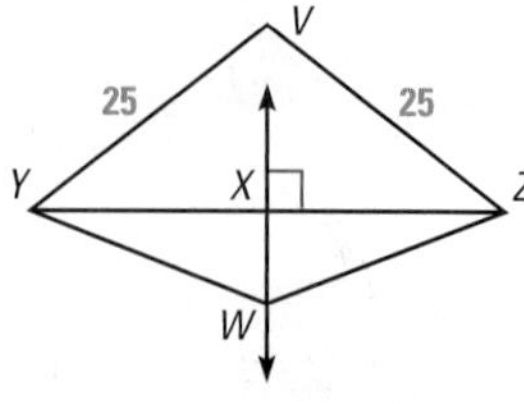

a. What segment lengths in the diagram are equal?

b. Is V on $\overleftrightarrow{WX}$?

Solution

a. $\overleftrightarrow{WX}$ bisects $\overline{YZ}$, so $XY = XZ$. Because W is on the perpendicular bisector of $\overline{YZ}$, $WY = WZ$ by Theorem 5.2. The diagram shows that $VY = VZ = 25$.

b. Because $VY = VZ$, V is equidistant from Y and Z. So, by the Converse of the Perpendicular Bisector Theorem, V is on the perpendicular bisector of $\overline{YZ}$, which is $\overleftrightarrow{WX}$.

Animated Geometry at classzone.com

✓ GUIDED PRACTICE for Examples 1 and 2

In the diagram, $\overleftrightarrow{JK}$ is the perpendicular bisector of $\overline{NL}$.

N, 8, 6x − 5, M, J, K, 8, 4x + 1, L

1. What segment lengths are equal? *Explain* your reasoning.
2. Find NK. **13**
3. *Explain* why M is on $\overleftrightarrow{JK}$.
Since *ML* = *MN*, *M* is equidistant from *N* and *L*, so by the Converse of the Perpendicular Bisector Theorem *M* is on the perpendicular bisector of $\overline{NL}$ which is $\overleftrightarrow{JK}$.

1. *NJ* = *LJ* since $\overleftrightarrow{JK}$ bisects $\overline{NL}$. *NK* = *LK* by the Perpendicular Bisector Theorem and the diagram shows *ML* = *MN*.

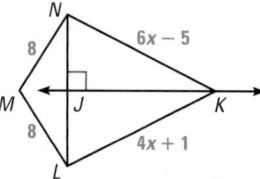

ACTIVITY FOLD THE PERPENDICULAR BISECTORS OF A TRIANGLE

QUESTION Where do the perpendicular bisectors of a triangle meet?

Materials:
- paper
- scissors
- ruler

Follow the steps below and answer the questions about perpendicular bisectors of triangles.

STEP 1 Cut four large acute scalene triangles out of paper. Make each one different.

STEP 2 Choose one triangle. Fold it to form the perpendicular bisectors of the sides. Do the three bisectors intersect at the same point? **Yes**

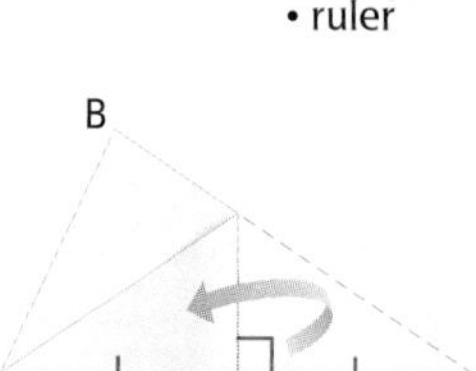

STEP 3 Repeat the process for the other three triangles. Make a conjecture about the perpendicular bisectors of a triangle. **The perpendicular bisectors of a triangle intersect at one point.**

STEP 4 Choose one triangle. Label the vertices A, B, and C. Label the point of intersection of the perpendicular bisectors as P. Measure $\overline{AP}$, $\overline{BP}$, and $\overline{CP}$. What do you observe? ***AP* = *BP* = *CP***

Differentiated Instruction

Below Level Students who have difficulty understanding the solution for **Example 2** may benefit from measuring the side lengths with a ruler. Ask them to verify the measurements. Then have them draw a segment 2 inches long and draw a line perpendicular to it at its midpoint. Ask them to draw triangles whose vertices are a point on the perpendicular bisector and the endpoints of the given segment and verify that the triangles are isosceles.

See also the *Geometry Toolkit* for more strategies.

CONCURRENCY When three or more lines, rays, or segments intersect in the same point, they are called **concurrent** lines, rays, or segments. The point of intersection of the lines, rays, or segments is called the **point of concurrency**.

READ VOCABULARY
The perpendicular bisector of a side of a triangle can be referred to as a *perpendicular bisector of the triangle.*

As you saw in the Activity on page 304, the three perpendicular bisectors of a triangle are concurrent and the point of concurrency has a special property.

THEOREM *For Your Notebook*

THEOREM 5.4 Concurrency of Perpendicular Bisectors of a Triangle

The perpendicular bisectors of a triangle intersect at a point that is equidistant from the vertices of the triangle.

If $\overline{PD}$, $\overline{PE}$, and $\overline{PF}$ are perpendicular bisectors, then $PA = PB = PC$.

Proof: p. 933

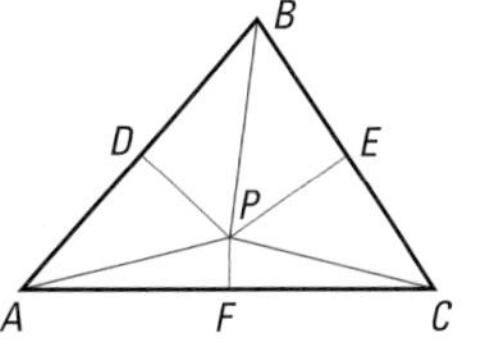

EXAMPLE 3 Use the concurrency of perpendicular bisectors

FROZEN YOGURT Three snack carts sell frozen yogurt from points A, B, and C outside a city. Each of the three carts is the same distance from the frozen yogurt distributor.

Find a location for the distributor that is equidistant from the three carts.

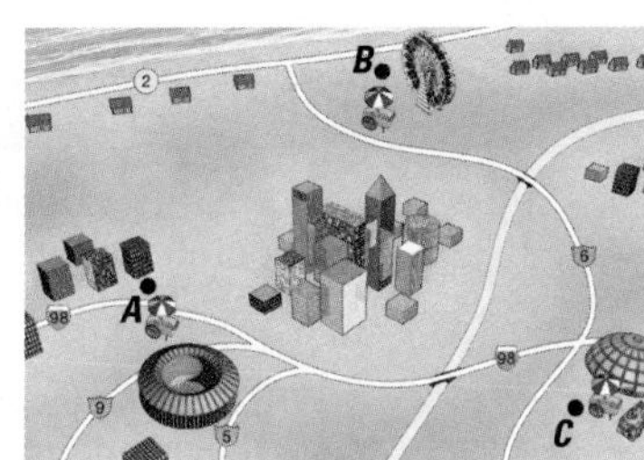

Solution

Theorem 5.4 shows you that you can find a point equidistant from three points by using the perpendicular bisectors of the triangle formed by those points.

Copy the positions of points A, B, and C and connect those points to draw $\triangle ABC$. Then use a ruler and protractor to draw the three perpendicular bisectors of $\triangle ABC$. The point of concurrency D is the location of the distributor.

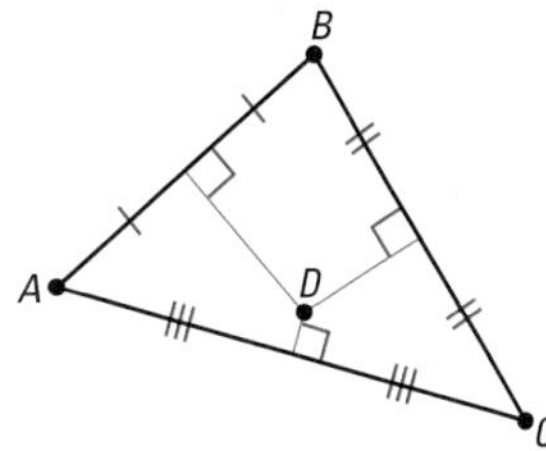

✓ **GUIDED PRACTICE** for Example 3

4. **WHAT IF?** Hot pretzels are sold from points A and B and also from a cart at point E. Where could the pretzel distributor be located if it is equidistant from those three points? Sketch the triangle and show the location.
Where the perpendicular bisectors of the triangle formed by *A*, *B*, and *C* intersect; see margin for art.

A• • E

Activity Note

The purpose of the activity is to demonstrate that the perpendicular bisectors of the sides of any triangle meet at a single point.

Extra Example 3

Each of three forest ranger stations is the same distance from the main office. Describe how to find the location of the office. **Draw the perpendicular bisectors of the three sides. Those three lines meet at a point, and that point is the location of the office.**

Key Question to Ask for Example 3

- Is the point of concurrency always inside the triangle? **No, it can be on or outside the triangle.**

Mathematical Reasoning

You can use the Concurrency of Perpendicular Bisectors Theorem to find the center of any circle. Choose any 3 points on the circle as the vertices of a triangle and find the point of concurrency for the 3 sides of the triangle. That point is equidistant from all the points on the circle, so it is the center of the circle.

Closing the Lesson

Have students summarize the major points of the lesson and answer the Essential Question: How do you find the point of concurrency of the perpendicular bisectors of the sides of a triangle?

- **A point on the perpendicular bisector of a segment is equidistant from the endpoints of the segments, and vice versa.**
- **The perpendicular bisectors of a triangle are concurrent.**

Draw each of the perpendicular bisectors and find their point of intersection.

Differentiated Instruction

Advanced Pose this question: Can you circumscribe a circle about any triangle? To answer the question, ask students to experiment with different triangles, including acute, right, and obtuse triangles, and find the point of concurrency for the perpendicular bisectors of the sides of the triangle. With that as center, use a compass to draw a circle through the vertices of the triangle.

See also the *Geometry Toolkit* for more strategies.

4.

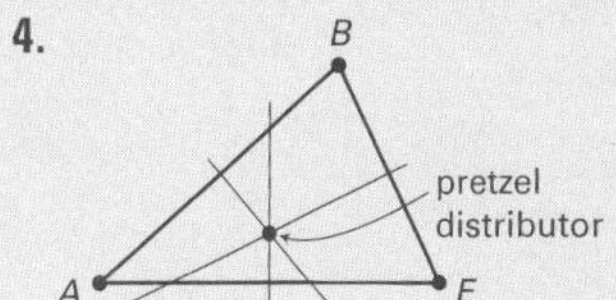

4 PRACTICE AND APPLY

Assignment Guide

Answer Transparencies available for all exercises

Basic:
Day 1: pp. 306–309
Exs. 1–15
Day 2: pp. 306–309
Exs. 16–19, 24–28, 34–41

Average:
Day 1: pp. 306–309
Exs. 1–10, 13–15, 18, 19
Day 2: pp. 306–309
Exs. 16, 17, 20–22, 24–30, 34–41

Advanced:
Day 1: pp. 306–309
Exs. 1–9, 13–15, 18, 19
Day 2: pp. 306–309
Exs. 16, 17, 20–33*, 34–40 even

Block:
pp. 306–309
Exs. 1–10, 13–22, 24–30, 34–41

Differentiated Instruction

See *Geometry Best Practices Toolkit* for suggestions on addressing the needs of a diverse classroom.

Homework Check

For a quick check of student understanding of key concepts, go over the following exercises:

Basic: 4, 12, 16, 24, 25
Average: 6, 13, 17, 26, 28
Advanced: 8, 14, 17, 27, 28

Extra Practice

- Student Edition, p. 904
- Chapter 5 Resource Book: Practice levels A, B, C, pp. 20–25

Practice Worksheet

An easily-readable reduced practice page (with answers) for this lesson can be found on p. 292C.

READ VOCABULARY
The prefix *circum-* means "around" or "about" as in *circumference* (distance around a circle).

CIRCUMCENTER The point of concurrency of the three perpendicular bisectors of a triangle is called the **circumcenter** of the triangle. The circumcenter P is equidistant from the three vertices, so P is the center of a circle that passes through all three vertices.

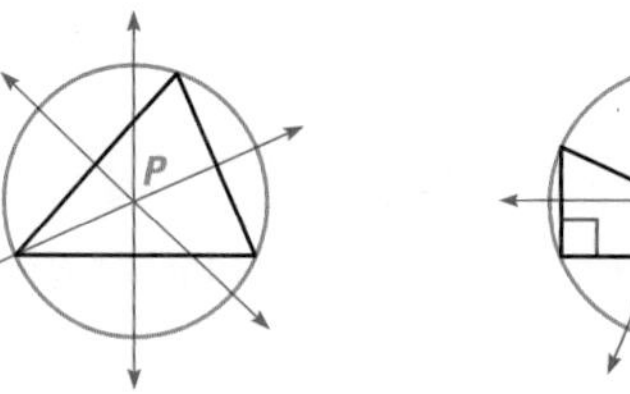

Acute triangle
***P* is inside triangle.**

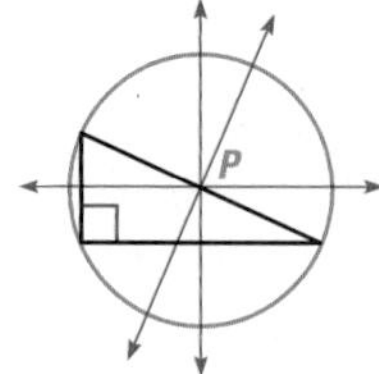

Right triangle
***P* is on triangle.**

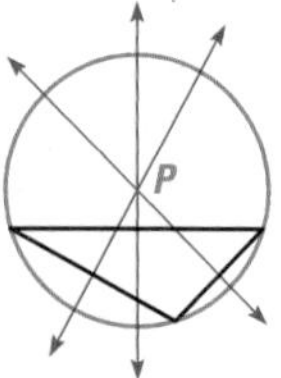

Obtuse triangle
***P* is outside triangle.**

As shown above, the location of P depends on the type of triangle. The circle with the center P is said to be *circumscribed* about the triangle.

5.2 EXERCISES

HOMEWORK KEY
○ = **WORKED-OUT SOLUTIONS on p. WS6 for Exs. 15, 17, and 25**
★ = **STANDARDIZED TEST PRACTICE Exs. 2, 9, 25, and 28**

SKILL PRACTICE

A

1. **VOCABULARY** Suppose you draw a circle with a compass. You choose three points on the circle to use as the vertices of a triangle. Copy and complete: The center of the circle is also the _?_ of the triangle. **circumcenter**

2. ★ **WRITING** Consider $\overline{AB}$. How can you *describe* the set of all points in a plane that are equidistant from A and B? **all points on the perpendicular bisector of $\overline{AB}$**

EXAMPLES 1 and 2
on pp. 303–304 for Exs. 3–15

ALGEBRA Find the length of $\overline{AB}$.

3. **15**

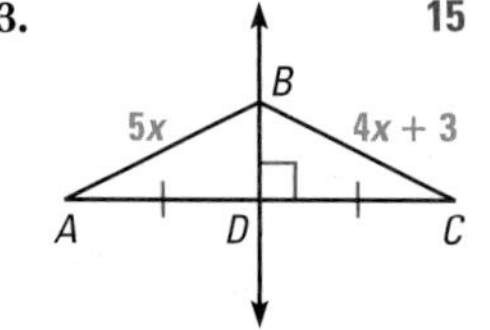

4. **30**

C
3x − 6
A
D
x + 18
B

5. **55**

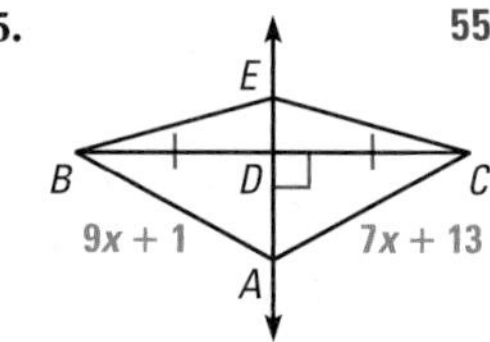

REASONING Tell whether the information in the diagram allows you to conclude that C is on the perpendicular bisector of $\overline{AB}$.

6.

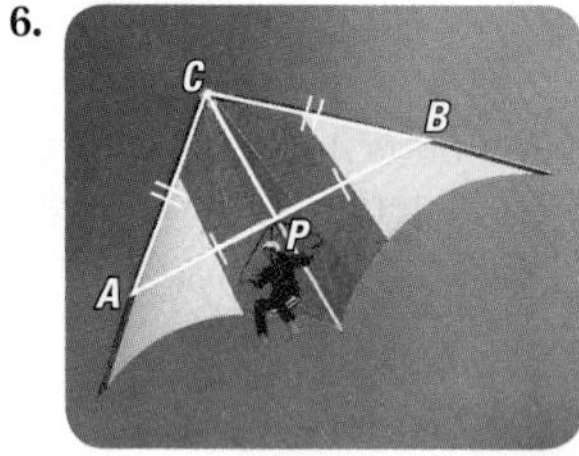

yes

7.

yes

8.

no

9. ★ **MULTIPLE CHOICE** Point P is inside $\triangle ABC$ and is equidistant from points A and B. On which of the following segments must P be located? **B**

Ⓐ $\overline{AB}$ Ⓑ The perpendicular bisector of $\overline{AB}$

Ⓒ The midsegment opposite $\overline{AB}$ Ⓓ The perpendicular bisector of $\overline{AC}$

10. **ERROR ANALYSIS** *Explain* why the conclusion is not correct given the information in the diagram.
You don't know that $EC = DC$.

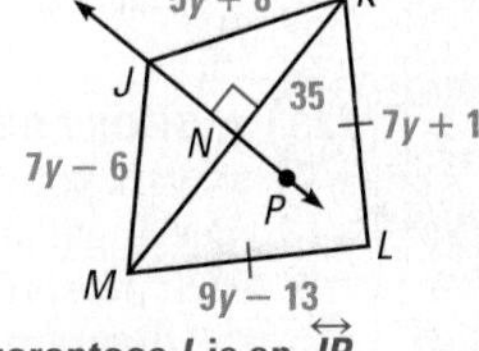

PERPENDICULAR BISECTORS In Exercises 11–15, use the diagram. $\overleftrightarrow{JN}$ is the perpendicular bisector of $\overline{MK}$.

11. Find NM. **35**
12. Find JK. **43**
13. Find KL. **50**
14. Find ML. **50**
15. Is L on $\overleftrightarrow{JP}$? *Explain* your reasoning.
Yes; the Converse of the Perpendicular Bisector Theorem guarantees L is on $\overleftrightarrow{JP}$.

EXAMPLE 3
on p. 305
for Exs. 16–17

USING CONCURRENCY In the diagram, the perpendicular bisectors of $\triangle ABC$ meet at point G and are shown in blue. Find the indicated measure.

16. Find BG. **9**

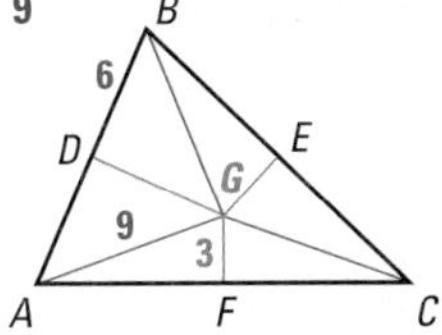

17. Find GA. **11**

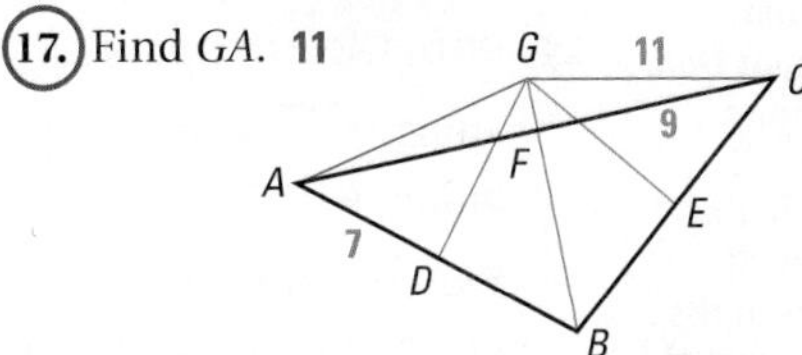

18. **Sample answer:** In the construction of the segment bisector four congruent triangles are created. In the process four pairs of congruent angles are formed which are right angles making the bisector perpendicular to the segment.

B

18. **CONSTRUCTING PERPENDICULAR BISECTORS** Use the construction shown on page 33 to construct the bisector of a segment. *Explain* why the bisector you constructed is actually the perpendicular bisector.

19. **CONSTRUCTION** Draw a right triangle. Use a compass and straightedge to find its circumcenter. Use a compass to draw the circumscribed circle. **See margin.**

ANALYZING STATEMENTS **Copy and complete the statement with *always, sometimes,* or *never. Justify* your answer.**

20. The circumcenter of a scalene triangle is __?__ inside the triangle.
Sometimes; a scalene triangle can be acute, right, or obtuse.
21. If the perpendicular bisector of one side of a triangle goes through the opposite vertex, then the triangle is __?__ isosceles.
Always; congruent sides are created.
22. The perpendicular bisectors of a triangle intersect at a point that is __?__ equidistant from the midpoints of the sides of the triangle.
Sometimes; consider an equilateral triangle and a scalene triangle.

C

23. **CHALLENGE** Prove the statements in parts (a) – (c).

GIVEN ▶ Plane P is a perpendicular bisector of $\overline{XZ}$ at Y.

PROVE ▶ a. $\overline{XW} \cong \overline{ZW}$ **a–c. See margin.**
b. $\overline{XV} \cong \overline{ZV}$
c. $\angle VXW \cong \angle VZW$

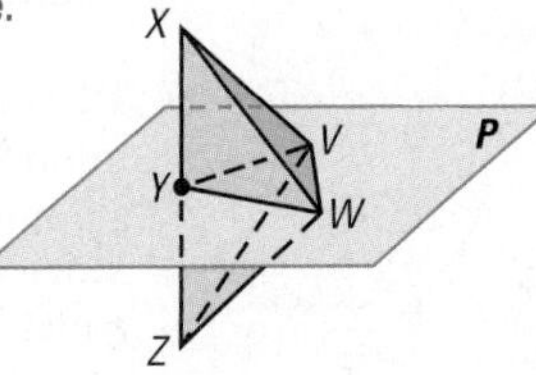

Avoiding Common Errors

Exercises 6–10 Students may consider any line drawn from a vertex to the opposite side of the triangle a perpendicular bisector. Caution them to verify that this line is not only perpendicular (Ex. 7), but it contains the midpoint of the opposite side (Ex. 8), and is equidistant from the endpoints of a segment (Exs. 7, 10).

Teaching Strategy

Exercises 18–19 Ask students to verify these constructions by measuring the segment lengths. Then have them label the points in the construction and use them for their explanation.

Mathematical Reasoning

Exercise 23 Postulate 10 guarantees that if W and Y are in plane P, then $\overleftrightarrow{WY}$ is also in P. Then since X, Y, Z, and W are coplanar, it can be shown that $\overleftrightarrow{WY}$ is the perpendicular bisector of $\overleftrightarrow{XZ}$ in the plane of X, Y, W, and Z. Similarly, $\overleftrightarrow{VY}$ is the perpendicular bisector of $\overleftrightarrow{XZ}$ in the plane of X, Y, V, and Z.

19. *Sample:*

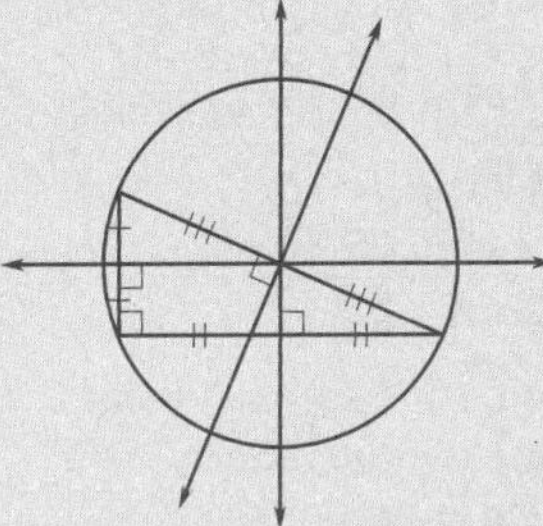

23a–c. Statements (Reasons)

1. P is a perpendicular bisector of $\overline{XZ}$ at Y, W and V lie in plane P. (Given)
2. $XW = ZW$, $XV = ZV$ (Perpendicular Bisector Theorem)
3. $\overline{XW} \cong \overline{ZW}$, $\overline{XV} \cong \overline{ZV}$ (Definition of segment congruence)
4. $\overline{WV} \cong \overline{WV}$ (Reflexive Property of Segment Congruence)
5. $\triangle VXW \cong \triangle VZW$ (SSS)
6. $\angle VXW \cong \angle VZW$ (Corr. parts of $\cong$ ▲ are $\cong$.)

Internet Reference

Exercise 24 For more information about cable-stayed bridges, visit www.pbs.org/wgbh/nova/bridge/meetcable.html

Exercise 28 Additional information about archaeology can be found at www.cr.nps.gov/archeology/sites/fedarch.htm

Study Strategy

Exercise 30 Tell students that they may want to look at their diagram for Exercise 42 on page 301 to help them understand this exercise.

26. Statements (Reasons)

1. $\overleftrightarrow{CP}$ is the perpendicular bisector of $\overline{AB}$. (Given)
2. $AP = BP$, $m\angle CPA = m\angle CPB = 90°$ (Definition of perpendicular bisector)
3. $\overline{AP} \cong \overline{BP}$ (Definition of segment congruence)
4. $\angle CPA \cong \angle CPB$ (Definition of angle congruence)
5. $\overline{CP} \cong \overline{CP}$ (Reflexive Property of Segment Congruence)
6. $\triangle CPA \cong \triangle CPB$ (SAS)
7. $\overline{CA} \cong \overline{CB}$ (Corr. parts of $\cong$ $\triangle$s are $\cong$.)
8. $CA = CB$ (Definition of segment congruence)

27. Statements (Reasons)

1. $CA = CB$ (Given)
2. Draw $\overleftrightarrow{PC} \perp \overline{AB}$ through point C. (Perpendicular Postulate)
3. $\overline{CA} \cong \overline{CB}$ (Definition of segment congruence)
4. $\overline{CP} \cong \overline{CP}$ (Reflexive Property of Segment Congruence)
5. $\angle CPA$ and $\angle CPB$ are right angles. (Definition of perpendicular lines)
6. $\triangle CPA$ and $\triangle CPB$ are right triangles. (Definition of right triangle)
7. $\triangle CPA \cong \triangle CPB$ (HL)
8. $\overline{PA} \cong \overline{PB}$ (Corr. parts of $\cong$ $\triangle$s are $\cong$.)
9. P is the midpoint of $\overline{AB}$. (Definition of midpoint)
10. C is on the perpendicular bisector of $\overline{AB}$. (Definition of perpendicular bisector)

PROBLEM SOLVING

A

24. BRIDGE A cable-stayed bridge is shown below. Two cable lengths are given. Find the lengths of the blue cables. *Justify* your answer.
59.6 m, 195.5 m; Perpendicular Bisector Theorem

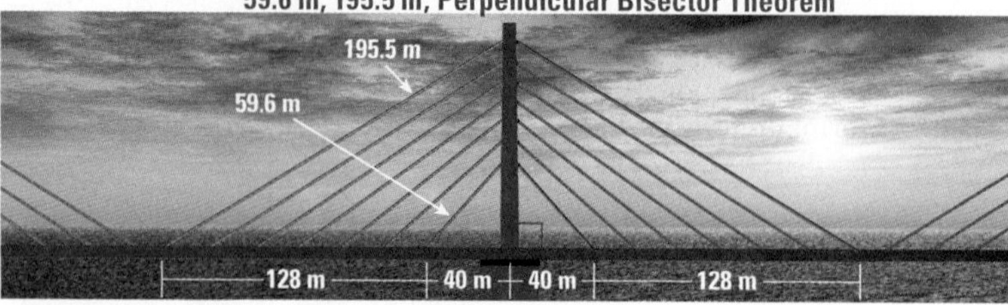

@HomeTutor for problem solving help at classzone.com

EXAMPLE 3 on p. 305 for Exs. 25, 28

25. Theorem 5.4 shows you that you can find a point equidistant from three points by using the perpendicular bisectors of the sides of the triangle formed by the three points.

(25.) ★ **SHORT RESPONSE** You and two friends plan to walk your dogs together. You want your meeting place to be the same distance from each person's house. *Explain* how you can use the diagram to locate the meeting place.

your house • Mike's house • Ken's house •

@HomeTutor for problem solving help at classzone.com

26. PROVING THEOREM 5.2 Prove the Perpendicular Bisector Theorem. **See margin.**

GIVEN ▶ $\overleftrightarrow{CP}$ is the perpendicular bisector of $\overline{AB}$.

PROVE ▶ $CA = CB$

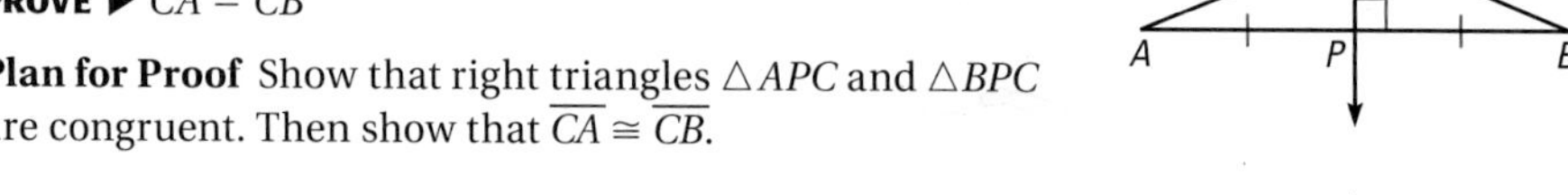

Plan for Proof Show that right triangles $\triangle APC$ and $\triangle BPC$ are congruent. Then show that $\overline{CA} \cong \overline{CB}$.

B

27. PROVING THEOREM 5.3 Prove the converse of Theorem 5.2. (*Hint:* Construct a line through C perpendicular to $\overline{AB}$.) **See margin.**

GIVEN ▶ $CA = CB$

PROVE ▶ C is on the perpendicular bisector of $\overline{AB}$.

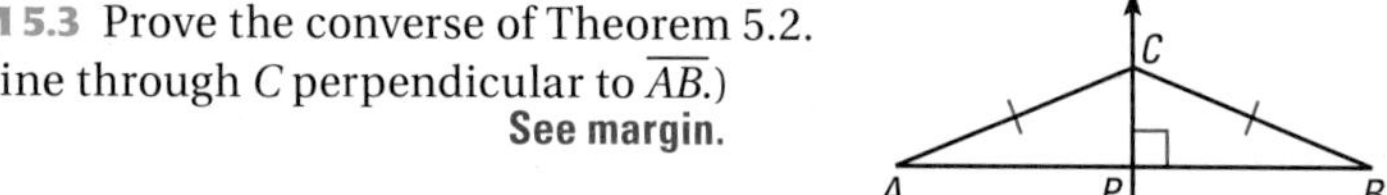

28a. Find the intersection of the perpendicular bisectors of the triangle formed by the three points.

28. ★ **EXTENDED RESPONSE** Archaeologists find three stones. They believe that the stones were once part of a circle of stones with a community firepit at its center. They mark the locations of Stones A, B, and C on a graph where distances are measured in feet.

a. *Explain* how the archaeologists can use a sketch to estimate the center of the circle of stones.

b. Copy the diagram and find the approximate coordinates of the point at which the archaeologists should look for the firepit. **approximately (7, 6.5)**

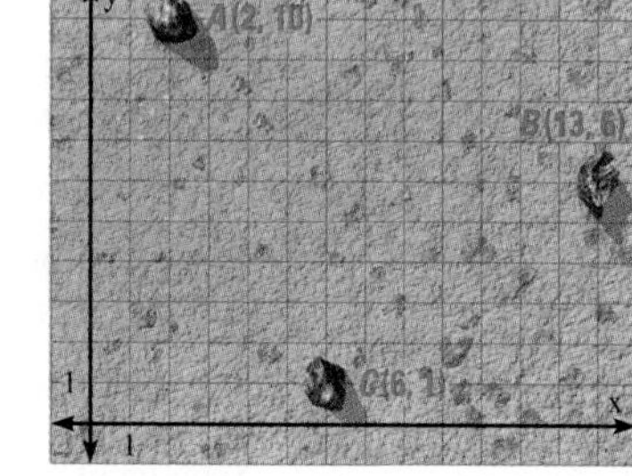

29. TECHNOLOGY Use geometry drawing software to construct $\overline{AB}$. Find the midpoint C. Draw the perpendicular bisector of $\overline{AB}$ through C. Construct a point D along the perpendicular bisector and measure $\overline{DA}$ and $\overline{DB}$. Move D along the perpendicular bisector. What theorem does this construction demonstrate? **Check students' work; Perpendicular Bisector Theorem.**

○ = WORKED-OUT SOLUTIONS on p. WS1 ★ = STANDARDIZED TEST PRACTICE

30. Midpoint of the hypotenuse. ***Sample answer:*** **Right triangle with vertices $A(2a, 0)$, $B(0, 2b)$, and $C(0, 0)$; the midpoint of $\overline{AC}$ is $(a, 0)$ and the midpoint of $\overline{BC}$ is $(0, b)$. The equations of the perpendicular bisectors of $\overline{AC}$ and $\overline{BC}$ are $x = a$ and $y = b$. These two lines intersect in the point (a, b), which is the midpoint of $\overline{AB}$.**

30. COORDINATE PROOF Where is the circumcenter located in any right triangle? Write a coordinate proof of this result. **See margin.**

C **PROOF** **Use the information in the diagram to prove the given statement.** **31, 32. See margin.**

31. $\overline{AB} \cong \overline{BC}$ if and only if D, E, and B are collinear.

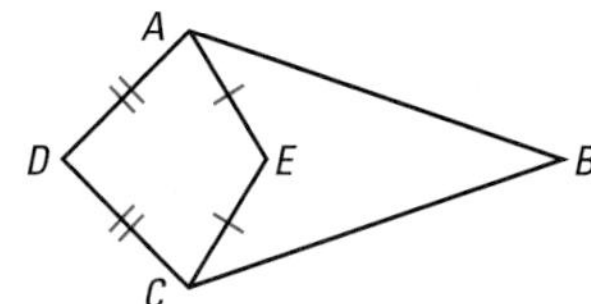

32. $\overline{PV}$ is the perpendicular bisector of $\overline{TQ}$ for regular polygon $PQRST$.

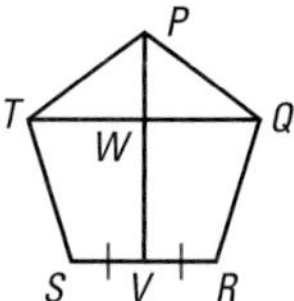

33. CHALLENGE The four towns on the map are building a common high school. They have agreed that the school should be an equal distance from each of the four towns. Is there a single point where they could agree to build the school? If so, find it. If not, *explain* why not. Use a diagram to *explain* your answer. **No; unless the four points determine a rectangle there is no single point to locate the school so that it is equidistant from the four towns. See margin for art.**

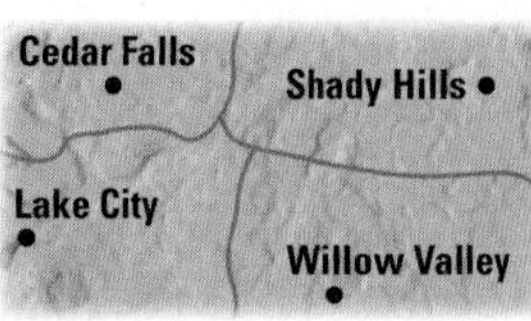

MIXED REVIEW

Solve the equation. Write your answer in simplest radical form. *(p. 882)*

34. $5^2 + x^2 = 13^2$ **±12**

35. $x^2 + 15^2 = 17^2$ **±8**

36. $x^2 + 10 = 38$ **$\pm 2\sqrt{7}$**

PREVIEW
Prepare for Lesson 5.3 in Exs. 37–38.

Ray $\overrightarrow{BD}$ bisects $\angle ABC$. Find the value of x. Then find $m\angle ABC$. *(p. 24)*

37. **18; 158°**

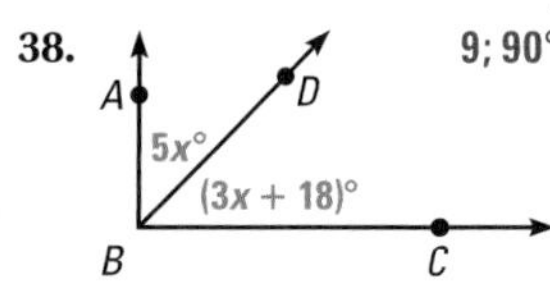

38. **9; 90°**

Describe **the pattern in the numbers. Write the next number.** *(p. 72)*

39. 21, 16, 11, 6, . . . **The numbers are decreasing by 5; 1.**

40. 2, 6, 18, 54, . . . **The next number in the sequence is the previous one multiplied by 3; 162.**

41. 3, 3, 4, 6, . . . **Starting with 3, zero is added to get 3, then one is added to get 4, then 2 is added to get 6, next add 3; 9.**

QUIZ *for Lessons 5.1–5.2*

Find the value of x. Identify the theorem used to find the answer. *(pp. 295, 303)*

1.

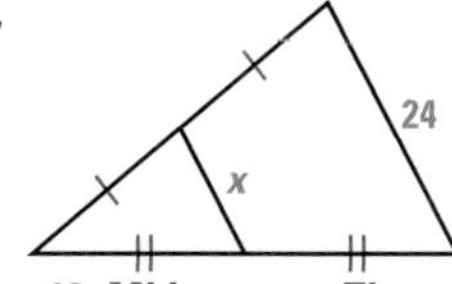

12; Midsegment Theorem

2.

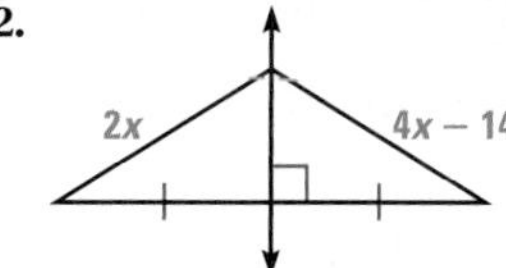

7; Perpendicular Bisector Theorem

3.

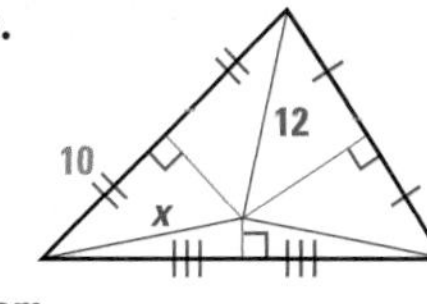

3. 12; Concurrency of Perpendicular Bisectors Theorem

4. Graph the triangle with vertices $R(2a, 0)$, $S(0, 2b)$, and $T(2a, 2b)$, where a and b are positive. Find RT and ST. Then find the slope of $\overline{SR}$ and the coordinates of the midpoint of $\overline{SR}$. *(p. 295)* **$2b$, $2a$; $-\frac{b}{a}$, (a, b); see margin for art.**

5 ASSESS AND RETEACH

Daily Homework Quiz

Transparency Available

In Exercises 1 and 2, find AB.

1. **25**

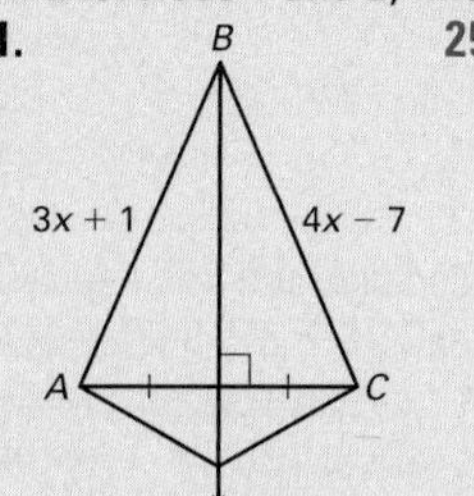

2. **24.5**

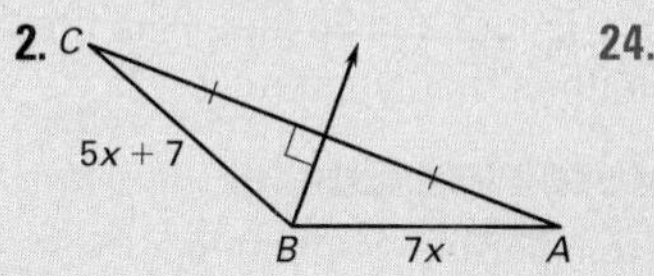

3. In this diagram, the perpendicular bisectors of $\triangle ABC$ meet at point G. Find EC and GC. **5; 7**

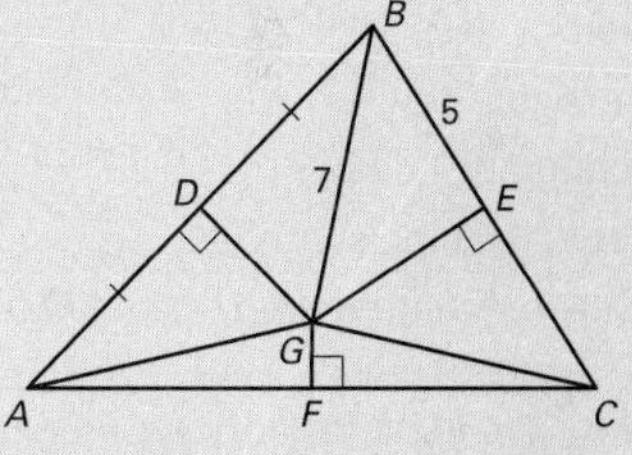

Available at **classzone.com**

Diagnosis/Remediation

- Practice A, B, C in Chapter 5 Resource Book, pp. 20–25
- Study Guide in Chapter 5 Resource Book, pp. 26–27
- Practice Workbook, pp. 88–90
- @HomeTutor

Challenge

Additional challenge is available in the Chapter 5 Resource Book, p. 30.

Quiz

An easily-readable reduced copy of the quiz (with answers) on Lessons 5.1–5.1 from the Assessment Book can be found on p. 292F.

31–33, Quiz 4. See Additional Answers beginning on p. AA1.

1 PLAN AND PREPARE

Warm-Up Exercises

Transparency Available

1. $\overrightarrow{AD}$ bisects $\angle BAC$. Find x. **20**

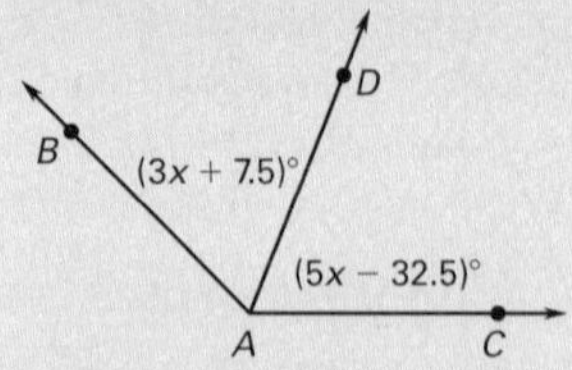

2. Solve $x^2 + 12^2 = 169$. **±5**
3. The legs of a right triangle measure 15 feet and 20 feet. Find the length of the hypotenuse. **25 ft**

Notetaking Guide

Transparency Available

Promotes interactive learning and notetaking skills, pp. 125–127.

Pacing

Basic: 1 day
Average: 1 day
Advanced: 1 day
Block: 0.5 block with 5.4
- See *Teaching Guide/Lesson Plan*.

2 FOCUS AND MOTIVATE

Essential Question

Big Idea 1, p. 293

When can you conclude that a point is on the bisector of an angle? **Tell students they will learn how to answer this question by applying the Angle Bisector Theorem and its converse.**

5.3 Use Angle Bisectors of Triangles

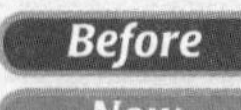

Before	You used angle bisectors to find angle relationships.
Now	You will use angle bisectors to find distance relationships.
Why?	So you can apply geometry in sports, as in Example 2.

Key Vocabulary
- **incenter**
- **angle bisector,** *p. 28*
- **distance from a point to a line,** *p. 192*

Remember that an *angle bisector* is a ray that divides an angle into two congruent adjacent angles. Remember also that the *distance from a point to a line* is the length of the perpendicular segment from the point to the line.

So, in the diagram, $\overrightarrow{PS}$ is the bisector of $\angle QPR$ and the distance from S to $\overrightarrow{PQ}$ is SQ, where $\overline{SQ} \perp \overrightarrow{PQ}$.

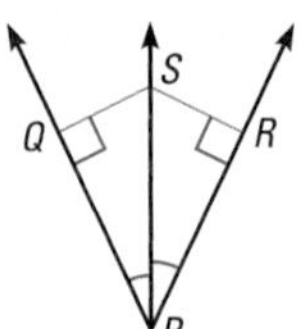

REVIEW DISTANCE
In Geometry, *distance* means the *shortest* length between two objects.

THEOREMS *For Your Notebook*

THEOREM 5.5 Angle Bisector Theorem

If a point is on the bisector of an angle, then it is equidistant from the two sides of the angle.

If $\overrightarrow{AD}$ bisects $\angle BAC$ and $\overline{DB} \perp \overrightarrow{AB}$ and $\overline{DC} \perp \overrightarrow{AC}$, then $DB = DC$.

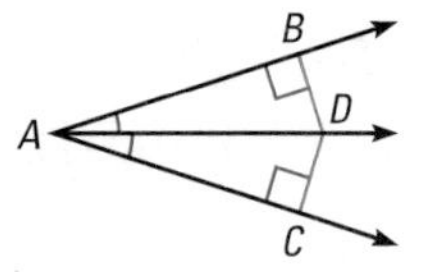

Proof: Ex. 34, p. 315

THEOREM 5.6 Converse of the Angle Bisector Theorem

If a point is in the interior of an angle and is equidistant from the sides of the angle, then it lies on the bisector of the angle.

If $\overline{DB} \perp \overrightarrow{AB}$ and $\overline{DC} \perp \overrightarrow{AC}$ and $DB = DC$, then $\overrightarrow{AD}$ bisects $\angle BAC$.

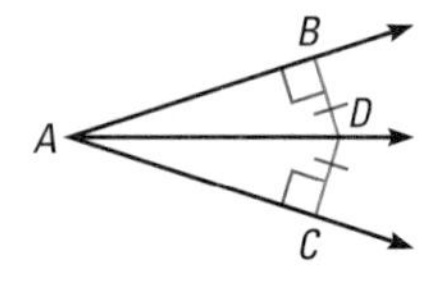

Proof: Ex. 35, p. 315

Standards
12.0 Students find and use measures of sides and of interior and exterior **angles of triangles** and polygons **to** classify figures and **solve problems.**

EXAMPLE 1 Use the Angle Bisector Theorems

Find the measure of $\angle GFJ$.

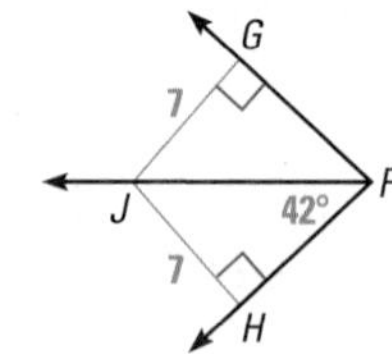

Solution

Because $\overline{JG} \perp \overrightarrow{FG}$ and $\overline{JH} \perp \overrightarrow{FH}$ and $JG = JH = 7$, $\overrightarrow{FJ}$ bisects $\angle GFH$ by the Converse of the Angle Bisector Theorem. So, $m\angle GFJ = m\angle HFJ = 42°$.

Resource Planning Guide

Chapter Resource Book
- Teaching Guide/Lesson Plan (pp. 31–32)
- Activity Master (p. 33)
- Practice levels A, B, C (pp. 34–39)
- Study Guide (pp. 40–41)
- Catch-up for Absent Students (p. 42)
- Problem Solving Workshop (p. 43)
- Challenge (p. 45)

Workbooks
- Notetaking Guide (pp. 125–127)
- Practice Workbook (pp. 91–93)

Teaching Options
- **Power Presentations CD-ROM** provides dynamic electronic teaching resources for the classroom.
- **Activity Generator CD-ROM** provides editable activities for all ability levels.

Interactive Technology
- Easy Planner
- Power Presentations CD-ROM
- Activity Generator CD-ROM
- Animated Geometry
- Test Generator CD-ROM
- Online Quiz
- eWorkbook
- eEdition
- @HomeTutor

Resources for English Learners
- Quick Reference for English Learners
- Spanish Study Guide
- Multi-Language Visual Glossary
- Student Resources in Spanish

See also the *Geometry Toolkit* for more strategies for meeting individual needs.

EXAMPLE 2 Solve a real-world problem

SOCCER A soccer goalie's position relative to the ball and goalposts forms congruent angles, as shown. Will the goalie have to move farther to block a shot toward the right goalpost R or the left goalpost L?

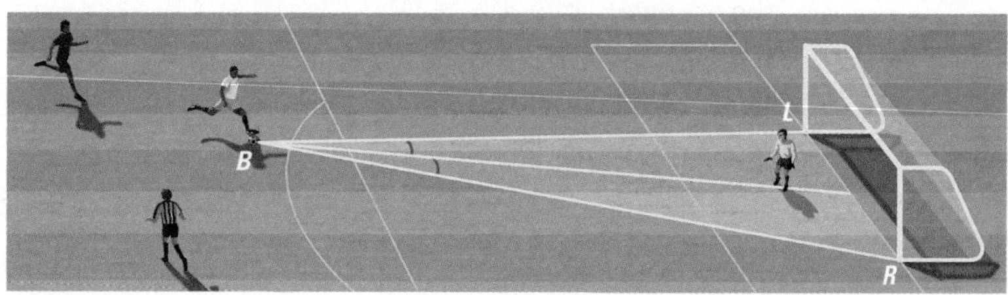

Solution

The congruent angles tell you that the goalie is on the bisector of $\angle LBR$. By the Angle Bisector Theorem, the goalie is equidistant from $\overrightarrow{BR}$ and $\overrightarrow{BL}$.

▶ So, the goalie must move the same distance to block either shot.

EXAMPLE 3 Use algebra to solve a problem

 ALGEBRA **For what value of x does P lie on the bisector of $\angle A$?**

Solution

From the Converse of the Angle Bisector Theorem, you know that P lies on the bisector of $\angle A$ if P is equidistant from the sides of $\angle A$, so when $BP = CP$.

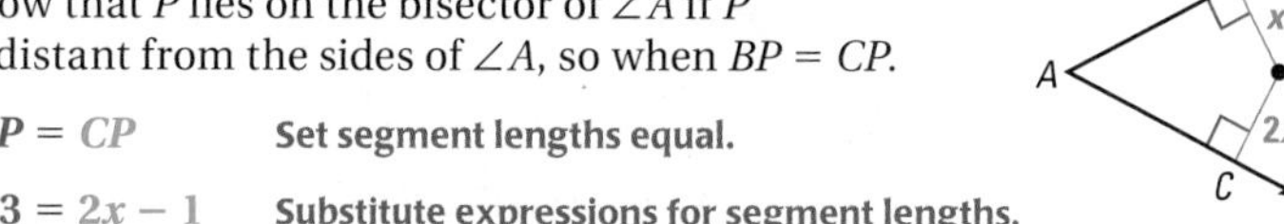

$BP = CP$	Set segment lengths equal.
$x + 3 = 2x - 1$	Substitute expressions for segment lengths.
$4 = x$	Solve for x.

▶ Point P lies on the bisector of $\angle A$ when $x = 4$.

 **GUIDED PRACTICE** for Examples 1, 2, and 3

In Exercises 1–3, find the value of x.

1. 15

x, 27°, 27°, 15

2. 11

$(3x + 5)°$, $(4x - 6)°$

3. 5

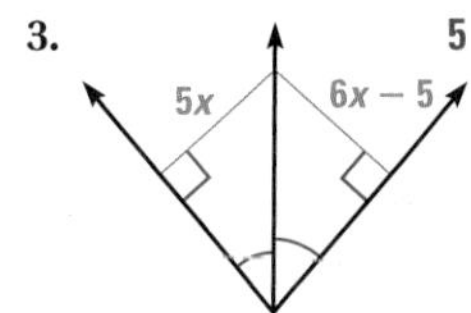

4. Do you have enough information to conclude that $\overrightarrow{QS}$ bisects $\angle PQR$? *Explain.*
No; you need to establish that $\overline{SR} \perp \overline{QR}$ and $\overline{SP} \perp \overline{QP}$.

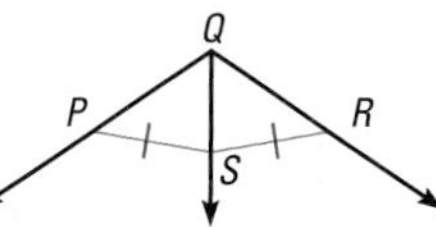

Motivating the Lesson

Show students a triangle, and ask them how they could draw circles that lie inside or on, but not outside, the triangle. Tell students that in this lesson they will learn how to draw a circle that just touches all three sides of the triangle.

3 TEACH

Extra Example 1

Find the measure of $\angle BAD$. **54°**

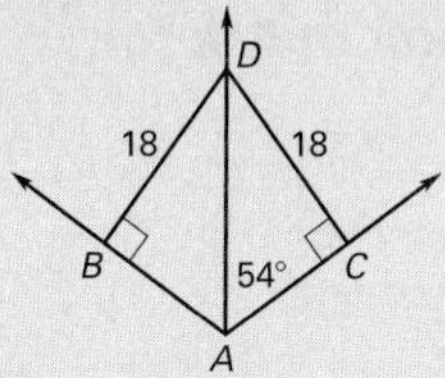

Key Question to Ask for Example 1

- If $JH \neq JG$, can you conclude that J is on the bisector of $\angle GFH$? **no**

Extra Example 2

Three spotlights form two congruent angles. Is the actor closer to the spotlighted area on the right or on the left?

The actor is the same distance from both spotlighted areas.

Extra Example 3

For what value of x does P lie on the bisector of $\angle A$? **7**

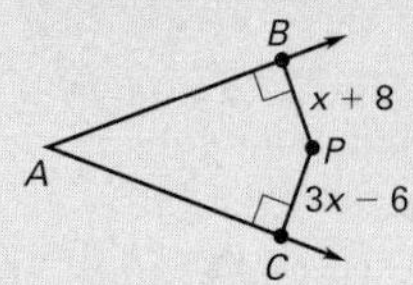

Differentiated Instruction

Visual Learners Before students read the solution in **Example 3**, have them draw the angle bisector of $\angle A$ by drawing a segment from point A that goes through point P. After students have solved for x, discuss with them what must be true of the segment they drew if they substitute any other number than 4 for x. Students should realize the segment they drew does not bisect the angle if x is any number other than 4.

See also the *Geometry Toolkit* for more strategies.

Extra Example 4

In the diagram, G is the incenter of $\triangle RST$. Find GW. **5**

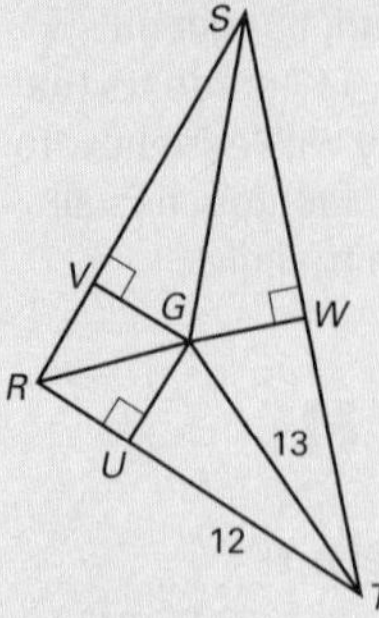

Key Question to Ask for Example 4

- Why does $NF = ND$? **The incenter is equidistant from the three sides of the triangle.**

An **Animated Geometry** activity is available on-line for **Example 4**. This activity is also available on the **Power Presentations CD-ROM**.

Vocabulary

Be sure students distinguish between a triangle's incenter, which is the intersection of the angle bisectors of the triangle, and its circumcenter, which is the intersection of the perpendicular bisectors of the sides.

Closing the Lesson

Have students summarize the major points of the lesson and answer the Essential Question: When can you conclude that a point is on the bisector of an angle?

- **If a point is on the bisector of an angle it is equidistant from the sides of the angle, and vice versa.**
- **The angle bisectors of a triangle intersect at a point equidistant from the triangle's sides.**

A point is on the bisector of an angle if it is in the interior of the angle and is equidistant from the sides of the angle.

READ VOCABULARY
An *angle bisector of a triangle* is the bisector of an interior angle of the triangle.

THEOREM *For Your Notebook*

THEOREM 5.7 Concurrency of Angle Bisectors of a Triangle

The angle bisectors of a triangle intersect at a point that is equidistant from the sides of the triangle.

If $\overline{AP}$, $\overline{BP}$, and $\overline{CP}$ are angle bisectors of $\triangle ABC$, then $PD = PE = PF$.

Proof: Ex. 36, p. 316

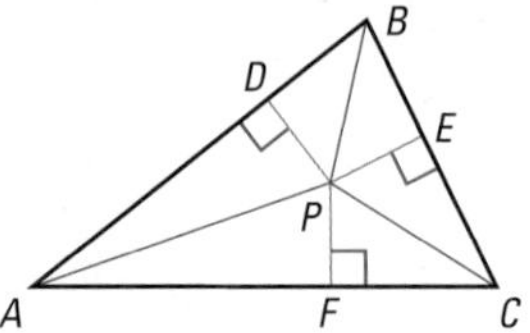

The point of concurrency of the three angle bisectors of a triangle is called the **incenter** of the triangle. The incenter always lies inside the triangle.

Because the incenter P is equidistant from the three sides of the triangle, a circle drawn using P as the center and the distance to one side as the radius will just touch the other two sides. The circle is said to be *inscribed* within the triangle.

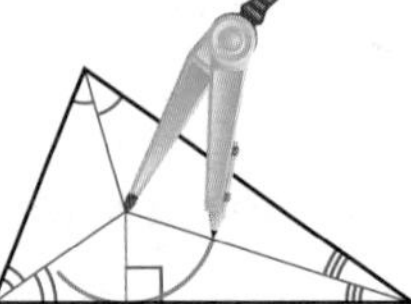

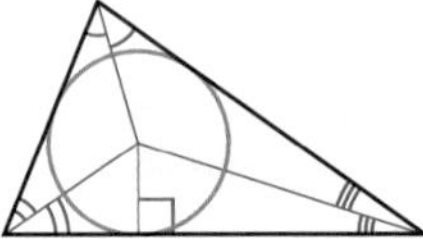

EXAMPLE 4 Use the concurrency of angle bisectors

In the diagram, N is the incenter of $\triangle ABC$. Find ND.

Solution

REVIEW QUADRATIC EQUATIONS
For help with solving a quadratic equation by taking square roots, see page 882. Use only the positive square root when finding a distance, as in Example 4.

By the Concurrency of Angle Bisectors of a Triangle Theorem, the incenter N is equidistant from the sides of $\triangle ABC$. So, to find ND, you can find NF in $\triangle NAF$. Use the Pythagorean Theorem stated on page 18.

$c^2 = a^2 + b^2$	**Pythagorean Theorem**
$20^2 = NF^2 + 16^2$	**Substitute known values.**
$400 = NF^2 + 256$	**Multiply.**
$144 = NF^2$	**Subtract 256 from each side.**
$12 = NF$	**Take the positive square root of each side.**

▶ Because $NF = ND$, $ND = 12$.

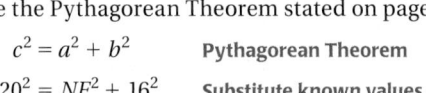

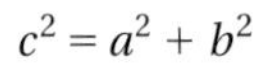 at classzone.com

GUIDED PRACTICE for Example 4

5. **WHAT IF?** In Example 4, suppose you are not given AF or AN, but you are given that $BF = 12$ and $BN = 13$. Find ND. **5**

5.3 EXERCISES

HOMEWORK KEY ○ = **WORKED-OUT SOLUTIONS** on p. WS6 for Exs. 7, 15, and 29
★ = **STANDARDIZED TEST PRACTICE** Exs. 2, 18, 23, 30, and 31

SKILL PRACTICE

1. **VOCABULARY** Copy and complete: Point C is in the interior of $\angle ABD$. If $\angle ABC$ and $\angle DBC$ are congruent, then $\overrightarrow{BC}$ is the _?_ of $\angle ABD$. **bisector**

2. ★ **WRITING** How are perpendicular bisectors and angle bisectors of a triangle different? How are they alike? **See margin.**

EXAMPLE 1 on p. 310 for Exs. 3–5

FINDING MEASURES **Use the information in the diagram to find the measure.**

3. Find $m\angle ABD$. **20°**

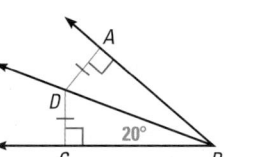

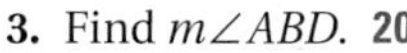

4. Find PS. **12**

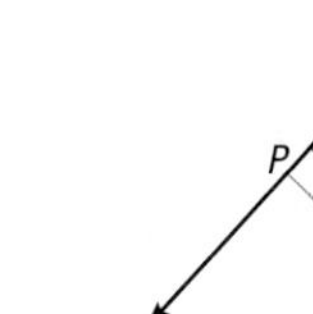

5. $m\angle YXW = 60°$. Find WZ. **9**

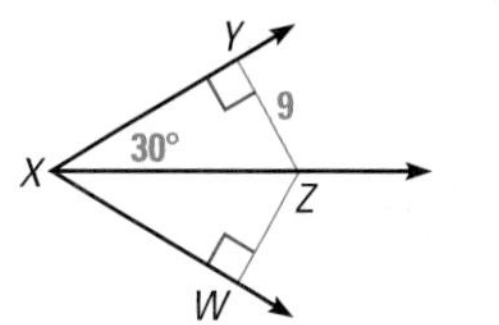

EXAMPLE 2 on p. 311 for Exs. 6–11

2. Perpendicular bisectors bisect line segments while angle bisectors bisect angles; both divide the segment or angle into two equal parts, and both have special points of intersection.

ANGLE BISECTOR THEOREM **Is $DB = DC$? Explain.** **6–8. See margin.**

6.

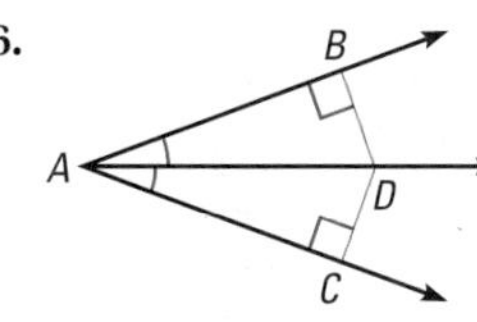

(7.)

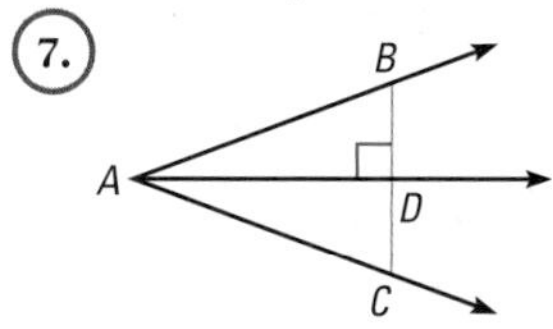

8.

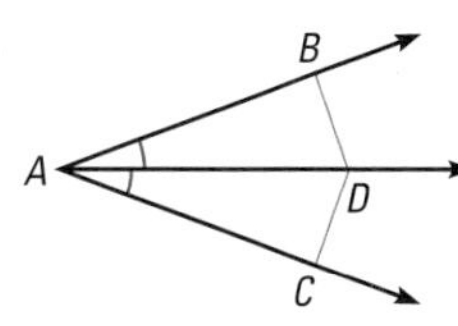

REASONING **Can you conclude that $\overrightarrow{EH}$ bisects $\angle FEG$? Explain.**

9. **No; you don't know that $\overline{HG} \cong \overline{HF}$, $\overline{HF} \perp \overrightarrow{EF}$, or $\overline{HG} \perp \overrightarrow{EG}$.**

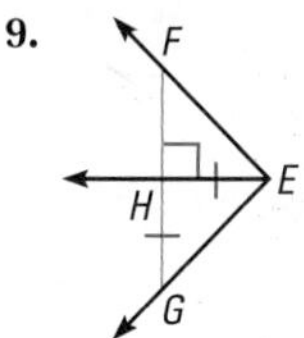

10. **Yes; Converse of Angle Bisector Theorem**

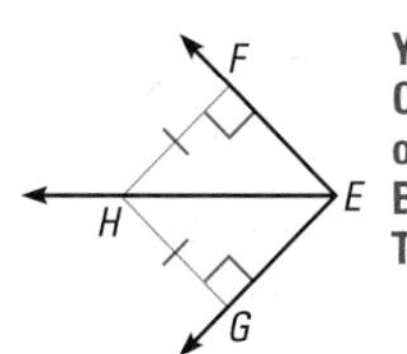

11. **No; you don't know that $\overline{HF} \perp \overrightarrow{EF}$ or $\overline{HG} \perp \overrightarrow{EG}$.**

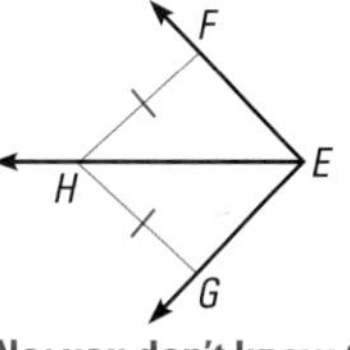

EXAMPLE 3 on p. 311 for Exs. 12–18

ALGEBRA **Find the value of x.**

12. **5**

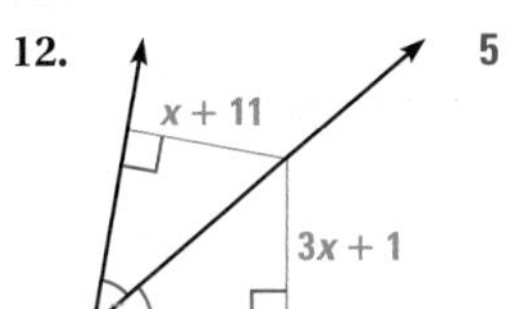

13. **4**

(7x)°
(3x + 16)°

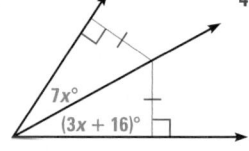

14. **8**

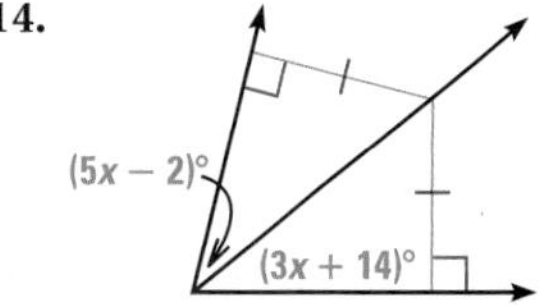

RECOGNIZING MISSING INFORMATION **Can you find the value of x? Explain.** **15–17. See margin.**

(15.)

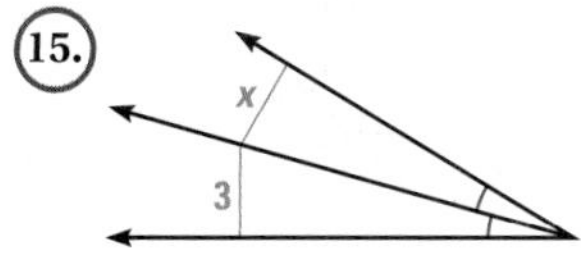

16.

40° x°

17.

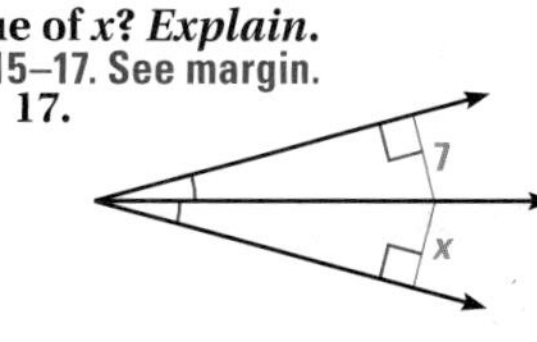

4 PRACTICE AND APPLY

Assignment Guide

Answer Transparencies available for all exercises

Basic:
Day 1: pp. 313–316
Exs. 1–17 odd, 18–24, 28–33, 39–47 odd

Average:
Day 1: pp. 313–316
Exs. 1, 2–22 even, 23–26, 28–36, 40–46 even

Advanced:
Day 1: pp. 313–316
Exs. 1, 2, 5, 8, 11, 14, 17–38*, 41, 44, 47

Block:
pp. 313–316
Exs. 1, 2–22 even, 23–26, 28–36, 40–46 even (with 5.4)

Differentiated Instruction

See *Geometry Best Practices Toolkit* for suggestions on addressing the needs of a diverse classroom.

Homework Check

For a quick check of student understanding of key concepts, go over the following exercises:

Basic: 3, 7, 13, 19, 28
Average: 4, 8, 14, 20, 29
Advanced: 5, 11, 17, 20, 30

Extra Practice

- Student Edition, p. 904
- Chapter 5 Resource Book: Practice levels A, B, C, pp. 34–39

Practice Worksheet

An easily-readable reduced practice page (with answers) for this lesson can be found on p. 292C.

6. Yes; $\angle BAD \cong \angle CAD$, $\overline{DB} \perp \overline{AB}$, and $\overline{DC} \perp \overline{AC}$ so by the Angle Bisector Theorem $DB = DC$.

7. No; you do not know that $\angle BAD \cong \angle CAD$.

8. No; you do not know that $\overline{DB} \perp \overline{AB}$ or $\overline{DC} \perp \overline{AC}$.

15. No; the segments with length x and 3 are not perpendicular to their respective rays.

16. No; you do not know that the perpendicular segment bisects the angle.

17. Yes; $x = 7$ using the Angle Bisector Theorem.

Avoiding Common Errors

Exercises 6–11 Applying the Angle Bisector Theorems can be confusing for some students. Point out that $\overline{BD}$ does not represent the distance from B to the angle bisector in Exercises 7 and 8, and $\overline{FH}$ does not represent the distance from F to the angle bisector in Exercises 9 and 11.

21. ***GD*** **is not the perpendicular distance from** ***G*** **to** $\overline{CE}$**. The same is true about** ***GF*****; the distance from** ***G*** **to each side of the triangle is the same.**

22. ***T*** **is not the incenter of △*UWY*.** ***Sample answer:*** ***TU = TW = TY***

26. ***Sample:***

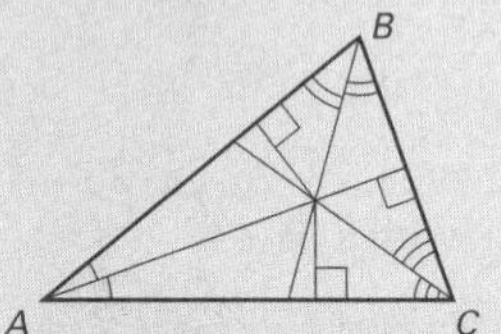

27. ***Sample answer:*** **Since △*ABC* is a right triangle, its area is** $\frac{1}{2}(AB \cdot AC)$**. The area of △*ABC* is also the sum of the areas of △*ABD*, △*ADC*, and △*DBC*. This sum is** $\frac{1}{2}x(AB) + \frac{1}{2}x(AC) + \frac{1}{2}x(BC)$**, or** $\frac{1}{2}x(AC + AB + BC)$**. Setting** $\frac{1}{2}(AB \cdot AC)$ **equal to** $\frac{1}{2}x(AC + AB + BC)$ **and solving for** ***x*** **gives** $x = \frac{AB \cdot AC}{AC + AB + BC}$**.**

18. ★ **MULTIPLE CHOICE** What is the value of x in the diagram? **B**

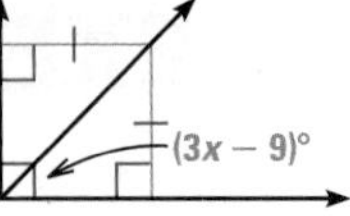

Ⓐ 13 Ⓑ 18

Ⓒ 33 Ⓓ Not enough information

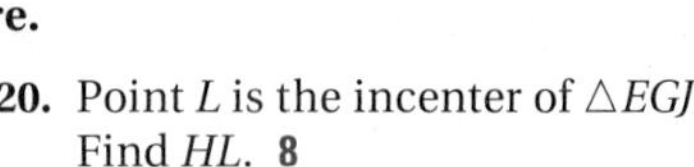

EXAMPLE 4 on p. 312 for Exs. 19–22

USING INCENTERS **Find the indicated measure.**

19. Point D is the incenter of $\triangle XYZ$. Find DB. **9**

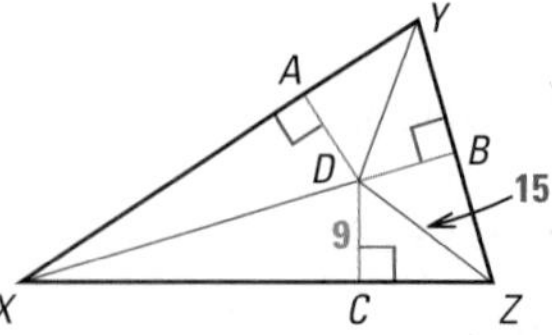

20. Point L is the incenter of $\triangle EGJ$. Find HL. **8**

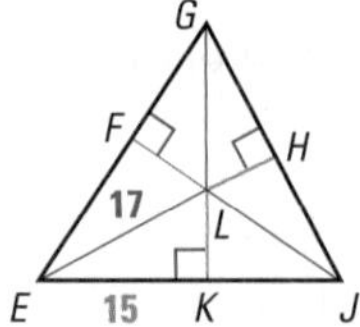

ERROR ANALYSIS ***Describe*** **the error in reasoning. Then state a correct conclusion about distances that can be deduced from the diagram.** **21, 22. See margin.**

21.

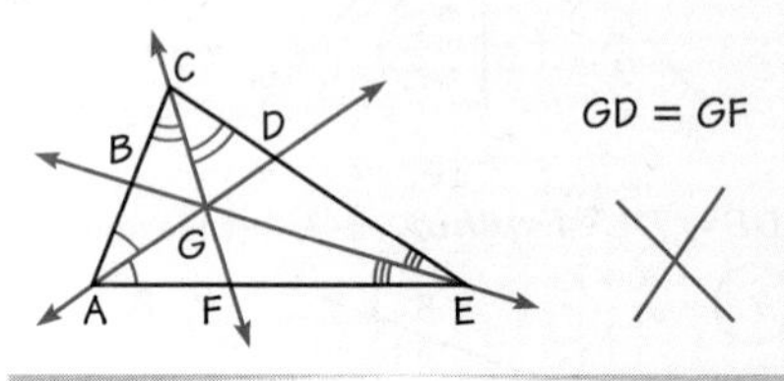

22.

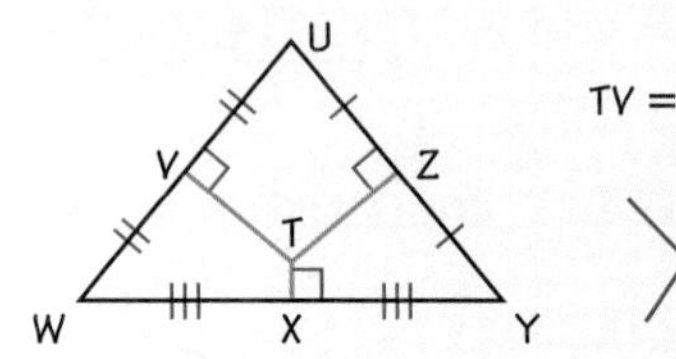

B **23.** ★ **MULTIPLE CHOICE** In the diagram, N is the incenter of $\triangle GHJ$. Which statement cannot be deduced from the given information? **C**

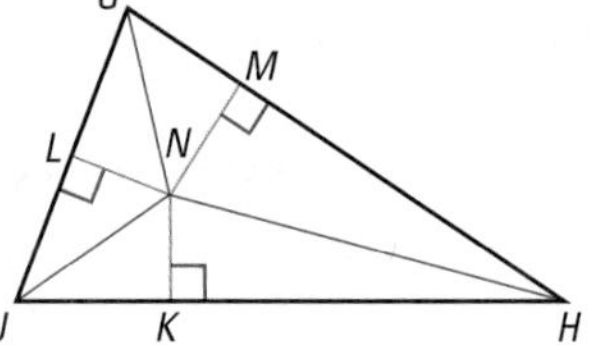

Ⓐ $\overline{NM} \cong \overline{NK}$ Ⓑ $\overline{NL} \cong \overline{NM}$

Ⓒ $\overline{NG} \cong \overline{NJ}$ Ⓓ $\overline{HK} \cong \overline{HM}$

ALGEBRA **Find the value of** x **that makes** N **the incenter of the triangle.**

24. **6**

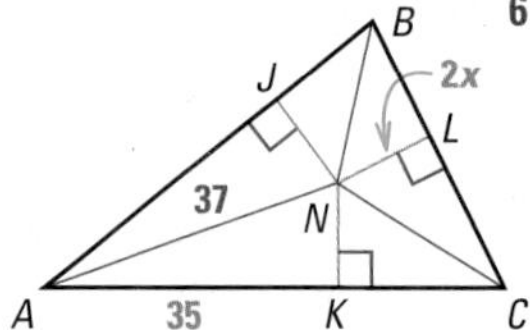

25. **0.5**

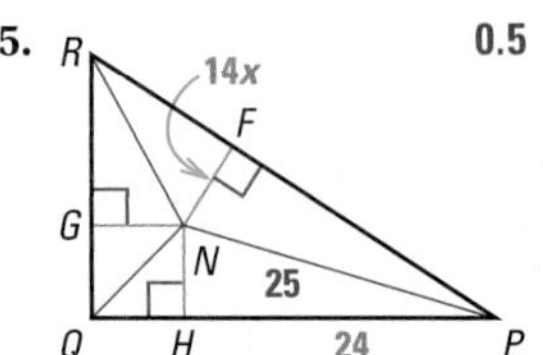

26. **CONSTRUCTION** Use a compass and a straightedge to draw $\triangle ABC$ with incenter D. Label the angle bisectors and the perpendicular segments from D to each of the sides of $\triangle ABC$. Measure each segment. What do you notice? What theorem have you verified for your $\triangle ABC$? **They all have the same length; Concurrency of Angle Bisectors of a Triangle Theorem; see margin for art.**

C **27.** **CHALLENGE** Point D is the incenter of $\triangle ABC$. Write an expression for the length x in terms of the three side lengths AB, AC, and BC. **See margin.**

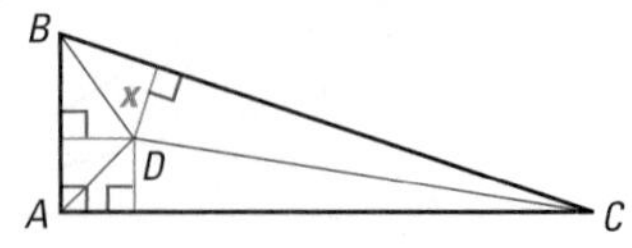

○ = **WORKED-OUT SOLUTIONS** on p. WS1 ★ = **STANDARDIZED TEST PRACTICE**

29.

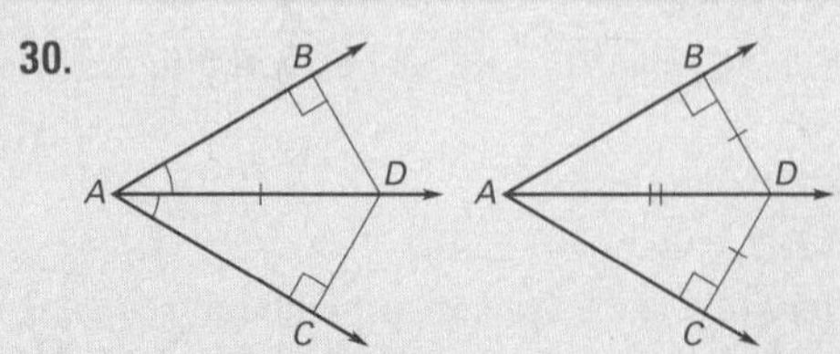

30.

PROBLEM SOLVING

EXAMPLE 2 A on p. 311 for Ex. 28

28. **FIELD HOCKEY** In a field hockey game, the goalkeeper is at point G and a player from the opposing team hits the ball from point B. The goal extends from left goalpost L to right goalpost R. Will the goalkeeper have to move farther to keep the ball from hitting L or R? *Explain.*

@HomeTutor for problem solving help at classzone.com

No; G is on the angle bisector of $\angle LBR$.

29. **KOI POND** You are constructing a fountain in a triangular koi pond. You want the fountain to be the same distance from each edge of the pond. Where should you build the fountain? *Explain* your reasoning. Use a sketch to support your answer.

@HomeTutor for problem solving help at classzone.com

At the incenter of the pond; see margin for art.

30. ★ **SHORT RESPONSE** What congruence postulate or theorem would you use to prove the Angle Bisector Theorem? to prove the Converse of the Angle Bisector Theorem? Use diagrams to show your reasoning. **AAS; HL; see margin for art.**

B

31. ★ **EXTENDED RESPONSE** Suppose you are given a triangle and are asked to draw all of its perpendicular bisectors and angle bisectors.

 a. For what type of triangle would you need the fewest segments? What is the minimum number of segments you would need? *Explain.*

 31a. Equilateral; 3; the angle bisector would also be the perpendicular bisector.

 b. For what type of triangle would you need the most segments? What is the maximum number of segments you would need? *Explain.* **Scalene; 6; each angle bisector would be different than the corresponding perpendicular bisector.**

CHOOSING A METHOD In Exercises 32 and 33, tell whether you would use *perpendicular bisectors* or *angle bisectors*. Then solve the problem.

32. **BANNER** To make a banner, you will cut a triangle from an $8\frac{1}{2}$ inch by 11 inch sheet of white paper and paste a red circle onto it as shown. The circle should just touch each side of the triangle. Use a model to decide whether the circle's radius should be *more* or *less* than $2\frac{1}{2}$ inches. Can you cut the circle from a 5 inch by 5 inch red square? *Explain.*

Angle bisector; more; no; the diameter of the inscribed circle is greater than 5 inches.

33. **CAMP** A map of a camp shows a pool at (10, 20), a nature center at (16, 2), and a tennis court at (2, 4). A new circular walking path will connect the three locations. Graph the points and find the approximate center of the circle. Estimate the radius of the circle if each unit on the grid represents 10 yards. Then use the formula $C = 2\pi r$ to estimate the length of the path. **Perpendicular bisectors; (10, 10); 100 yd; about 628 yd; see margin for art.**

PROVING THEOREMS 5.5 AND 5.6 Use Exercise 30 to prove the theorem. **34, 35. See margin.**

34. Angle Bisector Theorem

35. Converse of the Angle Bisector Theorem

Internet Reference

Exercise 28 For more information about field hockey, visit www.usfieldhockey.com/hockey/index.htm

Reading Strategy

Exercises 32–33 These exercises can help students distinguish between the incenter and the circumcenter of a triangle. Ask students to discuss the directions with a partner and their strategies for answering the questions.

Teaching Strategy

Exercise 38 Ask students to draw diagrams of different triangles, including obtuse ones, to help them plan their proof. Each diagram should be labeled with the same letters or variables so that the proof applies to all of them.

35. Statements (Reasons)

1. $\angle BAC$ with D in its interior, $\overline{DB} \perp \overline{AB}$, $\overline{DC} \perp \overline{AC}$, $DB = DC$. (Given)
2. $\angle ABD$ and $\angle ACD$ are right angles. (Definition of perpendicular lines)
3. $\triangle ABD$ and $\triangle ACD$ are right triangles. (Definition of right triangle)
4. $\overline{DB} \cong \overline{DC}$ (Definition of congruent segments)
5. $\overline{AD} \cong \overline{AD}$ (Reflexive Property of Segment Congruence)
6. $\triangle ABD \cong \triangle ACD$ (HL)
7. $\angle BAD \cong \angle CAD$ (Corr. parts of $\cong$ $\triangle$s are $\cong$.)
8. $\overrightarrow{AD}$ bisects $\angle BAC$. (Definition of angle bisector)

33.

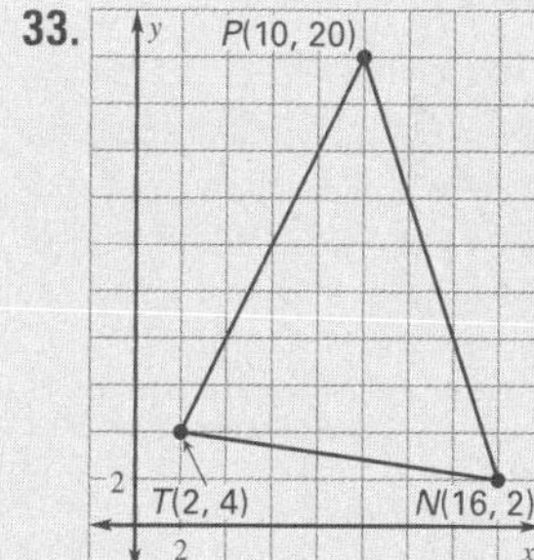

34. Statements (Reasons)

1. $\angle BAC$ is bisected by $\overline{AD}$, $\overline{DB} \perp \overline{AB}$, $\overline{DC} \perp \overline{AC}$. (Given)
2. $\angle BAD \cong \angle CAD$ (Definition of angle bisector)
3. $\angle DBA$ and $\angle DCA$ are right angles. (Definition of perpendicular lines)
4. $\angle DBA \cong \angle DCA$ (Right Angles Congruence Theorem)
5. $\overline{DA} \cong \overline{DA}$ (Reflexive Property of Segment Congruence)
6. $\triangle ABD \cong \triangle ACD$ (AAS)
7. $\overline{DB} \cong \overline{DC}$ (Corr. parts of $\cong$ $\triangle$s are $\cong$.)
8. $DB = DC$ (Definition of congruent segments)

5 ASSESS AND RETEACH

Daily Homework Quiz

Transparency Available

Find the value of x.

1. **12**

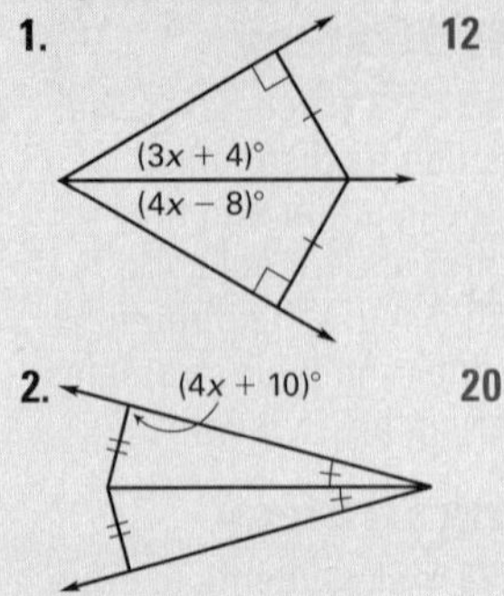

2. (4x + 10)° **20**

3. Point D is the incenter of $\triangle XYZ$. Find DB. **10**

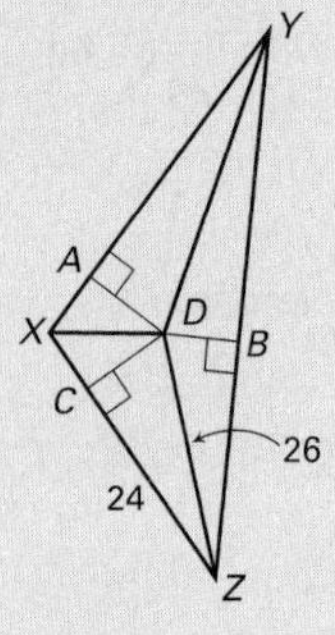

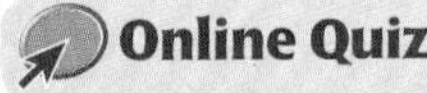

Online Quiz

Available at **classzone.com**

Diagnosis/Remediation

- Practice A, B, C in Chapter 5 Resource Book, pp. 34–39
- Study Guide in Chapter 5 Resource Book, pp. 40–41
- Practice Workbook, pp. 91–93
- @HomeTutor

Challenge

Additional challenge is available in the Chapter 5 Resource Book, p. 45.

36, 37a. See Additional Answers beginning on p. AA1.

36. PROVING THEOREM 5.7 Write a proof of the Concurrency of Angle Bisectors of a Triangle Theorem. **See margin.**

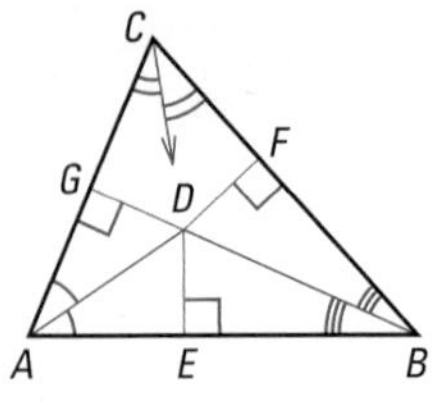

GIVEN ▶ $\triangle ABC$, $\overline{AD}$ bisects $\angle CAB$, $\overline{BD}$ bisects $\angle CBA$, $\overline{DE} \perp \overline{AB}$, $\overline{DF} \perp \overline{BC}$, $\overline{DG} \perp \overline{CA}$

PROVE ▶ The angle bisectors intersect at D, which is equidistant from $\overline{AB}$, $\overline{BC}$, and $\overline{CA}$.

C **37. CELEBRATION** You are planning a graduation party in the triangular courtyard shown. You want to fit as large a circular tent as possible on the site without extending into the walkway.

a. Copy the triangle and show how to place the tent so that it just touches each edge. Then *explain* how you can be sure that there is no place you could fit a larger tent on the site. Use sketches to support your answer.

37a. Use the Concurrency of Angle Bisectors of Triangle Theorem; if you move the circle to any other spot it will extend into the walkway; see margin for art.

b. Suppose you want to fit as large a tent as possible while leaving at least one foot of space around the tent. Would you put the center of the tent in the same place as you did in part (a)? *Justify* your answer.
Yes; the incenter will allow the largest tent possible.

38. CHALLENGE You have seen that there is a point inside any triangle that is equidistant from the three sides of the triangle. Prove that if you extend the sides of the triangle to form lines, you can find three points outside the triangle, each of which is equidistant from those three lines.
***Sample answer:* Construct three circles exterior to the triangle, each one tangent to one side of the triangle and the other two lines. The centers of the circles are the three points.**

Y
X
Z

MIXED REVIEW

PREVIEW
Prepare for Lesson 5.4 in Exs. 39–41.

Find the length of $\overline{AB}$ and the coordinates of the midpoint of $\overline{AB}$. *(p. 15)*

39. $A(-2, 2)$, $B(-10, 2)$ **8, (−6, 2)**

40. $A(0, 6)$, $B(5, 8)$ **$\sqrt{29}$, (2.5, 7)**

41. $A(-1, -3)$, $B(7, -5)$ **$2\sqrt{17}$, (3, −4)**

***Explain* how to prove the given statement.** *(p. 256)* **42–44. See margin.**

42. $\angle QNP \cong \angle LNM$

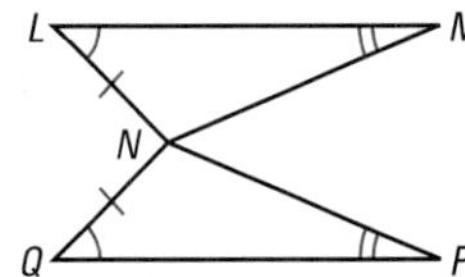

43. $\overline{JG}$ bisects $\angle FGH$.

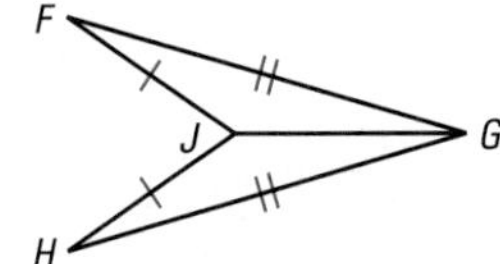

44. $\triangle ZWX \cong \triangle ZYX$

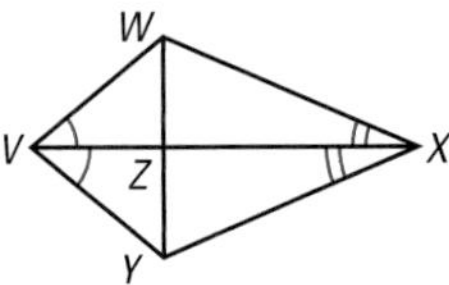

Find the coordinates of the red points in the figure if necessary. Then find OR and the coordinates of the midpoint M of $\overline{RT}$. *(p. 295)*

45.

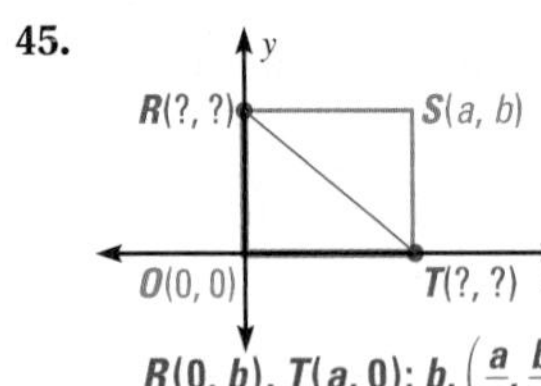

$R(0, b)$, $T(a, 0)$; b, $\left(\frac{a}{2}, \frac{b}{2}\right)$

46.

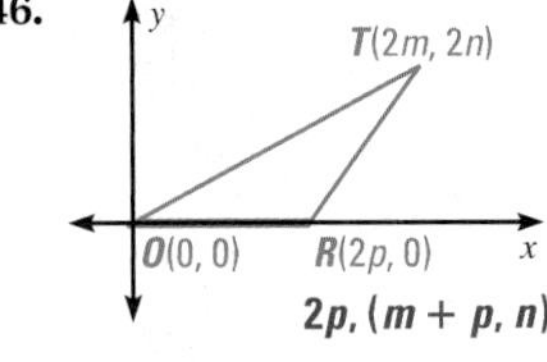

$2p$, $(m + p, n)$

47.

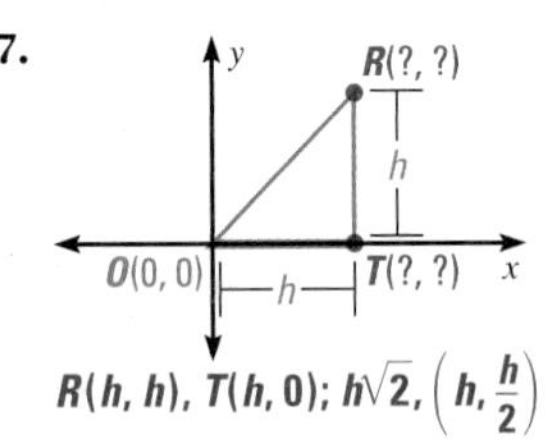

$R(h, h)$, $T(h, 0)$; $h\sqrt{2}$, $\left(h, \frac{h}{2}\right)$

42. $\triangle QNP \cong \triangle LNM$ **by AAS. Use corr. parts of ≅ ⚠ are ≅.**

43. $\triangle JFG \cong \triangle JHG$ **by SSS. Use corr. parts of ≅ ⚠ are ≅ and the definition of angle bisector.**

44. $\triangle VWX \cong \triangle VYX$ **by ASA.** $\overline{WX} \cong \overline{YX}$ **because corr. parts of ≅ ⚠ are ≅.** $\overline{ZX} \cong \overline{ZX}$ **by the Reflexive Property of Segment Congruence.** $\triangle ZWX \cong \triangle ZYX$ **by SAS.**

MIXED REVIEW of Problem Solving

Lessons 5.1–5.3

1. **SHORT RESPONSE** A committee has decided to build a park in Deer County. The committee agreed that the park should be equidistant from the three largest cities in the county, which are labeled X, Y, and Z in the diagram. *Explain* why this may not be the best place to build the park. Use a sketch to support your answer. ***Sample answer:* The park would be located outside of the county; see margin for art.**

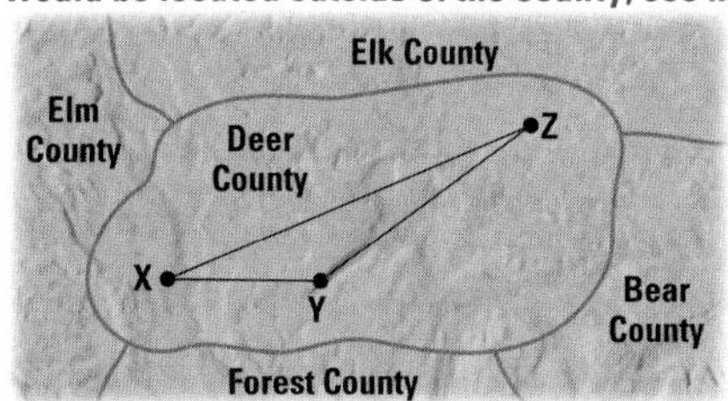

2. **EXTENDED RESPONSE** A woodworker is trying to cut as large a wheel as possible from a triangular scrap of wood. The wheel just touches each side of the triangle as shown below.

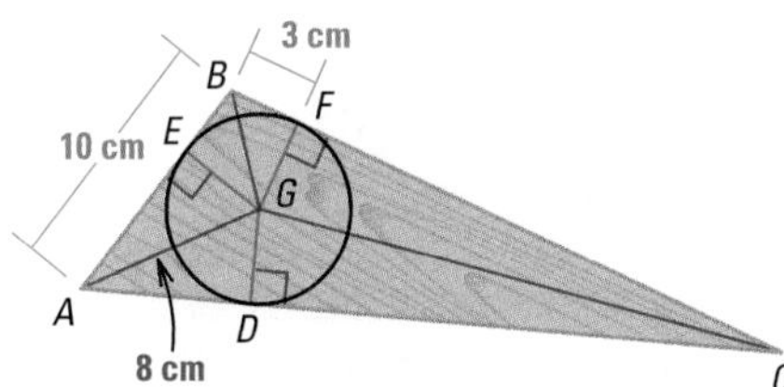

   a. Which point of concurrency is the woodworker using for the center of the circle? What type of special segment are $\overline{BG}$, $\overline{CG}$, and $\overline{AG}$? **incenter; angle bisectors**

   b. Which postulate or theorem can you use to prove that $\triangle BGF \cong \triangle BGE$? **HL**

   c. Find the radius of the wheel to the nearest tenth of a centimeter. *Explain* your reasoning. **3.9 cm; $(AE)^2 + (EG)^2 = (GA)^2$ or $7^2 + (EG)^2 = 8^2$**

3. **SHORT RESPONSE** Graph $\triangle GHJ$ with vertices $G(2, 2)$, $H(6, 8)$, and $J(10, 4)$ and draw its midsegments. Each midsegment is contained in a line. Which of those lines has the greatest y-intercept? Write the equation of that line. *Justify* your answer. **$\overleftrightarrow{AC}$; $y = -x + 9$; the y-intercepts are -6, 4, and 9. The slope of the line with 9 as the y-intercept is -1 so the equation of that line is $y = -1x + 9$; see margin for art.**

4. **GRIDDED ANSWER** Three friends are practicing disc golf, in which a flying disk is thrown into a set of targets. Each player is 15 feet from the target. Two players are 24 feet from each other along one edge of the nearby football field. How far is the target from that edge of the football field? **9 ft**

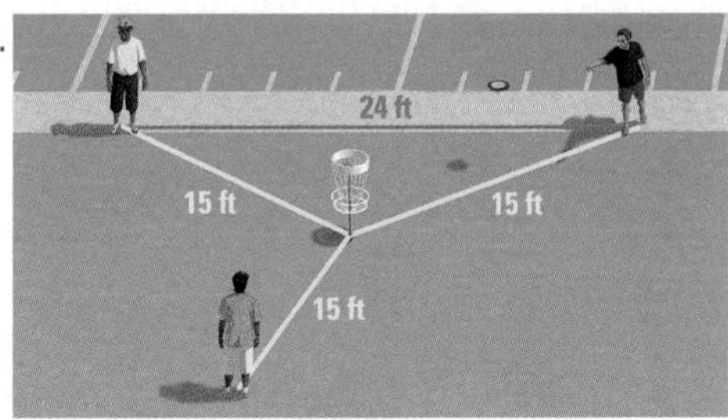

5. **MULTI-STEP PROBLEM** An artist created a large floor mosaic consisting of eight triangular sections. The grey segments are the midsegments of the two black triangles.

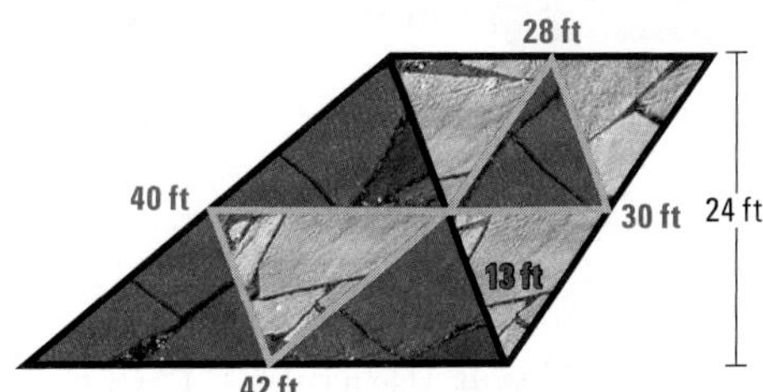

   a. The gray and black edging was created using special narrow tiles. What is the total length of all the edging used? **262 ft**

   b. What is the total area of the mosaic? **840 ft^2**

6. **OPEN-ENDED** If possible, draw a triangle whose incenter and circumcenter are the same point. *Describe* this triangle as specifically as possible. **Equilateral triangle; see margin for art.**

7. **SHORT RESPONSE** Points S, T, and U are the midpoints of the sides of $\triangle PQR$. Which angles are congruent to $\angle QST$? *Justify* your answer. **See margin.**

1.

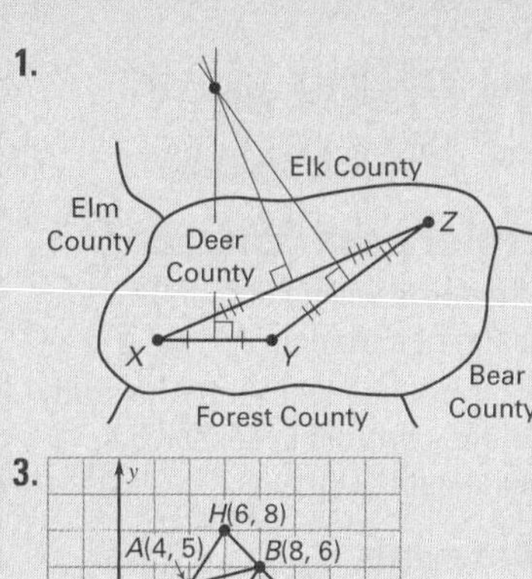

3.

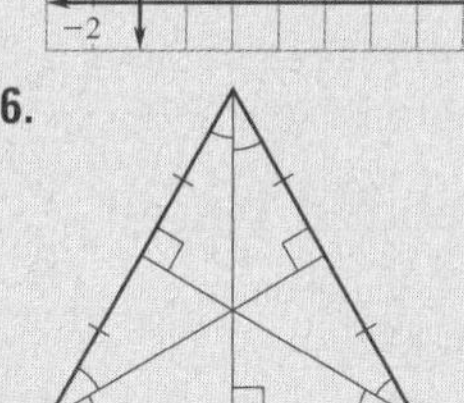

6.

7. $\angle QPR$, $\angle STU$, $\angle TUR$; $\overline{ST} \parallel \overline{PR}$ with $\overline{QP}$ a transversal, so $\angle QPR$ and $\angle QST$ are corresponding angles. $\overline{PQ} \parallel \overline{UT}$ with $\overline{ST}$ a transversal, so $\angle QST$ and $\angle STU$ are alternate interior angles. $\overline{ST} \parallel \overline{PR}$ with $\overline{TU}$ a transversal, so $\angle STU$ and $\angle TUR$ are alternate interior angles and $\angle QST \cong \angle TUR$ by the Transitive Property.

1 PLAN AND PREPARE

Explore the Concept

- Students will find the balance point of a triangle.
- This activity leads into the study of the centroid in Lesson 5.4, Example 1.

Materials

Each student or group of students will need:

- cardboard, straightedge
- scissors, metric ruler

Recommended Time

Work activity: 10 min

Discuss results: 5 min

Grouping

Students can work individually or in groups of two. In groups, students can alternate finding measurements.

2 TEACH

Tips for Success

Make sure students measure accurately so they can make valid conclusions.

Key Question

- What can you conclude about a line that contains a vertex and the balance point? **The line bisects the opposite side.**

Alternative Strategy

Show that the segment through the balance point, a vertex, and a point on the opposite side is a median.

Key Discovery

The medians of a triangle intersect in the balance point of a triangle.

3 ASSESS AND RETEACH

1. If P is the point of intersection of the medians of $\triangle ABC$ and $\overline{BF}$ is a median, how is BP related to PF? $BP = 2 \cdot PF$

5.4 Intersecting Medians

Standards

Prepare for 12.0 *Students find and use measures* of sides and of interior and exterior angles *of triangles* and polygons *to* classify figures and *solve problems.*

MATERIALS • cardboard • straightedge • scissors • metric ruler

QUESTION What is the relationship between segments formed by the medians of a triangle?

EXPLORE 1 Find the balance point of a triangle

STEP 1

Cut out triangle Draw a triangle on a piece of cardboard. Then cut it out.

STEP 2

Balance the triangle Balance the triangle on the eraser end of a pencil.

STEP 3

Mark the balance point Mark the point on the triangle where it balanced on the pencil.

EXPLORE 2 Construct the medians of a triangle

STEP 1

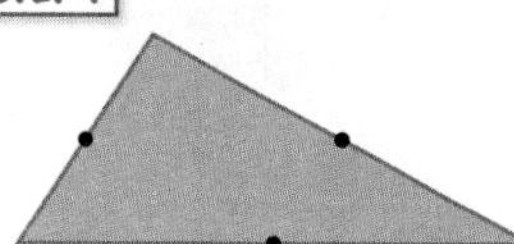

Find the midpoint Use a ruler to find the midpoint of each side of the triangle.

STEP 2

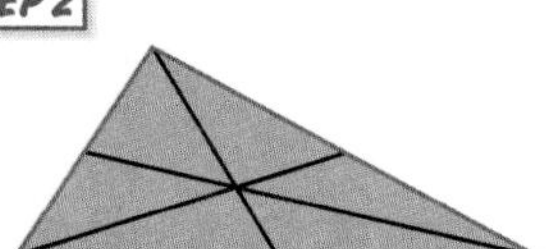

Draw medians Draw a segment, or *median*, from each midpoint to the vertex of the opposite angle.

STEP 3

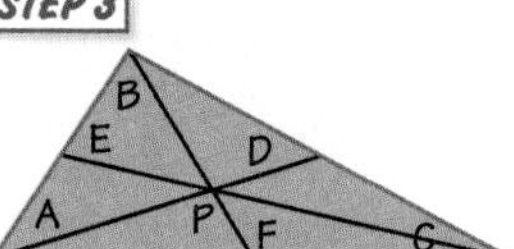

Label points Label your triangle as shown. What do you notice about point P and the balance point in Explore 1?

DRAW CONCLUSIONS Use your observations to complete these exercises

1. Copy and complete the table. Measure in millimeters. **See margin.**

Length of segment from vertex to midpoint of opposite side	$AD = ?$	$BF = ?$	$CE = ?$
Length of segment from vertex to P	$AP = ?$	$BP = ?$	$CP = ?$
Length of segment from P to midpoint	$PD = ?$	$PF = ?$	$PE = ?$

2. How does the length of the segment from a vertex to P compare with the length of the segment from P to the midpoint of the opposite side? **It is twice as long.**

3. How does the length of the segment from a vertex to P compare with the length of the segment from the vertex to the midpoint of the opposite side? **It is $\frac{2}{3}$ the length.**

1. ***Sample:*** **Row 1: 27, 15, 36; Row 2: 18, 10, 24; Row 3: 9, 5, 12**

5.4 Use Medians and Altitudes

Before You used perpendicular bisectors and angle bisectors of triangles.

Now You will use medians and altitudes of triangles.

Why? So you can find the balancing point of a triangle, as in Ex. 37.

Key Vocabulary
- median of a triangle
- centroid
- altitude of a triangle
- orthocenter

Standards

Prepare for 12.0 *Students find and use measures* of sides and of interior and exterior angles *of triangles* and polygons *to* classify figures and *solve problems.*

As shown by the Activity on page 318, a triangle will balance at a particular point. This point is the intersection of the *medians* of the triangle.

A **median of a triangle** is a segment from a vertex to the midpoint of the opposite side. The three medians of a triangle are concurrent. The point of concurrency, called the **centroid**, is inside the triangle.

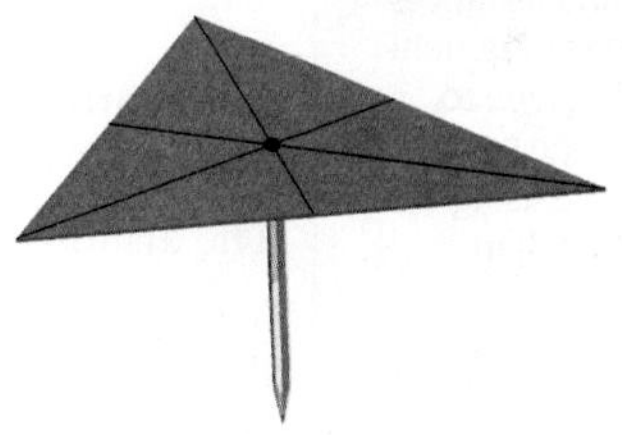

Three medians meet at the centroid.

THEOREM *For Your Notebook*

THEOREM 5.8 Concurrency of Medians of a Triangle

The medians of a triangle intersect at a point that is two thirds of the distance from each vertex to the midpoint of the opposite side.

The medians of $\triangle ABC$ meet at P and $AP = \frac{2}{3}AE$, $BP = \frac{2}{3}BF$, and $CP = \frac{2}{3}CD$.

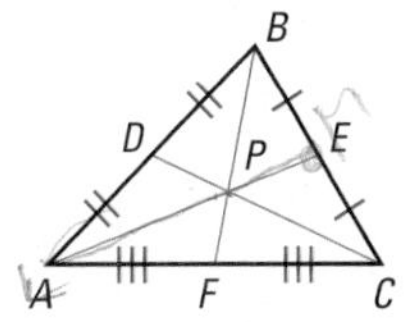

Proof: Ex. 32, p. 323; p. 934

EXAMPLE 1 Use the centroid of a triangle

In $\triangle RST$, Q is the centroid and $SQ = 8$. Find QW and SW.

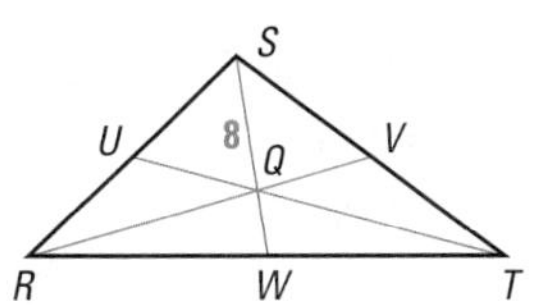

Solution

$SQ = \frac{2}{3}SW$	Concurrency of Medians of a Triangle Theorem
$8 = \frac{2}{3}SW$	Substitute 8 for SQ.
$12 = SW$	Multiply each side by the reciprocal, $\frac{3}{2}$.

Then $QW = SW - SQ = 12 - 8 = 4$.

▶ So, $QW = 4$ and $SW = 12$.

1 PLAN AND PREPARE

Warm-Up Exercises

Transparency Available

1. For $A(-4, 8)$ and $B(5, 8)$, find the midpoint of $\overline{AB}$. $\left(\frac{1}{2}, 8\right)$
2. For $A(-3, 2)$ and $B(4, -1)$, find the length of $\overline{AB}$. $\sqrt{58}$
3. For $A(0, 4)$ and $C(18, 4)$, find the length of $\overline{AB}$, where B is a point $\frac{2}{3}$ the distance from A to C. **12**

Notetaking Guide

Transparency Available

Promotes interactive learning and notetaking skills, pp. 128–131.

Pacing

Basic: 2 days
Average: 2 days
Advanced: 2 days
Block: 0.5 block with 5.3
0.5 block with 5.5
- See *Teaching Guide/Lesson Plan.*

2 FOCUS AND MOTIVATE

Essential Question

Big Idea 1, p. 293

How do you find the centroid of a triangle? **Tell students they will learn how to answer this question by finding the point where the medians of a triangle intersect.**

Resource Planning Guide

Chapter Resource Book
- Teaching Guide/Lesson Plan (pp. 46–47)
- Activity Master (p. 48)
- Practice levels A, B, C (pp. 51–56)
- Study Guide (pp. 57–58)
- Catch-up for Absent Students (p. 59)
- Problem Solving Workshop (p. 60)
- Challenge (p. 61)

Workbooks
- Notetaking Guide (pp. 128–131)
- Practice Workbook (pp. 94–96)

Teaching Options
- **Power Presentations CD-ROM** provides dynamic electronic teaching resources for the classroom.
- **Activity Generator CD-ROM** provides editable activities for all ability levels.

Interactive Technology
- Easy Planner
- Power Presentations CD-ROM
- Activity Generator CD-ROM
- Animated Geometry
- Test Generator CD-ROM
- Online Quiz
- eWorkbook
- eEdition
- @HomeTutor

Resources for English Learners
- Quick Reference for English Learners
- Spanish Study Guide
- Multi-Language Visual Glossary
- Student Resources in Spanish

See also the *Geometry Toolkit* for more strategies for meeting individual needs.

Motivating the Lesson

A microphone hangs on wires from two ceiling hooks. In the triangle formed by the hooks and the mike, what segment represents the distance from the mike to the ceiling? This lesson deals with that segment, the altitude, and other segments in triangles.

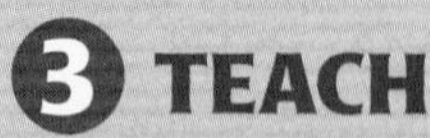

3 TEACH

Extra Example 1

In $\triangle HJK$, P is the centroid and $JP = 12$. Find PT and JT. **6; 18**

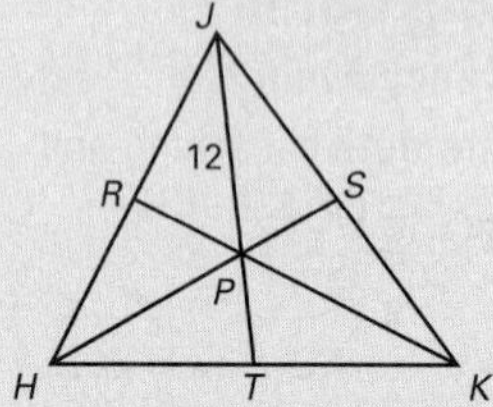

Key Questions to Ask for Example 1

- If $\triangle RST$ is scalene, does $SQ = RQ$? **no**
- Can the centroid and the incenter be the same point? **yes**

Extra Example 2

The vertices of $\triangle ABC$ are $A(1, 5)$, $B(5, 7)$, and $C(9, 3)$. Which ordered pair gives the coordinates of the centroid of $\triangle ABC$? **C**

Ⓐ (3, 6) Ⓑ (5, 4)
Ⓒ (5, 5) Ⓓ (7, 5)

Key Question to Ask for Example 2

- How would you find the coordinates of the centroid using the median from F? **The midpoint of $\overline{GH}$ is (5, 5) and the length of the segment from (5, 5) to F(2, 5) is 3 units. The centroid is $\frac{2}{3}$ of that distance along a horizontal line from F, which is P(4, 5).**

★ EXAMPLE 2 Standardized Test Practice

The vertices of $\triangle FGH$ are $F(2, 5)$, $G(4, 9)$, and $H(6, 1)$. Which ordered pair gives the coordinates of the centroid P of $\triangle FGH$?

Ⓐ (3, 5) Ⓑ (4, 5) Ⓒ (4, 7) Ⓓ (5, 3)

CHECK ANSWERS
Median $\overline{GK}$ was used in Example 2 because it is easy to find distances on a vertical segment. It is a good idea to check by finding the centroid using a different median.

Solution

Sketch $\triangle FGH$. Then use the Midpoint Formula to find the midpoint K of $\overline{FH}$ and sketch median $\overline{GK}$.

$$K\left(\frac{2+6}{2}, \frac{5+1}{2}\right) = K(4, 3).$$

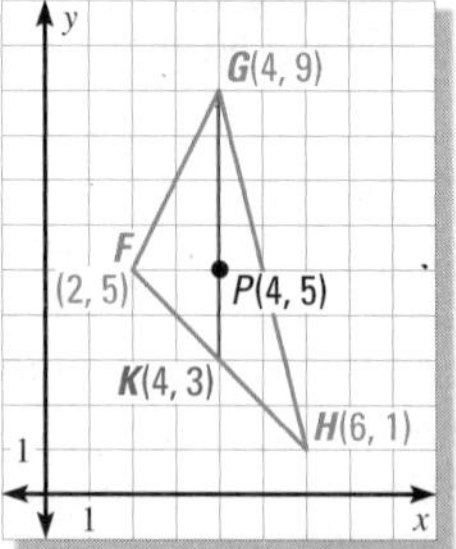

The centroid is two thirds of the distance from each vertex to the midpoint of the opposite side.

The distance from vertex $G(4, 9)$ to $K(4, 3)$ is $9 - 3 = 6$ units. So, the centroid is $\frac{2}{3}(6) = 4$ units down from G on $\overline{GK}$.

The coordinates of the centroid P are $(4, 9 - 4)$, or $(4, 5)$.

▶ The correct answer is B. Ⓐ Ⓑ Ⓒ Ⓓ

✓ GUIDED PRACTICE for Examples 1 and 2

There are three paths through a triangular park. Each path goes from the midpoint of one edge to the opposite corner. The paths meet at point P.

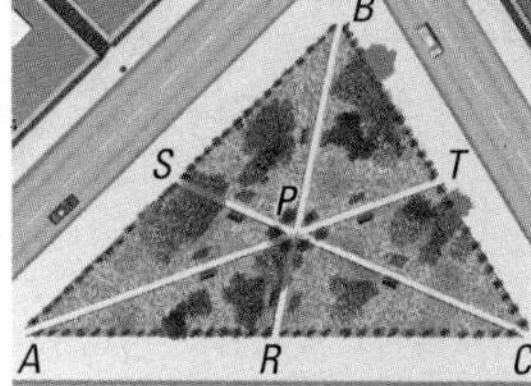

1. If $SC = 2100$ feet, find PS and PC. **700 ft, 1400 ft**
2. If $BT = 1000$ feet, find TC and BC. **1000 ft, 2000 ft**
3. If $PT = 800$ feet, find PA and TA. **1600 ft, 2400 ft**

MEASURES OF TRIANGLES
In the area formula for a triangle, $A = \frac{1}{2}bh$, you can use the length of any side for the base b. The height h is the length of the altitude to that side from the opposite vertex.

ALTITUDES An **altitude of a triangle** is the perpendicular segment from a vertex to the opposite side or to the line that contains the opposite side.

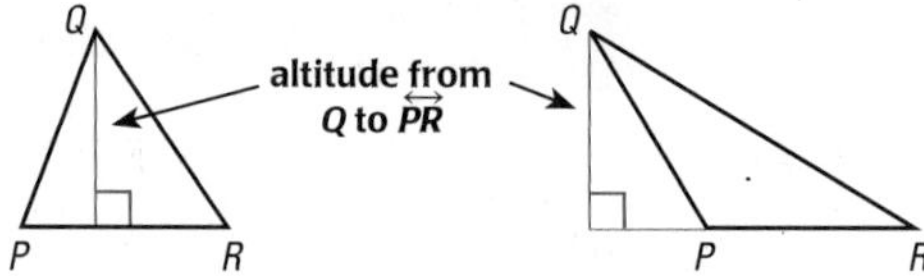

THEOREM *For Your Notebook*

THEOREM 5.9 Concurrency of Altitudes of a Triangle

The lines containing the altitudes of a triangle are concurrent.

The lines containing $\overline{AF}$, $\overline{BE}$, and $\overline{CD}$ meet at G.

Proof: Exs. 29–31, p. 323; p. 936

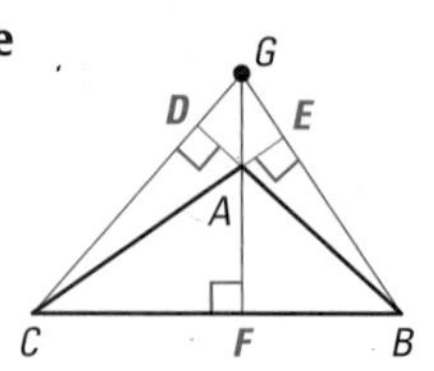

CONCURRENCY OF ALTITUDES The point at which the lines containing the three altitudes of a triangle intersect is called the **orthocenter** of the triangle.

EXAMPLE 3 Find the orthocenter

Find the orthocenter *P* in an acute, a right, and an obtuse triangle.

READ DIAGRAMS
The altitudes are shown in red. Notice that in the right triangle the legs are also altitudes. The altitudes of the obtuse triangle are extended to find the orthocenter.

Solution

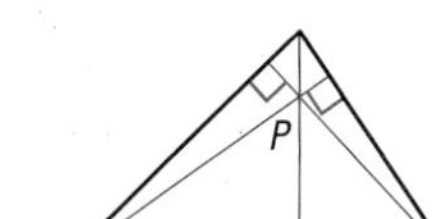

Acute triangle
***P* is inside triangle.**

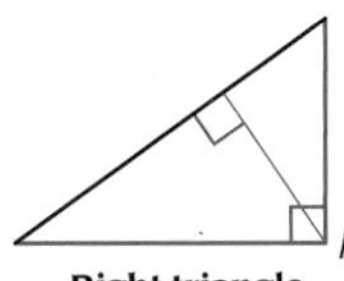

Right triangle
***P* is on triangle.**

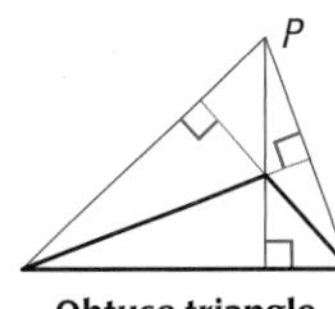

Obtuse triangle
***P* is outside triangle.**

Animated Geometry at classzone.com

ISOSCELES TRIANGLES In an isosceles triangle, the perpendicular bisector, angle bisector, median, and altitude from the vertex angle to the base are all the same segment. In an equilateral triangle, this is true for the special segment from any vertex.

EXAMPLE 4 Prove a property of isosceles triangles

Prove that the median to the base of an isosceles triangle is an altitude.

Solution

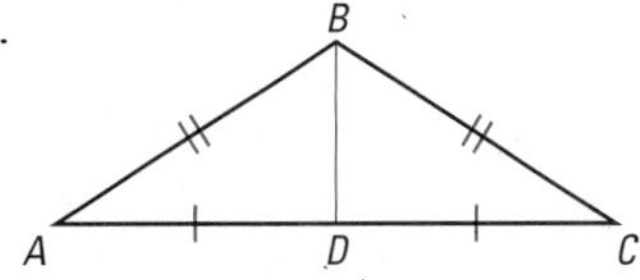

GIVEN ▶ $\triangle ABC$ is isosceles, with base $\overline{AC}$.
$\overline{BD}$ is the median to base $\overline{AC}$.

PROVE ▶ $\overline{BD}$ is an altitude of $\triangle ABC$.

Proof Legs $\overline{AB}$ and $\overline{BC}$ of isosceles $\triangle ABC$ are congruent. $\overline{CD} \cong \overline{AD}$ because $\overline{BD}$ is the median to $\overline{AC}$. Also, $\overline{BD} \cong \overline{BD}$. Therefore, $\triangle ABD \cong \triangle CBD$ by the SSS Congruence Postulate.

$\angle ADB \cong \angle CDB$ because corresponding parts of $\cong$ ⚠ are $\cong$. Also, $\angle ADB$ and $\angle CDB$ are a linear pair. $\overline{BD}$ and $\overline{AC}$ intersect to form a linear pair of congruent angles, so $\overline{BD} \perp \overline{AC}$ and $\overline{BD}$ is an altitude of $\triangle ABC$.

GUIDED PRACTICE for Examples 3 and 4

4. Copy the triangle in Example 4 and find its orthocenter. **See margin.**

5. **WHAT IF?** In Example 4, suppose you wanted to show that median $\overline{BD}$ is also an angle bisector. How would your proof be different?

5. $\triangle ABD \cong \triangle CBD$ by SSS making $\angle ABD \cong \angle CBD$ which leads to $\overline{BD}$ being an angle bisector.

6. Triangle PQR is an isoscleles triangle and segment $\overline{OQ}$ is an altitude. What else do you know about $\overline{OQ}$? What are the coordinates of P?

6. $\overline{OQ}$ is also a perpendicular bisector, angle bisector, and median; $(-h, 0)$.

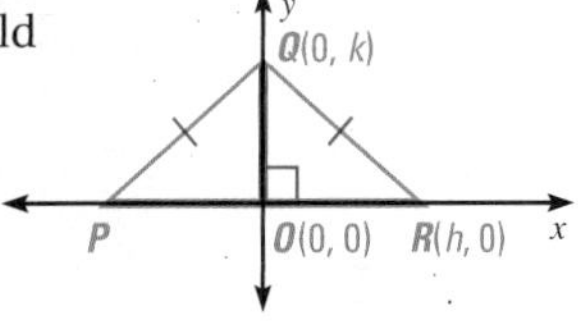

Differentiated Instruction

English Learners Students who are learning English may have difficulty distinguishing between the terms *bisector*, *median*, and *altitude* and between the names for the points where they intersect. On an index card, have students list the terms perpendicular bisector, angle bisector, median, and altitude, and draw a diagram to represent each as well as name the point where the lines intersect.

See also the *Geometry Toolkit* for more strategies.

4.

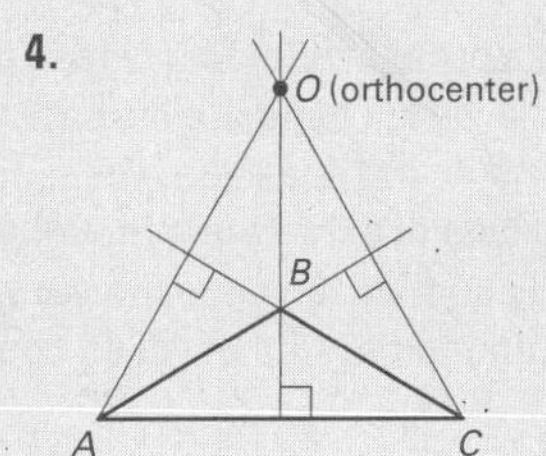

Extra Example 3

Show that the orthocenter can be inside, on, or outside the triangle.

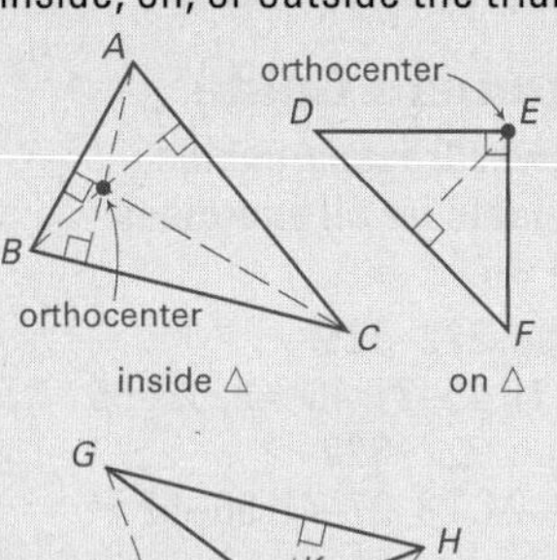

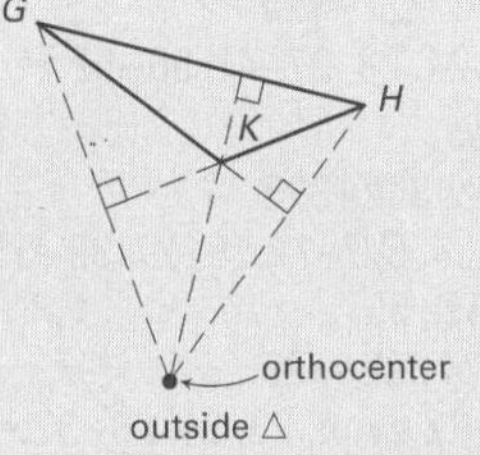

An **Animated Geometry** activity is available on-line for **Example 3**. This activity is also available on the **Power Presentations CD-ROM**.

Extra Example 4

Prove that if an angle bisector of a triangle is also an altitude, then the triangle is isosceles.

Given $\triangle ABC$, with $\overline{BD}$ an angle bisector and altitude to $\overline{AC}$.

Prove $\triangle ABC$ is isosceles.

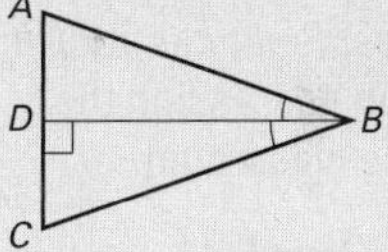

$\overline{BD}$ is an angle bisector and altitude, so $\angle ABD \cong \angle CBD$ and $\overline{BD} \perp \overline{AC}$. Then $\angle ADB$ and $\angle CDB$ are congruent right angles. Since $\overline{BD} \cong \overline{BD}$, $\triangle ABD \cong \triangle CBD$ by ASA. $\overline{AB} \cong \overline{CB}$ since they are corresponding parts of congruent triangles. So $\triangle ABC$ is isosceles.

Closing the Lesson

Have students summarize the major points of the lesson and answer the Essential Question: How do you find the centroid of a triangle?

- **The medians of a triangle intersect at the centroid.**

Find the midpoints of the sides and draw the medians. Locate the point where the medians intersect.

4 PRACTICE AND APPLY

Assignment Guide

Answer Transparencies available for all exercises

Basic:
Day 1: pp. 322–325
Exs. 1–11, 25–27, 46–49, 53–55
Day 2: pp. 322–325
Exs. 12–24, 28, 37–41, 50–52

Average:
Day 1: pp. 322–325
Exs. 1, 2, 4, 5, 7–11, 25–27, 33–35, 46–49, 53–55
Day 2: pp. 322–325
Exs. 12–22 even, 23, 24, 28–32, 37–44, 50–52

Advanced:
Day 1: pp. 322–325
Exs. 1, 2, 5–11, 25–27, 33–35, 46–49, 53–55
Day 2: pp. 322–325
Exs. 12, 14, 15, 21–24, 28–32, 36*, 39–45*, 50–52

Block:
pp. 322–325
Exs. 1, 2, 4, 5, 7–11, 25–27, 33–35, 46–49, 53–55 (with 5.3)
pp. 322–325
Exs. 12–22 even, 23, 24, 28–32, 37–44, 50–52 (with 5.5)

Differentiated Instruction

See *Geometry Best Practices Toolkit* for suggestions on addressing the needs of a diverse classroom.

Homework Check

For a quick check of student understanding of key concepts, go over the following exercises:

Basic: 3, 8, 13, 18, 38
Average: 4, 10, 14, 20, 42
Advanced: 6, 11, 15, 22, 42

Extra Practice

- Student Edition, p. 905
- Chapter 5 Resource Book: Practice levels A, B, C, pp. 51–56

Practice Worksheet

An easily-readable reduced practice page (with answers) for this lesson can be found on p. 292C.

5.4 EXERCISES

HOMEWORK KEY
○ = **WORKED-OUT SOLUTIONS on p. WS6 for Exs. 5, 21, and 39**
★ = **STANDARDIZED TEST PRACTICE Exs. 2, 7, 11, 12, 28, 40, and 44**

SKILL PRACTICE

A

1. VOCABULARY Name the four types of points of concurrency introduced in Lessons 5.2–5.4. When is each type inside the triangle? on the triangle? outside the triangle? **circumcenter: when it is an acute triangle, when it is a right triangle, when it is an obtuse triangle; incenter: always, never, never; centroid: always, never, never; orthocenter: when it is an acute triangle, when it is a right triangle, when it is an obtuse triangle**

2. ★ **WRITING** *Compare* a perpendicular bisector and an altitude of a triangle. *Compare* a perpendicular bisector and a median of a triangle. **See margin.**

EXAMPLE 1 on p. 319 for Exs. 3–7

FINDING LENGTHS **G is the centroid of $\triangle ABC$, $BG = 6$, $AF = 12$, and $AE = 15$. Find the length of the segment.**

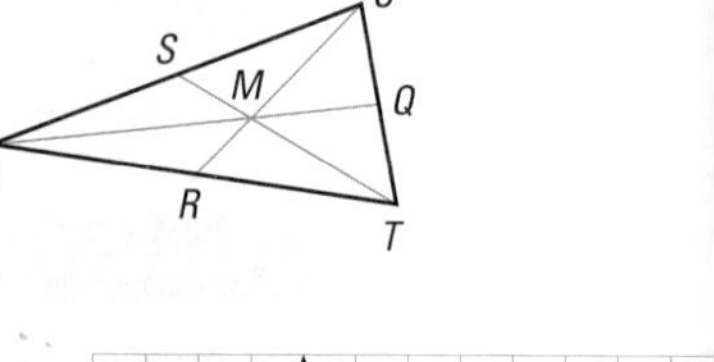

3. $\overline{FC}$ **12**
4. $\overline{BF}$ **9**
5.  $\overline{AG}$ **10**
6. $\overline{GE}$ **5**

7. ★ **MULTIPLE CHOICE** In the diagram, M is the centroid of $\triangle ACT$, $CM = 36$, $MQ = 30$, and $TS = 56$. What is AM? **D**

Ⓐ 15 Ⓑ 30 Ⓒ 36 Ⓓ 60

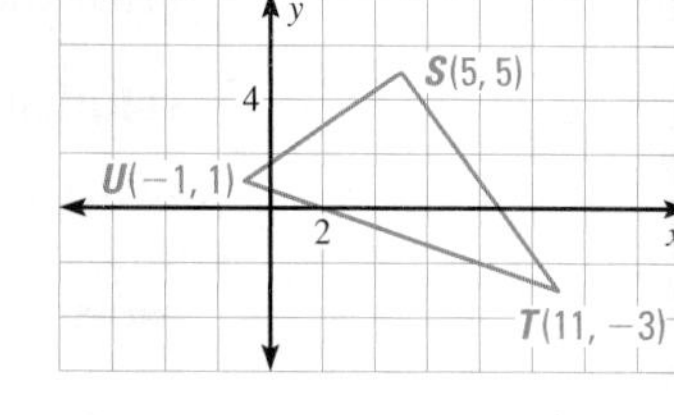

EXAMPLE 2 on p. 320 for Exs. 8–11

8. FINDING A CENTROID Use the graph shown.
   a. Find the coordinates of P, the midpoint of $\overline{ST}$. Use the median $\overline{UP}$ to find the coordinates of the centroid Q. **(8, 1); (5, 1)**
   b. Find the coordinates of R, the midpoint of $\overline{TU}$. Verify that $SQ = \frac{2}{3}SR$. **(5, −1); $SQ = 4$ and $SR = 6$ therefore $SQ = \frac{2}{3}SR$.**

GRAPHING CENTROIDS **Find the coordinates of the centroid P of $\triangle ABC$.**

9. $A(-1, 2)$, $B(5, 6)$, $C(5, -2)$ **(3, 2)**
10. $A(0, 4)$, $B(3, 10)$, $C(6, -2)$ **(3, 4)**

11. ★ **OPEN-ENDED MATH** Draw a large right triangle and find its centroid. **See margin.**

EXAMPLE 3 on p. 321 for Exs. 12–16

12. ★ **OPEN-ENDED MATH** Draw a large obtuse, scalene triangle and find its orthocenter. **See margin.**

IDENTIFYING SEGMENTS **Is $\overline{BD}$ a *perpendicular bisector* of $\triangle ABC$? Is $\overline{BD}$ a *median*? an *altitude*?**

13. 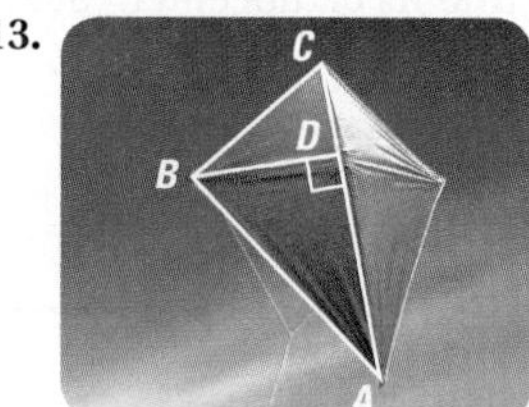

no; no; yes

14. 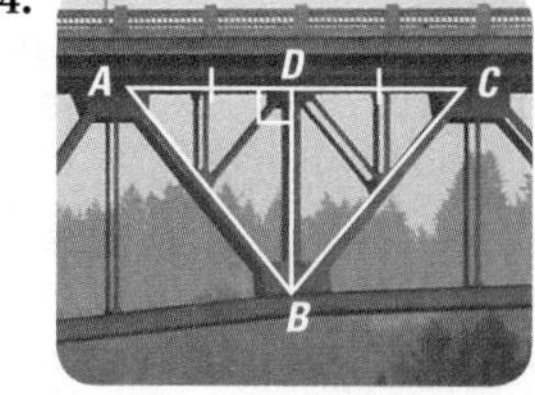

yes; yes; yes

15. 

no; yes; no

2. Both are perpendicular to a side of the triangle although the altitude contains the vertex opposite the side while a perpendicular bisector bisects the side but does not necessarily contain the opposite vertex; both bisect one side of a triangle although the perpendicular bisector does not necessarily contain the opposite vertex while the median is not necessarily perpendicular to the side but does contain the opposite vertex.

11. 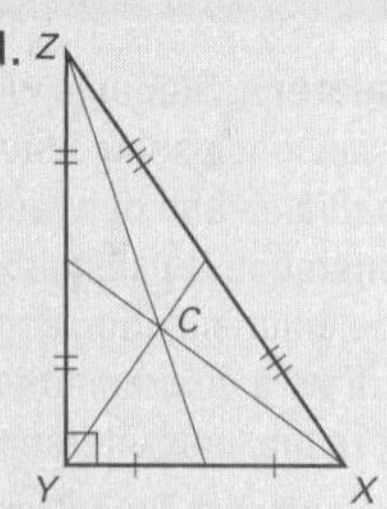

16. **ERROR ANALYSIS** A student uses the fact that T is a point of concurrency to conclude that $NT = \frac{2}{3}NQ$. *Explain* what is wrong with this reasoning.
T is the orthocenter, but the centroid is needed to reach the conclusion.

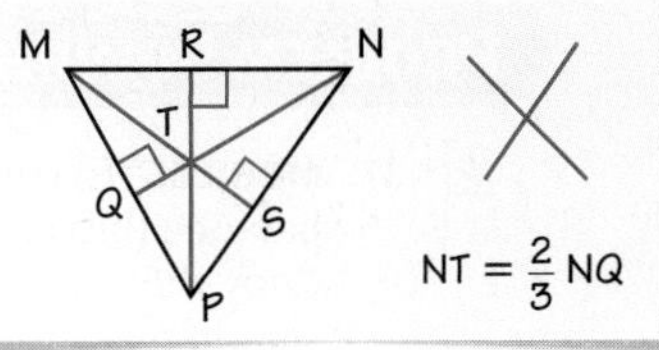

EXAMPLE 4
on p. 321
for Exs. 17–22

REASONING **Use the diagram shown and the given information to decide whether $\overline{YW}$ is a *perpendicular bisector*, an *angle bisector*, a *median*, or an *altitude* of $\triangle XYZ$. There may be more than one right answer.** **20–22. See margin.**

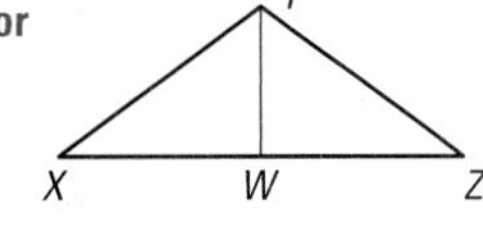

17. $\overline{YW} \perp \overline{XZ}$ **altitude**
18. $\angle XYW \cong \angle ZYW$ **angle bisector**
19. $\overline{XW} \cong \overline{ZW}$ **median**
20. $\overline{YW} \perp \overline{XZ}$ and $\overline{XW} \cong \overline{ZW}$
21. $\triangle XYW \cong \triangle ZYW$
22. $\overline{YW} \perp \overline{XZ}$ and $\overline{XY} \cong \overline{ZY}$

20. perpendicular bisector, angle bisector, median, altitude
21. perpendicular bisector, angle bisector, median, altitude
22. perpendicular bisector, angle bisector, median, altitude

B

ISOSCELES TRIANGLES **Find the measurements. *Explain* your reasoning.**

23. Given that $\overline{DB} \perp \overline{AC}$, find DC and $m\angle ABD$.
6, 22°; $\triangle ABD \cong \triangle CBD$ by HL, use Corr. parts of $\cong \triangle$s are $\cong$.
24. Given that $AD = DC$, find $m\angle ADB$ and $m\angle ABD$.
90°, 22°; $\triangle ABD \cong \triangle CBD$ by SSS, use definition of a linear pair and Corr. parts of $\cong \triangle$s are $\cong$.

RELATING LENGTHS **Copy and complete the statement for $\triangle DEF$ with medians $\overline{DH}$, $\overline{EJ}$, and $\overline{FG}$, and centroid K.**

25. $EJ =$ _?_ KJ **3**
26. $DK =$ _?_ KH **2**
27. $FG =$ _?_ KF $\mathbf{\frac{3}{2}}$

28. ★ **SHORT RESPONSE** Any isosceles triangle can be placed in the coordinate plane with its base on the x-axis and the opposite vertex on the y-axis as in Guided Practice Exercise 6 on page 321. *Explain* why. **If the base angles of the isosceles triangle are placed at $(-a, 0)$ and $(0, a)$, the vertex angle will be on the y-axis.**

CONSTRUCTION **Verify the Concurrency of Altitudes of a Triangle by drawing a triangle of the given type and constructing its altitudes.** (*Hint:* To construct an altitude, use the construction in Exercise 25 on page 195.) **29–31. See margin.**

29. Equilateral triangle
30. Right scalene triangle
31. Obtuse isosceles triangle

32. **VERIFYING THEOREM 5.8** Use Example 2 on page 320. Verify that Theorem 5.8, the Concurrency of Medians of a Triangle, holds for the median from vertex F and for the median from vertex H. **See margin.**

ALGEBRA **Point D is the centroid of $\triangle ABC$. Use the given information to find the value of x.**

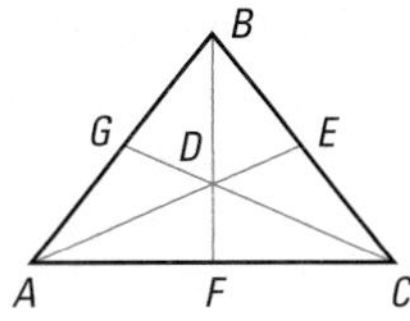

33. $BD = 4x + 5$ and $BF = 9x$ $\mathbf{\frac{5}{2}}$
34. $GD = 2x - 8$ and $GC = 3x + 3$ **9**
35. $AD = 5x$ and $DE = 3x - 2$ **4**

C

36. **CHALLENGE** $\overline{KM}$ is a median of $\triangle JKL$. Find the areas of $\triangle JKM$ and $\triangle LKM$. Compare the areas. Do you think that the two areas will always compare in this way, regardless of the shape of the triangle? *Explain*.
$\mathbf{\frac{9\sqrt{19}}{2}, \frac{9\sqrt{19}}{2}}$**; yes; the height and base of both triangles will always be the same.**

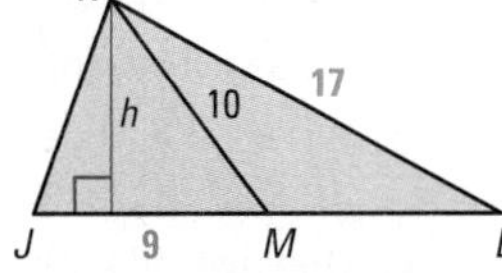

Vocabulary

Exercises 17–22 Have students review the definitions of the terms in italic before they do these exercises.

Avoiding Common Errors

Exercises 25–27 Some students may not be able to visualize the position of a centroid in a triangle. Encourage students to draw and label the centroid for each triangle.

Teaching Strategy

Exercise 36 Because M is a midpoint, the length of the bases of the two triangles are equal. If two triangles have the same base and same altitude to that base, they have the same area. Geometry software can be used to help students see this relationship for this exercise.

29.

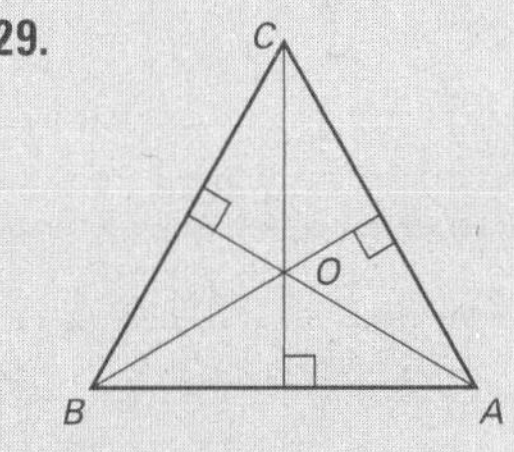

30.

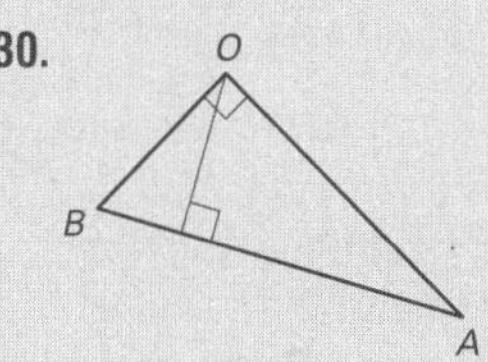

31.

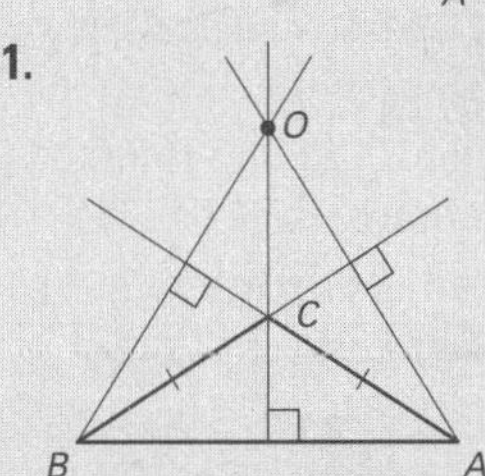

32. ***Sample answer:*** **The midpoint of $\overline{FG}$ is $L(3, 7)$, so the equation of the median from $H(6, 1)$ to $L(3, 7)$ is $y = -2x + 13$. $P(4, 5)$ lies on this median. The midpoint of $\overline{GH}$ is $J(5, 5)$, so the equation of the median from $F(2, 5)$ to $J(5, 5)$ is $y = 5$. $P(4, 5)$ lies on this median, so all three medians intersect at the centroid.**

12.

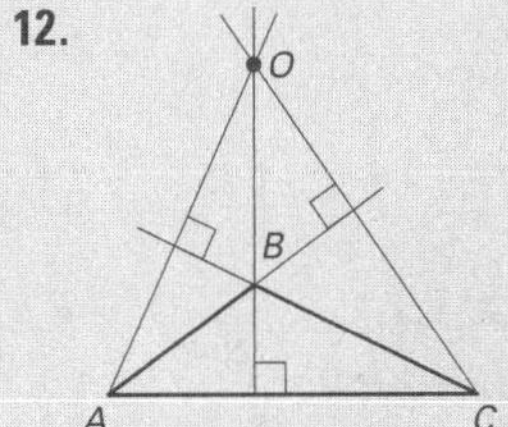

Teaching Strategy

Exercise 41 Students can start by graphing the lines and observing where they intersect. After students solve systems of pairs of the equations to find the exact coordinates of the vertices, they can use the midpoint formula to find equations of the three medians. Finally, students can solve a system for any two of the medians to find the centroid.

38. *Sample:*

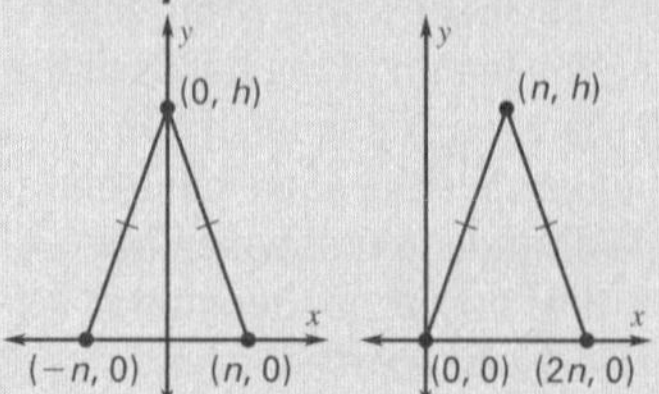

41.

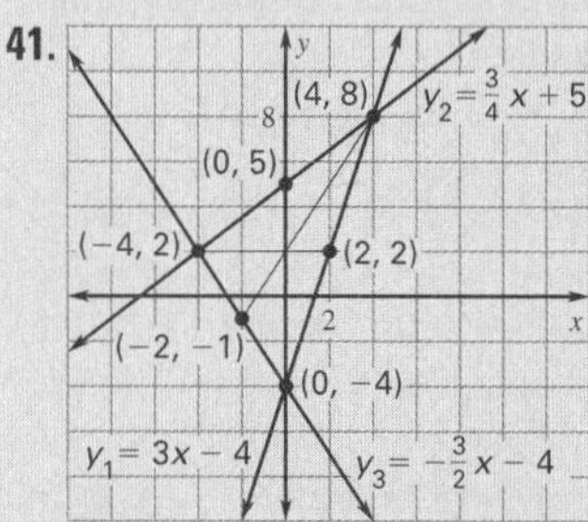

42a. Statements (Reasons)

1. $\triangle ABC$ is equilateral, $\overline{BD}$ is an altitude of $\triangle ABC$. (Given)
2. $\overline{AB} \cong \overline{BC}$ (Definition of equilateral triangle)
3. $\overline{BD} \cong \overline{BD}$ (Reflexive Property of Segment Congruence)
4. $\angle ADB$ and $\angle CDB$ are right angles. (Definition of altitude)
5. $\triangle ABD$ and $\triangle CBD$ are right triangles. (Definition of right triangle)
6. $\triangle ABD \cong \triangle CBD$ (HL)
7. $\overline{AD} \cong \overline{CD}$ (Corr. parts of $\cong$ △ are $\cong$.)
8. $AD = CD$ (Definition of congruent segments)
9. $\overline{BD}$ is a perpendicular bisector of $\overline{AC}$. (Definition of perpendicular bisector)

PROBLEM SOLVING

A **37. MOBILES** To complete the mobile, you need to balance the red triangle on the tip of a metal rod. Copy the triangle and decide if you should place the rod at *A* or *B*. *Explain.*

for problem solving help at classzone.com

B; it is the centroid of the triangle.

38. DEVELOPING PROOF Show two different ways that you can place an isosceles triangle with base $2n$ and height h on the coordinate plane. Label the coordinates for each vertex. **See margin.**

@HomeTutor for problem solving help at classzone.com

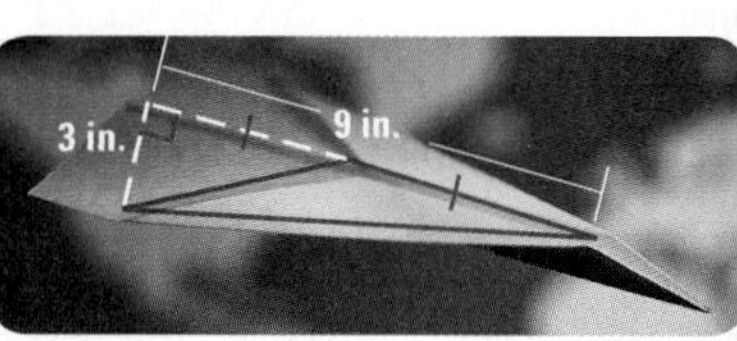

(39.) PAPER AIRPLANE Find the area of the triangular part of the paper airplane wing that is outlined in red. Which special segment of the triangle did you use?
6.75 in.^{2}; median

B **40. ★ SHORT RESPONSE** In what type(s) of triangle can a vertex of the triangle be one of the points of concurrency of the triangle? *Explain.*
Right; the orthocenter is on the right angle.

41. COORDINATE GEOMETRY Graph the lines on the same coordinate plane and find the centroid of the triangle formed by their intersections.
(0, 2); see margin for art.

$y_1 = 3x - 4$ $\quad$ $y_2 = \frac{3}{4}x + 5$ $\quad$ $y_3 = -\frac{3}{2}x - 4$

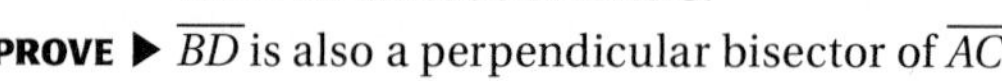

EXAMPLE 4 on p. 321 for Ex. 42

42. PROOF Write proofs using different methods. **See margin.**

GIVEN ▶ $\triangle ABC$ is equilateral. $\overline{BD}$ is an altitude of $\triangle ABC$.

PROVE ▶ $\overline{BD}$ is also a perpendicular bisector of $\overline{AC}$.

a. Write a proof using congruent triangles.

b. Write a proof using the Perpendicular Postulate on page 148.

43. TECHNOLOGY Use geometry drawing software.

a. Construct a triangle and its medians. Measure the areas of the blue, green, and red triangles. **Check students' work.**

b. What do you notice about the triangles? **Their areas are the same.**

c. If a triangle is of uniform thickness, what can you conclude about the weight of the three interior triangles? How does this support the idea that a triangle will balance on its centroid?

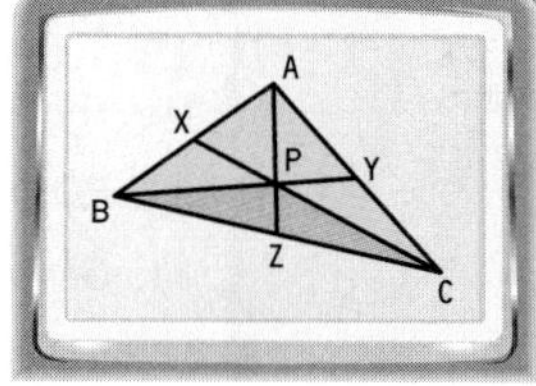

They weigh the same; it means the weight of $\triangle ABC$ is evenly distributed around its centroid.

44. ★ EXTENDED RESPONSE Use $P(0, 0)$, $Q(8, 12)$, and $R(14, 0)$.

a. What is the slope of the altitude from R to $\overline{PQ}$? $-\frac{2}{3}$

b. Write an equation for each altitude of $\triangle PQR$. Find the orthocenter by finding the ordered pair that is a solution of the three equations. **$y = \frac{1}{2}x$, $x = 8$, $y = -\frac{2}{3}x + \frac{28}{3}$; (8, 4)**

c. How would your steps change if you were finding the circumcenter? **Find the equation of each perpendicular bisector of each side and solve the system.**

○ = WORKED-OUT SOLUTIONS on p. WS1 $\quad$ ★ = STANDARDIZED TEST PRACTICE

42b. Statements (Reasons)

1. $\triangle ABC$ is equilateral. (Given)
2. $BA = BC$ (Definition of equilateral triangle)
3. $\overline{BD} \perp \overline{AC}$ (Definition of altitude)
4. B is on the perpendicular bisector of $\overline{AC}$. (Converse of the Perpendicular Bisector Theorem)
5. Only one line exists through B perpendicular to $\overline{AC}$, so the perpendicular bisector and the altitude are contained in the same line. (Perpendicular Postulate)

C **45. CHALLENGE** Prove the results in parts (a) – (c). **See margin.**

GIVEN ▶ $\overline{LP}$ and $\overline{MQ}$ are medians of scalene $\triangle LMN$. Point R is on $\overrightarrow{LP}$ such that $\overline{LP} \cong \overline{PR}$. Point S is on $\overrightarrow{MQ}$ such that $\overline{MQ} \cong \overline{QS}$.

PROVE ▶ **a.** $\overline{NS} \cong \overline{NR}$

b. $\overline{NS}$ and $\overline{NR}$ are both parallel to $\overline{LM}$.

c. R, N, and S are collinear.

MIXED REVIEW

In Exercises 46–48, write an equation of the line that passes through points *A* and *B*. *(p. 180)*

46. $A(0, 7), B(1, 10)$ **$y = 3x + 7$**

47. $A(4, -8), B(-2, -5)$ **$y = -\frac{1}{2}x - 6$**

48. $A(5, -21), B(0, 4)$ **$y = -5x + 4$**

49. In the diagram, $\triangle JKL \cong \triangle RST$. Find the value of x. *(p. 225)* **23**

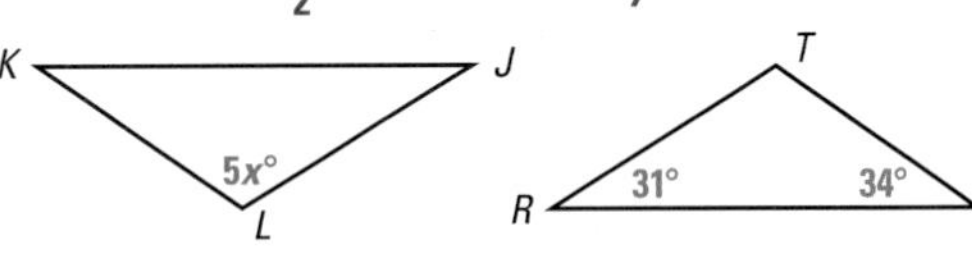

PREVIEW Prepare for Lesson 5.5 in Exs. 50–52.

Solve the inequality. *(p. 287)*

50. $2x + 13 < 35$ **$x < 11$**

51. $12 > -3x - 6$ **$x > -6$**

52. $6x < x + 20$ **$x < 4$**

In the diagram, $\overleftrightarrow{LM}$ is the perpendicular bisector of $\overline{PN}$. *(p. 303)*

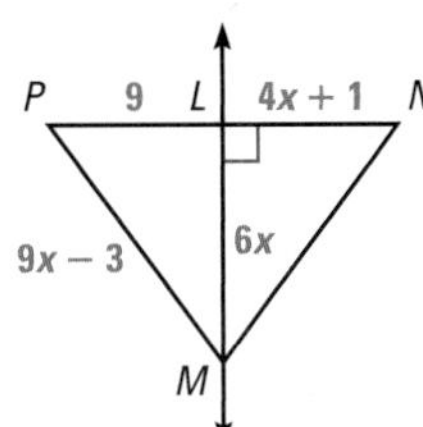

53. What segment lengths are equal?

54. What is the value of x? **2**

55. Find MN. **15**

53. *LP* and *LN*, *PM* and *NM*

QUIZ for Lessons 5.3–5.4

Find the value of x. Identify the theorem used to find the answer. *(p. 310)*

1.

3x − 4

2x + 6

10; Angle Bisector Theorem

2.

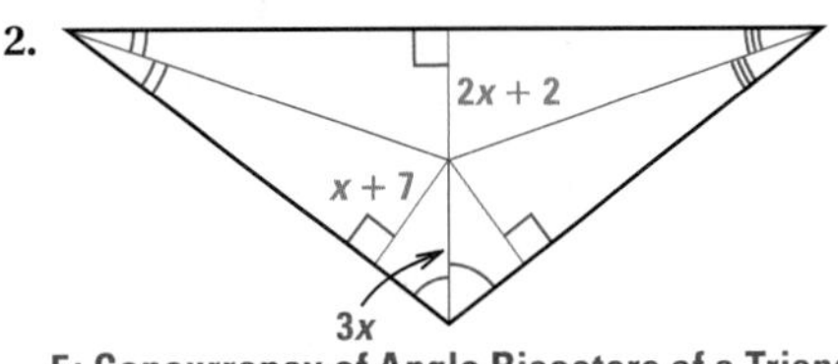

5; Concurrency of Angle Bisectors of a Triangle

In the figure, P is the centroid of $\triangle XYZ$, $YP = 12$, $LX = 15$, and $LZ = 18$. *(p. 319)*

3. Find the length of $\overline{LY}$. **15**

4. Find the length of $\overline{YN}$. **18**

5. Find the length of $\overline{LP}$. **6**

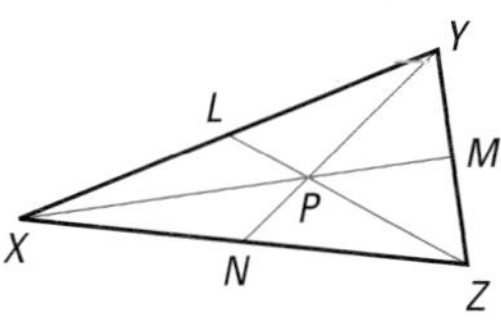

5 ASSESS AND RETEACH

Daily Homework Quiz

Transparency Available

For Exercises 1–3, use the diagram below. G is the centroid of $\triangle ABC$.

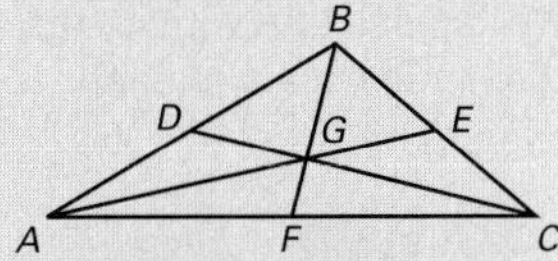

1. If $BG = 9$, find BF. **13.5**

2. If $BD = 12$, find AD. **12**

3. If $CD = 27$, find GC. **18**

4. Find the centroid of $\triangle ABC$. **(1, 1)**

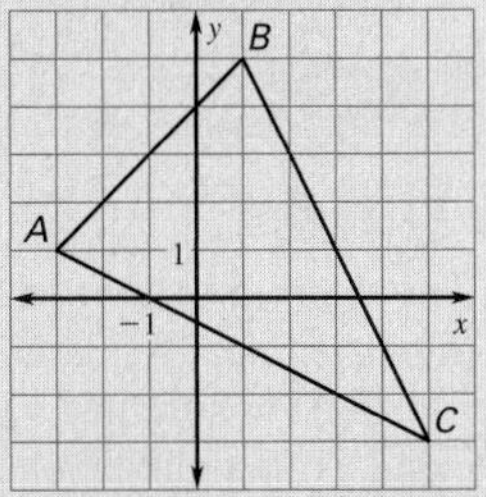

5. Which type of triangle has its orthocenter on the triangle? **a right triangle**

 **Online Quiz**

Available at **classzone.com**

Diagnosis/Remediation

- Practice A, B, C in Chapter 5 Resource Book, pp. 51–56
- Study Guide in Chapter 5 Resource Book, pp. 57–58
- Practice Workbook, pp. 94–96
- @HomeTutor

Challenge

Additional challenge is available in the Chapter 5 Resource Book, p. 61.

Quiz

An easily-readable reduced copy of the quiz (with answers) on Lessons 5.3–5.4 from the Assessment Book can be found on p. 292F.

45a–c. See Additional Answers beginning on p. AA1.

1 PLAN AND PREPARE

Learn the Method

- Students will draw the perpendicular bisectors, medians, and altitudes of a triangle.
- Students can use this activity to verify the concurrency of each type of segment.

Keystroke Help

Keystrokes for several models of calculators are available in blackline format in the *Chapter 5 Resource Book.*

2 TEACH

Tips for Success

Have students experiment with different types of triangles. Ask them to drag the vertices to see that points *D*, *E*, and *F* remain collinear.

Alternative Strategy

You may want to do this activity as a demonstration. Have students write conclusions in their notebooks and share them with the class.

Extra Example 1

Draw the perpendicular bisectors of a triangle. Label the point of concurrency *D*. Hide the lines.

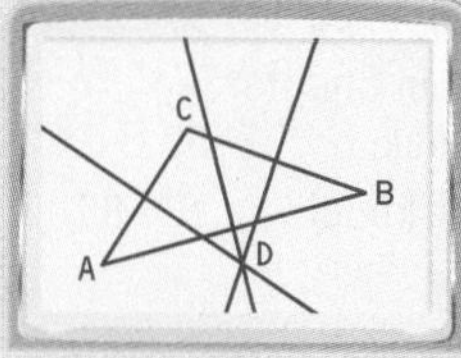

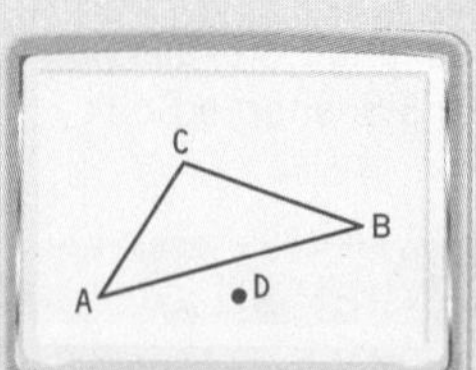

5.4 Investigate Points of Concurrency

MATERIALS • graphing calculator or computer

Standards

Enrichment Topic; not required by California Standards.

QUESTION How are the points of concurrency in a triangle related?

You can use geometry drawing software to investigate concurrency.

EXAMPLE 1 Draw the perpendicular bisectors of a triangle

STEP 1

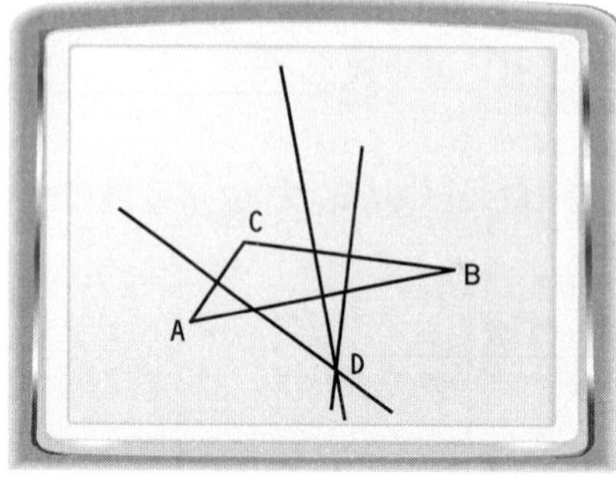

Draw perpendicular bisectors Draw a line perpendicular to each side of a $\triangle ABC$ at the midpoint. Label the point of concurrency *D*.

STEP 2

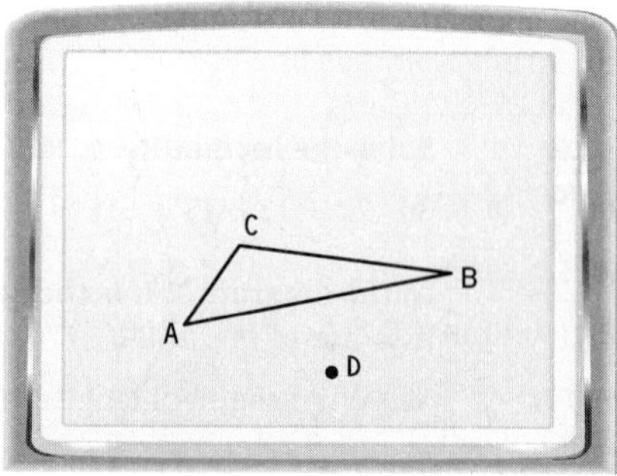

Hide the lines Use the *HIDE* feature to hide the perpendicular bisectors. Save as "EXAMPLE1."

EXAMPLE 2 Draw the medians of the triangle

STEP 1

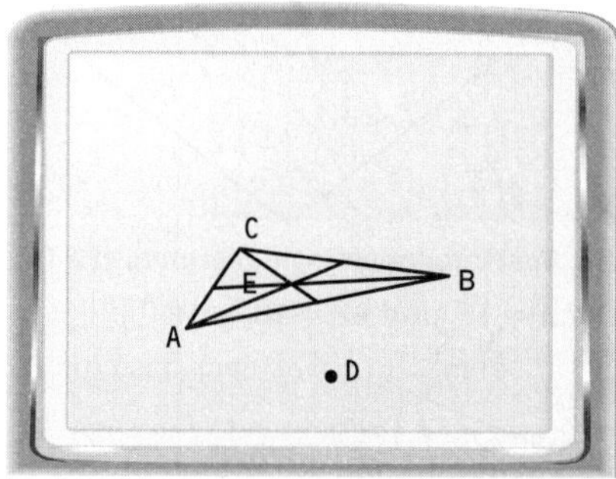

Draw medians Start with the figure you saved as "EXAMPLE1." Draw the medians of $\triangle ABC$. Label the point of concurrency *E*.

STEP 2

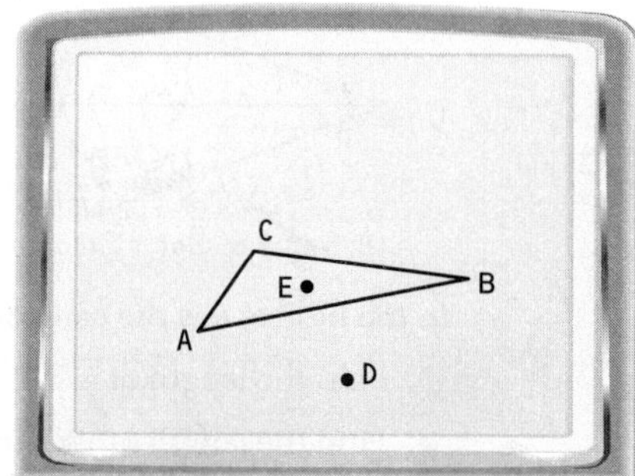

Hide the lines Use the *HIDE* feature to hide the medians. Save as "EXAMPLE2."

@HomeTutor
classzone.com
Keystrokes

EXAMPLE 3 Draw the altitudes of the triangle

STEP 1

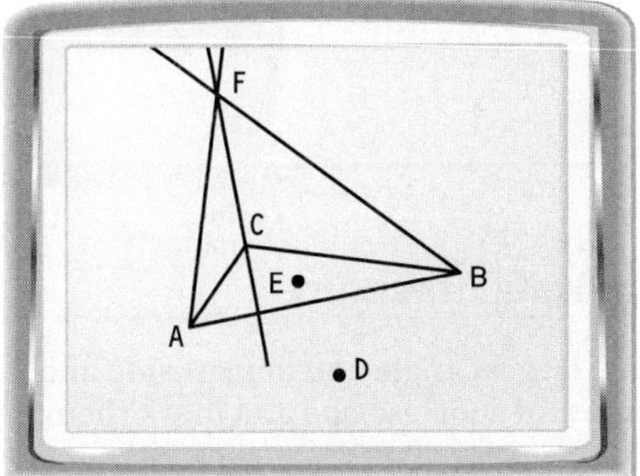

Draw altitudes Start with the figure you saved as "EXAMPLE2." Draw the altitudes of $\triangle ABC$. Label the point of concurrency F.

STEP 2

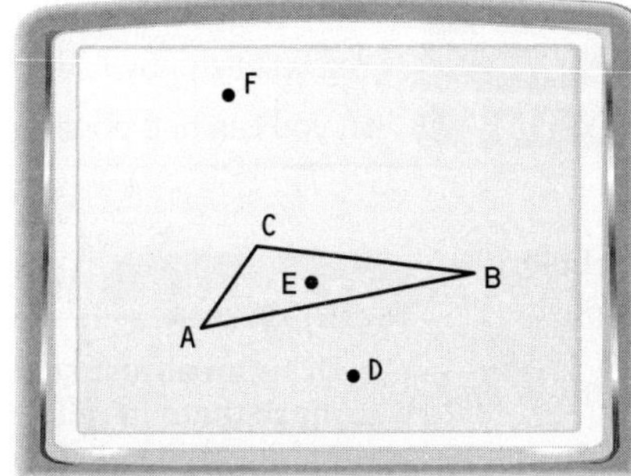

Hide the lines Use the *HIDE* feature to hide the altitudes. Save as "EXAMPLE3."

PRACTICE

1. Try to draw a line through points D, E, and F. Are the points collinear? **yes**
2. Try dragging point A. Do points D, E, and F remain collinear? **yes**

In Exercises 3–5, use the triangle you saved as "EXAMPLE3."

3. Draw the angle bisectors. Label the point of concurrency as point G. **See margin.**
4. How does point G relate to points D, E, and F? **It is not collinear to all three points.**
5. Try dragging point A. What do you notice about points D, E, F, and G? **D, E, and F remain collinear; G is not collinear.**

DRAW CONCLUSIONS

In 1765, Leonhard Euler (pronounced "oi′-ler") proved that the circumcenter, the centroid, and the orthocenter are all collinear. The line containing these three points is called *Euler's line*. Save the triangle from Exercise 5 as "EULER" and use that for Exercises 6–8.

6. Try moving the triangle's vertices. Can you verify that the same three points lie on Euler's line whatever the shape of the triangle? *Explain.*

6. Yes. *Sample answer:* After changing the shape of the triangle identify the circumcenter, centroid, and orthocenter to see that they remain collinear.

7. Notice that some of the four points can be outside of the triangle. Which points lie outside the triangle? Why? What happens when you change the shape of the triangle? Are there any points that never lie outside the triangle? Why? **See margin.**
8. Draw the three midsegments of the triangle. Which, if any, of the points seem contained in the triangle formed by the midsegments? Do those points stay there when the shape of the large triangle is changed? **Centroid, incenter; yes; see margin for art.**

Extra Example 2

Draw the medians of the triangle. Label the point of concurrency E. Hide the lines.

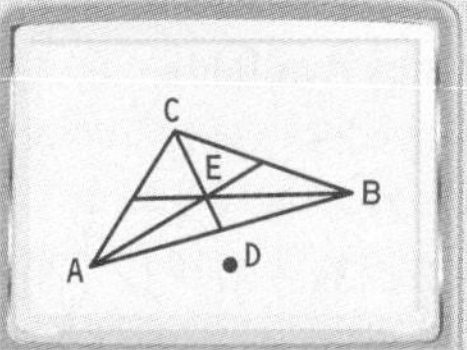

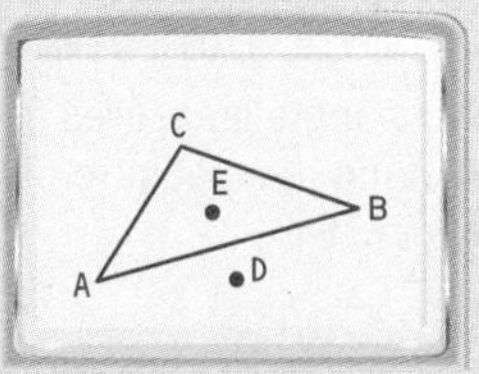

Extra Example 3

Draw the altitudes of the triangle. Label the point of concurrency F. Hide the lines.

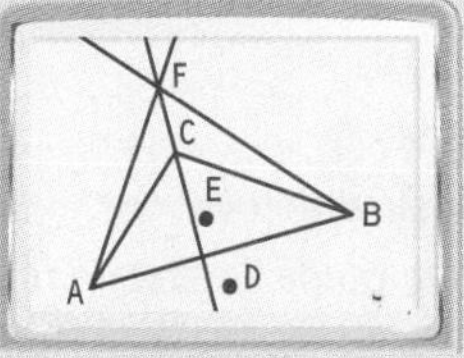

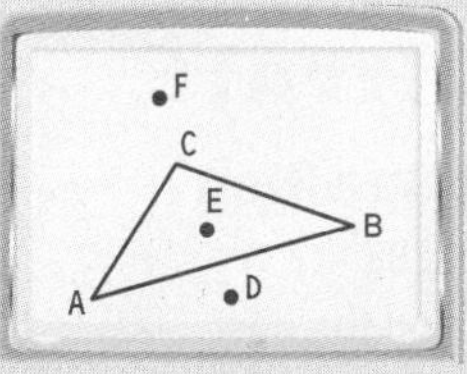

3 ASSESS AND RETEACH

1. Describe the position of the points of the Euler line for each type of triangle.
   a. acute isosceles triangle **the same as the altitude to the base**
   b. isosceles right triangle **the same as the altitude to the hypotenuse**

3. $\bullet F$

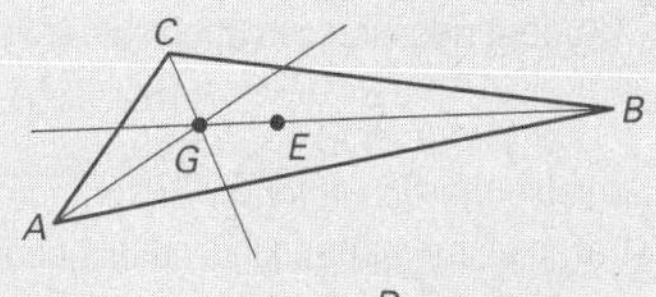

7. *Sample answer:* The circumcenter or orthocenter; the triangle is obtuse; if the triangle is acute, the circumcenter and orthocenter are inside. If the triangle is a right triangle, the circumcenter and orthocenter are on it. If the triangle is obtuse, the circumcenter and orthocenter are outside; the incenter and centroid; the medians and angle bisectors will always intersect in the interior of the triangle.

8. C B A

1 PLAN AND PREPARE

Warm-Up Exercises

Transparency Available

1. Solve $3x + 8 < 29$. $x < 7$
2. Solve $15 > -2x - 9$. $x > -12$
3. Solve $2x - 2 < (3x - 4) + (x - 8)$. $x > 5$
4. Find all integer solutions for $4 < x < 11$. **5, 6, 7, 8, 9, 10**
5. A triangle has angle measures 82° and 34°. Find the measure of the third angle. **64°**

Notetaking Guide

Transparency Available

Promotes interactive learning and notetaking skills, pp. 132–134.

Pacing

Basic: 1 day
Average: 1 day
Advanced: 1 day
Block: 0.5 block with 5.4
- See *Teaching Guide/Lesson Plan.*

2 FOCUS AND MOTIVATE

Essential Question

Big Idea 2, p. 293

How do you find the possible lengths of the third side of a triangle if you know the lengths of two sides? **Tell students they will learn how to answer this question by applying the Triangle Inequality Theorem.**

5.5 Use Inequalities in a Triangle

Before You found what combinations of angles are possible in a triangle.
Now You will find possible side lengths of a triangle.
Why? So you can find possible distances, as in Ex. 39.

Key Vocabulary
- **side opposite,** *p. 241*
- **inequality,** *p. 876*

Standards

6.0 Students know and are able to use the triangle inequality theorem.

12.0 Students find and use measures of sides and of interior and exterior **angles of triangles** and polygons **to classify figures and solve problems.**

EXAMPLE 1 Relate side length and angle measure

Draw an obtuse scalene triangle. Find the largest angle and longest side and mark them in red. Find the smallest angle and shortest side and mark them in blue. What do you notice?

Solution

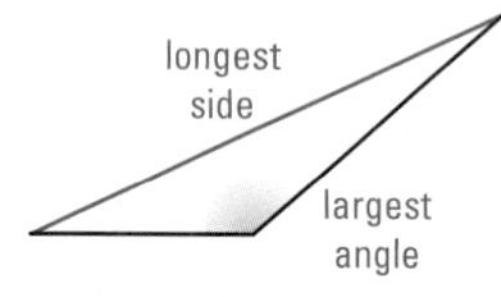

The longest side and largest angle are opposite each other.

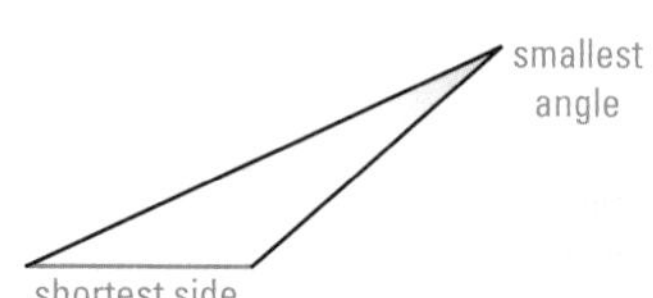

The shortest side and smallest angle are opposite each other.

The relationships in Example 1 are true for all triangles as stated in the two theorems below. These relationships can help you to decide whether a particular arrangement of side lengths and angle measures in a triangle may be possible.

AVOID ERRORS
Be careful not to confuse the symbol ∠ meaning *angle* with the symbol < meaning *is less than.* Notice that the bottom edge of the angle symbol is horizontal.

THEOREMS *For Your Notebook*

THEOREM 5.10

If one side of a triangle is longer than another side, then the angle opposite the longer side is larger than the angle opposite the shorter side.

Proof: p. 329

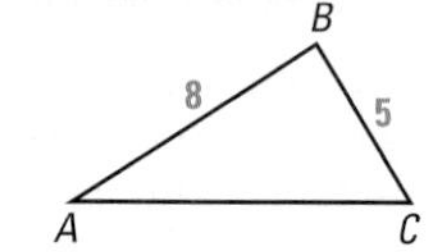

$AB > BC$, so $m\angle C > m\angle A$.

THEOREM 5.11

If one angle of a triangle is larger than another angle, then the side opposite the larger angle is longer than the side opposite the smaller angle.

Proof: Ex. 24, p. 340

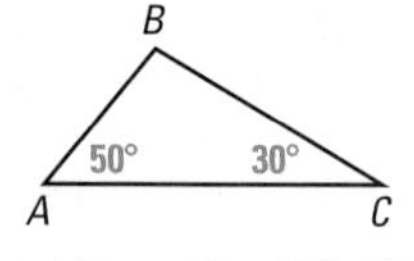

$m\angle A > m\angle C$, so $BC > AB$.

Resource Planning Guide

Chapter Resource Book
- Teaching Guide/Lesson Plan (pp. 62–63)
- Activity Master (p. 64)
- Practice levels A, B, C (pp. 66–71)
- Study Guide (pp. 72–73)
- Catch-up for Absent Students (p. 74)
- Application (p. 75)
- Challenge (p. 76)

Workbooks
- Notetaking Guide (pp. 132–134)
- Practice Workbook (pp. 97–99)

Teaching Options
- **Power Presentations CD-ROM** provides dynamic electronic teaching resources for the classroom.
- **Activity Generator CD-ROM** provides editable activities for all ability levels.

Interactive Technology
- Easy Planner
- Power Presentations CD-ROM
- Activity Generator CD-ROM
- Animated Geometry
- Test Generator CD-ROM
- Online Quiz
- eWorkbook
- eEdition
- @HomeTutor

Resources for English Learners
- Quick Reference for English Learners
- Spanish Study Guide
- Multi-Language Visual Glossary
- Student Resources in Spanish

See also the *Geometry Toolkit* for more strategies for meeting individual needs.

EXAMPLE 2 Standardized Test Practice

STAGE PROP You are constructing a stage prop that shows a large triangular mountain. The bottom edge of the mountain is about 27 feet long, the left slope is about 24 feet long, and the right slope is about 20 feet long. You are told that one of the angles is about 46° and one is about 59°. What is the angle measure of the peak of the mountain?

Ⓐ 46° Ⓑ 59° Ⓒ 75° Ⓓ 85°

ELIMINATE CHOICES
You can eliminate choice D because a triangle with a 46° angle and a 59° angle cannot have an 85° angle. The sum of the three angles in a triangle must be 180°, but the sum of 46, 59, and 85 is 190, not 180.

Solution

Draw a diagram and label the side lengths. The peak angle is opposite the longest side so, by Theorem 5.10, the peak angle is the largest angle.

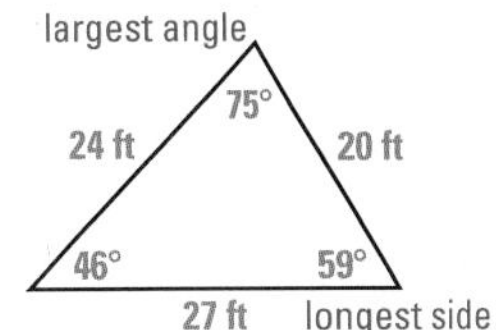

The angle measures sum is 180°, so the third angle measure is $180° - (46° + 59°) = 75°$. You can now label the angle measures in your diagram.

▶ The greatest angle measure is 75°, so the correct answer is C. Ⓐ Ⓑ Ⓒ Ⓓ

GUIDED PRACTICE for Examples 1 and 2

1. List the sides of $\triangle RST$ in order from shortest to longest. **$\overline{ST}$, $\overline{RS}$, $\overline{TR}$**

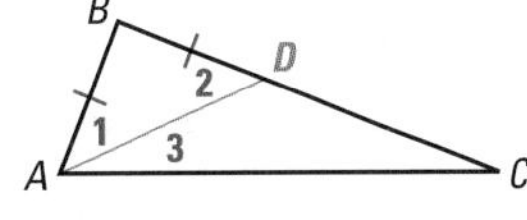

2. Another stage prop is a right triangle with sides that are 6, 8, and 10 feet long and angles of 90°, about 37°, and about 53°. Sketch and label a diagram with the shortest side on the bottom and the right angle at the left. **See margin.**

PROOF Theorem 5.10

GIVEN ▶ $BC > AB$
PROVE ▶ $m\angle BAC > m\angle C$

Locate a point D on $\overline{BC}$ such that $DB = BA$. Then draw $\overline{AD}$. In the isosceles triangle $\triangle ABD$, $\angle 1 \cong \angle 2$.

Because $m\angle BAC = m\angle 1 + m\angle 3$, it follows that $m\angle BAC > m\angle 1$. Substituting $m\angle 2$ for $m\angle 1$ produces $m\angle BAC > m\angle 2$.

By the Exterior Angle Theorem, $m\angle 2 = m\angle 3 + m\angle C$, so it follows that $m\angle 2 > m\angle C$ (see Exercise 27, page 332). Finally, because $m\angle BAC > m\angle 2$ and $m\angle 2 > m\angle C$, you can conclude that $m\angle BAC > m\angle C$.

Motivating the Lesson

Give each student three straws of various lengths, some of which form triangles and some of which do not. Have students investigate when three straws can form a triangle, and when then cannot. Tell students that they will describe and examine this property in this lesson.

3 TEACH

Extra Example 1

Draw an acute scalene triangle. Find and label the largest angle and the longest side. Find and label the smallest angle and shortest side. What do you notice? **The longest side and largest angle are opposite each other. The shortest side and smallest angle are opposite each other.**

Extra Example 2

Three wooden beams will be nailed together to form a brace for a wall. The bottom edge of the brace is about 8 feet, and the sides are about 12 feet and 14 feet. One of the angles measures about 86° and the other measures about 35°. What is the angle measure opposite the largest side of the brace? **C**

Ⓐ 35° Ⓑ 59°
Ⓒ 86° Ⓓ 96°

Key Question to Ask for Example 2

- How do you know that the greatest angle is opposite the 27 foot edge? **The 27 ft edge is the longest side.**

2.

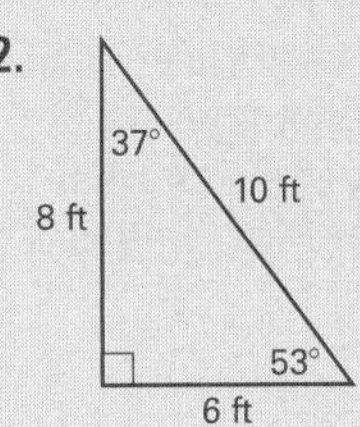

An **Animated Geometry** activity is available on-line for the **Triangle Inequality**. This activity is also available on the **Power Presentations CD-ROM**.

Extra Example 3

A triangle has one side of length 11 and another of length 6. Describe the possible lengths of the third side. **greater than 5 and less than 17**

Key Questions to Ask for Example 3

- Can the third side have a length of 21? **no**
- Can the third side have a length of 5.5? **yes**

Teaching Strategy

It is important that students know how to interpret the compound inequality $4 < x < 20$ in the solution of Example 3. Emphasize that it is a shorter way to write the two inequalities $x > 4$ and $x < 20$.

Closing the Lesson

Have students summarize the major points of the lesson and answer the Essential Question: How do you find the possible lengths of the third side of a triangle if you know the lengths of two sides?

- **In a triangle, the largest angle is opposite the longest side and the smallest angle is opposite the shortest side.**
- **The sum of the lengths of any two sides of a triangle is greater than the length of the third side.**

The length of the third side can be any value greater than the difference of the two lengths and less than the sum of the two lengths.

THE TRIANGLE INEQUALITY Not every group of three segments can be used to form a triangle. The lengths of the segments must fit a certain relationship.

For example, three attempted triangle constructions for sides with given lengths are shown below. Only the first set of side lengths forms a triangle.

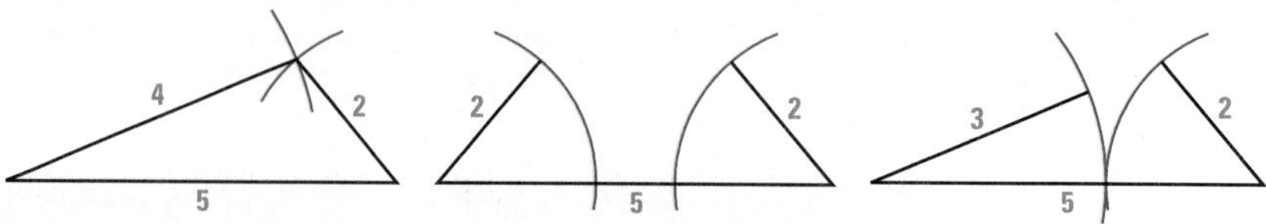

If you start with the longest side and attach the other two sides at its endpoints, you can see that the other two sides are not long enough to form a triangle in the second and third figures. This leads to the *Triangle Inequality Theorem.*

Animated Geometry at classzone.com

THEOREM *For Your Notebook*

THEOREM 5.12 Triangle Inequality Theorem

The sum of the lengths of any two sides of a triangle is greater than the length of the third side.

$AB + BC > AC$ $AC + BC > AB$ $AB + AC > BC$

Proof: Ex. 47, p. 334

EXAMPLE 3 Find possible side lengths

ALGEBRA A triangle has one side of length 12 and another of length 8. Describe the possible lengths of the third side.

Solution

Let x represent the length of the third side. Draw diagrams to help visualize the small and large values of x. Then use the Triangle Inequality Theorem to write and solve inequalities.

USE SYMBOLS
You can combine the two inequalities, $x > 4$ and $x < 20$, to write the compound inequality $4 < x < 20$. This can be read as *x is between 4 and 20.*

Small values of x | **Large values of x**

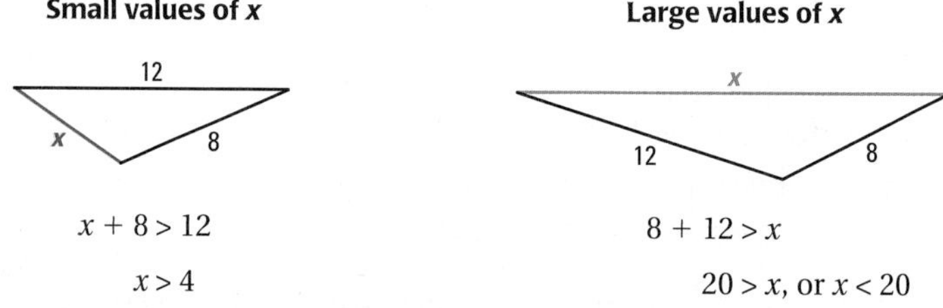

$x + 8 > 12$ | $8 + 12 > x$

$x > 4$ | $20 > x$, or $x < 20$

▶ The length of the third side must be greater than 4 and less than 20.

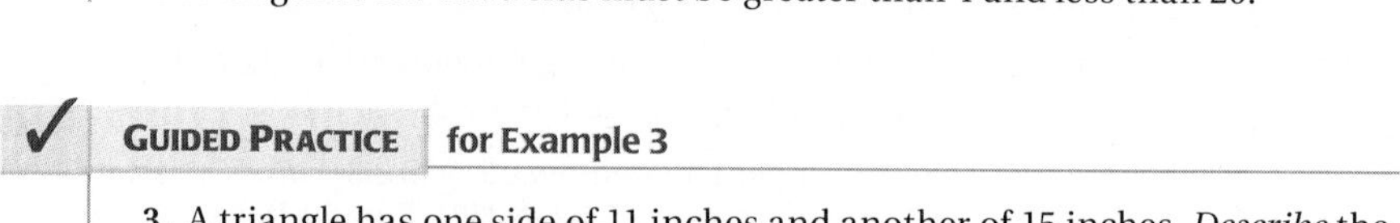

GUIDED PRACTICE for Example 3

3. A triangle has one side of 11 inches and another of 15 inches. *Describe* the possible lengths of the third side. **$4 < x < 26$**

Differentiated Instruction

Below Level Give students a number of straws and ask them to cut them into various lengths. Then have them measure each length. Ask them to make a table listing the measures of many possible combinations of the three lengths. Then have them manipulate the straws to see if they can form a triangle. Highlight sets of three measurements that do not form a triangle.

See also the *Geometry Toolkit* for more strategies.

5.5 EXERCISES

HOMEWORK KEY ○ = **WORKED-OUT SOLUTIONS** on p. WS6 for Exs. 9, 17, and 39
★ = **STANDARDIZED TEST PRACTICE** Exs. 2, 12, 20, 30, 39, and 45

SKILL PRACTICE

A

1. **VOCABULARY** Use the diagram at the right. For each angle, name the side that is *opposite* that angle. **∠A, $\overline{BC}$; ∠B, $\overline{CA}$; ∠C, $\overline{AB}$**

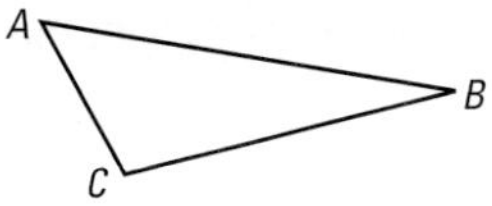

2. ★ **WRITING** How can you tell from the angle measures of a triangle which side of the triangle is the longest? the shortest?
It is opposite the largest angle; it is opposite the smallest angle.

EXAMPLE 1 on p. 328 for Exs. 3–5

MEASURING **Use a ruler and protractor to draw the given type of triangle. Mark the largest angle and longest side in red and the smallest angle and shortest side in blue. What do you notice?** **3–5. See margin.**

3. Acute scalene
4. Right scalene
5. Obtuse isosceles

EXAMPLE 2 on p. 329 for Exs. 6–15

WRITING MEASUREMENTS IN ORDER **List the sides and the angles in order from smallest to largest.**

6. 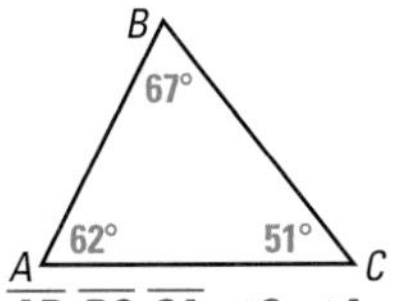

$\overline{AB}$, $\overline{BC}$, $\overline{CA}$; ∠C, ∠A, ∠B

7. 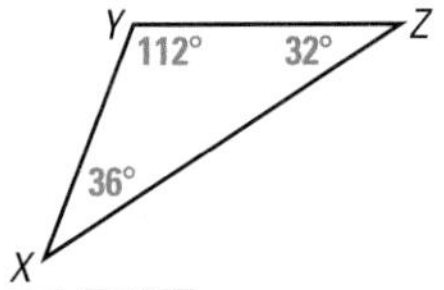

$\overline{XY}$, $\overline{YZ}$, $\overline{ZX}$; ∠Z, ∠X, ∠Y

8. 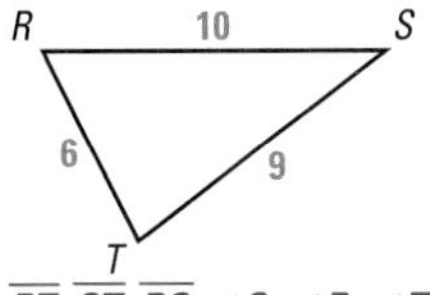

$\overline{RT}$, $\overline{ST}$, $\overline{RS}$; ∠S, ∠R, ∠T

(9.) 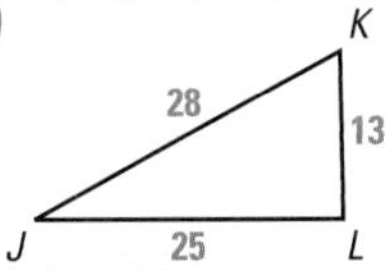

$\overline{KL}$, $\overline{JL}$, $\overline{JK}$; ∠J, ∠K, ∠L

10. 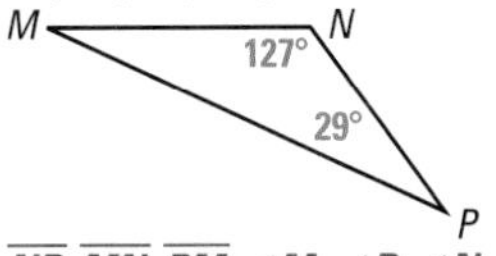

$\overline{NP}$, $\overline{MN}$, $\overline{PM}$; ∠M, ∠P, ∠N

11. 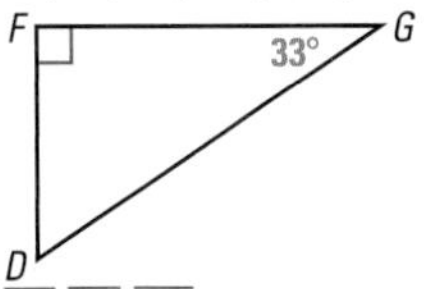

$\overline{DF}$, $\overline{FG}$, $\overline{GD}$; ∠G, ∠D, ∠F

12. ★ **MULTIPLE CHOICE** In △*RST*, which is a possible side length for *ST*? **C**

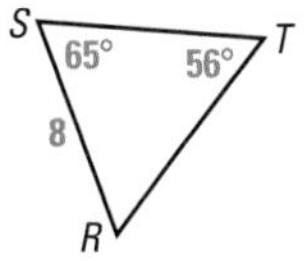

Ⓐ 7 Ⓑ 8

Ⓒ 9 Ⓓ Cannot be determined

DRAWING TRIANGLES **Sketch and label the triangle described.** **13–15. See margin.**

13. Side lengths: about 3 m, 7 m, and 9 m, with longest side on the bottom
Angle measures: 16°, 41°, and 123°, with smallest angle at the left

14. Side lengths: 37 ft, 35 ft, and 12 ft, with shortest side at the right
Angle measures: about 71°, about 19°, and 90°, with right angle at the top

15. Side lengths: 11 in., 13 in., and 14 in., with middle-length side at the left
Two angle measures: about 48° and 71°, with largest angle at the top

EXAMPLE 3 on p. 330 for Exs. 16–26

IDENTIFYING POSSIBLE TRIANGLES **Is it possible to construct a triangle with the given side lengths? If not, *explain* why not.**

16. 6, 7, 11 **yes**
(17.) 3, 6, 9 **No; 3 + 6 is not greater than 9.**
18. 28, 34, 39 **yes**
19. 35, 120, 125 **yes**

4 PRACTICE AND APPLY

Assignment Guide

Answer Transparencies available for all exercises

Basic:
Day 1: pp. 331–334
Exs. 1–9, 12–17, 20–28, 37–42, 49–53 odd

Average:
Day 1: pp. 331–334
Exs. 1–5, 7–9, 12–15, 17, 18, 20–26 even, 27–34, 38–45, 50, 52

Advanced:
Day 1: pp. 331–334
Exs. 1, 2, 5, 10–12, 15, 18–20, 25–36*, 39–48*, 50, 54

Block:
pp. 331–334
Exs. 1–5, 7–9, 12–15, 17, 18, 20–26 even, 27–34, 38–45, 50, 52 (with 5.4)

Differentiated Instruction

See *Geometry Best Practices Toolkit* for suggestions on addressing the needs of a diverse classroom.

Homework Check

For a quick check of student understanding of key concepts, go over the following exercises:

Basic: 3, 8, 16, 21, 39
Average: 4, 8, 22, 38, 39
Advanced: 5, 15, 26, 39, 40

Extra Practice

- Student Edition, p. 905
- Chapter 5 Resource Book: Practice levels A, B, C, pp. 66–71

Practice Worksheet

An easily-readable reduced practice page (with answers) for this lesson can be found on p. 292C.

3. ***Sample answer:*** The longest side is opposite the largest angle. The shortest side is opposite the smallest angle.
4. ***Sample answer:*** The largest angle is the right angle, and the longest side is the hypotenuse, opposite the right angle. The shortest side is opposite the smaller acute angle.
5. ***Sample answer:*** The longest side is opposite the obtuse angle, and the two angles with the same measure are opposite the sides with the same length.

13. 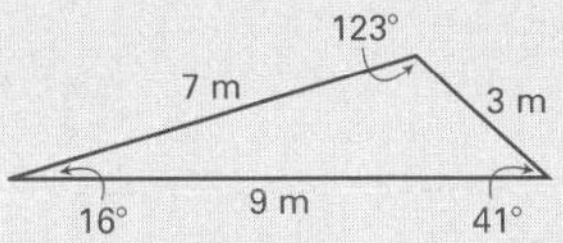

14. 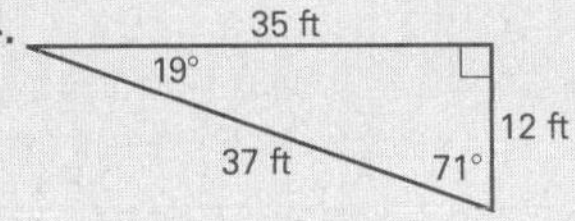

15. 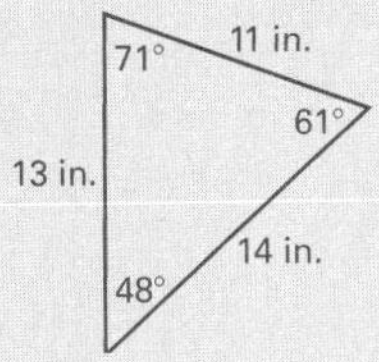

Study Strategy

Exercises 6–11 Some students may find it helpful to list all the angles and sides before doing these exercises. Then they can list the angles in order and write the side lengths opposite those angles.

Avoiding Common Errors

Exercises 13–15 Student should not attempt to make drawings "to scale" for these exercises. Have them start with a rough sketch and then refine it using all the conditions listed.

Teaching Strategy

Exercises 16–19 Ask students who are having difficulty with these problems to cut 3 strips of paper for each triangle with centimeter measures matching the side lengths. They can use their paper strips to try and form triangles.

Exercises 21–26 Ask students who are having difficulty with these problems to cut 2 strips of paper for each triangle with centimeter measures matching the side lengths. Then they can manipulate the sides to find the maximum and minimum lengths for the third side.

20. ★ **MULTIPLE CHOICE** Which group of side lengths can be used to construct a triangle? **B**

Ⓐ 3 yd, 4 ft, 5 yd Ⓑ 3 yd, 5 ft, 8 ft

Ⓒ 11 in., 16 in., 27 in. Ⓓ 2 ft, 11 in., 12 in.

B **POSSIBLE SIDE LENGTHS** ***Describe*** **the possible lengths of the third side of the triangle given the lengths of the other two sides.**

21. 5 inches, 12 inches **7 in. < x < 17 in.**

22. 3 meters, 4 meters **1 m < x < 7 m**

23. 12 feet, 18 feet **6 ft < x < 30 ft**

24. 10 yards, 23 yards **13 yd < x < 33 yd**

25. 2 feet, 40 inches **16 in. < x < 64 in.**

26. 25 meters, 25 meters **0 m < x < 50 m**

27. **EXTERIOR ANGLE INEQUALITY** Another triangle inequality relationship is given by the Exterior Angle Inequality Theorem. It states:

The measure of an exterior angle of a triangle is greater than the measure of either of the nonadjacent interior angles.

Use a relationship from Chapter 4 to *explain* how you know that $m\angle 1 > m\angle A$ and $m\angle 1 > m\angle B$ in $\triangle ABC$ with exterior angle $\angle 1$.

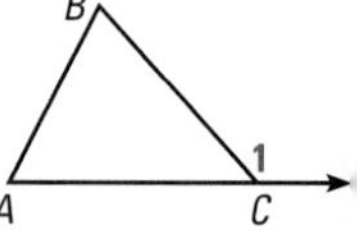

27. $\angle A$ and $\angle B$ are the nonadjacent interior angles to $\angle 1$ thus by the Exterior Angle Inequality Theorem $m\angle 1 = m\angle A + m\angle B$, which guarantees $m\angle 1 > m\angle A$ and $m\angle 1 > m\angle B$.

ERROR ANALYSIS **Use Theorems 5.10–5.12 and the theorem in Exercise 27 to** ***explain*** **why the diagram must be incorrect.**

28.

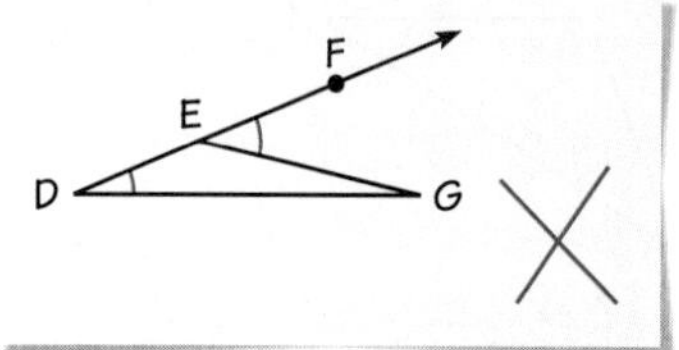

28. The diagram indicates that exterior angle of the triangle has the same measure as one of the nonadjacent interior angles, which cannot be.

29.

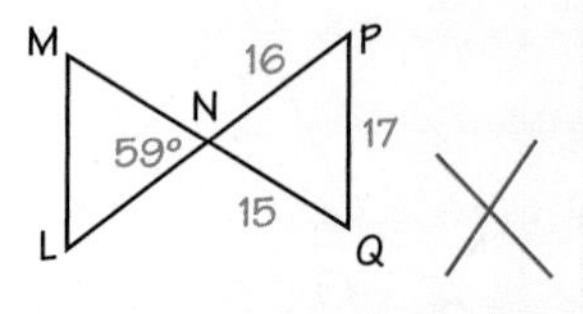

The longest side is not opposite the largest angle.

30. ★ **SHORT RESPONSE** *Explain* why the hypotenuse of a right triangle must always be longer than either leg. **The hypotenuse is opposite the 90° angle in a right triangle which is the largest angle in the triangle.**

ORDERING MEASURES **Is it possible to build a triangle using the given side lengths? If so, list the angles of the triangle in order from least to greatest measure.**

31. $PQ = \sqrt{58}$, $QR = 2\sqrt{13}$, $PR = 5\sqrt{2}$ **yes; $\angle Q, \angle P, \angle R$**

32. $ST = \sqrt{29}$, $TU = 2\sqrt{17}$, $SU = 13.9$ **no**

ALGEBRA ***Describe*** **the possible values of *x*.**

33. **$2 < x < 15$**

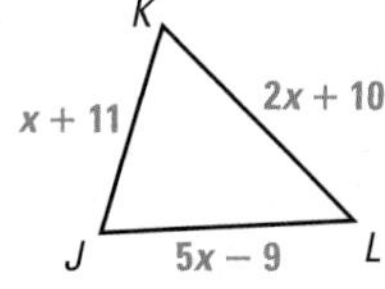

34. **$\frac{15}{7} < x < 13$**

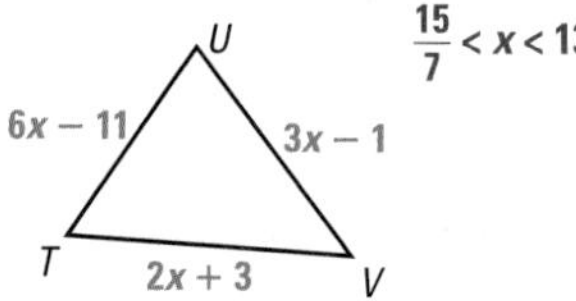

C **35.** **USING SIDE LENGTHS** Use the diagram at the right. Suppose $\overline{XY}$ bisects $\angle WYZ$. List all six angles of $\triangle XYZ$ and $\triangle WXY$ in order from smallest to largest. *Explain* your reasoning.

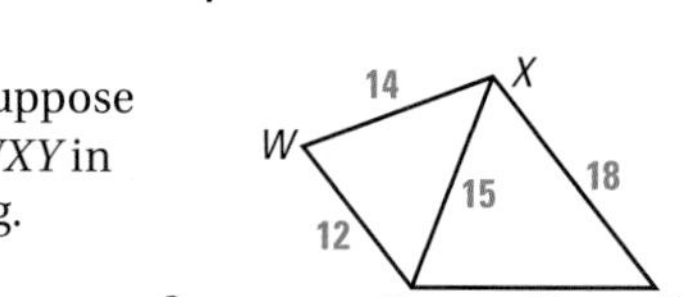

35. $\angle WXY$, $\angle Z$, $\angle ZXY$, $\angle WYX$ and $\angle ZYX$, $\angle W$; $\angle ZYX$ is the largest angle in $\triangle ZYX$ and $\angle WYX$ is the middle sized angle in $\triangle WXY$ making $\angle W$ the largest angle. $m\angle WXY + m\angle W = m\angle Z + m\angle ZXY$ making $\angle WXY$ the smallest.

36. **CHALLENGE** The perimeter of $\triangle HGF$ must be between what two integers? *Explain* your reasoning.

$4 < P < 24$; $2 < FG < 8$, $1 < GH < 7$, and $1 < HF < 9$

○ = WORKED-OUT SOLUTIONS on p. WS1 ★ = STANDARDIZED TEST PRACTICE

PROBLEM SOLVING

37. TRAY TABLE In the tray table shown, $\overline{PQ} \cong \overline{PR}$ and $QR < PQ$. Write two inequalities about the angles in $\triangle PQR$. What other angle relationship do you know? $m\angle P < m\angle Q$, $m\angle P < m\angle R$; $m\angle Q = m\angle R$

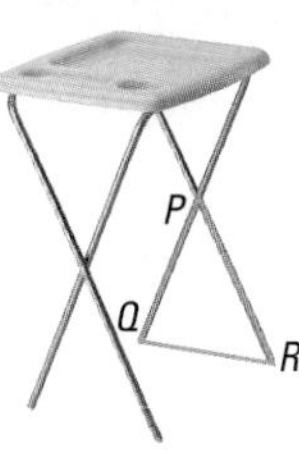

@HomeTutor for problem solving help at classzone.com

38. INDIRECT MEASUREMENT You can estimate the width of the river at point A by taking several sightings to the tree across the river at point B. The diagram shows the results for locations C and D along the riverbank. Using $\triangle BCA$ and $\triangle BDA$, what can you conclude about AB, the width of the river at point A? What could you do if you wanted a closer estimate?

38. 35 yd < AB < 50 yd *Sample answer:* Extend $\overrightarrow{BA}$ through E such that $m\angle ACE = 40°$, then measure $\overline{AE}$.

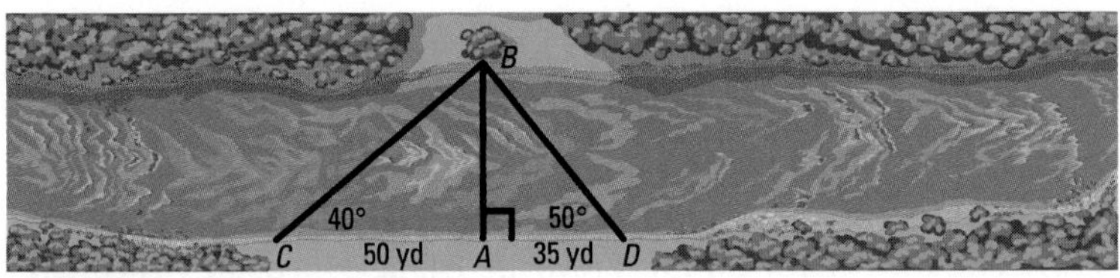

@HomeTutor for problem solving help at classzone.com

EXAMPLE 3 on p. 330 for Ex. 39

(39.) ★ EXTENDED RESPONSE You are planning a vacation to Montana. You want to visit the destinations shown in the map.

a. A brochure states that the distance between Granite Peak and Fort Peck Lake is 1080 kilometers. *Explain* how you know that this distance is a misprint.

39a. The sum of the other two side lengths is less than 1080.

b. Could the distance from Granite Peak to Fort Peck Lake be 40 kilometers? *Explain.*

39b. No; the sum of the distance from Granite Peak to Fort Peck Lake and Granite Peak to Glacier National Park must be more than 565.

c. Write two inequalities to represent the range of possible distances from Granite Peak to Fort Peck Lake. $d > 76$ km, $d < 1054$ km

d. What can you say about the distance between Granite Peak and Fort Peck Lake if you know that $m\angle 2 < m\angle 1$ and $m\angle 2 < m\angle 3$? The distance is less than 489 kilometers.

FORMING TRIANGLES In Exercises 40–43, you are given a 24 centimeter piece of string. You want to form a triangle out of the string so that the length of each side is a whole number. Draw figures accurately.

40. Can you decide if three side lengths form a triangle without checking all three inequalities shown for Theorem 5.12? If so, *describe* your shortcut. Yes; pick the two shortest sides and see if their sum is greater than the third side.

41. Draw four possible isosceles triangles and label each side length. Tell whether each of the triangles you formed is *acute, right,* or *obtuse.* See margin.

42. Draw three possible scalene triangles and label each side length. Try to form at least one scalene acute triangle and one scalene obtuse triangle. See margin.

43. List three combinations of side lengths that will not produce triangles. *Sample answer:* 3, 4, 17; 2, 5, 17; 4, 4, 16

Internet Reference

Exercise 39 More information about Montana can be found at www.state.mt.us

42. *Sample:*

7 cm, 6 cm, 11 cm
scalene obtuse

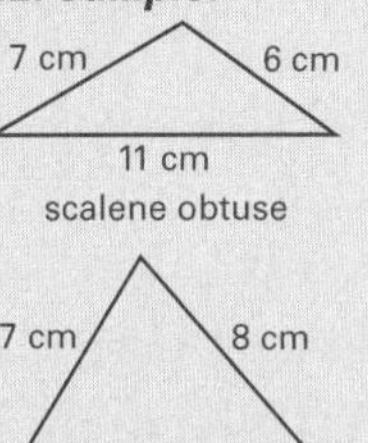

scalene acute

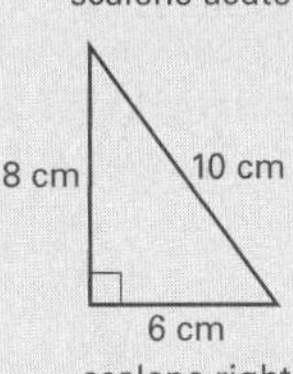

scalene right

41. *Sample:*

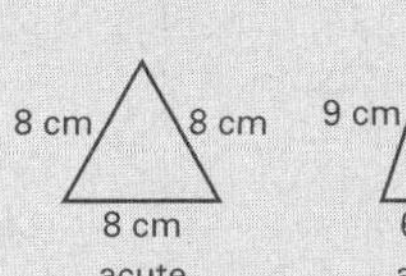

acute

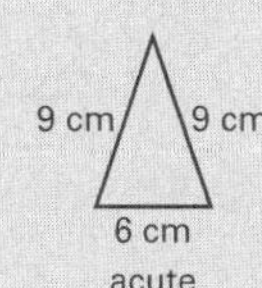

acute

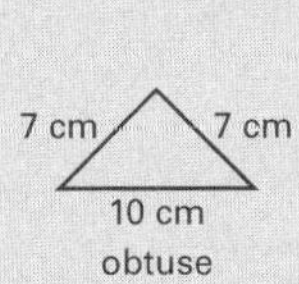

obtuse

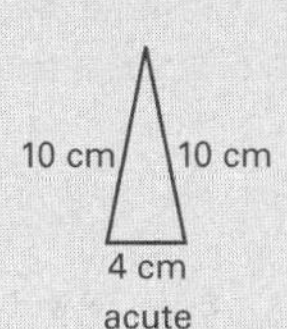

acute

5 ASSESS AND RETEACH

Daily Homework Quiz

Transparency Available

For Exercises 1 and 2, list the sides or angles in order from least to greatest.

1.

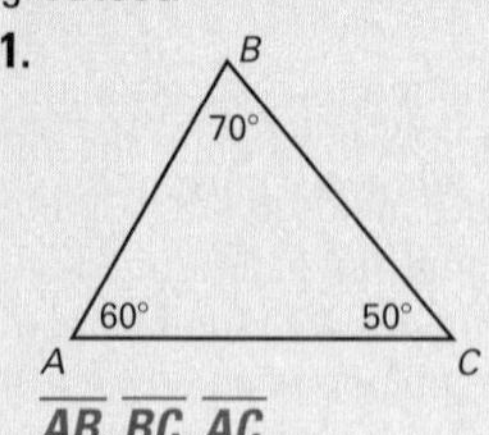

$\overline{AB}, \overline{BC}, \overline{AC}$

2.

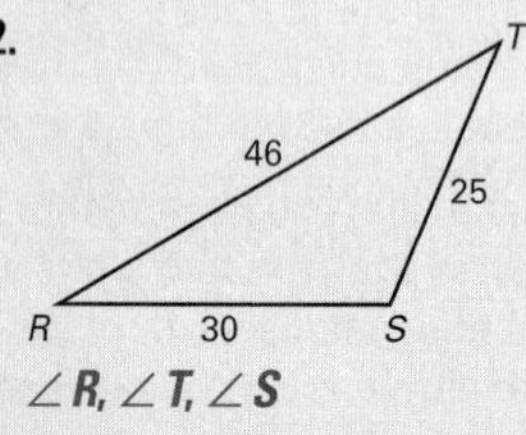

$\angle R, \angle T, \angle S$

Tell whether the side lengths can form a triangle.

3. 37 m, 35 m, 18 m **yes**

4. 3 ft, 3 ft, 6 ft **no**

5. Jeremy wants to build a triangular toy using sticks. He has one stick that is 12 inches and another that is 10 inches. What are the possible lengths of the third side of the triangle? **greater than 2 in. and less than 22 in.**

Online Quiz

Available at **classzone.com**

Diagnosis/Remediation

- Practice A, B, C in Chapter 5 Resource Book, pp. 66–71
- Study Guide in Chapter 5 Resource Book, pp. 72–73
- Practice Workbook, pp. 97–99
- @HomeTutor

Challenge

Additional challenge is available in the Chapter 5 Resource Book, p. 76.

47, 48a–b. See Additional Answers beginning on p. AA1.

45. $1\frac{1}{4}$ mi $\le d \le 2\frac{3}{4}$ mi; **if the locations are collinear then the distance could be $1\frac{1}{4}$ miles or $2\frac{3}{4}$ miles. If the locations are not collinear then the distance must be between $1\frac{1}{4}$ miles and $2\frac{3}{4}$ miles because of the Triangle Inequality Theorem.**

44. SIGHTSEEING You get off the Washington, D.C., subway system at the Smithsonian Metro station. First you visit the Museum of Natural History. Then you go to the Air and Space Museum. You record the distances you walk on your map as shown. *Describe* the range of possible distances you might have to walk to get back to the Smithsonian Metro station. **350 yd < *d* < 1068 yd**

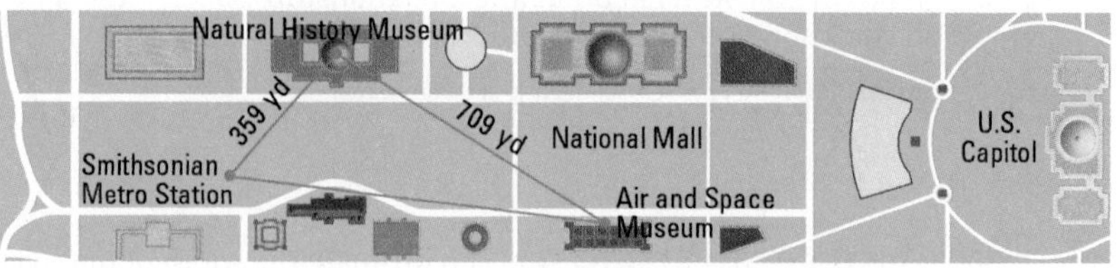

45. ★ SHORT RESPONSE Your house is 2 miles from the library. The library is $\frac{3}{4}$ mile from the grocery store. What do you know about the distance from your house to the grocery store? *Explain*. Include the special case when the three locations are all in a straight line.

C **46. ISOSCELES TRIANGLES** For what combinations of angle measures in an isosceles triangle are the congruent sides shorter than the base of the triangle? longer than the base of the triangle?
vertex angle: 60° < *x* < 180°; vertex angle: 0° < *x* < 60°

47. PROVING THEOREM 5.12 Prove the Triangle Inequality Theorem. **See margin.**

GIVEN ▶ $\triangle ABC$

PROVE ▶ (1) $AB + BC > AC$
(2) $AC + BC > AB$
(3) $AB + AC > BC$

Plan for Proof One side, say $\overline{BC}$, is longer than or at least as long as each of the other sides. Then (1) and (2) are true. To prove (3), extend $\overline{AC}$ to D so that $\overline{AB} \cong \overline{AD}$ and use Theorem 5.11 to show that $DC > BC$.

48. CHALLENGE Prove the following statements. **See margin.**

a. The length of any one median of a triangle is less than half the perimeter of the triangle.

b. The sum of the lengths of the three medians of a triangle is greater than half the perimeter of the triangle.

MIXED REVIEW

PREVIEW Prepare for Lesson 5.6 in Exs. 49–50.

In Exercises 49 and 50, write the if-then form, the converse, the inverse, and the contrapositive of the given statement. *(p. 79)* **49, 50. See margin.**

49. A redwood is a large tree. **50.** $5x - 2 = 18$, because $x = 4$.

51. A triangle has vertices $A(22, 21)$, $B(0, 0)$, and $C(22, 2)$. Graph $\triangle ABC$ and classify it by its sides. Then determine if it is a right triangle. *(p. 217)*
Scalene; not a right triangle; see margin for art.

Graph figure *LMNP* with vertices $L(-4, 6)$, $M(4, 8)$, $N(2, 2)$, and $P(-4, 0)$. Then draw its image after the transformation. *(p. 272)* **52–54. See margin.**

52. $(x, y) \to (x + 3, y - 4)$ **53.** $(x, y) \to (x, -y)$ **54.** $(x, y) \to (-x, y)$

49. If a tree is a redwood, then it is a large tree; if a tree is large, then it is a redwood; if a tree is not a redwood, then it is not large; if a tree is not large, then it is not a redwood.

50. If $x = 4$, then $5x - 2 = 18$; if $5x - 2 = 18$, then $x = 4$; if $x \neq 4$, then $5x - 2 \neq 18$; if $5x - 2 \neq 18$, then $x \neq 4$.

51.

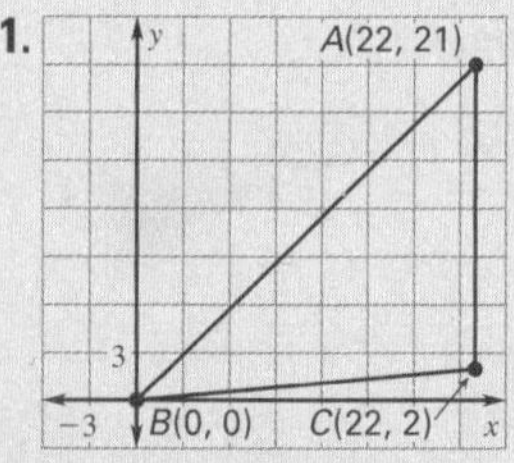

52–54. See Additional Answers beginning on p. AA1.

5.6 Inequalities in Two Triangles and Indirect Proof

Before You used inequalities to make comparisons in one triangle.
Now You will use inequalities to make comparisons in two triangles.
Why? So you can compare the distances hikers traveled, as in Ex. 22.

Key Vocabulary
- **indirect proof**
- **included angle,** *p. 240*

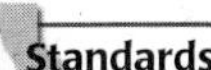

Standards
2.0 Students write geometric proofs, including proofs by contradiction.

Imagine a gate between fence posts A and B that has hinges at A and swings open at B.

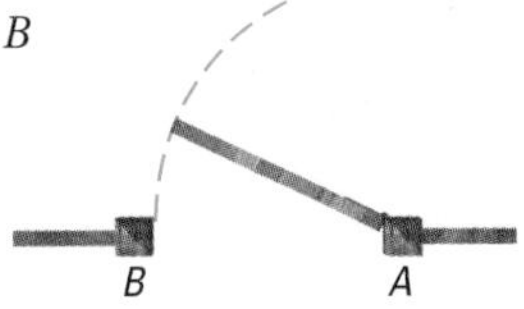

As the gate swings open, you can think of $\triangle ABC$, with side $\overline{AC}$ formed by the gate itself, side $\overline{AB}$ representing the distance between the fence posts, and side $\overline{BC}$ representing the opening between post B and the outer edge of the gate.

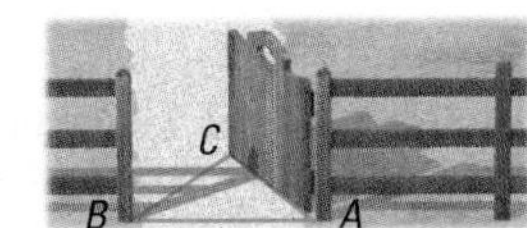

Notice that as the gate opens wider, both the measure of $\angle A$ and the distance CB increase. This suggests the *Hinge Theorem*.

THEOREMS *For Your Notebook*

THEOREM 5.13 Hinge Theorem

If two sides of one triangle are congruent to two sides of another triangle, and the included angle of the first is larger than the included angle of the second, then the third side of the first is longer than the third side of the second.

V W X 88° R S T 35°

$WX > ST$

Proof: Ex. 28, p. 341

THEOREM 5.14 Converse of the Hinge Theorem

If two sides of one triangle are congruent to two sides of another triangle, and the third side of the first is longer than the third side of the second, then the included angle of the first is larger than the included angle of the second.

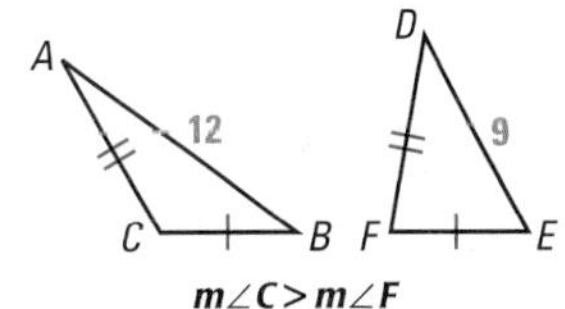

$m\angle C > m\angle F$

Proof: Example 4, p. 338

1 PLAN AND PREPARE

Warm-Up Exercises

Transparency Available

1. Write the if-then form, converse, inverse, and contrapositive of the given statement.
$3x - 8 = 22$ because $x = 10$.
If $x = 10$, then $3x - 8 = 22$.
If $3x - 8 = 22$, then $x = 10$.
If $x \neq 10$, then $3x - 8 \neq 22$.
If $3x - 8 \neq 22$, then $x \neq 10$.
2. In $\triangle ABC$, $BC = 18$, $AB = 13$, and $AC = 16$. List the angles of the triangle from least to greatest. **$\angle C$, $\angle B$, $\angle A$**

Notetaking Guide

Transparency Available

Promotes interactive learning and notetaking skills, pp. 135–137.

Pacing

Basic: 2 days
Average: 2 days
Advanced: 2 days
Block: 1 block
- See *Teaching Guide/Lesson Plan.*

2 FOCUS AND MOTIVATE

Essential Question

Big Idea 3, p. 293

How do you write an indirect proof? **Tell students they will learn how to answer this question by using the opposite of what they are trying to prove.**

Resource Planning Guide

Chapter Resource Book
- Teaching Guide/Lesson Plan (pp. 77–78)
- Activity Master (p. 79)
- Practice levels A, B, C (pp. 80–85)
- Study Guide (pp. 86–87)
- Catch-up for Absent Students (p. 88)
- Problem Solving Workshop (p. 89)
- Challenge (p. 90)

Workbooks
- Notetaking Guide (pp. 135–137)
- Practice Workbook (pp. 100–102)

Teaching Options
- **Power Presentations CD-ROM** provides dynamic electronic teaching resources for the classroom.
- **Activity Generator CD-ROM** provides editable activities for all ability levels.

Interactive Technology
- Easy Planner
- Power Presentations CD-ROM
- Activity Generator CD-ROM
- Animated Geometry
- Test Generator CD-ROM
- Online Quiz
- eWorkbook
- eEdition
- @HomeTutor

Resources for English Learners
- Quick Reference for English Learners
- Spanish Study Guide
- Multi-Language Visual Glossary
- Student Resources in Spanish

See also the *Geometry Toolkit* for more strategies for meeting individual needs.

Motivating the Lesson

A snake opens its jaws to swallow food. Discuss how the angle formed by its jaws is related to the size of the food. Tell students that this lesson explores the relationship between an angle of a triangle and the length of the side opposite that angle.

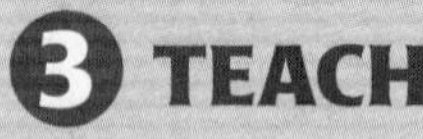

Extra Example 1

Given that $\overline{BC} \cong \overline{DC}$, how does $\angle ABC$ compare to $\angle ACD$?

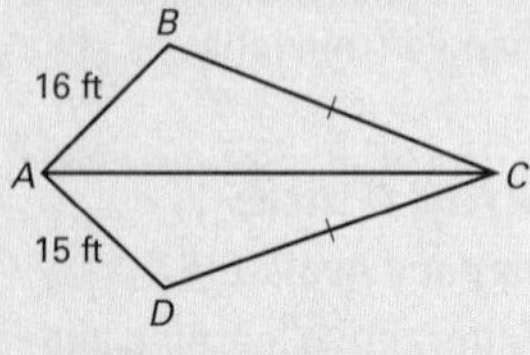

$\angle ACB > \angle ACD$

Key Question to Ask for Example 1

- What did you show in order to use the Converse of the Hinge Theorem. **Two pairs of corresponding sides are congruent and one third side is greater than the other third side.**

An **Animated Geometry** activity is available on-line for **Example 2**. This activity is also available on the **Power Presentations CD-ROM**.

EXAMPLE 1 Use the Converse of the Hinge Theorem

Given that $\overline{ST} \cong \overline{PR}$, how does $\angle PST$ compare to $\angle SPR$?

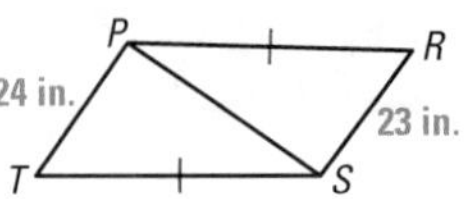

Solution

You are given that $\overline{ST} \cong \overline{PR}$ and you know that $\overline{PS} \cong \overline{PS}$ by the Reflexive Property. Because 24 inches > 23 inches, $PT > RS$. So, two sides of $\triangle STP$ are congruent to two sides of $\triangle PRS$ and the third side in $\triangle STP$ is longer.

▶ By the Converse of the Hinge Theorem, $m\angle PST > m\angle SPR$.

EXAMPLE 2 Solve a multi-step problem

BIKING Two groups of bikers leave the same camp heading in opposite directions. Each group goes 2 miles, then changes direction and goes 1.2 miles. Group A starts due east and then turns 45° toward north as shown. Group B starts due west and then turns 30° toward south.

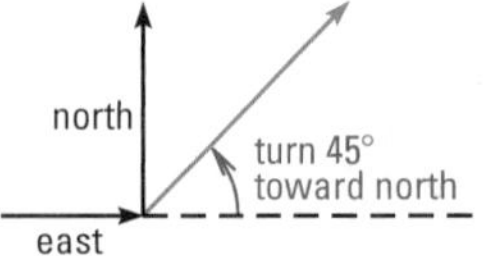

Which group is farther from camp? Explain your reasoning.

Solution

Draw a diagram and mark the given measures. The distances biked and the distances back to camp form two triangles, with congruent 2 mile sides and congruent 1.2 mile sides. Add the third sides of the triangles to your diagram.

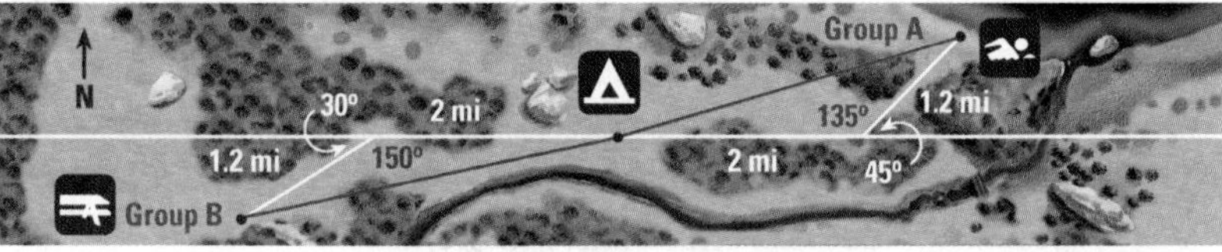

Next use linear pairs to find and mark the included angles of 150° and 135°.

▶ Because 150° > 135°, Group B is farther from camp by the Hinge Theorem.

Animated Geometry at classzone.com

GUIDED PRACTICE for Examples 1 and 2

Use the diagram at the right.

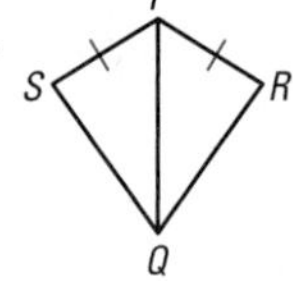

1. If $PR = PS$ and $m\angle QPR > m\angle QPS$, which is longer, $\overline{SQ}$ or $\overline{RQ}$? $\overline{\mathbf{RQ}}$
2. If $PR = PS$ and $RQ < SQ$, which is larger, $\angle RPQ$ or $\angle SPQ$? $\angle \mathbf{SPQ}$
3. **WHAT IF?** In Example 2, suppose Group C leaves camp and goes 2 miles due north. Then they turn 40° toward east and continue 1.2 miles. *Compare* the distances from camp for all three groups. **Group *B* is the farthest from camp, followed by Group *C*, and then Group *A* which is the closest.**

INDIRECT REASONING Suppose a student looks around the cafeteria, concludes that hamburgers are not being served, and explains as follows.

> *At first I assumed that we are having hamburgers because today is Tuesday and Tuesday is usually hamburger day.*
>
> *There is always ketchup on the table when we have hamburgers, so I looked for the ketchup, but I didn't see any.*
>
> *So, my assumption that we are having hamburgers must be false.*

The student used *indirect* reasoning. So far in this book, you have reasoned *directly* from given information to prove desired conclusions.

In an **indirect proof**, you start by making the temporary assumption that the desired conclusion is false. By then showing that this assumption leads to a logical impossibility, you prove the original statement true *by contradiction.*

KEY CONCEPT *For Your Notebook*

How to Write an Indirect Proof

STEP 1 **Identify** the statement you want to prove. **Assume** temporarily that this statement is false by assuming that its opposite is true.

STEP 2 **Reason** logically until you reach a contradiction.

STEP 3 **Point out** that the desired conclusion must be true because the contradiction proves the temporary assumption false.

EXAMPLE 3 Write an indirect proof

Write an indirect proof that an odd number is not divisible by 4.

GIVEN ▶ x is an odd number.

PROVE ▶ x is not divisible by 4.

Solution

STEP 1 Assume temporarily that x is divisible by 4. This means that $\frac{x}{4} = n$ for some whole number n. So, multiplying both sides by 4 gives $x = 4n$.

STEP 2 If x is odd, then, by definition, x cannot be divided evenly by 2. However, $x = 4n$ so $\frac{x}{2} = \frac{4n}{2} = 2n$. We know that $2n$ is a whole number because n is a whole number, so x *can* be divided evenly by 2. This contradicts the given statement that x is odd.

STEP 3 Therefore, the assumption that x is divisible by 4 must be false, which proves that x is not divisible by 4.

READ VOCABULARY
You have reached a *contradiction* when you have two statements that cannot both be true at the same time.

GUIDED PRACTICE for Example 3

4. Suppose you wanted to prove the statement "If $x + y \neq 14$ and $y = 5$, then $x \neq 9$." What temporary assumption could you make to prove the conclusion indirectly? How does that assumption lead to a contradiction?
Assume temporarily that $x = 9$; since $x + y \neq 14$ and $y = 5$ are given, letting $x = 9$ leads to the contradiction $9 + 5 \neq 14$.

Extra Example 2

Two runners start together and run in opposite directions. Each one goes 1.5 miles, changes direction, and goes 2.4 miles. The first runner starts due north and turns 100° towards the east. The other runner starts due south and turns 130° towards the west. Both runners return to the starting point. Which runner ran farther? *Explain.*

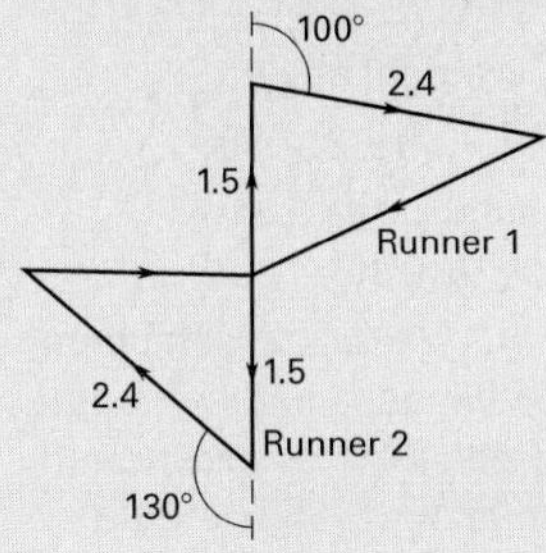

Each triangle has side lengths 1.5 mi and 2.4 mi, and the angles between those sides are 80° and 50°. By the Hinge Theorem, the third side of the triangle for Runner 1 is longer, so Runner 1 ran further.

Extra Example 3

Write an indirect proof to show that the sum of two odd numbers is even.

Given a and b are odd numbers.

Prove $a + b$ is an even number.

Step 1. Assume $a + b$ is not even, which is the same as assuming that $a + b$ is odd.

Step 2. If a and b are odd, then $a = 2m + 1$ and $b = 2n + 1$ for some m and n. Then $a + b = (2m + 1) + (2n + 1) = 2(m + n) + 2$, which is an even number. This contradicts the assumption that $a + b$ is odd.

Step 3. The assumption that $a + b$ is odd must be false. Therefore, $a + b$ must be an even number.

Extra Example 4

Write an indirect proof of the Corollary of the Triangle Sum Theorem, page 220, that the acute angles of a right triangle are complementary.

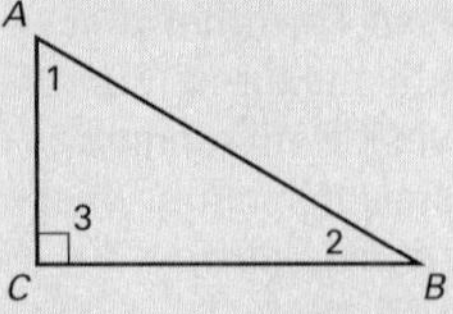

Given $\angle C$ is a right angle.

Prove $m\angle 1 + m\angle 2 = 90°$

Assume temporarily that $m\angle 1 + m\angle 2 \neq 90°$.

Case 1. If $m\angle 1 + m\angle 2 < 90°$, then $m\angle 3 > 90°$ because of the Triangle Sum Theorem. But this contradicts the statement that $\angle C$ is a right angle.

Case 2. If $m\angle 1 + m\angle 2 > 90°$, then $m\angle 3 < 90°$ because of the Triangle Sum Theorem. Again, this contradicts the statement that $\angle C$ is a right angle.

Therefore, $m\angle 1 + m\angle 2 = 90°$.

Key Question to Ask for Example 4

- Why are there two cases in the proof? **If $m\angle B$ is not greater than $m\angle E$, then there are two possibilities: $m\angle B = m\angle E$ or $m\angle B < m\angle E$.**

Closing the Lesson

Have students summarize the major points of the lesson and answer the Essential Question: How do you organize an indirect proof?

- **If two sides of one triangle are congruent to two sides of another triangle, and the included angle of the first is larger than the included angle of the second, then the third side of the first is longer than the third side of the second, and vice versa.**
- **To write an indirect proof, start by assuming the opposite of what you want to prove and then reason logically until you reach a contradiction.**

Assume the opposite of what you are trying to prove is true and then reason logically until you reach a contradiction.

EXAMPLE 4 Prove the Converse of the Hinge Theorem

Write an indirect proof of Theorem 5.14.

GIVEN ▶ $\overline{AB} \cong \overline{DE}$
$\overline{BC} \cong \overline{EF}$
$AC > DF$

PROVE ▶ $m\angle B > m\angle E$

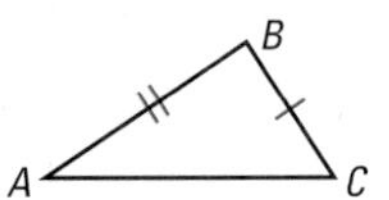

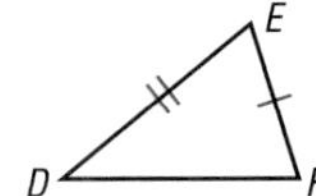

Proof Assume temporarily that $m\angle B \not> m\angle E$. Then, it follows that either $m\angle B = m\angle E$ or $m\angle B < m\angle E$.

Case 1 If $m\angle B = m\angle E$, then $\angle B \cong \angle E$. So, $\triangle ABC \cong \triangle DEF$ by the SAS Congruence Postulate and $AC = DF$.

Case 2 If $m\angle B < m\angle E$, then $AC < DF$ by the Hinge Theorem.

Both conclusions contradict the given statement that $AC > DF$. So, the temporary assumption that $m\angle B \not> m\angle E$ cannot be true. This proves that $m\angle B > m\angle E$.

✓ GUIDED PRACTICE for Example 4

5. Write a temporary assumption you could make to prove the Hinge Theorem indirectly. What two cases does that assumption lead to?
The third side of the first is less than or equal to the third side of the second; Case 1: Third side of the first equals the third side of the second. Case 2: Third side of the first is less than the third side of the second.

5.6 EXERCISES

HOMEWORK KEY
○ = **WORKED-OUT SOLUTIONS** on p. WS7 for Exs. 5, 7, and 23
★ = **STANDARDIZED TEST PRACTICE** Exs. 2, 9, 19, and 25

SKILL PRACTICE

A

1. **VOCABULARY** Why is indirect proof also called *proof by contradiction*?
You temporarily assume that the desired conclusion is false and this leads to a logical contradiction.

2. ★ **WRITING** *Explain* why the name "Hinge Theorem" is used for Theorem 5.13. ***Sample answer:*** **Consider opening a door; the wider you open it, the bigger the angle the door makes with the wall and the larger the opening.**

EXAMPLE 1 on p. 336 for Exs. 3–10

APPLYING THEOREMS **Copy and complete with <, >, or =. *Explain.***

3. AD _?_ CD >

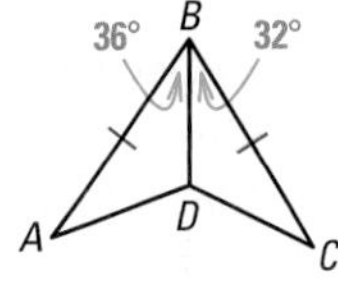

4. MN _?_ LK <

5. TR _?_ UR <

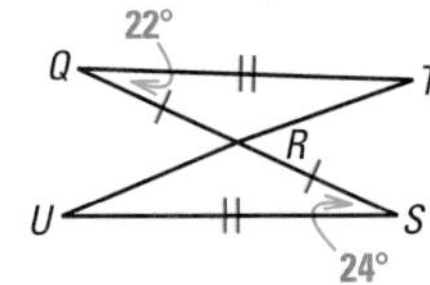

6. $m\angle 1$ _?_ $m\angle 2$ <

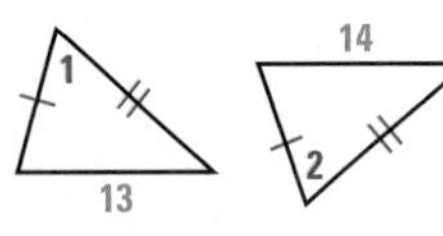

7. $m\angle 1$ _?_ $m\angle 2$ =

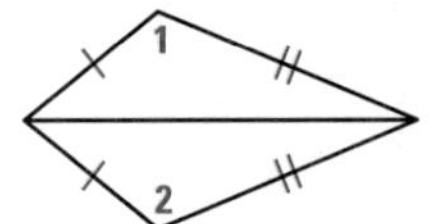

8. $m\angle 1$ _?_ $m\angle 2$ >

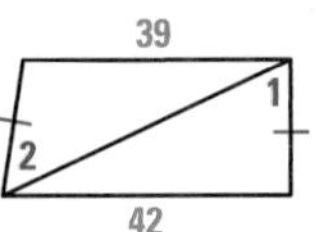

9. ★ **MULTIPLE CHOICE** Which is a possible measure for $\angle JKM$? **A**

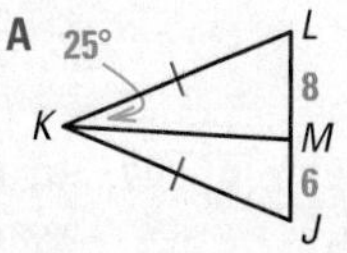
25°
L
8
K
M
6
J

Ⓐ 20° Ⓑ 25°

Ⓒ 30° Ⓓ Cannot be determined

10. **USING A DIAGRAM** The path from E to F is longer than the path from E to D. The path from G to D is the same length as the path from G to F. What can you conclude about the angles of the paths? *Explain* your reasoning. **$m\angle DGE < m\angle FGE$; Converse of the Hinge Theorem applies.**

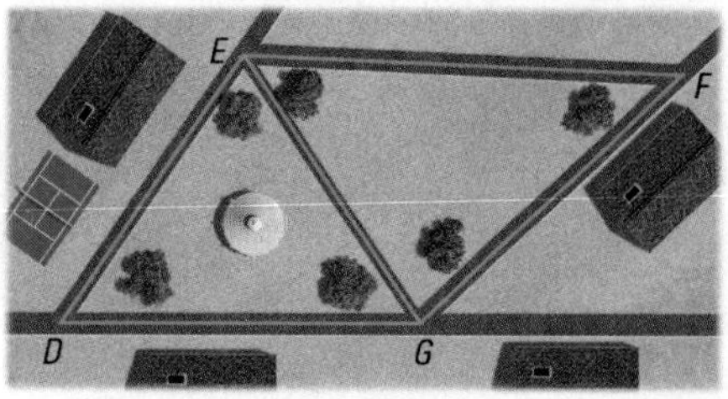
E
F
D
G

EXAMPLES B **3 and 4** on pp. 337–338 for Exs. 11–13

STARTING AN INDIRECT PROOF **In Exercises 11 and 12, write a temporary assumption you could make to prove the conclusion indirectly.**

11. If x and y are odd integers, then xy is odd. **Suppose xy is even.**

12. In $\triangle ABC$, if $m\angle A = 100°$, then $\angle B$ is not a right angle. **Suppose $\angle B$ is a right angle.**

13. **REASONING** Your study partner is planning to write an indirect proof to show that $\angle A$ is an obtuse angle. She states "Assume temporarily that $\angle A$ is an acute angle." What has your study partner overlooked? **$\angle A$ could be a right angle or a straight angle.**

ERROR ANALYSIS ***Explain*** **why the student's reasoning is not correct.**

14. To use the Hinge Theorem the angle must be the included angle between the two pairs of congruent sides.

14.

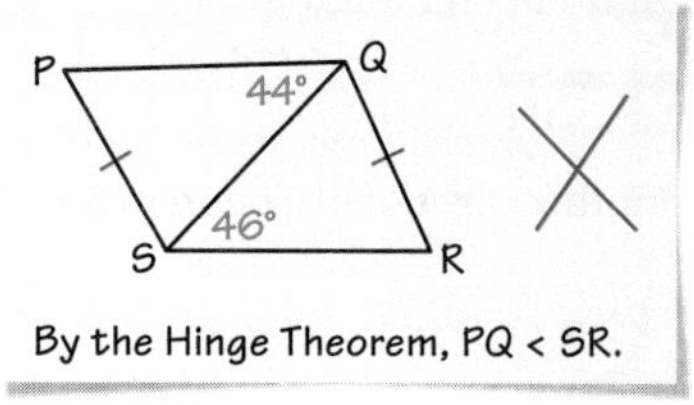
P
Q
44°
46°
S
R
By the Hinge Theorem, PQ < SR.

15.

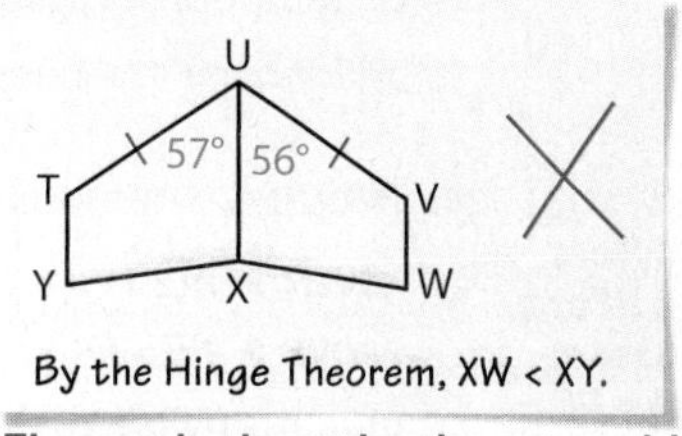
U
57°
56°
T
V
Y
X
W
By the Hinge Theorem, XW < XY.

The Hinge Theorem is about triangles not quadrilaterals.

xy **ALGEBRA** **Use the Hinge Theorem or its converse and properties of triangles to write and solve an inequality to describe a restriction on the value of x.**

16. **$x < 30\frac{1}{2}$**

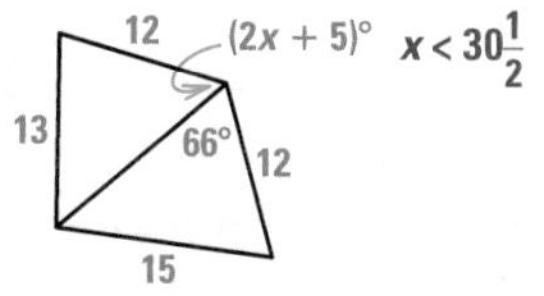
12
(2x + 5)°
13
66°
12
15

17. **$x > \frac{1}{2}$**

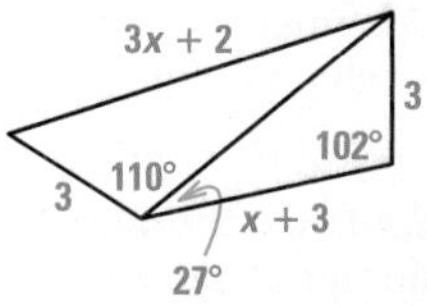
3x + 2
3
110°
102°
3
x + 3
27°

18. **$x > \frac{3}{2}$**

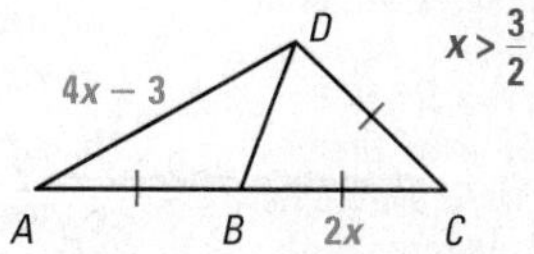
D
4x − 3
A
B
2x
C

C

19. ★ **SHORT RESPONSE** If $\overline{NR}$ is a median of $\triangle NPQ$ and $NQ > NP$, *explain* why $\angle NRQ$ is obtuse. **Using the Converse of the Hinge Theorem $\angle NRQ > \angle NRP$. Since $\angle NRQ$ and $\angle NRP$ are a linear pair $\angle NRQ$ must be obtuse and $\angle NRP$ must be acute.**

20. **ANGLE BISECTORS** In $\triangle EFG$, the bisector of $\angle F$ intersects the bisector of $\angle G$ at point H. *Explain* why $\overline{FG}$ must be longer than $\overline{FH}$ or $\overline{HG}$. **In $\triangle FHG$, $m\angle H > m\angle GFH$ or $m\angle FGH$ by Theorem 5.11.**

21. **CHALLENGE** In $\triangle ABC$, the altitudes from B and C meet at D. What is true about $\triangle ABC$ if $m\angle BAC > m\angle BDC$? *Justify* your answer. **$\triangle ABC$ is obtuse; the orthocenter of an obtuse triangle is always outside of the triangle, making the angle smaller outside than inside.**

4 PRACTICE AND APPLY

Assignment Guide

Answer Transparencies available for all exercises

Basic:
Day 1: pp. 338–341
Exs. 1–10, 22
Day 2: pp. 338–341
Exs. 11–14, 23–25, 29–35

Average:
Day 1: pp. 338–341
Exs. 1–10, 16–18, 22
Day 2: pp. 338–341
Exs. 11–15, 19, 23–26, 29–35

Advanced:
Day 1: pp. 338–341
Exs. 1–10, 16–18, 22
Day 2: pp. 338–341
Exs. 11–15, 19–21*, 23–28*, 30, 34, 35

Block:
pp. 338–341
Exs. 1–19, 22–26, 29–35

Differentiated Instruction

See *Geometry Best Practices Toolkit* for suggestions on addressing the needs of a diverse classroom.

Homework Check

For a quick check of student understanding of key concepts, go over the following exercises:

Basic: 4, 10, 11, 22, 23
Average: 6, 12, 16, 22, 24
Advanced: 8, 13, 17, 22, 24

Extra Practice

- Student Edition, p. 905
- Chapter 5 Resource Book: Practice levels A, B, C, pp. 80–85

Practice Worksheet

An easily-readable reduced practice page (with answers) for this lesson can be found on p. 292C.

Avoiding Common Errors

Exercises 11–12 A common error is to assume that the opposite of the *given* is false. Caution students to assume the opposite of the *conclusion* is false.

Teaching Strategy

Exercise 26 Point out that this proof depends on knowing that the largest angle of a right triangle is the right angle. Exercise 26 can also be proved indirectly by using the Triangle Sum Theorem.

Mathematical Reasoning

Exercise 27 Using symbolic notation (see page 94), the contrapositive of the conditional $p \to q$ is $\sim q \to \sim p$. If we know that both $\sim q \to \sim p$ and $\sim q$ are true, then the Law of Detachment lets us conclude that $\sim p$ must be true. If p is given, this is a contradiction because p and $\sim p$ cannot both be true.

Study Strategy

Exercise 28 Encourage students to list the key points of the plan for the proof of the Hinge Theorem. Then they can prove each statement in their list.

25c. ***Sample answer:*** **Since $NL = NK = NM$ and as $m\angle LNK$ increases KL increases, and $m\angle KNM$ decreases as KM decreases, you have two pairs of congruent sides with $m\angle LNK$ eventually greater than $m\angle KNM$. The Hinge Theorem guarantees KL will eventually be greater than KM.**

26. ***Sample answer:*** **Assume temporarily that $\overline{AB}$ is not the shortest segment from A to k. This implies that there is a point C on k such that $\overline{AC}$ is the shortest segment. $\triangle ABC$ is a right triangle with hypotenuse $\overline{AC}$. Since $\overline{AC}$ is opposite the right angle, the largest angle in a right triangle, Theorem 5.10 guarantees that $\overline{AC}$ is the longest side. This contradicts the assumption that $\overline{AC}$ is the shortest side, making $\overline{AB}$ the shortest side.**

PROBLEM SOLVING

EXAMPLE 2 [A] on p. 336 for Ex. 22

22. HIKING Two hikers start at the visitor center. The first hikes 4 miles due west, then turns 40° toward south and hikes 1.8 miles. The second hikes 4 miles due east, then turns 52° toward north and and hikes 1.8 miles. Which hiker is farther from the visitor center? *Explain* how you know. **the first hiker; the Hinge Theorem**

for problem solving help at classzone.com

EXAMPLES 3 and 4 on pp. 337–338 for Exs. 23–24

23. INDIRECT PROOF Arrange statements A–E in order to write an indirect proof of the corollary: If $\triangle PQR$ is *equilateral*, then it is *equiangular*. **E, A, D, B, C**

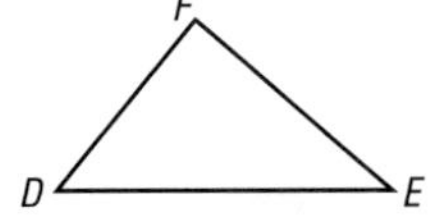

GIVEN ▶ $\triangle PQR$ is equilateral.

A. That means that for some pair of vertices, say P and Q, $m\angle P > m\angle Q$.

B. But this contradicts the given statement that $\triangle PQR$ is equilateral.

C. The contradiction shows that the temporary assumption that $\triangle PQR$ is not equiangular is false. This proves that $\triangle PQR$ is equiangular.

D. Then, by Theorem 5.11, you can conclude that $QR > PR$.

E. Temporarily assume that $\triangle PQR$ is not equiangular.

@HomeTutor for problem solving help at classzone.com

24. Assume temporarily that either $EF < DF$ or $EF = DF$. Case 1: Assume $EF < DF$. Using Theorem 5.10 you would get $m\angle D < m\angle E$ which contradicts the given statement. Case 2: Assume $EF = DF$. If $EF = DF$ then $\triangle FDE$ would be isosceles with $m\angle D = m\angle E$ which contradicts the given statement. Therefore, the assumption must be false. So, $EF > DF$.

[B]

24. PROVING THEOREM 5.11 Write an indirect proof of Theorem 5.11, page 328.

GIVEN ▶ $m\angle D > m\angle E$

PROVE ▶ $EF > DF$

Plan for Proof In Case 1, assume that $EF < DF$. In Case 2, assume that $EF = DF$.

F, D, E

25. ★ EXTENDED RESPONSE A scissors lift can be used to adjust the height of a platform. **It gets larger; it gets smaller.**

a. Interpret As the mechanism expands, $\overline{KL}$ gets longer. As KL increases, what happens to $m\angle LNK$? to $m\angle KNM$?

b. Apply Name a distance that decreases as $\overline{KL}$ gets longer. **KM**

c. Writing *Explain* how the adjustable mechanism illustrates the Hinge Theorem. **See margin.**

26. PROOF Write a proof that the shortest distance from a point to a line is the length of the perpendicular segment from the point to the line. **See margin.**

GIVEN ▶ Line k; point A not on k; point B on k such that $\overline{AB} \perp k$

PROVE ▶ $\overline{AB}$ is the shortest segment from A to k.

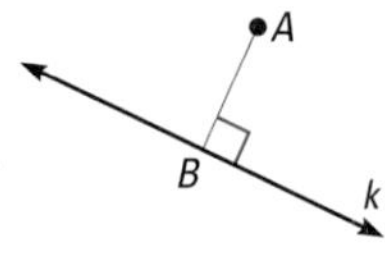

Plan for Proof Assume that there is a shorter segment from A to k and use Theorem 5.10 to show that this leads to a contradiction.

○ = WORKED-OUT SOLUTIONS on p. WS1 ★ = STANDARDIZED TEST PRACTICE

27. Prove: If x is divisible by 4, then x is even. Proof: Since x is divisible by 4, $x = 4a$. When you factor out a 2, you get $x = 2(2a)$ which is in the form $2n$, which implies x is an even number; your temporary assumption in the indirect proof is the same as your hypothesis in the direct proof.

C **27. USING A CONTRAPOSITIVE** Because the contrapositive of a conditional is equivalent to the original statement, you can prove the statement by proving its contrapositive. Look back at the conditional in Example 3 on page 337. Write a proof of the contrapositive that uses direct reasoning. How is your proof similar to the indirect proof of the original statement? **See margin.**

28. CHALLENGE Write a proof of Theorem 5.13, the Hinge Theorem. **See margin.**

GIVEN ▶ $\overline{AB} \cong \overline{DE}$, $\overline{BC} \cong \overline{EF}$, $m\angle ABC > m\angle DEF$

PROVE ▶ $AC > DF$

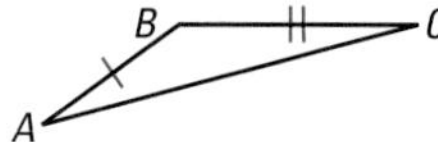

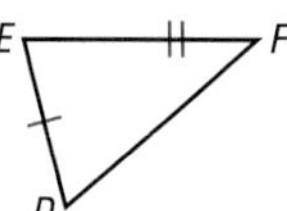

Plan for Proof

1. Because $m\angle ABC > m\angle DEF$, you can locate a point P in the interior of $\angle ABC$ so that $\angle CBP \cong \angle FED$ and $\overline{BP} \cong \overline{ED}$. Draw $\overline{BP}$ and show that $\triangle PBC \cong \triangle DEF$.
2. Locate a point H on $\overline{AC}$ so that $\overrightarrow{BH}$ bisects $\angle PBA$ and show that $\triangle ABH \cong \triangle PBH$.
3. Give reasons for each statement below to show that $AC > DF$.

$AC = AH + HC = PH + HC > PC = DF$

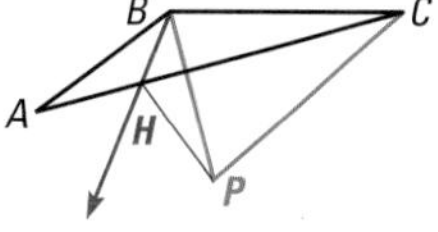

MIXED REVIEW

PREVIEW Prepare for Lesson 6.1 in Exs. 29–31.

Write the conversion factor you would multiply by to change units as specified. *(p. 886)*

29. inches to feet $\frac{1\text{ ft}}{12\text{ in.}}$
30. liters to kiloliters $\frac{1\text{ kL}}{1000\text{ L}}$
31. pounds to ounces $\frac{16\text{ oz}}{1\text{ lb}}$

Solve the equation. Write a reason for each step. *(p. 105)* **32–34. See margin.**

32. $1.5(x + 4) = 5(2.4)$
33. $-3(-2x + 5) = 12$
34. $2(5x) = 3(4x + 6)$

35. Simplify the expression $\frac{-6xy^2}{21x^2y}$ if possible. *(p. 139)* $-\frac{2y}{7x}$

QUIZ for Lessons 5.5–5.6

1. Is it possible to construct a triangle with side lengths 5, 6, and 12? If not, *explain* why not. *(p. 328)* **No; 5 + 6 must be greater than 12.**
2. The lengths of two sides of a triangle are 15 yards and 27 yards. *Describe* the possible lengths of the third side of the triangle. *(p. 328)* **12 yd < x < 42 yd**
3. In $\triangle PQR$, $m\angle P = 48°$ and $m\angle Q = 79°$. List the sides of $\triangle PQR$ in order from shortest to longest. *(p. 328)* $\overline{QR}, \overline{PQ}, \overline{PR}$

Copy and complete with <, >, or =. *(p. 335)*

4. BA _?_ DA >

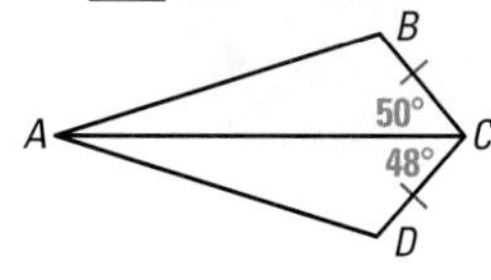

5. $m\angle 1$ _?_ $m\angle 2$ >

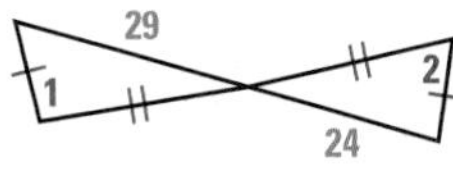

5 ASSESS AND RETEACH

Daily Homework Quiz

Transparency Available

Complete each statement with <, >, or =.

1. KL _?_ NP <

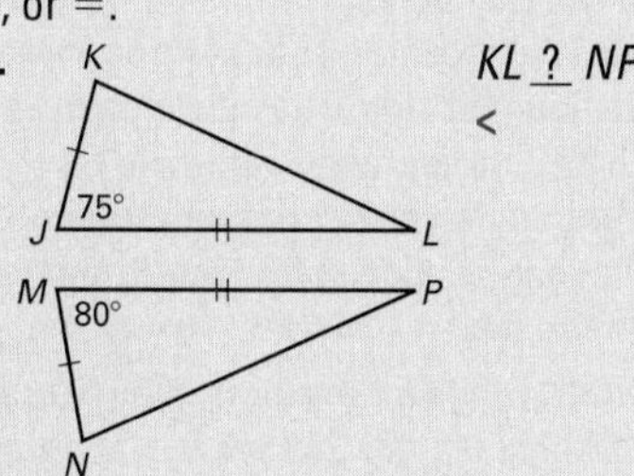

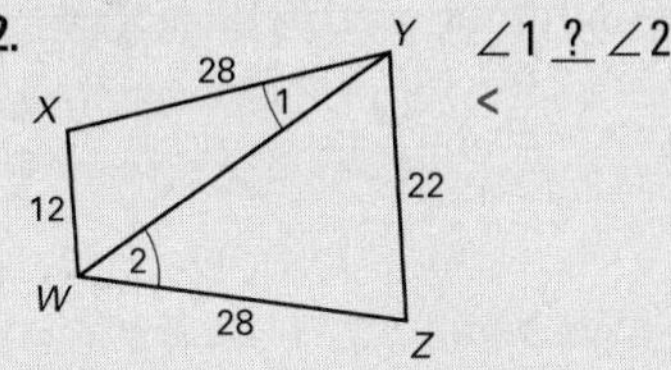

2. $\angle 1$ _?_ $\angle 2$ <

3. Suppose you want to write an indirect proof of this statement: "In $\triangle ABC$, if $m\angle A > 90$ then $\triangle ABC$ is not a right triangle." What temporary assumption should start your proof? **Assume $\triangle ABC$ is a right triangle.**

Online Quiz

Available at **classzone.com**

Diagnosis/Remediation

- Practice A, B, C in Chapter 5 Resource Book, pp. 80–85
- Study Guide in Chapter 5 Resource Book, pp. 86–87
- Practice Workbook, pp. 100–102
- @HomeTutor

Challenge

Additional challenge is available in the Chapter 5 Resource Book, p. 90.

Quiz

An easily-readable reduced copy of the quiz (with answers) on Lessons 5.5–5.6 from the Assessment Book can be found on p. 292F.

28. See Additional Answers beginning on p. AA1.

32. Equation (Reason)

$1.5(x + 4) = 5(2.4)$ (Given)
$1.5(x + 4) = 12$ (Simplify.)
$x + 4 = 8$ (Division Property of Equality)
$x = 4$ (Subtraction Property of Equality)

33. Equation (Reason)

$-3(-2x + 5) = 12$ (Given)
$-2x + 5 = -4$ (Division Property of Equality)
$-2x = -9$ (Subtraction Property of Equality)
$x = \frac{9}{2}$ (Division Property of Equality)

34. Equation (Reason)

$2(5x) = 3(4x + 6)$ (Given)
$10x = 3(4x + 6)$ (Simplify.)
$10x = 12x + 18$ (Distributive Property)
$-2x = 18$ (Subtraction Property of Equality)
$x = -9$ (Division Property of Equality)

2. Dawson. *Sample answer:* The Hinge Theorem guarantees that Allentown to Dawson is the shortest distance since the included angle is 120°, unlike Allentown to Bakersville where the included angle is 145°.

4. No. *Sample answer:* In a triangle the largest angle should be opposite the longest side. The side measuring 13.55 centimeters is opposite the right angle yet 13.7 centimeters is the longest side in the right triangle on the left.

5c. 24 ft by 16 ft by 32 ft; since two of the sides are 24 feet and 16 feet, the third side must be 32 feet so the dog can run at least 25 feet within the pen.

Lessons 5.4–5.6

1. **MULTI-STEP PROBLEM** In the diagram below, the entrance to the path is halfway between your house and your friend's house.

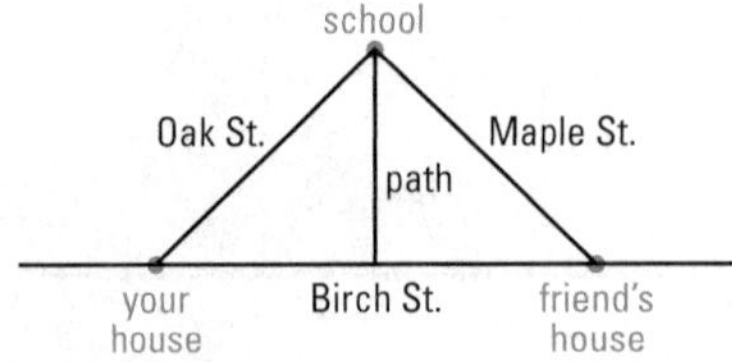

   a. Can you conclude that you and your friend live the same distance from the school if the path bisects the angle formed by Oak and Maple Streets? **no**

   b. Can you conclude that you and your friend live the same distance from the school if the path is perpendicular to Birch Street? **yes**

   c. Your answers to parts (a) and (b) show that a triangle must be isosceles if which two special segments are equal in length? **altitude and median**

2. **SHORT RESPONSE** The map shows your driving route from Allentown to Bakersville and from Allentown to Dawson. Which city, Bakersville or Dawson, is located closer to Allentown? *Explain* your reasoning. **See margin.**

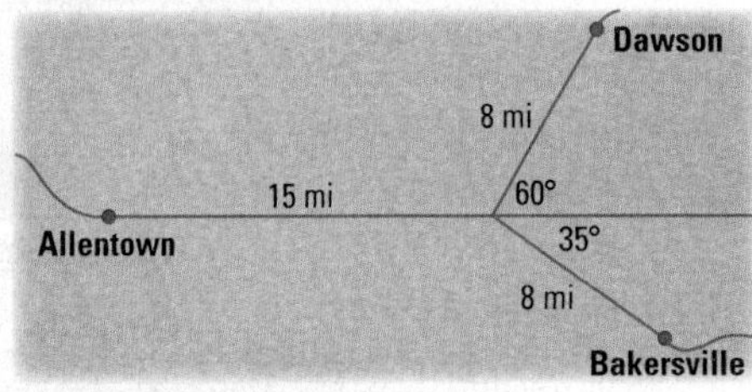

3. **GRIDDED RESPONSE** Find the length of $\overline{AF}$. **18**

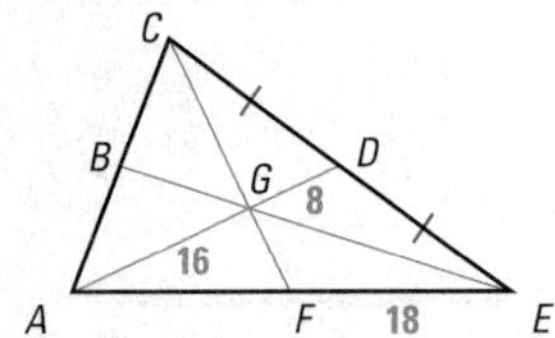

4. **SHORT RESPONSE** In the instructions for creating the terrarium shown, you are given a pattern for the pieces that form the roof. Does the diagram for the red triangle appear to be correct? *Explain* why or why not. **See margin.**

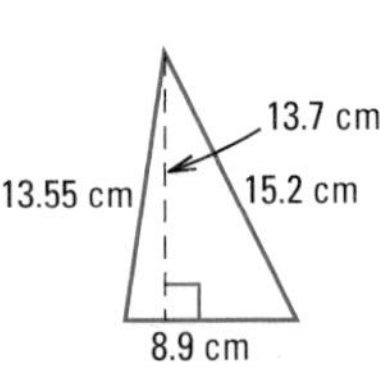

5. **EXTENDED RESPONSE** You want to create a triangular fenced pen for your dog. You have the two pieces of fencing shown, so you plan to move those to create two sides of the pen.

   a. *Describe* the possible lengths for the third side of the pen. **8 ft < ℓ < 40 ft**

   b. The fencing is sold in 8 foot sections. If you use whole sections, what lengths of fencing are possible for the third side? **16 ft, 24 ft, 32 ft**

   c. You want your dog to have a run within the pen that is at least 25 feet long. Which pen(s) could you use? *Explain.* **See margin.**

6. **OPEN-ENDED** In the gem shown, give a possible side length of $\overline{DE}$ if $m\angle EFD > 90°$, $DF = 0.4$ mm, and $EF = 0.63$ mm. **0.63 mm < DE < 1.03 mm**

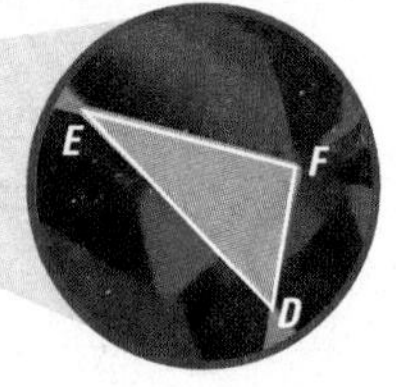

CHAPTER SUMMARY

BIG IDEAS — For Your Notebook

Using Properties of Special Segments in Triangles

Special segment	***Properties to remember***
Midsegment	Parallel to side opposite it and half the length of side opposite it
Perpendicular bisector	Concurrent at the circumcenter, which is: • equidistant from 3 vertices of △ • center of *circumscribed* circle that passes through 3 vertices of △
Angle bisector	Concurrent at the incenter, which is: • equidistant from 3 sides of △ • center of *inscribed* circle that just touches each side of △
Median (connects vertex to midpoint of opposite side)	Concurrent at the centroid, which is: • located two thirds of the way from vertex to midpoint of opposite side • balancing point of △
Altitude (perpendicular to side of △ through opposite vertex)	Concurrent at the orthocenter Used in finding area: If b is length of any side and h is length of altitude to that side, then $A = \frac{1}{2}bh$.

Using Triangle Inequalities to Determine What Triangles are Possible

Sum of lengths of any two sides of a △ is greater than length of third side.	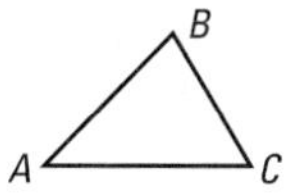 (triangle ABC)	$AB + BC > AC$ $AB + AC > BC$ $BC + AC > AB$
In a △, longest side is opposite largest angle and shortest side is opposite smallest angle.	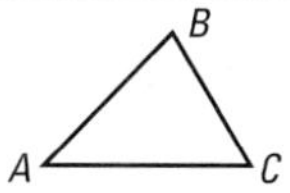 (triangle ABC)	If $AC > AB > BC$, then $m\angle B > m\angle C > m\angle A$. If $m\angle B > m\angle C > m\angle A$, then $AC > AB > BC$.
If two sides of a △ are ≅ to two sides of another △, then the △ with longer third side also has larger included angle.	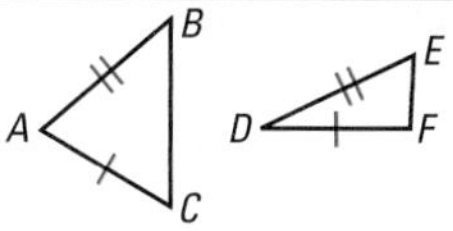 (triangles ABC and DEF)	If $BC > EF$, then $m\angle A > m\angle D$. If $m\angle A > m\angle D$, then $BC > EF$.

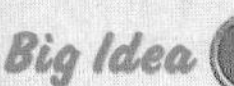

Extending Methods for Justifying and Proving Relationships

Coordinate proof uses the coordinate plane and variable coordinates. *Indirect proof* involves assuming the conclusion is false and then showing that the assumption leads to a contradiction.

Additional Resources

The following resources are available to help review the materials in this chapter.

Chapter 5 Resource Book

- Chapter Review Games and Activities, p. 91
- Cumulative Practice, Chs. 1–5, pp. 94–95

Student Resources in Spanish

eWorkbook

@HomeTutor

Vocabulary Practice

Vocabulary practice is available at **classzone.com**

Extra Example 5.1

In the diagram, $\overline{DF}$ is a midsegment of $\triangle ABC$. Find BC. **24**

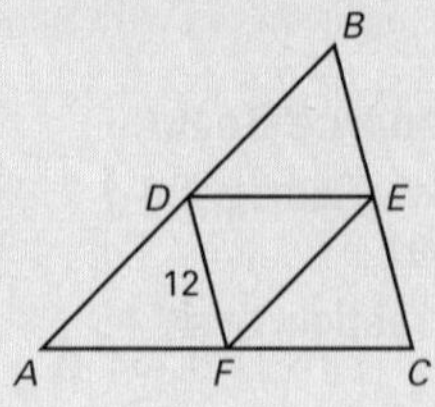

8.

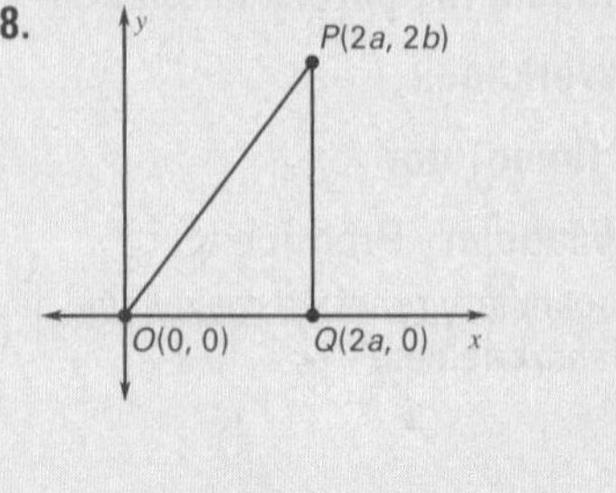

5 CHAPTER REVIEW

@HomeTutor
classzone.com
- Multi-Language Glossary
- Vocabulary practice

REVIEW KEY VOCABULARY

For a list of postulates and theorems, see pp. 926–931.

- midsegment of a triangle, *p. 295*
- coordinate proof, *p. 296*
- perpendicular bisector, *p. 303*
- equidistant, *p. 303*
- concurrent, *p. 305*
- point of concurrency, *p. 305*
- circumcenter, *p. 306*
- incenter, *p. 312*
- median of a triangle, *p. 319*
- centroid, *p. 319*
- altitude of a triangle, *p. 320*
- orthocenter, *p. 321*
- indirect proof, *p. 337*

VOCABULARY EXERCISES

1. Copy and complete: A __?__ is a segment, ray, line, or plane that is perpendicular to a segment at its midpoint. **perpendicular bisector**

2. **WRITING** *Explain* how to draw a circle that is circumscribed about a triangle. What is the center of the circle called? *Describe* its radius.

2. Find the intersection of three perpendicular bisectors of the triangle. Using this point as the center of the circle, draw a circle whose radius is the distance from the point to any of the vertices; circumcenter; the distance from the circumcenter to any of the vertices

In Exercises 3–5, match the term with the correct definition.

3. Incenter **B**
4. Centroid **A**
5. Orthocenter **C**

A. The point of concurrency of the medians of a triangle

B. The point of concurrency of the angle bisectors of a triangle

C. The point of concurrency of the altitudes of a triangle

REVIEW EXAMPLES AND EXERCISES

Use the review examples and exercises below to check your understanding of the concepts you have learned in each lesson of Chapter 5.

5.1 Midsegment Theorem and Coordinate Proof

pp. 295–301

EXAMPLE

In the diagram, $\overline{DE}$ is a midsegment of $\triangle ABC$. Find AC.

By the Midsegment Theorem, $DE = \frac{1}{2}AC$.

So, $AC = 2DE = 2(51) = 102$.

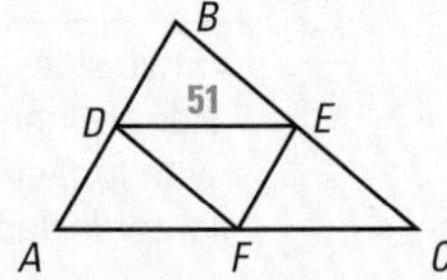

EXERCISES

EXAMPLES 1, 4, and 5 on pp. 295, 297 for Exs. 6–8

Use the diagram above where $\overline{DF}$ and $\overline{EF}$ are midsegments of $\triangle ABC$.

6. If $AB = 72$, find EF. **36**

7. If $DF = 45$, find EC. **45**

8. Graph $\triangle PQR$, with vertices $P(2a, 2b)$, $Q(2a, 0)$, and $O(0, 0)$. Find the coordinates of midpoint S of $\overline{PQ}$ and midpoint T of $\overline{QO}$. Show $\overline{ST} \parallel \overline{PO}$.
$S(2a, b)$, $T(a, 0)$; slope of $\overline{ST}$ is $\frac{b}{a}$ and slope of $\overline{OP}$ is $\frac{b}{a}$; see margin for art.

@HomeTutor
classzone.com
Chapter Review Practice

5.2 Use Perpendicular Bisectors

pp. 303–309

EXAMPLE

Use the diagram at the right to find XZ.

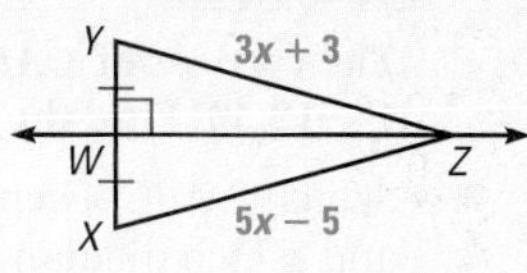

$\overleftrightarrow{WZ}$ is the perpendicular bisector of $\overline{XY}$.

$5x - 5 = 3x + 3$ **By the Perpendicular Bisector Theorem, $ZX = ZY$.**

$x = 4$ **Solve for x.**

▸ So, $XZ = 5x - 5 = 5(4) - 5 = 15$.

EXERCISES

EXAMPLES 1 and 2 on pp. 303–304 for Exs. 9–11

In the diagram, $\overleftrightarrow{BD}$ is the perpendicular bisector of $\overline{AC}$.

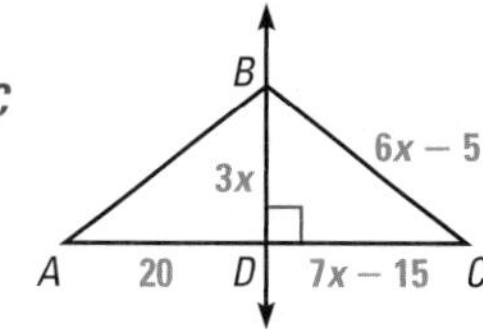

9. What segment lengths are equal? **BA and BC, DA and DC**

10. What is the value of x? **5**

11. Find AB. **25**

5.3 Use Angle Bisectors of Triangles

pp. 310–316

EXAMPLE

In the diagram, N is the incenter of $\triangle XYZ$. Find NL.

Use the Pythagorean Theorem to find NM in $\triangle NMY$.

$c^2 = a^2 + b^2$ **Pythagorean Theorem**

$30^2 = NM^2 + 24^2$ **Substitute known values.**

$900 = NM^2 + 576$ **Multiply.**

$324 = NM^2$ **Subtract 576 from each side.**

$18 = NM$ **Take positive square root of each side.**

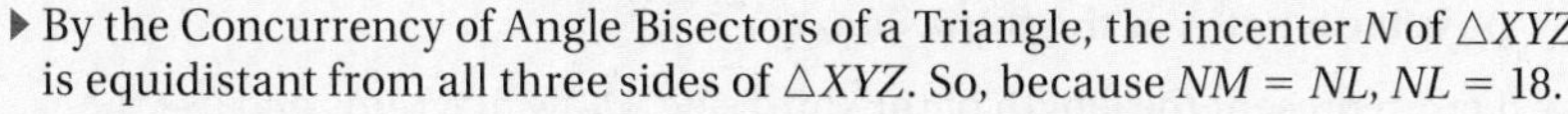

▸ By the Concurrency of Angle Bisectors of a Triangle, the incenter N of $\triangle XYZ$ is equidistant from all three sides of $\triangle XYZ$. So, because $NM = NL$, $NL = 18$.

EXERCISES

EXAMPLE 4 on p. 312 for Exs. 12–13

Point D is the incenter of the triangle. Find the value of x.

12. **5**

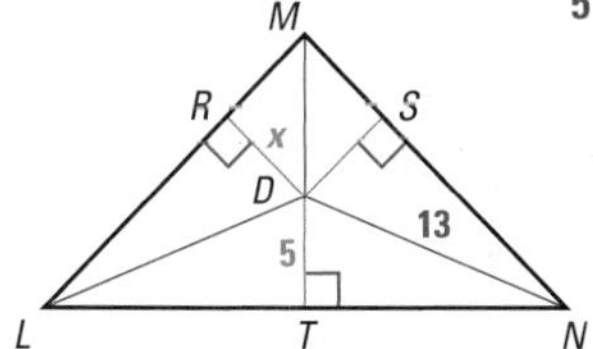

13. **15**

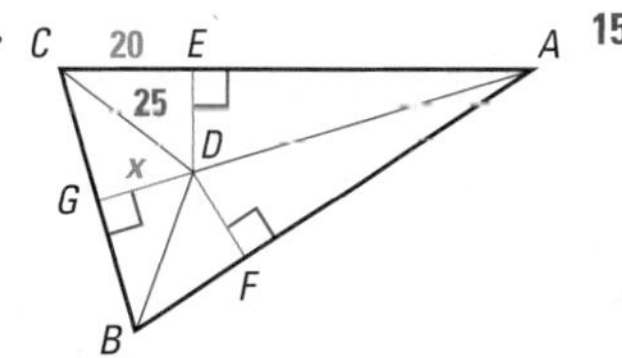

Extra Example 5.2

Uses the diagram to find RS. **29**

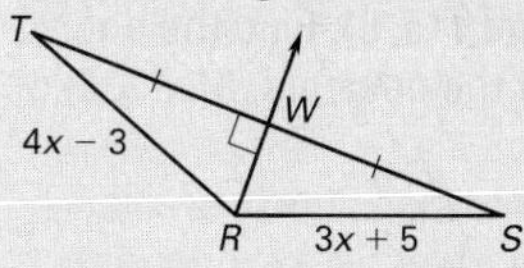

Extra Example 5.3

In the diagram, P is the incenter of $\triangle ABC$. Find PD. **14**

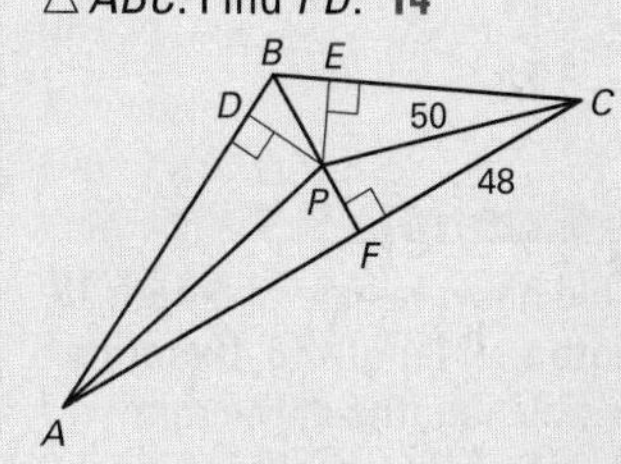

5 CHAPTER REVIEW

Extra Example 5.4

The vertices of $\triangle RST$ are $R(1, 4)$, $S(3, 8)$, and $T(5, 0)$. Find the coordinates of the centroid, M. **(3, 4)**

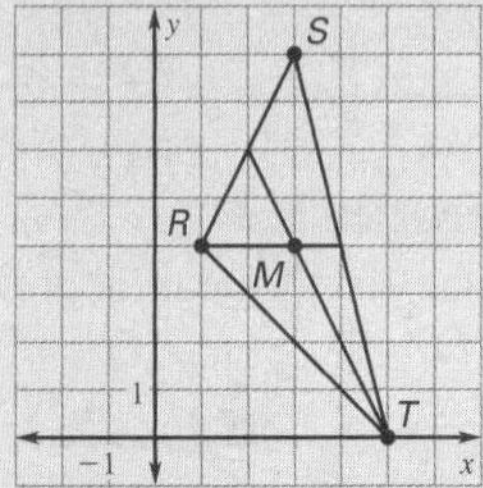

Extra Example 5.5

A triangle has one side of length 13 and another of length 18. Describe the possible lengths of the third side. **The length of the third side must be greater than 5 and less than 31.**

18. ***Sample:***

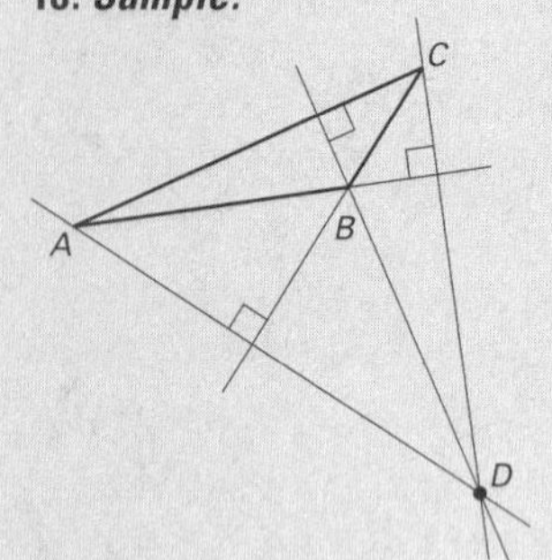

5.4 Use Medians and Altitudes

pp. 319–325

EXAMPLE

The vertices of $\triangle ABC$ are $A(-6, 8)$, $B(0, -4)$, and $C(-12, 2)$. Find the coordinates of its centroid P.

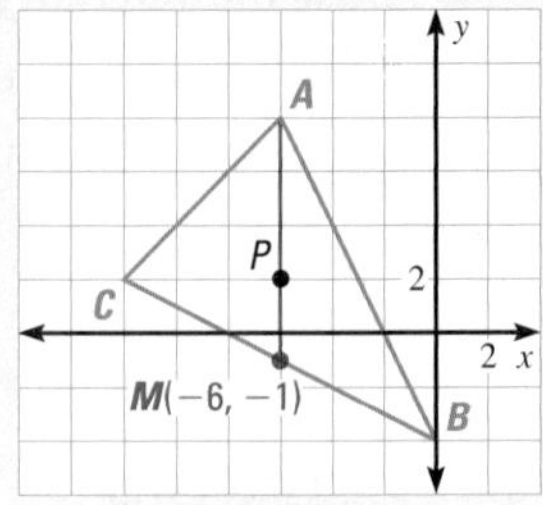

Sketch $\triangle ABC$. Then find the midpoint M of $\overline{BC}$ and sketch median $\overline{AM}$.

$$M\left(\frac{-12+0}{2}, \frac{2+(-4)}{2}\right) = M(-6, -1)$$

The centroid is two thirds of the distance from a vertex to the midpoint of the opposite side.

The distance from vertex $A(-6, 8)$ to midpoint $M(-6, -1)$ is $8 - (-1) = 9$ units.

So, the centroid P is $\frac{2}{3}(9) = 6$ units down from A on $\overline{AM}$.

▸ The coordinates of the centroid P are $(-6, 8 - 6)$, or $(-6, 2)$.

EXERCISES

EXAMPLES 1, 2, and 3 on pp. 319–321 for Exs. 14–18

Find the coordinates of the centroid D of $\triangle RST$.

14. $R(-4, 0)$, $S(2, 2)$, $T(2, -2)$ **(0, 0)**

15. $R(-6, 2)$, $S(-2, 6)$, $T(2, 4)$ **(−2, 4)**

Point Q is the centroid of $\triangle XYZ$.

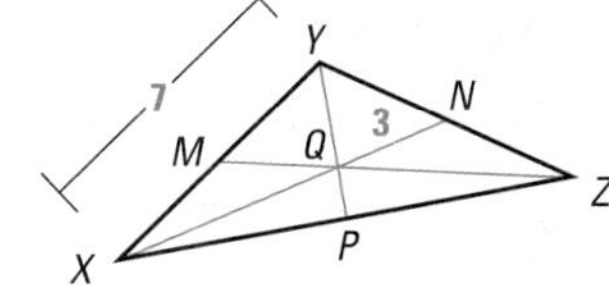

16. Find XQ. **6**

17. Find XM. **3.5**

18. Draw an obtuse $\triangle ABC$. Draw its three altitudes. Then label its orthocenter D. **See margin.**

5.5 Use Inequalities in a Triangle

pp. 328–334

EXAMPLE

A triangle has one side of length 9 and another of length 14. Describe the possible lengths of the third side.

Let x represent the length of the third side. Draw diagrams and use the Triangle Inequality Theorem to write inequalities involving x.

$x + 9 > 14$ $\qquad$ $9 + 14 > x$

$x > 5$ $\qquad$ $23 > x$, or $x < 23$

▸ The length of the third side must be greater than 5 and less than 23.

@HomeTutor
classzone.com
Chapter Review Practice

EXERCISES

EXAMPLES 1, 2, and 3 on pp. 328–330 for Exs. 19–24

Describe **the possible lengths of the third side of the triangle given the lengths of the other two sides.**

19. 4 inches, 8 inches
4 in. < ℓ < 12 in.

20. 6 meters, 9 meters
3 m < ℓ < 15 m

21. 12 feet, 20 feet
8 ft < ℓ < 32 ft

List the sides and the angles in order from smallest to largest.

22.

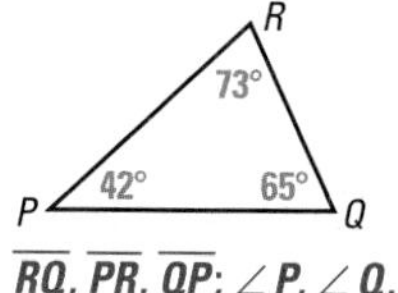

$\overline{RQ}$, $\overline{PR}$, $\overline{QP}$; $\angle P$, $\angle Q$, $\angle R$

23.

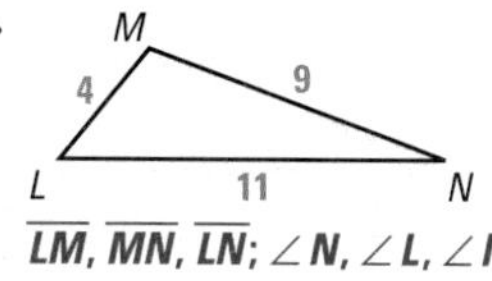

$\overline{LM}$, $\overline{MN}$, $\overline{LN}$; $\angle N$, $\angle L$, $\angle M$

24.

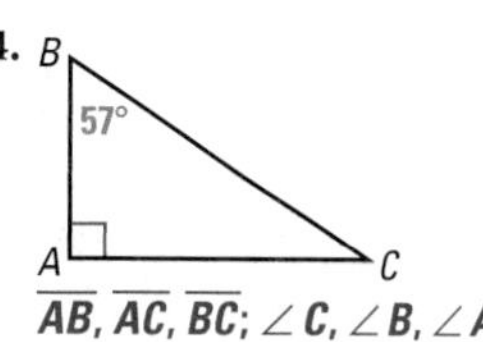

$\overline{AB}$, $\overline{AC}$, $\overline{BC}$; $\angle C$, $\angle B$, $\angle A$

5.6 Inequalities in Two Triangles and Indirect Proof

pp. 335–341

EXAMPLE

How does the length of $\overline{DG}$ compare to the length of $\overline{FG}$?

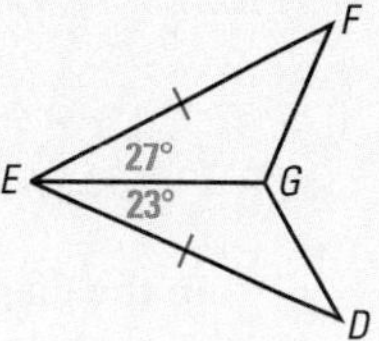

▸ Because 27° > 23°, $m\angle GEF > m\angle GED$. You are given that $\overline{DE} \cong \overline{FE}$ and you know that $\overline{EG} \cong \overline{EG}$. Two sides of $\triangle GEF$ are congruent to two sides of $\triangle GED$ and the included angle is larger so, by the Hinge Theorem, $FG > DG$.

EXERCISES

EXAMPLES 1, 3, and 4 on pp. 336–338 for Exs. 25–27

Copy and complete with <, >, or =.

25. $m\angle BAC$ _?_ $m\angle DAC$ **>**

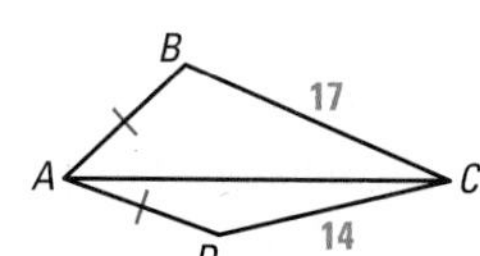

26. LM _?_ KN **=**

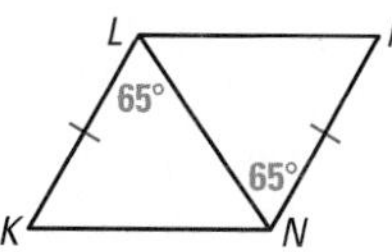

27. Arrange statements A–D in correct order to write an indirect proof of the statement: *If two lines intersect, then their intersection is exactly one point.* **C, B, A, D**

GIVEN ▸ Intersecting lines m and n

PROVE ▸ The intersection of lines m and n is exactly one point.

A. But this contradicts Postulate 5, which states that through any two points there is exactly one line.

B. Then there are two lines (m and n) through points P and Q.

C. Assume that there are two points, P and Q, where m and n intersect.

D. It is false that m and n can intersect in two points, so they must intersect in exactly one point.

Extra Example 5.6

How does the length of $\overline{CD}$ compare to the length of $\overline{CB}$? **$CD < CB$**

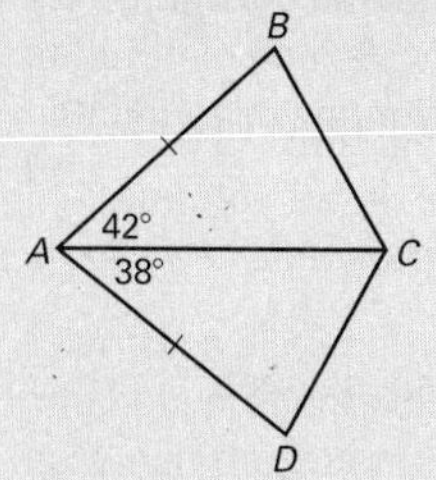

5 CHAPTER TEST

Additional Resources

Assessment Book

- Chapter Test, Levels A, B, C, pp. 64–69
- Standardized Chapter Test, pp. 70–71
- SAT/ACT Chapter Test, pp. 72–73
- Alternative Assessment, pp. 74–75

Test Generator CD-ROM

Chapter Test

Easily-readable reduced copies (with answers) of Chapter Test B, the Standardized Chapter Test, and the Alternative Assessment from the Assessment Book can be found on pp. 292G–292H.

13.

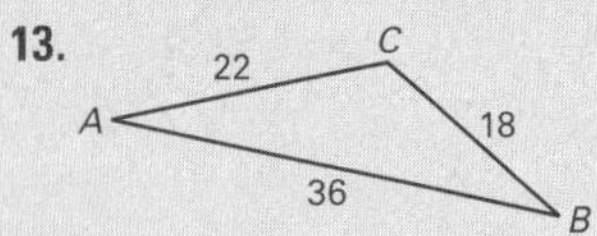

18.

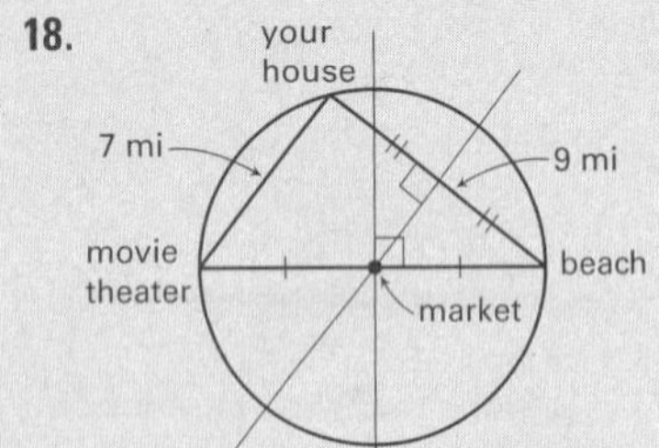

4. 2; $\triangle SWV \cong \triangle UWV$ so $SV = UV$.

5. 3; since $\overrightarrow{QS}$ bisects $\angle PSR$ the Angle Bisector Theorem guarantees $PQ = RQ$.

6. 7; since J is interior to $\angle HGK$ and equidistant from each side of the angle, the Converse of the Angle Bisector Theorem guarantees $m\angle HGJ = m\angle KGJ$.

Two midsegments of $\triangle ABC$ are $\overline{DE}$ and $\overline{DF}$.

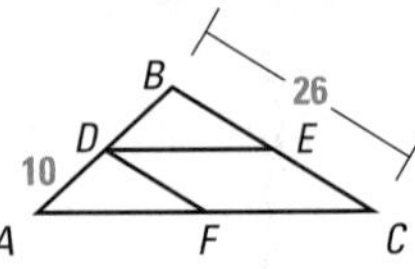

1. Find DB. **10**
2. Find DF. **13**
3. What can you conclude about $\overline{EF}$? **$\overline{EF}$ is a midsegment.**

Find the value of x. *Explain* your reasoning.

4.

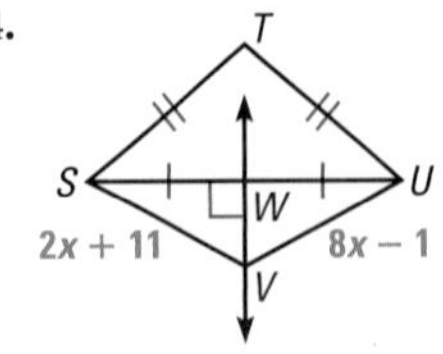

5.

6.

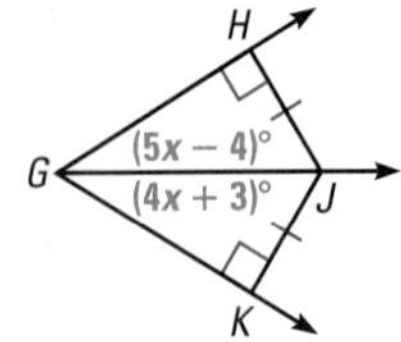

7. In Exercise 4, is point T on the perpendicular bisector of $\overline{SU}$? *Explain.* **Yes; $\triangle STU$ is isosceles.**
8. In the diagram at the right, the angle bisectors of $\triangle XYZ$ meet at point D. Find DB. **7**

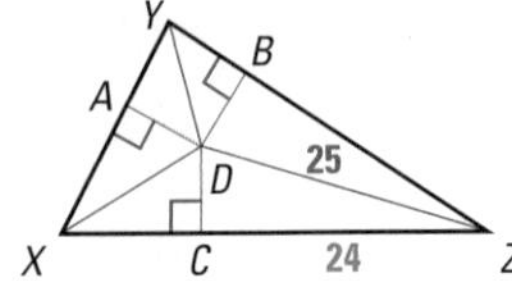

In the diagram at the right, P is the centroid of $\triangle RST$.

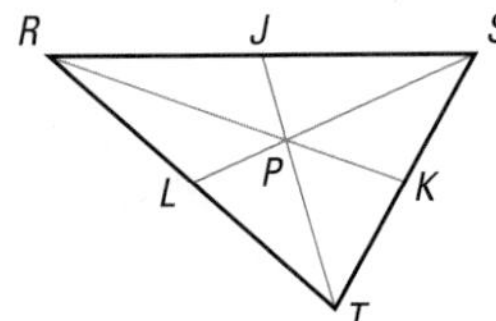

9. If $LS = 36$, find PL and PS. **12, 24**
10. If $TP = 20$, find TJ and PJ. **30, 10**
11. If $JR = 25$, find JS and RS. **25, 50**
12. Is it possible to construct a triangle with side lengths 9, 12, and 22? If not, *explain* why not. **No; the sum of the lengths of any two sides of a triangle must be greater than the length of the third side.**
13. In $\triangle ABC$, $AB = 36$, $BC = 18$, and $AC = 22$. Sketch and label the triangle. List the angles in order from smallest to largest. **$\angle A$, $\angle B$, $\angle C$; see margin for art.**

14. $\overline{MJ}$; the Hinge Theorem guarantees the longer side is opposite the larger angle.

15. $\angle LJK$; the Converse of the Hinge Theorem guarantees the larger angle is opposite the longer side.

In the diagram for Exercises 14 and 15, $JL = MK$. **See margin.**

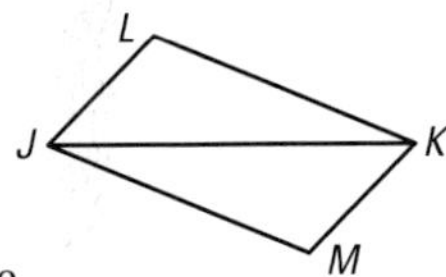

14. If $m\angle JKM > m\angle LJK$, which is longer, $\overline{LK}$ or $\overline{MJ}$? *Explain.*
15. If $MJ < LK$, which is larger, $\angle LJK$ or $\angle JKM$? *Explain.*
16. Write a temporary assumption you could make to prove the conclusion indirectly: *If $RS + ST \neq 12$ and $ST = 5$, then $RS \neq 7$.* **Assume that $RS = 7$.**

Use the diagram in Exercises 17 and 18.

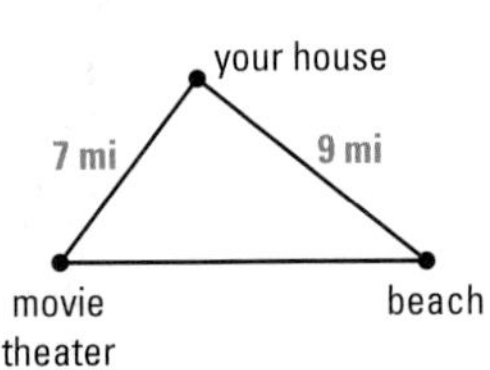

17. *Describe* the range of possible distances from the beach to the movie theater. **2 mi < d < 16 mi**
18. A market is the same distance from your house, the movie theater, and the beach. Copy the diagram and locate the market. **See margin.**

xy ALGEBRA REVIEW

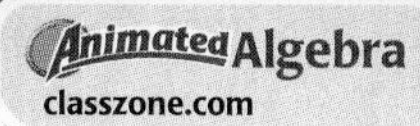

USE RATIOS AND PERCENT OF CHANGE

EXAMPLE 1 *Write a ratio in simplest form*

A team won 18 of its 30 games and lost the rest. Find its win-loss ratio.

The ratio of a to b, $b \neq 0$, can be written as a to b, $a:b$, and $\frac{a}{b}$.

$\frac{\text{wins}}{\text{losses}} = \frac{18}{30 - 18}$ **To find losses, subtract wins from total.**

$= \frac{18}{12} = \frac{3}{2}$ **Simplify.**

▶ The team's win-loss ratio is 3 : 2.

xy EXAMPLE 2 *Find and interpret a percent of change*

A \$50 sweater went on sale for \$28. What is the percent of change in price? The new price is what percent of the old price?

$$\text{Percent of change} = \frac{\text{Amount of increase or decrease}}{\text{Original amount}} = \frac{50 - 28}{50} = \frac{22}{50} = 0.44$$

▶ The price went down, so the change is a decrease. The percent of decrease is 44%. So, the new price is 100%−44% = 56% of the original price.

EXERCISES

EXAMPLE 1 for Exs. 1–3

1. A team won 12 games and lost 4 games. Write each ratio in simplest form.
   a. wins to losses $\frac{3}{1}$
   b. losses out of total games $\frac{1}{4}$
2. A scale drawing that is 2.5 feet long by 1 foot high was used to plan a mural that is 15 feet long by 6 feet high. Write each ratio in simplest form.
   a. length to height of mural $\frac{5}{2}$
   b. length of scale drawing to length of mural $\frac{1}{6}$
3. There are 8 males out of 18 members in the school choir. Write the ratio of females to males in simplest form. $\frac{5}{4}$

EXAMPLE 2 for Exs. 4–13

Find the percent of change.

4. From 75 campsites to 120 campsites **60% increase**
5. From 150 pounds to 136.5 pounds **9% decrease**
6. From \$480 to \$408 **15% decrease**
7. From 16 employees to 18 employees **12.5% increase**
8. From 24 houses to 60 houses **150% increase**
9. From 4000 ft^2 to 3990 ft^2 **0.25% decrease**

Write the percent comparing the new amount to the original amount. Then find the new amount.

10. 75 feet increased by 4% **104%; 78 ft**
11. 45 hours decreased by 16% **84%; 37.8 h**
12. \$16,500 decreased by 85% **15%; \$2475**
13. 80 people increased by 7.5% **107.5%; 86 people**

Extra Example 1

A softball player got 180 hits out of 500 times she batted. Find the ratio of the number of times she got a hit to the number of times she did not get a hit. **9:16**

Extra Example 2

A \$240 MP3 music player was on sale for \$180. What is the percent of change in price? The new price is what percent of the old price? **25%; 75%**

5 ★ Standardized TEST PREPARATION

Using Rubrics

The rubric given on the pupil page is a sample of a three-level rubric. Other rubrics may contain four, five, or six levels. For more information on rubrics, see the *Geometry Toolkit*.

Test-Taking Strategy

Drawing a graph when given coordinates is a useful strategy as it allows students to see what the figure appears to be (in this case, an equilateral triangle). Given the graph, students' calculations should indicate that the triangle is equilateral (or something close to it). If this is not the case, students should realize that either the graph or the calculations are incorrect.

Avoiding Common Errors

Students may simplify $\sqrt{(k-0)^2 + (k\sqrt{3} - 0)^2}$ as $\sqrt{k^2} + \sqrt{(k\sqrt{3})^2} = k + k\sqrt{3}$. Remind them that $\sqrt{a^2 + b^2} \neq \sqrt{a^2} + \sqrt{b^2}$ for nonzero values of a and b.

Study Strategy

Tell students to start by using sample values of k in points O, M, and N to practice using the distance formula. Then have them substitute in the variable k and calculate the distance formula with k.

Scoring Rubric

Full Credit
- solution is complete and correct

Partial Credit
- solution is complete but has errors,

  or
- solution is without error but incomplete

No Credit
- no solution is given,

  or
- solution makes no sense

SHORT RESPONSE QUESTIONS

PROBLEM

The coordinates of the vertices of a triangle are $O(0, 0)$, $M(k, k\sqrt{3})$, and $N(2k, 0)$. Classify $\triangle OMN$ by its side lengths. *Justify* your answer.

Below are sample solutions to the problem. Read each solution and the comments in blue to see why the sample represents full credit, partial credit, or no credit.

SAMPLE 1: Full credit solution

A sample triangle is graphed and an explanation is given.

Begin by graphing $\triangle OMN$ for a given value of k. I chose a value of k that makes $\triangle OMN$ easy to graph. In the diagram, $k = 4$, so the coordinates are $O(0, 0)$, $M(4, 4\sqrt{3})$, and $N(8, 0)$.

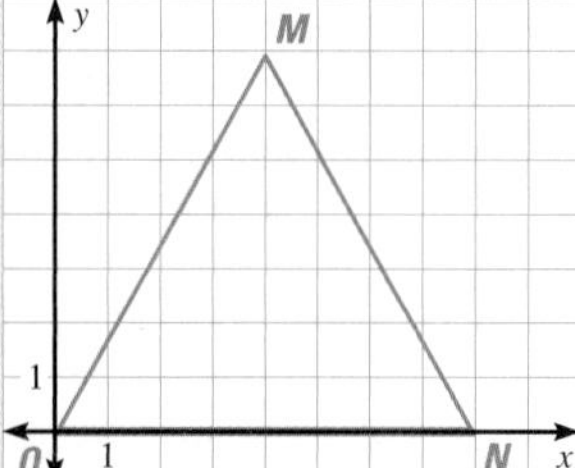

From the graph, it appears that $\triangle OMN$ is equilateral.

The Distance Formula is applied correctly.

To verify that $\triangle OMN$ is equilateral, use the Distance Formula. Show that $OM = MN = ON$ for all values of k.

$$OM = \sqrt{(k-0)^2 + (k\sqrt{3} - 0)^2} = \sqrt{k^2 + 3k^2} = \sqrt{4k^2} = 2|k|$$

$$MN = \sqrt{(2k-k)^2 + (0 - k\sqrt{3})^2} = \sqrt{k^2 + 3k^2} = \sqrt{4k^2} = 2|k|$$

$$ON = \sqrt{(2k-0)^2 + (0-0)^2} = \sqrt{4k^2} = 2|k|$$

The answer is correct.

Because all of its side lengths are equal, $\triangle OMN$ is an equilateral triangle.

SAMPLE 2: Partial credit solution

Use the Distance Formula to find the side lengths.

A calculation error is made in finding OM and MN. The value of $(k\sqrt{3})^2$ is $k^2 \cdot (\sqrt{3})^2$, or $3k^2$, not $9k^2$.

$$OM = \sqrt{(k-0)^2 + (k\sqrt{3} - 0)^2} = \sqrt{k^2 + 9k^2} = \sqrt{10k^2} = k\sqrt{10}$$

$$MN = \sqrt{(2k-k)^2 + (0 - k\sqrt{3})^2} = \sqrt{k^2 + 9k^2} = \sqrt{10k^2} = k\sqrt{10}$$

$$ON = \sqrt{(2k-0)^2 + (0-0)^2} = \sqrt{4k^2} = 2k$$

The answer is incorrect.

Two of the side lengths are equal, so $\triangle OMN$ is an isosceles triangle.

SAMPLE 3: Partial credit solution

The answer is correct, but the explanation does not justify the answer.

Graph $\triangle OMN$ and compare the side lengths.

From $O(0, 0)$, move right k units and up $k\sqrt{3}$ units to $M(k, k\sqrt{3})$. Draw $\overline{OM}$. To draw $\overline{MN}$, move k units right and $k\sqrt{3}$ units down from M to $N(2k, 0)$. Then draw $\overline{ON}$, which is $2k$ units long. All side lengths appear to be equal, so $\triangle OMN$ is equilateral.

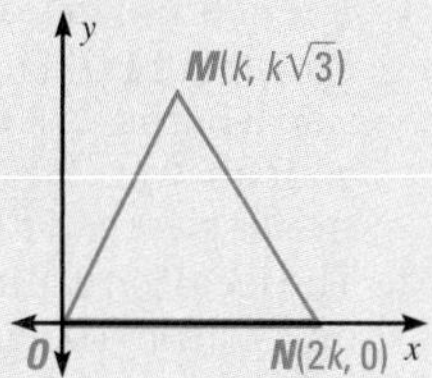

SAMPLE 4: No credit solution

The reasoning and the answer are incorrect.

You are not given enough information to classify $\triangle OMN$ because you need to know the value of k.

Standards

12.0 Students find and use measures of sides and of interior and exterior angles **of triangles** and polygons **to classify figures and solve problems.**

PRACTICE Apply the Scoring Rubric

Use the rubric on page 350 to score the solution to the problem below as *full credit, partial credit,* or *no credit. Explain* your reasoning.

PROBLEM You are a goalie guarding the goal $\overline{NQ}$. To make a goal, Player P must send the ball across $\overline{NQ}$. Is the distance you may need to move to block the shot greater if you stand at Position A or at Position B? *Explain.*

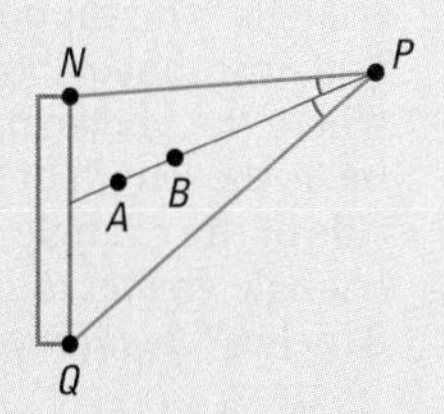

1. At either position, you are on the angle bisector of ∠NPQ. So, in both cases you are equidistant from the angle's sides. Therefore, the distance you need to move to block the shot from the two positions is the same.

1. Partial credit; the initial set-up of the problem is correct but no diagram is provided and the conclusion reached is incorrect.

2. Both positions lie on the angle bisector of ∠NPQ. So, each is equidistant from $\overline{PN}$ and $\overline{PQ}$.

The sides of an angle are farther from the angle bisector as you move away from the vertex. So, A is farther from $\overline{PN}$ and from $\overline{PQ}$ than B is.

The distance may be greater if you stand at Position A than if you stand at Position B.

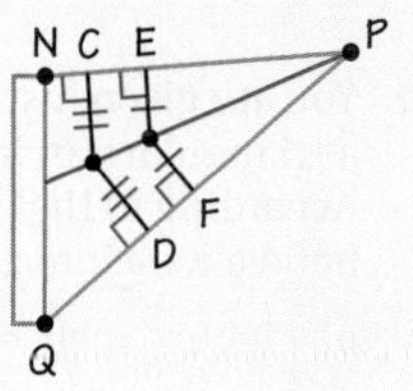

2. Full credit; the initial set-up of the problem is correct, a correct diagram is provided, and the answer is correct.

3. Because Position B is farther from the goal, you may need to move a greater distance to block the shot if you stand at Position B.

3. No credit; the reasoning and answer are incorrect.

Avoiding Common Errors

For the practice problem, students may assume that since A is closer to $\overline{NQ}$, then position A is automatically the correct answer. Remind them that the problem depends on properties of an angle bisector, so those properties must be considered.

2. 20 ft; the sides of the small triangle are the midsegments of the bigger triangle. You know that the perimeter of the bigger one is twice the perimeter of the smaller one by using the Midsegment Theorem.

5. $(-1, -4)$; the median from C is a segment on the vertical line $x = -1$. Since $(-1, 5)$ is the midpoint of $\overline{AB}$, the distance to the centroid is 3 units making point C 6 units from the centroid.

8. It is $\frac{1}{4}$ the area of the original triangle. *Sample answer:* Consider $\triangle ABC$ with vertices $A(2a, 0)$, $B(-2a, 0)$, and $C(0, 2a)$ whose area is $4a^2$ and $\triangle DEF$ (the triangle formed by the midsegments of $\triangle ABC$) with vertices $D(a, a)$, $E(0, 0)$, and $F(-a, a)$ whose area is a^2.

5 ★ Standardized TEST PRACTICE

SHORT RESPONSE

1. The coordinates of $\triangle OPQ$ are $O(0, 0)$, $P(a, a)$, and $Q(2a, 0)$. Classify $\triangle OPQ$ by its side lengths. Is $\triangle OPQ$ a right triangle? *Justify* your answer. **Isosceles; yes; the slope of $\overline{PQ}$ is -1 and the slope of $\overline{OP}$ is 1.**

2. The local gardening club is planting flowers on a traffic triangle. They divide the triangle into four sections, as shown. The perimeter of the middle triangle is 10 feet. What is the perimeter of the traffic triangle? *Explain* your reasoning. **See margin.**

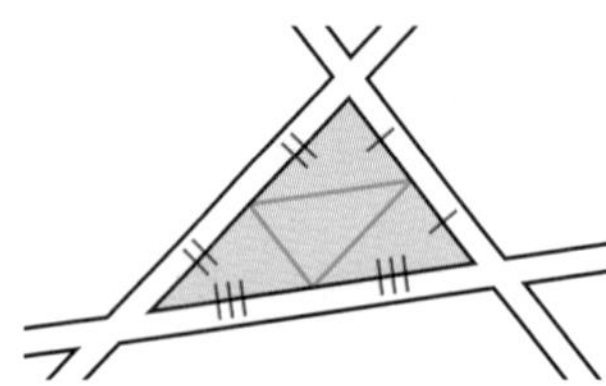

3. A wooden stepladder with a metal support is shown. The legs of the stepladder form a triangle. The support is parallel to the floor, and positioned about five inches above where the midsegment of the triangle would be. Is the length of the support from one side of the triangle to the other side of the triangle *greater than*, *less than*, or *equal to* 8 inches? *Explain* your reasoning.

Less than; if the support were the midsegment, it would measure 8 inches; since it is above the midsegment, it has to be smaller.

4. You are given instructions for making a triangular earring from silver wire. According to the instructions, you must first bend a wire into a triangle with side lengths of $\frac{3}{4}$ inch, $\frac{5}{8}$ inch, and $1\frac{1}{2}$ inches. *Explain* what is wrong with the first part of the instructions.
The sum of any two sides of a triangle must be greater than the third, in this example $\frac{3}{4}$ in. + $\frac{5}{8}$ in. < $1\frac{1}{2}$ in.

5. The centroid of $\triangle ABC$ is located at $P(-1, 2)$. The coordinates of A and B are $A(0, 6)$ and $B(-2, 4)$. What are the coordinates of vertex C? *Explain* your reasoning. **See margin.**

6. A college club wants to set up a booth to attract more members. They want to put the booth at a spot that is equidistant from three important buildings on campus. Without measuring, decide which spot, A or B, is the correct location for the booth. *Explain* your reasoning.
***B*; Concurrency of Perpendicular Bisectors Theorem**

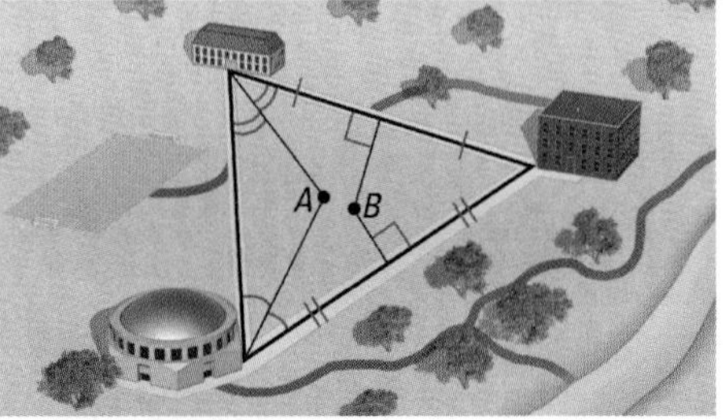

7. Contestants on a television game show must run to a well (point W), fill a bucket with water, empty it at either point A or B, and then run back to the starting point (point P). To run the shortest distance possible, which point should contestants choose, A or B? *Explain* your reasoning. ***A*; the Hinge Theorem guarantees $\overline{AP}$ is shorter than $\overline{BP}$.**

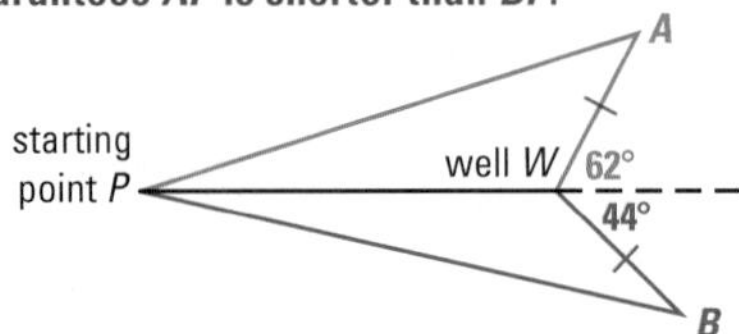

8. How is the area of the triangle formed by the midsegments of a triangle related to the area of the original triangle? Use an example to *justify* your answer. **See margin.**

9. You are bending an 18 inch wire to form an isosceles triangle. *Describe* the possible lengths of the base if the vertex angle is larger than 60°. *Explain* your reasoning.
6 in. < ℓ < 9 in.; the Hinge Theorem guarantees that the base must be longer than either side.

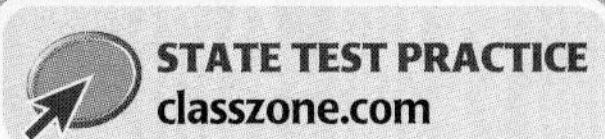

MULTIPLE CHOICE

10. If $\triangle ABC$ is obtuse, which statement is always true about its circumcenter P? **D**

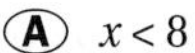

Ⓐ P is equidistant from $\overline{AB}$, $\overline{BC}$, and $\overline{AC}$.

Ⓑ P is inside $\triangle ABC$.

Ⓒ P is on $\triangle ABC$.

Ⓓ P is outside $\triangle ABC$.

11. Which conclusion about the value of x can be made from the diagram? **A**

Ⓐ $x < 8$

Ⓑ $x = 8$

Ⓒ $x > 8$

Ⓓ No conclusion can be made.

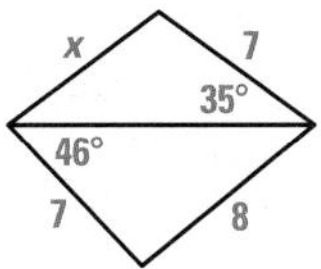

GRIDDED ANSWER

12. Find the perimeter of $\triangle RST$. **30.6**

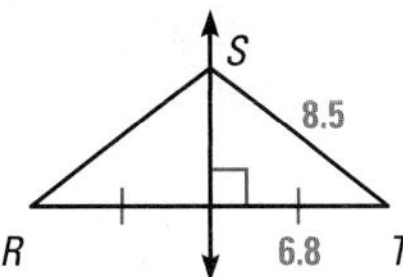

13. In the diagram, N is the incenter of $\triangle ABC$. Find NF. **5**

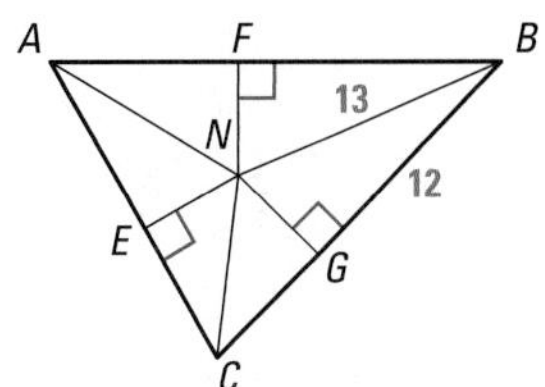

EXTENDED RESPONSE

14. A new sport is to be played on the triangular playing field shown with a basket located at a point that is equidistant from each side line.

a. Copy the diagram and show how to find the location of the basket. *Describe* your method. **See margin.**

b. What theorem can you use to verify that the location you chose in part (a) is correct? *Explain.* **Concurrency of Angle Bisectors Theorem; it states that the angle bisectors of a triangle intersect at a point that is equidistant from the sides of the triangle.**

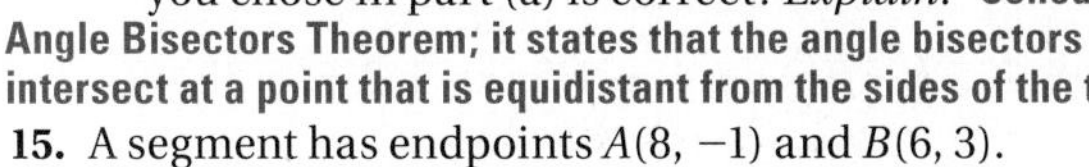

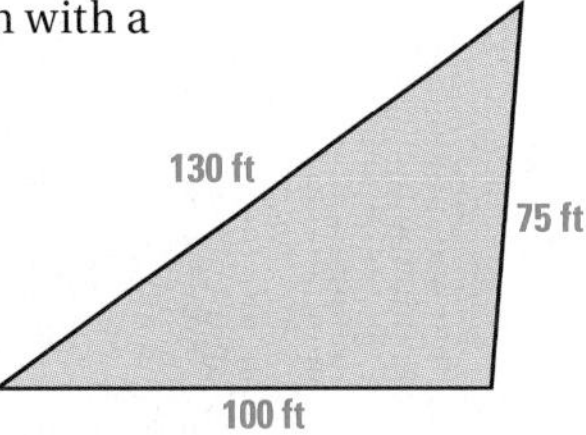

15. A segment has endpoints $A(8, -1)$ and $B(6, 3)$.

a. Graph $\overline{AB}$. Then find the midpoint C of $\overline{AB}$ and the slope of $\overline{AB}$. **$C(7, 1)$, -2; see margin for art.**

b. Use what you know about slopes of perpendicular lines to find the slope of the perpendicular bisector of $\overline{AB}$. Then sketch the perpendicular bisector of $\overline{AB}$ and write an equation of the line. *Explain* your steps. **See margin.**

c. Find a point D that is a solution to the equation you wrote in part (b). Find AD and BD. What do you notice? What theorem does this illustrate? ***Sample answer:* $(5, 0)$; $\sqrt{10}$, $\sqrt{10}$; $AD = BD$; Perpendicular Bisector Theorem**

16. The coordinates of $\triangle JKL$ are $J(-2, 2)$, $K(4, 8)$, and $L(10, -4)$.

a. Find the coordinates of the centroid M. Show your steps.

b. Find the mean of the x-coordinates of the three vertices and the mean of the y-coordinates of the three vertices. *Compare* these results with the coordinates of the centroid. What do you notice? **4, 2; they are the same as the x- and y-coordinates of the centroid.**

c. Is the relationship in part (b) true for $\triangle JKP$ with $P(1, -1)$? *Explain.* **Yes; the centroid of $\triangle JKP$ is $(1, 3)$. The mean of the x-coordinates is 1 and the mean of the y-coordinates is 3.**

16a. $(4, 2)$. *Sample answer:* The equation of the line passing through midpoint $(1, 5)$ of $\overline{JK}$ and L with slope -1 is $y = -x + 6$. The equation of the line passing through the midpoint $(4, -1)$ of $\overline{JL}$ and K with undefined slope is $x = 4$. The intersection is the centroid.

14a.

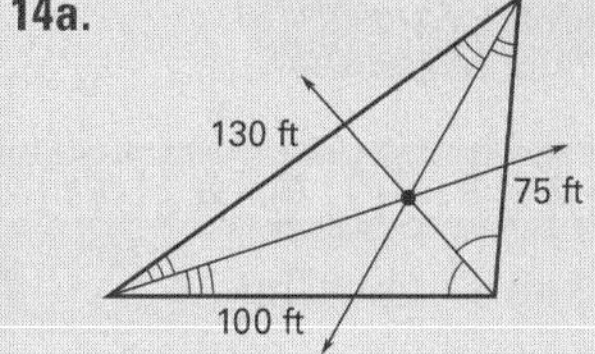

The angle bisectors will intersect in the point that is equidistant from each side.

15a.

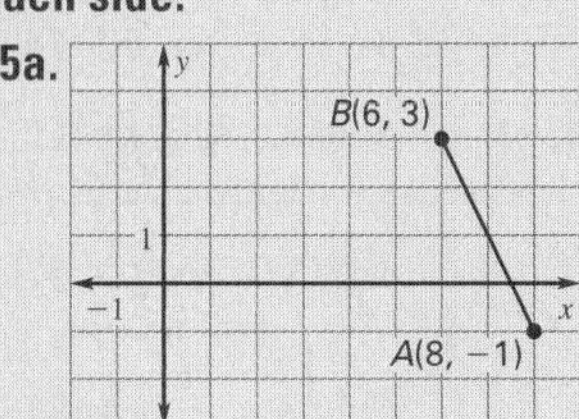

15b. $\frac{1}{2}$;

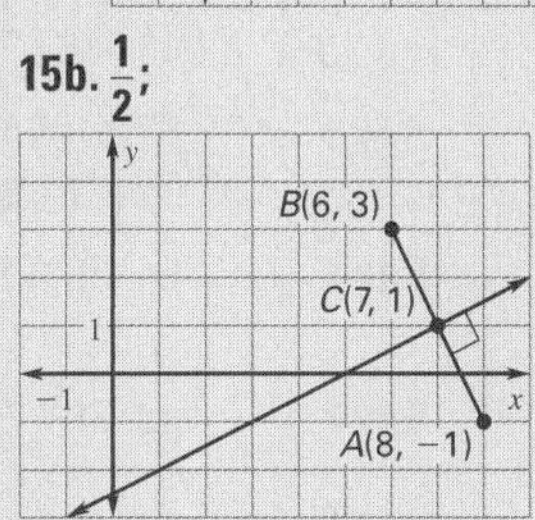

$y = \frac{1}{2}x - \frac{5}{2}$; using the point $(7, 1)$ and slope $\frac{1}{2}$ you get $y - 1 = \frac{1}{2}(x - 7)$.

6 Pacing and Assignment Guide

REGULAR SCHEDULE

Pre-AP For pacing and assignments for a Pre-AP course, see the *Geometry Toolkit*.

Lesson	Les. Day	BASIC	AVERAGE	ADVANCED
6.1	Day 1	EP p. 902 Exs. 4–6; pp. 360–363 Exs. 1–22, 38–41, 57, 76–80	pp. 360–363 Exs. 1, 2, 5–8, 11–22, 37–41, 46–51, 53, 57, 58	pp. 360–363 Exs. 1, 2, 8–10, 12, 13, 16–19, 21, 22, 37–41, 46–51, 53, 56*, 57
	Day 2	pp. 360–363 Exs. 23–37, 42–45, 59–64, 72–75	pp. 360–363 Exs. 25–28, 33–35, 42–45, 52, 54, 59–67, 72–80	pp. 360–363 Exs. 28–30, 34–36, 42–45, 52, 54, 55, 60–71*, 72–80 even
6.2	Day 1	SRH p. 875 Exs. 32–36; pp. 367–370 Exs. 1–16, 22–29, 38–40	pp. 367–370 Exs. 1, 2, 4–6, 8–18, 22–33, 38, 39	pp. 367–370 Exs. 1, 2, 5, 6, 9, 10–18 even, 19–38*, 40
6.3	Day 1	pp. 376–379 Exs. 1–10, 14–18, 31, 32	pp. 376–379 Exs. 1–10, 14–18, 23–26, 31, 32	pp. 376–379 Exs. 1, 2, 4–10, 14–18, 23–26, 29–32*
	Day 2	pp. 376–379 Exs. 11–13, 19–22, 33–35, 40–48	pp. 376–379 Exs. 11–13, 19–22, 27, 28, 33–36, 40–48 even	pp. 376–379 Exs. 11, 12, 19–22, 27, 28, 33–39*, 42, 45, 48
6.4	Day 1	EP p. 900 Exs. 7–11; pp. 384–387 Exs. 1–20, 31–35, 41–49 odd	pp. 384–387 Exs. 1, 2–12 even, 15–25, 31–37, 42–48 even	pp. 384–387 Exs. 1, 2, 3–7 odd, 11–14, 16–30*, 32, 34–40*, 44, 45, 49
6.5	Day 1	pp. 391–395 Exs. 1–6, 28–30, 32, 39–42	pp. 391–395 Exs. 1–6, 18–23, 28–30, 32, 40, 42	pp. 391–395 Exs. 1, 2, 5, 6, 18–23, 25–30*, 32, 41
	Day 2	pp. 391–395 Exs. 7–17, 31, 33, 34, 43, 44	pp. 391–395 Exs. 7–17, 24, 31, 33–37, 43	pp. 391–395 Exs. 8, 9, 11, 12, 14–17, 24, 31, 33–38*, 44
6.6	Day 1	pp. 400–403 Exs. 1–7, 13, 16, 22, 34–36	pp. 400–403 Exs. 1–7, 13, 16, 22, 30–36	pp. 400–403 Exs. 1–7, 13, 16, 22, 30–36
	Day 2	pp. 400–403 Exs. 8–12, 14, 15, 21, 23–26, 30–33	pp. 400–403 Exs. 8–12, 14, 15, 17–19, 21, 23–28	pp. 400–403 Exs. 8, 10, 11, 14, 15, 17–21*, 23–29*
6.7	Day 1	EP p. 903 Exs. 36–38; pp. 412–415 Exs. 1–8, 15–18, 35–40	pp. 412–415 Exs. 1–8, 15–18, 22, 35–40	pp. 412–415 Exs. 1, 2, 5–8, 15–18, 22–24*, 35–40
	Day 2	pp. 412–415 Exs. 9–14, 25–30, 41–43	pp. 412–415 Exs. 9–14, 19–21, 25–31, 42	pp. 412–415 Exs. 9–14, 19–21, 26–34*, 43
Review	Day 1	pp. 418–421 Exs. 1–21	pp. 418–421 Exs. 1–21	pp. 418–421 Exs. 1–21
Assess	Day 1	Chapter 6 Test	Chapter 6 Test	Chapter 6 Test
Yearly Pacing		Chapter 6 Total – 14 days	Chapters 1–6 Total – 80 days	Remaining – 80 days

*Challenge Exercises EP = Extra Practice SRH = Skills Review Handbook

BLOCK SCHEDULE

DAY 1	DAY 2	DAY 3	DAY 4	DAY 5	DAY 6	DAY 7
6.1	6.2	6.3 (CONT.)	6.5	6.6	6.7	REVIEW
pp. 360–363 Exs. 1, 2, 5–8, 11–22, 25–28, 33–35, 37–54, 57, 59–67, 72–80	pp. 367–370 Exs. 1, 2, 4–6, 8–18, 22–33, 38, 39	pp. 367–379 Exs. 11–13, 19–22, 27, 28, 33–36, 40–48 even	pp. 391–395 Exs. 1–24, 28–37, 40, 42, 43	pp. 400–403 Exs. 1–19, 21–28, 30–36	pp. 412–415 Exs. 1–22, 25–31, 35–40, 42	pp. 418–421 Exs. 1–21
	6.3	6.4				ASSESS
	pp. 367–379 Exs. 1–10, 14–18, 23–26, 31, 32	pp. 384–387 Exs. 1, 2–12 even, 15–25, 31–37, 42–48 even				Chapter 6 Test
Yearly Pacing	Chapter 6 Total – 7 days	Chapters 1–6 Total – 40 days	Remaining – 40 days			

Chapter Resource Guide 6

RESOURCE MANAGER

Chapter Resource Book							
CHAPTER SUPPORT							
Parents as Partners (Chapter Overview with home involvement exercises and activity)						p. 1	
LESSON SUPPORT	**6.1**	**6.2**	**6.3**	**6.4**	**6.5**	**6.6**	**6.7**
Teaching Guide/Lesson Plan	p. 3	p. 17	p. 30	p. 44	p. 57	p. 71	p. 85
Activity Masters	p. 5				p. 59		
Technology Activities & Keystrokes						p. 73	p. 87
Activity Support Masters							
Practice (3 levels)	p. 6	p. 19	p. 32	p. 46	p. 60	p. 74	p. 89
Study Guide	p. 12	p. 25	p. 38	p. 52	p. 66	p. 80	p. 95
Catch-Up for Absent Students	p. 14	p. 27	p. 40	p. 54	p. 68	p. 82	p. 97
Problem Solving/Application	p. 15	p. 28	p. 41	p. 55	p. 69	p. 83	p. 98
Challenge Practice	p. 16	p. 29	p. 43	p. 56	p. 70	p. 84	p. 99
REVIEW							
Chapter Review Games and Activities		p. 100		Cumulative Practice		p. 103	
Project with Rubric		p. 101		Resource Book Answers		A1	

Transparencies	*6.1*	*6.2*	*6.3*	*6.4*	*6.5*	*6.6*	*6.7*
Warm-Up/Daily Homework Quiz	✔	✔	✔	✔	✔	✔	✔
Notetaking Guide	✔	✔	✔	✔	✔	✔	✔
Teacher Support	✔			✔			✔
Answer Transparencies	✔	✔	✔	✔	✔	✔	✔

ASSESSMENT BOOK

Quizzes	p. 76	SAT/ACT Chapter Test	p. 87
Chapter Tests (3 levels)	p. 79	Alternative Assessment with Rubric	p. 89
Standardized Chapter Test	p. 85	Cumulative Test	p. 91

TECHNOLOGY

- Easy Planner
- Test and Practice Generator
- Power Presentations
- @HomeTutor
- Activity Generator
- Animated Geometry
- Classzone.com
- eEdition Plus Online
- eWorkbook Plus Online
- ML Assessment System

ADDITIONAL RESOURCES

- Worked-Out Solution Key
- Notetaking Guide
- Practice Wookbook
- Geometry Toolkit
- Benchmark Tests
- Remediation Book
- Spanish Study Guide
- Spanish Assessment Book
- Student Resources in Spanish
- Multi-Language Visual Glossary

LESSON 6.1 Practice B
For use with pages 356–363

Simplify the ratio.

1. \$12 : \$16   3 : 4
2. $\frac{32 \text{ in.}^2}{8 \text{ in.}^2}$ $\frac{4}{1}$
3. $\frac{6 \text{ cm}}{14 \text{ cm}}$ $\frac{3}{7}$
4. $\frac{10 \text{ in.}}{2 \text{ ft}}$ $\frac{5}{12}$
5. 3 gallons : 10 quarts   6 : 5
6. 28 oz : 2 lb $\frac{7}{8}$

Find the ratio of the width to the length of the rectangle. Then simplify the ratio.

7.
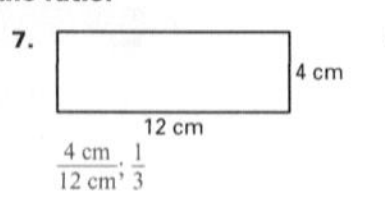

$\frac{4 \text{ cm}}{12 \text{ cm}}$; $\frac{1}{3}$

8.
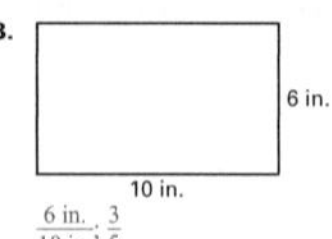

$\frac{6 \text{ in.}}{10 \text{ in.}}$; $\frac{3}{5}$

9.
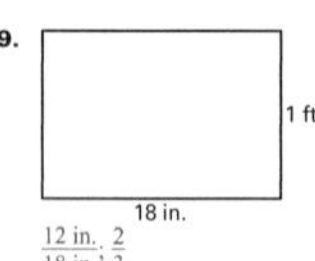

$\frac{12 \text{ in.}}{18 \text{ in.}}$; $\frac{2}{3}$

Use the number line to find the ratio of the distances.

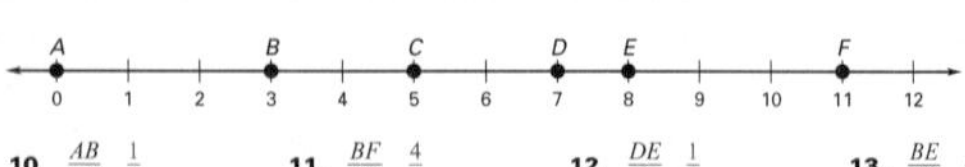

10. $\frac{AB}{CF}$ $\frac{1}{2}$
11. $\frac{BF}{CD}$ $\frac{4}{1}$
12. $\frac{DE}{AC}$ $\frac{1}{5}$
13. $\frac{BE}{AD}$ $\frac{5}{7}$

14. **Perimeter** The perimeter of a rectangle is 56 inches. The ratio of the length to the width is 6 : 1. Find the length and the width.   24 in., 4 in.

15. **Area** The area of a rectangle is 525 square centimeters. The ratio of the length to the width is 7 : 3. Find the length and the width.   35 cm, 15 cm

The measures of the angles of a triangle are in the extended ratio given. Find the measures of the angles of the triangle.

16. 1 : 7 : 10   10°, 70°, 100°
17. 5 : 6 : 7   50°, 60°, 70°
18. 7 : 14 : 15   35°, 70°, 75°

Solve the proportion.

19. $\frac{4}{5} = \frac{x}{15}$ 12
20. $\frac{5}{8} = \frac{20}{y}$ 32
21. $\frac{z+2}{4} = \frac{27}{12}$ 7
22. $\frac{3}{x} = \frac{1}{x-6}$ 9
23. $\frac{3}{m+5} = \frac{2}{m+1}$ 7
24. $\frac{2}{k-1} = \frac{5}{3k-4}$ 3

LESSON 6.1 Practice B *continued*
For use with pages 356–363

Find the geometric mean of the two numbers.

25. 2 and 8   4
26. 3 and 9 $3\sqrt{3}$
27. 7 and 14 $7\sqrt{2}$
28. 8 and 16 $8\sqrt{2}$
29. 10 and 12 $2\sqrt{30}$
30. 9 and 13 $3\sqrt{13}$

Let $x = 6$, $y = 3$, and $z = 2$. Write the ratio in simplest form.

31. $\frac{2x+y}{3}$ $\frac{5}{1}$
32. $\frac{4z-3}{x}$ $\frac{5}{6}$
33. $\frac{z+2y}{2x-4}$ $\frac{1}{1}$

Solve the proportion.

34. $\frac{12}{x} = \frac{x}{4}$ $\pm 4\sqrt{3}$
35. $\frac{y-2}{2} = \frac{2y-3}{5}$ 4
36. $\frac{8}{z-2} = \frac{z+2}{4}$ ± 6

In Exercises 37–39, the ratio of two side lengths for the triangle is given. Solve for the variable.

37. $AC:AB$ is 3 : 4.   9

C, x, A, 12, B

38. $AB:CB$ is 2 : 1.   3

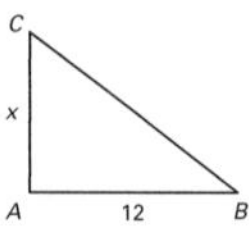

39. $AC:BC$ is 7 : 4.   4

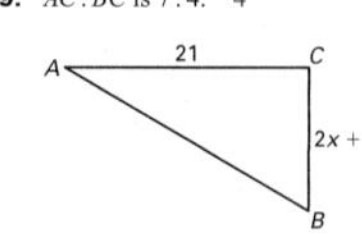

40. **Area** The perimeter of the rectangular front lawn of the library is 192 feet. The ratio of the length to the width is 5 : 3. Find the area of the lawn.   2160 ft^2

In Exercises 41 and 42, use the following information.

Golden Gate Bridge You purchase a scale model of the Golden Gate Bridge which is located near San Francisco, California. The model states that the scale is 1 inch : 50 feet. The actual length of the bridge is 8980 feet.

41. What is the length of the model?   179.6 in.

42. The model is approximately 15 inches tall. What is the actual height of the bridge?   750 ft

LESSON 6.2 Practice B
For use with pages 364–370

Copy and complete the statement.

1. If $\frac{6}{x} = \frac{5}{y}$, then $\frac{6}{5} = \frac{?}{?}$. $\frac{x}{y}$
2. If $\frac{x}{12} = \frac{y}{26}$, then $\frac{x}{y} = \frac{?}{?}$. $\frac{6}{13}$
3. If $\frac{x}{4} = \frac{7}{y}$, then $\frac{x+4}{4} = \frac{?}{?}$. $\frac{y+7}{y}$
4. If $\frac{9}{2} = \frac{x}{y}$, then $\frac{11}{2} = \frac{?}{?}$. $\frac{x+y}{y}$

Decide whether the statement is *true* or *false*.

5. If $\frac{x}{y} = \frac{8}{3}$, then $\frac{y}{x} = \frac{3}{8}$.   true
6. If $\frac{x}{y} = \frac{8}{3}$, then $\frac{3}{x} = \frac{y}{8}$.   false
7. If $\frac{x}{y} = \frac{8}{3}$, then $\frac{x}{8} = \frac{3}{y}$.   false
8. If $\frac{x}{y} = \frac{8}{3}$, then $\frac{x}{8} = \frac{y}{3}$.   true
9. If $\frac{x}{y} = \frac{8}{3}$, then $\frac{x+8}{8} = \frac{y+3}{3}$.   true
10. If $\frac{x}{y} = \frac{8}{3}$, then $\frac{x+2y}{y} = \frac{14}{3}$.   true

Use the diagram and the given information to find the unknown length.

11. Given $\frac{AB}{BC} = \frac{AE}{ED}$, find BC.   2

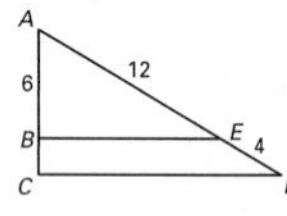

12. Given $\frac{AB}{BC} = \frac{AE}{ED}$, find BC.   10

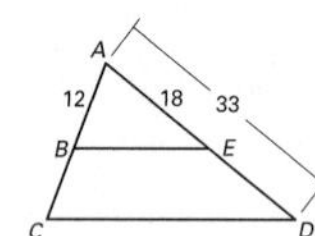

13. Given $\frac{FD}{FE} = \frac{CD}{BE}$, find BE.   12

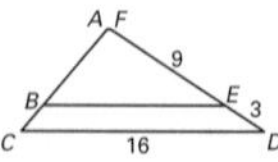

14. Given $\frac{AB}{BC} = \frac{FE}{ED}$, find AC. $\frac{25}{3}$

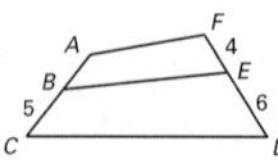

15. **Multiple Choice** If m, n, p, and q are four different numbers, and the proportion $\frac{m}{n} = \frac{p}{q}$ is true, which of the following is false?   B

A. $mq = pn$ **B.** $m = p$ and $n = q$ **C.** $\frac{n+m}{m} = \frac{q+p}{p}$

LESSON 6.2 Practice B *continued*
For use with pages 364–370

16. **Error Analysis** Describe and correct the error made in the reasoning.

If $\frac{a}{5} = \frac{b}{3}$, then $\frac{5}{a} = \frac{b}{3}$. ✗

If two ratios are equal, then their reciprocals are equal. If $\frac{a}{5} = \frac{b}{3}$, then $\frac{5}{a} = \frac{3}{b}$.

17. **Map Scale** On a map, two neighboring towns are 2.4 inches apart. The actual straight line distance between the two towns is 36 miles. What is the scale of the map?   1 in. : 15 mi

18. **Collinear Points** The points $(-3, -3)$, $(-1, 1)$, and $(2, y)$ are collinear. Find the value of y by solving the proportion: $\frac{1-(-3)}{-1-(-3)} = \frac{y-1}{2-(-1)}$.   7

19. **Sales Tax** You plan on purchasing a new \$25,000 vehicle. Recently, a friend bought a \$22,500 vehicle and paid an additional \$1575 in sales tax. Assuming the same sales tax rate applies, how much should you expect to pay in sales tax?   \$1750

In Exercises 20 and 21, use the following information.

Scale Model You purchase a scale model of a train. The model states that the scale is 1 inch : 5.4 feet.

20. If the model is 10 inches long, how long is the actual train?   54 ft

21. The actual height of the train is 13.5 feet, how tall is the model?   2.5 in.

In Exercises 22 and 23, use the following information.

Mexican Pesos In November, 2005, the exchange rate of Mexican pesos to American dollars was 10.77 to 1. While on vacation, you paid 205 pesos for a sombrero at a gift shop.

22. What was the price of the sombrero in American dollars?   \$19.03

23. If the exchange rate were 9.24 Mexican pesos to 1 American dollar, what would have the cost been in American dollars?   \$22.19

In Exercises 24 and 25, use the following information.

Canadian Dollars In November, 2005, the exchange rate of Canadian dollars to American dollars was 1 to 0.85. A Canadian citizen paid \$12.28 in American dollars for lunch while visiting New York City.

24. What was the price of the lunch in Canadian dollars?   \$14.45

25. If the exchange rate were 1.28 Canadian dollars to 1 American dollar, what would have the cost been in Canadian dollars?   \$15.72

LESSON 6.3
Practice B
For use with pages 371–379

List all pairs of congruent angles for the figures. Then write the ratios of the corresponding sides in a statement of proportionality.

1. $\triangle ABC \sim \triangle DFE$
$\angle A \cong \angle D, \angle B \cong \angle F, \angle C \cong \angle E$

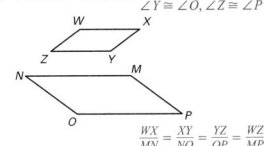

$\frac{AB}{DF} = \frac{BC}{FE} = \frac{AC}{DE}$

2. $\square WXYZ \sim \square MNOP$ $\angle W \cong \angle M, \angle X \cong \angle N, \angle Y \cong \angle O, \angle Z \cong \angle P$

$\frac{WX}{MN} = \frac{XY}{NO} = \frac{YZ}{OP} = \frac{WZ}{MP}$

3. Multiple Choice Triangles *ABC* and *DEF* are similar. Which statement is not correct? C

A. $\frac{AB}{DE} = \frac{BC}{EF}$ **B.** $\frac{CA}{FD} = \frac{AB}{DE}$ **C.** $\angle A \cong \angle F$

Determine whether the polygons are similar. If they are, write a similarity statement and find the scale factor.

4. no

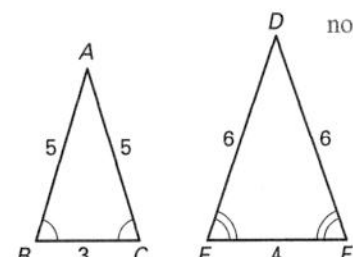

5. yes; $\square BCDA \sim \square WXYZ$; 4

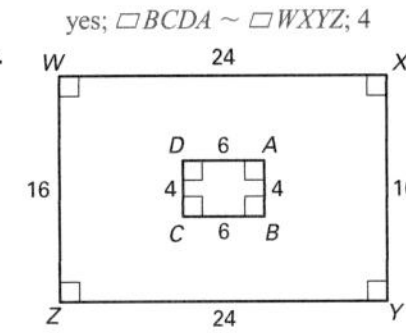

In the diagram, *WXYZ* ~ *MNOP*.

6. Find the scale factor of *WXYZ* to *MNOP*. $\frac{4}{5}$

7. Find the values of *x*, *y* and *z*. 15, 8, 135

8. Find the perimeter of *WXYZ*. 40

9. Find the perimeter of *MNOP*. 50

10. Find the ratio of the perimeter of *MNOP* to the perimeter of *WXYZ*. $\frac{5}{4}$

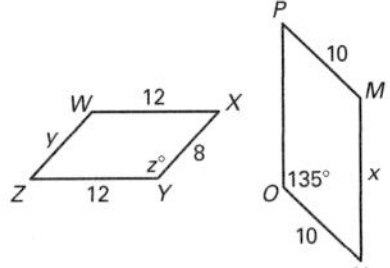

LESSON 6.3

LESSON 6.3
Practice B *continued*
For use with pages 371–379

The two triangles are similar. Find the value of the variables.

11. $m = 11, n = 4$

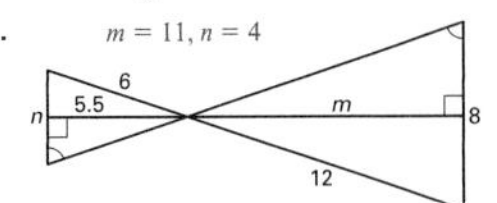

12. $m = 8$

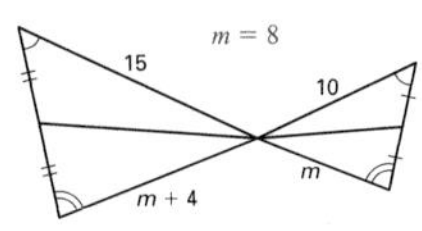

In Exercises 13 and 14, use the following information.

Similar Triangles Triangles *RST* and *WXY* are similar. The side lengths of $\triangle RST$ are 10 inches, 14 inches, and 20 inches, and the length of an altitude is 6.5 inches. The shortest side of $\triangle WXY$ is 15 inches long.

13. Find the lengths of the other two sides of $\triangle WXY$. $XY = 30$ in., $WY = 21$ in.

14. Find the length of the corresponding altitude in $\triangle WXY$. 9.75 in.

15. Multiple Choice The ratio of one side of $\triangle ABC$ to the corresponding side of a similar $\triangle DEF$ is 4 : 3. The perimeter of $\triangle DEF$ is 24 inches. What is the perimeter of $\triangle ABC$? C

A. 18 inches **B.** 24 inches **C.** 32 inches

In the diagram, $\triangle XYZ \sim \triangle MNP$.

16. Find the scale factor of $\triangle XYZ$ to $\triangle MNP$. $\frac{2}{5}$

17. Find the unknown side lengths of both triangles. $XY = 3.6, PN = 15$

18. Find the length of the altitude shown in $\triangle XYZ$. 2.32

19. Find and compare the areas of both triangles. Area of $\triangle XYZ = 6.96$; Area of $\triangle MNP = 43.5$; The area of similar triangles differ by the scale factor squared.

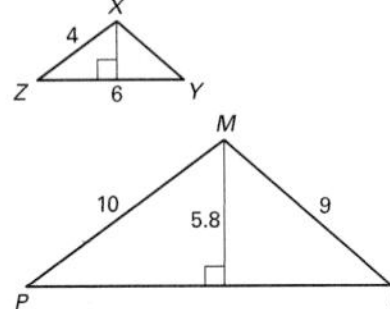

In Exercises 20–22, use the following information.

Swimming Pool The community park has a rectangular swimming pool enclosed by a rectangular fence for sunbathing. The shape of the pool is similar to the shape of the fence. The pool is 30 feet wide. The fence is 50 feet wide and 100 feet long.

20. What is the scale factor of the pool to the fence? $\frac{3}{5}$

21. What is the length of the pool? 60 ft

22. Find the area reserved strictly for sunbathing. 3200 ft²

LESSON 6.3

LESSON 6.4
Practice B
For use with pages 381–387

Use the diagram to complete the statement.

1. $\triangle ABC \sim$ __?__ $\triangle DEF$

2. $\frac{AB}{?} = \frac{?}{EF} = \frac{CA}{?}$ DE, BC, FD

3. $\angle B \cong$ __?__ $\angle E$

4. $\frac{?}{12} = \frac{8}{?}$ x, y

5. $x =$ __?__ $\frac{9}{2}$

6. $y =$ __?__ $\frac{64}{3}$

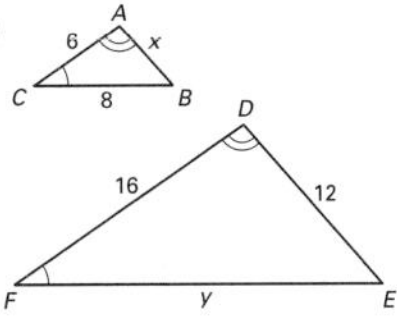

Determine whether the triangles are similar. If they are, write a similarity statement.

7. $\triangle ABC \sim \triangle ZYX$

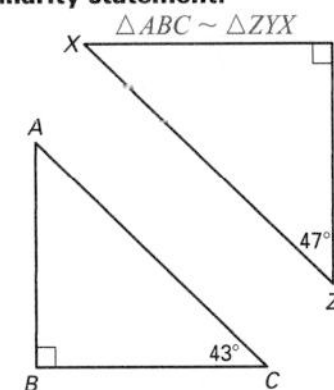

8. not similar

9. $\triangle JLK \sim \triangle YXZ$

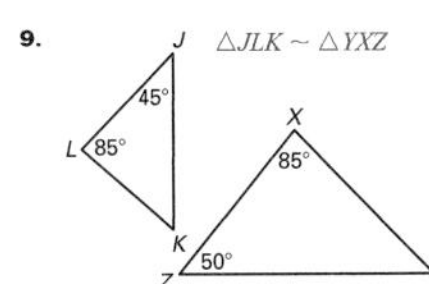

10. $\triangle JNK \sim \triangle JML$

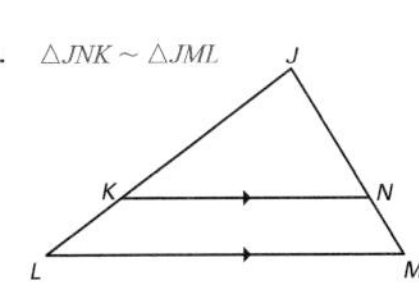

11. $\triangle PTQ \sim \triangle PRS$

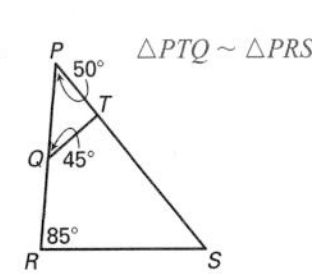

12. $\triangle KGH \sim \triangle KNM$

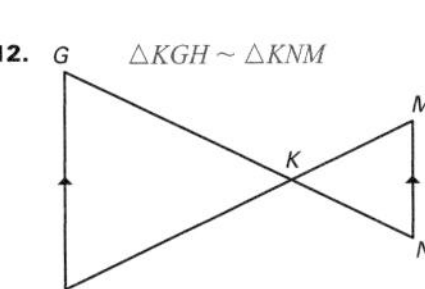

LESSON 6.4

LESSON 6.4
Practice B *continued*
For use with pages 381–387

13. Multiple Choice In the diagram at the right, find the length of *BC*. D

A. $\frac{28}{5}$ **B.** 6

C. 3 **D.** $\frac{20}{7}$

14. *Sample answer:* $\angle BAE \cong \angle DEA, \angle DCA \cong \angle BCE, \angle ADB \cong \angle EBD$

In Exercises 14–17, use the diagram at the right.

14. List three pairs of congruent angles. See above.

15. Name two pairs of similar triangles and write a similarity statement for each. *Sample answer:* $\triangle CAB \sim \triangle CED$, $\triangle ABD \sim \triangle EDB$

16. Is $\triangle ACD \sim \triangle BCE$? no

17. Is $\triangle AED \cong \triangle EAD$? yes

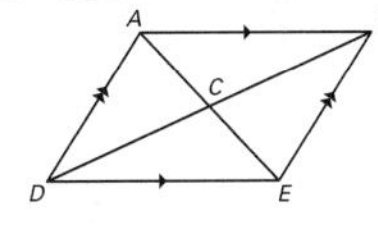

In Exercises 18–21, use the diagram at the right. Find the coordinates of point *Z* so that $\triangle RST \sim \triangle RXZ$.

18. $R(0, 0), S(0, 4), T(-8, 0), X(0, 2), Z(x, y)$ (4, 0)

19. $R(0, 0), S(0, 6), T(-6, 0), X(0, 2), Z(x, y)$ (2, 0)

20. $R(0, 0), S(0, 10), T(-20, 0), X(0, 6), Z(x, y)$ (12, 0)

21. $R(0, 0), S(0, 7), T(-9, 0), X(0, 4), Z(x, y)$ $\left(\frac{36}{7}, 0\right)$

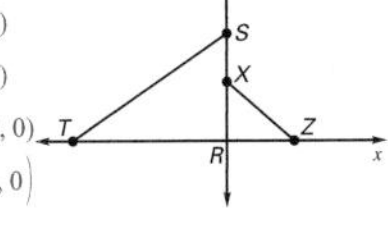

22. Multiple Choice Triangles *ABC* and *DEF* are right triangles that are similar. $\overline{AB}$ and $\overline{BC}$ are the legs of the first triangle. $\overline{DE}$ and $\overline{EF}$ are the legs of the second triangle. Which of the following is false? B

A. $\angle A \cong \angle D$ **B.** $AC = DF$ **C.** $\frac{AC}{DF} = \frac{AB}{DE}$

In Exercises 23–25, use the following information.

Flag Pole In order to estimate the height *h* of a flag pole, a 5 foot tall male student stands so that the tip of his shadow coincides with the tip of the flag pole's shadow. This scenario results in two similar triangles as shown in the diagram.

23. Why are the two overlapping triangles similar? See below.

24. Using the similar triangles, write a proportion that models the situation. $\frac{h}{5} = \frac{18}{6}$

25. What is the height *h* (in feet) of the flag pole? 15 ft

23. Both triangles are right triangles and have $\angle A$ in common. Because both triangles have two congruent angles, the triangles are similar.

LESSON 6.4

LESSON 6.5

Practice B

For use with pages 388–395

Is either $\triangle LMN$ or $\triangle RST$ similar to $\triangle ABC$?

1. $\triangle RST$

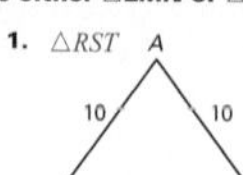
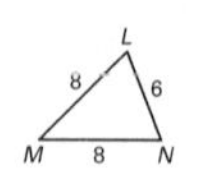
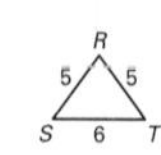

2. $\triangle LMN$

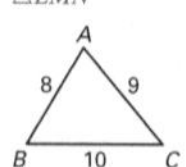
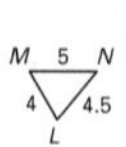
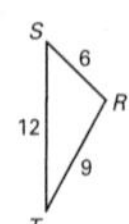

Determine whether the two triangles are similar. If they are similar, write a similarity statement and find the scale factor of $\triangle A$ to $\triangle B$.

3. $\triangle JLK \sim \triangle YXZ$; 1 : 4

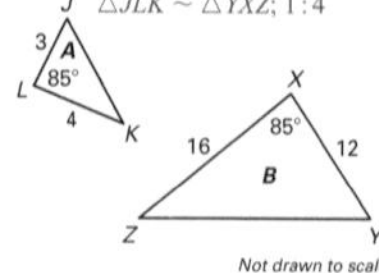

Not drawn to scale

4. not similar

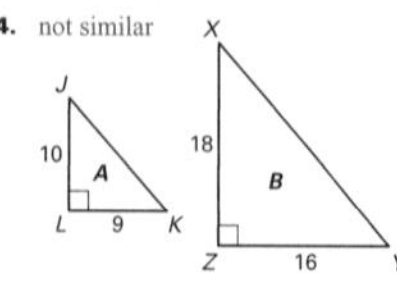

5. **Algebra** Find the value of m that makes $\triangle ABC \sim \triangle DEF$ when $AB = 3$, $BC = 4$, $DE = 2m$, $EF = m + 5$, and $\angle B \cong \angle E$. 3

Show that the triangles are similar and write a similarity statement. *Explain* your reasoning.

6.

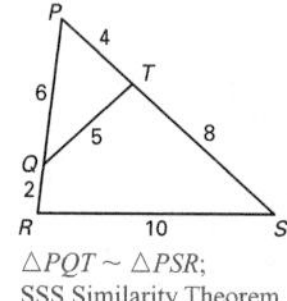

$\triangle PQT \sim \triangle PSR$; SSS Similarity Theorem

7.

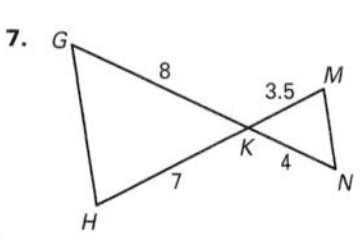

$\triangle KNM \sim \triangle KGH$; SAS Similarity Theorem

LESSON 6.5

Practice B *continued*

For use with pages 388–395

8. **Multiple Choice** In the diagram at the right, $\triangle ACE \sim \triangle DCB$. Find the length of AB. B

A. 12 **B.** 18

C. $\frac{35}{2}$ **D.** $\frac{30}{7}$

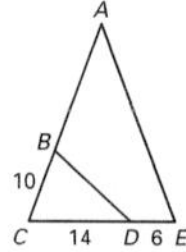

Sketch the triangles using the given description. *Explain* whether the two triangles can be similar.

9. The side lengths of $\triangle ABC$ are 8, 10 and 14. The side lengths of $\triangle DEF$ are 16, 20 and 26.

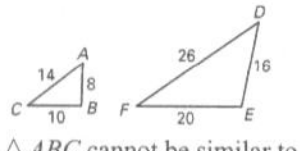

$\triangle ABC$ cannot be similar to $\triangle DEF$ because not all corresponding sides are proportional.

10. In $\triangle ABC$, $AB = 15$, $BC = 24$ and $m\angle B = 38°$. In $\triangle DEF$, $DE = 5$, $EF = 8$ and $m\angle E = 38°$.

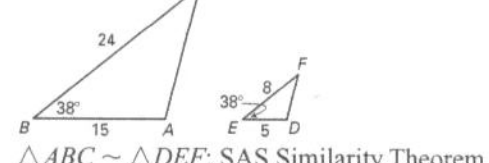

$\triangle ABC \sim \triangle DEF$; SAS Similarity Theorem

In Exercises 11–14, use the diagram at the right to copy and complete the statement.

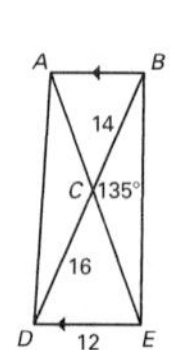

11. $\triangle ABC \sim$ __?__ $\triangle EDC$

12. $m\angle DCE =$ __?__ 45°

13. $AB =$ __?__ 10.5

14. $m\angle CAB + m\angle ABC =$ __?__ 135°

In Exercises 15 and 16, use the following information.

Pine Tree In order to estimate the height h of a tall pine tree, a student places a mirror on the ground and stands where she can see the top of the tree, as shown. The student is 6 feet tall and stands 3 feet from the mirror which is 11 feet from the base of the tree.

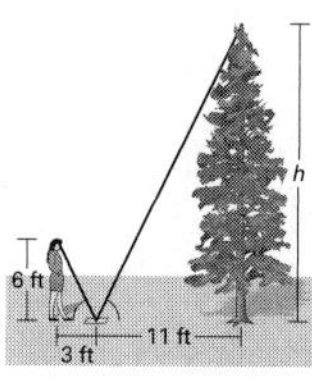

15. What is the height h (in feet) of the pine tree? 22 ft

16. Another student also wants to see the top of the tree. The other student is 5.5 feet tall. If the mirror is to remain 3 feet from the student's feet, how far from the base of the tree should the mirror be placed? 12 ft

LESSON 6.6

Practice B

For use with pages 396–403

Use the figure to complete the proportions.

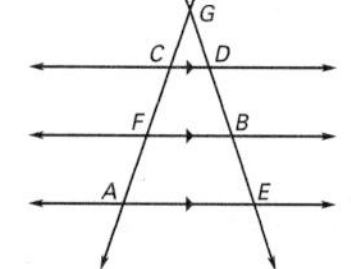

1. $\frac{GC}{CF} = \frac{?}{DB}$ GD

2. $\frac{AF}{FC} = \frac{?}{BD}$ EB

3. $\frac{CD}{FB} = \frac{GD}{?}$ GB

4. $\frac{AE}{CD} = \frac{GE}{?}$ GD

5. $\frac{FG}{AG} = \frac{FB}{?}$ AE

6. $\frac{GD}{GE} = \frac{?}{AE}$ CD

Use the given information to determine whether $\overline{BD} \parallel \overline{AE}$.

7. yes

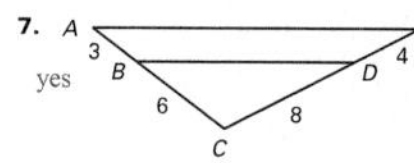

8. no

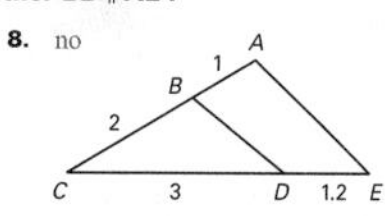

9. no

10. yes

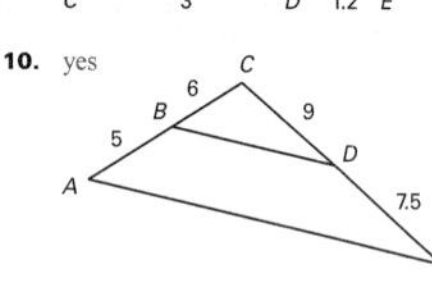

Determine the length of each segment.

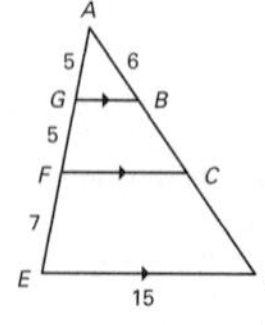

11. $\overline{BC}$ 6

12. $\overline{FC}$ $8\frac{14}{17}$

13. $\overline{GB}$ $4\frac{7}{17}$

14. $\overline{CD}$ $8\frac{2}{5}$

In Exercises 15–18, find the value of x.

15. 8

16. $2\frac{1}{3}$

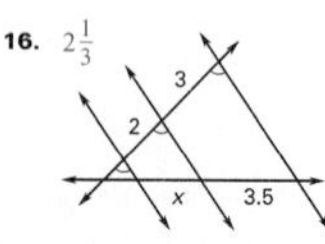

LESSON 6.6

Practice B *continued*

For use with pages 396–403

17. $5\sqrt{2}$

18. 21

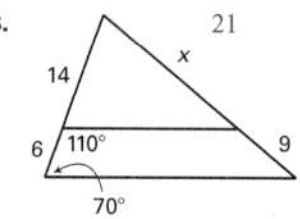

In Exercises 19–21, find the value of the variable.

19. x 2

20. m $3\frac{3}{4}$

21. a $1\frac{1}{4}$

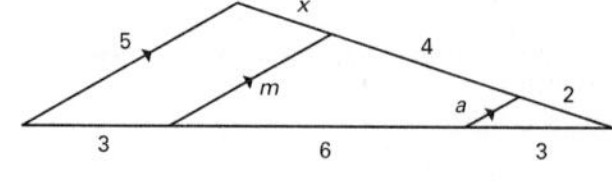

Use construction tools to divide the line segment into the given number of equal parts. 22–24. Check student's work.

22. 4

23. 3

24. 2

25. **Maps** On the map below, 51st Street and 52nd Street are parallel. Charlie walks from point A to point B and then from point B to point C. You walk directly from point A to point C.

a. How many more feet did Charlie walk than you? 600 ft

b. Park Avenue is perpendicular to 51st Street. Is Park Avenue perpendicular to 52nd Street? *Explain.* yes; If a transversal is perpendicular to one of two parallel lines, then it is perpendicular to the other.

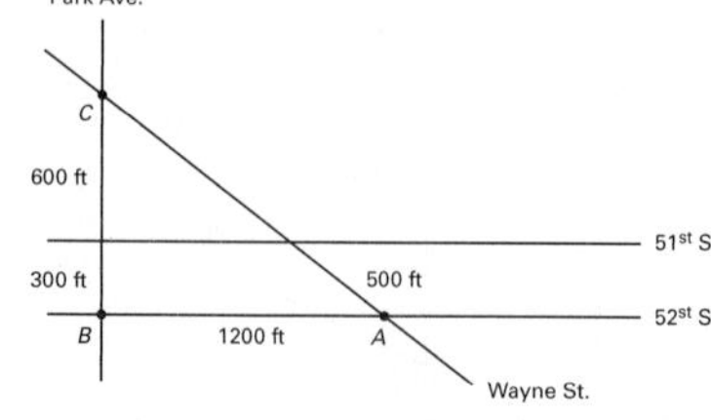

Practice B
For use with pages 408–415

Draw a dilation of the figure using the given scale factor.

1. $k = 2$ **2.** $k = \frac{1}{4}$

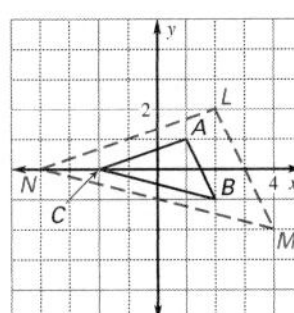

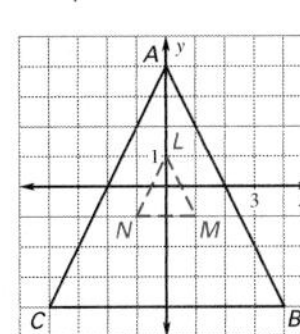

3. $k = \frac{1}{2}$ **4.** $k = 1\frac{1}{2}$

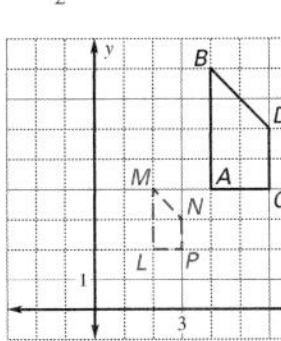

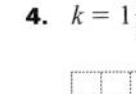

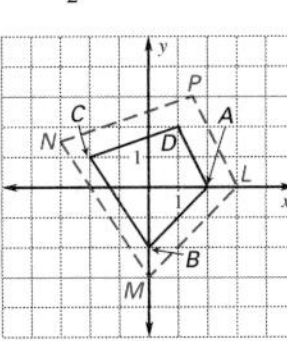

Determine whether the dilation from Figure A to Figure B is a *reduction* or an *enlargement*. Then, find the values of the variables.

5. reduction; $x = 1, y = 2, z = 1$

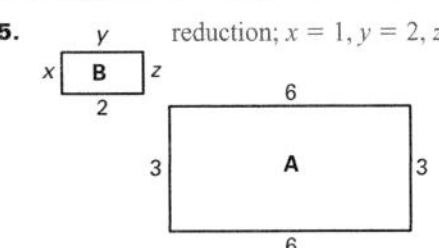

6. enlargement; $m = 16, n = 10$

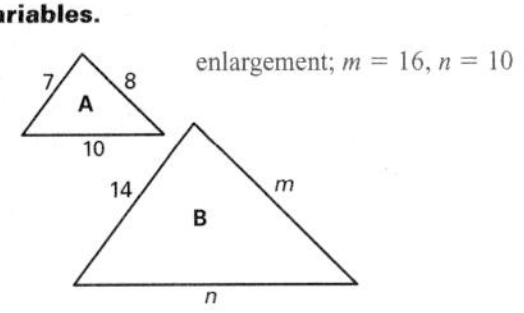

7. enlargement; $x = 3, y = 2, z = 3$

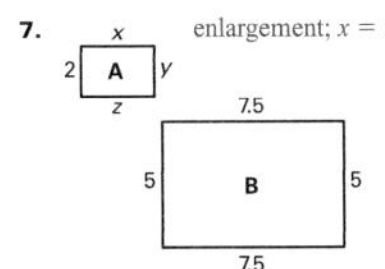

8. reduction; $m = 2, n = 1.5$

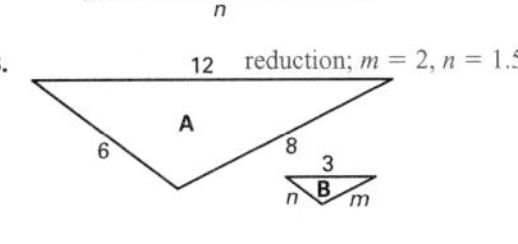

LESSON 6.7

LESSON 6.7
Practice B *continued*
For use with pages 408–415

Determine whether the transformation from Figure A to Figure B is a *translation, reflection, rotation,* or *dilation.*

9. dilation

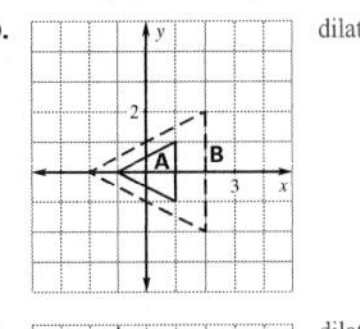

10. reflection

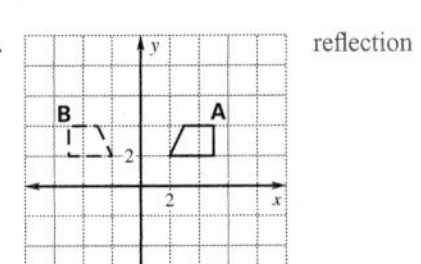

11. dilation

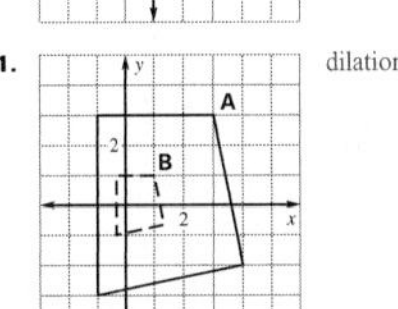

12. translation

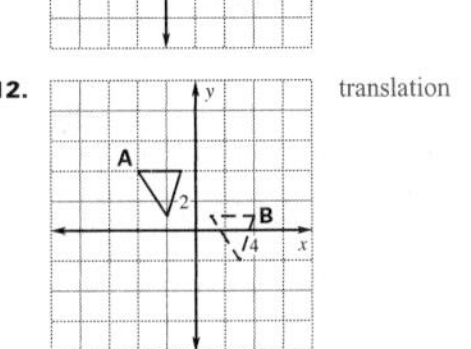

13. Overhead Projectors Your teacher draws a circle on an overhead projector. The projector then displays an enlargement of the circle on the wall. The circle drawn has a radius of 3 inches. The circle on the wall has a diameter of 4 feet. What is the scale factor of the enlargement? 8

14. Posters A poster is enlarged and then the enlargement is reduced as shown in the figure.

a. What is the scale factor of the enlargement? the reduction? $2; \frac{1}{4}$

b. A second poster is reduced directly from size A to size C. What is the scale factor of the reduction? $\frac{1}{2}$

c. How are the scale factors in part (a) related to the scale factor in part (b)? The scale factor in part (b) is the product of the scale factors in part (a).

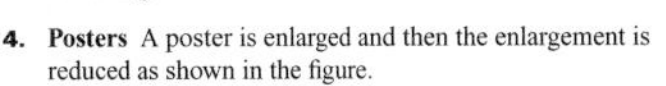

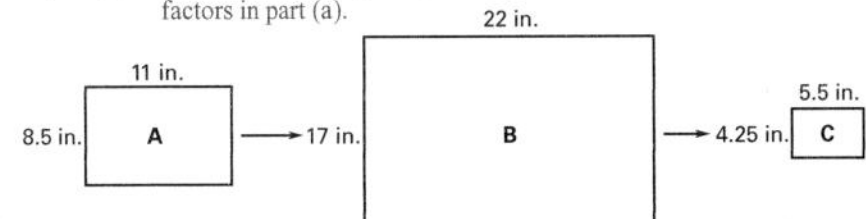

LESSON 6.7

CHAPTER 6 Quiz 1
For use after Lessons 6.1–6.2

Solve the proportion.

1. $\frac{14}{x} = \frac{7}{3}$
2. $\frac{s}{5} = \frac{9}{3}$
3. $\frac{2}{a-4} = \frac{3}{9}$

Complete the sentence.

4. If $\frac{x}{3} = \frac{7}{9}$, then $\frac{3}{x} = \frac{?}{?}$.
5. If $\frac{x}{8} = \frac{y}{12}$, then $\frac{x}{y} = \frac{?}{?}$.
6. If $\frac{x}{4} = \frac{y}{7}$, then $\frac{x+4}{4} = \frac{?}{?}$.
7. Given $\frac{CB}{BA} = \frac{DE}{EF}$, find BA.

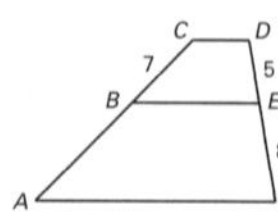

Answers

1. $x = 6$
2. $s = 15$
3. $a = 10$
4. $\frac{9}{7}$
5. $\frac{2}{3}$
6. $\frac{y+7}{7}$
7. 11.2

CHAPTER 6 Quiz 2
For use after Lessons 6.3–6.5

In the diagram, *DEFG* ~ *PQRS*.

D 36 E 122° 24 F 48 56 G; S y R 24 12 z° Q x P

1. Find the scale factor of $DEFG$ to $PQRS$.
2. Find the value of x.
3. Find the value of y.
4. Find the value of z.
5. Find the perimeter of each polygon.

Determine whether the triangles are similar. If they are similar, write a similarity statement.

6.

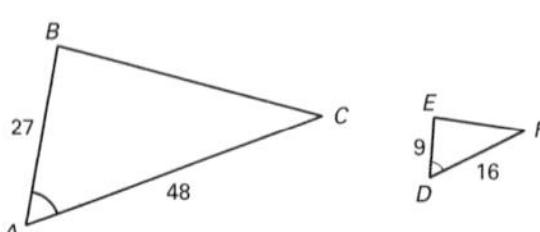

7.

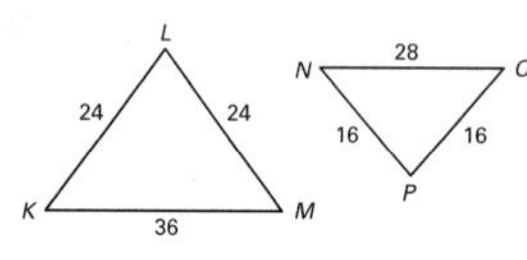
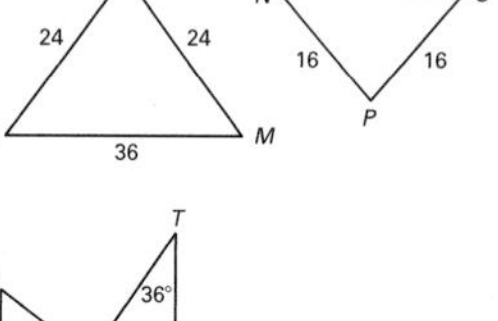

8.

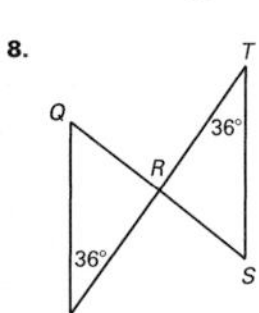

Answers

1. 2 : 1
2. 18
3. 28
4. 122
5. 164, 82
6. similar; $\triangle ABC \sim \triangle DEF$
7. not similar
8. similar; $\triangle PQR \sim \triangle TSR$

CHAPTER 6 Quiz 3
For use after Lessons 6.6–6.7

Find the value of *x*.

1. 12 9 36 x

2. 16 x 8 10

3.

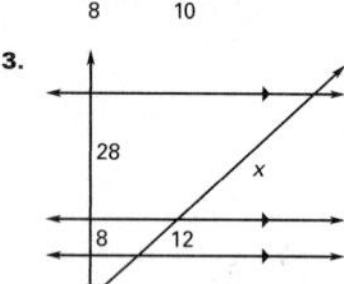

Draw a dilation of $\triangle ABC$ with the given vertices and the scale factor *k*.

4. $A(-6, 6)$, $B(-6, -6)$, $C(8, 0)$; $k = 0.5$

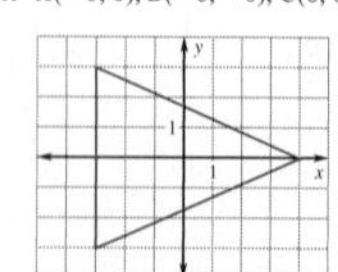

5. $A(4, -2)$, $B(8, -2)$, $C(4, -8)$; $k = 1.5$

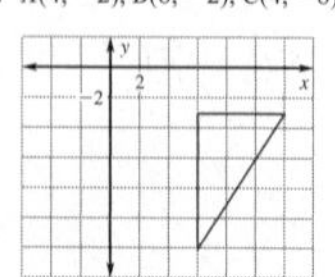

Answers

1. 27
2. 20
3. 42
4. See left.
5. See left.

CHAPTER 6 Chapter Test B
For use after Chapter 6

Simplify the ratio.

1. \$25 : \$5
2. $\frac{40 \text{ cm}}{2 \text{ cm}}$
3. $\frac{1 \text{ mi}}{10 \text{ ft}}$
4. $\frac{9 \text{ ft}}{12 \text{ in.}}$
5. 3 L : 100 ml
6. $\frac{3 \text{ gallons}}{4 \text{ quarts}}$

In the diagram, $\triangle ABC \sim \triangle XYZ$.

7. Find YZ.
8. Find AC.

B 4 3 A C; Y 6 X 7.5 Z

In the diagram, *ABCDE* ~ *FGHJK*.

9. Find the value of x.
10. Find the perimeter of $ABCDE$.

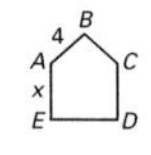

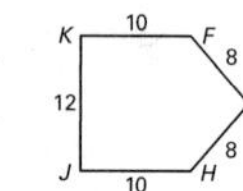

Determine whether the triangles are similar. If so, write a similarity statement and the postulate or theorem that justifies your answer.

11. B C 35° A E D

12.

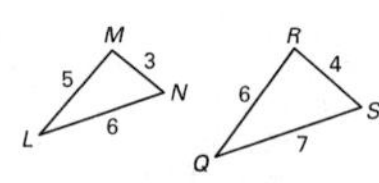

Determine the value of *x* that makes $\triangle ABC \sim \triangle XYZ$.

13.

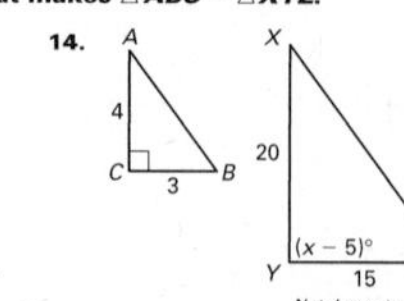

14.

Answers

1. 5 : 1
2. $\frac{20}{1}$
3. $\frac{528}{1}$
4. $\frac{9}{1}$
5. 30 : 1
6. $\frac{3}{1}$
7. 4.5
8. 5
9. 5
10. 24
11. $\triangle ABD \sim \triangle ECD$; AA Similarity Postulate
12. no
13. 22.5
14. 95

CHAPTER 6 Chapter Test B *continued*
For use after Chapter 6

In Exercises 15 and 16, find the length of $\overline{AB}$.

15. 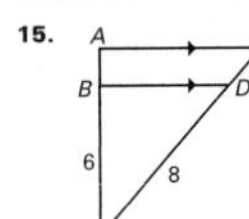

16. 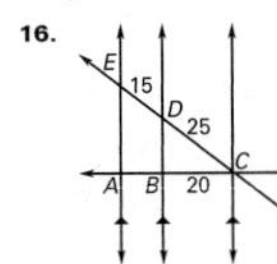

Determine whether the dilation from Figure A to Figure B is a *reduction* or an *enlargement*. Then find its scale factor.

17. 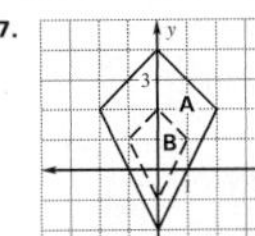

18. 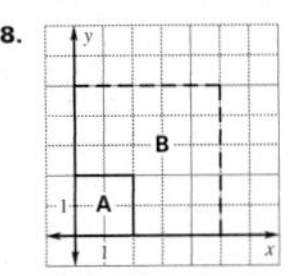

19. The perimeter of a rectangle is 24 inches. The ratio of the length to the width is 2 : 1. Find the length and the width.

20. The perimeter of a rectangle is 65 inches. The ratio of the length to the width is 4 : 1. Find the length and the width.

21. You are making a scale model of your neighborhood. The distance between two consecutive streets is 200 feet. You use a scale factor of $\frac{1}{80}$ to build your model. What is the distance between Catabay Street and Skelly Street on your model?

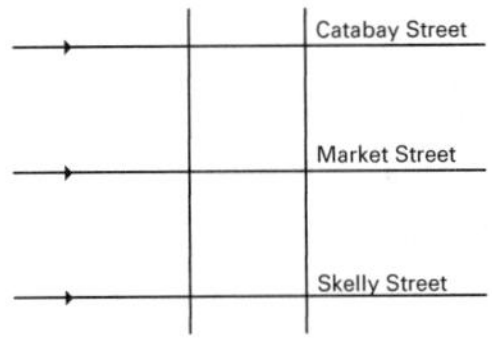

Answers

15. 1.5

16. 12

17. reduction; $k = \frac{1}{2}$

18. enlargement; $k = 2.5$

19. $\ell = 8, w = 4$

20. $\ell = 26, w = 6.5$

21. 5 ft

CHAPTER 6 Standardized Test
For use after Chapter 6

Multiple Choice

1. A rectangle is $\frac{5}{8}$ as wide as it is long. How wide is the rectangle if it is 10 inches long? D

Ⓐ 8 in. Ⓑ 16 in.
Ⓒ $5\frac{3}{4}$ in. Ⓓ $6\frac{1}{4}$ in.

2. Find the geometric mean of 8 and 32. B

Ⓐ 20 Ⓑ 16 Ⓒ 24 Ⓓ 12

3. One serving of a cookie recipe calls for 6 tablespoons of sugar. If one serving makes enough for 4 people, how much sugar is needed to serve 10 people? A

Ⓐ 15 Tbs Ⓑ 60 Tbs
Ⓒ 12 Tbs Ⓓ 24 Tbs

4. If the corresponding angles of two polygons are congruent and the corresponding side lengths are proportional, then the two polygons are __?__. C

Ⓐ regular Ⓑ concave
Ⓒ similar Ⓓ equilateral

5. Given $\triangle ABC \sim \triangle RST$, find the perimeter of $\triangle RST$ if the scale factor of $\triangle ABC$ to $\triangle RST$ is $\frac{3}{2}$. A

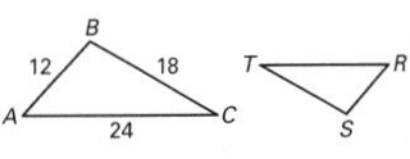

Ⓐ 36 Ⓑ 81 Ⓒ 54 Ⓓ 27

6. If two angles of one triangle are congruent to two angles of another triangle, then the triangles are __?__. D

Ⓐ equilateral Ⓑ congruent
Ⓒ equiangular Ⓓ similar

7. Use the Angle-Angle Similarity Postulate to determine which pair of triangles is *not* similar. D

Ⓐ 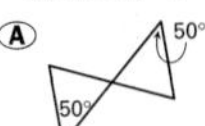

Ⓑ 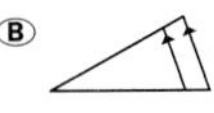

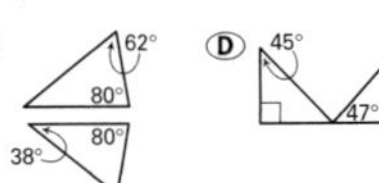

Ⓒ Ⓓ

8. Find x. B

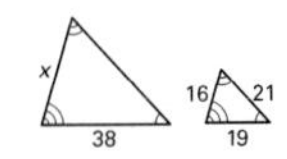

Ⓐ 2 Ⓑ 32 Ⓒ 42 Ⓓ 38

9. If $\triangle PQR \sim \triangle FGH$, find QR. C

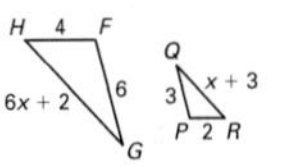

Ⓐ $\frac{3}{2}$ Ⓑ 2 Ⓒ 1 Ⓓ 3

10. Which Similarity Theorem can be used to show $\triangle ABC \sim \triangle DBE$? C

Ⓐ SSS
Ⓑ AA
Ⓒ SAS
Ⓓ AAS

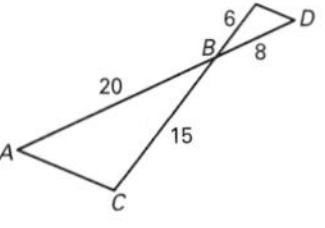

11. If a line parallel to one side of a triangle intersects the other two sides, then it divides the two sides __?__. B

Ⓐ equally Ⓑ proportionally
Ⓒ congruently Ⓓ perpendicularly

CHAPTER 6 Standardized Test *continued*
For use after Chapter 6

12. Use the Triangle Proportionality Theorem to find MK. B

Ⓐ 3
Ⓑ 3.75
Ⓒ 3.5
Ⓓ 3.25

13. Find SU. D

Ⓐ 12 Ⓑ 4 Ⓒ 6 Ⓓ 16

14. Find YZ. A

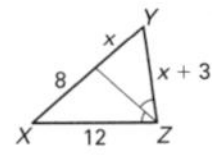

Ⓐ 9 Ⓑ 10 Ⓒ 6 Ⓓ 8

15. Which of the following set of points could form a dilation of a polygon with vertices $A(-3, 3)$, $B(-3, 1)$, $C(0, 1)$, and $D(6,6)$? C

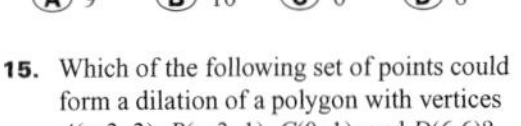

Ⓐ $W(3, -3)$, $X(3, -1)$, $Y(0, -1)$, $Z(-6, 6)$
Ⓑ $W(-2, 4)$, $X(-2, 2)$, $Y(1, 2)$, $Z(7, 7)$
Ⓒ $W(-6, 6)$, $X(-6, 2)$, $Y(0, 2)$, $Z(12, 12)$
Ⓓ $W(-3, 6)$, $X(-3, 2)$, $Y(0, 2)$, $Z(6, 12)$

Gridded Answer

16. Find m. 195

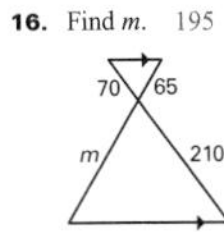

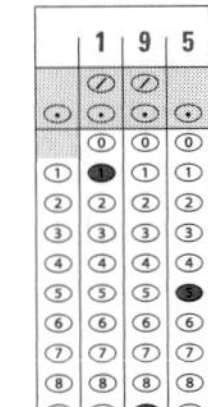

Short Response

17. Fold a 8.5 in. × 11 in. sheet of paper, lengthwise, 4 times. Find the ratios of length, width, and area of each congruent rectangle formed to that of the original sheet of paper. Find the same ratios for 5 folds and 6 folds. See below.

Extended Response

18. A photography company sells school picture packages as shown.

	Selections	Price
A	1 – 16 × 20	\$34
B	1 – 12 × 16	\$24
C	1 – 10 × 14	\$18
D	1 – 8 × 10	\$11
E	4 – 5 × 7	\$18
F	2 – 5 × 7	\$10
G	2 – 4 × 6	\$8
H	2 – 3 × 5	\$5
I	8 – 2 × 3	\$8
J	16 – 1.5 × 2	\$8

17. length is 1 : 1, width is 1 : 16, area is 1 : 16; After 5 folds: length is 1 : 1, width is 1 : 32, area is 1 : 32; After 6 folds: length is 1 : 1, width is 1 : 64, area is 1 : 64

a. Which selection(s) have a price to square inch ratio smaller than 13 : 1? A, B, C, E

b. Which portrait sizes are enlargement dilations of another size and by what scale factor? See below.

c. If each selection prints in its entirety on one sheet of paper, which selections could print on congruent rectangles?

b. The 16 × 20 is an enlargement dilation of the 8 × 10 by a scale factor of 2 : 1. The 10 × 14 is an enlargement dilation of the 5 × 7 by a scale factor of 2 : 1. The 4 × 6 is an enlargement dilation of the 2 × 3 by a scale factor of 2 : 1. The 12 × 16 is an enlargement dilation of the 1.5 × 2 by a scale factor of 8 : 1 **c.** C and E could print on a 10 × 14. G, I, and J could print on an 8 × 12.

CHAPTER 6 Alternative Assessment and Math Journal
For use after Chapter 6

Journal **1.** A triangle has the vertices $A(2, 2)$, $B(4, 6)$, and $C(6, 2)$. The image of $\triangle ABC$ after a dilation with a scale factor of $\frac{1}{2}$ is $\triangle DEF$. The image of $\triangle ABC$ after a dilation with a scale factor of 3 is $\triangle LMN$. Sketch all three triangles and verify that all three triangles are similar.

Multi-Step Problem **2.** A carpenter is building a custom wall unit, as shown in the scale drawing.

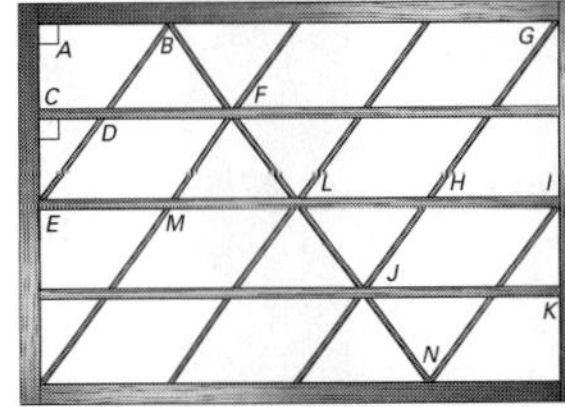

a. The scale used to create the drawing of the actual wall unit is 1 in. : 4 ft. Find the length and width of the actual wall unit.

b. Show that $\triangle ABE$ and $\triangle CDE$ are similar.

c. Suppose that $GH = 5$, $GI = 4$, $HI = 2x$, $GJ = x + 6$, $GK = 6$, and $JK = 6 - x$. Find the value of x that makes $\triangle GHI \sim \triangle GJK$.

d. Suppose that $\overline{BE} \parallel \overline{FM}$. What can you conclude about the sides of $\triangle LBE$?

e. Suppose that $HI = 3$, $LH = 3$, and $LJ = 2.5$. Explain the steps you would use to show that $\triangle LJH \sim \triangle LNI$.

1. Complete answers should include:

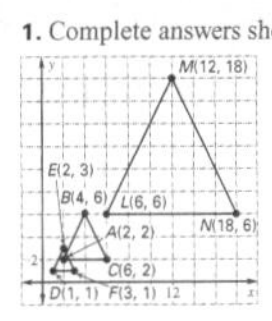

$\frac{AB}{DE} = \frac{BC}{EF} = \frac{AC}{DF} = 2$, so $\triangle ABC \sim \triangle DEF$;

$\frac{AB}{LM} = \frac{BC}{MN} = \frac{AC}{LN} = \frac{1}{3}$, so $\triangle ABC \sim \triangle LMN$;

$\frac{DE}{LM} = \frac{EF}{MN} = \frac{DF}{LN} = \frac{1}{6}$, so $\triangle DEF \sim \triangle LMN$.

2. a. 12 ft by 8 ft **b.** Because $\angle A$ and $\angle C$ are right angles, $\angle A \cong \angle C$. By the Reflexive Property, $\angle E \cong \angle E$. So $\triangle ABE$ and $\triangle CDE$ are similar by the AA Similarity Postulate. **c.** 1.5 **d.** $\frac{LF}{FB} = \frac{LM}{ME}$ **e.** First, use the Triangle Proportionality Theorem to find the length of $\overline{JN}$. Then find the lengths of $\overline{LN}$ and $\overline{LI}$. Finally, show that $\frac{LJ}{LN} = \frac{LH}{HI} = \frac{JH}{NI}$.

PLAN AND PREPARE

Main Ideas

In this chapter students use ratios, proportions, and geometric means to solve geometry problems. They use ratios to find the scale of a drawing and then use the scale to find the actual distance on a map or the actual height of a building. They use proportions to identify similar polygons and find the scale factor between two polygons, they use a scale factor to find corresponding lengths in similar polygons, and they use the AA Similarity Postulate, the SSS Similarity Theorem, or the SAS Similarity Theorem to determine whether two triangles are similar. Also, students use proportions and the Triangle Proportionality Theorem or its converse to find the lengths of segments related to triangles or parallel lines. Finally, students perform dilations that are reductions or enlargements and they verify that a figure is similar to its dilation.

Prerequisite Skills

- Reviewing the Alternate Interior Angles Theorem and the definition of congruent triangles
- Simplifying numeric expressions
- Finding the perimeter of a rectangle with given dimensions
- Finding the slope of a line parallel to a given line

Additional resources for reviewing prerequisite skills are:

- Skills Review Handbook, pp. 869–895
- @HomeTutor

6 Similarity

Before

In previous courses and in Chapters 1–5, you learned the following skills, which you'll use in Chapter 6: using properties of parallel lines, using properties of triangles, simplifying expressions, and finding perimeter.

Prerequisite Skills

VOCABULARY CHECK

1. The alternate interior angles formed when a transversal intersects two _?_ lines are congruent. **parallel**
2. Two triangles are congruent if and only if their corresponding parts are _?_. **congruent**

SKILLS AND ALGEBRA CHECK

Simplify the expression. *(Review pp. 870, 874 for 6.1.)*

3. $\frac{9 \cdot 20}{15}$ **12**
4. $\frac{15}{25}$ $\mathbf{\frac{3}{5}}$
5. $\frac{3+4+5}{6+8+10}$ $\mathbf{\frac{1}{2}}$
6. $\sqrt{5(5 \cdot 7)}$ $\mathbf{5\sqrt{7}}$

Find the perimeter of the rectangle with the given dimensions. *(Review p. 49 for 6.1, 6.2.)*

7. $\ell = 5$ in., $w = 12$ in. **34 in.**
8. $\ell = 30$ ft, $w = 10$ ft **80 ft**
9. $A = 56\text{ m}^2$, $\ell = 8$ m **30 m**
10. Find the slope of a line parallel to the line whose equation is $y - 4 = 7(x + 2)$. *(Review p. 171 for 6.5.)* **7**

@HomeTutor Prerequisite skills practice at classzone.com

Chapter Planning Guide

Chapter 6 Resource Book
- Teaching Guide/Lesson Plan (pp. 3, 17, 30, 44, 57, 71, 85)
- Project with Rubric (p. 101)

Assessment and Intervention
- Assessment Book (pp. 76–90)
- Benchmark Tests
- Remediation Book

Interactive Technology
- Easy Planner
- Power Presentations CD-ROM
- Activity Generator CD-ROM
- Animated Algebra
- Test Generator CD-ROM
- Online Quizzes
- eWorkbook
- eEdition
- @HomeTutor

Resources for English Learners
- Quick Reference for English Learners
- Spanish Study Guide
- Multi-Language Visual Glossary
- Student Resources in Spanish

California Standards for Chapter 6

Geometry: 4.0, 5.0, 7.0, 8.0, 11.0, 12.0

Now

In Chapter 6, you will apply the big ideas listed below and reviewed in the Chapter Summary on page 417. You will also use the key vocabulary listed below.

Big Ideas

1. **Using ratios and proportions to solve geometry problems**
2. **Showing that triangles are similar**
3. **Using indirect measurement and similarity**

KEY VOCABULARY

- ratio, *p. 356*
- proportion, *p. 358* means, extremes
- geometric mean, *p. 359*
- scale drawing, *p. 365*
- scale, *p. 365*
- similar polygons, *p. 372*
- scale factor of two similar polygons, *p. 373*
- dilation, *p. 409*
- center of dilation, *p. 409*
- scale factor of a dilation, *p. 409*
- reduction, *p. 409*
- enlargement, *p. 409*

Why?

You can use similarity to measure lengths indirectly. For example, you can use similar triangles to find the height of a tree.

Animated Geometry

The animation illustrated below for Exercise 33 on page 394 helps you answer this question: What is the height of the tree?

You can use proportional reasoning to estimate the height of a tall tree.

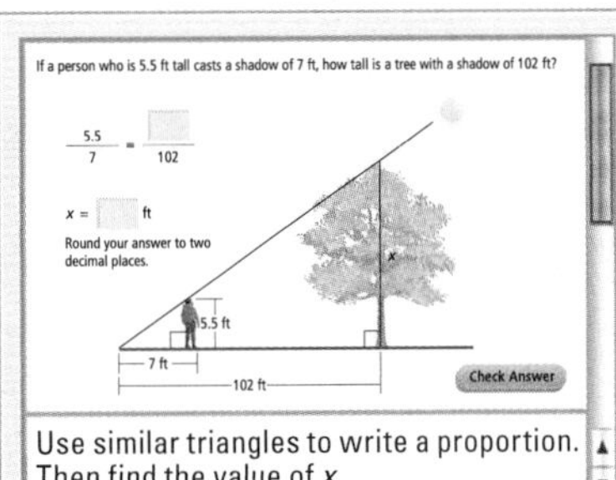

If a person who is 5.5 ft tall casts a shadow of 7 ft, how tall is a tree with a shadow of 102 ft?
5.5
7
102
x = ft
Round your answer to two decimal places.
5.5 ft
7 ft
102 ft
Check Answer

Use similar triangles to write a proportion. Then find the value of x.

Animated Geometry at classzone.com

Other animations for Chapter 6: pages 365, 375, 391, 407, and 414

Geometry Toolkit

- Reading Strategies for Chapter 6, pp. 19–20
- Differentiated Instruction Notes, pp. 59–62
- English Learners Notes, pp. 101–102
- Inclusion Notes, pp. 131–132
- Teaching Strategies with Sample Worksheets, pp. 145–168
- Using Technology in the Classroom, pp. 169–174
- Tips for New Teachers, pp. 185–186
- Math Background Notes, pp. 215–218
- Pre-AP Strategies and Copymasters, pp. 293–294, 349–354
- Teacher Survival Activities, pp. 431–432, 455–456
- Bulletin Board Idea, p. 474
- Teacher Tool Transparencies, following p. 480

1 PLAN AND PREPARE

Warm-Up Exercises

Transparency Available

1. Simplify $\frac{3x^2}{9x}$. $\frac{x}{3}$
2. Solve $2n = 18 \cdot 32$. **288**
3. Solve $4x = 2x + 12$. **6**
4. Solve $x = \sqrt{36 \cdot 16}$. **24**
5. A triangle has angle measures 18° and 82°. Find the measure of the third angle. **80°**

Notetaking Guide

Transparency Available

Promotes interactive learning and notetaking skills, pp. 140–144.

Pacing

Basic: 2 days
Average: 2 days
Advanced: 2 days
Block: 1 block
- See *Teaching Guide/Lesson Plan.*

2 FOCUS AND MOTIVATE

Essential Question

Big Idea 1, p. 355

How do you use ratios and proportions to solve a problem? **Tell students they will learn how to answer this question by using two ratios to write a proportion.**

6.1 Ratios, Proportions, and the Geometric Mean

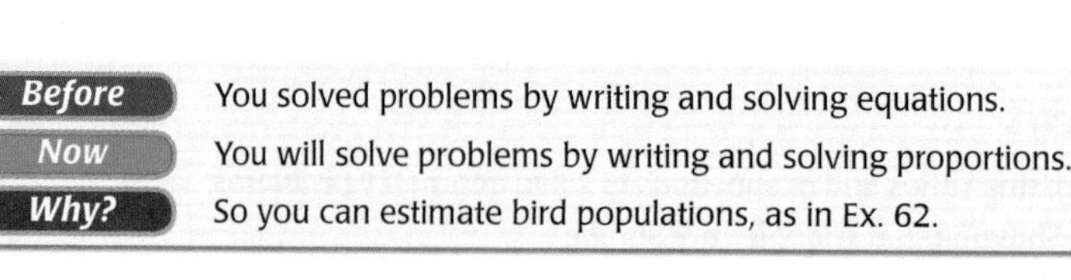

Before You solved problems by writing and solving equations.
Now You will solve problems by writing and solving proportions.
Why? So you can estimate bird populations, as in Ex. 62.

Key Vocabulary
- **ratio**
- **proportion**
  means, extremes
- **geometric mean**

Standards

Prepare for 8.0
Students know, derive, and *solve problems involving the perimeter,* circumference, *area,* volume, lateral area, and surface area *of common geometric figures.*

If a and b are two numbers or quantities and $b \neq 0$, then the **ratio of *a* to *b*** is $\frac{a}{b}$. The ratio of a to b can also be written as $a:b$.

For example, the ratio of a side length in $\triangle ABC$ to a side length in $\triangle DEF$ can be written as $\frac{2}{1}$ or 2 : 1.

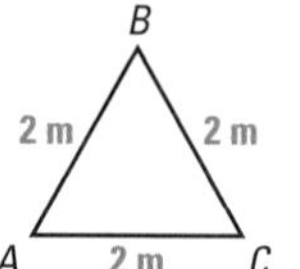

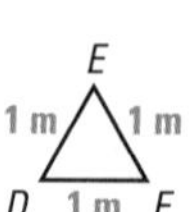

Ratios are usually expressed in simplest form. Two ratios that have the same simplified form are called *equivalent ratios.* The ratios 7 : 14 and 1 : 2 in the example below are *equivalent.*

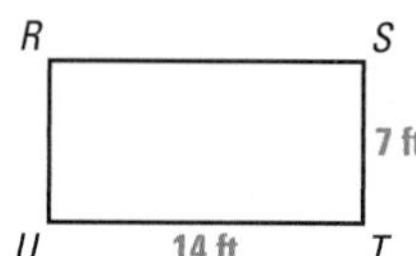

$$\frac{\text{width of } RSTU}{\text{length of } RSTU} = \frac{7 \text{ ft}}{14 \text{ ft}} = \frac{1}{2}$$

EXAMPLE 1 Simplify ratios

Simplify the ratio.

a. 64 m : 6 m

b. $\frac{5 \text{ ft}}{20 \text{ in.}}$

Solution

a. Write 64 m : 6 m as $\frac{64 \text{ m}}{6 \text{ m}}$. Then divide out the units and simplify.

$$\frac{64 \cancel{\text{m}}}{6 \cancel{\text{m}}} = \frac{32}{3} = 32:3$$

b. To simplify a ratio with unlike units, multiply by a conversion factor.

$$\frac{5 \text{ ft}}{20 \text{ in.}} = \frac{5 \cancel{\text{ft}}}{20 \cancel{\text{in.}}} \cdot \frac{12 \cancel{\text{in.}}}{1 \cancel{\text{ft}}} = \frac{60}{20} = \frac{3}{1}$$

REVIEW UNIT ANALYSIS

For help with measures and conversion factors, see p. 886 and the Table of Measures on p. 921.

GUIDED PRACTICE for Example 1

Simplify the ratio.

1. 24 yards to 3 yards **8 to 1**
2. 150 cm : 6 m **1 : 4**

Resource Planning Guide

Chapter Resource Book
- Teaching Guide/Lesson Plan (pp. 3–4)
- Activity Master (p. 5)
- Practice levels A, B, C (pp. 6–11)
- Study Guide (pp. 12–13)
- Catch-up for Absent Students (p. 14)
- Application (p. 15)
- Challenge (p. 16)

Workbooks
- Notetaking Guide (pp. 140–144)
- Practice Workbook (pp. 103–105)

Teaching Options
- **Power Presentations CD-ROM** provides dynamic electronic teaching resources for the classroom.
- **Activity Generator CD-ROM** provides editable activities for all ability levels.

Interactive Technology
- Easy Planner
- Power Presentations CD-ROM
- Activity Generator CD-ROM
- Animated Algebra
- Test Generator CD-ROM
- Online Quiz
- eWorkbook
- eEdition
- @HomeTutor

Resources for English Learners
- Quick Reference for English Learners
- Spanish Study Guide
- Multi-Language Visual Glossary
- Student Resources in Spanish

See also the *Geometry Toolkit* for more strategies for meeting individual needs.

EXAMPLE 2 Use a ratio to find a dimension

PAINTING You are planning to paint a mural on a rectangular wall. You know that the perimeter of the wall is 484 feet and that the ratio of its length to its width is 9 : 2. Find the area of the wall.

WRITE EXPRESSIONS

Because the ratio in Example 2 is 9 : 2, you can write an equivalent ratio to find expressions for the length and width.

$$\frac{\text{length}}{\text{width}} = \frac{9}{2} = \frac{9}{2} \cdot \frac{x}{x} = \frac{9x}{2x}.$$

Solution

STEP 1 **Write** expressions for the length and width. Because the ratio of length to width is 9 : 2, you can represent the length by $9x$ and the width by $2x$.

STEP 2 **Solve** an equation to find x.

$2\ell + 2w = P$	Formula for perimeter of rectangle
$2(9x) + 2(2x) = 484$	Substitute for ℓ, w, and P.
$22x = 484$	Multiply and combine like terms.
$x = 22$	Divide each side by 22.

STEP 3 **Evaluate** the expressions for the length and width. Substitute the value of x into each expression.

Length $= 9x = 9(22) = 198$ Width $= 2x = 2(22) = 44$

▶ The wall is 198 feet long and 44 feet wide, so its area is $198 \text{ ft} \cdot 44 \text{ ft} = 8712 \text{ ft}^2$.

EXAMPLE 3 Use extended ratios

ALGEBRA The measures of the angles in $\triangle CDE$ are in the *extended ratio* of 1 : 2 : 3. Find the measures of the angles.

Solution

Begin by sketching the triangle. Then use the extended ratio of 1 : 2 : 3 to label the measures as $x°$, $2x°$, and $3x°$.

C, E, D, $x°$, $3x°$, $2x°$

$x° + 2x° + 3x° = 180°$	Triangle Sum Theorem
$6x = 180$	Combine like terms.
$x = 30$	Divide each side by 6.

▶ The angle measures are $30°$, $2(30°) = 60°$, and $3(30°) = 90°$.

✓ **GUIDED PRACTICE** for Examples 2 and 3

3. The perimeter of a room is 48 feet and the ratio of its length to its width is 7 : 5. Find the length and width of the room. **14 ft, 10 ft**

4. A triangle's angle measures are in the extended ratio of 1 : 3 : 5. Find the measures of the angles. **20°, 60°, 100°**

Motivating the Lesson

An oatmeal cookie recipe for 24 cookies uses 2 cups of flour and $\frac{1}{2}$ cup of butter. If you want to know how much flour and butter you need to make other numbers of cookies, you can use ratios (cups/cookies) and set up and solve proportions.

3 TEACH

Extra Example 1

Simplify the ratio.

a. 12 km : 3 km **4 : 1**

b. 36 in. : 9 ft **1 : 3**

Key Question to Ask for Example 1

- Why do you multiply a ratio with unlike units by a conversion factor before simplifying? **The numerator and denominator must have the same units.**

Avoiding Common Errors

In **Example 1(b)**, a common error is to forget to multiply by a conversion factor. Point out that the units should be the same when simplifying a ratio.

Extra Example 2

The area of a rectangular garden is 108 square feet, and the ratio of the length to the width is 4 : 3. Find the length and width of fence needed to enclose the garden. **length: 12 ft; width: 9 ft**

Key Question to Ask for Example 2

- Why can the ratio of the length of the rectangle to the width be represented by $9x : 2x$? **$9x : 2x$ is equivalent to 9 : 2 because it can be reduced to 9 : 2.**

Extra Example 3

The measures of the angles of $\triangle RST$ are in the extended ratio 2 : 3 : 4. Find the measures of the angles.

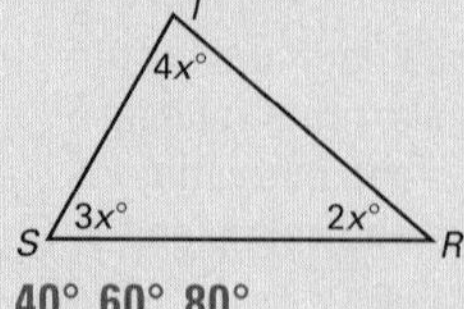

40°, 60°, 80°

Extra Example 4

Solve the proportion.

a. $\frac{8}{24} = \frac{x}{27}$ 9 b. $\frac{2}{x+3} = \frac{5}{4x}$ 5

PROPORTIONS An equation that states that two ratios are equal is called a **proportion**.

$$\text{extreme} \rightarrow a \quad c \leftarrow \text{mean}$$
$$\frac{a}{b} = \frac{c}{d}$$
$$\text{mean} \rightarrow b \quad d \leftarrow \text{extreme}$$

The numbers b and c are the **means** of the proportion. The numbers a and d are the **extremes** of the proportion.

The property below can be used to solve proportions. To *solve a proportion*, you find the value of any variable in the proportion.

PROPORTIONS You will learn more properties of proportions on p. 364.

KEY CONCEPT — *For Your Notebook*

A Property of Proportions

1. **Cross Products Property** In a proportion, the product of the extremes equals the product of the means.

If $\frac{a}{b} = \frac{c}{d}$ where $b \neq 0$ and $d \neq 0$, then $ad = bc$.

$\frac{2}{3} = \frac{4}{6}$ $\quad 3 \cdot 4 = 12$, $\quad 2 \cdot 6 = 12$

EXAMPLE 4 Solve proportions

ALGEBRA Solve the proportion.

a. $\frac{5}{10} = \frac{x}{16}$ b. $\frac{1}{y+1} = \frac{2}{3y}$

Solution

ANOTHER WAY In part (a), you could multiply each side by the denominator, 16. Then $16 \cdot \frac{5}{10} = 16 \cdot \frac{x}{16}$, so $8 = x$.

a.

$\frac{5}{10} = \frac{x}{16}$	Write original proportion.
$5 \cdot 16 = 10 \cdot x$	Cross Products Property
$80 = 10x$	Multiply.
$8 = x$	Divide each side by 10.

b.

$\frac{1}{y+1} = \frac{2}{3y}$	Write original proportion.
$1 \cdot 3y = 2(y+1)$	Cross Products Property
$3y = 2y + 2$	Distributive Property
$y = 2$	Subtract $2y$ from each side.

✓ GUIDED PRACTICE for Example 4

Solve the proportion.

5. $\frac{2}{x} = \frac{5}{8}$ $\frac{16}{5}$

6. $\frac{1}{x-3} = \frac{4}{3x}$ 12

7. $\frac{y-3}{7} = \frac{y}{14}$ 6

Differentiated Instruction

Visual Learners To help students visualize how two ratios make a proportion, draw a circle on the board. Divide it into ten equal sectors. Shade any five of the sectors. Ask students to write the ratio of the number of shaded regions of the circle to the total number regions. Then have them look at the proportion in **Example 4a**. Ask students to divide another circle of the same size into 16 sectors and solve the proportion by determining the correct number of sectors to shade in this new circle in order to have the same amount of this circle shaded as in the first circle. See also the *Geometry Toolkit* for more strategies.

EXAMPLE 5 Solve a real-world problem

SCIENCE As part of an environmental study, you need to estimate the number of trees in a 150 acre area. You count 270 trees in a 2 acre area and you notice that the trees seem to be evenly distributed. Estimate the total number of trees.

Solution

Write and solve a proportion involving two ratios that compare the number of trees with the area of the land.

$\frac{270}{2} = \frac{n}{150}$ ← number of trees / ← area in acres — **Write proportion.**

$270 \cdot 150 = 2 \cdot n$ — **Cross Products Property**

$20{,}250 = n$ — **Simplify.**

▶ There are about 20,250 trees in the 150 acre area.

KEY CONCEPT — *For Your Notebook*

Geometric Mean

The **geometric mean** of two positive numbers a and b is the positive number x that satisfies $\frac{a}{x} = \frac{x}{b}$. So, $x^2 = ab$ and $x = \sqrt{ab}$.

EXAMPLE 6 Find a geometric mean

Find the geometric mean of 24 and 48.

Solution

$x = \sqrt{ab}$ — **Definition of geometric mean**

$= \sqrt{24 \cdot 48}$ — **Substitute 24 for *a* and 48 for *b*.**

$= \sqrt{24 \cdot 24 \cdot 2}$ — **Factor.**

$= 24\sqrt{2}$ — **Simplify.**

▶ The geometric mean of 24 and 48 is $24\sqrt{2} \approx 33.9$.

GUIDED PRACTICE for Examples 5 and 6

8. WHAT IF? In Example 5, suppose you count 390 trees in a 3 acre area of the 150 acre area. Make a new estimate of the total number of trees. **19,500 trees**

Find the geometric mean of the two numbers.

9. 12 and 27 **18** **10.** 18 and 54 $18\sqrt{3}$ **11.** 16 and 18 $12\sqrt{2}$

Extra Example 5

As part of a science project, you need to estimate the number of blue spruce trees in a 50 acre forest. You count 36 trees in 3 acres and notice that the trees seem to be evenly distributed. Estimate the total number of blue spruce trees in the forest. **about 600 trees**

Key Questions to Ask for Example 5

- Why is the answer only an estimate? **You did not actually count all of the trees.**
- Is there another proportion you can solve? If so, what is it? **yes;** $\frac{270}{n} = \frac{2}{150}$

Extra Example 6

Find the geometric mean of 36 and 54. $18\sqrt{6}$

Closing the Lesson

Have students summarize the major points of the lesson and answer the Essential Question: How do you use ratios and proportions to solve a problem?

- **Write a proportion by writing two equal ratios comparing quantities in the problem.**
- **Use the Cross Products Property and solve for the variable.**

Write a proportion involving ratios from the problem and solve the proportion.

Differentiated Instruction

Below Level For **Example 5**, call students' attention to the phrase "270 trees in a 2 acre area." They can use this phrase to write the ratio $\frac{\text{number of trees}}{\text{number of acres}}$ and substitute to get two equal ratios $\frac{270 \text{ trees}}{2 \text{ acres}} = \frac{n \text{ trees}}{150 \text{ acres}}$. Then they can solve the proportion. See also the *Geometry Toolkit* for more strategies.

4 PRACTICE AND APPLY

Assignment Guide

Answer Transparencies available for all exercises

Basic:
Day 1: EP p. 902 Exs. 4–6
pp. 360–363
Exs. 1–22, 38–41, 57, 76–80
Day 2: pp. 360–363
Exs. 23–37, 42–45, 59–64, 72–75

Average:
Day 1: pp. 360–363
Exs. 1, 2, 5–8, 11–22, 37–41, 46–51, 53, 57, 58
Day 2: pp. 360–363
Exs. 25–28, 33–35, 42–45, 52, 54, 59–67, 72–80

Advanced:
Day 1: pp. 360–363
Exs. 1, 2, 8–10, 12, 13, 16–19, 21, 22, 37–41, 46–51, 53, 56*, 57
Day 2: pp. 360–363
Exs. 28–30, 34–36, 42–45, 52, 54, 55, 60–71*, 72–80 even

Block:
pp. 360–363
Exs. 1, 2, 5–8, 11–22, 25–28, 33–35, 37–54, 57, 59–67, 72–80

Differentiated Instruction

See *Geometry Best Practices Toolkit* for suggestions on addressing the needs of a diverse classroom.

Homework Check

For a quick check of student understanding of key concepts, go over the following exercises:

Basic: 6, 18, 24, 32, 62
Average: 12, 19, 26, 34, 62
Advanced: 16, 28, 36, 57, 62

Extra Practice

- Student Edition, p. 906
- Chapter 6 Resource Book: Practice levels A, B, C, pp. 6–11

Practice Worksheet

An easily-readable reduced practice page (with answers) for this lesson can be found on p. 354C.

6.1 EXERCISES

HOMEWORK KEY
○ = **WORKED-OUT SOLUTIONS** on p. WS7 for Exs. 5, 27, and 59
★ = **STANDARDIZED TEST PRACTICE** Exs. 2, 47, 48, 52, and 63
◆ = **MULTIPLE REPRESENTATIONS** Ex. 66

SKILL PRACTICE

A

1. **VOCABULARY** Copy the proportion $\frac{m}{n} = \frac{p}{q}$. Identify the means of the proportion and the extremes of the proportion. **means: *n* and *p*, extremes: *m* and *q***

2. ★ **WRITING** Write three ratios that are equivalent to the ratio 3 : 4. *Explain* how you found the ratios. ***Sample answer:* 6 : 8, 9 : 12, 12 : 16; multiply both numbers in the ratio by the same number.**

EXAMPLE 1 on p. 356 for Exs. 3–17

SIMPLIFYING RATIOS Simplify the ratio.

3. \$20 : \$5 **4 : 1**
4. $\frac{15\text{ cm}^2}{12\text{ cm}^2}$ $\frac{5}{4}$
5. 6 L : 10 mL **600 : 1**
6. $\frac{1\text{ mi}}{20\text{ ft}}$ $\frac{264}{1}$
7. $\frac{7\text{ ft}}{12\text{ in.}}$ $\frac{7}{1}$
8. $\frac{80\text{ cm}}{2\text{ m}}$ $\frac{2}{5}$
9. $\frac{3\text{ lb}}{10\text{ oz}}$ $\frac{24}{5}$
10. $\frac{2\text{ gallons}}{18\text{ quarts}}$ $\frac{4}{9}$

WRITING RATIOS Find the ratio of the width to the length of the rectangle. Then simplify the ratio.

11. 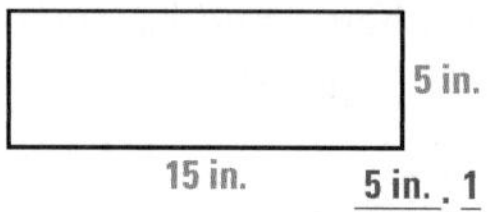

$\frac{5\text{ in.}}{15\text{ in.}}; \frac{1}{3}$

12. 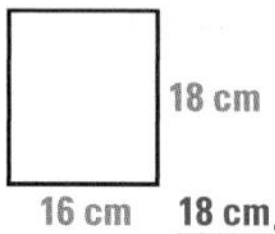

$\frac{18\text{ cm}}{16\text{ cm}}; \frac{9}{8}$

13. 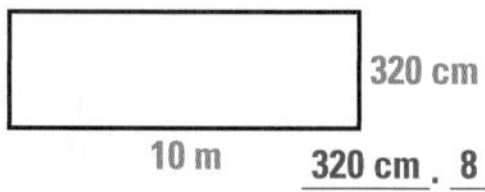

$\frac{320\text{ cm}}{1000\text{ cm}}; \frac{8}{25}$

FINDING RATIOS Use the number line to find the ratio of the distances.

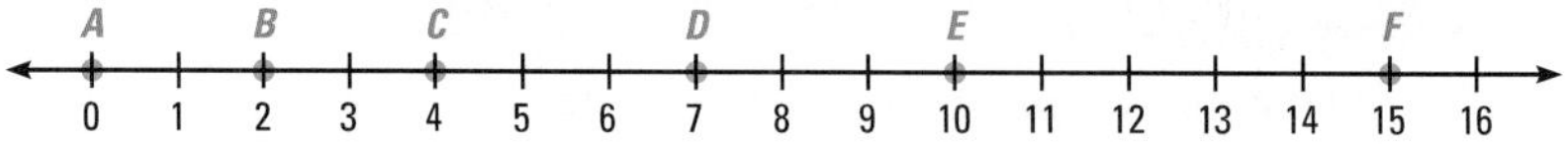

14. $\frac{AD}{CF}$ $\frac{7}{11}$
15. $\frac{BD}{AB}$ $\frac{5}{2}$
16. $\frac{CE}{EF}$ $\frac{6}{5}$
17. $\frac{BE}{CE}$ $\frac{4}{3}$

EXAMPLE 2 on p. 357 for Exs. 18–19

18. **PERIMETER** The perimeter of a rectangle is 154 feet. The ratio of the length to the width is 10 : 1. Find the length and the width. **70 ft, 7 ft**

19. **SEGMENT LENGTHS** In the diagram, $AB : BC$ is 2 : 7 and $AC = 36$. Find AB and BC. **8, 28**

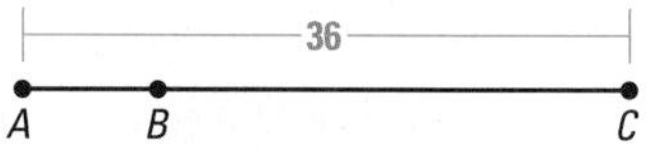

EXAMPLE 3 on p. 357 for Exs. 20–22

USING EXTENDED RATIOS The measures of the angles of a triangle are in the extended ratio given. Find the measures of the angles of the triangle.

20. 3 : 5 : 10 **30°, 50°, 100°**
21. 2 : 7 : 9 **20°, 70°, 90°**
22. 11 : 12 : 13 **55°, 60°, 65°**

EXAMPLE 4 on p. 358 for Exs. 23–30

ALGEBRA Solve the proportion.

23. $\frac{6}{x} = \frac{3}{2}$ **4**
24. $\frac{y}{20} = \frac{3}{10}$ **6**
25. $\frac{2}{7} = \frac{12}{z}$ **42**
26. $\frac{j+1}{5} = \frac{4}{10}$ **1**
27. $\frac{1}{c+5} = \frac{3}{24}$ **3**
28. $\frac{4}{a-3} = \frac{2}{5}$ **13**
29. $\frac{1+3b}{4} = \frac{5}{2}$ **3**
30. $\frac{3}{2p+5} = \frac{1}{9p}$ $\frac{1}{5}$

EXAMPLE 6
on p. 359
for Exs. 31–36

GEOMETRIC MEAN **Find the geometric mean of the two numbers.**

31. 2 and 18 **6**
32. 4 and 25 **10**
33. 32 and 8 **16**
34. 4 and 16 **8**
35. 2 and 25 **$5\sqrt{2}$**
36. 6 and 20 **$2\sqrt{30}$**

B

37. **ERROR ANALYSIS** A student incorrectly simplified the ratio. *Describe* and correct the student's error.

$$\frac{8 \text{ in.}}{3 \text{ ft}} = \frac{8 \text{ in.}}{3 \text{ ft}} \cdot \frac{12 \text{ in.}}{1 \text{ ft}} = \frac{96 \text{ in.}}{3 \text{ ft}} = \frac{32 \text{ in.}}{1 \text{ ft}}$$

The unit conversion should be $\frac{1 \text{ ft}}{12 \text{in.}}$; $\frac{8 \text{ in.}}{3 \text{ ft}} \cdot \frac{1 \text{ ft}}{12 \text{ in.}} = \frac{8}{36} = \frac{2}{9}$.

WRITING RATIOS **Let $x = 10$, $y = 3$, and $z = 8$. Write the ratio in simplest form.**

38. $x:z$ **5 : 4**
39. $\frac{8y}{x}$ **$\frac{12}{5}$**
40. $\frac{4}{2x + 2z}$ **$\frac{1}{9}$**
41. $\frac{2x - z}{3y}$ **$\frac{4}{3}$**

ALGEBRA **Solve the proportion.**

42. $\frac{2x + 5}{3} = \frac{x - 5}{4}$ **−7**
43. $\frac{2 - s}{3} = \frac{2s + 1}{5}$ **$\frac{7}{11}$**
44. $\frac{15}{m} = \frac{m}{5}$ **$\pm 5\sqrt{3}$**
45. $\frac{7}{q + 1} = \frac{q - 1}{5}$ **±6**

46. **ANGLE MEASURES** The ratio of the measures of two supplementary angles is 5 : 3. Find the measures of the angles. **112.5°, 67.5°**

47. ★ **SHORT RESPONSE** The ratio of the measure of an exterior angle of a triangle to the measure of the adjacent interior angle is 1 : 4. Is the triangle *acute* or *obtuse*? *Explain* how you found your answer. **Obtuse; since the angles are supplementary, $x + 4x = 180$. Find $x = 36$, so the measure of the interior angle is 144°.**

48. ★ **SHORT RESPONSE** Without knowing its side lengths, can you determine the ratio of the perimeter of a square to the length of one of its sides? *Explain.* **Yes; the ratio is $\frac{4x}{x} = \frac{4}{1}$.**

ALGEBRA **In Exercises 49–51, the ratio of two side lengths for the triangle is given. Solve for the variable.**

49. $AB:BC$ is 3 : 8. **9**

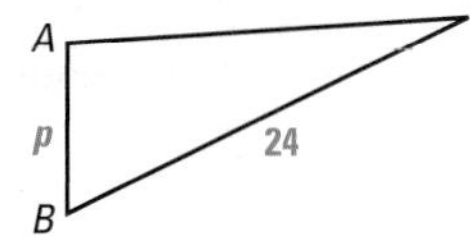

50. $AB:BC$ is 3 : 4. **6.5**

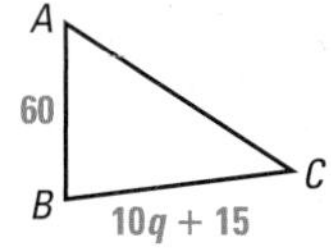

51. $AB:BC$ is 5 : 9. **5**

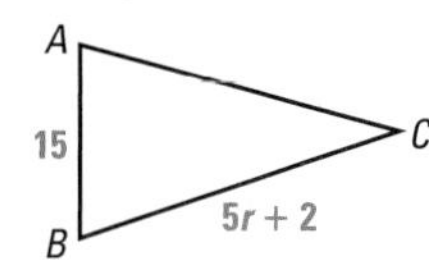

52. ★ **MULTIPLE CHOICE** What is a value of x that makes $\frac{x}{3} = \frac{4x}{x + 3}$ true? **C**

Ⓐ 3 Ⓑ 4 Ⓒ 9 Ⓓ 12

53. **AREA** The area of a rectangle is 4320 square inches. The ratio of the width to the length is 5 : 6. Find the length and the width. **72 in., 60 in.**

54. **COORDINATE GEOMETRY** The points (−3, 2), (1, 1), and (x, 0) are collinear. Use slopes to write a proportion to find the value of x. **$-\frac{1}{4} = \frac{1}{1 - x}$, $x = 5$**

C

55. **ALGEBRA** Use the proportions $\frac{a + b}{2a - b} = \frac{5}{4}$ and $\frac{b}{a + 9} = \frac{5}{9}$ to find a and b. **45, 30**

56. **CHALLENGE** Find the ratio of x to y given that $\frac{5}{y} + \frac{7}{x} = 24$ and $\frac{12}{y} + \frac{2}{x} = 24$. **5 : 7**

Avoiding Common Errors

Exercises 5–10 Some students forget that they need to have the same unit in a ratio. Point out that each of these exercises needs a conversion factor.

Vocabulary

Exercises 20–22 Students can refer to Example 3 if they are unsure of what "extended ratio" means.

Avoiding Common Errors

Exercise 47 Students will not be able to answer the question if they are not careful when they label the triangle in their drawings. That is, they should use $1x$ and $4x$ as angles in their drawing, but the angle whose measure is $1x$ should be the exterior angle, not the interior angle. The interior angle is 144°, so the triangle is obtuse.

Study Strategy

Exercise 54 Remind students that if points are collinear, the slope for each pair of points is the same. Students can use the first pair of points to find the slope of the line, then use the second pair of points and the calculated slope to find the value of x. Encourage them to check their value with the first and third points.

Reading Strategy

Exercise 61 Some students may be more familiar than others with batting averages, and can explain the idea to the rest of the class.

Internet Reference

Exercise 62 Additional information about the Red-tailed hawk can be found at www.birds.cornell.edu/programs/AllAboutBirds/BirdGuide/Red-tailed_Hawk_dtl.html

Exercise 63 Explain that computer screen resolutions are given as width by height, in pixels. Therefore, these numbers represent the left-to-right number of pixels by the up and down number of pixels.

PROBLEM SOLVING

EXAMPLE 2 A on p. 357 for Ex. 57

57. TILING The perimeter of a room is 66 feet. The ratio of its length to its width is 6 : 5. You want to tile the floor with 12 inch square tiles. Find the length and width of the room, and the area of the floor. How many tiles will you need? The tiles cost $1.98 each. What is the total cost to tile the floor? **18 ft, 15 ft, 270 ft^2; 270 tiles; $534.60**

@HomeTutor for problem solving help at classzone.com

58. GEARS The *gear ratio* of two gears is the ratio of the number of teeth of the larger gear to the number of teeth of the smaller gear. In a set of three gears, the ratio of Gear A to Gear B is equal to the ratio of Gear B to Gear C. Gear A has 36 teeth and Gear C has 16 teeth. How many teeth does Gear B have? **24 teeth**

@HomeTutor for problem solving help at classzone.com

(59.) TRAIL MIX You need to make 36 one-half cup bags of trail mix for a class trip. The recipe calls for peanuts, chocolate chips, and raisins in the extended ratio 5 : 1 : 4. How many cups of each item do you need? **9 c, 1.8 c, 7.2 c**

60. PAPER SIZES International standard paper sizes are commonly used all over the world. The various sizes all have the same width-to-length ratios. Two sizes of paper are shown, called A3 and A2. The distance labeled x is the geometric mean of 297 mm and 594 mm. Find the value of x. **about 420 mm**

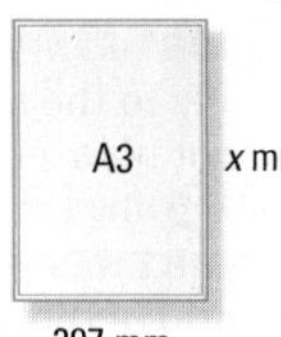

61. BATTING AVERAGE The batting average of a baseball player is the ratio of the number of hits to the number of official at-bats. In 2004, Johnny Damon of the Boston Red Sox had 621 official at-bats and a batting average of .304. Use the proportion to find the number of hits made by Johnny Damon. **about 189 hits**

$$\frac{\text{Number of hits}}{\text{Number of at-bats}} = \frac{\text{Batting average}}{1.000}$$

EXAMPLE 5 B on p. 359 for Ex. 62

62. MULTI-STEP PROBLEM The population of Red-tailed hawks is increasing in many areas of the United States. One long-term survey of bird populations suggests that the Red-tailed hawk population is increasing nationally by 2.7% each year.

a. Write the ratio of hawks in year n to hawks in year $(n - 1)$. **1027 : 1000**

b. In 2004, observers in Corpus Christi, TX, spotted 180 migrating Red-tailed hawks. Assuming this population follows the national trend, about how many Red-tailed hawks can they expect to see in 2005? **about 185 Red-tailed hawks**

c. Observers in Lipan Point, AZ, spotted 951 migrating Red-tailed hawks in 2004. Assuming this population follows the national trend, about how many Red-tailed hawks can they expect to see in 2006? **about 1003 Red-tailed hawks**

○ = WORKED-OUT SOLUTIONS on p. WS1 ★ = STANDARDIZED TEST PRACTICE

= MULTIPLE REPRESENTATIONS

66a. *Sample answer:*

x	1	2	3	4	6
y	36	18	12	9	6

66b. *Sample:*

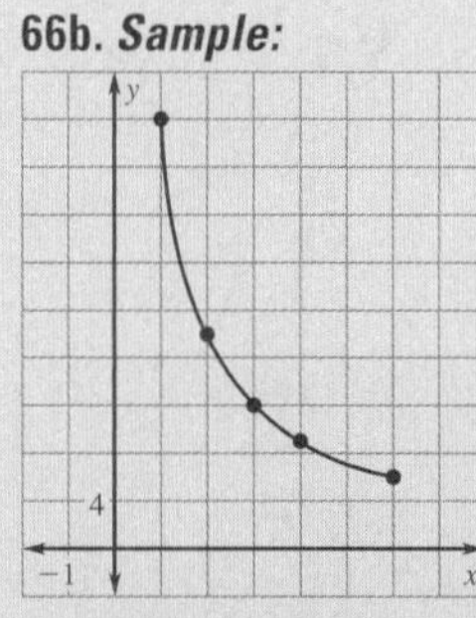

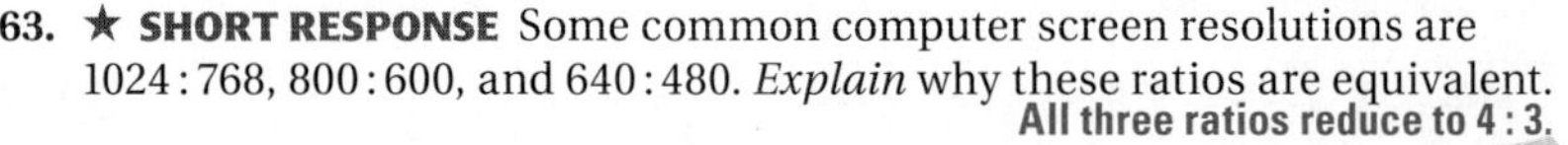

63. ★ **SHORT RESPONSE** Some common computer screen resolutions are 1024 : 768, 800 : 600, and 640 : 480. *Explain* why these ratios are equivalent. **All three ratios reduce to 4 : 3.**

64. **BIOLOGY** The larvae of the Mother-of-Pearl moth is the fastest moving caterpillar. It can run at a speed of 15 inches per second. When threatened, it can curl itself up and roll away 40 times faster than it can run. How fast can it run in miles per hour? How fast can it roll? **about 0.852 mph; about 34.1 mph**

65. **CURRENCY EXCHANGE** Emily took 500 U.S. dollars to the bank to exchange for Canadian dollars. The exchange rate on that day was 1.2 Canadian dollars per U.S. dollar. How many Canadian dollars did she get in exchange for the 500 U.S. dollars? **600 Canadian dollars**

66. **MULTIPLE REPRESENTATIONS** Let x and y be two positive numbers whose geometric mean is 6.

a. **Making a Table** Make a table of ordered pairs (x, y) such that $\sqrt{xy} = 6$.

b. **Drawing a Graph** Use the ordered pairs to make a scatter plot. Connect the points with a smooth curve. **a, b. See margin.**

c. **Analyzing Data** Is the data linear? Why or why not? **No; the graph of the equation is not a straight line.**

67. **ALGEBRA** Use algebra to verify Property 1, the Cross Products Property.

67. $\frac{a}{b} = \frac{c}{d}$, $b \neq 0$, $d \neq 0$,
$\frac{a}{b} \cdot bd = \frac{c}{d} \cdot bd$,
$ad = cb$,
$ad = bc$

C 68. **ALGEBRA** Show that the geometric mean of two numbers is equal to the arithmetic mean (or average) of the two numbers only when the numbers are equal. (*Hint*: Solve $\sqrt{xy} = \frac{x + y}{2}$ with $x, y \geq 0$.) **See margin.**

CHALLENGE In Exercises 69–71, use the given information to find the value(s) of x. Assume that the given quantities are nonnegative.

69. The geometric mean of the quantities $(\sqrt{x})$ and $(3\sqrt{x})$ is $(x - 6)$. **12**

70. The geometric mean of the quantities $(x + 1)$ and $(2x + 3)$ is $(x + 3)$. **3**

71. The geometric mean of the quantities $(2x + 1)$ and $(6x + 1)$ is $(4x - 1)$. **4**

MIXED REVIEW

PREVIEW Prepare for Lesson 6.2 in Exs. 72–75.

Find the reciprocal. *(p. 869)*

72. -6 $\;-\frac{1}{6}$ 73. $\frac{1}{13}$ $\;13$ 74. $\frac{-36}{3}$ $\;-\frac{3}{36}$ 75. -0.2 $\;-5$

Solve the quadratic equation. *(p. 882)*

76. $5x^2 = 35$ $\;\pm\sqrt{7}$ 77. $x^2 - 20 = 29$ $\;\pm 7$ 78. $(x - 3)(x + 3) = 27$ $\;\pm 6$

Write the equation of the line with the given description. *(p. 180)*

79. Parallel to $y = 3x - 7$, passing through (1, 2) $\;y = 3x - 1$

80. Perpendicular to $y = \frac{1}{4}x + 5$, passing through (0, 24) $\;y = -4x + 24$

5 ASSESS AND RETEACH

Daily Homework Quiz

Transparency Available

1. Simplify the ratio 1200 cm : 1.8 m. **2 : 3**
2. The perimeter of a rectangle is 528 millimeters. The ratio of the length to the width is 8 : 3. Find the length and the width. **192 mm, 72 mm**
3. Solve $\frac{1}{s + 8} = \frac{3}{36}$. **4**
4. Find the geometric mean of 42 and 12. $6\sqrt{14}$
5. The extended ratio of the angles of a triangle is 5 : 12 : 13. Find the angle measures of the triangle. **30°, 72°, 78°**
6. The area of a rectangle is 720 square inches. If the ratio of the length to width is 5 : 4, find the perimeter of the rectangle. **108 in.**

Online Quiz

Available at **classzone.com**

Diagnosis/Remediation

- Practice A, B, C in Chapter 6 Resource Book, pp. 6–11
- Study Guide in Chapter 6 Resource Book, pp. 12–13
- Practice Workbook, pp. 103–105
- @HomeTutor

Challenge

Additional challenge is available in the Chapter 6 Resource Book, p. 16.

68.
$$\sqrt{xy} = \frac{x + y}{2}$$
$$xy = \frac{x^2 + 2xy + y^2}{4}$$
$$4xy = x^2 + 2xy + y^2$$
$$0 = x^2 - 2xy + y^2$$
$$0 = (x - y)^2$$
$$0 = x - y$$
$$y = x$$

1 PLAN AND PREPARE

Warm-Up Exercises

Transparency Available

Solve each proportion.

1. $\frac{3}{8} = \frac{6}{x+1}$ **15**
2. $\frac{8}{3} = \frac{x+1}{6}$ **15**
3. $\frac{3}{6} = \frac{8}{x+1}$ **15**
4. The area of a rectangle is 750 square meters. The ratio of the width to the length is 5:6. Find the width and length. **width: 25 m; length: 30 m**

Notetaking Guide

Transparency Available

Promotes interactive learning and notetaking skills, pp. 145–148.

Pacing

Basic: 1 day
Average: 1 day
Advanced: 1 day
Block: 0.5 block with 6.3
- See *Teaching Guide/Lesson Plan.*

2 FOCUS AND MOTIVATE

Essential Question

Big Idea 1, p. 355

How do you calculate actual distance from a scale drawing? **Tell students they will learn how to answer this question by setting up and solving a proportion.**

6.2 Use Proportions to Solve Geometry Problems

Before You wrote and solved proportions.
Now You will use proportions to solve geometry problems.
Why? So you can calculate building dimensions, as in Ex. 22.

Key Vocabulary
- scale drawing
- scale

In Lesson 6.1, you learned to use the Cross Products Property to write equations that are equivalent to a given proportion. Three more ways to do this are given by the properties below.

REVIEW RECIPROCALS
For help with reciprocals, see p. 869.

Standards
12.0 Students find and use measures of **sides** and of interior and exterior angles **of triangles and polygons to** classify figures and **solve problems.**

KEY CONCEPT — *For Your Notebook*

Additional Properties of Proportions

2. **Reciprocal Property** If two ratios are equal, then their reciprocals are also equal. If $\frac{a}{b} = \frac{c}{d}$, then $\frac{b}{a} = \frac{d}{c}$.
3. If you interchange the means of a proportion, then you form another true proportion. If $\frac{a}{b} = \frac{c}{d}$, then $\frac{a}{c} = \frac{b}{d}$.
4. In a proportion, if you add the value of each ratio's denominator to its numerator, then you form another true proportion. If $\frac{a}{b} = \frac{c}{d}$, then $\frac{a+b}{b} = \frac{c+d}{d}$.

EXAMPLE 1 Use properties of proportions

In the diagram, $\frac{MN}{RS} = \frac{NP}{ST}$. Write four true proportions.

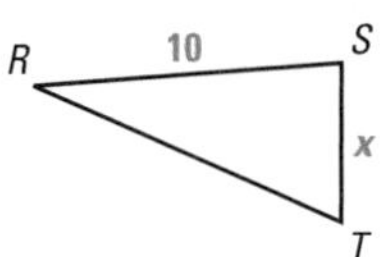

Solution

Because $\frac{MN}{RS} = \frac{NP}{ST}$, then $\frac{8}{10} = \frac{4}{x}$.

By the Reciprocal Property, the reciprocals are equal, so $\frac{10}{8} = \frac{x}{4}$.

By Property 3, you can interchange the means, so $\frac{8}{4} = \frac{10}{x}$.

By Property 4, you can add the denominators to the numerators, so $\frac{8+10}{10} = \frac{4+x}{x}$, or $\frac{18}{10} = \frac{4+x}{x}$.

Resource Planning Guide

Chapter Resource Book
- Teaching Guide/Lesson Plan (pp. 17–18)
- Practice levels A, B, C (pp. 19–24)
- Study Guide (pp. 25–26)
- Catch-up for Absent Students (p. 27)
- Problem Solving Workshop (p. 28)
- Challenge (p. 29)

Workbooks
- Notetaking Guide (pp. 145–148)
- Practice Workbook (pp. 106–108)

Teaching Options
- **Power Presentations CD-ROM** provides dynamic electronic teaching resources for the classroom.
- **Activity Generator CD-ROM** provides editable activities for all ability levels.

Interactive Technology
- Easy Planner
- Power Presentations CD-ROM
- Activity Generator CD-ROM
- Animated Algebra
- Test Generator CD-ROM
- Online Quiz
- eWorkbook
- eEdition
- @HomeTutor

Resources for English Learners
- Quick Reference for English Learners
- Spanish Study Guide
- Multi-Language Visual Glossary
- Student Resources in Spanish

See also the *Geometry Toolkit* for more strategies for meeting individual needs.

EXAMPLE 2 Use proportions with geometric figures

ALGEBRA **In the diagram, $\frac{BD}{DA} = \frac{BE}{EC}$. Find BA and BD.**

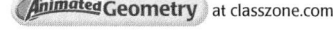

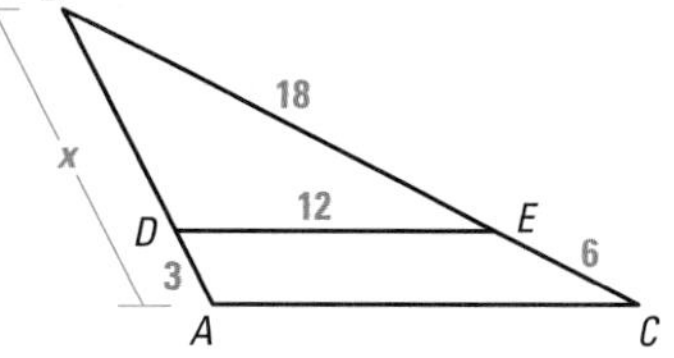

Solution

$\frac{BD}{DA} = \frac{BE}{EC}$ Given

$\frac{BD + DA}{DA} = \frac{BE + EC}{EC}$ Property of Proportions (Property 4)

$\frac{x}{3} = \frac{18 + 6}{6}$ Substitution Property of Equality

$6x = 3(18 + 6)$ Cross Products Property

$x = 12$ Solve for x.

▶ So, $BA = 12$ and $BD = 12 - 3 = 9$.

Animated Geometry at classzone.com

SCALE DRAWING A **scale drawing** is a drawing that is the same shape as the object it represents. The **scale** is a ratio that describes how the dimensions in the drawing are related to the actual dimensions of the object.

EXAMPLE 3 Find the scale of a drawing

BLUEPRINTS The blueprint shows a scale drawing of a cell phone. The length of the antenna on the blueprint is 5 centimeters. The actual length of the antenna is 2 centimeters. What is the scale of the blueprint?

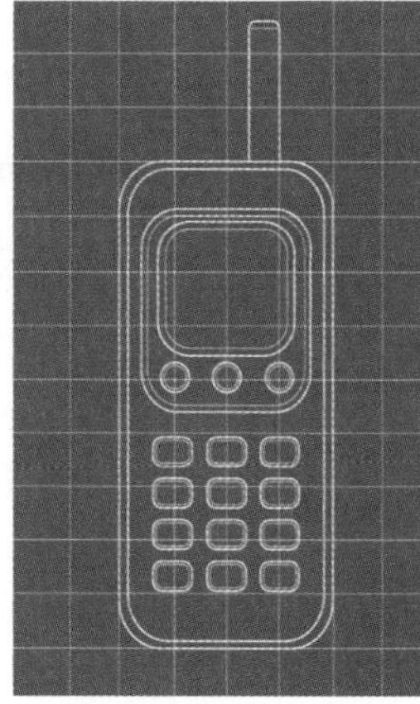

Solution

To find the scale, write the ratio of a length in the drawing to an actual length, then rewrite the ratio so that the denominator is 1.

$$\frac{\text{length on blueprint}}{\text{length of antenna}} = \frac{5 \text{ cm}}{2 \text{ cm}} = \frac{5 \div 2}{2 \div 2} = \frac{2.5}{1}$$

▶ The scale of the blueprint is 2.5 cm : 1 cm.

GUIDED PRACTICE for Examples 1, 2, and 3

1. In Example 1, find the value of x. **5**
2. In Example 2, $\frac{DE}{AC} = \frac{BE}{BC}$. Find AC. **16**
3. **WHAT IF?** In Example 3, suppose the length of the antenna on the blueprint is 10 centimeters. Find the new scale of the blueprint. $\frac{5 \text{ cm}}{1 \text{ cm}}$

Motivating the Lesson

Suppose you are driving to a vacation cabin and want to know how much further you need to drive. You can set up a proportion using lengths on a map and the map key to find the remaining distance.

3 TEACH

Extra Example 1

In the diagram $\frac{AB}{DE} = \frac{AC}{DF}$. Write four true proportions.

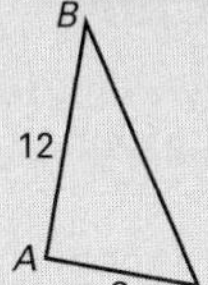

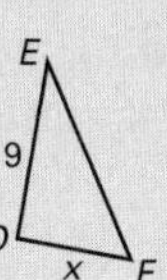

Sample answer: $\frac{12}{9} = \frac{8}{x}$; $\frac{9}{12} = \frac{x}{8}$; $\frac{12}{8} = \frac{9}{x}$; $\frac{12 + 9}{9} = \frac{8 + x}{x}$

Extra Example 2

In the diagram, $\frac{SV}{VT} = \frac{SU}{UR}$. Find ST and VT.

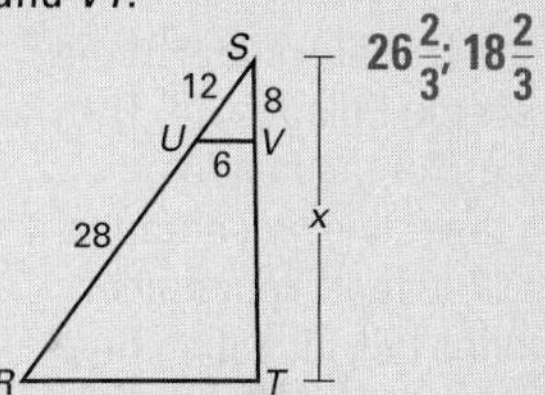

$26\frac{2}{3}$; $18\frac{2}{3}$

Key Question to Ask for Example 2

- Why was Property 4 of proportions used to solve this problem? ***BD + DA = x*; you need Property 4 because *x* is a sum.**

An **Animated Geometry** activity is available on-line for **Example 2**. This activity is also available on the **Power Presentations CD-ROM**.

Extra Example 3

The blueprint shows a scale drawing of an MP3 music player. The diameter of the round speaker on the blueprint is 0.4 inch. The actual length is 1.6 inches. What is the scale of the blueprint?

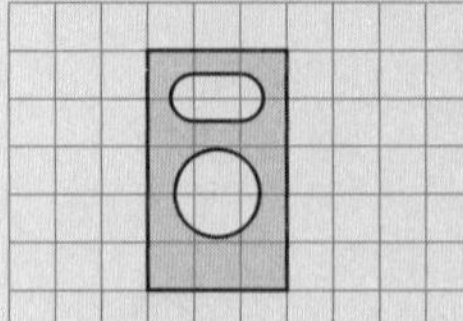

1 in.: 4 in.

Key Question to Ask for Example 3

- What does the unit 1 represent on the scale of the blueprint? **The unit 1 gives the side of one square of the blueprint.**

Extra Example 4

The scale of a map is 1 in.: 1440 ft. Find the actual length of a street if the distance on the map is 3 inches. **4320 feet**

Extra Example 5

You buy a 3-D scale model of the Sears Tower in Chicago, IL. The actual height of the building, including the television antenna on top, is 1703 feet. Your model is 29.4 inches tall, including the 4.4 inch antenna on top of the model.

a. What is the height of the actual antenna? **about 255 feet**

b. About how many times as tall as your model is the actual building, including the antenna? **695 times**

Closing the Lesson

Have students summarize the major points of the lesson and answer the Essential Question: How do you calculate actual distance from a scale drawing?

- **The proportion properties allow you to write true proportions in a number of ways.**
- **A scale drawing has a scale that relates the size of the drawing to the size of the actual object.**

Write a proportion with the scale of the drawing on one side of the equal sign and the ratio of the length in the drawing to the actual length on the other side. Solve the proportion.

EXAMPLE 4 Use a scale drawing

MAPS The scale of the map at the right is 1 inch : 26 miles. Find the actual distance from Pocahontas to Algona.

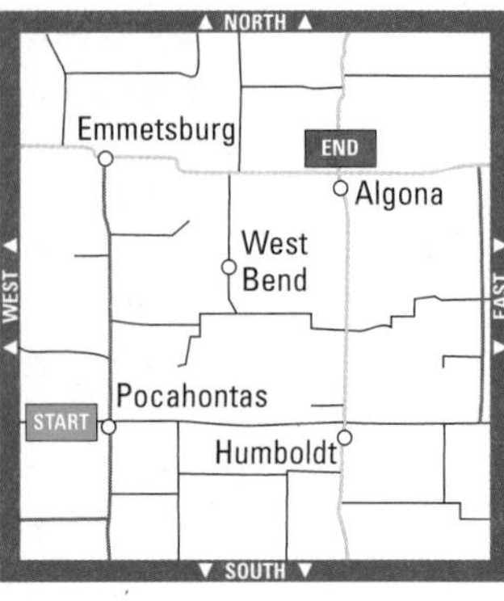

Solution

Use a ruler. The distance from Pocahontas to Algona on the map is about 1.25 inches. Let x be the actual distance in miles.

$$\frac{1.25 \text{ in.}}{x \text{ mi}} = \frac{1 \text{ in.}}{26 \text{ mi}}$$ ← **distance on map** / ← **actual distance**

$x = 1.25(26)$ **Cross Products Property**

$x = 32.5$ **Simplify.**

▶ The actual distance from Pocahontas to Algona is about 32.5 miles.

EXAMPLE 5 Solve a multi-step problem

SCALE MODEL You buy a 3-D scale model of the Reunion Tower in Dallas, TX. The actual building is 560 feet tall. Your model is 10 inches tall, and the diameter of the dome on your scale model is about 2.1 inches.

a. What is the diameter of the actual dome?

b. About how many times as tall as your model is the actual building?

Solution

a. $$\frac{10 \text{ in.}}{560 \text{ ft}} = \frac{2.1 \text{ in.}}{x \text{ ft}}$$ ← **measurement on model** / ← **measurement on actual building**

$10x = 1176$ **Cross Products Property**

$x = 117.6$ **Solve for x.**

▶ The diameter of the actual dome is about 118 feet.

b. To simplify a ratio with unlike units, multiply by a conversion factor.

$$\frac{560 \text{ ft}}{10 \text{ in.}} = \frac{560 \cancel{\text{ft}}}{10 \cancel{\text{in.}}} \cdot \frac{12 \cancel{\text{in.}}}{1 \cancel{\text{ft}}} = 672$$

▶ The actual building is 672 times as tall as the model.

✓ GUIDED PRACTICE for Examples 4 and 5

4. Two cities are 96 miles from each other. The cities are 4 inches apart on a map. Find the scale of the map. **1 in. : 24 mi**

5. **WHAT IF?** Your friend has a model of the Reunion Tower that is 14 inches tall. What is the diameter of the dome on your friend's model? **about 2.94 in.**

Differentiated Instruction

Kinesthetic Learners After discussing **Example 5**, have students measure and create a scale drawing of an object in the classroom. Tell them to write the scale on their drawing. When everyone is finished, ask them to exchange their drawing with another student. Direct students to find the actual dimensions of the object by using the drawing and its scale.

See also the *Geometry Toolkit* for more strategies.

6.2 EXERCISES

HOMEWORK KEY
○ = **WORKED-OUT SOLUTIONS** on p. WS7 for Exs. 11, 13, and 25
★ = **STANDARDIZED TEST PRACTICE** Exs. 2, 18, and 24

SKILL PRACTICE

A

1. VOCABULARY Copy and complete: A _?_ is a drawing that has the same shape as the object it represents. **scale drawing**

2. ★ WRITING Suppose the scale of a model of the Eiffel Tower is 1 inch : 20 feet. *Explain* how to determine how many times taller the actual tower is than the model. $\frac{20\text{ ft}}{1\text{ in.}} \cdot \frac{12\text{ in.}}{1\text{ ft}} = 240$ **times taller**

EXAMPLE 1 on p. 364 for Exs. 3–10

REASONING **Copy and complete the statement.**

3. If $\frac{8}{x} = \frac{3}{y}$, then $\frac{8}{3} = \frac{?}{?}$. $\frac{x}{y}$

4. If $\frac{x}{9} = \frac{y}{20}$, then $\frac{x}{y} = \frac{?}{?}$. $\frac{9}{20}$

5. If $\frac{x}{6} = \frac{y}{15}$, then $\frac{x+6}{6} = \frac{?}{?}$. $\frac{y+15}{15}$

6. If $\frac{14}{3} = \frac{x}{y}$, then $\frac{17}{3} = \frac{?}{?}$. $\frac{x+y}{y}$

REASONING **Decide whether the statement is *true* or *false*.**

7. If $\frac{8}{m} = \frac{n}{9}$, then $\frac{8+m}{m} = \frac{n+9}{9}$. **true**

8. If $\frac{5}{7} = \frac{a}{b}$, then $\frac{7}{5} = \frac{a}{b}$. **false**

9. If $\frac{d}{2} = \frac{g+10}{11}$, then $\frac{d}{g+10} = \frac{2}{11}$. **true**

10. If $\frac{4+x}{4} = \frac{3+y}{y}$, then $\frac{x}{4} = \frac{3}{y}$. **true**

EXAMPLE 2 on p. 365 for Exs. 11–12

PROPERTIES OF PROPORTIONS **Use the diagram and the given information to find the unknown length.**

(11.) Given $\frac{CB}{BA} = \frac{DE}{EF}$, find BA. **10.5**

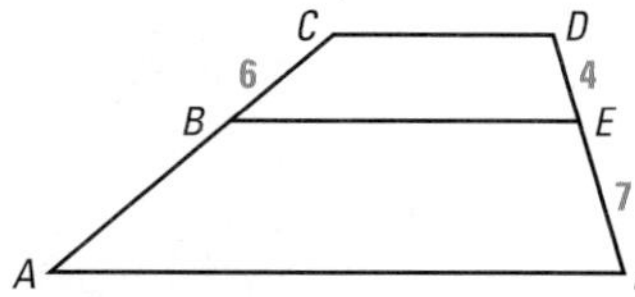

12. Given $\frac{XW}{XV} = \frac{YW}{ZV}$, find ZV. **34**

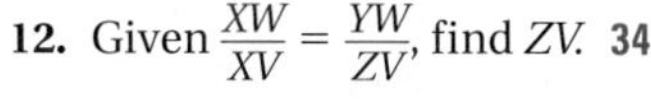

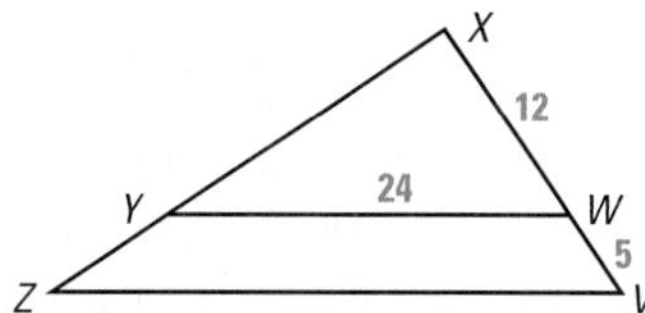

EXAMPLES 3 and 4 on pp. 365–366 for Exs. 13–14

SCALE DIAGRAMS **In Exercises 13 and 14, use the diagram of the field hockey field in which 1 inch = 50 yards. Use a ruler to approximate the dimension.**

(13.) Find the actual length of the field. **about 100 yd**

14. Find the actual width of the field. **about 60 yd**

15. ERROR ANALYSIS *Describe* and correct the error made in the reasoning.

If $\frac{a}{3} = \frac{c}{4}$, then $\frac{a+3}{3} = \frac{c+3}{4}$. ✗

4 should have been added to the numerator of the second fraction instead of 3; $\frac{a+3}{3} = \frac{c+4}{4}$.

4 PRACTICE AND APPLY

Assignment Guide

Answer Transparencies available for all exercises

Basic:
Day 1: SRH p. 875 Exs. 32–36
pp. 367–370
Exs. 1–16, 22–29, 38–40

Average:
Day 1: pp. 367–370
Exs. 1, 2, 4–6, 8–18, 22–33, 38, 39

Advanced:
Day 1: pp. 367–370
Exs. 1, 2, 5, 6, 9, 10–18 even, 19–38*, 40

Block:
pp. 367–370
Exs. 1, 2, 4–6, 8–18, 22–33, 38, 39 (with 6.3)

Differentiated Instruction

See *Geometry Best Practices Toolkit* for suggestions on addressing the needs of a diverse classroom.

Homework Check

For a quick check of student understanding of key concepts, go over the following exercises:

Basic: 4, 12, 14, 22, 26
Average: 6, 12, 14, 22, 28
Advanced: 10, 12, 14, 22, 30

Extra Practice

- Student Edition, p. 906
- Chapter 6 Resource Book: Practice levels A, B, C, pp. 19–24

Practice Worksheet

An easily-readable reduced practice page (with answers) for this lesson can be found on p. 354C.

Teaching Strategy

Exercises 23–24 Students may have difficulty knowing the steps to perform to find the scale of a map or model. Remind them that they need to write the ratio of a length in the drawing or model to the actual length.

B **PROPERTIES OF PROPORTIONS** **Use the diagram and the given information to find the unknown length.**

16. Given $\frac{CA}{CB} = \frac{AE}{BD}$, find BD. **12**

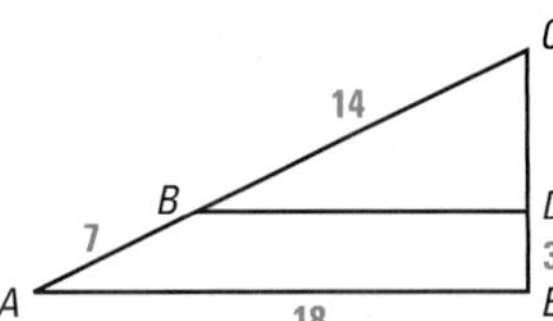
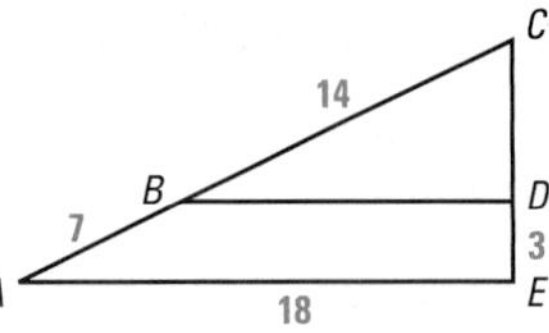

17. Given $\frac{SQ}{SR} = \frac{TV}{TU}$, find RQ. $\frac{49}{3}$

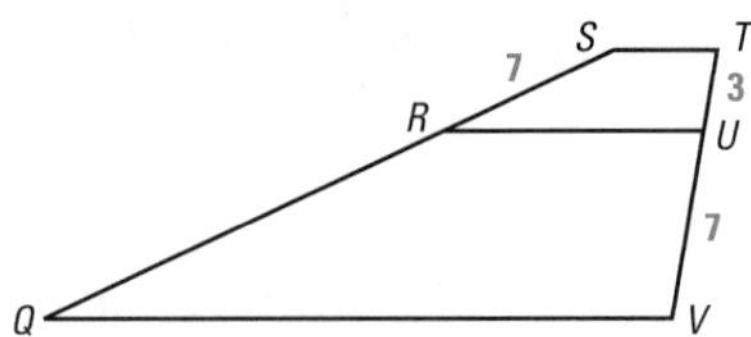

18. ★ **MULTIPLE CHOICE** If x, y, z, and q are four different numbers, and the proportion $\frac{x}{y} = \frac{z}{q}$ is true, which of the following is false? **C**

Ⓐ $\frac{y}{x} = \frac{q}{z}$ Ⓑ $\frac{x}{z} = \frac{y}{q}$ Ⓒ $\frac{y}{x} = \frac{z}{q}$ Ⓓ $\frac{x+y}{y} = \frac{z+q}{q}$

C **CHALLENGE** **Two number patterns are *proportional* if there is a nonzero number k such that $(a_1, b_1, c_1, \ldots) = k(a_2, b_2, c_2, \ldots) = ka_2, kb_2, kc_2, \ldots$.**

19. Given the relationship $(8, 16, 20) = k(2, 4, 5)$, find k. **4**

20. Given that $a_1 = ka_2$, $b_1 = kb_2$, and $c_1 = kc_2$, show that $\frac{a_1}{a_2} = \frac{b_1}{b_2} = \frac{c_1}{c_2}$.

21. Given that $a_1 = ka_2$, $b_1 = kb_2$, and $c_1 = kc_2$, show that $\frac{a_1 + b_1 + c_1}{a_2 + b_2 + c_2} = k$.

20. $\frac{a_1}{a_2} = k$, $\frac{b_1}{b_2} = k$, $\frac{c_1}{c_2} = k$, $\frac{a_1}{a_2} = \frac{b_1}{b_2} = \frac{c_1}{c_2}$

21. $a_1 + b_1 + c_1 = ka_2 + kb_2 + kc_2$, $a_1 + b_1 + c_1 = k(a_2 + b_2 + c_2)$, $\frac{a_1 + b_1 + c_1}{a_2 + b_2 + c_2} = k$

PROBLEM SOLVING

EXAMPLE 5 A on p. 366 for Ex. 22

22. **ARCHITECTURE** A basket manufacturer has headquarters in an office building that has the same shape as a basket they sell.

    a. The bottom of the basket is a rectangle with length 15 inches and width 10 inches. The base of the building is a rectangle with length 192 feet. What is the width of the base of the building? **128 ft**

    b. About how many times as long as the bottom of the basket is the base of the building? **153.6 times**

@HomeTutor for problem solving help at classzone.com

Longaberger Company Home Office Newark, Ohio

23. **MAP SCALE** A street on a map is 3 inches long. The actual street is 1 mile long. Find the scale of the map. **1 in. : $\frac{1}{3}$ mi**

@HomeTutor for problem solving help at classzone.com

24. ★ **MULTIPLE CHOICE** A model train engine is 12 centimeters long. The actual engine is 18 meters long. What is the scale of the model? **B**

Ⓐ 3 cm : 2 m Ⓑ 1 cm : 1.5 m Ⓒ 1 cm : 3 m Ⓓ 200 cm : 3 m

○ = WORKED-OUT SOLUTIONS on p. WS1

★ = STANDARDIZED TEST PRACTICE

MAP READING **The map of a hiking trail has a scale of 1 inch : 3.2 miles. Use a ruler to approximate the actual distance between the two shelters.**

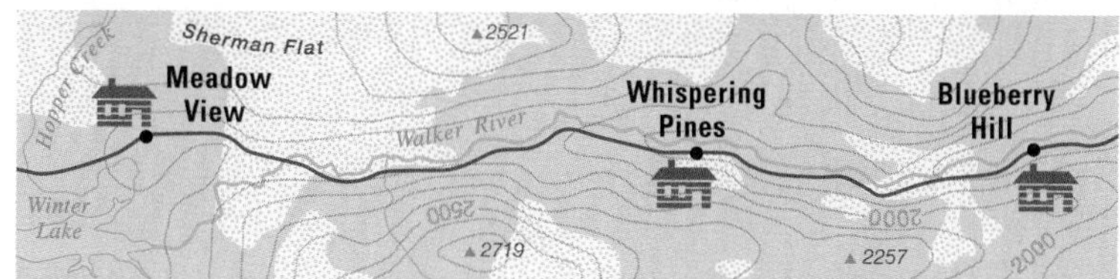

(25.) Meadow View and Whispering Pines **about 8 mi**

26. Whispering Pines and Blueberry Hill **about 4.5 mi**

B 27. **POLLEN** The photograph shows a particle of goldenrod pollen that has been magnified under a microscope. The scale of the photograph is 900 : 1. Use a ruler to estimate the width in millimeters of the particle. **about 0.022 mm**

RAMP DESIGN **Assume that the wheelchair ramps described each have a slope of $\frac{1}{12}$, which is the maximum slope recommended for a wheelchair ramp.**

28. A wheelchair ramp has a 21 foot run. What is its rise? **$1\frac{3}{4}$ ft**

29. A wheelchair ramp rises 4 feet. What is its run? **48 ft**

30. **STATISTICS** Researchers asked 4887 people to pick a number between 1 and 10. The results are shown in the table below.

Answer	1	2	3	4	5
Percent	4.2%	5.1%	11.4%	10.5%	10.7%
Answer	6	7	8	9	10
Percent	10.0%	27.2%	8.8%	6.0%	6.1%

a. Estimate the number of people who picked the number 3. **about 557 people**

b. You ask a participant what number she picked. Is the participant more likely to answer 6 or 7? *Explain.* **7; 27.2% is greater than 10%.**

c. Conduct this experiment with your classmates. Make a table in which you compare the new percentages with the ones given in the original survey. Why might they be different?
Check students' work. ***Sample answer:*** **A different group of people were polled.**

ALGEBRA Use algebra to verify the property of proportions.

31. Property 2

32. Property 3

33. Property 4

31. $\frac{a}{b} = \frac{c}{d}$, $\frac{a}{b} \cdot bd = \frac{c}{d} \cdot bd$, $ad = cb$, $ad \cdot \frac{1}{ac} = cb \cdot \frac{1}{ac}$, $\frac{d}{c} = \frac{b}{a}$

32. $\frac{a}{b} = \frac{c}{d}$, $\frac{a}{b} \cdot bd = \frac{c}{d} \cdot bd$, $ad = cb$, $ad \cdot \frac{1}{cd} = cb \cdot \frac{1}{cd}$, $\frac{a}{c} = \frac{b}{d}$

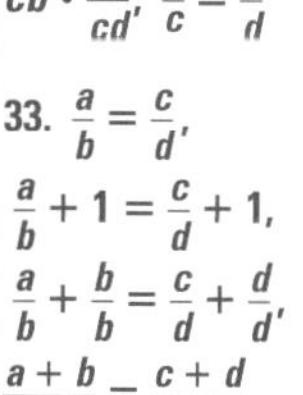

33. $\frac{a}{b} = \frac{c}{d}$, $\frac{a}{b} + 1 = \frac{c}{d} + 1$, $\frac{a}{b} + \frac{b}{b} = \frac{c}{d} + \frac{d}{d}$, $\frac{a+b}{b} = \frac{c+d}{d}$

Internet Reference

Exercise 27 For more information about pollen, visit www.pollenuk.co.uk/aero/pm/WIP.htm

Mathematical Reasoning

Exercise 30 Remind students that a percent is another way to write the ratio of a number to 100. So a proportion that would solve part (a) is $\frac{11.4}{100} = \frac{x}{4887}$.

Study Strategy

Exercises 31–33 It can be helpful to students if they understand that each of these exercises is based on the Cross Products Property for proportions or on the Addition Property of Equality.

5 ASSESS AND RETEACH

Daily Homework Quiz

Transparency Available

1. In the diagram, $\frac{RS}{XY} = \frac{ST}{YZ}$. Write four true proportions.

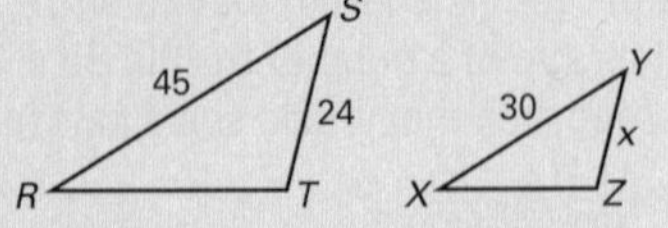

Sample answer: $\frac{45}{30} = \frac{24}{x}$; $\frac{30}{45} = \frac{x}{24}$; $\frac{45}{24} = \frac{30}{x}$; $\frac{45+30}{30} = \frac{24+x}{x}$

2. In the diagram, $\frac{MR}{RN} = \frac{PS}{SN}$. Find MN and MR. **48; 30**

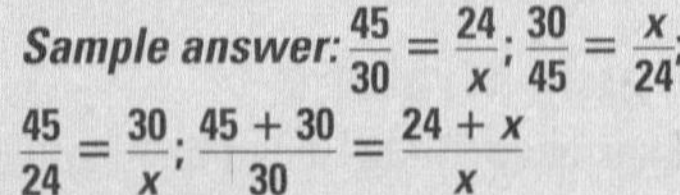

3. On a map, a street is 2 inches long. The actual length is 1 mile. Find the scale. **1 in. : 0.5 mi**

4. A map is scaled so that 1 cm represents 20 km. If two towns are 8.2 centimeters apart on the map, what is the actual distance between the towns? **164 km**

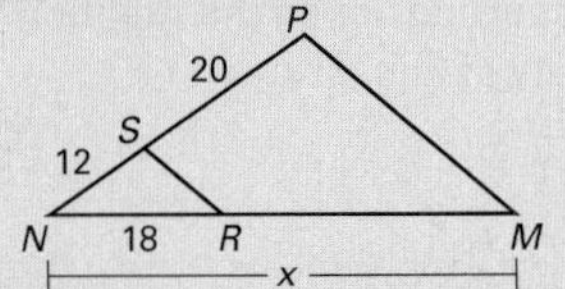

Available at **classzone.com**

Diagnosis/Remediation

- Practice A, B, C in Chapter 6 Resource Book, pp. 19–24
- Study Guide in Chapter 6 Resource Book, pp. 25–26
- Practice Workbook, pp. 106–108
- @HomeTutor

Challenge

Additional challenge is available in the Chapter 6 Resource Book, p. 29.

Quiz

An easily-readable reduced copy of the quiz (with answers) on Lessons 6.1–6.2 from the Assessment Book can be found on p. 354G.

34–36. See Additional Answers beginning on p. AA1.

C **REASONING** **Use algebra to *explain* why the property of proportions is true.** **34–36. See margin.**

34. If $\frac{a-b}{a+b} = \frac{c-d}{c+d}$, then $\frac{a}{b} = \frac{c}{d}$.

35. If $\frac{a+c}{b+d} = \frac{a-c}{b-d}$, then $\frac{a}{b} = \frac{c}{d}$.

36. If $\frac{a}{b} = \frac{c}{d} = \frac{e}{f}$, then $\frac{a+c+e}{b+d+f} = \frac{a}{b}$. (*Hint:* Let $\frac{a}{b} = r$.)

37. **CHALLENGE** When fruit is dehydrated, water is removed from the fruit. The water content in fresh apricots is about 86%. In dehydrated apricots, the water content is about 75%. Suppose 5 kilograms of raw apricots are dehydrated. How many kilograms of water are removed from the fruit? What is the approximate weight of the dehydrated apricots? **about 2.9 kg; about 2.1 kg**

MIXED REVIEW

38. Over the weekend, Claudia drove a total of 405 miles, driving twice as far on Saturday as on Sunday. How far did Claudia travel each day? *(p. 65)* **Saturday: 270 mi, Sunday: 135 mi**

PREVIEW Prepare for Lesson 6.3 in Exs. 39–40.

Identify all pairs of congruent corresponding parts. Then write another congruence statement for the figures. *(p. 225)*

39. $\triangle XYZ \cong \triangle LMN$

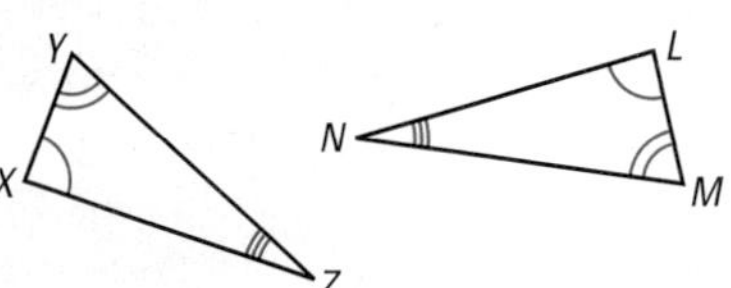

$\angle L \cong \angle X$, $\angle M \cong \angle Y$, $\angle N \cong \angle Z$, $\overline{XY} \cong \overline{LM}$, $\overline{YZ} \cong \overline{MN}$, $\overline{XZ} \cong \overline{LN}$. *Sample answer:* $\triangle YZX \cong \triangle MNL$

40. $DEFG \cong QRST$

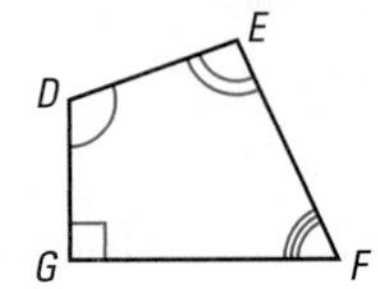

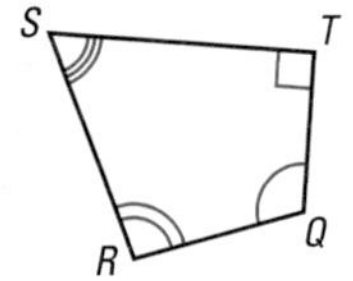

$\angle D \cong \angle Q$, $\angle E \cong \angle R$, $\angle F \cong \angle S$, $\angle G \cong \angle T$, $\overline{DE} \cong \overline{QR}$, $\overline{EF} \cong \overline{RS}$, $\overline{FG} \cong \overline{ST}$, $\overline{GD} \cong \overline{TQ}$. *Sample answer:* $EFGD \cong RSTQ$

QUIZ *for Lessons 6.1–6.2*

Solve the proportion. *(p. 356)*

1. $\frac{10}{y} = \frac{5}{2}$ **4**

2. $\frac{x}{6} = \frac{9}{3}$ **18**

3. $\frac{1}{a+3} = \frac{4}{16}$ **1**

4. $\frac{6}{d-6} = \frac{4}{8}$ **18**

Copy and complete the statement. *(p. 364)*

5. If $\frac{9}{x} = \frac{5}{2}$, then $\frac{9}{5} = \frac{?}{?}$. $\frac{x}{2}$

6. If $\frac{x}{15} = \frac{y}{21}$, then $\frac{x}{y} = \frac{?}{?}$. $\frac{15}{21}$

7. If $\frac{x}{8} = \frac{y}{12}$, then $\frac{x+8}{8} = \frac{?}{?}$. $\frac{y+12}{12}$

8. If $\frac{32}{5} = \frac{x}{y}$, then $\frac{37}{5} = \frac{?}{?}$. $\frac{x+y}{y}$

9. In the diagram, $AD = 10$, B is the midpoint of $\overline{AD}$, and AC is the geometric mean of AB and AD. Find AC. *(p. 364)* $5\sqrt{2}$

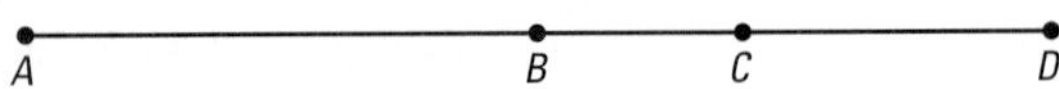

EXTRA PRACTICE for Lesson 6.2, p. 906

ONLINE QUIZ at classzone.com

6.3 Similar Polygons

MATERIALS • metric ruler • protractor

Standards

12.0 Students find and use measures of sides and of interior and exterior **angles of triangles and polygons** to classify figures and solve problems.

QUESTION **When a figure is reduced, how are the corresponding angles related? How are the corresponding lengths related?**

EXPLORE **Compare measures of lengths and angles in two photos**

STEP 1 ***Measure segments*** Photo 2 is a reduction of Photo 1. In each photo, find AB to the nearest millimeter. Write the ratio of the length of $\overline{AB}$ in Photo 1 to the length of $\overline{AB}$ in Photo 2.

STEP 2 ***Measure angles*** Use a protractor to find the measure of $\angle 1$ in each photo. Write the ratio of $m\angle 1$ in Photo 1 to $m\angle 1$ in Photo 2.

STEP 3 ***Find measurements*** Copy and complete the table. Use the same units for each measurement. Record your results in a table.

Photo 1

Photo 2

Measurement	Photo 1	Photo 2	$\frac{\text{Photo 1}}{\text{Photo 2}}$
AB	? 36 mm	? 26 mm	? 1.4
AC	? 14 mm	? 10 mm	? 1.4
DE	? 28 mm	? 20 mm	? 1.4
$m\angle 1$	? 60°	? 60°	? 1
$m\angle 2$	? 28°	? 28°	? 1

DRAW CONCLUSIONS **Use your observations to complete these exercises**

1. Make a conjecture about the relationship between corresponding lengths when a figure is reduced. **When a figure is reduced, the ratios of each pair of corresponding lengths are equal.**
2. Make a conjecture about the relationship between corresponding angles when a figure is reduced. **Corresponding angles are congruent.**
3. Suppose the measure of an angle in Photo 2 is 35°. What is the measure of the corresponding angle in Photo 1? **35°**
4. Suppose a segment in Photo 2 is 1 centimeter long. What is the measure of the corresponding segment in Photo 1? **about 1.4 cm**
5. Suppose a segment in Photo 1 is 5 centimeters long. What is the measure of the corresponding segment in Photo 2? **about 3.6 cm**

1 PLAN AND PREPARE

Explore the Concept

- Students will compare the measures of lengths and angles in two similar photos.
- This activity leads into the study of similar triangles in Lesson 6.3, Example 1.

Materials

Each student will need:

- metric ruler
- protractor

Recommended Time

Work activity: 10 min

Discuss results: 5 min

Grouping

Students should work individually.

2 TEACH

Tips for Success

Remind students to use the same units for each measurement. For Step 3, if the ratios are not equal, suggest that they re-measure the figures.

Alternative Strategy

Demonstrate how to do this activity by doing the steps on the overhead projector and asking students to make conjectures.

Key Discovery

If two polygons are similar, then the ratios of corresponding side lengths are the same and the corresponding angle measures are the same.

3 ASSESS AND RETEACH

1. One segment is twice as long as another in a photo. What is the relationship between the corresponding segments in an enlargement of the photo? **One is twice as long as the other.**

6.3 Use Similar Polygons

Before You used proportions to solve geometry problems.

Now You will use proportions to identify similar polygons.

Why? So you can solve science problems, as in Ex. 34.

1 PLAN AND PREPARE

Warm-Up Exercises

Transparency Available

1. Solve $\frac{12}{10} = \frac{x}{60}$. **72**
2. The scale of a map is 1 cm : 10 mi. The actual distance between two towns is 4.3 miles. Find the length on the map. **0.43 cm**
3. A model train is 9 centimeters long. The actual engine is 18 meters long. What is the scale of the model? **1 cm : 2 m**

Notetaking Guide

Transparency Available

Promotes interactive learning and notetaking skills, pp. 149–152.

Pacing

Basic: 2 days

Average: 2 days

Advanced: 2 days

Block: 0.5 block with 6.2
0.5 block with 6.4

• See *Teaching Guide/Lesson Plan.*

2 FOCUS AND MOTIVATE

Essential Question

Big Idea 1, p. 355

If two figures are similar, how do you find the length of a missing side? **Tell students they will learn how to answer this question by solving a proportion using the lengths of corresponding sides.**

Key Vocabulary
- **similar polygons**
- **scale factor**

Standards

5.0 Students prove that triangles are congruent or **similar, and they are able to use the concept of corresponding parts** of congruent triangles.

8.0 Students know, derive, and **solve problems involving the perimeter,** circumference, area, volume, lateral area, and surface area **of common geometric figures.**

11.0 Students determine how changes in dimensions affect the perimeter, area, and volume **of common geometric figures** and solids.

Two polygons are **similar polygons** if corresponding angles are congruent and corresponding side lengths are proportional.

In the diagram below, *ABCD* is similar to *EFGH*. You can write "*ABCD* is similar to *EFGH*" as $ABCD \sim EFGH$. Notice in the similarity statement that the corresponding vertices are listed in the same order.

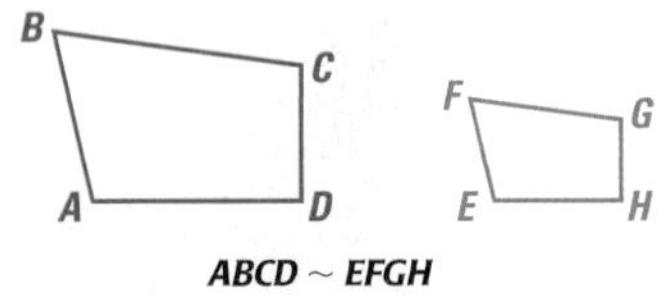

$ABCD \sim EFGH$

Corresponding angles

$\angle A \cong \angle E$, $\angle B \cong \angle F$, $\angle C \cong \angle G$, and $\angle D \cong \angle H$

Ratios of corresponding sides

$\frac{AB}{EF} = \frac{BC}{FG} = \frac{CD}{GH} = \frac{DA}{HE}$

EXAMPLE 1 Use similarity statements

In the diagram, $\triangle RST \sim \triangle XYZ$.

a. List all pairs of congruent angles.

b. Check that the ratios of corresponding side lengths are equal.

c. Write the ratios of the corresponding side lengths in a *statement of proportionality*.

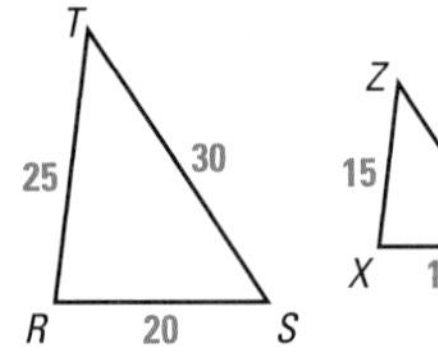

READ VOCABULARY
In a *statement of proportionality*, any pair of ratios forms a true proportion.

Solution

a. $\angle R \cong \angle X$, $\angle S \cong \angle Y$, and $\angle T \cong \angle Z$.

b. $\frac{RS}{XY} = \frac{20}{12} = \frac{5}{3}$ $\frac{ST}{YZ} = \frac{30}{18} = \frac{5}{3}$ $\frac{TR}{ZX} = \frac{25}{15} = \frac{5}{3}$

c. Because the ratios in part (b) are equal, $\frac{RS}{XY} = \frac{ST}{YZ} = \frac{TR}{ZX}$.

GUIDED PRACTICE for Example 1

1. Given $\triangle JKL \sim \triangle PQR$, list all pairs of congruent angles. Write the ratios of the corresponding side lengths in a statement of proportionality.
   $\angle J \cong \angle P$, $\angle K \cong \angle Q$, $\angle L \cong \angle R$; $\frac{JK}{PQ} = \frac{KL}{QR} = \frac{LJ}{RP}$

Resource Planning Guide

Chapter Resource Book
- Teaching Guide/Lesson Plan (pp. 30–31)
- Practice levels A, B, C (pp. 32–37)
- Study Guide (pp. 38–39)
- Catch-up for Absent Students (p. 40)
- Problem Solving Workshop (p. 41)
- Challenge (p. 43)

Workbooks
- Notetaking Guide (pp. 149–152)
- Practice Workbook (pp. 109–111)

Teaching Options
- **Power Presentations CD-ROM** provides dynamic electronic teaching resources for the classroom.
- **Activity Generator CD-ROM** provides editable activities for all ability levels.

Interactive Technology
- Easy Planner
- Power Presentations CD-ROM
- Activity Generator CD-ROM
- Animated Algebra
- Test Generator CD-ROM
- Online Quiz
- eWorkbook
- eEdition
- @HomeTutor

Resources for English Learners
- Quick Reference for English Learners
- Spanish Study Guide
- Multi-Language Visual Glossary
- Student Resources in Spanish

See also the *Geometry Toolkit* for more strategies for meeting individual needs.

SCALE FACTOR If two polygons are similar, then the ratio of the lengths of two corresponding sides is called the **scale factor**. In Example 1, the common ratio of $\frac{5}{3}$ is the scale factor of $\triangle RST$ to $\triangle XYZ$.

EXAMPLE 2 Find the scale factor

Determine whether the polygons are similar. If they are, write a similarity statement and find the scale factor of *ZYXW* to *FGHJ*.

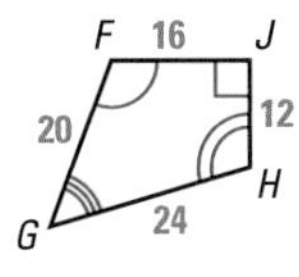

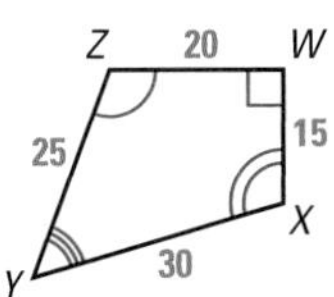

Solution

STEP 1 **Identify** pairs of congruent angles. From the diagram, you can see that $\angle Z \cong \angle F$, $\angle Y \cong \angle G$, and $\angle X \cong \angle H$. Angles W and J are right angles, so $\angle W \cong \angle J$. So, the corresponding angles are congruent.

STEP 2 **Show** that corresponding side lengths are proportional.

$\frac{ZY}{FG} = \frac{25}{20} = \frac{5}{4}$ $\frac{YX}{GH} = \frac{30}{24} = \frac{5}{4}$ $\frac{XW}{HJ} = \frac{15}{12} = \frac{5}{4}$ $\frac{WZ}{JF} = \frac{20}{16} = \frac{5}{4}$

The ratios are equal, so the corresponding side lengths are proportional.

▶ So $ZYXW \sim FGHJ$. The scale factor of $ZYXW$ to $FGHJ$ is $\frac{5}{4}$.

EXAMPLE 3 Use similar polygons

 **ALGEBRA In the diagram, $\triangle DEF \sim \triangle MNP$. Find the value of x.**

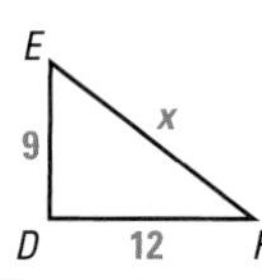

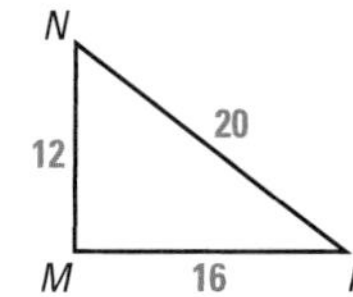

Solution

The triangles are similar, so the corresponding side lengths are proportional.

ANOTHER WAY
There are several ways to write the proportion. For example, you could write $\frac{DF}{MP} = \frac{EF}{NP}$.

$\frac{MN}{DE} = \frac{NP}{EF}$ Write proportion.

$\frac{12}{9} = \frac{20}{x}$ Substitute.

$12x = 180$ Cross Products Property

$x = 15$ Solve for x.

✓ **GUIDED PRACTICE** for Examples 2 and 3

In the diagram, *ABCD* ~ *QRST*.

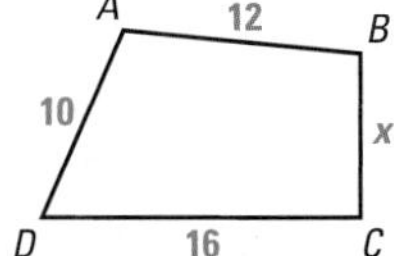

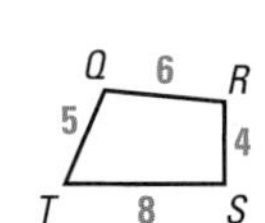

2. What is the scale factor of *QRST* to *ABCD*? $\frac{1}{2}$
3. Find the value of x. **8**

Differentiated Instruction

English Learners The word *similar* is often used in the English language to mean "alike." Similar is defined as "sharing some qualities, but not identical." Explain that in mathematics, the definition of *similar* is more specific—it describes geometric figures that differ in size, but are the same shape and have the same angle measures.

See also the *Geometry Toolkit* for more strategies.

Motivating the Lesson

Tell students that a football coach uses a whiteboard to show players new plays during the game. Ask students if they think the whiteboard should look like a scale drawing of the football field.

3 TEACH

Extra Example 1

In the diagram, $\triangle ABC \sim \triangle DEF$.

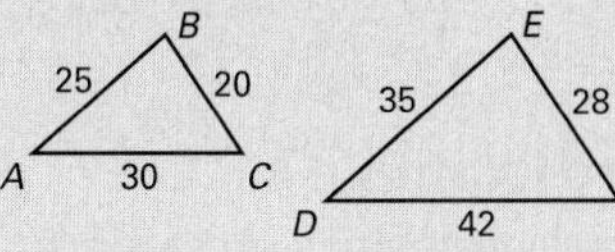

a. List all pairs of congruent angles. ***∠A ≅ ∠D; ∠B ≅ ∠E; ∠C ≅ ∠F***

b. Check that the ratios of corresponding side lengths are equal. $\frac{AB}{DE} = \frac{5}{7}, \frac{BC}{EF} = \frac{5}{7}, \frac{AC}{DF} = \frac{5}{7}$

c. Write the ratios of the corresponding side lengths in a statement of proportionality. $\frac{AB}{DE} = \frac{BC}{EF} = \frac{AC}{DF}$

Key Question to Ask for Example 1

- If the triangles were congruent, what would be the ratio of the corresponding sides? **1 : 1**

Extra Example 2

Determine whether the polygons are similar. If they are, write a similarity statement and find the scale factor of *RSTU* to *DEFG*.

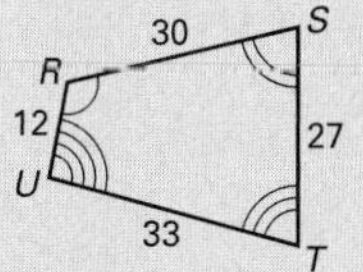

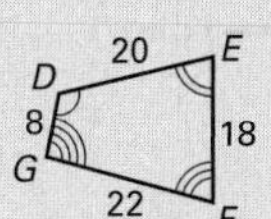

***RSTU ~ DEFG*; the scale factor is 3 : 2.**

Extra Example 3

In the diagram, $\triangle ABC \sim \triangle GHJ$. Find the value of x.

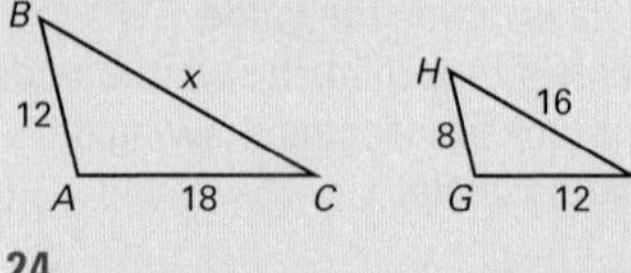

24

Key Question to Ask for Example 3

- What is another proportion you could write to solve the problem? ***Sample answer:*** $\frac{12}{16} = \frac{x}{20}$

Extra Example 4

You are constructing a rectangular play area. A playground is rectangular with length 25 meters and width 15 meters. The new play area will be similar in shape, but only 10 meters in length.

a. Find the scale factor of the new play area to the playground. **2:5**

b. Find the perimeter of the playground and the play area. **80 m; 32 m**

PERIMETERS The ratio of lengths in similar polygons is the same as the scale factor. Theorem 6.1 shows this is true for the perimeters of the polygons.

THEOREM *For Your Notebook*

THEOREM 6.1 Perimeters of Similar Polygons

If two polygons are similar, then the ratio of their perimeters is equal to the ratios of their corresponding side lengths.

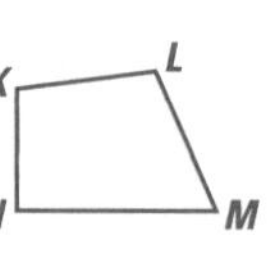

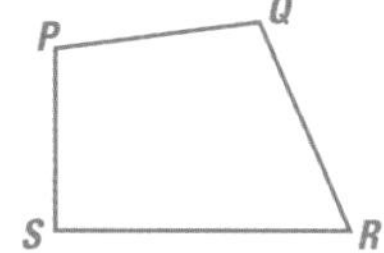

If $KLMN \sim PQRS$, then $\frac{KL + LM + MN + NK}{PQ + QR + RS + SP} = \frac{KL}{PQ} = \frac{LM}{QR} = \frac{MN}{RS} = \frac{NK}{SP}$.

Proof: Ex. 38, p. 379

EXAMPLE 4 Find perimeters of similar figures

SWIMMING A town is building a new swimming pool. An Olympic pool is rectangular with length 50 meters and width 25 meters. The new pool will be similar in shape, but only 40 meters long.

a. Find the scale factor of the new pool to an Olympic pool.

b. Find the perimeter of an Olympic pool and the new pool.

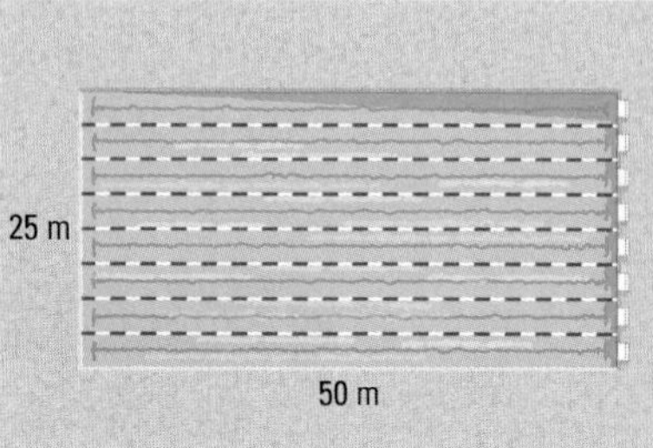

Solution

ANOTHER WAY
Another way to solve Example 4 is to write the scale factor as the decimal 0.8. Then, multiply the perimeter of the Olympic pool by the scale factor to get the perimeter of the new pool:
$0.8(150) = 120$.

a. Because the new pool will be similar to an Olympic pool, the scale factor is the ratio of the lengths, $\frac{40}{50} = \frac{4}{5}$.

b. The perimeter of an Olympic pool is $2(50) + 2(25) = 150$ meters. You can use Theorem 6.1 to find the perimeter x of the new pool.

$\frac{x}{150} = \frac{4}{5}$ **Use Theorem 6.1 to write a proportion.**

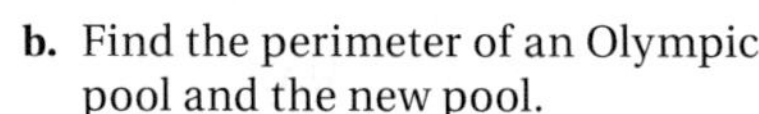

$x = 120$ **Multiply each side by 150 and simplify.**

▶ The perimeter of the new pool is 120 meters.

✓ GUIDED PRACTICE for Example 4

In the diagram, *ABCDE* ~ *FGHJK*.

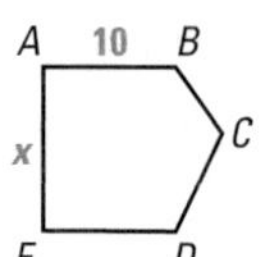

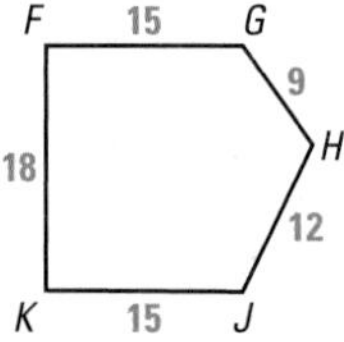

4. Find the scale factor of *FGHJK* to *ABCDE*. $\frac{3}{2}$
5. Find the value of x. **12**
6. Find the perimeter of *ABCDE*. **46**

SIMILARITY AND CONGRUENCE Notice that any two congruent figures are also similar. Their scale factor is 1 : 1. In $\triangle ABC$ and $\triangle DEF$, the scale factor is $\frac{5}{5} = 1$. You can write $\triangle ABC \sim \triangle DEF$ and $\triangle ABC \cong \triangle DEF$.

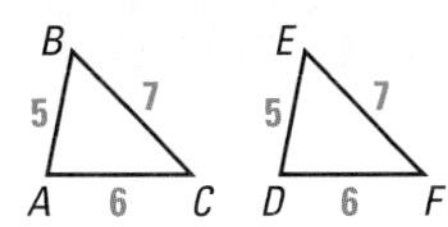

READ VOCABULARY
Corresponding lengths in similar triangles include side lengths, altitudes, medians, midsegments, and so on.

CORRESPONDING LENGTHS You know that perimeters of similar polygons are in the same ratio as corresponding side lengths. You can extend this concept to other segments in polygons.

KEY CONCEPT *For Your Notebook*

Corresponding Lengths in Similar Polygons

If two polygons are similar, then the ratio of any two corresponding lengths in the polygons is equal to the scale factor of the similar polygons.

EXAMPLE 5 Use a scale factor

In the diagram, $\triangle TPR \sim \triangle XPZ$. Find the length of the altitude $\overline{PS}$.

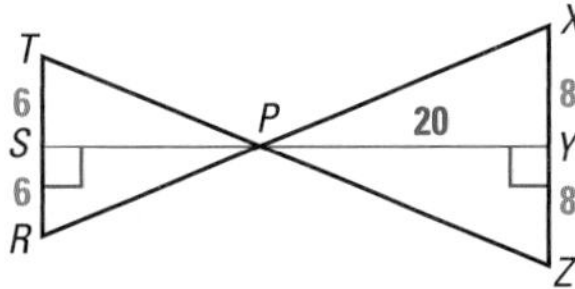

Solution

First, find the scale factor of $\triangle TPR$ to $\triangle XPZ$.

$$\frac{TR}{XZ} = \frac{6+6}{8+8} = \frac{12}{16} = \frac{3}{4}$$

Because the ratio of the lengths of the altitudes in similar triangles is equal to the scale factor, you can write the following proportion.

$\frac{PS}{PY} = \frac{3}{4}$ **Write proportion.**

$\frac{PS}{20} = \frac{3}{4}$ **Substitute 20 for *PY*.**

$PS = 15$ **Multiply each side by 20 and simplify.**

▶ The length of the altitude $\overline{PS}$ is 15.

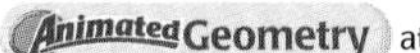 at classzone.com

✓ **GUIDED PRACTICE** for Example 5

7. In the diagram, $\triangle JKL \sim \triangle EFG$. Find the length of the median $\overline{KM}$. **42**

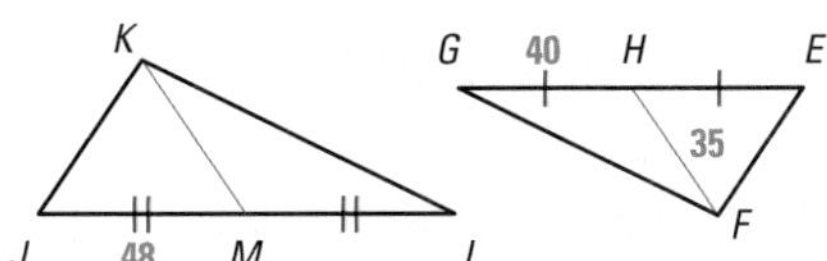

Extra Example 5

In the diagram, $\triangle MNP \sim \triangle RST$. Find the length of the altitude $\overline{NL}$.

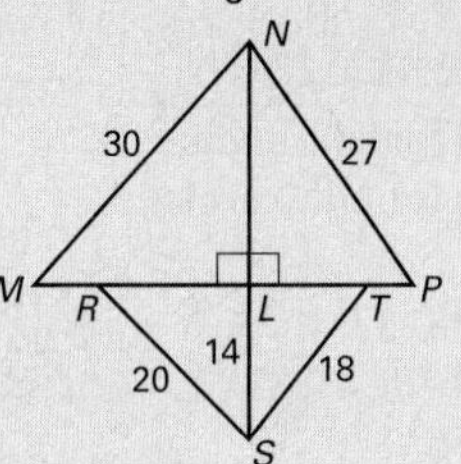

21

An **Animated Geometry** activity is available on-line for **Example 5**. This activity is also available on the **Power Presentations CD-ROM**.

Closing the Lesson

Have students summarize the major points of the lesson and answer the Essential Question: If two figures are similar, how do you find the length of a missing side?

- **Two polygons are similar if the corresponding angles are congruent and the corresponding side lengths are proportional. The ratio of corresponding lengths is the scale factor.**
- **If two polygons are similar, the ratio of any two corresponding lengths equals the scale factor.**

Write a proportion using the scale factor between the figures and the unknown side length. Then solve the proportion.

4 PRACTICE AND APPLY

Assignment Guide

Answer Transparencies available for all exercises

Basic:
Day 1: pp. 376–379
Exs. 1–10, 14–18, 31, 32
Day 2: pp. 376–379
Exs. 11–13, 19–22, 33–35, 40–48

Average:
Day 1: pp. 376–379
Exs. 1–10, 14–18, 23–26, 31, 32
Day 2: pp. 376–379
Exs. 11–13, 19–22, 27, 28, 33–36, 40–48 even

Advanced:
Day 1: pp. 376–379
Exs. 1, 2, 4–10, 14–18, 23–26, 29–32*
Day 2: pp. 376–379
Exs. 11, 12, 19–22, 27, 28, 33–39*, 42, 45, 48

Block:
pp. 376–379
Exs. 1–10, 14–18, 23–26, 31, 32 (with 6.2)
pp. 376–379
Exs. 11–13, 19–22, 27, 28, 33–36, 40–48 even (with 6.4)

Differentiated Instruction

See *Geometry Best Practices Toolkit* for suggestions on addressing the needs of a diverse classroom.

Homework Check

For a quick check of student understanding of key concepts, go over the following exercises:

Basic: 4, 8, 11, 21, 31
Average: 5, 9, 12, 22, 31
Advanced: 6, 10, 11, 22, 32

Extra Practice

- Student Edition, p. 906
- Chapter 6 Resource Book: Practice levels A, B, C, pp. 32–37

Practice Worksheet

An easily-readable reduced practice page (with answers) for this lesson can be found on p. 354C.

6.3 EXERCISES

HOMEWORK KEY
○ = **WORKED-OUT SOLUTIONS** on p. WS7 for Exs. 3, 7, and 31
★ = **STANDARDIZED TEST PRACTICE** Exs. 2, 6, 18, 27, 28, 35, 36, and 37
◆ = **MULTIPLE REPRESENTATIONS** Ex. 33

SKILL PRACTICE

A

1. **VOCABULARY** Copy and complete: Two polygons are similar if corresponding angles are __?__ and corresponding side lengths are __?__. **congruent, proportional**

2. ★ **WRITING** If two polygons are congruent, must they be similar? If two polygons are similar, must they be congruent? *Explain.* **See margin.**

EXAMPLE 1 on p. 372 for Exs. 3–6

USING SIMILARITY List all pairs of congruent angles for the figures. Then write the ratios of the corresponding sides in a statement of proportionality.

3. $\triangle ABC \sim \triangle LMN$

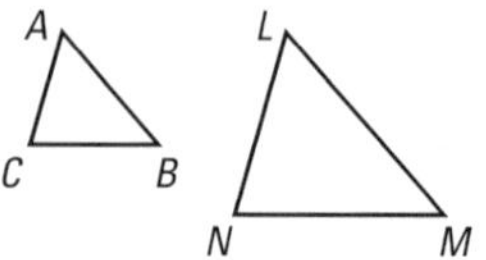

4. $DEFG \sim PQRS$

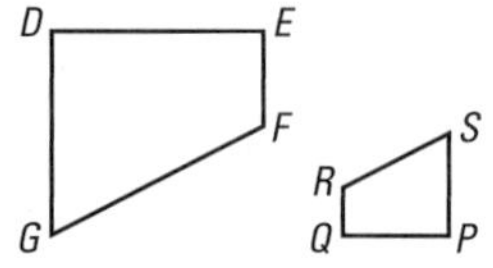

5. $HJKL \sim WXYZ$

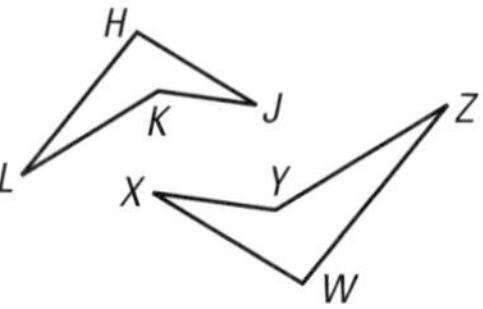

3. $\angle A \cong \angle L$, $\angle B \cong \angle M$, $\angle C \cong \angle N$; $\frac{AB}{LM} = \frac{BC}{MN} = \frac{CA}{NL}$

4. $\angle D \cong \angle P$, $\angle E \cong \angle Q$, $\angle F \cong \angle R$, $\angle G \cong \angle S$; $\frac{DE}{PQ} = \frac{EF}{QR} = \frac{FG}{RS} = \frac{GD}{SP}$

5. $\angle H \cong \angle W$, $\angle J \cong \angle X$, $\angle K \cong \angle Y$, $\angle L \cong \angle Z$; $\frac{HJ}{WX} = \frac{JK}{XY} = \frac{KL}{YZ} = \frac{LH}{ZW}$

6. ★ **MULTIPLE CHOICE** Triangles ABC and DEF are similar. Which statement is *not* correct? **D**

Ⓐ $\frac{BC}{EF} = \frac{AC}{DF}$ Ⓑ $\frac{AB}{DE} = \frac{CA}{FD}$ Ⓒ $\frac{CA}{FD} = \frac{BC}{EF}$ Ⓓ $\frac{AB}{EF} = \frac{BC}{DE}$

EXAMPLES 2 and 3 on p. 373 for Exs. 7–10

DETERMINING SIMILARITY Determine whether the polygons are similar. If they are, write a similarity statement and find the scale factor.

7.

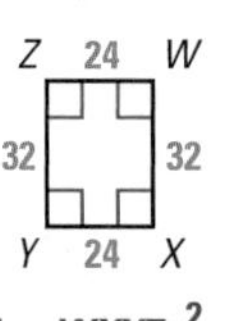

similar; $RSTU \sim WXYZ$, $\frac{2}{1}$

8.

similar; $\triangle CDE \sim \triangle TUV$, $\frac{5}{4}$

USING SIMILAR POLYGONS In the diagram, $JKLM \sim EFGH$.

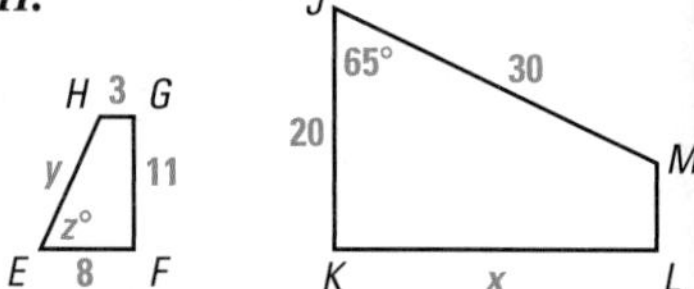

9. Find the scale factor of $JKLM$ to $EFGH$. $\frac{5}{2}$

10. Find the values of x, y, and z. **27.5, 12, 65**

EXAMPLE 4 on p. 374 for Exs. 11–13

11. Find the perimeter of each polygon. **85, 34**

12. **PERIMETER** Two similar FOR SALE signs have a scale factor of 5 : 3. The large sign's perimeter is 60 inches. Find the small sign's perimeter. **36 in.**

13. **ERROR ANALYSIS** The triangles are similar. *Describe* and correct the error in finding the perimeter of Triangle B. **The larger triangle's perimeter was doubled but should have been halved; perimeter of $B = 14$.**

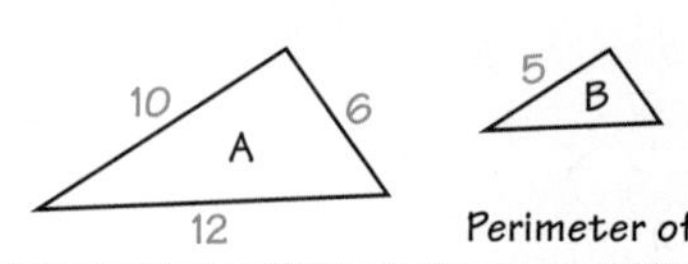

2. Yes; no; if two polygons are congruent, corresponding angles are congruent and the scale factor is 1. If they are similar, corresponding angles are congruent but one polygon can be larger than the other since the scale factor does not have to be 1.

B **REASONING** **Are the polygons *always, sometimes,* or *never* similar?**

14. Two isosceles triangles **sometimes**
15. Two equilateral triangles **always**
16. A right triangle and an isosceles triangle **sometimes**
17. A scalene triangle and an isosceles triangle **never**

18. ★ **SHORT RESPONSE** The scale factor of Figure A to Figure B is $1:x$. What is the scale factor of Figure B to Figure A? *Explain* your reasoning.
$x:1$; since the order of the figures switched, simply switch the ratio.

SIMILAR TRIANGLES **The black triangles are similar. Identify the type of special segment shown in blue, and find the value of the variable.**

19.

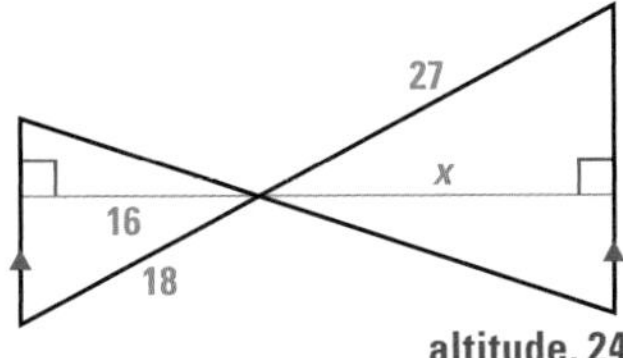

altitude, 24

20.

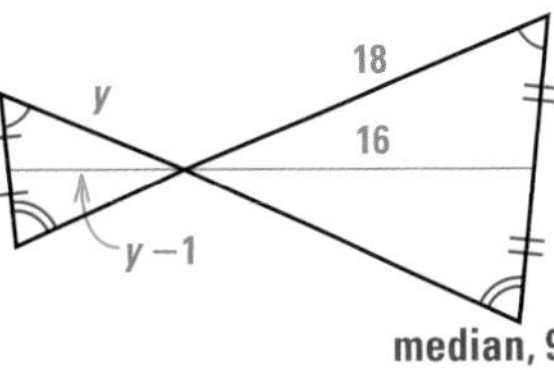

median, 9

EXAMPLE 5
on p. 375 for Exs. 21–22

USING SCALE FACTOR **Triangles *NPQ* and *RST* are similar. The side lengths of $\triangle NPQ$ are 6 inches, 8 inches, and 10 inches, and the length of an altitude is 4.8 inches. The shortest side of $\triangle RST$ is 8 inches long.**

21. Find the lengths of the other two sides of $\triangle RST$. **$10\frac{2}{3}$ in., $13\frac{1}{3}$ in.**
22. Find the length of the corresponding altitude in $\triangle RST$. **6.4 in.**

USING SIMILAR TRIANGLES **In the diagram, $\triangle ABC \sim \triangle DEF$.**

23. Find the scale factor of $\triangle ABC$ to $\triangle DEF$. **$\frac{11}{5}$**
24. Find the unknown side lengths in both triangles. **$AC = 22\frac{22}{25}$, $ED = 10$**

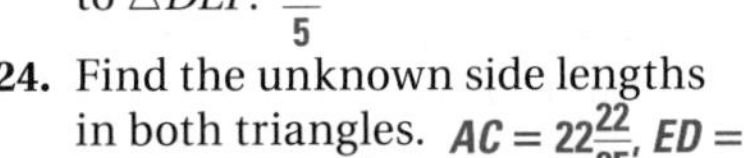

25. Find the length of the altitude shown in $\triangle ABC$. **$17\frac{3}{5}$**

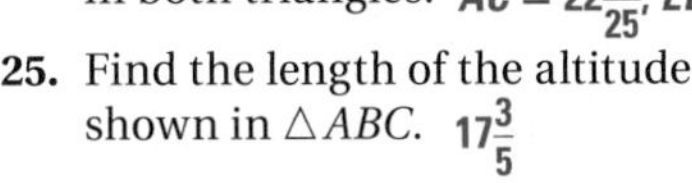

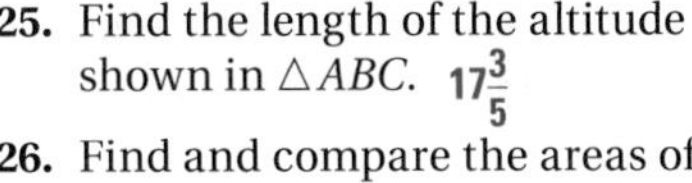

E, D, F, 8, 9, $10\frac{2}{5}$; B, A, C, 22, $19\frac{4}{5}$

26. Find and compare the areas of both triangles.
About 201, 41.6; the ratio of their areas is approximately equal to the scale factor squared.
27. ★ **SHORT RESPONSE** Suppose you are told that $\triangle PQR \sim \triangle XYZ$ and that the extended ratio of the angle measures in $\triangle PQR$ is $x:x+30:3x$. Do you need to know anything about $\triangle XYZ$ to be able to write its extended ratio of angle measures? *Explain* your reasoning.
No; in similar triangles corresponding angles are congruent.
28. ★ **MULTIPLE CHOICE** The lengths of the legs of right triangle *ABC* are 3 feet and 4 feet. The shortest side of $\triangle UVW$ is 4.5 feet and $\triangle UVW \sim \triangle ABC$. How long is the hypotenuse of $\triangle UVW$? **D**

Ⓐ 1.5 ft Ⓑ 5 ft Ⓒ 6 ft Ⓓ 7.5 ft

C 29. **CHALLENGE** Copy the figure at the right and divide it into two similar figures. **See margin.**

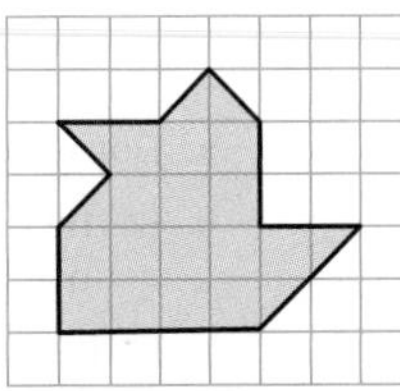

30. **REASONING** Is similarity reflexive? symmetric? transitive? Give examples to support your answers.
**Yes, yes, yes. *Sample answer:* $\triangle ABC \sim \triangle ABC$.
If $\triangle ABC \sim \triangle DEF$, then $\triangle DEF \sim \triangle ABC$.
If $\triangle ABC \sim \triangle DEF$ and $\triangle DEF \sim \triangle HJK$, then $\triangle ABC \sim \triangle HJK$.**

Avoiding Common Errors

Exercise 6 If students have difficulty with this exercise, remind them to match up the letters corresponding to the triangles in the order they are written. For example, *AB* uses the first two letters of $\triangle ABC$, so its corresponding side uses the first two letters of $\triangle DEF$.

Exercises 7–8 If students have difficulty with these exercises, suggest that they redraw the diagrams so that corresponding letters appear in corresponding positions.

Teaching Strategy

Exercises 14–17 Encourage students to draw examples to verify their answers to these exercises. Remind them that one counterexample eliminates the "always" choice. Suggest that they start by looking for counterexamples.

Mathematical Reasoning

Exercise 26 For a pair of similar figures, including a pair formed from an enlargement or reduction (a dilation), if the scale factor is $\frac{a}{b}$, then the corresponding sides, related segments, and perimeters all have the same scale factor, $\frac{a}{b}$, while the area has scale factor $\frac{a^2}{b^2}$.

29.

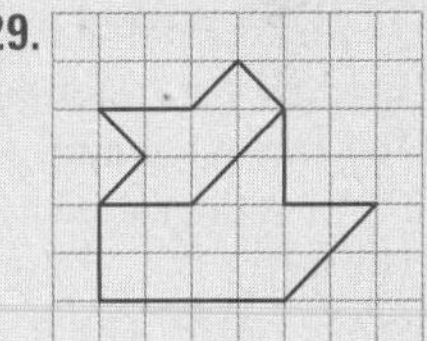

Study Strategy

Exercise 35 Encourage students to analyze this problem by substituting numbers for the variables and then using algebra to prove their conclusion.

Exercise 34 Additional information about solar eclipses can be found at csep10.phys.utk.edu/astr161/lect/time/eclipses.html

33b.

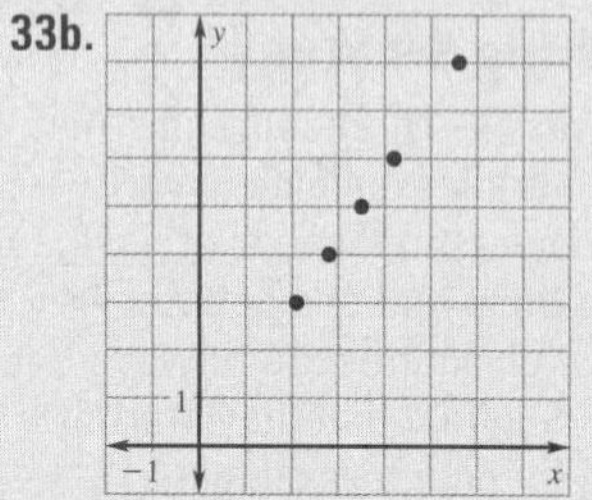

34a. See below.

37b. $\angle BOA \cong \angle DOC$ by the Vertical Angles Theorem; $\angle OBA \cong \angle ODC$ by the Alternate Interior Angles Theorem; $\angle BAO \cong \angle DCO$ by the Alternate Interior Angles Theorem.

37c. $A(-3, 0)$, $B(0, 4)$, $C(6, 0)$, $D(0, -8)$; $AO = 3$, $OB = 4$, $BA = 5$, $CO = 6$, $OD = 8$, $DC = 10$

38. *Sample answer:* $KLMN \sim PQRS$ is given. Since the rectangles are similar, let $\frac{x}{1}$ be the scale factor and let a, b, c, d be the lengths of the sides of $KLMN$ and ax, bx, cx, dx be the lengths of the corresponding sides of $PQRS$. Taking the ratio of perimeters you get

$$\frac{ax + bx + cx + dx}{a + b + c + d} = \frac{x(a + b + c + d)}{a + b + c + d} = x.$$

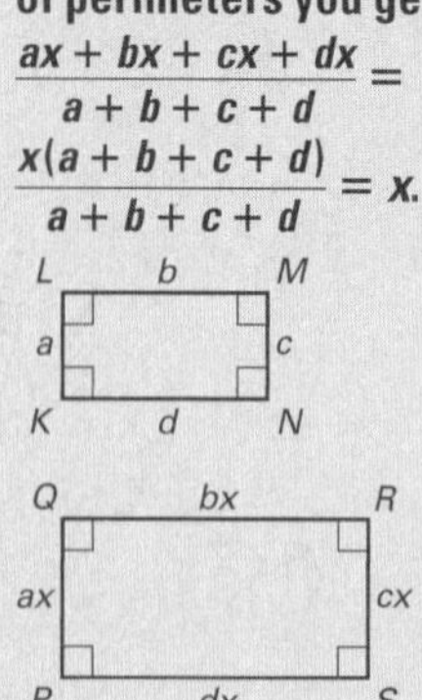

PROBLEM SOLVING

EXAMPLE 2 A on p. 373 for Exs. 31–32

31. **TENNIS** In table tennis, the table is a rectangle 9 feet long and 5 feet wide. A tennis court is a rectangle 78 feet long and 36 feet wide. Are the two surfaces similar? *Explain.* If so, find the scale factor of the tennis court to the table.

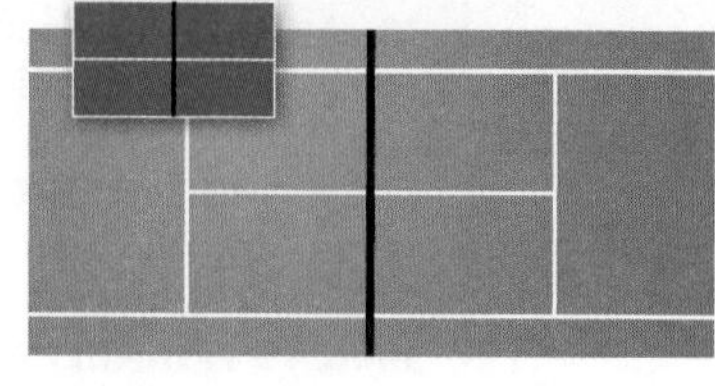

@HomeTutor for problem solving help at classzone.com

No; the lengths are not proportional.

32. **DIGITAL PROJECTOR** You are preparing a computer presentation to be digitally projected onto the wall of your classroom. Your computer screen is 13.25 inches wide and 10.6 inches high. The projected image on the wall is 53 inches wide and 42.4 inches high. Are the two shapes similar? If so, find the scale factor of the computer screen to the projected image. **yes; $\frac{1}{4}$**

@HomeTutor for problem solving help at classzone.com

33. ◆ **MULTIPLE REPRESENTATIONS** Use the similar figures shown. The scale factor of Figure 1 to Figure 2 is 7 : 10.

a. Making a Table Copy and complete the table.

	AB	BC	CD	DE	EA
Figure 1	3.5	? **2.8**	? **4.2**	? **5.6**	? **2.1**
Figure 2	5.0	4.0	6.0	8.0	3.0

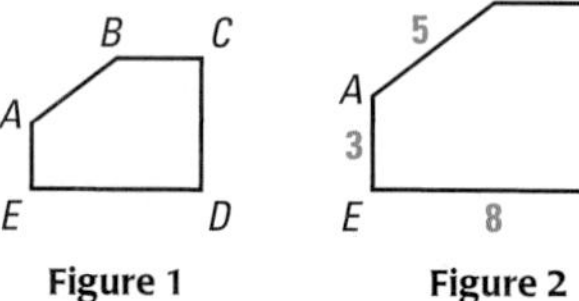

Figure 1 Figure 2

b. Drawing a Graph Graph the data in the table. Let x represent the length of a side in Figure 1 and let y represent the length of the corresponding side in Figure 2. Is the relationship linear? **See margin for art; yes.**

c. Writing an Equation Write an equation that relates x and y. What is its slope? How is the slope related to the scale factor? **$y = \frac{10}{7}x$; $\frac{10}{7}$; they are the same.**

34. **MULTI-STEP PROBLEM** During a total eclipse of the sun, the moon is directly in line with the sun and blocks the sun's rays. The distance ED between Earth and the moon is 240,000 miles, the distance DA between Earth and the sun is 93,000,000 miles, and the radius AB of the sun is 432,500 miles.

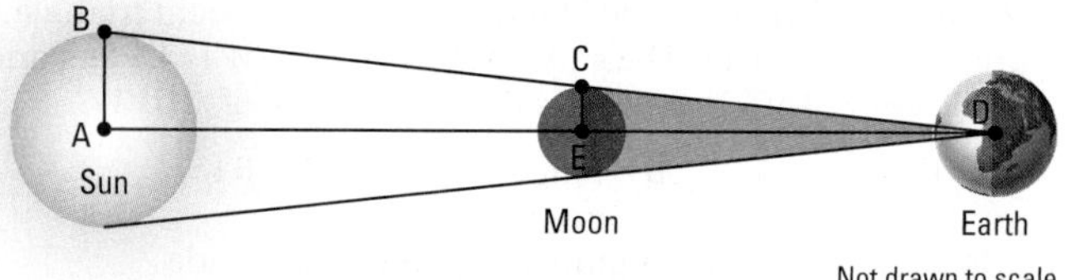

a. Copy the diagram and label the known distances. **See margin.**

b. In the diagram, $\triangle BDA \sim \triangle CDE$. Use this fact to explain a total eclipse of the sun.

c. Estimate the radius CE of the moon. **about 1116 mi**

34b. ***Sample answer:*** **Since the triangles are similar, the light from every point of the sun that is in $\triangle BDA$ is blocked by the moon before reaching Earth.**

○ = WORKED-OUT SOLUTIONS on p. WS1 ★ = STANDARDIZED TEST PRACTICE

34a.

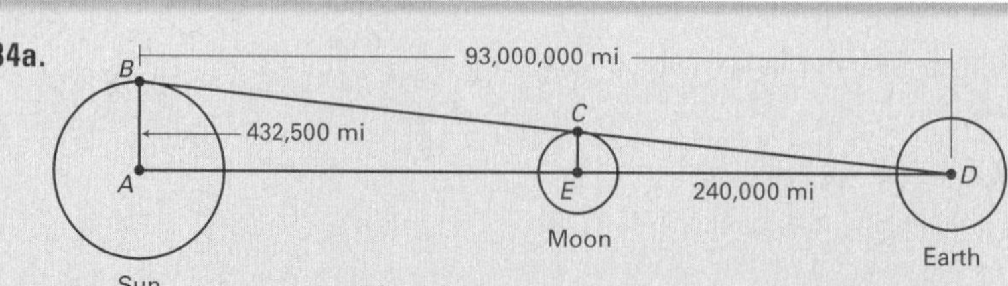

B 35. ★ **SHORT RESPONSE** A rectangular image is enlarged on each side by the same amount. The angles remain unchanged. Can the larger image be similar to the original? *Explain* your reasoning, and give an example to support your answer.

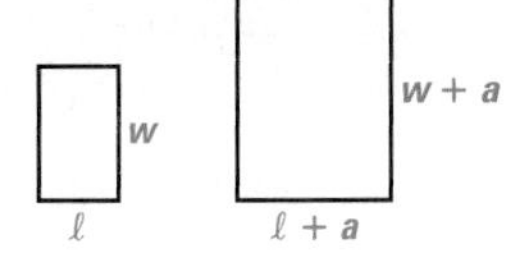

36. ★ **SHORT RESPONSE** How are the areas of similar rectangles related to the scale factor? Use examples to *justify* your reasoning.

C 37. ★ **EXTENDED RESPONSE** The equations of two lines in the coordinate plane are $y = \frac{4}{3}x + 4$ and $y = \frac{4}{3}x - 8$.

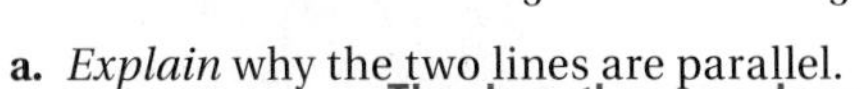

a. *Explain* why the two lines are parallel. **They have the same slope.**

b. Show that $\angle BOA \cong \angle DOC$, $\angle OBA \cong \angle ODC$, and $\angle BAO \cong \angle DCO$. **b, c. See margin.**

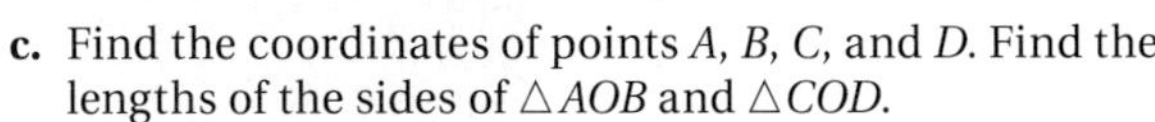

c. Find the coordinates of points *A*, *B*, *C*, and *D*. Find the lengths of the sides of $\triangle AOB$ and $\triangle COD$.

d. Show that $\triangle AOB \sim \triangle COD$. **Since corresponding angles are congruent and the ratios of corresponding sides are all the same the triangles are similar.**

38. **PROVING THEOREM 6.1** Prove the Perimeters of Similar Polygons Theorem for similar rectangles. Include a diagram in your proof. **See margin.**

39. **CHALLENGE** In the diagram, *PQRS* is a square, and $PLMS \sim LMRQ$. Find the exact value of *x*. This value is called the *golden ratio*. Golden rectangles have their length and width in this ratio. Show that the similar rectangles in the diagram are golden rectangles. **See margin.**

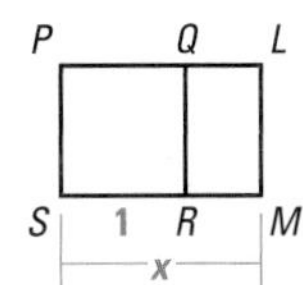

. Yes; if $\ell = w$ [the]n the larger [an]d smaller [im]age would be [si]milar. *Sample [an]swer:* [Le]t $\ell = 8$, $w = 8$, [an]d $a = 4$; $\frac{w}{w+a} = \frac{8}{12} = \frac{2}{3}$, $\frac{\ell}{\ell+a} = \frac{8}{12} = \frac{2}{3}$.

[36]. The ratio [o]f the areas of [si]milar figures [is] the square of [th]e scale factor. [S]ample answer: [C]onsider two [r]ectangles, one [2]x4 and the other [6]x12, with scale [f]actor $\frac{1}{3}$ and ratio [o]f areas $\frac{8}{72} = \frac{1}{9}$, $\left(\frac{1}{3}\right)^2 = \frac{1}{9}$.

MIXED REVIEW

PREVIEW Prepare for Lesson 6.4 in Exs. 40–42.

Given $A(1, 1)$, $B(3, 2)$, $C(2, 4)$, and $D\left(1, \frac{7}{2}\right)$, determine whether the following lines are *parallel*, *perpendicular*, or *neither*. *(p. 171)*

40. $\overleftrightarrow{AB}$ and $\overleftrightarrow{BC}$ **perpendicular**
41. $\overleftrightarrow{CD}$ and $\overleftrightarrow{AD}$ **neither**
42. $\overleftrightarrow{AB}$ and $\overleftrightarrow{CD}$ **parallel**

Find the measure of the exterior angle shown. *(p. 217)*

43. 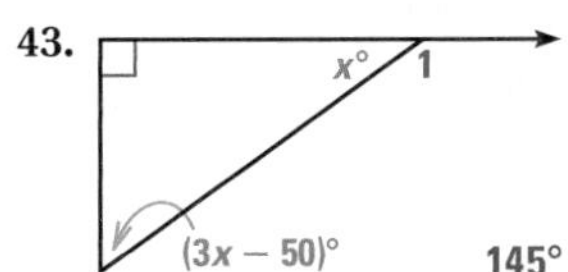

145°

44.

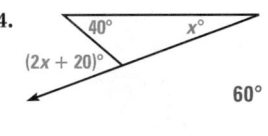

60°

45. 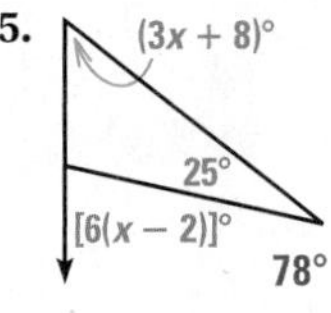

78°

Copy and complete the statement with <, >, or =. *(p. 335)*

46. $RS \underline{\ ?\ } TU$ **<**

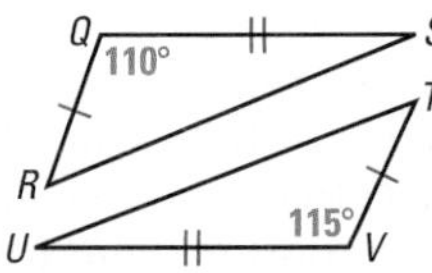

47. $FG \underline{\ ?\ } HD$ **=**

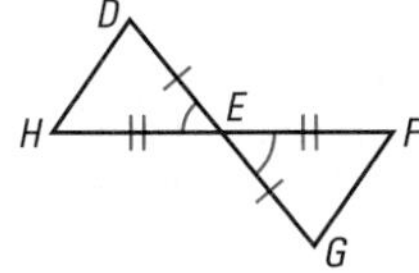

48. $WX \underline{\ ?\ } YX$ **>**

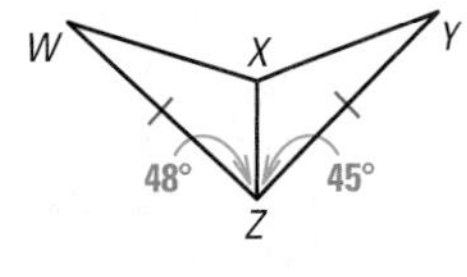

[3]9. $\frac{1+\sqrt{5}}{2}$; $\frac{1+\sqrt{5}}{2} \over 1$ = $\frac{1}{\frac{1+\sqrt{5}}{2} - 1}$

5 ASSESS AND RETEACH

Daily Homework Quiz

Transparency Available

1. Determine whether the polygons are similar. If they are, write a similarity statement and find the scale factor of *EFGH* to *KLMN*.

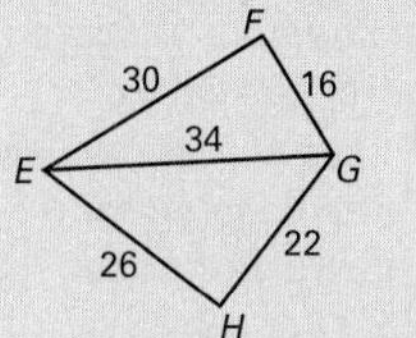

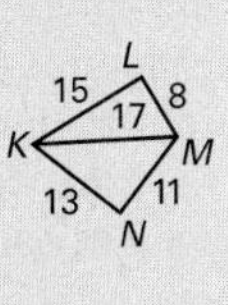

yes; $EFGH \sim KLMN$; the scale factor is 2 : 1.

2. In the diagram, $\triangle DEF \sim \triangle HJK$. Find the value of *x*.

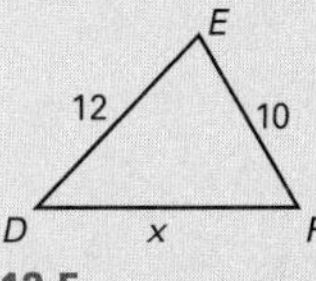

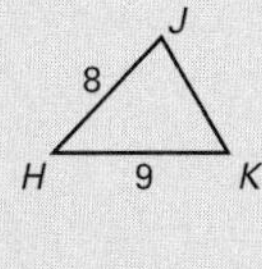

13.5

3. Two similar triangles have the scale factor 5 : 4. Find the ratio of their corresponding altitudes and medians. **5 : 4; 5 : 4**

4. Two similar triangles have the scale factor 3 : 7. Find the ratio of their corresponding perimeters and areas. **3 : 7; 9 : 49**

Online Quiz

Available at **classzone.com**

Diagnosis/Remediation

- Practice A, B, C in Chapter 6 Resource Book, pp. 32–37
- Study Guide in Chapter 6 Resource Book, pp. 38–39
- Practice Workbook, pp. 109–111
- @HomeTutor

Challenge

Additional challenge is available in the Chapter 6 Resource Book, p. 43.

3. *Sample:*

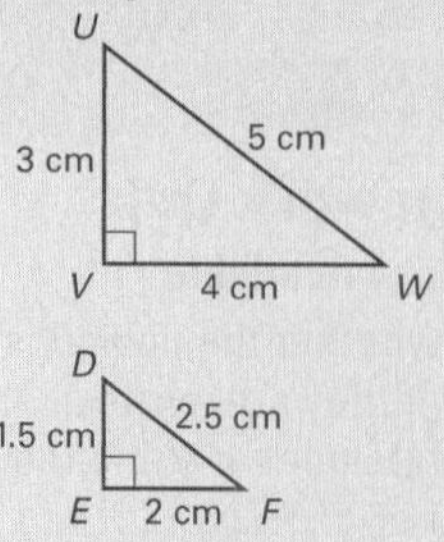

7d. Yes. ***Sample answer:*** **If apple production decreases due to weather conditions apples become less plentiful and the per capita consumption would decrease.**

MIXED REVIEW *of Problem Solving*

STATE TEST PRACTICE classzone.com

Lessons 6.1–6.3

1. **MULTI-STEP PROBLEM** In the diagram, $\triangle LMN \sim \triangle QRS$.

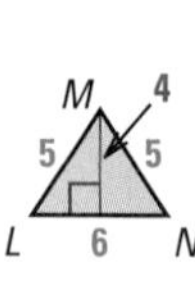

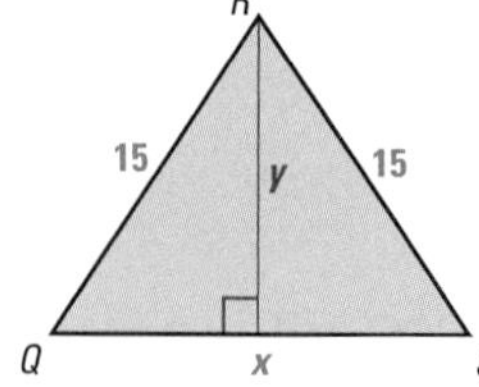

   a. Find the scale factor of $\triangle LMN$ to $\triangle QRS$. Then find the values of x and y. **$\frac{1}{3}$; 18, 12**

   b. Find the perimeters of $\triangle LMN$ and $\triangle QRS$. **16, 48**

   c. Find the areas of $\triangle LMN$ and $\triangle QRS$. **12, 108**

   d. *Compare* the ratio of the perimeters to the ratio of the areas of $\triangle LMN$ to $\triangle QRS$. What do you notice? **The ratio of areas is the square of the ratio of perimeters.**

2. **GRIDDED ANSWER** In the diagram, $AB : BC$ is $3 : 8$. Find AC. **1562**

3. **OPEN-ENDED** $\triangle UVW$ is a right triangle with side lengths of 3 cm, 4 cm, and 5 cm. Draw and label $\triangle UVW$. Then draw a triangle similar to $\triangle UVW$ and label its side lengths. What scale factor did you use? **See margin for art.** ***Sample answer:*** **$\frac{1}{2}$**

4. **MULTI-STEP PROBLEM** Kelly is going on a trip to England. She takes 600 U.S. dollars with her.

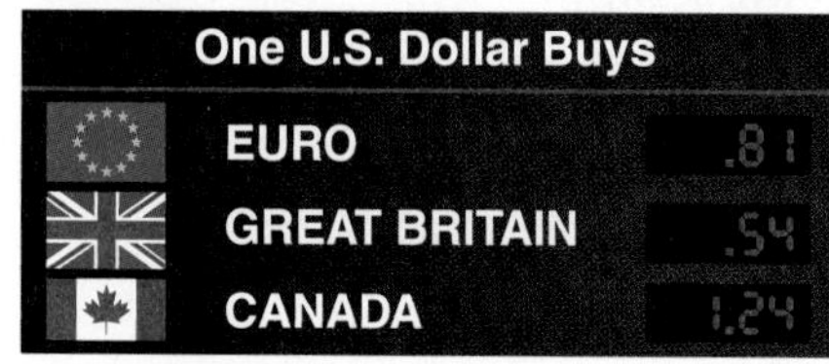

One U.S. Dollar Buys	
EURO	.81
GREAT BRITAIN	.54
CANADA	1.24

   a. In England, she exchanges her U.S. dollars for British pounds. During her stay, Kelly spends 150 pounds. How many British pounds does she have left? **174 British pounds**

   b. When she returns home, she exchanges her money back to U.S. dollars. How many U.S. dollars does she have at the end of her trip? **$322.22**

5. **SHORT RESPONSE** Kelly bought a 3-D scale model of the Tower Bridge in London, England. The towers of the model are 9 inches tall. The towers of the actual bridge are 206 feet tall, and there are two walkways that are 140 feet high.

   a. Approximate the height of the walkways on the model. **about 6 in.**

   b. About how many times as tall as the model is the actual structure? **about 275 times**

6. **GRIDDED ANSWER** In the diagram, $\triangle ABC \sim \triangle DEF$. The scale factor of $\triangle ABC$ to $\triangle DEF$ is $3 : 5$. Find AC. **7.2**

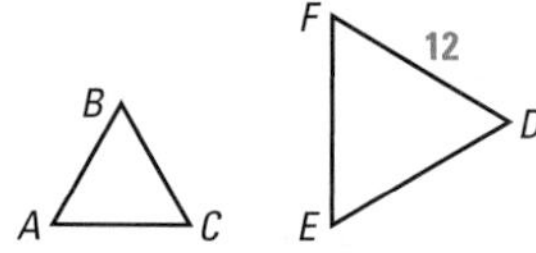

7. **EXTENDED RESPONSE** In the United States, 4634 million pounds of apples were consumed in 2002. The population of the United States in that year was 290 million.

   a. Divide the total number of apples consumed by the population to find the per capita consumption. **about 16 lb per person**

   b. About how many pounds of apples would a family of four have consumed in one year? in one month? **about 64 lb; about 5 lb**

   c. A medium apple weighs about 5 ounces. Estimate how many apples a family of four would have consumed in one month. **about 16 apples**

   d. Is it reasonable to assume that a family of four would have eaten that many apples? What other factors could affect the per capita consumption? *Explain.* **See margin.**

6.4 Prove Triangles Similar by AA

Before You used the AAS Congruence Theorem.
Now You will use the AA Similarity Postulate.
Why? So you can use similar triangles to understand aerial photography, as in Ex. 34.

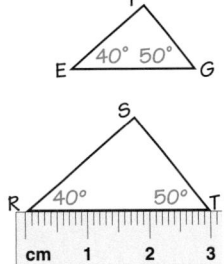

Key Vocabulary
- **similar polygons,** *p. 372*

Standards

5.0 Students prove that triangles are congruent or **similar, and they are able to use the concept of corresponding parts** of congruent triangles.

12.0 Students find and use measures of sides and of interior and exterior angles **of triangles** and polygons **to** classify figures and **solve problems.**

ACTIVITY ANGLES AND SIMILAR TRIANGLES

QUESTION What can you conclude about two triangles if you know two pairs of corresponding angles are congruent?

Materials:
- protractor
- metric ruler

STEP 1 **Draw** $\triangle EFG$ so that $m\angle E = 40°$ and $m\angle G = 50°$.

STEP 2 **Draw** $\triangle RST$ so that $m\angle R = 40°$ and $m\angle T = 50°$, and $\triangle RST$ is not congruent to $\triangle EFG$.

STEP 3 **Calculate** $m\angle F$ and $m\angle S$ using the Triangle Sum Theorem. Use a protractor to check that your results are true. **90°, 90°**

STEP 4 **Measure** and record the side lengths of both triangles. Use a metric ruler.

DRAW CONCLUSIONS

1. Are the triangles similar? Explain your reasoning. **See margin.**
2. Repeat the steps above using different angle measures. Make a conjecture about two triangles with two pairs of congruent corresponding angles. **See margin.**

1. Yes; the corresponding angles are congruent, and the corresponding side lengths are proportional.

2. Two triangles with two pairs of congruent corresponding angles are similar triangles.

TRIANGLE SIMILARITY The Activity suggests that two triangles are similar if two pairs of corresponding angles are congruent. In other words, you do not need to know the measures of the sides or the third pair of angles.

POSTULATE *For Your Notebook*

POSTULATE 22 Angle-Angle (AA) Similarity Postulate

If two angles of one triangle are congruent to two angles of another triangle, then the two triangles are similar.

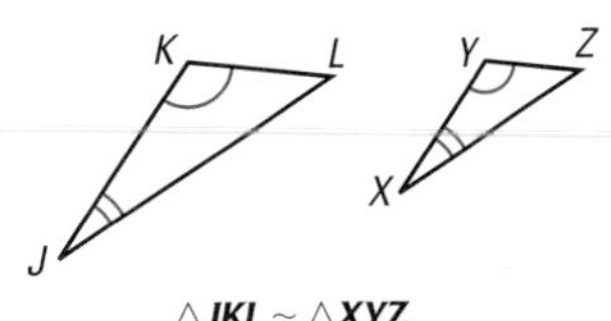

$\triangle JKL \sim \triangle XYZ$

1 PLAN AND PREPARE

Warm-Up Exercises

Transparency Available

1. In $\triangle ABC$ and $\triangle XZW$, $m\angle A = m\angle X$ and $m\angle B = m\angle Z$. What can you conclude about $m\angle C$ and $m\angle W$? **They are the same.**
2. Solve $\frac{x}{18} = \frac{54}{9}$. **108**
3. $\triangle ABC \sim \triangle DEF$. Find x. **10**

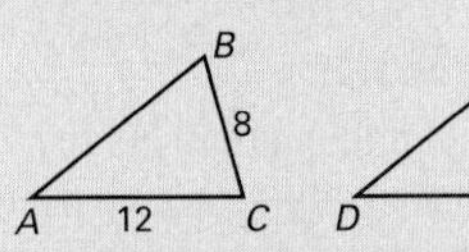

Notetaking Guide

Transparency Available

Promotes interactive learning and notetaking skills, pp. 153–155.

Pacing

Basic: 1 day
Average: 1 day
Advanced: 1 day
Block: 0.5 block with 6.3
- See *Teaching Guide/Lesson Plan.*

2 FOCUS AND MOTIVATE

Essential Question

Big Idea 2, p. 355

How can you show that two triangles are similar? **Tell students they will learn how to answer this question by showing that two pairs of angles are congruent.**

Resource Planning Guide

Chapter Resource Book
- Teaching Guide/Lesson Plan (pp. 44–45)
- Practice levels A, B, C (pp. 46–51)
- Study Guide (pp. 52–53)
- Catch-up for Absent Students (p. 54)
- Application (p. 55)
- Challenge (p. 56)

Workbooks
- Notetaking Guide (pp. 153–155)
- Practice Workbook (pp. 112–114)

Teaching Options
- **Power Presentations CD-ROM** provides dynamic electronic teaching resources for the classroom.
- **Activity Generator CD-ROM** provides editable activities for all ability levels.

Interactive Technology
- Easy Planner
- Power Presentations CD-ROM
- Activity Generator CD-ROM
- Animated Algebra
- Test Generator CD-ROM
- Online Quiz
- eWorkbook
- eEdition
- @HomeTutor

Resources for English Learners
- Quick Reference for English Learners
- Spanish Study Guide
- Multi-Language Visual Glossary
- Student Resources in Spanish

See also the *Geometry Toolkit* for more strategies for meeting individual needs.

Motivating the Lesson

Ask students how to describe the angles in two similar figures. Then ask them how they could check if two triangles in a design or graphic drawing are similar. They should be able to use the Triangle Sum theorem (page 218) to conclude that they need to check for just two pairs of congruent angles.

3 TEACH

Activity Note

The purpose of this activity is to show that if two angles in two triangles have the same angle measure, then the third angles must have the same measure and the corresponding sides are proportional.

Extra Example 1

Determine whether the triangles are similar. If they are, write a similarity statement. Explain your reasoning.

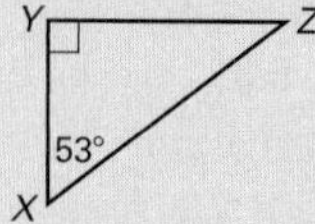

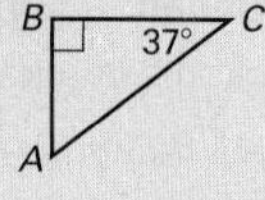

$\angle Y \cong \angle B$ because both are right angles. By the Triangle Sum Theorem, $m\angle Z = 37°$ so $m\angle Z \cong \angle C$. $\triangle XYZ \sim \triangle ABC$ by the AA Similarity Postulate.

Key Question to Ask for Example 1

- What is the name of the triangle that is similar to $\triangle EDC$? How do you know the order for the vertices? **$\triangle EDC \sim \triangle HGK$; corresponding vertices appear in the same position for each triangle.**

EXAMPLE 1 Use the AA Similarity Postulate

DRAW DIAGRAMS

H C D E G K

Use colored pencils to show congruent angles. This will help you write similarity statements.

Determine whether the triangles are similar. If they are, write a similarity statement. Explain your reasoning.

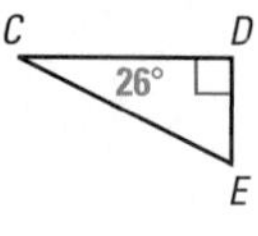

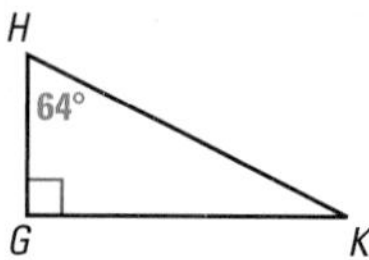

Solution

Because they are both right angles, $\angle D$ and $\angle G$ are congruent.

By the Triangle Sum Theorem, $26° + 90° + m\angle E = 180°$, so $m\angle E = 64°$. Therefore, $\angle E$ and $\angle H$ are congruent.

▶ So, $\triangle CDE \sim \triangle KGH$ by the AA Similarity Postulate.

EXAMPLE 2 Show that triangles are similar

Show that the two triangles are similar.

a. $\triangle ABE$ and $\triangle ACD$

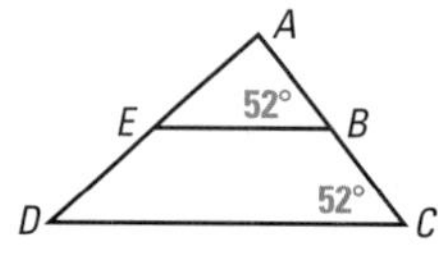

b. $\triangle SVR$ and $\triangle UVT$

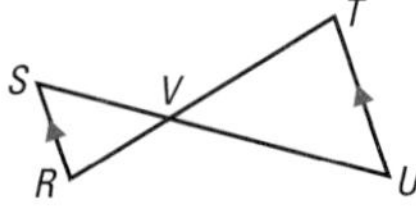

Solution

a. You may find it helpful to redraw the triangles separately.

Because $m\angle ABE$ and $m\angle C$ both equal 52°, $\angle ABE \cong \angle C$. By the Reflexive Property, $\angle A \cong \angle A$.

▶ So, $\triangle ABE \sim \triangle ACD$ by the AA Similarity Postulate.

b. You know $\angle SVR \cong \angle UVT$ by the Vertical Angles Congruence Theorem. The diagram shows $\overline{RS} \parallel \overline{UT}$ so $\angle S \cong \angle U$ by the Alternate Interior Angles Theorem.

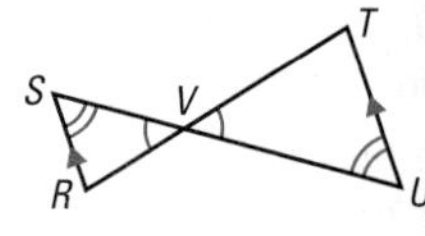

▶ So, $\triangle SVR \sim \triangle UVT$ by the AA Similarity Postulate.

✓ **GUIDED PRACTICE** for Examples 1 and 2

Show that the triangles are similar. Write a similarity statement.

1. $\triangle FGH$ and $\triangle RQS$

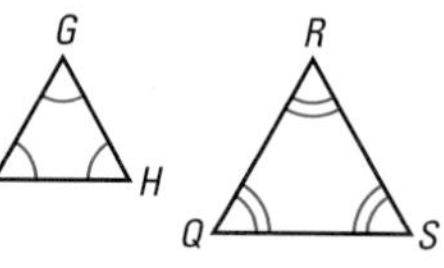

2. $\triangle CDF$ and $\triangle DEF$

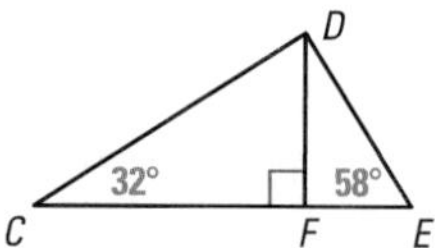

3. REASONING Suppose in Example 2, part (b), $\overline{SR} \nparallel \overline{TU}$. Could the triangles still be similar? *Explain.*
Yes; if $\angle S \cong \angle T$, the triangles are similar by the AA Similarity Postulate.

1. In each triangle all three angles measure 60°, so by the AA Similarity Postulate the triangles are similar; $\triangle FGH \sim \triangle QRS$.

2. Since $m\angle CDF = 58°$ by the Triangle Sum Theorem and $m\angle DFE = 90°$ by the Linear Pair Postulate the two triangles are similar by the AA Similarity Postulate; $\triangle CDF \sim \triangle DEF$.

Differentiated Instruction

Below Level Ask students to draw two scalene triangles. Then have them draw a segment connecting two sides of each triangle, parallel to the third side in one triangle and not parallel in the other triangle. Ask the students to make a conjecture about which drawing has similar triangles, then have them use protractors and rulers to verify their conjecture.

See also the *Geometry Toolkit* for more strategies.

INDIRECT MEASUREMENT In Lesson 4.6, you learned a way to use congruent triangles to find measurements indirectly. Another useful way to find measurements indirectly is by using similar triangles.

EXAMPLE 3 Standardized Test Practice

A flagpole casts a shadow that is 50 feet long. At the same time, a woman standing nearby who is five feet four inches tall casts a shadow that is 40 inches long. How tall is the flagpole to the nearest foot?

Ⓐ 12 feet Ⓑ 40 feet

Ⓒ 80 feet Ⓓ 140 feet

ELIMINATE CHOICES
Notice that the woman's height is greater than her shadow's length. So the flagpole must be taller than its shadow's length. Eliminate choices A and B.

Solution

The flagpole and the woman form sides of two right triangles with the ground, as shown below. The sun's rays hit the flagpole and the woman at the same angle. You have two pairs of congruent angles, so the triangles are similar by the AA Similarity Postulate.

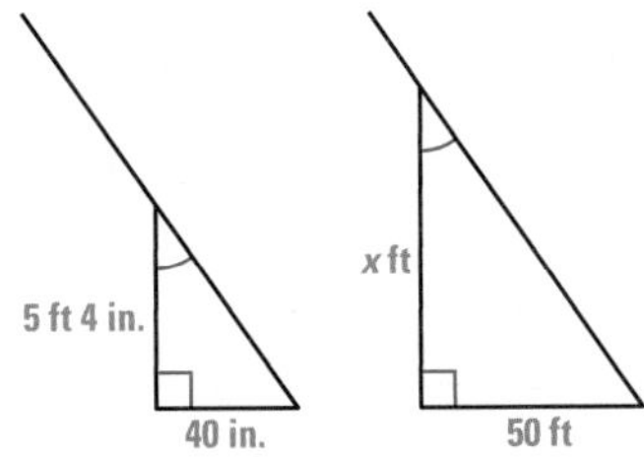

You can use a proportion to find the height x. Write 5 feet 4 inches as 64 inches so that you can form two ratios of feet to inches.

$\frac{x \text{ ft}}{64 \text{ in.}} = \frac{50 \text{ ft}}{40 \text{ in.}}$ **Write proportion of side lengths.**

$40x = 64(50)$ **Cross Products Property**

$x = 80$ **Solve for *x*.**

▶ The flagpole is 80 feet tall. The correct answer is C. Ⓐ Ⓑ Ⓒ Ⓓ

GUIDED PRACTICE for Example 3

4. **WHAT IF?** A child who is 58 inches tall is standing next to the woman in Example 3. How long is the child's shadow? **36.25 in.**

5. You are standing in your backyard, and you measure the lengths of the shadows cast by both you and a tree. Write a proportion showing how you could find the height of the tree. ***Sample answer:*** $\frac{\text{tree height}}{\text{your height}} = \frac{\text{length of tree shadow}}{\text{length of your shadow}}$

Extra Example 2

Show that the two triangles are similar.

a.

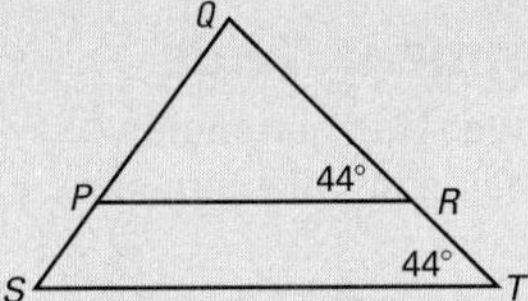

$m\angle QRP = 44°$ and $m\angle QTS = 44°$, so $\angle QRP \cong \angle QTS$. Also, $\angle Q \cong \angle Q$. So $\triangle QRP \sim \triangle QTS$ by the AA Similarity Postulate.

b.

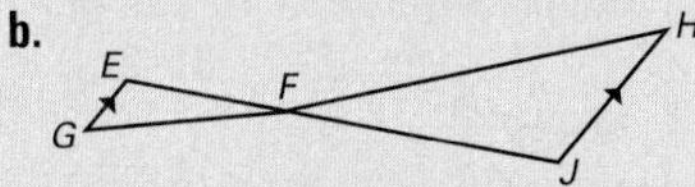

$\angle EFG \cong \angle JFH$ because they are vertical angles, and $\overline{EG} \parallel \overline{JH}$ so $\angle E \cong \angle J$ by the Alternate Interior Angles Theorem. So $\triangle EFG \sim \triangle JFH$ by the AA Similarity Postulate.

Study Strategy

For Example 2, instruct students to redraw $\triangle AEB$ and $\triangle ADC$ separately and mark the congruent parts.

Extra Example 3

A school building casts a shadow that is 26 feet long. At the same time a student standing nearby, who is 71 inches tall, casts a shadow that is 48 inches long. How tall is the building to the nearest foot? **C**

Ⓐ 18 ft Ⓑ 33 ft

Ⓒ 38 ft Ⓓ 131 ft

Teaching Strategy

Point out that the procedure used in Example 3 to find the height of an object indirectly is useful for vertical objects like buildings and trees. Encourage them to draw a diagram and label it carefully.

Closing the Lesson

Have students summarize the major points of the lesson and answer the Essential Question: How can you show that two triangles are similar?

- **If two pairs of angles of two triangles are congruent, you can use the AA Similarity Postulate to conclude that the triangles are similar.**

Show that two pairs of angles are congruent and apply the AA Similarity Postulate.

Differentiated Instruction

Kinesthetic Learners After discussing **Example 3**, take students outside on a sunny day to find and solve a problem similar to **Example 3**. Point out that they can use this strategy to find the height of any tall object, such as a tree or a building. Have students draw a diagram showing the two triangles. You may wish to have different groups of students use people of different heights to find the height of the same object and then compare their answers.

See also the *Geometry Toolkit* for more strategies.

4 PRACTICE AND APPLY

Assignment Guide

Answer Transparencies available for all exercises

Basic:
Day 1: EP p. 900 Exs. 7–11
pp. 384–387
Exs. 1–20, 31–35, 41–49 odd

Average:
Day 1: pp. 384–387
Exs. 1, 2–12 even, 15–25, 31–37, 42–48 even

Advanced:
Day 1: pp. 384–387
Exs. 1, 2, 3–7 odd, 11–14, 16–30*, 32, 34–40*, 44, 45, 49

Block:
pp. 384–387
Exs. 1, 2–12 even, 15–25, 31–37, 42–48 even (with 6.3)

Differentiated Instruction

See *Geometry Best Practices Toolkit* for suggestions on addressing the needs of a diverse classroom.

Homework Check

For a quick check of student understanding of key concepts, go over the following exercises:

Basic: 6, 12, 18, 31, 34
Average: 10, 12, 22, 32, 35
Advanced: 11, 16, 24, 32, 36

Extra Practice

- Student Edition, p. 907
- Chapter 6 Resource Book: Practice levels A, B, C, pp. 46–51

Practice Worksheet

An easily-readable reduced practice page (with answers) for this lesson can be found on p. 354C.

6.4 EXERCISES

HOMEWORK KEY ○ = **WORKED-OUT SOLUTIONS** on p. WS7 for Exs. 9, 13, and 33
★ = **STANDARDIZED TEST PRACTICE** Exs. 2, 16, 18, 19, 20, 33, and 38

SKILL PRACTICE

A

1. **VOCABULARY** Copy and complete: If two angles of one triangle are congruent to two angles of another triangle, then the triangles are _?_. **similar**

2. ★ **WRITING** Can you assume that corresponding sides and corresponding angles of any two similar triangles are congruent? *Explain.* **No; the ratio of corresponding sides would be the same but they would not necessarily be congruent.**

EXAMPLE 1 on p. 382 for Exs. 3–11

REASONING **Use the diagram to complete the statement.**

3. $\triangle ABC \sim$ _?_ **△FED**

4. $\frac{BA}{?} = \frac{AC}{?} = \frac{CB}{?}$ **EF, FD, DE**

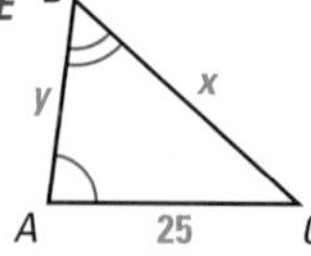

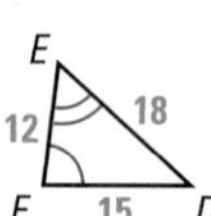

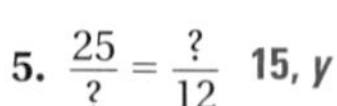

5. $\frac{25}{?} = \frac{?}{12}$ **15, y**

6. $\frac{?}{25} = \frac{18}{?}$ **15, x**

7. $y =$ _?_ **20**

8. $x =$ _?_ **30**

AA SIMILARITY POSTULATE **In Exercises 9–14, determine whether the triangles are similar. If they are, write a similarity statement.**

9.

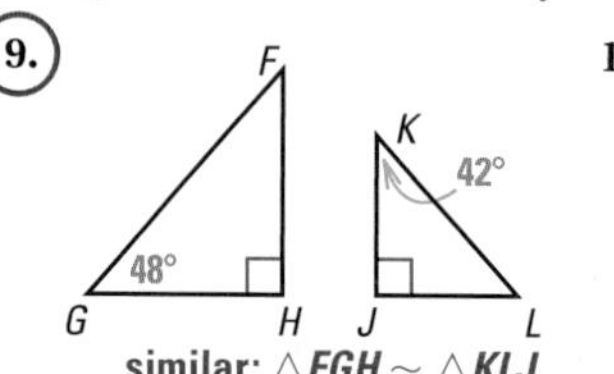

similar; △FGH ~ △KLJ

10. **similar; △NYM ~ △ZYX**

11. **not similar**

EXAMPLE 2 on p. 382 for Exs. 12–16

12. **similar; △CBD ~ △CAE**

13. **similar; △YZX ~ △YWU**

14.

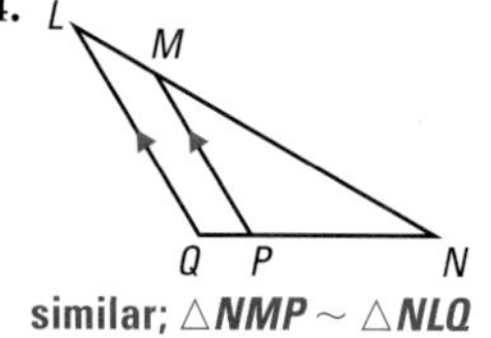

similar; △NMP ~ △NLQ

15. **ERROR ANALYSIS** *Explain* why the student's similarity statement is incorrect.

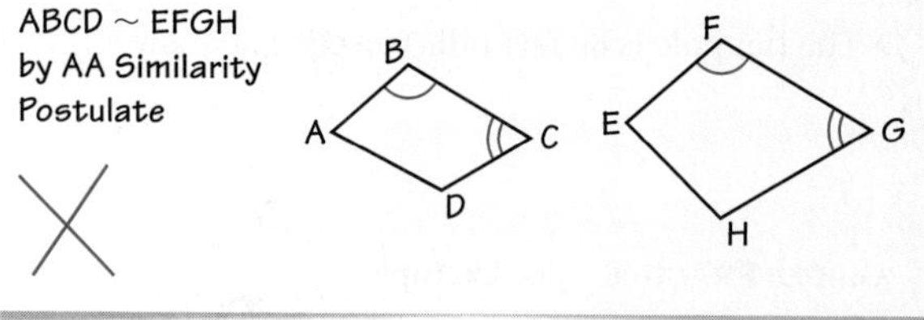

The AA Similarity Postulate is for triangles, not quadrilaterals.

16. ★ **MULTIPLE CHOICE** What is the value of p? **B**

Ⓐ 5   Ⓑ 20
Ⓒ 28.8   Ⓓ Cannot be determined

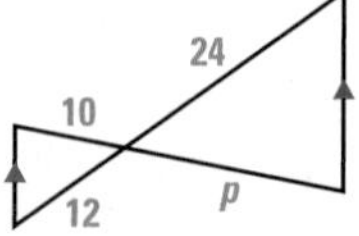

17. **ERROR ANALYSIS** A student uses the proportion $\frac{4}{6} = \frac{5}{x}$ to find the value of x in the figure. *Explain* why this proportion is incorrect and write a correct proportion. **5 should be replaced by 9, which is the length of the corresponding side of the larger triangle. *Sample answer:* $\frac{4}{6} = \frac{9}{x}$.**

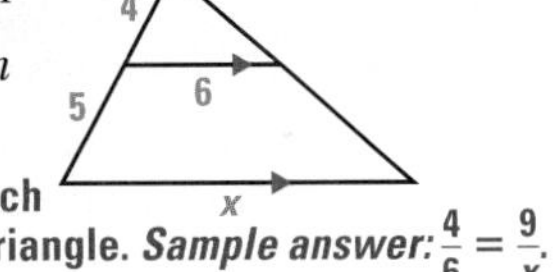

★ **OPEN-ENDED MATH In Exercises 18 and 19, make a sketch that can be used to show that the statement is false.** **18, 19. See margin.**

18. If two pairs of sides of two triangles are congruent, then the triangles are similar.

19. If the ratios of two pairs of sides of two triangles are proportional, then the triangles are similar.

20. ★ **MULTIPLE CHOICE** In the figure at the right, find the length of $\overline{BD}$. **A**

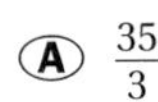

Ⓐ $\frac{35}{3}$ Ⓑ $\frac{37}{5}$

Ⓒ $\frac{20}{3}$ Ⓓ $\frac{12}{5}$

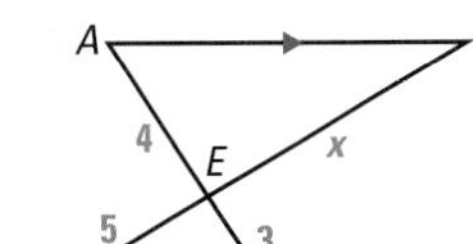

ALGEBRA Find coordinates for point E so that $\triangle ABC \sim \triangle ADE$.

21. $A(0, 0)$, $B(0, 4)$, $C(8, 0)$, $D(0, 5)$, $E(x, y)$ **(10, 0)**

22. $A(0, 0)$, $B(0, 3)$, $C(4, 0)$, $D(0, 7)$, $E(x, y)$ $\left(\frac{28}{3}, 0\right)$

23. $A(0, 0)$, $B(0, 1)$, $C(6, 0)$, $D(0, 4)$, $E(x, y)$ **(24, 0)**

24. $A(0, 0)$, $B(0, 6)$, $C(3, 0)$, $D(0, 9)$, $E(x, y)$ $\left(\frac{9}{2}, 0\right)$

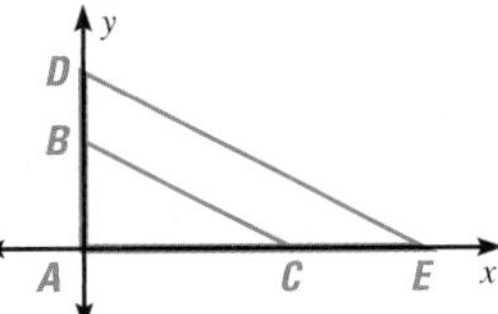

25. **MULTI-STEP PROBLEM** In the diagram, $\overleftrightarrow{AB} \parallel \overleftrightarrow{DC}$, $AE = 6$, $AB = 8$, $CE = 15$, and $DE = 10$.

a. Copy the diagram and mark all given information. **See margin.**

b. List two pairs of congruent angles in the diagram.

c. Name a pair of similar triangles and write a similarity statement. **$\triangle ABE$ and $\triangle CDE$, $\triangle ABE \sim \triangle CDE$**

d. Find BE and DC. **4, 20**

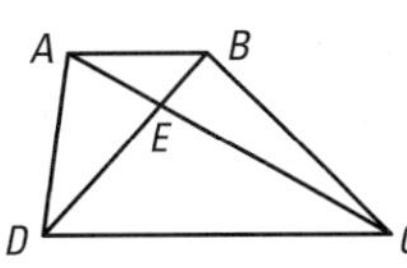

25b. *Sample answer:* $\angle ABE$ and $\angle CDE$, $\angle BAE$ and $\angle DCE$

C

REASONING In Exercises 26–29, is it possible for $\triangle JKL$ and $\triangle XYZ$ to be similar? *Explain* why or why not.

26. $m\angle J = 71°$, $m\angle K = 52°$, $m\angle X = 71°$, and $m\angle Z = 57°$
Yes; in $\triangle JKL$, $m\angle L = 57°$, making the triangles similar by the AA Similarity

27. $\triangle JKL$ is a right triangle and $m\angle X + m\angle Y = 150°$.
Yes; either $m\angle X$ or $m\angle Y$ could be 90°, and the other angles could be the same.

28. $m\angle J = 87°$ and $m\angle Y = 94°$
No; 87° + 94° = 181° is already greater then the possible total for three angles in a triangle.

29. $m\angle J + m\angle K = 85°$ and $m\angle Y + m\angle Z = 80°$

29. No; since $m\angle J + m\angle K = 85°$ then $m\angle L = 95°$. Since $m\angle Y + m\angle Z = 80°$ then $m\angle X = 100°$ and thus neither $\angle Y$ nor $\angle Z$ can measure 95°.

30. **CHALLENGE** If $PT = x$, $PQ = 3x$, and $SR = \frac{8}{3}x$, find PS in terms of x. *Explain* your reasoning.
$\frac{4}{3}x$; solve the proportion $\frac{a}{a + \frac{8}{3}x} = \frac{x}{3x}$ where $PS = a$.

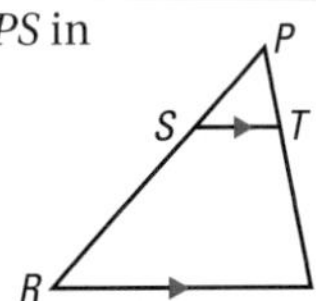

Avoiding Common Errors

Exercise 13 Students may assume that if $\overline{XZ}$ is not parallel to $\overline{WU}$ then the triangles are not similar. Caution them to find the measures of the third pair of angles before answering the question.

Study Strategy

Exercise 25 Encourage students to separate the triangles to help them see which pairs of angle of triangles are similar.

Exercises 26–29 Instruct students to look for counterexamples by drawing triangles for each of these exercises.

18. *Sample:*

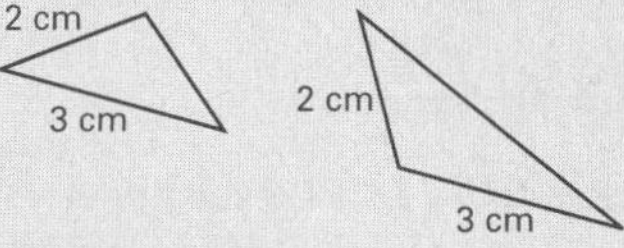

19. *Sample:*

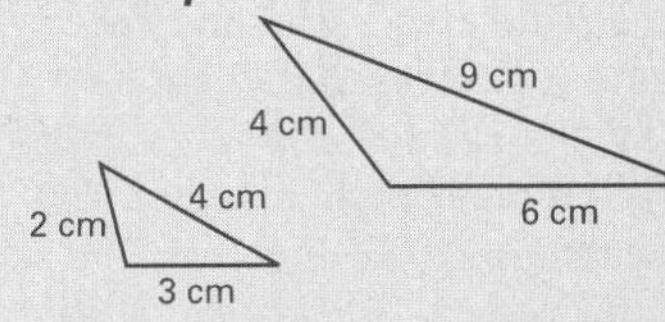

25a.

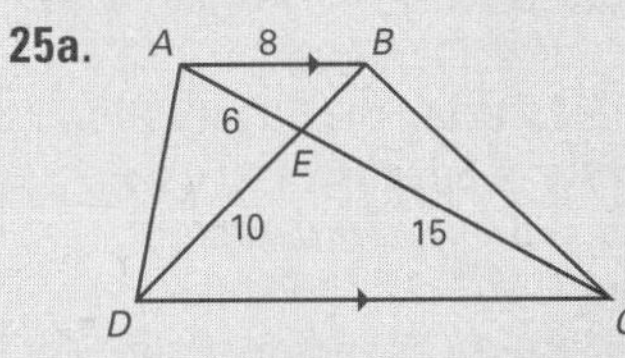

Mathematical Reasoning

Exercise 35 This exercise is a proof that if two triangles are similar, then the angle bisectors of corresponding angles have the same scale factor as the corresponding sides.

33.

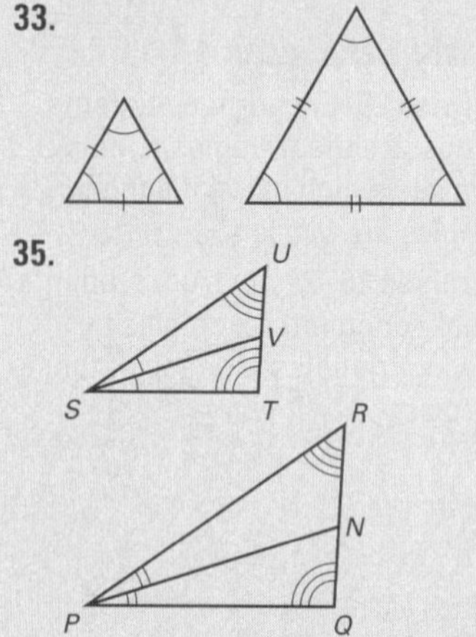

35.

Since $\triangle STU \sim \triangle PQR$ you know that $\angle T \cong \angle Q$ and $\angle UST \cong \angle RPQ$. Since $\overline{SV}$ bisects $\angle TSU$ and $\overline{PN}$ bisects $\angle QPR$ you know that $\angle USV \cong \angle VST$ and $\angle RPN \cong \angle NPQ$ by definition of angle bisector. You know that $m\angle USV + m\angle VST = m\angle UST$ and $m\angle RPN + m\angle NPQ = m\angle RPQ$, therefore $2m\angle VST = 2m\angle NPQ$ using the Substitution Property of Equality. You now have $\angle VST \cong \angle NPQ$, which makes $\triangle VST \sim \triangle NPQ$ using the AA Similarity Postulate. From this you know that $\frac{SV}{PN} = \frac{ST}{PQ}$.

37a. *Sample:*

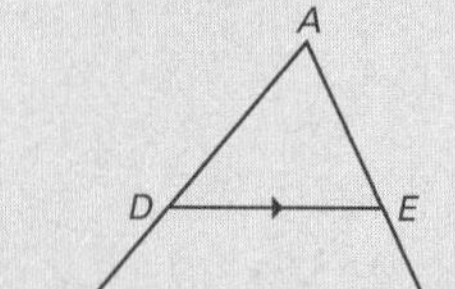

37e. The measures of the angles change, but the equalities remain the same. The lengths of the sides change, but they remain proportional; yes; the triangles remain similar by the AA Similarity Postulate.

PROBLEM SOLVING

EXAMPLE 3 A on p. 383 for Exs. 31–32

31. AIR HOCKEY An air hockey player returns the puck to his opponent by bouncing the puck off the wall of the table as shown. From physics, the angles that the path of the puck makes with the wall are congruent. What is the distance d between the puck and the wall when the opponent returns it? **about 30.8 in.**

@HomeTutor for problem solving help at classzone.com

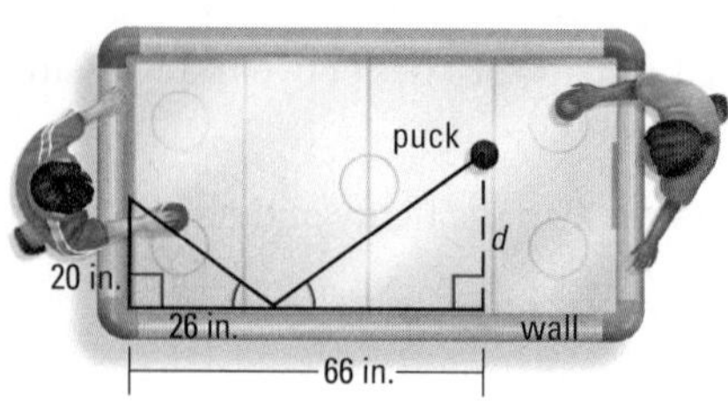

32a. Angle-Angle Similarity Postulate

32. LAKES You can measure the width of the lake using a surveying technique, as shown in the diagram.

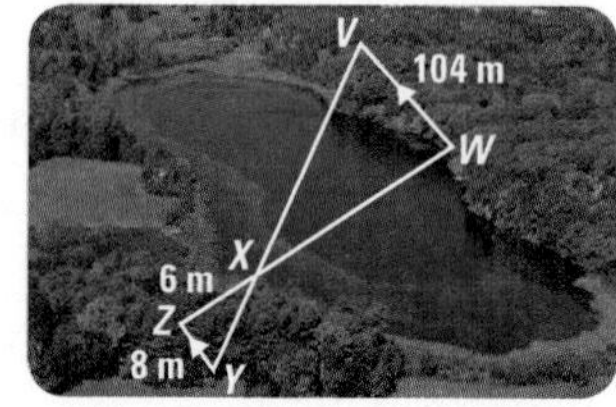

a. What postulate or theorem can you use to show that the triangles are similar?

b. Find the width of the lake, WX. **78 m**

c. If $XY = 10$ meters, find VX. **130 m**

@HomeTutor for problem solving help at classzone.com

33. The measure of all angles in an equilateral triangle is 60°; see margin for art.

33. ★ **SHORT RESPONSE** *Explain* why all equilateral triangles are similar. Include sketches in your answer.

B

34. AERIAL PHOTOGRAPHY Low-level aerial photos can be taken using a remote-controlled camera suspended from a blimp. You want to take an aerial photo that covers a ground distance g of 50 meters. Use the proportion $\frac{f}{h} = \frac{n}{g}$ to estimate the altitude h that the blimp should fly at to take the photo. In the proportion, use $f = 8$ centimeters and $n = 3$ centimeters. These two variables are determined by the type of camera used. **$133\frac{1}{3}$ m**

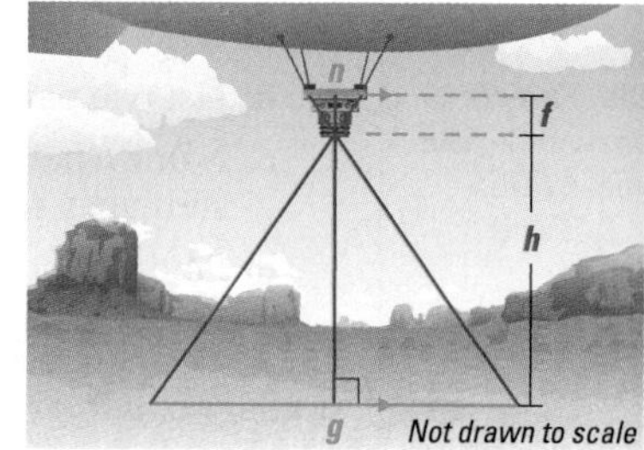

35. PROOF Use the given information to draw a sketch. Then write a proof. **See margin.**

GIVEN ▶ $\triangle STU \sim \triangle PQR$
Point V lies on $\overline{TU}$ so that $\overline{SV}$ bisects $\angle TSU$.
Point N lies on $\overline{QR}$ so that $\overline{PN}$ bisects $\angle QPR$.

PROVE ▶ $\frac{SV}{PN} = \frac{ST}{PQ}$

36. PROOF Prove that if an acute angle in one right triangle is congruent to an acute angle in another right triangle, then the triangles are similar.
Sample answer: If $\angle ACB$ and $\angle EFB$ are right angles, then they are congruent. This, along with the fact that $\angle A \cong \angle E$, makes $\triangle ABC \sim \triangle EDF$ by the AA Similarity Postulate.

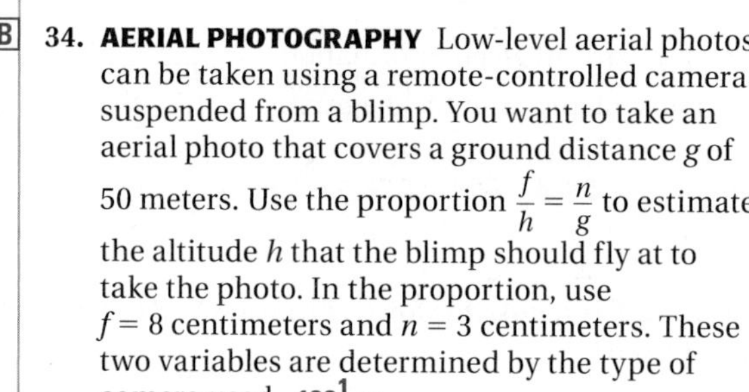

○ = WORKED-OUT SOLUTIONS on p. WS1 ★ = STANDARDIZED TEST PRACTICE

39. Let $\triangle ABC \sim \triangle DEF$, let $\overline{AN}$ bisect $\angle BAC$, and let $\overline{DM}$ bisect $\angle EDF$. By the definition of similar triangles, $\angle B \cong \angle E$ and $\angle BAC \cong \angle EDF$. By the definition of angle bisector, $\angle BAN \cong \angle NAC$ and $\angle EDM \cong \angle MDF$. The Angle Addition Postulate gives $m\angle BAN + m\angle NAC = m\angle BAC$ and $m\angle EDM + m\angle MDF = m\angle EDF$. By substitution we get $m\angle BAN + m\angle NAC = m\angle EDM + m\angle MDF$, and then $m\angle BAN + m\angle BAN = m\angle EDM + m\angle EDM$, and then $2m\angle BAN = 2m\angle EDM$, so $m\angle BAN = m\angle EDM$. Now, by the AA Similarity Postulate, $\triangle BAN \sim \triangle EDM$ so $\frac{AN}{DM} = \frac{AB}{DE}$ where $\frac{AB}{DE}$ is the scale factor.

7b. m∠ADE = m∠ACB and m∠AED = m∠ABC

30. The two right triangles formed by the altitudes and the two sides measuring a and b are similar by the AA Similarity Postulate. Since the ratio of the hypotenuses is $\frac{b}{a}$ then the ratio of corresponding sides, which are the altitudes of the original triangles is the same ratio by Corresponding Lengths in similar Polygons.

37. **TECHNOLOGY** Use a graphing calculator or computer.

a. Draw $\triangle ABC$. Draw $\overline{DE}$ through two sides of the triangle, parallel to the third side. **See margin.**

b. Measure $\angle ADE$ and $\angle ACB$. Measure $\angle AED$ and $\angle ABC$. What do you notice?

c. What does a postulate in this lesson tell you about $\triangle ADE$ and $\triangle ACB$? **$\triangle ADE \sim \triangle ACB$**

d. Measure all the sides. Show that corresponding side lengths are proportional. ***Sample answer:*** $\frac{AD}{AC} = \frac{AE}{AB} = \frac{DE}{CB} = \frac{1}{2}$

e. Move vertex A to form new triangles. How do your measurements in parts (b) and (d) change? Are the new triangles still similar? *Explain.* **See margin.**

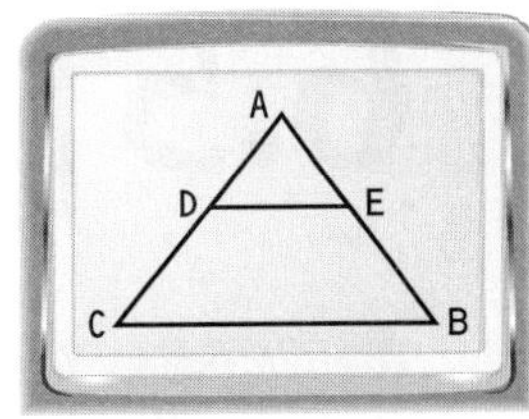

38. ★ **EXTENDED RESPONSE** *Explain* how you could use similar triangles to show that any two points on a line can be used to calculate its slope.

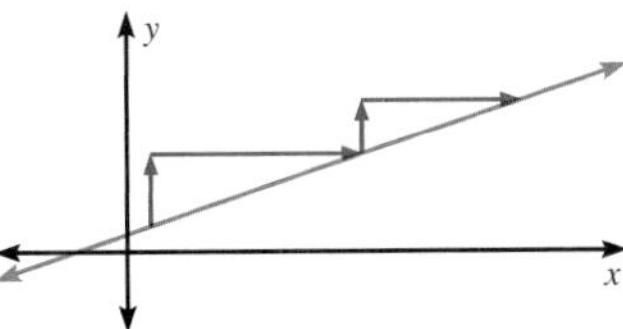

Since the two triangles are similar the ratio of corresponding sides are the same therefore compare the vertical rise to the horizontal run.

39. **CORRESPONDING LENGTHS** Without using the Corresponding Lengths Property on page 375, prove that the ratio of two corresponding angle bisectors in similar triangles is equal to the scale factor. **See margin.**

40. **CHALLENGE** Prove that if the lengths of two sides of a triangle are a and b respectively, then the lengths of the corresponding altitudes to those sides are in the ratio $\frac{b}{a}$.

MIXED REVIEW

PREVIEW
Prepare for Lesson 6.5 in Exs. 41–44.

In Exercises 41–44, use the diagram.

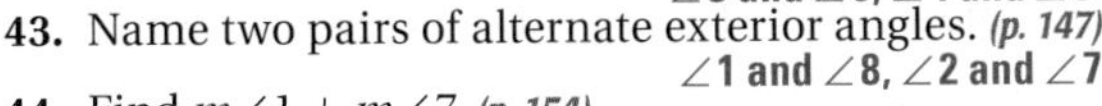

41. Name three pairs of corresponding angles. *(p. 147)*
Sample answer: **∠1 and ∠5, ∠3 and ∠7, ∠2 and ∠6**

42. Name two pairs of alternate interior angles. *(p. 147)*
∠3 and ∠6, ∠4 and ∠5

43. Name two pairs of alternate exterior angles. *(p. 147)*
∠1 and ∠8, ∠2 and ∠7

44. Find $m\angle 1 + m\angle 7$. *(p. 154)*
180°

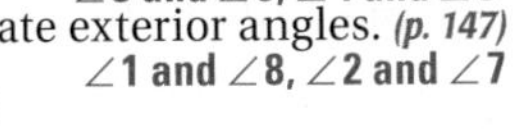

45. **CONGRUENCE** Explain why $\triangle ABE \cong \triangle CDE$. *(p. 240)*

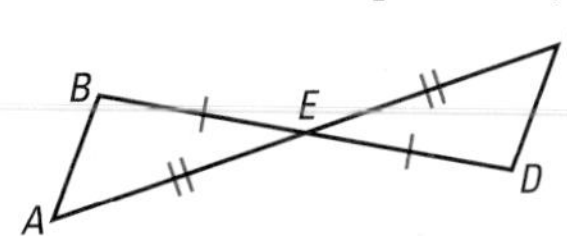

∠BEA ≅ ∠CED using the Vertical Angles Congruence Theorem making △ABE ≅ △CDE by the SAS Congruence Theorem.

Simplify the ratio. *(p. 356)*

46. $\frac{4}{20}$ **$\frac{1}{5}$**

47. $\frac{36}{18}$ **$\frac{2}{1}$**

48. 21 : 63 **1 : 3**

49. 42 : 28 **3 : 2**

EXTRA PRACTICE for Lesson 6.4, p. 907 **ONLINE QUIZ** at classzone.com

5 ASSESS AND RETEACH

Daily Homework Quiz

Transparency Available

Determine if the two triangles are similar. If they are, write a similarity statement.

1.

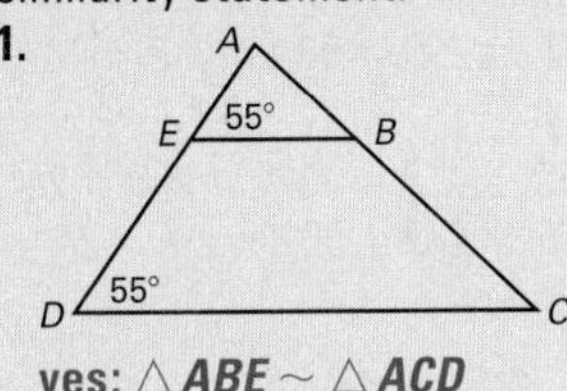

yes; △ABE ~ △ACD

2. **no**

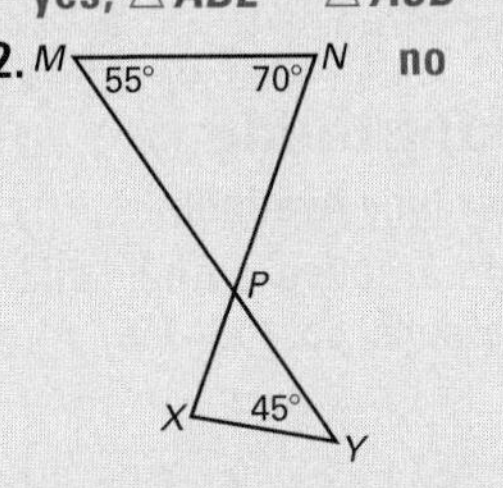

3. Find the length of $\overline{BC}$. **7.5**

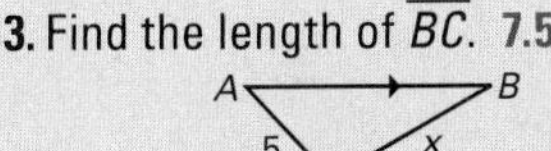

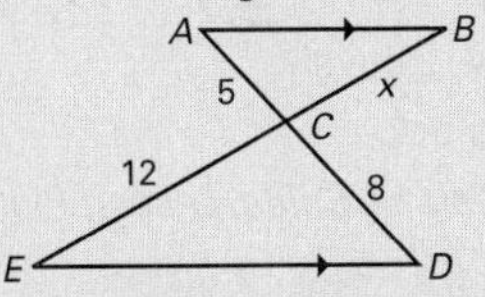

4. A tree casts a shadow that is 30 feet long. At the same time a person standing nearby, who is five feet two inches tall, casts a shadow that is 50 inches long. How tall is the tree to the nearest foot? **37 ft**

Available at **classzone.com**

Diagnosis/Remediation

- Practice A, B, C in Chapter 6 Resource Book, pp. 46–51
- Study Guide in Chapter 6 Resource Book, pp. 52–53
- Practice Workbook, pp. 112–114
- @HomeTutor

Challenge

Additional challenge is available in the Chapter 6 Resource Book, p. 56.

① PLAN AND PREPARE

Warm-Up Exercises

Transparency Available

Determine whether the two triangles are similar.

1. $\triangle ABC$: $m\angle A = 90°$, $m\angle B = 44°$; $\triangle DEF$: $m\angle D = 90°$, $m\angle E = 46°$ **similar**
2. $\triangle ABC$: $m\angle A = 132°$, $m\angle B = 24°$; $\triangle DEF$: $m\angle D = 90°$, $m\angle F = 24°$ **not similar**
3. Solve $\frac{6}{12} = \frac{x-1}{8}$. 5

Notetaking Guide

Transparency Available

Promotes interactive learning and notetaking skills, pp. 156–159.

Pacing

Basic: 2 days
Average: 2 days
Advanced: 2 days
Block: 1 block
- See *Teaching Guide/Lesson Plan.*

② FOCUS AND MOTIVATE

Essential Question

Big Idea 2, p. 355

How do you prove that two triangles are similar by using the SSS Similarity Theorem? **Tell students they will learn how to answer this question by using the ratios of pairs of sides.**

6.5 Prove Triangles Similar by SSS and SAS

Before You used the AA Similarity Postulate to prove triangles similar.
Now You will use the SSS and SAS Similarity Theorems.
Why? So you can show that triangles are similar, as in Ex. 28.

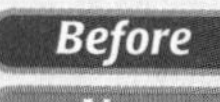

Key Vocabulary
- **ratio,** *p. 356*
- **proportion,** *p. 358*
- **similar polygons,** *p. 372*

Standards

4.0 Students prove basic theorems involving congruence and **similarity.**

5.0 Students prove that triangles are congruent or **similar, and they are able to use the concept of corresponding parts** of congruent triangles.

In addition to using congruent corresponding angles to show that two triangles are similar, you can use proportional corresponding side lengths.

THEOREM *For Your Notebook*

THEOREM 6.2 Side-Side-Side (SSS) Similarity Theorem

If the corresponding side lengths of two triangles are proportional, then the triangles are similar.

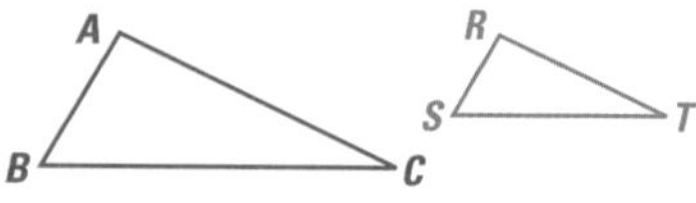

If $\frac{AB}{RS} = \frac{BC}{ST} = \frac{CA}{TR}$, then $\triangle ABC \sim \triangle RST$.

Proof: p. 389

EXAMPLE 1 Use the SSS Similarity Theorem

Is either $\triangle DEF$ or $\triangle GHJ$ similar to $\triangle ABC$?

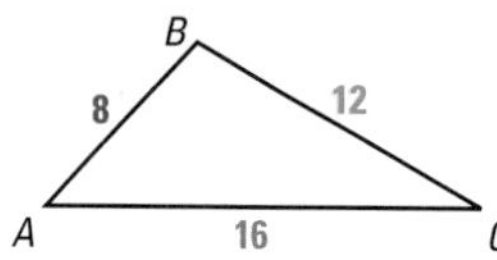

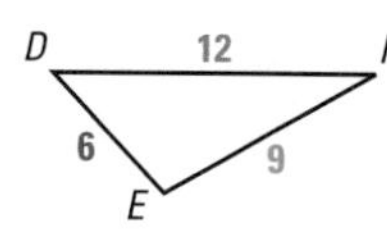

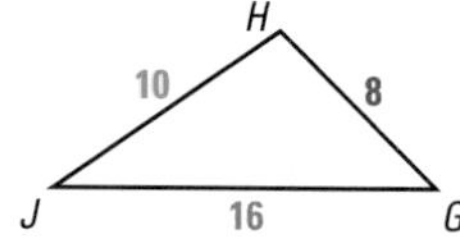

Solution

APPLY THEOREMS
When using the SSS Similarity Theorem, compare the shortest sides, the longest sides, and then the remaining sides.

Compare $\triangle ABC$ and $\triangle DEF$ by finding ratios of corresponding side lengths.

Shortest sides	Longest sides	Remaining sides
$\frac{AB}{DE} = \frac{8}{6} = \frac{4}{3}$	$\frac{CA}{FD} = \frac{16}{12} = \frac{4}{3}$	$\frac{BC}{EF} = \frac{12}{9} = \frac{4}{3}$

▶ All of the ratios are equal, so $\triangle ABC \sim \triangle DEF$.

Compare $\triangle ABC$ and $\triangle GHJ$ by finding ratios of corresponding side lengths.

Shortest sides	Longest sides	Remaining sides
$\frac{AB}{GH} = \frac{8}{8} = 1$	$\frac{CA}{JG} = \frac{16}{16} = 1$	$\frac{BC}{HJ} = \frac{12}{10} = \frac{6}{5}$

▶ The ratios are not all equal, so $\triangle ABC$ and $\triangle GHJ$ are not similar.

Resource Planning Guide

Chapter Resource Book
- Teaching Guide/Lesson Plan (pp. 57–58)
- Activity Master (p. 59)
- Practice levels A, B, C (pp. 60–65)
- Study Guide (pp. 66–67)
- Catch-up for Absent Students (p. 68)
- Application (p. 69)
- Challenge (p. 70)

Workbooks
- Notetaking Guide (pp. 156–159)
- Practice Workbook (pp. 115–117)

Teaching Options
- **Power Presentations CD-ROM** provides dynamic electronic teaching resources for the classroom.
- **Activity Generator CD-ROM** provides editable activities for all ability levels.

Interactive Technology
- Easy Planner
- Power Presentations CD-ROM
- Activity Generator CD-ROM
- Animated Algebra
- Test Generator CD-ROM
- Online Quiz
- eWorkbook
- eEdition
- @HomeTutor

Resources for English Learners
- Quick Reference for English Learners
- Spanish Study Guide
- Multi-Language Visual Glossary
- Student Resources in Spanish

See also the *Geometry Toolkit* for more strategies for meeting individual needs.

PROOF SSS Similarity Theorem

GIVEN ▶ $\frac{RS}{JK} = \frac{ST}{KL} = \frac{TR}{LJ}$

PROVE ▶ $\triangle RST \sim \triangle JKL$

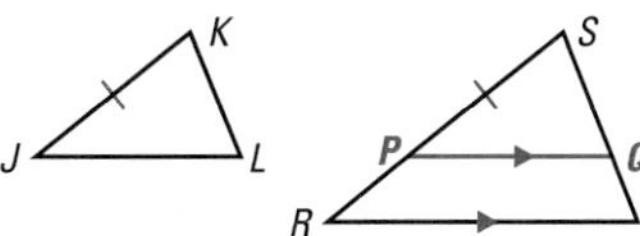

USE AN AUXILIARY LINE

The Parallel Postulate allows you to draw an auxiliary line $\overleftrightarrow{PQ}$ in $\triangle RST$. There is only one line through point P parallel to $\overleftrightarrow{RT}$, so you are able to draw it.

Locate P on $\overline{RS}$ so that $PS = JK$. Draw $\overline{PQ}$ so that $\overline{PQ} \parallel \overline{RT}$. Then $\triangle RST \sim \triangle PSQ$ by the AA Similarity Postulate, and $\frac{RS}{PS} = \frac{ST}{SQ} = \frac{TR}{QP}$.

You can use the given proportion and the fact that $PS = JK$ to deduce that $SQ = KL$ and $QP = LJ$. By the SSS Congruence Postulate, it follows that $\triangle PSQ \cong \triangle JKL$. Finally, use the definition of congruent triangles and the AA Similarity Postulate to conclude that $\triangle RST \sim \triangle JKL$.

EXAMPLE 2 Use the SSS Similarity Theorem

ALGEBRA Find the value of x that makes $\triangle ABC \sim \triangle DEF$.

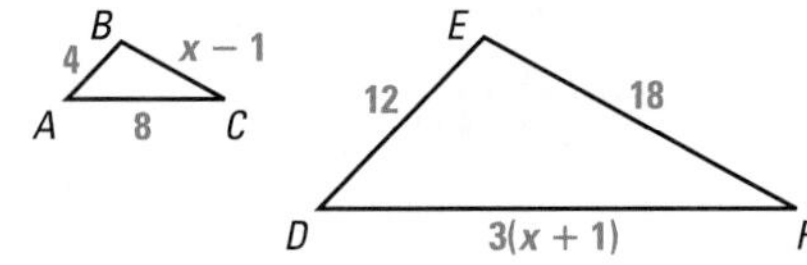

Solution

CHOOSE A METHOD

You can use either $\frac{AB}{DE} = \frac{BC}{EF}$ or $\frac{AB}{DE} = \frac{AC}{DF}$ in Step 1.

STEP 1 **Find** the value of x that makes corresponding side lengths proportional.

$\frac{4}{12} = \frac{x-1}{18}$	**Write proportion.**
$4 \cdot 18 = 12(x - 1)$	**Cross Products Property**
$72 = 12x - 12$	**Simplify.**
$7 = x$	**Solve for *x*.**

STEP 2 **Check** that the side lengths are proportional when $x = 7$.

$BC = x - 1 = 6$ $\qquad$ $DF = 3(x + 1) = 24$

$\frac{AB}{DE} \stackrel{?}{=} \frac{BC}{EF} \rightarrow \frac{4}{12} = \frac{6}{18}$ ✓ $\qquad$ $\frac{AB}{DE} \stackrel{?}{=} \frac{AC}{DF} \rightarrow \frac{4}{12} = \frac{8}{24}$ ✓

▶ When $x = 7$, the triangles are similar by the SSS Similarity Theorem.

✓ GUIDED PRACTICE for Examples 1 and 2

1. Which of the three triangles are similar? Write a similarity statement. **$\triangle MLN \sim \triangle ZYX$**
2. The shortest side of a triangle similar to $\triangle RST$ is 12 units long. Find the other side lengths of the triangle. **15, 16.5**

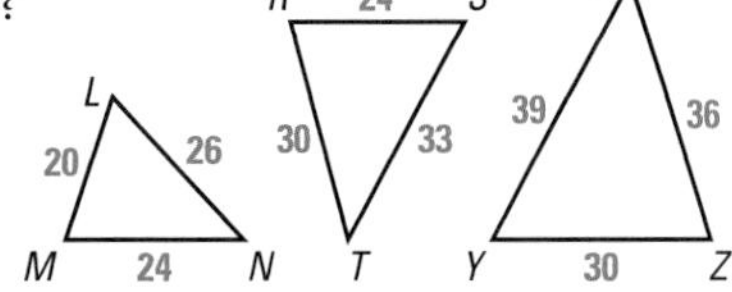

Motivating the Lesson

Ask students to draw a triangle and measure each side. Then have them draw a similar triangle with sides half as long. Discuss how they know that the smaller triangle is similar to the larger one.

3 TEACH

Extra Example 1

Is either $\triangle PQR$ or $\triangle STU$ similar to $\triangle XYZ$?

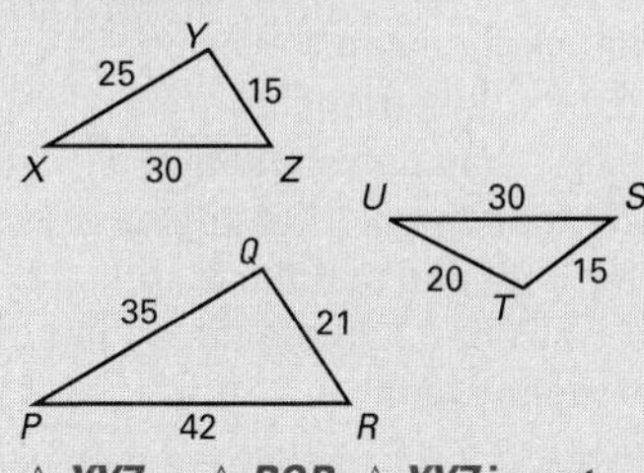

$\triangle XYZ \sim \triangle PQR$; $\triangle XYZ$ is not similar to $\triangle STU$.

Key Question to Ask for Example 1

- Do the ratios of all three pairs of corresponding sides have to be equal if the two triangles are similar? **yes**

Extra Example 2

Find the value of x that makes $\triangle XYZ \sim \triangle PQR$. **8**

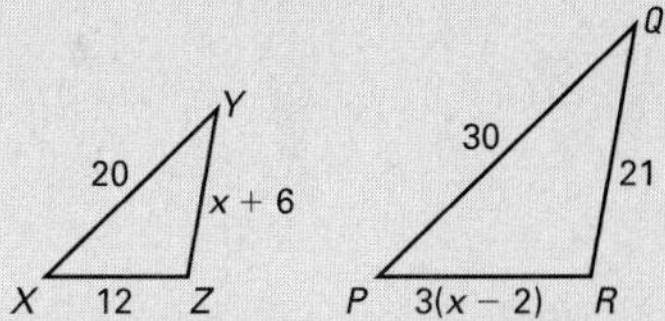

Key Questions to Ask for Example 2

- What is the scale factor for the triangles? **4:12 or 1:3**
- How is the scale factor used to find x? **You write and solve a proportion involving the scale factor and x.**

Extra Example 3

You enlarge $\triangle XYW$ to $\triangle JHK$ as shown. Is $\triangle XYW$ similar to $\triangle JHK$?

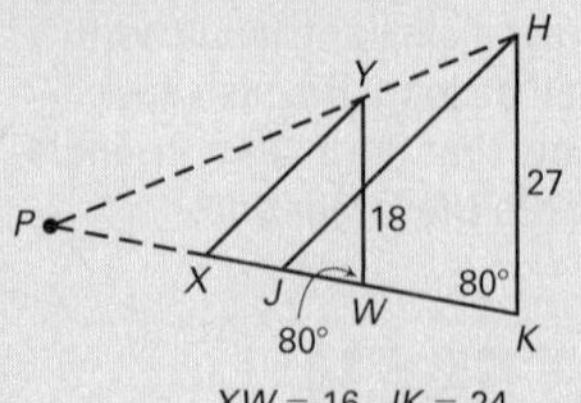

yes

Key Questions to Ask for Example 3

- What method can you use to show that the triangles are similar? **You can show that a corresponding pair of angles are congruent and that the lengths of the sides that include the angles are proportional.**
- Are the lengths of all three pairs of sides proportional? **yes**

THEOREM — *For Your Notebook*

THEOREM 6.3 Side-Angle-Side (SAS) Similarity Theorem

If an angle of one triangle is congruent to an angle of a second triangle and the lengths of the sides including these angles are proportional, then the triangles are similar.

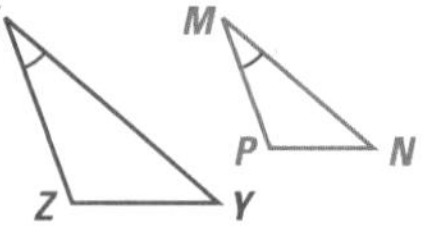

If $\angle X \cong \angle M$ and $\frac{ZX}{PM} = \frac{XY}{MN}$, then $\triangle XYZ \sim \triangle MNP$.

Proof: Ex. 37, p. 395

EXAMPLE 3 Use the SAS Similarity Theorem

LEAN-TO SHELTER You are building a lean-to shelter starting from a tree branch, as shown. Can you construct the right end so it is similar to the left end using the angle measure and lengths shown?

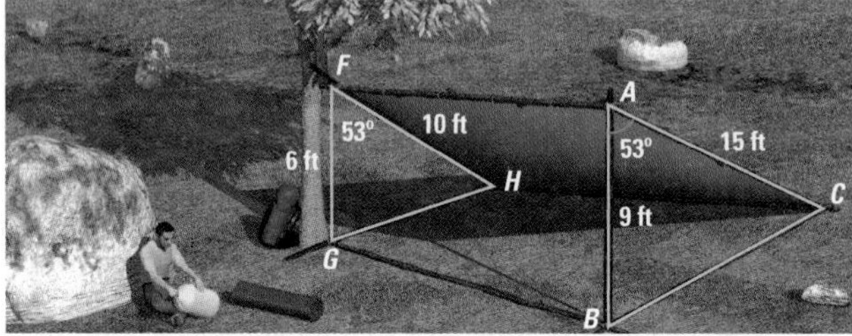

Solution

Both $m\angle A$ and $m\angle F$ equal 53°, so $\angle A \cong \angle F$. Next, compare the ratios of the lengths of the sides that include $\angle A$ and $\angle F$.

Shorter sides $\frac{AB}{FG} = \frac{9}{6} = \frac{3}{2}$ **Longer sides** $\frac{AC}{FH} = \frac{15}{10} = \frac{3}{2}$

The lengths of the sides that include $\angle A$ and $\angle F$ are proportional.

▶ So, by the SAS Similarity Theorem, $\triangle ABC \sim \triangle FGH$. Yes, you can make the right end similar to the left end of the shelter.

CONCEPT SUMMARY — *For Your Notebook*

Triangle Similarity Postulate and Theorems

AA Similarity Postulate

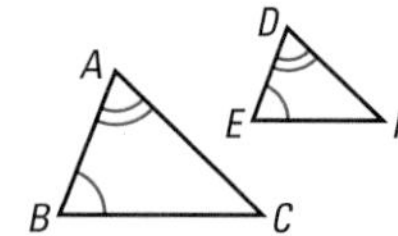

If $\angle A \cong \angle D$ and $\angle B \cong \angle E$, then $\triangle ABC \sim \triangle DEF$.

SSS Similarity Theorem

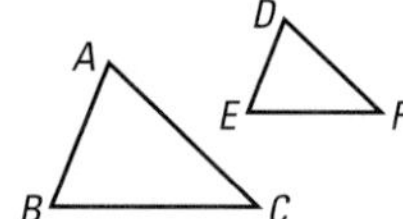

If $\frac{AB}{DE} = \frac{BC}{EF} = \frac{AC}{DF}$, then $\triangle ABC \sim \triangle DEF$.

SAS Similarity Theorem

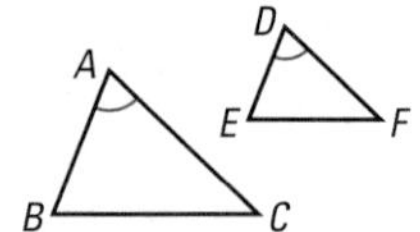

If $\angle A \cong \angle D$ and $\frac{AB}{DE} = \frac{AC}{DF}$, then $\triangle ABC \sim \triangle DEF$.

EXAMPLE 4 Choose a method

VISUAL REASONING

To identify corresponding parts, redraw the triangles so that the corresponding parts have the same orientation.

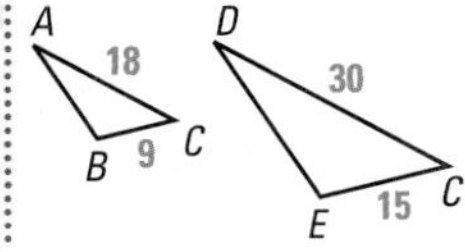

Tell what method you would use to show that the triangles are similar.

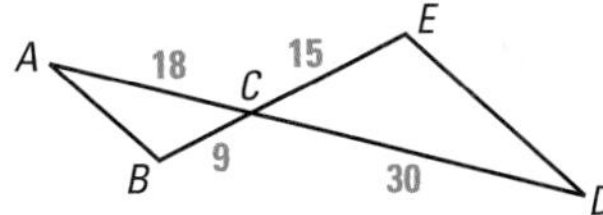

Solution

Find the ratios of the lengths of the corresponding sides.

Shorter sides $\frac{BC}{EC} = \frac{9}{15} = \frac{3}{5}$ **Longer sides** $\frac{CA}{CD} = \frac{18}{30} = \frac{3}{5}$

The corresponding side lengths are proportional. The included angles $\angle ACB$ and $\angle DCE$ are congruent because they are vertical angles. So, $\triangle ACB \sim \triangle DCE$ by the SAS Similarity Theorem.

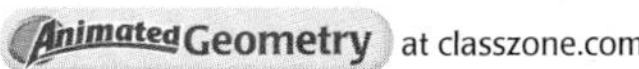 at classzone.com

GUIDED PRACTICE for Examples 3 and 4

Explain **how to show that the indicated triangles are similar.**

3. $\triangle SRT \sim \triangle PNQ$

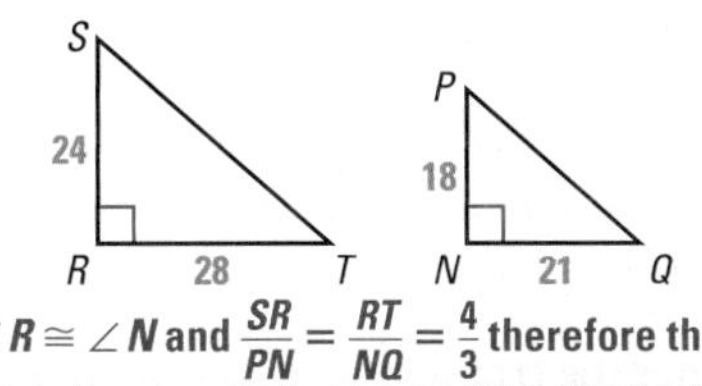

$\angle R \cong \angle N$ and $\frac{SR}{PN} = \frac{RT}{NQ} = \frac{4}{3}$ therefore the triangles are similar by the SAS Similarity Theorem.

4. $\triangle XZW \sim \triangle YZX$

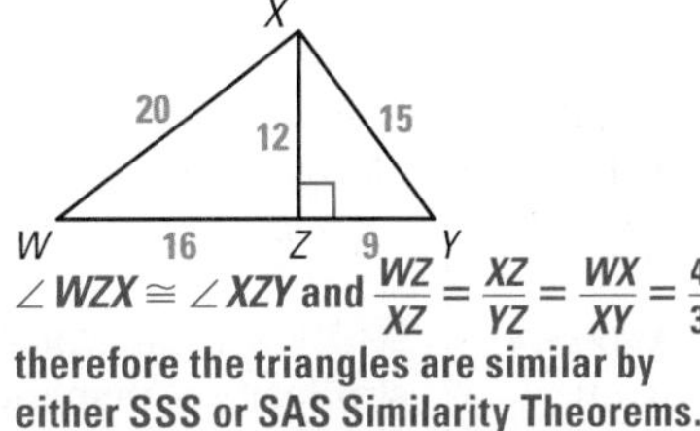

$\angle WZX \cong \angle XZY$ and $\frac{WZ}{XZ} = \frac{XZ}{YZ} = \frac{WX}{XY} = \frac{4}{3}$ therefore the triangles are similar by either SSS or SAS Similarity Theorems.

6.5 EXERCISES

HOMEWORK KEY

◯ = **WORKED-OUT SOLUTIONS** on p. WS7 for Exs. 3, 7, and 31

★ = **STANDARDIZED TEST PRACTICE** Exs. 2, 14, 32, 34, and 36

SKILL PRACTICE

A

1. VOCABULARY You plan to prove that $\triangle ACB$ is similar to $\triangle PXQ$ by the SSS Similarity Theorem. Copy and complete the proportion that is needed to use this theorem: $\frac{AC}{?} = \frac{?}{XQ} = \frac{AB}{?}$.

PX CB PQ

2. ★ WRITING If you know two triangles are similar by the SAS Similarity Theorem, what additional piece(s) of information would you need to know to show that the triangles are congruent?

You would need to know that one pair of corresponding sides is congruent.

EXAMPLES 1 and 2 on pp. 388–389 for Exs. 3–6

SSS SIMILARITY THEOREM Verify that $\triangle ABC \sim \triangle DEF$. Find the scale factor of $\triangle ABC$ to $\triangle DEF$.

3. $\triangle$**ABC:** $BC = 18$, $AB = 15$, $AC = 12$
$\triangle$**DEF:** $EF = 12$, $DE = 10$, $DF = 8$

$\frac{18}{12} = \frac{15}{10} = \frac{12}{8}, \frac{3}{2}$

4. $\triangle$**ABC:** $AB = 10$, $BC = 16$, $CA = 20$
$\triangle$**DEF:** $DE = 25$, $EF = 40$, $FD = 50$

$\frac{10}{25} = \frac{16}{40} = \frac{20}{50}, \frac{2}{5}$

Extra Example 4

Tell what method you would use to show that the triangles are similar.

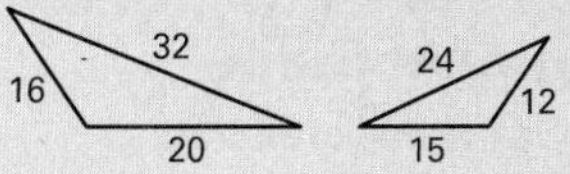

SSS Similarity Theorem

Teaching Strategy

Ask students to summarize the triangle similarity postulates and theorems by drawing and labeling a diagram for each and writing a conditional statement for each situation.

An **Animated Geometry** activity is available on-line for **Example 4**. This activity is also available on the **Power Presentations CD-ROM**.

Closing the Lesson

Have students summarize the major points of the lesson and answer the Essential Question: How do you prove that two triangles are similar using the SSS Similarity Theorem?

- **You can prove triangles are similar by the AA Similarity Postulate, the SSS Similarity Theorem, and the SAS Similarity Theorem.**

Compare the ratio of each pair of corresponding side lengths. If they are all equal, then the triangles are similar by the SSS Similarity Theorem.

4 PRACTICE AND APPLY

Assignment Guide

Answer Transparencies available for all exercises

Basic:
Day 1: pp. 391–395
Exs. 1–6, 28–30, 32, 39–42
Day 2: pp. 391–395
Exs. 7–17, 31, 33, 34, 43, 44

Average:
Day 1: pp. 391–395
Exs. 1–6, 18–23, 28–30, 32, 40, 42
Day 2: pp. 391–395
Exs. 7–17, 24, 31, 33–37, 43

Advanced:
Day 1: pp. 391–395
Exs. 1, 2, 5, 6, 18–23, 25–30*, 32, 41
Day 2: pp. 391–395
Exs. 8, 9, 11, 12, 14–17, 24, 31, 33–38*, 44

Block:
pp. 391–395
Exs. 1–24, 28–37, 40, 42, 43

Differentiated Instruction

See *Geometry Best Practices Toolkit* for suggestions on addressing the needs of a diverse classroom.

Homework Check

For a quick check of student understanding of key concepts, go over the following exercises:

Basic: 4, 8, 10, 29, 33
Average: 5, 8, 11, 30, 33
Advanced: 6, 9, 12, 32, 33

Extra Practice

- Student Edition, p. 907
- Chapter 6 Resource Book: Practice levels A, B, C, pp. 60–65

Practice Worksheet

An easily-readable reduced practice page (with answers) for this lesson can be found on p. 354C.

---

5. SSS SIMILARITY THEOREM Is either $\triangle JKL$ or $\triangle RST$ similar to $\triangle ABC$? **$\triangle RST$**

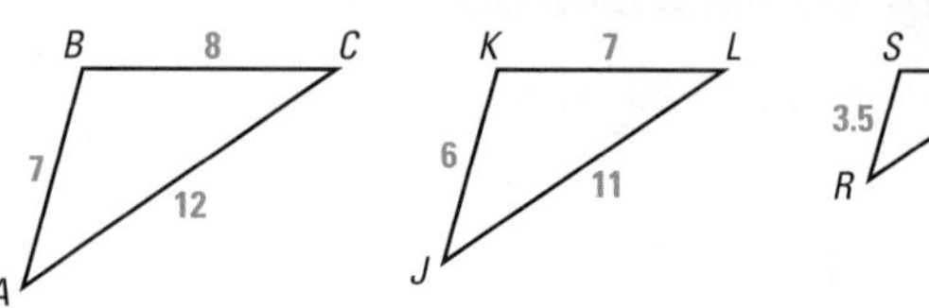

6. SSS SIMILARITY THEOREM Is either $\triangle JKL$ or $\triangle RST$ similar to $\triangle ABC$? **$\triangle JKL$**

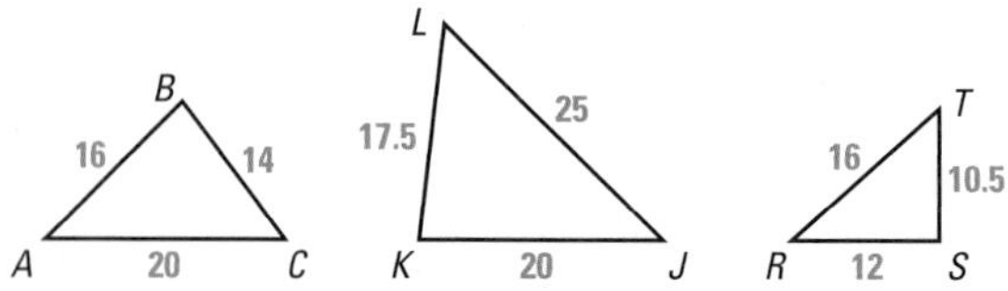

EXAMPLE 3 on p. 390 for Exs. 7–9

SAS SIMILARITY THEOREM Determine whether the two triangles are similar. If they are similar, write a similarity statement and find the scale factor of Triangle B to Triangle A.

7. similar; $\triangle FDE \sim \triangle XWY$; 2 : 3

8. not similar

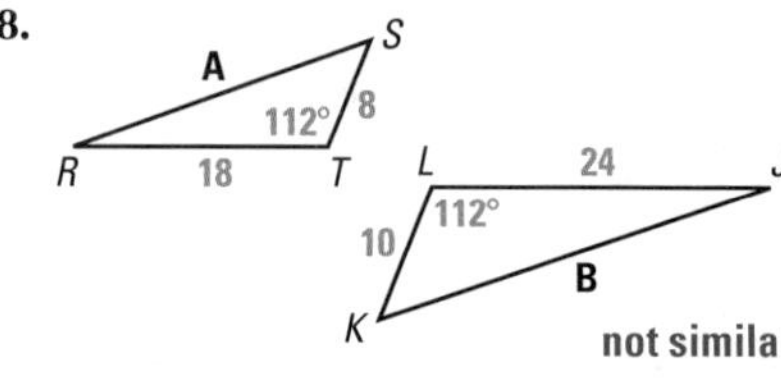

9. ALGEBRA Find the value of n that makes $\triangle PQR \sim \triangle XYZ$ when $PQ = 4$, $QR = 5$, $XY = 4(n + 1)$, $YZ = 7n - 1$, and $\angle Q \cong \angle Y$. Include a sketch. **3; see margin for art.**

EXAMPLE 4 on p. 391 for Exs. 10–12

SHOWING SIMILARITY Show that the triangles are similar and write a similarity statement. *Explain* your reasoning.

10. **11.** **12.**

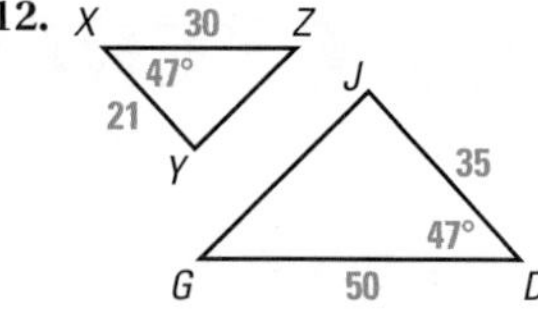

13. ERROR ANALYSIS *Describe* and correct the student's error in writing the similarity statement.
***Sample answer:* The triangle correspondence is not listed in the correct order; $\triangle ABC \sim \triangle RQP$.**

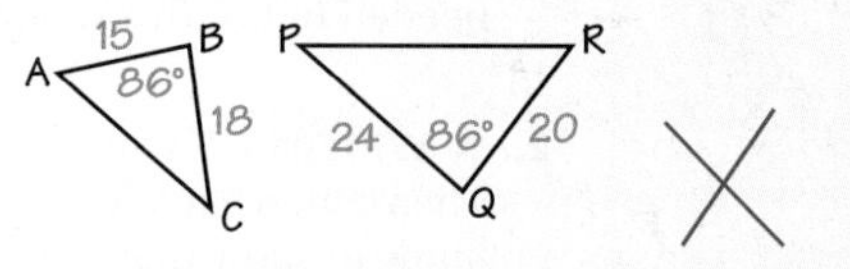
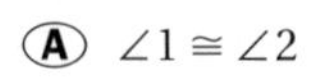
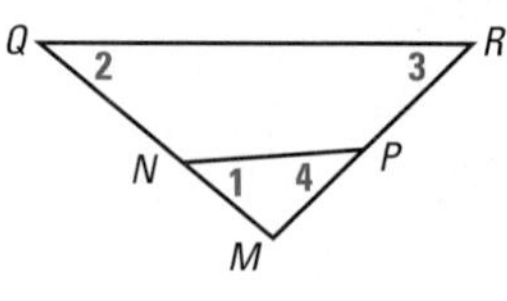

14. ★ MULTIPLE CHOICE In the diagram, $\frac{MN}{MR} = \frac{MP}{MQ}$. Which of the statements must be true? **D**

Ⓐ $\angle 1 \cong \angle 2$ Ⓑ $\overline{QR} \parallel \overline{NP}$
Ⓒ $\angle 1 \cong \angle 4$ Ⓓ $\triangle MNP \sim \triangle MRQ$

Margin answers:

10. $\triangle GHJ \sim \triangle FHK$; $\frac{FH}{GH} = \frac{HK}{HJ} = \frac{KF}{JG} = \frac{4}{3}$ thus the triangles are similar by the SSS Similarity Theorem.

11. $\triangle ABC \sim \triangle DEC$; $\angle ACB \cong \angle DCE$ by the Vertical Angles Congruence Theorem and $\frac{AC}{DC} = \frac{BC}{EC} = \frac{3}{2}$. The triangles are similar using the SAS Similarity Theorem.

12. $\triangle XYZ \sim \triangle DJG$; $\angle D \cong \angle X$ and $\frac{DG}{XZ} = \frac{DJ}{XY} = \frac{5}{3}$. The triangles are similar by the SAS Similarity Theorem.

○ = WORKED-OUT SOLUTIONS on p. WS1 ★ = STANDARDIZED TEST PRACTICE

9.

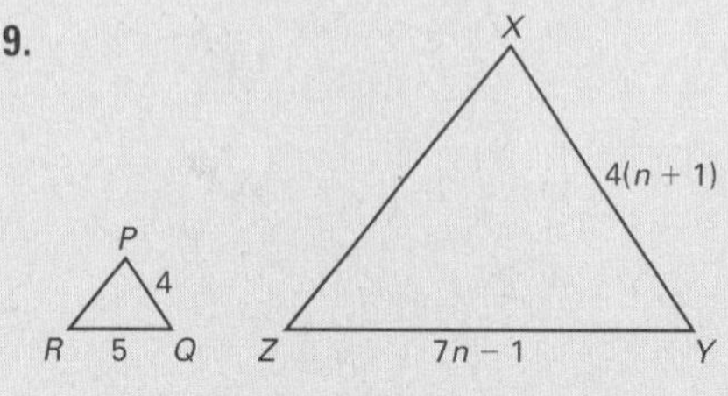

DRAWING TRIANGLES **Sketch the triangles using the given description. *Explain* whether the two triangles can be similar.** 15–17. See margin for art.

15. In $\triangle XYZ$, $m\angle X = 66°$ and $m\angle Y = 34°$. In $\triangle LMN$, $m\angle M = 34°$ and $m\angle N = 80°$. **They are similar by the AA Similarity Postulate.**

16. In $\triangle RST$, $RS = 20$, $ST = 32$, and $m\angle S = 16°$. In $\triangle FGH$, $GH = 30$, $HF = 48$, and $m\angle H = 24°$. **They are not similar since the larger side in $\triangle RST$ would not be opposite the largest angle.**

17. The side lengths of $\triangle ABC$ are 24, $8x$, and 54, and the side lengths of $\triangle DEF$ are 15, 25, and $7x$. **They are not similar since the ratio of corresponding sides is not constant for any arrangement of side lengths.**

FINDING MEASURES **In Exercises 18–23, use the diagram to copy and complete the statements.**

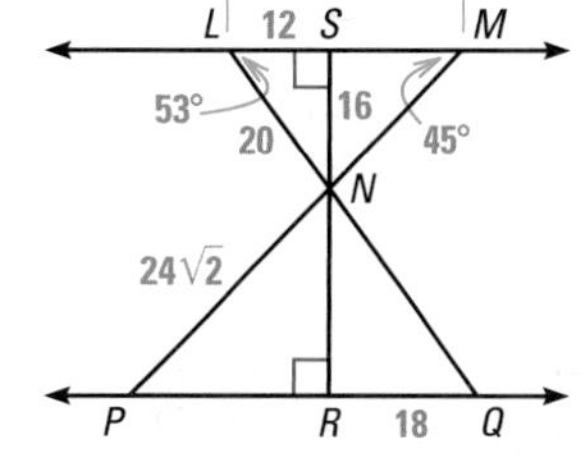

18. $m\angle NQP =$ __?__ **53°**
19. $m\angle QPN =$ __?__ **45°**
20. $m\angle PNQ =$ __?__ **82°**
21. $RN =$ __?__ **24**
22. $PQ =$ __?__ **42**
23. $NM =$ __?__ **$16\sqrt{2}$**

24. **SIMILAR TRIANGLES** In the diagram at the right, name the three pairs of triangles that are similar. **$\triangle NSM$ and $\triangle NRP$, $\triangle NSL$ and $\triangle NRQ$, $\triangle NLM$ and $\triangle NQP$**

27. In similar triangles the ratio of the areas is the square of the scale factor. *Sample answer:* Let the base and height of $\triangle VWX$ measure $3a$ and $3b$ and the base and height of $\triangle ABC$ measure $2a$ and $2b$. The ratio of their areas is $\frac{\frac{3a(3b)}{2}}{\frac{2a(2b)}{2}} = \frac{9}{4}$.

C **CHALLENGE** **In the figure at the right, $\triangle ABC \sim \triangle VWX$.**

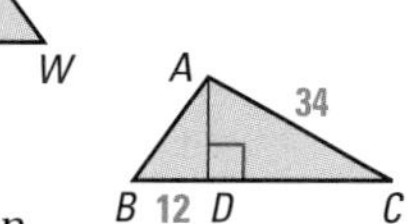

25. Find the scale factor of $\triangle VWX$ to $\triangle ABC$. $\frac{3}{2}$

26. Find the ratio of the area of $\triangle VWX$ to the area of $\triangle ABC$. $\frac{9}{4}$

27. Make a conjecture about the relationship between the scale factor in Exercise 25 and the ratio in Exercise 26. *Justify* your conjecture.

PROBLEM SOLVING

A 28. **RACECAR NET** Which postulate or theorem could you use to show that the three triangles that make up the racecar window net are similar? *Explain.*

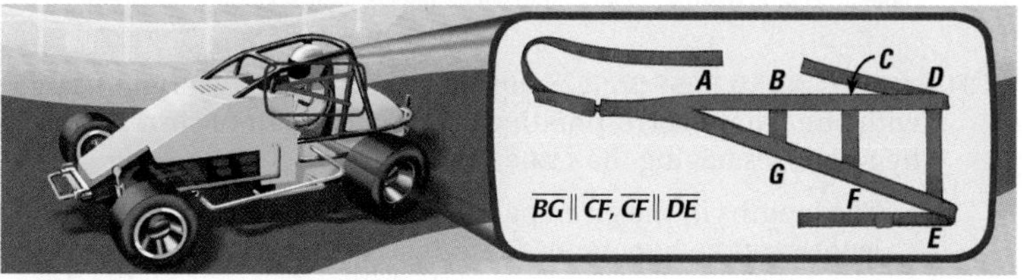

AA Similarity Postulate; in $\triangle AGB$ $\angle A$ and $\angle AGB$ are congruent to $\angle A$ and $\angle AFC$ in $\triangle AFC$. In $\triangle AFC$ $\angle A$ and $\angle AFC$ are congruent to $\angle A$ and $\angle AED$ in $\triangle AED$.

@HomeTutor for problem solving help at classzone.com

29. The triangle whose sides measure 4 inches, 4 inches, and 7 inches is similar to the triangle whose sides measure 3 inches, 3 inches, and 5.25 inches.

EXAMPLE 1 on p. 388 for Ex. 29

29. **STAINED GLASS** Certain sections of stained glass are sold in triangular *beveled* pieces. Which of the three beveled pieces, if any, are similar?

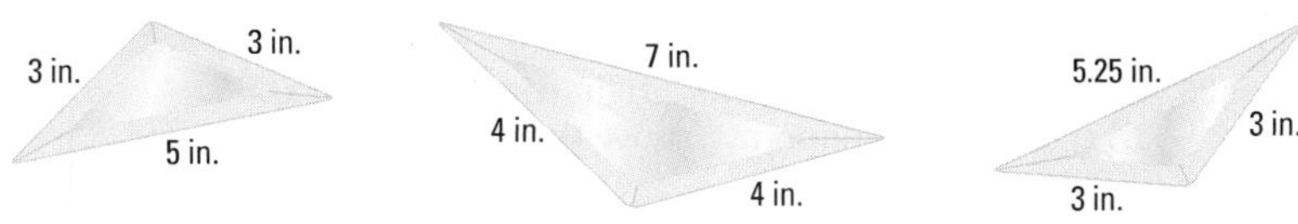

@HomeTutor for problem solving help at classzone.com

Teaching Strategy

Exercises 5, 6, 10–12, 15–17 Ask students to summarize the exercises by writing a paragraph explanation of when two triangles are similar or not similar.

Avoiding Common Errors

Exercises 11, 18–23 Students may have difficulty writing the correct ratio of corresponding lengths for these pairs of triangles. Encourage them to redraw the triangles separately and re-label them.

15.

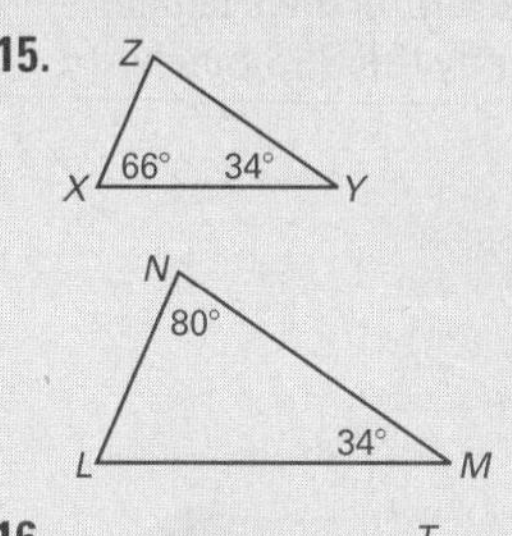

16.

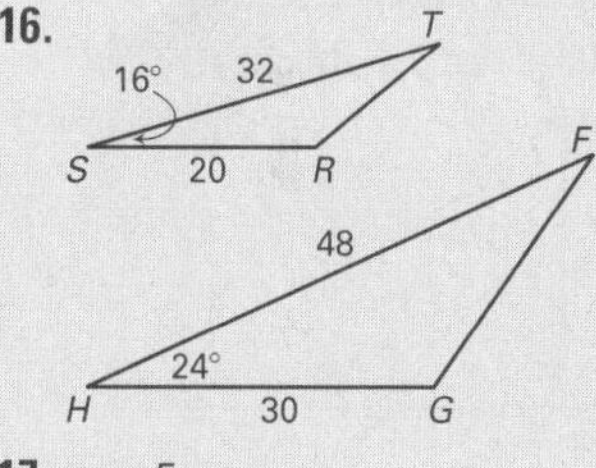

17.

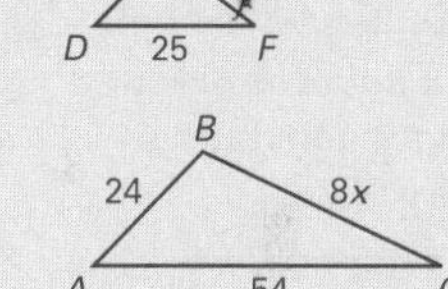

An **Animated Geometry** activity is available on-line for **Exercise 33**. This activity is also available on the **Power Presentations CD-ROM**.

Mathematical Reasoning

Exercise 34 In part (a), the Pythagorean Theorem will help students see that the ratio of the third pair of corresponding side lengths is the same as the other ratios. Therefore, the triangles are similar by the SSS Similarity Theorem.

32.

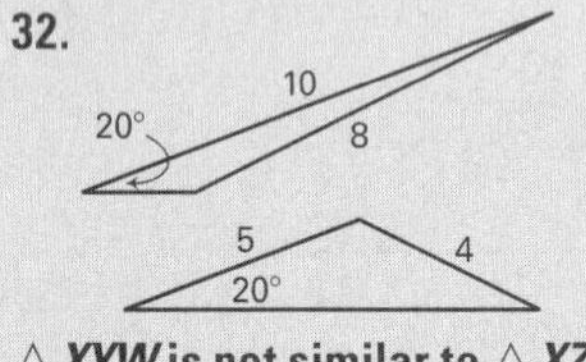

$\triangle XYW$ is not similar to $\triangle XZW$.

34a. 6, 10, 8; 18, 30, 24

36. Yes. *Sample answer:* All pairs of similar triangles have angle pairs whose measures are in proportion (with constant of proportionality 1).

37. *Sample answer:* Locate G on $\overline{AB}$ so that $GB = DE$. Draw $\overline{GH}$ so that $\overline{GH} \parallel \overline{AC}$. This makes $\triangle ABC \sim \triangle GBH$ by the AA Similarity Postulate. From this similarity you have $\frac{AB}{GB} = \frac{AC}{GH}$. This along with what's given you get $\frac{GH}{DF} = \frac{GB}{DE}$ which implies that $\overline{GH} \cong \overline{DF}$, making $\triangle GBH \cong \triangle DEF$. Finally, use the definition of congruent triangles and the AA Similarity Postulate to conclude $\triangle ABC \sim \triangle DEF$.

SHUFFLEBOARD **In the portion of the shuffleboard court shown, $\frac{BC}{AC} = \frac{BD}{AE}$.**

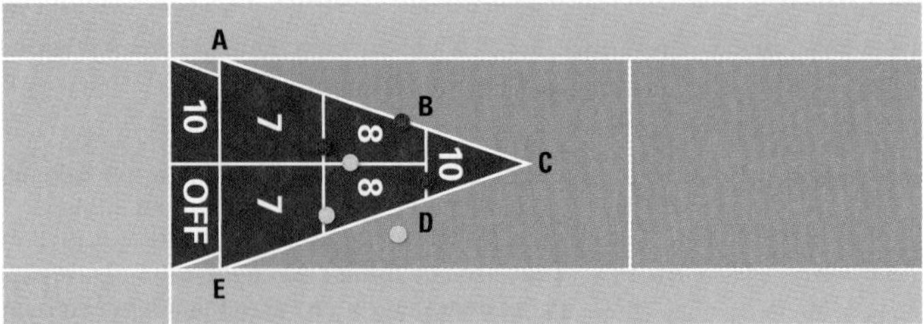

30. $\frac{CD}{CE}$ is the same scale factor as the other ratio.

30. What additional piece of information do you need in order to show that $\triangle BCD \sim \triangle ACE$ using the SSS Similarity Theorem?

31. What additional piece of information do you need in order to show that $\triangle BCD \sim \triangle ACE$ using the SAS Similarity Theorem? **$\angle CBD \cong \angle CAE$**

32. ★ **OPEN-ENDED MATH** Use a diagram to show why there is no Side-Side-Angle Similarity Postulate. **See margin.**

EXAMPLE 4 B on p. 391 for Ex. 33

33. **MULTI-STEP PROBLEM** Ruby is standing in her back yard and she decides to estimate the height of a tree. She stands so that the tip of her shadow coincides with the tip of the tree's shadow, as shown. Ruby is 66 inches tall. The distance from the tree to Ruby is 95 feet and the distance between the tip of the shadows and Ruby is 7 feet.

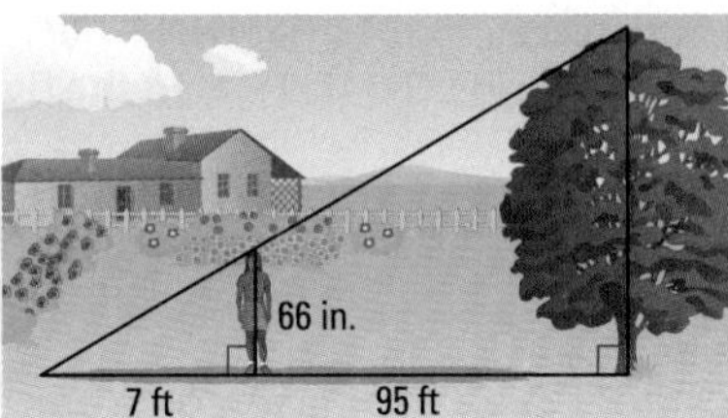

a. What postulate or theorem can you use to show that the triangles in the diagram are similar? **AA Similarity Postulate**

b. About how tall is the tree, to the nearest foot? **80 ft**

c. **What If?** Curtis is 75 inches tall. At a different time of day, he stands so that the tip of his shadow and the tip of the tree's shadow coincide, as described above. His shadow is 6 feet long. How far is Curtis from the tree? **70.8 ft**

Animated Geometry at classzone.com

34. ★ **EXTENDED RESPONSE** Suppose you are given two right triangles with one pair of corresponding legs and the pair of corresponding hypotenuses having the same length ratios.

a. The lengths of the given pair of corresponding legs are 6 and 18, and the lengths of the hypotenuses are 10 and 30. Use the Pythagorean Theorem to solve for the lengths of the other pair of corresponding legs. Draw a diagram. **8, 24; see margin for art.**

b. Write the ratio of the lengths of the second pair of corresponding legs. **$\frac{1}{3}$**

c. Are these triangles similar? Does this suggest a Hypotenuse-Leg Similarity Theorem for right triangles? **yes; yes**

35. *Sample answer:* Given that D and E are midpoints of $\overline{AB}$ and $\overline{BC}$ respectively the Midsegment Theorem guarantees that $\overline{AC} \parallel \overline{DE}$. By the Corresponding Angles Postulate $\angle A \cong \angle BDE$ and so $\angle BDE$ is a right angle. Reasoning similarly $\overline{AB} \parallel \overline{EF}$. By the Alternate Interior Angles Congruence Theorem $\angle BDE \cong \angle DEF$. This makes $\angle DEF$ a right angle that measures 90°.

35. **PROOF** Given that $\triangle ABC$ is a right triangle and D, E, and F are midpoints, prove that $m\angle DEF = 90°$.

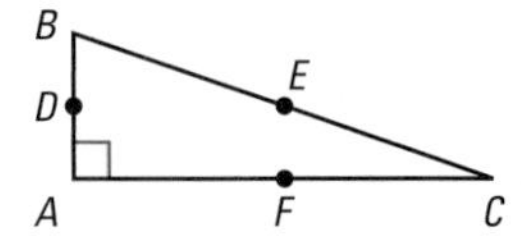

36. ★ **WRITING** Can two triangles have all pairs of corresponding angles in proportion? *Explain.* **See margin.**

○ = WORKED-OUT SOLUTIONS on p. WS1 ★ = STANDARDIZED TEST PRACTICE

37. **PROVING THEOREM 6.3** Write a paragraph proof of the SAS Similarity Theorem. **See margin.**

GIVEN ▶ $\angle A \cong \angle D, \frac{AB}{DE} = \frac{AC}{DF}$

PROVE ▶ $\triangle ABC \sim \triangle DEF$

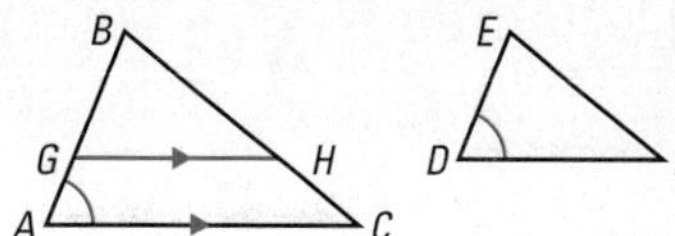

C 38. **CHALLENGE** A portion of a water slide in an amusement park is shown. Find the length of $\overline{EF}$. (*Note:* The posts form right angles with the ground.) **about 15.4 ft**

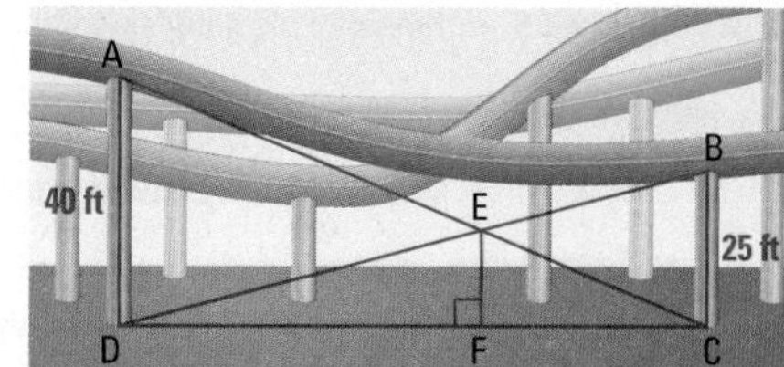

MIXED REVIEW

Find the slope of the line that passes through the given points. *(p. 171)*

39. (0, −8), (4, 16) **6**

40. (−2, −9), (1, −3) **2**

41. (−3, 9), (7, 2) $-\frac{7}{10}$

42. State the postulate or theorem you would use to prove the triangles congruent. Then write a congruence statement. *(p. 249)* **AAS Congruence Theorem; $\triangle QRT \sim \triangle STR$**

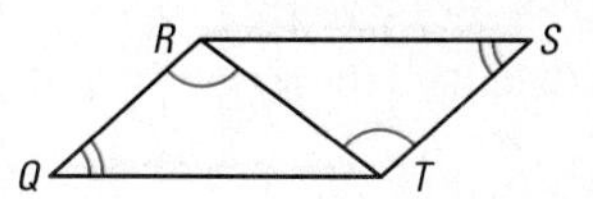

PREVIEW Prepare for Lesson 6.6 in Exs. 43–44.

Find the value of *x*.

43. $\overline{DE}$ is a midsegment of $\triangle ABC$. *(p. 295)* **7.5**

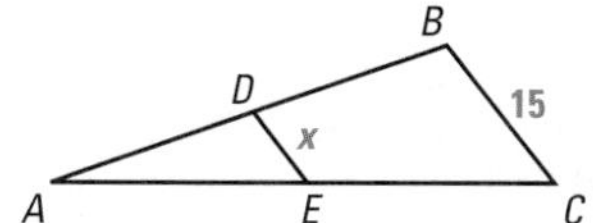

44. $\frac{GK}{GH} = \frac{JK}{FH}$ *(p. 364)* **24**

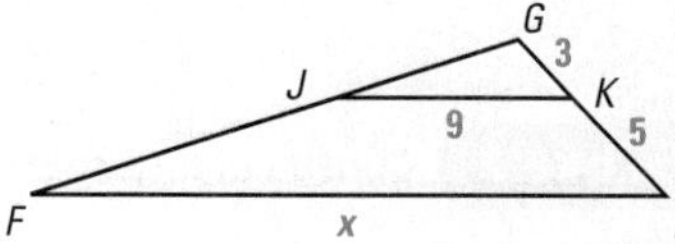

QUIZ *for Lessons 6.3–6.5*

In the diagram, *ABCD* ~ *KLMN*. *(p. 372)*

1. Find the scale factor of *ABCD* to *KLMN*. **5 : 3**
2. Find the values of *x*, *y*, and *z*. **42, 27, 85**
3. Find the perimeter of each polygon. $191\frac{2}{3}$**, 115**

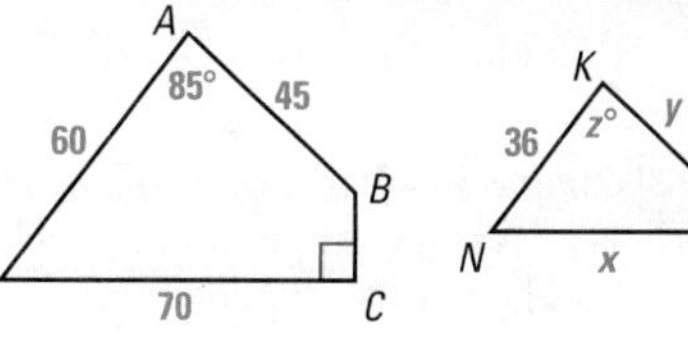

Determine whether the triangles are similar. If they are similar, write a similarity statement. *(pp. 381, 388)*

4. 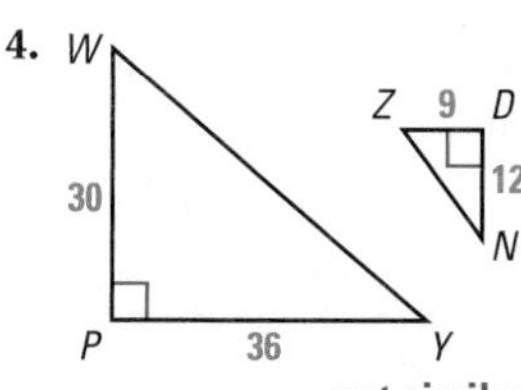

not similar

5. 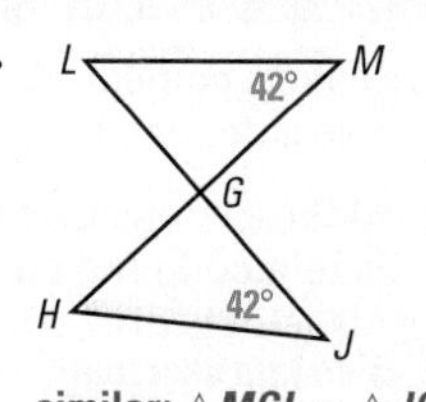

similar; $\triangle ACF \sim \triangle XRS$

6. L, M, 42°, G, H, 42°, J

similar; $\triangle MGL \sim \triangle JGH$

5 ASSESS AND RETEACH

Daily Homework Quiz

Transparency Available

1. Verify that $\triangle ABC \sim \triangle DEF$ for the given information. $\triangle ABC$: $AC = 6$, $AB = 9$, $BC = 12$; $\triangle DEF$: $DF = 2$, $DE = 3$, $EF = 4$
$\frac{AC}{DF} = \frac{AB}{DE} = \frac{BC}{EF} = \frac{3}{1}$. The ratios are equal, so $\triangle ABC \sim \triangle DEF$ by the SSS Similarity Theorem.
2. Show that the triangles are similar and write a similarity statement. Explain your reasoning.

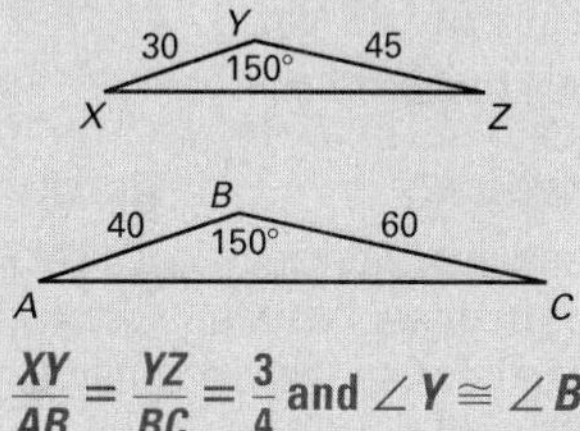

$\frac{XY}{AB} = \frac{YZ}{BC} = \frac{3}{4}$ and $\angle Y \cong \angle B$. So $\triangle XYZ \sim \triangle ABC$ by the SAS Similarity Theorem.

Available at **classzone.com**

Diagnosis/Remediation

- Practice A, B, C in Chapter 6 Resource Book, pp. 60–65
- Study Guide in Chapter 6 Resource Book, pp. 66–67
- Practice Workbook, pp. 115–117
- @HomeTutor

Challenge

Additional challenge is available in the Chapter 6 Resource Book, p. 70.

Quiz

An easily-readable reduced copy of the quiz (with answers) on Lessons 6.3–6.5 from the Assessment Book can be found on p. 354G.

1 PLAN AND PREPARE

Explore the Concept

- Students will compare segment lengths in triangles.
- This activity leads into the study of the proportionality theorems in Lesson 6.6, Examples 1 and 4.

Materials

Each student or group of students will need a graphing calculator or computer.

Recommended Time

Work activity: 15 min

Discuss results: 2 min

Grouping

Students can work individually or in groups of three. If students work in groups, they can share a computer.

2 TEACH

Tips for Success

If students are having difficulty, ask them to draw lines instead of segments and then measure the segment lengths.

Alternative Strategy

You may want to use an overhead graphing calculator or computer to demonstrate this activity. Have a student input the instructions while you discuss the steps with the class.

Key Discovery

If a line is parallel to one side of a triangle and intersects the other two sides, it divides them proportionally. An angle bisector of a triangle divides the opposite side into segments whose lengths are proportional to the lengths of the other two sides.

3 ASSESS AND RETEACH

1. In Exercise 2, which segments would be proportional if $\angle Q$ is bisected instead of $\angle P$? **If $\overrightarrow{QC}$ is the angle bisector, then $\frac{PC}{CR} = \frac{QP}{QR}$.**

Investigating Geometry ACTIVITY *Use before Lesson 6.6*

@HomeTutor
classzone.com
Keystrokes

6.6 Investigate Proportionality

MATERIALS • graphing calculator or computer

Standards
Prepare for 4.0
Students prove basic theorems involving congruence and similarity.

QUESTION **How can you use geometry drawing software to compare segment lengths in triangles?**

EXPLORE 1 **Construct a line parallel to a triangle's third side**

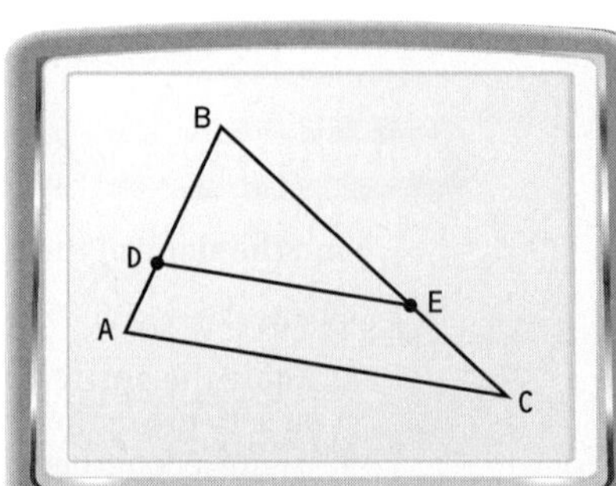

STEP 1 ***Draw a triangle*** Draw a triangle. Label the vertices *A*, *B*, and *C*. Draw a point on $\overline{AB}$. Label the point *D*.

STEP 2 ***Draw a parallel line*** Draw a line through *D* that is parallel to $\overline{AC}$. Label the intersection of the line and $\overline{BC}$ as point *E*.

STEP 3 ***Measure segments*** Measure $\overline{BD}$, $\overline{DA}$, $\overline{BE}$, and $\overline{EC}$. Calculate the ratios $\frac{BD}{DA}$ and $\frac{BE}{EC}$.

STEP 4 ***Compare ratios*** Move one or more of the triangle's vertices to change its shape. *Compare* the ratios from Step 3 as the shape changes. Save as "EXPLORE1."

EXPLORE 2 **Construct an angle bisector of a triangle**

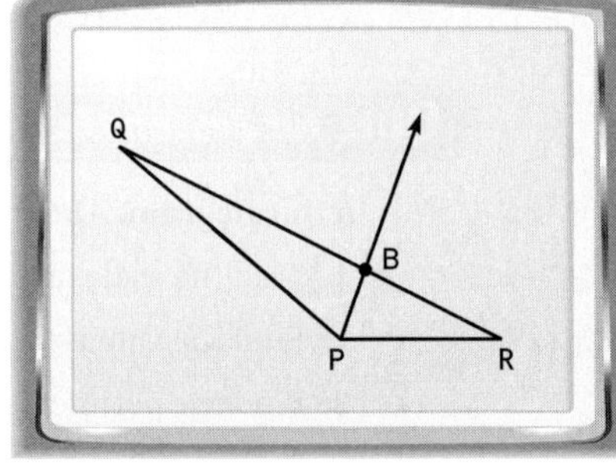

STEP 1 ***Draw a triangle*** Draw a triangle. Label the vertices *P*, *Q*, and *R*. Draw the angle bisector of $\angle QPR$. Label the intersection of the angle bisector and $\overline{QR}$ as point *B*.

STEP 2 ***Measure segments*** Measure $\overline{BR}$, $\overline{RP}$, $\overline{BQ}$, and $\overline{QP}$. Calculate the ratios $\frac{BR}{BQ}$ and $\frac{RP}{QP}$.

STEP 3 ***Compare ratios*** Move one or more of the triangle's vertices to change its shape. *Compare* the ratios from Step 3. Save as "EXPLORE2."

DRAW CONCLUSIONS **Use your observations to complete these exercises**

1. Make a conjecture about the ratios of the lengths of the segments formed when two sides of a triangle are cut by a line parallel to the triangle's third side. **The ratio of the segment lengths of the triangle sides is equal.**
2. Make a conjecture about how the ratio of the lengths of two sides of a triangle is related to the ratio of the lengths of the segments formed when an angle bisector is drawn to the third side. **An angle bisector of a triangle divides the opposite side into segments whose lengths are proportional to the lengths of the other two sides.**

6.6 Use Proportionality Theorems

Before You used proportions with similar triangles.
Now You will use proportions with a triangle or parallel lines.
Why? So you can use perspective drawings, as in Ex. 28.

Key Vocabulary
- **corresponding angles,** *p. 147*
- **ratio,** *p. 356*
- **proportion,** *p. 358*

Standards

4.0 Students prove basic theorems involving congruence and **similarity.**

7.0 Students prove and use theorems involving the properties of parallel lines cut by a transversal, the properties of quadrilaterals, and the properties of circles.

The Midsegment Theorem, which you learned on page 295, is a special case of the Triangle Proportionality Theorem and its converse.

THEOREMS — *For Your Notebook*

THEOREM 6.4 Triangle Proportionality Theorem

If a line parallel to one side of a triangle intersects the other two sides, then it divides the two sides proportionally.

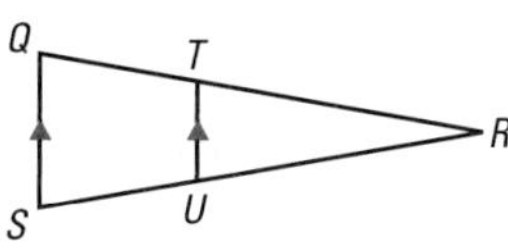

Proof: Ex. 22, p. 402

If $\overline{TU} \parallel \overline{QS}$, then $\frac{RT}{TQ} = \frac{RU}{US}$.

THEOREM 6.5 Converse of the Triangle Proportionality Theorem

If a line divides two sides of a triangle proportionally, then it is parallel to the third side.

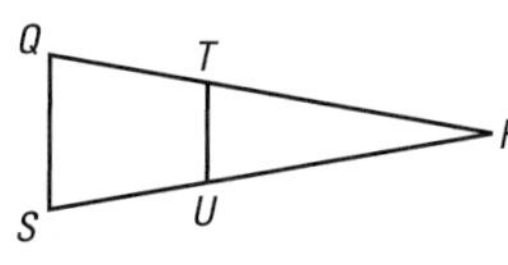

Proof: Ex. 26, p. 402

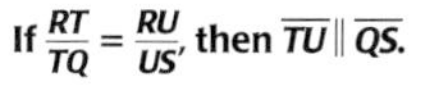

If $\frac{RT}{TQ} = \frac{RU}{US}$, then $\overline{TU} \parallel \overline{QS}$.

EXAMPLE 1 Find the length of a segment

In the diagram, $\overline{QS} \parallel \overline{UT}$, $RS = 4$, $ST = 6$, and $QU = 9$. What is the length of $\overline{RQ}$?

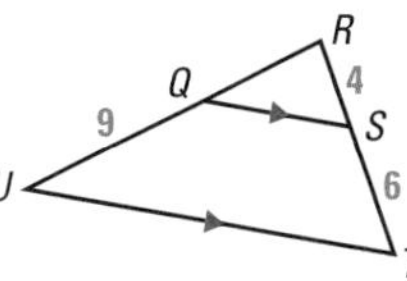

Solution

$\frac{RQ}{QU} = \frac{RS}{ST}$ — Triangle Proportionality Theorem

$\frac{RQ}{9} = \frac{4}{6}$ — Substitute.

$RQ = 6$ — Multiply each side by 9 and simplify.

1 PLAN AND PREPARE

Warm-Up Exercises

Transparency Available

1. Give the postulate or theorem that justifies why the triangles are similar.

80°
80°

AA Similarity Postulate

2. Solve $\frac{16}{32} = \frac{12 - x}{x}$. **8**

Notetaking Guide

Transparency Available

Promotes interactive learning and notetaking skills, pp. 160–163.

Pacing

Basic: 2 days
Average: 2 days
Advanced: 2 days
Block: 1 block
- See *Teaching Guide/Lesson Plan.*

2 FOCUS AND MOTIVATE

Essential Question

Big Idea 1, p. 355

What proportion can you write if a line is parallel to one side of a triangle? **Tell students they will learn how to answer this question by using a generalization of the Midsegment Theorem.**

Resource Planning Guide

Chapter Resource Book
- Teaching Guide/Lesson Plan (pp. 71–72)
- Practice levels A, B, C (pp. 74–79)
- Study Guide (pp. 80–81)
- Catch-up for Absent Students (p. 82)
- Problem Solving Workshop (p. 83)
- Challenge (p. 84)

Workbooks
- Notetaking Guide (pp. 160–163)
- Practice Workbook (pp. 118–120)

Teaching Options
- **Power Presentations CD-ROM** provides dynamic electronic teaching resources for the classroom.
- **Activity Generator CD-ROM** provides editable activities for all ability levels.

Interactive Technology
- Easy Planner
- Power Presentations CD-ROM
- Activity Generator CD-ROM
- Animated Algebra
- Test Generator CD-ROM
- Online Quiz
- eWorkbook
- eEdition
- @HomeTutor

Resources for English Learners
- Quick Reference for English Learners
- Spanish Study Guide
- Multi-Language Visual Glossary
- Student Resources in Spanish

See also the *Geometry Toolkit* for more strategies for meeting individual needs.

Motivating the Lesson

Show students this diagram of a wheelchair ramp.

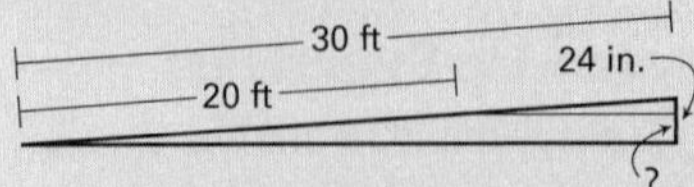

Ask them what vertical distance corresponds with going up 20 feet on the ramp. Discuss with them that $\frac{2}{3}$ of the ramp distance corresponds with $\frac{2}{3}$ of the vertical height. Tell students that in this lesson they will investigate other properties related to a line parallel to one side of a triangle.

3 TEACH

Extra Example 1

In the diagram, $\overline{RS} \parallel \overline{PN}$, $MS = 15$, $SN = 20$, and $RP = 12$. What is the length of $\overline{MR}$? **9**

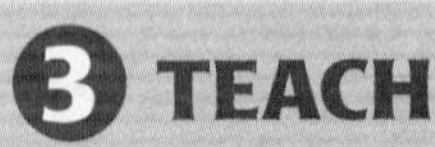

Extra Example 2

A brace is added to a tree house as shown. Explain why the brace is not parallel to the floor.

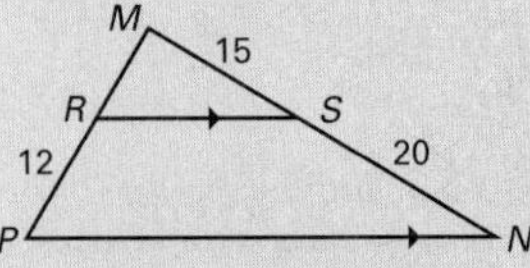

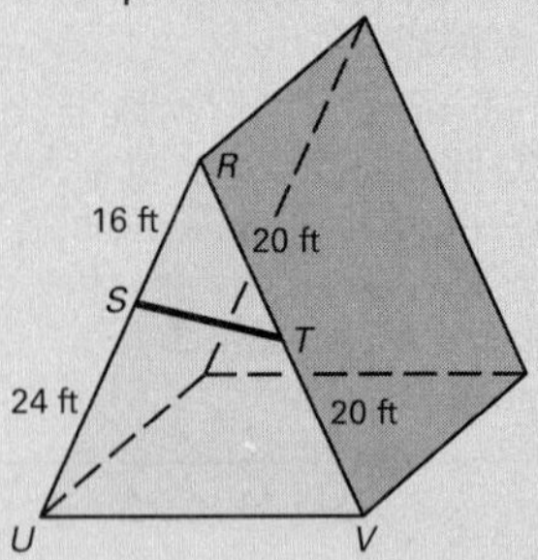

$\frac{RS}{SU} \neq \frac{RT}{TV}$ so $\overline{ST}$ is not parallel to $\overline{UV}$ and the brace is not parallel to the floor.

REASONING Theorems 6.4 and 6.5 also tell you that if the lines are *not* parallel, then the proportion is *not* true, and vice-versa.

So if $\overline{TU} \nparallel \overline{QS}$, then $\frac{RT}{TQ} \neq \frac{RU}{US}$. Also, if $\frac{RT}{TQ} \neq \frac{RU}{US}$, then $\overline{TU} \nparallel \overline{QS}$.

EXAMPLE 2 Solve a real-world problem

SHOERACK On the shoerack shown, $AB = 33$ cm, $BC = 27$ cm, $CD = 44$ cm, and $DE = 25$ cm. *Explain* why the gray shelf is not parallel to the floor.

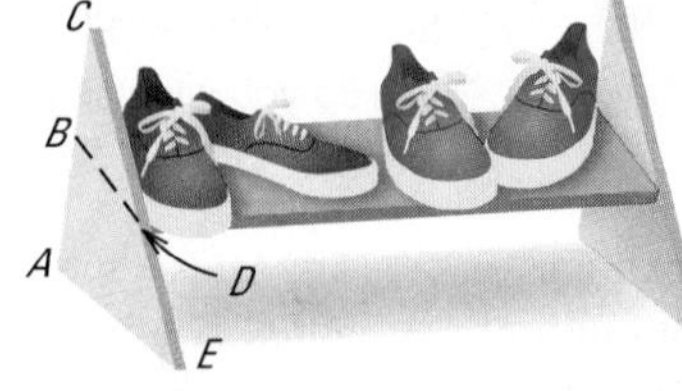

Solution

Find and simplify the ratios of lengths determined by the shoerack.

$\frac{CD}{DE} = \frac{44}{25}$ $\frac{CB}{BA} = \frac{27}{33} = \frac{9}{11}$

▶ Because $\frac{44}{25} \neq \frac{9}{11}$, $\overline{BD}$ is not parallel to $\overline{AE}$. So, the shelf is not parallel to the floor.

✓ GUIDED PRACTICE for Examples 1 and 2

1. Find the length of $\overline{YZ}$. **$\frac{315}{11}$**

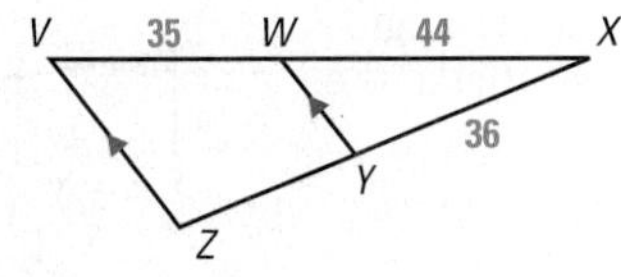

2. Determine whether $\overline{PS} \parallel \overline{QR}$. **parallel**

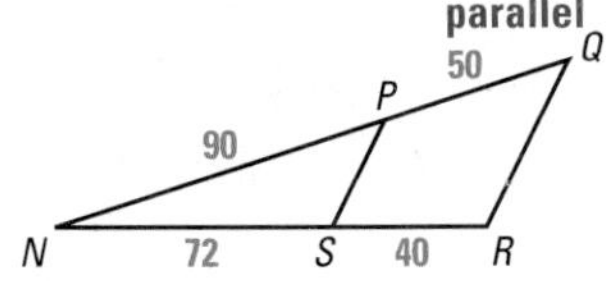

THEOREMS *For Your Notebook*

THEOREM 6.6

If three parallel lines intersect two transversals, then they divide the transversals proportionally.

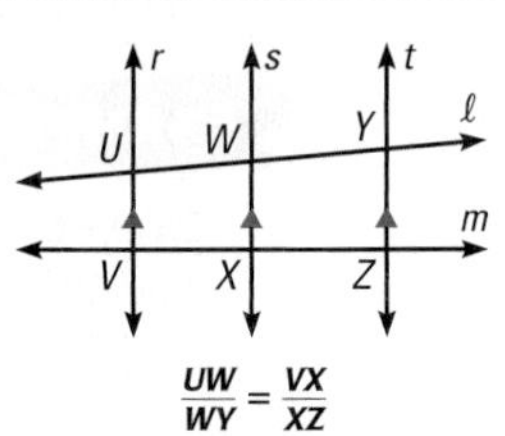

$\frac{UW}{WY} = \frac{VX}{XZ}$

Proof: Ex. 23, p. 402

THEOREM 6.7

If a ray bisects an angle of a triangle, then it divides the opposite side into segments whose lengths are proportional to the lengths of the other two sides.

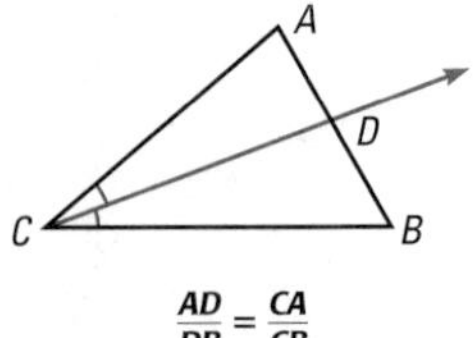

$\frac{AD}{DB} = \frac{CA}{CB}$

Proof: Ex. 27, p. 403

Differentiated Instruction

Auditory Learners Have students complete **Guided Practice Exercises 1 and 2** with a partner. Instruct them to talk about the problem as they work through it. They should work together to describe the steps they are taking to solve the problem as if they were describing a proof.

See also the *Geometry Toolkit* for more strategies.

EXAMPLE 3 Use Theorem 6.6

CITY TRAVEL In the diagram, $\angle 1$, $\angle 2$, and $\angle 3$ are all congruent and $GF = 120$ yards, $DE = 150$ yards, and $CD = 300$ yards. Find the distance HF between Main Street and South Main Street.

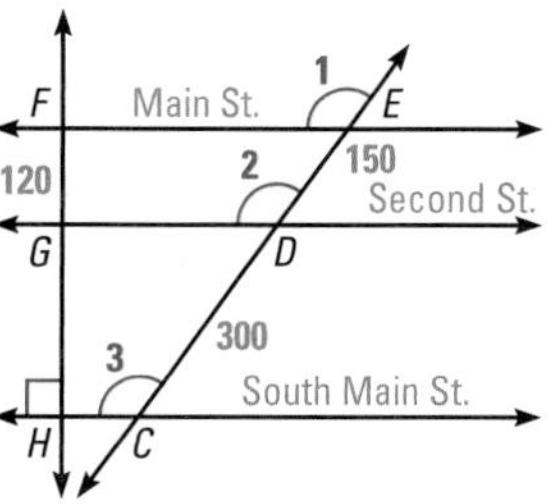

ANOTHER WAY
For alternative methods for solving the problem in Example 3, turn to page 404 for the **Problem Solving Workshop**.

Solution

Corresponding angles are congruent, so $\overleftrightarrow{FE}$, $\overleftrightarrow{GD}$, and $\overleftrightarrow{HC}$ are parallel. Use Theorem 6.6.

$\frac{HG}{GF} = \frac{CD}{DE}$ **Parallel lines divide transversals proportionally.**

$\frac{HG + GF}{GF} = \frac{CD + DE}{DE}$ **Property of proportions (Property 4)**

$\frac{HF}{120} = \frac{300 + 150}{150}$ **Substitute.**

$\frac{HF}{120} = \frac{450}{150}$ **Simplify.**

$HF = 360$ **Multiply each side by 120 and simplify.**

▶ The distance between Main Street and South Main Street is 360 yards.

EXAMPLE 4 Use Theorem 6.7

In the diagram, $\angle QPR \cong \angle RPS$. Use the given side lengths to find the length of $\overline{RS}$.

Solution

Because $\overrightarrow{PR}$ is an angle bisector of $\angle QPS$, you can apply Theorem 6.7. Let $RS = x$. Then $RQ = 15 - x$.

$\frac{RQ}{RS} = \frac{PQ}{PS}$ **Angle bisector divides opposite side proportionally.**

$\frac{15 - x}{x} = \frac{7}{13}$ **Substitute.**

$7x = 195 - 13x$ **Cross Products Property**

$x = 9.75$ **Solve for x.**

GUIDED PRACTICE for Examples 3 and 4

Find the length of $\overline{AB}$.

3.

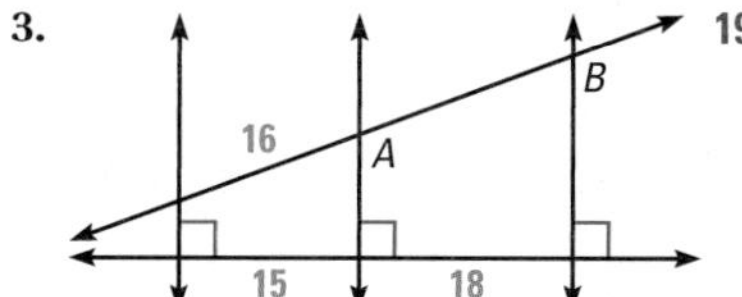

4. C, 4, D, 4, $4\sqrt{2}$, A, B, $4\sqrt{2}$

Extra Example 3

Using the information in the diagram, find the distance between First Street and Main Street.

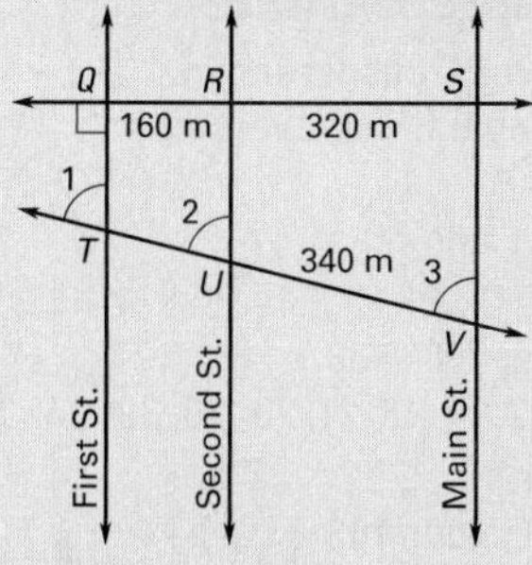

510 m

Key Question to Ask for Example 3

- Why is it important that $\angle 1 \cong \angle 2 \cong \angle 3$? **The streets need to be parallel to apply Theorem 6.6.**

Extra Example 4

In the diagram, $\angle ABD \cong \angle CBD$. Use the given side lengths to find the length of $\overline{DC}$.

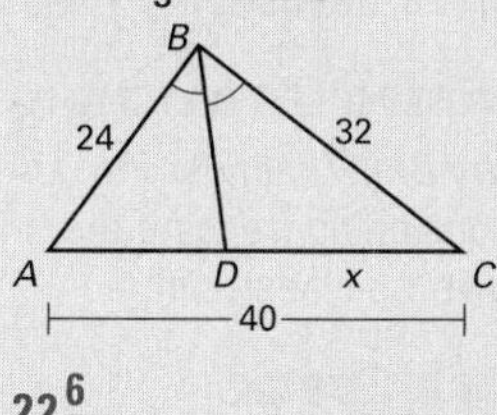

$22\frac{6}{7}$

Closing the Lesson

Have students summarize the major points of the lesson and answer the Essential Question: What proportion can you write if a line is parallel to one side of a triangle?

- **A line parallel to one side of a triangle intersecting the other sides divides those sides proportionally, and vice versa.**
- **Three parallel lines intersecting two transversals divide the transversals proportionally.**
- **An angle bisector of a triangle divides the opposite sides into segments whose lengths are proportional to the lengths of the other sides.**

In $\triangle ABC$, with D on $\overline{AB}$ and E on $\overline{AC}$, if $\overline{DE} \parallel \overline{BC}$ then $\frac{AD}{DB} = \frac{AE}{EC}$.

Differentiated Instruction

Below Level To help students remember how to write the proportion for Theorem 6.7, ask them to label $\overline{CA}$ as Side 1, $\overline{AD}$ as Part 1, $\overline{CB}$ as Side 2, and $\overline{DB}$ as Part 2. They should notice that Side 1 is adjacent to Part 1, and Side 2 is adjacent to Part 2. Then the correct proportion is $\frac{\text{Side 1}}{\text{Side 2}} = \frac{\text{Part 1}}{\text{Part 2}}$.

See also the *Geometry Toolkit* for more strategies.

6.6 EXERCISES

HOMEWORK KEY ○ = **WORKED-OUT SOLUTIONS** on p. WS8 for Exs. 5, 9, and 21
★ = **STANDARDIZED TEST PRACTICE** Exs. 2, 8, 13, 25, and 28

4 PRACTICE AND APPLY

Assignment Guide

Answer Transparencies available for all exercises

Basic:
Day 1: pp. 400–403
Exs. 1–7, 13, 16, 22, 34–36
Day 2: pp. 400–403
Exs. 8–12, 14, 15, 21, 23–26, 30–33

Average:
Day 1: pp. 400–403
Exs. 1–7, 13, 16, 22, 30–36
Day 2: pp. 400–403
Exs. 8–12, 14, 15, 17–19, 21, 23–28

Advanced:
Day 1: pp. 400–403
Exs. 1–7, 13, 16, 22, 30–36
Day 2: pp. 400–403
Exs. 8, 10, 11, 14, 15, 17–21*, 23–29*

Block:
pp. 400–403
Exs. 1–19, 21–28, 30–36

Differentiated Instruction

See *Geometry Best Practices Toolkit* for suggestions on addressing the needs of a diverse classroom.

Homework Check

For a quick check of student understanding of key concepts, go over the following exercises:

Basic: 3, 6, 8, 10, 22
Average: 4, 7, 8, 10, 23
Advanced: 7, 11, 16, 24, 25

Extra Practice

- Student Edition, p. 907
- Chapter 6 Resource Book: Practice levels A, B, C, pp. 74–79

Practice Worksheet

An easily-readable reduced practice page (with answers) for this lesson can be found on p. 354C.

SKILL PRACTICE

A

1. **VOCABULARY** State the Triangle Proportionality Theorem. Draw a diagram. **See margin.**

2. ★ **WRITING** *Compare* the Midsegment Theorem (see page 295) and the Triangle Proportionality Theorem. How are they related? **See margin.**

EXAMPLE 1 on p. 397 for Exs. 3–4

FINDING THE LENGTH OF A SEGMENT Find the length of $\overline{AB}$.

3. 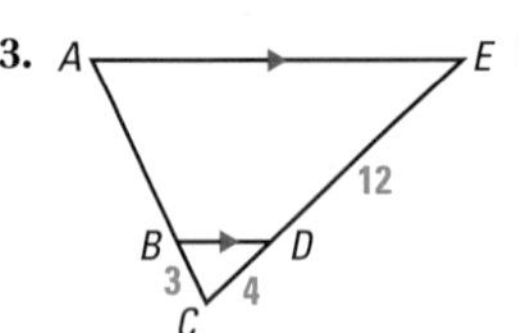

9

4. 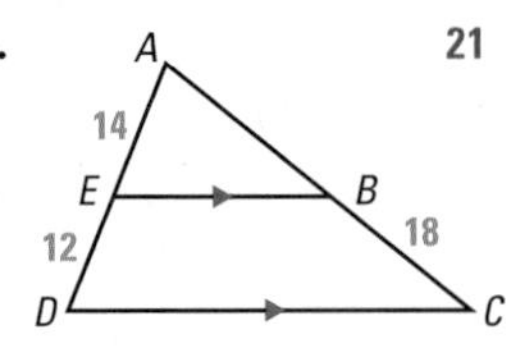

21

EXAMPLE 2 on p. 398 for Exs. 5–7

REASONING Use the given information to determine whether $\overline{KM} \parallel \overline{JN}$. *Explain* your reasoning. **5–7. See margin.**

5. 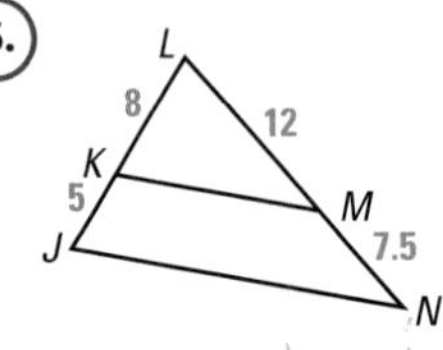

6. 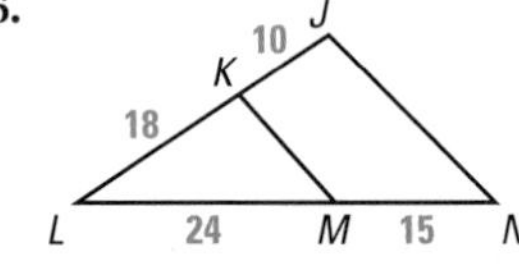

7. 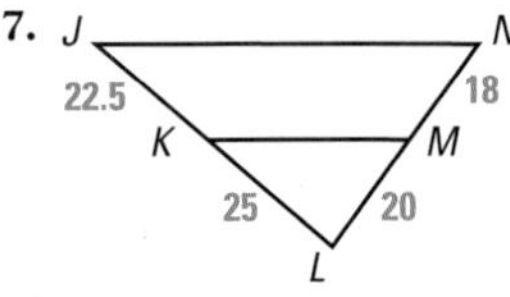

EXAMPLE 3 on p. 399 for Ex. 8

8. ★ **MULTIPLE CHOICE** For the figure at the right, which statement is *not* necessarily true? **C**

Ⓐ $\frac{PQ}{QR} = \frac{UT}{TS}$ Ⓑ $\frac{TS}{UT} = \frac{QR}{PQ}$

Ⓒ $\frac{QR}{RS} = \frac{TS}{RS}$ Ⓓ $\frac{PQ}{PR} = \frac{UT}{US}$

EXAMPLE 4 on p. 399 for Exs. 9–12

ALGEBRA Find the value of the variable.

9. 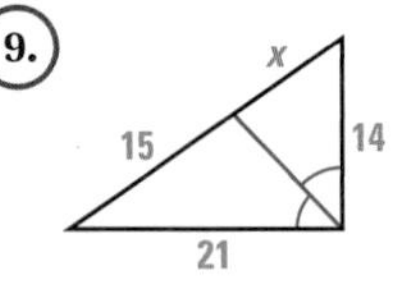

10

10. 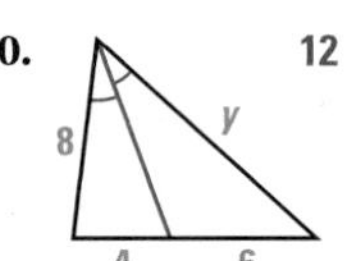

12

11. 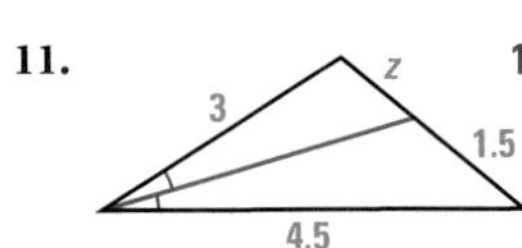

1

12. **ERROR ANALYSIS** A student begins to solve for the length of $\overline{AD}$ as shown. *Describe* and correct the student's error.
The length of $\overline{CD}$ is not 20; $\frac{10}{16} = \frac{20-x}{x}$.

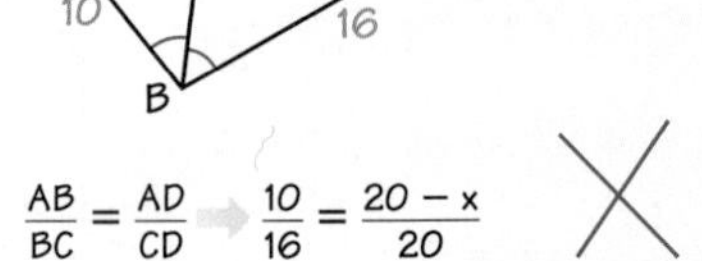

$\frac{AB}{BC} = \frac{AD}{CD} \Rightarrow \frac{10}{16} = \frac{20-x}{20}$

1. If a line parallel to one side of a triangle intersects the other two sides, then it divides the two sides proportionally.

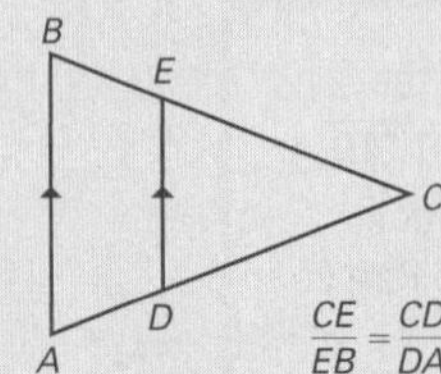

2. In the Midsegment Theorem, the segment connecting the midpoints of two sides of a triangle is parallel to the third side, which is a special case of the Converse of the Triangle Proportionality Theorem.

B 13. ★ **MULTIPLE CHOICE** Find the value of x. **C**

Ⓐ $\frac{1}{2}$ Ⓑ 1

Ⓒ 2 Ⓓ 3

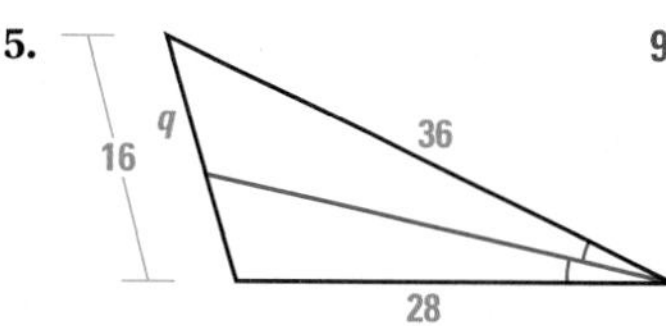

ALGEBRA Find the value of the variable.

14. **27**

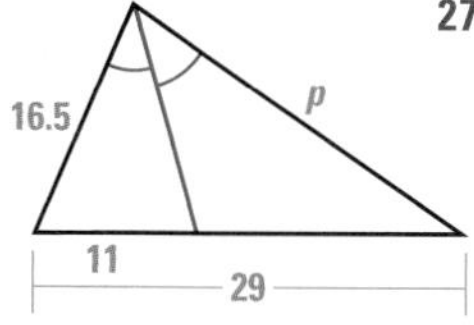

15. **9**

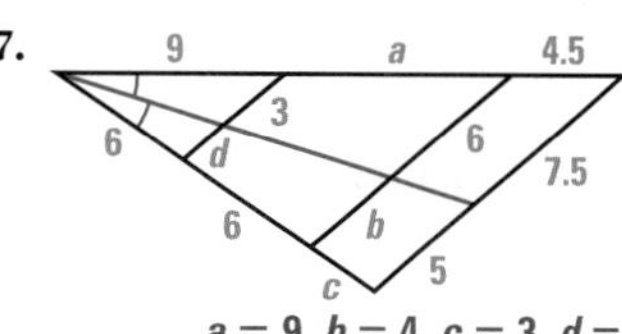

FINDING SEGMENT LENGTHS Use the diagram to find the value of each variable.

16.

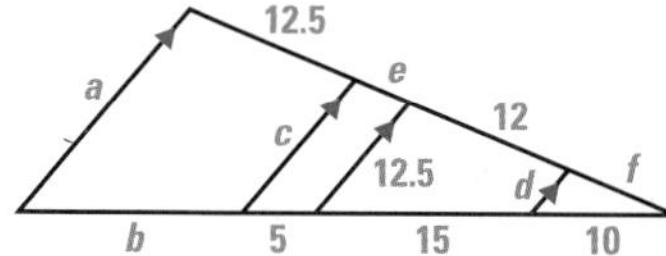

$a = 22.8125, b = 15.625, c = 15, d = 5, e = 4, f = 8$

17.

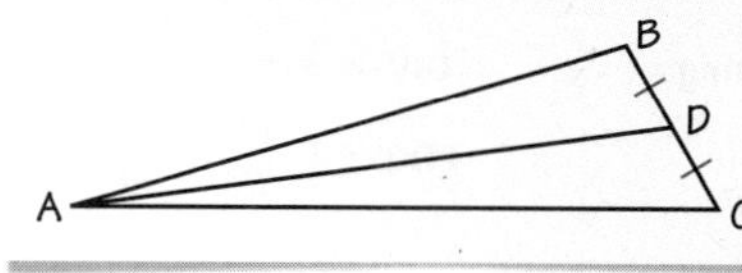

$a = 9, b = 4, c = 3, d = 2$

18. **ERROR ANALYSIS** A student claims that $AB = AC$ using the method shown. *Describe* and correct the student's error.
$\overline{AD}$ must bisect $\angle A$ to use Theorem 6.7.

By Theorem 6.7, $\frac{BD}{CD} = \frac{AB}{AC}$. Because $BD = CD$, it follows that $AB = AC$.

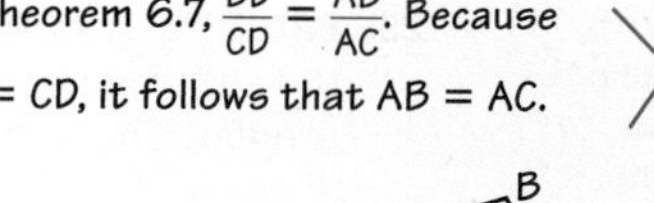

19. **CONSTRUCTION** Follow the instructions for constructing a line segment that is divided into four equal parts.

a. Draw a line segment that is about 3 inches long, and label its endpoints A and B. Choose any point C not on $\overline{AB}$. Draw $\overrightarrow{AC}$.
a, b. See figure in part (c).

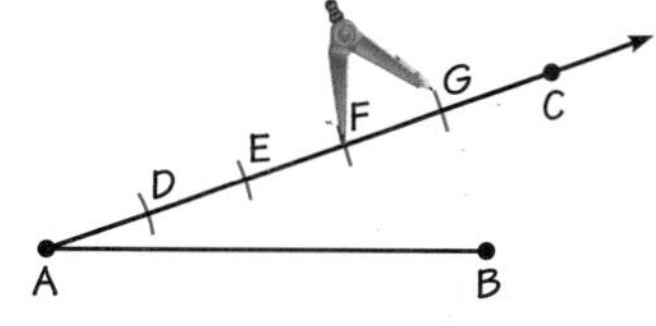

b. Using any length, place the compass point at A and make an arc intersecting $\overrightarrow{AC}$ at D. Using the same compass setting, make additional arcs on $\overrightarrow{AC}$. Label the points E, F, and G so that $AD = DE = EF = FG$.

c. Draw $\overline{GB}$. Construct a line parallel to $\overline{GB}$ through D. Continue constructing parallel lines and label the points as shown. *Explain* why $AJ = JK = KL = LB$.

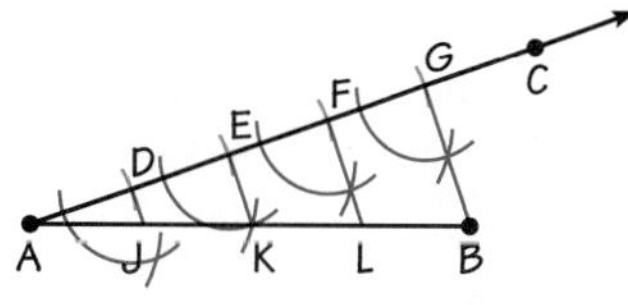

19c. See margin for art; Theorem 6.6 guarantees that parallel lines divide transversals proportionally. Since $\frac{AD}{DE} = \frac{DE}{EF} = \frac{EF}{FG} = 1$ implies $\frac{AJ}{JK} = \frac{JK}{KL} = \frac{KL}{LB} = 1$ which means $AJ = JK = KL = LB$.

C **20.** **CHALLENGE** Given segments with lengths r, s, and t, construct a segment of length x, such that $\frac{r}{s} = \frac{t}{x}$. **See margin.**

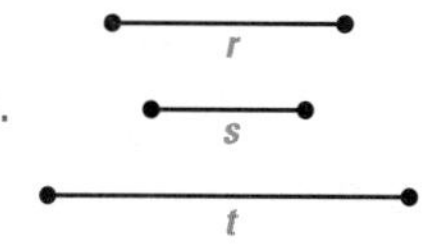

Vocabulary

Exercise 19 Students may need to review how to identify corresponding angles and that if corresponding angles are congruent, then the lines are parallel.

20.

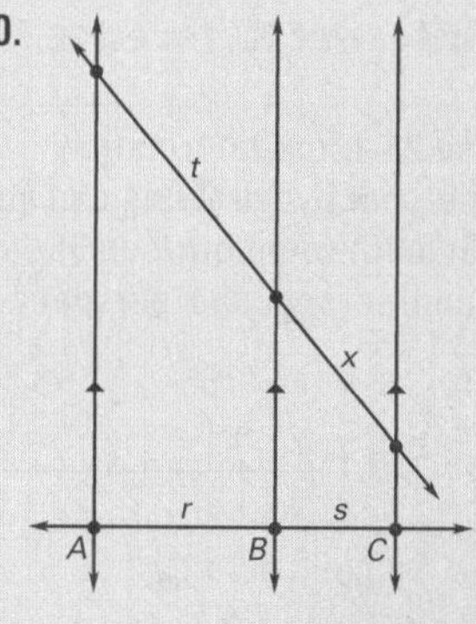

5. Parallel; $\frac{8}{5} = \frac{12}{7.5}$, so the Converse of the Triangle Proportionality Theorem applies.

6. not parallel; $\frac{24}{15} \neq \frac{18}{10}$

7. Parallel; $\frac{20}{18} = \frac{25}{22.5}$, so the Converse of the Triangle Proportionality Theorem applies.

19c.

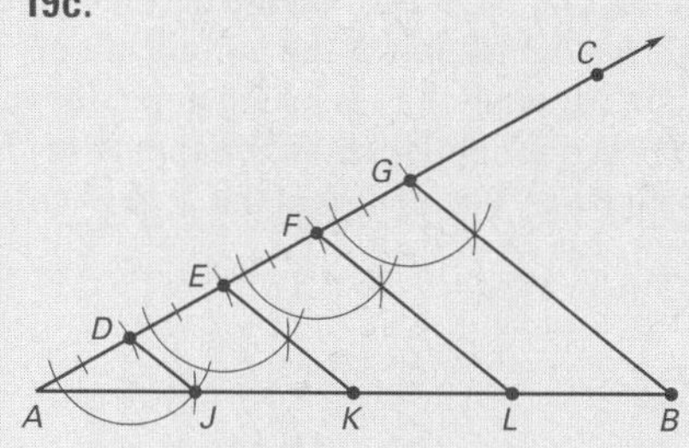

Teaching Strategy

Exercises 23, 27 Point out that an auxiliary line added to the diagram allows you to identify and use the proportionality theorems for triangles and parallel lines.

Internet Reference

Exercise 28 More information about perspective drawing can be found at mathforum.org/sum95/math_and/perspective/perspect.html

23. Draw $\overleftrightarrow{AD}$. (Through any two points, there is exactly one line.) Let G be the point of intersection of $\overleftrightarrow{AD}$ and $\overleftrightarrow{BE}$. Since $k_1 \parallel k_2$ and $k_2 \parallel k_3$, by the Triangle Proportionality Theorem $\frac{CB}{BA} = \frac{DG}{GA}$ and $\frac{DG}{GA} = \frac{DE}{EF}$. Using the Transitive Property of Equality, $\frac{CB}{BA} = \frac{DE}{EF}$.

25.

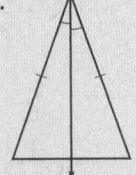

26. *Sample answer:* Begin by showing $\frac{RT + TQ}{TQ} = \frac{RU + US}{US}$ and simplifying this to $\frac{RQ}{TQ} = \frac{RS}{US}$. Use the proportions to solve for $\frac{TQ}{US}$ and use the Transitive Property of Equality. Show $\triangle RTU \sim \triangle RQS$ using the SAS Similarity Theorem and show $\angle RTU \cong \angle RQS$ by definition of similar triangles. Then use the Corresponding Angles Converse to show $\overline{QS} \parallel \overline{TU}$.

22. Since $\overline{QS} \parallel \overline{TU}$ $\angle S \cong \angle TUR$ and $\angle Q \cong \angle UTR$ using the Corresponding Angles Postulate. $\triangle SRQ \sim \triangle URT$ using the AA Similarity Postulate. $\frac{QR}{TR} = \frac{SR}{UR}$ using the definition of similarity. $QR = QT + TR$ and $SR = SU + UR$ by the Segment Addition Postulate. Substituting you get $\frac{QT + TR}{TR} = \frac{SU + UR}{UR}$ which simplifies to $\frac{QT}{TR} = \frac{SU}{UR}$.

24a. Lot A = 50.9 yd, Lot B = 58.4 yd, Lot C = 64.7 yd

25. See margin for art; in an isosceles triangle, the legs are congruent, so the ratio of their lengths is 1 : 1. By Theorem 6.7, this ratio is equal to the ratio of the lengths of the segments created by the ray, so it is also 1 : 1.

PROBLEM SOLVING

A

(21.) **CITY MAP** On the map below, Idaho Avenue bisects the angle between University Avenue and Walter Street. To the nearest yard, what is the distance along University Avenue from 12th Street to Washington Street? **350 yd**

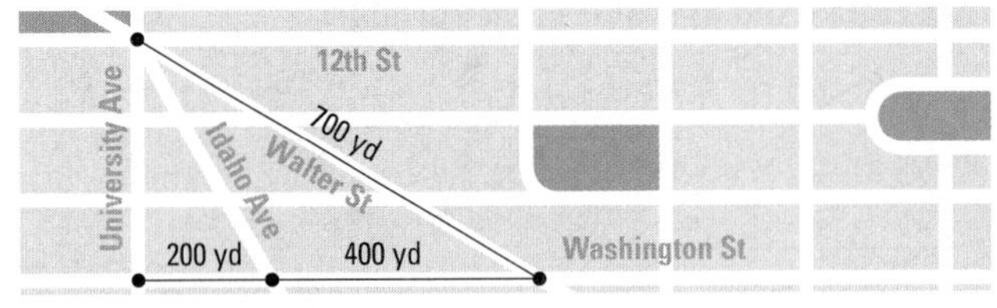

@HomeTutor for problem solving help at classzone.com

22. PROVING THEOREM 6.4 Prove the Triangle Proportionality Theorem.

GIVEN ▶ $\overline{QS} \parallel \overline{TU}$

PROVE ▶ $\frac{QT}{TR} = \frac{SU}{UR}$

@HomeTutor for problem solving help at classzone.com

23. PROVING THEOREM 6.6 Use the diagram with the auxiliary line drawn to write a paragraph proof of Theorem 6.6. **See margin.**

GIVEN ▶ $k_1 \parallel k_2$, $k_2 \parallel k_3$

PROVE ▶ $\frac{CB}{BA} = \frac{DE}{EF}$

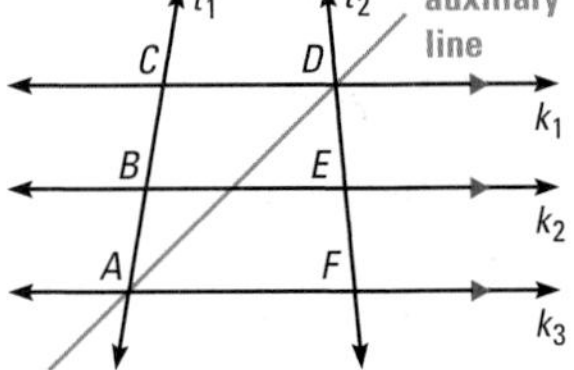

24. MULTI-STEP PROBLEM The real estate term *lake frontage* refers to the distance along the edge of a piece of property that touches a lake.

a. Find the lake frontage (to the nearest tenth of a yard) for each lot shown.

b. In general, the more lake frontage a lot has, the higher its selling price. Which of the lots should be listed for the highest price? **Lot C**

c. Suppose that lot prices are in the same ratio as lake frontages. If the least expensive lot is \$100,000, what are the prices of the other lots? *Explain* your reasoning.
About \$114,735; about \$127,112. *Sample answer:* Solve the ratio $\frac{50.9}{58.4} = \frac{100{,}000}{x}$ and $\frac{50.9}{64.7} = \frac{100{,}000}{x}$.

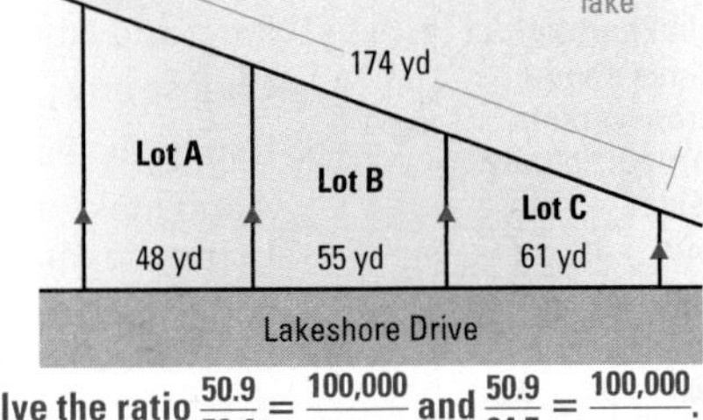

B

25. ★ SHORT RESPONSE Sketch an isosceles triangle. Draw a ray that bisects the angle opposite the base. This ray divides the base into two segments. By Theorem 6.7, the ratio of the legs is proportional to the ratio of these two segments. *Explain* why this ratio is 1 : 1 for an isosceles triangle.

26. PLAN FOR PROOF Use the diagram given for the proof of Theorem 6.4 in Exercise 22 to write a plan for proving Theorem 6.5, the Triangle Proportionality Converse. **See margin.**

○ = WORKED-OUT SOLUTIONS on p. WS1

★ = STANDARDIZED TEST PRACTICE

28b. *Sample answer:* The line connecting the top left to the bottom left of Car 1 is parallel to the line connecting the top left to the bottom left of Car 2; the triangle with vertices consisting of the vanishing point, the top left of Car 1, and the bottom left of Car 1 is similar to the triangle with vertices consisting of the vanishing point, the top left of Car 2, and the bottom left of Car 2.

7. Since $\overline{XW} \parallel \overline{AZ}$, $\angle XZA \cong \angle WXZ$ using the Alternate Interior Angles Congruence Theorem. This makes $\triangle AXZ$ isosceles because it is shown that $\angle A \cong \angle WXZ$ and by the Converse of the Base Angles Theorem, $AX = XZ$. Since $\overline{XW} \parallel \overline{AZ}$ using the Triangle Proportionality Theorem you get $\frac{YW}{WZ} = \frac{XY}{AX}$. Substituting you get $\frac{YW}{WZ} = \frac{XY}{XZ}$.

27. **PROVING THEOREM 6.7** Use the diagram with the auxiliary lines drawn to write a paragraph proof of Theorem 6.7.

GIVEN ▶ $\angle YXW \cong \angle WXZ$

PROVE ▶ $\frac{YW}{WZ} = \frac{XY}{XZ}$

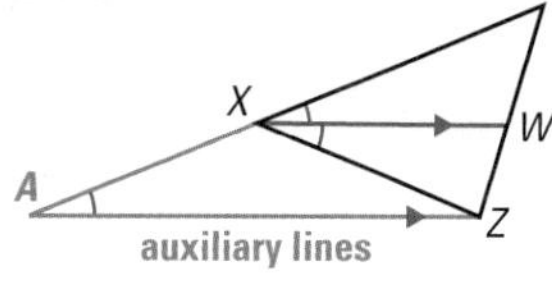

28. ★ **EXTENDED RESPONSE** In *perspective drawing,* lines that are parallel in real life must meet at a vanishing point on the horizon. To make the train cars in the drawing appear equal in length, they are drawn so that the lines connecting the opposite corners of each car are parallel.

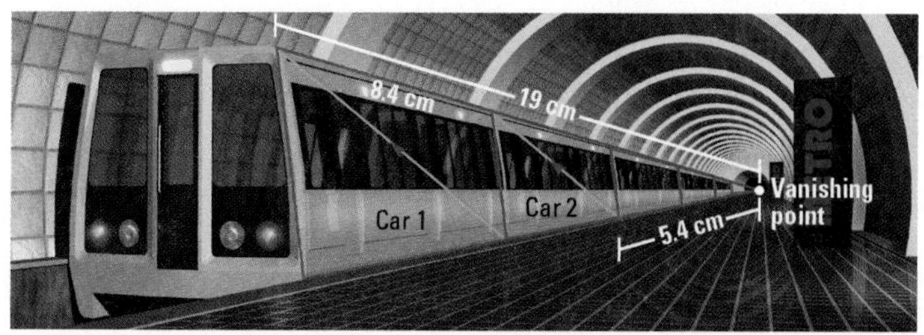

a. Use the dimensions given and the red parallel lines to find the length of the bottom edge of the drawing of Car 2. **about 4.3 cm**

b. What other set of parallel lines exist in the figure? *Explain* how these can be used to form a set of similar triangles. **See margin.**

c. Find the length of the top edge of the drawing of Car 2. **about 4.7 cm**

C 29. **CHALLENGE** Prove *Ceva's Theorem:* If *P* is any point inside $\triangle ABC$, then $\frac{AY}{YC} \cdot \frac{CX}{XB} \cdot \frac{BZ}{ZA} = 1$. (*Hint:* Draw lines parallel to $\overleftrightarrow{BY}$ through *A* and *C*. Apply Theorem 6.4 to $\triangle ACM$. Show that $\triangle APN \sim \triangle MPC$, $\triangle CXM \sim \triangle BXP$, and $\triangle BZP \sim \triangle AZN$.) **See margin.**

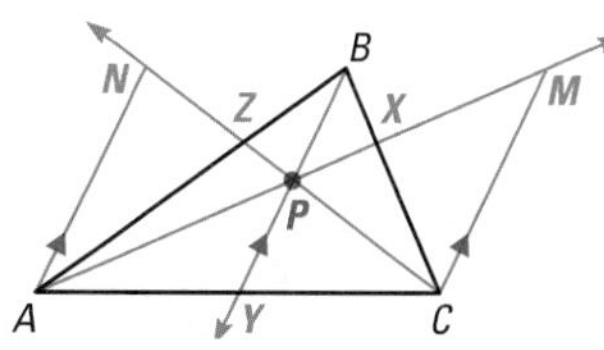

MIXED REVIEW

PREVIEW Prepare for Lesson 6.7 in Exs. 30–36.

Perform the following operations. Then simplify.

30. $(-3) \cdot \frac{7}{2}$ *(p. 869)* $-\frac{21}{2}$ 31. $\frac{4}{3} \cdot \frac{1}{2}$ *(p. 869)* $\frac{2}{3}$ 32. $5\left(\frac{1}{2}\right)^2$ *(p. 871)* $\frac{5}{4}$ 33. $\left(\frac{5}{4}\right)^3$ *(p. 871)* $\frac{125}{64}$

Describe **the translation in words and write the coordinate rule for the translation.** *(p. 272)*

34.

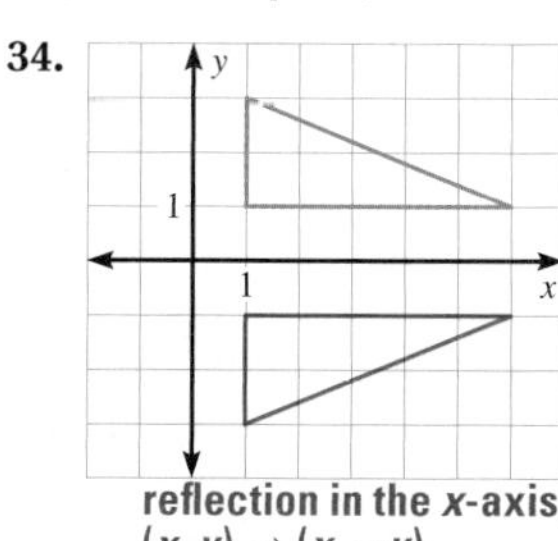

reflection in the *x*-axis, $(x, y) \rightarrow (x, -y)$

35.

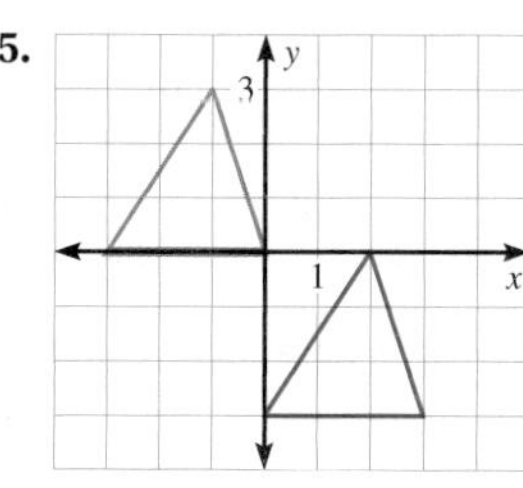

36.

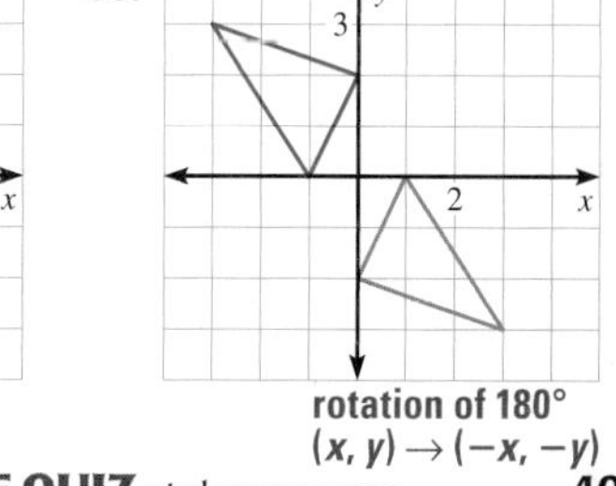

rotation of 180° $(x, y) \rightarrow (-x, -y)$

35. horizontal translation of 3 units to the right followed by a vertical translation of 3 units down, $(x, y) \rightarrow (x + 3, y - 3)$

5 ASSESS AND RETEACH

Daily Homework Quiz

Transparency Available

Find the value of the variable.

1. **12**

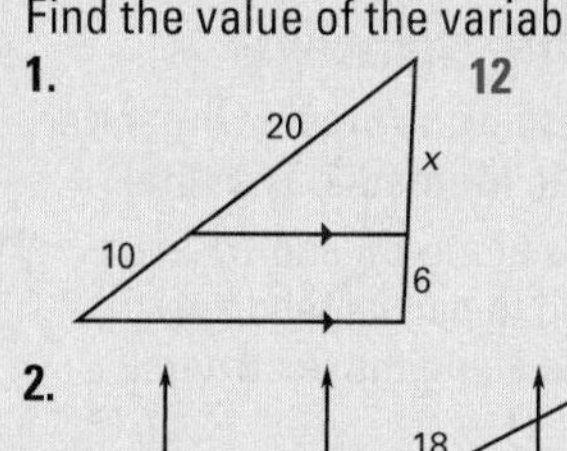

2. **13.5**

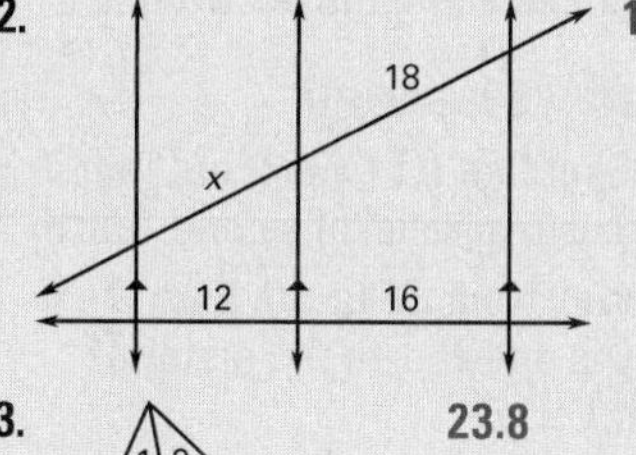

3. **23.8**

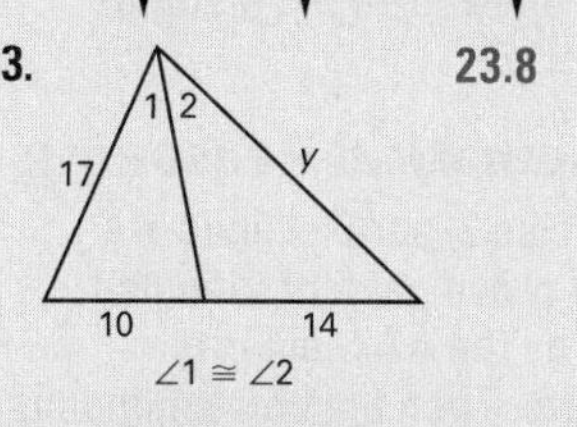

4. This diagram represents a tract of land being developed for homes. Which lot has the greatest perimeter? **Lot B**

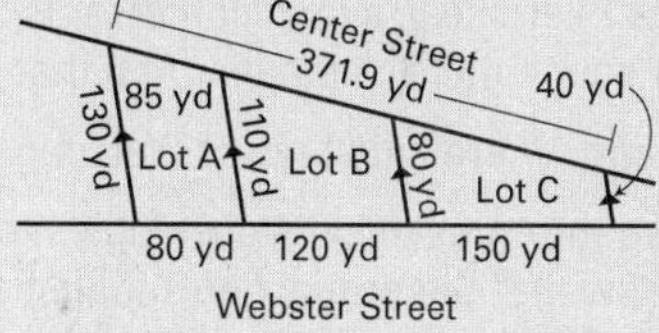

Available at **classzone.com**

Diagnosis/Remediation

- Practice A, B, C in Chapter 6 Resource Book, pp. 74–79
- Study Guide in Chapter 6 Resource Book, pp. 80–81
- Practice Workbook, pp. 118–120
- @HomeTutor

Challenge

Additional challenge is available in the Chapter 6 Resource Book, p. 84.

29. See Additional Answers beginning on p. AA1.

Using ALTERNATIVE METHODS

Alternative Strategy

Example 3 on page 399 can be solved by looking for and applying ratios in the diagram (Method 1) or by using a graphic organizer to set up a proposition (Method 2).

Teaching Strategy

Point out how the graphic organizer is set up in Method 2. The total distances along $\overleftrightarrow{CE}$ and $\overleftrightarrow{HF}$ are compared to partial (shorter) distances along those streets.

Study Strategy

For Exercise 1(b), point out that if there is a parallel alley one-fourth the way from $\overline{BE}$ to $\overline{CD}$, then the alley is one-fourth the distance from E to D.

Mathematical Reasoning

In Exercise 2, parallel lines are used to prove pairs of triangles similar by the AA Similarity Postulate. Then the corresponding side lengths for the pair of triangles can be used to write a proportion.

Avoiding Common Errors

For Exercise 5, a common error is to conclude from the diagram that $\frac{2}{5}$ and $\frac{1.5}{x}$ are equal ratios. You can use the sides of similar triangles to show that the proportion should be $\frac{2}{7} = \frac{1.5}{x}$.

Another Way to Solve Example 3, page 399

MULTIPLE REPRESENTATIONS In Lesson 6.6, you used proportionality theorems to find lengths of segments formed when transversals intersect two or more parallel lines. Now, you will learn two different ways to solve Example 3 on page 399.

PROBLEM

CITY TRAVEL In the diagram, $\angle 1$, $\angle 2$, and $\angle 3$ are all congruent and $GF = 120$ yards, $DE = 150$ yards, and $CD = 300$ yards. Find the distance HF between Main Street and South Main Street.

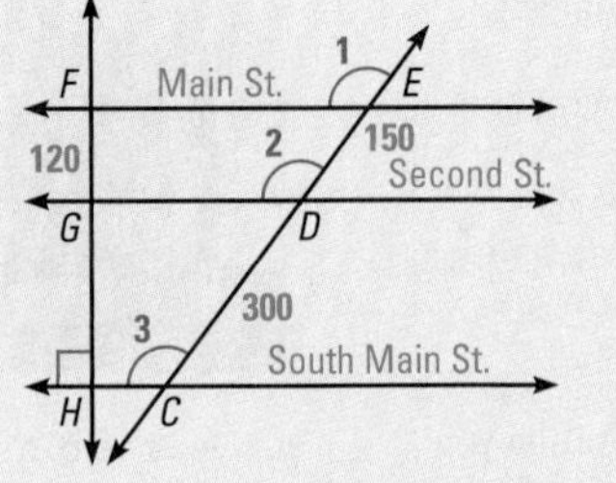

Standards

7.0 Students prove and **use theorems involving the properties of parallel lines cut by a transversal,** the properties of quadrilaterals, and the properties of circles.

METHOD 1

Applying a Ratio One alternative approach is to look for ratios in the diagram.

STEP 1 **Read** the problem. Because Main Street, Second Street, and South Main Street are all parallel, the lengths of the segments of the cross streets will be in proportion, so they have the same ratio.

STEP 2 **Apply** a ratio. Notice that on $\overleftrightarrow{CE}$, the distance CD between South Main Street and Second Street is twice the distance DE between Second Street and Main Street. So the same will be true for the distances HG and GF.

$HG = 2 \cdot GF$	**Write equation.**
$= 2 \cdot 120$	**Substitute.**
$= 240$	**Simplify.**

STEP 3 **Calculate** the distance. Line HF is perpendicular to both Main Street and South Main Street, so the distance between Main Street and South Main Street is this perpendicular distance, HF.

$HF = HG + GF$	**Segment Addition Postulate**
$= 120 + 240$	**Substitute.**
$= 360$	**Simplify.**

STEP 4 **Check** page 399 to verify your answer, and confirm that it is the same.

METHOD 2 **Writing a Proportion** Another alternative approach is to use a graphic organizer to set up a proportion.

STEP 1 **Make** a table to compare the distances.

	$\overleftrightarrow{CE}$	$\overleftrightarrow{HF}$
Total distance	300 + 150, or 450	x
Partial distance	150	120

STEP 2 **Write** and solve a proportion.

$\frac{450}{150} = \frac{x}{120}$ **Write proportion.**

$360 = x$ **Multiply each side by 120 and simplify.**

▶ The distance is 360 yards.

PRACTICE

1. **MAPS** Use the information on the map.

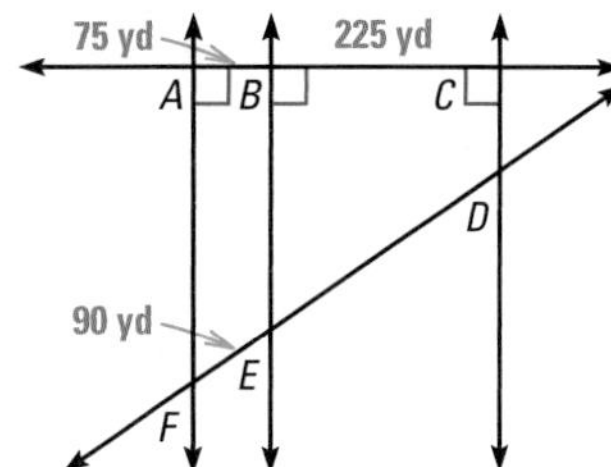

a. Find DE. **270 yd**

b. **What If?** Suppose there is an alley one fourth of the way from $\overline{BE}$ to $\overline{CD}$ and parallel to $\overline{BE}$. What is the distance from E to the alley along $\overleftrightarrow{FD}$? **67.5 yd**

2. **REASONING** Given the diagram below, *explain* why the three given proportions are true.

$\frac{a}{a+b} = \frac{d}{e}$

$\frac{a}{a+b+c} = \frac{d}{f}$

$\frac{a+b}{a+b+c} = \frac{e}{f}$

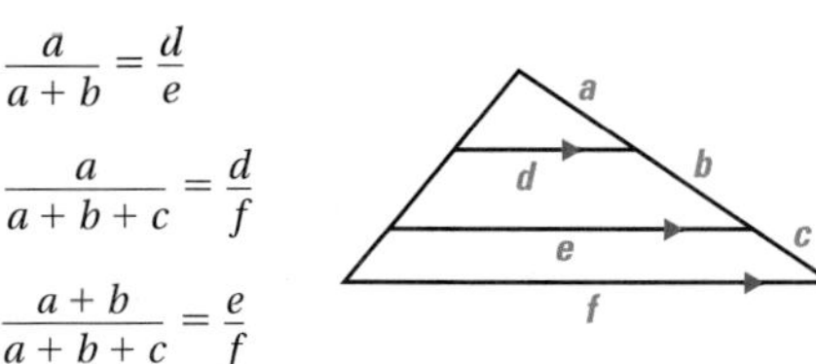

Since the three triangles are similar, the ratio of corresponding sides is the same.

3. **WALKING** Two people leave points A and B at the same time. They intend to meet at point C at the same time. The person who leaves point A walks at a speed of 3 miles per hour. How fast must the person who leaves point B walk? **4.5 mi/h**

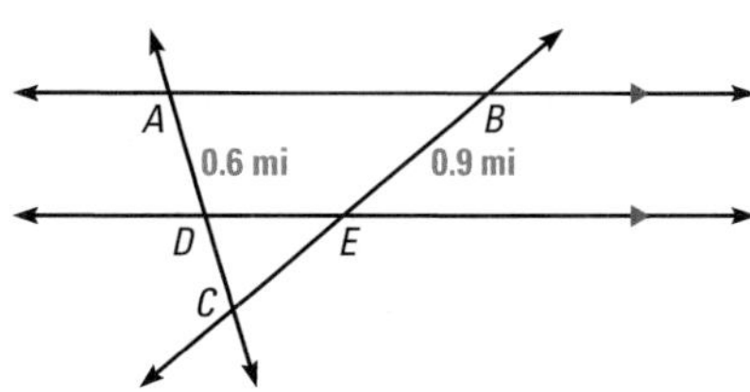

4. **ERROR ANALYSIS** A student who attempted to solve the problem in Exercise 3 claims that you need to know the length of $\overline{AC}$ to solve the problem. *Describe* and correct the error that the student made. **You only need to know that the ratio of the two distances is 2 : 3.**

5. **ALGEBRA** Use the diagram to find the values of x and y. **5.25, 7.5**

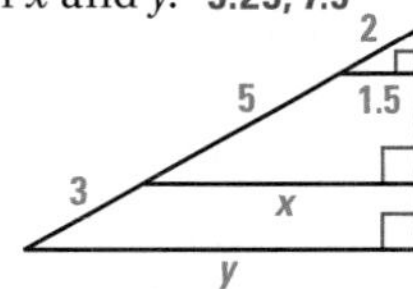

1 PLAN AND PREPARE

Warm-Up Exercises

1. Simplify 3^n for $n = 0, 1, 2, 3,$ and 4. **1, 3, 9, 27, 81**
2. Evaluate $3 \cdot 4^n$ for $n = 5$. **3072**

2 FOCUS AND MOTIVATE

Essential Question

Big Idea 3, p. 355

What is one way to generate a fractal? **Tell students they will learn how to answer this question by drawing a Stage 0 shape and then repeating the sequence of steps that define the fractal.**

3 TEACH

Extra Example 1

Draw a Sierpinski triangle: Start with an equilateral triangle. At each stage connect the midpoints of each side, forming a new equilateral triangle. Shade the triangle in the center with a different color.

Stage 0 Stage 1

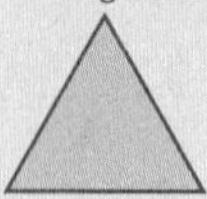

Stage 2 Stage 3

406

Extension Fractals

Use after Lesson 6.6

GOAL Explore the properties of fractals.

Key Vocabulary
- **fractal**
- **self-similarity**
- **iteration**

HISTORY NOTE

Computers made it easier to study mathematical iteration by reducing the time needed to perform calculations. Using fractals, mathematicians have been able to create better models of coastlines, clouds, and other natural objects.

Standards

11.0 Students determine how changes in dimensions affect the perimeter, area, and volume **of common geometric figures** and solids.

A **fractal** is an object that is *self-similar.* An object is **self-similar** if one part of the object can be enlarged to look like the whole object. In nature, fractals can be found in ferns and branches of a river. Scientists use fractals to map out clouds in order to predict rain.

A Mandelbrot fractal

Many fractals are formed by a repetition of a sequence of the steps called **iteration**. The first stage of drawing a fractal is considered Stage 0. Helge van Koch (1870–1924) described a fractal known as the *Koch snowflake*, shown in Example 1.

EXAMPLE 1 Draw a fractal

Use the directions below to draw a Koch snowflake.

Starting with an equilateral triangle, at each stage each side is divided into thirds and a new equilateral triangle is formed using the middle third as the triangle side length.

Solution

STAGE 0 **Draw** an equilateral triangle with a side length of one unit.

STAGE 1 **Replace** the middle third of each side with an equilateral triangle.

STAGE 2 **Repeat** Stage 1 with the six smaller equilateral triangles.

STAGE 3 **Repeat** Stage 1 with the eighteen smaller equilateral triangles.

MEASUREMENT Benoit Mandelbrot (b. 1924) was the first mathematician to formalize the idea of fractals when he observed methods used to measure the lengths of coastlines. Coastlines cannot be measured as straight lines because of the inlets and rocks. Mandelbrot used fractals to model coastlines.

EXAMPLE 2 Find lengths in a fractal

Make a table to study the lengths of the sides of a Koch snowflake at different stages.

Stage number	Edge length	Number of edges	Perimeter
0	1	3	3
1	$\frac{1}{3}$	$3 \cdot 4 = 12$	4
2	$\frac{1}{9}$	$12 \cdot 4 = 48$	$\frac{48}{9} = 5\frac{1}{3}$
3	$\frac{1}{27}$	$48 \cdot 4 = 192$	$\frac{192}{27} = 7\frac{1}{9}$
n	$\frac{1}{3^n}$	$3 \cdot 4^n$	$\frac{4^n}{3^{n-1}}$

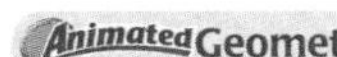

at classzone.com

PRACTICE

EXAMPLES 1 and 2 for Exs. 1–3

1. **PERIMETER** Find the ratio of the edge length of the triangle in Stage 0 of a Koch snowflake to the edge length of the triangle in Stage 1. How is the perimeter of the triangle in Stage 0 related to the perimeter of the triangle in Stage 1? *Explain.* **3 : 1. *Sample answer:* It's one unit longer; each of the three edges went from measuring one unit to four edges each measuring $\frac{1}{3}$ of a unit.**

2. **MULTI-STEP PROBLEM** Use the *Cantor set*, which is a fractal whose iteration consists of dividing a segment into thirds and erasing the middle third.
   a. Draw Stage 0 through Stage 5 of the Cantor set. Stage 0 has a length of one unit. **a, b. See margin.**
   b. Make a table showing the stage number, number of segments, segment length, and total length of the Cantor set.
   c. What is the total length of the Cantor set at Stage 10? Stage 20? Stage n?

3. **EXTENDED RESPONSE** A *Sierpinski carpet* starts with a square with side length one unit. At each stage, divide the square into nine equal squares with the middle square shaded a different color.
   a. Draw Stage 0 through Stage 3 of a Sierpinski carpet. **See margin.**
   b. *Explain* why the carpet is said to be *self-similar* by comparing the upper left hand square to the whole square.
   c. Make a table to find the total area of the colored squares at Stage 3. **See margin.**

2c. $\frac{1024}{59049}$, or about 0.01734 units; $\frac{1048576}{3486784401}$, or about 0.0003007 units; $\left(\frac{2}{3}\right)^n$

3b. *Sample answer:* The upper left square is simply a smaller version of the whole square.

Extra Example 2

Make a table of the lengths of the sides of the equilateral triangles in the Sierpinski triangle.

Stage Number	Edge Length	No. of Triangles with this Edge Length
0	1	1
1	$\frac{1}{2}$	3
2	$\frac{1}{4}$	9
3	$\frac{1}{8}$	27
n	$\left(\frac{1}{2}\right)^n$	3^n

Key Question to Ask for Example 2

- In the table, why are there $3 \cdot 4$ edges after Stage 1? **Each of 3 edges of the triangle in Stage 0 is replaced with 4 edges.**

An **Animated Geometry** activity is available on-line for **Example 2.** This activity is also available on the **Power Presentations CD-ROM**.

Closing the Lesson

Have students summarize the major points of the lesson and answer the Essential Question: What is one way to generate a fractal?

- **Draw Stage 0 for the fractal.**
- **Follow the directions and draw Stage 1.**
- **Repeat to draw more stages.**

Draw Stage 0 and repeat the sequence of steps that define the fractal.

4 PRACTICE AND APPLY

Vocabulary

Exercise 3(b) The idea of "self-similar" may be new to some students. One way to describe a self-similar figure is that it is formed by replicating itself using a scale other than 1.

2a–b, 3a, 3c. See Additional Answers beginning on p. AA1.

6.7 Dilations

MATERIALS • graph paper • straightedge • compass • ruler

Standards

Enrichment Topic; not required by California Standards.

QUESTION How can you construct a similar figure?

EXPLORE Construct a similar triangle

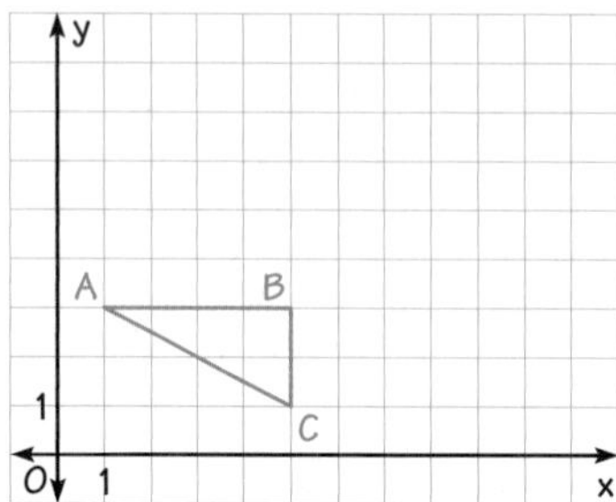

Draw a triangle Plot the points $A(1, 3)$, $B(5, 3)$, and $C(5, 1)$ in a coordinate plane. Draw $\triangle ABC$.

STEP 2

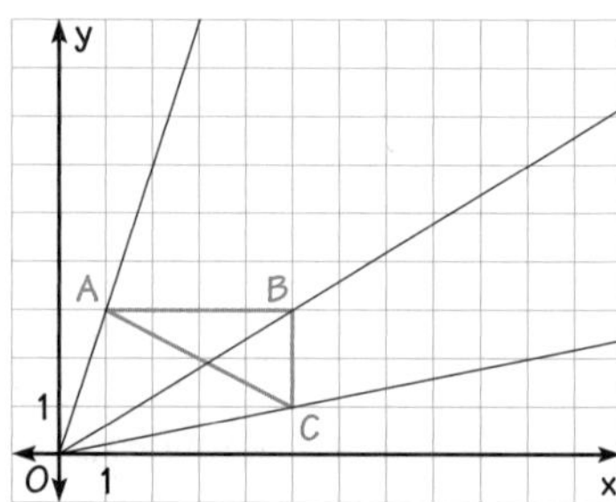

Draw rays Using the origin as an endpoint O, draw $\overrightarrow{OA}$, $\overrightarrow{OB}$, and $\overrightarrow{OC}$.

STEP 3

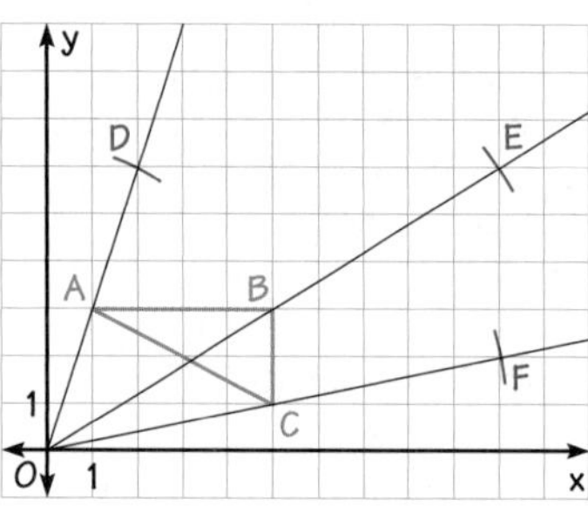

Draw equal segments Use a compass to mark a point D on $\overrightarrow{OA}$ so $OA = AD$. Mark a point E on $\overrightarrow{OB}$ so $OB = BE$. Mark a point F on $\overrightarrow{OC}$ so $OC = CF$.

STEP 4

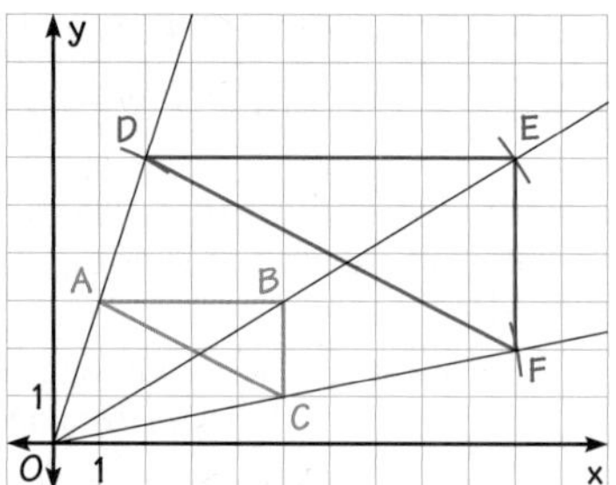

Draw the image Connect points D, E, and F to form a right triangle.

DRAW CONCLUSIONS Use your observations to complete these exercises

1. Measure $\overline{AB}$, $\overline{BC}$, $\overline{DE}$, and $\overline{EF}$. Calculate the ratios $\frac{DE}{AB}$ and $\frac{EF}{BC}$. Using this information, show that the two triangles are similar. **See margin.**
2. Repeat the steps in the Explore to construct $\triangle GHJ$ so that $3 \cdot OA = AG$, $3 \cdot OB = BH$, and $3 \cdot OC = CJ$. **See margin.**

1 PLAN AND PREPARE

Explore the Concept

- Students will construct similar triangles.
- This activity leads into the study of dilations in Lesson 6.7, Example 1.

Materials

Each student will need:

- graph paper
- compass
- straightedge
- ruler

Recommended Time

Work activity: 10 min

Discuss results: 5 min

Grouping

Students can work individually or in groups of two. If students work in groups, they can share their results.

2 TEACH

Tips for Success

Point out the importance of using a compass for step 3 of the dilation. This will help students learn how to perform a dilation independent of the units on the graph paper.

Alternative Strategy

You may want to do this activity as a demonstration with drawing software.

Key Discovery

Dilations create similar images.

3 ASSESS AND RETEACH

1. A right triangle with side lengths 5, 12, 13 is dilated with a scale factor of 3. What are the side lengths of the image? **15, 36, 39**
2. The vertices of an image with center (0, 0) has vertices that are $\frac{1}{2}$ the distance from the origin as the original vertices. What is the ratio of the side lengths between the original figure and its image? **2:1**

1. $\frac{DE}{AB} = \frac{EF}{BC}$ **or** $\frac{8}{4} = \frac{6}{3}$**; since the corresponding sides are proportional and the included angles, $\angle E$ and $\angle B$, are both 90°, $\triangle ABC \sim \triangle DEF$ by the SAS Similarity Theorem.**

2. **See Additional Answers beginning on p. AA1.**

6.7 Perform Similarity Transformations

Before You performed congruence transformations.
Now You will perform dilations.
Why? So you can solve problems in art, as in Ex. 26.

Key Vocabulary
- **dilation**
- **center of dilation**
- **scale factor of a dilation**
- **reduction**
- **enlargement**
- **transformation,** *p. 272*

Standards

5.0 Students prove that triangles are congruent or **similar, and they are able to use the concept of corresponding parts** of congruent triangles.

11.0 Students determine how changes in dimensions affect the perimeter, area, and volume **of common geometric figures** and solids.

A **dilation** is a transformation that stretches or shrinks a figure to create a similar figure. A dilation is a type of *similarity transformation.*

In a dilation, a figure is enlarged or reduced with respect to a fixed point called the **center of dilation**.

The **scale factor of a dilation** is the ratio of a side length of the image to the corresponding side length of the original figure. In the figure shown, $\triangle XYZ$ is the image of $\triangle ABC$. The center of dilation is (0, 0) and the scale factor is $\frac{XY}{AB}$.

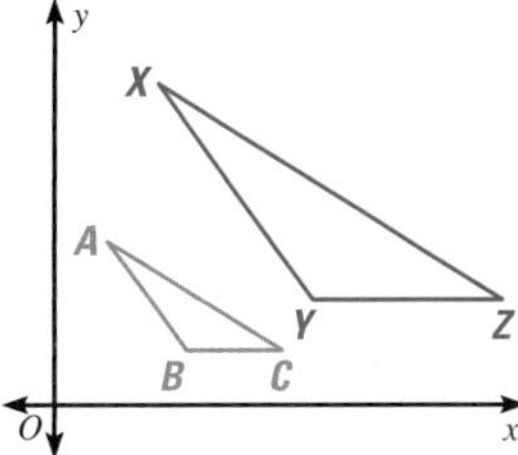

KEY CONCEPT *For Your Notebook*

Coordinate Notation for a Dilation

You can describe a dilation with respect to the origin with the notation $(x, y) \rightarrow (kx, ky)$, where k is the scale factor.

If $0 < k < 1$, the dilation is a **reduction**. If $k > 1$, the dilation is an **enlargement**.

EXAMPLE 1 **Draw a dilation with a scale factor greater than 1**

READ DIAGRAMS
All of the dilations in this lesson are in the coordinate plane and each center of dilation is the origin.

Draw a dilation of quadrilateral *ABCD* with vertices $A(2, 1)$, $B(4, 1)$, $C(4, -1)$, and $D(1, -1)$. Use a scale factor of 2.

Solution

First draw *ABCD*. Find the dilation of each vertex by multiplying its coordinates by 2. Then draw the dilation.

$(x, y) \rightarrow (2x, 2y)$

$A(2, 1) \rightarrow L(4, 2)$

$B(4, 1) \rightarrow M(8, 2)$

$C(4, -1) \rightarrow N(8, -2)$

$D(1, -1) \rightarrow P(2, -2)$

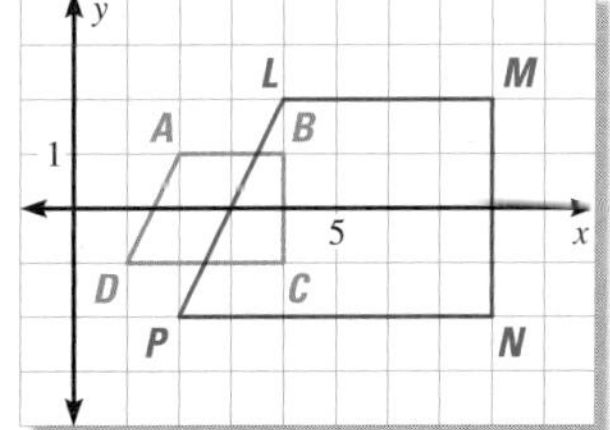

1 PLAN AND PREPARE

Warm-Up Exercises

Transparency Available

Give the coordinates of a point twice as far from the origin along a ray from (0, 0).

1. (3, 5) **(6, 10)**
2. (−2, 0) **(−4, 0)**
3. $\left(\frac{1}{2}, -\frac{1}{2}\right)$ **(1, −1)**

Give the coordinates of a point one-half as far from the origin along a ray from (0, 0).

4. (6, −4) **(3, −2)**
5. (0, −7) **(0, −3.5)**

Notetaking Guide

Transparency Available

Promotes interactive learning and notetaking skills, pp. 164–167.

Pacing

Basic: 2 days
Average: 2 days
Advanced: 2 days
Block: 1 block
- See *Teaching Guide/Lesson Plan.*

2 FOCUS AND MOTIVATE

Essential Question

Big Idea 3, p. 355

How do you dilate a figure in the coordinate plane? **Tell students they will learn how to answer this question by using the coordinates of the vertices of the figure.**

Resource Planning Guide

Chapter Resource Book
- Teaching Guide/Lesson Plan (pp. 85–86)
- Activity Master (p. 87)
- Practice levels A, B, C (pp. 89–94)
- Study Guide (pp. 95–96)
- Catch-up for Absent Students (p. 97)
- Problem Solving Workshop (p. 98)
- Challenge (p. 99)

Workbooks
- Notetaking Guide (pp. 164–167)
- Practice Workbook (pp. 121–123)

Teaching Options
- **Power Presentations CD-ROM** provides dynamic electronic teaching resources for the classroom.
- **Activity Generator CD-ROM** provides editable activities for all ability levels.

Interactive Technology
- Easy Planner
- Power Presentations CD-ROM
- Activity Generator CD-ROM
- Animated Algebra
- Test Generator CD-ROM
- Online Quiz
- eWorkbook
- eEdition
- @HomeTutor

Resources for English Learners
- Quick Reference for English Learners
- Spanish Study Guide
- Multi-Language Visual Glossary
- Student Resources in Spanish

See also the *Geometry Toolkit* for more strategies for meeting individual needs.

Motivating the Lesson

Place a flat object on the overhead projector and observe the image on the wall. Is the image similar to the object? Are they the same size? How could you find the scale factor? Tell students they will investigate these ideas in this lesson.

3 TEACH

Extra Example 1

Draw a dilation of quadrilateral *ABCD* with vertices $A(2, 2)$, $B(4, 2)$, $C(4, 0)$, $D(0, -2)$. Use a scale factor of 1.5 and label the image *FGHJ*.

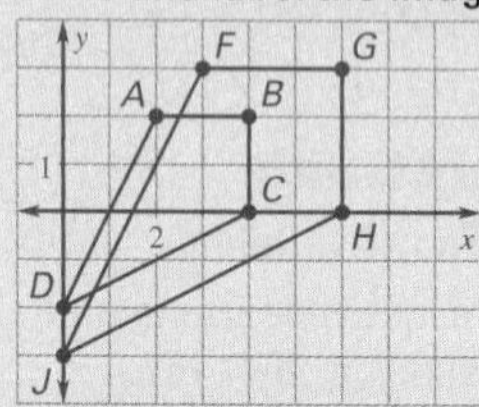

Extra Example 2

A triangle has vertices $A(2, 4)$, $B(8, 4)$, and $C(8, -4)$. The image of $\triangle ABC$ after a dilation with a scale factor of $\frac{1}{2}$ is $\triangle DEF$.

a. Sketch $\triangle ABC$ and $\triangle DEF$.

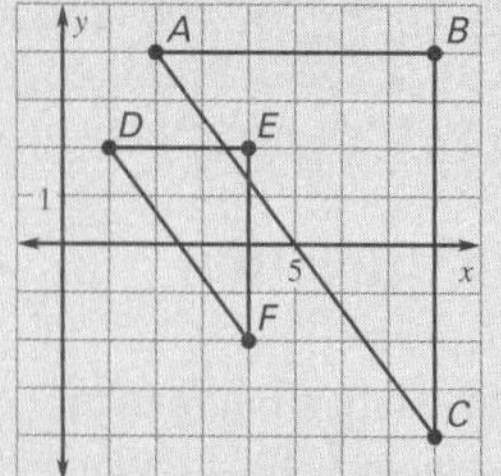

b. Verify that $\triangle ABC$ and $\triangle DEF$ are similar. ***Sample answer:*** **$\angle B$ and $\angle E$ are both right angles, so $\angle B \cong \angle E$. $\frac{AB}{DE} = \frac{6}{3} = 2$, and $\frac{BC}{EF} = \frac{8}{4} = 2$, so the lengths of the sides that include $\angle B$ and $\angle E$ are proportional. Therefore $\triangle ABC \sim \triangle DEF$ by the SAS Similarity Theorem.**

EXAMPLE 2 Verify that a figure is similar to its dilation

A triangle has the vertices $A(4, -4)$, $B(8, 2)$, and $C(8, -4)$. The image of $\triangle ABC$ after a dilation with a scale factor of $\frac{1}{2}$ is $\triangle DEF$.

a. Sketch $\triangle ABC$ and $\triangle DEF$.

b. Verify that $\triangle ABC$ and $\triangle DEF$ are similar.

Solution

a. The scale factor is less than one, so the dilation is a reduction.

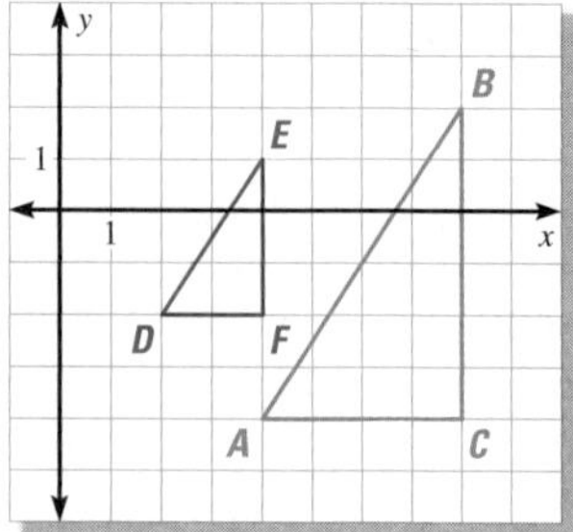

$$(x, y) \rightarrow \left(\frac{1}{2}x, \frac{1}{2}y\right)$$

$A(4, -4) \rightarrow D(2, -2)$

$B(8, 2) \rightarrow E(4, 1)$

$C(8, -4) \rightarrow F(4, -2)$

b. Because $\angle C$ and $\angle F$ are both right angles, $\angle C \cong \angle F$. Show that the lengths of the sides that include $\angle C$ and $\angle F$ are proportional. Find the horizontal and vertical lengths from the coordinate plane.

$$\frac{AC}{DF} \stackrel{?}{=} \frac{BC}{EF}$$  $$\frac{4}{2} = \frac{6}{3} \checkmark$$

So, the lengths of the sides that include $\angle C$ and $\angle F$ are proportional.

▸ Therefore, $\triangle ABC \sim \triangle DEF$ by the SAS Similarity Theorem.

✓ GUIDED PRACTICE for Examples 1 and 2

Find the coordinates of *L*, *M*, and *N* so that $\triangle LMN$ is a dilation of $\triangle PQR$ with a scale factor of *k*. Sketch $\triangle PQR$ and $\triangle LMN$. **1, 2. See margin for art.**

1. $P(-2, -1)$, $Q(-1, 0)$, $R(0, -1)$; $k = 4$ **$L(-8, -4)$, $M(-4, 0)$, $N(0, -4)$**
2. $P(5, -5)$, $Q(10, -5)$, $R(10, 5)$; $k = 0.4$ **$L(2, -2)$, $M(4, -2)$, $N(4, 2)$**

EXAMPLE 3 Find a scale factor

PHOTO STICKERS You are making your own photo stickers. Your photo is 4 inches by 4 inches. The image on the stickers is 1.1 inches by 1.1 inches. What is the scale factor of the reduction?

Solution

The scale factor is the ratio of a side length of the sticker image to a side length of the original photo, or $\frac{1.1 \text{ in.}}{4 \text{ in.}}$. In simplest form, the scale factor is $\frac{11}{40}$.

Differentiated Instruction

Visual Learners Instruct students to make use of different colored pencils when they are drawing their triangles in **Guided Practice Exercises 1 and 2**. Have them sketch the original figure in one color and the dilation of that figure in a different color. Point out that they can determine which figure in a set of two similar figures is a dilation of the other by looking at the scale factor to find out if it is a reduction or an enlargement of the original.

See also the *Geometry Toolkit* for more strategies.

READING DIAGRAMS Generally, for a center of dilation at the origin, a point of the figure and its image lie on the same ray from the origin. However, if a point of the figure *is* the origin, its image is also the origin.

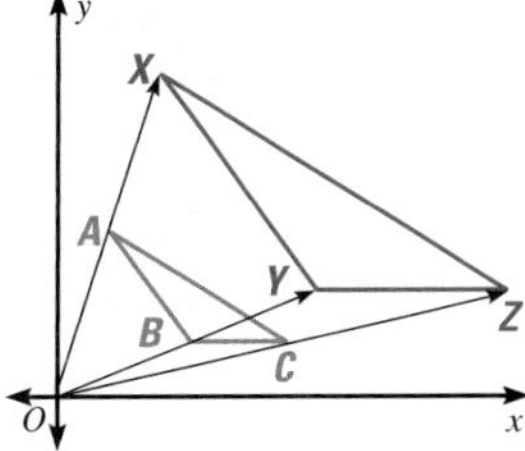

EXAMPLE 4 Standardized Test Practice

You want to create a quadrilateral *EFGH* that is similar to quadrilateral *PQRS*. What are the coordinates of *H*?

ELIMINATE CHOICES
You can eliminate choice A, because you can tell by looking at the graph that *H* is in Quadrant I. The point (12, −15) is in Quadrant IV.

Ⓐ (12, −15)

Ⓑ (7, 8)

Ⓒ (12, 15)

Ⓓ (15, 18)

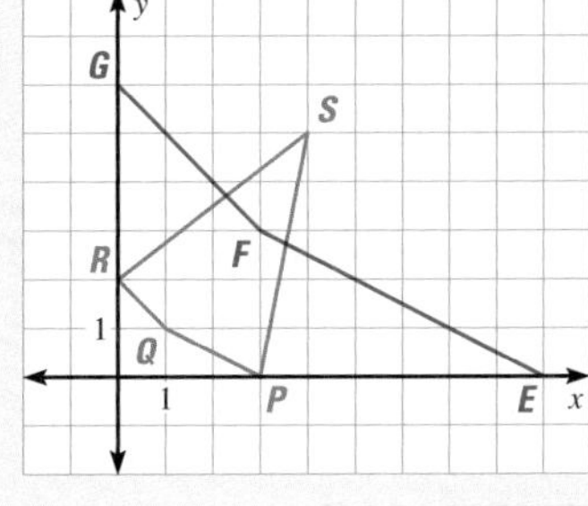

Solution

Determine if *EFGH* is a dilation of *PQRS* by checking whether the same scale factor can be used to obtain *E*, *F*, and *G* from *P*, *Q*, and *R*.

$(x, y) \rightarrow (kx, ky)$

$P(3, 0) \rightarrow E(9, 0)$ $\quad k = 3$

$Q(1, 1) \rightarrow F(3, 3)$ $\quad k = 3$

$R(0, 2) \rightarrow G(0, 6)$ $\quad k = 3$

Because k is the same in each case, the image is a dilation with a scale factor of 3. So, you can use the scale factor to find the image *H* of point *S*.

$S(4, 5) \rightarrow H(3 \cdot 4, 3 \cdot 5) = H(12, 15)$

▶ The correct answer is C. Ⓐ Ⓑ Ⓒ Ⓓ

CHECK Draw rays from the origin through each point and its image.

GUIDED PRACTICE for Examples 3 and 4

3. **WHAT IF?** In Example 3, what is the scale factor of the reduction if your photo is 5.5 inches by 5.5 inches? $\frac{1}{5}$

4. Suppose a figure containing the origin is dilated. *Explain* why the corresponding point in the image of the figure is also the origin.
A dilation with respect to the origin and scale factor k can be described as $(x, y) \rightarrow (kx, ky)$. If $(x, y) = (0, 0)$, then $(kx, ky) = (k \cdot 0, k \cdot 0) = (0, 0)$.

Extra Example 3

You are using a photo quality printer to enlarge a digital picture. The picture on the computer screen is 6 centimeters by 6 centimeters. The printed image is 15 centimeters by 15 centimeters. What is the scale factor of the enlargement? **2:5**

Key Question to Ask for Example 3

- If the image stickers are 1.1 inches by 2.2 inches, would the reduction be a dilation? **No, the image is not a square so it is not similar to the original.**

Extra Example 4

You want to create quadrilateral *RSTU* that is similar to quadrilateral *ABCD*. What are the coordinates of *U*? **D**

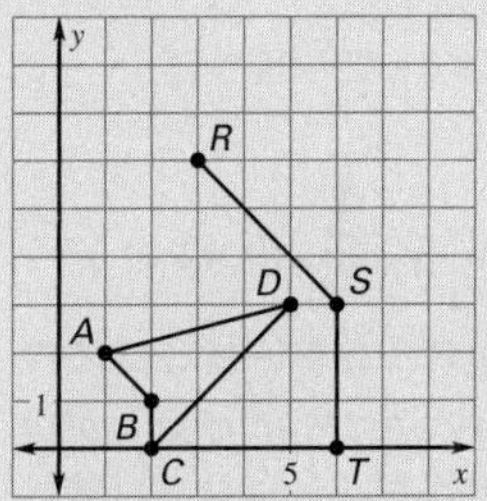

Ⓐ (15, −9) Ⓑ (8, 6)

Ⓒ (10, 6) Ⓓ (15, 9)

Closing the Lesson

Have students summarize the major points of the lesson and answer the Essential Question: How do you dilate a figure in the coordinate plane?

- **A dilation with respect to the origin can be described by $(x, y) \rightarrow (kx, ky)$ where k is the scale factor.**

Draw the figure, multiply each of the coordinates by the scale factor, and graph the new coordinates.

1.

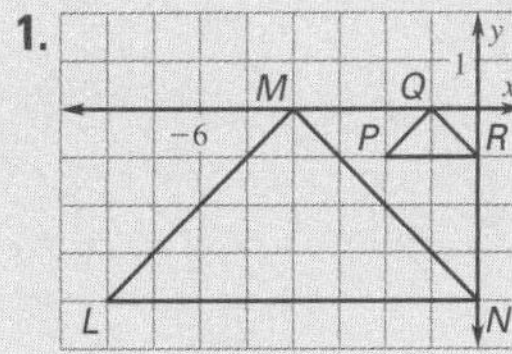

2.

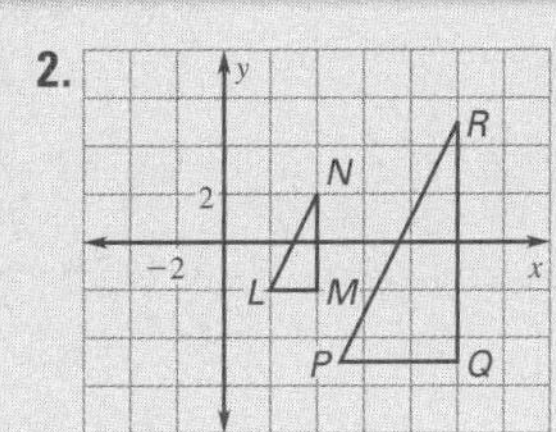

4 PRACTICE AND APPLY

Assignment Guide

Answer Transparencies available for all exercises

Basic:
Day 1: EP p. 903 Exs. 36–38
pp. 412–415
Exs. 1–8, 15–18, 35–40
Day 2: pp. 412–415
Exs. 9–14, 25–30, 41–43

Average:
Day 1: pp. 412–415
Exs. 1–8, 15–18, 22, 35–40
Day 2: pp. 412–415
Exs. 9–14, 19–21, 25–31, 42

Advanced:
Day 1: pp. 412–415
Exs. 1, 2, 5–8, 15–18, 22–24*, 35–40
Day 2: pp. 412–415
Exs. 9–14, 19–21, 26–34*, 43

Block:
pp. 412–415
Exs. 1–22, 25–31, 35–40, 42

Differentiated Instruction

See *Geometry Best Practices Toolkit* for suggestions on addressing the needs of a diverse classroom.

Homework Check

For a quick check of student understanding of key concepts, go over the following exercises:

Basic: 4, 9, 13, 25, 28
Average: 6, 10, 13, 26, 29
Advanced: 8, 12, 13, 26, 30

Extra Practice

- Student Edition, p. 907
- Chapter 6 Resource Book: Practice levels A, B, C, pp. 89–94

Practice Worksheet

An easily-readable reduced practice page (with answers) for this lesson can be found on p. 354C.

6.7 EXERCISES

HOMEWORK KEY
○ = **WORKED-OUT SOLUTIONS** on p. WS8 for Exs. 5, 11, and 27
★ = **STANDARDIZED TEST PRACTICE** Exs. 2, 13, 21, 22, 28, 30, and 31

SKILL PRACTICE

A

1. **VOCABULARY** Copy and complete: In a dilation, the image is ___?___ to the original figure. **similar**

2. ★ **WRITING** *Explain* how to find the scale factor of a dilation. How do you know whether a dilation is an enlargement or a reduction? **See margin.**

2. Find the ratio of a side length of the image to the corresponding side length of the original figure; suppose k is the scale factor, if $0 < k < 1$ the dilation is a reduction. If $k > 1$ the dilation is an enlargement.

EXAMPLES 1 and 2 on pp. 409–410 for Exs. 3–8

DRAWING DILATIONS **Draw a dilation of the polygon with the given vertices using the given scale factor k.** **3–8. See margin.**

3. $A(-2, 1), B(-4, 1), C(-2, 4); k = 2$
4. $A(-5, 5), B(-5, -10), C(10, 0); k = \frac{3}{5}$
5. $A(1, 1), B(6, 1), C(6, 3); k = 1.5$
6. $A(2, 8), B(8, 8), C(16, 4); k = 0.25$
7. $A(-8, 0), B(0, 8), C(4, 0), D(0, -4); k = \frac{3}{8}$
8. $A(0, 0), B(0, 3), C(2, 4), D(2, -1); k = \frac{13}{2}$

EXAMPLE 3 on p. 410 for Exs. 9–12

IDENTIFYING DILATIONS **Determine whether the dilation from Figure A to Figure B is a *reduction* or an *enlargement*. Then find its scale factor.**

9. **reduction; $\frac{1}{2}$**

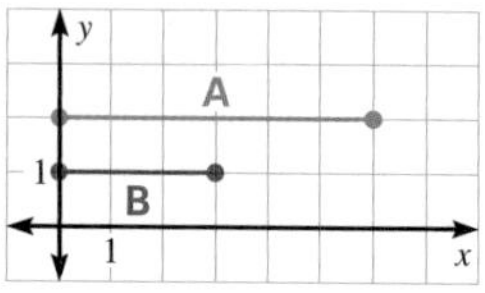

10. **enlargement; $\frac{3}{2}$**

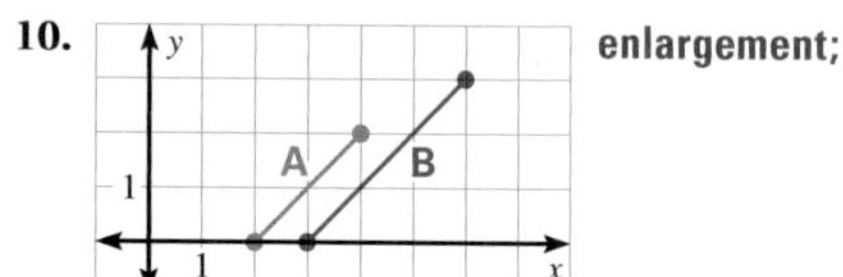

11. **enlargement; 3**

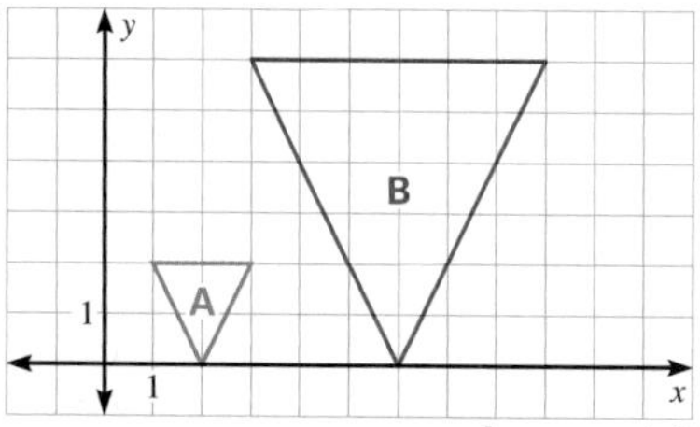

12. **reduction; $\frac{1}{3}$**

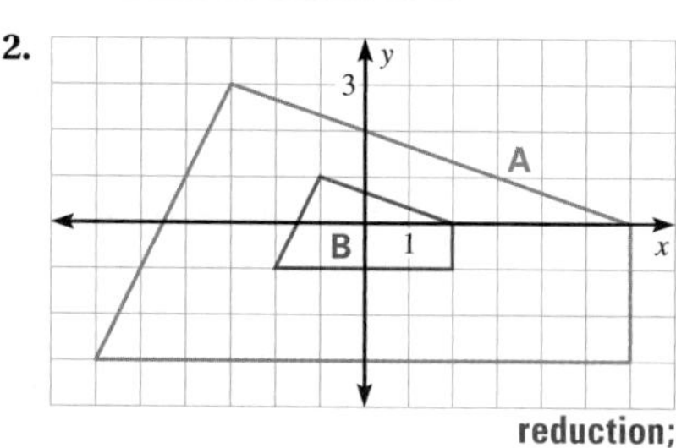

EXAMPLE 4 on p. 411 for Ex. 13

13. ★ **MULTIPLE CHOICE** You want to create a quadrilateral $PQRS$ that is similar to quadrilateral $JKLM$. What are the coordinates of S? **C**

Ⓐ (2, 4)　Ⓑ (4, −2)　Ⓒ (−2, −4)　Ⓓ (−4, −2)

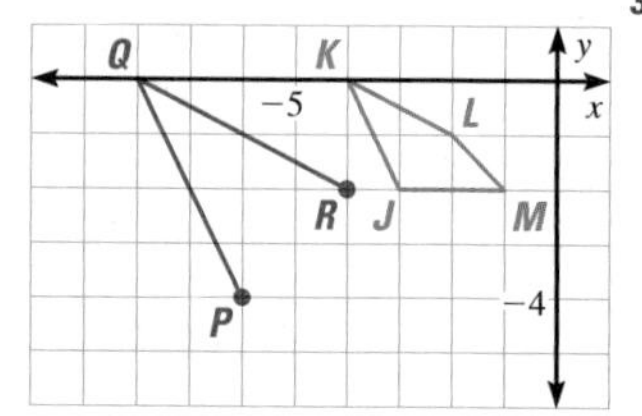

14. **ERROR ANALYSIS** A student found the scale factor of the dilation from $\overline{AB}$ to $\overline{CD}$ to be $\frac{2}{5}$. *Describe* and correct the student's error.
The scale factor should be the ratio of the image to the original rather than the ratio of the original to the image; $\frac{5}{2}$.

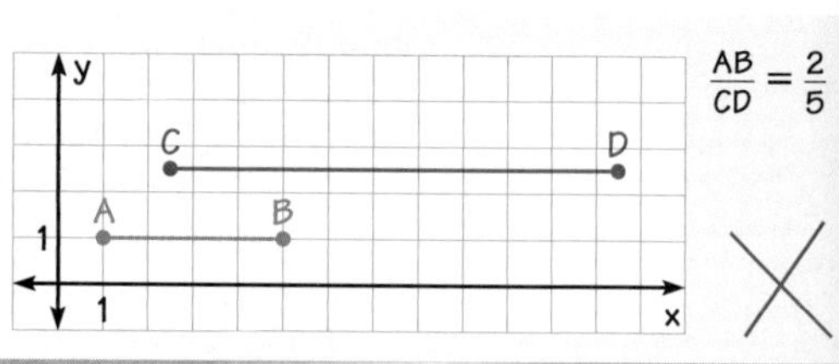

3.

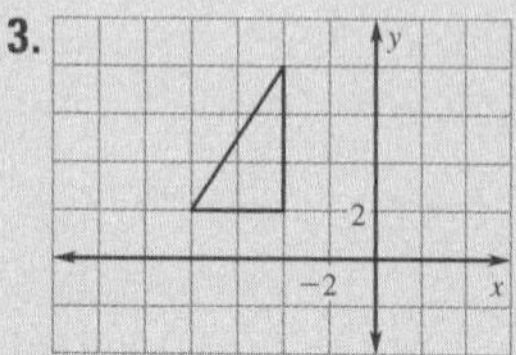

4.

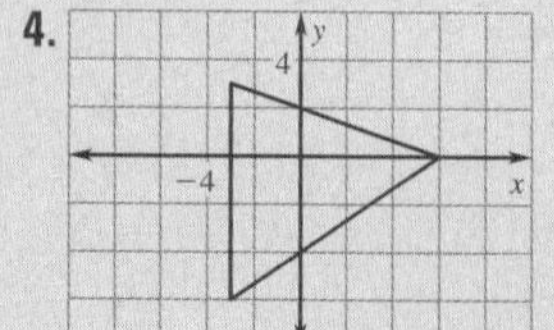

5.

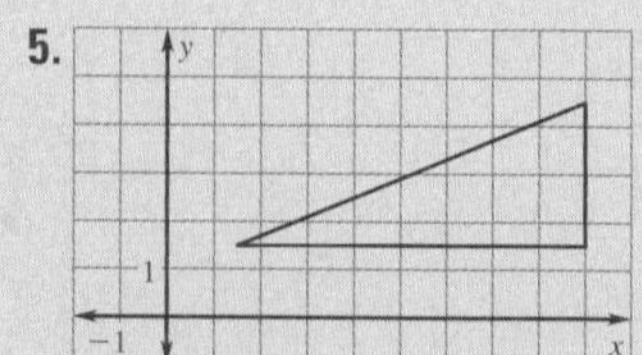

15. **ERROR ANALYSIS** A student says that the figure shown represents a dilation. What is wrong with this statement?
The figures are not similar.

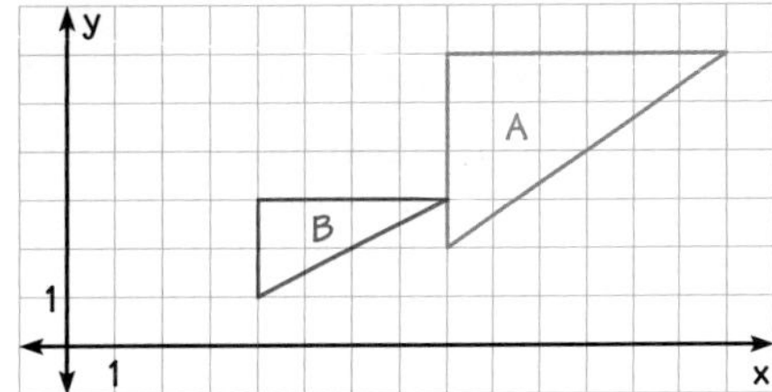

B **IDENTIFYING TRANSFORMATIONS** **Determine whether the transformation shown is a *translation, reflection, rotation,* or *dilation.***

16.

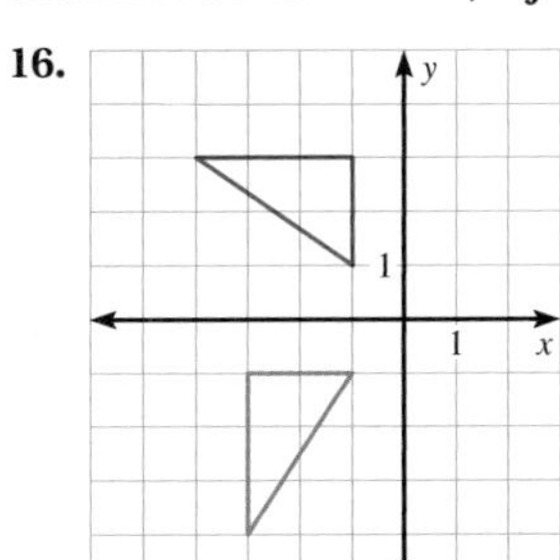

rotation

17.

reflection

18.

dilation

FINDING SCALE FACTORS **Find the scale factor of the dilation of Figure A to Figure B. Then give the unknown lengths of Figure A.**

19.

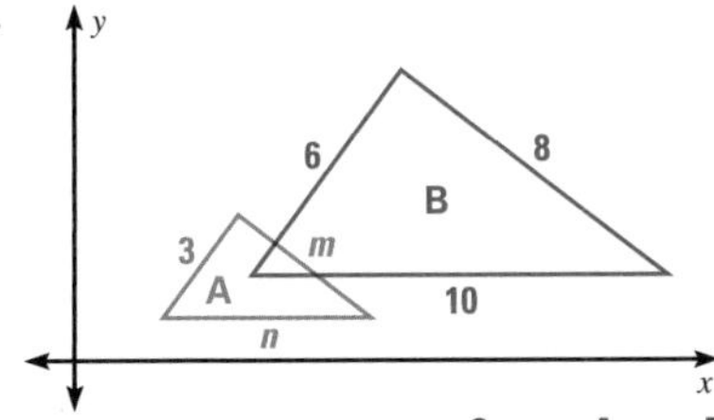

2; $m = 4$, $n = 5$

20.

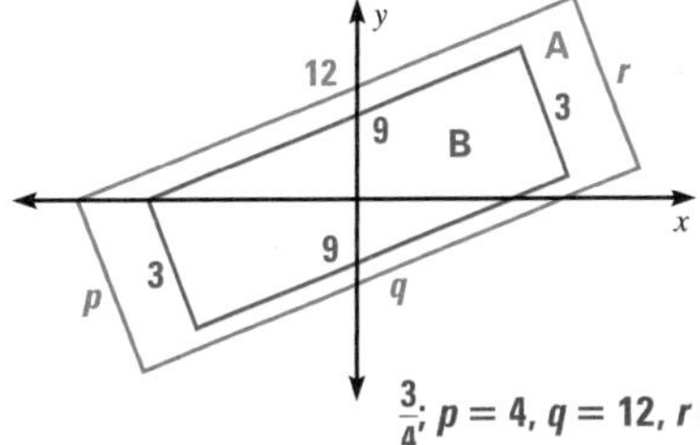

$\frac{3}{4}$; $p = 4$, $q = 12$, $r = 4$

21. ★ **MULTIPLE CHOICE** In the diagram shown, $\triangle ABO$ is a dilation of $\triangle DEO$. The length of a median of $\triangle ABO$ is what percent of the length of the corresponding median of $\triangle DEO$? **C**

(A) 50% (B) 75%

(C) $133\frac{1}{3}\%$ (D) 200%

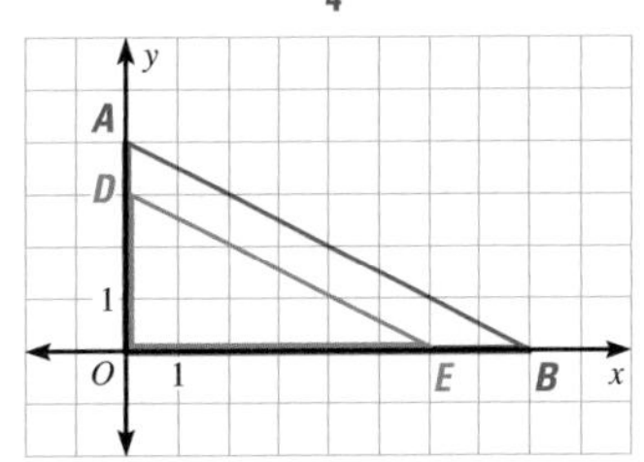

22. ★ **SHORT RESPONSE** Suppose you dilate a figure using a scale factor of 2. Then, you dilate the image using a scale factor of $\frac{1}{2}$. *Describe* the size and shape of this new image. **The result of both dilations is the original figure.**

C **CHALLENGE** ***Describe*** **the two transformations, the first followed by the second, that combined will transform $\triangle ABC$ into $\triangle DEF$.**

23. $A(-3, 3)$, $B(-3, 1)$, $C(0, 1)$
$D(6, 6)$, $E(6, 2)$, $F(0, 2)$
Sample answer: **$(x, y) \rightarrow (-x, y) \rightarrow (2x, 2y)$**

24. $A(6, 0)$, $B(9, 6)$, $C(12, 6)$
$D(0, 3)$, $E(1, 5)$, $F(2, 5)$
Sample answer: **$(x, y) \rightarrow \left(\frac{1}{3}x, \frac{1}{3}y\right) \rightarrow (x - 2, y + 3)$**

Avoiding Common Errors

Exercises 9–13, 19, 20 Students may make errors if they confuse which figure is the image and which is the original. Encourage them to redraw the figures, using different colors for the original and the image.

Teaching Strategy

Exercises 16–18 Review the properties of translations, reflections, rotations, and dilations for these exercises. Point out that reflections do not preserve orientation, so Exercise 17 must be a reflection.

Exercises 23–24 Encourage students to draw the original figure and the image before finding the transformations that fit these exercises. Tell them to guess and check the coordinates of the middle figure between the original and image.

6.

7.

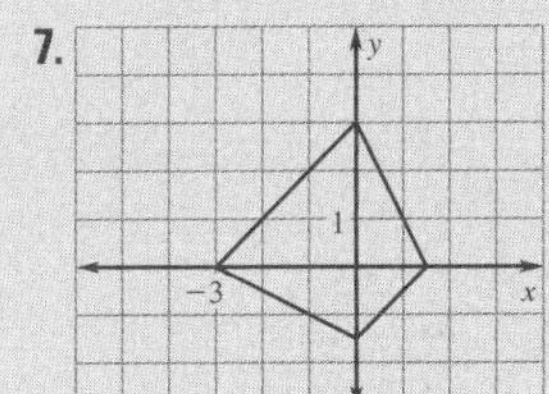

8.

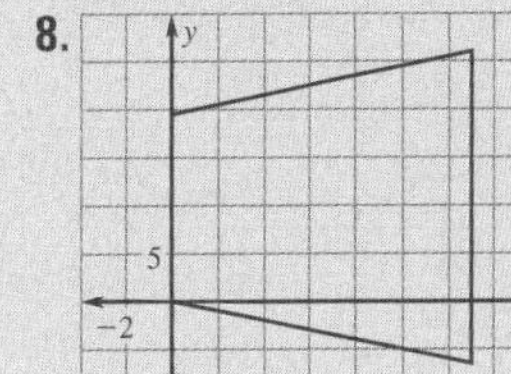

classzone.com

An **Animated Geometry** activity is available on-line for **Exercise 28.** This activity is also available on the **Power Presentations CD-ROM**.

Mathematical Reasoning

Exercise 29 The ratio of corresponding segment lengths in a dilation have the same scale factor as the dilation, including the altitudes and medians of a triangle. If the scale factor is $\frac{a}{b}$, then the perimeters will have the ratio $\frac{a}{b}$, and the areas will have the ratio $\frac{a^2}{b^2}$.

29a.

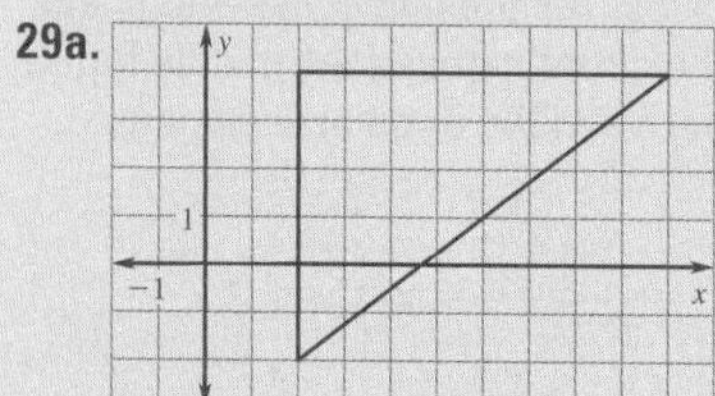

31.

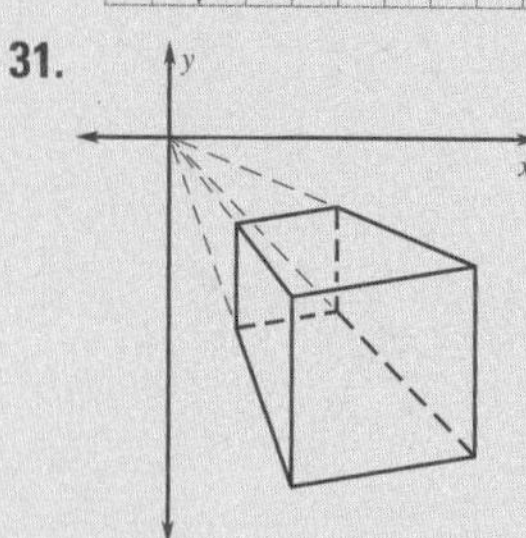

32. Let $P(a, b)$ and $Q(c, d)$ be the coordinates of the endpoints of $\overline{PQ}$ with midpoint $\left(\frac{a+c}{2}, \frac{b+d}{2}\right)$. Since $\overline{XY}$ is a dilation of $\overline{PQ}$ with scale factor k, you have $X(ka, kb)$ and $Y(kc, kd)$ with midpoint $\left(\frac{ka+kc}{2}, \frac{kb+kd}{2}\right)$. Thus, $k\left(\frac{a+c}{2}, \frac{b+d}{2}\right) = \left(\frac{ka+kc}{2}, \frac{kb+kd}{2}\right)$.

33. The slope of $\overline{PQ}$ is $\frac{d-b}{c-a}$ and the slope of $\overline{XY}$ is $\frac{kd-kb}{kc-ka} = \frac{k(d-b)}{k(c-a)} = \frac{d-b}{c-a}$. Since the slopes are the same, the lines are parallel.

PROBLEM SOLVING

EXAMPLE 3 A on p. 410 for Exs. 25–27

25. BILLBOARD ADVERTISEMENT A billboard advertising agency requires each advertisement to be drawn so that it fits in a 12-inch by 6-inch rectangle. The agency uses a scale factor of 24 to enlarge the advertisement to create the billboard. What are the dimensions of a billboard, in feet? **24 ft by 12 ft**

@HomeTutor for problem solving help at classzone.com

26. POTTERY Your pottery is used on a poster for a student art show. You want to make postcards using the same image. On the poster, the image is 8 inches in width and 6 inches in height. If the image on the postcard can be 5 inches wide, what scale should you use for the image on the postcard? $\frac{5}{8}$

@HomeTutor for problem solving help at classzone.com

27. SHADOWS You and your friend are walking at night. You point a flashlight at your friend, and your friend's shadow is cast on the building behind him. The shadow is an enlargement, and is 15 feet tall. Your friend is 6 feet tall. What is the scale factor of the enlargement? $\frac{5}{2}$

28. ★ OPEN-ENDED MATH *Describe* how you can use dilations to create the figure shown below.

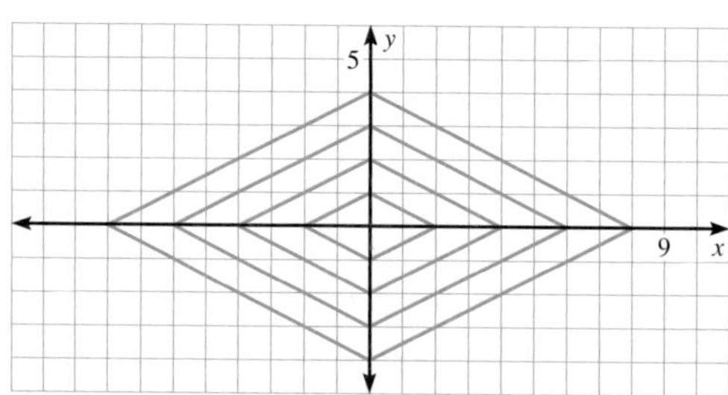

Multiply the coordinates of the smallest quadrilateral by 2, 3, and 4 to create each of the larger quadrilaterals.

Animated Geometry at classzone.com

B **29. MULTI-STEP PROBLEM** $\triangle ABC$ has vertices $A(3, -3)$, $B(3, 6)$, and $C(15, 6)$.

a. Draw a dilation of $\triangle ABC$ using a scale factor of $\frac{2}{3}$. **See margin.**

b. Find the ratio of the perimeter of the image to the perimeter of the original figure. How does this ratio compare to the scale factor? $\frac{2}{3}$**; they are the same.**

c. Find the ratio of the area of the image to the area of the original figure. How does this ratio compare to the scale factor? $\frac{4}{9}$**; it's the square of the scale factor.**

30. ★ EXTENDED RESPONSE Look at the coordinate notation for a dilation on page 409. Suppose the definition of dilation allowed $k < 0$.

a. *Describe* the dilation if $-1 < k < 0$. **It would be a reduction.**

b. *Describe* the dilation if $k < -1$. **It would be an enlargement.**

c. Use a rotation to describe a dilation with $k = -1$. **It would be a rotation of 180°.**

◯ = WORKED-OUT SOLUTIONS on p. WS1 ★ = STANDARDIZED TEST PRACTICE

Quiz, p. 415

4.

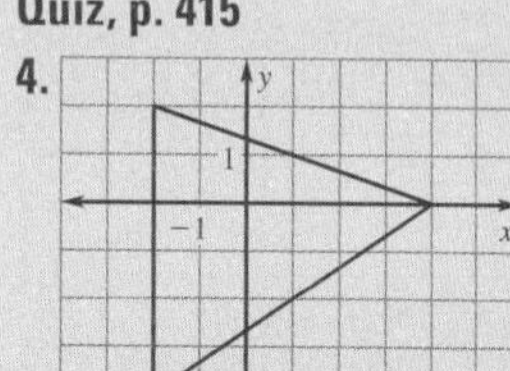

5.

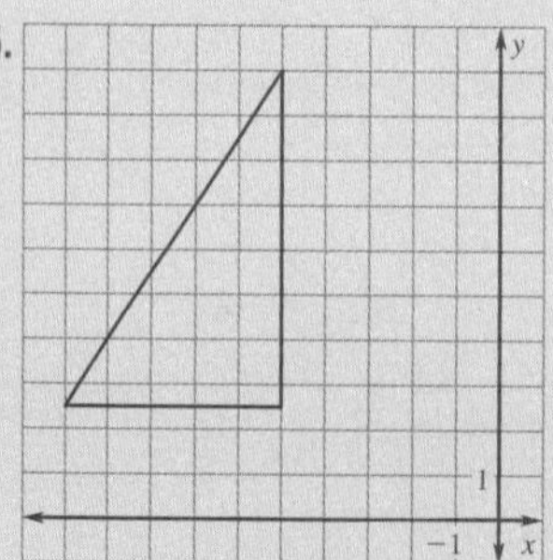

. Perspective awings use nverging es to give the usion that object three-mensional. nce the back the drawing similar to the ont, a dilation an be used create this lusion with the anishing point s the center f dilation; see argin for art.

31. ★ **SHORT RESPONSE** *Explain* how you can use dilations to make a perspective drawing with the center of dilation as a vanishing point. Draw a diagram.

C 32. **MIDPOINTS** Let $\overline{XY}$ be a dilation of $\overline{PQ}$ with scale factor k. Show that the image of the midpoint of $\overline{PQ}$ is the midpoint of $\overline{XY}$. **See margin.**

33. **REASONING** In Exercise 32, show that $\overline{XY} \parallel \overline{PQ}$. **See margin.**

34. **CHALLENGE** A rectangle has vertices $A(0, 0)$, $B(0, 6)$, $C(9, 6)$, and $D(9, 0)$. *Explain* how to dilate the rectangle to produce an image whose area is twice the area of the original rectangle. Make a conjecture about how to dilate any polygon to produce an image whose area is n times the area of the original polygon. **Use a scale factor of $\sqrt{2}$; use a scale factor of $\sqrt{n}$.**

MIXED REVIEW

Simplify the expression. *(p. 873)*

35. $(3x + 2)^2 + (x - 5)^2$ **$10x^2 + 2x + 29$**

36. $4\left(\frac{1}{2}ab\right) + (b - a)^2$ **$b^2 + a^2$**

37. $(a + b)^2 - (a - b)^2$ **$4ab$**

Find the distance between each pair of points. *(p. 15)*

38. $(0, 5)$ and $(4, 3)$ **$2\sqrt{5}$**

39. $(-3, 0)$ and $(2, 4)$ **$\sqrt{41}$**

40. $(-2, -4)$ and $(3, -2)$ **$\sqrt{29}$**

PREVIEW
Prepare for Lesson 7.1 in Exs. 41–43.

Find the value(s) of the variable(s).

41. Area = 6 in.^{2} *(p. 49)*

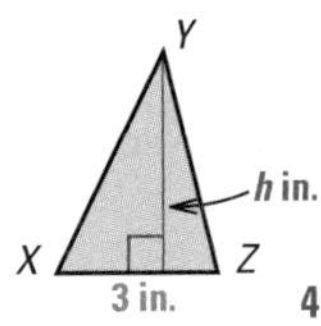

4

42. $\triangle ABC \cong \triangle DCB$ *(p. 256)*

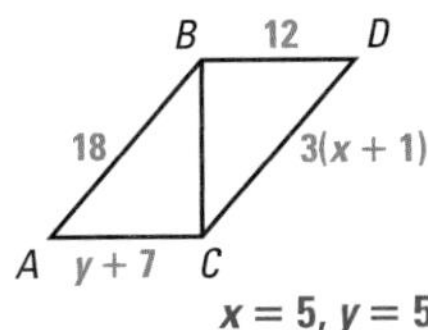

$x = 5, y = 5$

43. $\triangle PQR$ is isosceles. *(p. 303)*

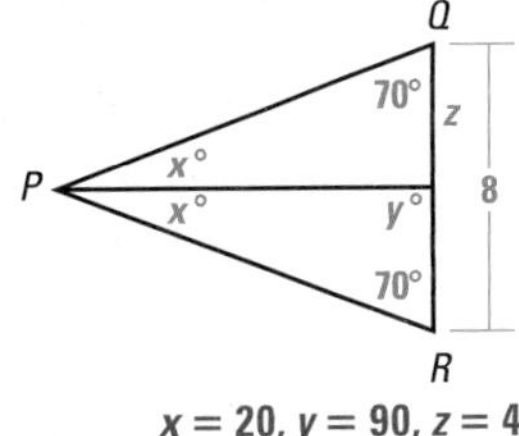

$x = 20, y = 90, z = 4$

QUIZ for Lessons 6.6–6.7

Find the value of x. *(p. 397)*

1. **8**

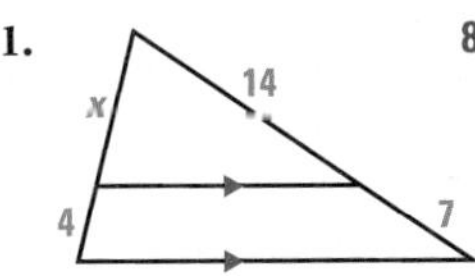

2. **21**

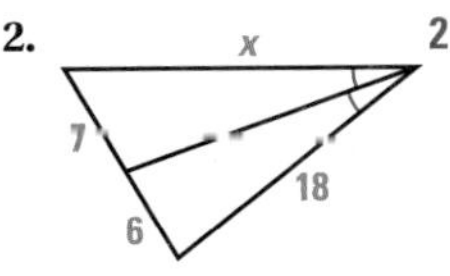

3. **$\frac{21}{2}$**

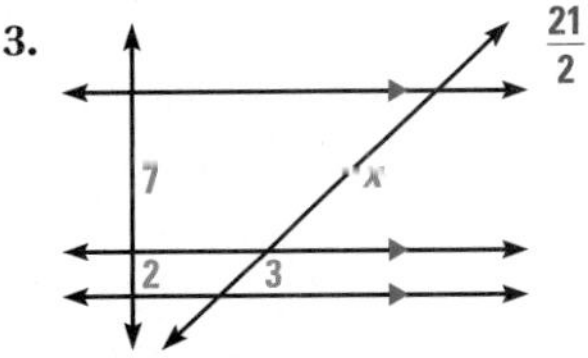

Draw a dilation of $\triangle ABC$ with the given vertices and scale factor k. *(p. 409)* **4, 5. See margin.**

4. $A(-5, 5)$, $B(-5, -10)$, $C(10, 0)$; $k = 0.4$

5. $A(-2, 1)$, $B(-4, 1)$, $C(-2, 4)$; $k = 2.5$

5 ASSESS AND RETEACH

Daily Homework Quiz

Transparency Available

1. Draw a dilation with scale factor 2 of $\triangle ABC$ with vertices $A(1, 0)$, $B(0, 3)$, and $C(3, 2)$. Label the image $\triangle DEF$.

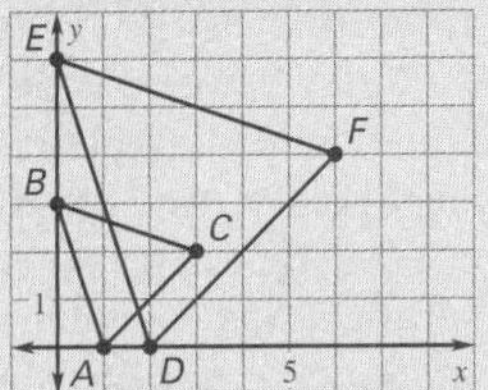

2. $\triangle ABC$ has vertices $A(0, 0)$, $B(0, 8)$, and $C(6, 0)$. Draw a dilation of $\triangle ABC$ using a scale factor of $\frac{1}{2}$. Label the image $\triangle DEF$.

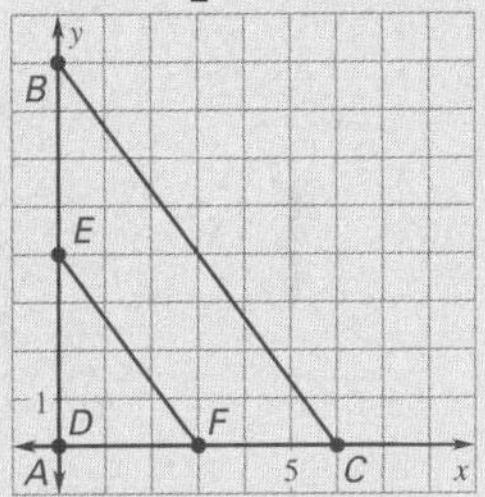

Online Quiz

Available at **classzone.com**

Diagnosis/Remediation

- Practice A, B, C in Chapter 6 Resource Book, pp. 89–94
- Study Guide in Chapter 6 Resource Book, pp. 95–96
- Practice Workbook, pp. 121–123
- @HomeTutor

Challenge

Additional challenge is available in the Chapter 6 Resource Book, p. 99.

Quiz

An easily-readable reduced copy of the quiz (with answers) on Lessons 6.6–6.7 from the Assessment Book can be found on p. 354G.

2a. Use the AA Similarity Postulate since $\angle D$ and $\angle B$ are right angles and $\angle ACB \cong \angle ECD$ by the Vertical Angles Congruence Theorem.

4. Sometimes. *Sample answer:* One possibility is for line ℓ_2 to be vertical with ℓ_1 and ℓ_3 being non-vertical lines so that the ratios of lengths $2x : x$ and $2y : y$ are achieved. In this case, ℓ_1, ℓ_2, and ℓ_3 are not parallel. It is also possible for lines ℓ_1, ℓ_2, and ℓ_3 to be parallel (as they appear in the diagram) with the line labeled with $2x$ and $2y$ drawn at enough of an angle to the three parallel lines so that the ratios of lengths $2x : x$ and $2y : y$ are achieved.

7a.

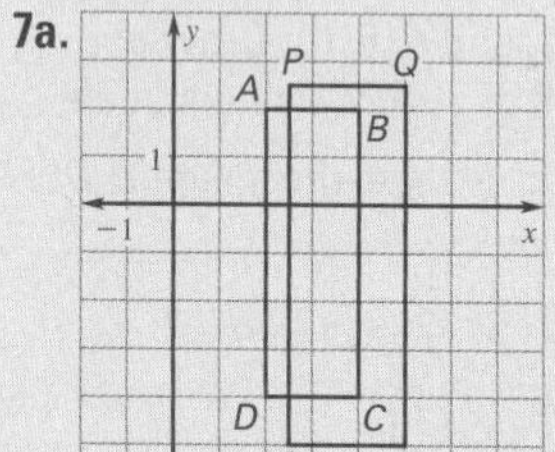

MIXED REVIEW of Problem Solving

STATE TEST PRACTICE
classzone.com

Lessons 6.4–6.7

1. **OPEN-ENDED** The diagram shows the front of a house. What information would you need in order to show that $\triangle WXY \sim \triangle VXZ$ using the SAS Similarity Theorem? $\frac{XW}{XV} = \frac{XY}{XZ}$

2. **EXTENDED RESPONSE** You leave your house to go to the mall. You drive due north 8 miles, due east 7.5 miles, and due north again 2 miles.

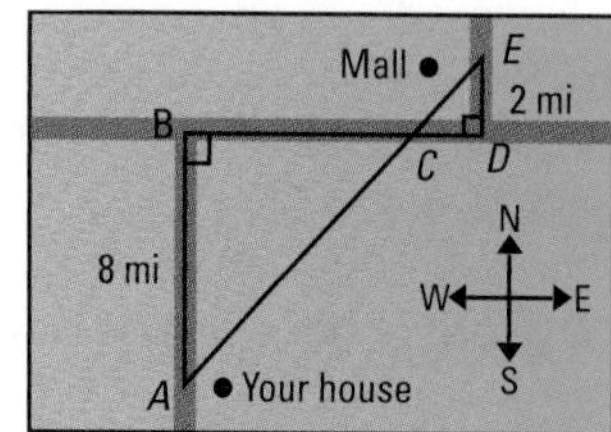

a. *Explain* how to prove that $\triangle ABC \sim \triangle EDC$. **See margin.**

b. Find CD. **1.5 mi**

c. Find AE, the distance between your house and the mall. **12.5 mi**

3. **SHORT RESPONSE** The Cardon cactus found in the Sonoran Desert in Mexico is the tallest type of cactus in the world. Marco stands 76 feet from the cactus so that his shadow coincides with the cactus' shadow. Marco is 6 feet tall and his shadow is 8 feet long. How tall is the Cardon cactus? *Explain.*

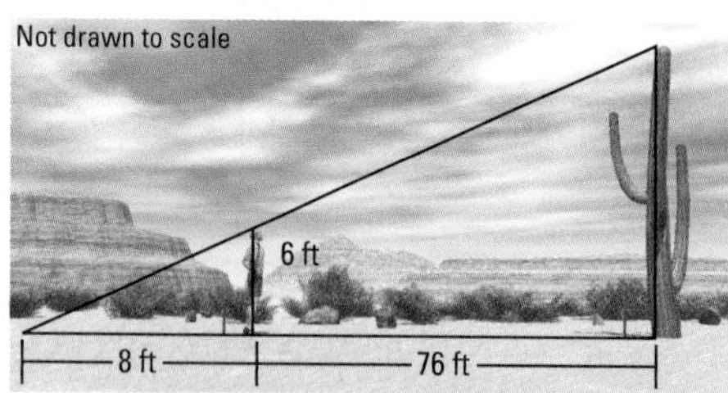

63 ft; set up the proportion $\frac{6}{8} = \frac{x}{84}$ and solve for x.

4. **SHORT RESPONSE** In the diagram, is it *always, sometimes,* or *never* true that $l_1 \parallel l_2 \parallel l_3$? *Explain.* **See margin.**

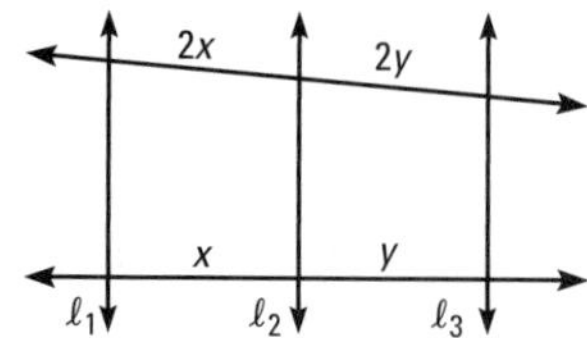

5. **GRIDDED ANSWER** In the diagram of the roof truss, $HK = 7$ meters, $KM = 8$ meters, $JL = 4.7$ meters, and $\angle 1 \cong \angle 2$. Find LM to the nearest tenth of a meter. **5.4 m**

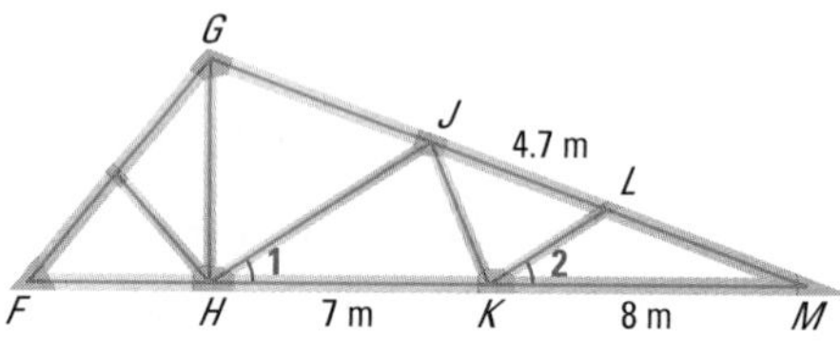

6. **GRIDDED ANSWER** You are designing a catalog for a greeting card company. The catalog features a $2\frac{4}{5}$ inch by 2 inch photograph of each card. The actual dimensions of a greeting card are 7 inches by 5 inches. What is the scale factor of the reduction? **0.4**

7. **MULTI-STEP PROBLEM** Rectangle $ABCD$ has vertices $A(2, 2)$, $B(4, 2)$, $C(4, -4)$, and $D(2, -4)$.

a. Draw rectangle $ABCD$. Then draw a dilation of rectangle $ABCD$ using a scale factor of $\frac{5}{4}$. Label the image $PQRS$. **See margin.**

b. Find the ratio of the perimeter of the image to the perimeter of the original figure. How does this ratio compare to the scale factor? **$\frac{5}{4}$; they are the same.**

c. Find the ratio of the area of the image to the area of the original figure. How does this ratio compare to the scale factor? **$\frac{25}{16}$; it's the square of the scale factor.**

6 CHAPTER SUMMARY

BIG IDEAS *For Your Notebook*

Big Idea 1

Using Ratios and Proportions to Solve Geometry Problems

You can use properties of proportions to solve a variety of algebraic and geometric problems.

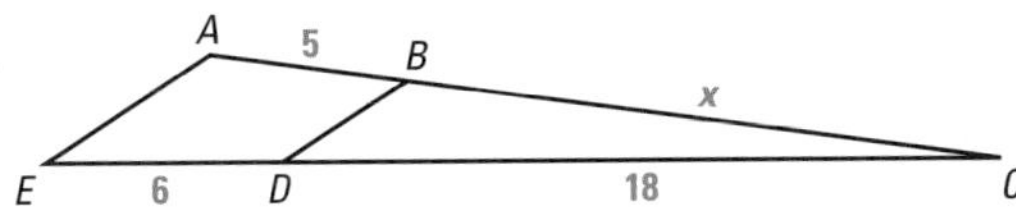

For example, in the diagram above, suppose you know that $\frac{AB}{BC} = \frac{ED}{DC}$. Then you can write any of the following relationships.

$\frac{5}{x} = \frac{6}{18}$ $\quad 5 \cdot 18 = 6x$ $\quad \frac{x}{5} = \frac{18}{6}$ $\quad \frac{5}{6} = \frac{x}{18}$ $\quad \frac{5+x}{x} = \frac{6+18}{18}$

Big Idea 2

Showing that Triangles are Similar

You learned three ways to prove two triangles are similar.

AA Similarity Postulate

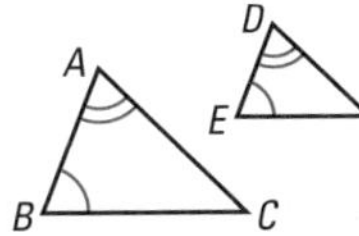

If $\angle A \cong \angle D$ and $\angle B \cong \angle E$, then $\triangle ABC \sim \triangle DEF$.

SSS Similarity Theorem

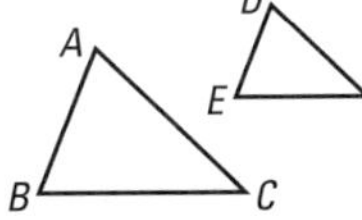

If $\frac{AB}{DE} = \frac{BC}{EF} = \frac{AC}{DF}$, then $\triangle ABC \sim \triangle DEF$.

SAS Similarity Theorem

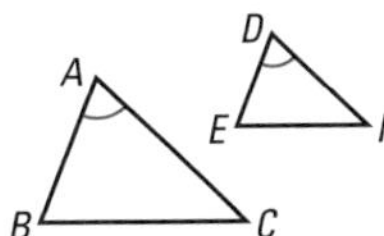

If $\angle A \cong \angle D$ and $\frac{AB}{DE} = \frac{AC}{DF}$, then $\triangle ABC \sim \triangle DEF$.

Big Idea 3

Using Indirect Measurement and Similarity

You can use triangle similarity theorems to apply indirect measurement in order to find lengths that would be inconvenient or impossible to measure directly.

Consider the diagram shown. Because the two triangles formed by the person and the tree are similar by the AA Similarity Postulate, you can write the following proportion to find the height of the tree.

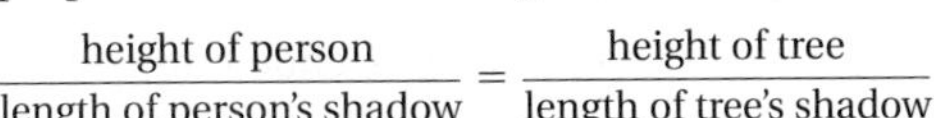

$$\frac{\text{height of person}}{\text{length of person's shadow}} = \frac{\text{height of tree}}{\text{length of tree's shadow}}$$

You also learned about dilations, a type of similarity transformation. In a dilation, a figure is either enlarged or reduced in size.

Additional Resources

The following resources are available to help review the materials in this chapter.

Chapter 6 Resource Book
- Chapter Review Games and Activities, p. 100
- Cumulative Practice, Chs. 1–6, pp. 103–104

Student Resources in Spanish

eWorkbook

@HomeTutor

Vocabulary Practice

Vocabulary practice is available at **classzone.com**

Extra Example 6.1

The measures of the angles in $\triangle ABC$ are in the extended ratio of 1 : 3 : 5. Find the measures of the angles. **20°; 60°; 100°**

6 CHAPTER REVIEW

@HomeTutor
classzone.com
- Multi-Language Glossary
- Vocabulary practice

REVIEW KEY VOCABULARY

For a list of postulates and theorems, see pp. 926–931.

- ratio, *p. 356*
- proportion, *p. 358* means, extremes
- geometric mean, *p. 359*
- scale drawing, *p. 365*
- scale, *p. 365*
- similar polygons, *p. 372*
- scale factor of two similar polygons, *p. 373*
- dilation, *p. 409*
- center of dilation, *p. 409*
- scale factor of a dilation, *p. 409*
- reduction, *p. 409*
- enlargement, *p. 409*

VOCABULARY EXERCISES

Copy and complete the statement.

1. A __?__ is a transformation in which the original figure and its image are similar. **dilation**
2. If $\triangle PQR \sim \triangle XYZ$, then $\frac{PQ}{XY} = \frac{?}{YZ} = \frac{?}{?}$. **QR**; $\frac{RP}{ZX}$
3. **WRITING** *Describe* the relationship between a ratio and a proportion. Give an example of each. **In a ratio two numbers are compared. In a proportion two ratios are set equal to one another. *Sample answer:*** $\frac{2}{4}$, $\frac{6}{10} = \frac{3}{5}$

REVIEW EXAMPLES AND EXERCISES

Use the review examples and exercises below to check your understanding of the concepts you have learned in each lesson of Chapter 6.

6.1 Ratios, Proportions, and the Geometric Mean *pp. 356–363*

EXAMPLE

The measures of the angles in $\triangle ABC$ are in the extended ratio of 3 : 4 : 5. Find the measures of the angles.

Use the extended ratio of 3 : 4 : 5 to label the angle measures as $3x°$, $4x°$, and $5x°$.

$3x° + 4x° + 5x° = 180°$	**Triangle Sum Theorem**
$12x = 180$	**Combine like terms.**
$x = 15$	**Divide each side by 12.**

So, the angle measures are $3(15°) = 45°$, $4(15°) = 60°$, and $5(15°) = 75°$.

EXERCISES

EXAMPLES 1, 3, and 6 on pp. 356–359 for Exs. 4–6

4. The length of a rectangle is 20 meters and the width is 15 meters. Find the ratio of the width to the length of the rectangle. Then simplify the ratio. $\frac{15}{20}$, $\frac{3}{4}$
5. The measures of the angles in $\triangle UVW$ are in the extended ratio of 1 : 1 : 2. Find the measures of the angles. **45°, 45°, 90°**
6. Find the geometric mean of 8 and 12. $4\sqrt{6}$

@HomeTutor
classzone.com
Chapter Review Practice

6.2 Use Proportions to Solve Geometry Problems

pp. 364–370

EXAMPLE

In the diagram, $\frac{BA}{DA} = \frac{BC}{EC}$. Find BD.

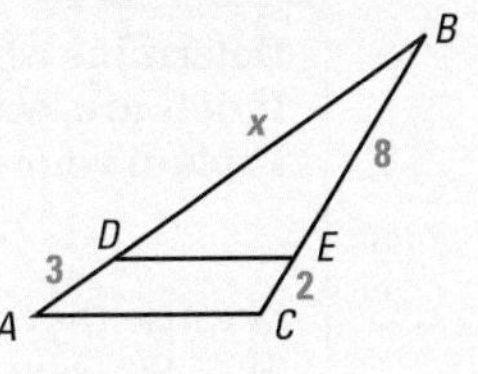

$\frac{x+3}{3} = \frac{8+2}{2}$ **Substitution Property of Equality**

$2x + 6 = 30$ **Cross Products Property**

$x = 12$ **Solve for x.**

EXERCISES

EXAMPLE 2 on p. 365 for Exs. 7–8

Use the diagram and the given information to find the unknown length.

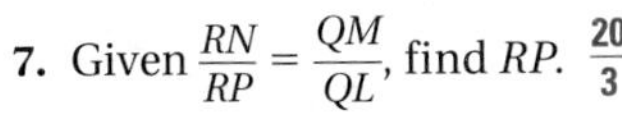

7. Given $\frac{RN}{RP} = \frac{QM}{QL}$, find RP. $\frac{20}{3}$

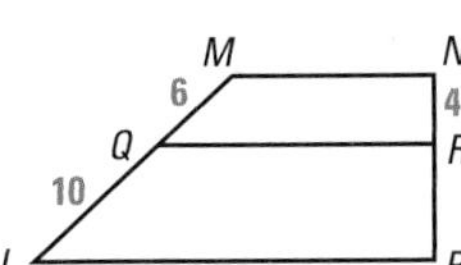

8. Given $\frac{CD}{DB} = \frac{CE}{EA}$, find CD. $\frac{25}{2}$

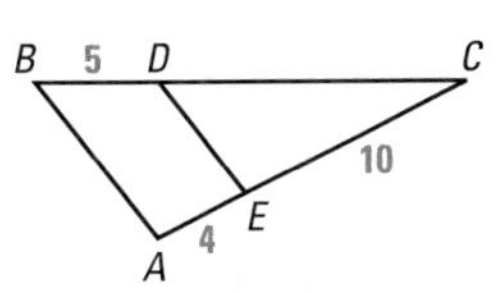

6.3 Use Similar Polygons

pp. 372–379

EXAMPLE

In the diagram, $EHGF \sim KLMN$. Find the scale factor.

From the diagram, you can see that $\overline{EH}$ and $\overline{KL}$ correspond. So, the scale factor of $EHGF$ to $KLMN$ is $\frac{EH}{KL} = \frac{12}{18} = \frac{2}{3}$.

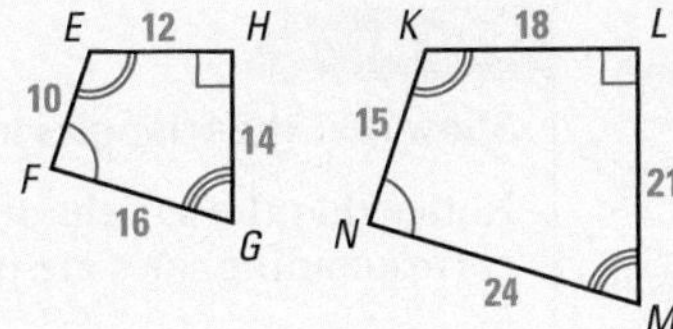

EXERCISES

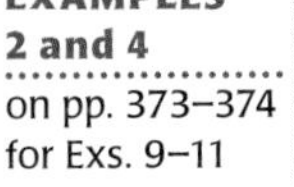

EXAMPLES 2 and 4 on pp. 373–374 for Exs. 9–11

In Exercises 9 and 10, determine whether the polygons are similar. If they are, write a similarity statement and find the scale factor.

9.

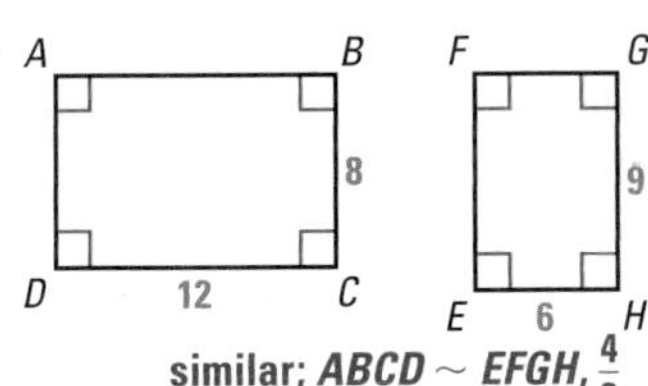

similar; $ABCD \sim EFGH$, $\frac{4}{3}$

10.

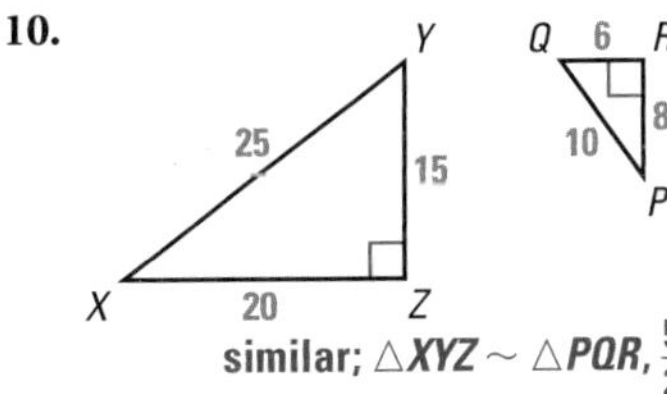

similar; $\triangle XYZ \sim \triangle PQR$, $\frac{5}{2}$

11. POSTERS Two similar posters have a scale factor of 4:5. The large poster's perimeter is 85 inches. Find the small poster's perimeter. **68 in.**

Extra Example 6.2

In the diagram, $\frac{SR}{UR} = \frac{ST}{VT}$. Find SV.

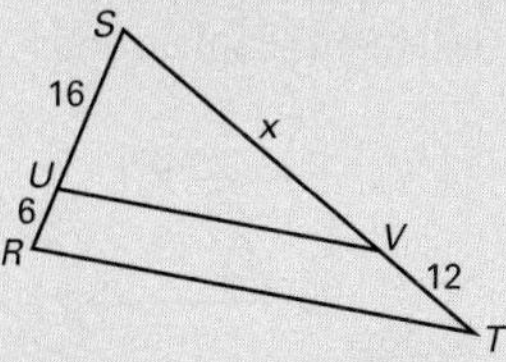

32

Extra Example 6.3

In the diagram, $ABCD \sim FGHJ$. Find the scale factor.

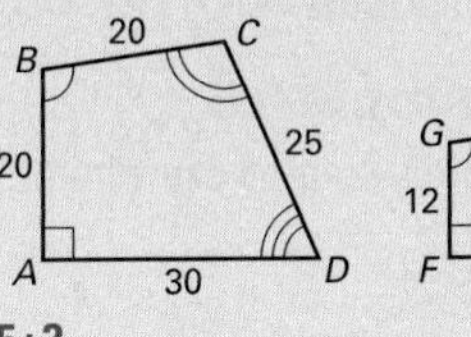

5:3

6 CHAPTER REVIEW

Extra Example 6.4

Determine whether the triangles are similar. If they are, write a similarity statement. Explain your reasoning.

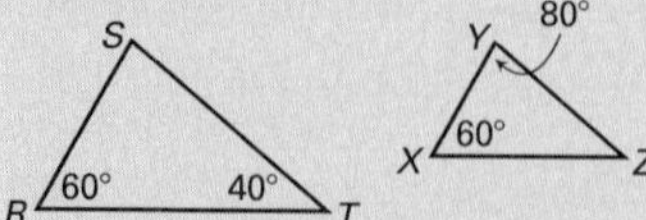

$\angle R \cong \angle X$. By the Triangle Sum Theorem, $40° + 60° + m\angle S = 180°$, so $m\angle S = 80°$, and $\angle S \cong \angle Y$. $\triangle RST \sim \triangle XYZ$ by the AA Similarity Postulate.

Extra Example 6.5

Show that the triangles are similar.

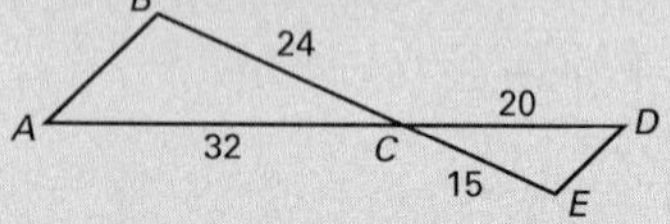

$\frac{AC}{DC} = \frac{32}{20} = \frac{8}{5}$ and $\frac{BC}{EC} = \frac{24}{15} = \frac{8}{5}$, so the sides are proportional. The included angles for these sides are vertical angles, so $\angle ACB \cong \angle DCE$. $\triangle ABC \sim \triangle DEC$ by the SAS Similarity Theorem.

15. Since $\frac{4}{8} = \frac{3.5}{7}$ and the included angle, $\angle C$, is congruent to itself, $\triangle BCD \sim \triangle ACE$ by the SAS Similarity Theorem.

16. Since $\frac{9}{13.5} = \frac{14}{21} = \frac{10}{15}$, $\triangle QRU \sim \triangle QST$ by the SSS Similarity Theorem.

6.4 Prove Triangles Similar by AA

pp. 381–387

12. $\angle RSQ \cong \angle UST$ by the Vertical Angles Theorem and it was given that $\angle Q \cong \angle T$ making $\triangle SQR \sim \triangle STU$ using the AA Similarity Theorem.

EXAMPLES 2 and 3 on pp. 382–383 for Exs. 12–14

EXAMPLE

Determine whether the triangles are similar. If they are, write a similarity statement. Explain your reasoning.

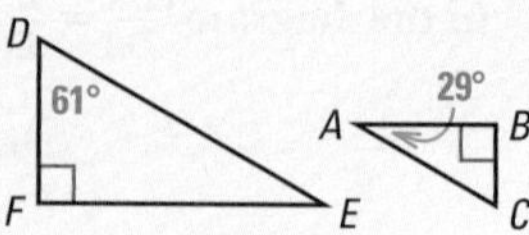

Because they are right angles, $\angle F \cong \angle B$. By the Triangle Sum Theorem, $61° + 90° + m\angle E = 180°$, so $m\angle E = 29°$ and $\angle E \cong \angle A$. Then, two angles of $\triangle DFE$ are congruent to two angles of $\triangle CBA$. So, $\triangle DFE \sim \triangle CBA$.

EXERCISES

Use the AA Similarity Postulate to show that the triangles are similar.

12.

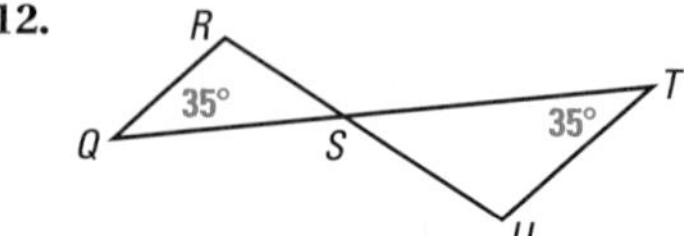

13.

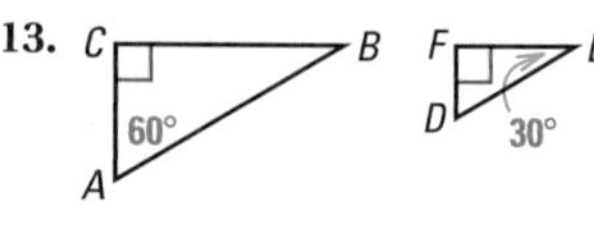

14. **CELL TOWER** A cellular telephone tower casts a shadow that is 72 feet long, while a tree nearby that is 27 feet tall casts a shadow that is 6 feet long. How tall is the tower? **324 ft**

6.5 Prove Triangles Similar by SSS and SAS

pp. 388–395

13. By the Triangle Sum Theorem, $m\angle D = 60°$ so $\angle A \cong \angle D$. $\angle C \cong \angle F$ by the Right Angles Congruence Theorem. So, $\triangle ABC \sim \triangle DEF$ using the AA Similarity Postulate.

EXAMPLE 4 on p. 391 for Exs. 15–16

EXAMPLE

Show that the triangles are similar.

Notice that the lengths of two pairs of corresponding sides are proportional.

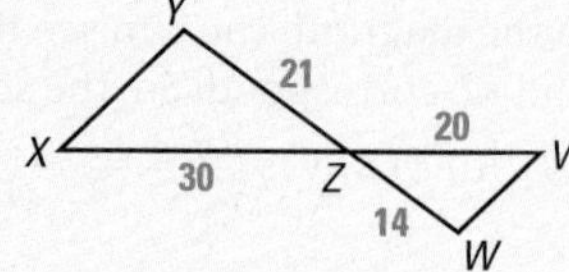

$$\frac{WZ}{YZ} = \frac{14}{21} = \frac{2}{3} \qquad \frac{VZ}{XZ} = \frac{20}{30} = \frac{2}{3}$$

The included angles for these sides, $\angle XZY$ and $\angle VZW$, are vertical angles, so $\angle XZY \cong \angle VZW$. Then $\triangle XYZ \sim \triangle VWZ$ by the SAS Similarity Theorem.

EXERCISES

Use the SSS Similarity Theorem or SAS Similarity Theorem to show that the triangles are similar. **15, 16. See margin.**

15.

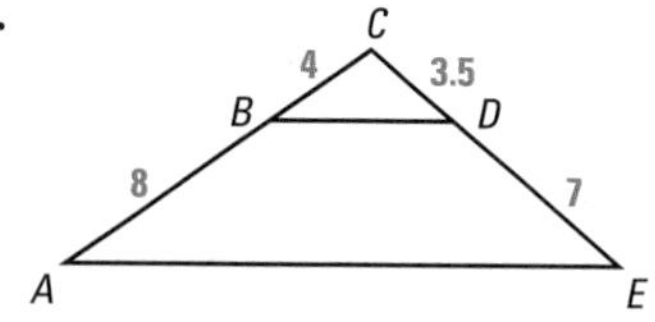

16.

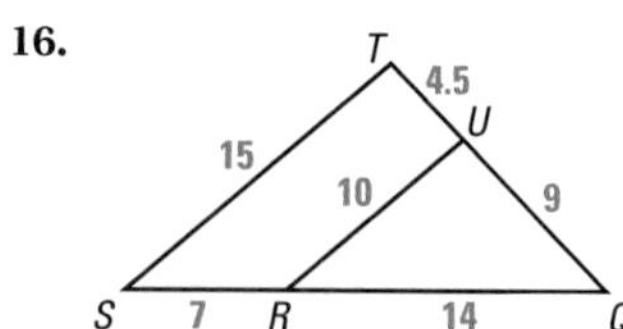

@HomeTutor
classzone.com
Chapter Review Practice

6.6 Use Proportionality Theorems *pp. 397–403*

EXAMPLE

Determine whether $\overline{MP} \parallel \overline{LQ}$.

Begin by finding and simplifying ratios of lengths determined by $\overline{MP}$.

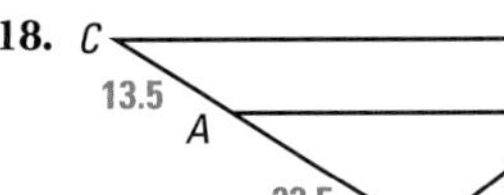

$\frac{NM}{ML} = \frac{8}{4} = \frac{2}{1}$ $\qquad$ $\frac{NP}{PQ} = \frac{24}{12} = \frac{2}{1}$

Because $\frac{NM}{ML} = \frac{NP}{PQ}$, $\overline{MP}$ is parallel to $\overline{LQ}$ by Theorem 6.5, the Triangle Proportionality Converse.

EXERCISES

EXAMPLE 2 on p. 398 for Exs. 17–18

Use the given information to determine whether $\overline{AB} \parallel \overline{CD}$.

17.

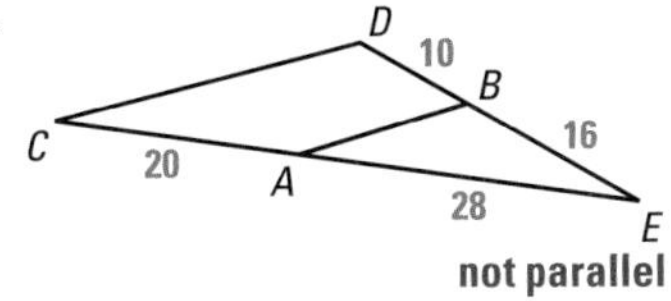

not parallel

18. C, D, 13.5, A, B, 12, 22.5, 20, E

parallel

6.7 Perform Similarity Transformations *pp. 409–415*

EXAMPLE

Draw a dilation of quadrilateral *FGHJ* with vertices *F*(1, 1), *G*(2, 2), *H*(4, 1), and *J*(2, −1). Use a scale factor of 2.

First draw *FGHJ*. Find the dilation of each vertex by multiplying its coordinates by 2. Then draw the dilation.

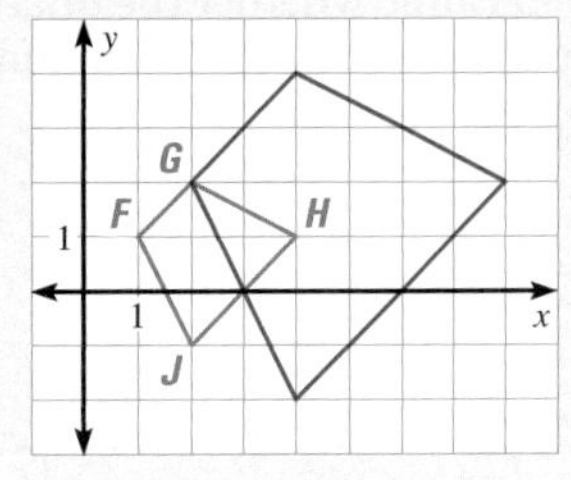

$(x, y) \rightarrow (2x, 2y)$

$F(1, 1) \rightarrow (2, 2)$

$G(2, 2) \rightarrow (4, 4)$

$H(4, 1) \rightarrow (8, 2)$

$J(2, -1) \rightarrow (4, -2)$

EXERCISES

EXAMPLE 1 on p. 409 for Exs. 19–21

Draw a dilation of the polygon with the given vertices using the given scale factor *k*. **19–21. See margin.**

19. $T(0, 8)$, $U(6, 0)$, $V(0, 0)$; $k = \frac{3}{2}$

20. $A(6, 0)$, $B(3, 9)$, $C(0, 0)$, $D(3, 1)$; $k = 4$

21. $P(8, 2)$, $Q(4, 0)$, $R(3, 1)$, $S(6, 4)$; $k = 0.5$

Extra Example 6.6

Determine whether $\overline{DE} \parallel \overline{AC}$.

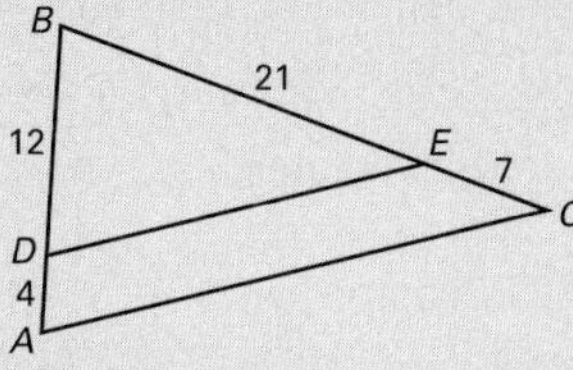

$\frac{BD}{DA} = \frac{12}{4} = \frac{3}{1}$; $\frac{BE}{EC} = \frac{21}{7} = \frac{3}{1}$. So $\frac{BD}{DA} = \frac{BE}{EC}$. $\overline{DE}$ is parallel to $\overline{AC}$ by Theorem 6.5.

Extra Example 6.7

Draw a dilation of quadrilateral *ABCD* with vertices *A*(0, 0), *B*(1, 1), *C*(2, 1), and *D*(2, −1). Label the image *RSTU*. Use a scale factor of 3.

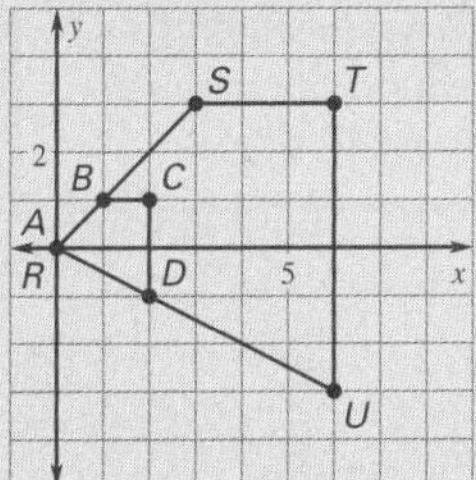

19.

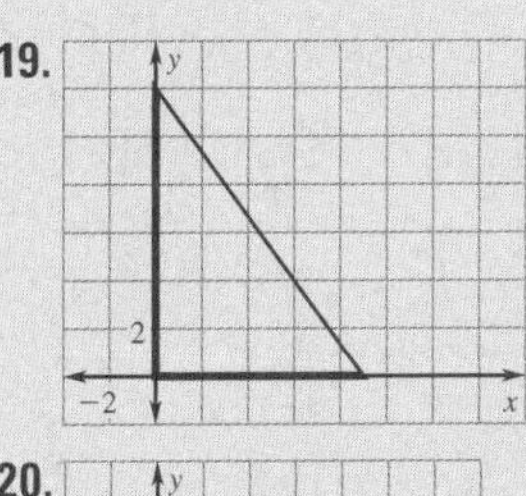

20.

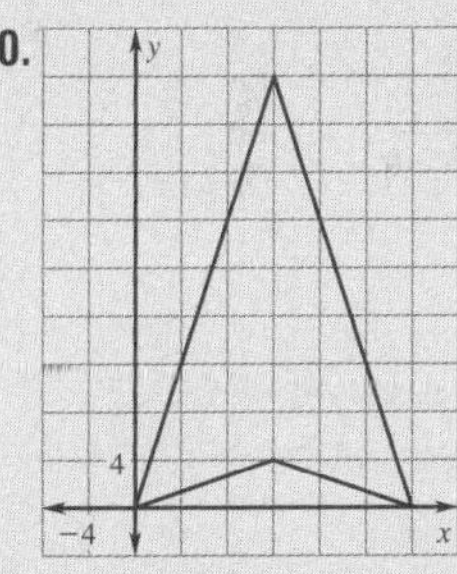

21.

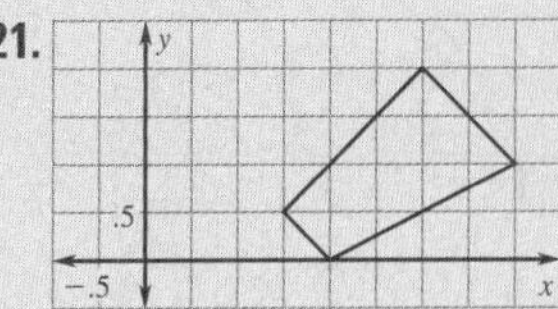

6 CHAPTER TEST

Additional Resources

Assessment Book

- Chapter Test, Levels A, B, C, pp. 79–84
- Standardized Chapter Test, pp. 85–86
- SAT/ACT Chapter Test, pp. 87–88
- Alternative Assessment, pp. 89–90

Test Generator CD-ROM

Chapter Test

Easily-readable reduced copies (with answers) of Chapter Test B, the Standardized Chapter Test, and the Alternative Assessment from the Assessment Book can be found on pp. 354G–354H.

Solve the proportion.

1. $\frac{6}{x} = \frac{9}{24}$ **16**
2. $\frac{5}{4} = \frac{y-5}{12}$ **20**
3. $\frac{3-2b}{4} = \frac{3}{2}$ $-\frac{3}{2}$
4. $\frac{7}{2a+8} = \frac{1}{a-1}$ **3**

In Exercises 5–7, use the diagram where $\triangle PQR \sim \triangle ABC$.

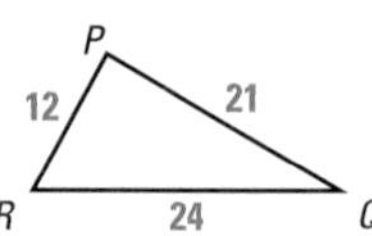

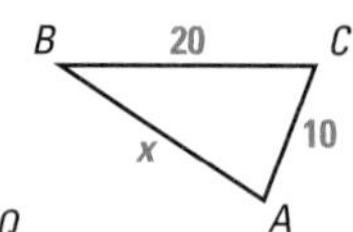

5. List all pairs of congruent angles. **$\angle P$ and $\angle A$, $\angle Q$ and $\angle B$, $\angle R$ and $\angle C$**
6. Write the ratios of the corresponding sides in a statement of proportionality. $\frac{x}{21} = \frac{20}{24} = \frac{10}{12}$
7. Find the value of x. **17.5**

Determine whether the triangles are similar. If so, write a similarity statement and the postulate or theorem that justifies your answer.

8.

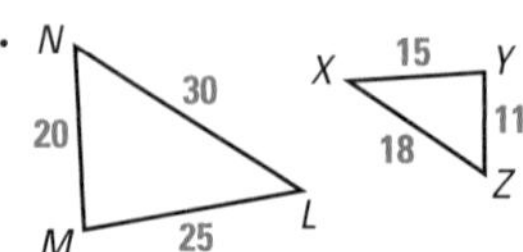

not similar

9.

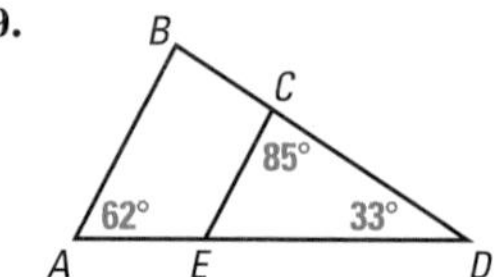

10.

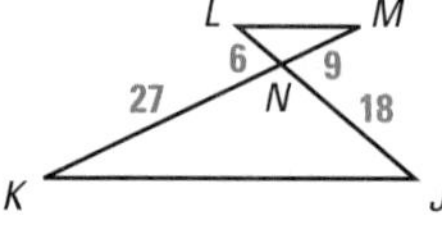

9. similar; $\triangle DEC \sim \triangle DAB$, AA Similarity Postulate

10. similar; $\triangle NKJ \sim \triangle NML$, SAS Similarity Theorem

In Exercises 11–13, find the length of $\overline{AB}$.

11.

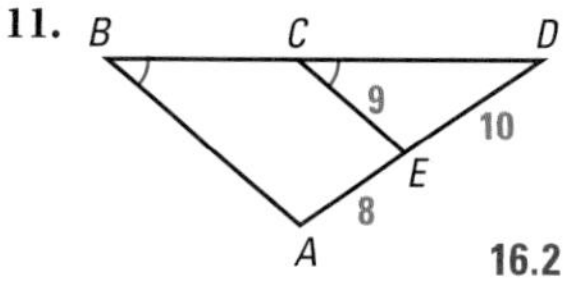

16.2

12.

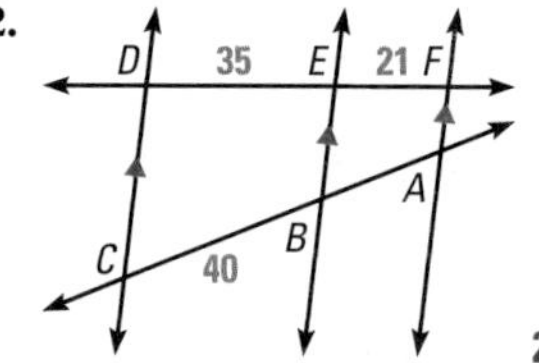

24

13.

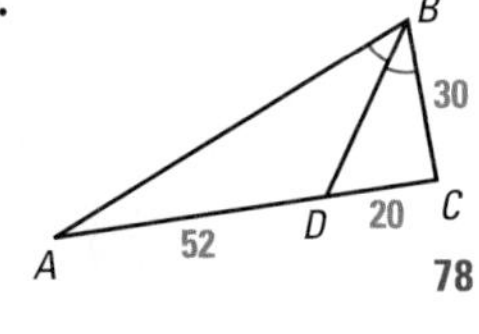

78

Determine whether the dilation from Figure A to Figure B is a *reduction* or an *enlargement*. Then find its scale factor.

14.

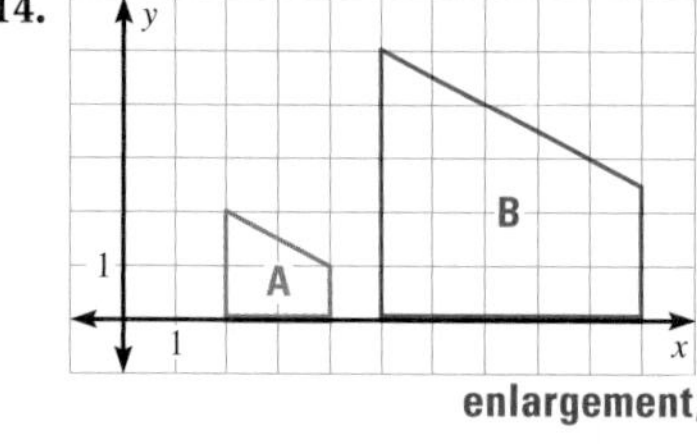

enlargement; $\frac{5}{2}$

15.

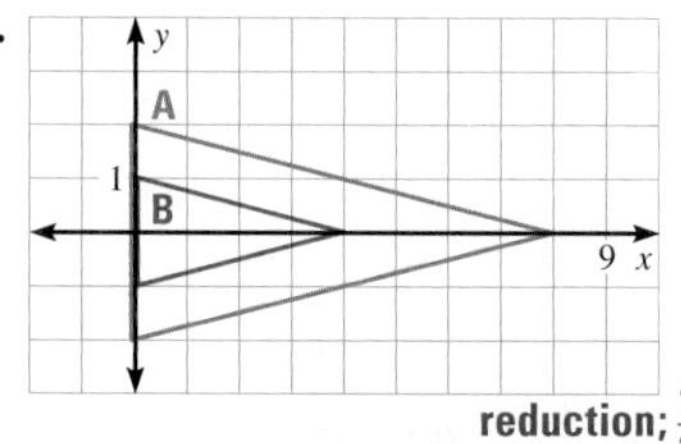

reduction; $\frac{1}{2}$

16. **SCALE MODEL** You are making a scale model of your school's baseball diamond as part of an art project. The distance between two consecutive bases is 90 feet. If you use a scale factor of $\frac{1}{180}$ to build your model, what will be the distance around the bases on your model? **2 ft**

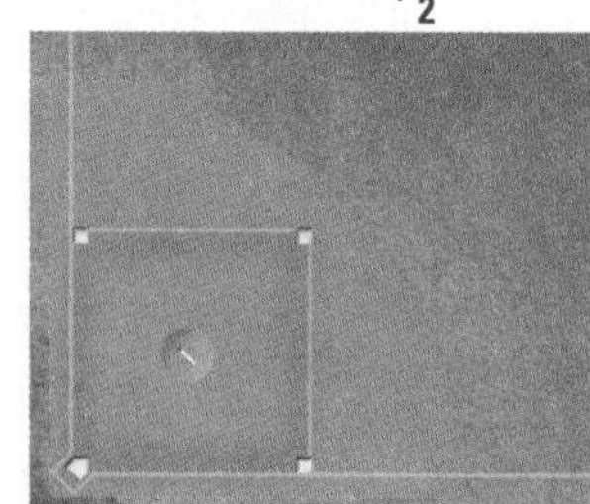

 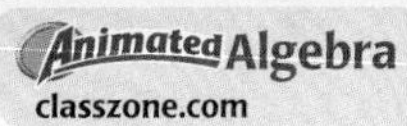

SOLVE QUADRATIC EQUATIONS AND SIMPLIFY RADICALS

A radical expression is *simplified* when the radicand has no perfect square factor except 1, there is no fraction in the radicand, and there is no radical in a denominator.

EXAMPLE 1 Solve quadratic equations by finding square roots

Solve the equation $4x^2 - 3 = 109$.

$4x^2 - 3 = 109$	**Write original equation.**
$4x^2 = 112$	**Add 3 to each side.**
$x^2 = 28$	**Divide each side by 4.**
$x = \pm\sqrt{28}$	$\sqrt{ab} = \sqrt{a} \cdot \sqrt{b}$, **so** $\sqrt{28} = \pm\sqrt{4} \cdot \sqrt{7}$.
$x = \pm 2\sqrt{7}$	**Simplify.**

EXAMPLE 2 Simplify quotients with radicals

Simplify the expression.

a. $\sqrt{\frac{10}{8}}$ **b.** $\sqrt{\frac{1}{5}}$

Solution

a. $\sqrt{\frac{10}{8}} = \sqrt{\frac{5}{4}}$ **Simplify fraction.**

$= \frac{\sqrt{5}}{\sqrt{4}}$ $\sqrt{\frac{a}{b}} = \frac{\sqrt{a}}{\sqrt{b}}$.

$= \frac{\sqrt{5}}{2}$ **Simplify.**

b. $\sqrt{\frac{1}{5}} = \frac{1}{\sqrt{5}}$ $\sqrt{\frac{a}{b}} = \frac{\sqrt{a}}{\sqrt{b}}$ **and** $\sqrt{1} = 1$.

$= \frac{1}{\sqrt{5}} \cdot \frac{\sqrt{5}}{\sqrt{5}}$ **Multiply numerator and denominator by** $\sqrt{5}$.

$= \frac{\sqrt{5}}{5}$ **Multiply fractions.** $\sqrt{a} \cdot \sqrt{a} = a$.

EXERCISES

EXAMPLE 1 for Exs. 1–9

Solve the equation or write *no solution*.

1. $x^2 + 8 = 108$ ± 10
2. $2x^2 - 1 = 49$ ± 5
3. $x^2 - 9 = 8$ $\pm\sqrt{17}$
4. $5x^2 + 11 = 1$ no solution
5. $2(x^2 - 7) = 6$ $\pm\sqrt{10}$
6. $9 = 21 + 3x^2$ no solution
7. $3x^2 - 17 = 43$ $\pm 2\sqrt{5}$
8. $56 - x^2 = 20$ ± 6
9. $-3(-x^2 + 5) = 39$ $\pm 3\sqrt{2}$

EXAMPLE 2 for Exs. 10–17

Simplify the expression.

10. $\sqrt{\frac{7}{81}}$ $\frac{\sqrt{7}}{9}$
11. $\sqrt{\frac{3}{5}}$ $\frac{\sqrt{15}}{5}$
12. $\sqrt{\frac{24}{27}}$ $\frac{2\sqrt{2}}{3}$
13. $\frac{3\sqrt{7}}{\sqrt{12}}$ $\frac{\sqrt{21}}{2}$
14. $\sqrt{\frac{75}{64}}$ $\frac{5\sqrt{3}}{8}$
15. $\frac{\sqrt{2}}{\sqrt{200}}$ $\frac{1}{10}$
16. $\frac{9}{\sqrt{27}}$ $\sqrt{3}$
17. $\sqrt{\frac{21}{42}}$ $\frac{\sqrt{2}}{2}$

Extra Example 1

Solve the equation $3x^2 + 20 = 140$. $\pm 2\sqrt{10}$

Extra Example 2

Simplify the expression.

a. $\sqrt{\frac{14}{18}}$ $\frac{\sqrt{7}}{3}$

b. $\sqrt{\frac{1}{3}}$ $\frac{\sqrt{3}}{3}$

Using Rubrics

The rubric given on the pupil page is a sample of a three-level rubric. Other rubrics may contain four, five, or six levels. For more information on rubrics, see the *Geometry Toolkit*.

Test-Taking Strategy

One strategy to help solve the extended response question is to make another drawing that is simplified. Separate the triangles and label each with points, dimensions, and any congruent pairs of corresponding parts. Students should note that $\angle QPR \cong \angle T$ because both are right angles and $\angle Q \cong \angle Q$ by the Reflexive Property. This lets them conclude that the triangles are similar by the AA Similarity Postulate. Then students should use the new drawing to help them write a proportion about the height of the tree.

Teaching Strategy

For part (c) of the Sample 1 solution, students may think that the student has to change his position as the position of the sun changes. Point out that it is the length of the shadow that changes, and that is reflected in the position of the point Q.

Scoring Rubric

Full Credit
- solution is complete and correct

Partial Credit
- solution is complete but has errors,

or
- solution is without error but is incomplete

No Credit
- no solution is given,

or
- solution makes no sense

5.0 Students prove that triangles are congruent or **similar, and they are able to use the concept of corresponding parts** of congruent triangles.

EXTENDED RESPONSE QUESTIONS

PROBLEM

To find the height of a tree, a student 63 inches in height measures the length of the tree's shadow and the length of his own shadow, as shown. The student casts a shadow 81 inches in length and the tree casts a shadow 477 inches in length.

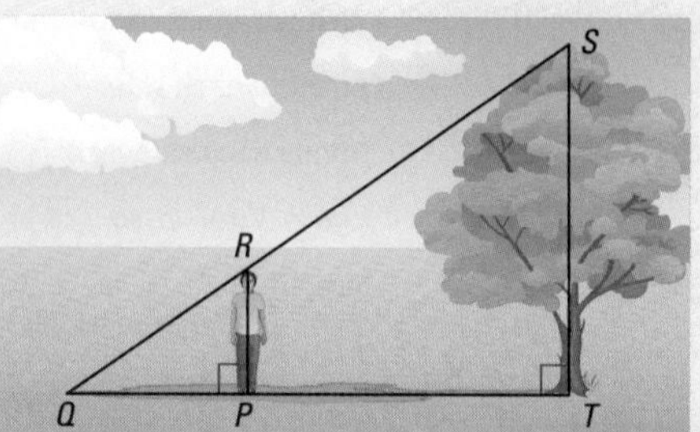

a. Explain why $\triangle PQR \sim \triangle TQS$.

b. Find the height of the tree.

c. Suppose the sun is a little lower in the sky. Can you still use this method to measure the height of the tree? *Explain.*

Below are sample solutions to the problem. Read each solution and the comments in blue to see why the sample represents full credit, partial credit, or no credit.

SAMPLE 1: Full credit solution

a. Because they are both right angles, $\angle QPR \cong \angle QTS$. Also, $\angle Q \cong \angle Q$ by the Reflexive Property. So, $\triangle PQR \sim \triangle TQS$ by the AA Similarity Postulate.

The reasoning is complete.

b.

$$\frac{PR}{PQ} = \frac{TS}{TQ}$$

$$\frac{63}{81} = \frac{TS}{477}$$

$$63(477) = 81 \cdot TS$$

$$371 = TS$$

The height of the tree is 371 inches.

The proportion and calculations are correct.

In part (b), the question is answered correctly.

c. As long as the sun creates two shadows, I can use this method. Angles RPQ and T will always be right angles. The measure of $\angle Q$ will change as the sun's position changes, but the angle will still be congruent to itself. So, $\triangle PQR$ and $\triangle TQS$ will still be similar, and I can write a proportion.

In part (c), the reasoning is complete and correct.

SAMPLE 2: Partial credit solution

In part (a), there is no explanation of why the postulate can be applied.

In part (b), the proportion is incorrect, which leads to an incorrect solution.

In part (c), a partial explanation is given.

a. $\triangle PQR \sim \triangle TQS$ by the Angle-Angle Similarity Postulate.

b. $\frac{PR}{PQ} = \frac{TS}{TP}$

$\frac{63}{81} = \frac{TS}{396}$

$308 = TS$

The height of the tree is 308 inches.

c. As long as the sun creates two shadows, I can use this method because the triangles will always be similar.

SAMPLE 3: No credit solution

The reasoning in part (a) is incomplete.

In part (b), no work is shown.

The answer in part (c) is incorrect.

a. The triangles are similar because the lines are parallel and the angles are congruent.

b. $TS = 371$ inches

c. No. The angles in the triangle will change, so you can't write a proportion.

PRACTICE Apply the Scoring Rubric

Partial credit. ***Sample answer:*** **In part a the student correctly identifies what is needed to prove the triangles similar but does not identify the theorem or postulate used. In part b the student sets up the incorrect proportion and gets the wrong answer. The proportion should be $\frac{PR}{PQ} = \frac{TS}{TQ}$. Part c is correct.**

1. A student's solution to the problem on the previous page is given below. Score the solution as *full credit, partial credit,* or *no credit. Explain* your reasoning. If you choose *partial credit* or *no credit, explain* how you would change the solution so that it earns a score of full credit.

a. $\angle QPR \cong \angle PTS$, and $\angle Q$ is in both triangles. So, $\triangle PQR \sim \triangle TQS$.

b. $\frac{PR}{PQ} = \frac{QT}{ST}$

$\frac{63}{81} = \frac{477}{x}$

$63x = 81(477)$

$x \approx 613.3$

The tree is about 613.3 inches tall.

c. The method will still work because the triangles will still be similar if the sun changes position. The right angles will stay right angles, and $\angle Q$ is in both triangles, so it does not matter if its measure changes.

425

1a. $\angle ACB \cong \angle ECD$ by the Vertical Angles Congruence Theorem, $\angle B \cong \angle D$ is given, so $\triangle ABC \sim \triangle EDC$ by the AA Similarity Postulate.

2a. 41 in., 30 in., 11 in.; since $\overline{AG} \cong \overline{BD}$ and $AG = 41$ inches, then $BD = 41$ inches. Theorem 6.6 along with $\overline{AG} \cong \overline{BD}$ guarantees $BC = 30$ inches and $CD = 11$ inches.

2c. No. *Sample answer:* The ratio $\frac{AM}{AM}$ is not equivalent to $\frac{NH}{PG'}$, $\frac{MN}{MP'}$ or $\frac{AH}{AG'}$ so all corresponding sides are not in proportion.

3a. Yes; $\frac{2}{3}$; corresponding angles are congruent and the ratios of corresponding sides are equal.

4a. AA Similarity; both triangles have $\angle O$, and $\angle PSO$ and $\angle QRS$ are right angles so they are congruent which makes the triangles similar by AA.

4b. $\left(9, \frac{27}{5}\right)$; solve the proportion $\frac{5}{9} = \frac{3}{x}$.

4c. $\frac{3}{5}a$; equation of the line is $y = \frac{3}{5}x$.

EXTENDED RESPONSE

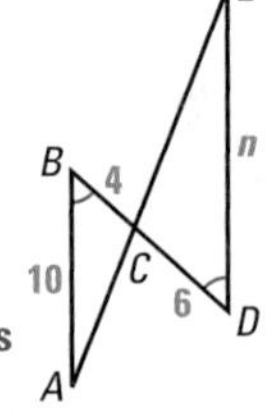

1. Use the diagram.
   a. *Explain* how you know that $\triangle ABC \sim \triangle EDC$. **See margin.**
   b. Find the value of n. **15**
   c. The perimeter of $\triangle ABC$ is 22. What is the perimeter of $\triangle EDC$? *Justify* your answer. **33; the ratio of the perimeters of the two triangles is the same as the ratio of the lengths of corresponding sides in the triangles.**

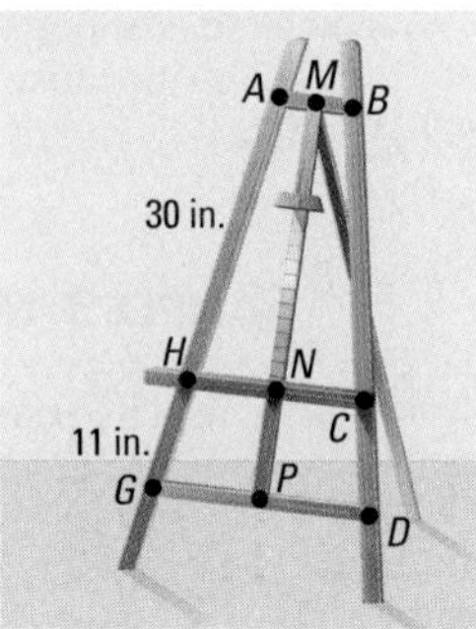

2. On the easel shown at the right, $\overline{AB} \parallel \overline{HC} \parallel \overline{GD}$, and $\overline{AG} \cong \overline{BD}$.
   a. Find BD, BC, and CD. *Justify* your answer. **See margin.**
   b. On the easel, $\overline{MP}$ is a support bar attached to $\overline{AB}$, $\overline{HC}$, and $\overline{GD}$. On this support bar, $NP = 10$ inches. Find the length of $\overline{MP}$ to the nearest inch. *Justify* your answer. **27 in.; using Theorem 6.6 $\frac{PN}{NM} = \frac{GH}{HA}$.**
   c. The support bar $\overline{MP}$ bisects $\overline{AB}$, $\overline{HC}$, and $\overline{GD}$. Does this mean that polygons $AMNH$ and $AMPG$ are similar? *Explain.* **See margin.**

3. A handmade rectangular rug is available in two sizes at a rug store. A small rug is 24 inches long and 16 inches wide. A large rug is 36 inches long and 24 inches wide.
   a. Are the rugs similar? If so, what is the ratio of their corresponding sides? *Explain.* **See margin.**
   b. Find the perimeter and area of each rug. Then find the ratio of the perimeters (large rug to small rug) and the ratio of the areas (large rug to small rug). **120 in., 864 in.^{2}; 80 in., 384 in.^{2}; $\frac{3}{2}$, $\frac{9}{4}$**
   c. It takes 250 feet of wool yarn to make 1 square foot of either rug. How many inches of yarn are used for each rug? *Explain.* **8,000 in., 18,000 in.; divide each area by 144, then multiply by 250 • 12.**
   d. The price of a large rug is 1.5 times the price of a small rug. The store owner wants to change the prices for the rugs, so that the price for each rug is based on the amount of yarn used to make the rug. If the owner changes the prices, about how many times as much will the price of a large rug be than the price of a small rug? *Explain.* **2.25 times greater; the large rug uses 2.25 times as much yarn.**

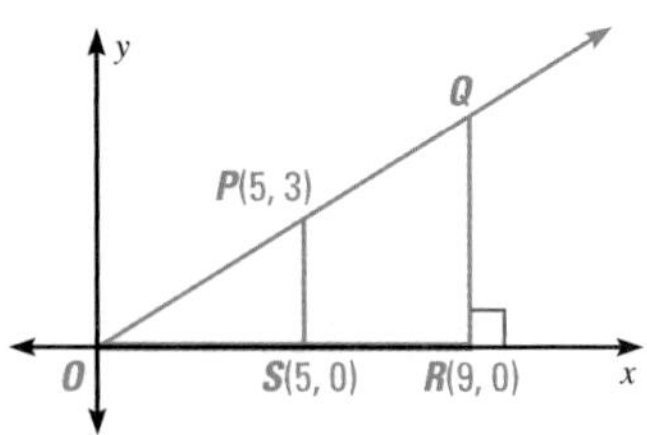

4. In the diagram shown at the right, $\overleftrightarrow{OQ}$ passes through the origin. **a–c. See margin.**
   a. Explain how you know that $\triangle OPS \sim \triangle OQR$.
   b. Find the coordinates of point Q. *Justify* your answer.
   c. The x-coordinate of a point on $\overleftrightarrow{OQ}$ is a. Write the y-coordinate of this point in terms of a. *Justify* your answer.

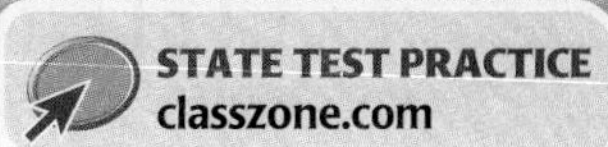
STATE TEST PRACTICE
classzone.com

MULTIPLE CHOICE

5. If $\triangle PQR \sim \triangle STU$, which proportion is not necessarily true? **B**

Ⓐ $\frac{PQ}{QR} = \frac{ST}{TU}$ Ⓑ $\frac{PQ}{SU} = \frac{PR}{TU}$

Ⓒ $\frac{PR}{SU} = \frac{QR}{TU}$ Ⓓ $\frac{PQ}{PR} = \frac{ST}{SU}$

6. On a map, the distance between two cities is $2\frac{3}{4}$ inches. The scale on the map is 1 in.:80 mi. What is the actual distance between the two cities? **D**

Ⓐ 160 mi Ⓑ 180 mi

Ⓒ 200 mi Ⓓ 220 mi

7. In the diagram, what is the scale factor of the dilation from $\triangle PQR$ to $\triangle TUV$? **B**

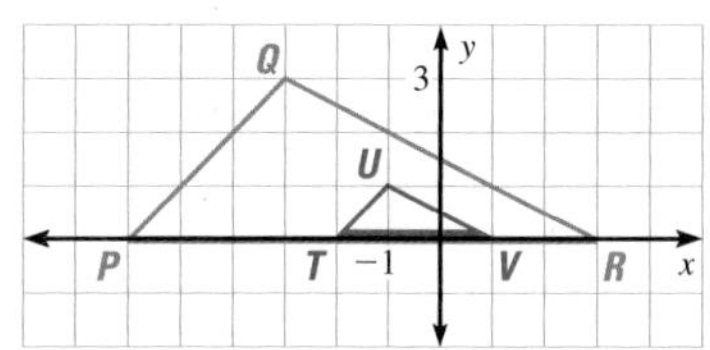

Ⓐ $\frac{1}{2}$ Ⓑ $\frac{1}{3}$

Ⓒ 2 Ⓓ 3

GRIDDED ANSWER

8. Find the value of x. **6**

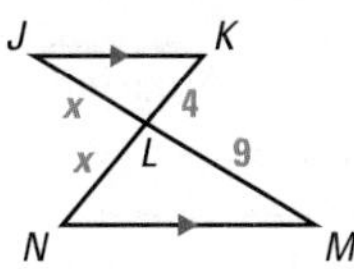

9. In the diagram below, $\triangle PQM \sim \triangle NMR$, and $\overline{MR} \cong \overline{QR}$. If $NR = 12$, find PM. **24**

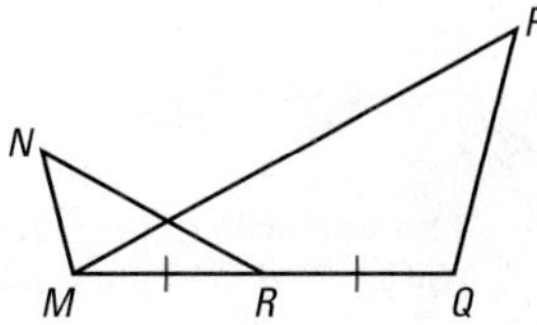

10. Given $GE = 10$, find HE. **3.75**

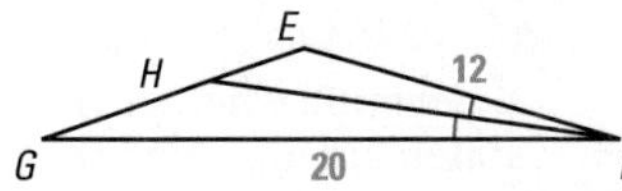

11. In an acute isosceles triangle, the measures of two of the angles are in the ratio 4 : 1. Find the measure of a base angle in the triangle. **80°**

SHORT RESPONSE

12. On a school campus, the gym is 400 feet from the art studio.

a. Suppose you draw a map of the school campus using a scale of $\frac{1}{4}$ inch: 100 feet. How far will the gym be from the art studio on your map? **1 in.**

b. Suppose you draw a map of the school campus using a scale of $\frac{1}{2}$ inch : 100 feet. Will the distance from the gym to the art studio on this map be *greater than* or *less than* the distance on the map in part (a)? *Explain.* **Greater than. *Sample answer:* The distance will be 2 inches.**

13. Rectangles $ABCD$ and $EFGH$ are similar, and the ratio of AB to EF is 1 : 3. In each rectangle, the length is twice the width. The area of $ABCD$ is 32 square inches. Find the length, width, and area of $EFGH$. *Explain.*
24 in., 12 in., 288 in.^{2}; use the area and the fact that the length is twice the width to find the length and width of *ABCD* to be 8 inches and 4 inches. Use the ratio of 1 : 3 to find the length and width of *EFGH* to be 24 inches and 12 inches and the area to be 288 square inches.

Additional Resources

The following resources are available to help review the materials in Chapters 1–6.

Chapter Resource Books

- Chapter 4 CRB, Cumulative Review, pp. 119–120
- Chapter 5 CRB, Cumulative Review, pp. 94–95
- Chapter 6 CRB, Cumulative Review, pp. 103–104

Assessment Book

- Cumulative Test, Chapters 1–6, pp. 91–94

5. Equation (Reason)

$3x - 19 = 47$ (Given)

$3x = 66$ (Addition Property of Equality)

$x = 22$ (Division Property of Equality)

6. Equation (Reason)

$30 - 4(x - 3) = -x + 18$ (Given)

$-4(x - 3) = -x - 12$ (Subtraction Property of Equality)

$-4x + 12 = -x - 12$ (Distributive Property)

$-3x + 12 = -12$ (Addition Property of Equality)

$-3x = -24$ (Subtraction Property of Equality)

$x = 8$ (Division Property of Equality)

7. Equation (Reason)

$-5(x + 2) = 25$ (Given)

$x + 2 = -5$ (Division Property of Equality)

$x = -7$ (Subtraction Property of Equality)

Find $m\angle 2$ if $\angle 1$ and $\angle 2$ are (a) complementary angles and (b) supplementary angles. *(p. 35)*

1. $m\angle 1 = 57°$ a. 33° b. 123°
2. $m\angle 1 = 23°$ a. 67° b. 157°
3. $m\angle 1 = 88°$ a. 2° b. 92°
4. $m\angle 1 = 46°$ a. 44° b. 134°

Solve the equation and write a reason for each step. *(p. 105)* 5–7. See margin.

5. $3x - 19 = 47$
6. $30 - 4(x - 3) = -x + 18$
7. $-5(x + 2) = 25$

State the postulate or theorem that justifies the statement. *(pp. 147, 154)*

8. $\angle 1 \cong \angle 8$
9. $\angle 3 \cong \angle 6$
10. $m\angle 3 + m\angle 5 = 180°$
11. $\angle 3 \cong \angle 7$
12. $\angle 2 \cong \angle 3$ Vertical Angles Theorem
13. $m\angle 7 + m\angle 8 = 180°$ Linear Pair Postulate

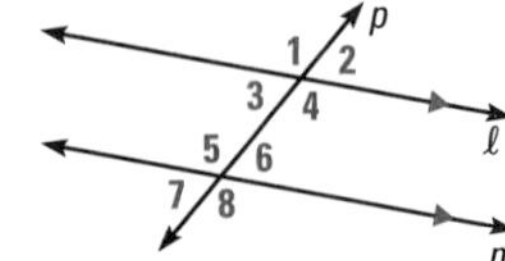

8. Alternate Exterior Angles Theorem
9. Alternate Interior Angles Theorem
10. Consecutive Interior Angles Theorem
11. Corresponding Angles Postulate

The variable expressions represent the angle measures of a triangle. Find the measure of each angle. Then classify the triangle by its angles. *(p. 217)*

14. $m\angle A = x°$, $m\angle B = 3x°$, $m\angle C = 4x°$ 22.5°, 67.5°, 90°; right
15. $m\angle A = 2x°$, $m\angle B = 2x°$, $m\angle C = (x - 15)°$ 78°, 78°, 24°; acute
16. $m\angle A = (3x - 15)°$, $m\angle B = (x + 5)°$, $m\angle C = (x - 20)°$ 111°, 47°, 22°; obtuse

Determine whether the triangles are congruent. If so, write a congruence statement and state the postulate or theorem you used. *(pp. 234, 240, 249)*

17.

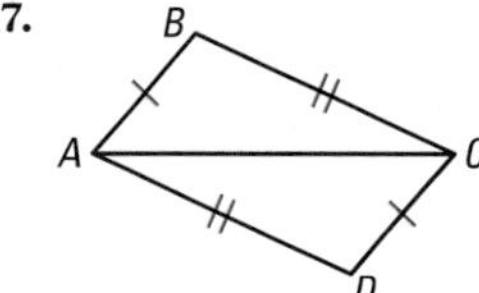

18.

19.

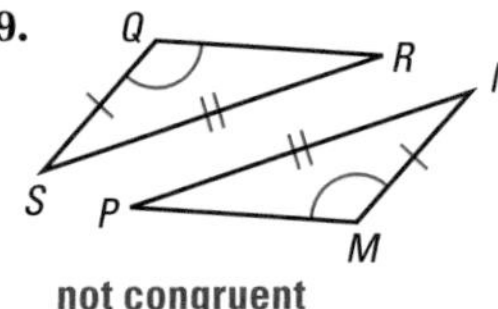

not congruent

17. congruent; $\triangle ABC \cong \triangle CDA$, SSS Congruence Theorem

18. congruent; $\triangle VXW \cong \triangle ZXY$, SAS Congruence Theorem

Find the value of x. *(pp. 295, 303, 310)*

20. 5

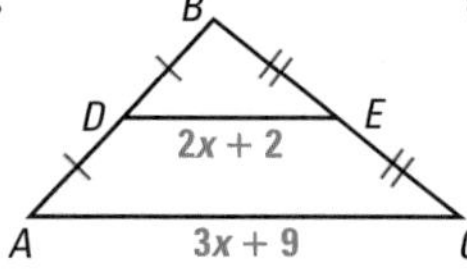

21. 8

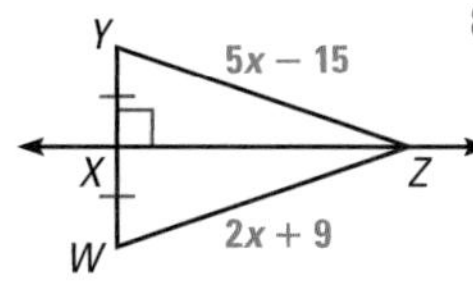

22. 20

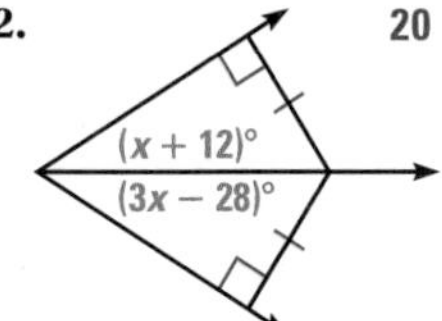

Determine whether the triangles are similar. If they are, write a similarity statement and state the postulate or theorem you used. *(pp. 381, 388)*

23.

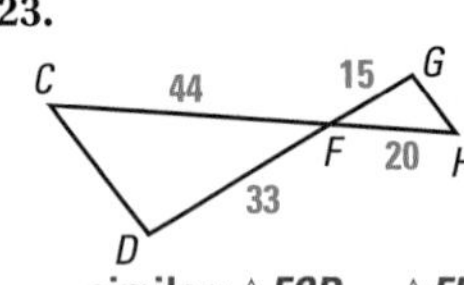

similar; $\triangle FCD \sim \triangle FHG$, SAS Similarity Theorem

24.

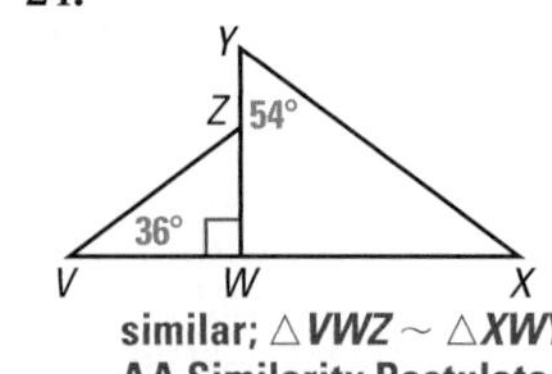

similar; $\triangle VWZ \sim \triangle XWY$, AA Similarity Postulate

25.

not similar

27b. The slope is the monthly membership and the y-intercept is the initial cost to join the club.

28. *Sample answer:* Using the Reflexive Property of Segment Congruence you know that $\overline{HG} \cong \overline{HG}$. Since it is given that $\overline{FG} \cong \overline{HJ}$ you can use the Addition Property for Equality to show that $FH = JG$ which implies they are congruent. $\overline{MF} \perp \overline{FJ}$ and $\overline{KJ} \perp \overline{FJ}$ implies $\angle F$ and $\angle J$ are right angles and therefore are congruent. Since it is given that $\overline{MH} \cong \overline{KG}$, $\triangle FHM \cong \triangle JGK$ using *HL*.

29. *Sample answer:* Since $\overline{BC} \parallel \overline{AD}$ you know that $\angle CBD \cong \angle ADB$ by the Alternate Interior Angles Theorem. $\overline{BD} \cong \overline{BD}$ by the Reflexive Property of Segment Congruence and with $\overline{BC} \cong \overline{AD}$ given, then $\triangle BCD \cong \triangle DAB$ by the SAS Congruence Theorem.

26. PROFITS A company's profits for two years are shown in the table. Plot and connect the points (x, y). Use the Midpoint Formula to estimate the company's profits in 2003. (Assume that profits followed a linear pattern.) *(p. 15)*
See margin for art; $28,625.

Years since 2000, x	1	5
Profit, y (in dollars)	21,000	36,250

27. TENNIS MEMBERSHIP The graph at the right models the accumulated cost for an individual adult tennis club membership for several months. *(p. 180)*

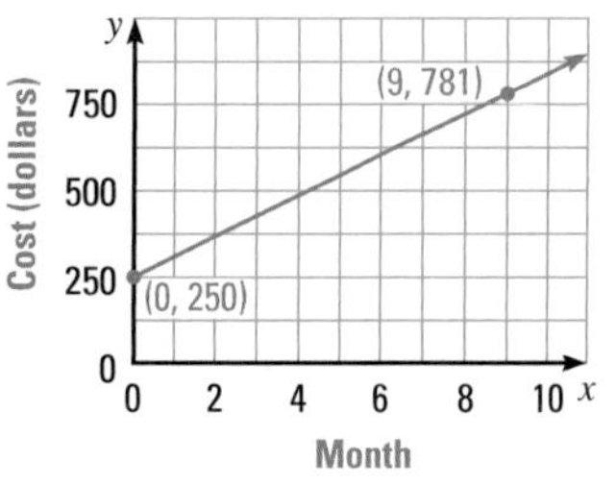

a. Write an equation of the line. **$y = 59x + 250$**

b. Tell what the slope and y-intercept mean in this situation.

c. Find the accumulated cost for one year. **$958**

PROOF **Write a two-column proof or a paragraph proof.** *(pp. 234, 240, 249)*

28. GIVEN ▶ $\overline{FG} \cong \overline{HJ}$, $\overline{MH} \cong \overline{KG}$, $\overline{MF} \perp \overline{FJ}$, $\overline{KJ} \perp \overline{FJ}$

PROVE ▶ $\triangle FHM \cong \triangle JGK$

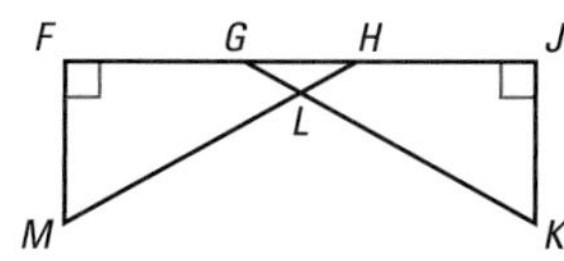

29. GIVEN ▶ $\overline{BC} \parallel \overline{AD}$, $\overline{BC} \cong \overline{AD}$

PROVE ▶ $\triangle BCD \cong \triangle DAB$

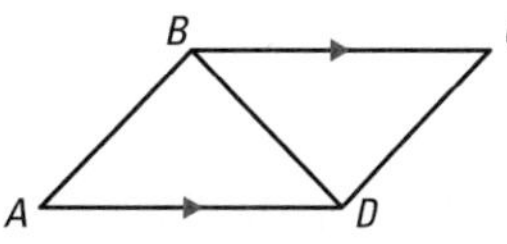

30. COMMUNITY CENTER A building committee needs to choose a site for a new community center. The committee decides that the new center should be located so that it is the same distance from each of the three local schools. Use the diagram to make a sketch of the triangle formed by the three schools. *Explain* how you can use this triangle to locate the site for the new community center. *(p. 303)*
See margin.

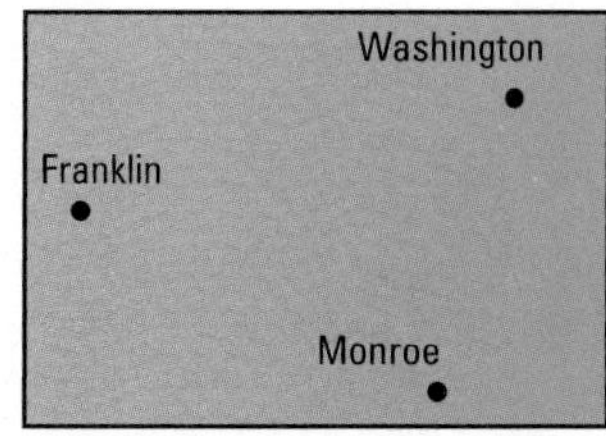

31. GEOGRAPHY The map shows the distances between three cities in North Dakota. *Describe* the range of possible distances from Bowman to Ellendale. *(p. 328)*
43 mi < d < 397 mi

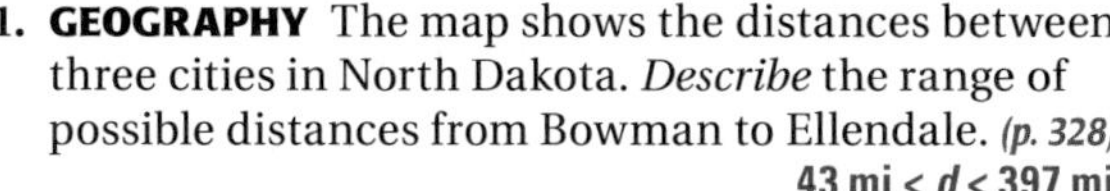

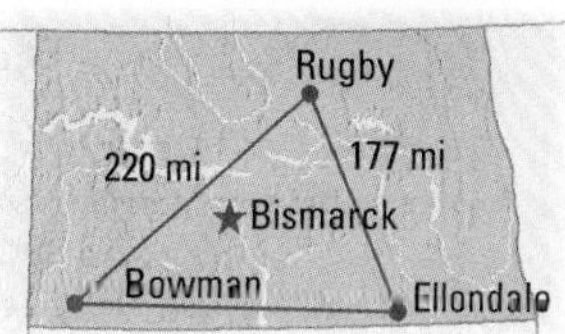

32. CALENDAR You send 12 photos to a company that makes personalized wall calendars. The company enlarges the photos and inserts one for each month on the calendar. Each photo is 4 inches by 6 inches. The image for each photo on the calendar is 10 inches by 15 inches. What is the scale factor of the enlargement? *(p. 409)* **$\frac{5}{2}$**

26.

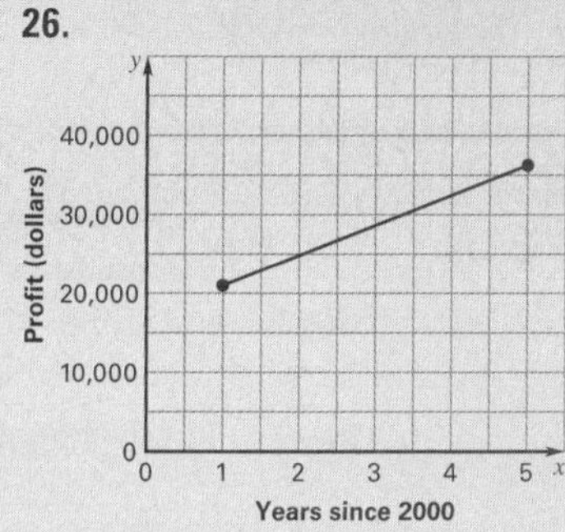

30.

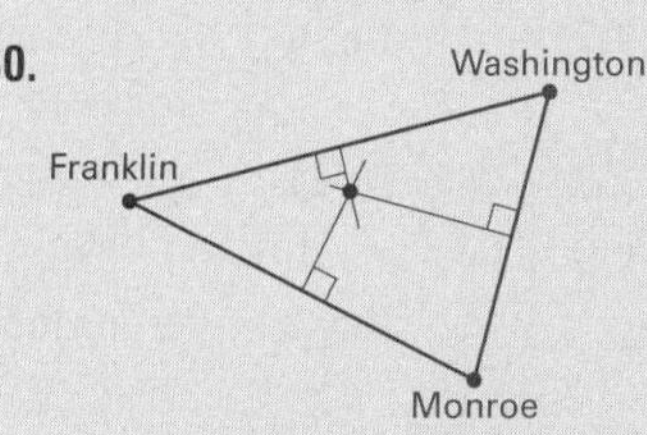

Construct the perpendicular bisectors of each side of the triangle. The point of concurrency will be equidistant from the vertices, which are the locations of the three schools.

7 Pacing and Assignment Guide

REGULAR SCHEDULE

Pre-AP For pacing and assignments for a Pre-AP course, see the *Geometry Toolkit*.

Lesson	Les. Day	BASIC	AVERAGE	ADVANCED
7.1	Day 1	SRH p. 874 Exs. 1–4, 6, 7; pp. 436–439 Exs. 1–10, 31–33, 49, 50	pp. 436–439 Exs. 1, 2, 4–9, 24–26, 31–33, 49, 50	pp. 436–439 Exs. 1, 2, 4, 5, 9, 10, 24–26, 31–33, 36–38*, 49, 50
	Day 2	pp. 436–439 Exs. 11–23, 34, 35, 39–48	pp. 436–439 Exs. 12, 13, 15–17, 20–22, 27, 28, 34–37, 40, 44, 47	pp. 436–439 Exs. 13, 16, 17, 21–23, 27–30*, 34, 35, 42, 48
7.2	Day 1	pp. 444–447 Exs. 1–7, 9–11, 15–18, 24–28, 35–40, 46–52	pp. 444–447 Exs. 1, 2, 5–7, 10–12, 18–20, 24–31, 35–44, 47, 50, 52	pp. 444–447 Exs. 1, 2, 7, 8, 12–14, 21–25, 27–35*, 37–45*, 48, 51, 52
7.3	Day 1	EP p. 906 Exs. 5, 6, 13–16; pp. 453–456 Exs. 1–7, 13–15, 39–49	pp. 453–456 Exs. 1–7, 13–15, 19, 20, 39–49	pp. 453–456 Exs. 1–7, 13–15, 19, 20, 28*, 39–49
	Day 2	pp. 453–456 Exs. 8–12, 16–21, 29–33	pp. 453–456 Exs. 8–12, 16–18, 22–26, 30–37	pp. 453–456 Exs. 9, 10, 17, 18, 21–27, 31–38*
7.4	Day 1	SRH p. 874 Exs. 17, 18, 22–24; pp. 461–464 Exs. 1–7, 11, 29, 30, 36–44	pp. 461–464 Exs. 1–7, 11, 29, 30, 33, 36–44	pp. 461–464 Exs. 1–7, 11, 29, 30, 33, 36–44
	Day 2	pp. 461–464 Exs. 8–10, 12–19, 27, 28, 31	pp. 461–464 Exs. 8–10, 12, 16–25, 27, 28, 31, 32	pp. 461–464 Exs. 9, 10, 17–28*, 31, 32, 34, 35*
7.5	Day 1	SRH p. 874 Exs. 25–28; pp. 469–472 Exs. 1–20, 31–35, 39–47 odd	pp. 469–472 Exs. 1, 2, 4–12 even, 13–26, 31–37, 40, 42, 46	pp. 469–472 Exs. 1, 4–12 even, 15–30*, 32–38*, 41, 44, 47
7.6	Day 1	pp. 477–480 Exs. 1–15, 42–44	pp. 477–480 Exs. 1, 2, 4–6, 8, 9, 11–13, 19–27	pp. 477–480 Exs. 1, 2, 4, 5, 8, 9, 13–15, 19–27, 30, 31
	Day 2	pp. 477–480 Exs. 16–21, 33–38, 45–48	pp. 477–480 Exs. 16–18, 28, 29, 34–39, 42–48 even	pp. 477–480 Exs. 16–18, 28, 29, 32*, 35–41*, 44–48 even
7.7	Day 1	pp. 485–489 Exs. 1–9, 19–24, 37	pp. 485–489 Exs. 1, 2, 4, 5, 7–9, 19–28, 37, 47, 48	pp. 485–489 Exs. 1, 2, 4, 5, 8, 9, 19–28, 31, 32, 37, 47, 48
	Day 2	pp. 485–489 Exs. 10–18, 34–36, 38, 39, 43–48	pp. 485–489 Exs. 12–16, 29–31, 34–36, 38–41, 43–46	pp. 485–489 Exs. 14–18, 29, 30, 33*, 35, 36, 38–42*, 43, 46
Review	Day 1	pp. 494–497 Exs. 1–33	pp. 494–497 Exs. 1–33	pp. 494–497 Exs. 1–33
Assess	Day 1	Chapter 7 Test	Chapter 7 Test	Chapter 7 Test
Yearly Pacing		Chapter 7 Total – 14 days	Chapters 1–7 Total – 94 days	Remaining – 66 days

*Challenge Exercises   EP = Extra Practice   SRH = Skills Review Handbook

BLOCK SCHEDULE

DAY 1	DAY 2	DAY 3	DAY 4	DAY 5	DAY 6	DAY 7
7.1	**7.2**	**7.3 (CONT.)**	**7.4 (CONT.)**	**7.6**	**7.7**	**REVIEW**
pp. 436–439 Exs. 1, 2, 4–9, 12, 13, 15–17, 20–22, 24–28, 31–37, 40, 44, 47, 49, 50	pp. 444–447 Exs. 1, 2, 5–7, 10–12, 18–20, 24–31, 35–44, 47, 50, 52	pp. 453–456 Exs. 8–12, 16–18, 22–26, 30–37	pp. 461–464 Exs. 8–10, 12, 16–25, 27, 28, 31, 32	pp. 477–480 Exs. 1, 2, 4–6, 8, 9, 11–13, 16–29, 34–39, 42–48 even	pp. 485–489 Exs. 1, 2, 4, 5, 7–9, 12–16, 19–31, 34–41, 43–48	pp. 494–497 Exs. 1–33
	7.3	**7.4**	**7.5**			**ASSESS**
	pp. 453–456 Exs. 1–7, 13–15, 19, 20, 39–49	pp. 461–464 Exs. 1–7, 11, 29, 30, 33, 36–44	pp. 469–472 Exs. 1, 2, 4–12 even, 13–26, 31–37, 40, 42, 46			Chapter 7 Test
Yearly Pacing	Chapter 7 Total – 7 days		Chapters 1–7 Total – 47 days		Remaining – 33 days	

Chapter Resource Guide 7

RESOURCE MANAGER

Chapter Resource Book							
CHAPTER SUPPORT							
Parents as Partners (Chapter Overview with home involvement exercises and activity)						p. 1	
LESSON SUPPORT	**7.1**	**7.2**	**7.3**	**7.4**	**7.5**	**7.6**	**7.7**
Teaching Guide/Lesson Plan	p. 3	p. 19	p. 33	p. 46	p. 61	p. 74	p. 89
Activity Masters	p. 5			p. 48			p. 91
Technology Activities & Keystrokes		p. 21				p. 76	
Activity Support Masters	p. 7						
Practice (3 levels)	p. 8	p. 22	p. 35	p. 49	p. 63	p. 78	p. 92
Study Guide	p. 14	p. 28	p. 41	p. 55	p. 69	p. 84	p. 98
Catch-Up for Absent Students	p. 16	p. 30	p. 43	p. 57	p. 71	p. 86	p. 100
Problem Solving/Application	p. 17	p. 31	p. 44	p. 58	p. 72	p. 87	p. 101
Challenge Practice	p. 18	p. 32	p. 45	p. 60	p. 73	p. 88	p. 102
REVIEW							
Chapter Review Games and Activities		p. 103		Cumulative Practice		p. 106	
Project with Rubric		p. 104		Resource Book Answers		A1	

Transparencies	*7.1*	*7.2*	*7.3*	*7.4*	*7.5*	*7.6*	*7.7*
Warm-Up/Daily Homework Quiz	✔	✔	✔	✔	✔	✔	✔
Notetaking Guide	✔	✔	✔	✔	✔	✔	✔
Teacher Support							
Answer Transparencies	✔	✔	✔	✔	✔	✔	✔

ASSESSMENT BOOK

Quizzes	p. 95	SAT/ACT Chapter Test	p. 106
Chapter Tests (3 levels)	p. 98	Alternative Assessment with Rubric	p. 108
Standardized Chapter Test	p. 104		

TECHNOLOGY

- Easy Planner
- Test and Practice Generator
- Power Presentations
- @HomeTutor
- Activity Generator
- Animated Geometry
- Classzone.com
- eEdition Plus Online
- eWorkbook Plus Online
- ML Assessment System

ADDITIONAL RESOURCES

- Worked-Out Solution Key
- Notetaking Guide
- Practice Wookbook
- Geometry Toolkit
- Benchmark Tests
- Remediation Book
- Spanish Study Guide
- Spanish Assessment Book
- Student Resources in Spanish
- Multi-Language Visual Glossary

Practice B

For use with pages 432–439

Use $\triangle ABC$ to determine if the equation is *true* or *false*.

1. $b^2 + a^2 = c^2$ true
2. $c^2 - a^2 = b^2$ true
3. $b^2 - c^2 = a^2$ false
4. $c^2 = a^2 - b^2$ false
5. $c^2 = b^2 + a^2$ true
6. $a^2 = c^2 - b^2$ true

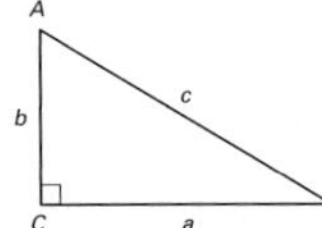

Find the unknown side length. Simplify answers that are radicals. Tell whether the side lengths form a Pythagorean triple.

7. $2\sqrt{3}$; no

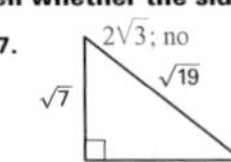

8. 5; yes

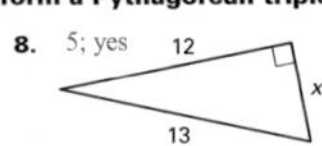

9. $\sqrt{61}$; no

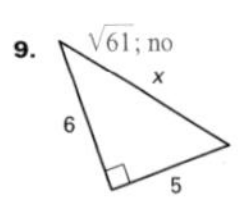

10. 26; yes

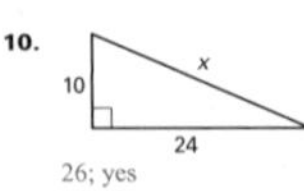

11. 8; no

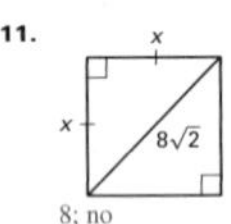

12. $3\sqrt{21}$; no

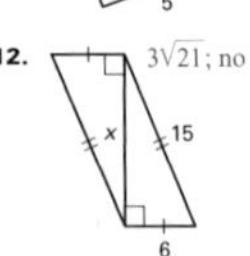

The given lengths are two sides of a right triangle. All three side lengths of the triangle are integers and together form a Pythagorean triple. Find the length of the third side and tell whether it is a leg or the hypotenuse.

13. 40 and 41 9; leg
14. 12 and 35 37; hypotenuse
15. 63 and 65 16; leg
16. 28 and 45 53; hypotenuse
17. 56 and 65 33; leg
18. 20 and 29 21; leg
19. 80 and 89 39; leg
20. 48 and 55 73; hypotenuse
21. 65 and 72 97; hypotenuse

Find the area of a right triangle with given leg ℓ and hypotenuse h. Round decimal answers to the nearest tenth.

22. $\ell = 8$ m, $h = 16$ m 55.4 m^2
23. $\ell = 9$ yd, $h = 12$ yd 35.7 yd^2
24. $\ell = 3.5$ ft, $h = 9$ ft 14.5 ft^2
25. $\ell = 9$ mi, $h = 10$ mi 19.6 mi^2
26. $\ell = 21$ in., $h = 29$ in. 210 in.^{2}
27. $\ell = 13$ cm, $h = 17$ cm 71.2 cm^2

Practice B *continued*

For use with pages 432–439

Find the area of the figure. Round decimal answers to the nearest tenth.

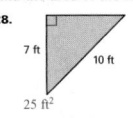

28. 25 ft^2
29. 45.3 cm^2
30. 217 in.^{2}
31. 1056 m^2
32. 32 in.^{2}
33. 312 ft^2

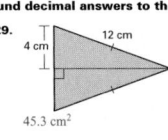

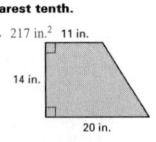

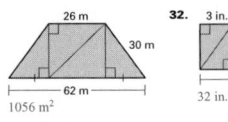

34. **Softball** In slow-pitch softball, the distance of the paths between each pair of consecutive bases is 65 feet and the paths form right angles. Find the distance the catcher must throw a baseball from 3 feet behind home plate to second base. about 95 ft

35. **Flight Distance** A small commuter airline flies to three cities whose locations form the vertices of a right triangle. The total flight distance (from city A to city B to city C and back to city A) is 1400 miles. It is 600 miles between the two cities that are furthest apart. Find the other two distances between cities.

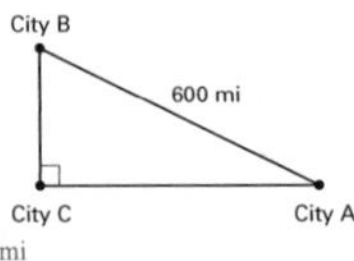

$400 + 100\sqrt{2} \approx 541.4$ mi, $400 - 100\sqrt{2} \approx 258.6$ mi

In Exercises 36–38, use the following information.

Garden You have a garden that is in the shape of a right triangle with the dimensions shown.

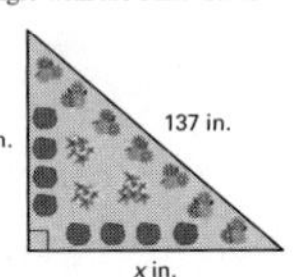

36. Find the perimeter of the garden. 330 in.
37. You are going to plant a post every 15 inches around the garden's perimeter. How many posts do you need? 22 posts
38. You plan to attach fencing to the posts to enclose the garden. If each post costs \$1.25 and each foot of fencing costs \$.70, how much will it cost to enclose the garden? *Explain.*

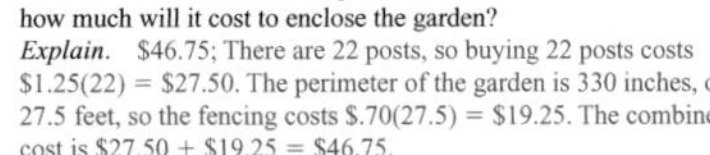

\$46.75; There are 22 posts, so buying 22 posts costs \$1.25(22) = \$27.50. The perimeter of the garden is 330 inches, or 27.5 feet, so the fencing costs \$.70(27.5) = \$19.25. The combined cost is \$27.50 + \$19.25 = \$46.75.

Practice B

For use with pages 440–447

Decide whether the numbers can represent the side lengths of a triangle. If they can, classify the triangle as *right, acute,* or *obtuse.*

1. 5, 12, 13 yes; right
2. $\sqrt{8}$, 4, 6 yes; obtuse
3. 20, 21, 28 yes; acute
4. 15, 36, 39 yes; right
5. $\sqrt{13}$, 10, 12 yes; obtuse
6. 14, 48, 50 yes; right

Graph points *A, B,* and *C*. Connect the points to form $\triangle ABC$. Decide whether $\triangle ABC$ is *right, acute,* or *obtuse.*

7. $A(-3, 5), B(0, -2), C(4, 1)$ acute

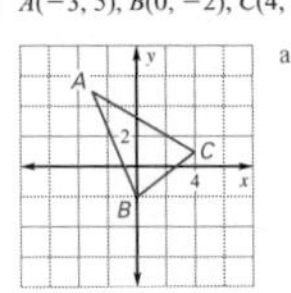

8. $A(-8, -4), B(-5, -2), C(-1, -7)$ obtuse

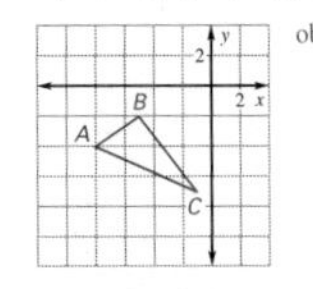

9. $A(4, 1), B(7, -2), C(2, -4)$ acute

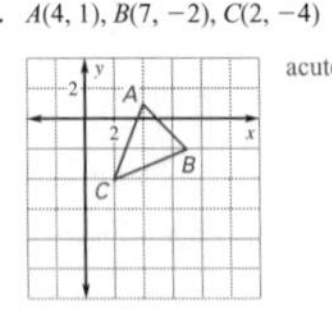

10. $A(-2, 2), B(6, 4), C(-4, 10)$ right

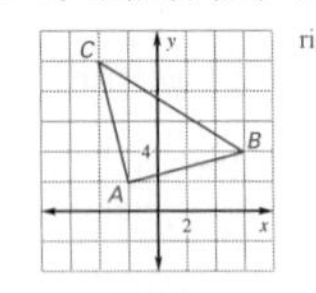

11. $A(0, 5), B(3, 6), C(5, 1)$ obtuse

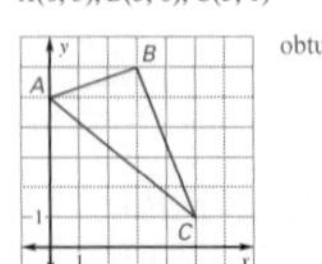

12. $A(-2, 4), B(2, 0), C(5, 2)$ obtuse

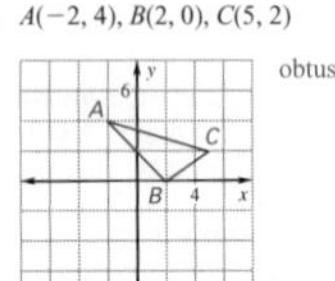

In Exercises 13 and 14, copy and complete the statement with <, >, or =, if possible. If it is not possible, *explain* why.

13. $m\angle J$? $m\angle R$ >
14. $m\angle K + m\angle L$? $m\angle S + m\angle T$ <

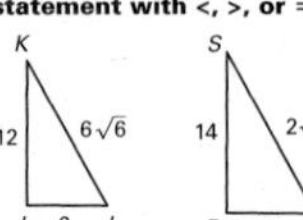
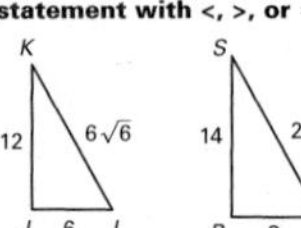
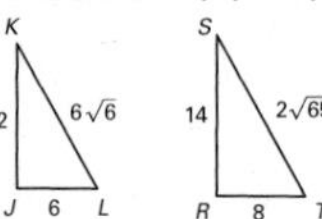

Practice B *continued*

For use with pages 440–447

The sides and classification of a triangle are given below. The length of the longest side is the integer given. What value(s) of x make the triangle?

15. $x, x, 8$; right $x = 4\sqrt{2}$
16. $x, x, 12$; obtuse $0 < x < 6\sqrt{2}$
17. $x, x, 6$; acute $x > 3\sqrt{2}$
18. $x, x + 3, 15$; obtuse $0 < x < 9$
19. $x, x - 8, 40$; right $x = 32$
20. $x + 2, x + 3, 29$; acute $x > 18$

In Exercises 21 and 22, use the diagram and the following information.

Roof The roof shown in the diagram at the right is shown from the front of the house. The slope of the roof is $\frac{5}{12}$. The height of the roof is 15 feet.

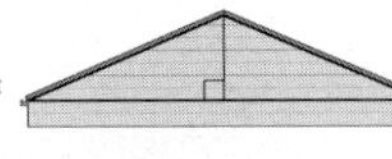

21. What is the length from gutter to peak of the roof? 39 ft

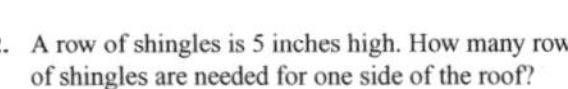

22. A row of shingles is 5 inches high. How many rows of shingles are needed for one side of the roof? about 94 rows

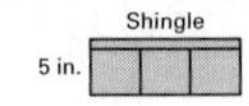

In Exercises 23–25, you will use two different methods for determining whether $\triangle ABC$ is a right triangle. See below.

23. **Method 1** Find the slope of $\overline{AC}$ and the slope of $\overline{BC}$. What do the slopes tell you about $\angle ACB$? Is $\triangle ABC$ a right triangle? How do you know?
24. **Method 2** Use the Distance Formula and the Converse of the Pythagorean Theorem to determine whether $\triangle ABC$ is a right triangle.
25. **Compare** Which method would you use to determine whether a given triangle is right, acute, or obtuse? *Explain.*

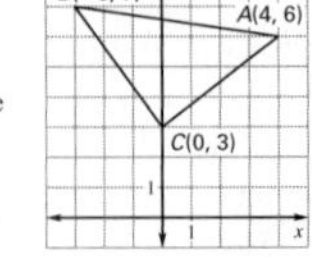

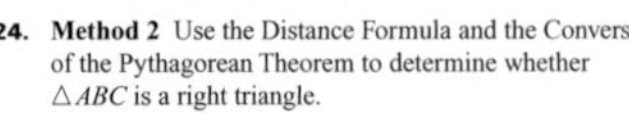

23. $\frac{3}{4}; -\frac{4}{3}$; Because $\left(\frac{3}{4}\right)\left(-\frac{4}{3}\right) = -1$, $\overline{AC} \perp \overline{BC}$.

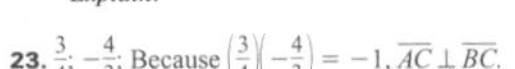

So $\angle ACB$ is a right angle. Therefore $\triangle ABC$ is a right triangle by the definition of a right triangle.

24. $(AC)^2 + (BC)^2 = 25 + 25 = 50 = (AB)^2$, so by the Converse of the Pythagorean Theorem, $\triangle ABC$ is a right triangle.

25. Start by finding the slopes to see if the triangle is a right triangle. If no two slopes lead to perpendicular line segments, then find the distances to determine whether the triangle is acute or obtuse.

LESSON 7.3

Practice B

For use with pages 448–456

Complete and solve the proportion.

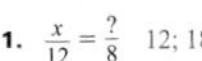

1. $\frac{x}{12} = \frac{?}{8}$ 12; 18 **2.** $\frac{15}{x} = \frac{x}{?}$ 5; $5\sqrt{3}$ **3.** $\frac{9}{x} = \frac{x}{?}$ 20; $6\sqrt{5}$

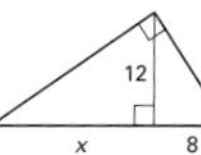

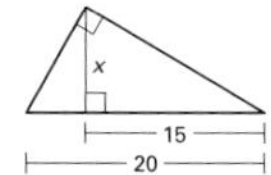

Find the value(s) of the variable(s).

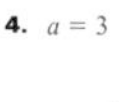

4. $a = 3$ **5.** $x = 4\sqrt{3}$ **6.** $b = \frac{25}{6}$

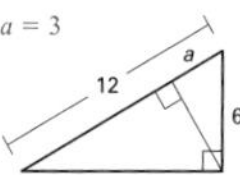

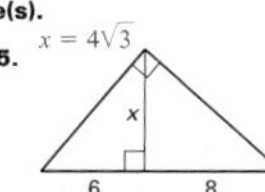

7. $w = 3$ **8.** $x = 12.25$, $y = 3.75$, $z = \frac{7\sqrt{15}}{4}$ **9.** $a = 42\frac{2}{3}$, $b = 40$, $c = 53\frac{1}{3}$

Tell whether the triangle is a right triangle. If so, find the length of the altitude to the hypotenuse. Round decimal answers to the nearest tenth.

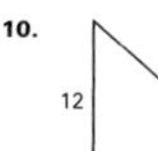

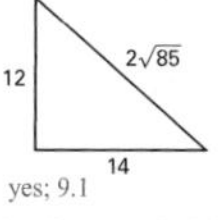

10. yes; 9.1

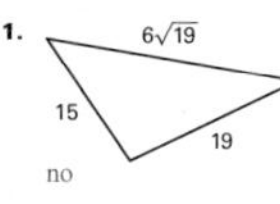

11. no

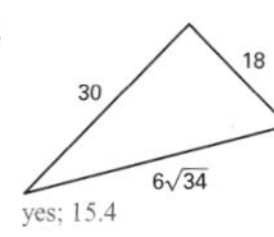

12. yes; 15.4

Use the Geometric Mean Theorems to find *AC* and *BD*.

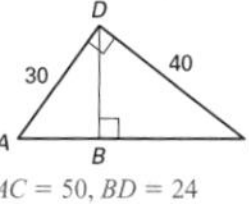

13. $AC = 50$, $BD = 24$

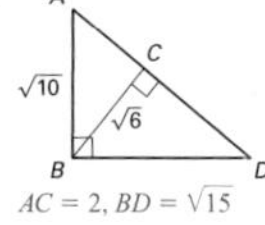

14. $AC = 2$, $BD = \sqrt{15}$

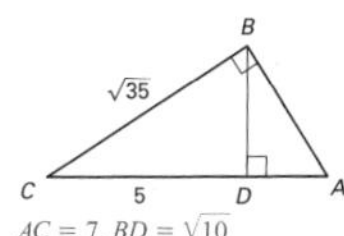

15. $AC = 7$, $BD = \sqrt{10}$

LESSON 7.3

Practice B *continued*

For use with pages 448–456

16. Complete the proof.

GIVEN: $\triangle XYZ$ is a right triangle with $m\angle XYZ = 90°$; $\overline{VW} \parallel \overline{XY}$, $\overline{YU}$ is an altitude of $\triangle XYZ$.

PROVE: $\triangle YUZ \sim \triangle VWZ$

Statements	Reasons
1. $\triangle XYZ$ is a right $\triangle$ with altitude $\overline{YU}$.	1. __?__ Given
2. $\triangle XYZ \sim \triangle YUZ$	2. __?__ Theorem 7.5
3. $\overline{VW} \parallel \overline{XY}$	3. __?__ Given
4. $\angle VWZ \cong \angle XYZ$	4. __?__ Corresponding Angles Postulate
5. $\angle Z \cong \angle Z$	5. __?__ Reflexive Property of Congruence
6. __?__ $\triangle XYZ \sim \triangle VWZ$	6. AA Similarity Postulate
7. $\triangle YUZ \sim \triangle VWZ$	7. __?__ Transitive Property

In Exercises 17–19, use the diagram.

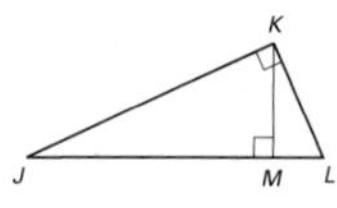

17. Sketch the three similar triangles in the diagram. Label the vertices.

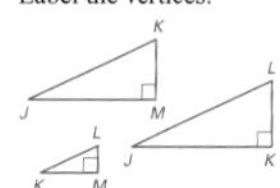

18. Write similarity statements for the three triangles. $\triangle LKJ \sim \triangle KMJ$, $\triangle LKJ \sim \triangle LMK$, $\triangle KMJ \sim \triangle LMK$

19. Which segment's length is the geometric mean of *LM* and *JM*? *KM*

20. Kite Design You are designing a diamond-shaped kite. You know that $AB = 38.4$ centimeters, $BC = 72$ centimeters, and $AC = 81.6$ centimeters. You want to use a straight crossbar $\overline{BD}$. About how long should it be? about 67.8 cm

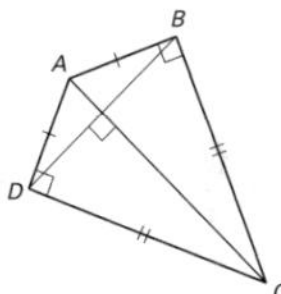

LESSON 7.4

Practice B

For use with pages 457–464

Find the value of *x*. Write your answer in simplest radical form.

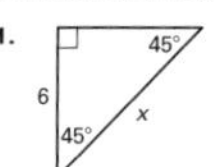

1. $6\sqrt{2}$

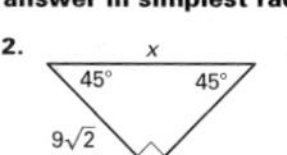

2. 18

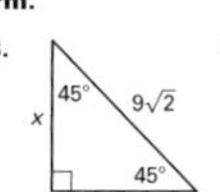

3. 9

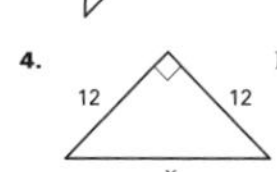

4. $12\sqrt{2}$

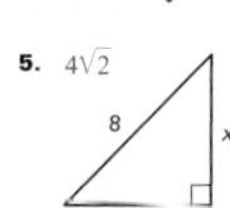

5. $4\sqrt{2}$

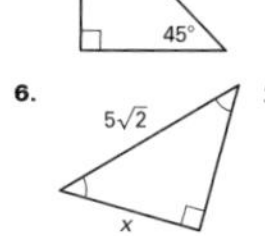

6. 5

Find the value of each variable. Write your answers in simplest radical form.

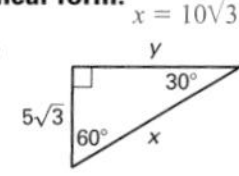

7. $x = 10\sqrt{3}$, $y = 15$

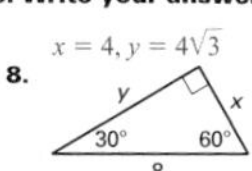

8. $x = 4$, $y = 4\sqrt{3}$

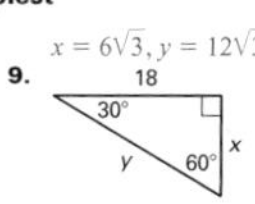

9. $x = 6\sqrt{3}$, $y = 12\sqrt{3}$

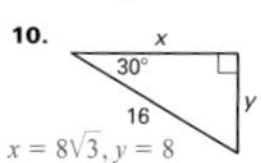

10. $x = 8\sqrt{3}$, $y = 8$

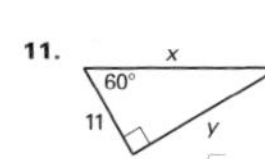

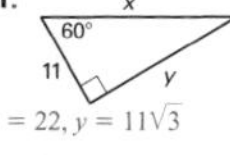

11. $x = 22$, $y = 11\sqrt{3}$

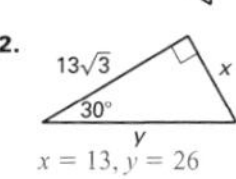

12. $x = 13$, $y = 26$

Complete the table.

13.

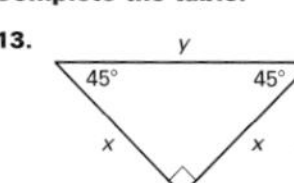

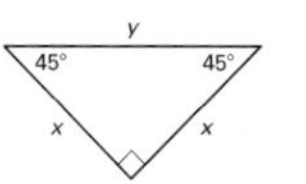

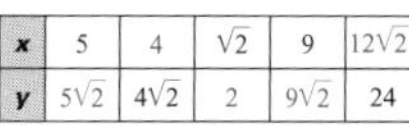

x	5	4	$\sqrt{2}$	9	$12\sqrt{2}$
y	$5\sqrt{2}$	$4\sqrt{2}$	2	$9\sqrt{2}$	24

14.

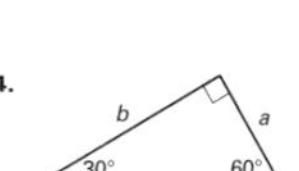

a	9	$3\sqrt{3}$	5	11	8
b	$9\sqrt{3}$	9	$5\sqrt{3}$	$11\sqrt{3}$	$8\sqrt{3}$
c	18	$6\sqrt{3}$	10	22	16

LESSON 7.4

Practice B *continued*

For use with pages 457–464

Find the value of each variable. Write your answers in simplest radical form.

15. $r = 10\sqrt{2}$, $s = 10$

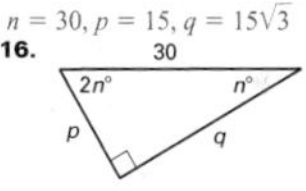

16. $n = 30$, $p = 15$, $q = 15\sqrt{3}$

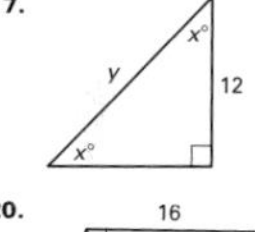

17. $x = 45$, $y = 12\sqrt{2}$

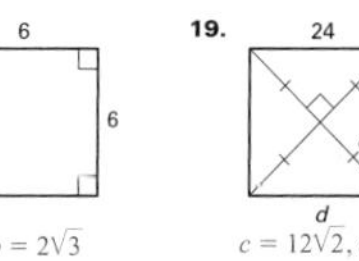

18. $a = 4\sqrt{3}$, $b = 2\sqrt{3}$

19. $c = 12\sqrt{2}$, $d = 24$

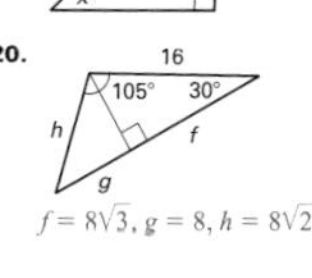

20. $f = 8\sqrt{3}$, $g = 8$, $h = 8\sqrt{2}$

The side lengths of a triangle are given. Determine whether it is a *45°-45°-90° triangle*, a *30°-60°-90° triangle*, or *neither*.

21. 5, 10, $5\sqrt{3}$ 30°-60°-90° **22.** 7, 7, $7\sqrt{3}$ neither **23.** 6, 6, $6\sqrt{2}$ 45°-45°-90°

24. Roofing You are replacing the roof on the house shown, and you want to know the total area of the roof. The roof has a 1-1 pitch on both sides, which means that it slopes upward at a rate of 1 vertical unit for each 1 horizontal unit.

a. Find the values of *x* and *y* in the diagram. $x = y = 12\sqrt{2}$ ft

b. Find the total area of the roof to the nearest square foot. 1188 ft²

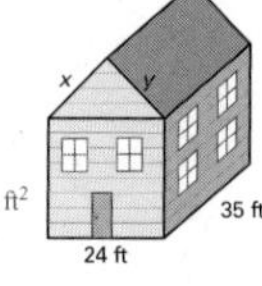

25. Skateboard Ramp You are using wood to build a pyramid-shaped skateboard ramp. You want each ramp surface to incline at an angle of 30° and the maximum height to be 56 centimeters as shown.

a. Use the relationships shown in the diagram to determine the lengths *a*, *b*, *c*, and *d* to the nearest centimeter. $a \approx 97$ cm, $b = d \approx 112$ cm, $c \approx 158$ cm

b. Suppose you want to build a second pyramid ramp with a 45° angle of incline and a maximum height of 56 inches. You can use the diagram shown by simply changing the 30° angle to 45°. Determine the lengths *a*, *b*, *c*, and *d* to the nearest centimeter for this ramp. $a = 56$ cm, $b = d \approx 79$ cm, $c = 112$ cm

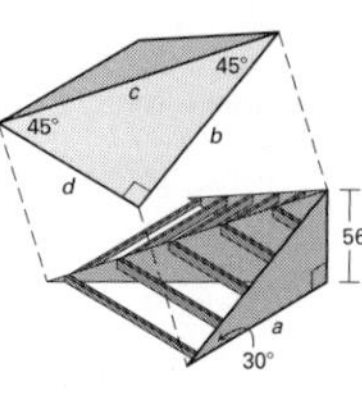

LESSON 7.5 Practice B

For use with pages 466–472

Find tan *A* and tan *B*. Write each answer as a decimal rounded to four decimal places.

1. 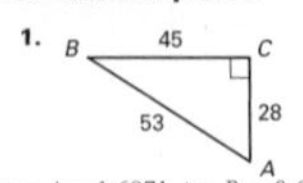

$\tan A = 1.6071, \tan B = 0.6222$

2. 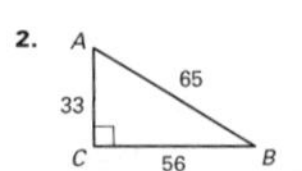

$\tan A = 1.6970, \tan B = 0.5893$

3. 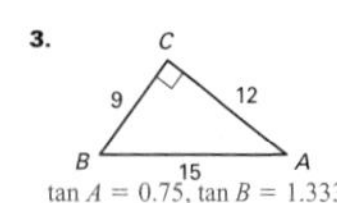

$\tan A = 0.75, \tan B = 1.3333$

Find the value of *x* to the nearest tenth.

4. 10.9 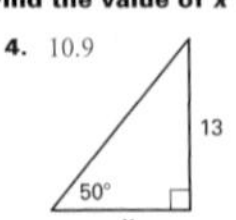

5. 20.2 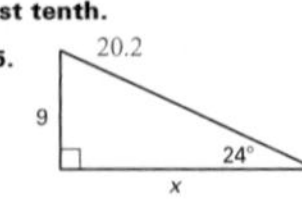

6. 13.9 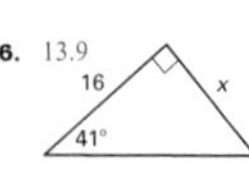

7. 47.0 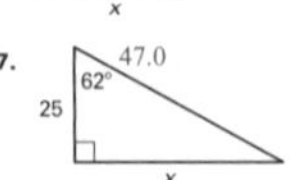

8. 31.1 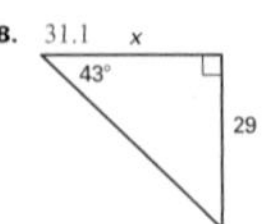

9. 110.8 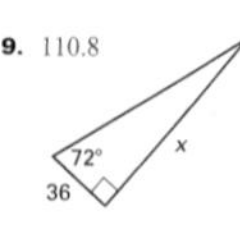

Find the value of *x* using the definition of tangent. Then find the value of *x* using the 45°-45°-90° Triangle Theorem or the 30°-60°-90° Triangle Theorem. *Compare* the results.

10. 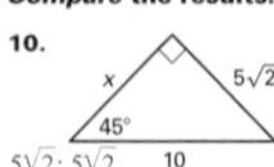

$5\sqrt{2}$; $5\sqrt{2}$

11. 12; 12 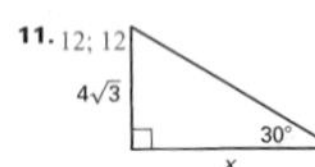

12. 25; 25 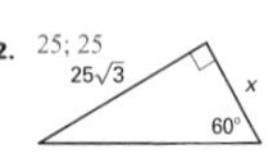

For acute $\angle A$ of a right triangle, find tan *A* by using the 45°-45°-90° Triangle Theorem or the 30°-60°-90° Triangle Theorem.

13. $m\angle A = 30°$ $\frac{\sqrt{3}}{3}$

14. $m\angle A = 45°$ 1

15. $m\angle A = 60°$ $\sqrt{3}$

Use a tangent ratio to find the value of *x*. Round to the nearest tenth.

16. 8.3 (17, 64°, x)

17. 38.6 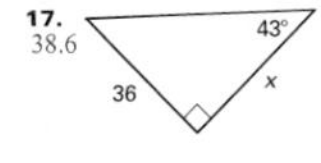

18. 22.5 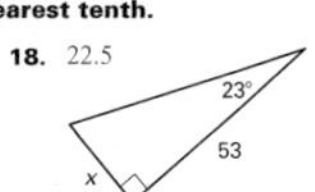

LESSON 7.5

LESSON 7.5 Practice B *continued*

For use with pages 466–472

Find the area of the triangle. Round your answer to the nearest tenth.

19. 72.1 m² 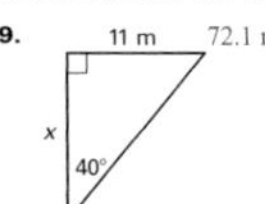

20. 180.0 ft² 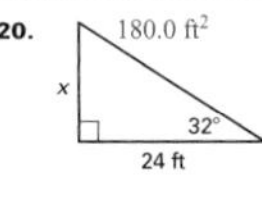

21. 1186.0 in.² 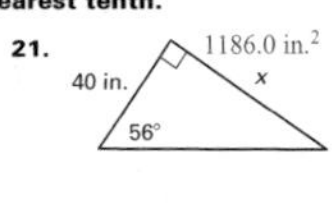

Find the perimeter of the triangle. Round to the nearest tenth.

22. 145.2 in. 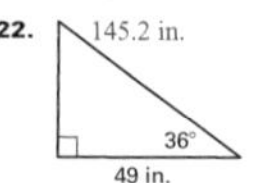

23. 81.7 ft 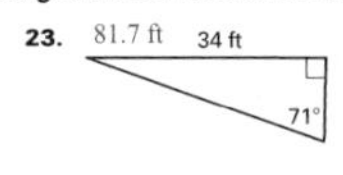

24. 215.5 ft 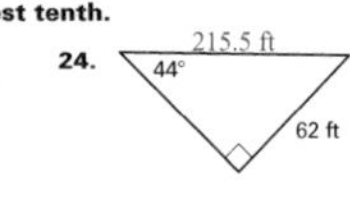

25. Model Rockets To calculate the height *h* reached by a model rocket, you move 100 feet from the launch point and record the angle of elevation θ to the rocket at its highest point. The values of θ for three flights are given below. Find the rocket's height to the nearest foot for the given θ in each flight.

a. $\theta = 77°$ 433 ft

b. $\theta = 81°$ 631 ft

c. $\theta = 83°$ 814 ft

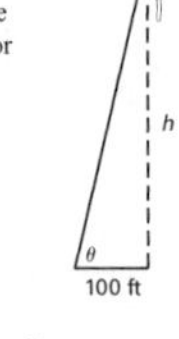

26. Drive-in Movie You are 50 feet from the screen at a drive-in movie. Your eye is on a horizontal line with the bottom of the screen and the angle of elevation to the top of the screen is 58°. How tall is the screen? 80 ft

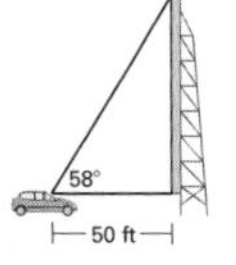

27. Skyscraper You are a block away from a skyscraper that is 780 feet tall. Your friend is between the skyscraper and yourself. The angle of elevation from your position to the top of the skyscraper is 42°. The angle of elevation from your friend's position to the top of the skyscraper is 71°. To the nearest foot, how far are you from your friend? 598 ft

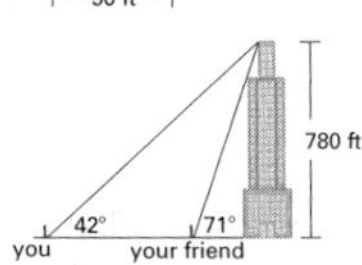

LESSON 7.5

LESSON 7.6 Practice B

For use with pages 473–480

7. $\cos A = \frac{12}{13} \approx 0.9231, \cos B = \frac{5}{13} \approx 0.3846$

8. $\cos A = \frac{12}{37} \approx 0.3243, \cos B = \frac{35}{37} \approx 0.9459$

Find sin *R* and sin *S*. Write each answer as a fraction and as a decimal. Round to four decimal places, if necessary.

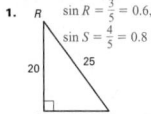

1. (R, T, S; 20, 15, 25) $\sin R = \frac{3}{5} = 0.6$, $\sin S = \frac{4}{5} = 0.8$

2. 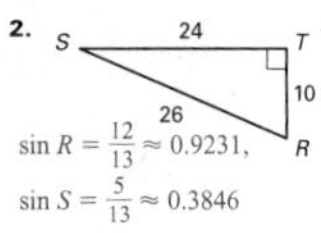

$\sin R = \frac{12}{13} \approx 0.9231$, $\sin S = \frac{5}{13} \approx 0.3846$

3. 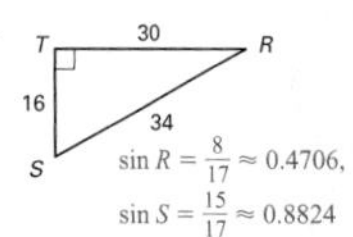

$\sin R = \frac{8}{17} \approx 0.4706$, $\sin S = \frac{15}{17} \approx 0.8824$

4. 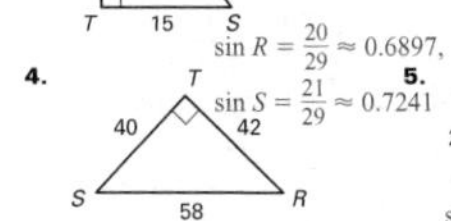

$\sin R = \frac{20}{29} \approx 0.6897$, $\sin S = \frac{21}{29} \approx 0.7241$

5. 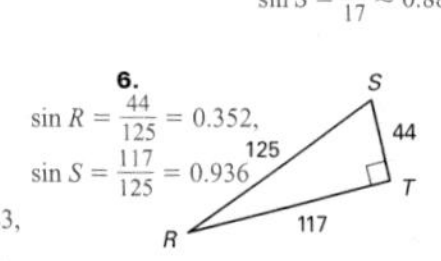

$\sin R = \frac{28}{53} \approx 0.5283$, $\sin S = \frac{45}{53} \approx 0.8491$

6. (S, T, R; 44, 125, 117) $\sin R = \frac{44}{125} = 0.352$, $\sin S = \frac{117}{125} = 0.936$

Find cos *A* and cos *B*. Write each answer as a fraction and as a decimal. Round to four decimal places, if necessary.

7. See above. (B, A, C; 52, 20, 48)

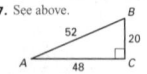

8. See above. 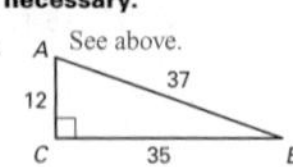

9. 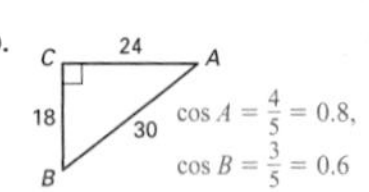

$\cos A = \frac{4}{5} = 0.8$, $\cos B = \frac{3}{5} = 0.6$

10. 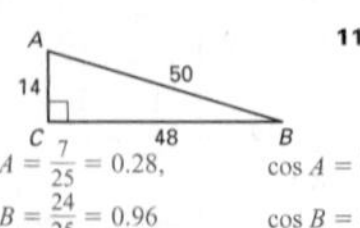

$\cos A = \frac{7}{25} = 0.28$, $\cos B = \frac{24}{25} = 0.96$

11. 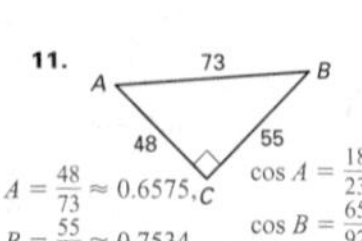

$\cos A = \frac{48}{73} \approx 0.6575$, $\cos B = \frac{55}{73} \approx 0.7534$

12. 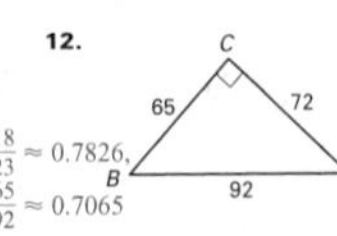

$\cos A = \frac{18}{23} \approx 0.7826$, $\cos B = \frac{65}{92} \approx 0.7065$

Use a cosine or sine ratio to find the value of each variable. Round decimals to the nearest tenth.

13. (57°, a, b, 14) $a \approx 9.1, b \approx 16.7$

14. 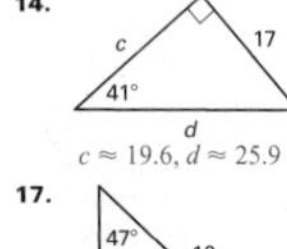

$c \approx 19.6, d \approx 25.9$

15. (r, 36°, s, 21) $r \approx 28.9, s \approx 35.7$

16. 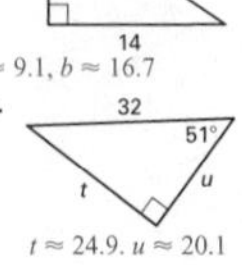

$t \approx 24.9, u \approx 20.1$

17. (47°, 12, x, y) $x \approx 8.2, y \approx 8.8$

18. 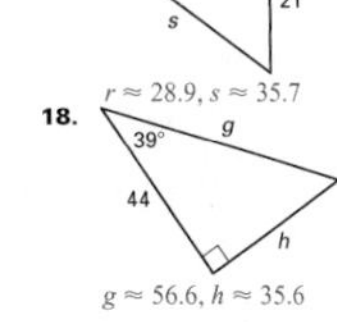

$g \approx 56.6, h \approx 35.6$

LESSON 7.6

LESSON 7.6 Practice B *continued*

For use with pages 473–480

Use the 45°-45°-90° Triangle Theorem or the 30°-60°-90° Triangle Theorem to find the sine and cosine of the angle.

19. a 30° angle $\sin 30° = 0.5, \cos 30° = \frac{\sqrt{3}}{2}$

20. a 45° angle $\sin 45° = \cos 45° = \frac{\sqrt{2}}{2}$

21. a 60° angle $\sin 60° = \frac{\sqrt{3}}{2}, \cos 60° = 0.5$

Find the unknown side length. Then find sin *A* and cos *A*. Write each answer as a fraction in simplest form and as a decimal. Round to four decimal places, if necessary.

22. 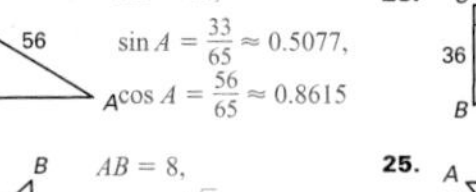

$AB = 65$, $\sin A = \frac{33}{65} \approx 0.5077$, $\cos A = \frac{56}{65} \approx 0.8615$

23. 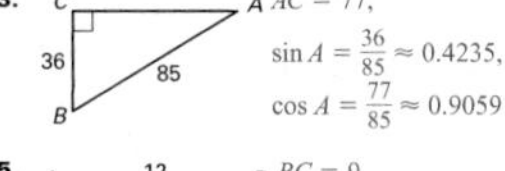

$AC = 77$, $\sin A = \frac{36}{85} \approx 0.4235$, $\cos A = \frac{77}{85} \approx 0.9059$

24. 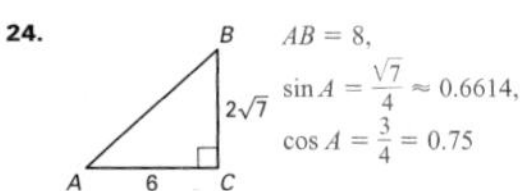

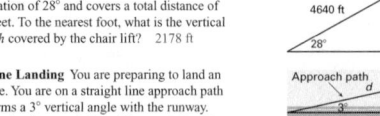

$AB = 8$, $\sin A = \frac{\sqrt{7}}{4} \approx 0.6614$, $\cos A = \frac{3}{4} = 0.75$

25. 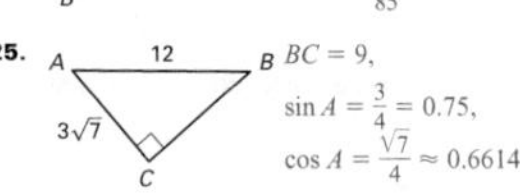

$BC = 9$, $\sin A = \frac{3}{4} = 0.75$, $\cos A = \frac{\sqrt{7}}{4} \approx 0.6614$

26. Ski Lift A chair lift on a ski slope has an angle of elevation of 28° and covers a total distance of 4640 feet. To the nearest foot, what is the vertical height *h* covered by the chair lift? 2178 ft

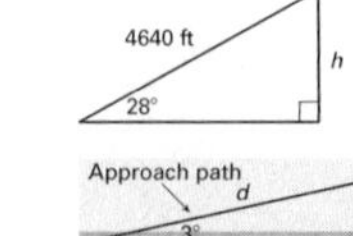

27. Airplane Landing You are preparing to land an airplane. You are on a straight line approach path that forms a 3° vertical angle with the runway. What is the distance *d* along this approach path to your touchdown point when you are 500 feet above the ground? Round your answer to the nearest foot. about 9554 ft

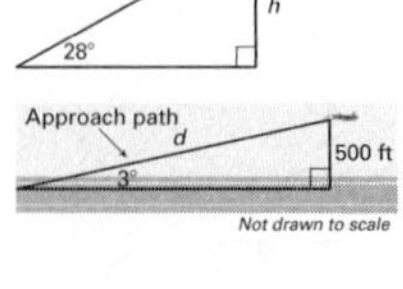

28. Extension Ladders You are using extension ladders to paint a chimney that is 33 feet tall. The length of an extension ladder ranges in one-foot increments from its minimum length to its maximum length. For safety, you should always use an angle of about 75.5° between the ground and the ladder.

a. Your smallest extension ladder has a maximum length of 17 feet. How high does this ladder safely reach on a vertical wall? about 16.5 ft

b. You place the base of the ladder 3 feet from the chimney. How many feet long should the ladder be? 12 ft

c. To reach the top of the chimney, you need a ladder that reaches 30 feet high. How many feet long should the ladder be? 31 ft

LESSON 7.6

LESSON 7.7

Practice B

For use with pages 483–489

Use the diagram to find the indicated measurement. Round your answer to the nearest tenth.

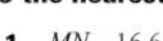

1. MN 16.6
2. $m\angle M$ 65
3. $m\angle N$ 25

Solve the right triangle. Round decimal answers to the nearest tenth.

4. 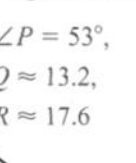

$m\angle P = 53°$, $PQ \approx 13.2$, $QR \approx 17.6$

5. 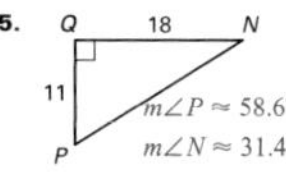
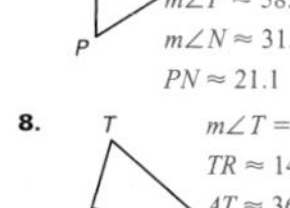

$m\angle P \approx 58.6°$, $m\angle N \approx 31.4°$, $PN \approx 21.1$

6. 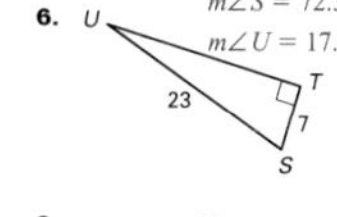

$TU \approx 21.9$, $m\angle S = 72.3°$, $m\angle U = 17.7°$

7. 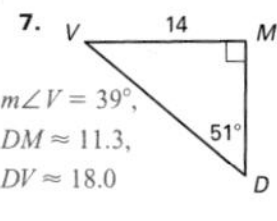

$m\angle V = 39°$, $DM \approx 11.3$, $DV \approx 18.0$

8. 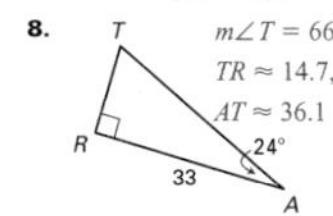

$m\angle T = 66°$, $TR \approx 14.7$, $AT \approx 36.1$

9. 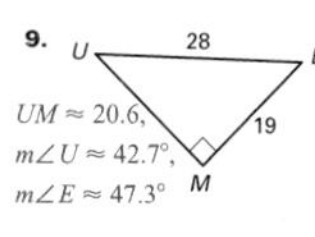

$UM \approx 20.6$, $m\angle U \approx 42.7°$, $m\angle E \approx 47.3°$

10. 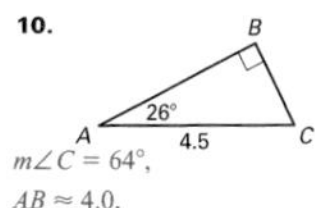

$m\angle C = 64°$, $AB \approx 4.0$, $BC \approx 2.0$

11. 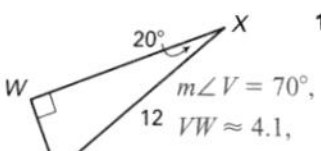

$m\angle V = 70°$, $VW \approx 4.1$, $WX \approx 11.3$

12. 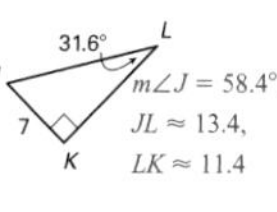

$m\angle J = 58.4°$, $JL \approx 13.4$, $LK \approx 11.4$

Let $\angle A$ be an acute angle in a right triangle. Approximate the measure of $\angle A$ to the nearest tenth of a degree.

13. $\sin A = 0.36$ 21.1°
14. $\tan A = 0.8$ 38.7°
15. $\sin A = 0.27$ 15.7°
16. $\cos A = 0.35$ 69.5°
17. $\tan A = 0.42$ 22.8°
18. $\cos A = 0.11$ 83.7°
19. $\sin A = 0.94$ 70.1°
20. $\cos A = 0.77$ 39.6°

21. **Office Buildings** The angle of depression from the top of a 320 foot office building to the top of a 200 foot office building is 55°. How far apart are the buildings? about 84.02 ft

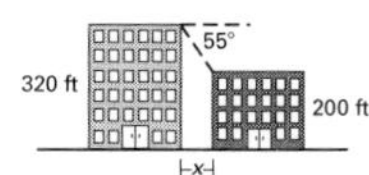

LESSON 7.7

LESSON 7.7

Practice B *continued*

For use with pages 483–489

22. **Suspension Bridge** Use the diagram to find the distance across the suspension bridge. about 499.30 ft

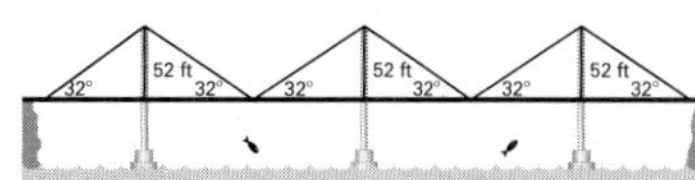

In Exercises 23 and 24, use the following information.

Ramps The Uniform Federal Accessibility Standards specify that the ramp angle used for a wheelchair ramp must be less than or equal to 4.78°.

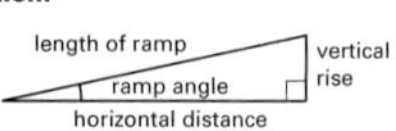

23. The length of one ramp is 16 feet. The vertical rise is 14 inches. Estimate the ramp's horizontal distance and its ramp angle. Does this ramp meet the Uniform Federal Accessibility Standards? about 191.5 in. or about 15 ft 11.5 in.; about 4.2°; Yes, the angle is less than 4.78°.
24. You want to build a ramp with a vertical rise of 6 inches. You want to minimize the horizontal distance taken up by the ramp. Draw a sketch showing the approximate dimensions of your ramp.

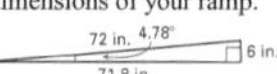

In Exercises 25–27, use the following information.

Hot Air Balloon You are in a hot air balloon that is 600 feet above the ground where you can see two people.

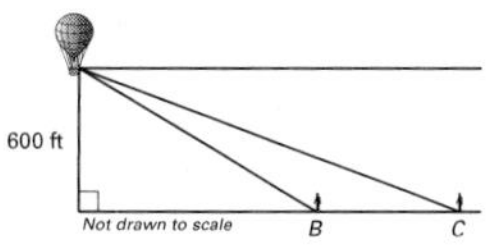

25. If the angle of depression from your line of sight to the person at B is 30°, how far is the person from the point on the ground below the hot air balloon? about 1039.2 ft
26. If the angle of depression from your line of sight to the person at C is 20°, how far is the person from the point on the ground below the hot air balloon? about 1648.5 ft
27. How far apart are the two people? about 609.3 ft

LESSON 7.7

7 Assessment

CHAPTER 7 Quiz 1
For use after Lessons 7.1–7.2

Find the unknown side length. Write your answer in simplest radical form.

1.
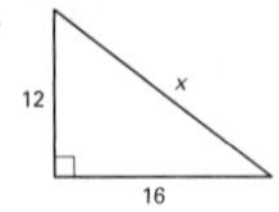

2.
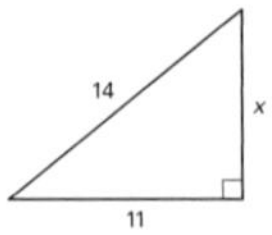

3.
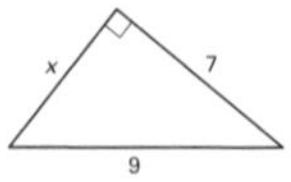

Classify the triangle formed by the side lengths as *right, acute,* or *obtuse.*

4. 4, 5, 6
5. 9, 12, 15
6. 11, 13, 23
7. 8, $8\sqrt{3}$, 16
8. 16, 20, 24

Answers

1. 20
2. $5\sqrt{3}$
3. $4\sqrt{2}$
4. acute
5. right
6. obtuse
7. right
8. acute

CHAPTER 7 Quiz 2
For use after Lessons 7.3–7.4

In Exercises 1–3, use the diagram.

1. Find *BD*.
2. Find *AD*.
3. Find *AB*.

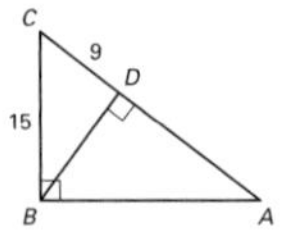

Find the value(s) of the variable(s). Write your answer(s) in simplest radical form.

4.
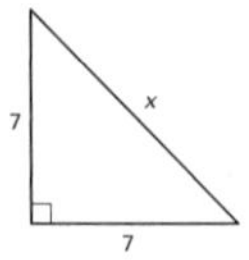

5.
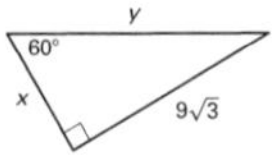

6.
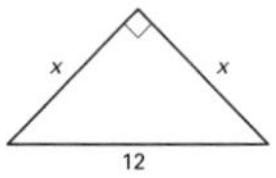

Answers

1. 12
2. 16
3. 20
4. $x = 7\sqrt{2}$
5. $x = 9, y = 18$
6. $x = 6\sqrt{2}$

CHAPTER 7 Quiz 3
For use after Lessons 7.5–7.7

Find the value of *x* to the nearest tenth.

1.
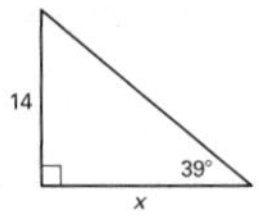

2.
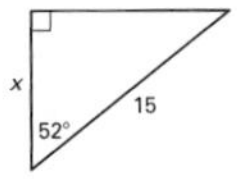

3.
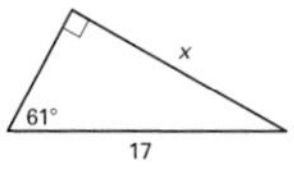

Solve the right triangles. Round decimal answers to the nearest tenth.

4.
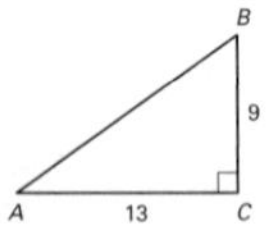

5.
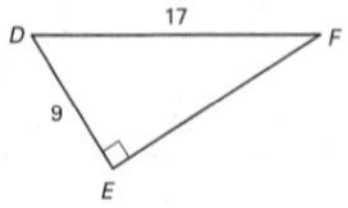

6.
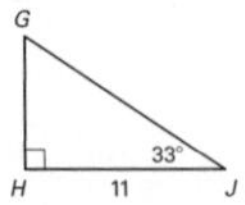

Answers

1. 17.3
2. 9.2
3. 14.9
4. $\angle A = 34.7°$, $\angle B = 55.3°$, $AB = 15.8$
5. $\angle D = 58.0°$, $\angle F = 32.0°$, $EF = 14.4$
6. $\angle G = 57°$, $GH = 7.1$, $GJ = 13.1$

CHAPTER 7 Chapter Test B
For use after Chapter 7

Find the value of *x*. Write your answer in simplest radical form.

1.
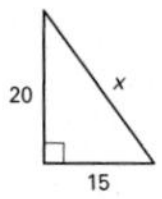

2.
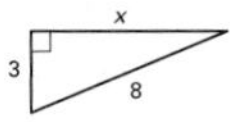

3.
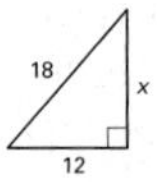

4.
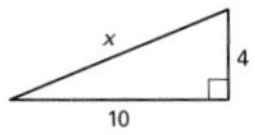

Classify the triangle as *acute, right,* or *obtuse.*

5. 5, 7, 9
6. 3, 5, $\sqrt{34}$
7. 3.1, 4.5, 5.2
8. 9, 15, $10\sqrt{3}$

Find the exact value of *x*.

9.
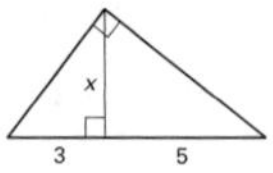

10.
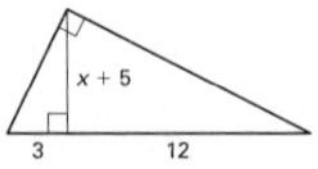

11.
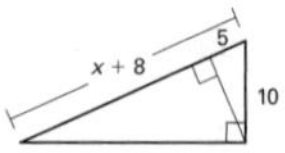

12.
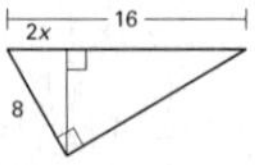

Find the value of each variable. Write your answer in simplest radical form.

13.
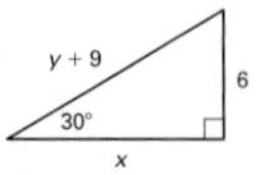

14.
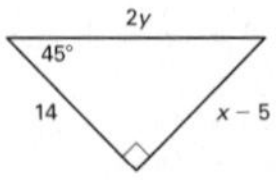

15.
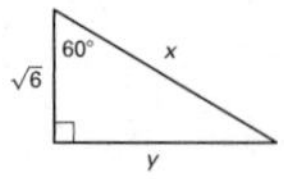

16.
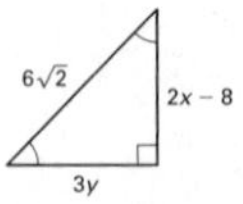

Answers

1. 25
2. $\sqrt{55}$
3. $6\sqrt{5}$
4. $2\sqrt{29}$
5. obtuse
6. right
7. acute
8. acute
9. $\sqrt{15}$
10. 1
11. 12
12. 2
13. $x = 6\sqrt{3}, y = 3$
14. $x = 19, y = 7\sqrt{2}$
15. $x = 2\sqrt{6}, y = 3\sqrt{2}$
16. $x = 7, y = 2$

Chapter Test B *continued*

For use after Chapter 7

Find the value of *x*. Round your answer to the nearest tenth.

17.

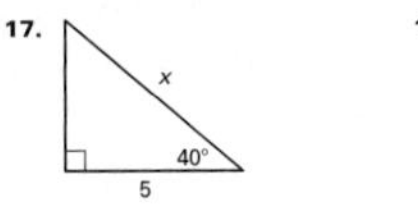

18.

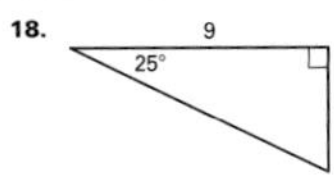

19.

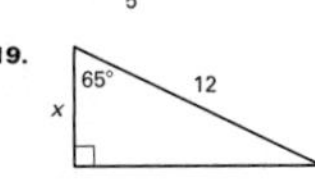

20.

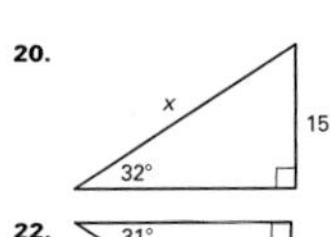

21. 20, x, 55°

22.

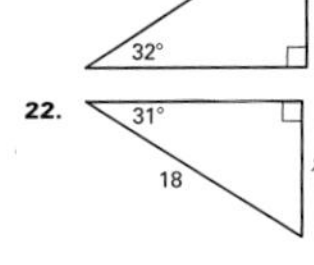

Solve the right triangle. Round your answer to the nearest tenth.

23.

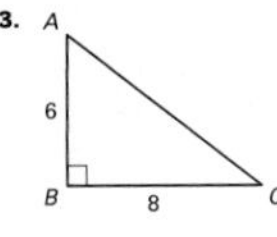

24.

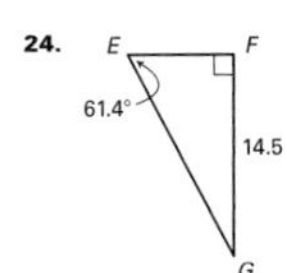

25. A balloon rises to the ceiling of a gymnasium. You want to find the distance from the ground to the balloon. You use a cardboard square to line up the balloon and the ground. Your friend measures the vertical distance from the ground to your eye and the distance from you to the gym wall. Approximate the distance from the ground to the balloon.

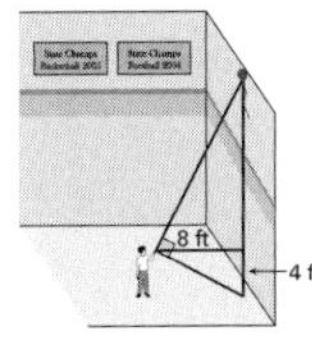

Answers

17. $x \approx 6.5$
18. $x \approx 4.2$
19. $x \approx 5.1$
20. $x \approx 28.3$
21. $x \approx 14.0$
22. $x \approx 9.3$
23. $AC = 10$, $m\angle A \approx 53.1°$, $m\angle C \approx 36.9°$
24. $EG \approx 16.5$, $EF \approx 7.9$, $m\angle G = 28.6°$
25. 20 ft

Standardized Test *continued*

For use after Chapter 7

Multiple Choice

1. Which equation is *not* correct? B

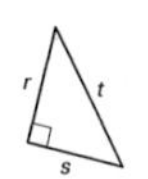

Ⓐ $t^2 - r^2 = s^2$ Ⓑ $t^2 + r^2 = s^2$
Ⓒ $s^2 - t^2 = -r^2$ Ⓓ $t^2 - s^2 = r^2$

2. A 25-foot ladder leans against a wall 7 feet from the base of the wall. How high up the wall does the ladder touch? A

Ⓐ 24 ft Ⓑ 18 ft Ⓒ 20 ft Ⓓ 21.5 ft

3. Find the area of the rectangle. D

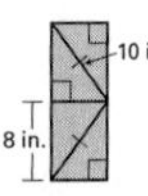

Ⓐ 192 in.^{2} Ⓑ 48 in.^{2}
Ⓒ 24 in.^{2} Ⓓ 96 in.^{2}

4. If the square of the length of the longest side of a triangle is greater than the sum of the squares of the lengths of the other two sides, then the triangle is: D

Ⓐ equilateral. Ⓑ a right triangle.
Ⓒ acute. Ⓓ none of these

5. Classify $\triangle ABC$ if the vertices are $A(-12, 5)$, $B(12, 5)$, and $C(10,17)$? C

Ⓐ right scalene Ⓑ obtuse scalene
Ⓒ acute scalene Ⓓ none of these

6. Find x. A

Ⓐ $4\sqrt{3}$ Ⓑ $2\sqrt{3}$ Ⓒ $3\sqrt{3}$ Ⓓ $5\sqrt{3}$

7. Find a, b, and c. C

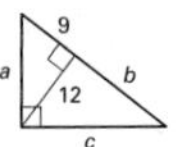

Ⓐ $a = 20, b = 25, c = 15$
Ⓑ $a = 15, b = 25, c = 20$
Ⓒ $a = 15, b = 16, c = 20$
Ⓓ $a = 16, b = 20, c = 25$

8. In a 45°-45°-90° triangle, the hypotenuse is __?__ times as long as each leg? B

Ⓐ $\sqrt{3}$ Ⓑ $\sqrt{2}$ Ⓒ $\frac{\sqrt{2}}{2}$ Ⓓ $\frac{3}{2}$

9. Find x and y. D

y, 60°, x, $6\sqrt{3}$, 30°

Ⓐ $x = 6, y = 12$ Ⓑ $x = 12\sqrt{3}, y = 6$
Ⓒ $x = 8\sqrt{3}, y = 8$ Ⓓ $x = 12, y = 6$

10. Find tan A and tan B. B

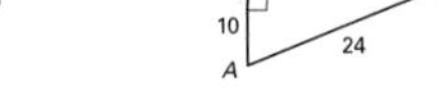

Ⓐ $\tan A \approx 0.38$, $\tan B = 2.6$
Ⓑ $\tan A = 2.6$, $\tan B \approx 0.38$
Ⓒ $\tan A \approx 1.08$, $\tan B \approx 0.42$
Ⓓ $\tan A \approx 0.92$, $\tan B = 2.4$

11. Find the approximate area of the triangle. A

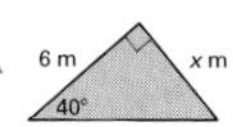

Ⓐ 15.1 m^2 Ⓑ 5.03 m^2
Ⓒ 45.3 m^2 Ⓓ 30.2 m^2

Standardized Test *continued*

For use after Chapter 7

12. Find sin F and sin G. D

H, 96, G, 28, 100, F

Ⓐ $\sin F = 0.28$, $\sin G = 0.96$
Ⓑ $\sin F \approx 3.57$, $\sin G \approx 1.04$
Ⓒ $\sin F \approx 1.04$, $\sin G \approx 3.57$
Ⓓ $\sin F = 0.96$, $\sin G = 0.28$

13. Which expression could be used to find the value of x in the diagram? A

x, 12, 35°

Ⓐ $\cos 55° = \frac{12}{x}$ Ⓑ $\cos 35° = \frac{x}{12}$
Ⓒ $\cos 35° = \frac{12}{x}$ Ⓓ $\cos 55° = \frac{x}{12}$

14. Which is *not* enough given information needed to solve a right triangle? B

Ⓐ two acute angles and one side length
Ⓑ measure of the hypotenuse
Ⓒ two side lengths
Ⓓ one side length and the measure of one acute angle

15. Find $m\angle A$. B

B, x, 3.5, A, 6.5, C

Ⓐ 28.3° Ⓑ 32.58°
Ⓒ 57.42° Ⓓ 45°

Gridded Answer

16. Given a side length of 18 inches, find the height of a stop sign rounded to the nearest tenth.

18

Grid answer: 4 3 . 5

Short Response

17. You are cleaning the gutters on your house. Some bushes extend 7 feet from the wall of the house. The gutters are at a height of 24 feet. What is the minimum length of ladder you will need? If you have a 50 foot ladder, what is the minimum angle the ladder can form with the ground?
25 ft; 28.69°

Extended Response

18. An architect creates a rough blue print for a new warehouse as shown.

30 ft, 55°, 75 ft, 150 ft

a. How many square feet of carpet will you need? 11,250 ft^2

b. If you paint the interior walls, how much area will you cover? 13,500 ft^2

c. How many square feet of shingles will you need to cover the roof? 15,668 ft^2

d. You decide to divide the warehouse into two rooms by building a vertical wall to the peak of the roof. What is the area of the larger room? 7548.86 ft^2

Alternative Assessment and Math Journal

For use after Chapter 7

Journal **1.** Describe how you would find a missing side length or a missing angle measure of a right triangle if you were given (a) the lengths of two sides or (b) the measure of one angle and the length of one side.

Multi-Step Problem **2.** A kitchen designer is planning the work triangle in a new kitchen. A work triangle is the triangle formed by the positions of the sink, the stove, and the refrigerator. The first design being considered is shown below.

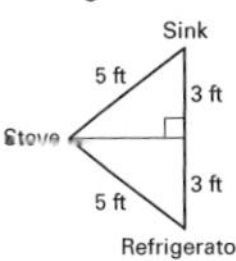

a. Classify the work triangle as *acute*, *right*, or *obtuse*.

b. Find the distance between the stove and the wall that the sink and refrigerator sit on.

c. Find the measure of the angle whose vertex is the stove.
The second design being considered is shown below.

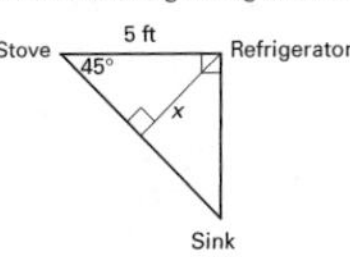

d. Find the distance from the stove to the sink. Round your answer to the nearest tenth.

e. Find the length of x.

f. Find the sine, cosine, and tangent of the angle whose vertex is the sink.

g. Which design do you think is the best? *Explain* your reasoning.

1. Complete answers should include: given two side lengths, the missing side length should be found using the Pythagorean Theorem; given two side lengths, the missing angle should be found by using a trigonometric ratio; given one side length and one angle measure, the missing side length should be found by using a trigonometric ratio; given one side length and one angle measure, the missing angle measure should be found by using the Triangle Sum Theorem

2. a. acute **b.** 4 ft **c.** 73.7398° **d.** about 7.1 ft **e.** about 3.5 ft
f. $\sin 45° = \frac{\sqrt{2}}{2}$; $\cos 45° = \frac{\sqrt{2}}{2}$; $\tan 45° = 1$ **g.** Answers will vary.

PLAN AND PREPARE

Main Ideas

In this chapter students investigate side lengths and angles in triangles. They start by using the Pythagorean theorem to find the length of the third side in a right triangle, then use the Converse of the Pythagorean Theorem, and other theorems, to decide if three given sides lengths form an acute, right, or obtuse triangle. Students explore ratios of lengths formed by an altitude to the hypotenuse of a right triangle and use the ratios of side lengths for a 45°-45°-90° triangle and a 30°-60°-90° triangle. Finally, students apply trigonometric ratios, the Law of Sines, and the Law of Cosines to find side lengths and angle measures in triangles.

Prerequisite Skills

- Classifying triangles
- Simplifying radicals
- Solving proportions

Additional resources for reviewing prerequisite skills are:

- Skills Review Handbook, pp. 869–895
- @HomeTutor

7 Right Triangles and Trigonometry

Before

In previous courses and in Chapters 1–6, you learned the following skills, which you'll use in Chapter 7: classifying triangles, simplifying radicals, and solving proportions.

Prerequisite Skills

VOCABULARY CHECK

Classify the triangle shown.

1. equilateral

2. 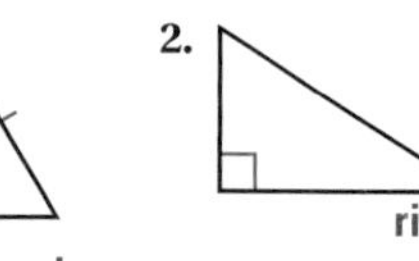 right

3. 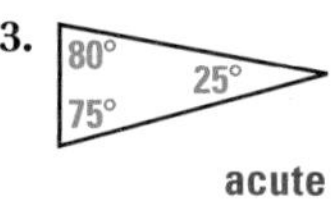

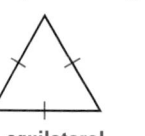

acute

4. 135° obtuse, isosceles

SKILLS AND ALGEBRA CHECK

Simplify the radical. *(Review p. 874 for 7.1, 7.2, 7.4.)*

5. $\sqrt{45}$ **$3\sqrt{5}$** **6.** $(3\sqrt{7})^2$ **63** **7.** $\sqrt{3} \cdot \sqrt{5}$ **$\sqrt{15}$** **8.** $\frac{7}{\sqrt{2}}$ **$\frac{7\sqrt{2}}{2}$**

Solve the proportion. *(Review p. 356 for 7.3, 7.5–7.7.)*

9. $\frac{3}{x} = \frac{12}{16}$ **4** **10.** $\frac{2}{3} = \frac{x}{18}$ **12** **11.** $\frac{x+5}{4} = \frac{1}{2}$ **−3** **12.** $\frac{x+4}{x-4} = \frac{6}{5}$ **44**

@HomeTutor Prerequisite skills practice at classzone.com

Chapter Planning Guide

Chapter 7 Resource Book
- Teaching Guide/Lesson Plan (pp. 3, 19, 33, 46, 61, 74, 89)
- Project with Rubric (p. 104)

Assessment and Intervention
- Assessment Book (pp. 95–109)
- Benchmark Tests
- Remediation Book

Interactive Technology
- Easy Planner
- Power Presentations CD-ROM
- Activity Generator CD-ROM
- Animated Geometry
- Test Generator CD-ROM
- Online Quizzes
- eWorkbook
- eEdition
- @HomeTutor

Resources for English Learners
- Quick Reference for English Learners
- Spanish Study Guide
- Multi-Language Visual Glossary
- Student Resources in Spanish

California Standards for Chapter 7

Geometry: 4.0, 5.0, 12.0, 14.0, 15.0, 18.0, 19.0, 20.0

Now

In Chapter 7, you will apply the big ideas listed below and reviewed in the Chapter Summary on page 493. You will also use the key vocabulary listed below.

Big Ideas

1. **Using the Pythagorean Theorem and its converse**
2. **Using special relationships in right triangles**
3. **Using trigonometric ratios to solve right triangles**

KEY VOCABULARY

- Pythagorean triple, *p. 435*
- trigonometric ratio, *p. 466*
- tangent, *p. 466*
- sine, *p. 473*
- cosine, *p. 473*
- angle of elevation, *p. 475*
- angle of depression, *p. 475*
- solve a right triangle, *p. 483*
- inverse tangent, *p. 483*
- inverse sine, *p. 483*
- inverse cosine, *p. 483*

Why?

You can use trigonometric ratios to find unknown side lengths and angle measures in right triangles. For example, you can find the length of a ski slope.

Animated Geometry

The animation illustrated below for Example 4 on page 475 helps you answer this question: How far will you ski down the mountain?

Start
You can use right triangles to find the distance you ski down a mountain.

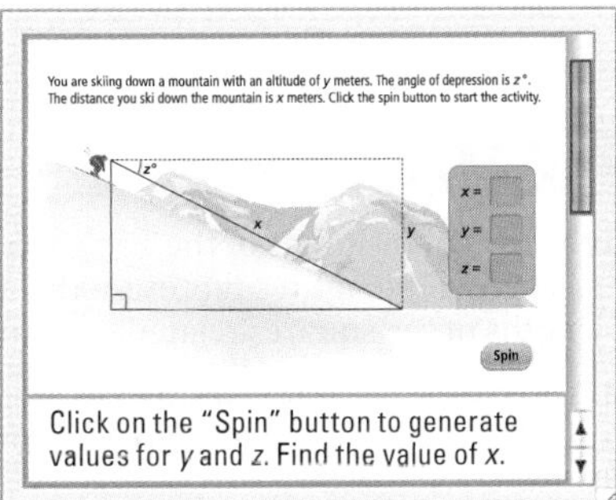

You are skiing down a mountain with an altitude of y meters. The angle of depression is z°. The distance you ski down the mountain is x meters. Click the spin button to start the activity.
z°
x
y
x =
y =
z =
Spin
Click on the "Spin" button to generate values for y and z. Find the value of x.

Animated Geometry at classzone.com

Other animations for Chapter 7: pages 434, 442, 450, 460, and 462

Geometry Toolkit

- Reading Strategies for Chapter 7, pp. 21–22
- Differentiated Instruction Notes, pp. 63–66
- English Learners Notes, pp. 103–104
- Inclusion Notes, pp. 133–134
- Teaching Strategies with Sample Worksheets, pp. 145–168
- Using Technology in the Classroom, pp. 169–174
- Tips for New Teachers, pp. 187–188
- Math Background Notes, pp. 219–221
- Pre-AP Strategies and Copymasters, pp. 295–296, 355–360
- Teacher Survival Activities, pp. 433–434, 457–458
- Bulletin Board Idea, p. 475
- Teacher Tool Transparencies, following p. 480

1 PLAN AND PREPARE

Explore the Concept

- Students will make a tangram set to develop the Pythagorean Theorem.
- This activity leads into the study of the Pythagorean Theorem in Lesson 7.1.

Materials

Each student will need:

- graph paper
- ruler
- scissors
- Activity Support Master (*Chapter 7 Resource Book*, p. 7)

Recommended Time

Work activity: 15 min

Discuss results: 5 min

Grouping

Students should work individually.

2 TEACH

Tips for Success

Remind the students that to find the area of each square they can count the number of squares along one edge and square that number.

Alternative Strategy

Provide students with tangram sets already cut out of graph paper. Have them do Steps 3 and 4, then go over the exercises as a class.

Key Discovery

The sum of the squares of the lengths of the legs of a right triangle is equal to the square of the length of the hypotenuse.

3 ASSESS AND RETEACH

1. Draw a right triangle and label the lengths of the sides a, b, and c, where c is the hypotenuse. What equation relates a, b, and c? $a^2 + b^2 = c^2$

7.1 Pythagorean Theorem

MATERIALS • graph paper • ruler • pencil • scissors

Standards

14.0 Students prove the Pythagorean theorem.

QUESTION What relationship exists among the sides of a right triangle?

Recall that a square is a four sided figure with four right angles and four congruent sides.

EXPLORE Make and use a tangram set

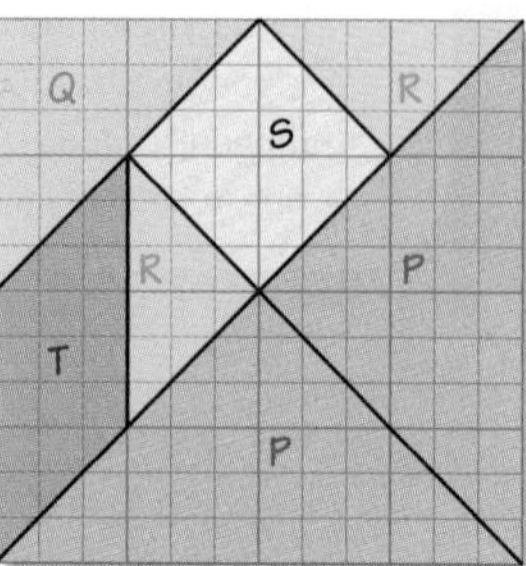

STEP 1 ***Make a tangram set*** On your graph paper, copy the tangram set as shown. Label each piece with the given letters. Cut along the solid black lines to make seven pieces.

STEP 2 ***Trace a triangle*** On another piece of paper, trace one of the large triangles P of the tangram set.

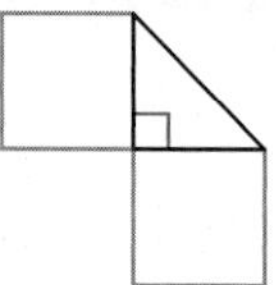

STEP 3 ***Assemble pieces along the legs*** Use all of the tangram pieces to form two squares along the legs of your triangle so that the length of each leg is equal to the side length of the square. Trace all of the pieces.

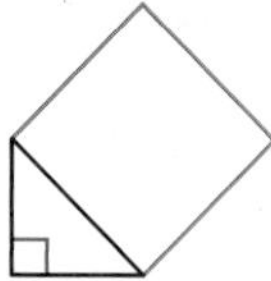

STEP 4 ***Assemble pieces along the hypotenuse*** Use all of the tangram pieces to form a square along the hypotenuse so that the side length of the square is equal to the length of the hypotenuse. Trace all of the pieces.

DRAW CONCLUSIONS Use your observations to complete these exercises

1. Find the sum of the areas of the two squares formed in Step 3. Let the letters labeling the figures represent the area of the figure. How are the side lengths of the squares related to Triangle P? **144 units^2; the side length of the square is the same as the length of the leg of Triangle P.**
2. Find the area of the square formed in Step 4. How is the side length of the square related to Triangle P? **144 units^2; the side length of the square is the same as the hypotenuse of Triangle P.**
3. Compare your answers from Exercises 1 and 2. Make a conjecture about the relationship between the legs and hypotenuse of a right triangle.
4. The triangle you traced in Step 2 is an isosceles right triangle. Why? Do you think that your conjecture is true for all isosceles triangles? Do you think that your conjecture is true for all right triangles? *Justify* your answers. **See margin.**

3. The sum of the squares of the legs of a right triangle is equal to the square of the hypotenuse.

4. The legs of the triangles are congruent and they meet to form a right angle; no; yes; not all isosceles triangles are right triangles; for any triangle, if you construct a square on each leg and find the sum of their areas, it will be equal to the area of the square formed on the hypotenuse.

7.1 Apply the Pythagorean Theorem

Before You learned about the relationships within triangles.
Now You will find side lengths in right triangles.
Why? So you can find the shortest distance to a campfire, as in Ex. 35.

Key Vocabulary
- **Pythagorean triple**
- **right triangle,** *p. 217*
- **leg of a right triangle,** *p. 241*
- **hypotenuse,** *p. 241*

Standards

15.0 Students use the Pythagorean theorem to determine distance and find missing lengths of sides of right triangles.

14.0 Students prove the Pythagorean theorem.

One of the most famous theorems in mathematics is the Pythagorean Theorem, named for the ancient Greek mathematician Pythagoras (around 500 B.C.). This theorem can be used to find information about the lengths of the sides of a right triangle.

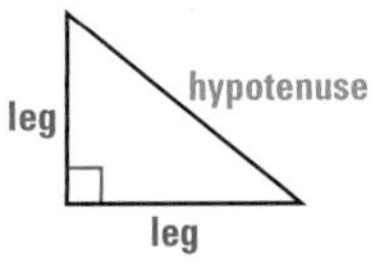

THEOREM *For Your Notebook*

THEOREM 7.1 Pythagorean Theorem

In a right triangle, the square of the length of the hypotenuse is equal to the sum of the squares of the lengths of the legs.

Proof: p. 434; Ex. 32, p. 455

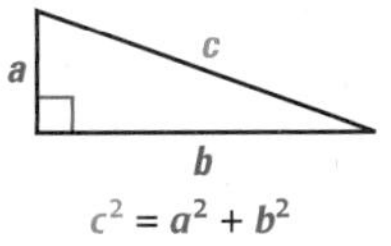

$c^2 = a^2 + b^2$

EXAMPLE 1 Find the length of a hypotenuse

Find the length of the hypotenuse of the right triangle.

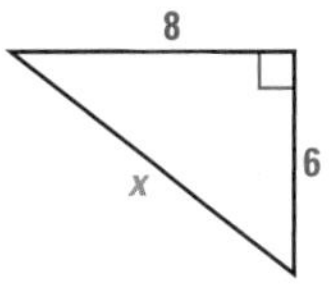

Solution

ABBREVIATE In the equation for the Pythagorean Theorem, "length of hypotenuse" and "length of leg" was shortened to "hypotenuse" and "leg".

$(\text{hypotenuse})^2 = (\text{leg})^2 + (\text{leg})^2$	Pythagorean Theorem
$x^2 = 6^2 + 8^2$	Substitute.
$x^2 = 36 + 64$	Multiply.
$x^2 = 100$	Add.
$x = 10$	Find the positive square root.

✓ **GUIDED PRACTICE** for Example 1

Identify the unknown side as a *leg* or *hypotenuse*. Then, find the unknown side length of the right triangle. Write your answer in simplest radical form.

1. 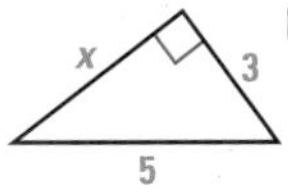

leg; 4

2. 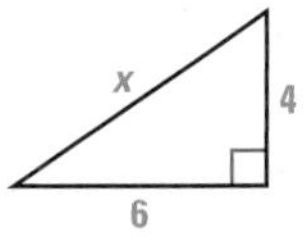

hypotenuse; $2\sqrt{13}$

1 PLAN AND PREPARE

Warm-Up Exercises

Transparency Available

1. Solve $x^2 = 100$. **10, −10**
2. Solve $x^2 + 9 = 25$ **4, −4**
3. Simplify $\sqrt{20}$. **$2\sqrt{5}$**
4. Find x. **6 cm**

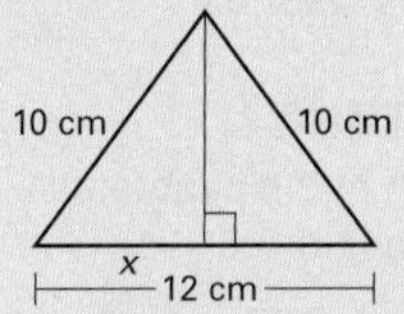

Notetaking Guide

Transparency Available

Promotes interactive learning and notetaking skills, pp. 170–173.

Pacing

Basic: 2 days
Average: 2 days
Advanced: 2 days
Block: 1 block
- See *Teaching Guide/Lesson Plan.*

2 FOCUS AND MOTIVATE

Essential Question

Big Idea 1, p. 431

If you know the lengths of two sides of a right triangle, how do you find the length of the third side? **Tell students they will learn how to answer this question by using the Pythagorean Theorem.**

Resource Planning Guide

Chapter Resource Book
- Teaching Guide/Lesson Plan (pp. 3–4)
- Activity Master (p. 5)
- Practice levels A, B, C (pp. 8–13)
- Study Guide (pp. 14–15)
- Catch-up for Absent Students (p. 16)
- Application (p. 17)
- Challenge (p. 18)

Workbooks
- Notetaking Guide (pp. 170–173)
- Practice Workbook (pp. 124–126)

Teaching Options
- **Power Presentations CD-ROM** provides dynamic electronic teaching resources for the classroom.
- **Activity Generator CD-ROM** provides editable activities for all ability levels.

Interactive Technology
- Easy Planner
- Power Presentations CD-ROM
- Activity Generator CD-ROM
- Animated Geometry
- Test Generator CD-ROM
- Online Quiz
- eWorkbook
- eEdition
- @HomeTutor

Resources for English Learners
- Quick Reference for English Learners
- Spanish Study Guide
- Multi-Language Visual Glossary
- Student Resources in Spanish

See also the *Geometry Toolkit* for more strategies for meeting individual needs.

Motivating the Lesson

You are at one corner of a football field and your friend is at the opposite corner. Is it shorter to walk diagonally across the field or to walk around it? In this lesson students will learn how to find the length of a diagonal of a rectangle.

3 TEACH

Extra Example 1

Find the length of the hypotenuse of the right triangle. **13**

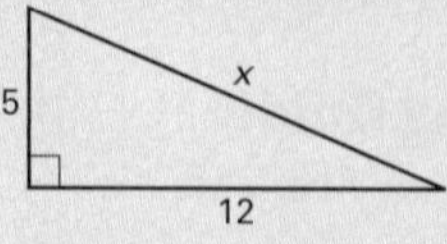

Extra Example 2

Randy made a ramp for his dog to get into his truck. The ramp is 6 feet long and the bed of the truck is 3 feet above the ground. Approximately how far from the back of the truck does the ramp touch the ground? **C**

Ⓐ 3 ft Ⓑ 4 ft
Ⓒ 5.2 ft Ⓓ 6.7 ft

Animated Geometry
classzone.com

An **Animated Geometry** activity is available on-line for **Proving the Pythagorean Theorem**. This activity is also available on the **Power Presentations CD-ROM**.

EXAMPLE 2 Standardized Test Practice

A 16 foot ladder rests against the side of the house, and the base of the ladder is 4 feet away. Approximately how high above the ground is the top of the ladder?

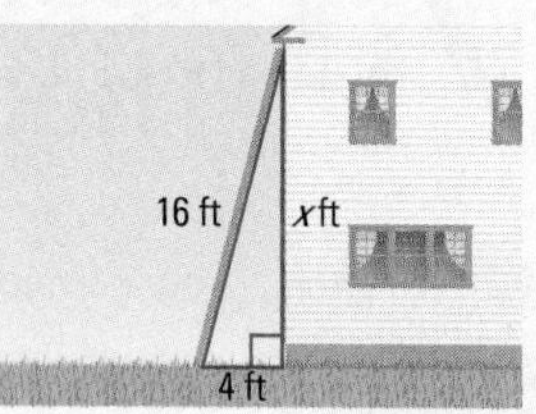

Ⓐ 240 feet Ⓑ 20 feet
Ⓒ 16.5 feet Ⓓ 15.5 feet

Solution

$\left(\text{Length of ladder}\right)^2 = \left(\text{Distance from house}\right)^2 + \left(\text{Height of ladder}\right)^2$

$16^2 = 4^2 + x^2$ **Substitute.**

$256 = 16 + x^2$ **Multiply.**

$240 = x^2$ **Subtract 16 from each side.**

$\sqrt{240} = x$ **Find positive square root.**

$15.491 \approx x$ **Approximate with a calculator.**

APPROXIMATE
In real-world applications, it is usually appropriate to use a calculator to approximate the square root of a number. Round your answer to the nearest tenth.

The ladder is resting against the house at about 15.5 feet above the ground.

▶ The correct answer is D. Ⓐ Ⓑ Ⓒ Ⓓ

✓ GUIDED PRACTICE for Example 2

3. The top of a ladder rests against a wall, 23 feet above the ground. The base of the ladder is 6 feet away from the wall. What is the length of the ladder? **about 23.8 ft**

4. The Pythagorean Theorem is only true for what type of triangle? **right triangle**

PROVING THE PYTHAGOREAN THEOREM There are many proofs of the Pythagorean Theorem. An informal proof is shown below. You will write another proof in Exercise 32 on page 455.

In the figure at the right, the four right triangles are congruent, and they form a small square in the middle. The area of the large square is equal to the area of the four triangles plus the area of the smaller square.

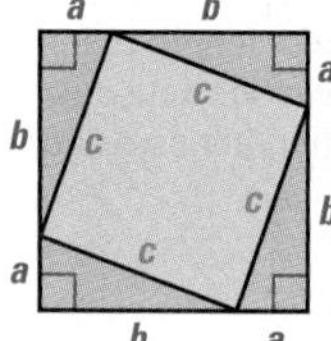

$(\text{Area of large square}) = (\text{Area of four triangles}) + (\text{Area of smaller square})$

$(a + b)^2 = 4\left(\frac{1}{2}ab\right) + c^2$ **Use area formulas.**

$a^2 + 2ab + b^2 = 2ab + c^2$ **Multiply.**

$a^2 + b^2 = c^2$ **Subtract $2ab$ from each side.**

REVIEW AREA
Recall that the area of a square with side length s is $A = s^2$. The area of a triangle with base b and height h is $A = \frac{1}{2}bh$.

Animated Geometry at classzone.com

Differentiated Instruction

Kinesthetic Learners After discussing **Example 2**, set up a similar problem in the classroom. For example, have students find the height of a stack of textbooks indirectly by leaning a ruler from the desktop to the top of the stack. Have them measure the distance from the base of the stack of books to the bottom of the ruler. Instruct them to use the Pythagorean Theorem to find the height of the stack of books.

See also the *Geometry Toolkit* for more strategies.

EXAMPLE 3 Find the area of an isosceles triangle

Find the area of the isosceles triangle with side lengths 10 meters, 13 meters, and 13 meters.

Solution

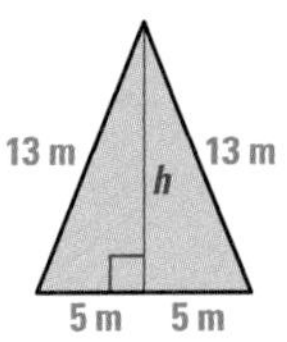

STEP 1 **Draw** a sketch. By definition, the length of an altitude is the height of a triangle. In an isosceles triangle, the altitude to the base is also a perpendicular bisector. So, the altitude divides the triangle into two right triangles with the dimensions shown.

STEP 2 **Use** the Pythagorean Theorem to find the height of the triangle.

$c^2 = a^2 + b^2$	Pythagorean Theorem
$13^2 = 5^2 + h^2$	Substitute.
$169 = 25 + h^2$	Multiply.
$144 = h^2$	Subtract 25 from each side.
$12 = h$	Find the positive square root.

STEP 3 **Find** the area.

$$\text{Area} = \frac{1}{2}(\text{base})(\text{height}) = \frac{1}{2}(10)(12) = 60 \text{ m}^2$$

▸ The area of the triangle is 60 square meters.

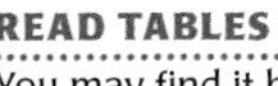

READ TABLES

You may find it helpful to use the Table of Squares and Square Roots on p. 924.

✓ **GUIDED PRACTICE** for Example 3

Find the area of the triangle.

5. 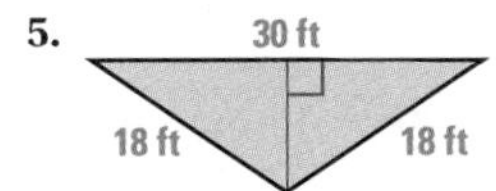

about 149.2 ft^2

6. 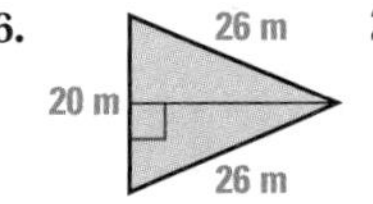

240 m^2

PYTHAGOREAN TRIPLES A **Pythagorean triple** is a set of three positive integers a, b, and c that satisfy the equation $c^2 = a^2 + b^2$.

KEY CONCEPT *For Your Notebook*

Common Pythagorean Triples and Some of Their Multiples

3, 4, 5	**5, 12, 13**	**8, 15, 17**	**7, 24, 25**
6, 8, 10	10, 24, 26	16, 30, 34	14, 48, 50
9, 12, 15	15, 36, 39	24, 45, 51	21, 72, 75
30, 40, 50	50, 120, 130	80, 150, 170	70, 240, 250
$3x$, $4x$, $5x$	$5x$, $12x$, $13x$	$8x$, $15x$, $17x$	$7x$, $24x$, $25x$

The most common Pythagorean triples are in bold. The other triples are the result of multiplying each integer in a bold face triple by the same factor.

STANDARDIZED TESTS

You may find it helpful to memorize the basic Pythagorean triples, shown in **bold**, for standardized tests.

Extra Example 3

Find the area of the isosceles triangle with side lengths 20 in., 20 in., and 24 in. **192 in.^2**

Key Question to Ask for Example 3

- How do you know that the altitude bisects the base? ***Sample answer:*** **The vertex from which the altitude to the base of an isosceles triangle is drawn is equidistant from the endpoints of the base. By the Converse of the Perpendicular Bisector Theorem, the vertex lies on the perpendicular bisector of the base.**

Avoiding Common Errors

In the Key Concept about Pythagorean triples, be sure students understand that if the two legs of a right triangle have lengths 3 and 5, the hypotenuse is *not* 4. The hypotenuse must be the longest side of the triangle.

Extra Example 4

Find the length of the hypotenuse of the right triangle. **75**

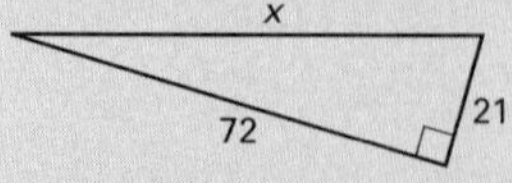

Key Question to Ask for Example 4

- If the legs were 2.5 and 6, how could you find the length of the hypotenuse without using the Pythagorean Theorem? **Using the Pythagorean triple 5, 12, 13, the lengths 2.5 and 6 are half of 5 and 12, so the hypotenuse must be half of 13.**

Closing the Lesson

Have students summarize the major points of the lesson and answer the Essential Question: If you know the lengths of two sides of a right triangle, how do you find the length of the third side?

- **In a right triangle, the square of the length of the hypotenuse is equal to the sum of the squares of the lengths of the two legs.**
- **A Pythagorean triple, such as 3, 4, 5 or 5, 12, 13, is a set of three positive integers that satisfy the Pythagorean Theorem.**

If you know the lengths of two sides of a right triangle, use the Pythagorean Theorem or a Pythagorean triple to find the length of the third side.

EXAMPLE 4 Find the length of a hypotenuse using two methods

Find the length of the hypotenuse of the right triangle.

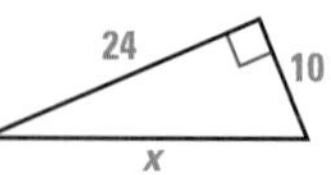

Solution

Method 1: Use a Pythagorean triple.

A common Pythagorean triple is 5, 12, 13. Notice that if you multiply the lengths of the legs of the Pythagorean triple by 2, you get the lengths of the legs of this triangle: $5 \cdot 2 = 10$ and $12 \cdot 2 = 24$. So, the length of the hypotenuse is $13 \cdot 2 = 26$.

Method 2: Use the Pythagorean Theorem.

$x^2 = 10^2 + 24^2$	Pythagorean Theorem
$x^2 = 100 + 576$	Multiply.
$x^2 = 676$	Add.
$x = 26$	Find the positive square root.

✓ GUIDED PRACTICE for Example 4

Find the unknown side length of the right triangle using the Pythagorean Theorem. Then use a Pythagorean triple.

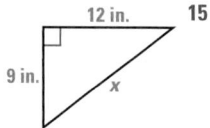

7. 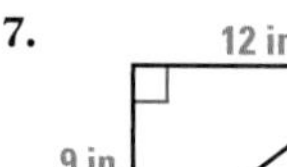

15 in.

8. 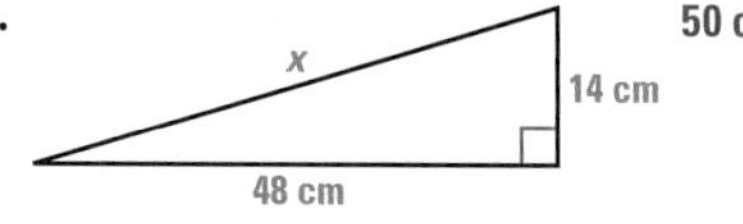

50 cm

7.1 EXERCISES

HOMEWORK KEY
- ○ = **WORKED-OUT SOLUTIONS** on p. WS8 for Exs. 9, 11, and 33
- ★ = **STANDARDIZED TEST PRACTICE** Exs. 2, 17, 27, 33, and 36
- ◆ = **MULTIPLE REPRESENTATIONS** Ex. 35

SKILL PRACTICE

A

1. **VOCABULARY** Copy and complete: A set of three positive integers *a*, *b*, and *c* that satisfy the equation $c^2 = a^2 + b^2$ is called a _?_. **Pythagorean triple**

2. ★ **WRITING** *Describe* the information you need to have in order to use the Pythagorean Theorem to find the length of a side of a triangle. **A right triangle, the measure of a leg of the triangle, and the measure of either the hypotenuse or the other leg.**

EXAMPLE 1 on p. 433 for Exs. 3–7

 **ALGEBRA** **Find the length of the hypotenuse of the right triangle.**

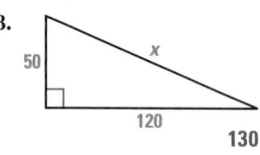

3. Triangle with legs 50 and 120, hypotenuse x. **130**

4. 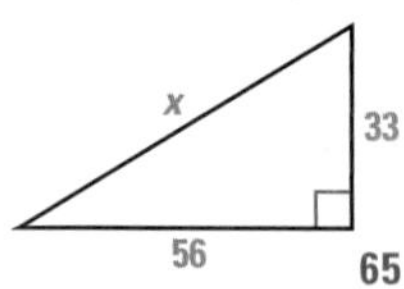

65

5. 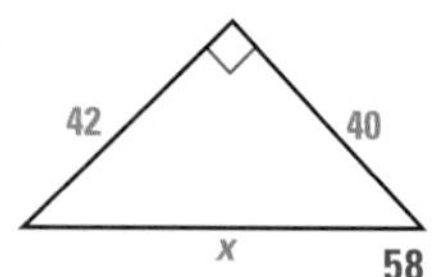

58

ERROR ANALYSIS *Describe* **and correct the error in using the Pythagorean Theorem.**

6.

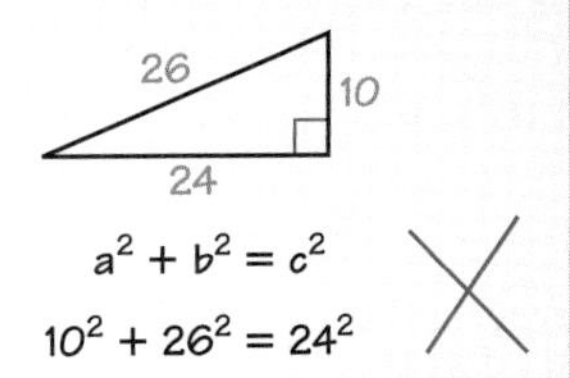

a and *b* represent the legs of the triangle, but 26 is the hypotenuse; $10^2 + 24^2 = 26^2$.

7.

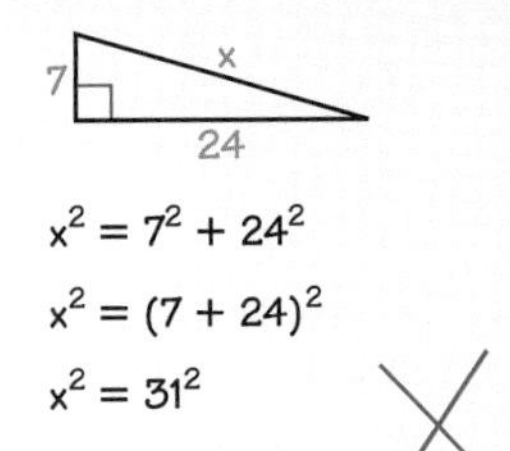

In step 2, the Distributive Property was used incorrectly; $x^2 = 49 + 576$ $x^2 = 625$ $x = 25$.

EXAMPLE 2 on p. 434 for Exs. 8–10

FINDING A LENGTH **Find the unknown leg length *x*.**

8.

about 14.1 ft

9.

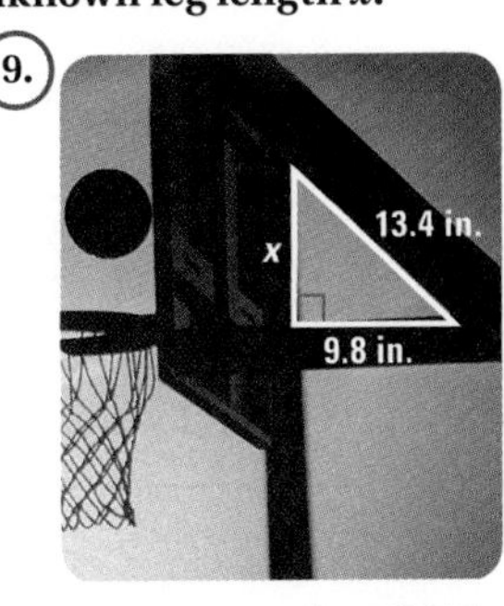

about 9.14 in.

10.

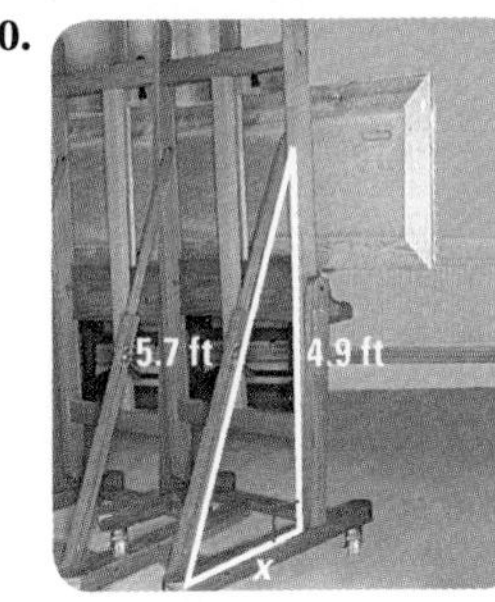

about 2.91 ft

EXAMPLE 3 on p. 435 for Exs. 11–13

FINDING THE AREA **Find the area of the isosceles triangle.**

11.

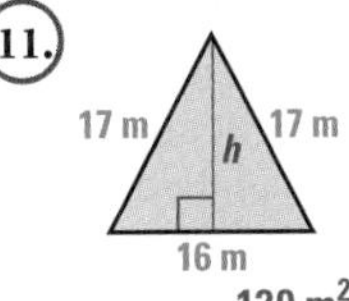

120 m^2

12.

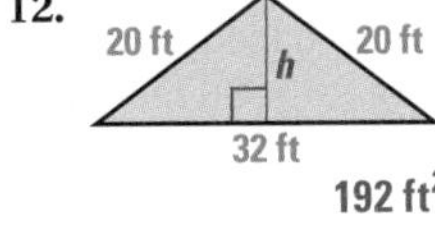

192 ft^2

13.

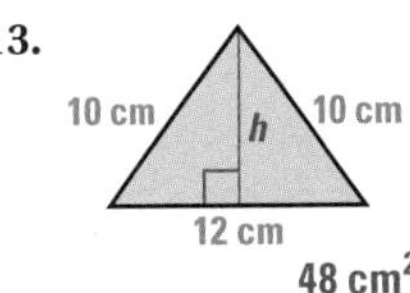

48 cm^2

EXAMPLE 4 on p. 436 for Exs. 14–17

FINDING SIDE LENGTHS **Find the unknown side length of the right triangle using the Pythagorean Theorem or a Pythagorean triple.**

14. (72, 21, x) 75

15.

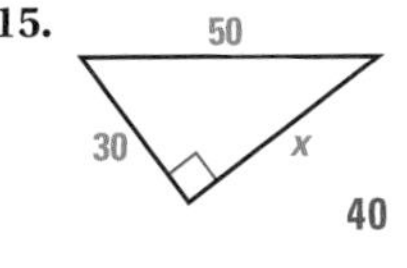

40

16.

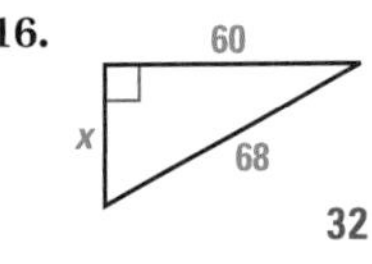

32

17. ★ **MULTIPLE CHOICE** What is the length of the hypotenuse of a right triangle with leg lengths of 8 inches and 15 inches? **B**

Ⓐ 13 inches Ⓑ 17 inches Ⓒ 21 inches Ⓓ 25 inches

PYTHAGOREAN TRIPLES **The given lengths are two sides of a right triangle. All three side lengths of the triangle are integers and together form a Pythagorean triple. Find the length of the third side and tell whether it is a leg or the hypotenuse.**

B

18. 24 and 51 **45, leg**

19. 20 and 25 **15, leg**

20. 28 and 96 **100, hypotenuse**

21. 20 and 48 **52, hypotenuse**

22. 75 and 85 **40, leg**

23. 72 and 75 **21, leg**

4 PRACTICE AND APPLY

Assignment Guide

Answer Transparencies available for all exercises

Basic:
Day 1: SRH p. 874 Exs. 1–4, 6, 7
pp. 436–439
Exs. 1–10, 31–33, 49, 50
Day 2: pp. 436–439
Exs. 11–23, 34, 35, 39–48

Average:
Day 1: pp. 436–439
Exs. 1, 2, 4–9, 24–26, 31–33, 49, 50
Day 2: pp. 436–439
Exs. 12, 13, 15–17, 20–22, 27, 28, 34–37, 40, 44, 47

Advanced:
Day 1: pp. 436–439
Exs. 1, 2, 4, 5, 9, 10, 24–26, 31–33, 36–38*, 49, 50
Day 2: pp. 436–439
Exs. 13, 16, 17, 21–23, 27–30*, 34, 35, 42, 48

Block:
pp. 436–439
Exs. 1, 2, 4–9, 12, 13, 15–17, 20–22, 24–28, 31–37, 40, 44, 47, 49, 50

Differentiated Instruction

See *Geometry Best Practices Toolkit* for suggestions on addressing the needs of a diverse classroom.

Homework Check

For a quick check of student understanding of key concepts, go over the following exercises:
Basic: 3, 8, 12, 14, 31
Average: 4, 8, 12, 15, 32
Advanced: 5, 10, 13, 16, 34

Extra Practice

- Student Edition, p. 908
- Chapter 7 Resource Book: Practice levels A, B, C, pp. 8–13

Practice Worksheet

An easily-readable reduced practice page (with answers) for this lesson can be found on p. 430C.

Study Strategy

Exercises 3–5, 11–17 Identify which exercises use Pythagorean triples or their multiples. For example, the lengths in Exercise 3 are 10 times the numbers in the Pythagorean triple 5, 12, 13.

35a–b. See below.

35c.

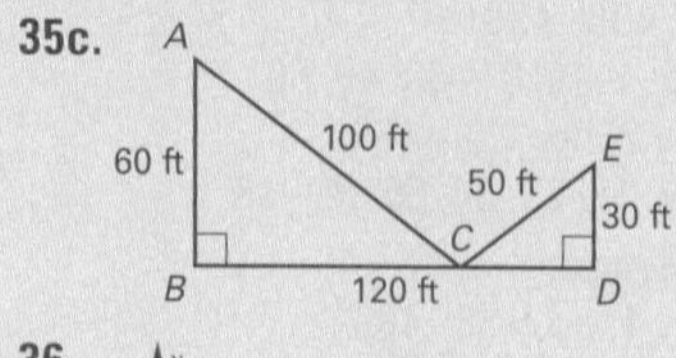

36.

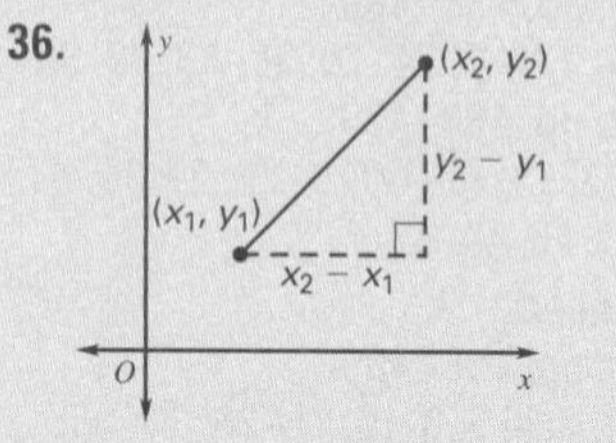

37. *Sample answer:*

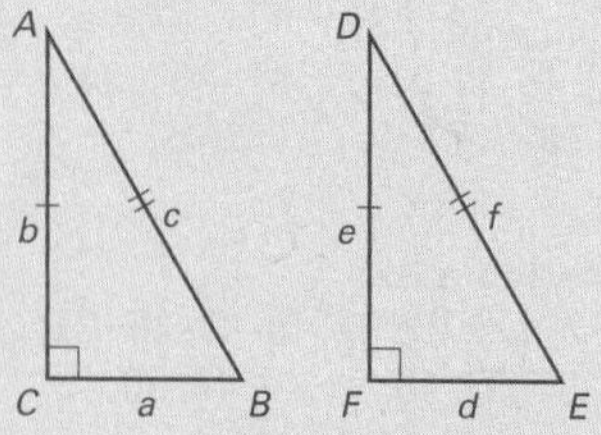

Given: $\triangle ABC$ and $\triangle DEF$ are right triangles; $\overline{AB} \cong \overline{DE}$, $\overline{AC} \cong \overline{DF}$.

Prove: $\triangle ABC \cong \triangle DEF$

Statements (Reasons)

1. **$\triangle ABC$ and $\triangle DEF$ are right triangles; $\overline{AB} \cong \overline{DE}$, $\overline{AC} \cong \overline{DF}$. (Given)**
2. **$c = f$, $b = e$ (Definition of segment congruence)**
3. **$a^2 + b^2 = c^2$, $d^2 + e^2 = f^2$ (Pythagorean Theorem)**
4. **$a^2 + b^2 = f^2$ (Substitution Property of Equality)**
5. **$a^2 + b^2 = d^2 + e^2$ (Substitution Property of Equality)**
6. **$a^2 + e^2 = d^2 + e^2$ (Substitution Property of Equality)**
7. **$a^2 = d^2$ (Subtraction Property of Equality)**
8. **$a = d$ (A property of square roots)**
9. **$\overline{BC} \cong \overline{EF}$ (Definition of segment congruence)**
10. **$\angle C \cong \angle F$ (Right Angle Congruence Theorem)**
11. **$\triangle ABC \cong \triangle DEF$ (SAS Congruence Postulate)**

FINDING SIDE LENGTHS **Find the unknown side length x. Write your answer in simplest radical form.**

24. 6, 6, 3, x **$3\sqrt{5}$**

25. **$11\sqrt{2}$**

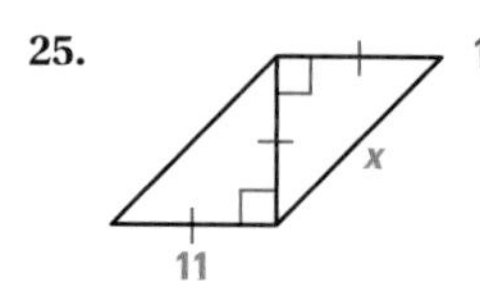

26. **$\sqrt{65}$**

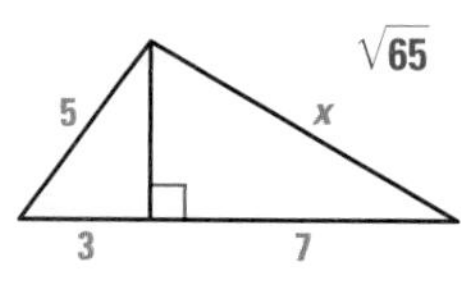

27. ★ **MULTIPLE CHOICE** What is the area of a right triangle with a leg length of 15 feet and a hypotenuse length of 39 feet? **A**

Ⓐ 270 ft^2 Ⓑ 292.5 ft^2 Ⓒ 540 ft^2 Ⓓ 585 ft^2

28. **ALGEBRA** Solve for x if the lengths of the two legs of a right triangle are $2x$ and $2x + 4$, and the length of the hypotenuse is $4x - 4$. **6**

CHALLENGE **In Exercises 29 and 30, solve for x.**

C **29.** **$2\sqrt{13}$**

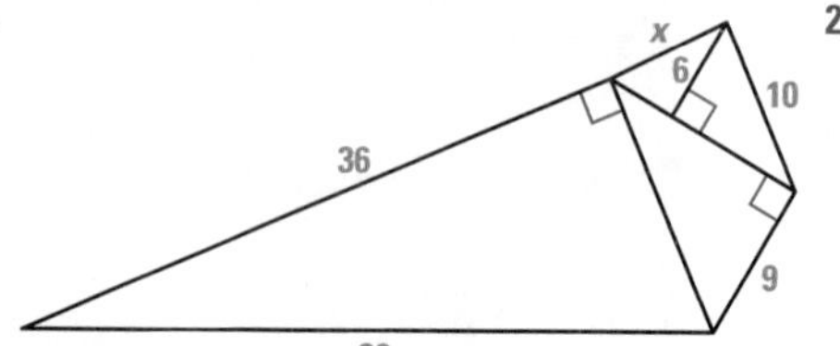

30. 13, 15, x, 14 **12**

PROBLEM SOLVING

EXAMPLE 2 A on p. 434 for Exs. 31–32

31. BASEBALL DIAMOND In baseball, the distance of the paths between each pair of consecutive bases is 90 feet and the paths form right angles. How far does the ball need to travel if it is thrown from home plate directly to second base? **about 127 ft**

@HomeTutor for problem solving help at classzone.com

32. APPLE BALLOON You tie an apple balloon to a stake in the ground. The rope is 10 feet long. As the wind picks up, you observe that the balloon is now 6 feet away from the stake. How far above the ground is the balloon now? **8 ft**

@HomeTutor for problem solving help at classzone.com

33. ★ **SHORT RESPONSE** Three side lengths of a right triangle are 25, 65, and 60. *Explain* how you know which side is the hypotenuse. **The longest side of the triangle is opposite the largest angle, which in a right triangle is the right angle.**

34. MULTI-STEP PROBLEM In your town, there is a field that is in the shape of a right triangle with the dimensions shown.

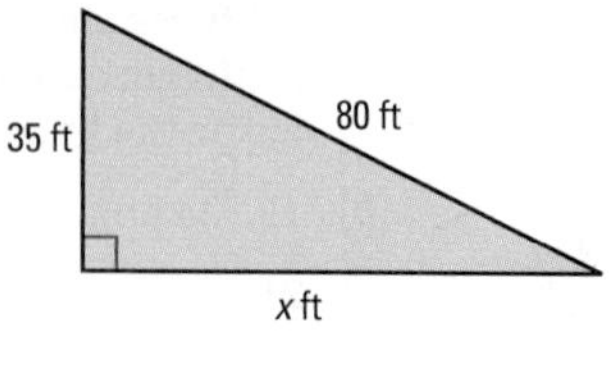

a. Find the perimeter of the field. **about 187 ft**

b. You are going to plant dogwood seedlings about every ten feet around the field's edge. How many trees do you need? **about 19 trees**

c. If each dogwood seedling sells for \$12, how much will the trees cost? **about \$228**

◯ = WORKED-OUT SOLUTIONS on p. WS1 ★ = STANDARDIZED TEST PRACTICE ◆ = MULTIPLE REPRESENTATIONS

35a–b.

BC	10	20	30	40	50	60	70	80	90	100	110	120
AC	60.8	63.2	67.1	72.1	78.1	84.9	92.2	100	108.2	116.6	125.3	134.2
CE	114.0	104.4	94.9	85.4	76.2	67.1	58.3	50	42.4	36.1	31.6	30
AC + CE	174.8	167.6	162	157.5	154.3	152	150.5	150	150.6	152.7	156.9	164.2

B 35. MULTIPLE REPRESENTATIONS As you are gathering leaves for a science project, you look back at your campsite and see that the campfire is not completely out. You want to get water from a nearby river to put out the flames with the bucket you are using to collect leaves. Use the diagram and the steps below to determine the shortest distance you must travel.

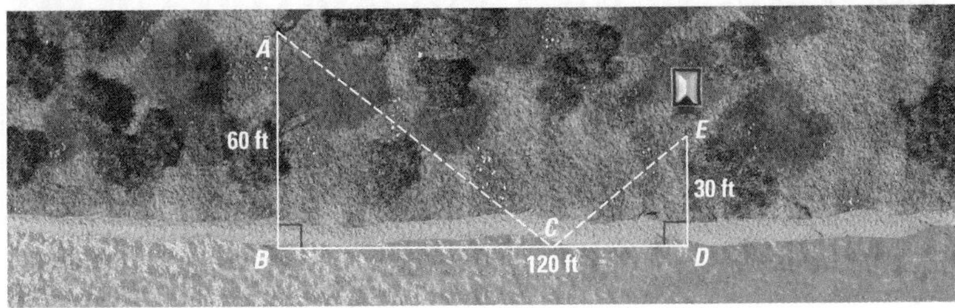

a. **Making a Table** Make a table with columns labeled BC, AC, CE, and $AC + CE$. Enter values of BC from 10 to 120 in increments of 10. **See margin.**

b. **Calculating Values** Calculate AC, CE, and $AC + CE$ for each value of BC, and record the results in the table. Then, use your table of values to determine the shortest distance you must travel. **150 ft**

c. **Drawing a Picture** Draw an accurate picture to scale of the shortest distance. **See margin.**

36. ★ **SHORT RESPONSE** *Justify* the Distance Formula using the Pythagorean Theorem. **See margin for art; by the Pythagorean Theorem, $(x_2 - x_1)^2 + (y_2 - y_1)^2 = d^2$ so $d = \sqrt{(x_2 - x_1)^2 + (y_2 - y_1)^2}$.**

37. PROVING THEOREM 4.5 Find the Hypotenuse-Leg (HL) Congruence Theorem on page 241. Assign variables for the side lengths in the diagram. Use your variables to write GIVEN and PROVE statements. Use the Pythagorean Theorem and congruent triangles to prove Theorem 4.5. **See margin.**

C 38. CHALLENGE Trees grown for sale at nurseries should stand at least five feet from one another while growing. If the trees are grown in parallel rows, what is the smallest allowable distance between rows? **about 4.3 ft**

MIXED REVIEW

PREVIEW Prepare for Lesson 7.2 in Exs. 39–42.

Evaluate the expression. *(p. 874)*

39. $(\sqrt{7})^2$ **7** 40. $(4\sqrt{3})^2$ **48** 41. $(-6\sqrt{81})^2$ **2916** 42. $(-8\sqrt{2})^2$ **128**

Describe **the possible lengths of the third side of the triangle given the lengths of the other two sides.** *(p. 328)*

43. 3 feet, 6 feet **3 ft < ℓ < 9 ft**
44. 5 inches, 11 inches **6 in. < ℓ < 16 in.**
45. 14 meters, 21 meters **7 m < ℓ < 35 m**
46. 12 inches, 27 inches **15 in. < ℓ < 39 in.**
47. 18 yards, 18 yards **0 yd < ℓ < 36 yd**
48. 27 meters, 39 meters **12 m < ℓ < 66 m**

Determine whether the two triangles are similar. If they are similar, write a similarity statement and find the scale factor of Triangle B to Triangle A. *(p. 388)*

49.
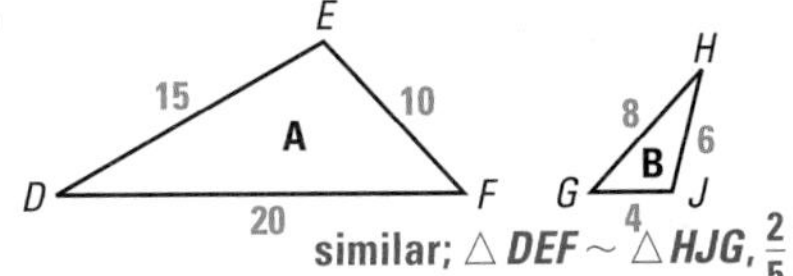

similar; $\triangle DEF \sim \triangle HJG$, $\frac{2}{5}$

50.
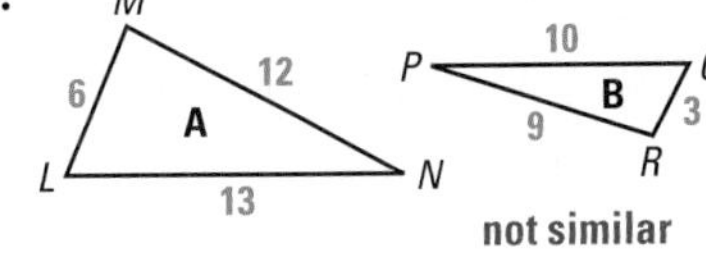

not similar

5 ASSESS AND RETEACH

Daily Homework Quiz

Transparency Available

1. Find the length of the hypotenuse of the right triangle. **39**

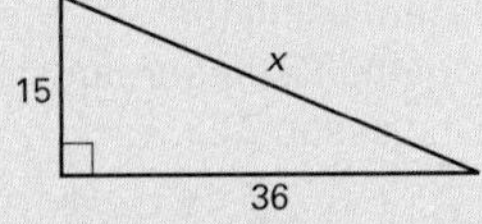

2. Find the area of the isosceles triangle. **1080 cm²**

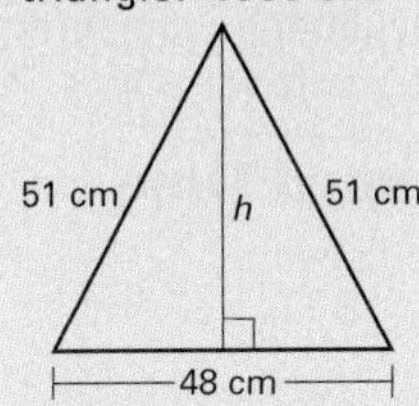

3. Find the unknown side length x. Write your answer in simplest radical form. **$4\sqrt{13}$**

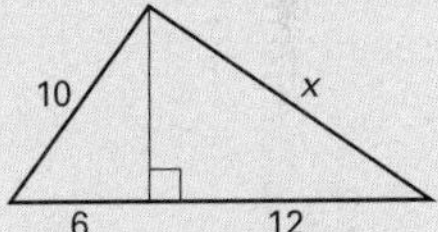

Available at **classzone.com**

Diagnosis/Remediation

- Practice A, B, C in Chapter 7 Resource Book, pp. 8–13
- Study Guide in Chapter 7 Resource Book, pp. 14–15
- Practice Workbook, pp. 124–126
- @HomeTutor

Challenge

Additional challenge is available in the Chapter 7 Resource Book, p. 18.

1 PLAN AND PREPARE

Explore the Concept

- Students will use the Converse of the Pythagorean Theorem to classify a triangle.
- This leads into using the Converse of the Pythagorean Theorem in Lesson 7.2.

Materials

Each student will need:

- graphing calculator or computer with geometry software

Recommended Time

Work activity: 15 min
Discuss results: 5 min

Grouping

Students can work individually or in pairs. If students work in pairs, one can measure while the other records the results.

2 TEACH

Tips for Success

If possible, let the software do the calculations and print results.

Alternative Strategy

Do the activity as a demonstration on a computer. Have students take turns doing the calculations.

Key Discovery

Compare AB^2 to $AC^2 + CB^2$. If AB^2 is greater, the triangle is obtuse; if AB^2 is less, the triangle is acute; if AB^2 is equal, the triangle is right.

3 ASSESS AND RETEACH

1. If $AB^2 = 31$ and $AC^2 + CB^2 = 26$, what type of triangle is $\triangle ABC$? **obtuse**

@HomeTutor
classzone.com
Keystrokes

7.2 Converse of the Pythagorean Theorem

MATERIALS • graphing calculator or computer

Standards

12.0 Students find and use measures of sides and of interior and exterior angles **of triangles** and polygons **to classify figures** and solve problems.

QUESTION **How can you use the side lengths in a triangle to classify the triangle by its angle measures?**

You can use geometry drawing software to construct and measure triangles.

EXPLORE **Construct a triangle**

STEP 1 ***Draw a triangle*** Draw any $\triangle ABC$ with the largest angle at C. Measure $\angle C$, $\overline{AB}$, $\overline{AC}$, and $\overline{CB}$. **Check students' work.**

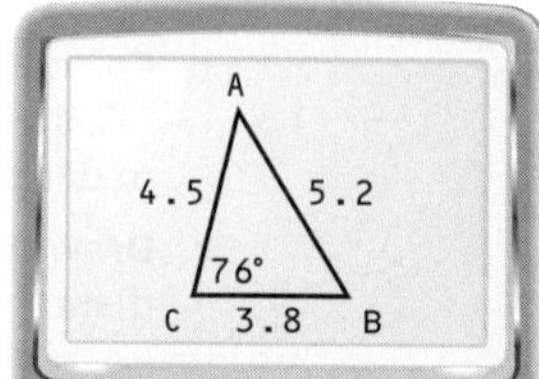

STEP 2 ***Calculate*** Use your measurements to calculate AB^2, AC^2, CB^2, and $(AC^2 + CB^2)$. **Check students' work.**

STEP 3 ***Complete a table*** Copy the table below and record your results in the first row. Then move point A to different locations and record the values for each triangle in your table. Make sure $\overline{AB}$ is always the longest side of the triangle. Include triangles that are acute, right, and obtuse. **Check students' work.**

$m\angle C$	AB	AB^2	AC	CB	$AC^2 + CB^2$
76°	5.2	27.04	4.5	3.8	34.69
?	?	?	?	?	?
?	?	?	?	?	?

DRAW CONCLUSIONS **Use your observations to complete these exercises**

1. The Pythagorean Theorem states that "In a right triangle, the square of the length of the hypotenuse is equal to the sum of the squares of the lengths of the legs." Write the Pythagorean Theorem in if-then form. Then write its converse. **See margin.**
2. Is the converse of the Pythagorean Theorem true? *Explain.* **Yes; because the theorem can be stated as an equation, it will be true in either direction.**
3. Make a conjecture about the relationship between the measure of the largest angle in a triangle and the squares of the side lengths. **Check students' work.**

Copy and complete the statement.

4. If $AB^2 > AC^2 + CB^2$, then the triangle is a(n) __?__ triangle. **obtuse**
5. If $AB^2 < AC^2 + CB^2$, then the triangle is a(n) __?__ triangle. **acute**
6. If $AB^2 = AC^2 + CB^2$, then the triangle is a(n) __?__ triangle. **right**

1. If a triangle is a right triangle, then the square of the length of the hypotenuse is equal to the sum of the squares of the lengths of the legs; if the square of the length of the hypotenuse is equal to the sum of the squares of the lengths of the legs, then the triangle is a right triangle.

7.2 Use the Converse of the Pythagorean Theorem

Before You used the Pythagorean Theorem to find missing side lengths.

Now You will use its converse to determine if a triangle is a right triangle.

Why? So you can determine if a volleyball net is set up correctly, as in Ex. 38.

Key Vocabulary
- **acute triangle,** *p. 217*
- **obtuse triangle,** *p. 217*

Standards

12.0 Students find and use measures of sides and of interior and exterior angles **of triangles** and polygons **to classify figures** and solve problems.

The converse of the Pythagorean Theorem is also true. You can use it to verify that a triangle with given side lengths is a right triangle.

THEOREM *For Your Notebook*

THEOREM 7.2 **Converse of the Pythagorean Theorem**

If the square of the length of the longest side of a triangle is equal to the sum of the squares of the lengths of the other two sides, then the triangle is a right triangle.

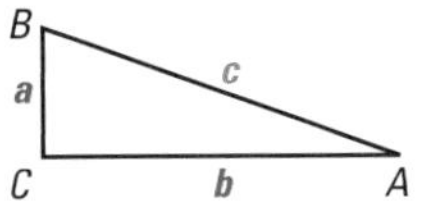

If $c^2 = a^2 + b^2$, then $\triangle ABC$ is a right triangle.

Proof: Ex. 42, p. 446

EXAMPLE 1 Verify right triangles

Tell whether the given triangle is a right triangle.

a.

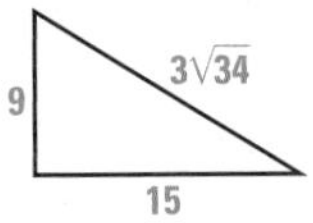

b.

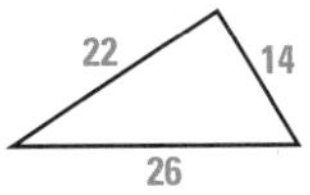

Let c represent the length of the longest side of the triangle. Check to see whether the side lengths satisfy the equation $c^2 = a^2 + b^2$.

a. $(3\sqrt{34})^2 \stackrel{?}{=} 9^2 + 15^2$

$9 \cdot 34 \stackrel{?}{=} 81 + 225$

$306 = 306$ ✓

The triangle is a right triangle.

b. $26^2 \stackrel{?}{=} 22^2 + 14^2$

$676 \stackrel{?}{=} 484 + 196$

$676 \neq 680$

The triangle is not a right triangle.

REVIEW ALGEBRA

Use a square root table or a calculator to find the decimal representation. So, $3\sqrt{34} \approx 17.493$ is the length of the longest side in part (a).

✓ **GUIDED PRACTICE** for Example 1

Tell whether a triangle with the given side lengths is a right triangle.

1. 4, $4\sqrt{3}$, 8 **right triangle**
2. 10, 11, and 14 **not a right triangle**
3. 5, 6, and $\sqrt{61}$ **right triangle**

1 PLAN AND PREPARE

Warm-Up Exercises

Transparency Available

1. Find x. $\sqrt{29}$

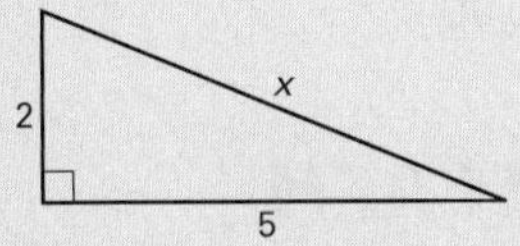

2. Simplify $(5\sqrt{3})^2$. **75**
3. Find x. **9**

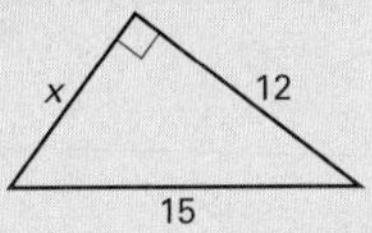

Notetaking Guide

Transparency Available

Promotes interactive learning and notetaking skills, pp. 174–177.

Pacing

Basic: 1 day

Average: 1 day

Advanced: 1 day

Block: 0.5 block with 7.3

- See *Teaching Guide/Lesson Plan.*

2 FOCUS AND MOTIVATE

Essential Question

Big Idea 1, p. 431

How can you use the sides of a triangle to determine if it is right? **Tell students they will learn how to answer this question by using theorems about the sides of a triangle.**

Resource Planning Guide

Chapter Resource Book
- Teaching Guide/Lesson Plan (pp. 19–20)
- Practice levels A, B, C (pp. 22–27)
- Study Guide (pp. 28–29)
- Catch-up for Absent Students (p. 30)
- Application (p. 31)
- Challenge (p. 32)

Workbooks
- Notetaking Guide (pp. 174–177)
- Practice Workbook (pp. 127–129)

Teaching Options
- **Power Presentations CD-ROM** provides dynamic electronic teaching resources for the classroom.
- **Activity Generator CD-ROM** provides editable activities for all ability levels.

Interactive Technology
- Easy Planner
- Power Presentations CD-ROM
- Activity Generator CD-ROM
- Animated Geometry
- Test Generator CD-ROM
- Online Quiz
- eWorkbook
- eEdition
- @HomeTutor

Resources for English Learners
- Quick Reference for English Learners
- Spanish Study Guide
- Multi-Language Visual Glossary
- Student Resources in Spanish

See also the *Geometry Toolkit* for more strategies for meeting individual needs.

Motivating the Lesson

You want to put in a fence post and be sure it is perpendicular to the ground. In this lesson you will learn how to use the lengths of sides of a triangle to determine whether or not one side is perpendicular to another side.

3 TEACH

Extra Example 1

Tell whether the given triangle is a right triangle.

a.

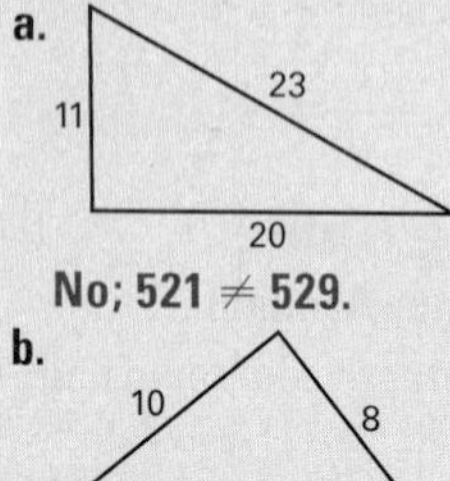

No; 521 ≠ 529.

b.

Yes; 164 = 164.

Extra Example 2

Can segments with lengths of 11.2 inches, 6.5 inches, and 7.1 inches form a triangle? If so, would the triangle be acute, right, or obtuse? **Yes; obtuse**

Animated Geometry classzone.com

An **Animated Geometry** activity is available on-line for **Example 2**. This activity is also available on the **Power Presentations CD-ROM**.

CLASSIFYING TRIANGLES The Converse of the Pythagorean Theorem is used to verify that a given triangle is a right triangle. The theorems below are used to verify that a given triangle is acute or obtuse.

THEOREMS *For Your Notebook*

THEOREM 7.3

If the square of the length of the longest side of a triangle is less than the sum of the squares of the lengths of the other two sides, then the triangle is an acute triangle.

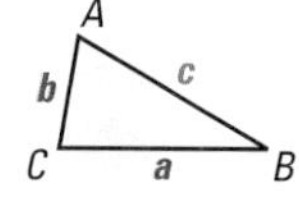

If $c^2 < a^2 + b^2$, then the triangle is acute.

Proof: Ex. 40, p. 446

THEOREM 7.4

If the square of the length of the longest side of a triangle is greater than the sum of the squares of the lengths of the other two sides, then the triangle is an obtuse triangle.

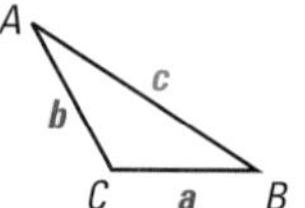

If $c^2 > a^2 + b^2$, then triangle ABC is obtuse.

Proof: Ex. 41, p. 446

EXAMPLE 2 Classify triangles

Can segments with lengths of 4.3 feet, 5.2 feet, and 6.1 feet form a triangle? If so, would the triangle be *acute, right,* or *obtuse*?

Solution

APPLY THEOREMS The Triangle Inequality Theorem on page 330 states that the sum of the lengths of any two sides of a triangle is greater than the length of the third side.

STEP 1 **Use** the Triangle Inequality Theorem to check that the segments can make a triangle.

$4.3 + 5.2 = 9.5$ $\quad$ $4.3 + 6.1 = 10.4$ $\quad$ $5.2 + 6.1 = 11.3$

$9.5 > 6.1$ $\quad$ $10.4 > 5.2$ $\quad$ $11.3 > 4.3$

▶ The side lengths 4.3 feet, 5.2 feet, and 6.1 feet can form a triangle.

STEP 2 **Classify** the triangle by comparing the square of the length of the longest side with the sum of squares of the lengths of the shorter sides.

$c^2 \ \underline{\ ?\ }\ a^2 + b^2$	Compare c^2 with $a^2 + b^2$.
$6.1^2 \ \underline{\ ?\ }\ 4.3^2 + 5.2^2$	Substitute.
$37.21 \ \underline{\ ?\ }\ 18.49 + 27.04$	Simplify.
$37.21 < 45.53$	c^2 is less than $a^2 + b^2$.

▶ The side lengths 4.3 feet, 5.2 feet, and 6.1 feet form an acute triangle.

Animated Geometry at classzone.com

EXAMPLE 3 Use the Converse of the Pythagorean Theorem

CATAMARAN You are part of a crew that is installing the mast on a catamaran. When the mast is fastened properly, it is perpendicular to the trampoline deck. How can you check that the mast is perpendicular using a tape measure?

Solution

To show a line is perpendicular to a plane you must show that the line is perpendicular to two lines in the plane.

Think of the mast as a line and the deck as a plane. Use a 3-4-5 right triangle and the Converse of the Pythagorean Theorem to show that the mast is perpendicular to different lines on the deck.

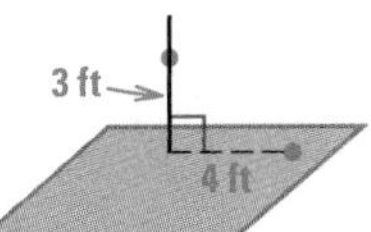

First place a mark 3 feet up the mast and a mark on the deck 4 feet from the mast.

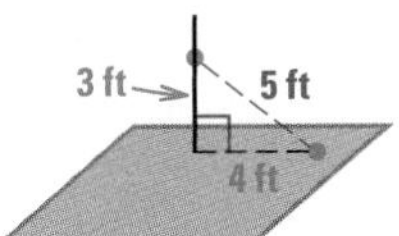

Use the tape measure to check that the distance between the two marks is 5 feet. The mast makes a right angle with the line on the deck.

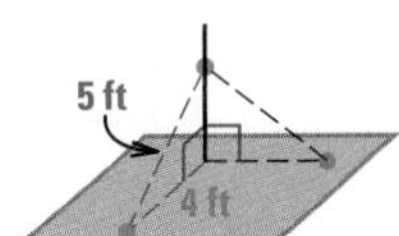

Finally, repeat the procedure to show that the mast is perpendicular to another line on the deck.

 **GUIDED PRACTICE** for Examples 2 and 3

4. Show that segments with lengths 3, 4, and 6 can form a triangle and classify the triangle as *acute, right,* or *obtuse.* **$3 + 4 > 6, 4 + 6 > 3, 6 + 3 > 4$, obtuse**

5. **WHAT IF?** In Example 3, could you use triangles with side lengths 2, 3, and 4 to verify that you have perpendicular lines? *Explain.* **No; in order to verify that you have perpendicular lines, the triangle would have to be a right triangle, and a 2-3-4 triangle is not a right triangle.**

CLASSIFYING TRIANGLES You can use the theorems from this lesson to classify a triangle as acute, right, or obtuse based on its side lengths.

CONCEPT SUMMARY *For Your Notebook*

Methods for Classifying a Triangle by Angles Using its Side Lengths

Theorem 7.2

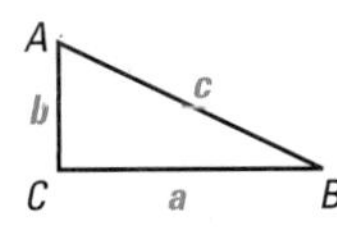

If $c^2 = a^2 + b^2$, then $m\angle C = 90°$ and $\triangle ABC$ is a right triangle.

Theorem 7.3

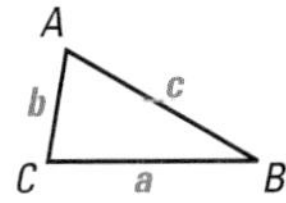

If $c^2 < a^2 + b^2$, then $m\angle C < 90°$ and $\triangle ABC$ is an acute triangle.

Theorem 7.4

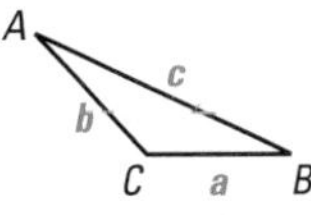

If $c^2 > a^2 + b^2$, then $m\angle C > 90°$ and $\triangle ABC$ is an obtuse triangle.

Extra Example 3

You are planting a tree and want it to be perpendicular to the ground. How can you check this using a meter stick? ***Sample answer:*** **Mark a point 80 cm off the ground on the tree and put several stakes in the ground 60 cm from the base of the tree. Adjust the angle of the tree until the 80-cm mark is exactly 100 cm from each of the stakes.**

Key Questions to Ask for Example 3

- How do you show that a line is perpendicular to a plane? **Show that it is perpendicular to 2 lines in the plane.**
- What are the lengths of the segments on the mast and on the deck? **3 ft and 4 ft**

Closing the Lesson

Have students summarize the major points of the lesson and answer the Essential Question: How can you use the sides of a triangle to determine if it is right?

- **Let c be the length of the longest side and let a and b be the lengths of the other two sides. Then:**
  If $c^2 < a^2 + b^2$, the triangle is an acute triangle.
  If $c^2 = a^2 + b^2$, the triangle is a right triangle.
  If $c^2 > a^2 + b^2$, the triangle is an obtuse triangle.

A triangle is a right triangle if the square of its longest side is equal to the sum of the squares of its two other sides.

Differentiated Instruction

Kinesthetic Learners Create a model for **Example 3** using a piece of cardboard, a pencil, and two 5-inch long pieces of string. The cardboard will be the boat and the pencil will be the mast. Attach the strings 3 inches up from one end of the pencil. Then attach each end to two separate points on the cardboard, 4 inches away from where the pencil rests on the cardboard. Students should see that the pencil must be perpendicular to the cardboard.

See also the *Geometry Toolkit* for more strategies.

4 PRACTICE AND APPLY

Assignment Guide

Answer Transparencies available for all exercises

Basic:
Day 1: pp. 444–447
Exs. 1–7, 9–11, 15–18, 24–28, 35–40, 46–52

Average:
Day 1: pp. 444–447
Exs. 1, 2, 5–7, 10–12, 18–20, 24–31, 35–44, 47, 50, 52

Advanced:
Day 1: pp. 444–447
Exs. 1, 2, 7, 8, 12–14, 21–25, 27–35*, 37–45*, 48, 51, 52

Block:
pp. 444–447
Exs. 1, 2, 5–7, 10–12, 18–20, 24–31, 35–44, 47, 50, 52 (with 7.3)

Differentiated Instruction

See *Geometry Best Practices Toolkit* for suggestions on addressing the needs of a diverse classroom.

Homework Check

For a quick check of student understanding of key concepts, go over the following exercises:

Basic: 4, 10, 16, 35, 36
Average: 6, 12, 20, 35, 38
Advanced: 8, 14, 22, 35, 40

Extra Practice

- Student Edition, p. 908
- Chapter 7 Resource Book: Practice levels A, B, C, pp. 22–27

Practice Worksheet

An easily-readable reduced practice page (with answers) for this lesson can be found on p. 430C.

7.2 EXERCISES

HOMEWORK KEY
○ = **WORKED-OUT SOLUTIONS on p. WS8 for Exs. 7, 17, and 37**
★ = **STANDARDIZED TEST PRACTICE Exs. 2, 24, 25, 32, 38, 39, and 43**

SKILL PRACTICE

A

1. **VOCABULARY** What is the longest side of a right triangle called? **hypotenuse**

2. ★ **WRITING** *Explain* how the side lengths of a triangle can be used to classify it as acute, right, or obtuse. **See margin.**

EXAMPLE 1 on p. 441 for Exs. 3–14

VERIFYING RIGHT TRIANGLES **Tell whether the triangle is a right triangle.**

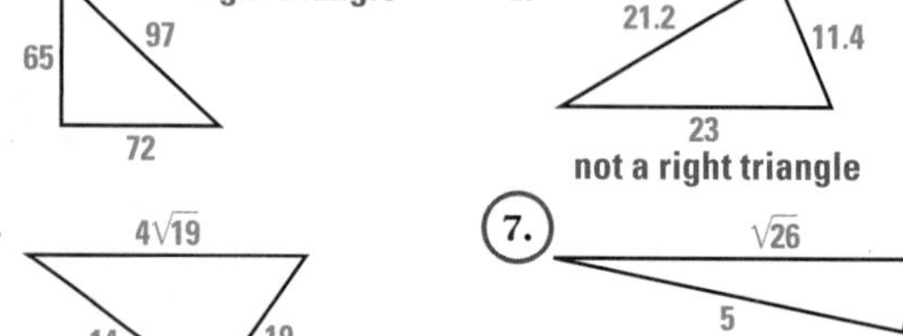

3. (sides 65, 72, 97) **right triangle**
4. (sides 21.2, 11.4, 23) **not a right triangle**
5. (sides 2, 6, $3\sqrt{5}$) **not a right triangle**
6. (sides $4\sqrt{19}$, 14, 10) **not a right triangle**
7. (sides $\sqrt{26}$, 5, 1) **right triangle**
8. (sides 89, 80, 39) **right triangle**

VERIFYING RIGHT TRIANGLES **Tell whether the given side lengths of a triangle can represent a right triangle.**

9. 9, 12, and 15 **right triangle**
10. 9, 10, and 15 **not a right triangle**
11. 36, 48, and 60 **right triangle**
12. 6, 10, and $2\sqrt{34}$ **right triangle**
13. 7, 14, and $7\sqrt{5}$ **right triangle**
14. 10, 12, and 20 **not a right triangle**

EXAMPLE 2 on p. 442 for Exs. 15–23

CLASSIFYING TRIANGLES **In Exercises 15–23, decide if the segment lengths form a triangle. If so, would the triangle be *acute, right,* or *obtuse?***

15. 10, 11, and 14 **triangle; acute**
16. 10, 15, and $5\sqrt{13}$ **triangle; right**
17. 24, 30, and $6\sqrt{43}$ **triangle; obtuse**
18. 5, 6, and 7 **triangle; acute**
19. 12, 16, and 20 **triangle; right**
20. 8, 10, and 12 **triangle; acute**
21. 15, 20, and 36 **not a triangle**
22. 6, 8, and 10 **triangle; right**
23. 8.2, 4.1, and 12.2 **triangle; obtuse**

24. ★ **MULTIPLE CHOICE** Which side lengths do not form a right triangle? **B**

(A) 5, 12, 13 (B) 10, 24, 28 (C) 15, 36, 39 (D) 50, 120, 130

25. ★ **MULTIPLE CHOICE** What type of triangle has side lengths of 4, 7, and 9? **C**

(A) Acute scalene (B) Right scalene
(C) Obtuse scalene (D) None of the above

B

26. **ERROR ANALYSIS** A student tells you that if you double all the sides of a right triangle, the new triangle is obtuse. *Explain* why this statement is incorrect.

26. ***Sample answer:*** **If a triangle with sides *a*, *b*, and *c* is a right triangle with $a^2 + b^2 = c^2$, then a triangle with double side lengths would be 2*a*, 2*b*, and 2*c*, and $(2a)^2 + (2b)^2 = (2c)^2$, $4a^2 + 4b^2 = 4c^2$, simplify to $a^2 + b^2 = c^2$, so if the sides of a right triangle are doubled, the new triangle is also a right triangle.**

GRAPHING TRIANGLES **Graph points *A*, *B*, and *C*. Connect the points to form △*ABC*. Decide whether △*ABC* is *acute, right,* or *obtuse.*** **27, 28. See margin for art.**

27. $A(-2, 4)$, $B(6, 0)$, $C(-5, -2)$ **right**
28. $A(0, 2)$, $B(5, 1)$, $C(1, -1)$ **acute**

2. The relationship of the longest side squared to the sum of the squares of the other two sides determines the angle classification. If the longest side squared is greater than the sum of the other two sides, then the triangle is obtuse; if they are equal, the triangle is a right triangle; if the longest side squared is less than the sum of the square of the other two sides, then the triangle is acute.

29. **ALGEBRA** Tell whether a triangle with side lengths $5x$, $12x$, and $13x$ (where $x > 0$) is *acute, right,* or *obtuse.* **right**

USING DIAGRAMS In Exercises 30 and 31, copy and complete the statement with <, >, or =, if possible. If it is not possible, *explain* why.

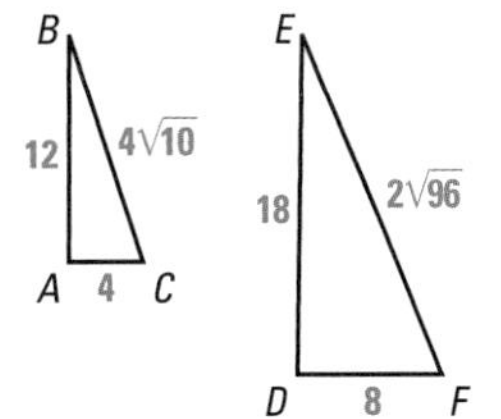

30. $m\angle A$ _?_ $m\angle D$ >

31. $m\angle B + m\angle C$ _?_ $m\angle E + m\angle F$ <

C 32. ★ **OPEN-ENDED MATH** The side lengths of a triangle are 6, 8, and x (where $x > 0$). What are the values of x that make the triangle a right triangle? an acute triangle? an obtuse triangle?
$2\sqrt{7}$ and 10; $2\sqrt{7} < x < 10$; $2 < x < 2\sqrt{7}$ or $10 < x < 14$

33. **ALGEBRA** The sides of a triangle have lengths x, $x + 4$, and 20. If the length of the longest side is 20, what values of x make the triangle acute? **$8 < x < 12$**

34. **CHALLENGE** The sides of a triangle have lengths $4x + 6$, $2x + 1$, and $6x - 1$. If the length of the longest side is $6x - 1$, what values of x make the triangle obtuse? **$x > 4.5$**

PROBLEM SOLVING

EXAMPLE 3 A on p. 443 for Ex. 35

35. **PAINTING** You are making a canvas frame for a painting using stretcher bars. The rectangular painting will be 10 inches long and 8 inches wide. Using a ruler, how can you be certain that the corners of the frame are 90°?

@HomeTutor for problem solving help at classzone.com

Measure diagonally across the painting and it should be about 12.8 inches.

36. **WALKING** You walk 749 feet due east to the gym from your home. From the gym you walk 800 feet southwest to the library. Finally, you walk 305 feet from the library back home. Do you live directly north of the library? *Explain.* **no; $749^2 + 305^2 \neq 800^2$**

@HomeTutor for problem solving help at classzone.com

37. **MULTI-STEP PROBLEM** Use the diagram shown.

a. Find BC. **5**

b. Use the Converse of the Pythagorean Theorem to show that $\triangle ABC$ is a right triangle.

c. Draw and label a similar diagram where $\triangle DBC$ remains a right triangle, but $\triangle ABC$ is not. **See margin.**

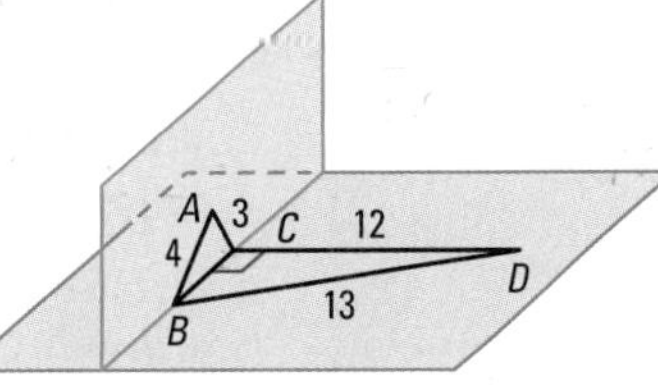

37b. $3^2 + 4^2 = 5^2$ therefore $\triangle ABC$ is a right triangle.

Avoiding Common Errors

Exercise 6 When evaluating $(4\sqrt{19})^2$, some students may calculate it as $16 + 19$ or as $4 \cdot 19$. Review that $(4\sqrt{19})^2$ means $4\sqrt{19} \cdot 4\sqrt{19}$, or $16 \cdot 19$, which is 304.

Study Strategy

Exercises 27–28 Encourage students to check their answers by drawing the triangles on graph paper and using a protractor.

Mathematical Reasoning

Exercise 32 Have students think about whether x needs to be the length of the longest side. Students should realize that to solve this problem they must break it into two cases: (1) $6^2 + 8^2 = x^2$ and (2) $6^2 + x^2 = 8^2$.

Avoiding Common Errors

Exercise 33 Students may forget the middle term when they evaluate $(x + 4)^2$. Review that $(x + 4)(x + 4) = x^2 + 8x + 16$.

37c. *Sample:*

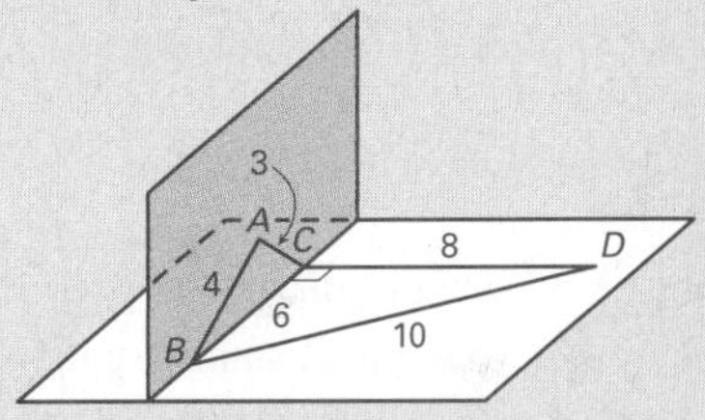

27.

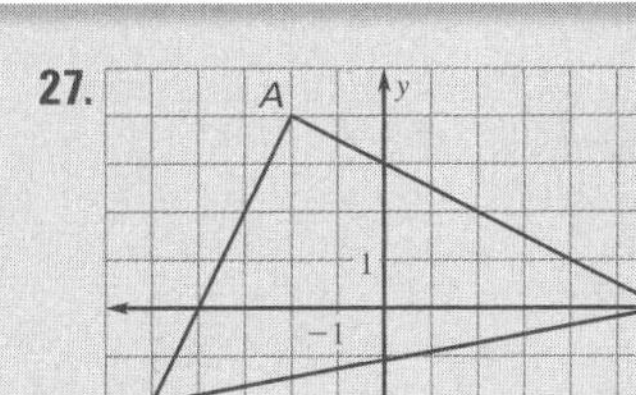

28.

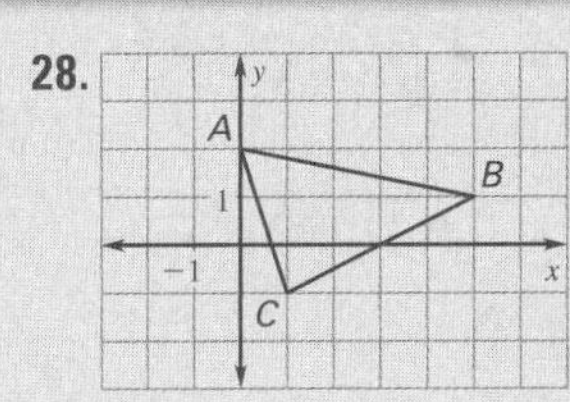

Exercise 38 Additional information about volleyball can be found at www.volleyball.org/general/index/html

Teaching Strategy

Exercise 40 Review all the theorems involving inequalities that students have learned in earlier chapters of this course, especially the Triangle Inequality Theorem, the Hinge Theorem, and the Converse of the Hinge Theorem.

41. Given: In $\triangle ABC$, $c^2 > a^2 + b^2$ where c is the length of the longest side.
Prove: $\triangle ABC$ is obtuse.

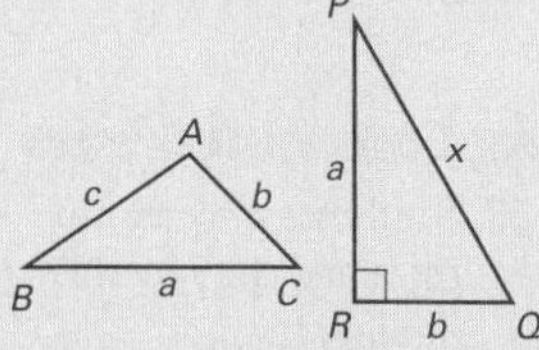

Statements (Reasons)

1. **In $\triangle ABC$, $c^2 > a^2 + b^2$ where c is the length of the longest side. In $\triangle PQR$, $\angle R$ is a right angle. (Given)**
2. **$a^2 + b^2 = x^2$ (Pythagorean Theorem)**
3. **$c^2 > x^2$ (Substitution)**
4. **$c > x$ (A property of square roots)**
5. **$m\angle R = 90°$ (Definition of a right angle)**
6. **$m\angle C > m\angle R$ (Converse of the Hinge Theorem)**
7. **$m\angle C > 90°$ (Substitution Property of Equality)**
8. **$\angle C$ is an obtuse angle. (Definition of an obtuse angle)**
9. **$\triangle ABC$ is an obtuse triangle. (Definition of an obtuse triangle)**

38. No; $7^2 + 4^2 \neq \left(\frac{25}{3}\right)^2$. ***Sample answer:*** **Use about 8.1 feet of rope instead of $8\frac{1}{3}$ feet.**

38. ★ **SHORT RESPONSE** You are setting up a volleyball net. To stabilize the pole, you tie one end of a rope to the pole 7 feet from the ground. You tie the other end of the rope to a stake that is 4 feet from the pole. The rope between the pole and stake is about 8 feet 4 inches long. Is the pole perpendicular to the ground? *Explain.* If it is not, how can you fix it?

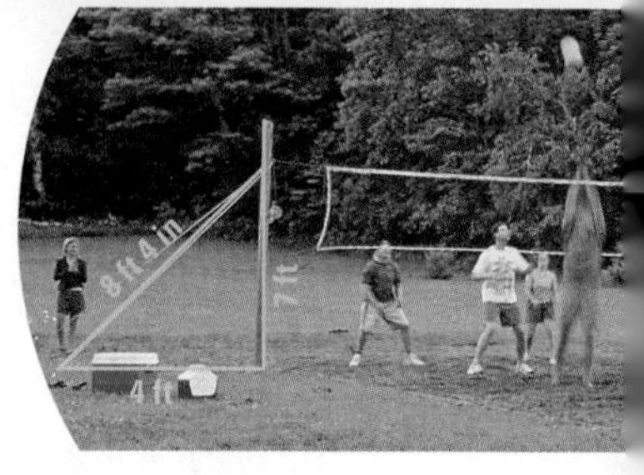

B **39.** ★ **EXTENDED RESPONSE** You are considering buying a used car. You would like to know whether the frame is sound. A sound frame of the car should be rectangular, so it has four right angles. You plan to measure the shadow of the car on the ground as the sun shines directly on the car.

a. You make a triangle with three tape measures on one corner. It has side lengths 12 inches, 16 inches, and 20 inches. Is this a right triangle? *Explain.* **yes; $12^2 + 16^2 = 20^2$**

b. You make a triangle on a second corner with side lengths 9 inches, 12 inches, and 18 inches. Is this a right triangle? *Explain.* **no; $9^2 + 12^2 \neq 18^2$**

c. The car owner says the car was never in an accident. Do you believe this claim? *Explain.* **No; if the car was not in an accident, the angles should form a right triangle.**

40. **PROVING THEOREM 7.3** Copy and complete the proof of Theorem 7.3.

GIVEN ▶ In $\triangle ABC$, $c^2 < a^2 + b^2$ where c is the length of the longest side.

PROVE ▶ $\triangle ABC$ is an acute triangle.

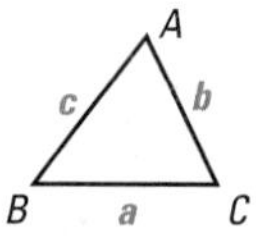

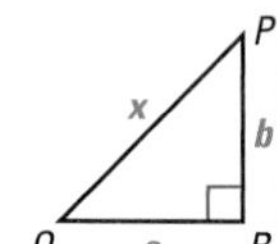

Plan for Proof Draw right $\triangle PQR$ with side lengths a, b, and x, where $\angle R$ is a right angle and x is the length of the longest side. Compare lengths c and x.

STATEMENTS	REASONS
1. In $\triangle ABC$, $c^2 < a^2 + b^2$ where c is the length of the longest side. In $\triangle PQR$, $\angle R$ is a right angle.	**1.** ? **Given**
2. $a^2 + b^2 = x^2$	**2.** ? **Pythagorean Theorem**
3. $c^2 < x^2$	**3.** ? **Substitution Property**
4. $c < x$	**4.** A property of square roots
5. $m\angle R = 90°$	**5.** ? **Definition of a right angle**
6. $m\angle C < m\angle$? **R**	**6.** Converse of the Hinge Theorem
7. $m\angle C < 90°$	**7.** ? **Substitution Property**
8. $\angle C$ is an acute angle.	**8.** ? **Definition of acute angle**
9. $\triangle ABC$ is an acute triangle.	**9.** ? **Definition of acute triangle**

41. **PROVING THEOREM 7.4** Prove Theorem 7.4. Include a diagram and GIVEN and PROVE statements. (*Hint*: Look back at Exercise 40.) **See margin.**

42. **PROVING THEOREM 7.2** Prove the Converse of the Pythagorean Theorem. **See margin.**

GIVEN ▶ In $\triangle LMN$, $\overline{LM}$ is the longest side, and $c^2 = a^2 + b^2$.

PROVE ▶ $\triangle LMN$ is a right triangle.

Plan for Proof Draw right $\triangle PQR$ with side lengths a, b, and x. Compare lengths c and x.

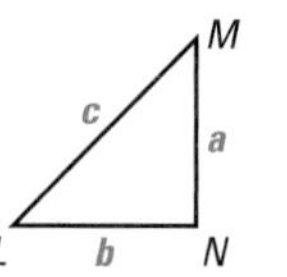

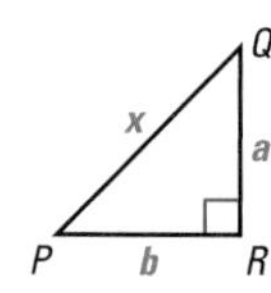

★ = **STANDARDIZED TEST PRACTICE**

42. Statements (Reasons)

1. **In $\triangle LMN$, $\overline{LM}$ is the longest side, and $c^2 = a^2 + b^2$. In $\triangle PQR$, $\angle R$ is a right angle. (Given)**
2. **$a^2 + b^2 = x^2$ (Pythagorean Theorem)**
3. **$c^2 = x^2$ (Substitution Property of Equality)**
4. **$c = x$ (A property of square roots)**
5. **$\triangle LMN \cong \triangle PQR$ (SSS Congruence Postulate)**
6. **$\angle N \cong \angle R$ (Corr. parts of $\cong$ △s are $\cong$.)**
7. **$m\angle N = 90°$ (Definition of congruent angles)**
8. **$\triangle LMN$ is a right triangle. (Definition of a right triangle)**

44a, 44c. See Additional Answers beginning on p. AA1.

4b. $\triangle ABC$ is not a right triangle; $\overline{AB}$ is the longest side, so $\angle C$ would have to be the right angle, but the slopes of $\overline{AC}$ and $\overline{BC}$ are not opposite reciprocals, so the line segments are not perpendicular and therefore, there is no right angle.

43. ★ **SHORT RESPONSE** *Explain* why $\angle D$ must be a right angle. **$\triangle ABC \sim \triangle DEC$, $\angle BAC$ is 90°, so $\angle EDC$ must also be 90°.**

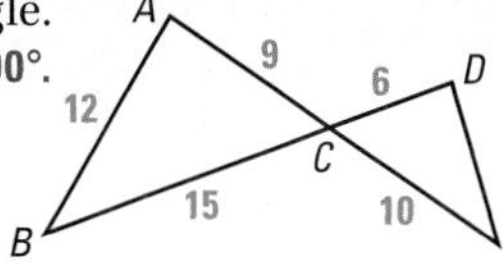

44. **COORDINATE PLANE** Use graph paper.

a. Graph $\triangle ABC$ with $A(-7, 2)$, $B(0, 1)$ and $C(-4, 4)$. **See margin.**

b. Use the slopes of the sides of $\triangle ABC$ to determine whether it is a right triangle. *Explain.*

c. Use the lengths of the sides of $\triangle ABC$ to determine whether it is a right triangle. *Explain.* **See margin.**

d. Did you get the same answer in parts (b) and (c)? If not, *explain* why. **yes**

C 45. **CHALLENGE** Find the values of x and y. $x = \sqrt{5}$, $y = \frac{12}{5}\sqrt{5}$

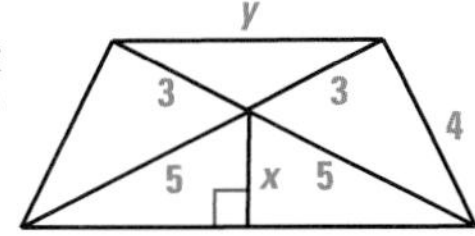

MIXED REVIEW

PREVIEW
Prepare for Lesson 7.3 in Exs. 46–48.

In Exercises 46–48, copy the triangle and draw one of its altitudes. *(p. 319)* **46–48. See margin.**

46. 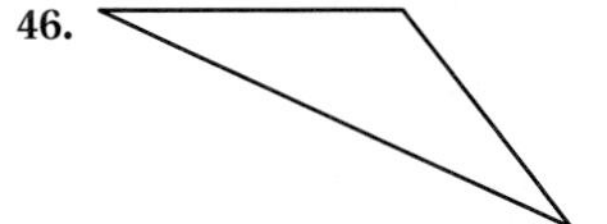

47. 

48. 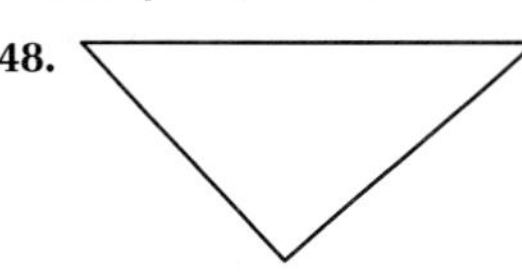

Copy and complete the statement. *(p. 364)*

49. If $\frac{10}{x} = \frac{7}{y}$, then $\frac{10}{7} = \frac{?}{?}$. $\frac{x}{y}$

50. If $\frac{x}{15} = \frac{y}{2}$, then $\frac{x}{y} = \frac{?}{?}$. $\frac{15}{2}$

51. If $\frac{x}{8} = \frac{y}{9}$, then $\frac{x+8}{8} = \frac{?}{?}$. $\frac{y+9}{9}$

52. The perimeter of a rectangle is 135 feet. The ratio of the length to the width is 8 : 1. Find the length and the width. *(p. 372)* **60 ft, 7.5 ft**

QUIZ for Lessons 7.1–7.2

Find the unknown side length. Write your answer in simplest radical form. *(p. 433)*

1. 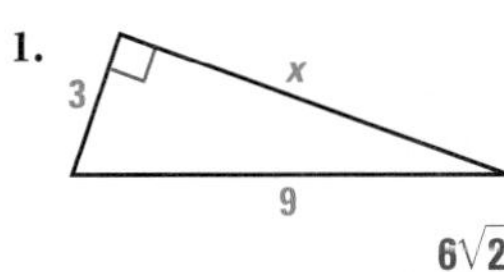

$6\sqrt{2}$

2. 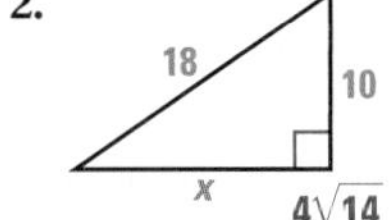

$4\sqrt{14}$

3. 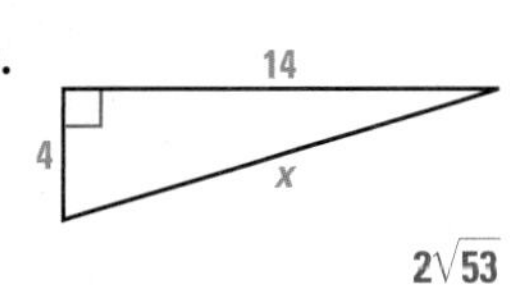

$2\sqrt{53}$

Classify the triangle formed by the side lengths as *acute, right,* or *obtuse.* *(p. 441)*

4. 6, 7, and 9 **acute**
5. 10, 12, and 16 **obtuse**
6. 8, 16, and $8\sqrt{6}$ **obtuse**
7. 20, 21, and 29 **right**
8. 8, 3, $\sqrt{73}$ **right**
9. 8, 10, and 12 **acute**

46–48. Sample answers are given.

46. 

47. 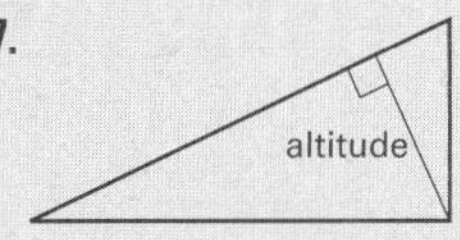

48. 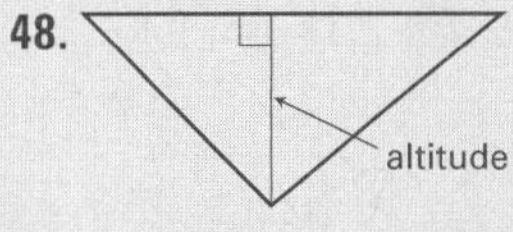

5 ASSESS AND RETEACH

Daily Homework Quiz

Transparency Available

1. Tell whether the triangle is a right triangle. **yes**

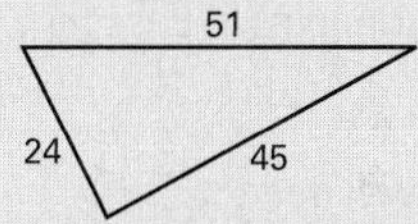

Decide if the segment lengths can form a triangle. If so, tell whether the triangle is acute, right, or obtuse.

2. 7, 11, $3\sqrt{17}$ **yes; acute because 153 < 170**

3. 4.1, 9.2, 5.6 **yes; obtuse because 84.64 > 48.17**

4. A playground has a slide, a swing, and a sandbox. The slide and the swing are 50 feet apart, the swing and sandbox are 32 feet apart, and the slide and sandbox are 48 feet apart. Do the three pieces of apparatus form a right triangle? **no**

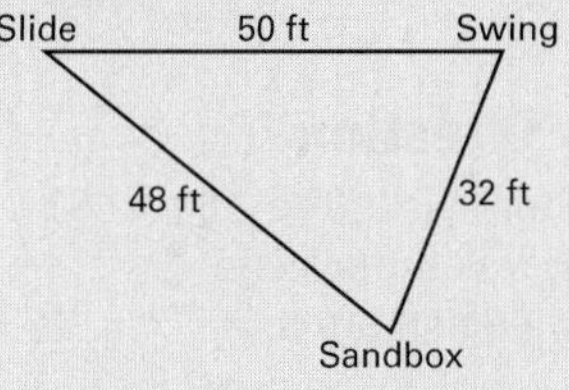

Available at **classzone.com**

Diagnosis/Remediation

- Practice A, B, C in Chapter 7 Resource Book, pp. 22–27
- Study Guide in Chapter 7 Resource Book, pp. 28–29
- Practice Workbook, pp. 127–129
- @HomeTutor

Challenge

Additional challenge is available in the Chapter 7 Resource Book, p. 32.

Quiz

An easily-readable reduced copy of the quiz (with answers) on Lessons 7.1–7.2 from the Assessment Book can be found on p. 430G.

1 PLAN AND PREPARE

Explore the Concept

- Students will explore geometric means in right triangles.
- This activity leads into studying similar right triangles in Lesson 7.3.

Materials

Each student will need:

- straight edge
- scissors

Recommended Time

Work activity: 10 min

Discuss results: 5 min

Grouping

Students should work individually.

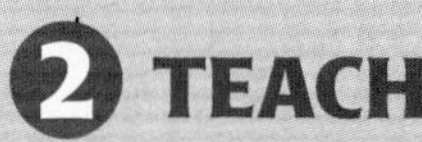

TEACH

Tips for Success

Before cutting apart the triangles in Step 3, be sure students label all the angles.

Key Question

- In Step 4, is $\angle 3 \cong \angle 6 \cong \angle 9$? Why? **Yes, each is complementary to $\angle 7$.**

Alternative Strategy

Start with a single right triangle and cut it along the altitude to the hypotenuse. Show that the two triangles are similar. Then show that each is similar to the original triangle.

Key Discovery

The altitude to the hypotenuse forms two triangles, similar to each other and to the original.

3 ASSESS AND RETEACH

1. If you drew the altitudes from the right angles in each of the triangles in Step 3 and then cut along those altitudes, how would the six new triangles be related? **They would all be similar to each other.**

7.3 Similar Right Triangles

Standards

5.0 Students prove that triangles are congruent or **similar, and they are able to use the concept of corresponding parts** of congruent triangles.

MATERIALS • rectangular piece of paper • ruler • scissors • colored pencils

QUESTION **How are geometric means related to the altitude of a right triangle?**

EXPLORE **Compare right triangles**

STEP 1

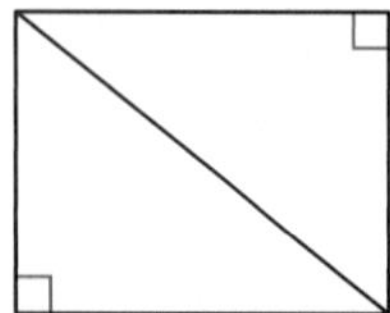

Draw a diagonal Draw a diagonal on your rectangular piece of paper to form two congruent right triangles.

STEP 2

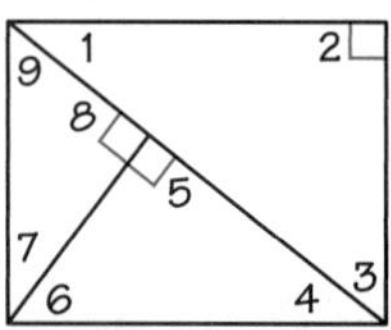

Draw an altitude Fold the paper to make an altitude to the hypotenuse of one of the triangles.

STEP 3

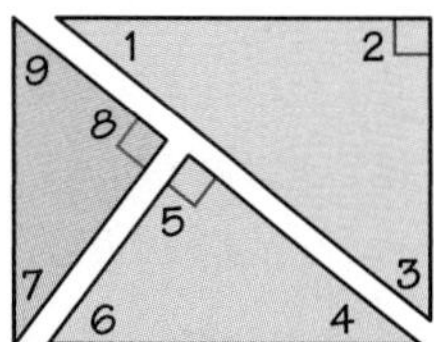

Cut and label triangles Cut the rectangle into the three right triangles that you drew. Label the angles and color the triangles as shown.

STEP 4

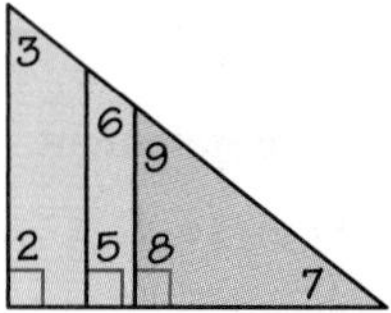

Arrange the triangles Arrange the triangles so $\angle 1$, $\angle 4$, and $\angle 7$ are on top of each other as shown.

DRAW CONCLUSIONS **Use your observations to complete these exercises**

1. How are the two smaller right triangles related to the large triangle? **They are similar to it.**
2. *Explain* how you would show that the green triangle is similar to the red triangle. **Show that corresponding sides have a constant proportion.**
3. *Explain* how you would show that the red triangle is similar to the blue triangle. **Show that corresponding sides have a constant proportion.**
4. The *geometric mean* of a and b is x if $\frac{a}{x} = \frac{x}{b}$. Write a proportion involving the side lengths of two of your triangles so that one side length is the geometric mean of the other two lengths in the proportion. **Check students' work.**

7.3 Use Similar Right Triangles

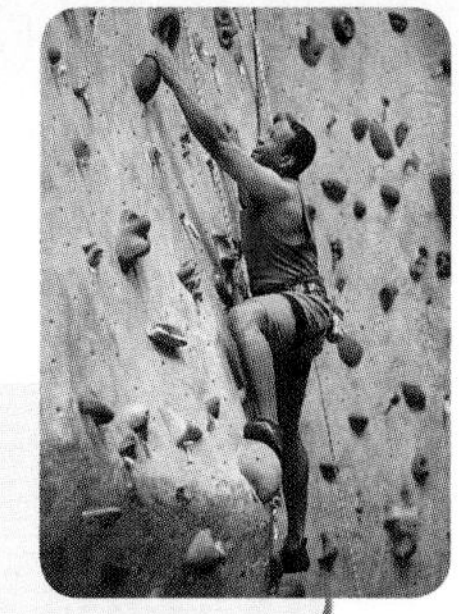

Before You identified the altitudes of a triangle.

Now You will use properties of the altitude of a right triangle.

Why? So you can determine the height of a wall, as in Example 4.

Key Vocabulary
- **altitude of a triangle,** *p. 320*
- **geometric mean,** *p. 359*
- **similar polygons,** *p. 372*

Standards

4.0 Students prove basic theorems involving congruence and **similarity.**

12.0 Students find and use measures of sides and of interior and exterior angles **of triangles** and polygons **to classify figures and solve problems.**

When the altitude is drawn to the hypotenuse of a right triangle, the two smaller triangles are similar to the original triangle and to each other.

THEOREM *For Your Notebook*

THEOREM 7.5

If the altitude is drawn to the hypotenuse of a right triangle, then the two triangles formed are similar to the original triangle and to each other.

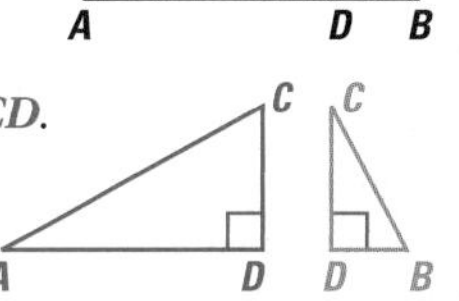

$\triangle CBD \sim \triangle ABC$, $\triangle ACD \sim \triangle ABC$, and $\triangle CBD \sim \triangle ACD$.

Proof: below; Ex. 35, p. 456

Plan for Proof of Theorem 7.5 First prove that $\triangle CBD \sim \triangle ABC$. Each triangle has a right angle and each triangle includes $\angle B$. The triangles are similar by the AA Similarity Postulate. Use similar reasoning to show that $\triangle ACD \sim \triangle ABC$.

To show $\angle CBD \sim \triangle ACD$, begin by showing $\angle ACD \cong \angle B$ because they are both complementary to $\angle DCB$. Each triangle also has a right angle, so you can use the AA Similarity Postulate.

EXAMPLE 1 Identify similar triangles

Identify the similar triangles in the diagram.

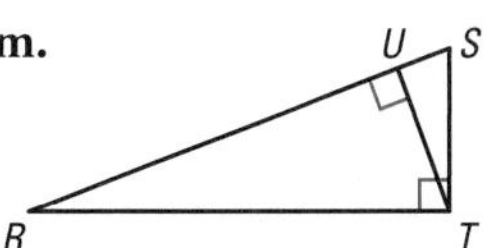

Solution

Sketch the three similar right triangles so that the corresponding angles and sides have the same orientation.

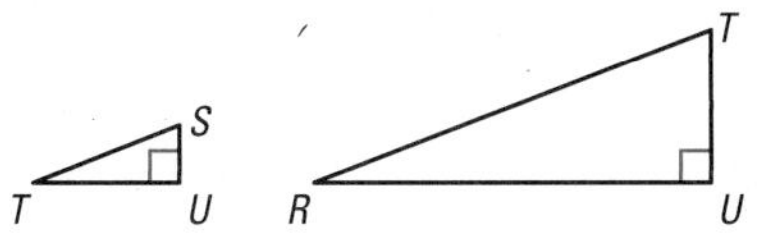

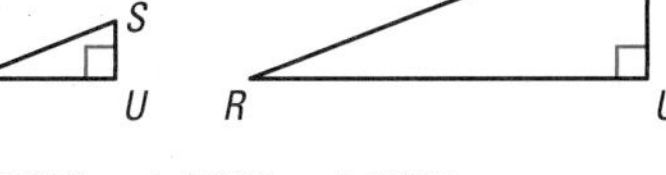

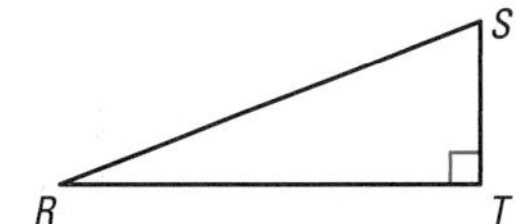

▶ $\triangle TSU \sim \triangle RTU \sim \triangle RST$

1 PLAN AND PREPARE

Warm-Up Exercises

Transparency Available

1. Are these triangles similar? If so, give the reason.

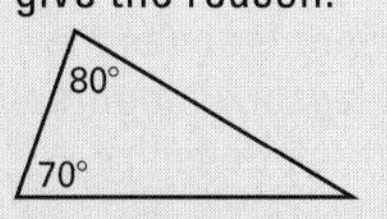

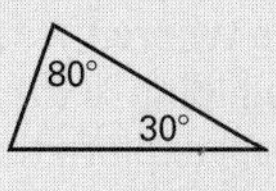

Yes; the AA Similarity Postulate

2. Find *x*. **50**

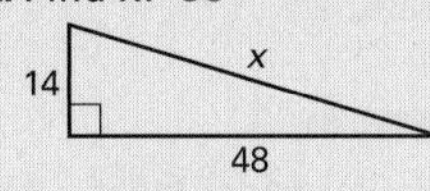

Notetaking Guide

Transparency Available

Promotes interactive learning and notetaking skills, pp. 178–181.

Pacing

Basic: 2 days
Average: 2 days
Advanced: 2 days
Block: 0.5 block with 7.2
0.5 block with 7.4
- See *Teaching Guide/Lesson Plan*.

2 FOCUS AND MOTIVATE

Essential Question

Big Idea 2, p. 431

How can you find the length of the altitude to the hypotenuse of a right triangle? **Tell students they will learn how to answer this question by using properties of the altitude of a right triangle.**

Resource Planning Guide

Chapter Resource Book
- Teaching Guide/Lesson Plan (pp. 33–34)
- Practice levels A, B, C (pp. 35–40)
- Study Guide (pp. 41–42)
- Catch-up for Absent Students (p. 43)
- Problem Solving Workshop (p. 44)
- Challenge (p. 45)

Workbooks
- Notetaking Guide (pp. 178–181)
- Practice Workbook (pp. 130–132)

Teaching Options
- **Power Presentations CD-ROM** provides dynamic electronic teaching resources for the classroom.
- **Activity Generator CD-ROM** provides editable activities for all ability levels.

Interactive Technology
- Easy Planner
- Power Presentations CD-ROM
- Activity Generator CD-ROM
- Animated Geometry
- Test Generator CD-ROM
- Online Quiz
- eWorkbook
- eEdition
- @HomeTutor

Resources for English Learners
- Quick Reference for English Learners
- Spanish Study Guide
- Multi-Language Visual Glossary
- Student Resources in Spanish

See also the *Geometry Toolkit* for more strategies for meeting individual needs.

Motivating the Lesson

A ladder rests against a building. The length of a piece of rope from the base of the building and perpendicular to the ladder is related to two other distances: from the base of the ladder to the building, and from the base of the building to where the ladder touches the building. In this lesson students will explore that relationship.

3 TEACH

Extra Example 1

Identify the similar triangles in the diagram.

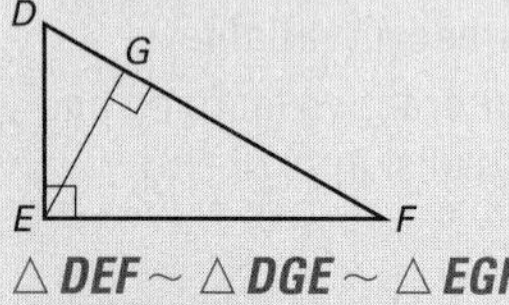

$\triangle DEF \sim \triangle DGE \sim \triangle EGF$

Key Question to Ask for Example 1

- How would you use the AA Similarity Postulate to show the triangles are similar? **The three triangles all have right angles. $\triangle RUT$ and $\triangle RTS$ both have acute $\angle R$, and $\triangle RTS$ and $\triangle STU$ both have acute $\angle S$. So the triangles are similar by the AA Similarity Postulate.**

Extra Example 2

The figure shows the side view of a tool shed. What is the maximum height, h, of the shed? **16.1 ft**

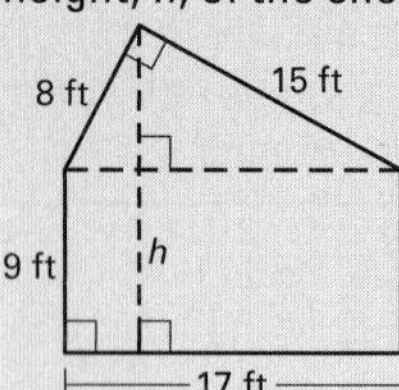

AVOID ERRORS

Notice that if you tried to write a proportion using $\triangle RTM$ and $\triangle TSM$, there would be two unknowns, so you would not be able to solve for h.

EXAMPLE 2 Find the length of the altitude to the hypotenuse

SWIMMING POOL The diagram below shows a cross-section of a swimming pool. What is the maximum depth of the pool?

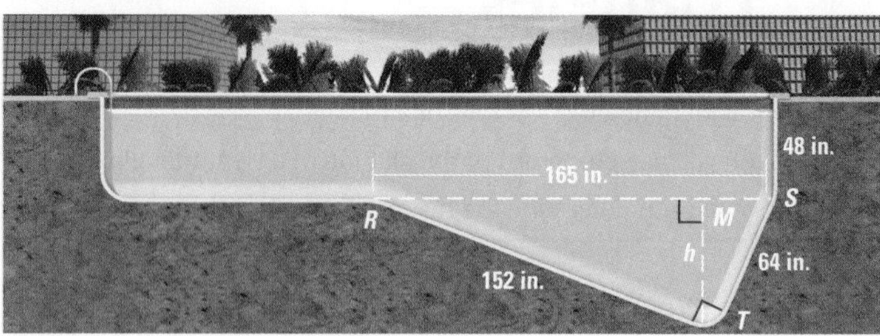

Solution

STEP 1 **Identify** the similar triangles and sketch them.

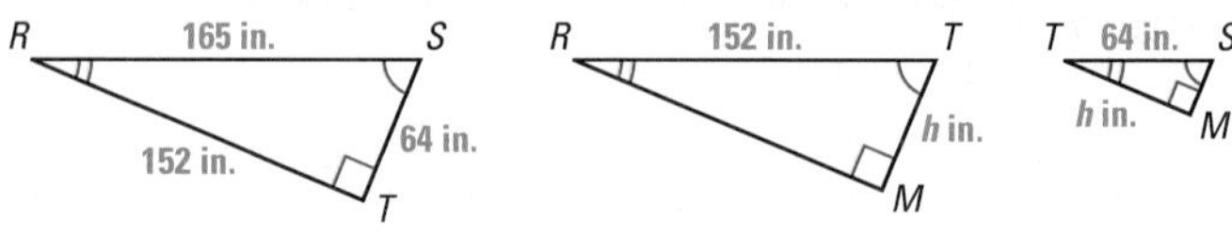

$\triangle RST \sim \triangle RTM \sim \triangle TSM$

STEP 2 **Find** the value of h. Use the fact that $\triangle RST \sim \triangle RTM$ to write a proportion.

$\frac{TM}{ST} = \frac{TR}{SR}$	**Corresponding side lengths of similar triangles are in proportion.**
$\frac{h}{64} = \frac{152}{165}$	**Substitute.**
$165h = 64(152)$	**Cross Products Property**
$h \approx 59$	**Solve for h.**

STEP 3 **Read** the diagram above. You can see that the maximum depth of the pool is $h + 48$, which is about $59 + 48 = 107$ inches.

▶ The maximum depth of the pool is about 107 inches.

AnimatedGeometry at classzone.com

GUIDED PRACTICE for Examples 1 and 2

Identify the similar triangles. Then find the value of x.

1. **$\triangle EGF \sim \triangle GHF \sim \triangle EHG$; $\frac{12}{5}$**

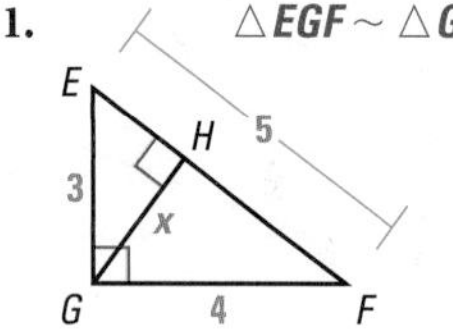

2.

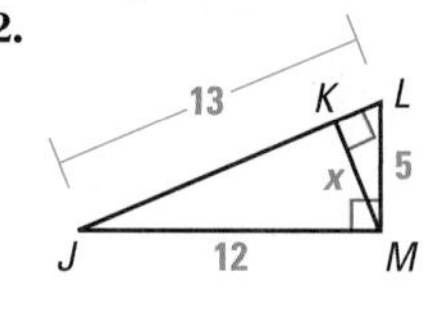

$\triangle LMJ \sim \triangle MKJ \sim \triangle LKM$; $\frac{60}{13}$

GEOMETRIC MEANS In Lesson 6.1, you learned that the *geometric mean* of two numbers a and b is the positive number x such that $\frac{a}{x} = \frac{x}{b}$. Consider right $\triangle ABC$. From Theorem 7.5, you know that altitude $\overline{CD}$ forms two smaller triangles so that $\triangle CBD \sim \triangle ACD \sim \triangle ABC$.

READ SYMBOLS
Remember that an altitude is defined as a segment. So, $\overline{CD}$ refers to an altitude in $\triangle ABC$ and CD refers to its length.

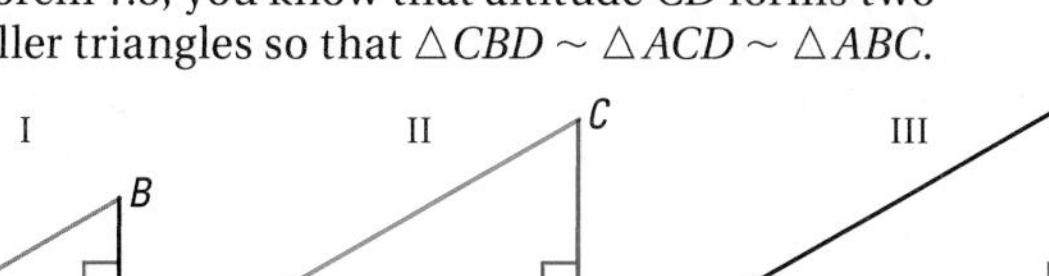

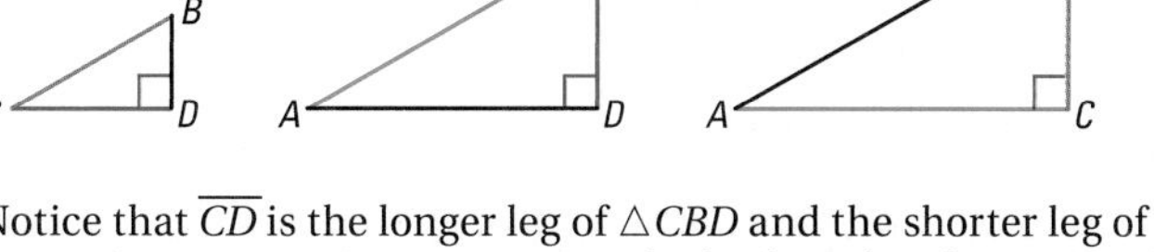

Notice that $\overline{CD}$ is the longer leg of $\triangle CBD$ and the shorter leg of $\triangle ACD$. When you write a proportion comparing the leg lengths of $\triangle CBD$ and $\triangle ACD$, you can see that CD is the geometric mean of BD and AD. As you see below, CB and AC are also geometric means of segment lengths in the diagram.

Proportions Involving Geometric Means in Right $\triangle ABC$

length of shorter leg of I / length of shorter leg of II →	$\frac{BD}{CD} = \frac{CD}{AD}$	← length of longer leg of I / length of longer leg of II
length of hypotenuse of III / length of hypotenuse of I →	$\frac{AB}{CB} = \frac{CB}{DB}$	← length of shorter leg of III / length of shorter leg of I
length of hypotenuse of III / length of hypotenuse of II →	$\frac{AB}{AC} = \frac{AC}{AD}$	← length of longer leg of III / length of longer leg of II

EXAMPLE 3 Use a geometric mean

Find the value of y. Write your answer in simplest radical form.

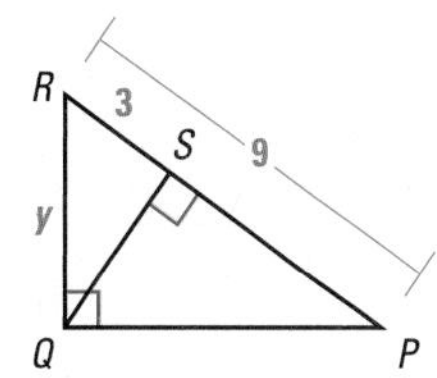

Solution

REVIEW SIMILARITY
Notice that $\triangle RQS$ and $\triangle RPQ$ both contain the side with length y, so these are the similar triangles to use to solve for y.

STEP 1 **Draw** the three similar triangles.

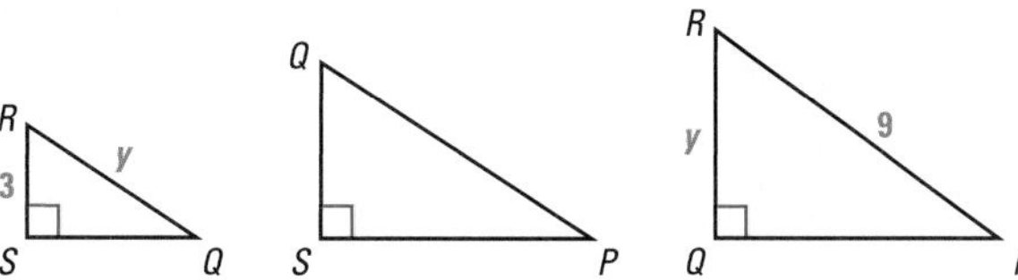

STEP 2 **Write** a proportion.

$$\frac{\text{length of hyp. of } \triangle RPQ}{\text{length of hyp. of } \triangle RQS} = \frac{\text{length of shorter leg of } \triangle RPQ}{\text{length of shorter leg of } \triangle RQS}$$

$\frac{9}{y} = \frac{y}{3}$ **Substitute.**

$27 = y^2$ **Cross Products Property**

$\sqrt{27} = y$ **Take the positive square root of each side.**

$3\sqrt{3} = y$ **Simplify.**

Animated Geometry classzone.com

An **Animated Geometry** activity is available on-line for **Example 2**. This activity is also available on the **Power Presentations CD-ROM**.

Extra Example 3

Find the value of k. $2\sqrt{5}$

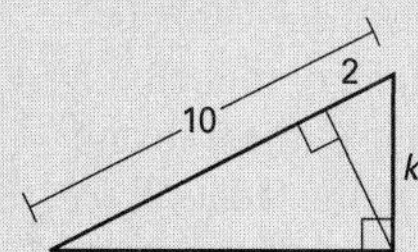

Differentiated Instruction

Kinesthetic Learners Some students may have difficulty visualizing how to sketch similar triangles from a diagram. Have these students use tracing paper to trace each of the three triangles in the diagram in **Example 3**. Ask them to cut each triangle out. Have them arrange the triangles as they were in the diagram and then manipulate each one by rotating and/or flipping it to show all three similar triangles in the same orientation.

See also the *Geometry Toolkit* for more strategies.

Reading Strategy

Theorem 7.6 Students can think of the proportion as "part of the hypotenuse is to the altitude as the altitude is to the other part of the hypotenuse."

Extra Example 4

You are standing by a tree as shown in the diagram. A 25 foot ladder is leaning against the tree. What is the length of a piece of rope that goes from the base of the tree and is perpendicular to the ladder? **4.9 ft**

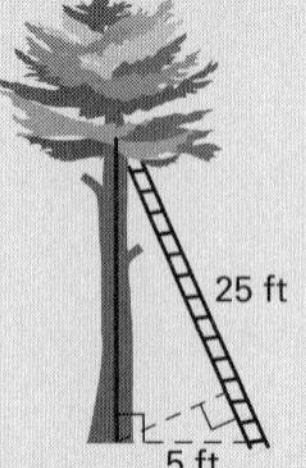

Closing the Lesson

Have students summarize the major points of the lesson and answer the Essential Question: How can you find the length of the altitude to the hypotenuse of a right triangle?

- **The altitude to the hypotenuse in a right triangle divides the triangle into 2 triangles, each similar to the other and each similar to the original triangle.**
- **The altitude to the hypotenuse in a right triangle is the geometric mean of the two parts of the hypotenuse.**

Write and solve the proportion $\frac{\text{part of hyp.}}{\text{altitude}} = \frac{\text{altitude}}{\text{other part of hyp.}}$

WRITE PROOFS In Exercise 32 on page 455, you will use the geometric mean theorems to prove the Pythagorean Theorem.

THEOREMS — *For Your Notebook*

THEOREM 7.6 Geometric Mean (Altitude) Theorem

In a right triangle, the altitude from the right angle to the hypotenuse divides the hypotenuse into two segments.

The length of the altitude is the geometric mean of the lengths of the two segments.

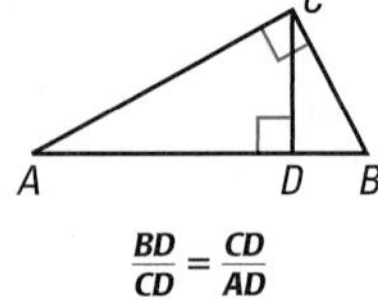

$\frac{BD}{CD} = \frac{CD}{AD}$

Proof: Ex. 36, p. 456

THEOREM 7.7 Geometric Mean (Leg) Theorem

In a right triangle, the altitude from the right angle to the hypotenuse divides the hypotenuse into two segments.

The length of each leg of the right triangle is the geometric mean of the lengths of the hypotenuse and the segment of the hypotenuse that is adjacent to the leg.

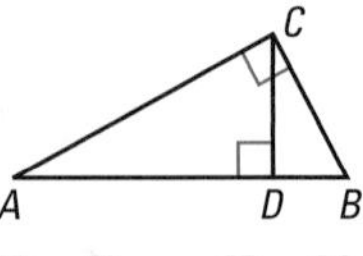

$\frac{AB}{CB} = \frac{CB}{DB}$ and $\frac{AB}{AC} = \frac{AC}{AD}$

Proof: Ex. 37, p. 456

EXAMPLE 4 Find a height using indirect measurement

ROCK CLIMBING WALL To find the cost of installing a rock wall in your school gymnasium, you need to find the height of the gym wall.

You use a cardboard square to line up the top and bottom of the gym wall. Your friend measures the vertical distance from the ground to your eye and the distance from you to the gym wall. Approximate the height of the gym wall.

Solution

By Theorem 7.6, you know that 8.5 is the geometric mean of w and 5.

$\frac{w}{8.5} = \frac{8.5}{5}$ **Write a proportion.**

$w \approx 14.5$ **Solve for w.**

▶ So, the height of the wall is $5 + w \approx 5 + 14.5 = 19.5$ feet.

GUIDED PRACTICE for Examples 3 and 4

3. In Example 3, which theorem did you use to solve for y? *Explain.*

3. Theorem 7.7; set the ratios hypotenuse of the large triangle to the shorter leg and the hypotenuse of the small triangle to the shorter leg equal to each other.

4. Mary is 5.5 feet tall. How far from the wall in Example 4 would she have to stand in order to measure its height? **about 8.77 ft**

Differentiated Instruction

Below Level Encourage students to rewrite Theorems 7.6 and 7.7 in the form $(\text{altitude})^2 = (\text{part of hypotenuse}) \times (\text{other part of hypotenuse})$ and $(\text{leg})^2 = (\text{hypotenuse}) \times (\text{part of hypotenuse closer to leg})$.

See also the *Geometry Toolkit* for more strategies.

7.3 EXERCISES

HOMEWORK KEY ◯ = **WORKED-OUT SOLUTIONS** on p. WS8 for Exs. 5, 15, and 29
★ = **STANDARDIZED TEST PRACTICE** Exs. 2, 19, 20, 31, and 34

SKILL PRACTICE

A

1. **VOCABULARY** Copy and complete: Two triangles are _?_ if their corresponding angles are congruent and their corresponding side lengths are proportional. **similar**

2. ★ **WRITING** In your own words, explain *geometric mean*. **See margin.**

EXAMPLE 1 on p. 449 for Exs. 3–4

IDENTIFYING SIMILAR TRIANGLES Identify the three similar right triangles in the given diagram.

3. 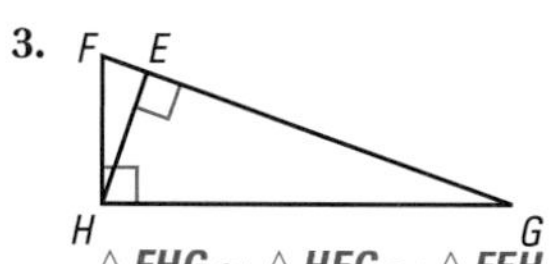

△FHG ~ △HEG ~ △FEH

4. 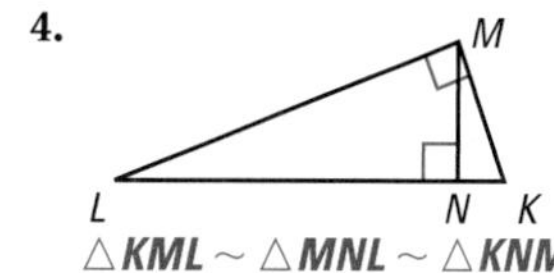

△KML ~ △MNL ~ △KNM

EXAMPLE 2 on p. 450 for Exs. 5–7

FINDING ALTITUDES Find the length of the altitude to the hypotenuse. Round decimal answers to the nearest tenth.

5. 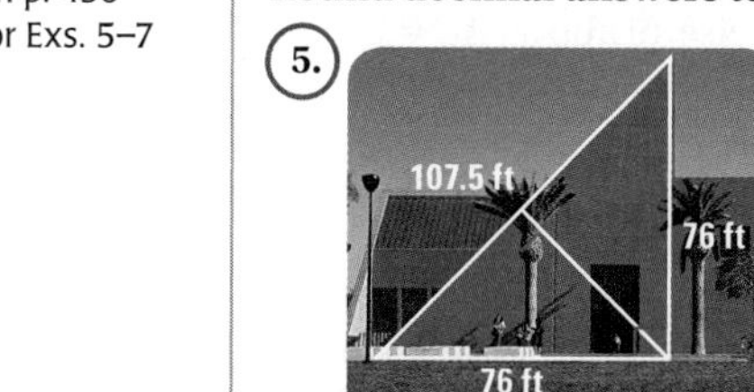

53.7 ft

6. 26.6 ft, 12.8 ft, 23 ft, x **11.1 ft**

7. 

6.7 ft

EXAMPLES 3 and 4 on pp. 451–452 for Exs. 8–18

COMPLETING PROPORTIONS Write a similarity statement for the three similar triangles in the diagram. Then complete the proportion.

8. $\frac{XW}{?} = \frac{ZW}{YW}$ **△YZX ~ △ZWX ~ △YWZ; ZW**

9. $\frac{?}{SQ} = \frac{SQ}{TQ}$ **△QSR ~ △STR ~ △QTS; RQ**

10. $\frac{EF}{EG} = \frac{EG}{?}$

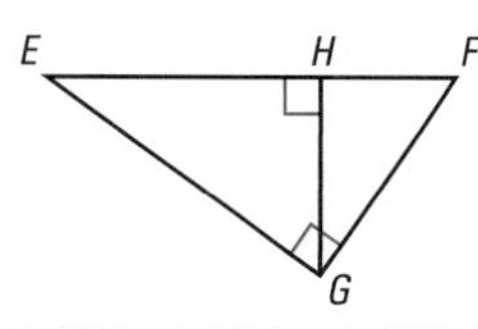

△GEF ~ △HEG ~ △HGF; EH

ERROR ANALYSIS ***Describe*** **and correct the error in writing a proportion for the given diagram.**

11. 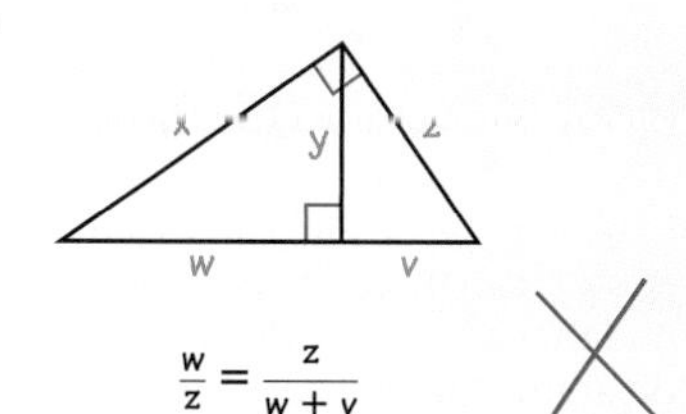

12. e, f, g, d, h

$\frac{e}{d} = \frac{d}{f}$

11. ***Sample answer:*** **The proportion must compare corresponding parts;** $\frac{v}{z} = \frac{z}{w+v}$.

12. **When using the altitude and parts of the hypotenuse, you must use both pieces of the large triangle's hypotenuse,** $\frac{e}{d} = \frac{d}{g}$.

2. *Sample answer:* If a proportion is formed such that the same value is in the numerator of one fraction and in the denominator of the other fraction, this value is the geometric mean of the other two numbers in the proportion.

4 PRACTICE AND APPLY

Assignment Guide

Answer Transparencies available for all exercises

Basic:
Day 1: EP p. 906 Exs. 5, 6, 13–16
pp. 453–456
Exs. 1–7, 13–15, 39–49
Day 2: pp. 453–456
Exs. 8–12, 16–21, 29–33

Average:
Day 1: pp. 453–456
Exs. 1–7, 13–15, 19, 20, 39–49
Day 2: pp. 453–456
Exs. 8–12, 16–18, 22–26, 30–37

Advanced:
Day 1: pp. 453–456
Exs. 1–7, 13–15, 19, 20, 28*, 39–49
Day 2: pp. 453–456
Exs. 9, 10, 17, 18, 21–27, 31–38*

Block:
pp. 453–456
Exs. 1–7, 13–15, 19, 20, 39–49 (with 7.2)
pp. 453–456
Exs. 8–12, 16–18, 22–26, 30–37 (with 7.4)

Differentiated Instruction

See *Geometry Best Practices Toolkit* for suggestions on addressing the needs of a diverse classroom.

Homework Check

For a quick check of student understanding of key concepts, go over the following exercises:
Basic: 3, 6, 10, 30, 31
Average: 4, 6, 16, 31, 33
Advanced: 4, 7, 18, 31, 34

Extra Practice

- Student Edition, p. 908
- Chapter 7 Resource Book: Practice levels A, B, C, pp. 35–40

Practice Worksheet

An easily-readable reduced practice page (with answers) for this lesson can be found on p. 430D.

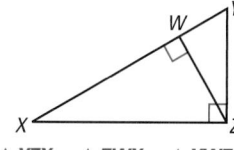

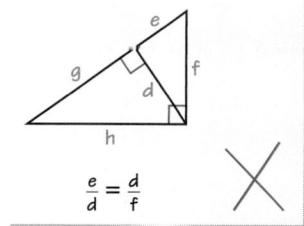

Avoiding Common Errors

Exercises 9–10 Students may use the wrong part of the hypotenuse in their proportion. Have them redraw the three triangles side-by-side so corresponding angles are in the same relative positions before they write the similarity statements. If they draw the triangles so they do not look isosceles, it will be easier for them to tell which is the longer leg in each triangle.

Teaching Strategy

Exercises 13–18 Encourage students to start writing the proportions by filling in the geometric means, such as $\frac{\ }{x} = \frac{x}{\ }$ for Exercise 13 and $\frac{\ }{18} = \frac{18}{\ }$ for Exercise 14. Then they can fill in the proportion and solve it.

28.

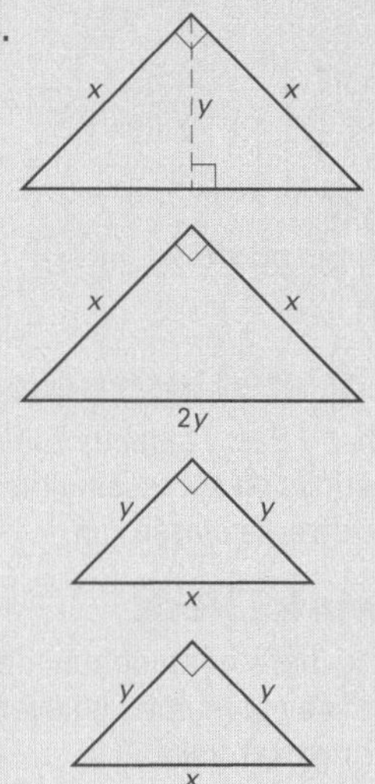

FINDING LENGTHS **Find the value of the variable. Round decimal answers to the nearest tenth.**

13.

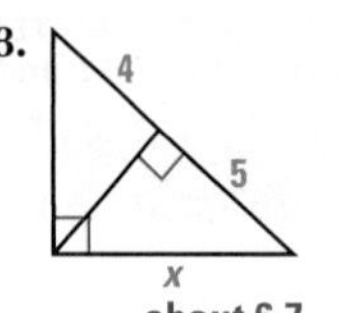

about 6.7

14.

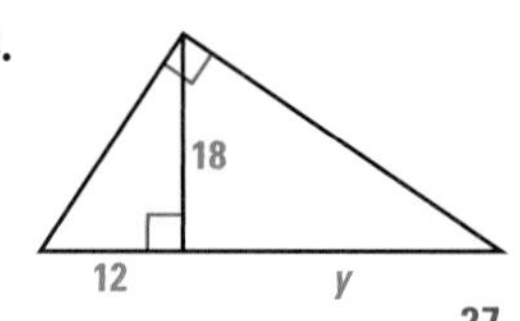

27

15.

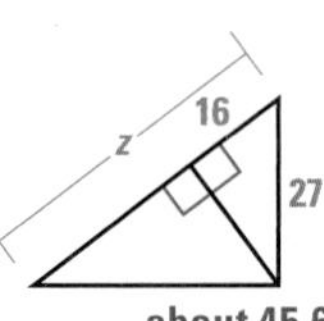

about 45.6

16.

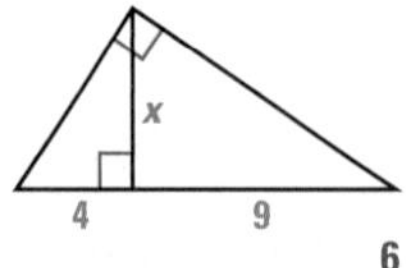

6

17.

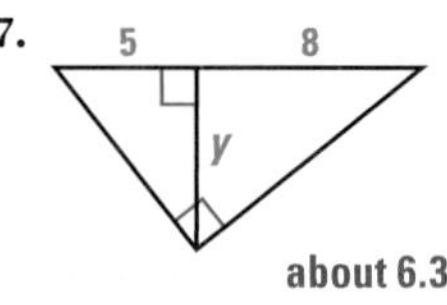

about 6.3

18.

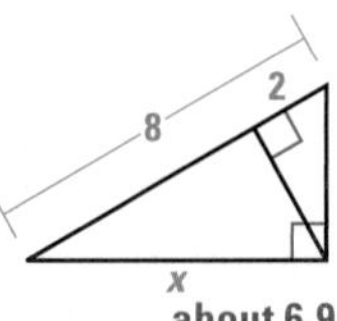

about 6.9

B **19.** ★ **MULTIPLE CHOICE** Use the diagram at the right. Decide which proportion is false. **C**

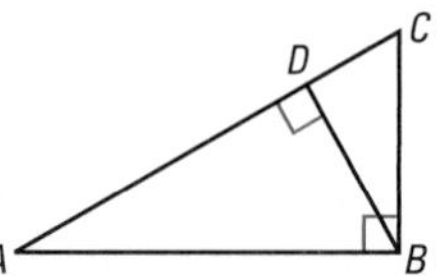

Ⓐ $\frac{DB}{DC} = \frac{DA}{DB}$ Ⓑ $\frac{CA}{AB} = \frac{AB}{AD}$

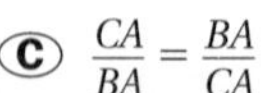

Ⓒ $\frac{CA}{BA} = \frac{BA}{CA}$ Ⓓ $\frac{DC}{BC} = \frac{BC}{CA}$

20. ★ **MULTIPLE CHOICE** In the diagram in Exercise 19 above, $AC = 36$ and $BC = 18$. Find AD. If necessary, round to the nearest tenth. **C**

Ⓐ 9   Ⓑ 15.6   Ⓒ 27   Ⓓ 31.2

ALGEBRA **Find the value(s) of the variable(s).**

21.

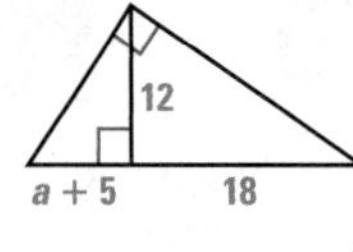

3

22.

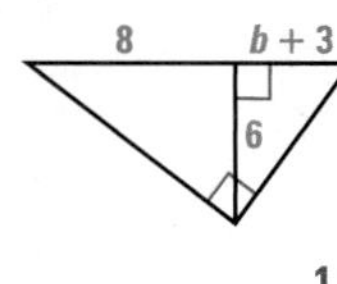

1.5

23.

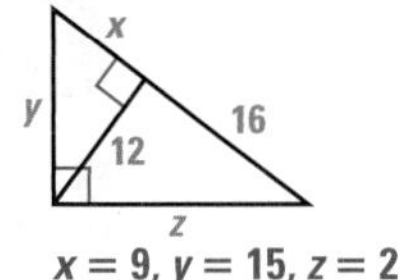

$x = 9$, $y = 15$, $z = 20$

USING THEOREMS **Tell whether the triangle is a right triangle. If so, find the length of the altitude to the hypotenuse. Round decimal answers to the nearest tenth.**

24.

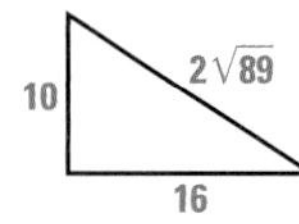

right triangle; about 8.5

25.

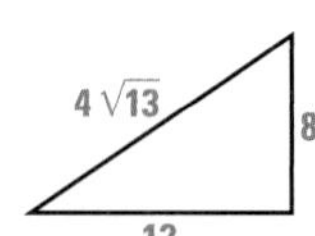

right triangle; about 6.7

26.

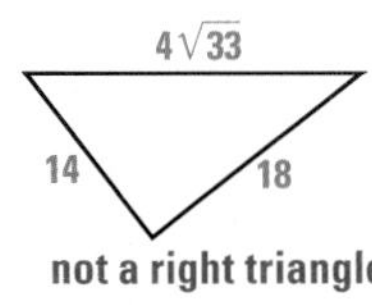

not a right triangle

C **27.** **FINDING LENGTHS** Use the Geometric Mean Theorems to find AC and BD. **25, 12**

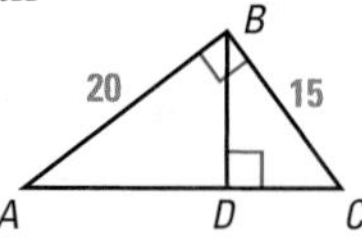

28. **CHALLENGE** Draw a right isosceles triangle and label the two leg lengths x. Then draw the altitude to the hypotenuse and label its length y. Now draw the three similar triangles and label any side length that is equal to either x or y. What can you conclude about the relationship between the two smaller triangles? *Explain.* **See margin for art. *Sample answer:* The two smaller triangles are congruent to each other and are also isosceles triangles.**

○ = **WORKED-OUT SOLUTIONS** on p. WS1   ★ = **STANDARDIZED TEST PRACTICE**

PROBLEM SOLVING

A (29.) **DOGHOUSE** The peak of the doghouse shown forms a right angle. Use the given dimensions to find the height of the roof. **about 1.1 ft**

@HomeTutor for problem solving help at classzone.com

EXAMPLE 4 on p. 452 for Exs. 30–31

30. **MONUMENT** You want to determine the height of a monument at a local park. You use a cardboard square to line up the top and bottom of the monument. Mary measures the vertical distance from the ground to your eye and the distance from you to the monument. Approximate the height of the monument (as shown at the left below). **about 14.9 ft**

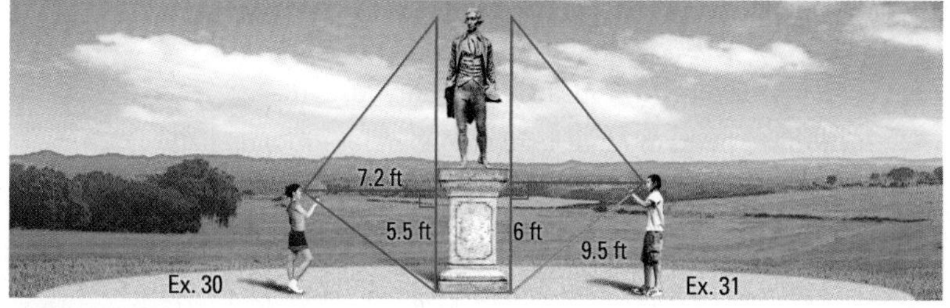

@HomeTutor for problem solving help at classzone.com

31. about 15 ft; no; the values are slightly off because the measurements are not exact.

31. ★ **SHORT RESPONSE** Paul is standing on the other side of the monument in Exercise 30 (as shown at the right above). He has a piece of rope staked at the base of the monument. He extends the rope to the cardboard square he is holding lined up to the top and bottom of the monument. Use the information in the diagram above to approximate the height of the monument. Do you get the same answer as in Exercise 30? *Explain.*

B 32. **PROVING THEOREM 7.1** Use the diagram of $\triangle ABC$. Copy and complete the proof of the Pythagorean Theorem.

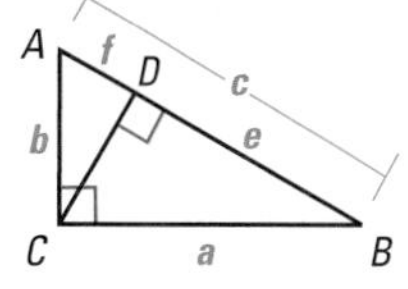

GIVEN ▶ In $\triangle ABC$, $\angle BCA$ is a right angle.

PROVE ▶ $c^2 = a^2 + b^2$

STATEMENTS	REASONS
1. Draw $\triangle ABC$. $\angle BCA$ is a right angle.	1. ? **Given**
2. Draw a perpendicular from C to $\overline{AB}$.	2. Perpendicular Postulate
3. $\frac{c}{a} = \frac{a}{e}$ and $\frac{c}{b} = \frac{b}{f}$	3. ? **Geometric Mean (leg) Theorem**
4. $ce = a^2$ and $cf = b^2$	4. ? **Cross Products Property**
5. $ce + b^2 =$? $+ b^2$ **a^2**	5. Addition Property of Equality
6. $ce + cf = a^2 + b^2$	6. ? **Substitution Property of Equality**
7. $c(e + f) = a^2 + b^2$	7. ? **Distributive Property**
8. $e + f =$? **c**	8. Segment Addition Postulate
9. $c \cdot c = a^2 + b^2$	9. ? **Substitution Property of Equality**
10. $c^2 = a^2 + b^2$	10. Simplify.

Avoiding Common Errors

Exercise 29 Some students may write $\frac{1.5}{x} = \frac{x}{1.5}$ as the proportion. Remind them that they must use the two parts of the hypotenuse, so the first step is to use the Pythagorean Theorem to find the complete hypotenuse. Then they can use the Pythagorean Theorem or Geometric Mean Theorem to find x.

Mathematical Reasoning

Exercise 32 To identify each Reason, students should try to determine what was done to each previous Statement to obtain the new Statement.

5 ASSESS AND RETEACH

Daily Homework Quiz

Transparency Available

1. Identify the three similar right triangles in the diagram.

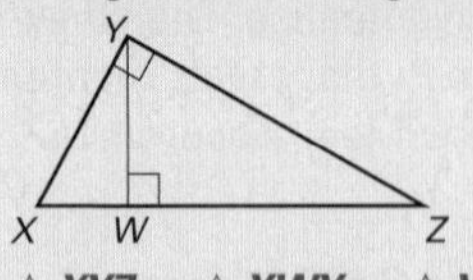

$\triangle XYZ \sim \triangle XWY \sim \triangle YWZ$

Find the values of the variable.

2. $3\sqrt{5}$

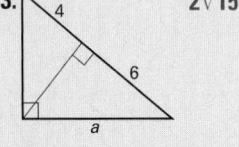

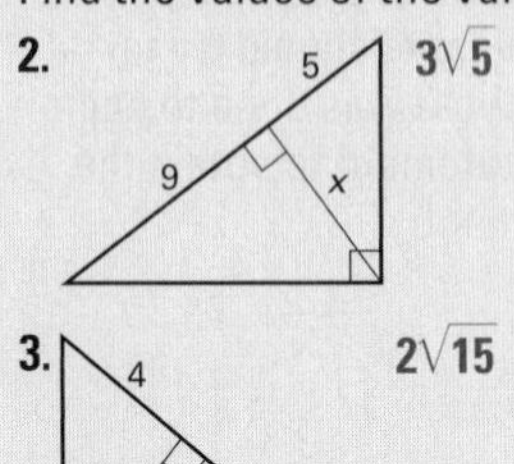

3. $2\sqrt{15}$

Online Quiz

Available at **classzone.com**

Diagnosis/Remediation

- Practice A, B, C in Chapter 7 Resource Book, pp. 35–40
- Study Guide in Chapter 7 Resource Book, pp. 41–42
- Practice Workbook, pp. 130–132
- @HomeTutor

Challenge

Additional challenge is available in the Chapter 7 Resource Book, p. 45.

34a.

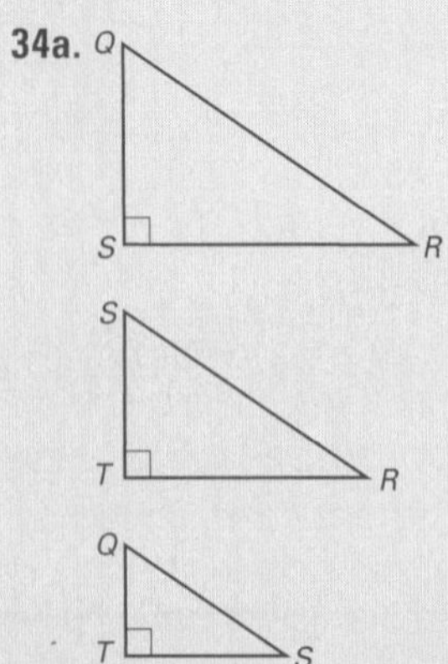

35–37. See Additional Answers beginning on p. AA1.

33a. $\overline{FH}$, $\overline{GF}$, $\overline{EF}$; each segment has a vertex as an endpoint and is perpendicular to the opposite side.

34a. See margin for art; the right angles correspond and from there you find the shorter leg and the longer leg, keeping in mind which way you choose and being consistent with all three triangles.

34c. $\overline{RS}$. *Sample answer:* $\overline{RQ}$ is the hypotenuse of the large triangle and $\overline{RT}$ is the long leg of the medium triangle, so the relationship for the geometric mean requires a segment that is a hypotenuse and a long leg.

33. MULTI-STEP PROBLEM Use the diagram.

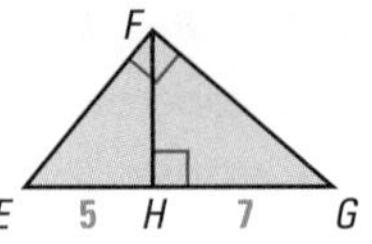

a. Name all the altitudes in $\triangle EGF$. *Explain.*

b. Find FH. $\sqrt{35}$

c. Find the area of the triangle. **about 35.5**

34. ★ EXTENDED RESPONSE Use the diagram.

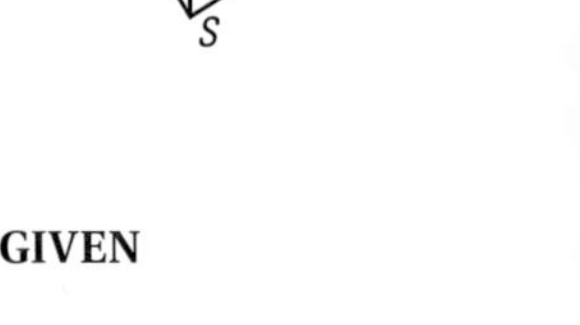

a. Sketch the three similar triangles in the diagram. Label the vertices. *Explain* how you know which vertices correspond.

b. Write similarity statements for the three triangles. $\triangle QSR \sim \triangle STR \sim \triangle QTS$

c. Which segment's length is the geometric mean of RT and RQ? *Explain* your reasoning.

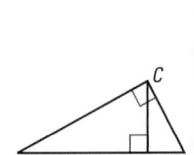

PROVING THEOREMS In Exercises 35–37, use the diagram and GIVEN statements below. 35–37. See margin.

GIVEN ▶ $\triangle ABC$ is a right triangle.
Altitude $\overline{CD}$ is drawn to hypotenuse $\overline{AB}$.

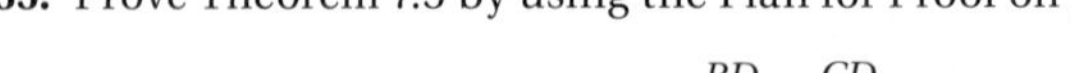

35. Prove Theorem 7.5 by using the Plan for Proof on page 449.

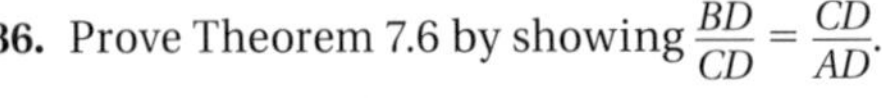

36. Prove Theorem 7.6 by showing $\frac{BD}{CD} = \frac{CD}{AD}$.

37. Prove Theorem 7.7 by showing $\frac{AB}{CB} = \frac{CB}{DB}$ and $\frac{AB}{AC} = \frac{AC}{AD}$.

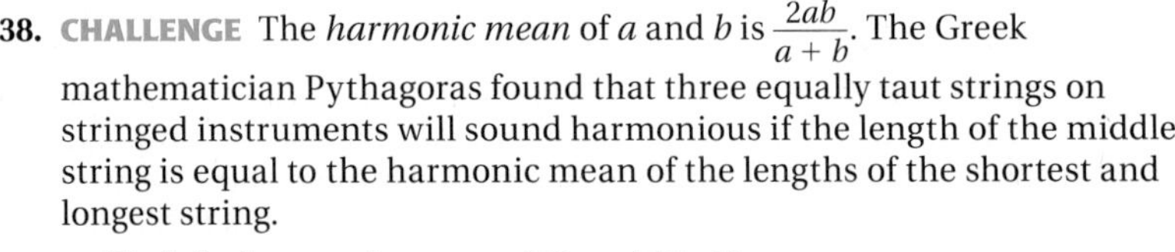

38. **CHALLENGE** The *harmonic mean* of a and b is $\frac{2ab}{a + b}$. The Greek mathematician Pythagoras found that three equally taut strings on stringed instruments will sound harmonious if the length of the middle string is equal to the harmonic mean of the lengths of the shortest and longest string.

a. Find the harmonic mean of 10 and 15. **12**

b. Find the harmonic mean of 6 and 14. **8.4**

c. Will equally taut strings whose lengths have the ratio 4 : 6 : 12 sound harmonious? *Explain* your reasoning. **Yes; when you compute the harmonic mean using 4 and 12, you get 6.**

MIXED REVIEW

PREVIEW Prepare for Lesson 7.4 in Exs. 39–46.

Simplify the expression. *(p. 874)*

39. $\sqrt{27} \cdot \sqrt{2}$ $3\sqrt{6}$

40. $\sqrt{8} \cdot \sqrt{10}$ $4\sqrt{5}$

41. $\sqrt{12} \cdot \sqrt{7}$ $2\sqrt{21}$

42. $\sqrt{18} \cdot \sqrt{12}$ $6\sqrt{6}$

43. $\frac{5}{\sqrt{7}}$ $\frac{5\sqrt{7}}{7}$

44. $\frac{8}{\sqrt{11}}$ $\frac{8\sqrt{11}}{11}$

45. $\frac{15}{\sqrt{27}}$ $\frac{5\sqrt{3}}{3}$

46. $\frac{12}{\sqrt{24}}$ $\sqrt{6}$

Tell whether the lines through the given points are *parallel, perpendicular,* or *neither. Justify* your answer. *(p. 171)* **47–49. See margin.**

47. **Line 1:** (2, 4), (4, 2)
Line 2: (3, 5), (−1, 1)

48. **Line 1:** (0, 2), (−1, −1)
Line 2: (3, 1), (1, −5)

49: **Line 1:** (1, 7), (4, 7)
Line 2: (5, 2), (7, 4)

47. Perpendicular; the slope of line 1 is −1, the slope of line 2 is 1, and $-1 \cdot 1 = -1$.

48. Parallel; the slope of each line is 3.

49. Neither; the slope of line 1 is 0, the slope of line 2 is 1, and $0 \neq 1$ and $0 \cdot 1 \neq -1$.

7.4 Special Right Triangles

Before You found side lengths using the Pythagorean Theorem.

Now You will use the relationships among the sides in special right triangles.

Why? So you can find the height of a drawbridge, as in Ex. 28.

Key Vocabulary
- **isosceles triangle,** *p. 217*

A 45°-45°-90° triangle is an *isosceles right triangle* that can be formed by cutting a square in half as shown.

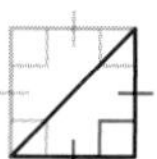

USE RATIOS
The extended ratio of the side lengths of a 45°-45°-90° triangle is $1:1:\sqrt{2}$.

THEOREM — *For Your Notebook*

THEOREM 7.8 45°-45°-90° Triangle Theorem

In a 45°-45°-90° triangle, the hypotenuse is $\sqrt{2}$ times as long as each leg.

hypotenuse = leg • $\sqrt{2}$

Proof: Ex. 30, p. 463

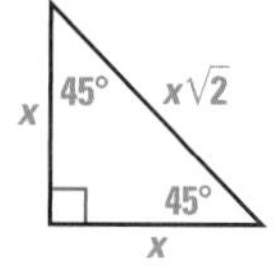

Standards
20.0 Students know and are able to use angle and side relationships in problems with special right triangles, such as 30°, 60°, and 90° triangles and 45°, 45°, and 90° triangles.

EXAMPLE 1 Find hypotenuse length in a 45°-45°-90° triangle

Find the length of the hypotenuse.

a.

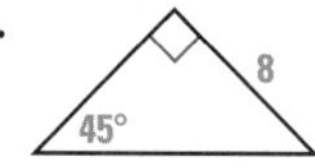

b.

Solution

a. By the Triangle Sum Theorem, the measure of the third angle must be 45°. Then the triangle is a 45°-45°-90° triangle, so by Theorem 7.8, the hypotenuse is $\sqrt{2}$ times as long as each leg.

hypotenuse = leg • $\sqrt{2}$ — **45°-45°-90° Triangle Theorem**

= $8\sqrt{2}$ — **Substitute.**

b. By the Base Angles Theorem and the Corollary to the Triangle Sum Theorem, the triangle is a 45°-45°-90° triangle.

hypotenuse = leg • $\sqrt{2}$ — **45°-45°-90° Triangle Theorem**

= $3\sqrt{2} \cdot \sqrt{2}$ — **Substitute.**

= 3 • 2 — **Product of square roots**

= 6 — **Simplify.**

REVIEW ALGEBRA
Remember the following properties of radicals:
$\sqrt{a} \cdot \sqrt{b} = \sqrt{a \cdot b}$
$\sqrt{a \cdot a} = a$
For a review of radical expressions, see p. 874.

1 PLAN AND PREPARE

Warm-Up Exercises

Transparency Available

Simplify.

1. $6\sqrt{2} \cdot \sqrt{2}$ 12 **2.** $\frac{6}{\sqrt{3}}$ $2\sqrt{3}$

3. $\frac{5}{\sqrt{2}}$ $\frac{5\sqrt{2}}{2}$

4. Find $m\angle DBC$ in square *ABCD*. 45°

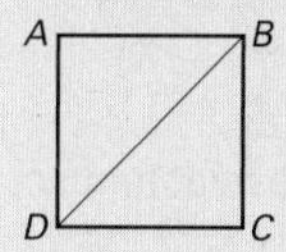

Notetaking Guide

Transparency Available

Promotes interactive learning and notetaking skills, pp. 182–185.

Pacing

Basic: 2 days
Average: 2 days
Advanced: 2 days
Block: 0.5 block with 7.3
0.5 block with 7.5
- See *Teaching Guide/Lesson Plan.*

2 FOCUS AND MOTIVATE

Essential Question

Big Idea 2, p. 431

How do you find the lengths of the sides of a 30°-60°-90° triangle and a 45°-45°-90° triangle? **Tell students they will learn how to answer this question by learning about two special right triangles.**

Resource Planning Guide

Chapter Resource Book
- Teaching Guide/Lesson Plan (pp. 46–47)
- Activity Master (p. 48)
- Practice levels A, B, C (pp. 49–54)
- Study Guide (pp. 55–56)
- Catch-up for Absent Students (p. 57)
- Problem Solving Workshop (p. 58)
- Challenge (p. 60)

Workbooks
- Notetaking Guide (pp. 182–185)
- Practice Workbook (pp. 133–135)

Teaching Options
- **Power Presentations CD-ROM** provides dynamic electronic teaching resources for the classroom.
- **Activity Generator CD-ROM** provides editable activities for all ability levels.

Interactive Technology
- Easy Planner
- Power Presentations CD-ROM
- Activity Generator CD-ROM
- Animated Geometry
- Test Generator CD-ROM
- Online Quiz
- eWorkbook
- eEdition
- @HomeTutor

Resources for English Learners
- Quick Reference for English Learners
- Spanish Study Guide
- Multi-Language Visual Glossary
- Student Resources in Spanish

See also the *Geometry Toolkit* for more strategies for meeting individual needs.

Motivating the Lesson

In an equilateral triangle, how does the length of an altitude compare to the length of a side? In a square, how does the length of a diagonal compare to the length of a side? In this lesson students will learn how to answer these questions by studying 45°-45°-90° triangles and 30°-60°-90° triangles.

3 TEACH

Extra Example 1

Find the length of the hypotenuse.

a.

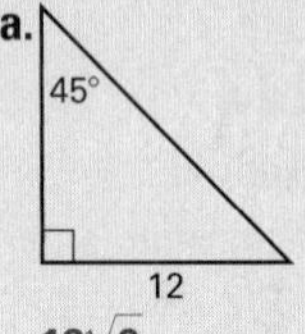

$12\sqrt{2}$

b.

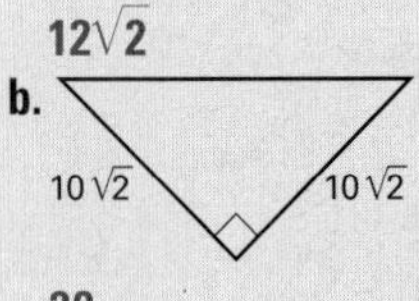

20

Extra Example 2

Find the length of the legs in the triangle. **15**

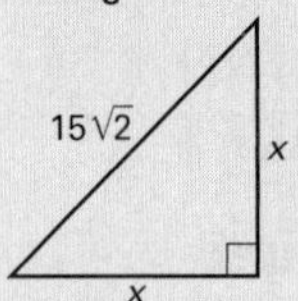

Extra Example 3

$\triangle MNP$ is a right triangle. Find the length of $\overline{MP}$. **D**

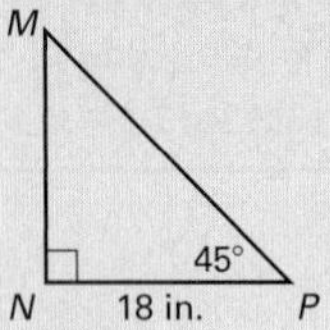

Ⓐ 18 in. Ⓑ $9\sqrt{2}$ in.

Ⓒ 36 in. Ⓓ $18\sqrt{2}$ in.

EXAMPLE 2 Find leg lengths in a 45°-45°-90° triangle

Find the lengths of the legs in the triangle.

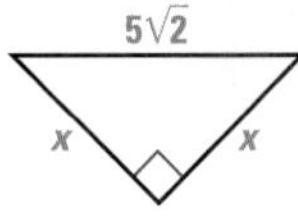

Solution

By the Base Angles Theorem and the Corollary to the Triangle Sum Theorem, the triangle is a 45°-45°-90° triangle.

hypotenuse $=$ leg $\cdot \sqrt{2}$ — **45°-45°-90° Triangle Theorem**

$5\sqrt{2} = x \cdot \sqrt{2}$ — **Substitute.**

$\frac{5\sqrt{2}}{\sqrt{2}} = \frac{x\sqrt{2}}{\sqrt{2}}$ — **Divide each side by $\sqrt{2}$.**

$5 = x$ — **Simplify.**

★ EXAMPLE 3 Standardized Test Practice

Triangle *WXY* is a right triangle. Find the length of $\overline{WX}$.

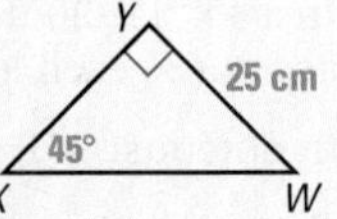

Ⓐ 50 cm Ⓑ $25\sqrt{2}$ cm

Ⓒ 25 cm Ⓓ $\frac{25\sqrt{2}}{2}$ cm

ELIMINATE CHOICES
You can eliminate choices C and D because the hypotenuse has to be longer than the leg.

Solution

By the Corollary to the Triangle Sum Theorem, the triangle is a 45°-45°-90° triangle.

hypotenuse $=$ leg $\cdot \sqrt{2}$ — **45°-45°-90° Triangle Theorem**

$WX = 25\sqrt{2}$ — **Substitute.**

▶ The correct answer is B. Ⓐ Ⓑ Ⓒ Ⓓ

GUIDED PRACTICE for Examples 1, 2, and 3

Find the value of the variable.

1.

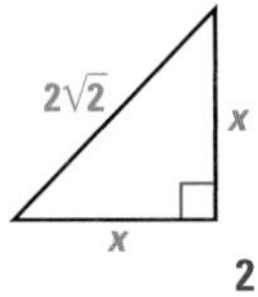

2

2.

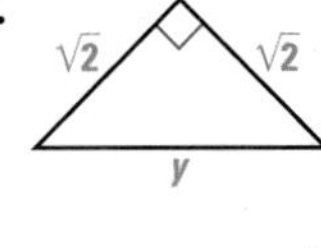

2

3.

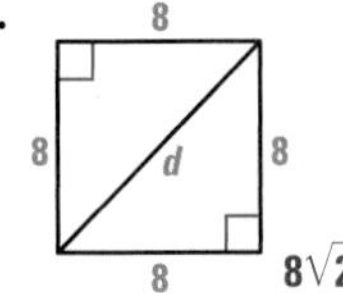

$8\sqrt{2}$

4. Find the leg length of a 45°-45°-90° triangle with a hypotenuse length of 6. **$3\sqrt{2}$**

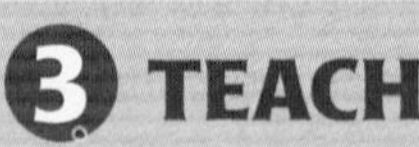

Differentiated Instruction

Auditory Learners Have students work with a partner. As one student reads Theorem 7.9 aloud, his or her partner should sketch a triangle to show the length of each leg and the hypotenuse, and also the measure of each angle. Have them change roles so each student has a chance to make a sketch. Have them repeat the process with Theorem 7.8 on page 457.

See also the *Geometry Toolkit* for more strategies.

A 30°-60°-90° triangle can be formed by dividing an equilateral triangle in half.

USE RATIOS
The extended ratio of the side lengths of a 30°-60°-90° triangle is $1 : \sqrt{3} : 2$.

THEOREM *For Your Notebook*

THEOREM 7.9 30°-60°-90° Triangle Theorem

In a 30°-60°-90° triangle, the hypotenuse is twice as long as the shorter leg, and the longer leg is $\sqrt{3}$ times as long as the shorter leg.

hypotenuse = 2 • shorter leg

longer leg = shorter leg • $\sqrt{3}$

Proof: Ex. 32, p. 463

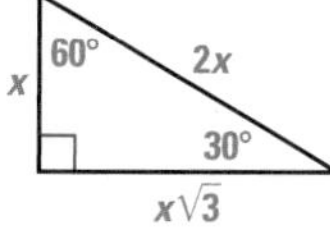

EXAMPLE 4 Find the height of an equilateral triangle

LOGO The logo on the recycling bin at the right resembles an equilateral triangle with side lengths of 6 centimeters. What is the approximate height of the logo?

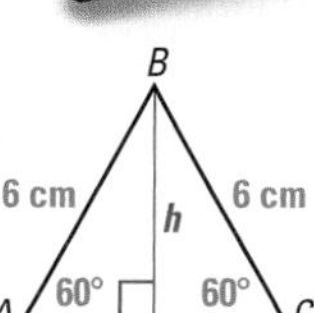

Solution

REVIEW MEDIAN
Remember that in an equilateral triangle, the altitude to a side is also the median to that side. So, altitude $\overline{BD}$ bisects $\overline{AC}$.

Draw the equilateral triangle described. Its altitude forms the longer leg of two 30°-60°-90° triangles. The length h of the altitude is approximately the height of the logo.

longer leg = shorter leg • $\sqrt{3}$

$h = 3 \cdot \sqrt{3} \approx 5.2$ cm

EXAMPLE 5 Find lengths in a 30°-60°-90° triangle

Find the values of x and y. Write your answer in simplest radical form.

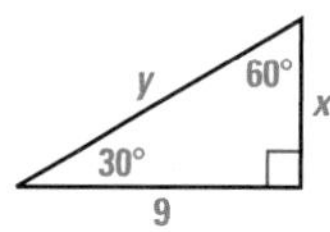

STEP 1 **Find** the value of x.

longer leg = shorter leg • $\sqrt{3}$	**30°-60°-90° Triangle Theorem**
$9 = x\sqrt{3}$	**Substitute.**
$\frac{9}{\sqrt{3}} = x$	**Divide each side by $\sqrt{3}$.**
$\frac{9}{\sqrt{3}} \cdot \frac{\sqrt{3}}{\sqrt{3}} = x$	**Multiply numerator and denominator by $\sqrt{3}$.**
$\frac{9\sqrt{3}}{3} = x$	**Multiply fractions.**
$3\sqrt{3} = x$	**Simplify.**

STEP 2 **Find** the value of y.

hypotenuse = 2 • shorter leg	**30°-60°-90° Triangle Theorem**
$y = 2 \cdot 3\sqrt{3} = 6\sqrt{3}$	**Substitute and simplify.**

Key Question to Ask for Example 3

- When do you multiply by $\sqrt{2}$? When do you divide by $\sqrt{2}$? **You multiply by $\sqrt{2}$ when you are given the length of one leg of a 45°-45°-90° triangle and you are asked to find the length of the hypotenuse. You divide by $\sqrt{2}$ when you are given the hypotenuse and are asked to find the leg.**

Extra Example 4

Alex has a team logo patch in the shape of an equilateral triangle. If the sides of the patch are $2\frac{1}{2}$ inches long, what is the approximate height of the patch? **2.2 in.**

Extra Example 5

Find the values of a and b. Write your answer in simplest radical form.

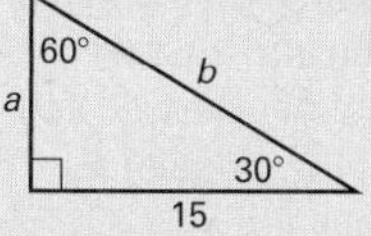

$5\sqrt{3}$, $10\sqrt{3}$

Key Question to Ask for Example 5

- Which is the shorter leg in a 30°-60°-90° triangle? How do you know? **The shorter leg is opposite the smaller angle. *Sample explanation:* Theorem 5.11, page 328: In a triangle, the side opposite a larger angle is longer than the side opposite a smaller angle.**

Differentiated Instruction

Below Level In Example 5, students have to solve for x in the equation $9 = x\sqrt{3}$. Some students may find this method easier: Multiply both sides by $\sqrt{3}$ to get $9\sqrt{3} = 3x$, then divide both sides by 3 to get $3\sqrt{3} = x$.

See also the *Geometry Toolkit* for more strategies.

Extra Example 6

A kite is attached to a 100 foot string as shown in the diagram. How far above the ground is the kite when the string forms the given angle?

a. $m\angle 1 = 45°$ **$50\sqrt{2} \approx 70.71$ ft**

b. $m\angle 1 = 30°$ **50 ft**

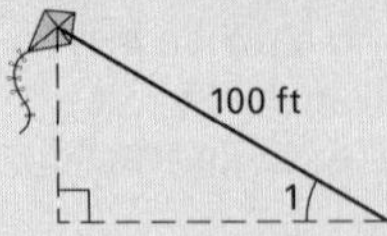

Animated Geometry
classzone.com

An **Animated Geometry** activity is available on-line for **Example 6**. This activity is also available on the **Power Presentations CD-ROM**.

Closing the Lesson

Have students summarize the major points of the lesson and answer the Essential Question: How do you find the lengths of the sides of a 30°-60°-90° triangle and a 45°-45°-90° triangle?

- **In a 45°-45°-90° triangle, the length of the hypotenuse is $\sqrt{2}$ times the length of each leg.**
- **In a 30°-60°-90° triangle, the length of the hypotenuse is 2 times the length of the shorter leg, and the length of the longer leg is $\sqrt{3}$ times the length of the shorter leg.**

In a 30°-60°-90° triangle the ratio of the sides is $x : x\sqrt{3} : 2x$. In a 45°-45°-90° triangle the ratio of the sides is $x : x : x\sqrt{2}$.

EXAMPLE 6 Find a height

DUMP TRUCK The body of a dump truck is raised to empty a load of sand. How high is the 14 foot body from the frame when it is tipped upward at the given angle?

a. 45° angle **b.** 60° angle

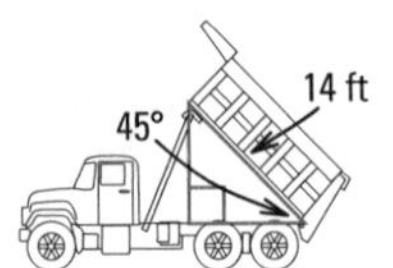

Solution

a. When the body is raised 45° above the frame, the height h is the length of a leg of a 45°-45°-90° triangle. The length of the hypotenuse is 14 feet.

$14 = h \cdot \sqrt{2}$	**45°-45°-90° Triangle Theorem**
$\frac{14}{\sqrt{2}} = h$	**Divide each side by $\sqrt{2}$.**
$9.9 \approx h$	**Use a calculator to approximate.**

(Diagram: 45°, 14 ft)

REWRITE MEASURES
To write 9.9 ft in feet and inches, multiply the decimal part by 12.
$12 \cdot 0.9 = 10.8$
So, 9.9 ft is about 9 feet 11 inches.

▶ When the angle of elevation is 45°, the body is about 9 feet 11 inches above the frame.

b. When the body is raised 60°, the height h is the length of the longer leg of a 30°-60°-90° triangle. The length of the hypotenuse is 14 feet.

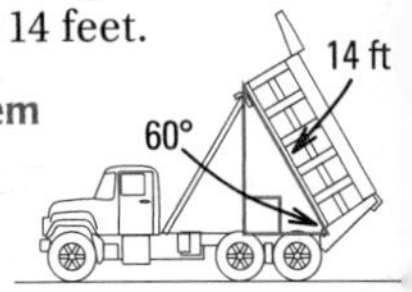

hypotenuse = 2 • shorter leg	**30°-60°-90° Triangle Theorem**
$14 = 2 \cdot s$	**Substitute.**
$7 = s$	**Divide each side by 2.**
longer leg = shorter leg • $\sqrt{3}$	**30°-60°-90° Triangle Theorem**
$h = 7\sqrt{3}$	**Substitute.**
$h \approx 12.1$	**Use a calculator to approximate.**

(Diagram: 60°, 14 ft)

▶ When the angle of elevation is 60°, the body is about 12 feet 1 inch above the frame.

Animated Geometry at classzone.com

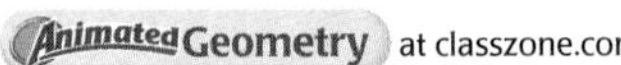

GUIDED PRACTICE for Examples 4, 5, and 6

Find the value of the variable.

5. **3**

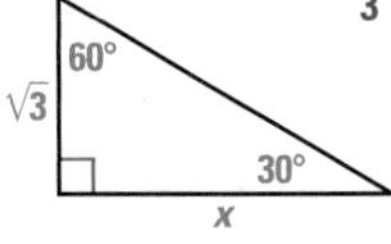

6. **$2\sqrt{3}$**

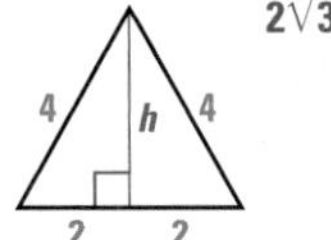

7. WHAT IF? In Example 6, what is the height of the body of the dump truck if it is raised 30° above the frame? **7 ft**

8. In a 30°-60°-90° triangle, *describe* the location of the shorter side. *Describe* the location of the longer side? ***Sample answer:* The shorter side is adjacent to the 60° angle; the longer side is adjacent to the 30° angle.**

7.4 EXERCISES

HOMEWORK KEY ○ = **WORKED-OUT SOLUTIONS** on p. WS8 for Exs. 5, 9, and 27
★ = **STANDARDIZED TEST PRACTICE** Exs. 2, 6, 19, 22, 29, and 34

SKILL PRACTICE

A

1. **VOCABULARY** Copy and complete: A triangle with two congruent sides and a right angle is called _?_. **an isosceles right triangle**

2. ★ **WRITING** *Explain* why the acute angles in an isosceles right triangle always measure 45°. **See margin.**

EXAMPLES 1 and 2 on pp. 457–458 for Exs. 3–5

45°-45°-90° TRIANGLES Find the value of x. Write your answer in simplest radical form.

3. 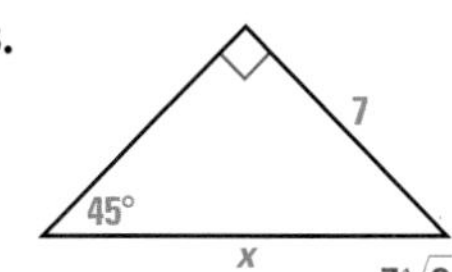
$7\sqrt{2}$

4. 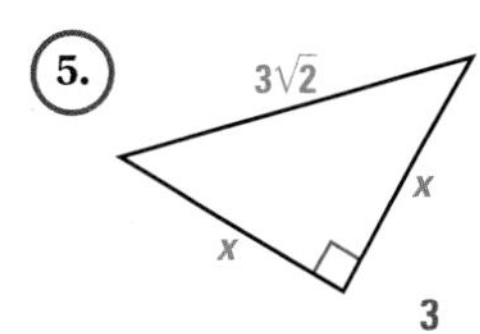
10

5.
3

EXAMPLE 3 on p. 458 for Exs. 6–7

6. ★ **MULTIPLE CHOICE** Find the length of $\overline{AC}$. **C**

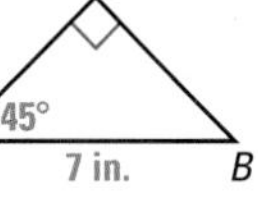

Ⓐ $7\sqrt{2}$ in.   Ⓑ $2\sqrt{7}$ in.

Ⓒ $\frac{7\sqrt{2}}{2}$ in.   Ⓓ $\sqrt{14}$ in.

7. **ISOSCELES RIGHT TRIANGLE** The square tile shown has painted corners in the shape of congruent 45°-45°-90° triangles. What is the value of x? What is the side length of the tile? **2; 4 in.**

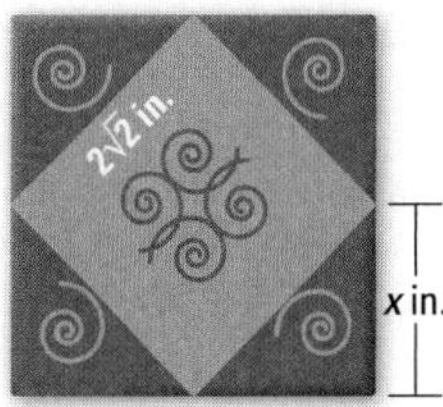

EXAMPLES 4 and 5 on p. 459 for Exs. 8–10

30°-60°-90° TRIANGLES Find the value of each variable. Write your answers in simplest radical form.

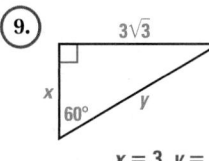

8. 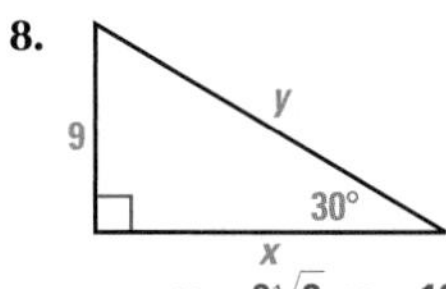
$x = 9\sqrt{3}$, $y = 18$

9. 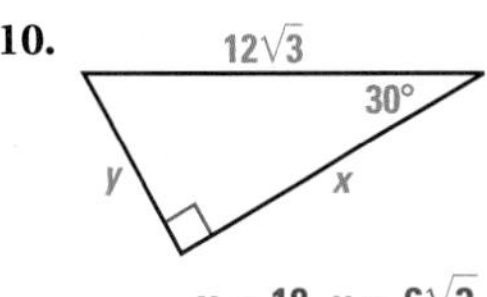
$x = 3$, $y = 6$

10.
$x = 18$, $y = 6\sqrt{3}$

SPECIAL RIGHT TRIANGLES Copy and complete the table. **11, 12. See margin.**

B

11. 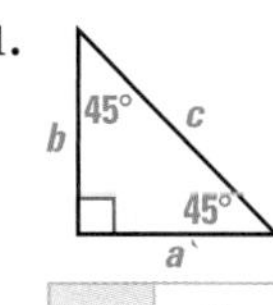

a	7	?	?	?	$\sqrt{5}$
b	?	11	?	?	?
c	?	?	10	$6\sqrt{2}$	?

12. 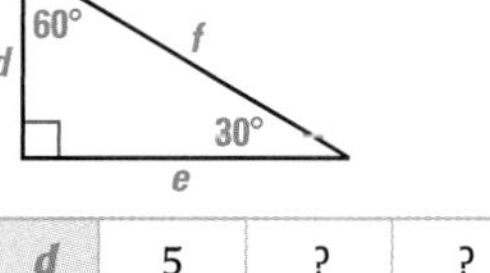

d	5	?	?	?	?
e	?	?	$8\sqrt{3}$	?	12
f	?	14	?	$18\sqrt{3}$	?

4 PRACTICE AND APPLY

Assignment Guide

Answer Transparencies available for all exercises

Basic:
Day 1: SRH p. 874 Exs. 17, 18, 22–24
pp. 461–464
Exs. 1–7, 11, 29, 30, 36–44
Day 2: pp. 461–464
Exs. 8–10, 12–19, 27, 28, 31

Average:
Day 1: pp. 461–464
Exs. 1–7, 11, 29, 30, 33, 36–44
Day 2: pp. 461–464
Exs. 8–10, 12, 16–25, 27, 28, 31, 32

Advanced:
Day 1: pp. 461–464
Exs. 1–7, 11, 29, 30, 33, 36–44
Day 2: pp. 461–464
Exs. 9, 10, 17–28*, 31, 32, 34, 35*

Block:
pp. 461–464
Exs. 1–7, 11, 29, 30, 33, 36–44 (with 7.3)
pp. 461–464
Exs. 8–10, 12, 16–25, 27, 28, 31, 32 (with 7.5)

Differentiated Instruction

See *Geometry Best Practices Toolkit* for suggestions on addressing the needs of a diverse classroom.

Homework Check

For a quick check of student understanding of key concepts, go over the following exercises:
Basic: 3, 6, 8, 27, 28
Average: 4, 6, 9, 27, 29
Advanced: 4, 7, 10, 27, 30

Extra Practice

- Student Edition, p. 908
- Chapter 7 Resource Book: Practice levels A, B, C, pp. 49–54

Practice Worksheet

An easily-readable reduced practice page (with answers) for this lesson can be found on p. 430D.

2. The sum of the interior angles of a triangle is 180°; if one angle is 90°, then the other two angles must total 90°. Since the triangle is isosceles, these angles must be congruent. Therefore each angle must be half of 90° or 45°.

11.

a	7	11	$5\sqrt{2}$	6	$\sqrt{5}$
b	7	11	$5\sqrt{2}$	6	$\sqrt{5}$
c	$7\sqrt{2}$	$11\sqrt{2}$	10	$6\sqrt{2}$	$\sqrt{10}$

12.

d	5	7	8	$9\sqrt{3}$	$4\sqrt{3}$
e	$5\sqrt{3}$	$7\sqrt{3}$	$8\sqrt{3}$	27	12
f	10	14	16	$18\sqrt{3}$	$8\sqrt{3}$

Reading Strategy

Exercises 4–5 Even though no angle measures are given, students should notice that two sides of each triangle are congruent so they are 45°-45°-90° triangles.

Avoiding Common Errors

Exercise 10 Some students may be confused because they think that the $\sqrt{3}$ must be on the side of the triangle across from the 60° angle. Show students a triangle where the shorter leg is $2\sqrt{3}$, and have them see that the longer leg is 6 and the hypotenuse is $4\sqrt{3}$. Similarly, show them a 45°-45°-90° triangle where the length of a leg is a multiple of $\sqrt{2}$.

An **Animated Geometry** activity is available on-line for **Exercises 13–18**. This activity is also available on the **Power Presentations CD-ROM**.

ALGEBRA Find the value of each variable. Write your answers in simplest radical form.

13. 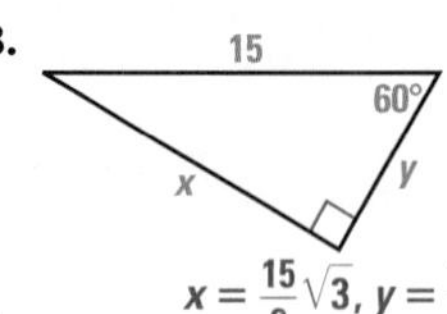

$x = \frac{15}{2}\sqrt{3}, y = \frac{15}{2}$

14. $\sqrt{6}$, m, n

$m = \sqrt{3}, n = \sqrt{3}$

15. 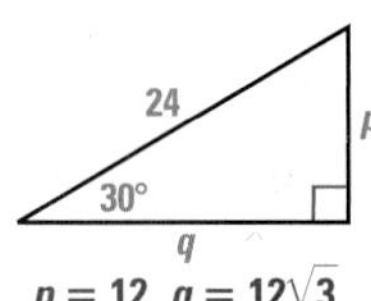

$p = 12, q = 12\sqrt{3}$

16. 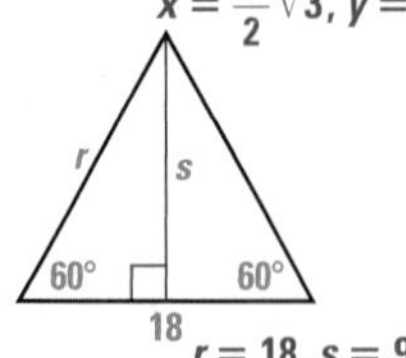

$r = 18, s = 9\sqrt{3}$

17. 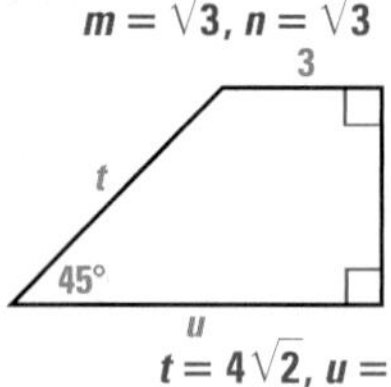

$t = 4\sqrt{2}, u = 7$

18. 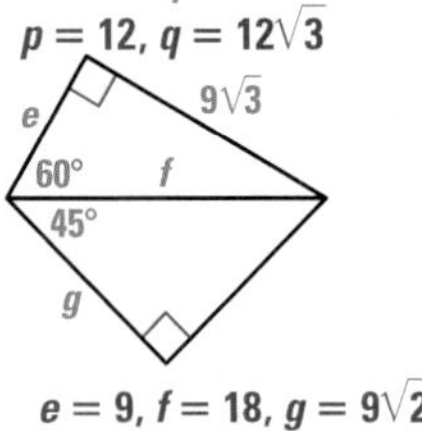

$e = 9, f = 18, g = 9\sqrt{2}$

Animated Geometry at classzone.com

19. ★ **MULTIPLE CHOICE** Which side lengths do *not* represent a 30°-60°-90° triangle? **C**

Ⓐ $\frac{1}{2}, \frac{\sqrt{3}}{2}, 1$　　Ⓑ $\sqrt{2}, \sqrt{6}, 2\sqrt{2}$

Ⓒ $\frac{5}{2}, \frac{5\sqrt{3}}{2}, 10$　　Ⓓ $3, 3\sqrt{3}, 6$

ERROR ANALYSIS ***Describe*** **and correct the error in finding the length of the hypotenuse.**

20. 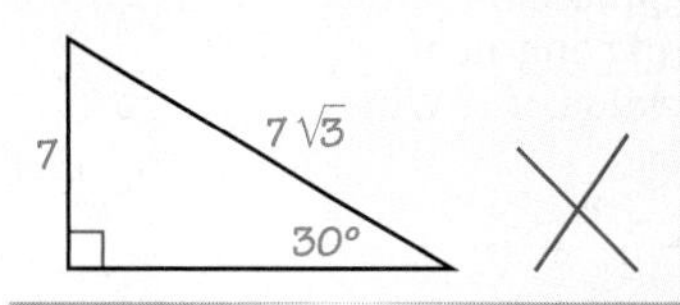

20. The hypotenuse of a 30°-60°-90° triangle should be $2x$ not $x\sqrt{3}$; if $x = 7$, then the hypotenuse is 14.

21. 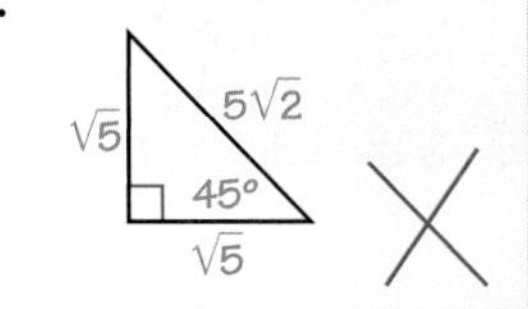

The hypotenuse of a 45°-45°-90° triangle should be $x\sqrt{2}$; if $x = \sqrt{5}$, then the hypotenuse is $\sqrt{10}$.

22. ★ **WRITING** Abigail solved Example 5 on page 459 in a different way. Instead of dividing each side by $\sqrt{3}$, she multiplied each side by $\sqrt{3}$. Does her method work? *Explain* why or why not. **Yes. *Sample answer:* After she multiplies by $\sqrt{3}$ she would have to divide by 3 to solve for x and find $x = 3\sqrt{3}$.**

ALGEBRA Find the value of each variable. Write your answers in simplest radical form.

23. 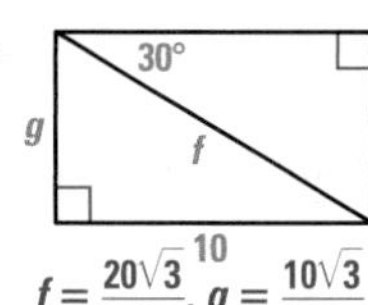

$f = \frac{20\sqrt{3}}{3}, g = \frac{10\sqrt{3}}{3}$

24. 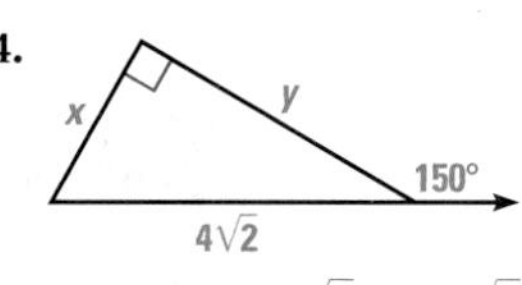

$x = 2\sqrt{2}, y = 2\sqrt{6}$

25. 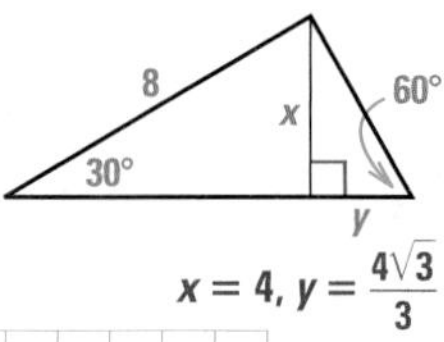

$x = 4, y = \frac{4\sqrt{3}}{3}$

C **26.** **CHALLENGE** $\triangle ABC$ is a 30°-60°-90° triangle. Find the coordinates of A. **about (1.5, 1.60)**

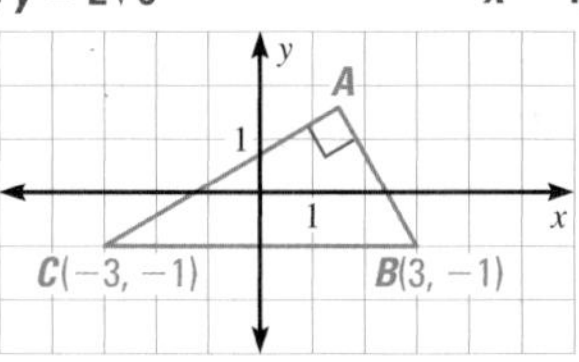

○ = WORKED-OUT SOLUTIONS on p. WS1　　★ = STANDARDIZED TEST PRACTICE

PROBLEM SOLVING

EXAMPLE 6 A on p. 460 for Ex. 27

27. KAYAK RAMP A ramp is used to launch a kayak. What is the height of an 11 foot ramp when its angle is 30° as shown? **5.5 ft**

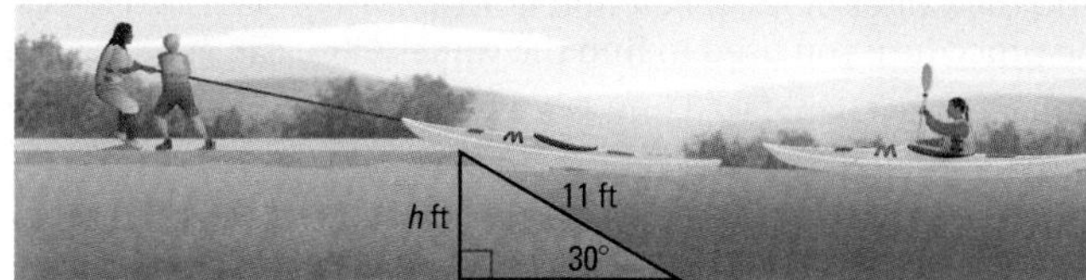

@HomeTutor for problem solving help at classzone.com

28. DRAWBRIDGE Each half of the drawbridge is about 284 feet long, as shown. How high does a seagull who is on the end of the drawbridge rise when the angle with measure $x°$ is 30°? 45°? 60°?

@HomeTutor for problem solving help at classzone.com

142 ft, $142\sqrt{2}$ ft, $142\sqrt{3}$ ft

29. ★ SHORT RESPONSE *Describe* two ways to show that all isosceles right triangles are similar to each other. **See margin.**

30. PROVING THEOREM 7.8 Write a paragraph proof of the 45°-45°-90° Triangle Theorem. **See margin.**

GIVEN ▶ $\triangle DEF$ is a 45°-45°-90° triangle.

PROVE ▶ The hypotenuse is $\sqrt{2}$ times as long as each leg.

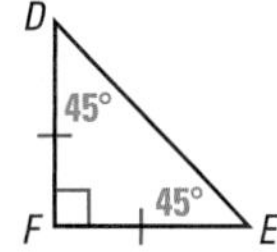

B **31. EQUILATERAL TRIANGLE** If an equilateral triangle has a side length of 20 inches, find the height of the triangle. **$10\sqrt{3}$ in.**

32. PROVING THEOREM 7.9 Write a paragraph proof of the 30°-60°-90° Triangle Theorem. **See margin.**

GIVEN ▶ $\triangle JKL$ is a 30°-60°-90° triangle.

PROVE ▶ The hypotenuse is twice as long as the shorter leg and the longer leg is $\sqrt{3}$ times as long as the shorter leg.

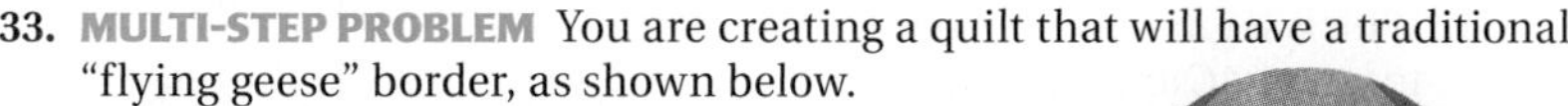

Plan for Proof Construct $\triangle JML$ congruent to $\triangle JKL$. Then prove that $\triangle JKM$ is equilateral. Express the lengths of $\overline{JK}$ and $\overline{JL}$ in terms of x.

33. MULTI-STEP PROBLEM You are creating a quilt that will have a traditional "flying geese" border, as shown below.

a. Find all the angle measures of the small blue triangles and the large orange triangles. **45°-45°-90° for all triangles**

b. The width of the border is to be 3 inches. To create the large triangle, you cut a square of fabric in half. Not counting any extra fabric needed for seams, what size square do you need? **$\frac{3\sqrt{2}}{2}$ in. × $\frac{3\sqrt{2}}{2}$ in.**

c. What size square do you need to create each small triangle? **1.5 in. × 1.5 in.**

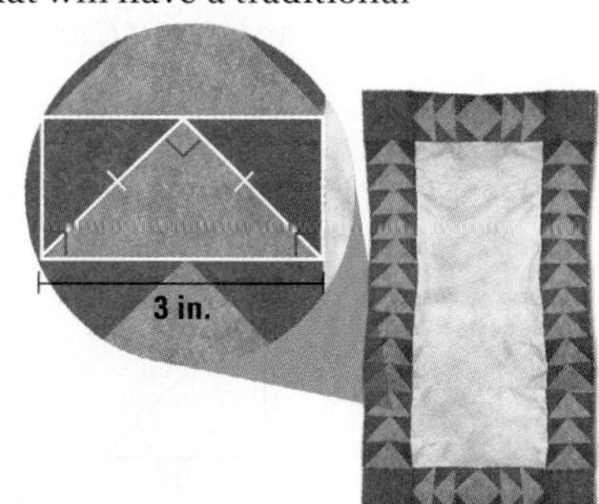

Avoiding Common Errors

Exercise 32 Some students may write the square of the hypotenuse as $2x^2$, forgetting to write it as $(2x)^2$. Encourage them to start by writing $(\ \ )^2 + (\ \ )^2 = (\ \ )^2$, and then filling in expressions for the lengths of the three sides.

30. It is given that $\angle D \cong \angle E$, and $\angle F$ is a right angle, so by the Converse of the Base Angles Theorem, $\overline{DF} \cong \overline{EF}$. Then by the Pythagorean Theorem, $DF^2 + EF^2 = DE^2$. By substitution, the equation becomes $DF^2 + DF^2 = DE^2$. By addition, we get $2DF^2 = DE^2$ and a property of square roots allows us to state that $DE = DF \cdot \sqrt{2}$ or by substitution, $DE = EF \cdot \sqrt{2}$.

32. It is given that $\triangle JKL$ is a 30°-60°-90° triangle with x as the side opposite the 30° angle and $\triangle JKL \cong \triangle JML$. Since $m\angle KJL$ is 30° and $m\angle MJL$ is also 30°, angle addition shows that $\angle KJM$ measures 60°. In addition, the definition of an equiangular triangle shows that $\triangle JKM$ is equiangular and since $\triangle JKM$ is equiangular, it is also equilateral. This allows us to state that since $KM = 2x$, then $JK = 2x$. Therefore, JK which is the hypotenuse of $\triangle JKL$ is twice as long as the shorter leg of this triangle. Using $\triangle JKL$, the Pythagorean Theorem states that $JL^2 + LK^2 = JK^2$. The Substitution Property of Equality allows us to rewrite this equation as $JL^2 + x^2 = (2x)^2$. A property of exponents simplifies the equation to $JL^2 + x^2 = 4x^2$, and subtraction simplifies the equation to $JL^2 = 3x^2$. Finally, a property of square roots simplifies the equation to $JL = x\sqrt{3}$.

29. ***Sample answer:*** Method 1. Use the Angle-Angle Similarity Postulate, because by definition of an isosceles triangle, the base angles must be the same and in a right isosceles triangle, the angles are 45°. Method 2. Use the Side-Angle-Side Similarity Theorem, because a right angle is always congruent to another right angle and the ratio of the lengths of the corresponding sides of two isosceles right triangles will always be the same.

5 ASSESS AND RETEACH

Daily Homework Quiz

Transparency Available

Use these triangles for Exercises 1–4.

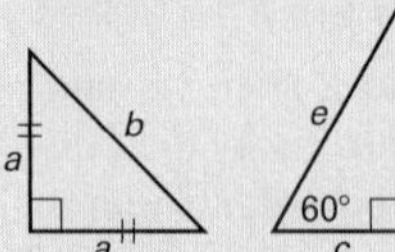

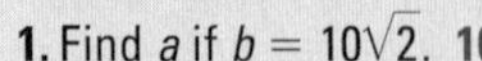

1. Find a if $b = 10\sqrt{2}$. **10**

2. Find b if $a = 19$. **$19\sqrt{2}$**

3. Find d and e if $c = 4$. **$d = 4\sqrt{3}$, $e = 8$**

4. Find c and d if $e = 50\sqrt{3}$. **$c = 25\sqrt{3}$, $d = 75$**

5. Find x, y, and z.

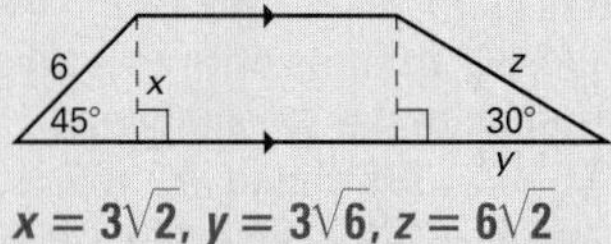

$x = 3\sqrt{2}$, $y = 3\sqrt{6}$, $z = 6\sqrt{2}$

Available at **classzone.com**

Diagnosis/Remediation

- Practice A, B, C in Chapter 7 Resource Book, pp. 49–54
- Study Guide in Chapter 7 Resource Book, pp. 55–56
- Practice Workbook, pp. 133–135
- @HomeTutor

Challenge

Additional challenge is available in the Chapter 7 Resource Book, p. 60.

Quiz

An easily-readable reduced copy of the quiz (with answers) on Lessons 7.3–7.4 from the Assessment Book can be found on p. 430G.

34a, 35a. See Additional Answers beginning on p. AA1.

C **34.** ★ **EXTENDED RESPONSE** Use the figure at the right. You can use the fact that the converses of the 45°-45°-90° Triangle Theorem and the 30°-60°-90° Triangle Theorem are true.

a. Find the values of r, s, t, u, v, and w. *Explain* the procedure you used to find the values. **See margin.**

b. Which of the triangles, if any, is a 45°-45°-90° triangle? *Explain.*

c. Which of the triangles, if any, is a 30°-60°-90° triangle? *Explain.* **The triangle with t as the hypotenuse; the side lengths fit those given in Theorem 7.9.**

34b. The left most triangle with sides of 1; the triangle must be a 45°–45°–90° triangle because it is an isosceles right triangle.

35. **CHALLENGE** In quadrilateral $QRST$, $m\angle R = 60°$, $m\angle T = 90°$, $QR = RS$, $ST = 8$, $TQ = 8$, and $\overline{RT}$ and $\overline{QS}$ intersect at point Z.

a. Draw a diagram. **See margin.**

b. *Explain* why $\triangle RQT \cong \triangle RST$. **Side-Side-Side Congruence Postulate**

c. Which is longer, QS or RT? *Explain.* **RT; $QS = 8\sqrt{2}$ and $RT = 4\sqrt{6} + 4\sqrt{2}$.**

MIXED REVIEW

In the diagram, $\overleftrightarrow{BD}$ is the perpendicular bisector of $\overline{AC}$. *(p. 303)*

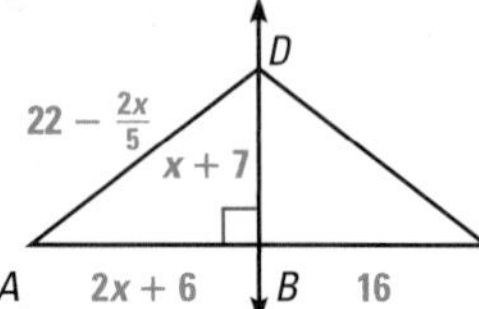

36. Which pairs of segment lengths are equal? **$AB = BC$, $AD = CD$**

37. What is the value of x? **5**

38. Find CD. **20**

Is it possible to build a triangle using the given side lengths? *(p. 328)*

39. 4, 4, and 7 **yes**

40. 3, 3, and $9\sqrt{2}$ **no**

41. 7, 15, and 21 **yes**

PREVIEW Prepare for Lesson 7.5 in Exs. 42–44.

Tell whether the given side lengths form a right triangle. *(p. 441)*

42. 21, 22, and $5\sqrt{37}$ **right triangle**

43. $\frac{3}{2}$, 2, and $\frac{5}{2}$ **right triangle**

44. 8, 10, and 14 **not a right triangle**

QUIZ for Lessons 7.3–7.4

In Exercises 1 and 2, use the diagram. *(p. 449)*

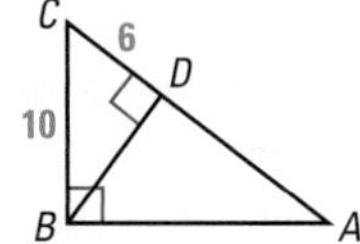

1. Which segment's length is the geometric mean of AC and CD? **CB**

2. Find BD, AD, and AB. **8, $\frac{32}{3}$, $\frac{40}{3}$**

Find the values of the variable(s). Write your answer(s) in simplest radical form. *(p. 457)*

3. (8, 8, x) **$8\sqrt{2}$**

4.

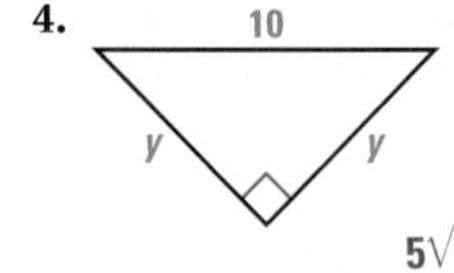

$5\sqrt{2}$

5.

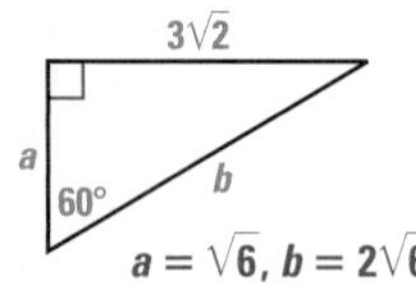

$a = \sqrt{6}$, $b = 2\sqrt{6}$

MIXED REVIEW *of Problem Solving*

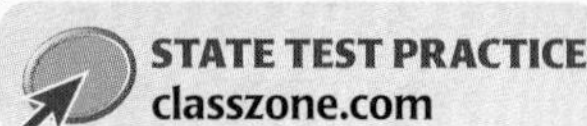

Lessons 7.1–7.4

1. **GRIDDED ANSWER** Find the direct distance, in paces, from the treasure to the stump. **51**

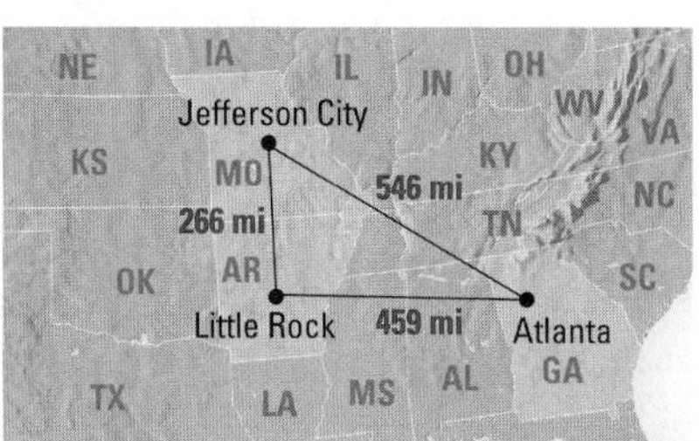

From the old stump,
take 30 paces east,
then 20 paces north,
6 paces west, and then
another 25 paces north
to find the hidden treasure.
N
W
E
S

2. **MULTI-STEP PROBLEM** On a map of the United States, you put a pushpin on three state capitols you want to visit: Jefferson City, Missouri; Little Rock, Arkansas; and Atlanta, Georgia.

a. Draw a diagram to model the triangle. **See margin.**

b. Do the pushpins form a right triangle? If not, what type of triangle do they form? **no; obtuse triangle**

3. **SHORT RESPONSE** Bob and John started running at 10 A.M. Bob ran east at 4 miles per hour while John ran south at 5 miles per hour. How far apart were they at 11:30 A.M.? *Describe* how you calculated the answer. **See margin.**

4. **EXTENDED RESPONSE** Give all values of x that make the statement true for the given diagram. **a–e. See margin.**

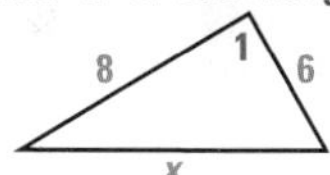

a. $\angle 1$ is a right angle. *Explain.*

b. $\angle 1$ is an obtuse angle. *Explain.*

c. $\angle 1$ is an acute angle. *Explain.*

d. The triangle is isosceles. *Explain.*

e. No triangle is possible. *Explain.*

5. **EXTENDED RESPONSE** A Chinese checker board is made of triangles. Use the picture below to answer the questions.

a. Count the marble holes in the purple triangle. What kind of triangle is it? **equilateral triangle**

b. If a side of the purple triangle measures 8 centimeters, find the area of the purple triangle. $\mathbf{16\sqrt{3}\ cm^2}$

c. How many marble holes are in the center hexagon? Assuming each marble hole takes up the same amount of space, what is the relationship between the purple triangle and center hexagon? **See margin.**

d. Find the area of the center hexagon. *Explain* your reasoning. **See margin.**

6. **MULTI-STEP PROBLEM** You build a beanbag toss game. The game is constructed from a sheet of plywood supported by two boards. The two boards form a right angle and their lengths are 3 feet and 2 feet.

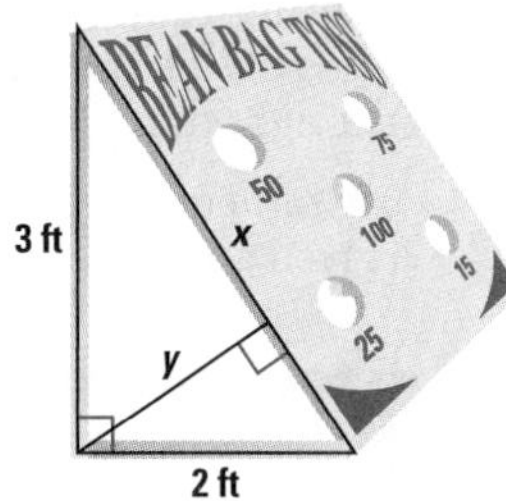

a. Find the length x of the plywood. $\mathbf{\sqrt{13}\ ft}$

b. You put in a support that is the altitude y to the hypotenuse of the right triangle. What is the length of the support? $\mathbf{\frac{6\sqrt{13}}{13}\ ft}$

c. Where does the support attach to the plywood? *Explain.* **See margin.**

2a.

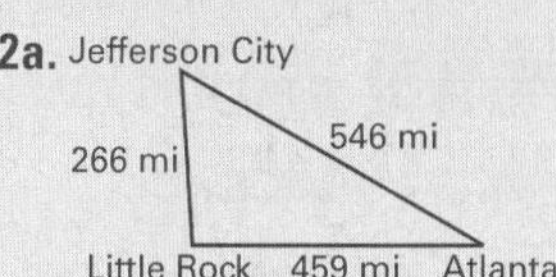

3. About 9.6 mi; I determined that they had been running 1.5 hours and used this to find the number of miles each person ran. These values form a right triangle. I then used the Pythagorean Theorem to find their distance apart.

4a. 10; if $m\angle 1 = 90°$, the Pythagorean Theorem gives 10.

4b. $10 < x < 14$; according to Theorem 7.4 the hypotenuse squared must be greater than the sum of the squares of the legs and the Triangle Inequality Theorem indicates that the side cannot exceed 14.

4c. $2 < x < 10$; according to Theorem 7.3 the hypotenuse squared must be less than the sum of the squares of the legs and the Triangle Inequality Theorem indicates that the side must not be less than 2.

4d. 6 or 8; an isosceles triangle must have two sides of the same measure.

4e. $x < 2$ or $x > 14$; the Triangle Inequality Theorem states that the sum of the lengths of any two sides of a triangle must be greater than the third.

5c. 61 marble holes; the purple triangle is $\frac{1}{6}$ of the center hexagon.

5d. $96\sqrt{3}$ cm²; since the purple triangle is $\frac{1}{6}$ of the center hexagon and the purple triangle has an area of $16\sqrt{3}$ square centimeters, the area of the hexagon is $6 \cdot 16\sqrt{3} = 96\sqrt{3}$ square centimeters.

6c. $\frac{4\sqrt{13}}{13}$ feet from the bottom of the plywood along the hypotenuse; since the brace forms a right triangle with the front and base, the Pythagorean Theorem allows you to determine the distance from the ground.

1 PLAN AND PREPARE

Warm-Up Exercises

Transparency Available

Find the values of the variables.

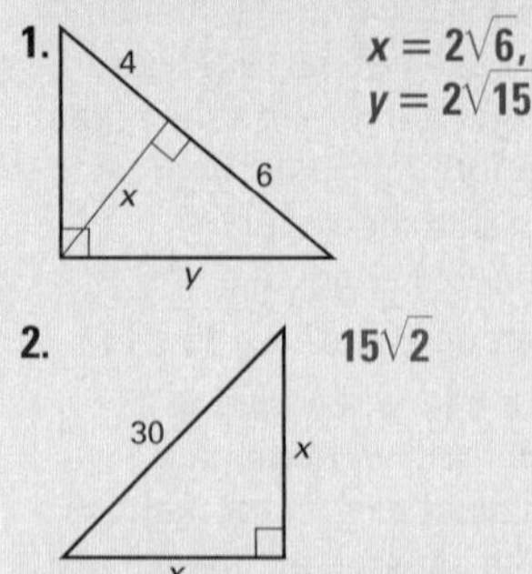

1. $x = 2\sqrt{6}$, $y = 2\sqrt{15}$

2. $15\sqrt{2}$

Notetaking Guide

Transparency Available

Promotes interactive learning and notetaking skills, pp. 186–188.

Pacing

Basic: 1 day
Average: 1 day
Advanced: 1 day
Block: 0.5 block with 7.4
• See *Teaching Guide/Lesson Plan.*

2 FOCUS AND MOTIVATE

Essential Question

Big Idea 3, p. 431

How can you find a leg of a right triangle when you know the other leg and one acute angle? **Tell students they will learn how to answer this question by using the tangent ratio.**

7.5 Apply the Tangent Ratio

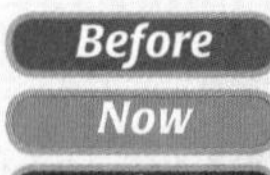

Before You used congruent or similar triangles for indirect measurement.
Now You will use the tangent ratio for indirect measurement.
Why? So you can find the height of a roller coaster, as in Ex. 32.

Key Vocabulary
• **trigonometric ratio**
• **tangent**

ACTIVITY RIGHT TRIANGLE RATIO

Materials: metric ruler, protractor, calculator

STEP 1 **Draw** a 30° angle and mark a point every 5 centimeters on a side as shown. Draw perpendicular segments through the 3 points.

STEP 2 **Measure** the legs of each right triangle. Copy and complete the table.

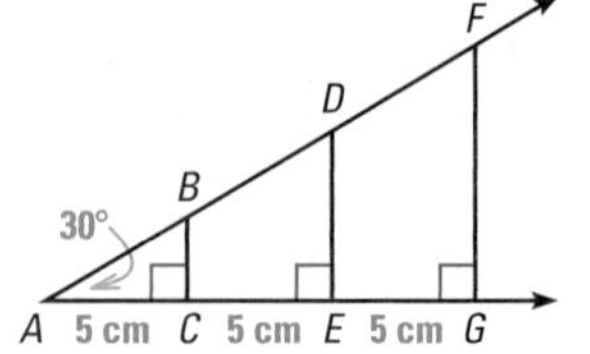

Triangle	Adjacent leg	Opposite leg	Opposite leg / Adjacent leg
$\triangle ABC$	5 cm	about ? 2.9 cm	? 0.58
$\triangle ADE$	10 cm	about ? 5.8 cm	? 0.58
$\triangle AFG$	15 cm	about ? 8.7 cm	? 0.58

STEP 3 **Explain** why the proportions $\frac{BC}{DE} = \frac{AC}{AE}$ and $\frac{BC}{AC} = \frac{DE}{AE}$ are true.

STEP 4 **Make** a conjecture about the ratio of the lengths of the legs in a right triangle. Test your conjecture by using different acute angle measures.

Step 3. Since $\triangle ABC \sim \triangle ADE$ by the AA Similarity Postulate, the proportions are true.

Step 4. The ratio of the lengths of the legs in similar right triangles is constant.

A **trigonometric ratio** is a ratio of the lengths of two sides in a right triangle. You will use trigonometric ratios to find the measure of a side or an acute angle in a right triangle.

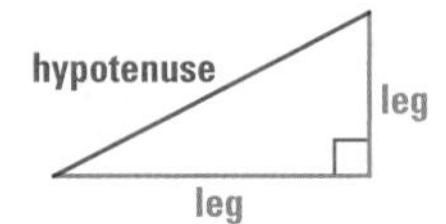

The ratio of the lengths of the legs in a right triangle is constant for a given angle measure. This ratio is called the **tangent** of the angle.

ABBREVIATE
Remember these abbreviations:
tangent → tan
opposite → opp.
adjacent → adj.

KEY CONCEPT *For Your Notebook*

Tangent Ratio

Let $\triangle ABC$ be a right triangle with acute $\angle A$. The tangent of $\angle A$ (written as $\tan A$) is defined as follows:

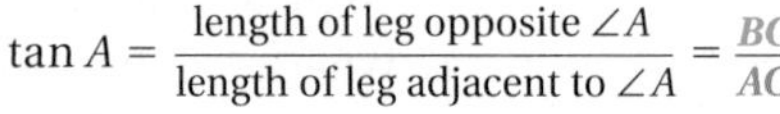

$$\tan A = \frac{\text{length of leg opposite } \angle A}{\text{length of leg adjacent to } \angle A} = \frac{BC}{AC}$$

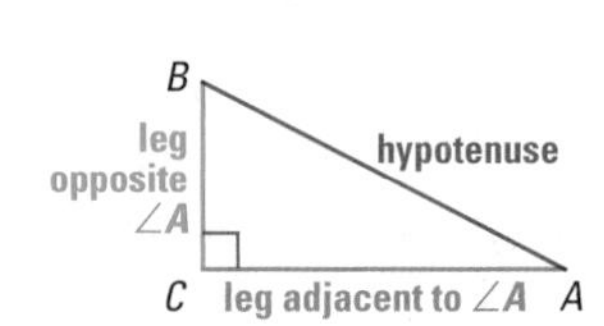

Resource Planning Guide

Chapter Resource Book
• Teaching Guide/Lesson Plan (pp. 61–62)
• Practice levels A, B, C (pp. 63–68)
• Study Guide (pp. 69–70)
• Catch-up for Absent Students (p. 71)
• Problem Solving Workshop (p. 72)
• Challenge (p. 73)

Workbooks
• Notetaking Guide (pp. 186–188)
• Practice Workbook (pp. 136–138)

Teaching Options
• **Power Presentations CD-ROM** provides dynamic electronic teaching resources for the classroom.
• **Activity Generator CD-ROM** provides editable activities for all ability levels.

Interactive Technology
• Easy Planner
• Power Presentations CD-ROM
• Activity Generator CD-ROM
• Animated Geometry
• Test Generator CD-ROM
• Online Quiz
• eWorkbook
• eEdition
• @HomeTutor

Resources for English Learners
• Quick Reference for English Learners
• Spanish Study Guide
• Multi-Language Visual Glossary
• Student Resources in Spanish

See also the *Geometry Toolkit* for more strategies for meeting individual needs.

COMPLEMENTARY ANGLES In the right triangle, $\angle A$ and $\angle B$ are complementary so you can use the same diagram to find the tangent of $\angle A$ and the tangent of $\angle B$. Notice that the leg adjacent to $\angle A$ is the leg *opposite* $\angle B$ and the leg opposite $\angle A$ is the leg *adjacent* to $\angle B$.

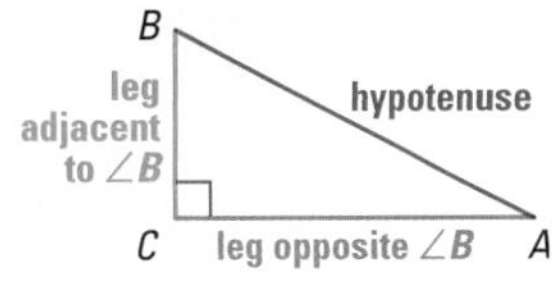

EXAMPLE 1 Find tangent ratios

Find tan *S* and tan *R*. Write each answer as a fraction and as a decimal rounded to four places.

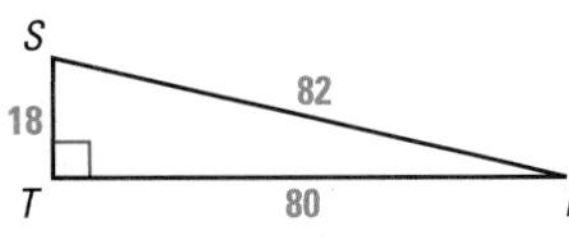

Solution

$$\tan S = \frac{\text{opp. } \angle S}{\text{adj. to } \angle S} = \frac{RT}{ST} = \frac{80}{18} = \frac{40}{9} \approx 4.4444$$

$$\tan R = \frac{\text{opp. } \angle R}{\text{adj. to } \angle R} = \frac{ST}{RT} = \frac{18}{80} = \frac{9}{40} = 0.2250$$

APPROXIMATE
Unless told otherwise, you should round the values of trigonometric ratios to the ten-thousandths' place and round lengths to the tenths' place.

✓ **GUIDED PRACTICE** for Example 1

Find tan *J* and tan *K*. Round to four decimal places.

1. 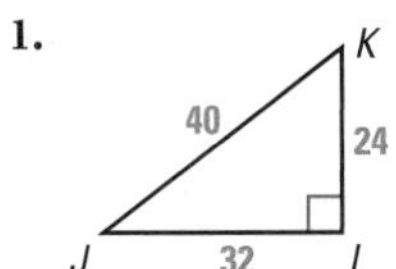

0.7500, 1.3333

2. 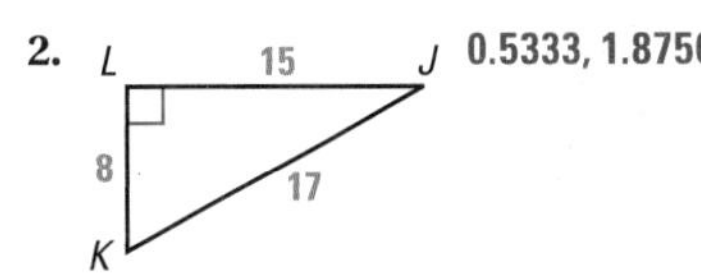

0.5333, 1.8750

Standards

18.0 Students know the definitions of the basic trigonometric functions defined by the angles of a right triangle. They also know and are able to use elementary relationships between them. For example, $\tan(x) = \frac{\sin(x)}{\cos(x)}$, $(\sin(x))^2 + (\cos(x))^2 = 1$.

19.0 Students use trigonometric functions to solve for an unknown length of a side of a right triangle, given an angle and a length of a side.

20.0 Students know and are able to use angle and side relationships in problems with special right triangles, such as 30°, 60°, and 90° triangles and 45°, 45°, and 90° triangles.

EXAMPLE 2 Find a leg length

xy ALGEBRA Find the value of *x*.

Solution

Use the tangent of an acute angle to find a leg length.

$\tan 32° = \frac{\text{opp.}}{\text{adj.}}$	**Write ratio for tangent of 32°.**
$\tan 32° = \frac{11}{x}$	**Substitute.**
$x \cdot \tan 32° = 11$	**Multiply each side by *x*.**
$x = \frac{11}{\tan 32°}$	**Divide each side by tan 32°.**
$x \approx \frac{11}{0.6249}$	**Use a calculator to find tan 32°.**
$x \approx 17.6$	**Simplify.**

ANOTHER WAY
You can also use the Table of Trigonometric Ratios on p. 925 to find the decimal values of trigonometric ratios.

Motivating the Lesson

A wire supports a tree. The wire is staked into the ground 10 feet from the tree and it forms an angle of 70° with the tree. In this lesson students will learn how to use the tangent ratio to determine how high up the tree the wire is attached.

3 TEACH

Activity Note

It may be helpful to some students to identify each opposite leg by name $(\overline{BC}, \overline{DE}, \overline{FG})$ before entering the measurements in their tables. Also, point out that the 60° angles formed at points *B*, *D*, and *F*, can be used to complete the second part of Step 4.

Extra Example 1

Find tan *D* and tan *F*. Write each answer as a fraction and as a decimal rounded to four places.

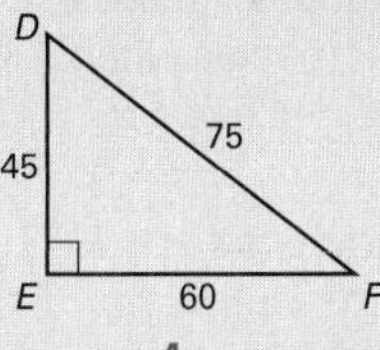

$\tan F = \frac{4}{3} \approx 1.3333$; $\tan D = \frac{3}{4} = 0.7500$

Key Questions to Ask for Example 1

- Describe side $\overline{ST}$ in two ways. **It is the leg adjacent to ∠*S* and it is the leg opposite ∠*R*.**
- Describe side $\overline{TR}$ in two ways. **It is the leg adjacent to ∠*R* and it is the leg opposite ∠*S*.**

Extra Example 2

Find the value of *x*. **29.4**

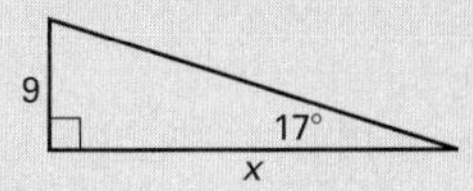

Extra Example 3

Find the height of the flagpole to the nearest foot. **51 ft**

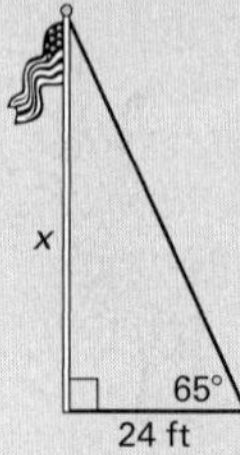

Extra Example 4

Use a special right triangle to find the tangent of a 45° angle. **tan 45° = 1**

Key Question to Ask for Example 4

- What is the tangent of a 30° angle?

$\tan 30° = \frac{\sqrt{3}}{3}$

Closing the Lesson

Have students summarize the major points of the lesson and answer the Essential Question: How can you find a leg of a right triangle when you know the other leg and one acute angle?

- **The tangent ratio for an acute angle of a right triangle is the length of the leg opposite the angle divided by the length of the leg adjacent to the angle.**

Use the tangent ratio. Solve for the unknown side length.

EXAMPLE 3 Estimate height using tangent

LAMPPOST Find the height h of the lamppost to the nearest inch.

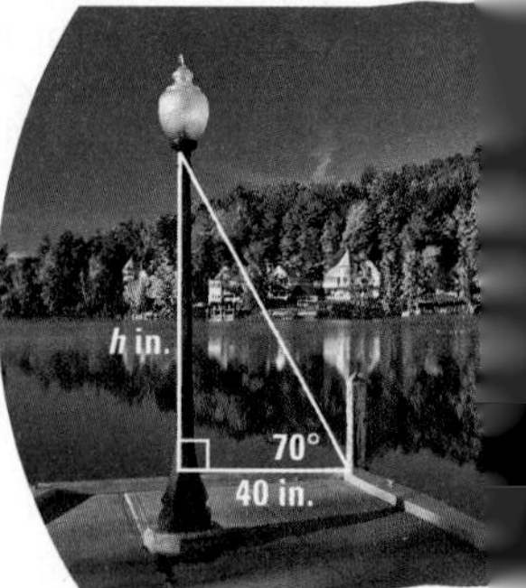

$\tan 70° = \frac{\text{opp.}}{\text{adj.}}$ — Write ratio for tangent of 70°.

$\tan 70° = \frac{h}{40}$ — Substitute.

$40 \cdot \tan 70° = h$ — Multiply each side by 40.

$109.9 \approx h$ — Use a calculator to simplify.

▶ The lamppost is about 110 inches tall.

SPECIAL RIGHT TRIANGLES You can find the tangent of an acute angle measuring 30°, 45°, or 60° by applying what you know about special right triangles.

EXAMPLE 4 Use a special right triangle to find a tangent

Use a special right triangle to find the tangent of a 60° angle.

SIMILAR TRIANGLES
The tangents of all 60° angles are the same constant ratio. Any right triangle with a 60° angle can be used to determine this value.

STEP 1 **Because** all 30°-60°-90° triangles are similar, you can simplify your calculations by choosing 1 as the length of the shorter leg. Use the 30°-60°-90° Triangle Theorem to find the length of the longer leg.

longer leg = shorter leg $\cdot \sqrt{3}$ — 30°-60°-90° Triangle Theorem

$x = 1 \cdot \sqrt{3}$ — Substitute.

$x = \sqrt{3}$ — Simplify.

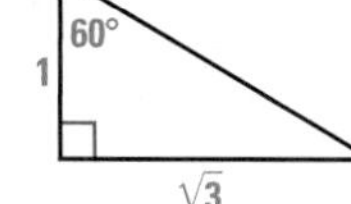

STEP 2 **Find** tan 60°.

$\tan 60° = \frac{\text{opp.}}{\text{adj.}}$ — Write ratio for tangent of 60°.

$\tan 60° = \frac{\sqrt{3}}{1}$ — Substitute.

$\tan 60° = \sqrt{3}$ — Simplify.

▶ The tangent of any 60° angle is $\sqrt{3} \approx 1.7321$.

✓ GUIDED PRACTICE for Examples 2, 3, and 4

Find the value of x. Round to the nearest tenth.

3. 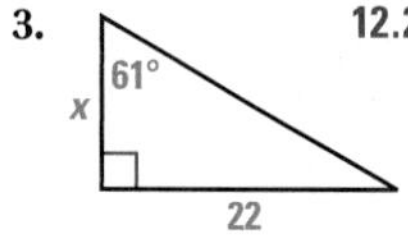

12.2

4. 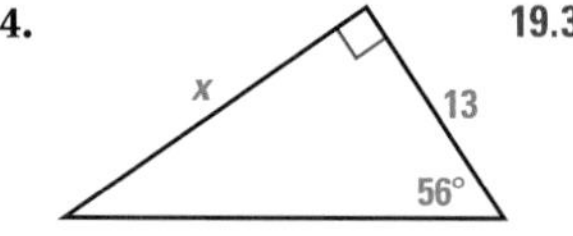

19.3

5. **WHAT IF?** In Example 4, suppose the side length of the shorter leg is 5 instead of 1. Show that the tangent of 60° is still equal to $\sqrt{3}$.

shorter leg = 5, longer leg = $5\sqrt{3}$, $\tan 60° = \frac{5\sqrt{3}}{5} = \sqrt{3}$

7.5 EXERCISES

HOMEWORK KEY
○ = **WORKED-OUT SOLUTIONS** on p. WS9 for Exs. 5, 7, and 31
★ = **STANDARDIZED TEST PRACTICE** Exs. 2, 15, 16, 17, 35, and 37

SKILL PRACTICE

A

1. **VOCABULARY** Copy and complete: The tangent ratio compares the length of _?_ to the length of _?_. **the opposite leg, the adjacent leg**

2. ★ **WRITING** *Explain* how you know that all right triangles with an acute angle measuring $n°$ are similar to each other. **See margin.**

EXAMPLE 1 on p. 467 for Exs. 3–5

FINDING TANGENT RATIOS **Find tan *A* and tan *B*. Write each answer as a fraction and as a decimal rounded to four places.**

3. 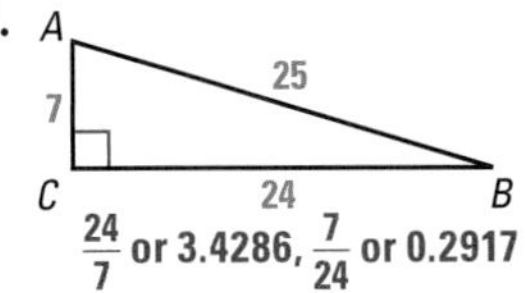

$\frac{24}{7}$ **or 3.4286,** $\frac{7}{24}$ **or 0.2917**

4. 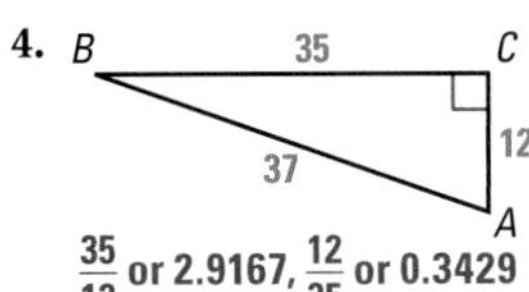

$\frac{35}{12}$ **or 2.9167,** $\frac{12}{35}$ **or 0.3429**

(5.) 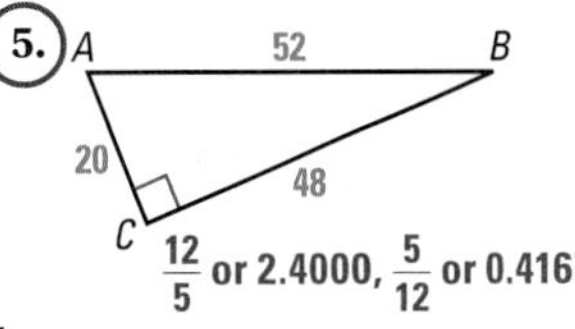

$\frac{12}{5}$ **or 2.4000,** $\frac{5}{12}$ **or 0.4167**

EXAMPLE 2 on p. 467 for Exs. 6–8

FINDING LEG LENGTHS **Find the value of *x* to the nearest tenth.**

6. 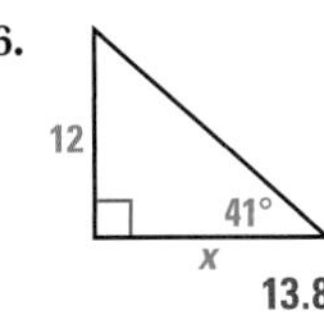

13.8

(7.) 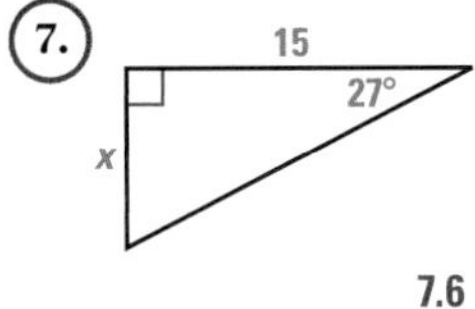

7.6

8. 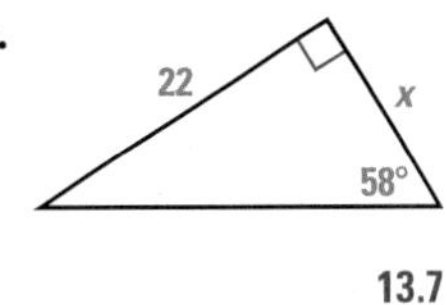

13.7

EXAMPLE 4 on p. 468 for Exs. 9–12

FINDING LEG LENGTHS **Find the value of *x* using the definition of tangent. Then find the value of *x* using the 45°-45°-90° Theorem or the 30°-60°-90° Theorem. *Compare* the results.**

9. 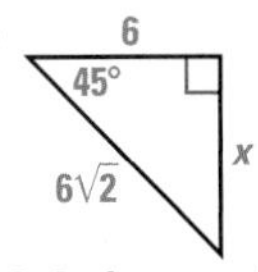

6; 6; they are the same.

10. 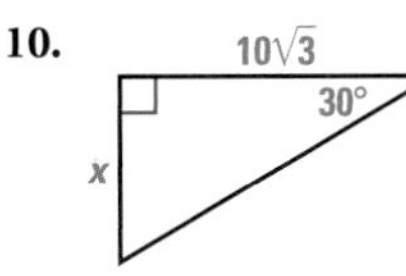

10; 10; they are the same.

11. 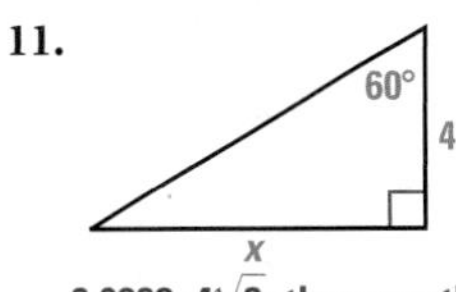

6.9282; $4\sqrt{3}$; they are the same.

12. **SPECIAL RIGHT TRIANGLES** Find tan 30° and tan 45° using the 45°-45°-90° Triangle Theorem and the 30°-60°-90° Triangle Theorem. $\tan 30 = \frac{x}{x\sqrt{3}} = \frac{1}{\sqrt{3}} = \frac{\sqrt{3}}{3}$, $\tan 45 = \frac{x}{x} = 1$

B

ERROR ANALYSIS ***Describe*** **the error in the statement of the tangent ratio. Correct the statement, if possible. Otherwise, write *not possible*.**

13. 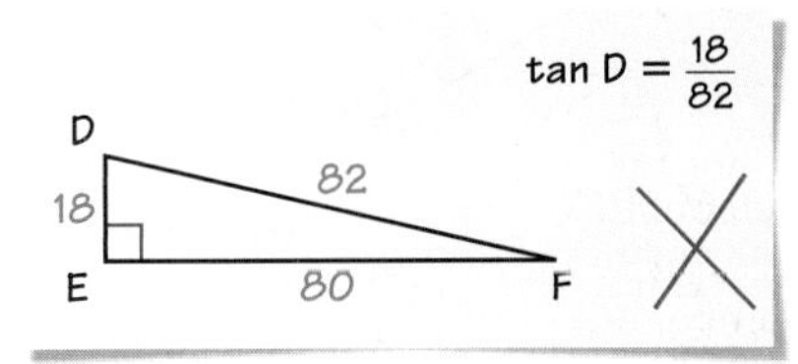

14. 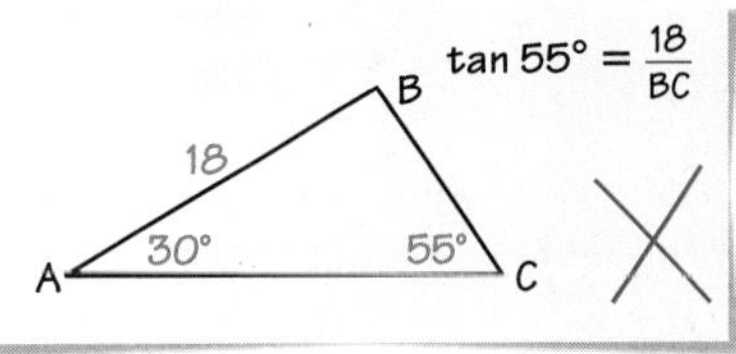

13. Tangent is the ratio of the opposite and the adjacent side, not adjacent to hypotenuse; $\frac{80}{18}$.

14. The triangle is not a right triangle and the tangent ratio only applies to right triangles; not possible.

15. ★ **WRITING** *Describe* what you must know about a triangle in order to use the tangent ratio. **You need to know: that the triangle is a right triangle, which angle you will be applying the ratio to, and the lengths of the opposite side and the adjacent side to the angle.**

4 PRACTICE AND APPLY

Assignment Guide

Answer Transparencies available for all exercises

Basic:
Day 1: SRH p. 874 Exs. 25–28
pp. 469–472
Exs. 1–20, 31–35, 39–47 odd

Average:
Day 1: pp. 469–472
Exs. 1, 2, 4–12 even, 13–26, 31–37, 40, 42, 46

Advanced:
Day 1: pp. 469–472
Exs. 1, 4–12 even, 15–30*, 32–38*, 41, 44, 47

Block:
pp. 469–472
Exs. 1, 2, 4–12 even, 13–26, 31–37, 40, 42, 46 (with 7.4)

Differentiated Instruction

See *Geometry Best Practices Toolkit* for suggestions on addressing the needs of a diverse classroom.

Homework Check

For a quick check of student understanding of key concepts, go over the following exercises:
Basic: 3, 6, 9, 31, 32
Average: 4, 6, 10, 32, 33
Advanced: 4, 8, 12, 32, 34

Extra Practice

- Student Edition, p. 909
- Chapter 7 Resource Book: Practice levels A, B, C, pp. 63–68

Practice Worksheet

An easily-readable reduced practice page (with answers) for this lesson can be found on p. 430E.

2. ***Sample answer:*** **All right triangles with an acute angle measuring *n*° also have an acute angle measuring (90 − *n*)°. Therefore all the triangles with these measures will be similar.**

Avoiding Common Errors

Exercise 6 After the students write $\tan 41° = \frac{12}{x}$, they may mistakenly write "$x = \frac{\tan 41°}{12}$". Have them multiply both sides of $\tan 41° = \frac{12}{x}$ by x to get $x \cdot \tan 41° = 12$ and then divide by $\tan 41°$ to get $x = \frac{12}{\tan 41°}$.

Reading Strategy

Exercises 27–29 Encourage students to look carefully at the diagrams and to notice that the large triangles are not marked as right triangles.

16. ★ **MULTIPLE CHOICE** Which expression can be used to find the value of x in the triangle shown? **C**

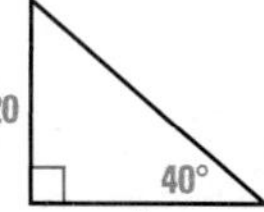

Ⓐ $x = 20 \cdot \tan 40°$ Ⓑ $x = \frac{\tan 40°}{20}$

Ⓒ $x = \frac{20}{\tan 40°}$ Ⓓ $x = \frac{20}{\tan 50°}$

17. ★ **MULTIPLE CHOICE** What is the approximate value of x in the triangle shown? **C**

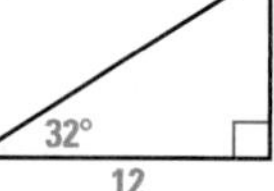

Ⓐ 0.4   Ⓑ 2.7

Ⓒ 7.5   Ⓓ 19.2

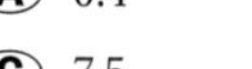

FINDING LEG LENGTHS **Use a tangent ratio to find the value of x. Round to the nearest tenth. Check your solution using the tangent of the other acute angle.**

18.
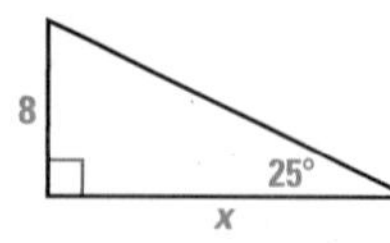

17.2

19.
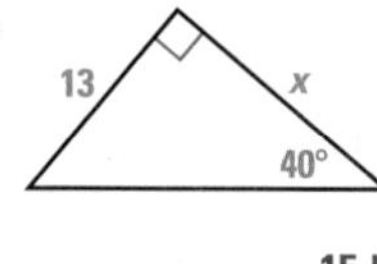

15.5

20.
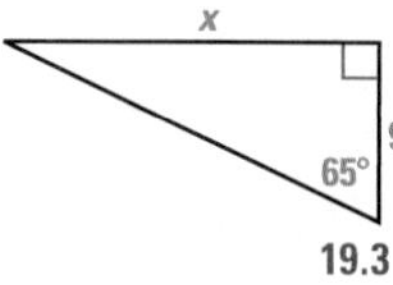

19.3

FINDING AREA **Find the area of the triangle. Round to the nearest tenth.**

21.
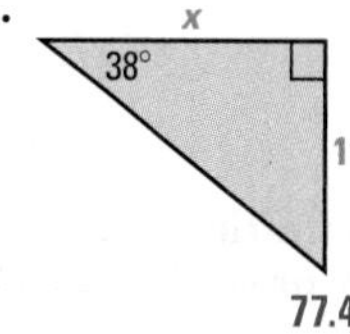

77.4

22.
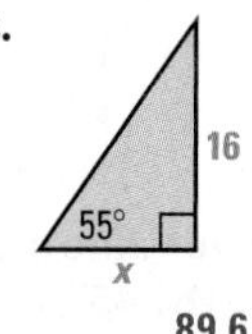

89.6

23.
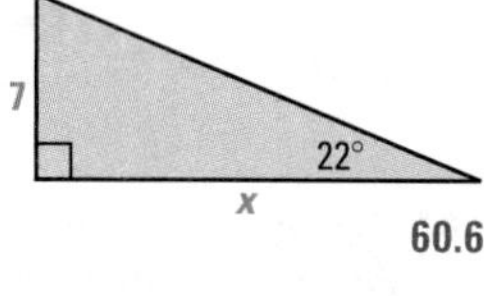

60.6

FINDING PERIMETER **Find the perimeter of the triangle. Round to the nearest tenth.**

24.
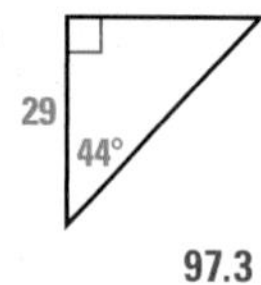

97.3

25.
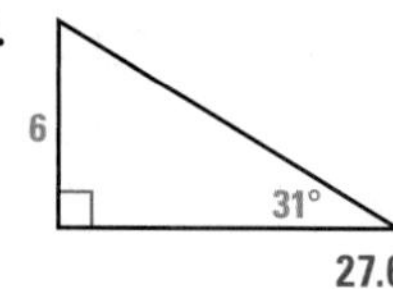

27.6

26.
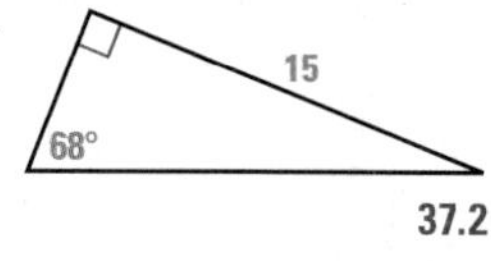

37.2

C **FINDING LENGTHS** **Find y. Then find z. Round to the nearest tenth.**

27.
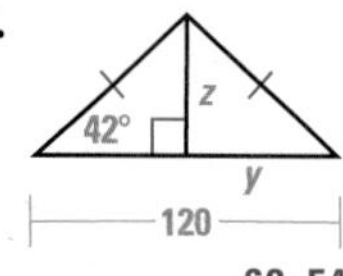

60; 54.0

28.
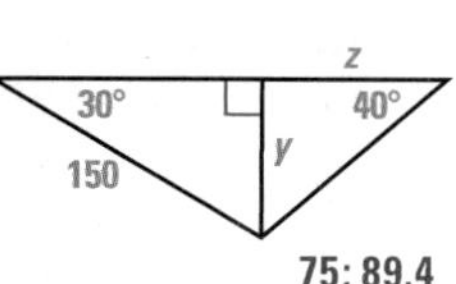

75; 89.4

29.
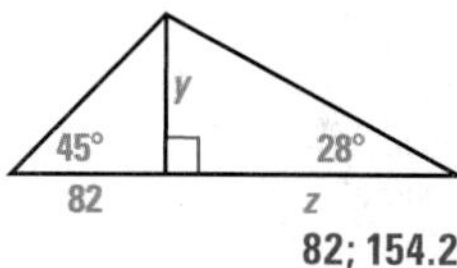

82; 154.2

30. **CHALLENGE** Find the perimeter of the figure at the right, where $AC = 26$, $AD = BF$, and D is the midpoint of $\overline{AC}$. **about 128**

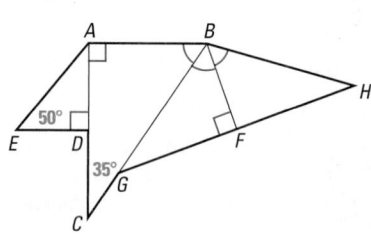

○ = WORKED-OUT SOLUTIONS on p. WS1   ★ = STANDARDIZED TEST PRACTICE

PROBLEM SOLVING

EXAMPLE 3 [A] on p. 468 for Exs. 31–32

31. **WASHINGTON MONUMENT** A surveyor is standing 118 feet from the base of the Washington Monument. The surveyor measures the angle between the ground and the top of the monument to be 78°. Find the height h of the Washington Monument to the nearest foot. **555 ft**

@HomeTutor for problem solving help at classzone.com

32. **ROLLER COASTERS** A roller coaster makes an angle of 52° with the ground. The horizontal distance from the crest of the hill to the bottom of the hill is about 121 feet, as shown. Find the height h of the roller coaster to the nearest foot. **155 ft**

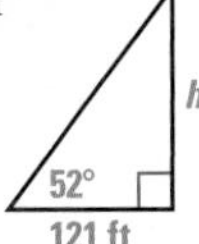

@HomeTutor for problem solving help at classzone.com

CLASS PICTURE Use this information and diagram for Exercises 33 and 34.

Your class is having a class picture taken on the lawn. The photographer is positioned 14 feet away from the center of the class. If she looks toward either end of the class, she turns 50°.

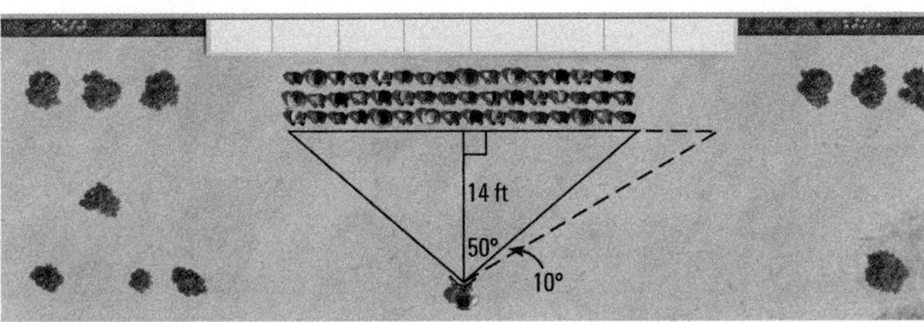

33. **ISOSCELES TRIANGLE** What is the distance between the ends of the class? **about 33.4 ft**

34. **MULTI-STEP PROBLEM** The photographer wants to estimate how many more students can fit at the end of the first row. The photographer turns 50° to see the last student and another 10° to see the end of the camera range.
    a. Find the distance from the center to the last student in the row. **about 16.7 ft**
    b. Find the distance from the center to the end of the camera range. **about 24.2 ft**
    c. Use the results of parts (a) and (b) to estimate the length of the empty space. **about 7.5 ft**
    d. If each student needs 2 feet of space, about how many more students can fit at the end of the first row? *Explain* your reasoning. **3; 7.5 ÷ 2 is 3.75, but there is not enough room for 4 students, so round down.**

[B] 35. ★ **SHORT RESPONSE** Write expressions for the tangent of each acute angle in the triangle. *Explain* how the tangent of one acute angle is related to the tangent of the other acute angle. What kind of angle pair are $\angle A$ and $\angle B$?

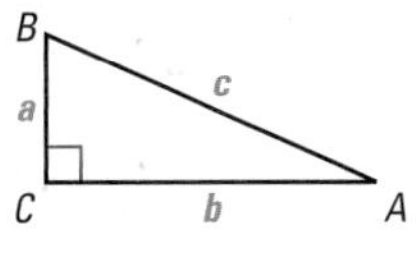

$\tan A = \frac{a}{b}$, $\tan B = \frac{b}{a}$; the tangent of one acute angle is the reciprocal of the other acute angle; complementary.

Study Strategy

Exercise 34 Have students draw and label a diagram for the problem. Remind them that in order to use the tangent ratio they must have a right triangle. Therefore, for part (c) finding the empty space means finding the difference of the values they found in part (a) and part (b).

Internet Reference

Exercise 31 More information about the Washington Monument can be found by visiting the website www.nps.gov/wamo/home.htm and clicking on the "Stones and Mortar" link.

Exercise 37 Additional information about the Americans with Disabilities Act can be found at www.usdoj.gov/crt/ada/adahom1.htm

5 ASSESS AND RETEACH

Daily Homework Quiz

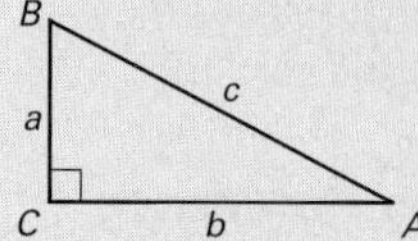

Transparency Available

Use this diagram for Exercises 1–4.

1. If $a = 18$, $b = 80$, and $c = 82$, find tan B and tan A. Write each answer as a fraction and a decimal rounded to 4 places.
   $\tan B = \frac{40}{9} \approx 4.4444$;
   $\tan A = \frac{9}{40} = 0.2250$
2. If $a = 17$ and $m\angle A = 31°$, find b to the nearest tenth. **28.3**
3. If $a = 9$ and $m\angle B = 74°$, find b to the nearest tenth. **31.4**
4. If $a = 5$ and $m\angle B = 79°$, find the number of square units in the area of $\triangle ABC$ to the nearest tenth. **64.3**

Online Quiz

Available at **classzone.com**

Diagnosis/Remediation

- Practice A, B, C in Chapter 7 Resource Book, pp. 63–68
- Study Guide in Chapter 7 Resource Book, pp. 69–70
- Practice Workbook, pp. 136–138
- @HomeTutor

Challenge

Additional challenge is available in the Chapter 7 Resource Book, p. 73.

37b. See Additional Answers beginning on p. AA1.

36. **EYE CHART** You are looking at an eye chart that is 20 feet away. Your eyes are level with the bottom of the "E" on the chart. To see the top of the "E," you look up 1°. How tall is the "E"? **about 4.2 in.**

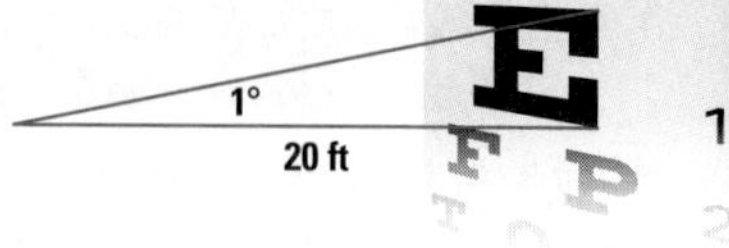

37. ★ **EXTENDED RESPONSE** According to the Americans with Disabilities Act, a ramp cannot have an incline that is greater than 5°. The regulations also state that the maximum rise of a ramp is 30 inches. When a ramp needs to reach a height greater than 30 inches, a series of ramps connected by 60 inch landings can be used, as shown below.

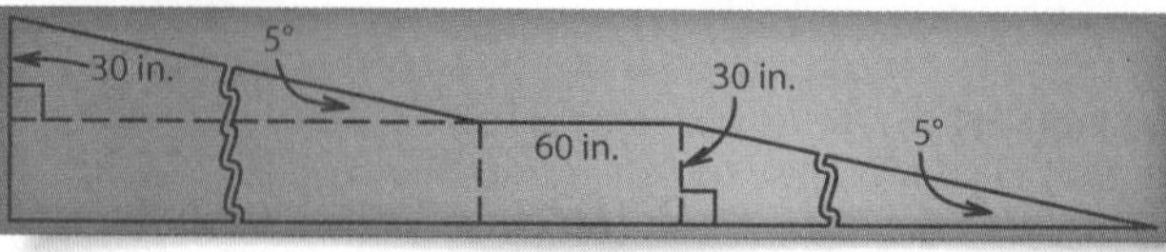

   a. What is the maximum horizontal length of the base of one ramp, in feet? Round to the nearest foot. **29 ft**

   b. If a doorway is 7.5 feet above the ground, what is the least number of ramps and landings you will need to lead to the doorway? Draw and label a diagram to *justify* your answer. **3 ramps and 2 landings; see margin for art.**

   c. To the nearest foot, what is the total length of the base of the system of ramps and landings in part (b)? **96 ft**

C 38. **CHALLENGE** The road salt shown is stored in a cone-shaped pile. The base of the cone has a circumference of 80 feet. The cone rises at an angle of 32°. Find the height h of the cone. Then find the length s of the cone-shaped pile. **about 8 ft; about 15 ft**

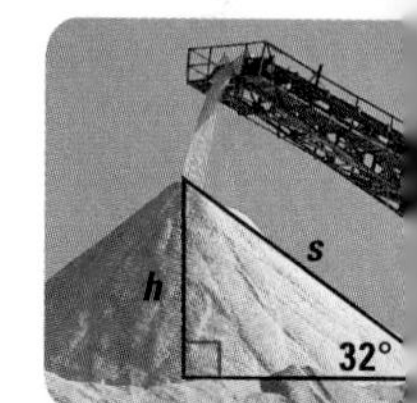

MIXED REVIEW

The expressions given represent the angle measures of a triangle. Find the measure of each angle. Then classify the triangle by its angles. *(p. 217)*

39. $m\angle A = x°$
    $m\angle B = 4x°$
    $m\angle C = 4x°$
    20°, 80°, 80°; acute

40. $m\angle A = x°$
    $m\angle B = x°$
    $m\angle C = (5x - 60)°$

41. $m\angle A = (x + 20)°$
    $m\angle B = (3x + 15)°$
    $m\angle C = (x - 30)°$
    55°, 120°, 5°; obtuse

40. about 34.3°, about 34.3°, about 111.4°; obtuse

Copy and complete the statement with <, >, or =. *Explain.* *(p. 335)* **42–44. See margin.**

42. $m\angle 1$ __?__ $m\angle 2$

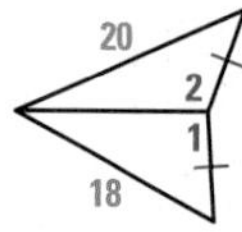

43. $m\angle 1$ __?__ $m\angle 2$

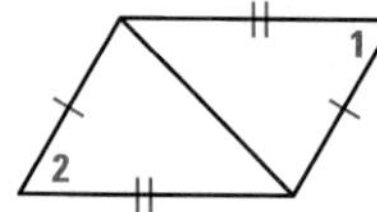

44. $m\angle 1$ __?__ $m\angle 2$

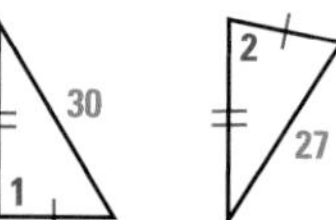

PREVIEW
Prepare for Lesson 7.6 in Exs. 45–47.

Find the unknown side length of the right triangle. *(p. 433)*

45.
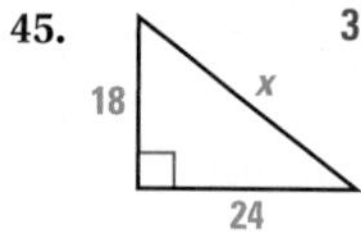

46.
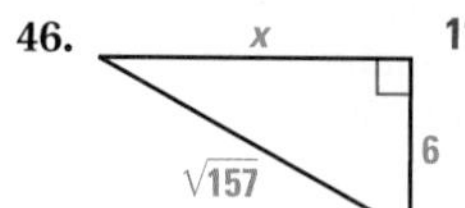

47.
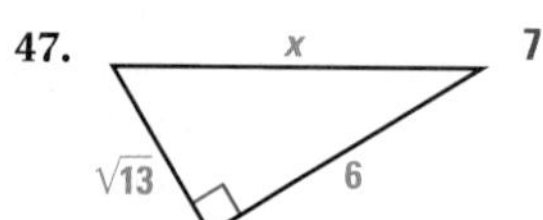

42. <; since 18 < 20, by the Converse of the Hinge Theorem, $m\angle 1 < m\angle 2$.

43. =; by the SSS Similarity Theorem, the two triangles are similar; by the definition of similar polygons, corresponding angles are congruent; and by the definition of congruent angles, the measures of the angles are equal.

44. >; since 30 > 27, by the Converse of the Hinge Theorem, $m\angle 1 > m\angle 2$.

7.6 Apply the Sine and Cosine Ratios

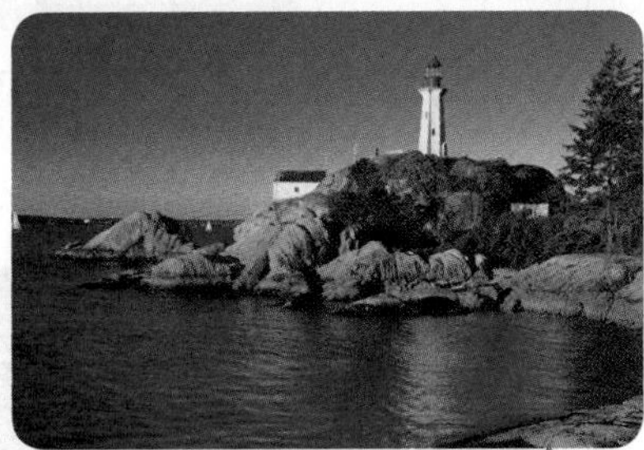

Before You used the tangent ratio.
Now You will use the sine and cosine ratios.
Why So you can find distances, as in Ex. 39.

Key Vocabulary
sine
cosine
angle of elevation
angle of depression

The **sine** and **cosine** ratios are trigonometric ratios for acute angles that involve the lengths of a leg and the hypotenuse of a right triangle.

ABBREVIATE
Remember these abbreviations:
sine → sin
cosine → cos
hypotenuse → hyp

KEY CONCEPT *For Your Notebook*

Sine and Cosine Ratios

Let $\triangle ABC$ be a right triangle with acute $\angle A$. The sine of $\angle A$ and cosine of $\angle A$ (written $\sin A$ and $\cos A$) are defined as follows:

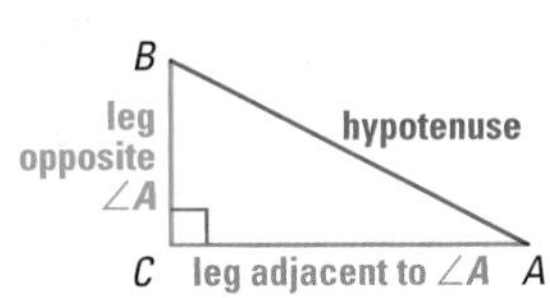

$$\sin A = \frac{\text{length of leg opposite } \angle A}{\text{length of hypotenuse}} = \frac{BC}{AB}$$

$$\cos A = \frac{\text{length of leg adjacent to } \angle A}{\text{length of hypotenuse}} = \frac{AC}{AB}$$

EXAMPLE 1 **Find sine ratios**

Find sin *S* and sin *R*. Write each answer as a fraction and as a decimal rounded to four places.

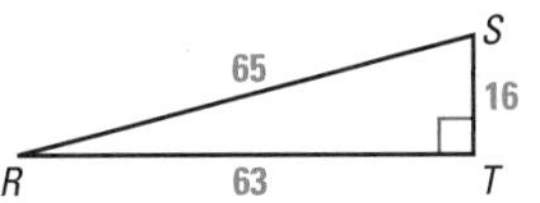

Solution

$$\sin S = \frac{\text{opp. } \angle S}{\text{hyp.}} = \frac{RT}{SR} = \frac{63}{65} \approx 0.9692$$

$$\sin R = \frac{\text{opp. } \angle R}{\text{hyp.}} = \frac{ST}{SR} = \frac{16}{65} \approx 0.2462$$

✓ **GUIDED PRACTICE** for Example 1

Find sin *X* and sin *Y*. Write each answer as a fraction and as a decimal. Round to four decimal places, if necessary.

1. 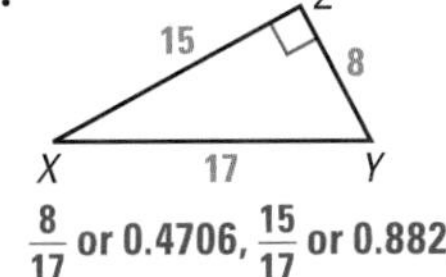

$\frac{8}{17}$ **or 0.4706,** $\frac{15}{17}$ **or 0.8824**

2. 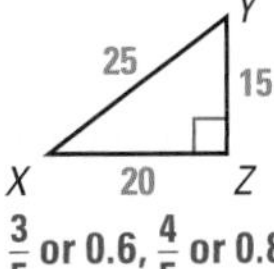

$\frac{3}{5}$ **or 0.6,** $\frac{4}{5}$ **or 0.8**

1 PLAN AND PREPARE

Warm-Up Exercises

Transparency Available

Use this diagram for Exercises 1–4.

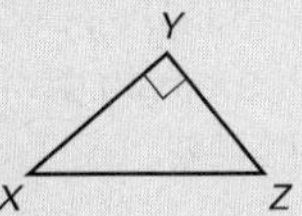

1. Name the hypotenuse. $\overline{XZ}$
2. Name the leg opposite $\angle X$. $\overline{YZ}$
3. Name the leg adjacent to $\angle X$. $\overline{XY}$
4. If $XY = 17$ and $m\angle X = 41°$, find YZ. **14.78**

Notetaking Guide

Transparency Available

Promotes interactive learning and notetaking skills, pp. 189–193.

Pacing

Basic: 2 days
Average: 2 days
Advanced: 2 days
Block: 1 block
• See *Teaching Guide/Lesson Plan.*

2 FOCUS AND MOTIVATE

Essential Question

Big Idea 3, p. 431

How can you find the lengths of the sides of a right triangle when you are given the length of the hypotenuse and one acute angle? **Tell students they will learn how to answer this question by using trigonometric ratios.**

Resource Planning Guide

Chapter Resource Book
- Teaching Guide/Lesson Plan (pp. 74–75)
- Activity Master (p. 76)
- Practice levels A, B, C (pp. 78–83)
- Study Guide (pp. 84–85)
- Catch-up for Absent Students (p. 86)
- Application (p. 87)
- Challenge (p. 88)

Workbooks
- Notetaking Guide (pp. 189–193)
- Practice Workbook (pp. 139–141)

Teaching Options
- **Power Presentations CD-ROM** provides dynamic electronic teaching resources for the classroom.
- **Activity Generator CD-ROM** provides editable activities for all ability levels.

Interactive Technology
- Easy Planner
- Power Presentations CD-ROM
- Activity Generator CD-ROM
- Animated Geometry
- Test Generator CD-ROM
- Online Quiz
- eWorkbook
- eEdition
- @HomeTutor

Resources for English Learners
- Quick Reference for English Learners
- Spanish Study Guide
- Multi-Language Visual Glossary
- Student Resources in Spanish

See also the *Geometry Toolkit* for more strategies for meeting individual needs.

Motivating the Lesson

A long ladder rests against a building, forming an angle of 80° at the ground. If you know one of three lengths—the ladder, the horizontal distance from the base of the building to the ladder, or the height reached by the ladder—you can use the methods in this lesson to find the other two lengths.

3 TEACH

Extra Example 1

Find sin A and sin B. Write each answer as a fraction and as a decimal rounded to four places.

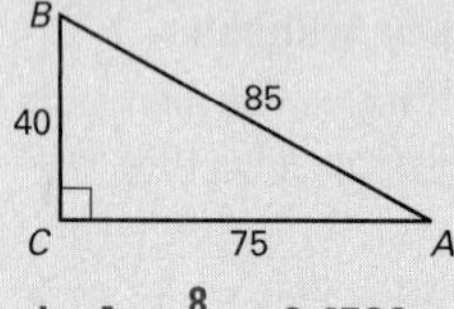

$\sin A = \frac{8}{17} \approx 0.4706$;

$\sin B = \frac{15}{17} \approx 0.8824$

Extra Example 2

Find cos P and cos R. Write each answer as a fraction and as a decimal.

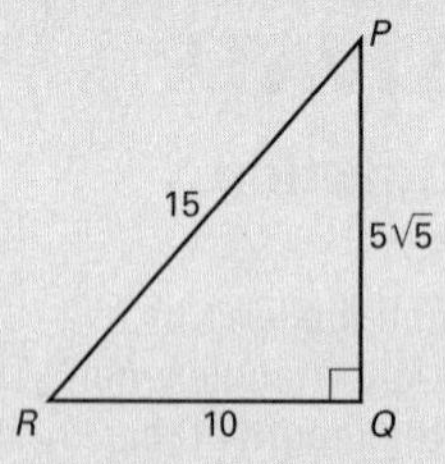

$\cos P = \frac{\sqrt{5}}{3} \approx 0.7454$;

$\cos R = \frac{2}{3} \approx 0.6667$

Standards

18.0 Students know the definitions of the basic trigonometric functions defined by the angles of a right triangle. They also know and are able to use elementary relationships between them. For example, $\tan(x) = \frac{\sin(x)}{\cos(x)}$, $(\sin(x))^2 + (\cos(x))^2 = 1$.

19.0 Students use trigonometric functions to solve for an unknown length of a side of a right triangle, given an angle and a length of a side.

20.0 Students know and are able to use angle and side relationships in problems with special right triangles, such as 30°, 60°, and 90° triangles and 45°, 45°, and 90° triangles.

EXAMPLE 2 Find cosine ratios

Find cos U and cos W. Write each answer as a fraction and as a decimal.

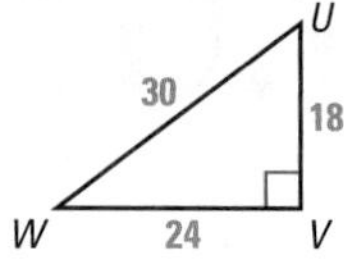

Solution

$$\cos U = \frac{\text{adj. to } \angle U}{\text{hyp.}} = \frac{UV}{UW} = \frac{18}{30} = \frac{3}{5} = 0.6000$$

$$\cos W = \frac{\text{adj. to } \angle W}{\text{hyp.}} = \frac{WV}{UW} = \frac{24}{30} = \frac{4}{5} = 0.8000$$

EXAMPLE 3 Use a trigonometric ratio to find a hypotenuse

DOG RUN You want to string cable to make a dog run from two corners of a building, as shown in the diagram. Write and solve a proportion using a trigonometric ratio to approximate the length of cable you will need.

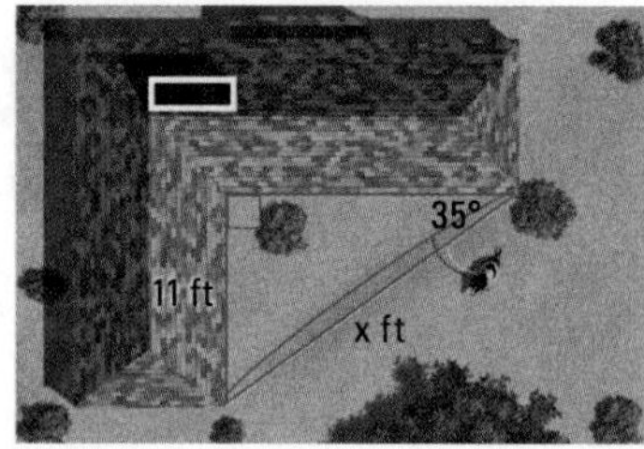

Solution

$\sin 35° = \frac{\text{opp.}}{\text{hyp.}}$	Write ratio for sine of 35°.
$\sin 35° = \frac{11}{x}$	Substitute.
$x \cdot \sin 35° = 11$	Multiply each side by x.
$x = \frac{11}{\sin 35°}$	Divide each side by sin 35°.
$x \approx \frac{11}{0.5736}$	Use a calculator to find sin 35°.
$x \approx 19.2$	Simplify.

▶ You will need a little more than 19 feet of cable.

✓ GUIDED PRACTICE for Examples 2 and 3

In Exercises 3 and 4, find cos R and cos S. Write each answer as a decimal. Round to four decimal places, if necessary.

3. 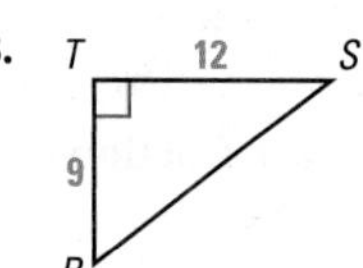

0.6, 0.8

4. 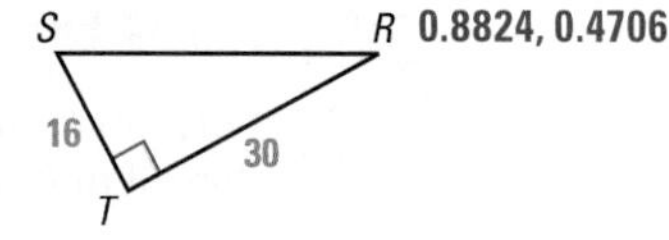

0.8824, 0.4706

5. In Example 3, use the cosine ratio to find the length of the other leg of the triangle formed. **about 15.7 ft**

ANGLES If you look up at an object, the angle your line of sight makes with a horizontal line is called the **angle of elevation**. If you look down at an object, the angle your line of sight makes with a horizontal line is called the **angle of depression**.

APPLY THEOREMS
Notice that the angle of elevation and the angle of depression are congruent by the Alternate Interior Angles Theorem on page 155.

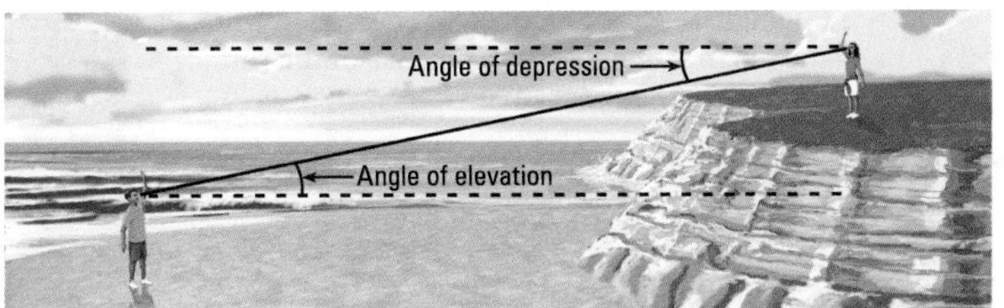

EXAMPLE 4 Find a hypotenuse using an angle of depression

SKIING You are skiing on a mountain with an altitude of 1200 meters. The angle of depression is 21°. About how far do you ski down the mountain?

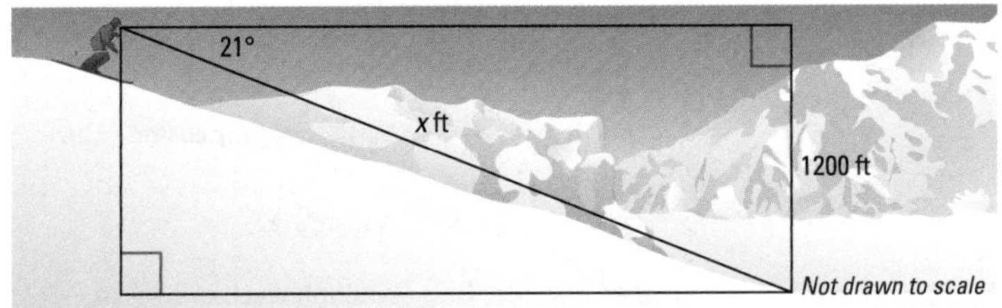

Solution

$\sin 21° = \frac{\text{opp.}}{\text{hyp.}}$	Write ratio for sine of 21°.
$\sin 21° = \frac{1200}{x}$	Substitute.
$x \cdot \sin 21° = 1200$	Multiply each side by x.
$x = \frac{1200}{\sin 21°}$	Divide each side by sin 21°.
$x \approx \frac{1200}{0.3584}$	Use a calculator to find sin 21°.
$x \approx 3348.2$	Simplify.

▶ You ski about 3348 meters down the mountain.

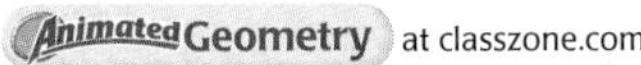

at classzone.com

GUIDED PRACTICE for Example 4

6. **WHAT IF?** Suppose the angle of depression in Example 4 is 28°. About how far would you ski? **about 2556 m**

Extra Example 3

A rope, staked 20 feet from the base of a building, goes to the roof and forms an angle of 58° with the ground. To the nearest tenth of a foot, how long is the rope? **37.7 ft**

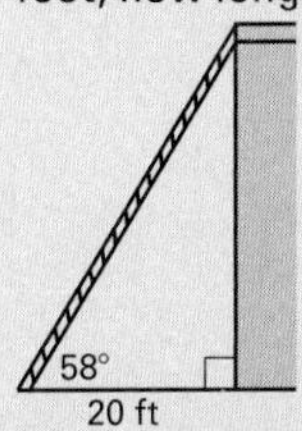

Key Question to Ask for Example 3

- How could you solve this problem using the cosine ratio? *Explain.* **The other acute angle is 55°, so $\cos 55° = \frac{11}{x}$. Then $x \cdot \cos 55° = 11$ and $x = \frac{11}{\cos 55°} \approx 19.2$ ft.**

Extra Example 4

A pilot is looking at an airport from her plane. The angle of depression is 29°. If the plane is at an altitude of 10,000 feet, approximately how far is it from the airport? **20,627 ft**

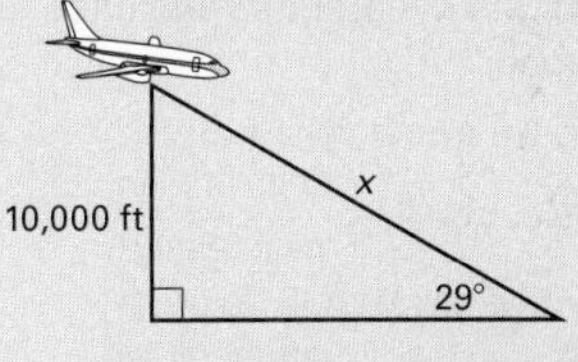

An **Animated Geometry** activity is available on-line for **Example 4**. This activity is also available on the **Power Presentations CD-ROM**.

Vocabulary

One memory device to remember the three trig ratios is "soh-cah-toa." This stands for **s**ine: **o**pposite over **h**ypotenuse; **c**osine: **a**djacent over **h**ypotenuse; **t**angent: **o**pposite over **a**djacent.

Differentiated Instruction

Advanced Have the students draw a circle with center (0, 0) and radius 1 (in trigonometry, this is called the "unit circle"). Have them draw a radius forming a 30° central angle with the positive x-axis. Identify the point (x, y) where the radius meets the circle. Ask them to find the values of x and y. Then have them repeat this procedure for a 45° central angle and a 60° central angle. The coordinates are $\left(\frac{\sqrt{3}}{2}, \frac{1}{2}\right)$, $\left(\frac{\sqrt{2}}{2}, \frac{\sqrt{2}}{2}\right)$, and $\left(\frac{1}{2}, \frac{\sqrt{3}}{2}\right)$.

See also the *Geometry Toolkit* for more strategies.

Extra Example 5

A dog is looking at a squirrel at the top of a tree. The distance between the two animals is 55 feet and the angle of elevation is 64°. How high is the squirrel and how far is the dog from the base of the tree?

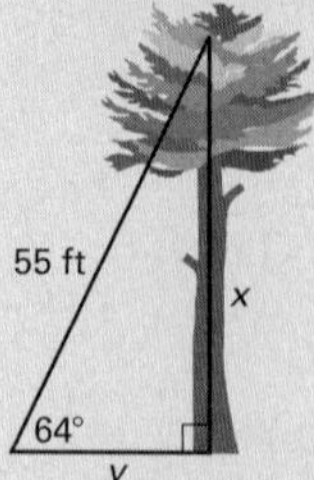

49.4 ft high; 24.1 ft from tree

Extra Example 6

Use a special right triangle to find the sine and cosine of a 45° angle.

$\sin 45° = \frac{\sqrt{2}}{2}$; $\cos 45° = \frac{\sqrt{2}}{2}$

Closing the Lesson

Have students summarize the major points of the lesson and answer the Essential Question: How can you find the lengths of the legs of a right triangle when you are given the length of the hypotenuse and one acute angle?

- **For acute angle A in a right triangle, $\sin A = \frac{\text{opposite leg}}{\text{hypotenuse}}$.**
- **For acute angle A in a right triangle, $\cos A = \frac{\text{adjacent leg}}{\text{hypotenuse}}$.**

If you know one of the acute angles in a right triangle and the length of the hypotenuse, you can use the sine ratio and cosine ratio to find the lengths of the other two sides.

EXAMPLE 5 Find leg lengths using an angle of elevation

SKATEBOARD RAMP You want to build a skateboard ramp with a length of 14 feet and an angle of elevation of 26°. You need to find the height and length of the base of the ramp.

ANOTHER WAY
For alternative methods for solving the problem in Example 5, turn to page 481 for the **Problem Solving Workshop**.

Solution

STEP 1 **Find** the height.

$\sin 26° = \frac{\text{opp.}}{\text{hyp.}}$ — **Write ratio for sine of 26°.**

$\sin 26° = \frac{x}{14}$ — **Substitute.**

$14 \cdot \sin 26° = x$ — **Multiply each side by 14.**

$6.1 \approx x$ — **Use a calculator to simplify.**

▸ The height is about 6.1 feet.

STEP 2 **Find** the length of the base.

$\cos 26° = \frac{\text{adj.}}{\text{hyp.}}$ — **Write ratio for cosine of 26°.**

$\cos 26° = \frac{y}{14}$ — **Substitute.**

$14 \cdot \cos 26° = y$ — **Multiply each side by 14.**

$12.6 \approx y$ — **Use a calculator to simplify.**

▸ The length of the base is about 12.6 feet.

EXAMPLE 6 Use a special right triangle to find a sine and cosine

Use a special right triangle to find the sine and cosine of a 60° angle.

DRAW DIAGRAMS
As in Example 4 on page 468, to simplify calculations you can choose 1 as the length of the shorter leg.

Solution

Use the 30°-60°-90° Triangle Theorem to draw a right triangle with side lengths of 1, $\sqrt{3}$, and 2. Then set up sine and cosine ratios for the 60° angle.

$$\sin 60° = \frac{\text{opp.}}{\text{hyp.}} = \frac{\sqrt{3}}{2} \approx 0.8660$$

$$\cos 60° = \frac{\text{adj.}}{\text{hyp.}} = \frac{1}{2} = 0.5000$$

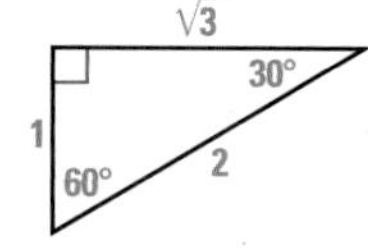

 **GUIDED PRACTICE** for Examples 5 and 6

7. **WHAT IF?** In Example 5, suppose the angle of elevation is 35°. What is the new height and base length of the ramp? **about 8 ft, about 11.5 ft**

8. Use a special right triangle to find the sine and cosine of a 30° angle. **$\frac{1}{2}, \frac{\sqrt{3}}{2}$**

Differentiated Instruction

English Learners Distinguishing between *sine* and *cosine* may be challenging for some students. Explain that the prefix *co-* can mean "together" as it does in the word cooperate. Point out that the cosine ratio for an acute angle of a triangle involves the adjacent leg. Tell students to remember this by thinking of the adjacent leg as coming "together" with the hypotenuse to form the angle.

See also the *Geometry Toolkit* for more strategies.

7.6 EXERCISES

HOMEWORK KEY

- ○ = **WORKED-OUT SOLUTIONS** on p. WS9 for Exs. 5, 9, and 33
- ★ = **STANDARDIZED TEST PRACTICE** Exs. 2, 17, 18, 29, 35, and 37
- ◆ = **MULTIPLE REPRESENTATIONS** Ex. 39

SKILL PRACTICE

A

1. VOCABULARY Copy and complete: The sine ratio compares the length of _?_ to the length of _?_. **the opposite leg, the hypotenuse**

2. ★ WRITING *Explain* how to tell which side of a right triangle is adjacent to an angle and which side is the hypotenuse. **The adjacent side is the side that forms part of the angle and is not opposite the right angle; the hypotenuse is the side opposite the right angle.**

EXAMPLE 1 on p. 473 for Exs. 3–6

FINDING SINE RATIOS **Find sin D and sin E. Write each answer as a fraction and as a decimal. Round to four decimal places, if necessary.**

3.

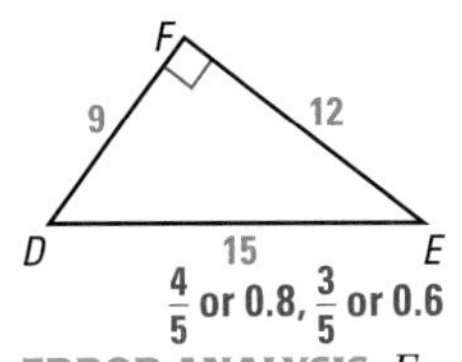

$\frac{4}{5}$ **or 0.8,** $\frac{3}{5}$ **or 0.6**

4. $\frac{35}{37}$ **or 0.9459,** $\frac{12}{37}$ **or 0.3243**

(5.)

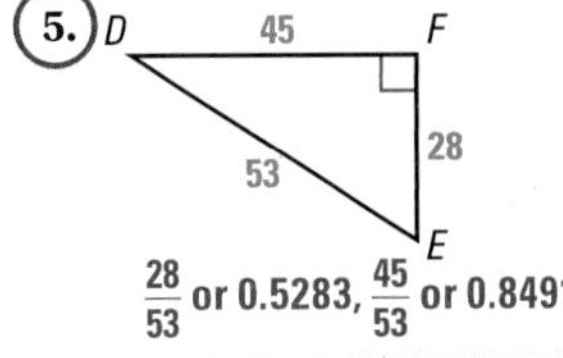

$\frac{28}{53}$ **or 0.5283,** $\frac{45}{53}$ **or 0.8491**

6. ERROR ANALYSIS *Explain* why the student's statement is incorrect. Write a correct statement for the sine of the angle. **The ratio for sine is opposite over hypotenuse, not adjacent over hypotenuse;** $\sin A = \frac{12}{13}$.

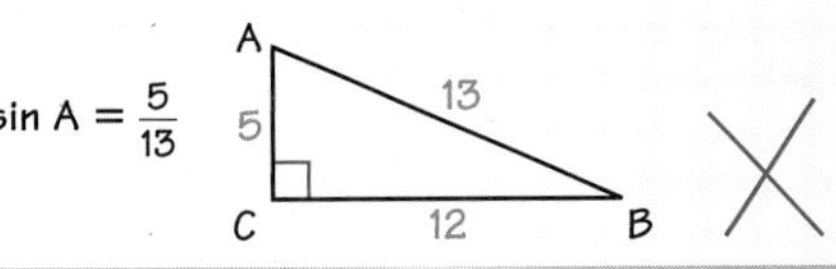

EXAMPLE 2 on p. 474 for Exs. 7–9

FINDING COSINE RATIOS **Find cos X and cos Y. Write each answer as a fraction and as a decimal. Round to four decimal places, if necessary.**

7.

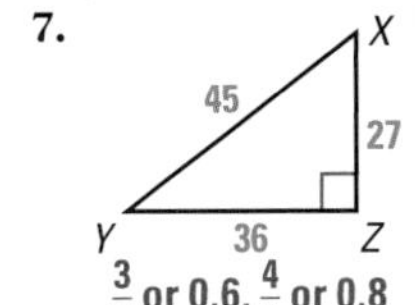

$\frac{3}{5}$ **or 0.6,** $\frac{4}{5}$ **or 0.8**

8.

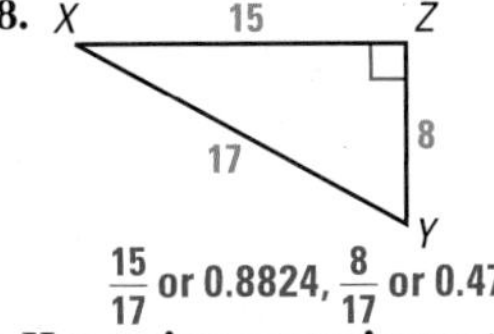

$\frac{15}{17}$ **or 0.8824,** $\frac{8}{17}$ **or 0.4706**

(9.)

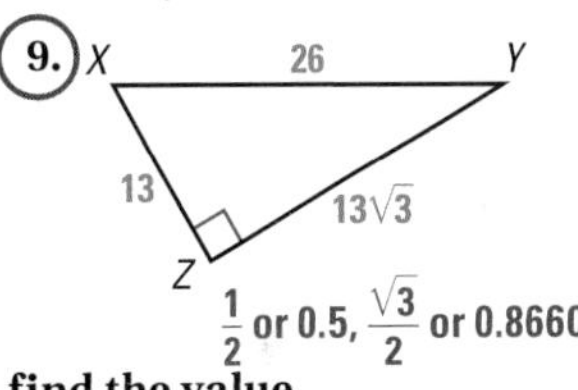

$\frac{1}{2}$ **or 0.5,** $\frac{\sqrt{3}}{2}$ **or 0.8660**

EXAMPLE 3 on p. 474 for Exs. 10–15

USING SINE AND COSINE RATIOS **Use a sine or cosine ratio to find the value of each variable. Round decimals to the nearest tenth.**

10.

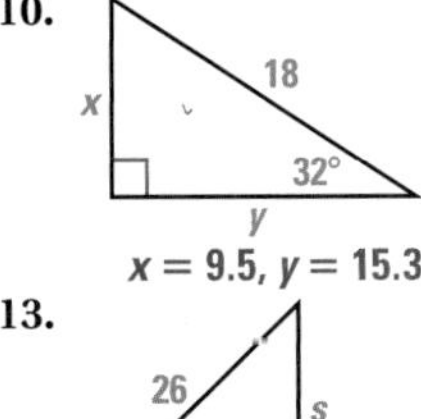

$x = 9.5$, $y = 15.3$

11. $a = 14.9$, $b = 11.1$

12. $v = 5.3$, $w = 1.7$

13. $r = 19.0$, $s = 17.7$

14.

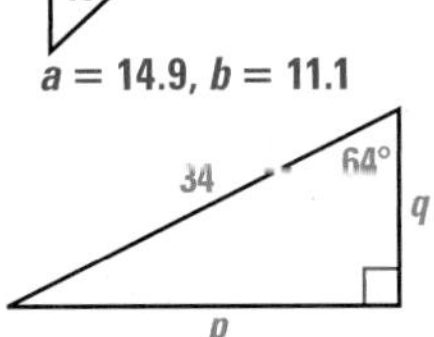

$p = 30.6$, $q = 14.9$

15.

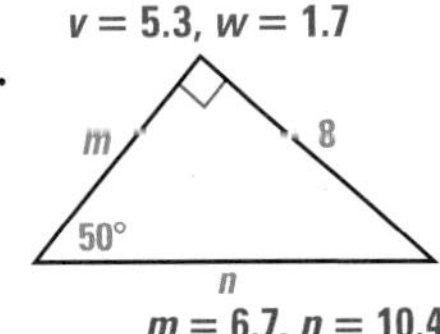

$m = 6.7$, $n = 10.4$

EXAMPLE 6 on p. 476 for Ex. 16

16. SPECIAL RIGHT TRIANGLES Use the 45°-45°-90° Triangle Theorem to find the sine and cosine of a 45° angle. $\frac{\sqrt{2}}{2}, \frac{\sqrt{2}}{2}$

4 PRACTICE AND APPLY

Assignment Guide

Answer Transparencies available for all exercises

Basic:
Day 1: pp. 477–480
Exs. 1–15, 42–44
Day 2: pp. 477–480
Exs. 16–21, 33–38, 45–48

Average:
Day 1: pp. 477–480
Exs. 1, 2, 4–6, 8, 9, 11–13, 19–27
Day 2: pp. 477–480
Exs. 16–18, 28, 29, 34–39, 42–48 even

Advanced:
Day 1: pp. 477–480
Exs. 1, 2, 4, 5, 8, 9, 13–15, 19–27, 30, 31
Day 2: pp. 477–480
Exs. 16–18, 28, 29, 32*, 35–41*, 44–48 even

Block:
pp. 477–480
Exs. 1, 2, 4–6, 8, 9, 11–13, 16–29, 34–39, 42–48 even

Differentiated Instruction

See *Geometry Best Practices Toolkit* for suggestions on addressing the needs of a diverse classroom.

Homework Check

For a quick check of student understanding of key concepts, go over the following exercises:

Basic: 3, 7, 10, 34, 35
Average: 4, 8, 12, 34, 36
Advanced: 4, 8, 14, 35, 36

Extra Practice

- Student Edition, p. 909
- Chapter 7 Resource Book: Practice levels A, B, C, pp. 78–83

Practice Worksheet

An easily-readable reduced practice page (with answers) for this lesson can be found on p. 430E.

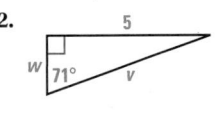

Graphing Calculator

Exercise 16 Have the students find the sine and cosine of a 30°, 45°, and 60° angle on their calculator. Have them compare these values to the ones they found using special right triangles.

Mathematical Reasoning

Exercise 29 Students should understand that the sine or cosine of an angle cannot be greater than 1 because it is the ratio of a leg length to the hypotenuse length, and the hypotenuse is the longest side in a right triangle.

32a.

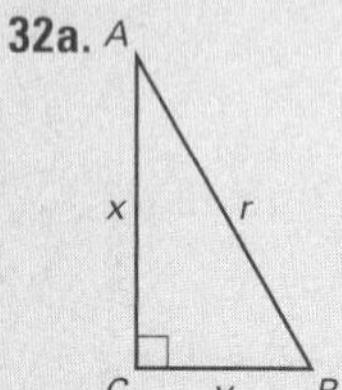

$\sin A = \frac{y}{r} \rightarrow y = r\sin A$

$\cos A = \frac{x}{r} \rightarrow x = r\cos A$

$\tan A = \frac{y}{x} = \frac{\sin A}{\cos A}$

32b.

$$x^2 + y^2 = r^2$$
$$(r\cos A)^2 + (r\sin A)^2 = r^2$$
$$r^2\cos^2 A + r^2\sin^2 A = r^2$$
$$r^2(\cos^2 A + \sin^2 A) = r^2$$
$$\cos^2 A + \sin^2 A = 1$$

B

17. ★ **WRITING** *Describe* what you must know about a triangle in order to use the sine ratio and the cosine ratio. **The triangle must be a right triangle, and you need either an acute angle measure and the length of one side or the lengths of two sides of the triangle.**

18. ★ **MULTIPLE CHOICE** In $\triangle PQR$, which expression can be used to find PQ? **C**

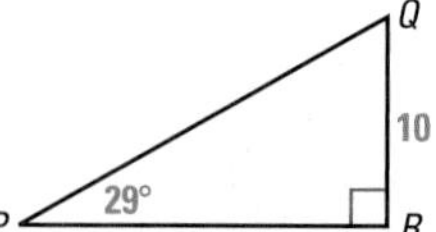

Ⓐ $10 \cdot \cos 29°$ Ⓑ $10 \cdot \sin 29°$

Ⓒ $\frac{10}{\sin 29°}$ Ⓓ $\frac{10}{\cos 29°}$

ALGEBRA **Find the value of x. Round decimals to the nearest tenth.**

19. **3.0**

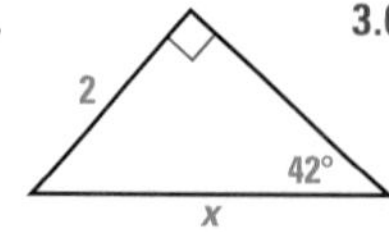

20. **13.8**

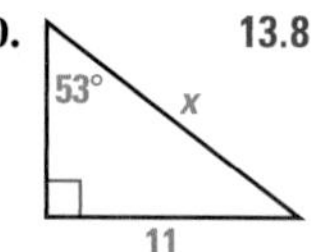

21. **20.2**

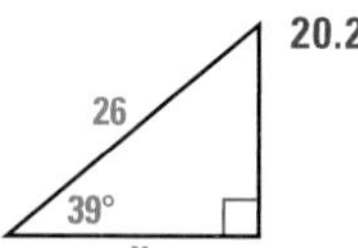

FINDING SINE AND COSINE RATIOS **Find the unknown side length. Then find $\sin X$ and $\cos X$. Write each answer as a fraction in simplest form and as a decimal. Round to four decimal places, if necessary.**

22.

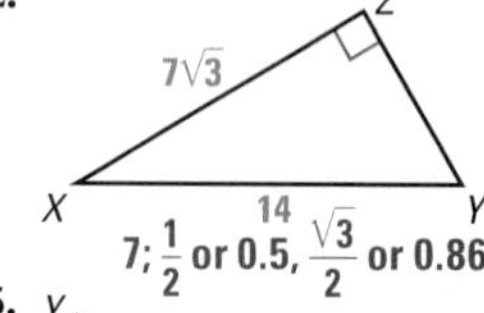

7; $\frac{1}{2}$ or 0.5, $\frac{\sqrt{3}}{2}$ or 0.8660

23.

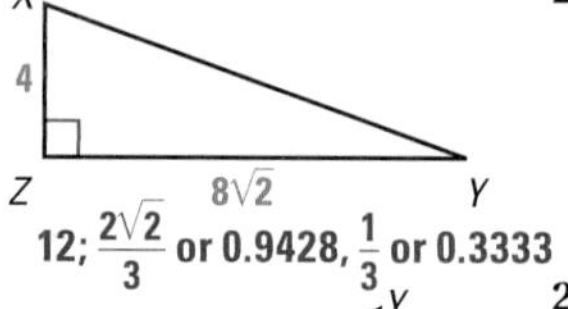

12; $\frac{2\sqrt{2}}{3}$ or 0.9428, $\frac{1}{3}$ or 0.3333

24.

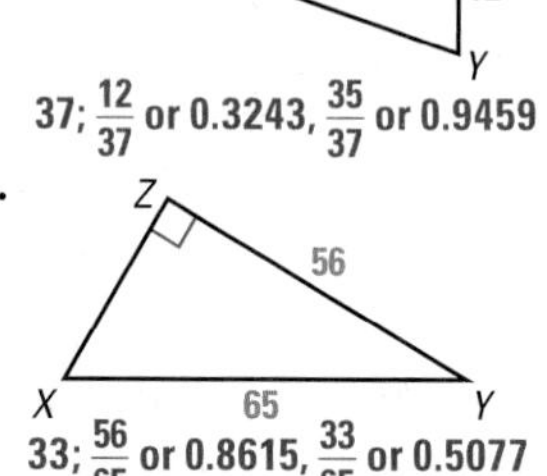

37; $\frac{12}{37}$ or 0.3243, $\frac{35}{37}$ or 0.9459

25. (Y; $3\sqrt{5}$; Z; 6; X)

3; $\frac{\sqrt{5}}{5}$ or 0.4472, $\frac{2\sqrt{5}}{5}$ or 0.8944

26. (Y; 16; X; 30; Z)

34; $\frac{8}{17}$ or 0.4706, $\frac{15}{17}$ or 0.8824

27. (Z; 56; X; 65; Y)

33; $\frac{56}{65}$ or 0.8615, $\frac{33}{65}$ or 0.5077

28. **ANGLE MEASURE** Make a prediction about how you could use trigonometric ratios to find angle measures in a triangle. ***Sample answer:*** **You can use $\sin^{-1}$, $\cos^{-1}$, or $\tan^{-1}$ to determine the angle measure when you have the appropriate ratio.**

29. ★ **MULTIPLE CHOICE** In $\triangle JKL$, $m\angle L = 90°$. Which statement about $\triangle JKL$ *cannot* be true? **D**

Ⓐ $\sin J = 0.5$ Ⓑ $\sin J = 0.1071$

Ⓒ $\sin J = 0.8660$ Ⓓ $\sin J = 1.1$

C

PERIMETER **Find the approximate perimeter of the figure.**

30.

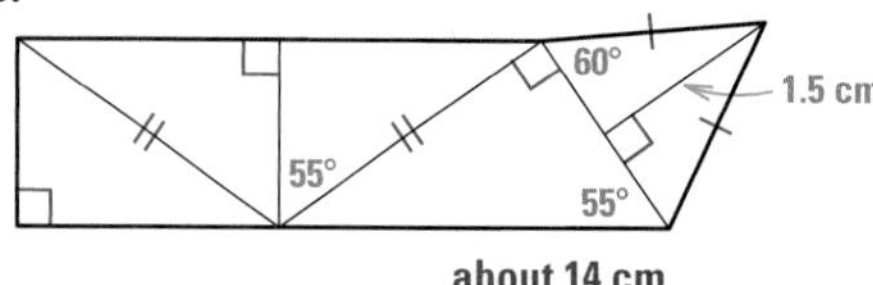

about 14 cm

31.

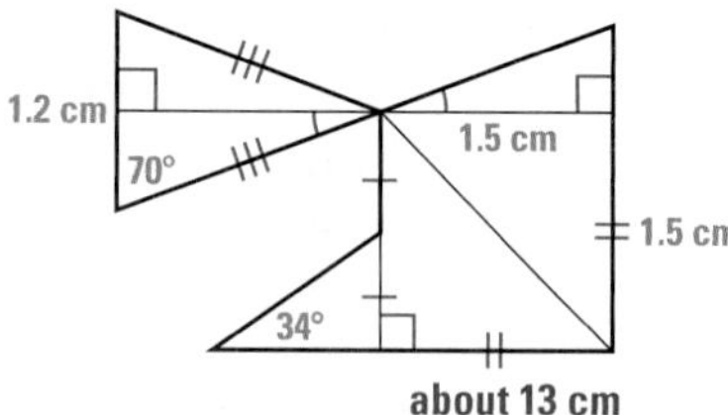

about 13 cm

32. **CHALLENGE** Let A be any acute angle of a right triangle. Show that (a) $\tan A = \frac{\sin A}{\cos A}$ and (b) $(\sin A)^2 + (\cos A)^2 = 1$. **See margin.**

PROBLEM SOLVING

EXAMPLES 4 and 5 on pp. 475–476 for Exs. 33–36

33. AIRPLANE RAMP The airplane door is 19 feet off the ground and the ramp has a 31° angle of elevation. What is the length y of the ramp? **about 36.9 ft**

@HomeTutor for problem solving help at classzone.com

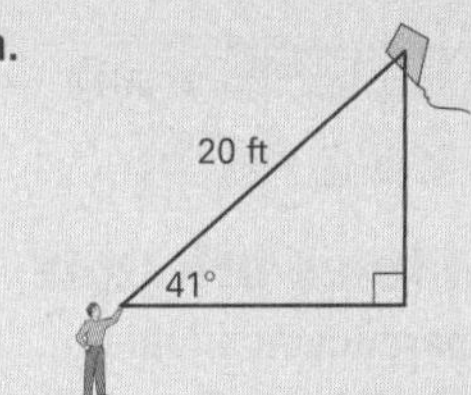

35a.

34. BLEACHERS Find the horizontal distance h the bleachers cover. Round to the nearest foot. **16 ft**

@HomeTutor for problem solving help at classzone.com

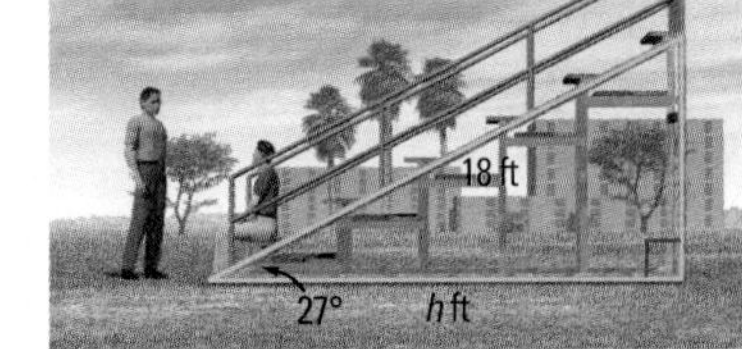

35. ★ SHORT RESPONSE You are flying a kite with 20 feet of string extended. The angle of elevation from the spool of string to the kite is 41°.

a. Draw and label a diagram to represent the situation. **See margin.**

b. How far off the ground is the kite if you hold the spool 5 feet off the ground? *Describe* how the height where you hold the spool affects the height of the kite. **About 18.1 ft; the height that the spool is off the ground has to be added.**

36. MULTI-STEP PROBLEM You want to hang a banner that is 29 feet tall from the third floor of your school. You need to know how tall the wall is, but there is a large bush in your way.

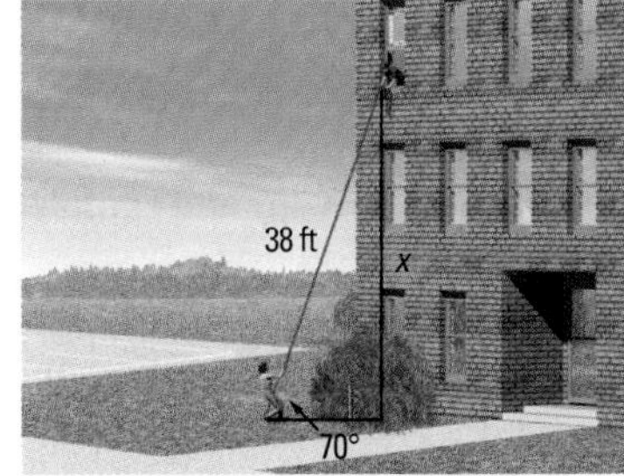

a. You throw a 38 foot rope out of the window to your friend. She extends it to the end and measures the angle of elevation to be 70°. How high is the window? **about 35.7 ft**

b. The bush is 6 feet tall. Will your banner fit above the bush? **yes**

c. **What If?** Suppose you need to find how far from the school your friend needs to stand. Which trigonometric ratio should you use? **cosine**

37. ★ SHORT RESPONSE Nick uses the equation $\sin 49° = \frac{x}{16}$ to find BC in $\triangle ABC$. Tim uses the equation $\cos 41° = \frac{x}{16}$. Which equation produces the correct answer? *Explain.* **Both; since different angles are used in each ratio, both the sine and cosine relationships can be used to correctly answer the question.**

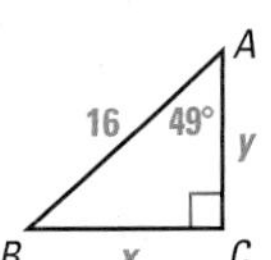

B **38. TECHNOLOGY** Use geometry drawing software to construct an angle. Mark three points on one side of the angle and construct segments perpendicular to that side at the points. Measure the legs of each triangle and calculate the sine of the angle. Is the sine the same for each triangle? **yes**

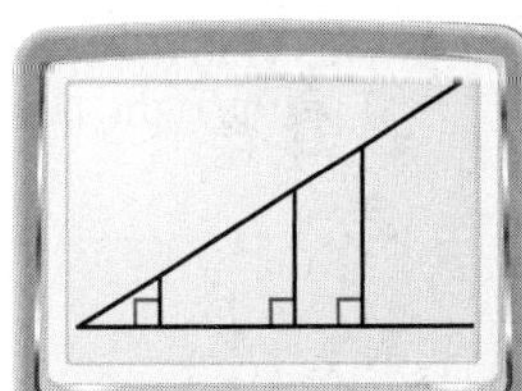

5 ASSESS AND RETEACH

Daily Homework Quiz

Transparency Available

Use this diagram for Exercises 1–3.

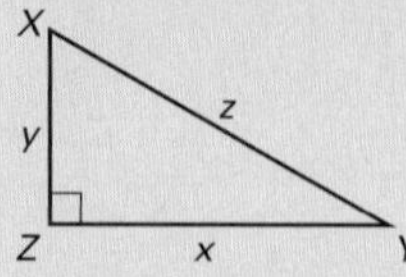

1. If $x = 4\sqrt{5}$, $y = 4$, and $z = 4\sqrt{6}$, find sin X, sin Y, cos X, and cos Y.
   $\sin X = \frac{\sqrt{30}}{6} \approx 0.9129$,
   $\sin Y = \frac{\sqrt{6}}{6} \approx 0.4082$,
   $\cos X = \frac{\sqrt{6}}{6} \approx 0.4082$,
   $\cos Y = \frac{\sqrt{30}}{6} \approx 0.9129$
2. If $y = 10$ and $m\angle Y = 15°$, find z to the nearest tenth. **38.6**
3. If $z = 12$ and $m\angle X = 84°$, find y to the nearest tenth. **1.3**
4. A lamppost is 11 feet tall. If the angle of elevation through the top of the lamppost to the sun is 49°, approximately how far is the top of the lamppost from the tip of its shadow? **14.6 ft**

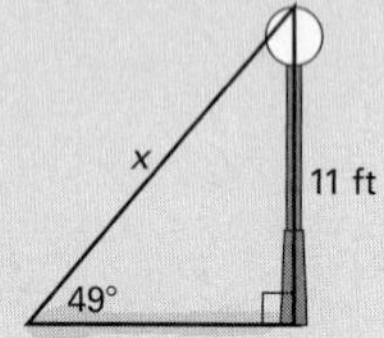

Available at **classzone.com**

Diagnosis/Remediation

- Practice A, B, C in Chapter 7 Resource Book, pp. 78–83
- Study Guide in Chapter 7 Resource Book, pp. 84–85
- Practice Workbook, pp. 139–141
- @HomeTutor

Challenge

Additional challenge is available in the Chapter 7 Resource Book, p. 88.

39a–c, 40, 41a. See Additional Answers beginning on p. AA1.

39. **MULTIPLE REPRESENTATIONS** You are standing on a cliff 30 feet above an ocean. You see a sailboat on the ocean.
    a. **Drawing a Diagram** Draw and label a diagram of the situation. **a–c. See margin.**
    b. **Making a Table** Make a table showing the angle of depression and the length of your line of sight. Use the angles 40°, 50°, 60°, 70°, and 80°.
    c. **Drawing a Graph** Graph the values you found in part (b), with the angle measures on the x-axis.
    d. **Making a Prediction** Predict the length of the line of sight when the angle of depression is 30°. ***Sample answer:* 60 ft**

C 40. **ALGEBRA** If $\triangle EQU$ is equilateral and $\triangle RGT$ is a right triangle with $RG = 2$, $RT = 1$, and $m\angle T = 90°$, show that $\sin E = \cos G$. **See margin.**

41. **CHALLENGE** Make a conjecture about the relationship between sine and cosine values.
    a. Make a table that gives the sine and cosine values for the acute angles of a 45°-45°-90° triangle, a 30°-60°-90° triangle, a 34°-56°-90° triangle, and a 17°-73°-90° triangle. **See margin.**
    b. Compare the sine and cosine values. What pattern(s) do you notice? **For complementary angles, the sine and cosine values are reversed, *i.e.* sin 30 = cos 60.**
    c. Make a conjecture about the sine and cosine values in part (b). **If *A* and *B* are complementary, then sin *A* = cos *B*.**
    d. Is the conjecture in part (c) true for right triangles that are not special right triangles? *Explain.* **Check students' work.**

MIXED REVIEW

Rewrite the equation so that x is a function of y. *(p. 877)*

42. $y = \sqrt{x}$ **$x = y^2, y > 0$**

43. $y = 3x - 10$ **$x = \frac{y + 10}{3}$**

44. $y = \frac{x}{9}$ **$x = 9y$**

PREVIEW
Prepare for Lesson 7.7 in Exs. 45–47.

Copy and complete the table. *(p. 884)*

45.

x	$\sqrt{x}$
? 0	0
? 1	1
? 2	$\sqrt{2}$
? 4	2
? 16	4

46.

x	$\frac{1}{x}$
? 1	1
? 2	$\frac{1}{2}$
? $\frac{1}{3}$	3
? $\frac{7}{2}$	$\frac{2}{7}$
? $\frac{1}{7}$	7

47.

x	$\frac{2}{7}x + 4$
? −14	0
? −7	2
? 7	6
? 14	8
? 21	10

48. Find the values of x and y in the triangle at the right. *(p. 449)* **$3\sqrt{13}, 2\sqrt{13}$**

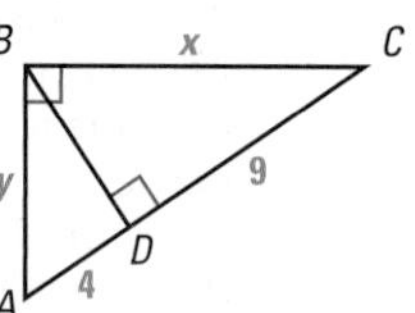

EXTRA PRACTICE for Lesson 7.6, p. 909 **ONLINE QUIZ** at classzone.com

Using ALTERNATIVE METHODS

Another Way to Solve Example 5, page 476

MULTIPLE REPRESENTATIONS You can use the Pythagorean Theorem, tangent ratio, sine ratio, or cosine ratio to find the length of an unknown side of a right triangle. The decision of which method to use depends upon what information you have. In some cases, you can use more than one method to find the unknown length.

PROBLEM

SKATEBOARD RAMP You want to build a skateboard ramp with a length of 14 feet and an angle of elevation of 26°. You need to find the height and base of the ramp.

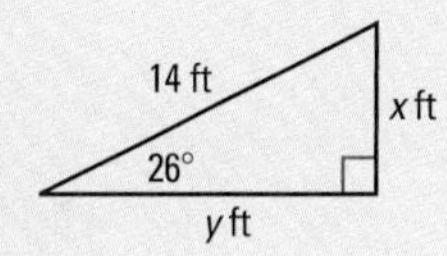

METHOD 1

Using a Cosine Ratio and the Pythagorean Theorem

Standards

19.0 Students use trigonometric functions to solve for an unknown length of a side of a right triangle, given an angle and a length of a side.

15.0 Students use the Pythagorean theorem to determine distance and find missing lengths of sides of right triangles.

STEP 1 **Find** the measure of the third angle.

$26° + 90° + m\angle 3 = 180°$	Triangle Sum Theorem
$116° + m\angle 3 = 180°$	Combine like terms.
$m\angle 3 = 64°$	Subtact 116° from each side.

STEP 2 **Use** the cosine ratio to find the height of the ramp.

$\cos 64° = \frac{\text{adj.}}{\text{hyp.}}$	Write ratio for cosine of 64°.
$\cos 64° = \frac{x}{14}$	Substitute.
$14 \cdot \cos 64° = x$	Multiply each side by 14.
$6.1 \approx x$	Use a calculator to simplify.

▸ The height is about 6.1 feet.

STEP 3 **Use** the Pythagorean Theorem to find the length of the base of the ramp.

$(\text{hypotenuse})^2 = (\text{leg})^2 + (\text{leg})^2$	Pythagorean Theorem
$14^2 = 6.1^2 + y^2$	Substitute.
$196 = 37.21 + y^2$	Multiply.
$158.79 = y^2$	Subtract 37.21 from each side.
$12.6 \approx y$	Find the positive square root.

▸ The length of the base is about 12.6 feet.

Alternative Strategy

Example 5 on page 476 can be solved by using the Pythagorean Theorem instead of a trigonometric ratio. The third angle can also be found and used for the trigonometric ratios instead of the given angle. Students may feel more comfortable using the Pythagorean Theorem than a trigonometric ratio and may be less likely to make mistakes.

Avoiding Common Errors

Method 2 Encourage students to show all the steps when they solve $\tan 26° = \frac{6.1}{y}$: $y \cdot \tan 26° = 6.1$ and $y = \frac{6.1}{\tan 26°}$. That way they are less likely to write the incorrect statement that y is $\frac{\tan 26°}{6.1}$.

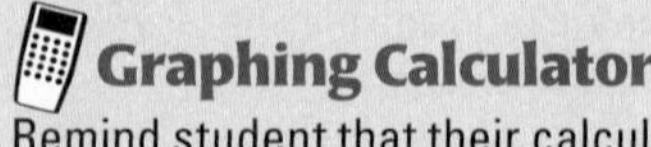

Graphing Calculator

Remind student that their calculator must be set on degrees, not radians, to get the correct values for sine, cosine, and tangent ratios.

4. If you have 2 of the 3 side lengths of a right triangle, then you would use the Pythagorean Theorem. If you have one angle and one side of the triangle, then you would use the trigonometric ratios.

5. The cosine ratio is the adjacent side over the hypotenuse, not opposite over adjacent; $\cos A = \frac{7}{25}$.

6a. About 56 ft; I drew a picture and saw that the height, angle, and distance form the tangent ratio, so I solved $\tan 75° = \frac{h}{15}$.

6b. *Sample answer:* You would need another triangle that would be similar to the given information, such as another tree that is in the same path with measurements to support the fact that the triangles are similar.

6c. You do not know the distance from the top of the tree to the end of the shadow, which forms the hypotenuse of the triangle.

482

METHOD 2 Using a Tangent Ratio

Use the tangent ratio and $h = 6.1$ feet to find the length of the base of the ramp.

$\tan 26° = \frac{\text{opp.}}{\text{adj.}}$	**Write ratio for tangent of 26°.**
$\tan 26° = \frac{6.1}{y}$	**Substitute.**
$y \cdot \tan 26° = 6.1$	**Multiply each side by y.**
$y = \frac{6.1}{\tan 26°}$	**Divide each side by tan 26°.**
$y \approx 12.5$	**Use a calculator to simplify.**

▶ The length of the base is about 12.5 feet.

Notice that when using the Pythagorean Theorem, the length of the base is 12.6 feet, but when using the tangent ratio, the length of the base is 12.5 feet. The tenth of a foot difference is due to the rounding error introduced when finding the height of the ramp and using that rounded value to calculate the length of the base.

PRACTICE

1. **WHAT IF?** Suppose the length of the skateboard ramp is 20 feet. Find the height and base of the ramp. **about 8.8 ft, about 18 ft**

2. **SWIMMER** The angle of elevation from the swimmer to the lifeguard is 35°. Find the distance x from the swimmer to the base of the lifeguard chair. Find the distance y from the swimmer to the lifeguard. **about 8.6 ft, about 10.5 ft**

3. **ALGEBRA** Use the triangle below to write three different equations you can use to find the unknown leg length. ***Sample answer:*** **$\cos 34° = \frac{x}{17}$, $\tan 34° = \frac{9.5}{x}$, $x^2 + 9.5^2 = 17^2$**

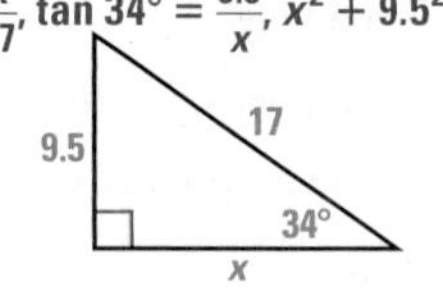

4. **SHORT RESPONSE** *Describe* how you would decide whether to use the Pythagorean Theorem or trigonometric ratios to find the lengths of unknown sides of a right triangle. **See margin.**

5. **ERROR ANALYSIS** *Explain* why the student's statement is incorrect. Write a correct statement for the cosine of the angle.

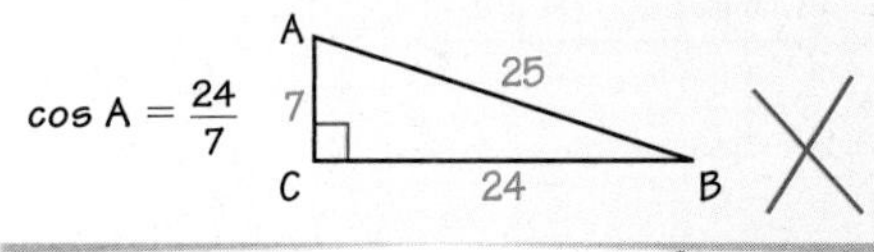

See margin.

6. **EXTENDED RESPONSE** You want to find the height of a tree in your yard. The tree's shadow is 15 feet long and you measure the angle of elevation from the end of the shadow to the top of tree to be 75°. **a–c. See margin.**
   a. Find the height of the tree. *Explain* the method you chose to solve the problem.
   b. What else would you need to know to solve this problem using similar triangles.
   c. *Explain* why you cannot use the sine ratio to find the height of the tree.

7.7 Solve Right Triangles

Before You used tangent, sine, and cosine ratios.
Now You will use inverse tangent, sine, and cosine ratios.
Why? So you can build a saddlerack, as in Ex. 39.

Key Vocabulary
- **solve a right triangle**
- **inverse tangent**
- **inverse sine**
- **inverse cosine**

To **solve a right triangle** means to find the measures of all of its sides and angles. You can solve a right triangle if you know either of the following:

- Two side lengths
- One side length and the measure of one acute angle

In Lessons 7.5 and 7.6, you learned how to use the side lengths of a right triangle to find trigonometric ratios for the acute angles of the triangle. Once you know the tangent, the sine, or the cosine of an acute angle, you can use a calculator to find the measure of the angle.

READ VOCABULARY
The expression "$\tan^{-1} x$" is read as "the inverse tangent of x."

KEY CONCEPT *For Your Notebook*

Inverse Trigonometric Ratios

Let $\angle A$ be an acute angle.

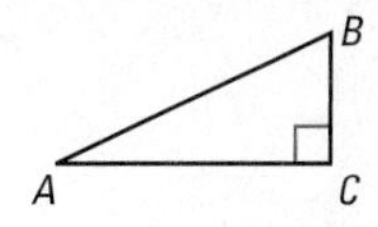

Inverse Tangent If $\tan A = x$, then $\tan^{-1} x = m\angle A$. $\tan^{-1} \frac{BC}{AC} = m\angle A$

Inverse Sine If $\sin A = y$, then $\sin^{-1} y = m\angle A$. $\sin^{-1} \frac{BC}{AB} = m\angle A$

Inverse Cosine If $\cos A = z$, then $\cos^{-1} z = m\angle A$. $\cos^{-1} \frac{AC}{AB} = m\angle A$

Standards

19.0 Students use trigonometric functions to solve for an unknown length of a side of a right triangle, given an angle and a length of a side.

12.0 Students find and use measures of sides and of interior and exterior angles of triangles and polygons to classify figures and solve problems.

EXAMPLE 1 **Use an inverse tangent to find an angle measure**

Use a calculator to approximate the measure of $\angle A$ to the nearest tenth of a degree.

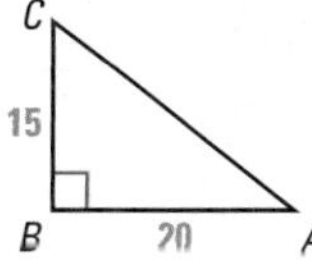

Solution

Because $\tan A = \frac{15}{20} = \frac{3}{4} = 0.75$, $\tan^{-1} 0.75 = m\angle A$. Use a calculator.

$\tan^{-1} 0.75 \approx 36.86989765 \cdots$

▶ So, the measure of $\angle A$ is approximately 36.9°.

1 PLAN AND PREPARE

Warm-Up Exercises

Transparency Available

Use this diagram for Exercises 1–4.

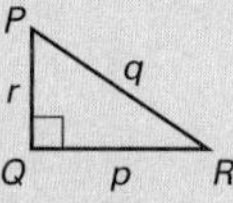

1. If $PR = 12$ and $m\angle R = 19°$, find p. **11.3**
2. If $m\angle P = 58°$ and $r = 5$, find p. **8.0**
3. If $m\angle P = 60°$, and $p = 9$, find q. **10.4**
4. If $r = 8$ and $p = 12$, find q. **14.4**

Notetaking Guide

Transparency Available

Promotes interactive learning and notetaking skills, pp. 194–196.

Pacing

Basic: 2 days
Average: 2 days
Advanced: 2 days
Block: 1 block
- See *Teaching Guide/Lesson Plan.*

2 FOCUS AND MOTIVATE

Essential Question

Big Idea 3, p. 431

In a right triangle, how can you find all the sides and angles of the triangle? **Tell students they will learn how to answer this question by "solving" the triangle.**

Resource Planning Guide

Chapter Resource Book
- Teaching Guide/Lesson Plan (pp. 89–90)
- Activity Master (p. 91)
- Practice levels A, B, C (pp. 92–97)
- Study Guide (pp. 98–99)
- Catch-up for Absent Students (p. 100)
- Problem Solving Workshop (p. 101)
- Challenge (p. 102)

Workbooks
- Notetaking Guide (pp. 194–196)
- Practice Workbook (pp. 142–144)

Teaching Options
- **Power Presentations CD-ROM** provides dynamic electronic teaching resources for the classroom.
- **Activity Generator CD-ROM** provides editable activities for all ability levels.

Interactive Technology
- Easy Planner
- Power Presentations CD-ROM
- Activity Generator CD-ROM
- Animated Geometry
- Test Generator CD-ROM
- Online Quiz
- eWorkbook
- eEdition
- @HomeTutor

Resources for English Learners
- Quick Reference for English Learners
- Spanish Study Guide
- Multi-Language Visual Glossary
- Student Resources in Spanish

See also the *Geometry Toolkit* for more strategies for meeting individual needs.

Motivating the Lesson

Suppose you are 5 feet tall and your shadow is 8 feet long. What is the angle of elevation of the sun? In this lesson students will learn how to find the measure of an acute angle of a right triangle if they know the lengths of two of the sides.

3 TEACH

Extra Example 1

Use a calculator to approximate the measure of $\angle Q$ to the nearest tenth of a degree. **56.3°**

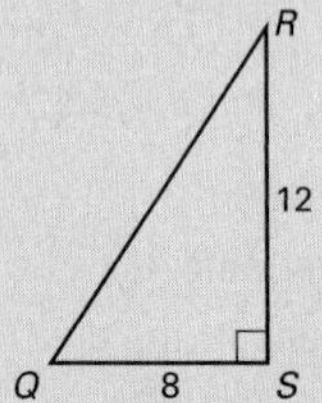

Extra Example 2

Let $\angle C$ be an acute angle in a right triangle. Use a calculator to approximate the measure of $\angle C$ to the nearest tenth of a degree.

a. $\sin C = 0.24$ **13.9°**

b. $\cos C = 0.37$ **68.3°**

Extra Example 3

Solve the right triangle formed by the water slide shown in the figure. Round decimal answers to the nearest tenth.

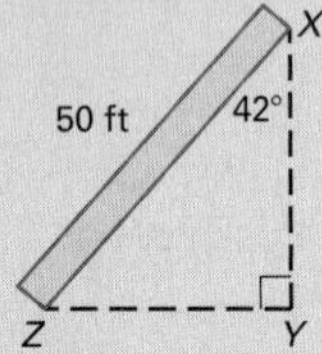

The angles are 42°, 48°, and 90°; the sides are 50 ft, about 33.5 ft, and about 37.2 ft.

EXAMPLE 2 Use an inverse sine and an inverse cosine

ANOTHER WAY
You can use the Table of Trigonometric Ratios on p. 925 to approximate $\sin^{-1} 0.87$ to the nearest degree. Find the number closest to 0.87 in the sine column and read the angle measure at the left.

Let $\angle A$ and $\angle B$ be acute angles in a right triangle. Use a calculator to approximate the measures of $\angle A$ and $\angle B$ to the nearest tenth of a degree.

a. $\sin A = 0.87$ **b.** $\cos B = 0.15$

Solution

a. $m\angle A = \sin^{-1} 0.87 \approx 60.5°$ **b.** $m\angle B = \cos^{-1} 0.15 \approx 81.4°$

✓ GUIDED PRACTICE for Examples 1 and 2

1. Look back at Example 1. Use a calculator and an inverse tangent to approximate $m\angle C$ to the nearest tenth of a degree. **53.1°**
2. Find $m\angle D$ to the nearest tenth of a degree if $\sin D = 0.54$. **32.7°**

EXAMPLE 3 Solve a right triangle

Solve the right triangle. Round decimal answers to the nearest tenth.

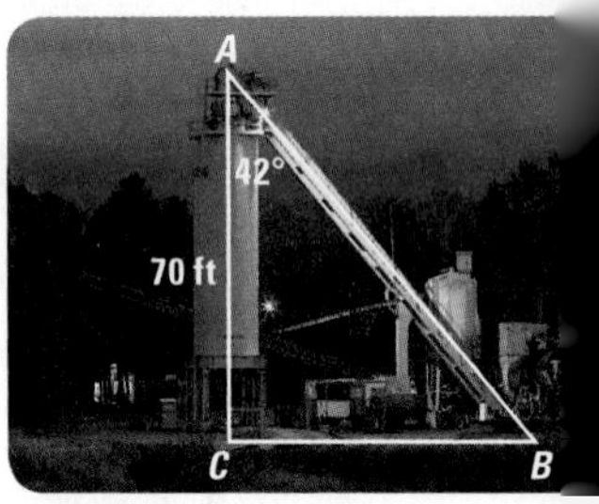

Solution

STEP 1 **Find** $m\angle B$ by using the Triangle Sum Theorem.

$180° = 90° + 42° + m\angle B$

$48° = m\angle B$

STEP 2 **Approximate** BC by using a tangent ratio.

$\tan 42° = \frac{BC}{70}$ Write ratio for tangent of 42°.

$70 \cdot \tan 42° = BC$ Multiply each side by 70.

$70 \cdot 0.9004 \approx BC$ Approximate tan 42°.

$63 \approx BC$ Simplify and round answer.

ANOTHER WAY
You could also find *AB* by using the Pythagorean Theorem, or a sine ratio.

STEP 3 **Approximate** AB using a cosine ratio.

$\cos 42° = \frac{70}{AB}$ Write ratio for cosine of 42°.

$AB \cdot \cos 42° = 70$ Multiply each side by *AB*.

$AB = \frac{70}{\cos 42°}$ Divide each side by cos 42°.

$AB \approx \frac{70}{0.7431}$ Use a calculator to find cos 42°.

$AB \approx 94.2$ Simplify.

▸ The angle measures are 42°, 48°, and 90°. The side lengths are 70 feet, about 63 feet, and about 94 feet.

EXAMPLE 4 Solve a real-world problem

READ VOCABULARY
A *raked stage* slants upward from front to back to give the audience a better view.

THEATER DESIGN Suppose your school is building a *raked stage*. The stage will be 30 feet long from front to back, with a total rise of 2 feet. A rake (angle of elevation) of 5° or less is generally preferred for the safety and comfort of the actors. Is the raked stage you are building within the range suggested?

Solution

Use the sine and inverse sine ratios to find the degree measure x of the rake.

$$\sin x° = \frac{\text{opp.}}{\text{hyp.}} = \frac{2}{30} \approx 0.0667$$

$$x \approx \sin^{-1} 0.0667 \approx 3.824$$

▶ The rake is about 3.8°, so it is within the suggested range of 5° or less.

GUIDED PRACTICE for Examples 3 and 4

3. Solve a right triangle that has a 40° angle and a 20 inch hypotenuse. **40°, 50°, and 90°, about 12.9 in., about 15.3 in. and 20 in.**
4. **WHAT IF?** In Example 4, suppose another raked stage is 20 feet long from front to back with a total rise of 2 feet. Is this raked stage safe? *Explain.* **No; the rake is 5.7° so it is slightly larger than the suggested range.**

7.7 EXERCISES

HOMEWORK KEY
○ = **WORKED-OUT SOLUTIONS** on p. WS9 for Exs. 5, 13, and 35
★ = **STANDARDIZED TEST PRACTICE** Exs. 2, 9, 29, 30, 35, 40, and 41
◆ = **MULTIPLE REPRESENTATIONS** Ex. 39

SKILL PRACTICE

A

1. **VOCABULARY** Copy and complete: To solve a right triangle means to find the measures of all of its _?_ and _?_. **angles, sides**

2. ★ **WRITING** *Explain* when to use a trigonometric ratio to find a side length of a right triangle and when to use the Pythagorean Theorem. **See margin.**

EXAMPLE 1 on p. 483 for Exs. 3–5

USING INVERSE TANGENTS Use a calculator to approximate the measure of $\angle A$ to the nearest tenth of a degree.

3. **33.7°**

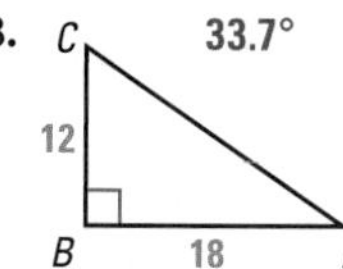

4. **24.4°**

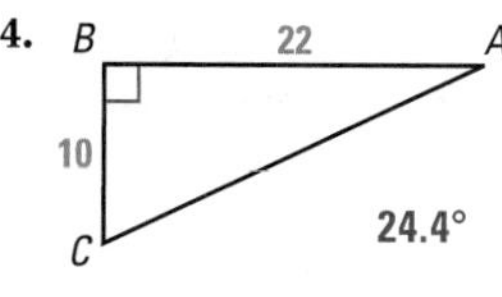

(5.) **74.1°**

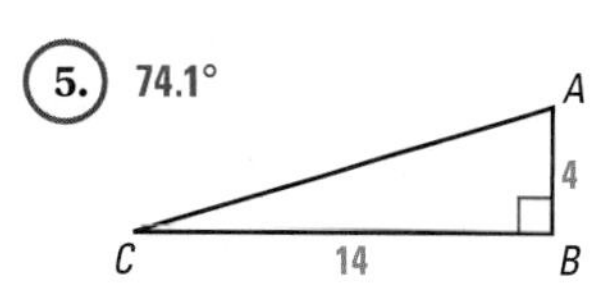

Key Question to Ask for Example 3

- In Step 3, find *AB* by the Pythagorean Theorem. Do you get the same answer? *Explain.* **Both answers round to 94.2. They differ slightly because of the rounding error in the approximation of *BC*.**

Extra Example 4

A road rises 10 feet in a horizontal distance of 200 feet. What is the angle of inclination? **2.9°**

Vocabulary

The expression $\tan^{-1} x$ is a short way to indicate "the angle whose tangent ratio is x." "Be sure students understand that the raised "−1" is *not* an exponent, and that $\tan^{-1} x$ does not mean $\frac{1}{\tan x}$. Stress that this applies to $\sin^{-1} x$ and $\cos^{-1} x$ as well.

Closing the Lesson

Have students summarize the major points of the lesson and answer the Essential Question: In a right triangle, how can you find all the sides and angles of the triangle?

- **To "solve a triangle" means to find the measures of all the angles and all the sides.**
- **If you know the measures of a side length and an acute angle, you can use trig ratios to find the lengths of the other two sides.**
- **If you know the lengths of two sides, you can use an inverse trig ratio to find the measure of an angle and you can use the Pythagorean Theorem to find the length of the third side.**

You use the sine, cosine, and tangent ratios to find the length of a side of a right triangle. You can use the inverse sine, inverse cosine, or inverse tangent ratio to find the measures of the angles.

2. Use the Pythagorean Theorem if you have two sides of the triangle. Use a trigonometric ratio if you have an angle measure and a side length.

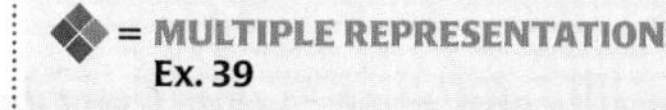

4 PRACTICE AND APPLY

Assignment Guide

Answer Transparencies available for all exercises

Basic:
Day 1: pp. 485–489
Exs. 1–9, 19–24, 37
Day 2: pp. 485–489
Exs. 10–18, 34–36, 38, 39, 43–48

Average:
Day 1: pp. 485–489
Exs. 1, 2, 4, 5, 7–9, 19–28, 37, 47, 48
Day 2: pp. 485–489
Exs. 12–16, 29–31, 34–36, 38–41, 43–46

Advanced:
Day 1: pp. 485–489
Exs. 1, 2, 4, 5, 8, 9, 19–28, 31, 32, 37, 47, 48
Day 2: pp. 485–489
Exs. 14–18, 29, 30, 33*, 35, 36, 38–42*, 43, 46

Block:
pp. 485–489
Exs. 1, 2, 4, 5, 7–9, 12–16, 19–31, 34–41, 43–48

Differentiated Instruction

See *Geometry Best Practices Toolkit* for suggestions on addressing the needs of a diverse classroom.

Homework Check

For a quick check of student understanding of key concepts, go over the following exercises:

Basic: 3, 6, 12, 34, 36
Average: 4, 7, 14, 36, 37
Advanced: 4, 8, 16, 36, 38

Extra Practice

- Student Edition, p. 909
- Chapter 7 Resource Book: Practice levels A, B, C, pp. 92–97

Practice Worksheet

An easily-readable reduced practice page (with answers) for this lesson can be found on p. 430F.

EXAMPLE 2 on p. 484 for Exs. 6–9

USING INVERSE SINES AND COSINES **Use a calculator to approximate the measure of $\angle A$ to the nearest tenth of a degree.**

6. 27.0°

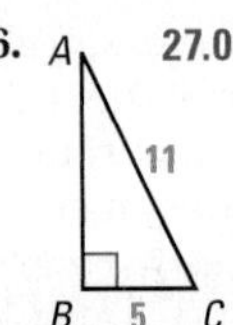

7. 53.1°

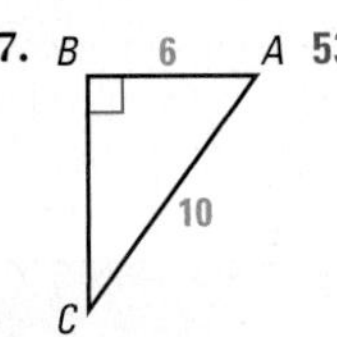

8. 54.3°

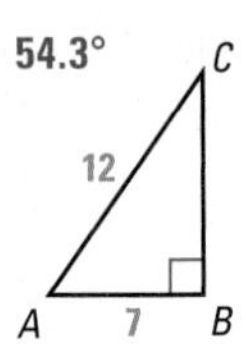

9. ★ **MULTIPLE CHOICE** Which expression is correct? **B**

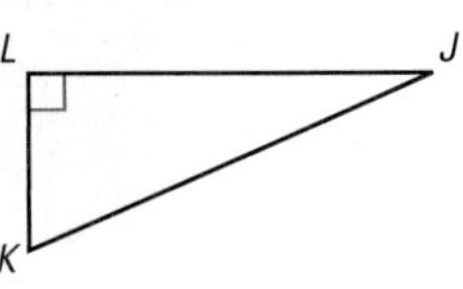

Ⓐ $\sin^{-1}\frac{JL}{JK} = m\angle J$ Ⓑ $\tan^{-1}\frac{KL}{JL} = m\angle J$

Ⓒ $\cos^{-1}\frac{JL}{JK} = m\angle K$ Ⓓ $\sin^{-1}\frac{JL}{KL} = m\angle K$

EXAMPLE 3 on p. 484 for Exs. 10–18

SOLVING RIGHT TRIANGLES **Solve the right triangle. Round decimal answers to the nearest tenth.**

10.

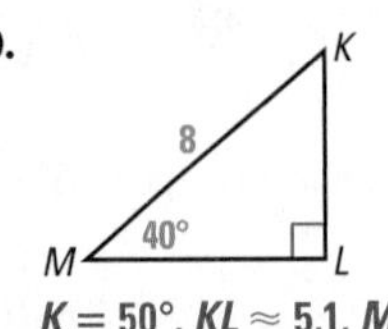

***K* = 50°, *KL* ≈ 5.1, *ML* ≈ 6.1**

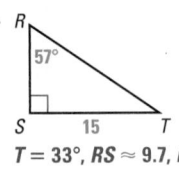

11.

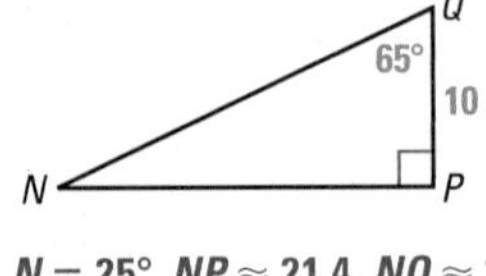

***N* = 25°, *NP* ≈ 21.4, *NQ* ≈ 23.7**

12. R, 57°, S, 15, T

***T* = 33°, *RS* ≈ 9.7, *RT* ≈ 17.9**

13.

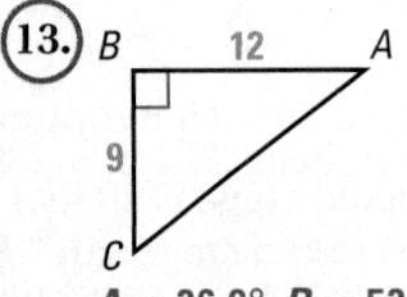

***A* ≈ 36.9°, *B* ≈ 53.1°, *AC* = 15**

14.

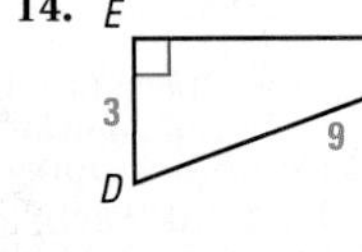

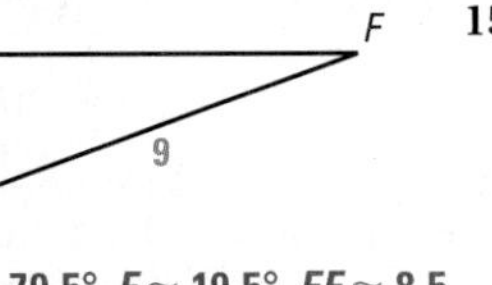

***D* ≈ 70.5°, *F* ≈ 19.5°, *EF* ≈ 8.5**

15.

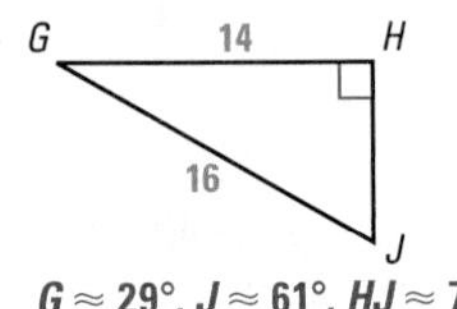

***G* ≈ 29°, *J* ≈ 61°, *HJ* ≈ 7.7**

16. C, 5.2, 43.6°, B, A

***A* = 46.4°, *AB* ≈ 7.2, *AC* ≈ 5.0**

17.

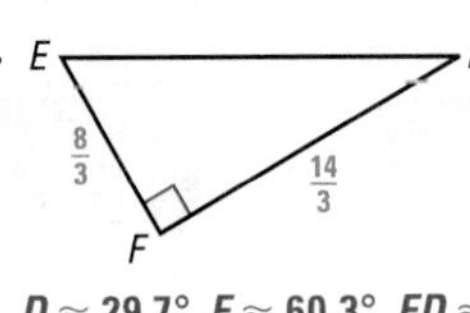

***D* ≈ 29.7°, *E* ≈ 60.3°, *ED* ≈ 5.4**

18.

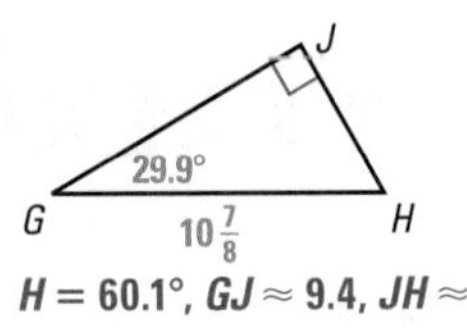

***H* = 60.1°, *GJ* ≈ 9.4, *JH* ≈ 5.4**

B **ERROR ANALYSIS** ***Describe*** **and correct the student's error in using an inverse trigonometric ratio.**

19.

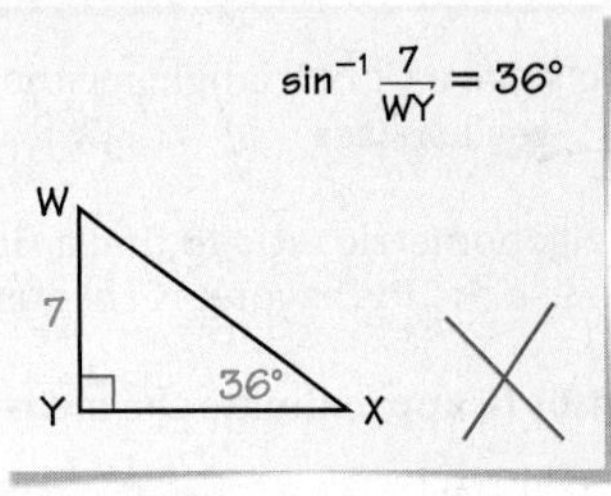

19. ***WX* should have been used instead of *WY*; $\sin^{-1}\frac{7}{WX} = 36°$.**

20. $\cos^{-1}\frac{8}{15} = m\angle T$; V, 15, 8, T, 17, U

20. To determine the measure of angle *T* using cosine, the ratio is adjacent over hypotenuse; $\cos^{-1}\frac{15}{17} = T$.

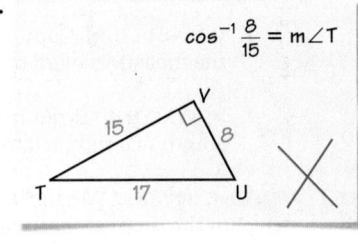

CALCULATOR **Let $\angle A$ be an acute angle in a right triangle. Approximate the measure of $\angle A$ to the nearest tenth of a degree.**

21. $\sin A = 0.5$ **30°**
22. $\sin A = 0.75$ **48.6°**
23. $\cos A = 0.33$ **70.7°**
24. $\cos A = 0.64$ **50.2°**
25. $\tan A = 1.0$ **45°**
26. $\tan A = 0.28$ **15.6°**
27. $\sin A = 0.19$ **11.0°**
28. $\cos A = 0.81$ **35.9°**

○ = **WORKED-OUT SOLUTIONS on p. WS1** ★ = **STANDARDIZED TEST PRACTICE**

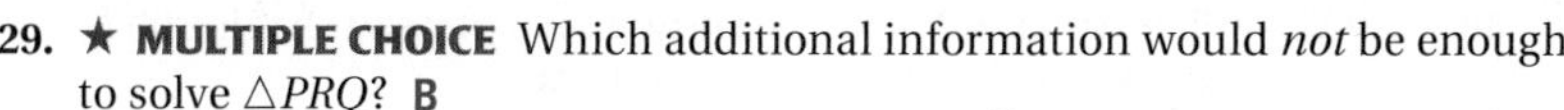

29. ★ **MULTIPLE CHOICE** Which additional information would *not* be enough to solve $\triangle PRQ$? **B**

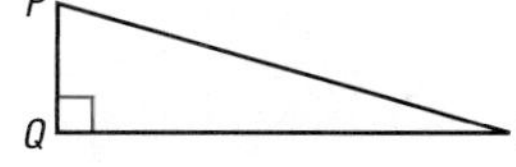

Ⓐ $m\angle P$ and PR Ⓑ $m\angle P$ and $m\angle R$

Ⓒ PQ and PR Ⓓ $m\angle P$ and PQ

30. ★ **WRITING** *Explain* why it is incorrect to say that $\tan^{-1} x = \frac{1}{\tan x}$. **$\tan^{-1}$ is the function which is used to determine the measure of an angle given the proper ratio of sides.**

C 31. **SPECIAL RIGHT TRIANGLES** If $\sin A = \frac{1}{2}\sqrt{2}$, what is $m\angle A$? If $\sin B = \frac{1}{2}\sqrt{3}$, what is $m\angle B$? **45°; 60°**

32. **TRIGONOMETRIC VALUES** Use the *Table of Trigonometric Ratios* on page 925 to answer the questions.

   a. What angles have nearly the same sine and tangent values? **0 to 10°**

   b. What angle has the greatest difference in its sine and tangent value? **89°**

   c. What angle has a tangent value that is double its sine value? **60°**

   d. Is $\sin 2x$ equal to $2 \cdot \sin x$? **no**

33. **CHALLENGE** The perimeter of rectangle *ABCD* is 16 centimeters, and the ratio of its width to its length is 1 : 3. Segment *BD* divides the rectangle into two congruent triangles. Find the side lengths and angle measures of one of these triangles. **6 cm, 2cm, $2\sqrt{10}$ cm, 90°, about 18.4°, about 71.6°**

PROBLEM SOLVING

EXAMPLE 4 on p. 485 for Exs. 34–36

A 34. **SOCCER** A soccer ball is placed 10 feet away from the goal, which is 8 feet high. You kick the ball and it hits the crossbar along the top of the goal. What is the angle of elevation of your kick? **about 38.7°**

@HomeTutor for problem solving help at classzone.com

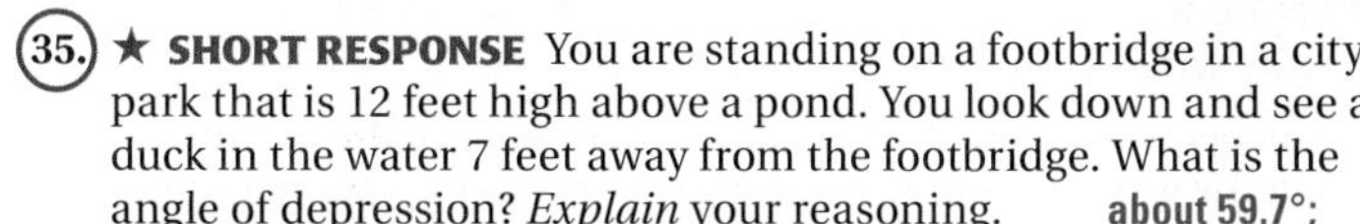

35. ★ **SHORT RESPONSE** You are standing on a footbridge in a city park that is 12 feet high above a pond. You look down and see a duck in the water 7 feet away from the footbridge. What is the angle of depression? *Explain* your reasoning. **about 59.7°; $90 - \tan^{-1}\frac{7}{12} \approx 59.7°$**

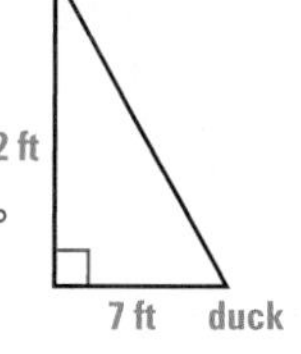

@HomeTutor for problem solving help at classzone.com

37. $\tan^{-1}\frac{BC}{AC}$; the information needed to determine the measure of *A* is given. If you used the tangent ratio, this will make the answer more accurate since no rounding has occurred.

36. **CLAY** In order to unload clay easily, the body of a dump truck must be elevated to at least 55°. If the body of the dump truck is 14 feet long and has been raised 10 feet, will the clay pour out easily? **no**

37. **REASONING** For $\triangle ABC$ shown, each of the expressions $\sin^{-1}\frac{BC}{AB}$, $\cos^{-1}\frac{AC}{AB}$, and $\tan^{-1}\frac{BC}{AC}$ can be used to approximate the measure of $\angle A$. Which expression would you choose? *Explain* your choice.

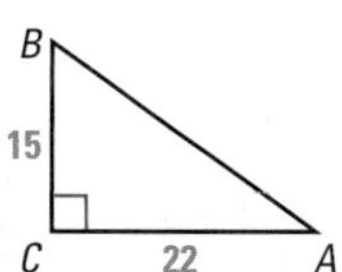

Avoiding Common Errors

Exercise 41 Students may assume that for part (c) the wire will be half as long as the wire for part (b) since it only reaches halfway up the tower. Make sure they calculate both lengths. Review that the triangles are not similar so the ratio of their hypotenuses is not 1 : 2.

39a. See below.

39b.

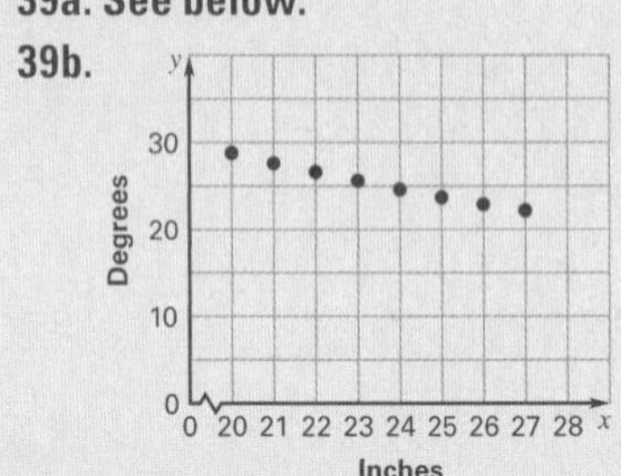

42. Statements (Reasons)

1. $\triangle ABC$ with altitude $\overline{CD}$ (Given)
2. $\sin A = \frac{CD}{b}$ and $\sin B = \frac{CD}{a}$ (Definition of sine)
3. $CD = b \sin A$ and $CD = a \sin B$ (Multiplication Property of Equality)
4. $b \sin A = a \sin B$ (Substitution Property of Equality)
5. $\frac{\sin A}{a} = \frac{\sin B}{b}$ (Division Property of Equality)

B **38. MULTI-STEP PROBLEM** You are standing on a plateau that is 800 feet above a basin where you can see two hikers.

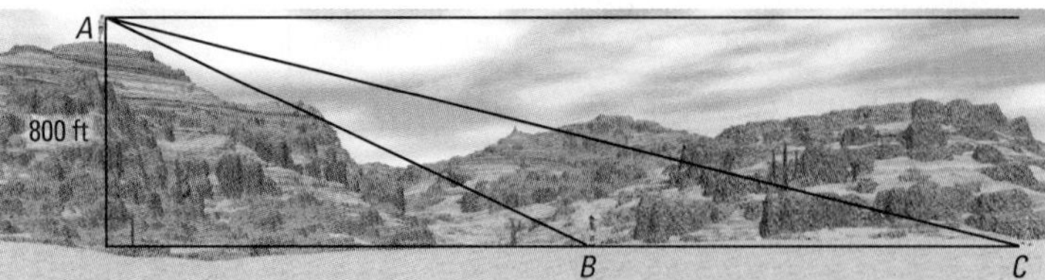

a. If the angle of depression from your line of sight to the hiker at B is 25°, how far is the hiker from the base of the plateau? **about 1716 ft**

b. If the angle of depression from your line of sight to the hiker at C is 15°, how far is the hiker from the base of the plateau? **about 2986 ft**

c. How far apart are the two hikers? *Explain.* **About 1270 ft; subtract the two distances to find out how far the two hikers are from each other.**

39. MULTIPLE REPRESENTATIONS A local ranch offers trail rides to the public. It has a variety of different sized saddles to meet the needs of horse and rider. You are going to build saddle racks that are 11 inches high. To save wood, you decide to make each rack fit each saddle.

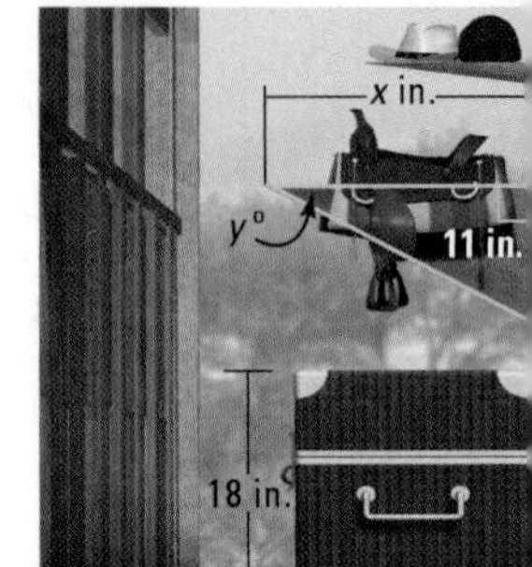

a. **Making a Table** The lengths of the saddles range from 20 inches to 27 inches. Make a table showing the saddle rack length x and the measure of the adjacent angle $y°$.

b. **Drawing a Graph** Use your table to draw a scatterplot. **a, b. See margin.**

c. **Making a Conjecture** Make a conjecture about the relationship between the length of the rack and the angle needed. ***Sample answer:*** **The longer the rack, the closer to 20° the angle gets.**

40. *Sample answer:* **You want to know how tall your town's water tower is. You are standing 40 feet away from the base of the tower and the angle of elevation is 60°. How tall is the water tower?**

40. ★ OPEN-ENDED MATH *Describe* a real-world problem you could solve using a trigonometric ratio.

41. ★ EXTENDED RESPONSE Your town is building a wind generator to create electricity for your school. The builder wants your geometry class to make sure that the guy wires are placed so that the tower is secure. By safety guidelines, the distance along the ground from the tower to the guy wire's connection with the ground should be between 50% to 75% of the height of the guy wire's connection with the tower.

a. The tower is 64 feet tall. The builders plan to have the distance along the ground from the tower to the guy wire's connection with the ground be 60% of the height of the tower. How far apart are the tower and the ground connection of the wire? **38.4 ft**

b. How long will a guy wire need to be that is attached 60 feet above the ground? **about 71.2 ft**

c. How long will a guy wire need to be that is attached 30 feet above the ground? **about 48.7 ft**

d. Find the angle of elevation of each wire. Are the right triangles formed by the ground, tower, and wires *congruent*, *similar*, or *neither*? *Explain.*

e. *Explain* which trigonometric ratios you used to solve the problem. **I used tangent because the height and the distance along the ground form a tangent relationship for the angle of elevation.**

41d. **about 57.4°, about 38.0°; neither; the sides are not the same, so the triangles are not congruent, and the angles are not the same, so the triangles are not similar.**

 = WORKED-OUT SOLUTIONS on p. WS1 ★ = STANDARDIZED TEST PRACTICE ◆ = MULTIPLE REPRESENTATIONS

39a.

x (inches)	20	21	22	23	24	25	26	27
y (degrees)	28.8	27.6	26.6	25.6	24.6	23.7	22.9	22.2

C **42. CHALLENGE** Use the diagram of $\triangle ABC$.

GIVEN ▶ $\triangle ABC$ with altitude $\overline{CD}$.

PROVE ▶ $\frac{\sin A}{a} = \frac{\sin B}{b}$ **See margin.**

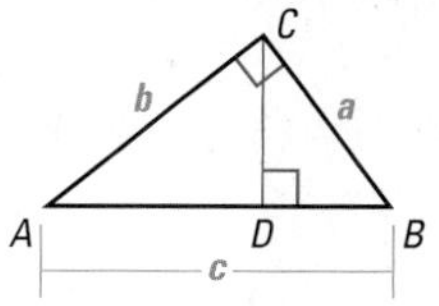

MIXED REVIEW

PREVIEW
Prepare for Lesson 8.1 in Ex. 43.

43. Copy and complete the table. *(p. 42)* **See margin.**

Number of sides	Type of polygon
5	?
12	?
?	Octagon
?	Triangle
7	?

Number of sides	Type of polygon
?	*n*-gon
?	Quadrilateral
10	?
9	?
?	Hexagon

A point on an image and the transformation are given. Find the corresponding point on the original figure. *(p. 272)*

44. Point on image: (5, 1); translation: $(x, y) \to (x + 3, y - 2)$ **(2, 3)**

45. Point on image: (4, −6); reflection: $(x, y) \to (x, -y)$ **(4, 6)**

46. Point on image: (−2, 3); translation: $(x, y) \to (x - 5, y + 7)$ **(3, −4)**

Draw a dilation of the polygon with the given vertices using the given scale factor *k*. *(p. 409)* **47–48. See margin.**

47. $A(2, 2), B(-1, -3), C(5, -3); k = 2$

48. $A(-4, -2), B(-2, 4), C(3, 6), D(6, 3); k = \frac{1}{2}$

QUIZ *for Lessons 7.5–7.7*

Find the value of *x* to the nearest tenth.

1. *(p. 466)* **8.4**

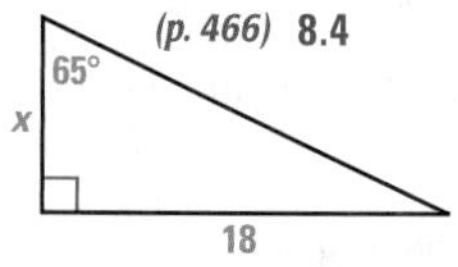

2. *(p. 473)* **6.5**

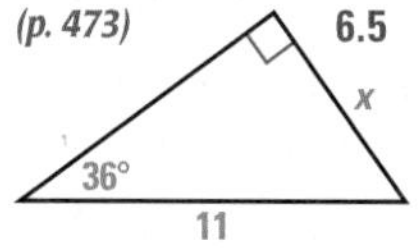

3. *(p. 473)* **25.7**

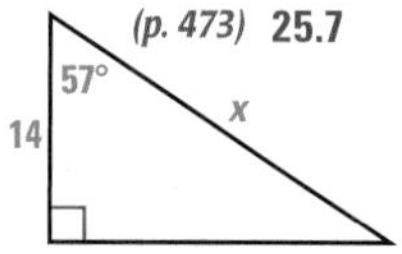

Solve the right triangle. Round decimal answers to the nearest tenth. *(p. 483)*

4.

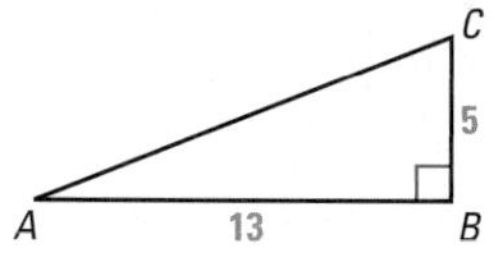

$A \approx 21.0°, C \approx 69.0°, AC \approx 13.9$

5.

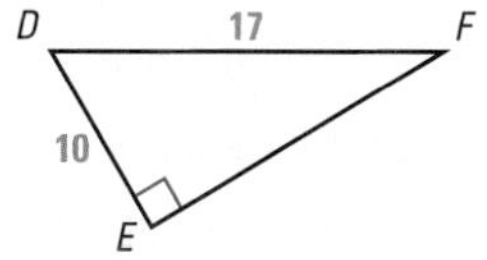

$D \approx 54°, F \approx 36°, EF \approx 13.7$

6.

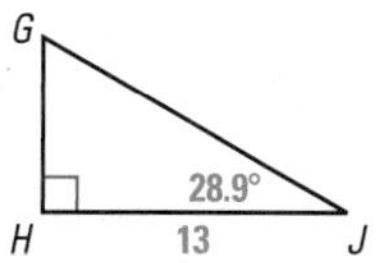

$G = 61.1°, GH \approx 7.2, JG \approx 14.8$

5 ASSESS AND RETEACH

Daily Homework Quiz

Transparency Available

Use this diagram for Exercises 1–3.

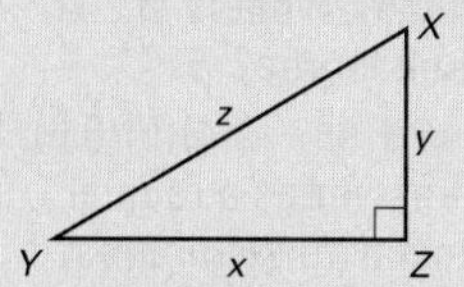

1. If $x = 9$ and $z = 11$, find $m\angle X$ to the nearest tenth of a degree. **54.9°**

2. If $y = 5$ and $z = 12$, find $m\angle X$ to the nearest tenth of a degree. **65.4°**

3. If $m\angle Y = 17.4°$ and $z = 12$, solve $\triangle XYZ$. **The angles are 17.4°, 72.6°, and 90°; the sides are 12, about 3.6, and about 11.5.**

Online Quiz

Available at **classzone.com**

Diagnosis/Remediation

- Practice A, B, C in Chapter 7 Resource Book, pp. 92–97
- Study Guide in Chapter 7 Resource Book, pp. 98–99
- Practice Workbook, pp. 142–144
- @HomeTutor

Challenge

Additional challenge is available in the Chapter 7 Resource Book, p. 102.

Quiz

An easily-readable reduced copy of the quiz (with answers) on Lessons 7.5–7.7 from the Assessment Book can be found on p. 430G.

43. See Additional Answers beginning on p. AA1.

47.

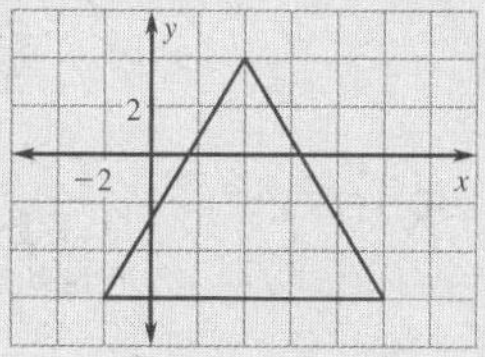

48.

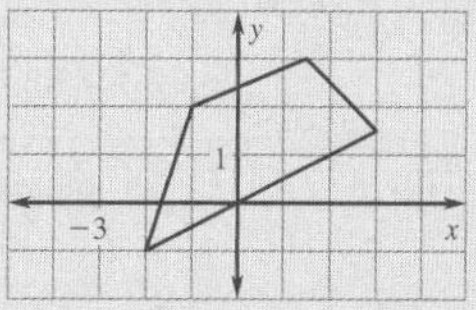

1 PLAN AND PREPARE

Warm-Up Exercises

1. Solve $\frac{x}{5} = \frac{6}{3}$. **10**
2. If $\sin A = 0.8357$, what is $m\angle A$ to the nearest degree? **57°**
3. Solve $x^2 = 4^2 + 5^2 - 2(4)(5)(0.6)$. Write your answer as a radical and as a decimal to the nearest hundredth. **$\pm\sqrt{17} \approx \pm 4.12$**

2 FOCUS AND MOTIVATE

Essential Question

Big Idea 3, p. 431

How do you find sides and angles in acute and obtuse triangles? **Tell students they will learn how to answer this question by using two properties called the Law of Sines and the Law of Cosines.**

3 TEACH

Extra Example 1

Use the information in the diagram to find how much closer, to the nearest hundredth mile, Jimmy lives to school than Adolph does. **1.79 mi**

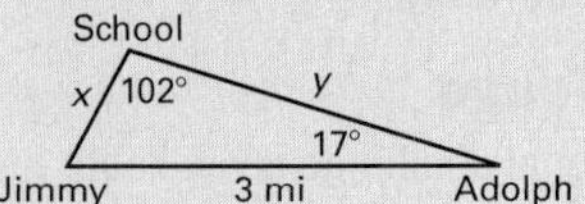

Extension: Law of Sines and Law of Cosines

Use after Lesson 7.7

Standards

19.0 Students use trigonometric functions to solve for an unknown length of a side of a right triangle, given an angle and a length of a side.

12.0 Students find and use measures of sides and of interior and exterior **angles of triangles** and polygons **to** classify figures and **solve problems.**

GOAL Use trigonometry with acute and obtuse triangles.

The trigonometric ratios you have seen so far in this chapter can be used to find angle and side measures in right triangles. You can use the Law of Sines to find angle and side measures in *any* triangle.

KEY CONCEPT *For Your Notebook*

Law of Sines

If $\triangle ABC$ has sides of length a, b, and c as shown, then $\frac{\sin A}{a} = \frac{\sin B}{b} = \frac{\sin C}{c}$.

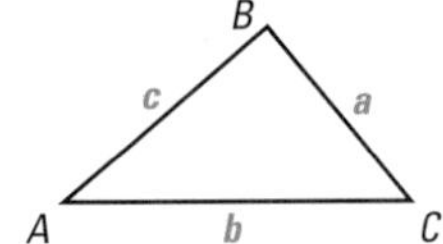

EXAMPLE 1 Find a distance using Law of Sines

DISTANCE Use the information in the diagram to determine how much closer you live to the music store than your friend does.

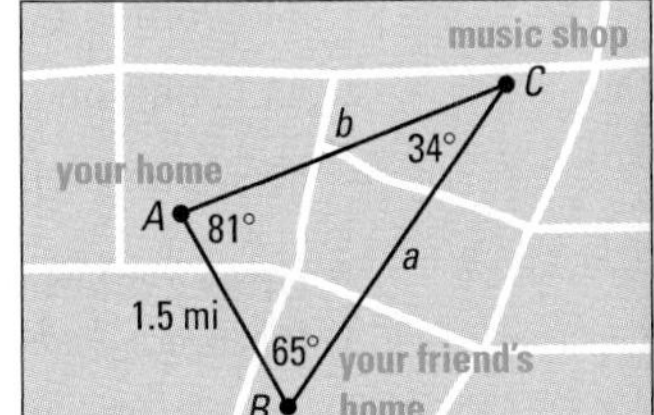

Solution

STEP 1 **Use** the Law of Sines to find the distance a from your friend's home to the music store.

$\frac{\sin A}{a} = \frac{\sin C}{c}$ **Write Law of Sines.**

$\frac{\sin 81°}{a} = \frac{\sin 34°}{1.5}$ **Substitute.**

$a \approx 2.6$ **Solve for *a*.**

STEP 2 **Use** the Law of Sines to find the distance b from your home to the music store.

$\frac{\sin B}{b} = \frac{\sin C}{c}$ **Write Law of Sines.**

$\frac{\sin 65°}{b} = \frac{\sin 34°}{1.5}$ **Substitute.**

$b \approx 2.4$ **Solve for *b*.**

STEP 3 **Subtract** the distances.

$a - b \approx 2.6 - 2.4 = 0.2$

▶ You live about 0.2 miles closer to the music store.

LAW OF COSINES You can also use the Law of Cosines to solve any triangle.

KEY CONCEPT *For Your Notebook*

Law of Cosines

If $\triangle ABC$ has sides of length a, b, and c, then:

$a^2 = b^2 + c^2 - 2bc \cos A$

$b^2 = a^2 + c^2 - 2ac \cos B$

$c^2 = a^2 + b^2 - 2ab \cos C$

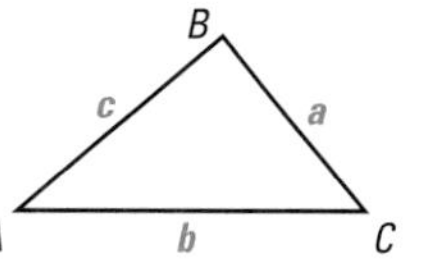

EXAMPLE 2 Find an angle measure using Law of Cosines

In $\triangle ABC$ at the right, $a = 11$ cm, $b = 17$ cm, and $c = 19$ cm. Find $m\angle C$.

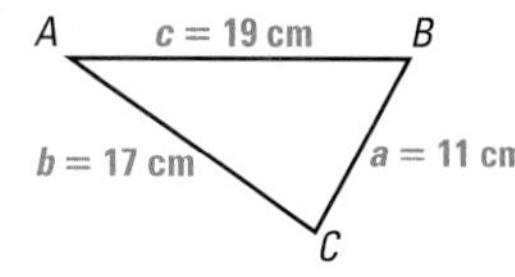

Solution

$c^2 = a^2 + b^2 - 2ab \cos C$ — **Write Law of Cosines.**

$19^2 = 11^2 + 17^2 - 2(11)(17) \cos C$ — **Substitute.**

$0.1310 = \cos C$ — **Solve for cos C.**

$m\angle C \approx 82°$ — **Find $\cos^{-1}$ (0.1310).**

PRACTICE

EXAMPLE 1 for Exs. 1–3

LAW OF SINES **Use the Law of Sines to solve the triangle. Round decimal answers to the nearest tenth.**

1. 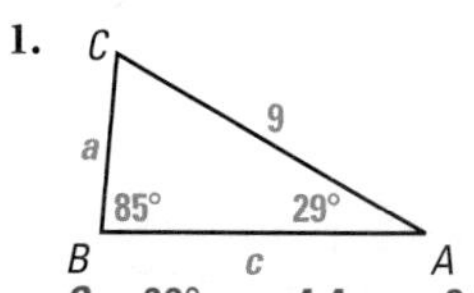

$C = 66°$, $a \approx 4.4$, $c \approx 8.3$

2. 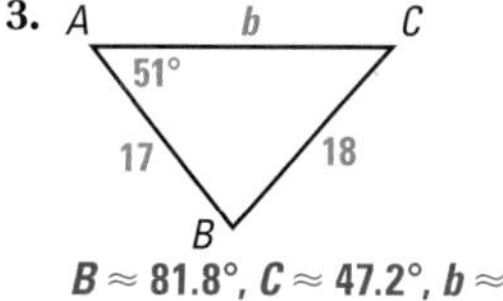

$A = 29°$, $b \approx 19.4$, $c \approx 20.4$

3. A b C, 51°, 17, 18, B
$B \approx 81.8°$, $C \approx 47.2°$, $b \approx 22.9$

EXAMPLE 2 for Exs. 4–7

LAW OF COSINES **Use the Law of Cosines to solve the triangle. Round decimal answers to the nearest tenth.**

4. 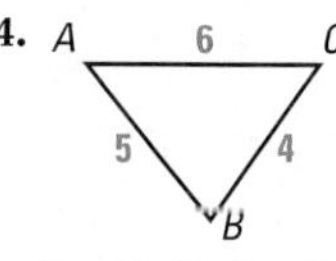

$B \approx 82.8°$, $C \approx 55.8°$, $A \approx 41.4°$

5. 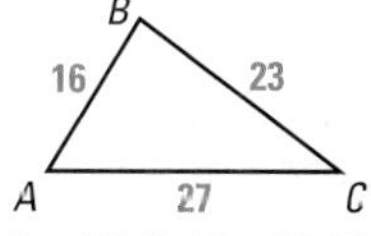

$A \approx 58.1°$, $B \approx 85.6°$, $C \approx 36.2$

6. 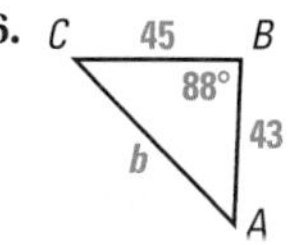

$A \approx 47.4°$, $C \approx 44.7°$, $b \approx 61.1$

7. **DISTANCE** Use the diagram at the right. Find the straight distance between the zoo and movie theater. **about 10 blocks**

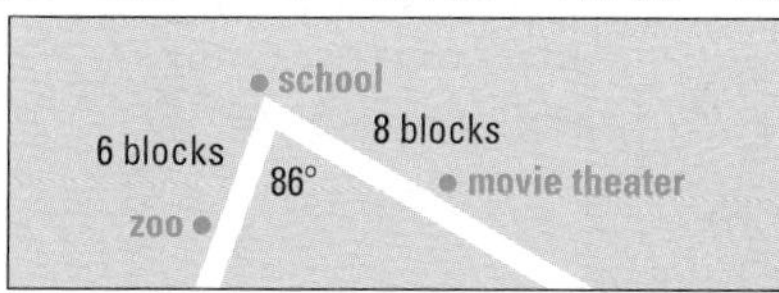

Study Strategy

The Law of Sines can be used to to find missing parts of a triangle when the given information can be represented as ASA, AAS, or SSA (there may be more than 1 solution for an SSA situation). The Law of Cosines can be used when you are given SAS or SSS.

Extra Example 2

In $\triangle DEF$, $d = 9$ in., $e = 12$ in., and $m\angle F = 46°$. Find f to the nearest hundredth. **8.66 in.**

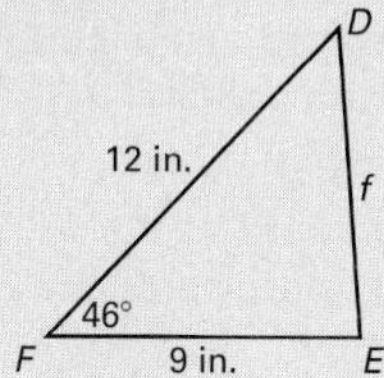

Avoiding Common Errors

Example 2 When students see the equation $19^2 = 11^2 + 17^2 - 2(11)(17) \cos C$, some may subtract $2(11)(17)$ from $11^2 + 17^2$. Show them a simpler statement having the same structure, such as $a = b + c - dx$, and ask them what operations they would perform to solve for x.

Closing the Lesson

Have students summarize the major points of the lesson and answer the Essential Question: How do you find sides or angles in acute and obtuse triangles?

- **The Law of Sines is the property that $\frac{\sin A}{a} = \frac{\sin B}{b} = \frac{\sin C}{c}$.**
- **The Law of Cosines is the property that $a^2 = b^2 + c^2 - 2bc \cos A$.**

Use the Law of Sines or the Law of Cosines.

4 PRACTICE AND APPLY

Teaching Strategy

Exercise 5 When solving a triangle given three sides and no angles, students should start by using the Law of Cosines to find the largest angle, in case it is obtuse. Then they can use the Law of Sines to find another angle.

2a. friend 10 m you
85°
rock

5a. $9\sqrt{3}$. *Sample answer:* I used the Pythagorean Theorem with $\triangle AEC$. Since $\triangle ACD$ is isosceles, and $\overline{AD}$ is bisected by $\overline{EC}$, $\overline{EC}$ is the altitude and is therefore perpendicular to the base.

5b. About 10.9°. *Sample answer:* I found the measure of $\angle ACE$ using the sine ratio, then I found the measure of $\angle ACB$ because it is supplementary to $\angle ACE$. The Law of Cosines allowed me to find AB and then I used the Law of Sines to find the measure of $\angle ABC$.

5c. *Sample answer:* Part (a): Since the hypotenuse is 18 and the given leg is half of that, the triangle must be a 30°-60°-90° triangle and therefore, the other leg must be $9\sqrt{3}$; part (b): EB must equal $3x$ and since $x = 9\sqrt{3}$, $EB = 27\sqrt{3}$. Now you can use the inverse tangent function to determine the measure of $\angle ABC$.

MIXED REVIEW of Problem Solving

Lessons 7.5–7.7

1. **MULTI-STEP PROBLEM** A *reach stacker* is a vehicle used to lift objects and move them between ships and land.

   a. The vehicle's arm is 10.9 meters long. The maximum measure of $\angle A$ is 60°. What is the greatest height h the arm can reach if the vehicle is 3.6 meters tall? **about 13.0 m**

   b. The vehicle's arm can extend to be 16.4 meters long. What is the greatest height its extended arm can reach? **about 17.8 m**

   c. What is the difference between the two heights the arm can reach above the ground? **about 4.8 m**

2. **EXTENDED RESPONSE** You and a friend are standing the same distance from the edge of a canyon. Your friend looks directly across the canyon at a rock. You stand 10 meters from your friend and estimate the angle between your friend and the rock to be 85°.

   a. Sketch the situation. **See margin.**

   b. *Explain* how to find the distance across the canyon. **Use the tangent ratio.**

   c. Suppose the actual angle measure is 87°. How far off is your estimate of the distance? **about 76.5 m**

3. **SHORT RESPONSE** The international rules of basketball state the rim of the net should be 3.05 meters above the ground. If your line of sight to the rim is 34° and you are 1.7 meters tall, what is the distance from you to the rim? *Explain* your reasoning.
   about 2.4 m; $\sin 34° = \frac{1.35}{x}$

4. **GRIDDED ANSWER** The specifications for a *yield ahead* pavement marking are shown. Find the height h in feet of this isosceles triangle to the nearest tenth. **18.9**

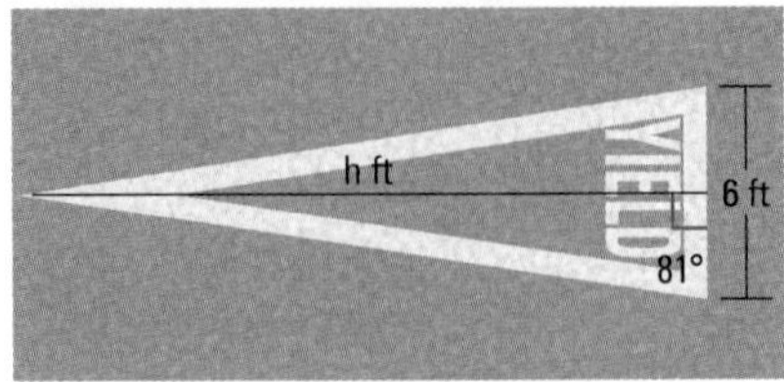

5. **EXTENDED RESPONSE** Use the diagram to answer the questions. **a–c. See margin.**

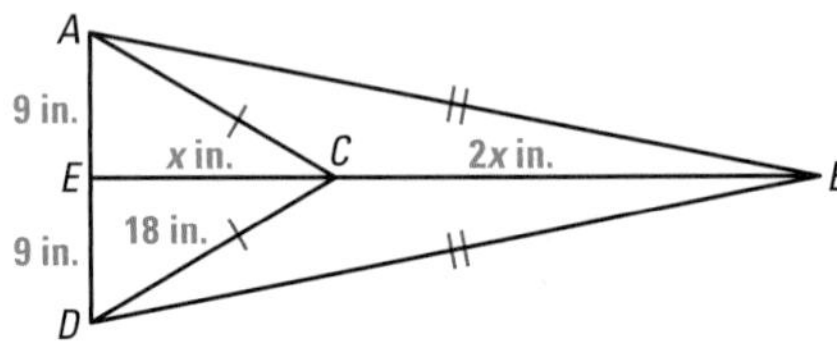

   a. Solve for x. *Explain* the method you chose.

   b. Find $m\angle ABC$. *Explain* the method you chose.

   c. *Explain* a different method for finding each of your answers in parts (a) and (b).

6. **SHORT RESPONSE** The triangle on the staircase below has a 52° angle and the distance along the stairs is 14 feet. What is the height h of the staircase? What is the length b of the base of the staircase?

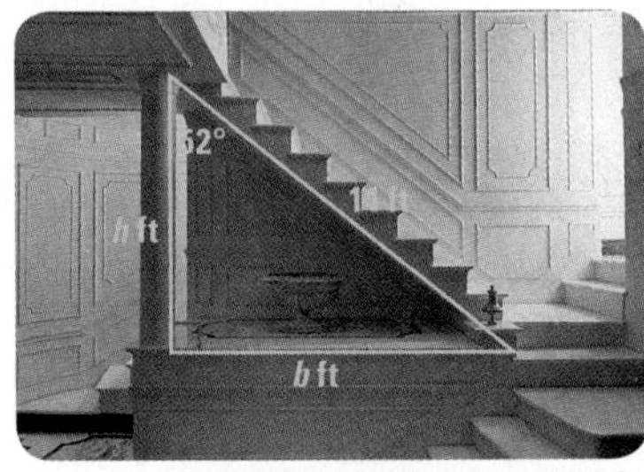

   about 8.6 ft; about 11.0 ft

7. **GRIDDED ANSWER** The base of an isosceles triangle is 70 centimeters long. The altitude to the base is 75 centimeters long. Find the measure of a base angle to the nearest degree. **65**

7 CHAPTER SUMMARY

BIG IDEAS

For Your Notebook

Big Idea 1

Using the Pythagorean Theorem and Its Converse

The Pythagorean Theorem states that in a right triangle the square of the length of the hypotenuse c is equal to the sum of the squares of the lengths of the legs a and b, so that $c^2 = a^2 + b^2$.

The Converse of the Pythagorean Theorem can be used to determine if a triangle is a right triangle.

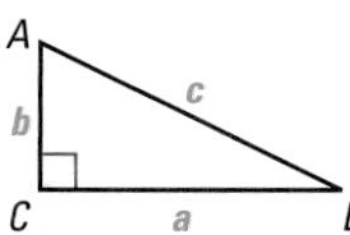

If $c^2 = a^2 + b^2$, then $m\angle C = 90°$ and $\triangle ABC$ is a right triangle.

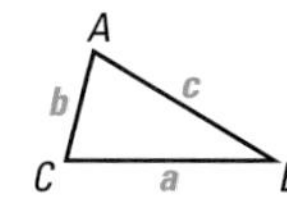

If $c^2 < a^2 + b^2$, then $m\angle C < 90°$ and $\triangle ABC$ is an acute triangle.

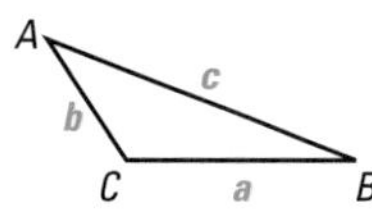

If $c^2 > a^2 + b^2$, then $m\angle C > 90°$ and $\triangle ABC$ is an obtuse triangle.

Using Special Relationships in Right Triangles

GEOMETRIC MEAN In right $\triangle ABC$, altitude $\overline{CD}$ forms two smaller triangles so that $\triangle CBD \sim \triangle ACD \sim \triangle ABC$.

Also, $\frac{BD}{CD} = \frac{CD}{AD}$, $\frac{AB}{CB} = \frac{CB}{DB}$, and $\frac{AB}{AC} = \frac{AC}{AD}$.

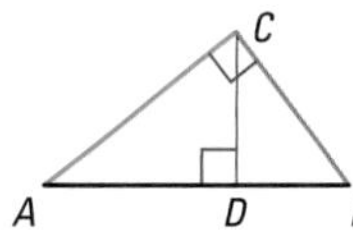

SPECIAL RIGHT TRIANGLES

45°-45°-90° Triangle

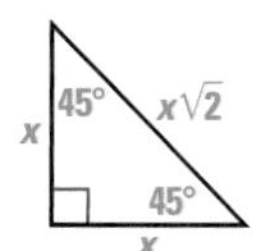

hypotenuse = leg • $\sqrt{2}$

30°-60°-90° Triangle

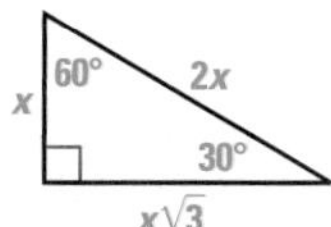

hypotenuse = 2 • shorter leg

longer leg = shorter leg • $\sqrt{3}$

Using Trigonometric Ratios to Solve Right Triangles

The tangent, sine, and cosine ratios can be used to find unknown side lengths and angle measures of right triangles. The values of tan $x°$, sin $x°$, and cos $x°$ depend only on the angle measure and not on the side length.

$\tan A = \frac{\text{opp.}}{\text{adj.}} = \frac{BC}{AC}$ $\qquad \tan^{-1} \frac{BC}{AC} = m\angle A$

$\sin A = \frac{\text{opp.}}{\text{hyp.}} = \frac{BC}{AB}$ $\qquad \sin^{-1} \frac{BC}{AB} = m\angle A$

$\cos A = \frac{\text{adj.}}{\text{hyp.}} = \frac{AC}{AB}$ $\qquad \cos^{-1} \frac{AC}{AB} = m\angle A$

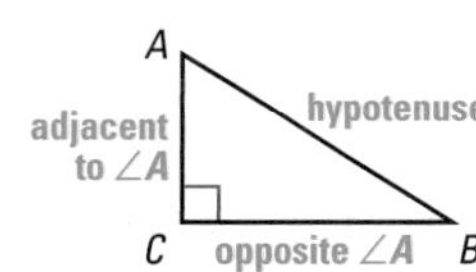

Additional Resources

The following resources are available to help review the materials in this chapter.

Chapter 7 Resource Book

- Chapter Review Games and Activities, p. 103
- Cumulative Practice, Chs. 1–7, pp. 106–107

Student Resources in Spanish

eWorkbook

@HomeTutor

Vocabulary Practice

Vocabulary practice is available at **classzone.com**

Extra Example 7.1

Find the value of x. **41**

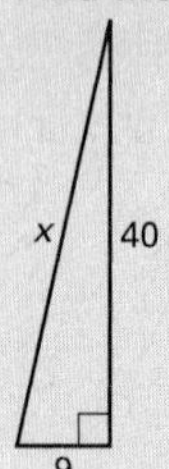

7 CHAPTER REVIEW

@HomeTutor
classzone.com
• Multi-Language Glossary
• Vocabulary practice

REVIEW KEY VOCABULARY

For a list of postulates and theorems, see pp. 926–931.

VOCABULARY EXERCISES

1. Copy and complete: A Pythagorean triple is a set of three positive integers a, b, and c that satisfy the equation _?_. $a^2 + b^2 = c^2$
2. **WRITING** What does it mean to solve a right triangle? What do you need to know to solve a right triangle? **To find the measure of all three sides and all three angles; 2 side lengths, or 1 side length and 1 acute angle.**
3. **WRITING** *Describe* the difference between an angle of depression and an angle of elevation. ***Sample answer:*** **The difference is your perspective on the situation. The angle of depression is the measure from your line of sight down, and the angle of elevation is the measure from your line of sight up, but if you construct the parallel lines in any situation, the angles are alternate interior angles and are congruent by Theorem 3.1.**

REVIEW EXAMPLES AND EXERCISES

Use the review examples and exercises below to check your understanding of the concepts you have learned in each lesson of Chapter 7.

7.1 Apply the Pythagorean Theorem

pp. 433–439

EXAMPLE

Find the value of x.

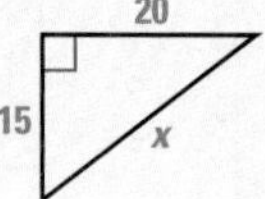

Because x is the length of the hypotenuse of a right triangle, you can use the Pythagorean Theorem to find its value.

$(\text{hypotenuse})^2 = (\text{leg})^2 + (\text{leg})^2$ **Pythagorean Theorem**

$x^2 = 15^2 + 20^2$ **Substitute.**

$x^2 = 625$ **Simplify.**

$x = 25$ **Find the positive square root.**

EXERCISES

EXAMPLES 1 and 2 on pp. 433–434 for Exs. 4–6

Find the unknown side length x.

4. **20**

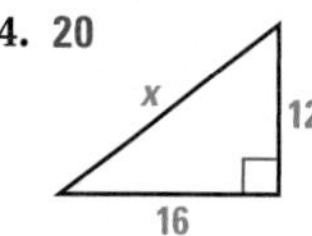

5.

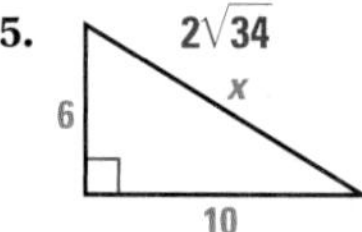

6. **15**

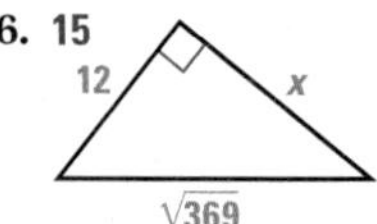

@HomeTutor
classzone.com
Chapter Review Practice

7.2 Use the Converse of the Pythagorean Theorem *pp. 441–447*

EXAMPLE

Tell whether the given triangle is a right triangle.

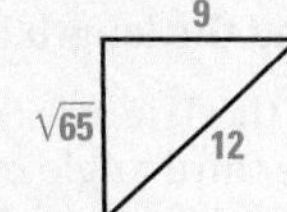

Check to see whether the side lengths satisfy the equation $c^2 = a^2 + b^2$.

$12^2 \stackrel{?}{=} (\sqrt{65})^2 + 9^2$

$144 \stackrel{?}{=} 65 + 81$

$144 < 146$

The triangle is not a right triangle. It is an acute triangle.

EXERCISES

EXAMPLE 2 on p. 442 for Exs. 7–12

Classify the triangle formed by the side lengths as *acute, right,* or *obtuse.*

7. 6, 8, 9 **acute**   **8.** 4, 2, 5 **obtuse**   **9.** 10, $2\sqrt{2}$, $6\sqrt{3}$ **right**

10. 15, 20, 15 **acute**   **11.** 3, 3, $3\sqrt{2}$ **right**   **12.** 13, 18, $3\sqrt{55}$ **obtuse**

7.3 Use Similar Right Triangles *pp. 449–456*

EXAMPLE

Find the value of *x*.

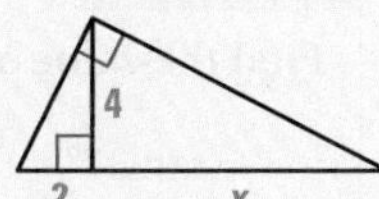

By Theorem 7.6, you know that 4 is the geometric mean of x and 2.

$\frac{x}{4} = \frac{4}{2}$ **Write a proportion.**

$2x = 16$ **Cross Products Property**

$x = 8$ **Divide.**

EXERCISES

EXAMPLES 2 and 3 on pp. 450–451 for Exs. 13–18

Find the value of *x*.

13. **13.5**

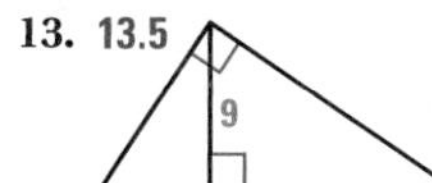

14. **4 6**

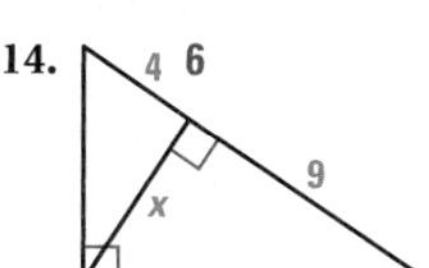

15. **$2\sqrt{10}$**

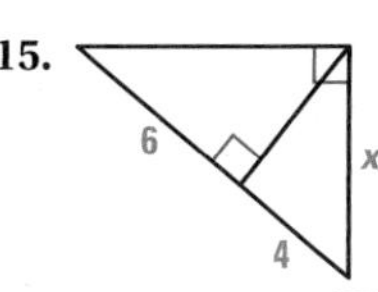

16. **2 $\sqrt{14}$**

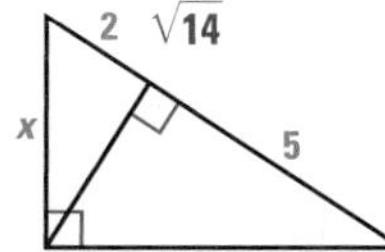

17. **9**

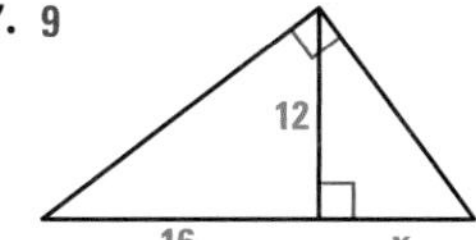

18. **16**

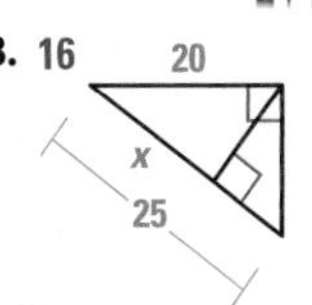

Extra Example 7.2

Tell whether the given triangle is a right triangle.

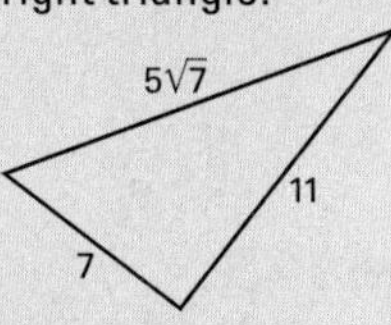

No, the triangle is obtuse.

Extra Example 7.3

Find the value of x. **27**

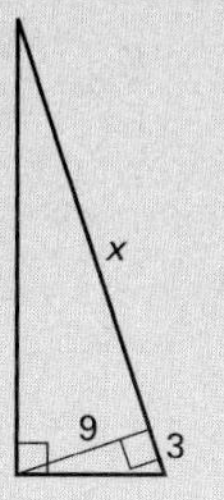

Extra Example 7.4

Find the length of the hypotenuse. **14**

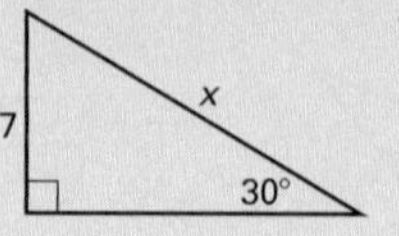

Extra Example 7.5

Find the value of x. **9.38**

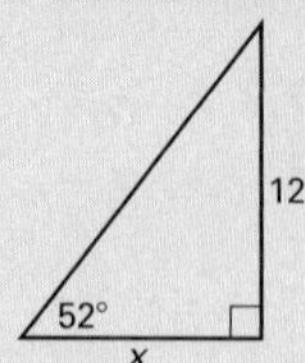

7 CHAPTER REVIEW

7.4 Special Right Triangles *pp. 457–464*

EXAMPLE

Find the length of the hypotenuse.

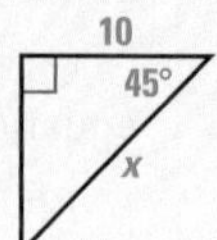

By the Triangle Sum Theorem, the measure of the third angle must be 45°. Then the triangle is a 45°-45°-90° triangle.

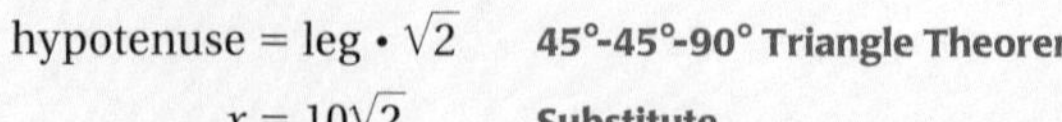

hypotenuse = leg • $\sqrt{2}$ **45°-45°-90° Triangle Theorem**

$x = 10\sqrt{2}$ **Substitute.**

EXERCISES

EXAMPLES 1, 2, and 5 on pp. 457–459 for Exs. 19–21

Find the value of x. Write your answer in simplest radical form.

19. **$6\sqrt{2}$**

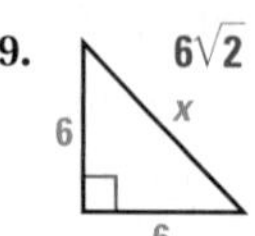

20. **7**

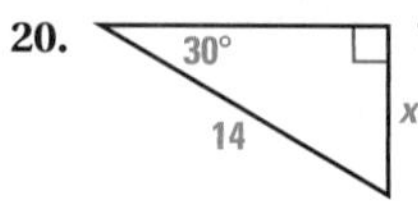

21. **$16\sqrt{3}$**

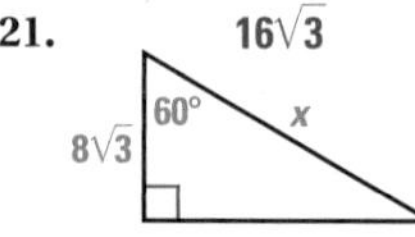

7.5 Apply the Tangent Ratio *pp. 466–472*

EXAMPLE

Find the value of x.

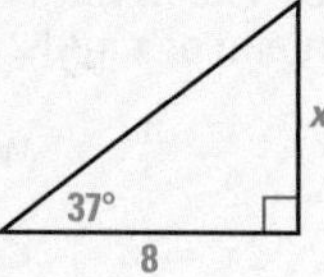

$\tan 37° = \frac{\text{opp.}}{\text{adj.}}$ **Write ratio for tangent of 37°.**

$\tan 37° = \frac{x}{8}$ **Substitute.**

$8 \cdot \tan 37° = x$ **Multiply each side by 8.**

$6 \approx x$ **Use a calculator to simplify.**

EXERCISES

EXAMPLE 2 on p. 467 for Exs. 22–26

In Exercises 22 and 23, use the diagram.

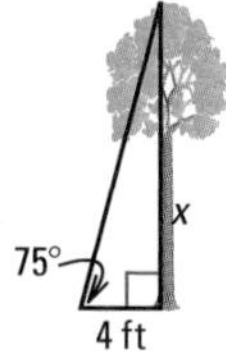

22. The angle between the bottom of a fence and the top of a tree is 75°. The tree is 4 feet from the fence. How tall is the tree? Round your answer to the nearest foot. **15 ft**

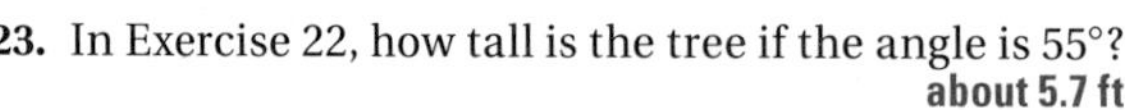

23. In Exercise 22, how tall is the tree if the angle is 55°? **about 5.7 ft**

Find the value of x to the nearest tenth.

24. **44.0** (triangle: 32, 54°, x)

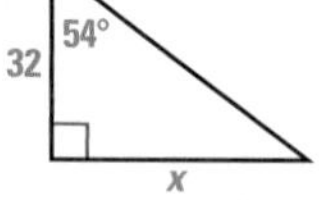

25. **9.3**

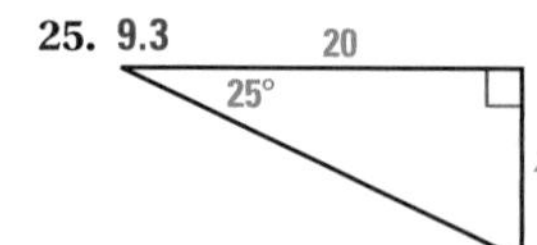

26. **12.8**

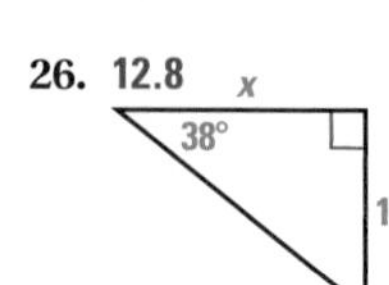

@HomeTutor
classzone.com
Chapter Review Practice

7.6 Apply the Sine and Cosine Ratios *pp. 473–480*

EXAMPLE

Find sin *A* and sin *B*.

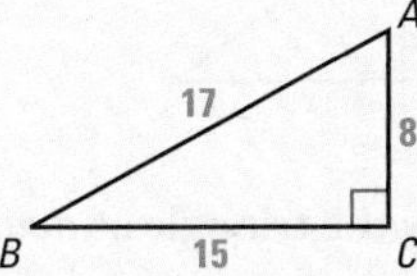

$\sin A = \frac{\text{opp.}}{\text{hyp.}} = \frac{BC}{BA} = \frac{15}{17} \approx 0.8824$

$\sin B = \frac{\text{opp.}}{\text{hyp.}} = \frac{AC}{AB} = \frac{8}{17} \approx 0.4706$

EXERCISES

EXAMPLES 1 and 2 on pp. 473–474 for Exs. 27–29

Find sin *X* and cos *X*. Write each answer as a fraction, and as a decimal. Round to four decimals places, if necessary.

27. $\frac{3}{5} = 0.6, \frac{4}{5} = 0.8$

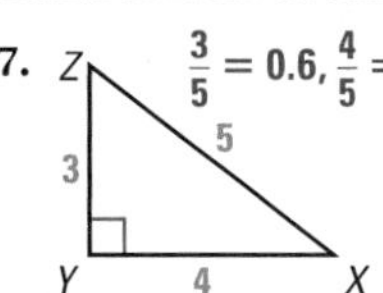

28.

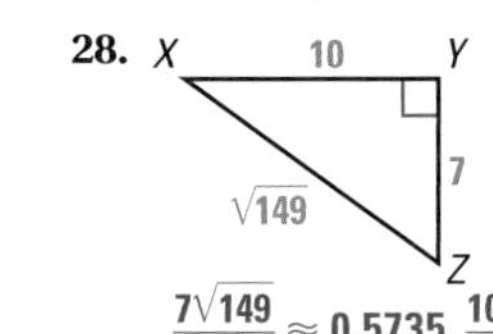

$\frac{7\sqrt{149}}{149} \approx 0.5735, \frac{10\sqrt{149}}{149} \approx 0.8192$

29.

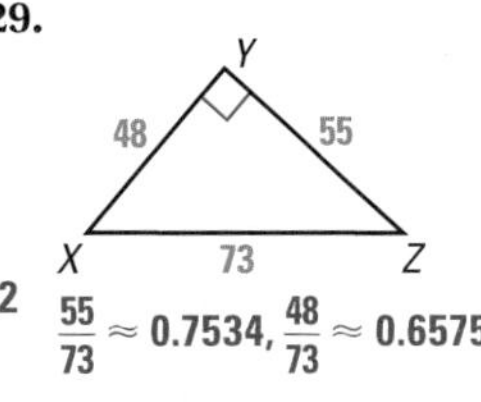

$\frac{55}{73} \approx 0.7534, \frac{48}{73} \approx 0.6575$

7.7 Solve Right Triangles *pp. 483–489*

EXAMPLE

Use a calculator to approximate the measure of $\angle A$ to the nearest tenth of a degree.

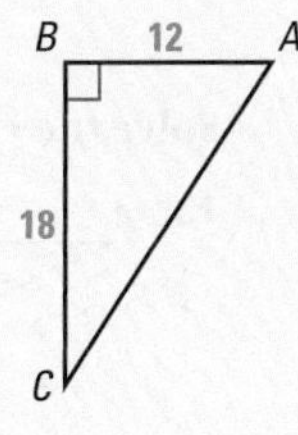

Because $\tan A = \frac{18}{12} = \frac{3}{2} = 1.5$, $\tan^{-1} 1.5 = m\angle A$.

Use a calculator to evaluate this expression.

$\tan^{-1} 1.5 \approx 56.3099324\ldots$

So, the measure of $\angle A$ is approximately 56.3°.

EXERCISES

EXAMPLE 3 on p. 484 for Exs. 30–33

Solve the right triangle. Round decimal answers to the nearest tenth.

30.

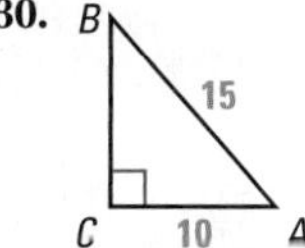

$A \approx 48.2°, B \approx 41.8°, BC \approx 11.2$

31.

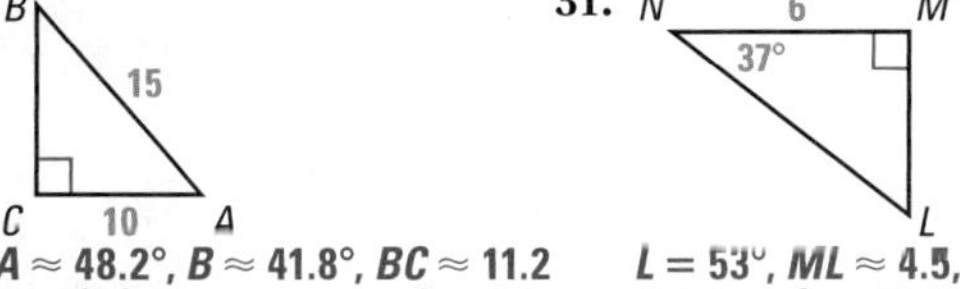

$L = 53°, ML \approx 4.5, NL \approx 7.5$

32.

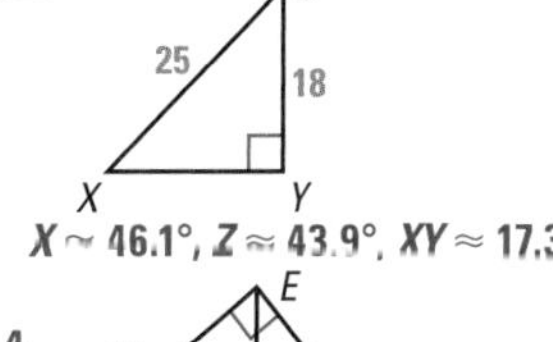

$X \approx 46.1°, Z \approx 43.9°, XY \approx 17.3$

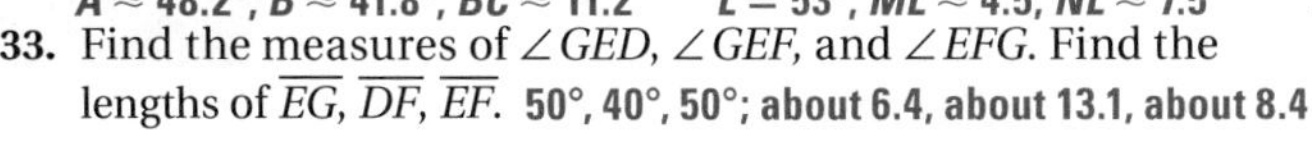

33. Find the measures of $\angle GED$, $\angle GEF$, and $\angle EFG$. Find the lengths of $\overline{EG}$, $\overline{DF}$, $\overline{EF}$. **50°, 40°, 50°; about 6.4, about 13.1, about 8.4**

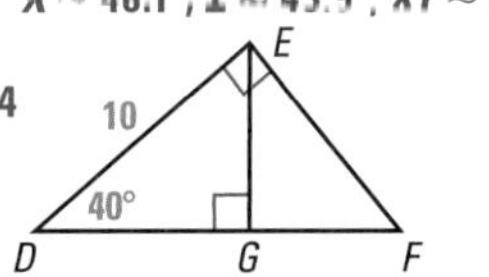

Extra Example 7.6

Find cos *A* and cos *B*.

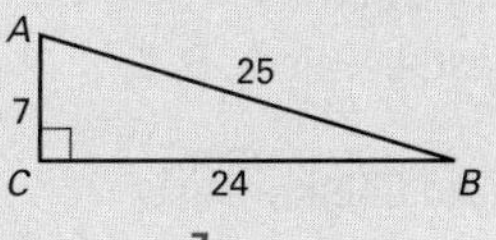

$\cos A = \frac{7}{25} = 0.28;$

$\cos B = \frac{24}{25} = 0.96$

Extra Example 7.7

Use a calculator to approximate the measure of $\angle A$ to the nearest tenth of a degree. **40.8°**

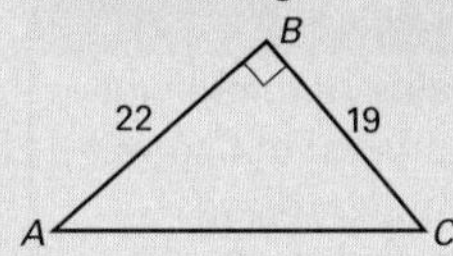

7 CHAPTER TEST

Additional Resources

Assessment Book

- Chapter Test, Levels A, B, C, pp. 98–103
- Standardized Chapter Test, pp. 104–105
- SAT/ACT Chapter Test, pp. 106–107
- Alternative Assessment, pp. 108–109

Test Generator CD-ROM

Chapter Test

Easily-readable reduced copies (with answers) of Chapter Test B, the Standardized Chapter Test, and the Alternative Assessment from the Assessment Book can be found on pp. 430G–430H.

Find the value of x. Write your answer in simplest radical form.

1. 16

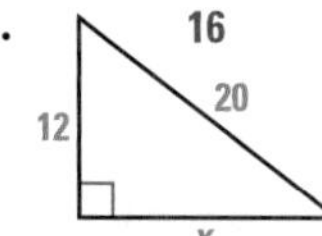

2. $5\sqrt{10}$

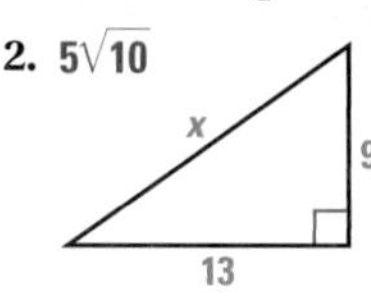

3. $6\sqrt{6}$

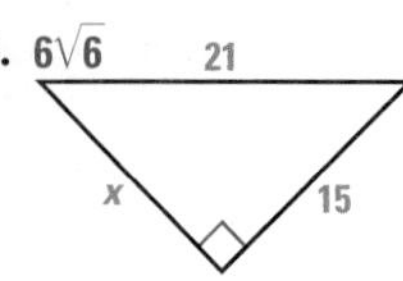

Classify the triangle as *acute, right,* or *obtuse.*

4. 5, 15, $5\sqrt{10}$ **right**
5. 4.3, 6.7, 8.2 **obtuse**
6. 5, 7, 8 **acute**

Find the value of x. Round decimal answers to the nearest tenth.

7. 10

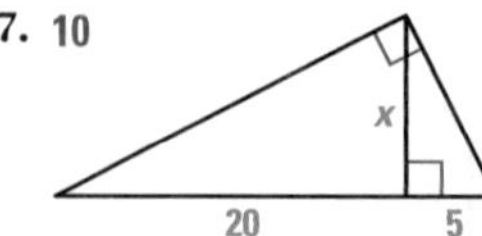

8. 9.2

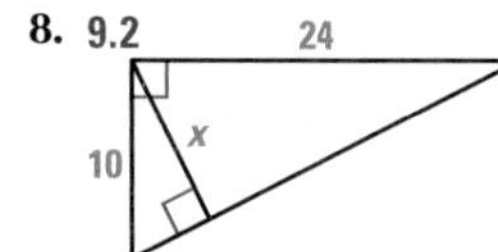

9. 13.4

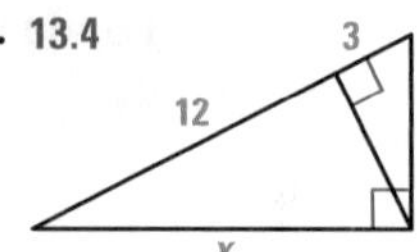

Find the value of each variable. Write your answer in simplest radical form.

10. $x = 4\sqrt{3}$, $y = 8$

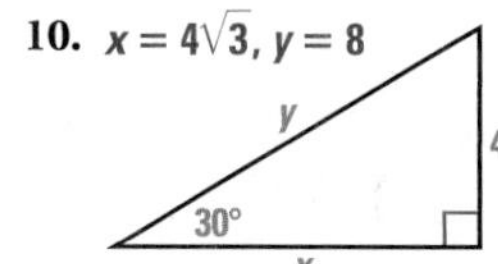

11. $x = 24$, $y = 24\sqrt{2}$

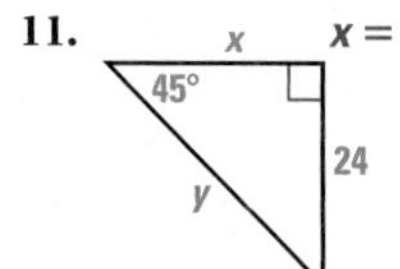

12.

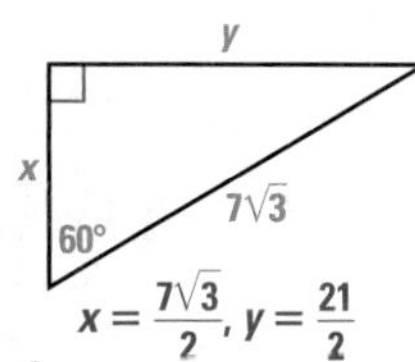

$x = \frac{7\sqrt{3}}{2}$, $y = \frac{21}{2}$

Solve the right triangle. Round decimal answers to the nearest tenth.

13.

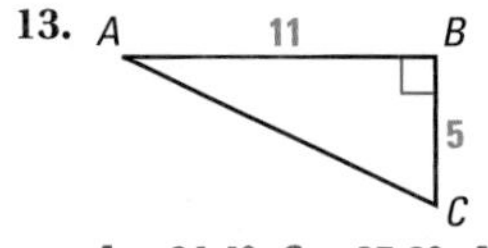

$A \approx 24.4°$, $C \approx 65.6°$, $AC \approx 12.1$

14.

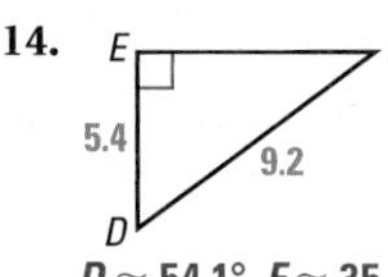

$D \approx 54.1°$, $F \approx 35.9°$, $EF \approx 7.4$

15.

$G = 36.8°$, $GH \approx 18.7$, $GJ \approx 23.4$

16. **FLAGPOLE** Julie is 6 feet tall. If she stands 15 feet from the flagpole and holds a cardboard square, the edges of the square line up with the top and bottom of the flagpole. Approximate the height of the flagpole. **about 43.5 ft**

17. **HILLS** The length of a hill in your neighborhood is 2000 feet. The height of the hill is 750 feet. What is the angle of elevation of the hill? **about 22°**

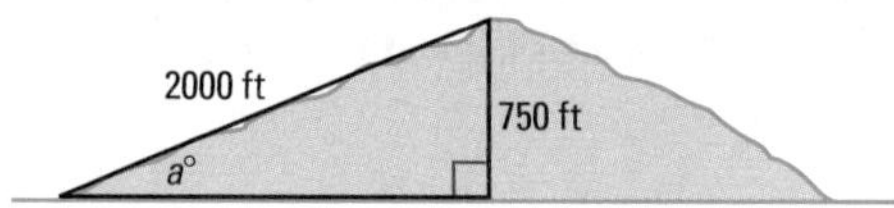

ALGEBRA REVIEW

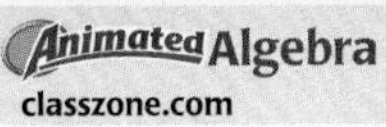

GRAPH AND SOLVE QUADRATIC EQUATIONS

The graph of $y = ax^2 + bx + c$ is a parabola that opens upward if $a > 0$ and opens downward if $a < 0$. The x-coordinate of the vertex is $-\frac{b}{2a}$. The axis of symmetry is the vertical line $x = -\frac{b}{2a}$.

EXAMPLE 1 Graph a quadratic function

Graph the equation $y = -x^2 + 4x - 3$.

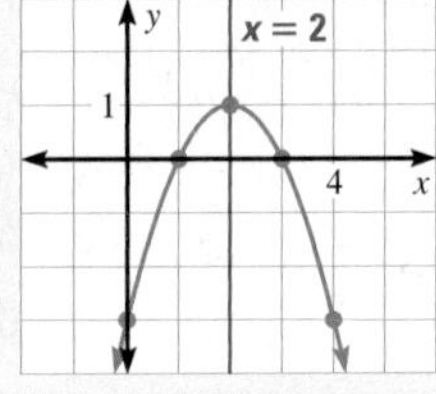

Because $a = -1$ and $-1 < 0$, the graph opens downward.

The vertex has x-coordinate $-\frac{b}{2a} = -\frac{4}{2(-1)} = 2$.

The y-coordinate of the vertex is $-(2)^2 + 4(2) - 3 = 1$.

So, the vertex is (2, 1) and the axis of symmetry is $x = 2$.

Use a table of values to draw a parabola through the plotted points.

EXAMPLE 2 Solve a quadratic equation by graphing

Solve the equation $x^2 - 2x = 3$.

Write the equation in the standard form $ax^2 + bx + c = 0$:

$x^2 - 2x - 3 = 0.$

Graph the related quadratic function $y = x^2 - 2x - 3$, as shown.

The x-intercepts of the graph are -1 and 3.

So, the solutions of $x^2 - 2x = 3$ are -1 and 3.

Check the solution algebraically.

$(-1)^2 - 2(-1) \stackrel{?}{=} 3 \rightarrow 1 + 2 = 3$ $\qquad (3)^2 - 2(3) \stackrel{?}{=} 3 \rightarrow 9 - 6 = 3$ ✓

EXERCISES

EXAMPLE 1 for Exs. 1–6

Graph the quadratic function. Label the vertex and axis of symmetry. 1–6. See margin.

1. $y = x^2 - 6x + 8$
2. $y = -x^2 - 4x + 2$
3. $y = 2x^2 - x - 1$
4. $y = 3x^2 - 9x + 2$
5. $y = \frac{1}{2}x^2 - x + 3$
6. $y = -4x^2 + 6x - 5$

EXAMPLE 2 for Exs. 7–18

Solve the quadratic equation by graphing. Check solutions algebraically.

7. $x^2 = x + 6$ **−2, 3.**
8. $4x + 4 = -x^2$ **−2**
9. $2x^2 = -8$ **no solution**
10. $3x^2 + 2 = 14$ **−2, 2**
11. $-x^2 + 4x - 5 = 0$ **no solution**
12. $2x - x^2 = -15$ **−3, 5**
13. $\frac{1}{4}x^2 = 2x$ **0, 8**
14. $x^2 + 3x = 4$ **−4, 1**
15. $x^2 + 8 = 6x$ **2, 4**
16. $x^2 = 9x - 1$ **about 0.113, about 8.89**
17. $-25 = x^2 + 10x$ **−5**
18. $x^2 + 6x = 0$ **−6, 0**

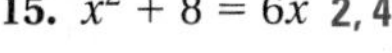

1.
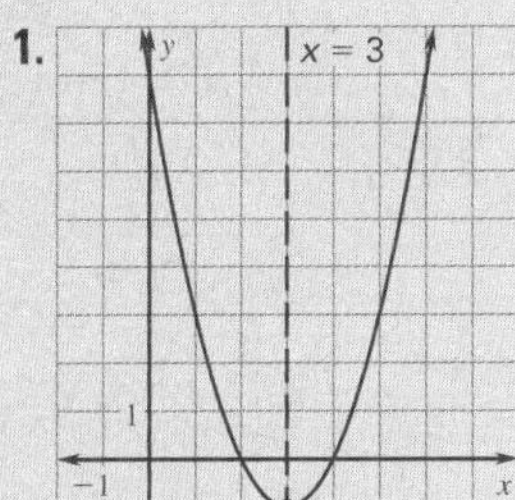

2.
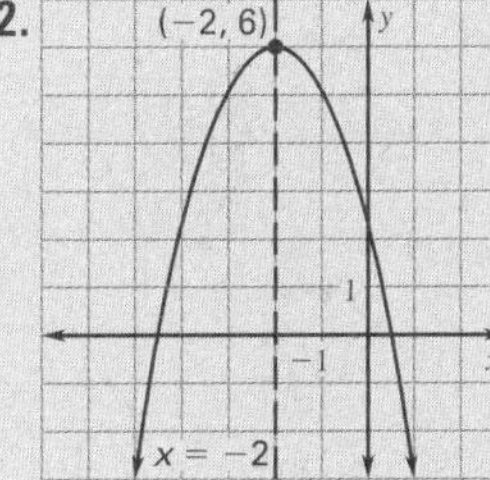

3.
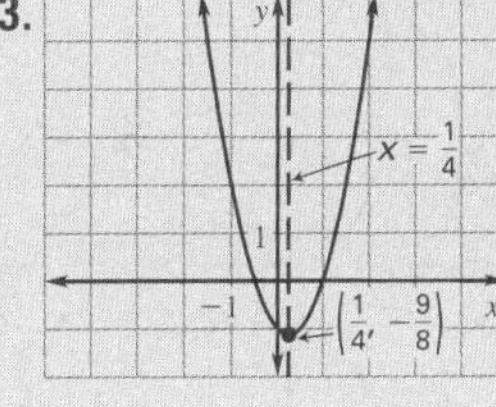

Extra Example 1

Graph the equation $y = x^2 + 8x + 12$.

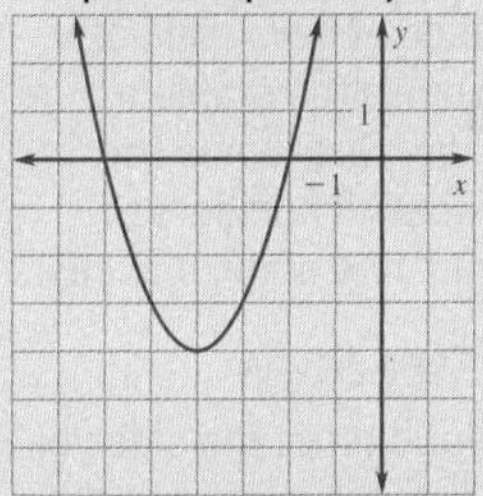

Extra Example 2

Solve the equation $x^2 + 2x = 8$.
−4, 2

4.
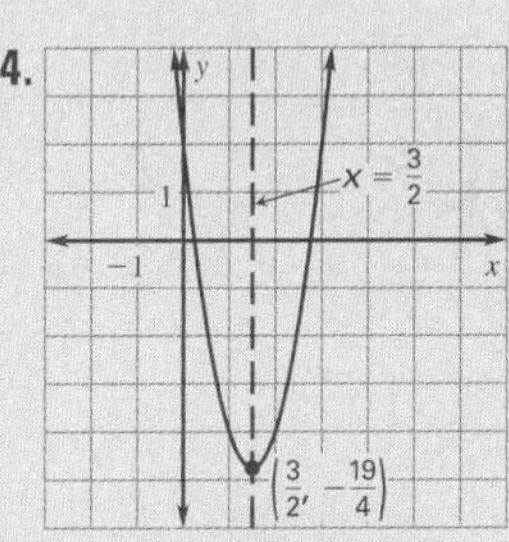

5.
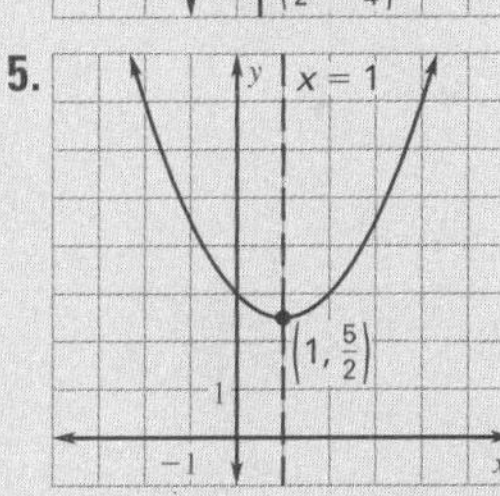

6.
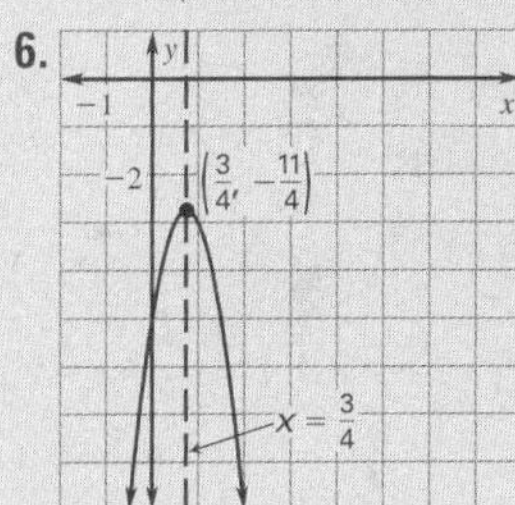

Test-Taking Strategy

Eliminate as many incorrect answer choices as you can. If you do not know how to solve the problem directly, you can sometimes use common sense with numbers to eliminate all but one of the choices.

Reading Strategy

Problem 1 Notice that the sides of $\triangle JKL$ are labeled in miles, but the question asks for the time in hours. Encourage students to read the problem carefully and find what is given and what is to be found.

MULTIPLE CHOICE QUESTIONS

If you have difficulty solving a multiple choice question directly, you may be able to use another approach to eliminate incorrect answer choices and obtain the correct answer.

Standards

15.0 Students use the Pythagorean theorem to determine distance and find missing lengths of sides of right triangles.

20.0 Students know and are able to use angle and side relationships in problems with special right triangles, such as 30°, 60°, and 90° triangles and 45°, 45°, and 90° triangles.

PROBLEM 1

You ride your bike at an average speed of 10 miles per hour. How long does it take you to ride one time around the triangular park shown in the diagram?

Ⓐ 0.1 h Ⓑ 0.2 h
Ⓒ 0.3 h Ⓓ 0.4 h

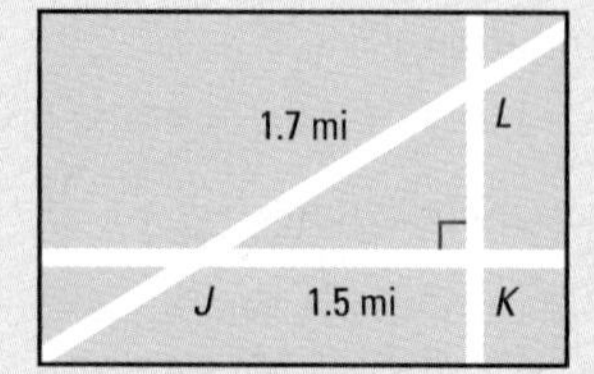

METHOD 1

SOLVE DIRECTLY The park is a right triangle. Use the Pythagorean Theorem to find KL. Find the perimeter of $\triangle JKL$. Then find how long it takes to ride around the park.

STEP 1 **Find** KL. Use the Pythagorean Theorem.

$$JK^2 + KL^2 = JL^2$$
$$1.5^2 + KL^2 = 1.7^2$$
$$2.25 + KL^2 = 2.89$$
$$KL^2 = 0.64$$
$$KL = 0.8$$

STEP 2 **Find** the perimeter of $\triangle JKL$.

$$P = JK + JL + KL$$
$$= 1.5 + 1.7 + 0.8$$
$$= 4 \text{ mi}$$

STEP 3 **Find** the time t (in hours) it takes you to go around the park.

Rate × Time = Distance

$$(10 \text{ mi/h}) \cdot t = 4 \text{ mi}$$
$$t = 0.4 \text{ h}$$

The correct answer is D. Ⓐ Ⓑ Ⓒ Ⓓ

METHOD 2

ELIMINATE CHOICES Another method is to find how far you can travel in the given times to eliminate choices that are not reasonable.

STEP 1 **Find** how far you will travel in each of the given times. Use the formula $rt = d$.

Choice A: $0.1(10) = 1$ mi

Choice B: $0.2(10) = 2$ mi

Choice C: $0.3(10) = 3$ mi

Choice D: $0.4(10) = 4$ mi

The distance around two sides of the park is $1.5 + 1.7 = 3.2$ mi. But you need to travel around all three sides, which is longer.

Since $1 < 3.2$, $2 < 3.2$, and $3 < 3.2$. You can eliminate choices A, B, and C.

STEP 2 **Check** that D is the correct answer. If the distance around the park is 4 miles, then

$$KL = 4 - JK - JL$$
$$= 4 - 1.5 - 1.7 = 0.8 \text{ mi.}$$

Apply the Converse of the Pythagorean Theorem.

$$0.8^2 + 1.5^2 \stackrel{?}{=} 1.7^2$$
$$0.64 + 2.25 \stackrel{?}{=} 2.89$$
$$2.89 = 2.89 \checkmark$$

The correct answer is D. Ⓐ Ⓑ Ⓒ Ⓓ

PROBLEM 2

What is the height of $\triangle WXY$?

(A) 4 (B) $4\sqrt{3}$

(C) 8 (D) $8\sqrt{3}$

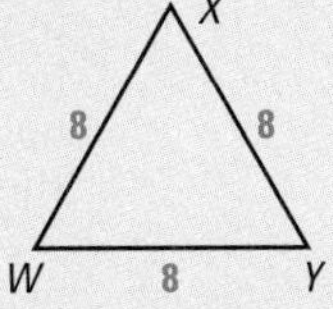

METHOD 1

SOLVE DIRECTLY Draw altitude $\overline{XZ}$ to form two congruent 30°-60°-90° triangles.

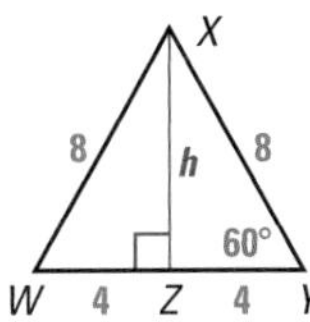

Let h be the length of the longer leg of $\triangle XZY$. The length of the shorter leg is 4.

longer leg $= \sqrt{3} \cdot$ shorter leg

$h = 4\sqrt{3}$

The correct answer is B.  

METHOD 2

ELIMINATE CHOICES Another method is to use theorems about triangles to eliminate incorrect choices. Draw altitude $\overline{XZ}$ to form two congruent right triangles.

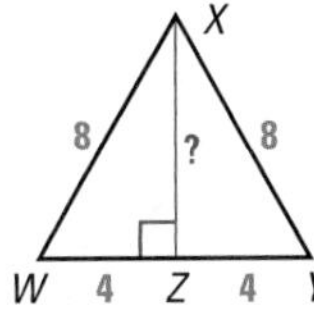

Consider $\triangle XZW$. By the Triangle Inequality Theorem, $XW < WZ + XZ$. So, $8 < 4 + XZ$ and $XZ > 4$. You can eliminate choice A. Also, XZ must be less than the hypotenuse of $\triangle XWZ$. You can eliminate choices C and D.

The correct answer is B. (A) (B) (C) (D)

PRACTICE

Explain **why you can eliminate the highlighted answer choice.**

1. In the figure shown, what is the length of $\overline{EF}$?

   (A) 9 (B) ~~$9\sqrt{2}$~~

   (C) 18 (D) $9\sqrt{5}$

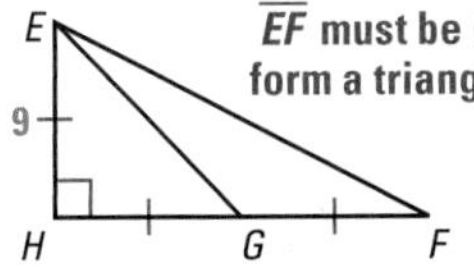

$\overline{EF}$ must be longer than 18 for the points to form a triangle.

2. Which of the following lengths are side lengths of a right triangle? **See margin.**

   (A) ~~2, 21, 23~~ (B) 3, 4, 5 (C) 9, 16, 18 (D) 11, 16, 61

3. In $\triangle PQR$, $PQ = QR = 13$ and $PR = 10$. What is the length of the altitude drawn from vertex Q? **The altitude must be less than the hypotenuse, which is 13.**

   (A) 10 (B) 11 (C) 12 (D) ~~13~~

Reading Strategy

Problem 2 Students should understand that an altitude of a triangle goes from a vertex to the opposite side and is perpendicular to that side. It is not equal to a side of the triangle unless the triangle is a right triangle. Also, students should notice that the triangle is equilateral, so any altitude will form two 30°-60°-90° triangles.

2. 2 + 21 = 23 and in order for the sides to form a triangle the sum of the lengths of any two sides must be greater than the length of the third side. So these lengths do not form a triangle.

MULTIPLE CHOICE

1. Which expression gives the correct length for XW in the diagram below? **B**

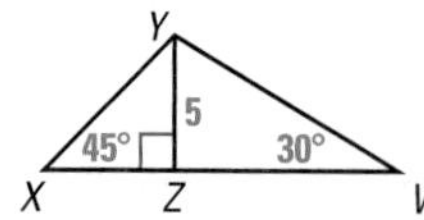

Ⓐ $5 + 5\sqrt{2}$ Ⓑ $5 + 5\sqrt{3}$

Ⓒ $5\sqrt{3} + 5\sqrt{2}$ Ⓓ $5 + 10$

2. The area of $\triangle EFG$ is 400 square meters. To the nearest tenth of a meter, what is the length of side $\overline{EG}$? **C**

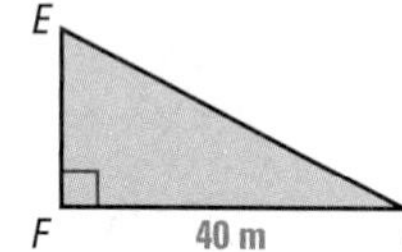

Ⓐ 10.0 meters Ⓑ 20.0 meters

Ⓒ 44.7 meters Ⓓ 56.7 meters

3. Which expression can be used to find the value of x in the diagram below? **D**

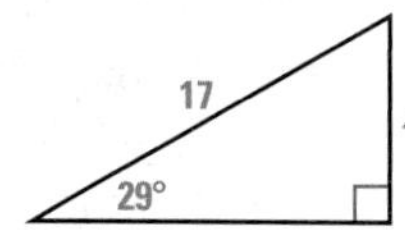

Ⓐ $\tan 29° = \frac{x}{17}$ Ⓑ $\cos 29° = \frac{x}{17}$

Ⓒ $\tan 61° = \frac{x}{17}$ Ⓓ $\cos 61° = \frac{x}{17}$

4. A fire station, a police station, and a hospital are not positioned in a straight line. The distance from the police station to the fire station is 4 miles. The distance from the fire station to the hospital is 3 miles. Which of the following could *not* be the distance from the police station to the hospital? **A**

Ⓐ 1 mile Ⓑ 2 miles

Ⓒ 5 miles Ⓓ 6 miles

5. It takes 14 minutes to walk from your house to your friend's house on the path shown in red. If you walk at the same speed, about how many minutes will it take on the path shown in blue? **C**

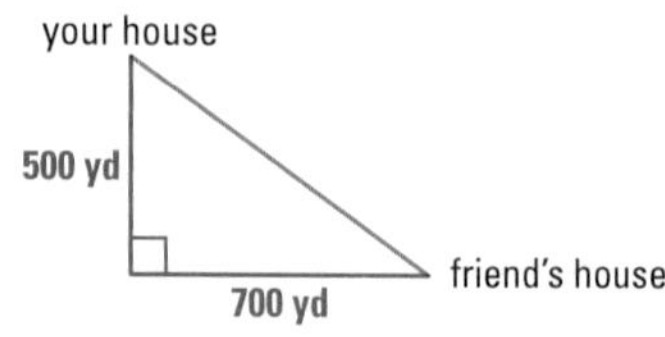

Ⓐ 6 minutes Ⓑ 8 minutes

Ⓒ 10 minutes Ⓓ 13 minutes

6. Which equation can be used to find QR in the diagram below? **A**

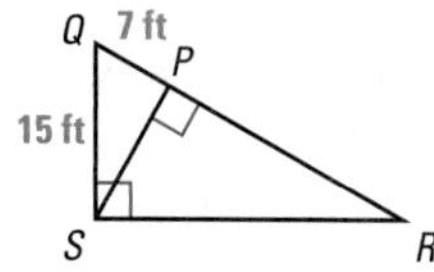

Ⓐ $\frac{QR}{15} = \frac{15}{7}$

Ⓑ $\frac{15}{QR} = \frac{QR}{8}$

Ⓒ $QR = \sqrt{15^2 + 27^2}$

Ⓓ $\frac{QR}{7} = \frac{7}{15}$

7. Stitches are sewn along the black line segments in the potholder shown below. There are 10 stitches per inch. Which is the closest estimate of the number of stitches used? **D**

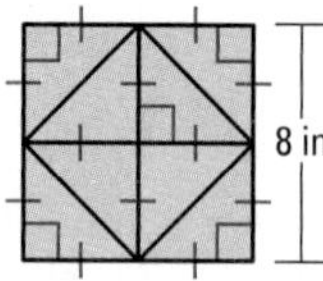

Ⓐ 480 Ⓑ 550

Ⓒ 656 Ⓓ 700

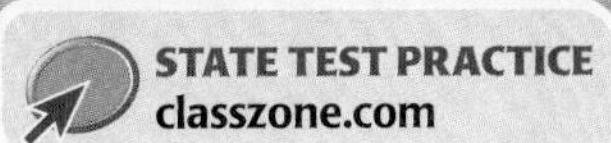

GRIDDED ANSWER

8. A design on a T-shirt is made of a square and four equilateral triangles. The side length of the square is 4 inches. Find the distance (in inches) from point A to point B. Round to the nearest tenth. **10.9**

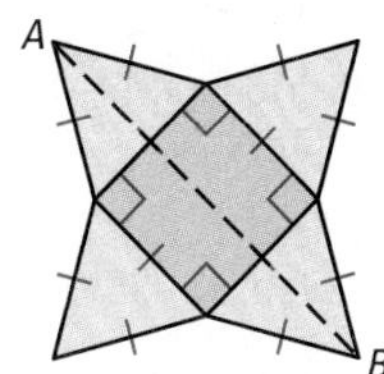

9. Use the diagram below. Find KM to the nearest tenth of a unit. **18.6**

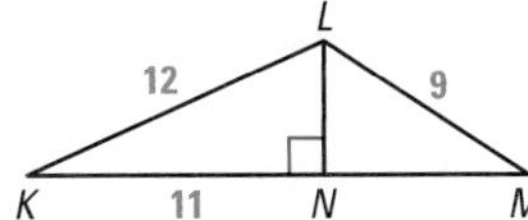

SHORT RESPONSE

10. The diagram shows the side of a set of stairs. In the diagram, the smaller right triangles are congruent. *Explain* how to find the lengths x, y, and z. **See margin.**

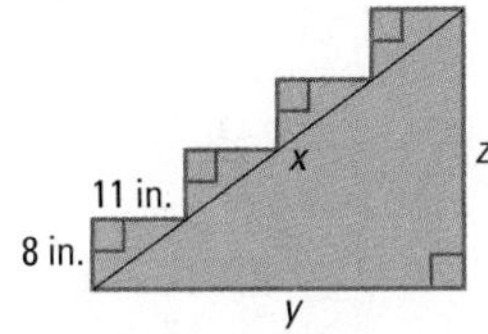

11. You drive due north from Dalton to Bristol. Next, you drive from Bristol to Hilldale. Finally, you drive from Hilldale to Dalton. Is Hilldale due west of Bristol? *Explain.*

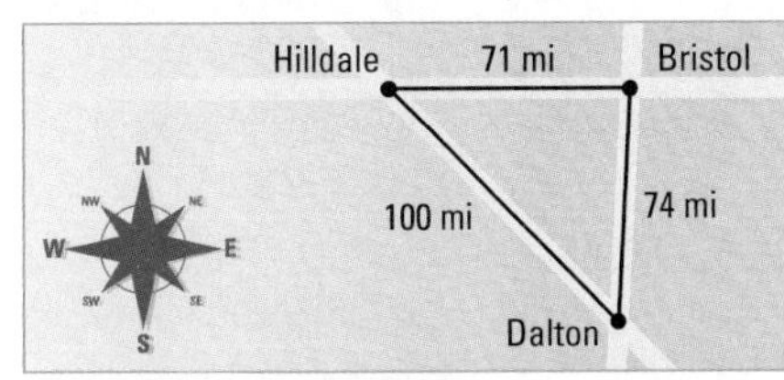

No. ***Sample answer:*** **If you use the law of cosines to determine the angle, you get about 87°. Since this is not 90°, Hilldale is not due west of Bristol.**

EXTENDED RESPONSE

12. The design for part of a water ride at an amusement park is shown. The ride carries people up a track along ramp $\overline{AB}$. Then riders travel down a water chute along ramp $\overline{BC}$. **a, b. See margin.**

a. How high is the ride above point D? *Explain.*

b. What is the total distance from point A to point B to point C? *Explain.*

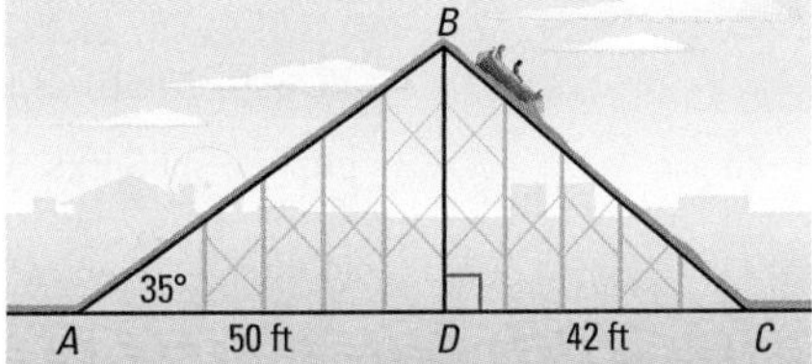

13. A formula for the area A of a triangle is *Heron's Formula.* For a triangle with side lengths EF, FG, and EG, the formula is

$$A = \sqrt{s(s - EF)(s - FG)(s - EG)}, \text{ where } s = \frac{1}{2}(EF + FG + EG).$$

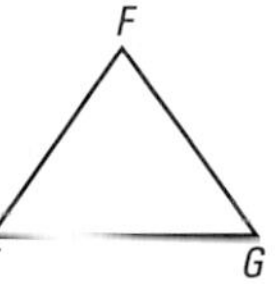

a. In $\triangle EFG$ shown, $EF = FG = 15$, and $EG = 18$. Use Heron's formula to find the area of $\triangle EFG$. **108**

b. Use the formula $A = \frac{1}{2}bh$ to find the area of $\triangle EFG$. **108**

c. Use Heron's formula to *justify* that the area of an equilateral triangle with side length x is $A = \frac{x^2}{4}\sqrt{3}$. **See margin.**

10. Use the Pythagorean Theorem to find the length of the hypotenuse of the smaller triangle and since there are 4 such triangles, x is 4 times one hypotenuse. y is equivalent to 4 times the length of one small triangle and z is equivalent to 4 times the height of one small triangle.

12a. About 35 ft; the tangent ratio is used here to find the length of the side opposite the 35° angle, which represents the height of the triangle.

12b. About 116 ft; use the height and the Pythagorean Theorem to find AB, then use the height and DC to find BC, and then find the sum of the distances.

13c. $x = \frac{1}{2}(x + x + x) = \frac{3}{2}x$, so

$A =$

$\sqrt{\frac{3}{2}x\left(\frac{3}{2}x - x\right)\left(\frac{3}{2}x - x\right)\left(\frac{3}{2}x - x\right)}$

$= \sqrt{\frac{3}{2}x\left(\frac{1}{2}x\right)\left(\frac{1}{2}x\right)\left(\frac{1}{2}x\right)}$

$= \sqrt{\frac{3}{16}x^4}$

$= \frac{x^2}{4}\sqrt{3}$

8 Pacing and Assignment Guide

REGULAR SCHEDULE

Pre-AP For pacing and assignments for a Pre-AP course, see the *Geometry Toolkit*.

Lesson	Les. Day	BASIC	AVERAGE	ADVANCED
8.1	Day 1	EP p. 899 Exs. 25–30; pp. 510–513 Exs. 1–10, 28, 29, 42–47	pp. 510–513 Exs. 1–10, 28, 29, 33, 34, 42–46 even	pp. 510–513 Exs. 1–10, 28, 29, 33, 34, 43–47 odd
	Day 2	pp. 510–513 Exs. 11–23, 30–34, 39–41	pp. 510–513 Exs. 13–15, 17–25, 30–32, 35–37, 39–41	pp. 510–513 Exs. 14–16, 18–27*, 30–32, 35–38*, 40
8.2	Day 1	EP p. 897 Exs. 35–40; pp. 518–521 Exs. 1–5, 9–19, 23–25, 38–41, 47–57 odd	pp. 518–521 Exs. 1, 2, 5–7, 10–12, 14–16, 17–29 odd, 30–35, 38–43, 46, 50, 52, 56	pp. 518–521 Exs. 1, 2, 7, 8, 10–12, 14–16, 20–28 even, 29–38*, 40–45*, 48, 54, 57
8.3	Day 1	pp. 526–529 Exs. 1–7, 19–22, 31, 32, 46, 47	pp. 526–529 Exs. 1–7, 19–23, 31, 32, 46	pp. 526–529 Exs. 1, 2, 4–7, 19–23, 30–32*, 47
	Day 2	pp. 526–529 Exs. 8–18, 33–37, 43–45	pp. 526–529 Exs. 9, 10, 12–14, 16–18, 24–28, 33–40, 44	pp. 526–529 Exs. 10, 13, 14, 16–18, 24–29, 34–42*, 45
8.4	Day 1	EP p. 898 Exs. 12–17; pp. 537–540 Exs. 1–17, 54, 66–70	pp. 537–540 Exs. 1, 2, 5–7, 10–12, 16, 17, 25–29, 54, 66–70	pp. 537–540 Exs. 1, 2, 7, 8, 12–14, 16, 17, 26–29, 52–54*, 66–70 even
	Day 2	pp. 537–540 Exs. 18–37, 55–59, 65	pp. 537–540 Exs. 18, 21, 22, 30, 31, 32–50 even, 55–62, 65	pp. 537–540 Exs. 18, 23, 24, 30, 31, 33–51 odd, 55, 58–65*
8.5	Day 1	pp. 546–549 Exs. 1–12, 44–46	pp. 546–549 Exs. 1, 2, 4–6, 8–12, 28, 38, 39, 44–46	pp. 546–549 Exs. 1, 2, 4–6, 8–12, 28, 37–39, 43–45*
	Day 2	pp. 546–549 Exs. 13–24, 34–38, 47, 48	pp. 546–549 Exs. 14–17, 19, 20, 22–27, 29–31, 34–37, 40, 41, 47	pp. 546–549 Exs. 15, 16, 19, 20, 22–27, 29–36*, 40–42, 48
8.6	Day 1	pp. 554–557 Exs. 1–15, 17–19, 21, 22, 33–38, 43–49 odd	pp. 554–557 Exs. 1–13, 15–17, 19, 20, 23–28, 35–40, 43, 45, 48	pp. 554–557 Exs. 1–11, 13, 16, 17, 20, 23–32*, 36–42*, 44, 46, 50
Review	Day 1	pp. 560–563 Exs. 1–28	pp. 560–563 Exs. 1–28	pp. 560–563 Exs. 1–28
Assess	Day 1	Chapter 8 Test	Chapter 8 Test	Chapter 8 Test
Yearly Pacing		Chapter 8 Total – 12 days	Chapters 1–8 Total – 106 days	Remaining – 54 days

*Challenge Exercises EP = Extra Practice SRH = Skills Review Handbook

BLOCK SCHEDULE

DAY 1	DAY 2	DAY 3	DAY 4	DAY 5	DAY 6
8.1	8.2	8.3 (CONT.)	8.4 (CONT.)	8.5 (CONT.)	REVIEW
pp. 510–513 Exs. 1–10, 13–15, 17–25, 28–37, 39–41, 42–46 even	pp. 518–521 Exs. 1, 2, 5–7, 10–12, 14–16, 17–29 odd, 30–35, 38–43, 46, 50, 52, 56	pp. 526–529 Exs. 9, 10, 12–14, 16–18, 24–28, 33–40, 44	pp. 537–540 Exs. 18, 21, 22, 30, 31, 32–50 even, 55–62, 65	pp. 546–549 Exs. 14–17, 19, 20, 22–27, 29–31, 34–37, 40, 41, 47	pp. 560–563 Exs. 1–28
	8.3	8.4	8.5	8.6	ASSESS
	pp. 526–529 Exs. 1–7, 19–23, 31, 32, 46	pp. 537–540 Exs. 1, 2, 5–7, 10–12, 16, 17, 25–29, 54, 66–70	pp. 546–549 Exs. 1, 2, 4–6, 8–12, 28, 38, 39, 44–46	pp. 554–557 Exs. 1–13, 15–17, 19, 20, 23–28, 35–40, 43, 45, 48	Chapter 8 Test
Yearly Pacing	Chapter 8 Total – 6 days	Chapters 1–8 Total – 53 days	Remaining – 27 days		

Chapter Resource Guide 8

RESOURCE MANAGER

Chapter Resource Book						
CHAPTER SUPPORT						
Parents as Partners (Chapter Overview with home involvement exercises and activity)					p. 1	
LESSON SUPPORT	**8.1**	**8.2**	**8.3**	**8.4**	**8.5**	**8.6**
Teaching Guide/Lesson Plan	p. 3	p. 16	p. 30	p. 45	p. 60	p. 74
Activity Masters			p. 32			p. 76
Technology Activities & Keystrokes		p. 18		p. 47	p. 62	
Activity Support Masters						
Practice (3 levels)	p. 5	p. 19	p. 33	p. 49	p. 63	p. 77
Study Guide	p. 11	p. 25	p. 39	p. 55	p. 69	p. 83
Catch-Up for Absent Students	p. 13	p. 27	p. 41	p. 57	p. 71	p. 85
Problem Solving/Application	p. 14	p. 28	p. 42	p. 58	p. 72	p. 86
Challenge Practice	p. 15	p. 29	p. 44	p. 59	p. 73	p. 87
REVIEW						
Chapter Review Games and Activities		p. 88	Cumulative Practice			p. 91
Project with Rubric		p. 89	Resource Book Answers			A1

Transparencies	*8.1*	*8.2*	*8.3*	*8.4*	*8.5*	*8.6*
Warm-Up/Daily Homework Quiz	✔	✔	✔	✔	✔	✔
Notetaking Guide	✔	✔	✔	✔	✔	✔
Teacher Support		✔	✔		✔	
Answer Transparencies	✔	✔	✔	✔	✔	✔

ASSESSMENT BOOK

Quizzes	p. 110	SAT/ACT Chapter Test	p. 121
Chapter Tests (3 levels)	p. 113	Alternative Assessment with Rubric	p. 123
Standardized Chapter Test	p. 119		

TECHNOLOGY

- Easy Planner
- Test and Practice Generator
- Power Presentations
- @HomeTutor
- Activity Generator
- Animated Geometry
- Classzone.com
- eEdition Plus Online
- eWorkbook Plus Online
- ML Assessment System

ADDITIONAL RESOURCES

- Worked-Out Solution Key
- Notetaking Guide
- Practice Wookbook
- Geometry Toolkit
- Benchmark Tests
- Remediation Book
- Spanish Study Guide
- Spanish Assessment Book
- Student Resources in Spanish
- Multi-Language Visual Glossary

LESSON 8.1 Practice B
For use with pages 506–513

Find the sum of the measures of the interior angles of the indicated convex polygon.

1. Hexagon 720°　**2.** Dodecagon 1800°　**3.** 11-gon 1620°

4. 15-gon 2340°　**5.** 20-gon 3240°　**6.** 40-gon 6840°

The sum of the measures of the interior angles of a convex polygon is given. Classify the polygon by the number of sides.

7. 180° triangle　**8.** 540° pentagon　**9.** 900° heptagon

10. 1800° dodecagon　**11.** 2520° 16-gon　**12.** 3960° 24-gon

13. 5040° 30-gon　**14.** 5940° 35-gon　**15.** 8640° 50-gon

Find the value of *x*.

16. 121

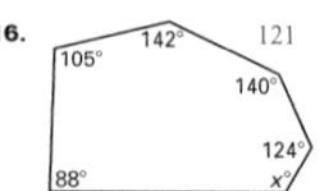

17. 56

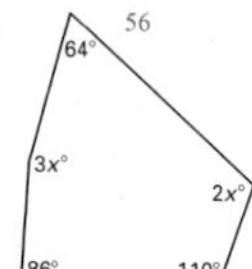

18. 5

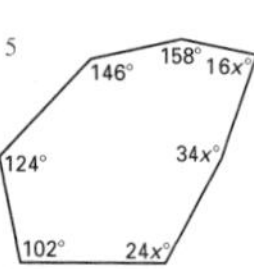

19. 64

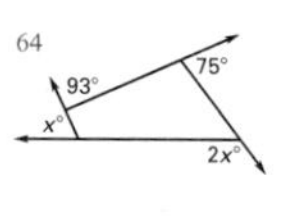

20. 30

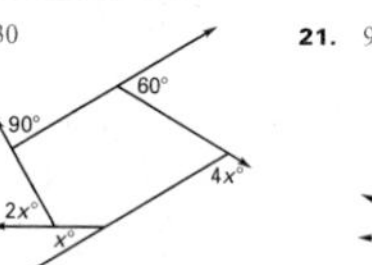

21. 9

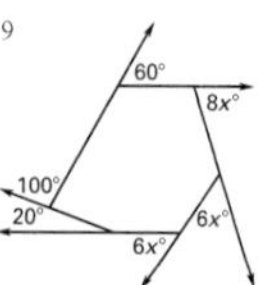

22. What is the measure of each exterior angle of a regular nonagon? 40°

23. The measures of the exterior angles of a convex quadrilateral are 90°, $10x°$, $5x°$, and 45°. What is the measure of the largest exterior angle? 150°

24. The measures of the interior angles of a convex octagon are $45x°$, $40x°$, 155°, 120°, 155°, $38x°$, 158°, and $41x°$. What is the measure of the smallest interior angle? 114°

Find the measures of an interior angle and an exterior angle of the indicated polygon.

25. Regular triangle 60°; 120°　**26.** Regular octagon 135°; 45°　**27.** Regular 16-gon 157.5°; 22.5°

28. Regular 45-gon 172°; 8°　**29.** Regular 60-gon 174°; 6°　**30.** Regular 100-gon 176.4°; 3.6°

LESSON 8.1 Practice B *continued*
For use with pages 506–513

In Exercises 31–34, find the value of *n* for each regular *n*-gon described.

31. Each interior angle of the regular *n*-gon has a measure of 140°. 9

32. Each interior angle of the regular *n*-gon has a measure of 175.2°. 75

33. Each exterior angle of the regular *n*-gon has a measure of 45°. 8

34. Each exterior angle of the regular *n*-gon has a measure of 3°. 120

35. Houses The side view of a storage shed is shown below. Find the value of *x*. Then determine the measure of each angle. $x = 60$; $m\angle A = m\angle B = m\angle E = 120°$ and $m\angle C = m\angle D = 90°$

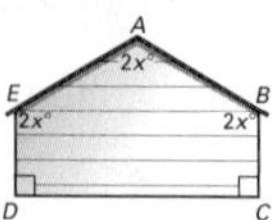

36. Tents The front view of a camping tent is shown below. Find the value of *x*. Then determine the measure of each angle. $x = 70$; $m\angle M = m\angle S = 70°$, $m\angle N = m\angle R = 160°$, $m\angle O = m\angle Q = 150°$, and $m\angle P = 140°$

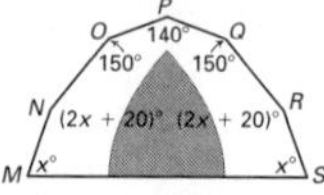

37. Proof Because all the interior angle measures of a regular *n*-gon are congruent, you can find the measure of each individual interior angle. The measure of each interior angle of a regular *n*-gon is $\frac{(n-2)\cdot 180}{n}$. Write a paragraph proof to prove this statement.

Let *A* be a regular *n*-gon and $x°$ be the measure of each interior ∠. Then the sum of the interior ∠s is $n \cdot x°$. By the Polygon Interior ∠s Theorem, the sum of the measures of the interior ∠s of *A* is $(n-2)\cdot 180°$.

So, $n \cdot x° = (n-2)\cdot$ w180°, or $x = \frac{(n-2)\cdot 180}{n}$.

LESSON 8.2 Practice B
For use with pages 514–521

Find the measure of the indicated angle in the parallelogram.

1. Find $m\angle B$. 116°　**2.** Find $m\angle G$. 48°　**3.** Find $m\angle M$. 96°

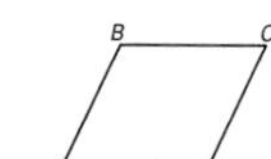

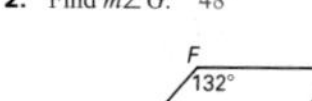

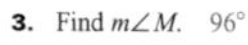

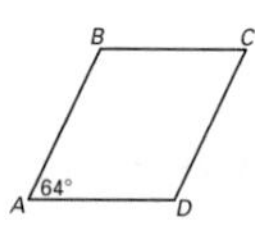

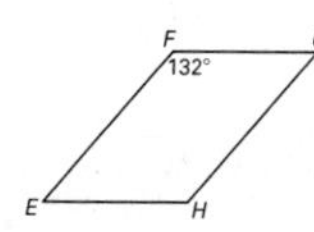

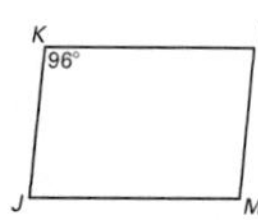

Find the value of each variable in the parallelogram.

4. $a = 9$; $b = 11$

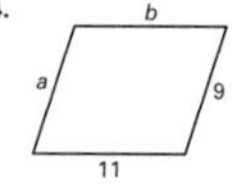

5. $x = 2$; $y = 17$

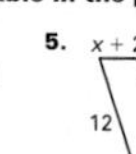

6. $x = 4$; $y = 116$

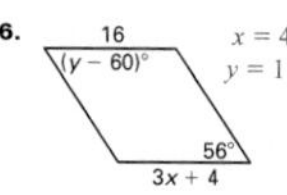

7.

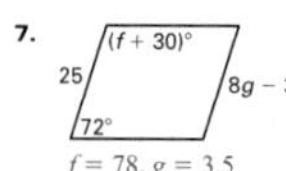

$f = 78$, $g = 3.5$

8.

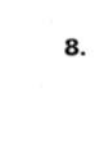

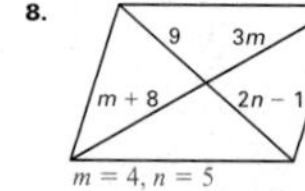

$m = 4$, $n = 5$

9.

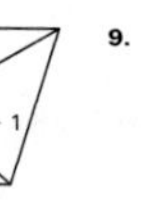

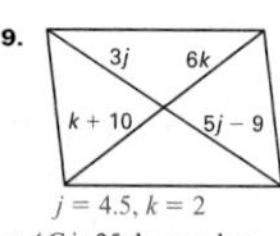

$j = 4.5$, $k = 2$

10. In ▱*WXYZ*, $m\angle W$ is 50 degrees more than $m\angle X$. Sketch ▱*WXYZ*. Find the measure of each interior angle. Then label each angle with its measure.

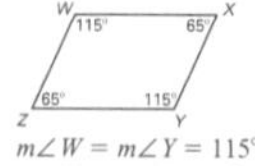

$m\angle W = m\angle Y = 115°$, $m\angle X = m\angle Z = 65°$

11. In ▱*EFGH*, $m\angle G$ is 25 degrees less than $m\angle H$. Sketch ▱*EFGH*. Find the measure of each interior angle. Then label each angle with its measure.

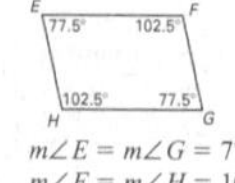

$m\angle E = m\angle G = 77.5°$, $m\angle F = m\angle H = 102.5°$

Find the indicated measure in ▱*ABCD*.

12. $m\angle AEB$ 117°　**13.** $m\angle BAE$ 40°

14. $m\angle AED$ 63°　**15.** $m\angle ECB$ 80°

16. $m\angle BAD$ 120°　**17.** $m\angle DCE$ 40°

18. $m\angle ADC$ 60°　**19.** $m\angle DCB$ 120°

LESSON 8.2 Practice B *continued*
For use with pages 514–521

Use the diagram of ▱*MNOP*. Points *Q*, *R*, *S*, and *T* are midpoints of $\overline{MX}$, $\overline{NX}$, $\overline{OX}$, and $\overline{PX}$. Find the indicated measure. (Diagram is not drawn to scale.)

20. *PN* 12

21. *MQ* 5

22. *XO* 10

23. $m\angle NMQ$ 18°

24. $m\angle NXO$ 48°

25. $m\angle MNP$ 30°

26. $m\angle NPO$ 30°

27. $m\angle NOP$ 55°

28. Movie Equipment The scissor lift shown at the right is sometimes used by camera crews to film movie scenes. The lift can be raised or lowered so that the camera can get a variety of views of one scene. In the figure, points *E*, *F*, *G*, and *H* are the vertices of a parallelogram.

a. If $m\angle E = 45°$, find $m\angle F$. 135°

b. What happens to ∠*E* and ∠*F* when the lift is raised? *Explain.*

As the lift is raised, vertices *F* and *H* of the parallelogram become farther apart causing the measure of ∠*F* to decrease and the measure of ∠*E* to increase.

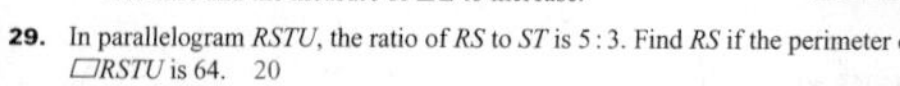

29. In parallelogram *RSTU*, the ratio of *RS* to *ST* is 5 : 3. Find *RS* if the perimeter of ▱*RSTU* is 64. 20

30. Parallelogram *MNOP* and parallelogram *PQRO* share a common side, as shown. Using a two-column proof, prove that segment *MN* is congruent to segment *QR*.

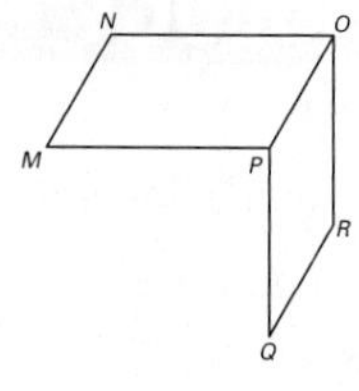

GIVEN: *MNOP* and *PQRO* are parallelograms.

PROVE: $\overline{MN} \cong \overline{QR}$

Statements	Reasons
1. *MNOP* and *PQRO*	1. Given are ▱'s.
2. $\overline{MN} \cong \overline{OP}$; $\overline{OP} \cong \overline{QR}$	2. Opp. sides of a ▱ are ≅.
3. $\overline{MN} \cong \overline{QR}$	3. Transitive prop. of congruence.

LESSON 8.3

Practice B
For use with pages 522–529

What theorem can you use to show that the quadrilateral is a parallelogram?

1. 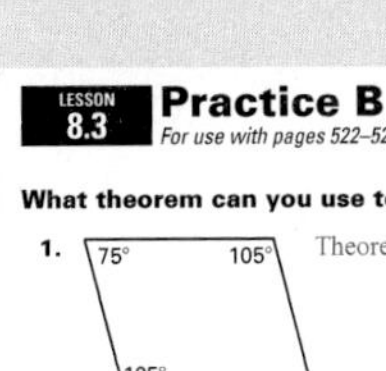

Theorem 8.8

2. 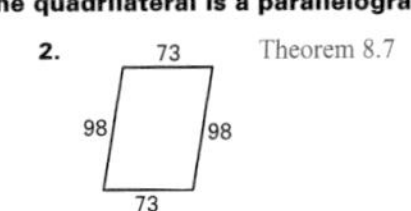

Theorem 8.7

3. 

Theorem 8.10

4. Theorem 8.9

For what value of *x* is the quadrilateral a parallelogram?

5. 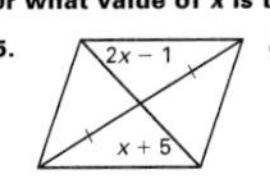

6

6. 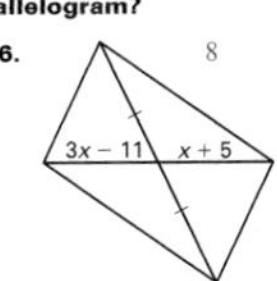

8

7. 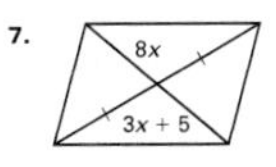

1

8. 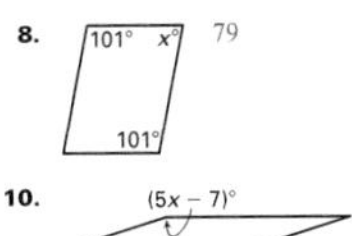

79

9. 20

10. 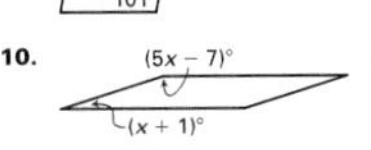

31

LESSON 8.3

LESSON 8.3

Practice B *continued*
For use with pages 522–529

The vertices of quadrilateral *ABCD* are given. Draw *ABCD* in a coordinate plane and show that it is a parallelogram.

11. $A(-2, -3), B(0, 5), C(6, 5), D(4, -3)$

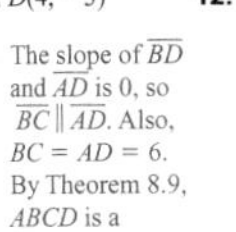

The slope of $\overline{BD}$ and $\overline{AD}$ is 0, so $\overline{BC} \parallel \overline{AD}$. Also, $BC = AD = 6$. By Theorem 8.9, $ABCD$ is a parallelogram.

12. $A(-3, -4), B(-1, 2), C(7, 0), D(5, -6)$

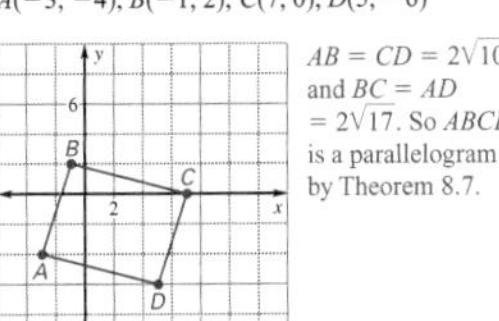

$AB = CD = 2\sqrt{10}$ and $BC = AD = 2\sqrt{17}$. So $ABCD$ is a parallelogram by Theorem 8.7.

***Describe* how to prove that *ABCD* is a parallelogram.**

13. 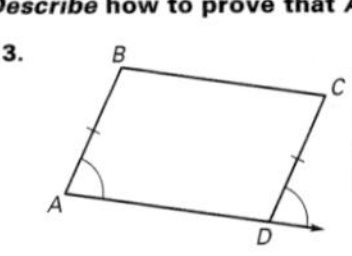

Use Corresponding Angles Converse to show $\overline{AB} \parallel \overline{CD}$, then apply Theorem 8.9.

14. 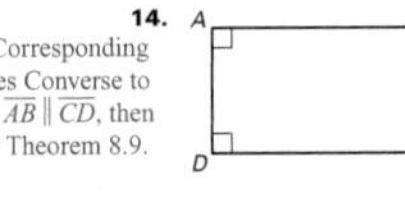

Use Right Angle Congruence Theorem, then apply Theorem 8.8.

15. Three vertices of $\square ABCD$ are $A(-1, 4)$, $B(4, 4)$, and $C(11, -3)$. Find the coordinates of point D. $D(6, -3)$

16. **History** The diagram shows a battering ram which was used in ancient times to break through walls. A log is suspended on ropes of equal length ($\overline{GF}$ and $\overline{HJ}$). The log swings, causing quadrilateral $FGHJ$ to shift. In the diagram, $\overline{GH} \cong \overline{FJ}$ and $\overline{GH}$ is parallel to the ground.

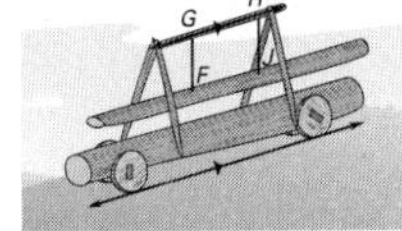

a. Identify $FGHJ$. *Explain.* See below.

b. *Explain* why the log is always parallel to the ground. See below.

17. **Proof** Use the diagram at the right.

GIVEN: $\triangle ABC \cong \triangle CDA$

PROVE: $ABCD$ is a parallelogram.

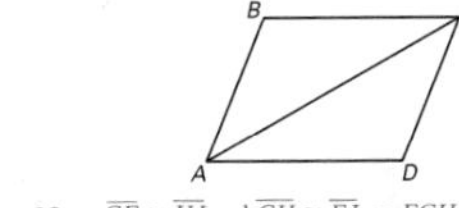

Statements	Reasons
1. $\triangle ABC \cong \triangle CDA$	1. Given
2. $\overline{AB} \cong \overline{CD}$, $\overline{CB} \cong \overline{AD}$	2. Corresp. sides of $\cong$ triangles are $\cong$.
3. $ABCD$ is a $\square$.	3. Theorem 8.7

16. **a.** $\overline{GF} \cong \overline{HJ}$ and $\overline{GH} \cong \overline{FJ}$, so $FGHJ$ is a parallelogram by Theorem 8.7. **b.** $FGHJ$ is always a $\square$, so $\overline{GH} \parallel \overline{FJ}$. Because $\overline{GH}$ is parallel to the ground, then $\overline{FJ}$ is also parallel to the ground by the Transitive Property of Parallel Lines. So, the moving log is always parallel to the ground.

LESSON 8.4

Practice B
For use with pages 533–540

For any rhombus *ABCD*, decide whether the statement is *always* or *sometimes* true. Draw a diagram and *explain* your reasoning.

1. $\angle ABC \cong \angle CDA$

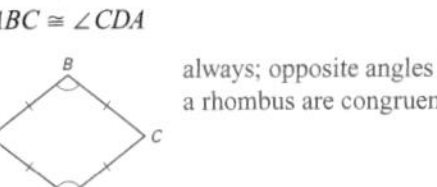

always; opposite angles in a rhombus are congruent.

2. $\overline{CA} \cong \overline{DB}$

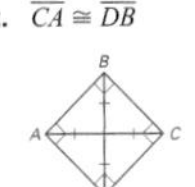

sometimes; if a rhombus is also a square, then its diagonals are congruent.

For any rectangle *FGHJ*, decide whether the statement is *always* or *sometimes* true. Draw a diagram and *explain* your reasoning.

3. $\angle F \cong \angle H$ always; every angle in a rectangle is a right angle.

4. $\overline{GH} \cong \overline{HJ}$ sometimes; if a rectangle is a square, then consecutive sides are congruent.

Classify the quadrilateral. *Explain* your reasoning.

5. rhombus; all sides are congruent.

6. 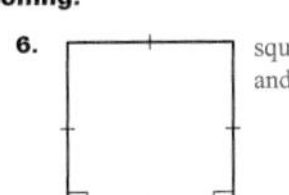
square; all sides are congruent and all angles are right angles.

Name each quadrilateral—*parallelogram, rectangle, rhombus,* and *square*—for which the statement is true.

7. It is equilateral. rhombus, square

8. The diagonals are congruent. rectangle, square

9. It can contain obtuse angles. parallelogram, rhombus

10. It contains no acute angles. rectangle, square

Classify the special quadrilateral. *Explain* your reasoning. Then find the values of *x* and *y*.

11. 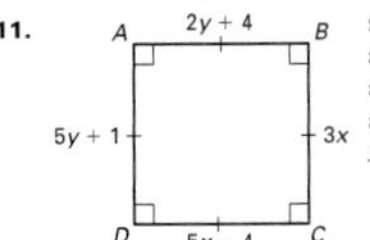

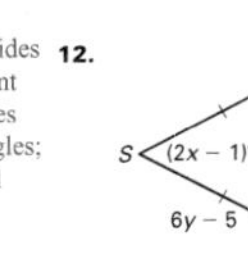

square; all sides are congruent and all angles are right angles; $x = 2, y = 1$

12. 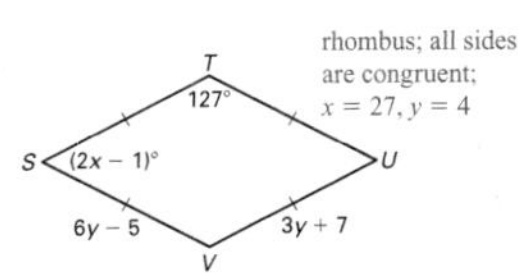

rhombus; all sides are congruent; $x = 27, y = 4$

LESSON 8.4

LESSON 8.4

Practice B *continued*
For use with pages 533–540

The diagonals of rhombus *PQRS* intersect at *T*. Given that $\angle RPS = 30°$ and $RT = 6$, find the indicated measure.

13. $m\angle QPR$ 30°

14. $m\angle QTP$ 90°

15. RP 12

16. QT $2\sqrt{3}$

The diagonals of rectangle *WXYZ* intersect at *P*. Given that $\angle YXZ = 50°$ and $XZ = 12$, find the indicated measure.

17. $m\angle WXZ$ 40°

18. $m\angle WPX$ 100°

19. PY 6

20. WX about 9.2

The diagonals of square *DEFG* intersect at *H*. Given that $EH = 5$, find the indicated measure.

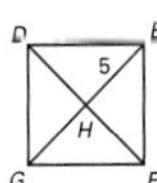

21. $m\angle GHF$ 90°

22. $m\angle DGH$ 45°

23. HF 5

24. DE $5\sqrt{2}$

25. **Windows** In preparation for a storm, a window is protected by nailing boards along its diagonals. The lengths of the boards are the same. Can you conclude that the window is square? *Explain.* No; the diagonals of all rectangles are congruent, so the window may not be square.

26. **Clothing** The side view of a wooden clothes dryer is shown at the right. Measurements shown are in inches.

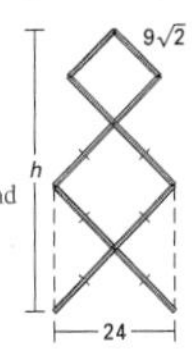

a. The uppermost quadrilateral is a square. Classify the quadrilateral below the square. *Explain* your reasoning. square; 4 congruent sides and 4 right angles

b. Find the height h of the clothes dryer. 54 in.

27. **Proof** The diagonals of rhombus $ABCD$ form several triangles. Using a two-column proof, prove that $\triangle BFA \cong \triangle DFC$.

GIVEN: $ABCD$ is a rhombus.

PROVE: $\triangle BFA \cong \triangle DFC$

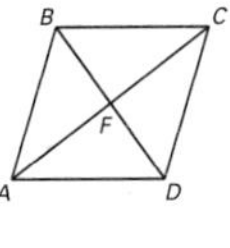

Statements	Reasons
1. $ABCD$ is a rhom.	1. Given
2. $\angle ABF \cong \angle CDF$, $\angle BAF \cong \angle DCF$	2. Theorem 8.12
3. $\overline{BA} \cong \overline{DC}$	3. Definition of a rhom.
4. $\triangle BFA \cong \triangle DFC$	4. ASA Cong. Postulate

8 Lesson Practice Level B

LESSON 8.5 Practice B

For use with pages 541–549

Points *A, B, C,* and *D* are the vertices of a quadrilateral. Determine whether *ABCD* is a trapezoid.

1. $A(-2, 3), B(3, 3), C(-1, -2), D(2, -2)$ trapezoid
2. $A(-3, 2), B(3, 0), C(4, 3), D(-2, 5)$ not a trapezoid
3. $A(-5, -3), B(-1, -1), C(-1, 3), D(-3, 2)$ trapezoid

Find $m\angle F$, $m\angle G$, and $m\angle H$.

4. 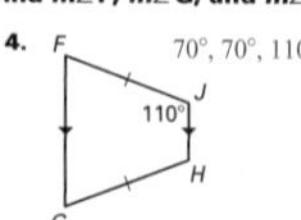

70°, 70°, 110°

5. 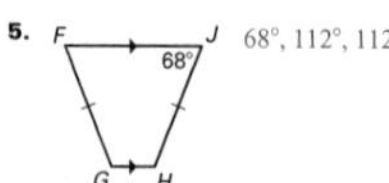

68°, 112°, 112°

Find the length of the midsegment of the trapezoid.

6. 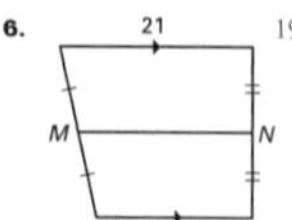

19

7. 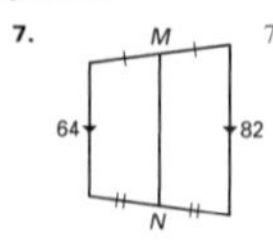

73

***JKLM* is a kite. Find $m\angle K$.**

8. 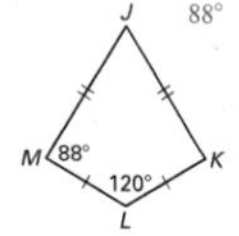

88°

9. 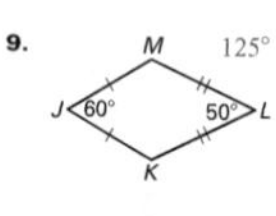

125°

Use Theorem 8.18 and the Pythagorean Theorem to find the side lengths of the kite. Write the lengths in simplest radical form.

10. 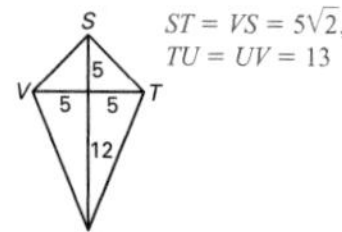

$ST = VS = 5\sqrt{2}$, $TU = UV = 13$

11. S, V, T, U; 8, 9, 9, 7
$ST = VS = \sqrt{145}$, $TU = UV = \sqrt{130}$

LESSON 8.5 Practice B *continued*

For use with pages 541–549

Find the value of *x*.

12. 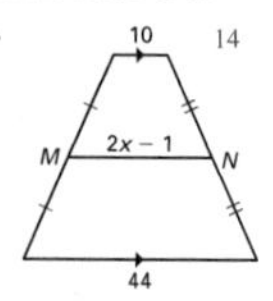

14

13. 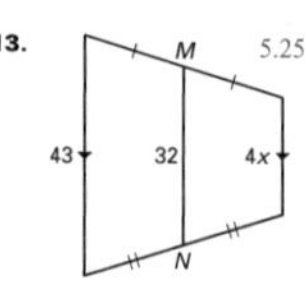

5.25

14. 2x; M; 17.1; N; 8x + 3.2
3.1

15. 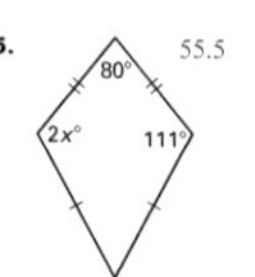

55.5

16. **Maps** Use the map shown at the right. The lines represent a sidewalk connecting the locations on the map.

Pool, Tennis court, Miniature golf course, Arcade, Basketball court, Restaurant

a. Is the sidewalk in the shape of a kite? *Explain.* No; none of the side lengths are congruent.

b. A sidewalk is built that connects the arcade, tennis court, miniature golf course, and restaurant. What is the shape of the sidewalk? trapezoid

c. What is the length of the midsegment of the sidewalk in part (b)? $\frac{3\sqrt{13}}{2}$ units

17. **Kite** You cut out a piece of fabric in the shape of a kite so that the congruent angles of the kite are 100°. Of the remaining two angles, one is 4 times larger than the other. What is the measure of the largest angle in the kite? 128°

18. **Proof** $\overline{MN}$ is the midsegment of isosceles trapezoid *FGHJ*. Write a paragraph proof to show that *FMNJ* is an isosceles trapezoid.

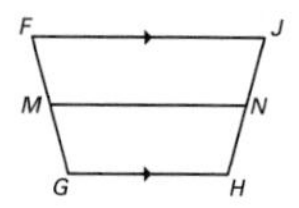

$\overline{MN}$ is the midsegment of isosceles trapezoid *FGHJ*, so $FM = MG = JN = NH$. Also, $\overline{MN} \parallel \overline{FJ}$ by Theorem 8.17. So, *FMNJ* is an isosceles trapezoid because it has one pair of parallel sides ($\overline{MN} \parallel \overline{FJ}$) and the legs are congruent ($FM = JN$).

LESSON 8.6 Practice B

For use with pages 552–557

Complete the chart. Put an X in the box if the shape *always* has the given property.

	Property	▱	Rectangle	Rhombus	Square	Kite	Trapezoid
1.	Both pairs of opposite sides are congruent.	X	X	X	X		
2.	Both pairs of opposite angles are congruent.	X	X	X	X		
3.	Exactly one pair of opposite sides are congruent.						
4.	Exactly one pair of opposite sides are parallel.						X
5.	Exactly one pair of opposite angles are congruent.					X	
6.	Consecutive angles are supplementary.	X	X	X	X		

Give the most specific name for the quadrilateral. *Explain.*

7. 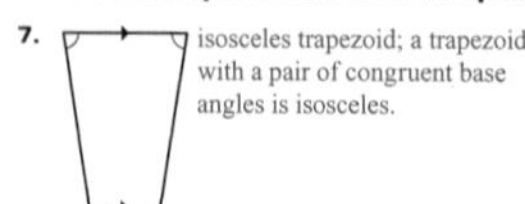
isosceles trapezoid; a trapezoid with a pair of congruent base angles is isosceles.

8. 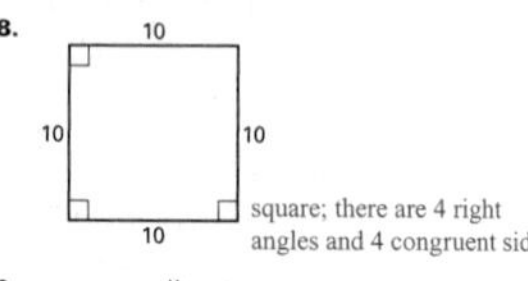

square; there are 4 right angles and 4 congruent sides.

9. kite; there are two pairs of consecutive congruent sides, but opposite sides are not congruent.

10. 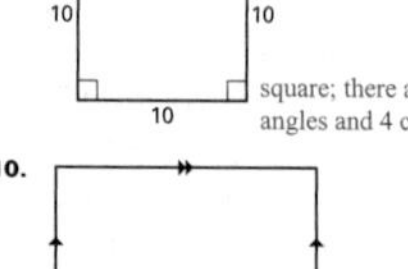
parallelogram; both pairs of opposite sides are parallel.

LESSON 8.6 Practice B *continued*

For use with pages 552–557

Tell whether enough information is given in the diagram to classify the quadrilateral by the indicated name.

11. Rectangle yes; Theorem 8.13

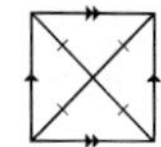

12. Isosceles trapezoid yes; Theorem 8.15

13. Rhombus no

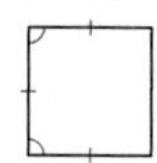

14. Kite no

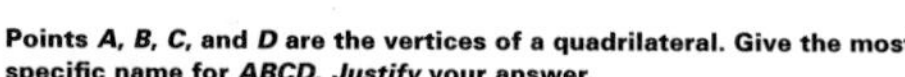

Points *A, B, C,* and *D* are the vertices of a quadrilateral. Give the most specific name for *ABCD*. *Justify* your answer.

15. $A(2, 2), B(4, 6), C(6, 5), D(4, 1)$
rectangle; opposite sides are congruent and contains 4 right angles.

16. $A(-5, 1), B(0, -6), C(5, 1), D(0, 3)$
kite; there are two pairs of consecutive congruent sides, but opposite sides are not congruent.

In Exercises 17 and 18, which two segments or angles must be congruent so that you can prove that *FGHJ* is the indicated quadrilateral? There may be more than one right answer.

17. Kite $\overline{FG}$ and $\overline{HJ}$

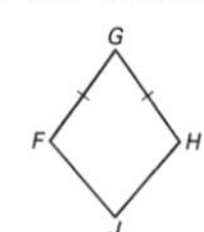

18. Isosceles trapezoid *Sample answer:* $\angle FJH$ and $\angle JHG$

19. **Picture Frame** What type of special quadrilateral is the stand of the picture frame at the right? trapezoid

20. **Painting** A painter uses a quadrilateral shaped piece of canvas. The artist begins by painting lines that represent the diagonals of the canvas. If the lengths of the painted lines are congruent, what types of quadrilaterals could represent the shape of the canvas? If the painted lines are also perpendicular, what type of quadrilateral represents the shape of the canvas? rectangle, square, isosceles trapezoid; square

CHAPTER 8

Quiz 1

For use after Lessons 8.1–8.2

Find the value of *x*.

1.

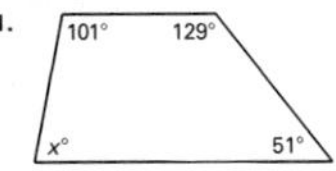

2.

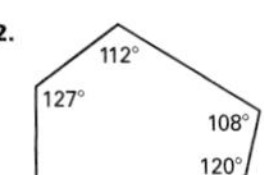

3.

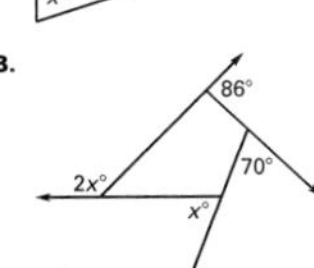

Find the value of each variable in the parallelogram.

4.

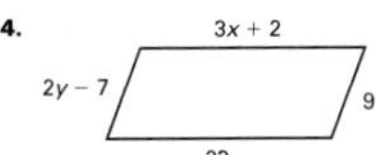

5.

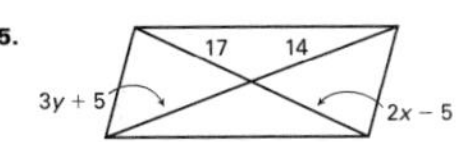

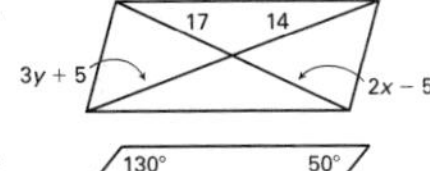

6.

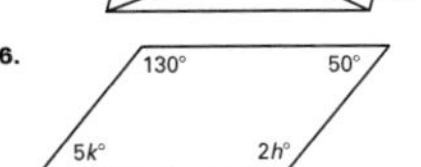

Answers

1. 79
2. 73
3. 68
4. $x = 7,\ y = 8$
5. $x = 11, y = 3$
6. $h = 65, k = 10$

CHAPTER 8

Quiz 2

For use after Lessons 8.3–8.4

For what value of *x* is the quadrilateral a parallelogram?

1. 2x + 9; 5x − 3

2. (2x + 25)°; (4x − 15)°

3. 5x; 7x − 60

Classify the quadrilateral. *Explain* your reasoning.

4.

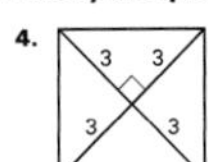

5.

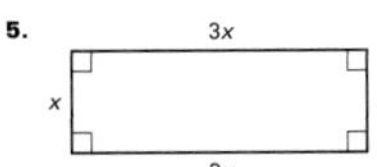

6.

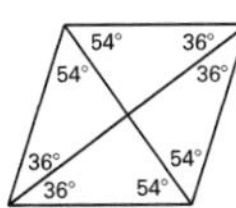

Answers

1. 4
2. 20
3. 30
4. Square; it is both a rhombus and a rectangle.
5. rectangle; Rectangle Corollary
6. rhombus; Theorem 8.12

CHAPTER 8

Quiz 3

For use after Lessons 8.5–8.6

Find the unknown angle measures.

1.

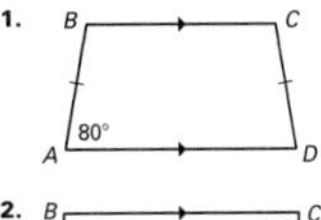

2.

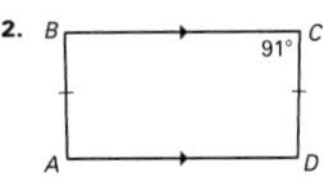

3.

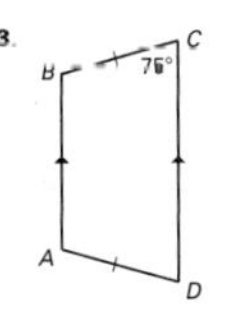

Give the most specific name for the quadrilateral.

4.

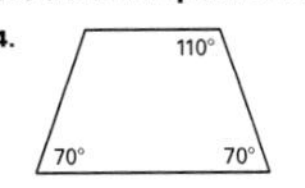

5.

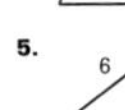

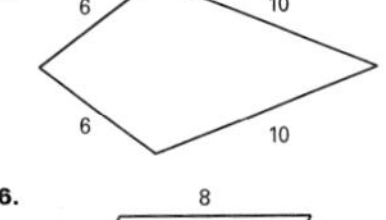

6.

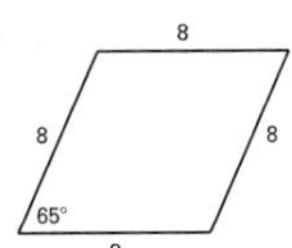

Answers

1. $\angle B = 100°$; $\angle C = 100°$; $\angle D = 80°$
2. $\angle A = 89°$; $\angle B = 91°$; $\angle D = 89°$
3. $\angle A = 105°$; $\angle B = 105°$; $\angle D = 75°$
4. isosceles trapezoid
5. kite
6. rhombus

8 Assessment

Chapter Test B
For use after Chapter 8

Find the value of x.

1. 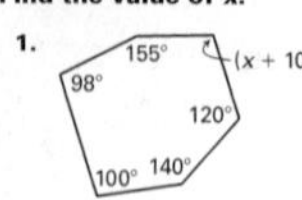

2. 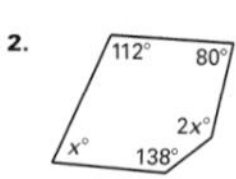

3. 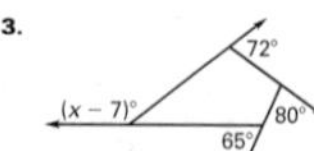

4. 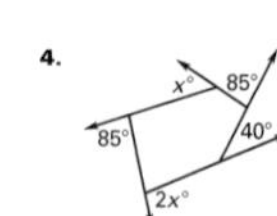

Find the value of x in the parallelogram.

5. 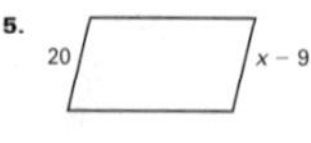

6. 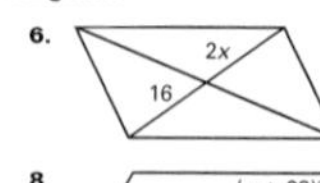

7. 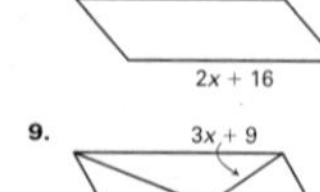

8. 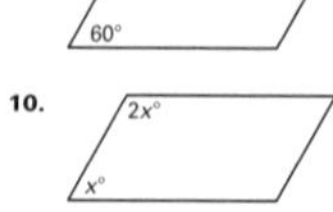

9.

10.

Three of the vertices of ▱ABCD are given. Find the coordinates of point D.

11. $A(3, 6), B(6, 7), C(6, 3), D(x, y)$
12. $A(-3, -4), B(-3, 2), C(-1, 4), D(x, y)$
13. $A(6, 0), B(0, 4), C(-4, 2), D(x, y)$
14. $A(-1, 0), B(4, -1), C(2, -4), D(x, y)$

Answers

1. 97
2. 70
3. 150
4. 50
5. 29
6. 8
7. 6
8. 37
9. 3
10. 60
11. (3, 2)
12. (−1, −2)
13. (2, −2)
14. (−3, −3)

Chapter Test B *continued*
For use after Chapter 8

For any rectangle CMXZ, decide whether the statement is *always, sometimes,* or *never* true.

15. $\overline{CM} \cong \overline{MX}$
16. $\overline{ZX} \cong \overline{CM}$
17. $\angle Z \cong \angle M$
18. $\overline{ZM} \cong \overline{CX}$
19. $\overline{CM} \perp \overline{ZX}$
20. $\angle CMZ \cong \angle XZM$

Find the value of x.

21. 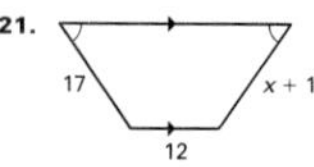

22. 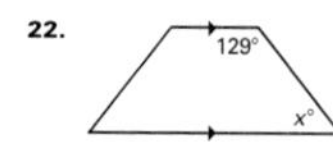

23. 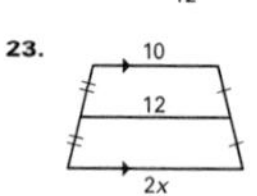

24. 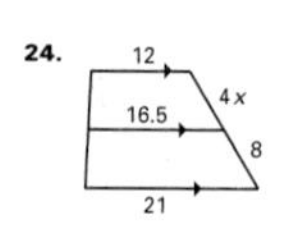

Give the most specific name for the quadrilateral.

25. 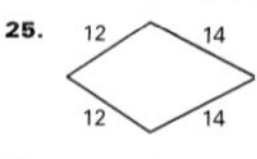

26. 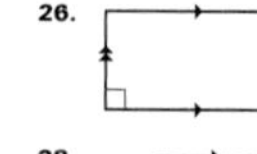

27. 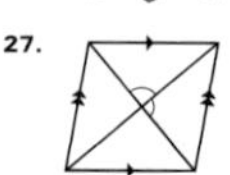

28. 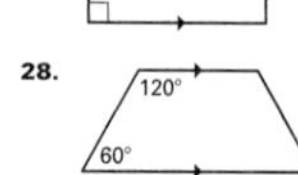

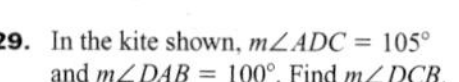

29. In the kite shown, $m\angle ADC = 105°$ and $m\angle DAB = 100°$. Find $m\angle DCB$.

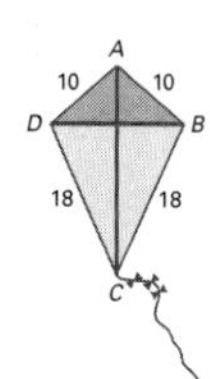

Answers

15. sometimes
16. always
17. always
18. always
19. never
20. always
21. 6
22. 51
23. 7
24. 2
25. kite
26. rectangle
27. rhombus
28. trapezoid
29. 50°

Standardized Test
For use after Chapter 8

Multiple Choice

1. A segment of a polygon that joins two nonconsecutive vertices is called a _?_. B
   (A) transversal (B) diagonal
   (C) hypotenuse (D) geometric mean

2. What is the sum of the measures of the interior angles of the figure shown? A

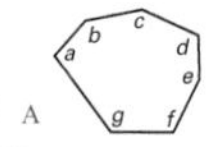

   (A) 900° (B) 1260°
   (C) 720° (D) 1080°

3. Find *x*. D
   (A) 27°
   (B) 36°
   (C) 9°
   (D) 18°

4. Which is *not* true of a parallelogram? B
   (A) opposite angles are congruent
   (B) consecutive angles are complementary
   (C) opposite sides are congruent
   (D) diagonals bisect each other

5. Find *p* and *q*. C

   (A) $p = 108, q = 29$ (B) $p = -28, q = 21$
   (C) $p = 8, q = 29$ (D) $p = 108, q = 21$

6. Find *a* and *b*. C

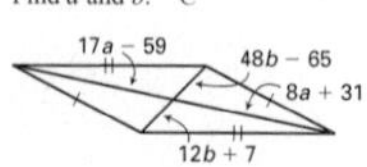

   (A) $a = 111, b = 31$ (B) $a = 2, b = 10$
   (C) $a = 10, b = 2$ (D) $a = 31, b = 111$

7. Which statement would *not* prove that *ABCD* is a parallelogram? A

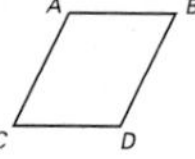

   (A) $\overline{AC} \cong \overline{CD}$ and $\overline{AB} \cong \overline{BD}$
   (B) $\overline{AD}$ and $\overline{BC}$ bisect each other
   (C) $\angle A \cong \angle D$ and $\angle B \cong \angle C$
   (D) $\overline{AB} \parallel \overline{CD}$ and $\overline{AB} \cong \overline{CD}$

8. What value of *x* makes quadrilateral *STUV* a parallelogram? D
   (A) 14
   (B) 102
   (C) 51
   (D) 7

9. Which statement is false? B
   (A) A parallelogram is a rectangle if and only if its diagonals are congruent.
   (B) A parallelogram is a rhombus if and only if its diagonals are congruent.
   (C) A quadrilateral is a square if and only if it is a rhombus and a rectangle.
   (D) A quadrilateral is a rectangle if and only if it has four right angles.

10. A quadrilateral with exactly one pair of parallel sides is a _?_. C
   (A) rhombus (B) parallelogram
   (C) trapezoid (D) square

11. Which statement about isosceles trapezoids is false? A
   (A) The base segments are congruent.
   (B) It has a pair of congruent base angles.
   (C) Its diagonals are congruent.
   (D) Each pair of base angles is congruent.

Standardized Test *continued*
For use after Chapter 8

12. Which statement about kites is false? B
   (A) A kite's diagonals are perpendicular.
   (B) A kite's opposite sides are congruent.
   (C) A kite has two pairs of consecutive congruent sides.
   (D) A kite has exactly one pair of opposite angles that are congruent.

13. Find the length of the midsegment of the trapezoid shown. A

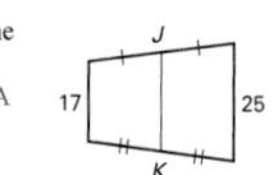
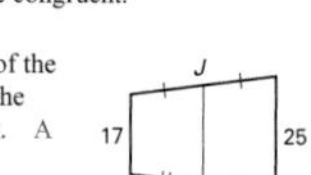

   (A) 21 (B) 19 (C) 20 (D) 22

14. *WXYZ* is a kite. Find $m\angle W$. D
   (A) 160°
   (B) 200°
   (C) 95°
   (D) 100°

15. Points $A(3, 2), B(7, 2), C(6, 9)$ and $D(4, 9)$ are the vertices of a quadrilateral. What is the most specific name for *ABCD*? D

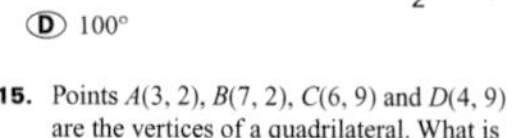

   (A) parallelogram (B) trapezoid
   (C) rectangle (D) isosceles trapezoid

Gridded Answer

16. Find the perimeter of kite *PQRS* to the nearest tenth.

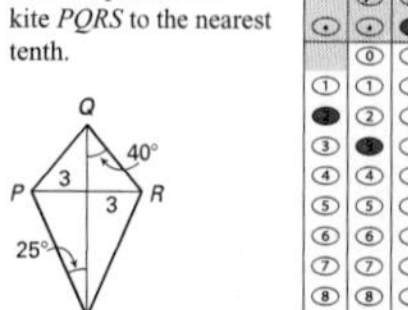
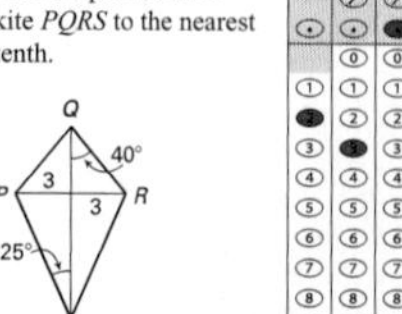

Grid: 2 3 . 5

Short Response

17. In the section of the suspension bridge shown, $\overline{GL}$ is the midsegment of trapezoid *FHKM* and $\overline{HK}$ is the midsegment of trapezoid *GIJL*.

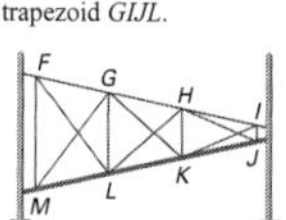

$FM = 70$ ft, $IJ = 10$ ft

   a. If $HK = 30$ ft and $GL = 50$ ft, how much cable is needed for $\overline{FM}$ and $\overline{IJ}$?
   b. If all trapezoids shown are isosceles trapezoids and $FG = 60$ ft, $GH = 40$ ft, and $HI = 20$ ft, find the length of all 16 segments to determine the total amount of linear cable feet needed. 732.8 ft

Extended Response

18. A water trough has two congruent isosceles trapezoids as ends and two congruent rectangles as sides.

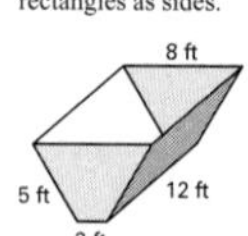

   a. Find the exterior surface area of the trough. 184 ft²
   b. Find the volume of the trough in cubic feet. 240 ft³
   c. If the trough is emptied until the water level is even with the midsegment of the trapezoidal ends, how much water is left in the trough? 84 ft³

CHAPTER 8 Alternative Assessment and Math Journal

For use after Chapter 8

Journal 1. Draw a Venn diagram that shows the relationship between different kinds of special quadrilaterals. Explain how these special quadrilaterals can be classified in their properties.

Multi-Step Problem 2. The surface of a gemstone is cut into flat faces called facets. Each facet is a polygon. The way a gemstone is cut affects the way light is reflected and refracted. The top part of a cut gem is called the crown and the bottom part is called the pavilion.

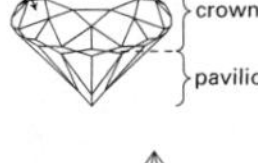

a. In the triangular gem at the right, the top view of the pavilion cut is shown. Quadrilateral *ABCD* is a rhombus. List everything you know about this quadrilateral.

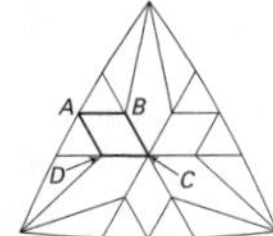

b. In the top view of the crown cut of the rectangular gem shown at the right, $\overline{EF}$ is the midsegment of trapezoid *ABCD*, $\overline{AD}$ is the midsegment of trapezoid *EFGH*, $BC = 4$ millimeters, and $AD = 8$ millimeters. Find *EF*. Then find *HG*.

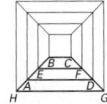

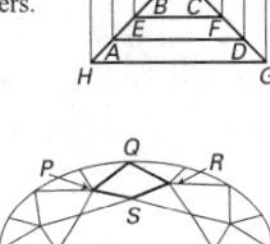

c. In the top view of the crown cut of the oval gem shown at the right, the very top facet is called the table. What is the sum of the measures of the angles of the polygon that is the table?

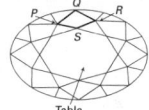

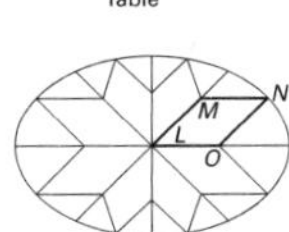

d. In quadrilateral *PQRS*, $\angle P$ and $\angle R$ are congruent. What is the most specific name for quadrilateral *PQRS*?

e. In the pavilion cut of the oval gem shown at the right, quadrilateral *LMNO* is a parallelogram and $m\angle L = 41°$. Find $m\angle M$. *Explain* your reasoning.

f. Which gem, the rectangular or the oval, do you think is more brilliant. *Explain* your reasoning.

1. Complete answers should include: a Venn diagram that shows the relationship between different kinds of quadrilaterals; an explanation of how the quadrilaterals can be classified by their properties (see the Chapter Summary for Chapter 8 in the text).

2. a. $\overline{AB} \cong \overline{BC} \cong \overline{CD} \cong \overline{AD}$; $\overline{AC} \perp \overline{BD}$; $\overline{AC}$ bisects $\angle BCD$ and $\angle BAD$; $\overline{BD}$ bisects $\angle ABC$ and $\angle ADC$ **b.** $EF = 6$ mm; $HG = 10$ mm **c.** 1080° **d.** kite **e.** 139°; Because the quadrilateral is a parallelogram, $\angle L$ and $\angle M$ are supplementary. So $\angle M = (180 - 41)° = 139°$ **f.** Answers will vary.

CHAPTER 8 Alternative Assessment Rubric *continued*

For use after Chapter 8

Journal Solution 1. Complete answers should include:

- a Venn diagram that shows the relationship between different kinds of quadrilaterals.
- an explanation of how the quadrilaterals can be classified by their properties (see the Chapter Summary for Chapter 8 in the text).

Multi-Step Problem Solution 2. a. $\overline{AB} \cong \overline{BC} \cong \overline{CD} \cong \overline{AD}$; $\overline{AC} \perp \overline{BD}$; $\overline{AC}$ bisects $\angle BCD$ and $\angle BAD$; $\overline{BD}$ bisects $\angle ABC$ and $\angle ADC$

b. $EF = 6$ mm; $HG = 10$ mm

c. 1080°

d. kite

e. 139°; Because the quadrilateral is a parallelogram, $\angle L$ and $\angle M$ are supplementary. So $\angle M = (180 - 41)° = 139°$

f. Answers will vary.

Multi-Step Problem Rubric

4 The student answers all parts of the problem correctly and completely. The student shows all work. The student's work is neat.

3 The student answers all parts of the problem. The student's work may have an error in the Venn diagram and one or two errors in calculations for the segment lengths or angles. The student shows most work. The student's work is neat.

2 The student answers all parts of the problem. The student's work contains multiple errors, but the student shows most work. The student's work is sloppy.

1 The student does not complete all parts of the problem. The work contains many errors in logic. The student's work is sloppy, or no work is shown.

PLAN AND PREPARE

Main Ideas

In this chapter students will find angle measures in polygons. They will investigate properties of parallelograms and learn what information they can use to conclude that a quadrilateral is a parallelogram. Students will also study special quadrilaterals such as rhombuses, rectangles, squares, trapezoids, and kites.

Prerequisite Skills

- Identifying angle pairs
- Using the Triangle Sum Theorem
- Using parallel lines

Additional resources for reviewing prerequisite skills are:

- Skills Review Handbook, pp. 869–895
- @HomeTutor

8 Quadrilaterals

Before

In previous chapters, you learned the following skills, which you'll use in Chapter 8: identifying angle pairs, using the Triangle Sum Theorem, and using parallel lines.

Prerequisite Skills

VOCABULARY CHECK

Copy and complete the statement.

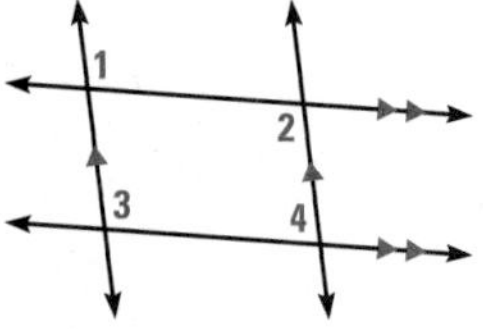

1. $\angle 1$ and _?_ are vertical angles. **$\angle 4$**
2. $\angle 3$ and _?_ are consecutive interior angles. **$\angle 5$**
3. $\angle 7$ and _?_ are corresponding angles. **$\angle 3$**
4. $\angle 5$ and _?_ are alternate interior angles. **$\angle 4$**

SKILLS AND ALGEBRA CHECK

5. In $\triangle ABC$, $m\angle A = x°$, $m\angle B = 3x°$, and $m\angle C = (4x - 12)°$. Find the measures of the three angles. *(Review p. 217 for 8.1.)* **24°, 72°, 84°**

Find the measure of the indicated angle. *(Review p. 154 for 8.2–8.5.)*

6. If $m\angle 3 = 105°$, then $m\angle 2 =$ _?_. **105°**
7. If $m\angle 1 = 98°$, then $m\angle 3 =$ _?_. **98°**
8. If $m\angle 4 = 82°$, then $m\angle 1 =$ _?_. **98°**
9. If $m\angle 2 = 102°$, then $m\angle 4 =$ _?_. **78°**

@HomeTutor Prerequisite skills practice at classzone.com

Chapter Planning Guide

Chapter 8 Resource Book
- Teaching Guide/Lesson Plan (pp. 3, 16, 30, 45, 60, 74)
- Project with Rubric (p. 89)

Assessment and Intervention
- Assessment Book (pp. 110–124)
- Benchmark Tests
- Remediation Book

Interactive Technology
- Easy Planner
- Power Presentations CD-ROM
- Activity Generator CD-ROM
- Animated Geometry
- Test Generator CD-ROM
- Online Quizzes
- eWorkbook
- eEdition
- @HomeTutor

Resources for English Learners
- Quick Reference for English Learners
- Spanish Study Guide
- Multi-Language Visual Glossary
- Student Resources in Spanish

California Standards for Chapter 8

Geometry: 7.0, 12.0, 17.0

Now

In Chapter 8, you will apply the big ideas listed below and reviewed in the Chapter Summary on page 559. You will also use the key vocabulary listed below.

Big Ideas

1. **Using angle relationships in polygons**
2. **Using properties of parallelograms**
3. **Classifying quadrilaterals by their properties**

KEY VOCABULARY

- diagonal, *p. 507*
- parallelogram, *p. 515*
- rhombus, *p. 533*
- rectangle, *p. 533*
- square, *p. 533*
- trapezoid, *p. 542* bases, base angles, legs
- isosceles trapezoid, *p. 543*
- midsegment of a trapezoid, *p. 544*
- kite, *p. 545*

Why?

You can use properties of quadrilaterals and other polygons to find side lengths and angle measures.

Animated Geometry

The animation illustrated below for Example 4 on page 545 helps you answer this question: How can classifying a quadrilateral help you draw conclusions about its sides and angles?

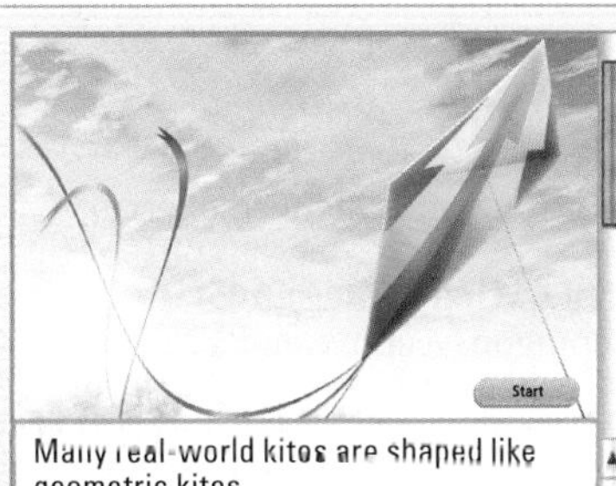

Start
Many real-world kites are shaped like geometric kites.

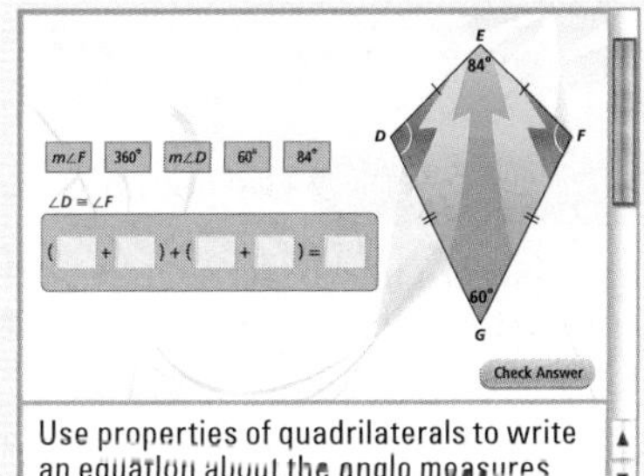

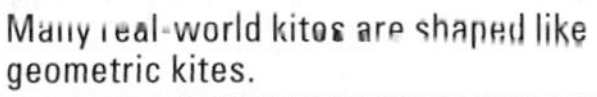

Other animations for Chapter 8: pages 509, 519, 527, 535, 551, and 553

Geometry Toolkit

- Reading Strategies for Chapter 8, pp. 23–24
- Differentiated Instruction Notes, pp. 67–70
- English Learners Notes, pp. 105–106
- Inclusion Notes, pp. 135–136
- Teaching Strategies with Sample Worksheets, pp. 145–168
- Using Technology in the Classroom, pp. 169–174
- Tips for New Teachers, pp. 189–190
- Math Background Notes, pp. 222–225
- Pre-AP Strategies and Copymasters, pp. 297–298, 361–366
- Teacher Survival Activities, pp. 435–436, 459–460
- Bulletin Board Idea, p. 476
- Teacher Tool Transparencies, following p. 480

8.1 Investigate Angle Sums in Polygons

MATERIALS • straightedge • ruler

QUESTION **What is the sum of the measures of the interior angles of a convex n-gon?**

Recall from page 43 that an n-gon is a polygon with n sides and n vertices.

Standards

12.0 Students find and use measures of sides and **of interior** and exterior **angles of triangles and polygons** to classify figures and solve problems.

EXPLORE **Find sums of interior angle measures**

STEP 1 ***Draw polygons*** Use a straightedge to draw convex polygons with three sides, four sides, five sides, and six sides. An example is shown.

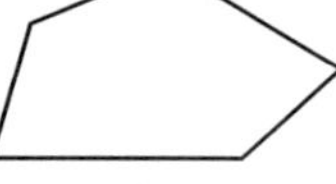

STEP 2 ***Draw diagonals*** In each polygon, draw all the diagonals from one vertex. A *diagonal* is a segment that joins two nonconsecutive vertices. Notice that the diagonals divide the polygon into triangles.

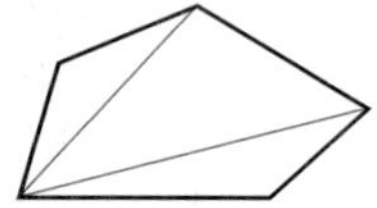

STEP 3 ***Make a table*** Copy the table below. By the Triangle Sum Theorem, the sum of the measures of the interior angles of a triangle is 180°. Use this theorem to complete the table.

Polygon	Number of sides	Number of triangles	Sum of measures of interior angles	
Triangle	3	1	$1 \cdot 180° = 180°$	
Quadrilateral	? 4	? 2	$2 \cdot 180° = 360°$	
Pentagon	? 5	? 3	?	**$3 \cdot 180° = 540°$**
Hexagon	? 6	? 4	?	**$4 \cdot 180° = 720°$**

DRAW CONCLUSIONS **Use your observations to complete these exercises**

1. Look for a pattern in the last column of the table. What is the sum of the measures of the interior angles of a convex heptagon? a convex octagon? *Explain* your reasoning. **900°, 1080°; as the number of sides of a polygon increases by 1, the sum of the measures of the interior angles increases by 180°.**
2. Write an expression for the sum of the measures of the interior angles of a convex n-gon. **$(n - 2) \cdot 180°$**
3. Measure the side lengths in the hexagon you drew. Compare the lengths with those in hexagons drawn by other students. Do the side lengths affect the sum of the interior angle measures of a hexagon? *Explain.* **Check students work; no; the number of interior triangles will always remain the same, so the sum of the measures of the interior angles does not depend on side length.**

1 PLAN AND PREPARE

Explore the Concept

- Students will find an expression for the sum of the measures of the interior angles of a convex polygon.
- This activity leads into the study of the measures of interior angles of convex polygons in Example 1 in Lesson 8.1.

Materials

Each student will need:

- straightedge
- ruler

Recommended Time

Work activity: 10 min

Discuss results: 5 min

Grouping

Students should work individually.

2 TEACH

Tips for Success

Be sure students draw all the diagonals from one vertex and no others.

Alternative Strategy

Draw each polygon on the board and draw the diagonals from one vertex. Have students volunteer answers for filling in the table.

Key Discovery

The sum of the measures of the interior angles of a convex polygon with n sides is $(n - 2)180°$.

3 ASSESS AND RETEACH

Explain how the expression $(n - 2)180°$ is obtained. **Draw all diagonals of a polygon from one vertex; multiply the number of triangles formed by 180°.**

8.1 Find Angle Measures in Polygons

Before You classified polygons.
Now You will find angle measures in polygons.
Why? So you can describe a baseball park, as in Exs. 28–29.

Key Vocabulary
- diagonal
- interior angle, *p. 218*
- exterior angle, *p. 218*

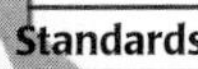

Standards

12.0 Students find and use measures of sides and of interior and exterior angles of triangles and polygons to classify figures and solve problems.

In a polygon, two vertices that are endpoints of the same side are called *consecutive vertices*. A **diagonal** of a polygon is a segment that joins two *nonconsecutive vertices*. Polygon $ABCDE$ has two diagonals from vertex B, $\overline{BD}$ and $\overline{BE}$.

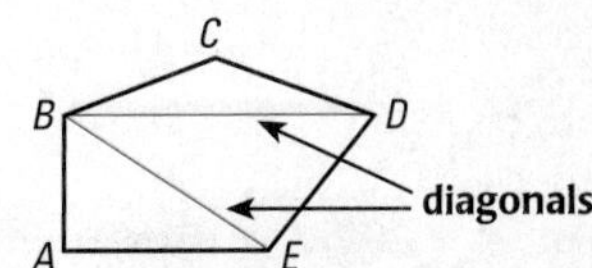

As you can see, the diagonals from one vertex form triangles. In the Activity on page 506, you used these triangles to find the sum of the interior angle measures of a polygon. Your results support the following theorem and corollary.

THEOREMS *For Your Notebook*

THEOREM 8.1 Polygon Interior Angles Theorem

The sum of the measures of the interior angles of a convex n-gon is $(n - 2) \cdot 180°$.

$m\angle 1 + m\angle 2 + \cdots + m\angle n = (n - 2) \cdot 180°$

Proof: Ex. 33, p. 512 (for pentagons)

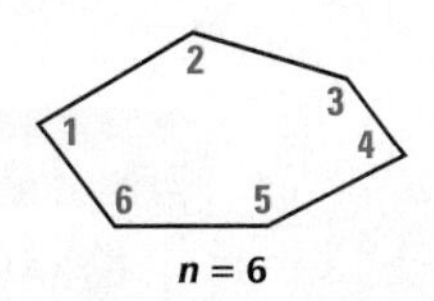

COROLLARY TO THEOREM 8.1 Interior Angles of a Quadrilateral

The sum of the measures of the interior angles of a quadrilateral is 360°.

Proof: Ex. 34, p. 512

EXAMPLE 1 Find the sum of angle measures in a polygon

Find the sum of the measures of the interior angles of a convex octagon.

Solution

An octagon has 8 sides. Use the Polygon Interior Angles Theorem.

$(n - 2) \cdot 180° = (8 - 2) \cdot 180°$ **Substitute 8 for *n*.**

$= 6 \cdot 180°$ **Subtract.**

$= 1080°$ **Multiply.**

▶ The sum of the measures of the interior angles of an octagon is 1080°.

1 PLAN AND PREPARE

Warm-Up Exercises

Transparency Available

1. If the measures of two angles of a triangle are 19° and 80°, find the measure of the third angle. **81°**
2. Solve $(x - 2)180 = 1980$ **13**
3. Find the value of x. **126**

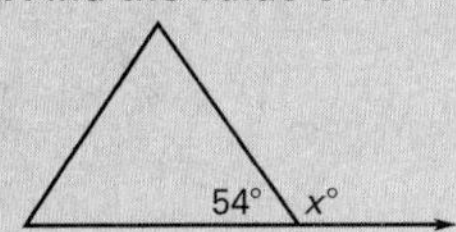

Notetaking Guide

Transparency Available

Promotes interactive learning and notetaking skills, pp. 198–201.

Pacing

Basic: 2 days
Average: 2 days
Advanced: 2 days
Block: 1 block
- See *Teaching Guide/Lesson Plan.*

2 FOCUS AND MOTIVATE

Essential Question

Big Idea 1, p. 504

How do you find a missing angle measure in a convex polygon?
Tell students they will learn how to answer this question by using the Polygon Interior Angles Theorem.

Resource Planning Guide

Chapter Resource Book
- Teaching Guide/Lesson Plan (pp. 3–4)
- Practice levels A, B, C (pp. 5–10)
- Study Guide (pp. 11–12)
- Catch-up for Absent Students (p. 13)
- Problem Solving Workshop (p. 14)
- Challenge (p. 15)

Workbooks
- Notetaking Guide (pp. 198–201)
- Practice Workbook (pp. 145–147)

Teaching Options
- **Power Presentations CD-ROM** provides dynamic electronic teaching resources for the classroom.
- **Activity Generator CD-ROM** provides editable activities for all ability levels.

Interactive Technology
- Easy Planner
- Power Presentations CD-ROM
- Activity Generator CD-ROM
- Animated Geometry
- Test Generator CD-ROM
- Online Quiz
- eWorkbook
- eEdition
- @HomeTutor

Resources for English Learners
- Quick Reference for English Learners
- Spanish Study Guide
- Multi-Language Visual Glossary
- Student Resources in Spanish

See also the *Geometry Toolkit* for more strategies for meeting individual needs.

Motivating the Lesson

Have students imagine that they need to make a regular hexagon to use in a quilt pattern. Observe that they will need to know how many degrees are in each angle of the hexagon. Tell students that in this lesson they will learn how to find the measures of the interior angles of a regular polygon.

3 TEACH

Extra Example 1

Find the sum of the measures of the interior angles of a convex decagon. **1440°**

Extra Example 2

The sum of the measures of the interior angles of a convex polygon is 2340°. Classify the polygon by the number of sides. **15-gon**

Key Question to Ask for Example 2

- How could you solve the equation without first dividing both sides by 180? **Distribute 180 to get $180n - 360 = 900$. Then solve in the usual way.**

Extra Example 3

Find the value of x in the diagram shown. **154**

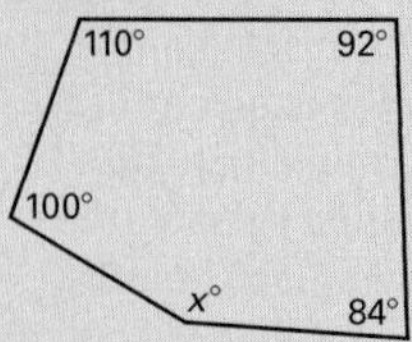

Key Question to Ask for Example 3

- Are there any special relationships between sides of the quadrilateral? **Yes; the top and bottom sides are parallel, since $121° + 59° = 180°$.**

EXAMPLE 2 Find the number of sides of a polygon

The sum of the measures of the interior angles of a convex polygon is 900°. Classify the polygon by the number of sides.

Solution

Use the Polygon Interior Angles Theorem to write an equation involving the number of sides n. Then solve the equation to find the number of sides.

$(n - 2) \cdot 180° = 900°$	**Polygon Interior Angles Theorem**
$n - 2 = 5$	**Divide each side by 180°.**
$n = 7$	**Add 2 to each side.**

▶ The polygon has 7 sides. It is a heptagon.

✓ **GUIDED PRACTICE** for Examples 1 and 2

1. The coin shown is in the shape of a regular 11-gon. Find the sum of the measures of the interior angles. **1620°**

2. The sum of the measures of the interior angles of a convex polygon is 1440°. Classify the polygon by the number of sides. **decagon**

EXAMPLE 3 Find an unknown interior angle measure

 ALGEBRA **Find the value of x in the diagram shown.**

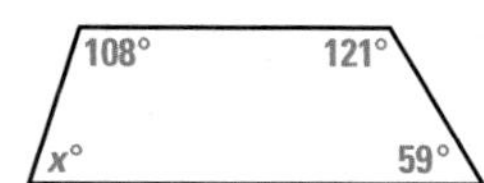

Solution

The polygon is a quadrilateral. Use the Corollary to the Polygon Interior Angles Theorem to write an equation involving x. Then solve the equation.

$x° + 108° + 121° + 59° = 360°$	**Corollary to Theorem 8.1**
$x + 288 = 360$	**Combine like terms.**
$x = 72$	**Subtract 288 from each side.**

▶ The value of x is 72.

✓ **GUIDED PRACTICE** for Example 3

3. Use the diagram at the right. Find $m\angle S$ and $m\angle T$. **103°, 103°**

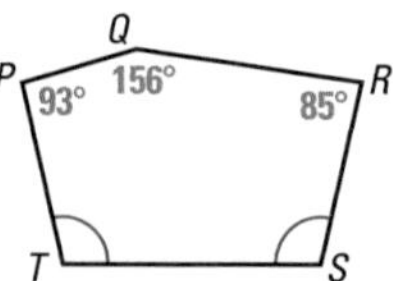

4. The measures of three of the interior angles of a quadrilateral are 89°, 110°, and 46°. Find the measure of the fourth interior angle. **115°**

Differentiated Instruction

Advanced Have students find the formula for the number of diagonals of a convex polygon with n sides: $\frac{(n-3)n}{2}$. Each vertex can be connected to $n - 3$ vertices (neither to itself nor to the one on either side). But this counts each vertex twice, so $(n - 3)n$ must be divided by 2. Have students find the number of diagonals of various polygons. Then have them figure out the number of sides of a convex polygon given the number of diagonals. This will require solving a quadratic equation.

See also the *Geometry Toolkit* for more strategies.

EXTERIOR ANGLES Unlike the sum of the interior angle measures of a convex polygon, the sum of the exterior angle measures does *not* depend on the number of sides of the polygon. The diagrams below suggest that the sum of the measures of the exterior angles, one at each vertex, of a pentagon is 360°. In general, this sum is 360° for any convex polygon.

VISUALIZE IT
A circle contains two straight angles. So, there are 180° + 180°, or 360°, in a circle.

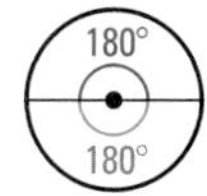

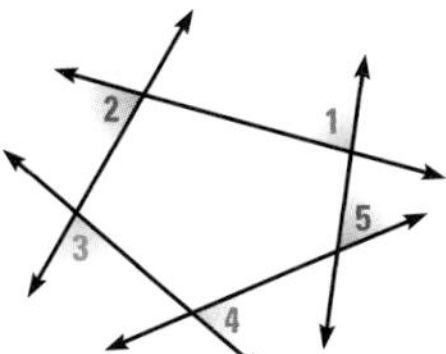

STEP 1 **Shade** one exterior angle at each vertex.

STEP 2 **Cut** out the exterior angles.

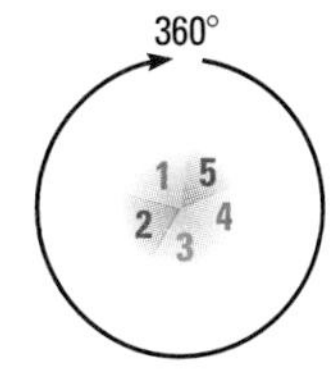

STEP 3 **Arrange** the exterior angles to form 360°.

Animated Geometry at classzone.com

THEOREM — *For Your Notebook*

THEOREM 8.2 Polygon Exterior Angles Theorem

The sum of the measures of the exterior angles of a convex polygon, one angle at each vertex, is 360°.

$m\angle 1 + m\angle 2 + \cdots + m\angle n = 360°$

Proof: Ex. 35, p. 512

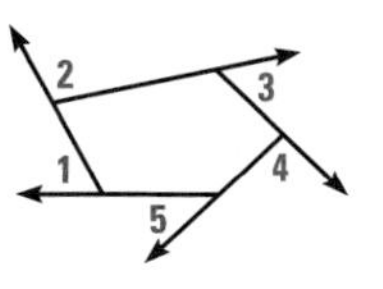

EXAMPLE 4 Standardized Test Practice

What is the value of *x* in the diagram shown?

Ⓐ 67 Ⓑ 68

Ⓒ 91 Ⓓ 136

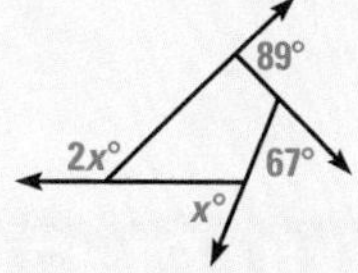

ELIMINATE CHOICES
You can quickly eliminate choice *D*. If *x* were equal to 136, then the sum of only two of the angle measures ($x°$ and $2x°$) would be greater than 360°.

Solution

Use the Polygon Exterior Angles Theorem to write and solve an equation.

$x° + 2x° + 89° + 67° = 360°$ **Polygon Exterior Angles Theorem**

$3x + 156 = 360$ **Combine like terms.**

$x = 68$ **Solve for *x*.**

▶ The correct answer is B. Ⓐ Ⓑ Ⓒ Ⓓ

GUIDED PRACTICE for Example 4

5. A convex hexagon has exterior angles with measures 34°, 49°, 58°, 67°, and 75°. What is the measure of an exterior angle at the sixth vertex? **77°**

Animated Geometry classzone.com

An **Animated Geometry** activity is available on-line for **Example 3**. This activity is also available on the **Power Presentations CD-ROM**.

Extra Example 4

What is the value of *x* in the diagram shown? **B**

Ⓐ 61

Ⓑ 66

Ⓒ 90

Ⓓ 96

$(x + 20)°$, $x°$, 96°, 112°

Key Questions to Ask for Example 4

- How many exterior angles are there at each vertex of a convex polygon? **2**
- How are exterior angles at the same vertex related to each other? **They are congruent.**

Differentiated Instruction

Visual Learners To begin work on **Guided Practice Exercise 4** on page 508, have students draw the quadrilateral using a protractor to correctly draw each angle. Have them show the known angle measures on the figure. Direct them to find the measure of the fourth angle using the Polygon Interior Angles Theorem and then check their calculations by measuring the fourth angle with a protractor.

See also the *Geometry Toolkit* for more strategies.

Extra Example 5

A stop sign is shaped like a regular octagon. Find (a) the measure of each interior angle and (b) the measure of each exterior angle. **135°, 45°**

Key Question to Ask for Example 5

- Is it easier to first find the measure of each interior angle or of each exterior angle of a regular polygon? **each exterior angle, $\frac{360}{n}$ is easier to evaluate than $\frac{(n-2)180}{n}$.**

Teaching Strategy

Teach students that to find the measure of each interior angle of a regular polygon, they can divide the sum of the measures of the interior angles by the number of angles. Therefore, an expression for the measure of each interior angle of a regular n-gon is $\frac{(n-2)180°}{n}$.

Closing the Lesson

Have students summarize the major points of the lesson and answer the Essential Question: How do you find a missing angle measure in a convex polygon?

- **The sum of the measures of the interior angles of a convex n-gon is $(n-2)180°$.**
- **The sum of the measures of the exterior angles of a convex polygon, one angle at each vertex, is 360°.**

Find the sum of the measures of the interior angles by using the expression $(n-2)180°$, then subtract the angle measures that you know to find the missing measure.

1. *Sample:*

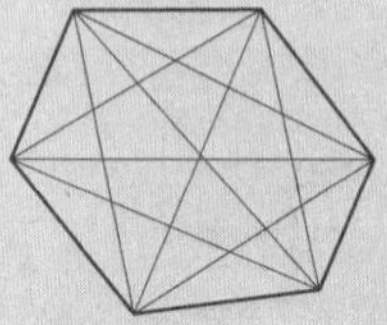

EXAMPLE 5 Find angle measures in regular polygons

READ VOCABULARY
Recall that a *dodecagon* is a polygon with 12 sides and 12 vertices.

TRAMPOLINE The trampoline shown is shaped like a regular dodecagon. Find (a) the measure of each interior angle and (b) the measure of each exterior angle.

Solution

a. Use the Polygon Interior Angles Theorem to find the sum of the measures of the interior angles.

$$(n-2) \cdot 180° = (12-2) \cdot 180° = 1800°$$

Then find the measure of one interior angle. A regular dodecagon has 12 congruent interior angles. Divide 1800° by 12: $1800° \div 12 = 150°$.

▶ The measure of each interior angle in the dodecagon is 150°.

b. By the Polygon Exterior Angles Theorem, the sum of the measures of the exterior angles, one angle at each vertex, is 360°. Divide 360° by 12 to find the measure of one of the 12 congruent exterior angles: $360° \div 12 = 30°$.

▶ The measure of each exterior angle in the dodecagon is 30°.

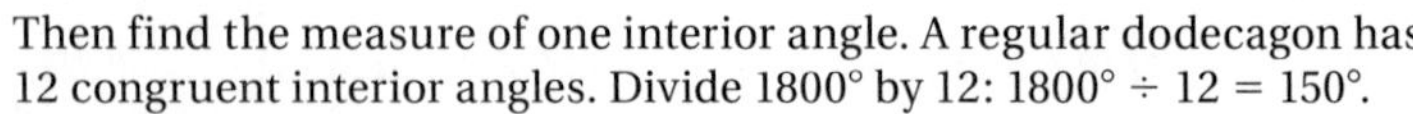

✓ **GUIDED PRACTICE** for Example 5

6. An interior angle and an adjacent exterior angle of a polygon form a linear pair. How can you use this fact as another method to find the exterior angle measure in Example 5? **Linear pairs are supplementary. Since the interior angle measures 150°, the exterior angle must measure 30°.**

8.1 EXERCISES

HOMEWORK KEY
○ = **WORKED-OUT SOLUTIONS** on p. WS9 for Exs. 9, 11, and 29
★ = **STANDARDIZED TEST PRACTICE** Exs. 2, 18, 23, and 37
◆ = **MULTIPLE REPRESENTATIONS** Ex. 36

SKILL PRACTICE

A

1. **VOCABULARY** Sketch a convex hexagon. Draw all of its diagonals. **See margin.**

2. ★ **WRITING** How many exterior angles are there in an n-gon? Are all the exterior angles considered when you use the Polygon Exterior Angles Theorem? *Explain.* **2n; no; only n angles are considered**

EXAMPLES 1 and 2
on pp. 507–508 for Exs. 3–10

INTERIOR ANGLE SUMS Find the sum of the measures of the interior angles of the indicated convex polygon.

3. Nonagon **1260°** 4. 14-gon **2160°** 5. 16-gon **2520°** 6. 20-gon **3240°**

FINDING NUMBER OF SIDES The sum of the measures of the interior angles of a convex polygon is given. Classify the polygon by the number of sides.

7. 360° **quadrilateral** 8. 720° **hexagon** (9.) 1980° **13-gon** 10. 2340° **15-gon**

EXAMPLES 3 and 4 on pp. 508–509 for Exs. 11–18

ALGEBRA **Find the value of x.**

11.
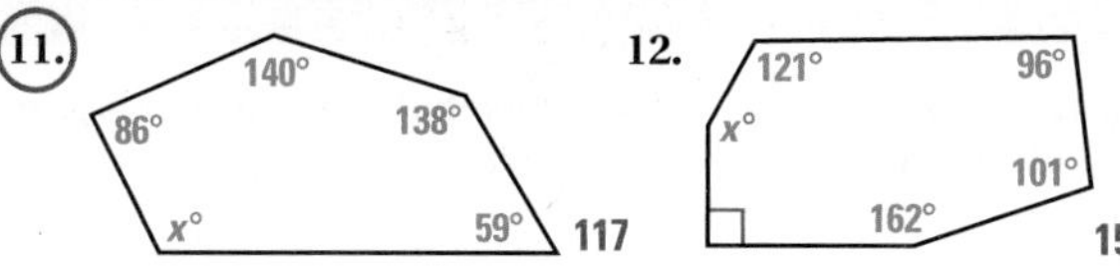

117

12.
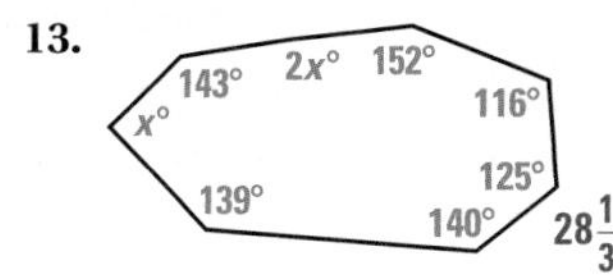

150

13. 143° 2x° 152° x° 116° 125° 139° 140° $28\frac{1}{3}$

14.
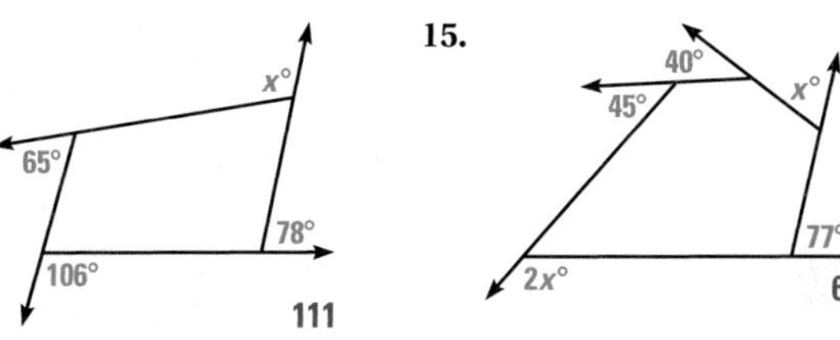

111

15.
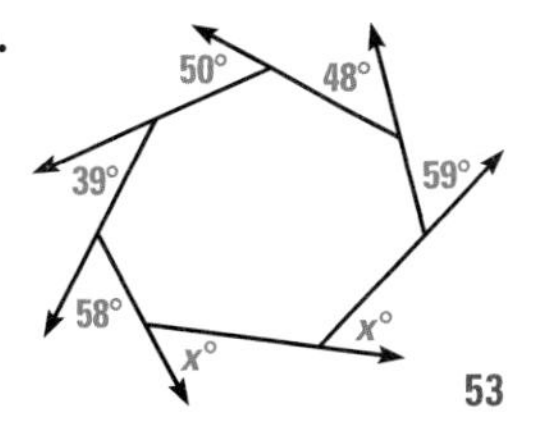

66

16. 50° 48° 39° 59° 58° x° x° 53

7. The student thinks that because an octagon has 8 exterior angles while a hexagon has only 6 exterior angles, the sum of the measures of the 8 angles must be greater than the sum of the measures of the 6 angles. The sum of the measures of the exterior angles of any convex n-gon is always 360°.

17. **ERROR ANALYSIS** A student claims that the sum of the measures of the exterior angles of an octagon is greater than the sum of the measures of the exterior angles of a hexagon. The student justifies this claim by saying that an octagon has two more sides than a hexagon. *Describe* and correct the error the student is making.

18. ★ **MULTIPLE CHOICE** The measures of the interior angles of a quadrilateral are $x°$, $2x°$, $3x°$, and $4x°$. What is the measure of the largest interior angle? **B**

Ⓐ 120° Ⓑ 144° Ⓒ 160° Ⓓ 360°

EXAMPLE 5 on p. 510 for Exs. 19–21

REGULAR POLYGONS **Find the measures of an interior angle and an exterior angle of the indicated regular polygon.**

19. Regular pentagon **108°, 72°**

20. Regular 18-gon **160°, 20°**

21. Regular 90-gon **176°, 4°**

B **22.** **DIAGONALS OF SIMILAR FIGURES** Hexagons $RSTUVW$ and $JKLMNP$ are similar. $\overline{RU}$ and $\overline{JM}$ are diagonals. Given $ST = 6$, $KL = 10$, and $RU = 12$, find JM. **20**

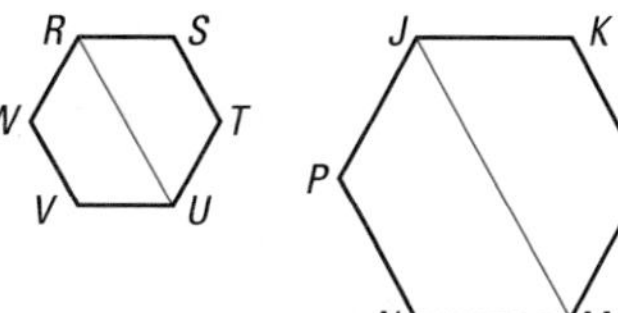

J K P L N M

23. The interior angle measures are the same in both pentagons and the ratios of corresponding sides would be the same.

23. ★ **SHORT RESPONSE** *Explain* why any two regular pentagons are similar.

REGULAR POLYGONS **Find the value of n for each regular n-gon described.**

24. Each interior angle of the regular n-gon has a measure of 156°. **15**

25. Each exterior angle of the regular n-gon has a measure of 9°. **40**

C **26.** **POSSIBLE POLYGONS** Determine if it is possible for a regular polygon to have an interior angle with the given angle measure. *Explain* your reasoning. **a–d. See margin.**

a. 165° **b.** 171° **c.** 75° **d.** 40°

27. **CHALLENGE** Sides are added to a convex polygon so that the sum of its interior angle measures is increased by 540°. How many sides are added to the polygon? *Explain* your reasoning. **3 sides; solve the equation $(n + x - 2) \cdot 180 = 540 + (n - 2) \cdot 180$ for x where n is the number of original sides and x is the number of sides added.**

26a. Yes; the number of sides would be 24.

26b. Yes; the number of sides would be 40.

26c. No; solving the equation $(n - 2) \cdot 180 = 75n$ does not yield a positive integer greater than or equal to 3.

26d. No; solving the equation $(n - 2) \cdot 180 = 40n$ does not yield a positive integer greater than or equal to 3.

4 PRACTICE AND APPLY

Assignment Guide

Answer Transparencies available for all exercises

Basic:
Day 1: EP p. 899 Exs. 25–30
pp. 510–513
Exs. 1–10, 28, 29, 42–47
Day 2: pp. 510–513
Exs. 11–23, 30–34, 39–41

Average:
Day 1: pp. 510–513
Exs. 1–10, 28, 29, 33, 34, 42–46 even
Day 2: pp. 510–513
Exs. 13–15, 17–25, 30–32, 35–37, 39–41

Advanced:
Day 1: pp. 510–513
Exs. 1–10, 28, 29, 33, 34, 43–47 odd
Day 2: pp. 510–513
Exs. 14–16, 18–27*, 30–32, 35–38*, 40

Block:
pp. 510–513
Exs. 1–10, 13–15, 17–25, 28–37, 39–41, 42–46 even

Differentiated Instruction

See *Geometry Best Practices Toolkit* for suggestions on addressing the needs of a diverse classroom.

Homework Check

For a quick check of student understanding of key concepts, go over the following exercises:

Basic: 4, 7, 12, 19, 30
Average: 5, 8, 14, 20, 30
Advanced: 6, 10, 16, 21, 31

Extra Practice

- Student Edition, p. 910
- Chapter 8 Resource Book: Practice levels A, B, C, pp. 5–10

Practice Worksheet

An easily-readable reduced practice page (with answers) for this lesson can be found on p. 504C.

Avoiding Common Errors

Exercises 3–6 Some students may not correctly recall the expression for the sum of the angle measures of a convex n-gon. If this is the case, have them sketch a convex pentagon, draw the diagonals from one vertex, and note that they get 3 triangles, 2 less than 5 (the number of sides). This should help them recall the general expression $(n - 2)180°$.

Mathematical Reasoning

Exercise 26 Ask students how they could use exterior angles to solve these problems. For part a, they could note that each exterior angle would need to have a measure of $180° - 165°$, or $15°$. Since $\frac{360}{15} = 24$, a regular polygon with 24 sides will have interior angles of measure 165°.

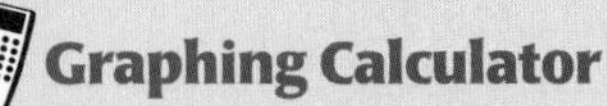

Graphing Calculator

Exercise 36 Students can enter the lists $L_1 = \{3, 4, 5, 6, 7, 8\}$ and $L_2 = \{180, 360, 540, 720, 900, 1080\}$ and use the STAT PLOT feature to display a scatter plot.

32a.

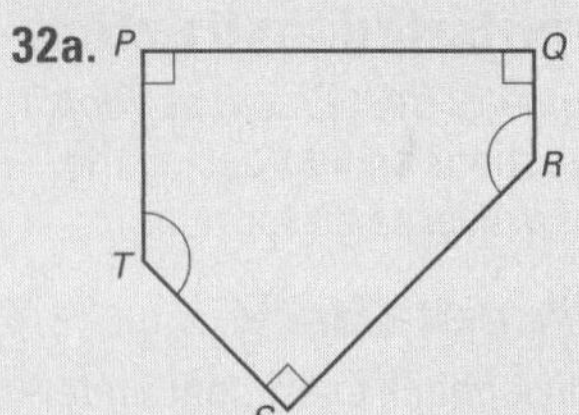

34. In a quadrilateral, draw all the diagonals from one vertex. Observe that the polygon is divided up into two triangles. Since the sum of the measures of the interior angles of each triangle is 180°, the sum of the measures of the interior angles of the quadrilateral is $2 \cdot 180° = 360°$.

PROBLEM SOLVING

EXAMPLE 1 A on p. 507 for Exs. 28–29

BASEBALL The outline of the playing field at a baseball park is a polygon, as shown. Find the sum of the measures of the interior angles of the polygon.

28.

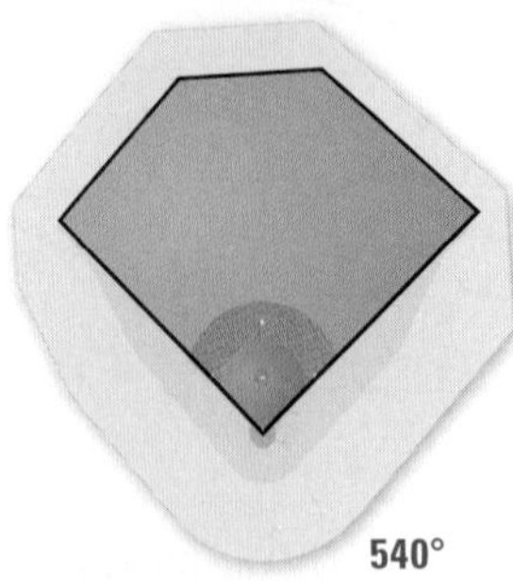

540°

(29.)

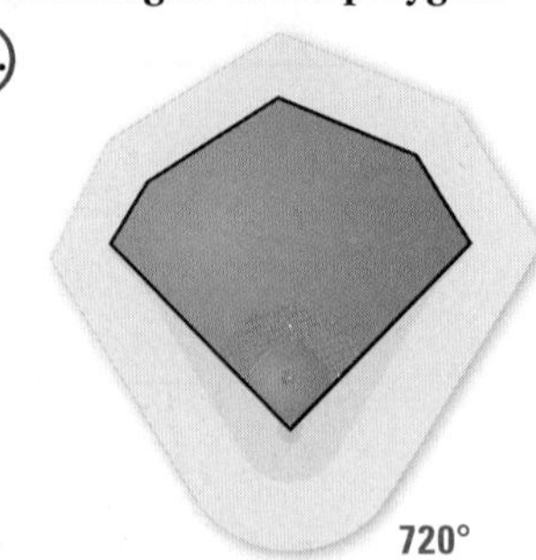

720°

@HomeTutor for problem solving help at classzone.com

EXAMPLE 5 on p. 510 for Exs. 30–31

30. JEWELRY BOX The base of a jewelry box is shaped like a regular hexagon. What is the measure of each interior angle of the hexagon? **120°**

@HomeTutor for problem solving help at classzone.com

31. GREENHOUSE The floor of the greenhouse shown is a shaped like a regular decagon. Find the measure of an interior angle of the regular decagon. Then find the measure of an exterior angle. **144°; 36°**

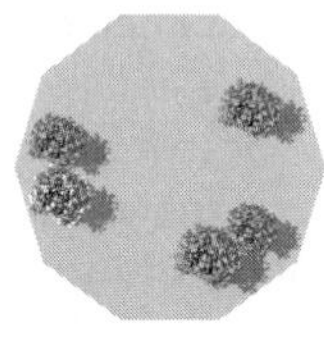

32. MULTI-STEP PROBLEM In pentagon $PQRST$, $\angle P$, $\angle Q$, and $\angle S$ are right angles, and $\angle R \cong \angle T$.

a. **Draw a Diagram** Sketch pentagon $PQRST$. Mark the right angles and the congruent angles. **See margin.**

b. **Calculate** Find the sum of the interior angle measures of $PQRST$. **540°**

c. **Calculate** Find $m\angle R$ and $m\angle T$. **135°, 135°**

33. In a pentagon draw all the diagonals from one vertex. Observe that the polygon is divided up into three triangles. Since the sum of the measures of the interior angles of each triangle is 180° the sum of the measures of the interior angles of the pentagon is $(5 - 2) \cdot 180° = 3 \cdot 180° = 540°$.

B

33. PROVING THEOREM 8.1 FOR PENTAGONS The Polygon Interior Angles Theorem states that the sum of the measures of the interior angles of an n-gon is $(n - 2) \cdot 180°$. Write a paragraph proof of this theorem for the case when $n = 5$.

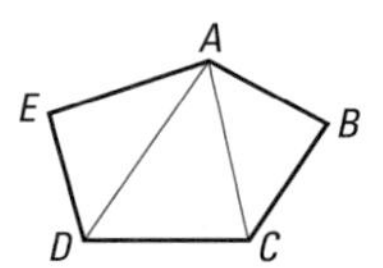

34. PROVING A COROLLARY Write a paragraph proof of the Corollary to the Polygon Interior Angles Theorem. **See margin.**

35. PROVING THEOREM 8.2 Use the plan below to write a paragraph proof of the Polygon Exterior Angles Theorem.

Plan for Proof In a convex n-gon, the sum of the measures of an interior angle and an adjacent exterior angle at any vertex is 180°. Multiply by n to get the sum of all such sums at each vertex. Then subtract the sum of the interior angles derived by using the Polygon Interior Angles Theorem. **See margin.**

○ = WORKED-OUT SOLUTIONS on p. WS1 ★ = STANDARDIZED TEST PRACTICE

= MULTIPLE REPRESENTATIONS

35. ***Sample answer:*** **In a convex n-gon the sum of the measures of the n interior angles is $(n - 2) \cdot 180°$ using the Polygon Interior Angles Theorem. Since each of the n interior angles forms a linear pair with its corresponding exterior angle, you know that the sum of the measures of the n interior and exterior angles is $180n°$. Subtracting the sum of the interior angle measures from the sum of the measures of the linear pairs $(180n° - [(n - 2) \cdot 180°])$, you get 360°.**

36c.

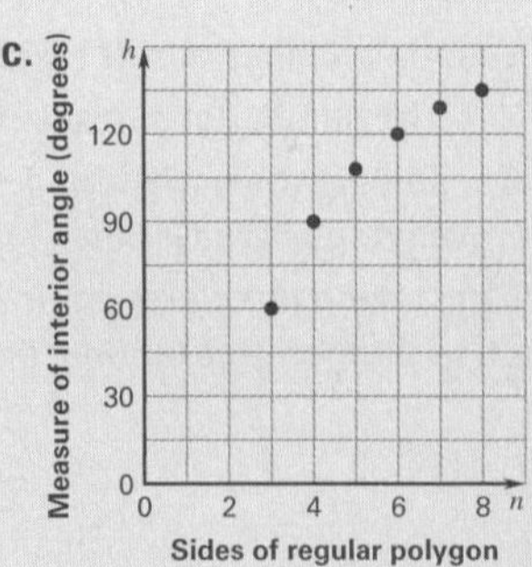

36. **MULTIPLE REPRESENTATIONS** The formula for the measure of each interior angle in a regular polygon can be written in function notation.

a. **Writing a Function** Write a function $h(n)$, where n is the number of sides in a regular polygon and $h(n)$ is the measure of any interior angle in the regular polygon. $h(n) = \frac{(n-2) \cdot 180°}{n}$

b. **Using a Function** Use the function from part (a) to find $h(9)$. Then use the function to find n if $h(n) = 150°$. **140°; 12**

c. **Graphing a Function** Graph the function from part (a) for $n = 3, 4, 5, 6, 7$, and 8. Based on your graph, *describe* what happens to the value of $h(n)$ as n increases. *Explain* your reasoning. **See margin for art; $h(n)$ increases but its growth rate is slowing down.**

37. ★ **EXTENDED RESPONSE** In a concave polygon, at least one interior angle measure is greater than 180°. For example, the measure of the shaded angle in the concave quadrilateral below is 210°.

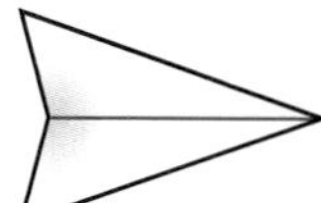  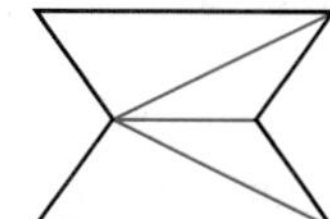 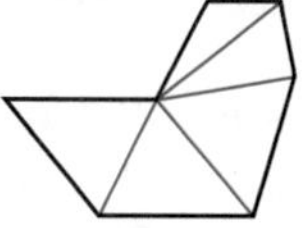

a. In the diagrams above, the interiors of a concave quadrilateral, pentagon, hexagon, and heptagon are divided into triangles. Make a table like the one in the Activity on page 506. For each of the polygons shown above, record the number of sides, the number of triangles, and the sum of the measures of the interior angles. **See margin.**

b. Write a function that you can use to find the sum of the measures of the interior angles of a concave polygon. *Explain.* **$s(n) = (n-2) \cdot 180°$; the table shows that the number of triangles is two less than the number of sides.**

38. 90°; the measure of each interior angle is 135°. This makes the measure of each exterior angle 45°. Since the interior angles of △BPC contain two exterior angles and ∠BPC, m∠BPC = 90°; see margin for art.

38. **CHALLENGE** Polygon $ABCDEFGH$ is a regular octagon. Suppose sides $\overline{AB}$ and $\overline{CD}$ are extended to meet at a point P. Find $m\angle BPC$. *Explain* your reasoning. Include a diagram with your answer.

MIXED REVIEW

PREVIEW
Prepare for Lesson 8.2 in Exs. 39–41.

Find $m\angle 1$ and $m\angle 2$. *Explain* your reasoning. *(p. 154)* **39–41. See margin.**

39.

40.

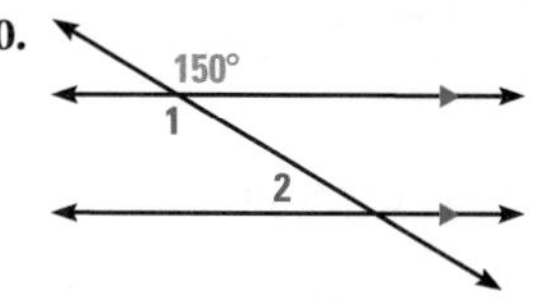

41.

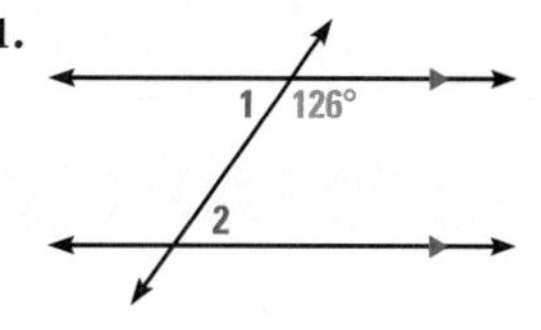

42. Quadrilaterals $JKLM$ and $PQRS$ are similar. If $JK = 3.6$ centimeters and $PQ = 1.2$ centimeters, find the scale factor of $JKLM$ to $PQRS$. *(p. 372)* $\frac{3}{1}$

43. Quadrilaterals $ABCD$ and $EFGH$ are similar. The scale factor of $ABCD$ to $EFGH$ is 8 : 5, and the perimeter of $ABCD$ is 90 feet. Find the perimeter of $EFGH$. *(p. 372)* **56.25 ft**

Let $\angle A$ be an acute angle in a right triangle. Approximate the measure of $\angle A$ to the nearest tenth of a degree. *(p. 483)*

44. $\sin A = 0.77$ **50.4°** 45. $\sin A = 0.35$ **20.5°** 46. $\cos A = 0.81$ **35.9°** 47. $\cos A = 0.23$ **76.7°**

39. 82°, 82°; $m\angle 2 + 98° = 180°$ since they are a linear pair and $\angle 1 \cong \angle 2$ using the Corresponding Angles Postulate.

40. 150°, 30°; $m\angle 1 = 150°$ using vertical angles and $m\angle 2 = 30°$ using the Consecutive Interior Angles Theorem.

41. 54°, 54°; $m\angle 1 + 126° = 180°$ since they are a linear pair and $\angle 1 \cong \angle 2$ using the Alternate Interior Angles Theorem.

5 ASSESS AND RETEACH

Daily Homework Quiz

Transparency Available

1. Find the sum of the measures of the interior angles of a convex 24-gon. **3960°**
2. The sum of the measures of the interior angles of a convex polygon is 5040°. Classify the polygon by the number of sides. **30-gon**
3. Find the value of x. **33**

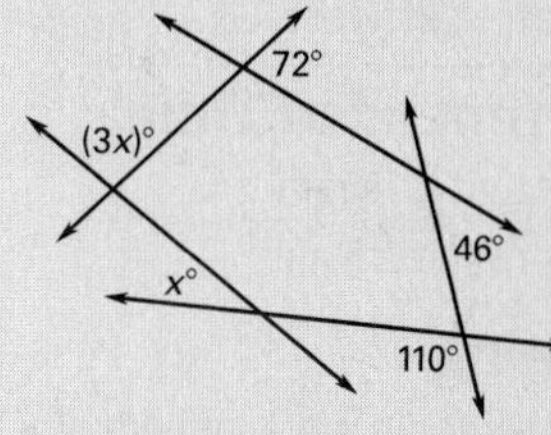

4. Find the measure of an interior angle and an exterior angle of a regular 36-gon. **170°, 10°**

Online Quiz

Available at **classzone.com**

Diagnosis/Remediation

- Practice A, B, C in Chapter 8 Resource Book, pp. 5–10
- Study Guide in Chapter 8 Resource Book, pp. 11–12
- Practice Workbook, pp. 145–147
- @HomeTutor

Challenge

Additional challenge is available in the Chapter 8 Resource Book, p. 15.

37. See Additional Answers beginning on p. AA1.

38.

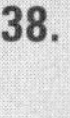

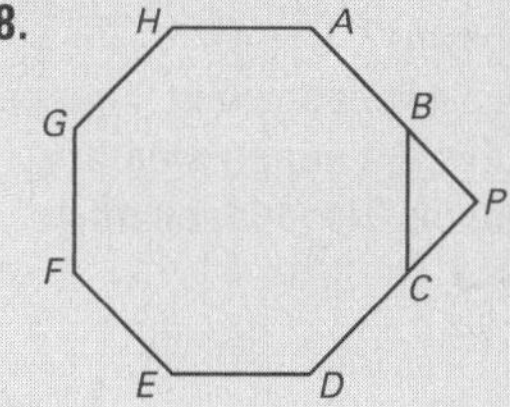

@HomeTutor
classzone.com
Keystrokes

1 PLAN AND PREPARE

Explore the Concept

- Students will investigate properties of a parallelogram.
- This activity leads into the study of using the properties of parallelograms in Examples 1 and 2 in Lesson 8.2.

Materials

Each student will need:

- graphing calculator or computer
- geometry software

Recommended Time

Work activity: 15 min

Discuss results: 5 min

Grouping

Students should work individually.

2 TEACH

Tips for Success

Urge students not to "eyeball" it but to use the construction features of the software to draw the parallel lines.

Alternative Strategy

Have students construct a parallelogram with compass and straightedge and measure the parts.

Key Discovery

In a parallelogram, opposite sides and angles are congruent and diagonals bisect each other.

3 ASSESS AND RETEACH

What are the main properties of parallelograms? **Opposite sides and angles are congruent, consecutive angles are supplementary, and diagonals bisect each other.**

8.2 Investigate Parallelograms

MATERIALS • graphing calculator or computer

Standards

Prepare for 7.0 *Students prove* and use *theorems involving the properties of parallel lines cut by a transversal, the properties of quadrilaterals,* and the properties of circles.

QUESTION What are some of the properties of a parallelogram?

You can use geometry drawing software to investigate relationships in special quadrilaterals.

EXPLORE Draw a quadrilateral

STEP 1 ***Draw parallel lines*** Construct $\overleftrightarrow{AB}$ and a line parallel to $\overleftrightarrow{AB}$ through point C. Then construct $\overleftrightarrow{BC}$ and a line parallel to $\overleftrightarrow{BC}$ through point A. Finally, construct a point D at the intersection of the line drawn parallel to $\overleftrightarrow{AB}$ and the line drawn parallel to $\overleftrightarrow{BC}$.

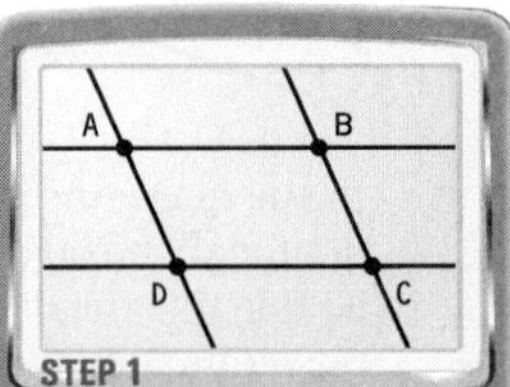

STEP 2 ***Draw quadrilateral*** Construct segments to form the sides of quadrilateral $ABCD$. After you construct $\overline{AB}$, $\overline{BC}$, $\overline{CD}$, and $\overline{DA}$, hide the parallel lines that you drew in Step 1.

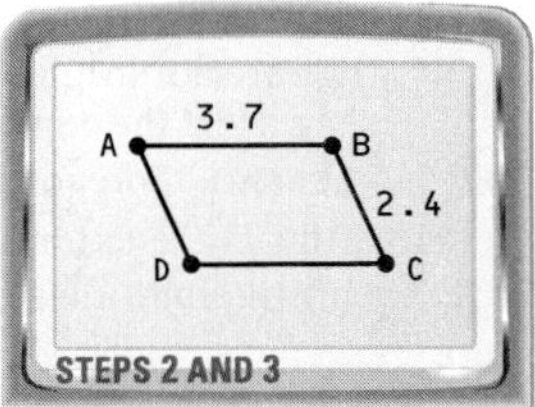

STEP 3 ***Measure side lengths*** Measure the side lengths AB, BC, CD, and DA. Drag point A or point B to change the side lengths of $ABCD$. What do you notice about the side lengths? **Opposite sides have the same length.**

STEP 4 ***Measure angles*** Find the measures of $\angle A$, $\angle B$, $\angle C$, and $\angle D$. Drag point A or point B to change the angle measures of $ABCD$. What do you notice about the angle measures? **Opposite angles have the same measure.**

DRAW CONCLUSIONS Use your observations to complete these exercises

1. The quadrilateral you drew in the Explore is called a *parallelogram*. Why do you think this type of quadrilateral has this name? **The opposite sides are parallel.**
2. Based on your observations, make a conjecture about the side lengths of a parallelogram and a conjecture about the angle measures of a parallelogram. **Opposite sides are congruent and opposite angles are congruent.**
3. **REASONING** Draw a parallelogram and its diagonals. Measure the distance from the intersection of the diagonals to each vertex of the parallelogram. Make and test a conjecture about the diagonals of a parallelogram. **Check students' work; the diagonals of a parallelogram bisect each other.**

8.2 Use Properties of Parallelograms

Before You used a property of polygons to find angle measures.

Now You will find angle and side measures in parallelograms.

Why? So you can solve a problem about airplanes, as in Ex. 38.

Key Vocabulary
- parallelogram

Standards

7.0 Students prove and use theorems involving the properties of parallel lines cut by a transversal, the properties of quadrilaterals, and the properties of circles.

A **parallelogram** is a quadrilateral with both pairs of opposite sides parallel. The term "parallelogram *PQRS*" can be written as ▱*PQRS*. In ▱*PQRS*, $\overline{PQ} \parallel \overline{RS}$ and $\overline{QR} \parallel \overline{PS}$ by definition. The theorems below describe other properties of parallelograms.

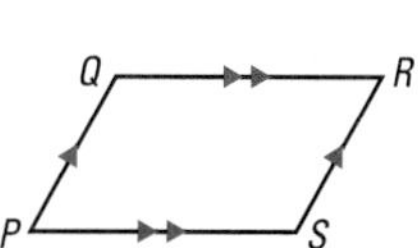

THEOREMS *For Your Notebook*

THEOREM 8.3

If a quadrilateral is a parallelogram, then its opposite sides are congruent.

If *PQRS* is a parallelogram, then $\overline{PQ} \cong \overline{RS}$ and $\overline{QR} \cong \overline{PS}$.

Proof: p. 516

THEOREM 8.4

If a quadrilateral is a parallelogram, then its opposite angles are congruent.

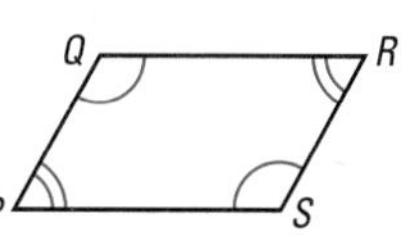

If *PQRS* is a parallelogram, then $\angle P \cong \angle R$ and $\angle Q \cong \angle S$.

Proof: Ex. 42, p. 520

EXAMPLE 1 Use properties of parallelograms

ALGEBRA Find the values of x and y.

ABCD is a parallelogram by the definition of a parallelogram. Use Theorem 8.3 to find the value of x.

$AB = CD$	**Opposite sides of a ▱ are ≅.**
$x + 4 = 12$	**Substitute $x + 4$ for AB and 12 for CD.**
$x = 8$	**Subtract 4 from each side.**

By Theorem 8.4, $\angle A \cong \angle C$, or $m\angle A = m\angle C$. So, $y° = 65°$.

▶ In ▱*ABCD*, $x = 8$ and $y = 65$.

1 PLAN AND PREPARE

Warm-Up Exercises

Transparency Available

1. Find the value of x. **60**

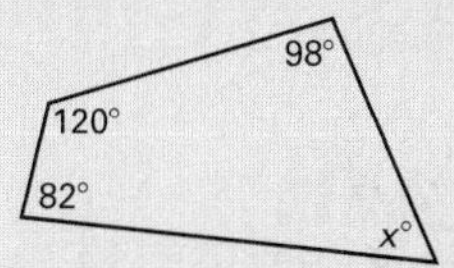

2. Find the coordinates of the midpoint of $\overline{AB}$ with endpoints $A(-2, 6)$ and $B(10, 4)$. **(4, 5)**
3. Find the distance between $(-2, 6)$ and $(10, 4)$. $\mathbf{2\sqrt{37}}$

Notetaking Guide

Transparency Available

Promotes interactive learning and notetaking skills, pp. 202–204.

Pacing

Basic: 1 day

Average: 1 day

Advanced: 1 day

Block: 0.5 block with 8.3

- See *Teaching Guide/Lesson Plan.*

2 FOCUS AND MOTIVATE

Essential Question

Big Idea 2, p. 504

How do you find angle and side measures in a parallelogram? **Tell students they will learn how to answer this question by studying the theorems about parallelograms.**

Resource Planning Guide

Chapter Resource Book
- Teaching Guide/Lesson Plan (pp. 16–17)
- Practice levels A, B, C (pp. 19–24)
- Study Guide (pp. 25–26)
- Catch-up for Absent Students (p. 27)
- Application (p. 28)
- Challenge (p. 29)

Workbooks
- Notetaking Guide (pp. 202–204)
- Practice Workbook (pp. 148–150)

Teaching Options
- **Power Presentations CD-ROM** provides dynamic electronic teaching resources for the classroom.
- **Activity Generator CD-ROM** provides editable activities for all ability levels.

Interactive Technology
- Easy Planner
- Power Presentations CD-ROM
- Activity Generator CD-ROM
- Animated Geometry
- Test Generator CD-ROM
- Online Quiz
- eWorkbook
- eEdition
- @HomeTutor

Resources for English Learners
- Quick Reference for English Learners
- Spanish Study Guide
- Multi-Language Visual Glossary
- Student Resources in Spanish

See also the *Geometry Toolkit* for more strategies for meeting individual needs.

Motivating the Lesson

On the board, sketch a piece of land that has opposite sides parallel. Tell students that in this lesson, they will learn how to find all the side lengths and angle measures of the piece of land by measuring only two sides and one angle.

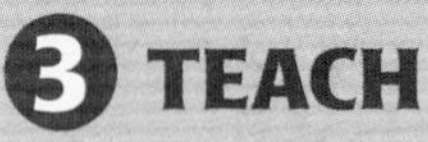

3 TEACH

Extra Example 1

Find the values of x and y. **72, 44**

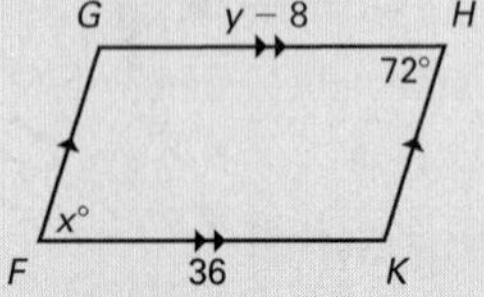

Key Question to Ask for Example 1

- What are $m\angle B$ and $m\angle D$? How do you know? **115° because consecutive angles are supplementary by the Consecutive Interior Angles Theorem.**

Vocabulary

Urge students to be careful with the definition of *parallelogram*. Saying "a quadrilateral with parallel sides" is not the same as saying "a quadrilateral with both pairs of opposite sides parallel." The first phrase could mean that it is sufficient for only one pair of sides to be parallel.

PROOF Theorem 8.3

If a quadrilateral is a parallelogram, then its opposite sides are congruent.

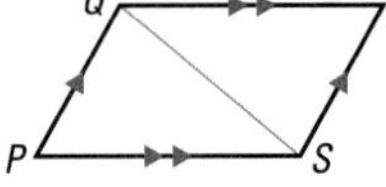

GIVEN ▶ *PQRS* is a parallelogram.

PROVE ▶ $\overline{PQ} \cong \overline{RS}$, $\overline{QR} \cong \overline{PS}$

Plan for Proof

a. Draw diagonal $\overline{QS}$ to form $\triangle PQS$ and $\triangle RSQ$.

b. Use the ASA Congruence Postulate to show that $\triangle PQS \cong \triangle RSQ$.

c. Use congruent triangles to show that $\overline{PQ} \cong \overline{RS}$ and $\overline{QR} \cong \overline{PS}$.

Plan in Action

	STATEMENTS	REASONS
a.	1. *PQRS* is a ▱.	1. Given
	2. Draw $\overline{QS}$.	2. Through any 2 points there exists exactly 1 line.
	3. $\overline{PQ} \parallel \overline{RS}$, $\overline{QR} \parallel \overline{PS}$	3. Definition of parallelogram
b.	4. $\angle PQS \cong \angle RSQ$, $\angle PSQ \cong \angle RQS$	4. Alternate Interior Angles Theorem
	5. $\overline{QS} \cong \overline{QS}$	5. Reflexive Property of Congruence
	6. $\triangle PQS \cong \triangle RSQ$	6. ASA Congruence Postulate
c.	7. $\overline{PQ} \cong \overline{RS}$, $\overline{QR} \cong \overline{PS}$	7. Corresp. parts of ≅ △ are ≅.

✓ GUIDED PRACTICE for Example 1

1. Find *FG* and $m\angle G$. **8, 60°**

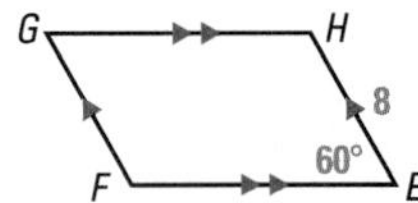

2. Find the values of x and y. **25, 15**

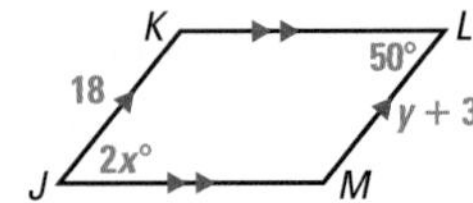

INTERIOR ANGLES The Consecutive Interior Angles Theorem (page 155) states that if two parallel lines are cut by a transversal, then the pairs of consecutive interior angles formed are supplementary.

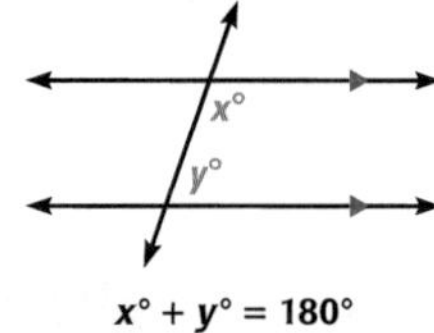

A pair of consecutive angles in a parallelogram are like a pair of consecutive interior angles between parallel lines. This similarity suggests Theorem 8.5.

THEOREM — *For Your Notebook*

THEOREM 8.5

If a quadrilateral is a parallelogram, then its consecutive angles are supplementary.

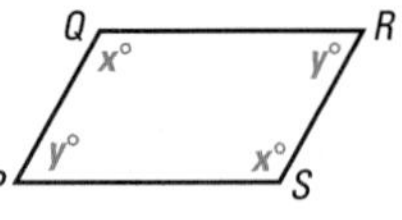

If *PQRS* is a parallelogram, then $x° + y° = 180°$.

Proof: Ex. 43, p. 520

Differentiated Instruction

Auditory Learners Instruct students to complete **Guided Practice Exercises 1 and 2** with a partner. As the students work together to complete each problem, direct them to discuss which theorems allow them to reach the conclusions they make to solve each problem.

See also the *Geometry Toolkit* for more strategies.

EXAMPLE 2 Use properties of a parallelogram

DESK LAMP As shown, part of the extending arm of a desk lamp is a parallelogram. The angles of the parallelogram change as the lamp is raised and lowered. Find $m\angle BCD$ when $m\angle ADC = 110°$.

Solution

By Theorem 8.5, the consecutive angle pairs in $\square ABCD$ are supplementary. So, $m\angle ADC + m\angle BCD = 180°$. Because $m\angle ADC = 110°$, $m\angle BCD = 180° - 110° = 70°$.

THEOREM *For Your Notebook*

THEOREM 8.6

If a quadrilateral is a parallelogram, then its diagonals bisect each other.

Proof: Ex. 44, p. 521

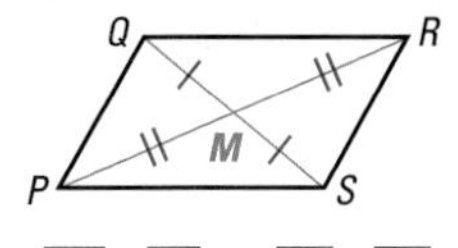

$\overline{QM} \cong \overline{SM}$ and $\overline{PM} \cong \overline{RM}$

EXAMPLE 3 Standardized Test Practice

The diagonals of $\square LMNO$ intersect at point *P*. What are the coordinates of *P*?

Ⓐ $\left(\frac{7}{2}, 2\right)$ Ⓑ $\left(2, \frac{7}{2}\right)$

Ⓒ $\left(\frac{5}{2}, 2\right)$ Ⓓ $\left(2, \frac{5}{2}\right)$

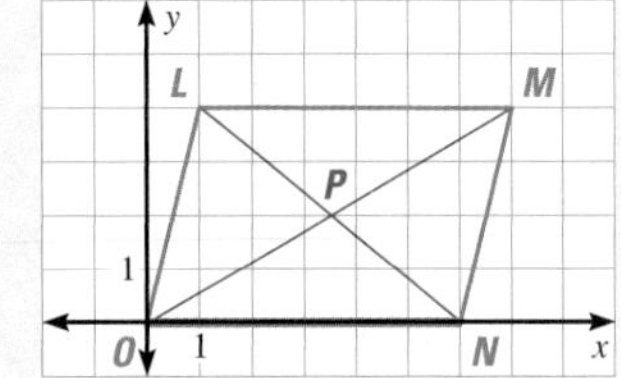

SIMPLIFY CALCULATIONS

In Example 3, you can use either diagonal to find the coordinates of *P*. Using $\overline{OM}$ simplifies calculations because one endpoint is (0, 0).

Solution

By Theorem 8.6, the diagonals of a parallelogram bisect each other. So, *P* is the midpoint of diagonals $\overline{LN}$ and $\overline{OM}$. Use the Midpoint Formula.

Coordinates of midpoint *P* of $\overline{OM} = \left(\frac{7+0}{2}, \frac{4+0}{2}\right) = \left(\frac{7}{2}, 2\right)$

▸ The correct answer is A. Ⓐ Ⓑ Ⓒ Ⓓ

GUIDED PRACTICE for Examples 2 and 3

Find the indicated measure in $\square JKLM$.

3. *NM* 2

4. *KM* 4

5. $m\angle JML$ 70°

6. $m\angle KML$ 40°

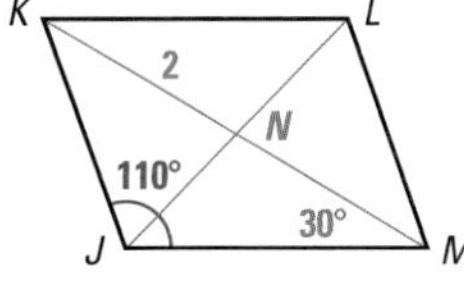

Extra Example 2

A metal screen is used to cover a shop window when the shop is closed. The sections of the screen are parallelograms. If $m\angle LMN = 110°$, what is $m\angle MNO$? **70°**

Extra Example 3

The diagonals of $\square PQRS$ intersect at point *T*. What are the coordinates of point *T*? **C**

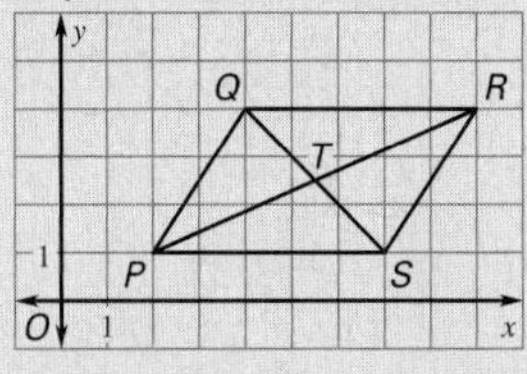

Ⓐ $\left(\frac{9}{2}, \frac{5}{2}\right)$ Ⓑ $\left(\frac{9}{2}, \frac{7}{2}\right)$

Ⓒ $\left(\frac{11}{2}, \frac{5}{2}\right)$ Ⓓ $\left(\frac{11}{2}, \frac{7}{2}\right)$

Key Question to Ask for Example 3

- Which other points could you have used to find the coordinates of *P*? ***L* and *N***

Closing the Lesson

Have students summarize the major points of the lesson and answer the Essential Question: How do you find angle and side measures in a parallelogram?

- **Opposite sides and angles of a parallelogram are congruent.**
- **Consecutive angles of a parallelogram are supplementary.**
- **The diagonals of a parallelogram bisect each other.**

If you know the length of a side of a parallelogram, then you know that the opposite side has the same measure. If you know the measure of an angle of the parallelogram, then you know that the opposite angle has the same measure and that the other two angle measures can be found by subtracting the given measure from 180°.

8.2 EXERCISES

HOMEWORK KEY
○ = **WORKED-OUT SOLUTIONS** on p. WS1 for Exs. 9, 13, and 39
★ = **STANDARDIZED TEST PRACTICE** Exs. 2, 16, 29, 35, and 41

4 PRACTICE AND APPLY

Assignment Guide

Answer Transparencies available for all exercises

Basic:
Day 1: EP p. 897 Exs. 35–40
pp. 518–521
Exs. 1–5, 9–19, 23–25, 38–41, 47–57 odd

Average:
Day 1: pp. 518–521
Exs. 1, 2, 5–7, 10–12, 14–16, 17–29 odd, 30–35, 38–43, 46, 50, 52, 56

Advanced:
Day 1: pp. 518–521
Exs. 1, 2, 7, 8, 10–12, 14–16, 20–28 even, 29–38*, 40–45*, 48, 54, 57

Block:
pp. 518–521
Exs. 1, 2, 5–7, 10–12, 14–16, 17–29 odd, 30–35, 38–43, 46, 50, 52, 56 (with 8.3)

Differentiated Instruction

See *Geometry Best Practices Toolkit* for suggestions on addressing the needs of a diverse classroom.

Homework Check

For a quick check of student understanding of key concepts, go over the following exercises:
Basic: 4, 10, 14, 18, 38
Average: 6, 11, 15, 25, 40
Advanced: 8, 12, 16, 30, 41

Extra Practice

- Student Edition, p. 910
- Chapter 8 Resource Book: Practice levels A, B, C, pp. 19–24

Practice Worksheet

An easily-readable reduced practice page (with answers) for this lesson can be found on p. 504C.

SKILL PRACTICE

A

1. **VOCABULARY** What property of a parallelogram is included in the definition of a parallelogram? What properties are described by the theorems in this lesson? **See margin.**

2. ★ **WRITING** In parallelogram *ABCD*, $m\angle A = 65°$. *Explain* how you would find the other angle measures of ▱*ABCD*. **$m\angle B = 115°$ since consecutive angles are supplementary and $m\angle C = 65°$ and $m\angle D = 115°$ since opposite angles are congruent.**

EXAMPLE 1 on p. 515 for Exs. 3–8

ALGEBRA Find the value of each variable in the parallelogram.

3.
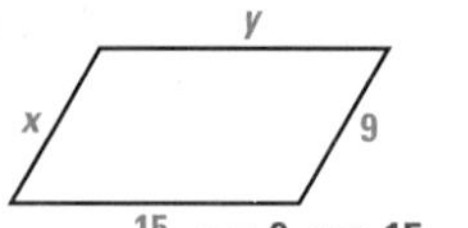

x = 9, y = 15

4.
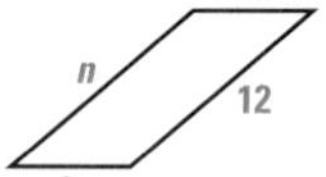

m = 5, n = 12

5.
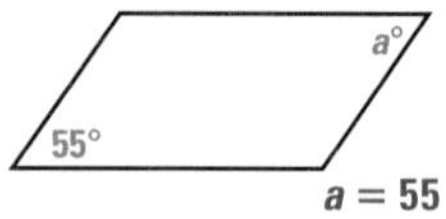

a = 55

6.
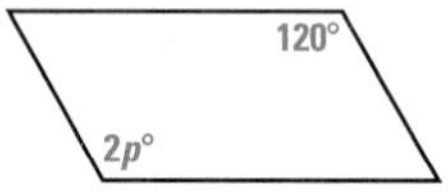

p = 60

7.
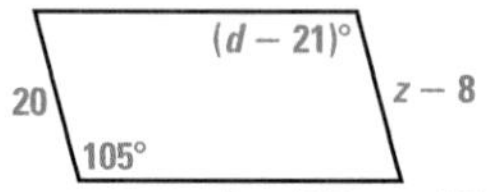

d = 126, z = 28

8.
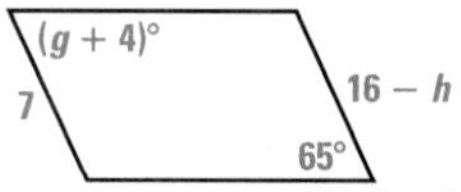

g = 61, h = 9

EXAMPLE 2 on p. 517 for Exs. 9–12

FINDING ANGLE MEASURES Find the measure of the indicated angle in the parallelogram.

9. Find $m\angle B$. **129°**
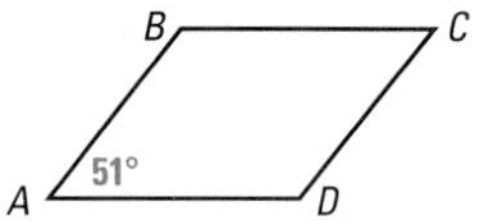

10. Find $m\angle L$. **85°**
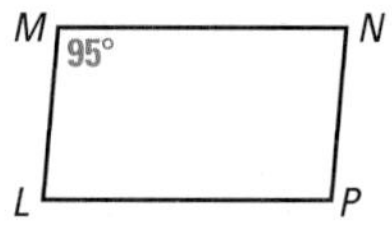

11. Find $m\angle Y$. **61°**
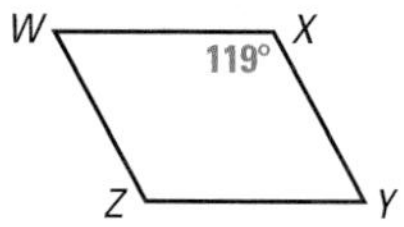

12. **SKETCHING** In ▱*PQRS*, $m\angle R$ is 24 degrees more than $m\angle S$. Sketch ▱*PQRS*. Find the measure of each interior angle. Then label each angle with its measure. **See margin for art; $m\angle S = 78°$, $m\angle P = 102°$, $m\angle Q = 78°$, $m\angle R = 102°$.**

EXAMPLE 3 on p. 517 for Exs. 13–16

ALGEBRA Find the value of each variable in the parallelogram.

13.
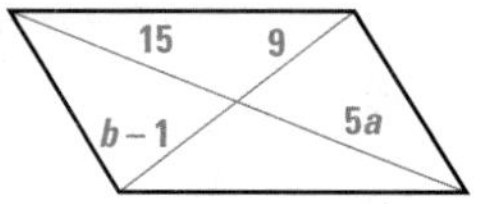

a = 3, b = 10

14.
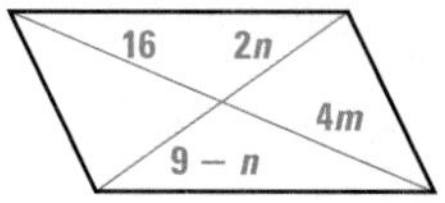

m = 4, n = 3

15.
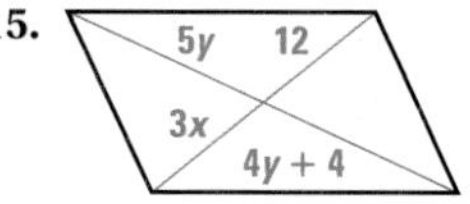

x = 4, y = 4

16. ★ **MULTIPLE CHOICE** The diagonals of parallelogram *OPQR* intersect at point *M*. What are the coordinates of point *M*? **A**

Ⓐ $\left(1, \frac{5}{2}\right)$ Ⓑ $\left(2, \frac{5}{2}\right)$

Ⓒ $\left(1, \frac{3}{2}\right)$ Ⓓ $\left(2, \frac{3}{2}\right)$

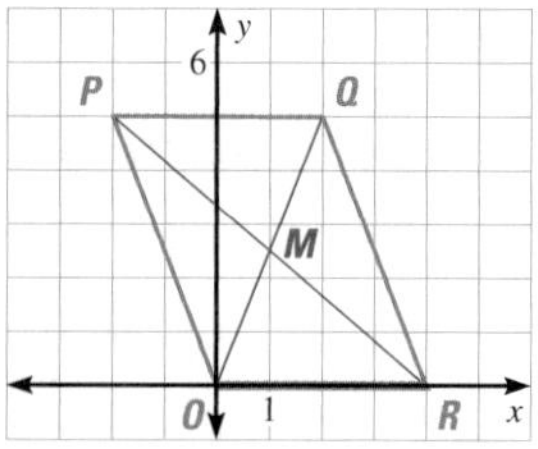

1. A parallelogram is a quadrilateral with both pairs of opposite sides parallel; opposite sides are congruent, opposite angles are congruent, consecutive angles are supplementary, and the diagonals bisect each other.

12.
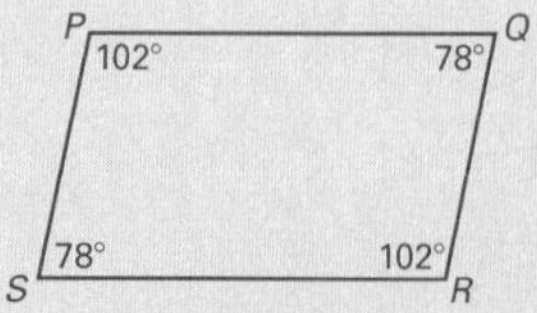

B **REASONING** **Use the photo to copy and complete the statement. *Explain.*** **17–22. See margin.**

17. $\overline{AD} \cong$ _?_
18. $\angle DAB \cong$ _?_
19. $\angle BCA \cong$ _?_
20. $m\angle ABC =$ _?_
21. $m\angle CAB =$ _?_
22. $m\angle CAD =$ _?_

USING A DIAGRAM **Find the indicated measure in $\square EFGH$. *Explain.*** **23–28. See margin.**

23. $m\angle EJF$
24. $m\angle EGF$
25. $m\angle HFG$
26. $m\angle GEF$
27. $m\angle HGF$
28. $m\angle EHG$

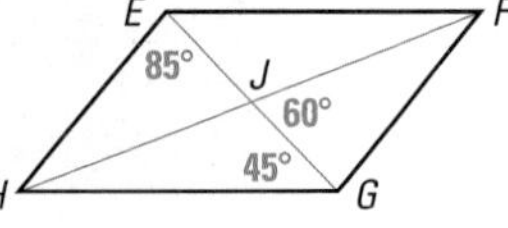

Animated Geometry at classzone.com

29. ★ **MULTIPLE CHOICE** In parallelogram $ABCD$, $AB = 14$ inches and $BC = 20$ inches. What is the perimeter (in inches) of $\square ABCD$? **C**

Ⓐ 28 Ⓑ 40 Ⓒ 68 Ⓓ 280

30. **ALGEBRA** The measure of one interior angle of a parallelogram is 0.25 times the measure of another angle. Find the measure of each angle. **36°, 144°**

31. **ALGEBRA** The measure of one interior angle of a parallelogram is 50 degrees more than 4 times the measure of another angle. Find the measure of each angle. **26°, 154°**

32. **ERROR ANALYSIS** In $\square ABCD$, $m\angle B = 50°$. A student says that $m\angle A = 50°$. *Explain* why this statement is incorrect. **$\angle B$ and $\angle A$ are consecutive angles and thus are supplementary which makes $m\angle A = 130°$.**

33. **USING A DIAGRAM** In the diagram, $QRST$ and $STUV$ are parallelograms. Find the values of x and y. *Explain* your reasoning. **20, 60°; $UV = TS = QR$ using the fact that opposite sides are congruent and the Transitive Property of Equality. $\angle TUS \cong \angle VSU$ by the Alternate Interior Angles Congruence Theorem and $m\angle TSU = 60°$ by the Triangle Sum Theorem.**

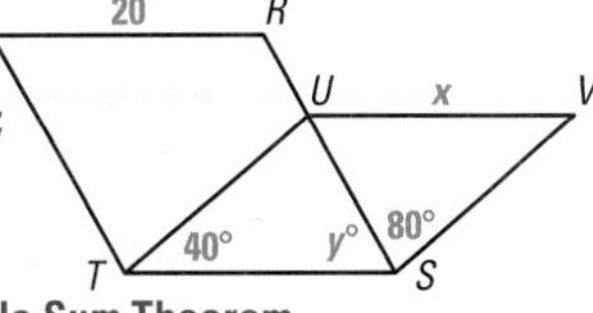

34. **FINDING A PERIMETER** The sides of $\square MNPQ$ are represented by the expressions below. Sketch $\square MNPQ$ and find its perimeter. **See margin for art; 52**

$MQ = -2x + 37$ $QP = y + 14$ $NP = x - 5$ $MN = 4y + 5$

35. ★ **SHORT RESPONSE** In $ABCD$, $m\angle B = 124°$, $m\angle A = 66°$, and $m\angle C = 124°$. *Explain* why $ABCD$ cannot be a parallelogram. ***Sample answer:* In a parallelogram, opposite angles are congruent. $\angle A$ and $\angle C$ are opposite angles but not congruent.**

C 36. **FINDING ANGLE MEASURES** In $\square LMNP$ shown at the right, $m\angle MLN = 32°$, $m\angle NLP = (x^2)°$, $m\angle MNP = 12x°$, and $\angle MNP$ is an acute angle. Find $m\angle NLP$. **16°**

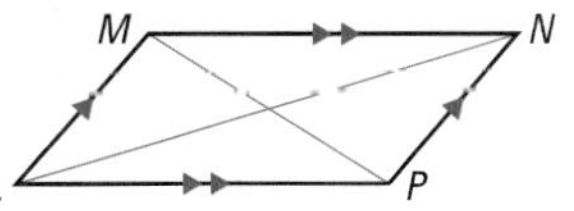

37. **CHALLENGE** Points $A(1, 2)$, $B(3, 6)$, and $C(6, 4)$ are three vertices of a parallelogram. Find the coordinates of each point that could be vertex D. Sketch each possible parallelogram in a separate coordinate plane. *Justify* your answers. **(−2, 4), (4, 0), (8,8); see margin for art; in each quadrilateral each pair of opposite sides is parallel.**

Avoiding Common Errors

Exercises 5–8 Students may treat opposite angles of the parallelogram as supplementary rather than congruent. Review Theorems 8.4 and 8.5. Also suggest that students inspect the diagrams carefully.

An **Animated Geometry** activity is available on-line for **Exercises 23–28**. This activity is also available on the **Power Presentations CD-ROM**.

Teaching Strategy

Exercises 23–28 Have students copy the diagram, and before they attempt to answer the exercises, have them use a second color to fill in the measures of all angles of the four smallest triangles.

Mathematical Reasoning

Exercises 30–31 Draw and label a parallelogram that shows the measures of the angles. Point out that the given angles must be consecutive angles since they are not congruent. Have the students write algebraic expressions for the angle measures before writing an equation.

23. 120°; $\angle EJF$ and $\angle FJG$ are a linear pair.

24. 85°; Alternate Interior Angles Theorem with $\angle HEG$

25. 35°; Triangle Sum Theorem

26. 45°; Alternate Interior Angles Theorem with $\angle HGE$

27. 130°; sum of the measures of $\angle HGE$ and $\angle EGF$

28. 50°; consecutive angles $\angle HGF$ and $\angle EHG$ are supplementary.

34.

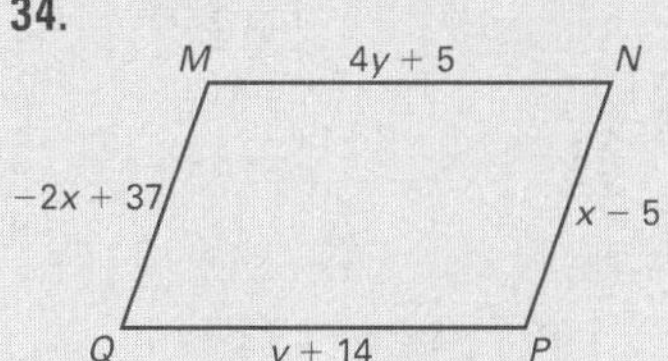

37. See Additional Answers beginning on p. AA1.

17. $\overline{BC}$; opposite sides of a parallelogram are congruent.

18. $\angle BCD$; opposite angles of a parallelogram are congruent.

19. $\angle DAC$; alternate interior angles are congruent.

20. 47°; opposite angles of a parallelogram are congruent.

21. 47°; consecutive angles of a parallelogram are supplementary and alternate interior angles are congruent.

22. 86°; alternate interior angles are congruent.

Study Strategy

Exercise 39 Have the students make a model of $PQRS$ with toothpicks. For part c, have them move the toothpicks and watch how $m\angle P$ and QS change when $m\angle Q$ increases or decreases. If students have access to geometry software, have them use the software instead.

Teaching Strategy

Exercise 40 Have the students use $4x$ for LM and $3x$ for MN and then write the equation $4x + 3x + 4x + 3x = 28$ to express the fact that the perimeter is 28. Be sure students understand that after they solve for x, they need to substitute the solution in the expression $4x$ to find LM.

41. See below.

42. Statements (Reasons)

1. $ABCD$ is a parallelogram. (Given)
2. $\overline{BD} \parallel \overline{AC}$, $\overline{AB} \parallel \overline{CD}$ (Definition of a parallelogram)
3. $\angle CBD \cong \angle ADB$, $\angle CDB \cong \angle ABD$ (Alternate Interior Angles Congruence Theorem)
4. $\overline{BD} \cong \overline{BD}$ (Reflexive Property of Segment Congruence)
5. $\triangle ABD \cong \triangle CDB$ (ASA)
6. $\angle A \cong \angle C$, $\angle B \cong \angle D$ (Corr. parts of $\cong$ △s are $\cong$.)

43. *Sample answer:* Given that $PQRS$ is a parallelogram, you know that $\overline{QR} \parallel \overline{PS}$ with $\overline{QP}$ being a transversal. By definition and the fact that they are consecutive interior angles, $\angle Q$ and $\angle P$ are supplementary by the Consecutive Interior Angles Theorem. So $x° + y° = 180°$ by the definition of supplementary angles.

PROBLEM SOLVING

EXAMPLE 2 on p. 517 for Ex. 38

38. AIRPLANE The diagram shows the mechanism for opening the canopy on a small airplane. Two pivot arms attach at four pivot points A, B, C, and D. These points form the vertices of a parallelogram. Find $m\angle D$ when $m\angle C = 40°$. *Explain* your reasoning. **140°; $\angle C$ and $\angle D$ are consecutive angles and therefore are supplementary.**

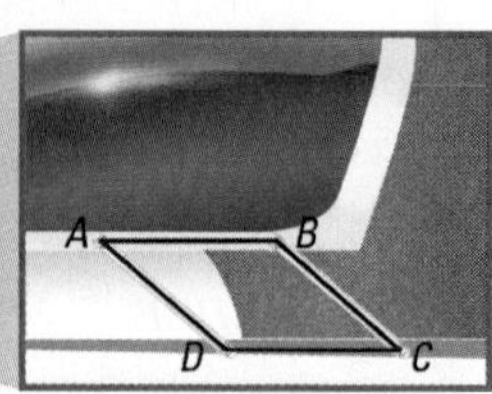

 for problem solving help at classzone.com

39. MIRROR The mirror shown is attached to the wall by an arm that can extend away from the wall. In the figure, points P, Q, R, and S are the vertices of a parallelogram. This parallelogram is one of several that change shape as the mirror is extended.

a. If $PQ = 3$ inches, find RS. **3 in.**

b. If $m\angle Q = 70°$, what is $m\angle S$? **70°**

c. What happens to $m\angle P$ as $m\angle Q$ increases? What happens to QS as $m\angle Q$ decreases? *Explain.*

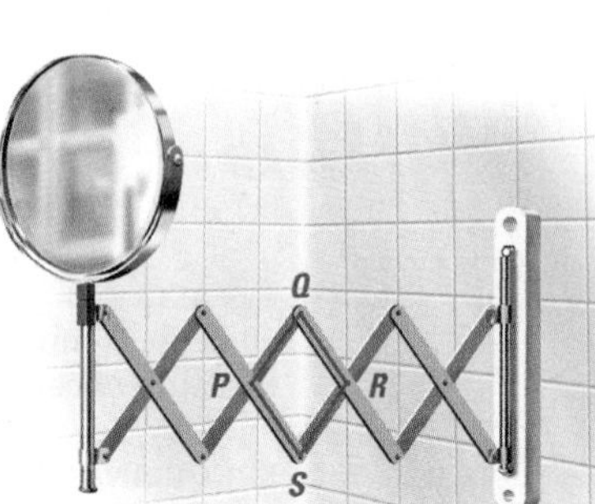

@HomeTutor for problem solving help at classzone.com

39c. It decreases; it gets longer; the sum of the measures of the interior angles always is 360°. As $m\angle Q$ increases so does $m\angle S$ therefore $m\angle P$ must decrease to maintain the sum of 360°. As $m\angle Q$ decreases $m\angle P$ increases, moving Q farther away from S.

40. USING RATIOS In ▱$LMNO$, the ratio of LM to MN is 4:3. Find LM if the perimeter of $LMNO$ is 28. **8**

41. ★ OPEN-ENDED MATH Draw a triangle. Copy the triangle and combine the two triangles to form a quadrilateral. Show that the quadrilateral is a parallelogram. Then show how you can make additional copies of the triangle to form a larger parallelogram that is similar to the first parallelogram. *Justify* your method. **See margin.**

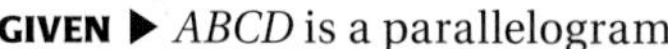

42. PROVING THEOREM 8.4 Use the diagram of quadrilateral $ABCD$ with the auxiliary line segment drawn to write a two-column proof of Theorem 8.4. **See margin.**

GIVEN ▶ $ABCD$ is a parallelogram.

PROVE ▶ $\angle A \cong \angle C$, $\angle B \cong \angle D$

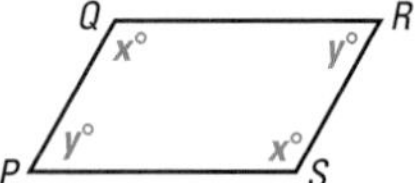

43. PROVING THEOREM 8.5 Use properties of parallel lines to prove Theorem 8.5. **See margin.**

GIVEN ▶ $PQRS$ is a parallelogram.

PROVE ▶ $x° + y° = 180°$

Q R P S x° y° y° x°

◯ = WORKED-OUT SOLUTIONS on p. WS1 ★ = STANDARDIZED TEST PRACTICE

41. *Sample:*

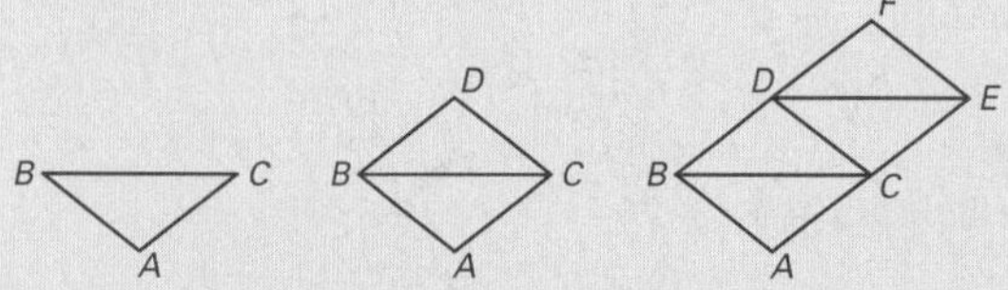

Since $\triangle ABC \cong \triangle DCB$ you know $\angle ACB \cong \angle DBC$ and $\angle ABC \cong \angle DCB$. By the Alternate Interior Angles Converse, $\overline{BD} \parallel \overline{AC}$ and $\overline{AB} \parallel \overline{CD}$, thus making $ABDC$ a parallelogram. If two more triangles are positioned the same as the first two, you can line up the pair of congruent sides and form a larger parallelogram because corresponding angles are congruent, and the ratios of the lengths of the corresponding sides are equal, so ▱$ABCD \sim$ ▱$ABFE$ by definition.

C 44. **PROVING THEOREM 8.6** Theorem 8.6 states that if a quadrilateral is a parallelogram, then its diagonals bisect each other. Write a two-column proof of Theorem 8.6. **See margin.**

45. **CHALLENGE** Suppose you choose a point on the base of an isosceles triangle. You draw segments from that point perpendicular to the legs of the triangle. Prove that the sum of the lengths of those segments is equal to the length of the altitude drawn to one leg. **See margin.**

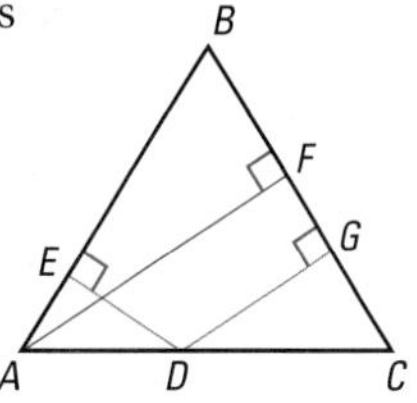

GIVEN ▶ $\triangle ABC$ is isosceles with base $\overline{AC}$, $\overline{AF}$ is the altitude drawn to $\overline{BC}$, $\overline{DE} \perp \overline{AB}$, $\overline{DG} \perp \overline{BC}$

PROVE ▶ For D anywhere on $\overline{AC}$, $DE + DG = AF$.

MIXED REVIEW

PREVIEW
Prepare for Lesson 8.3 in Exs. 46–48.

Tell whether the lines through the given points are *parallel, perpendicular,* or *neither. Justify* your answer. *(p. 171)* **46–48. See margin.**

46. **Line 1:** (2, 4), (4, 1)
Line 2: (5, 7), (9, 0)

47. **Line 1:** (−6, 7), (−2, 3)
Line 2: (9, −1), (2, 6)

48. **Line 1:** (−3, 0), (−6, 5)
Line 2: (3, −5), (5, −10)

Decide if the side lengths form a triangle. If so, would the triangle be *acute, right,* or *obtuse*? *(p. 441)*

49. 9, 13, and 6 **triangle; obtuse**

50. 10, 12, and 7 **triangle; acute**

51. 5, 9, and $\sqrt{106}$ **triangle; right**

52. 8, 12, and 4 **not a triangle**

53. 24, 10, and 26 **triangle; right**

54. 9, 10, and 11 **triangle; acute**

Find the value of *x*. Write your answer in simplest radical form. *(p. 457)*

55. 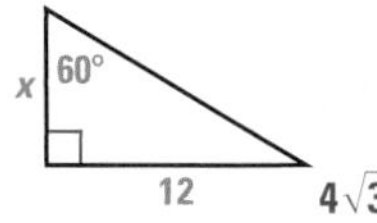

$4\sqrt{3}$

56. 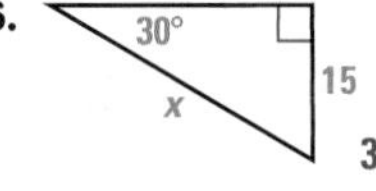

30

57. 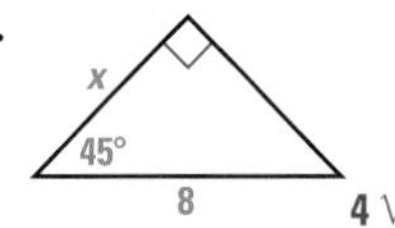

$4\sqrt{2}$

QUIZ *for Lessons 8.1–8.2*

Find the value of *x*. *(p. 507)*

1. 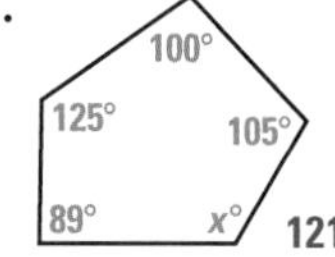

121

2. 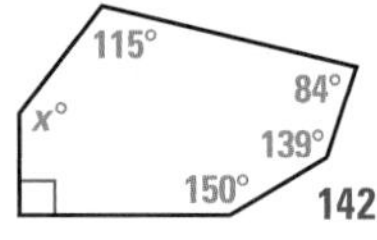

142

3. 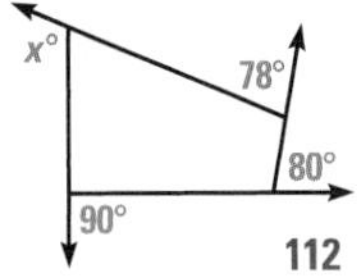

112

Find the value of each variable in the parallelogram. *(p. 515)*

4. 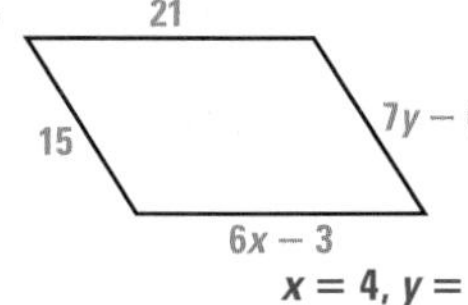

$x = 4, y = 3$

5. 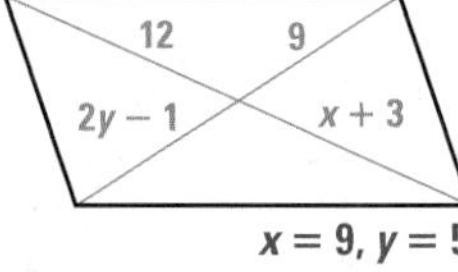

$x = 9, y = 5$

6. 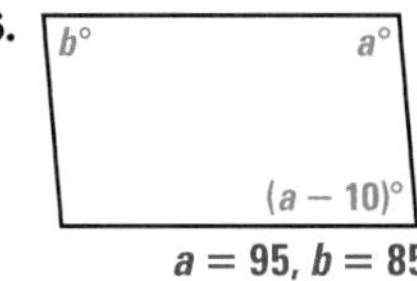

$a = 95, b = 85$

46. Neither; the slope of line 1 is $-\frac{3}{2}$ and the slope of line 2 is $-\frac{7}{4}$.

47. Parallel; the slope of both lines is −1.

48. Neither; the slope of line 1 is $-\frac{5}{3}$ and the slope of line 2 is $-\frac{5}{2}$.

5 ASSESS AND RETEACH

Daily Homework Quiz

Transparency Available

1. Find the values of *a* and *b* in the parallelogram. **42, 26**

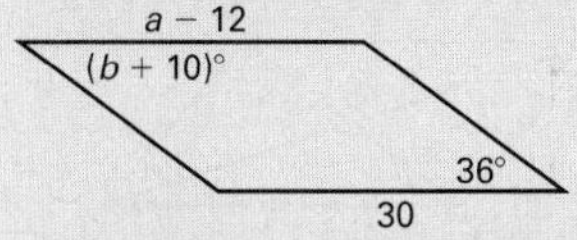

2. Find the measure of $\angle K$ in the parallelogram. **116°**

Find the indicated measures in parallelogram *ABCD*.

3. $m\angle BCD$ **43°**

4. If $BE = 9$, find BD. **18**

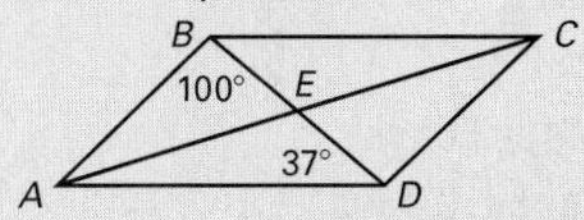

Available at **classzone.com**

Diagnosis/Remediation

- Practice A, B, C in Chapter 8 Resource Book, pp. 19–24
- Study Guide in Chapter 8 Resource Book, pp. 25–26
- Practice Workbook, pp. 148–150
- @HomeTutor

Challenge

Additional challenge is available in the Chapter 8 Resource Book, p. 29.

Quiz

An easily-readable reduced copy of the quiz (with answers) on Lessons 8.1–8.2 from the Assessment Book can be found on p. 504F.

44, 45. See Additional Answers beginning on p. AA1.

1 PLAN AND PREPARE

Warm-Up Exercises

Transparency Available

1. What congruence postulate shows that $\triangle ABE \cong \triangle CDE$? **SAS**

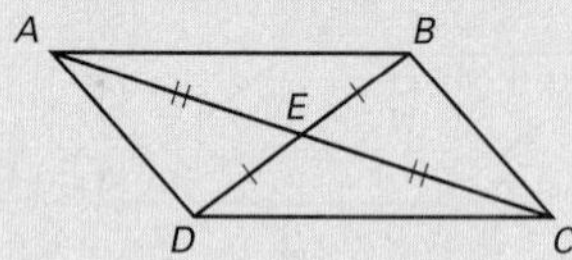

2. If $\angle E \cong \angle G$, find $m\angle E$. **118°**

G H 62° 62° F E

Notetaking Guide

Transparency Available

Promotes interactive learning and notetaking skills, pp. 205–208.

Pacing

Basic: 2 days

Average: 2 days

Advanced: 2 days

Block: 0.5 block with 8.2
0.5 block with 8.4

• See *Teaching Guide/Lesson Plan*.

2 FOCUS AND MOTIVATE

Essential Question

Big Idea 2, p. 504

How can you prove that a quadrilateral is a parallelogram? **Tell students they will learn how to answer this question by studying the theorems in this lesson.**

8.3 Show that a Quadrilateral is a Parallelogram

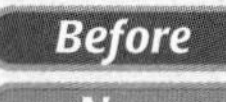

Before You identified properties of parallelograms.

Now You will use properties to identify parallelograms.

Why? So you can describe how a music stand works, as in Ex. 32.

Key Vocabulary

• **parallelogram,** *p. 515*

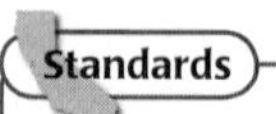

Standards

7.0 Students prove and use theorems involving the properties of parallel lines cut by a transversal, the properties of quadrilaterals, and the properties of circles.

Given a parallelogram, you can use Theorem 8.3 and Theorem 8.4 to prove statements about the angles and sides of the parallelogram. The converses of Theorem 8.3 and Theorem 8.4 are stated below. You can use these and other theorems in this lesson to prove that a quadrilateral with certain properties is a parallelogram.

THEOREMS *For Your Notebook*

THEOREM 8.7

If both pairs of opposite sides of a quadrilateral are congruent, then the quadrilateral is a parallelogram.

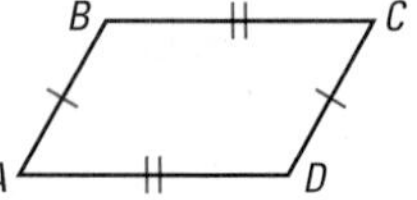

If $\overline{AB} \cong \overline{CD}$ and $\overline{BC} \cong \overline{AD}$, then $ABCD$ is a parallelogram.

Proof: below

THEOREM 8.8

If both pairs of opposite angles of a quadrilateral are congruent, then the quadrilateral is a parallelogram.

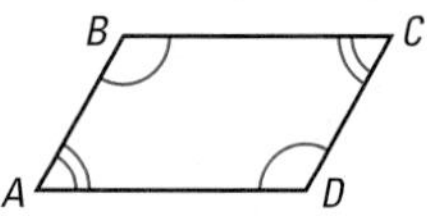

If $\angle A \cong \angle C$ and $\angle B \cong \angle D$, then $ABCD$ is a parallelogram.

Proof: Ex. 38, p. 529

PROOF Theorem 8.7

GIVEN ▶ $\overline{AB} \cong \overline{CD}$, $\overline{BC} \cong \overline{AD}$

PROVE ▶ $ABCD$ is a parallelogram.

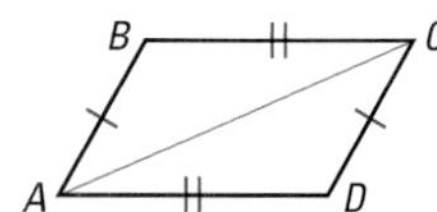

Proof Draw $\overline{AC}$, forming $\triangle ABC$ and $\triangle CDA$. You are given that $\overline{AB} \cong \overline{CD}$ and $\overline{BC} \cong \overline{AD}$. Also, $\overline{AC} \cong \overline{AC}$ by the Reflexive Property of Congruence. So, $\triangle ABC \cong \triangle CDA$ by the SSS Congruence Postulate. Because corresponding parts of congruent triangles are congruent, $\angle BAC \cong \angle DCA$ and $\angle BCA \cong DAC$. Then, by the Alternate Interior Angles Converse, $\overline{AB} \parallel \overline{CD}$ and $\overline{BC} \parallel \overline{AD}$. By definition, $ABCD$ is a parallelogram.

Resource Planning Guide

Chapter Resource Book
• Teaching Guide/Lesson Plan (pp. 30–31)
• Activity Master (p. 32)
• Practice levels A, B, C (pp. 33–38)
• Study Guide (pp. 39–40)
• Catch-up for Absent Students (p. 41)
• Problem Solving Workshop (p. 42)
• Challenge (p. 44)

Workbooks
• Notetaking Guide (pp. 205–208)
• Practice Workbook (pp. 151–153)

Teaching Options
• **Power Presentations CD-ROM** provides dynamic electronic teaching resources for the classroom.
• **Activity Generator CD-ROM** provides editable activities for all ability levels.

Interactive Technology
• Easy Planner
• Power Presentations CD-ROM
• Activity Generator CD-ROM
• Animated Geometry
• Test Generator CD-ROM
• Online Quiz
• eWorkbook
• eEdition
• @HomeTutor

Resources for English Learners
• Quick Reference for English Learners
• Spanish Study Guide
• Multi-Language Visual Glossary
• Student Resources in Spanish

See also the *Geometry Toolkit* for more strategies for meeting individual needs.

EXAMPLE 1 Solve a real-world problem

RIDE An amusement park ride has a moving platform attached to four swinging arms. The platform swings back and forth, higher and higher, until it goes over the top and around in a circular motion. In the diagram below, $\overline{AD}$ and $\overline{BC}$ represent two of the swinging arms, and $\overline{DC}$ is parallel to the ground (line ℓ). *Explain* why the moving platform $\overline{AB}$ is always parallel to the ground.

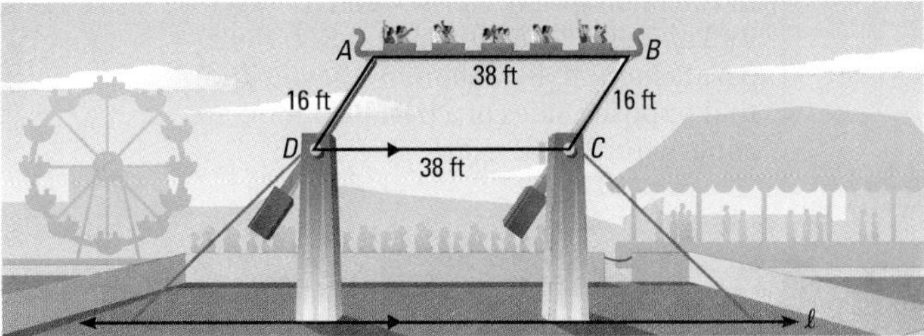

Solution

The shape of quadrilateral *ABCD* changes as the moving platform swings around, but its side lengths do not change. Both pairs of opposite sides are congruent, so *ABCD* is a parallelogram by Theorem 8.7.

By the definition of a parallelogram, $\overline{AB} \parallel \overline{DC}$. Because $\overline{DC}$ is parallel to line ℓ, $\overline{AB}$ is also parallel to line ℓ by the Transitive Property of Parallel Lines. So, the moving platform is parallel to the ground.

GUIDED PRACTICE for Example 1

1. In quadrilateral *WXYZ*, $m\angle W = 42°$, $m\angle X = 138°$, $m\angle Y = 42°$. Find $m\angle Z$. Is *WXYZ* a parallelogram? *Explain* your reasoning. **138°; yes; the sum of the measures of the interior angles in a quadrilateral is 360°, so the measure of $\angle Z$ is 138°. Since opposite angles of the quadrilateral are congruent, *WXYZ* is a parallelogram.**

THEOREMS *For Your Notebook*

THEOREM 8.9

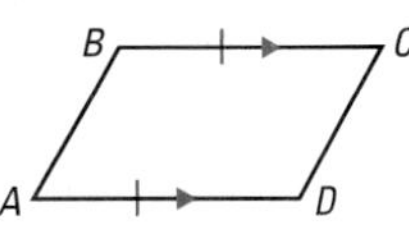

If one pair of opposite sides of a quadrilateral are congruent and parallel, then the quadrilateral is a parallelogram.

If $\overline{BC} \parallel \overline{AD}$ and $\overline{BC} \cong \overline{AD}$, then *ABCD* is a parallelogram.

Proof: Ex. 33, p. 528

THEOREM 8.10

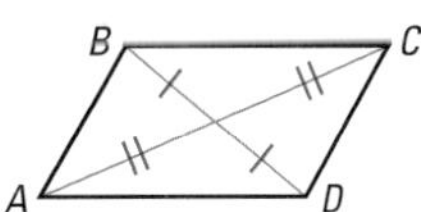

If the diagonals of a quadrilateral bisect each other, then the quadrilateral is a parallelogram.

If $\overline{BD}$ and $\overline{AC}$ bisect each other, then *ABCD* is a parallelogram.

Proof: Ex. 39, p. 529

Motivating the Lesson

Review briefly the theorems about parallelograms that were proved in Lesson 8.2. Ask students to state the converse of each theorem and to tell whether or not they think the converse is true. Tell students that in this lesson, they will examine these converses and how they can be used.

3 TEACH

Extra Example 1

The figure shows part of a stair railing. Explain how you know the support bars $\overline{MP}$ and $\overline{NQ}$ are parallel.

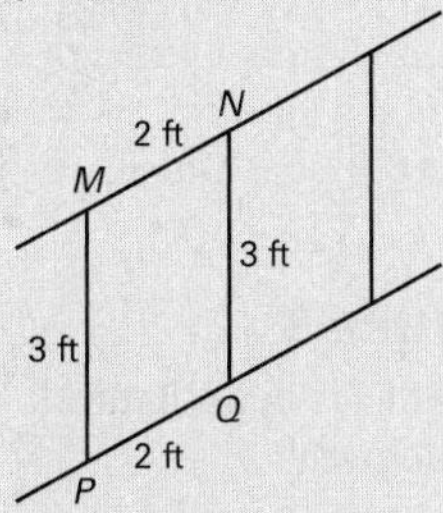

$MP = NQ$ and $MN = PQ$, so *MNQP* is a parallelogram. Therefore, $\overline{MP} \parallel \overline{NQ}$.

Key Question to Ask for Example 1

- How high above $\overline{DC}$ can a rider be? Explain. **16 ft; When $\overline{AD}$ and $\overline{BC}$ are perpendicular to $\overline{DC}$, the length of $\overline{AD}$ gives the maximum height.**

Extra Example 2

Suppose you place two straight, narrow strips of paper of equal length on top of two lines of a sheet of notebook paper. If you draw a segment to join their left ends and a segment to join their right ends, will the resulting figure be a parallelogram? Explain.

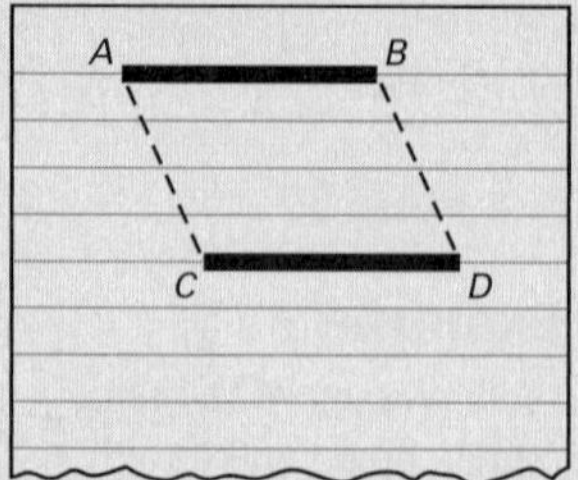

Yes. Since $AB = CD$, you know that $\overline{AB} \cong \overline{CD}$. The segments are parallel since the lines on the notebook paper are parallel. So, by Theorem 8.9, $ABCD$ is a parallelogram.

Extra Example 3

For what value of x is quadrilateral $RSTU$ a parallelogram? **8**

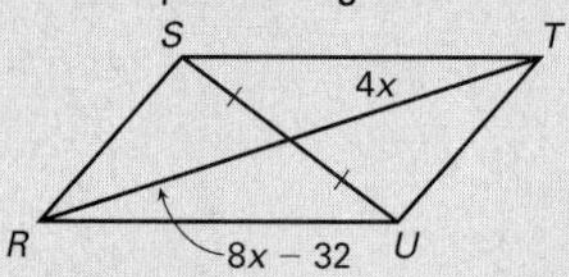

Key Question to Ask for Example 3

- When $x = 4$, can you find the lengths of $\overline{DF}$ and $\overline{CE}$? Explain. **No. You can find the lengths of $\overline{DN}$, $\overline{NF}$, and $\overline{DF}$ by using the value 4 for x and the Segment Addition Postulate. But there is no specific information about other lengths, so the best you can say about CE is that $CE = 2(NC) = 2(NE)$.**

EXAMPLE 2 Identify a parallelogram

ARCHITECTURE The doorway shown is part of a building in England. Over time, the building has leaned sideways. *Explain* how you know that $SV = TU$.

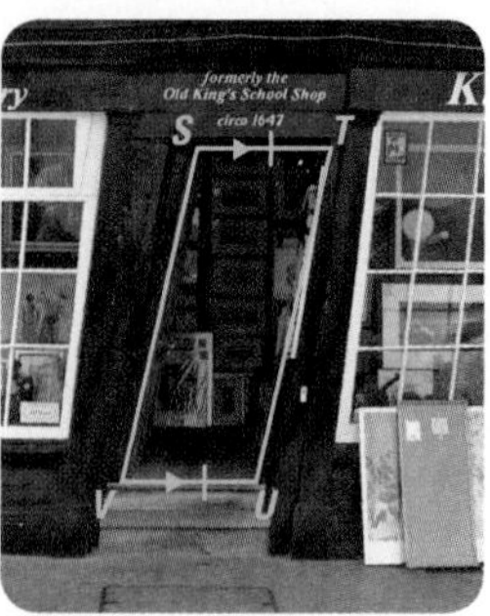

Solution

In the photograph, $\overline{ST} \parallel \overline{UV}$ and $\overline{ST} \cong \overline{UV}$. By Theorem 8.9, quadrilateral $STUV$ is a parallelogram. By Theorem 8.3, you know that opposite sides of a parallelogram are congruent. So, $SV = TU$.

EXAMPLE 3 Use algebra with parallelograms

ALGEBRA For what value of x is quadrilateral $CDEF$ a parallelogram?

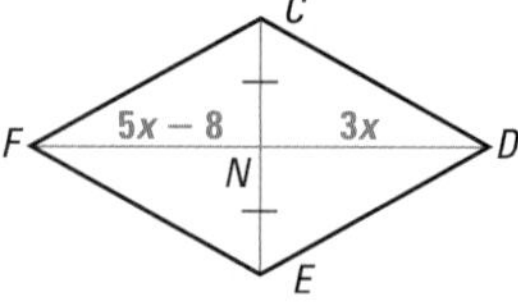

Solution

By Theorem 8.10, if the diagonals of $CDEF$ bisect each other, then it is a parallelogram. You are given that $\overline{CN} \cong \overline{EN}$. Find x so that $\overline{FN} \cong \overline{DN}$.

$FN = DN$	**Set the segment lengths equal.**
$5x - 8 = 3x$	**Substitute $5x - 8$ for FN and $3x$ for DN.**
$2x - 8 = 0$	**Subtract $3x$ from each side.**
$2x = 8$	**Add 8 to each side.**
$x = 4$	**Divide each side by 2.**

When $x = 4$, $FN = 5(4) - 8 = 12$ and $DN = 3(4) = 12$.

▶ Quadrilateral $CDEF$ is a parallelogram when $x = 4$.

GUIDED PRACTICE for Examples 2 and 3

What theorem can you use to show that the quadrilateral is a parallelogram?

2.
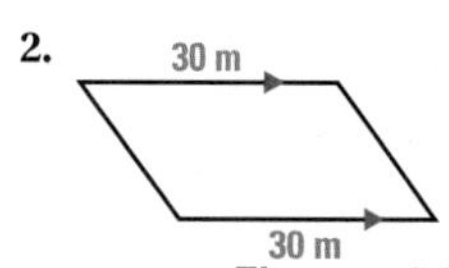

Theorem 8.9

3.
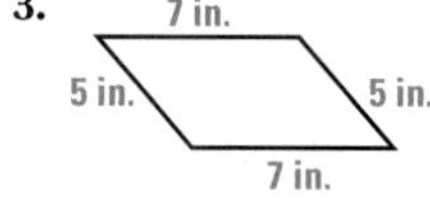

Theorem 8.7

4.
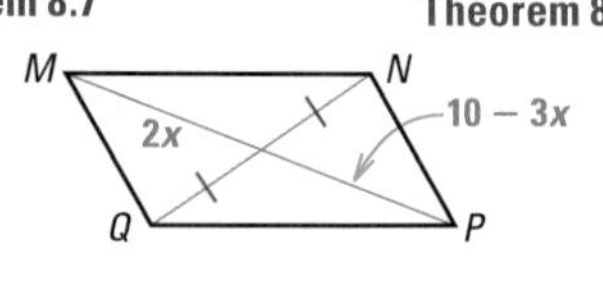

Theorem 8.8

5. For what value of x is quadrilateral $MNPQ$ a parallelogram? *Explain* your reasoning. **2; the diagonals of a parallelogram bisect each other so solve $2x = 10 - 3x$ for x.**

M, N, 2x, 10 − 3x, Q, P

CONCEPT SUMMARY — *For Your Notebook*

Ways to Prove a Quadrilateral is a Parallelogram

1. Show both pairs of opposite sides are parallel.
   (DEFINITION)
   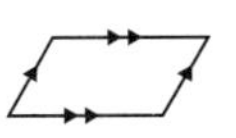

2. Show both pairs of opposite sides are congruent.
   (THEOREM 8.7)
   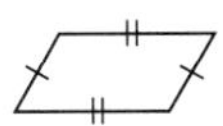

3. Show both pairs of opposite angles are congruent.
   (THEOREM 8.8)
   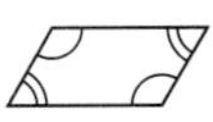

4. Show one pair of opposite sides are congruent and parallel.
   (THEOREM 8.9)
   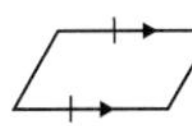

5. Show the diagonals bisect each other.
   (THEOREM 8.10)
   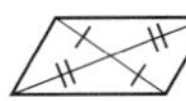

EXAMPLE 4 Use coordinate geometry

Show that quadrilateral *ABCD* is a parallelogram.

ANOTHER WAY
For alternative methods for solving the problem in Example 4, turn to page 530 for the **Problem Solving Workshop**.

Solution

One way is to show that a pair of sides are congruent and parallel. Then apply Theorem 8.9.

First use the Distance Formula to show that $\overline{AB}$ and $\overline{CD}$ are congruent.

$$AB = \sqrt{[2-(-3)]^2 + (5-3)^2} = \sqrt{29} \qquad CD = \sqrt{(5-0)^2 + (2-0)^2} = \sqrt{29}$$

Because $AB = CD = \sqrt{29}$, $\overline{AB} \cong \overline{CD}$.

Then use the slope formula to show that $\overline{AB} \parallel \overline{CD}$.

$$\text{Slope of } \overline{AB} = \frac{5-(3)}{2-(-3)} = \frac{2}{5} \qquad \text{Slope of } \overline{CD} = \frac{2-0}{5-0} = \frac{2}{5}$$

Because $\overline{AB}$ and $\overline{CD}$ have the same slope, they are parallel.

▶ $\overline{AB}$ and $\overline{CD}$ are congruent and parallel. So, *ABCD* is a parallelogram by Theorem 8.9.

6. Find the slopes of all four sides and show that opposite sides are parallel. A second way is to find the length of each side and show that opposite sides are congruent. A third way is to find the point of intersection of the diagonals and show the diagonals bisect each other.

✓ **GUIDED PRACTICE** for Example 4

6. Refer to the Concept Summary above. *Explain* how other methods can be used to show that quadrilateral *ABCD* in Example 4 is a parallelogram.

Differentiated Instruction

Inclusion Some students may need help answering **Guided Practice Exercise 6**. Divide students into four groups. Assign each group one of the ways to prove a quadrilateral is a parallelogram, except for Theorem 8.9, from the Concept Summary box. Have students work together to plan and give a brief presentation to the class about how their method can be used to show quadrilateral *ABCD* is a parallelogram.

See also the *Geometry Toolkit* for more strategies.

Extra Example 4

Show that *FGHJ* is a parallelogram.

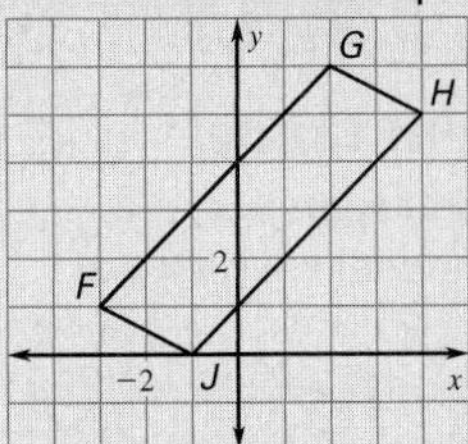

$FJ = GH = \sqrt{5}$, slope of $\overline{FJ}$ = slope of $\overline{GH} = -\frac{1}{2}$. Since a pair of opposite sides are parallel and congruent, *FGHJ* is a parallelogram.

Key Question to Ask for Example 4

- How else could you have proved that *ABCD* is a parallelogram? **Find the lengths of all four sides and show that both pairs of opposite sides are congruent; find the slopes of all four sides and show that both pairs of opposite sides are parallel; find the midpoints of both diagonals and show that the diagonals bisect each other.**

Closing the Lesson

Have students summarize the major points of the lesson and answer the Essential Question: How can you prove that a quadrilateral is a parallelogram?

- **If a quadrilateral has a pair of parallel and congruent sides, then it is a parallelogram.**
- **If a quadrilateral has two pairs of congruent opposite sides or two pairs of congruent opposite angles, then it is a parallelogram.**
- **If the diagonals of a quadrilateral bisect each other, then it is a parallelogram.**
- **If opposite sides of a quadrilateral are parallel, then, by definition, the quadrilateral is a parallelogram.**

You can prove a quadrilateral is a parallelogram by showing that all opposite sides or opposite angles are congruent, by showing that a pair of opposite sides are congruent and parallel, or by showing that the diagonals bisect each other. You can also use the definition of a parallelogram if you know that both pairs of opposite sides are parallel.

4 PRACTICE AND APPLY

Assignment Guide

Answer Transparencies available for all exercises

Basic:
Day 1: pp. 526–529
Exs. 1–7, 19–22, 31, 32, 46, 47
Day 2: pp. 526–529
Exs. 8–18, 33–37, 43–45

Average:
Day 1: pp. 526–529
Exs. 1–7, 19–23, 31, 32, 46
Day 2: pp. 526–529
Exs. 9, 10, 12–14, 16–18, 24–28, 33–40, 44

Advanced:
Day 1: pp. 526–529
Exs. 1, 2, 4–7, 19–23, 30–32*, 47
Day 2: pp. 526–529
Exs. 10, 13, 14, 16–18, 24–29, 34–42*, 45

Block:
pp. 526–529
Exs. 1–7, 19–23, 31, 32, 46 (with 8.2)
pp. 526–529
Exs. 9, 10, 12–14, 16–18, 24–28, 33–40, 44 (with 8.4)

Differentiated Instruction

See *Geometry Best Practices Toolkit* for suggestions on addressing the needs of a diverse classroom.

Homework Check

For a quick check of student understanding of key concepts, go over the following exercises:
Basic: 4, 8, 12, 16, 32
Average: 6, 9, 13, 20, 33
Advanced: 7, 10, 14, 26, 34

Extra Practice

- Student Edition, p. 910
- Chapter 8 Resource Book: Practice levels A, B, C, pp. 33–38

Practice Worksheet

An easily-readable reduced practice page (with answers) for this lesson can be found on p. 504D.

11–14. See Additional Answers beginning on p. AA1.

8.3 EXERCISES

HOMEWORK KEY
◯ = WORKED-OUT SOLUTIONS on p. WS9 for Exs. 5, 11, and 31
★ = STANDARDIZED TEST PRACTICE Exs. 2, 7, 18, and 37

SKILL PRACTICE

1. The definition of a parallelogram is that it is a quadrilateral with opposite pairs of parallel sides. Since $\overline{AB}$, $\overline{CD}$, and $\overline{AD}$, $\overline{BC}$ are opposite pairs of parallel sides, quadrilateral *ABCD* is a parallelogram.

A

1. **VOCABULARY** *Explain* how knowing that $\overline{AB} \parallel \overline{CD}$ and $\overline{AD} \parallel \overline{BC}$ allows you to show that quadrilateral *ABCD* is a parallelogram.

2. ★ **WRITING** A quadrilateral has four congruent sides. Is the quadrilateral a parallelogram? *Justify* your answer. **Yes; both pairs of opposite sides are congruent.**

3. **ERROR ANALYSIS** A student claims that because two pairs of sides are congruent, quadrilateral *DEFG* shown at the right is a parallelogram. *Describe* the error that the student is making. **The congruent sides must be opposite one another.**

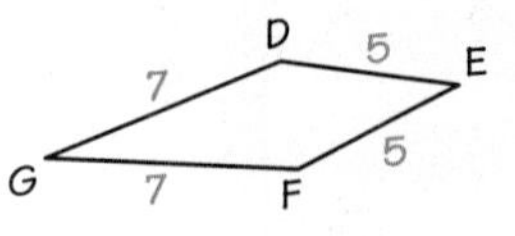

DEFG is a parallelogram.

EXAMPLES 1 and 2 on pp. 523–524 for Exs. 4–7

REASONING **What theorem can you use to show that the quadrilateral is a parallelogram?**

4. 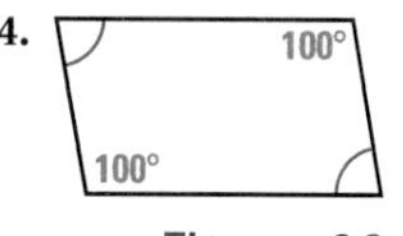

Theorem 8.8

(5.) 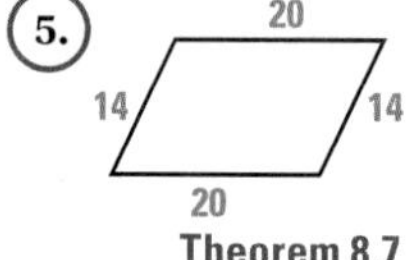

Theorem 8.7

6. 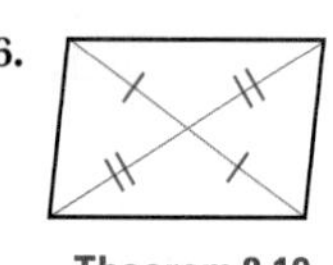
Theorem 8.10

7. Since both pairs of opposite sides of *JKLM* always remain congruent, *JKLM* is always a parallelogram and $\overline{JK}$ remains parallel to $\overline{ML}$.

7. ★ **SHORT RESPONSE** When you shift gears on a bicycle, a mechanism called a *derailleur* moves the chain to a new gear. For the derailleur shown below, $JK = 5.5$ cm, $KL = 2$ cm, $ML = 5.5$ cm, and $MJ = 2$ cm. *Explain* why $\overline{JK}$ and $\overline{ML}$ are always parallel as the derailleur moves.

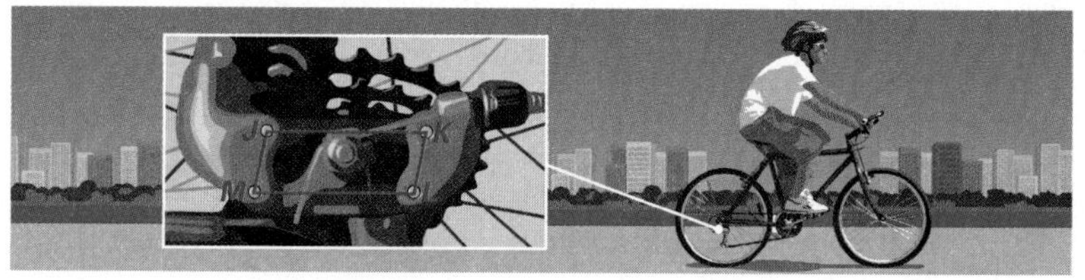

EXAMPLE 3 on p. 524 for Exs. 8–10

ALGEBRA **For what value of *x* is the quadrilateral a parallelogram?**

8. 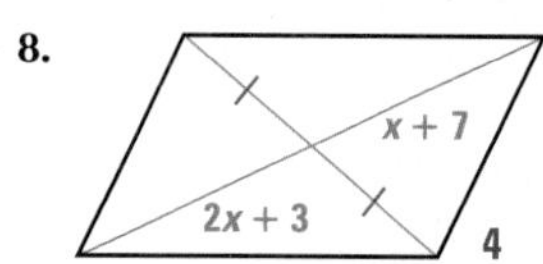

4

9. 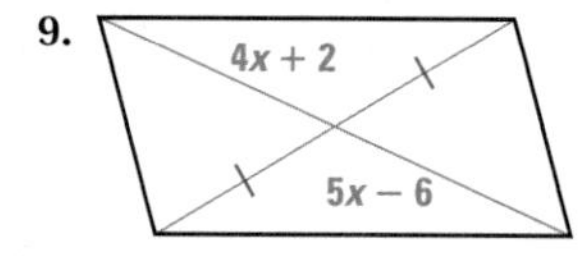

8

10. 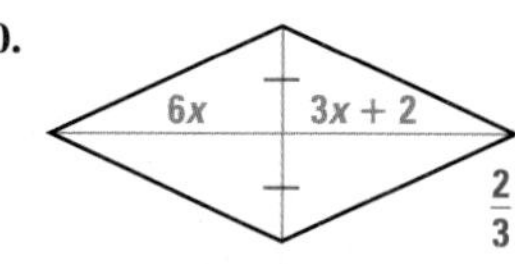

$\frac{2}{3}$

EXAMPLE 4 on p. 525 for Exs. 11–14

COORDINATE GEOMETRY **The vertices of quadrilateral *ABCD* are given. Draw *ABCD* in a coordinate plane and show that it is a parallelogram.** **11–14. See margin.**

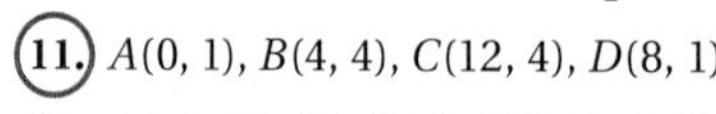
(11.) $A(0, 1), B(4, 4), C(12, 4), D(8, 1)$

12. $A(-3, 0), B(-3, 4), C(3, -1), D(3, -5)$

13. $A(-2, 3), B(-5, 7), C(3, 6), D(6, 2)$

14. $A(-5, 0), B(0, 4), C(3, 0), D(-2, -4)$

16. ***Sample answer:*** **Show $\triangle ADB \cong \triangle CBD$ using the ASA Congruence Theorem. This makes $\overline{AB} \cong \overline{CD}$ and $\overline{AD} \cong \overline{CB}$ using corresponding parts of congruent triangles are congruent.**

17. ***Sample answer:*** **Show $\overline{AB} \parallel \overline{DC}$ by the Alternate Interior Angles Converse, and show $\overline{AD} \parallel \overline{BC}$ by the Corresponding Angles Converse.**

REASONING ***Describe*** **how to prove that $ABCD$ is a parallelogram.**

15\. 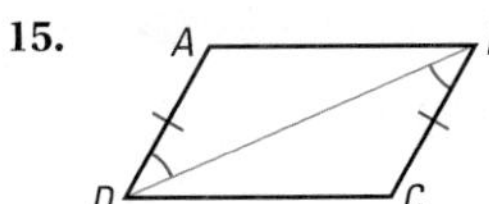

16\. 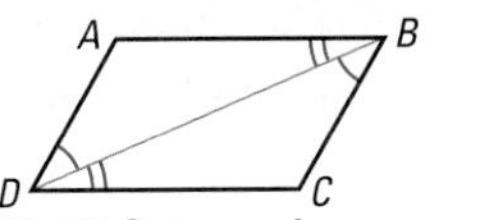

17\. 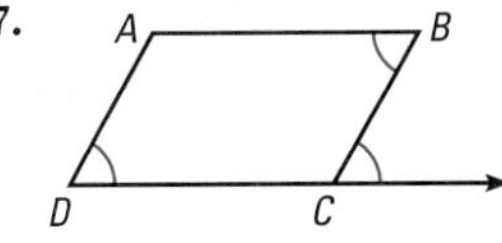

16–17. See margin.

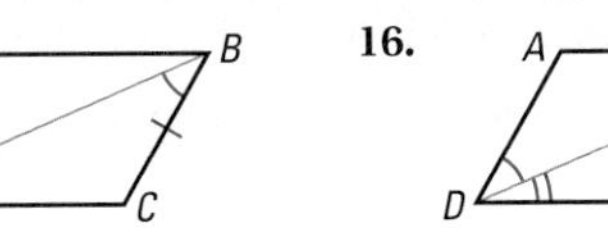 at classzone.com

15\. Sample answer: Show $\triangle ADB \cong \triangle CBD$ using the SAS Congruence Postulate. This makes $\overline{AD} \cong \overline{CB}$ and $\overline{BA} \cong \overline{CD}$ using corresponding parts of congruent triangles are congruent.

B 18. ★ **MULTIPLE CHOICE** In quadrilateral $WXYZ$, $\overline{WZ}$ and $\overline{XY}$ are congruent and parallel. Which statement below is not necessarily true? **A**

(A) $m\angle Y + m\angle W = 180°$ (B) $\angle X \cong \angle Z$

(C) $\overline{WX} \cong \overline{ZY}$ (D) $\overline{WX} \parallel \overline{ZY}$

ALGEBRA **For what value of x is the quadrilateral a parallelogram?**

19\. 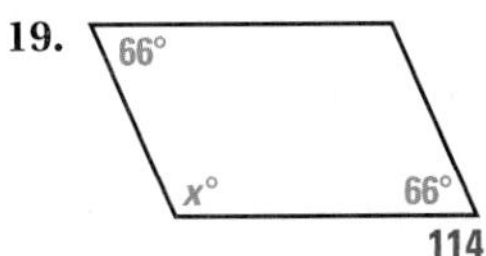

114

20\. 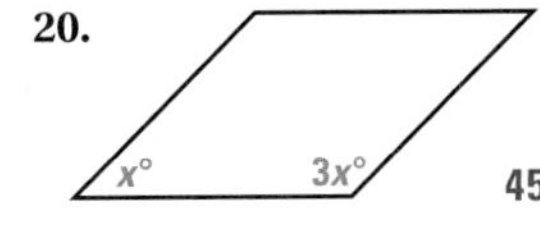

45

21\. 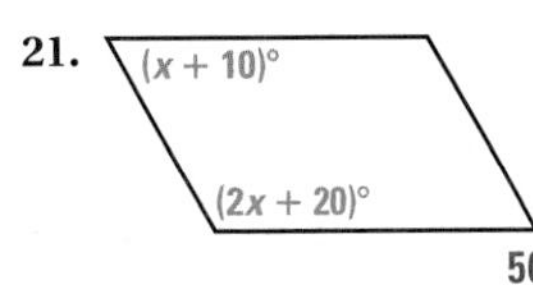

50

BICONDITIONALS **Write the indicated theorems as a biconditional statement.**

22\. Theorem 8.3, page 515 and Theorem 8.7, page 522

23\. Theorem 8.4, page 515 and Theorem 8.8, page 522

22\. $PQRS$ is a parallelogram if and only if $\overline{PQ} \cong \overline{RS}$ and $\overline{QR} \cong \overline{PS}$.

23\. $PQRS$ is a parallelogram if and only if $\angle P \cong \angle R$ and $\angle Q \cong \angle S$.

24\. **REASONING** Follow the steps below to draw a parallelogram. *Explain* why this method works. State a theorem to support your answer. **Joining the endpoints of the two line segments that bisect one another forms a quadrilateral. Using Theorem 8.10 you know that it is a parallelogram.**

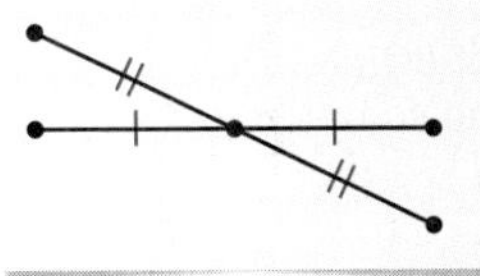

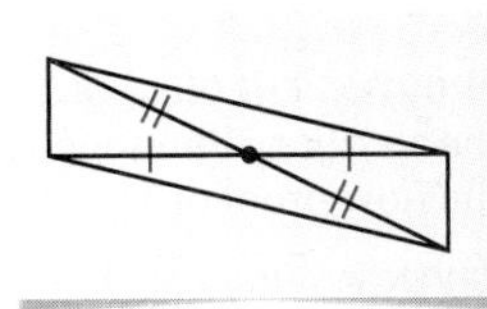

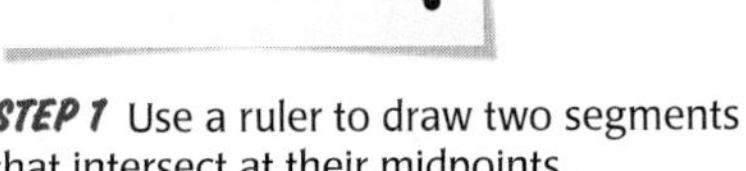

STEP 1 Use a ruler to draw two segments that intersect at their midpoints.

STEP 2 Connect the endpoints of the segments to form a quadrilateral.

COORDINATE GEOMETRY **Three of the vertices of $\square ABCD$ are given. Find the coordinates of point D. Show your method.** **25–28. See margin.**

25\. $A(-2, -3)$, $B(4, -3)$, $C(3, 2)$, $D(x, y)$

26\. $A(-4, 1)$, $B(-1, 5)$, $C(6, 5)$, $D(x, y)$

27\. $A(-4, 4)$, $B(4, 6)$, $C(3, -1)$, $D(x, y)$

28\. $A(-1, 0)$, $B(0, -4)$, $C(8, -6)$, $D(x, y)$

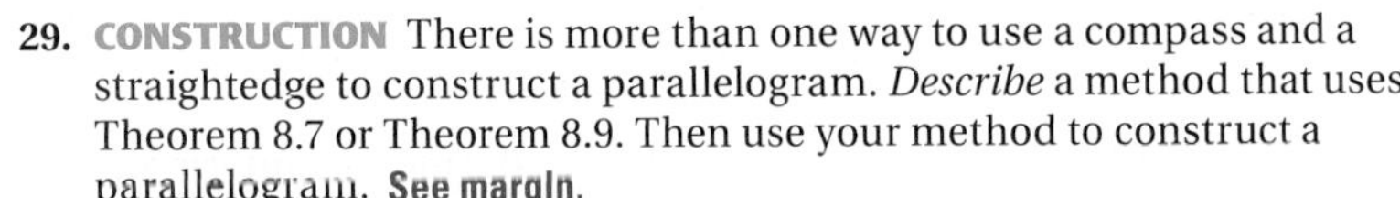

C 29. **CONSTRUCTION** There is more than one way to use a compass and a straightedge to construct a parallelogram. *Describe* a method that uses Theorem 8.7 or Theorem 8.9. Then use your method to construct a parallelogram. **See margin.**

30\. **CHALLENGE** In the diagram, $ABCD$ is a parallelogram, $BF = DE = 12$, and $CF = 8$. Find AE. *Explain* your reasoning. **See margin.**

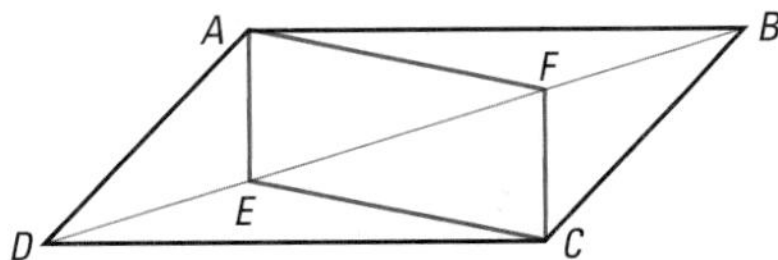

An **Animated Geometry** activity is available on-line for **Exercises 15–17.** This activity is also available on the **Power Presentations CD-ROM**.

Teaching Strategy

Exercises 15–17 Have the students discuss different ways of proving that $ABCD$ is a parallelogram. Discuss whether all of the five methods could be used or not. Ask students if one method would be easier to use than the others in a particular case.

Mathematical Reasoning

Exercise 24 Have students write a description of how they can use a compass and straightedge to obtain the two segments in Step 1.

Avoiding Common Errors

Exercises 25–28 Some students may have errors because they are not paying careful attention to the order of the letters in the name of the parallelogram. For example, in Exercise 25, they may think that the fourth vertex could be $D(-1, -8)$. The points A, B, C, and D would be the vertices of a parallelogram, but the parallelogram would be $DACB$, not $ABCD$. Point out the importance of the order in which the vertices are listed, and ask students to correct their work.

29. See Additional Answers beginning on p. AA1.

30. 8; since $ABCD$ is a parallelogram you know that $\overline{AD} \cong \overline{CB}$ and $\overline{AD} \parallel \overline{CB}$. $\angle ADE \cong \angle CBF$ using the Alternate Interior Angles Congruence Theorem. It was given that $\overline{BF} \cong \overline{DE}$, therefore $\triangle ADE \cong \triangle CBF$ by the SAS Congruence Theorem. Using corresponding parts of congruent triangles are congruent, you know that $CF = EA = 8$.

25. $(-3, 2)$; since $\overline{DA}$ must be parallel and congruent to $\overline{BC}$, use the slope and length of $\overline{BC}$ to find point D by starting at point A.

26. $(3, 1)$; since $\overline{AB}$ must be parallel and congruent to $\overline{CD}$, use the slope and length of $\overline{AB}$ to find point D by starting at point C.

27. $(-5, -3)$; since $\overline{DA}$ must be parallel and congruent to $\overline{BC}$, use the slope and length of $\overline{BC}$ to find point D by starting at point A.

28. $(7, -2)$; since $\overline{AB}$ must be parallel and congruent to $\overline{CD}$, use the slope and length of $\overline{AB}$ to find point D starting at point C.

Teaching Strategy

Exercises 34–36 It may help to have students model each situation by using pens or strips of cardboard.

Mathematical Reasoning

Exercise 41 Ask students to conjecture how the perimeter of the inner parallelogram is related to the diagonals of the outer quadrilateral.

34. 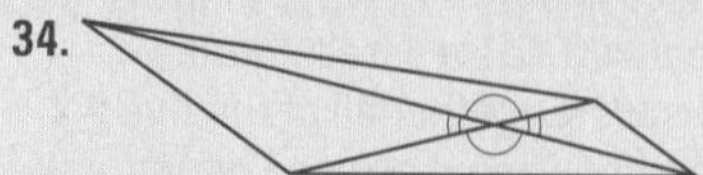

The point of intersection of the diagonals is not necessarily their midpoint.

35. 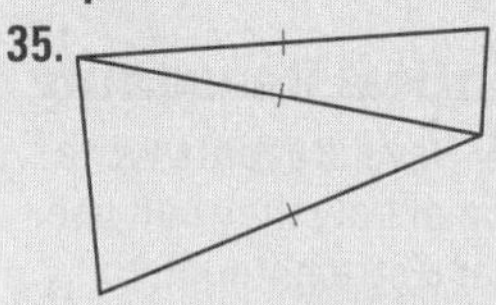

The opposite sides that are not marked in the given diagram are not necessarily the same length.

36. 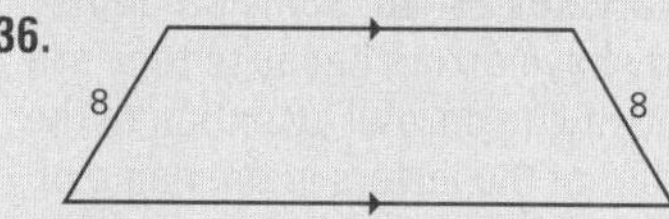

The sides of length 8 are not necessarily parallel.

37. In a quadrilateral, if consecutive angles are supplementary, then the quadrilateral is a parallelogram. In *ABCD* you are given $\angle A$ and $\angle B$ are supplementary, and $\angle C$ and $\angle B$ are supplementary, which gives you $m\angle A = m\angle C$. Also $\angle B$ and $\angle C$ are supplementary, and $\angle C$ and $\angle D$ are supplementary which gives you $m\angle B = m\angle D$. So *ABCD* is a parallelogram by Theorem 8.8.

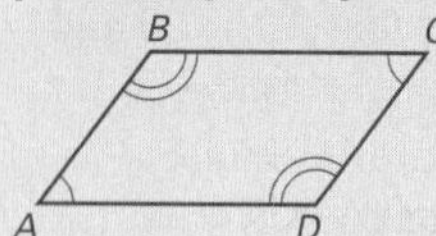

PROBLEM SOLVING

EXAMPLES 1 and 2 on pp. 523–524 for Exs. 31–32

31a. *EFJK, FGHJ, EGHK*; in each case opposite pairs of sides are congruent.

31b. Since *EGHK* is a parallelogram, opposite sides are parallel.

(31.) **AUTOMOBILE REPAIR** The diagram shows an automobile lift. A bus drives on to the ramp ($\overline{EG}$). Levers ($\overline{EK}$, $\overline{FJ}$, and $\overline{GH}$) raise the bus. In the diagram, $\overline{EG} \cong \overline{KH}$ and $EK = FJ = GH$. Also, F is the midpoint of $\overline{EG}$, and J is the midpoint of $\overline{KH}$.

a. Identify all the quadrilaterals in the automobile lift. *Explain* how you know that each one is a parallelogram.

b. *Explain* why $\overline{EG}$ is always parallel to $\overline{KH}$.

@HomeTutor for problem solving help at classzone.com

32. **MUSIC STAND** A music stand can be folded up, as shown below. In the diagrams, $\angle A \cong \angle EFD$, $\angle D \cong \angle AEF$, $\angle C \cong \angle BEF$, and $\angle B \cong \angle CFE$. *Explain* why $\overline{AD}$ and $\overline{BC}$ remain parallel as the stand is folded up. Which other labeled segments remain parallel? **AEFD and EBCF are parallelograms by Theorem 8.8 so $\overline{AD}$ and $\overline{BC}$ both remain parallel to $\overline{EF}$; AE and DF, BE and CF.**

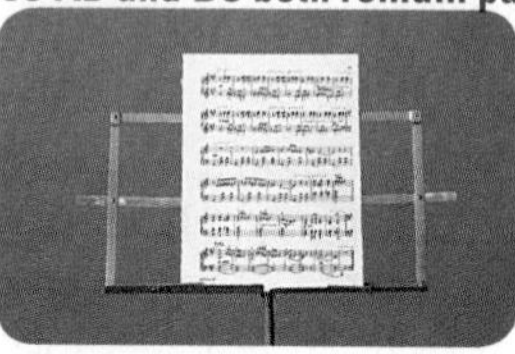

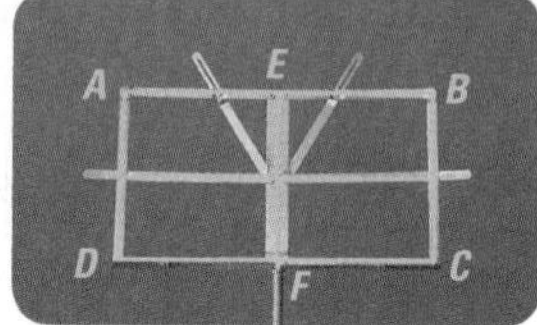

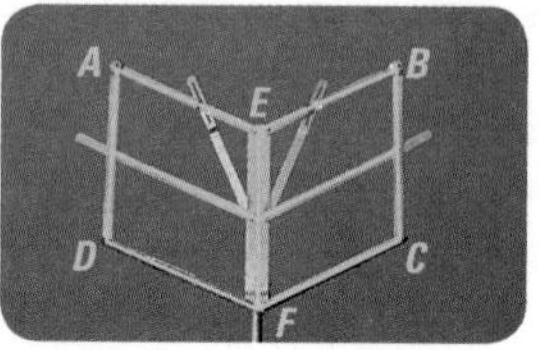

@HomeTutor for problem solving help at classzone.com

33. **PROVING THEOREM 8.9** Use the diagram of *PQRS* with the auxiliary line segment drawn. Copy and complete the flow proof of Theorem 8.9.

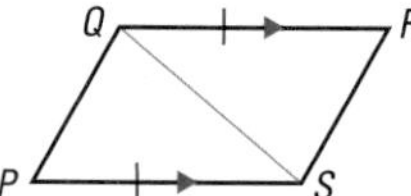

GIVEN ▶ $\overline{QR} \parallel \overline{PS}$, $\overline{QR} \cong \overline{PS}$

PROVE ▶ *PQRS* is a parallelogram.

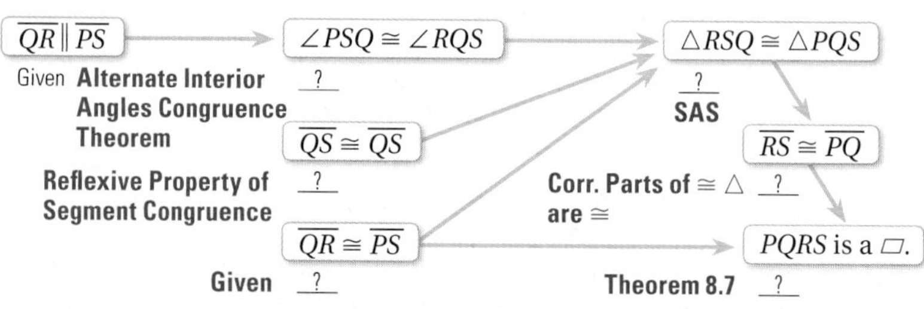

REASONING **A student claims incorrectly that the marked information can be used to show that the figure is a parallelogram. Draw a quadrilateral with the marked properties that is clearly *not* a parallelogram. *Explain*.** 34–36. See margin.

34. 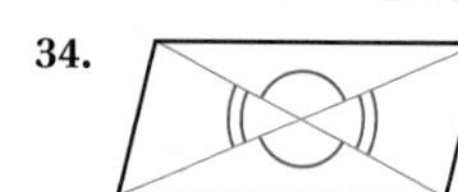

35.

36. 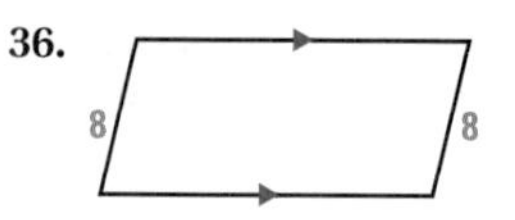

○ = **WORKED-OUT SOLUTIONS on p. WS1**

★ = **STANDARDIZED TEST PRACTICE**

38. It is given that $\angle A \cong \angle C$ and $\angle B \cong \angle D$. Let $m\angle A = m\angle C = x$ and $m\angle B = m\angle D = y$. Since *ABCD* is a quadrilateral, you know that $2x + 2y = 360$ using the Polygon Interior Angles Theorem, so $x + y = 180$. Using the definition of supplementary angles, $\angle A$ and $\angle B$, $\angle B$ and $\angle C$, $\angle C$ and $\angle D$, and $\angle D$ and $\angle A$ are supplementary. Using Theorem 8.5, *ABCD* is a parallelogram.

39. It is given that $\overline{KP} \cong \overline{MP}$ and $\overline{JP} \cong \overline{LP}$ by definition of segment bisector. $\angle KPL \cong \angle MPJ$ and $\angle KPJ \cong \angle MPL$ since they are vertical angles. $\triangle KPL \cong \triangle MPJ$ and $\triangle KPJ \cong \triangle MPL$ by the SAS Congruence Postulate. Using corresponding parts of congruent triangles are congruent, $\overline{KJ} \cong \overline{ML}$ and $\overline{JM} \cong \overline{LK}$. Using Theorem 8.7, *JKLM* is a parallelogram.

40–42. See Additional Answers beginning on p. AA1.

37. ★ **EXTENDED RESPONSE** Theorem 8.5 states that if a quadrilateral is a parallelogram, then its consecutive angles are supplementary. Write the converse of Theorem 8.5. Then write a plan for proving the converse of Theorem 8.5. Include a diagram. **See margin.**

38. **PROVING THEOREM 8.8** Prove Theorem 8.8.

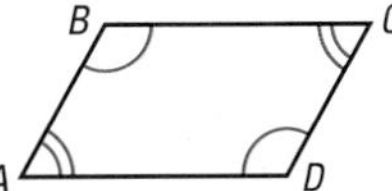

GIVEN ▶ $\angle A \cong \angle C$, $\angle B \cong \angle D$

PROVE ▶ $ABCD$ is a parallelogram.

Hint: Let $x°$ represent $m\angle A$ and $m\angle C$, and let $y°$ represent $m\angle B$ and $m\angle D$. Write and simplify an equation involving x and y. **See margin.**

39. **PROVING THEOREM 8.10** Prove Theorem 8.10.

GIVEN ▶ Diagonals $\overline{JL}$ and $\overline{KM}$ bisect each other.

PROVE ▶ $JKLM$ is a parallelogram. **See margin.**

40. **PROOF** Use the diagram at the right.

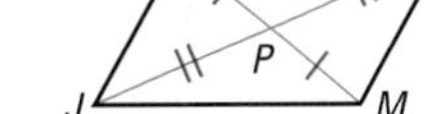

GIVEN ▶ $DEBF$ is a parallelogram, $AE = CF$

PROVE ▶ $ABCD$ is a parallelogram. **See margin.**

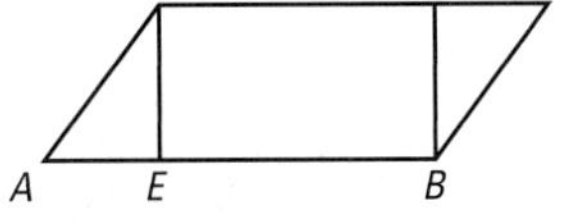

C 41. **REASONING** In the diagram, the midpoints of the sides of a quadrilateral have been joined to form what appears to be a parallelogram. Show that a quadrilateral formed by connecting the midpoints of the sides of any quadrilateral is *always* a parallelogram. (*Hint:* Draw a diagram. Include a diagonal of the larger quadrilateral. Show how two sides of the smaller quadrilateral are related to the diagonal.) **See margin.**

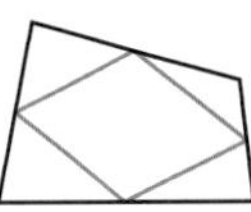

42. **CHALLENGE** Show that if $ABCD$ is a parallelogram with its diagonals intersecting at E, then you can connect the midpoints F, G, H, and J of $\overline{AE}$, $\overline{BE}$, $\overline{CE}$, and $\overline{DE}$, respectively, to form another parallelogram, $FGHJ$. **See margin.**

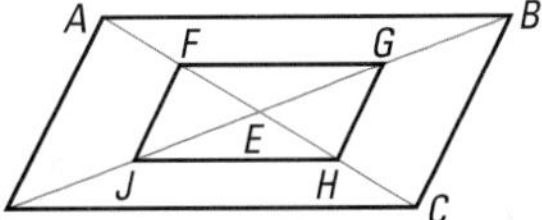

MIXED REVIEW

PREVIEW
Prepare for Lesson 8.4 in Exs. 43–45.

In Exercises 43–45, draw a figure that fits the description. *(p. 42)* **43–45. See margin.**

43. A quadrilateral that is equilateral but not equiangular

44. A quadrilateral that is equiangular but not equilateral

45. A quadrilateral that is concave

46. The width of a rectangle is 4 centimeters less than its length. The perimeter of the rectangle is 42 centimeters. Find its area. *(p. 49)* **106.25 cm²**

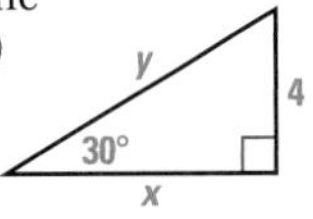

47. Find the values of x and y in the triangle shown at the right. Write your answers in simplest radical form. *(p. 457)* **$4\sqrt{3}$, 8**

43.

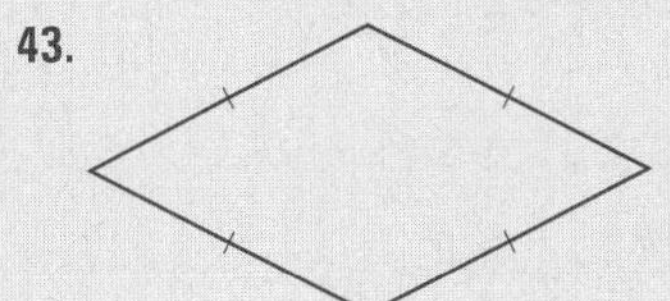

44.

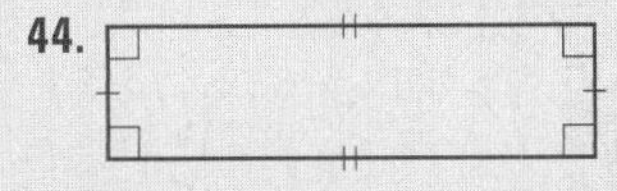

45.

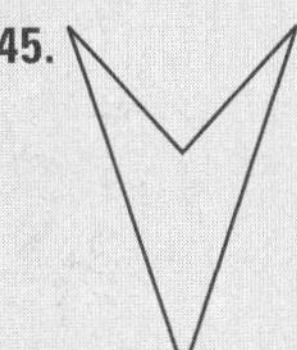

5 ASSESS AND RETEACH

Daily Homework Quiz

Transparency Available

Tell how you know that the quadrilateral is a parallelogram.

1.

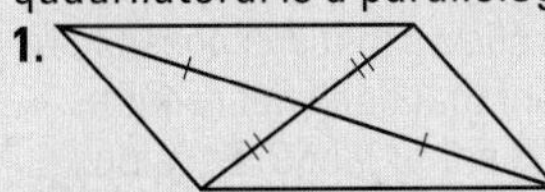

The diagonals bisect each other.

2.

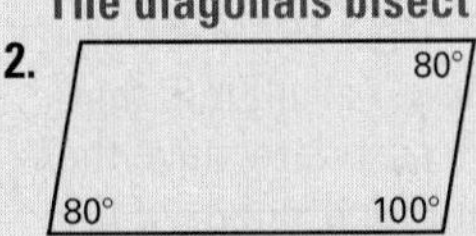

Both pairs of opposite angles are congruent. You can also conclude that both pairs of opposite sides are parallel and use the definition of a parallelogram.

3. For what value of x is the quadrilateral a parallelogram? **50**

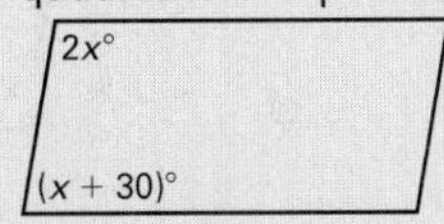

4. In a coordinate plane, draw the quadrilateral $ABCD$ with vertices $A(-1, 3)$, $B(7, -1)$, $C(6, -4)$, and $D(-2, 0)$. Show that $ABCD$ is a parallelogram.

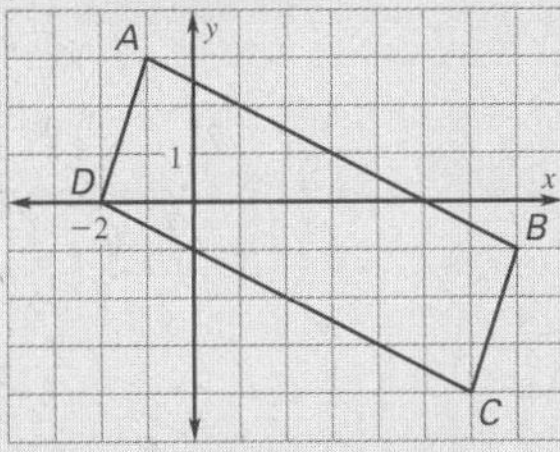

$AB = CD = 4\sqrt{5}$ and $BC = AD = \sqrt{10}$, so both pairs of opposite sides are congruent.

Available at **classzone.com**

Diagnosis/Remediation

- Practice A, B, C in Chapter 8 Resource Book, pp. 33–38
- Study Guide in Chapter 8 Resource Book, pp. 39–40
- Practice Workbook, pp. 151–153
- @HomeTutor

Challenge

Additional challenge is available in the Chapter 8 Resource Book, p. 44.

Alternative Strategy

Example 4 on page 525 can be solved by showing that both pairs of opposite sides are congruent or by showing that the diagonals bisect each other. Method 1 helps students see how to prove the desired result without using the concept of slope. Method 2 shows that it is possible to give a proof that does not require calculating either lengths or slopes.

Graphing Calculator

If students have calculators that use geometry software, have them find the lengths and slopes of the sides of the parallelogram by using the software.

Using ALTERNATIVE METHODS

Another Way to Solve Example 4, page 525

MULTIPLE REPRESENTATIONS In Example 4 on page 525, the problem is solved by showing that one pair of opposite sides are congruent and parallel using the Distance Formula and the slope formula. There are other ways to show that a quadrilateral is a parallelogram.

PROBLEM

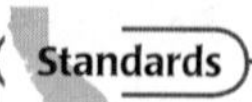

Standards

7.0 Students prove and **use theorems involving** the properties of parallel lines cut by a transversal, **the properties of quadrilaterals**, and the properties of circles.

Show that quadrilateral *ABCD* is a parallelogram.

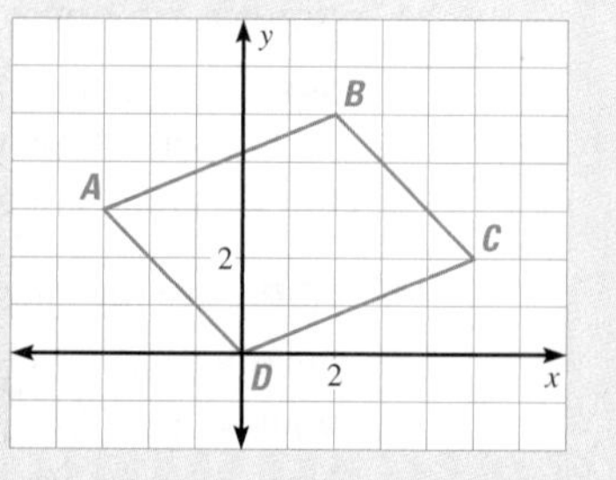

METHOD 1

Use Opposite Sides You can show that both pairs of opposite sides are congruent.

STEP 1 **Draw** two right triangles. Use $\overline{AB}$ as the hypotenuse of $\triangle AEB$ and $\overline{CD}$ as the hypotenuse of $\triangle CFD$.

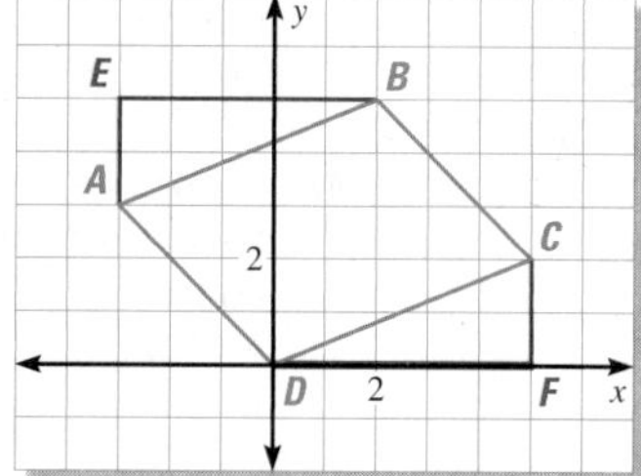

STEP 2 **Show** that $\triangle AEB \cong \triangle CFD$. From the graph, $AE = 2$, $BE = 5$, and $\angle E$ is a right angle. Similarly, $CF = 2$, $DF = 5$, and $\angle F$ is a right angle. So, $\triangle AEB \cong \triangle CFD$ by the SAS Congruence Postulate.

STEP 3 **Use** the fact that corresponding parts of congruent triangles are congruent to show that $\overline{AB} \cong \overline{CD}$.

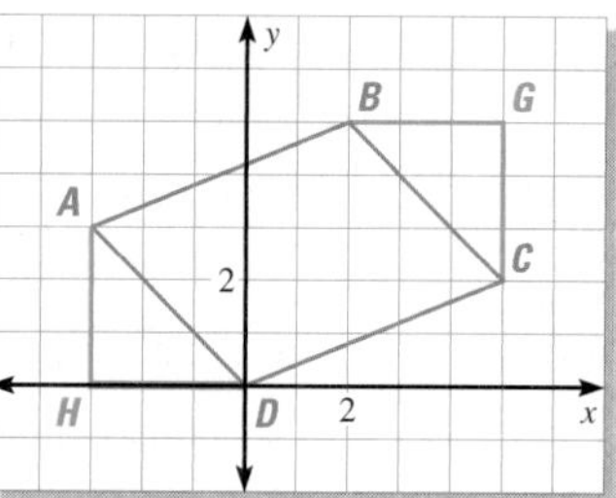

STEP 4 **Repeat** Steps 1–3 for sides $\overline{AD}$ and $\overline{BC}$. You can prove that $\triangle AHD \cong \triangle CGB$. So, $\overline{AD} \cong \overline{CB}$.

▶ The pairs of opposite sides, $\overline{AB}$ and $\overline{CD}$ and $\overline{AD}$ and $\overline{CB}$, are congruent. So, *ABCD* is a parallelogram by Theorem 8.7.

METHOD 2 **Use Diagonals** You can show that the diagonals bisect each other.

STEP 1 **Use** the Midpoint Formula to find the midpoint of diagonal $\overline{AC}$.

The coordinates of the endpoints of $\overline{AC}$ are $A(-3, 3)$ and $C(5, 2)$.

$$\left(\frac{x_1 + x_2}{2}, \frac{y_1 + y_2}{2}\right) = \left(\frac{-3 + 5}{2}, \frac{3 + 2}{2}\right) = \left(\frac{2}{2}, \frac{5}{2}\right) = \left(1, \frac{5}{2}\right)$$

STEP 2 **Use** the Midpoint Formula to find the midpoint of diagonal $\overline{BD}$.

The coordinates of the endpoints of $\overline{BD}$ are $B(2, 5)$ and $D(0, 0)$.

$$\left(\frac{x_1 + x_2}{2}, \frac{y_1 + y_2}{2}\right) = \left(\frac{2 + 0}{2}, \frac{5 + 0}{2}\right) = \left(\frac{2}{2}, \frac{5}{2}\right) = M\left(1, \frac{5}{2}\right)$$

▶ Because the midpoints of both diagonals are the same point, the diagonals bisect each other. So, *ABCD* is a parallelogram by Theorem 8.10.

PRACTICE

1. **SLOPE** Show that quadrilateral *ABCD* in the problem on page 530 is a parallelogram by showing that both pairs of opposite sides are parallel. **See margin.**

2. **PARALLELOGRAMS** Use two methods to show that *EFGH* is a parallelogram.

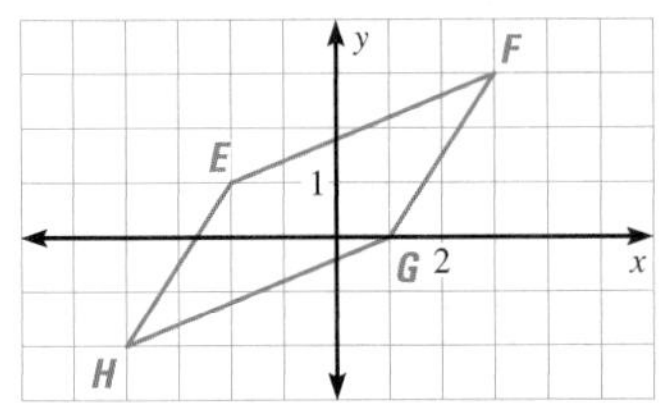

See margin.

3. **MAP** Do the four towns on the map form the vertices of a parallelogram? *Explain.*

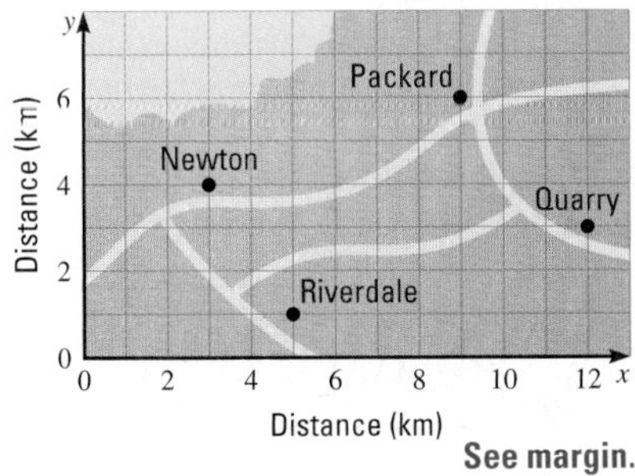

See margin.

4. **QUADRILATERALS** Is the quadrilateral a parallelogram? *Justify* your answer. **See margin.**

   a. $A(1, 0)$, $B(5, 0)$, $C(7, 2)$, $D(3, 2)$

   b. $E(3, 4)$ $F(6, 8)$, $G(9, 5)$, $H(6, 0)$

   c. $J(-1, 0)$, $K(2, -2)$, $L(2, 2)$, $M(-1, 4)$

5. **ERROR ANALYSIS** Quadrilateral *PQRS* has vertices $P(2, 2)$, $Q(3, 4)$, $R(6, 5)$, and $S(5, 3)$. A student makes the conclusion below. *Describe* and correct the error(s) made by the student. **See margin.**

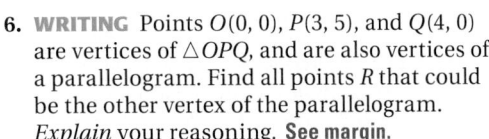

> $\overline{PQ}$ and $\overline{QR}$ are opposite sides, so they should be congruent.
>
> $PQ = \sqrt{(3-2)^2 + (4-2)^2} = \sqrt{5}$
>
> $QR = \sqrt{(6-3)^2 + (5-4)^2} = \sqrt{10}$
>
> But $\overline{PQ} \not\cong \overline{QR}$. So, PQRS is not a parallelogram.

6. **WRITING** Points $O(0, 0)$, $P(3, 5)$, and $Q(4, 0)$ are vertices of $\triangle OPQ$, and are also vertices of a parallelogram. Find all points *R* that could be the other vertex of the parallelogram. *Explain* your reasoning. **See margin.**

Mathematical Reasoning

Multiple Representations In Method 1, students can show that the opposite sides are congruent by using the distance formula to find the lengths of all four sides.

Teaching Strategy

Exercise 2 Instead of using the slope and distance formulas, you can have the students count squares. From *H* to *E* you move right 2 and up 3. From *G* to *F*, you also move right 2 and up 3. Therefore, the slopes are the same. The lengths are also the same since $\overline{HE}$ and $\overline{GF}$ can be seen as the hypotenuses of congruent right triangles.

Avoiding Common Errors

Exercise 4 In part a, students may not use the vertices in the correct order. Have students graph and label the points to be sure which order is necessary to obtain a quadrilateral.

1. The slope of $\overline{AB}$ and $\overline{CD}$ is $\frac{2}{5}$ and the slope of $\overline{BC}$ and $\overline{DA}$ is -1. *ABCD* is a parallelogram by definition.

2. *Sample answer:* Method 1: The slope of $\overline{EF}$ and $\overline{GH}$ is $\frac{2}{5}$ and the slope of $\overline{FG}$ and $\overline{HE}$ is $\frac{3}{2}$. *EFGH* is a parallelogram by definition. Method 2: $EF = GH = \sqrt{29}$ and $FG = HE = \sqrt{13}$, making $\overline{EF} \cong \overline{GH}$ and $\overline{FG} \cong \overline{HE}$. *EFGH* is a parallelogram using Theorem 8.3.

3. No; the slope of the line segment joining Newton to Packard is $\frac{1}{3}$ while the slope of the line segment joining Riverdale to Quarry is $\frac{2}{7}$.

4a. Yes. *Sample answer:* $\overline{AD} \cong \overline{BC}$ and $\overline{AB} \cong \overline{CD}$

4b. No. *Sample answer:* $\overline{EF}$ is not parallel to $\overline{HG}$.

4c. Yes. *Sample answer:* $\overline{MJ} \parallel \overline{KL}$ and $\overline{KJ} \parallel \overline{LM}$

5. $\overline{PQ}$ and $\overline{QR}$ are not opposite sides. $\overline{PQ}$ and $\overline{RS}$ are opposite sides, so they should be parallel and congruent. The slope of $\overline{PQ}$ is $\frac{4-2}{3-2} = 2$. The slope of $\overline{RS}$ is $\frac{5-3}{6-5} = 2$. They are parallel, so *PQRS* is a parallelogram.

6. $(-1, 5)$, $(1, -5)$, $(7, 5)$. *Sample answer:* To find $(-1, 5)$, use the slope from point *Q* to point *P*. To locate point *R*, start at *O* and use the slope and length of $\overline{QP}$. Repeat the process for the other two points.

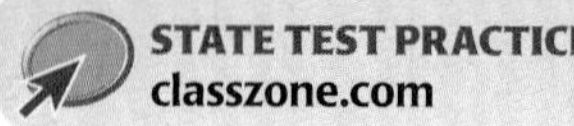

2. The sum of the interior angles of *ABCDE* is 540°. To find $m\angle A$ and $m\angle C$, subtract 270° from 540° and then divide by 2.

5. In a parallelogram, consecutive interior angles are supplementary. Solve $x + 3x - 12 = 180$ for x. Use the value of x to find the degree measure of the two consecutive angles. In a parallelogram, the angle opposite each of these known angles has the same measure.

6a. *EFGH* is a parallelogram by Theorem 8.9. As *EFGH* changes shape, $\angle E$ and $\angle G$ remain congruent, and $\angle H$ and $\angle F$ remain congruent, keeping $\overline{FG} \parallel \overline{EH}$.

6b. $m\angle E$ and $m\angle G$ decrease from 55° to 50°. $m\angle H$ and $m\angle F$ change from 125° to 130°. Since *EFGH* is always a parallelogram, $m\angle F$ and $m\angle H$ are always the same and $m\angle E$ and $m\angle G$ are always the same. Since $\angle E$ is always supplementary to $\angle F$, the sum of their measures must be 180°.

7a. Since the slope of $\overline{MN}$ and $\overline{PQ}$ is $\frac{3}{11}$ and the slope of $\overline{NP}$ and $\overline{QM}$ is $-\frac{5}{4}$, it is a parallelogram by definition.

7b. $MN = PQ = \sqrt{130}$ making $\overline{MN} \cong \overline{PQ}$ and $NP = QM = \sqrt{41}$ making $\overline{NP} \cong \overline{QM}$. Using Theorem 8.3, *MNPQ* is a parallelogram.

8. $\overline{BX} \parallel \overline{DY}$ using the Lines Perpendicular to a Transversal Theorem. Since $\overline{BX} \perp \overline{AC}$ and $\overline{DY} \perp \overline{AC}$, then $\angle BXA$ and $\angle DYC$ are right angles making $\angle BXA \cong \angle DYC$. Using the Alternate Interior Angles Congruence Theorem, $\angle BAX \cong \angle DCY$. $\overline{AB} \cong \overline{CD}$ since opposite sides of a parallelogram are congruent. $\triangle BXA \cong \triangle DYC$ by the AAS Congruence Theorem, making $\overline{BX} \cong \overline{DY}$ using corresponding parts of congruent triangles are congruent. Use Theorem 8.9 to show *XBYD* is a parallelogram.

Lessons 8.1–8.3

1. **MULTI-STEP PROBLEM** The shape of Iowa can be approximated by a polygon, as shown.

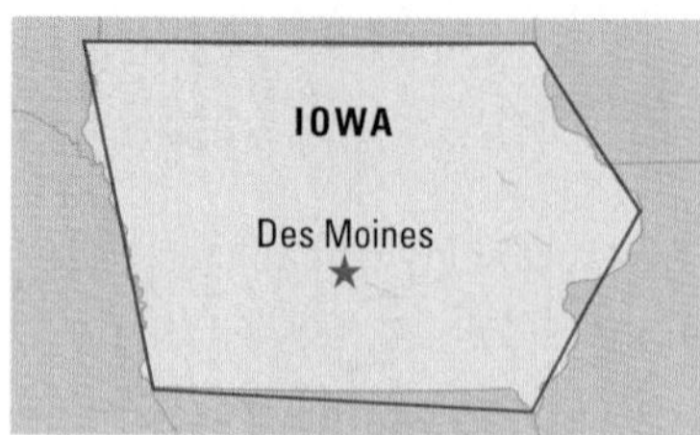

   a. How many sides does the polygon have? Classify the polygon. **5; pentagon**
   b. What is the sum of the measures of the interior angles of the polygon? **540°**
   c. What is the sum of the measures of the exterior angles of the polygon? **360°**

2. **SHORT RESPONSE** A graphic designer is creating an electronic image of a house. In the drawing, $\angle B$, $\angle D$, and $\angle E$ are right angles, and $\angle A \cong \angle C$. *Explain* how to find $m\angle A$ and $m\angle C$. **See margin.**

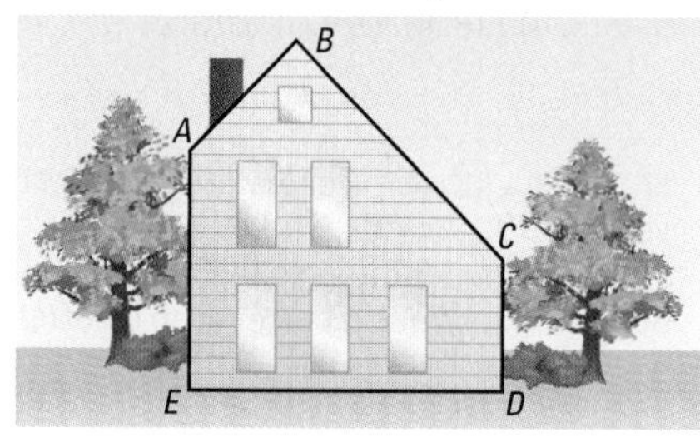

3. **SHORT RESPONSE** Quadrilateral *STUV* shown below is a parallelogram. Find the values of x and y. *Explain* your reasoning.

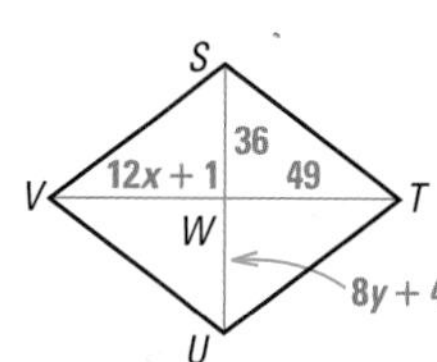

$x = 4$, $y = 4$; the diagonals of a parallelogram bisect each other. Set $12x + 1 = 49$ and $8y + 4 = 36$ and solve for x and y.

4. **GRIDDED ANSWER** A convex decagon has interior angles with measures 157°, 128°, 115°, 162°, 169°, 131°, 155°, 168°, x°, and $2x$°. Find the value of x. **85**

5. **SHORT RESPONSE** The measure of an angle of a parallelogram is 12 degrees less than 3 times the measure of an adjacent angle. Explain how to find the measures of all the interior angles of the parallelogram. **See margin.**

6. **EXTENDED RESPONSE** A stand to hold binoculars in place uses a quadrilateral in its design. Quadrilateral *EFGH* shown below changes shape as the binoculars are moved. In the photograph, $\overline{EF}$ and $\overline{GH}$ are congruent and parallel.

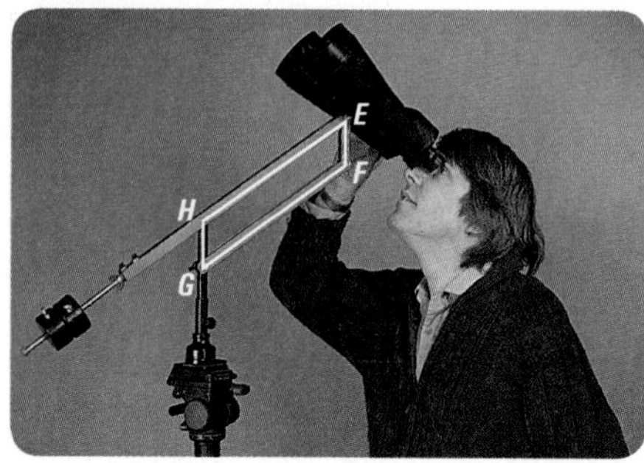

a, b. See margin.

   a. *Explain* why $\overline{EF}$ and $\overline{GH}$ remain parallel as the shape of *EFGH* changes. *Explain* why $\overline{EH}$ and $\overline{FG}$ remain parallel.
   b. As *EFGH* changes shape, $m\angle E$ changes from 55° to 50°. *Describe* how $m\angle F$, $m\angle G$, and $m\angle H$ will change. *Explain.*

7. **EXTENDED RESPONSE** The vertices of quadrilateral *MNPQ* are $M(-8, 1)$, $N(3, 4)$, $P(7, -1)$, and $Q(-4, -4)$. **a, b. See margin.**
   a. Use what you know about slopes of lines to prove that *MNPQ* is a parallelogram. *Explain* your reasoning.
   b. Use the Distance Formula to show that *MNPQ* is a parallelogram. *Explain.*

8. **EXTENDED RESPONSE** In ▱*ABCD*, $\overline{BX} \perp \overline{AC}$, $\overline{DY} \perp \overline{AC}$. Show that *XBYD* is a parallelogram. **See margin.**

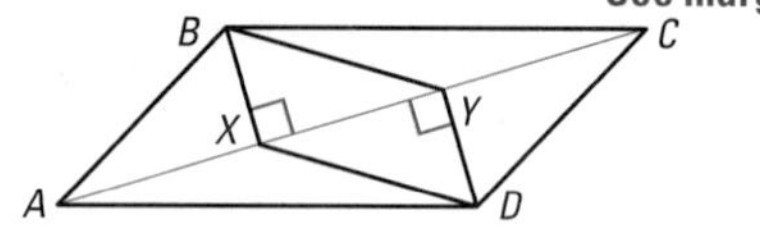

8.4 Properties of Rhombuses, Rectangles, and Squares

Before You used properties of parallelograms.

Now You will use properties of rhombuses, rectangles, and squares.

Why? So you can solve a carpentry problem, as in Example 4.

Key Vocabulary
- rhombus
- rectangle
- square

Standards

7.0 Students prove and use theorems involving the properties of parallel lines cut by a transversal, **the properties of quadrilaterals**, and the properties of circles.

17.0 Students prove theorems by using coordinate geometry, including the midpoint of a line segment, **the distance formula**, and various forms of equations of lines and circles.

In this lesson, you will learn about three special types of parallelograms: *rhombuses*, *rectangles*, and *squares*.

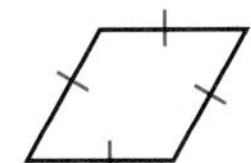

A rhombus is a parallelogram with four congruent sides.

A rectangle is a parallelogram with four right angles.

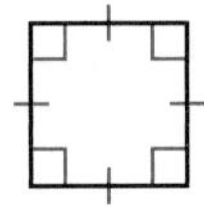

A square is a parallelogram with four congruent sides and four right angles.

You can use the corollaries below to prove that a quadrilateral is a rhombus, rectangle, or square, without first proving that the quadrilateral is a parallelogram.

COROLLARIES *For Your Notebook*

RHOMBUS COROLLARY

A quadrilateral is a rhombus if and only if it has four congruent sides.

ABCD is a rhombus if and only if $\overline{AB} \cong \overline{BC} \cong \overline{CD} \cong \overline{AD}$.

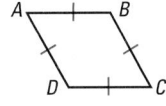

Proof: Ex. 57, p. 539

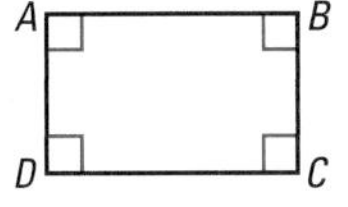

RECTANGLE COROLLARY

A quadrilateral is a rectangle if and only if it has four right angles.

ABCD is a rectangle if and only if $\angle A$, $\angle B$, $\angle C$, and $\angle D$ are right angles.

Proof: Ex. 58, p. 539

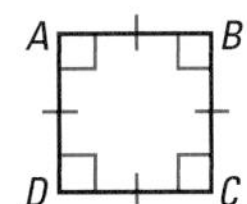

SQUARE COROLLARY

A quadrilateral is a square if and only if it is a rhombus and a rectangle.

ABCD is a square if and only if $\overline{AB} \cong \overline{BC} \cong \overline{CD} \cong \overline{AD}$ and $\angle A$, $\angle B$, $\angle C$, and $\angle D$ are right angles.

Proof: Ex. 59, p. 539

1 PLAN AND PREPARE

Warm-Up Exercises

Transparency Available

1. Give five ways to prove that a quadrilateral is a parallelogram. **opp. sides ∥, opp. sides ≅, diags. bisect each other, opp. angles ≅, a pair of opp. sides ∥ and ≅**
2. Find *x* in the parallelogram. **14**

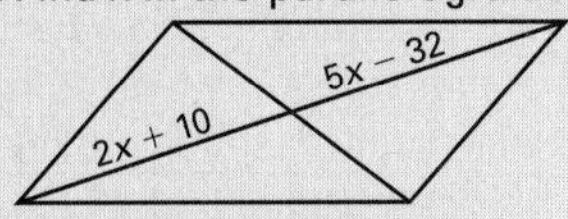

Notetaking Guide

Transparency Available

Promotes interactive learning and notetaking skills, pp. 209–212.

Pacing

Basic: 2 days
Average: 2 days
Advanced: 2 days
Block: 0.5 block with 8.3
0.5 block with 8.5
- See *Teaching Guide/Lesson Plan.*

2 FOCUS AND MOTIVATE

Essential Question

Big Idea 2, p. 504

What are the properties of parallelograms that have all sides or all angles congruent? **Tell students they will learn how to answer this question by studying three special kinds of parallelograms.**

Resource Planning Guide

Chapter Resource Book
- Teaching Guide/Lesson Plan (pp. 45–46)
- Activity Master (p. 47)
- Practice levels A, B, C (pp. 49–54)
- Study Guide (pp. 55–56)
- Catch-up for Absent Students (p. 57)
- Application (p. 58)
- Challenge (p. 59)

Workbooks
- Notetaking Guide (pp. 209–212)
- Practice Workbook (pp. 154–156)

Teaching Options
- **Power Presentations CD-ROM** provides dynamic electronic teaching resources for the classroom.
- **Activity Generator CD-ROM** provides editable activities for all ability levels.

Interactive Technology
- Easy Planner
- Power Presentations CD-ROM
- Activity Generator CD-ROM
- Animated Geometry
- Test Generator CD-ROM
- Online Quiz
- eWorkbook
- eEdition
- @HomeTutor

Resources for English Learners
- Quick Reference for English Learners
- Spanish Study Guide
- Multi-Language Visual Glossary
- Student Resources in Spanish

See also the *Geometry Toolkit* for more strategies for meeting individual needs.

Motivating the Lesson

Tell students that in this lesson, they will focus their attention on some of the parallelograms that are often used in architecture, construction, and the decorative arts.

3 TEACH

Extra Example 1

For any rectangle $ABCD$, decide whether the statement is *always* or *sometimes* true. Draw a sketch and explain your reasoning. **Check students' sketches.**

a. $\overline{AB} \cong \overline{CD}$ **always; All rectangles are parallelograms, and opposite sides of a parallelogram are congruent.**

b. $\overline{AB} \cong \overline{BC}$ **sometimes;** $\overline{AB} \cong \overline{BC}$ **provided the rectangle *ABCD* is a square. But not all rectangles are squares.**

Extra Example 2

Classify the special quadrilateral. Explain your reasoning.

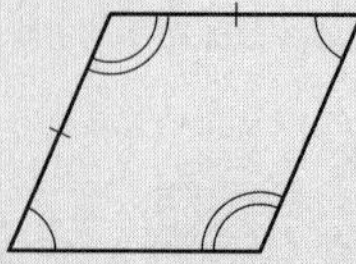

rhombus; It is a parallelogram because opposite angles are congruent. Since a pair of adjacent sides are congruent, all four sides are congruent.

Key Questions to Ask for Example 2

- Do all the properties for a rhombus hold for a square? **yes**
- Do all the properties for a square hold for a rhombus? Explain. **No, every square is a rhombus, but it is not true that every rhombus is a square.**

The *Venn diagram* below illustrates some important relationships among parallelograms, rhombuses, rectangles, and squares. For example, you can see that a square is a rhombus because it is a parallelogram with four congruent sides. Because it has four right angles, a square is also a rectangle.

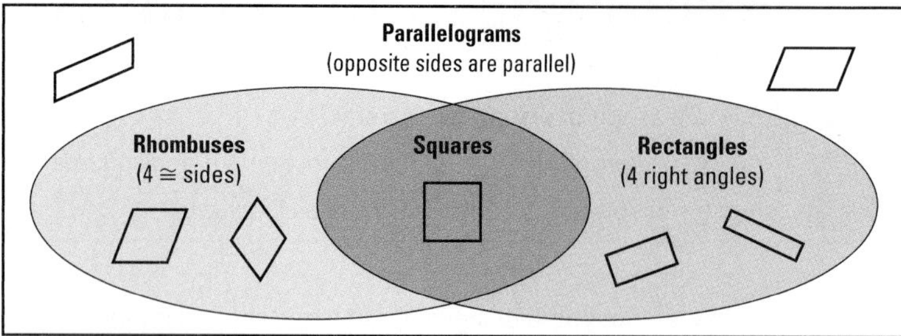

EXAMPLE 1 Use properties of special quadrilaterals

For any rhombus *QRST*, decide whether the statement is *always* or *sometimes* true. Draw a sketch and explain your reasoning.

a. $\angle Q \cong \angle S$ **b.** $\angle Q \cong \angle R$

Solution

a. By definition, a rhombus is a parallelogram with four congruent sides. By Theorem 8.4, opposite angles of a parallelogram are congruent. So, $\angle Q \cong \angle S$. The statement is *always* true.

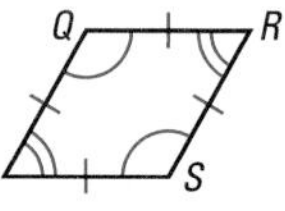

b. If rhombus $QRST$ is a square, then all four angles are congruent right angles. So, $\angle Q \cong \angle R$ if $QRST$ is a square. Because not all rhombuses are also squares, the statement is *sometimes* true.

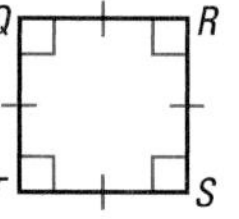

EXAMPLE 2 Classify special quadrilaterals

Classify the special quadrilateral. Explain your reasoning.

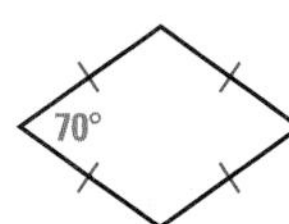

Solution

The quadrilateral has four congruent sides. One of the angles is not a right angle, so the rhombus is not also a square. By the Rhombus Corollary, the quadrilateral is a rhombus.

GUIDED PRACTICE for Examples 1 and 2

1. For any rectangle $EFGH$, is it *always* or *sometimes* true that $\overline{FG} \cong \overline{GH}$? *Explain* your reasoning. **Sometimes; this is only true if *EFGH* is a square.**
2. A quadrilateral has four congruent sides and four congruent angles. Sketch the quadrilateral and classify it. **See margin for art; square.**

Differentiated Instruction

Below Level Have students use narrow cardboard strips and fasteners to make a rhombus and to make a parallelogram that is clearly not a rhombus. Have them vary the angles to illustrate definitions and theorems of the lesson. Have them devise ways to illustrate the theorems about diagonals.

See also the *Geometry Toolkit* for more strategies.

DIAGONALS The theorems below describe some properties of the diagonals of rhombuses and rectangles.

THEOREMS *For Your Notebook*

THEOREM 8.11

A parallelogram is a rhombus if and only if its diagonals are perpendicular.

$\square ABCD$ is a rhombus if and only if $\overline{AC} \perp \overline{BD}$.

Proof: p. 536; Ex. 56, p. 539

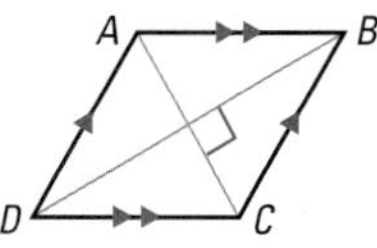

THEOREM 8.12

A parallelogram is a rhombus if and only if each diagonal bisects a pair of opposite angles.

$\square ABCD$ is a rhombus if and only if $\overline{AC}$ bisects $\angle BCD$ and $\angle BAD$ and $\overline{BD}$ bisects $\angle ABC$ and $\angle ADC$.

Proof: Exs. 60–61, p. 539

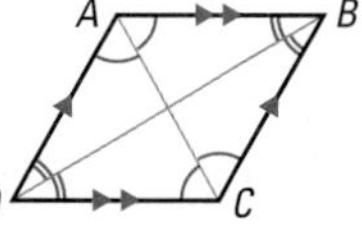

THEOREM 8.13

A parallelogram is a rectangle if and only if its diagonals are congruent.

$\square ABCD$ is a rectangle if and only if $\overline{AC} \cong \overline{BD}$.

Proof: Exs. 63–64, p. 540

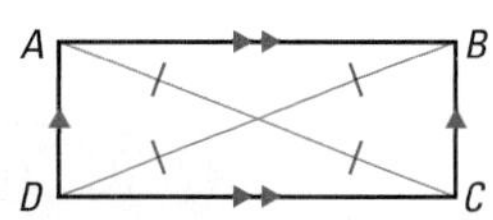

EXAMPLE 3 List properties of special parallelograms

Sketch rectangle *ABCD*. List everything that you know about it.

Solution

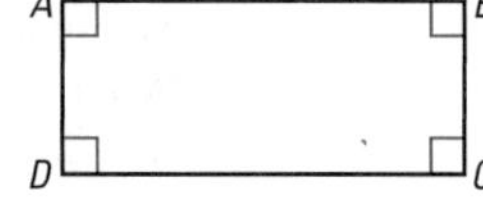

By definition, you need to draw a figure with the following properties:

- The figure is a parallelogram.
- The figure has four right angles.

Because *ABCD* is a parallelogram, it also has these properties:

- Opposite sides are parallel and congruent.
- Opposite angles are congruent. Consecutive angles are supplementary.
- Diagonals bisect each other.

By Theorem 8.13, the diagonals of *ABCD* are congruent.

Animated Geometry at classzone.com

3. See margin for art; *PQRS* is a parallelogram, rectangle, and a rhombus. Opposite pairs of sides are parallel and all four sides are congruent. All four angles are right angles. Diagonals are congruent and bisect each other.

✓ **GUIDED PRACTICE** for Example 3

3. Sketch square *PQRS*. List everything you know about the square.

Extra Example 3

Sketch a square *EFGH*. List everything that you know about it.

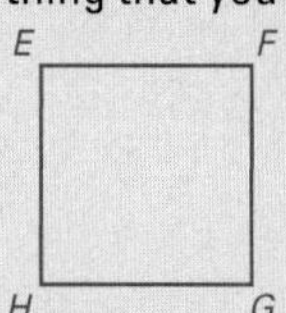

Opposite sides are parallel; all sides are congruent; all angles are congruent right angles; the diagonals are congruent and perpendicular, and they bisect each other; each diagonal bisects a pair of opposite angles.

Key Question to Ask for Example 3

- Under what conditions would the diagonals be perpendicular? **if the rectangle is a square**

An **Animated Geometry** activity is available on-line for **Example 3**. This activity is also available on the **Power Presentations CD-ROM**.

Study Strategy

Have the students make flash cards that they can use with a friend to practice stating the properties of rectangles, squares, and rhombuses.

3.
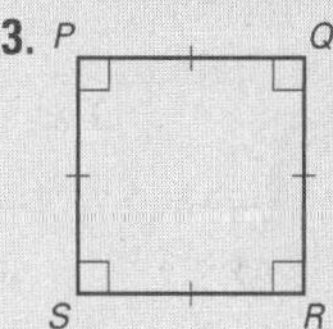

Differentiated Instruction

Kinesthetic Learners Challenge students to find a parallelogram in their classroom or school building. Have them work with a partner to sketch the parallelogram after measuring its four angles and four sides. Instruct them to list as many properties of the parallelogram as they can based on the information they obtain. Have students describe their parallelogram to the class.

See also the *Geometry Toolkit* for more strategies.

2.
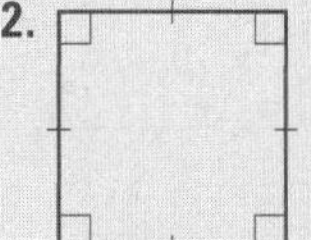

Extra Example 4

You are building a case with glass shelves for collectibles.

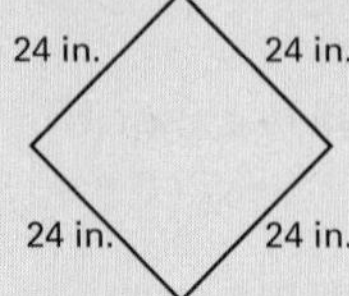

a. Given the shelf measurements in the diagram, can you assume that the shelf is a square? Explain. **No. It has four congruent sides so it is a rhombus. However, we do not know whether the angles are right angles.**

b. You measure the diagonals and find they are both 33.94 inches. What can you conclude about the shape? **It is a square.**

Key Question to Ask for Example 4

- If the figure were to be a rectangle, how long should the diagonals be? How do you know? **55 in.; Pythagorean Theorem**

Closing the Lesson

Have students summarize the major points of the lesson and answer the Essential Question: What are the properties of parallelograms that have all sides or all angles congruent?

- **A rhombus is a parallelogram with four congruent sides.**
- **A rectangle is a parallelogram with four right angles.**
- **A square is a parallelogram with four congruent sides and four right angles.**

A quadrilateral that has all its sides congruent is a rhombus; the diagonals are perpendicular bisectors of each other, and each bisects a pair of opposite angles of the rhombus. A quadrilateral with four congruent angles is a rectangle; the diagonals are congruent and bisect each other. A quadrilateral that has all four sides congruent and all four angles congruent is a square; it has all the properties of rhombuses and all the properties of rectangles.

BICONDITIONALS Recall that biconditionals such as Theorem 8.11 can be rewritten as two parts. To prove a biconditional, you must prove both parts.

Conditional statement If the diagonals of a parallelogram are perpendicular, then the parallelogram is a rhombus.

Converse If a parallelogram is a rhombus, then its diagonals are perpendicular.

PROOF Part of Theorem 8.11

PROVE THEOREMS
You will prove the other part of Theorem 8.11 in Exercise 56 on page 539.

If the diagonals of a parallelogram are perpendicular, then the parallelogram is a rhombus.

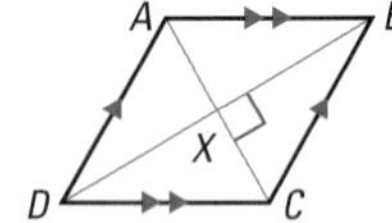

GIVEN ▶ *ABCD* is a parallelogram; $\overline{AC} \perp \overline{BD}$

PROVE ▶ *ABCD* is a rhombus.

Proof *ABCD* is a parallelogram, so $\overline{AC}$ and $\overline{BD}$ bisect each other, and $\overline{BX} \cong \overline{DX}$. Also, $\angle BXC$ and $\angle CXD$ are congruent right angles, and $\overline{CX} \cong \overline{CX}$. So, $\triangle BXC \cong \triangle DXC$ by the SAS Congruence Postulate. Corresponding parts of congruent triangles are congruent, so $\overline{BC} \cong \overline{DC}$. Opposite sides of a ▱*ABCD* are congruent, so $\overline{AD} \cong \overline{BC} \cong \overline{DC} \cong \overline{AB}$. By definition, *ABCD* is a rhombus.

EXAMPLE 4 Solve a real-world problem

CARPENTRY You are building a frame for a window. The window will be installed in the opening shown in the diagram.

a. The opening must be a rectangle. Given the measurements in the diagram, can you assume that it is? *Explain.*

b. You measure the diagonals of the opening. The diagonals are 54.8 inches and 55.3 inches. What can you conclude about the shape of the opening?

Solution

a. No, you cannot. The boards on opposite sides are the same length, so they form a parallelogram. But you do not know whether the angles are right angles.

b. By Theorem 8.13, the diagonals of a rectangle are congruent. The diagonals of the quadrilateral formed by the boards are not congruent, so the boards do not form a rectangle.

GUIDED PRACTICE for Example 4

4. Suppose you measure only the diagonals of a window opening. If the diagonals have the same measure, can you conclude that the opening is a rectangle? *Explain.* **yes; Theorem 8.13**

8.4 EXERCISES

HOMEWORK KEY
○ = WORKED-OUT SOLUTIONS on p. WS10 for Exs. 7, 15, and 55
★ = STANDARDIZED TEST PRACTICE Exs. 2, 30, 31, and 62

SKILL PRACTICE

A

1. **VOCABULARY** What is another name for an equilateral rectangle? **square**

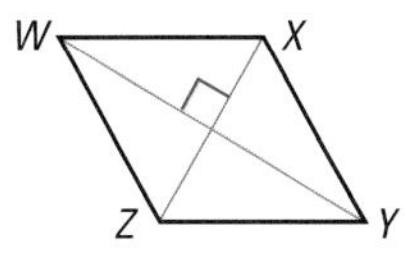

2. ★ **WRITING** Do you have enough information to identify the figure at the right as a rhombus? *Explain.* **No; WXYZ is not known to be a parallelogram.**

EXAMPLES 1, 2, and 3 on pp. 534–535 for Exs. 3–25

RHOMBUSES For any rhombus $JKLM$, decide whether the statement is *always* or *sometimes* true. Draw a diagram and *explain* your reasoning. 3–8. See margin.

3. $\angle L \cong \angle M$
4. $\angle K \cong \angle M$
5. $\overline{JK} \cong \overline{KL}$
6. $\overline{JM} \cong \overline{KL}$
7. $\overline{JL} \cong \overline{KM}$
8. $\angle JKM \cong \angle LKM$

RECTANGLES For any rectangle $WXYZ$, decide whether the statement is *always* or *sometimes* true. Draw a diagram and *explain* your reasoning. 9–14. See margin.

9. $\angle W \cong \angle X$
10. $\overline{WX} \cong \overline{YZ}$
11. $\overline{WX} \cong \overline{XY}$
12. $\overline{WY} \cong \overline{XZ}$
13. $\overline{WY} \perp \overline{XZ}$
14. $\angle WXZ \cong \angle YXZ$

CLASSIFYING Classify the quadrilateral. *Explain* your reasoning. 15–17. See margin.

15. 

16. 

17. 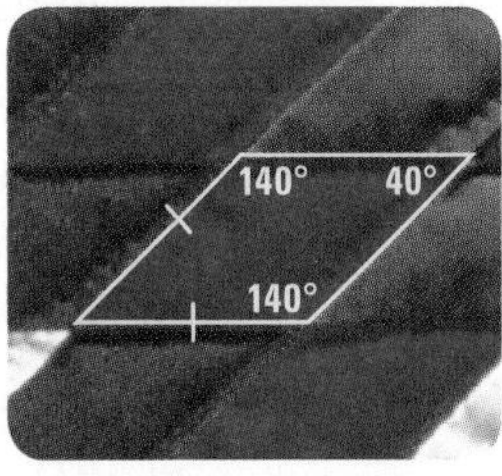

18. **USING PROPERTIES** Sketch rhombus $STUV$. *Describe* everything you know about the rhombus.

18. See margin for art; *STUV* is a parallelogram with four congruent sides, opposite pairs of sides are parallel, opposite pairs of angles are congruent, and perpendicular diagonals bisect each other and bisect opposite angles.

USING PROPERTIES Name each quadrilateral—*parallelogram, rectangle, rhombus,* and *square*—for which the statement is true.

19. It is equiangular. **rectangle, square**
20. It is equiangular and equilateral. **square**
21. Its diagonals are perpendicular. **rhombus, square**
22. Opposite sides are congruent. **parallelogram, rectangle, rhombus, square**
23. The diagonals bisect each other. **parallelogram, rectangle, rhombus, square**
24. The diagonals bisect opposite angles. **rhombus, square**
25. **ERROR ANALYSIS** Quadrilateral $PQRS$ is a rectangle. *Describe* and correct the error made in finding the value of x. **$7x - 4$ is not necessarily equal to $3x + 14$; $(7x - 4) + (3x + 4) = 90$, $10x = 90$, $x = 9$.**

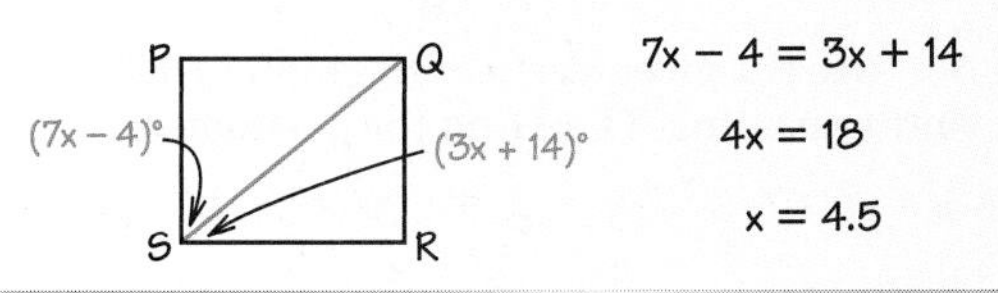

3–8. Check students' diagrams.
3. Sometimes; *JKLM* would need to be a square.
4. Always; in a rhombus opposite pairs of angles are always congruent.
5. Always; in a rhombus all four sides are congruent.
6. Always; in a rhombus all four sides are congruent.
7. Sometimes; diagonals are congruent if the rhombus is a square.
8. Always; diagonals of a rhombus bisect the interior angles.
9–18. See Additional Answers beginning on p. AA1.

4 PRACTICE AND APPLY

Assignment Guide

Answer Transparencies available for all exercises

Basic:
Day 1: EP p. 898 Exs. 12–17
pp. 537–540
Exs. 1–17, 54, 66–70
Day 2: pp. 537–540
Exs. 18–37, 55–59, 65

Average:
Day 1: pp. 537–540
Exs. 1, 2, 5–7, 10–12, 16, 17, 25–29, 54, 66–70
Day 2: pp. 537–540
Exs. 18, 21, 22, 30, 31, 32–50 even, 55–62, 65

Advanced:
Day 1: pp. 537–540
Exs. 1, 2, 7, 8, 12–14, 16, 17, 26–29, 52–54*, 66–70 even
Day 2: pp. 537–540
Exs. 18, 23, 24, 30, 31, 33–51 odd, 55, 58–65*

Block:
pp. 537–540
Exs. 1, 2, 5–7, 10–12, 16, 17, 25–29, 54, 66–70 (with 8.3)
pp. 537–540
Exs. 18, 21, 22, 30, 31, 32–50 even, 55–62, 65 (with 8.5)

Differentiated Instruction

See *Geometry Best Practices Toolkit* for suggestions on addressing the needs of a diverse classroom.

Homework Check

For a quick check of student understanding of key concepts, go over the following exercises:
Basic: 4, 10, 16, 26, 55
Average: 6, 12, 17, 28, 55
Advanced: 8, 14, 18, 30, 55

Extra Practice

- Student Edition, p. 911
- Chapter 8 Resource Book: Practice levels A, B, C, pp. 49–54

Practice Worksheet

An easily-readable reduced practice page (with answers) for this lesson can be found on p. 504D.

Avoiding Common Errors

Exercises 3–14 Students may draw a rhombus or rectangle that looks like a square and then believe that more of these statements are true than really are. Encourage them to draw the rhombus and rectangle so they do not look like squares and to use a protractor or ruler to check congruences of angles or sides. A common misconception is that the diagonals of a rhombus are congruent. Be sure students draw a slanted rhombus and measure both diagonals to convince themselves that they are not congruent.

Teaching Strategy

Exercises 32–49 You can provide additional practice by varying the data provided for the diagram.

50. 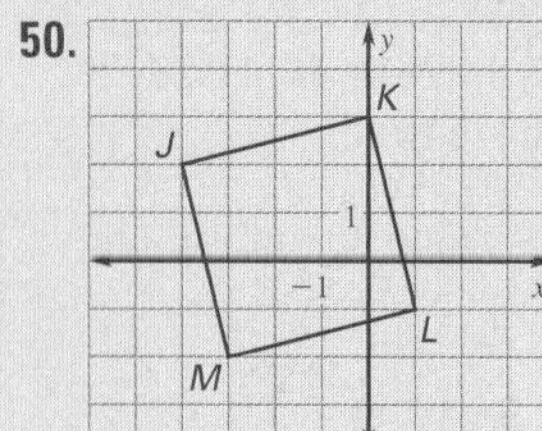

51. 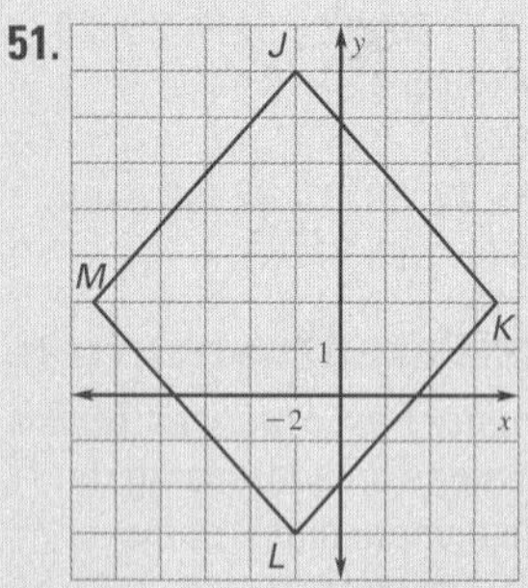

52. No; yes; two rhombuses do not have to have the same angle measures; all squares have the same angle measures, and the ratios of the lengths of their sides will be equal.

53. $AB = BC = CD = DA = \sqrt{89}$; $m\angle ABC = m\angle ADC = 64°$, $m\angle DAB = m\angle BCD = 116°$. The diagonals of a rhombus bisect each other and intersect at a right angle to form four congruent right triangles. The Pythagorean Theorem is used to find the side lengths and the tangent ratio is used to compute the measures of the angles of the rhombus.

B **ALGEBRA Classify the special quadrilateral. *Explain* your reasoning. Then find the values of x and y.**

26. 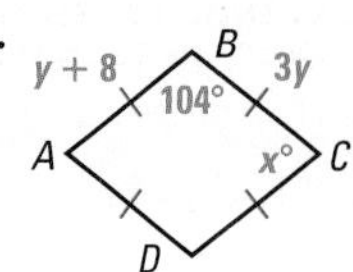

Rhombus; *ABCD* is a quadrilateral with four congruent sides; 76, 4.

27. 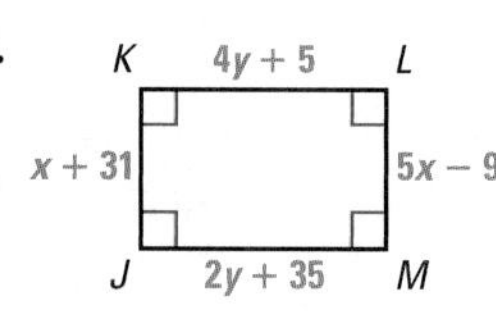

Rectangle; *JKLM* is a quadrilateral with four right angles; 10, 15.

28. 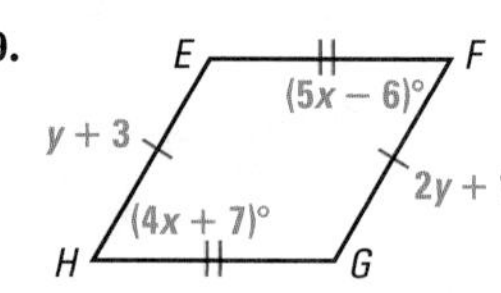

Square; *PQRS* is a quadrilateral with four right angles and perpendicular diagonals; 9, 5.

29. E, F, G, H; $(5x - 6)°$, $y + 3$, $2y + 1$, $(4x + 7)°$
Parallelogram; *EFGH* is a quadrilateral with opposite pairs of sides congruent; 13, 2.

30. ★ **SHORT RESPONSE** The diagonals of a rhombus are 6 inches and 8 inches. What is the perimeter of the rhombus? *Explain.*
20 in.; four 3-4-5 right triangles are created by the diagonals.

31. ★ **MULTIPLE CHOICE** Rectangle $ABCD$ is similar to rectangle $FGHJ$. If $AC = 5$, $CD = 4$, and $FM = 5$, what is HJ? **C**

Ⓐ 4 Ⓑ 5
Ⓒ 8 Ⓓ 10

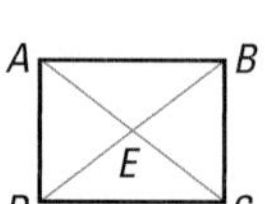

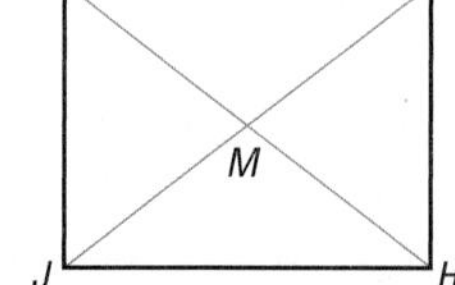

RHOMBUS The diagonals of rhombus *ABCD* intersect at *E*. Given that $m\angle BAC = 53°$ and $DE = 8$, find the indicated measure.

32. $m\angle DAC$ **53°**
33. $m\angle AED$ **90°**
34. $m\angle ADC$ **74°**
35. DB **16**
36. AE **about 6.0**
37. AC **about 12.0**

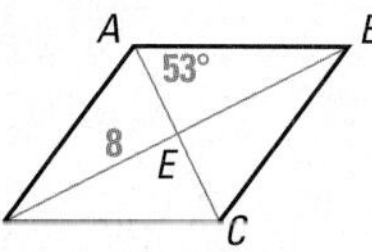

RECTANGLE The diagonals of rectangle *QRST* intersect at *P*. Given that $m\angle PTS = 34°$ and $QS = 10$, find the indicated measure.

38. $m\angle SRT$ **56°**
39. $m\angle QPR$ **112°**
40. QP **5**
41. RP **5**
42. QR **about 8.3**
43. RS **about 5.6**

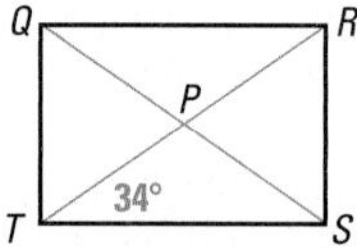

SQUARE The diagonals of square *LMNP* intersect at *K*. Given that $LK = 1$, find the indicated measure.

44. $m\angle MKN$ **90°**
45. $m\angle LMK$ **45°**
46. $m\angle LPK$ **45°**
47. KN **1**
48. MP **2**
49. LP **$\sqrt{2}$**

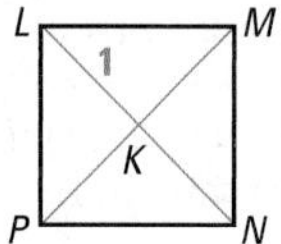

COORDINATE GEOMETRY Use the given vertices to graph ▱*JKLM*. Classify ▱*JKLM* and *explain* your reasoning. Then find the perimeter of ▱*JKLM*.

50. $J(-4, 2)$, $K(0, 3)$, $L(1, -1)$, $M(-3, -2)$
51. $J(-2, 7)$, $K(7, 2)$, $L(-2, -3)$, $M(-11, 2)$

50. See margin for art; square; opposite sides are parallel, adjacent sides are perpendicular, and all four sides are congruent; $4\sqrt{17}$.

51. See margin for art; rhombus; four congruent sides and opposite sides are parallel; $4\sqrt{106}$.

○ = **WORKED-OUT SOLUTIONS on p. WS1** ★ = **STANDARDIZED TEST PRACTICE**

54a. Rhombus, rectangle; *HBDF* is a rhombus since all four sides are congruent and *ACEG* is a rectangle since all four angles are right angles.

54b. They are congruent; they are congruent; the diagonals of a rectangle are congruent and they bisect each other.

C 52. **REASONING** Are all rhombuses similar? Are all squares similar? *Explain* your reasoning. **See margin.**

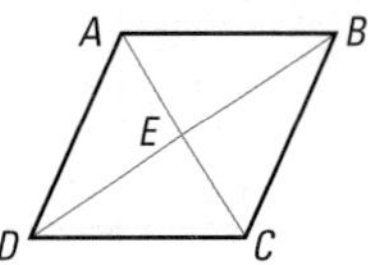

53. **CHALLENGE** Quadrilateral *ABCD* shown at the right is a rhombus. Given that $AC = 10$ and $BD = 16$, find all side lengths and angle measures. *Explain* your reasoning. **See margin.**

PROBLEM SOLVING

EXAMPLE 2 on p. 534 for Ex. 54

A 54. **MULTI-STEP PROBLEM** In the window shown at the right, $\overline{BD} \cong \overline{DF} \cong \overline{BH} \cong \overline{HF}$. Also, $\angle HAB$, $\angle BCD$, $\angle DEF$, and $\angle FGH$ are right angles. **a, b. See margin.**

a. Classify *HBDF* and *ACEG*. *Explain* your reasoning.

b. What can you conclude about the lengths of the diagonals $\overline{AE}$ and $\overline{GC}$? Given that these diagonals intersect at *J*, what can you conclude about the lengths of $\overline{AJ}$, $\overline{JE}$, $\overline{CJ}$, and $\overline{JG}$? *Explain*.

@HomeTutor for problem solving help at classzone.com

EXAMPLE 4 on p. 536 for Ex. 55

55. **PATIO** You want to mark off a square region in your yard for a patio. You use a tape measure to mark off a quadrilateral on the ground. Each side of the quadrilateral is 2.5 meters long. *Explain* how you can use the tape measure to make sure that the quadrilateral you drew is a square. **Measure the diagonals. If they are the same, it is a square.**

@HomeTutor for problem solving help at classzone.com

56. **PROVING THEOREM 8.11** Use the plan for proof below to write a paragraph proof for the converse statement of Theorem 8.11.

A B X D C

GIVEN ▶ *ABCD* is a rhombus.

PROVE ▶ $\overline{AC} \perp \overline{BD}$

Plan for Proof Because *ABCD* is a parallelogram, its diagonals bisect each other at *X*. Show that $\triangle AXB \cong \triangle CXB$. Then show that $\overline{AC}$ and $\overline{BD}$ intersect to form congruent adjacent angles, $\angle AXB$ and $\angle CXB$.

56. Since the diagonals of a parallelogram bisect each other $AX = XC$. $BX = BX$ by the Reflexive Property, and it is given that $AB = BC$. $\triangle AXB \cong \triangle CXB$ by the SSS Congruence Theorem. Because corresponding parts of congruent triangles are congruent $\angle AXB \cong \angle CXB$ and since they are a linear pair, they both must be 90°, which means $\overline{AC} \perp \overline{BD}$.

B **PROVING COROLLARIES** **Write the corollary as a conditional statement and its converse. Then *explain* why each statement is true.** **57–59. See margin.**

57. Rhombus Corollary

58. Rectangle Corollary

59. Square Corollary

PROVING THEOREM 8.12 **In Exercises 60 and 61, prove both parts of Theorem 8.12.** **60, 61. See margin.**

60. **GIVEN ▶** *PQRS* is a parallelogram. $\overline{PR}$ bisects $\angle SPQ$ and $\angle QRS$. $\overline{SQ}$ bisects $\angle PSR$ and $\angle RQP$.

PROVE ▶ *PQRS* is a rhombus.

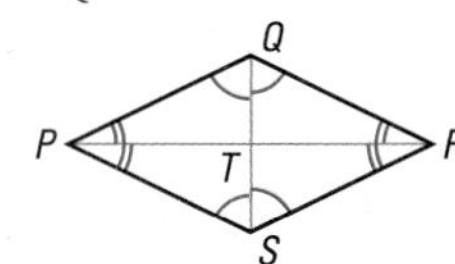

61. **GIVEN ▶** *WXYZ* is a rhombus.

PROVE ▶ $\overline{WY}$ bisects $\angle ZWX$ and $\angle XYZ$. $\overline{ZX}$ bisects $\angle WZY$ and $\angle YXW$.

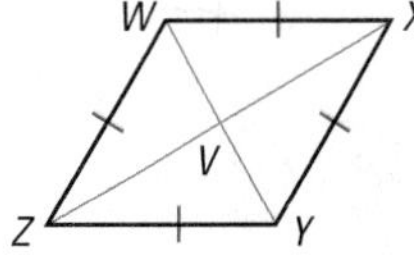

Study Strategy

Exercises 60–61 For each proof, encourage students to think about all the properties of the type of figure that is given. Ask what triangles they can prove congruent so that corresponding parts can be used to prove the desired result.

59. If a quadrilateral is a square, then it is a rhombus and a rectangle; if a quadrilateral is a rhombus and a rectangle, then it is a square; the conditional statement is true since a square is a parallelogram with four right angles and four congruent sides; the converse is true since a rhombus has four congruent sides and a rectangle has four right angles and is therefore a square.

60. Since *PQRS* is a parallelogram the diagonals bisect each other, making $\overline{PT} \cong \overline{RT}$. This along with what is given implies $\triangle PQT \cong \triangle RQT \cong \triangle RST \cong \triangle PST$ using the AAS Congruence Theorem. It follows that $\overline{QR} \cong \overline{SR} \cong \overline{SP} \cong \overline{QP}$ using corresponding parts of congruent triangles are congruent. Since all four sides of the parallelogram are congruent, it is a rhombus.

61. Since *WXYZ* is a rhombus, $\overline{WX} \cong \overline{XY} \cong \overline{YZ} \cong \overline{ZW}$. Using Theorem 8.6, $\overline{WV} \cong \overline{YV}$ and $\overline{ZV} \cong \overline{XV}$. Now $\triangle WVX \cong \triangle WVZ \cong \triangle YVX \cong \triangle YVZ$ by SSS. Using corresponding parts of congruent triangles are congruent, $\angle WVZ \cong \angle WVX$ and $\angle YVZ \cong \angle YVX$, which shows $\overline{WY}$ bisects $\angle ZWX$ and $\angle XYZ$. Similarly, $\angle VZW \cong \angle VZY$ and $\angle VXW \cong \angle VXY$. This shows $\overline{ZX}$ bisects $\angle WZY$ and $\angle YXW$.

57. If a quadrilateral is a rhombus, then it has four congruent sides; if a quadrilateral has four congruent sides, then it is a rhombus; the conditional statement is true since a quadrilateral is a parallelogram and a rhombus is a parallelogram with four congruent sides; the converse is true since a quadrilateral with four congruent sides is also a parallelogram with four congruent sides making it a rhombus.

58. If a quadrilateral is a rectangle, then it has four right angles; if a quadrilateral has four right angles, then it is a rectangle; the conditional statement is true since the definition of a rectangle includes four right angles; the converse is true since four right angles will lead to parallel sides.

5 ASSESS AND RETEACH

Daily Homework Quiz

Transparency Available

Name each type of quadrilateral – parallelogram, rectangle, rhombus, and square – for which the statement is true.

1. Both pairs of opposite angles are congruent. **parallelogram, rectangle, rhombus, square**
2. The quadrilateral is equilateral. **rhombus, square**
3. Given rhombus *MNOP*, find $m\angle NPO$. **48°**

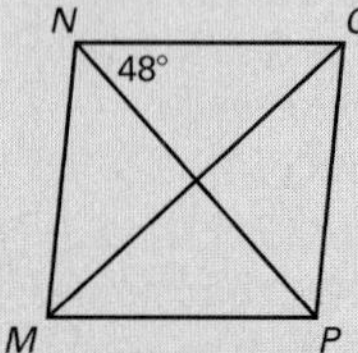

4. Given rectangle *QRST*, find $m\angle RUS$. **128°**

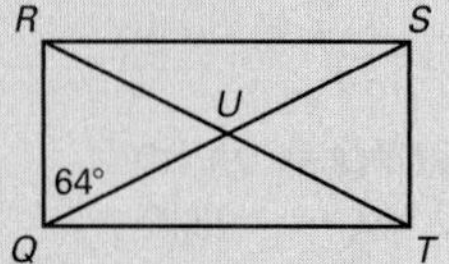

Online Quiz

Available at **classzone.com**

Diagnosis/Remediation

- Practice A, B, C in Chapter 8 Resource Book, pp. 49–54
- Study Guide in Chapter 8 Resource Book, pp. 55–56
- Practice Workbook, pp. 154–156
- @HomeTutor

Challenge

Additional challenge is available in the Chapter 8 Resource Book, p. 59.

Quiz

An easily-readable reduced copy of the quiz (with answers) on Lessons 8.3–8.4 from the Assessment Book can be found on p. 504F.

62a–b, 63, 64. See Additional Answers beginning on p. AA1.

62. ★ **EXTENDED RESPONSE** In *ABCD*, $\overline{AB} \parallel \overline{CD}$, and $\overline{DB}$ bisects $\angle ADC$.

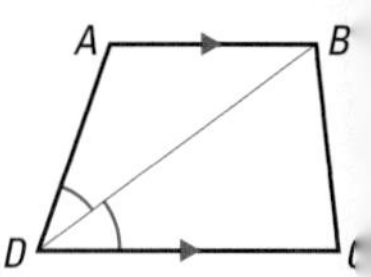

a. Show that $\angle ABD \cong \angle CDB$. What can you conclude about $\angle ADB$ and $\angle ABD$? What can you conclude about $\overline{AB}$ and $\overline{AD}$? *Explain.*

b. Suppose you also know that $\overline{AD} \parallel \overline{BC}$. Classify *ABCD*. *Explain.* **a, b. See margin.**

C 63. **PROVING THEOREM 8.13** Write a coordinate proof of the following statement, which is part of Theorem 8.13.

If a quadrilateral is a rectangle, then its diagonals are congruent. **See margin.**

64. **CHALLENGE** Write a coordinate proof of part of Theorem 8.13.

GIVEN ▶ *DFGH* is a parallelogram, $\overline{DG} \cong \overline{HF}$

PROVE ▶ *DFGH* is a rectangle.

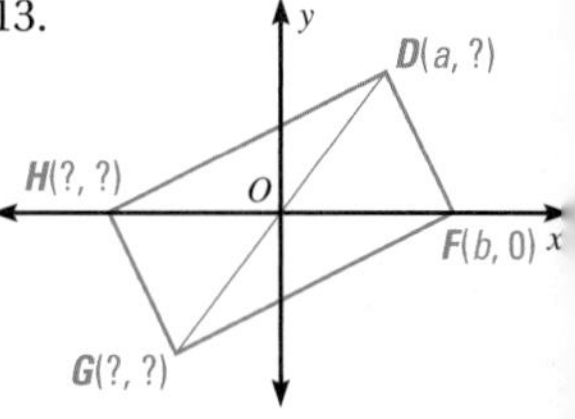

Plan for Proof Write the coordinates of the vertices in terms of *a* and *b*. Find and compare the slopes of the sides. **See margin.**

MIXED REVIEW

PREVIEW Prepare for Lesson 8.5 in Ex. 65.

65. In $\triangle JKL$, $KL = 54.2$ centimeters. Point *M* is the midpoint of $\overline{JK}$ and *N* is the midpoint of $\overline{JL}$. Find *MN*. *(p. 295)* **27.1 cm**

Find the sine and cosine of the indicated angle. Write each answer as a fraction and a decimal. *(p. 473)*

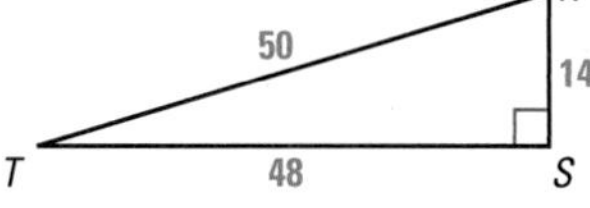

66. $\angle R$ **$\frac{24}{25}$ or 0.96, $\frac{7}{25}$ or 0.28**

67. $\angle T$ **$\frac{7}{25}$ or 0.28, $\frac{24}{25}$ or 0.96**

Find the value of *x*. *(p. 507)*

68. 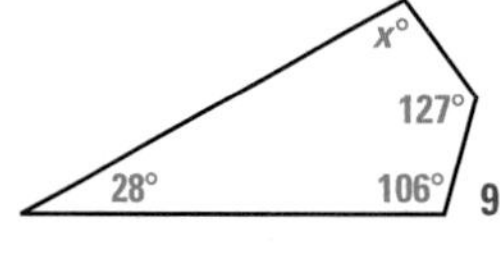

99

69. 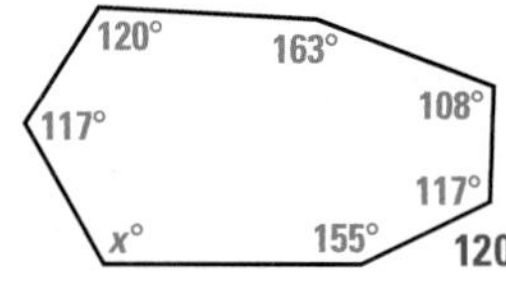

120

70. 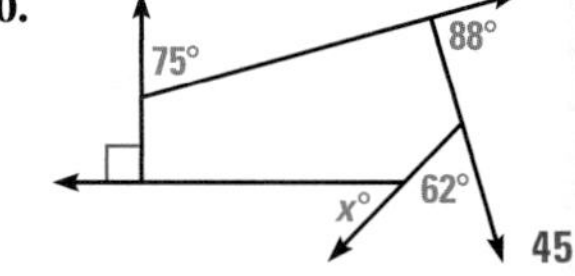

45

QUIZ *for Lessons 8.3–8.4*

For what value of *x* is the quadrilateral a parallelogram? *(p. 522)*

1. **4**

2. **16**

3. **24**

Classify the quadrilateral. *Explain* your reasoning. *(p. 533)*

4. 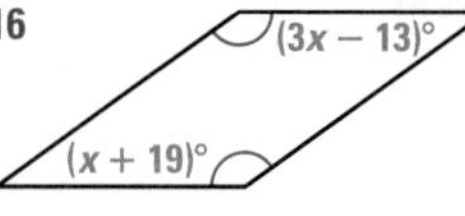

Square; it is both a rhombus and a rectangle.

5. 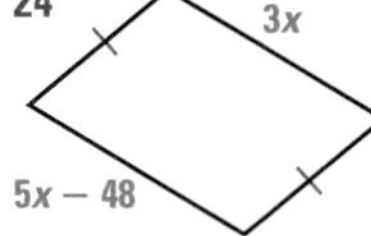

rhombus; Theorem 8.12

6. 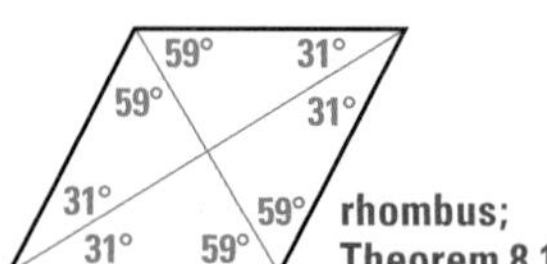 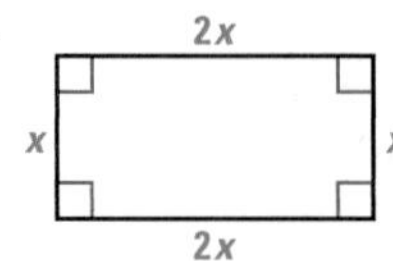

6. rectangle; Rectangle Corollary

@HomeTutor
classzone.com
Keystrokes

8.5 Midsegment of a Trapezoid

MATERIALS • graphing calculator or computer

Standards

Prepare for
7.0 *Students prove* and use *theorems involving* the properties of parallel lines cut by a transversal, *the properties of quadrilaterals,* and the properties of circles.

QUESTION **What are the properties of the midsegment of a trapezoid?**

You can use geometry drawing software to investigate properties of trapezoids.

EXPLORE **Draw a trapezoid and its midsegment**

STEP 1 ***Draw parallel lines*** Draw $\overleftrightarrow{AB}$. Draw a point C not on $\overleftrightarrow{AB}$ and construct a line parallel to $\overleftrightarrow{AB}$ through point C.

A B C
STEP 1

STEP 2 ***Draw trapezoid*** Construct a point D on the same line as point C. Then draw $\overline{AD}$ and $\overline{BC}$ so that the segments are not parallel. Draw $\overline{AB}$ and $\overline{DC}$. Quadrilateral $ABCD$ is called a *trapezoid*. A trapezoid is a quadrilateral with exactly one pair of parallel sides.

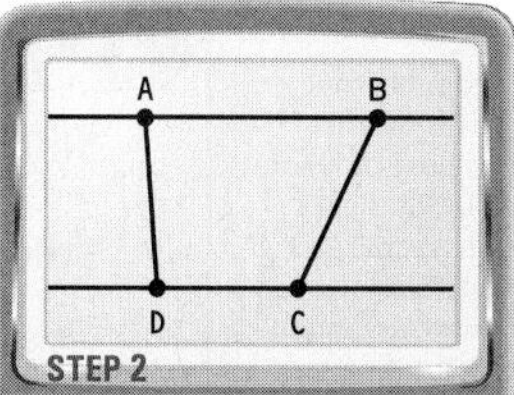

STEP 3 ***Draw midsegment*** Construct the midpoints of $\overline{AD}$ and $\overline{BC}$. Label the points E and F. Draw $\overline{EF}$. $\overline{EF}$ is called a *midsegment* of trapezoid $ABCD$. The midsegment of a trapezoid connects the midpoints of its nonparallel sides.

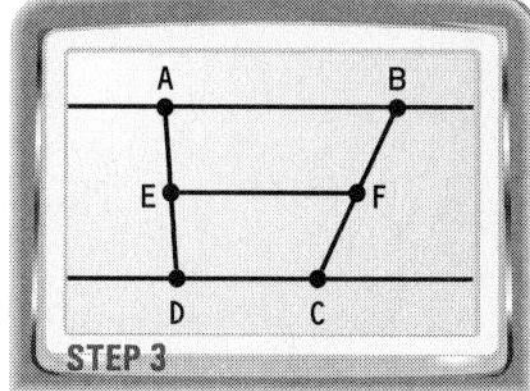

STEP 4 ***Measure lengths*** Measure $\overline{AB}$, $\overline{DC}$, and $\overline{EF}$.

STEP 5 ***Compare lengths*** The average of AB and DC is $\frac{AB + DC}{2}$. Calculate and compare this average to EF. What do you notice? Drag point A or point B to change the shape of trapezoid $ABCD$. Do not allow $\overline{AD}$ to intersect $\overline{BC}$. What do you notice about EF and $\frac{AB + DC}{2}$?

DRAW CONCLUSIONS **Use your observations to complete these exercises**

1. Make a conjecture about the length of the midsegment of a trapezoid. **The length of the midsegment is equal to half the sum of the lengths of the parallel sides.**
2. The midsegment of a trapezoid is parallel to the two parallel sides of the trapezoid. What measurements could you make to show that the midsegment in the *Explore* is parallel to $\overline{AB}$ and $\overline{CD}$? *Explain.* **See margin.**
3. In Lesson 5.1 (page 295), you learned a theorem about the midsegment of a triangle. How is the midsegment of a trapezoid similar to the midsegment of a triangle? How is it different? **It divides two sides of the polygon into congruent segments; in the triangle, the length of the midsegment is half the length of the third side. In the trapezoid, the length of the midsegment is half the sum of the lengths of the parallel sides.**

2. *Sample answer:* Measure $\angle BAE$ and $\angle FED$. If the angles are congruent then $\overline{AB} \parallel \overline{EF}$ using the Corresponding Angles Converse Postulate and $\overline{EF} \parallel \overline{CD}$ using the Transitive Property of Parallel Lines.

1 PLAN AND PREPARE

Explore the Concept

- Students will investigate the properties of the midsegment of a trapezoid.
- This activity leads into the study of the midsegment of a trapezoid in Example 3 in Lesson 8.5.

Materials

Each student will need:

- graphing calculator or computer
- geometry software

Recommended Time

Work activity: 10 min
Discuss results: 5 min

Grouping

Students should work individually.

2 TEACH

Tips for Success

Be sure students use the construction features to draw the line parallel to $\overleftrightarrow{AB}$. It is not good enough to "eyeball" it.

Alternative Strategy

Have students construct a trapezoid and its midsegment with compass and straightedge and measure the lengths with a ruler.

Key Discovery

The length of the midsegment of a trapezoid is equal to the average of the lengths of the two bases.

3 ASSESS AND RETEACH

How could you find the length of the midsegment of a trapezoid when you are given the lengths of the bases? **Add the lengths, then divide by 2.**

1 PLAN AND PREPARE

Warm-Up Exercises

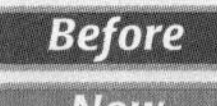 **Transparency Available**

Use the figure to answer the questions.

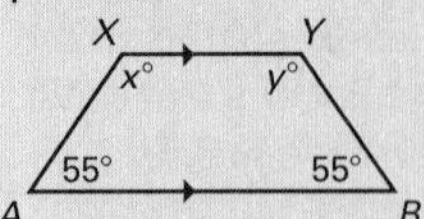

1. What are the values of x and y? **125, 125**
2. If $\overrightarrow{AX}$ and $\overrightarrow{BY}$ intersect at point P, what kind of triangle is $\triangle XPY$? **isosceles**

Notetaking Guide

Transparency Available

Promotes interactive learning and notetaking skills, pp. 213–217.

Pacing

Basic: 2 days

Average: 2 days

Advanced: 2 days

Block: 0.5 block with 8.4
0.5 block with 8.6

- See *Teaching Guide/Lesson Plan.*

2 FOCUS AND MOTIVATE

Essential Question

Big Idea 3, p. 504

What are the main properties of trapezoids and kites? **Tell students they will learn how to answer this question by studying the definitions and theorems of this lesson.**

8.5 Use Properties of Trapezoids and Kites

Before You used properties of special parallelograms.

Now You will use properties of trapezoids and kites.

Why? So you can measure part of a building, as in Example 2.

Key Vocabulary
- **trapezoid**
  bases, base angles, legs
- **isosceles trapezoid**
- **midsegment of a trapezoid**
- **kite**

A **trapezoid** is a quadrilateral with exactly one pair of parallel sides. The parallel sides are the **bases**.

A trapezoid has two pairs of **base angles**. For example, in trapezoid $ABCD$, $\angle A$ and $\angle D$ are one pair of base angles, and $\angle B$ and $\angle C$ are the second pair. The nonparallel sides are the **legs** of the trapezoid.

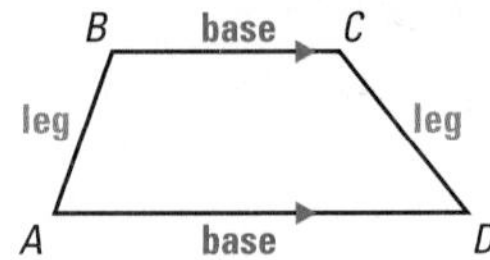

Standards

7.0 Students prove and use theorems involving the properties of parallel lines cut by a transversal, **the properties of quadrilaterals,** and the properties of circles.

EXAMPLE 1 Use a coordinate plane

Show that *ORST* is a trapezoid.

Solution

Compare the slopes of opposite sides.

Slope of $\overline{RS} = \frac{4-3}{2-0} = \frac{1}{2}$

Slope of $\overline{OT} = \frac{2-0}{4-0} = \frac{2}{4} = \frac{1}{2}$

The slopes of $\overline{RS}$ and $\overline{OT}$ are the same, so $\overline{RS} \parallel \overline{OT}$.

Slope of $\overline{ST} = \frac{2-4}{4-2} = \frac{-2}{2} = -1$

Slope of $\overline{OR} = \frac{3-0}{0-0} = \frac{3}{0}$, which is undefined.

The slopes of $\overline{ST}$ and $\overline{OR}$ are not the same, so $\overline{ST}$ is not parallel to $\overline{OR}$.

▸ Because quadrilateral *ORST* has exactly one pair of parallel sides, it is a trapezoid.

GUIDED PRACTICE for Example 1

1. **WHAT IF?** In Example 1, suppose the coordinates of point S are (4, 5). What type of quadrilateral is *ORST*? *Explain.*
   Parallelogram; opposite pairs of sides are parallel.
2. In Example 1, which of the interior angles of quadrilateral *ORST* are supplementary angles? *Explain* your reasoning.
   $\angle O$ and $\angle R$, $\angle T$ and $\angle S$; Consecutive Interior Angles Theorem

Resource Planning Guide

Chapter Resource Book
- Teaching Guide/Lesson Plan (pp. 60–61)
- Practice levels A, B, C (pp. 63–68)
- Study Guide (pp. 69–70)
- Catch-up for Absent Students (p. 71)
- Problem Solving Workshop (p. 72)
- Challenge (p. 73)

Workbooks
- Notetaking Guide (pp. 213–217)
- Practice Workbook (pp. 157–159)

Teaching Options
- **Power Presentations CD-ROM** provides dynamic electronic teaching resources for the classroom.
- **Activity Generator CD-ROM** provides editable activities for all ability levels.

Interactive Technology
- Easy Planner
- Power Presentations CD-ROM
- Activity Generator CD-ROM
- Animated Geometry
- Test Generator CD-ROM
- Online Quiz
- eWorkbook
- eEdition
- @HomeTutor

Resources for English Learners
- Quick Reference for English Learners
- Spanish Study Guide
- Multi-Language Visual Glossary
- Student Resources in Spanish

See also the *Geometry Toolkit* for more strategies for meeting individual needs.

ISOSCELES TRAPEZOIDS If the legs of a trapezoid are congruent, then the trapezoid is an **isosceles trapezoid**.

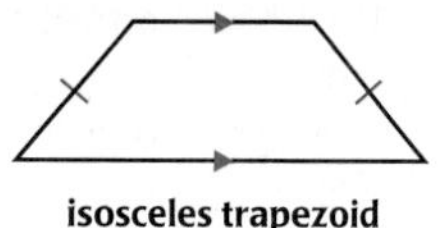

isosceles trapezoid

THEOREMS *For Your Notebook*

THEOREM 8.14

If a trapezoid is isosceles, then each pair of base angles is congruent.

If trapezoid $ABCD$ is isosceles, then $\angle A \cong \angle D$ and $\angle B \cong \angle C$.

Proof: Ex. 37, p. 548

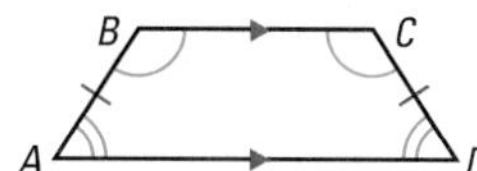

THEOREM 8.15

If a trapezoid has a pair of congruent base angles, then it is an isosceles trapezoid.

If $\angle A \cong \angle D$ (or if $\angle B \cong \angle C$), then trapezoid $ABCD$ is isosceles.

Proof: Ex. 38, p. 548

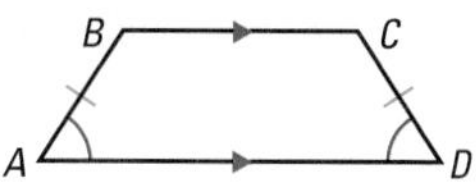

THEOREM 8.16

A trapezoid is isosceles if and only if its diagonals are congruent.

Trapezoid $ABCD$ is isosceles if and only if $\overline{AC} \cong \overline{BD}$.

Proof: Exs. 39 and 43, p. 549

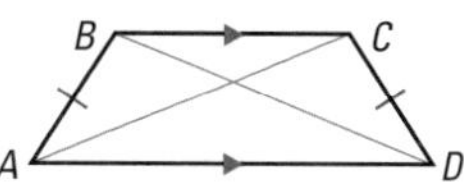

EXAMPLE 2 Use properties of isosceles trapezoids

ARCH The stone above the arch in the diagram is an isosceles trapezoid. Find $m\angle K$, $m\angle M$, and $m\angle J$.

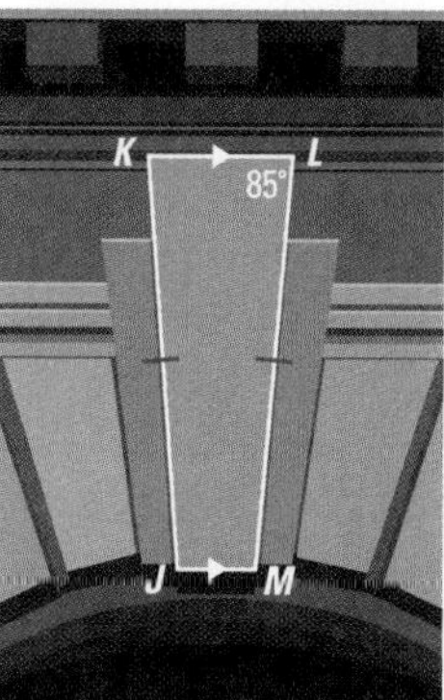

Solution

STEP 1 **Find** $m\angle K$. $JKLM$ is an isosceles trapezoid, so $\angle K$ and $\angle L$ are congruent base angles, and $m\angle K = m\angle L = 85°$.

STEP 2 **Find** $m\angle M$. Because $\angle L$ and $\angle M$ are consecutive interior angles formed by $\overleftrightarrow{LM}$ intersecting two parallel lines, they are supplementary. So, $m\angle M = 180° - 85° = 95°$.

STEP 3 **Find** $m\angle J$. Because $\angle J$ and $\angle M$ are a pair of base angles, they are congruent, and $m\angle J = m\angle M = 95°$.

▶ So, $m\angle J = 95°$, $m\angle K = 85°$, and $m\angle M = 95°$.

Motivating the Lesson

Ask students if they have ever flown a kite. Tell them that the word kite is also a term used in geometry. Tell them that this is one of the figures they will study in this lesson.

3 TEACH

Extra Example 1

Show that $XYZW$ is a trapezoid.

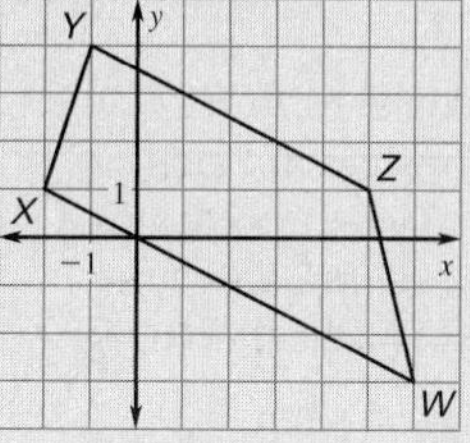

slope $\overline{YZ}$ = slope $\overline{XW} = -\frac{1}{2}$, slope $\overline{XY} = 3$, and slope $\overline{ZW} = -4$. Therefore, $\overline{YZ} \parallel \overline{XW}$ and $\overline{XY} \nparallel \overline{ZW}$. Since exactly one pair of sides are parallel, $XYZW$ is a trapezoid.

Key Question to Ask for Example 1

- Why is it not sufficient simply to show that $\overline{RS}$ is parallel to $\overline{OT}$? **If more than one pair of sides is parallel, then the quadrilateral would be a parallelogram and not a trapezoid.**

Extra Example 2

The top of the table in the diagram is an isosceles trapezoid. Find $m\angle N$, $m\angle O$, and $m\angle P$. **115°, 115°, 65°**

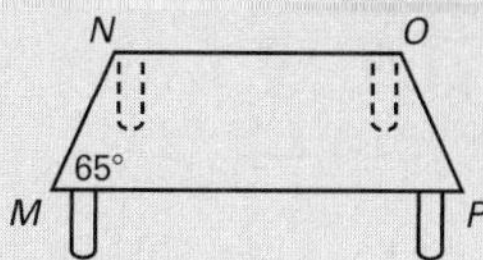

Differentiated Instruction

Advanced Have students investigate what type of figure is formed when consecutive midpoints of the sides of a parallelogram, rectangle, rhombus, square, kite, trapezoid, and isosceles trapezoid are connected. Each figure must at least be a parallelogram. Ask when the parallelogram will be a rhombus, rectangle, or square. Have students explain their answers.

See also the *Geometry Toolkit* for more strategies.

Extra Example 3

In the diagram, $\overline{HK}$ is the midsegment of trapezoid *DEFG*. Find *HK*. **12 cm**

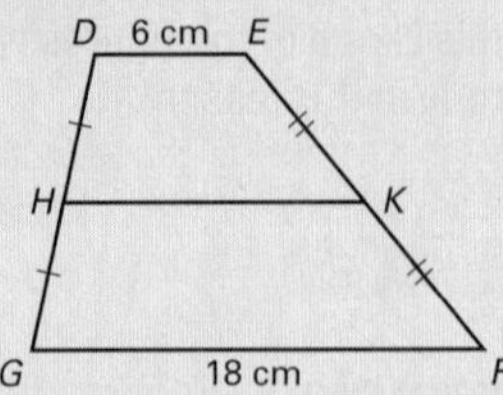

Key Question to Ask for Example 3

- Is *PQNM* similar to *PQRS*? Explain. **They are not similar trapezoids. The corresponding angles are congruent but the sides are not proportional. For example, $\frac{PM}{PS} = \frac{1}{2}$ but $\frac{MN}{SR} = \frac{5}{7}$.**

Extra Example 4

Find $m\angle C$ in the kite shown. **68°**

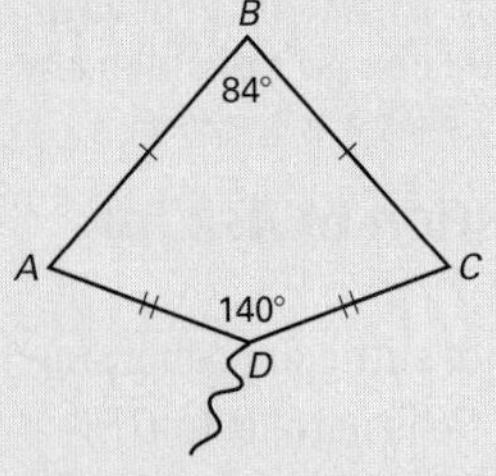

Key Questions to Ask for Example 4

- Is a kite a parallelogram? **no**
- Is a rhombus a kite? **no**

5.

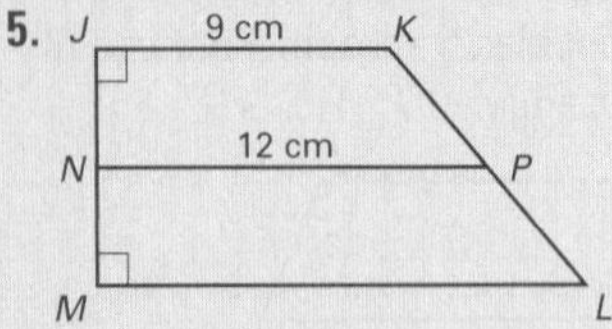

READ VOCABULARY

The midsegment of a trapezoid is sometimes called the *median* of the trapezoid.

MIDSEGMENTS Recall that a midsegment of a triangle is a segment that connects the midpoints of two sides of the triangle. The **midsegment of a trapezoid** is the segment that connects the midpoints of its legs.

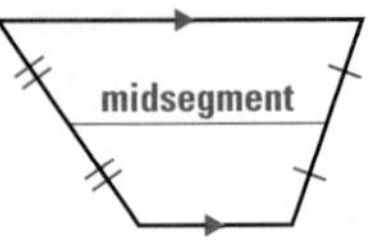

The theorem below is similar to the Midsegment Theorem for Triangles.

THEOREM *For Your Notebook*

THEOREM 8.17 Midsegment Theorem for Trapezoids

The midsegment of a trapezoid is parallel to each base and its length is one half the sum of the lengths of the bases.

If $\overline{MN}$ is the midsegment of trapezoid *ABCD*, then $\overline{MN} \parallel \overline{AB}$, $\overline{MN} \parallel \overline{DC}$, and $MN = \frac{1}{2}(AB + CD)$.

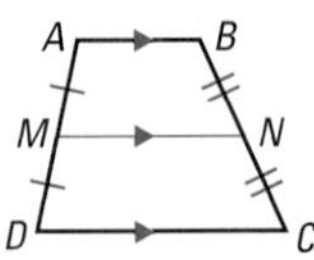

Justification: Ex. 40, p. 549
Proof: p. 937

EXAMPLE 3 Use the midsegment of a trapezoid

In the diagram, $\overline{MN}$ is the midsegment of trapezoid *PQRS*. Find *MN*.

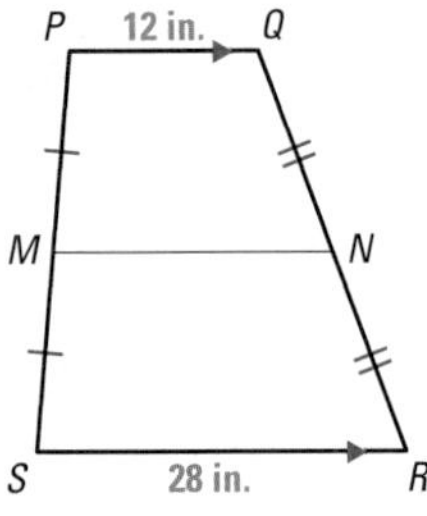

Solution

Use Theorem 8.17 to find *MN*.

$MN = \frac{1}{2}(PQ + SR)$ **Apply Theorem 8.17.**

$= \frac{1}{2}(12 + 28)$ **Substitute 12 for *PQ* and 28 for *XU*.**

$= 20$ **Simplify.**

▶ The length *MN* is 20 inches.

✓ GUIDED PRACTICE for Examples 2 and 3

In Exercises 3 and 4, use the diagram of trapezoid *EFGH*.

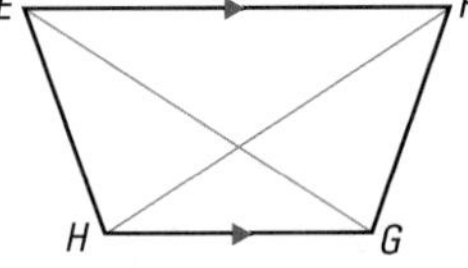

3. If $EG = FH$, is trapezoid *EFGH* isosceles? *Explain.* **yes; Theorem 8.16**

4. If $m\angle HEF = 70°$ and $m\angle FGH = 110°$, is trapezoid *EFGH* isosceles? *Explain.*

4. Yes. *Sample answer:* $m\angle EFG = 70°$ by Consecutive Interior Angles Theorem making *EFGH* an isosceles trapezoid by Theorem 8.15.

5. In trapezoid *JKLM*, $\angle J$ and $\angle M$ are right angles, and $JK = 9$ cm. The length of the midsegment $\overline{NP}$ of trapezoid *JKLM* is 12 cm. Sketch trapezoid *JKLM* and its midsegment. Find *ML*. *Explain* your reasoning. **See margin for art; 15 cm; solve $\frac{1}{2}(9 + x) = 12$ for *x* to find *ML*.**

Differentiated Instruction

English Learners It may be helpful for students learning English to break mathematical terms into smaller parts to help them remember the meanings of the terms. Point out that *iso-* in *isosceles* means equal. Other terms with *iso-* also have meanings regarding something that is equal. Explain that many words may have the same word part. For example, words related to trapezoid include trapeze and trapezium, which are related by trapezoid-like shapes.

See also the *Geometry Toolkit* for more strategies.

KITES A **kite** is a quadrilateral that has two pairs of consecutive congruent sides, but opposite sides are not congruent.

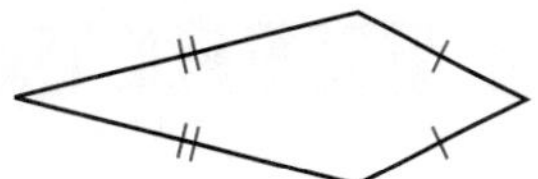

THEOREMS — *For Your Notebook*

THEOREM 8.18

If a quadrilateral is a kite, then its diagonals are perpendicular.

If quadrilateral $ABCD$ is a kite, then $\overline{AC} \perp \overline{BD}$.

Proof: Ex. 41, p. 549

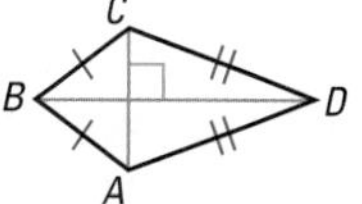

THEOREM 8.19

If a quadrilateral is a kite, then exactly one pair of opposite angles are congruent.

If quadrilateral $ABCD$ is a kite and $\overline{BC} \cong \overline{BA}$, then $\angle A \cong \angle C$ and $\angle B \not\cong \angle D$.

Proof: Ex. 42, p. 549

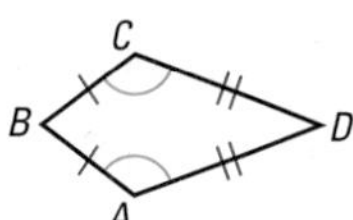

EXAMPLE 4 Apply Theorem 8.19

Find $m\angle D$ in the kite shown at the right.

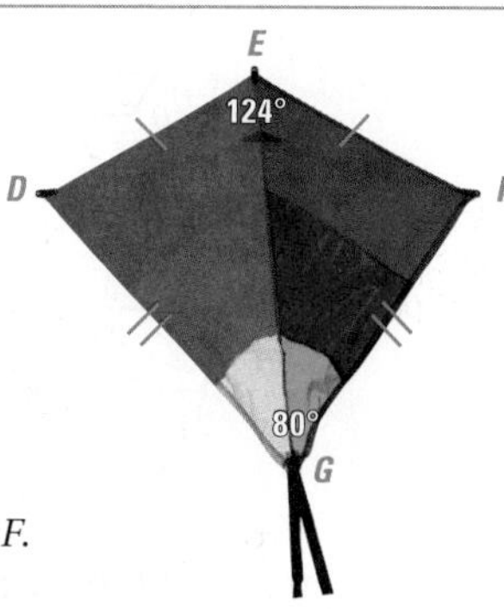

Solution

By Theorem 8.19, $DEFG$ has exactly one pair of congruent opposite angles. Because $\angle E \not\cong \angle G$, $\angle D$ and $\angle F$ must be congruent. So, $m\angle D = m\angle F$. Write and solve an equation to find $m\angle D$.

$m\angle D + m\angle F + 124° + 80° = 360°$ **Corollary to Theorem 8.1**

$m\angle D + m\angle D + 124° + 80° = 360°$ **Substitute $m\angle D$ for $m\angle F$.**

$2(m\angle D) + 204° = 360°$ **Combine like terms.**

$m\angle D = 78°$ **Solve for $m\angle D$.**

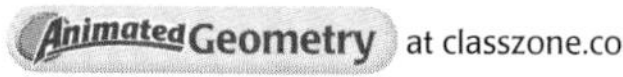 at classzone.com

 **GUIDED PRACTICE** for Example 4

6. In a kite, the measures of the angles are $3x°$, 75°, 90°, and 120°. Find the value of x. What are the measures of the angles that are congruent? **25; 75°**

An **Animated Geometry** activity is available on-line for **Example 4**. This activity is also available on the **Power Presentations CD-ROM**.

Study Strategy

If students have made flash cards for properties of parallelograms, have them add cards with properties of trapezoids, isosceles trapezoids, and kites.

Vocabulary

As an aid to building vocabulary and remembering logical connections, ask students to modify the Venn diagram on page 534 to include trapezoids, isosceles trapezoids, and kites.

Closing the Lesson

Have students summarize the major points of the lesson and answer the Essential Question: What are the main properties of trapezoids and kites?

- **A trapezoid is a quadrilateral with exactly one pair of parallel sides. The midsegment is the segment that joins the midpoints of the legs.**
- **An isosceles trapezoid is a trapezoid with congruent legs.**
- **A kite is a quadrilateral with two pairs of consecutive congruent sides, but opposite sides are not congruent.**

The length of the midsegment of a trapezoid is the average of the lengths of the bases. The base angles and diagonals of an isosceles trapezoid are congruent. The diagonals of a kite are perpendicular; exactly one pair of opposite angles are congruent.

8.5 EXERCISES

HOMEWORK KEY ○ = **WORKED-OUT SOLUTIONS** on p. WS10 for Exs. 11, 19, and 35
★ = **STANDARDIZED TEST PRACTICE** Exs. 2, 16, 28, 31, and 36

4 PRACTICE AND APPLY

Assignment Guide

Answer Transparencies available for all exercises

Basic:
Day 1: pp. 546–549
Exs. 1–12, 44–46
Day 2: pp. 546–549
Exs. 13–24, 34–38, 47, 48

Average:
Day 1: pp. 546–549
Exs. 1, 2, 4–6, 8–12, 28, 38, 39, 44–46
Day 2: pp. 546–549
Exs. 14–17, 19, 20, 22–27, 29–31, 34–37, 40, 41, 47

Advanced:
Day 1: pp. 546–549
Exs. 1, 2, 4–6, 8–12, 28, 37–39, 43–45*
Day 2: pp. 546–549
Exs. 15, 16, 19, 20, 22–27, 29–36*, 40–42, 48

Block:
pp. 546–549
Exs. 1, 2, 4–6, 8–12, 28, 38, 39, 44–46 (with 8.4)
pp. 546–549
Exs. 14–17, 19, 20, 22–27, 29–31, 34–37, 40, 41, 47 (with 8.6)

Differentiated Instruction

See *Geometry Best Practices Toolkit* for suggestions on addressing the needs of a diverse classroom.

Homework Check

For a quick check of student understanding of key concepts, go over the following exercises:
Basic: 4, 8, 14, 18, 34
Average: 5, 10, 15, 20, 36
Advanced: 6, 12, 16, 22, 37

Extra Practice

- Student Edition, p. 911
- Chapter 8 Resource Book: Practice levels A, B, C, pp. 63–68

Practice Worksheet

An easily-readable reduced practice page (with answers) for this lesson can be found on p. 504E.

SKILL PRACTICE

A

1. **VOCABULARY** In trapezoid $PQRS$, $\overline{PQ} \parallel \overline{RS}$. Sketch $PQRS$ and identify its bases and its legs. **See margin.**

2. ★ **WRITING** *Describe* the differences between a kite and a trapezoid.

2. A trapezoid has one pair of parallel sides and at most one pair of congruent opposite sides. A kite has two pairs of consecutive congruent sides and opposite sides are not congruent.

EXAMPLES 1 and 2 on pp. 542–543 for Exs. 3–12

COORDINATE PLANE **Points A, B, C, and D are the vertices of a quadrilateral. Determine whether $ABCD$ is a trapezoid.**

3. $A(0, 4)$, $B(4, 4)$, $C(8, -2)$, $D(2, 1)$ **trapezoid**
4. $A(-5, 0)$, $B(2, 3)$, $C(3, 1)$, $D(-2, -2)$ **not a trapezoid**
5. $A(2, 1)$, $B(6, 1)$, $C(3, -3)$, $D(-1, -4)$ **not a trapezoid**
6. $A(-3, 3)$, $B(-1, 1)$, $C(1, -4)$, $D(-3, 0)$ **trapezoid**

FINDING ANGLE MEASURES **Find $m\angle J$, $m\angle L$, and $m\angle M$.**

7. 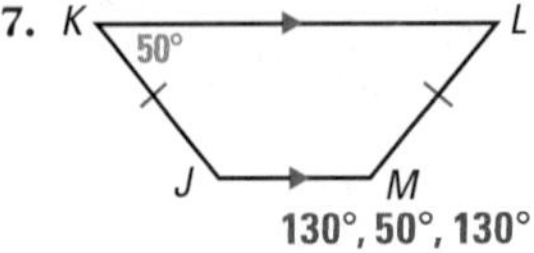

130°, 50°, 130°

8. 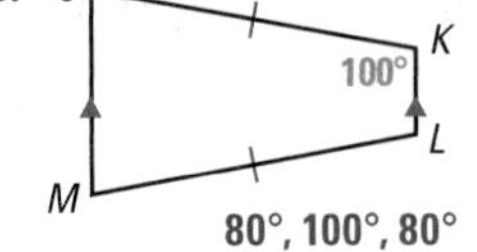

80°, 100°, 80°

9. 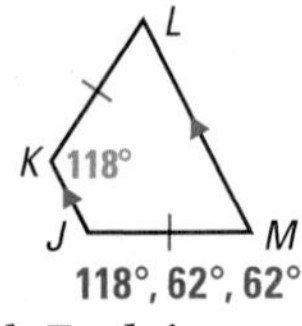

118°, 62°, 62°

REASONING **Determine whether the quadrilateral is a trapezoid. *Explain.*** **10–12. See margin.**

10. 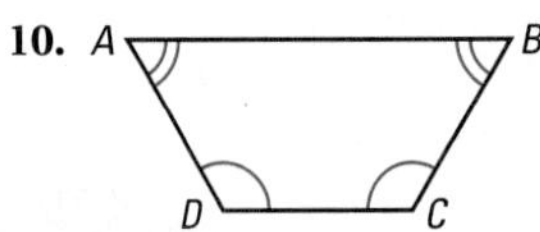

11. 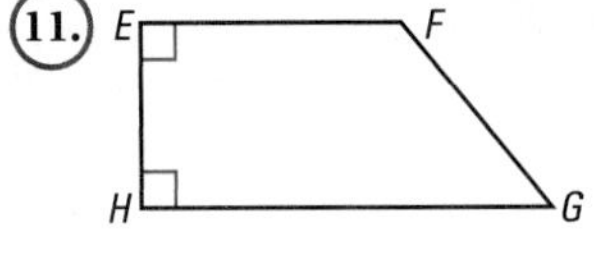

12. 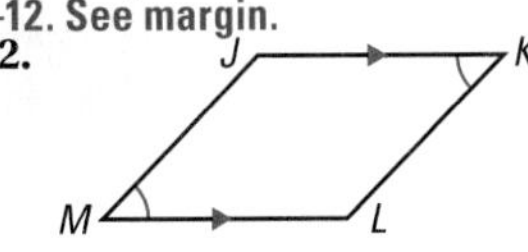

EXAMPLE 3 on p. 544 for Exs. 13–16

FINDING MIDSEGMENTS **Find the length of the midsegment of the trapezoid.**

13. 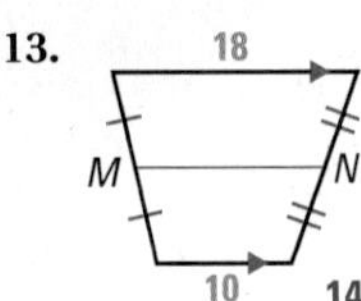

14

14. 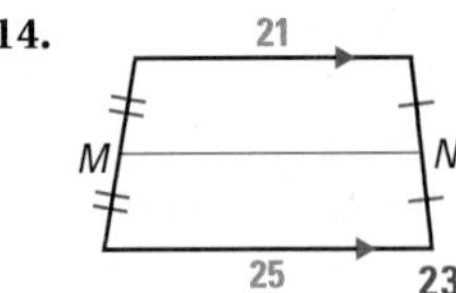

23

15. 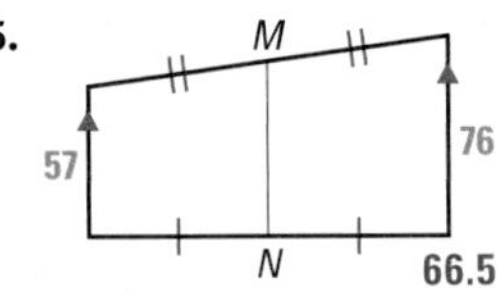

66.5

16. ★ **MULTIPLE CHOICE** Which statement is not always true? **D**

Ⓐ The base angles of an isosceles trapezoid are congruent.

Ⓑ The midsegment of a trapezoid is parallel to the bases.

Ⓒ The bases of a trapezoid are parallel.

Ⓓ The legs of a trapezoid are congruent.

EXAMPLE 4 on p. 545 for Exs. 17–20

17. **ERROR ANALYSIS** *Describe* and correct the error made in finding $m\angle A$. **Only one pair of opposite angles in a kite is congruent. In this case $m\angle B = m\angle D = 120°$; $m\angle A + m\angle B + m\angle C + m\angle D = 360°$, $m\angle A + 120° + 50° + 120° = 360°$, so $m\angle A = 70°$.**

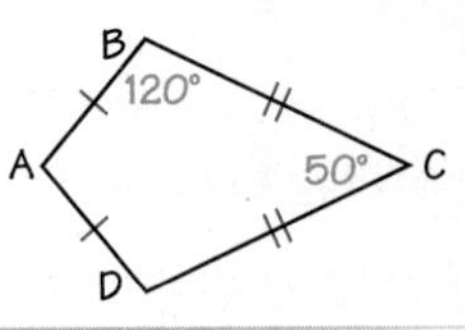

1. 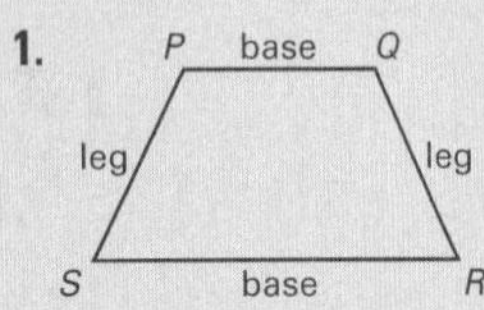

10. Trapezoid; both pairs of base angles are congruent, so $\angle A$ and $\angle D$, $\angle B$ and $\angle C$ are supplementary angles. By the Consecutive Interior Angles Theorem, $\overline{AB} \parallel \overline{DC}$.

11. Trapezoid; $\overline{EF} \parallel \overline{HG}$ since they are both perpendicular to $\overline{EH}$

12. Trapezoid; $\overline{JK} \parallel \overline{ML}$

ANGLES OF KITES ***EFGH*** **is a kite. Find** $m\angle G$**.**

18. 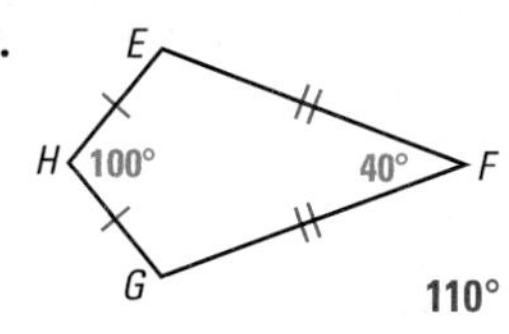

110°

(19.) 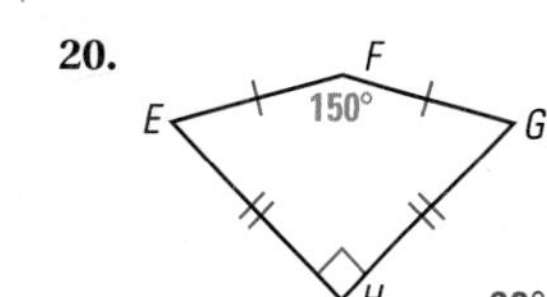

80°

20. E F 150° G H **60°**

B **DIAGONALS OF KITES** **Use Theorem 8.18 and the Pythagorean Theorem to find the side lengths of the kite. Write the lengths in simplest radical form.**

21. 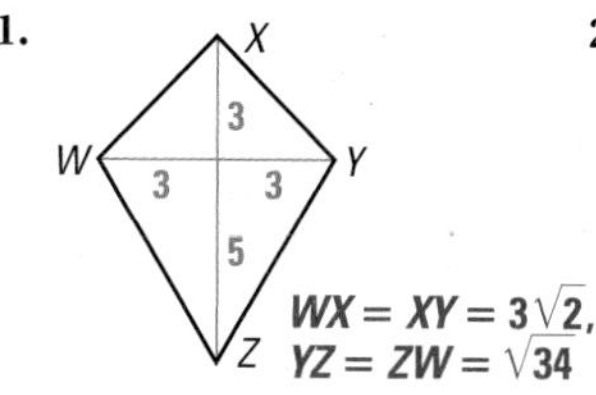

$WX = XY = 3\sqrt{2}$, $YZ = ZW = \sqrt{34}$

22. 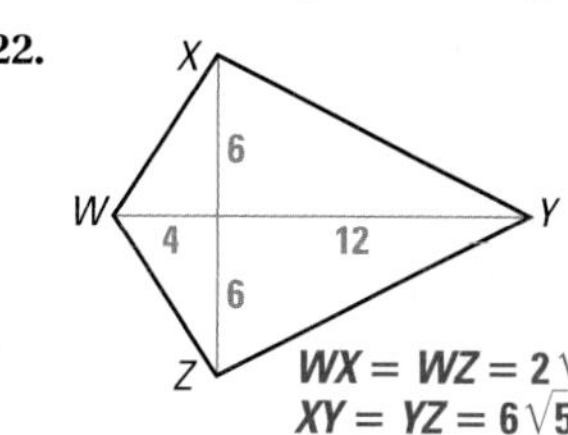

$WX = WZ = 2\sqrt{13}$, $XY = YZ = 6\sqrt{5}$

23. 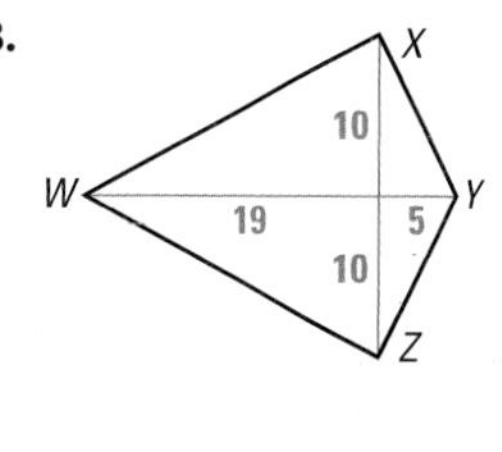

3. **$XY = YZ =$ $\sqrt{5}$, $WX = WZ =$ $\sqrt{461}$**

24. **ERROR ANALYSIS** In trapezoid *ABCD*, $\overline{MN}$ is the midsegment. *Describe* and correct the error made in finding *DC*. **$DC = 2MN - AB$ since $MN = \frac{AB + DC}{2}$; $DC = 2(8) - 14$, $DC = 2$.**

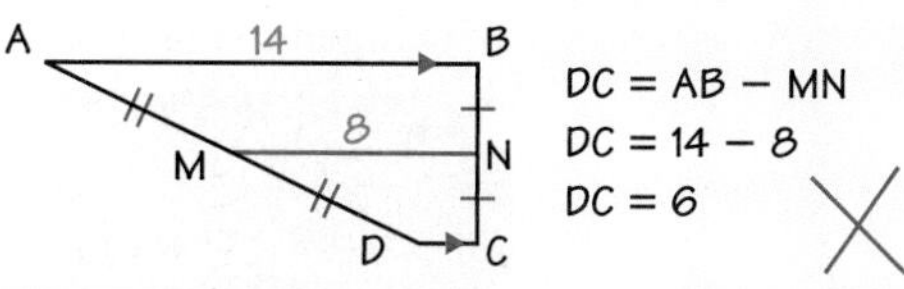

ALGEBRA **Find the value of** x**.**

25. 10 7 $2x$ **2**

26. 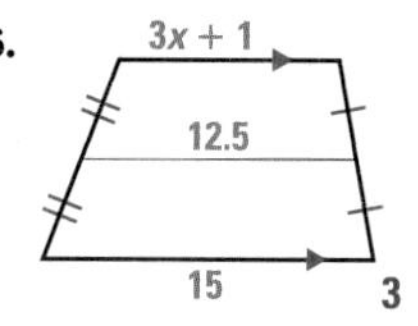

3

27. 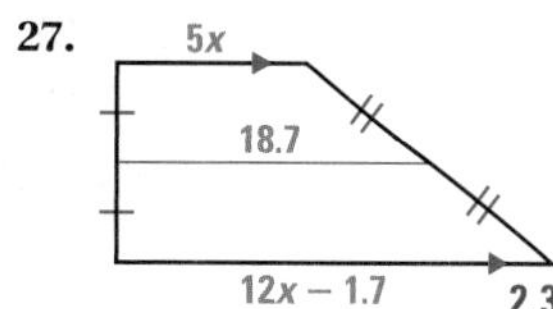

2.3

28. ★ **SHORT RESPONSE** The points $M(-3, 5)$, $N(-1, 5)$, $P(3, -1)$, and $Q(-5, -1)$ form the vertices of a trapezoid. Draw *MNPQ* and find *MP* and *NQ*. What do your results tell you about the trapezoid? *Explain.* **See margin for art; $MP = 6\sqrt{2}$, $NQ = 2\sqrt{13}$; *MNPQ* is not isosceles; Theorem 8.16.**

29. **DRAWING** In trapezoid *JKLM*, $\overline{JK} \parallel \overline{LM}$ and $JK = 17$. The midsegment of *JKLM* is $\overline{XY}$, and $XY = 37$. Sketch *JKLM* and its midsegment. Then find *LM*. **See margin for art; 57.**

30. **RATIOS** The ratio of the lengths of the bases of a trapezoid is 1 : 3. The length of the midsegment is 24. Find the lengths of the bases. **12, 36**

31. ★ **MULTIPLE CHOICE** In trapezoid *PQRS*, $\overline{PQ} \parallel \overline{RS}$ and $\overline{MN}$ is the midsegment of *PQRS*. If $RS = 5 \cdot PQ$, what is the ratio of *MN* to *RS*? **A**

Ⓐ 3 : 5 Ⓑ 5 : 3 Ⓒ 2 : 1 Ⓓ 3 : 1

C 32. **CHALLENGE** The figure shown at the right is a trapezoid with its midsegment. Find all the possible values of x. What is the length of the midsegment? *Explain.* (The figure may not be drawn to scale.)

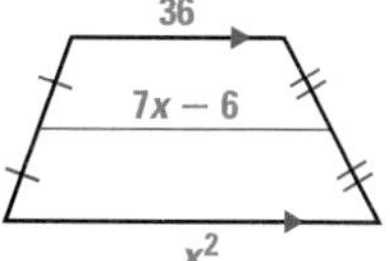

32. 6, 8; 50; solve the equation $\frac{x^2 + 36}{2} = 7x - 6$, the solution $x = 6$ must be rejected because the midsegment will equal 36 and that is not possible.

33. **REASONING** *Explain* why a kite and a general quadrilateral are the only quadrilaterals that can be concave. ***Sample answer:*** **A kite or a quadrilateral that is not a parallelogram or a trapezoid would have no pair of opposite sides parallel. So, no consecutive angles would be supplementary. So, the measure of an interior angle could be greater than 180°.**

Avoiding Common Errors

Exercises 24–27 Some students may have errors of exactly the sort that Exercise 24 warns against. In that case, discuss Exercise 24 with the students. Then have them correct their work.

Reading Strategy

Exercise 29 Have students explain the diagram. Ask whether the wording of the exercise lets us say with certainty which side contains point *X* and which contains point *Y*.

28. 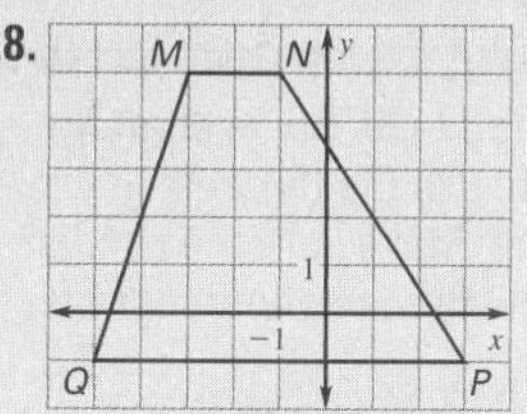

29. 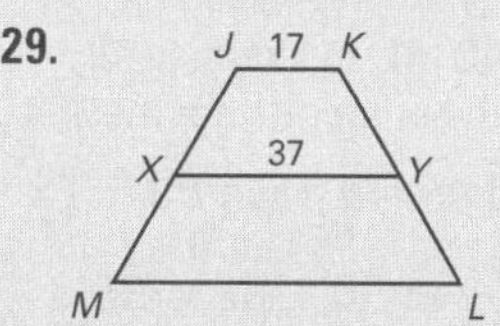

Exercise 36 Additional information about this bridge can be found at www.construction.com/NewsCenter/Headlines/AR/20041207r.asp

Vocabulary

Exercises 37–38 Students may need to review what is meant by an *auxiliary segment*. Have students identify the auxiliary segment in each exercise.

Avoiding Common Errors

Exercises 37–39 Some students may try to use the theorem in its own proof. Make sure they understand why this is not permissible.

Teaching Strategy

Exercises 40–41 In Exercise 40 suggest to the students that they let $CD = x$ and $AF = y$. Then $BG = \frac{1}{2}x$ and $GE = \frac{1}{2}y$ so $BG + GE = BE = \frac{1}{2}x + \frac{1}{2}y = \frac{1}{2}(x + y)$. For Exercise 41, discuss how they could do the proof without using congruent triangles. Review how the Converse of the Perpendicular Bisector Theorem would make the proof much shorter.

Mathematical Reasoning

Exercise 42 Discuss with students why an indirect proof is the best approach in this situation.

35. *Sample:*

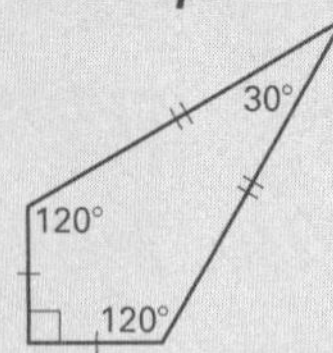

PROBLEM SOLVING

EXAMPLES A **3 and 4** on pp. 544–545 for Exs. 34–35

34. FURNITURE In the photograph of a chest of drawers, $\overline{HC}$ is the midsegment of trapezoid $ABDG$, $\overline{GD}$ is the midsegment of trapezoid $HCEF$, $AB = 13.9$ centimeters, and $GD = 50.5$ centimeters. Find HC. Then find FE. **32.2 cm, 68.8 cm**

@HomeTutor for problem solving help at classzone.com

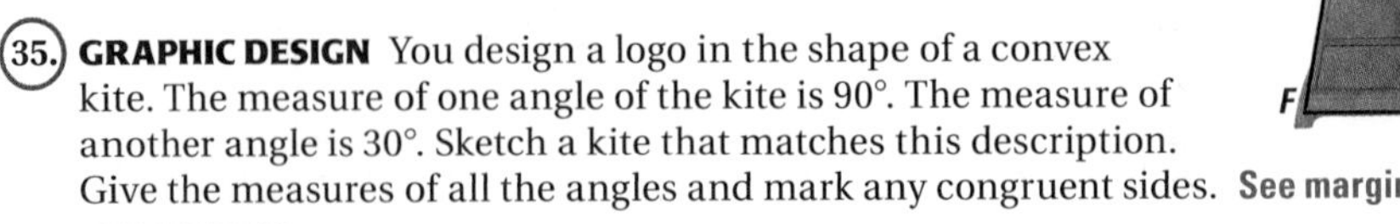

(35.) GRAPHIC DESIGN You design a logo in the shape of a convex kite. The measure of one angle of the kite is 90°. The measure of another angle is 30°. Sketch a kite that matches this description. Give the measures of all the angles and mark any congruent sides. **See margin.**

@HomeTutor for problem solving help at classzone.com

36. ★ EXTENDED RESPONSE The bridge below is designed to fold up into an octagon shape. The diagram shows a section of the bridge.

a. Classify the quadrilaterals shown in the diagram. **isosceles trapezoid, kite**

b. As the bridge folds up, what happens to the length of $\overline{BF}$? What happens to $m\angle BAF$, $m\angle ABC$, $m\angle BCF$, and $m\angle CFA$?

c. Given $m\angle CFE = 65°$, find $m\angle DEF$, $m\angle FCD$, and $m\angle CDE$. *Explain.* **65°, 115°, 115°; in an isosceles trapezoid base angles are congruent.**

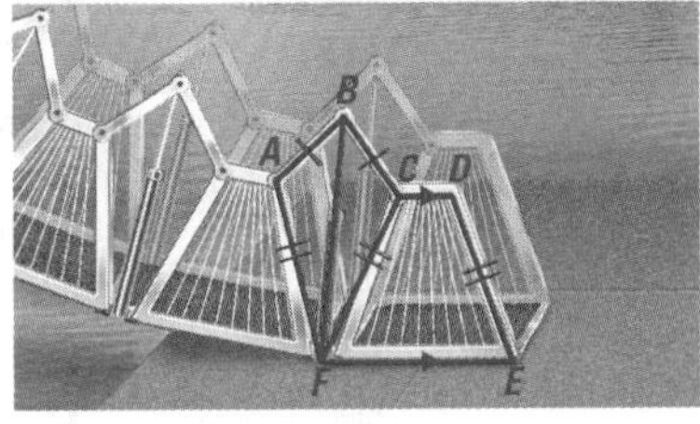

36b. It increases; $m\angle BAF$ approaches 180°, $m\angle ABC$ approaches 0°, $m\angle BCF$ approaches 180°, and $m\angle CFA$ approaches 0°.

B **37. PROVING THEOREM 8.14** Use the diagram and the auxiliary segment to prove Theorem 8.14. In the diagram, $\overline{EC}$ is drawn parallel to $\overline{AB}$. **See margin.**

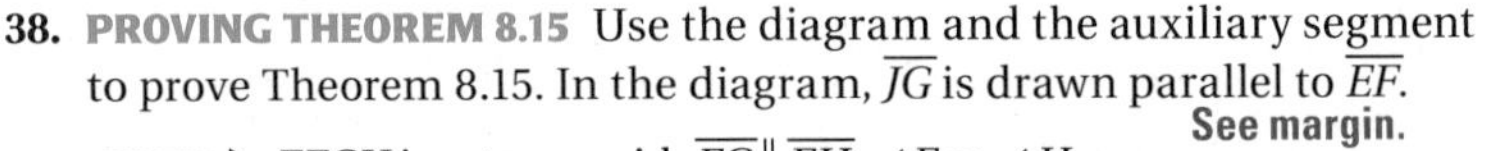

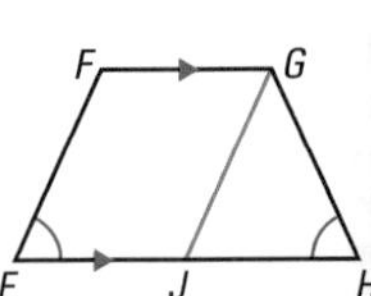

GIVEN ▶ $ABCD$ is an isosceles trapezoid, $\overline{BC} \parallel \overline{AD}$

PROVE ▶ $\angle A \cong \angle D$, $\angle B \cong \angle BCD$

Hint: Find a way to show that $\triangle ECD$ is an isosceles triangle.

38. PROVING THEOREM 8.15 Use the diagram and the auxiliary segment to prove Theorem 8.15. In the diagram, $\overline{JG}$ is drawn parallel to $\overline{EF}$. **See margin.**

GIVEN ▶ $EFGH$ is a trapezoid, $\overline{FG} \parallel \overline{EH}$, $\angle E \cong \angle H$

PROVE ▶ $EFGH$ is an isosceles trapezoid.

Hint: Find a way to show that $\triangle JGH$ is an isosceles triangle.

○ = WORKED-OUT SOLUTIONS on p. WS1 ★ = STANDARDIZED TEST PRACTICE

37. Since $\overline{BC} \parallel \overline{AE}$ and $\overline{AB} \parallel \overline{EC}$, $ABCE$ is a parallelogram which makes $\overline{AB} \cong \overline{EC}$. Using the Transitive Property of Segment Congruence, $\overline{CE} \cong \overline{CD}$ making $\triangle ECD$ isosceles. Since $\triangle ECD$ is isosceles $\angle D \cong \angle CED$. $\angle A \cong \angle CED$ using the Corresponding Angles Congruence Postulate, therefore $\angle A \cong \angle D$ using the Transitive Property of Angle Congruence. $\angle CED$ and $\angle CEA$ form a linear pair and therefore are supplementary. $\angle A$ and $\angle ABC$ are supplementary, and $\angle CEA$ and $\angle ECB$ are supplementary since they are consecutive pairs of angles in a parallelogram. Using the Congruent Supplements Theorem, $\angle A \cong \angle D$ and $\angle B \cong \angle BCD$.

38. See Additional Answers beginning on p. AA1.

39. **PROVING THEOREM 8.16** Prove part of Theorem 8.16. **See margin.**

GIVEN ▶ $JKLM$ is an isosceles trapezoid. $\overline{KL} \parallel \overline{JM}$, $\overline{JK} \cong \overline{LM}$

PROVE ▶ $\overline{JL} \cong \overline{KM}$

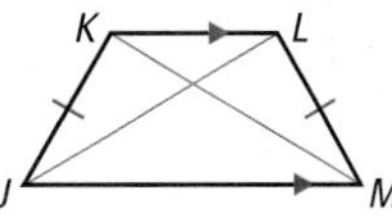

40. **REASONING** In the diagram below, $\overline{BG}$ is the midsegment of $\triangle ACD$ and $\overline{GE}$ is the midsegment of $\triangle ADF$. *Explain* why the midsegment of trapezoid $ACDF$ is parallel to each base and why its length is one half the sum of the lengths of the bases. **See margin.**

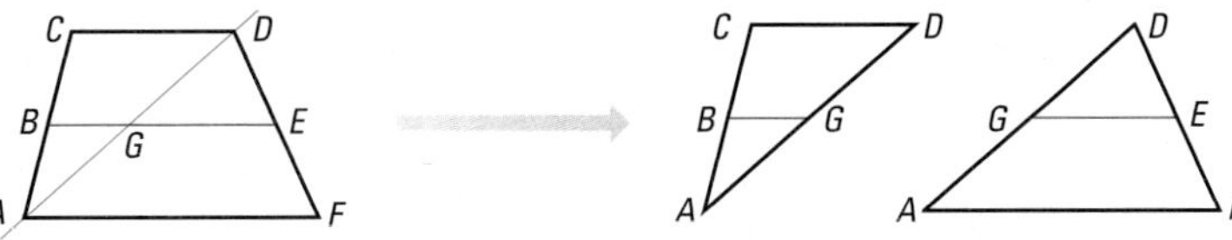

41. **PROVING THEOREM 8.18** Prove Theorem 8.18. **See margin.**

GIVEN ▶ $ABCD$ is a kite. $\overline{AB} \cong \overline{CB}$, $\overline{AD} \cong \overline{CD}$

PROVE ▶ $\overline{AC} \perp \overline{BD}$

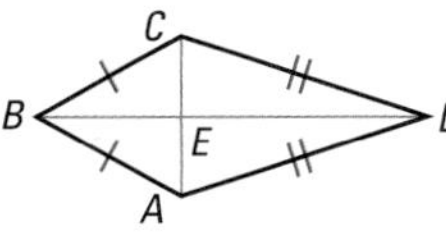

C 42. **PROVING THEOREM 8.19** Write a paragraph proof of Theorem 8.19. **See margin.**

GIVEN ▶ $EFGH$ is a kite. $\overline{EF} \cong \overline{GF}$, $\overline{EH} \cong \overline{GH}$

PROVE ▶ $\angle E \cong \angle G$, $\angle F \not\cong \angle H$

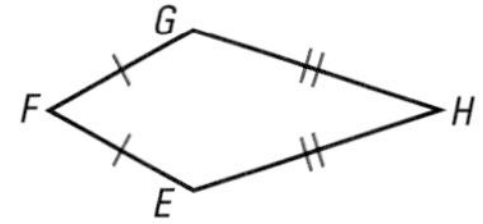

Plan for Proof First show that $\angle E \cong \angle G$. Then use an indirect argument to show that $\angle F \not\cong \angle H$: If $\angle F \cong \angle H$, then $EFGH$ is a parallelogram. But opposite sides of a parallelogram are congruent. This result contradicts the definition of a kite.

43. **CHALLENGE** In Exercise 39, you proved that part of Theorem 8.16 is true. Write the other part of Theorem 8.16 as a conditional statement. Then prove that the statement is true. **See margin.**

MIXED REVIEW

44. Place a right triangle in a coordinate plane in a way that is convenient for finding side lengths. Assign coordinates to each vertex. *(p. 295)* **See margin.**

Use the diagram to complete the proportion. *(p. 449)*

45. $\frac{AB}{AC} = \frac{?}{AB}$ **AD**

46. $\frac{AB}{BC} = \frac{BD}{?}$ **CD**

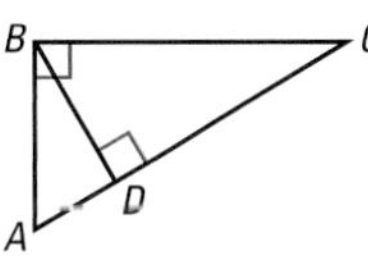

PREVIEW Prepare for Lesson 8.6 in Exs. 47–48.

Three of the vertices of $\square ABCD$ are given. Find the coordinates of point D. Show your method. *(p. 522)* **47, 48. See margin for art.**

47. $A(-1, -2)$, $B(4, -2)$, $C(6, 2)$, $D(x, y)$ **(1, 2)**

48. $A(1, 4)$, $B(0, 1)$, $C(4, 1)$, $D(x, y)$ **(5, 4)**

44. Sample:

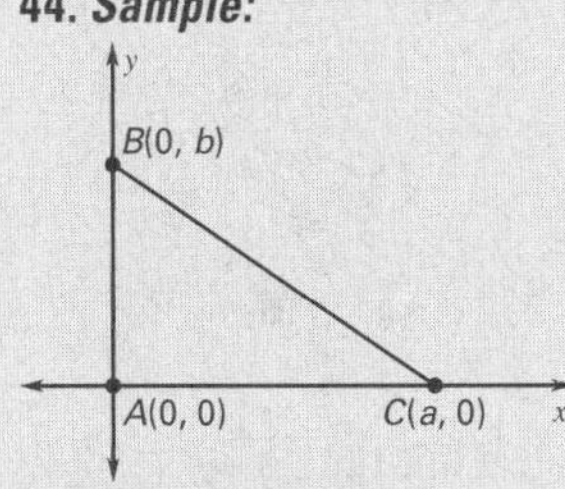

(0, 0), (a, 0), (0, b)

47.

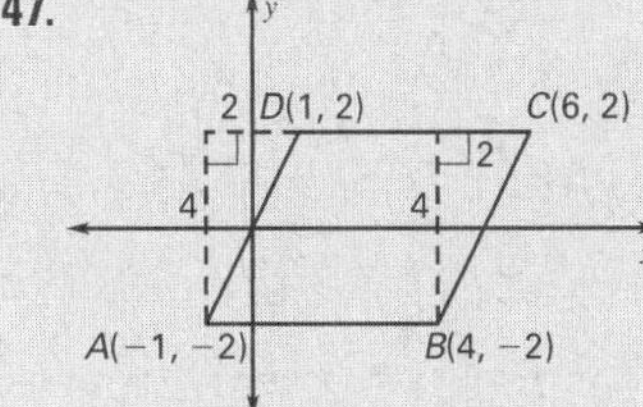

48.

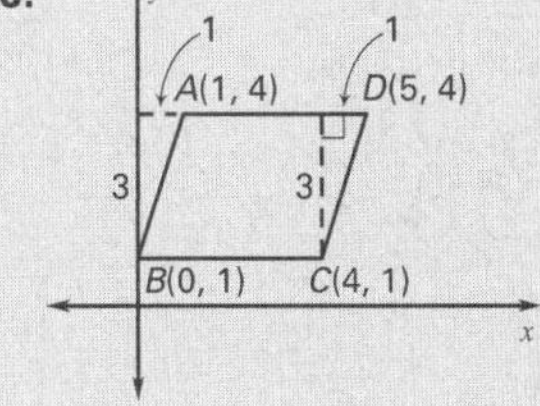

5 ASSESS AND RETEACH

Daily Homework Quiz

Transparency Available

1. Find $m\angle A$, $m\angle C$, and $m\angle D$. **124°, 56°, 124°**

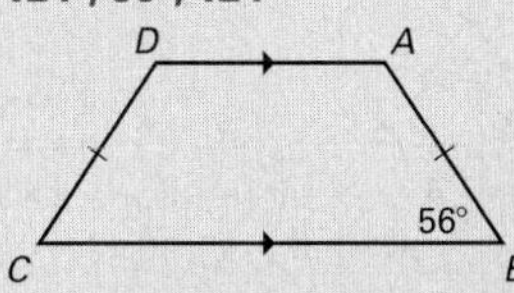

2. Find the length of the midsegment of the trapezoid. **25**

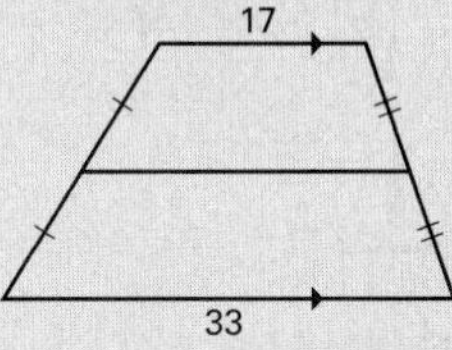

For Exercises 3 and 4, use the figure to find the indicated measures.

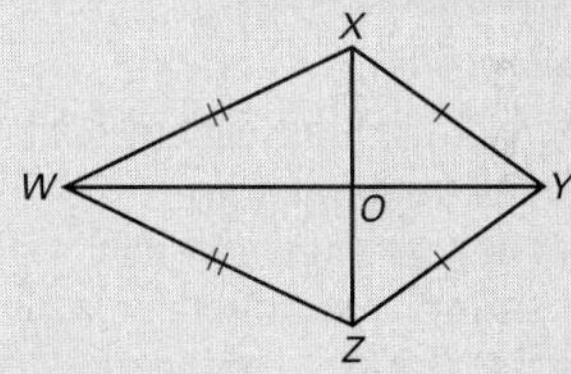

3. If $m\angle XYZ = 80°$ and $m\angle XWZ = 48°$, find $m\angle YZW$. **116°**

4. If $XO = 2$, $OZ = 2$, $YO = 6$, and $OW = 8$, find the lengths of the sides of the kite. $\mathbf{2\sqrt{10}, 2\sqrt{17}}$

Online Quiz

Available at **classzone.com**

Diagnosis/Remediation

- Practice A, B, C in Chapter 8 Resource Book, pp. 63–68
- Study Guide in Chapter 8 Resource Book, pp. 69–70
- Practice Workbook, pp. 157–159
- @HomeTutor

Challenge

Additional challenge is available in the Chapter 8 Resource Book, p. 73.

39–43. See Additional Answers beginning on p. AA1.

1 PLAN AND PREPARE

Warm-Up Exercises

1. Draw a parallelogram.

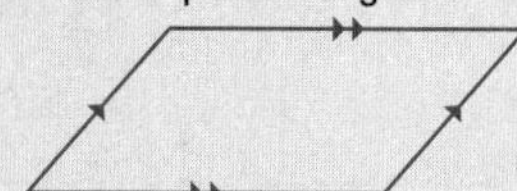

2. What shapes are used to form the surfaces of this object? **two equilateral triangles, three rectangles**

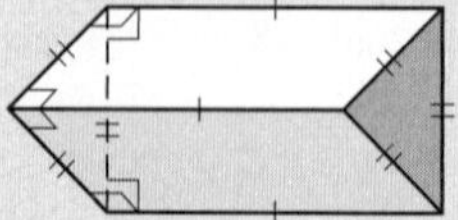

2 FOCUS AND MOTIVATE

Essential Question

Big Idea 2, p. 504

How do you draw three-dimensional figures? **Tell students they will learn how to answer this question by learning how to create an isometric drawing and an orthographic projection.**

3 TEACH

Extra Example 1

Sketch a cube.

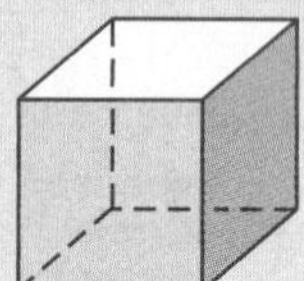

Extension
Use after Lesson 8.5

Draw Three-Dimensional Figures

GOAL Create isometric drawings and orthographic projections of three-dimensional figures.

Key Vocabulary
- **isometric drawing**
- **orthographic projection**

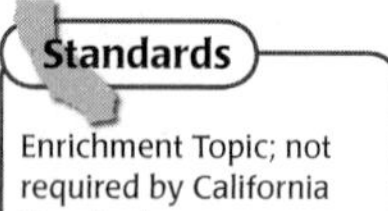

Technical drawings are drawings that show different viewpoints of an object. Engineers and architects create technical drawings of products and buildings before actually constructing the actual objects.

EXAMPLE 1 Draw a rectangular box

Draw a rectangular box.

Solution

STEP 1 **Draw** the bases. They are rectangular, but you need to draw them tilted.

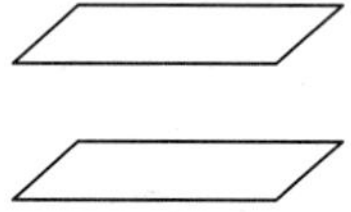

STEP 2 **Connect** the bases using vertical lines.

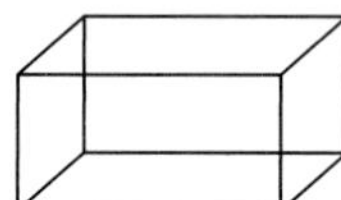

STEP 3 **Erase** parts of the hidden edges so that they are dashed lines.

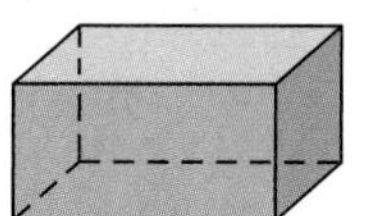

ISOMETRIC DRAWINGS Technical drawings may include **isometric drawings**. These drawings look three-dimensional and can be created on a grid of dots using three axes that intersect to form 120° angles.

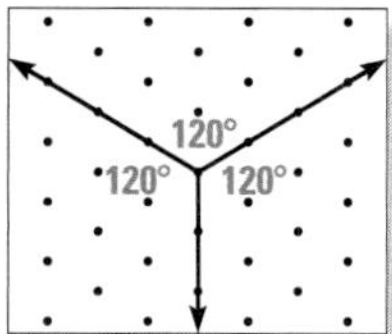

EXAMPLE 2 Create an isometric drawing

Create an isometric drawing of the rectangular box in Example 1.

Solution

STEP 1 **Draw** three axes on isometric dot paper.

STEP 2 **Draw** the box so that the edges of the box are parallel to the three axes.

STEP 3 **Add** depth to the drawing by using different shading for the front, top, and sides.

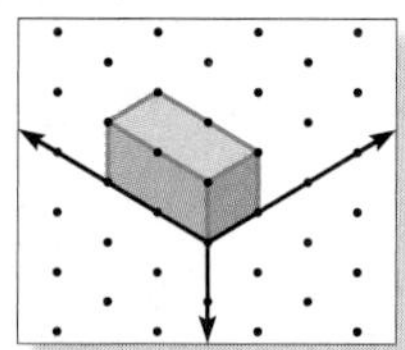

ANOTHER VIEW Technical drawings may also include an *orthographic projection*. An **orthographic projection** is a two-dimensional drawing of the front, top, and side views of an object. The interior lines in these two-dimensional drawings represent edges of the object.

EXAMPLE 3 Create an orthographic projection

Create an orthographic projection of the solid.

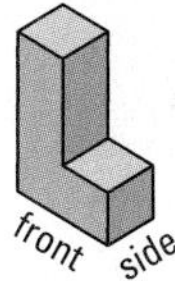

VISUAL REASONING

In this Extension, you can think of the solids as being constructed from cubes. You can assume there are no cubes hidden from view except those needed to support the visible ones.

Solution

On graph paper, draw the front, top, and side views of the solid.

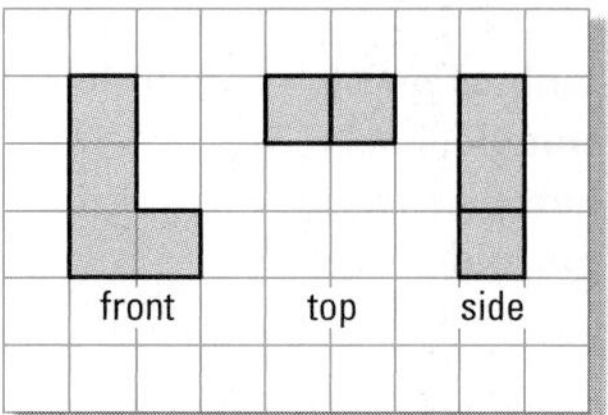

Animated Geometry at classzone.com

PRACTICE

EXAMPLE 1 on p. 550 for Exs. 1–3

DRAWING BOXES **Draw a box with the indicated base.** 1–3. See margin.

1. Equilateral triangle
2. Regular hexagon
3. Square

EXAMPLES 2 and 3 on pp. 550–551 for Exs. 4–12

DRAWING SOLIDS **Create an isometric drawing of the solid. Then create an orthographic projection of the solid.** 4–9. See margin.

4. 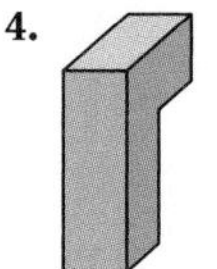

5. 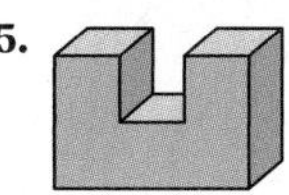

6. 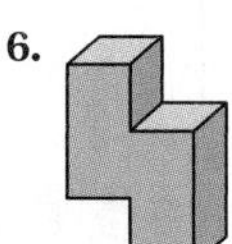

7. 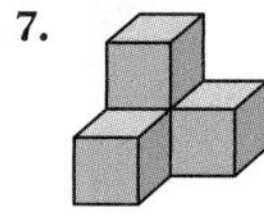

8. 

9. 

CREATING ISOMETRIC DRAWINGS **Create an isometric drawing of the orthographic projection.** 10–12. See margin.

10. 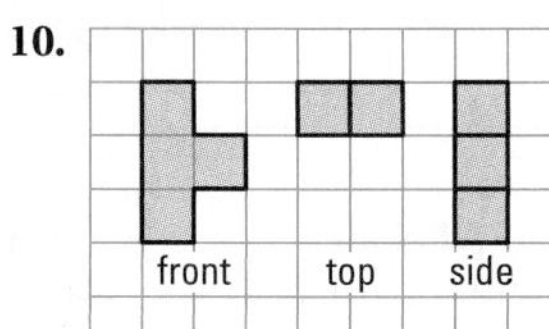

11. 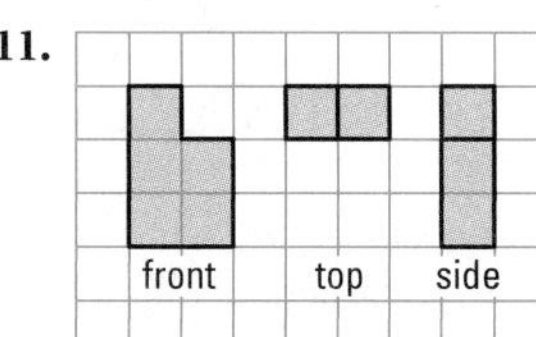

12. 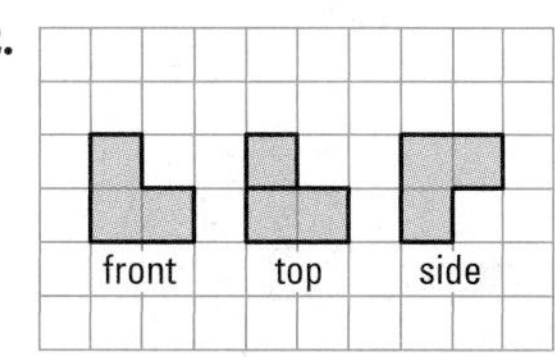

1.

2. 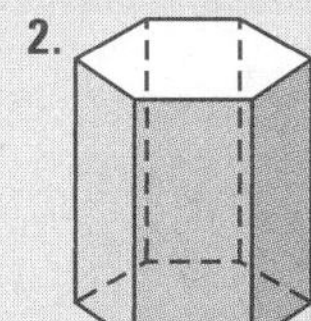

3. 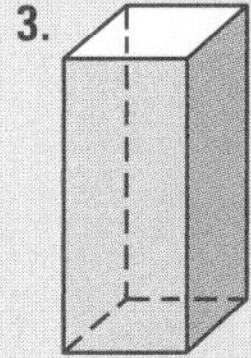

4–12. See Additional Answers beginning on p. AA1.

Extra Example 2

Create an isometric drawing of a cube.

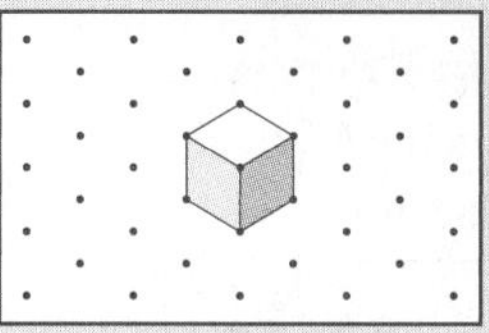

Extra Example 3

Create an orthographic projection of this solid.

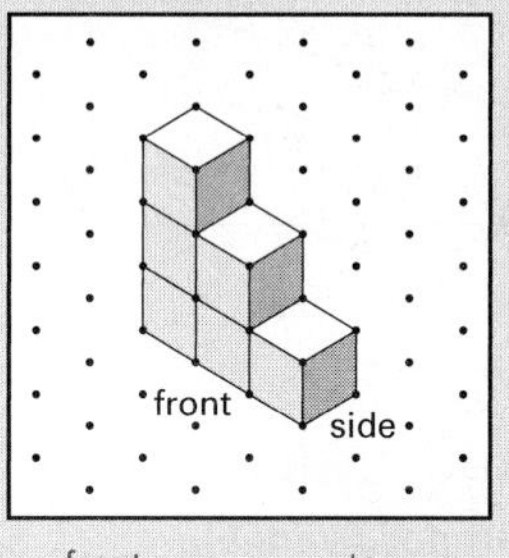

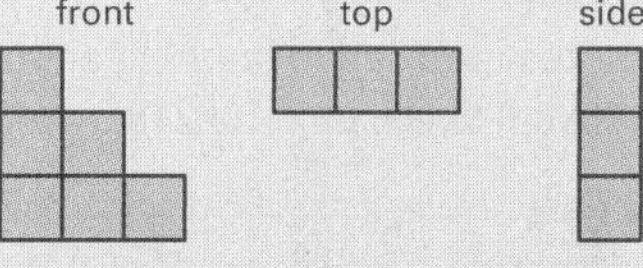

An **Animated Geometry** activity is available on-line for **Example 3**. This activity is also available on the **Power Presentations CD-ROM**.

Closing the Lesson

Have students summarize the major points of the lesson and answer the Essential Question: How do you draw three-dimensional figures?

- **Technical drawings are drawings that show different views of an object.**

A three-dimensional figure can be drawn by sketching it, making an isometric drawing on a dot grid, or by drawing front, top, and side views of an object for an orthographic projection.

4 PRACTICE AND APPLY

Avoiding Common Errors

Exercises 1–3 Students may forget to make hidden edges dashed. Help them identify these edges so they can correct their work.

1 PLAN AND PREPARE

Warm-Up Exercises

Transparency Available

Find the value of *x*.

1. 65
2. 120
3. 70

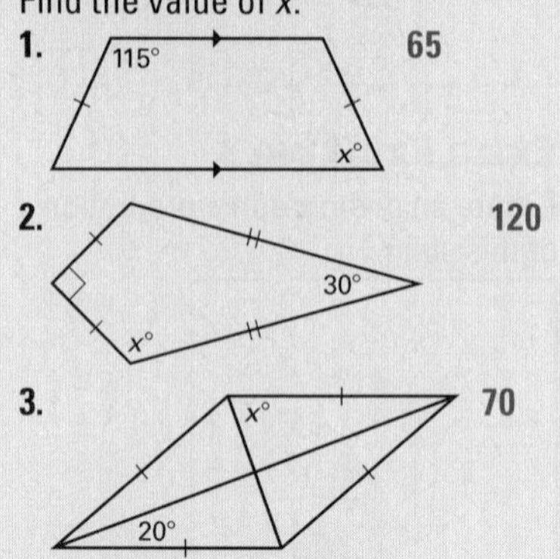

Notetaking Guide

Transparency Available

Promotes interactive learning and notetaking skills, pp. 218–219.

Pacing

Basic: 1 day
Average: 1 day
Advanced: 1 day
Block: 0.5 block with 8.5
- See *Teaching Guide/Lesson Plan.*

2 FOCUS AND MOTIVATE

Essential Question

Big Idea 3, p. 504

How can you identify special quadrilaterals? **Tell students they will learn how to answer this question by using the quadrilateral chart.**

8.6 Identify Special Quadrilaterals

Before You identified polygons.
Now You will identify special quadrilaterals.
Why? So you can describe part of a pyramid, as in Ex. 36.

Key Vocabulary
- **parallelogram,** *p. 515*
- **rhombus,** *p. 533*
- **rectangle,** *p. 533*
- **square,** *p. 533*
- **trapezoid,** *p. 542*
- **kite,** *p. 545*

Standards

7.0 Students prove and **use theorems involving the properties of parallel lines cut by a transversal, the properties of quadrilaterals,** and the properties of circles.

12.0 Students find and use measures of sides and of interior and exterior **angles of triangles and polygons to classify figures** and solve problems.

The diagram below shows relationships among the special quadrilaterals you have studied in Chapter 8. Each shape in the diagram has the properties of the shapes linked above it. For example, a rhombus has the properties of a parallelogram and a quadrilateral.

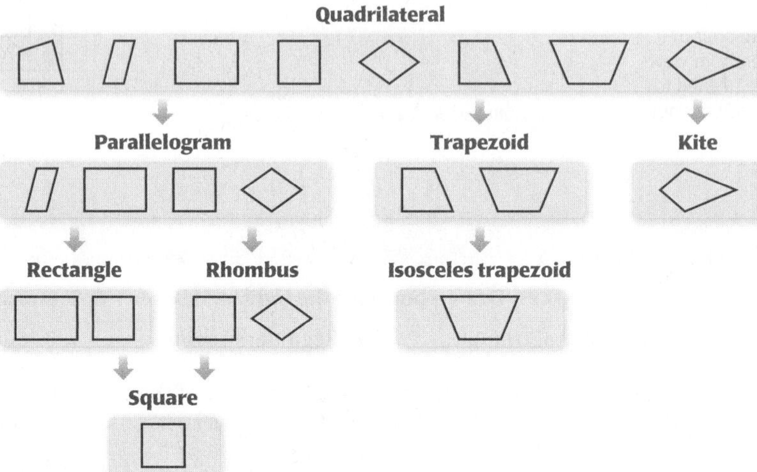

EXAMPLE 1 Identify quadrilaterals

Quadrilateral *ABCD* has at least one pair of opposite angles congruent. What types of quadrilaterals meet this condition?

Solution

There are many possibilities.

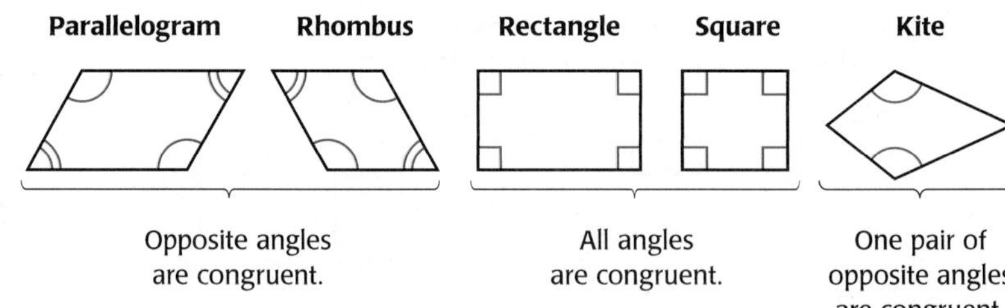

Resource Planning Guide

Chapter Resource Book
- Teaching Guide/Lesson Plan (pp. 74–75)
- Activity Master (p. 76)
- Practice levels A, B, C (pp. 77–82)
- Study Guide (pp. 83–84)
- Catch-up for Absent Students (p. 85)
- Problem Solving Workshop (p. 86)
- Challenge (p. 87)

Workbooks
- Notetaking Guide (pp. 218–219)
- Practice Workbook (pp. 160–162)

Teaching Options
- **Power Presentations CD-ROM** provides dynamic electronic teaching resources for the classroom.
- **Activity Generator CD-ROM** provides editable activities for all ability levels.

Interactive Technology
- Easy Planner
- Power Presentations CD-ROM
- Activity Generator CD-ROM
- Animated Geometry
- Test Generator CD-ROM
- Online Quiz
- eWorkbook
- eEdition
- @HomeTutor

Resources for English Learners
- Quick Reference for English Learners
- Spanish Study Guide
- Multi-Language Visual Glossary
- Student Resources in Spanish

See also the *Geometry Toolkit* for more strategies for meeting individual needs.

EXAMPLE 2 Standardized Test Practice

AVOID ERRORS
In Example 2, *ABCD* is shaped like a square. But you must rely only on marked information when you interpret a diagram.

What is the most specific name for quadrilateral *ABCD*?

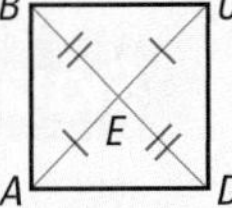

Ⓐ Parallelogram Ⓑ Rhombus

Ⓒ Square Ⓓ Rectangle

Solution

The diagram shows $\overline{AE} \cong \overline{CE}$ and $\overline{BE} \cong \overline{DE}$. So, the diagonals bisect each other. By Theorem 8.10, *ABCD* is a parallelogram.

Rectangles, rhombuses and squares are also parallelograms. However, there is no information given about the side lengths or angle measures of *ABCD*. So, you cannot determine whether it is a rectangle, a rhombus, or a square.

▶ The correct answer is A. Ⓐ Ⓑ Ⓒ Ⓓ

EXAMPLE 3 Identify a quadrilateral

Is enough information given in the diagram to show that quadrilateral *PQRS* is an isosceles trapezoid? Explain.

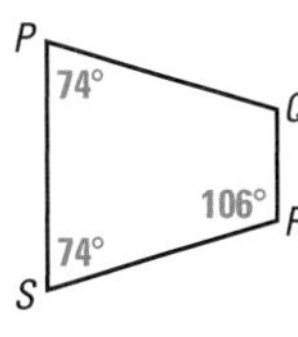

Solution

STEP 1 **Show** that *PQRS* is a trapezoid. $\angle R$ and $\angle S$ are supplementary, but $\angle P$ and $\angle S$ are not. So, $\overline{PS} \parallel \overline{QR}$, but $\overline{PQ}$ is not parallel to $\overline{SR}$. By definition, *PQRS* is a trapezoid.

STEP 2 **Show** that trapezoid *PQRS* is isosceles. $\angle P$ and $\angle S$ are a pair of congruent base angles. So, *PQRS* is an isosceles trapezoid by Theorem 8.15.

▶ Yes, the diagram is sufficient to show that *PQRS* is an isosceles trapezoid.

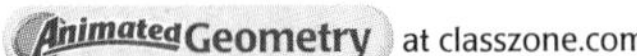

at classzone.com

✓ **GUIDED PRACTICE** for Examples 1, 2, and 3

1. Quadrilateral *DEFG* has at least one pair of opposite sides congruent. What types of quadrilaterals meet this condition?
   parallelogram, rectangle, square, rhombus, trapezoid

Give the most specific name for the quadrilateral. *Explain* your reasoning.

2. (Quadrilateral *RSTU* with side labels 50, 50, 51, 51)

3. 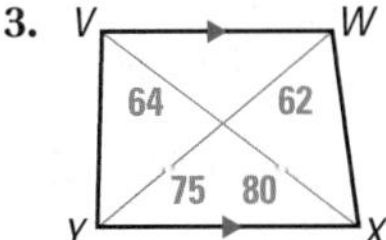

4. 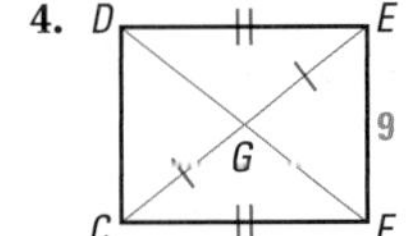

5. **ERROR ANALYSIS** A student knows the following information about quadrilateral *MNPQ*: $\overline{MN} \parallel \overline{PQ}$, $\overline{MP} \cong \overline{NQ}$, and $\angle P \cong \angle Q$. The student concludes that *MNPQ* is an isosceles trapezoid. *Explain* why the student cannot make this conclusion. **It's possible that *MNPQ* could be a rectangle or a square since you don't know the relationship between $\overline{MQ}$ and $\overline{NP}$.**

2. Kite; there are two pair of consecutive congruent sides.

3. Trapezoid; there is only one pair of parallel sides, and because the diagonals do not bisect each other, it is not a parallelogram.

4. Quadrilateral; there is not enough information to be more specific.

Motivating the Lesson

Have students think of quadrilaterals they have seen in tile patterns. Tell them that in this lesson they will learn to classify these shapes.

Extra Example 1

STUV has at least one pair of consecutive sides congruent. What types of quadrilaterals meet this condition? **rhombus, square, kite**

Extra Example 2

What is the most specific name for quadrilateral *WXYZ*? **D**

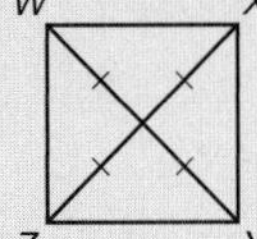

Ⓐ parallelogram

Ⓑ rhombus

Ⓒ square

Ⓓ rectangle

Extra Example 3

Is enough information given in the diagram to show that quadrilateral *ABCD* is a square? Explain.

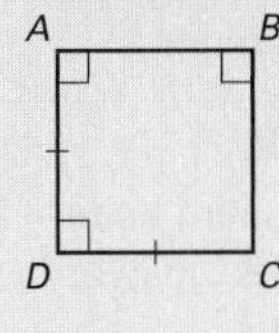

Yes; 3 rt. ∠s are shown, so $m\angle C = 90°$ and *ABCD* is a rect. There is a pair of consec. ≅ sides, so *ABCD* is a square.

Animated Geometry
classzone.com

An **Animated Geometry** activity is available on-line for **Example 3**. This activity is also available on the **Power Presentations CD-ROM**.

Closing the Lesson

Have students summarize the major points of the lesson and answer the Essential Question: How can you identify special quadrilaterals?

- **Each quad. has the properties of the shapes above it in the chart.**

You use the properties of the figure and those above it in the chart.

Differentiated Instruction

Visual Learners For **Guided Practice Exercise 1**, have students draw a visual representation of each quadrilateral that meets the condition of having at least one pair of opposite sides congruent. Remind students to clearly mark the opposite sides that are congruent. Have them identify which theorem or definition states that the quadrilateral meets the condition.

See also the *Geometry Toolkit* for more strategies.

4 PRACTICE AND APPLY

Assignment Guide

Answer Transparencies available for all exercises

Basic:
Day 1: pp. 554–557
Exs. 1–15, 17–19, 21, 22, 33–38, 43–49 odd

Average:
Day 1: pp. 554–557
Exs. 1–13, 15–17, 19, 20, 23–28, 35–40, 43, 45, 48

Advanced:
Day 1: pp. 554–557
Exs. 1–11, 13, 16, 17, 20, 23–32*, 36–42*, 44, 46, 50

Block:
pp. 554–557
Exs. 1–13, 15–17, 19, 20, 23–28, 35–40, 43, 45, 48 (with 8.5)

Differentiated Instruction

See *Geometry Best Practices Toolkit* for suggestions on addressing the needs of a diverse classroom.

Homework Check

For a quick check of student understanding of key concepts, go over the following exercises:

Basic: 4, 14, 18, 34, 36
Average: 6, 16, 19, 23, 37
Advanced: 10, 17, 20, 26, 38

Extra Practice

- Student Edition, p. 911
- Chapter 8 Resource Book: Practice levels A, B, C, pp. 77–82

Practice Worksheet

An easily-readable reduced practice page (with answers) for this lesson can be found on p. 504E.

8.6 EXERCISES

HOMEWORK KEY ○ = **WORKED-OUT SOLUTIONS** on p. WS10 for Exs. 3, 15, and 33
★ = **STANDARDIZED TEST PRACTICE** Exs. 2, 13, 37, and 38

SKILL PRACTICE

A

1. **VOCABULARY** Copy and complete: A quadrilateral that has exactly one pair of parallel sides and diagonals that are congruent is a(n) __?__.
isosceles trapezoid

2. ★ **WRITING** *Describe* three methods you could use to prove that a parallelogram is a rhombus. **Prove its diagonals are perpendicular, each diagonal bisects a pair of opposite angles, or it has four congruent sides.**

EXAMPLE 1 on p. 552 for Exs. 3–12

PROPERTIES OF QUADRILATERALS **Copy the chart. Put an X in the box if the shape *always* has the given property.**

	Property	▱	Rectangle	Rhombus	Square	Kite	Trapezoid
3.	All sides are ≅.	?	?	? x	? x	?	?
4.	Both pairs of opp. sides are ≅.	? x	? x	? x	? x	?	?
5.	Both pairs of opp. sides are ∥.	? x	? x	? x	? x	?	?
6.	Exactly 1 pair of opp. sides are ∥.	?	?	?	?	?	? x
7.	All ∠s are ≅.	?	? x	?	? x	?	?
8.	Exactly 1 pair of opp. ∠s are ≅.	?	?	?	?	? x	?
9.	Diagonals are ⊥.	?	?	? x	? x	? x	?
10.	Diagonals are ≅.	?	? x	?	? x	?	?
11.	Diagonals bisect each other.	? x	? x	? x	? x	?	?

12. **ERROR ANALYSIS** *Describe* and correct the error in classifying the quadrilateral.

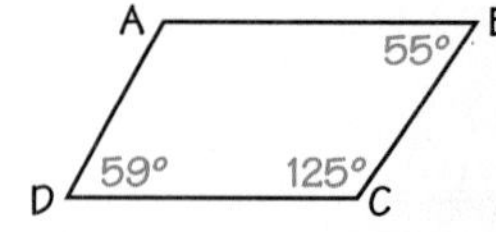

∠B and ∠C are supplements, so $\overline{AB} \parallel \overline{CD}$. So, ABCD is a parallelogram.

12. The fact that ∠*B* and ∠*C* are supplementary does not guarantee *ABCD* is a parallelogram. ∠*D* and ∠*C* are not supplementary, so $\overline{AD}$ is not parallel to $\overline{BC}$. So, *ABCD* is not a quadrilateral.

EXAMPLE 2 on p. 553 for Exs. 13–17

13. ★ **MULTIPLE CHOICE** What is the most specific name for the quadrilateral shown at the right? **A**

Ⓐ Rectangle Ⓑ Parallelogram
Ⓒ Trapezoid Ⓓ Isosceles trapezoid

CLASSIFYING QUADRILATERALS **Give the most specific name for the quadrilateral. *Explain.***

14.

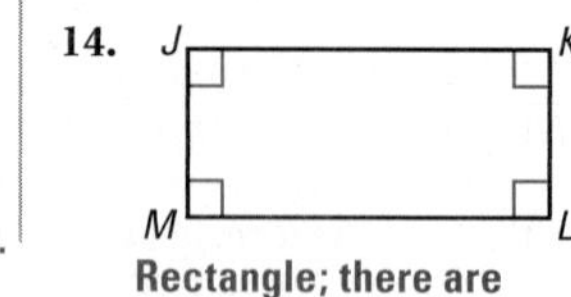

Rectangle; there are four right angles.

15. Q P 111° S R

Trapezoid; there is one pair of parallel sides.

16.

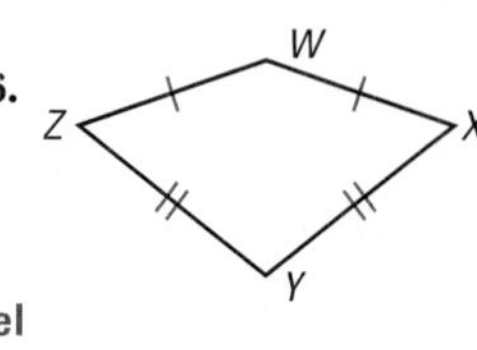

16. Kite; there are two pair of consecutive congruent sides.

17. **DRAWING** Draw a quadrilateral with congruent diagonals and exactly one pair of congruent sides. What is the most specific name for this quadrilateral? **See margin for art; isosceles trapezoid.**

IDENTIFYING QUADRILATERALS Tell whether enough information is given in the diagram to classify the quadrilateral by the indicated name. *Explain.*

EXAMPLE 3
on p. 553
for Exs. 18–20

18. Rhombus

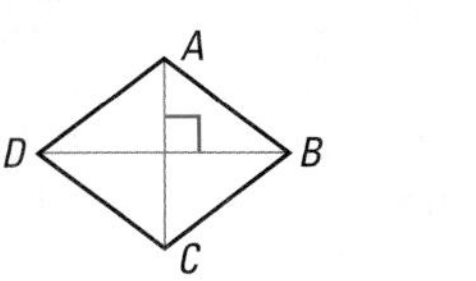

No; it could be a kite.

19. Isosceles trapezoid

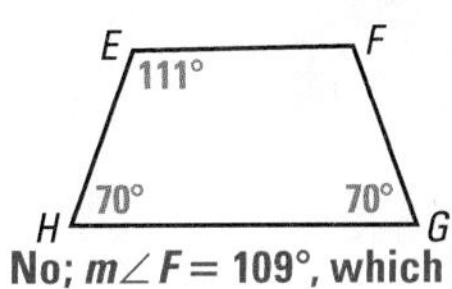

No; $m\angle F = 109°$, which is not equal to $m\angle E$.

20. Square

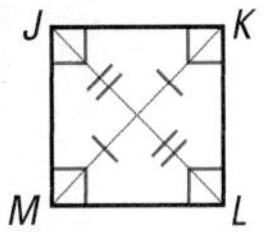

No; it could be a rectangle.

COORDINATE PLANE Points *P*, *Q*, *R*, and *S* are the vertices of a quadrilateral. Give the most specific name for *PQRS*. *Justify* your answer.

21. $P(1, 0), Q(1, 2), R(6, 5), S(3, 0)$

22. $P(2, 1), Q(6, 1), R(5, 8), S(3, 8)$

23. $P(2, 7), Q(6, 9), R(9, 3), S(5, 1)$

24. $P(1, 7), Q(5, 8), R(6, 2), S(2, 1)$

25. **TECHNOLOGY** Use geometry drawing software to draw points *A*, *B*, *C*, and segments AC and BC. Draw a circle with center *A* and radius AC. Draw a circle with center *B* and radius BC. Label the other intersection of the circles *D*. Draw $\overline{BD}$ and $\overline{AD}$.

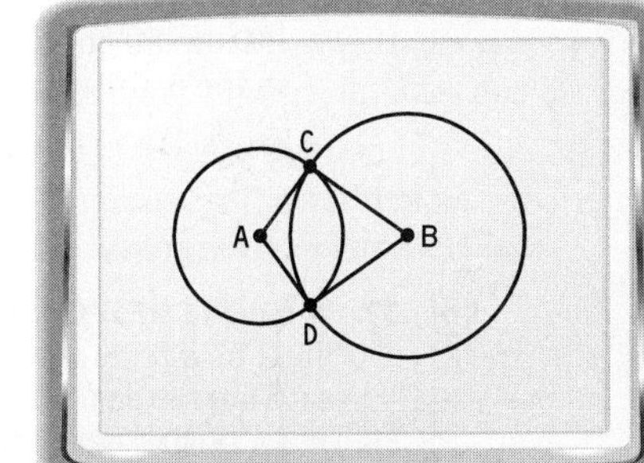

a. Drag point *A*, *B*, *C*, or *D* to change the shape of *ABCD*. What types of quadrilaterals can be formed? **rhombus, square, kite**

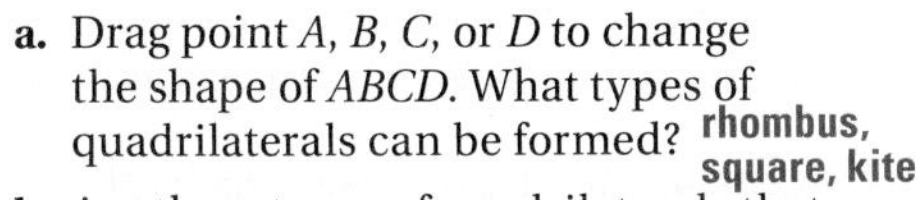

b. Are there types of quadrilaterals that cannot be formed? *Explain.* **Parallelogram, rectangle, trapezoid; two consecutive pairs of sides are always congruent and one pair of opposite angles remain congruent.**

DEVELOPING PROOF Which pairs of segments or angles must be congruent so that you can prove that *ABCD* is the indicated quadrilateral? *Explain.* There may be more than one right answer. **26–28. Sample answers are given.**

26. Square

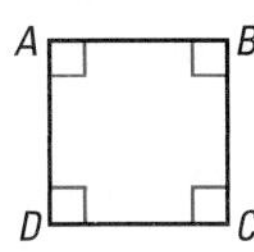

27. Isosceles trapezoid

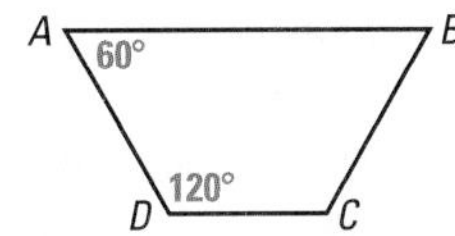

28. Parallelogram

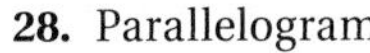

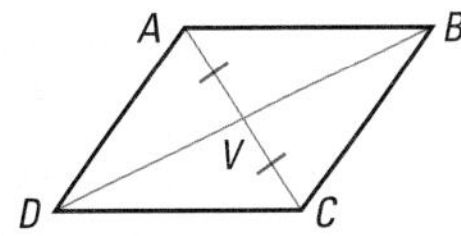

TRAPEZOIDS In Exercises 29–31, determine whether there is enough information to prove that *JKLM* is an isosceles trapezoid. *Explain.*

29. **GIVEN** ▶ $\overline{JK} \parallel \overline{LM}$, $\angle JKL \cong \angle KJM$ **See margin.**

30. **GIVEN** ▶ $\overline{JK} \parallel \overline{LM}$, $\angle JML \cong \angle KLM$, $m\angle KLM \neq 90°$

31. **GIVEN** ▶ $\overline{JL} \cong \overline{KM}$, $\overline{JK} \parallel \overline{LM}$, $JK > LM$
Yes; *JKLM* has one pair of non-congruent parallel sides with congruent diagonals.

32. **CHALLENGE** Draw a rectangle and bisect its angles. What type of quadrilateral is formed by the intersecting bisectors? *Justify* your answer. **See margin.**

1. Kite; it has two pair of consecutive congruent sides.

2. Isosceles trapezoid; it has one pair of parallel sides and its diagonals are congruent

3. Rectangle; opposite sides are parallel with four right angles.

4. Parallelogram; opposite sides are parallel but all four sides are not congruent and there is no right angle.

26. $\overline{AB} \cong \overline{BC}$; all 4 sides are congruent and there are 4 right angles.

27. $m\angle B = 60°$ or $m\angle C = 120°$; then $\overline{AB} \parallel \overline{DC}$ and the base angles would be congruent.

28. $\overline{DV} \cong \overline{BV}$; then the diagonals bisect each other.

30. Yes; *JKLM* has one pair of congruent base angles and only one pair of parallel sides.

Teaching Strategy

Exercises 3–11 Have students work in groups to complete the chart. Have groups present their results to the class. Discuss the results.

Avoiding Common Errors

Exercises 18–20 Students may answer on the basis of the appearance of the diagram. You may need to review what it is and is not permissible to assume from a diagram.

17.

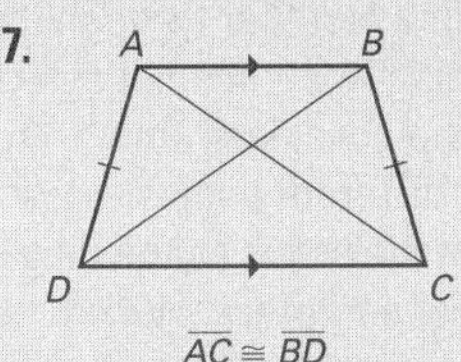

$\overline{AC} \cong \overline{BD}$

29. No; if $m\angle JKL = m\angle KJM = 90°$, *JKLM* would be a rectangle.

32.

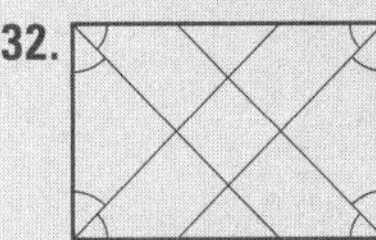

Square; when the rectangle's angles are bisected, the resulting angle measures are 45°. The triangles created all have angle measures 45°-45°-90° and are similar. So the quadrilateral has four right angles since each is one of a pair of vertical angles where the other angle is a right angle. Pairs of angle bisectors are parallel since they are perpendicular to the same line (one of the other angle bisectors). Therefore, the quadrilateral is a parallelogram, making its opposite sides congruent. Consecutive sides of the quadrilateral can be shown congruent using congruent triangles and the Subtraction Property of Equality. Therefore, the quadrilateral has four congruent sides and four right angles, which makes it a square.

Internet Reference

Exercise 36 More information about the Pyramid of Kukulcan at Chichen Itza can be found at sacredsites.com/americas/mexico/chichen_itza.html

Study Strategy

Exercise 40 Have students model this situation with thin strips of cardboard of the same length. They can place one strip on top of the other and put a fastener through the two strips, but *not* at the midpoint of the strips. They can easily move the strips to get different angles. Have them think of the strips as the diagonals of the quadrilateral *WXYZ*.

38a.

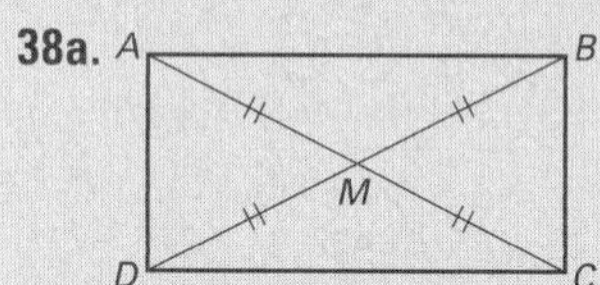

$\overline{AC}$ and $\overline{BD}$ are the diagonals of quadrilateral *ABCD*. Since they are congruent, *ABCD* is either a rectangle or a square; since they are not perpendicular, *ABCD* must be a rectangle.

38b.

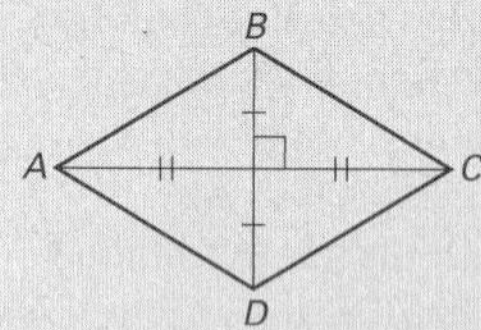

Since $\overline{AC}$ and $\overline{BD}$ are perpendicular, quadrilateral *ABCD* is a rhombus, square, or kite; since they are not congruent, *ABCD* is a rhombus or a kite. However, the diagonals of a kite do not bisect each other, so *ABCD* must be a rhombus.

PROBLEM SOLVING

A **REAL-WORLD OBJECTS** **What type of special quadrilateral is outlined?**

33. trapezoid

(33.)

34.

kite

35.

parallelogram

@HomeTutor for problem solving help at classzone.com

36. PYRAMID Use the photo of the Pyramid of Kukulcan in Mexico.

a. $\overline{EF} \parallel \overline{HG}$, and $\overline{EH}$ and $\overline{FG}$ are not parallel. What shape is this part of the pyramid? **trapezoid**

b. $\overline{AB} \parallel \overline{DC}$, $\overline{AD} \parallel \overline{BC}$, and $\angle A$, $\angle B$, $\angle C$, and $\angle D$ are all congruent to each other. What shape is this part of the pyramid? **rectangle**

@HomeTutor for problem solving help at classzone.com

B **37.** ★ **SHORT RESPONSE** *Explain* why a parallelogram with one right angle must be a rectangle. **Consecutive interior angles are supplementary making each interior angle 90°.**

38. ★ **EXTENDED RESPONSE** Segments *AC* and *BD* bisect each other. **a, b. See margin.**

a. Suppose that $\overline{AC}$ and $\overline{BD}$ are congruent, but not perpendicular. Draw quadrilateral *ABCD* and classify it. *Justify* your answer.

b. Suppose that $\overline{AC}$ and $\overline{BD}$ are perpendicular, but not congruent. Draw quadrilateral *ABCD* and classify it. *Justify* your answer.

39. MULTI-STEP PROBLEM Polygon *QRSTUV* shown at the right is a regular hexagon, and $\overline{QU}$ and $\overline{RT}$ are diagonals. Follow the steps below to classify quadrilateral *QRTU*. *Explain* your reasoning in each step. **a–d. See margin.**

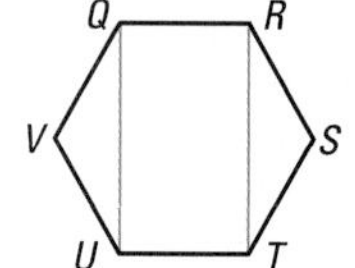

a. Show that $\triangle QVU$ and $\triangle RST$ are congruent isosceles triangles.

b. Show that $\overline{QR} \cong \overline{UT}$ and that $\overline{QU} \cong \overline{RT}$.

c. Show that $\angle UQR \cong \angle QRT \cong \angle RTU \cong \angle TUQ$. Find the measure of each of these angles.

d. Classify quadrilateral *QRTU*.

40. REASONING In quadrilateral *WXYZ*, $\overline{WY}$ and $\overline{XZ}$ intersect each other at point *V*. $\overline{WV} \cong \overline{XV}$ and $\overline{YV} \cong \overline{ZV}$, but $\overline{WY}$ and $\overline{XZ}$ do not bisect each other. Draw $\overline{WY}$, $\overline{XY}$, and *WXYZ*. What special type of quadrilateral is *WXYZ*? Write a plan for a proof of your answer. **See margin for art; isosceles trapezoid; show $\overline{WX} \parallel \overline{ZY}$ by showing $\triangle WVX \sim \triangle YVZ$ which leads to $\angle XWV \cong \angle ZYV$. Now show $\angle ZWX \cong \angle YXW$ using $\triangle ZVW \cong \triangle YVX$ and $\angle XWV \cong \angle WXV$.**

○ = WORKED-OUT SOLUTIONS on p. WS1 ★ = STANDARDIZED TEST PRACTICE

39a. Using the definition of a regular hexagon, $\overline{UV} \cong \overline{VQ} \cong \overline{RS} \cong \overline{ST}$ and $\angle V \cong \angle S$. So $\triangle QVU$ and $\triangle RST$ are isosceles. Using the SAS Congruence Postulate, $\triangle QVU \cong \triangle RST$.

39b. Using the definition of a regular hexagon, $\overline{QR} \cong \overline{UT}$. Using corresponding parts of congruent triangles are congruent, $\overline{QU} \cong \overline{RT}$.

39c. Since $\angle Q \cong \angle R \cong \angle T \cong \angle U$ and $\angle VUQ \cong \angle VQU \cong \angle STR \cong \angle SRT$, you know that $\angle UQR \cong \angle QRT \cong \angle RTU \cong \angle TUQ$ by the Angle Addition Postulate; 90°.

39d. Rectangle; there are 4 right angles and opposite sides are congruent.

40.

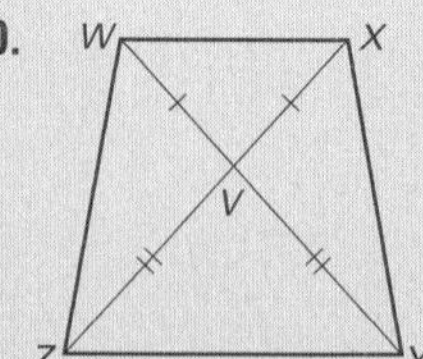

41, 42. See Additional Answers beginning on p. AA1.

C **CHALLENGE What special type of quadrilateral is *EFGH*? Write a paragraph proof to show that your answer is correct.** 41, 42. See margin.

41. GIVEN ▶ *PQRS* is a square. *E, F, G,* and *H* are midpoints of the sides of the square.

PROVE ▶ *EFGH* is a _?_.

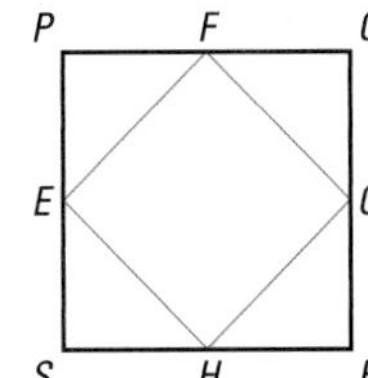

42. GIVEN ▶ In the three-dimensional figure, $\overline{JK} \cong \overline{LM}$; *E, F, G,* and *H* are the midpoints of $\overline{JL}$, $\overline{KL}$, $\overline{KM}$, and $\overline{JM}$.

PROVE ▶ *EFGH* is a _?_.

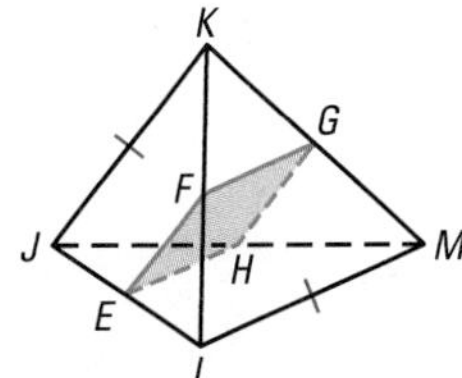

MIXED REVIEW

In Exercises 43 and 44, use the diagram. *(p. 264)*

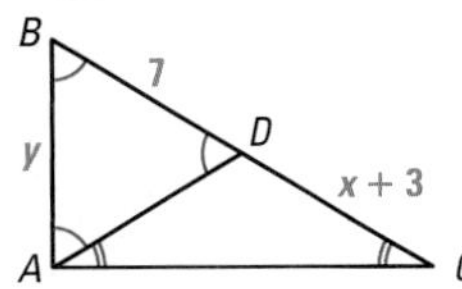

43. Find the values of *x* and *y*. *Explain* your reasoning. See margin.

44. Find $m\angle ADC$, $m\angle DAC$, and $m\angle DCA$. *Explain* your reasoning. See margin.

PREVIEW
Prepare for Lesson 9.1 in Exs. 45–46.

The vertices of quadrilateral *ABCD* are *A*(−2, 1), *B*(2, 5), *C*(3, 2), and *D*(1, −1). Draw *ABCD* in a coordinate plane. Then draw its image after the indicated translation. *(p. 272)* 45, 46. See margin.

45. $(x, y) \to (x + 1, y - 3)$

46. $(x, y) \to (x - 2, y - 2)$

Use the diagram of ▱*WXYZ* to find the indicated length. *(p. 515)*

47. *YZ* 12

48. *WZ* 5

49. *XV* 4

50. *XZ* 8

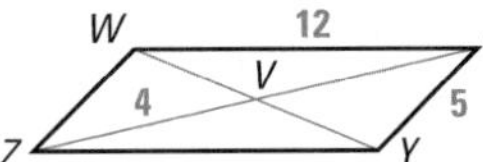

QUIZ for Lessons 8.5–8.6

Find the unknown angle measures. *(p. 542)*

1.

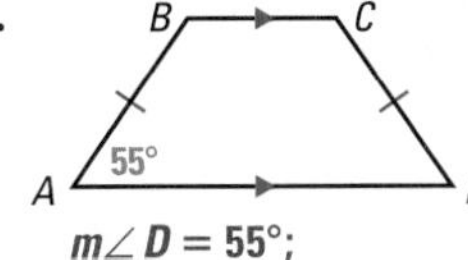

$m\angle D = 55°$;
$m\angle B = m\angle C = 125°$

2.

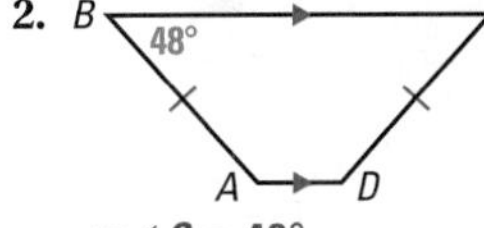

$m\angle C = 48°$,
$m\angle A = m\angle D = 132°$

3.

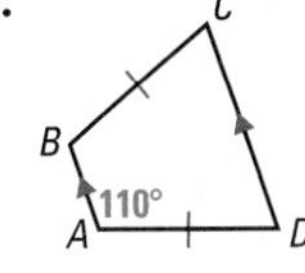

3. $m\angle B = 110°$,
$m\angle C =$
$m\angle D = 70°$

4. The diagonals of quadrilateral *ABCD* are congruent and bisect each other. What types of quadrilaterals match this description? *(p. 552)* rectangle, square

5. In quadrilateral *EFGH*, $\angle E \cong \angle G$, $\angle F \cong \angle H$, and $\overline{EF} \cong \overline{EH}$. What is the most specific name for quadrilateral *EFGH*? *(p. 552)* rhombus

43. 4, 7; since △*ABD* is equilateral, all three sides are congruent and are 7 units long. Since △*ADC* is isosceles, *AD* = 7 = *CD*, thus *x* + 3 = 7 or *x* = 4.

44. 120°, 30°, 30°; since △*ABD* is equiangular, $m\angle BDA = 60°$ making $m\angle ADC = 120°$ by definition of a linear pair. Since $m\angle DAC = m\angle DCA$ and $m\angle ADC = 120°$, by the Triangle Sum Theorem $m\angle DAC = m\angle DCA = 30°$.

45, 46. See Additional Answers beginning on p. AA1.

5 ASSESS AND RETEACH

Daily Homework Quiz

Transparency Available

Write *true* or *false*.

1. The diagonals of a rectangle are perpendicular. **false**

2. The diagonals of a rhombus are always congruent. **false**

3. One pair of opposite angles of a kite are congruent. **true**

4. Give the most specific name for the quadrilateral. Explain.

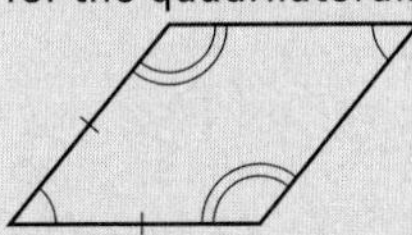

Rhombus; it is a ▱ since two pairs of opp. ∠s are ≅. Since two consec. sides are ≅, all sides are ≅.

5. Points *A*(1, 4), *B*(6, −1), *C*(1, −6), and *D*(−4, −1) are the vertices of a quadrilateral. Give the most specific name for *ABCD*. Explain. **Square; slope of $\overline{AB}$ = slope of $\overline{CD}$ = −1, slope of $\overline{BC}$ = slope of $\overline{AD}$ = 1. Opp. sides are ∥, so *ABCD* is a ▱. Two consec. sides are ⊥ and *AB* = *BC* = $5\sqrt{2}$, so *ABCD* is a square.**

Online Quiz

Available at **classzone.com**

Diagnosis/Remediation

- Practice A, B, C in Chapter 8 Resource Book, pp. 77–82
- Study Guide in Chapter 8 Resource Book, pp. 83–84
- Practice Workbook, pp. 160–162
- @HomeTutor

Challenge

Additional challenge is available in the Chapter 8 Resource Book, p. 87.

Quiz

An easily-readable reduced copy of the quiz (with answers) on Lessons 8.5–8.6 from the Assessment Book can be found on p. 504F.

Lessons 8.4–8.6

1. **MULTI-STEP PROBLEM** In the photograph shown below, quadrilateral *ABCD* represents the front view of the roof.

   a. *Explain* how you know that the shape of the roof is a trapezoid. **ABCD has one pair of parallel sides.**

   b. Do you have enough information to determine that the roof is an isosceles trapezoid? *Explain* your reasoning. **Yes; the base angles are congruent.**

2. **SHORT RESPONSE** Is enough information given in the diagram to show that quadrilateral *JKLM* is a square? *Explain* your reasoning. **Yes; since the four triangles are congruent right triangles you know that $\overline{JK} \cong \overline{KL} \cong \overline{LM} \cong \overline{MJ}$ with $\angle J \cong \angle K \cong \angle L \cong \angle M$ each measuring 90°.**

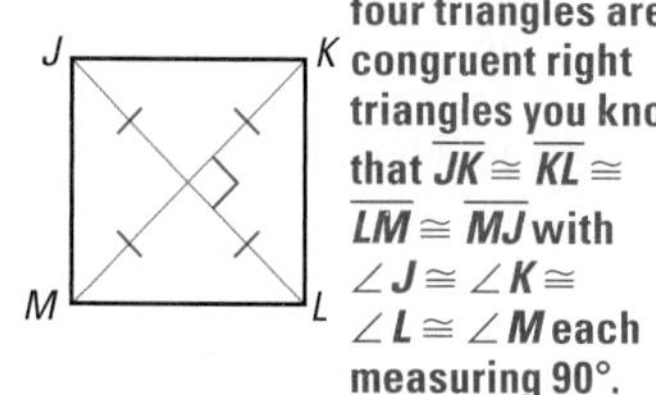

3. **EXTENDED RESPONSE** In the photograph, quadrilateral *QRST* is a kite.

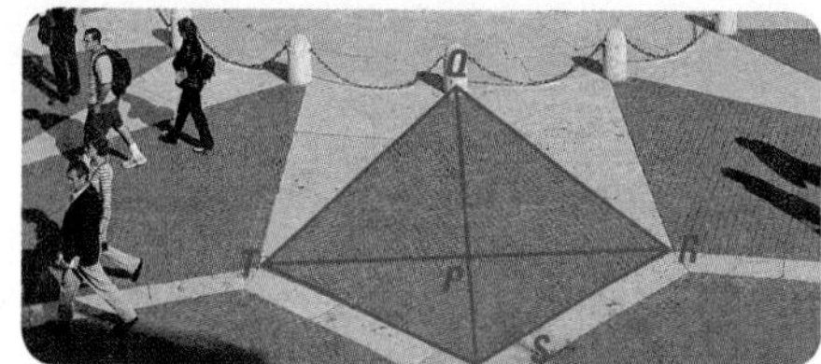

a, b. See margin.

   a. If $m\angle TQR = 102°$ and $m\angle RST = 125°$, find $m\angle QTS$. *Explain* your reasoning.

   b. If $QS = 11$ ft, $TR = 14$ ft, and $\overline{TP} \cong \overline{QP} \cong \overline{RP}$, find *QR*, *RS*, *ST*, and *TQ*. Round your answers to the nearest foot. Show your work.

4. **GRIDDED ANSWER** The top of the table shown is shaped like an isosceles trapezoid. In *ABCD*, $AB = 48$ inches, $BC = 19$ inches, $CD = 24$ inches, and $DA = 19$ inches. Find the length (in inches) of the midsegment of *ABCD*. **36**

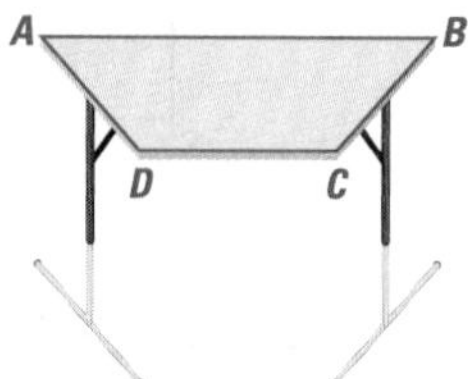

5. **SHORT RESPONSE** Rhombus *PQRS* is similar to rhombus *VWXY*. In the diagram below, $QS = 32$, $QR = 20$, and $WZ = 20$. Find *WX*. *Explain* your reasoning. **See margin.**

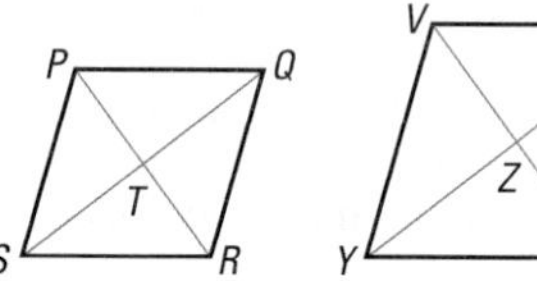

6. **OPEN-ENDED** In quadrilateral *MNPQ*, $\overline{MP} \cong \overline{NQ}$. **a, b. See margin.**

   a. What types of quadrilaterals could *MNPQ* be? Use the most specific names. *Explain*.

   b. For each of your answers in part (a), tell what additional information would allow you to conclude that *MNPQ* is that type of quadrilateral. *Explain* your reasoning. (There may be more than one correct answer.)

7. **EXTENDED RESPONSE** Three of the vertices of quadrilateral *EFGH* are $E(0, 4)$, $F(2, 2)$, and $G(4, 4)$. **a, b. See margin.**

   a. Suppose that *EFGH* is a rhombus. Find the coordinates of vertex *H*. *Explain* why there is only one possible location for *H*.

   b. Suppose that *EFGH* is a convex kite. Show that there is more than one possible set of coordinates for vertex *H*. *Describe* what all the possible sets of coordinates have in common.

3a. 66.5°; in a kite one pair of opposite angles have the same measure, therefore $m\angle QTS = m\angle QRS$. Now $2m\angle QTS = 360° - (120° + 105°)$ making $m\angle QTS = 66.5°$.

3b. $7\sqrt{2}$ ft, $\sqrt{65}$ ft, $\sqrt{65}$ ft, $7\sqrt{2}$ ft; since $TR = TP + RP = 14$ and $TP = QP + RP$, this makes each of these segments 7 feet long and $PS = 4$ feet. Use the Pythagorean Theorem to find the lengths of the sides of the kite.

5. 25; since the rhombuses are similar, corresponding parts are proportional. Solve $\frac{32}{40} = \frac{20}{x}$ to find *WX*.

6a. Rectangle, square, isosceles trapezoid; the diagonals of these three quadrilaterals are congruent.

6b. For a rectangle you need to know that opposite sides are congruent. For a square you need to know that opposite sides are congruent and that consecutive sides are congruent. For an isosceles trapezoid you need to know that only one pair of opposite sides are parallel.

7a. $H(2, 6)$; if *H* is at $(2, 6)$ $HG = GF = FE = EH$, $\overline{HG} \parallel \overline{FE}$, and $\overline{EH} \parallel \overline{FG}$. If *H* is at $(-2, 2)$, both pairs of opposite sides are parallel and congruent, but the quadrilateral is *EGFH*, not *EFGH*.

7b. *Sample answer:* The coordinates of *H* could be $(2, 10)$ or $(2, 14)$. Both points allow *EFGH* to meet the definition of a kite. The points lie on the line with equation $x = 2$ excluding $(2, 4)$ and $(2, 2)$.

CHAPTER SUMMARY

BIG IDEAS

For Your Notebook

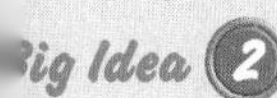

Using Angle Relationships in Polygons

You can use theorems about the interior and exterior angles of convex polygons to solve problems.

Polygon Interior Angles Theorem	Polygon Exterior Angles Theorem
The sum of the interior angle measures of a convex n-gon is $(n - 2) \cdot 180°$.	The sum of the exterior angle measures of a convex n-gon is $360°$.

Big Idea 2

Using Properties of Parallelograms

By definition, a parallelogram is a quadrilateral with both pairs of opposite sides parallel. Other properties of parallelograms:

- Opposite sides are congruent.
- Opposite angles are congruent.
- Diagonals bisect each other.
- Consecutive angles are supplementary.

Ways to show that a quadrilateral is a parallelogram:

- Show both pairs of opposite sides are parallel.
- Show both pairs of opposite sides or opposite angles are congruent.
- Show one pair of opposite sides are congruent and parallel.
- Show the diagonals bisect each other.

Classifying Quadrilaterals by Their Properties

Special quadrilaterals can be classified by their properties. In a parallelogram, both pairs of opposite sides are parallel. In a trapezoid, only one pair of sides are parallel. A kite has two pairs of consecutive congruent sides, but opposite sides are not congruent.

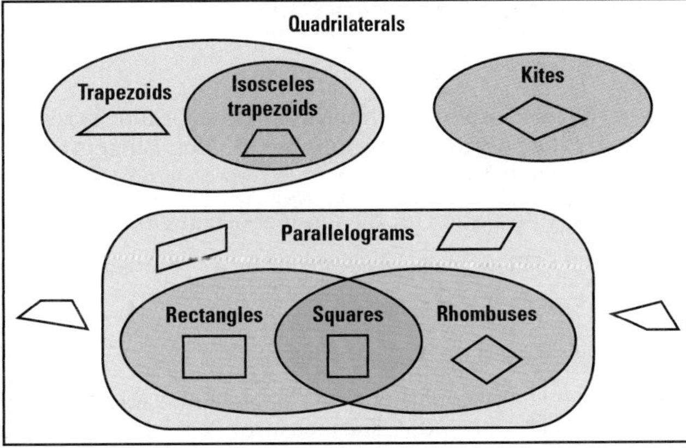

Additional Resources

The following resources are available to help review the materials in this chapter.

Chapter 8 Resource Book

- Chapter Review Games and Activities, p. 88
- Cumulative Practice, Chs. 1–8, pp. 91–92

Student Resources in Spanish

eWorkbook

@HomeTutor

Vocabulary Practice

Vocabulary practice is available at **classzone.com**

Extra Example 8.1

The sum of the measures of the interior angles of a convex regular polygon is 1260°. Classify the polygon by the number of sides. What is the measure of each interior angle? **nonagon, 140°**

8 CHAPTER REVIEW

@HomeTutor
classzone.com
• Multi-Language Glossary
• Vocabulary practice

REVIEW KEY VOCABULARY

For a list of postulates and theorems, see pp. 926–931.

- diagonal, *p. 507*
- parallelogram, *p. 515*
- rhombus, *p. 533*
- rectangle, *p. 533*
- square, *p. 533*
- trapezoid, *p. 542*
- bases of a trapezoid, *p. 542*
- base angles of a trapezoid, *p. 542*
- legs of a trapezoid, *p. 542*
- isosceles trapezoid, *p. 543*
- midsegment of a trapezoid, *p. 544*
- kite, *p. 545*

VOCABULARY EXERCISES

In Exercises 1 and 2, copy and complete the statement.

1. The _?_ of a trapezoid is parallel to the bases. **midsegment**
2. A(n) _?_ of a polygon is a segment whose endpoints are nonconsecutive vertices. **diagonal**
3. WRITING *Describe* the different ways you can show that a trapezoid is an isosceles trapezoid. **Prove the trapezoid has a pair of congruent base angles or the diagonals are congruent.**

In Exercises 4–6, match the figure with the most specific name.

4. 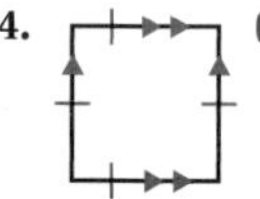 C

5. 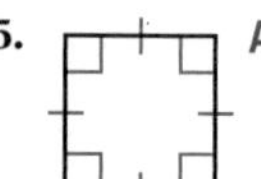 A

6. 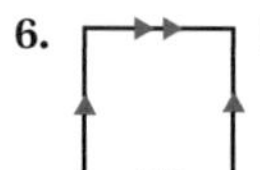 B

A. Square **B.** Parallelogram **C.** Rhombus

REVIEW EXAMPLES AND EXERCISES

Use the review examples and exercises below to check your understanding of the concepts you have learned in each lesson of Chapter 8.

8.1 Find Angle Measures in Polygons *pp. 507–513*

EXAMPLE

The sum of the measures of the interior angles of a convex regular polygon is 1080°. Classify the polygon by the number of sides. What is the measure of each interior angle?

Write and solve an equation for the number of sides n.

$(n - 2) \cdot 180° = 1080°$ **Polygon Interior Angles Theorem**

$n = 8$ **Solve for n.**

The polygon has 8 sides, so it is an octagon.

A regular octagon has 8 congruent interior angles, so divide to find the measure of each angle: $1080° \div 8 = 135°$. The measure of each interior angle is 135°.

@HomeTutor
classzone.com
Chapter Review Practice

EXERCISES

EXAMPLES 2, 3, 4, and 5 on pp. 508–510 for Exs. 7–11

7. The sum of the measures of the interior angles of a convex regular polygon is 3960°. Classify the polygon by the number of sides. What is the measure of each interior angle? **24-gon; 165°**

In Exercises 8–10, find the value of *x*.

8. **133**

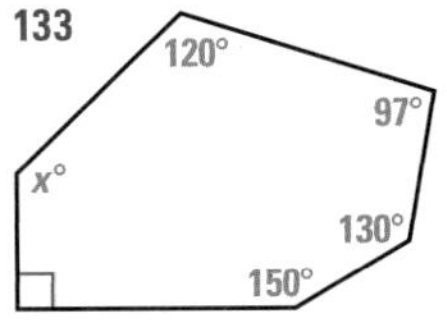

9. **82**

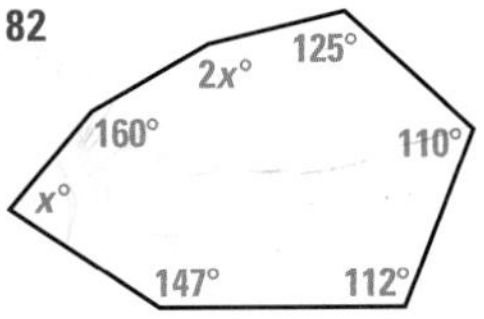

10. **20**

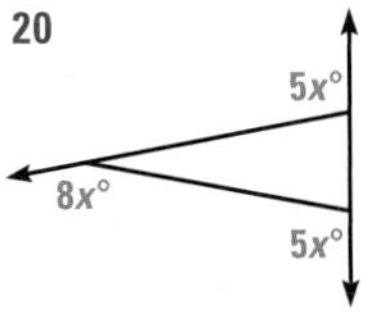

11. In a regular nonagon, the exterior angles are all congruent. What is the measure of one of the exterior angles? *Explain.* **40°; the sum of the measures of the exterior angles is always 360°, and there are nine congruent external angles in a nonagon.**

8.2 Use Properties of Parallelograms *pp. 515–521*

EXAMPLE

Quadrilateral *WXYZ* is a parallelogram. Find the values of *x* and *y*.

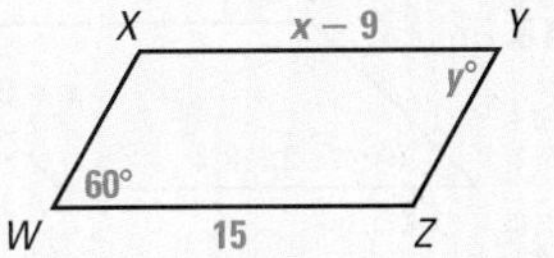

To find the value of *x*, apply Theorem 8.3.

$XY = WZ$ **Opposite sides of a ▱ are ≅.**

$x - 9 = 15$ **Substitute.**

$x = 24$ **Add 9 to each side.**

By Theorem 8.4, $\angle W \cong \angle Y$, or $m\angle W = m\angle Y$. So, $y = 60$.

EXERCISES

EXAMPLES 1, 2, and 3 on pp. 515, 517 for Exs. 12–17

Find the value of each variable in the parallelogram.

12.

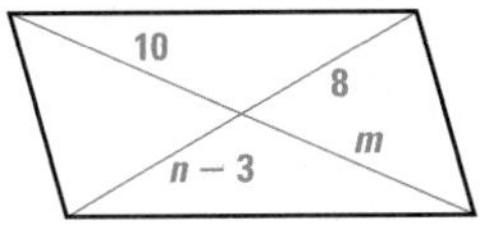

$m = 10$, $n = 11$

13.

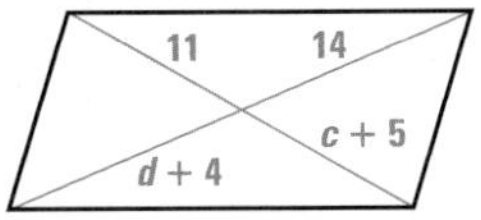

$c = 6$, $d = 10$

14.

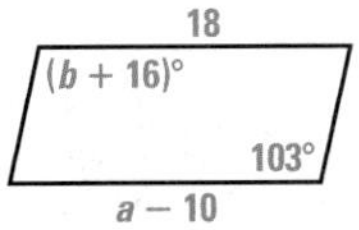

$a = 28$, $b = 87$

15. In ▱*PQRS*, *PQ* = 5 centimeters, *QR* = 10 centimeters, and $m\angle PQR = 36°$. Sketch *PQRS*. Find and label all of its side lengths and interior angle measures. **See margin.**

16. The perimeter of ▱*EFGH* is 16 inches. If *EF* is 5 inches, find the lengths of all the other sides of *EFGH*. *Explain* your reasoning. **See margin.**

17. In ▱*JKLM*, the ratio of the measure of ∠*J* to the measure of ∠*M* is 5 : 4. Find $m\angle J$ and $m\angle M$. *Explain* your reasoning. **100°, 80°; solve $5x + 4x = 180$ for *x*.**

Extra Example 8.2

Quadrilateral *ABCD* is a parallelogram. Find the values of *x* and *y*.
82, 18

15.

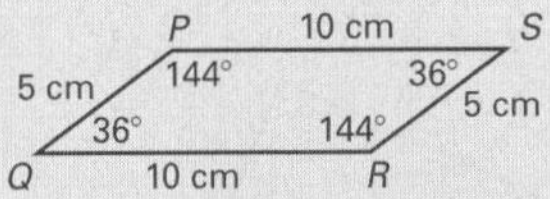

16. *FG* = 3 in., *GH* = 5 in., *HE* = 3 in.; in a parallelogram opposite sides have the same measure, therefore *EF* = *GH* = 5 inches. This leaves 6 inches for both $\overline{FG}$ and $\overline{HE}$. Since *FG* = *HE*, they both are 3 inches in length.

8 CHAPTER REVIEW

Extra Example 8.3

For what value of x is quadrilateral $MNPQ$ a parallelogram? **4**

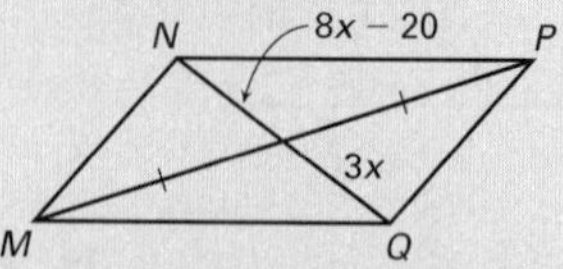

Extra Example 8.4

Classify the special quadrilateral. **rectangle**

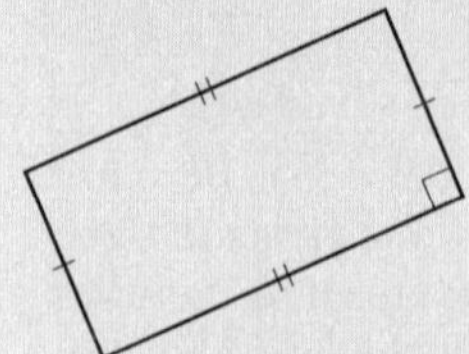

8.3 Show that a Quadrilateral is a Parallelogram

pp. 522–529

EXAMPLE

For what value of x is quadrilateral $ABCD$ a parallelogram?

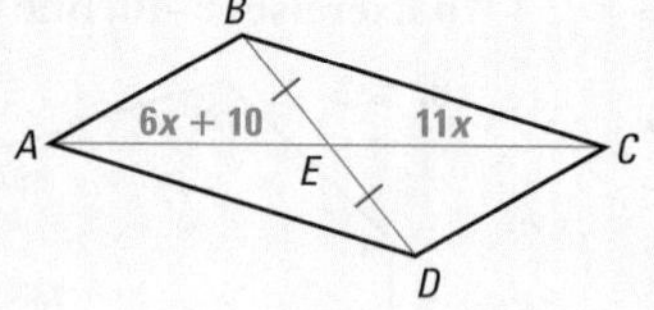

If the diagonals bisect each other, then $ABCD$ is a parallelogram. The diagram shows that $\overline{BE} \cong \overline{DE}$. You need to find the value of x that makes $\overline{AE} \cong \overline{CE}$.

$AE = CE$ **Set the segment lengths equal.**

$6x + 10 = 11x$ **Substitute expressions for the lengths.**

$x = 2$ **Solve for x.**

When $x = 2$, $AE = 6(2) + 10 = 22$ and $CE = 11(2) = 22$. So, $\overline{AE} \cong \overline{CE}$.

Quadrilateral $ABCD$ is a parallelogram when $x = 2$.

EXERCISES

EXAMPLE 3 on p. 524 for Exs. 18–19

For what value of x is the quadrilateral a parallelogram?

18. **5**

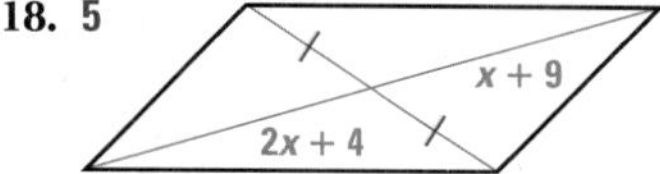

19. **3**

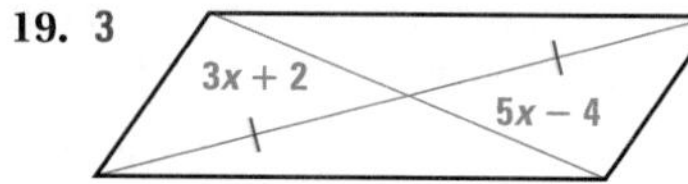

8.4 Properties of Rhombuses, Rectangles, and Squares

pp. 533–540

EXAMPLE

Classify the special quadrilateral.

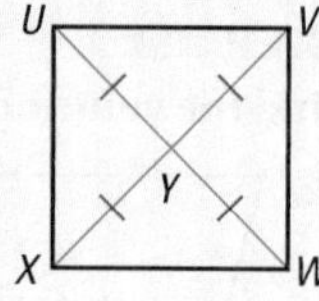

In quadrilateral $UVWX$, the diagonals bisect each other. So, $UVWX$ is a parallelogram. Also, $\overline{UY} \cong \overline{VY} \cong \overline{WY} \cong \overline{XY}$. So, $UY + YW = VY + XY$. Because $UY + YW = UW$, and $VY + XY = VX$, you can conclude that $\overline{UW} \cong \overline{VX}$. By Theorem 8.13, $UVWX$ is a rectangle.

EXERCISES

EXAMPLES 2 and 3 on pp. 534–535 for Exs. 20–22

Classify the special quadrilateral. Then find the values of x and y.

20.

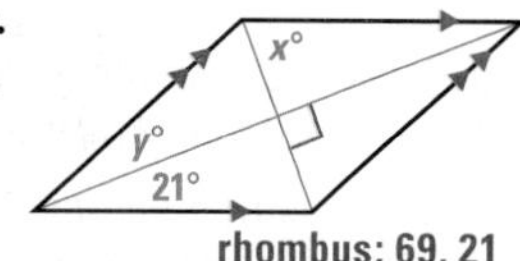

rhombus; 69, 21

21.

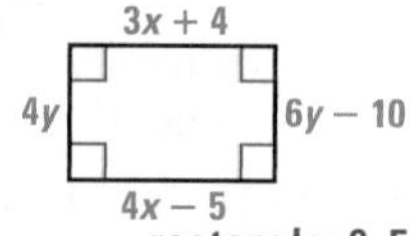

rectangle; 9, 5

22. The diagonals of a rhombus are 10 centimeters and 24 centimeters. Find the length of a side. *Explain.* **13 cm; the diagonals of a rhombus are perpendicular and form four 5-12-13 right triangles.**

@HomeTutor
classzone.com
Chapter Review Practice

8.5 Use Properties of Trapezoids and Kites

pp. 542–549

EXAMPLE

Quadrilateral $ABCD$ is a kite. Find $m\angle B$ and $m\angle D$.

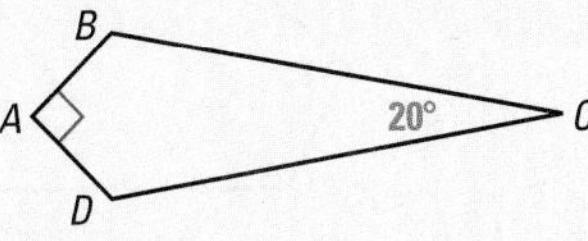

A kite has exactly one pair of congruent opposite angles. Because $\angle A \not\cong \angle C$, $\angle B$ and $\angle D$ must be congruent. Write and solve an equation.

$90° + 20° + m\angle B + m\angle D = 360°$ **Corollary to Theorem 8.1**

$110° + m\angle B° + m\angle D = 360°$ **Combine like terms.**

$m\angle B + m\angle D = 250°$ **Subtract 110° from each side.**

Because $\angle B \cong \angle D$, you can substitute $m\angle B$ for $m\angle D$ in the last equation. Then $m\angle B + m\angle B = 250°$, and $m\angle B = m\angle D = 125°$.

EXERCISES

EXAMPLES 2 and 3 on pp. 543–544 for Exs. 20–22

In Exercises 23 and 24, use the diagram of a recycling container. One end of the container is an isosceles trapezoid with $\overline{FG} \parallel \overline{JH}$ and $m\angle F = 79°$.

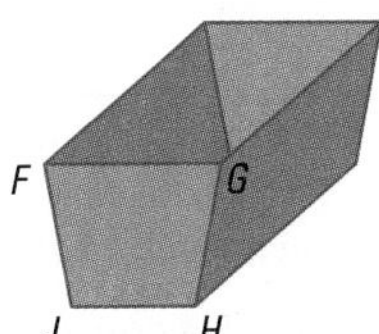

23. Find $m\angle G$, $m\angle H$, and $m\angle J$. **79°, 101°, 101°**

24. Copy trapezoid $FGHJ$ and sketch its midsegment. If the midsegment is 16.5 inches long and $\overline{FG}$ is 19 inches long, find JH. **See margin for art; 14 in.**

8.6 Identify Special Quadrilaterals

pp. 552–557

EXAMPLE

Give the most specific name for quadrilateral $LMNP$.

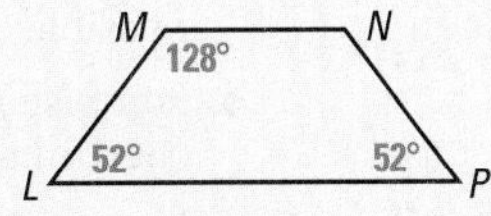

In $LMNP$, $\angle L$ and $\angle M$ are supplementary, but $\angle L$ and $\angle P$ are not. So, $\overline{MN} \parallel \overline{LP}$, but $\overline{LM}$ is not parallel to $\overline{NP}$. By definition, $LMNP$ is a trapezoid.

Also, $\angle L$ and $\angle P$ are a pair of base angles and $\angle L \cong \angle P$. So, $LMNP$ is an isosceles trapezoid by Theorem 8.15.

EXERCISES

EXAMPLE 2 on p. 553 for Exs. 25–28

Give the most specific name for the quadrilateral. *Explain* your reasoning.

25.

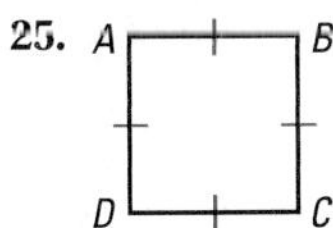

26.

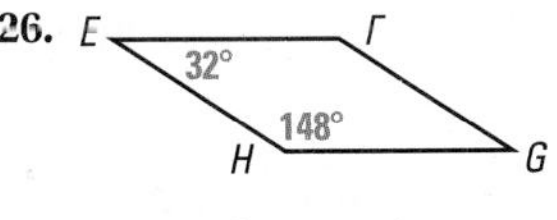

27.

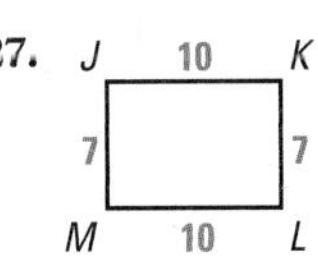

26, 27. See margin.

28. In quadrilateral $RSTU$, $\angle R$, $\angle T$, and $\angle U$ are right angles, and $RS = ST$. What is the most specific name for quadrilateral $RSTU$? *Explain.* **See margin.**

25. Rhombus; since all four sides are congruent it is a rhombus. There are no known right angles.

Extra Example 8.5

Quadrilateral $DEFG$ is a trapezoid. Find $m\angle G$ and $m\angle E$. **70°, 155°**

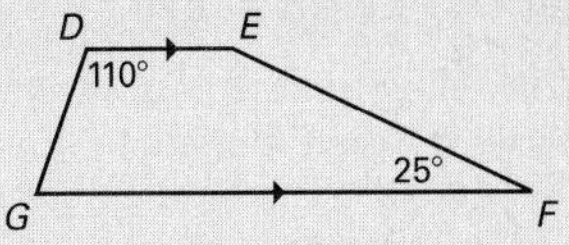

Extra Example 8.6

Give the most specific name for quadrilateral $XYZW$. **kite**

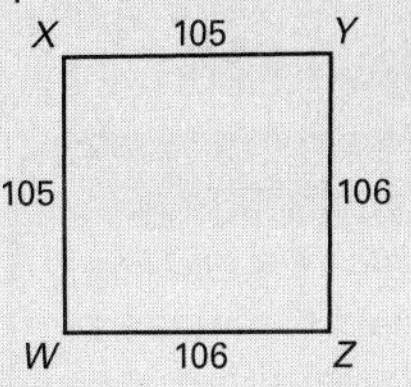

24.

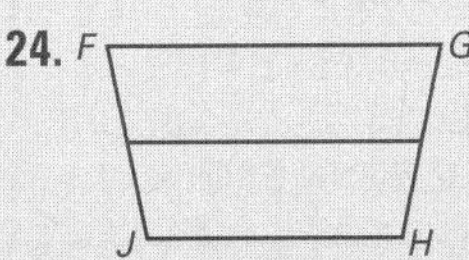

26. Trapezoid; since consecutive interior angles are supplementary, $\overline{EF} \parallel \overline{HG}$ but you do not know that $\overline{EH}$ is parallel to $\overline{FG}$.

27. Parallelogram; since opposite pairs of sides are congruent, it is a parallelogram. There are no known right angles.

28. Square; since three interior angles measure 90°, the measure of the fourth angle is 90°. It is a parallelogram with consecutive sides congruent, so all 4 sides are congruent which makes it a square.

8 CHAPTER TEST

Additional Resources

Assessment Book

- Chapter Test, Levels A, B, C, pp. 113–118
- Standardized Chapter Test, pp. 119–120
- SAT/ACT Chapter Test, pp. 121–122
- Alternative Assessment, pp. 123–124

Test Generator CD-ROM

Chapter Test

Easily-readable reduced copies (with answers) of Chapter Test B, the Standardized Chapter Test, and the Alternative Assessment from the Assessment Book can be found on pp. 504G–504H.

4.

12.

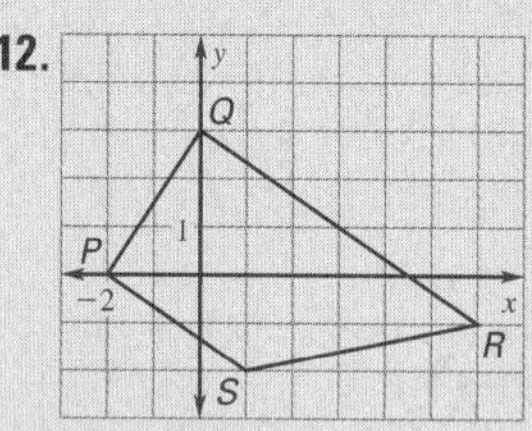

14. Trapezoid; only one pair of opposite sides are known to be parallel.

15. Rhombus; $m\angle FJG = 180° - 33° - 57° = 90°$, so $\overline{FH} \perp \overline{EG}$. The diagonals of a rhombus are perpendicular but you don't know that the angle measure of the vertices is 90°.

16. Kite; *JKLM* has a pair of consecutive congruent sides and the angle is bisected.

Find the value of *x*.

1. **118**

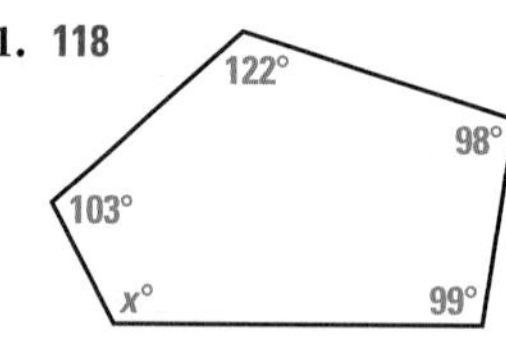

2. **31**

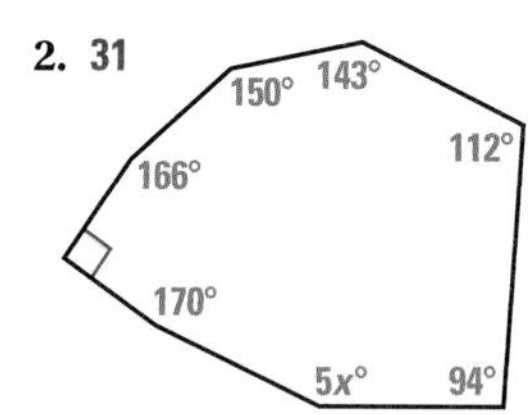

3. **71**

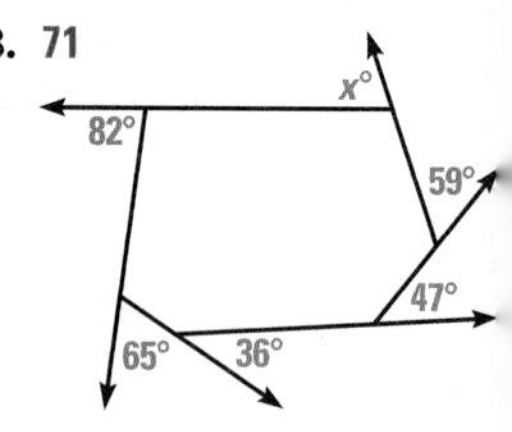

4. In ▱*EFGH*, $m\angle F$ is 40° greater than $m\angle G$. Sketch ▱*EFGH* and label each angle with its correct angle measure. *Explain* your reasoning. **See margin for art; Consecutive angles are supplementary, therefore $x + (x + 40) = 180$.**

Are you given enough information to determine whether the quadrilateral is a parallelogram? *Explain* your reasoning.

5. 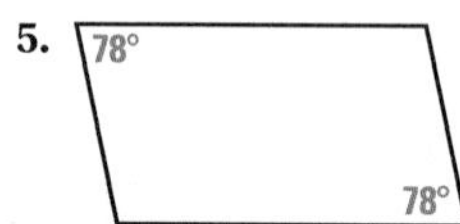

No; the sides might not be parallel.

6. 6, 8, 8, 6

Yes; diagonals bisect one another.

7. 10, 10

No; it could be a trapezoid.

In Exercises 8–11, list each type of quadrilateral—*parallelogram, rectangle, rhombus,* and *square*—for which the statement is always true.

8. It is equilateral. **rhombus, square**
9. Its interior angles are all right angles. **rectangle, square**
10. The diagonals are congruent. **rectangle, square**
11. Opposite sides are parallel. **parallelogram, rectangle, rhombus, square**
12. The vertices of quadrilateral *PQRS* are $P(-2, 0)$, $Q(0, 3)$, $R(6, -1)$, and $S(1, -2)$. Draw *PQRS* in a coordinate plane. Show that it is a trapezoid. **See margin for art; $\overline{PS} \parallel \overline{QR}$ and $\overline{SR}$ is not parallel to $\overline{PQ}$.**
13. One side of a quadrilateral *JKLM* is longer than another side.
    a. Suppose *JKLM* is an isosceles trapezoid. In a coordinate plane, find possible coordinates for the vertices of *JKLM*. *Justify* your answer.
    b. Suppose *JKLM* is a kite. In a coordinate plane, find possible coordinates for the vertices of *JKLM*. *Justify* your answer.
    c. Name other special quadrilaterals that *JKLM* could be. **trapezoid, parallelogram, rectangle**

13a. *Sample answer:* $J(4, 0)$, $K(2, 2)$, $L(-2, 2)$, $M(-4, 0)$; $\overline{JM} \parallel \overline{KL}$, $\overline{JK} \cong \overline{LM}$, and $\overline{JK}$ is not parallel to $\overline{LM}$.

13b. *Sample answer:* $J(2, 0)$, $K(0, 1)$, $L(-2, 0)$, $M(0, -5)$; two consecutive pairs of sides are congruent.

Give the most specific name for the quadrilateral. *Explain* your reasoning. **14–16. See margin.**

14. 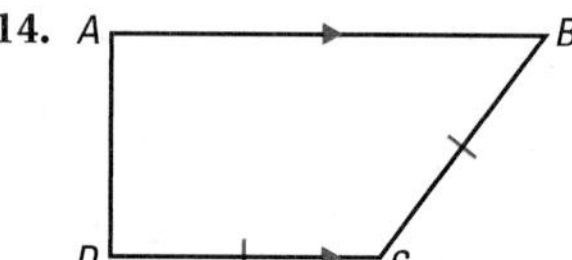

15. 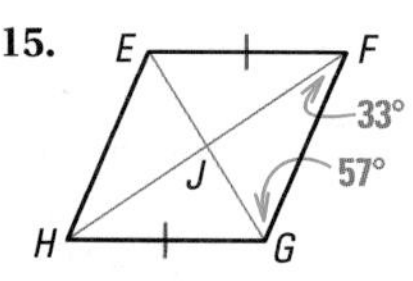

16. 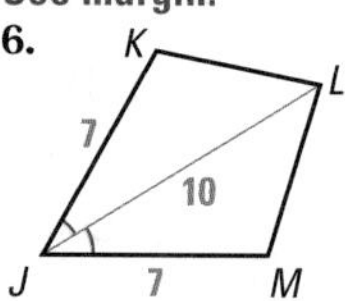

17. In trapezoid *WXYZ*, $\overline{WX} \parallel \overline{YZ}$, and $YZ = 4.25$ centimeters. The midsegment of trapezoid *WXYZ* is 2.75 centimeters long. Find *WX*. **1.25 cm**
18. In ▱*RSTU*, $\overline{RS}$ is 3 centimeters shorter than $\overline{ST}$. The perimeter of ▱*RSTU* is 42 centimeters. Find *RS* and *ST*. **9 cm, 12 cm**

8 xy ALGEBRA REVIEW

GRAPH NONLINEAR FUNCTIONS

EXAMPLE 1 Graph a quadratic function in vertex form

Graph $y = 2(x - 3)^2 - 1$.

The *vertex form* of a quadratic function is $y = a(x - h)^2 + k$. Its graph is a parabola with vertex at (h, k) and axis of symmetry $x = h$.

The given function is in vertex form. So, $a = 2$, $h = 3$, and $k = -1$. Because $a > 0$, the parabola opens up.

Graph the vertex at $(3, -1)$. Sketch the axis of symmetry, $x = 3$. Use a table of values to find points on each side of the axis of symmetry. Draw a parabola through the points.

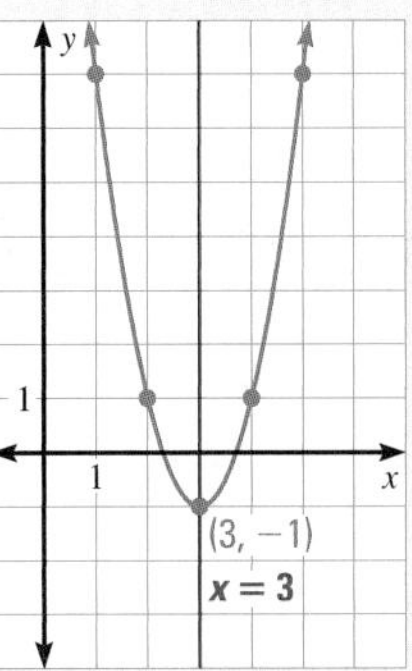

x	3	1	2	4	5
y	−1	7	1	1	7

EXAMPLE 2 Graph an exponential function

Graph $y = 2^x$.

Make a table by choosing a few values for x and finding the values for y. Plot the points and connect them with a smooth curve.

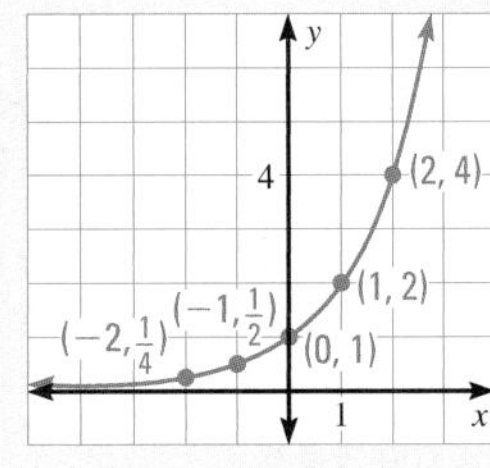

x	−2	−1	0	1	2
y	$\frac{1}{4}$	$\frac{1}{2}$	1	2	4

EXERCISES

EXAMPLE 1 for Exs. 1–6

Graph the quadratic function. Label the vertex and sketch the axis of symmetry. **1–6. See margin.**

1. $y = 3x^2 + 5$
2. $y = -2x^2 + 4$
3. $y = 0.5x^2 - 3$
4. $y = 3(x + 3)^2 - 3$
5. $y = -2(x - 4)^2 - 1$
6. $y = \frac{1}{2}(x - 4)^2 + 3$

EXAMPLE 2 for Exs. 7–10

Graph the exponential function. **7–10. See margin.**

7. $y = 3^x$
8. $y = 8^x$
9. $y = 2.2^x$
10. $y = \left(\frac{1}{3}\right)^x$

Use a table of values to graph the cubic or absolute value function. **11–16. See margin.**

11. $y = x^3$
12. $y = x^3 - 2$
13. $y = 3x^3 - 1$
14. $y = 2|x|$
15. $y = 2|x| - 4$
16. $y = -|x| - 1$

Extra Example 1

Graph $y = \frac{1}{2}(x + 1)^2 - 3$.

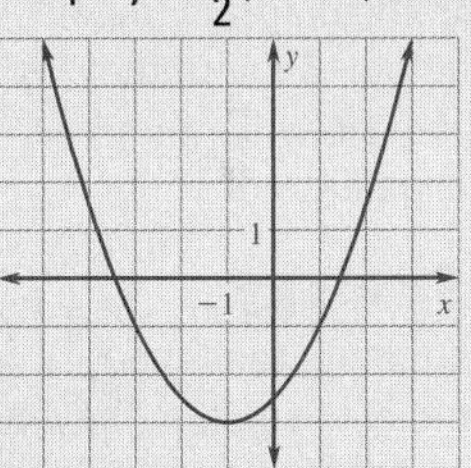

Extra Example 2

Graph $y = 3|x| + 1$.

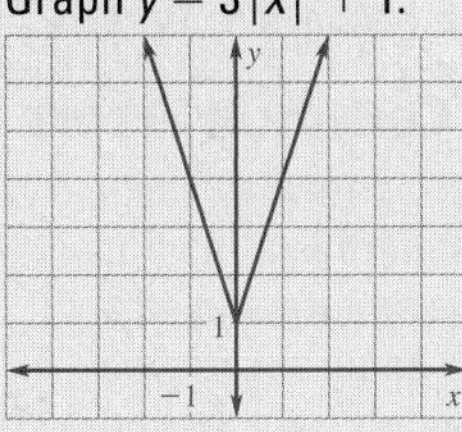

4.

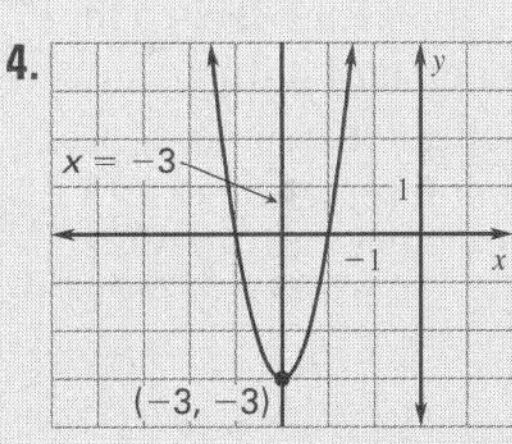

5.

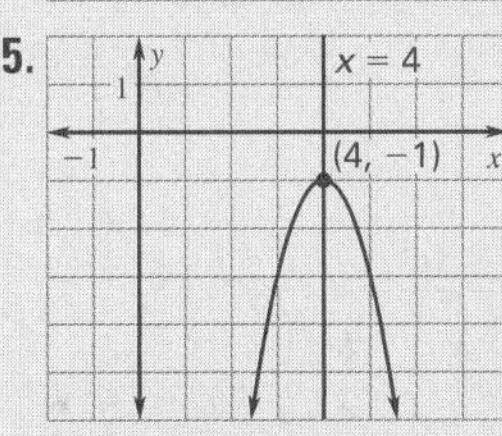

6.

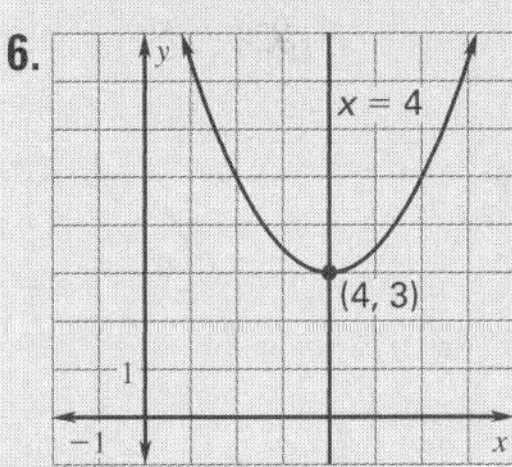

7–16. See Additional Answers beginning on p. AA1.

1.

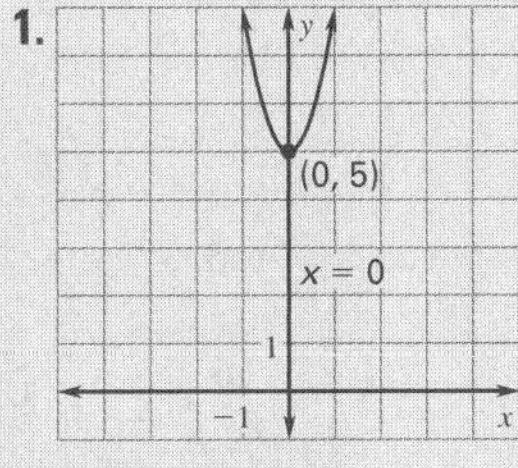

2.

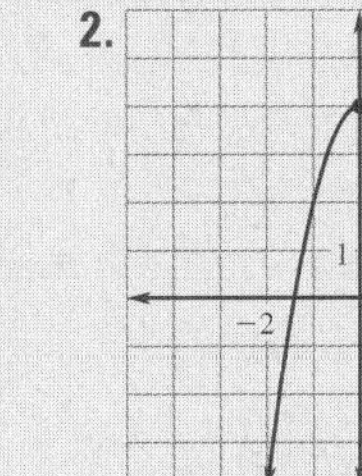

3.

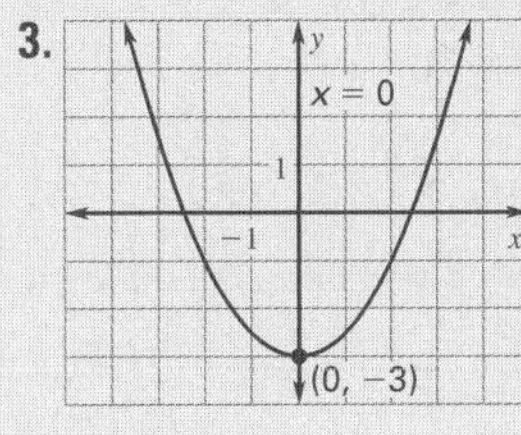

Test-Taking Strategy

Make certain students use the information in the diagram to help solve the problem. Be sure they look at the diagram while they are reading the problem.

Reading Strategy

Be sure the students read the problem carefully to see that they are looking for a statement which is NOT always true. You may need to discuss the difference between *not always true* and *always not true.*

Avoiding Common Errors

Problem 1 Students may assume that since a square is a rhombus, a rhombus is a square and so a property for a square would be true for a rhombus, which is not necessarily the case. Review the hierarchy of quadrilaterals and the way properties hold true for special quadrilaterals.

Standards

7.0 Students prove and **use theorems involving** the properties of parallel lines cut by a transversal, **the properties of quadrilaterals**, and the properties of circles.

12.0 Students find and use measures of sides and of interior and exterior **angles of triangles and polygons to** classify figures and **solve problems.**

CONTEXT-BASED MULTIPLE CHOICE QUESTIONS

Some of the information you need to solve a context-based multiple choice question may appear in a table, a diagram, or a graph.

PROBLEM 1

Which of the statements about the rhombus-shaped ring is not always true?

Ⓐ $m\angle SPT = m\angle TPQ$ Ⓑ $PT = TR$

Ⓒ $m\angle STR = 90°$ Ⓓ $PR = SQ$

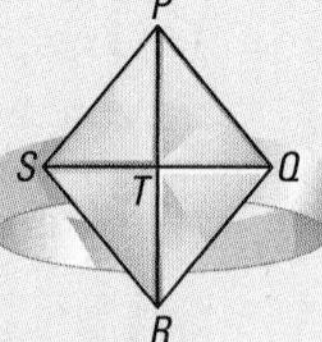

Plan

INTERPRET THE DIAGRAM The diagram shows rhombus *PQRS* with its diagonals intersecting at point *T*. Use properties of rhombuses to figure out which statement is not always true.

Solution

STEP 1 Evaluate choice A.

Consider choice A: $m\angle SPT = m\angle TPQ$.

Each diagonal of a rhombus bisects each of a pair of opposite angles. The diagonal $\overline{PR}$ bisects $\angle SPQ$, so $m\angle SPT = m\angle TPQ$. Choice A is true.

STEP 2 Evaluate choice B.

Consider choice B: $PT = TR$.

The diagonals of a parallelogram bisect each other. A rhombus is also a parallelogram, so the diagonals of *PQRS* bisect each other. So, $PT = TR$. Choice B is true.

STEP 3 Evaluate choice C.

Consider choice C: $m\angle STR = 90°$.

The diagonals of a rhombus are perpendicular. *PQRS* is a rhombus, so its diagonals are perpendicular. Therefore, $m\angle STR = 90°$. Choice C is true.

STEP 3 Evaluate choice D.

Consider choice D: $PR = SQ$.

If the diagonals of a parallelogram are congruent, then it is a rectangle. But *PQRS* is a rhombus. Only in the special case where it is also a square (a type of rhombus that is also a rectangle), would choice D be true. So, choice D is not always true.

The correct answer is D. Ⓐ Ⓑ Ⓒ Ⓓ

PROBLEM 2

The official dimensions of home plate in professional baseball are shown on the diagram. What is the value of x?

Ⓐ 90　　Ⓑ 108

Ⓒ 135　　Ⓓ 150

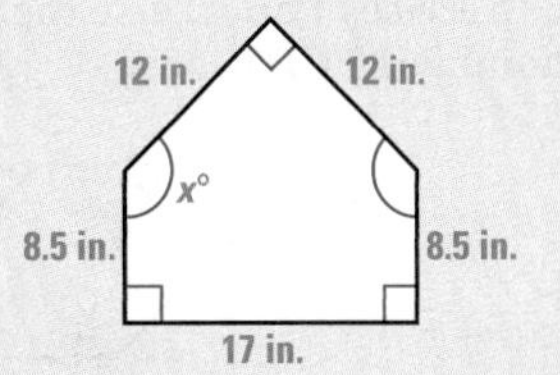

Plan

INTERPRET THE DIAGRAM From the diagram, you can see that home plate is a pentagon. Use what you know about the interior angles of a polygon and the markings given on the diagram to find the value of x.

Solution

STEP 1 Find the sum of the measures of the interior angles.

Home plate has 5 sides. Use the Polygon Interior Angles Theorem to find the sum of the measures of the interior angles.

$(n - 2) \cdot 180° = (5 - 2) \cdot 180°$　**Substitute 5 for *n*.**

$= 3 \cdot 180°$　**Subtract.**

$= 540°$　**Multiply.**

STEP 2 Write and solve an equation.

From the diagram, you know that three interior angles are right angles. The two other angles are congruent, including the one whose measure is $x°$. Use this information to write an equation. Then solve the equation.

$3 \cdot 90° + 2 \cdot x° = 540°$　**Write equation.**

$270 + 2x = 540$　**Multiply.**

$2x = 270$　**Subtract 270 from each side.**

$x = 135$　**Divide each side by 2.**

The correct answer is C. Ⓐ Ⓑ Ⓒ Ⓓ

PRACTICE

In Exercises 1 and 2, use the part of the quilt shown.

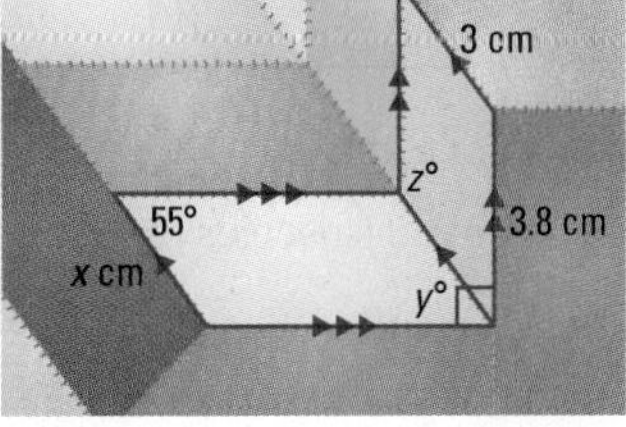

1. What is the value of x? **A**

 Ⓐ 3　　Ⓑ 3.4

 Ⓒ 3.8　　Ⓓ 5.5

2. What is the value of z? **D**

 Ⓐ 35　　Ⓑ 55

 Ⓒ 125　　Ⓓ 145

Mathematical Reasoning

Problem 2 Ask students how they could use an auxiliary segment to solve the problem. They may see that if they draw an auxiliary segment with endpoints at the vertices of the angles marked with arcs, then the segment will divide the figure into a rectangle and a 45°-45°-90° right triangle. The Angle Addition Postulate shows that each angle marked with an arc has a measure of $45° + 90°$, or 135°.

MULTIPLE CHOICE

In Exercises 1 and 2, use the diagram of rhombus *ABCD* below.

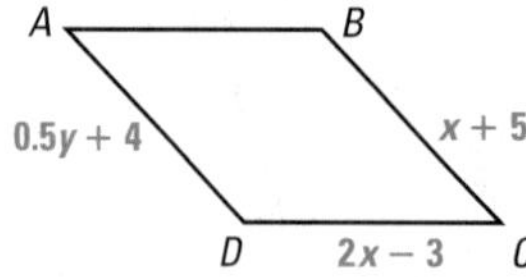

1. What is the value of x? C

Ⓐ 2 Ⓑ 4.6

Ⓒ 8 Ⓓ 13

2. What is the value of y? D

Ⓐ 1.8 Ⓑ 2

Ⓒ 8 Ⓓ 18

3. In the design shown below, a green regular hexagon is surrounded by yellow equilateral triangles and blue isosceles triangles. What is the measure of $\angle 1$? A

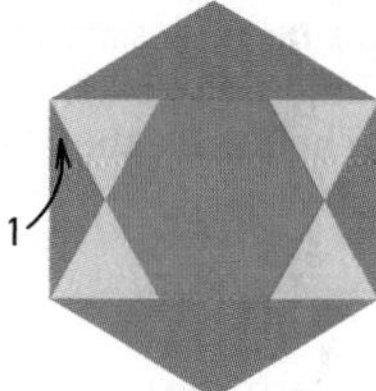

Ⓐ 30° Ⓑ 40°

Ⓒ 50° Ⓓ 60°

4. Which statement about *EFGH* can be concluded from the given information? A

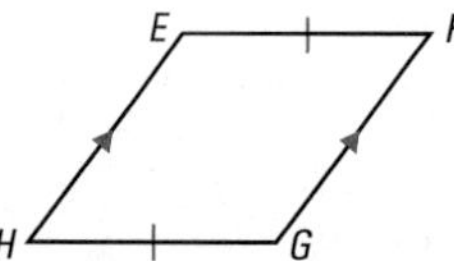

Ⓐ It is not a kite.

Ⓑ It is not an isosceles trapezoid.

Ⓒ It is not a square.

Ⓓ It is not a rhombus.

5. What is the most specific name for quadrilateral *FGHJ*? B

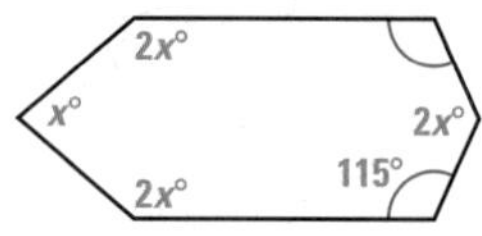

Ⓐ Parallelogram

Ⓑ Rhombus

Ⓒ Rectangle

Ⓓ Square

6. What is the measure of the smallest interior angle of the hexagon shown? C

$2x°$, $x°$, $2x°$, $2x°$, $115°$

Ⓐ 50° Ⓑ 60°

Ⓒ 70° Ⓓ 80°

In Exercises 7 and 8, use the diagram of a cardboard container. In the diagram, $\angle S \cong \angle R$, $\overline{PQ} \parallel \overline{SR}$, and $\overline{PS}$ and $\overline{QR}$ are not parallel.

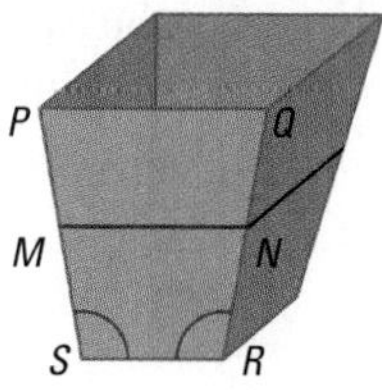

7. Which statement is true? A

Ⓐ $PR = SQ$

Ⓑ $m\angle S + m\angle R = 180°$

Ⓒ $PQ = 2 \cdot SR$

Ⓓ $PQ = QR$

8. The bases of trapezoid *PQRS* are $\overline{PQ}$ and $\overline{SR}$, and the midsegment is $\overline{MN}$. Given $PQ = 9$ centimeters, and $MN = 7.2$ centimeters, what is SR? A

Ⓐ 5.4 cm Ⓑ 8.1 cm

Ⓒ 10.8 cm Ⓓ 12.6 cm

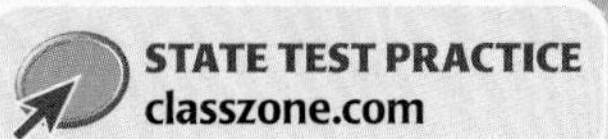

GRIDDED ANSWER

9. How many degrees greater is the measure of an interior angle of a regular octagon than the measure of an interior angle of a regular pentagon? **27°**

10. Parallelogram *ABCD* has vertices $A(-3, -1)$, $B(-1, 3)$, $C(4, 3)$, and $D(2, -1)$. What is the sum of the *x*- and *y*-coordinates of the point of intersection of the diagonals of *ABCD*? **1.5**

11. For what value of *x* is the quadrilateral shown below a parallelogram? **25**

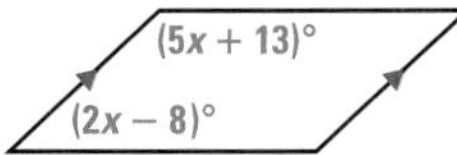

12. In kite *JKLM*, the ratio of *JK* to *KL* is 3 : 2. The perimeter of *JKLM* is 30 inches. Find the length (in inches) of $\overline{JK}$. **9 in.**

SHORT RESPONSE

13. The vertices of quadrilateral *EFGH* are $E(-1, -2)$, $F(-1, 3)$, $G(2, 4)$, and $H(3, 1)$. What type of quadrilateral is *EFGH*? *Explain.* **See margin.**

14. In the diagram below, *PQRS* is an isosceles trapezoid with $\overline{PQ} \parallel \overline{RS}$. *Explain* how to show that $\triangle PTS \cong \triangle QTR$. **See margin.**

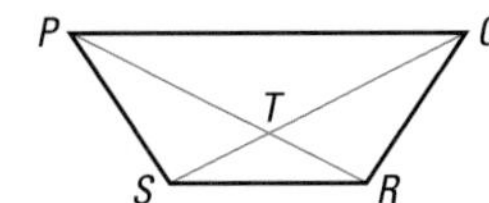

15. In trapezoid *ABCD*, $\overline{AB} \parallel \overline{CD}$, $\overline{XY}$ is the midsegment of *ABCD*, and $\overline{CD}$ is twice as long as $\overline{AB}$. Find the ratio of *XY* to *AB*. *Justify* your answer.

$\frac{3}{2}$. *Sample answer:* Let $AB = x$ and $DC = 2x$, then $XY = \frac{3x}{2}$. The ratio of *XY* to *AB* is $\frac{\frac{3x}{2}}{x} = \frac{3}{2}$.

EXTENDED RESPONSE

16. The diagram shows a regular pentagon and diagonals drawn from vertex *F*. **a–c. See margin.**
   a. The diagonals divide the pentagon into three triangles. Classify the triangles by their angles and side measures. *Explain* your reasoning.
   b. Which triangles are congruent? *Explain* how you know.
   c. For each triangle, find the interior angle measures. *Explain* your reasoning.

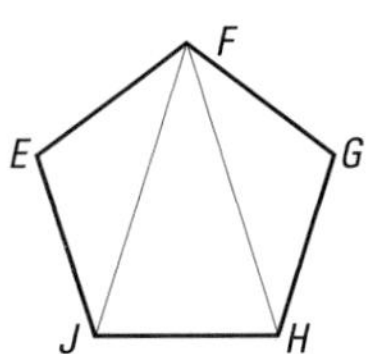

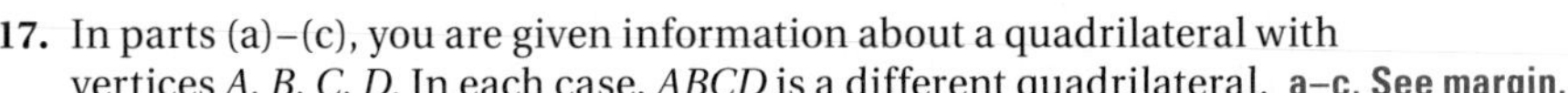

17. In parts (a)–(c), you are given information about a quadrilateral with vertices *A*, *B*, *C*, *D*. In each case, *ABCD* is a different quadrilateral. **a–c. See margin.**
   a. Suppose that $\overline{AB} \parallel \overline{CD}$, $AB = DC$, and $\angle C$ is a right angle. Draw quadrilateral *ABCD* and give the most specific name for *ABCD*. *Justify* your answer.
   b. Suppose that $\overline{AB} \parallel \overline{CD}$ and *ABCD* has *exactly* two right angles, one of which is $\angle C$. Draw quadrilateral *ABCD* and give the most specific name for *ABCD*. *Justify* your answer.
   c. Suppose you are given only that $\overline{AB} \parallel \overline{CD}$. What additional information would you need to know about $\overline{AC}$ and $\overline{BD}$ to conclude that *ABCD* is a rhombus? *Explain.*

16a. $\triangle FEJ$ and $\triangle FGH$ are obtuse isosceles triangles since $m\angle E = m\angle G = 108°$ and $\overline{EF} \cong \overline{EJ} \cong \overline{FG} \cong \overline{GH}$. $\triangle JFH$ is an acute isosceles triangle since all angles are less than 90° and $\overline{FJ} \cong \overline{FH}$.

16b. $\triangle JEF$ and $\triangle FGH$; since *EFGHJ* is a regular pentagon, $\angle E \cong \angle G$ and $\overline{EF} \cong \overline{EJ} \cong \overline{FG} \cong \overline{GH}$. Using the SAS Congruence Theorem, $\triangle JEF \cong \triangle FGH$.

16c. $m\angle E = 108°$, $m\angle EFJ = m\angle EJF = 36°$; $m\angle JFH = 36°$, $m\angle FJH = m\angle FHJ = 72°$; $m\angle G = 108°$, $m\angle GFH = m\angle GHF = 36°$; each of the five angles in the pentagon measure 108°. Since $\triangle JEF$ and $\triangle FGH$ are congruent and isosceles, the base angles measure 36°. Since $\triangle JFH$ is isosceles, the base angles are congruent. Subtracting 36° from 108° leaves the base angles measuring 72°. The third angle measures 36°.

17a.

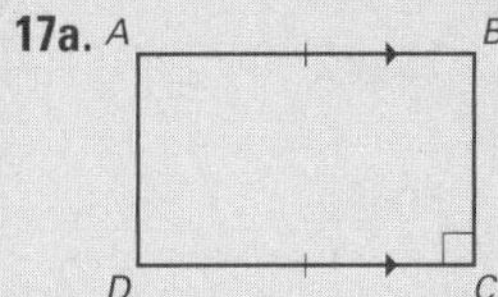

Rectangle; using the Consecutive Interior Angles Theorem, $m\angle B = 90°$. Using the HL Congruence Theorem, $\triangle ABC \cong \triangle CDA$. Using corresponding parts of congruent triangles are congruent, $\angle D \cong \angle B$ and $\overline{AD} \cong \overline{BC}$. *ABCD* is a rectangle.

17b.

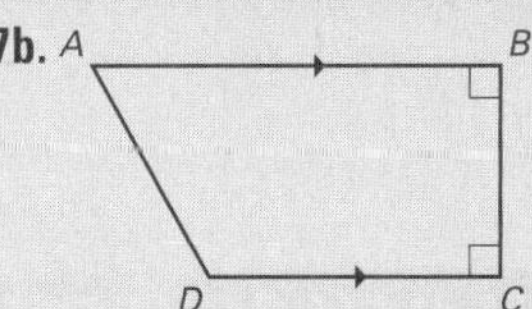

Trapezoid; $\overline{AD}$ is not parallel to $\overline{BC}$.

17c. $\overline{AC} \perp \overline{BD}$; **in a rhombus the diagonals are perpendicular.**

14. Since *PQRS* is an isosceles trapezoid, $\overline{PS} \cong \overline{QR}$ and $\overline{QS} \cong \overline{PR}$. $\overline{SR} \cong \overline{SR}$ by the Reflexive Property of Segment Congruence. Using the SSS Congruence Postulate, $\triangle PSR \cong \triangle QRS$. Using corresponding parts of congruent triangles are congruent, $\angle SQR \cong \angle RPS$. Using the Vertical Angles Theorem, $\angle PTS \cong \angle QTR$. Therefore, $\triangle PTS \cong \triangle QTR$ by the AAS Congruence Theorem.

9 Pacing and Assignment Guide

REGULAR SCHEDULE

Pre-AP For pacing and assignments for a Pre-AP course, see the *Geometry Toolkit.*

Lesson	Les. Day	BASIC	AVERAGE	ADVANCED
9.1	Day 1	pp. 576–579 Exs. 1–14, 28, 29, 33, 34, 51, 53	pp. 576–579 Exs. 1–6, 8–10, 12, 14, 28–31, 33, 34, 51, 54	pp. 576–579 Exs. 1–6, 8–10, 12, 14, 28–34*, 51, 54
	Day 2	pp. 576–579 Exs. 15–27, 35–40, 47–50	pp. 576–579 Exs. 16, 17, 19–27, 36–43, 47, 49	pp. 576–579 Exs. 16, 17, 20–27, 37–46*, 50
9.2	Day 1	SRH p. 870 Exs. 1–8; pp. 584–587 Exs. 1–17	pp. 584–587 Exs. 1–6, 8–12, 14–17, 27, 28	pp. 584–587 Exs. 1, 2, 3–6, 8–12, 14–17, 27–30*
	Day 2	pp. 584–587 Exs. 18–25, 31–34, 38–45	pp. 584–587 Exs. 18–26, 29, 31–36, 38–44 even	pp. 584–587 Exs. 18–26, 31–37*, 39–45 odd
9.3	Day 1	EP p. 901 Exs. 24–26; pp. 593–596 Exs. 1–12, 44–46	pp. 593–596 Exs. 1, 2, 6–12, 26–28, 44–46	pp. 593–596 Exs. 1, 2, 7–12, 26–30*, 46
	Day 2	pp. 593–596 Exs. 13–21, 31–37, 42, 43	pp. 593–596 Exs. 15–25, 32–40, 42	pp. 593–596 Exs. 16–25, 34–41*, 43
9.4	Day 1	EP p. 903 Exs. 39, 40; pp. 602–605 Exs. 1–14, 44–46	pp. 602–605 Exs. 1–8, 10, 11, 13, 14, 23, 24, 45, 46	pp. 602–605 Exs. 1, 2, 6–8, 10, 11, 13, 14, 25–28*, 46
	Day 2	pp. 602–605 Exs. 15–23, 29–35, 41–43	pp. 602–605 Exs. 16–22, 29–37, 41–43	pp. 602–605 Exs. 15–17, 20–24, 31–43*
9.5	Day 1	pp. 611–615 Exs. 1–14, 27–30	pp. 611–615 Exs. 1, 2, 4–6, 8–14, 23, 24, 27–30	pp. 611–615 Exs. 1, 2, 4–6, 9–14, 23, 24, 26–30*
	Day 2	pp. 611–615 Exs. 15–23, 31–35, 42–48	pp. 611–615 Exs. 15–22, 25, 31–39, 42–48	pp. 611–615 Exs. 15–22, 25, 31–41*, 44, 46
9.6	Day 1	pp. 621–624 Exs. 1–8, 10–18, 27–32, 37–45	pp. 621–624 Exs. 1, 2, 4, 5, 7–16, 19–23, 28–35, 37–45 odd	pp. 621–624 Exs. 1, 2, 4, 5, 8–14, 19–26*, 29–36*, 38–44 even
9.7	Day 1	EP p. 907 Exs. 41, 42; pp. 629–632 Exs. 1–10, 15–25, 33–38, 43–49 odd	pp. 629–632 Exs. 1, 2, 4–6, 10–12, 16, 17, 19–30, 34–41, 44, 46	pp. 629–632 Exs. 1, 2, 4, 5, 13–16, 20–24 even, 25–32*, 35–42*, 45, 48
Review	Day 1	pp. 636–639 Exs. 1–21	pp. 636–639 Exs. 1–21	pp. 636–639 Exs. 1–21
Assess	Day 1	Chapter 9 Test	Chapter 9 Test	Chapter 9 Test
Yearly Pacing		Chapter 9 Total – 14 days	Chapters 1–9 Total – 120 days	Remaining – 40 days

*Challenge Exercises EP = Extra Practice SRH = Skills Review Handbook

BLOCK SCHEDULE

DAY 1	DAY 2	DAY 3	DAY 4	DAY 5	DAY 6	DAY 7
9.1	9.2	9.3	9.4	9.5	9.6	REVIEW
pp. 576–579 Exs. 1–6, 8–10, 12, 14, 16, 17, 19–31, 33, 34, 36–43, 47, 49, 51, 54	pp. 584–587 Exs. 1–6, 8–12, 14–29, 31–36, 38–44 even	pp. 593–596 Exs. 1, 2, 6–12, 15–28, 32–40, 42, 44–46	pp. 602–605 Exs. 1–8, 10, 11, 13, 14, 16–24, 29–37, 41–43, 45, 46	pp. 611–615 Exs. 1, 2, 4–6, 8–25, 27–39, 42–48	pp. 621–624 Exs. 1, 2, 4, 5, 7–16, 19–23, 28–35, 37–45 odd	pp. 636–639 Exs. 1–21
					9.7	ASSESS
					pp. 629–632 Exs. 1, 2, 4–6, 10–12, 16, 17, 19–30, 34–41, 44, 46	Chapter 9 Test
Yearly Pacing	Chapter 9 Total – 7 days		Chapters 1–9 Total – 60 days		Remaining – 20 days	

Chapter Resource Guide 9

RESOURCE MANAGER

Chapter Resource Book

CHAPTER SUPPORT							
Parents as Partners (Chapter Overview with home involvement exercises and activity)						p. 1	
LESSON SUPPORT	**9.1**	**9.2**	**9.3**	**9.4**	**9.5**	**9.6**	**9.7**
Teaching Guide/Lesson Plan	p. 3	p. 18	p. 31	p. 45	p. 59	p. 73	p. 87
Activity Masters				p. 47		p. 75	
Technology Activities & Keystrokes	p. 5				p. 61		p. 89
Activity Support Masters							
Practice (3 levels)	p. 7	p. 20	p. 33	p. 48	p. 62	p. 76	p. 90
Study Guide	p. 13	p. 26	p. 39	p. 54	p. 68	p. 82	p. 96
Catch-Up for Absent Students	p. 15	p. 28	p. 41	p. 56	p. 70	p. 84	p. 98
Problem Solving/Application	p. 16	p. 29	p. 42	p. 57	p. 71	p. 85	p. 99
Challenge Practice	p. 17	p. 30	p. 44	p. 58	p. 72	p. 86	p. 100

REVIEW			
Chapter Review Games and Activities	p. 101	Cumulative Practice	p. 104
Project with Rubric	p. 102	Resource Book Answers	A1

Transparencies	*9.1*	*9.2*	*9.3*	*9.4*	*9.5*	*9.6*	*9.7*
Warm-Up/Daily Homework Quiz	✔	✔	✔	✔	✔	✔	✔
Notetaking Guide	✔	✔	✔	✔	✔	✔	✔
Teacher Support	✔	✔	✔	✔	✔		✔
Answer Transparencies	✔	✔	✔	✔	✔	✔	✔

ASSESSMENT BOOK

Quizzes	p. 125	SAT/ACT Chapter Test	p. 136
Chapter Tests (3 levels)	p. 128	Alternative Assessment with Rubric	p. 138
Standardized Chapter Test	p. 134		

TECHNOLOGY

- Easy Planner
- Test and Practice Generator
- Power Presentations
- @HomeTutor
- Activity Generator
- Animated Geometry
- Classzone.com
- eEdition Plus Online
- eWorkbook Plus Online
- ML Assessment System

ADDITIONAL RESOURCES

- Worked-Out Solution Key
- Notetaking Guide
- Practice Wookbook
- Geometry Toolkit
- Benchmark Tests
- Remediation Book
- Spanish Study Guide
- Spanish Assessment Book
- Student Resources in Spanish
- Multi-Language Visual Glossary

9 Lesson Practice Level B

LESSON 9.1 Practice B
For use with pages 572–579

Use the translation $(x, y) \to (x + 6, y - 3)$.

1. What is the image of $A(3, 2)$? $A'(9, -1)$
2. What is the image of $B(-4, 1)$? $B'(2, -2)$
3. What is the preimage of $C'(2, -7)$? $C(-4, -4)$
4. What is the preimage of $D'(-3, -2)$? $D(-9, 1)$

The vertices of $\triangle ABC$ are $A(-1, 1)$, $B(4, -1)$, and $C(2, 4)$. Graph the image of the triangle using prime notation.

5. $(x, y) \to (x - 3, y + 5)$

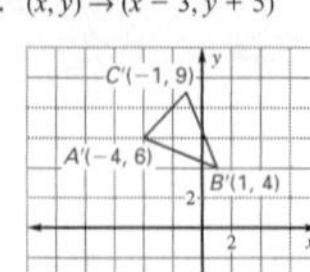

6. $(x, y) \to (x - 4, y - 2)$

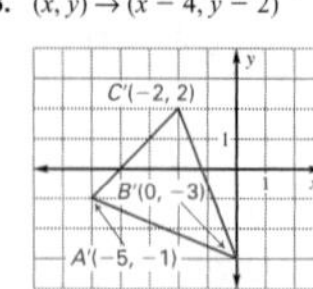

$\triangle A'B'C'$ is the image of $\triangle ABC$ after a translation. Write a rule for the translation. Then verify that the translation is an isometry.

7.

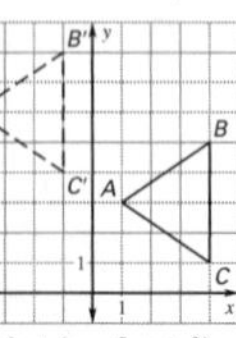

$(x, y) \to (x - 5, y + 3)$

8.

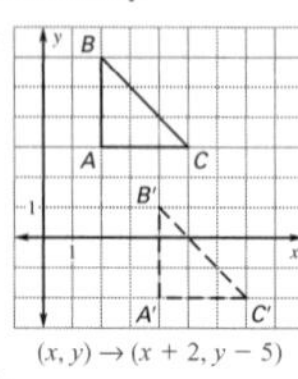

$(x, y) \to (x + 2, y - 5)$

Name the vector and its component form.

9.

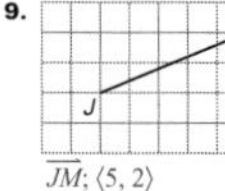

$\overrightarrow{JM}$; $\langle 5, 2\rangle$

10.

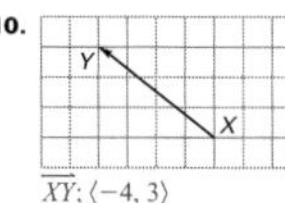

$\overrightarrow{XY}$; $\langle -4, 3\rangle$

11.

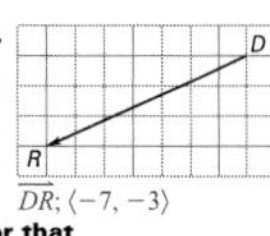

$\overrightarrow{DR}$; $\langle -7, -3\rangle$

Use the point $P(5, -2)$. Find the component form of the vector that describes the translation to P'.

12. $P'(2, 0)$ $\langle -3, 2\rangle$
13. $P'(8, -3)$ $\langle 3, -1\rangle$
14. $P'(0, 4)$ $\langle -5, 6\rangle$
15. $P'(-5, -4)$ $\langle -10, -2\rangle$

LESSON 9.1 Practice B *continued*
For use with pages 572–579

The vertices of $\triangle ABC$ are $A(1, 2)$, $B(2, 6)$, and $C(3, 1)$. Translate $\triangle ABC$ using the given vector. Graph $\triangle ABC$ and its image.

16. $\langle 8, 2\rangle$

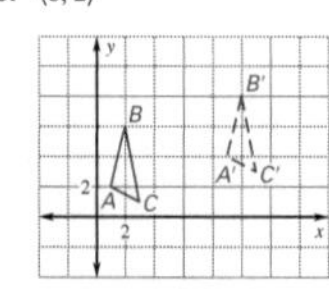

17. $\langle -7, -3\rangle$

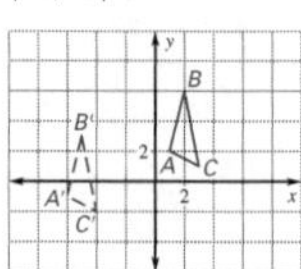

Find the value of each variable in the translation.

18. $a = 80$, $b = 4$, $c = 13$, $d = 20$

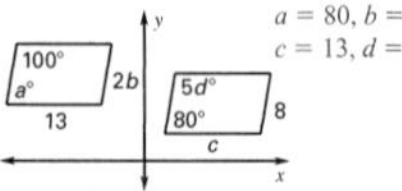

19. $a = 59$, $b = 17$, $c = 6$

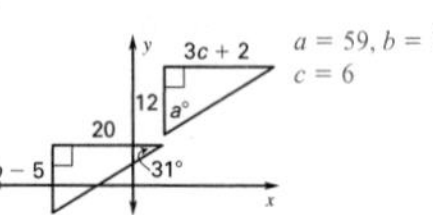

20. **Navigation** A hot air balloon is flying from point A to point D. After the balloon travels 6 miles east and 3 miles north, the wind direction changes at point B. The balloon travels to point C as shown in the diagram.

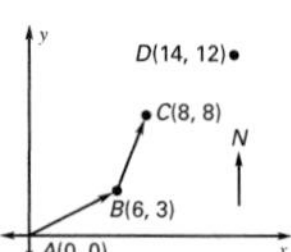

a. Write the component form for $\overrightarrow{AB}$ and $\overrightarrow{BC}$. $\langle 6, 3\rangle$, $\langle 2, 5\rangle$

b. The wind direction changes and the balloon travels from point C to point D. Write the component form for $\overrightarrow{CD}$. $\langle 6, 4\rangle$

c. What is the total distance the balloon travels? about 19.3 mi

d. Suppose the balloon went straight from A to D. Write the component form of the vector that describes this path. What is this distance? $\langle 14, 12\rangle$, about 18.4 mi

LESSON 9.2 Practice B
For use with pages 580–587

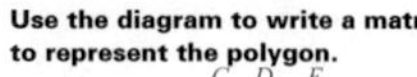

Use the diagram to write a matrix to represent the polygon.

1. $\triangle CDE$
2. $\triangle ABF$
3. Quadrilateral $BCEF$
4. Hexagon $ABCDEF$

1. $\begin{array}{c} \begin{matrix} C & D & E \end{matrix} \\ \begin{bmatrix} 5 & 7 & 5 \\ 4 & 2 & -2 \end{bmatrix} \end{array}$ 2. $\begin{array}{c} \begin{matrix} A & B & F \end{matrix} \\ \begin{bmatrix} -2 & 2 & 2 \\ 3 & 4 & -3 \end{bmatrix} \end{array}$

3. $\begin{array}{c} \begin{matrix} B & C & E & F \end{matrix} \\ \begin{bmatrix} 2 & 5 & 5 & 2 \\ 4 & 4 & -2 & -3 \end{bmatrix} \end{array}$

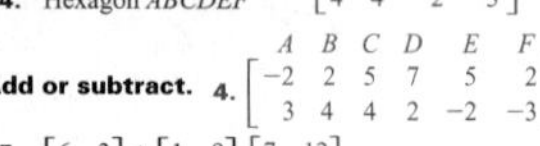

Add or subtract.

4. $\begin{array}{c} \begin{matrix} A & B & C & D & E & F \end{matrix} \\ \begin{bmatrix} -2 & 2 & 5 & 7 & 5 & 2 \\ 3 & 4 & 4 & 2 & -2 & -3 \end{bmatrix} \end{array}$

5. $\begin{bmatrix} 6 & 3 \end{bmatrix} + \begin{bmatrix} 1 & 9 \end{bmatrix}$ $\begin{bmatrix} 7 & 12 \end{bmatrix}$

6. $\begin{bmatrix} -8 & 4 \\ 4 & -5 \end{bmatrix} + \begin{bmatrix} 4 & 6 \\ 6 & -1 \end{bmatrix}$ $\begin{bmatrix} -4 & 10 \\ 10 & -6 \end{bmatrix}$

7. $\begin{bmatrix} 5 & -2 \\ 2 & 4 \\ -7 & 2 \end{bmatrix} + \begin{bmatrix} 1 & 3 \\ 6 & -4 \\ 6 & -1 \end{bmatrix}$ $\begin{bmatrix} 6 & 1 \\ 8 & 0 \\ -1 & 1 \end{bmatrix}$

8. $\begin{bmatrix} -0.3 & 1.8 \end{bmatrix} - \begin{bmatrix} 0.6 & 2.7 \end{bmatrix}$ $\begin{bmatrix} -0.9 & -0.9 \end{bmatrix}$

9. $\begin{bmatrix} -1 & -9 \\ 0 & 2 \end{bmatrix} - \begin{bmatrix} 5 & 9 \\ -6 & -7 \end{bmatrix}$ $\begin{bmatrix} -6 & -18 \\ 6 & 9 \end{bmatrix}$

10. $\begin{bmatrix} 1.4 & 1.3 \\ -5 & -6.5 \\ 2 & 4 \end{bmatrix} - \begin{bmatrix} -1.4 & -3 \\ 3.9 & 4 \\ 1.3 & 3.9 \end{bmatrix}$ $\begin{bmatrix} 2.8 & 4.3 \\ -8.9 & -10.5 \\ 0.7 & 0.1 \end{bmatrix}$

Find the image matrix that represents the translation of the polygon. Then graph the polygon and its image.

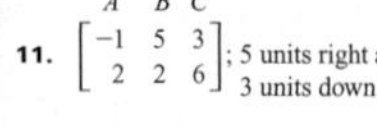

11. $\begin{array}{c} \begin{matrix} A & B & C \end{matrix} \\ \begin{bmatrix} -1 & 5 & 3 \\ 2 & 2 & 6 \end{bmatrix} \end{array}$; 5 units right and 3 units down

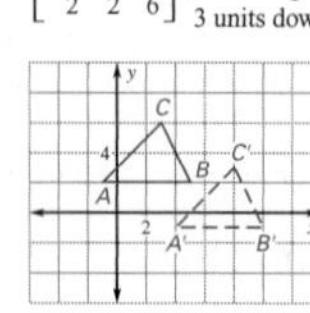

12. $\begin{array}{c} \begin{matrix} M & N & O & P \end{matrix} \\ \begin{bmatrix} 3 & 7 & 5 & 1 \\ 1 & 2 & 6 & 5 \end{bmatrix} \end{array}$; 6 units left and 2 units up

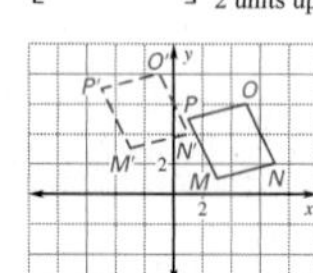

Multiply.

13. $\begin{bmatrix} 4 & -3 \end{bmatrix}\begin{bmatrix} -6 \\ 2 \end{bmatrix}$ $\begin{bmatrix} -30 \end{bmatrix}$

14. $\begin{bmatrix} -0.8 & 4 \end{bmatrix}\begin{bmatrix} 3 \\ -1.6 \end{bmatrix}$ $\begin{bmatrix} -8.8 \end{bmatrix}$

15. $\begin{bmatrix} -2 & 3 \\ 5 & -4 \end{bmatrix}\begin{bmatrix} -1 & 4 \\ 7 & 5 \end{bmatrix}$ $\begin{bmatrix} 23 & 7 \\ -33 & 0 \end{bmatrix}$

16. $\begin{bmatrix} 0.9 & 5 \\ -4 & 2 \end{bmatrix}\begin{bmatrix} 3 & 0 \\ -4 & -3 \end{bmatrix}$ $\begin{bmatrix} -17.3 & -15 \\ -20 & -6 \end{bmatrix}$

17. $\begin{bmatrix} -3 & 2 & 6 \end{bmatrix}\begin{bmatrix} -5 \\ 0 \\ -3 \end{bmatrix}$ $\begin{bmatrix} -3 \end{bmatrix}$

18. $\begin{bmatrix} 2 & 5 & 5 \\ 1 & 0 & 3 \end{bmatrix}\begin{bmatrix} 0 \\ -4 \\ 2 \end{bmatrix}$ $\begin{bmatrix} -10 \\ 6 \end{bmatrix}$

LESSON 9.2 Practice B *continued*
For use with pages 580–587

Use the described translation and the graph of the image to find the matrix that represents the preimage.

19. 3 units right and 4 units up See below.

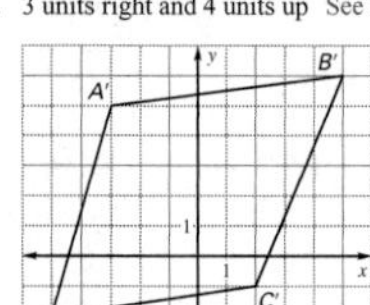

20. 2 units left and 3 units down See below.

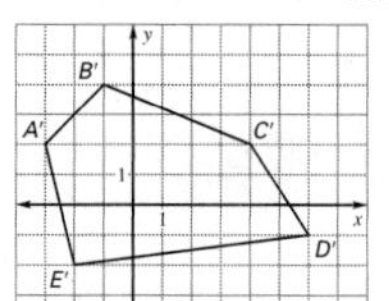

21. **Matrix Equation** Use the description of a translation of a triangle to find the value of each variable. What are the coordinates of the vertices of the image triangle?

$$\begin{bmatrix} -8 & x & -8 \\ 4 & 4 & y \end{bmatrix} + \begin{bmatrix} -2 & b & c \\ d & -5 & 2 \end{bmatrix} = \begin{bmatrix} r & -4 & -3 \\ 7 & s & 6 \end{bmatrix}$$

$x = -8$, $y = 4$, $b = 4$, $c = 5$, $d = 3$, $r = -10$, $s = -1$; $(-10, 7)$, $(-4, -1)$, $(-3, 6)$

22. **Office Supplies** Two offices submit supply lists. A weekly planner costs $8, a chairmat costs $90, and a desk tray costs $5. Use matrix multiplication to find the total cost of supplies for each office. Office 1: $670; Office 2: $890

Office 1	Office 2
15 weekly planners	25 weekly planners
5 chair mats	6 chair mats
20 desk trays	30 desk trays

23. **School Play** The school play was performed on three evenings. The attendance on each evening is shown in the table. Adult tickets sold for $5 and student tickets sold for $3.50.

Night	Adults	Students
First	340	250
Second	425	360
Third	440	390

a. Use matrix addition to find the total number of people that attended each night of the school play. First night: 590, second night: 785, third night: 830

b. Use matrix multiplication to find how much money was collected from all tickets each night. First night: $2575, second night: $3385, third night: $3565

19. $\begin{array}{c} \begin{matrix} A & B & C & D \end{matrix} \\ \begin{bmatrix} -6 & 2 & -1 & -8 \\ 1 & 2 & -5 & -6 \end{bmatrix} \end{array}$

20. $\begin{array}{c} \begin{matrix} A & B & C & D & E \end{matrix} \\ \begin{bmatrix} -1 & 1 & 6 & 8 & 0 \\ 5 & 7 & 5 & 2 & 1 \end{bmatrix} \end{array}$

LESSON 9.3 Practice B
For use with pages 588–596

Graph the reflection of the polygon in the given line.

1. x-axis
2. y-axis
3. $x = -1$

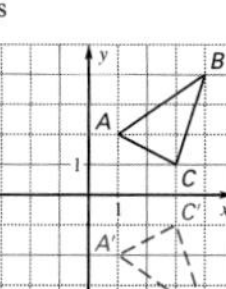
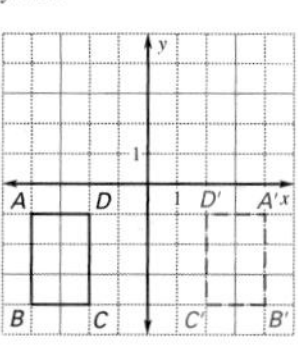
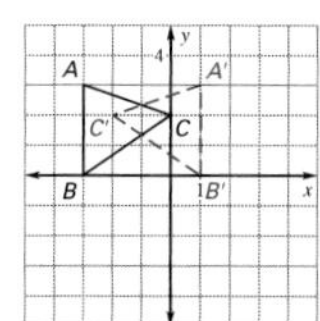

4. $y = 1$
5. $y = -x$
6. $y = x$

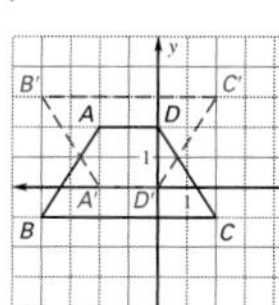
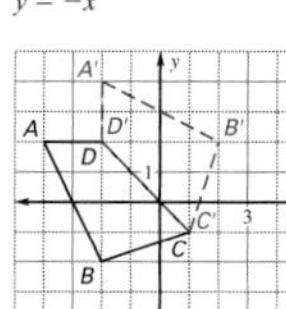
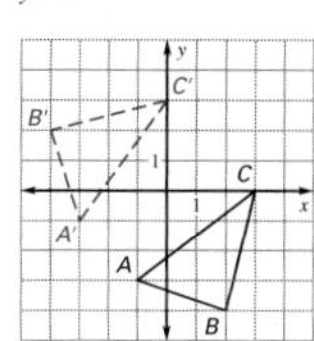

Use matrix multiplication to find the image. Graph the polygon and its image.

7. Reflect $\begin{bmatrix} -3 & 1 & 6 \\ 4 & 7 & 2 \end{bmatrix}$ (columns A, B, C) in the x-axis.

8. Reflect $\begin{bmatrix} 2 & 5 & 7 & 1 \\ 6 & 4 & -5 & -3 \end{bmatrix}$ (columns A, B, C, D) in the y-axis.

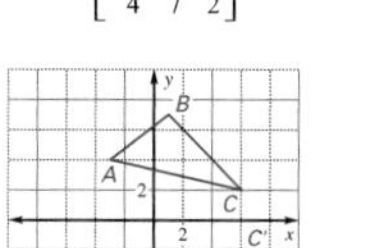
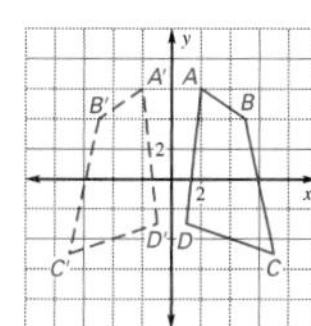

LESSON 9.3

LESSON 9.3 Practice B *continued*
For use with pages 588–596

Write a matrix for the polygon. Then find the image matrix that represents the polygon after a reflection in the given line. 9–11. See below.

9. x-axis
10. y-axis
11. x-axis

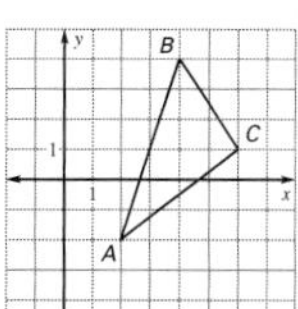
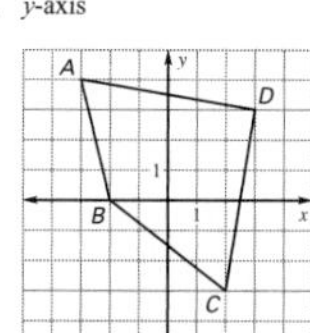
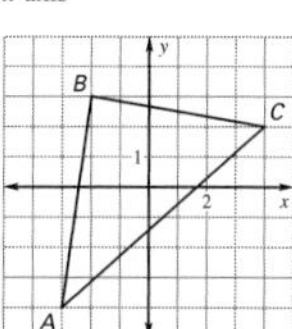

Find point C on the x-axis so $AC + BC$ is a minimum.

12. $A(2, -2)$, $B(11, -4)$ (5, 0)
13. $A(-1, 4)$, $B(6, 3)$ (3, 0)
14. $A(-3, 2)$, $B(-6, -4)$ (0, 0)

The vertices of $\triangle ABC$ are $A(-2, 1)$, $B(3, 4)$, and $C(3, 1)$. Reflect $\triangle ABC$ in the first line. Then reflect $\triangle A'B'C'$ in the second line. Graph $\triangle A'B'C'$ and $\triangle A''B''C''$.

15. In $y = 1$, then in $y = -2$
16. In $x = 4$, then in $y = -1$
17. In $y = x$, then in $x = -2$

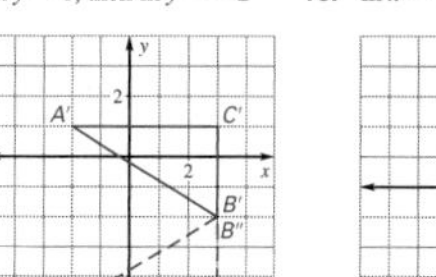
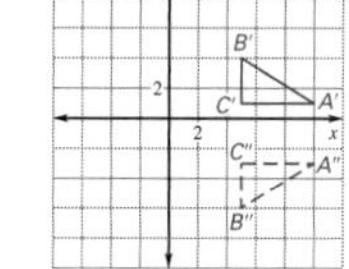
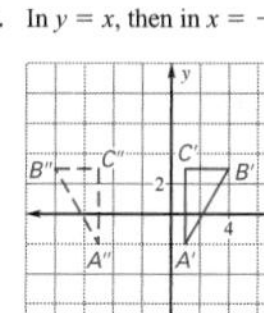

18. **Laying Cable** Underground electrical cable is being laid for two new homes. Where along the road (line m) should the transformer box be placed so that there is a minimum distance from the box to each of the homes?

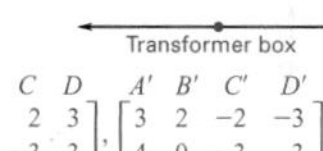

9. $\begin{bmatrix} 2 & 4 & 6 \\ -2 & 4 & 1 \end{bmatrix}$, $\begin{bmatrix} 2 & 4 & 6 \\ 2 & -4 & -1 \end{bmatrix}$ (columns A, B, C; A', B', C')

10. $\begin{bmatrix} -3 & -2 & 2 & 3 \\ 4 & 0 & -3 & 3 \end{bmatrix}$, $\begin{bmatrix} 3 & 2 & -2 & -3 \\ 4 & 0 & -3 & 3 \end{bmatrix}$ (columns A, B, C, D; A', B', C', D')

11. $\begin{bmatrix} -3 & -2 & 4 \\ -4 & 3 & 2 \end{bmatrix}$, $\begin{bmatrix} -3 & -2 & 4 \\ 4 & -3 & -2 \end{bmatrix}$ (columns A, B, C; A', B', C')

LESSON 9.3

LESSON 9.4 Practice B
For use with pages 598–605

LESSON 9.4

Match the diagram with the angle of rotation.

1. C
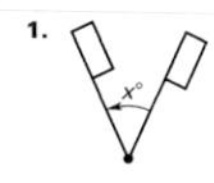

2. A
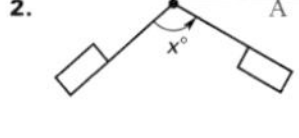

3. B
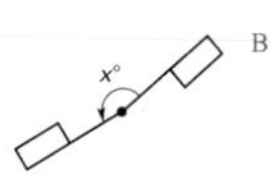

A. 110°
B. 170°
C. 50°

Trace the polygon and point P on paper. Then draw a rotation of the polygon the given number of degrees about P.

4. 45°
5. 120°
6. 135°

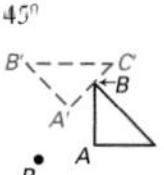
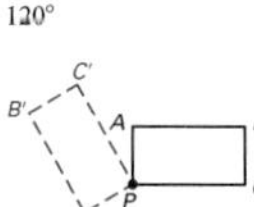
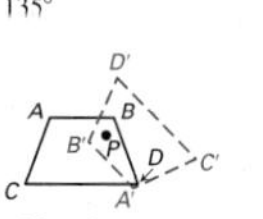

Rotate the figure the given number of degrees about the origin. List the coordinates of the vertices of the image.

7. 90° $A'(-1, -3)$, $B'(-3, -3)$, $C'(-3, 1)$, $D'(-1, 1)$
8. 180° $A'(2, 0)$, $B'(3, -2)$, $C'(2, -4)$, $D'(1, -2)$
9. 270° $A'(2, 0)$, $B'(4, -1)$, $C'(4, -6)$, $D'(2, -5)$

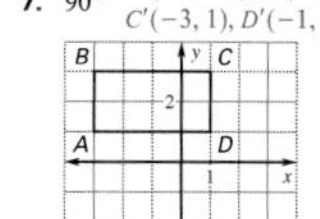
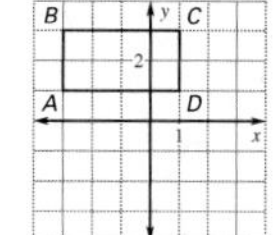
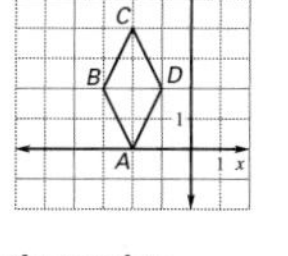
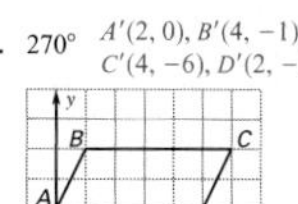
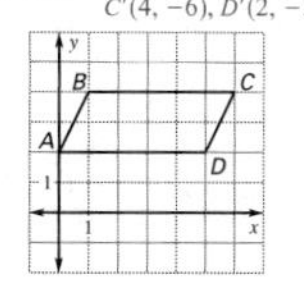

Find the value of each variable in the rotation.

10.
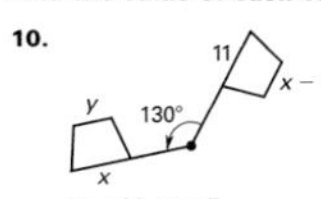
$x = 11$, $y = 7$

11.
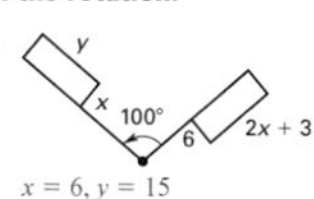
$x = 6$, $y = 15$

12.
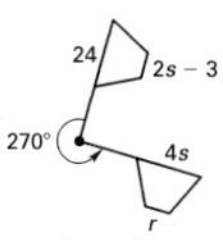
$r = 9$, $s = 6$

LESSON 9.4 Practice B *continued*
For use with pages 598–605

LESSON 9.4

Find the image matrix that represents the rotation of the polygon about the origin. Then graph the polygon and its image.

13. $\begin{bmatrix} 1 & 4 & 3 \\ 2 & 2 & 4 \end{bmatrix}$; 90° $\begin{bmatrix} -2 & -2 & -4 \\ 1 & 4 & 3 \end{bmatrix}$ (columns A, B, C; A', B', C')

14. $\begin{bmatrix} 0 & 4 & 2 \\ -1 & 0 & 3 \end{bmatrix}$; 180° $\begin{bmatrix} 0 & -4 & -2 \\ 1 & 0 & -3 \end{bmatrix}$ (columns A, B, C; A', B', C')

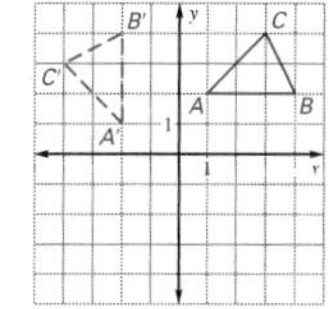
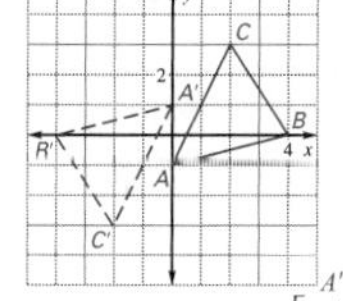

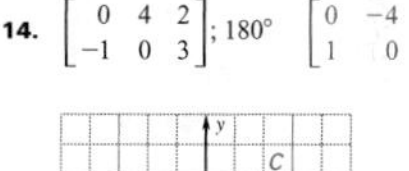
$\begin{bmatrix} -4 & -1 & -1 & -4 \\ 3 & 2 & -2 & -1 \end{bmatrix}$ (columns A', B', C', D')

15. $\begin{bmatrix} 1 & 2 & 4 & 5 \\ -1 & 3 & 3 & -1 \end{bmatrix}$; 90° $\begin{bmatrix} 1 & -3 & -3 & 1 \\ 1 & 2 & 4 & 5 \end{bmatrix}$ (columns A, B, C, D; A', B', C', D')

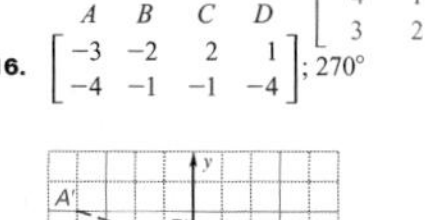
16. $\begin{bmatrix} -3 & -2 & 2 & 1 \\ -4 & -1 & -1 & -4 \end{bmatrix}$; 270° (columns A, B, C, D)

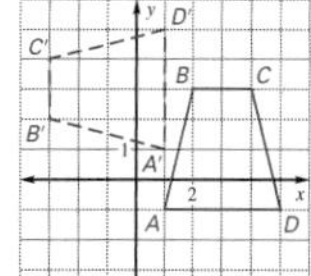
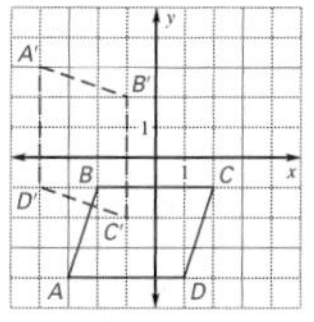

The endpoints of $\overline{CD}$ are $C(2, 1)$ and $D(4, 5)$. Graph $\overline{C'D'}$ and $\overline{C''D''}$ after the given rotations.

17. **Rotation:** 90° about the origin
Rotation: 270° about (2, 0)

18. **Rotation:** 180° about the origin
Rotation: 90° about (0, −3)

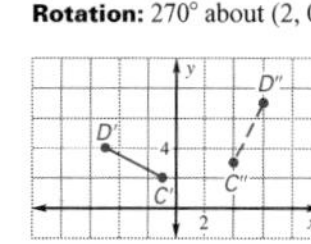
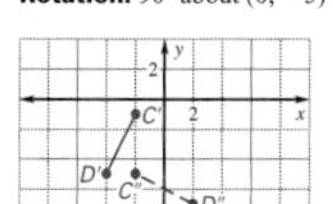

LESSON 9.5 Practice B

For use with pages 607–615

The endpoints of $\overline{CD}$ are $C(1, 2)$ and $D(5, 4)$. Graph the image of $\overline{CD}$ after the glide reflection.

1. **Translation:** $(x, y) \rightarrow (x - 4, y)$
Reflection: in the x-axis

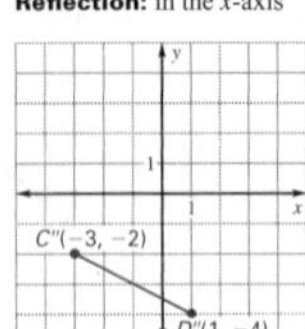

2. **Translation:** $(x, y) \rightarrow (x, y + 2)$
Reflection: in $y = x$

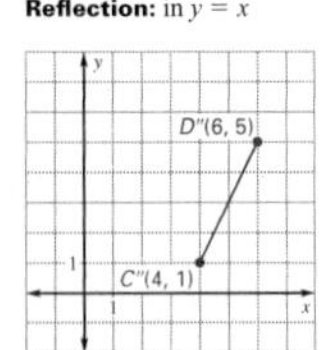

The vertices of $\triangle ABC$ are $A(3, 1)$, $B(1, 5)$, and $C(5, 3)$. Graph the image of $\triangle ABC$ after a composition of the transformations in the order they are listed.

3. **Translation:** $(x, y) \rightarrow (x + 3, y - 5)$
Reflection: in the y-axis

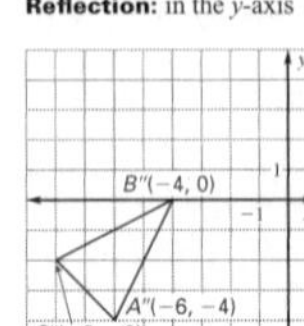

4. **Translation:** $(x, y) \rightarrow (x - 6, y + 1)$
Rotation: 90° about the origin

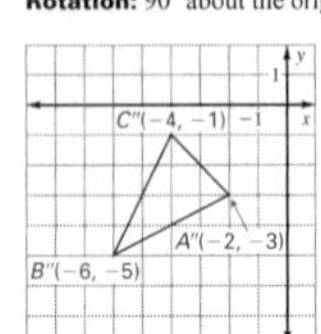

Graph $\overline{F''G''}$ after a composition of the transformations in the order they are listed. Then perform the transformations in reverse order. Does the order affect the final image $\overline{F''G''}$?

5. $F(4, -4)$, $G(1, -2)$
Rotation: 90° about the origin
Reflection: in the y-axis

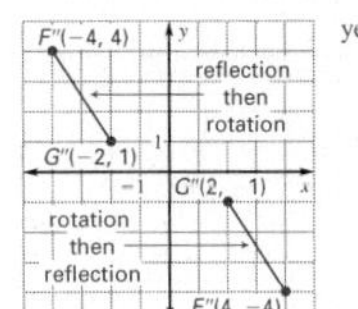

yes

6. $F(-1, -3)$, $G(-4, -2)$
Reflection: in the line $x = 1$
Translation: $(x, y) \rightarrow (x + 2, y + 10)$

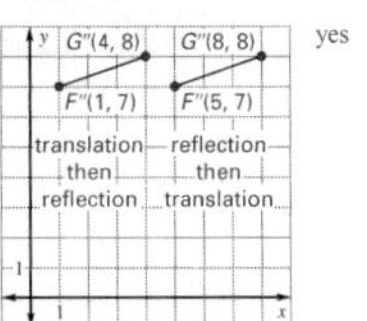

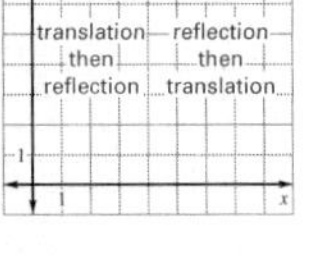

yes

LESSON 9.5 Practice B *continued*

For use with pages 607–615

Describe the composition of transformations.

7.

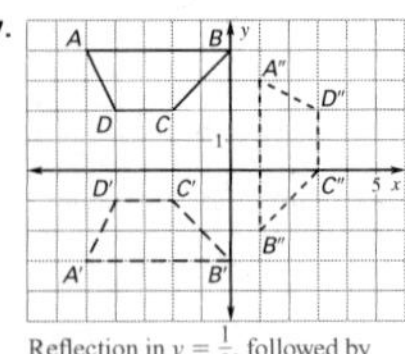

Reflection in $y = \frac{1}{2}$, followed by 270° rotation about $(1, -3)$.

8. 270° rotation about $(-2, -1)$, followed by the translation $(x, y) \rightarrow (x + 5, y - 2)$.

In the diagram, $k \parallel m$, $\overline{AB}$ is reflected in line k, and $\overline{A'B'}$ is reflected in line m.

9. A translation maps $\overline{AB}$ onto which segment? $\overline{A''B''}$

10. Which lines are perpendicular to $\overleftrightarrow{BB''}$? k and m

11. Name two segments parallel to $\overline{AA''}$. $\overleftrightarrow{BB'}$, $\overleftrightarrow{BB''}$

12. If the distance between k and m is 2.7 centimeters, what is the length of $\overline{AA''}$? 5.4 cm

13. Is the distance from A' to m the same as the distance from A'' to m? *Explain.* yes; definition of reflection

Find the angle of rotation that maps A onto A''.

14. 120°

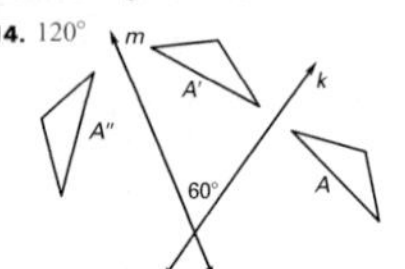

15. 90°

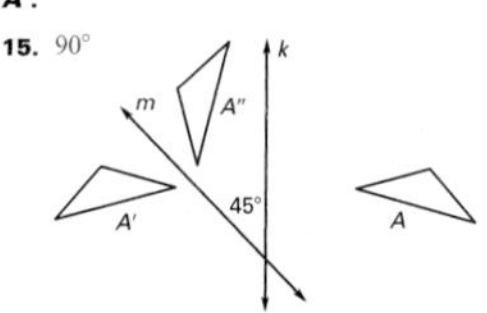

16. Stenciling a Border The border pattern below was made with a stencil. Describe how the border was created using one stencil four times.

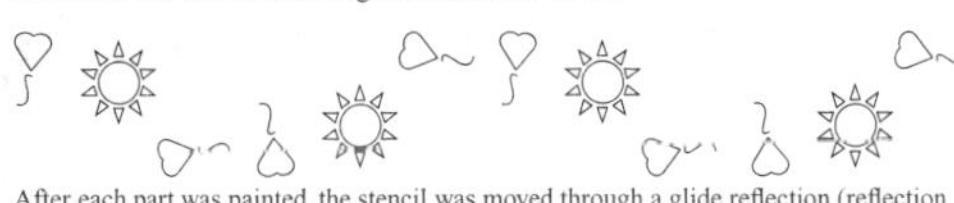

After each part was painted, the stencil was moved through a glide reflection (reflection in a horizontal line and translation to the right) to paint the next part.

LESSON 9.6 Practice B

For use with pages 619–624

Determine whether the figure has rotational symmetry. If so, describe the rotations that map the figure onto itself. 1–4. See below.

1.

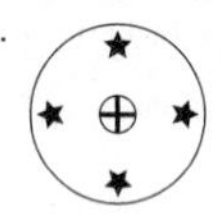

2.

3.

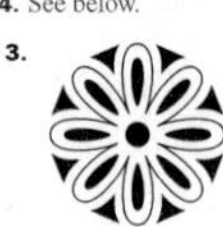

4.

Does the figure have the rotational symmetry shown? If not, does the figure have any rotational symmetry?

5. 120° yes

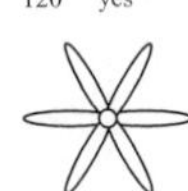

6. 180° no; no

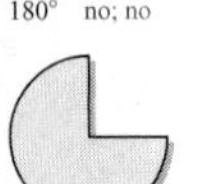

7. 45° yes

8. 36° no; yes, 40°

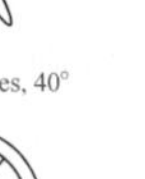

9. 180° yes

10. 90° no; no

In Exercises 11–16, draw a figure for the description. If not possible, write *not possible*.

11. A triangle with exactly two lines of symmetry not possible

12. A quadrilateral with exactly two lines of symmetry

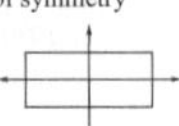

13. A pentagon with exactly two lines of symmetry not possible

14. A hexagon with exactly two lines of symmetry

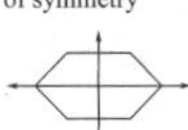

1. yes; a rotation of 90° or 180° about its center
2. yes; a rotation of 60°, 120°, or 180° about its center
3. yes; a rotation of 45°, 90°, 135°, or 180° about its center
4. yes; a rotation of 45°, 90°, 135°, or 180° about its center

LESSON 9.6 Practice B *continued*

For use with pages 619–624

15. An octagon with exactly two lines of symmetry

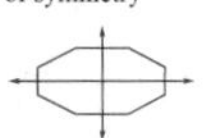

16. A quadrilateral with exactly four lines of symmetry

17. Paper Folding A piece of paper is folded in half and some cuts are made, as shown. Which figure represents the piece of paper unfolded? B

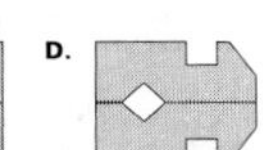

A. **B.** **C.** **D.**

In Exercises 18 and 19, use the following information.

Taj Mahal The Taj Mahal, located in India, was built between 1631 and 1653 by the emperor Shah Jahan as a monument to his wife. The floor map of the Taj Mahal is shown.

18. How many lines of symmetry does the floor map have? 4

19. Does the floor map have rotational symmetry? If so, describe a rotation that maps the pattern onto itself. Yes. The floor map can be rotated 90° or 180° about its center.

In Exercises 20 and 21, use the following information.

Drains Refer to the diagram below of a drain in a sink.

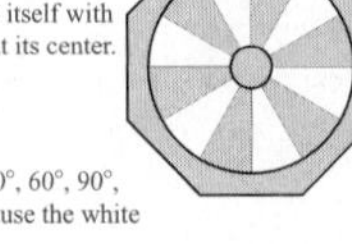

20. Does the drain have rotational symmetry? If so, describe the rotations that map the image onto itself. Yes. The image can be mapped onto itself with a rotation of 60°, 120°, or 180° about its center.

21. Would your answer to Exercise 20 change if you disregard the shading of the figures? *Explain* your reasoning.

Yes, the answer would change to a rotation of 30°, 60°, 90°, 120°, 150°, or 180° about its center. This is because the white figures can be mapped onto the shaded figures.

LESSON 9.7 Practice B

For use with pages 625–633

Find the scale factor. Tell whether the dilation is a *reduction* or an *enlargement*. Then find the values of the variables.

1.

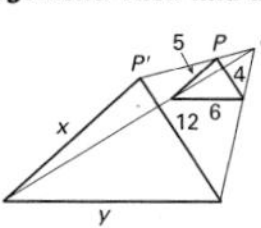

$k = 3$; enlargement; $x = 15$, $y = 18$

2.

12
5
P'
P
C
x
6

$k = \frac{5}{12}$; reduction; $x = 2.5$

Use the origin as the center of the dilation and the given scale factor to find the coordinates of the vertices of the image of the polygon.

3. $k = 3$ $M'(0, 9), N'(6, 12), L'(12, 0)$

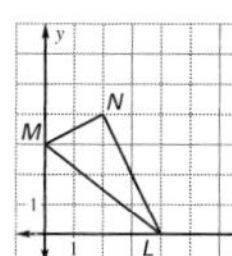

4. $k = \frac{1}{3}$ $G'\left(\frac{5}{3}, \frac{7}{3}\right), H'(3, 1), I'\left(1, \frac{1}{3}\right)$

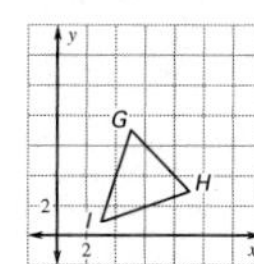

5. $k = 2$ $A'(2, 8), B'(6, 4), C'(12, 6), D'(8, 10)$

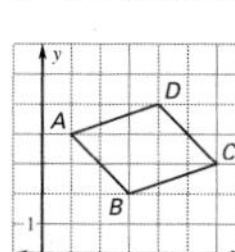

6. $k = \frac{5}{2}$ $P'\left(-\frac{5}{2}, -\frac{5}{2}\right), Q'(-10, 5), R'\left(-\frac{5}{2}, 10\right), S'\left(5, \frac{5}{2}\right)$

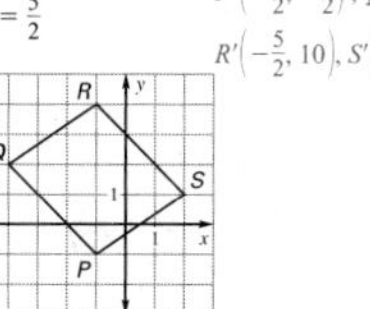

A dilation maps *A* to *A'* and *B* to *B'*. Find the scale factor of the dilation. Find the center of the dilation.

7. $A(4, 2), A'(5, 1), B(10, 6), B'(8, 3)$ $k = \frac{1}{2}$, $C(6, 0)$

8. $A(1, 6), A'(3, 2), B(2, 12), B'(6, 20)$ $k = 3$, $C(0, 8)$

9. $A(3, 6), A'(6, 3), B(11, 10), B'(8, 4)$ $k = \frac{1}{4}$, $C(7, 2)$

10. $A(-4, 1), A'(-5, 3), B(-1, 0), B'(1, 1)$ $k = 2$, $C(-3, -1)$

LESSON 9.7

LESSON 9.7 Practice B *continued*

For use with pages 625–633

The vertices of ▱*ABCD* are *A*(1, 1), *B*(3, 5), *C*(11, 5), and *D*(9, 1). Graph the image of the parallelogram after a composition of the transformations in the order they are listed.

11. **Translation:** $(x, y) \rightarrow (x + 5, y - 2)$

Dilation: centered at the origin with a scale factor of $\frac{3}{5}$

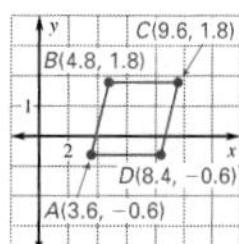

12. **Dilation:** centered at the origin with a scale factor of 2

Reflection: in the x-axis

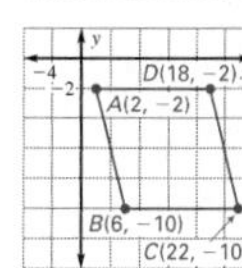

In Exercises 13–15, use the following information.

Flashlight Image You are projecting images onto a wall with a flashlight. The lamp of the flashlight is 8.3 centimeters away from the wall. The preimage is imprinted onto a clear cap that fits over the end of the flashlight. This cap has a diameter of 3 centimeters. The preimage has a height of 2 centimeters and the lamp of the flashlight is located 2.7 centimeters from the preimage.

13. Sketch a diagram of the dilation.

bulb
preimage
image
circle of light

14. Find the diameter of the circle of light projected onto the wall from the flashlight. about 9.22 cm

15. Find the height of the image projected onto the wall. about 6.15 cm

LESSON 9.7

9 Assessment

CHAPTER 9 Quiz 1
For use after Lessons 9.1–9.2

1. In the diagram shown, name the vector and write its component form.

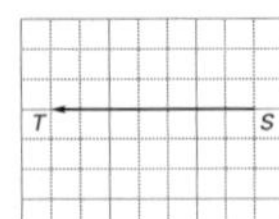

Use the translation $(x, y) \to (x + 4, y - 3)$.

2. What is the image of $(-2, 4)$?
3. What is the image of $(7, 2)$?
4. What is the preimage of $(-6, -1)$?

Add, subtract, or multiply.

5. $\begin{bmatrix} 6 & -2 \\ 9 & -1 \end{bmatrix} + \begin{bmatrix} -10 & -5 \\ 3 & -8 \end{bmatrix}$ $\begin{bmatrix} -4 & -7 \\ 12 & -9 \end{bmatrix}$

6. $\begin{bmatrix} -5 & 2 \\ 4 & 13 \end{bmatrix} - \begin{bmatrix} 5 & 16 \\ -6 & 9 \end{bmatrix}$ $\begin{bmatrix} -10 & -14 \\ 10 & 4 \end{bmatrix}$

7. $\begin{bmatrix} 4 & 2 \end{bmatrix} \begin{bmatrix} -4 \\ -1 \end{bmatrix}$ $\begin{bmatrix} -18 \end{bmatrix}$

8. $\begin{bmatrix} 2 & 1 \\ 5 & 6 \end{bmatrix} \begin{bmatrix} 3 & -4 \\ -2 & 7 \end{bmatrix}$ $\begin{bmatrix} 4 & -1 \\ 3 & 22 \end{bmatrix}$

Answers

1. $\overrightarrow{ST}$, $\langle -7, 0 \rangle$
2. $(2, 1)$
3. $(11, -1)$
4. $(-10, 2)$
5. See left.
6. See left.
7. See left.
8. See left.

CHAPTER 9 Quiz 2
For use after Lessons 9.3–9.5

The vertices of $\triangle ABC$ are $A(6, 2)$, $B(4, 3)$, and $C(9, 8)$. Graph the reflection in the line.

1. x-axis

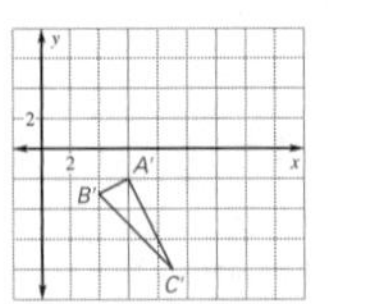

2. $y = -2$

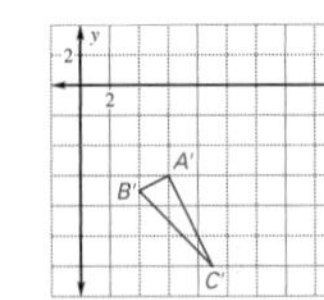

Find the coordinates of the image of $P(3, -4)$ after the rotation about the origin.

3. 90° rotation
4. 180° rotation
5. 270° rotation

The vertices of $\triangle LMN$ are $L(-9, 7)$, $M(-6, -1)$, and $M(-2, 2)$. Graph the image of $\triangle LMN$ after a composition of the transformations in the order they are listed.

6. Translation: $(x, y) \to (x + 8, y)$

Reflection: in the y-axis

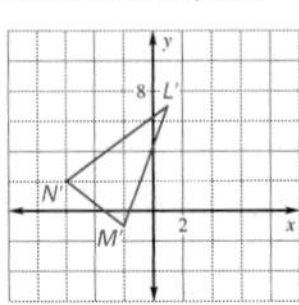

7. Rotation: $(x, y) \to 90°$ about the origin

Translation: $(x, y) \to (x + 3, y - 4)$

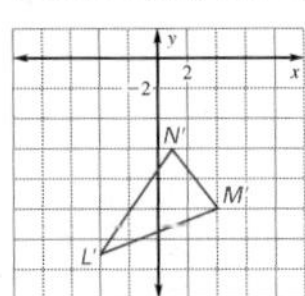

Answers

1. See left.
2. See left.
3. $P'(4, 3)$
4. $P'(-3, 4)$
5. $P'(-4, -3)$
6. See left.
7. See left.

CHAPTER 9 Quiz 3
For use after Lessons 9.6–9.7

Determine whether the figure has line symmetry. If possible, identify the number of lines of symmetry.

1.
2.
3.
4.

Tell whether the dilation is a *reduction* or an *enlargement* and find its scale factor.

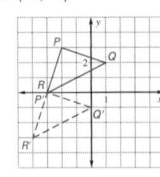

5.

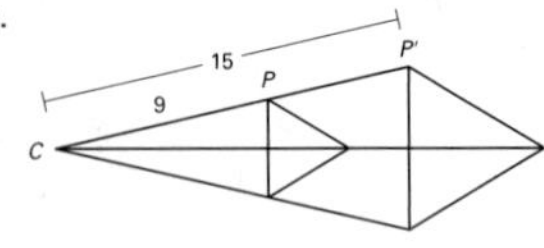

6.

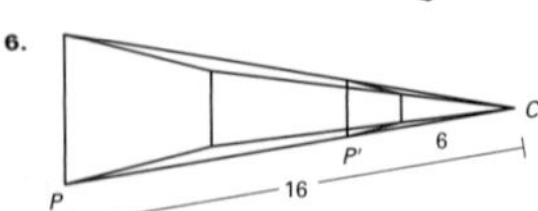

Find the image matrix that represents a dilation of the polygon centered at the origin with the given scale factor.

7. $\begin{matrix} D & E & F \end{matrix}$ $\begin{bmatrix} 3 & 4 & 6 \\ 2 & 7 & 5 \end{bmatrix}$; $k = 3$ $\begin{bmatrix} 9 & 12 & 18 \\ 6 & 21 & 15 \end{bmatrix}$

8. $\begin{matrix} G & H & J \end{matrix}$ $\begin{bmatrix} -3 & -1 & 5 \\ -5 & 1 & -1 \end{bmatrix}$; $k = \frac{1}{4}$ $\begin{bmatrix} -\frac{3}{4} & -\frac{1}{4} & \frac{5}{4} \\ -\frac{5}{4} & \frac{1}{4} & -\frac{1}{4} \end{bmatrix}$

Answers

1. yes; 2
2. yes; 8
3. yes; 1
4. no
5. enlargement; $\frac{5}{3}$
6. reduction; $\frac{3}{8}$
7. See left.
8. See left.

CHAPTER 9 Chapter Test B
For use after Chapter 9

Quadrilateral $A'B'C'D'$ is the image of $ABCD$ after a translation. Write a rule for the translation.

1.

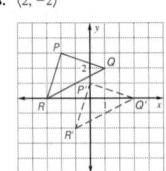

2.

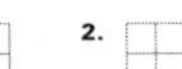

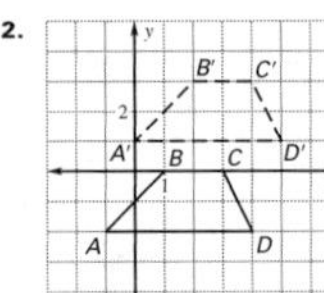

The vertices of $\triangle PQR$ are $P(-2, 3)$, $Q(1, 2)$, and $R(-3, 0)$. Translate $\triangle PQR$ using the given vector. Graph $\triangle PQR$ and its image.

3. $\langle 2, -2 \rangle$
4. $\langle -1, -3 \rangle$

Add, subtract, or multiply.

5. $\begin{bmatrix} -6 & 2 \end{bmatrix} + \begin{bmatrix} 13 & -9 \end{bmatrix}$

6. $\begin{bmatrix} 3.5 & -4.7 \end{bmatrix} - \begin{bmatrix} 5.6 & -1.2 \end{bmatrix}$

7. $\begin{bmatrix} 2 & 5 \\ -3 & -1 \end{bmatrix} + \begin{bmatrix} 6 & 1 \\ 4 & -8 \end{bmatrix}$

8. $\begin{bmatrix} 7 & -2 \\ 0 & 3 \end{bmatrix} \begin{bmatrix} -1 & 5 \\ 4 & -4 \end{bmatrix}$

Find the image matrix that represents the polygon shown after a reflection in the given line.

9. x-axis

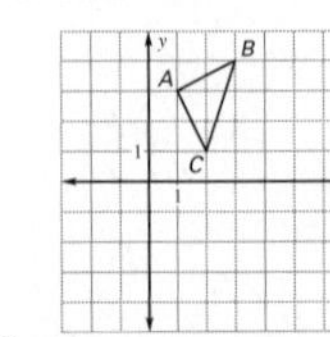

10. y-axis

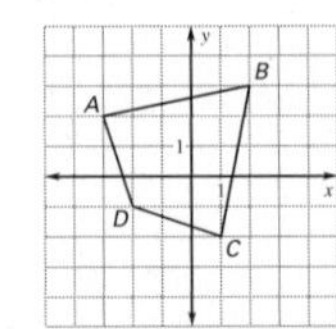

Answers

1. $(x, y) \to (x - 5, y - 2)$
2. $(x, y) \to (x + 1, y + 3)$
3. See left.
4. See left.
5. $\begin{bmatrix} 7 & -7 \end{bmatrix}$
6. $\begin{bmatrix} -2.1 & -3.5 \end{bmatrix}$
7. $\begin{bmatrix} 8 & 6 \\ 1 & -9 \end{bmatrix}$
8. $\begin{bmatrix} -15 & 43 \\ 12 & -12 \end{bmatrix}$
9. $\begin{bmatrix} 1 & 3 & 2 \\ -3 & -4 & -1 \end{bmatrix}$
10. $\begin{bmatrix} 3 & -2 & -1 & 2 \\ 2 & 3 & -2 & -1 \end{bmatrix}$

CHAPTER 9

Chapter Test B *continued*

For use after Chapter 9

Quadrilateral *STUV* has vertices *S*(−4, −2), *T*(−1, −1), *U*(1, −3), and *V*(−2, −5). Find the vertices of *S'T'U'V'* after the given counterclockwise rotation about the origin.

11. 90° **12.** 180° **13.** 270°

In Exercises 14–16, the vertices of quadrilateral *ABCD* are *A*(−4, 3), *B*(−1, 3), *C*(−3, 1), and *D*(−4, 1). Find the vertices of *A''B''C''D''* after a composition of the transformations in the order they are listed.

14. **Translation:** $(x, y) \rightarrow (x + 2, y - 3)$

Translation: $(x, y) \rightarrow (x - 1, y + 5)$

15. **Translation:** $(x, y) \rightarrow (x + 4, y + 1)$

Reflection: in the *x*-axis

16. **Reflection:** in the *y*-axis

Rotation: 180° about the origin

17. How many lines of symmetry does the figure shown have?

18. Draw a pentagon with one line of symmetry.

Sample answer:

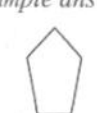

19. Draw a hexagon that has rotational symmetry.

Sample answer:

Simplify the product.

20. $-7\begin{bmatrix} -1 & 4 & -3 \\ 0 & -5 & 11 \end{bmatrix}$

21. $\frac{1}{4}\begin{bmatrix} 0 & -8 & -2 & -16 \\ 4 & 12 & -4 & 8 \end{bmatrix}$

The vertices of quadrilateral *JKLM* are *J*(0, 6), *K*(2, 8), *L*(6, 8), and *M*(6, 4). Find the vertices of *J''K''L''M''* after a composition of the transformations in the order they are listed.

22. **Translation:** $(x, y) \rightarrow (x - 4, y - 2)$

Dilation: centered at the origin with a scale factor of 2

23. **Dilation:** centered at the origin with a scale factor of $\frac{1}{2}$

Reflection: in the *x*-axis

Answers

11. $S'(2, -4), T'(1, -1), U'(3, 1), V'(5, -2)$
12. $S'(4, 2), T'(1, 1), U'(-1, 3), V'(2, 5)$
13. $S'(-2, 4), T'(-1, 1), U'(-3, -1), V'(-5, 2)$
14. $A''(-3, 5), B''(0, 5), C''(-2, 3), D''(-3, 3)$
15. $A''(0, -4), B''(3, -4), C''(1, -2), D''(0, -2)$
16. $A''(-4, -3), B''(-1, -3), C''(-3, -1), D''(-4, -1)$
17. 2
18. See left.
19. See left.
20. $\begin{bmatrix} 7 & -28 & 21 \\ 0 & 35 & -77 \end{bmatrix}$
21. $\begin{bmatrix} 0 & -2 & -\frac{1}{2} & -4 \\ 1 & 3 & -1 & 2 \end{bmatrix}$
22. $J''(-8, 8), K''(-4, 12), L''(4, 12), M''(4, 4)$
23. $J''(0, -3), K''(1, -4), L''(3, -4), M''(3, 2)$

CHAPTER 9

Standardized Test *continued*

For use after Chapter 9

Multiple Choice

1. What is the image of *P*(11, −4) using the translation $(x, y) \rightarrow (x - 17, y + 2)$? A

Ⓐ $P'(-6, -2)$ Ⓑ $P'(6, 2)$
Ⓒ $P'(-11, 4)$ Ⓓ $P'(-4, 11)$

2. Points *F*(2, 5), *G*(4, 4), and *H*(−1, −2) are the vertices of △*FGH*. Find the vertices of △*F'G'H'* by using the vector ⟨−3, −2⟩. C

Ⓐ $F'(-6, -10), G'(-12, -8), H'(3, 4)$
Ⓑ $F'(5, 7), G'(7, 6), H'(2, 0)$
Ⓒ $F'(-1, 3), G'(1, 2), H'(-4, -4)$
Ⓓ $F'(0, 2), G'(2, 1), H'(-3, -5)$

3. Add $\begin{bmatrix} 4 & -2 & 9 \\ -3 & 7 & 0 \\ 1 & 4 & 5 \end{bmatrix} + \begin{bmatrix} 0 & 3 & -4 \\ 6 & 1 & 8 \\ -2 & 1 & 5 \end{bmatrix}$. A

Ⓐ $\begin{bmatrix} 4 & 1 & 5 \\ 3 & 8 & 8 \\ -1 & 5 & 10 \end{bmatrix}$

Ⓑ $\begin{bmatrix} 4 & 0 & -3 \\ 0 & 8 & 1 \\ -7 & 5 & 6 \end{bmatrix}$

Ⓒ $\begin{bmatrix} 4 & -5 & 13 \\ -9 & 6 & -8 \\ 3 & 3 & 10 \end{bmatrix}$

Ⓓ $\begin{bmatrix} 4 & 5 & 13 \\ 9 & 8 & 8 \\ 3 & 5 & 10 \end{bmatrix}$

4. Multiply $\begin{bmatrix} 6 \\ -1 \end{bmatrix}\begin{bmatrix} -3 & 2 \end{bmatrix}$. A

Ⓐ $\begin{bmatrix} -18 & 12 \\ 3 & -2 \end{bmatrix}$ Ⓑ $\begin{bmatrix} 3 & 8 \\ -4 & 1 \end{bmatrix}$

Ⓒ $\begin{bmatrix} -6 \\ 1 \end{bmatrix}$ Ⓓ $\begin{bmatrix} -20 \end{bmatrix}$

5. Which statement is false? D

Ⓐ If (*a*, *b*) is reflected in the *x*-axis, its image is the point (*a*, −*b*).
Ⓑ If (*a*, *b*) is reflected in the *y*-axis, its image is the point (−*a*, *b*).
Ⓒ If (*a*, *b*) is reflected in the line *y* = *x*, its image is the point (*b*, *a*).
Ⓓ If (*a*, *b*) is reflected in the line *y* = −*x*, its image is the point (−*a*, −*b*).

6. The vertices of △*PQR* are *P*(3, −1), *Q*(−2, 7), and *R*(6, 5). Find the reflection matrix of △*P'Q'R'* in the line *y* = *x*. B

Ⓐ $\begin{bmatrix} 1 & -7 & -5 \\ -3 & 2 & -6 \end{bmatrix}$

Ⓑ $\begin{bmatrix} -1 & 7 & 5 \\ 3 & -2 & 6 \end{bmatrix}$

Ⓒ $\begin{bmatrix} -3 & 2 & -6 \\ -1 & 7 & 5 \end{bmatrix}$

Ⓓ $\begin{bmatrix} 3 & -2 & 6 \\ 1 & -7 & -5 \end{bmatrix}$

7. Which statement describes the image? C

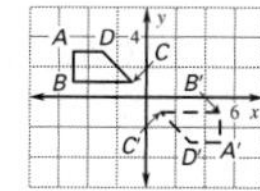

Ⓐ Reflection in the line *y* = *x*
Ⓑ Rotation of 180° about point (−1, 1)
Ⓒ Rotation of 180° about the origin
Ⓓ Translation right two units, down 2 units

CHAPTER 9

Standardized Test

For use after Chapter 9

8. Which of the following could make a regular tessellation? A

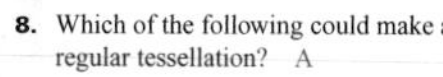

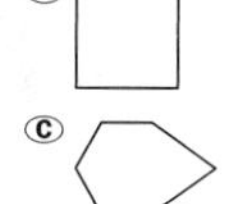

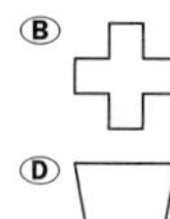

9. Which figure has rotational symmetry? D

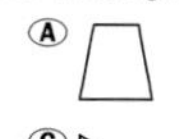

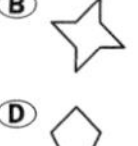

10. Vertices of quadrilateral *EFGH* are *E*(−2, −1), *F*(1, 2), *G*(6, 0), and *H*(2, −2). Find the scale factor if an image of *EFGH* has vertices $E'\left(-3, -\frac{3}{2}\right), F'\left(\frac{3}{2}, 3\right), G'(9, 0)$, and *H'*(3, −3). D

Ⓐ $\frac{2}{3}$ Ⓑ $-\frac{3}{2}$ Ⓒ $-\frac{2}{3}$ Ⓓ $\frac{3}{2}$

Gridded Answer

11. Find the product:

$\begin{bmatrix} 12 & -4 & 7 & -6 \end{bmatrix}\begin{bmatrix} 8 \\ -3 \\ 5 \\ -2 \end{bmatrix}$.

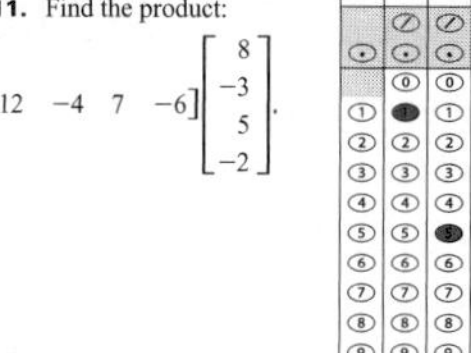

Short Response

12. A picture hangs on a wall as shown. See below.

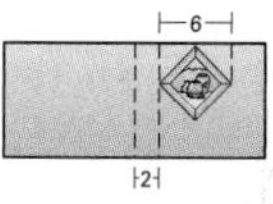

a. Describe a transformation that could move the picture to the symmetrical location on the left side of the wall.

b. Would the results of a reflection about the wall's vertical midsegment be desirable? *Explain.*

c. Would the results of a rotation about a point on the wall's vertical midsegment be desirable? *Explain.*

Extended Response

13. Quadrilateral *ABCD* has vertices See below.

$A\left(-\frac{7}{2}, \frac{7}{2}\right), B(-3, 1), C\left(1, \frac{5}{2}\right)$, and $D\left(0, -\frac{3}{2}\right)$.

a. Find the vertices *A'*, *B'*, *C'*, and *D'* of the image after a dilation with a scale factor of 2.

b. Graph the image and preimage.

c. Show the image matrix after reflecting *A'B'C'D'* in the line *y* = *x*.

d. Now rotate the reflection 270°. Find the new image matrix.

12. a. $(x, y) \rightarrow (x - 10, y)$ **b.** No, because the picture would be facing the wall. **c.** No, because the picture would be upside down.

13. a. $A'(-7, 7)$, $B'(-6, 2)$, $C'(2, 5)$, $D'(0, -3)$ **b.**

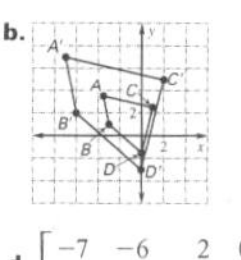

c. $\begin{bmatrix} 7 & 2 & 5 & -3 \\ -7 & -6 & 2 & 0 \end{bmatrix}$ **d.** $\begin{bmatrix} -7 & -6 & 2 & 0 \\ 7 & -2 & -5 & 3 \end{bmatrix}$

CHAPTER 9

Alternative Assessment and Math Journal

For use after Chapter 9

Journal **1.** Use the triangle with vertices *A*(−1, 1), *B*(3, 1), and *C*(2, 4) to demonstrate each different kind of transformation. Then describe each transformation in coordinate notation and in matrix notation.

Multi-Step Problem **2.** The walls of a day care center are being painted with different geometric shapes. The beginning of the design on one wall is shown below with a grid superimposed over top of it.

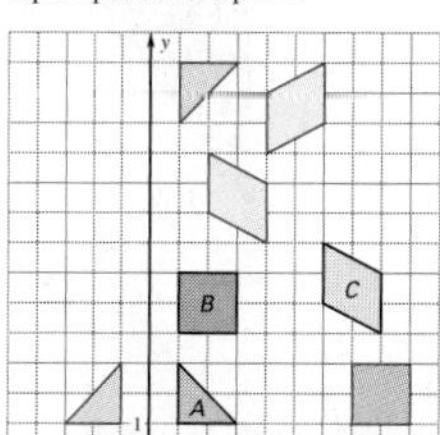

a. Graph the image of square B after the translation $(x, y) \rightarrow (x + 6, y - 3)$. Then list the coordinates of the image.

b. Write the matrix that represents parallelogram C. Then find the image matrix that represents a translation of 4 units left and 3 units up of parallelogram C.

c. Graph the image parallelogram from part (b).

d. Graph the reflection of triangle A in the line given by *y* = 7. Then list the coordinates of the image.

e. Find the image matrix that represents the 90° rotation of triangle A about the origin. Then graph the image.

f. Graph the image of parallelogram C after the glide reflection.
Translation: $(x, y) \rightarrow (x, y + 6)$
Reflection: in the line given by *x* = 6

g. Find the image matrix that represents a dilation of square B centered at the origin and a scale factor of $\frac{1}{2}$.

h. Determine whether parallelogram C has line symmetry and/or rotational symmetry. Identify the number of lines of symmetry and/or the rotations that map the figure onto itself.

1. Complete answers should include: examples of a translation, a reflection, and a dilation and descriptions of each type of transformation in coordinate notation and in matrix notation.

2. a. See graph; (7, 1), (9, 1), (9, 3), (7, 3)

b. $\begin{bmatrix} 6 & 8 & 8 & 6 \\ 5 & 4 & 6 & 7 \end{bmatrix}$; $\begin{bmatrix} 2 & 4 & 4 & 2 \\ 8 & 7 & 10 & 9 \end{bmatrix}$

c. See graph.

d. See graph; (1, 11), (1, 13), (3, 13)

e. See graph; $\begin{bmatrix} -1 & -3 & -1 \\ 1 & 1 & 3 \end{bmatrix}$

f. See graph.

g. $\begin{bmatrix} \frac{1}{2} & \frac{3}{2} & \frac{1}{2} & \frac{3}{2} \\ \frac{2}{2} & \frac{2}{2} & \frac{3}{2} & \frac{3}{2} \end{bmatrix}$ **h.** no line symmetry; rotational symmetry: 180°

PLAN AND PREPARE

Main Ideas

In Chapter 9 students will perform translations with vectors, algebra and matrices. They will reflect figures in a given line, rotate figures about a point, identify line and rotational symmetry, and perform dilations using drawing tools and matrices.

Prerequisite Skills

- Translating, reflecting, rotating and dilating polygons
- Using similar triangles

Additional resources for reviewing prerequisite skills are:

- Skills Review Handbook, pp. 869–895
- @HomeTutor

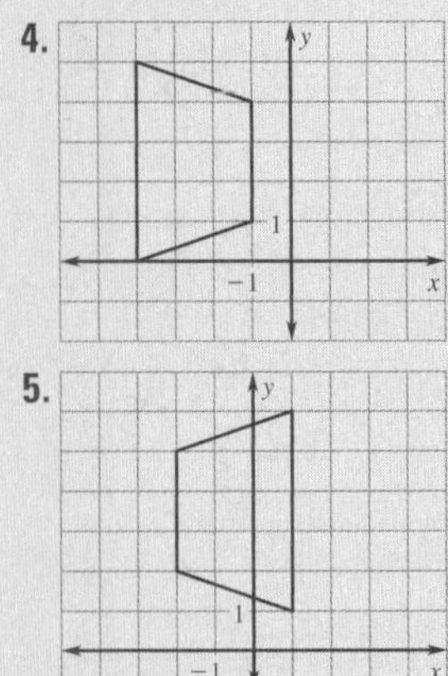

9 Properties of Transformations

Before

In previous chapters, you learned the following skills, which you'll use in Chapter 9: translating, reflecting, and rotating polygons, and using similar triangles.

Prerequisite Skills

VOCABULARY CHECK

Match the transformation of Triangle A with its graph.

1. Translation of Triangle A **Triangle B**
2. Reflection of Triangle A **Triangle D**
3. Rotation of Triangle A **Triangle C**

SKILLS AND ALGEBRA CHECK

The vertices of $JKLM$ are $J(-1, 6)$, $K(2, 5)$, $L(2, 2)$, and $M(-1, 1)$. Graph its image after the transformation described. *(Review p. 272 for 9.1, 9.3.)* **4, 5. See margin.**

4. Translate 3 units left and 1 unit down.
5. Reflect in the y-axis.

In the diagram, $ABCD \sim EFGH$.
(Review p. 372 for 9.7.)

6. Find the scale factor of $ABCD$ to $EFGH$. $\frac{2}{3}$
7. Find the values of x, y, and z. **90, 9, 8**

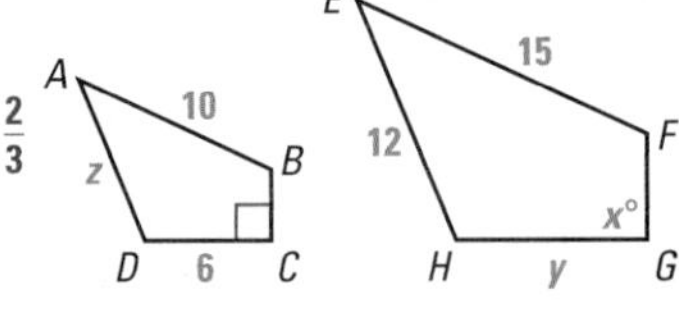

@HomeTutor Prerequisite skills practice at classzone.com

Chapter Planning Guide

Chapter 9 Resource Book
- Teaching Guide/Lesson Plan (pp. 3, 18, 31, 45, 59, 73, 87)
- Project with Rubric (p. 102)

Assessment and Intervention
- Assessment Book (pp. 125–139)
- Benchmark Tests
- Remediation Book

Interactive Technology
- Easy Planner
- Power Presentations CD-ROM
- Activity Generator CD-ROM
- Animated Geometry
- Test Generator CD-ROM
- Online Quizzes
- eWorkbook
- eEdition
- @HomeTutor

Resources for English Learners
- Quick Reference for English Learners
- Spanish Study Guide
- Multi-Language Visual Glossary
- Student Resources in Spanish

California Standards for Chapter 9

Geometry: 5.0, 16.0, 17.0, 22.0

Now

In Chapter 9, you will apply the big ideas listed below and reviewed in the Chapter Summary on page 635. You will also use the key vocabulary listed below.

Big Ideas

1. **Performing congruence and similarity transformations**
2. **Making real-world connections to symmetry and tessellations**
3. **Applying matrices and vectors in Geometry**

KEY VOCABULARY

- image, *p. 572*
- preimage, *p. 572*
- isometry, *p. 573*
- vector, *p. 574*
- component form, *p. 574*
- matrix, *p. 580*
- element, *p. 580*
- dimensions, *p. 580*
- line of reflection, *p. 589*
- center of rotation, *p. 598*
- angle of rotation, *p. 598*
- glide reflection, *p. 608*
- composition of transformations, *p. 609*
- line symmetry, *p. 619*
- rotational symmetry, *p. 620*
- scalar multiplication, *p. 627*

Why?

You can use properties of shapes to determine whether shapes tessellate. For example, you can use angle measurements to determine which shapes can be used to make a tessellation.

Animated Geometry

The animation illustrated below for Example 3 on page 617 helps you answer this question: How can you use tiles to tessellate a floor?

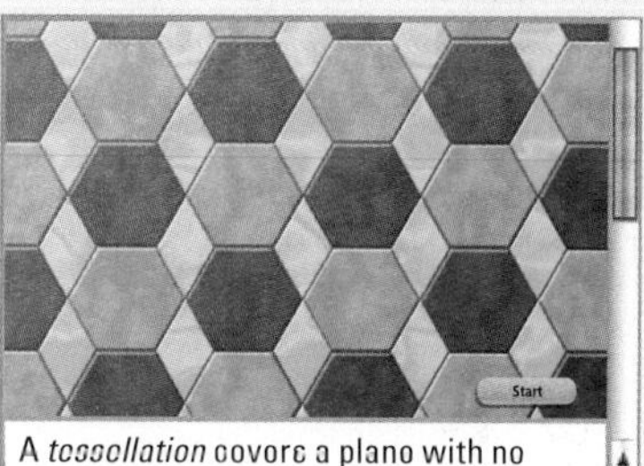
Start
A *tessellation* covers a plane with no gaps or overlaps.

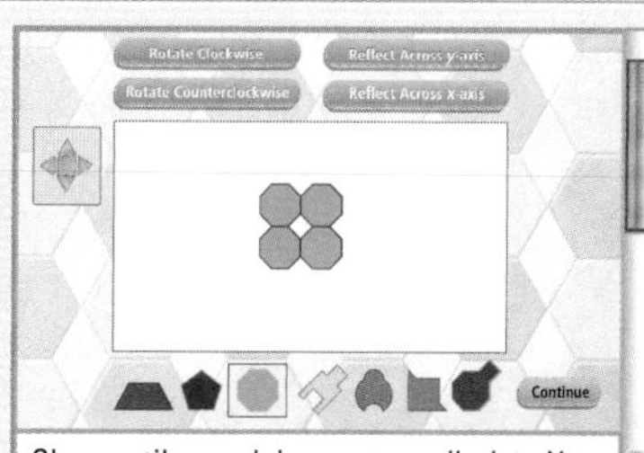
Continue
Choose tiles and draw a tessellation. You may translate, reflect, and rotate tiles.

Animated Geometry at classzone.com

Other animations for Chapter 9: pages 582, 590, 599, 602, 611, 619, and 626

Geometry Toolkit

- Reading Strategies for Chapter 9, pp. 25–26
- Differentiated Instruction Notes, pp. 71–74
- English Learners Notes, pp. 107–108
- Inclusion Notes, pp. 137–138
- Teaching Strategies with Sample Worksheets, pp. 145–168
- Using Technology in the Classroom, pp. 169–174
- Tips for New Teachers, pp. 191–192
- Math Background Notes, pp. 226–229
- Pre-AP Strategies and Copymasters, pp. 299–300, 367–376
- Teacher Survival Activities, pp. 437–438, 461–462
- Bulletin Board Idea, p. 477
- Teacher Tool Transparencies, following p. 480

9.1 Translate Figures and Use Vectors

Before You used a coordinate rule to translate a figure.

Now You will use a vector to translate a figure.

Why? So you can find a distance covered on snowshoes, as in Exs. 35–37.

Key Vocabulary
- **image**
- **preimage**
- **isometry**
- **vector**
  initial point, terminal point, horizontal component, vertical component
- **component form**
- **translation,** *p. 272*

In Lesson 4.8, you learned that a *transformation* moves or changes a figure in some way to produce a new figure called an **image**. Another name for the original figure is the **preimage**.

Recall that a *translation* moves every point of a figure the same distance in the same direction. More specifically, a translation maps, or moves, the points P and Q of a plane figure to the points P' (read "*P prime*") and Q', so that one of the following statements is true:

- $PP' = QQ'$ and $\overline{PP'} \parallel \overline{QQ'}$, or
- $PP' = QQ'$ and $\overline{PP'}$ and $\overline{QQ'}$ are collinear.

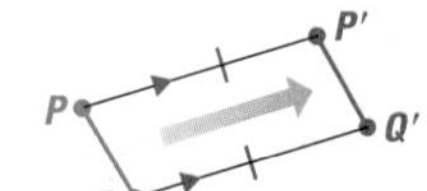

EXAMPLE 1 Translate a figure in the coordinate plane

Graph quadrilateral $ABCD$ with vertices $A(-1, 2)$, $B(-1, 5)$, $C(4, 6)$, and $D(4, 2)$. Find the image of each vertex after the translation $(x, y) \to (x + 3, y - 1)$. Then graph the image using prime notation.

Solution

USE NOTATION
You can use *prime notation* to name an image. For example, if the preimage is $\triangle ABC$, then its image is $\triangle A'B'C'$, read as *"triangle A prime, B prime, C prime."*

First, draw $ABCD$. Find the translation of each vertex by adding 3 to its x-coordinate and subtracting 1 from its y-coordinate. Then graph the image.

$$(x, y) \to (x + 3, y - 1)$$

$A(-1, 2) \to A'(2, 1)$

$B(-1, 5) \to B'(2, 4)$

$C(4, 6) \to C'(7, 5)$

$D(4, 2) \to D'(7, 1)$

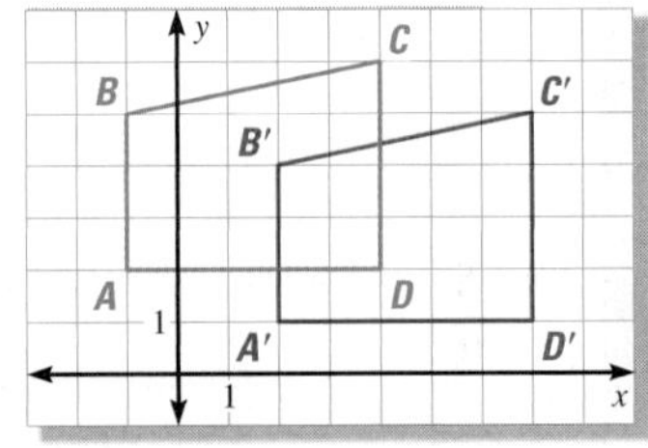

✓ GUIDED PRACTICE for Example 1

1. Draw $\triangle RST$ with vertices $R(2, 2)$, $S(5, 2)$, and $T(3, 5)$. Find the image of each vertex after the translation $(x, y) \to (x + 1, y + 2)$. Graph the image using prime notation. **See margin for art; $R'(3, 4)$, $S'(6, 4)$, $T'(4, 7)$.**

2. The image of $(x, y) \to (x + 4, y - 7)$ is $\overline{P'Q'}$ with endpoints $P'(-3, 4)$ and $Q'(2, 1)$. Find the coordinates of the endpoints of the preimage. **$P(-7, 11)$, $Q(-2, 8)$**

1 PLAN AND PREPARE

Warm-Up Exercises

Transparency Available

1. What is a translation? **a transformation that moves every point of a figure the same distance in the same direction**
2. Translate $A(3, 5)$ 4 units right and 2 units down. What are the coordinates of the image? **(7, 3)**
3. Find the length of $\overline{BC}$ with endpoints $B(-3, 5)$ and $C(1, 2)$. **5**
4. If you translate the points $M(4, 7)$ and $N(-1, 5)$ by using $(x, y) \to (x - 3, y + 6)$, what is the distance from M' to N'? **$\sqrt{29}$**

Notetaking Guide

Transparency Available

Promotes interactive learning and notetaking skills, pp. 221–225.

Pacing

Basic: 2 days
Average: 2 days
Advanced: 2 days
Block: 1 block
- See *Teaching Guide/Lesson Plan.*

2 FOCUS AND MOTIVATE

Essential Question

Big Idea 3, p. 571

How do you translate a figure using a vector? **Tell students they will learn how to answer this question by studying vectors.**

Resource Planning Guide

Chapter Resource Book
- Teaching Guide/Lesson Plan (pp. 3–4)
- Activity Master (p. 5)
- Practice levels A, B, C (pp. 7–12)
- Study Guide (pp. 13–14)
- Catch-up for Absent Students (p. 15)
- Problem Solving Workshop (p. 16)
- Challenge (p. 17)

Workbooks
- Notetaking Guide (pp. 221–225)
- Practice Workbook (pp. 163–165)

Teaching Options
- **Power Presentations CD-ROM** provides dynamic electronic teaching resources for the classroom.
- **Activity Generator CD-ROM** provides editable activities for all ability levels.

Interactive Technology
- Easy Planner
- Power Presentations CD-ROM
- Activity Generator CD-ROM
- Animated Geometry
- Test Generator CD-ROM
- Online Quiz
- eWorkbook
- eEdition
- @HomeTutor

Resources for English Learners
- Quick Reference for English Learners
- Spanish Study Guide
- Multi-Language Visual Glossary
- Student Resources in Spanish

See also the *Geometry Toolkit* for more strategies for meeting individual needs.

ISOMETRY An **isometry** is a transformation that preserves length and angle measure. Isometry is another word for congruence transformation (page 272).

EXAMPLE 2 Write a translation rule and verify congruence

READ DIAGRAMS
In this book, the preimage is always shown in blue, and the image is always shown in red.

Write a rule for the translation of $\triangle ABC$ to $\triangle A'B'C'$. Then verify that the transformation is an isometry.

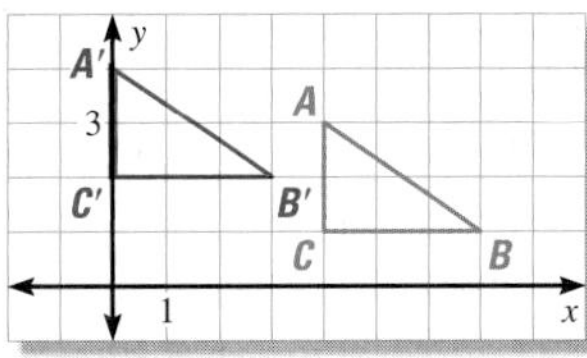

Solution

To go from A to A', move 4 units left and 1 unit up. So, a rule for the translation is $(x, y) \rightarrow (x - 4, y + 1)$.

Use the SAS Congruence Postulate. Notice that $CB = C'B' = 3$, and $AC = A'C' = 2$. The slopes of $\overline{CB}$ and $\overline{C'B'}$ are 0, and the slopes of $\overline{CA}$ and $\overline{C'A'}$ are undefined, so the sides are perpendicular. Therefore, $\angle C$ and $\angle C'$ are congruent right angles. So, $\triangle ABC \cong \triangle A'B'C'$. The translation is an isometry.

GUIDED PRACTICE for Example 2

3. In Example 2, write a rule to translate $\triangle A'B'C'$ back to $\triangle ABC$.
$(x, y) \rightarrow (x + 4, y - 1)$

Standards

17.0 Students prove theorems by using coordinate geometry, including the midpoint of a line segment, **the distance formula,** and various forms of equations of lines and circles.

22.0 Students know the effect of rigid motions on figures in the coordinate plane and space, including rotations, **translations,** and reflections.

THEOREM *For Your Notebook*

THEOREM 9.1 Translation Theorem

A translation is an isometry.

Proof: below; Ex. 46, p. 579

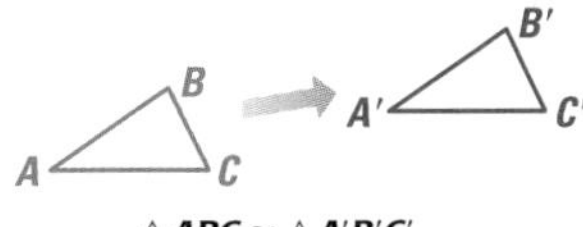

$\triangle ABC \cong \triangle A'B'C'$

PROOF Translation Theorem

A translation is an isometry.

GIVEN ▶ $P(a, b)$ and $Q(c, d)$ are two points on a figure translated by $(x, y) \rightarrow (x + s, y + t)$.

PROVE ▶ $PQ = P'Q'$

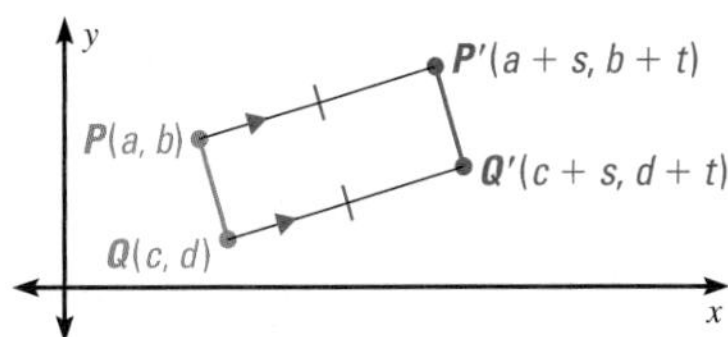

The translation maps $P(a, b)$ to $P'(a + s, b + t)$ and $Q(c, d)$ to $Q'(c + s, d + t)$.

Use the Distance Formula to find PQ and $P'Q'$. $PQ = \sqrt{(c - a)^2 + (d - b)^2}$.

$$P'Q' = \sqrt{[(c + s) - (a + s)]^2 + [(d + t) - (b + t)]^2}$$
$$= \sqrt{(c + s - a - s)^2 + (d + t - b - t)^2}$$
$$= \sqrt{(c - a)^2 + (d - b)^2}$$

Therefore, $PQ = P'Q'$ by the Transitive Property of Equality.

Motivating the Lesson

Ask students to imagine that an airplane is traveling at a constant velocity when it encounters a strong wind. Tell students that in this lesson they will study vectors and that vectors can be used to describe the effect of the wind on the path of the airplane.

3 TEACH

Extra Example 1

Graph quadrilateral *KLMN* with vertices $K(0, -2)$, $L(4, 3)$, $M(5, 2)$, and $N(6, -1)$. Find the image of each vertex after the translation $(x, y) \rightarrow (x - 4, y + 2)$. Then graph the image using prime notation.

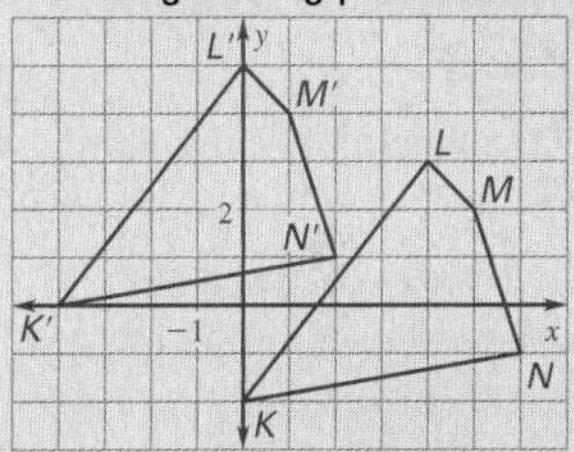

Extra Example 2

Write a rule for the translation of $\triangle DEF$ to $\triangle D'E'F'$. Then verify that the transformation is an isometry.

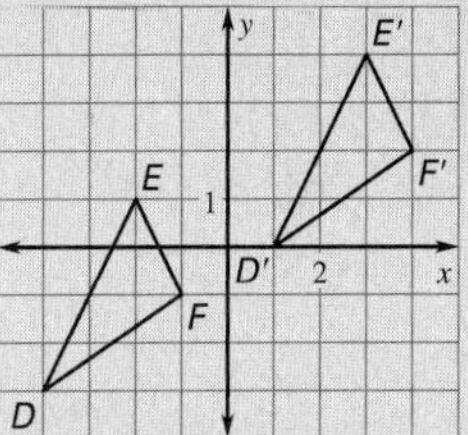

$(x, y) \rightarrow (x + 5, y + 3)$; $DE = D'E' = 2\sqrt{5}$, $EF = E'F' = \sqrt{5}$, $DF = D'F' = \sqrt{13}$, so the triangles are congruent by the SSS congruence Postulate.

1. See Additional Answers beginning on p. AA1.

Extra Example 3

Name the vector and write its component form.

a.

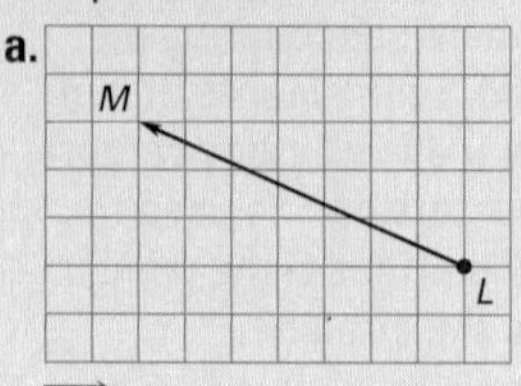

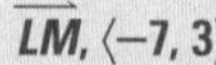

$\overrightarrow{LM}$, $\langle -7, 3\rangle$

b.

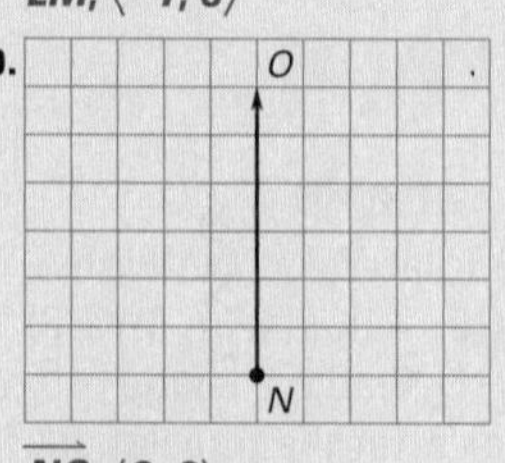

$\overrightarrow{NO}$, $\langle 0, 6\rangle$

Key Question to Ask for Example 3

- Is $\overrightarrow{BC}$ the same as $\overrightarrow{CB}$? Explain. **No, $\overrightarrow{BC}$ starts at *B* and ends at *C*, while $\overrightarrow{CB}$ starts at *C* and ends at *B*. They have the same length but opposite directions.**

Extra Example 4

The vertices of $\triangle DEF$ are $D(-2, 0)$, $E(-1, 3)$, and $F(2, -1)$. Translate $\triangle DEF$ using the vector $\langle 2, -3\rangle$.

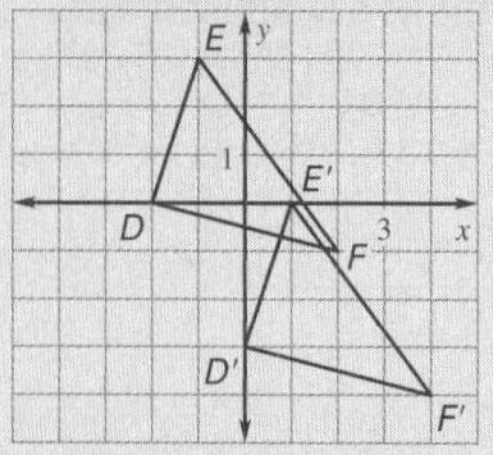

Avoiding Common Errors

Students may forget to use the brackets for the components of a vector. Instead, they will write the components as an ordered pair in parentheses. Show them that there are infinitely many arrows that model the vector $\langle 5, 3\rangle$ but only one point for the ordered pair $(5, 3)$. Stress the correct vector notation throughout the chapter.

VECTORS Another way to describe a translation is by using a vector. A **vector** is a quantity that has both direction and *magnitude*, or size. A vector is represented in the coordinate plane by an arrow drawn from one point to another.

USE NOTATION

Use brackets to write the component form of the vector $\langle r, s\rangle$. Use parentheses to write the coordinates of the point (p, q).

y
$\langle r, s\rangle$
(p, q)
x

KEY CONCEPT *For Your Notebook*

Vectors

The diagram shows a vector named $\overrightarrow{FG}$, read as "vector *FG*."

The **initial point**, or starting point, of the vector is *F*.

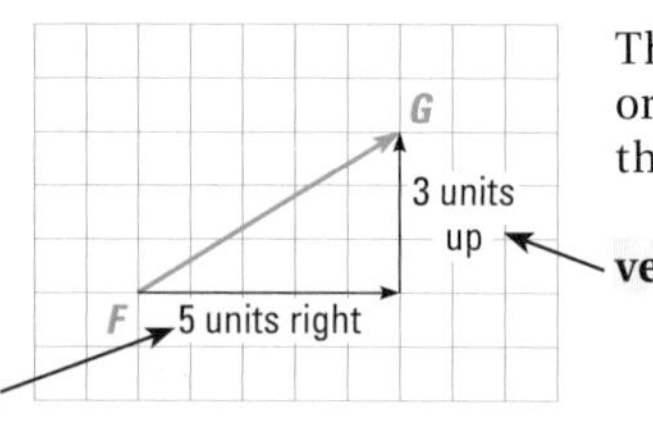

The **terminal point**, or ending point, of the vector is *G*.

vertical component

horizontal component

The **component form** of a vector combines the horizontal and vertical components. So, the component form of $\overrightarrow{FG}$ is $\langle 5, 3\rangle$.

EXAMPLE 3 Identify vector components

Name the vector and write its component form.

a.

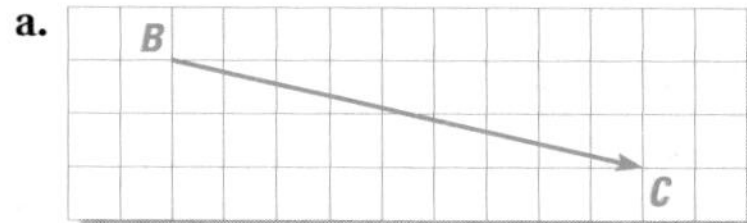

b.

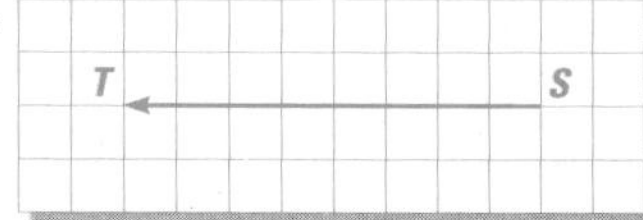

Solution

a. The vector is $\overrightarrow{BC}$. From initial point *B* to terminal point *C*, you move 9 units right and 2 units down. So, the component form is $\langle 9, -2\rangle$.

b. The vector is $\overrightarrow{ST}$. From initial point *S* to terminal point *T*, you move 8 units left and 0 units vertically. The component form is $\langle -8, 0\rangle$.

EXAMPLE 4 Use a vector to translate a figure

The vertices of $\triangle ABC$ are $A(0, 3)$, $B(2, 4)$, and $C(1, 0)$. Translate $\triangle ABC$ using the vector $\langle 5, -1\rangle$.

USE VECTORS

Notice that the vector can have different initial points. The vector describes only the direction and magnitude of the translation.

Solution

First, graph $\triangle ABC$. Use $\langle 5, -1\rangle$ to move each vertex 5 units to the right and 1 unit down. Label the image vertices. Draw $\triangle A'B'C'$. Notice that the vectors drawn from preimage to image vertices are parallel.

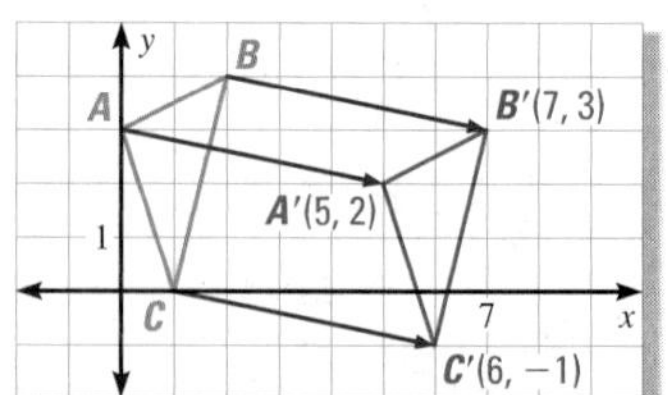

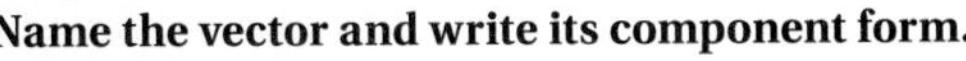

GUIDED PRACTICE for Examples 3 and 4

$\overrightarrow{RS}$, ⟨5, 0⟩

$\overrightarrow{TX}$, ⟨0, 3⟩

$\overrightarrow{BK}$, ⟨−5, 2⟩

Name the vector and write its component form.

4. 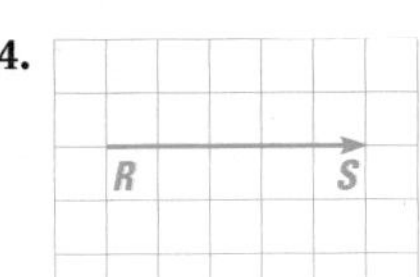

5. 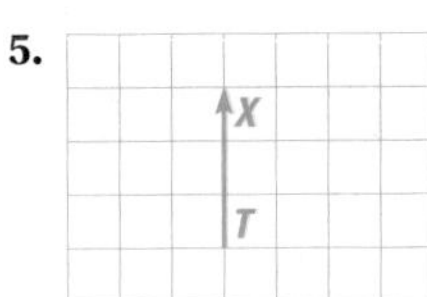

6. 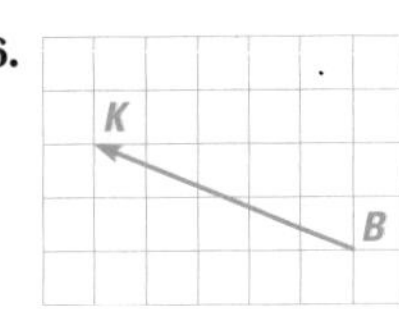

7. The vertices of $\triangle LMN$ are $L(2, 2)$, $M(5, 3)$, and $N(9, 1)$. Translate $\triangle LMN$ using the vector ⟨−2, 6⟩. **L′(0, 8), M′(3, 9), N′(7, 7)**

EXAMPLE 5 Solve a multi-step problem

NAVIGATION A boat heads out from point A on one island toward point D on another. The boat encounters a storm at B, 12 miles east and 4 miles north of its starting point. The storm pushes the boat off course to point C, as shown.

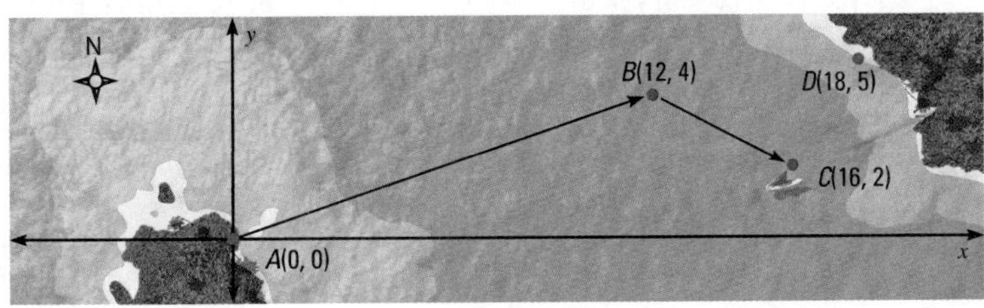

a. Write the component form of $\overrightarrow{AB}$.

b. Write the component form of $\overrightarrow{BC}$.

c. Write the component form of the vector that describes the straight line path from the boat's current position C to its intended destination D.

Solution

a. The component form of the vector from $A(0, 0)$ to $B(12, 4)$ is

$$\overrightarrow{AB} = \langle 12 - 0, 4 - 0 \rangle = \langle 12, 4 \rangle.$$

b. The component form of the vector from $B(12, 4)$ to $C(16, 2)$ is

$$\overrightarrow{BC} = \langle 16 - 12, 2 - 4 \rangle = \langle 4, -2 \rangle.$$

c. The boat is currently at point C and needs to travel to D. The component form of the vector from $C(16, 2)$ to $D(18, 5)$ is

$$\overrightarrow{CD} = \langle 18 - 16, 5 - 2 \rangle = \langle 2, 3 \rangle.$$

GUIDED PRACTICE for Example 5

8. WHAT IF? In Example 5, suppose there is no storm. Write the component form of the vector that describes the straight path from the boat's starting point A to its final destination D. **⟨18, 5⟩**

Extra Example 5

Ingrid hit a golf ball from the tee toward the hole. After she hit the ball, it got as far as point Y when a freak gust of wind blew it to point X.

a. Write the component form of $\overrightarrow{TY}$. **⟨220, 85⟩**

b. Write the component form of $\overrightarrow{YX}$. **⟨20, −35⟩**

c. Write the component form of the vector that describes the straight-line path from the point X where the ball landed to the hole H.

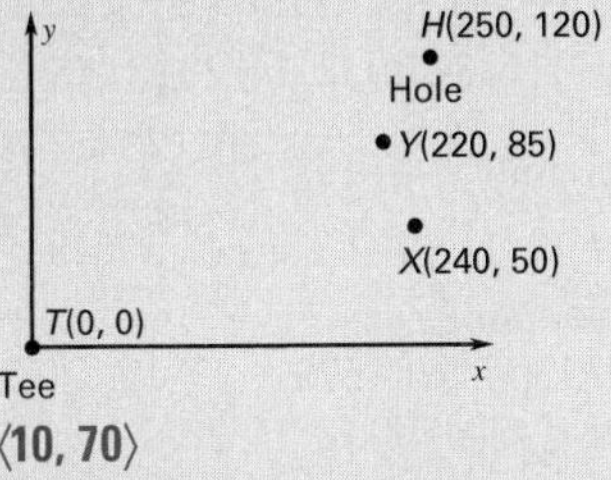

⟨10, 70⟩

Key Question to Ask for Example 5

- Find the component form of $\overrightarrow{AC}$. **⟨16, 2⟩**

Closing the Lesson

Have students summarize the major points of the lesson and answer the Essential Question: How do you translate a figure using a vector?

- **A translation is an isometry.**
- **A vector is a quantity with magnitude and direction.**

You add the vector components to the preimage coordinates to get the image coordinates.

Differentiated Instruction

Kinesthetic Learners In a wide, open area, choose a middle point to be the origin of a coordinate grid. Mark the x-axis and y-axis with masking tape or string. Have students begin at the origin. For **Guided Practice Exercises 4–6**, have them follow the path of the vector on the grid, each step representing one unit on the grid. Have them count the number of units they move up or down and left or right from the origin to determine the component form of each vector.

See also the *Geometry Toolkit* for more strategies.

4 PRACTICE AND APPLY

Assignment Guide

Answer Transparencies available for all exercises

Basic:
Day 1: pp. 576–579
Exs. 1–14, 28, 29, 33, 34, 51, 53
Day 2: pp. 576–579
Exs. 15–27, 35–40, 47–50

Average:
Day 1: pp. 576–579
Exs. 1–6, 8–10, 12, 14, 28–31, 33, 34, 51, 54
Day 2: pp. 576–579
Exs. 16, 17, 19–27, 36–43, 47, 49

Advanced:
Day 1: pp. 576–579
Exs. 1–6, 8–10, 12, 14, 28–34*, 51, 54
Day 2: pp. 576–579
Exs. 16, 17, 20–27, 37–46*, 50

Block:
pp. 576–579
Exs. 1–6, 8–10, 12, 14, 16, 17, 19–31, 33, 34, 36–43, 47, 49, 51, 54

Differentiated Instruction

See *Geometry Best Practices Toolkit* for suggestions on addressing the needs of a diverse classroom.

Homework Check

For a quick check of student understanding of key concepts, go over the following exercises:
Basic: 4, 12, 16, 33, 36
Average: 6, 13, 20, 34, 36
Advanced: 10, 14, 22, 34, 37

Extra Practice

- Student Edition, p. 912
- Chapter 9 Resource Book: Practice levels A, B, C, pp. 7–12

Practice Worksheet

An easily-readable reduced practice page (with answers) for this lesson can be found on p. 570C.

9.1 EXERCISES

HOMEWORK KEY
○ = WORKED-OUT SOLUTIONS on p. WS10 for Exs. 7, 11, and 35
★ = STANDARDIZED TEST PRACTICE Exs. 2, 14, and 42

SKILL PRACTICE

A

1. **VOCABULARY** Copy and complete: A _?_ is a quantity that has both _?_ and magnitude. **vector, direction**

2. ★ **WRITING** *Describe* the difference between a vector and a ray. **See margin.**

EXAMPLE 1 on p. 572 for Exs. 3–10

IMAGE AND PREIMAGE Use the translation $(x, y) \to (x - 8, y + 4)$.

3. What is the image of $A(2, 6)$? $A'(-6, 10)$
4. What is the image of $B(-1, 5)$? $B'(-9, 9)$
5. What is the preimage of $C'(-3, -10)$? $C(5, -14)$
6. What is the preimage of $D'(4, -3)$? $D(12, -7)$

GRAPHING AN IMAGE The vertices of $\triangle PQR$ are $P(-2, 3)$, $Q(1, 2)$, and $R(3, -1)$. Graph the image of the triangle using prime notation. **7–10. See margin.**

7. $(x, y) \to (x + 4, y + 6)$
8. $(x, y) \to (x + 9, y - 2)$
9. $(x, y) \to (x - 2, y - 5)$
10. $(x, y) \to (x - 1, y + 3)$

EXAMPLE 2 on p. 573 for Exs. 11–14

WRITING A RULE $\triangle A'B'C'$ is the image of $\triangle ABC$ after a translation. Write a rule for the translation. Then *verify* that the translation is an isometry. **11, 12. See margin.**

11. 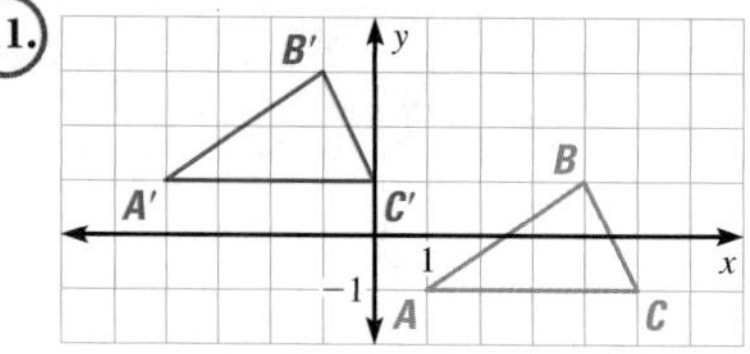

12. 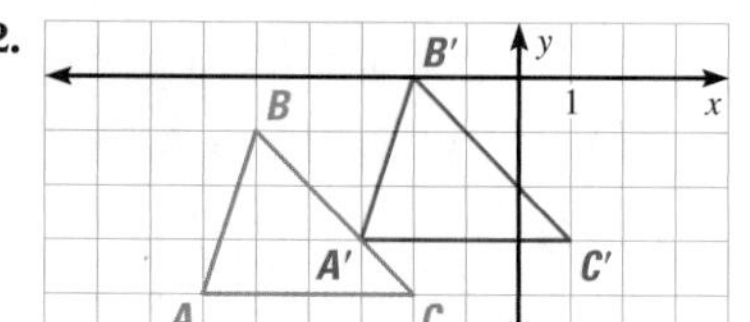

13. **ERROR ANALYSIS** *Describe* and correct the error in graphing the translation of quadrilateral *EFGH*.
The image should be 1 unit to the left instead of right and 2 units down instead of up; see margin for art.

$(x, y) \to (x - 1, y - 2)$

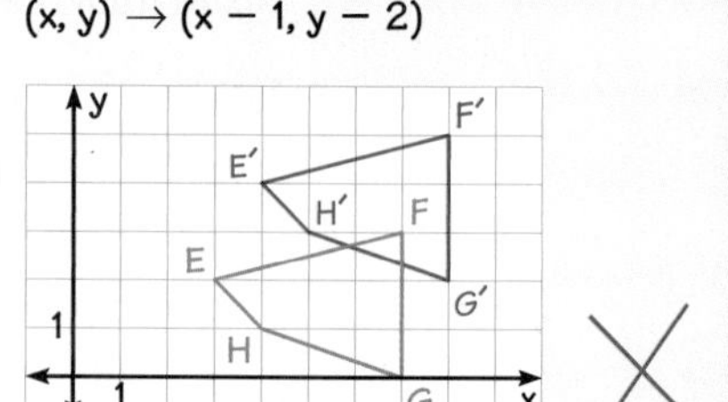

14. ★ **MULTIPLE CHOICE** Translate $Q(0, -8)$ using $(x, y) \to (x - 3, y + 2)$. **C**

Ⓐ $Q'(-2, 5)$ Ⓑ $Q'(3, -10)$ Ⓒ $Q'(-3, -6)$ Ⓓ $Q'(2, -11)$

EXAMPLE 3 on p. 574 for Exs. 15–23

IDENTIFYING VECTORS Name the vector and write its component form.

15. 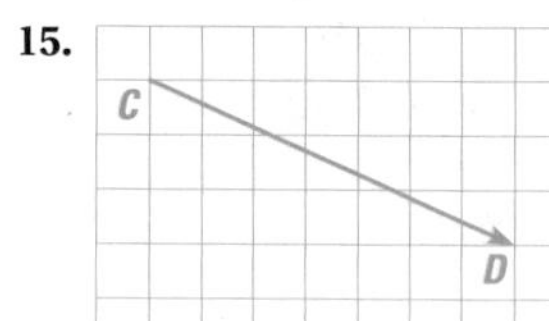

16.
R
T

17. 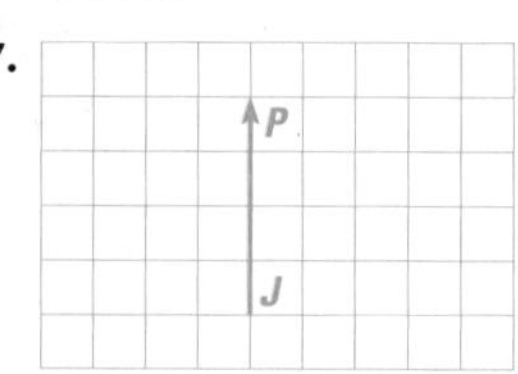

15. $\overrightarrow{CD}$, $\langle 7, -3\rangle$
16. $\overrightarrow{RT}$, $\langle -2, -4\rangle$
17. $\overrightarrow{JP}$, $\langle 0, 4\rangle$

2. A vector is a quantity that has both direction and magnitude. A ray, $\overrightarrow{AB}$, consists of an initial point A and all points on $\overleftrightarrow{AB}$ that are on the same side of A as point B.

7–10. See Additional Answers beginning on p. AA1.

11. $(x, y) \to (x - 5, y + 2)$; $AB = A'B' = \sqrt{13}$, $AC = A'C' = 4$, and $BC = B'C' = \sqrt{5}$. $\triangle ABC \cong \triangle A'B'C'$ using the SSS Congruence Postulate.

12. $(x, y) \to (x + 3, y + 1)$; $AB = A'B' = \sqrt{10}$, $AC = A'C' = 4$, and $BC = B'C' = 3\sqrt{2}$. $\triangle ABC \cong \triangle A'B'C'$ using the SSS Congruence Postulate.

13. See Additional Answers beginning on p. AA1.

.The vertical
mponent is 0
nce the bottles
e translated
ft or right but
ot up or down.

. The vertical
mponent is
e distance
om the ground
 to the plane
ntrance.

EXAMPLE 4
on p. 574
for Exs. 24–27

VECTORS **Use the point $P(-3, 6)$. Find the component form of the vector that describes the translation to P'.**

18. $P'(0, 1)$ **⟨3, −5⟩** **19.** $P'(-4, 8)$ **⟨−1, 2⟩** **20.** $P'(-2, 0)$ **⟨1, −6⟩** **21.** $P'(-3, -5)$ **⟨0, −11⟩**

TRANSLATIONS **Think of each translation as a vector. *Describe* the vertical component of the vector. *Explain.***

22.

23.

TRANSLATING A TRIANGLE **The vertices of $\triangle DEF$ are $D(2, 5)$, $E(6, 3)$, and $F(4, 0)$. Translate $\triangle DEF$ using the given vector. Graph $\triangle DEF$ and its image.** **24–27. See margin.**

24. ⟨6, 0⟩ **25.** ⟨5, −1⟩ **26.** ⟨−3, −7⟩ **27.** ⟨−2, −4⟩

B **ALGEBRA** **Find the value of each variable in the translation.**

28.

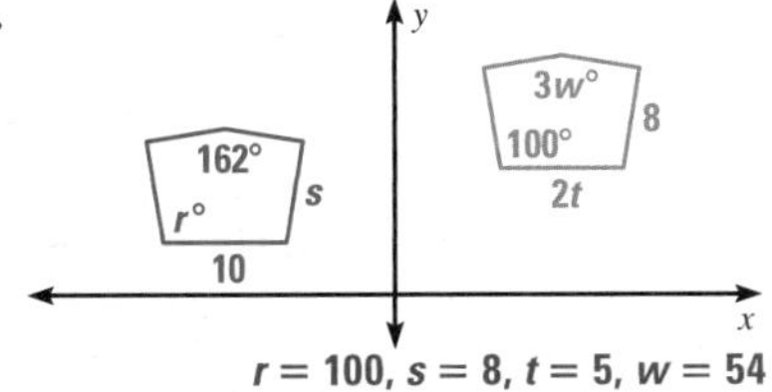

$r = 100, s = 8, t = 5, w = 54$

29.

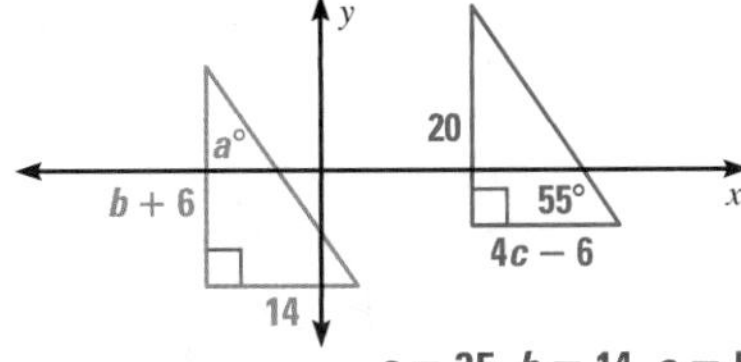

$a = 35, b = 14, c = 5$

30. **ALGEBRA** Translation A maps (x, y) to $(x + n, y + m)$. Translation B maps (x, y) to $(x + s, y + t)$.

a. Translate a point using Translation A, then Translation B. Write a rule for the final image of the point. **$(x, y) \to (x + n, y + m) \to (x + n + s, y + m + t)$**

b. Translate a point using Translation B, then Translation A. Write a rule for the final image of the point. **$(x, y) \to (x + s, y + t) \to (x + s + n, y + t + m)$**

c. *Compare* the rules you wrote in parts (a) and (b). Does it matter which translation you do first? *Explain.* **They are the same; no; $s + n = n + s$, $m + t = t + m$.**

31. **MULTI-STEP PROBLEM** The vertices of a rectangle are $Q(2, -3)$, $R(2, 4)$, $S(5, 4)$, and $T(5, -3)$.

a. Translate $QRST$ 3 units left and 2 units down. Find the areas of $QRST$ and $Q'R'S'T'$. **$Q'(-1, -5)$, $R'(-1, 2)$, $S'(2, 2)$, $T'(2, -5)$; 21, 21**

b. *Compare* the areas. Make a conjecture about the areas of a preimage and its image after a translation. **The areas are the same; the area of an image and its preimage under a translation are the same.**

C **32.** **CHALLENGE** The vertices of $\triangle ABC$ are $A(2, 2)$, $B(4, 2)$, and $C(3, 4)$. **a, b. See margin for art.**

a. Graph the image of $\triangle ABC$ after the transformation $(x, y) \to (x + y, y)$. Is the transformation an isometry? *Explain.* Are the areas of $\triangle ABC$ and $\triangle A'B'C'$ the same? **No; $\triangle ABC$ is not congruent to $\triangle A'B'C'$; yes.**

b. Graph a new triangle, $\triangle DEF$, and its image after the transformation given in part (a). Are the areas of $\triangle DEF$ and $\triangle D'E'F'$ the same? **yes**

Avoiding Common Errors

Exercises 5–6 Students may do these just as they did Exercises 3 and 4. Explain that in Exercises 5 and 6, the given point is the image, not the preimage. Discuss how they can work back from the image to find the preimage.

Teaching Strategy

Exercises 18–21 Have students graph P and P'. Draw $\overrightarrow{PP'}$. Explain that P is the initial point and P' the terminal point, so the vector components are obtained by subtracting the coordinates of the initial point from the coordinates of the terminal point.

Mathematical Reasoning

Exercise 30 Have students replace n, m, s, and t with whole numbers and complete parts (a) and (b) of this exercise. Then have them generalize back to the variable expressions.

27. $D'(0, 1)$, $E'(4, -1)$, $F'(2, -4)$;

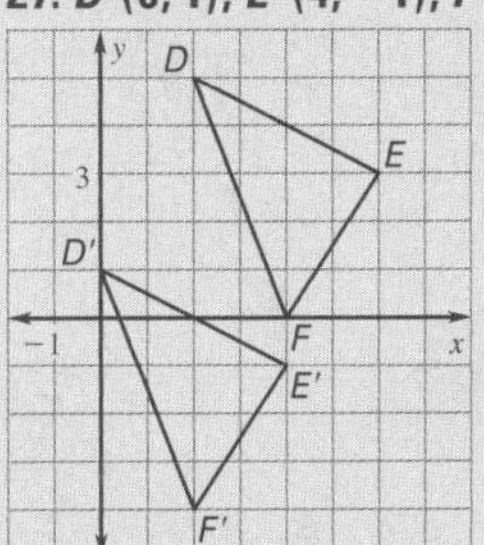

32a.

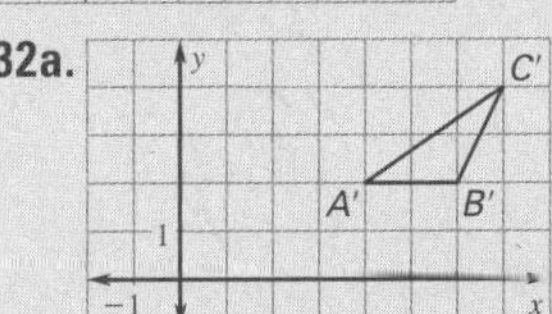

32b. *Sample:*

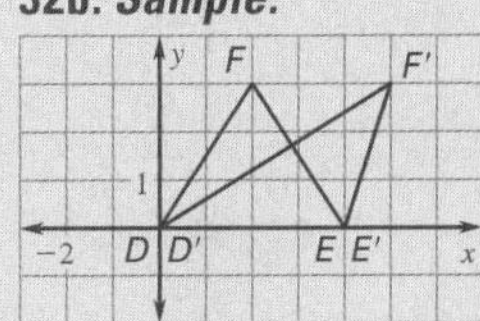

24. $D'(8, 5)$, $E'(12, 3)$, $F'(10, 0)$;

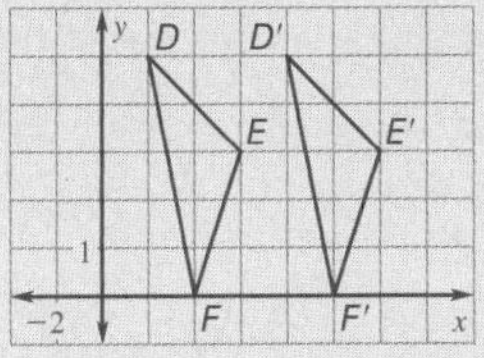

25. $D'(7, 4)$, $E'(11, 2)$, $F'(9, -1)$;

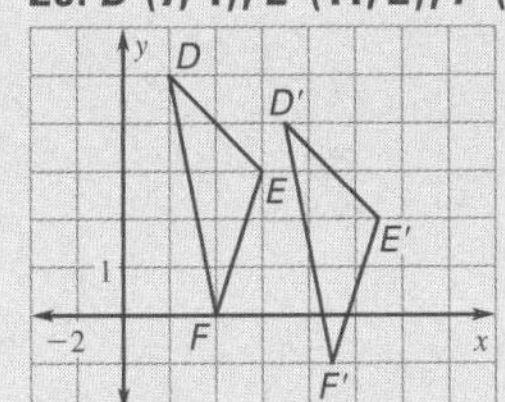

26. $D'(-1, -2)$, $E'(3, -4)$, $F'(1, -7)$;

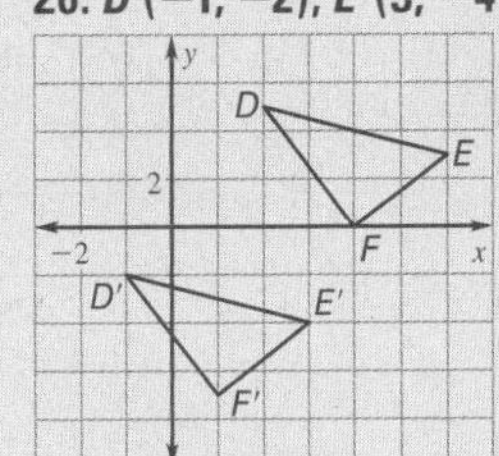

Reading Strategy

Exercise 43 Ask students to examine the diagram carefully. Discuss how the diagram provides visual clues that help explain what is meant by a *grid-indexed microscope slide.*

Teaching Strategy

Exercise 44 It may help students if you discuss how to relate each equation and graph to the graph of $y = x^2$.

42a.
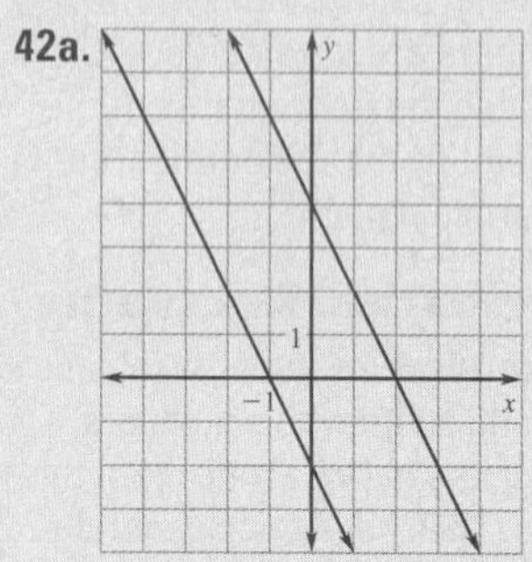

PROBLEM SOLVING

EXAMPLE 2 on p. 573 for Exs. 33–34

HOME DESIGN Designers can use computers to make patterns in fabrics or floors. On the computer, a copy of the design in Rectangle A is used to cover an entire floor. The translation $(x, y) \to (x + 3, y)$ maps Rectangle A to Rectangle B.

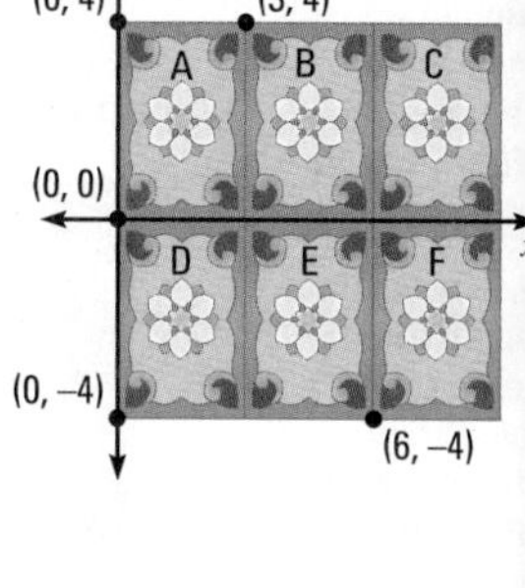

A 33. Use coordinate notation to describe the translations that map Rectangle A to Rectangles C, D, E, and F.

33. $(x, y) \to (x + 6, y)$, $(x, y) \to (x, y - 4)$, $(x, y) \to (x + 3, y - 4)$, $(x, y) \to (x + 6, y - 4)$

@HomeTutor for problem solving help at classzone.com

34. Write a rule to translate Rectangle F back to Rectangle A. $(x, y) \to (x - 6, y + 4)$

@HomeTutor for problem solving help at classzone.com

EXAMPLE 5 on p. 575 for Exs. 35–37

SNOWSHOEING You are snowshoeing in the mountains. The distances in the diagram are in miles. Write the component form of the vector.

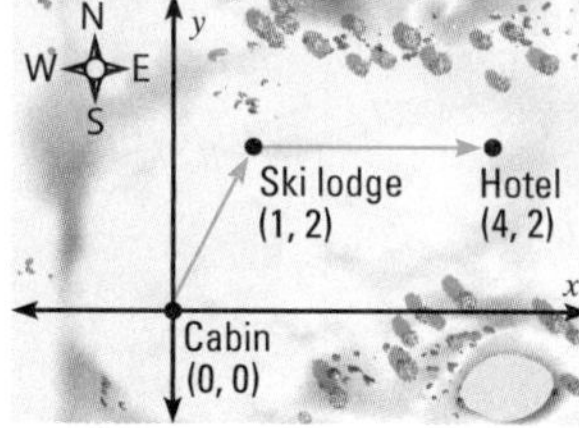

35. From the cabin to the ski lodge $\langle 1, 2\rangle$

36. From the ski lodge to the hotel $\langle 3, 0\rangle$

37. From the hotel back to your cabin $\langle -4, -2\rangle$

HANG GLIDING A hang glider travels from point A to point D. At point B, the hang glider changes direction, as shown in the diagram. The distances in the diagram are in kilometers.

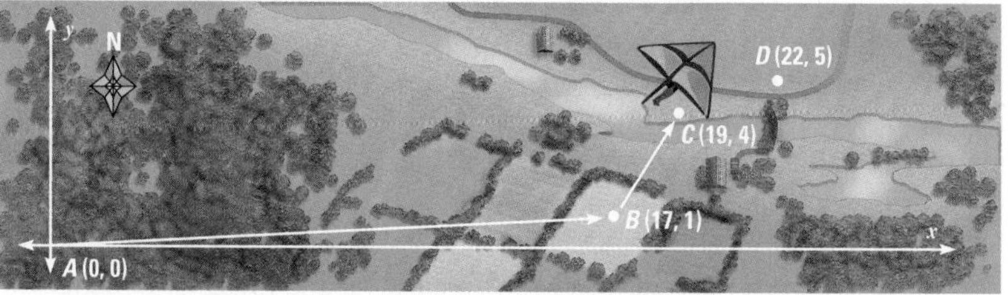

B 38. Write the component form for $\overrightarrow{AB}$ and $\overrightarrow{BC}$. $\langle 17, 1\rangle$, $\langle 2, 3\rangle$

39. Write the component form of the vector that describes the path from the hang glider's current position C to its intended destination D. $\langle 3, 1\rangle$

40. What is the total distance the hang glider travels? **about 23.8 km**

41. Suppose the hang glider went straight from A to D. Write the component form of the vector that describes this path. What is this distance? $\langle 22, 5\rangle$; **about 22.6 km**

42. ★ **EXTENDED RESPONSE** Use the equation $2x + y = 4$.

a. Graph the line and its image after the translation $\langle -5, 4\rangle$. What is an equation of the image of the line? **See margin for art; $2x + y = -2$.**

b. *Compare* the line and its image. What are the slopes? the y-intercepts? the x-intercepts? $-2, -2$; $(0, 4), (0, -2)$; $(2, 0), (-1, 0)$

c. Write an equation of the image of $2x + y = 4$ after the translation $\langle 2, -6\rangle$ *without* using a graph. *Explain* your reasoning.
$2x + y = 2$. ***Sample answer:*** Translate the y-intercept, $(0, 4)$ and x-intercept, $(2, 0)$, using the translation $\langle 2, -6\rangle$. Use these points to find the equation of the image.

◯ = WORKED-OUT SOLUTIONS on p. WS1 ★ = STANDARDIZED TEST PRACTICE

3a. 5 squares to the right followed by 4 squares down.

3b. about 12.8 mm

43. **SCIENCE** You are studying an amoeba through a microscope. Suppose the amoeba moves on a grid-indexed microscope slide in a straight line from square B3 to square G7.

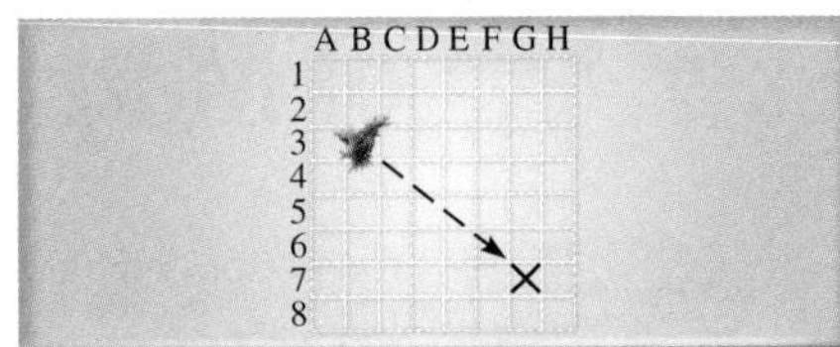

a. *Describe* the translation.

b. Each grid square is 2 millimeters on a side. How far does the amoeba travel?

c. Suppose the amoeba moves from B3 to G7 in 24.5 seconds. What is its speed in millimeters per second? **about 0.522 mm/sec**

C 44. **MULTI-STEP PROBLEM** You can write the equation of a parabola in the form $y = (x - h)^2 + k$, where (h, k) is the *vertex* of the parabola. In the graph, an equation of Parabola 1 is $y = (x - 1)^2 + 3$, with vertex (1, 3). Parabola 2 is the image of Parabola 1 after a translation.

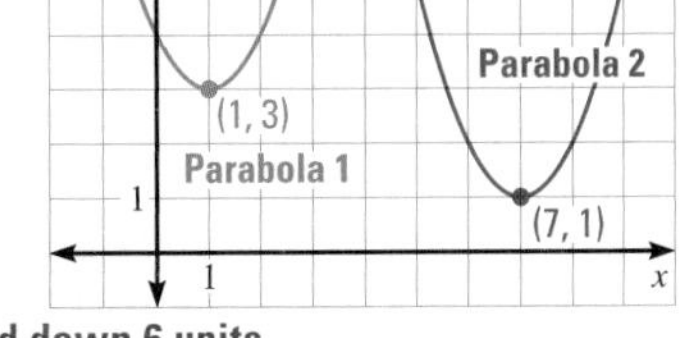

a. Write a rule for the translation. $(x, y) \rightarrow (x + 6, y - 2)$

b. Write an equation of Parabola 2. $y = (x - 7)^2 + 1$

c. Suppose you translate Parabola 1 using the vector $\langle -4, 8 \rangle$. Write an equation of the image.

d. An equation of Parabola 3 is $y = (x + 5)^2 - 3$. Write a rule for the translation of Parabola 1 to Parabola 3. *Explain* your reasoning.
$(x, y) \rightarrow (x - 6, y - 6)$; **the graph is moved left 6 units and down 6 units.**

44c. $y = (x + 3)^2 + 11$

45. **TECHNOLOGY** The standard form of an exponential equation is $y = a^x$, where $a > 0$ and $a \neq 1$. Use the equation $y = 2^x$.

a. Use a graphing calculator to graph $y = 2^x$ and $y = 2^x - 4$. *Describe* the translation from $y = 2^x$ to $y = 2^x - 4$. **The graph is 4 units lower.**

b. Use a graphing calculator to graph $y = 2^x$ and $y = 2^{x-4}$. *Describe* the translation from $y = 2^x$ to $y = 2^{x-4}$. **The graph is 4 units to the right.**

46. **CHALLENGE** Use properties of congruent triangles to prove part of Theorem 9.1, that a translation preserves angle measure.

46. After a translation, a triangle and its image remain congruent using the SSS Congruence Postulate. Since the triangles are congruent, corresponding angles are congruent.

MIXED REVIEW

PREVIEW Prepare for Lesson 9.2 in Exs. 47–50.

Find the sum, difference, product, or quotient. *(p. 869)*

47. $-16 - 7$ **−23**
48. $6 + (-12)$ **−6**
49. $(13)(-2)$ **−26**
50. $16 \div (-4)$ **−4**

Determine whether the two triangles are similar. If they are, write a similarity statement. *(pp. 381, 388)*

51.

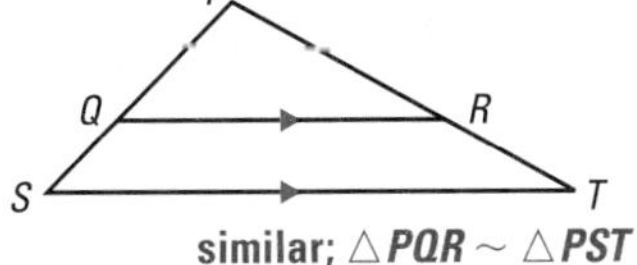

similar; $\triangle PQR \sim \triangle PST$

52.

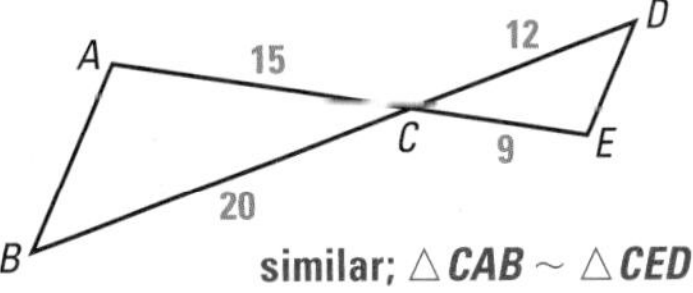

similar; $\triangle CAB \sim \triangle CED$

Points *A, B, C,* and *D* are the vertices of a quadrilateral. Give the most specific name for *ABCD*. *Justify* your answer. *(p. 552)*

53. $A(2, 0), B(7, 0), C(4, 4), D(2, 4)$
Trapezoid; *ABCD* is a quadrilateral with one pair of parallel sides.

54. $A(3, 0), B(7, 2), C(3, 4), D(1, 2)$
Kite; *ABCD* has two pairs of consecutive congruent sides.

5 ASSESS AND RETEACH

Daily Homework Quiz

Transparency Available

1. The vertices of $\triangle XYZ$ are $X(-3, 2)$, $Y(1, 1)$, and $Z(-1, -3)$. Graph the image of the triangle using prime notation after the translation $(x, y) \rightarrow (x + 1, y - 2)$.

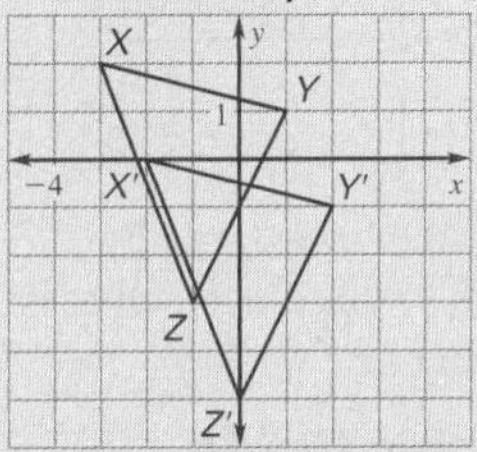

2. Translate $A(-8, 6)$ using $(x, y) \rightarrow (x - 7, y + 10)$. **(−15, 16)**

3. Name the vector and write it in component form. $\overrightarrow{CD}$, $\langle 4, 6 \rangle$

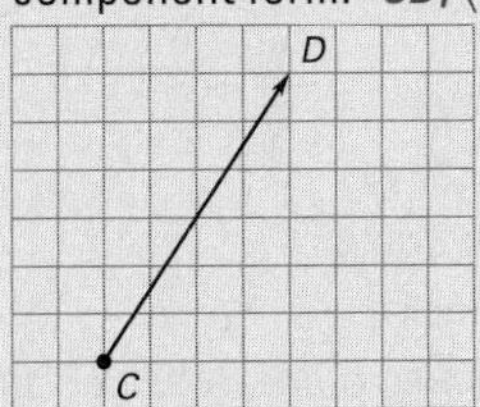

4. Use the point $M(8, -2)$. Find the component form of the vector that describes the translation to $M'(7, 5)$. $\langle -1, 7 \rangle$

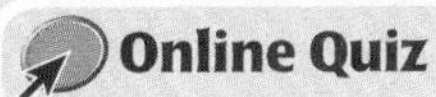

Available at **classzone.com**

Diagnosis/Remediation

- Practice A, B, C in Chapter 9 Resource Book, pp. 7–12
- Study Guide in Chapter 9 Resource Book, pp. 13–14
- Practice Workbook, pp. 163–165
- @HomeTutor

Challenge

Additional challenge is available in the Chapter 9 Resource Book, p. 17.

1 PLAN AND PREPARE

Warm-Up Exercises

Transparency Available

1. Write the component form of the vector that translates $\triangle ABC$ to $\triangle A'B'C'$. **$\langle -6, -1\rangle$**

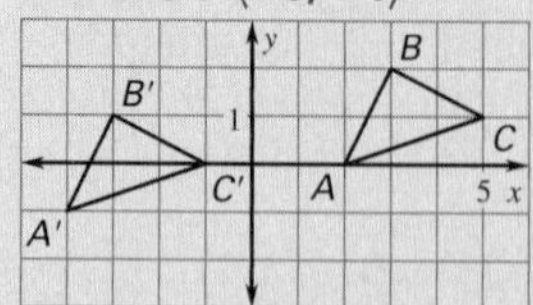

2. If $P(-8, 4)$ is translated by $(x, y) \rightarrow (x + 6, y + 1)$, what is the image of P? **$(-2, 5)$**

Notetaking Guide

Transparency Available

Promotes interactive learning and notetaking skills, pp. 226–230.

Pacing

Basic: 2 days
Average: 2 days
Advanced: 2 days
Block: 1 block

- See *Teaching Guide/Lesson Plan.*

2 FOCUS AND MOTIVATE

Essential Question

Big Idea 3, p. 571

How do you use matrix operations to translate a figure? **Tell students they will learn how to answer this question by studying matrices that represent figures and transformations.**

9.2 Use Properties of Matrices

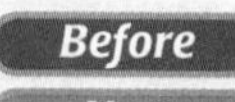

Before You performed translations using vectors.
Now You will perform translations using matrix operations.
Why? So you can calculate the total cost of art supplies, as in Ex. 36.

Key Vocabulary
- **matrix**
- **element**
- **dimensions**

A **matrix** is a rectangular arrangement of numbers in rows and columns. (The plural of matrix is *matrices.*) Each number in a matrix is called an **element**.

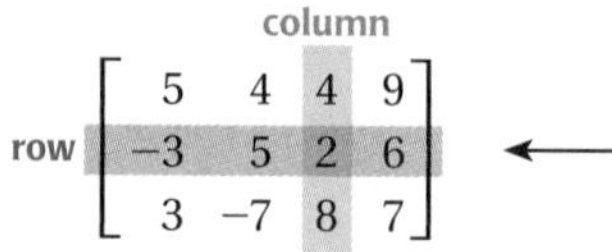

READ VOCABULARY
An element of a matrix may also be called an *entry.*

The **dimensions** of a matrix are the numbers of rows and columns. The matrix above has three rows and four columns, so the dimensions of the matrix are 3×4 (read "3 by 4").

You can represent a figure in the coordinate plane using a matrix with two rows. The first row has the x-coordinate(s) of the vertices. The second row has the corresponding y-coordinate(s). Each column represents a vertex, so the number of columns depends on the number of vertices of the figure.

Standards
Prepare for 22.0
Students know the effect of rigid motions on figures in the coordinate plane and space, including rotations, translations, and reflections.

EXAMPLE 1 Represent figures using matrices

Write a matrix to represent the point or polygon.

a. Point A

b. Quadrilateral $ABCD$

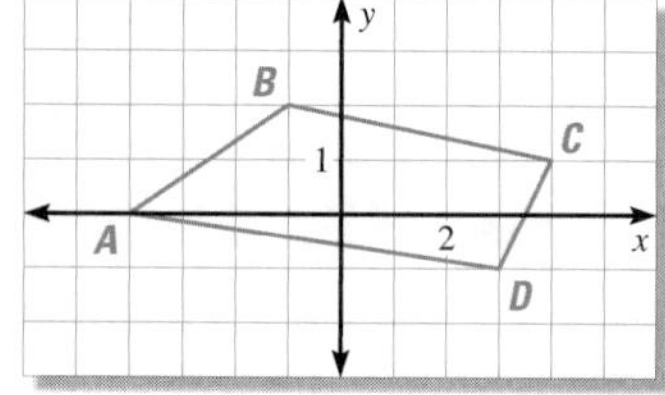

Solution

AVOID ERRORS
The columns in a polygon matrix follow the consecutive order of the vertices of the polygon.

a. Point matrix for A

$$\begin{bmatrix} -4 \\ 0 \end{bmatrix} \begin{matrix} \leftarrow x\text{-coordinate} \\ \leftarrow y\text{-coordinate} \end{matrix}$$

b. Polygon matrix for $ABCD$

$$\begin{matrix} & A & B & C & D \\ & \end{matrix}$$
$$\begin{bmatrix} -4 & -1 & 4 & 3 \\ 0 & 2 & 1 & -1 \end{bmatrix} \begin{matrix} \leftarrow x\text{-coordinates} \\ \leftarrow y\text{-coordinates} \end{matrix}$$

✓ GUIDED PRACTICE for Example 1

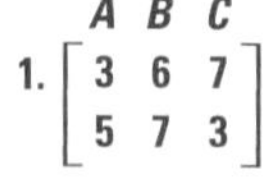

1. $\begin{bmatrix} 3 & 6 & 7 \\ 5 & 7 & 3 \end{bmatrix}$ (columns A, B, C)

1. Write a matrix to represent $\triangle ABC$ with vertices $A(3, 5)$, $B(6, 7)$ and $C(7, 3)$.
2. How many rows and columns are in a matrix for a hexagon? **2 rows, 6 columns**

Resource Planning Guide

Chapter Resource Book
- Teaching Guide/Lesson Plan (pp. 18–19)
- Practice levels A, B, C (pp. 20–25)
- Study Guide (pp. 26–27)
- Catch-up for Absent Students (p. 28)
- Problem Solving Workshop (p. 29)
- Challenge (p. 30)

Workbooks
- Notetaking Guide (pp. 226–230)
- Practice Workbook (pp. 166–168)

Teaching Options
- **Power Presentations CD-ROM** provides dynamic electronic teaching resources for the classroom.
- **Activity Generator CD-ROM** provides editable activities for all ability levels.

Interactive Technology
- Easy Planner
- Power Presentations CD-ROM
- Activity Generator CD-ROM
- Animated Geometry
- Test Generator CD-ROM
- Online Quiz
- eWorkbook
- eEdition
- @HomeTutor

Resources for English Learners
- Quick Reference for English Learners
- Spanish Study Guide
- Multi-Language Visual Glossary
- Student Resources in Spanish

See also the *Geometry Toolkit* for more strategies for meeting individual needs.

ADDING AND SUBTRACTING To add or subtract matrices, you add or subtract corresponding elements. The matrices must have the same dimensions.

EXAMPLE 2 Add and subtract matrices

a. $\begin{bmatrix} 5 & -3 \\ 6 & -6 \end{bmatrix} + \begin{bmatrix} 1 & 2 \\ 3 & -4 \end{bmatrix} = \begin{bmatrix} 5+1 & -3+2 \\ 6+3 & -6+(-4) \end{bmatrix} = \begin{bmatrix} 6 & -1 \\ 9 & -10 \end{bmatrix}$

b. $\begin{bmatrix} 6 & 8 & 5 \\ 4 & 9 & -1 \end{bmatrix} - \begin{bmatrix} 1 & -7 & 0 \\ 4 & -2 & 3 \end{bmatrix} = \begin{bmatrix} 6-1 & 8-(-7) & 5-0 \\ 4-4 & 9-(-2) & -1-3 \end{bmatrix} = \begin{bmatrix} 5 & 15 & 5 \\ 0 & 11 & -4 \end{bmatrix}$

TRANSLATIONS You can use matrix addition to represent a translation in the coordinate plane. The image matrix for a translation is the sum of the translation matrix and the matrix that represents the preimage.

EXAMPLE 3 Represent a translation using matrices

The matrix $\begin{bmatrix} 1 & 5 & 3 \\ 1 & 0 & -1 \end{bmatrix}$ represents $\triangle ABC$. Find the image matrix that represents the translation of $\triangle ABC$ 1 unit left and 3 units up. Then graph $\triangle ABC$ and its image.

Solution

The translation matrix is $\begin{bmatrix} -1 & -1 & -1 \\ 3 & 3 & 3 \end{bmatrix}$.

Add this to the polygon matrix for the preimage to find the image matrix.

$$\underset{\text{Translation matrix}}{\begin{bmatrix} -1 & -1 & -1 \\ 3 & 3 & 3 \end{bmatrix}} + \underset{\text{Polygon matrix}}{\overset{\begin{matrix} A & B & C \end{matrix}}{\begin{bmatrix} 1 & 5 & 3 \\ 1 & 0 & -1 \end{bmatrix}}} = \underset{\text{Image matrix}}{\overset{\begin{matrix} A' & B' & C' \end{matrix}}{\begin{bmatrix} 0 & 4 & 2 \\ 4 & 3 & 2 \end{bmatrix}}}$$

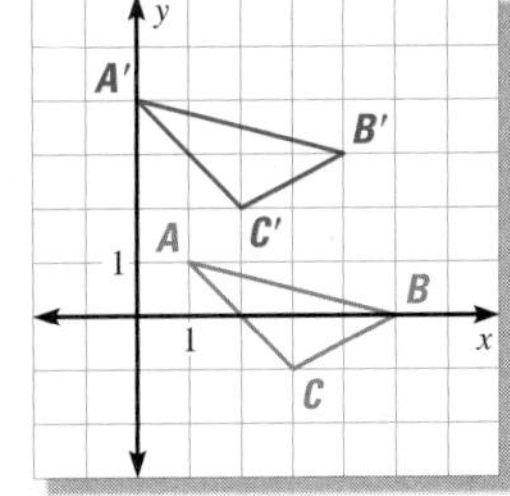

AVOID ERRORS
In order to add two matrices, they must have the same dimensions, so the translation matrix here must have three columns like the polygon matrix.

✓ GUIDED PRACTICE for Examples 2 and 3

In Exercises 3 and 4, add or subtract.

3. $[-3 \;\; 7] + [2 \;\; -5]$ $[-1 \;\; 2]$

4. $\begin{bmatrix} 1 & -4 \\ 3 & -5 \end{bmatrix} - \begin{bmatrix} 2 & 3 \\ 7 & 8 \end{bmatrix}$ $\begin{bmatrix} -1 & -7 \\ -4 & -13 \end{bmatrix}$

5. The matrix $\begin{bmatrix} 1 & 2 & 6 & 7 \\ 2 & -1 & 1 & 3 \end{bmatrix}$ represents quadrilateral $JKLM$. Write the translation matrix and the image matrix that represents the translation of $JKLM$ 4 units right and 2 units down. Then graph $JKLM$ and its image. **See margin.**

Motivating the Lesson

Remind students that they have used ordered pairs of numbers to represent individual points. Tell them that in this lesson they will learn to use arrays of numbers called matrices to represent points, polygons, and translations.

3 TEACH

Extra Example 1

Write a matrix that represents the point or polygon.

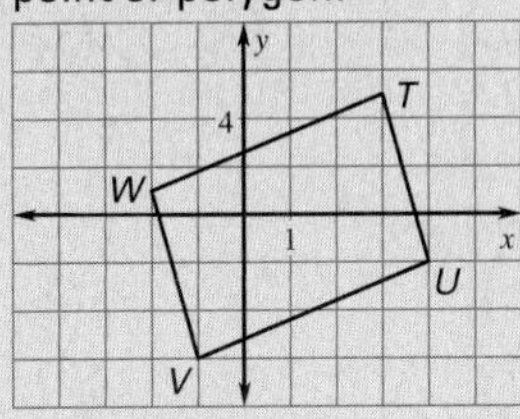

a. Point T $\begin{bmatrix} 3 \\ 5 \end{bmatrix}$

b. Quadrilateral $TUVW$

$$\overset{\begin{matrix} T & U & V & W \end{matrix}}{\begin{bmatrix} 3 & 4 & -1 & -2 \\ 5 & -2 & -6 & 1 \end{bmatrix}}$$

Extra Example 2

Add or subtract.

a. $\begin{bmatrix} 7 & 2 \\ -5 & 9 \end{bmatrix} + \begin{bmatrix} -8 & 1 \\ 4 & 0 \end{bmatrix}$ $\begin{bmatrix} -1 & 3 \\ -1 & 9 \end{bmatrix}$

b. $\begin{bmatrix} 2 & 3 & 5 \\ 7 & -1 & 8 \end{bmatrix} - \begin{bmatrix} 12 & -2 & 1 \\ 6 & 3 & -4 \end{bmatrix}$

$\begin{bmatrix} -10 & 5 & 4 \\ 1 & -4 & 12 \end{bmatrix}$

5. **See Additional Answers beginning on p. AA1.**

Differentiated Instruction

Auditory Learners Adding and subtracting matrices requires adding or subtracting several corresponding elements. Encourage students to say the numbers they are adding or subtracting aloud as they add or subtract the matrices. Describing the process aloud will help ensure they have added or subtracted the correct corresponding elements.

See also the *Geometry Toolkit* for more strategies.

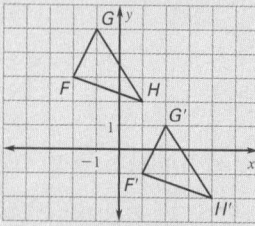

MULTIPLYING MATRICES The product of two matrices A and B is defined only when the number of columns in A is equal to the number of rows in B. If A is an $m \times n$ matrix and B is an $n \times p$ matrix, then the product AB is an $m \times p$ matrix.

USE NOTATION
Recall that the dimensions of a matrix are always written as rows × columns.

$$\begin{array}{ccccc} A & \cdot & B & = & AB \\ (m \text{ by } n) & \cdot & (n \text{ by } p) & = & (m \text{ by } p) \end{array}$$

equal — **dimensions of *AB***

You will use matrix multiplication in later lessons to represent transformations.

EXAMPLE 4 Multiply matrices

Multiply $\begin{bmatrix} 1 & 0 \\ 4 & 5 \end{bmatrix}\begin{bmatrix} 2 & -3 \\ -1 & 8 \end{bmatrix}$.

Solution

The matrices are both 2×2, so their product is defined. Use the following steps to find the elements of the product matrix.

STEP 1 **Multiply** the numbers in the first row of the first matrix by the numbers in the first column of the second matrix. Put the result in the first row, first column of the product matrix.

$$\begin{bmatrix} 1 & 0 \\ 4 & 5 \end{bmatrix}\begin{bmatrix} 2 & -3 \\ -1 & 8 \end{bmatrix} = \begin{bmatrix} 1(2) + 0(-1) & ? \\ ? & ? \end{bmatrix}$$

STEP 2 **Multiply** the numbers in the first row of the first matrix by the numbers in the second column of the second matrix. Put the result in the first row, second column of the product matrix.

$$\begin{bmatrix} 1 & 0 \\ 4 & 5 \end{bmatrix}\begin{bmatrix} 2 & -3 \\ -1 & 8 \end{bmatrix} = \begin{bmatrix} 1(2) + 0(-1) & 1(-3) + 0(8) \\ ? & ? \end{bmatrix}$$

STEP 3 **Multiply** the numbers in the second row of the first matrix by the numbers in the first column of the second matrix. Put the result in the second row, first column of the product matrix.

$$\begin{bmatrix} 1 & 0 \\ 4 & 5 \end{bmatrix}\begin{bmatrix} 2 & -3 \\ -1 & 8 \end{bmatrix} = \begin{bmatrix} 1(2) + 0(-1) & 1(-3) + 0(8) \\ 4(2) + 5(-1) & ? \end{bmatrix}$$

STEP 4 **Multiply** the numbers in the second row of the first matrix by the numbers in the second column of the second matrix. Put the result in the second row, second column of the product matrix.

$$\begin{bmatrix} 1 & 0 \\ 4 & 5 \end{bmatrix}\begin{bmatrix} 2 & -3 \\ -1 & 8 \end{bmatrix} = \begin{bmatrix} 1(2) + 0(-1) & 1(-3) + 0(8) \\ 4(2) + 5(-1) & 4(-3) + 5(8) \end{bmatrix}$$

STEP 5 **Simplify** the product matrix.

$$\begin{bmatrix} 1(2) + 0(-1) & 1(-3) + 0(8) \\ 4(2) + 5(-1) & 4(-3) + 5(8) \end{bmatrix} = \begin{bmatrix} 2 & -3 \\ 3 & 28 \end{bmatrix}$$

Animated Geometry at classzone.com

Avoiding Common Errors

If students write matrices for polygons in two columns rather than two rows, point out the error and have them correct their work. Tell them that the reason for using two rows will become clear when they use matrices to perform other types of transformations.

Extra Example 3

The matrix $\begin{bmatrix} -2 & -1 & 1 \\ 3 & 5 & 2 \end{bmatrix}$ represents $\triangle FGH$. Find the image matrix that represents the translation of $\triangle FGH$ 3 units right and 4 units down. Then graph $\triangle FGH$ and its image.

$\begin{bmatrix} 1 & 2 & 4 \\ -1 & 1 & -2 \end{bmatrix}$

Extra Example 4

Multiply $\begin{bmatrix} 3 & -5 \\ 1 & 4 \end{bmatrix}\begin{bmatrix} 2 & -1 \\ 0 & 6 \end{bmatrix}$.

$\begin{bmatrix} 6 & -33 \\ 2 & 23 \end{bmatrix}$

An **Animated Geometry** activity is available on-line for **Example 4**. This activity is also available on the **Power Presentations CD-ROM**.

Study Strategy

Students may find it helpful to remember the following description of how to find the matrix product $A \cdot B$. To find the first row of $A \cdot B$, multiply the first row of A by each column of B. To find the second row of $A \cdot B$, multiply the second row of A by each column of B.

EXAMPLE 5 Solve a real-world problem

SOFTBALL Two softball teams submit equipment lists for the season. A bat costs $20, a ball costs $5, and a uniform costs $40. Use matrix multiplication to find the total cost of equipment for each team.

Women's Team	Men's Team
13 bats	15 bats
42 balls	45 balls
16 uniforms	18 uniforms

Solution

First, write the equipment lists and the costs per item in matrix form. You will use matrix multiplication, so you need to set up the matrices so that the number of columns of the equipment matrix matches the number of rows of the cost per item matrix.

EQUIPMENT · **COST** = **TOTAL COST**

$$\begin{array}{c|ccc} & \text{Bats} & \text{Balls} & \text{Uniforms} \\ \text{Women} & 13 & 42 & 16 \\ \text{Men} & 15 & 45 & 18 \end{array} \cdot \begin{array}{c|c} & \text{Dollars} \\ \text{Bats} & 20 \\ \text{Balls} & 5 \\ \text{Uniforms} & 40 \end{array} = \begin{array}{c|c} & \text{Dollars} \\ \text{Women} & ? \\ \text{Men} & ? \end{array}$$

You can find the total cost of equipment for each team by multiplying the equipment matrix by the cost per item matrix. The equipment matrix is 2×3 and the cost per item matrix is 3×1, so their product is a 2×1 matrix.

$$\begin{bmatrix} 13 & 42 & 16 \\ 15 & 45 & 18 \end{bmatrix}\begin{bmatrix} 20 \\ 5 \\ 40 \end{bmatrix} = \begin{bmatrix} 13(20) + 42(5) + 16(40) \\ 15(20) + 45(5) + 18(40) \end{bmatrix} = \begin{bmatrix} 1110 \\ 1245 \end{bmatrix}$$

▶ The total cost of equipment for the women's team is $1110, and the total cost for the men's team is $1245.

ANOTHER WAY

You could solve this problem arithmetically, multiplying the number of bats by the price of bats, and so on, then adding the costs for each team.

✓ GUIDED PRACTICE for Examples 4 and 5

Use the matrices below. Is the product defined? *Explain.*

$$A = \begin{bmatrix} -3 \\ 4 \end{bmatrix} \qquad B = \begin{bmatrix} 2 & 1 \end{bmatrix} \qquad C = \begin{bmatrix} 6.7 & 0 \\ -9.3 & 5.2 \end{bmatrix}$$

6. AB

7. BA **Yes; the number of columns in *B* is equal to the number of rows in *A*.**

8. AC **No; the number of columns in *A* is not equal to the number of rows in *C*.**

Multiply.

9. $\begin{bmatrix} 1 & 0 \\ 0 & -1 \end{bmatrix}\begin{bmatrix} 3 & 8 \\ -4 & 7 \end{bmatrix}$

10. $\begin{bmatrix} 5 & 1 \end{bmatrix}\begin{bmatrix} -3 \\ -2 \end{bmatrix}$ $[-17]$

11. $\begin{bmatrix} 5 & 1 \\ 1 & -1 \end{bmatrix}\begin{bmatrix} 2 & -4 \\ 5 & 1 \end{bmatrix}$

12. WHAT IF? In Example 5, find the total cost for each team if a bat costs $25, a ball costs $4, and a uniform costs $35. **women: $1053, men: $1185**

6. Yes, the number of columns in *A* is equal to the number of rows in *B*.

9. $\begin{bmatrix} 3 & 8 \\ 4 & -7 \end{bmatrix}$

11. $\begin{bmatrix} 15 & -19 \\ -3 & -5 \end{bmatrix}$

Extra Example 5

Jenny and Arthur are going to the store to buy tomatoes, peppers, and cucumbers. If a tomato costs $.89, a pepper $.59, and a cucumber $.45, use matrix multiplication to find the total amount each person spent.

Jenny	Arthur
3 tomatoes	7 tomatoes
2 peppers	4 peppers
4 cucumbers	2 cucumbers

Jenny: $5.65; Arthur: $9.49

Key Question to Ask for Example 5

- Could you multiply the matrices in reverse order? Explain. **No; there is one element in each row of the cost matrix, but there are two elements in each column of the equipment matrix.**

Closing the Lesson

Have students summarize the major points of the lesson and answer the Essential Question: How do you use matrix operations to translate a figure?

- **A matrix is a rectangular array of numbers in rows and columns.**
- **To add or subtract matrices, first check that the dimensions are the same. Then add or subtract corresponding elements.**
- **To multiply matrices the number of columns of the first matrix must be equal to the number of rows of the second matrix.**

To translate a figure, add the matrix for the point or polygon to the translation matrix.

4 PRACTICE AND APPLY

Assignment Guide

Answer Transparencies available for all exercises

Basic:
Day 1: SRH p. 870 Exs. 1–8
pp. 584–587
Exs. 1–17
Day 2: pp. 584–587
Exs. 18–25, 31–34, 38–45

Average:
Day 1: pp. 584–587
Exs. 1–6, 8–12, 14–17, 27, 28
Day 2: pp. 584–587
Exs. 18–26, 29, 31–36, 38–44 even

Advanced:
Day 1: pp. 584–587
Exs. 1, 2, 3–6, 8–12, 14–17, 27–30*
Day 2: pp. 584–587
Exs. 18–26, 31–37*, 39–45 odd

Block:
pp. 584–587
Exs. 1–6, 8–12, 14–29, 31–36, 38–44 even

Differentiated Instruction

See *Geometry Best Practices Toolkit* for suggestions on addressing the needs of a diverse classroom.

Homework Check

For a quick check of student understanding of key concepts, go over the following exercises:

Basic: 4, 8, 14, 18, 31
Average: 5, 10, 15, 20, 31
Advanced: 6, 12, 16, 22, 31

Extra Practice

- Student Edition, p. 912
- Chapter 9 Resource Book: Practice levels A, B, C, pp. 20–25

Practice Worksheet

An easily-readable reduced practice page (with answers) for this lesson can be found on p. 570C.

9.2 EXERCISES

HOMEWORK KEY
○ = **WORKED-OUT SOLUTIONS on p. WS11 for Exs. 13, 19, and 31**
★ = **STANDARDIZED TEST PRACTICE Exs. 2, 17, 24, 25, and 35**

SKILL PRACTICE

A

1. **VOCABULARY** Copy and complete: To find the sum of two matrices, add corresponding __?__. **elements**

2. ★ **WRITING** How can you determine whether two matrices can be added? How can you determine whether two matrices can be multiplied? **See margin.**

EXAMPLE 1 on p. 580 for Exs. 3–6

USING A DIAGRAM **Use the diagram to write a matrix to represent the given polygon.** **3–6. See margin.**

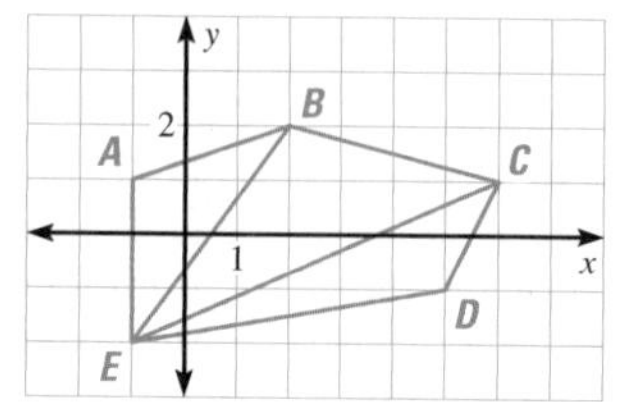

3. $\triangle EBC$
4. $\triangle ECD$
5. Quadrilateral $BCDE$
6. Pentagon $ABCDE$

EXAMPLE 2 on p. 581 for Exs. 7–12

MATRIX OPERATIONS **Add or subtract.**

7. $\begin{bmatrix} 3 & 5 \end{bmatrix} + \begin{bmatrix} 9 & 2 \end{bmatrix}$ $\begin{bmatrix} 12 & 7 \end{bmatrix}$

8. $\begin{bmatrix} -12 & 5 \\ 1 & -4 \end{bmatrix} + \begin{bmatrix} 2 & -3 \\ 0 & 8 \end{bmatrix}$

9. $\begin{bmatrix} 9 & 8 \\ -2 & 3 \\ 0 & -4 \end{bmatrix} + \begin{bmatrix} 7 & 1 \\ 2 & -3 \\ -5 & 1 \end{bmatrix}$

10. $\begin{bmatrix} 4.6 & 8.1 \end{bmatrix} - \begin{bmatrix} 3.8 & -2.1 \end{bmatrix}$ $\begin{bmatrix} 0.8 & 10.2 \end{bmatrix}$

11. $\begin{bmatrix} -5 & 6 \\ -8 & 9 \end{bmatrix} - \begin{bmatrix} 8 & 10 \\ 4 & -7 \end{bmatrix}$

12. $\begin{bmatrix} 1.2 & 6 \\ 5.3 & 1.1 \end{bmatrix} - \begin{bmatrix} 2.5 & -3.3 \\ 7 & 4 \end{bmatrix}$

Answers: 8. $\begin{bmatrix} -10 & 2 \\ 1 & 4 \end{bmatrix}$ 9. $\begin{bmatrix} 16 & 9 \\ 0 & 0 \\ -5 & -3 \end{bmatrix}$ 11. $\begin{bmatrix} -13 & -4 \\ -12 & 16 \end{bmatrix}$ 12. $\begin{bmatrix} -1.3 & 9.3 \\ -1.7 & -2.9 \end{bmatrix}$

EXAMPLE 3 on p. 581 for Exs. 13–17

TRANSLATIONS **Find the image matrix that represents the translation of the polygon. Then graph the polygon and its image.** **13–16. See margin.**

13. $\begin{bmatrix} -2 & 2 & 1 \\ 4 & 1 & -3 \end{bmatrix}$ (columns A, B, C); 4 units up

14. $\begin{bmatrix} 2 & 5 & 8 & 5 \\ 2 & 3 & 1 & -1 \end{bmatrix}$ (columns F, G, H, J); 2 units left and 3 units down

15. $\begin{bmatrix} 2 & 0 & 2 & 3 \\ -1 & 3 & 3 & -1 \end{bmatrix}$ (columns L, M, N, P); 4 units right and 2 units up

16. $\begin{bmatrix} -5 & 0 & 1 \\ 1 & 4 & 2 \end{bmatrix}$ (columns Q, R, S); 3 units right and 1 unit down

17. ★ **MULTIPLE CHOICE** The matrix that represents quadrilateral $ABCD$ is $\begin{bmatrix} 3 & 8 & 9 & 7 \\ 3 & 7 & 3 & 1 \end{bmatrix}$. Which matrix represents the image of the quadrilateral after translating it 3 units right and 5 units up? **A**

Ⓐ $\begin{bmatrix} 6 & 11 & 12 & 10 \\ 8 & 12 & 8 & 6 \end{bmatrix}$ Ⓑ $\begin{bmatrix} 0 & 5 & 6 & 4 \\ 8 & 12 & 8 & 6 \end{bmatrix}$

Ⓒ $\begin{bmatrix} 6 & 11 & 12 & 10 \\ -2 & 2 & -2 & -4 \end{bmatrix}$ Ⓓ $\begin{bmatrix} 0 & 6 & 6 & 4 \\ -2 & 3 & -2 & -4 \end{bmatrix}$

2. If they have the same dimensions they can be added; if the number of columns in the first matrix matches the number of rows in the second matrix they can be multiplied.

3. $\begin{bmatrix} -1 & 2 & 6 \\ -2 & 2 & 1 \end{bmatrix}$ (E, B, C) **4.** $\begin{bmatrix} -1 & 6 & 5 \\ -2 & 1 & -1 \end{bmatrix}$ (E, C, D) **5.** $\begin{bmatrix} 2 & 6 & 5 & -1 \\ 2 & 1 & -1 & -2 \end{bmatrix}$ (B, C, D, E) **6.** $\begin{bmatrix} -1 & 2 & 6 & 5 & -1 \\ 1 & 2 & 1 & -1 & -2 \end{bmatrix}$ (A, B, C, D, E)

13–16. See Additional Answers beginning on p. AA1.

EXAMPLE 4 B
on p. 582
for Exs. 18–26

MATRIX OPERATIONS Multiply.

18. $\begin{bmatrix} 5 & 2 \end{bmatrix}\begin{bmatrix} 4 \\ 3 \end{bmatrix}$ **[26]**

(19.) $\begin{bmatrix} 1.2 & 3 \end{bmatrix}\begin{bmatrix} -2 \\ -1.5 \end{bmatrix}$ **[−6.9]**

20. $\begin{bmatrix} 6 & 7 \\ -5 & 8 \end{bmatrix}\begin{bmatrix} 2 & 1 \\ 9 & -3 \end{bmatrix}$

21. $\begin{bmatrix} 0.4 & 6 \\ -6 & 2.3 \end{bmatrix}\begin{bmatrix} 5 & 8 \\ -1 & 2 \end{bmatrix}$ **See margin.**

22. $\begin{bmatrix} 4 & 8 & -1 \end{bmatrix}\begin{bmatrix} 3 \\ 2 \\ 5 \end{bmatrix}$ **[23]**

23. $\begin{bmatrix} 9 & 1 & 2 \\ 8 & -1 & 4 \end{bmatrix}\begin{bmatrix} 4 \\ 0 \\ 1 \end{bmatrix}$ $\begin{bmatrix} \mathbf{38} \\ \mathbf{36} \end{bmatrix}$

24. ★ **MULTIPLE CHOICE** Which product is not defined? **C**

Ⓐ $\begin{bmatrix} 1 & 7 \\ 3 & 12 \end{bmatrix}\begin{bmatrix} 6 \\ 15 \end{bmatrix}$ Ⓑ $\begin{bmatrix} 3 & 20 \end{bmatrix}\begin{bmatrix} 9 \\ 30 \end{bmatrix}$ Ⓒ $\begin{bmatrix} 15 \\ -3 \end{bmatrix}\begin{bmatrix} 1 & 6 \\ 4 & 0 \end{bmatrix}$ Ⓓ $\begin{bmatrix} 30 \\ -7 \end{bmatrix}\begin{bmatrix} 5 & 5 \end{bmatrix}$

25. ★ **OPEN-ENDED MATH** Write two matrices that have a defined product. Then find the product.

26. **ERROR ANALYSIS** *Describe* and correct the error in the computation.

$$\begin{bmatrix} 9 & -2 \\ 4 & 10 \end{bmatrix}\begin{bmatrix} -6 & 12 \\ 3 & -6 \end{bmatrix} = \begin{bmatrix} 9(-6) & -2(12) \\ 4(3) & 10(-6) \end{bmatrix}$$ ✗

Corresponding elements were multiplied rather than rows and columns; $\begin{bmatrix} 9(-6) + -2(3) & 9(12) + -2(-6) \\ 4(-6) + 10(3) & 4(12) + 10(-6) \end{bmatrix}$

TRANSLATIONS Use the described translation and the graph of the image to find the matrix that represents the preimage. **27, 28. See margin.**

27. 4 units right and 2 units down

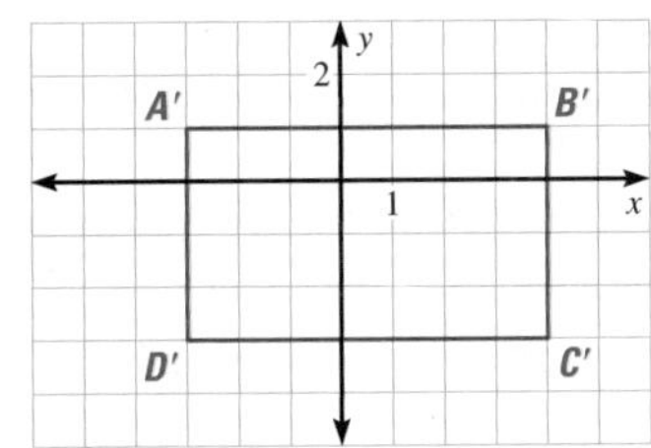

28. 6 units left and 5 units up

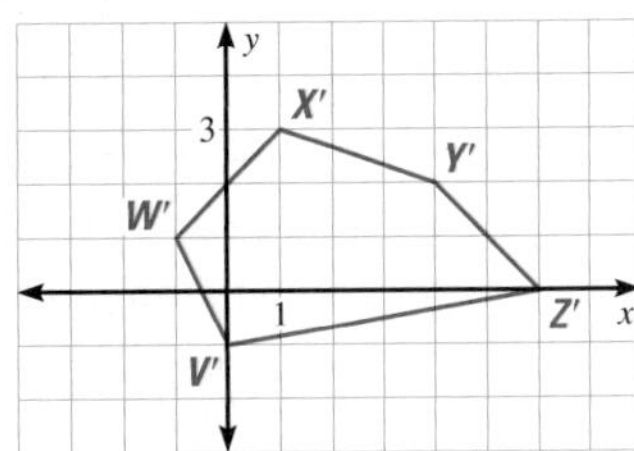

29. **MATRIX EQUATION** Use the description of a translation of a triangle to find the value of each variable. *Explain* your reasoning. What are the coordinates of the vertices of the image triangle? **See margin.**

$$\begin{bmatrix} 12 & 12 & w \\ -7 & v & -7 \end{bmatrix} + \begin{bmatrix} 9 & a & b \\ 6 & -2 & c \end{bmatrix} = \begin{bmatrix} m & 20 & -8 \\ n & -9 & 13 \end{bmatrix}$$

C

30. **CHALLENGE** A point in space has three coordinates (x, y, z), as shown at the right. From the origin, a point can be forward or back on the x-axis, left or right on the y-axis, and up or down on the z-axis.

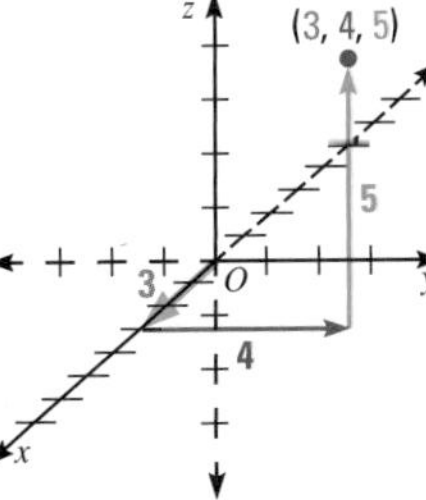

a. You translate a point three units forward, four units right, and five units up. Write a translation matrix for the point.

b. You translate a figure that has five vertices. Write a translation matrix to move the figure five units back, ten units left, and six units down. **See margin.**

Margin (left):

0. $\begin{bmatrix} 75 & -15 \\ 62 & -29 \end{bmatrix}$

5. *Sample answer:* $\begin{bmatrix} -2 & 1 \\ 0 & 4 \end{bmatrix}$, $\begin{bmatrix} 1 & 1 \\ 2 & 1 \end{bmatrix}$; $\begin{bmatrix} 0 & -1 \\ 8 & 4 \end{bmatrix}$

30a. $\begin{bmatrix} 3 \\ 4 \\ 5 \end{bmatrix}$

Graphing Calculator

Exercises 7–12, 18–23 Teach students how to enter matrices on their graphing calculators and then how to add, subtract, and multiply matrices using the calculator.

Avoiding Common Errors

Exercises 18–23 Students sometimes think that matrix multiplication is an application of the Distributive Property of multiplication over addition. Help them by reviewing Example 4 carefully. Point out that none of the sums in the matrix equation in Step 4 could be the result of applying the Distributive Property.

21. $\begin{bmatrix} -4 & 15.2 \\ -32.3 & -43.4 \end{bmatrix}$

27. $\begin{array}{cccc} A & B & C & D \end{array}$ $\begin{bmatrix} -7 & 0 & 0 & -7 \\ 3 & 3 & -1 & -1 \end{bmatrix}$

28. $\begin{array}{ccccc} V & W & X & Y & Z \end{array}$ $\begin{bmatrix} 6 & 5 & 7 & 10 & 12 \\ -6 & -4 & -2 & -3 & -5 \end{bmatrix}$

29. $a = 8, b = -20, c = 20, m = 21, n = -1, v = -7, w = 12$; **the sum of the corresponding elements on the left equals the corresponding elements on the right; (21, −1), (20, −9), (−8, 13).**

30b. $\begin{bmatrix} -5 & -5 & -5 & -5 & -5 \\ -10 & -10 & -10 & -10 & -10 \\ -6 & -6 & -6 & -6 & -6 \end{bmatrix}$

Vocabulary

Exercises 33–35 Review the Commutative, Associative, and Distributive Properties for whole numbers before having the students complete these exercises. Be sure they know what the properties mean and understand how to check whether the properties extend to matrices.

33b. $\begin{bmatrix} -3 & 15 \\ -14 & 30 \end{bmatrix}, \begin{bmatrix} 25 & -7 \\ 10 & 2 \end{bmatrix},$ $AB \neq BA$

34b. $\begin{bmatrix} -81 & 3 \\ -178 & -26 \end{bmatrix}, \begin{bmatrix} -81 & 3 \\ -178 & -26 \end{bmatrix},$ $A(BC) = (AB)C$

35. $\begin{bmatrix} 2 & 36 \\ 16 & 68 \end{bmatrix}, \begin{bmatrix} 2 & 36 \\ 16 & 68 \end{bmatrix},$ **the Distributive Property holds for matrices.**

PROBLEM SOLVING

EXAMPLE 5 A on p. 583 for Ex. 31

31. COMPUTERS Two computer labs submit equipment lists. A mouse costs \$10, a package of CDs costs \$32, and a keyboard costs \$15. Use matrix multiplication to find the total cost of equipment for each lab.

Lab 1	Lab 2
25 Mice	15 Mice
10 CDs	20 CDs
18 Keyboards	12 Keyboards

31. Lab 1: \$840, Lab 2: \$970

@HomeTutor for problem solving help at classzone.com

32. SWIMMING Two swim teams submit equipment lists. The women's team needs 30 caps and 26 goggles. The men's team needs 15 caps and 25 goggles. A cap costs \$10 and goggles cost \$15.

a. Use matrix addition to find the total number of caps and the total number of goggles for each team. **32a. 45 caps, 51 goggles**

b. Use matrix multiplication to find the total equipment cost for each team. **Women: \$690; Men: \$525**

c. Find the total cost for both teams. **\$1215**

@HomeTutor for problem solving help at classzone.com

B **MATRIX PROPERTIES In Exercises 33–35, use matrices *A*, *B*, and *C*.**

$$A = \begin{bmatrix} 5 & 1 \\ 10 & -2 \end{bmatrix} \quad B = \begin{bmatrix} -1 & 3 \\ 2 & 0 \end{bmatrix} \quad C = \begin{bmatrix} 2 & 4 \\ -5 & 1 \end{bmatrix}$$

33. MULTI-STEP PROBLEM Use the 2×2 matrices above to explore the Commutative Property of Multiplication.

a. What does it mean that multiplication is *commutative*? **$AB = BA$**

b. Find and *compare* AB and BA. **See margin.**

c. Based on part (b), make a conjecture about whether matrix multiplication is commutative. **Matrix multiplication is not commutative.**

34. MULTI-STEP PROBLEM Use the 2×2 matrices above to explore the Associative Property of Multiplication.

a. What does it mean that multiplication is *associative*? **$A(BC) = (AB)C$**

b. Find and *compare* $A(BC)$ and $(AB)C$. **See margin.**

c. Based on part (b), make a conjecture about whether matrix multiplication is associative. **Matrix multiplication is associative.**

35. ★ SHORT RESPONSE Find and *compare* $A(B + C)$ and $AB + AC$. Make a conjecture about matrices and the Distributive Property. **See margin.**

36. ART Two art classes are buying supplies. A brush is \$4 and a paint set is \$10. Each class has only \$225 to spend. Use matrix multiplication to find the maximum number of brushes Class A can buy and the maximum number of paint sets Class B can buy. *Explain.* **26 brushes, 15 paint sets; solve $4x + 120 \leq 225$ and $72 + 10y \leq 225$.**

Class A	Class B
x brushes	18 brushes
12 paint sets	*y* paint sets

a. 2002: Iowa about 1928 million, Illinois about 1471 million, Nebraska about 942 million, Minnesota about 1049 million; 2003: Iowa about 1881 million, Illinois about 1810 million, Nebraska about 1123 million, Minnesota about 971 million.

C **37. CHALLENGE** The total United States production of corn was 8,967 million bushels in 2002, and 10,114 million bushels in 2003. The table shows the percents of the total grown by four states.

	2002	2003
Iowa	21.5%	18.6%
Illinois	16.4%	17.9%
Nebraska	10.5%	11.1%
Minnesota	11.7%	9.6%

a. Use matrix multiplication to find the number of bushels (in millions) harvested in each state each year.

b. How many bushels (in millions) were harvested in these two years in Iowa? **about 3809 million bushels**

c. The price for a bushel of corn in Nebraska was \$2.32 in 2002, and \$2.45 in 2003. Use matrix multiplication to find the total value of corn harvested in Nebraska in these two years. **about \$4935 million**

MIXED REVIEW

PREVIEW Prepare for Lesson 9.3 in Exs. 38–39.

Copy the figure and draw its image after the reflection. *(p. 272)* **38, 39. See margin.**

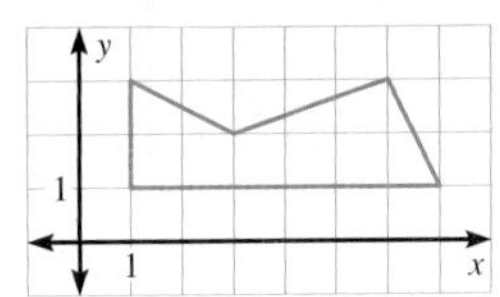

38. Reflect the figure in the x-axis.

39. Reflect the figure in the y-axis.

Find the value of x to the nearest tenth. *(p. 466)*

40. 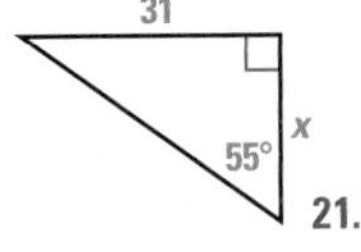

21.7

41. 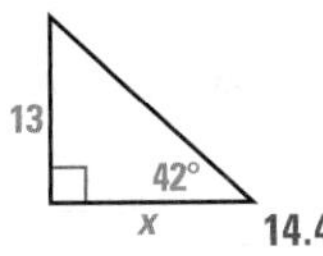

14.4

42. 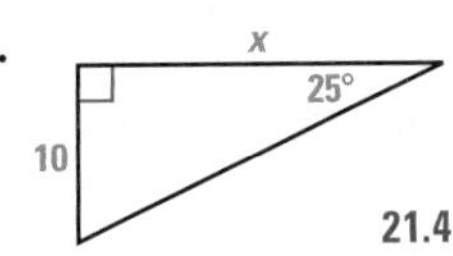

21.4

The diagonals of rhombus $WXYZ$ intersect at V. Given that $m\angle XYW = 62°$, find the indicated measure. *(p. 533)*

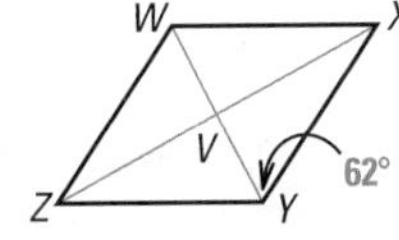

43. $m\angle ZYW = \underline{?}$ **62°** **44.** $m\angle WXY = \underline{?}$ **56°** **45.** $m\angle XVY = \underline{?}$ **90°**

QUIZ for Lessons 9.1–9.2

1. In the diagram shown, name the vector and write its component form. *(p. 572)* $\overrightarrow{ML}$, $\langle -4, -3\rangle$

Use the translation $(x, y) \to (x + 3, y - 2)$. *(p. 572)*

2. What is the image of $(-1, 5)$? **(2, 3)**

3. What is the image of $(6, 3)$? **(9, 1)**

4. What is the preimage of $(-4, -1)$? **(−7, 1)**

Add, subtract, or multiply. *(p. 580)*

5. $\begin{bmatrix} 5 & -3 \\ 8 & -2 \end{bmatrix} + \begin{bmatrix} -9 & 6 \\ 4 & -7 \end{bmatrix}$ **6.** $\begin{bmatrix} -6 & 1 \\ 3 & 12 \end{bmatrix} - \begin{bmatrix} 4 & 15 \\ -7 & 8 \end{bmatrix}$ **7.** $\begin{bmatrix} 7 & -6 & 2 \\ 8 & 3 & 5 \end{bmatrix}\begin{bmatrix} 5 & 2 \\ -9 & 0 \\ 3 & -7 \end{bmatrix}$

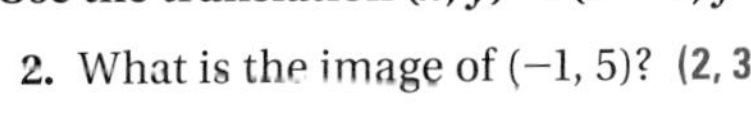
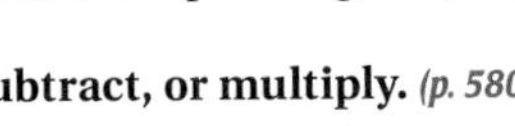

5. $\begin{bmatrix} -4 & 3 \\ 12 & -9 \end{bmatrix}$
6. $\begin{bmatrix} -10 & -14 \\ 10 & 4 \end{bmatrix}$
7. $\begin{bmatrix} 95 & 0 \\ 28 & -19 \end{bmatrix}$

38. 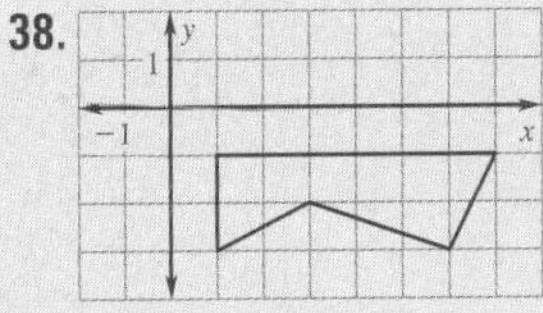

39. 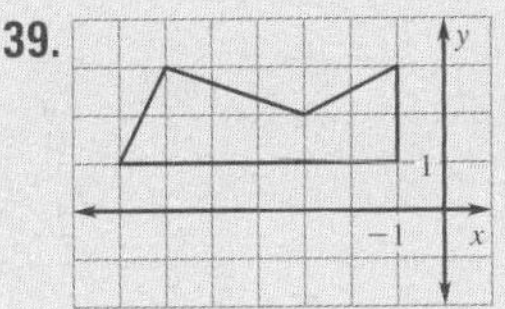

5 ASSESS AND RETEACH

Daily Homework Quiz

Transparency Available

Add or subtract

1. $[2.8\ \ -9.2] + [3.5\ \ 6.1]$ $[6.3\ \ -3.1]$

2. $\begin{bmatrix} 8 & -2 \\ -3 & 5 \end{bmatrix} - \begin{bmatrix} 4 & 3 \\ 1 & -7 \end{bmatrix}$ $\begin{bmatrix} 4 & -5 \\ -4 & 12 \end{bmatrix}$

3. Triangle ABC has vertices $A(2, -1)$, $B(1, 3)$, and $C(-2, -2)$. Write a matrix equation that shows how to find the image matrix that represents the translation of $\triangle ABC$ 4 units left and 5 units up.
$\begin{bmatrix} -4 & -4 & -4 \\ 5 & 5 & 5 \end{bmatrix} + \begin{bmatrix} 2 & 1 & -2 \\ -1 & 3 & -2 \end{bmatrix} = \begin{bmatrix} -2 & -3 & -6 \\ 4 & 8 & 3 \end{bmatrix}$

4. Multiply $\begin{bmatrix} 2 & -5 \\ 1 & 0 \end{bmatrix}\begin{bmatrix} 6 & -1 \\ 3 & -2 \end{bmatrix}$. $\begin{bmatrix} -3 & 8 \\ 6 & -1 \end{bmatrix}$

Online Quiz

Available at **classzone.com**

Diagnosis/Remediation

- Practice A, B, C in Chapter 9 Resource Book, pp. 20–25
- Study Guide in Chapter 9 Resource Book, pp. 26–27
- Practice Workbook, pp. 166–168
- @HomeTutor

Challenge

Additional challenge is available in the Chapter 9 Resource Book, p. 30.

Quiz

An easily-readable reduced copy of the quiz (with answers) on Lessons 9.1–9.2 from the Assessment Book can be found on p. 570G.

1 PLAN AND PREPARE

Explore the Concept

- Students will investigate the relationships between the line of reflection and the segment connecting a point and its image.
- This activity leads into the study of relationships in reflections in Example 1 in Lesson 9.3.

Materials

Each student will need:

- graph paper
- straightedge

Recommended Time

Work activity: 10 min
Discuss results: 5 min

Grouping

Students should work individually.

2 TEACH

Tips for Success

Students need to be very accurate when measuring the segments and angles.

Key Question

- What term describes a line that contains the midpoint of a segment? **bisector**

Alternative Strategy

Have students use a computer with geometric software to do this activity.

Key Discovery

The line of reflection is the perpendicular bisector of the segment connecting a point and its image.

3 ASSESS AND RETEACH

1. If you reflect a point in a line, how will the distance from the point to the line and from the image to the line compare? **equal**
2. How is the line of reflection related to the segment joining the point and its image? **perpendicular bisector**

9.3 Reflections in the Plane

MATERIALS • graph paper • straightedge

Standards
22.0 Students know the effect of rigid motions on figures in the coordinate plane and space, including rotations, translations, and reflections.

QUESTION What is the relationship between the line of reflection and the segment connecting a point and its image?

EXPLORE Graph a reflection of a triangle

STEP 1

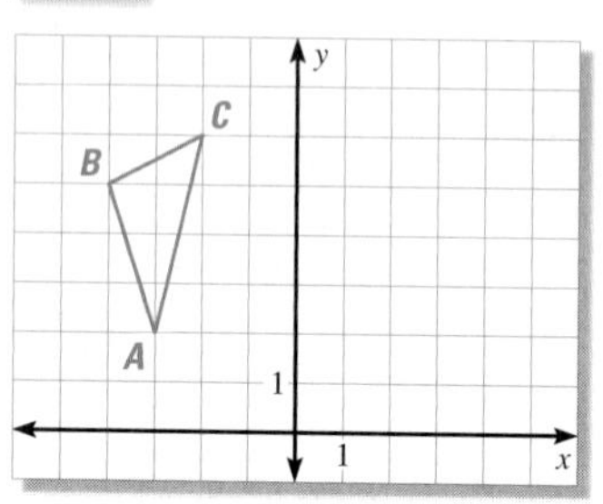

Draw a triangle Graph $A(-3, 2)$, $B(-4, 5)$, and $C(-2, 6)$. Connect the points to form $\triangle ABC$.

STEP 2

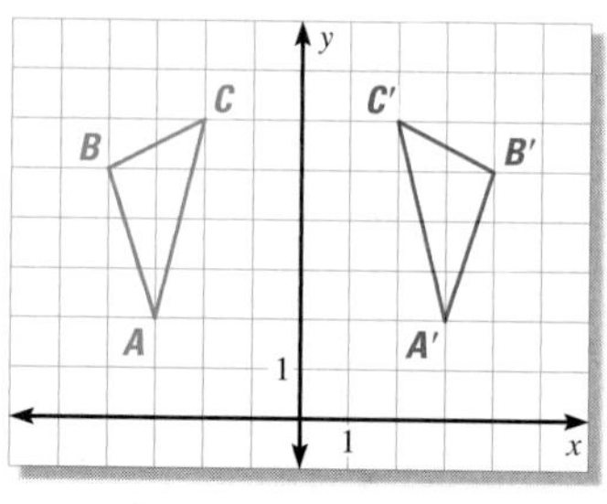

Graph a reflection Reflect $\triangle ABC$ in the y-axis. Label points A', B', and C' appropriately.

STEP 3

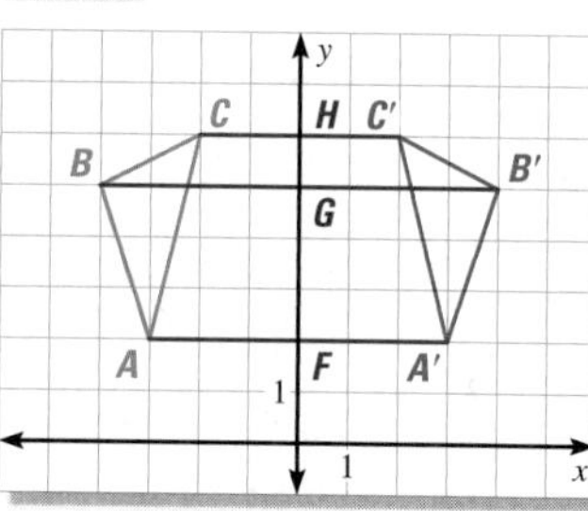

Draw segments Draw $\overline{AA'}$, $\overline{BB'}$, and $\overline{CC'}$. Label the points where these segments intersect the y-axis as F, G, and H, respectively.

DRAW CONCLUSIONS Use your observations to complete these exercises

1. Find the lengths of $\overline{CH}$ and $\overline{HC'}$, $\overline{BG}$ and $\overline{GB'}$, and $\overline{AF}$ and $\overline{FA'}$. *Compare* the lengths of each pair of segments. **2, 2; 4, 4; 3, 3; each pair of segments is the same.**
2. Find the measures of $\angle CHG$, $\angle BGF$, and $\angle AFG$. *Compare* the angle measures. **90°, 90°, 90°; they all measure 90°.**
3. How is the y-axis related to $\overline{AA'}$, $\overline{BB'}$, and $\overline{CC'}$? **It is perpendicular to and bisects each line segment.**
4. Use the graph at the right. **a, b. See margin.**
   a. $\overline{K'L'}$ is the reflection of $\overline{KL}$ in the x-axis. Copy the diagram and draw $\overline{K'L'}$.
   b. Draw $\overline{KK'}$ and $\overline{LL'}$. Label the points where the segments intersect the x-axis as J and M.
   c. How is the x-axis related to $\overline{KK'}$ and $\overline{LL'}$? **It is perpendicular to and bisects each line segment.**
5. How is the line of reflection related to the segment connecting a point and its image? **It is perpendicular to and bisects each line segment.**

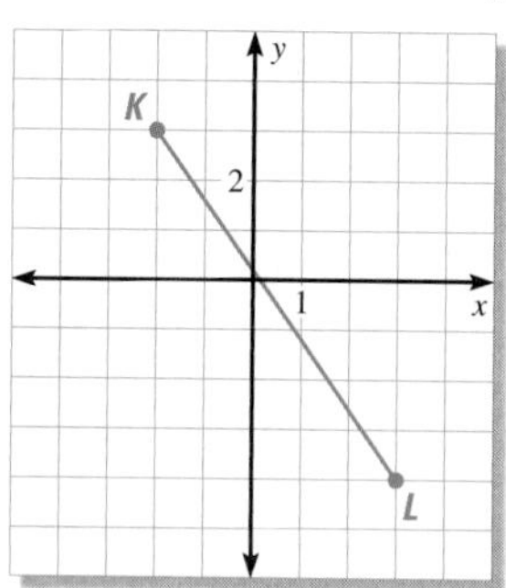

4a.

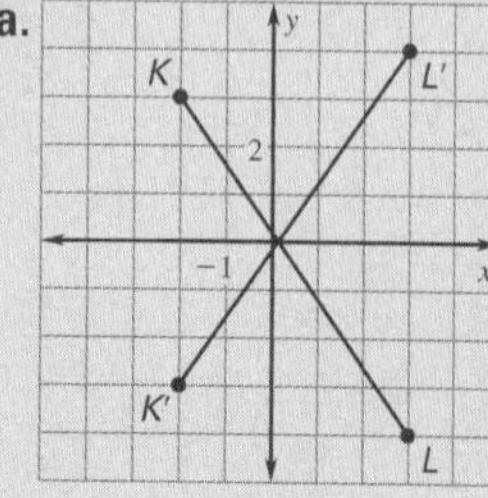

4b.

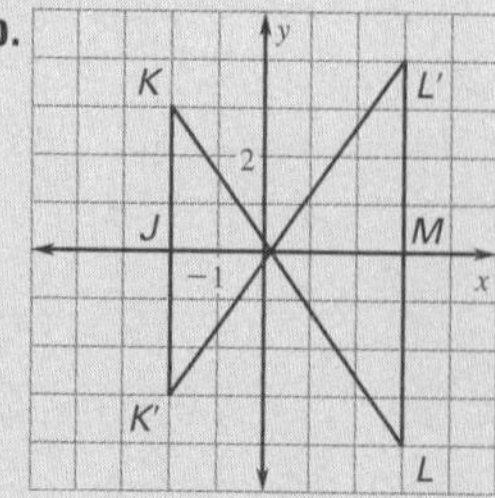

9.3 Perform Reflections

Before	You reflected a figure in the *x*- or *y*-axis.
Now	You will reflect a figure in any given line.
Why?	So you can identify reflections, as in Exs. 31–33.

Key Vocabulary
- **line of reflection**
- **reflection,** *p. 272*

Standards

22.0 Students know the effect of rigid motions on figures in the coordinate plane and space, including rotations, translations, **and reflections.**

In Lesson 4.8, you learned that a *reflection* is a transformation that uses a line like a mirror to reflect an image. The mirror line is called the **line of reflection.**

A reflection in a line m maps every point P in the plane to a point P', so that for each point one of the following properties is true:

- If P is not on m, then m is the perpendicular bisector of $\overline{PP'}$, or
- If P is on m, then $P = P'$.

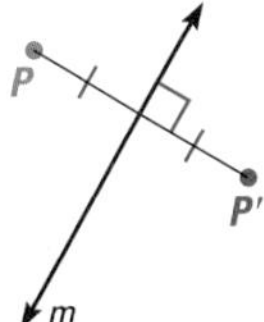

Point *P* not on *m*

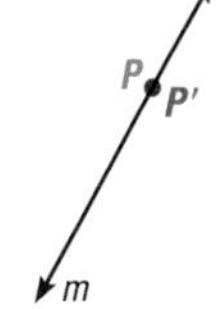

Point *P* on *m*

EXAMPLE 1 Graph reflections in horizontal and vertical lines

The vertices of $\triangle ABC$ are $A(1, 3)$, $B(5, 2)$, and $C(2, 1)$. Graph the reflection of $\triangle ABC$ described.

a. In the line n: $x = 3$

b. In the line m: $y = 1$

Solution

a. Point A is 2 units left of n, so its reflection A' is 2 units right of n at (5, 3). Also, B' is 2 units left of n at (1, 2), and C' is 1 unit right of n at (4, 1).

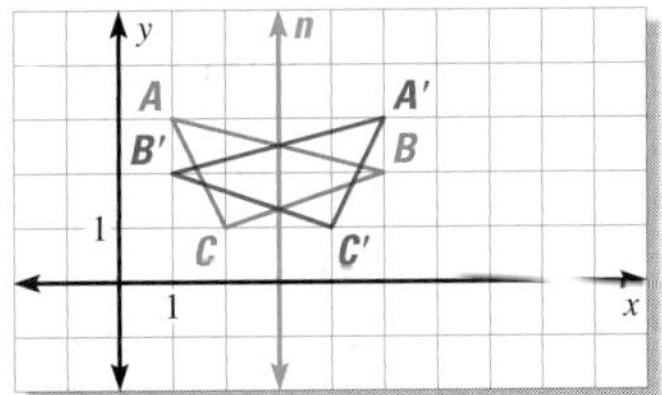

b. Point A is 2 units above m, so A' is 2 units below m at (1, −1). Also, B' is 1 unit below m at (5, 0). Because point C is on line m, you know that $C = C'$.

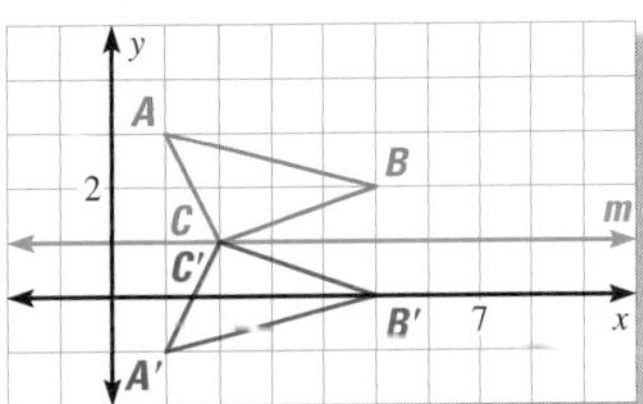

GUIDED PRACTICE for Example 1

Graph a reflection of $\triangle ABC$ from Example 1 in the given line.

1–3. See Additional Answers beginning on p. AA1.

1. $y = 4$ **2.** $x = -3$ **3.** $y = 2$

1 PLAN AND PREPARE

Warm-Up Exercises

Transparency Available

1. The *y*-axis is the perpendicular bisector of $\overline{AB}$. If point *A* is at (−3, 5), what is the location of point *B*? **(3, 5)**

2. What is the slope of the segment with endpoints at (−7, 4) and (4, −7)? **−1**

3. Multiply $\begin{bmatrix} -1 & 0 \\ 0 & 1 \end{bmatrix}\begin{bmatrix} 6 & -2 & 1 \\ 3 & 4 & 7 \end{bmatrix}$.

$\begin{bmatrix} -6 & 2 & -1 \\ 3 & 4 & 7 \end{bmatrix}$

Notetaking Guide

Transparency Available

Promotes interactive learning and notetaking skills, pp. 231–235.

Pacing

Basic: 2 days

Average: 2 days

Advanced: 2 days

Block: 1 block

- See *Teaching Guide/Lesson Plan.*

2 FOCUS AND MOTIVATE

Essential Question

Big Idea 1, p. 571

How do you reflect a figure in the line $y = x$? **Tell students they will learn how to answer this question by studying coordinate rules and matrices for reflections.**

Resource Planning Guide

Chapter Resource Book
- Teaching Guide/Lesson Plan (pp. 31–32)
- Practice levels A, B, C (pp. 33–38)
- Study Guide (pp. 39–40)
- Catch-up for Absent Students (p. 41)
- Problem Solving Workshop (p. 42)
- Challenge (p. 44)

Workbooks
- Notetaking Guide (pp. 231–235)
- Practice Workbook (pp. 169–171)

Teaching Options
- **Power Presentations CD-ROM** provides dynamic electronic teaching resources for the classroom.
- **Activity Generator CD-ROM** provides editable activities for all ability levels.

Interactive Technology
- Easy Planner
- Power Presentations CD-ROM
- Activity Generator CD-ROM
- Animated Geometry
- Test Generator CD-ROM
- Online Quiz
- eWorkbook
- eEdition
- @HomeTutor

Resources for English Learners
- Quick Reference for English Learners
- Spanish Study Guide
- Multi-Language Visual Glossary
- Student Resources in Spanish

See also the *Geometry Toolkit* for more strategies for meeting individual needs.

Motivating the Lesson

Have students imagine that they are playing miniature golf and want to hit the ball off a wall so it will land in the hole. Tell students that in this lesson they will learn about geometric transformations that can help solve this problem.

3 TEACH

Extra Example 1

The vertices of $\triangle DEF$ are $D(0, 2)$, $E(1, 4)$, and $F(3, 1)$. Graph the reflection of $\triangle DEF$ described.

a. In the line m: $y = 2$

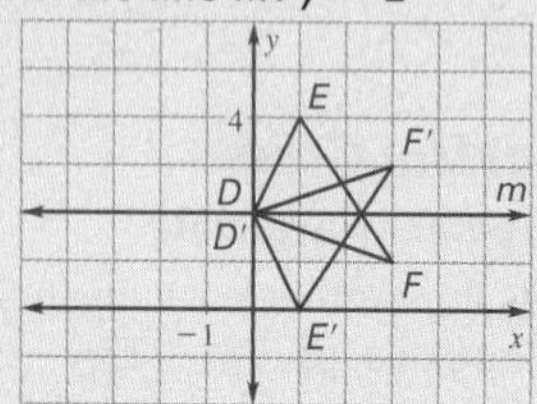

b. In the line n: $x = 4$

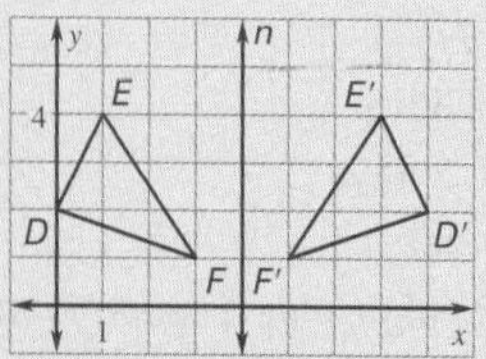

Extra Example 2

The endpoints of $\overline{AB}$ are $A(3, 2)$ and $B(4, 1)$. Reflect the segment in the line $y = x$. Graph the segment and its image.

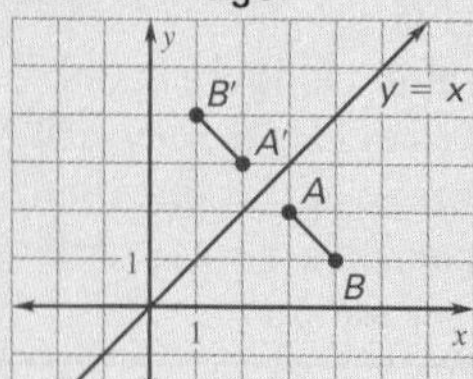

EXAMPLE 2 Graph a reflection in $y = x$

The endpoints of $\overline{FG}$ are $F(-1, 2)$ and $G(1, 2)$. Reflect the segment in the line $y = x$. Graph the segment and its image.

Solution

REVIEW SLOPE
The product of the slopes of perpendicular lines is -1.

The slope of $y = x$ is 1. The segment from F to its image, $\overline{FF'}$, is perpendicular to the line of reflection $y = x$, so the slope of $\overline{FF'}$ will be -1 (because $1(-1) = -1$). From F, move 1.5 units right and 1.5 units down to $y = x$. From that point, move 1.5 units right and 1.5 units down to locate $F'(2, -1)$.

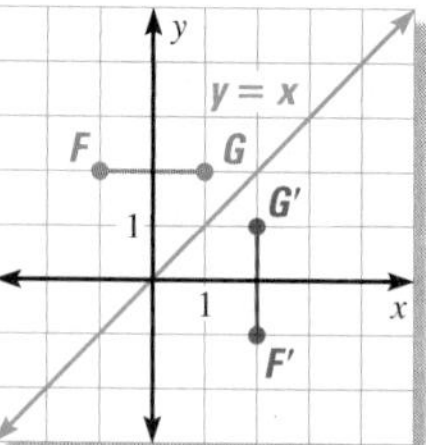

The slope of $\overline{GG'}$ will also be -1. From G, move 0.5 units right and 0.5 units down to $y = x$. Then move 0.5 units right and 0.5 units down to locate $G'(2, 1)$.

COORDINATE RULES You can use coordinate rules to find the images of points reflected in four special lines.

KEY CONCEPT *For Your Notebook*

Coordinate Rules for Reflections

- If (a, b) is reflected in the x-axis, its image is the point $(a, -b)$.
- If (a, b) is reflected in the y-axis, its image is the point $(-a, b)$.
- If (a, b) is reflected in the line $y = x$, its image is the point (b, a).
- If (a, b) is reflected in the line $y = -x$, its image is the point $(-b, -a)$.

EXAMPLE 3 Graph a reflection in $y = -x$

Reflect $\overline{FG}$ from Example 2 in the line $y = -x$. Graph $\overline{FG}$ and its image.

Solution

Use the coordinate rule for reflecting in $y = -x$.

$$(a, b) \rightarrow (-b, -a)$$

$F(-1, 2) \rightarrow F'(-2, 1)$

$G(1, 2) \rightarrow G'(-2, -1)$

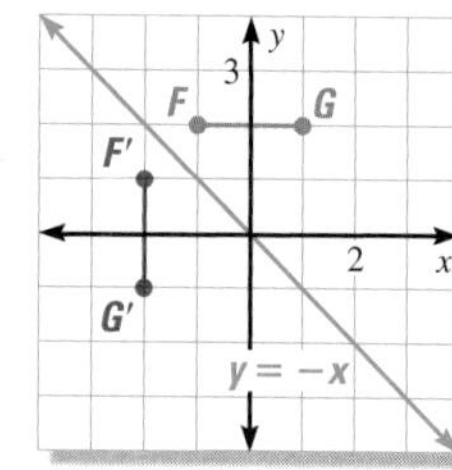

AnimatedGeometry at classzone.com

GUIDED PRACTICE for Examples 2 and 3

4. Graph $\triangle ABC$ with vertices $A(1, 3)$, $B(4, 4)$, and $C(3, 1)$. Reflect $\triangle ABC$ in the lines $y = -x$ and $y = x$. Graph each image. **See margin.**
5. In Example 3, *verify* that $\overline{FF'}$ is perpendicular to $y = -x$.

5. Slope of $y = -x$ is -1. The slope of $\overline{FF'}$ is 1. The product of their slopes is -1 making them perpendicular.

REFLECTION THEOREM You saw in Lesson 9.1 that the image of a translation is congruent to the original figure. The same is true for a reflection.

THEOREM *For Your Notebook*

THEOREM 9.2 Reflection Theorem

A reflection is an isometry.

$\triangle ABC \cong \triangle A'B'C'$

Proof: Exs. 35–38, p. 595

WRITE PROOFS
Some theorems, such as the Reflection Theorem, have more than one case. To prove this type of theorem, each case must be proven.

PROVING THE THEOREM To prove the Reflection Theorem, you need to show that a reflection preserves the length of a segment. Consider a segment $\overline{PQ}$ that is reflected in a line m to produce $\overline{P'Q'}$. There are four cases to prove:

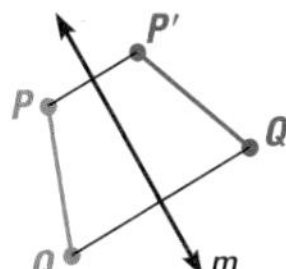

Case 1 P and Q are on the same side of m.

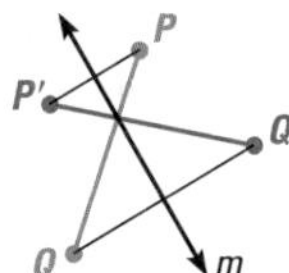

Case 2 P and Q are on opposite sides of m.

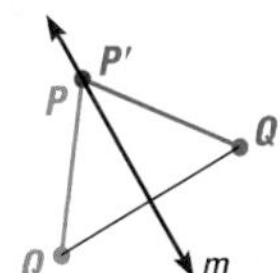

Case 3 P lies on m, and $\overline{PQ}$ is not $\perp$ to m.

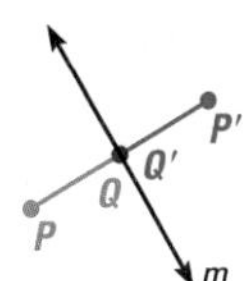

Case 4 Q lies on m, and $\overline{PQ} \perp m$.

EXAMPLE 4 Find a minimum distance

PARKING You are going to buy books. Your friend is going to buy CDs. Where should you park to minimize the distance you both will walk?

Solution

Reflect B in line m to obtain B'. Then draw $\overline{AB'}$. Label the intersection of $\overline{AB'}$ and m as C. Because AB' is the shortest distance between A and B' and $BC = B'C$, park at point C to minimize the combined distance, $AC + BC$, you both have to walk.

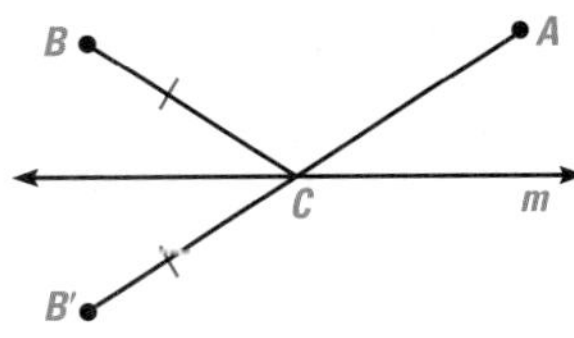

GUIDED PRACTICE for Example 4

6. Look back at Example 4. Answer the question by using a reflection of point A instead of point B. **Reflect A in line m obtaining A'. Then draw $\overline{A'B}$. Label the intersection of m and $\overline{A'B}$ as C. Because $A'B$ is the shortest distance between A' and B and $AC = A'C$, park at point C to minimize the combined distance, $AC + BC$, you both have to walk.**

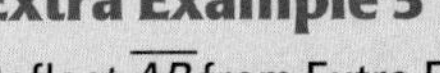

Extra Example 3

Reflect $\overline{AB}$ from Extra Example 2 in the line $y = -x$. Graph $\overline{AB}$ and its image.

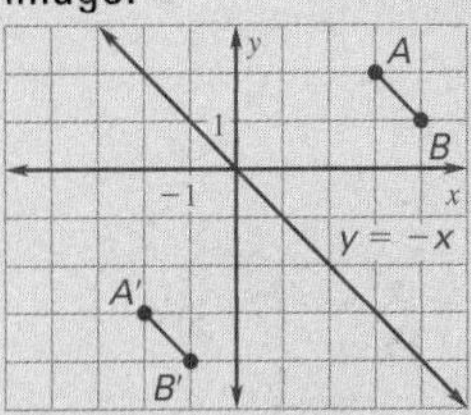

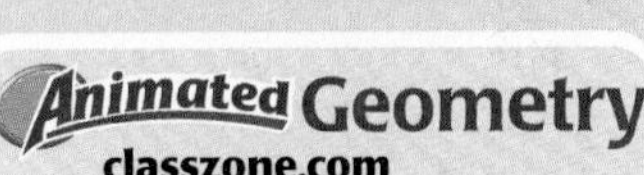

An **Animated Geometry** activity is available on-line for **Example 3.** This activity is also available on the **Power Presentations CD-ROM.**

Key Questions to Ask for Examples 2 and 3

- If a point and its image are in the same quadrant after a reflection in the line $y = x$, in which quadrant is the point located? **I or III**
- If a point and its image are in the same quadrant after a reflection in the line $y = -x$, in which quadrant is the point located? **II or IV**

Extra Example 4

Jan and Lula are going to meet on the beach shoreline. Where will they meet to minimize the distance they both must walk?

•*L* Lula's house

•*J* Jan's house

Beach shoreline

at the point where the beach shoreline intersects $\overline{LJ'}$, where J' is the image of J in the shoreline

Study Strategy

Have the students create a way to help them remember the Coordinate Rules for Reflections.

4.
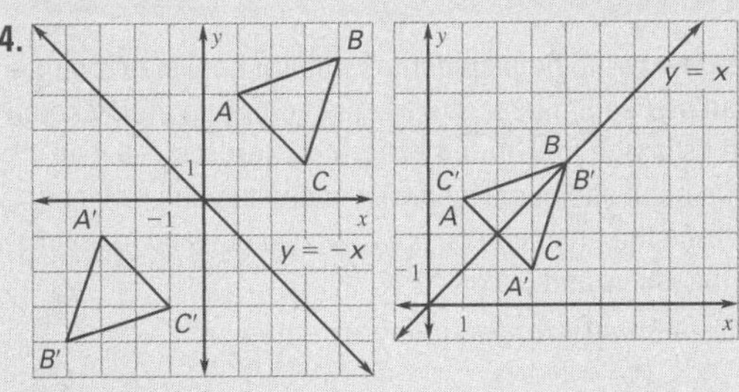

REFLECTION MATRIX You can find the image of a polygon reflected in the x-axis or y-axis using matrix multiplication. Write the reflection matrix to the *left* of the polygon matrix, then multiply.

Notice that because matrix multiplication is not commutative, the order of the matrices in your product is important. The reflection matrix must be first followed by the polygon matrix.

KEY CONCEPT *For Your Notebook*

Reflection Matrices

Reflection in the x-axis	Reflection in the y-axis
$\begin{bmatrix} 1 & 0 \\ 0 & -1 \end{bmatrix}$	$\begin{bmatrix} -1 & 0 \\ 0 & 1 \end{bmatrix}$

EXAMPLE 5 Use matrix multiplication to reflect a polygon

The vertices of $\triangle DEF$ are $D(1, 2)$, $E(3, 3)$, and $F(4, 0)$. Find the reflection of $\triangle DEF$ in the y-axis using matrix multiplication. Graph $\triangle DEF$ and its image.

Solution

STEP 1 **Multiply** the polygon matrix by the matrix for a reflection in the y-axis.

$$\underset{\text{Reflection matrix}}{\begin{bmatrix} -1 & 0 \\ 0 & 1 \end{bmatrix}} \underset{\text{Polygon matrix}}{\overset{D \;\; E \;\; F}{\begin{bmatrix} 1 & 3 & 4 \\ 2 & 3 & 0 \end{bmatrix}}} = \begin{bmatrix} -1(1) + 0(2) & -1(3) + 0(3) & -1(4) + 0(0) \\ 0(1) + 1(2) & 0(3) + 1(3) & 0(4) + 1(0) \end{bmatrix}$$

$$= \overset{D' \;\; E' \;\; F'}{\begin{bmatrix} -1 & -3 & -4 \\ 2 & 3 & 0 \end{bmatrix}} \quad \text{Image matrix}$$

STEP 2 **Graph** $\triangle DEF$ and $\triangle D'E'F'$.

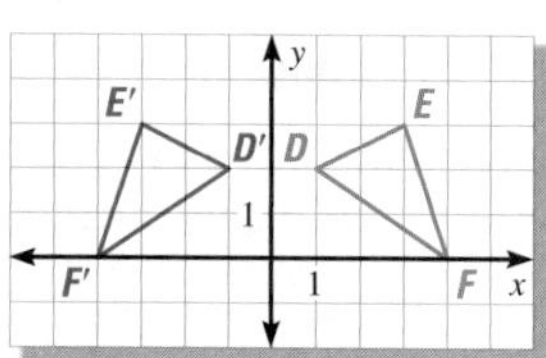

GUIDED PRACTICE for Example 5

The vertices of $\triangle LMN$ are $L(-3, 3)$, $M(1, 2)$, and $N(-2, 1)$. Find the described reflection using matrix multiplication.

7. Reflect $\triangle LMN$ in the x-axis. **$L'(-3, -3)$, $M'(1, -2)$, $N'(-2, -1)$**

8. Reflect $\triangle LMN$ in the y-axis. **$L'(3, 3)$, $M'(-1, 2)$, $N'(2, 1)$**

Extra Example 5

The vertices of $\triangle PQR$ are $P(-3, 6)$, $Q(-5, 3)$, and $R(-1, 2)$. Find the reflection of $\triangle PQR$ in the x-axis. Graph $\triangle PQR$ and its image.

$$\overset{P' \;\; Q' \;\; R'}{\begin{bmatrix} -3 & -5 & -1 \\ -6 & -3 & -2 \end{bmatrix}}$$

Key Question to Ask for Example 5

- How do the coordinates of the image compare to the coordinates of the preimage? **The x-coordinates are opposites, the y-coordinates are the same.**

Closing the Lesson

Have students summarize the major points of the lesson and answer the Essential Question: How do you reflect a figure in the line $y = x$?

- **Coordinate Rules for Reflections can be used to find the images of points reflected in the x-axis, y-axis, $y = x$, and $y = -x$.**
- **Matrices can be used to find the images of points reflected in the x-axis and y-axis.**

To reflect a figure in the line $y = x$, switch the x- and y-coordinates of each point of the figure.

Differentiated Instruction

Visual Learners To help students visualize how matrix multiplication can be used to describe a reflection, have them sketch $\triangle LMN$ and its image for **Guided Practice Exercises 7–8**. For students who need additional help with understanding reflections, have them trace the preimage of $\triangle LMN$, cut it out, and manually reflect it in the x-axis and y-axis.

See also the *Geometry Toolkit* for more strategies.

9.3 EXERCISES

HOMEWORK KEY
○ = **WORKED-OUT SOLUTIONS** on p. WS11 for Exs. 5, 13, and 33
★ = **STANDARDIZED TEST PRACTICE** Exs. 2, 12, 25, and 40

SKILL PRACTICE

A

1. **VOCABULARY** What is a *line of reflection*?
 a line which acts like a mirror to reflect an image across the line
2. ★ **WRITING** *Explain* how to find the distance from a point to its image if you know the distance from the point to the line of reflection. **See margin.**

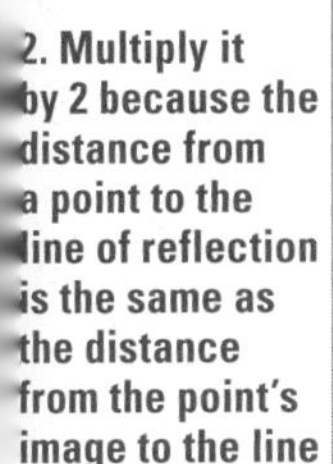

2. Multiply it by 2 because the distance from a point to the line of reflection is the same as the distance from the point's image to the line of reflection.

EXAMPLE 1 on p. 589 for Exs. 3–8

REFLECTIONS **Graph the reflection of the polygon in the given line.** **3–11. See margin.**

3. x-axis

4. y-axis

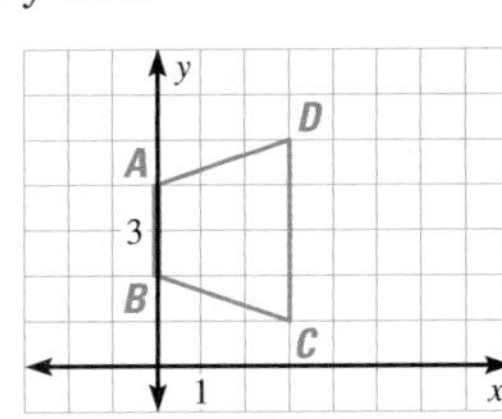

(5.) $y = 2$

6. $x = -1$

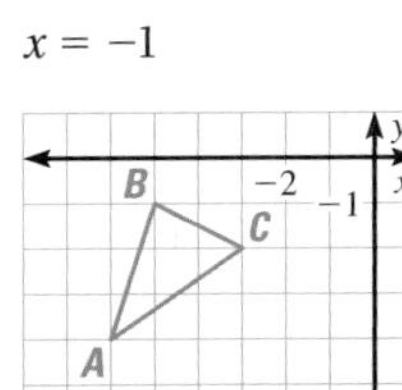

7. y-axis

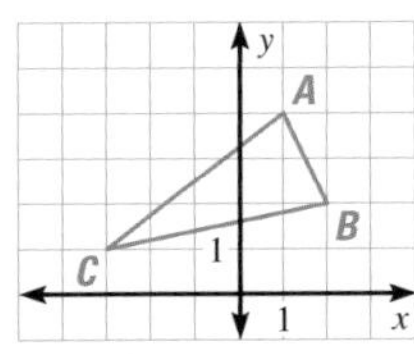

8. $y = -3$

EXAMPLES 2 and 3 on p. 590 for Exs. 9–12

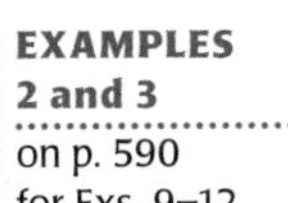

9. $y = x$

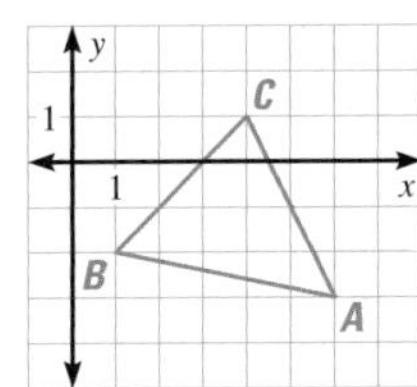

10. $y = -x$

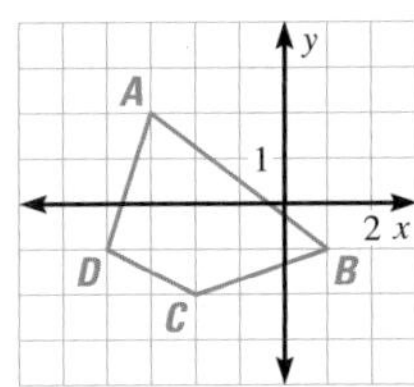

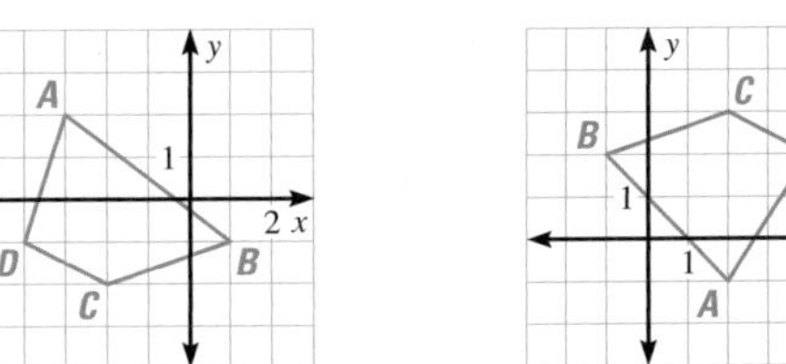

11. $y = x$

12. ★ **MULTIPLE CHOICE** What is the line of reflection for $\triangle ABC$ and its image? **D**

Ⓐ $y = 0$ (the x-axis) Ⓑ $y = -x$

Ⓒ $x - 1$ Ⓓ $y = x$

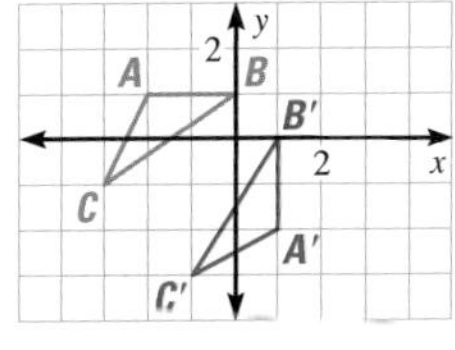

EXAMPLE 5 on p. 592 for Exs. 13–17

USING MATRIX MULTIPLICATION **Use matrix multiplication to find the image. Graph the polygon and its image.** **13, 14. See margin.**

(13.) Reflect $\begin{bmatrix} -2 & 3 & 4 \\ 5 & -3 & 6 \end{bmatrix}$ (columns A, B, C) in the x-axis.

14. Reflect $\begin{bmatrix} 2 & 6 & 5 & 2 \\ -2 & -3 & -8 & -5 \end{bmatrix}$ (columns P, Q, R, S) in the y-axis.

4 PRACTICE AND APPLY

Assignment Guide

Answer Transparencies available for all exercises

Basic:
Day 1: EP p. 901 Exs. 24–26
pp. 593–596
Exs. 1–12, 44–46
Day 2: pp. 593–596
Exs. 13–21, 31–37, 42, 43

Average:
Day 1: pp. 593–596
Exs. 1, 2, 6–12, 26–28, 44–46
Day 2: pp. 593–596
Exs. 15–25, 32–40, 42

Advanced:
Day 1: pp. 593–596
Exs. 1, 2, 7–12, 26–30*, 46
Day 2: pp. 593–596
Exs. 16–25, 34–41*, 43

Block:
pp. 593–596
Exs. 1, 2, 6–12, 15–28, 32–40, 42, 44–46

Differentiated Instruction

See *Geometry Best Practices Toolkit* for suggestions on addressing the needs of a diverse classroom.

Homework Check

For a quick check of student understanding of key concepts, go over the following exercises:
Basic: 4, 9, 14, 31, 34
Average: 6, 10, 16, 32, 34
Advanced: 8, 11, 17, 34, 35

Extra Practice

- Student Edition, p. 912
- Chapter 9 Resource Book: Practice levels A, B, C, pp. 33–38

Practice Worksheet

An easily-readable reduced practice page (with answers) for this lesson can be found on p. 570C.

3–11, 13, 14. See Additional Answers beginning on p. AA1.

B **FINDING IMAGE MATRICES** **Write a matrix for the polygon. Then find the image matrix that represents the polygon after a reflection in the given line.** 15–17. See margin.

15. y-axis

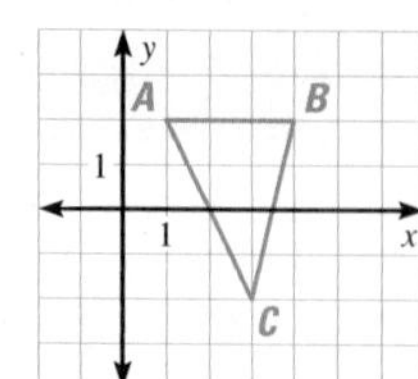

16. x-axis

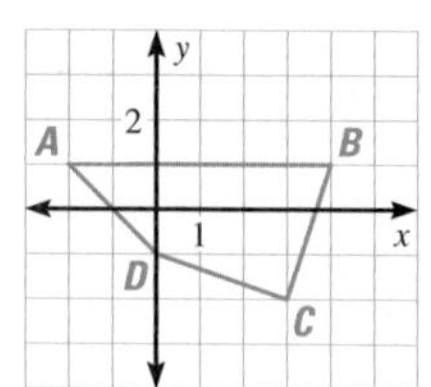

17. y-axis

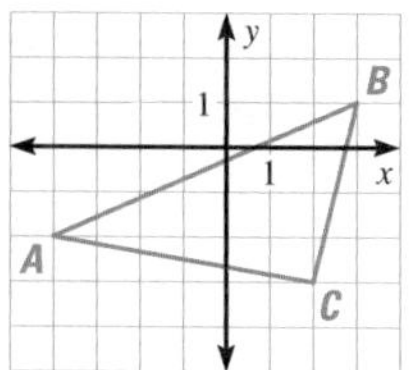

18. **ERROR ANALYSIS** *Describe* and correct the error in finding the image matrix of $\triangle PQR$ reflected in the y-axis. See margin.

$$\begin{bmatrix} 1 & 0 \\ 0 & -1 \end{bmatrix}\begin{bmatrix} -5 & 4 & -2 \\ 4 & 8 & -1 \end{bmatrix} = \begin{bmatrix} -5 & 4 & -2 \\ -4 & -8 & -1 \end{bmatrix}$$

MINIMUM DISTANCE **Find point C on the x-axis so $AC + BC$ is a minimum.**

19. $A(1, 4)$, $B(6, 1)$ $C(5, 0)$

20. $A(4, -3)$, $B(12, -5)$ $C(7, 0)$

21. $A(-8, 4)$, $B(-1, 3)$ $C(-4, 0)$

TWO REFLECTIONS **The vertices of $\triangle FGH$ are $F(3, 2)$, $G(1, 5)$, and $H(-1, 2)$. Reflect $\triangle FGH$ in the first line. Then reflect $\triangle F'G'H'$ in the second line. Graph $\triangle F'G'H'$ and $\triangle F''G''H''$.** 22–24. See margin.

22. In $y = 2$, then in $y = -1$

23. In $y = -1$, then in $x = 2$

24. In $y = x$, then in $x = -3$

25. ★ **SHORT RESPONSE** Use your graphs from Exercises 22–24. What do you notice about the order of vertices in the preimages and images? **The order is reversed.**

26. **CONSTRUCTION** Use these steps to construct a reflection of $\triangle ABC$ in line m using a straightedge and a compass. See margin.

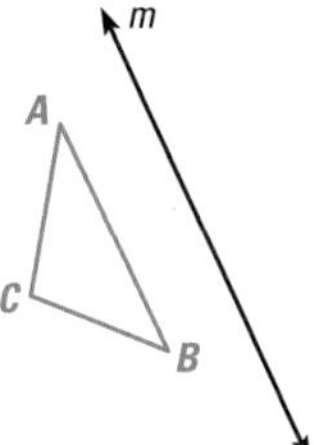

STEP 1 **Draw** $\triangle ABC$ and line m.

STEP 2 **Use** one compass setting to find two points that are equidistant from A on line m. Use the same compass setting to find a point on the other side of m that is the same distance from line m. Label that point A'.

STEP 3 **Repeat** Step 2 to find points B' and C'. Draw $\triangle A'B'C'$.

27. **ALGEBRA** The line $y = 3x + 2$ is reflected in the line $y = -1$. What is the equation of the image? $y = -3x - 4$

28. **ALGEBRA** Reflect the graph of the quadratic equation $y = 2x^2 - 5$ in the x-axis. What is the equation of the image? $y = -2x^2 + 5$

C 29. **REFLECTING A TRIANGLE** Reflect $\triangle MNQ$ in the line $y = -2x$. See margin.

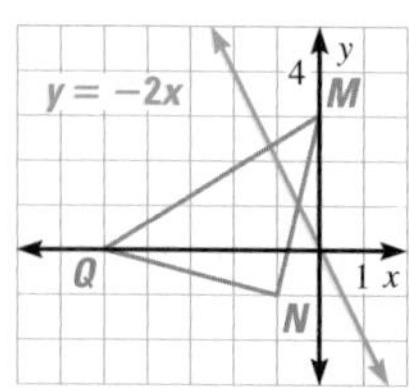

30. **CHALLENGE** Point $B'(1, 4)$ is the image of $B(3, 2)$ after a reflection in line c. Write an equation of line c. $y = x + 1$

○ = WORKED-OUT SOLUTIONS on p. WS1

★ = STANDARDIZED TEST PRACTICE

Teaching Strategy

Exercises 3–11 Students will do better with these exercises if they use a graph to find the image of each vertex in the given line. This will help give meaning to the coordinate rules stated on page 590. Urge students to use their graphs to confirm the coordinate rules.

Avoiding Common Errors

Exercises 19–21 Students may find the midpoint between the points rather than finding a point on the x-axis. Or they may find the point on the x-axis where the x-coordinate is the average of the x-coordinates of the given points. Have them graph the points, reflect one point over the x-axis, and see where the line joining the image to the other point intersects the x-axis.

Study Strategy

Exercise 26 Relate this construction to the construction of a line perpendicular to a given line through a point not on the line. When you reflect A over m you are constructing a point A' such that $\overline{AA'}$ is perpendicular to m.

15. $A\ B\ C$: $\begin{bmatrix} 1 & 4 & 3 \\ 2 & 2 & -2 \end{bmatrix}$; $A'\ B'\ C'$: $\begin{bmatrix} -1 & -4 & -3 \\ 2 & 2 & -2 \end{bmatrix}$

16. $A\ B\ C\ D$: $\begin{bmatrix} -2 & 4 & 3 & 0 \\ 1 & 1 & -2 & -1 \end{bmatrix}$; $A'\ B'\ C'\ D'$: $\begin{bmatrix} -2 & 4 & 3 & 0 \\ -1 & -1 & 2 & 1 \end{bmatrix}$

17. $A\ B\ C$: $\begin{bmatrix} -4 & 3 & 2 \\ -2 & 1 & -3 \end{bmatrix}$; $A'\ B'\ C'$: $\begin{bmatrix} 4 & -3 & -2 \\ -2 & 1 & -3 \end{bmatrix}$

18. The reflection matrix should be $\begin{bmatrix} -1 & 0 \\ 0 & 1 \end{bmatrix}$, not $\begin{bmatrix} 1 & 0 \\ 0 & -1 \end{bmatrix}$; $\begin{bmatrix} -1 & 0 \\ 0 & 1 \end{bmatrix}\begin{bmatrix} -5 & 4 & 2 \\ 4 & 8 & -1 \end{bmatrix} = \begin{bmatrix} 5 & -4 & 2 \\ 4 & 8 & -1 \end{bmatrix}$.

22–24, 26. See Additional Answers beginning on p. AA1.

29.

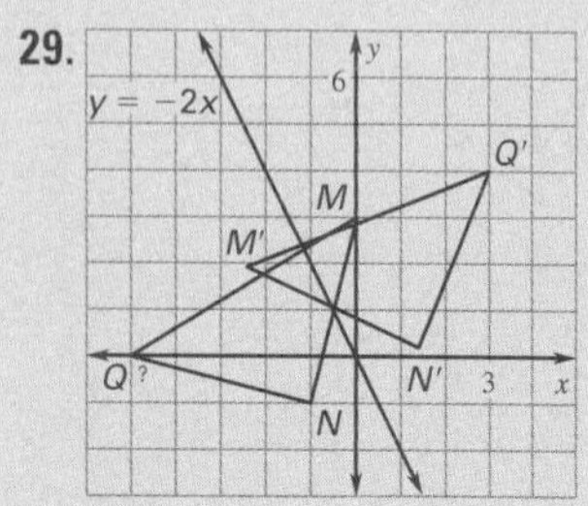

Differentiated Instruction

Advanced Extend **Exercise 27** by having students generalize. If the line $y = mx + b$ is reflected in the line $y = k$, what is the equation of the image? Also generalize on **Exercise 28** finding the equation of $y = ax^2 + c$ reflected in the x-axis or the y-axis and finding the equation of the image.

See also the *Geometry Toolkit* for more strategies.

Problem Solving

A **REFLECTIONS Identify the case of the Reflection Theorem represented.**

31. 

Case 4

32. 

Case 3

33. 

Case 1

EXAMPLE 4 on p. 591 for Ex. 34

34. **DELIVERING PIZZA** You park at some point K on line n. You deliver a pizza to house H, go back to your car, and deliver a pizza to house J. Assuming that you can cut across both lawns, how can you determine the parking location K that minimizes the total walking distance?

@HomeTutor for problem solving help at classzone.com

34. *Sample answer:* Reflect point H across line n and label it H'. Draw $\overline{JH'}$. Label the point where line n intersects at P. Park the car at P.

35. **PROVING THEOREM 9.2** Prove Case 1 of the Reflection Theorem.

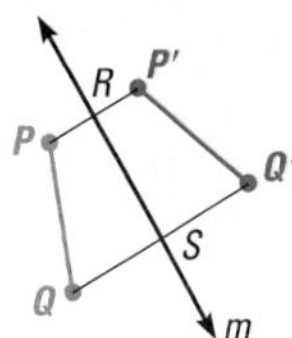

Case 1 The segment does not intersect the line of reflection.

GIVEN ▶ A reflection in m maps P to P' and Q to Q'.

PROVE ▶ $PQ = P'Q'$

Plan for Proof a, b. See margin.

a. Draw $\overline{PP'}$, $\overline{QQ'}$, $\overline{RQ}$, and $\overline{RQ'}$. Prove that $\triangle RSQ \cong \triangle RSQ'$.

b. Use the properties of congruent triangles and perpendicular bisectors to prove that $PQ = P'Q'$.

@HomeTutor for problem solving help at classzone.com

B **PROVING THEOREM 9.2 In Exercises 36–38, write a proof for the given case of the Reflection Theorem. (Refer to the diagrams on page 591.)** 36–38. See margin.

36. **Case 2** The segment intersects the line of reflection.

GIVEN ▶ A reflection in m maps P to P' and Q to Q'. Also, $\overline{PQ}$ intersects m at point R.

PROVE ▶ $PQ = P'Q'$

37. **Case 3** One endpoint is on the line of reflection, and the segment is not perpendicular to the line of reflection.

GIVEN ▶ A reflection in m maps P to P' and Q to Q'. Also, P lies on line m, and $\overline{PQ}$ is not perpendicular to m.

PROVE ▶ $PQ = P'Q'$

38. **Case 4** One endpoint is on the line of reflection, and the segment is perpendicular to the line of reflection.

GIVEN ▶ A reflection in m maps P to P' and Q to Q'. Also, Q lies on line m, and $\overline{PQ}$ is perpendicular to line m.

PROVE ▶ $PQ = P'Q'$

Teaching Strategy

Exercise 30 Elicit that the line of reflection c is the perpendicular bisector of the segment $\overline{BB'}$. Ask students how they could find the coordinates of a point on line c. Then ask how they could find the slope of line c.

Mathematical Reasoning

Exercises 35–38 Ask students if they can think of yet another special case of the Reflection Theorem. Ask them to explain why this case does not merit a complete proof. **the case in which $\overline{PQ}$ is contained in line m; $\overline{P'Q'}$ and $\overline{PQ}$ coincide, so it is trivially true that $\overline{P'Q'} \cong \overline{PQ}$.**

Internet Reference

Exercises 40–41 For more information about the Law of Reflection, visit acept.la.asu.edu/PiN/rdg/reflection/reflection.shtml

35b. Using corresponding parts of congruent triangles are congruent, $\overline{RQ} \cong \overline{RQ'}$. Using the definition of a line of reflection, $\overline{PR} \cong \overline{P'R}$. Since $\overline{PP'}$ and $\overline{QQ'}$ are both perpendicular to m, they are parallel. Using the Alternate Interior Angles Theorem, $\angle SQ'R \cong \angle P'RQ'$ and $\angle SQR \cong \angle PRQ$. Using corresponding parts of congruent triangles are congruent, $\angle SQ'R \cong \angle SQR$. Using the Transitive Property of Angle Congruence, $\angle P'RQ' \cong \angle PRQ$. $\triangle PRQ \cong \triangle P'RQ'$ using the SAS Congruence Postulate. Using corresponding parts of congruent triangles are congruent, $\overline{PQ} \cong \overline{P'Q'}$ which implies $PQ = P'Q'$.

36–38. See Additional Answers beginning on p. AA1.

35a.

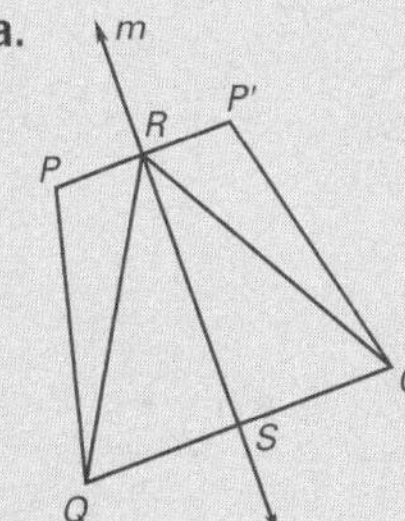

Given: A reflection in m maps P to P' and Q to Q'. Using the definition of a line of reflection, $\overline{QS} \cong \overline{Q'S}$ and $\angle QSR \cong \angle Q'SR$. Using the Reflexive Property of Segment Congruence, $\overline{RS} \cong \overline{RS}$. Using the SAS Congruence Postulate, $\triangle RSQ \cong \triangle RSQ'$.

5 ASSESS AND RETEACH

Daily Homework Quiz

Transparency Available

Graph the polygon and its reflection in the given line.

1. Quadrilateral with vertices $A(-2, 1)$, $B(1, 4)$, $C(3, 1)$, $D(2, -1)$ over $y = 1$

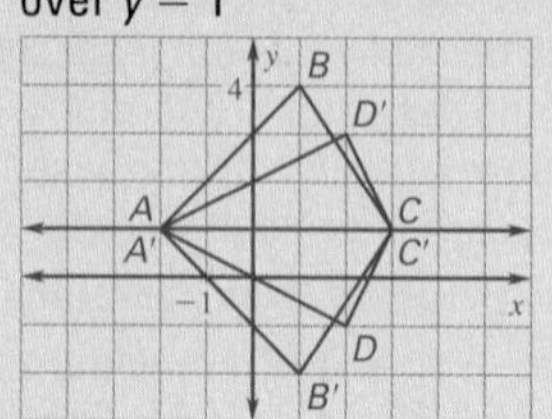

2. Triangle $P(-2, 2)$, $Q(3, 4)$, $R(4, 1)$ over $y = x$

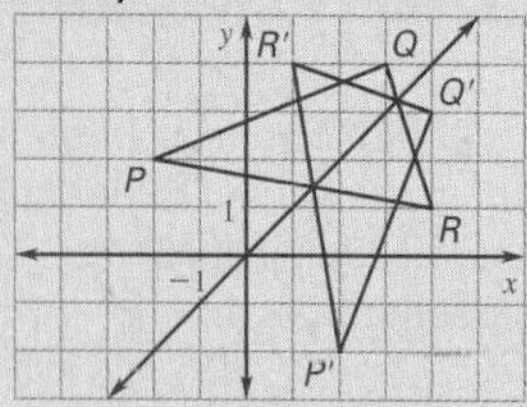

3. Use matrix multiplication to find the image matrix when $\triangle ABC$ is reflected in the y-axis.

$$\begin{matrix} A & B & C \\ \end{matrix} \quad \begin{matrix} A' & B' & C' \end{matrix}$$
$$\begin{bmatrix} 2 & -1 & 0 \\ 3 & 4 & -1 \end{bmatrix} \begin{bmatrix} -2 & 1 & 0 \\ 3 & 4 & -1 \end{bmatrix}$$

4. Find point C on the x-axis so $AC + BC$ is a minimum for $A(2, 5)$ and $B(7, 3)$. $\left(\frac{41}{8}, 0\right)$

Online Quiz

Available at **classzone.com**

Diagnosis/Remediation

- Practice A, B, C in Chapter 9 Resource Book, pp. 33–38
- Study Guide in Chapter 9 Resource Book, pp. 39–40
- Practice Workbook, pp. 169–171
- @HomeTutor

Challenge

Additional challenge is available in the Chapter 9 Resource Book, p. 44.

40. Yes. *Sample answer:* Starting at (0, 3) the ball would follow the following path: (1, 4), (5, 0), (8, 3), (7, 4), (3, 0) and end up at (0, 3).

41a. at a point that is directly across from the midpoint of the distance between your eye and your foot

41b. at a point that is directly across the midpoint of the distance between your eye and the top of your head

41c. The top of the mirror F is directly across from the point that is halfway between the top of your head and your eye, and the bottom of the mirror E is directly across from the point that is halfway between your eye and your foot. So, the height of the mirror EF is half your height.

39. REFLECTING POINTS Use $C(1, 3)$.

a. Point A has coordinates $(-1, 1)$. Find point B on $\overrightarrow{AC}$ so $AC = CB$. **$B(3, 5)$**

b. The endpoints of $\overline{FG}$ are $F(2, 0)$ and $G(3, 2)$. Find point H on $\overrightarrow{FC}$ so $FC = CH$. Find point J on $\overrightarrow{GC}$ so $GC = CJ$. **$H(0, 6)$; $J(-1, 4)$**

c. Explain why parts (a) and (b) can be called *reflection in a point.* **In each case point C bisects each line segment.**

PHYSICS The Law of Reflection states that the angle of incidence is congruent to the angle of reflection. Use this information in Exercises 40 and 41.

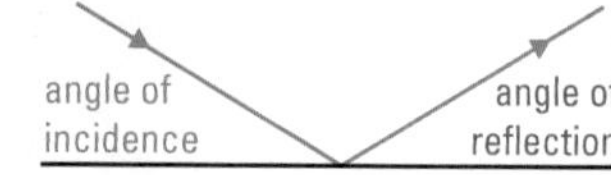

40. ★ SHORT RESPONSE Suppose a billiard table has a coordinate grid on it. If a ball starts at the point (0, 1) and rolls at a 45° angle, it will eventually return to its starting point. Would this happen if the ball started from other points on the y-axis between (0, 0) and (0, 4)? *Explain.*

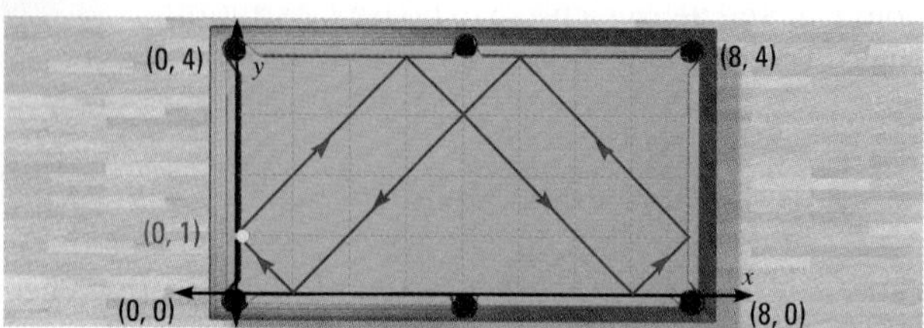

41. CHALLENGE Use the diagram to prove that you can see your full self in a mirror that is only half of your height. Assume that you and the mirror are both perpendicular to the floor.

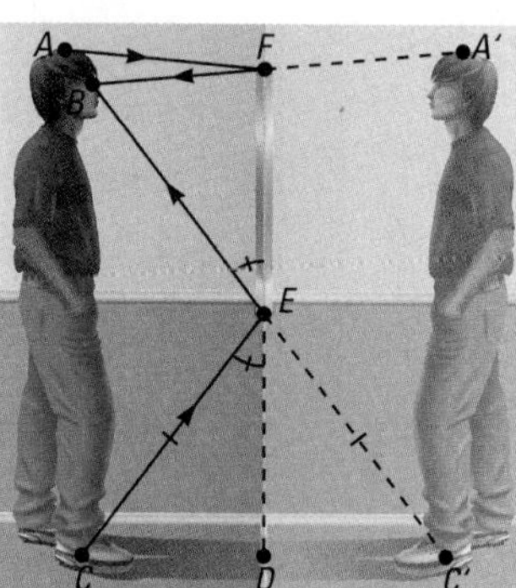

a. Think of a light ray starting at your foot and reflected in a mirror. Where does it have to hit the mirror in order to reflect to your eye?

b. Think of a light ray starting at the top of your head and reflected in a mirror. Where does it have to hit the mirror in order to reflect to your eye?

c. Show that the distance between the points you found in parts (a) and (b) is half your height. **The distance from the midpoint of your torso to the top of your head is half your height.**

MIXED REVIEW

PREVIEW
Prepare for Lesson 9.4 in Exs. 42–43.

42. Perpendicular; Line 1 is horizontal and Line 2 is vertical.

Tell whether the lines through the given points are *parallel, perpendicular,* or *neither. Justify* your answer. *(p. 171)*

42. Line 1: (3, 7) and (9, 7)
Line 2: (−2, 8) and (−2, 1)

43. Line 1: (−4, −1) and (−8, −4)
Line 2: (1, −3) and (5, 0)
Parallel; both slopes are $\frac{3}{4}$.

Quadrilateral *EFGH* is a kite. Find $m\angle G$. *(p. 542)*

44. **102.5°**

45.

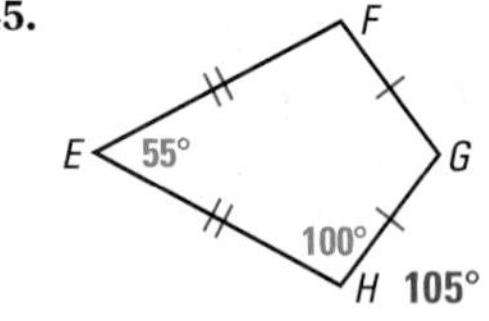

105°

46.

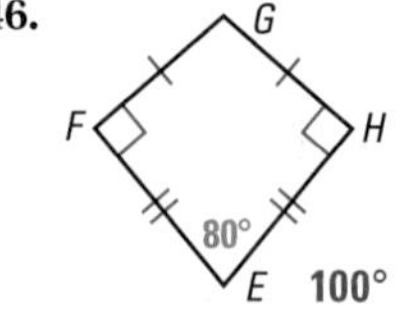

100°

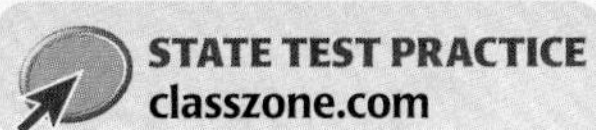

Lessons 9.1–9.3

1. **MULTI-STEP PROBLEM** $\triangle R'S'T'$ is the image of $\triangle RST$ after a translation.

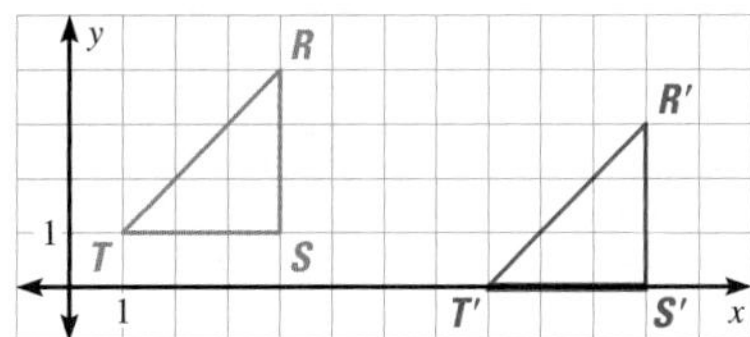

 a. Write a rule for the translation. **$(x, y) \to (x + 7, y - 1)$**
 b. *Verify* that the transformation is an isometry. **See margin.**
 c. Suppose $\triangle R'S'T'$ is translated using the rule $(x, y) \to (x + 4, y - 2)$. What are the coordinates of the vertices of $\triangle R''S''T''$? **$R''(15, 1)$, $S''(15, -2)$, $T''(12, -2)$**

2. **SHORT RESPONSE** During a marching band routine, a band member moves directly from point A to point B. Write the component form of the vector $\overrightarrow{AB}$. *Explain* your answer. **See margin.**

3. **SHORT RESPONSE** Trace the picture below. Reflect the image in line m. How is the distance from X to line m related to the distance from X' to line m? Write the property that makes this true.

The distances are the same; if X is not on line m then line m is the perpendicular bisector of $\overline{XX'}$.

4. **SHORT RESPONSE** The endpoints of $\overline{AB}$ are $A(2, 4)$ and $B(4, 0)$. The endpoints of $\overline{CD}$ are $C(3, 3)$ and $D(7, -1)$. Is the transformation from $\overline{AB}$ to $\overline{CD}$ an isometry? *Explain.* **No; the transformation did not preserve segment length.**

5. **GRIDDED ANSWER** The vertices of $\triangle FGH$ are $F(-4, 3)$, $G(3, -1)$, and $H(1, -2)$. The coordinates of F' are $(-1, 4)$ after a translation. What is the x-coordinate of G'? **6**

6. **OPEN-ENDED** Draw a triangle in a coordinate plane. Reflect the triangle in an axis. Write the reflection matrix that would yield the same result. **See margin.**

7. **EXTENDED RESPONSE** Two cross-country teams submit equipment lists for a season. A pair of running shoes costs \$60, a pair of shorts costs \$18, and a shirt costs \$15.

Women's Team	Men's Team
14 pairs of shoes	10 pairs of shoes
16 pairs of shorts	13 pairs of shorts
16 shirts	13 shirts

a, b. See margin.

 a. Use matrix multiplication to find the total cost of equipment for each team.
 b. How much money will the teams need to raise if the school gives each team \$200?
 c. Repeat parts (a) and (b) if a pair of shoes costs \$65 and a shirt costs \$10. Does the change in prices change which team needs to raise more money? *Explain.* **No; the women still need to raise more money.**

8. **MULTI-STEP PROBLEM** Use the polygon as the preimage.

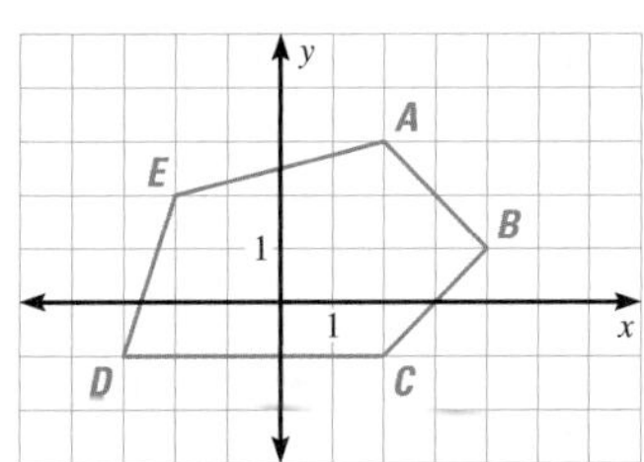

a, b. See margin.

 a. Reflect the preimage in the y-axis.
 b. Reflect the preimage in the x-axis.
 c. *Compare* the order of vertices in the preimage with the order in each image. **The order is reversed.**

1b. $ST = S'T' = 3$, $RS = R'S' = 3$, $TR = T'R' = 3\sqrt{2}$

2. $\langle 3, -2 \rangle$; **the band member moved 3 units to the right and 2 units down.**

6. ***Sample:***

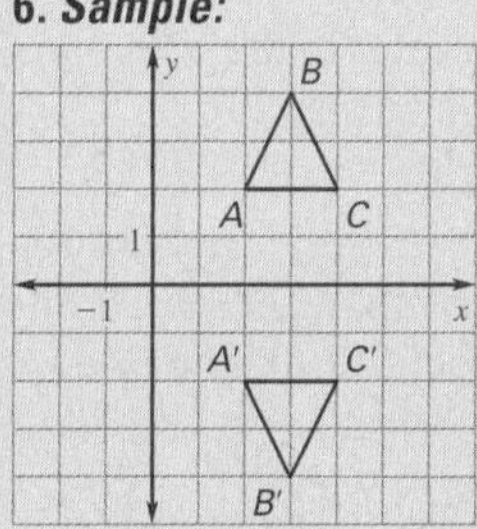

$$\begin{bmatrix} 1 & 0 \\ 0 & -1 \end{bmatrix}$$

7a. Women: \$1368, Men: \$1029

7b. Women: \$1168, Men: \$829

8a.

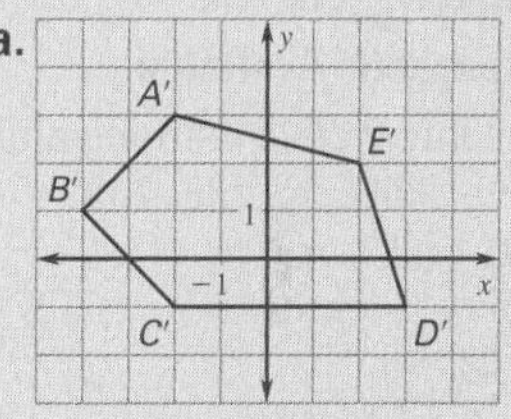

8b.

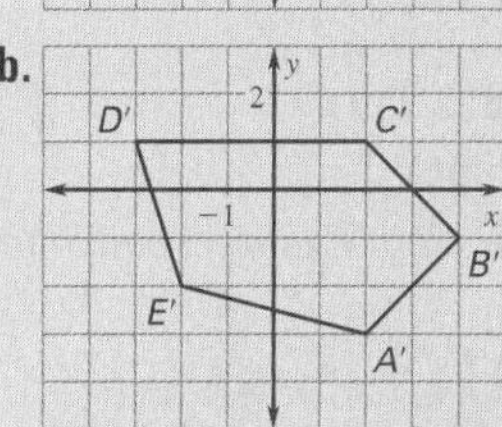

1 PLAN AND PREPARE

Warm-Up Exercises

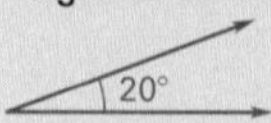

Transparency Available

1. Use a protractor to draw an angle with measure 20°.

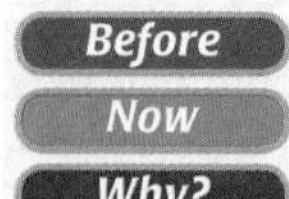

2. Given the points $A(3, 5)$, $B(-5, 3)$, and the origin $O(0, 0)$, find OA, OB, and $m\angle BOA$. **$\sqrt{34}$, $\sqrt{34}$, 90°**

3. Multiply $\begin{bmatrix} 0 & 1 \\ -1 & 0 \end{bmatrix}\begin{bmatrix} 2 & 3 \\ 5 & -7 \end{bmatrix}$.

$\begin{bmatrix} 5 & -7 \\ -2 & -3 \end{bmatrix}$

Notetaking Guide

Transparency Available

Promotes interactive learning and notetaking skills, pp. 236–239.

Pacing

Basic: 2 days
Average: 2 days
Advanced: 2 days
Block: 1 block
• See *Teaching Guide/Lesson Plan.*

2 FOCUS AND MOTIVATE

Essential Question

Big Idea 1, p. 571

How do you rotate a figure 90°, 180°, or 270° about the origin?
Tell students they will learn how to answer this question by using rules and matrices.

9.4 Perform Rotations

Before You rotated figures about the origin.
Now You will rotate figures about a point.
Why? So you can classify transformations, as in Exs. 3–5.

Key Vocabulary
- **center of rotation**
- **angle of rotation**
- **rotation,** *p. 272*

Recall from Lesson 4.8 that a *rotation* is a transformation in which a figure is turned about a fixed point called the **center of rotation**. Rays drawn from the center of rotation to a point and its image form the **angle of rotation**.

A rotation about a point P through an angle of $x°$ maps every point Q in the plane to a point Q' so that one of the following properties is true:

- If Q is not the center of rotation P, then $QP = Q'P$ and $m\angle QPQ' = x°$, or
- If Q is the center of rotation P, then the image of Q is Q.

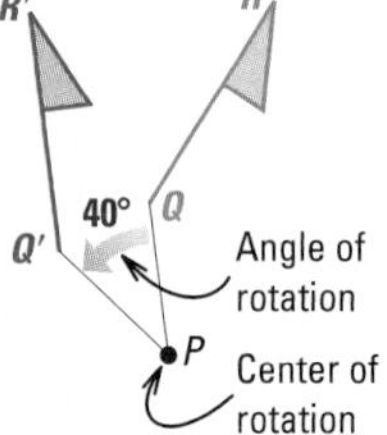

A 40° counterclockwise rotation is shown at the right. Rotations can be *clockwise* or *counterclockwise*. In this chapter, all rotations are counterclockwise.

DIRECTION OF ROTATION

clockwise

counterclockwise

Standards

22.0 Students know the effect of rigid motions on figures in the coordinate plane and space, including rotations, translations, and reflections.

EXAMPLE 1 Draw a rotation

Draw a 120° rotation of $\triangle ABC$ about P.

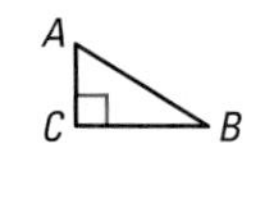

Solution

STEP 1 **Draw** a segment from A to P.

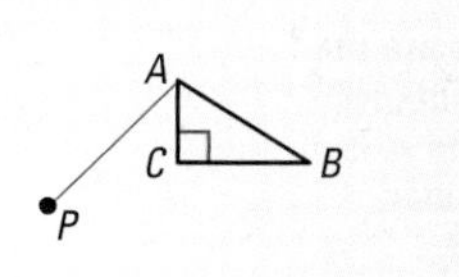
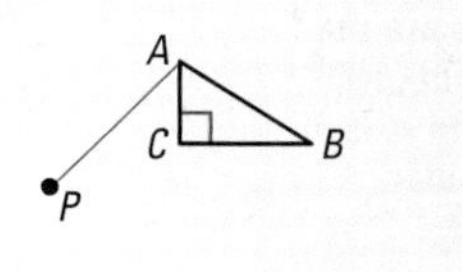

STEP 2 **Draw** a ray to form a 120° angle with $\overline{PA}$.

STEP 3 **Draw** A' so that $PA' = PA$.

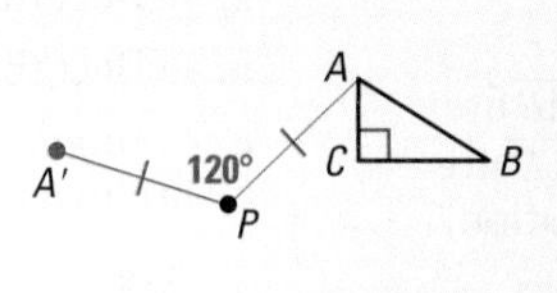

STEP 4 **Repeat** Steps 1–3 for each vertex. Draw $\triangle A'B'C'$.

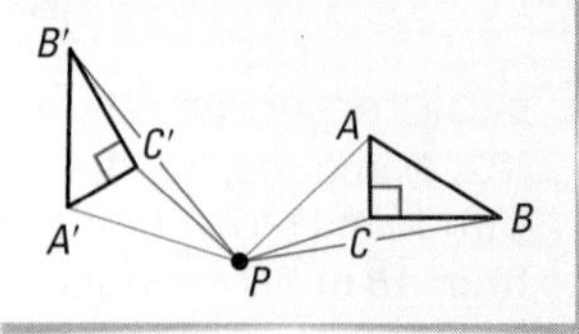

Resource Planning Guide

Chapter Resource Book
- Teaching Guide/Lesson Plan (pp. 45–46)
- Activity Master (p. 47)
- Practice levels A, B, C (pp. 48–53)
- Study Guide (pp. 54–55)
- Catch-up for Absent Students (p. 56)
- Application (p. 57)
- Challenge (p. 58)

Workbooks
- Notetaking Guide (pp. 236–239)
- Practice Workbook (pp. 172–174)

Teaching Options
- **Power Presentations CD-ROM** provides dynamic electronic teaching resources for the classroom.
- **Activity Generator CD-ROM** provides editable activities for all ability levels.

Interactive Technology
- Easy Planner
- Power Presentations CD-ROM
- Activity Generator CD-ROM
- Animated Geometry
- Test Generator CD-ROM
- Online Quiz
- eWorkbook
- eEdition
- @HomeTutor

Resources for English Learners
- Quick Reference for English Learners
- Spanish Study Guide
- Multi-Language Visual Glossary
- Student Resources in Spanish

See also the *Geometry Toolkit* for more strategies for meeting individual needs.

USE ROTATIONS
You can rotate a figure more than 360°. However, the effect is the same as rotating the figure by the angle minus 360°.

ROTATIONS ABOUT THE ORIGIN You can rotate a figure more than 180°. The diagram shows rotations of point A 130°, 220°, and 310° about the origin. A rotation of 360° returns a figure to its original coordinates.

There are coordinate rules that can be used to find the coordinates of a point after rotations of 90°, 180°, or 270° about the origin.

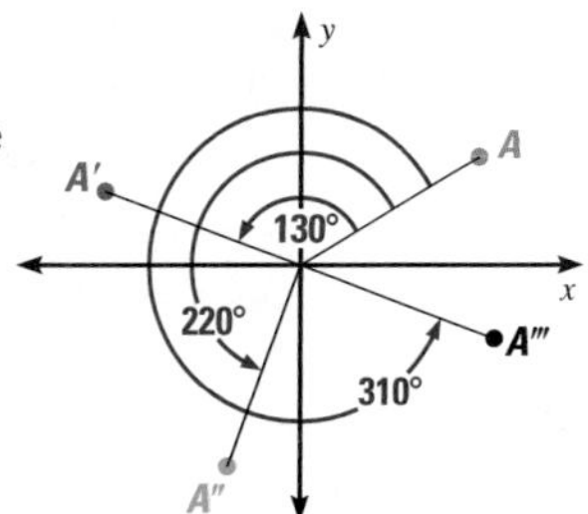

KEY CONCEPT — For Your Notebook

Coordinate Rules for Rotations about the Origin

When a point (a, b) is rotated counterclockwise about the origin, the following are true:

1. For a rotation of 90°, $(a, b) \to (-b, a)$.
2. For a rotation of 180°, $(a, b) \to (-a, -b)$.
3. For a rotation of 270°, $(a, b) \to (b, -a)$.

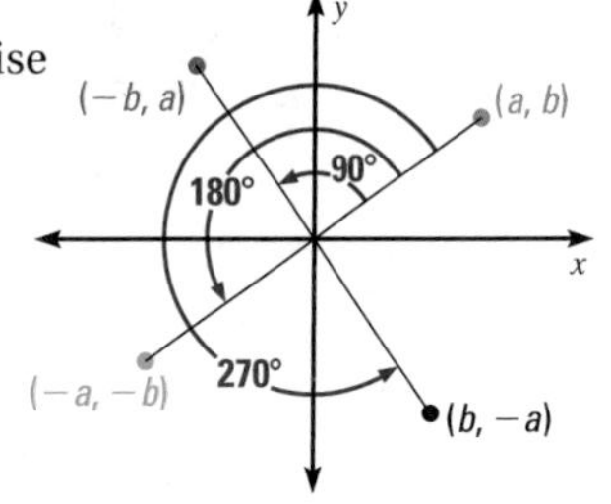

EXAMPLE 2 Rotate a figure using the coordinate rules

Graph quadrilateral $RSTU$ with vertices $R(3, 1)$, $S(5, 1)$, $T(5, -3)$, and $U(2, -1)$. Then rotate the quadrilateral 270° about the origin.

ANOTHER WAY
For an alternative method for solving the problem in Example 2, turn to page 606 for the **Problem Solving Workshop**.

Solution

Graph $RSTU$. Use the coordinate rule for a 270° rotation to find the images of the vertices.

$(a, b) \to (b, -a)$

$R(3, 1) \to R'(1, -3)$

$S(5, 1) \to S'(1, -5)$

$T(5, -3) \to T'(-3, -5)$

$U(2, -1) \to U'(-1, -2)$

Graph the image $R'S'T'U'$.

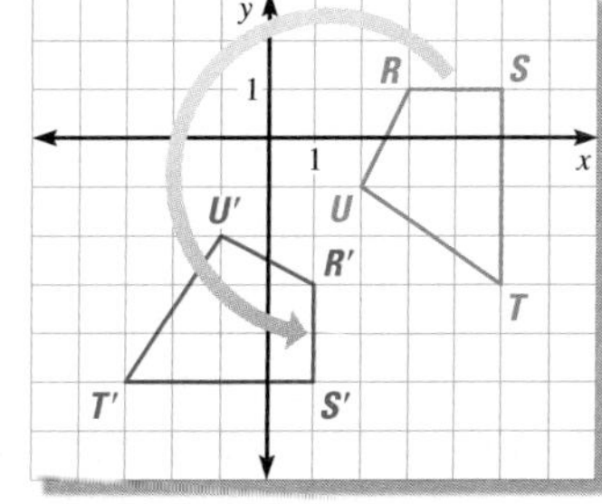

✓ **GUIDED PRACTICE** for Examples 1 and 2

1. Trace $\triangle DEF$ and P. Then draw a 50° rotation of $\triangle DEF$ about P. **See margin.**

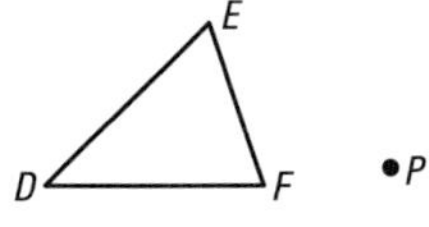

2. Graph $\triangle JKL$ with vertices $J(3, 0)$, $K(4, 3)$, and $L(6, 0)$. Rotate the triangle 90° about the origin. **See margin.**

Motivating the Lesson

Have students think of devices in everyday life that have parts that turn around a fixed point. Tell them that in this lesson they will learn how to describe the motion of the turning parts of such devices.

3 TEACH

Extra Example 1

Draw a 150° rotation of $\triangle XYZ$ about P.

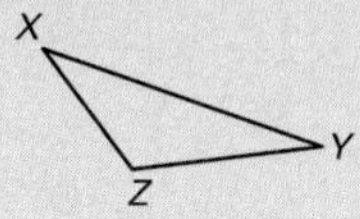

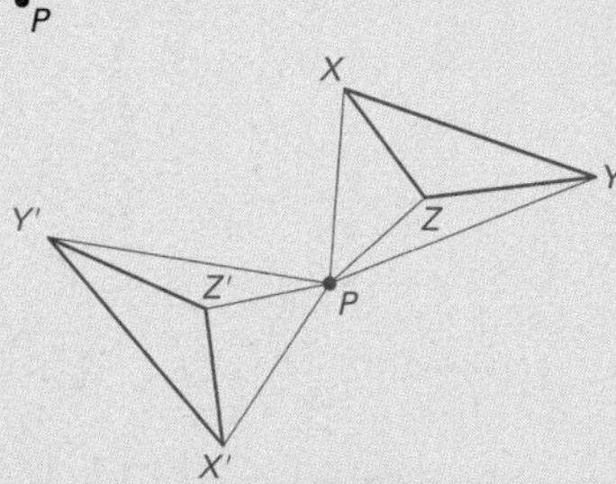

Extra Example 2

Graph quadrilateral $ABCD$ with vertices $A(-2, 4)$, $B(-4, -1)$, $C(-3, -3)$, and $D(-1, 0)$. Then rotate the quadrilateral 90° about the origin.

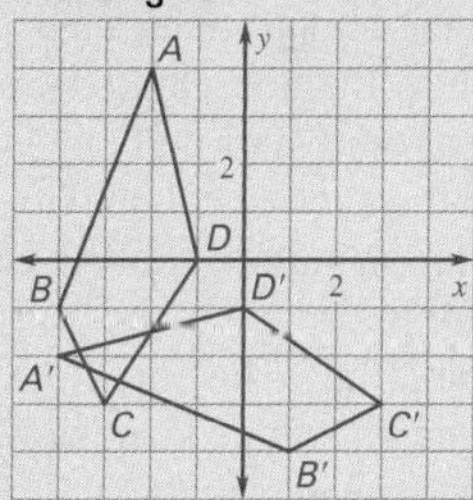

1–2. See Additional Answers beginning on p. AA1.

An **Animated Geometry** activity is available on-line for **Example 2**. This activity is also available on the **Power Presentations CD-ROM**.

Extra Example 3

Trapezoid *PQRS* has vertices $P(2, 5)$, $Q(4, 4)$, $R(4, -1)$, and $S(2, -2)$. Find the image matrix for a 270° rotation about the origin. Graph *PQRS* and its image.

$$\begin{array}{cccc} P' & Q' & R' & S' \end{array}$$
$$\begin{bmatrix} 5 & 4 & -1 & -2 \\ -2 & -4 & -4 & -2 \end{bmatrix}$$

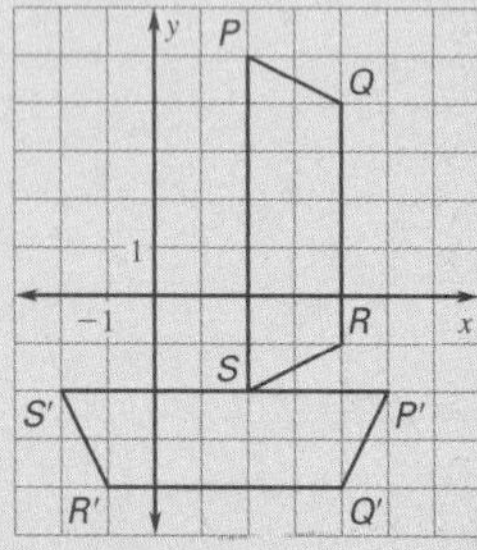

Teaching Strategy

After class discussion of Example 3, you may wish to show students how they can easily find the rotation matrices on page 600 without memorizing them. This method also works for reflection matrices. In the first column of the transformation matrix, show the coordinates for the image of the x-axis unit point $(1, 0)$. In the second column of the transformation matrix, show the coordinates for the image of the y-axis unit point $(0, 1)$. The coordinates of the image points can easily be found from a rough sketch. Illustrate the method with the rotation matrices on page 600. Encourage students to verify that the method also works for the reflection matrices in Lesson 9.3.

Vocabulary

Have students write their own explanations of the terms rotation matrix, reflection matrix, polygon matrix, and image matrix.

USING MATRICES You can find certain images of a polygon rotated about the origin using matrix multiplication. Write the rotation matrix to the left of the polygon matrix, then multiply.

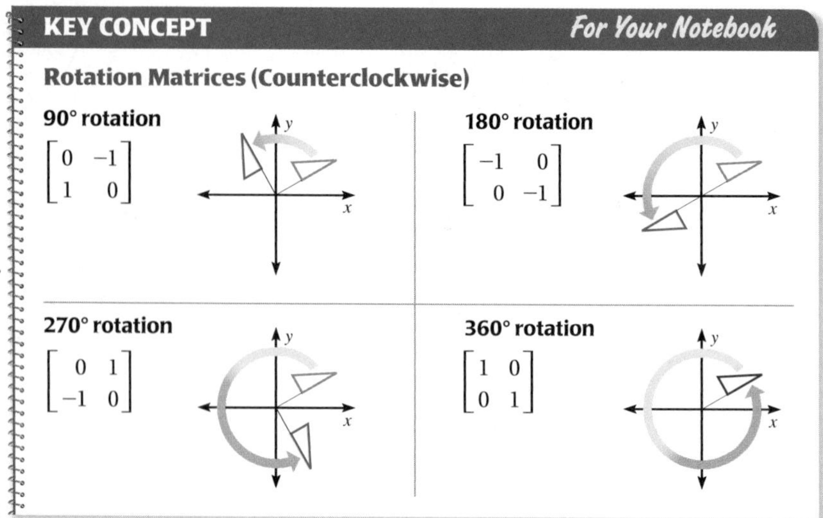

READ VOCABULARY
Notice that a 360° rotation returns the figure to its original position. Multiplying by the matrix that represents this rotation gives you the polygon matrix you started with, which is why it is also called the *identity matrix*.

EXAMPLE 3 Use matrices to rotate a figure

Trapezoid *EFGH* has vertices $E(-3, 2)$, $F(-3, 4)$, $G(1, 4)$, and $H(2, 2)$. Find the image matrix for a 180° rotation of *EFGH* about the origin. Graph *EFGH* and its image.

Solution

STEP 1 **Write** the polygon matrix: $\begin{array}{c} \begin{array}{cccc} E & F & G & H \end{array} \\ \begin{bmatrix} -3 & -3 & 1 & 2 \\ 2 & 4 & 4 & 2 \end{bmatrix} \end{array}$

STEP 2 **Multiply** by the matrix for a 180° rotation.

$$\begin{bmatrix} -1 & 0 \\ 0 & -1 \end{bmatrix} \overset{\begin{array}{cccc} E & F & G & H \end{array}}{\begin{bmatrix} -3 & -3 & 1 & 2 \\ 2 & 4 & 4 & 2 \end{bmatrix}} = \overset{\begin{array}{cccc} E' & F' & G' & H' \end{array}}{\begin{bmatrix} 3 & 3 & -1 & -2 \\ -2 & -4 & -4 & -2 \end{bmatrix}}$$

Rotation matrix — Polygon matrix — Image matrix

STEP 3 **Graph** the preimage *EFGH*.
Graph the image *E′F′G′H′*.

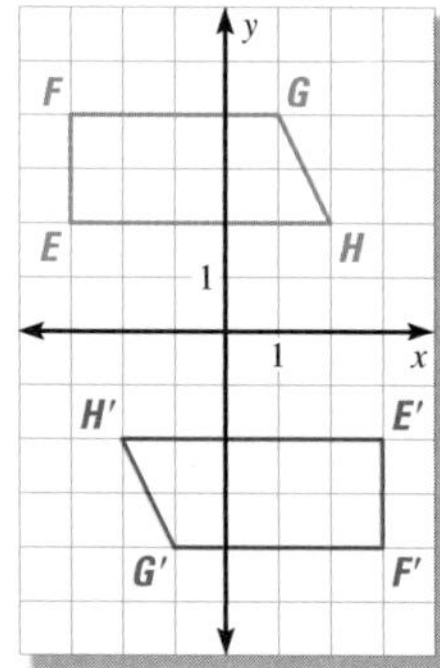

AVOID ERRORS
Because matrix multiplication is not commutative, you should always write the rotation matrix first, then the polygon matrix.

✓ GUIDED PRACTICE for Example 3

Use the quadrilateral *EFGH* in Example 3. Find the image matrix after the rotation about the origin. Graph the image. **3–5. See margin.**

3. 90° **4.** 270° **5.** 360°

3. $\overset{\begin{array}{cccc} E' & F' & G' & H' \end{array}}{\begin{bmatrix} -2 & -4 & -4 & -2 \\ -3 & -3 & 1 & 2 \end{bmatrix}}$;

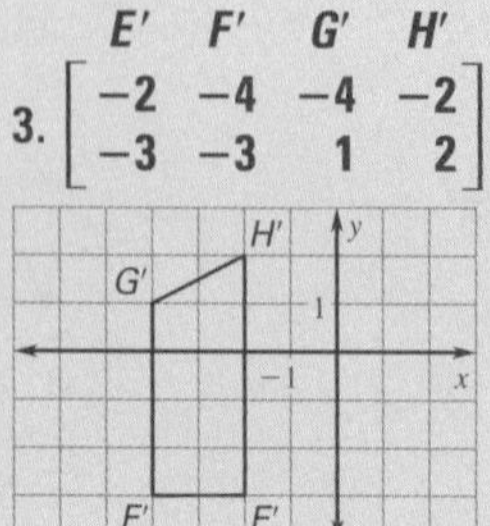

4. $\overset{\begin{array}{cccc} E' & F' & G' & H' \end{array}}{\begin{bmatrix} 2 & 4 & 4 & 2 \\ 3 & 3 & -1 & -2 \end{bmatrix}}$;

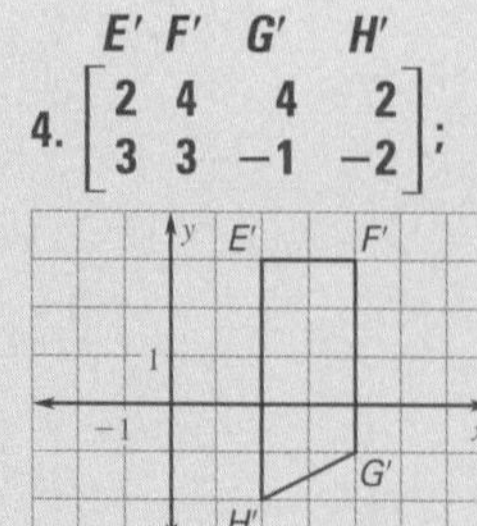

5. $\overset{\begin{array}{cccc} E' & F' & G' & H' \end{array}}{\begin{bmatrix} -3 & -3 & 1 & 2 \\ 2 & 4 & 4 & 2 \end{bmatrix}}$;

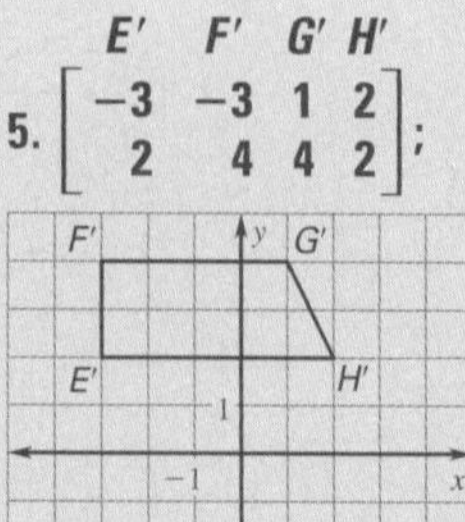

THEOREM — *For Your Notebook*

THEOREM 9.3 Rotation Theorem

A rotation is an isometry.

Proof: Exs. 33–35, p. 604

$\triangle ABC \cong \triangle A'B'C'$

CASES OF THEOREM 9.3 To prove the Rotation Theorem, you need to show that a rotation preserves the length of a segment. Consider a segment $\overline{QR}$ rotated about point P to produce $\overline{Q'R'}$. There are three cases to prove:

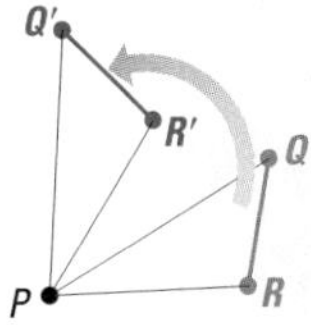

Case 1 R, Q, and P are noncollinear.

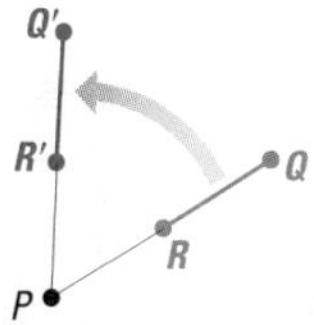

Case 2 R, Q, and P are collinear.

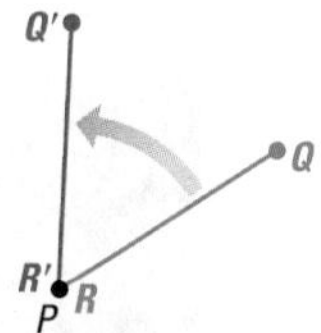

Case 3 P and R are the same point.

EXAMPLE 4 Standardized Test Practice

The quadrilateral is rotated about P. What is the value of y?

Ⓐ $\frac{8}{5}$ Ⓑ 2

Ⓒ 3 Ⓓ 10

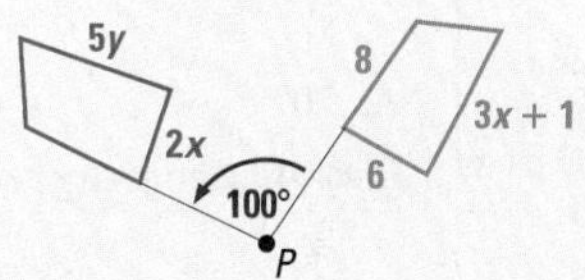

Solution

By Theorem 9.3, the rotation is an isometry, so corresponding side lengths are equal. Then $2x = 6$, so $x = 3$. Now set up an equation to solve for y.

$5y = 3x + 1$	**Corresponding lengths in an isometry are equal.**
$5y = 3(3) + 1$	**Substitute 3 for x.**
$y = 2$	**Solve for y.**

▶ The correct answer is B. Ⓐ Ⓑ Ⓒ Ⓓ

GUIDED PRACTICE for Example 4

6. Find the value of r in the rotation of the triangle. **B**

Ⓐ 3 Ⓑ 5

Ⓒ 6 Ⓓ 15

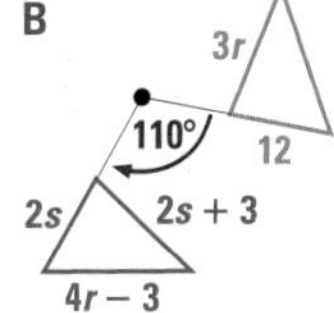

Extra Example 4

The quadrilateral is rotated about P. What is the value of x? **D**

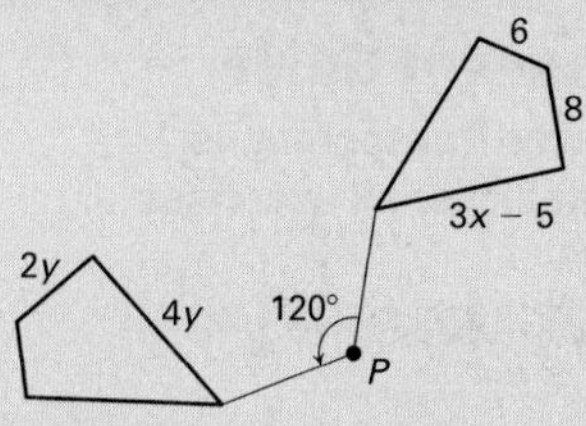

Ⓐ 2 Ⓑ 4

Ⓒ $\frac{17}{3}$ Ⓓ 7

Closing the Lesson

Have students summarize the major points of the lesson and answer the Essential Question: How do you rotate a figure 90°, 180°, or 270° about the origin?

- **A figure can be rotated 90° about the origin using the rule $(a, b) \to (-b, a)$ or the matrix $\begin{bmatrix} 0 & -1 \\ 1 & 0 \end{bmatrix}$.**
- **A figure can be rotated 180° about the origin using the rule $(a, b) \to (-a, -b)$ or the matrix $\begin{bmatrix} -1 & 0 \\ 0 & -1 \end{bmatrix}$.**
- **A figure can be rotated 270° about the origin using the rule $(a, b) \to (b, -a)$ or the matrix $\begin{bmatrix} 0 & 1 \\ -1 & 0 \end{bmatrix}$.**
- **A rotation is an isometry.**

You rotate a figure 90°, 180°, or 270° about the origin by multiplying the coefficient matrix by the rotation matrix or by using the coordinate rules for rotations about the origin.

Differentiated Instruction

Below Level Have students use their graphing calculators to enter and save the matrices for reflections in the x-axis, y-axis, $y = x$, and $y = -x$ and the matrices for rotations of 90°, 180°, and 270° about the origin. Teach them how to enter the coefficient matrix and multiply it by the matrix for the specific transformation they wish to perform.

See also the *Geometry Toolkit* for more strategies.

4 PRACTICE AND APPLY

Assignment Guide

Answer Transparencies available for all exercises

Basic:
Day 1: EP p. 903 Exs. 39, 40
pp. 602–605
Exs. 1–14, 44–46
Day 2: pp. 602–605
Exs. 15–23, 29–35, 41–43

Average:
Day 1: pp. 602–605
Exs. 1–8, 10, 11, 13, 14, 23, 24, 45, 46
Day 2: pp. 602–605
Exs. 16–22, 29–37, 41–43

Advanced:
Day 1: pp. 602–605
Exs. 1, 2, 6–8, 10, 11, 13, 14, 25–28*, 46
Day 2: pp. 602–605
Exs. 15–17, 20–24, 31–43*

Block:
pp. 602–605
Exs. 1–8, 10, 11, 13, 14, 16–24, 29–37, 41–43, 45, 46

Differentiated Instruction

See *Geometry Best Practices Toolkit* for suggestions on addressing the needs of a diverse classroom.

Homework Check

For a quick check of student understanding of key concepts, go over the following exercises:

Basic: 4, 12, 16, 20, 30
Average: 8, 14, 18, 21, 31
Advanced: 10, 14, 17, 21, 32

Extra Practice

- Student Edition, p. 912
- Chapter 9 Resource Book: Practice levels A, B, C, pp. 48–53

Practice Worksheet

An easily-readable reduced practice page (with answers) for this lesson can be found on p. 570D.

9.4 EXERCISES

HOMEWORK KEY ○ = **WORKED-OUT SOLUTIONS** on p. WS11 for Exs. 13, 15, and 29
★ = **STANDARDIZED TEST PRACTICE** Exs. 2, 20, 21, 23, 24, and 37

SKILL PRACTICE

A

1. **VOCABULARY** What is a *center of rotation*? **a point which a figure is turned about during a rotation transformation**
2. ★ **WRITING** *Compare* the coordinate rules and the rotation matrices for a rotation of 90°. **In the coordinate rotation the *x* and the *y* values are switched with the new *x* value being the opposite of the old *y* value. The rotation matrix for 90° has the same result.**

EXAMPLE 1 on p. 598 for Exs. 3–11

IDENTIFYING TRANSFORMATIONS **Identify the type of transformation, *translation*, *reflection*, or *rotation*, in the photo. *Explain* your reasoning.**

3. 
4. 
5. 

3. Reflection; the horses are reflected across the edge of the stream which acts like a line of symmetry.

4. Rotation; as the steering wheel turns everything rotates around the center point.

5. Translation; the train moves horizontally from right to left.

ANGLE OF ROTATION **Match the diagram with the angle of rotation.**

6. **C** 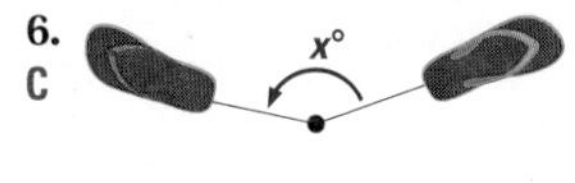

7. **A** 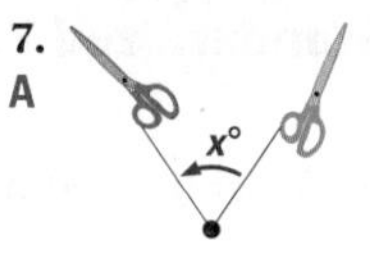

8. **B** 

A. 70° B. 100° C. 150°

Animated Geometry at classzone.com

ROTATING A FIGURE **Trace the polygon and point *P* on paper. Then draw a rotation of the polygon the given number of degrees about *P*.** **9–11. See margin.**

9. 30° 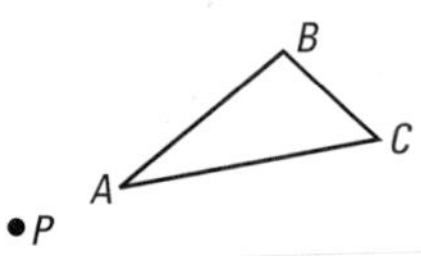

10. 150° 

11. 130° 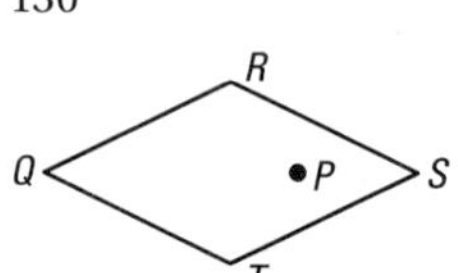

EXAMPLE 2 on p. 599 for Exs. 12–14

USING COORDINATE RULES **Rotate the figure the given number of degrees about the origin. List the coordinates of the vertices of the image.** **12–14. See margin for art.**

12. 90° **$A'(-2, -3)$, $B'(-4, 2)$, $C'(-1, 3)$**
13. 180° **$J'(-1, -4)$, $K'(-5, -5)$, $L'(-7, -2)$, $M'(-2, -2)$**
14. 270° **$Q'(-3, 6)$, $R'(0, 5)$, $S'(0, 3)$, $T'(-3, 1)$**

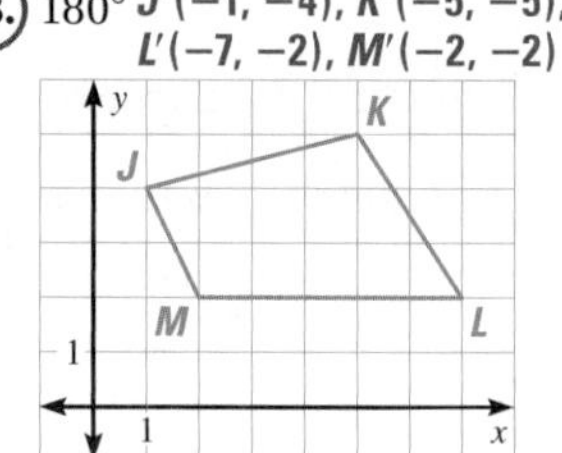

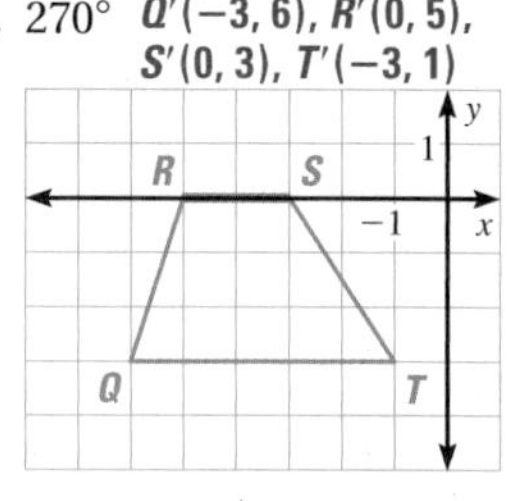

9. 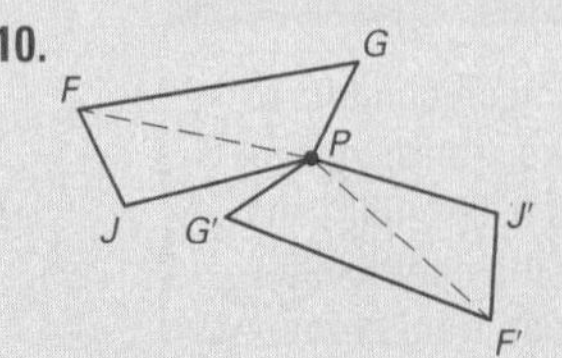
10. 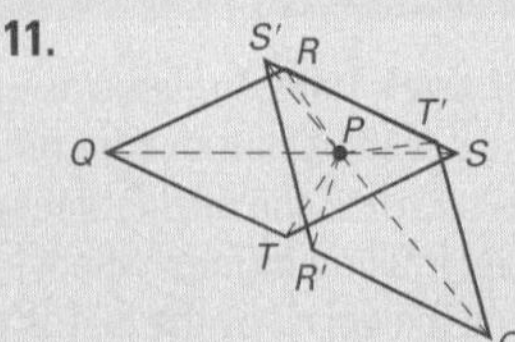
11.

12–14. See Additional Answers beginning on p. AA1.

EXAMPLE 3 on p. 600 for Exs. 15–19

USING MATRICES **Find the image matrix that represents the rotation of the polygon about the origin. Then graph the polygon and its image.** **15–17. See margin.**

15. $\begin{matrix} A & B & C \end{matrix}$ $\begin{bmatrix} 1 & 5 & 4 \\ 4 & 6 & 3 \end{bmatrix}$; 90°

16. $\begin{matrix} J & K & L \end{matrix}$ $\begin{bmatrix} 1 & 2 & 0 \\ 1 & -1 & -3 \end{bmatrix}$; 180°

17. $\begin{matrix} P & Q & R & S \end{matrix}$ $\begin{bmatrix} -4 & 2 & 2 & -4 \\ -4 & -2 & -5 & -7 \end{bmatrix}$; 270°

ERROR ANALYSIS **The endpoints of $\overline{AB}$ are $A(-1, 1)$ and $B(2, 3)$. *Describe* and correct the error in setting up the matrix multiplication for a 270° rotation about the origin.** **18, 19. See margin.**

18.

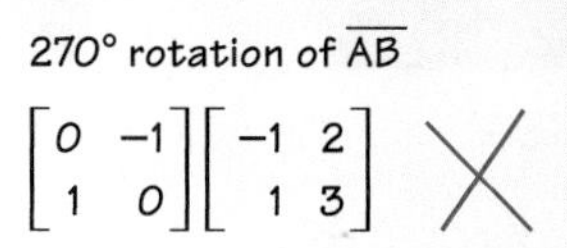

19.

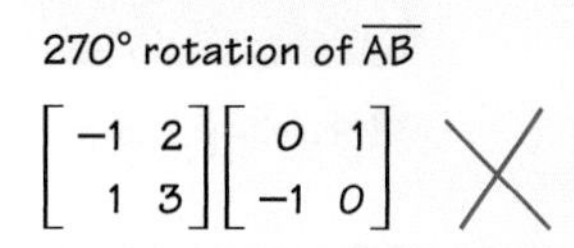

EXAMPLE 4 on p. 601 for Exs. 20–21

20. ★ **MULTIPLE CHOICE** What is the value of y in the rotation of the triangle about P? **A**

Ⓐ 4 Ⓑ 5 Ⓒ $\frac{17}{3}$ Ⓓ 10

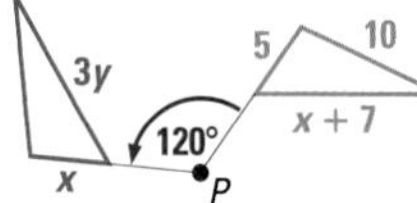

21. ★ **MULTIPLE CHOICE** Suppose quadrilateral $QRST$ is rotated 180° about the origin. In which quadrant is Q'? **C**

Ⓐ I Ⓑ II Ⓒ III Ⓓ IV

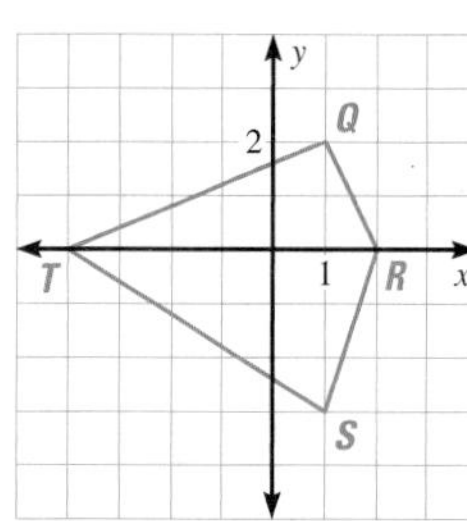

B 22. **FINDING A PATTERN** The vertices of $\triangle ABC$ are $A(2, 0)$, $B(3, 4)$, and $C(5, 2)$. Make a table to show the vertices of each image after a 90°, 180°, 270°, 360°, 450°, 540°, 630°, and 720° rotation. What would be the coordinates of A' after a rotation of 1890°? *Explain.*
See margin for table; (0, 2); divide 1890 by 360 and use the remainder as your rotation.

23. ★ **MULTIPLE CHOICE** A rectangle has vertices at (4, 0), (4, 2), (7, 0), and (7, 2). Which image has a vertex at the origin? **D**

Ⓐ Translation right 4 units and down 2 units

Ⓑ Rotation of 180° about the origin

Ⓒ Reflection in the line $x = 4$

Ⓓ Rotation of 180° about the point (2, 0)

24. ★ **SHORT RESPONSE** Rotate the triangle in Exercise 12 90° about the origin. Show that corresponding sides of the preimage and image are perpendicular. *Explain.* **See margin.**

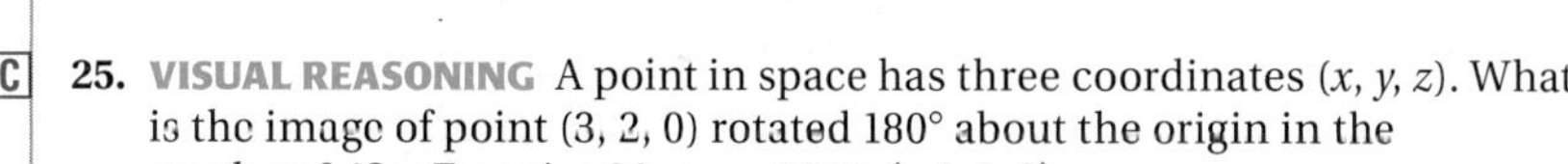

C 25. **VISUAL REASONING** A point in space has three coordinates (x, y, z). What is the image of point (3, 2, 0) rotated 180° about the origin in the xz-plane? (*See* Exercise 30, page 585.) **(−3, 2, 0)**

CHALLENGE **Rotate the line the given number of degrees (a) about the x-intercept and (b) about the y-intercept. Write the equation of each image.**

26. $y = 2x - 3$; 90°
a. $y = -\frac{1}{2}x + \frac{3}{4}$ **b.** $y = -\frac{1}{2}x - 3$

27. $y = -x + 8$; 180°
a. $y = -x + 8$ **b.** $y = -x + 8$

28. $y = \frac{1}{2}x + 5$; 270°
a. $y = -2x - 20$ **b.** $y = -2x + 5$

Avoiding Common Errors

Exercises 9–11 Some students may rotate the figures clockwise. Remind them of our convention to use counterclockwise rotations except when there is an explicit instruction to do otherwise.

Teaching Strategy

Exercises 12–17 Use these as examples and have students show that the result is the same regardless of the method used to obtain the image. Have them use a drawing, the coordinate rules, and matrix multiplication.

Avoiding Common Errors

Exercises 15–17 Students will run into trouble if they write the matrices in the wrong order when they set up the matrix multiplication expression. Be sure students write the rotation matrix to the left of the coordinate matrix in order to multiply.

Mathematical Reasoning

Exercise 25 Have students make a model of a 3-dimensional coordinate system to show the point and its image after the rotation.

17. $\begin{matrix} P' & Q' & R' & S' \end{matrix}$ $\begin{bmatrix} -4 & -2 & -5 & -7 \\ 4 & -2 & -2 & 4 \end{bmatrix}$;

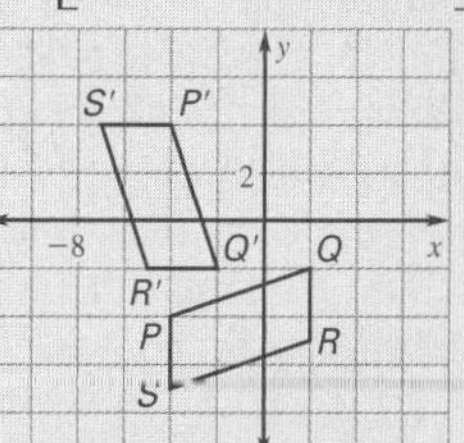

18. The wrong rotation matrix is being used; $\begin{bmatrix} 0 & 1 \\ -1 & 0 \end{bmatrix}\begin{bmatrix} -1 & 2 \\ 1 & 3 \end{bmatrix}$.

19. The rotation matrix should be first; $\begin{bmatrix} 0 & 1 \\ -1 & 0 \end{bmatrix}\begin{bmatrix} -1 & 2 \\ 1 & 3 \end{bmatrix}$.

22. See Additional Answers beginning on p. AA1.

24. The slope of $\overline{AB}$ is $\frac{2}{5}$ and the slope of $\overline{A'B'}$ is $-\frac{5}{2}$; the slope of $\overline{BC}$ is −3 and the slope of $\overline{B'C'}$ is $\frac{1}{3}$; the slope of $\overline{AC}$ is $-\frac{1}{6}$ and the slope of $\overline{A'C'}$ is 6. They are perpendicular since the product of the corresponding slopes is −1.

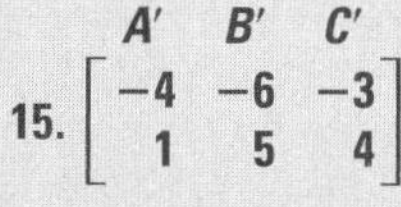

15. $\begin{matrix} A' & B' & C' \end{matrix}$ $\begin{bmatrix} -4 & -6 & -3 \\ 1 & 5 & 4 \end{bmatrix}$;

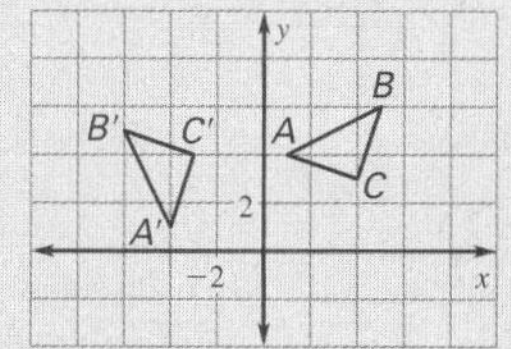

16. $\begin{matrix} J' & K' & L' \end{matrix}$ $\begin{bmatrix} -1 & -2 & 0 \\ -1 & 1 & 3 \end{bmatrix}$;

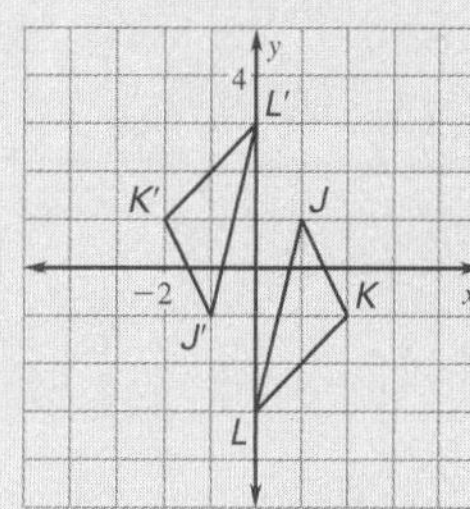

Teaching Strategy

Exercise 36 Have students locate two points on the line, write a coordinate matrix for those two points, and multiply by the appropriate rotation matrix. To graph the image line, they need only graph the two image points and draw a line through them. Have students write an equation for their new line. Compare the slopes and y-intercepts of the original line and the new line.

30. 180°; A' and A are on opposite sides of a line segment containing the point of rotation.

31. 120°; the line segment joining A' to the center of rotation is rotated $\frac{1}{3}$ of a circle from the line segment joining A to the center of rotation.

34. Given: A rotation about P maps Q to Q' and R to R'. P, Q, and R are collinear. Using the definition of rotation about a point P, $PR = PR'$ and $PQ = PQ'$. Using the Segment Addition Postulate, $PQ = PR + RQ$ and $PQ' = PR' + R'Q'$. Using the Transitive Property of Equality, $PR + RQ = PR' + R'Q'$. Using the Subtraction Property of Equality, $RQ = R'Q'$.

35. Given: A rotation about P maps Q to Q' and R to R'. P and R are the same point. Using the definition of rotation about a point P, $PQ = PQ'$ and P, R, and R' are the same point. Substituting R for P on the left and R' for P on the right side, you get $RQ = R'Q'$.

36a. Rotating 90° produces perpendicular lines. Rotating 180° produces parallel lines. Rotating 270° produces perpendicular lines. Rotating 360° produces the same line.

PROBLEM SOLVING

29. 270°; the line segment joining A' to the center of rotation is perpendicular to the line segment joining A to the center of rotation.

A **ANGLE OF ROTATION Use the photo to find the angle of rotation that maps A onto A'. *Explain* your reasoning.** 30, 31. See margin.

(29.)

30. 

31. 

@HomeTutor for problem solving help at classzone.com

32. **REVOLVING DOOR** You enter a revolving door and rotate the door 180°. What does this mean in the context of the situation? Now, suppose you enter a revolving door and rotate the door 360°. What does this mean in the context of the situation? *Explain.*

@HomeTutor for problem solving help at classzone.com

If you started inside the building you will end up outside, and if you started outside the building you will end up inside; you will end up back where you started.

33. **PROVING THEOREM 9.3** Copy and complete the proof of Case 1.

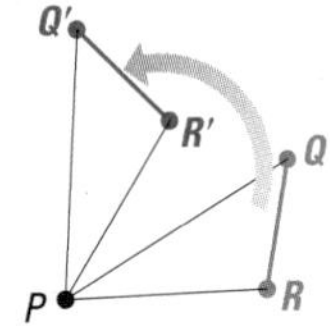

Case 1 The segment is noncollinear with the center of rotation.

GIVEN ▶ A rotation about P maps Q to Q' and R to R'.

PROVE ▶ $QR = Q'R'$

STATEMENTS	REASONS
1. $PQ = PQ'$, $PR = PR'$, $m\angle QPQ' = m\angle RPR'$	1. Definition of _?_ a rotation about a point
2. $m\angle QPQ' = m\angle QPR' + m\angle R'PQ'$ $m\angle RPR' = m\angle RPQ + m\angle QPR'$	2. _?_ Angle Addition Postulate
3. $m\angle QPR' + m\angle R'PQ' = m\angle RPQ + m\angle QPR'$	3. _?_ Property of Equality Transitive
4. $m\angle QPR = m\angle Q'PR'$	4. _?_ Property of Equality Subtraction
5. _?_ ≅ _?_ $\triangle RPQ \cong \triangle R'PQ'$	5. SAS Congruence Postulate
6. $\overline{QR} \cong \overline{Q'R'}$	6. _?_ Corr. Parts of ≅ ▲ are ≅
7. $QR = Q'R'$	7. _?_ definition of segment congruence

B **PROVING THEOREM 9.3 Write a proof for Case 2 and Case 3. (Refer to the diagrams on page 601.)** 34, 35. See margin.

34. **Case 2** The segment is collinear with the center of rotation.

GIVEN ▶ A rotation about P maps Q to Q' and R to R'. P, Q, and R are collinear.

PROVE ▶ $QR = Q'R'$

35. **Case 3** The center of rotation is one endpoint of the segment.

GIVEN ▶ A rotation about P maps Q to Q' and R to R'. P and R are the same point.

PROVE ▶ $QR = Q'R'$

○ = WORKED-OUT SOLUTIONS on p. WS1 ★ = STANDARDIZED TEST PRACTICE

37a.
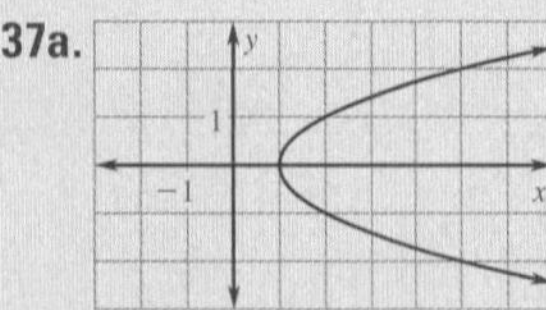

38.
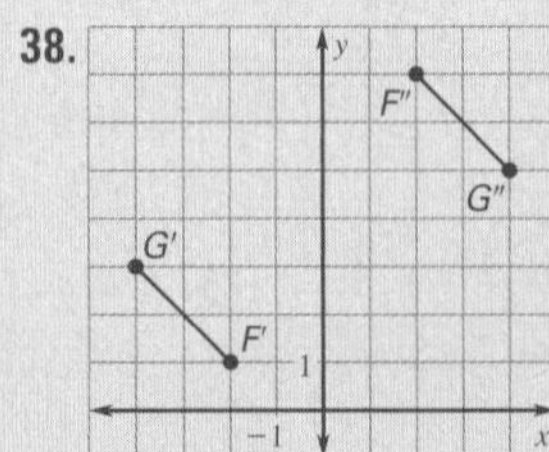

39.
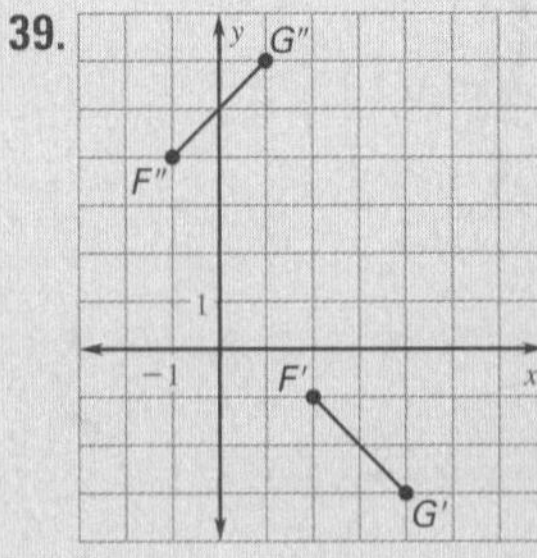

b. Yes; choose two points on the line and rotate the two points and look at the slope of each image.

36. **MULTI-STEP PROBLEM** Use the graph of $y = 2x - 3$.

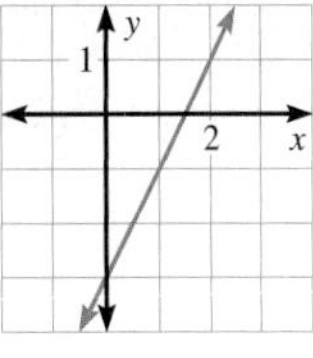

a. Rotate the line 90°, 180°, 270°, and 360° about the origin. *Describe* the relationship between the equation of the preimage and each image. **See margin.**

b. Do you think that the relationships you described in part (a) are true for *any* line? *Explain* your reasoning.

37. ★ **EXTENDED RESPONSE** Use the graph of the quadratic equation $y = x^2 + 1$ at the right.

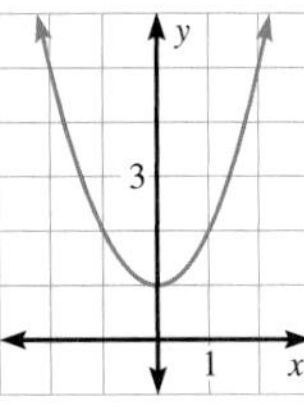

a. Rotate the *parabola* by replacing y with x and x with y in the original equation, then graph this new equation. **See margin.**

b. What is the angle of rotation? **270°**

c. Are the image and the preimage both functions? *Explain.* **No; the image does not pass the vertical line test.**

C **TWO ROTATIONS** **The endpoints of $\overline{FG}$ are $F(1, 2)$ and $G(3, 4)$. Graph $\overline{F'G'}$ and $\overline{F''G''}$ after the given rotations.** **38, 39. See margin.**

38. **Rotation:** 90° about the origin
Rotation: 180° about (0, 4)

39. **Rotation:** 270° about the origin
Rotation: 90° about (−2, 0)

40. **CHALLENGE** A polar coordinate system locates a point in a plane by its distance from the origin O and by the measure of an angle with its vertex at the origin. For example, the point $A(2, 30°)$ at the right is 2 units from the origin and $m\angle XOA = 30°$. What are the polar coordinates of the image of point A after a 90° rotation? 180° rotation? 270° rotation? *Explain.*
(2, 120°); (2, 210°); (2, 300°); the distance from the origin to *A* never changes. Add 90°, 180°, and 270° to 30° to find each angle measure.

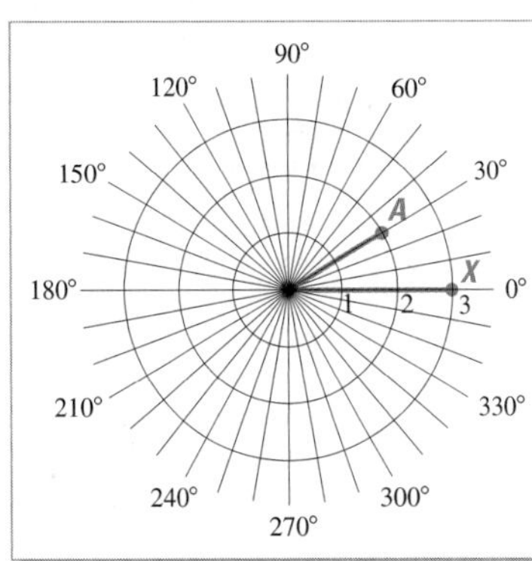

MIXED REVIEW

PREVIEW
Prepare for Lesson 9.5 in Exs. 41–43.

In the diagram, $\overrightarrow{DC}$ is the perpendicular bisector of $\overline{AB}$. *(p. 303)*

41. What segment lengths are equal?

41. $\overline{AC}$ and $\overline{BC}$, $\overline{AD}$ and $\overline{BD}$

42. What is the value of x? **4**

43. Find BD. *(p. 433)* **34**

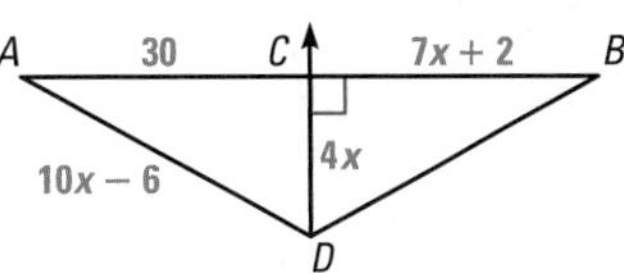

Use a sine or cosine ratio to find the value of each variable. Round decimals to the nearest tenth. *(p. 473)*

44.

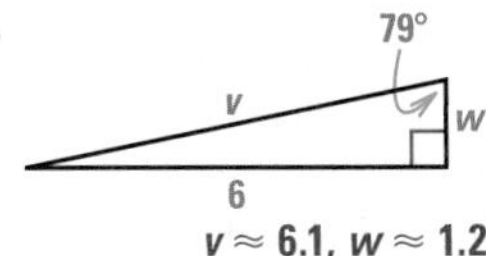

$v \approx 6.1$, $w \approx 1.2$

45.

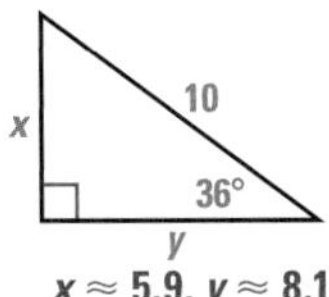

$x \approx 5.9$, $y \approx 8.1$

46.

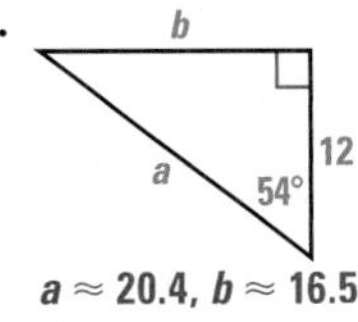

$a \approx 20.4$, $b \approx 16.5$

5 ASSESS AND RETEACH

Daily Homework Quiz

Transparency Available

1. Construct an equilateral triangle DEF. Then draw the image of $\triangle DEF$ for a 30° rotation about the center C of the triangle.

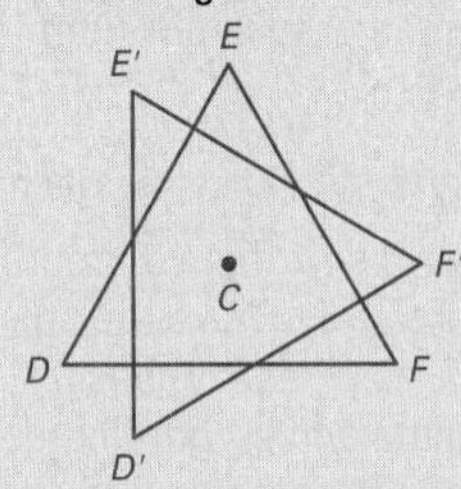

For Exercises 2 and 3, use the quadrilateral $HIJK$ with vertices $H(3, 0)$, $I(1, -4)$, $J(0, -4)$, and $K(-1, -3)$.

2. Use the coordinate rules to name the vertices of the image of $HIJK$ for a rotation of 180° about the origin. **$H'(-3, 0)$, $I'(-1, 4)$, $J'(0, 4)$, $K'(1, 3)$**

3. Use matrix multiplication to find the image matrix that represents a 270° rotation of $HIJK$ about the origin. Then graph the polygon and its image.

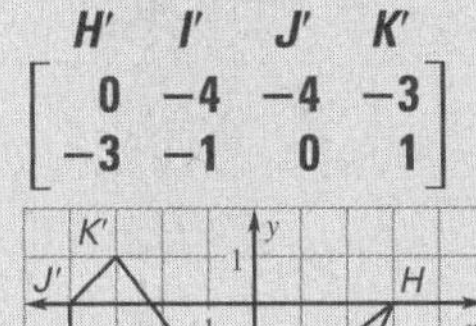

$$\begin{array}{cccc} H' & I' & J' & K' \end{array}$$
$$\begin{bmatrix} 0 & -4 & -4 & -3 \\ -3 & -1 & 0 & 1 \end{bmatrix}$$

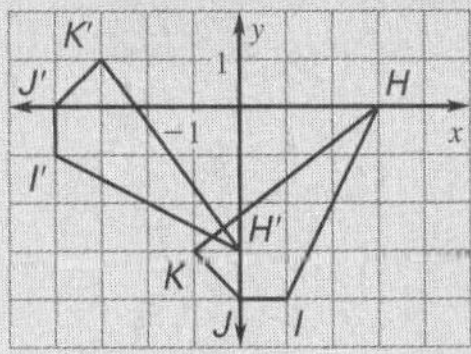

Available at **classzone.com**

Diagnosis/Remediation

- Practice A, B, C in Chapter 9 Resource Book, pp. 48–53
- Study Guide in Chapter 9 Resource Book, pp. 54–55
- Practice Workbook, pp. 172–174
- @HomeTutor

Challenge

Additional challenge is available in the Chapter 9 Resource Book, p. 58.

Using ALTERNATIVE METHODS

Alternative Strategy

Example 2 on page 599 can be solved by using tracing paper. This method allows the student to visualize how the figure is rotating about the point.

Avoiding Common Errors

Students need to be sure to keep the intersection of the axes on the tracing paper in the same place as the origin on the graph in Practice Exercises 1–3.

Mathematical Reasoning

Multiple Representations Extend Practice Exercise 5 to have the students generalize what happens to the x-coordinate and y-coordinate of a point when it is rotated 90° about the origin. **The x-coordinate becomes the opposite of the original y-coordinate and the y-coordinate becomes the original x-coordinate.**

1.
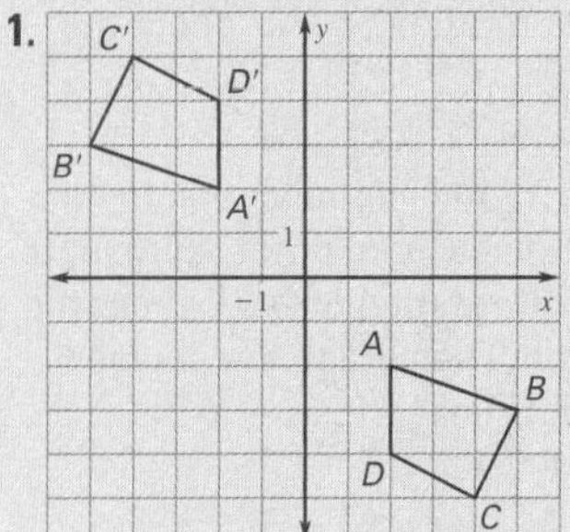

2.
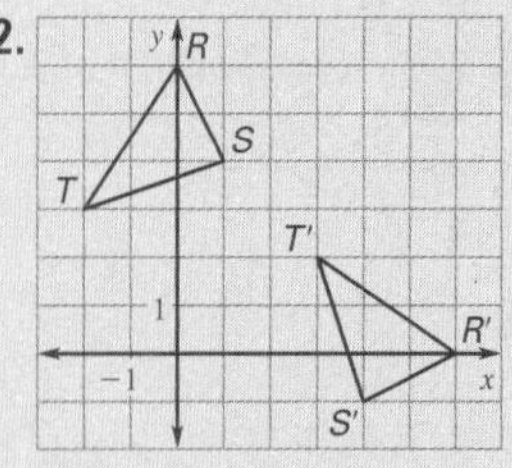

4. Trace the figure then reflect the figure across the line of reflection.

6.
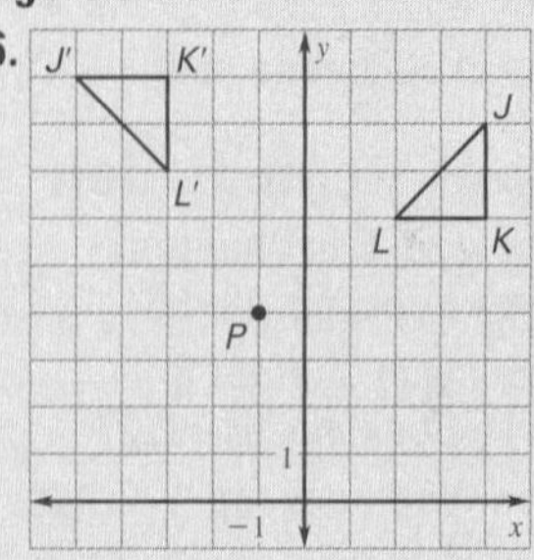

Another Way to Solve Example 2, page 599

MULTIPLE REPRESENTATIONS In Example 2 on page 599, you saw how to use a coordinate rule to rotate a figure. You can also *use tracing paper* and move a copy of the figure around the coordinate plane.

PROBLEM

Graph quadrilateral $RSTU$ with vertices $R(3, 1)$, $S(5, 1)$, $T(5, -3)$, and $U(2, -1)$. Then rotate the quadrilateral 270° about the origin.

METHOD

Using Tracing Paper You can use tracing paper to rotate a figure.

Standards

22.0 Students know the effect of rigid motions on figures in the coordinate plane and space, including rotations, translations, and reflections.

STEP 1 **Graph** the original figure in the coordinate plane.

STEP 2 **Trace** the quadrilateral and the axes on tracing paper.

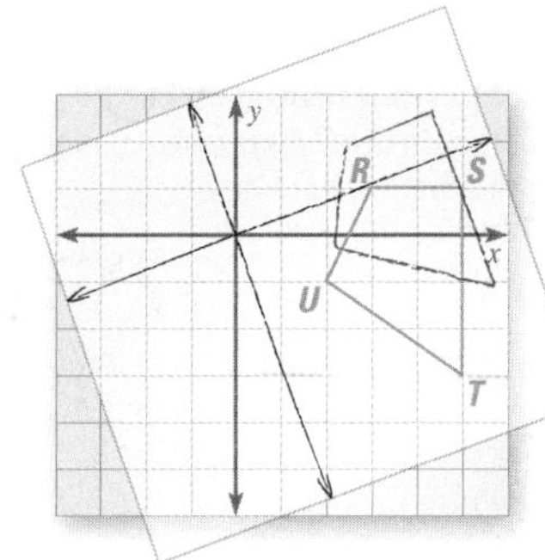

STEP 3 **Rotate** the tracing paper 270°. Then transfer the resulting image onto the graph paper.

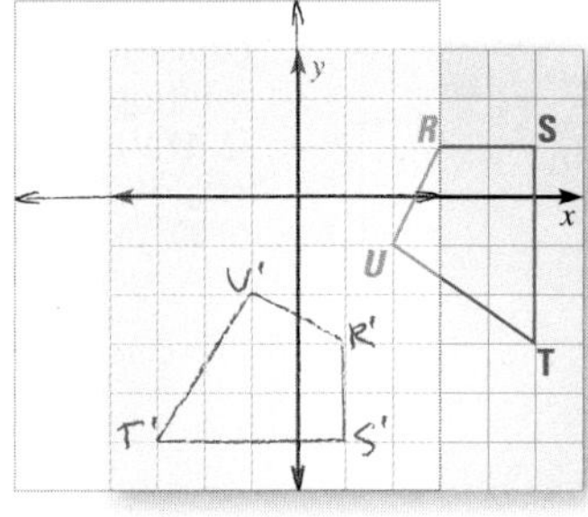

PRACTICE

1. **GRAPH** Graph quadrilateral $ABCD$ with vertices $A(2, -2)$, $B(5, -3)$, $C(4, -5)$, and $D(2, -4)$. Then rotate the quadrilateral 180° about the origin using tracing paper. **See margin.**
2. **GRAPH** Graph $\triangle RST$ with vertices $R(0, 6)$, $S(1, 4)$, and $T(-2, 3)$. Then rotate the triangle 270° about the origin using tracing paper. **See margin.**
3. **SHORT RESPONSE** *Explain* why rotating a figure 90° clockwise is the same as rotating the figure 270° counterclockwise. **Since they are rotating in opposite directions they will each place you at 90° below your reference line.**
4. **SHORT RESPONSE** *Explain* how you could use tracing paper to do a reflection. **See margin.**
5. **REASONING** If you rotate the point (3, 4) 90° about the origin, what happens to the x-coordinate? What happens to the y-coordinate? **The x-coordinate is now −4; the y-coordinate is now 3.**
6. **GRAPH** Graph $\triangle JKL$ with vertices $J(4, 8)$, $K(4, 6)$, and $L(2, 6)$. Then rotate the triangle 90° about the point $(-1, 4)$ using tracing paper. **See margin.**

@HomeTutor
classzone.com
Keystrokes

9.5 Double Reflections

MATERIALS • graphing calculator or computer

Standards

22.0 Students know the effect of rigid motions on figures in the coordinate plane and space, including rotations, translations, and reflections.

QUESTION What happens when you reflect a figure in two lines in a plane?

EXPLORE 1 Double reflection in parallel lines

STEP 1 ***Draw a scalene triangle*** Construct a scalene triangle like the one at the right. Label the vertices D, E, and F.

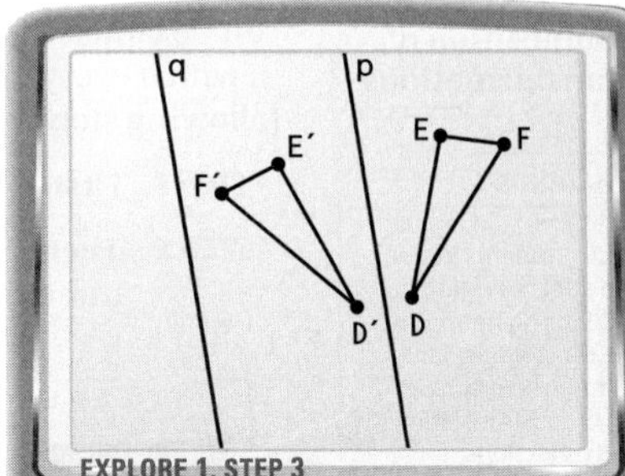

STEP 2 ***Draw parallel lines*** Construct two parallel lines p and q on one side of the triangle. Make sure that the lines do not intersect the triangle. Save as "EXPLORE1".

STEP 3 ***Reflect triangle*** Reflect $\triangle DEF$ in line p. Reflect $\triangle D'E'F'$ in line q. How is $\triangle D''E''F''$ related to $\triangle DEF$?

STEP 4 ***Make conclusion*** Drag line q. Does the relationship appear to be true if p and q are not on the same side of the figure?

EXPLORE 2 Double reflection in intersecting lines

STEP 1 ***Draw intersecting lines*** Follow Step 1 in Explore 1 for $\triangle ABC$. Change Step 2 from parallel lines to intersecting lines k and m. Make sure that the lines do not intersect the triangle. Label the point of intersection of lines k and m as P. Save as "EXPLORE2".

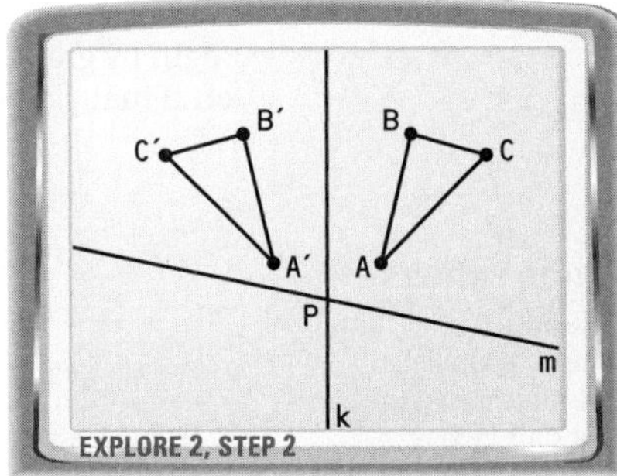

STEP 2 ***Reflect triangle*** Reflect $\triangle ABC$ in line k. Reflect $\triangle A'B'C'$ in line m. How is $\triangle A''B''C''$ related to $\triangle ABC$?

STEP 3 ***Measure angles*** Measure $\angle APA''$ and the acute angle formed by lines k and m. What is the relationship between these two angles? Does this relationship remain true when you move lines k and m?

DRAW CONCLUSIONS Use your observations to complete these exercises

1. What other transformation maps a figure onto the same image as a reflection in two parallel lines? **translation**
2. What other transformation maps a figure onto the same image as a reflection in two intersecting lines? **rotation**

1 PLAN AND PREPARE

Explore the Concept

- Students will reflect a figure in two lines in a plane.
- This activity leads into the study of finding the image of a reflection in two lines in Example 3 in Lesson 9.5.

Materials

Each student will need:

- graphing calculator or computer
- geometry software

Recommended Time

Work activity: 15 min
Discuss results: 5 min

Grouping

Students should work individually.

2 TEACH

Tips for Success

Students must use the construction features to draw the parallel lines.

Key Questions

- How does the distance between each point and its image compare to the distance between the parallel lines? **double**
- How does the angle of rotation compare to the acute angle between the intersecting lines? **double**

Alternative Strategy

Students can use graph paper and a straightedge and draw the image of a triangle under two reflections.

Key Discovery

A reflection in two parallel lines is a translation. A reflection in two intersecting lines is a rotation.

3 ASSESS AND RETEACH

What transformation results from reflecting a figure in two parallel lines? in two intersecting lines? **translation; rotation**

1 PLAN AND PREPARE

Warm-Up Exercises

Transparency Available

Find the image of (2, 3) under each transformation.

1. translation $(x, y) \rightarrow (x - 6, y - 2)$ **(−4, 1)**
2. reflection in the y-axis **(−2, 3)**
3. reflection in the line $y = 6$ **(2, 9)**
4. rotation 90° about the origin **(−3, 2)**

Notetaking Guide

Transparency Available

Promotes interactive learning and notetaking skills, pp. 240–243.

Pacing

Basic: 2 days
Average: 2 days
Advanced: 2 days
Block: 1 block
• See *Teaching Guide/Lesson Plan.*

2 FOCUS AND MOTIVATE

Essential Question

Big Idea 1, p. 571

What is a glide reflection? **Tell students they will learn how to answer this question by studying compositions of two or more transformations.**

9.5 Apply Compositions of Transformations

Before You performed rotations, reflections, or translations.
Now You will perform combinations of two or more transformations.
Why? So you can describe the transformations that represent a rowing crew, as in Ex. 30.

Key Vocabulary
- **glide reflection**
- **composition of transformations**

Standards
22.0 Students know the effect of rigid motions on figures in the coordinate plane and space, including rotations, translations, and reflections.

A translation followed by a reflection can be performed one after the other to produce a *glide reflection.* A translation can be called a glide. A **glide reflection** is a transformation in which every point P is mapped to a point P'' by the following steps.

STEP 1 **First,** a translation maps P to P'.

STEP 2 **Then,** a reflection in a line k parallel to the direction of the translation maps P' to P''.

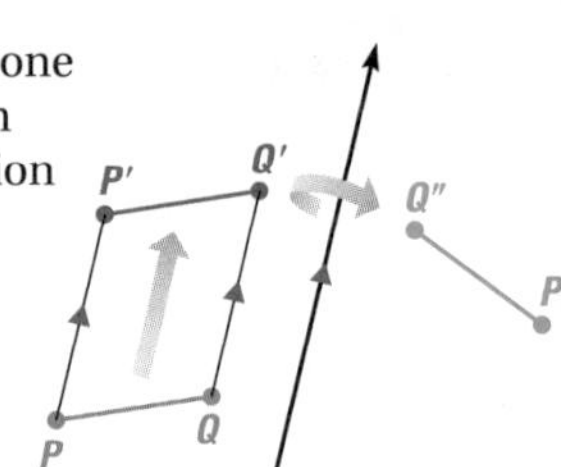

EXAMPLE 1 Find the image of a glide reflection

The vertices of $\triangle ABC$ are $A(3, 2)$, $B(6, 3)$, and $C(7, 1)$. Find the image of $\triangle ABC$ after the glide reflection.

Translation: $(x, y) \rightarrow (x - 12, y)$
Reflection: in the x-axis

Solution

Begin by graphing $\triangle ABC$. Then graph $\triangle A'B'C'$ after a translation 12 units left. Finally, graph $\triangle A''B''C''$ after a reflection in the x-axis.

AVOID ERRORS
The line of reflection must be parallel to the direction of the translation to be a glide reflection.

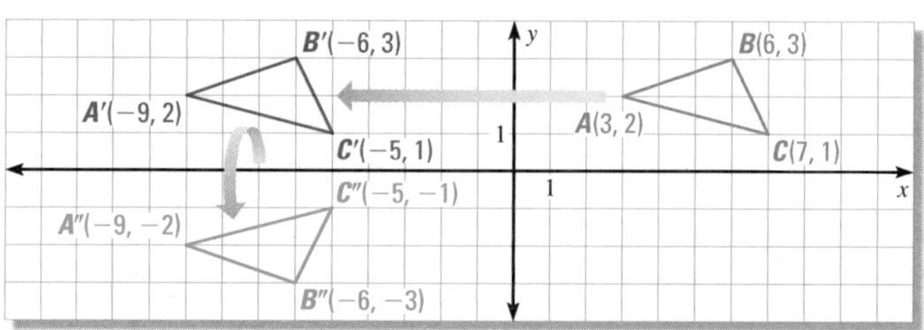

✓ GUIDED PRACTICE for Example 1

1. Suppose $\triangle ABC$ in Example 1 is translated 4 units down, then reflected in the y-axis. What are the coordinates of the vertices of the image? **A(−3, −2), B(−6, −1), C(−7, −3)**
2. In Example 1, *describe* a glide reflection from $\triangle A''B''C''$ to $\triangle ABC$. **(x, y) → (x + 12, y) followed by a reflection in x.**

Resource Planning Guide

Chapter Resource Book
- Teaching Guide/Lesson Plan (pp. 59–60)
- Practice levels A, B, C (pp. 62–67)
- Study Guide (pp. 68–69)
- Catch-up for Absent Students (p. 70)
- Application (p. 71)
- Challenge (p. 72)

Workbooks
- Notetaking Guide (pp. 240–243)
- Practice Workbook (pp. 175–177)

Teaching Options
- **Power Presentations CD-ROM** provides dynamic electronic teaching resources for the classroom.
- **Activity Generator CD-ROM** provides editable activities for all ability levels.

Interactive Technology
- Easy Planner
- Power Presentations CD-ROM
- Activity Generator CD-ROM
- Animated Geometry
- Test Generator CD-ROM
- Online Quiz
- eWorkbook
- eEdition
- @HomeTutor

Resources for English Learners
- Quick Reference for English Learners
- Spanish Study Guide
- Multi-Language Visual Glossary
- Student Resources in Spanish

See also the *Geometry Toolkit* for more strategies for meeting individual needs.

COMPOSITIONS When two or more transformations are combined to form a single transformation, the result is a **composition of transformations.** A glide reflection is an example of a composition of transformations.

In this lesson, a composition of transformations uses isometries, so the final image is congruent to the preimage. This suggests the Composition Theorem.

THEOREM *For Your Notebook*

THEOREM 9.4 Composition Theorem

The composition of two (or more) isometries is an isometry.

Proof: Exs. 35–36, p. 614

EXAMPLE 2 Find the image of a composition

The endpoints of $\overline{RS}$ are $R(1, -3)$ and $S(2, -6)$. Graph the image of $\overline{RS}$ after the composition.

Reflection: in the y-axis
Rotation: 90° about the origin

Solution

STEP 1 **Graph** $\overline{RS}$.

STEP 2 **Reflect** $\overline{RS}$ in the y-axis. $\overline{R'S'}$ has endpoints $R'(-1, -3)$ and $S'(-2, -6)$.

STEP 3 **Rotate** $\overline{R'S'}$ 90° about the origin. $\overline{R''S''}$ has endpoints $R''(3, -1)$ and $S''(6, -2)$.

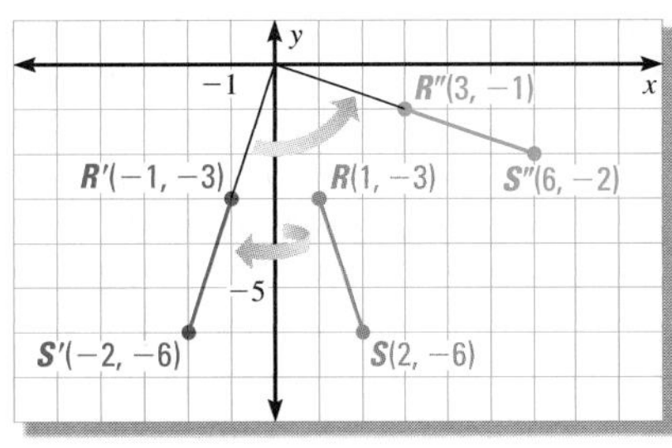

AVOID ERRORS
Unless you are told otherwise, do the transformations in the order given.

TWO REFLECTIONS Compositions of two reflections result in either a translation or a rotation, as described in Theorems 9.5 and 9.6.

THEOREM *For Your Notebook*

THEOREM 9.5 Reflections in Parallel Lines Theorem

If lines k and m are parallel, then a reflection in line k followed by a reflection in line m is the same as a translation.

If P'' is the image of P, then:

1. $\overline{PP''}$ is perpendicular to k and m, and
2. $PP'' = 2d$, where d is the distance between k and m.

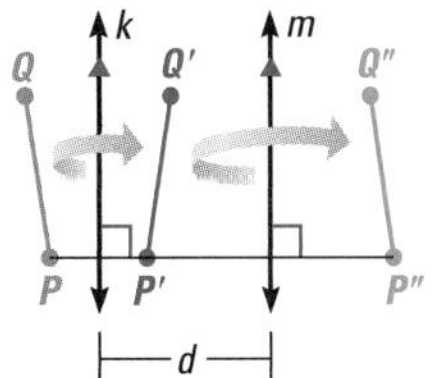

Proof: Ex. 37, p. 614

Motivating the Lesson

Tell students that patterns in tiled floors are often created by combining reflections, translations, and rotations. Tell students that in this lesson they will learn about the results of performing more than one transformation.

3 TEACH

Extra Example 1

The vertices of $\triangle PQR$ are $P(2, 6)$, $Q(4, -2)$, and $R(-3, -3)$. Find the image of $\triangle PQR$ after the glide reflection.
Translation: $(x, y) \rightarrow (x + 4, y)$;
Reflection: in the x-axis

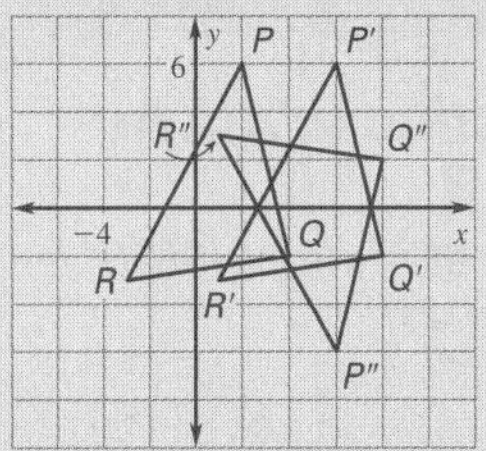

Extra Example 2

The endpoints of $\overline{MN}$ are $M(-2, 1)$ and $N(3, 4)$. Graph the image of $\overline{MN}$ after the composition.
Reflection: in the line (x, y)
Rotation: 180° about the origin

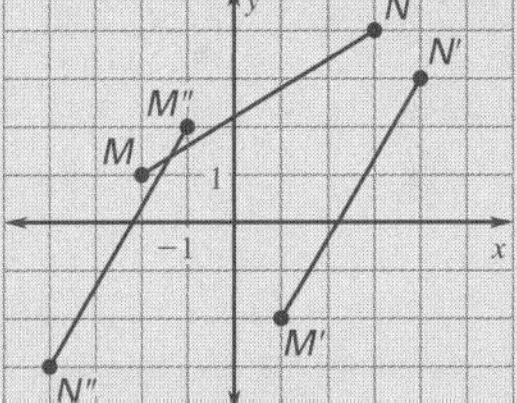

Key Question to Ask for Example 2

- Would you get the same result if you performed the rotation first? Explain. **No; the final image would have endpoints at $(-3, 1)$ and $(-6, 2)$.**

Extra Example 3

In the diagram, a reflection in line a maps $\overline{XY}$ to $\overline{X'Y'}$. A reflection in line b maps $\overline{X'Y'}$ to $\overline{X''Y''}$. Also, $XD = 6$ and $EX'' = 9$.

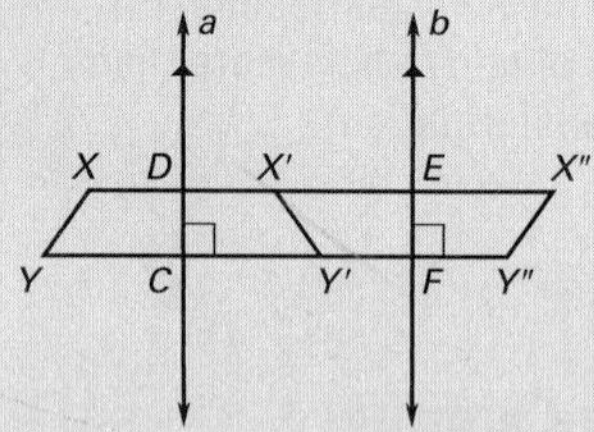

a. Name any segments congruent to each segment: $\overline{XY}$, $\overline{XD}$, and $\overline{YC}$. **$\overline{X'Y'}$, $\overline{X''Y''}$; $\overline{DX'}$; $\overline{Y'C}$**

b. Does $CF = DE$? Explain. **Yes, *CDEF* is a rectangle.**

c. What is the length of $\overline{YY''}$? **30**

Key Question to Ask for Example 3

- What type of figure is $HGG''H''$? **parallelogram**

3. 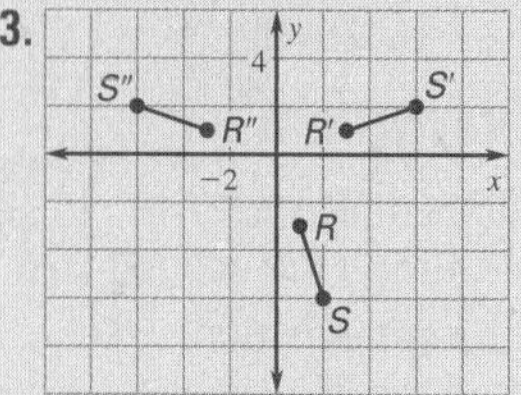

EXAMPLE 3 Use Theorem 9.5

In the diagram, a reflection in line k maps $\overline{GH}$ to $\overline{G'H'}$. A reflection in line m maps $\overline{G'H'}$ to $\overline{G''H''}$. Also, $HB = 9$ and $DH'' = 4$.

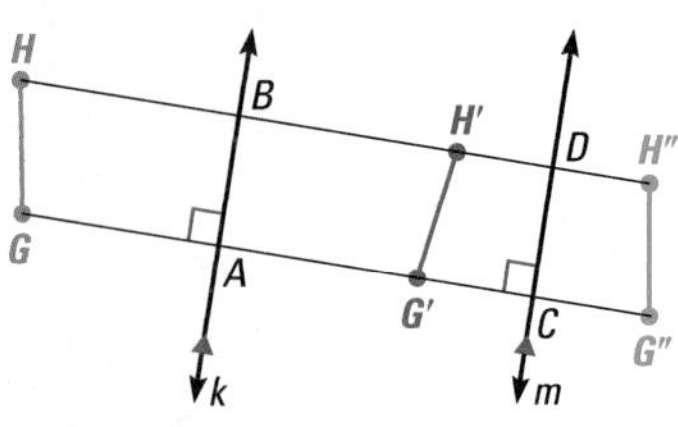

a. Name any segments congruent to each segment: $\overline{HG}$, $\overline{HB}$, and $\overline{GA}$.

b. Does $AC = BD$? Explain.

c. What is the length of $\overline{GG''}$?

Solution

a. $\overline{HG} \cong \overline{H'G'}$, and $\overline{HG} \cong \overline{H''G''}$. $\overline{HB} \cong \overline{H'B}$. $\overline{GA} \cong \overline{G'A}$.

b. Yes, $AC = BD$ because $\overline{GG''}$ and $\overline{HH''}$ are perpendicular to both k and m, so $\overline{BD}$ and $\overline{AC}$ are opposite sides of a rectangle.

c. By the properties of reflections, $H'B = 9$ and $H'D = 4$. Theorem 9.5 implies that $GG'' = HH'' = 2 \cdot BD$, so the length of $\overline{GG''}$ is $2(9 + 4)$, or 26 units.

GUIDED PRACTICE for Examples 2 and 3

3. See margin for art; yes; the resulting segment $R''S''$ is not the same.

3. Graph $\overline{RS}$ from Example 2. Do the rotation first, followed by the reflection. Does the order of the transformations matter? *Explain.*

4. In Example 3, part (c), *explain* how you know that $GG'' = HH''$. **They are opposite sides of a parallelogram.**

Use the figure below for Exercises 5 and 6. The distance between line k and line m is 1.6 centimeters.

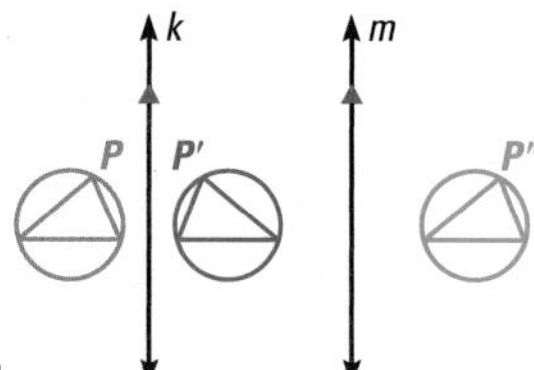

5. The preimage is reflected in line k, then in line m. *Describe* a single transformation that maps the blue figure to the green figure. **translation**

6. What is the distance between P and P''? If you draw $\overline{PP'}$, what is its relationship with line k? *Explain.* **3.2 cm; they are perpendicular.**

THEOREM *For Your Notebook*

THEOREM 9.6 Reflections in Intersecting Lines Theorem

If lines k and m intersect at point P, then a reflection in k followed by a reflection in m is the same as a rotation about point P.

The angle of rotation is $2x°$, where $x°$ is the measure of the acute or right angle formed by k and m.

Proof: Ex. 38, p. 614

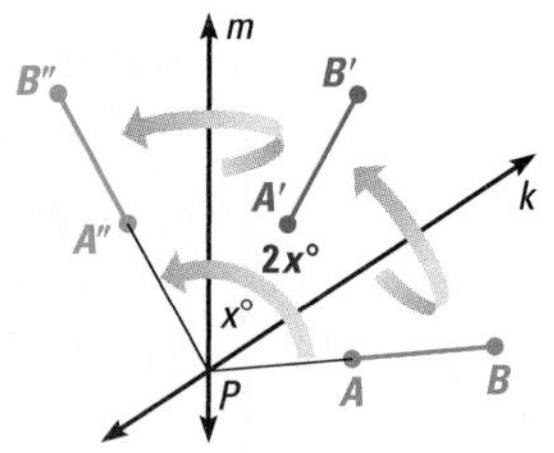

$m\angle BPB'' = 2x°$

Differentiated Instruction

Inclusion Some students may have difficulty grasping how two reflections can result in a translation. Assist students with **Guided Practice Exercise 5** by having them trace the preimage *P*. Ask them to cut out the preimage and place it over *P* on the page. Then have them manipulate *P* to create *P''*. Help them to describe in words how *P* is transformed to create *P''*.

See also the *Geometry Toolkit* for more strategies.

EXAMPLE 4 Use Theorem 9.6

In the diagram, the figure is reflected in line k. The image is then reflected in line m. Describe a single transformation that maps F to F''.

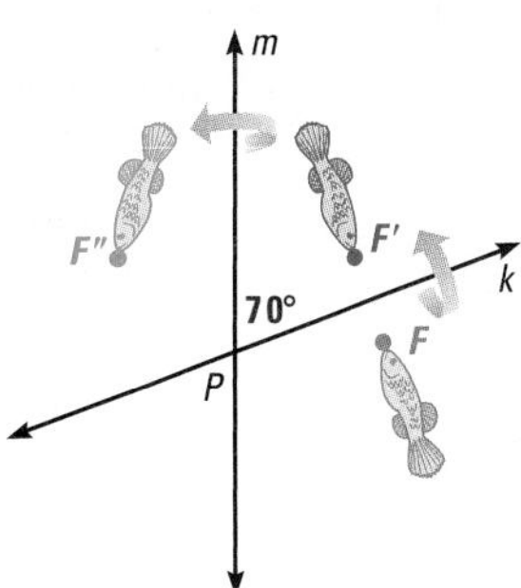

Solution

The measure of the acute angle formed between lines k and m is 70°. So, by Theorem 9.6, a single transformation that maps F to F'' is a 140° rotation about point P.

You can check that this is correct by tracing lines k and m and point F, then rotating the point 140°.

 at classzone.com

✓ **GUIDED PRACTICE** for Example 4

a rotation of 160° about point P

7. In the diagram at the right, the preimage is reflected in line k, then in line m. *Describe* a single transformation that maps the blue figure onto the green figure.

8. A rotation of 76° maps C to C'. To map C to C' using two reflections, what is the angle formed by the intersecting lines of reflection? **38°**

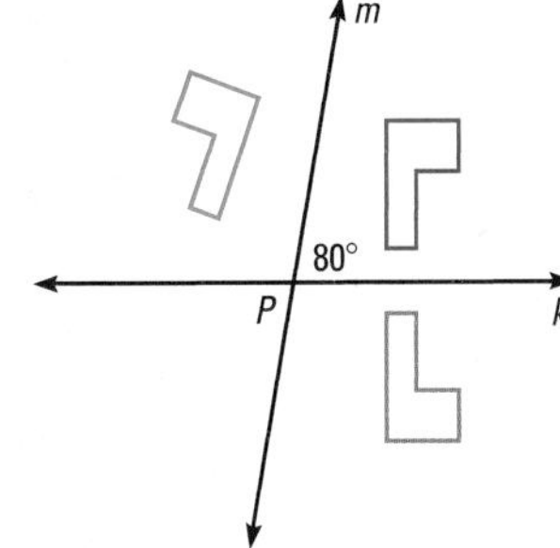

9.5 EXERCISES

HOMEWORK KEY
○ = **WORKED-OUT SOLUTIONS** on p. WS12 for Exs. 7, 17, and 27
★ = **STANDARDIZED TEST PRACTICE** Exs. 2, 25, 29, and 34

SKILL PRACTICE

A

1. **VOCABULARY** Copy and complete: In a glide reflection, the direction of the translation must be _?_ to the line of reflection. **parallel**

2. ★ **WRITING** *Explain* why a glide reflection is an isometry. **It preserves length and angle measure.**

EXAMPLE 1 on p. 608 for Exs. 3–6

GLIDE REFLECTION The endpoints of $\overline{CD}$ are $C(2, -5)$ and $D(4, 0)$. Graph the image of $\overline{CD}$ after the glide reflection. **3–6. See margin.**

3. **Translation:** $(x, y) \to (x, y - 1)$
   Reflection: in the y-axis

4. **Translation:** $(x, y) \to (x - 3, y)$
   Reflection: in $y = -1$

5. **Translation:** $(x, y) \to (x, y + 4)$
   Reflection: in $x = 3$

6. **Translation:** $(x, y) \to (x + 2, y + 2)$
   Reflection: in $y = x$

Extra Example 4

In the diagram, the figure is reflected in line a. The image is then reflected in line b. Describe a single transformation that maps H to H''. **100° rotation about P**

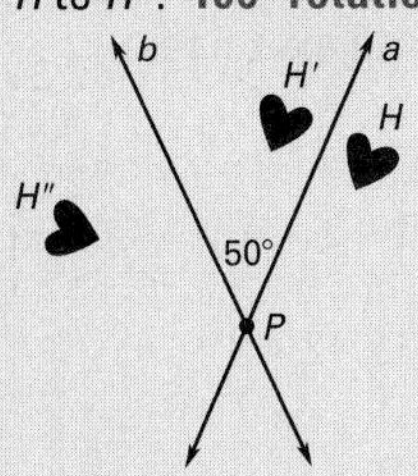

Animated Geometry
classzone.com

An **Animated Geometry** activity is available on-line for **Example 4**. This activity is also available on the **Power Presentations CD-ROM**.

Closing the Lesson

Have students summarize the major points of the lesson and answer the Essential Question: What is a glide reflection?

- **The composition of two or more isometries is an isometry.**
- **Successive reflections in two parallel lines give a translation.**
- **Successive reflections in two intersecting lines give a rotation.**

A glide reflection is a translation followed by a reflection over a line parallel to the direction of the translation.

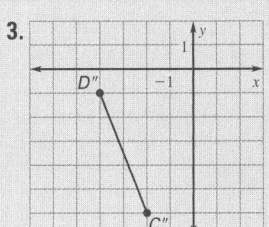

3. D'' C'' (graph)

4.

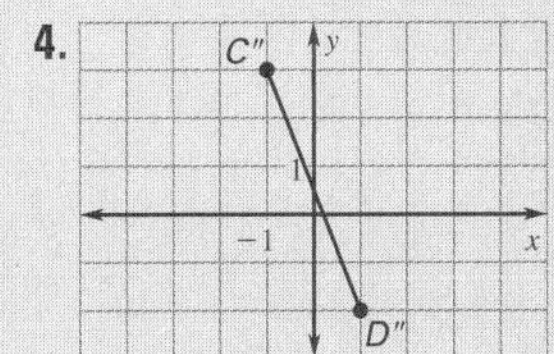

5.

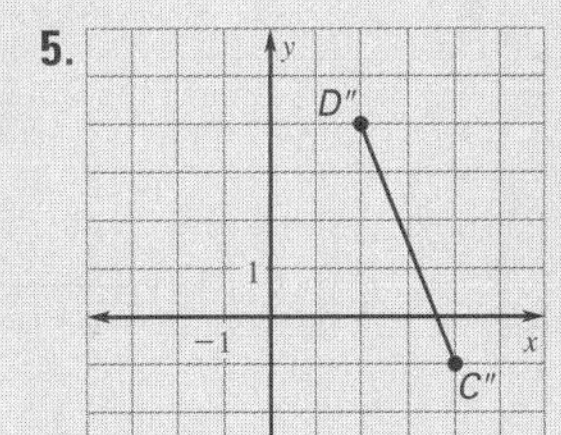

6.

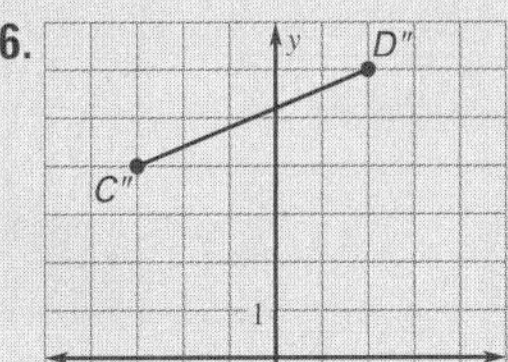

4 PRACTICE AND APPLY

Assignment Guide

Answer Transparencies available for all exercises

Basic:
Day 1: pp. 611–615
Exs. 1–14, 27–30
Day 2: pp. 611–615
Exs. 15–23, 31–35, 42–48

Average:
Day 1: pp. 611–615
Exs. 1, 2, 4–6, 8–14, 23, 24, 27–30
Day 2: pp. 611–615
Exs. 15–22, 25, 31–39, 42–48

Advanced:
Day 1: pp. 611–615
Exs. 1, 2, 4–6, 9–14, 23, 24, 26–30*
Day 2: pp. 611–615
Exs. 15–22, 25, 31–41*, 44, 46

Block:
pp. 611–615
Exs. 1, 2, 4–6, 8–25, 27–39, 42–48

Differentiated Instruction

See *Geometry Best Practices Toolkit* for suggestions on addressing the needs of a diverse classroom.

Homework Check

For a quick check of student understanding of key concepts, go over the following exercises:

Basic: 4, 8, 16, 20, 27
Average: 5, 12, 18, 21, 28
Advanced: 6, 14, 19, 21, 30

Extra Practice

- Student Edition, p. 913
- Chapter 9 Resource Book: Practice levels A, B, C, pp. 62–67

Practice Worksheet

An easily-readable reduced practice page (with answers) for this lesson can be found on p. 570E.

EXAMPLE 2 on p. 609 for Exs. 7–14

GRAPHING COMPOSITIONS **The vertices of $\triangle PQR$ are $P(2, 4)$, $Q(6, 0)$, and $R(7, 2)$. Graph the image of $\triangle PQR$ after a composition of the transformations in the order they are listed.** **7–10. See margin.**

7. **Translation:** $(x, y) \to (x, y - 5)$
   Reflection: in the y-axis
8. **Translation:** $(x, y) \to (x - 3, y + 2)$
   Rotation: 90° about the origin
9. **Translation:** $(x, y) \to (x + 12, y + 4)$
   Translation: $(x, y) \to (x - 5, y - 9)$
10. **Reflection:** in the x-axis
    Rotation: 90° about the origin

REVERSING ORDERS **Graph $\overline{F''G''}$ after a composition of the transformations in the order they are listed. Then perform the transformations in reverse order. Does the order affect the final image $\overline{F''G''}$?** **11, 12. See margin for art.**

11. $F(-5, 2)$, $G(-2, 4)$
    Translation: $(x, y) \to (x + 3, y - 8)$
    Reflection: in the x-axis **yes**
12. $F(-1, -8)$, $G(-6, -3)$
    Reflection: in the line $y = 2$
    Rotation: 90° about the origin **yes**

DESCRIBING COMPOSITIONS ***Describe*** **the composition of transformations.**

13.

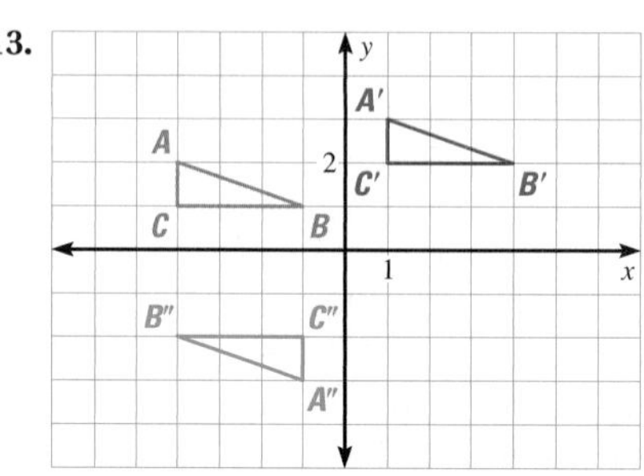

14.

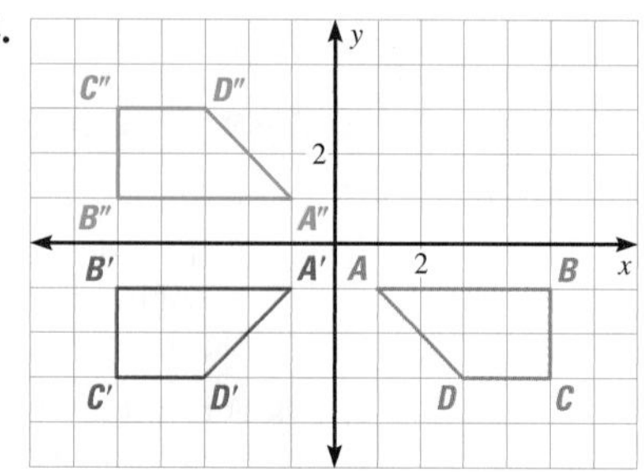

13. $(x, y) \to (x + 5, y + 1)$ followed by a rotation of 180° about the origin.

14. a reflection in the y-axis followed by a reflection in the x-axis

EXAMPLE 3 on p. 610 for Exs. 15–19

USING THEOREM 9.5 **In the diagram, $k \parallel m$, $\triangle ABC$ is reflected in line k, and $\triangle A'B'C'$ is reflected in line m.**

15. A translation maps $\triangle ABC$ onto which triangle? **$\triangle A''B''C''$**
16. Which lines are perpendicular to $\overleftrightarrow{AA''}$? **line k and line m**
17. Name two segments parallel to $\overleftrightarrow{BB''}$. ***Sample answer:* $\overline{AA'}$, $\overline{AA''}$**
18. If the distance between k and m is 2.6 inches, what is the length of $\overline{CC''}$? **5.2 in.**
19. Is the distance from B' to m the same as the distance from B'' to m? *Explain.*
    yes; definition of reflection of a point over a line

EXAMPLE 4 on p. 611 for Exs. 20–21

USING THEOREM 9.6 **Find the angle of rotation that maps A onto A''.**

20. **110°**

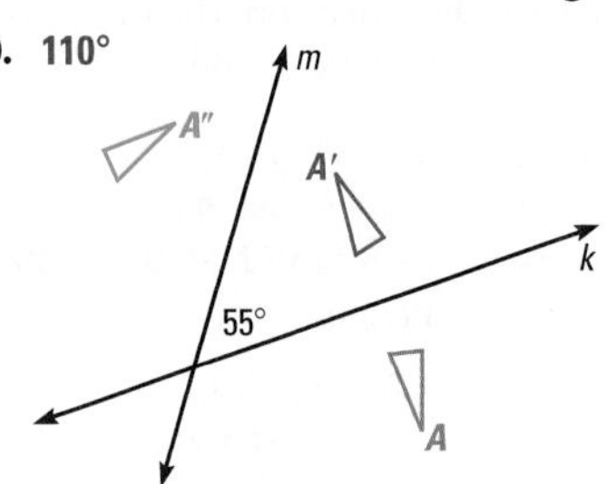

21. **30°**

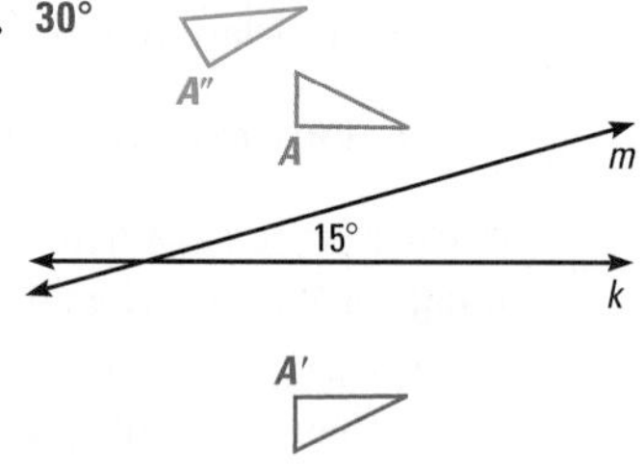

○ = WORKED-OUT SOLUTIONS on p. WS1 ★ = STANDARDIZED TEST PRACTICE

7.

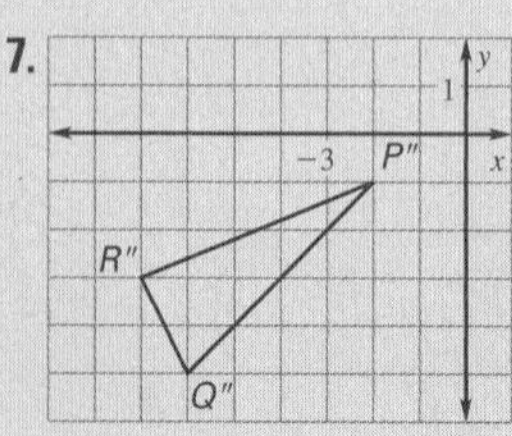

8.

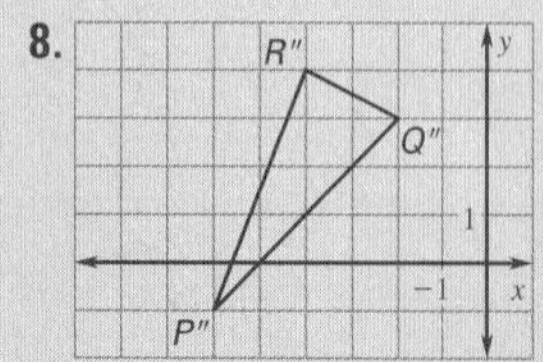

9.

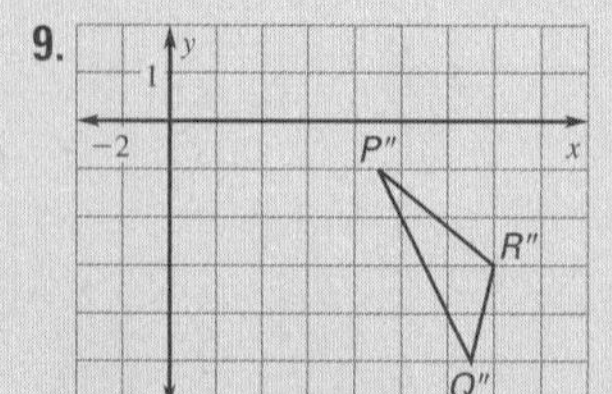

10.

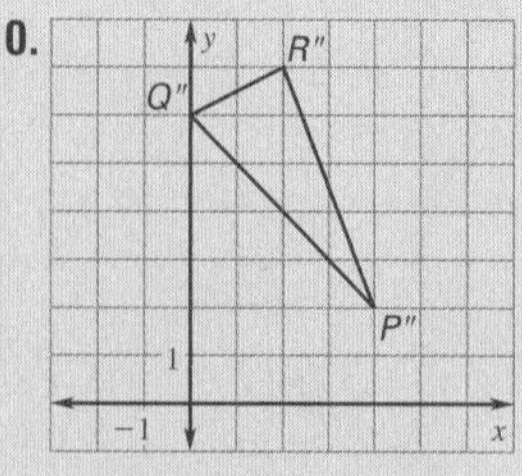

2. The line of eflection is not arallel to the irection of the anslation; this not a glide eflection.

5. Check tudents work. ince the three ansformations re isometries, ne preimage nd the final mage are ongruent ecause an sometry reserves ength and angle neasure.

B **22. ERROR ANALYSIS** A student described the translation of $\overline{AB}$ to $\overline{A'B'}$ followed by the reflection of $\overline{A'B'}$ to $\overline{A''B''}$ in the y-axis as a glide reflection. *Describe* and correct the student's error.

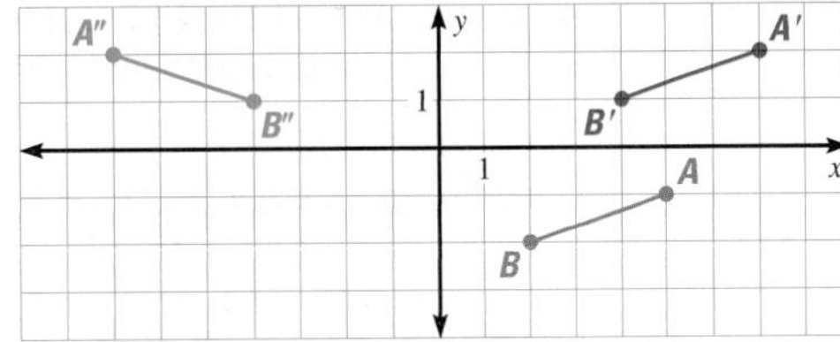

USING MATRICES The vertices of $\triangle PQR$ are $P(1, 4)$, $Q(3, -2)$, and $R(7, 1)$. Use matrix operations to find the image matrix that represents the composition of the given transformations. Then graph $\triangle PQR$ and its image. **23, 24. See margin.**

23. Translation: $(x, y) \to (x, y + 5)$
Reflection: in the y-axis

24. Reflection: in the x-axis
Translation: $(x, y) \to (x - 9, y - 4)$

25. ★ OPEN-ENDED MATH Sketch a polygon. Apply three transformations of your choice on the polygon. What can you say about the congruence of the preimage and final image after multiple transformations? *Explain.*

C **26. CHALLENGE** The vertices of $\triangle JKL$ are $J(1, -3)$, $K(2, 2)$, and $L(3, 0)$. Find the image of the triangle after a 180° rotation about the point $(-2, 2)$, followed by a reflection in the line $y = -x$. **$J''(-7, 5)$, $K''(-2, 6)$, $L''(-4, 7)$**

Problem Solving

EXAMPLE 1 **A**
on p. 608 for Exs. 27–30

ANIMAL TRACKS The left and right prints in the set of animal tracks can be related by a glide reflection. Copy the tracks and *describe* a translation and reflection that combine to create the glide reflection.

27. bald eagle (2 legs)

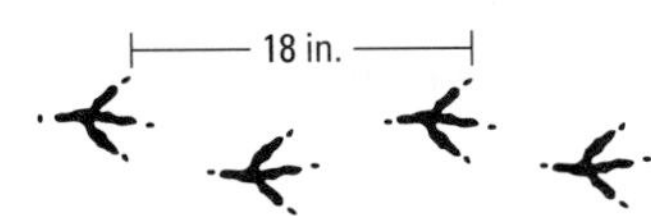

27. ***Sample answer:*** **$(x, y) \to (x + 9, y)$, reflected over a horizontal line that separates the left and right prints**

28. armadillo (4 legs)

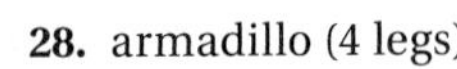

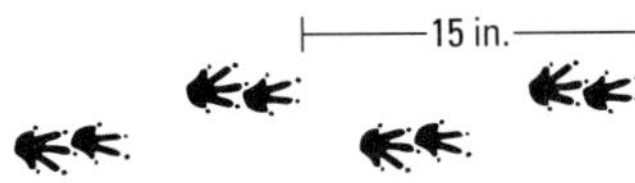

Sample answer: **$(x, y) \to (x + 7.5, y)$, reflected over a horizontal line that separates the left and right prints**

@HomeTutor for problem solving help at classzone.com

29. ★ MULTIPLE CHOICE Which is *not* a glide reflection? **C**

Ⓐ The teeth of a closed zipper

Ⓑ The tracks of a walking duck

Ⓒ The keys on a computer keyboard

Ⓓ The red squares on two adjacent rows of a checkerboard

@HomeTutor for problem solving help at classzone.com

30. ROWING *Describe* the transformations that are combined to represent an eight-person rowing shell. **glide reflection**

Avoiding Common Errors

Exercises 23–24 Some students may attempt to use matrix multiplication to perform the translations. Remind them that translations are performed by using matrix addition.

23. $\begin{array}{c} \quad P' \quad Q' \quad R' \\ \begin{bmatrix} -1 & -3 & -7 \\ 9 & 3 & 6 \end{bmatrix}; \end{array}$

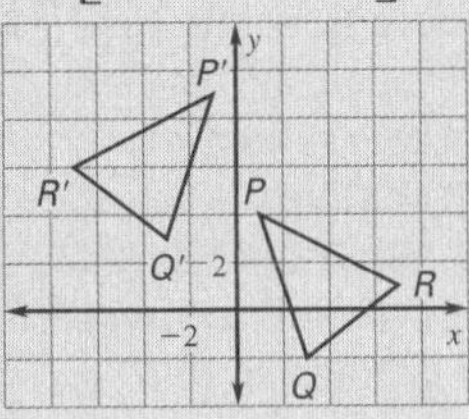

24. $\begin{array}{c} \quad P' \quad Q' \quad R' \\ \begin{bmatrix} -8 & -6 & -2 \\ -8 & -2 & -5 \end{bmatrix}; \end{array}$

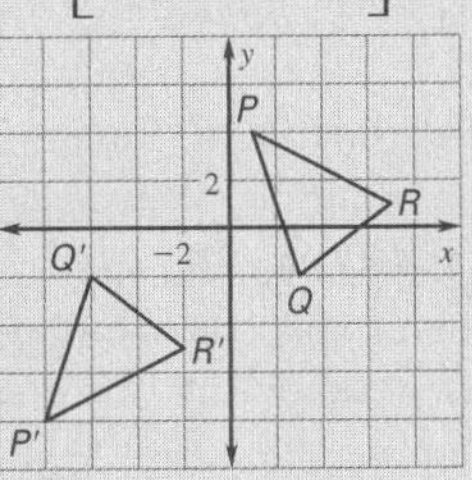

11.

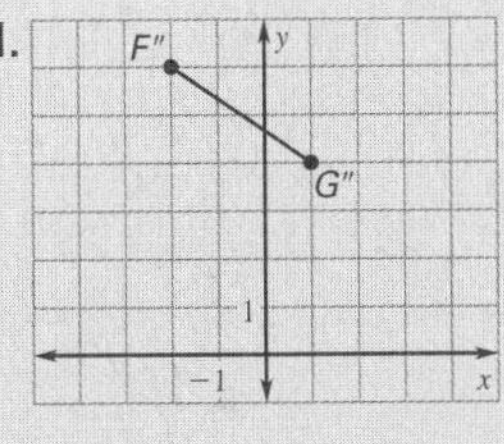

12.

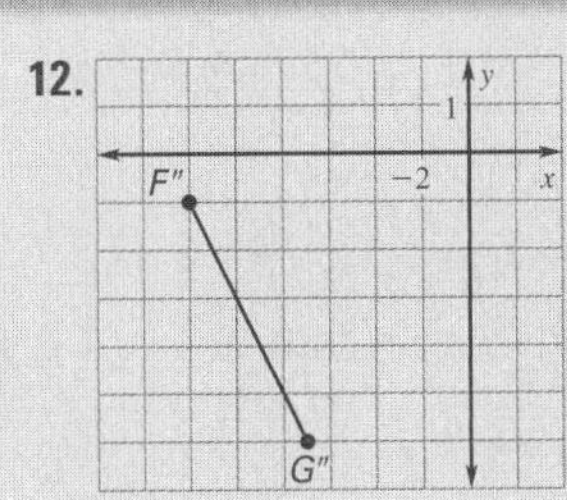

Teaching Strategy

Exercises 35–38 Divide the students into groups and assign one problem to each group. Have them present their proofs to the class.

36. A reflection followed by a rotation, a reflection followed by a translation, a rotation followed by a translation, a rotation followed by a reflection, a translation followed by a rotation, or a translation followed by a reflection. ***Sample answer:*** **Given: a reflection in m mapping P to P' and Q to Q' followed by a rotation about R mapping P' to P'' and Q' to Q''. Using the Reflection Theorem, $PQ = P'Q'$. Using the Rotation Theorem, $P'Q' = P''Q''$. Using the Transitive Property of Equality, $PQ = P''Q''$.**

37a. Given: A reflection in ℓ maps $\overline{JK}$ to $\overline{J'K'}$, a reflection in m maps $\overline{J'K'}$ to $\overline{J''K''}$, $\ell \parallel m$, and the distance between ℓ and m is d. Using the definition of reflection, ℓ is the perpendicular bisector of $\overline{KK'}$ and m is the perpendicular bisector of $\overline{K'K''}$. Using the Segment Addition Postulate, $KK' + K'K'' = KK''$. It follows that $\overline{KK''}$ is perpendicular to ℓ and m.

37b. Using the definition of reflection, the distance from K to ℓ is the same as the distance from ℓ to K' and the distance from K' to m is the same as the distance from m to K''. Since the distance from ℓ to K' plus the distance from K' to m is d, it follows that $K'K'' = 2d$.

38a–b. See Additional Answers beginning on p. AA1.

34. Reflect the object across two parallel lines, and then reflect it across a third line perpendicular to the first two lines.

39b. One transformation is not followed by the second. They are done simultaneously.

B **SWEATER PATTERNS In Exercises 31–33, *describe* the transformations that are combined to make each sweater pattern.**

31. 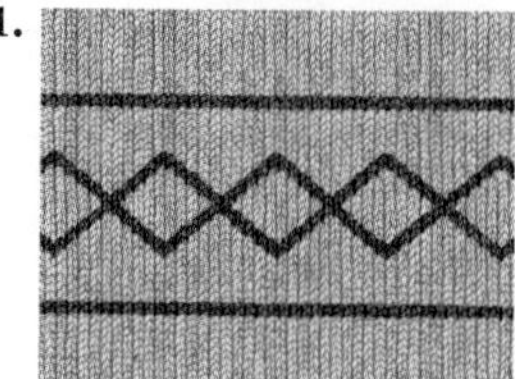
reflection and translation

32. 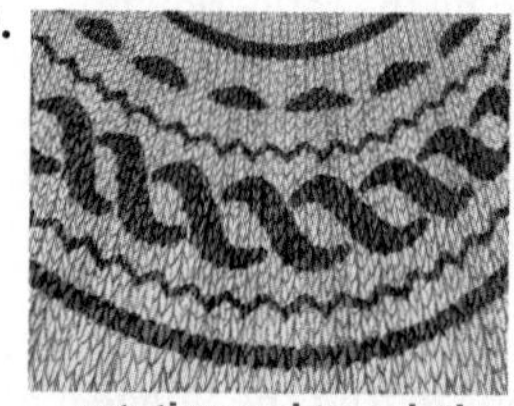
rotation and translation

33. 
translation and reflection

34. ★ **SHORT RESPONSE** Use Theorem 9.5 to *explain* how you can make a glide reflection using three reflections. How are the lines of reflection related?

35. PROVING THEOREM 9.4 Write a plan for proof for one case of the Composition Theorem.

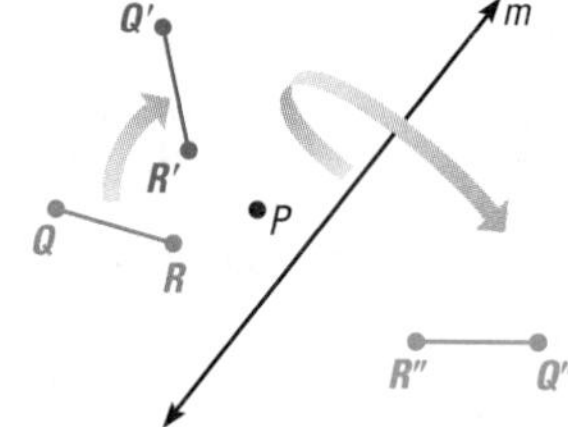

GIVEN ▶ A rotation about P maps Q to Q' and R to R'. A reflection in m maps Q' to Q'' and R' to R''.

PROVE ▶ $QR = Q''R''$

Use the Rotation Theorem followed by the Reflection Theorem.

36. PROVING THEOREM 9.4 A composition of a rotation and a reflection, as in Exercise 35, is one case of the Composition Theorem. List all possible cases, and prove the theorem for another pair of compositions. **See margin.**

37. PROVING THEOREM 9.5 Prove the Reflection in Parallel Lines Theorem. **See margin.**

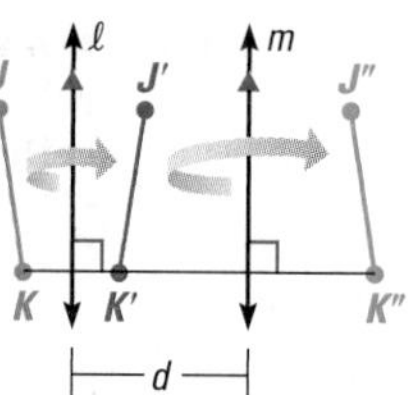

GIVEN ▶ A reflection in line ℓ maps $\overline{JK}$ to $\overline{J'K'}$, a reflection in line m maps $\overline{J'K'}$ to $\overline{J''K''}$, and $\ell \parallel m$.

PROVE ▶ a. $\overleftrightarrow{KK''}$ is perpendicular to ℓ and m.

b. $KK'' = 2d$, where d is the distance between ℓ and m.

38. PROVING THEOREM 9.6 Prove the Reflection in Intersecting Lines Theorem. **See margin.**

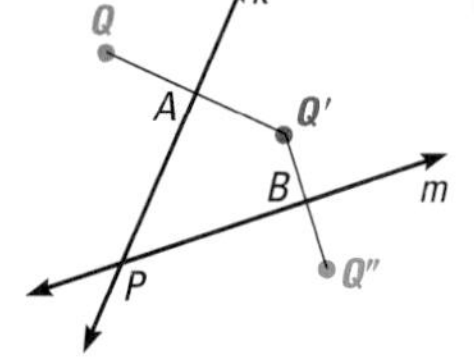

GIVEN ▶ Lines k and m intersect at point P. Q is any point not on k or m.

PROVE ▶ a. If you reflect point Q in k, and then reflect its image Q' in m, Q'' is the image of Q after a rotation about point P.

b. $m\angle QPQ'' = 2(m\angle APB)$

Plan for Proof First show $k \perp \overline{QQ'}$ and $\overline{QA} \cong \overline{Q'A}$. Then show $\triangle QAP \cong \triangle Q'AP$. In the same way, show $\triangle Q'BP \cong \triangle Q''BP$. Use congruent triangles and substitution to show that $\overline{QP} \cong \overline{Q''P}$. That proves part (a) by the definition of a rotation. Then use congruent triangles to prove part (b).

39. VISUAL REASONING You are riding a bicycle along a flat street.

a. What two transformations does the wheel's motion use? **translation and a rotation**

b. *Explain* why this is not a composition of transformations.

★ = STANDARDIZED TEST PRACTICE

41. *Sample answer:* The conjecture is not always true. Consider reflection of point (a, b) in the x-axis followed by a reflection in the line $y = x$.

C **40. MULTI-STEP PROBLEM** A point in space has three coordinates (x, y, z). From the origin, a point can be forward or back on the x-axis, left or right on the y-axis, and up or down on the z-axis. The endpoints of segment $\overline{AB}$ in space are $A(2, 0, 0)$ and $B(2, 3, 0)$, as shown at the right.

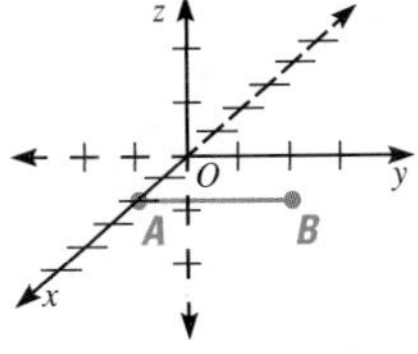

a. Rotate $\overline{AB}$ 90° about the x-axis with center of rotation A. What are the coordinates of $\overline{A'B'}$? **$A'(2, 0, 0)$, $B'(2, 0, 3)$**

b. Translate $\overline{A'B'}$ using the vector $\langle 4, 0, -1\rangle$. What are the coordinates of $\overline{A''B''}$? **$A''(6, 0, -1)$, $B''(6, 0, 2)$**

41. CHALLENGE *Justify* the following conjecture or provide a counterexample.

Conjecture When performing a composition of two transformations of the *same type*, order does not matter.

MIXED REVIEW

Find the unknown side length. Write your answer in simplest radical form. (p. 433)

42.

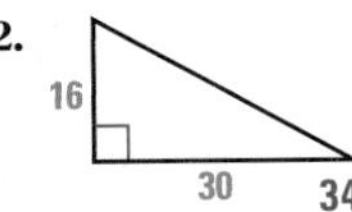

43.

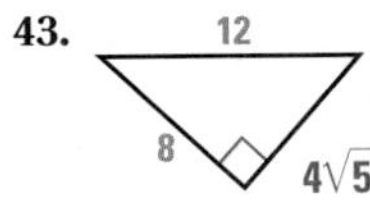

44.

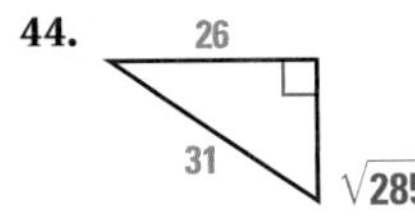

PREVIEW
Prepare for Lesson 9.6 in Exs. 45–48.

The coordinates of $\triangle PQR$ are $P(3, 1)$, $Q(3, 3)$, and $R(6, 1)$. Graph the image of the triangle after the translation. (p. 572) **45–48. See margin.**

45. $(x, y) \to (x + 3, y)$

46. $(x, y) \to (x - 3, y)$

47. $(x, y) \to (x, y + 2)$

48. $(x, y) \to (x + 3, y + 2)$

QUIZ *for Lessons 9.3–9.5*

The vertices of $\triangle ABC$ are $A(7, 1)$, $B(3, 5)$, and $C(10, 7)$. Graph the reflection in the line. (p. 589) **1–3. See margin.**

1. y-axis

2. $x = -4$

3. $y = -x$

Find the coordinates of the image of $P(2, -3)$ after the rotation about the origin. (p. 598)

4. 180° rotation **$(-2, 3)$**

5. 90° rotation **$(3, 2)$**

6. 270° rotation **$(-3, -2)$**

The vertices of $\triangle PQR$ are $P(-8, 8)$, $Q(-5, 0)$, and $R(-1, 3)$. Graph the image of $\triangle PQR$ after a composition of the transformations in the order they are listed. (p. 608) **7–10. See margin.**

7. Translation: $(x, y) \to (x + 6, y)$
Reflection: in the y-axis

8. Reflection: in the line $y = -2$
Rotation: 90° about the origin

9. Translation: $(x, y) \to (x - 5, y)$
Translation: $(x, y) \to (x + 2, y + 7)$

10. Rotation: 180° about the origin
Translation: $(x, y) \to (x + 4, y - 3)$

45–48. See Additional Answers beginning on p. AA1.

5 ASSESS AND RETEACH

Daily Homework Quiz

Transparency Available

1. The endpoints of $\overline{AB}$ are $A(3, 2)$ and $B(1, 4)$. Graph the image of $\overline{AB}$ after the glide reflection.
Translation: $(x, y) \to (x, y - 2)$
Reflection: in the line $x = 1$

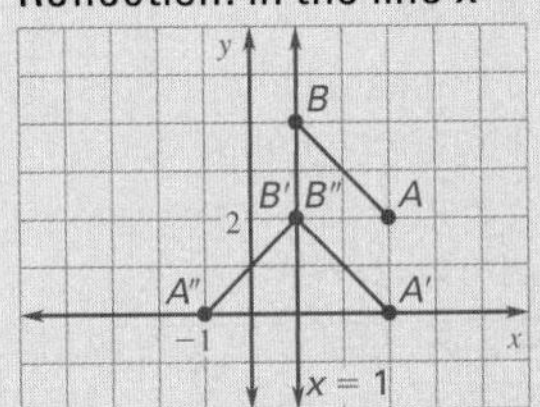

2. The vertices of $\triangle MNK$ are $M(1, 1)$, $N(2, 3)$, and $K(0, 2)$. Graph the image of $\triangle MNK$ after the composition of the reflection followed by the rotation.
Reflection: in the y-axis
Rotation: 180° about the origin

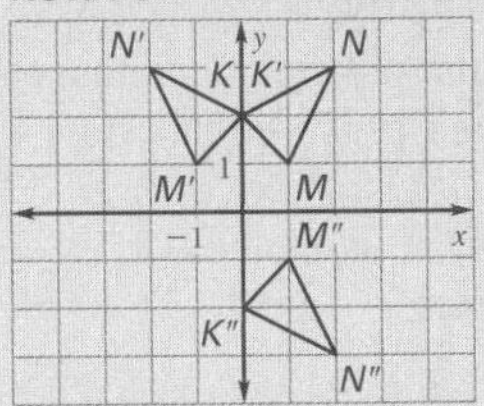

Available at **classzone.com**

Diagnosis/Remediation

- Practice A, B, C in Chapter 9 Resource Book, pp. 62–67
- Study Guide in Chaptor 9 Resource Book, pp. 68–69
- Practice Workbook, pp. 175–177
- @HomeTutor

Challenge

Additional challenge is available in the Chapter 9 Resource Book, p. 72.

Quiz

An easily-readable reduced copy of the quiz (with answers) on Lessons 9.3–9.5 from the Assessment Book can be found on p. 570G.

Quiz 1–3, 7–10. See Additional Answers beginning on p. AA1.

1 PLAN AND PREPARE

Warm-Up Exercises

What is the measure of each interior angle of each regular polygon?

1. equilateral triangle 60°
2. pentagon 108°
3. hexagon 120°
4. octagon 135°
5. Draw a trapezoid and its image for a reflection in one base.

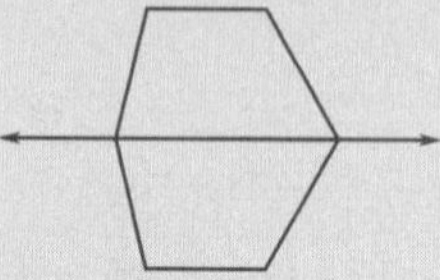

2 FOCUS AND MOTIVATE

Essential Question

Big Idea 2, p. 571

What regular polygons can tessellate a plane? **Tell students they will learn how to answer this question by studying how to make tessellations.**

3 TEACH

Extra Example 1

Does the shape tessellate? If so, tell whether the tessellation is regular.

a. rectangle **yes; not unless the rectangle is a square**

b. regular decagon **no**

c. equilateral triangle **yes; regular**

Extension Tessellations

Use after Lesson 9.5

Key Vocabulary
- **tessellation**

Standards

22.0 Students know the effect of rigid motions on figures in the coordinate plane and space, including rotations, translations, and reflections.

GOAL Make tessellations and discover their properties.

A **tessellation** is a collection of figures that cover a plane with no gaps or overlaps. You can use transformations to make tessellations.

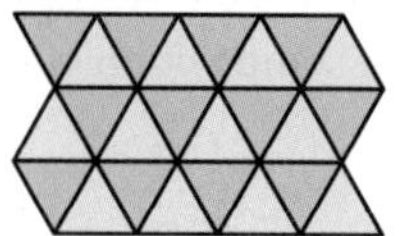

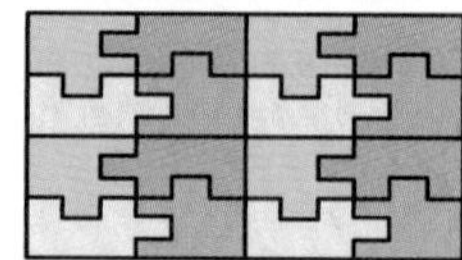

A *regular tessellation* is a tessellation of congruent regular polygons. In the figures above, the tessellation of equilateral triangles is a regular tessellation.

AVOID ERRORS

The sum of the angles surrounding every vertex of a tessellation is 360°. This means that no regular polygon with more than six sides can be used in a *regular* tesssellation.

EXAMPLE 1 Determine whether shapes tessellate

Does the shape tessellate? If so, tell whether the tessellation is regular.

a. Regular octagon

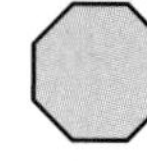

b. Trapezoid

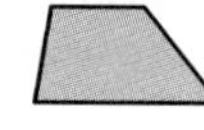

c. Regular hexagon

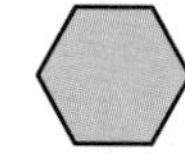

Solution

a. A regular octagon does not tessellate.

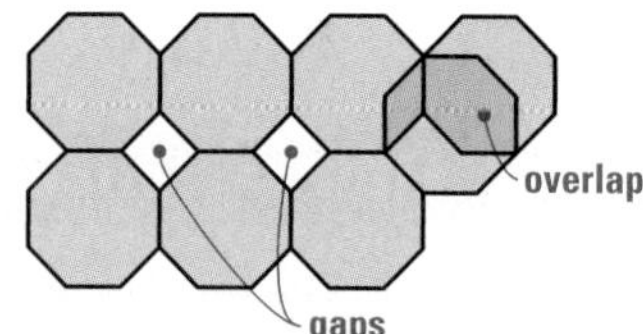

b. The trapezoid tessellates. The tessellation is not regular because the trapezoid is not a regular polygon.

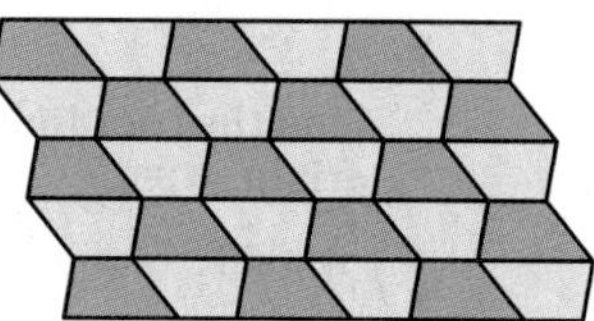

c. A regular hexagon tessellates using translations. The tessellation is regular because it is made of congruent regular hexagons.

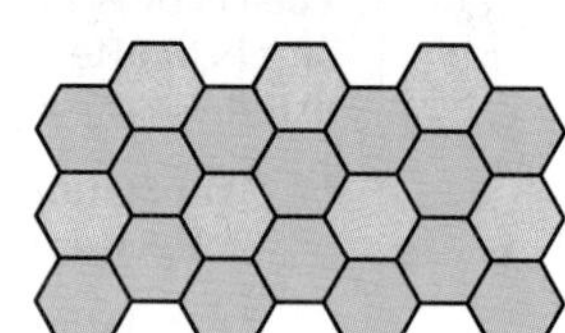

EXAMPLE 2 Draw a tessellation using one shape

Change a triangle to make a tessellation.

Solution

STEP 1

Cut a piece from the triangle.

STEP 2

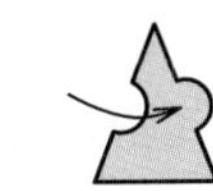

Slide the piece to another side.

STEP 3

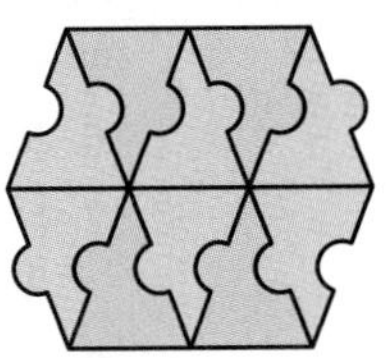

Translate and reflect the figure to make a tessellation.

EXAMPLE 3 Draw a tessellation using two shapes

Draw a tessellation using the given floor tiles.

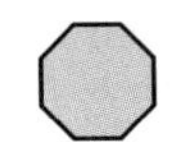 

Solution

STEP 1

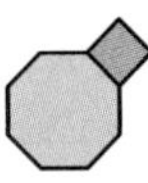

Combine one octagon and one square by connecting sides of the same length.

STEP 2

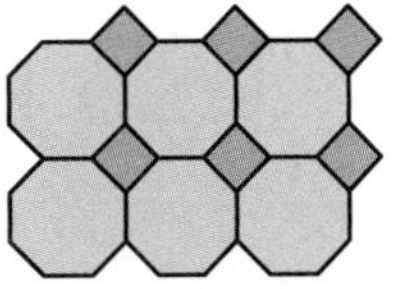

Translate the pair of polygons to make a tessellation

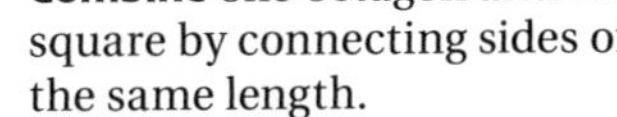

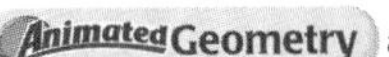

Animated Geometry at classzone.com

READ VOCABULARY

Notice that in the tessellation in Example 3, the same combination of regular polygons meet at each vertex. This type of tessellation is called *semi-regular*.

PRACTICE

EXAMPLE 1 on p. 616 for Exs. 1–4

REGULAR TESSELLATIONS Does the shape tessellate? If so, tell whether the tessellation is regular.

1. Equilateral triangle **yes; regular**

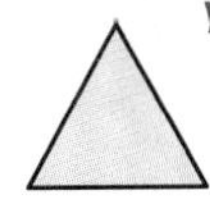

2. Circle **no**

3. Kite **yes; not regular**

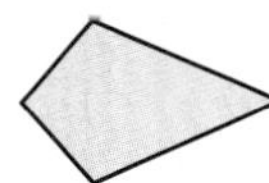

4. ★ **OPEN-ENDED MATH** Draw a rectangle. Use the rectangle to make two different tessellations. **See margin.**

4. *Sample:*

Key Question to Ask for Example 1

- Why can a regular polygon with more than six sides not tessellate a plane? **The measure of each angle will not be a factor of 360°.**

Extra Example 2

Change a quadrilateral to make a tessellation. **Cut a piece from the quadrilateral, slide it to another side, and translate the figure.**

Step 1

Step 2

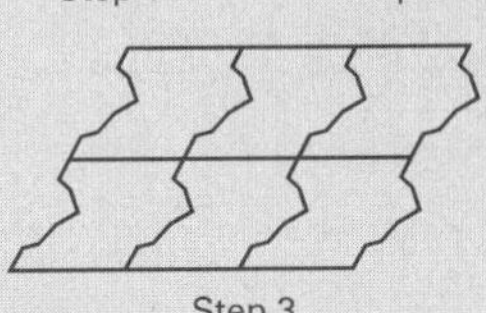

Step 3

Extra Example 3

Draw a tessellation using the given polygons.

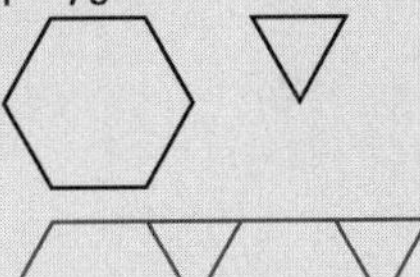

Teaching Strategy

Have the students bring in real world examples of tessellations. For example, floor tile patterns, brick patterns, patio paver stone patterns, and so on. Have students discuss these tessellations in class.

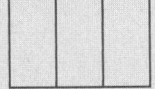

Closing the Lesson

Have students summarize the major points of the lesson and answer the Essential Question: What regular polygons can tessellate a plane?

- **A tessellation is a collection of figures that cover a plane.**
- **A regular tessellation is a tessellation of congruent regular polygons.**

An equilateral triangle, square, and regular hexagon can tessellate a plane.

4 PRACTICE AND APPLY

Study Strategy

Exercises 6–9 Have students make these figures from cardboard or construction paper so they can move the figures around and see the tessellations rather than just trying to visualize them.

6. ***Sample:***

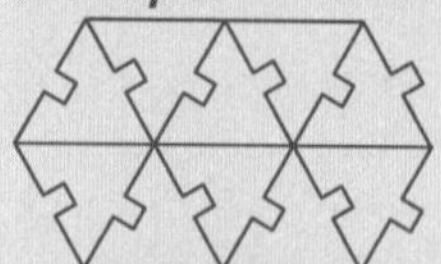

7. ***Sample:***

8. ***Sample:***

9a.

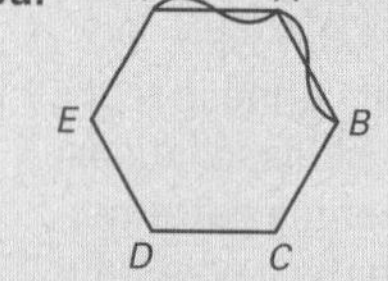

9b.

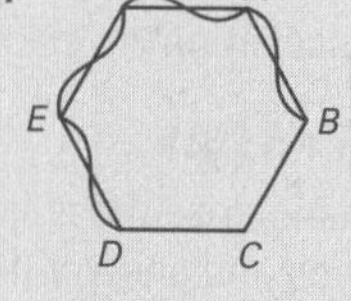

9c.

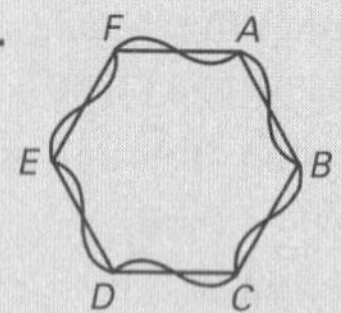

9d.

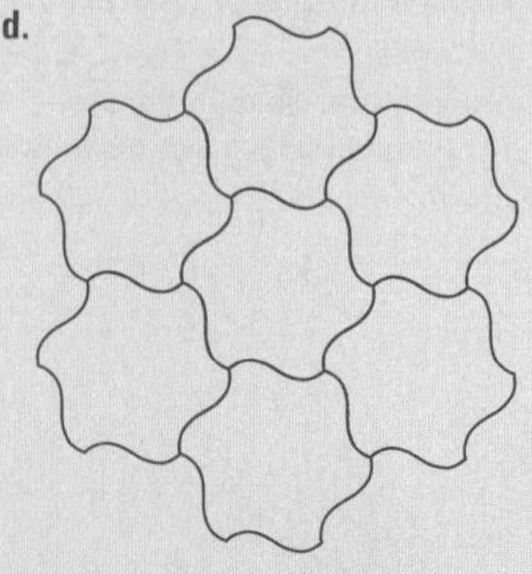

5. MULTI-STEP PROBLEM Choose a tessellation and measure the angles at three vertices.

a. What is the sum of the measures of the angles? What can you conclude? **360°; the sum of the angle measures at any vertex is 360°.**

b. *Explain* how you know that any *quadrilateral* will tessellate. **The sum of the measures of the interior angles is 360°.**

EXAMPLE 2 on p. 617 for Exs. 6–9

DRAWING TESSELLATIONS In Exercises 6–8, use the steps in Example 2 to make a figure that will tessellate. **6–8. See margin.**

6. Make a tessellation using a triangle as the base figure.

7. Make a tessellation using a square as the base figure. Change both pairs of opposite sides.

8. Make a tessellation using a hexagon as the base figure. Change all three pairs of opposite sides.

9. **ROTATION TESSELLATION** Use these steps to make another tessellation based on a regular hexagon $ABCDEF$. **a–d. See margin.**

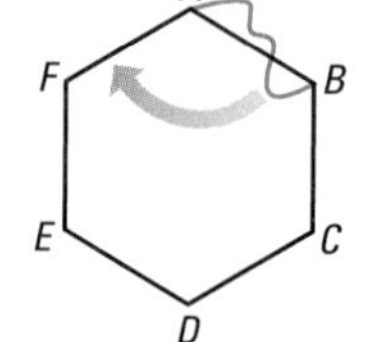

a. Connect points A and B with a curve. Rotate the curve 120° about A so that B coincides with F.

b. Connect points E and F with a curve. Rotate the curve 120° about E so that F coincides with D.

c. Connect points C and D with a curve. Rotate the curve 120° about C so that D coincides with B.

d. Use this figure to draw a tessellation.

EXAMPLE 3 on p. 617 for Exs. 10–12

USING TWO POLYGONS Draw a tessellation using the given polygons. **10–12. See margin.**

10. 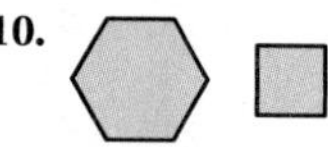 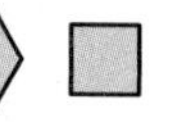

11. 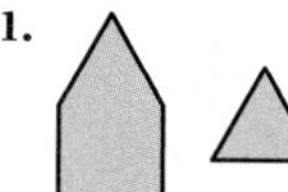

12. 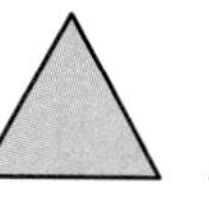 

13. ★ **OPEN-ENDED MATH** Draw a tessellation using three different polygons. **See margin.**

TRANSFORMATIONS ***Describe*** **the transformation(s) used to make the tessellation.**

14. 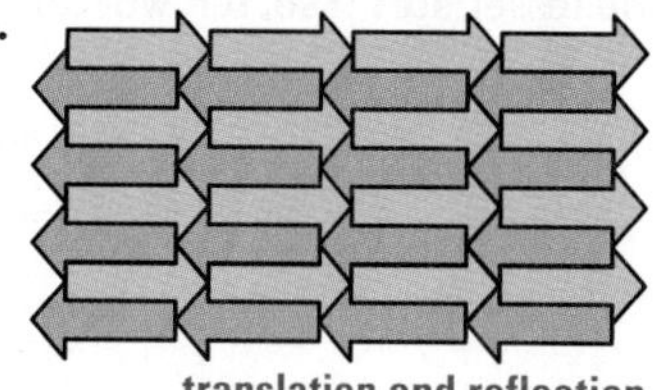

rotation and translation

15. 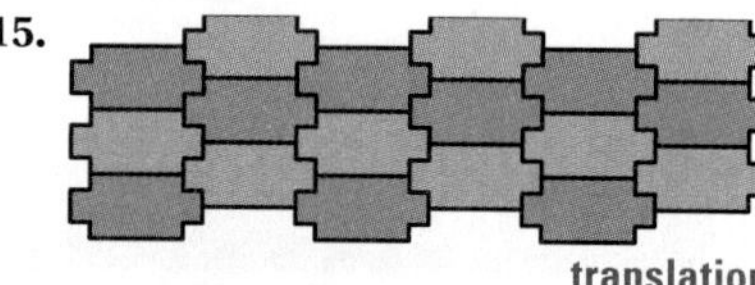

translation

16.

translation and reflection

17. 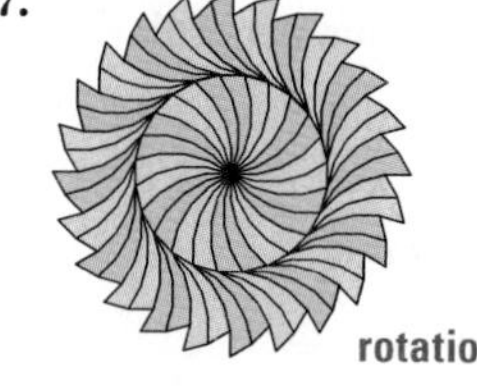

rotation

18. **USING SHAPES** On graph paper, outline a capital H. Use this shape to make a tessellation. What transformations did you use? ***Sample answer:*** **translation and reflection**

10–12. See Additional Answers beginning on p. AA1.

13. ***Sample:***

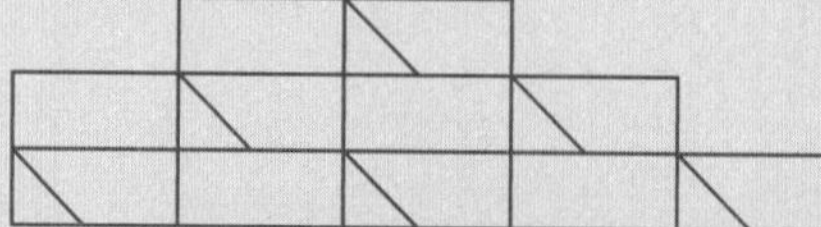

9.6 Identify Symmetry

Before You reflected or rotated figures.
Now You will identify line and rotational symmetries of a figure.
Why? So you can identify the symmetry in a bowl, as in Ex. 11.

Key Vocabulary
- line symmetry
- line of symmetry
- rotational symmetry
- center of symmetry

A figure in the plane has **line symmetry** if the figure can be mapped onto itself by a reflection in a line. This line of reflection is a **line of symmetry**, such as line m at the right. A figure can have more than one line of symmetry.

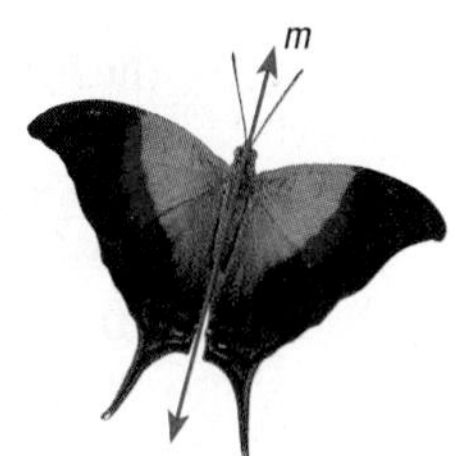

EXAMPLE 1 Identify lines of symmetry

How many lines of symmetry does the hexagon have?

a. 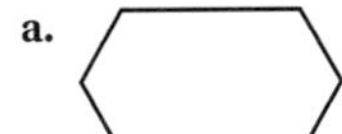 **b.** 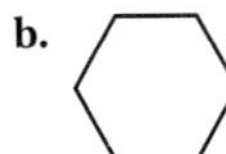 **c.** 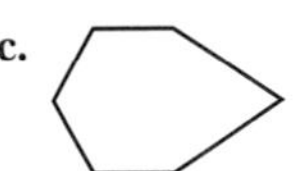

Solution

a. Two lines of symmetry

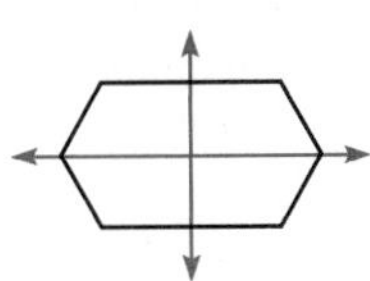

b. Six lines of symmetry

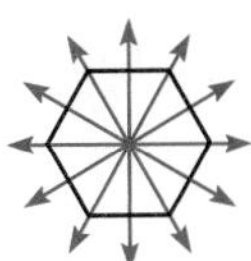

c. One line of symmetry

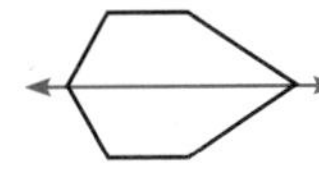

REVIEW REFLECTION
Notice that the lines of symmetry are also lines of reflection.

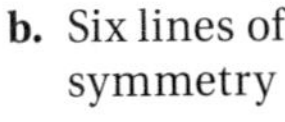

at classzone.com

✓ GUIDED PRACTICE for Example 1

How many lines of symmetry does the object appear to have?

1.  8

2.  5

3.  1

4. Draw a hexagon with no lines of symmetry. **See margin.**

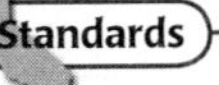

22.0 Students know the effect of rigid motions on figures in the coordinate plane and space, including rotations, translations, **and reflections.**

1 PLAN AND PREPARE

Warm-Up Exercises

Transparency Available

Find the coordinates of the image of $A(-3, 8)$ for each transformation.

1. Reflection in the line $y = x$ **(8, −3)**

2. Rotation of 90° about the origin **(−8, −3)**

3. Translation 4 units down **(−3, 4)**

Notetaking Guide

Transparency Available

Promotes interactive learning and notetaking skills, pp. 244–246.

Pacing

Basic: 1 day
Average: 1 day
Advanced: 1 day
Block: 0.5 block with 9.7
- See *Teaching Guide/Lesson Plan.*

2 FOCUS AND MOTIVATE

Essential Question

Big Idea 2, p. 571

When does a figure have line symmetry? **Tell students they will learn how to answer this question by studying how to draw symmetry lines.**

4. See Additional Answers beginning on p. AA1.

Resource Planning Guide

Chapter Resource Book
- Teaching Guide/Lesson Plan (pp. 73–74)
- Activity Master (p. 75)
- Practice levels A, B, C (pp. 76–81)
- Study Guide (pp. 82–83)
- Catch-up for Absent Students (p. 84)
- Application (p. 85)
- Challenge (p. 86)

Workbooks
- Notetaking Guide (pp. 244–246)
- Practice Workbook (pp. 178–180)

Teaching Options
- **Power Presentations CD-ROM** provides dynamic electronic teaching resources for the classroom.
- **Activity Generator CD-ROM** provides editable activities for all ability levels.

Interactive Technology
- Easy Planner
- Power Presentations CD-ROM
- Activity Generator CD-ROM
- Animated Geometry
- Test Generator CD-ROM
- Online Quiz
- eWorkbook
- eEdition
- @HomeTutor

Resources for English Learners
- Quick Reference for English Learners
- Spanish Study Guide
- Multi-Language Visual Glossary
- Student Resources in Spanish

See also the *Geometry Toolkit* for more strategies for meeting individual needs.

Motivating the Lesson

Tell students that artists use symmetry to create designs. Tell them that in this lesson they will study line symmetry and rotational symmetry of various figures.

3 TEACH

Extra Example 1

How many lines of symmetry does each octagon have?

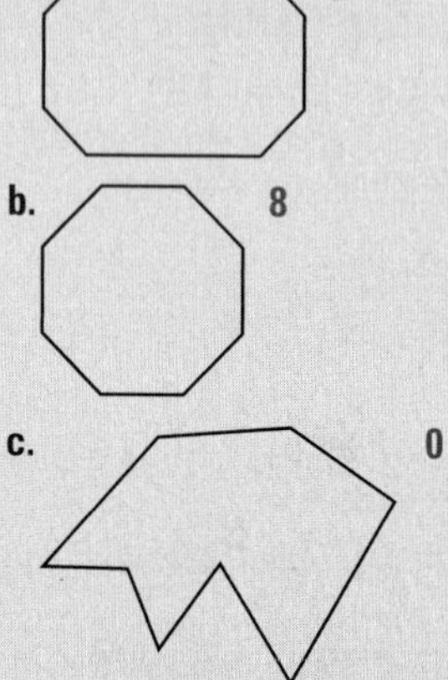

c. 0

Key Question to Ask for Example 1

- How many lines of symmetry will a regular polygon with n sides have? Describe them. **It will have n symmetry lines. If n is even, then half of them will be perpendicular bisectors of a pair of sides and the others will pass through a pair of vertices. If n is odd, then the lines of symmetry will be the perpendicular bisectors of the sides.**

An **Animated Geometry** activity is available on-line for **Example 1**. This activity is also available on the **Power Presentations CD-ROM**.

ROTATIONAL SYMMETRY A figure in a plane has **rotational symmetry** if the figure can be mapped onto itself by a rotation of 180° or less about the center of the figure. This point is the **center of symmetry**. Note that the rotation can be either clockwise or counterclockwise.

REVIEW ROTATION
For a figure with rotational symmetry, the *angle of rotation* is the smallest angle that maps the figure onto itself.

For example, the figure below has rotational symmetry, because a rotation of either 90° or 180° maps the figure onto itself (although a rotation of 45° does not).

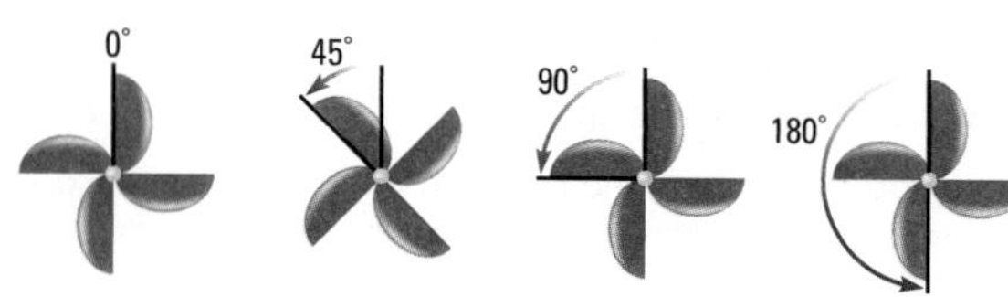

The figure above also has *point symmetry*, which is 180° rotational symmetry.

EXAMPLE 2 Identify rotational symmetry

Does the figure have rotational symmetry? If so, describe any rotations that map the figure onto itself.

a. Parallelogram

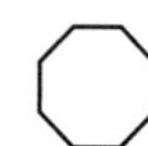

b. Regular octagon

c. Trapezoid

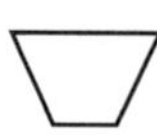

Solution

a. The parallelogram has rotational symmetry. The center is the intersection of the diagonals. A 180° rotation about the center maps the parallelogram onto itself.

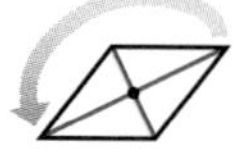

b. The regular octagon has rotational symmetry. The center is the intersection of the diagonals. Rotations of 45°, 90°, 135°, or 180° about the center all map the octagon onto itself.

c. The trapezoid does not have rotational symmetry because no rotation of 180° or less maps the trapezoid onto itself.

GUIDED PRACTICE for Example 2

Does the figure have rotational symmetry? If so, *describe* any rotations that map the figure onto itself.

5. Rhombus **yes; 180° about the center**

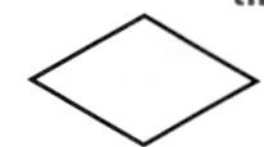

6. Octagon **yes; 90° or 180° about the center**

7. Right triangle **no**

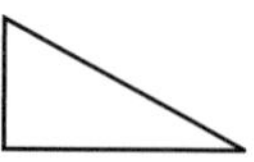

 **EXAMPLE 3** Standardized Test Practice

Identify the line symmetry and rotational symmetry of the equilateral triangle at the right.

Ⓐ 3 lines of symmetry, 60° rotational symmetry

Ⓑ 3 lines of symmetry, 120° rotational symmetry

Ⓒ 1 line of symmetry, 180° rotational symmetry

Ⓓ 1 line of symmetry, no rotational symmetry

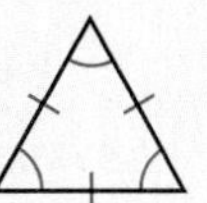

Solution

ELIMINATE CHOICES
An equilateral triangle can be mapped onto itself by reflecting over any of three different lines. So, you can eliminate choices C and D.

The triangle has line symmetry. Three lines of symmetry can be drawn for the figure.

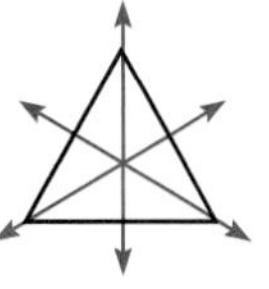

For a figure with s lines of symmetry, the smallest rotation that maps the figure onto itself has the measure $\frac{360°}{s}$. So, the equilateral triangle has $\frac{360°}{3}$, or 120° rotational symmetry.

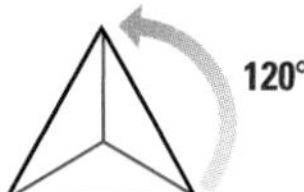

▶ The correct answer is B. 

 **GUIDED PRACTICE** for Example 3

8. *Describe* the lines of symmetry and rotational symmetry of a non-equilateral isosceles triangle.
the altitude, no rotational symmetry

9.6 EXERCISES

HOMEWORK KEY
○ = **WORKED-OUT SOLUTIONS** on p. WS12 for Exs. 7, 13, and 31
★ = **STANDARDIZED TEST PRACTICE** Exs. 2, 13, 14, 21, and 23

SKILL PRACTICE

1. **VOCABULARY** What is a *center of symmetry*?
If a figure has rotational symmetry it is the point about which the figure is rotated.

2. ★ **WRITING** Draw a figure that has one line of symmetry and does not have rotational symmetry. Can a figure have two lines of symmetry and no rotational symmetry? **See margin for art; no.**

EXAMPLE 1 on p. 619 for Exs. 3–5

LINE SYMMETRY **How many lines of symmetry does the triangle have?**

3. 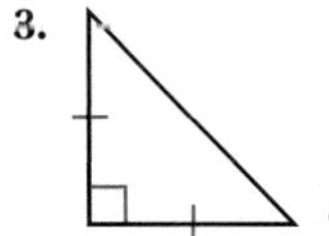 **1**

4. 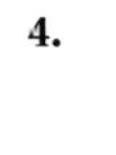 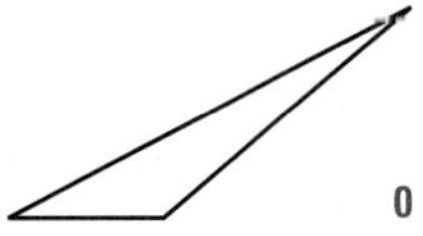 **0**

5. 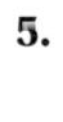 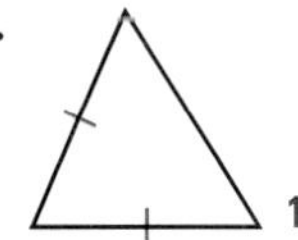 **1**

Differentiated Instruction

Kinesthetic Learners Have students work with a partner to find an object in the classroom that has both line symmetry and rotational symmetry. Have them determine how many lines of symmetry the object has and what the angle of rotation is. Invite pairs of students to describe their findings to the class.

See also the *Geometry Toolkit* for more strategies.

2. *Sample:* 

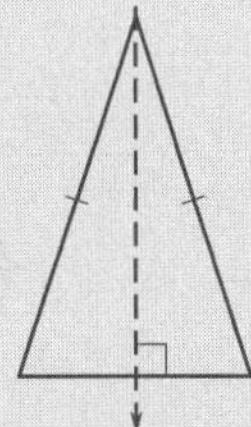

Extra Example 2

Does the figure have rotational symmetry? If so, describe the rotations that map the figure onto itself.

a. rectangle

yes, 180° about the intersection of the diagonals

b. regular hexagon

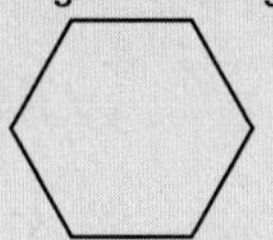

yes, 60°, 120°, 180° about the center

c. kite **no**

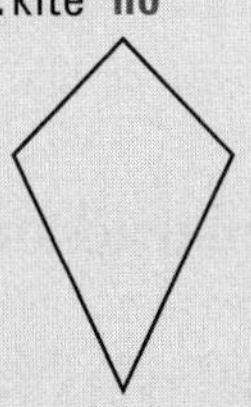

Extra Example 3

Identify the line symmetry and rotational symmetry of the square shown. **A**

Ⓐ 4 lines of symmetry, 90° rotational symmetry

Ⓑ 4 lines of symmetry, 45° rotational symmetry

Ⓒ 2 lines of symmetry, 90° rotational symmetry

Ⓓ 2 lines of symmetry, no rotational symmetry

Closing the Lesson

Have students summarize the major points of the lesson and answer the Essential Question: When does a figure have line symmetry?

- **A line of symmetry for a figure is a line in which you can reflect the figure to map it onto itself.**
- **A figure has rotational symmetry if it can be mapped onto itself by a rotation of 180° or less about the center of the figure.**

A figure has line symmetry when it can be mapped onto itself by a reflection in a line.

4 PRACTICE AND APPLY

Assignment Guide

Answer Transparencies available for all exercises

Basic:
Day 1: pp. 621–624
Exs. 1–8, 10–18, 27–32, 37–45

Average:
Day 1: pp. 621–624
Exs. 1, 2, 4, 5, 7–16, 19–23, 28–35, 37–45 odd

Advanced:
Day 1: pp. 621–624
Exs. 1, 2, 4, 5, 8–14, 19–26*, 29–36*, 38–44 even

Block:
pp. 621–624
Exs. 1, 2, 4, 5, 7–16, 19–23, 28–35, 37–45 odd (with 9.7)

Differentiated Instruction

See *Geometry Best Practices Toolkit* for suggestions on addressing the needs of a diverse classroom.

Homework Check

For a quick check of student understanding of key concepts, go over the following exercises:

Basic: 3, 6, 10, 17, 28
Average: 4, 8, 11, 20, 29
Advanced: 5, 9, 12, 20, 30

Extra Practice

- Student Edition, p. 913
- Chapter 9 Resource Book: Practice levels A, B, C, pp. 76–81

Practice Worksheet

An easily-readable reduced practice page (with answers) for this lesson can be found on p. 570C.

11. Line symmetry, rotational symmetry; there are four lines of symmetry, two passing through the outer opposite pairs of leaves and two passing through the inner opposite pairs of leaves; 90° or 180° about the center.

EXAMPLE 2 on p. 620 for Exs. 6–9

ROTATIONAL SYMMETRY Does the figure have rotational symmetry? If so, *describe* any rotations that map the figure onto itself.

6.

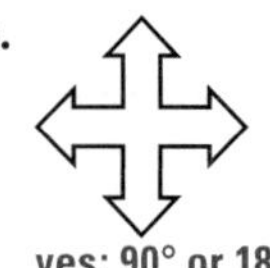

yes; 90° or 180° about the center

7. **8.**

yes; 72° or 144° about the center

yes; 45°, 90°, 135°, or 180° about the center

9. **no**

EXAMPLE 3 on p. 621 for Exs. 10–16

SYMMETRY Determine whether the figure has *line symmetry* and whether it has *rotational symmetry.* Identify all lines of symmetry and angles of rotation that map the figure onto itself.

10.

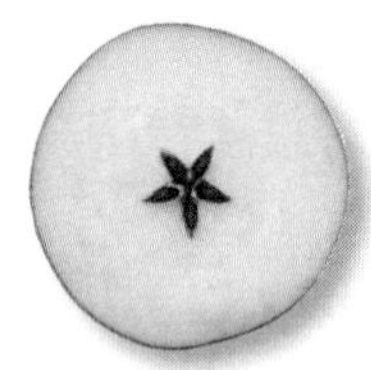

11. **See margin.**

12.

10. Line symmetry, rotational symmetry; the 5 lines of symmetry run through the center of each seed; 72° or 144° about the center.

12. Line symmetry, no rotational symmetry; the line of symmetry runs through the violin between the 2 center strings.

13. ★ **MULTIPLE CHOICE** Identify the line symmetry and rotational symmetry of the figure at the right. **C**

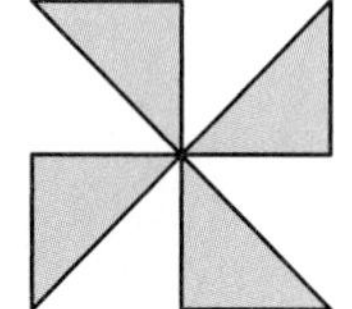

Ⓐ 1 line of symmetry, no rotational symmetry
Ⓑ 1 line of symmetry, 180° rotational symmetry
Ⓒ No lines of symmetry, 90° rotational symmetry
Ⓓ No lines of symmetry, no rotational symmetry

14. ★ **MULTIPLE CHOICE** Which statement best describes the rotational symmetry of a square? **D**

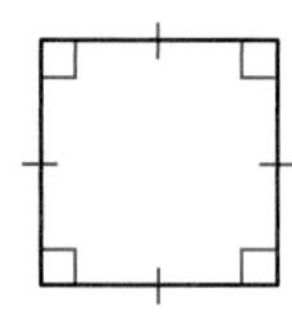

Ⓐ The square has no rotational symmetry.
Ⓑ The square has 90° rotational symmetry.
Ⓒ The square has point symmetry.
Ⓓ Both B and C are correct.

ERROR ANALYSIS *Describe* and correct the error made in describing the symmetry of the figure.

15.

The figure has 1 line of symmetry and 180° rotational symmetry.

16.

The figure has 1 line of symmetry and 180° rotational symmetry.

15. There is no rotational symmetry; the figure has 1 line of symmetry but no rotational symmetry.

16. There are 2 lines of symmetry; the figure has 2 lines of symmetry and 180° rotational symmetry.

B

DRAWING FIGURES In Exercises 17–20, use the description to draw a figure. If not possible, write *not possible.*

17. A quadrilateral with no line of symmetry **See margin.**

18. An octagon with exactly two lines of symmetry **not possible**

19. A hexagon with no point symmetry **See margin.**

20. A trapezoid with rotational symmetry **not possible**

○ = WORKED-OUT SOLUTIONS on p. WS1 ★ = STANDARDIZED TEST PRACTICE

17. *Sample:*

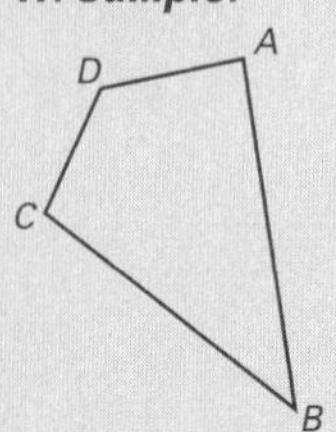

19. *Sample:*

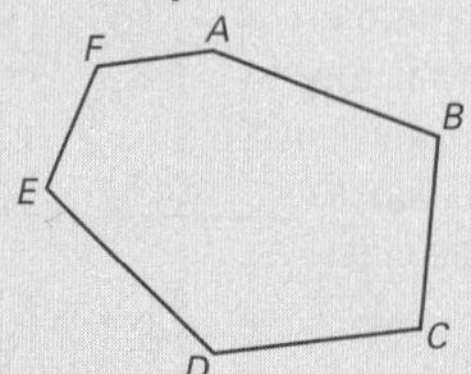

21. ★ **OPEN-ENDED MATH** Draw a polygon with 180° rotational symmetry and with exactly two lines of symmetry. **See margin.**

22. **POINT SYMMETRY** In the graph, $\overline{AB}$ is reflected in the point C to produce the image $\overline{A'B'}$. To make a reflection in a point C for each point N on the preimage, locate N' so that $N'C = NC$ and N' is on $\overleftrightarrow{NC}$. *Explain* what kind of rotation would produce the same image. What kind of symmetry does quadrilateral $AB'A'B$ have?
a rotation of 180° about *C*; rotational symmetry of 180°

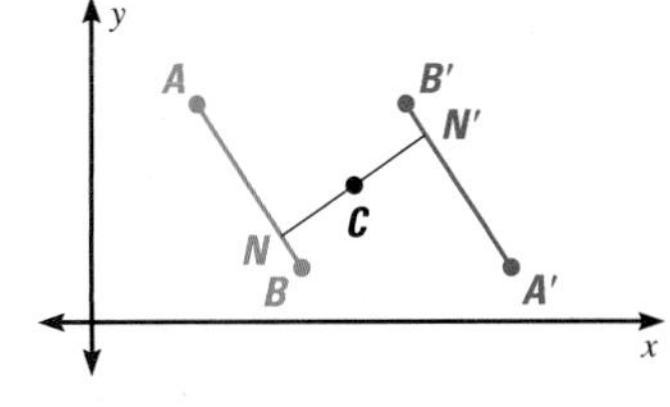

23. ★ **SHORT RESPONSE** A figure has more than one line of symmetry. Can two of the lines of symmetry be parallel? *Explain.*

C 24. **REASONING** How many lines of symmetry does a circle have? How many angles of rotational symmetry does a circle have? *Explain.* **See margin.**

25. **VISUAL REASONING** How many planes of symmetry does a cube have? **5 planes**

26. **CHALLENGE** What can you say about the rotational symmetry of a regular polygon with n sides? *Explain.*
The regular polygon would have rotational symmetry about the center of the *n*-gon and the smallest angle of rotation would be $\frac{360°}{n}$.

3. No; what's n the left and ight of the first ine would ave to be the same as what's n the left and ight of the second line which is not possible.

PROBLEM SOLVING

EXAMPLES A
1 and 2
on pp. 619–620 for Exs. 27–30

WORDS Identify the line symmetry and rotational symmetry (if any) of each word.

27. MOW 28. RADAR 29. OHIO 30. pod

No line symmetry, it has rotational symmetry of 180° about the center of o.

@HomeTutor for problem solving help at classzone.com

27. No line symmetry, rotational symmetry of 180° about the center of the letter O.

28. No line symmetry, no rotational symmetry

29. It has a line of symmetry passing horizontally through the center of each O, no rotational symmetry.

KALEIDOSCOPES In Exercises 31–33, use the following information about kaleidoscopes.

Inside a kaleidoscope, two mirrors are placed next to each other to form a V, as shown at the right. The angle between the mirrors determines the number of lines of symmetry in the image. Use the formula $n(m\angle 1) = 180°$ to find the measure of $\angle 1$ between the mirrors or the number n of lines of symmetry in the image.

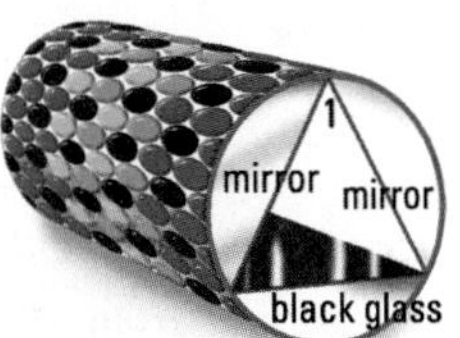

B **Calculate the angle at which the mirrors must be placed for the image of a kaleidoscope to make the design shown.**

(31.)

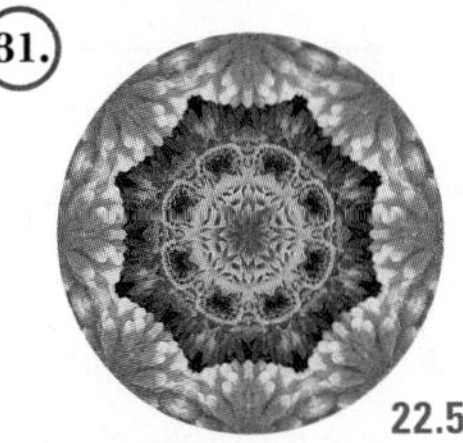

22.5°

32.

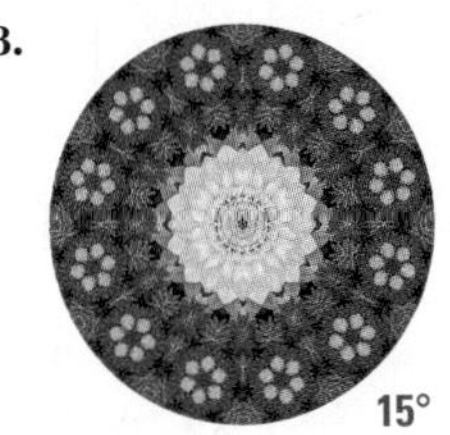

30°

33.

15°

@HomeTutor for problem solving help at classzone.com

Avoiding Common Errors

Exercise 9 Students may think this figure can be rotated 180° onto itself. Have them copy it onto tracing paper and rotate it so they can see the image does not match the original figure.

Mathematical Reasoning

Exercise 25 Challenge students to devise models to illustrate the planes of symmetry of a cube.

Exercise 35 More information about the Castillo de San Marcos can be found at www.nps.gov/casa

21. ***Sample:***

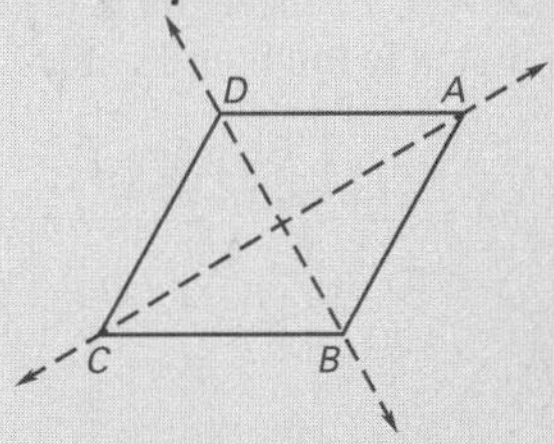

24. Infinitely many; infinitely many; any line passing through the center of the circle is a line of symmetry and any rotation about the center is rotational symmetry. There are an infinite number in both cases.

5 ASSESS AND RETEACH

Daily Homework Quiz

Transparency Available

How many lines of symmetry does each figure have?

1. a rhombus that is not a square **2**

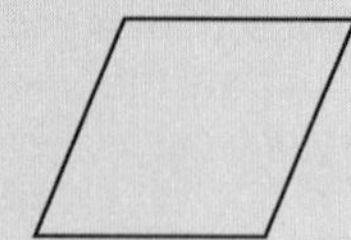

2. equilateral triangle **3**

Does the figure have rotational symmetry? If so, describe the rotations that map the figure onto itself.

3. **yes; 72°, 144°**

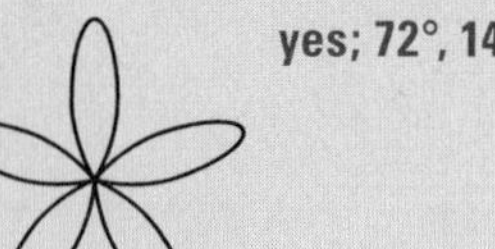

4. **no**

Online Quiz

Available at **classzone.com**

Diagnosis/Remediation

- Practice A, B, C in Chapter 9 Resource Book, pp. 76–81
- Study Guide in Chapter 9 Resource Book, pp. 82–83
- Practice Workbook, pp. 178–180
- @HomeTutor

Challenge

Additional challenge is available in the Chapter 9 Resource Book, p. 86.

34. The molecules are reflections of each other; one is a mirror image of the other.

34. **CHEMISTRY** The diagram at the right shows two forms of the amino acid *alanine*. One form is laevo-alanine and the other is dextro-alanine. How are the structures of these two molecules related? *Explain.*

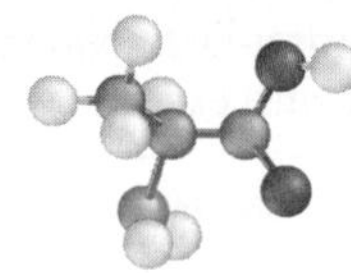

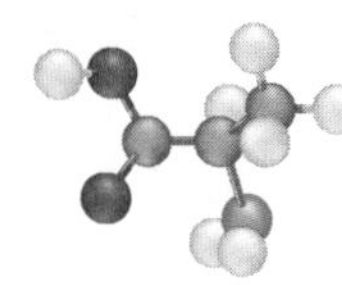

35. **MULTI-STEP PROBLEM** The *Castillo de San Marcos* in St. Augustine, Florida, has the shape shown.

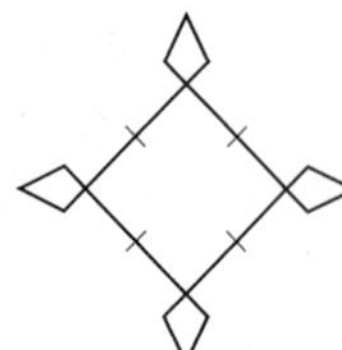

a. What kind(s) of symmetry does the shape of the building show? **line symmetry and rotational symmetry**

b. Imagine the building on a three-dimensional coordinate system. Copy and complete the following statement: The lines of symmetry in part (a) are now described as _?_ of symmetry and the rotational symmetry about the center is now described as rotational symmetry about the _?_. **planes, z-axis**

36. Translation, rotation; the left spiral is counter-clockwise rotation and the right spiral is clockwise rotation.

C 36. **CHALLENGE** Spirals have a type of symmetry called spiral, or helical, symmetry. *Describe* the two transformations involved in a spiral staircase. Then *explain* the difference in transformations between the two staircases at the right.

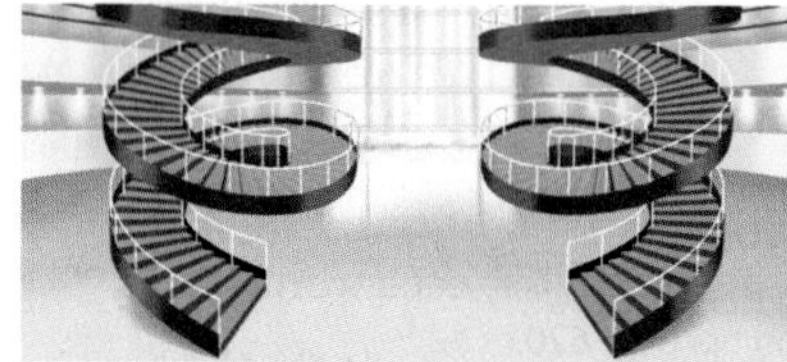

MIXED REVIEW

PREVIEW Prepare for Lesson 9.7 in Exs. 37–39.

Solve the proportion. *(p. 356)*

37. $\frac{5}{x} = \frac{15}{27}$ **9**

38. $\frac{a+4}{7} = \frac{49}{56}$ **$\frac{17}{8}$**

39. $\frac{5}{2b-3} = \frac{1}{3b+1}$ **$-\frac{8}{13}$**

Determine whether the dilation from Figure A to Figure B is a *reduction* or an *enlargement*. Then find its scale factor. *(p. 409)*

40.

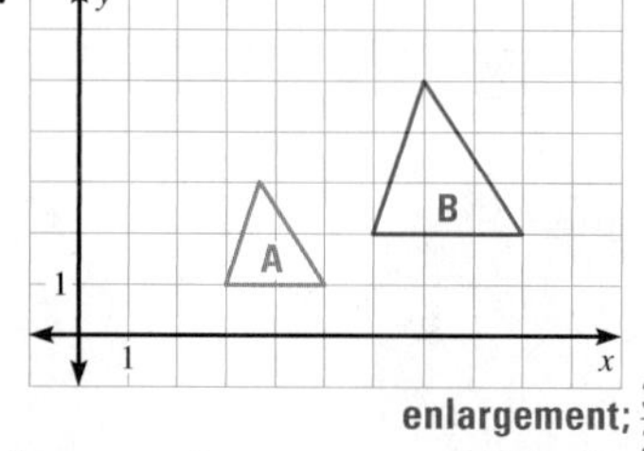

enlargement; $\frac{3}{2}$

41.

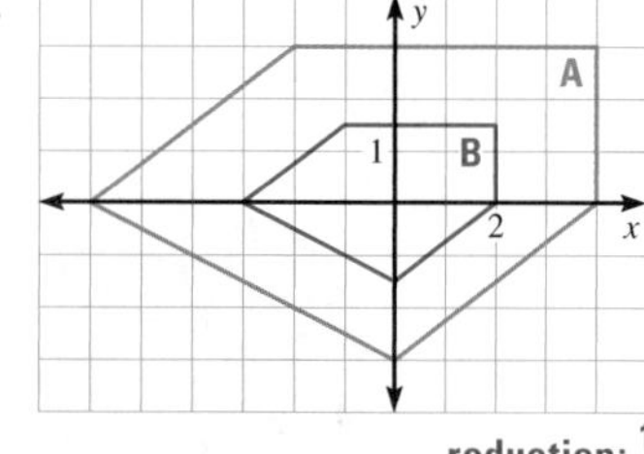

reduction; $\frac{1}{2}$

Write a matrix to represent the given polygon. *(p. 580)* **42–45. See margin.**

42. Triangle A in Exercise 40

43. Triangle B in Exercise 40

44. Pentagon A in Exercise 41

45. Pentagon B in Exercise 41

42–45. Sample answers are given.

42. $\begin{bmatrix} 3 & \frac{11}{3} & 5 \\ 1 & 3 & 1 \end{bmatrix}$

43. $\begin{bmatrix} 6 & 7 & 9 \\ 2 & 5 & 2 \end{bmatrix}$

44. $\begin{bmatrix} 4 & 4 & -2 & -6 & 0 \\ 0 & 3 & 3 & 0 & -3 \end{bmatrix}$

45. $\begin{bmatrix} 2 & 2 & -1 & -3 & 0 \\ 0 & 1.5 & 1.5 & 0 & -1.5 \end{bmatrix}$

9.7 Investigate Dilations

MATERIALS • straightedge • compass • ruler

Standards

16.0 Students perform basic constructions with a straightedge and compass, such as angle bisectors, perpendicular bisectors, and the line parallel to a given line through a point off the line.

5.0 Students prove that triangles are congruent or **similar, and they are able to use the concept of corresponding parts** of congruent triangles.

QUESTION **How do you construct a dilation of a figure?**

Recall from Lesson 6.7 that a dilation enlarges or reduces a figure to make a similar figure. You can use construction tools to make enlargement dilations.

EXPLORE **Construct an enlargement dilation**

Use a compass and straightedge to construct a dilation of $\triangle PQR$ with a scale factor of 2, using a point C outside the triangle as the center of dilation.

STEP 1

Draw a triangle Draw $\triangle PQR$ and choose the center of the dilation C outside the triangle. Draw lines from C through the vertices of the triangle.

STEP 2

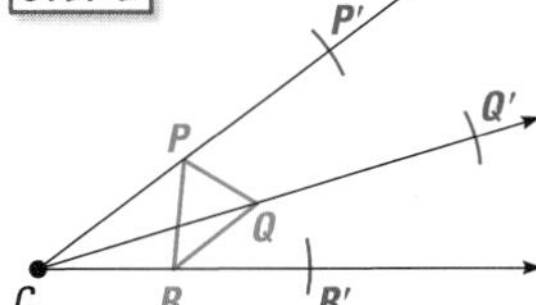

Use a compass Use a compass to locate P' on $\overrightarrow{CP}$ so that $CP' = 2(CP)$. Locate Q' and R' in the same way.

STEP 3

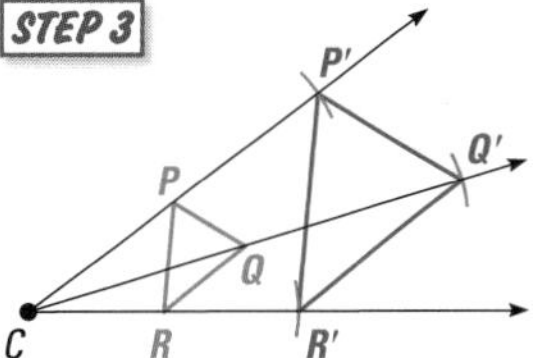

Connect points Connect points P', Q', and R' to form $\triangle P'Q'R'$.

DRAW CONCLUSIONS **Use your observations to complete these exercises**

1. Find the ratios of corresponding side lengths of $\triangle PQR$ and $\triangle P'Q'R'$. Are the triangles similar? *Explain.* $\frac{1}{2}$; **yes; use the SSS Similarity Theorem.**
2. Draw $\triangle DEF$. Use a compass and straightedge to construct a dilation with a scale factor of 3, using point D on the triangle as the center of dilation. **See margin.**
3. Find the ratios of corresponding side lengths of $\triangle DEF$ and $\triangle D'E'F'$. Are the triangles similar? *Explain.* $\frac{1}{3}$; **yes; use the SSS Similarity Theorem.**
4. Draw $\triangle JKL$. Use a compass and straightedge to construct a dilation with a scale factor of 2, using a point A inside the triangle as the center of dilation. **See margin.**
5. Find the ratios of corresponding side lengths of $\triangle JKL$ and $\triangle J'K'L'$. Are the triangles similar? *Explain.* $\frac{1}{2}$; **yes; use the SSS Similarity Theorem.**
6. What can you conclude about the corresponding angle measures of a triangle and an enlargement dilation of the triangle? **The measures of corresponding angles are the same.**

2, 4. See Additional Answers beginning on p. AA1.

1 PLAN AND PREPARE

Explore the Concept

- Students will construct a dilation of a figure.
- This activity leads into the study of drawing a dilation in Example 2 in Lesson 9.7.

Materials

Each student will need:

- compass
- ruler
- straightedge

Recommended Time

Work activity: 10 min
Discuss results: 5 min

Grouping

Students should work individually.

2 TEACH

Tips for Success

Have students use their compasses rather than their rulers to locate point P'.

Key Question

- What other scale factors would it be easy to use with this method? **whole numbers greater than 2**

Alternative Strategy

Have the students use a computer with geometry software to complete this activity.

Key Discovery

A dilation can be constructed by drawing lines through the vertices from a given point and multiplying distances by the scale factor.

3 ASSESS AND RETEACH

Show an example of dilating a triangle with scale factor 4. Explain your work. **Check students' work.**

1 PLAN AND PREPARE

Warm-Up Exercises

Transparency Available

If $\triangle ABC \sim \triangle DEF$, find each value.

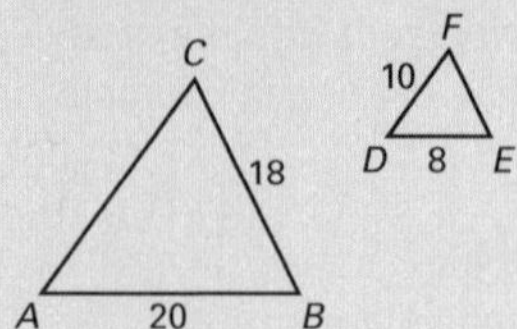

1. EF $\frac{36}{5}$
2. AC 25
3. scale factor $\frac{5}{2}$

Notetaking Guide

Transparency Available

Promotes interactive learning and notetaking skills, pp. 247–250.

Pacing

Basic: 1 day
Average: 1 day
Advanced: 1 day
Block: 0.5 block with 9.6
• See *Teaching Guide/Lesson Plan.*

2 FOCUS AND MOTIVATE

Essential Question

Big Idea 1, p. 571

How do you use matrices to draw a dilation? **Tell students they will learn how to answer this question by studying how to use matrices to find the coordinates of the image of a dilation.**

9.7 Identify and Perform Dilations

Before You used a coordinate rule to draw a dilation.
Now You will use drawing tools and matrices to draw dilations.
Why? So you can determine the scale factor of a photo, as in Ex. 37.

Key Vocabulary
• **scalar multiplication**
• **dilation,** *p. 409*
• **reduction,** *p. 409*
• **enlargement,** *p. 409*

Standards
Enrichment Topic; not required by California Standards.

Recall from Lesson 6.7 that a dilation is a transformation in which the original figure and its image are similar.

A dilation with center C and scale factor k maps every point P in a figure to a point P' so that one of the following statements is true:

• If P is not the center point C, then the image point P' lies on $\overrightarrow{CP}$. The scale factor k is a positive number such that $k = \frac{CP'}{CP}$ and $k \neq 1$, or

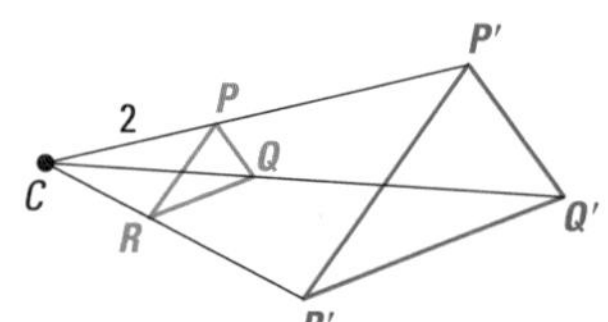

• If P is the center point C, then $P = P'$.

As you learned in Lesson 6.7, the dilation is a *reduction* if $0 < k < 1$ and it is an *enlargement* if $k > 1$.

EXAMPLE 1 Identify dilations

Find the scale factor of the dilation. Then tell whether the dilation is a *reduction* or an *enlargement*.

a.

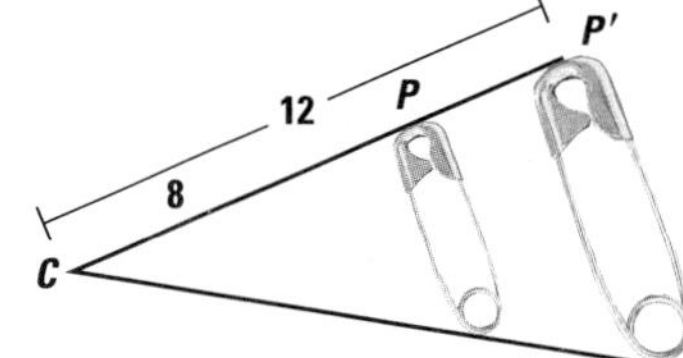

b.

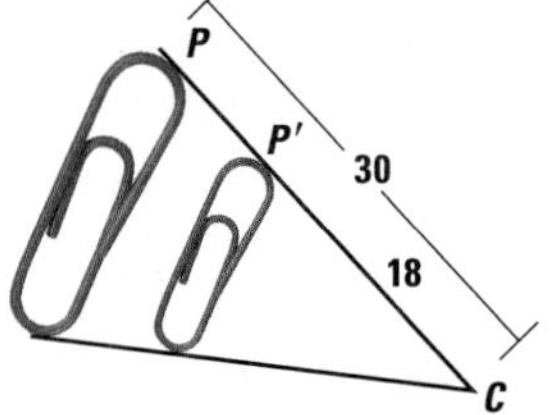

Solution

a. Because $\frac{CP'}{CP} = \frac{12}{8}$, the scale factor is $k = \frac{3}{2}$. The image P' is an enlargement.

b. Because $\frac{CP'}{CP} = \frac{18}{30}$, the scale factor is $k = \frac{3}{5}$. The image P' is a reduction.

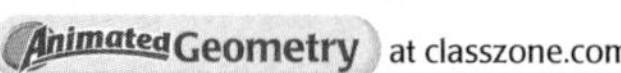

at classzone.com

Resource Planning Guide

Chapter Resource Book
• Teaching Guide/Lesson Plan (pp. 87–88)
• Practice levels A, B, C (pp. 90–95)
• Study Guide (pp. 96–97)
• Catch-up for Absent Students (p. 98)
• Problem Solving Workshop (p. 99)
• Challenge (p. 100)

Workbooks
• Notetaking Guide (pp. 247–250)
• Practice Workbook (pp. 181–183)

Teaching Options
• **Power Presentations CD-ROM** provides dynamic electronic teaching resources for the classroom.
• **Activity Generator CD-ROM** provides editable activities for all ability levels.

Interactive Technology
• Easy Planner
• Power Presentations CD-ROM
• Activity Generator CD-ROM
• Animated Geometry
• Test Generator CD-ROM
• Online Quiz
• eWorkbook
• eEdition
• @HomeTutor

Resources for English Learners
• Quick Reference for English Learners
• Spanish Study Guide
• Multi-Language Visual Glossary
• Student Resources in Spanish

See also the *Geometry Toolkit* for more strategies for meeting individual needs.

EXAMPLE 2 Draw a dilation

Draw and label ▱*DEFG*. Then construct a dilation of ▱*DEFG* with point *D* as the center of dilation and a scale factor of 2.

Solution

STEP 1

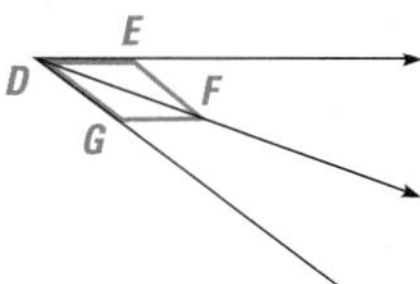

Draw *DEFG*. Draw rays from *D* through vertices *E*, *F*, and *G*.

STEP 2

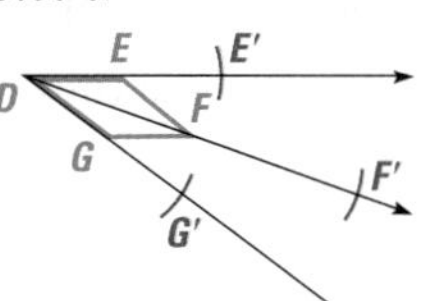

Open the compass to the length of $\overline{DE}$. Locate *E'* on $\overrightarrow{DE}$ so $DE' = 2(DE)$. Locate *F'* and *G'* the same way.

STEP 3

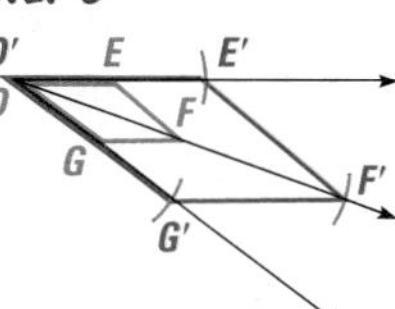

Add a second label *D'* to point *D*. Draw the sides of *D'E'F'G'*.

GUIDED PRACTICE for Examples 1 and 2

1. In a dilation, $CP' = 3$ and $CP = 12$. Tell whether the dilation is a *reduction* or an *enlargement* and find its scale factor. **reduction, $\frac{1}{4}$**
2. Draw and label △*RST*. Then construct a dilation of △*RST* with *R* as the center of dilation and a scale factor of 3. **See margin.**

MATRICES **Scalar multiplication** is the process of multiplying each element of a matrix by a real number or *scalar.*

EXAMPLE 3 Scalar multiplication

Simplify the product: $4\begin{bmatrix} 3 & 0 & 1 \\ 2 & -1 & -3 \end{bmatrix}$.

Solution

$$4\begin{bmatrix} 3 & 0 & 1 \\ 2 & -1 & -3 \end{bmatrix} = \begin{bmatrix} 4(3) & 4(0) & 4(1) \\ 4(2) & 4(-1) & 4(-3) \end{bmatrix}$$ **Multiply each element in the matrix by 4.**

$$= \begin{bmatrix} 12 & 0 & 4 \\ 8 & -4 & -12 \end{bmatrix}$$ **Simplify.**

GUIDED PRACTICE for Example 3

Simplify the product.

3. $5\begin{bmatrix} 2 & 1 & -10 \\ 3 & -4 & 7 \end{bmatrix}$ $\begin{bmatrix} 10 & 5 & -50 \\ 15 & -20 & 35 \end{bmatrix}$

4. $-2\begin{bmatrix} -4 & 1 & 0 \\ 9 & -5 & -7 \end{bmatrix}$ $\begin{bmatrix} 8 & -2 & 0 \\ -18 & 10 & 14 \end{bmatrix}$

Motivating the Lesson

Tell students that enlarging a photograph involves creating a dilation with a scale factor greater than 1. Tell them that in this lesson they will learn two methods for creating dilations of geometric figures.

3 TEACH

Extra Example 1

Find the scale factor of the dilation. Then tell whether the dilation is a reduction or an enlargement.

a. $\frac{2}{3}$, reduction

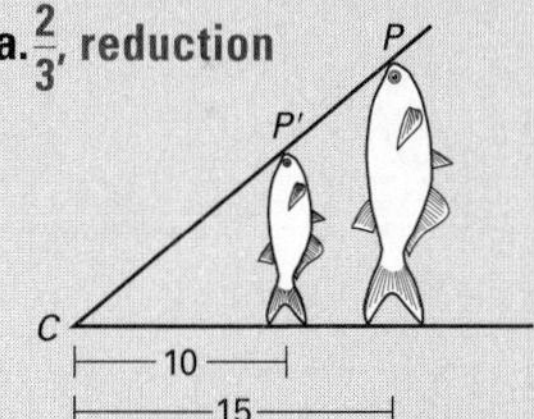

b. $\frac{5}{2}$, enlargement

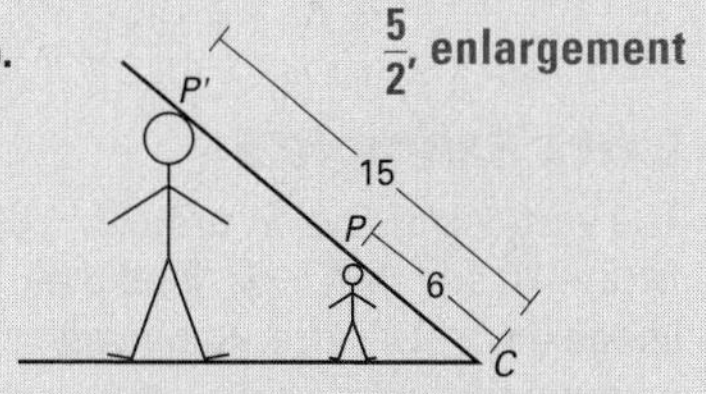

An **Animated Geometry** activity is available on-line for **Example 1**. This activity is also available on the **Power Presentations CD-ROM**.

Extra Example 2

Draw and label parallelogram *ABCD*. Then construct a dilation of *ABCD* with point *C* as the center and a scale factor of 3.

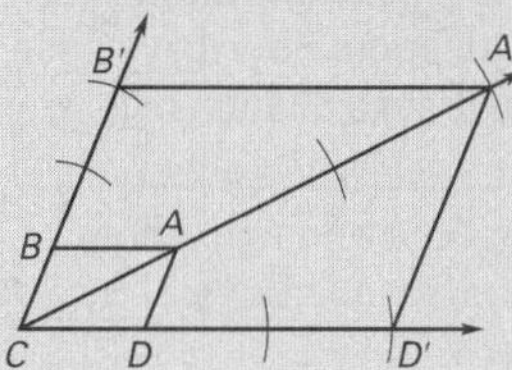

2. Sample:

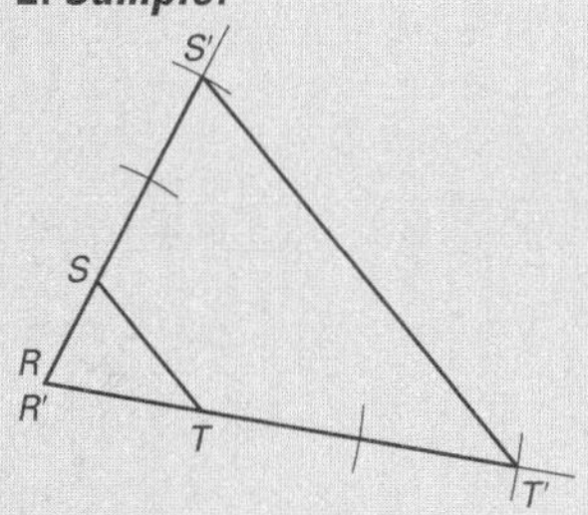

Extra Example 3

Simplify the product:

$$7\begin{bmatrix} 2 & -1 & 5 \\ 3 & 4 & -2 \end{bmatrix}. \begin{bmatrix} 14 & -7 & 35 \\ 21 & 28 & -14 \end{bmatrix}$$

Extra Example 4

The vertices of $XYZW$ are $X(-4, 4)$, $Y(2, 8)$, $Z(6, 2)$, and $W(-2, -4)$. Use scalar multiplication to find the image of $XYZW$ after a dilation with its center at the origin and a scale factor of $\frac{1}{2}$. Graph $XYZW$ and its image.

$$\begin{matrix} X' & Y' & Z' & W' \end{matrix}$$
$$\begin{bmatrix} -2 & 1 & 3 & -1 \\ 2 & 4 & 1 & -2 \end{bmatrix}$$

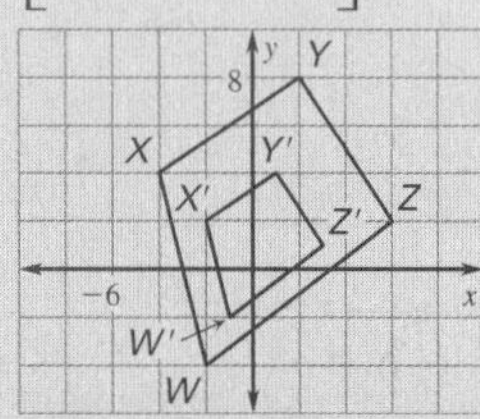

Extra Example 5

The vertices of $\triangle LMN$ are $L(2, -3)$, $M(3, -1)$, and $N(4, -2)$. Find the image of $\triangle LMN$ after the given composition.
Translation: $(x, y) \to (x - 3, y + 2)$
Dilation: centered at the origin with a scale factor of 3

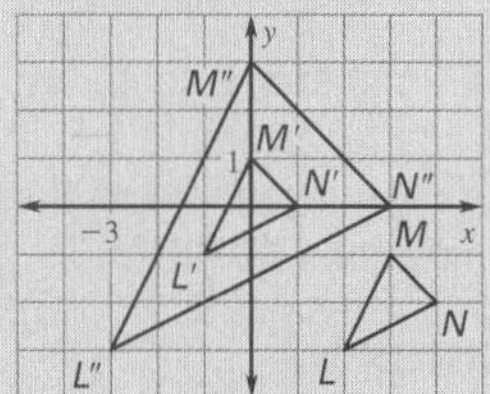

Closing the Lesson

Have students summarize the major points of the lesson and answer the Essential Question: How do you use matrices to draw a dilation?

- **A dilation results in an image similar to the preimage. Lines through corresponding points are concurrent.**
- **A dilation can be found by scalar multiplication.**

Multiply each element of the matrix for the preimage by the scale factor. Then use the resulting matrix to draw the image.

DILATIONS USING MATRICES You can use scalar multiplication to represent a dilation centered at the origin in the coordinate plane. To find the image matrix for a dilation centered at the origin, use the scale factor as the scalar.

EXAMPLE 4 Use scalar multiplication in a dilation

The vertices of quadrilateral $KLMN$ are $K(-6, 6)$, $L(-3, 6)$, $M(0, 3)$, and $N(-6, 0)$. Use scalar multiplication to find the image of $KLMN$ after a dilation with its center at the origin and a scale factor of $\frac{1}{3}$. Graph $KLMN$ and its image.

Solution

$$\frac{1}{3}\begin{matrix} K & L & M & N \\ \begin{bmatrix} -6 & -3 & 0 & -6 \\ 6 & 6 & 3 & 0 \end{bmatrix} \end{matrix} = \begin{matrix} K' & L' & M' & N' \\ \begin{bmatrix} -2 & -1 & 0 & -2 \\ 2 & 2 & 1 & 0 \end{bmatrix} \end{matrix}$$

Scale factor — Polygon matrix — Image matrix

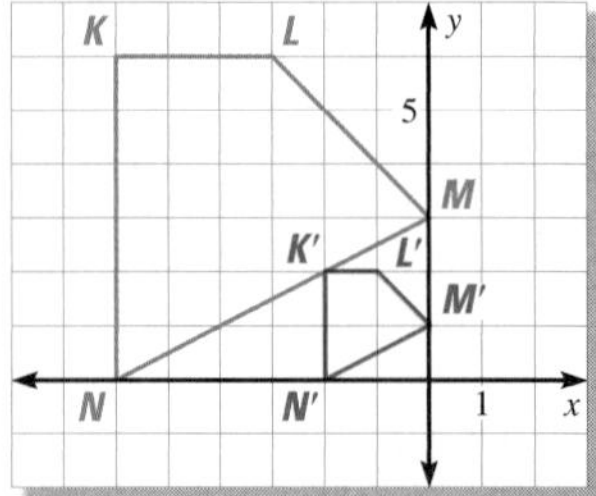

EXAMPLE 5 Find the image of a composition

The vertices of $\triangle ABC$ are $A(-4, 1)$, $B(-2, 2)$, and $C(-2, 1)$. Find the image of $\triangle ABC$ after the given composition.

Translation: $(x, y) \to (x + 5, y + 1)$
Dilation: centered at the origin with a scale factor of 2

Solution

STEP 1 **Graph** the preimage $\triangle ABC$ on the coordinate plane.

STEP 2 **Translate** $\triangle ABC$ 5 units to the right and 1 unit up. Label it $\triangle A'B'C'$.

STEP 3 **Dilate** $\triangle A'B'C'$ using the origin as the center and a scale factor of 2 to find $\triangle A''B''C''$.

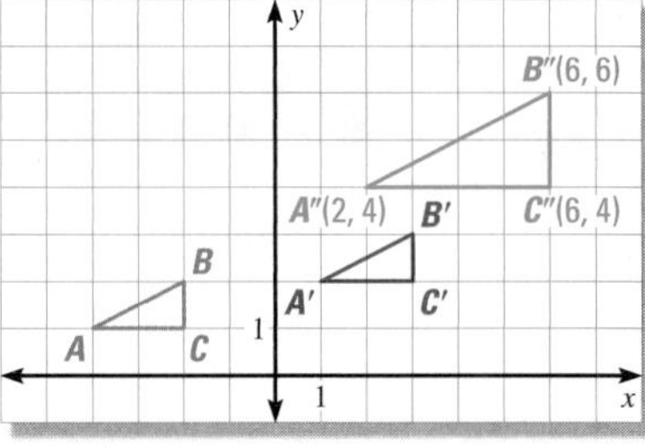

✓ GUIDED PRACTICE for Examples 4 and 5

5. The vertices of $\triangle RST$ are $R(1, 2)$, $S(2, 1)$, and $T(2, 2)$. Use scalar multiplication to find the vertices of $\triangle R'S'T'$ after a dilation with its center at the origin and a scale factor of 2. **$R'(2, 4)$, $S'(4, 2)$, $T'(4, 4)$**

6. A segment has the endpoints $C(-1, 1)$ and $D(1, 1)$. Find the image of $\overline{CD}$ after a 90° rotation about the origin followed by a dilation with its center at the origin and a scale factor of 2. **$C'(-2, -2)$, $D'(-2, 2)$**

9.7 EXERCISES

HOMEWORK KEY
○ = **WORKED-OUT SOLUTIONS** on p. WS12 for Exs. 7, 19, and 35
★ = **STANDARDIZED TEST PRACTICE** Exs. 2, 24, 25, 27, 29, and 38

SKILL PRACTICE

A

1. **VOCABULARY** What is a *scalar*? **a real number**

2. ★ **WRITING** If you know the scale factor, *explain* how to determine if an image is larger or smaller than the preimage. **If the scale factor is greater than 1, the image is larger. If the scale factor is between 0 and 1, the image is smaller.**

EXAMPLE 1 on p. 626 for Exs. 3–6

IDENTIFYING DILATIONS **Find the scale factor. Tell whether the dilation is a *reduction* or an *enlargement*. Find the value of *x*.**

3.
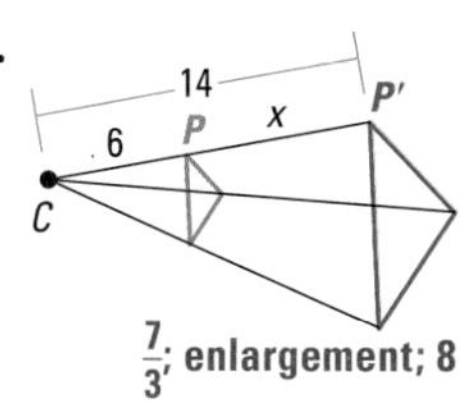

$\frac{7}{3}$; enlargement; 8

4.
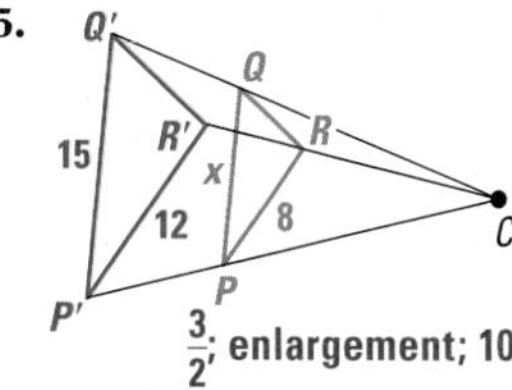

$\frac{2}{5}$; reduction; 6

5. Q′ Q R′ R 15 x 12 8 P P′ C
$\frac{3}{2}$; enlargement; 10

6. **ERROR ANALYSIS** *Describe* and correct the error in finding the scale factor *k* of the dilation. **The ratio should be $\frac{CP'}{CP}$; $k = \frac{CP'}{CP} = \frac{3}{12} = \frac{1}{4}$.**

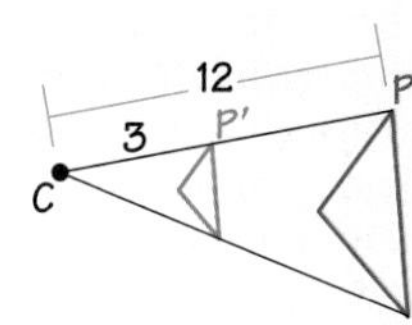

$k = \frac{CP}{CP'}$

$k = \frac{12}{3} = 4$ ✗

EXAMPLE 2 on p. 627 for Exs. 7–14

CONSTRUCTION **Copy the diagram. Then draw the given dilation.** **7–14. See margin.**

7. Center *H*; $k = 2$
8. Center *H*; $k = 3$
9. Center *J*; $k = 2$
10. Center *F*; $k = 2$
11. Center *J*; $k = \frac{1}{2}$
12. Center *F*; $k = \frac{3}{2}$
13. Center *D*; $k = \frac{3}{2}$
14. Center *G*; $k = \frac{1}{2}$

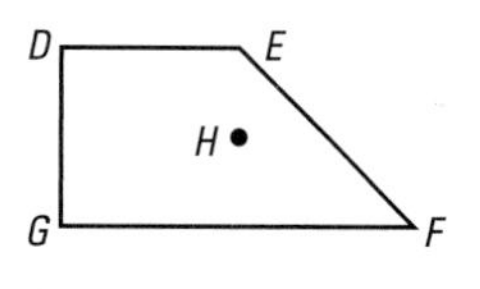

EXAMPLE 3 on p. 627 for Exs. 15–17

SCALAR MULTIPLICATION **Simplify the product.** **15–17. See margin.**

15. $4\begin{bmatrix} 3 & 7 & 4 \\ 0 & 9 & -1 \end{bmatrix}$

16. $-5\begin{bmatrix} -2 & -5 & 7 & 3 \\ 1 & 4 & 0 & -1 \end{bmatrix}$

17. $9\begin{bmatrix} 0 & 3 & 2 \\ -1 & 7 & 0 \end{bmatrix}$

EXAMPLE 4 on p. 628 for Exs. 18–20

DILATIONS WITH MATRICES **Find the image matrix that represents a dilation of the polygon centered at the origin with the given scale factor. Then graph the polygon and its image.** **18–20. See margin.**

18. $\begin{bmatrix} 2 & 3 & 5 \\ 1 & 6 & 4 \end{bmatrix}$ (columns D, E, F); $k = 2$

19. $\begin{bmatrix} -2 & 0 & 6 \\ -4 & 2 & -2 \end{bmatrix}$ (columns G, H, J); $k = \frac{1}{2}$

20. $\begin{bmatrix} -6 & -3 & 3 & 3 \\ 0 & 3 & 0 & -3 \end{bmatrix}$ (columns J, L, M, N); $k = \frac{2}{3}$

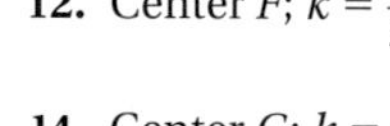

4 PRACTICE AND APPLY

Assignment Guide

Answer Transparencies available for all exercises

Basic:
Day 1: EP p. 907 Exs. 41, 42
pp. 629–632
Exs. 1–10, 15–25, 33–38, 43–49 odd

Average:
Day 1: pp. 629–632
Exs. 1, 2, 4–6, 10–12, 16, 17, 19–30, 34–41, 44, 46

Advanced:
Day 1: pp. 629–632
Exs. 1, 2, 4, 5, 13–16, 20–24 even, 25–32*, 35–42*, 45, 48

Block:
pp. 629–632
Exs. 1, 2, 4–6, 10–12, 16, 17, 19–30, 34–41, 44, 46 (with 9.6)

Differentiated Instruction

See *Geometry Best Practices Toolkit* for suggestions on addressing the needs of a diverse classroom.

Homework Check

For a quick check of student understanding of key concepts, go over the following exercises:
Basic: 8, 15, 18, 21, 33
Average: 10, 16, 20, 22, 34
Advanced: 14, 16, 20, 22, 35

Extra Practice

- Student Edition, p. 913
- Chapter 9 Resource Book: Practice levels A, B, C, pp. 90–95

Practice Worksheet

An easily-readable reduced practice page (with answers) for this lesson can be found on p. 570C.

4–11. See Additional Answers beginning on p. AA1.

15. $\begin{bmatrix} 12 & 28 & 16 \\ 0 & 36 & -4 \end{bmatrix}$

16. $\begin{bmatrix} 10 & 25 & -35 & -15 \\ -5 & -20 & 0 & 5 \end{bmatrix}$

17. $\begin{bmatrix} 0 & 27 & 18 \\ -9 & 63 & 0 \end{bmatrix}$

18–20. See Additional Answers beginning on p. AA1.

Mathematical Reasoning

Exercise 29 Students may have difficulty with this exercise. Since x is multiplied in choice A and y is multiplied in choice B, they may not realize that both coordinates must be multiplied by the same number to be a dilation. Have them experiment by graphing a point and its image under the transformations in choices A and B to see whether the line through the image and preimage passes through the origin.

21.
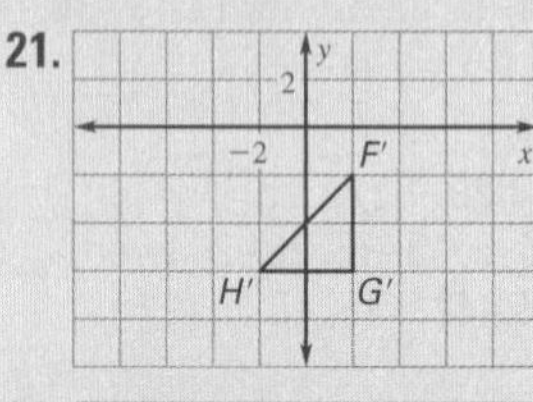

22.
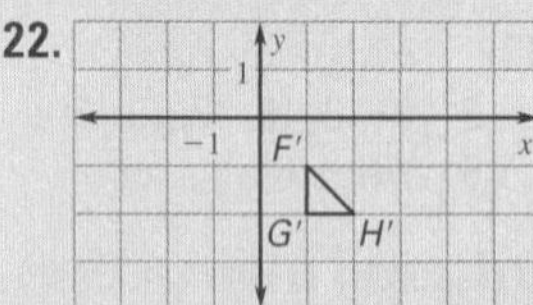

23.
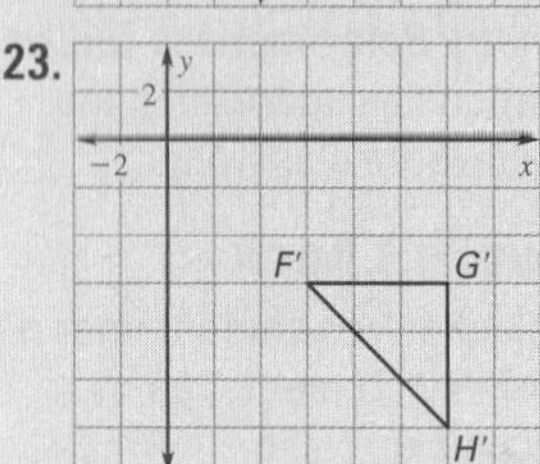

27. *Sample:*
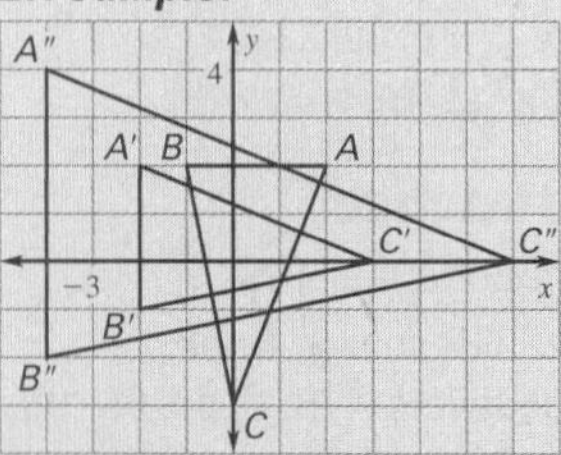

30. *Sample:*
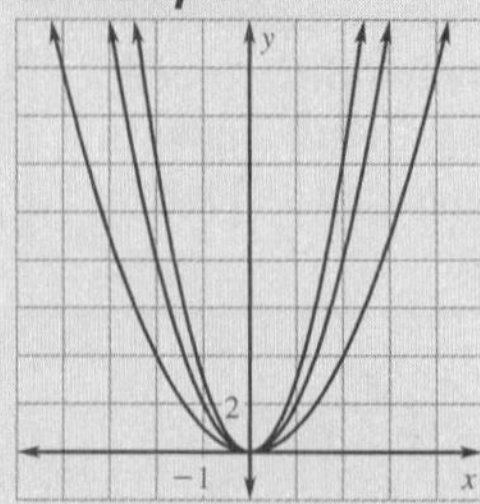

EXAMPLE 5 B on p. 628 for Exs. 21–23

COMPOSING TRANSFORMATIONS **The vertices of $\triangle FGH$ are $F(-2, -2)$, $G(-2, -4)$, and $H(-4, -4)$. Graph the image of the triangle after a composition of the transformations in the order they are listed.** **21–23. See margin.**

21. **Translation:** $(x, y) \rightarrow (x + 3, y + 1)$
    Dilation: centered at the origin with a scale factor of 2

22. **Dilation:** centered at the origin with a scale factor of $\frac{1}{2}$
    Reflection: in the y-axis

23. **Rotation:** 90° about the origin
    Dilation: centered at the origin with a scale factor of 3

24. ★ **WRITING** Is a composition of transformations that includes a dilation ever an isometry? *Explain.* **No; dilation does not preserve length.**

25. ★ **MULTIPLE CHOICE** In the diagram, the center of the dilation of ▱$PQRS$ is point C. The length of a side of ▱$P'Q'R'S'$ is what percent of the length of the corresponding side of ▱$PQRS$? **A**

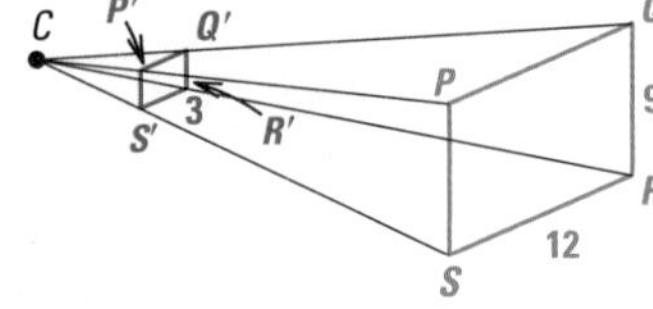

Ⓐ 25% Ⓑ 33% Ⓒ 300% Ⓓ 400%

26. **REASONING** The distance from the center of dilation to the image of a point is shorter than the distance from the center of dilation to the preimage. Is the dilation a *reduction* or an *enlargement*? *Explain.* **Reduction; the ratio of corresponding image to preimage lengths is between 0 and 1.**

27. ★ **SHORT RESPONSE** Graph a triangle in the coordinate plane. Rotate the triangle, then dilate it. Then do the same dilation first, followed by the rotation. In this composition of transformations, does it matter in which order the triangle is dilated and rotated? *Explain* your answer. **See margin for art; no; the result is the same.**

28. **REASONING** A dilation maps $A(5, 1)$ to $A'(2, 1)$ and $B(7, 4)$ to $B'(6, 7)$.
    a. Find the scale factor of the dilation. **2**
    b. Find the center of the dilation. **(8, 1)**

29. ★ **MULTIPLE CHOICE** Which transformation of (x, y) is a dilation? **C**

Ⓐ $(3x, y)$ Ⓑ $(-x, 3y)$ Ⓒ $(3x, 3y)$ Ⓓ $(x + 3, y + 3)$

30. **ALGEBRA** Graph parabolas of the form $y = ax^2$ using three different values of a. Describe the effect of changing the value of a. Is this a dilation? *Explain.* **See margin for art; as *a* increases the parabola becomes steeper; no; there is no center of dilation.**

31. No; the ratio of the lengths of corresponding sides is not the same.

C

31. **REASONING** In the graph at the right, determine whether $\triangle D'E'F'$ is a dilation of $\triangle DEF$. *Explain.*

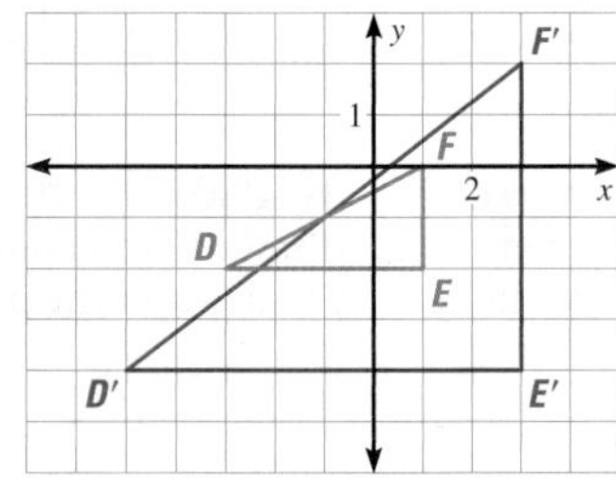

32. **CHALLENGE** $\triangle ABC$ has vertices $A(4, 2)$, $B(4, 6)$, and $C(7, 2)$. Find the vertices that represent a dilation of $\triangle ABC$ centered at (4, 0) with a scale factor of 2. ***A'*(4, 4), *B'*(4, 12), *C'*(10, 4)**

PROBLEM SOLVING

EXAMPLE 1 on p. 626 for Exs. 33–35

A

SCIENCE You are using magnifying glasses. Use the length of the insect and the magnification level to determine the length of the image seen through the magnifying glass.

33. Emperor moth **300 mm**
magnification 5x

34. Ladybug **45 mm**
magnification 10x

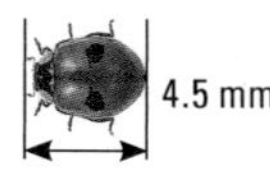

35. Dragonfly **940 mm**
magnification 20x

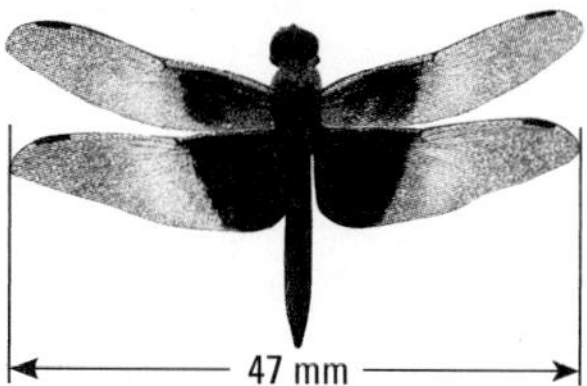

@HomeTutor for problem solving help at classzone.com

36. MURALS A painter sketches plans for a mural. The plans are 2 feet by 4 feet. The actual mural will be 25 feet by 50 feet. What is the scale factor? Is this a dilation? *Explain.* **$\frac{25}{2}$; yes; the center point is (0, 0) with scale factor $\frac{25}{2}$.**

@HomeTutor for problem solving help at classzone.com

B

37. PHOTOGRAPHY By adjusting the distance between the negative and the enlarged print in a photographic enlarger, you can make prints of different sizes. In the diagram shown, you want the enlarged print to be 9 inches wide ($A'B'$). The negative is 1.5 inches wide (AB), and the distance between the light source and the negative is 1.75 inches (CD).

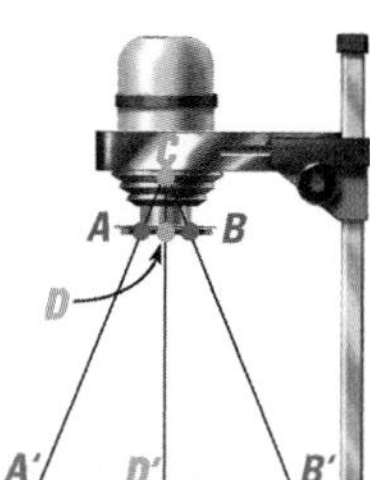

a. What is the scale factor of the enlargement? **$\frac{6}{1}$**

b. What is the distance between the negative and the enlarged print? **8.75 in.**

38. ★ OPEN-ENDED MATH Graph a polygon in a coordinate plane. Draw a figure that is similar but not congruent to the polygon. What is the scale factor of the dilation you drew? What is the center of the dilation? **See margin.**

39. MULTI-STEP PROBLEM Use the figure at the right.

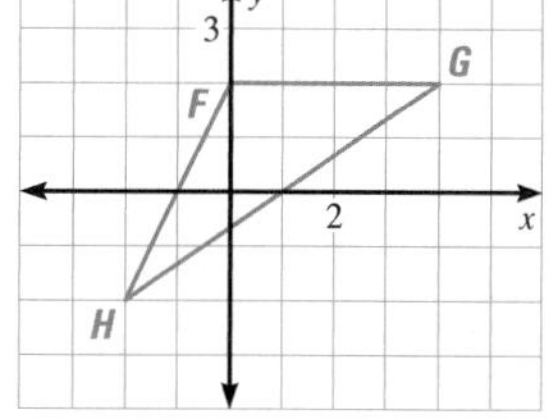

a. Write a polygon matrix for the figure. Multiply the matrix by the scalar −2. **a–c. See margin.**

b. Graph the polygon represented by the new matrix.

c. Repeat parts (a) and (b) using the scalar $-\frac{1}{2}$.

d. Make a conjecture about the effect of multiplying a polygon matrix by a negative scale factor.
A reflection in both the x-axis and y-axis occurs as well as dilation.

40. AREA You have an 8 inch by 10 inch photo.

a. What is the area of the photo? **80 in.^{2}**

b. You photocopy the photo at 50%. What are the dimensions of the image? What is the area of the image? **4 in. by 5 in.; 20 in.^{2}**

c. How many images of this size would you need to cover the original photo? **4 images**

Mathematical Reasoning

Exercise 39 Have students rotate the given figure by 180° and then dilate the image with a scale factor of 2. How does the final image compare with the image obtained in parts (a) and (b)? **The images are the same.**

Internet Reference

Exercise 33 More information about the Emperor moth can be found at www.arkive.org/species/ARK/invertebrates_terrestrial_and_freshwater/Saturnia_pavonia/more_info.html

38. *Sample:*

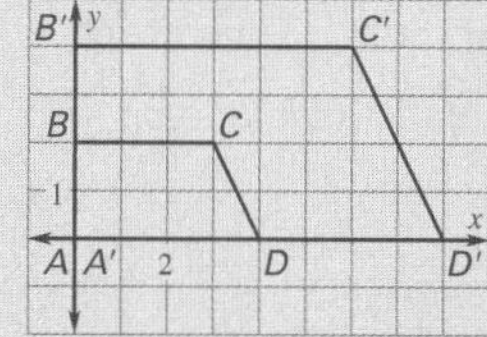

2; (0, 0)

39a. $\begin{bmatrix} 0 & 4 & -2 \\ 2 & 2 & -2 \end{bmatrix}$ (columns F, G, H); $\begin{bmatrix} 0 & -8 & 4 \\ -4 & -4 & 4 \end{bmatrix}$ (columns F', G', H')

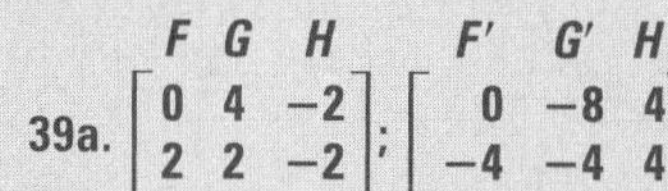

39b.

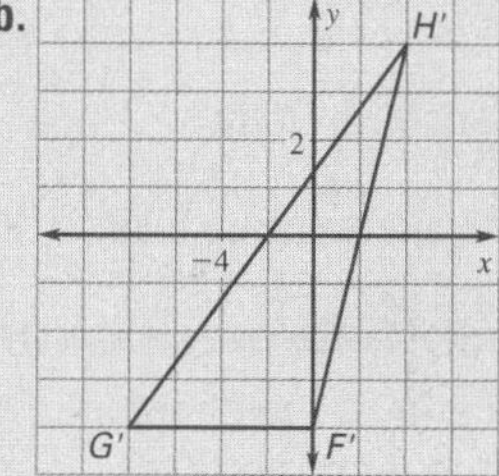

39c. $\begin{bmatrix} 0 & -2 & 1 \\ -1 & -1 & 1 \end{bmatrix}$ (columns F'', G'', H'');

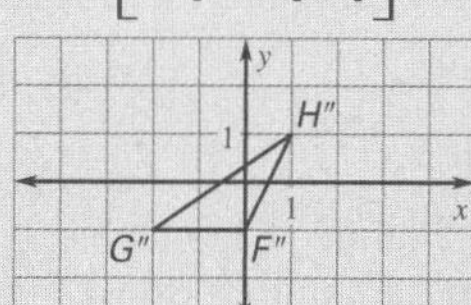

5 ASSESS AND RETEACH

Daily Homework Quiz

Transparency Available

1. Find the scale factor. Tell whether the dilation is a reduction or an enlargement. Find the value of *x*.

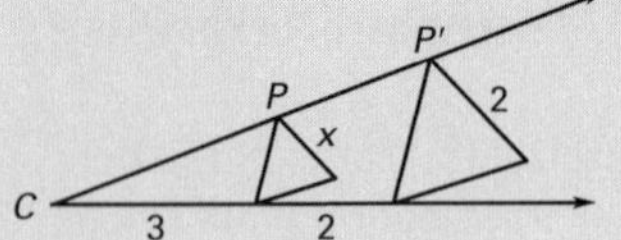

$\frac{5}{3}$; enlargement; 1.2

2. Find the image matrix that represents a dilation of $\triangle XYZ$ with vertices $X(3, 2)$, $Y(8, -1)$, and $Z(-1, -1)$ centered at the origin with scale factor $\frac{1}{2}$. Then graph the polygon and its image.

$$\begin{matrix} X' & Y' & Z' \end{matrix}$$
$$\begin{bmatrix} 1.5 & 4 & -0.5 \\ 1 & -0.5 & -0.5 \end{bmatrix}$$

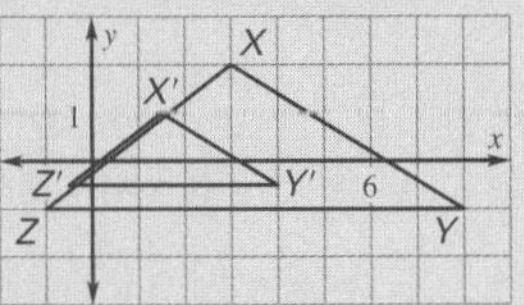

Available at **classzone.com**

Diagnosis/Remediation

- Practice A, B, C in Chapter 9 Resource Book, pp. 90–95
- Study Guide in Chapter 9 Resource Book, pp. 96–97
- Practice Workbook, pp. 181–183
- @HomeTutor

Challenge

Additional challenge is available in the Chapter 9 Resource Book, p. 100.

Quiz

An easily-readable reduced copy of the quiz (with answers) on Lessons 9.6–9.7 from the Assessment Book can be found on p. 570G.

42. See Additional Answers beginning on p. AA1.

41. REASONING You put a reduction of a page on the original page. *Explain* why there is a point that is in the same place on both pages. **It's the center point of the dilation.**

C **42. CHALLENGE** Draw two concentric circles with center *A*. Draw $\overline{AB}$ and $\overline{AC}$ to the larger circle to form a 45° angle. Label points *D* and *F*, where $\overline{AB}$ and $\overline{AC}$ intersect the smaller circle. Locate point *E* at the intersection of $\overline{BF}$ and $\overline{CD}$. Choose a point *G* and draw quadrilateral *DEFG*. Use *A* as the center of the dilation and a scale factor of $\frac{1}{2}$. Dilate *DEFG*, $\triangle DBE$, and $\triangle CEF$ two times. Sketch each image on the circles. *Describe* the result.

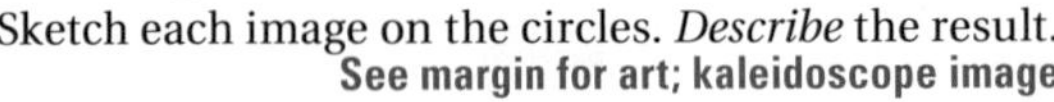
See margin for art; kaleidoscope image.

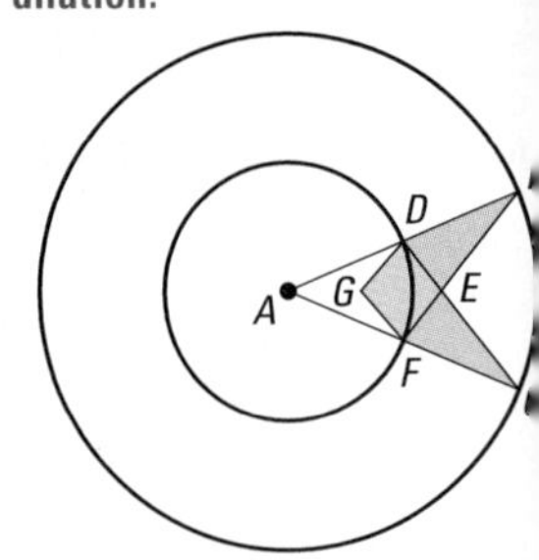

MIXED REVIEW

PREVIEW
Prepare for Lesson 10.1 in Exs. 43–45.

Find the unknown leg length *x*. *(p. 433)*

43. 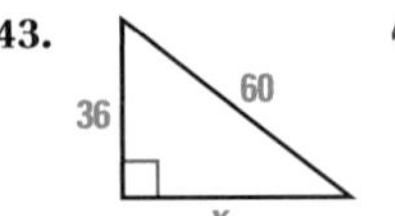

48

44. 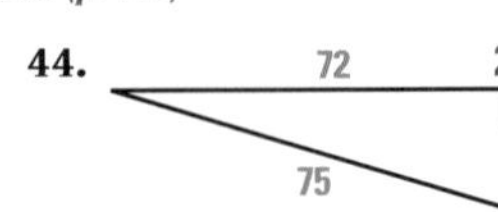

21

45. 

300

Find the sum of the measures of the interior angles of the indicated convex polygon. *(p. 507)*

46. Hexagon **720°**
47. 13-gon **1980°**
48. 15-gon **2340°**
49. 18-gon **2880°**

QUIZ for Lessons 9.6–9.7

Determine whether the figure has *line symmetry* and/or *rotational symmetry*. Identify the number of lines of symmetry and/or the rotations that map the figure onto itself. *(p. 619)*

1. 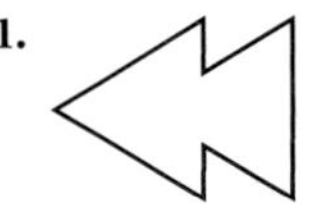

2. 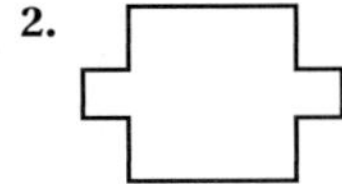

3. 

4. 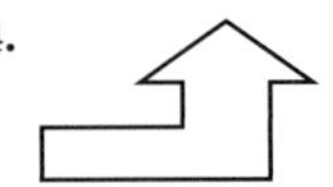

1. line symmetry, no rotational symmetry; one

2. line symmetry, rotational symmetry; two, 180° about the center

3. line symmetry, rotational symmetry; four, 90° or 180° about the center

4. no line symmetry, no rotational symmetry

Tell whether the dilation is a *reduction* or an *enlargement* and find its scale factor. *(p. 626)*

5. 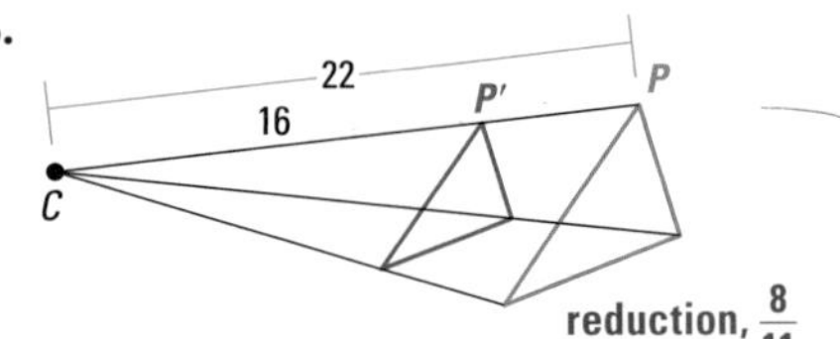

reduction, $\frac{8}{11}$

6. 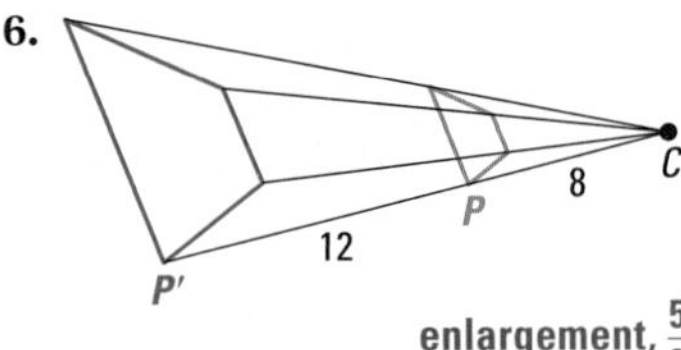

enlargement, $\frac{5}{2}$

7. The vertices of $\triangle RST$ are $R(3, 1)$, $S(0, 4)$, and $T(-2, 2)$. Use scalar multiplication to find the image of the triangle after a dilation centered at the origin with scale factor $4\frac{1}{2}$. *(p. 626)* **$R'\left(13\frac{1}{2}, 4\frac{1}{2}\right)$, $S'(0, 18)$, $T'(-9, 9)$**

EXTRA PRACTICE for Lesson 9.7, p. 913

 **ONLINE QUIZ** at classzone.com

9.7 Compositions With Dilations

MATERIALS • graphing calculator or computer

Standards
Enrichment Topic; not required by California Standards.

QUESTION How can you graph compositions with dilations?

You can use geometry drawing software to perform compositions with dilations.

EXAMPLE Perform a reflection and dilation

STEP 1 ***Draw triangle*** Construct a scalene triangle like $\triangle ABC$ at the right. Label the vertices A, B, and C. Construct a line that does not intersect the triangle. Label the line p.

STEP 2 ***Reflect triangle*** Select Reflection from the F4 menu. To reflect $\triangle ABC$ in line p, choose the triangle, then the line.

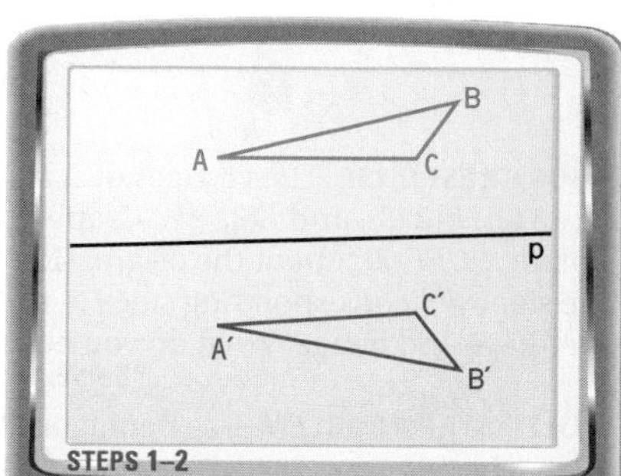

STEP 3 ***Dilate triangle*** Select Hide/Show from the F5 menu and show the axes. To set the scale factor, select Alpha-Num from the F5 menu, press ENTER when the cursor is where you want the number, and then enter 0.5 for the scale factor.

Next, select Dilation from the F4 menu. Choose the image of $\triangle ABC$, then choose the origin as the center of dilation, and finally choose 0.5 as the scale factor to dilate the triangle. Save this as "DILATE".

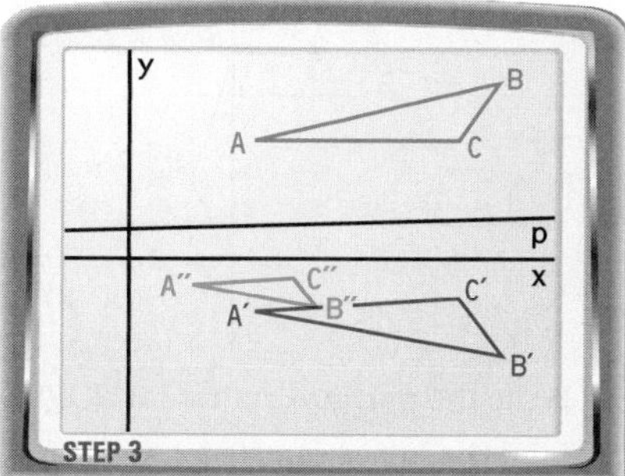

PRACTICE

1. Move the line of reflection. How does the final image change? **The new image is congruent to the final image but its relationship to line p changes as line p changes its relationship to $\triangle ABC$.**
2. To change the scale factor, select the Alpha-Num tool. Place the cursor over the scale factor. Press ENTER, then DELETE. Enter a new scale. How does the final image change? **If the scale factor is greater than 1 the figure enlarges. If the scale factor is between 0 and 1 it is a reduction.**
3. Dilate with a center not at the origin. How does the final image change? **The new image is similar to the final image.**
4. Use $\triangle ABC$ and line p, and the dilation and reflection from the Example. Dilate the triangle first, then reflect it. How does the final image change? **It is the same.**

1 PLAN AND PREPARE

Learn the Method

- Students will use geometry software to perform a composition with dilations.

Keystroke Help

Keystrokes for several models of calculators are available in blackline format in the *Chapter 9 Resource Book*.

2 TEACH

Tips for Success

Students need to follow directions carefully step by step in order.

Alternative Strategy

Do a demonstration on a classroom computer for students to see the results.

Extra Example 1

Perform a rotation and a dilation. **Use the software to draw and label a triangle. Mark a point as the center of rotation. Specify the number of degrees for the rotation. Select Rotate and perform the rotation. Then mark a point as the center for the dilation. Specify the scale factor. Select Dilate and perform the dilation.**

3 ASSESS AND RETEACH

How do you use geometry software to graph a composition with a dilation? Give an example and explain. **Students should choose a reflection, rotation, or translation and a dilation and explain the steps appropriate for their example.**

Lessons 9.4–9.7

1. **GRIDDED ANSWER** What is the angle of rotation, in degrees, that maps A to A' in the photo of the ceiling fan below? **216**

2. **SHORT RESPONSE** The vertices of $\triangle DEF$ are $D(-3, 2)$, $E(2, 3)$, and $F(3, -1)$. Graph $\triangle DEF$. Rotate $\triangle DEF$ 90° about the origin. Compare the slopes of corresponding sides of the preimage and image. What do you notice? **See margin.**

3. **MULTI-STEP PROBLEM** Use pentagon $PQRST$ shown below.

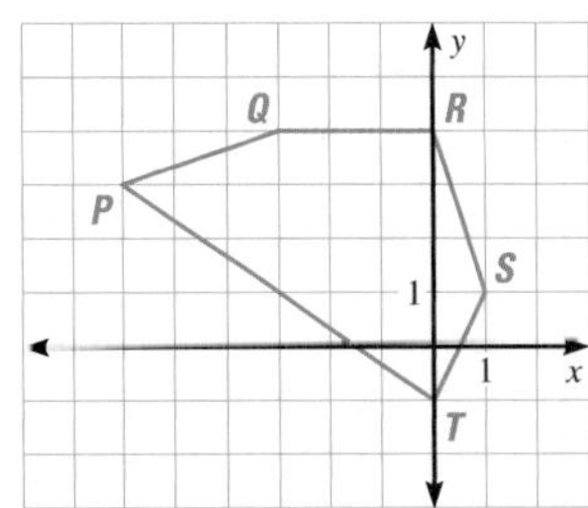

a–c. See margin.

   a. Write the polygon matrix for $PQRST$.

   b. Find the image matrix for a 270° rotation about the origin.

   c. Graph the image.

4. **SHORT RESPONSE** *Describe* the transformations that can be found in the quilt pattern below.

translation, rotation and reflection

5. **MULTI-STEP PROBLEM** The diagram shows the pieces of a puzzle.

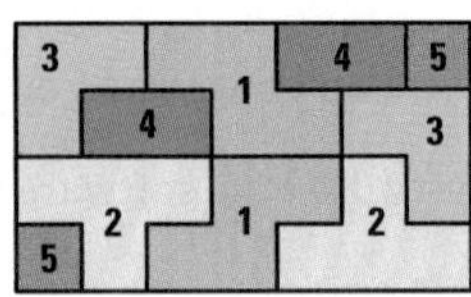

   a. Which pieces are translated? **4, 5**

   b. Which pieces are reflected? **1**

   c. Which pieces are glide reflected? **2, 3**

6. **OPEN-ENDED** Draw a figure that has the given type(s) of symmetry. **a–c. See margin.**

   a. Line symmetry only

   b. Rotational symmetry only

   c. Both line symmetry and rotational symmetry

7. **EXTENDED RESPONSE** In the graph below, $\triangle A'B'C'$ is a dilation of $\triangle ABC$.

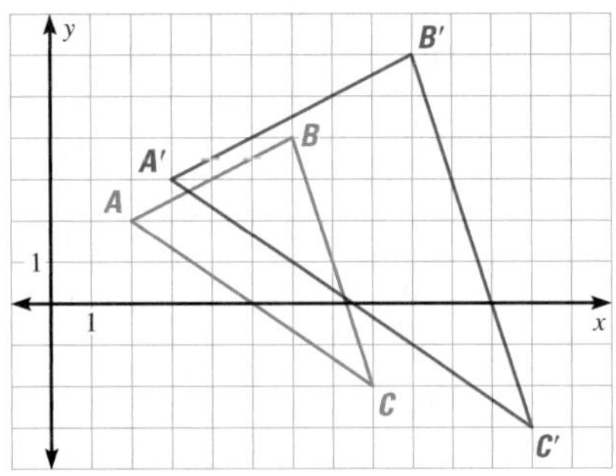

   a. Is the dilation a *reduction* or an *enlargement*? **enlargement**

   b. What is the scale factor? *Explain* your steps. **b–d. See margin.**

   c. What is the polygon matrix? What is the image matrix?

   d. When you perform a composition of a dilation and a translation on a figure, does order matter? *Justify* your answer using the translation $(x, y) \to (x + 3, y - 1)$ and the dilation of $\triangle ABC$.

2. They are negative reciprocals of each other.

3a. $\begin{matrix} P & Q & R & S & T \end{matrix}$ $\begin{bmatrix} -6 & -3 & 0 & 1 & 0 \\ 3 & 4 & 4 & 1 & -1 \end{bmatrix}$

3b. $\begin{matrix} P' & Q' & R' & S' & T' \end{matrix}$ $\begin{bmatrix} 3 & 4 & 4 & 1 & -1 \\ 6 & 3 & 0 & -1 & 0 \end{bmatrix}$

3c.

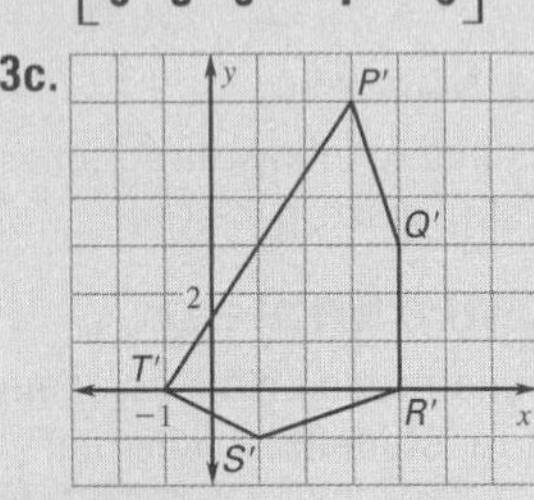

6a. *Sample:*

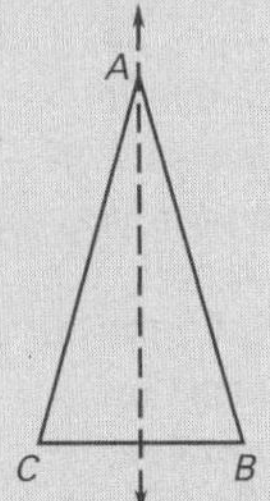

6b. *Sample:*

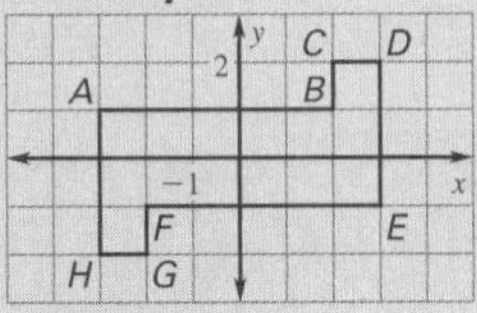

6c. *Sample:*

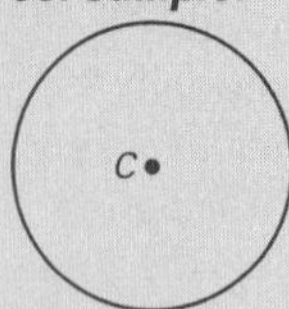

7b. $\frac{3}{2}$; find $\frac{A'B'}{AB} = \frac{3\sqrt{5}}{2\sqrt{5}} = \frac{3}{2}$

7c. $\begin{matrix} A & B & C \end{matrix}$ $\begin{bmatrix} 2 & 6 & 8 \\ 2 & 4 & -2 \end{bmatrix}$; $\begin{matrix} A' & B' & C' \end{matrix}$ $\begin{bmatrix} 3 & 9 & 12 \\ 3 & 6 & -3 \end{bmatrix}$

7d. yes; $\begin{bmatrix} 2 & 6 & 8 \\ 2 & 4 & -2 \end{bmatrix} \to \begin{bmatrix} 5 & 9 & 11 \\ 1 & 3 & -3 \end{bmatrix} \to \begin{bmatrix} 7.5 & 13.5 & 16.5 \\ 1.5 & 4.5 & -4.5 \end{bmatrix}$; $\begin{bmatrix} 2 & 6 & 8 \\ 2 & 4 & -2 \end{bmatrix} \to \begin{bmatrix} 3 & 9 & 12 \\ 3 & 6 & -3 \end{bmatrix} \to \begin{bmatrix} 6 & 12 & 15 \\ 2 & 5 & -4 \end{bmatrix}$

BIG IDEAS

For Your Notebook

Big Idea 1

Performing Congruence and Similarity Transformations

Translation

Translate a figure right or left, up or down.

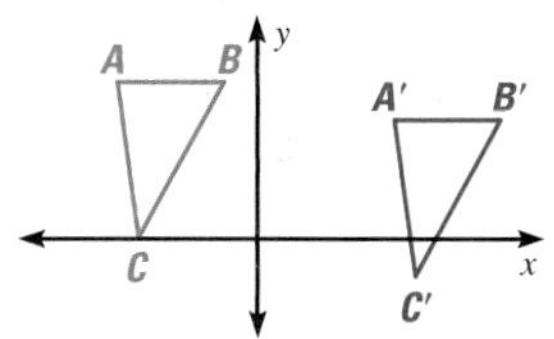

Reflection

Reflect a figure in a line.

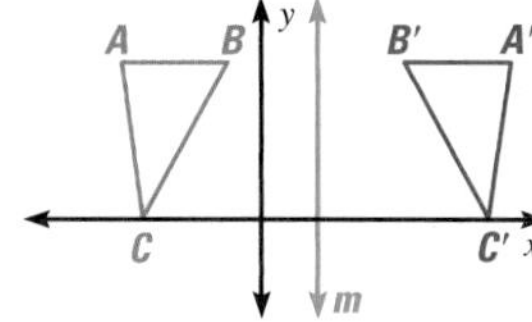

Rotation

Rotate a figure about a point.

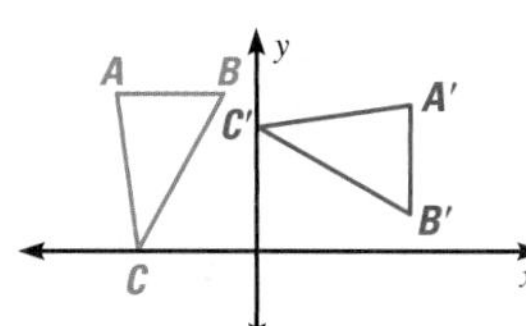

Dilation

Dilate a figure to change the size but not the shape.

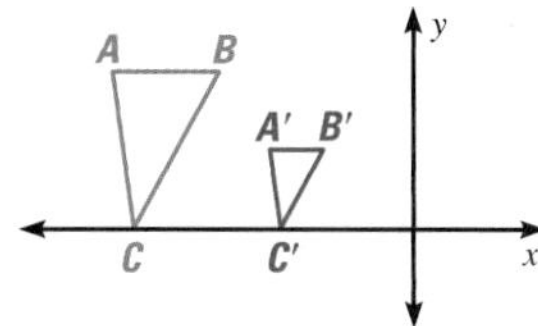

You can combine congruence and similarity transformations to make a composition of transformations, such as a glide reflection.

Big Idea 2

Making Real-World Connections to Symmetry and Tessellations

Line symmetry

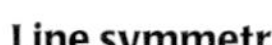

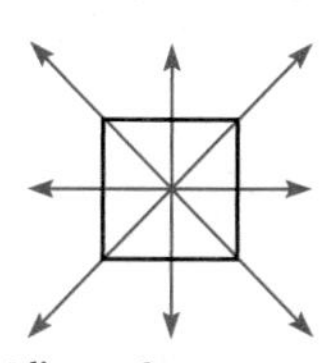

4 lines of symmetry

Rotational symmetry

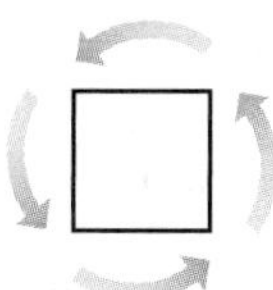

90° rotational symmetry

Big Idea 3

Applying Matrices and Vectors in Geometry

You can use matrices to represent points and polygons in the coordinate plane. Then you can use matrix addition to represent translations, matrix multiplication to represent reflections and rotations, and scalar multiplication to represent dilations. You can also use vectors to represent translations.

Additional Resources

The following resources are available to help review the materials in this chapter.

Chapter 9 Resource Book

- Chapter Review Games and Activities, p. 101
- Cumulative Practice, Chs. 1–9, pp. 104–105

Student Resources in Spanish

eWorkbook

@HomeTutor

Vocabulary Practice

Vocabulary practice is available at **classzone.com**

Extra Example 9.1

Name the vector and write its component form. $\overrightarrow{XY}$, $\langle 3, 2\rangle$

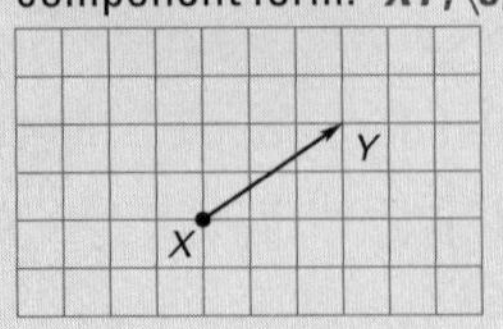

2. *Sample:*

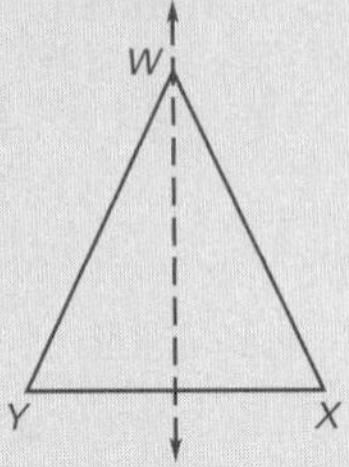

3. Count the number of rows, *n*, and the number of columns, *m*. The dimensions are $n \times m$.

Sample answer: $\begin{bmatrix} 2 & 0 & 3 \\ -1 & 4 & 7 \end{bmatrix}$ is 2×3.

6. 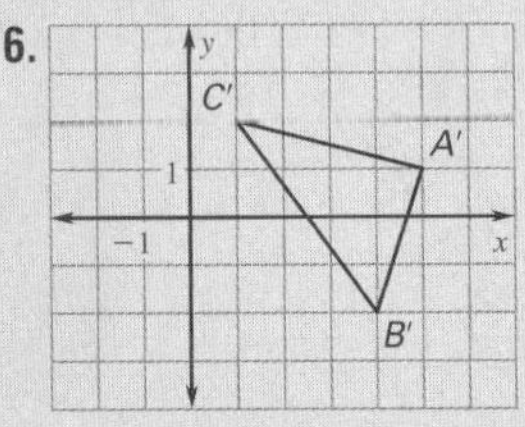

7. 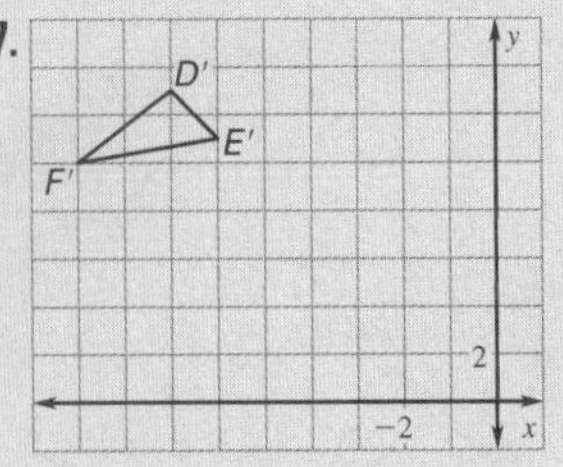

9 CHAPTER REVIEW

@HomeTutor
classzone.com
- Multi-Language Glossary
- Vocabulary practice

REVIEW KEY VOCABULARY

For a list of postulates and theorems, see pp. 926–931.

- image, *p. 572*
- preimage, *p. 572*
- isometry, *p. 573*
- vector, *p. 574*
  initial point, terminal point, horizontal component, vertical component
- component form, *p. 574*
- matrix, *p. 580*
- element, *p. 580*
- dimensions, *p. 580*
- line of reflection, *p. 589*
- center of rotation, *p. 598*
- angle of rotation, *p. 598*
- glide reflection, *p. 608*
- composition of transformations, *p. 609*
- line symmetry, *p. 619*
- line of symmetry, *p. 619*
- rotational symmetry, *p. 620*
- center of symmetry, *p. 620*
- scalar multiplication, *p. 627*

VOCABULARY EXERCISES

1. Copy and complete: A(n) __?__ is a transformation that preserves lengths. **isometry**
2. Draw a figure with exactly one line of symmetry. **See margin.**
3. **WRITING** *Explain* how to identify the dimensions of a matrix. Include an example with your explanation. **See margin.**

Match the point with the appropriate name on the vector.

4. *T* **B**   A. Initial point
5. *H* **A**   B. Terminal point

REVIEW EXAMPLES AND EXERCISES

Use the review examples and exercises below to check your understanding of the concepts you have learned in each lesson of Chapter 9.

9.1 Translate Figures and Use Vectors *pp. 572–579*

EXAMPLE

Name the vector and write its component form.

The vector is $\overrightarrow{EF}$. From initial point *E* to terminal point *F*, you move 4 units right and 1 unit down. So, the component form is $\langle 4, 1\rangle$.

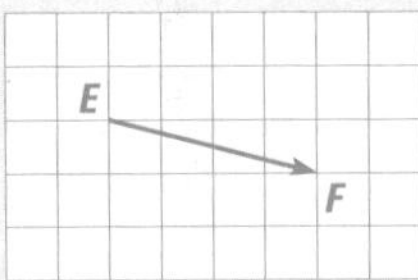

EXERCISES

EXAMPLES 1 and 4 on pp. 572, 574 for Exs. 6–7

6. The vertices of $\triangle ABC$ are $A(2, 3)$, $B(1, 0)$, and $C(-2, 4)$. Graph the image of $\triangle ABC$ after the translation $(x, y) \rightarrow (x + 3, y - 2)$. **See margin.**
7. The vertices of $\triangle DEF$ are $D(-6, 7)$, $E(-5, 5)$, and $F(-8, 4)$. Graph the image of $\triangle DEF$ after the translation using the vector $\langle -1, 6\rangle$. **See margin.**

9.2 Use Properties of Matrices
pp. 580–587

EXAMPLE

Add $\begin{bmatrix} -9 & 12 \\ 5 & -4 \end{bmatrix} + \begin{bmatrix} 20 & 18 \\ 11 & 25 \end{bmatrix}$.

These two matrices have the same dimensions, so you can perform the addition. To add matrices, you add corresponding elements.

$$\begin{bmatrix} -9 & 12 \\ 5 & -4 \end{bmatrix} + \begin{bmatrix} 20 & 18 \\ 11 & 25 \end{bmatrix} = \begin{bmatrix} -9+20 & 12+18 \\ 5+11 & -4+25 \end{bmatrix} = \begin{bmatrix} 11 & 30 \\ 16 & 21 \end{bmatrix}$$

EXERCISES

EXAMPLE 3 on p. 581 for Exs. 8–9

Find the image matrix that represents the translation of the polygon. Then graph the polygon and its image. 8, 9. See margin.

8. $\begin{matrix} A & B & C \end{matrix}$ $\begin{bmatrix} 2 & 8 & 1 \\ 4 & 3 & 2 \end{bmatrix}$; 5 units up and 3 units left

9. $\begin{matrix} D & E & F & G \end{matrix}$ $\begin{bmatrix} -2 & 3 & 4 & -1 \\ 3 & 6 & 4 & -1 \end{bmatrix}$; 2 units down

9.3 Perform Reflections
pp. 589–596

EXAMPLE

The vertices of $\triangle MLN$ are $M(4, 3)$, $L(6, 3)$, and $N(5, 1)$. Graph the reflection of $\triangle MLN$ in the line p with equation $x = 2$.

Point M is 2 units to the right of p, so its reflection M' is 2 units to the left of p at (0, 3). Similarly, L' is 4 units to the left of p at (−2, 3) and N' is 3 units to the left of p at (−1, 1).

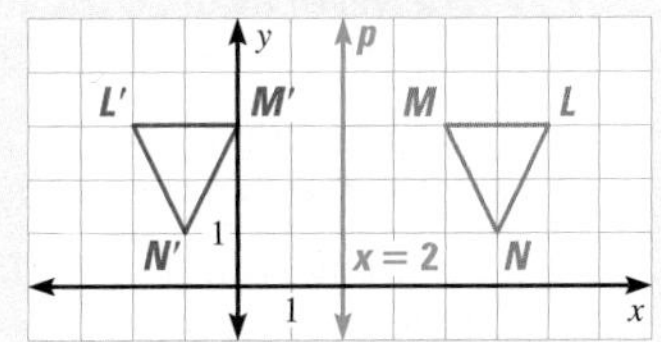

EXERCISES

EXAMPLES 1 and 2 on pp. 589–590 for Exs. 10–12

Graph the reflection of the polygon in the given line. 10–12. See margin.

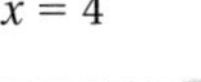

10. $x = 4$

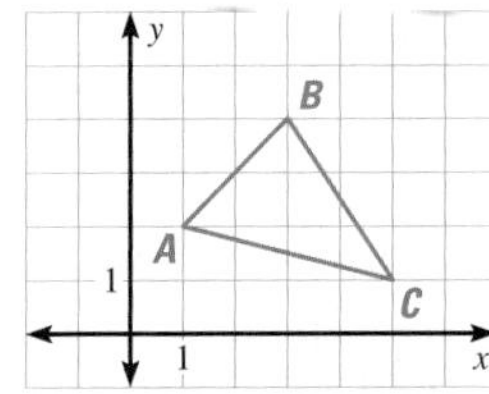

11. $y = 3$

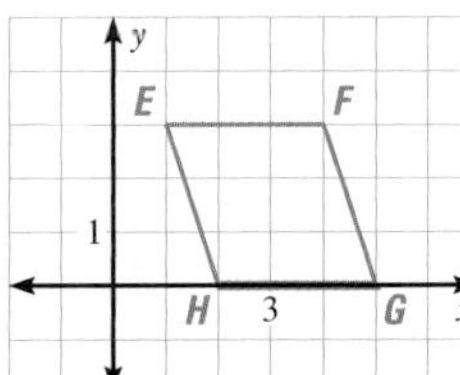

12. $y = x$

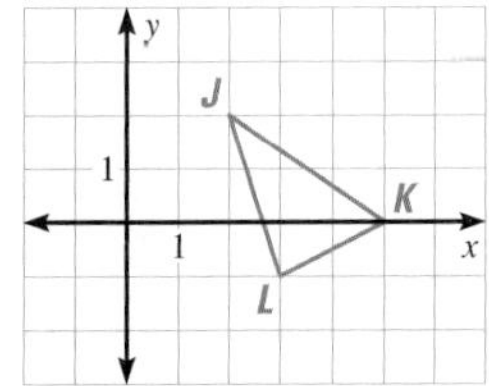

Extra Example 9.2

Subtract $\begin{bmatrix} 6 & 7 \\ -2 & 5 \end{bmatrix} - \begin{bmatrix} 16 & -9 \\ -11 & 3 \end{bmatrix}$.

$\begin{bmatrix} -10 & 16 \\ 9 & 2 \end{bmatrix}$

Extra Example 9.3

The vertices of $\triangle ABC$ are $A(3, 7)$, $B(4, 9)$, and $C(6, 6)$. Graph the reflection of $\triangle ABC$ in the line q with equation $y = 4$.

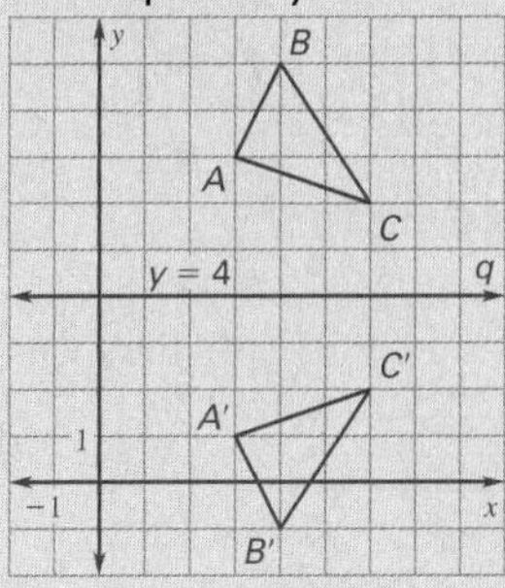

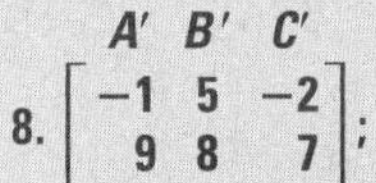

8. $\begin{matrix} A' & B' & C' \end{matrix}$ $\begin{bmatrix} -1 & 5 & -2 \\ 9 & 8 & 7 \end{bmatrix}$;

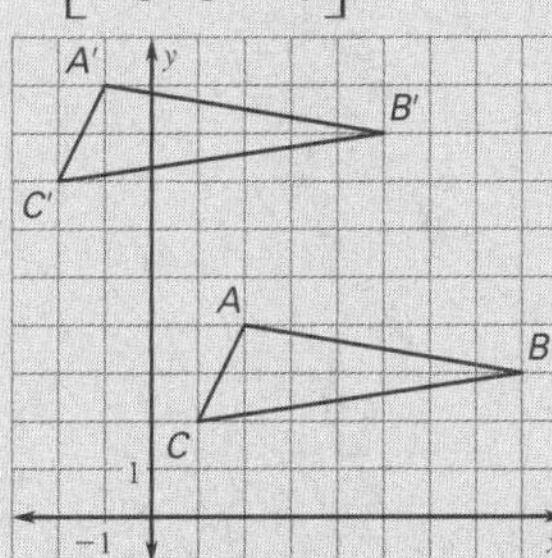

9. $\begin{matrix} D' & E' & F' & G' \end{matrix}$ $\begin{bmatrix} -2 & 3 & 4 & -1 \\ 1 & 4 & 2 & -3 \end{bmatrix}$;

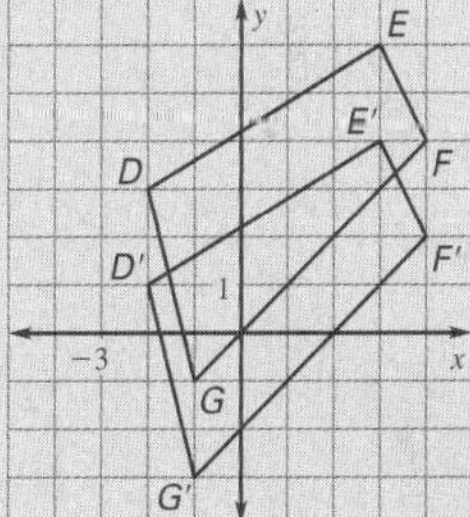

10.

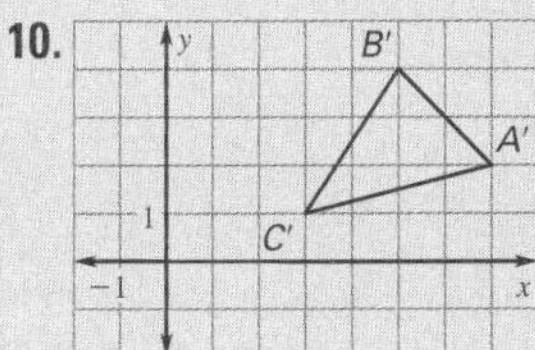

11.

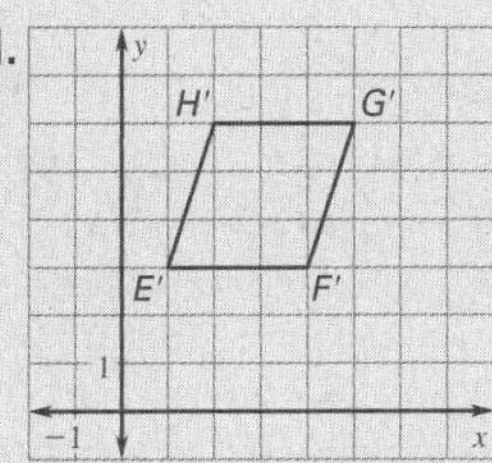

12.

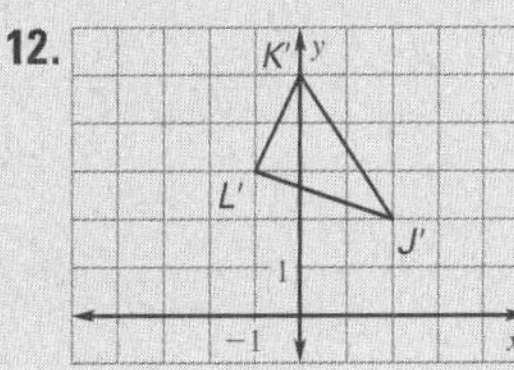

9 CHAPTER REVIEW

9.4 Perform Rotations

pp. 598–605

EXAMPLE

Find the image matrix that represents the 90° rotation of *ABCD* about the origin.

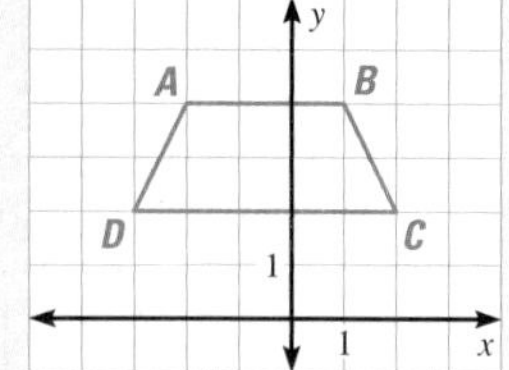

The polygon matrix for *ABCD* is $\begin{bmatrix} -2 & 1 & 2 & -3 \\ 4 & 4 & 2 & 2 \end{bmatrix}$.

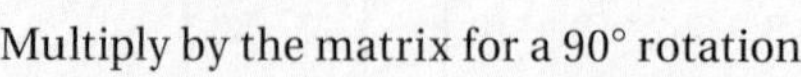

Multiply by the matrix for a 90° rotation.

$$\begin{bmatrix} 0 & -1 \\ 1 & 0 \end{bmatrix} \overset{\begin{matrix} A & B & C & D \end{matrix}}{\begin{bmatrix} -2 & 1 & 2 & -3 \\ 4 & 4 & 2 & 2 \end{bmatrix}} = \overset{\begin{matrix} A' & B' & C' & D' \end{matrix}}{\begin{bmatrix} -4 & -4 & -2 & -2 \\ -2 & 1 & 2 & -3 \end{bmatrix}}$$

EXERCISES

EXAMPLE 3 on p. 600 for Exs. 13–14

Find the image matrix that represents the given rotation of the polygon about the origin. Then graph the polygon and its image. 13, 14. See margin.

13. $\overset{\begin{matrix} Q & R & S \end{matrix}}{\begin{bmatrix} 3 & 4 & 1 \\ 0 & 5 & -2 \end{bmatrix}}$; 180°

14. $\overset{\begin{matrix} L & M & N & P \end{matrix}}{\begin{bmatrix} -1 & 3 & 5 & -2 \\ 6 & 5 & 0 & -3 \end{bmatrix}}$; 270°

9.5 Apply Compositions of Transformations

pp. 608–615

EXAMPLE

The vertices of $\triangle ABC$ are $A(4, -4)$, $B(3, -2)$, and $C(8, -3)$. Graph the image of $\triangle ABC$ after the glide reflection.

Translation: $(x, y) \to (x, y + 5)$
Reflection: in the *y*-axis

Begin by graphing $\triangle ABC$. Then graph the image $\triangle A'B'C'$ after a translation of 5 units up. Finally, graph the image $\triangle A''B''C''$ after a reflection in the *y*-axis.

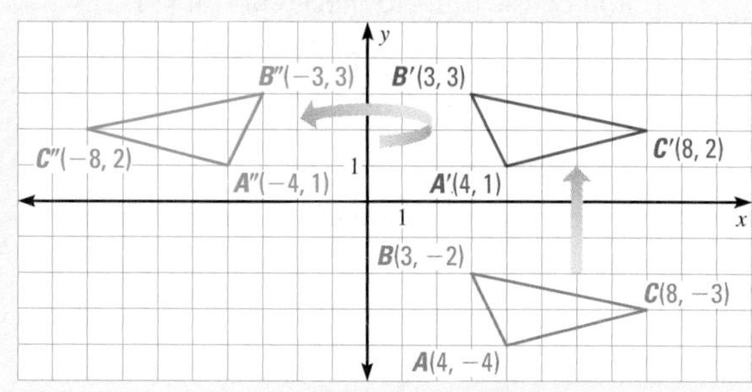

EXERCISES

EXAMPLE 1 on p. 608 for Exs. 15–16

Graph the image of $H(-4, 5)$ after the glide reflection. 15, 16. See margin.

15. Translation: $(x, y) \to (x + 6, y - 2)$
Reflection: in $x = 3$

16. Translation: $(x, y) \to (x - 4, y - 5)$
Reflection: in $y = x$

Extra Example 9.4

Find the image matrix that represents the 90° rotation of *EFGH* about the origin.

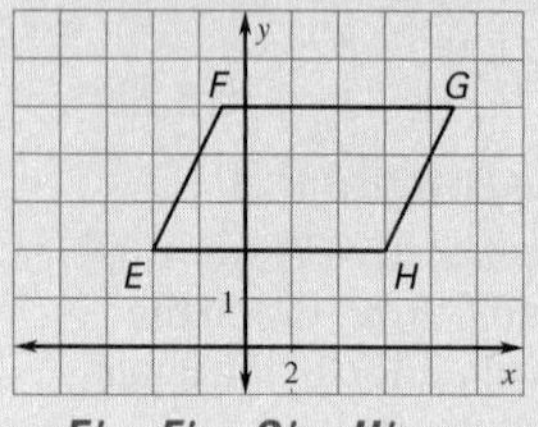

$\overset{\begin{matrix} E' & F' & G' & H' \end{matrix}}{\begin{bmatrix} -2 & -5 & -5 & -2 \\ -4 & -1 & 9 & 6 \end{bmatrix}}$

Extra Example 9.5

The vertices of $\triangle XYZ$ are $X(-5, -1)$, $Y(-3, 4)$, and $Z(2, 1)$. Graph the image of $\triangle XYZ$ after the glide reflection.

Translation: $(x, y) \to (x - 2, y)$
Reflection: in the *x*-axis

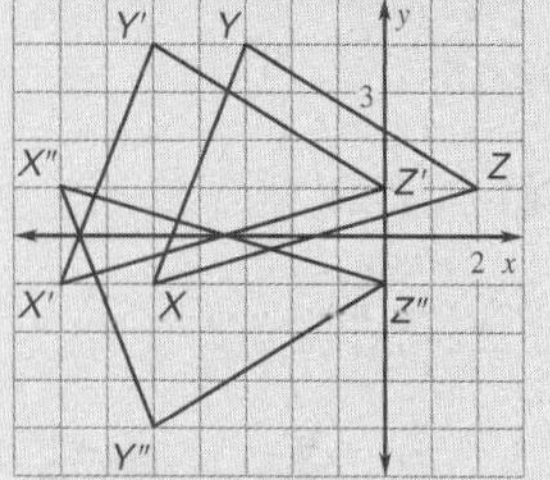

13. $\overset{\begin{matrix} Q' & R' & S' \end{matrix}}{\begin{bmatrix} -3 & -4 & -1 \\ 0 & -5 & 2 \end{bmatrix}}$;

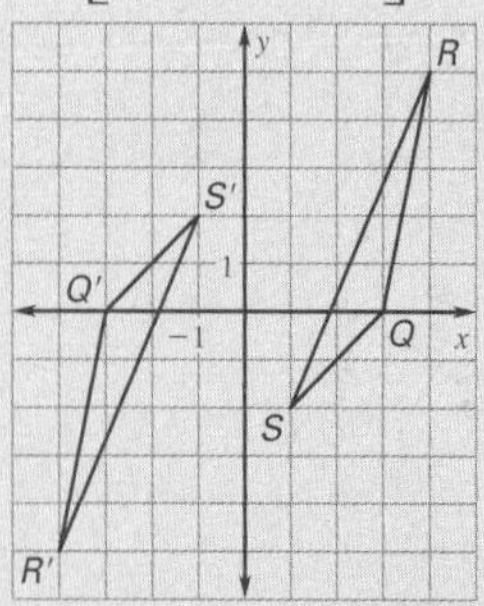

14. $\overset{\begin{matrix} L' & M' & N' & P' \end{matrix}}{\begin{bmatrix} 6 & 5 & 0 & -3 \\ 1 & -3 & -5 & 2 \end{bmatrix}}$;

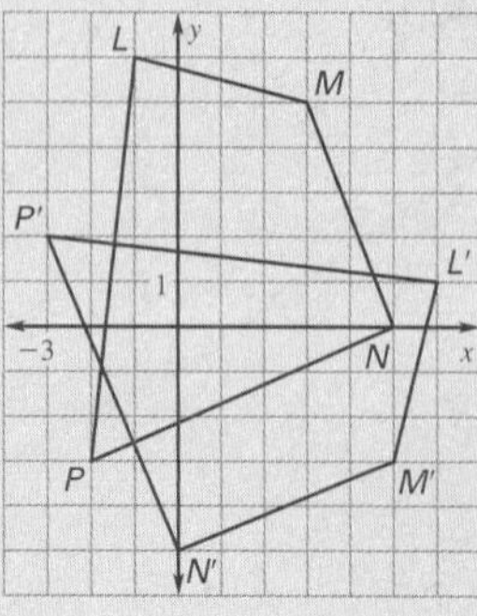

15.

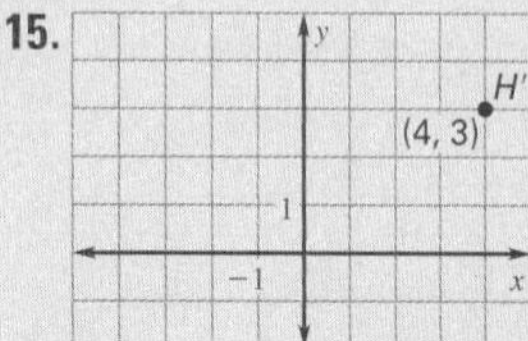

16.

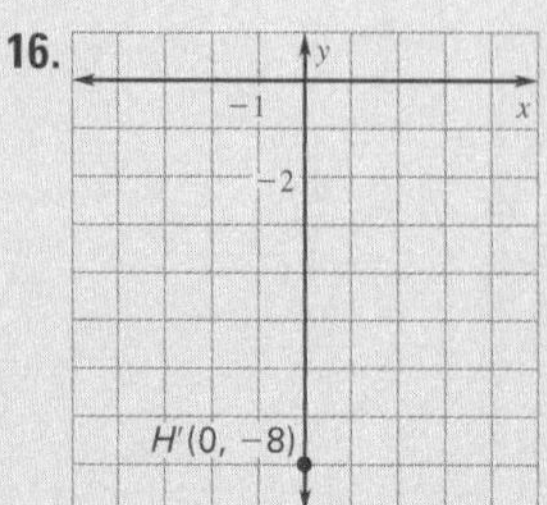

@HomeTutor
classzone.com
Chapter Review Practice

9.6 Identify Symmetry
pp. 619–624

EXAMPLE

Determine whether the rhombus has *line symmetry* and/or *rotational symmetry*. Identify the number of lines of symmetry and/or the rotations that map the figure onto itself.

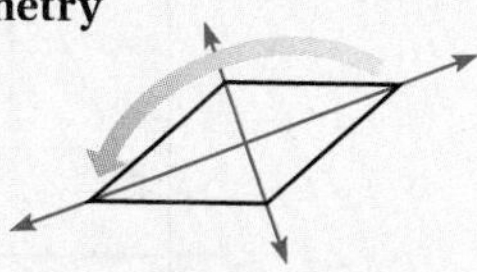

The rhombus has two lines of symmetry. It also has rotational symmetry, because a 180° rotation maps the rhombus onto itself.

EXERCISES

EXAMPLES 1 and 2 on pp. 619–620 for Exs. 17–19

Determine whether the figure has *line symmetry* and/or *rotational symmetry*. Identify the number of lines of symmetry and/or the rotations that map the figure onto itself.

17.

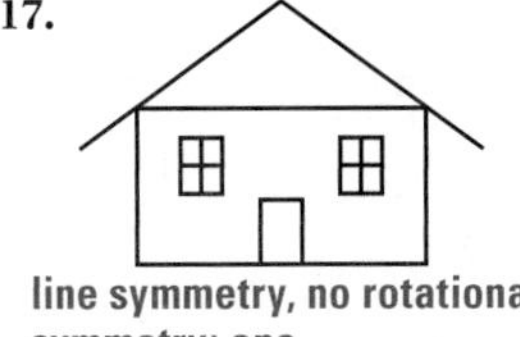

line symmetry, no rotational symmetry; one

18.

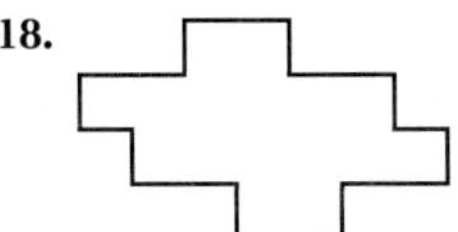

no line symmetry, rotational symmetry; 180° about the center

19.

line symmetry, rotational symmetry; two, 180° about the center

9.7 Identify and Perform Dilations
pp. 626–632

EXAMPLE

Quadrilateral *ABCD* has vertices *A*(1, 1), *B*(1, 3), *C*(3, 2), and *D*(3, 1). Use scalar multiplication to find the image of *ABCD* after a dilation with its center at the origin and a scale factor of 2. Graph *ABCD* and its image.

To find the image matrix, multiply each element of the polygon matrix by the scale factor.

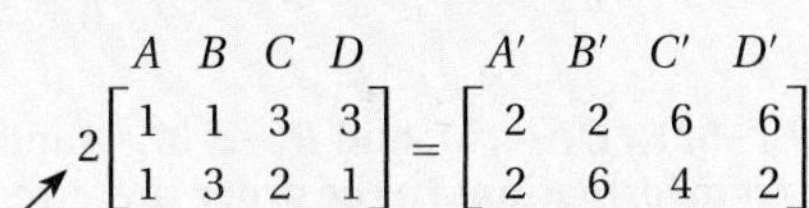

$$2\begin{bmatrix} 1 & 1 & 3 & 3 \\ 1 & 3 & 2 & 1 \end{bmatrix} = \begin{bmatrix} 2 & 2 & 6 & 6 \\ 2 & 6 & 4 & 2 \end{bmatrix}$$

(Columns A B C D; A′ B′ C′ D′.) Scale factor, Polygon matrix, Image matrix

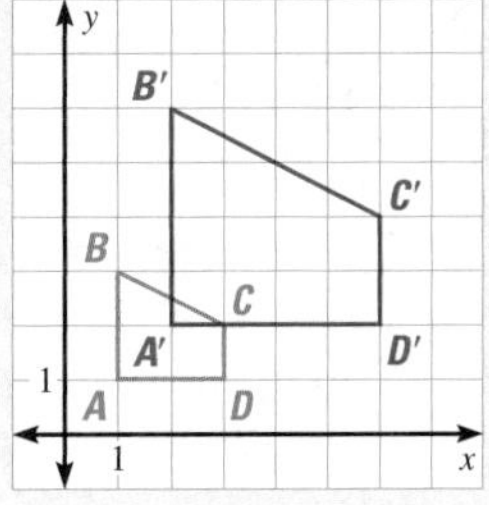

EXERCISES

EXAMPLE 4 on p. 628 for Exs. 20–21

Find the image matrix that represents a dilation of the polygon centered at the origin with the given scale factor. Then graph the polygon and its image. 20, 21. See margin.

20. $\begin{bmatrix} 2 & 4 & 8 \\ 2 & 4 & 2 \end{bmatrix}$ (Q R S); $k = \frac{1}{4}$

21. $\begin{bmatrix} -1 & 1 & 2 \\ -2 & 3 & 4 \end{bmatrix}$ (L M N); $k = 3$

Extra Example 9.6

Determine whether the rectangle has line symmetry and/or rotational symmetry. Identify the number of lines of symmetry and/or the rotations that map the figure onto itself.

2 lines of symmetry, 180° rotational symmetry

Extra Example 9.7

Quadrilateral *PQRS* has vertices *P*(2, 6), *Q*(4, 4), *R*(2, 0), and *S*(−2, 2). Use scalar multiplication to find the image of *PQRS* after a dilation with its center at the origin and a scale factor of $\frac{1}{2}$. Graph *PQRS* and its image.

$\begin{bmatrix} 1 & 2 & 1 & -1 \\ 3 & 2 & 0 & 1 \end{bmatrix}$ (P′ Q′ R′ S′)

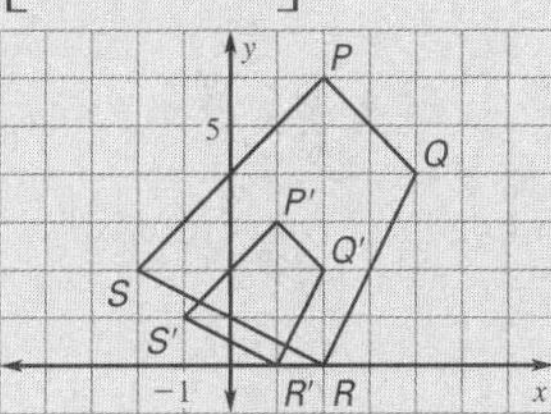

20. $\begin{bmatrix} \frac{1}{2} & 1 & 2 \\ \frac{1}{2} & 1 & \frac{1}{2} \end{bmatrix}$ (Q′ R′ S′);

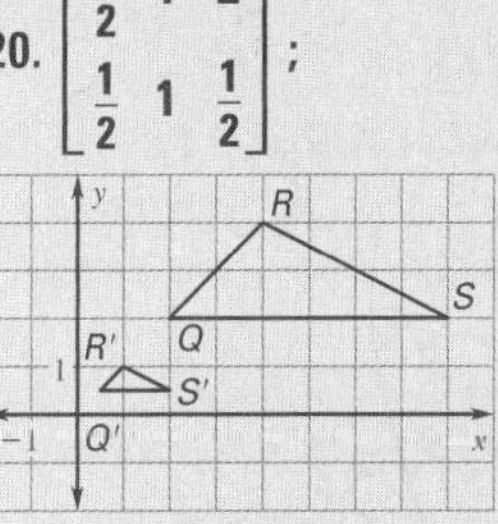

21. $\begin{bmatrix} -3 & 3 & 6 \\ -6 & 9 & 12 \end{bmatrix}$ (L′ M′ N′);

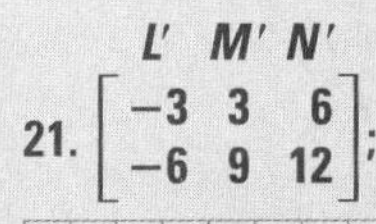

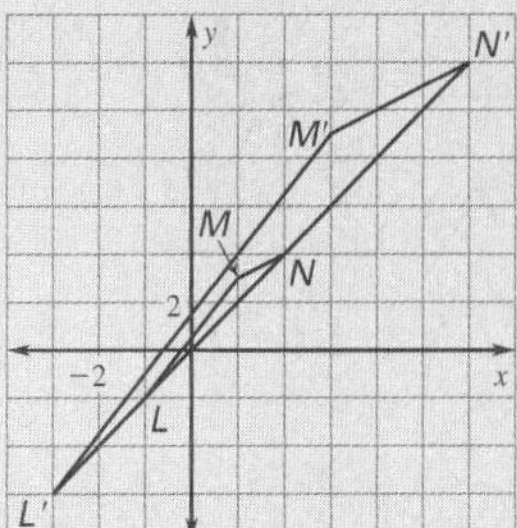

9 CHAPTER TEST

Additional Resources

Assessment Book

- Chapter Test, Levels A, B, C, pp. 128–133
- Standardized Chapter Test, pp. 134–135
- SAT/ACT Chapter Test, pp. 136–137
- Alternative Assessment, pp. 138–139

Test Generator CD-ROM

Chapter Test

Easily-readable reduced copies (with answers) of Chapter Test B, the Standardized Chapter Test, and the Alternative Assessment from the Assessment Book can be found on pp. 570G–570H.

1. $(x, y) \to (x + 3, y - 1)$; $AB = A'B' = 2\sqrt{5}$, $AC = A'C' = 2$, $BC = B'C' = 4$, so $\triangle ABC \cong \triangle A'B'C'$ by the SSS Congruence Postulate.
2. $(x, y) \to (x - 4, y + 3)$; $AB = A'B' = \sqrt{5}$, $AC = A'C' = 3$, $BC = B'C' = 2\sqrt{2}$, so $\triangle ABC \cong \triangle A'B'C'$ by the SSS Congruence Postulate.
3. $(x, y) \to (x - 2, y)$; $AB = A'B' = 4$, $AC = A'C' = \sqrt{10}$, $BC = B'C' = 3\sqrt{2}$, so $\triangle ABC \cong \triangle A'B'C'$ by the SSS Congruence Postulate.

7. 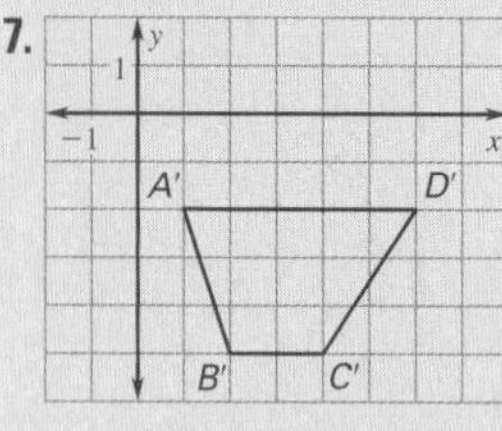

8. 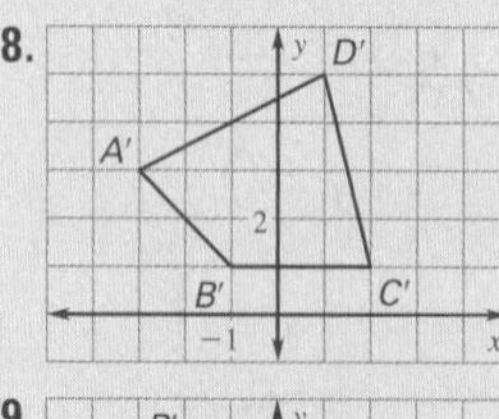

9. 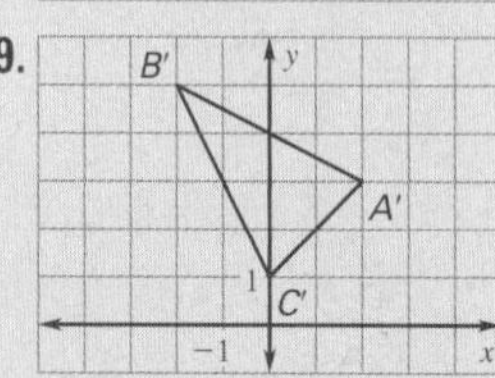

4. $\begin{bmatrix} -7 & -6 \\ 14.1 & -0.7 \end{bmatrix}$

5. $\begin{bmatrix} -8 & -6.4 \\ 1.8 & 1 \end{bmatrix}$

6. $\begin{bmatrix} 13 \\ -7 \end{bmatrix}$

Write a rule for the translation of $\triangle ABC$ to $\triangle A'B'C'$. Then verify that the translation is an isometry. 1–3. See margin.

1. 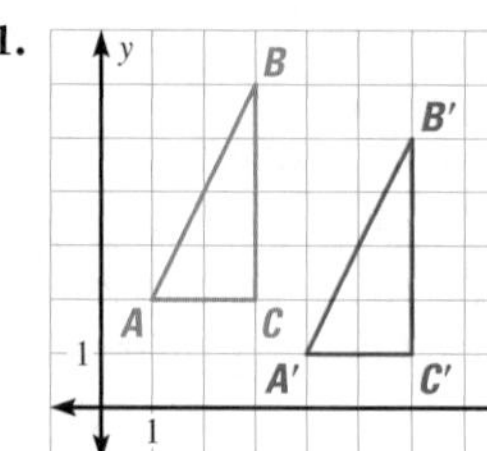
2. 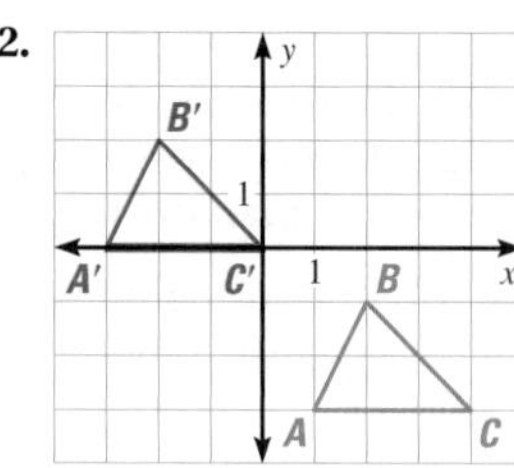
3. 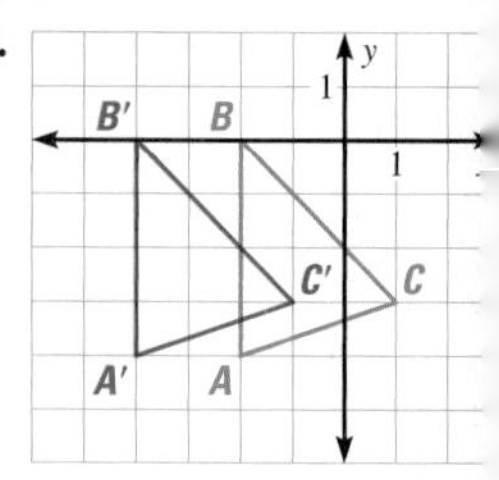

Add, subtract, or multiply.

4. $\begin{bmatrix} 3 & -8 \\ 9 & 4.3 \end{bmatrix} + \begin{bmatrix} -10 & 2 \\ 5.1 & -5 \end{bmatrix}$

5. $\begin{bmatrix} -2 & 2.6 \\ 0.8 & 4 \end{bmatrix} - \begin{bmatrix} 6 & 9 \\ -1 & 3 \end{bmatrix}$

6. $\begin{bmatrix} 7 & -3 & 2 \\ 5 & 1 & -4 \end{bmatrix}\begin{bmatrix} 1 \\ 0 \\ 3 \end{bmatrix}$

Graph the image of the polygon after the reflection in the given line. 7–9. See margin.

7. x-axis

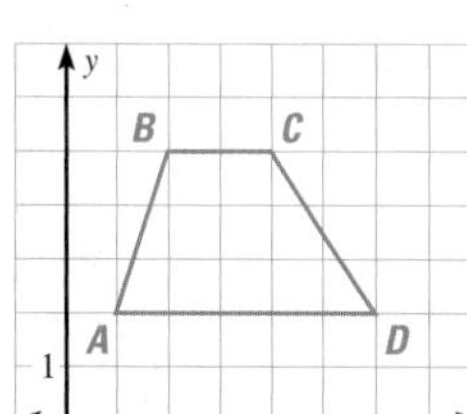

8. $y = 3$

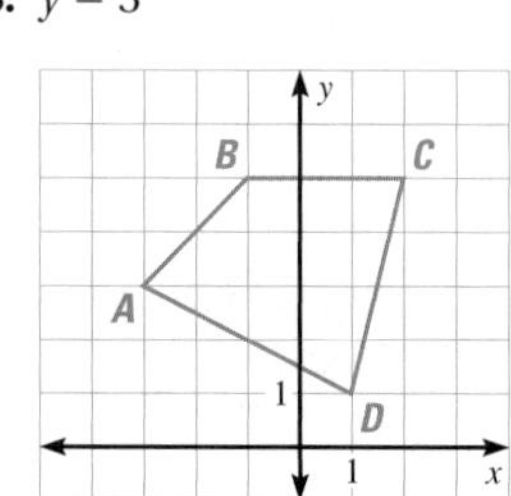

9. $y = -x$

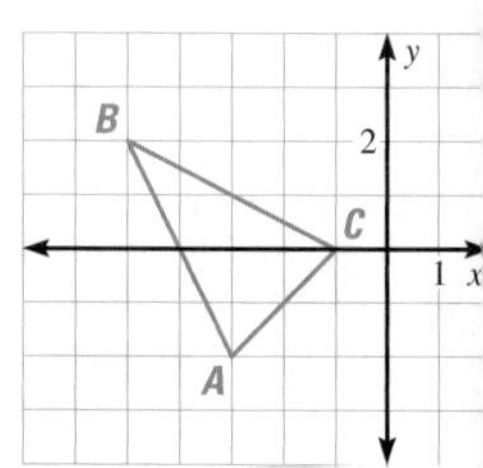

Find the image matrix that represents the rotation of the polygon. Then graph the polygon and its image. 10, 11. See margin.

10. $\triangle ABC$: $\begin{bmatrix} 2 & 4 & 6 \\ 2 & 5 & 1 \end{bmatrix}$; 90° rotation

11. $KLMN$: $\begin{bmatrix} -5 & -2 & -3 & -5 \\ 0 & 3 & -1 & -3 \end{bmatrix}$; 180° rotation

The vertices of $\triangle PQR$ are $P(-5, 1)$, $Q(-4, 6)$, and $R(-2, 3)$. Graph $\triangle P''Q''R''$ after a composition of the transformations in the order they are listed. 12, 13. See margin.

12. **Translation:** $(x, y) \to (x - 8, y)$
    Dilation: centered at the origin, $k = 2$

13. **Reflection:** in the y-axis
    Rotation: 90° about the origin

Determine whether the flag has *line symmetry* and/or *rotational symmetry*. Identify all lines of symmetry and/or angles of rotation that map the figure onto itself. 14–16. See margin.

14. 

15. 

16. 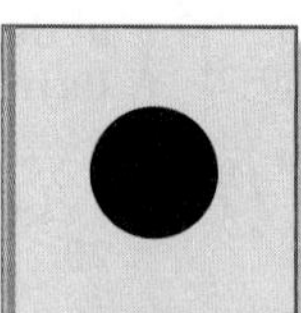

10. $\begin{matrix} A' & B' & C' \end{matrix}$ $\begin{bmatrix} -2 & -5 & -1 \\ 2 & 4 & 6 \end{bmatrix}$;

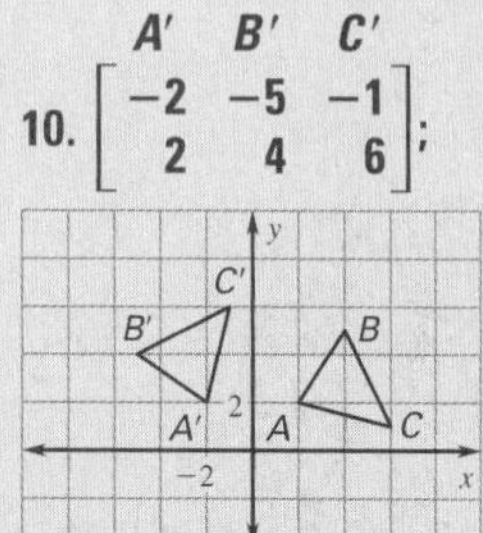

11. $\begin{matrix} K' & L' & M' & N' \end{matrix}$ $\begin{bmatrix} 5 & 2 & 3 & 5 \\ 0 & -3 & 1 & 3 \end{bmatrix}$;

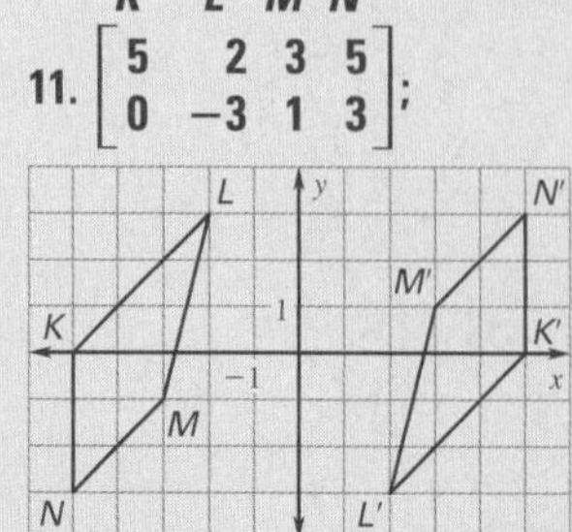

12. 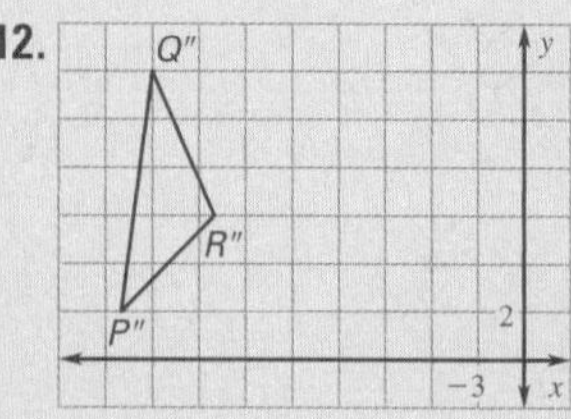

xy ALGEBRA REVIEW

Animated Algebra
classzone.com

MULTIPLY BINOMIALS AND USE QUADRATIC FORMULA

xy **EXAMPLE 1** *Multiply binomials*

Find the product $(2x + 3)(x - 7)$.

Solution

Use the **FOIL** pattern: Multiply the **F**irst, **O**uter, **I**nner, and **L**ast terms.

	First	Outer	Inner	Last	
$(2x + 3)(x - 7) =$	$2x(x)$	$+ 2x(-7)$	$+ 3(x)$	$+ 3(-7)$	**Write the products of terms.**

$= 2x^2 - 14x + 3x - 21$ **Multiply.**

$= 2x^2 - 11x - 21$ **Combine like terms.**

EXAMPLE 2 *Solve a quadratic equation using the quadratic formula*

Solve $2x^2 + 1 = 5x$.

Solution

Write the equation in standard form to be able to use the quadratic formula.

$2x^2 + 1 = 5x$ **Write the original equation.**

$2x^2 - 5x + 1 = 0$ **Write in standard form.**

$x = \frac{-b \pm \sqrt{b^2 - 4ac}}{2a}$ **Write the quadratic formula.**

$x = \frac{-(-5) \pm \sqrt{(-5)^2 - 4(2)(1)}}{2(2)}$ **Substitute values in the quadratic formula: $a = 2$, $b = -5$, and $c = 1$.**

$x = \frac{5 \pm \sqrt{25 - 8}}{4} = \frac{5 \pm \sqrt{17}}{4}$ **Simplify.**

▶ The solutions are $\frac{5 + \sqrt{17}}{4} \approx 2.28$ and $\frac{5 - \sqrt{17}}{4} \approx 0.22$.

EXERCISES

EXAMPLE 1 for Exs. 1–9

Find the product.

1. $(x + 3)(x - 2)$ $x^2 + x - 6$
2. $(x - 8)^2$ $x^2 - 16x + 64$
3. $(x + 4)(x - 4)$ $x^2 - 16$
4. $(x - 5)(x - 1)$ $x^2 - 6x + 5$
5. $(7x + 6)^2$ $49x^2 + 84x + 36$
6. $(3x - 1)(x + 9)$ $3x^2 + 26x - 9$
7. $(2x + 1)(2x - 1)$ $4x^2 - 1$
8. $(-3x + 1)^2$ $9x^2 - 6x + 1$
9. $(x + y)(2x + y)$ $2x^2 + 3xy + y^2$

4. $\frac{-2 \pm \sqrt{34}}{3}$

EXAMPLE 2 for Exs. 10–18

Use the quadratic formula to solve the equation.

10. $3x^2 - 2x - 5 = 0$ $\frac{5}{3}, -1$
11. $x^2 - 7x + 12 = 0$ 3, 4
12. $x^2 + 5x - 2 = 0$ $\frac{-5 \pm \sqrt{33}}{2}$
13. $4x^2 + 9x + 2 = 0$ $-2, -\frac{1}{4}$
14. $3x^2 + 4x - 10 = 0$
15. $x^2 + x = 7$ $\frac{-1 \pm \sqrt{29}}{2}$
16. $3x^2 = 5x - 1$ $\frac{5 \pm \sqrt{13}}{6}$
17. $x^2 = -11x - 4$
18. $5x^2 + 6 = 17x$ $\frac{2}{5}, 3$

7. $\frac{-11 \pm \sqrt{105}}{2}$

Extra Example 1

Find the product $(4x - 5)(2x + 1)$.
$8x^2 - 6x - 5$

Extra Example 2

Solve $3x^2 + 2 = 8x$.
$\frac{4 + \sqrt{10}}{3} \approx 2.39$, $\frac{4 - \sqrt{10}}{3} \approx 0.28$

Chapter Test, p. 640

13.

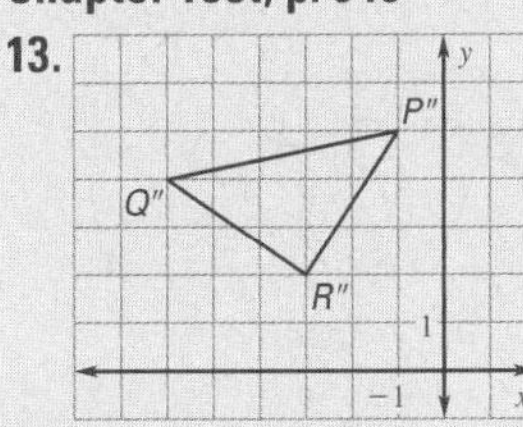

14. line symmetry, rotational symmetry; two lines of symmetry, one down each of the diagonals, 180° about the center

15. line symmetry, no rotational symmetry; one horizontal line of symmetry passing through the center

16. line symmetry, rotational symmetry; four lines of symmetry, one down each of the diagonals, one vertically down the center, and one horizontally through the center, 90° or 180° about the center

Using Rubrics

The rubric given on the pupil page is a sample of a three-level rubric. Other rubrics may contain four, five, or six levels. For more information on rubrics, see the *Geometry Toolkit*.

Test-Taking Strategy

Have students write out a complete solution. They should draw a graph to illustrate the solution. They should also check to be sure their math is correct and that their explanations are clear. They should not assume that the person reading the solution already knows how to do the problem.

Teaching Strategy

Have students read their solutions aloud to the class. Discuss what is good and bad about each solution and ask for suggestions on how to improve it.

Scoring Rubric

Full Credit
- solution is complete and correct

Partial Credit
- solution is complete but has errors,
  or
- solution is without error but incomplete

No Credit
- no solution is given,
  or
- solution makes no sense

SHORT RESPONSE QUESTIONS

PROBLEM

The vertices of $\triangle PQR$ are $P(1, -1)$, $Q(4, -1)$, and $R(0, -3)$. What are the coordinates of the image of $\triangle PQR$ after the given composition? *Describe* your steps. Include a graph with your answer.

Translation: $(x, y) \to (x - 6, y)$
Reflection: in the x-axis

Below are sample solutions to the problem. Read each solution and the comments in blue to see why the sample represents full credit, partial credit, or no credit.

SAMPLE 1: Full credit solution

The reasoning is correct, and the graphs are correct.

Standards

22.0 Students know the effect of rigid motions on figures in the coordinate plane and space, including rotations, **translations,** and reflections.

First, graph $\triangle PQR$. Next, to translate $\triangle PQR$ 6 units left, subtract 6 from the x-coordinate of each vertex.

$P(1, -1) \to P'(-5, -1)$

$Q(4, -1) \to Q'(-2, -1)$

$R(0, -3) \to R'(-6, -3)$

Finally, reflect $\triangle P'Q'R'$ in the x-axis by multiplying the y-coordinates by -1.

$P'(-5, -1) \to P''(-5, 1)$

$Q'(-2, -1) \to Q''(-2, 1)$

$R'(-6, -3) \to R''(-6, 3)$

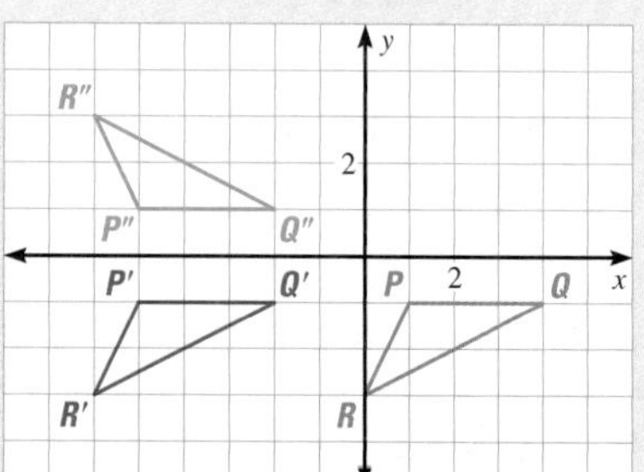

SAMPLE 2: Partial credit solution

Each transformation is performed correctly. However, the transformations are not performed in the order given in the problem.

First, graph $\triangle PQR$. Next, reflect $\triangle PQR$ over the x-axis by multiplying each y-coordinate by -1. Finally, to translate $\triangle P'Q'R'$ 6 units left, subtract 6 from each x-coordinate.

The coordinates of the image of $\triangle PQR$ after the composition are $P''(-5, 1)$, $Q''(-2, 1)$, and $R''(-6, 3)$.

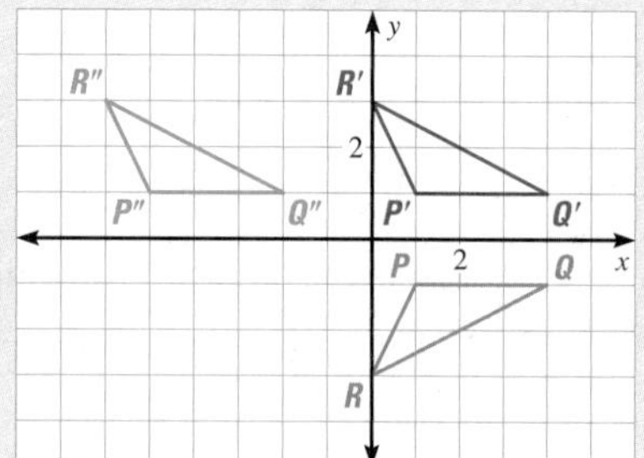

SAMPLE 3: Partial credit solution

The reasoning is correct, but the student does not show a graph.

First subtract 6 from each x-coordinate. So, $P'(1 - 6, -1) = P'(-5, -1)$, $Q'(4 - 6, -1) = Q'(-2, -1)$, and $R'(0 - 6, -3) = R'(-6, -3)$. Then reflect the triangle in the x-axis by multiplying each y-coordinate by -1. So, $P''(-5, -1 \cdot (-1)) = P''(-5, 1)$, $Q''(-2, -1 \cdot (-1)) = Q''(-2, 1)$, and $R''(-6, -1 \cdot (-3)) = R''(-6, 3)$.

SAMPLE 4: No credit solution

The reasoning is incorrect, and the student does not show a graph.

Translate $\triangle PQR$ 6 units by adding 6 to each x-coordinate. Then multiply each x-coordinate by -1 to reflect the image over the x-axis. The resulting $\triangle P'Q'R'$ has vertices $P'(-7, -1)$, $Q'(-10, -1)$, and $R'(-6, -3)$.

PRACTICE Apply Scoring Rubric

Use the rubric on page 642 to score the solution to the problem below as *full credit, partial credit,* or *no credit. Explain* your reasoning.

PROBLEM The vertices of $ABCD$ are $A(-6, 2)$, $B(-2, 3)$, $C(-1, 1)$, and $D(-5, 1)$. Graph the reflection of $ABCD$ in line m with equation $x = 1$.

1. Full credit; the reasoning is correct and the graphs are correct.

1. First, graph ABCD. Because m is a vertical line, the reflection will not change the y-coordinates. A is 7 units left of m, so A′ is 7 units right of m, at A′(8, 2). Since B is 3 units left of m, B′ is 3 units right of m, at B′(4, 3). The images of C and D are C′(3, 1) and D′(7, 1).

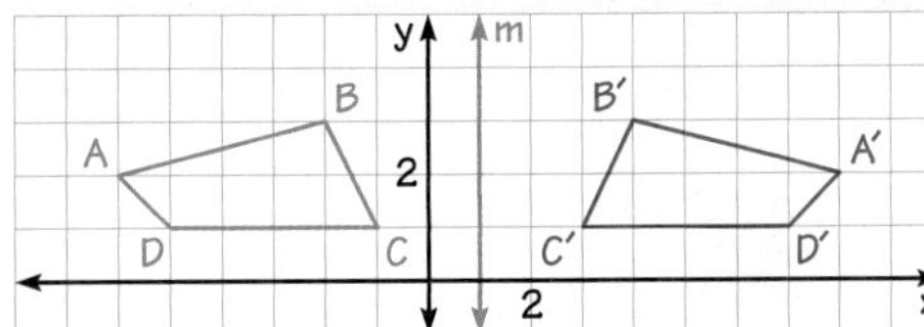

2. Partial credit; the student has an understanding of reflection but reflects the polygon across the incorrect line.

2. First, graph ABCD. The reflection is in a vertical line, so only the x-coordinates change. Multiply the x-coordinates in ABCD by −1 to get A′(6, 2), B′(2, 3), C′(1, 1), and D′(5, 1). Graph A′B′C′D′.

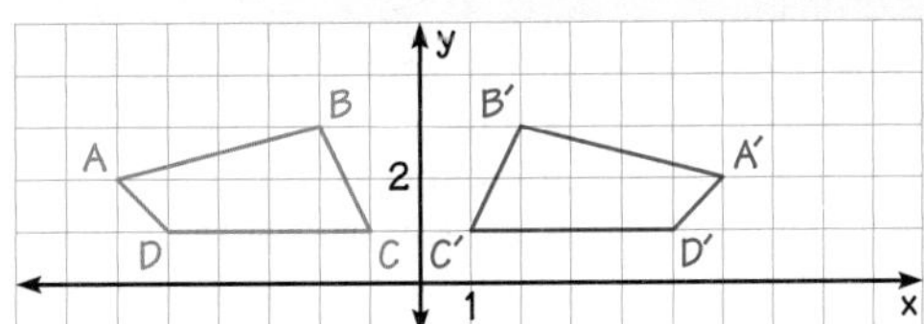

Avoiding Common Errors

Be sure the students actually do the problem to check whether the math in each solution is correct.

1a.

2.

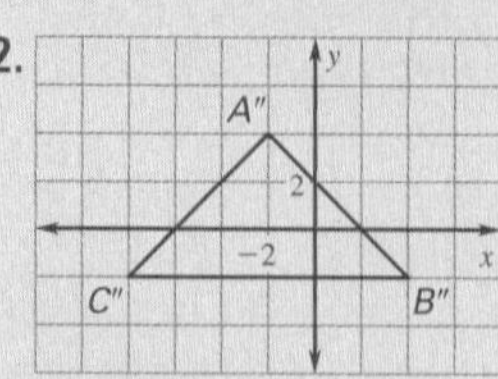

5. **60°, 60°, 120°, 120°; the sum of the 6 angles that meet at the center is 360°. Since they are all congruent, one measures 60°. Since the trapezoid is isosceles, the other angles must measure 60°, 120°, and 120°.**

7. ***Sample:***

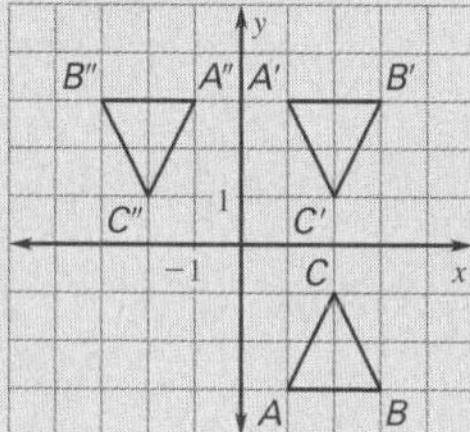

9 ★ *Standardized* TEST PRACTICE

SHORT RESPONSE

1. Use the square window shown below.

   a. Draw a sketch showing all the lines of symmetry in the window design. **See margin.**

   b. Does the design have rotational symmetry? If so, *describe* the rotations that map the design onto itself. **Yes; it has rotational symmetry of 90° and 180° about the center.**

2. The vertices of a triangle are $A(0, 2)$, $B(2, 0)$, and $C(-2, 0)$. What are the coordinates of the image of $\triangle ABC$ after the given composition? Include a graph with your answer.

   Dilation: $(x, y) \to (3x, 3x)$
   Translation: $(x, y) \to (x - 2, y - 2)$
   $A''(-2, 4)$, $B''(4, -2)$, $C''(-8, -2)$; see margin for art.

3. The red square is the image of the blue square after a single transformation. *Describe* three different transformations that could produce the image. **rotation of 180°, a translation, a reflection in $y = -x$**

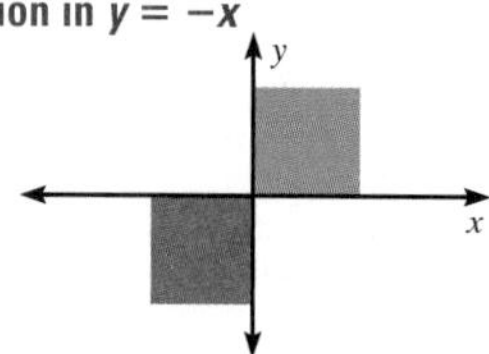

4. At a stadium concession stand, a hotdog costs \$3.25, a soft drink costs \$2.50, and a pretzel costs \$3. The Johnson family buys 5 hotdogs, 3 soft drinks, and 1 pretzel. The Scott family buys 4 hotdogs, 4 soft drinks, and 2 pretzels. Use matrix multiplication to find the total amount spent by each family. Which family spends more money? *Explain.* **\$26.75, \$29; Scott; \$29 is greater than \$26.75.**

5. The design below is made of congruent isosceles trapezoids. Find the measures of the four interior angles of one of the trapezoids. *Explain* your reasoning. **See margin.**

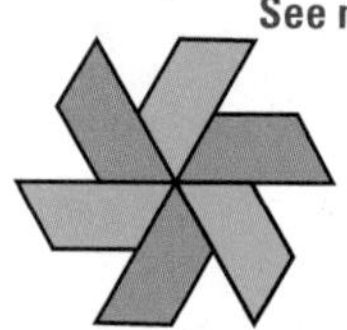

6. Two swimmers design a race course near a beach. The swimmers must move from point A to point B. Then they swim from point B to point C. Finally, they swim from point C to point D. Write the component form of the vectors shown in the diagram, $\overrightarrow{AB}$, $\overrightarrow{BC}$, and $\overrightarrow{CD}$. Then write the component form of $\overrightarrow{AD}$. **⟨9, 6⟩, ⟨8, −6⟩, ⟨7, 16⟩; ⟨24, 16⟩**

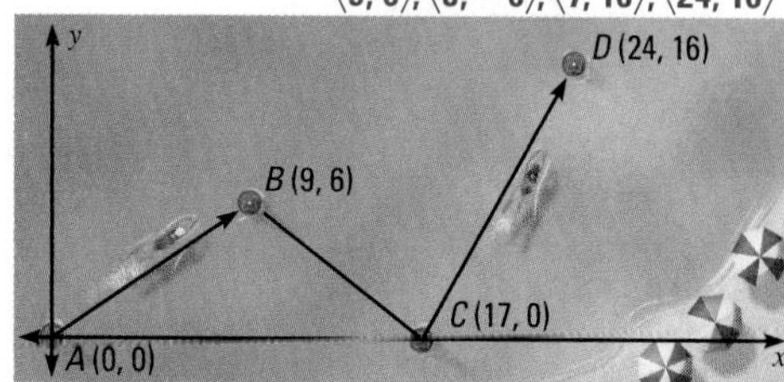

7. A polygon is reflected in the x-axis and then reflected in the y-axis. *Explain* how you can use a rotation to obtain the same result as this composition of transformations. Draw an example. **A rotation of 180° is the same as the two reflections; see margin for art.**

8. In rectangle $PQRS$, one side is twice as long as the other side. Rectangle $P'Q'R'S'$ is the image of $PQRS$ after a dilation centered at P with a scale factor of 0.5. The area of $P'Q'R'S'$ is 32 square inches.

   a. Find the lengths of the sides of $PQRS$. *Explain.* **8 in. by 16 in.; solve the equation $0.5x^2 = 32$.**

   b. Find the ratio of the area of $PQRS$ to the area of $P'Q'R'S'$. $\frac{4}{1}$

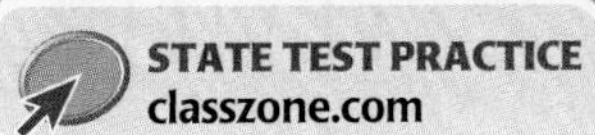

MULTIPLE CHOICE

9. Which matrix product is equivalent to the product $\begin{bmatrix} 3 & -1 \end{bmatrix}\begin{bmatrix} 7 \\ 4 \end{bmatrix}$? **B**

Ⓐ $\begin{bmatrix} -3 & 1 \end{bmatrix}\begin{bmatrix} -7 \\ 4 \end{bmatrix}$

Ⓑ $\begin{bmatrix} 1 & 3 \end{bmatrix}\begin{bmatrix} -4 \\ 7 \end{bmatrix}$

Ⓒ $\begin{bmatrix} -1 & 3 \end{bmatrix}\begin{bmatrix} 7 \\ 4 \end{bmatrix}$

Ⓓ $\begin{bmatrix} 1 & -3 \end{bmatrix}\begin{bmatrix} 4 \\ -7 \end{bmatrix}$

10. Which transformation is *not* an isometry? **D**

Ⓐ Translation Ⓑ Reflection

Ⓒ Rotation Ⓓ Dilation

GRIDDED ANSWER

11. Line p passes through points $J(2, 5)$ and $K(-4, 13)$. Line q is the image of line p after line p is reflected in the x-axis. Find the slope of line q. $\frac{4}{3}$

12. The red triangle is the image of the blue triangle after it is rotated about point P. What is the value of y? $\frac{1}{4}$

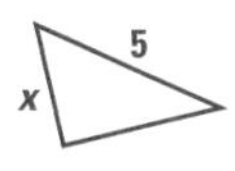

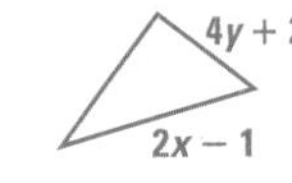

•P

13. The vertices of $\triangle PQR$ are $P(1, 4)$, $Q(2, 0)$, and $R(4, 5)$. What is the x-coordinate of Q' after the given composition? **0**

Translation: $(x, y) \to (x - 2, y + 1)$
Dilation: centered at (0, 0) with $k = 2$

EXTENDED RESPONSE

14. An equation of line ℓ is $y = 3x$.

a. Graph line ℓ. Then graph the image of line ℓ after it is reflected in the line $y = x$. **See margin.**

b. Find the equation of the image. $y = \frac{1}{3}x$

c. Suppose a line has an equation of the form $y = ax$. Make a conjecture about the equation of the image of that line when it is reflected in the line $y = x$. Use several examples to support your conjecture. **See margin.**

15. The vertices of $\triangle EFG$ are $E(4, 2)$, $F(-2, 1)$, and $G(0, -3)$.

a. Find the coordinates of the vertices of $\triangle E'F'G'$, the image of $\triangle EFG$ after a dilation centered at the origin with a scale factor of 2. Graph $\triangle EFG$ and $\triangle E'F'G'$ in the same coordinate plane. **$E'(8, 4)$, $F'(-4, 2)$, $G'(0, -6)$; see graph in part (b).**

b. Find the coordinates of the vertices of $\triangle E''F''G''$, the image of $\triangle E'F'G'$ after a dilation centered at the origin with a scale factor of 2.5. Graph $\triangle E''F''G''$ in the same coordinate plane you used in part (a). **$E''(20, 10)$, $F''(-10, 5)$, $G''(0, -15)$; see margin for art.**

c. What is the dilation that maps $\triangle EFG$ to $\triangle E''F''G''$? **dilation centered at the origin with scale factor 5**

d. What is the scale factor of a dilation that is equivalent to the composition of two dilations described below? *Explain.*

Dilation: centered at (0, 0) with a scale factor of a
Dilation: centered at (0, 0) with a scale factor of b
***ab*; it's the product of the two scale factors.**

14a.

14c. The equation of the image is $y = \frac{1}{a}x$. *Sample answer:* $y = 2x$ and $y = \frac{1}{2}x$ or $y = -5x$ and $y = -\frac{1}{5}x$ are reflections of one another in the line $y = x$.

15b.

Additional Resources

The following resources are available to help review the materials in Chapters 1–9.

Chapter Resource Books

- Chapter 7 CRB, Cumulative Review, pp. 106–107
- Chapter 8 CRB, Cumulative Review, pp. 91–92
- Chapter 9 CRB, Cumulative Review, pp. 104–105

Tell whether the lines through the given points are *parallel*, *perpendicular*, or *neither*. *(p. 171)*

1. Line 1: (3, 5), (−2, 6)
Line 2: (−3, 5), (−4, 10) **neither**

2. Line 1: (2, −10), (9, −8)
Line 2: (8, 6), (1, 4) **parallel**

Write an equation of the line shown. *(p. 180)*

3.

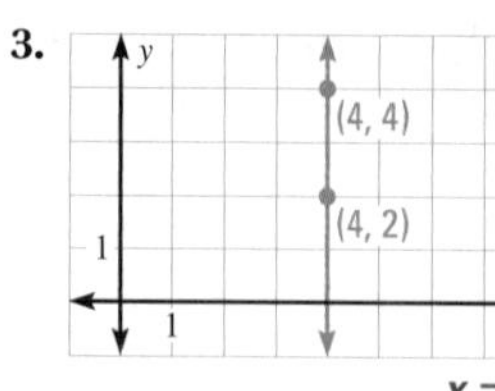

$x = 4$

4. **$y = -\frac{3}{2}x + 1$**

5.

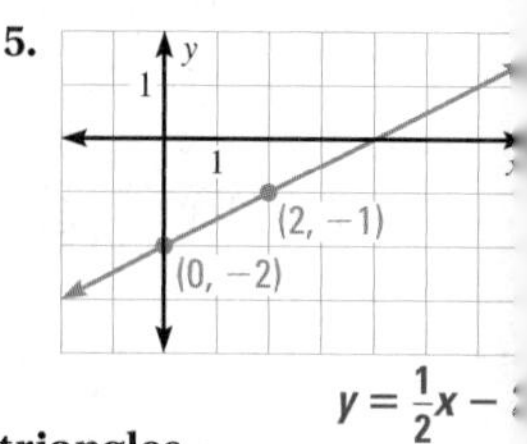

$y = \frac{1}{2}x -$

State the third congruence that must be given to prove that the triangles are congruent using the given postulate or theorem. *(pp. 234, 240, and 249)*

6. SSS Congruence Post.

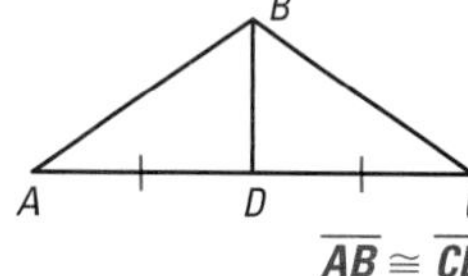

$\overline{AB} \cong \overline{CB}$

7. SAS Congruence Post.

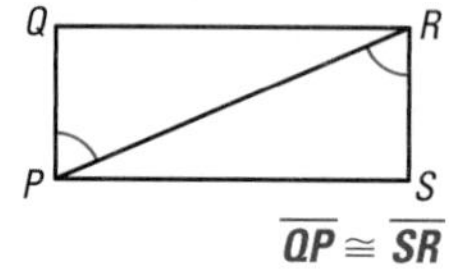

$\overline{QP} \cong \overline{SR}$

8. AAS Congruence Thm

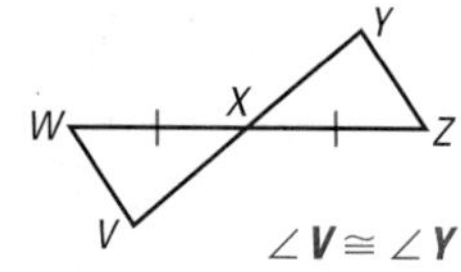

$\angle V \cong \angle Y$

Determine whether $\overline{BD}$ is a *perpendicular bisector, median,* or *altitude* of $\triangle ABC$. *(p. 319)*

9.

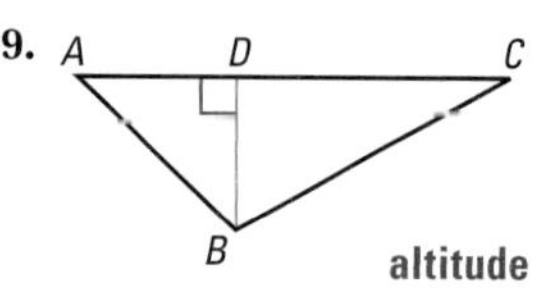

altitude

10. **perpendicular bisector**

11.

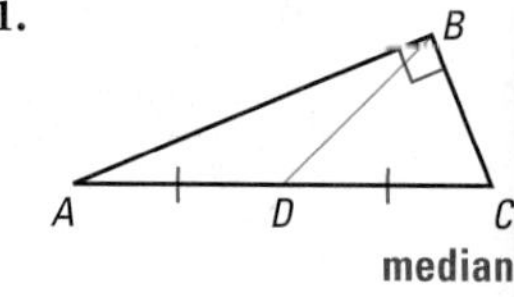

median

Determine whether the segment lengths form a triangle. If so, would the triangle be *acute, right,* or *obtuse*? *(pp. 328 and 441)*

12. 11, 11, 15 **triangle; acute**

13. 33, 44, 55 **triangle; right**

14. 9, 9, 13 **triangle; obtuse**

15. 7, 8, 16 **not a triangle**

16. 9, 40, 41 **triangle; right**

17. 0.5, 1.2, 1.3 **triangle; right**

Classify the special quadrilateral. *Explain* your reasoning. Then find the values of x and y. *(p. 533)*

18. **Rhombus; all 4 sides are congruent; 82, 4.**

19. **Rectangle; the diagonals are congruent and they bisect each other; 5, 3.**

20. **Parallelogram; two pair of opposite congruent sides; 15, 22.**

Graph the image of the triangle after the composition of the transformations in the order they are listed. *(p. 608)* **21, 22. See margin.**

21. $P(-5, 2)$, $Q(-2, 4)$, $R(0, 0)$
Translation: $(x, y) \rightarrow (x - 2, y + 5)$
Reflection: in the x-axis

22. $F(-1, -8)$, $G(-6, -3)$, $R(0, 0)$
Reflection: in the line $x = 2$
Rotation: 90° about the origin

FIRE ESCAPE In the diagram, the staircases on the fire escape are parallel. The measure of ∠1 is 48°. *(p. 154)*

23. Identify the angle(s) congruent to ∠1. **∠4, ∠5, ∠8**

24. Identify the angle(s) congruent to ∠2. **∠3, ∠6, ∠7**

25. What is $m\angle 2$? **132°**

26. What is $m\angle 6$? **132°**

27. **BAHAMA ISLANDS** The map of some of the Bahamas has a scale of $\frac{1}{2}$ inch : 60 miles. Use a ruler to estimate the actual distance from Freeport to Nassau. *(p. 364)* **about 135 mi**

28. **ANGLE OF ELEVATION** You are standing 12 feet away from your house and the angle of elevation is 65° from your foot. How tall is your house? Round to the nearest foot. *(p. 473)* **26 ft**

29. **PURSE** You are decorating 8 trapezoid-shaped purses to sell at a craft show. You want to decorate the front of each purse with a string of beads across the midsegment. On each purse, the length of the bottom is 5.5 inches and the length of the top is 9 inches. If the beading costs \$1.59 per foot, how much will it cost to decorate the 8 purses? *(p. 542)* **\$7.69**

TILE PATTERNS ***Describe*** **the transformations that are combined to make the tile pattern.** *(p. 607)*

30. 
translation and reflection

31. 

translation and rotation

32. 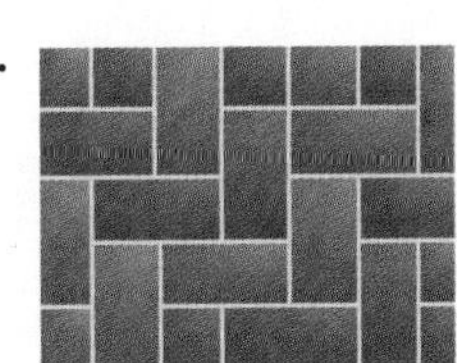
translation and rotation

21.

22.

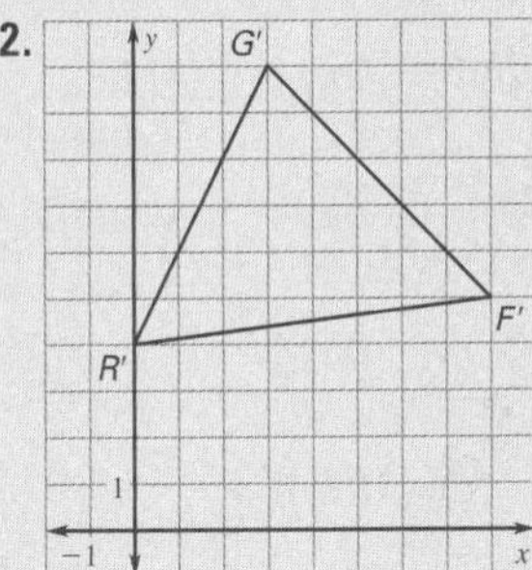

10 Pacing and Assignment Guide

REGULAR SCHEDULE

Pre-AP For pacing and assignments for a Pre-AP course, see the *Geometry Toolkit.*

Lesson	Les. Day	BASIC	AVERAGE	ADVANCED
10.1	Day 1	pp. 655–658 Exs. 1–17, 35, 36	pp. 655–658 Exs. 1–17, 27, 28, 35, 36	pp. 655–658 Exs. 1–10, 12–17, 27, 28, 35, 36
	Day 2	pp. 655–658 Exs. 18–29, 37–39, 43–47	pp. 655–658 Exs. 18–26, 29–33, 37–41, 43–47 odd	pp. 655–658 Exs. 18–20, 23–26, 29–34*, 37–43*, 46, 47
10.2	Day 1	EP p. 896 Exs. 30–32; pp. 661–663 Exs. 1–17, 22–24, 26–34	pp. 661–663 Exs. 1–19, 22–24, 26–34	pp. 661–663 Exs. 1, 2, 4–10 even, 11–25*, 26–34 even
10.3	Day 1	pp. 667–670 Exs. 1–18, 25–28, 35–37	pp. 667–670 Exs. 1, 2–14 even, 15–22, 25–30, 35–37	pp. 667–670 Exs. 1, 2, 3–15 odd, 16–35*, 37
10.4	Day 1	pp. 676–679 Exs. 1–12, 43–47	pp. 676–679 Exs. 1, 2, 4–7, 9–12, 16–18, 43–47	pp. 676–679 Exs. 1, 2, 5–8, 10–12, 16–18, 43–47
	Day 2	pp. 676–679 Exs. 13–19, 27–33, 40–42	pp. 676–679 Exs. 13–15, 19–25, 28–36, 41	pp. 676–679 Exs. 14, 15, 19–26*, 28, 29, 34–39*, 42
10.5	Day 1	pp. 683–686 Exs. 1–16, 22–27, 32–39	pp. 683–686 Exs. 1–6, 9–11, 13–19, 22–29, 32–39	pp. 683–686 Exs. 1–6, 10–13, 15–21*, 23–31*, 32–38 even
10.6	Day 1	SRH p. 873 Exs. 1–7; pp. 692–695 Exs. 1–15, 20–23, 29–41 odd	pp. 692–695 Exs. 1–5, 7–10, 12–18, 20–26, 30–42 even	pp. 692–695 Exs. 1–5, 7, 8, 10, 11, 13–28*, 30, 32, 36, 39, 42
10.7	Day 1	pp. 702–705 Exs. 1–16, 49–54	pp. 702–705 Exs. 1, 2, 4–7, 10–13, 15, 16, 31–34, 49–54	pp. 702–705 Exs. 1, 2, 5–8, 11–14, 16, 31–35*, 49–54
	Day 2	pp. 702–705 Exs. 17–28, 36–40, 46–48	pp. 702–705 Exs. 18–23, 26–30, 36–43, 47	pp. 702–705 Exs. 18, 19, 22–30, 36–45*, 48
Review	Day 1	pp. 708–711 Exs. 1–32	pp. 708–711 Exs. 1–32	pp. 708–711 Exs. 1–32
Assess	Day 1	Chapter 10 Test	Chapter 10 Test	Chapter 10 Test
Yearly Pacing		Chapter 10 Total – 12 days	Chapters 1–10 Total – 132 days	Remaining – 28 days

*Challenge Exercises EP = Extra Practice SRH = Skills Review Handbook

BLOCK SCHEDULE

DAY 1	DAY 2	DAY 3	DAY 4	DAY 5	DAY 6
10.1	**10.2**	**10.4**	**10.5**	**10.7**	**REVIEW**
pp. 655–658 Exs. 1–33, 35–41, 43–47 odd	pp. 661–663 Exs. 1–19, 22–24, 26–34	pp. 676–679 Exs. 1, 2, 4–7, 9–25, 28–36, 41, 43–47	pp. 683–686 Exs. 1–6, 9–11, 13–19, 22–29, 32–39	pp. 702–705 Exs. 1, 2, 4–7, 10–13, 15, 16, 18–23, 26–34, 36–43, 47, 49–54	pp. 708–711 Exs. 1–32
	10.3		**10.6**		**ASSESS**
	pp. 667–670 Exs. 1, 2–14 even, 15–22, 25–30, 35–37		pp. 692–695 Exs. 1–5, 7–10, 12–18, 20–26, 30–42 even		Chapter 10 Test
Yearly Pacing	Chapter 10 Total – 6 days	Chapters 1–10 Total – 66 days	Remaining – 14 days		

Chapter Resource Guide 10

RESOURCE MANAGER

Chapter Resource Book							
CHAPTER SUPPORT							
Parents as Partners (Chapter Overview with home involvement exercises and activity)						p. 1	
LESSON SUPPORT	**10.1**	**10.2**	**10.3**	**10.4**	**10.5**	**10.6**	**10.7**
Teaching Guide/Lesson Plan	p. 3	p. 16	p. 30	p. 45	p. 58	p. 73	p. 87
Activity Masters		p. 18			p. 60		p. 89
Technology Activities & Keystrokes			p. 32			p. 75	
Activity Support Masters							
Practice (3 levels)	p. 5	p. 19	p. 34	p. 47	p. 61	p. 76	p. 90
Study Guide	p. 11	p. 25	p. 40	p. 53	p. 67	p. 82	p. 96
Catch-Up for Absent Students	p. 13	p. 27	p. 42	p. 55	p. 69	p. 84	p. 98
Problem Solving/Application	p. 14	p. 28	p. 43	p. 56	p. 70	p. 85	p. 99
Challenge Practice	p. 15	p. 29	p. 44	p. 57	p. 72	p. 86	p. 100
REVIEW							
Chapter Review Games and Activities		p. 101		Cumulative Practice		p. 104	
Project with Rubric		p. 102		Resource Book Answers		A1	

Transparencies	*10.1*	*10.2*	*10.3*	*10.4*	*10.5*	*10.6*	*10.7*
Warm-Up/Daily Homework Quiz	✔	✔	✔	✔	✔	✔	✔
Notetaking Guide	✔	✔	✔	✔	✔	✔	✔
Teacher Support	✔						✔
Answer Transparencies	✔	✔	✔	✔	✔	✔	✔

ASSESSMENT BOOK

Quizzes	p. 140	SAT/ACT Chapter Test	p. 151
Chapter Tests (3 levels)	p. 143	Alternative Assessment with Rubric	p. 153
Standardized Chapter Test	p. 149		

TECHNOLOGY

- Easy Planner
- Test and Practice Generator
- Power Presentations
- @HomeTutor
- Activity Generator
- Animated Geometry
- Classzone.com
- eEdition Plus Online
- eWorkbook Plus Online
- ML Assessment System

ADDITIONAL RESOURCES

- Worked-Out Solution Key
- Notetaking Guide
- Practice Wookbook
- Geometry Toolkit
- Benchmark Tests
- Remediation Book
- Spanish Study Guide
- Spanish Assessment Book
- Student Resources in Spanish
- Multi-Language Visual Glossary

10 Lesson Practice Level B

LESSON 10.1 Practice B
For use with pages 650–658

Use $\odot P$ to draw the described part of the circle.

1. Draw a diameter and label it AB. *Sample answer:*

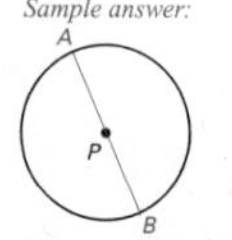

2. Draw a tangent ray and label it CD. *Sample answer:*

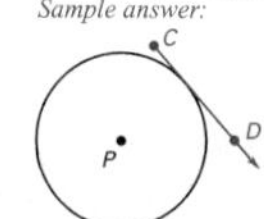

3. Draw a secant and label it EF. *Sample answer:*

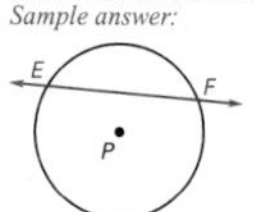

4. Draw a chord and label it GH. *Sample answer:*

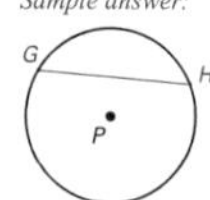

Use the diagram to determine if the statement is *true* or *false*.

5. The distance between the centers of the circles is equal to the length of the diameter of each circle. true
6. The lines $y = 0$ and $y = 4$ represent all the common tangents of the two circles. false
7. The circles intersect at the point $(6, 3)$. true
8. Suppose the two circles shown are inscribed in a rectangle. The perimeter of the rectangle is 36 units. true

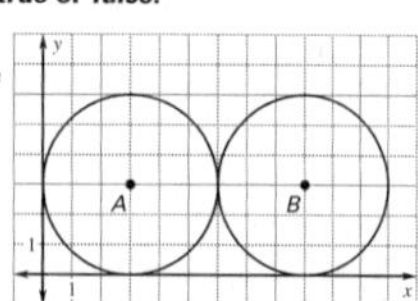

Draw two circles that have the given number of common tangents.

9. 3 *Sample answer:*
10. 2 *Sample answer:*
11. 0 *Sample answer:*

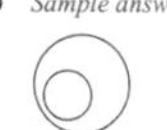

In Exercises 12–17, $\overline{BC}$ is a radius of $\odot C$ and $\overline{AB}$ is tangent to $\odot C$. Find the value of x.

12. 28

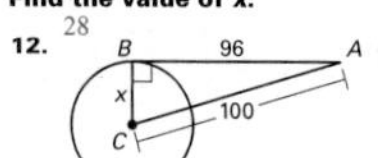

13. 117

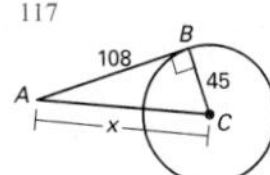

14. 64

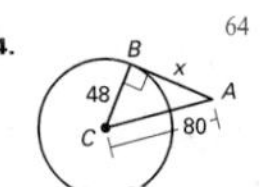

LESSON 10.1 Practice B *continued*
For use with pages 650–658

15. 24

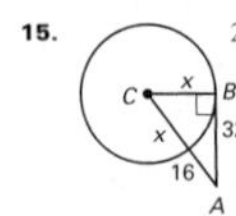

16. 33

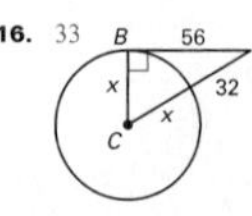

17. 16

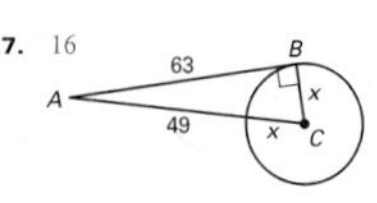

The points K and M are points of tangency. Find the value(s) of x.

18. 5

19. 3, −3

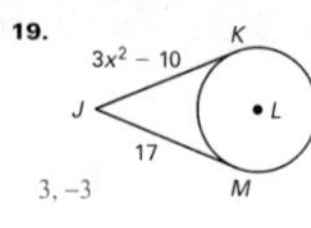

20. $1, -\frac{5}{2}$

21. **Swimming Pool** You are standing 36 feet from a circular swimming pool. The distance from you to a point of tangency on the pool is 48 feet as shown. What is the radius of the swimming pool? 14 ft

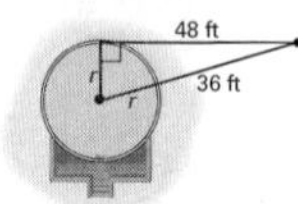

22. **Space Shuttle** Suppose a space shuttle is orbiting about 180 miles above Earth. What is the distance d from the shuttle to the horizon? The radius of Earth is about 4000 miles. Round your answer to the nearest tenth. 1213.4 mi

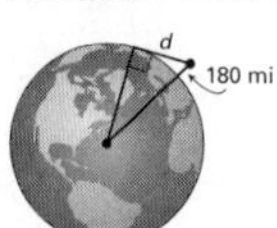

In Exercises 23 and 24, use the following information.

Golf A green on a golf course is in the shape of a circle. Your golf ball is 8 feet from the edge of the green and 32 feet from a point of tangency on the green as shown in the figure.

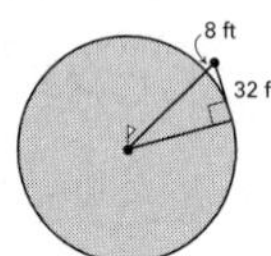

23. Assuming the green is flat, what is the radius of the green? 60 ft
24. How far is your golf ball from the cup at the center of the green? 68 ft

LESSON 10.2 Practice B
For use with pages 659–663

In $\odot F$, determine whether the given arc is a *minor arc*, *major arc*, or *semicircle*.

1. $\widehat{AB}$ minor arc
2. $\widehat{AE}$ minor arc
3. $\widehat{EAC}$ semicircle
4. $\widehat{ACD}$ major arc
5. $\widehat{CAD}$ major arc
6. $\widehat{DEB}$ semicircle
7. $\widehat{BAE}$ minor arc
8. $\widehat{DEC}$ major arc

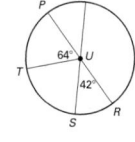

In the figure, $\overline{PR}$ and $\overline{QS}$ are diameters of $\odot U$. Find the measure of the indicated arc.

9. $m\widehat{PQ}$ 42°
10. $m\widehat{ST}$ 74°
11. $m\widehat{TPS}$ 286°
12. $m\widehat{RT}$ 116°
13. $m\widehat{RQS}$ 318°
14. $m\widehat{QR}$ 138°
15. $m\widehat{PQS}$ 222°
16. $m\widehat{TQR}$ 244°
17. $m\widehat{PS}$ 138°
18. $m\widehat{PTR}$ 180°

$\widehat{PQ}$ has a measure of 90° in $\odot R$. Find the length of $\overline{PQ}$.

19. $7\sqrt{2}$

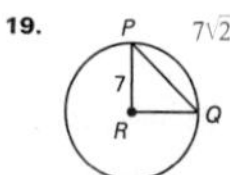

20. $10\sqrt{2}$

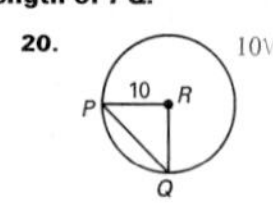

Find the indicated arc measure.

21. $m\widehat{AC}$ 135°
22. $m\widehat{ACB}$ 240°
23. $m\widehat{DAB}$ 225°

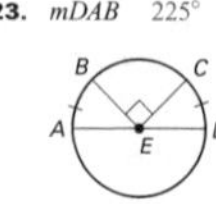

Two diameters of $\odot T$ are $\overline{PQ}$ and $\overline{RS}$. Find the given arc measure if $m\widehat{PR} = 35°$.

24. $m\widehat{PS}$ 145°
25. $m\widehat{PSR}$ 325°
26. $m\widehat{PRQ}$ 180°
27. $m\widehat{PRS}$ 215°

LESSON 10.2 Practice B *continued*
For use with pages 659–663

Two diameters of $\odot N$ are $\overline{JK}$ and $\overline{LM}$. Find the given arc measure if $m\widehat{JM} = 165°$.

28. $m\widehat{JL}$ 15°
29. $m\widehat{JMK}$ 180°
30. $m\widehat{JLM}$ 195°
31. $m\widehat{KLM}$ 345°

Tell whether the given arcs are congruent.

32. $\widehat{JK}$ and $\widehat{QR}$ no

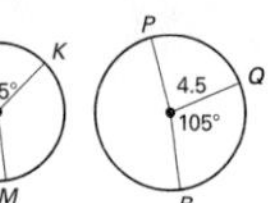

33. $\widehat{AB}$ and $\widehat{CD}$ yes

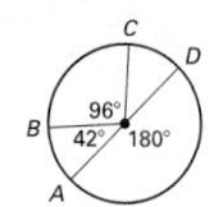

34. $\widehat{EF}$ and $\widehat{GH}$ no

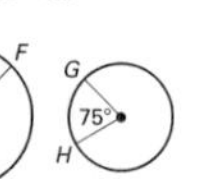

35. $\widehat{STV}$ and $\widehat{UVT}$ no

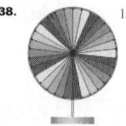

Game Shows Each game show wheel shown is divided into congruent sections. Find the measure of each arc.

36. 24°

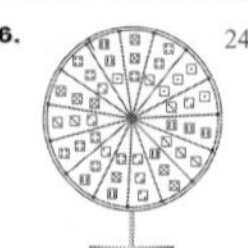

37. 15°

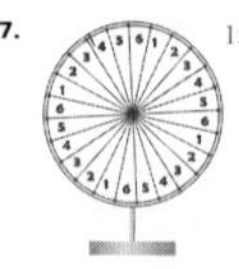

38. 12°

In Exercises 39 and 40, use the following information.

Sprinkler A water sprinkler covers the area shown in the figure. It moves through the covered area at a rate of about 5° per second.

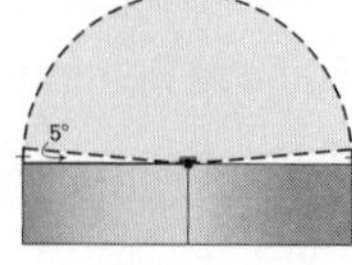

39. What is the measure of the arc covered by the sprinkler? 170°
40. If the sprinkler starts at the far left position, how long will it take for the sprinkler to reach the far right position? 34 sec

LESSON 10.3 Practice B
For use with pages 664–670

Find the measure of the given arc or chord.

1. $m\widehat{BC}$ 122°
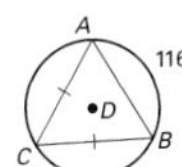

2. $m\widehat{LM}$ 90°
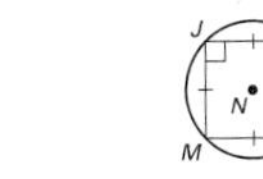

3. $\overline{QS}$ 22
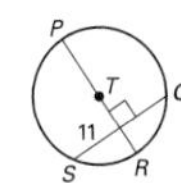

4. $m\widehat{AC}$ 115°
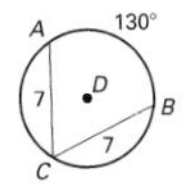

5. $m\widehat{PQR}$ 80°
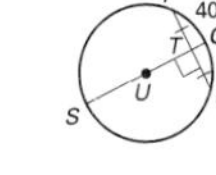

6. $m\widehat{KLM}$ 180°

Find the value of x.

7. 1
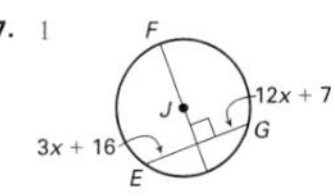

8. 10
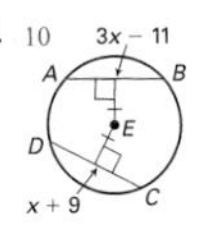

9. 4
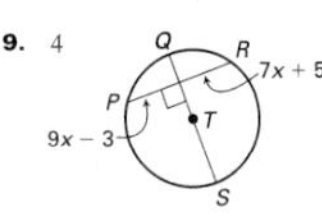

10. 9
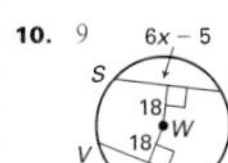

11. 4
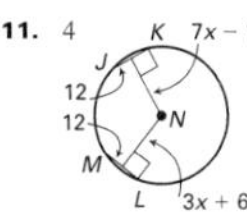

12. 6
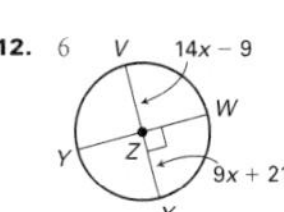

In Exercises 13–16, determine whether $\overline{PR}$ is a diameter of the circle.

13. no
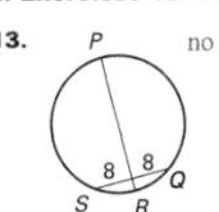

14. no
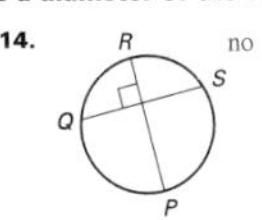

LESSON 10.3 Practice B continued
For use with pages 664–670

15. yes

16. no
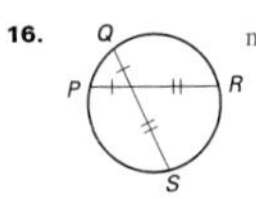

17. **Proof** Complete the proof.

GIVEN: $\overline{AC}$ is a diameter of $\odot F$. $\overline{AC} \perp \overline{BD}$

PROVE: $\widehat{AD} \cong \widehat{AB}$

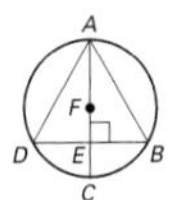

Statements	Reasons
1. $\overline{AC}$ is a diameter of $\odot F$, $\overline{AC} \perp \overline{BD}$	1. ? Given
2. ? $\angle AED \cong \angle AEB$	2. Perpendicular angles are congruent.
3. $\overline{DE} \cong \overline{BE}$	3. ? Theorem 10.5
4. $\overline{AE} \cong \overline{AE}$	4. ? Reflexive property of segment congruence
5. $\triangle AED \cong \triangle AEB$	5. ? SAS Congruence Postulate
6. ? $\overline{AD} \cong \overline{AB}$	6. Corresponding parts of congruent triangles are congruent.
7. $\widehat{AD} \cong \widehat{AB}$	7. ? Theorem 10.3

18. **Proof** Complete the proof.

GIVEN: $\overline{PQ}$ is a diameter of $\odot U$. $\widehat{PT} \cong \widehat{QS}$

PROVE: $\triangle PUT \cong \triangle QUS$

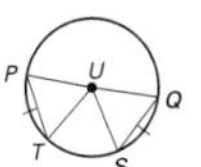

Statements	Reasons
1. $\widehat{PT} \cong \widehat{QS}$	1. ? Given
2. ? $\overline{PT} \cong \overline{QS}$	2. Theorem 10.3
3. $\overline{UP} \cong \overline{UQ} \cong \overline{UT} \cong \overline{US}$	3. ? Definition of radius
4. $\triangle PUT \cong \triangle QUS$	4. ? SSS Congruence Postulate

19. Briefly explain what other congruence postulate you could use to prove that $\triangle PUT \cong \triangle QUS$ in Exercise 18.
Show that all radii are equal, then use definition of measure of minor arc to show that $\angle PUT \cong \angle QUS$, then use SAS Congruence Postulate.

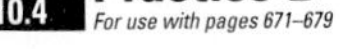

LESSON 10.4 Practice B
For use with pages 671–679

1. **Multiple Choice** In the figure shown, which statement is true? B

A. $\angle SPR \cong \angle PSQ$ B. $\angle RQS \cong \angle RPS$
C. $\angle RPS \cong \angle PRQ$ D. $\angle PRQ \cong \angle SQR$

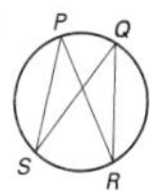

Find the measure of the indicated angle or arc in $\odot P$.

2. $m\widehat{ST}$ 58°

3. $m\widehat{AB}$ 140°

4. $m\angle JLM$ 46°

5. $m\angle A$ 63°

6. $m\angle K$ 28°

7. $m\widehat{VST}$ 123°
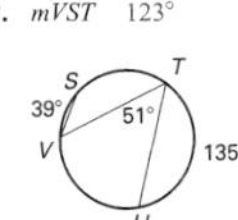

Find the measure of the indicated angle or arc in $\odot P$, given $m\widehat{LM} = 84°$ and $m\widehat{KN} = 116°$.

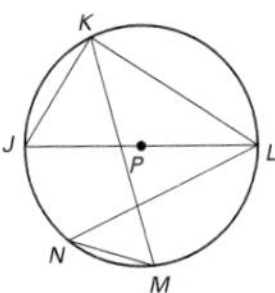

8. $m\angle JKL$ 90° 9. $m\angle MKL$ 42°
10. $m\angle KMN$ 58° 11. $m\angle JKM$ 48°
12. $m\angle KLN$ 58° 13. $m\angle LNM$ 42°
14. $m\widehat{MJ}$ 96° 15. $m\widehat{LKJ}$ 180°

Find the values of the variables.

16. $x = 14, y = 38$
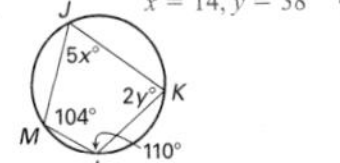
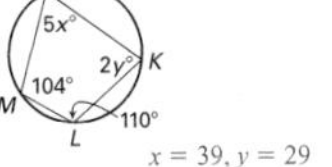

17. $x = 58, y = 29$
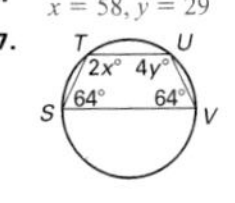

18. $x = 72, y = 90$

19. $x = 39, y = 29$
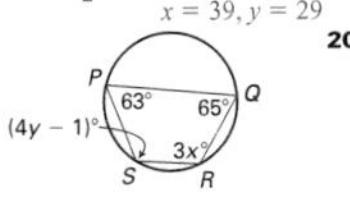

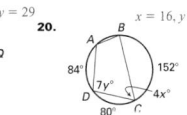

20. $x = 16, y = 14$
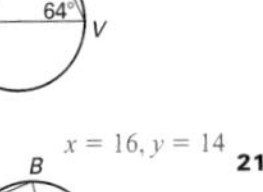

21. $x = 6, y = 36.5$
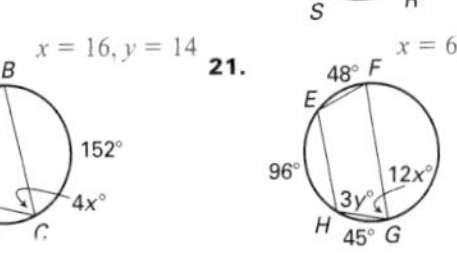

LESSON 10.4 Practice B continued
For use with pages 671–679

22. **Multiple Choice** What is the value of x in the figure shown? D

A. 7 B. 12
C. 16 D. 21

23. **Proof** Complete the proof.

GIVEN: $\odot P$

PROVE: $\triangle AED \sim \triangle BEC$

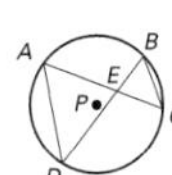

Statements	Reasons
1. $\odot P$	1. Given
2. ? $\angle AED \cong \angle BEC$	2. Vertical Angles Theorem
3. $\angle CAD \cong \angle DBC$	3. ? Theorem 10.8
4. $\triangle AED \sim \triangle BEC$	4. ? Angle-Angle Similarity Postulate

24. Name two other angles that could be used in Step 3 of Exercise 23. $\angle ADB$ and $\angle ACB$

25. **Proof** Complete the proof.

GIVEN: $m\widehat{AB} \cong m\widehat{CD}$

PROVE: $\triangle ABE \cong \triangle DCE$

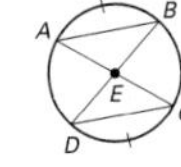

Statements	Reasons
1. $m\widehat{AB} \cong m\widehat{CD}$	1. ? Given
2. ? $\overline{AB} \cong \overline{CD}$	2. Theorem 10.3
3. ? $\angle AEB \cong \angle DEC$	3. Vertical Angles Theorem
4. $\angle BDC \cong \angle CAB$	4. ? Theorem 10.8
5. $\triangle ABE \cong \triangle DCE$	5. ? AAS Congruence Theorem

10 Lesson Practice Level B

LESSON 10.5 Practice B
For use with pages 680–686

Find the indicated arc measure.

1. $m\widehat{AB}$ 202° 

2. $m\widehat{FH}$ 102° 

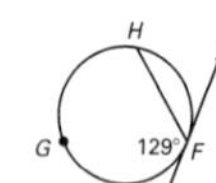

3. $m\widehat{JKL}$ 240°

Find $m\angle 1$.

4. 56°

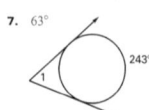

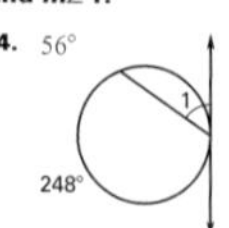

5. 128°

6. 37°

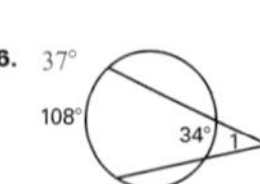

7. 63°

8. 120° 109°

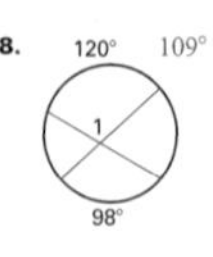

9. 133°

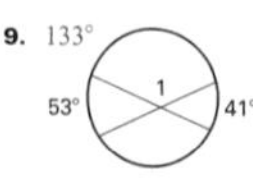

10. 26°

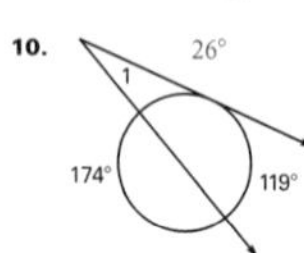

11. 42°

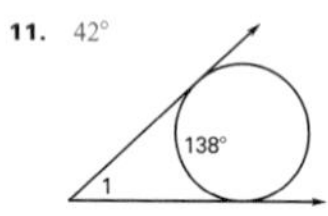

12. 35° 104°

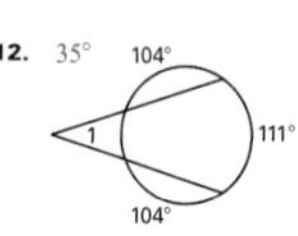

In Exercises 13–18, find the value of *x*.

13. 67

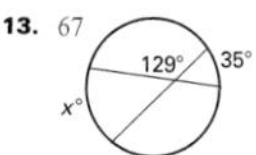

14. 70

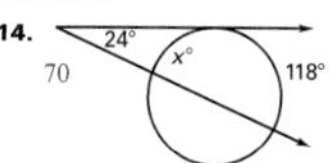

15. 61

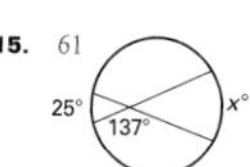

LESSON 10.5 Practice B *continued*
For use with pages 680–686

16. 24

17. 7

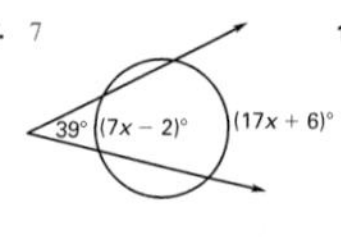

18. 16

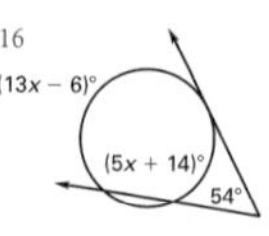

19. In the diagram shown, *m* is tangent to the circle at the point *S*. Find the measures of all the numbered angles.
$m\angle 1 = 97°, m\angle 2 = 83°, m\angle 3 = 63°, m\angle 4 = 117°$

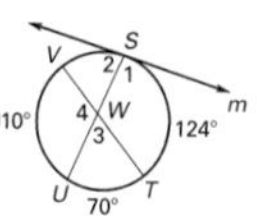

Use the diagram shown to find the measure of the angle.

20. $m\angle CAF$ 60° 21. $m\angle AFB$ 30°

22. $m\angle CEF$ 60° 23. $m\angle CFB$ 60°

24. $m\angle DCF$ 30° 25. $m\angle BCD$ 60°

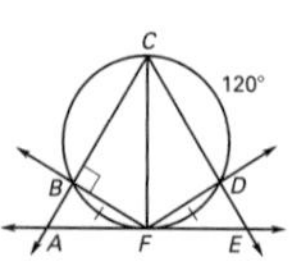

In Exercises 26 and 27, the circles are concentric. Find the value of *x*.

26. 128

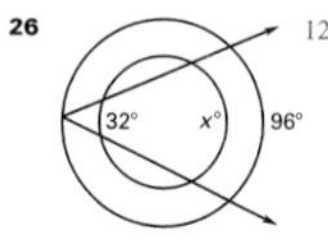

27. 43

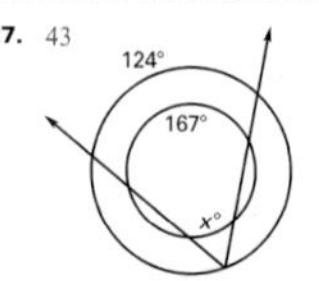

28. **Transportation** A plane is flying at an altitude of about 7 miles above Earth. What is the measure of arc *TV* that represents the part of Earth you can see? The radius of Earth is about 4000 miles.
about 6.8°

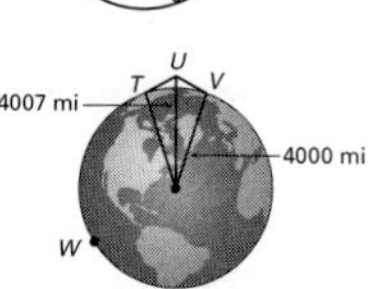

29. **Mountain Climbing** A mountain climber is standing on top of a mountain that is about 4.75 miles above sea level. Use the information from Exercise 28 to find the measure of the arc that represents the part of Earth the mountain climber can see.
about 5.6°

LESSON 10.6 Practice B
For use with pages 688–695

Find the value of *x*.

1. 15

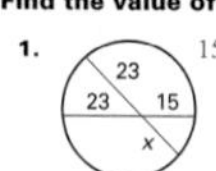

2. 2

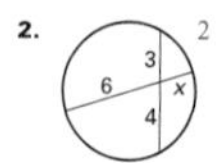

3. 4

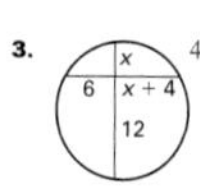

Find *AB* and *DE*.

4. $AB = 16$, $DE = 17$

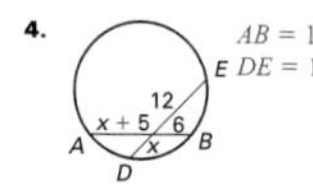

5. $AB = 21$, $DE = 23$

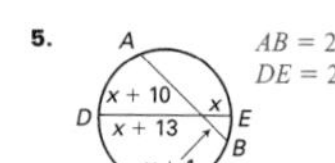

6. $AB = 32$, $DE = 24$

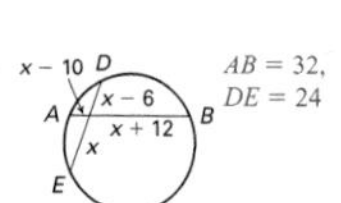

Find the value of *x*.

7. 5

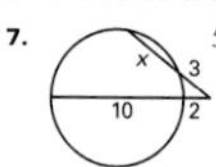

8. 6

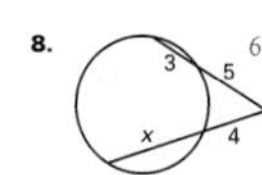

9. 7

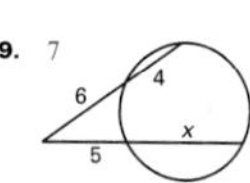

Find *RT* and *TV*.

10. $RT = 20$, $TV = 16$

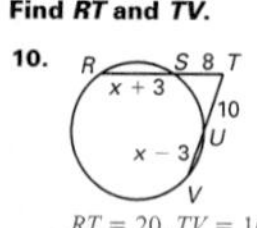

11. $RT = 35$, $TV = 45$

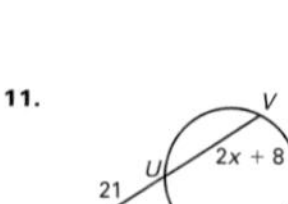

12. $RT = 36$, $TV = 27$

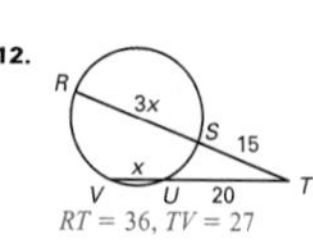

Find the value of *x*.

13. 15

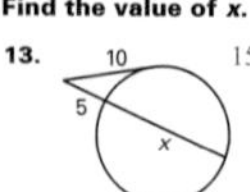

14. 12

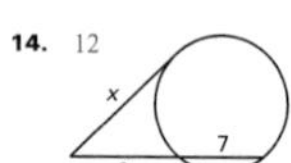

15. 4

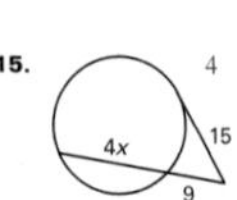

Find *PQ*.

16. 18

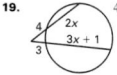

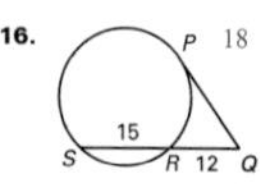

17. 30

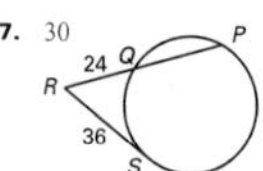

18. 50

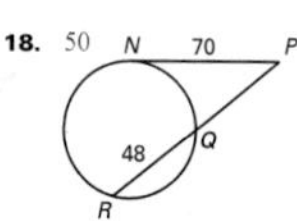

LESSON 10.6 Practice B *continued*
For use with pages 688–695

Find the value of *x*.

19. 4

20. 8

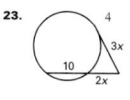

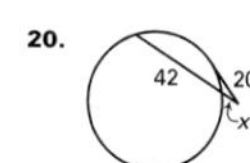

21. 10

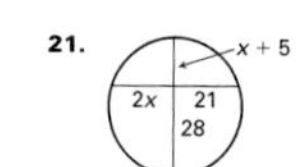

22. 8

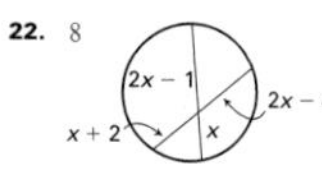

23. 4

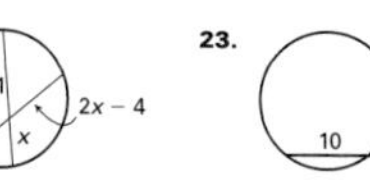

24. 6

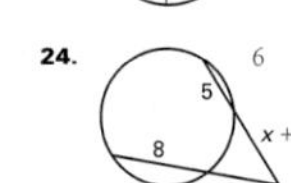

25. 15

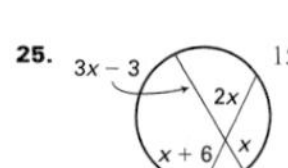

26. 8

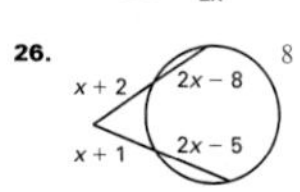

27. 4

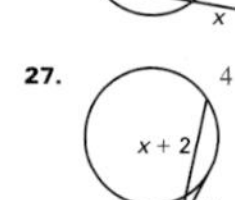

28. **Winch** A large industrial winch is enclosed as shown. There are 15 inches of the cable hanging free off of the winch's spool and the distance from the end of the cable to the spool is 8 inches. What is the diameter of the spool?
20.125 in.

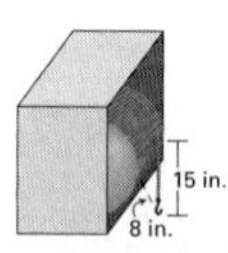

29. **Storm Drain** The diagram shows a cross-section of a large storm drain pipe with a small amount of standing water. The distance across the surface of the water is 48 inches and the water is 4.25 inches deep at its deepest point. To the nearest inch, what is the diameter of the storm drain pipe?
140 in.

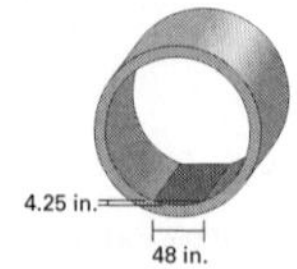

30. **Basketball** The Xs show the positions of two basketball teammates relative to the circular "key" on a basketball court. The player outside the key passes the ball to the player on the key. To the nearest tenth of a foot, how long is the pass? 14.2 ft

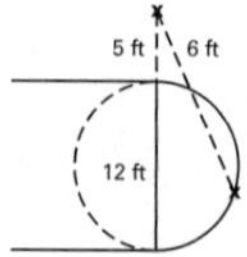

LESSON 10.7

Practice B

For use with pages 699–705

Write the standard equation of the circle.

1. 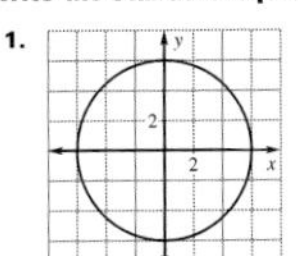 $x^2 + y^2 = 36$

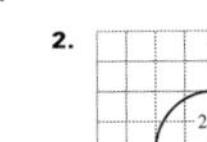

2. 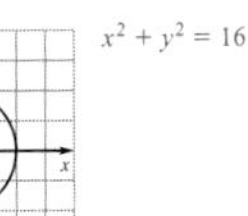 $x^2 + y^2 = 16$

3. $(x - 1)^2 + (y - 1)^2 = 1$

4. 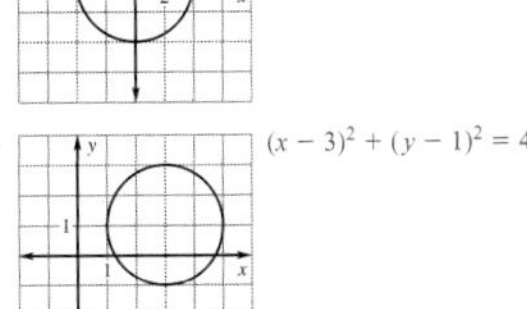 $(x - 3)^2 + (y - 1)^2 = 4$

Write the standard equation of the circle with the given center and radius.

5. Center (0, 0), radius 9 $x^2 + y^2 = 81$
6. Center (1, 3), radius 4 $(x - 1)^2 + (y - 3)^2 = 16$
7. Center (−3, 0), radius 5 $(x + 3)^2 + y^2 = 25$
8. Center (4, −7), radius 13 $(x - 4)^2 + (y + 7)^2 = 169$
9. Center (0, 14), radius 14 $x^2 + (y - 14)^2 = 196$
10. Center (−12, 7), radius 6 $(x + 12)^2 + (y - 7)^2 = 36$

Use the given information to write the standard equation of the circle.

11. The center is (0, 0), and a point on the circle is (4, 0). $x^2 + y^2 = 16$
12. The center is (0, 0), and a point on the circle is (3, −4). $x^2 + y^2 = 25$
13. The center is (2, 4), and a point on the circle is (−3, 16). $(x - 2)^2 + (y - 4)^2 = 169$
14. The center is (3, −2), and a point on the circle is (23, 19). $(x - 3)^2 + (y + 2)^2 = 841$
15. The center is (−43, 5), and a point on the circle is (−34, 17). $(x + 43)^2 + (y - 5)^2 = 225$
16. The center is (17, 24), and a point on the circle is (−3, 9). $(x - 17)^2 + (y - 24)^2 = 625$

Determine the diameter of the circle with the given equation.

17. $x^2 + y^2 = 100$ 20
18. $(x - 12)^2 + (y + 5)^2 = 64$ 16
19. $(x - 2)^2 + (y - 9)^2 = 4$ 4
20. $(x + 16)^2 + (y + 15)^2 = 81$ 18

LESSON 10.7

Practice B *continued*

For use with pages 699–705

Graph the equation.

21. 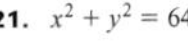 $x^2 + y^2 = 64$

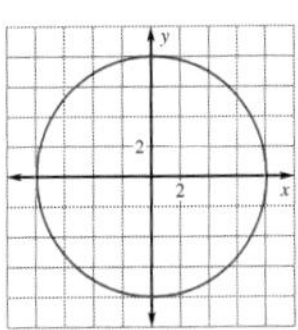

22.  $(x - 4)^2 + (y + 1)^2 = 16$

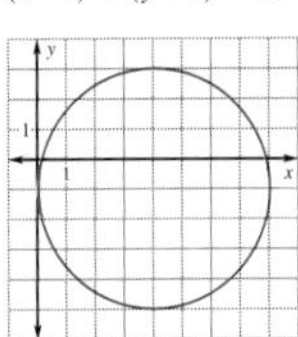

Determine whether the point lies on the circle described by the equation $(x - 3)^2 + (y - 8)^2 = 100$.

23. (0, 0) no
24. (13, 8) yes
25. (−5, 2) yes
26. (11, 5) no

27. **Earthquakes** After an earthquake, you are given seismograph readings from three locations, where the coordinate units are miles.

At *A*(2, 1), the epicenter is 5 miles away.
At *B*(−2, −2), the epicenter is 6 miles away.
At *C*(−6, 4), the epicenter is 4 miles away.

a. Graph three circles in one coordinate plane to represent the possible epicenter locations determined by each of the seismograph readings.

b. What are the coordinates of the epicenter? (−2, 4)

c. People could feel the earthquake up to 9 miles from its epicenter. Could a person at (4, −5) feel it? *Explain.* No; The given coordinates are about 10.8 miles from the epicenter.

28. **Olympic Flag** You are using a math software program to design a pattern for an Olympic flag. In addition to the dimensions shown in the diagram, the distance between any two adjacent rings in the same row is 3 inches. See below.

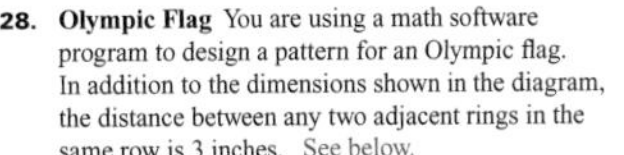

a. Use the given dimensions to write equations representing the outer circles of the five rings. Use inches as units in a coordinate plane with the lower left corner of the flag at the origin.

b. Each ring is 3 inches thick. Explain how you can adjust the equations of the outer circles to write equations representing the inner circles.

a. $(x - 28)^2 + (y - 44)^2 = 169$; $(x - 42.5)^2 + (y - 31)^2 = 169$; $(x - 57)^2 + (y - 44)^2 = 169$; $(x - 71.5)^2 + (y - 31)^2 = 169$; $(x - 86)^2 + (y - 44)^2 = 169$

b. Change the right side of each equation from 169 to 100.

CHAPTER 10 Quiz 1

For use after Lessons 10.1–10.3

Determine whether $\overline{AB}$ is tangent to $\odot C$. *Explain* your reasoning.

1.

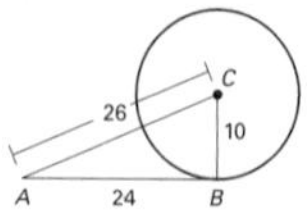

2.

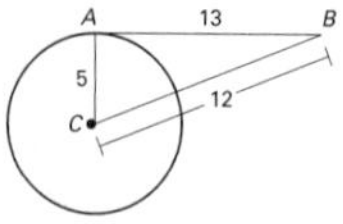

Find the measure of each arc of $\odot P$, where $\overline{RT}$ is a diameter.

3. $m\widehat{RS}$

4. $m\widehat{ST}$

5. $m\widehat{RTS}$

6. $m\widehat{RST}$

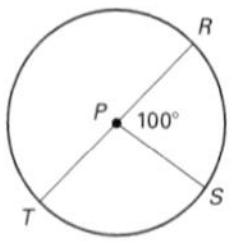

Find the value of x in $\odot Q$.

7.

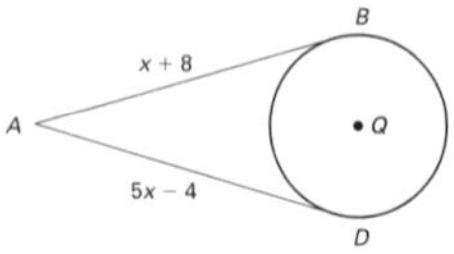

8.

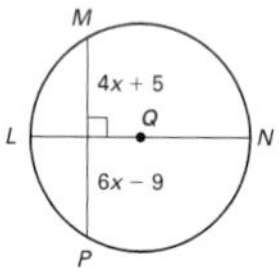

Answers

1. Yes, $24^2 + 10^2 = 26^2$; $\overline{BC} \perp \overline{AB}$
2. No, $5^2 + 13^2 \neq 12^2$; $\overline{BC}$ is not $\perp \overline{AB}$
3. 100°
4. 80°
5. 260°
6. 180°
7. 3
8. 7

CHAPTER 10 Quiz 2

For use after Lessons 10.4–10.5

Find the value(s) of the variable(s).

1. $m\widehat{ABC} = z°$

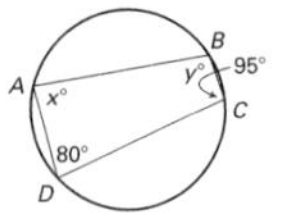

2. $m\widehat{HEF} = z°$

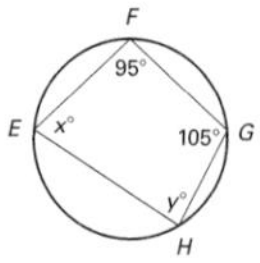

3.

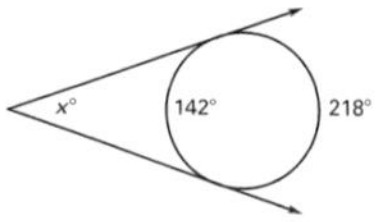

4.

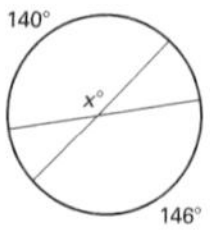

5.

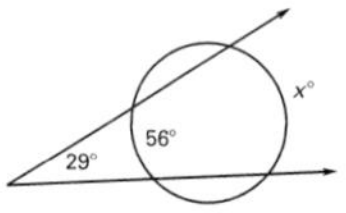

6.

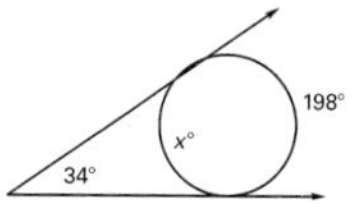

Answers

1. $x = 85, y = 100,$ $z = 160$
2. $x = 75, y = 85,$ $z = 210$
3. 38
4. 143
5. 114
6. 130

CHAPTER 10 Quiz 3

For use after Lessons 10.6–10.7

Find the value of x.

1.

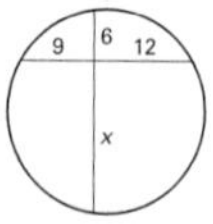

2.

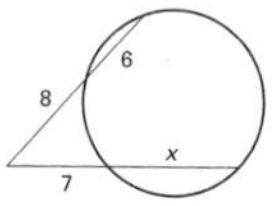

3.

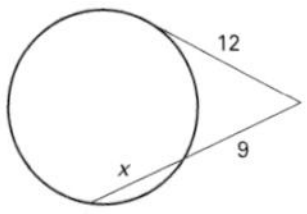

Use the given information to write the standard equation of the circle.

4. The center is (0, 0) and the radius is 5.

5. The center is (−1, 6) and the radius is 7.

6. The center is (4, −8) and a point on the circle is (6, −2).

Answers

1. 18
2. 9
3. 7
4. $x^2 + y^2 = 25$
5. $(x + 1)^2 + (y - 6)^2 = 49$
6. $(x - 4)^2 + (y + 8)^2 = 40$

CHAPTER 10 Chapter Test B

For use after Chapter 10

Tell how many common tangents the given circles have.

1.

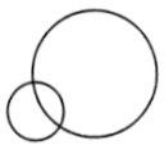

2.

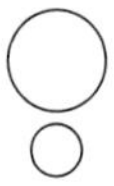

$\overline{QR}$ is a radius of $\odot R$ and $\overline{PQ}$ is tangent to $\odot R$. Find the value of x.

3.

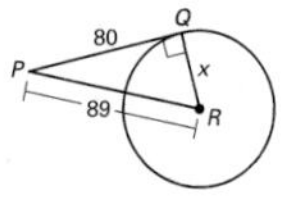

4.

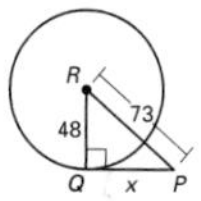

5.

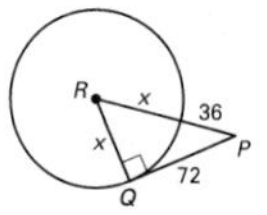

6.

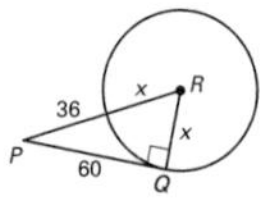

$\overline{JM}$ and $\overline{KN}$ are diameters of $\odot P$. Identify the given arc as a *major arc, minor arc,* or *semicircle.* Then find the measure of the arc.

7. $m\widehat{MN}$

8. $m\widehat{LM}$

9. $m\widehat{KLN}$

10. $m\widehat{JLN}$

11. $m\widehat{JN}$

12. $m\widehat{NJL}$

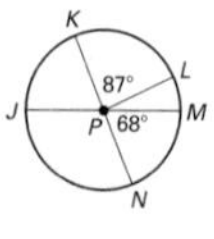

Find the measure of the given arc.

13. $m\widehat{AC}$

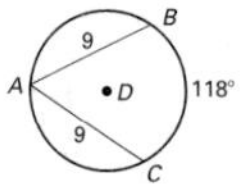

14. $m\widehat{QRS}$

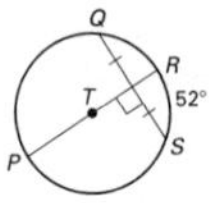

Answers

1. 2
2. 4
3. $x = 39$
4. $x = 55$
5. $x = 54$
6. $x = 32$
7. minor arc, 68°
8. minor arc, 25°
9. semicircle, 180°
10. major arc, 248°
11. minor arc, 112°
12. major arc, 267°
13. 121°
14. 104°

CHAPTER 10

Chapter Test B *continued*

For use after Chapter 10

Find the value(s) of the variable(s).

15. 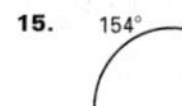

16. 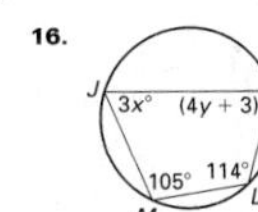

17. 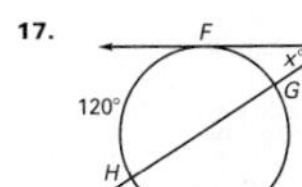

18. 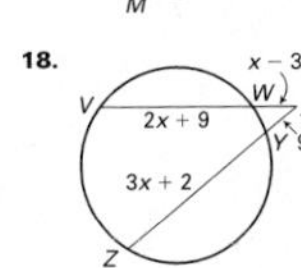

Write the standard equation of the circle with the given center and radius.

19. Center $(-4, 7)$, radius 6

20. Center $(3, -9)$, radius 8.4

Graph the equation.

21. $(x - 3)^2 + (y - 2)^2 = 1$

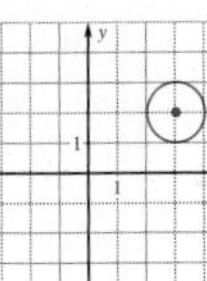

22. $(x - 4)^2 + (y + 4)^2 = 2$

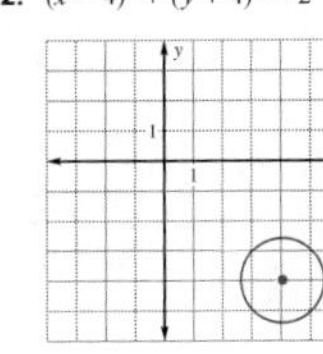

23. You are standing 9 meters from a circular pond. The distance from you to a point of tangency on the pond is 51 meters. What is the radius of the pond?

24. A wagon wheel has 14 spokes. What is the measure of the angle between any two spokes? Round your answer to the nearest tenth.

25. Two spokes in the wagon wheel in Exercise 24 form a central angle of about 128.5°. How many spokes are between the two spokes?

Answers

15. $x = 77$
16. $x = 22, y = 18$
17. $x = 32$
18. $x = 13$
19. $(x + 4)^2 + (y - 7)^2 = 36$
20. $(x - 3)^2 + (y + 9)^2 = 70.56$
21. See left.
22. See left.
23. 140 m
24. 25.7°
25. 4 spokes

CHAPTER 10

Standardized Test

For use after Chapter 10

Multiple Choice

1. Find radius x of $\odot A$. A

Ⓐ 5 Ⓑ 3 Ⓒ 4 Ⓓ 6

2. Which term best describes $\overline{XY}$? C

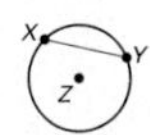

Ⓐ tangent Ⓑ secant
Ⓒ chord Ⓓ diameter

3. Find $m\widehat{FGH}$. A

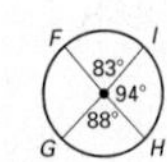

Ⓐ 183° Ⓑ 95°
Ⓒ 182° Ⓓ 92°

4. Which pair of arcs is congruent? D

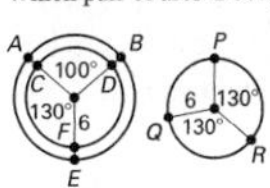

Ⓐ $\widehat{AB} \cong \widehat{CD}$ Ⓑ $\widehat{AE} \cong \widehat{PR}$
Ⓒ $\widehat{BE} \cong \widehat{QR}$ Ⓓ $\widehat{CD} \cong \widehat{PQ}$

5. If $m\widehat{KM} = 112°$, find $m\widehat{LM}$. B

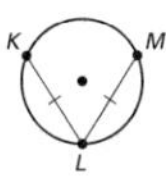

Ⓐ 100° Ⓑ 124°
Ⓒ 112° Ⓓ 236°

6. In the same circle, or in congruent circles, two chords are congruent if and only if _?_. A

Ⓐ they are equidistant from the center
Ⓑ they are parallel
Ⓒ their endpoints form two pairs of congruent arcs
Ⓓ the same diameter perpendicularly bisects both chords

7. Find $m\widehat{AE}$ and $m\widehat{CD}$. D

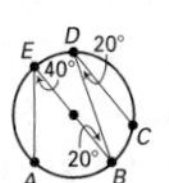

Ⓐ 80°; 80° Ⓑ 80°; 100°
Ⓒ 100°; 80° Ⓓ 100°; 100°

8. Which statement is not necessarily true of $\odot W$? C

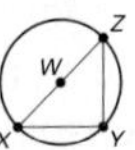

Ⓐ $m\angle XYZ = 90°$ Ⓑ $\overline{WZ} \cong \overline{WX}$
Ⓒ $\overline{XY} \cong \overline{YZ}$ Ⓓ $m\widehat{XZ} = 180°$

9. Find x and y. B

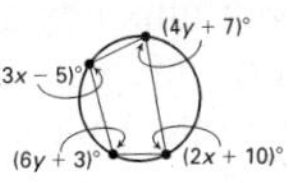

Ⓐ 17; 35 Ⓑ 35; 17
Ⓒ $\frac{17}{2}; \frac{35}{2}$ Ⓓ $\frac{35}{2}; \frac{17}{2}$

10. Find $m\widehat{PQR}$. C

Ⓐ 285° Ⓑ 105° Ⓒ 210° Ⓓ 185°

CHAPTER 10

Standardized Test *continued*

For use after Chapter 10

11. Find $m\widehat{KM}$. D

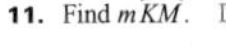

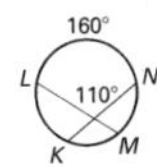

Ⓐ 70° Ⓑ 20° Ⓒ 110° Ⓓ 60°

12. Find XY and WZ. A

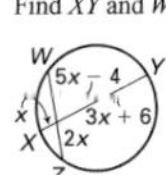

Ⓐ 14; 10 Ⓑ 12; 10
Ⓒ $19\frac{1}{3}; 19\frac{1}{3}$ Ⓓ 10; 14

13. Find RS. D

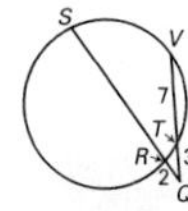

Ⓐ 10 Ⓑ 8 Ⓒ 12 Ⓓ 13

14. Write the standard equation of the circle with center P. B

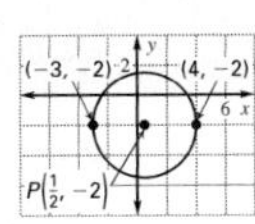

Ⓐ $(x - 2)^2 - \left(y + \frac{1}{2}\right) = 49$

Ⓑ $\left(x - \frac{1}{2}\right)^2 + (y + 2)^2 = \frac{49}{4}$

Ⓒ $\left(x + \frac{1}{2}\right)^2 + (y - 2) = 49$

Ⓓ $(x + 2)^2 - \left(y - \frac{1}{2}\right) = \frac{49}{4}$

Gridded Answer

15. Find $m\widehat{AD}$.

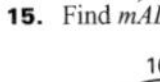

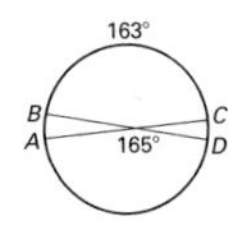

Gridded answer: 1 6 7

Short Response

16. You have a pizza with a 16 inch diameter cut into 16 equal slices.

a. What is the side length of a piece of pizza? 8 in.

b. What is the arc measure of a single slice? 22.5°

c. If the pieces are numbered consecutively, find the measures of the major arc and minor arc between the second and eighth piece. 202.5°; 112.5°

Extended Response

17. $\odot A$ has center $P(3, -5)$. Point $Q(7, 0)$ lies on the circle.

a. Write an equation of the circle in standard form. $(x - 3)^2 + (y + 5)^2 = 41$

b. Write the equation of the circle concentric to $\odot A$ containing point $R(1, -1)$. $(x - 3)^2 + (y + 5)^2 = 20$

c. Find the radius of each circle. 6.4; 4.47

d. Find QR. 6.08

CHAPTER 10

Alternative Assessment and Math Journal

For use after Chapter 10

Journal **1.** Describe the measures of angles formed inside, outside, and on circles in terms of arcs on circles.

Multi-Step Problem **2.** You can use a circle to create string art. Draw a circle on a piece of wood and place push pins or tacks on the circle. Then wrap a piece of string around the tacks. A completed string art piece is shown at the right. Use the incomplete string art piece to answer the questions below.

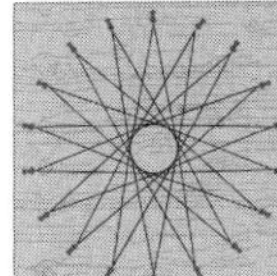

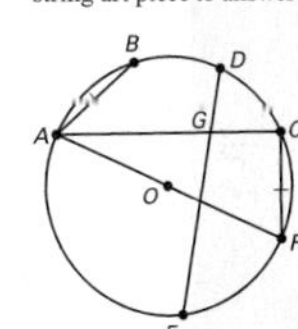

a. Identify the segments in the figure as chords, diameters, or tangents.

b. Suppose that $m\angle AOB = 47°$. Find $m\widehat{BCF}$ and $m\widehat{BAF}$.

c. Suppose that $m\angle AEB = 22°$. Find $m\widehat{FC}$.

d. Suppose that $m\widehat{ABD} = 90°$ and $m\widehat{CFE} = 100°$. Find $m\angle CGE$.

e. Suppose that $AG = x + 7$, $GC = x$, $DG = x + 1$, and $GE = x + 5$. Find DE and AC.

f. You are using a sheet of graph paper to create your own string art. You draw a set of axes and place the center at the origin. Your circle has a radius of 5 units. Can you place a pin at $(-3, 4)$? *Explain* why or why not.

1. Complete answers should include: an explanation of how to find measures of angles formed on circles, an explanation of how to find measures of angles formed inside circles, an explanation of how to find measures of angles formed outside circles (see the Chapter Summary for Chapter 10 in the text).

2. **a.** Chords: $\overline{AB}, \overline{AC}, \overline{DE}, \overline{CF}$; Diameter: $\overline{AF}$
b. 133°; 227° **c.** 44° **d.** 95°
e. 17 units; 16 units
f. Yes. The equation of the circle is $x^2 + y^2 = 25$ and $(-3, 4)$ is a solution because $(-3)^2 + 4^2 = 9 + 16 = 25$.

PLAN AND PREPARE

Main Ideas

In this chapter students investigate aspects of circles. They start by drawing tangents to circles and seeing how a tangent to a circle is related to the radius at the point of tangency. They use intercepted arcs of circles to measure angles formed by chords in a circle and to measure angles formed by secants and tangents to a circle. They explore relationships between segment lengths of chords that intersect in a circle, and they investigate relationships between segment lengths of secants and tangents to a circle. Finally, they use the standard equation of a circle to graph and describe circles in a coordinate plane.

Prerequisite Skills

- Reviewing similar triangles, linear pairs, and the definition of interior of an angle
- Classifying a triangle using the Converse of the Pythagorean Theorem
- Finding the measures of vertical angles and supplementary angles

Additional resources for reviewing prerequisite skills are:

- Skills Review Handbook, pp. 869–895
- @HomeTutor

10 Properties of Circles

Before

In previous chapters, you learned the following skills, which you'll use in Chapter 10: classifying triangles, finding angle measures, and solving equations.

Prerequisite Skills

VOCABULARY CHECK

Copy and complete the statement.

1. Two similar triangles have congruent corresponding angles and __?__ corresponding sides. **proportional**
2. Two angles whose sides form two pairs of opposite rays are called __?__. **vertical angles**
3. The __?__ of an angle is all of the points between the sides of the angle. **interior**

SKILLS AND ALGEBRA CHECK

Use the Converse of the Pythagorean Theorem to classify the triangle. *(Review p. 441 for 10.1.)*

4. 0.6, 0.8, 0.9 **acute**
5. 11, 12, 17 **obtuse**
6. 1.5, 2, 2.5 **right**

Find the value of the variable. *(Review pp. 24, 35 for 10.2, 10.4.)*

7. 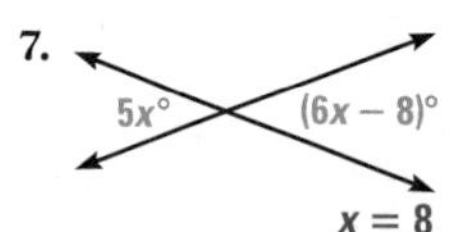

$x = 8$

8. 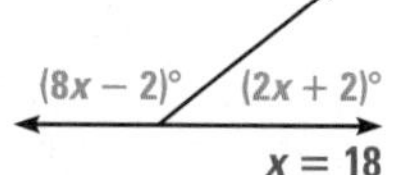

$x = 18$

9. 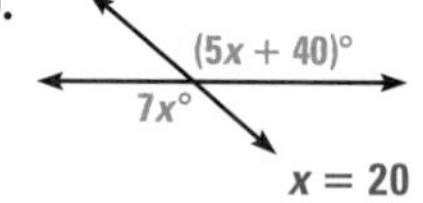

$x = 20$

@HomeTutor Prerequisite skills practice at classzone.com

648

Chapter Planning Guide

Chapter 10 Resource Book
- Teaching Guide/Lesson Plan (pp. 3, 16, 30, 45, 58, 73, 87)
- Project with Rubric (p. 102)

Assessment and Intervention
- Assessment Book (pp. 140–154)
- Benchmark Tests
- Remediation Book

Interactive Technology
- Easy Planner
- Power Presentations CD-ROM
- Activity Generator CD-ROM
- Animated Geometry
- Test Generator CD-ROM
- Online Quizzes
- eWorkbook
- eEdition
- @HomeTutor

Resources for English Learners
- Quick Reference for English Learners
- Spanish Study Guide
- Multi-Language Visual Glossary
- Student Resources in Spanish

California Standards for Chapter 10

Geometry: 5.0, 7.0, 17.0, 21.0

Now

In Chapter 10, you will apply the big ideas listed below and reviewed in the Chapter Summary on page 707. You will also use the key vocabulary listed below.

Big Ideas

1. **Using properties of segments that intersect circles**
2. **Applying angle relationships in circles**
3. **Using circles in the coordinate plane**

KEY VOCABULARY

- circle, *p. 651* center, radius, diameter
- chord, *p. 651*
- secant, *p. 651*
- tangent, *p. 651*
- central angle, *p. 659*
- minor arc, *p. 659*
- major arc, *p. 659*
- semicircle, *p. 659*
- congruent circles, *p. 660*
- congruent arcs, *p. 660*
- inscribed angle, *p. 672*
- intercepted arc, *p. 672*
- standard equation of a circle, *p. 699*

Why?

Circles can be used to model a wide variety of natural phenomena. You can use properties of circles to investigate the Northern Lights.

Animated Geometry

The animation illustrated below for Example 4 on page 682 helps you answer this question: From what part of Earth are the Northern Lights visible?

Start
Your goal is to determine from what part of Earth you can see the Northern Lights.

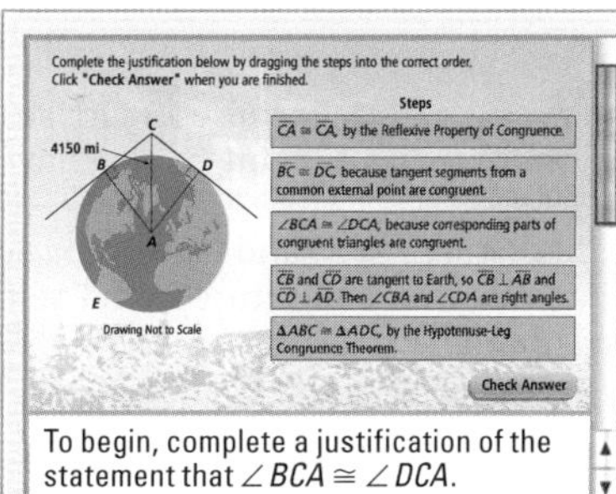

Animated Geometry at classzone.com

Other animations for Chapter 10: pages 655, 661, 671, 691, and 701

649

Geometry Toolkit

- Reading Strategies for Chapter 10, pp. 27–28
- Differentiated Instruction Notes, pp. 75–78
- English Learners Notes, pp. 109–110
- Inclusion Notes, pp. 139–140
- Teaching Strategies with Sample Worksheets, pp. 145–168
- Using Technology in the Classroom, pp. 169–174
- Tips for New Teachers, pp. 193–194
- Math Background Notes, pp. 230–233
- Pre-AP Strategies and Copymasters, pp. 301–302, 377–382
- Teacher Survival Activities, pp. 439–440, 463–464
- Bulletin Board Idea, p. 478
- Teacher Tool Transparencies, following p. 480

1 PLAN AND PREPARE

Explore the Concept

- Students will draw tangents and measure tangent segments.
- This activity leads into the study of tangents in Lesson 10.1, Example 6.

Materials

Each student will need:

- compass
- ruler

Recommended Time

Work activity: 10 min

Discuss results: 5 min

Grouping

Students should work individually.

2 TEACH

Tips for Success

Ask students to discuss how a line may intersect a circle in 0, 1, or 2 points. For Step 3, ask them to also find other pairs of tangents from different external points.

Key Question

- How many tangents to circle P can be drawn containing point A? **one**

Alternative Strategy

Demonstrate this activity by doing the steps on the overhead projector.

Key Discovery

The two tangent segments through a point outside a circle have the same length.

3 ASSESS AND RETEACH

1. If $\overline{AC}$ and $\overline{BC}$ are tangent segments from C to circle O, what must be true? $AC = BC$

10.1 Explore Tangent Segments

MATERIALS • compass • ruler

Standards

21.0 Students prove and solve problems regarding relationships among chords, secants, **tangents,** inscribed angles, and inscribed and circumscribed polygons **of circles.**

QUESTION How are the lengths of tangent segments related?

A line can intersect a circle at 0, 1, or 2 points. If a line is in the plane of a circle and intersects the circle at 1 point, the line is a *tangent*.

EXPLORE Draw tangents to a circle

STEP 1

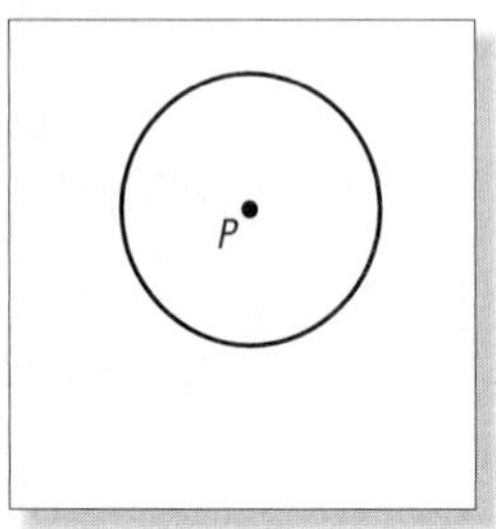

Draw a circle Use a compass to draw a circle. Label the center *P*.

STEP 2

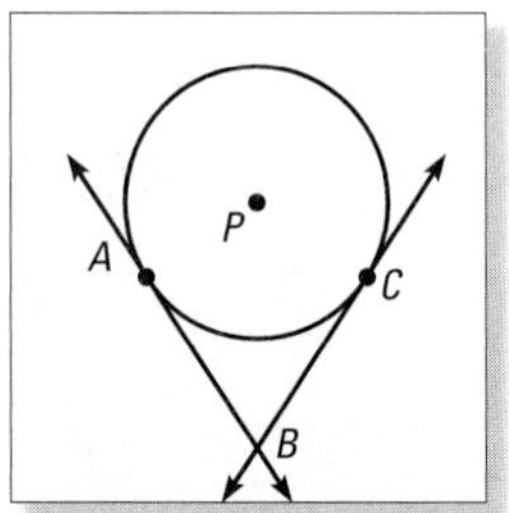

Draw tangents Draw lines $\overleftrightarrow{AB}$ and $\overleftrightarrow{CB}$ so that they intersect $\odot P$ only at A and C, respectively. These lines are called *tangents*.

STEP 3

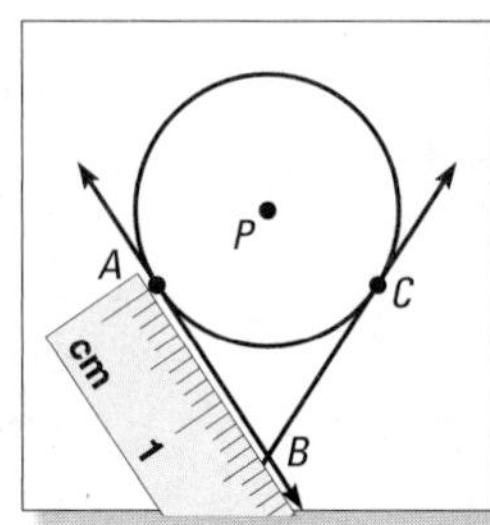

Measure segments $\overline{AB}$ and $\overline{CB}$ are called *tangent segments*. Measure and compare the lengths of the tangent segments.

DRAW CONCLUSIONS Use your observations to complete these exercises

1. Repeat Steps 1–3 with three different circles. **Check students' work.**
2. Use your results from Exercise 1 to make a conjecture about the lengths of tangent segments that have a common endpoint. **Tangent segments from a common external point are congruent.**
3. In the diagram, L, Q, N, and P are points of tangency. Use your conjecture from Exercise 2 to find LQ and NP if $LM = 7$ and $MP = 5.5$. **12.5, 12.5**

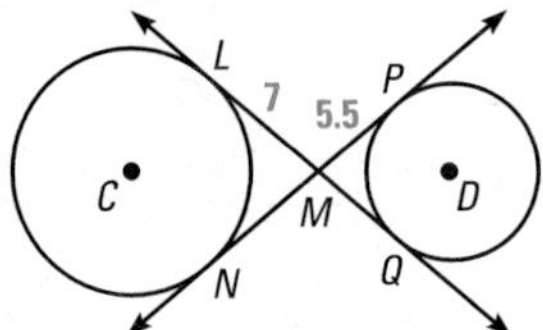

4. In the diagram below, A, B, D, and E are points of tangency. Use your conjecture from Exercise 2 to explain why $\overline{AB} \cong \overline{ED}$. **Since $AC = EC$ and $BC = DC$, it follows that $AB = ED$ which makes $\overline{AB} \cong \overline{ED}$.**

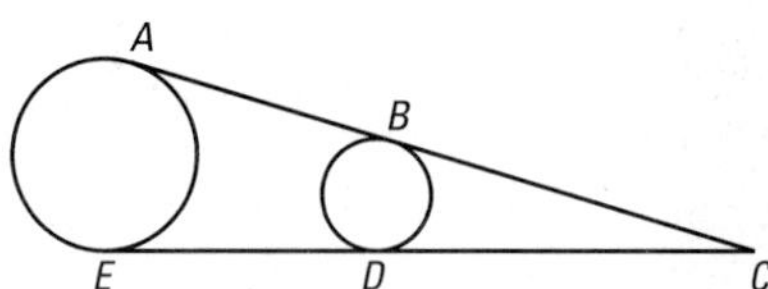

10.1 Use Properties of Tangents

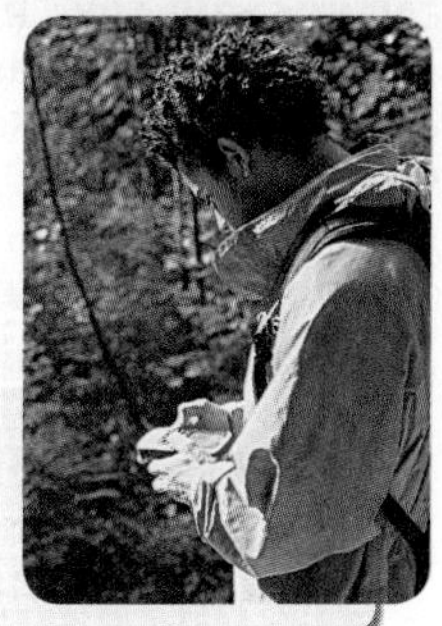

Before You found the circumference and area of circles.

Now You will use properties of a tangent to a circle.

Why? So you can find the range of a GPS satellite, as in Ex. 37.

Key Vocabulary
- **circle**
  center, radius, diameter
- **chord**
- **secant**
- **tangent**

Standards

7.0 Students prove and use theorems involving the properties of parallel lines cut by a transversal, the properties of quadrilaterals, and **the properties of circles.**

21.0 Students prove and solve problems regarding relationships among chords, secants, **tangents,** inscribed angles, and inscribed and circumscribed polygons **of circles.**

A **circle** is the set of all points in a plane that are equidistant from a given point called the **center** of the circle. A circle with center P is called "circle P" and can be written $\odot P$. A segment whose endpoints are the center and any point on the circle is a **radius**.

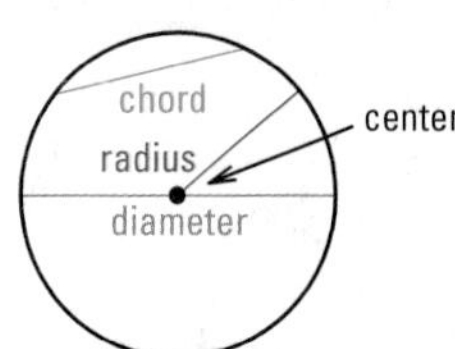

A **chord** is a segment whose endpoints are on a circle. A **diameter** is a chord that contains the center of the circle.

A **secant** is a line that intersects a circle in two points. A **tangent** is a line in the plane of a circle that intersects the circle in exactly one point, the *point of tangency*. The *tangent ray* $\overrightarrow{AB}$ and the *tangent segment* $\overline{AB}$ are also called tangents.

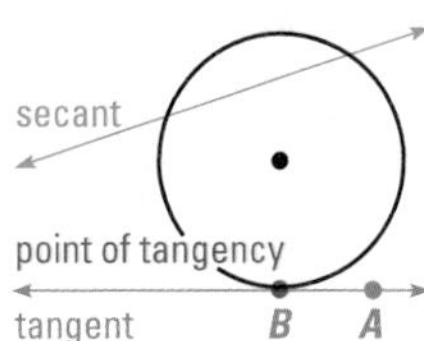

EXAMPLE 1 Identify special segments and lines

Tell whether the line, ray, or segment is best described as a *radius, chord, diameter, secant,* or *tangent* of $\odot C$.

a. $\overline{AC}$ **b.** $\overline{AB}$

c. $\overrightarrow{DE}$ **d.** $\overleftrightarrow{AE}$

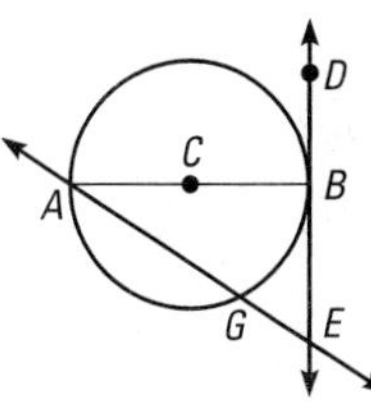

Solution

a. $\overline{AC}$ is a radius because C is the center and A is a point on the circle.

b. $\overline{AB}$ is a diameter because it is a chord that contains the center C.

c. $\overrightarrow{DE}$ is a tangent ray because it is contained in a line that intersects the circle at only one point.

d. $\overleftrightarrow{AE}$ is a secant because it is a line that intersects the circle in two points.

✓ **GUIDED PRACTICE for Example 1**

1. In Example 1, what word best describes $\overline{AG}$? $\overline{CB}$? **chord; radius**
2. In Example 1, name a tangent and a tangent segment. ***Sample answer:*** $\overleftrightarrow{DE}$, $\overline{DB}$

1 PLAN AND PREPARE

Warm-Up Exercises
Transparency Available

1. What measure is needed to find the circumference or area of a circle? **radius or diameter**
2. Find the radius of a circle with diameter 8 centimeters. **4 cm**
3. A right triangle has legs with lengths 5 inches and 12 inches. Find the length of the hypotenuse. **13 in.**
4. Solve $6x + 15 = 33$. **3**
5. Solve $(x + 18)^2 = x^2 + 24^2$. **7**

Notetaking Guide
Transparency Available

Promotes interactive learning and notetaking skills, pp. 253–257.

Pacing
Basic: 2 days
Average: 2 days
Advanced: 2 days
Block: 1 block
- See *Teaching Guide/Lesson Plan.*

2 FOCUS AND MOTIVATE

Essential Question
Big Idea 1, p. 649

How can you verify that a segment is tangent to a circle? **Tell students they will learn how to answer this question by using the Converse of the Pythagorean Theorem.**

Resource Planning Guide

Chapter Resource Book
- Teaching Guide/Lesson Plan (pp. 3–4)
- Practice levels A, B, C (pp. 5–10)
- Study Guide (pp. 11–12)
- Catch-up for Absent Students (p. 13)
- Application (p. 14)
- Challenge (p. 15)

Workbooks
- Notetaking Guide (pp. 253–257)
- Practice Workbook (pp. 184–186)

Teaching Options
- **Power Presentations CD-ROM** provides dynamic electronic teaching resources for the classroom.
- **Activity Generator CD-ROM** provides editable activities for all ability levels.

Interactive Technology
- Easy Planner
- Power Presentations CD-ROM
- Activity Generator CD-ROM
- Animated Geometry
- Test Generator CD-ROM
- Online Quiz
- eWorkbook
- eEdition
- @HomeTutor

Resources for English Learners
- Quick Reference for English Learners
- Spanish Study Guide
- Multi-Language Visual Glossary
- Student Resources in Spanish

See also the *Geometry Toolkit* for more strategies for meeting individual needs.

Motivating the Lesson

Draw a diagram of two separate different-size circles, with segments forming the common external tangents, to represent bicycle gears and the chain. Ask students to describe the relationship between the chain and the radii where they meet. Tell students they will investigate circles, radii, and tangents to circles in this lesson.

3 TEACH

Extra Example 1

Tell whether the line or segment is best described as a radius, chord, diameter, secant, or tangent of ⊙ C.

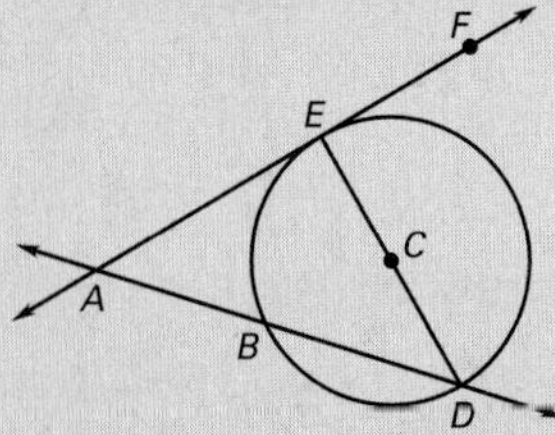

a. $\overline{DC}$ **radius** **b.** $\overline{BD}$ **secant**
c. $\overline{DE}$ **diameter** **d.** $\overleftrightarrow{AE}$ **tangent**

Key Questions to Ask for Example 1

- Why is $\overleftrightarrow{AG}$ a secant? **It is a line that intersects the circle in 2 points.**
- Why isn't $\overleftrightarrow{AG}$ a chord? **A chord is a segment, not a line.**
- Using the points in the diagram, what are other secants that are not drawn? $\overleftrightarrow{AB}$, $\overleftrightarrow{AD}$, $\overleftrightarrow{BG}$, $\overleftrightarrow{CD}$, $\overleftrightarrow{CE}$, $\overleftrightarrow{CG}$, $\overleftrightarrow{DG}$

Vocabulary

It may be helpful to use "a radius" or "a diameter" to refer to the segments and "the radius" or "the diameter" to refer to the lengths of the segments.

READ VOCABULARY
The plural of radius is *radii.* All radii of a circle are congruent.

RADIUS AND DIAMETER The words *radius* and *diameter* are used for lengths as well as segments. For a given circle, think of *a radius* and *a diameter* as segments and *the radius* and *the diameter* as lengths.

EXAMPLE 2 Find lengths in circles in a coordinate plane

Use the diagram to find the given lengths.

a. Radius of ⊙A

b. Diameter of ⊙A

c. Radius of ⊙B

d. Diameter of ⊙B

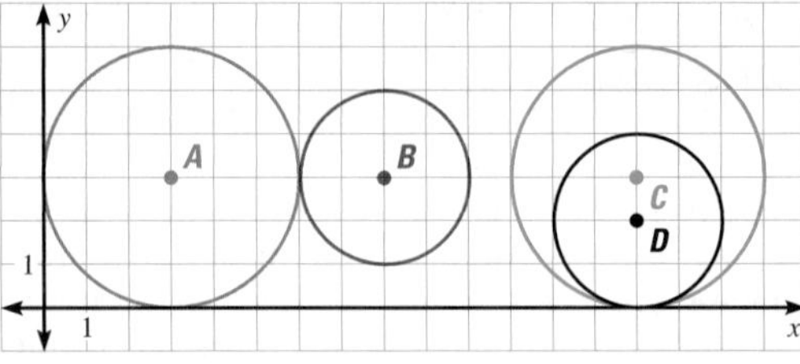

Solution

a. The radius of ⊙A is 3 units.

b. The diameter of ⊙A is 6 units.

c. The radius of ⊙B is 2 units.

d. The diameter of ⊙B is 4 units.

GUIDED PRACTICE for Example 2

3. Use the diagram in Example 2 to find the radius and diameter of ⊙C and ⊙D. **3, 6; 2, 4**

COPLANAR CIRCLES Two circles can intersect in two points, one point, or no points. Coplanar circles that intersect in one point are called *tangent circles.* Coplanar circles that have a common center are called *concentric.*

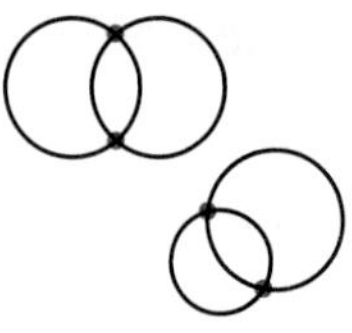

2 points of intersection

1 point of intersection (tangent circles)

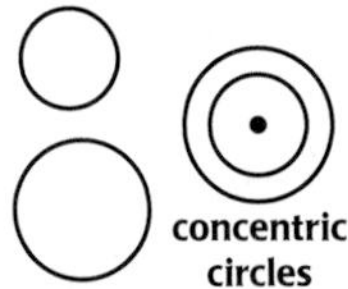

no points of intersection

READ VOCABULARY
A line that intersects a circle in exactly one point is said to be *tangent* to the circle.

COMMON TANGENTS A line, ray, or segment that is tangent to two coplanar circles is called a *common tangent.*

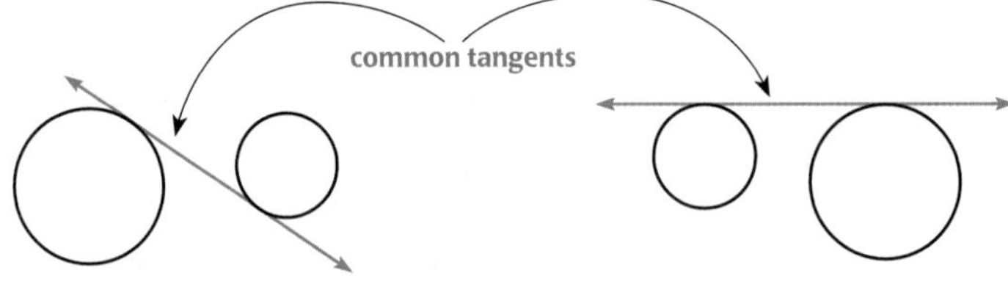

EXAMPLE 3 Draw common tangents

Tell how many common tangents the circles have and draw them.

a. 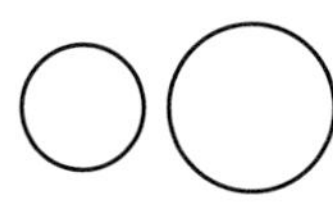

b. 

c. 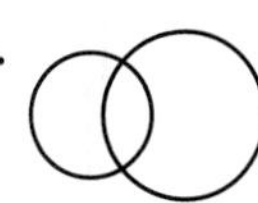

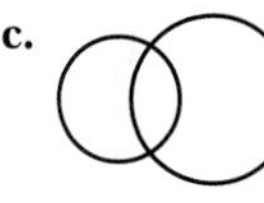

Solution

a. 4 common tangents

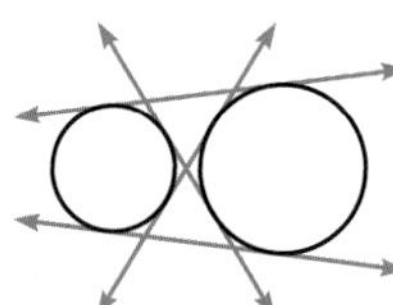

b. 3 common tangents

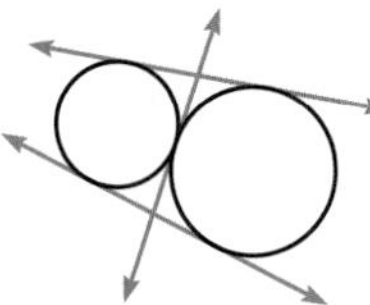

c. 2 common tangents

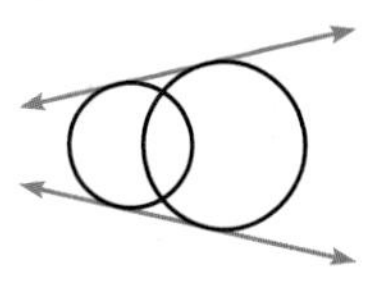

GUIDED PRACTICE for Example 3

Tell how many common tangents the circles have and draw them.

4, 5. See margin for art.

4. 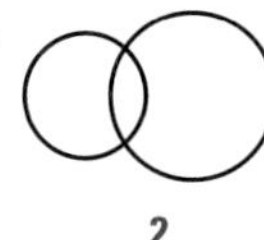 2

5. 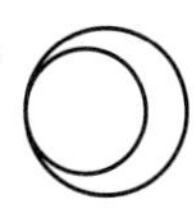 1

6.  0

THEOREM *For Your Notebook*

THEOREM 10.1

In a plane, a line is tangent to a circle if and only if the line is perpendicular to a radius of the circle at its endpoint on the circle.

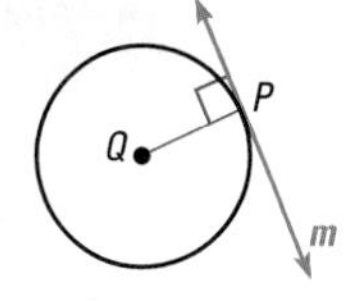

Line m is tangent to $\odot Q$ if and only if $m \perp \overline{QP}$.

Proof: Exs. 39–40, p. 658

EXAMPLE 4 Verify a tangent to a circle

In the diagram, $\overline{PT}$ is a radius of $\odot P$. Is $\overline{ST}$ tangent to $\odot P$?

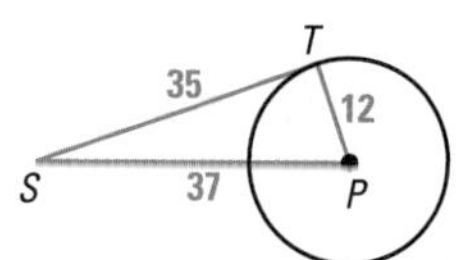

Solution

Use the Converse of the Pythagorean Theorem. Because $12^2 + 35^2 = 37^2$, $\triangle PST$ is a right triangle and $\overline{ST} \perp \overline{PT}$. So, $\overline{ST}$ is perpendicular to a radius of $\odot P$ at its endpoint on $\odot P$. By Theorem 10.1, $\overline{ST}$ is tangent to $\odot P$.

4.

5.

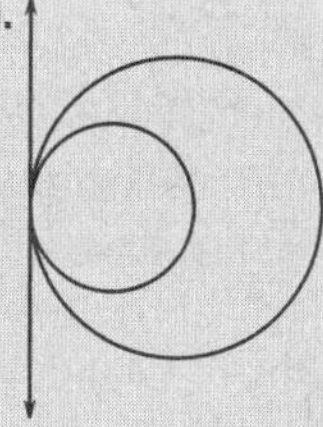

Extra Example 2

Use the diagram to find the given lengths.

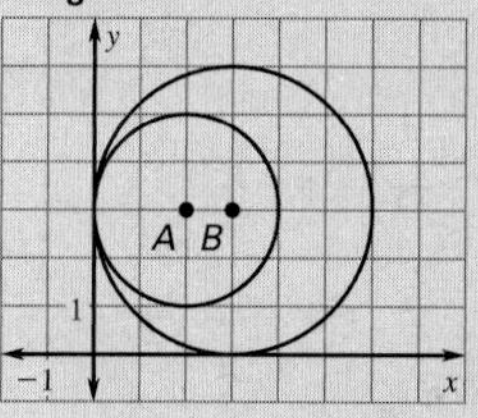

a. Radius of $\odot B$ **3 units**

b. Diameter of $\odot A$ **4 units**

c. Radius of $\odot A$ **2 units**

d. Diameter of $\odot B$ **6 units**

Extra Example 3

Tell how many common tangents the circles have and draw them.

a.

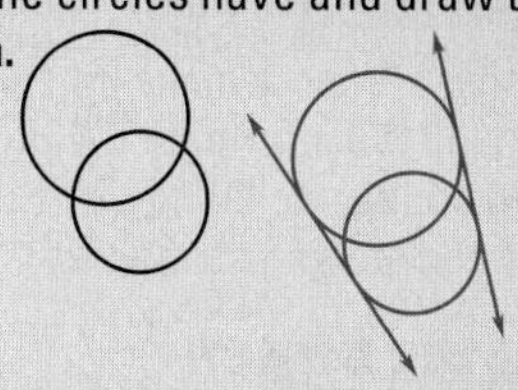

b.

c.

a. 2 common tangents
b. 4 common tangents
c. 3 common tangents

Extra Example 4

In the diagram, $\overline{AB}$ is a radius of $\odot A$. Is $\overline{BC}$ tangent to $\odot A$? Explain.

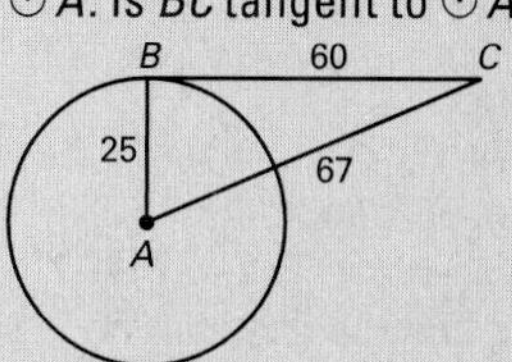

No, $25^2 + 60^2 = 4225$, but $67^2 = 4489$.

Extra Example 5

In the diagram, S is a point of tangency. Find the radius r of $\odot T$. **14 cm**

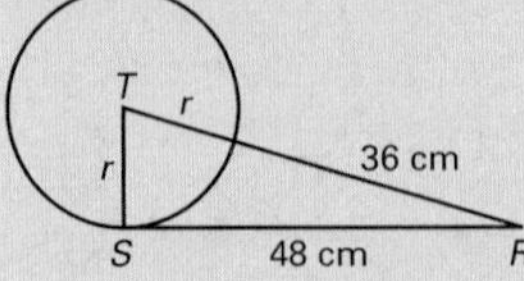

Extra Example 6

In $\odot C$, $\overline{DA}$ is tangent at A and $\overline{DB}$ is tangent at B. Find x. **5.5**

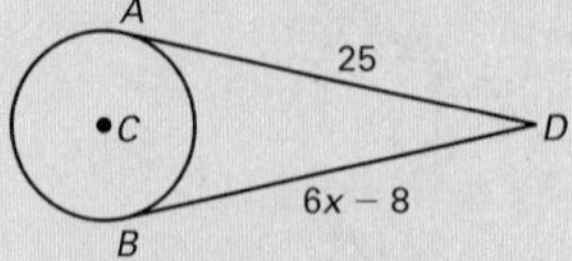

Study Strategy

Suggest that students make note cards with all the information related to circles, including examples and solving strategies.

Closing the Lesson

Have students summarize the major points of the lesson and answer the Essential Question: How can you verify that a segment is tangent to a circle?

- **A circle is the set of all points in a plane equidistant from a given point called the center. A segment from the center to the circle is a radius.**
- **A chord is a segment whose endpoints are on the circle. A diameter is a chord that passes through the center. A line that intersects a circle in two points is a secant.**
- **A tangent is a line that intersects a circle in one point. A radius to that point is perpendicular to the tangent. Tangent segments from a common external point are congruent.**

Use the Converse of the Pythagorean Theorem to verify that a segment is perpendicular to a radius, and then use Theorem 10.1 to conclude that the segment is tangent to the circle.

EXAMPLE 5 Find the radius of a circle

In the diagram, B is a point of tangency. Find the radius r of $\odot C$.

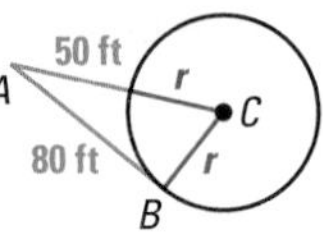

Solution

You know from Theorem 10.1 that $\overline{AB} \perp \overline{BC}$, so $\triangle ABC$ is a right triangle. You can use the Pythagorean Theorem.

$AC^2 = BC^2 + AB^2$	**Pythagorean Theorem**
$(r + 50)^2 = r^2 + 80^2$	**Substitute.**
$r^2 + 100r + 2500 = r^2 + 6400$	**Multiply.**
$100r = 3900$	**Subtract from each side.**
$r = 39$ ft	**Divide each side by 100.**

THEOREM *For Your Notebook*

THEOREM 10.2

Tangent segments from a common external point are congruent.

Proof: Ex. 41, p. 658

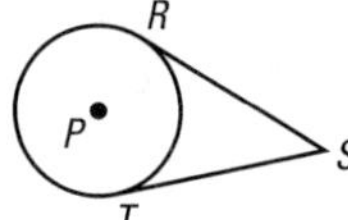

If $\overline{SR}$ and $\overline{ST}$ are tangent segments, then $\overline{SR} \cong \overline{ST}$.

EXAMPLE 6 Use properties of tangents

$\overline{RS}$ is tangent to $\odot C$ at S and $\overline{RT}$ is tangent to $\odot C$ at T. Find the value of x.

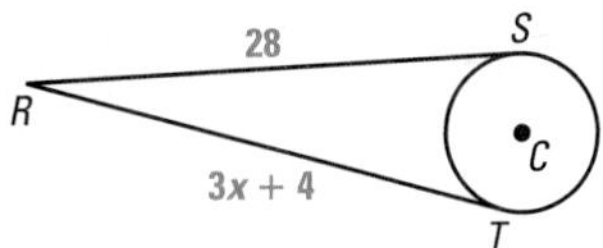

Solution

$RS = RT$	**Tangent segments from the same point are $\cong$.**
$28 = 3x + 4$	**Substitute.**
$8 = x$	**Solve for x.**

✓ GUIDED PRACTICE for Examples 4, 5, and 6

7. Is $\overline{DE}$ tangent to $\odot C$? **yes**

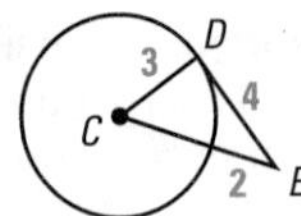

8. $\overline{ST}$ is tangent to $\odot Q$. Find the value of r. **7**

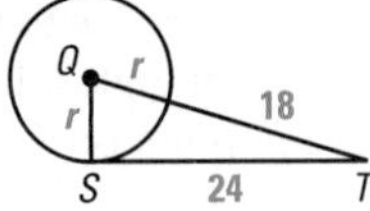

9. Find the value(s) of x. **±3**

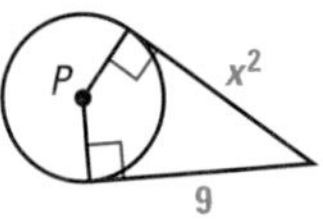

Differentiated Instruction

Advanced Have students refer to the diagram for Example 6. Have them show that $\triangle RSC$ and $\triangle RTC$ are congruent. **$\overline{RS} \cong \overline{RT}$ by Theorem 10.2, $\overline{CS} \cong \overline{CT}$ because they are radii of the same circle, and $\overline{RC} \cong \overline{RC}$ by the Reflexive Property of Congruence. The triangles are congruent by the SSS Postulate.**

See also the *Geometry Toolkit* for more strategies.

10.1 EXERCISES

HOMEWORK KEY
○ = **WORKED-OUT SOLUTIONS** on p. WS12 for Exs. 7, 19, and 37
★ = **STANDARDIZED TEST PRACTICE** Exs. 2, 29, 33, and 38

SKILL PRACTICE

A

1. **VOCABULARY** Copy and complete: The points A and B are on $\odot C$. If C is a point on $\overline{AB}$, then $\overline{AB}$ is a _?_. **diameter**

2. ★ **WRITING** Explain how you can determine from the context whether the words *radius* and *diameter* are referring to a segment or a length. **If a measure is being asked for then you are referring to length otherwise you are referring to a segment.**

EXAMPLE 1 on p. 651 for Exs. 3–11

MATCHING TERMS **Match the notation with the term that best describes it.**

3. B **G**
4. $\overleftrightarrow{BH}$ **H**
5. $\overline{AB}$ **C**
6. $\overleftrightarrow{AB}$ **E**
7. $\overleftrightarrow{AE}$ **F**
8. G **A**
9. $\overline{CD}$ **B**
10. $\overline{BD}$ **D**

A. Center
B. Radius
C. Chord
D. Diameter
E. Secant
F. Tangent
G. Point of tangency
H. Common tangent

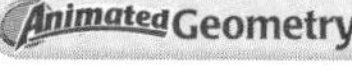

at classzone.com

11. **ERROR ANALYSIS** *Describe* and correct the error in the statement about the diagram. **$\overline{AB}$ is not a secant, it is a chord; the length of chord $\overline{AB}$ is 6.**

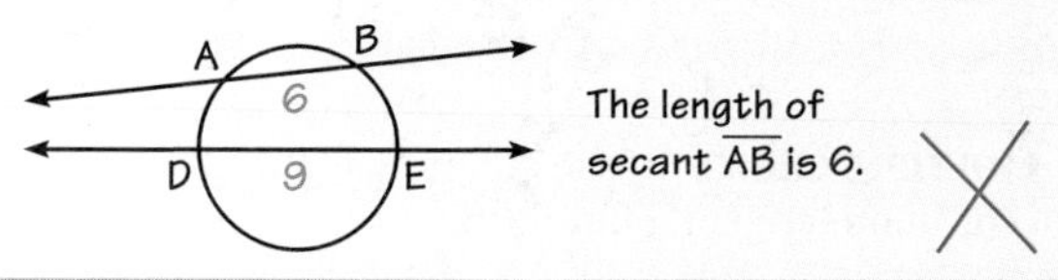

EXAMPLES 2 and 3 on pp. 652–653 for Exs. 12–17

COORDINATE GEOMETRY **Use the diagram at the right.**

12. What are the radius and diameter of $\odot C$? **9, 18**

13. What are the radius and diameter of $\odot D$? **6, 12**

14. Copy the circles. Then draw all the common tangents of the two circles. **See margin.**

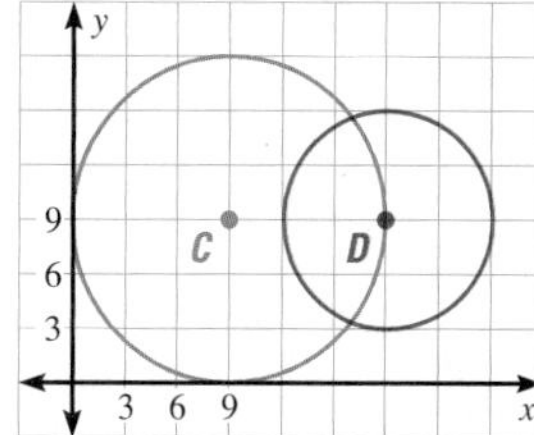

DRAWING TANGENTS **Copy the diagram. Tell how many common tangents the circles have and draw them.**

15. **4; see margin for art.**

16. **0**

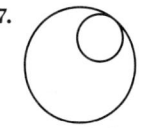

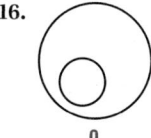

17. **1; see margin for art.**

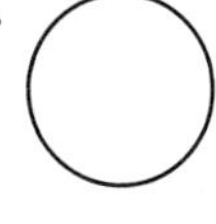

14. 15. 17.

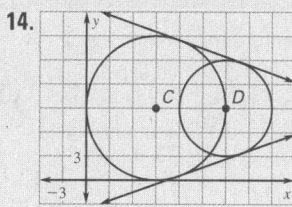

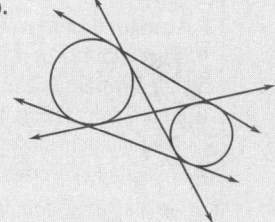

4 PRACTICE AND APPLY

Assignment Guide

Answer Transparencies available for all exercises

Basic:
Day 1: pp. 655–658
Exs. 1–17, 35, 36
Day 2: pp. 655–658
Exs. 18–29, 37–39, 43–47

Average:
Day 1: pp. 655–658
Exs. 1–17, 27, 28, 35, 36
Day 2: pp. 655–658
Exs. 18–26, 29–33, 37–41, 43–47 odd

Advanced:
Day 1: pp. 655–658
Exs. 1–10, 12–17, 27, 28, 35, 36
Day 2: pp. 655–658
Exs. 18–20, 23–26, 29–34*, 37–43*, 46, 47

Block:
pp. 655–658
Exs. 1–33, 35–41, 43–47 odd

Differentiated Instruction

See *Geometry Best Practices Toolkit* for suggestions on addressing the needs of a diverse classroom.

Homework Check

For a quick check of student understanding of key concepts, go over the following exercises:
Basic: 4, 12, 18, 22, 37
Average: 6, 14, 18, 24, 37
Advanced: 10, 16, 20, 26, 37

Extra Practice

- Student Edition, p. 914
- Chapter 10 Resource Book: Practice levels A, B, C, pp. 5–10

Practice Worksheet

An easily-readable reduced practice page (with answers) for this lesson can be found on p. 648C.

Animated Geometry
classzone.com

An **Animated Geometry** activity is available on-line for **Exercises 3–10**. This activity is also available on the **Power Presentations CD-ROM**.

Teaching Strategy

Exercises 3–10 Remind students that a diameter is also a chord, but a radius is not a chord.

Reading Strategy

Exercises 3–10 You may want to ask students to verbalize these exercises as they are reading them to reinforce the importance of the notation for points, lines, and segments.

Avoiding Common Errors

Exercise 29 A common error is to assume $RS = 8$, the sum of the radii. Encourage students to draw an auxiliary line segment parallel to $\overline{RS}$. This should help them see a rectangle with vertices R, S, and P and a fourth vertex on $\overline{QR}$.

EXAMPLE 4 on p. 653 for Exs. 18–20

DETERMINING TANGENCY **Determine whether $\overline{AB}$ is tangent to $\odot C$. *Explain.***
18–20. See margin.

18.

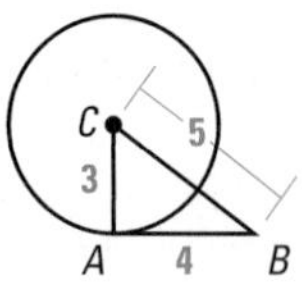

(19.)

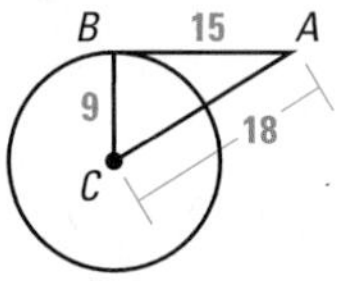

20.

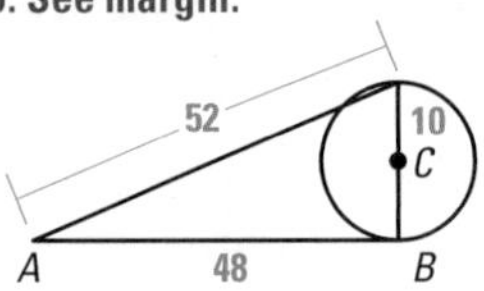

EXAMPLES 5 and 6 on p. 654 for Exs. 21–26

18. Tangent; by the Converse of the Pythagorean Theorem, $\triangle ABC$ is a right triangle which implies $\overline{CA} \perp \overline{AB}$. By Theorem 10.1, $\overline{AB}$ is tangent to $\odot C$.

19. not tangent; $9^2 + 15^2 \neq 18^2$

20. Tangent; the diameter of $\odot C$ is 20, and by the Converse of the Pythagorean Theorem, the triangle is a right triangle which implies that $\overline{CB} \perp \overline{BA}$. By Theorem 10.1, $\overline{AB}$ is tangent to $\odot C$.

ALGEBRA **Find the value(s) of the variable. In Exercises 24–26, B and D are points of tangency.**

21.

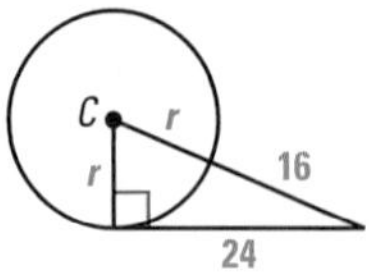

10

22.

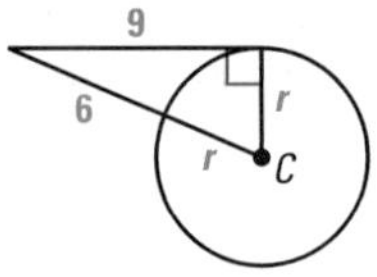

3.75

23.

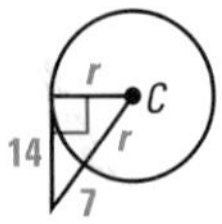

10.5

24.

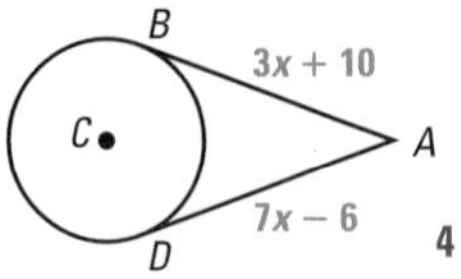

4

25.

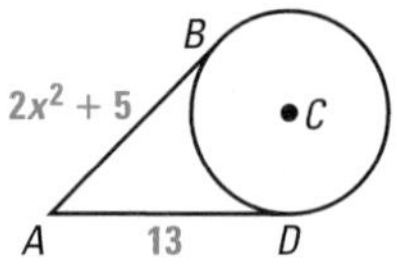

±2

26.

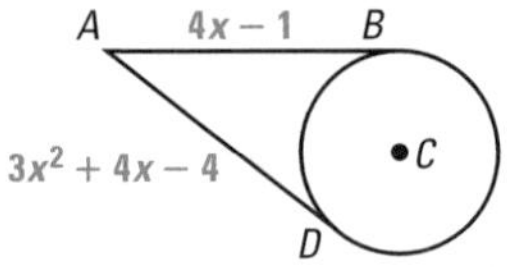

B **COMMON TANGENTS** **A *common internal tangent* intersects the segment that joins the centers of two circles. A *common external* tangent does not intersect the segment that joins the centers of the two circles. Determine whether the common tangents shown are *internal* or *external*.**

27.

external

28.

internal

29. ★ **MULTIPLE CHOICE** In the diagram, $\odot P$ and $\odot Q$ are tangent circles. $\overline{RS}$ is a common tangent. Find RS. **C**

Ⓐ $-2\sqrt{15}$

Ⓑ 4

Ⓒ $2\sqrt{15}$

Ⓓ 8

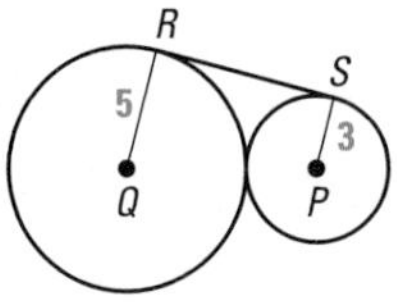

30. **REASONING** In the diagram, $\overrightarrow{PB}$ is tangent to $\odot Q$ and $\odot R$. *Explain* why $\overline{PA} \cong \overline{PB} \cong \overline{PC}$ even though the radius of $\odot Q$ is not equal to the radius of $\odot R$.
Using Theorem 10.2, $\overline{PA} \cong \overline{PB}$ and $\overline{PB} \cong \overline{PC}$. Using the Transitive Property of Segment Congruence, $\overline{PA} \cong \overline{PB} \cong \overline{PC}$.

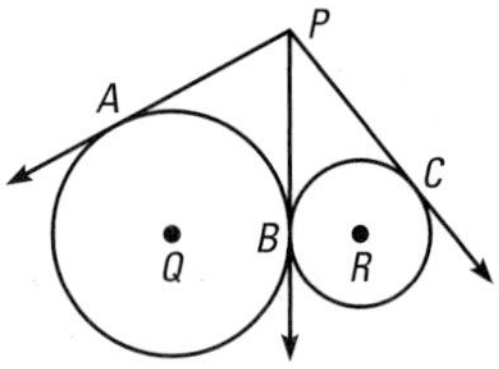

31. They will be parallel if they are tangent to opposite endpoints of the same diameter; lines perpendicular to the same line are parallel.

31. **TANGENT LINES** When will two lines tangent to the same circle not intersect? Use Theorem 10.1 to *explain* your answer.

○ = **WORKED-OUT SOLUTIONS** on p. WS1

★ = **STANDARDIZED TEST PRACTICE**

Differentiated Instruction

Auditory Learners Have students work through **Exercises 18–26** with a partner. Students should explain to their partner how they solve each exercise. Direct them to describe the theorems that allow them to draw conclusions that help them solve the exercise. Have students alternate explaining exercises to each other.

See also the *Geometry Toolkit* for more strategies.

3. No; no; no
atter what the
istance the
xternal point is
om the circle
here will
lways be
wo tangents.

32. **ANGLE BISECTOR** In the diagram at right, A and D are points of tangency on $\odot C$. *Explain* how you know that $\overrightarrow{BC}$ bisects $\angle ABD$. (*Hint*: Use Theorem 5.6, page 310.)
C is in the interior of $\angle ABD$ and $AC = DC$, using Theorem 5.6, $\overrightarrow{BC}$ bisects $\angle ABD$.

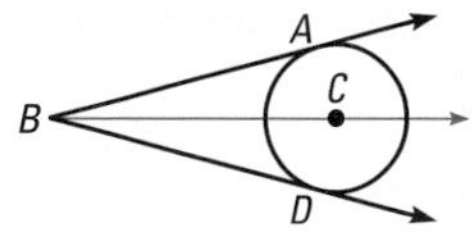

33. ★ **SHORT RESPONSE** For any point outside of a circle, is there ever only one tangent to the circle that passes through the point? Are there ever more than two such tangents? *Explain* your reasoning.

C **34.** **CHALLENGE** In the diagram at the right, $AB = AC = 12$, $BC = 8$, and all three segments are tangent to $\odot P$. What is the radius of $\odot P$? $2\sqrt{2}$

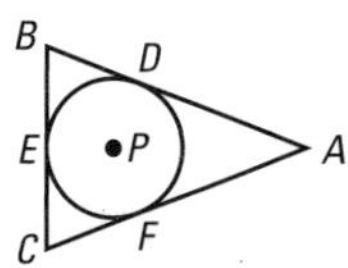

PROBLEM SOLVING

A **BICYCLES On modern bicycles, rear wheels usually have *tangential spokes*. Occasionally, front wheels have *radial spokes*. Use the definitions of *tangent* and *radius* to determine if the wheel shown has *tangential spokes* or *radial spokes*.**

35.

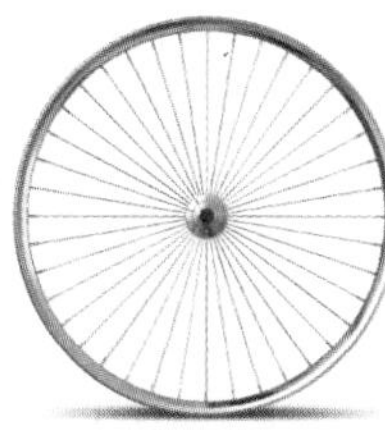

radial spokes

36.

tangential spokes

@HomeTutor for problem solving help at classzone.com

EXAMPLE 4
on p. 653
for Ex. 37

37. **GLOBAL POSITIONING SYSTEM (GPS)** GPS satellites orbit about 11,000 miles above Earth. The mean radius of Earth is about 3959 miles. Because GPS signals cannot travel through Earth, a satellite can transmit signals only as far as points A and C from point B, as shown. Find BA and BC to the nearest mile.
14,426 mi

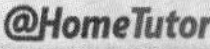 for problem solving help at classzone.com

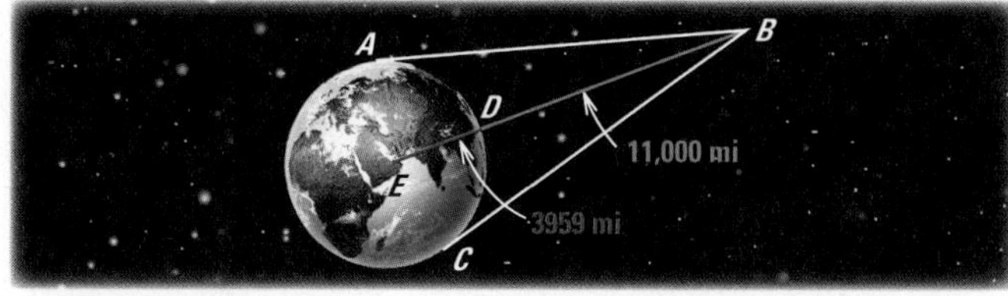

B **38.** ★ **SHORT RESPONSE** In the diagram, $\overline{RS}$ is a common internal tangent (see Exercises 27–28) to $\odot A$ and $\odot B$. Use similar triangles to *explain* why $\frac{AC}{BC} = \frac{RC}{SC}$.
$\triangle ARC \sim \triangle BSC$ by the AA Similarity Postulate, thus the ratio of corresponding sides is the same.

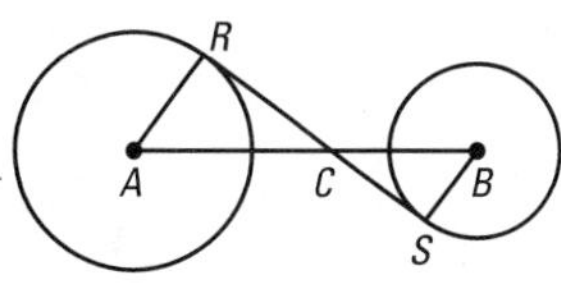

Internet Reference

Exercise 37 For additional information about the Global Positioning System, visit www.navcen.uscg.gov/gps/default.htm

5 ASSESS AND RETEACH

Daily Homework Quiz

Transparency Available

1. Give the name that best describes the figure.

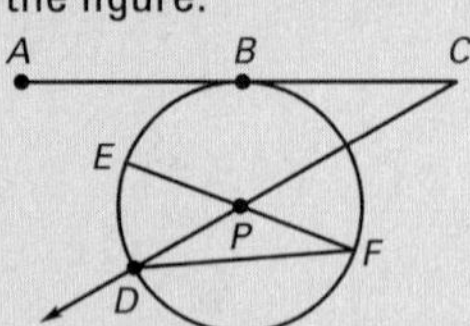

a. $\overleftrightarrow{CD}$ secant b. $\overleftrightarrow{AB}$ tangent
c. $\overline{FD}$ chord d. $\overline{EP}$ radius

2. Tell how many common tangents the circles have.

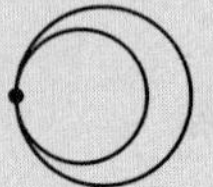

One tangent; it is a vertical line through the point of tangency.

3. Is $\overline{AB}$ tangent to $\odot C$? Explain.

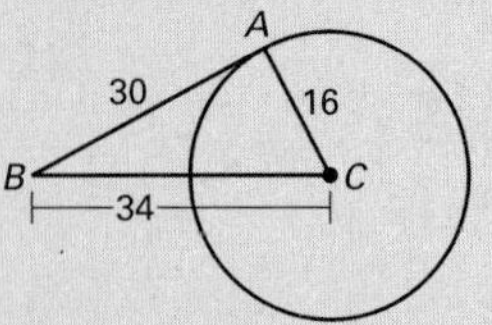

Yes; $16^2 + 30^2 = 1156 = 34^2$ so $\overline{AB} \perp \overline{AC}$, and a line $\perp$ to a radius at its endpoint is tangent to the circle.

4. Find x. 12

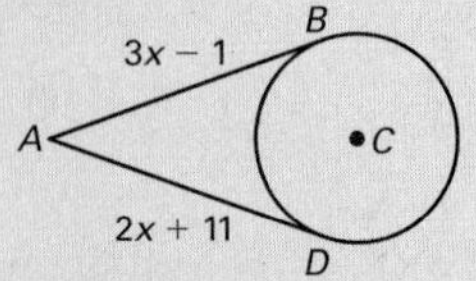

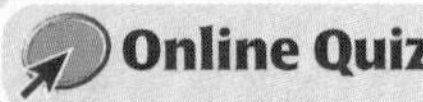

Available at **classzone.com**

Diagnosis/Remediation

- Practice A, B, C in Chapter 10 Resource Book, pp. 5–10
- Study Guide in Chapter 10 Resource Book, pp. 11–12
- Practice Workbook, pp. 184–186
- @HomeTutor

Challenge

Additional challenge is available in the Chapter 10 Resource Book, p. 15.

40, 41. See Additional Answers beginning on p. AA1.

39a. Since R is exterior to $\odot Q$, $QR > QP$.

39b. Since $\overline{QR}$ is perpendicular to m it must be the shortest distance from Q to m, thus $QR < QP$.

39c. It was assumed $\overline{QP}$ was not perpendicular to m but $\overline{QR}$ was perpendicular to m. Since R is outside of $\odot Q$ you know that $QR > QP$, but problem 39b tells you that $QR < QP$ which is a contradiction. Therefore m is perpendicular to $\overline{QP}$.

39. PROVING THEOREM 10.1 Use parts (a)–(c) to prove indirectly that if a line is tangent to a circle, then it is perpendicular to a radius.

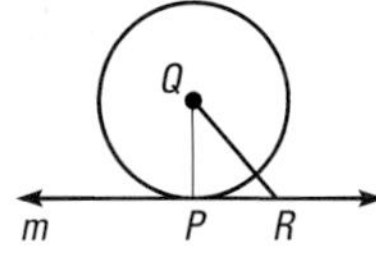

GIVEN ▶ Line m is tangent to $\odot Q$ at P.

PROVE ▶ $m \perp \overline{QP}$

a. Assume m is not perpendicular to $\overline{QP}$. Then the perpendicular segment from Q to m intersects m at some other point R. Because m is a tangent, R cannot be inside $\odot Q$. *Compare* the length QR to QP.

b. Because $\overline{QR}$ is the perpendicular segment from Q to m, $\overline{QR}$ is the shortest segment from Q to m. Now *compare* QR to QP.

c. Use your results from parts (a) and (b) to complete the indirect proof.

40. PROVING THEOREM 10.1 Write an indirect proof that if a line is perpendicular to a radius at its endpoint, the line is a tangent. **See margin.**

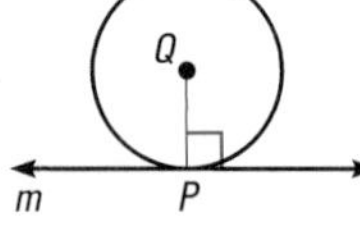

GIVEN ▶ $m \perp \overline{QP}$

PROVE ▶ Line m is tangent to $\odot Q$.

41. PROVING THEOREM 10.2 Write a proof that tangent segments from a common external point are congruent. **See margin.**

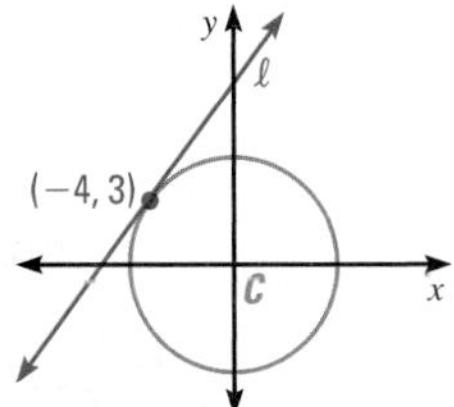

GIVEN ▶ $\overline{SR}$ and $\overline{ST}$ are tangent to $\odot P$.

PROVE ▶ $\overline{SR} \cong \overline{ST}$

Plan for Proof Use the Hypotenuse–Leg Congruence Theorem to show that $\triangle SRP \cong \triangle STP$.

C **42. CHALLENGE** Point C is located at the origin. Line ℓ is tangent to $\odot C$ at $(-4, 3)$. Use the diagram at the right to complete the problem.

a. Find the slope of line ℓ. $\frac{4}{3}$

b. Write the equation for ℓ. $y = \frac{4}{3}x + \frac{25}{3}$

c. Find the radius of $\odot C$. 5

d. Find the distance from ℓ to $\odot C$ along the y-axis. $\frac{10}{3}$

MIXED REVIEW

PREVIEW Prepare for Lesson 10.2 in Ex. 43.

43. D is in the interior of $\angle ABC$. If $m\angle ABD = 25°$ and $m\angle ABC = 70°$, find $m\angle DBC$. *(p. 24)* 45°

Find the values of *x* and *y*. *(p. 154)*

44.

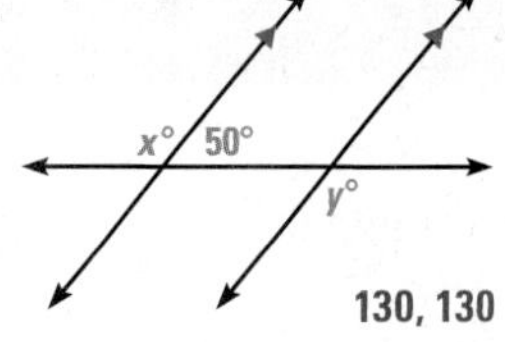

130, 130

45.

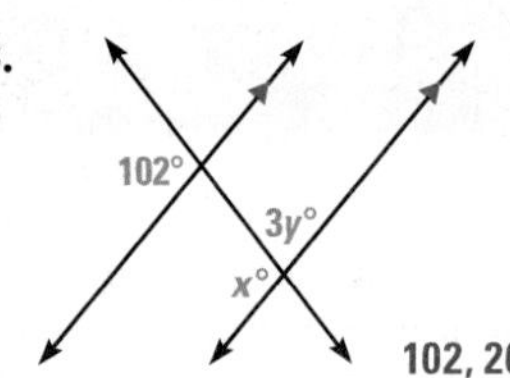

102, 26

46.

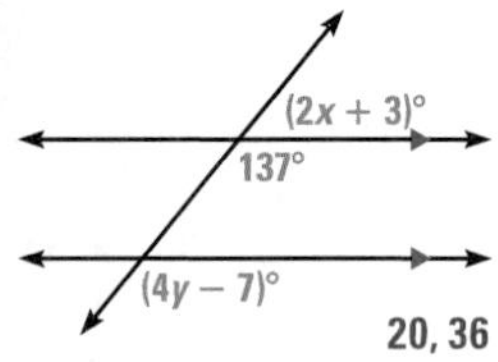

20, 36

47. A triangle has sides of lengths 8 and 13. Use an inequality to describe the possible length of the third side. What if two sides have lengths 4 and 11? *(p. 328)* $5 < x < 21$; $7 < x < 15$

10.2 Find Arc Measures

Before You found angle measures.

Now You will use angle measures to find arc measures.

Why? So you can describe the arc made by a bridge, as in Ex. 22.

Key Vocabulary
- central angle
- minor arc
- major arc
- semicircle
- measure
  - minor arc, major arc
- congruent circles
- congruent arcs

Standards

7.0 Students prove and use theorems involving the properties of parallel lines cut by a transversal, the properties of quadrilaterals, and **the properties of circles.**

A **central angle** of a circle is an angle whose vertex is the center of the circle. In the diagram, $\angle ACB$ is a central angle of $\odot C$.

If $m\angle ACB$ is less than 180°, then the points on $\odot C$ that lie in the interior of $\angle ACB$ form a **minor arc** with endpoints A and B. The points on $\odot C$ that do not lie on minor arc $\overset{\frown}{AB}$ form a **major arc** with endpoints A and B. A **semicircle** is an arc with endpoints that are the endpoints of a diameter.

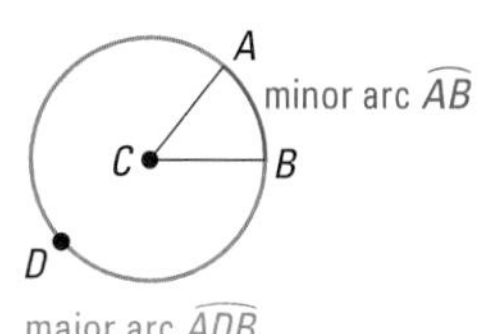

NAMING ARCS Minor arcs are named by their endpoints. The minor arc associated with $\angle ACB$ is named $\overset{\frown}{AB}$. Major arcs and semicircles are named by their endpoints and a point on the arc. The major arc associated with $\angle ACB$ can be named $\overset{\frown}{ADB}$.

KEY CONCEPT *For Your Notebook*

Measuring Arcs

The **measure of a minor arc** is the measure of its central angle. The expression $m\overset{\frown}{AB}$ is read as "the measure of arc AB."

The measure of the entire circle is 360°. The **measure of a major arc** is the difference between 360° and the measure of the related minor arc. The measure of a semicircle is 180°.

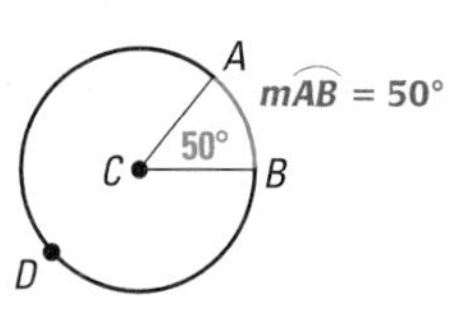

EXAMPLE 1 Find measures of arcs

Find the measure of each arc of $\odot P$, where $\overline{RT}$ is a diameter.

a. $\overset{\frown}{RS}$ **b.** $\overset{\frown}{RTS}$ **c.** $\overset{\frown}{RST}$

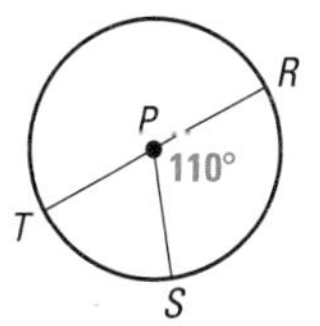

Solution

a. $\overset{\frown}{RS}$ is a minor arc, so $m\overset{\frown}{RS} = m\angle RPS = 110°$.

b. $\overset{\frown}{RTS}$ is a major arc, so $m\overset{\frown}{RTS} = 360° - 110° = 250°$.

c. $\overline{RT}$ is a diameter, so $\overset{\frown}{RST}$ is a semicircle, and $m\overset{\frown}{RST} = 180°$.

1 PLAN AND PREPARE

Warm-Up Exercises

Transparency Available

Find x and y.

1.

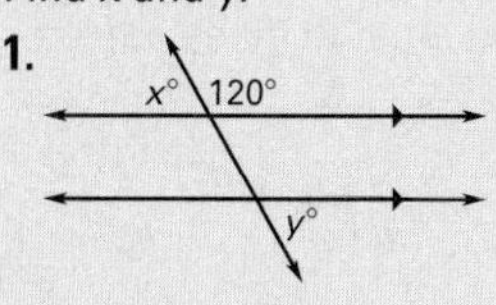

$x = 60$; $y = 60$

2.

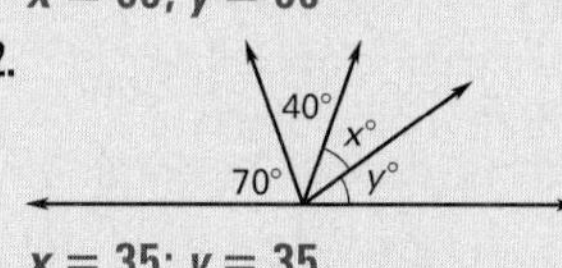

$x = 35$; $y = 35$

Notetaking Guide

Transparency Available

Promotes interactive learning and notetaking skills, pp. 258–260.

Pacing

Basic: 1 day
Average: 1 day
Advanced: 1 day
Block: 0.5 block with 10.3
- See *Teaching Guide/Lesson Plan.*

2 FOCUS AND MOTIVATE

Essential Question

Big Idea 2, p. 649

How do you find the measure of an arc of a circle? **Tell students they will learn how to answer this question by relating arc measure to the central angle of the arc.**

Resource Planning Guide

Chapter Resource Book
- Teaching Guide/Lesson Plan (pp. 16–17)
- Activity Master (p. 18)
- Practice levels A, B, C (pp. 19–24)
- Study Guide (pp. 25–26)
- Catch-up for Absent Students (p. 27)
- Problem Solving Workshop (p. 28)
- Challenge (p. 29)

Workbooks
- Notetaking Guide (pp. 258–260)
- Practice Workbook (pp. 187–189)

Teaching Options
- **Power Presentations CD-ROM** provides dynamic electronic teaching resources for the classroom.
- **Activity Generator CD-ROM** provides editable activities for all ability levels.

Interactive Technology
- Easy Planner
- Power Presentations CD-ROM
- Activity Generator CD-ROM
- Animated Geometry
- Test Generator CD-ROM
- Online Quiz
- eWorkbook
- eEdition
- @HomeTutor

Resources for English Learners
- Quick Reference for English Learners
- Spanish Study Guide
- Multi-Language Visual Glossary
- Student Resources in Spanish

See also the *Geometry Toolkit* for more strategies for meeting individual needs.

Motivating the Lesson

A pizza is cut into 6, 8, or 10 equal slices. Ask students how they would find the measure of the angle at the "point" of each slice. Tell students that in this lesson they will relate the measure of each curved crust to those angles.

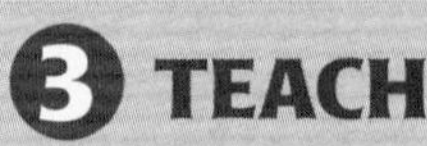

3 TEACH

Extra Example 1

Find the measure of each arc of $\odot C$, where $\overline{AB}$ is a diameter.

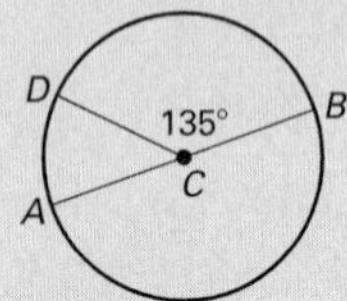

a. $\overset{\frown}{DB}$ **135°**
b. $\overset{\frown}{DAB}$ **225°**
c. $\overset{\frown}{ADB}$ **180°**

Key Question to Ask for Example 1

- How would you find the measure of $\overset{\frown}{ST}$? **Find $m\angle TPS$ by finding $180° - 110° = 70°$. Then $m\overset{\frown}{ST} = m\angle TPS = 70°$.**

Extra Example 2

A result of a survey about the ages of people in a town are shown. Find the indicated arc measures.

Ages of People (Years)

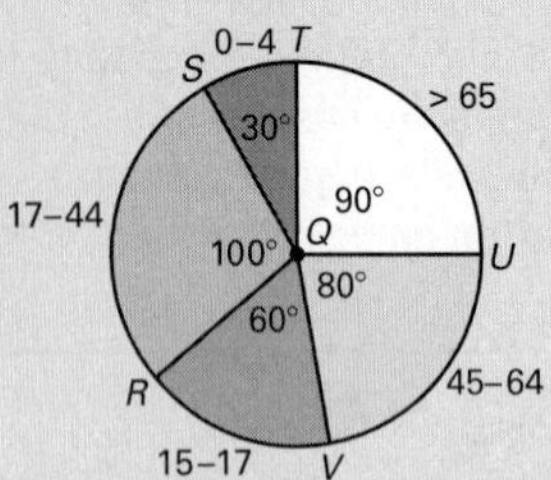

a. $m\overset{\frown}{RU}$ **140°** **b.** $m\overset{\frown}{RST}$ **130°**
c. $m\overset{\frown}{RVT}$ **230°** **d.** $m\overset{\frown}{UST}$ **270°**

ADJACENT ARCS Two arcs of the same circle are *adjacent* if they have a common endpoint. You can add the measures of two adjacent arcs.

POSTULATE *For Your Notebook*

POSTULATE 23 Arc Addition Postulate

The measure of an arc formed by two adjacent arcs is the sum of the measures of the two arcs.

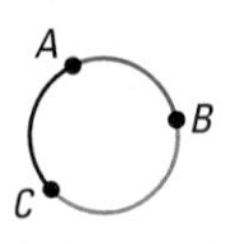

$m\overset{\frown}{ABC} = m\overset{\frown}{AB} + m\overset{\frown}{BC}$

EXAMPLE 2 Find measures of arcs

SURVEY A recent survey asked teenagers if they would rather meet a famous musician, athlete, actor, inventor, or other person. The results are shown in the circle graph. Find the indicated arc measures.

Whom Would You Rather Meet?

C, Musician, Athlete, 108°, 83°, D, B, 61°, 29°, 79°, Other, Inventor, A, E, Actor

a. $m\overset{\frown}{AC}$ **b.** $m\overset{\frown}{ACD}$
c. $m\overset{\frown}{ADC}$ **d.** $m\overset{\frown}{EBD}$

Solution

ARC MEASURES
The measure of a minor arc is less than 180°. The measure of a major arc is greater than 180°.

a. $m\overset{\frown}{AC} = m\overset{\frown}{AB} + m\overset{\frown}{BC} = 29° + 108° = 137°$

b. $m\overset{\frown}{ACD} = m\overset{\frown}{AC} + m\overset{\frown}{CD} = 137° + 83° = 220°$

c. $m\overset{\frown}{ADC} = 360° - m\overset{\frown}{AC} = 360° - 137° = 223°$

d. $m\overset{\frown}{EBD} = 360° - m\overset{\frown}{ED} = 360° - 61° = 299°$

✓ **GUIDED PRACTICE** for Examples 1 and 2

Identify the given arc as a *major arc, minor arc,* or *semicircle,* and find the measure of the arc.

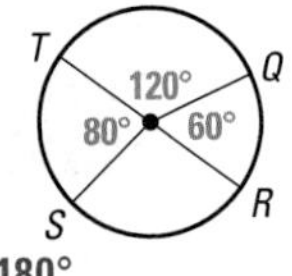

1. $\overset{\frown}{TQ}$ **minor arc, 120°**
2. $\overset{\frown}{QRT}$ **major arc, 240°**
3. $\overset{\frown}{TQR}$
4. $\overset{\frown}{QS}$ **minor arc, 160°**
5. $\overset{\frown}{TS}$ **minor arc, 80°**
6. $\overset{\frown}{RST}$ **semicircle, 180°**

3. semicircle, 180°

CONGRUENT CIRCLES AND ARCS Two circles are **congruent circles** if they have the same radius. Two arcs are **congruent arcs** if they have the same measure and they are arcs of the same circle or of congruent circles. If $\odot C$ is congruent to $\odot D$, then you can write $\odot C \cong \odot D$.

Differentiated Instruction

Visual Learners As you discuss **Example 2**, have students use colored pencils to create a copy of the circle graph. Instruct them to draw the arcs listed in parts (a)–(d) on their sketch. As students draw along the circle to form the larger arcs, they will be able to see the smaller arcs that are included in each of the larger arcs.

See also the *Geometry Toolkit* for more strategies.

EXAMPLE 3 Identify congruent arcs

Tell whether the red arcs are congruent. Explain why or why not.

a.

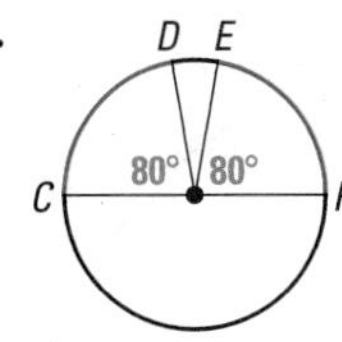

b.

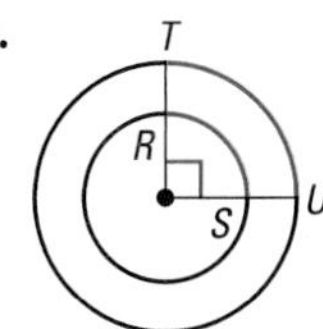

c.

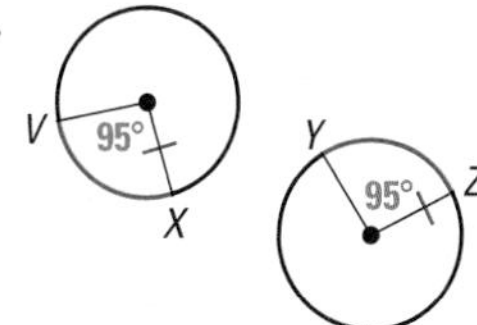

Solution

a. $\widehat{CD} \cong \widehat{EF}$ because they are in the same circle and $m\widehat{CD} = m\widehat{EF}$.

b. $\widehat{RS}$ and $\widehat{TU}$ have the same measure, but are not congruent because they are arcs of circles that are not congruent.

c. $\widehat{VX} \cong \widehat{YZ}$ because they are in congruent circles and $m\widehat{VX} = m\widehat{YZ}$.

Animated Geometry at classzone.com

GUIDED PRACTICE for Example 3

Tell whether the red arcs are congruent. *Explain* why or why not.

7.

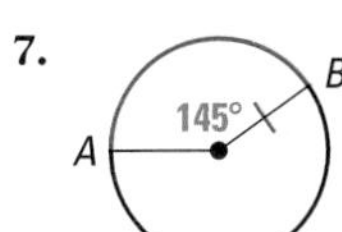

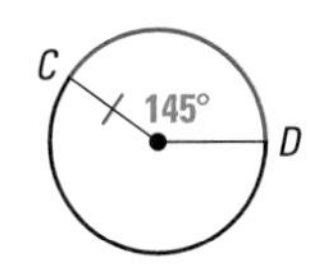

Congruent; $\widehat{AB} \cong \widehat{CD}$ since the two circles are congruent and $m\widehat{AB} = m\widehat{CD}$.

8.

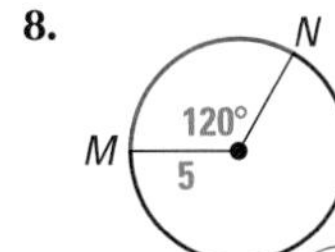

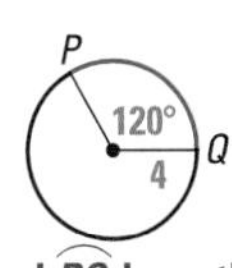

Not congruent; $\widehat{MN}$ and $\widehat{PQ}$ have the same measure but they are not congruent because the two circles are not congruent.

10.2 EXERCISES

HOMEWORK KEY

○ = **WORKED-OUT SOLUTIONS** on p. WS12 for Exs. 5, 13, and 23

★ = **STANDARDIZED TEST PRACTICE** Exs. 2, 11, 17, 18, and 24

SKILL PRACTICE

A

1. **VOCABULARY** Copy and complete: If $\angle ACB$ and $\angle DCE$ are congruent central angles of $\odot C$, then $\widehat{AB}$ and $\widehat{DE}$ are __?__. congruent

2. ★ **WRITING** What do you need to know about two circles to show that they are congruent? *Explain.* The length of their radii must be the same.

EXAMPLES 1 and 2 on pp. 659–660 for Exs. 3–11

MEASURING ARCS $\overline{AC}$ **and** $\overline{BE}$ **are diameters of** $\odot F$**. Determine whether the arc is a *minor arc*, a *major arc*, or a *semicircle* of** $\odot F$**. Then find the measure of the arc.**

3. $\widehat{BC}$ minor arc; 70°
4. $\widehat{DC}$ minor arc; 65°
5. $\widehat{DB}$ minor arc; 135°
6. $\widehat{AE}$ minor arc; 70°
7. $\widehat{AD}$ minor arc; 115°
8. $\widehat{ABC}$ semicircle; 180°
9. $\widehat{ACD}$ major arc; 245°
10. $\widehat{EAC}$ major arc; 250°

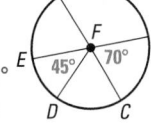

Extra Example 3

Tell whether arcs $\widehat{CD}$ and $\widehat{EF}$ are congruent. Explain why or why not.

a.

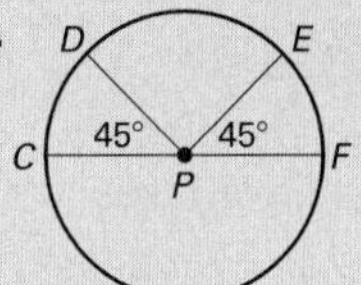

b.

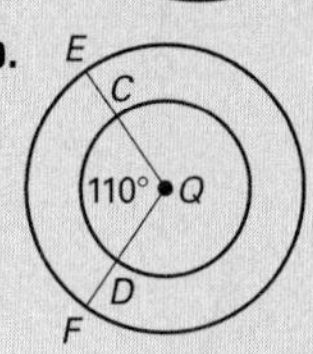

c.

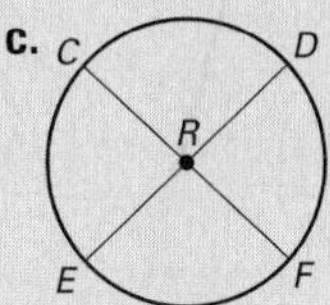

a. $\widehat{CD} \cong \widehat{EF}$; they are in the same circle and $m\widehat{CD} = m\widehat{EF}$.

b. $\widehat{CD}$ and $\widehat{EF}$ have the same measure, but they are not congruent because they are arcs of circles that are not congruent.

c. $\widehat{CD} \cong \widehat{EF}$ because they are in the same circle and vertical angles $\angle CRD$ and $\angle ERF$ are congruent.

An **Animated Geometry** activity is available on-line for **Example 3.** This activity is also available on the **Power Presentations CD-ROM**.

Closing the Lesson

Have students summarize the major points of the lesson and answer the Essential Question: How do you find the measure of an arc of a circle?

- The measure of a minor arc is the same as the measure of its related central angle.
- The measure of an arc formed by two adjacent arcs is the sum of their measures.
- Two circles are congruent if they have the same radius. Two arcs are congruent if they have the same measure and are part of the same circle or congruent circles.

Find the measure of the related central angle. That is the measure of the arc.

4 PRACTICE AND APPLY

Assignment Guide

Answer Transparencies available for all exercises

Basic:
Day 1: EP p. 896 Exs. 30–32
pp. 661–663
Exs. 1–17, 22–24, 26–34

Average:
Day 1: pp. 661–663
Exs. 1–19, 22–24, 26–34

Advanced:
Day 1: pp. 661–663
Exs. 1, 2, 4–10 even, 11–25*, 26–34 even

Block:
pp. 661–663
Exs. 1–19, 22–24, 26–34 (with 10.3)

Differentiated Instruction

See *Geometry Best Practices Toolkit* for suggestions on addressing the needs of a diverse classroom.

Homework Check

For a quick check of student understanding of key concepts, go over the following exercises:

Basic: 4, 9, 12, 22, 23
Average: 6, 8, 14, 22, 23
Advanced: 6, 10, 14, 22, 24

Extra Practice

- Student Edition, p. 914
- Chapter 10 Resource Book: Practice levels A, B, C, pp. 19–24

Practice Worksheet

An easily-readable reduced practice page (with answers) for this lesson can be found on p. 648C.

---

11. ★ **MULTIPLE CHOICE** In the diagram, $\overline{QS}$ is a diameter of $\odot P$. Which arc represents a semicircle? **C**

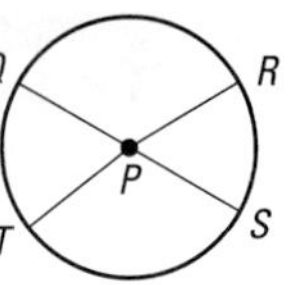

Ⓐ $\overparen{QR}$ Ⓑ $\overparen{RQT}$
Ⓒ $\overparen{QRS}$ Ⓓ $\overparen{QRT}$

EXAMPLE 3 on p. 661 for Exs. 12–14

CONGRUENT ARCS **Tell whether the red arcs are congruent. *Explain* why or why not.**

12. 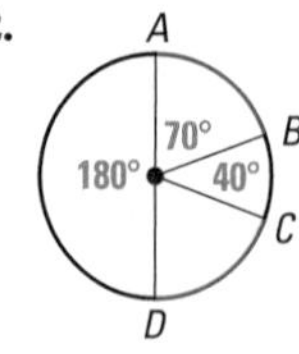

13. 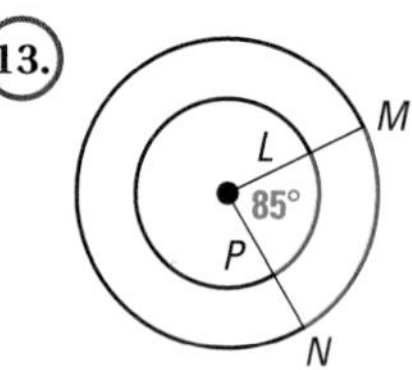

14. 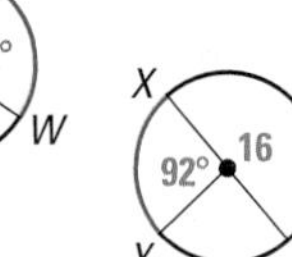

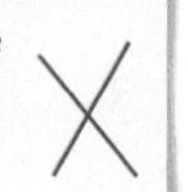

12. Congruent; $\overparen{AB} \cong \overparen{CD}$ because they are in the same circle and $m\overparen{AB} = m\overparen{CD}$.

13. Not congruent; they are arcs of circles that are not congruent.

14. Congruent; $\overparen{VW} \cong \overparen{XY}$ because they are in congruent circles and $m\overparen{VW} \cong m\overparen{XY}$.

B

15. **ERROR ANALYSIS** *Explain* what is wrong with the statement.

You can tell that the circles are congruent since they have the same radius $\overline{CD}$.

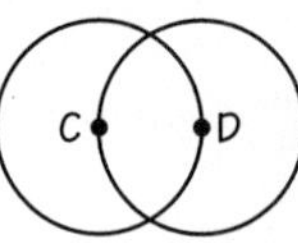

You cannot tell if $\odot C \cong \odot D$ because the radii are not given.

16. **ARCS** Two diameters of $\odot P$ are $\overline{AB}$ and $\overline{CD}$. If $m\overparen{AD} = 20°$, find $m\overparen{ACD}$ and $m\overparen{AC}$. **340°, 160°**

17. ★ **MULTIPLE CHOICE** $\odot P$ has a radius of 3 and $\overparen{AB}$ has a measure of 90°. What is the length of $\overline{AB}$? **A**

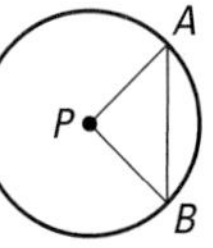

Ⓐ $3\sqrt{2}$ Ⓑ $3\sqrt{3}$
Ⓒ 6 Ⓓ 9

18. ★ **SHORT RESPONSE** On $\odot C$, $m\overparen{EF} = 100°$, $m\overparen{FG} = 120°$, and $m\overparen{EFG} = 220°$. If H is on $\odot C$ so that $m\overparen{GH} = 150°$, *explain* why H must be on $\overparen{EF}$. **Since $m\overparen{GE} = 140°$, H must be 10° beyond E placing it between E and F, or H must be 20° beyond F placing it between E and F.**

19. **REASONING** In $\odot R$, $m\overparen{AB} = 60°$, $m\overparen{BC} = 25°$, $m\overparen{CD} = 70°$, and $m\overparen{DE} = 20°$. Find two possible values for $m\overparen{AE}$. ***Sample answer:* 15°, 175°**

C

20. **CHALLENGE** In the diagram shown, $\overline{PQ} \perp \overline{AB}$, $\overline{QA}$ is tangent to $\odot P$, and $m\overparen{AVB} = 60°$. What is $m\overparen{AUB}$? **120°**

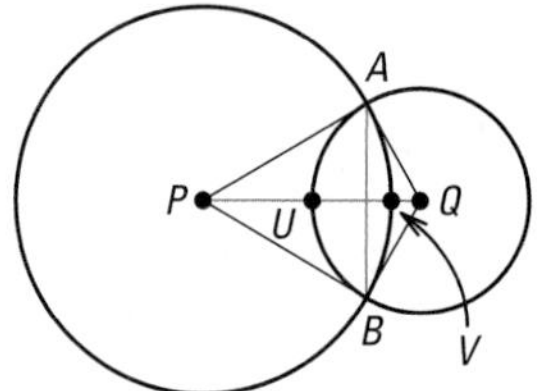

21. **CHALLENGE** In the coordinate plane shown, C is at the origin. Find the following arc measures on $\odot C$.

a. $m\overparen{BD}$ **about 36.9°**
b. $m\overparen{AD}$ **about 53.1°**
c. $m\overparen{AB}$ **about 16.2°**

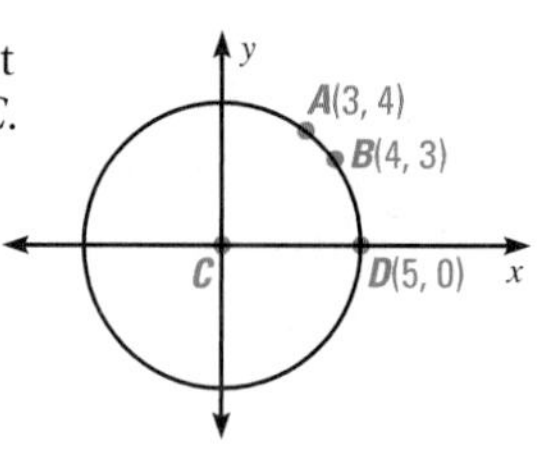

○ = WORKED-OUT SOLUTIONS on p. WS1 ★ = STANDARDIZED TEST PRACTICE

PROBLEM SOLVING

EXAMPLE 1 on p. 659 for Ex. 22

A 22. **BRIDGES** The deck of a bascule bridge creates an arc when it is moved from the closed position to the open position. Find the measure of the arc. **60°**

@HomeTutor for problem solving help at classzone.com

23. **DARTS** On a regulation dartboard, the outermost circle is divided into twenty congruent sections. What is the measure of each arc in this circle? **18°**

@HomeTutor for problem solving help at classzone.com

B 24. ★ **EXTENDED RESPONSE** A surveillance camera is mounted on a corner of a building. It rotates clockwise and counterclockwise continuously between Wall A and Wall B at a rate of 10° per minute.

a. What is the measure of the arc surveyed by the camera? **270°**

b. How long does it take the camera to survey the entire area once? **27 min**

c. If the camera is at an angle of 85° from Wall B while rotating counterclockwise, how long will it take for the camera to return to that same position? **37 min**

d. The camera is rotating counterclockwise and is 50° from Wall A. Find the location of the camera after 15 minutes. **100° from Wall A**

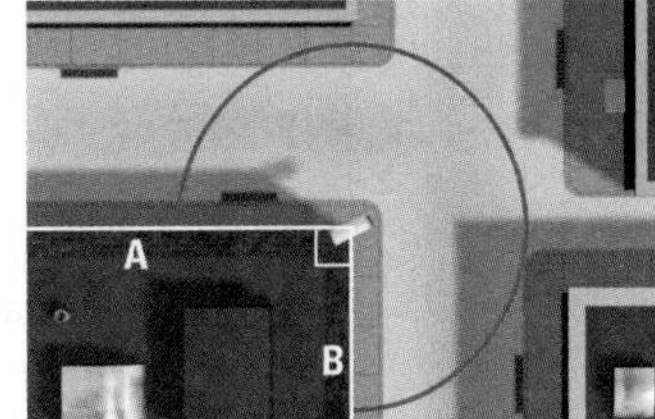

C 25. **CHALLENGE** A clock with hour and minute hands is set to 1:00 P.M.

a. After 20 minutes, what will be the measure of the minor arc formed by the hour and minute hands? **80°**

b. At what time before 2:00 P.M., to the nearest minute, will the hour and minute hands form a diameter? **1:38 P.M.**

MIXED REVIEW

PREVIEW Prepare for Lesson 10.3 in Exs. 26–27.

Determine if the lines with the given equations are parallel. *(p. 180)*

26. $y = 5x + 2, y = 5(1 - x)$ **not parallel**

27. $2y + 2x = 5, y = 4 - x$ **parallel**

28. Trace $\triangle XYZ$ and point P. Draw a counterclockwise rotation of $\triangle XYZ$ 145° about P. *(p. 598)* **See margin.**

Find the product. *(p. 641)*

29. $(x + 2)(x + 3)$ $x^2 + 5x + 6$

30. $(2y - 5)(y + 7)$ $2y^2 + 9y - 35$

31. $(x + 6)(x - 6)$ $x^2 - 36$

32. $(z - 3)^2$ $z^2 - 6z + 9$

33. $(3x + 7)(5x + 4)$ $15x^2 + 47x + 28$

34. $(z - 1)(z - 4)$ $z^2 - 5z + 4$

5 ASSESS AND RETEACH

Daily Homework Quiz

Transparency Available

Use this diagram of ⊙F for Exercises 1–4.

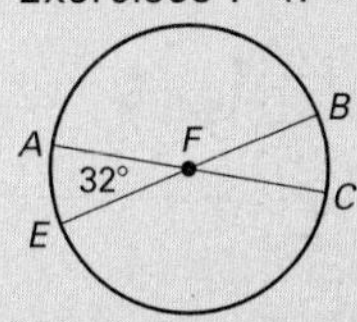

Describe each arc as a minor arc, major arc, or semicircle. Find the arc measure.

1. $\overset{\frown}{BC}$ **minor arc, 32°**
2. $\overset{\frown}{CBE}$ **major arc, 212°**
3. $\overset{\frown}{BCE}$ **semicircle, 180°**
4. Explain why $\overset{\frown}{AE} \cong \overset{\frown}{BC}$. **$m\angle AFE = m\angle BFC$ because the angles are vertical angles, so $\angle AFE \cong \angle BFC$. Then arcs $\overset{\frown}{AE}$ and $\overset{\frown}{BC}$ are arcs that have the same measure in the same circle. By definition $\overset{\frown}{AE} \cong \overset{\frown}{BC}$.**
5. Two diameters of ⊙P are $\overline{AB}$ and $\overline{CD}$. If $m\overset{\frown}{AD} = 50°$, find $m\overset{\frown}{ACD}$ and $m\overset{\frown}{AC}$. **310°; 130°**

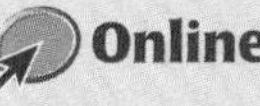

Online Quiz

Available at **classzone.com**

Diagnosis/Remediation

- Practice A, B, C in Chapter 10 Resource Book, pp. 19–24
- Study Guide in Chapter 10 Resource Book, pp. 25–26
- Practice Workbook, pp. 187–189
- @HomeTutor

Challenge

Additional challenge is available in the Chapter 10 Resource Book, p. 29.

28.

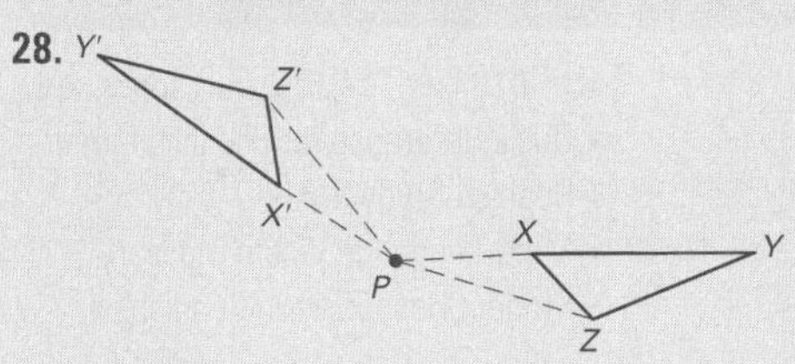

1 PLAN AND PREPARE

Warm-Up Exercises

Transparency Available

Tell whether the segment is best described as a radius, chord, or diameter of $\odot C$.

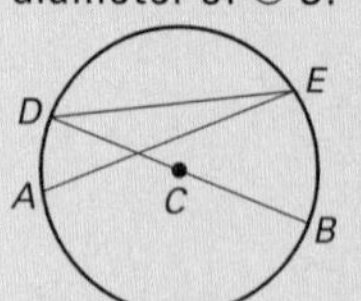

1. $\overline{DC}$ **radius**
2. $\overline{BD}$ **diameter**
3. $\overline{DE}$ **chord**
4. $\overline{AE}$ **chord**
5. Solve $4x = 8x - 12$. **3**
6. Solve $3x + 2 = 6x - 4$. **2**

Notetaking Guide

Transparency Available

Promotes interactive learning and notetaking skills, pp. 261–263.

Pacing

Basic: 1 day

Average: 1 day

Advanced: 1 day

Block: 0.5 block with 10.2

- See *Teaching Guide/Lesson Plan*.

2 FOCUS AND MOTIVATE

Essential Question

Big Idea 1, p. 649

How can you tell if two chords in a circle are congruent? **Tell students they will learn how to answer this question by looking at minor arcs or at the distance between the center and each chord.**

10.3 Apply Properties of Chords

Before You used relationships of central angles and arcs in a circle.

Now You will use relationships of arcs and chords in a circle.

Why? So you can design a logo for a company, as in Ex. 25.

Key Vocabulary
- **chord,** *p. 651*
- **arc,** *p. 659*
- **semicircle,** *p. 659*

Standards

21.0 Students prove and solve problems regarding relationships among chords, secants, tangents, inscribed angles, and inscribed and circumscribed polygons **of circles.**

7.0 Students prove and use theorems involving the properties of parallel lines cut by a transversal, the properties of quadrilaterals, and **the properties of circles.**

Recall that a *chord* is a segment with endpoints on a circle. Because its endpoints lie on the circle, any chord divides the circle into two arcs. A diameter divides a circle into two semicircles. Any other chord divides a circle into a minor arc and a major arc.

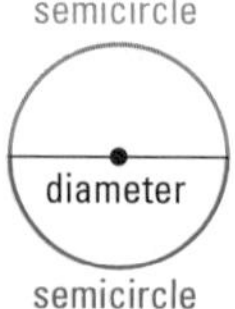

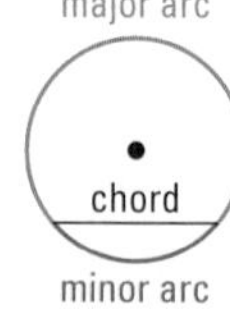

THEOREM *For Your Notebook*

THEOREM 10.3

In the same circle, or in congruent circles, two minor arcs are congruent if and only if their corresponding chords are congruent.

Proof: Exs. 27–28, p. 669

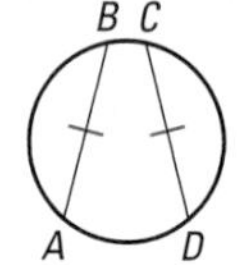

$\overset{\frown}{AB} \cong \overset{\frown}{CD}$ if and only if $\overline{AB} \cong \overline{CD}$.

EXAMPLE 1 Use congruent chords to find an arc measure

In the diagram, $\odot P \cong \odot Q$, $\overline{FG} \cong \overline{JK}$, and $m\overset{\frown}{JK} = 80°$. Find $m\overset{\frown}{FG}$.

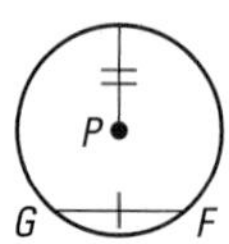

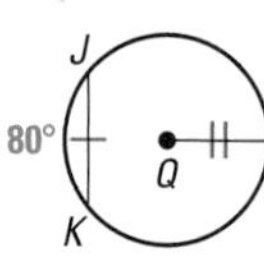

Solution

Because $\overline{FG}$ and $\overline{JK}$ are congruent chords in congruent circles, the corresponding minor arcs $\overset{\frown}{FG}$ and $\overset{\frown}{JK}$ are congruent.

▶ So, $m\overset{\frown}{FG} = m\overset{\frown}{JK} = 80°$.

GUIDED PRACTICE for Example 1

Use the diagram of $\odot D$.

1. If $m\overset{\frown}{AB} = 110°$, find $m\overset{\frown}{BC}$. **110°**
2. If $m\overset{\frown}{AC} = 150°$, find $m\overset{\frown}{AB}$. **105°**

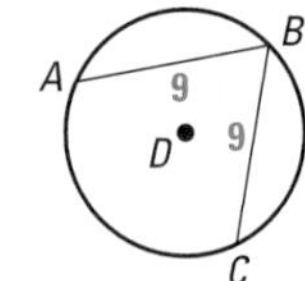

Resource Planning Guide

Chapter Resource Book
- Teaching Guide/Lesson Plan (pp. 30–31)
- Activity Master (p. 32)
- Practice levels A, B, C (pp. 34–39)
- Study Guide (pp. 40–41)
- Catch-up for Absent Students (p. 42)
- Application (p. 43)
- Challenge (p. 44)

Workbooks
- Notetaking Guide (pp. 261–263)
- Practice Workbook (pp. 190–192)

Teaching Options
- **Power Presentations CD-ROM** provides dynamic electronic teaching resources for the classroom.
- **Activity Generator CD-ROM** provides editable activities for all ability levels.

Interactive Technology
- Easy Planner
- Power Presentations CD-ROM
- Activity Generator CD-ROM
- Animated Geometry
- Test Generator CD-ROM
- Online Quiz
- eWorkbook
- eEdition
- @HomeTutor

Resources for English Learners
- Quick Reference for English Learners
- Spanish Study Guide
- Multi-Language Visual Glossary
- Student Resources in Spanish

See also the *Geometry Toolkit* for more strategies for meeting individual needs.

BISECTING ARCS If $\widehat{XY} \cong \widehat{YZ}$, then the point Y, and any line, segment, or ray that contains Y, *bisects* $\widehat{XYZ}$.

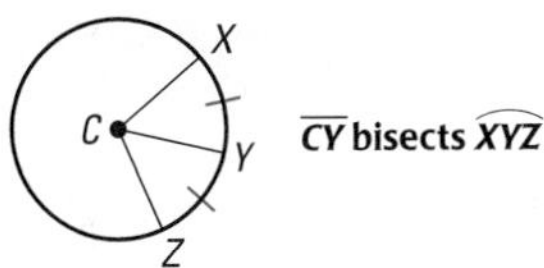

$\overline{CY}$ bisects $\widehat{XYZ}$.

THEOREMS *For Your Notebook*

THEOREM 10.4

If one chord is a perpendicular bisector of another chord, then the first chord is a diameter.

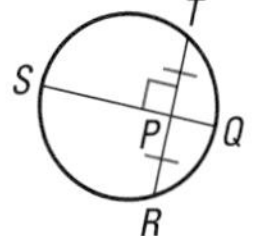

If $\overline{QS}$ is a perpendicular bisector of $\overline{TR}$, then $\overline{QS}$ is a diameter of the circle.

Proof: Ex. 31, p. 670

THEOREM 10.5

If a diameter of a circle is perpendicular to a chord, then the diameter bisects the chord and its arc.

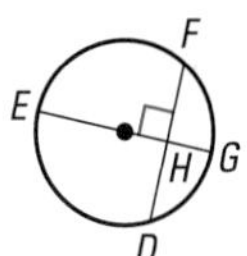

If $\overline{EG}$ is a diameter and $\overline{EG} \perp \overline{DF}$, then $\overline{HD} \cong \overline{HF}$ and $\widehat{GD} \cong \widehat{GF}$.

Proof: Ex. 32, p. 670

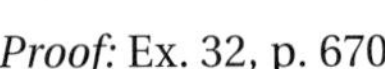

EXAMPLE 2 Use perpendicular bisectors

GARDENING Three bushes are arranged in a garden as shown. Where should you place a sprinkler so that it is the same distance from each bush?

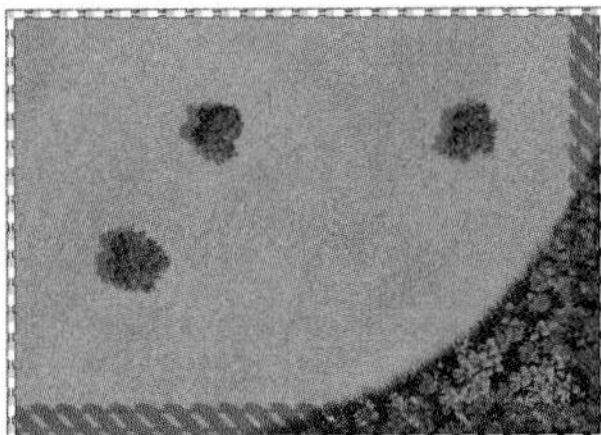

Solution

STEP 1

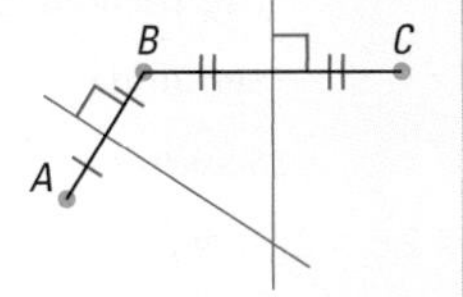

Label the bushes A, B, and C, as shown. Draw segments $\overline{AB}$ and $\overline{BC}$.

STEP 2

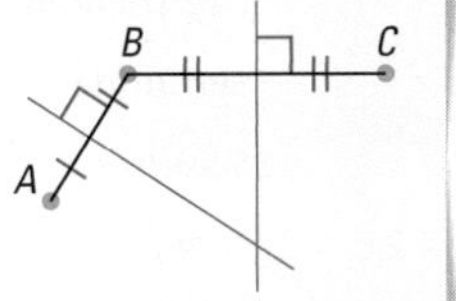

Draw the perpendicular bisectors of $\overline{AB}$ and $\overline{BC}$. By Theorem 10.4, these are diameters of the circle containing A, B, and C.

STEP 3

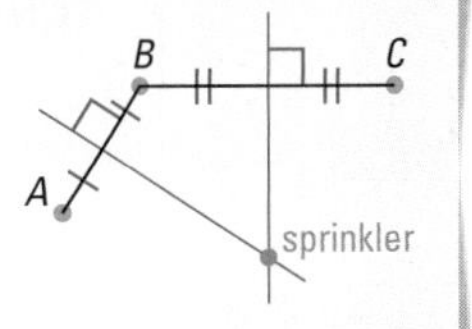

Find the point where these bisectors intersect. This is the center of the circle through A, B, and C, and so it is equidistant from each point.

Motivating the Lesson

Discuss with students that there are many circles that contain any two given points. Then ask them to describe the locations of the centers of all those circles. They should see that the centers are on the perpendicular bisector of the segment joining the two given points. Tell students that this lesson explores chords in circles and explores radii and diameters perpendicular to the chords.

3 TEACH

Extra Example 1

In $\odot R$, $\overline{AB} \cong \overline{CD}$ and $m\widehat{AB} = 108°$. Find $m\widehat{CD}$. **108°**

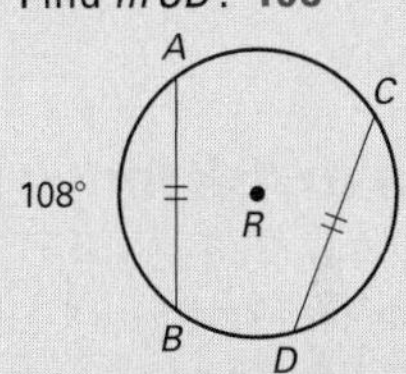

Extra Example 2

Three props are placed on a stage at points P, Q, and R as shown. Describe how to find the location of a table so it is the same distance from each prop.

Draw the perpendicular bisectors of any two of $\overline{PQ}$, $\overline{QR}$, and $\overline{PR}$. The intersection of the two perpendicular bisectors is the desired location.

Differentiated Instruction

Kinesthetic Learners After discussing **Example 2**, have students recreate the problem in the classroom. Have them place three chairs randomly in the middle of the classroom and have three of the students sit in them. Ask the students to find a point where the teacher could stand that is the same distance from each of the three students. Have them use yarn or string to create the circle that contains the three chairs and "draw" perpendicular bisectors.

See also the *Geometry Toolkit* for more strategies.

Extra Example 3

Use the diagram of $\odot C$ to find the length of $\overline{BF}$. Tell what theorem you used. **10; Theorem 10.5**

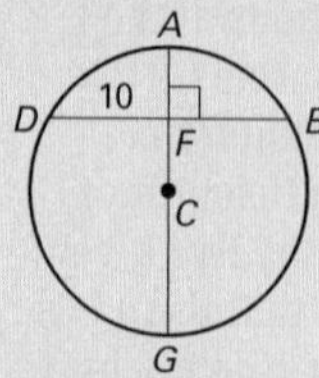

Extra Example 4

In the diagram of $\odot P$, $PV = PW$, $QR = 2x + 6$, and $ST = 3x - 1$. Find QR. **20**

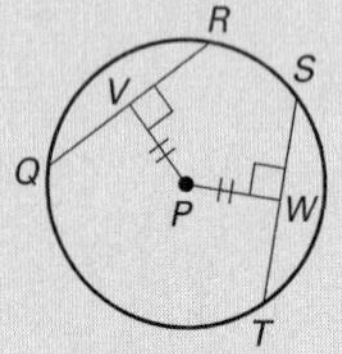

Key Question to Ask for Example 4

- Why can you say that $2x = 5x - 9$? **The chords are congruent in the same circle, CV and CU are the distances from the center for each chord, and Theorem 10.6 says those distances are equal.**

Closing the Lesson

Have students summarize the major points of the lesson and answer the Essential Question: How can you tell if two chords in a circle are congruent?

- **Two chords have congruent minor arcs if and only if they are congruent.**
- **If a diameter is perpendicular to a chord, then it bisects the chord and its arc.**
- **Two chords are equidistant from the center if and only if they are congruent.**

Determine whether the chords have congruent minor arcs or if they are equidistant from the center. If either condition is true, the chords are congruent.

EXAMPLE 3 Use a diameter

Use the diagram of $\odot E$ to find the length of $\overline{AC}$. Tell what theorem you use.

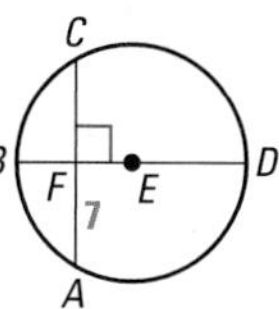

Solution

Diameter $\overline{BD}$ is perpendicular to $\overline{AC}$. So, by Theorem 10.5, $\overline{BD}$ bisects $\overline{AC}$, and $CF = AF$. Therefore, $AC = 2(AF) = 2(7) = 14$.

✓ GUIDED PRACTICE for Examples 2 and 3

Find the measure of the indicated arc in the diagram.

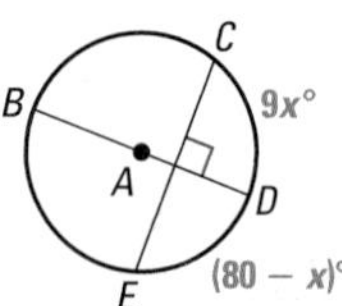

3. $\overset{\frown}{CD}$ **72°**
4. $\overset{\frown}{DE}$ **72°**
5. $\overset{\frown}{CE}$ **144°**

THEOREM — *For Your Notebook*

THEOREM 10.6

In the same circle, or in congruent circles, two chords are congruent if and only if they are equidistant from the center.

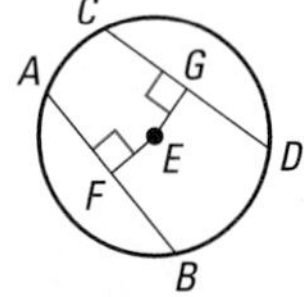

$\overline{AB} \cong \overline{CD}$ if and only if $EF = EG$.

Proof: Ex. 33, p. 670

EXAMPLE 4 Use Theorem 10.6

In the diagram of $\odot C$, $QR = ST = 16$. Find CU.

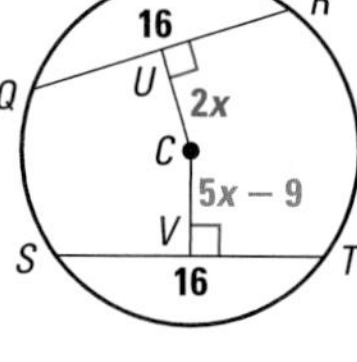

Solution

Chords $\overline{QR}$ and $\overline{ST}$ are congruent, so by Theorem 10.6 they are equidisant from C. Therefore, $CU = CV$.

$CU = CV$	**Use Theorem 10.6.**
$2x = 5x - 9$	**Substitute.**
$x = 3$	**Solve for *x*.**

▶ So, $CU = 2x = 2(3) = 6$.

✓ GUIDED PRACTICE for Example 4

In the diagram in Example 4, suppose $ST = 32$, and $CU = CV = 12$. Find the given length.

6. QR **32**
7. QU **16**
8. The radius of $\odot C$ **20**

10.3 EXERCISES

HOMEWORK KEY
○ = **WORKED-OUT SOLUTIONS** on p. WS13 for Exs. 7, 9, and 25
★ = **STANDARDIZED TEST PRACTICE** Exs. 2, 15, 22, and 26

SKILL PRACTICE

A

1. **VOCABULARY** *Describe* what it means to *bisect* an arc.
   Sample answer: **Point *Y* bisects $\overset{\frown}{XZ}$ if $\overset{\frown}{XY} \cong \overset{\frown}{YZ}$.**
2. ★ **WRITING** Two chords of a circle are perpendicular and congruent. Does one of them have to be a diameter? *Explain* your reasoning. **No. *Sample answer:* Inscribe a square in a circle using the intersection of the square's diagonals as the center of the circle.**

EXAMPLES 1 and 3 on pp. 664, 666 for Exs. 3–5

FINDING ARC MEASURES **Find the measure of the red arc or chord in $\odot C$.**

3.
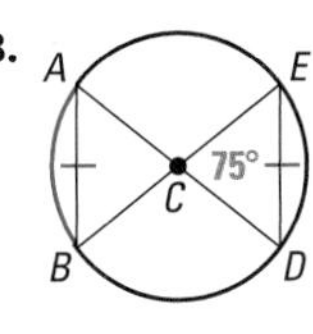

75°

4. A, B, C, D, 128°, 34, 34 **116°**

5.
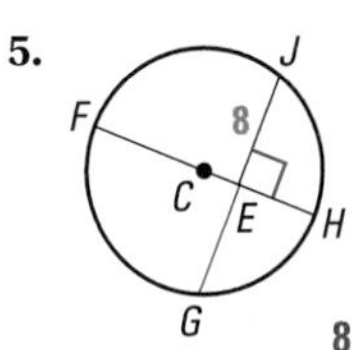

8

EXAMPLES 3 and 4 on p. 666 for Exs. 6–11

ALGEBRA **Find the value of *x* in $\odot Q$. *Explain* your reasoning.**

6.
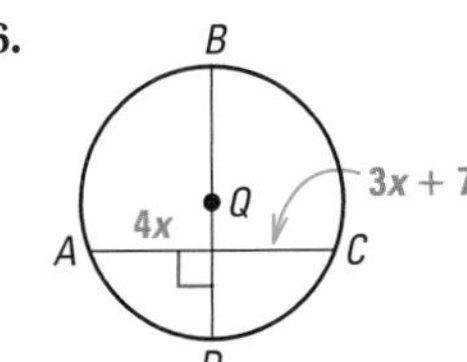

7.
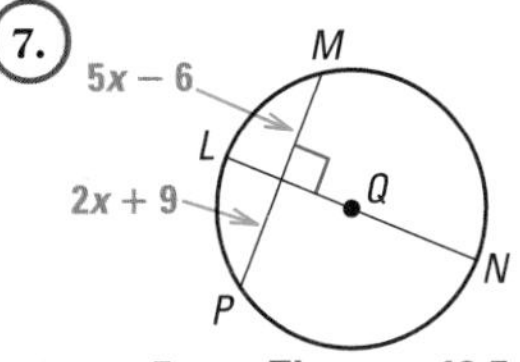

5; use Theorem 10.5 and solve $5x - 6 = 2x + 9$.

8.
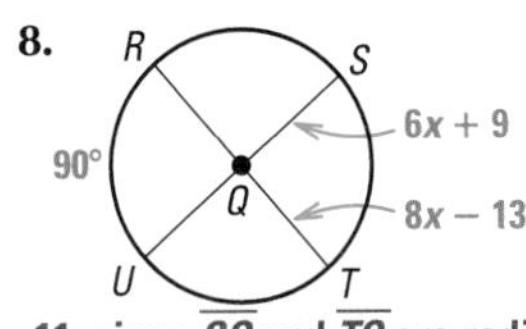

11; since $\overline{SQ}$ and $\overline{TQ}$ are radii they have the same measure. Solve $6x + 9 = 8x - 13$.

9. B, 18, Q, A, D, C, 5x − 7
5; use Theorem 10.6 and solve $18 = 5x - 7$.

10. 3x + 2, A, B, D, 6, Q, 6, 22, C

11.
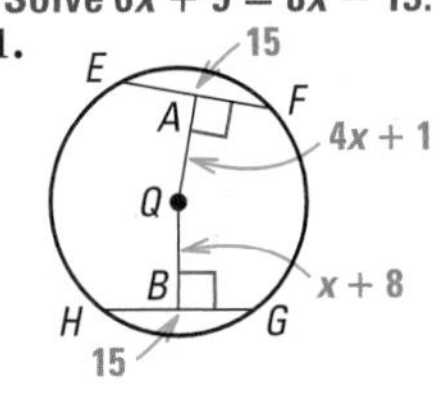

. 7; use Theorem 0.5 and solve $x = 3x + 7$.

0. 3; use Theorem 10.6 and 0.5 and solve $x + 4 = 22$.

1. $\frac{7}{3}$; use Theorem 10.6 and solve $x + 1 = x + 8$.

REASONING **In Exercises 12–14, what can you conclude about the diagram shown? State a theorem that justifies your answer.**

12.
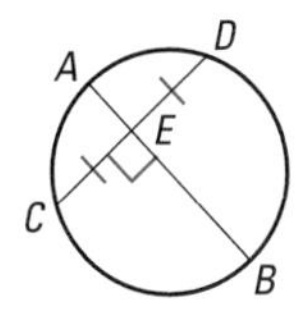

13. J, F, Q, H, G
$\overline{JH}$ bisects $\overline{FG}$ and $\overset{\frown}{FG}$; Theorem 10.5.

14.
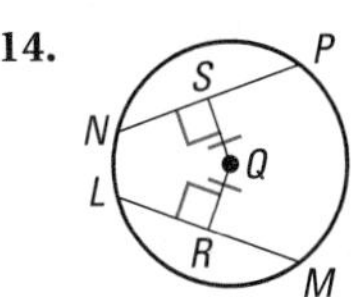

$\overline{NP} \cong \overline{LM}$; Theorem 10.6.

12. $\overline{AB}$ is a diameter of the circle; Theorem 10.4.

15. ★ **MULTIPLE CHOICE** In the diagram of $\odot R$, which congruence relation is not necessarily true? **D**
   Ⓐ $\overline{PQ} \cong \overline{QN}$ Ⓑ $\overline{NL} \cong \overline{LP}$
   Ⓒ $\overset{\frown}{MN} \cong \overset{\frown}{MP}$ Ⓓ $\overline{PN} \cong \overline{PL}$

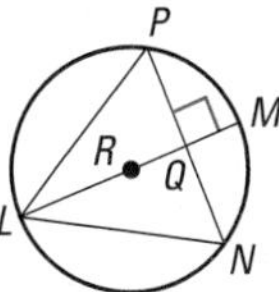

4 PRACTICE AND APPLY

Assignment Guide

Answer Transparencies available for all exercises

Basic:
Day 1: pp. 667–670
Exs. 1–18, 25–28, 35–37

Average:
Day 1: pp. 667–670
Exs. 1, 2–14 even, 15–22, 25–30, 35–37

Advanced:
Day 1: pp. 667–670
Exs. 1, 2, 3–15 odd, 16–35*, 37

Block:
pp. 667–670
Exs. 1, 2–14 even, 15–22, 25–30, 35–37 (with 10.2)

Differentiated Instruction

See *Geometry Best Practices Toolkit* for suggestions on addressing the needs of a diverse classroom.

Homework Check

For a quick check of student understanding of key concepts, go over the following exercises:
Basic: 3, 6, 9, 18, 26
Average: 4, 8, 10, 19, 26
Advanced: 5, 7, 11, 20, 26

Extra Practice

- Student Edition, p. 914
- Chapter 10 Resource Book: Practice levels A, B, C, pp. 34–39

Practice Worksheet

An easily-readable reduced practice page (with answers) for this lesson can be found on p. 648D.

Teaching Strategy

Exercises 6–14 Ask students to explain each exercise by writing the theorem that applies as a conditional statement.

Exercise 19 If students need help starting this exercise, suggest that congruent triangles can be used to show that $\overline{AB}$ is the perpendicular bisector of $\overline{CD}$. Ask students to label the intersection point of $\overline{AB}$ and $\overline{CD}$.

Mathematical Reasoning

Exercise 23 Since congruent chords in the same circle have congruent arcs, $m\overset{\frown}{AB}$ must be $360° -$ twice $m\overset{\frown}{AC}$. Since this expression is divisible by 2, $m\overset{\frown}{AB}$ (and therefore the measure of x) must be an even number.

22a. If the diameter of a circle bisects a chord of the circle and its arc, then the diameter is perpendicular to the chord; in the converse of Theorem 10.5 you are given the diameter, while in Theorem 10.4 you are to prove that the first chord is the diameter.

22b.

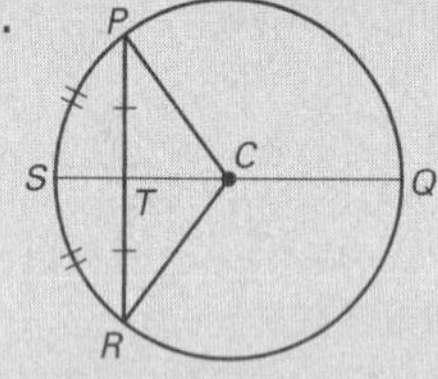

$\overline{PC} \cong \overline{RC}$ since they are both radii of the same circle. $\overline{CT} \cong \overline{CT}$ by the Reflexive Property of Congruence. $\triangle CPT \cong \triangle CRT$ by the SSS Congruence Postulate. Since $\angle RTP$ is a straight angle and $m\angle RTC = m\angle PTC$, both angles must be 90°, which makes $\overline{SQ} \perp \overline{PR}$.

22c. Since $\overline{SQ}$ is a diameter of $\odot C$ and it bisects both $\overline{PR}$ and $\overset{\frown}{PR}$, $\overline{SQ}$ is a perpendicular bisector of $\overline{PR}$. Therefore, any point on $\overline{SQ}$ is equidistant from the endpoints of the segment, so $QP = QR$.

16. $\overline{CD}$ should equal $\overline{EF}$ using Theorem 10.6.

17. You don't know that $\overline{AC} \perp \overline{DB}$ therefore you can't show $\overset{\frown}{BC} \cong \overset{\frown}{CD}$.

19. Diameter; the two triangles are congruent by the SAS Congruence Postulate which makes $\overline{AB}$ the perpendicular bisector of $\overline{CD}$. Use Theorem 10.4.

20. Not a diameter; if $\overline{AB}$ were a diameter CE would equal DE.

21. Using the facts that $\triangle APB$ is equilateral which makes it equiangular and that $m\overset{\frown}{AC} = 30°$, you can conclude that $m\angle APD = m\angle BPD = 30°$. You now know that $m\overset{\frown}{BC} = 30°$ which makes $\overline{AC} \cong \overline{BC}$. $\triangle APD \cong \triangle BPD$ by the SAS Congruence Postulate since $\overline{BP} \cong \overline{AP}$ and $\overline{PD} \cong \overline{PD}$. Because corresponding parts of congruent triangles are congruent, $\overline{AD} \cong \overline{BD}$. Along with $\overline{DC} \cong \overline{DC}$ you have $\triangle ADC \cong \triangle BDC$ by the SSS Congruence Postulate.

B

16. **ERROR ANALYSIS** *Explain* what is wrong with the diagram of $\odot P$.

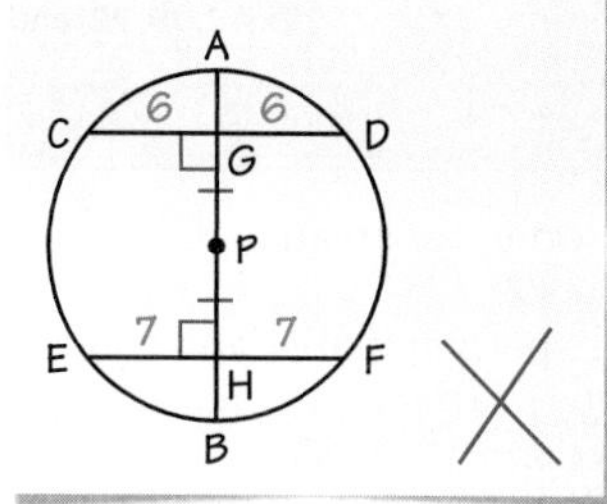

17. **ERROR ANALYSIS** *Explain* why the congruence statement is wrong.

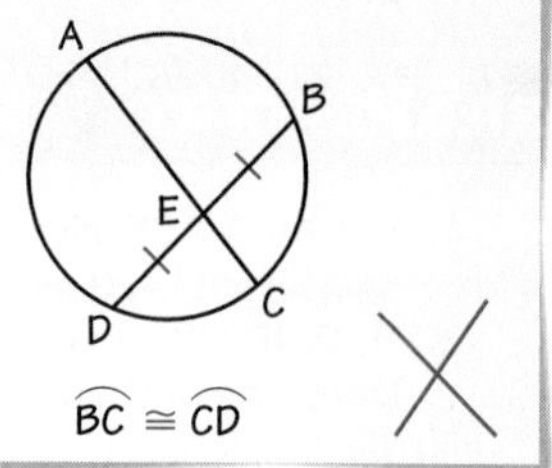

IDENTIFYING DIAMETERS **Determine whether $\overline{AB}$ is a diameter of the circle. *Explain* your reasoning.**

18.

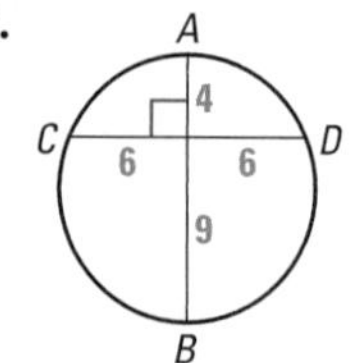

Diameter; use Theorem 10.4.

19.

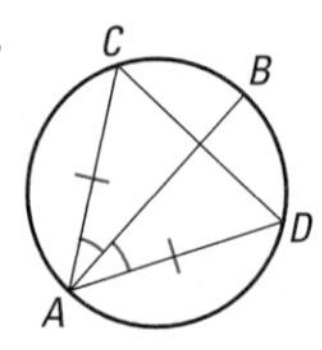

20.

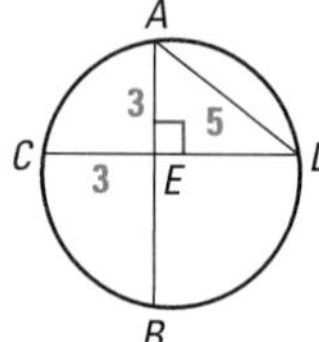

21. **REASONING** In the diagram of semicircle $\overset{\frown}{QCR}$, $\overline{PC} \cong \overline{AB}$ and $m\overset{\frown}{AC} = 30°$. *Explain* how you can conclude that $\triangle ADC \cong \triangle BDC$.

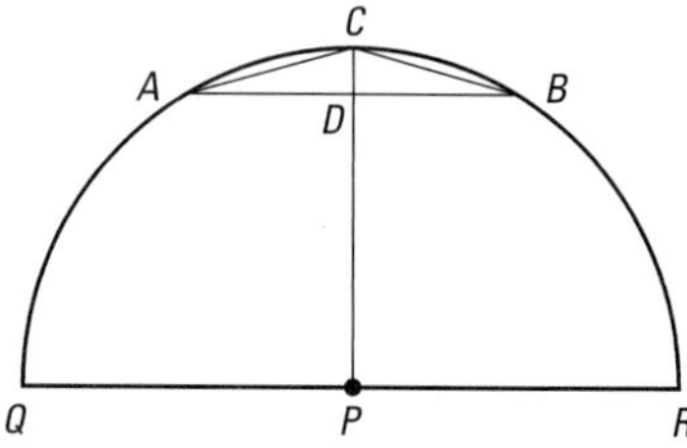

22. ★ **WRITING** Theorem 10.4 is nearly the converse of Theorem 10.5.

a. Write the converse of Theorem 10.5. *Explain* how it is different from Theorem 10.4. **a–c. See margin.**

b. Copy the diagram of $\odot C$ and draw auxiliary segments $\overline{PC}$ and $\overline{RC}$. Use congruent triangles to prove the converse of Theorem 10.5.

c. Use the converse of Theorem 10.5 to show that $QP = QR$ in the diagram of $\odot C$.

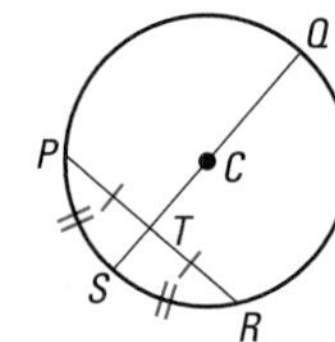

C

23. **ALGEBRA** In $\odot P$ below, $\overline{AC}$, $\overline{BC}$, and all arcs have integer measures. Show that x must be even. **See margin.**

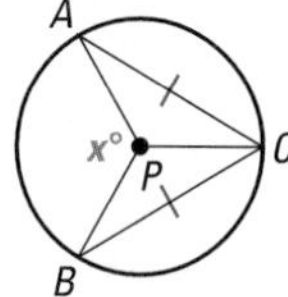

24. **CHALLENGE** In $\odot P$ below, the lengths of the parallel chords are 20, 16, and 12. Find $m\overset{\frown}{AB}$. **about 16.3°**

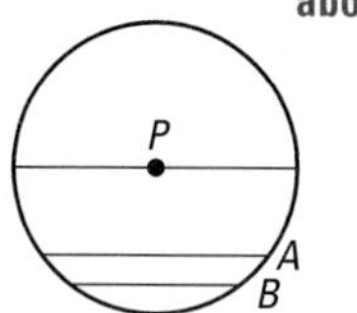

○ = WORKED-OUT SOLUTIONS on p. WS1 ★ = STANDARDIZED TEST PRACTICE

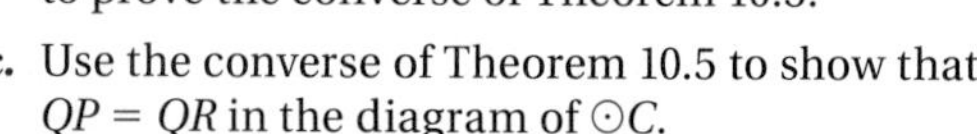

23. From the diagram, $m\overset{\frown}{AC} = m\overset{\frown}{CB}$ and $m\overset{\frown}{AB} = x°$, so you know that $m\overset{\frown}{AC} + m\overset{\frown}{CB} + x° = 360°$. Replacing $m\overset{\frown}{CB}$ by $m\overset{\frown}{AC}$ and solving for $m\overset{\frown}{AC}$, you get $m\overset{\frown}{AC} = \frac{360° - x°}{2}$. This along with the fact that all arcs have integer measures implies that x is even.

PROBLEM SOLVING

25. AB should be congruent to BC.

A **25. LOGO DESIGN** The owner of a new company would like the company logo to be a picture of an arrow inscribed in a circle, as shown. For symmetry, she wants $\overparen{AB}$ to be congruent to $\overparen{BC}$. How should $\overline{AB}$ and $\overline{BC}$ be related in order for the logo to be exactly as desired?

@HomeTutor for problem solving help at classzone.com

EXAMPLE 2 on p. 665 for Ex. 26

26. ★ OPEN-ENDED MATH In the cross section of the submarine shown, the control panels are parallel and the same length. *Explain* two ways you can find the center of the cross section. **(1) Construct the perpendicular bisector of the control panel, extend this segment to the other control panel, and then find the midpoint of the segment. (2) Draw the 2 diagonals from the top of one control panel to the bottom of the other. The center will be at their intersection.**

@HomeTutor for problem solving help at classzone.com

PROVING THEOREM 10.3 In Exercises 27 and 28, prove Theorem 10.3.

27. Given $\overline{AB} \cong \overline{CD}$. Since $\overline{PA}$, $\overline{PB}$, $\overline{PC}$, and $\overline{PD}$ are radii of $\odot P$, they are congruent. By the SSS Congruence Postulate, $\triangle PCD \cong \triangle PAB$. Because corresponding parts of congruent triangles are congruent, $\angle CPD \cong \angle APB$. With $m\angle CPD = m\angle APB$ and the fact they are both central angles, you now have $m\overparen{CD} = m\overparen{AB}$ which leads to $\overparen{CD} \cong \overparen{AB}$.

B **27. GIVEN ▶** $\overline{AB}$ and $\overline{CD}$ are congruent chords.
PROVE ▶ $\overparen{AB} \cong \overparen{CD}$

28. GIVEN ▶ $\overline{AB}$ and $\overline{CD}$ are chords and $\overparen{AB} \cong \overparen{CD}$.
PROVE ▶ $\overline{AB} \cong \overline{CD}$ **See margin.**

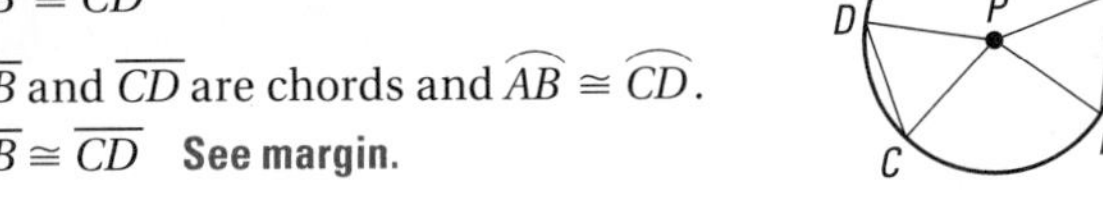

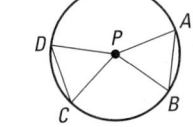

29. CHORD LENGTHS Make and prove a conjecture about chord lengths.

a. Sketch a circle with two noncongruent chords. Is the *longer* chord or the *shorter* chord closer to the center of the circle? Repeat this experiment several times. **See margin for art; longer chord.**

b. Form a conjecture related to your experiment in part (a).

c. Use the Pythagorean Theorem to prove your conjecture. **See margin.**

29b. The length of a chord in a circle increases as the distance from the center of the circle to the chord decreases.

30. MULTI-STEP PROBLEM If a car goes around a turn too quickly, it can leave tracks that form an arc of a circle. By finding the radius of the circle, accident investigators can estimate the speed of the car.

a. To find the radius, choose points A and B on the tire marks. Then find the midpoint C of $\overline{AB}$. Measure $\overline{CD}$, as shown. Find the radius r of the circle. **200 ft**

b. The formula $S = 3.86\sqrt{fr}$ can be used to estimate a car's speed in miles per hours, where f is the *coefficient of friction* and r is the radius of the circle in feet. The coefficient of friction measures how slippery a road is. If $f = 0.7$, estimate the car's speed in part (a). **about 45.7 mi/h**

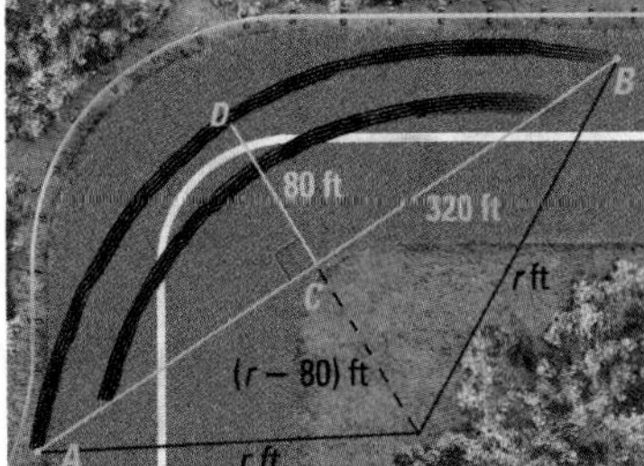

Not drawn to scale

Teaching Strategy

Exercise 29 Be sure students remember that the distance from the center of a circle to a chord is represented by a segment that is perpendicular to the chord.

28. Given: $\overline{AB}$ and $\overline{CD}$ are chords and $\overparen{AB} \cong \overparen{CD}$. From this, $m\overparen{AB} = m\overparen{CD}$, which implies $m\angle APB = m\angle CPD$, which implies $\angle APB \cong \angle CPD$. $\overline{PA}$, $\overline{PB}$, $\overline{PC}$, and $\overline{PD}$ are radii of $\odot P$, so they are congruent. Using the SAS Congruence Postulate, $\triangle APB \cong \triangle DPC$. Using corresponding parts of congruent triangles are congruent, $\overline{AB} \cong \overline{CD}$.

29a.

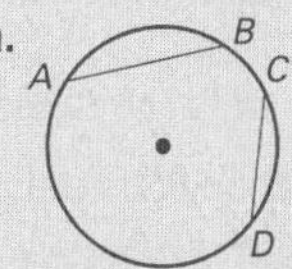

29c. Given: Radius r and real numbers a and b such that $r > a > b > 0$. Let a be the distance from one chord to the center of the circle and b be the distance from a second chord to the center of the circle. Using the Pythagorean Theorem, the length of the chord a units away from the center is $2\sqrt{r^2 - a^2}$ and the length of the chord b units away from the center is $2\sqrt{r^2 - b^2}$. Using properties of real numbers, $\sqrt{r^2 - b^2} > \sqrt{r^2 - a^2}$.

5 ASSESS AND RETEACH

Daily Homework Quiz

Transparency Available

Find the value of x in $\odot C$. Explain.

1. 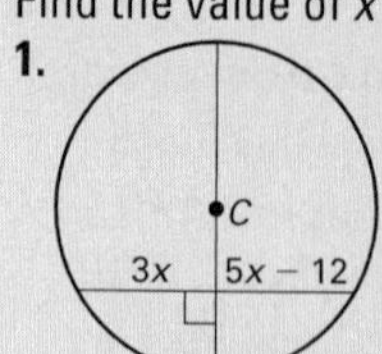

6; If a diameter of a circle is ⊥ to a chord, then the diameter bisects the chord and its arc.

2. 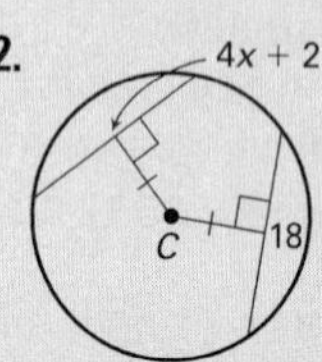

4; In the same circle, if two chords are equidistant from the center, then they are ≅.

3. Determine whether $\overline{RS}$ is a diameter. Explain.
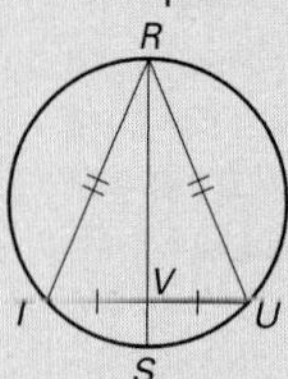

Yes. *Sample answer:* $\overline{RS}$ is the ⊥ bisector of $\overline{TU}$ by Theorem 5.3. Then $\overline{RS}$ is a diameter of the circle by Theorem 10.4.

Online Quiz

Available at **classzone.com**

Diagnosis/Remediation

- Practice A, B, C in Chapter 10 Resource Book, pp. 34–39
- Study Guide in Chapter 10 Resource Book, pp. 40–41
- Practice Workbook, pp. 190–192
- @HomeTutor

Challenge

Additional challenge is available in the Chapter 10 Resource Book, p. 44.

Quiz

An easily-readable reduced copy of the quiz (with answers) on Lessons 10.1–10.3 from the Assessment Book can be found on p. 648G.

32–34. See Additional Answers beginning on p. AA1.

31. Given: $\overline{QS}$ is perpendicular bisector of $\overline{RT}$ in $\odot L$. Suppose center L is not on $\overline{QS}$. Since $\overline{LT}$ and $\overline{LR}$ are radii of the circle they are congruent. With $\overline{PL} \cong \overline{PL}$, $\triangle RLP \cong \triangle TLP$ by the SSS Congruence Postulate. $\angle RPL$ and $\angle TPL$ are congruent and they form a linear pair. This makes them right angles and leads to $\overline{PL}$ being perpendicular to $\overline{RT}$. By the Perpendicular Postulate, L must be on $\overline{QS}$ and thus $\overline{QS}$ must be a diameter.

C **PROVING THEOREMS 10.4 AND 10.5** Write proofs.

31. **GIVEN ▶** $\overline{QS}$ is the perpendicular bisector of $\overline{RT}$.
PROVE ▶ $\overline{QS}$ is a diameter of $\odot L$.
Plan for Proof Use indirect reasoning. Assume center L is not on $\overline{QS}$. Prove that $\triangle RLP \cong \triangle TLP$, so $\overline{PL} \perp \overline{RT}$. Then use the Perpendicular Postulate.

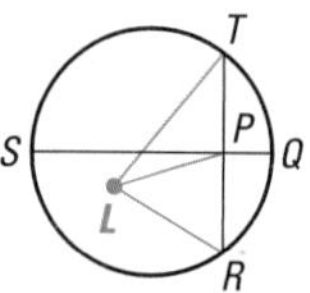

32. **GIVEN ▶** $\overline{EG}$ is a diameter of $\odot L$. $\overline{EG} \perp \overline{DF}$
PROVE ▶ $\overline{CD} \cong \overline{CF}$, $\widehat{DG} \cong \widehat{FG}$
Plan for Proof Draw $\overline{LD}$ and $\overline{LF}$. Use congruent triangles to show $\overline{CD} \cong \overline{CF}$ and $\angle DLG \cong \angle FLG$. Then show $\widehat{DG} \cong \widehat{FG}$. **See margin.**

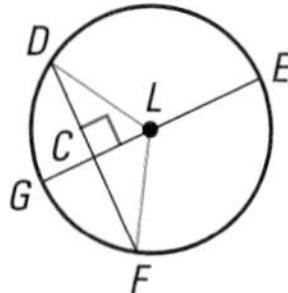

33. **PROVING THEOREM 10.6** For Theorem 10.6, prove both cases of the biconditional. Use the diagram shown for the theorem on page 666. **See margin.**

34. **CHALLENGE** A car is designed so that the rear wheel is only partially visible below the body of the car, as shown. The bottom panel is parallel to the ground. Prove that the point where the tire touches the ground bisects $\widehat{AB}$. **See margin.**

MIXED REVIEW

PREVIEW
Prepare for Lesson 10.4 in Exs. 35–37.

35. The measures of the interior angles of a quadrilateral are 100°, 140°, $(x + 20)°$, and $(2x + 10)°$. Find the value of x. *(p. 507)* **30**

Quadrilateral *JKLM* is a parallelogram. Graph ▱*JKLM*. Decide whether it is best described as a *rectangle*, a *rhombus*, or a *square*. *(p. 552)* **36, 37. See margin for art.**

36. $J(-3, 5)$, $K(2, 5)$, $L(2, -1)$, $M(-3, -1)$ **rectangle**

37. $J(-5, 2)$, $K(1, 1)$, $L(2, -5)$, $M(-4, -4)$ **rhombus**

QUIZ for Lessons 10.1–10.3

Determine whether $\overline{AB}$ is tangent to $\odot C$. *Explain* your reasoning. *(p. 651)*

1. 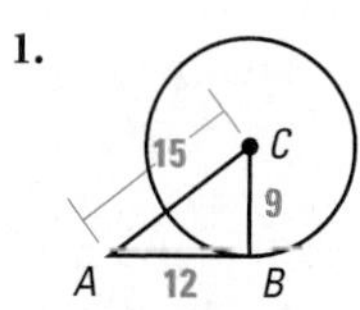

Tangent; $9^2 + 12^2 = 15^2$, $m\angle ABC = 90°$ therefore radius $\overline{CB}$ is perpendicular to $\overline{AB}$ at B.

2. 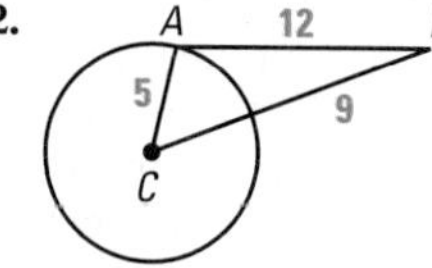

Not tangent; $5^2 + 12^2 \neq 14^2$, $m\angle BAC \neq 90°$ therefore radius $\overline{CA}$ is not perpendicular to $\overline{AB}$ at A.

3. If $m\widehat{EFG} = 195°$, and $m\widehat{EF} = 80°$, find $m\widehat{FG}$ and $m\widehat{EG}$. *(p. 659)* **115°, 165°**

4. The points A, B, and D are on $\odot C$, $\overline{AB} \cong \overline{BD}$, and $m\widehat{ABD} = 194°$. What is the measure of $\widehat{AB}$? *(p. 664)* **97°**

EXTRA PRACTICE for Lesson 10.3, p. 914   **ONLINE QUIZ** at classzone.com

36. 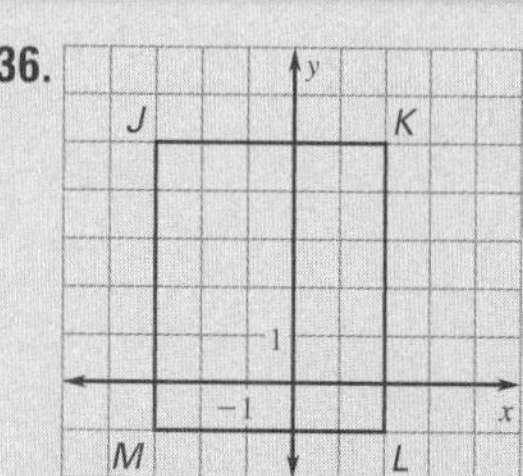

37. 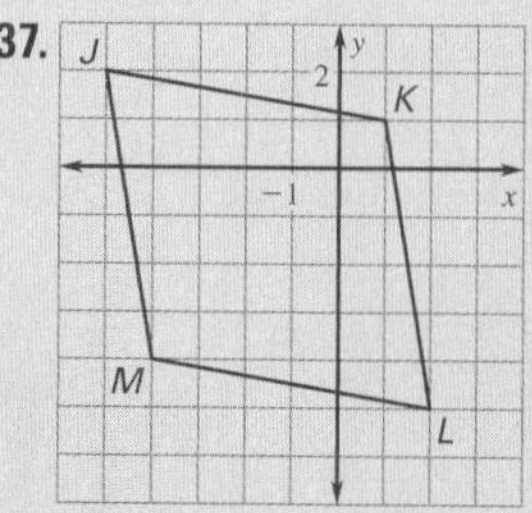

10.4 Explore Inscribed Angles

MATERIALS • compass • straightedge • protractor

Standards
Prepare for
21.0 *Students prove* and solve *problems regarding relationships among* chords, secants, tangents, *inscribed angles,* and inscribed and circumscribed polygons *of circles.*

QUESTION How are inscribed angles related to central angles?

The vertex of a central angle is at the center of the circle. The vertex of an *inscribed angle* is on the circle, and its sides form chords of the circle.

EXPLORE Construct inscribed angles of a circle

STEP 1

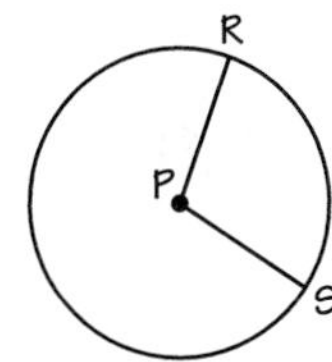

Draw a central angle Use a compass to draw a circle. Label the center *P*. Use a straightedge to draw a central angle. Label it $\angle RPS$.

STEP 2

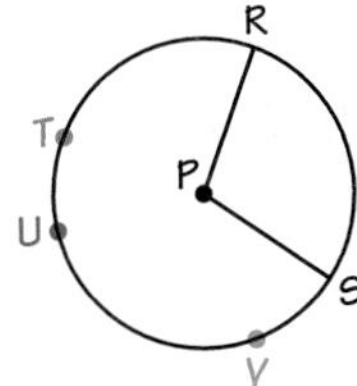

Draw points Locate three points on $\odot P$ in the exterior of $\angle RPS$ and label them *T*, *U*, and *V*.

STEP 3

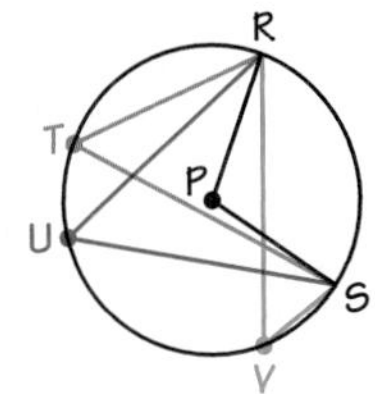

Measure angles Draw $\angle RTS$, $\angle RUS$, and $\angle RVS$. These are called *inscribed angles*. Measure each angle.

Animated Geometry at classzone.com

DRAW CONCLUSIONS Use your observations to complete these exercises

1. Copy and complete the table. **Check students' work.**

	Central angle	Inscribed angle 1	Inscribed angle 2	Inscribed angle 3
Name	$\angle RPS$	$\angle RTS$	$\angle RUS$	$\angle RVS$
Measure	?	?	?	?

2. Draw two more circles. Repeat Steps 1–3 using different central angles. Record the measures in a table similar to the one above. **Check students' work.**

3. Use your results to make a conjecture about how the measure of an inscribed angle is related to the measure of the corresponding central angle. **The measure of an inscribed angle is one half the measure of the corresponding central angle.**

1 PLAN AND PREPARE

Explore the Concept

- Students will construct inscribed angles of a circle.
- This activity leads into the study of inscribed angles in Lesson 10.4, Example 1.

Materials

Each student will need:

- compass
- straightedge
- protractor

Recommended Time

Work activity: 10 min
Discuss results: 5 min

Grouping

Students should work individually.

2 TEACH

Key Question

- If *X* and *Y* are points on a major arc with endpoints *R* and *S*, is $m\angle RXS = m\angle RYS$? **yes**

Alternative Strategy

You may want to use geometry software to demonstrate this activity.

An **Animated Geometry** activity is available on-line for the **Explore** activity. This activity is also available on the **Power Presentations CD-ROM**.

Key Discovery

The measure of an inscribed angle is half the measure of the corresponding central angle.

3 ASSESS AND RETEACH

1. A central angle measures $x°$. What is the measure of any angle inscribed in its major arc? $\frac{1}{2}x°$

1 PLAN AND PREPARE

Warm-Up Exercises

Transparency Available

1. The measure of the interior angles of a quadrilateral are 80°, 100°, 55°, and $5x°$. Find the value of x. **25**
2. Two supplementary angles have measures $6x°$ and $12x°$. Find each angle measure. **60°; 120°**
3. Solve $3x = \frac{1}{2}(4x + 12)$. **6**
4. Solve $80 = \frac{1}{2}(360 - 2x)$. **100**

Notetaking Guide

Transparency Available

Promotes interactive learning and notetaking skills, pp. 264–267.

Pacing

Basic: 2 days

Average: 2 days

Advanced: 2 days

Block: 1 block

- See *Teaching Guide/Lesson Plan.*

2 FOCUS AND MOTIVATE

Essential Question

Big Idea 2, p. 649

How do you find the measure of an inscribed angle? **Tell students they will learn how to answer this question by relating the inscribed angle to its intercepted arc.**

10.4 Use Inscribed Angles and Polygons

Before You used central angles of circles.

Now You will use inscribed angles of circles.

Why? So you can take a picture from multiple angles, as in Example 4.

Key Vocabulary
- **inscribed angle**
- **intercepted arc**
- **inscribed polygon**
- **circumscribed circle**

An **inscribed angle** is an angle whose vertex is on a circle and whose sides contain chords of the circle. The arc that lies in the interior of an inscribed angle and has endpoints on the angle is called the **intercepted arc** of the angle.

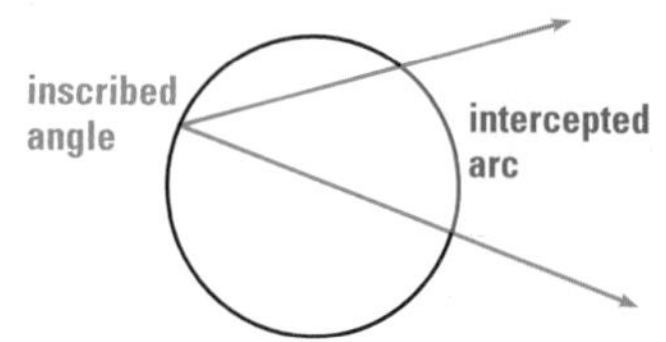

Standards

21.0 Students prove and solve problems regarding relationships among chords, secants, tangents, **inscribed angles, and inscribed and circumscribed polygons of circles.**

7.0 Students prove and use theorems involving the properties of parallel lines cut by a transversal, the properties of quadrilaterals, and **the properties of circles.**

THEOREM *For Your Notebook*

THEOREM 10.7 Measure of an Inscribed Angle Theorem

The measure of an inscribed angle is one half the measure of its intercepted arc.

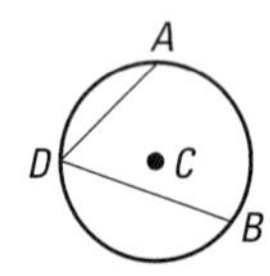

$m\angle ADB = \frac{1}{2}m\overset{\frown}{AB}$

Proof: Exs. 31–33, p. 678

The proof of Theorem 10.7 in Exercises 31–33 involves three cases.

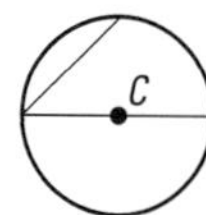

Case 1 Center C is on a side of the inscribed angle.

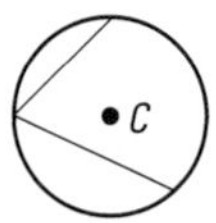

Case 2 Center C is inside the inscribed angle.

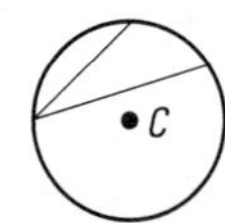

Case 3 Center C is outside the inscribed angle.

EXAMPLE 1 Use inscribed angles

Find the indicated measure in $\odot P$.

a. $m\angle T$ **b.** $m\overset{\frown}{QR}$

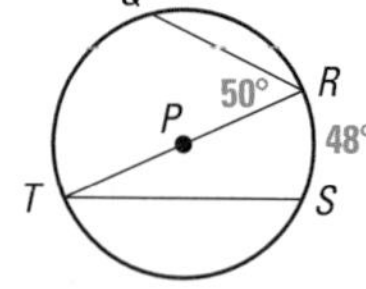

Solution

a. $m\angle T = \frac{1}{2}m\overset{\frown}{RS} = \frac{1}{2}(48°) = 24°$

b. $m\overset{\frown}{TQ} = 2m\angle R = 2 \cdot 50° = 100°$. Because $\overset{\frown}{TQR}$ is a semicircle, $m\overset{\frown}{QR} = 180° - m\overset{\frown}{TQ} = 180° - 100° = 80°$. So, $m\overset{\frown}{QR} = 80°$.

Resource Planning Guide

Chapter Resource Book
- Teaching Guide/Lesson Plan (pp. 45–46)
- Practice levels A, B, C (pp. 47–52)
- Study Guide (pp. 53–54)
- Catch-up for Absent Students (p. 55)
- Application (p. 56)
- Challenge (p. 57)

Workbooks
- Notetaking Guide (pp. 264–267)
- Practice Workbook (pp. 193–195)

Teaching Options
- **Power Presentations CD-ROM** provides dynamic electronic teaching resources for the classroom.
- **Activity Generator CD-ROM** provides editable activities for all ability levels.

Interactive Technology
- Easy Planner
- Power Presentations CD-ROM
- Activity Generator CD-ROM
- Animated Geometry
- Test Generator CD-ROM
- Online Quiz
- eWorkbook
- eEdition
- @HomeTutor

Resources for English Learners
- Quick Reference for English Learners
- Spanish Study Guide
- Multi-Language Visual Glossary
- Student Resources in Spanish

See also the *Geometry Toolkit* for more strategies for meeting individual needs.

EXAMPLE 2 Find the measure of an intercepted arc

Find $m\widehat{RS}$ and $m\angle STR$. What do you notice about $\angle STR$ and $\angle RUS$?

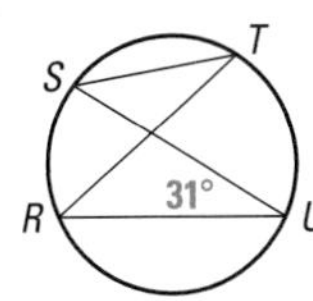

Solution

From Theorem 10.7, you know that $m\widehat{RS} = 2m\angle RUS = 2(31°) = 62°$.

Also, $m\angle STR = \frac{1}{2}m\widehat{RS} = \frac{1}{2}(62°) = 31°$. So, $\angle STR \cong \angle RUS$.

INTERCEPTING THE SAME ARC Example 2 suggests Theorem 10.8.

THEOREM *For Your Notebook*

THEOREM 10.8

If two inscribed angles of a circle intercept the same arc, then the angles are congruent.

Proof: Ex. 34, p. 678

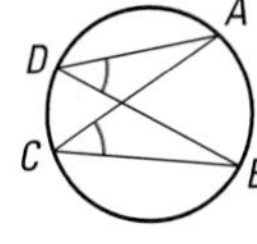

$\angle ADB \cong \angle ACB$

EXAMPLE 3 Standardized Test Practice

Name two pairs of congruent angles in the figure.

Ⓐ $\angle JKM \cong \angle KJL$, $\angle JLM \cong \angle KML$

Ⓑ $\angle JLM \cong \angle KJL$, $\angle JKM \cong \angle KML$

Ⓒ $\angle JKM \cong \angle JLM$, $\angle KJL \cong \angle KML$

Ⓓ $\angle JLM \cong \angle KJL$, $\angle JLM \cong \angle JKM$

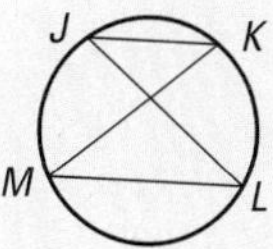

Solution

ELIMINATE CHOICES
You can eliminate choices A and B, because they do not include the pair $\angle JKM \cong \angle JLM$.

Notice that $\angle JKM$ and $\angle JLM$ intercept the same arc, and so $\angle JKM \cong \angle JLM$ by Theorem 10.8. Also, $\angle KJL$ and $\angle KML$ intercept the same arc, so they must also be congruent. Only choice C contains both pairs of angles.

▶ So, by Theorem 10.8, the correct answer is C. Ⓐ Ⓑ Ⓒ Ⓓ

GUIDED PRACTICE for Examples 1, 2, and 3

Find the measure of the red arc or angle.

1.

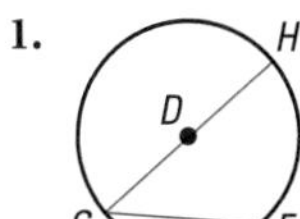

45°

2.

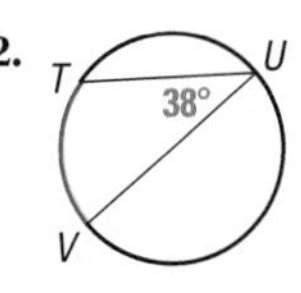

76°

3.

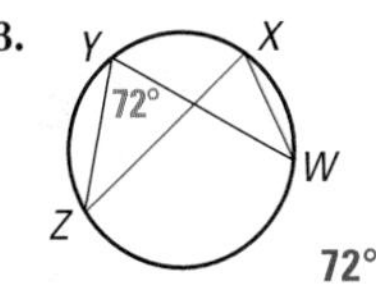

72°

Motivating the Lesson

Show students a diagram of several soccer players standing on a circle that contains the posts of the goal. Discuss with them if any player has the greatest "kicking angle" for the goal. Tell them that in this lesson they will see why each player has the same "kicking angle."

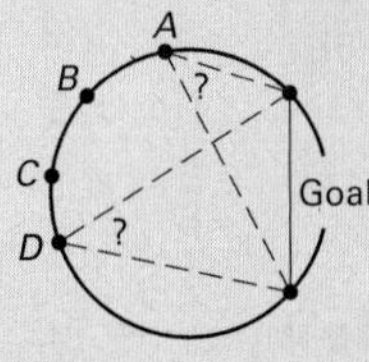

3 TEACH

Extra Example 1

Find the indicated measure in ⊙ C.

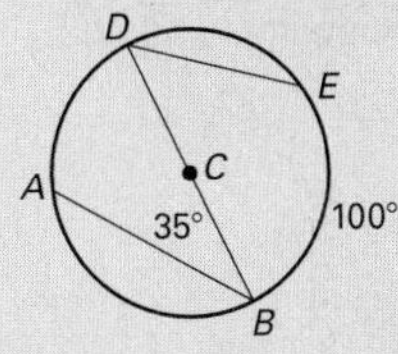

a. $m\angle D$ **50°** **b.** $m\widehat{AB}$ **110°**

Extra Example 2

Find $m\widehat{KN}$ and $m\angle KMN$. What do you notice about $\angle KMN$ and $\angle KLN$?

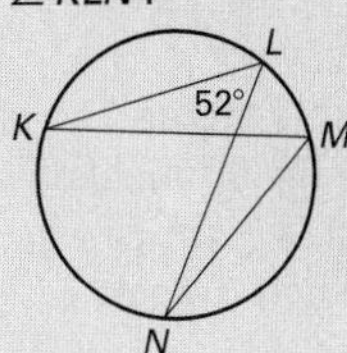

104°; 52°; $\angle KMN \cong \angle KLN$

Key Question to Ask for Example 2

- Which arc is intercepted by both $\angle STR$ and $\angle SUR$? $\widehat{RS}$

Extra Example 3

Name two pairs of congruent angles in the figure. **A**

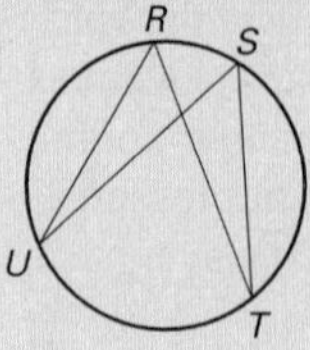

Ⓐ $\angle R \cong \angle S$, $\angle U \cong \angle T$ Ⓑ $\angle R \cong \angle T$, $\angle U \cong \angle S$

Ⓒ $\angle R \cong \angle U$, $\angle S \cong \angle T$ Ⓓ $\angle R \cong \angle T$, $\angle R \cong \angle S$

Extra Example 4

A graphic design software program was used in a home improvement store to design kitchen cabinets. The designer showed a wall of cabinets with a 90° viewing angle at *P*. From what other positions would the cabinets fill a 90° viewing window?

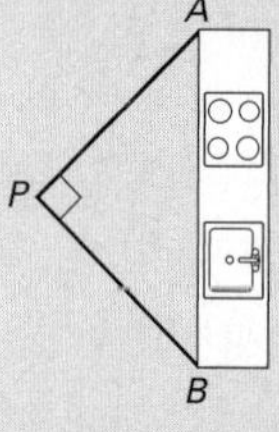

from any position on a semicircle that has $\overline{AB}$ as a diameter

Key Question to Ask for Example 4

- Why do all the points on the semicircle satisfy the 90° field of vision? **All triangles inscribed in a semicircle are right triangles.**

POLYGONS A polygon is an **inscribed polygon** if all of its vertices lie on a circle. The circle that contains the vertices is a **circumscribed circle**.

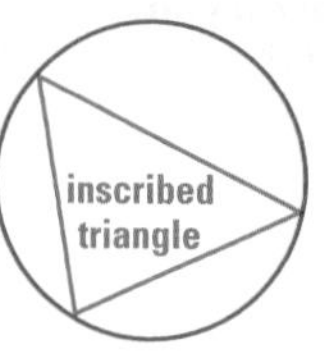

circumscribed circles

THEOREM *For Your Notebook*

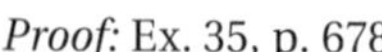

THEOREM 10.9

If a right triangle is inscribed in a circle, then the hypotenuse is a diameter of the circle. Conversely, if one side of an inscribed triangle is a diameter of the circle, then the triangle is a right triangle and the angle opposite the diameter is the right angle.

Proof: Ex. 35, p. 678

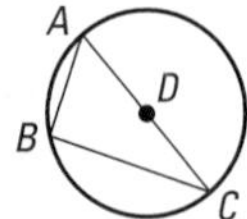

$m\angle ABC = 90°$ if and only if $\overline{AC}$ is a diameter of the circle.

EXAMPLE 4 Use a circumscribed circle

PHOTOGRAPHY Your camera has a 90° field of vision and you want to photograph the front of a statue. You move to a spot where the statue is the only thing captured in your picture, as shown. You want to change your position. Where else can you stand so that the statue is perfectly framed in this way?

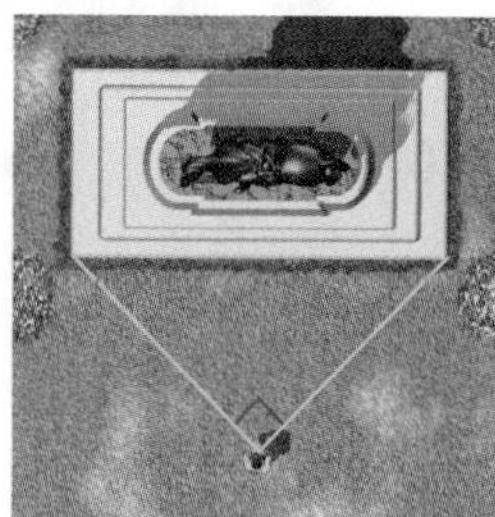

Solution

From Theorem 10.9, you know that if a right triangle is inscribed in a circle, then the hypotenuse of the triangle is a diameter of the circle. So, draw the circle that has the front of the statue as a diameter. The statue fits perfectly within your camera's 90° field of vision from any point on the semicircle in front of the statue.

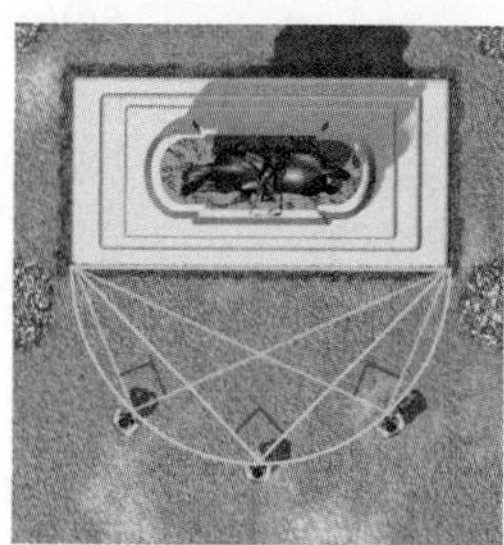

 **GUIDED PRACTICE** for Example 4

4. **WHAT IF?** In Example 4, *explain* how to find locations if you want to frame the front and left side of the statue in your picture.
Make the diameter of your circle the diagonal of the rectangular base.

Differentiated Instruction

Below Level To verify that a circle can be circumscribed about any triangle, ask students to draw a scalene triangle, an isosceles triangle, and an equilateral triangle. Then have them find the intersection point of the perpendicular bisectors of two sides of each triangle. Tell them to use that point as the center, and any vertex, to draw each circumscribed circle.

See also the *Geometry Toolkit* for more strategies.

INSCRIBED QUADRILATERAL Only certain quadrilaterals can be inscribed in a circle. Theorem 10.10 describes these quadrilaterals.

THEOREM *For Your Notebook*

THEOREM 10.10

A quadrilateral can be inscribed in a circle if and only if its opposite angles are supplementary.

D, E, F, and *G* lie on $\odot C$ if and only if $m\angle D + m\angle F = m\angle E + m\angle G = 180°$.

Proof: Ex. 30, p. 678; p. 938

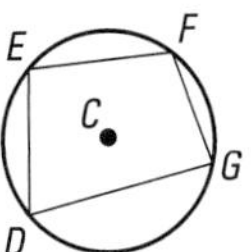

EXAMPLE 5 Use Theorem 10.10

Find the value of each variable.

a.

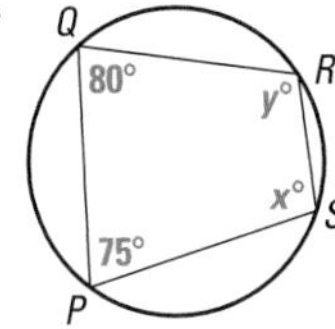

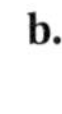

b.

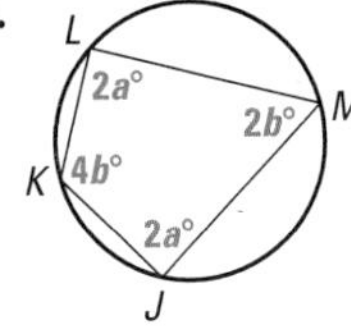

Solution

a. *PQRS* is inscribed in a circle, so opposite angles are supplementary.

$m\angle P + m\angle R = 180°$ $\qquad$ $m\angle Q + m\angle S = 180°$

$75° + y° = 180°$ $\qquad$ $80° + x° = 180°$

$y = 105$ $\qquad$ $x = 100$

b. *JKLM* is inscribed in a circle, so opposite angles are supplementary.

$m\angle J + m\angle L = 180°$ $\qquad$ $m\angle K + m\angle M = 180°$

$2a° + 2a° = 180°$ $\qquad$ $4b° + 2b° = 180°$

$4a = 180$ $\qquad$ $6b = 180$

$a = 45$ $\qquad$ $b = 30$

GUIDED PRACTICE for Example 5

Find the value of each variable.

5.

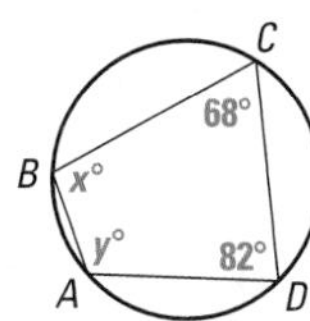

x = 98, y = 112

6.

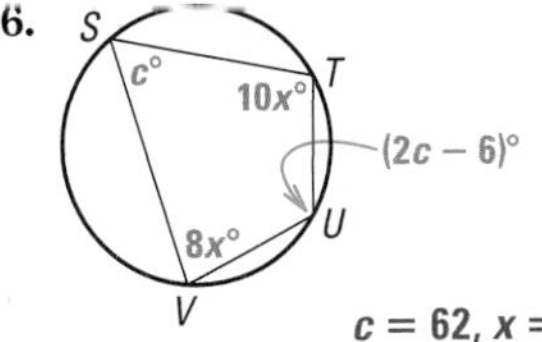

c = 62, x = 10

Extra Example 5

Find the value of each variable.

a.

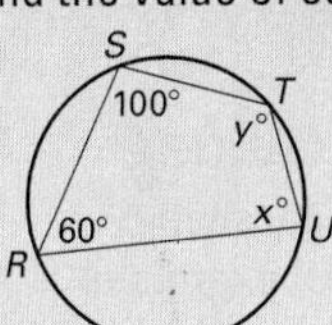

b.

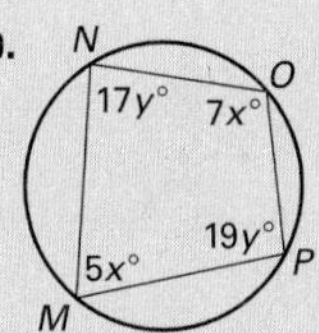

a. x = 80; y = 120; b. x = 15; y = 5

Key Questions to Ask for Example 5

- Why are the opposite angles supplementary? **The opposite angles are inscribed angles, and the sum of their intercepted arcs is 360°. So the sum of the opposite inscribed angles is 180°.**
- Are opposite angles supplementary in any quadrilateral? **No, only for a quadrilateral that can be inscribed in a circle.**

Closing the Lesson

Have students summarize the major points of the lesson and answer the Essential Question: How do you find the measure of an inscribed angle?

- **The measure of an inscribed angle is one half the measure of its intercepted arc.**
- **If two inscribed angles intercept the same arc, they are congruent.**
- **A right triangle is inscribed in a circle if and only if the hypotenuse is a diameter.**

The measure of an inscribed angle is one half of the measure of its intercepted arc.

Differentiated Instruction

Kinesthetic Learners Theorems 10.9 and 10.10 may become more concrete to students if they work out examples to support the theorems. For example, for Theorem 10.9, have students inscribe triangles in a circle so that one side of each triangle is a diameter of the circle. Then have them measure the angle opposite that side. Students will see that the angle is always a right angle.

See also the *Geometry Toolkit* for more strategies.

4 PRACTICE AND APPLY

Assignment Guide

Answer Transparencies available for all exercises

Basic:
Day 1: pp. 676–679
Exs. 1–12, 43–47
Day 2: pp. 676–679
Exs. 13–19, 27–33, 40–42

Average:
Day 1: pp. 676–679
Exs. 1, 2, 4–7, 9–12, 16–18, 43–47
Day 2: pp. 676–679
Exs. 13–15, 19–25, 28–36, 41

Advanced:
Day 1: pp. 676–679
Exs. 1, 2, 5–8, 10–12, 16–18, 43–47
Day 2: pp. 676–679
Exs. 14, 15, 19–26*, 28, 29, 34–39*, 42

Block:
pp. 676–679
Exs. 1, 2, 4–7, 9–25, 28–36, 41, 43–47

Differentiated Instruction

See *Geometry Best Practices Toolkit* for suggestions on addressing the needs of a diverse classroom.

Homework Check

For a quick check of student understanding of key concepts, go over the following exercises:

Basic: 4, 10, 14, 17, 28
Average: 6, 11, 14, 20, 28
Advanced: 8, 12, 15, 22, 28

Extra Practice

- Student Edition, p. 915
- Chapter 10 Resource Book: Practice levels A, B, C, pp. 47–52

Practice Worksheet

An easily-readable reduced practice page (with answers) for this lesson can be found on p. 648D.

10.4 EXERCISES

HOMEWORK KEY
○ = **WORKED-OUT SOLUTIONS** on p. WS13 for Exs. 11, 13, and 29
★ = **STANDARDIZED TEST PRACTICE** Exs. 2, 16, 18, 29, and 36

SKILL PRACTICE

A

1. **VOCABULARY** Copy and complete: If a circle is circumscribed about a polygon, then the polygon is _?_ in the circle. **inscribed**

2. ★ **WRITING** *Explain* why the diagonals of a rectangle inscribed in a circle are diameters of the circle. **The diagonals of a rectangle create two right triangles. Theorem 10.9 tells you the hypotenuse of each of these triangles is a diameter of the circle.**

EXAMPLES 1 and 2 on pp. 672–673 for Exs. 3–9

INSCRIBED ANGLES Find the indicated measure.

3. $m\angle A$ **42°**

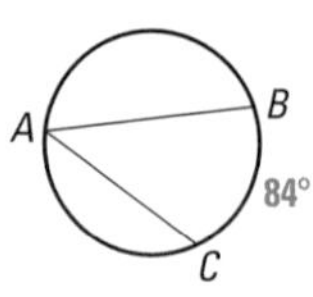

4. $m\angle G$ **85°**

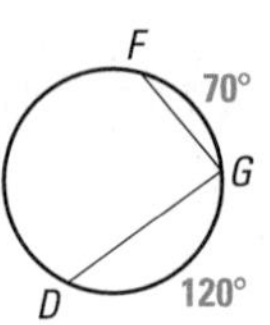

5. $m\angle N$ **10°**

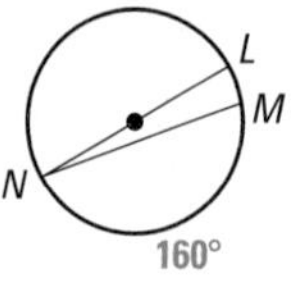

6. $m\overset{\frown}{RS}$ **134°**

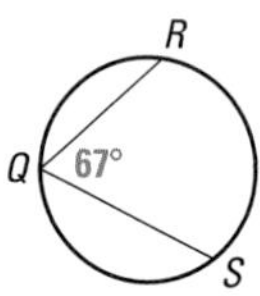

7. $m\overset{\frown}{VU}$ **120°**

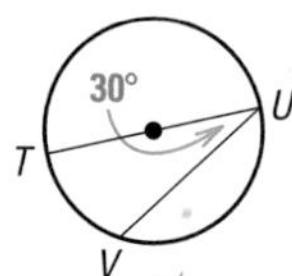

8. $m\overset{\frown}{WX}$ **100°**

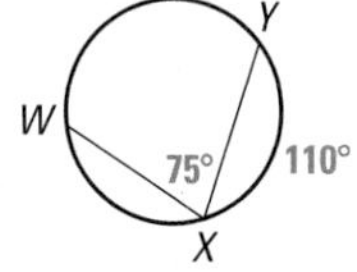

9. **ERROR ANALYSIS** *Describe* the error in the diagram of ⊙C. Find two ways to correct the error. **The measure of the arcs add up to 370°; change the measure of ∠Q to 40° or change the measure of $\overset{\frown}{QS}$ to 90°.**

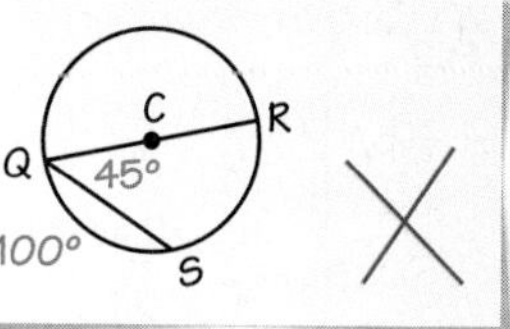

EXAMPLE 3 on p. 673 for Exs. 10–12

CONGRUENT ANGLES Name two pairs of congruent angles.

10. 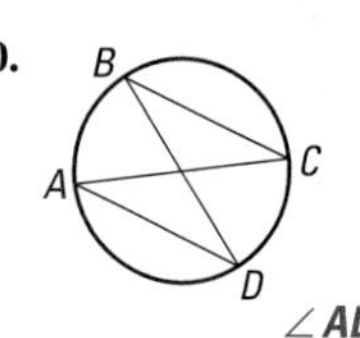

∠ADB, ∠ACB and ∠CAD, ∠DBC

11. 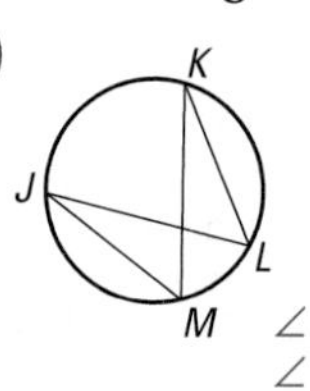

∠JMK, ∠JLK and ∠LKM, ∠LJM

12. W X Z Y
∠WXZ, ∠WYZ and ∠XWY, ∠XZY

EXAMPLE 5 on p. 675 for Exs. 13–15

ALGEBRA Find the values of the variables.

13. 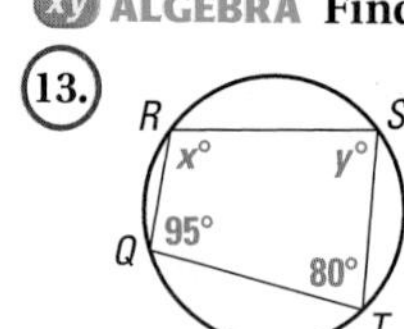

x = 100, y = 85

14. 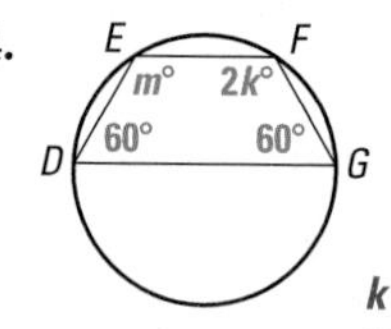

k = 60, m = 120

15. 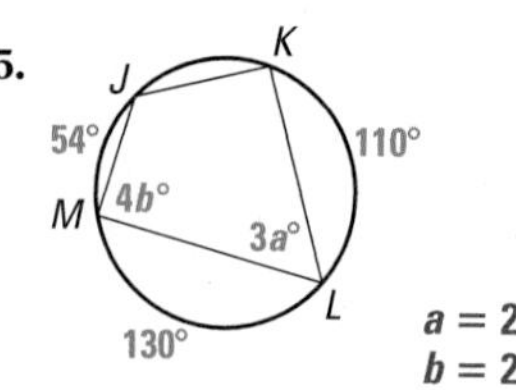

a = 20, b = 22

16. ★ **MULTIPLE CHOICE** In the diagram, $\angle ADC$ is a central angle and $m\angle ADC = 60°$. What is $m\angle ABC$? **B**

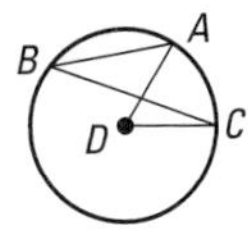

Ⓐ 15° Ⓑ 30° Ⓒ 60° Ⓓ 120°

B 17. **INSCRIBED ANGLES** In each star below, all of the inscribed angles are congruent. Find the measure of an inscribed angle for each star. Then find the sum of all the inscribed angles for each star.

a.  **36°; 180°**

b. 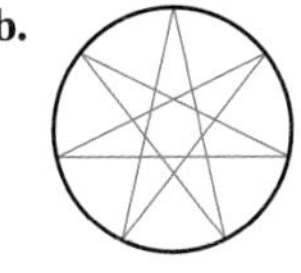 **about 25.7°; 180°**

c.  **20°; 180°**

18. ★ **MULTIPLE CHOICE** What is the value of x? **A**

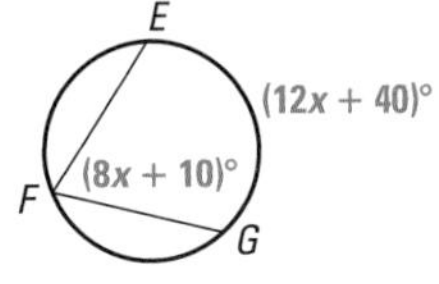

Ⓐ 5 Ⓑ 10 Ⓒ 13 Ⓓ 15

19. **PARALLELOGRAM** Parallelogram $QRST$ is inscribed in $\odot C$. Find $m\angle R$. **90°**

REASONING **Determine whether the quadrilateral can always be inscribed in a circle. *Explain* your reasoning.**

20. Square 21. Rectangle 22. Parallelogram **No; opposite angles are not always supplementary.**

23. Kite 24. Rhombus 25. Isosceles trapezoid **Yes; opposite angles are supplementary.**

20. Yes; opposite angles are 90° and thus are supplementary.

21. Yes; opposite angles are 90° and thus are supplementary.

23. No; opposite angles are not supplementary.

24. No; opposite angles are not supplementary.

C 26. **CHALLENGE** In the diagram, $\angle C$ is a right angle. If you draw the smallest possible circle through C and tangent to $\overline{AB}$, the circle will intersect $\overline{AC}$ at J and $\overline{BC}$ at K. Find the exact length of $\overline{JK}$. $\mathbf{\frac{12}{5}}$

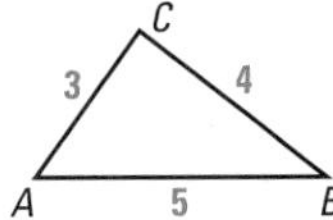

PROBLEM SOLVING

A 27. **ASTRONOMY** Suppose three moons A, B, and C orbit 100,000 kilometers above the surface of a planet. Suppose $m\angle ABC = 90°$, and the planet is 20,000 kilometers in diameter. Draw a diagram of the situation. How far is moon A from moon C? **See margin for art; 220,000 km.**

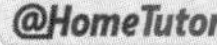 for problem solving help at classzone.com

EXAMPLE 4 on p. 674 for Ex. 28

28. **CARPENTER** A *carpenter's square* is an L-shaped tool used to draw right angles. You need to cut a circular piece of wood into two semicircles. How can you use a carpenter's square to draw a diameter on the circular piece of wood?

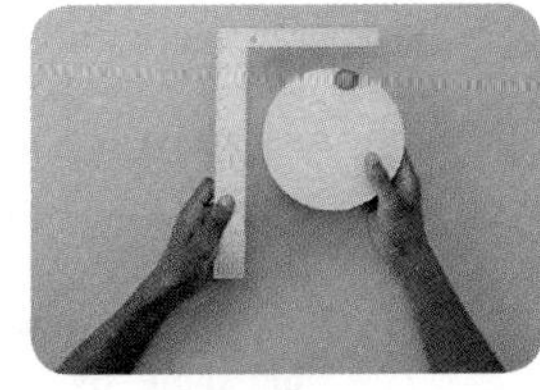

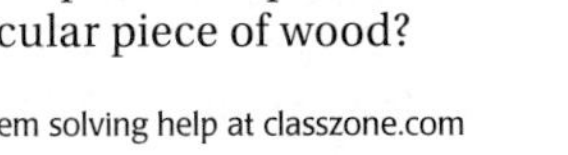 for problem solving help at classzone.com

Place the carpenter's square so the endpoints of the square and the vertex of the square are on the circumference of the circle, then connect the endpoints.

Avoiding Common Errors

Exercises 10–12 Caution students to make sure they match the inscribed angle with its correct intercepted arc.

Study Strategy

Exercises 10–12 Students can redraw the diagrams and use colored pencils to mark inscribed angles and their intercepted arcs.

Mathematical Reasoning

Exercise 17 Point out that since the total inscribed arcs constitute the entire circle, the sum of each set of inscribed angles must be 180°. The number of angles does not affect the sum.

Exercises 19, 22, 24 Point out that since the opposite sides of an inscribed quadrilateral must be supplementary, the only rhombus or parallelogram that can be inscribed is one with opposite angles supplementary, and those quadrilaterals are squares and rectangles.

Teaching Strategy

Exercise 28 Point out that the carpenter's square can be placed in several positions so that the diameter can be located. Each position used forms a right triangle with the diameter as hypotenuse.

27. 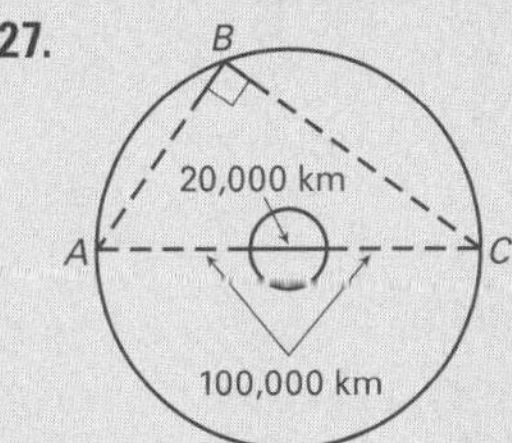

Internet Reference

Exercise 39 More information about the space shuttle's solid rocket boosters can be found at science.ksc.nasa.gov/shuttle/technology/sts-newsref/srb.html

31. Given: $\angle B$ is inscribed in $\odot Q$. Let $m\angle B = x°$. Point Q lies on $\overline{BC}$. Since all radii of a circle are congruent, $\overline{AQ} \cong \overline{BQ}$. Using the Base Angles Theorem, $\angle B \cong \angle A$ which implies $m\angle A = x°$. Using the Exterior Angles Theorem, $m\angle AQC = 2x°$ which implies $m\overset{\frown}{AC} = 2x°$. Solving for x, you get $\frac{1}{2}m\overset{\frown}{AC} = x°$. Substituting you get $\frac{1}{2}m\overset{\frown}{AC} = m\angle B$.

33. Given: $\angle ABC$ is inscribed in $\odot Q$. Point Q is in the exterior of $\angle ABC$; Prove: $m\angle ABC = \frac{1}{2}m\overset{\frown}{AC}$; construct the diameter $\overline{BD}$ of $\odot Q$ and show $m\angle ABD = \frac{1}{2}m\overset{\frown}{AD}$ and $m\angle CBD = \frac{1}{2}m\overset{\frown}{CD}$. Use the Arc Addition Postulate and the Angle Addition Postulate to show $m\angle ABD - m\angle CBD = m\angle ABC$. Then use substitution to show $2m\angle ABC = m\overset{\frown}{AC}$.

34.

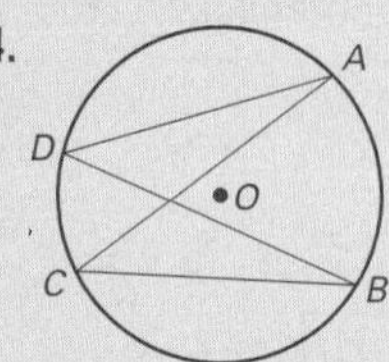

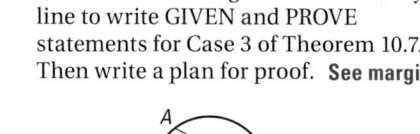

Given: $\odot O$ with inscribed $\angle C$ and $\angle D$ both intercepting $\overset{\frown}{AB}$; Prove: $\angle C \cong \angle D$; using the Measure of an Inscribed Angle Theorem, $m\angle C = \frac{1}{2}m\overset{\frown}{AB}$ and $m\angle D = \frac{1}{2}m\overset{\frown}{AB}$.

Using the Transitive Property of Equality, $m\angle C = m\angle D$ which implies $\angle C \cong \angle D$.

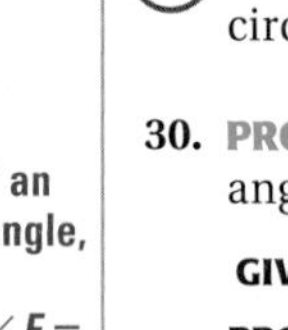

30. $m\overset{\frown}{GDE}$, Measure of an Inscribed Angle, $2m\angle F$, $m\angle D + m\angle F =$ 180° and thus are supplementary, $\angle E$ and $\angle G$ are supplementary

32. Given: $\angle ABC$ is inscribed in $\odot Q$. Point Q is in the interior of $\angle ABC$; Prove: $m\angle ABC = \frac{1}{2}m\overset{\frown}{AC}$; construct the diameter $\overline{BD}$ of $\odot Q$ and show $m\angle ABD = \frac{1}{2}m\overset{\frown}{AD}$ and $m\angle DBC = \frac{1}{2}m\overset{\frown}{DC}$. Use the Arc Addition Postulate and the Angle Addition Postulate to show $2m\angle ABC = m\overset{\frown}{AD} + m\overset{\frown}{DC}$.

29. ★ **WRITING** A right triangle is inscribed in a circle and the radius of the circle is given. *Explain* how to find the length of the hypotenuse.
Double the length of the radius.

30. PROVING THEOREM 10.10 Copy and complete the proof that opposite angles of an inscribed quadrilateral are supplementary.

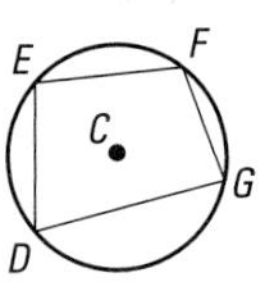

GIVEN ▶ $\odot C$ with inscribed quadrilateral $DEFG$

PROVE ▶ $m\angle D + m\angle F = 180°$, $m\angle E + m\angle G = 180°$.

By the Arc Addition Postulate, $m\overset{\frown}{EFG}$ + __?__ = 360° and $m\overset{\frown}{FGD} + m\overset{\frown}{DEF} = 360°$. Using the __?__ Theorem, $m\overset{\frown}{EDG} = 2m\angle F$, $m\overset{\frown}{EFG} = 2m\angle D$, $m\overset{\frown}{DEF} = 2m\angle G$, and $m\overset{\frown}{FGD} = 2m\angle E$. By the Substitution Property, $2m\angle D$ + __?__ = 360°, so __?__ . Similarly, __?__.

B **PROVING THEOREM 10.7 If an angle is inscribed in $\odot Q$, the center Q can be on a side of the angle, in the interior of the angle, or in the exterior of the angle. In Exercises 31–33, you will prove Theorem 10.7 for each of these cases.**

31. Case 1 Prove Case 1 of Theorem 10.7. **See margin.**

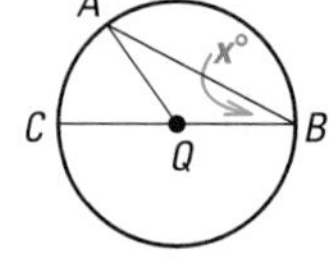

GIVEN ▶ $\angle B$ is inscribed in $\odot Q$. Let $m\angle B = x°$. Point Q lies on $\overline{BC}$.

PROVE ▶ $m\angle B = \frac{1}{2}m\overset{\frown}{AC}$

Plan for Proof Show that $\triangle AQB$ is isosceles. Use the Base Angles Theorem and the Exterior Angles Theorem to show that $m\angle AQC = 2x°$. Then, show that $m\overset{\frown}{AC} = 2x°$. Solve for x, and show that $m\angle B = \frac{1}{2}m\overset{\frown}{AC}$.

32. Case 2 Use the diagram and auxiliary line to write GIVEN and PROVE statements for Case 2 of Theorem 10.7. Then write a plan for proof.

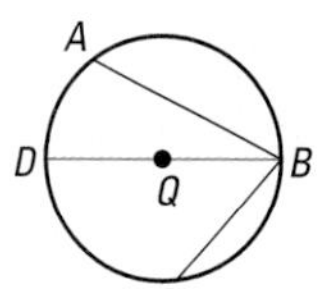

33. Case 3 Use the diagram and auxiliary line to write GIVEN and PROVE statements for Case 3 of Theorem 10.7. Then write a plan for proof. **See margin.**

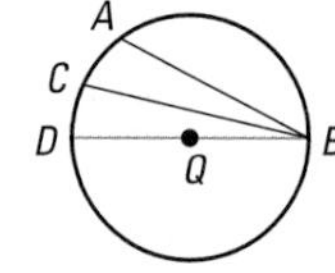

34. PROVING THEOREM 10.8 Write a paragraph proof of Theorem 10.8. First draw a diagram and write GIVEN and PROVE statements. **See margin.**

35. PROVING THEOREM 10.9 Theorem 10.9 is written as a conditional statement and its converse. Write a plan for proof of each statement. **See margin.**

36. ★ **EXTENDED RESPONSE** In the diagram, $\odot C$ and $\odot M$ intersect at B, and $\overline{AC}$ is a diameter of $\odot M$. *Explain* why $\overleftrightarrow{AB}$ is tangent to $\odot C$.
In the figure $\triangle ABC$ is a right triangle with $\angle ABC$ being the right angle. By Theorem 10.1, since $\overleftrightarrow{AB}$ is perpendicular to radius $\overline{BC}$, it is tangent to $\odot C$ at point B.

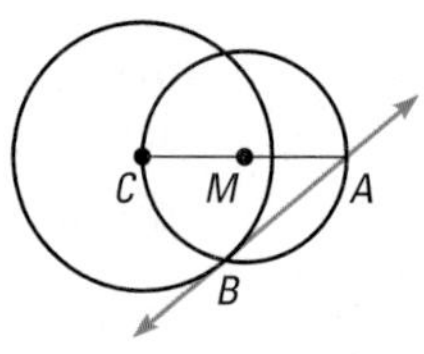

○ = WORKED-OUT SOLUTIONS on p. WS1 ★ = STANDARDIZED TEST PRACTICE

35. Case 1: Given: $\odot D$ with inscribed $\triangle ABC$ where $\overline{AC}$ is a diameter of $\odot D$; Prove: $\triangle ABC$ is a right triangle; let E be a point on $\overset{\frown}{AC}$. Show that $m\overset{\frown}{AEC} = 180°$ and then that $m\angle B = 90°$. Case 2: Given: $\odot D$ with inscribed $\triangle ABC$ with $\angle B$ a right angle; Prove: $\overline{AC}$ is a diameter of $\odot D$; using the Measure of an Inscribed Angle Theorem, show that $m\overset{\frown}{AC} = 180°$.

C CHALLENGE **In Exercises 37 and 38, use the following information.**

You are making a circular cutting board. To begin, you glue eight 1 inch by 2 inch boards together, as shown at the right. Then you draw and cut a circle with an 8 inch diameter from the boards.

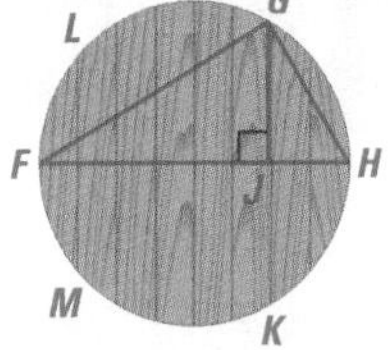

37. $\overline{FH}$ is a diameter of the circular cutting board. Write a proportion relating GJ and JH. State a theorem to justify your answer.

37. $\frac{HJ}{GJ} = \frac{GJ}{FJ}$; in a right triangle, the altitude from the right angle to the hypotenuse divides the hypotenuse into two segments. The length of the altitude is the geometric mean of the lengths of these two segments.

38. Find FJ, JH, and JG. What is the length of the cutting board seam labeled $\overline{GK}$? **6 in., 2 in., $2\sqrt{3}$ in.; $4\sqrt{3}$ in.**

39. **SPACE SHUTTLE** To maximize thrust on a NASA space shuttle, engineers drill an 11-point star out of the solid fuel that fills each booster. They begin by drilling a hole with radius 2 feet, and they would like each side of the star to be 1.5 feet. Is this possible if the fuel cannot have angles greater than 45° at its points? **yes**

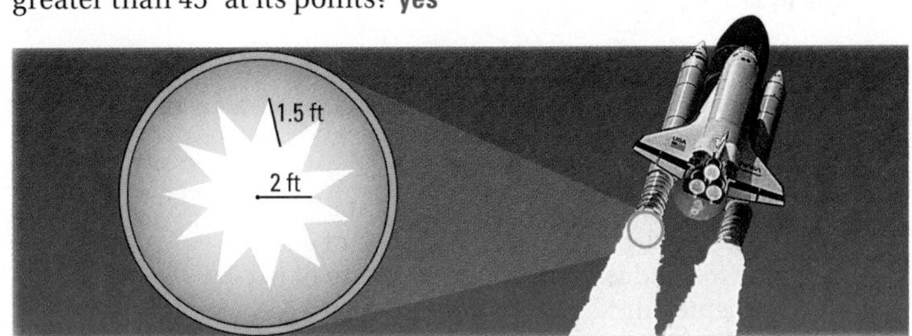

MIXED REVIEW

PREVIEW
Prepare for Lesson 10.5 in Exs. 40–42.

Find the approximate length of the hypotenuse. Round your answer to the nearest tenth. *(p. 433)*

40. **81.4**

41. 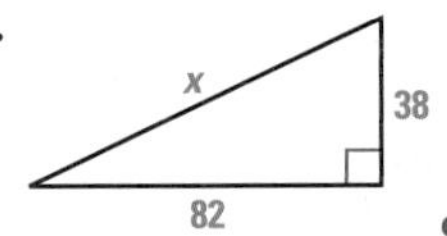

90.4

42. 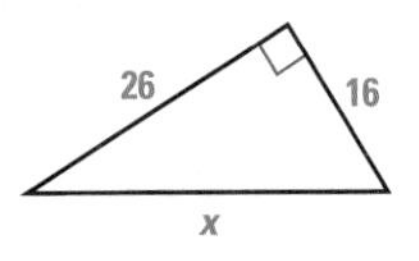

30.5

Graph the reflection of the polygon in the given line. *(p. 589)* **43–45. See margin.**

43. y-axis

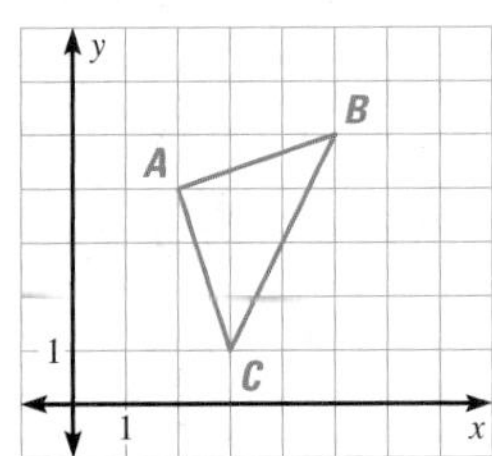

44. $x = 3$

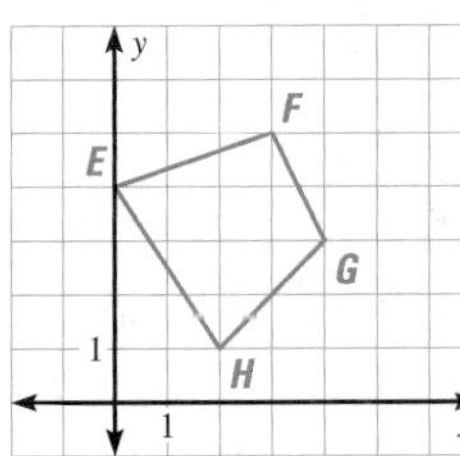

45. $y = 2$

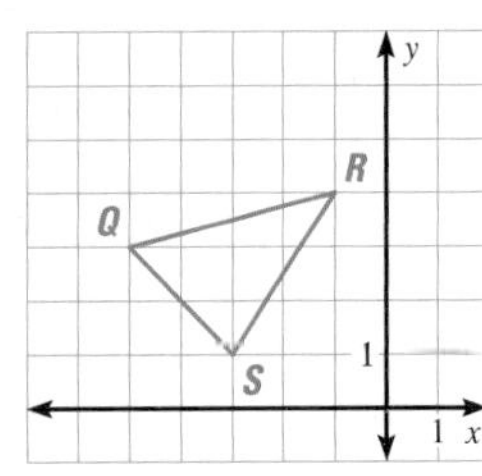

Sketch the image of $A(3, -4)$ after the described glide reflection. *(p. 608)* **46, 47. See margin.**

46. **Translation:** $(x, y) \rightarrow (x, y - 2)$
Reflection: in the y-axis

47. **Translation:** $(x, y) \rightarrow (x + 1, y + 4)$
Reflection: in $y = 4x$

43. 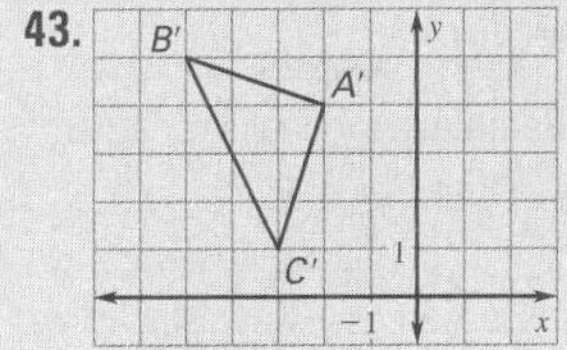

44. 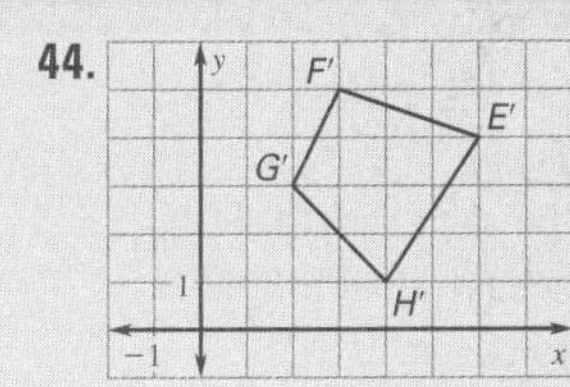

45. 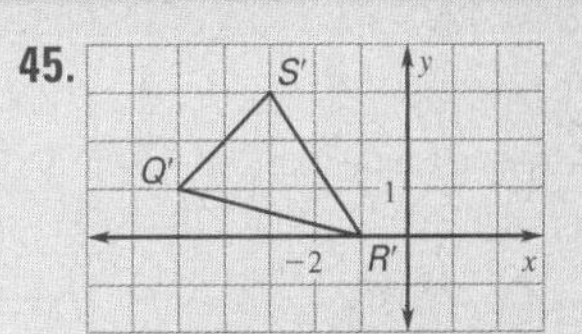

46–47. See Additional Answers beginning on p. AA1.

5 ASSESS AND RETEACH

Daily Homework Quiz

Transparency Available

Find the value of x.

1. **38**

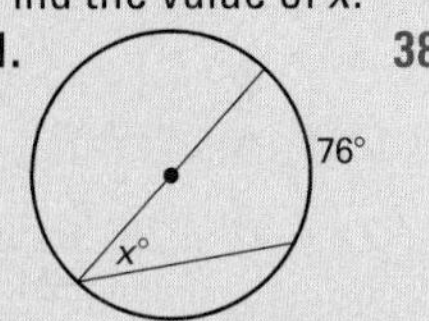

2. **56**

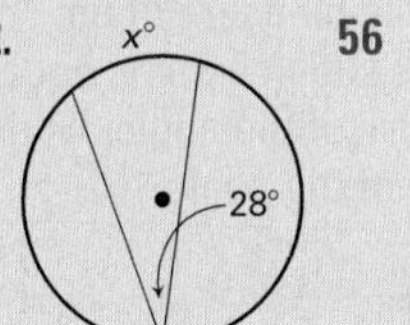

3. **44**

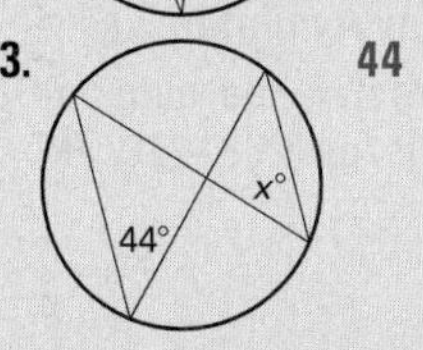

Find the value of each variable.

4. **$x = 54$; $y = 20$**

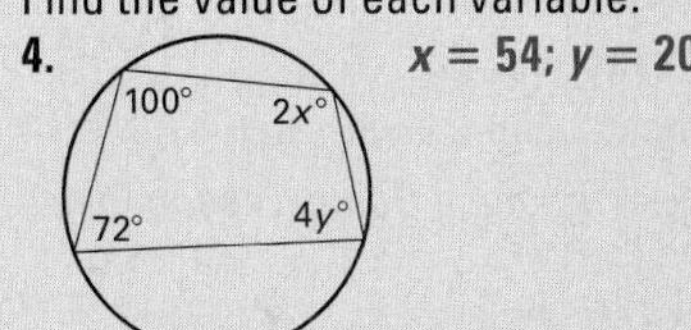

5. **$x = 5$; $y = 10$**

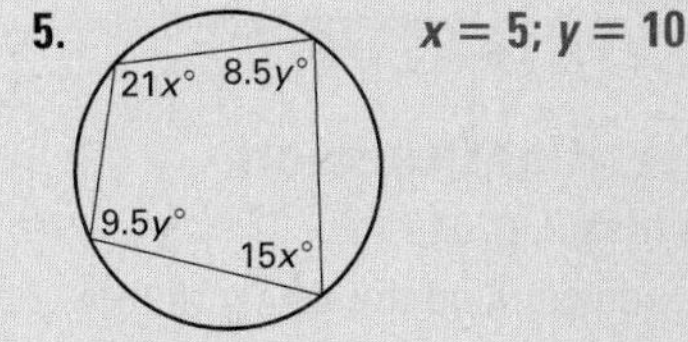

Online Quiz

Available at **classzone.com**

Diagnosis/Remediation

- Practice A, B, C in Chapter 10 Resource Book, pp. 47–52
- Study Guide in Chapter 10 Resource Book, pp. 53–54
- Practice Workbook, pp. 193–195
- @HomeTutor

Challenge

Additional challenge is available in the Chapter 10 Resource Book, p. 57.

1 PLAN AND PREPARE

Warm-Up Exercises

Transparency Available

Solve for x.

1. $2x = 84 + 32$ **58**
2. $x = \frac{1}{2}(360 - 120)$ **120**
3. $180 - x = \frac{1}{2}((2x + 4) + 28)$ **82**
4. One-half of the measure of an angle plus its supplement is equal to the measure of the angle. Find the measure of the angle. **120°**

Notetaking Guide

Transparency Available

Promotes interactive learning and notetaking skills, pp. 268–270.

Pacing

Basic: 1 day
Average: 1 day
Advanced: 1 day
Block: 0.5 block with 10.6

- See *Teaching Guide/Lesson Plan.*

2 FOCUS AND MOTIVATE

Essential Question

Big Idea 2, p. 649

How do you find the measure of an angle formed by two chords that intersect inside a circle? **Tell students they will learn how to answer this question by using the measures of intercepted arcs.**

10.5 Apply Other Angle Relationships in Circles

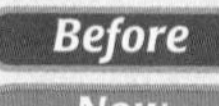

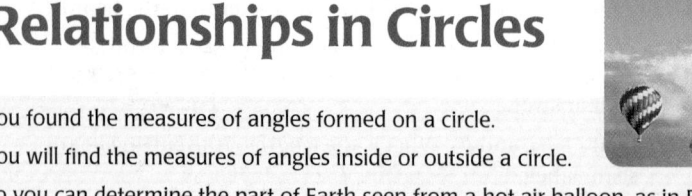

Before You found the measures of angles formed on a circle.

Now You will find the measures of angles inside or outside a circle.

Why So you can determine the part of Earth seen from a hot air balloon, as in Ex. 25.

Key Vocabulary
- **chord,** *p. 651*
- **secant,** *p. 651*
- **tangent,** *p. 651*

Standards

21.0 Students prove and solve problems regarding relationships among chords, secants, tangents, inscribed angles, and inscribed and circumscribed polygons **of circles.**

7.0 Students prove and use theorems involving the properties of parallel lines cut by a transversal, the properties of quadrilaterals, and **the properties of circles.**

You know that the measure of an inscribed angle is half the measure of its intercepted arc. This is true even if one side of the angle is tangent to the circle.

THEOREM *For Your Notebook*

THEOREM 10.11

If a tangent and a chord intersect at a point on a circle, then the measure of each angle formed is one half the measure of its intercepted arc.

Proof: Ex. 27, p. 685

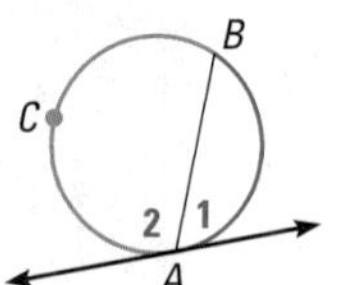

$m\angle 1 = \frac{1}{2}m\overset{\frown}{AB}$ $m\angle 2 = \frac{1}{2}m\overset{\frown}{BCA}$

EXAMPLE 1 **Find angle and arc measures**

Line m is tangent to the circle. Find the measure of the red angle or arc.

a.

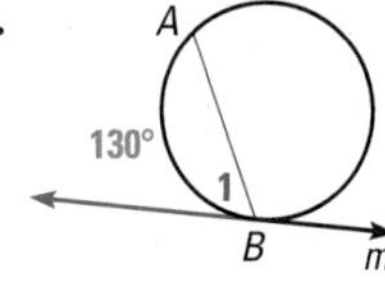

b.

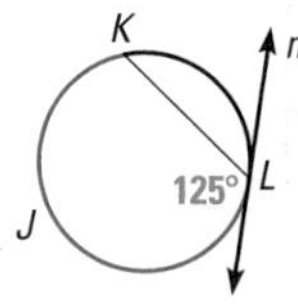

Solution

a. $m\angle 1 = \frac{1}{2}(130°) = 65°$

b. $m\overset{\frown}{KJL} = 2(125°) = 250°$

✓ **GUIDED PRACTICE** for Example 1

Find the indicated measure.

1. $m\angle 1$ **105°**

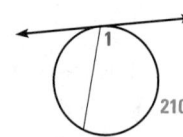

210°

2. $m\overset{\frown}{RST}$ **196°**

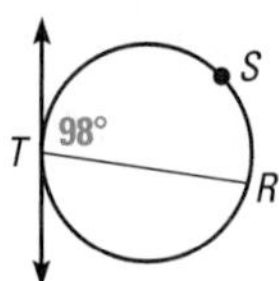

3. $m\overset{\frown}{XY}$ **160°**

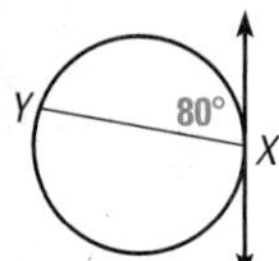

Resource Planning Guide

Chapter Resource Book
- Teaching Guide/Lesson Plan (pp. 58–59)
- Activity Master (p. 60)
- Practice levels A, B, C (pp. 61–66)
- Study Guide (pp. 67–68)
- Catch-up for Absent Students (p. 69)
- Problem Solving Workshop (p. 70)
- Challenge (p. 72)

Workbooks
- Notetaking Guide (pp. 268–270)
- Practice Workbook (pp. 196–198)

Teaching Options
- **Power Presentations CD-ROM** provides dynamic electronic teaching resources for the classroom.
- **Activity Generator CD-ROM** provides editable activities for all ability levels.

Interactive Technology
- Easy Planner
- Power Presentations CD-ROM
- Activity Generator CD-ROM
- Animated Geometry
- Test Generator CD-ROM
- Online Quiz
- eWorkbook
- eEdition
- @HomeTutor

Resources for English Learners
- Quick Reference for English Learners
- Spanish Study Guide
- Multi-Language Visual Glossary
- Student Resources in Spanish

See also the *Geometry Toolkit* for more strategies for meeting individual needs.

INTERSECTING LINES AND CIRCLES If two lines intersect a circle, there are three places where the lines can intersect.

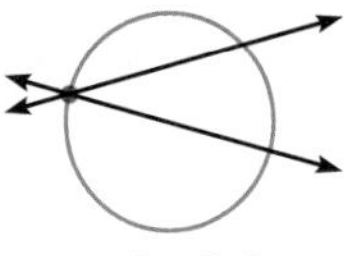

on the circle

inside the circle

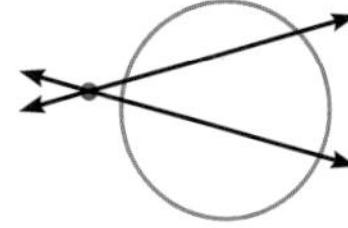

outside the circle

You can use Theorems 10.12 and 10.13 to find measures when the lines intersect *inside* or *outside* the circle.

THEOREMS — *For Your Notebook*

THEOREM 10.12 Angles Inside the Circle Theorem

If two chords intersect *inside* a circle, then the measure of each angle is one half the *sum* of the measures of the arcs intercepted by the angle and its vertical angle.

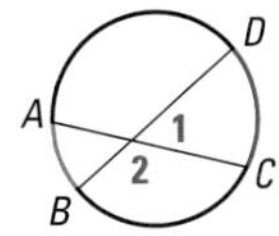

$m\angle 1 = \frac{1}{2}(m\overset{\frown}{DC} + m\overset{\frown}{AB})$,

$m\angle 2 = \frac{1}{2}(m\overset{\frown}{AD} + m\overset{\frown}{BC})$

Proof: Ex. 28, p. 685

THEOREM 10.13 Angles Outside the Circle Theorem

If a tangent and a secant, two tangents, or two secants intersect *outside* a circle, then the measure of the angle formed is one half the *difference* of the measures of the intercepted arcs.

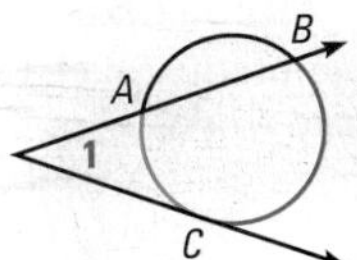

$m\angle 1 = \frac{1}{2}(m\overset{\frown}{BC} - m\overset{\frown}{AC})$

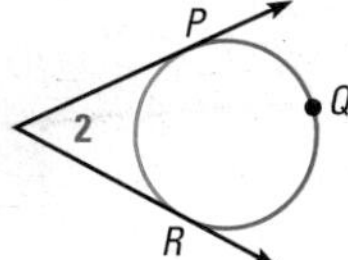

$m\angle 2 = \frac{1}{2}(m\overset{\frown}{PQR} - m\overset{\frown}{PR})$

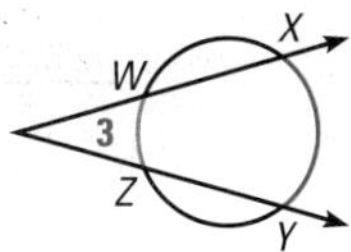

$m\angle 3 = \frac{1}{2}(m\overset{\frown}{XY} - m\overset{\frown}{WZ})$

Proof: Ex. 29, p. 685

EXAMPLE 2 Find an angle measure inside a circle

Find the value of x.

130° M L J x° K 156°

Solution

The chords $\overline{JL}$ and $\overline{KM}$ intersect inside the circle.

$x° = \frac{1}{2}(m\overset{\frown}{JM} + m\overset{\frown}{LK})$ **Use Theorem 10.12.**

$x° = \frac{1}{2}(130° + 156°)$ **Substitute.**

$x = 143$ **Simplify.**

Motivating the Lesson

Ask students why a sailor would climb to the top of a mast to watch for land. Tell them that in this lesson they will investigate how the height of the mast is related to the distance that can be seen.

3 TEACH

Extra Example 1

Line m is tangent to the circle. Find x or y. **a. 114; b. 236**

a.

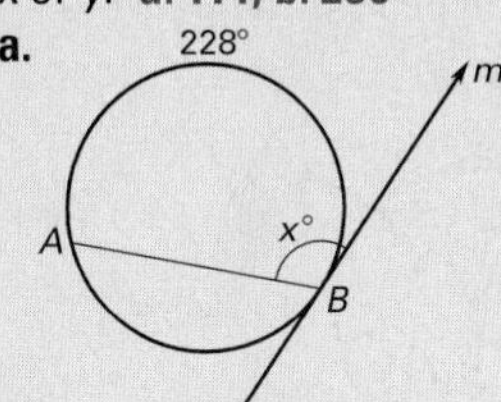

b.

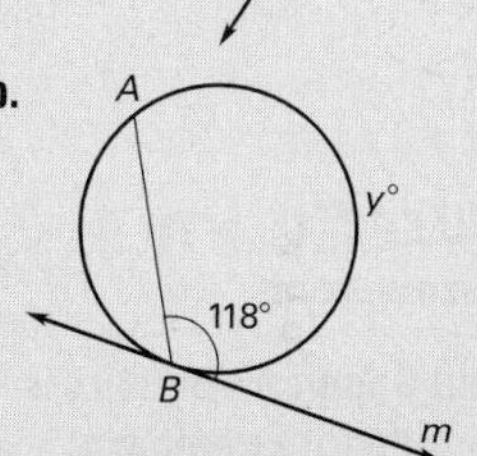

Key Question to Ask for Example 1

- In part (b), how do you find the measure of $\overset{\frown}{KL}$? $m\overset{\frown}{KL} = 360° - m\overset{\frown}{KJL} = 360° - 250° = 110°$

Extra Example 2

Find the value of x. **76**

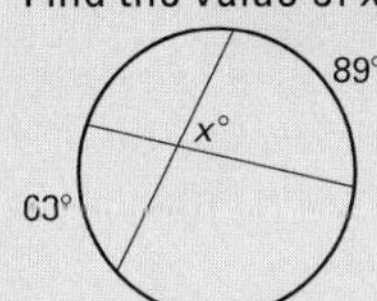

Extra Example 3

Find the value of x. **18**

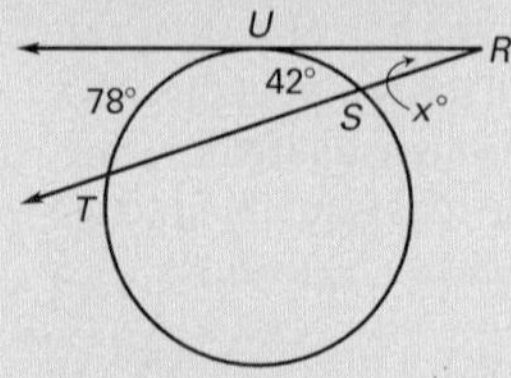

Extra Example 4

The Space Shuttle typically orbits at a height of 600 kilometers. Suppose an astronaut takes a picture from point S. What is the measure of $\widehat{RQ}$? **48°**

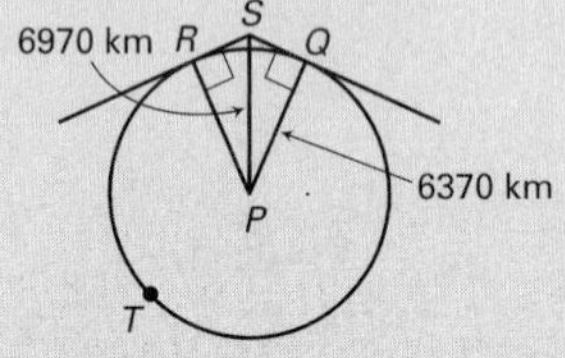

An **Animated Geometry** activity is available on-line for **Example 4**. This activity is also available on the **Power Presentations CD-ROM**.

Closing the Lesson

Have students summarize the major points of the lesson and answer the Essential Question: How do you find the measure of an angle formed by two chords that intersect inside a circle?

- **If a chord and a tangent intersect on a circle, the measure of the angle formed is one half that of the intercepted arc.**
- **The measure of an angle formed by two chords that intersect inside a circle is one half the sum of the measures of the intercepted arcs.**
- **The measure of an angle formed outside a circle by tangents and/or secants is one half the difference of the measures of the intercepted arcs.**

The measure of an angle formed by two chords that intersect inside a circle is one-half the sum of the measures of the intercepted arcs.

EXAMPLE 3 Find an angle measure outside a circle

Find the value of x.

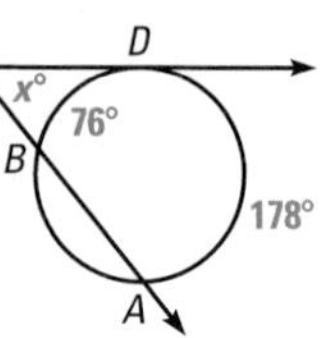

Solution

The tangent $\overrightarrow{CD}$ and the secant $\overrightarrow{CB}$ intersect outside the circle.

$m\angle BCD = \frac{1}{2}(m\widehat{AD} - m\widehat{BD})$ **Use Theorem 10.13.**

$x° = \frac{1}{2}(178° - 76°)$ **Substitute.**

$x = 51$ **Simplify.**

EXAMPLE 4 Solve a real-world problem

SCIENCE The Northern Lights are bright flashes of colored light between 50 and 200 miles above Earth. Suppose a flash occurs 150 miles above Earth. What is the measure of arc BD, the portion of Earth from which the flash is visible? (Earth's radius is approximately 4000 miles.)

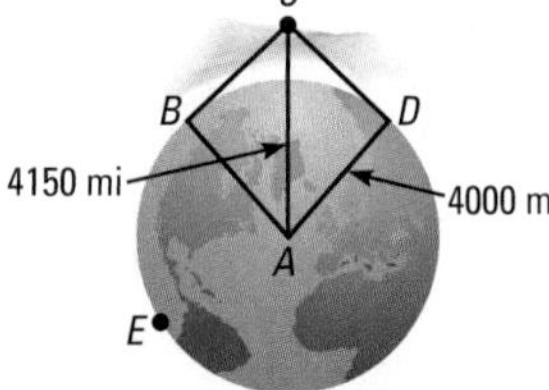

Not drawn to scale

Solution

Because $\overline{CB}$ and $\overline{CD}$ are tangents, $\overline{CB} \perp \overline{AB}$ and $\overline{CD} \perp \overline{AD}$. Also, $\overline{BC} \cong \overline{DC}$ and $\overline{CA} \cong \overline{CA}$. So, $\triangle ABC \cong \triangle ADC$ by the Hypotenuse-Leg Congruence Theorem, and $\angle BCA \cong \angle DCA$. Solve right $\triangle CBA$ to find that $m\angle BCA \approx 74.5°$. So, $m\angle BCD \approx 2(74.5°) \approx 149°$. Let $m\widehat{BD} = x°$.

$m\angle BCD = \frac{1}{2}(m\widehat{DEB} - m\widehat{BD})$ **Use Theorem 10.13.**

$149° \approx \frac{1}{2}[(360° - x°) - x°]$ **Substitute.**

$x \approx 31$ **Solve for x.**

AVOID ERRORS
Because the value for $m\angle BCD$ is an approximation, use the symbol $\approx$ instead of $=$.

▶ The measure of the arc from which the flash is visible is about 31°.

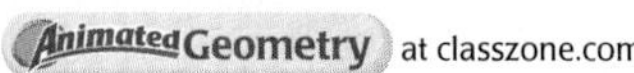

GUIDED PRACTICE for Examples 2, 3, and 4

Find the value of the variable.

4. (A, B, C, D; $y°$; 102°; 95°) **61**

5.

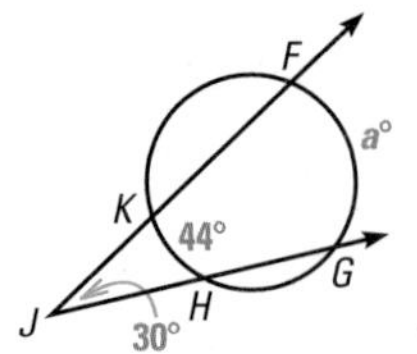

104

6.

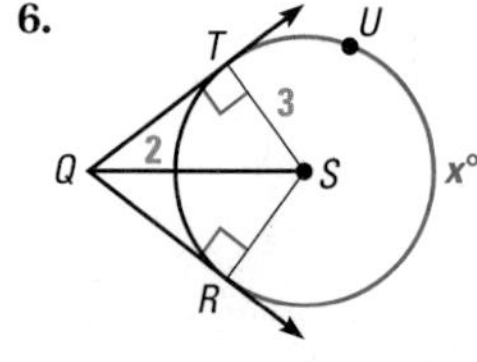

about 253.7

10.5 EXERCISES

HOMEWORK KEY
○ = **WORKED-OUT SOLUTIONS** on p. WS13 for Exs. 3, 9, and 23
★ = **STANDARDIZED TEST PRACTICE** Exs. 2, 6, 13, 15, 19, and 26

SKILL PRACTICE

A

1. VOCABULARY Copy and complete: The points A, B, C, and D are on a circle and $\overleftrightarrow{AB}$ intersects $\overleftrightarrow{CD}$ at P. If $m\angle APC = \frac{1}{2}(m\widehat{BD} - m\widehat{AC})$, then P is _?_ (*inside*, *on*, or *outside*) the circle. **outside**

2. ★ WRITING What does it mean in Theorem 10.12 if $m\widehat{AB} = 0°$? Is this consistent with what you learned in Lesson 10.4? *Explain* your answer. **See margin.**

EXAMPLE 1 on p. 680 for Exs. 3–6

FINDING MEASURES **Line t is tangent to the circle. Find the indicated measure.**

3. $m\widehat{AB}$ **130°**

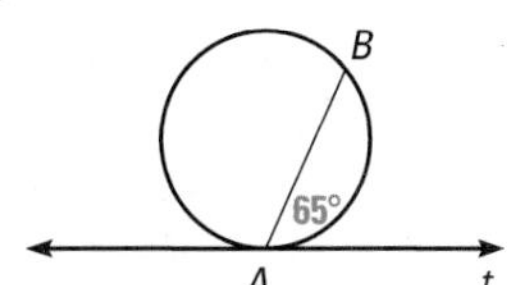

4. $m\widehat{DEF}$ **234°**

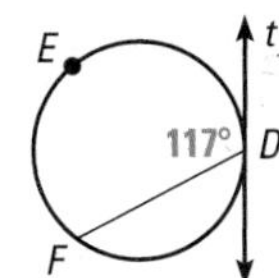

5. $m\angle 1$ **130°**

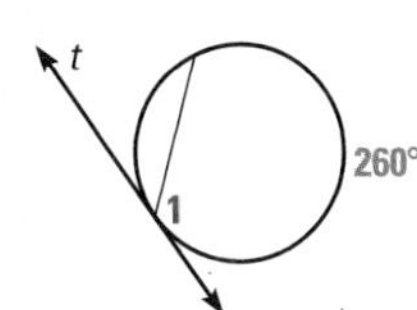

6. ★ MULTIPLE CHOICE The diagram at the right is not drawn to scale. $\overline{AB}$ is any chord that is not a diameter of the circle. Line m is tangent to the circle at point A. Which statement must be true? **D**

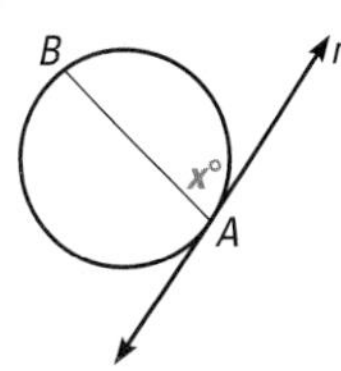

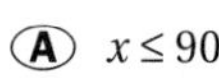

Ⓐ $x \le 90$ Ⓑ $x \ge 90$

Ⓒ $x = 90$ Ⓓ $x \ne 90$

FINDING MEASURES **Find the value of x.**

EXAMPLE 2 on p. 681 for Exs. 7–9

7. C, B, 145°, 85°, x°, A, D **115**

8.

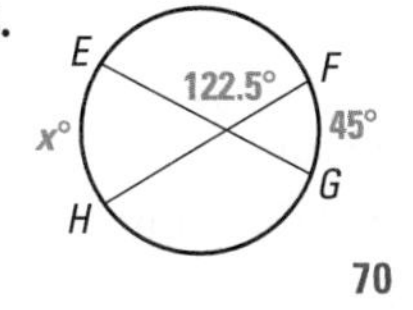

70

9.

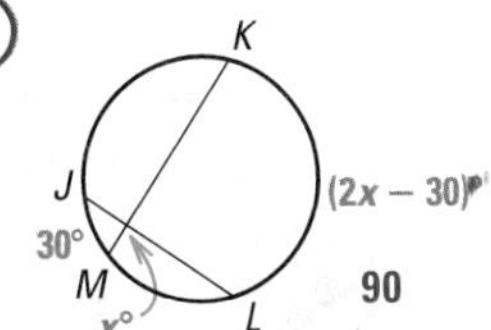

90

EXAMPLE 3 on p. 682 for Exs. 10–13

10.

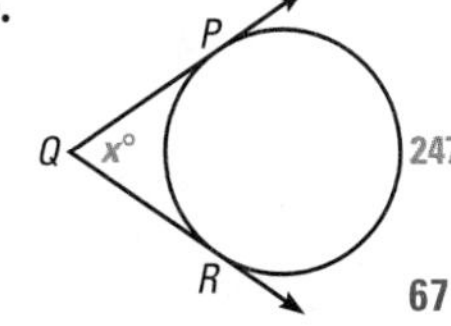

67

11.

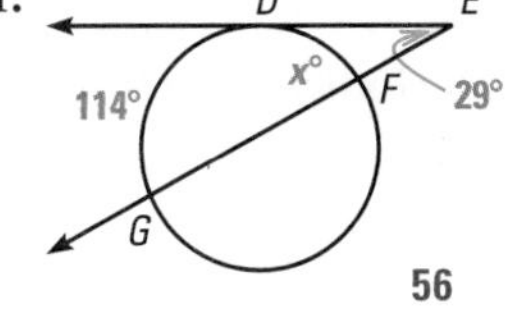

56

12.

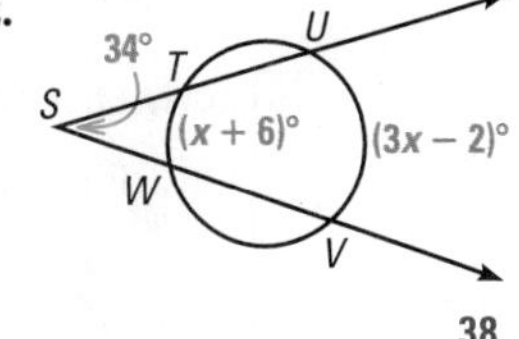

38

13. ★ MULTIPLE CHOICE In the diagram, ℓ is tangent to the circle at P. Which relationship is not true? **D**

Ⓐ $m\angle 1 = 110°$ Ⓑ $m\angle 2 = 70°$

Ⓒ $m\angle 3 = 80°$ Ⓓ $m\angle 4 = 90°$

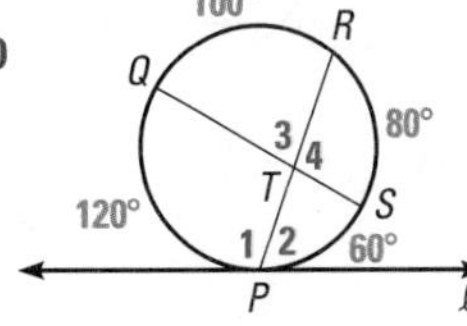

4 PRACTICE AND APPLY

Assignment Guide

Answer Transparencies available for all exercises

Basic:
Day 1: pp. 683–686
Exs. 1–16, 22–27, 32–39

Average:
Day 1: pp. 683–686
Exs. 1–6, 9–11, 13–19, 22–29, 32–39

Advanced:
Day 1: pp. 683–686
Exs. 1–6, 10–13, 15–21*, 23–31*, 32–38 even

Block:
pp. 683–686
Exs. 1–6, 9–11, 13–19, 22–29, 32–39 (with 10.6)

Differentiated Instruction

See *Geometry Best Practices Toolkit* for suggestions on addressing the needs of a diverse classroom.

Homework Check

For a quick check of student understanding of key concepts, go over the following exercises:

Basic: 4, 7, 10, 22, 25
Average: 5, 10, 11, 24, 25
Advanced: 6, 11, 12, 25, 26

Extra Practice

- Student Edition, p. 915
- Chapter 10 Resource Book: Practice levels A, B, C, pp. 61–66

Practice Worksheet

An easily-readable reduced practice page (with answers) for this lesson can be found on p. 648E.

2. If $m\widehat{AB} = 0$, then $m\widehat{CD} = 0$; yes; it means $m\widehat{AB} = m\widehat{CD} = 180°$, which is consistent with what you know since two semicircles are created.

Avoiding Common Errors

Exercise 9 If students have difficulty solving this problem, point out that they will find the supplement of x if they find half the sum of arcs $\overparen{KL}$ and $\overparen{JM}$.

Mathematical Reasoning

Exercise 16a One way to start is to let y equal the inscribed angle for the larger circle. The intercepted arc is 110°, so $y = \frac{1}{2}(110) = 55°$. Then students can use 55° as the measure of an angle formed by two secants of the smaller circle.

19a.

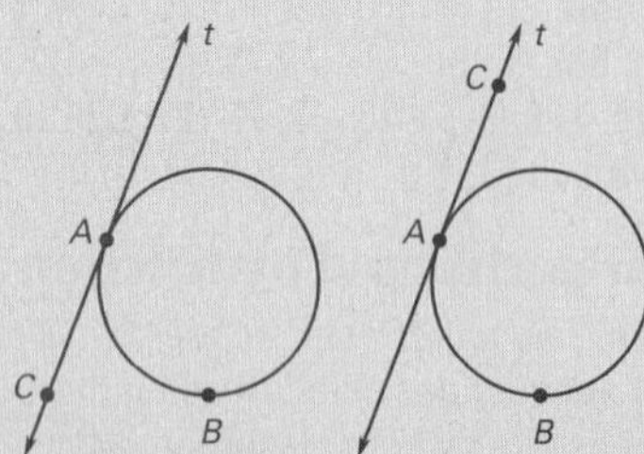

27. Given: $\overleftrightarrow{CA}$ tangent to $\odot Q$ at A and diameter $\overline{AB}$. Using Theorem 10.1, $\overline{AB}$ is perpendicular to $\overleftrightarrow{CA}$. It follows that $m\angle CAB = 90°$. This is half of 180°, which is $m\overparen{AB}$. Case 1: The center of the circle is interior to $\angle CAB$. Case 2: The center of the circle is exterior to $\angle CAB$.

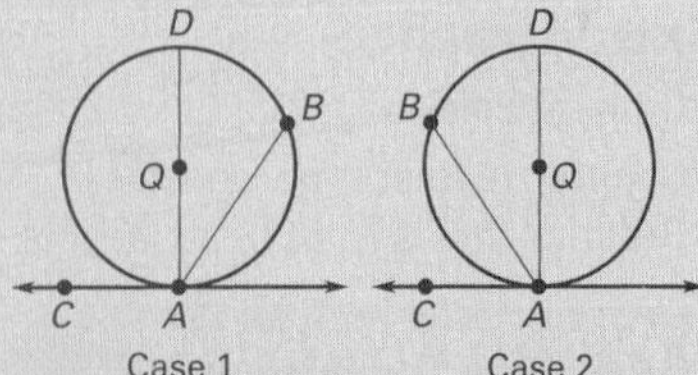

Construct diameter $\overline{AD}$. Case 1: Let B be a point on the right semicircle. Use Theorem 10.1 to show $m\angle CAB = 90°$. Use the Angle Addition Postulate and the Arc Addition Postulate to show that $m\angle CAD = \frac{1}{2}m\overparen{AB}$. Case 2: Let B be a point on the left semicircle. Prove similarly to Case 1.

B

14. **ERROR ANALYSIS** *Describe* the error in the diagram below. **The given measurements imply that $m\overparen{BE} = 40°$ using Theorem 10.12 or $m\overparen{BE} = 30°$ using Theorem 10.13.**

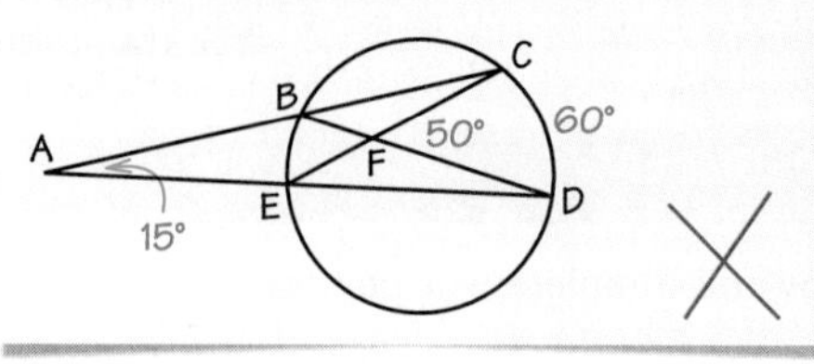

15. ★ **SHORT RESPONSE** In the diagram at the right, $\overrightarrow{PL}$ is tangent to the circle and $\overline{KJ}$ is a diameter. What is the range of possible angle measures of $\angle LPJ$? *Explain.*

15. $m\angle LPJ \le 90°$; if $\overrightarrow{PL}$ is perpendicular to $\overline{KJ}$ at K, then $m\angle LPJ = 90°$, otherwise it would measure less than 90°.

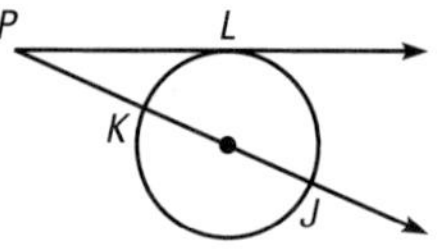

16. **CONCENTRIC CIRCLES** The circles below are concentric.

a. Find the value of x. **150°**

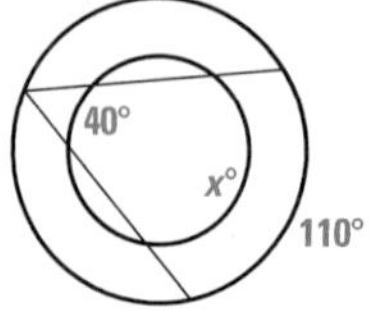

b. Express c in terms of a and b. **$c = b - a$**

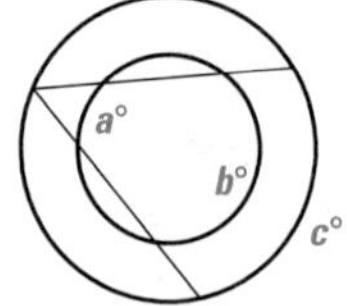

17. **INSCRIBED CIRCLE** In the diagram, the circle is inscribed in $\triangle PQR$. Find $m\overparen{EF}$, $m\overparen{FG}$, and $m\overparen{GE}$. **120°, 100°, 140°**

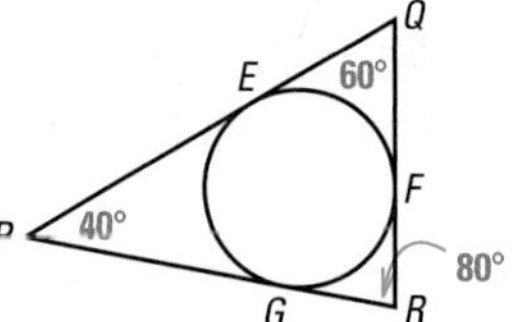

18. **ALGEBRA** In the diagram, $\overrightarrow{BA}$ is tangent to $\odot E$. Find $m\overparen{CD}$. **160°**

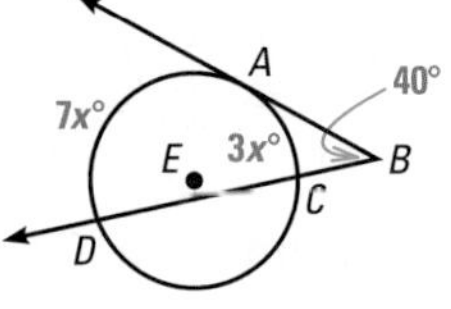

19. ★ **WRITING** Points A and B are on a circle and t is a tangent line containing A and another point C.

a. Draw two different diagrams that illustrate this situation. **See margin.**

b. Write an equation for $m\overparen{AB}$ in terms of $m\angle BAC$ for each diagram. **$m\overparen{AB} = 2m\angle BAC$, $m\overparen{AB} = 2(180 - m\angle BAC)$**

c. When will these equations give the same value for $m\overparen{AB}$? **when $\overline{AB}$ is perpendicular to t at point A**

C **CHALLENGE** **Find the indicated measure(s).**

20. Find $m\angle P$ if $m\overparen{WZY} = 200°$. **20°**

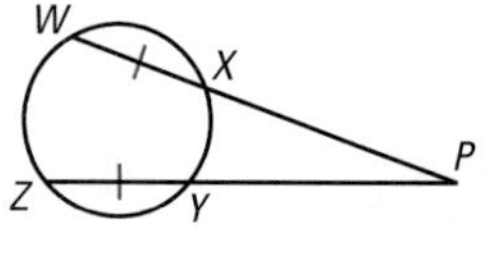

21. Find $m\overparen{AB}$ and $m\overparen{ED}$. **85°, 75°**

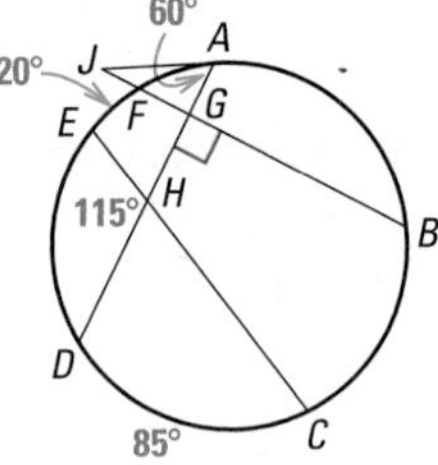

○ = WORKED-OUT SOLUTIONS on p. WS1

★ = STANDARDIZED TEST PRACTICE

PROBLEM SOLVING

A **VIDEO RECORDING In the diagram at the right, television cameras are positioned at *A*, *B*, and *C* to record what happens on stage. The stage is an arc of ⊙*A*. Use the diagram for Exercises 22–24.**

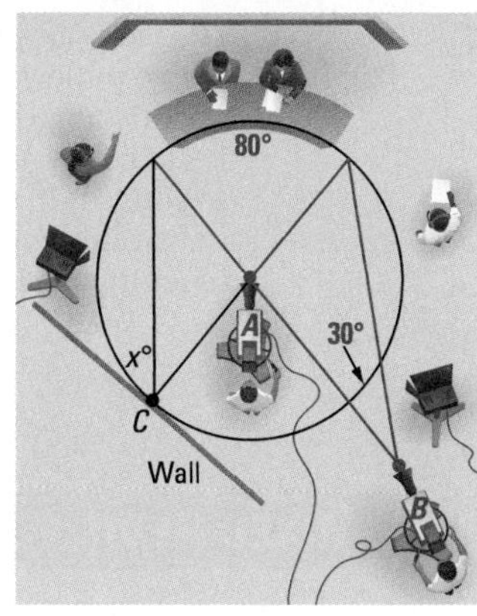

22. Find $m\angle A$, $m\angle B$, and $m\angle C$. **80°, 25°, 40°**

@HomeTutor for problem solving help at classzone.com

23. The wall is tangent to the circle. Find x without using the measure of $\angle C$. **50°**

@HomeTutor for problem solving help at classzone.com

24. You would like Camera *B* to have a 30° view of the stage. Should you move the camera closer or further away from the stage? *Explain.*

4. Closer; the arc measuring 80° must be reduced to an arc measuring 30°.

EXAMPLE 4 on p. 682 for Ex. 25

25. **HOT AIR BALLOON** You are flying in a hot air balloon about 1.2 miles above the ground. Use the method from Example 4 to find the measure of the arc that represents the part of Earth that you can see. The radius of Earth is about 4000 miles. **about 2.8°**

B

26. ★ **EXTENDED RESPONSE** A cart is resting on its handle. The angle between the handle and the ground is 14° and the handle connects to the center of the wheel. What are the measures of the arcs of the wheel between the ground and the cart? *Explain.*

26. 76°, 104°; The handle and ground form an angle outside the circle. Let one arc measure $x°$ and the other arc measure $(180 - x)°$. Use Theorem 10.13 to find each arc length.

27. **PROVING THEOREM 10.11** The proof of Theorem 10.11 can be split into three cases. The diagram at the right shows the case where $\overline{AB}$ contains the center of the circle. Use Theorem 10.1 to write a paragraph proof for this case. What are the other two cases? (*Hint:* See Exercises 31–33 on page 678.) Draw a diagram and write plans for proof for the other cases. **See margin.**

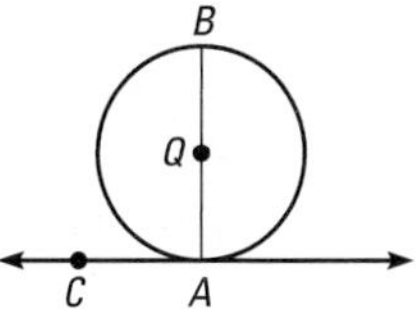

28. **PROVING THEOREM 10.12** Write a proof of Theorem 10.12. **See margin.**

GIVEN ▶ Chords $\overline{AC}$ and $\overline{BD}$ intersect.

PROVE ▶ $m\angle 1 = \frac{1}{2}(m\overset{\frown}{DC} + m\overset{\frown}{AB})$

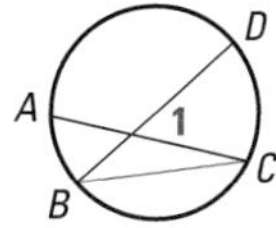

29. **PROVING THEOREM 10.13** Use the diagram at the right to prove Theorem 10.13 for the case of a tangent and a secant. Draw $\overline{BC}$. *Explain* how to use the Exterior Angle Theorem in the proof of this case. Then copy the diagrams for the other two cases from page 681, draw appropriate auxiliary segments, and write plans for proof for these cases. **See margin.**

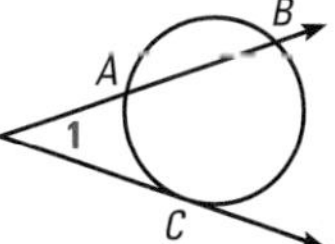

28. Given: Chords $\overline{AC}$ and $\overline{BD}$ intersect. Using the Exterior Angle Theorem, $m\angle 1 = m\angle DBC + m\angle ACB$. Using the Measure of an Inscribed Angle Theorem, $m\angle ACB = \frac{1}{2}m\overset{\frown}{AB}$ and $m\angle DBC = \frac{1}{2}m\overset{\frown}{DC}$. Substituting, you get $m\angle 1 = \frac{1}{2}m\overset{\frown}{AB} + \frac{1}{2}m\overset{\frown}{DC} = \frac{1}{2}(m\overset{\frown}{AB} + m\overset{\frown}{DC})$.

Teaching Strategy

Exercise 28 Students can plan their proof by noticing that $\angle 1$ is an exterior angle of a triangle, and the two remote interior angles of the triangle intercept arcs $\overset{\frown}{DC}$ and $\overset{\frown}{AB}$.

29. Given: A tangent and a secant to a circle intersecting outside of the circle. Construct $\overline{BC}$ and label the angle intercepting $\overset{\frown}{BC}$ as $\angle 2$. Using the Exterior Angle Theorem, $m\angle 2 = m\angle 1 + m\angle ABC$ which implies $m\angle 1 = m\angle 2 - m\angle ABC$. Using Theorem 10.11, $m\angle 2 = \frac{1}{2}m\overset{\frown}{BC}$. Using Theorem 10.7, $m\angle ABC = \frac{1}{2}m\overset{\frown}{AC}$. Substituting, you get $m\angle 1 = \frac{1}{2}m\overset{\frown}{BC} - \frac{1}{2}m\overset{\frown}{AC} = \frac{1}{2}(m\overset{\frown}{BC} - m\overset{\frown}{AC})$.

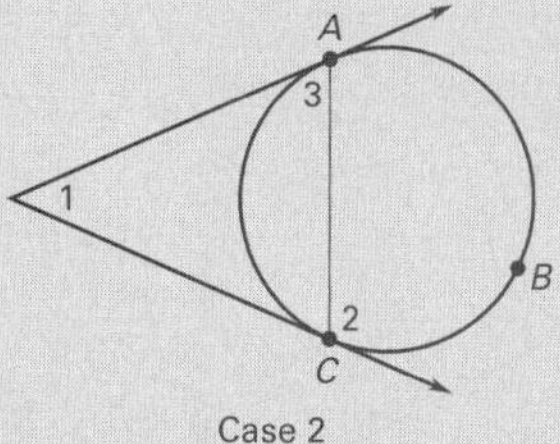

Case 2

Case 2: Construct $\overline{AC}$. Using the Exterior Angle Theorem, $m\angle 2 = m\angle 1 + m\angle 3$ which implies $m\angle 1 = m\angle 2 - m\angle 3$. Now use Theorem 10.11 to show $m\angle 2 = \frac{1}{2}m\overset{\frown}{ABC}$ and $m\angle 3 = \frac{1}{2}m\overset{\frown}{AC}$, which leads to $m\angle 1 = \frac{1}{2}m\overset{\frown}{ABC} - \frac{1}{2}m\overset{\frown}{AC} = \frac{1}{2}(m\overset{\frown}{ABC} - m\overset{\frown}{AC})$.

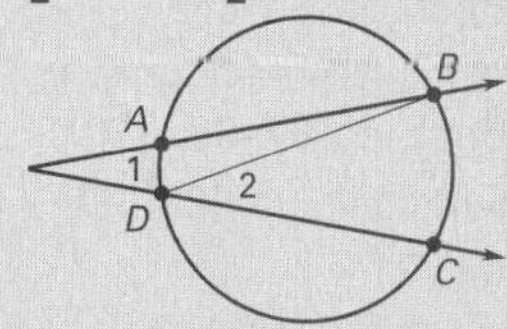

Case 3

Case 3: Construct $\overline{BD}$. Using the Exterior Angle Theorem, $m\angle 2 = m\angle 1 + m\angle ABD$ which implies $m\angle 1 = m\angle 2 - m\angle ABD$. Now use the Measure of an Inscribed Angle Theorem to show $m\angle 2 = \frac{1}{2}m\overset{\frown}{BC}$ and $m\angle ABD = \frac{1}{2}m\overset{\frown}{AD}$ which leads to $m\angle 1 = \frac{1}{2}m\overset{\frown}{BC} - \frac{1}{2}m\overset{\frown}{AD} = \frac{1}{2}(m\overset{\frown}{BC} - m\overset{\frown}{AD})$.

5 ASSESS AND RETEACH

Daily Homework Quiz

Transparency Available

Line t is tangent to the circle. Find the values of x and y.

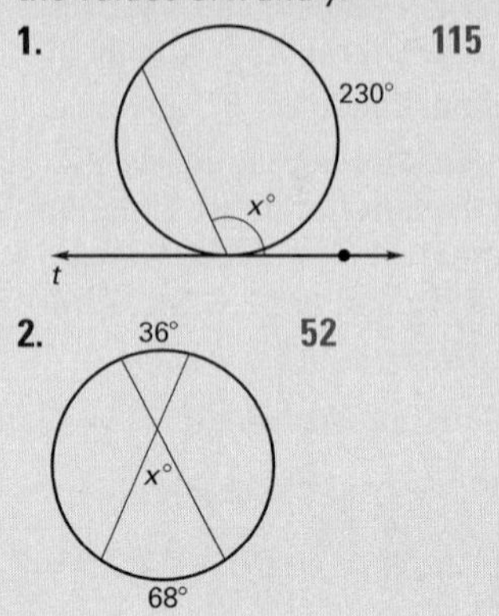

1. 115
2. 52

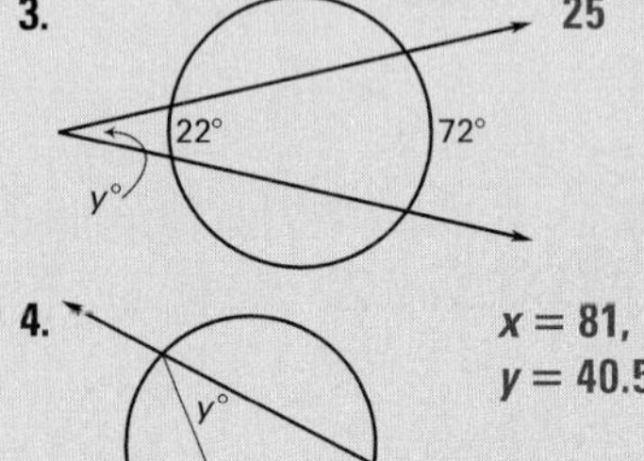

3. 25
4. $x = 81$, $y = 40.5$

Online Quiz

Available at **classzone.com**

Diagnosis/Remediation

- Practice A, B, C in Chapter 10 Resource Book, pp. 61–66
- Study Guide in Chapter 10 Resource Book, pp. 67–68
- Practice Workbook, pp. 196–198
- @HomeTutor

Challenge

Additional challenge is available in the Chapter 10 Resource Book, p. 72.

Quiz

An easily-readable reduced copy of the quiz (with answers) on Lessons 10.4–10.5 from the Assessment Book can be found on p. 648G.

30. See Additional Answers beginning on p. AA1.

C 30. **PROOF** Q and R are points on a circle. P is a point outside the circle. $\overline{PQ}$ and $\overline{PR}$ are tangents to the circle. Prove that $\overline{QR}$ is not a diameter. **See margin.**

31. **CHALLENGE** A block and tackle system composed of two pulleys and a rope is shown at the right. The distance between the centers of the pulleys is 113 centimeters and the pulleys each have a radius of 15 centimeters. What percent of the circumference of the bottom pulley is not touching the rope? **about 48%**

MIXED REVIEW

Classify the dilation and find its scale factor. *(p. 626)*

32.

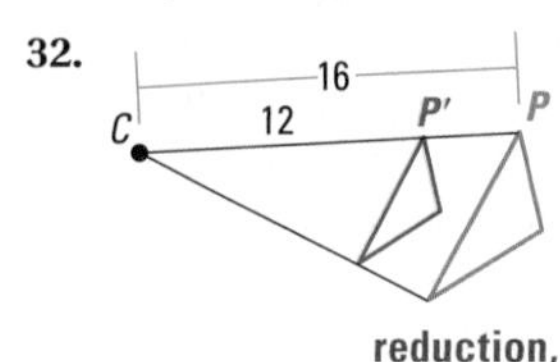

reduction, $\frac{3}{4}$

33.

enlargement, $\frac{5}{3}$

PREVIEW
Prepare for Lesson 10.6 in Exs. 34–39.

Use the quadratic formula to solve the equation. Round decimal answers to the nearest hundredth. *(pp. 641, 883)*

34. $x^2 + 7x + 6 = 0$ **−6, −1**
35. $x^2 - x - 12 = 0$ **−3, 4**
36. $x^2 + 16 = 8x$ **4**
37. $x^2 + 6x = 10$ **−7.36, 1.36**
38. $5x + 9 = 2x^2$ **−1.21, 3.71**
39. $4x^2 + 3x - 11 = 0$ **−2.08, 1**

QUIZ for Lessons 10.4–10.5

Find the value(s) of the variable(s).

1. $m\widehat{ABC} = z°$ *(p. 672)*
2. $m\widehat{GHE} = z°$ *(p. 672)*
3. $m\widehat{JKL} = z°$ *(p. 672)*

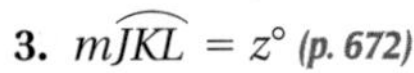

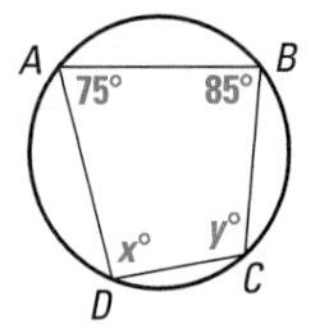

$x = 95$, $y = 105$, $z = 190$

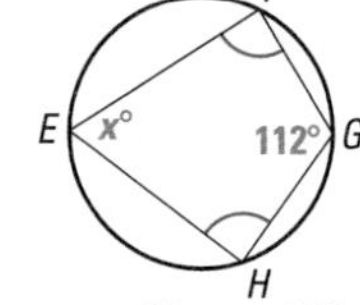

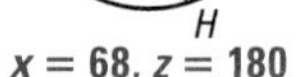

$x = 68$, $z = 180$

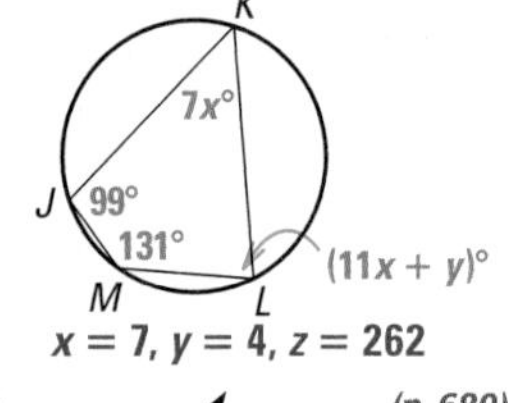

$x = 7$, $y = 4$, $z = 262$

4. *(p. 680)*

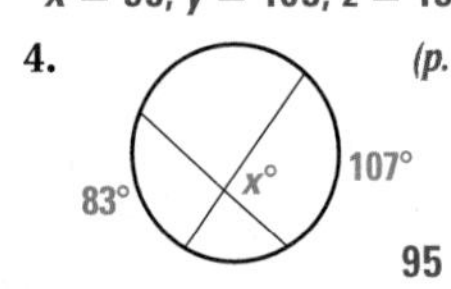

95

5. *(p. 680)*

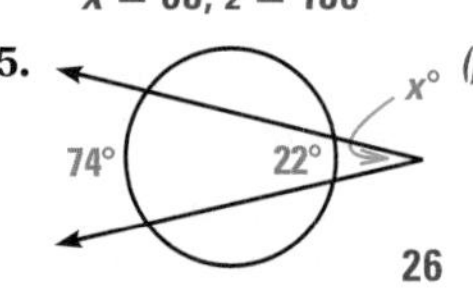

26

6. *(p. 680)*

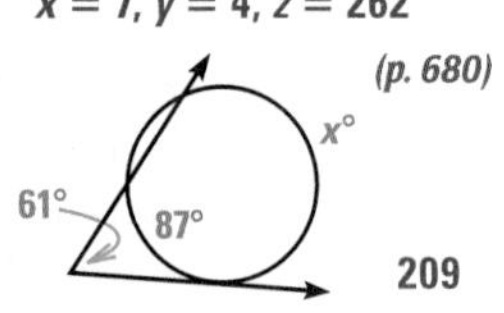

209

7. **MOUNTAIN** You are on top of a mountain about 1.37 miles above sea level. Find the measure of the arc that represents the part of Earth that you can see. Earth's radius is approximately 4000 miles. *(p. 680)* **about 3°**

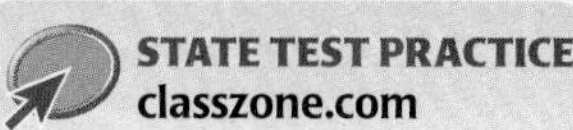

Lessons 10.1–10.5

1. **MULTI-STEP PROBLEM** An official stands 2 meters from the edge of a discus circle and 3 meters from a point of tangency.

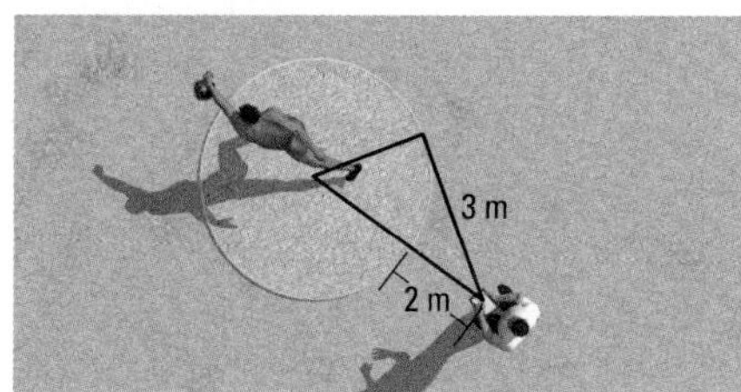

   a. Find the radius of the discus circle. **1.25 m**

   b. How far is the official from the center of the discus circle? **3.25 m**

2. **GRIDDED ANSWER** In the diagram, $\overline{XY} \cong \overline{YZ}$ and $m\overset{\frown}{XQZ} = 199°$. Find $m\overset{\frown}{YZ}$ in degrees. **80.5°**

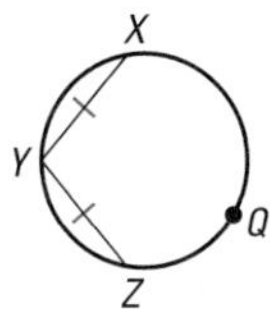

3. **MULTI-STEP PROBLEM** A wind turbine has three equally spaced blades that are each 131 feet long.

   a. What is the measure of the arc between any two blades? **120°**

   b. The highest point reached by a blade is 361 feet above the ground. Find the distance x between the lowest point reached by the blades and the ground. **99 ft**

   c. What is the distance y from the tip of one blade to the tip of another blade? Round your answer to the nearest tenth. **226.9 ft**

4. **EXTENDED RESPONSE** The Navy Pier Ferris Wheel in Chicago is 150 feet tall and has 40 spokes.

   a. Find the measure of the angle between any two spokes. **9°**

   b. Two spokes form a central angle of 72°. How many spokes are between the two spokes? **7 spokes**

   c. The bottom of the wheel is 10 feet from the ground. Find the diameter and radius of the wheel. *Explain* your reasoning. **See margin.**

5. **OPEN-ENDED** Draw a quadrilateral inscribed in a circle. Measure two consecutive angles. Then find the measures of the other two angles algebraically. **See margin.**

6. **MULTI-STEP PROBLEM** Use the diagram.

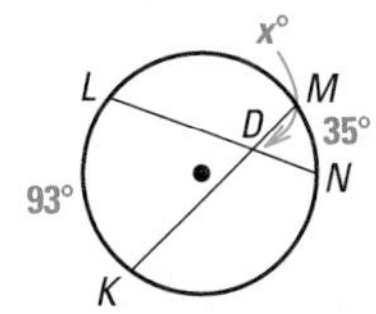

   a. Find the value of x. **64**

   b. Find the measures of the other three angles formed by the intersecting chords. **116°, 64°, 116°**

7. **SHORT RESPONSE** Use the diagram to show that $m\overset{\frown}{DA} = y° - x°$. **See margin.**

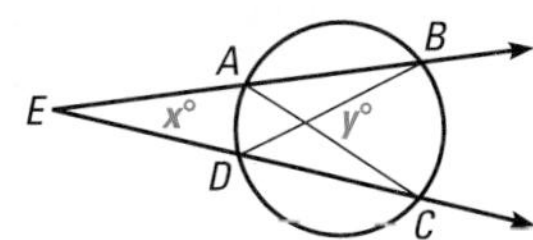

4c. 140 ft, 70 ft; since the ferris wheel is 150 feet high and is 10 feet off the ground, the wheel's diameter can only be 140 feet, and the radius is half the diameter.

5. Check students' work. Each unmeasured angle is supplementary to the measured angle opposite it.

7. $x° = \frac{1}{2}(m\overset{\frown}{BC} - m\overset{\frown}{DA})$ and $y° = \frac{1}{2}(m\overset{\frown}{BC} + m\overset{\frown}{DA})$ which leads to $y° - x° = m\overset{\frown}{DA}$.

1 PLAN AND PREPARE

Explore the Concept

- Students will investigate the lengths of parts of chords.
- This activity leads into the study of chord segment lengths in Lesson 10.6, Example 1.

Materials

Each student will need a graphing calculator or computer.

Recommended Time

Work activity: 15 min
Discuss results: 5 min

Grouping

Students should work individually.

2 TEACH

Tips for Success

Students can repeat the activity with circles of different radii to verify the relationship between the lengths of segments of intersecting chords.

Key Question

- Do the positions of points A, B, C, or D, affect the relationship between the chord segments? **no**

Key Discovery

If two chords intersect in a circle, the product of the lengths of the segments of one chord equals the product of the lengths of the segments in the other chord.

3 ASSESS AND RETEACH

1. In the diagram for the Explore activity, if $AE \cdot EC = 12.5$, what is the product of the lengths of the segments for any other chord that goes through point E? **12.5**

@HomeTutor
classzone.com
Keystrokes

10.6 Investigate Segment Lengths

MATERIALS • graphing calculator or computer

Standards

Prepare for
21.0 *Students prove* and solve problems regarding *relationships among chords,* secants, tangents, inscribed angles, and inscribed and circumscribed polygons *of circles.*

QUESTION **What is the relationship between the lengths of segments in a circle?**

You can use geometry drawing software to find a relationship between the segments formed by two intersecting chords.

EXPLORE **Draw a circle with two chords**

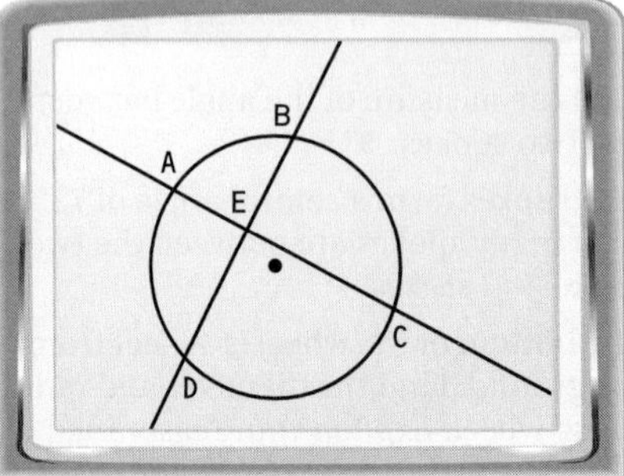

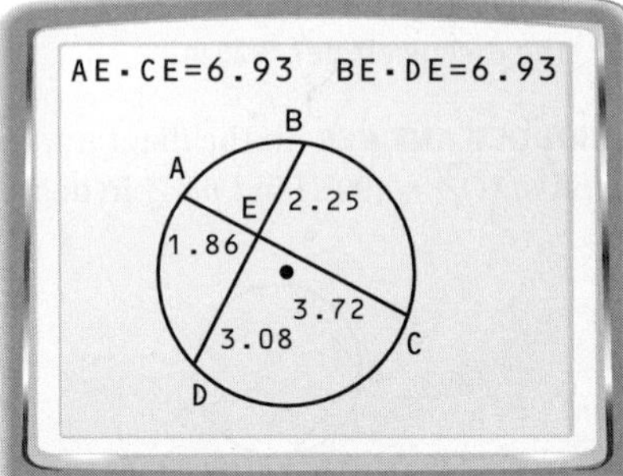

STEP 1 ***Draw a circle*** Draw a circle and choose four points on the circle. Label them A, B, C, and D.

STEP 2 ***Draw secants*** Draw secants $\overleftrightarrow{AC}$ and $\overleftrightarrow{BD}$ and label the intersection point E.

STEP 3 ***Measure segments*** Note that $\overline{AC}$ and $\overline{BD}$ are chords. Measure $\overline{AE}$, $\overline{CE}$, $\overline{BE}$, and $\overline{DE}$ in your diagram.

STEP 4 ***Perform calculations*** Calculate the products $AE \cdot CE$ and $BE \cdot DE$.

DRAW CONCLUSIONS **Use your observations to complete these exercises**

1. What do you notice about the products you found in Step 4? **Their products are the same.**
2. Drag points A, B, C, and D, keeping point E inside the circle. What do you notice about the new products from Step 4? **Their products are the same.**
3. Make a conjecture about the relationship between the four chord segments. $\boldsymbol{AE \cdot CE = BE \cdot DE}$
4. Let $\overline{PQ}$ and $\overline{RS}$ be two chords of a circle that intersect at the point T. If $PT = 9$, $QT = 5$, and $RT = 15$, use your conjecture from Exercise 3 to find ST. **3**

10.6 Find Segment Lengths in Circles

Before You found angle and arc measures in circles.
Now You will find segment lengths in circles.
Why? So you can find distances in astronomy, as in Example 4.

Key Vocabulary
- segments of a chord
- secant segment
- external segment

Standards

21.0 Students prove and solve problems regarding relationships among chords, secants, tangents, inscribed angles, and inscribed and circumscribed polygons of circles.

When two chords intersect in the interior of a circle, each chord is divided into two segments that are called **segments of the chord**.

THEOREM *For Your Notebook*

THEOREM 10.14 Segments of Chords Theorem

If two chords intersect in the interior of a circle, then the product of the lengths of the segments of one chord is equal to the product of the lengths of the segments of the other chord.

Proof: Ex. 21, p. 694

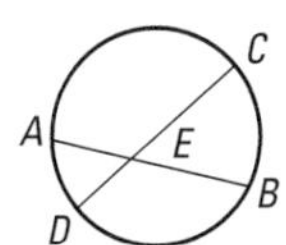

$EA \cdot EB = EC \cdot ED$

Plan for Proof To prove Theorem 10.14, construct two similar triangles. The lengths of the corresponding sides are proportional, so $\frac{EA}{ED} = \frac{EC}{EB}$. By the Cross Products Property, $EA \cdot EB = EC \cdot ED$.

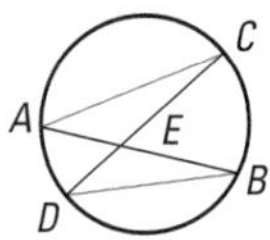

EXAMPLE 1 Find lengths using Theorem 10.14

xy ALGEBRA **Find ML and JK.**

M, x + 2, N, J, K, x, x + 4, x + 1, L

Solution

$NK \cdot NJ = NL \cdot NM$	Use Theorem 10.14.
$x \cdot (x + 4) = (x + 1) \cdot (x + 2)$	Substitute.
$x^2 + 4x = x^2 + 3x + 2$	Simplify.
$4x = 3x + 2$	Subtract x^2 from each side.
$x = 2$	Solve for x.

Find ML and JK by substitution.

$ML = (x + 2) + (x + 1)$ $\quad JK = x + (x + 4)$
$= 2 + 2 + 2 + 1$ $\quad = 2 + 2 + 4$
$= 7$ $\quad = 8$

1 PLAN AND PREPARE

Warm-Up Exercises

Transparency Available

Solve the equation.

1. $x^2 + 4x + 3 = 0$ **−1, −3**
2. $6x - 9 = x^2$ **3**
3. $3(x + 4) = (2 + 4)(4)$ **4**
4. $21(x - 4) = (2x - 7)(x + 2)$ **5, 7**
5. If 10 is multiplied by 10 more than a number, the product is the square of 24. Find the number. **47.6**

Notetaking Guide

Transparency Available

Promotes interactive learning and notetaking skills, pp. 271–274.

Pacing

Basic: 1 day
Average: 1 day
Advanced: 1 day
Block: 0.5 block with 10.5
• See *Teaching Guide/Lesson Plan.*

2 FOCUS AND MOTIVATE

Essential Question

Big Idea 1, p. 649

What are some properties of chords, secants, and tangents to a circle? **Tell students they will learn how to answer this question by looking at the lengths of the segments of the chords, secants, and tangents.**

Resource Planning Guide

Chapter Resource Book
- Teaching Guide/Lesson Plan (pp. 73–74)
- Practice levels A, B, C (pp. 76–81)
- Study Guide (pp. 82–83)
- Catch-up for Absent Students (p. 84)
- Application (p. 85)
- Challenge (p. 86)

Workbooks
- Notetaking Guide (pp. 271–274)
- Practice Workbook (pp. 199–201)

Teaching Options
- **Power Presentations CD-ROM** provides dynamic electronic teaching resources for the classroom.
- **Activity Generator CD-ROM** provides editable activities for all ability levels.

Interactive Technology
- Easy Planner
- Power Presentations CD-ROM
- Activity Generator CD-ROM
- Animated Geometry
- Test Generator CD-ROM
- Online Quiz
- eWorkbook
- eEdition
- @HomeTutor

Resources for English Learners
- Quick Reference for English Learners
- Spanish Study Guide
- Multi-Language Visual Glossary
- Student Resources in Spanish

See also the *Geometry Toolkit* for more strategies for meeting individual needs.

Motivating the Lesson

Four swimmers are together in a circular pool. Two of them swim toward the edge of the pool, in opposite directions. Then the other two swim to the edge of the pool, also in opposite directions from each other. Ask students how the four swimming distances are related. Tell students they will investigate this question by looking at the lengths of the segments of chords that intersect in the interior of a circle.

3 TEACH

Extra Example 1

Find RT and SU. $RT = 13$, $SU = 15$

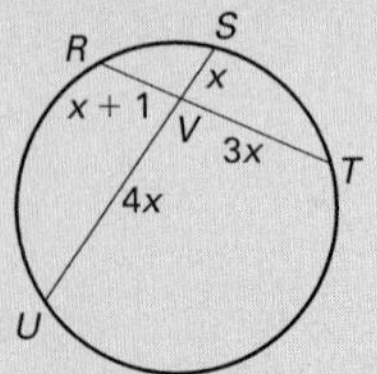

Extra Example 2

What is the value of x? C

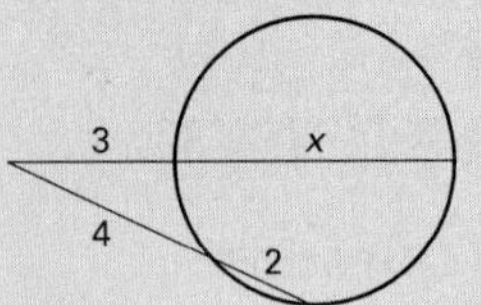

Ⓐ 2 Ⓑ $2\frac{2}{3}$

Ⓒ 5 Ⓓ 8

TANGENTS AND SECANTS A **secant segment** is a segment that contains a chord of a circle, and has exactly one endpoint outside the circle. The part of a secant segment that is outside the circle is called an **external segment**.

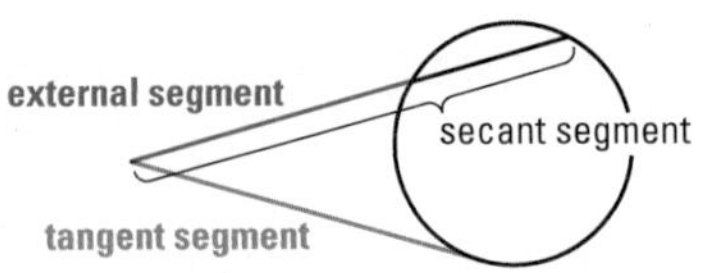

THEOREM *For Your Notebook*

THEOREM 10.15 Segments of Secants Theorem

If two secant segments share the same endpoint outside a circle, then the product of the lengths of one secant segment and its external segment equals the product of the lengths of the other secant segment and its external segment.

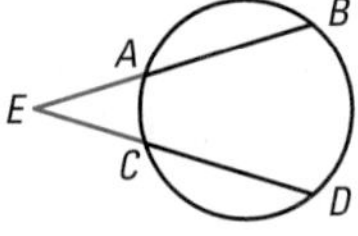

$EA \cdot EB = EC \cdot ED$

Proof: Ex. 25, p. 694

★ EXAMPLE 2 Standardized Test Practice

What is the value of x?

Ⓐ 6 Ⓑ $6\frac{2}{3}$

Ⓒ 8 Ⓓ 9

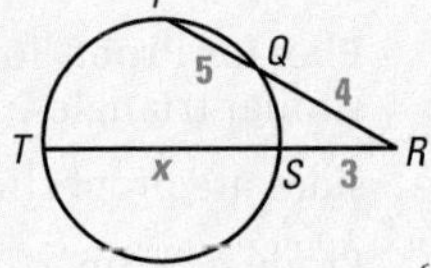

Solution

$RQ \cdot RP = RS \cdot RT$	Use Theorem 10.15.
$4 \cdot (5 + 4) = 3 \cdot (x + 3)$	Substitute.
$36 = 3x + 9$	Simplify.
$9 = x$	Solve for x.

▶ The correct answer is D. Ⓐ Ⓑ Ⓒ Ⓓ

GUIDED PRACTICE for Examples 1 and 2

Find the value(s) of x.

1. 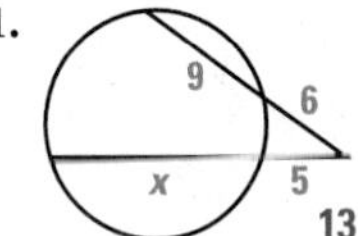

13

2. 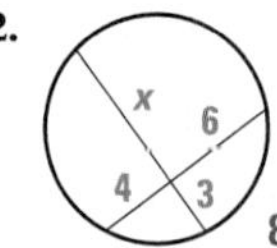

8

3. 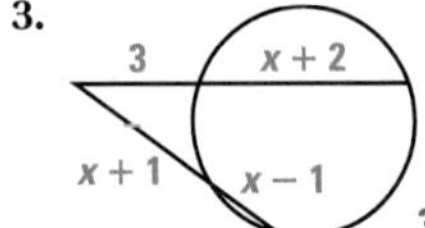

3

THEOREM — For Your Notebook

THEOREM 10.16 Segments of Secants and Tangents Theorem

If a secant segment and a tangent segment share an endpoint outside a circle, then the product of the lengths of the secant segment and its external segment equals the square of the length of the tangent segment.

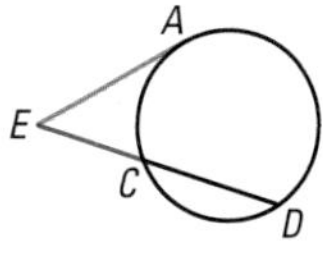

$EA^2 = EC \cdot ED$

Proof: Ex. 26, p. 694

EXAMPLE 3 Find lengths using Theorem 10.16

Use the figure at the right to find *RS*.

ANOTHER WAY
For an alternative method for solving the problem in Example 3, turn to page 696 for the **Problem Solving Workshop**.

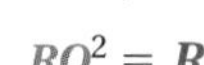

Solution

$RQ^2 = RS \cdot RT$ — Use Theorem 10.16.

$16^2 = x \cdot (x + 8)$ — Substitute.

$256 = x^2 + 8x$ — Simplify.

$0 = x^2 + 8x - 256$ — Write in standard form.

$x = \frac{-8 \pm \sqrt{8^2 - 4(1)(-256)}}{2(1)}$ — Use quadratic formula.

$x = -4 \pm 4\sqrt{17}$ — Simplify.

Use the positive solution, because lengths cannot be negative.

▶ So, $x = -4 + 4\sqrt{17} \approx 12.49$, and $RS \approx 12.49$.

 at classzone.com

✓ **GUIDED PRACTICE** for Example 3

Find the value of *x*.

4. 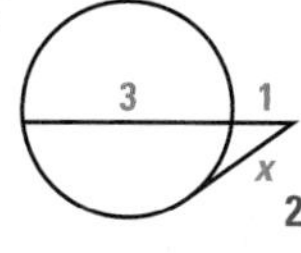

5. 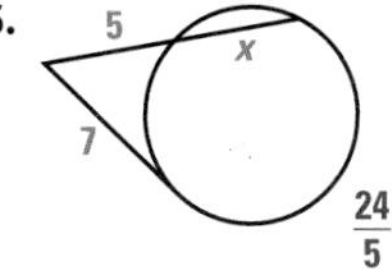

6. 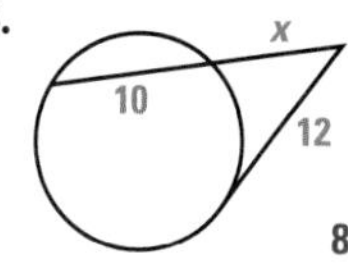

Determine which theorem you would use to find *x*. Then find the value of *x*.

7. 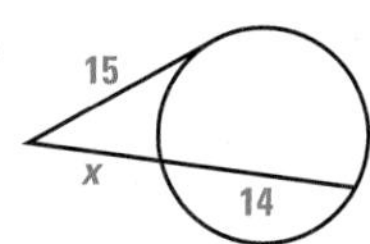

Theorem 10.16; $-7 + \sqrt{274}$

8. 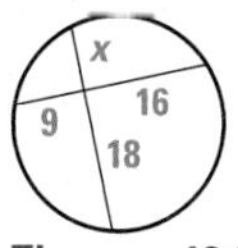

Theorem 10.14; 8

9. 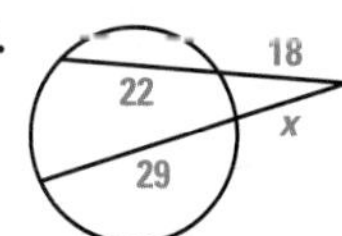

Theorem 10.15; 16

10. In the diagram for Theorem 10.16, what must be true about *EC* compared to *EA*? **$EC < EA$**

Extra Example 3

Use the figure to find *AB*. **20**

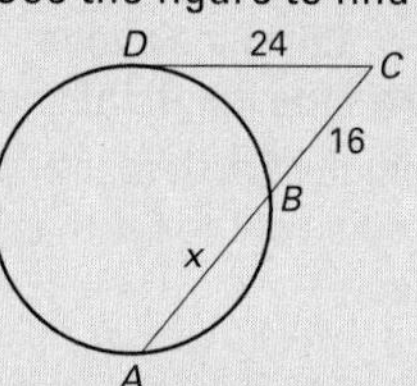

Key Question to Ask for Example 3

- What kind of segment is $\overline{RQ}$? **tangent**

An **Animated Geometry** activity is available on-line for **Example 3**. This activity is also available on the **Power Presentations CD-ROM**.

Extra Example 4

Suppose the Space Shuttle is positioned at point S, 150 miles above the Earth. What is the length of line segment $\overline{ES}$ from the Earth to the shuttle? (The radius of the Earth is about 4000 miles.)

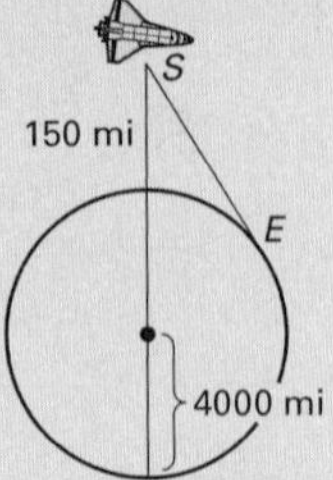

about 1106 miles

Closing the Lesson

Have students summarize the major points of the lesson and answer the Essential Question: What are some properties of chords, secants, and tangents to a circle?

- **Two chords: The products of the lengths of the segments of one chord is equal to the product of the lengths of the segments of the other chord.**
- **Two secants: The product of the lengths of one secant segment and its external segment equals the product of the lengths of the other secant segment and its external segment.**
- **A secant and a tangent: The product of the lengths of the secant segment and its external segment equals the square of the length of the tangent segment.**

For chords, secants, and tangents to a circle, the products of pairs of lengths are equal, as stated above.

EXAMPLE 4 Solve a real-world problem

SCIENCE Tethys, Calypso, and Telesto are three of Saturn's moons. Each has a nearly circular orbit 295,000 kilometers in radius. The Cassini-Huygens spacecraft entered Saturn's orbit in July 2004. Telesto is on a point of tangency. Find the distance DB from Cassini to Tethys.

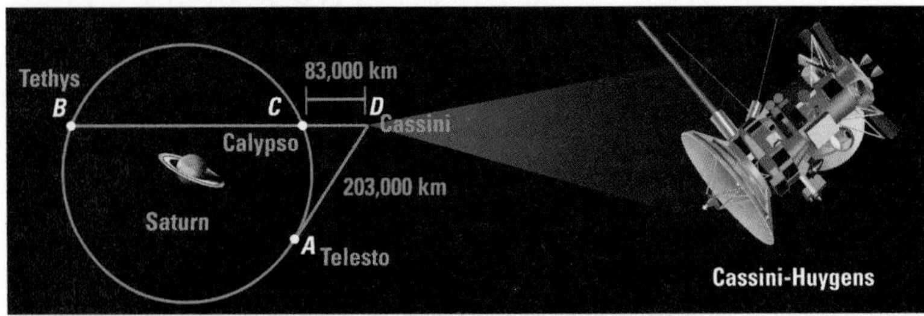

Solution

$DC \cdot DB = AD^2$	Use Theorem 10.16.
$83{,}000 \cdot DB \approx 203{,}000^2$	Substitute.
$DB \approx 496{,}494$	Solve for DB.

▶ Cassini is about 496,494 kilometers from Tethys.

GUIDED PRACTICE for Example 4

11. Why is it appropriate to use the approximation symbol $\approx$ in the last two steps of the solution to Example 4? **The given distances are not exact, so the calculations are approximations.**

10.6 EXERCISES

HOMEWORK KEY
○ = **WORKED-OUT SOLUTIONS** on p. WS13 for Exs. 3, 9, and 21
★ = **STANDARDIZED TEST PRACTICE** Exs. 2, 16, 24, and 27

SKILL PRACTICE

A

1. **VOCABULARY** Copy and complete: The part of the secant segment that is outside the circle is called a(n) __?__. **external segment**

2. ★ **WRITING** *Explain* the difference between a tangent segment and a secant segment. **A tangent segment intersects the circle in only one point while the secant segment intersects the circle in two points.**

EXAMPLE 1 on p. 689 for Exs. 3–5

FINDING SEGMENT LENGTHS Find the value of x.

3. 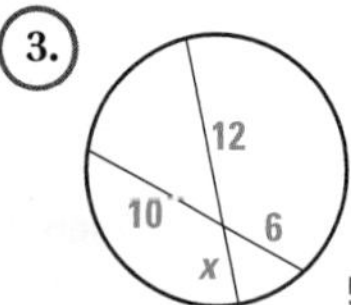

5

4. 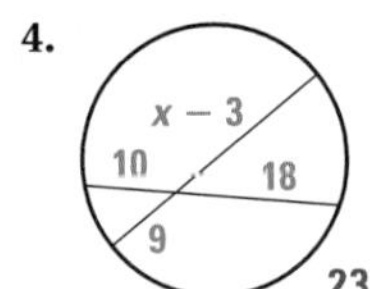

23

5. 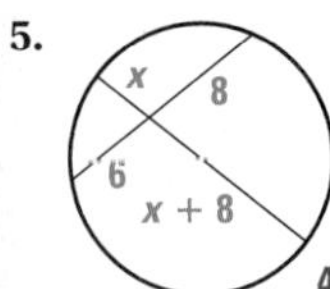

4

XAMPLE 2 on p. 690 for Exs. 6–8

XAMPLE 3 on p. 691 for Exs. 9–11

FINDING SEGMENT LENGTHS **Find the value of x.**

6. 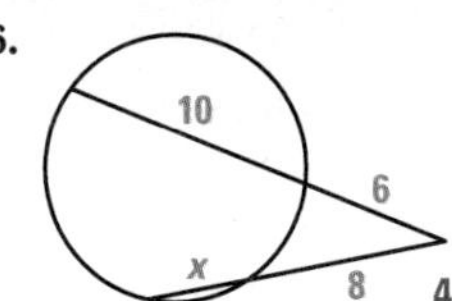

7. 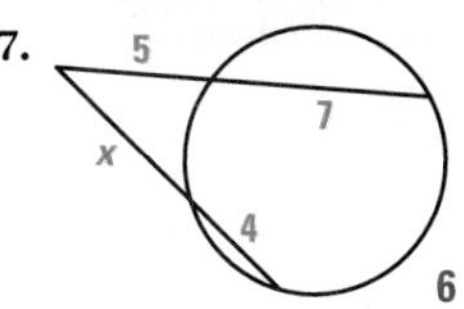

8. 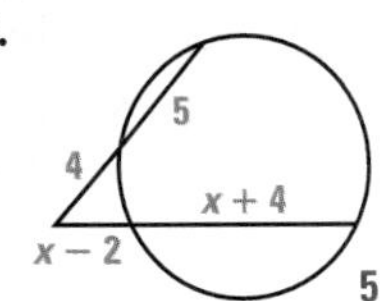

9. 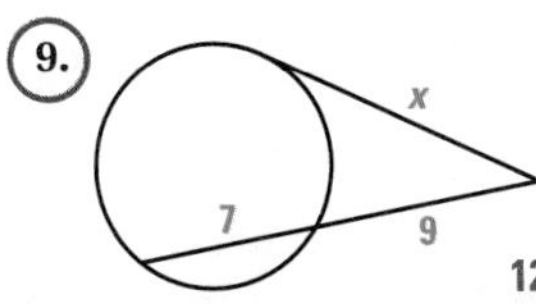

10. 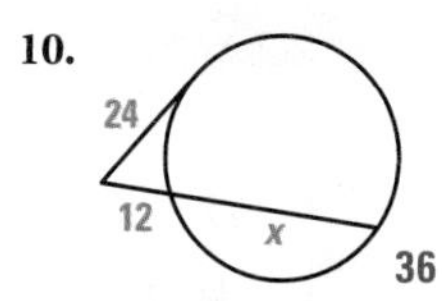

11. 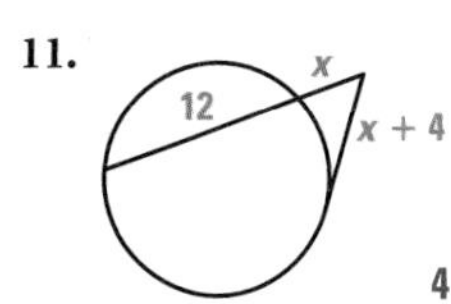

12. **ERROR ANALYSIS** *Describe* and correct the error in finding CD.

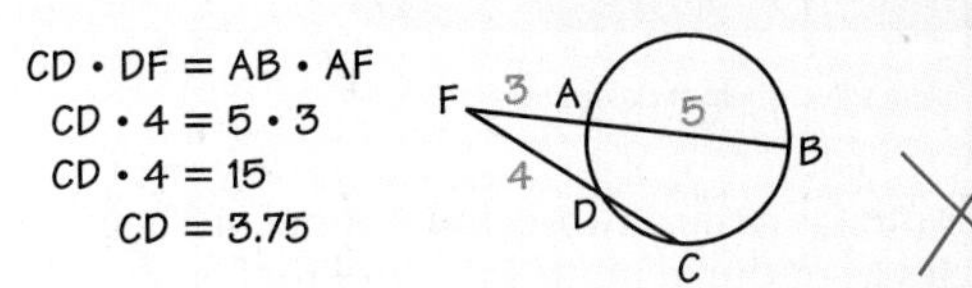

The wrong segment lengths are being multiplied together; $FD \cdot CF = AF \cdot BF$, $4 \cdot CF = 3 \cdot 8$, $CF = 6$, $CD + DF = CF$, $CD + 4 = 6$, $CD = 2$.

B **FINDING SEGMENT LENGTHS** **Find the value of x. Round to the nearest tenth.**

13. 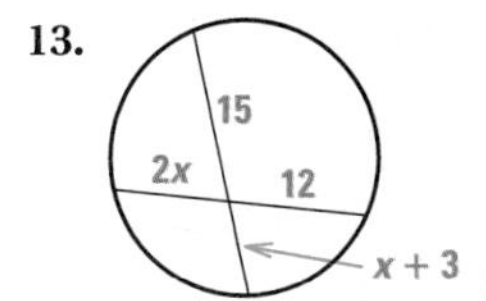

14. 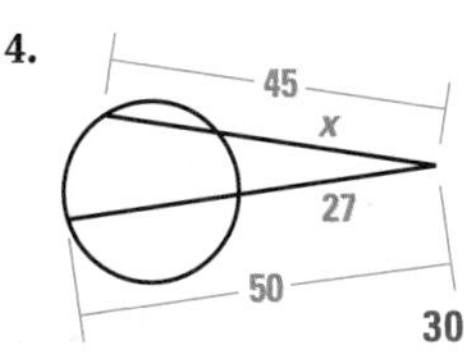

15. 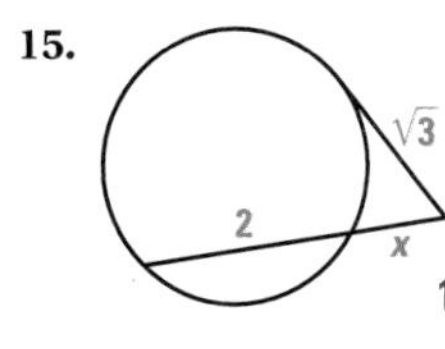

16. ★ **MULTIPLE CHOICE** Which of the following is a possible value of x? **D**

Ⓐ −2 Ⓑ 4

Ⓒ 5 Ⓓ 6

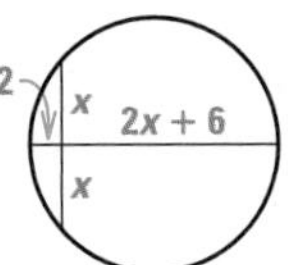

FINDING LENGTHS **Find PQ. Round your answers to the nearest tenth.**

17. 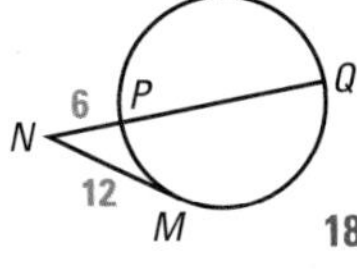

18. 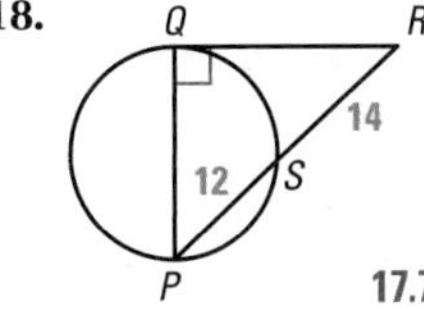

C 19. **CHALLENGE** In the figure, $AB = 12$, $BC = 8$, $DE = 6$, $PD = 4$, and A is a point of tangency. Find the radius of $\odot P$. **$2\sqrt{10}$**

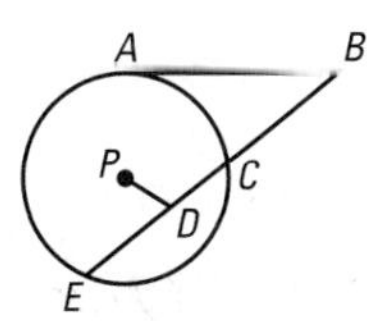

4 PRACTICE AND APPLY

Assignment Guide

Answer Transparencies available for all exercises

Basic:
Day 1: SRH p. 873 Exs. 1–7
pp. 692–695
Exs. 1–15, 20–23, 29–41 odd

Average:
Day 1: pp. 692–695
Exs. 1–5, 7–10, 12–18, 20–26, 30–42 even

Advanced:
Day 1: pp. 692–695
Exs. 1–5, 7, 8, 10, 11, 13–28*, 30, 32, 36, 39, 42

Block:
pp. 692–695
Exs. 1–5, 7–10, 12–18, 20–26, 30–42 even (with 10.5)

Differentiated Instruction

See *Geometry Best Practices Toolkit* for suggestions on addressing the needs of a diverse classroom.

Homework Check

For a quick check of student understanding of key concepts, go over the following exercises:

Basic: 4, 6, 10, 20, 21
Average: 4, 7, 10, 20, 22
Advanced: 5, 8, 11, 20, 24

Extra Practice

- Student Edition, p. 915
- Chapter 10 Resource Book: Practice levels A, B, C, pp. 76–81

Practice Worksheet

An easily-readable reduced practice page (with answers) for this lesson can be found on p. 648E.

Study Strategy

Exercise 14 Encourage students to get in the habit of drawing and labeling the entire secant as well as the external secant segment, as shown in this exercise. This will help them avoid errors in setting up the segment length equations.

Teaching Strategy

Exercise 26 Point out that after drawing segments $\overline{AD}$ and $\overline{AC}$, students can show that $\triangle EAD \sim \triangle ECA$, which will give them the proportion $\frac{EA}{ED} = \frac{EC}{EA}$.

21. Statements (Reasons)

1. Two intersecting chords in the same circle. (Given)

2. Draw $\overline{AC}$ and $\overline{BD}$. (Two points determine a line.)

3. $\angle ACD \cong \angle ABD$, $\angle CAB \cong \angle CDB$ (If two inscribed angles of a circle intercept the same arc, then the angles are congruent.)

4. $\triangle AEC \sim \triangle DEB$ (AA Similarity Postulate)

5. $\frac{EA}{ED} = \frac{EC}{EB}$ (If two triangles are similar, then the ratios of corresponding sides are equal.)

6. $EA \cdot EB = EC \cdot ED$ (Cross Products Property)

PROBLEM SOLVING

EXAMPLE 4 A on p. 692 for Ex. 20

20. **ARCHAEOLOGY** The circular stone mound in Ireland called Newgrange has a diameter of 250 feet. A passage 62 feet long leads toward the center of the mound. Find the perpendicular distance x from the end of the passage to either side of the mound. **about 108 ft**

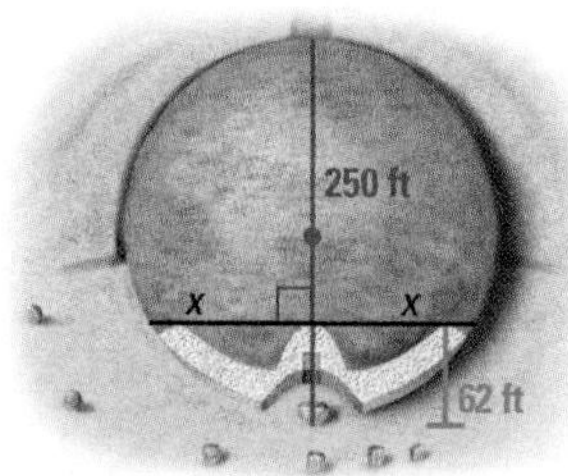

@HomeTutor for problem solving help at classzone.com

21. **PROVING THEOREM 10.14** Write a two-column proof of Theorem 10.14. Use similar triangles as outlined in the Plan for Proof on page 689. **See margin.**

@HomeTutor for problem solving help at classzone.com

B

22. **WELLS** In the diagram of the water well, AB, AD, and DE are known. Write an equation for BC using these three measurements. $BC = \frac{AD \cdot (AD + DE)}{AB} - AB$

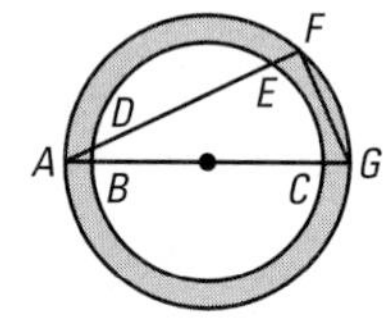

23. **PROOF** Use Theorem 10.1 to prove Theorem 10.16 for the special case when the secant segment contains the center of the circle. **See margin.**

24. 4 cm/sec; by the Segments of Chords Theorem, $6 \cdot 8 = 4 \cdot CN$, so $CN = 12$ cm. It takes 3 sec for sparkles to move the 6 cm from C to D, so the sparkles need to travel 12 cm in 3 sec, or 4 cm/sec.

24. ★ **SHORT RESPONSE** You are designing an animated logo for your website. Sparkles leave point C and move to the circle along the segments shown so that all of the sparkles reach the circle at the same time. Sparkles travel from point C to point D at 2 centimeters per second. How fast should sparkles move from point C to point N? *Explain.*

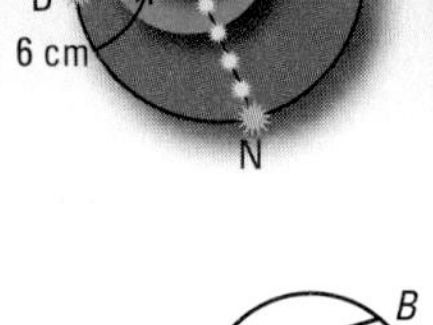

25. **PROVING THEOREM 10.15** Use the plan to prove Theorem 10.15.

GIVEN ▶ $\overline{EB}$ and $\overline{ED}$ are secant segments.

PROVE ▶ $EA \cdot EB = EC \cdot ED$

Plan for Proof Draw $\overline{AD}$ and $\overline{BC}$. Show that $\triangle BCE$ and $\triangle DAE$ are similar. Use the fact that corresponding side lengths in similar triangles are proportional. **See margin.**

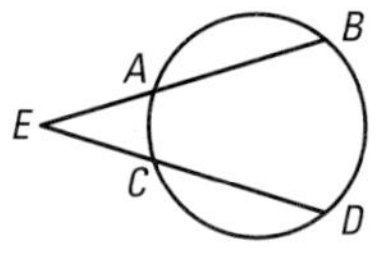

26. **PROVING THEOREM 10.16** Use the plan to prove Theorem 10.16.

GIVEN ▶ $\overline{EA}$ is a tangent segment. $\overline{ED}$ is a secant segment.

PROVE ▶ $EA^2 - EC \cdot ED$

Plan for Proof Draw $\overline{AD}$ and $\overline{AC}$. Use the fact that corresponding side lengths in similar triangles are proportional. **See margin.**

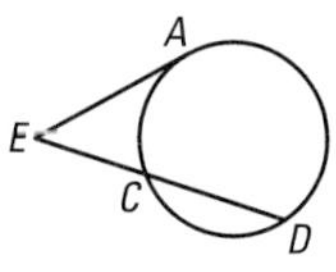

○ = WORKED-OUT SOLUTIONS on p. WS1 ★ = STANDARDIZED TEST PRACTICE

23. Given: EA is a tangent segment to circle P, ED is a secant segment of circle P, and ED is a diameter of circle P. Prove: $EA^2 = EC \cdot ED$. By Theorem 10.1, $EA \perp AP$, so $\triangle EAP$ is a right triangle. By the Pythagorean Theorem, $(y + r)^2 = x^2 + r^2$. So, $y^2 + 2yr + r^2 = x^2 + r^2$. By the subtrction Property of Equality, $y^2 + 2yr = x^2$. Factoring, this $y(y + 2r) = x^2$, or $EC \cdot ED = EA^2$.

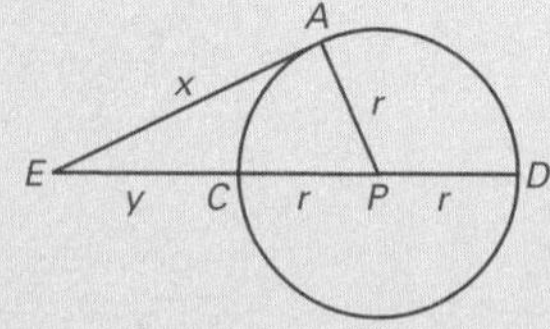

25, 26. See Additional Answers beginning on p. AA1.

'b. Using the
ertical Angles
ieorem,
$\angle ACB \cong \angle FCE$.
ince
$\angle CAB = 60°$
nd
$\angle EFD = 60°$,
ien $\angle CAB \cong$
$\angle EFD$. Using the
A Similarity
ostulate,
$\triangle ABC \sim \triangle FEC$.

C **27. ★ EXTENDED RESPONSE** In the diagram, $\overline{EF}$ is a tangent segment, $m\widehat{AD} = 140°$, $m\widehat{AB} = 20°$, $m\angle EFD = 60°$, $AC = 6$, $AB = 3$, and $DC = 10$.

a. Find $m\angle CAB$. **60°**

b. Show that $\triangle ABC \sim \triangle FEC$.

c. Let $EF = y$ and $DF = x$. Use the results of part (b) to write a proportion involving x and y. Solve for y. $\frac{y}{3} = \frac{x+10}{6}$; $y = \frac{x+10}{2}$

d. Use a theorem from this section to write another equation involving both x and y. $y^2 = x(x + 16)$

e. Use the results of parts (c) and (d) to solve for x and y. **2, 6**

f. *Explain* how to find CE. Since $\frac{CE}{CB} = \frac{2}{1}$, let $CE = 2x$ and $CB = x$. Using Theorem 10.14, $2x^2 = 60$ which implies $x = \sqrt{30}$ which implies $CE = 2\sqrt{30}$.

28. CHALLENGE Stereographic projection is a map-making technique that takes points on a sphere with radius one unit (Earth) to points on a plane (the map). The plane is tangent to the sphere at the origin.

The map location for each point P on the sphere is found by extending the line that connects N and P. The point's projection is where the line intersects the plane. Find the distance d from the point P to its corresponding point $P'(4, -3)$ on the plane. $\frac{25\sqrt{29}}{29}$

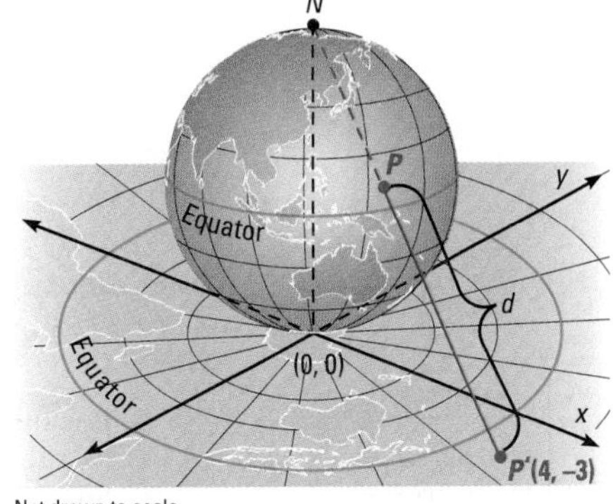

Not drawn to scale

MIXED REVIEW

PREVIEW
Prepare for Lesson 10.7 in Exs. 29–32.

Evaluate the expression. *(p. 874)*

29. $\sqrt{(-10)^2 - 8^2}$ **6**

30. $\sqrt{-5 + (-4) + (6 - 1)^2}$ **4**

31. $\sqrt{[-2 - (-6)]^2 + (3 - 6)^2}$ **5**

32. In right $\triangle PQR$, $PQ = 8$, $m\angle Q = 40°$, and $m\angle R = 50°$. Find QR and PR to the nearest tenth. *(p. 473)* **10.4, 6.7**

33. $\overleftrightarrow{EF}$ is tangent to $\odot C$ at E. The radius of $\odot C$ is 5 and $EF = 8$. Find FC. *(p. 651)* $\sqrt{89}$

Find the indicated measure. $\overline{AC}$ and $\overline{BE}$ are diameters. *(p. 659)*

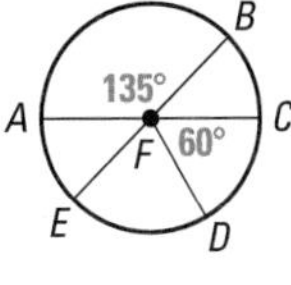

34. $m\widehat{AB}$ **135°**

35. $m\widehat{CD}$ **60°**

36. $m\widehat{BCA}$ **225°**

37. $m\widehat{CBD}$ **300°**

38. $m\widehat{CDA}$ **180°**

39. $m\widehat{BAE}$ **180°**

Determine whether $\overline{AB}$ is a diameter of the circle. *Explain.* *(p. 664)*

40.

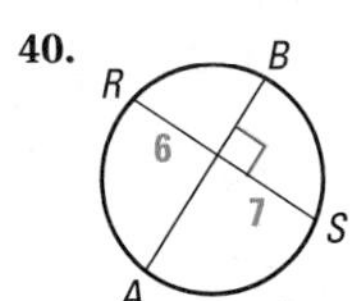

Not a diameter; if $\overline{AB}$ was a diameter it would bisect chord $\overline{RS}$.

41.

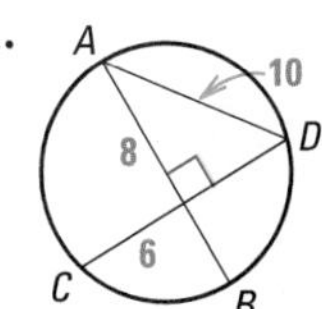

Diameter; $\overline{AB}$ bisects and is perpendicular to chord $\overline{CD}$.

42.

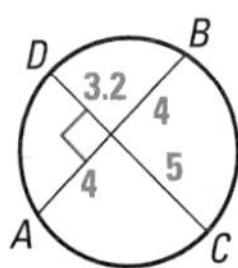

Not a diameter; if $\overline{AB}$ was a diameter it would bisect chord $\overline{DC}$.

5 ASSESS AND RETEACH

Daily Homework Quiz

Transparency Available

Find the value of x. Round to the nearest tenth, if necessary.

1. **2**

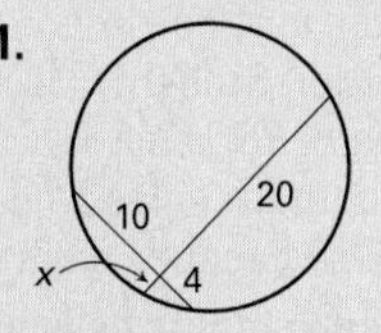

2. **8**

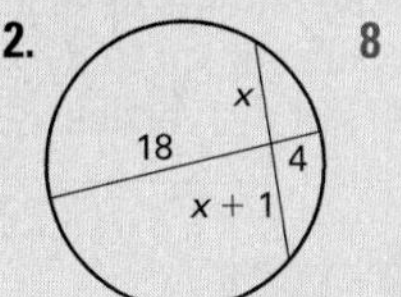

3. **15**

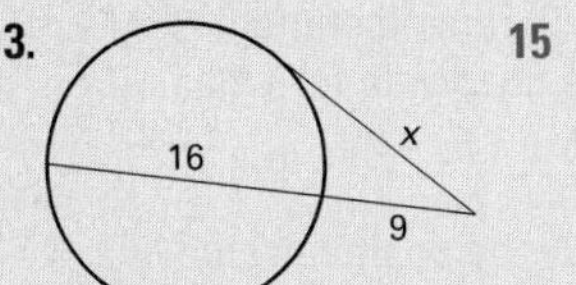

4. **20.25**

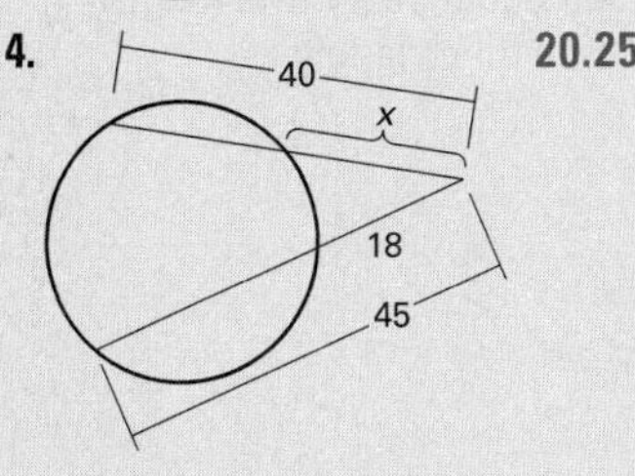

5. **11.3**

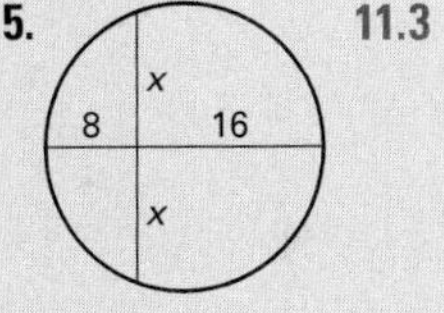

Online Quiz

Available at **classzone.com**

Diagnosis/Remediation

- Practice A, B, C in Chapter 10 Resource Book, pp. 76–81
- Study Guide in Chapter 10 Resource Book, pp. 82–83
- Practice Workbook, pp. 199–201
- @HomeTutor

Challenge

Additional challenge is available in the Chapter 10 Resource Book, p. 86.

Alternative Strategy

The length of the external secant segment in Example 3 on page 691 can be found by using proportions in similar triangles.

Avoiding Common Errors

A key is to write the similarity statement with the vertices in corresponding order. Students should see that in $\triangle RSQ$ and $\triangle RQT$, $\angle R$ is in both triangles, and $m\angle RQS = m\angle RTQ$ because each is half of $\widehat{SQ}$. Once students have a correct similarity statement, they can use the orders of the vertices to write a proportion.

Teaching Strategy

In Step 2, remind students that the quadratic formula is $x = \frac{-b \pm \sqrt{b^2 - 4ac}}{2a}$. Point out that only the positive value of x is used because x is the length of a side of a triangle.

2a.

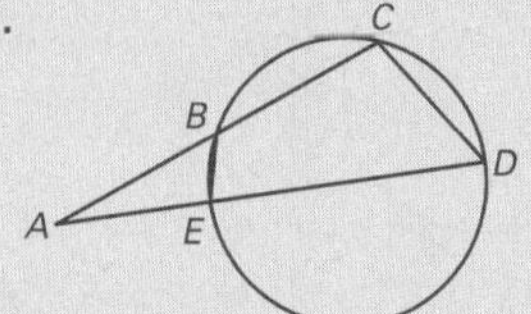

Another Way to Solve Example 3, page 691

MULTIPLE REPRESENTATIONS You can use similar triangles to find the length of an external secant segment.

PROBLEM

Use the figure at the right to find RS.

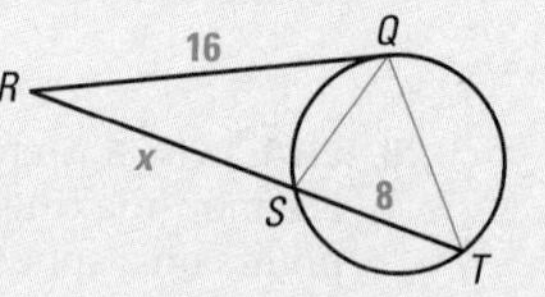

METHOD

Using Similar Triangles

Standards

21.0 Students prove and **solve problems regarding relationships among chords, secants, tangents,** inscribed angles, and inscribed and circumscribed polygons **of circles.**

5.0 Students prove that triangles are congruent or **similar, and they are able to use the concept of corresponding parts** of congruent triangles.

STEP 1 **Draw** segments $\overline{QS}$ and $\overline{QT}$, and identify the similar triangles.

Because they both intercept the same arc, $\angle RQS \cong \angle RTQ$.
By the Reflexive Property of Angle Congruence, $\angle QRS \cong \angle TRQ$.
So, $\triangle RSQ \sim \triangle RQT$ by the AA Similarity Postulate.

STEP 2 **Use** a proportion to solve for RS.

$$\frac{RS}{RQ} = \frac{RQ}{RT} \quad \Rightarrow \quad \frac{x}{16} = \frac{16}{x + 8}$$

▶ By the Cross Products Property, $x^2 + 8x = 256$. Use the quadratic formula to find that $x = -4 \pm 4\sqrt{17}$. Taking the positive solution, $x = -4 + 4\sqrt{17}$ and $RS = 12.49$.

PRACTICE

1. **WHAT IF?** Find RQ in the problem above if the known lengths are $RS = 4$ and $ST = 9$. $2\sqrt{13}$

2. **MULTI-STEP PROBLEM** Copy the diagram.

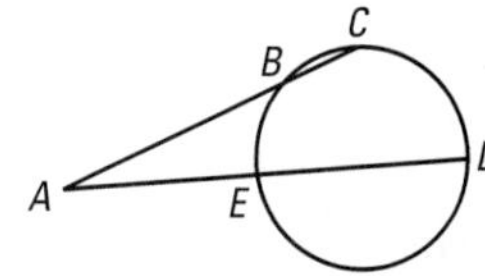

   a. Draw auxiliary segments $\overline{BE}$ and $\overline{CD}$. Name two similar triangles. See margin for art; $\triangle AEB \sim \triangle ACD$

   b. If $AB = 15$, $BC = 5$, and $AE = 12$, find DE. 13

3. **CHORD** Find the value of x. $\frac{24}{5}$

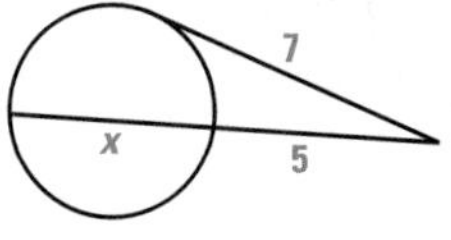

4. **SEGMENTS OF SECANTS** Use the Segments of Secants Theorem to write an expression for w in terms of x, y, and z. $w = \frac{y(z + y)}{x} - x$

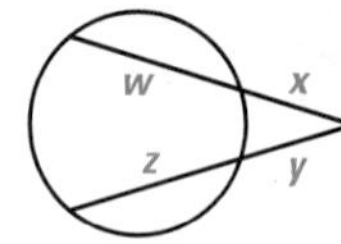

Extension
Use after Lesson 10.6

Draw a Locus

GOAL Draw the locus of points satisfying certain conditions.

ey Vocabulary
locus

Standards
nrichment Topic; not equired by California tandards.

A **locus** in a plane is the set of all points in a plane that satisfy a given condition or a set of given conditions. The word *locus* is derived from the Latin word for "location." The plural of locus is *loci*, pronounced "low-sigh."

A locus is often described as the path of an object moving in a plane. For example, the reason that many clock faces are circular is that the locus of the end of a clock's minute hand is a circle.

EXAMPLE 1 Find a locus

Draw a point C on a piece of paper. Draw and describe the locus of all points on the paper that are 1 centimeter from C.

Solution

STEP 1

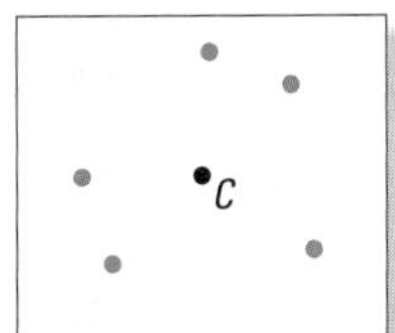

Draw point C. Locate several points 1 centimeter from C.

STEP 2

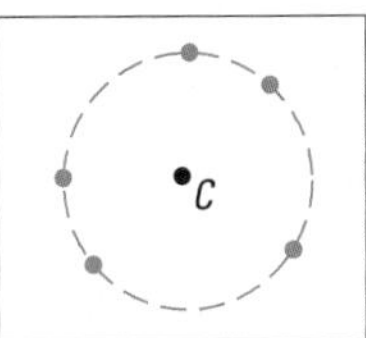

Recognize a pattern: the points lie on a circle.

STEP 3

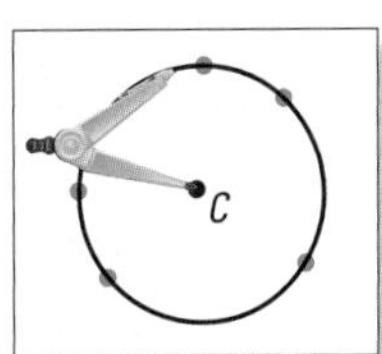

Draw the circle.

▶ The locus of points on the paper that are 1 centimeter from C is a circle with center C and radius 1 centimeter.

KEY CONCEPT — *For Your Notebook*

How to Find a Locus

To find the locus of points that satisfy a given condition, use the following steps.

STEP 1 **Draw** any figures that are given in the statement of the problem. Locate several points that satisfy the given condition.

STEP 2 **Continue** drawing points until you can recognize the pattern.

STEP 3 **Draw** the locus and describe it in words.

1 PLAN AND PREPARE

Warm-Up Exercises

1. Define *circle.* **A circle is the set of all points in a plane that are equidistant from a given point.**
2. What does it mean if point A is *equidistant* from the endpoints of segment $\overline{XY}$? **$AX = AY$**

2 FOCUS AND MOTIVATE

Essential Question

Big Idea 1, p. 649

How do you draw and describe a locus? **Tell students they will learn how to answer this question by identifying a pattern in the points that fit a particular condition.**

3 TEACH

Extra Example 1

Draw a circle with radius 5 cm on a piece of paper. Describe and draw the locus of all points on the paper that are 2 cm from the points of the circle. **The locus is two circles, with the same center as the original circle, having radii 3 cm and 7 cm.**

Key Question to Ask for Example 1

- Will the locus of all points a fixed distance from C always be a circle? **Yes, as long as you are restricted to points in a plane.**

LOCI SATISFYING TWO OR MORE CONDITIONS To find the locus of points that satisfy two or more conditions, first find the locus of points that satisfy each condition alone. Then find the intersection of these loci.

EXAMPLE 2 Draw a locus satisfying two conditions

Points A and B lie in a plane. What is the locus of points in the plane that are equidistant from points A and B and are a distance of AB from B?

Solution

STEP 1

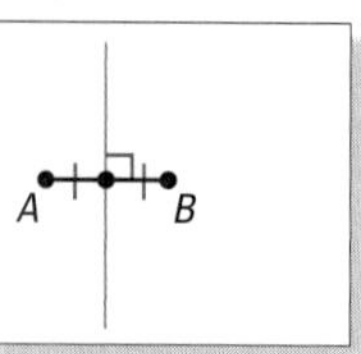

The locus of all points that are equidistant from A and B is the perpendicular bisector of $\overline{AB}$.

STEP 2

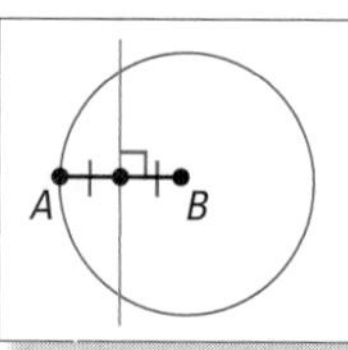

The locus of all points that are a distance of AB from B is the circle with center B and radius AB.

STEP 3

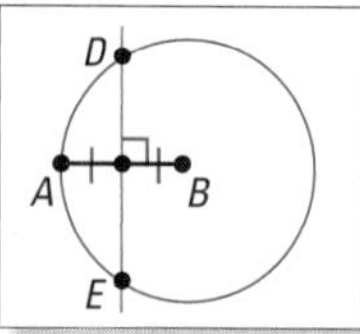

These loci intersect at D and E. So D and E form the locus of points that satisfy both conditions.

PRACTICE

EXAMPLE 1 on p. 697 for Exs. 1–4

DRAWING A LOCUS **Draw the figure. Then sketch the locus of points on the paper that satisfy the given condition.** **1–4. See margin.**

1. Point P, the locus of points that are 1 inch from P
2. Line k, the locus of points that are 1 inch from k
3. Point C, the locus of points that are at least 1 inch from C
4. Line j, the locus of points that are no more than 1 inch from j

EXAMPLE 2 on p. 698 for Exs. 5–9

WRITING **Write a description of the locus. Include a sketch.** **5–8. See margin.**

5. Point P lies on line ℓ. What is the locus of points on ℓ and 3 cm from P?
6. Point Q lies on line m. What is the locus of points 5 cm from Q and 3 cm from m?
7. Point R is 10 cm from line k. What is the locus of points that are within 10 cm of R, but further than 10 cm from k?
8. Lines ℓ and m are parallel. Point P is 5 cm from both lines. What is the locus of points between ℓ and m and no more than 8 cm from P?
9. **DOG LEASH** A dog's leash is tied to a stake at the corner of its doghouse, as shown at the right. The leash is 9 feet long. Make a scale drawing of the doghouse and sketch the locus of points that the dog can reach. **See margin.**

Vocabulary

Make sure students understand that a locus can be any set of points, and it may consist of a combination of one or more points, segments, rays, lines, or planes.

Extra Example 2

Point A is halfway between parallel lines m and n. Draw and describe the locus of points on m and n that are a given distance from point A.

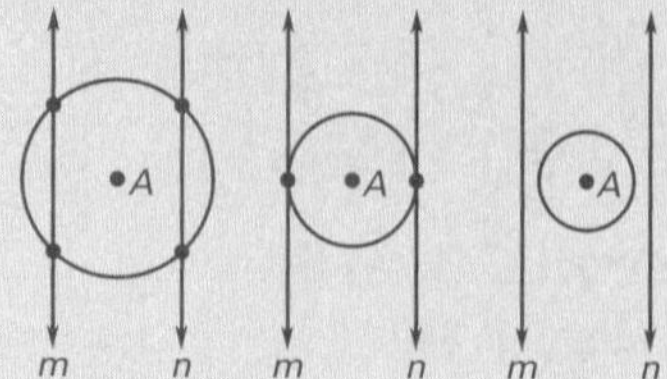

The locus may consist of 4 points, 2 points, or 0 points, depending on whether the given distance is greater than, equal to, or less than the distance between A and each of the two parallel lines.

Closing the Lesson

Have students summarize the major points of the lesson and answer the Essential Question: How do you draw and describe a locus?

- **A locus in a plane is the set of all points in the plane that satisfy a given condition or set of conditions.**
- **To find the locus of points that satisfy two or more conditions, find each locus separately and then find their intersection.**

Draw figures for given conditions until you recognize a pattern for each set of points. Draw and describe all of the the points that satisfy all of the conditions.

4 PRACTICE AND APPLY

Avoiding Common Errors

Exercises 3–4 Be sure students understand that the phrases "at least" and "no more than" mean the locus will be a region rather than a line.

1.

2.

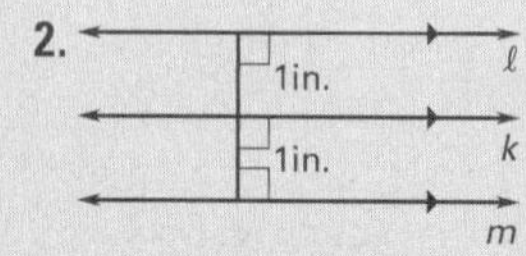

3.

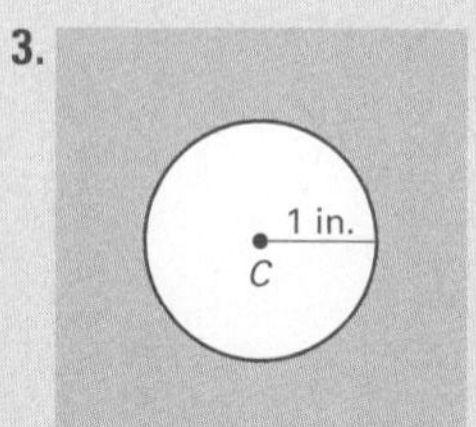

4.

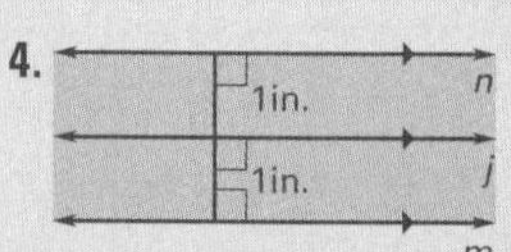

5–9. See Additional Answers beginning on p. AA1.

10.7 Write and Graph Equations of Circles

Before You wrote equations of lines in the coordinate plane.

Now You will write equations of circles in the coordinate plane.

Why? So you can determine zones of a commuter system, as in Ex. 36.

Key Vocabulary
- standard equation of a circle

Standards

17.0 Students prove theorems by using coordinate geometry, including the midpoint of a line segment, the distance formula, and **various forms of equations of lines and circles.**

Let (x, y) represent any point on a circle with center at the origin and radius r. By the Pythagorean Theorem,

$$x^2 + y^2 = r^2.$$

This is the equation of a circle with radius r and center at the origin.

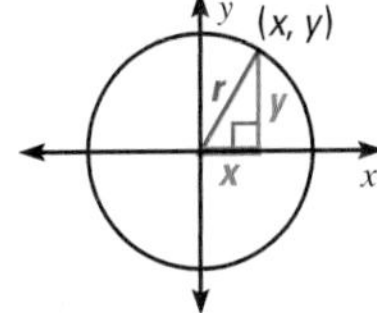

EXAMPLE 1 Write an equation of a circle

Write the equation of the circle shown.

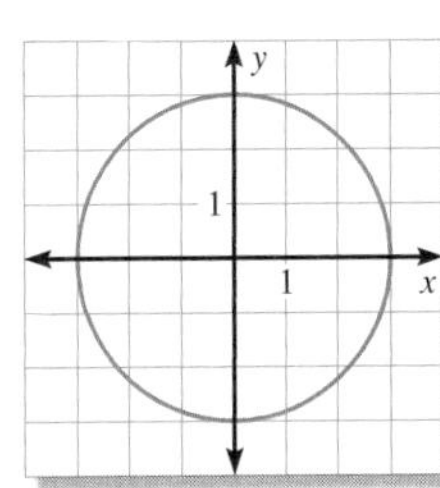

Solution

The radius is 3 and the center is at the origin.

$x^2 + y^2 = r^2$ **Equation of circle**

$x^2 + y^2 = 3^2$ **Substitute.**

$x^2 + y^2 = 9$ **Simplify.**

▶ The equation of the circle is $x^2 + y^2 = 9$.

CIRCLES CENTERED AT (h, k) You can write the equation of *any* circle if you know its radius and the coordinates of its center.

Suppose a circle has radius r and center (h, k). Let (x, y) be a point on the circle. The distance between (x, y) and (h, k) is r, so by the Distance Formula

$$\sqrt{(x - h)^2 + (y - k)^2} = r.$$

Square both sides to find the **standard equation of a circle**.

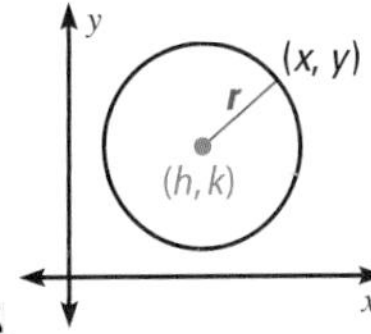

KEY CONCEPT *For Your Notebook*

Standard Equation of a Circle

The standard equation of a circle with center (h, k) and radius r is:

$$(x - h)^2 + (y - k)^2 = r^2$$

1 PLAN AND PREPARE

Warm-Up Exercises

Transparency Available

Evaluate each expression.

1. $\sqrt{(10 - 2)^2 + (8 + 7)^2}$ **17**

2. $\sqrt{(-3 - 2)^2 + (-8 - 4)^2}$ **13**

3. In a map on a coordinate grid, two towns are at coordinates (2, 3) and (−1, 4). If each unit on the grid is 1 kilometer, what is the distance between the towns? **$\sqrt{10}$ km or 3.16 km**

Notetaking Guide

Transparency Available

Promotes interactive learning and notetaking skills, pp. 275–278.

Pacing

Basic: 2 days

Average: 2 days

Advanced: 2 days

Block: 1 block

- See *Teaching Guide/Lesson Plan.*

2 FOCUS AND MOTIVATE

Essential Question

Big Idea 3, p. 649

What do you need to know to write the standard equation of a circle? **Tell students they will learn how to answer this question by writing the equation for a circle with a given center and a given radius.**

Resource Planning Guide

Chapter Resource Book
- Teaching Guide/Lesson Plan (pp. 87–88)
- Activity Master (p. 89)
- Practice levels A, B, C (pp. 90–95)
- Study Guide (pp. 96–97)
- Catch-up for Absent Students (p. 98)
- Problem Solving Workshop (p. 99)
- Challenge (p. 100)

Workbooks
- Notetaking Guide (pp. 275–278)
- Practice Workbook (pp. 202–204)

Teaching Options
- **Power Presentations CD-ROM** provides dynamic electronic teaching resources for the classroom.
- **Activity Generator CD-ROM** provides editable activities for all ability levels.

Interactive Technology
- Easy Planner
- Power Presentations CD-ROM
- Activity Generator CD-ROM
- Animated Geometry
- Test Generator CD-ROM
- Online Quiz
- eWorkbook
- eEdition
- @HomeTutor

Resources for English Learners
- Quick Reference for English Learners
- Spanish Study Guide
- Multi-Language Visual Glossary
- Student Resources in Spanish

See also the *Geometry Toolkit* for more strategies for meeting individual needs.

Motivating the Lesson

Suppose your school is located at the point (5, 2) on a grid. Ask students to find ordered pairs that are 3 units from the school. If necessary, help them come up with the ordered pairs (2, 2), (8, 2), (5, 5), and (5, −1). Tell students that in this lesson they will explore the equation that describes *all* the points that are 3 units from the school.

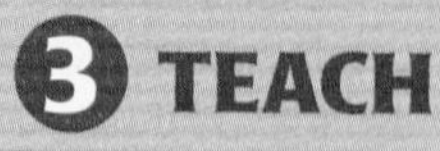

Extra Example 1

Write the equation of the circle shown. **$x^2 + y^2 = 16$**

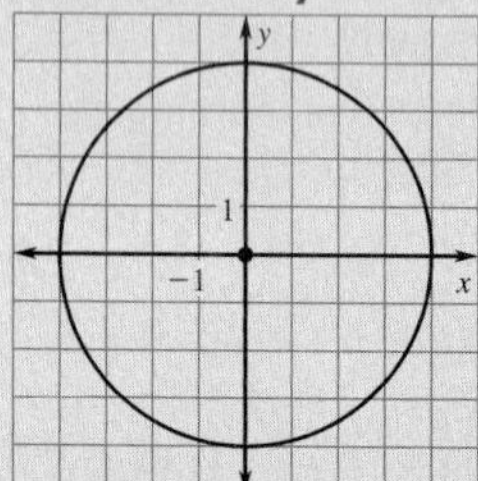

Extra Example 2

Write the standard equation of a circle with center (−2, 3) and radius 3.8. **$(x + 2)^2 + (y - 3)^2 = 14.44$**

Key Question to Ask for Example 2

- Why is there a positive sign in $(y + 9)^2$? **The expression $(y - (-9))^2$ is simplified to $(y + 9)^2$.**

Extra Example 3

The point (8, −1) is on a circle with center (4, 2). Write the standard equation of the circle. **$(x - 4)^2 + (y - 2)^2 = 25$**

Key Question to Ask for Example 3

- Will any point on the circle result in the same standard equation for the circle? **yes**

EXAMPLE 2 Write the standard equation of a circle

Write the standard equation of a circle with center (0, −9) and radius 4.2.

Solution

$(x - h)^2 + (y - k)^2 = r^2$ Standard equation of a circle

$(x - 0)^2 + (y - (-9))^2 = 4.2^2$ Substitute.

$x^2 + (y + 9)^2 = 17.64$ Simplify.

GUIDED PRACTICE for Examples 1 and 2

Write the standard equation of the circle with the given center and radius.

1. Center (0, 0), radius 2.5 **$x^2 + y^2 = 6.25$**
2. Center (−2, 5), radius 7 **$(x + 2)^2 + (y - 5)^2 = 49$**

EXAMPLE 3 Write the standard equation of a circle

The point (−5, 6) is on a circle with center (−1, 3). Write the standard equation of the circle.

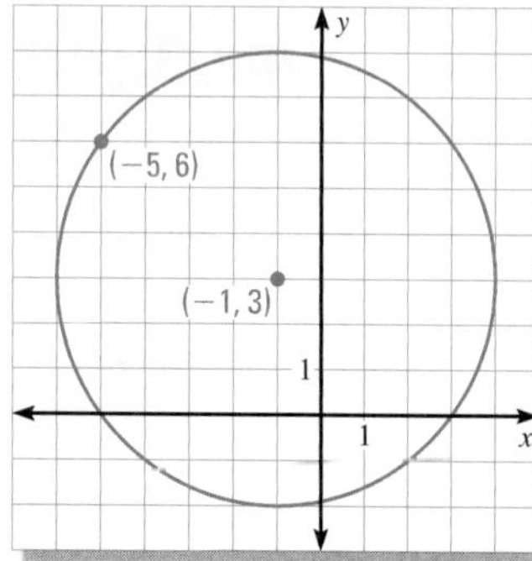

Solution

To write the standard equation, you need to know the values of h, k, and r. To find r, find the distance between the center and the point (−5, 6) on the circle.

$r = \sqrt{[-5 - (-1)]^2 + (6 - 3)^2}$ Distance Formula

$= \sqrt{(-4)^2 + 3^2}$ Simplify.

$= 5$ Simplify.

Substitute $(h, k) = (-1, 3)$ and $r = 5$ into the standard equation of a circle.

$(x - h)^2 + (y - k)^2 = r^2$ Standard equation of a circle

$[x - (-1)]^2 + (y - 3)^2 = 5^2$ Substitute.

$(x + 1)^2 + (y - 3)^2 = 25$ Simplify.

▶ The standard equation of the circle is $(x + 1)^2 + (y - 3)^2 = 25$.

GUIDED PRACTICE for Example 3

3. The point (3, 4) is on a circle whose center is (1, 4). Write the standard equation of the circle. **$(x - 1)^2 + (y - 4)^2 = 4$**
4. The point (−1, 2) is on a circle whose center is (2, 6). Write the standard equation of the circle. **$(x - 2)^2 + (y - 6)^2 = 25$**

Differentiated Instruction

Advanced Inform students that the set-builder notation mentioned on page 181 can be used to represent nonlinear equations like those for the circles in this lesson. For example, the set of points that lie on the circle shown in **Example 1** on page 699 can be given in set-builder notation as $\{(x, y) \mid x^2 + y^2 = 9\}$, which is read "the set of all ordered pairs (x, y) such that x^2 plus y^2 equals 9." Ask students to suggest set-builder notations for the circles found in **Examples 2 and 3**.

See also the *Geometry Toolkit* for more strategies.

EXAMPLE 4 Graph a circle

USE EQUATIONS
If you know the equation of a circle, you can graph the circle by identifying its center and radius.

The equation of a circle is $(x - 4)^2 + (y + 2)^2 = 36$. Graph the circle.

Solution

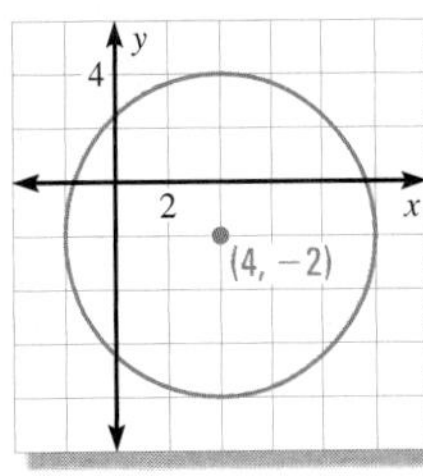

Rewrite the equation to find the center and radius.

$$(x - 4)^2 + (y + 2)^2 = 36$$

$$(x - 4)^2 + [y - (-2)]^2 = 6^2$$

The center is $(4, -2)$ and the radius is 6. Use a compass to graph the circle.

Extra Example 4

The equation of a circle is $(x + 1)^2 + (y - 3)^2 = 4$. Graph the circle.

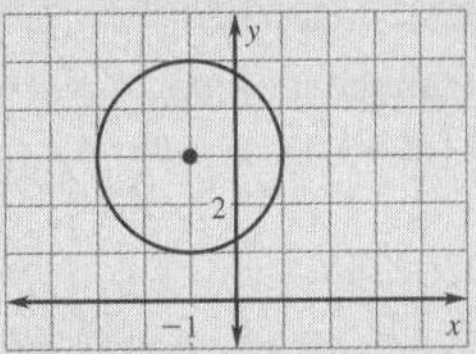

EXAMPLE 5 Use graphs of circles

EARTHQUAKES The epicenter of an earthquake is the point on Earth's surface directly above the earthquake's origin. A seismograph can be used to determine the distance to the epicenter of an earthquake. Seismographs are needed in three different places to locate an earthquake's epicenter.

Use the seismograph readings from locations A, B, and C to find the epicenter of an earthquake.

- The epicenter is 7 miles away from $A(-2, 2.5)$.
- The epicenter is 4 miles away from $B(4, 6)$.
- The epicenter is 5 miles away from $C(3, -2.5)$.

Solution

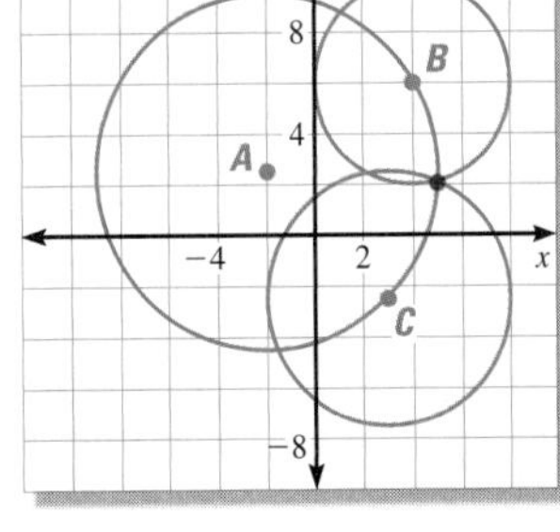

The set of all points equidistant from a given point is a circle, so the epicenter is located on each of the following circles.

⊙A with center $(-2, 2.5)$ and radius 7

⊙B with center $(4, 6)$ and radius 4

⊙C with center $(3, -2.5)$ and radius 5

To find the epicenter, graph the circles on a graph where units are measured in miles. Find the point of intersection of all three circles.

▶ The epicenter is at about $(5, 2)$.

Animated Geometry at classzone.com

Extra Example 5

Three forest ranger stations are at $A(-3, 2)$, $B(2, 2)$, and $C(-1, -1.5)$. A fire is 2 miles from A, 3 miles from B, and 3.5 miles from C. Find the location of the fire by graphing. **(−1, 2)**

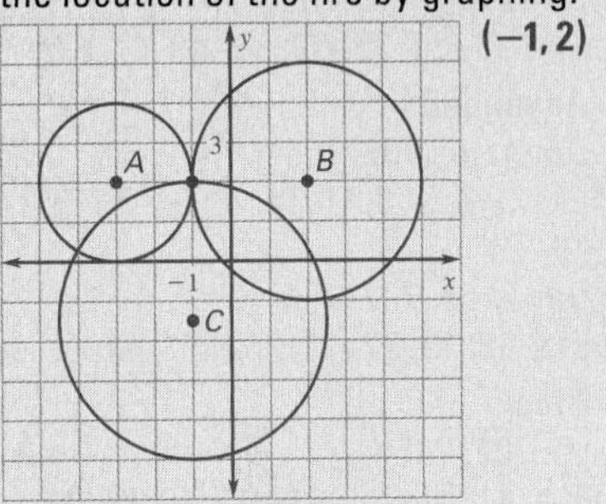

An **Animated Geometry** activity is available on-line for **Example 5**. This activity is also available on the **Power Presentations CD-ROM**.

Closing the Lesson

Have students summarize the major points of the lesson and answer the Essential Question: What do you need to know to write the standard equation of a circle?

- **The standard equation of a circle is $(x - h)^2 + (y - k)^2 = r^2$.**
- **In the standard equation, (h, k) is the center and r is the radius.**

To write the standard equation of a circle, you need to know the center and the radius. If the center is (h, k) and the radius is r, then the standard equation is $(x - h)^2 + (y - k)^2 = r^2$.

GUIDED PRACTICE for Examples 4 and 5

5. The equation of a circle is $(x - 4)^2 + (y + 3)^2 = 16$. Graph the circle. **See margin.**
6. The equation of a circle is $(x + 8)^2 + (y + 5)^2 = 121$. Graph the circle. **See margin.**
7. Why are three seismographs needed to locate an earthquake's epicenter?

7. Two circles intersect in two points. You would not know which one is the epicenter, so you need the third circle to know which one it is.

5.

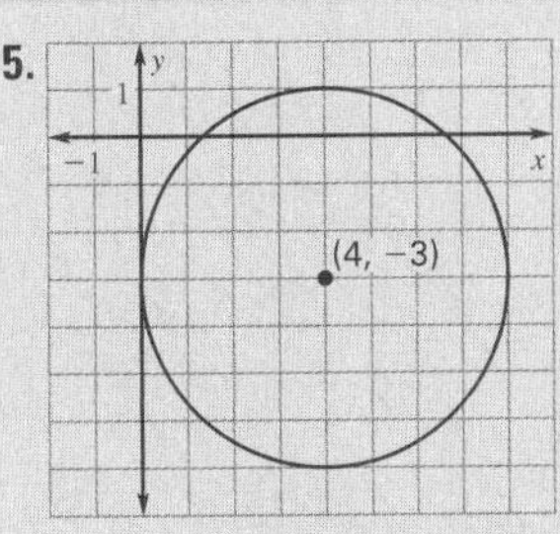

6.

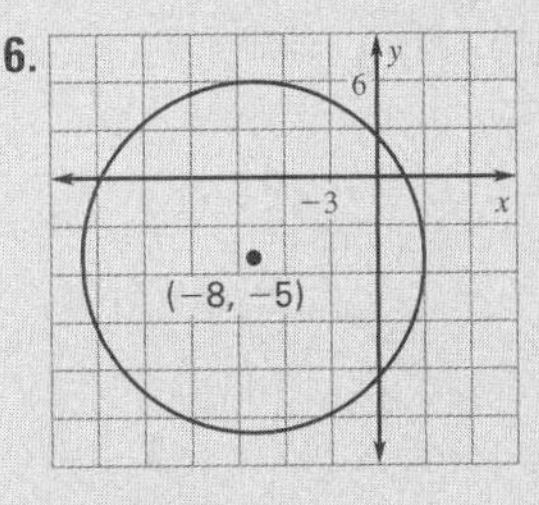

10.7 EXERCISES

HOMEWORK KEY
○ = **WORKED-OUT SOLUTIONS** on p. WS13 for Exs. 7, 17, and 37
★ = **STANDARDIZED TEST PRACTICE** Exs. 2, 16, 26, and 42

4 PRACTICE AND APPLY

Assignment Guide

Answer Transparencies available for all exercises

Basic:
Day 1: pp. 702–705
Exs. 1–16, 49–54
Day 2: pp. 702–705
Exs. 17–28, 36–40, 46–48

Average:
Day 1: pp. 702–705
Exs. 1, 2, 4–7, 10–13, 15, 16, 31–34, 49–54
Day 2: pp. 702–705
Exs. 18–23, 26–30, 36–43, 47

Advanced:
Day 1: pp. 702–705
Exs. 1, 2, 5–8, 11–14, 16, 31–35*, 49–54
Day 2: pp. 702–705
Exs. 18, 19, 22–30, 36–45*, 48

Block:
pp. 702–705
Exs. 1, 2, 4–7, 10–13, 15, 16, 18–23, 26–34, 36–43, 47, 49–54

Differentiated Instruction

See *Geometry Best Practices Toolkit* for suggestions on addressing the needs of a diverse classroom.

Homework Check

For a quick check of student understanding of key concepts, go over the following exercises:
Basic: 4, 10, 18, 20, 36
Average: 6, 12, 18, 22, 36
Advanced: 8, 14, 19, 24, 36

Extra Practice

- Student Edition, p. 915
- Chapter 10 Resource Book: Practice levels A, B, C, pp. 90–95

Practice Worksheet

An easily-readable reduced practice page (with answers) for this lesson can be found on p. 648F.

SKILL PRACTICE

A

1. **VOCABULARY** Copy and complete: The standard equation of a circle can be written for any circle with known __?__ and __?__. **center, radius**

2. ★ **WRITING** *Explain* why the location of the center and one point on a circle is enough information to draw the rest of the circle.
The distance from the center to the known point is the radius of the circle.

EXAMPLES 1 and 2 on pp. 699–700 for Exs. 3–16

WRITING EQUATIONS Write the standard equation of the circle.

3. 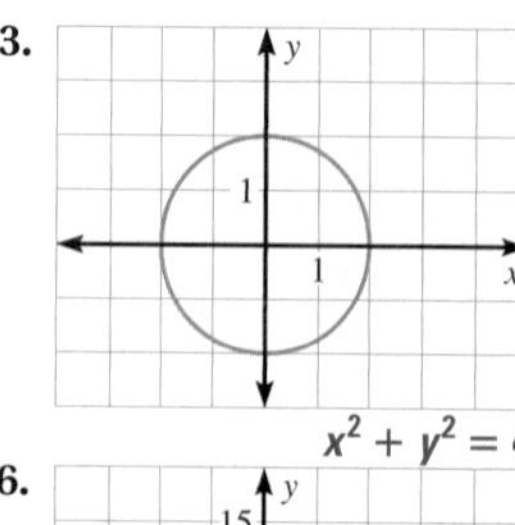
$x^2 + y^2 = 4$

4. 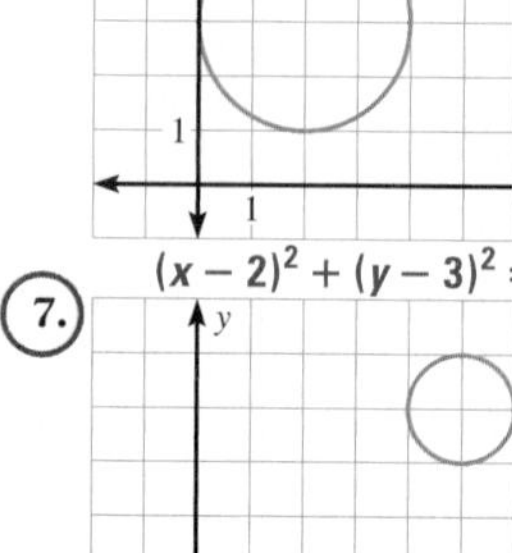
$(x - 2)^2 + (y - 3)^2 = 4$

5. 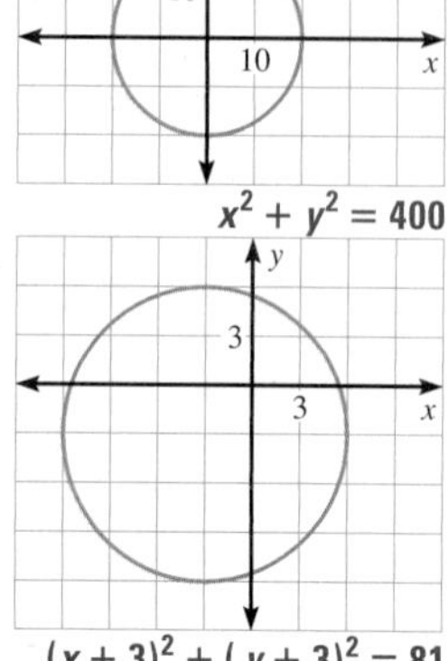
$x^2 + y^2 = 400$

6. $(x - 5)^2 + y^2 = 100$

7. $(x - 50)^2 + (y - 50)^2 = 100$

8. $(x + 3)^2 + (y + 3)^2 = 81$

WRITING EQUATIONS Write the standard equation of the circle with the given center and radius.

9. Center (0, 0), radius 7 $x^2 + y^2 = 49$
10. Center (−4, 1), radius 1 $(x + 4)^2 + (y - 1)^2 = 1$
11. Center (7, −6), radius 8 $(x - 7)^2 + (y + 6)^2 = 64$
12. Center (4, 1), radius 5 $(x - 4)^2 + (y - 1)^2 = 25$
13. Center (3, −5), radius 7 $(x - 3)^2 + (y + 5)^2 = 49$
14. Center (−3, 4), radius 5 $(x + 3)^2 + (y - 4)^2 = 25$

15. **ERROR ANALYSIS** *Describe* and correct the error in writing the equation of a circle.
If (h, k) is the center of a circle with a radius r, the equation of the circle should be $(x - h)^2 + (y - k)^2 = r^2$; $(x + 3)^2 + (y + 5)^2 = 9$.

An equation of a circle with center (−3, −5) and radius 3 is $(x - 3)^2 + (y - 5)^2 = 9$.

16. ★ **MULTIPLE CHOICE** The standard equation of a circle is $(x - 2)^2 + (y + 1)^2 = 16$. What is the diameter of the circle? **C**

Ⓐ 2 Ⓑ 4 Ⓒ 8 Ⓓ 16

EXAMPLE 3 on p. 700 for Exs. 17–19

WRITING EQUATIONS Use the given information to write the standard equation of the circle.

17. The center is (0, 0), and a point on the circle is (0, 6). $x^2 + y^2 = 36$
18. The center is (1, 2), and a point on the circle is (4, 2). $(x - 1)^2 + (y - 2)^2 = 9$
19. The center is (−3, 5), and a point on the circle is (1, 8). $(x + 3)^2 + (y - 5)^2 = 25$

EXAMPLE 4 on p. 701 for Exs. 20–25

GRAPHING CIRCLES **Graph the equation.** 20–25. See margin.

20. $x^2 + y^2 = 49$
21. $(x - 3)^2 + y^2 = 16$
22. $x^2 + (y + 2)^2 = 36$
23. $(x - 4)^2 + (y - 1)^2 = 1$
24. $(x + 5)^2 + (y - 3)^2 = 9$
25. $(x + 2)^2 + (y + 6)^2 = 25$

B 26. ★ **MULTIPLE CHOICE** Which of the points does not lie on the circle described by the equation $(x + 2)^2 + (y - 4)^2 = 25$? D

Ⓐ $(-2, -1)$ Ⓑ $(1, 8)$ Ⓒ $(3, 4)$ Ⓓ $(0, 5)$

ALGEBRA **Determine whether the given equation defines a circle. If the equation defines a circle, rewrite the equation in standard form.**

27. $x^2 + y^2 - 6y + 9 = 4$ circle; $x^2 + (y - 3)^2 = 4$
28. $x^2 - 8x + 16 + y^2 + 2y + 4 = 25$ circle; $(x - 4)^2 + (y + 1)^2 = 22$
29. $x^2 + y^2 + 4y + 3 = 16$ circle; $x^2 + (y + 2)^2 = 17$
30. $x^2 - 2x + 5 + y^2 = 81$ circle; $(x - 1)^2 + y^2 = 77$

IDENTIFYING TYPES OF LINES **Use the given equations of a circle and a line to determine whether the line is a *tangent, secant, secant that contains a diameter,* or none of these.**

31. **Circle:** $(x - 4)^2 + (y - 3)^2 = 9$
Line: $y = -3x + 6$ secant
32. **Circle:** $(x + 2)^2 + (y - 2)^2 = 16$
Line: $y = 2x - 4$ none of these
33. **Circle:** $(x - 5)^2 + (y + 1)^2 = 4$
Line: $y = \frac{1}{5}x - 3$ secant
34. **Circle:** $(x + 3)^2 + (y - 6)^2 = 25$
Line: $y = -\frac{4}{3}x + 2$ secant that contains a diameter

C 35. **CHALLENGE** Four tangent circles are centered on the x-axis. The radius of $\odot A$ is twice the radius of $\odot O$. The radius of $\odot B$ is three times the radius of $\odot O$. The radius of $\odot C$ is four times the radius of $\odot O$. All circles have integer radii and the point (63, 16) is on $\odot C$. What is the equation of $\odot A$? $(x - 15)^2 + y^2 = 100$

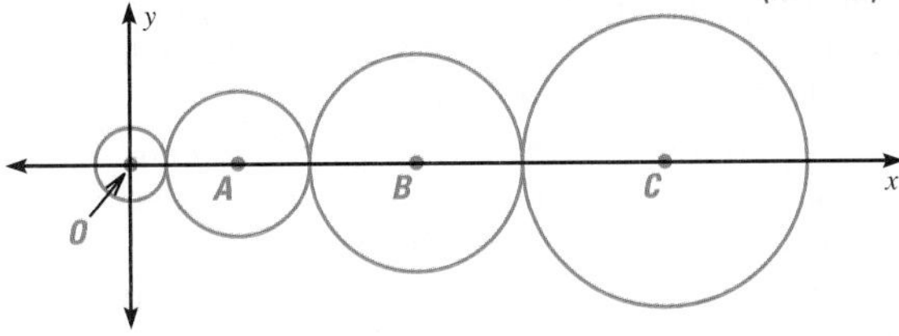

PROBLEM SOLVING

EXAMPLE 5 A on p. 701 for Ex. 36

36. **COMMUTER TRAINS** A city's commuter system has three zones covering the regions described. Zone 1 covers people living within three miles of the city center. Zone 2 covers those between three and seven miles from the center, and Zone 3 covers those over seven miles from the center.

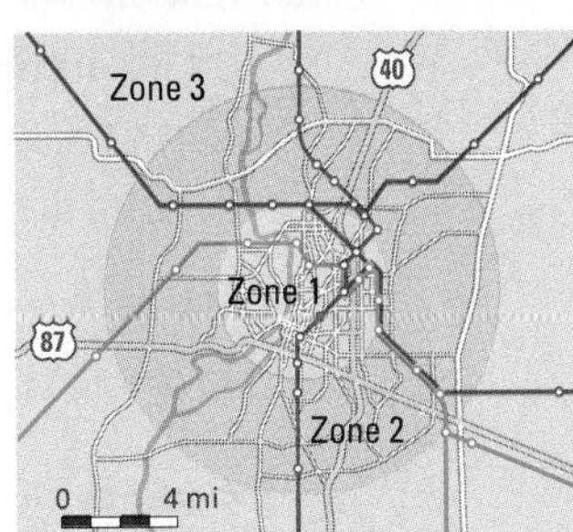

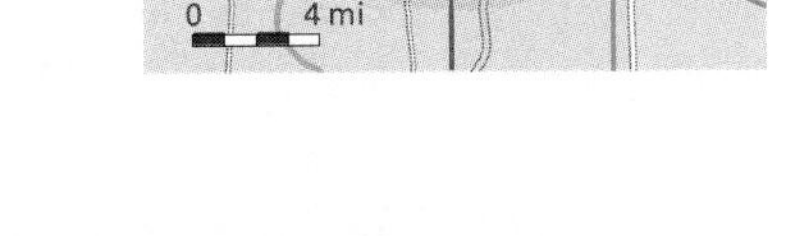

a. Graph this situation with the city center at the origin, where units are measured in miles. See margin.
b. Find which zone covers people living at (3, 4), (6, 5), (1, 2), (0, 3), and (1, 6).

36b. Zone 2, Zone 3, Zone 1, Zone 1, Zone 2

@HomeTutor for problem solving help at classzone.com

Teaching Strategy

Exercises 17–18 Encourage students to check whether the center and a point are on the same vertical or horizontal line. If so, the students do not need to use the distance formula to find the radius.

23.
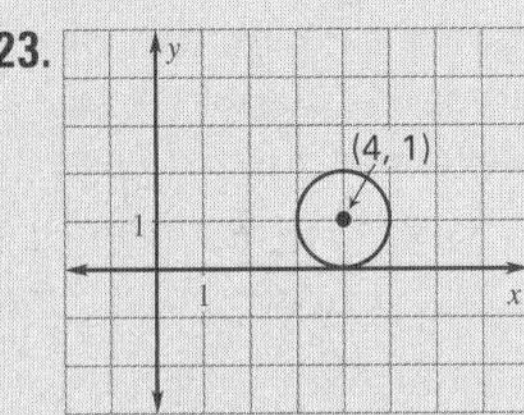

24.
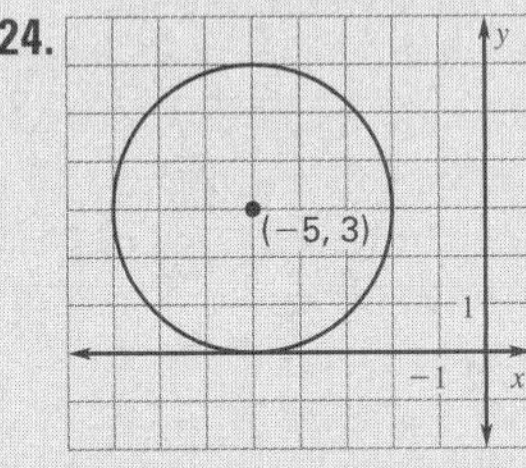

25.
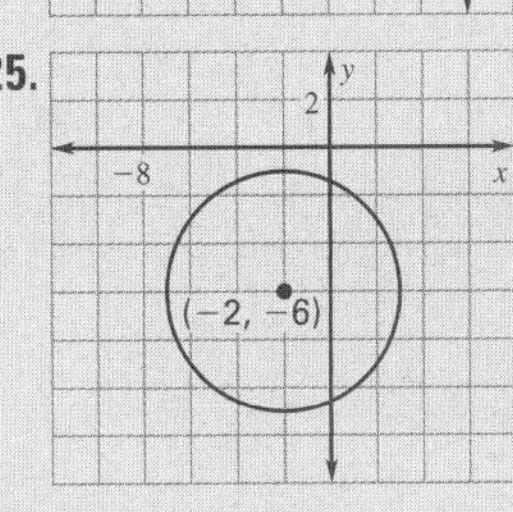

36a.
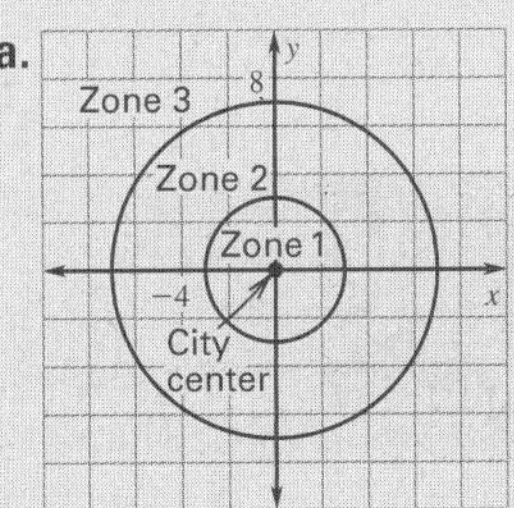

20.
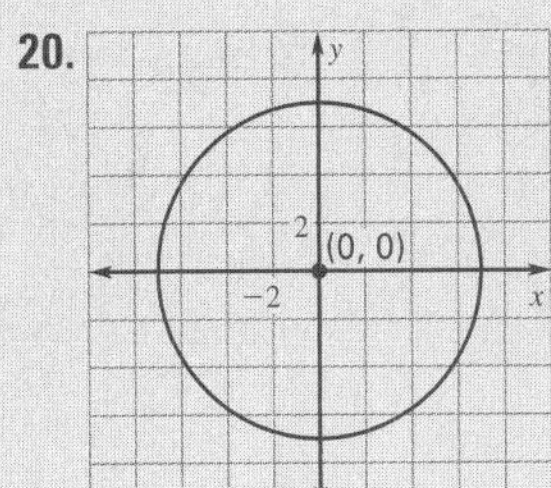

21.
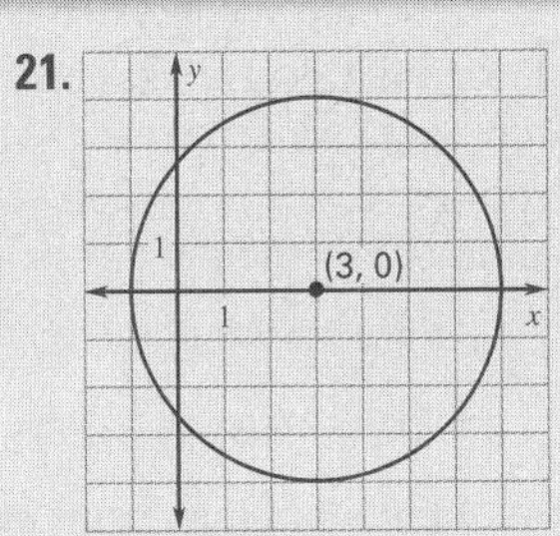

22.
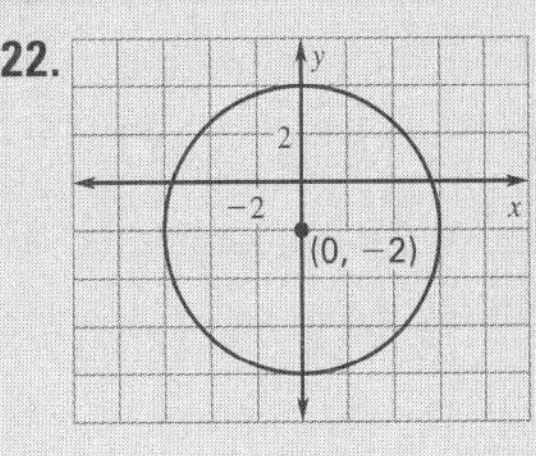

(37.) **COMPACT DISCS** The diameter of a CD is about 4.8 inches. The diameter of the hole in the center is about 0.6 inches. You place a CD on the coordinate plane with center at (0, 0). Write the equations for the outside edge of the disc and the edge of the hole in the center. **$x^2 + y^2 = 5.76$, $x^2 + y^2 = 0.09$**

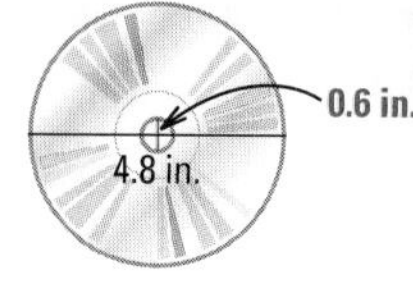

@HomeTutor for problem solving help at classzone.com

B **REULEAUX POLYGONS** **In Exercises 38–41, use the following information.**

The figure at the right is called a *Reuleaux polygon.* It is not a true polygon because its sides are not straight. $\triangle ABC$ is equilateral.

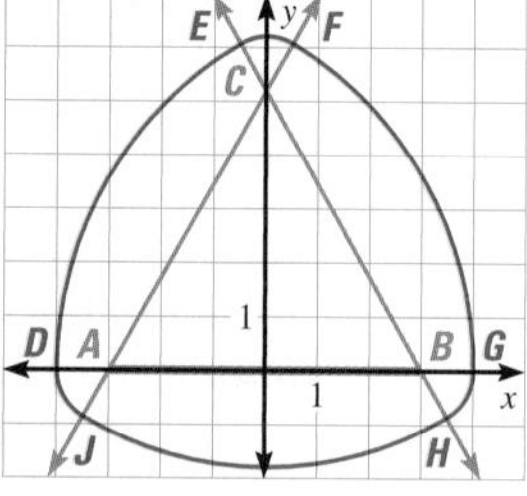

38. $\widehat{JD}$ lies on a circle with center A and radius AD. Write an equation of this circle. **$(x + 3)^2 + y^2 = 1$**

39. $\widehat{DE}$ lies on a circle with center B and radius BD. Write an equation of this circle. **$(x - 3)^2 + y^2 = 49$**

40. **CONSTRUCTION** The remaining arcs of the polygon are constructed in the same way as $\widehat{JD}$ and $\widehat{DE}$ in Exercises 38 and 39. Construct a Reuleaux polygon on a piece of cardboard. **Check students' work.**

41. Cut out the Reuleaux polygon from Exercise 40. Roll it on its edge like a wheel and measure its height when it is in different orientations. *Explain* why a Reuleaux polygon is said to have constant width.
The height (or width) always remains the same as the figure is rolled on its edge.

42. ★ **EXTENDED RESPONSE** Telecommunication towers can be used to transmit cellular phone calls. Towers have a range of about 3 km. A graph with units measured in kilometers shows towers at points (0, 0), (0, 5), and (6, 3).

a. Draw the graph and locate the towers. Are there any areas that may receive calls from more than one tower? **Yes; see margin for art.**

b. Suppose your home is located at (2, 6) and your school is at (2.5, 3). Can you use your cell phone at either or both of these locations?

c. City A is located at (−2, 2.5) and City B is at (5, 4). Each city has a radius of 1.5 km. Which city seems to have better cell phone coverage? *Explain.*

42b. You can use it at home but you cannot use it at school.

42c. City *B*; it is located well within the range of the tower located at (6, 3). City *A* is only partially in the range of the other two towers.

43. **REASONING** The lines $y = \frac{3}{4}x + 2$ and $y = -\frac{3}{4}x + 16$ are tangent to $\odot C$ at the points (4, 5) and (4, 13), respectively.

a. Find the coordinates of C and the radius of $\odot C$. *Explain* your steps. **See margin.**

b. Write the standard equation of $\odot C$ and draw its graph. **See margin for art; $(x - 1)^2 + (y - 9)^2 = 25$.**

C 44. **PROOF** Write a proof. **See margin.**

GIVEN ▶ A circle passing through the points (−1, 0) and (1, 0)

PROVE ▶ The equation of the circle is $x^2 - 2yk + y^2 = 1$ with center at (0, k).

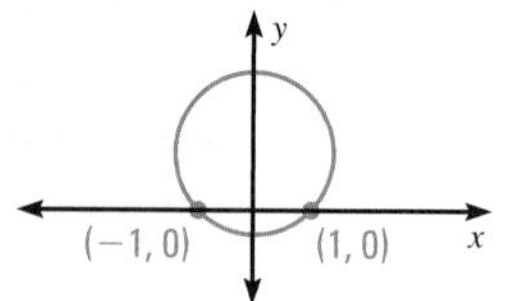

○ = **WORKED-OUT SOLUTIONS on p. WS1** ★ = **STANDARDIZED TEST PRACTICE**

42a.

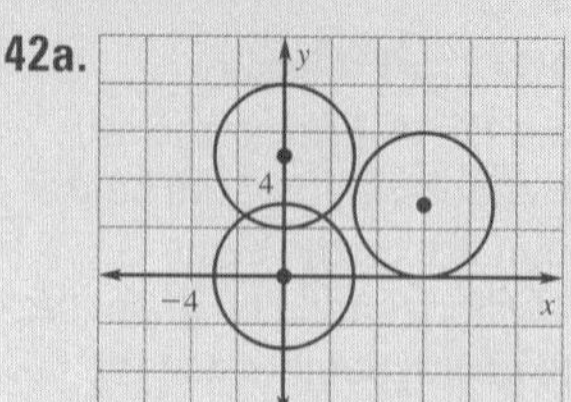

43a. (1, 9), 5; since the lines passing through the center of the circle must be perpendicular at the two points of tangency, their slopes must be $-\frac{4}{3}$ and $\frac{4}{3}$, respectively. Using the slopes and the points of tangency in the point-slope form of an equation of a line gives the equations for the lines that contain the two diameters as $4x + 3y = 31$ and $-4x + 3y = 23$, respectively. Finding the point of intersection of these two lines gives the center of the circle to be (1, 9). Using the distance formula and either point of tangency gives the radius of the circle to be 5.

43b.

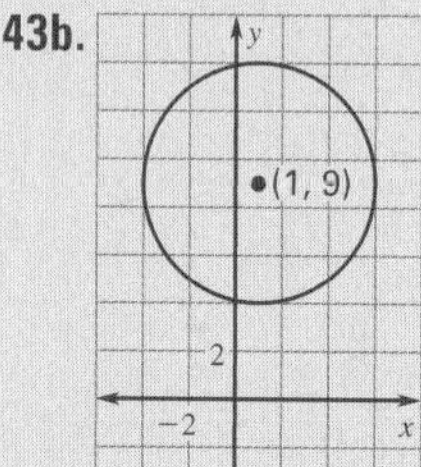

44. Given: A circle passing through the points (−1, 0) and (1, 0). Construct the perpendicular bisector of the chord with the endpoints (−1, 0) and (1, 0). Using Theorem 10.4, this new chord is a diameter of the circle. Since the new chord is a segment of the *y*-axis, the center of the circle is located at some point (0, *k*) which makes the equation of the circle $x^2 + (y - k)^2 = r^2$ or $x^2 + y^2 - 2yk = r^2 - k^2$. Now consider the right triangle whose vertices are (0, 0), (0, *k*), and (1, 0) with the distance from (0, *k*) to (1, 0) being *r*, the radius of the circle. Using the Pythagorean Theorem, you get $k^2 + 1^2 = r^2$ or $r^2 - k^2 = 1$. Substituting you get $x^2 - 2yk + y^2 = 1$.

45a. If $r = 2$, there are two possible points of intersection. If the center of the circle is (8, 8), then the point of intersection is (10, 6). If the center of the circle is (10, 6), then the point of intersection is (8, 8). If $r = 10$, there are also two possible points of intersection. If the center of the circle is (16, 0), then the point of intersection is $\left(8\frac{6}{7}, 7\frac{1}{7}\right)$. If the center of the circle is (2, 14), then the point of intersection is $\left(9\frac{1}{7}, 6\frac{6}{7}\right)$. *Sample answer:* They are collinear, and they lie on the perpendicular bisector of the segment joining the points (8, 6) and (10, 8).

45. **CHALLENGE** The intersecting lines m and n are tangent to $\odot C$ at the points (8, 6) and (10, 8), respectively.

a. What is the intersection point of m and n if the radius r of $\odot C$ is 2? What is their intersection point if r is 10? What do you notice about the two intersection points and the center C? **See margin.**

b. Write the equation that describes the locus of intersection points of m and n for all possible values of r. $x + y - 16 = 0$

MIXED REVIEW

PREVIEW
Prepare for Lesson 11.1 in Exs. 46–48.

Find the perimeter of the figure.

46. *(p. 49)*

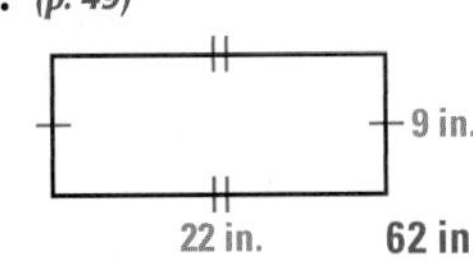

62 in.

47. *(p. 49)*

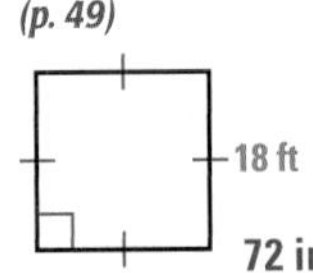

72 in.

48. *(p. 433)*

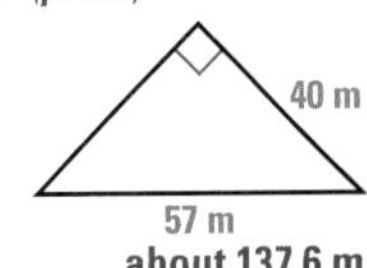

about 137.6 m

Find the circumference of the circle with given radius r or diameter d. Use $\pi = 3.14$. *(p. 49)*

49. $r = 7$ cm **43.96 cm**

50. $d = 160$ in. **502.4 in.**

51. $d = 48$ yd **150.72 yd**

Find the radius r of $\odot C$. *(p. 651)*

52.

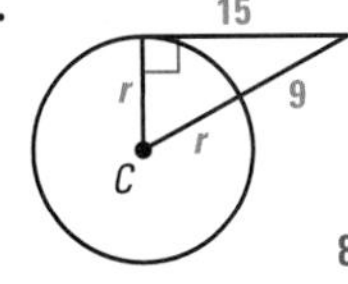

8

53.

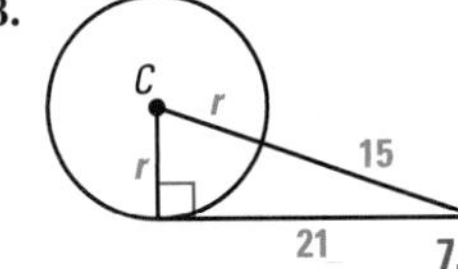

7.2

54.

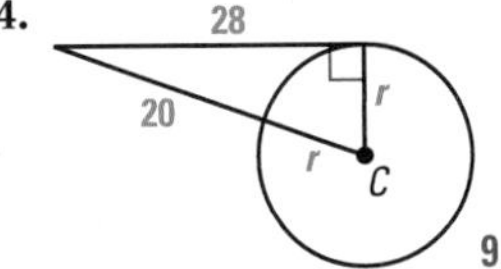

9.6

QUIZ *for Lessons 10.6–10.7*

Find the value of x. *(p. 689)*

1.

12

2.

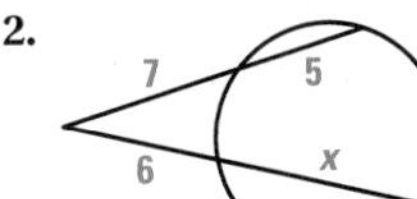

8

3.

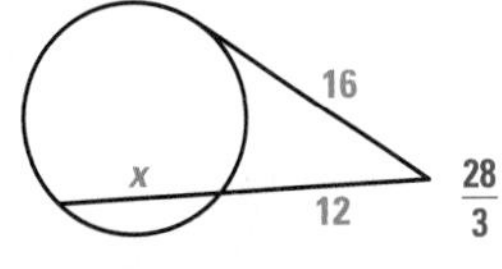

$\frac{28}{3}$

In Exercises 4 and 5, use the given information to write the standard equation of the circle. *(p. 699)*

4. The center is (1, 4), and the radius is 6. $(x - 1)^2 + (y - 4)^2 = 36$

5. The center is (5, −7), and a point on the circle is (5, −3). $(x - 5)^2 + (y + 7)^2 = 16$

6. **TIRES** The diameter of a certain tire is 24.2 inches. The diameter of the rim in the center is 14 inches. Draw the tire in a coordinate plane with center at (−4, 3). Write the equations for the outer edge of the tire and for the rim where units are measured in inches. *(p. 699)*
See margin for art; $(x + 4)^2 + (y - 3)^2 = 146.41$, $(x + 4)^2 + (y - 3)^2 = 49$

5 ASSESS AND RETEACH

Daily Homework Quiz

Transparency Available

1. Write the standard equation of a circle with center (−3, 5) and radius 2. $(x + 3)^2 + (y - 5)^2 = 4$
2. Graph the circle $(x + 1)^2 + (y - 3)^2 = 9$.

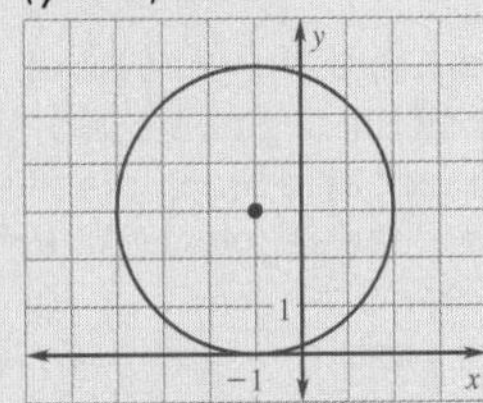

3. The line $x = 2$ is tangent to the circle in Exercise 2. Find the coordinates of the point of tangency. **(2, 3)**
4. A circle has equation $x^2 + y^2 = 4$. Determine whether line $y = -x + 2$ is a secant, tangent, or neither. **secant**

Available at **classzone.com**

Diagnosis/Remediation

- Practice A, B, C in Chapter 10 Resource Book, pp. 90–95
- Study Guide in Chapter 10 Resource Book, pp. 96–97
- Practice Workbook, pp. 202–204
- @HomeTutor

Challenge

Additional challenge is available in the Chapter 10 Resource Book, p. 100.

Quiz

An easily-readable reduced copy of the quiz (with answers) on Lessons 10.6–10.7 from the Assessment Book can be found on p. 648G.

Quiz 6. See Additional Answers beginning on p. AA1.

STATE TEST PRACTICE classzone.com

2a.

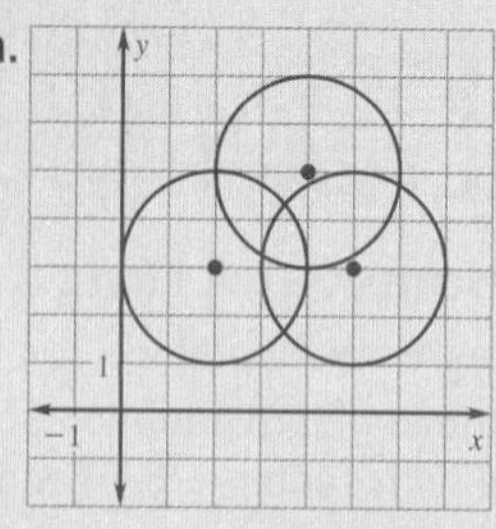

2b. You can use the phone at your house, but not at your friend's house.

3. It is not a circle; the product of the lengths of the segments of one chord is not equal to the product of the lengths of the segments of the second chord.

5a.

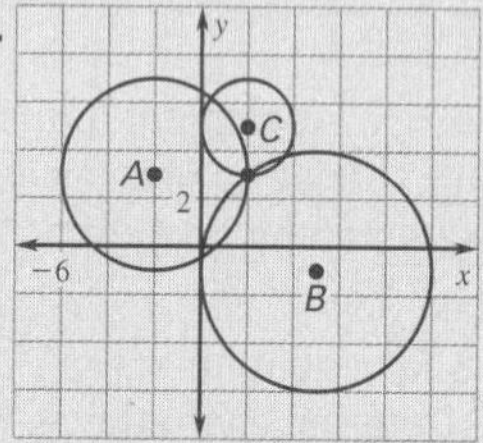

5c. No; the area that could feel the earthquake can be represented by the inequality $(x-2)^2 + (y-3)^2 \le 144$. The point (14, 16) is not a solution to the inequality.

Lessons 10.6–10.7

1. **SHORT RESPONSE** A local radio station can broadcast its signal 20 miles. The station is located at the point (20, 30) where units are measured in miles.

   a. Write an inequality that represents the area covered by the radio station. $(x-20)^2 + (y-30)^2 \le 400$

   b. Determine whether you can receive the radio station's signal when you are located at each of the following points: $E(25, 25)$, $F(10, 10)$, $G(20, 16)$, and $H(35, 30)$. yes, no, yes, yes

2. **EXTENDED RESPONSE** Cell phone towers are used to transmit calls. An area has cell phone towers at points (2, 3), (4, 5), and (5, 3) where units are measured in miles. Each tower has a transmission radius of 2 miles.

   a. Draw the area on a graph and locate the three cell phone towers. Are there any areas that can transmit calls using more than one tower? Yes; see margin for art.

   b. Suppose you live at (3, 5) and your friend lives at (1, 7). Can you use your cell phone at either or both of your homes? See margin.

   c. City A is located at (−1, 1) and City B is located at (4, 7). Each city has a radius of 5 miles. Which city has better coverage from the cell phone towers? City B

3. **SHORT RESPONSE** You are standing at point P inside a go-kart track. To determine if the track is a circle, you measure the distance to four points on the track, as shown in the diagram. What can you conclude about the shape of the track? *Explain.* See margin.

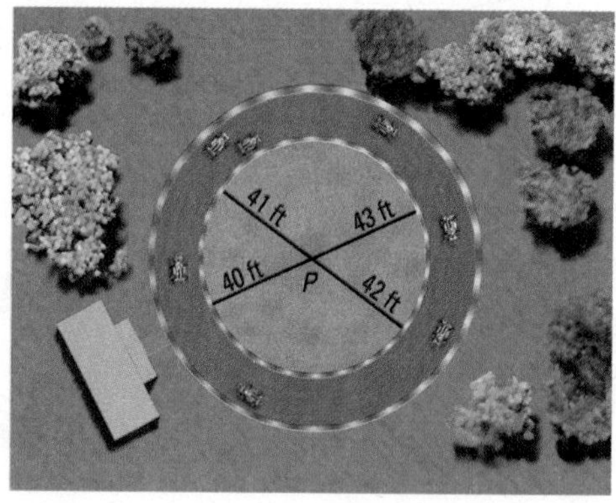

4. **SHORT RESPONSE** You are at point A, about 6 feet from a circular aquarium tank. The distance from you to a point of tangency on the tank is 17 feet.

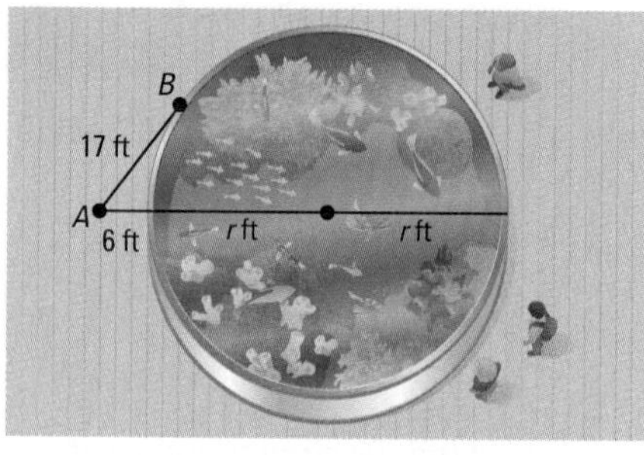

   a. What is the radius of the tank? about 21.1 ft

   b. Suppose you are standing 4 feet from another aquarium tank that has a diameter of 12 feet. How far, in feet, are you from a point of tangency? 8 ft

5. **EXTENDED RESPONSE** You are given seismograph readings from three locations.
   - At $A(-2, 3)$, the epicenter is 4 miles away.
   - At $B(5, -1)$, the epicenter is 5 miles away.
   - At $C(2, 5)$, the epicenter is 2 miles away.

   a. Graph circles centered at A, B, and C with radii of 4, 5, and 2 miles, respectively. See margin.

   b. Locate the epicenter. (2, 3)

   c. The earthquake could be felt up to 12 miles away. If you live at (14, 16), could you feel the earthquake? *Explain.* See margin.

6. **MULTI-STEP PROBLEM** Use the diagram.

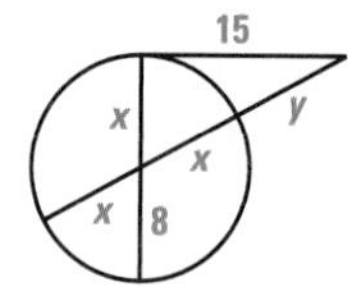

   a. Use Theorem 10.16 and the quadratic formula to write an equation for y in terms of x. $y = \frac{-2x + \sqrt{4x^2 + 900}}{2}$

   b. Find the value of x. 8

   c. Find the value of y. 9

10 CHAPTER SUMMARY

BIG IDEAS *For Your Notebook*

Big Idea 1

Using Properties of Segments that Intersect Circles

You learned several relationships between tangents, secants, and chords.

Some of these relationships can help you determine that two chords or tangents are congruent. For example, tangent segments from the same exterior point are congruent.

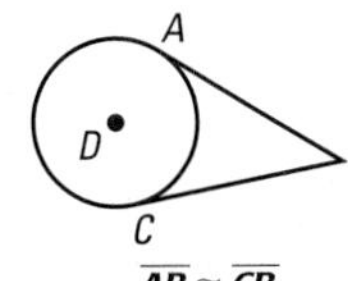

$\overline{AB} \cong \overline{CB}$

Other relationships allow you to find the length of a secant or chord if you know the length of related segments. For example, with the Segments of a Chord Theorem you can find the length of an unknown chord segment.

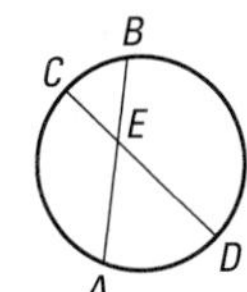

$EA \cdot EB = EC \cdot ED$

Big Idea 2

Applying Angle Relationships in Circles

You learned to find the measures of angles formed inside, outside, and on circles.

Angles formed on circles

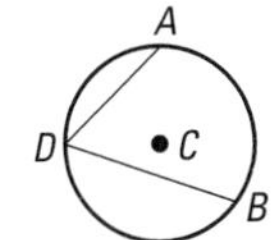

$m\angle ADB = \frac{1}{2}m\overset{\frown}{AB}$

Angles formed inside circles

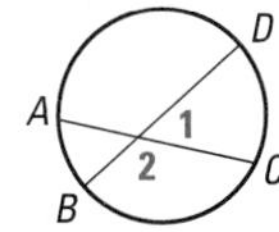

$m\angle 1 = \frac{1}{2}(m\overset{\frown}{AB} + m\overset{\frown}{CD})$,

$m\angle 2 = \frac{1}{2}(m\overset{\frown}{AD} + m\overset{\frown}{BC})$

Angles formed outside circles

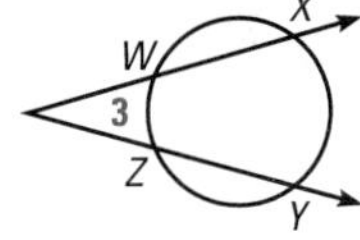

$m\angle 3 = \frac{1}{2}(m\overset{\frown}{XY} - m\overset{\frown}{WZ})$

Big Idea 3

Using Circles in the Coordinate Plane

The standard equation of $\odot C$ is:

$(x - h)^2 + (y - k)^2 = r^2$

$(x - 2)^2 + (y - 1)^2 = 2^2$

$(x - 2)^2 + (y - 1)^2 = 4$

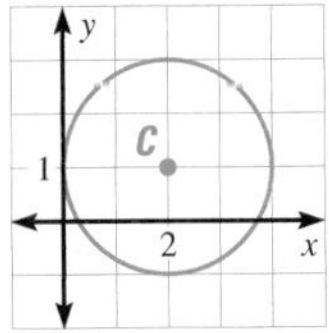

Additional Resources

The following resources are available to help review the materials in this chapter.

Chapter 10 Resource Book

- Chapter Review Games and Activities, p. 101
- Cumulative Practice, Chs. 1–10, pp. 104–105

Student Resources in Spanish

eWorkbook

@HomeTutor

Vocabulary Practice

Vocabulary practice is available at **classzone.com**

@HomeTutor
classzone.com
- Multi-Language Glossary
- Vocabulary practice

Extra Example 10.1

In the diagram, R and Q are points of tangency on $\odot S$. Find the value of x. **3**

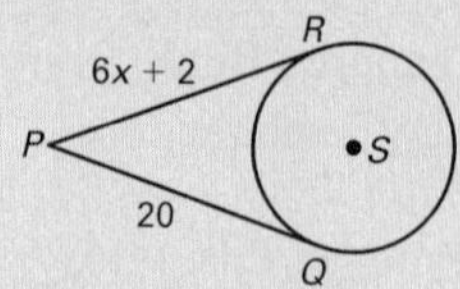

2.

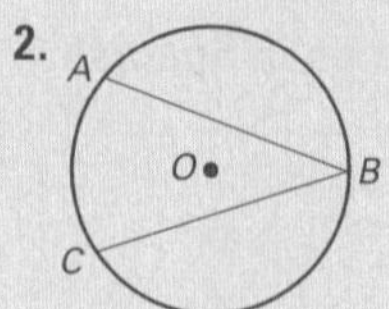

REVIEW KEY VOCABULARY

For a list of postulates and theorems, see pp. 926–931.

- circle, *p. 651* center, radius, diameter
- chord, *p. 651*
- secant, *p. 651*
- tangent, *p. 651*
- central angle, *p. 659*
- minor arc, *p. 659*
- major arc, *p. 659*
- semicircle, *p. 659*
- measure of a minor arc, *p. 659*
- measure of a major arc, *p. 659*
- congruent circles, *p. 660*
- congruent arcs, *p. 660*
- inscribed angle, *p. 672*
- intercepted arc, *p. 672*
- inscribed polygon, *p. 674*
- circumscribed circle, *p. 674*
- segments of a chord, *p. 689*
- secant segment, *p. 690*
- external segment, *p. 690*
- standard equation of a circle, *p. 69*

VOCABULARY EXERCISES

2. See margin for art; an inscribed angle is an angle whose vertex is on the circle and whose sides contain chords of the circle. The arc that lies in the interior of an inscribed angle and has endpoints on the angle is called the intercepted arc of the angle.

1. Copy and complete: If a chord passes through the center of a circle, then it is called a(n) _?_. **diameter**
2. Draw and *describe* an inscribed angle and an intercepted arc.
3. **WRITING** *Describe* how the measure of a central angle of a circle relates to the measure of the minor arc and the measure of the major arc created by the angle. **The measure of the central angle and the corresponding minor arc are the same. The measure of the major arc is 360° minus the measure of the minor arc.**

In Exercises 4–6, match the term with the appropriate segment.

4. Tangent segment **B**   **A.** $\overline{LM}$
5. Secant segment **C**   **B.** $\overline{KL}$
6. External segment **A**   **C.** $\overline{LN}$

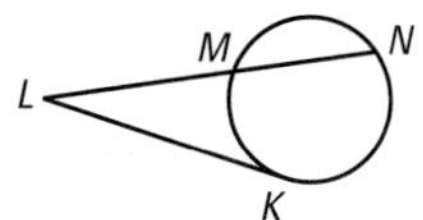

REVIEW EXAMPLES AND EXERCISES

Use the review examples and exercises below to check your understanding of the concepts you have learned in each lesson of Chapter 10.

10.1 Use Properties of Tangents

pp. 651–658

EXAMPLE

In the diagram, B and D are points of tangency on $\odot C$. Find the value of x.

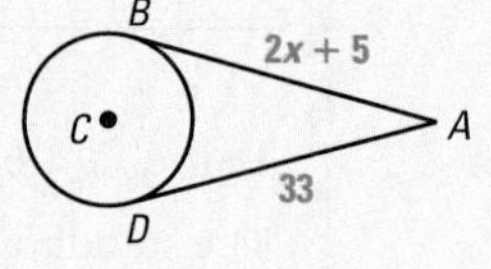

Use Theorem 10.2 to find x.

$AB = AD$ **Tangent segments from the same point are ≅.**

$2x + 5 = 33$ **Substitute.**

$x = 14$ **Solve for x.**

@HomeTutor
classzone.com
Chapter Review Practice

EXERCISES

EXAMPLES 5 and 6
on p. 654
for Exs. 7–9

Find the value of the variable. *Y* and *Z* are points of tangency on ⊙*W*.

7. 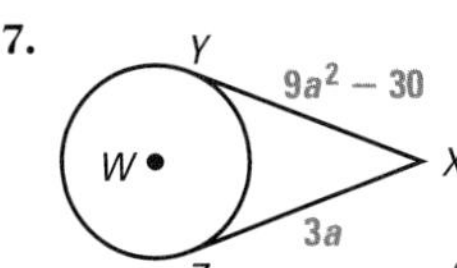

2

8. 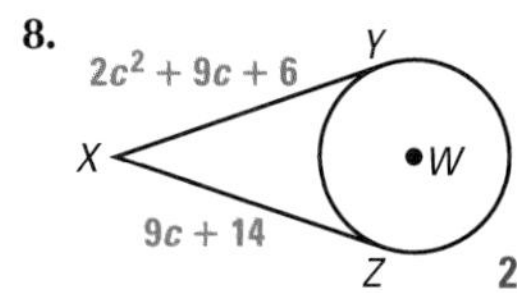

2

9. 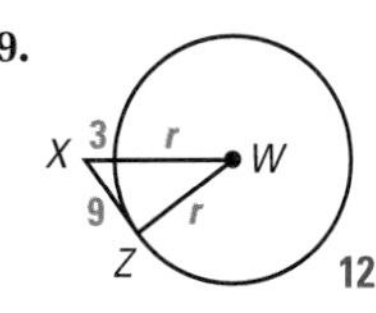

12

10.2 Find Arc Measures

pp. 659–663

EXAMPLE

Find the measure of the arc of ⊙*P*. In the diagram, $\overline{LN}$ is a diameter.

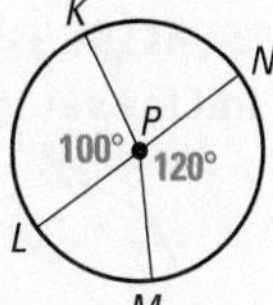

a. $\overparen{MN}$ b. $\overparen{NLM}$ c. $\overparen{NML}$

a. $\overparen{MN}$ is a minor arc, so $m\overparen{MN} = m\angle MPN = 120°$.

b. $\overparen{NLM}$ is a major arc, so $m\overparen{NLM} = 360° - 120° = 240°$.

c. $\overparen{NML}$ is a semicircle, so $m\overparen{NML} = 180°$.

EXERCISES

EXAMPLES 1 and 2
on pp. 659–660
for Exs. 10–13

Use the diagram above to find the measure of the indicated arc.

10. $\overparen{KL}$ 100° 11. $\overparen{LM}$ 60° 12. $\overparen{KM}$ 160° 13. $\overparen{KN}$ 80°

10.3 Apply Properties of Chords

pp. 664–670

EXAMPLE

In the diagram, ⊙*A* ≅ ⊙*B*, $\overline{CD} \cong \overline{FE}$, and $m\overparen{FE} = 75°$. Find $m\overparen{CD}$.

By Theorem 10.3, $\overline{CD}$ and $\overline{FE}$ are congruent chords in congruent circles, so the corresponding minor arcs $\overparen{FE}$ and $\overparen{CD}$ are congruent. So, $m\overparen{CD} = m\overparen{FE} = 75°$.

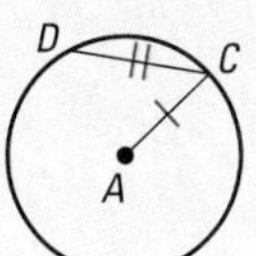

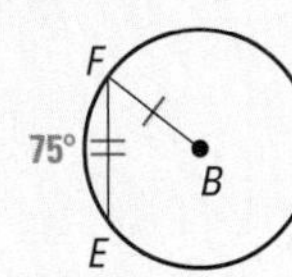

EXERCISES

EXAMPLES 1, 3, and 4
on pp. 664, 666
for Exs. 14–16

Find the measure of $\overparen{AB}$.

14. 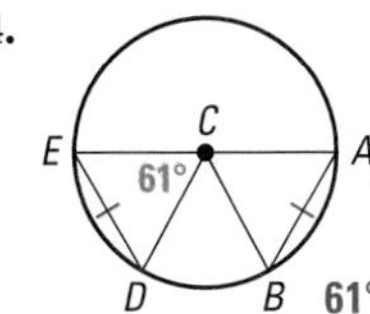

61°

15. 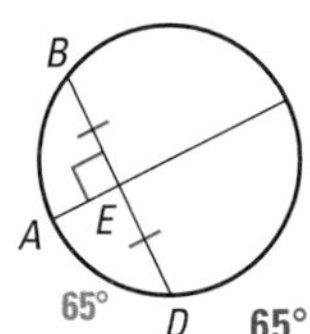

65°

16. 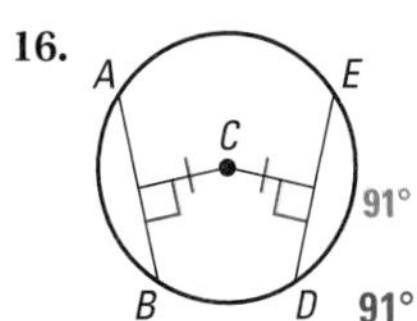

91°

Extra Example 10.2

Find the measure of the arc in ⊙ *P*. In the diagram, $\overline{US}$ is a diameter.

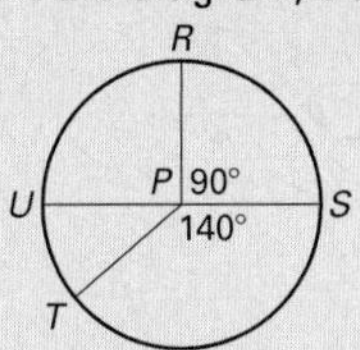

a. $\overparen{RS}$ 90°

b. $\overparen{RST}$ 230°

c. $\overparen{STU}$ 180°

Extra Example 10.3

In the diagram of ⊙ *J*, $CD = 3x + 1$ and $EF = 5x$. Find *CD*. 2.5

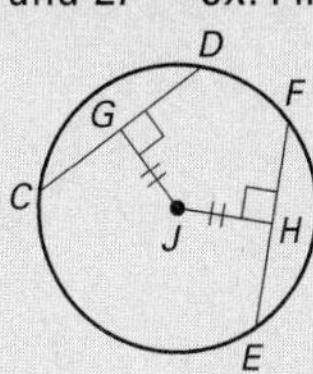

Extra Example 10.4

Find the value of each variable.

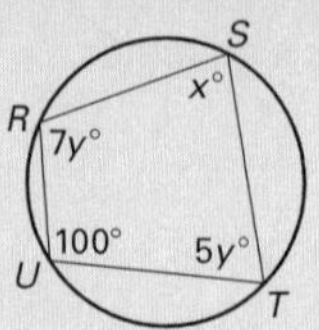

$x = 80$; $y = 15$

Extra Example 10.5

Find the value of x. **32**

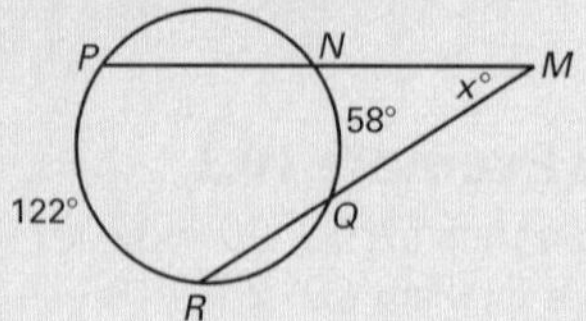

10 CHAPTER REVIEW

10.4 Use Inscribed Angles and Polygons

pp. 672–679

EXAMPLE

Find the value of each variable.

LMNP is inscribed in a circle, so by Theorem 10.10, opposite angles are supplementary.

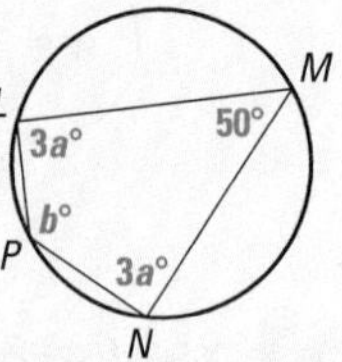

$m\angle L + m\angle N = 180°$ $\qquad$ $m\angle P + m\angle M = 180°$

$3a° + 3a° = 180°$ $\qquad$ $b° + 50° = 180°$

$6a = 180$ $\qquad$ $b = 130$

$a = 30$

EXERCISES

EXAMPLES 1, 2, and 5 on pp. 672–675 for Exs. 17–19

Find the value(s) of the variable(s).

17.

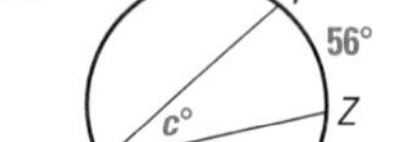

$c = 28$

18.

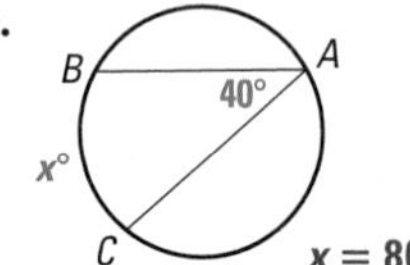

$x = 80$

19.

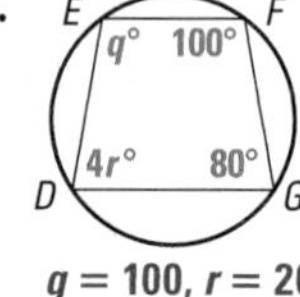

$q = 100$, $r = 20$

10.5 Apply Other Angle Relationships in Circles

pp. 680–686

EXAMPLE

Find the value of *y*.

The tangent $\overrightarrow{RQ}$ and secant $\overrightarrow{RT}$ intersect outside the circle, so you can use Theorem 10.13 to find the value of *y*.

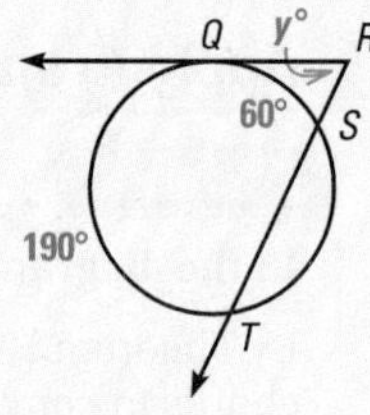

$y° = \frac{1}{2}(m\widehat{QT} - m\widehat{SQ})$ **Use Theorem 10.13.**

$y° = \frac{1}{2}(190° - 60°)$ **Substitute.**

$y = 65$ **Simplify.**

EXERCISES

EXAMPLES 2 and 3 on pp. 681–682 for Exs. 20–22

Find the value of *x*.

20.

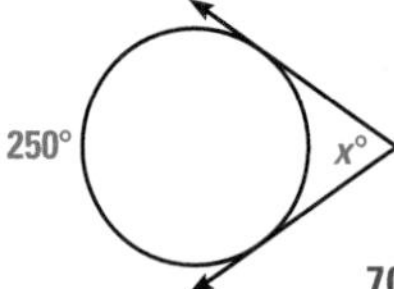

70

21.

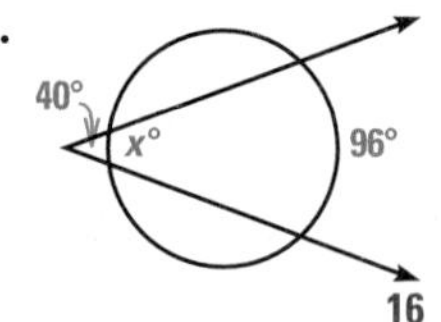

16

22.

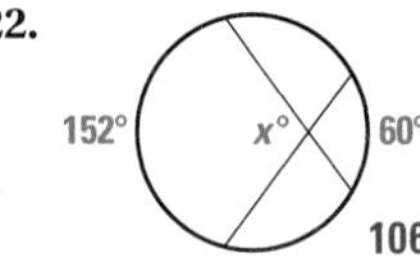

106

@HomeTutor
classzone.com
Chapter Review Practice

10.6 Find Segment Lengths in Circles
pp. 689–695

EXAMPLE

Find the value of x.

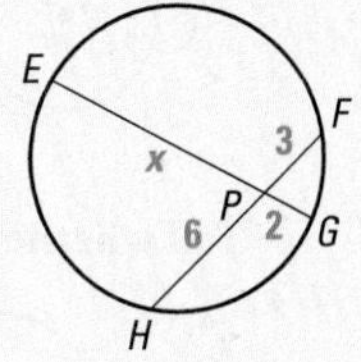

The chords $\overline{EG}$ and $\overline{FH}$ intersect inside the circle, so you can use Theorem 10.14 to find the value of x.

$EP \cdot PG = FP \cdot PH$ **Use Theorem 10.14.**

$x \cdot 2 = 3 \cdot 6$ **Substitute.**

$x = 9$ **Solve for x.**

EXERCISE

EXAMPLE 4 on p. 692 for Ex. 23

23. **SKATING RINK** A local park has a circular ice skating rink. You are standing at point A, about 12 feet from the edge of the rink. The distance from you to a point of tangency on the rink is about 20 feet. Estimate the radius of the rink. $10\frac{2}{3}$ ft

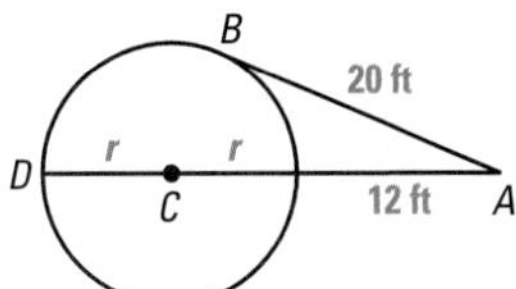

10.7 Write and Graph Equations of Circles
pp. 699–705

EXAMPLE

Write an equation of the circle shown.

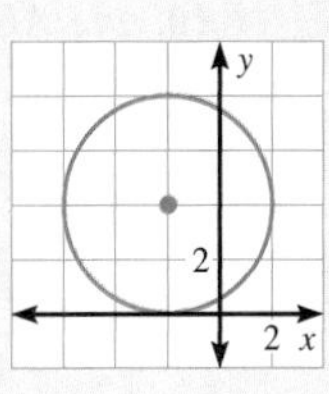

The radius is 4 and the center is at $(-2, 4)$.

$(x - h)^2 + (y - k)^2 = r^2$ **Standard equation of a circle**

$(x - (-2))^2 + (y - 4)^2 = 4^2$ **Substitute.**

$(x + 2)^2 + (y - 4)^2 = 16$ **Simplify.**

EXERCISES

EXAMPLES 1, 2, and 3 on pp. 699–700 for Exs. 24–32

Write an equation of the circle shown.

24. 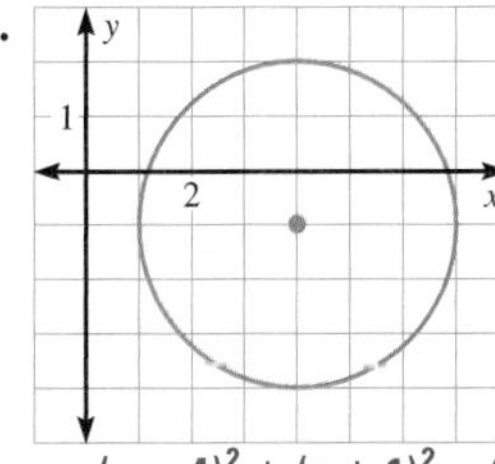

$(x - 4)^2 + (y + 1)^2 = 9$

25. 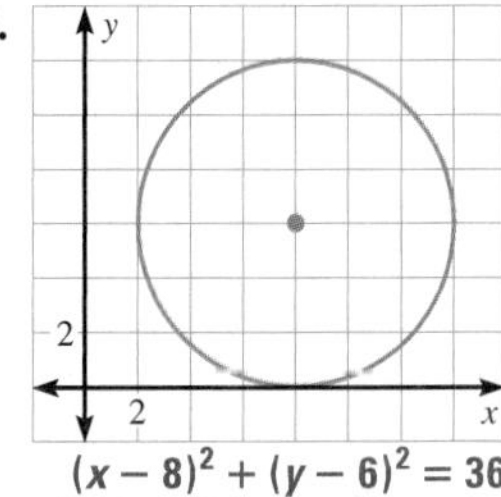

$(x - 8)^2 + (y - 6)^2 = 36$

26. 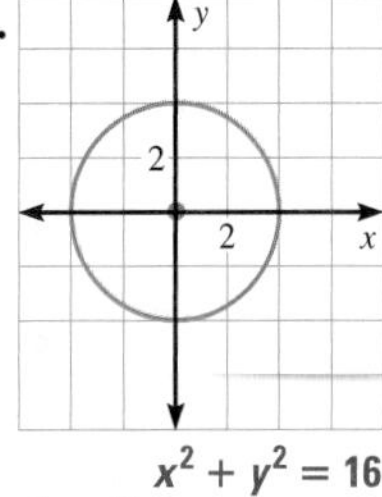

$x^2 + y^2 = 16$

Write the standard equation of the circle with the given center and radius.

27. Center $(0, 0)$, radius 9 $x^2 + y^2 = 81$
28. Center $(-5, 2)$, radius 1.3 $(x + 5)^2 + (y - 2)^2 = 1.69$
29. Center $(6, 21)$, radius 4 $(x - 6)^2 + (y - 21)^2 = 16$
30. Center $(-3, 2)$, radius 16 $(x + 3)^2 + (y - 2)^2 = 256$
31. Center $(10, 7)$, radius 3.5 $(x - 10)^2 + (y - 7)^2 = 12.25$
32. Center $(0, 0)$, radius 5.2 $x^2 + y^2 = 27.04$

Extra Example 10.6

Find the value of x. 6

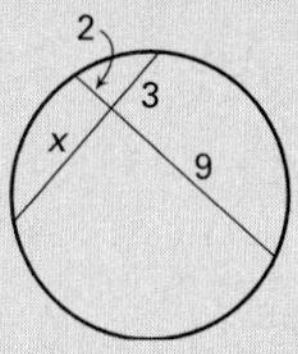

Extra Example 10.7

Write an equation of the circle shown.

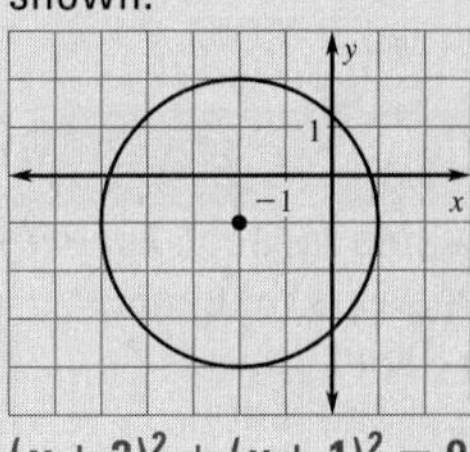

$(x + 2)^2 + (y + 1)^2 = 9$

Additional Resources

Assessment Book

- Chapter Test, Levels A, B, C, pp. 143–148
- Standardized Chapter Test, pp. 149–150
- SAT/ACT Chapter Test, pp. 151–152
- Alternative Assessment, pp. 153–154

Test Generator CD-ROM

Chapter Test

Easily-readable reduced copies (with answers) of Chapter Test B, the Standardized Chapter Test, and the Alternative Assessment from the Assessment Book can be found on pp. 648G–648H.

4. Congruent; the measure of the central angle is the same as the measure of the intercepted arc.

5. Congruent; the circles are congruent and $m\overset{\frown}{JL} = 136°$.

6. Not congruent; the circles are not congruent.

7. Diameter; $\overline{AB}$ bisects and is perpendicular to chord $\overline{CD}$.

8. Diameter; $\overline{AB}$ bisects and is perpendicular to chord $\overline{CD}$.

9. Not a diameter; if $\overline{AB}$ were a diameter it would bisect chord $\overline{XY}$, and $YZ = 15$ by the Pythagorean Theorem.

10 CHAPTER TEST

In $\odot C$, B and D are points of tangency. Find the value of the variable.

1.

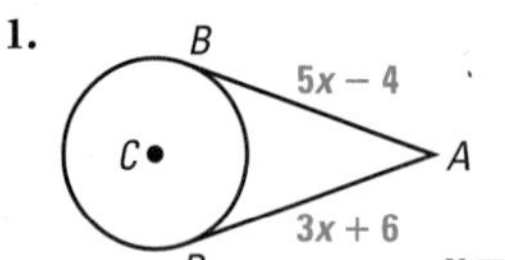

$x = 5$

2.

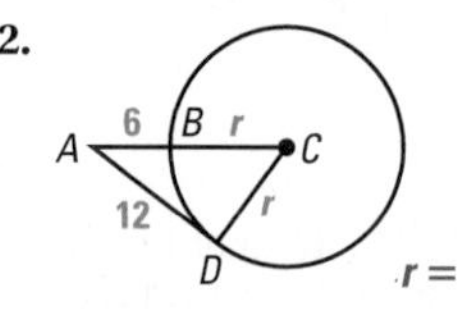

$r = 9$

3.

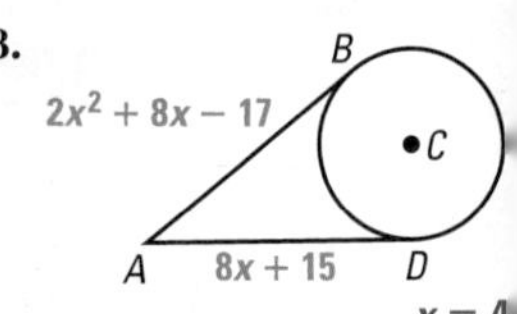

$x = 4$

Tell whether the red arcs are congruent. *Explain* why or why not. 4–6. See margin.

4.

5.

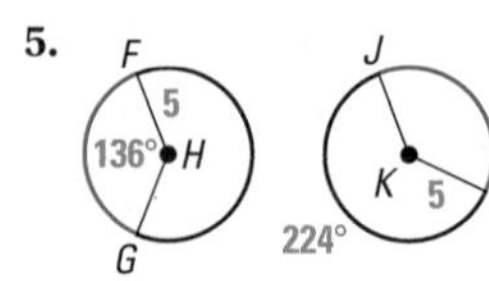

6.

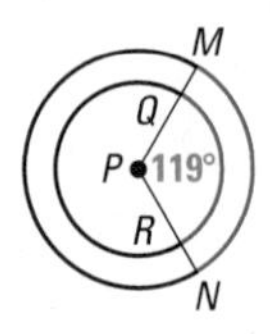

Determine whether $\overline{AB}$ is a diameter of the circle. *Explain* your reasoning. 7–9. See margin.

7.

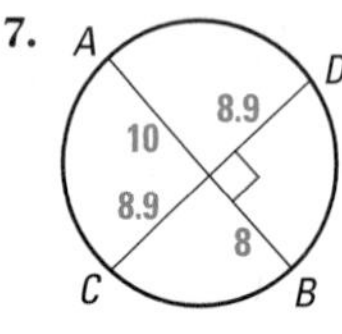

8.

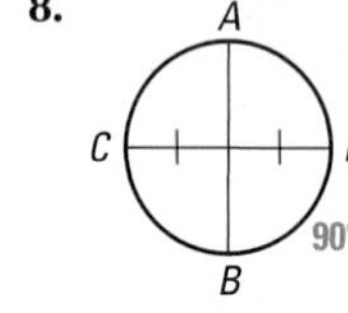

9.

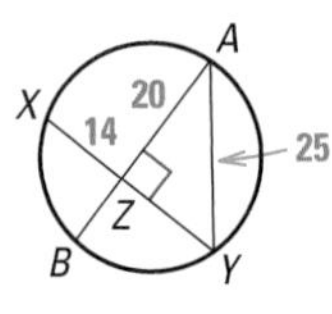

Find the indicated measure.

10. $m\angle ABC$ 53°

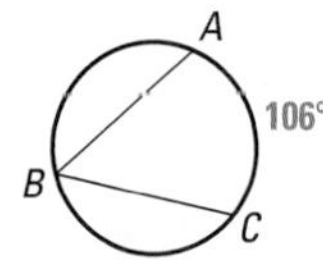

11. $m\overset{\frown}{DF}$ 164°

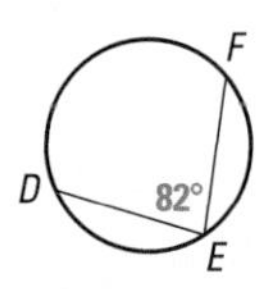

12. $m\overset{\frown}{GHJ}$ 274°

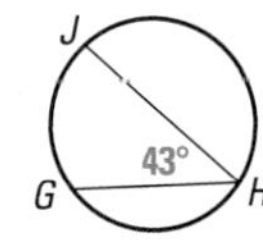

13. $m\angle 1$ 119°

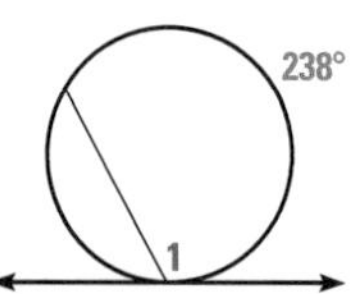

14. $m\angle 2$ 82°

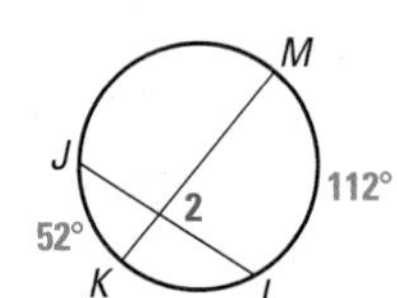

15. $m\overset{\frown}{AC}$ 84°

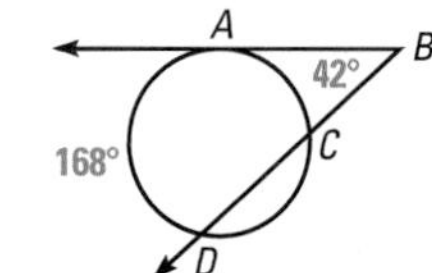

Find the value of x. Round decimal answers to the nearest tenth.

16. 7

17.

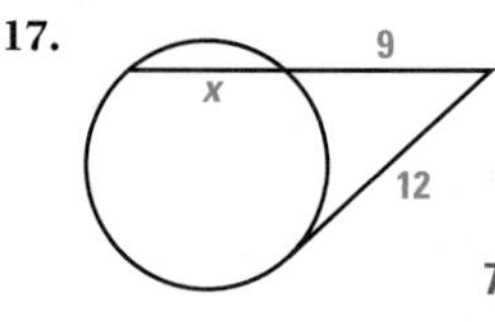

7

18.

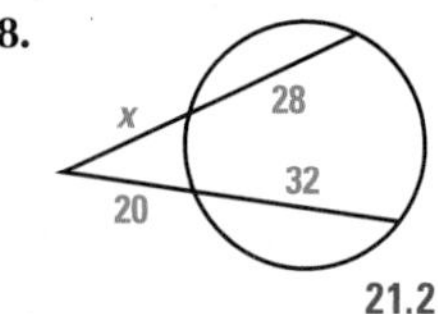

21.2

19. Find the center and radius of a circle that has the standard equation $(x + 2)^2 + (y - 5)^2 = 169$. (−2, 5), 13

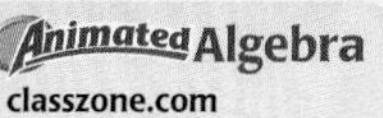

FACTOR BINOMIALS AND TRINOMIALS

Extra Example 1

Factor $3y^4 + 9y^2$. $3y^2(y^2 + 3)$

Extra Example 2

Factor.

a. $3x^2 + 11x - 4$ $(3x - 1)(x + 4)$

b. $25 - x^2$ $(5 + x)(5 - x)$

xy EXAMPLE 1 Factor using greatest common factor

Factor $2x^3 + 6x^2$.

Identify the *greatest common factor* of the terms. The greatest common factor (GCF) is the product of all the common factors.

First, factor each term. $2x^3 = 2 \cdot x \cdot x \cdot x$ and $6x^2 = 2 \cdot 3 \cdot x \cdot x$

Then, write the product of the common terms. $\text{GCF} = 2 \cdot x \cdot x = 2x^2$

Finally, use the distributive property with the GCF. $2x^3 + 6x^2 = 2x^2(x + 3)$

xy EXAMPLE 2 Factor binomials and trinomials

Factor.

a. $2x^2 - 5x + 3$ b. $x^2 - 9$

Solution

a. Make a table of possible factorizations. Because the middle term, $-5x$, is negative, both factors of the third term, 3, must be negative.

Factors of 2	Factors of 3	Possible factorization	Middle term when multiplied	
1, 2	−3, −1	$(x - 3)(2x - 1)$	$-x - 6x = -7x$	✗
1, 2	−1, −3	$(x - 1)(2x - 3)$	$-3x - 2x = -5x$	← Correct

b. Use the special factoring pattern $a^2 - b^2 = (a + b)(a - b)$.

$x^2 - 9 = x^2 - 3^2$ **Write in the form $a^2 - b^2$.**

$= (x + 3)(x - 3)$ **Factor using the pattern.**

EXERCISES

Factor.

EXAMPLE 1 for Exs. 1–9

1. $6x^2 + 18x^4$ $6x^2(3x^2 + 1)$
2. $16a^2 - 24b$ $8(2a^2 - 3b)$
3. $9r^2 - 15rs$ $3r(3r - 5s)$
4. $14x^5 + 27x^3$ $x^3(14x^2 + 27)$
5. $8t^4 + 6t^2 - 10t$ $2t(4t^3 + 3t - 5)$
6. $9z^3 + 3z + 21z^2$ $3z(3z^2 + 7z + 1)$
7. $5y^6 - 4y^5 + 2y^3$ $y^3(5y^3 - 4y^2 + 2)$
8. $30v^7 - 25v^5 - 10v^4$ $5v^4(6v^3 - 5v - 2)$
9. $6x^3y + 15x^2y^3$ $3x^2y(2x + 5y^2)$

EXAMPLE 2 for Exs. 10–24

10. $x^2 + 6x + 8$ $(x + 2)(x + 4)$
11. $y^2 - y - 6$ $(y - 3)(y + 2)$
12. $a^2 - 64$ $(a - 8)(a + 8)$
13. $z^2 - 8z + 16$ $(z - 4)^2$
14. $3s^2 + 2s - 1$ $(3s - 1)(s + 1)$
15. $5b^2 - 16b + 3$ $(5b - 1)(b - 3)$
16. $4x^4 - 49$ $(2x^2 - 7)(2x^2 + 7)$
17. $25r^2 - 81$ $(5r - 9)(5r + 9)$
18. $4x^2 + 12x + 9$ $(2x + 3)^2$
19. $x^2 + 10x + 21$ — 19. $(x + 3)(x + 7)$
20. $z^2 - 121$ $(z - 11)(z + 11)$
21. $y^2 + y - 6$ $(y + 3)(y - 2)$
22. $z^2 + 12z + 36$ $(z + 6)^2$
23. $x^2 - 49$ $(x - 7)(x + 7)$
24. $2x^2 - 12x - 14$ $2(x + 1)(x - 7)$

Test-Taking Strategy

One strategy to help solve the multiple choice question shown is to solve directly using the Arc Addition Postulate and the fact that if two chords are congruent, their corresponding arcs are congruent. Separate the circle into 3 arcs, two of which are congruent. Therefore $m\overset{\frown}{QR} + m\overset{\frown}{QP} + m\overset{\frown}{PR} = 360°$. The arcs must be in the ratio 4 : 7 : 7, so $4x° + 7x° + 7x° = 360°$. Solve to get $x = 20$. Then $m\overset{\frown}{QR} = 4(20) = 80°$. The answer is C.

MULTIPLE CHOICE QUESTIONS

If you have difficulty solving a multiple choice question directly, you may be able to use another approach to eliminate incorrect answer choices and obtain the correct answer.

Standards

21.0 Students prove and **solve problems regarding relationships among chords, secants, tangents, inscribed angles, and inscribed and** circumscribed **polygons of circles.**

PROBLEM 1

In the diagram, $\triangle PQR$ is inscribed in a circle. The ratio of the angle measures of $\triangle PQR$ is 4 : 7 : 7. What is $m\overset{\frown}{QR}$?

Ⓐ 20° Ⓑ 40°

Ⓒ 80° Ⓓ 140°

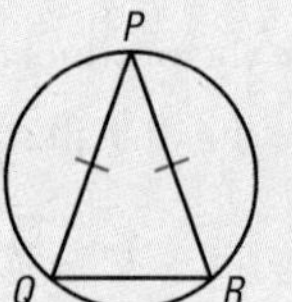

METHOD 1

SOLVE DIRECTLY Use the Interior Angles Theorem to find $m\angle QPR$. Then use the fact that $\angle QPR$ intercepts $\overset{\frown}{QR}$ to find $m\overset{\frown}{QR}$.

STEP 1 **Use** the ratio of the angle measures to write an equation. Because $\triangle PQR$ is isosceles, its base angles are congruent. Let $4x° = m\angle QPR$. Then $m\angle Q = m\angle R = 7x°$. You can write:

$$m\angle QPR + m\angle Q + m\angle R = 180°$$
$$4x° + 7x° + 7x° = 180°$$

STEP 2 **Solve** the equation to find the value of x.

$$4x° + 7x° + 7x° = 180°$$
$$18x° = 180°$$
$$x = 10$$

STEP 3 **Find** $m\angle QPR$. From Step 1, $m\angle QPR = 4x°$, so $m\angle QPR = 4 \cdot 10° = 40°$.

STEP 4 **Find** $m\overset{\frown}{QR}$. Because $\angle QPR$ intercepts $\overset{\frown}{QR}$, $m\overset{\frown}{QR} = 2 \cdot m\angle QPR$. So, $m\overset{\frown}{QR} = 2 \cdot 40° = 80°$.

The correct answer is C. Ⓐ Ⓑ Ⓒ Ⓓ

METHOD 2

ELIMINATE CHOICES Because $\angle QPR$ intercepts $\overset{\frown}{QR}$, $m\angle QPR = \frac{1}{2} \cdot m\overset{\frown}{QR}$. Also, because $\triangle PQR$ is isosceles, its base angles, $\angle Q$ and $\angle R$, are congruent. For each choice, find $m\angle QPR$, $m\angle Q$, and $m\angle R$. Determine whether the ratio of the angle measures is 4 : 7 : 7.

Choice A: If $m\overset{\frown}{QR} = 20°$, $m\angle QPR = 10°$. So, $m\angle Q + m\angle R = 180° - 10° = 170°$, and $m\angle Q = m\angle R = \frac{170}{2} = 85°$. The angle measures 10°, 85°, and 85° are not in the ratio 4 : 7 : 7, so Choice A is not correct.

Choice B: If $m\overset{\frown}{QR} = 40°$, $m\angle QPR = 20°$. So, $m\angle Q + m\angle R = 180° - 20° = 160°$, and $m\angle Q = m\angle R = 80°$. The angle measures 20°, 80°, and 80° are not in the ratio 4 : 7 : 7, so Choice B is not correct.

Choice C: If $m\overset{\frown}{QR} = 80°$, $m\angle QPR = 40°$. So, $m\angle Q + m\angle R = 180° - 40° = 140°$, and $m\angle Q = m\angle R = 70°$. The angle measures 40°, 70°, and 70° are in the ratio 4 : 7 : 7. So, $m\overset{\frown}{QR} = 80°$.

The correct answer is C. Ⓐ Ⓑ Ⓒ Ⓓ

PROBLEM 2

In the circle shown, $\overline{JK}$ intersects $\overline{LM}$ at point N. What is the value of x?

Ⓐ −1 Ⓑ 2

Ⓒ 7 Ⓓ 10

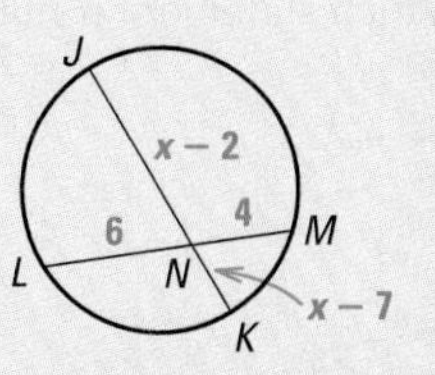

METHOD 1

SOLVE DIRECTLY Write and solve an equation.

STEP 1 **Write** an equation. By the Segments of a Chord Theorem, $NJ \cdot NK = NL \cdot NM$. You can write $(x - 2)(x - 7) = 6 \cdot 4 = 24$.

STEP 2 **Solve** the equation.

$$(x - 2)(x - 7) = 24$$
$$x^2 - 9x + 14 = 24$$
$$x^2 - 9x - 10 = 0$$
$$(x - 10)(x + 1) = 0$$

So, $x = 10$ or $x = -1$.

STEP 3 **Decide** which value makes sense.
If $x = -1$, then $NJ = -1 - 2 = -3$. But a distance cannot be negative.
If $x = 10$, then $NJ = 10 - 2 = 8$, and $NK = 10 - 7 = 3$. So, $x = 10$.

The correct answer is D. Ⓐ Ⓑ Ⓒ Ⓓ

METHOD 2

ELIMINATE CHOICES Check to see if any choices do not make sense.

STEP 1 **Check** to see if any choices give impossible values for NJ and NK. Use the fact that $NJ = x - 2$ and $NK = x - 7$.

Choice A: If $x = -1$, then $NJ = -3$ and $NK = -8$. A distance cannot be negative, so you can eliminate Choice A.

Choice B: If $x = 2$, then $NJ = 0$ and $NK = -5$. A distance cannot be negative or 0, so you can eliminate Choice B.

Choice C: If $x = 7$, then $NJ = 5$ and $NK = 0$. A distance cannot be 0, so you can eliminate Choice C.

STEP 2 **Verify** that Choice D is correct. By the Segments of a Chord Theorem, $(x - 7)(x - 2) = 6(4)$. This equation is true when $x = 10$.

The correct answer is D. Ⓐ Ⓑ Ⓒ Ⓓ

EXERCISES

Explain **why you can eliminate the highlighted answer choice.**

1. In the diagram, what is $m\overset{\frown}{NQ}$?

   Ⓐ ✗ 20° Ⓑ 26°

   Ⓒ 40° Ⓓ 52°

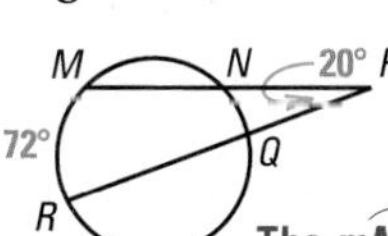

The $m\overset{\frown}{NQ}$ must be greater than $m\angle P$.

2. Isosceles trapezoid $EFGH$ is inscribed in a circle, $m\angle E = (x + 8)°$, and $m\angle G = (3x + 12)°$. What is the value of x? **If $x = -17$, then the measure of $\angle E$ would be negative.**

   Ⓐ ✗ −17 Ⓑ 10 Ⓒ 40 Ⓓ 72

Avoiding Common Errors

When using Method 2 for Problem 2, students may think that Choice A is valid because the product $(-3)(-8) = 24 = (6)(4)$. Make sure they understand the answer is only acceptable if it makes sense in the context of the problem. In this case −3 and −8 cannot be lengths of segments, so choice A can be eliminated.

Teaching Strategy

Exercise 2 Remind students that the order of vertices is determined by how the polygon is labeled. For trapezoid $EFGH$, vertices E and G have to be opposite each other.

10 ★ Standardized TEST PRACTICE

MULTIPLE CHOICE

1. In $\odot L$, $\overline{MN} \cong \overline{PQ}$. Which statement is not necessarily true? **C**

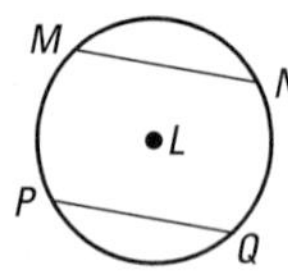

Ⓐ $\widehat{MN} \cong \widehat{PQ}$ Ⓑ $\widehat{NQP} \cong \widehat{QNM}$

Ⓒ $\widehat{MP} \cong \widehat{NQ}$ Ⓓ $\widehat{MPQ} \cong \widehat{NMP}$

2. In $\odot T$, $PV = 5x - 2$ and $PR = 4x + 14$. What is the value of x? **B**

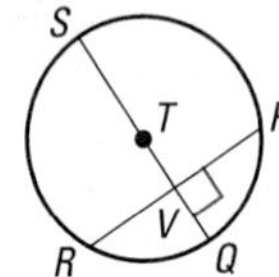

Ⓐ -10 Ⓑ 3

Ⓒ 12 Ⓓ 16

3. What are the coordinates of the center of a circle with equation $(x + 2)^2 + (y - 4)^2 = 9$? **B**

Ⓐ $(-2, -4)$ Ⓑ $(-2, 4)$

Ⓒ $(2, -4)$ Ⓓ $(2, 4)$

4. In the circle shown below, what is $m\widehat{QR}$? **D**

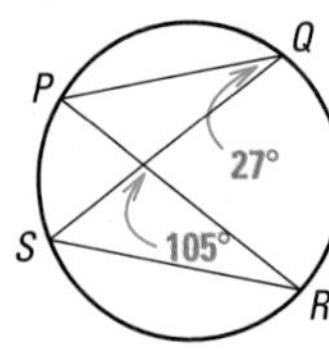

Ⓐ 24° Ⓑ 27°

Ⓒ 48° Ⓓ 96°

5. Regular hexagon $FGHJKL$ is inscribed in a circle. What is $m\widehat{KL}$? **B**

Ⓐ 6° Ⓑ 60°

Ⓒ 120° Ⓓ 240°

6. In the design for a jewelry store sign, $STUV$ is inscribed inside a circle, $ST = TU =$ 12 inches, and $SV = UV =$ 18 inches. What is the approximate diameter of the circle? **B**

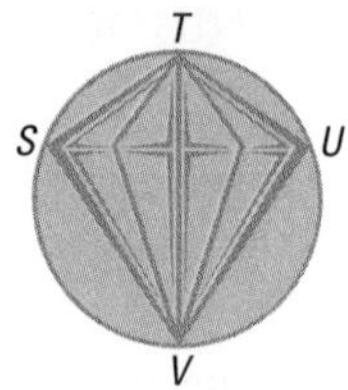

Ⓐ 17 in. Ⓑ 22 in.

Ⓒ 25 in. Ⓓ 30 in.

7. In the diagram shown, $\overleftrightarrow{QS}$ is tangent to $\odot N$ at R. What is $m\widehat{RPT}$? **D**

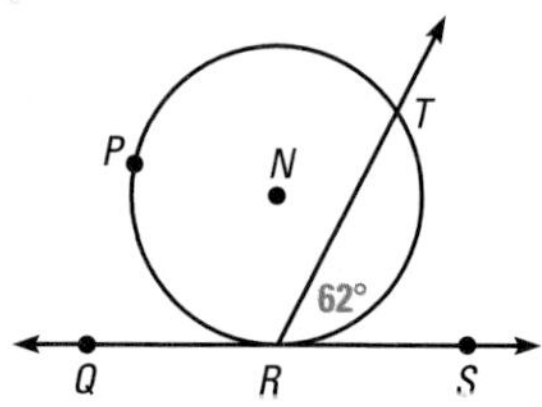

Ⓐ 62° Ⓑ 118°

Ⓒ 124° Ⓓ 236°

8. Two distinct circles intersect. What is the maximum number of common tangents? **C**

Ⓐ 1 Ⓑ 2

Ⓒ 3 Ⓓ 4

9. In the circle shown, $m\widehat{EFG} = 146°$ and $m\widehat{FGH} = 172°$. What is the value of x? **B**

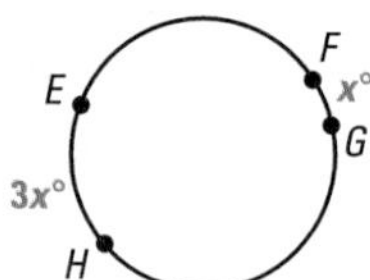

Ⓐ 10.5 Ⓑ 21

Ⓒ 42 Ⓓ 336

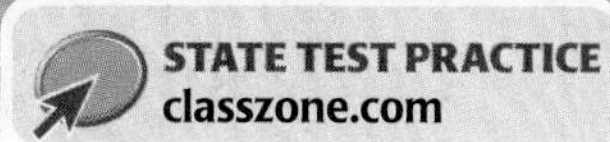

GRIDDED ANSWER

10. $\overline{LK}$ is tangent to $\odot T$ at K. $\overline{LM}$ is tangent to $\odot T$ at M. Find the value of x. **12**

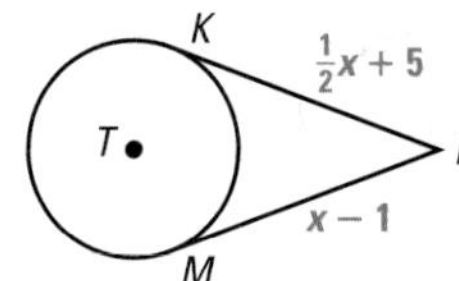

11. In $\odot H$, find $m\angle AHB$ in degrees. **69°**

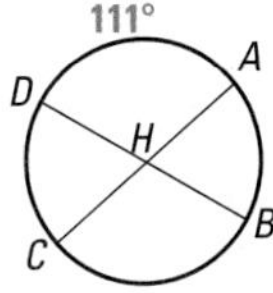

12. Find the value of x. **5**

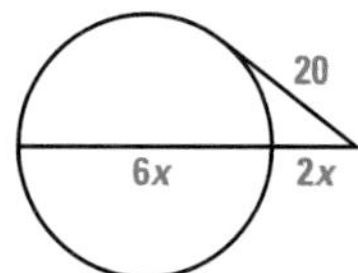

SHORT RESPONSE

13. *Explain* why $\triangle PSR$ is similar to $\triangle TQR$. **See margin.**

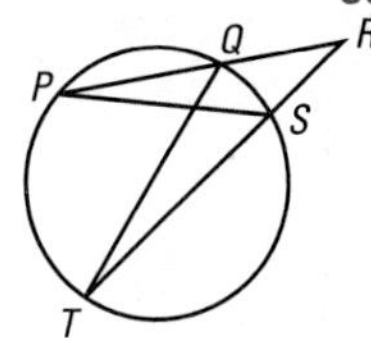

14. Let $x°$ be the measure of an inscribed angle, and let $y°$ be the measure of its intercepted arc. Graph y as a function of x for all possible values of x. Give the slope of the graph. **See margin for art; 2.**

15. In $\odot J$, $\overline{JD} \cong \overline{JH}$. Write two true statements about congruent arcs and two true statements about congruent segments in $\odot J$. *Justify* each statement. **See margin.**

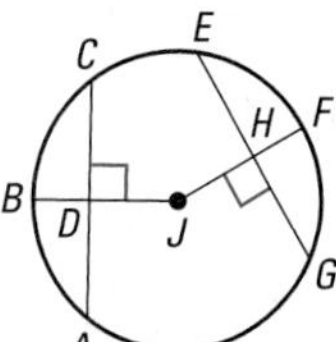

EXTENDED RESPONSE

16. The diagram shows a piece of broken pottery found by an archaeologist. The archaeologist thinks that the pottery is part of a circular plate and wants to estimate the diameter of the plate.

a. Trace the outermost arc of the diagram on a piece of paper. Draw any two chords whose endpoints lie on the arc. **See margin.**

b. Construct the perpendicular bisector of each chord. Mark the point of intersection of the perpendiculars bisectors. How is this point related to the circular plate? **It is the center of the plate; see margin for art.**

c. Based on your results, *describe* a method the archaeologist could use to estimate the diameter of the actual plate. *Explain* your reasoning. **Double the radius found in part b; the diameter is always twice the radius.**

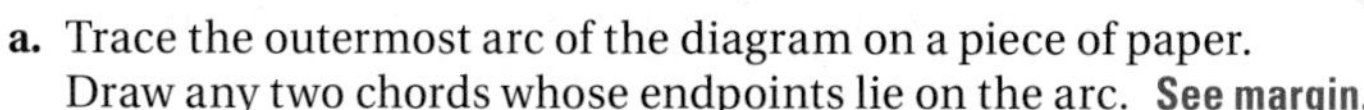

17. The point $P(3, -8)$ lies on a circle with center $C(-2, 4)$.

a. Write an equation for $\odot C$. $(x + 2)^2 + (y - 4)^2 = 169$

b. Write an equation for the line that contains radius $\overline{CP}$. *Explain.* **b, c. See margin.**

c. Write an equation for the line that is tangent to $\odot C$ at point P. *Explain.*

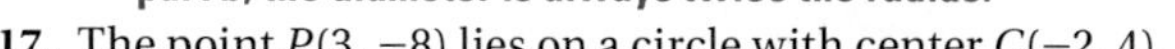

13. $\angle P \cong \angle T$ since they both intercept $\overset{\frown}{QS}$ and $\angle R \cong \angle R$ by the Reflexive Property of Congruence, so $\triangle PQR \sim \triangle TQR$ by the AA Similarity Postulate.

14.

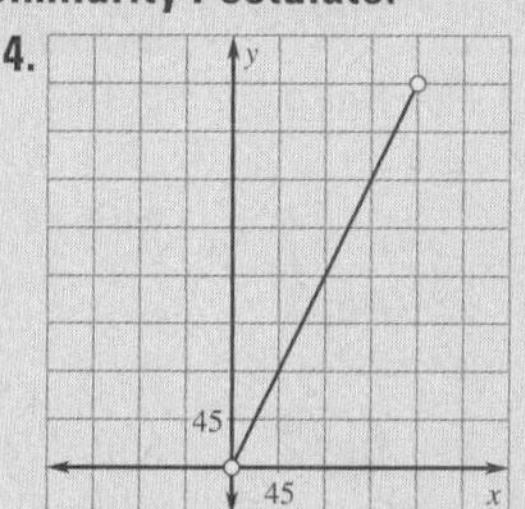

15. *Sample answer:* $\overset{\frown}{AC} \cong \overset{\frown}{EG}$ using Theorem 10.3, $\overset{\frown}{AB} \cong \overset{\frown}{CB}$ using Theorem 10.5, $\overline{AC} \cong \overline{EG}$ using Theorem 10.6, $\overline{JB} \cong \overline{JF}$ since they are radii of $\odot J$.

16a. *Sample:*

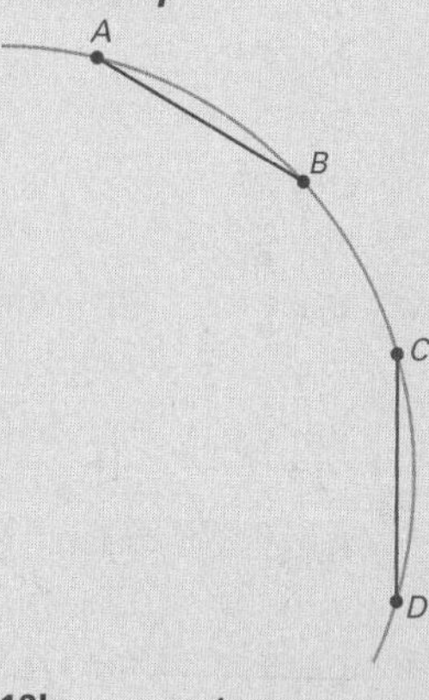

16b.

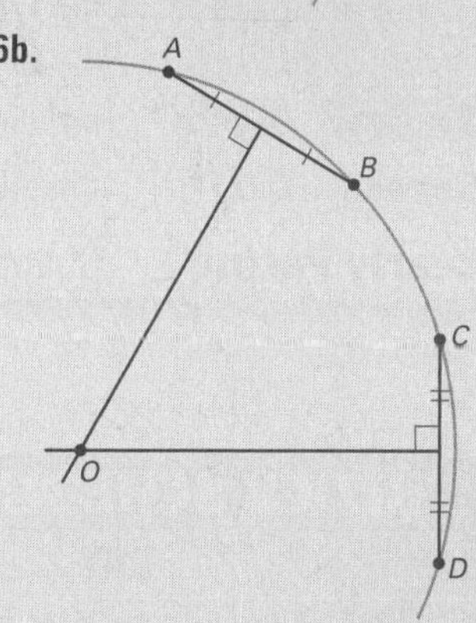

17b. $y = -\frac{12}{5}x - \frac{4}{5}$; the slope of $\overline{CP}$ is $-\frac{12}{5}$. Use the slope and one of the points to find the equation of the line.

17c. $y = \frac{5}{12}x - \frac{37}{4}$; the slope of the tangent line is the negative reciprocal of the slope of $\overline{CP}$. Using a slope of $\frac{5}{12}$ and point P find the equation of the line.

11 Pacing and Assignment Guide

REGULAR SCHEDULE

Pre-AP For pacing and assignments for a Pre-AP course, see the *Geometry Toolkit*.

Lesson	Les. Day	BASIC	AVERAGE	ADVANCED
11.1	Day 1	SRH p. 883 Exs. 1, 4, 5, 8; pp. 723–726 Exs. 1–5, 9–13, 16–24, 28, 36–42, 48–54	pp. 723–726 Exs. 1, 2, 5–7, 9–11, 14–17, 19–21, 25–33, 37–45, 49–53 odd	pp. 723–726 Exs. 1, 2, 7–9, 14, 15, 17–21, 26–35*, 37, 39–47*, 50, 54
11.2	Day 1	pp. 733–736 Exs. 1–14, 22, 23, 34, 35	pp. 733–736 Exs. 1–6, 8–11, 13, 14, 22–26, 34, 35	pp. 733–736 Exs. 1–6, 9–12, 22–29, 34, 35
	Day 2	pp. 733–736 Exs. 15–21, 24–26, 36–38, 44–48	pp. 733–736 Exs. 15–21, 27–32, 36–41, 44–48 even	pp. 733–736 Exs. 15–21, 30–33*, 36–43*, 46–48
11.3	Day 1	EP p. 906 Exs. 23–25; pp. 740–743 Exs. 1–20, 26–30, 35–41	pp. 740–743 Exs. 1–4, 6–8, 10–22, 27–33, 35–41	pp. 740–743 Exs. 1, 2, 6–14, 16–25*, 27–34*, 35–41 odd
11.4	Day 1	pp. 749–752 Exs. 1–10, 26–29, 37, 46–48	pp. 749–752 Exs. 1–10, 26–29, 37, 38, 46–48	pp. 749–752 Exs. 1–10, 26–29, 33*, 37, 38, 48
	Day 2	pp. 749–752 Exs. 11–25, 35, 36, 38, 42–45	pp. 749–752 Exs. 11–14, 18–25, 30–32, 35, 36, 39, 42–45	pp. 749–752 Exs. 11–13, 19–25, 30–32, 34, 39–42*, 44
11.5	Day 1	pp. 758–761 Exs. 1–13, 37, 38, 48–51	pp. 758–761 Exs. 1, 2, 4–6, 8–13, 33, 34, 37, 38, 48–51	pp. 758–761 Exs. 1, 2, 4–6, 8, 9, 11–13, 33–38*, 48, 50
	Day 2	pp. 758–761 Exs. 14–28, 39–41, 45–47	pp. 758–761 Exs. 14–19, 23–32, 39–43, 46	pp. 758–761 Exs. 15–19, 24–32, 39–44*, 47
11.6	Day 1	EP p. 909 Exs. 40–45; pp. 765–768 Exs. 1–13, 47–52	pp. 765–768 Exs. 1–13, 47–52	pp. 765–768 Exs. 1–13, 47–52
	Day 2	pp. 765–768 Exs. 14–24, 26–30 even, 36–40	pp. 765–768 Exs. 15–18, 20–22, 24–26, 27–33 odd, 34, 36–44	pp. 765–768 Exs. 16–30 even, 31–36*, 38–46*
11.7	Day 1	SRH p. 893 Exs. 1–5; pp. 774–777 Exs. 1–7, 16–19, 31–33, 42–44	pp. 774–777 Exs. 1–7, 16–19, 31–33, 36, 42–44	pp. 774–777 Exs. 1–7, 16–19, 29*, 31–33, 36, 42, 44
	Day 2	pp. 774–777 Exs. 8–15, 20–22, 30, 34, 35, 39–41	pp. 774–777 Exs. 8–15, 21–26, 30, 34, 35–39 odd	pp. 774–777 Exs. 8–10, 13–15, 22–28, 30, 34, 35, 37, 38*, 41
Review	Day 1	pp. 780–783 Exs. 1–26	pp. 780–783 Exs. 1–26	pp. 780–783 Exs. 1–26
Assess	Day 1	Chapter 11 Test	Chapter 11 Test	Chapter 11 Test
Yearly Pacing		Chapter 11 Total – 14 days	Chapters 1–11 Total – 146 days	Remaining – 14 days

*Challenge Exercises EP = Extra Practice SRH = Skills Review Handbook

BLOCK SCHEDULE

DAY 1	DAY 2	DAY 3	DAY 4	DAY 5	DAY 6	DAY 7
11.1	**11.2 (CONT.)**	**11.4**	**11.5**	**11.6**	**11.7**	**REVIEW**
pp. 723–726 Exs. 1, 2, 5–7, 9–11, 14–17, 19–21, 25–33, 37–45, 49–53 odd	pp. 733–736 Exs. 15–21, 27–32, 36–41, 44–48 even	pp. 749–752 Exs. 1–14, 18–32, 35–39, 42–48	pp. 758–761 Exs. 1, 2, 4–6, 8–19, 23–34, 37–43, 46, 48–51	pp. 765–768 Exs. 1–13, 15–18, 20–22, 24–26, 27–33 odd, 34, 36–44, 47–52	pp. 774–777 Exs. 1–19, 21–26, 30–37, 39, 42–44	pp. 780–783 Exs. 1–26
11.2	**11.3**					**ASSESS**
pp. 733–736 Exs. 1–6, 8–11, 13, 14, 22–26, 34, 35	pp. 740–743 Exs. 1–4, 6–8, 10–22, 27–33, 35–41					Chapter 11 Test
Yearly Pacing	Chapter 11 Total – 7 days		Chapters 1–11 Total – 73 days		Remaining – 7 days	

Chapter Resource Guide 11

RESOURCE MANAGER

Chapter Resource Book							
CHAPTER SUPPORT							
Parents as Partners (Chapter Overview with home involvement exercises and activity)						p. 1	
LESSON SUPPORT	**11.1**	**11.2**	**11.3**	**11.4**	**11.5**	**11.6**	**11.7**
Teaching Guide/Lesson Plan	p. 3	p. 18	p. 31	p. 46	p. 60	p. 75	p. 89
Activity Masters			p. 33	p. 48			
Technology Activities & Keystrokes	p. 5				p. 62	p. 77	
Activity Support Masters							p. 91
Practice (3 levels)	p. 7	p. 20	p. 34	p. 49	p. 64	p. 78	p. 92
Study Guide	p. 13	p. 26	p. 40	p. 55	p. 70	p. 84	p. 98
Catch-Up for Absent Students	p. 15	p. 28	p. 42	p. 57	p. 72	p. 86	p. 100
Problem Solving/Application	p. 16	p. 29	p. 43	p. 58	p. 73	p. 87	p. 101
Challenge Practice	p. 17	p. 30	p. 45	p. 59	p. 74	p. 88	p. 102
REVIEW							
Chapter Review Games and Activities		p. 103		Cumulative Practice		p. 106	
Project with Rubric		p. 104		Resource Book Answers		A1	

Transparencies	*11.1*	*11.2*	*11.3*	*11.4*	*11.5*	*11.6*	*11.7*
Warm-Up/Daily Homework Quiz	✔	✔	✔	✔	✔	✔	✔
Notetaking Guide	✔	✔	✔	✔	✔	✔	✔
Teacher Support		✔					✔
Answer Transparencies	✔	✔	✔	✔	✔	✔	✔

ASSESSMENT BOOK

Quizzes	p. 155	SAT/ACT Chapter Test	p. 166
Chapter Tests (3 levels)	p. 158	Alternative Assessment with Rubric	p. 168
Standardized Chapter Test	p. 164		

TECHNOLOGY

- Easy Planner
- Test and Practice Generator
- Power Presentations
- @HomeTutor
- Activity Generator
- Animated Geometry
- Classzone.com
- eEdition Plus Online
- eWorkbook Plus Online
- ML Assessment System

ADDITIONAL RESOURCES

- Worked-Out Solution Key
- Notetaking Guide
- Practice Wookbook
- Geometry Toolkit
- Benchmark Tests
- Remediation Book
- Spanish Study Guide
- Spanish Assessment Book
- Student Resources in Spanish
- Multi-Language Visual Glossary

11 Lesson Practice Level B

LESSON 11.1

Practice B
For use with pages 720–726

Find the area of the polygon.

1. 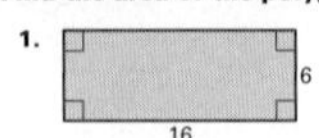

96 square units

2. 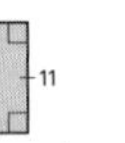

121 square units

3. 9, 14
126 square units

4. 8, 12
96 square units

5. 15, 19
142.5 square units

6. 7, 13, 18
91 square units

The lengths of the hypotenuse and one leg of a right triangle are given. Find the perimeter and area of the triangle.

7. Hypotenuse: 26 cm; leg: 24 cm 60 cm; 120 cm²
8. Hypotenuse: 50 mm; leg: 14 mm 112 mm; 336 mm²
9. Hypotenuse: 37 ft; leg: 12 ft 84 ft; 210 ft²
10. Hypotenuse: 85 in.; leg: 77 in. 198 in.; 1386 in.²

Find the value of *x*.

11. $A = 153$ ft² 9
x ft, 17 ft

12. $A = 528$ cm² 16
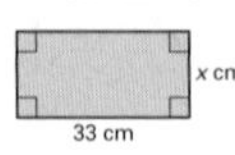

13. $A = 399$ in.² 38
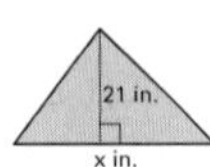

Find the area of the shaded polygon.

14. 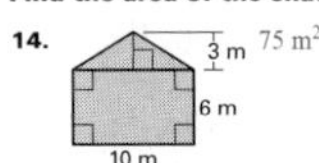

75 m²

15. 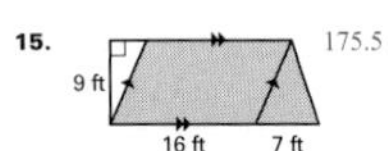

175.5 ft²

16. 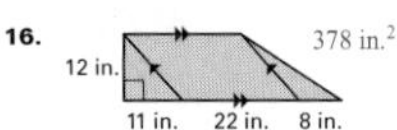

378 in.²

17. 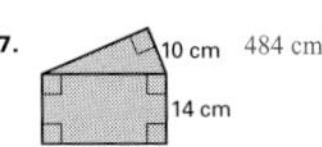

484 cm²

18. 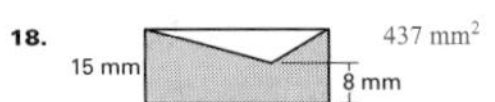

437 mm²

19. 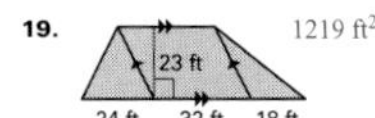

1219 ft²

LESSON 11.1

Practice B *continued*
For use with pages 720–726

Graph the points and connect them to form a polygon. Find the area of the polygon.

20. $A(2, 2), B(3, 6), C(5, 6), D(4, 2)$
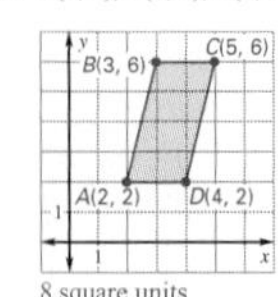

8 square units

21. $P(-4, -4), Q(-1, -1), R(5, -4)$
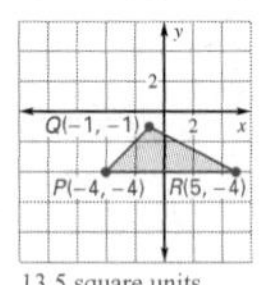

13.5 square units

Find the height and area of the polygon.

22. 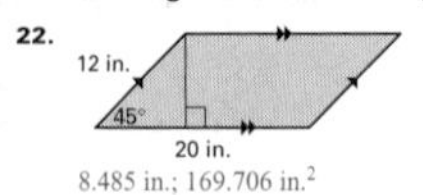

8.485 in.; 169.706 in.²

23. 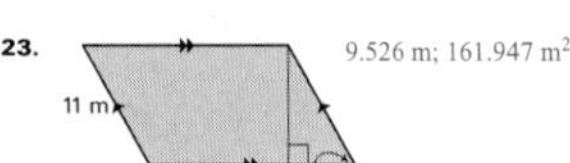

9.526 m; 161.947 m²

24. **Envelopes** You have an envelope that is 9.5 inches by 4.2 inches and has a triangular flap with a height of 2.4 inches. What is the area of the envelope shown in the diagram? 51.3 in.²

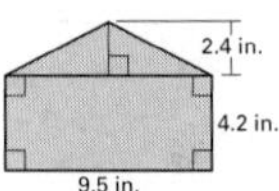

25. **Floor Tile** You have a piece of floor tile in the shape of a parallelogram that has a base of 6 feet and a height of 2.5 feet. You cut a triangular piece of tile with a base of 2 feet to fit next to the other piece, as shown. Find the total area of the tile in square feet and square inches. 17.5 ft²; 2520 in.²

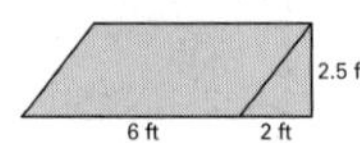

26. **Painting** A painter is painting the back of your garage, which has the measurements shown. The painter can paint 200 square feet per hour and charges $25 per hour. How much will you have to pay if the painter rounds the time spent painting to the nearest half hour? $125

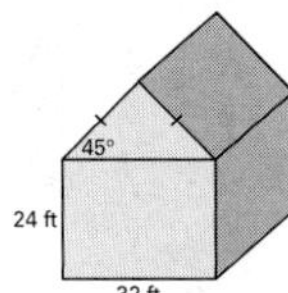

LESSON 11.2

Practice B
For use with pages 729–736

Find the area of the trapezoid.

1. 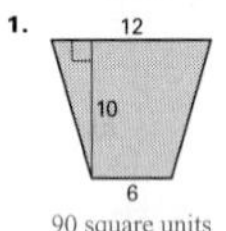

90 square units

2. 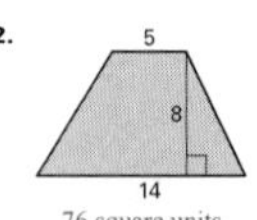

76 square units

3. 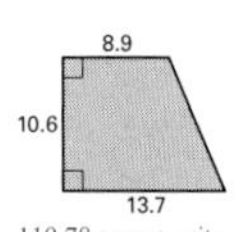

119.78 square units

Find the area of the rhombus or kite.

4. 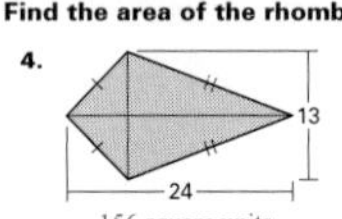

156 square units

5. 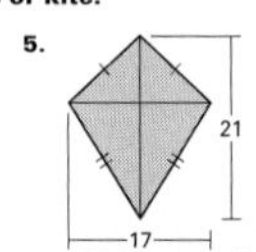

178.5 square units

6. 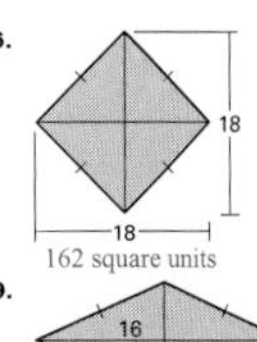

162 square units

7. 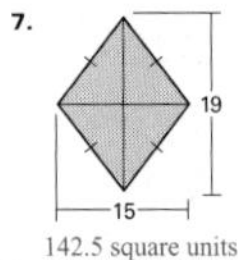

142.5 square units

8. 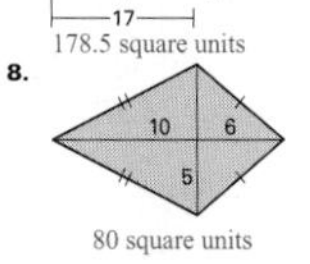

80 square units

9. 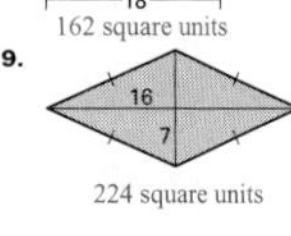

224 square units

Use the given information to find the value of *x*.

10. Area = 330 in.² 11 in.
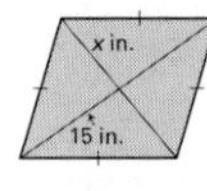

11. Area = 196 ft² 8 ft
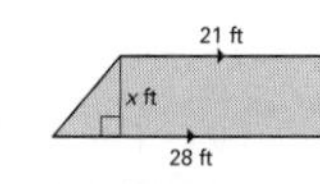

12. Area = 187 cm² 16 cm
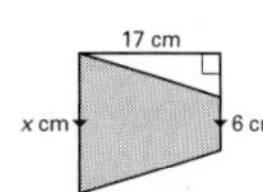

Find the area of the figure.

13. 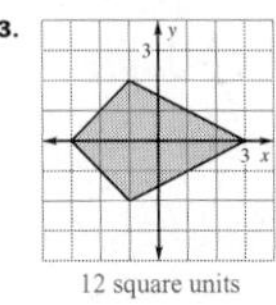

12 square units

14. 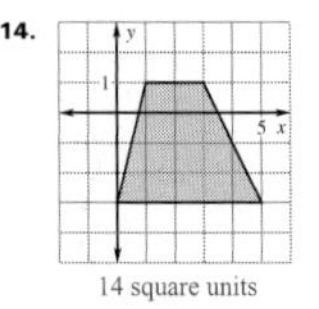

14 square units

15. 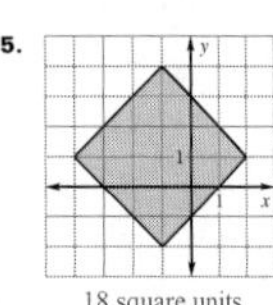

18 square units

LESSON 11.2

Practice B *continued*
For use with pages 729–736

Find the area of the polygon.

16. 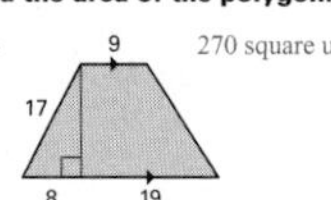

270 square units

17. 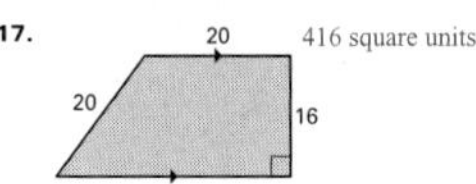

416 square units

18. 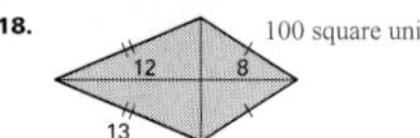

100 square units

19. 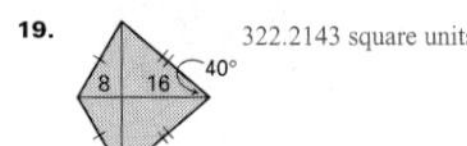

322.2143 square units

20. 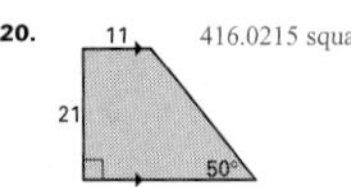

416.0215 square units

21. 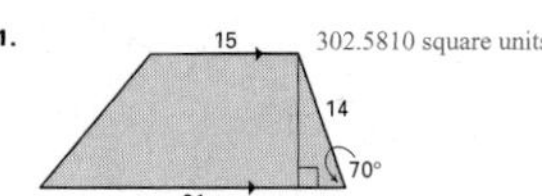

302.5810 square units

22. **Washing Windows** You are going to wash a large glass window in the shape of a trapezoid. The lengths of the bases of the window are 10 feet and 14 feet. The height is 8 feet. You can wash 6 square feet of the window in 1 minute. How long will it take you to wash the entire window? 16 min

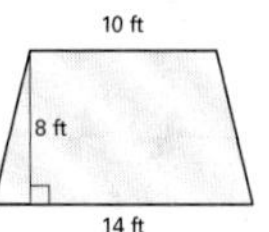

23. **Company Logo** A company has a logo that is in the shape of a rhombus. The company wants to put its logo on a sign outside the building. On the sign, the diagonals of the rhombus will be 72 and 36 inches long. Find the area of the logo. 1296 in.²

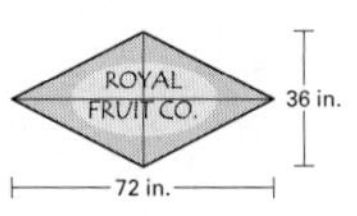

24. **Flower Decoration** You are making a flower decoration for your house in the shape of a kite. The area of the decoration is 450 square centimeters and the length of one diagonal is 25 centimeters. Find the length of the other diagonal. 36 cm

LESSON 11.3 Practice B
For use with pages 737–743

Complete the table of ratios for similar polygons.

	Ratio of corresponding side lengths	Ratio of perimeters	Ratio of areas
1.	5 : 8	5 : 8	25 : 64
2.	4 : 7	4 : 7	16 : 49
3.	13 : 6	13 : 6	169 : 36
4.	66 : 18 = ? 11 : 3	11 : 3	121 : 9

Corresponding lengths in similar figures are given. Find the ratios (shaded to unshaded) of the perimeters and areas. Find the unknown area.

5. 2 : 5; 4 : 25; 12.5 ft²

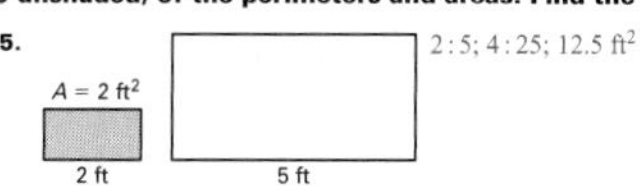

6. 7 : 10; 49 : 100; 196 in.²

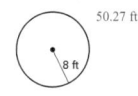

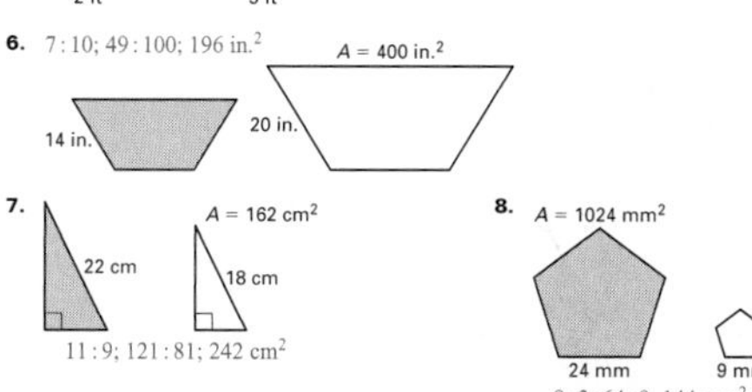

7. 11 : 9; 121 : 81; 242 cm²

A = 162 cm², 22 cm, 18 cm

8. 8 : 3; 64 : 9; 144 mm²

A = 1024 mm², 24 mm, 9 mm

The ratio of the areas of two similar figures is given. Write the ratio of the lengths of corresponding sides.

9. Ratio of areas = 16 : 81 4 : 9

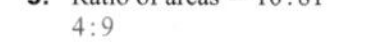

10. Ratio of areas = 25 : 196 5 : 14

11. Ratio of areas = 144 : 49 12 : 7

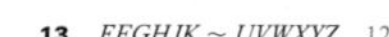

Use the given area to find *XY*.

12. *ABCD* ~ *WXYZ* 5 in.

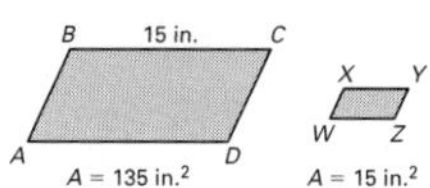

13. *EFGHJK* ~ *UVWXYZ* 12 cm

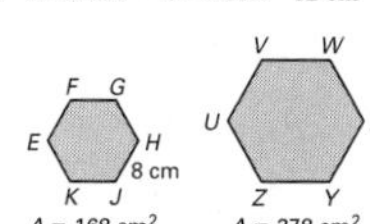

LESSON 11.3 Practice B *continued*
For use with pages 737–743

14. Regular octagon *ABCDEFGH* has a side length of 10 millimeters and an area of 160 square millimeters. Regular octagon *JKLMNOPQ* has a perimeter of 200 millimeters. Find its area. 1000 mm²

15. Kites *RSTU* and *VWXY* are similar. The area of *RSTU* is 162 square feet. The diagonals of *VWXY* are 32 feet long and 18 feet long. Find the area of *VWXY*. Then use the ratio of the areas to find the lengths of the diagonals of *RSTU*. 288 ft²; 24 ft and 13.5 ft

16. $\triangle ABC$ and $\triangle DEF$ are similar. The height of $\triangle ABC$ is 42 inches. The base of $\triangle DEF$ is 7 inches and the area is 42 square inches. Find the ratio of the area of $\triangle ABC$ to the area of $\triangle DEF$. 49 : 4

17. Rectangles *ABCD* and *EFGH* are similar. The width of *ABCD* is 18 centimeters and the perimeter is 120 centimeters. The length of *EFGH* is 91 centimeters. Find the ratio of the side lengths of *ABCD* to the side lengths of *EFGH*. 6 : 13

18. Posters Your school had a car wash to raise money. A poster that was used to attract customers is shown. You decide that you will have the car wash again next year. You will have a similar poster but you will increase the length to 6 feet to try to attract more customers. Find the area of the new poster. 18 ft²

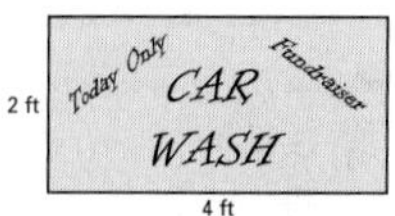

19. Rug Costs You are comparing the two rugs shown below. You want to be sure that the large rug is priced fairly. The price of the small rug is $84. The price of the large rug is $210.

a. What are the areas of the two rugs? What is the ratio of the area of the small rug to the area of the large rug? 40 ft² and 120 ft²; 1 : 3

b. Compare the rug costs. Do you think the large rug is a good buy? *Explain.*

Yes; the area of the larger rug is 3 times the area of the smaller rug, but it is only 2.5 times the cost.

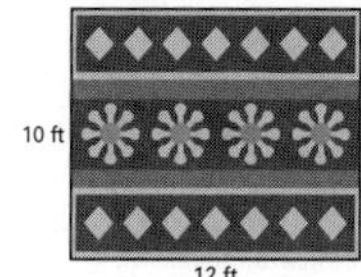

LESSON 11.4 Practice B
For use with pages 746–752

Use the diagram to find the indicated measure.

1. Find the circumference. 50.27 ft (8 ft)

2. Find the circumference. 40.84 in. (13 in.)

3. Find the radius. 10.50 cm ($C = 65.98$ cm)

Find the indicated measure.

4. The exact radius of a circle with circumference 42 meters $\frac{21}{\pi}$ m

5. The exact diameter of a circle with circumference 39 centimeters $\frac{39}{\pi}$ cm

6. The exact circumference of a circle with diameter 15 inches 15π in.

7. The exact circumference of a circle with radius 27 feet 54π ft

Find the length of $\widehat{AB}$.

8. 6.28 cm

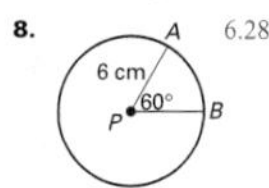

9. 47.12 in.

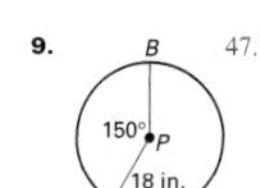

10. 7.33 ft

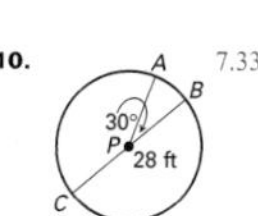

In ⊙*D* shown below, $\angle EDF \cong \angle FDG$. Find the indicated measure.

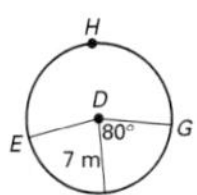

11. $m\widehat{EFG}$ 160°

12. $m\widehat{EHG}$ 200°

13. Length of $\widehat{EFG}$ 19.55 m

14. Length of $\widehat{EHG}$ 24.43 m

15. $m\widehat{EHF}$ 280°

16. Length of $\widehat{FEG}$ 34.21 m

Find the indicated measure.

17. $m\widehat{AB}$ 114.02°

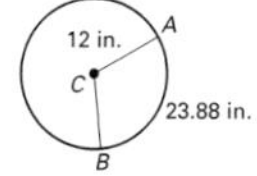

18. Circumference of ⊙*F* 58.03 ft

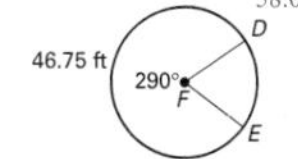

19. Radius of ⊙*J* 20.53 cm

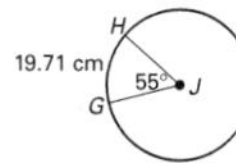

LESSON 11.4 Practice B *continued*
For use with pages 746–752

Find the perimeter of the region.

20. 45.71 mm

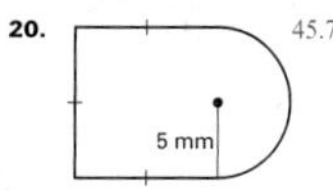

21. 138.56 in.

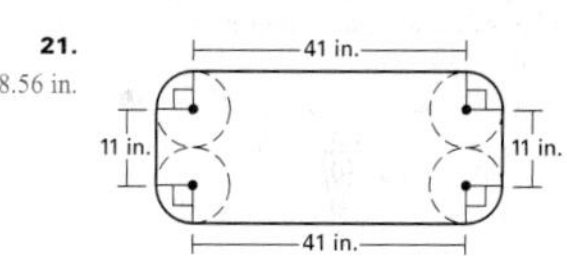

22. In the table below, $\widehat{AB}$ refers to the arc of a circle. Complete the table.

Radius	4	11	9.79	4.81	9.5	10.7
$m\widehat{AB}$	30°	43.02°	105°	75°	88.24°	270°
Length of $\widehat{AB}$	2.09	8.26	17.94	6.3	14.63	50.42

23. Bicycles The chain of a bicycle travels along the front and rear sprockets, as shown. The circumference of each sprocket is given.

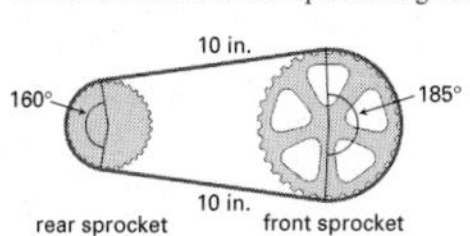

a. About how long is the chain? about 35.61 in.

b. On a chain, the teeth are spaced in $\frac{1}{2}$ inch intervals. About how many teeth are there on this chain? about 71 teeth

24. Enclosing a Garden You have planted a circular garden adjacent to one of the corners of your garage, as shown. You want to fence in your garden. About how much fencing do you need? about 56.55 ft

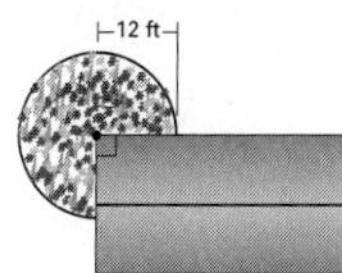

11 Lesson Practice Level B

LESSON 11.5 Practice B
For use with pages 755–761

Find the exact area of the circle. Then find the area to the nearest hundredth.

1. 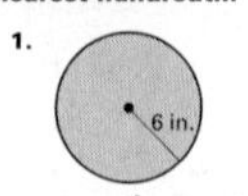

36π in.^{2}; 113.10 in.^{2}

2. 10.5 ft
110.25π ft^2; 346.36 ft^2

3. 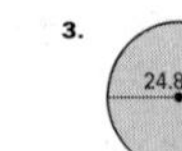

153.76π cm^2; 483.05 cm^2

Find the indicated measure.

4. The area of a circle is 173 square inches. Find the radius. 7.42 in.

5. The area of a circle is 290 square meters. Find the radius. 9.61 m

6. The area of a circle is 654 square centimeters. Find the diameter. 28.86 cm

7. The area of a circle is 528 square feet. Find the diameter. 25.93 ft

Find the areas of the sectors formed by $\angle ACB$.

8. 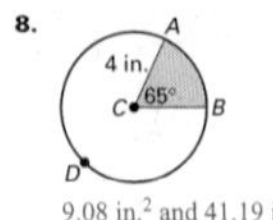

9.08 in.^{2} and 41.19 in.^{2}

9. 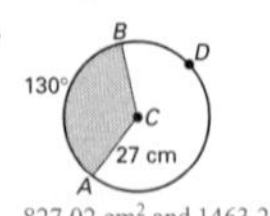

827.02 cm^2 and 1463.20 cm^2

10. 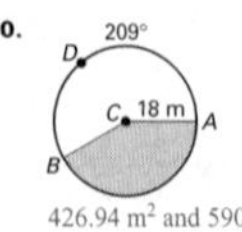

426.94 m^2 and 590.93 m^2

Use the diagram to find the indicated measure.

11. Find the area of $\odot H$. 107.06 ft^2

$A = 23.79$ ft^2

12. Find the radius of $\odot H$. 6.89 in.

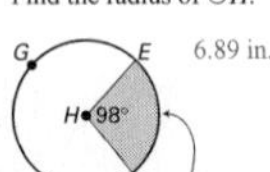

13. Find the diameter of $\odot H$. 6.83 m

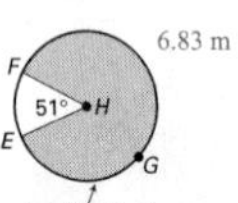

The area of $\odot R$ is 295.52 square inches. The area of sector PRQ is 55 square inches. Find the indicated measure.

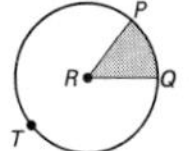

14. Radius of $\odot R$ 9.70 in.

15. Circumference of $\odot R$ 60.94 in.

16. $m\widehat{PQ}$ 67°

17. Length of $\widehat{PQ}$ 11.34 in.

18. Perimeter of shaded region 30.74 in.

19. Perimeter of unshaded region 69.01 in.

LESSON 11.5 Practice B *continued*
For use with pages 755–761

Find the area of the shaded region.

20. 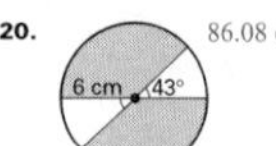

86.08 cm^2

21. 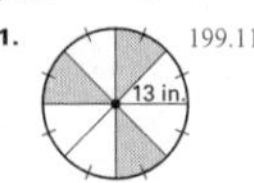

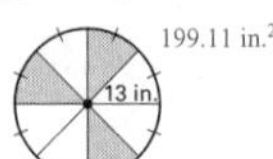
199.11 in.^{2}

22. 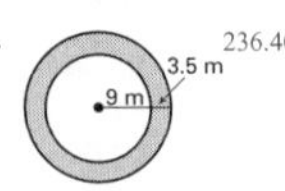

236.40 m^2

23. 10 ft, 2 ft
37.70 ft^2

24. 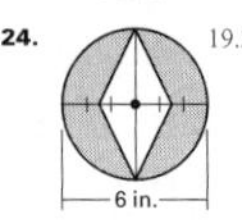

19.27 in.^{2}

25. 8 cm
117.92 cm^2

26. Fountain A circular water fountain has a diameter of 42 feet. Find the area of the fountain. 1385.44 ft^2

27. Landscaping The diagram at the right shows the area of a lawn covered by a water sprinkler.

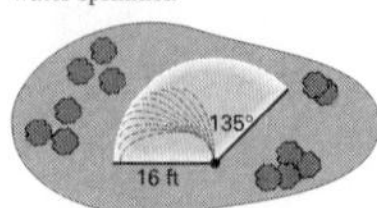

a. What is the area of the lawn that is covered by the sprinkler? 301.59 ft^2

b. The water pressure is weakened so that the radius is 10 feet. What is the area of lawn that will be covered? 117.81 ft^2

28. Window Design The window shown is in the shape of a semicircle. Find the area of the glass in the shaded region. 10.60 m^2

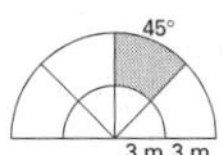

LESSON 11.6 Practice B
For use with pages 762–769

Find the measure of a central angle of a regular polygon with the given number of sides. Round answers to the nearest tenth of a degree, if necessary.

1. 20 sides 18°

2. 36 sides 10°

3. 120 sides 3°

4. 23 sides 15.7°

Find the given angle measure for the regular dodecagon shown.

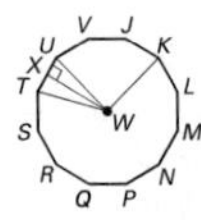

5. $m\angle TWU$ 30°

6. $m\angle TWX$ 15°

7. $m\angle XUW$ 75°

8. $m\angle TWK$ 120°

9. $m\angle UWK$ 90°

10. $m\angle XWK$ 105°

11. Multiple Choice Which expression gives the apothem for a regular nonagon with side length 10.5? C

A. $a = \dfrac{5.25}{\tan 40°}$

B. $a = \dfrac{10.5}{\tan 20°}$

C. $a = \dfrac{5.25}{\tan 20°}$

D. $a = 5.25 \cdot \tan 20°$

12. A regular hexagon has a diameter 22 inches. What is the length of its apothem? Round your answer to the nearest tenth. 9.5 in.

13. A regular octagon has a diameter 8.5 feet. What is the length of its apothem? Round your answer to the nearest tenth. 3.9 ft

Find the perimeter and area of the regular polygon. Round answers to the nearest tenth, if necessary.

14. 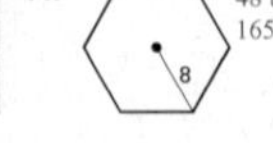

48 units; 165.6 square units

15. 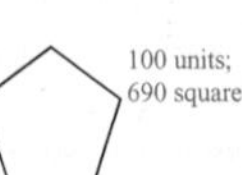

100 units; 690 square units

16. 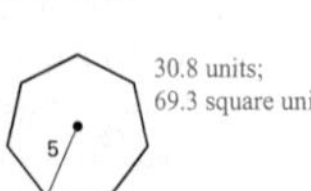

30.8 units; 69.3 square units

17. 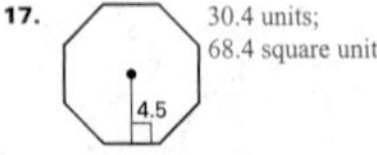

30.4 units; 68.4 square units

18. 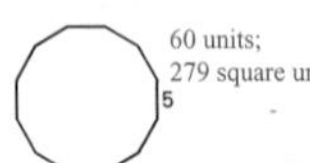

60 units; 279 square units

19. 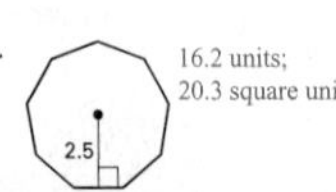

16.2 units; 20.3 square units

20. What is the area of a regular 18-gon with a side length of 8 meters? Round your answer to the nearest tenth, if necessary. 1634.4 m^2

LESSON 11.6 Practice B *continued*
For use with pages 762–769

21. What is the area of a regular 24-gon with a side length of 10 inches? Round your answer to the nearest tenth, if necessary. 4560 in.^{2}

22. What is the area of a regular 30-gon with a radius of 20 feet? Round your answer to the nearest tenth, if necessary. 1253.7 ft^2

23. Find the area of a regular pentagon inscribed in a circle whose equation is given by $(x - 4) + (y - 6) = 16$. 38.4 square units

24. Find the area of a regular octagon inscribed in a circle whose equation is given by $(x - 2) + (y + 3) = 25$. 69.9 square units

Find the area of the shaded region. Round answers to the nearest tenth, if necessary.

25. 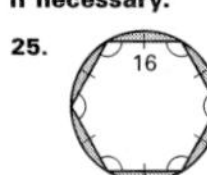

139.1 square units

26. 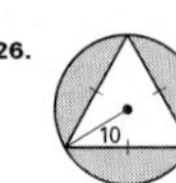

183.7 square units

27. 12, 40°
4 square units

28. 72°, 16
28.2 square units

In Exercises 29 and 30, use the following information.

Tiles You are tiling the floor of a hallway with tiles that are regular hexagons as shown.

6 in.

29. What is the area of each tile? 93.6 in.^{2}

30. The hallway has a width of 5 feet and a length of 12 feet. At least how many tiles will you need?

31. A cup saucer is shaped like a regular decagon with a diameter of 5.5 inches as shown. at least 93 tiles

a. What is the length of the apothem of the saucer? Round your answer to the nearest tenth. 2.6 in.

b. What is the perimeter and area of the saucer? Round your answers to the nearest tenth. 17.9 in.; 23.3 square units

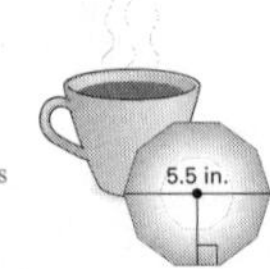

LESSON 11.7

Practice B

For use with pages 770–777

Find the probability that a point K, selected randomly on $\overline{AE}$, is on the given segment. Express your answer as a fraction, decimal, and percent.

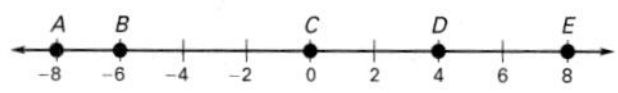

1. $\overline{BC}$ $\frac{3}{8}$; 0.375; 37.5%
2. $\overline{BD}$ $\frac{5}{8}$; 0.625; 62.5%
3. $\overline{CE}$ $\frac{1}{2}$; 0.5; 50%
4. $\overline{AD}$ $\frac{3}{4}$; 0.75; 75%

Find the probability that a randomly chosen point in the figure lies in the shaded region.

5. about 47.6%

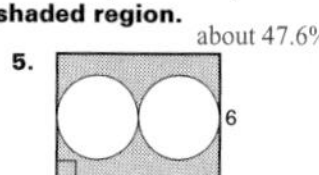

6. 68.75%

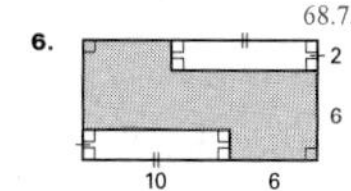

7. 25%

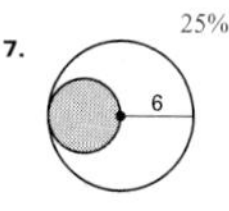

8. 25%

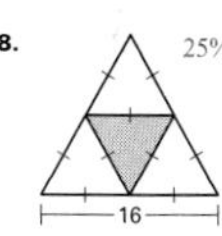

9. about 56.95%

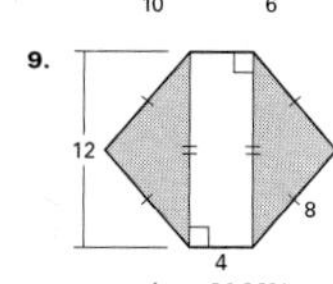

10. about 17.3%

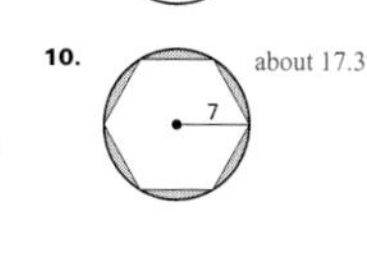

Find the probability that a point chosen at random on the segment satisfies the inequality.

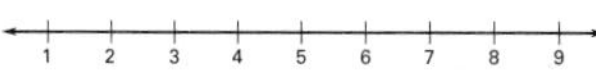

11. $x + 3 \leq 5$ 12.5%
12. $2x - 3 \leq 3$ 25%
13. $3x + 5 \geq 17$ 62.5%
14. $2x - 12 \geq 8$ 0%

Use the scale drawing.

15. What is the approximate area of the shaded figure in the scale drawing? 49.5
16. Find the probability that a randomly chosen point lies in the shaded region. about 28.1%
17. Find the probability that a randomly chosen point lies outside of the shaded region. about 71.9%
18. **Boxes and Buckets** A circular bucket with a diameter of 18 inches is placed inside a two foot cubic box. A small ball is thrown into the box. Find the probability that the ball lands in the bucket. about 44.2%

LESSON 11.7

Practice B *continued*

For use with pages 770–777

In Exercises 19 and 20, use the following information.

Arcs and Sectors The diagram to the right shows a circle with a sector that intercepts an arc of 60°.

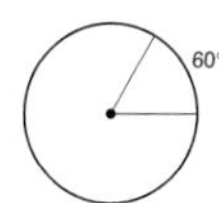

19. Find the probability that a randomly chosen point on the circle lies on the arc. about 16.7%
20. Find the probability that a randomly chosen point in the circle lies in the sector. about 16.7%

Find the probability that a randomly chosen point in the figure lies in the shaded region.

21.

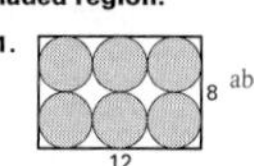

about 78.5%

22. 32%

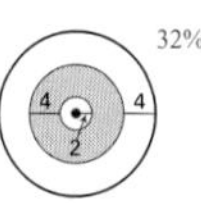

23. 50%

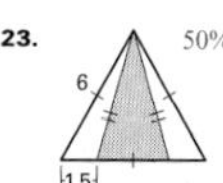

24. **Multiple Choice** A point X is chosen at random in region A, and A includes region B and region C. What is the probability that X is not in B? C

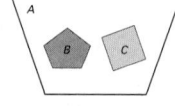

   A. $\dfrac{\text{Area of } A + \text{Area of } C}{\text{Area of } A}$

   B. $\dfrac{\text{Area of } A + \text{Area of } C - \text{Area of } B}{\text{Area of } A + \text{Area of } C}$

   C. $\dfrac{\text{Area of } A - \text{Area of } B}{\text{Area of } A}$

25. **Subway** At the local subway station, a subway train is scheduled to arrive every 15 minutes. The train waits for 2 minutes while passengers get off and on, and then departs for the next station. What is the probability that there is a train waiting when a pedestrian arrives at the station at a random time? about 13.3%

In Exercises 26–28, use the following information.

School Day The school day consists of six block classes with each being 60 minutes long. Lunch is 25 minutes. Transfer time between classes and/or lunch is 3 minutes. There is a fire drill scheduled to happen at a random time during the day.

26. What is the probability that the fire drill begins during lunch? about 6.2%
27. What is the probability that the fire drill begins during transfer time? about 4.5%
28. If you are 2 hours late to school, what is the probability that you missed the fire drill? about 29.8%

CHAPTER 11

Quiz 1

For use after Lessons 11.1–11.3

Find the area of the figure.

1.
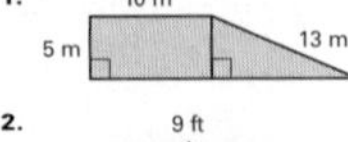

2.
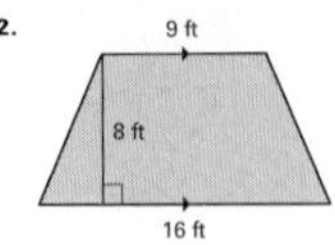

3.
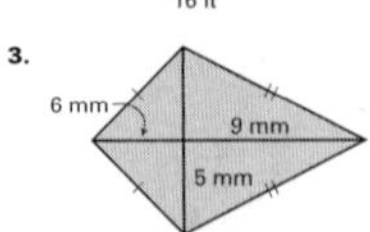

Find the value of *x*.

4. $A = 108\text{ ft}^2$

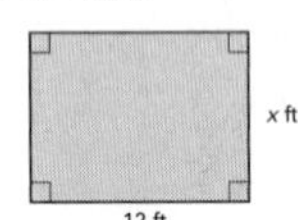

5. $A = 96\text{ cm}^2$

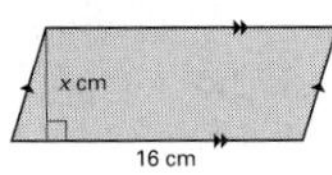

6. The ratio of the lengths of corresponding sides of two similar octagons is 8 : 9. Find the ratio of their perimeters and their areas.

Answers

1. 80 m^2
2. 100 ft^2
3. 75 mm^2
4. 9
5. 6
6. 8 : 9, 64 : 81

CHAPTER 11

Quiz 2

For use after Lessons 11.4–11.5

Find the indicated measure.

1. Circumference

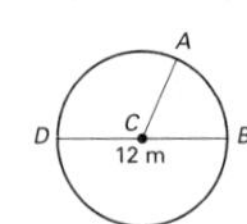

2. Length of $\widehat{JK}$

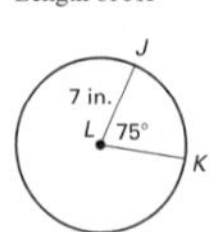

3. Radius

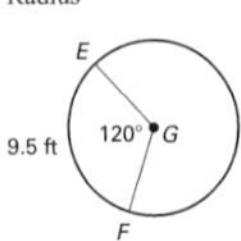

Find the area of the shaded region.

4.
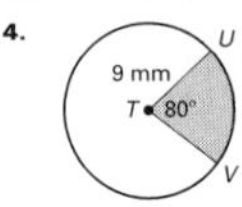

5.
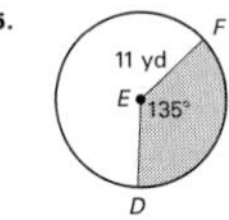

6. 7 cm, 13 cm

7.
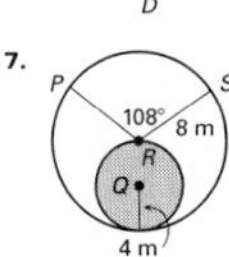

Answers

1. 37.7 m
2. 9.16 in.
3. 4.54 ft
4. 56.55 mm^2
5. 142.55 yd^2
6. 377 cm^2
7. 50.27 m^2

CHAPTER 11

Quiz 3

For use after Lessons 11.6–11.7

Find the area of the regular polygon.

1.
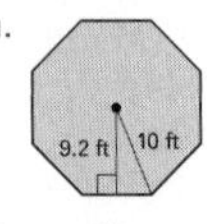
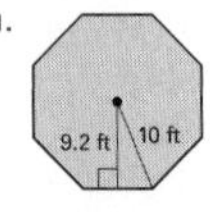

2.
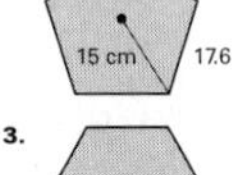

3.
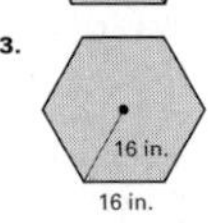
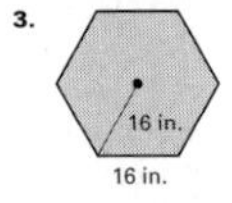

Find the probability that a randomly chosen point in the figure lies in the shaded region.

4.
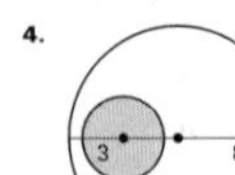

5.
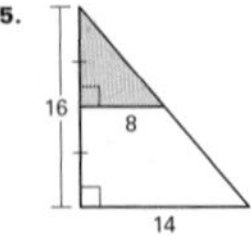

Answers

1. 288.5 ft^2
2. 534.5 cm^2
3. 665.1 in.^2
4. $\frac{9}{64}$
5. $\frac{2}{7}$

CHAPTER 11

Chapter Test B

For use after Chapter 11

Find the area of the shaded region. Round answers to the nearest tenth, if necessary.

1. 24, 40, 35
2. 24, 37, 42, 12
3. 9, 12
4. 26, 36, 24
5. 25, 25
6. 12
7. 7
8. 6
9. 5

10. Regular hexagon *PQRSTU* has a perimeter of 120 meters. What is the area of *PQRSTU*? Round your answer to the nearest meter.

Find the indicated measure. Round answers to the nearest tenth.

11. Length of $\widehat{AB}$

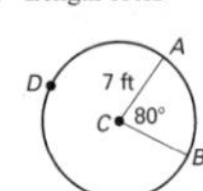

12. Circumference of $\odot L$

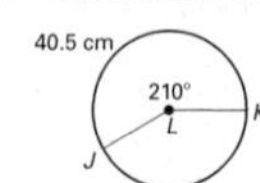

13. Radius of $\odot R$

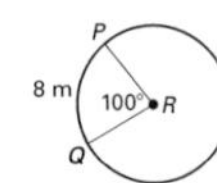

14. Length of $\widehat{XY}$

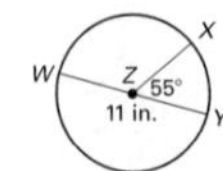

Answers

1. 1784 square units
2. 2100 square units
3. 216 square units
4. 600 square units
5. 268.3 square units
6. 695.3 square units
7. 141.7 square units
8. 98.5 square units
9. 13.6 square units
10. 1039 m^2
11. 9.8 ft
12. 69.4 cm
13. 4.6 m
14. 5.3 in.

CHAPTER 11 Chapter Test B *continued*
For use after Chapter 11

The equation of a circle is given. Find the circumference of the circle. Write the circumference in terms of π.

15. $x^2 + y^2 = 40$ **16.** $(x - 1)^2 + (y + 6)^2 = 15$

The area of $\odot D$ is 113.1 square meters. The area of sector *ADB* is 34.6 square meters. Find the indicated measure.

17. Radius of $\odot D$

18. Circumference of $\odot D$

19. $m\widehat{AB}$

20. Length of $\widehat{ACB}$

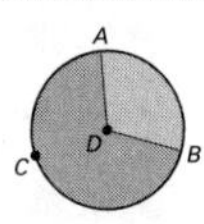

Find the area of the shaded region. Round answers to the nearest tenth, if necessary.

21.

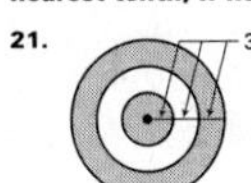

22.

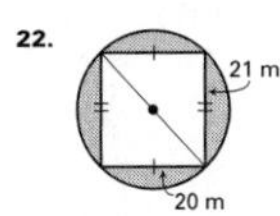

23. What is the area of a regular 15-gon that has a radius of 10 feet? Round your answer to the nearest tenth.

24. What is the area of a regular 20-gon with a side length of 12 centimeters? Round your answer to the nearest tenth.

Find the probability that a randomly chosen point in the figure lies in the shaded region.

25.

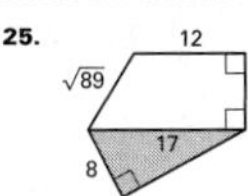

26.

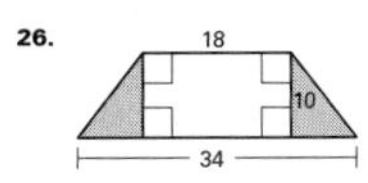

27. A bike tire has a diameter of about 26 inches. You ride a straight distance of about 75 feet. About how many revolutions does the tire make along this distance?

28. A park walkway surrounds a fountain as shown. Find the area of the walkway. Round your answer to the nearest foot.

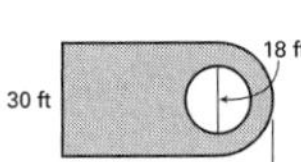

Answers

15. $4\pi\sqrt{10}$

16. $2\pi\sqrt{15}$

17. 6 m

18. 37.7 m

19. 110°

20. 26.2 m

21. 169.6 ft^2

22. 240.5 m^2

23. 305.1 ft^2

24. 4545.9 cm^2

25. $\frac{15}{44} \approx 34.1\%$

26. $\frac{4}{13} \approx 30.8\%$

27. about 11 rev

28. 1374 ft^2

CHAPTER 11 Standardized Test
For use after Chapter 11

Multiple Choice

1. Which statement is false? C

Ⓐ Either pair of parallel sides can be used as the bases of a parallelogram.

Ⓑ If two polygons are congruent, they have the same area.

Ⓒ The height of a parallelogram is the longer distance between the bases.

Ⓓ If you transform a rectangle to form other parallelograms with the same base and height, the area stays the same.

2. Find the area of the polygon. A

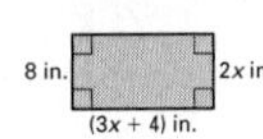

Ⓐ 128 in.^{2} Ⓑ 64 in.^{2}

Ⓒ 256 in.^{2} Ⓓ 96 in.^{2}

3. Find the height of a triangle with a base of 10 cm and an area of 230 cm^2. B

Ⓐ 23 cm Ⓑ 46 cm

Ⓒ 92 cm Ⓓ 69 cm

4. Find the area of the polygon. B

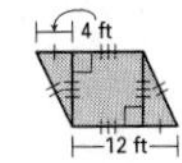

Ⓐ 32 ft^2 Ⓑ 96 ft^2

Ⓒ 80 ft^2 Ⓓ 128 ft^2

5. Find the area (in square meters) of a rhombus with vertices $A(1, 4)$, $B(6, -1)$, $C(1, -6)$, and $D(-4, -1)$. A

Ⓐ 50 m^2 Ⓑ 100 m^2

Ⓒ 20 m^2 Ⓓ 10 m^2

6. Find the area of the kite. C

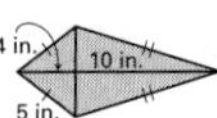

Ⓐ 40 in.^{2} Ⓑ 100 in.^{2}

Ⓒ 42 in.^{2} Ⓓ 70 in.^{2}

7. A plot of land 500 feet wide and 2000 feet long borders a similar, but smaller plot of land only 4% of the size of the larger plot. Find the area of the smaller plot. D

Ⓐ 40,000 ft^2 Ⓑ 160,000 ft^2

Ⓒ 4000 ft^2 Ⓓ 1600 ft^2

8. Find the diameter of a ball that rolls 100 feet after 60 revolutions. Round to the nearest hundredth. A

Ⓐ 0.53 ft Ⓑ 0.27 ft

Ⓒ 5.24 ft Ⓓ 2.62 ft

9. Find the length of $\widehat{PQ}$ to the nearest hundredth. B

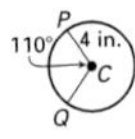

Ⓐ 2.44 in. Ⓑ 7.68 in.

Ⓒ 15.35 in. Ⓓ 3.84 in.

10. Find the circumference of $\odot K$. B

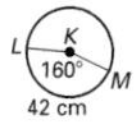

Ⓐ 100 cm Ⓑ 94.5 cm

Ⓒ 117.2 cm Ⓓ 138 cm

11. Find the area of the figure, rounded to the nearest hundredth. C

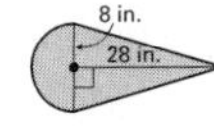

Ⓐ 130.48 in.^{2} Ⓑ 212.48 in.^{2}

Ⓒ 324.53 in.^{2} Ⓓ 280.96 in.^{2}

CHAPTER 11 Standardized Test *continued*
For use after Chapter 11

12. The apothem of a regular polygon inscribed in a circle is the: A

Ⓐ distance from the center to any side of the polygon.

Ⓑ center of the polygon.

Ⓒ arc length intercepted by each side of the polygon.

Ⓓ central angle of the polygon.

13. Find the side length of a 15-sided regular polygon with apothem $a = 6$ inches and area $A = 282$ square inches. C

Ⓐ $18\frac{4}{5}$ in. Ⓑ 94 in.

Ⓒ $6\frac{4}{15}$ in. Ⓓ $12\frac{8}{15}$ in.

14. Which is *not* true about the probability of an event? D

Ⓐ It can be expressed as a fraction, decimal, or percent.

Ⓑ It is the measure of the likelihood that an event will occur.

Ⓒ The probability of event *A* can be written as $P(A)$.

Ⓓ It is a number x such that $0 < x < 1$.

15. Find the probability that a randomly chosen point in the circle also lies in the triangle. B

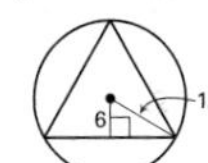

Ⓐ 28% Ⓑ 41%

Ⓒ 56% Ⓓ 45%

Gridded Answer

16. Find the area of the figure. Round your answer to the nearest inch.

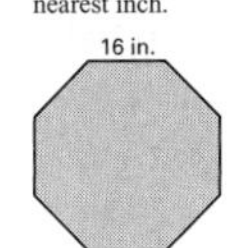

1 2 3 6

Short Response

17. You own a warehouse that is 240 feet long and 160 feet wide. You want to build a new warehouse that is 50% longer and 50% wider than the other warehouse.

a. Find the area of the new warehouse. 86,400 ft^2

b. Is it 50% more area than the smaller warehouse? *Explain.* See below.

Extended Response

18. You have a circular clock with an 8-inch radius.

a. Find the circumference of the clock. 50.27 in.

b. Find the area of the clock. 201.1 in.^{2}

c. Find the smaller arc length created by the hands of the clock when it is 10:30. 18.85 in.

d. Find the area of the large sector formed when it is 1:30. 125.66 in.^{2}

17. b. No; the length and width ratio of the new warehouse to the old warehouse is 3 : 2, so the area ratio is 9 : 4.

CHAPTER 11 Alternative Assessment and Math Journal
For use after Chapter 11

Journal **1.** Describe the relationships that can be formed from different ratios of similar figures.

Multi-Step Problem **2.** A community has a recreation center that has several soccer fields, baseball fields, basketball courts, and a concession stand.

a. The center has many adult soccer fields and youth soccer fields. The rectangular adult soccer field is 130 yards long and 100 yards wide. The rectangular youth soccer field is similar to the adult field and has an area of 8320 square yards. Find the length and width of the youth soccer field.

b. Find the shaded area of the soccer field shown.

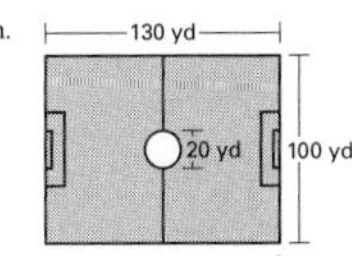

c. The bleachers on the side of the soccer field sit on a trapezoidal piece of land as shown. Find the area of this piece of land.

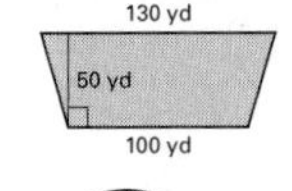

d. A circular concession stand is located at the center of the soccer fields. The juice bar is contained in the shaded sector. Find the area of the juice bar.

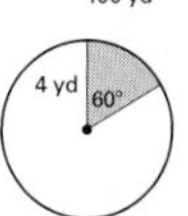

e. There is a large soccer tournament being held at the recreation center. The parking at the center can not accommodate the number of people attending, so a shuttle bus is being provided to and from a large parking lot nearby. Buses arrive at the parking lot every 12 minutes. They wait for 5 minutes while passengers get on and get off. Then the buses depart. Explain how you can find the probability that there is a bus waiting when a passenger arrives at a random time. Then find the probability.

1. If the ratio of the side lengths is $a : b$, then the ratio of the perimeters is $a : b$ and the ratio of the areas is $a^2 : b^2$. If the ratio of the perimeters is $c : d$, then the ratio of the side lengths is $c : d$ and the ratio of the areas is $c^2 : d^2$. If the ratio of the areas is $e : f$, then the ratio of the side lengths is $\sqrt{e} : \sqrt{f}$ and the ratio of the perimeters is $\sqrt{e} : \sqrt{f}$.

2. a. 104 yd; 80 yd **b.** about 12,685.84 yd^2 **c.** 5750 yd^2 **d.** about 8.38 yd^2

e. The probability is the ratio of the favorable waiting time to the maximum waiting time; $\frac{5}{12}$.

PLAN AND PREPARE

Main Ideas

In this chapter, students develop and use formulas for the area of triangles, parallelograms, trapezoids, and other polygons. They use ratios to find areas of similar polygons, and they use ratios of areas to find missing lengths in similar figures. Students explore circles, relating arc lengths and circumferences to areas of sectors, and they develop and use a formula for the area of a regular polygon. Finally, students use lengths of segments and areas of regions to calculate probabilities.

Prerequisite Skills

- Finding the radius and diameter of a circle and the measure of an arc
- Finding the width of a rectangle given the perimeter and the length
- Finding a side length of a right triangle
- Identifying properties of quadrilaterals
- Using proportions to find side lengths of similar triangles

Additional resources for reviewing prerequisite skills are:

- Skills Review Handbook, pp. 869–895
- @HomeTutor

11 Measuring Length and Area

Before

In previous chapters, you learned the following skills, which you'll use in Chapter 11: applying properties of circles and polygons, using formulas, solving for lengths in right triangles, and using ratios and proportions.

Prerequisite Skills

VOCABULARY CHECK

Give the indicated measure for $\odot P$.

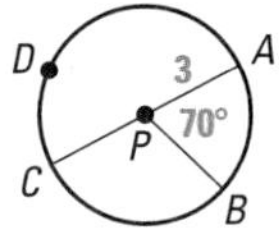

1. The radius **3**
2. The diameter **6**
3. $m\widehat{ADB}$ **290°**

SKILLS AND ALGEBRA CHECK

4. Use a formula to find the width w of the rectangle that has a perimeter of 24 centimeters and a length of 9 centimeters. *(Review p. 49 for 11.1.)* **3 cm**

In $\triangle ABC$, angle C is a right angle. Use the given information to find AC. *(Review pp. 433, 457, 473 for 11.1, 11.6.)*

5. $AB = 14, BC = 6$ **$4\sqrt{10}$**
6. $m\angle A = 35°, AB = 25$ **about 20.5**
7. $m\angle B = 60°, BC = 5$ **$5\sqrt{3}$**

8. Which special quadrilaterals have diagonals that bisect each other? *(Review pp. 533, 542 for 11.2.)* **parallelogram, rectangle, rhombus, square**

9. Use a proportion to find XY if $\triangle UVW \sim \triangle XYZ$. *(Review p. 372 for 11.3.)* **7.5**

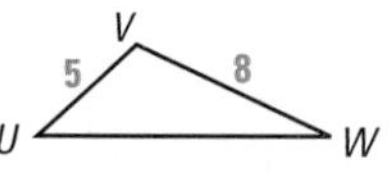

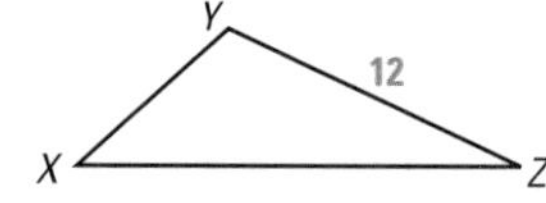

@HomeTutor Prerequisite skills practice at classzone.com

Chapter Planning Guide

Chapter 11 Resource Book
- Teaching Guide/Lesson Plan (pp. 3, 18, 31, 46, 60, 75, 89)
- Project with Rubric (p. 104)

Assessment and Intervention
- Assessment Book (pp. 155–169)
- Benchmark Tests
- Remediation Book

Interactive Technology
- Easy Planner
- Power Presentations CD-ROM
- Activity Generator CD-ROM
- Animated Geometry
- Test Generator CD-ROM
- Online Quizzes
- eWorkbook
- eEdition
- @HomeTutor

Resources for English Learners
- Quick Reference for English Learners
- Spanish Study Guide
- Multi-Language Visual Glossary
- Student Resources in Spanish

California Standards for Chapter 11

Geometry: 8.0, 10.0, 11.0, 21.0

Now

In Chapter 11, you will apply the big ideas listed below and reviewed in the Chapter Summary on page 779. You will also use the key vocabulary listed below.

Big Ideas

1. **Using area formulas for polygons**
2. **Relating length, perimeter, and area ratios in similar polygons**
3. **Comparing measures for parts of circles and the whole circle**

KEY VOCABULARY

- bases of a parallelogram, *p. 720*
- height of a parallelogram, *p. 720*
- height of a trapezoid, *p. 730*
- circumference, *p. 746*
- arc length, *p. 747*
- sector of a circle, *p. 756*
- center of a polygon, *p. 762*
- radius of a polygon, *p. 762*
- apothem of a polygon, *p. 762*
- central angle of a regular polygon, *p. 762*
- probability, *p. 771*
- geometric probability, *p. 771*

Why?

You can apply formulas for perimeter, circumference, and area to find and compare measures. To find lengths along a running track, you can break the track into straight sides and semicircles.

Animated Geometry

The animation illustrated below for Example 5 on page 749 helps you answer this question: How far does a runner travel to go around a track?

Start
Your goal is to find the distances traveled by two runners in different track lanes.

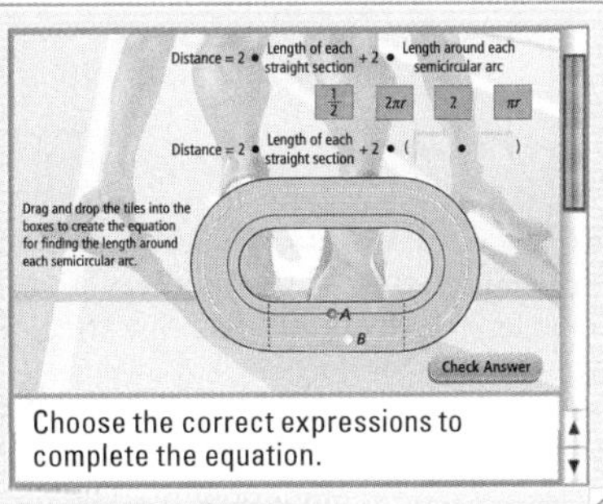

Animated Geometry at classzone.com

Other animations for Chapter 11: pages 720, 739, 759, 765, and 771

Geometry Toolkit

- Reading Strategies for Chapter 11, pp. 29–30
- Differentiated Instruction Notes, pp. 79–82
- English Learners Notes, pp. 111–112
- Inclusion Notes, pp. 141–142
- Teaching Strategies with Sample Worksheets, pp. 145–168
- Using Technology in the Classroom, pp. 169–174
- Tips for New Teachers, pp. 195–196
- Math Background Notes, pp. 234–237
- Pre-AP Strategies and Copymasters, pp. 303–304, 383–392
- Teacher Survival Activities, pp. 441–442, 465–466
- Bulletin Board Idea, p. 479
- Teacher Tool Transparencies, following p. 480

1 PLAN AND PREPARE

Warm-Up Exercises

Transparency Available

1. List the properties that make a quadrilateral a parallelogram. **Opposite sides are congruent and parallel; opposite angles are congruent; consecutive angles are supplementary; diagonals bisect each other**
2. Solve $x^2 + x^2 = 102$. $\sqrt{51}$
3. Solve $28 = \frac{1}{2}x(8)$. 7
4. Solve $12x = 84$. 7

Notetaking Guide

Transparency Available

Promotes interactive learning and notetaking skills, pp. 281–283.

Pacing

Basic: 1 day

Average: 1 day

Advanced: 1 day

Block: 0.5 block with 11.2

- See *Teaching Guide/Lesson Plan.*

2 FOCUS AND MOTIVATE

Essential Question

Big Idea 1, p. 719

How do you find the area of a parallelogram? **Tell students they will learn how to answer this question by developing a formula for the area of a parallelogram.**

11.1 Areas of Triangles and Parallelograms

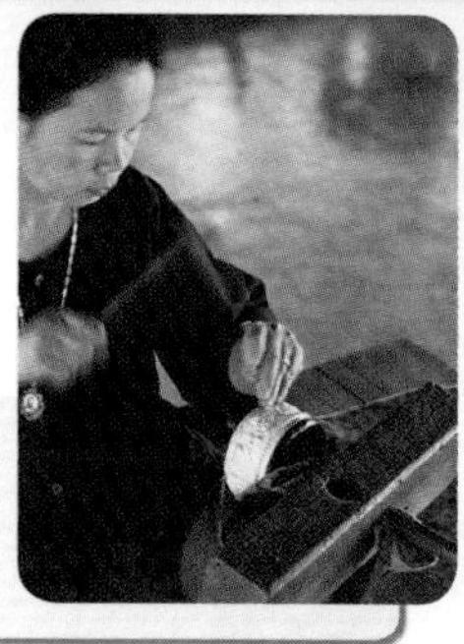

Before You learned properties of triangles and parallelograms.

Now You will find areas of triangles and parallelograms.

Why? So you can plan a jewelry making project, as in Ex. 44.

Key Vocabulary
- **bases of a parallelogram**
- **height of a parallelogram**
- **area,** *p. 49*
- **perimeter,** *p. 49*

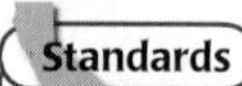

Standards

8.0 Students know, derive, and solve problems involving the perimeter, circumference, **area,** volume, lateral area, and surface area **of common geometric figures.**

10.0 Students compute areas of polygons, including rectangles, scalene triangles, equilateral triangles, rhombi, **parallelograms,** and trapezoids.

POSTULATES *For Your Notebook*

POSTULATE 24 Area of a Square Postulate

The area of a square is the square of the length of its side.

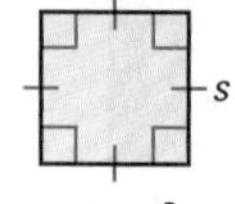

POSTULATE 25 Area Congruence Postulate

If two polygons are congruent, then they have the same area.

POSTULATE 26 Area Addition Postulate

The area of a region is the sum of the areas of its nonoverlapping parts.

RECTANGLES A rectangle that is b units by h units can be split into $b \cdot h$ unit squares, so the area formula for a rectangle follows from Postulates 24 and 26.

THEOREM *For Your Notebook*

THEOREM 11.1 Area of a Rectangle

The area of a rectangle is the product of its base and height.

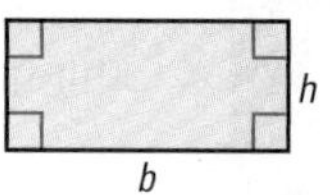

Justification: Ex. 46, p. 726

READ DIAGRAMS
The word *base* can refer to a segment or to its length. The segment used for the height must be perpendicular to the bases used.

PARALLELOGRAMS Either pair of parallel sides can be used as the **bases** of a parallelogram. The **height** is the perpendicular distance between these bases.

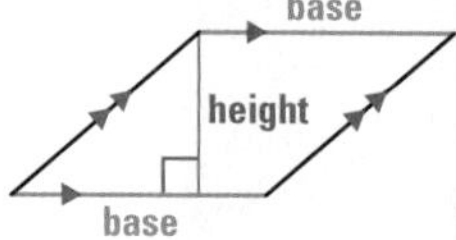

If you transform a rectangle to form other parallelograms with the same base and height, the area stays the same.

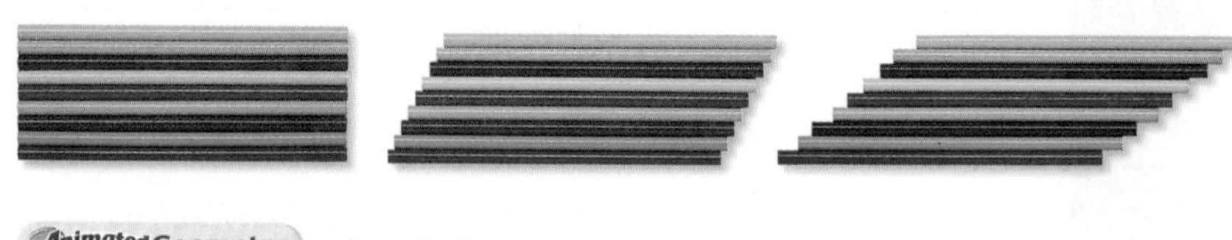

Animated Geometry at classzone.com

Resource Planning Guide

Chapter Resource Book
- Teaching Guide/Lesson Plan (pp. 3–4)
- Activity Master (p. 5)
- Practice levels A, B, C (pp. 7–12)
- Study Guide (pp. 13–14)
- Catch-up for Absent Students (p. 15)
- Problem Solving Workshop (p. 16)
- Challenge (p. 17)

Workbooks
- Notetaking Guide (pp. 281–283)
- Practice Workbook (pp. 205–207)

Teaching Options
- **Power Presentations CD-ROM** provides dynamic electronic teaching resources for the classroom.
- **Activity Generator CD-ROM** provides editable activities for all ability levels.

Interactive Technology
- Easy Planner
- Power Presentations CD-ROM
- Activity Generator CD-ROM
- Animated Geometry
- Test Generator CD-ROM
- Online Quiz
- eWorkbook
- eEdition
- @HomeTutor

Resources for English Learners
- Quick Reference for English Learners
- Spanish Study Guide
- Multi-Language Visual Glossary
- Student Resources in Spanish

See also the *Geometry Toolkit* for more strategies for meeting individual needs.

READ VOCABULARY

The *height* of a triangle is the length of the altitude drawn to the given *base*.

THEOREMS — *For Your Notebook*

THEOREM 11.2 Area of a Parallelogram

The area of a parallelogram is the product of a base and its corresponding height.

Justification: Ex. 42, p. 725

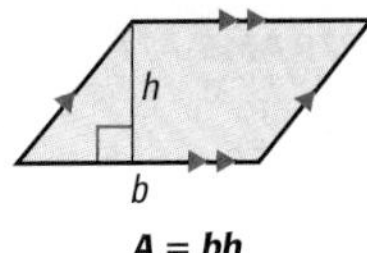

$A = bh$

THEOREM 11.3 Area of a Triangle

The area of a triangle is one half the product of a base and its corresponding height.

Justification: Ex. 43, p. 726

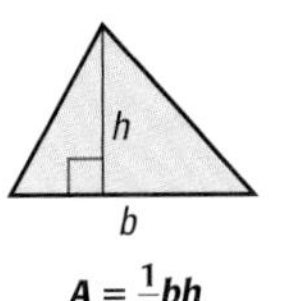

$A = \frac{1}{2}bh$

RELATING AREA FORMULAS As illustrated below, the area formula for a parallelogram is related to the formula for a rectangle, and the area formula for a triangle is related to the formula for a parallelogram. You will write a justification of these relationships in Exercises 42 and 43 on pages 725–726.

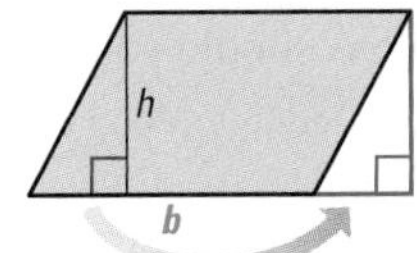

Area of ▱ = Area of Rectangle

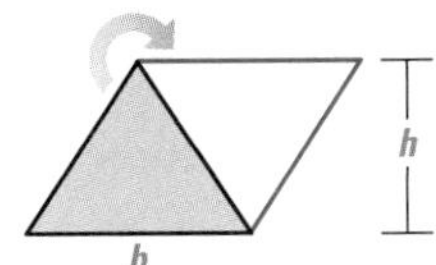

Area of △ = $\frac{1}{2}$ • Area of ▱

EXAMPLE 1 Use a formula to find area

Find the area of ▱*PQRS*.

Solution

Method 1 Use $\overline{PS}$ as the base.
The base is extended to measure the height *RU*. So, $b = 6$ and $h = 8$.

Area $= bh = 6(8) = 48$ square units

Method 2 Use $\overline{PQ}$ as the base.
Then the height is *QT*. So, $b = 12$ and $h = 4$.

Area $= bh = 12(4) = 48$ square units

GUIDED PRACTICE for Example 1

Find the perimeter and area of the polygon.

1. 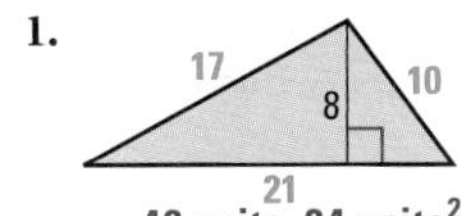

48 units, 84 units^2

2. 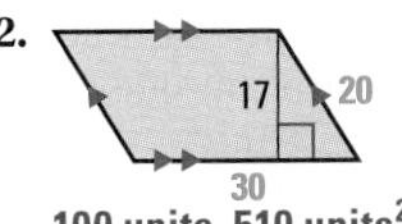

100 units, 510 units^2

3. 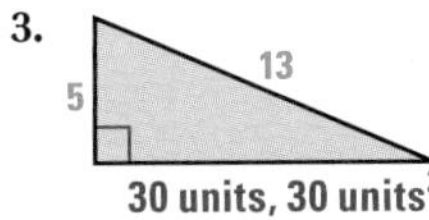

30 units, 30 units^2

Motivating the Lesson

Ask students to cut out two congruent right triangles, and then arrange the two triangles to form a rectangle, a parallelogram, and a triangle. Ask them to compare the areas of the three figures. Then tell students that in this lesson they will generate formulas for the area of a triangle and the area of a parallelogram.

3 TEACH

An **Animated Geometry** activity is available on-line for the transformation of a rectangle to a parallelogram. This activity is also available on the **Power Presentations CD-ROM**.

Extra Example 1

Find the area of ▱ *RSTU*.

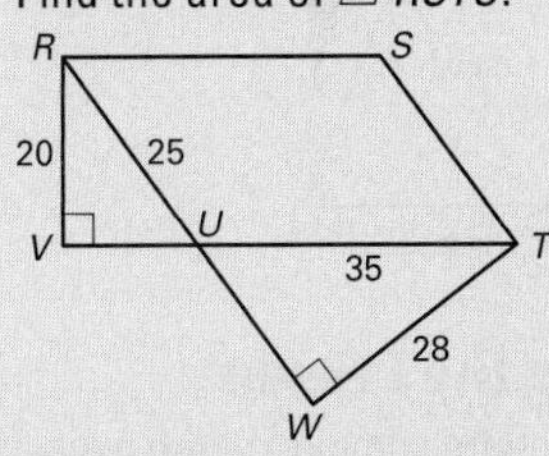

700 square units

Avoiding Common Errors

When finding the area of a parallelogram, a common error is to multiply the lengths of two consecutive sides. Point out the area formula uses one side and the height, which is the perpendicular distance between two parallel sides.

Differentiated Instruction

Kinesthetic Learners Ask students to imagine that their classroom is getting new flooring. Have them work in small groups to create a scale drawing of the floor of the classroom. Students should then calculate how much flooring to order to cover the floor. Have groups compare their results.

See also the *Geometry Toolkit* for more strategies.

Extra Example 2

The base of a triangle is one half the height. The area of the triangle is 64 square centimeters. Find the base and height. **8 cm; 16 cm**

Key Questions to Ask for Example 2

- If two triangles have the same base and height, must they be congruent? **no**
- If two triangles have the same base and height, must they have the same area? **yes**

Extra Example 3

You need to buy paint so you can cover the back of an A-frame house and the top of a deck. A gallon of paint covers 275 square feet. How many gallons should you buy? **3 gal**

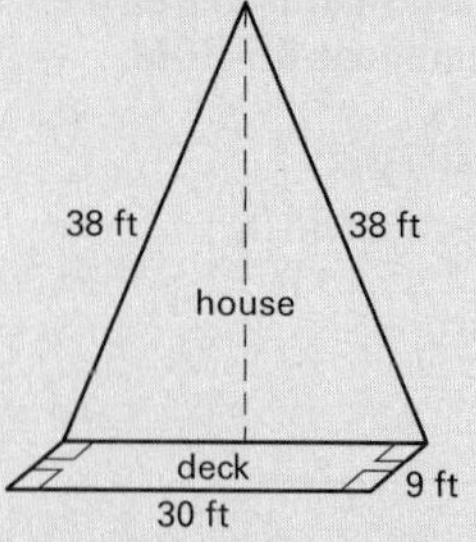

Closing the Lesson

Have students summarize the major points of the lesson and answer the Essential Question: How do you find the area of a parallelogram?

- **For a square with side length s, $A = s^2$.**
- **For a rectangle with base b and height h, $A = bh$.**
- **For a parallelogram with base b and height h, $A = bh$.**
- **For a triangle with base b and height h, $A = \frac{1}{2}bh$.**

Find the length of a base and the corresponding height, and use the area formula $A = bh$.

EXAMPLE 2 Solve for unknown measures

DRAW DIAGRAMS
Note that there are other ways you can draw the triangle described in Example 2.

ALGEBRA The base of a triangle is twice its height. The area of the triangle is 36 square inches. Find the base and height.

Let h represent the height of the triangle. Then the base is $2h$.

$A = \frac{1}{2}bh$ — **Write formula.**

$36 = \frac{1}{2}(2h)(h)$ — **Substitute 36 for A and $2h$ for b.**

$36 = h^2$ — **Simplify.**

$6 = h$ — **Find positive square root of each side.**

▶ The height of the triangle is 6 inches, and the base is $6 \cdot 2 = 12$ inches.

EXAMPLE 3 Solve a multi-step problem

PAINTING You need to buy paint so that you can paint the side of a barn. A gallon of paint covers 350 square feet. How many gallons should you buy?

Solution

You can use a right triangle and a rectangle to approximate the area of the side of the barn.

ANOTHER WAY
In Example 3, you have a 45°-45°-90° triangle, so you can also find x by using trigonometry or special right angles.

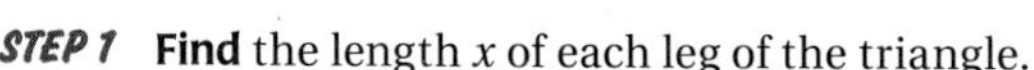

STEP 1 **Find** the length x of each leg of the triangle.

$26^2 = x^2 + x^2$ — **Use Pythagorean Theorem.**

$676 = 2x^2$ — **Simplify.**

$\sqrt{338} = x$ — **Solve for the positive value of x.**

STEP 2 **Find** the approximate area of the side of the barn.

Area = **Area of rectangle** + **Area of triangle**

$= 26(18) + \frac{1}{2} \cdot [(\sqrt{338})(\sqrt{338})] = 637 \text{ ft}^2$

STEP 3 **Determine** how many gallons of paint you need.

$637 \text{ ft}^2 \cdot \frac{1 \text{ gal}}{350 \text{ ft}^2} \approx 1.82 \text{ gal}$ — **Use unit analysis.**

▶ Round up so you will have enough paint. You need to buy 2 gallons of paint.

GUIDED PRACTICE for Examples 2 and 3

4. A parallelogram has an area of 153 square inches and a height of 17 inches. What is the length of the base? **9 in.**

5. **WHAT IF?** In Example 3, suppose there is a 5 foot by 10 foot rectangular window on the side of the barn. What is the approximate area you need to paint? **587 ft²**

Differentiated Instruction

Below Level Ask students to cut a sheet of $8\frac{1}{2}$ by 11 inch paper along one diagonal. Ask them for form a non-rectangular parallelogram using the two triangles and to find measurements for the base and height of the parallelogram. Have the students calculate and compare the areas of the original rectangle, the parallelogram, and one of the triangles.

See also the *Geometry Toolkit* for more strategies.

11.1 EXERCISES

HOMEWORK KEY ○ = **WORKED-OUT SOLUTIONS** on p. WS14 for Exs. 7, 23, and 37
★ = **STANDARDIZED TEST PRACTICE** Exs. 2, 21, 30, 39, and 45

SKILL PRACTICE

A

1. **VOCABULARY** Copy and complete: Either pair of parallel sides of a parallelogram can be called its _?_, and the perpendicular distance between these sides is called the _?_. **bases, height**

2. ★ **WRITING** What are the two formulas you have learned for the area of a rectangle? *Explain* why these formulas give the same results. **$A = \ell \cdot w$ or $A = b \cdot h$; ℓ and b represent the same side of a rectangle, as do w and h.**

EXAMPLE 1 on p. 721 for Exs. 3–15

FINDING AREA **Find the area of the polygon.**

3. 4, 7 — **28 units^2**

4. 12, 14 — **168 units^2**

5. 15 — **225 units^2**

6. 13, 10 — **65 units^2**

7. 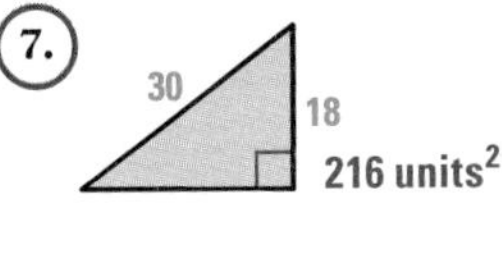

216 units^2

8. 9, 15 — **67.5 units^2**

9. **COMPARING METHODS** Show two different ways to calculate the area of parallelogram *ABCD*. *Compare* your results. **$A = 10(16) = 160$ units^2 or $A = 8(20) = 160$ units^2; the results are the same.**

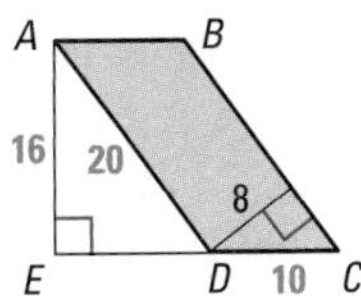

ERROR ANALYSIS ***Describe*** **and correct the error in finding the area of the parallelogram.**

10. 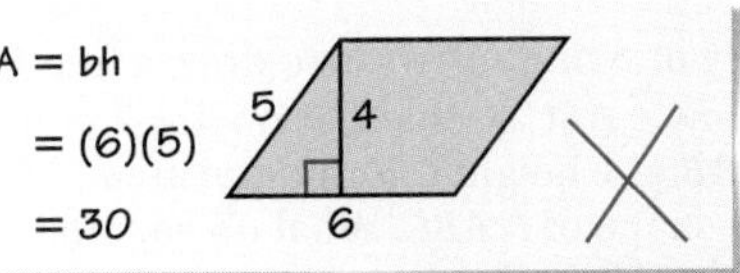

11. 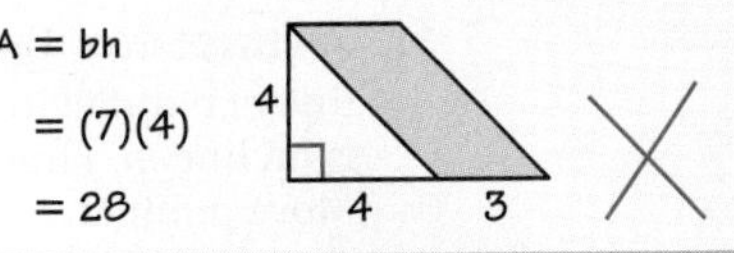

10. 5 is not the height of the parallelogram; $A = bh = 6(4) = 24$.

11. 7 is not the base of the parallelogram; $A = bh = 3(4) = 12$.

PYTHAGOREAN THEOREM **The lengths of the hypotenuse and one leg of a right triangle are given. Find the perimeter and area of the triangle.**

12. Hypotenuse: 15 in.; leg: 12 in. **36 in., 54 in.^{2}**

13. Hypotenuse: 34 ft; leg: 16 ft **80 ft, 240 ft^2**

14. Hypotenuse: 85 m; leg: 84 m **182 m, 546 m^2**

15. Hypotenuse: 29 cm; leg: 20 cm **70 cm, 210 cm^2**

EXAMPLE 2 on p. 722 for Exs. 16–21

ALGEBRA **Find the value of *x*.**

16. $A = 36$ in.^{2}

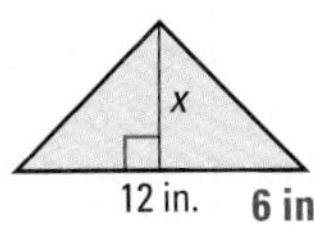

6 in.

17. $A = 276$ ft^2

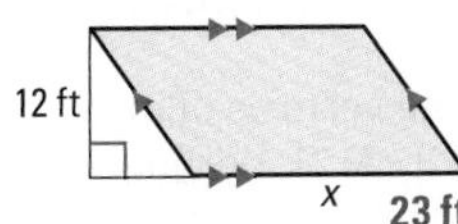

23 ft

18. $A = 476$ cm^2

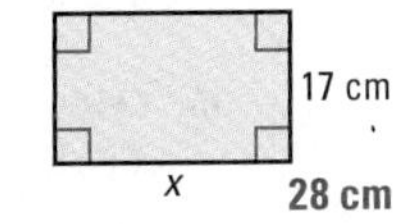

28 cm

4 PRACTICE AND APPLY

Assignment Guide

Answer Transparencies available for all exercises

Basic:
Day 1: SRH p. 883 Exs. 1, 4, 5, 8
pp. 723–726
Exs. 1–5, 9–13, 16–24, 28, 36–42, 48–54

Average:
Day 1: pp. 723–726
Exs. 1, 2, 5–7, 9–11, 14–17, 19–21, 25–33, 37–45, 49–53 odd

Advanced:
Day 1: pp. 723–726
Exs. 1, 2, 7–9, 14, 15, 17–21, 26–35*, 37, 39–47*, 50, 54

Block:
pp. 723–726
Exs. 1, 2, 5–7, 9–11, 14–17, 19–21, 25–33, 37–45, 49–53 odd (with 11.2)

Differentiated Instruction

See *Geometry Best Practices Toolkit* for suggestions on addressing the needs of a diverse classroom.

Homework Check

For a quick check of student understanding of key concepts, go over the following exercises:

Basic: 4, 16, 22, 36, 37
Average: 6, 16, 25, 37, 38
Advanced: 14, 20, 26, 37, 40

Extra Practice

- Student Edition, p. 916
- Chapter 11 Resource Book: Practice levels A, B, C, pp. 7–12

Practice Worksheet

An easily-readable reduced practice page (with answers) for this lesson can be found on p. 718C.

Avoiding Common Errors

Exercise 16 Students may use the equation $12x = 36$ to solve for x. Caution them to use the correct formula $A = \frac{1}{2}bh$ or $36 = \left(\frac{1}{2}\right)(12x)$.

Teaching Strategy

Exercises 22–26 Point out that each shaded polygon is the sum of two or more polygons and that the area addition postulate should be used to justify finding the total area.

Exercises 28–29 Suggest that students estimate the area calculations by counting the number of square units in the polygon.

Mathematical Reasoning

Exercise 31 For each triangle, the height is the distance between lines ℓ and m. Since all the triangles have the same base, $\overline{AB}$, and the same height, all the triangles must have the same area.

21. See Additional Answers beginning on p. AA1.

28.

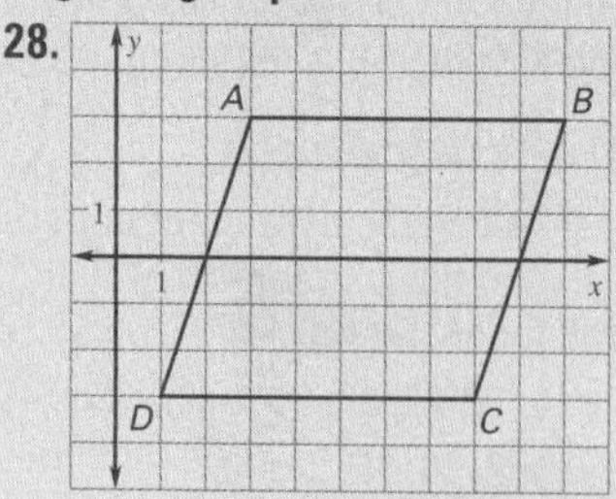

29.

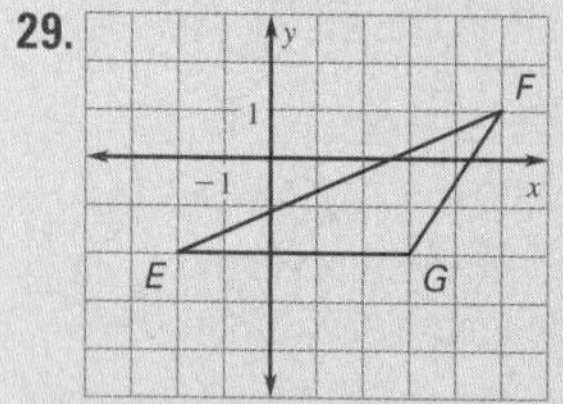

19. ALGEBRA The area of a triangle is 4 square feet. The height of the triangle is half its base. Find the base and the height. **4 ft, 2 ft**

20. ALGEBRA The area of a parallelogram is 507 square centimeters, and its height is three times its base. Find the base and the height. **13 cm, 39 cm**

21. ★ **OPEN-ENDED MATH** A polygon has an area of 80 square meters and a height of 10 meters. Make scale drawings of three different triangles and three different parallelograms that match this description. Label the base and the height. **See margin.**

EXAMPLE 3 B on p. 722 for Exs. 22–27

FINDING AREA **Find the area of the shaded polygon.**

22.

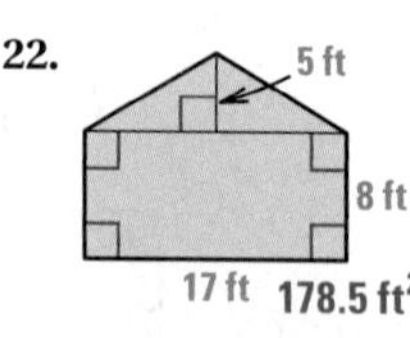

(23.)

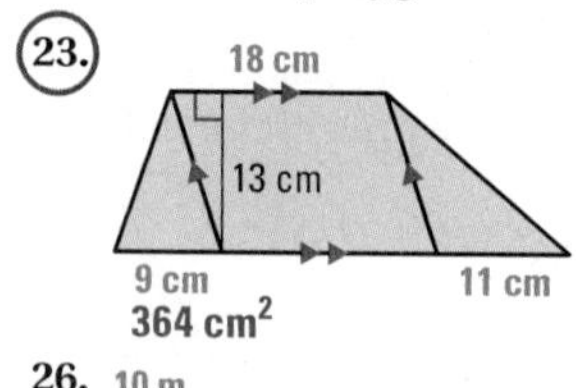

24.

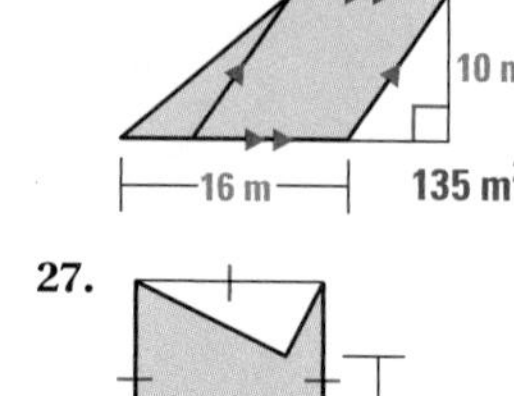

25.

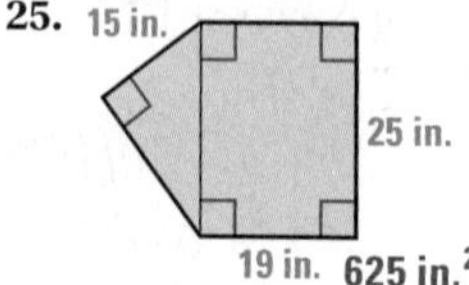

26.

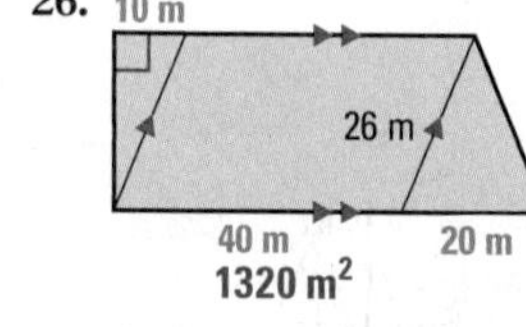

27.

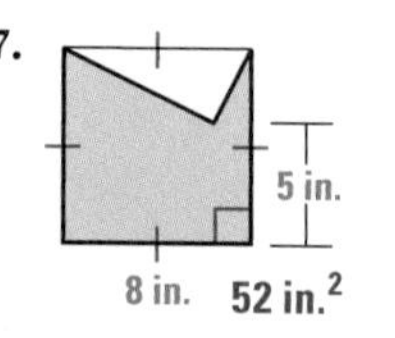

COORDINATE GRAPHING **Graph the points and connect them to form a polygon. Find the area of the polygon.** **28, 29. See margin for art.**

28. $A(3, 3)$, $B(10, 3)$, $C(8, -3)$, $D(1, -3)$ **42 units²**

29. $E(-2, -2)$, $F(5, 1)$, $G(3, -2)$ **7.5 units²**

30. ★ **MULTIPLE CHOICE** What is the area of the parallelogram shown at the right? **D**

Ⓐ $8\text{ ft}^2\ 6\text{ in.}^2$ Ⓑ 1350 in.

Ⓒ 675 in.^2 Ⓓ 9.375 ft^2

2 ft 3 in.
4 ft 2 in.

31. TECHNOLOGY Use geometry drawing software to draw a line ℓ and a line m parallel to ℓ. Then draw $\triangle ABC$ so that C is on line ℓ and $\overline{AB}$ is on line m. Find the base AB, the height CD, and the area of $\triangle ABC$. Move point C to change the shape of $\triangle ABC$. What do you notice about the base, height, and area of $\triangle ABC$? **Check students' work; the base remains the same, and the height remains the same, so the area also remains the same.**

32. USING TRIGONOMETRY In $\square ABCD$, base AD is 15 and AB is 8. What are the height and area of $\square ABCD$ if $m\angle DAB$ is 20°? if $m\angle DAB$ is 50°? **about 2.74 units, about 41 units²; about 6.13 units, about 92 units²**

33. ALGEBRA Find the area of a right triangle with side lengths 12 centimeters, 35 centimeters, and 37 centimeters. Then find the length of the altitude drawn to the hypotenuse. **210 cm²; about 11.4 cm**

C

34. ALGEBRA Find the area of a triangle with side lengths 5 feet, 5 feet, and 8 feet. Then find the lengths of all three altitudes of the triangle. **12 ft²; 3 ft, 4.8 ft, 4.8 ft**

35. CHALLENGE The vertices of quadrilateral $ABCD$ are $A(2, -2)$, $B(6, 4)$, $C(-1, 5)$, and $D(-5, 2)$. Without using the Distance Formula, find the area of $ABCD$. Show your steps. **41.5 units²; construct a rectangle so that *A*, *B*, *C*, and *D* are all on the sides of the rectangle. The area of the rectangle is 77 square units. Now subtract the right triangle formed on each corner of the rectangle that is not part of quadrilateral *ABCD*.**

○ = **WORKED-OUT SOLUTIONS on p. WS1** ★ = **STANDARDIZED TEST PRACTICE**

PROBLEM SOLVING

A **36. SAILING** Sails A and B are right triangles. The lengths of the legs of Sail A are 65 feet and 35 feet. The lengths of the legs of Sail B are 29.5 feet and 10.5 feet. Find the area of each sail to the nearest square foot. About how many times as great is the area of Sail A as the area of Sail B? **Sail A: 1138 ft^2, Sail B: 155 ft^2; about 7.3 times**

@HomeTutor for problem solving help at classzone.com

EXAMPLE 3 on p. 722 for Ex. 37

37. MOWING You can mow 10 square yards of grass in one minute. How long does it take you to mow a triangular plot with height 25 yards and base 24 yards? How long does it take you to mow a rectangular plot with base 24 yards and height 36 yards? **30 min; 86.4 min**

@HomeTutor for problem solving help at classzone.com

38. CARPENTRY You are making a tabletop in the shape of a parallelogram to replace an old 24 inch by 15 inch rectangular one. You want the areas of the tabletops to be equal. The base of the parallelogram is 20 inches. What should the height be? **18 in.**

39. ★ SHORT RESPONSE A *4 inch square* is a square that has a side length of 4 inches. Does a 4 inch square have an area of 4 square inches? If not, what size square does have an area of 4 square inches? *Explain.* **No; 2 inch square; the area of a square is side length squared, so $2^2 = 4$.**

B **40. PAINTING** You are earning money by painting a shed. You plan to paint two sides of the shed today. Each of the two sides has the dimensions shown at the right. You can paint 200 square feet per hour, and you charge $20 per hour. About how much will you get paid for painting those two sides of the shed? **about $20**

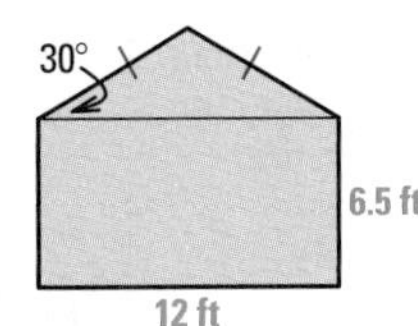

41. ENVELOPES The pattern below shows how to make an envelope to fit a card that is 17 centimeters by 14 centimeters. What are the dimensions of the rectangle you need to start with? What is the area of the paper that is actually used in the envelope? of the paper that is cut off? **23 cm × 34 cm; 611 cm^2; 171 cm^2**

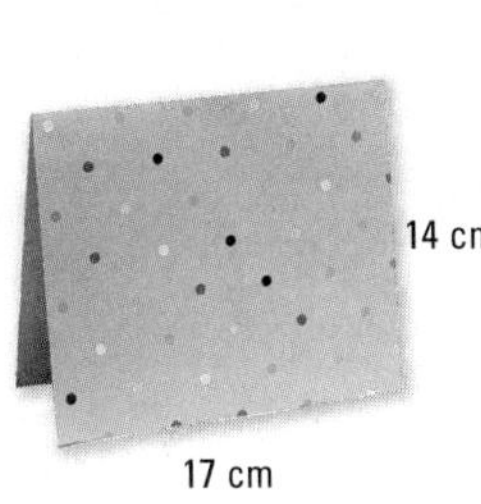

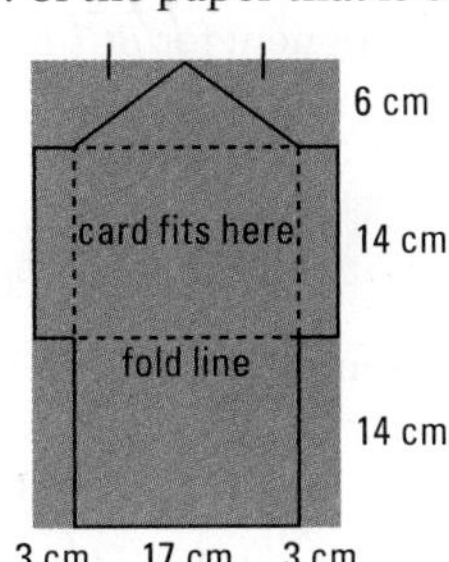

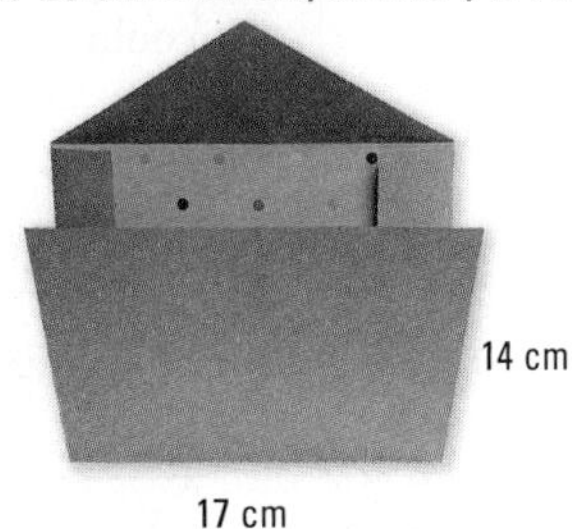

42. JUSTIFYING THEOREM 11.2 You can use the area formula for a rectangle to justify the area formula for a parallelogram. First draw ▱*PQRS* with base *b* and height *h*, as shown. Then draw a segment perpendicular to $\overleftrightarrow{PS}$ through point *R*. Label point *V*. **a, b. See margin.**

a. In the diagram, *explain* how you know that $\triangle PQT \cong \triangle SRV$.

b. *Explain* how you know that the area of *PQRS* is equal to the area of *QRVT*. How do you know that Area of *PQRS* = *bh*?

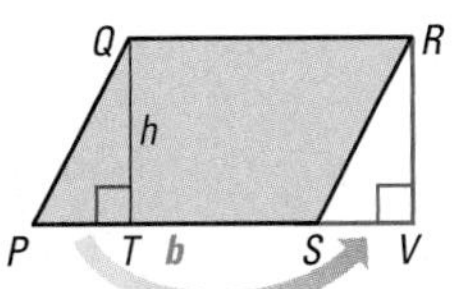

42a. $\overline{PQ} \cong \overline{SR}$ **by definition of a parallelogram and so** $\overline{QT} \cong \overline{RV}$**.** $\angle PPQ$ **and** $\angle V$ **are both right angles so by the HL Congruence Theorem the triangles are congruent.**

42b. Since $\triangle PQT$ **is shifted over to become** $\triangle SRV$**, then the areas are the same; since the area of** *PQRS* **is equal to the area of** *QRVT***, the formulas for determining the areas can be interchanged as well.**

5 ASSESS AND RETEACH

Daily Homework Quiz

Transparency Available

Find the area of the polygon.

1. 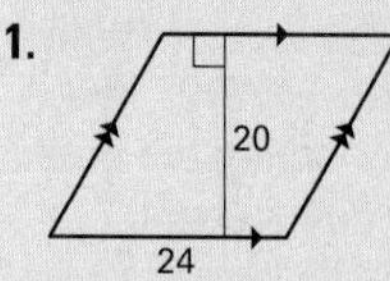

480 square units

2. 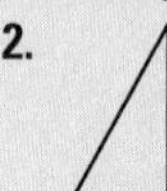 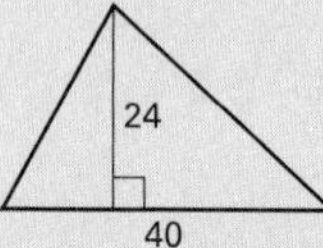

480 square units

3. $ABCE$ 375.4 square units

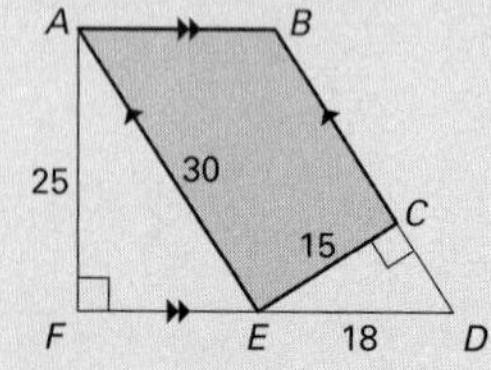

4. 973.5 ft²

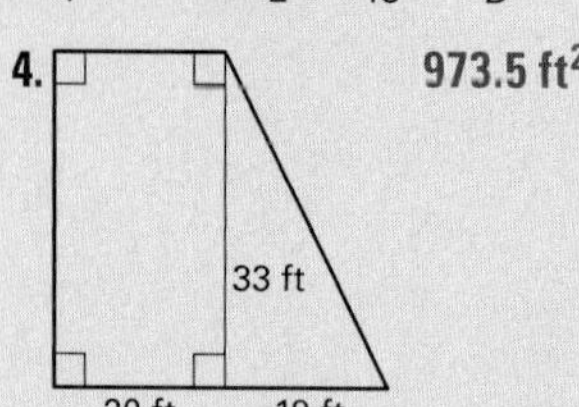

5. Find the area of a triangle with side lengths 13 inches, 13 inches, and 10 inches. 60 in.²

Online Quiz

Available at **classzone.com**

Diagnosis/Remediation

- Practice A, B, C in Chapter 11 Resource Book, pp. 7–12
- Study Guide in Chapter 11 Resource Book, pp. 13–14
- Practice Workbook, pp. 205–207
- @HomeTutor

Challenge

Additional challenge is available in the Chapter 11 Resource Book, p. 17.

46a–b, 47. See Additional Answers beginning on p. AA1.

43. Opposite pairs of sides are congruent so $XYZW$ is a parallelogram. The area of the parallelogram is bh, and since the parallelogram is made of two congruent triangles, the area of one triangle, $\triangle XYW$, is $\frac{1}{2}bh$.

45. The base and the height are not necessarily side lengths of the parallelogram; yes; no; if the base and height represent a rectangle, then the perimeter is 20 ft, the greatest possible perimeter cannot be determined from the given data.

43. JUSTIFYING THEOREM 11.3 You can use the area formula for a parallelogram to justify the area formula for a triangle. Start with two congruent triangles with base b and height h. Place and label them as shown. *Explain* how you know that $XYZW$ is a parallelogram and that Area of $\triangle XYW = \frac{1}{2}bh$.

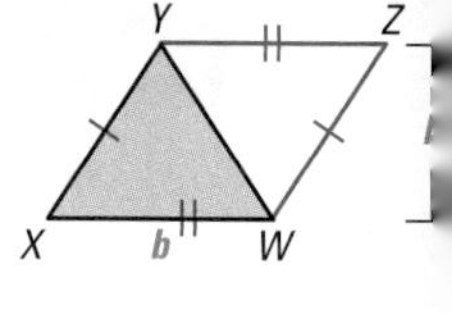

44. MULTI-STEP PROBLEM You have enough silver to make a pendant with an area of 4 square centimeters. The pendant will be an equilateral triangle. Let s be the side length of the triangle.

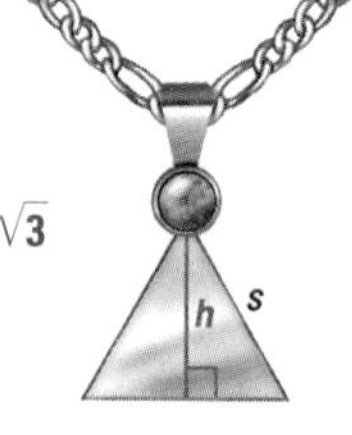

a. Find the height h of the triangle in terms of s. Then write a formula for the area of the triangle in terms of s. $\frac{1}{2}s\sqrt{3}$; $A = \frac{1}{4}s^2\sqrt{3}$

b. Find the side length of the triangle. Round to the nearest centimeter. **3 cm**

45. ★ EXTENDED RESPONSE The base of a parallelogram is 7 feet and the height is 3 feet. *Explain* why the perimeter cannot be determined from the given information. Is there a least possible perimeter for the parallelogram? Is there a greatest possible perimeter? *Explain.*

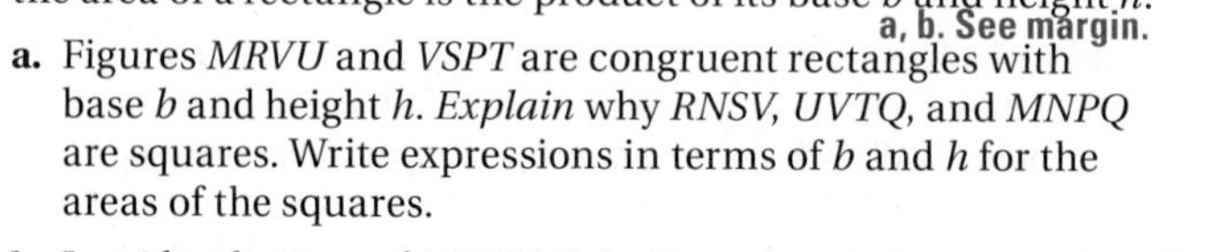

46. JUSTIFYING THEOREM 11.1 You can use the diagram to show that the area of a rectangle is the product of its base b and height h. **a, b. See margin.**

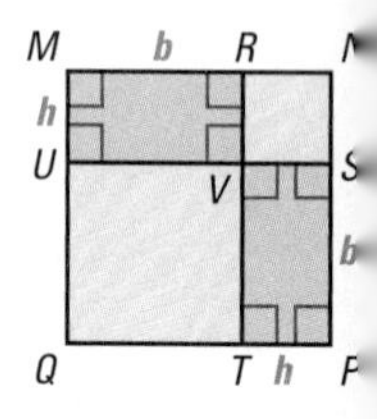

a. Figures $MRVU$ and $VSPT$ are congruent rectangles with base b and height h. *Explain* why $RNSV$, $UVTQ$, and $MNPQ$ are squares. Write expressions in terms of b and h for the areas of the squares.

b. Let A be the area of $MRVU$. Substitute A and the expressions from part (a) into the equation below. Solve to find an expression for A.

Area of $MNPQ$ = Area of $MRVU$ + Area of $UVTQ$ + Area of $RNSV$ + Area of $VSPT$

47. CHALLENGE An equation of $\overleftrightarrow{AB}$ is $y = x$. An equation of $\overleftrightarrow{AC}$ is $y = 2$. Suppose $\overleftrightarrow{BC}$ is placed so that $\triangle ABC$ is isosceles with an area of 4 square units. Find two different lines that fit these conditions. Give an equation for each line. Is there another line that could fit this requirement for $\overleftrightarrow{BC}$? *Explain.* **See margin.**

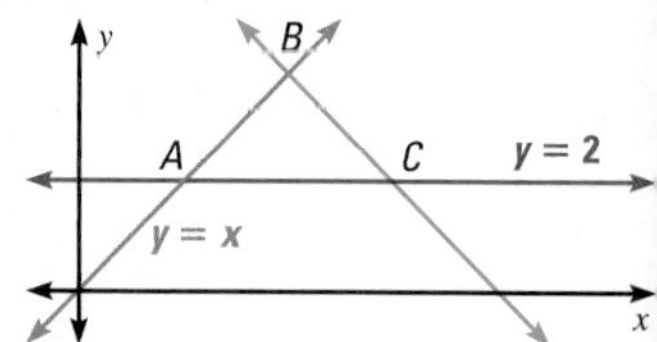

MIXED REVIEW

PREVIEW

Prepare for Lesson 11.2 in Exs. 48–50.

Find the length of the midsegment $\overline{MN}$ of the trapezoid. *(p. 542)*

48. 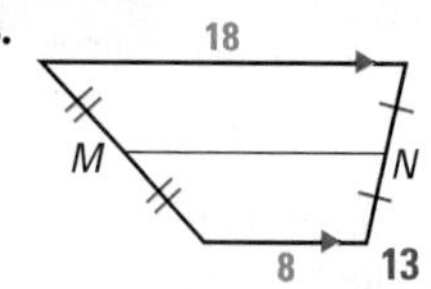

13

49. 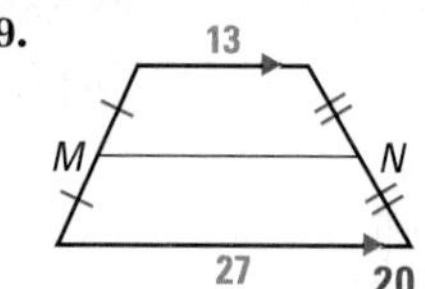

20

50. 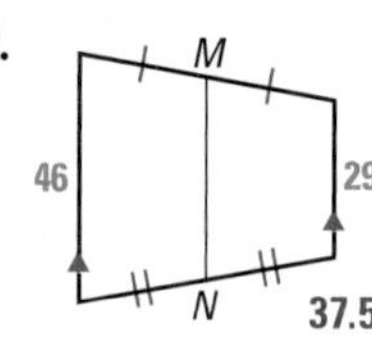

37.5

The coordinates of $\triangle PQR$ are $P(-4, 1)$, $Q(2, 5)$, and $R(1, -4)$. Graph the image of the triangle after the translation. Use prime notation. *(p. 572)* **51–54. See margin.**

51. $(x, y) \to (x + 1, y + 4)$

52. $(x, y) \to (x + 3, y - 5)$

53. $(x, y) \to (x - 3, y - 2)$

54. $(x, y) \to (x - 2, y + 3)$

51. 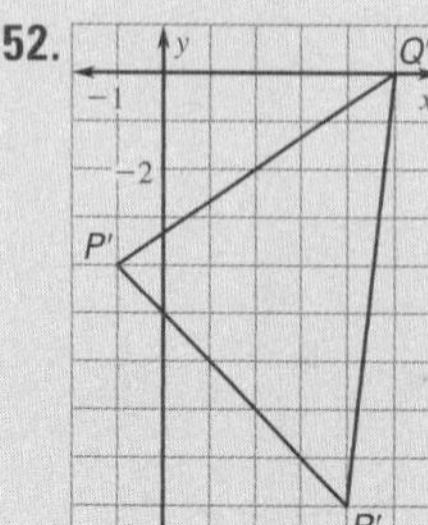

52. 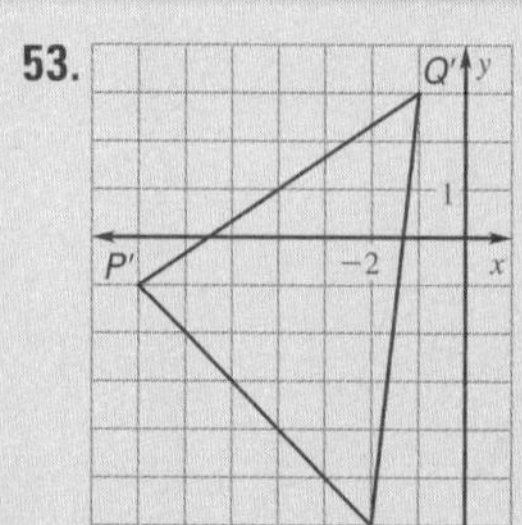

53. 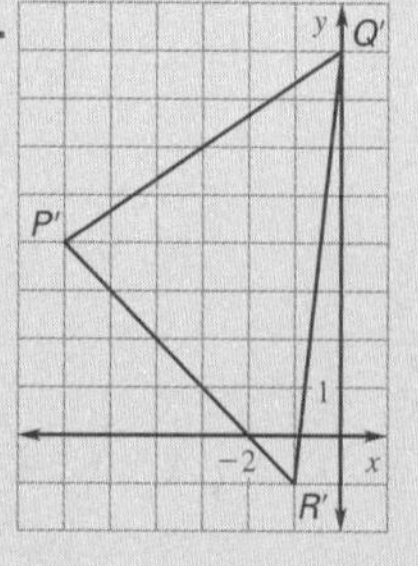

54.

Extension
Use after Lesson 11.1

Determine Precision and Accuracy

GOAL Determine the precision and accuracy of measurements.

Key Vocabulary
- unit of measure
- greatest possible error
- relative error

Standards
Enrichment topic; not required by the California Standards.

All measurements are approximations. The length of each segment below, *to the nearest inch*, is 2 inches. The measurement is to the nearest inch, so the **unit of measure** is 1 inch.

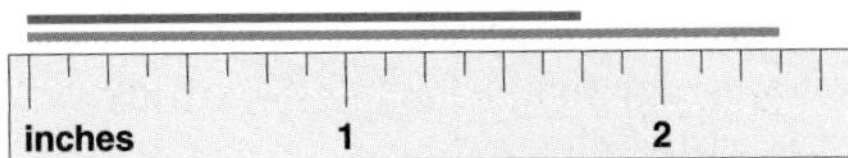

If you are told that an object is 2 inches long, you know that its exact length is between $1\frac{1}{2}$ inches and $2\frac{1}{2}$ inches, or within $\frac{1}{2}$ inch of 2 inches. The **greatest possible error** of a measurement is equal to one half of the unit of measure.

When the unit of measure is smaller, the greatest possible error is smaller and the measurement is *more precise*. Using one-eighth inch as the unit of measure for the segments above gives lengths of $1\frac{6}{8}$ inches and $2\frac{3}{8}$ inches and a greatest possible error of $\frac{1}{16}$ inch.

EXAMPLE 1 Find greatest possible error

AMUSEMENT PARK The final drop of a log flume ride is listed in the park guide as 52.3 feet. Find the unit of measure and the greatest possible error.

Solution

The measurement 52.3 feet is given to the nearest tenth of a foot. So, the unit of measure is $\frac{1}{10}$ foot. The greatest possible error is half the unit of measure. Because $\frac{1}{2}\left(\frac{1}{10}\right) = \frac{1}{20} = 0.05$, the greatest possible error is 0.05 foot.

READ VOCABULARY
The *precision* of a measurement depends only on the unit of measure. The *accuracy* of a measurement depends on both the unit of measure and on the size of the object being measured.

RELATIVE ERROR The diameter of a bicycle tire is 26 inches. The diameter of a key ring is 1 inch. In each case, the greatest possible error is $\frac{1}{2}$ inch, but a half-inch error has a much greater effect on the diameter of a smaller object. The **relative error** of a measurement is the ratio $\frac{\text{greatest possible error}}{\text{measured length}}$.

Bicycle tire diameter	Key ring diameter
Rel. error $= \frac{0.5 \text{ in.}}{26 \text{ in.}} \approx 0.01923 \approx 1.9\%$	Rel. error $= \frac{0.5 \text{ in.}}{1 \text{ in.}} = 0.5 = 50\%$

The measurement with the smaller relative error is said to be *more accurate.*

1 PLAN AND PREPARE

Warm-Up Exercises

Round to the nearest whole unit.

1. $2\frac{3}{4}$ in. **3 in.** **2.** 7.38 cm **7 cm**

Round to the nearest half unit.

3. $3\frac{3}{8}$ feet **$3\frac{1}{2}$ ft** **4.** $1\frac{1}{8}$ in. **1 in.**

5. A recipe calls for $\frac{3}{8}$ c of sugar. How much sugar do you need if you are making one half of the recipe? **$\frac{3}{16}$ c**

2 FOCUS AND MOTIVATE

Essential Question

Big Idea 1, p. 719

What does "relative error" mean and how do you evaluate it? **Tell students they will learn how to answer this question by finding the greatest possible error, which is one half of the unit used for the measurement.**

3 TEACH

Extra Example 1

The Navajo Bridge is a pedestrian bridge near Marble Canyon, Arizona, that is 143.3 meters over the Colorado River. Find the unit of measure and the greatest possible error. **0.1 m; 0.05 m**

Extra Example 2

A soccer field is 390 feet long and a soccer goal is 25 feet wide. Find the relative error of each measurement. Which measurement is more accurate? **field: $\frac{0.5}{390} = 0.00128 = 0.13\%$; goal: $\frac{0.5}{25} = 0.02 = 2\%$; the measurement of the field is more accurate.**

Closing the Lesson

Have students summarize the major points of the lesson and answer the Essential Question: What does "relative error" mean and how do you evaluate it?

- **One half of the unit used is called the greatest possible error.**
- **The ratio $\frac{\text{greatest possible error}}{\text{measured length}}$ is called the relative error.**

The relative error of a measurement is one half of the unit used for the measurement divided by the actual measurement.

4 PRACTICE AND APPLY

Vocabulary

Exercises 12–15 Make sure students understand that a measurement is *more precise* if $\frac{1}{2}$ the unit of measure is smaller, while a measurement is *more accurate* if $\frac{1}{2}$ the unit of measure divided by the measured length is smaller.

Mathematical Reasoning

Exercise 16 Since each side of the eraser has a greatest possible error of 0.05 centimeter, the length of the eraser can be 5.1 ± 0.05, or 5.05 centimeters to 5.15 centimeters, and the width can be 1.4 ± 0.05, or 1.35 centimeters to 1.45 centimeters. Students can use these lengths to find the greatest and least possible perimeter.

EXAMPLE 2 Find relative error

PLAYING AREAS An air hockey table is 3.7 feet wide. An ice rink is 85 feet wide. Find the relative error of each measurement. Which measurement is more accurate?

	Air hockey table (3.7 feet)	Ice rink (85 feet)
Unit of measure	0.1 ft	1 ft
Greatest possible error $\frac{1}{2}$ • (unit of measure)	$\frac{1}{2}(0.1\text{ ft}) = 0.05\text{ ft}$	$\frac{1}{2}(1\text{ ft}) = 0.5\text{ ft}$
Relative error $\frac{\text{greatest possible error}}{\text{measured length}}$	$\frac{0.05\text{ ft}}{3.7\text{ ft}} \approx 0.0135 \approx 1.4\%$	$\frac{0.5\text{ ft}}{85\text{ ft}} \approx 0.00588 \approx 0.6\%$

▶ The ice rink width has the smaller relative error, so it is more accurate.

PRACTICE

1. **VOCABULARY** *Describe* the difference between the *precision* of a measurement and the *accuracy* of a measurement. Give an example that illustrates the difference. **See margin.**

EXAMPLE 1 on p. 727 for Exs. 2–5

GREATEST POSSIBLE ERROR Find the unit of measure. Then find the greatest possible error.

2. 14.6 in. **0.1 in.; 0.05 in.**
3. 6 m **1 m; 0.5 m**
4. 8.217 km **0.001 km; 0.0005 km**
5. $4\frac{5}{16}$ yd **$\frac{1}{16}$ yd; $\frac{1}{32}$ yd**

EXAMPLE 2 on p. 728 for Exs. 6–9

RELATIVE ERROR Find the relative error of the measurement.

6. 4.0 cm **about 1.3%**
7. 28 in. **about 1.8%**
8. 4.6 m **about 1.1%**
9. 12.16 mm **about 0.04%**

10. **CHOOSING A UNIT** You are estimating the amount of paper needed to make book covers for your textbooks. Which unit of measure, 1 foot, 1 inch, or $\frac{1}{16}$ inch, should you use to measure your textbooks? *Explain.* **1 in.; you are estimating the amount of paper, so a greatest possible error of $\frac{1}{2}$ inch is precise enough.**

11. **REASONING** The greatest possible error of a measurement is $\frac{1}{16}$ inch. *Explain* how such a measurement could be more accurate in one situation than in another situation. **This measurement is more accurate if you are measuring large items; if you are measuring small items, this would not be very accurate.**

PRECISION AND ACCURACY Tell which measurement is more precise. Then tell which of the two measurements is more accurate. 12–15. See margin.

12. 17 cm; 12 cm
13. 18.65 ft; 25.6 ft
14. 6.8 in.; 13.4 ft
15. 3.5 ft; 35 in.

16. **PERIMETER** A side of the eraser shown is a parallelogram. What is the greatest possible error for the length of each side of the parallelogram? for the perimeter of the parallelogram? Find the greatest and least possible perimeter of the parallelogram. **0.05 cm; 0.5 cm; 13.2 cm, 12.8 cm**

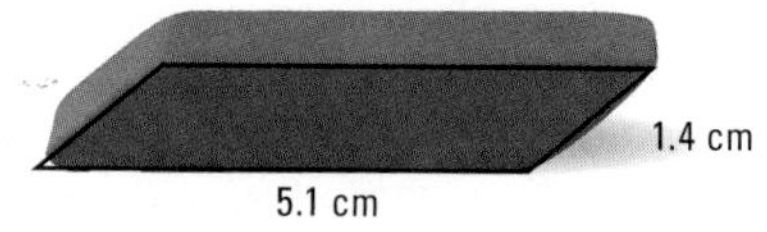

1. Precision depends on the greatest possible error while accuracy depends on the relative error. *Sample answer:* Consider a target: if you are consistently hitting the same area, that is precision; if you hit the bull's eye, that is accuracy.

12. Same level of precision; 17 centimeters is more accurate.
13. 18.65 feet is more precise; 18.65 feet is more accurate.
14. 6.8 inches is more precise; 13.4 feet is more accurate.
15. 35 in. is more precise; they are about the same level of accuracy.

11.2 Areas of Trapezoids and Kites

MATERIALS • graph paper • straightedge • scissors • tape

Standards
8.0 Students know, **derive**, and solve problems involving the perimeter, circumference, **area**, volume, lateral area, and surface area **of common geometric figures.**

QUESTION How can you use a parallelogram to find other areas?

A trapezoid or a kite can be cut out and rearranged to form a parallelogram.

EXPLORE 1 Use two congruent trapezoids to form a parallelogram

STEP 1

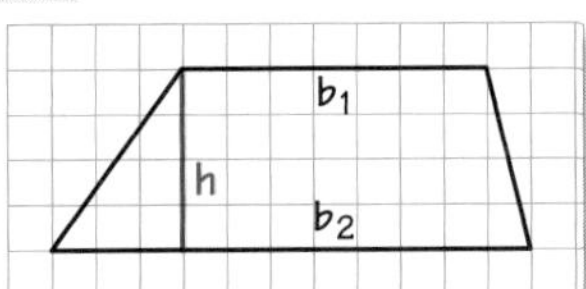

Draw a trapezoid Fold graph paper in half and draw a trapezoid. Cut out two congruent trapezoids. Label as shown.

STEP 2

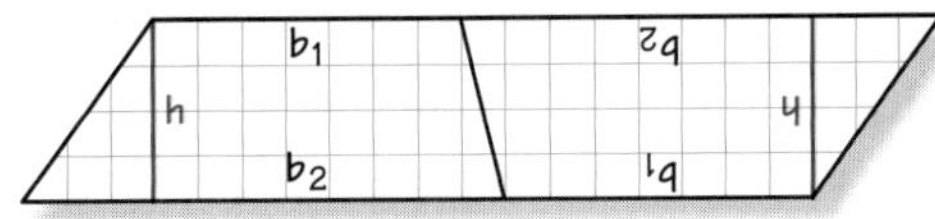

Create a parallelogram Arrange the two trapezoids from Step 1 to form a parallelogram. Then tape them together.

EXPLORE 2 Use one kite to form a rectangle

STEP 1

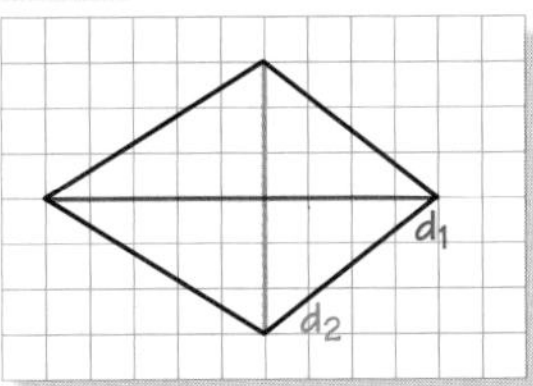

Draw a kite Draw a kite and its perpendicular diagonals. Label the diagonal that is a line of symmetry d_1. Label the other diagonal d_2.

STEP 2

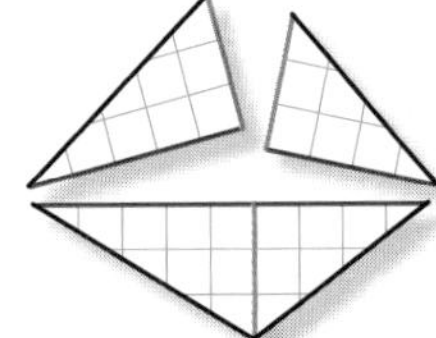

Cut triangles Cut out the kite. Cut along d_1 to form two congruent triangles. Then cut one triangle along part of d_2 to form two right triangles.

STEP 3

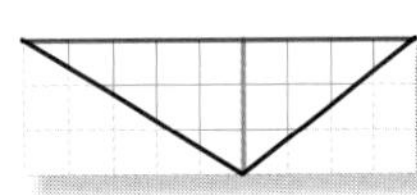

Create a rectangle Turn over the right triangles. Place each with its hypotenuse along a side of the larger triangle to form a rectangle. Then tape the pieces together.

DRAW CONCLUSIONS Use your observations to complete these exercises

1. In Explore 1, how does the area of one trapezoid compare to the area of the parallelogram formed from two trapezoids? Write expressions in terms of b_1, b_2, and h for the base, height, and area of the parallelogram. Then write a formula for the area of a trapezoid. **See margin.**

2. In Explore 2, how do the base and height of the rectangle compare to d_1 and d_2? Write an expression for the area of the rectangle in terms of d_1 and d_2. Then use that expression to write a formula for the area of a kite.
base $= d_1$, height $= \frac{1}{2}d_2$; $A = d_1\left(\frac{1}{2}d_2\right) = \frac{1}{2}d_1 d_2$

1. The area of the parallelogram is twice the area of the trapezoid; base $= b_1 + b_2$, height $= h$, $A = h(b_1 + b_2)$; $A_{trapezoid} = \frac{1}{2}h(b_1 + b_2)$.

1 PLAN AND PREPARE

Explore the Concept

- Students will use a parallelogram to find the areas of other figures.
- This activity leads into the study of the area of a trapezoid in Lesson 11.2, Example 1.

Materials

Each student or group of students will need:

- graph paper
- straightedge
- scissors
- tape

Recommended Time

Work activity: 10 min
Discuss results: 5 min

Grouping

Students can work individually or in groups of two. If students work in groups, they can each do one of the Explore activities.

2 TEACH

Alternative Strategy

You may want to do this activity as a demonstration. Repeat the activity with different trapezoids and kites.

Key Discovery

The area of a trapezoid is $\frac{1}{2}$ the height times the sum of the bases. The area of a kite is $\frac{1}{2}$ the product of the diagonals.

3 ASSESS AND RETEACH

1. What size rectangle can you make with a kite with diagonal lengths 8 and 12? **4 by 12**

1 PLAN AND PREPARE

Warm-Up Exercises

Transparency Available

1. Find the area of a parallelogram with height 12 feet and base 8 feet. **96 ft^2**
2. Find the area of an isosceles triangle with sides 20, 20, and 24 units. **192 square units**
3. What is the length of the midsegment of a trapezoid with bases 10 inches and 15 inches? **12.5 in.**
4. Solve $200 = \frac{1}{2}x(18 + 22)$. **10**

Notetaking Guide

Transparency Available

Promotes interactive learning and notetaking skills, pp. 284–287.

Pacing

Basic: 2 days
Average: 2 days
Advanced: 2 days
Block: 0.5 block with 11.1
0.5 block with 11.3

- See *Teaching Guide/Lesson Plan.*

2 FOCUS AND MOTIVATE

Essential Question

Big Idea 1, p. 719

How do you find the area of a trapezoid, a kite, and a rhombus? **Tell students they will learn how to answer this question by developing formulas for these figures.**

11.2 Areas of Trapezoids, Rhombuses, and Kites

Before	You found areas of triangles and parallelograms.
Now	You will find areas of other types of quadrilaterals.
Why?	So you can solve a problem in sports, as in Example 1.

Key Vocabulary
- **height of a trapezoid**
- **diagonal,** *p. 507*
- **bases of a trapezoid,** *p. 542*

Standards

8.0 Students know, derive, and solve problems involving the perimeter, circumference, **area,** volume, lateral area, and surface area **of common geometric figures.**

10.0 Students compute areas of polygons, including rectangles, scalene triangles, equilateral triangles, **rhombi,** parallelograms, **and trapezoids.**

As you saw in the Activity on page 729, you can use the area formula for a parallelogram to develop area formulas for other special quadrilaterals. The areas of the figures below are related to the lengths of the marked segments.

The **height of a trapezoid** is the perpendicular distance between its bases.

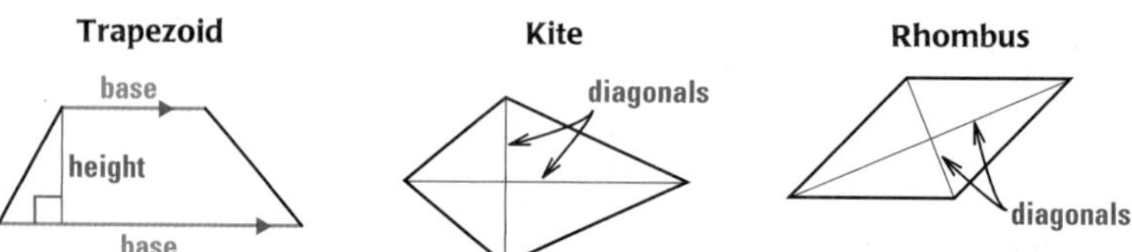

THEOREM — *For Your Notebook*

THEOREM 11.4 Area of a Trapezoid

The area of a trapezoid is one half the product of the height and the sum of the lengths of the bases.

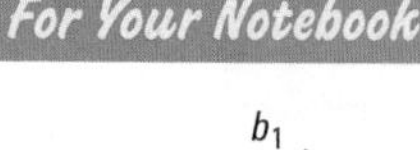

$A = \frac{1}{2}h(b_1 + b_2)$

Proof: Ex. 40, p. 736

EXAMPLE 1 Find the area of a trapezoid

BASKETBALL The free-throw lane on an international basketball court is shaped like a trapezoid. Find the area of the free-throw lane.

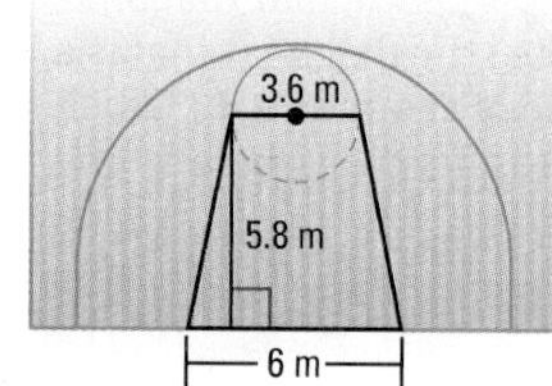

ANOTHER WAY
In a trapezoid, the average of the lengths of the bases is also the length of the midsegment. So, you can also find the area by multiplying the midsegment by the height.

Solution

The height of the trapezoid is 5.8 meters. The lengths of the bases are 3.6 meters and 6 meters.

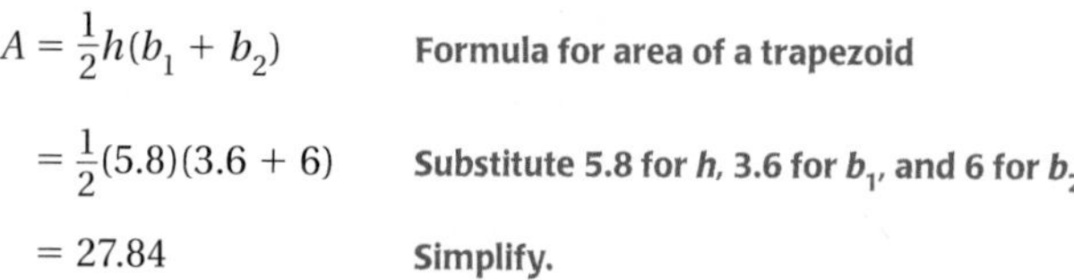

$A = \frac{1}{2}h(b_1 + b_2)$ **Formula for area of a trapezoid**

$= \frac{1}{2}(5.8)(3.6 + 6)$ **Substitute 5.8 for h, 3.6 for b_1, and 6 for b_2.**

$= 27.84$ **Simplify.**

▶ The area of the free-throw lane is about 27.8 square meters.

Resource Planning Guide

Chapter Resource Book
- Teaching Guide/Lesson Plan (pp. 18–19)
- Practice levels A, B, C (pp. 20–25)
- Study Guide (pp. 26–27)
- Catch-up for Absent Students (p. 28)
- Problem Solving Workshop (p. 29)
- Challenge (p. 30)

Workbooks
- Notetaking Guide (pp. 284–287)
- Practice Workbook (pp. 208–210)

Teaching Options
- **Power Presentations CD-ROM** provides dynamic electronic teaching resources for the classroom.
- **Activity Generator CD-ROM** provides editable activities for all ability levels.

Interactive Technology
- Easy Planner
- Power Presentations CD-ROM
- Activity Generator CD-ROM
- Animated Geometry
- Test Generator CD-ROM
- Online Quiz
- eWorkbook
- eEdition
- @HomeTutor

Resources for English Learners
- Quick Reference for English Learners
- Spanish Study Guide
- Multi-Language Visual Glossary
- Student Resources in Spanish

See also the *Geometry Toolkit* for more strategies for meeting individual needs.

THEOREMS *For Your Notebook*

ANOTHER WAY
Remember that a rhombus is also a parallelogram, so you can also use the formula $A = bh$.

THEOREM 11.5 Area of a Rhombus

The area of a rhombus is one half the product of the lengths of its diagonals.

Justification: Ex. 39, p. 735

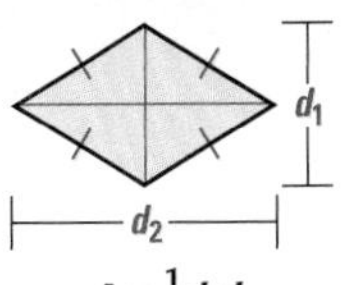

$A = \frac{1}{2}d_1d_2$

THEOREM 11.6 Area of a Kite

The area of a kite is one half the product of the lengths of its diagonals.

Proof: Ex. 41, p. 736

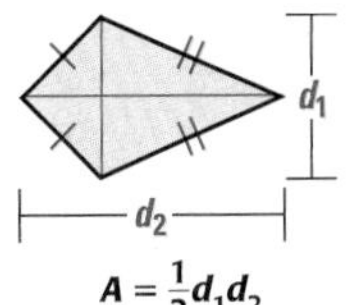

$A = \frac{1}{2}d_1d_2$

EXAMPLE 2 Find the area of a rhombus

MUSIC Rhombus $PQRS$ represents one of the inlays on the guitar in the photo. Find the area of the inlay.

READ DIAGRAMS
When you read a diagram, look for information you need to find. The diagram gives the lengths of $\overline{QN}$ and $\overline{PN}$, but not the lengths of $\overline{QS}$ and $\overline{PR}$.

Solution

STEP 1 **Find** the length of each diagonal. The diagonals of a rhombus bisect each other, so $QN = NS$ and $PN = NR$.

$QS = QN + NS = 9 + 9 = 18$ mm

$PR = PN + NR = 12 + 12 = 24$ mm

STEP 2 **Find** the area of the rhombus. Let d_1 represent QS and d_2 represent PR.

$A = \frac{1}{2}d_1d_2$ **Formula for area of a rhombus**

$= \frac{1}{2}(18)(24)$ **Substitute.**

$= 216$ **Simplify.**

▶ The area of the inlay is 216 square millimeters.

✓ GUIDED PRACTICE for Examples 1 and 2

Find the area of the figure.

1. 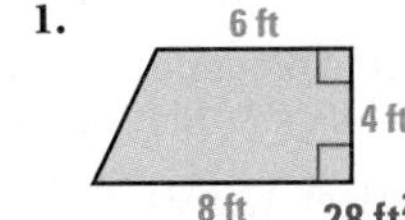

28 ft^2

2. 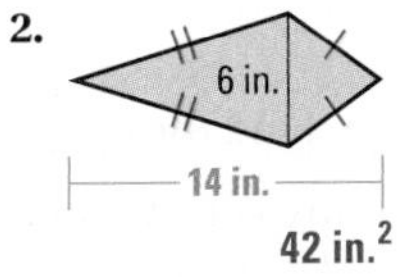

42 in.^{2}

3. 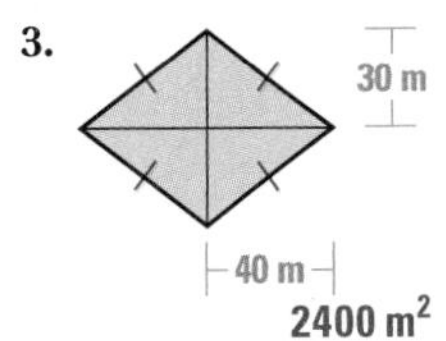

2400 m^2

Motivating the Lesson

Show students a trapezoid and tell them that this is the shape of a large lawn that needs fertilizer. Ask them how they could estimate the area of the trapezoid, and discuss their responses. Tell the students that this lesson develops a formula for the area of a trapezoid.

3 TEACH

Extra Example 1

The front of a decorative chest is a trapezoid, as shown. Find the area of the front of the chest. **300 in.^{2}**

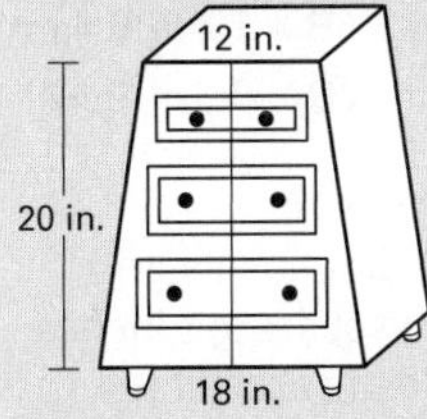

Mathematical Reasoning

Multiple Representations In Example 1, you can use the Area Addition Postulate to find the area of the trapezoid by breaking it up into a rectangle with base 3.6 m and height 5.8 m, and two congruent right triangles with base 1.2 m and height 5.8 m. Ask students to verify that this method gives the same area.

Extra Example 2

Rhombus $ABCD$ is part of a quilt. Find the area of the rhombus.

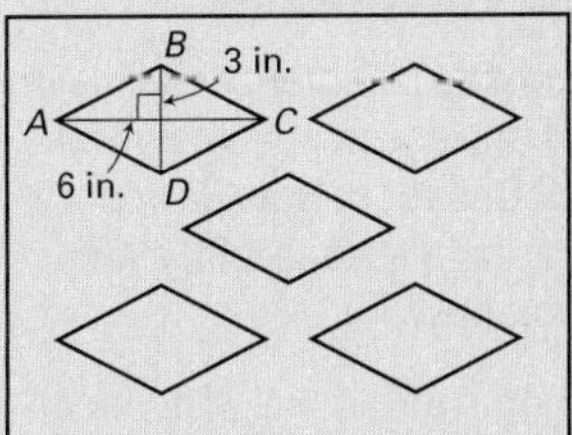

36 in.^{2}

Differentiated Instruction

English Learners Students who are learning English may have heard the word *kite* in reference to flying kites. Point out that the most basic flying kite has the shape of a geometric kite. Point out that the names for many objects in English, such as kite, have meanings referring to their shape or use. Challenge students to think of some other words that do this. Examples include *light* and *glass*.

See also the *Geometry Toolkit* for more strategies.

Key Questions to Ask for Example 2

- What is another way to find the area of the rhombus? **Add the areas of 4 right triangles with legs 9 millimeters and 12 millimeters.**
- How do you know the length of $\overline{RN}$ is 12 millimeters? **The diagonals of a rhombus bisect each other.**

Extra Example 3

One diagonal of a kite is $\frac{1}{3}$ as long as the other. The area of the kite is 0.24 m². What are the lengths of the diagonals? **B**

Ⓐ 1.2 m, 1.2 m Ⓑ 1.2 m, 0.4 m
Ⓒ 0.8 m, 0.3 m Ⓓ 0.6 m, 0.4 m

Extra Example 4

A logo design is drawn on a grid, where each grid square is 5 inches by 5 inches. Find the area of the design. **650 in.²**

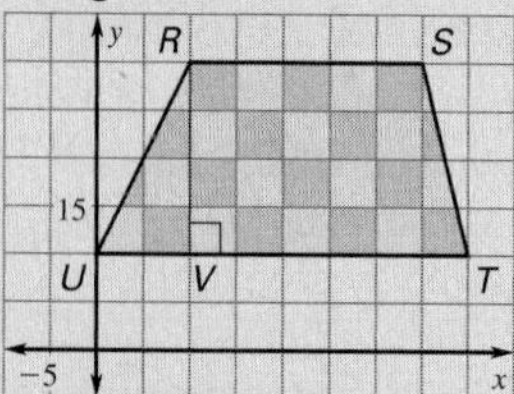

Study Strategy

Ask students to organize the area formulas in their notes by drawing an example of each shape, labeling the shape with variables, and writing the appropriate area formula.

Closing the Lesson

Have students summarize the major points of the lesson and answer the Essential Question: How do you find the area of a trapezoid, a kite, and a rhombus?

- **For a trapezoid, $A = \frac{1}{2}h(b_1 + b_2)$.**
- **For a kite or rhombus, $A = \frac{1}{2}d_1d_2$.**

Substitute the values for the bases b_1 and b_2 and the height h, or for the diagonals d_1 and d_2, into the appropriate formula and simplify.

EXAMPLE 3 Standardized Test Practice

One diagonal of a kite is twice as long as the other diagonal. The area of the kite is 72.25 square inches. What are the lengths of the diagonals?

Ⓐ 6 in., 6 in. Ⓑ 8.5 in., 8.5 in. Ⓒ 8.5 in., 17 in. Ⓓ 6 in., 12 in.

ELIMINATE CHOICES
In Example 3, you can eliminate choices A and B because in each case, one diagonal is not twice as long as the other diagonal.

Solution

Draw and label a diagram. Let x be the length of one diagonal. The other diagonal is twice as long, so label it $2x$. Use the formula for the area of a kite to find the value of x.

$A = \frac{1}{2}d_1d_2$	**Formula for area of a kite**
$72.25 = \frac{1}{2}(x)(2x)$	**Substitute 72.25 for A, x for d_1, and $2x$ for d_2.**
$72.25 = x^2$	**Simplify.**
$8.5 = x$	**Find the positive square root of each side.**

The lengths of the diagonals are 8.5 inches and $2(8.5) = 17$ inches.

▶ The correct answer is C. Ⓐ Ⓑ Ⓒ Ⓓ

EXAMPLE 4 Find an area in the coordinate plane

CITY PLANNING You have a map of a city park. Each grid square represents a 10 meter by 10 meter square. Find the area of the park.

Solution

STEP 1 **Find** the lengths of the bases and the height of trapezoid $ABCD$.

$b_1 = BC = |70 - 30| = 40$ m

$b_2 = AD = |80 - 10| = 70$ m

$h = BE = |60 - 10| = 50$ m

STEP 2 **Find** the area of $ABCD$.

$$A = \frac{1}{2}h(b_1 + b_2) = \frac{1}{2}(50)(40 + 70) = 2750$$

▶ The area of the park is 2750 square meters.

✓ **GUIDED PRACTICE** for Examples 3 and 4

4. The area of a kite is 80 square feet. One diagonal is 4 times as long as the other. Find the diagonal lengths. **$d_1 = 2\sqrt{10}$ ft, $d_2 = 8\sqrt{10}$ ft**
5. Find the area of a rhombus with vertices $M(1, 3)$, $N(5, 5)$, $P(9, 3)$, and $Q(5, 1)$. **16 units²**

Differentiated Instruction

Advanced Refer students to Example 4 and ask them to enclose the trapezoid in a rectangle with coordinates (10, 10), (10, 60), (80, 60), and (80, 10). Then tell them find the area of the enclosing rectangle and to subtract the areas of the two triangles formed by the rectangle and the trapezoid. Ask them to verify that the result is the area as calculated in Example 4.

See also the *Geometry Toolkit* for more strategies.

11.2 EXERCISES

HOMEWORK KEY

○ = **WORKED-OUT SOLUTIONS** on p. WS14 for Exs. 9, 17, and 35

★ = **STANDARDIZED TEST PRACTICE** Exs. 2, 15, 30, 39, and 42

SKILL PRACTICE

A

1. **VOCABULARY** Copy and complete: The perpendicular distance between the bases of a trapezoid is called the _?_ of the trapezoid. **height**

2. ★ **WRITING** Sketch a kite and its diagonals. *Describe* what you know about the segments and angles formed by the intersecting diagonals. **See margin.**

EXAMPLE 1 on p. 730 for Exs. 3–6

FINDING AREA **Find the area of the trapezoid.**

3.
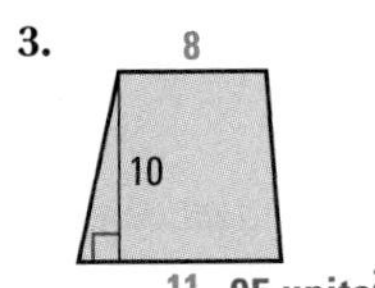

95 units²

4.
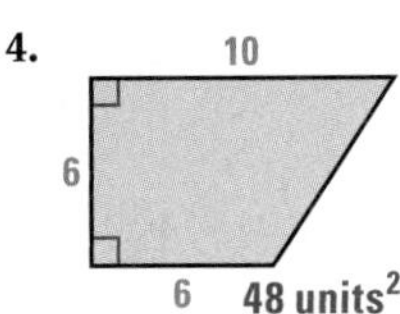

48 units²

5.
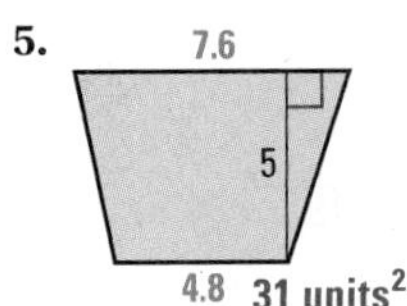

31 units²

6. **DRAWING DIAGRAMS** The lengths of the bases of a trapezoid are 5.4 centimeters and 10.2 centimeters. The height is 8 centimeters. Draw and label a trapezoid that matches this description. Then find its area. **See margin for art; 62.4 cm².**

EXAMPLE 2 on p. 731 for Exs. 7–14

FINDING AREA **Find the area of the rhombus or kite.**

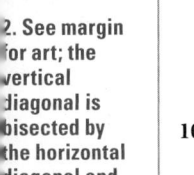

7. 50, 60 **1500 units²**

8.
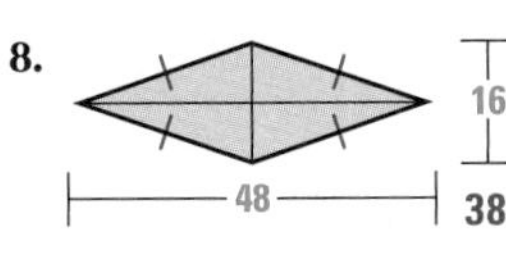

384 units²

9.
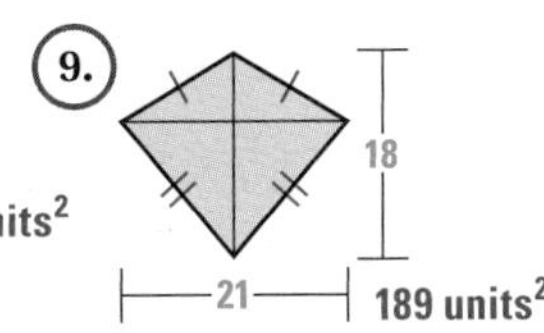

189 units²

10. 10, 19 **95 units²**

11.
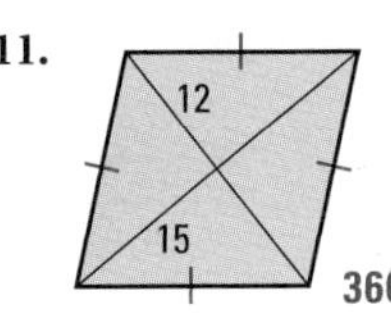

360 units²

12.
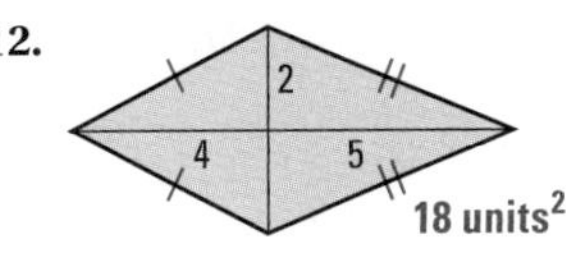

18 units²

ERROR ANALYSIS ***Describe*** **and correct the error in finding the area.** **13, 14. See margin.**

13.
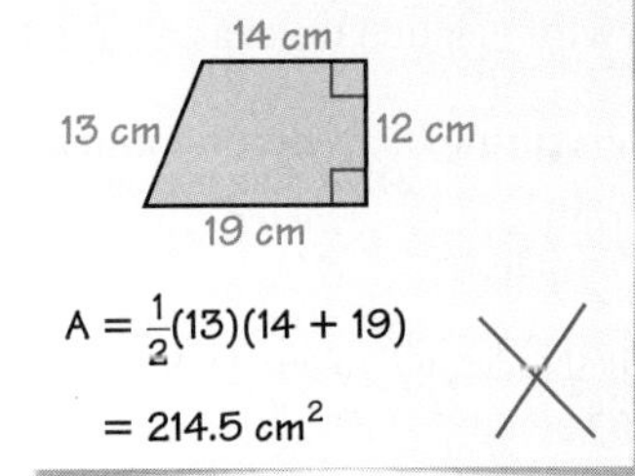

$A = \frac{1}{2}(13)(14 + 19)$

$= 214.5 \text{ cm}^2$

14.
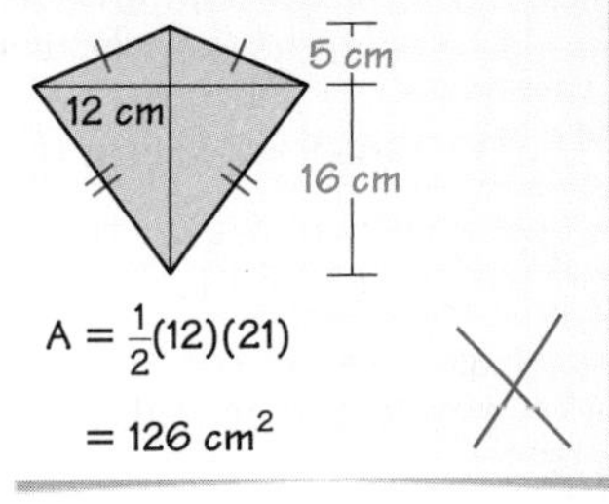

$A = \frac{1}{2}(12)(21)$

$= 126 \text{ cm}^2$

EXAMPLE 3 on p. 732 for Exs. 15–18

15. ★ **MULTIPLE CHOICE** One diagonal of a rhombus is three times as long as the other diagonal. The area of the rhombus is 24 square feet. What are the lengths of the diagonals? **B**

Ⓐ 8 ft, 11 ft Ⓑ 4 ft, 12 ft Ⓒ 2 ft, 6 ft Ⓓ 6 ft, 24 ft

2. See margin for art; the vertical diagonal is bisected by the horizontal diagonal and the angles are all right angles.

4 PRACTICE AND APPLY

Assignment Guide

Answer Transparencies available for all exercises

Basic:
Day 1: pp. 733–736
Exs. 1–14, 22, 23, 34, 35
Day 2: pp. 733–736
Exs. 15–21, 24–26, 36–38, 44–48

Average:
Day 1: pp. 733–736
Exs. 1–6, 8–11, 13, 14, 22–26, 34, 35
Day 2: pp. 733–736
Exs. 15–21, 27–32, 36–41, 44–48 even

Advanced:
Day 1: pp. 733–736
Exs. 1–6, 9–12, 22–29, 34, 35
Day 2: pp. 733–736
Exs. 15–21, 30–33*, 36–43*, 46–48

Block:
pp. 733–736
Exs. 1–6, 8–11, 13, 14, 22–26, 34, 35 (with 11.1)
pp. 733–736
Exs. 15–21, 27–32, 36–41, 44–48 even (with 11.3)

Differentiated Instruction

See *Geometry Best Practices Toolkit* for suggestions on addressing the needs of a diverse classroom.

Homework Check

For a quick check of student understanding of key concepts, go over the following exercises:

Basic: 3, 8, 15, 19, 34
Average: 4, 10, 16, 20, 35
Advanced: 6, 12, 18, 21, 36

Extra Practice

- Student Edition, p. 916
- Chapter 11 Resource Book: Practice levels A, B, C, pp. 20–25

Practice Worksheet

An easily-readable reduced practice page (with answers) for this lesson can be found on p. 718C.

2. d_2 d_1

6.
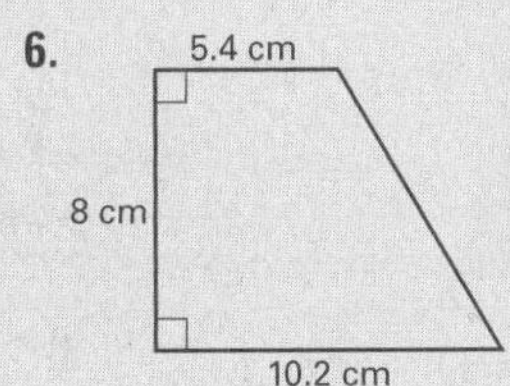

13. 13 is not the height of the trapezoid; $A = \frac{1}{2}(12)(14 + 19)$, $A = 198 \text{ cm}^2$.

14. 12 is not the length of the horizontal diagonal; $A = \frac{1}{2}(24)(21)$, $A = 252 \text{ cm}^2$.

Avoiding Common Errors

Exercises 7–12 If students are confused that the same formula can apply to each of these exercises, ask them to review Theorems 11.5 and 11.6, including the proofs of the theorems in Exercises 39 and 41.

Teaching Strategy

Exercises 24–29 Remind students that they can use the Area Addition Postulate to find the area of a figure formed by different shapes.

30. ***Sample:***

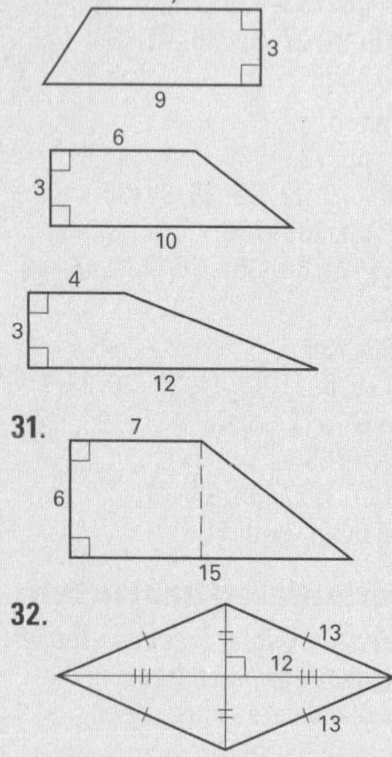

33. 122 units². ***Sample answer:*** **After drawing the two auxiliary lines, let *X* be the point where the line through *A* intersects $\overline{BF}$ and let *Y* be the point where the line through *D* intersects $\overline{CH}$. After showing that $\angle BAX \cong \angle CDY$, $\triangle ABX$ and $\triangle DCY$ can be shown congruent by AAS. This fact leads to $GH = 8$ and $DG = 9 - 6$, or 3. The area of parallelogram *ABCD* can then by found by finding the sum of the areas of trapezoids *ABFE* and *FBCH*, and subtracting the sum of the areas of trapezoids *ADGE* and *GDCH*.**

ALGEBRA **Use the given information to find the value of x.**

16. Area = 108 ft^2 **17.** Area = 300 m^2 **18.** Area = 100 yd^2

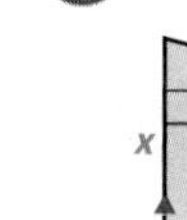

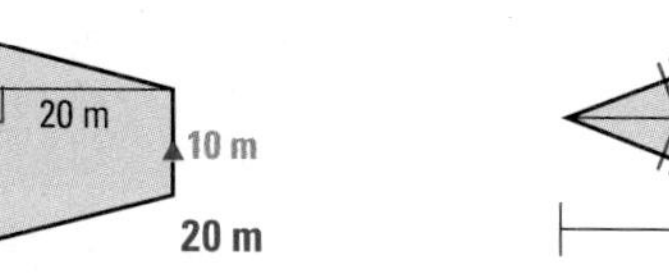

22 ft, x, 14 ft, **6 ft**; 20 m, x, 10 m, **20 m**; 10 yd, x, **20 yd**

EXAMPLE 4 on p. 732 for Exs. 19–21

COORDINATE GEOMETRY **Find the area of the figure.**

19. **10.5 units²** **20.** **8 units²** **21.** **10 units²**

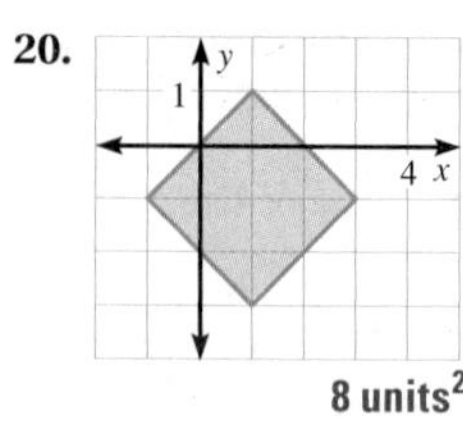

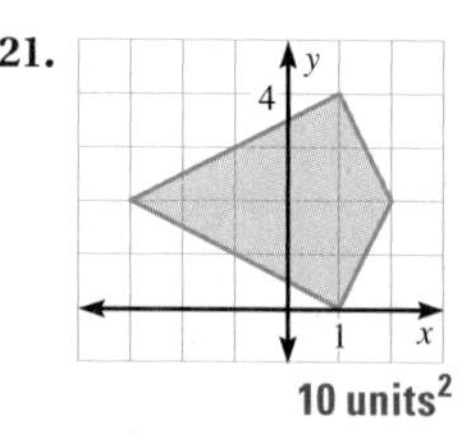

B **ALGEBRA** **Find the lengths of the bases of the trapezoid described.**

22. The height is 3 feet. One base is twice as long as the other base. The area is 13.5 square feet. **3 ft and 6 ft**

23. One base is 8 centimeters longer than the other base. The height is 6 centimeters and the area is 54 square centimeters. **5 cm and 13 cm**

FINDING AREA **Find the area of the shaded region.**

24.

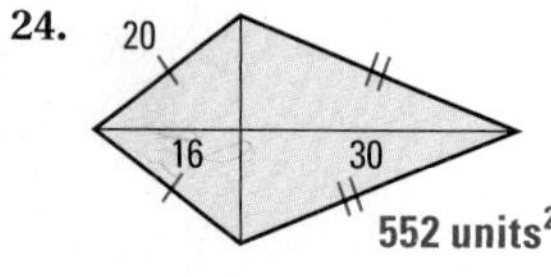

552 units²

25.

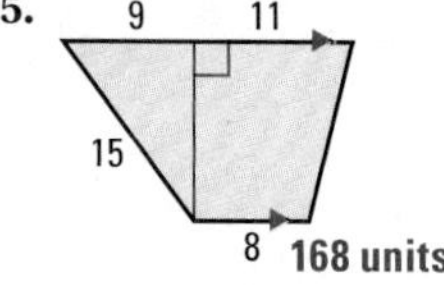

168 units²

26.

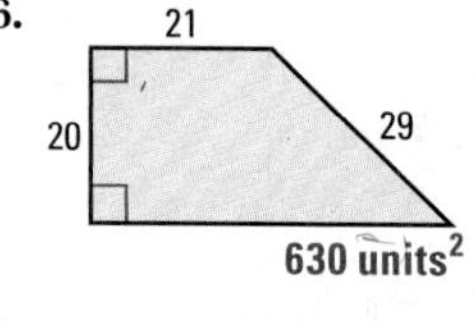

630 units²

27. 7, 5, 7, 10 **67 units²**

28.

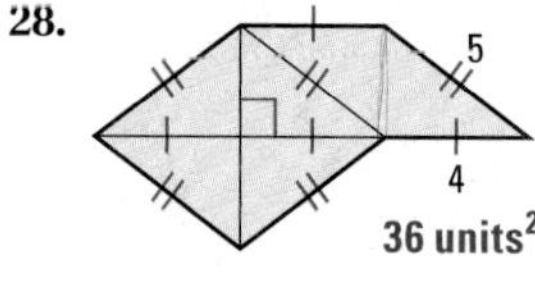

36 units²

29.

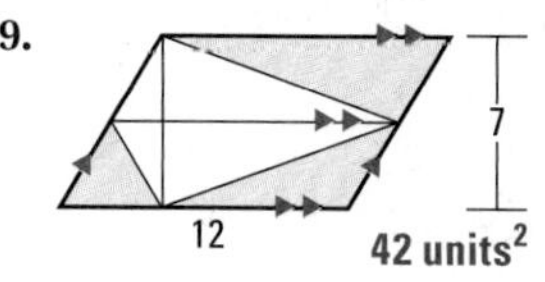

42 units²

30. ★ **OPEN-ENDED MATH** Draw three examples of trapezoids that match this description: The height of the trapezoid is 3 units and its area is the same as the area of a parallelogram with height 3 units and base 8 units. **See margin.**

VISUALIZING **Sketch the figure. Then determine its perimeter and area.** **31, 32. See margin for art.**

31. The figure is a trapezoid. It has two right angles. The lengths of its bases are 7 and 15. Its height is 6. **38 units, 66 units²**

32. The figure is a rhombus. Its side length is 13. The length of one of its diagonals is 24. **52 units, 120 units²**

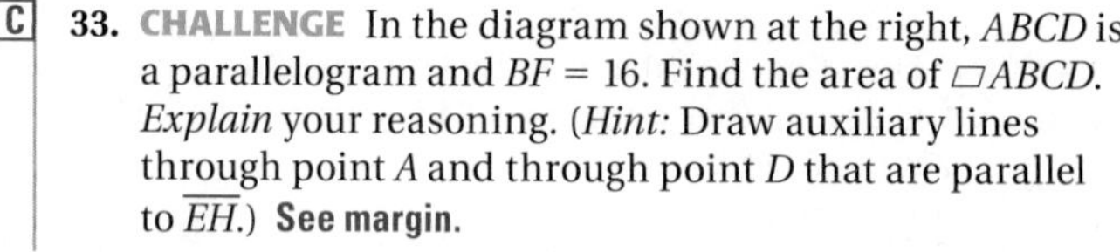

C **33.** **CHALLENGE** In the diagram shown at the right, *ABCD* is a parallelogram and $BF = 16$. Find the area of $\square ABCD$. *Explain* your reasoning. (*Hint:* Draw auxiliary lines through point *A* and through point *D* that are parallel to $\overline{EH}$.) **See margin.**

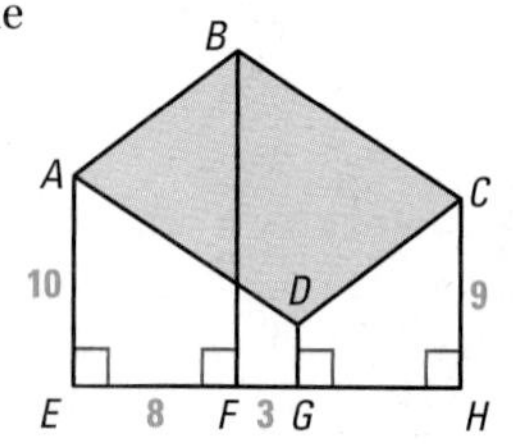

○ = **WORKED-OUT SOLUTIONS** on p. WS1 ★ = **STANDARDIZED TEST PRACTICE**

PROBLEM SOLVING

EXAMPLE 1 on p. 730 for Ex. 34

A

34. TRUCKS The windshield in a truck is in the shape of a trapezoid. The lengths of the bases of the trapezoid are 70 inches and 79 inches. The height is 35 inches. Find the area of the glass in the windshield. **2607.5 in.^{2}**

@HomeTutor for problem solving help at classzone.com

EXAMPLE 2 on p. 731 for Ex. 35

(35.) INTERNET You are creating a kite-shaped logo for your school's website. The diagonals of the logo are 8 millimeters and 5 millimeters long. Find the area of the logo. Draw two different possible shapes for the logo. **20 mm^2; see margin for art.**

@HomeTutor for problem solving help at classzone.com

36. DESIGN You are designing a wall hanging that is in the shape of a rhombus. The area of the wall hanging is 432 square inches and the length of one diagonal is 36 inches. Find the length of the other diagonal. **24 in.**

B

37. MULTI-STEP PROBLEM As shown, a baseball stadium's playing field is shaped like a pentagon. To find the area of the playing field shown at the right, you can divide the field into two smaller polygons.

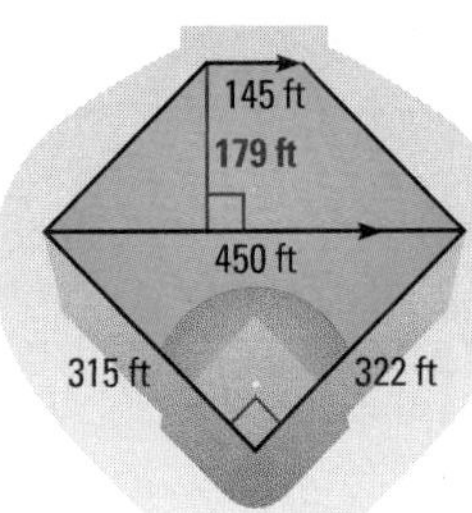

a. Classify the two polygons. **right triangle and trapezoid**

b. Find the area of the playing field in square feet. Round to the nearest square foot. Then express your answer in square yards. **103,968 ft^2; 11,552 yd^2**

38. VISUAL REASONING Follow the steps in parts (a)–(c).

a. **Analyze** Copy the table and extend it to include a column for $n = 5$. Complete the table for $n = 4$ and $n = 5$. **4; 8; 5; 10; see margin for art.**

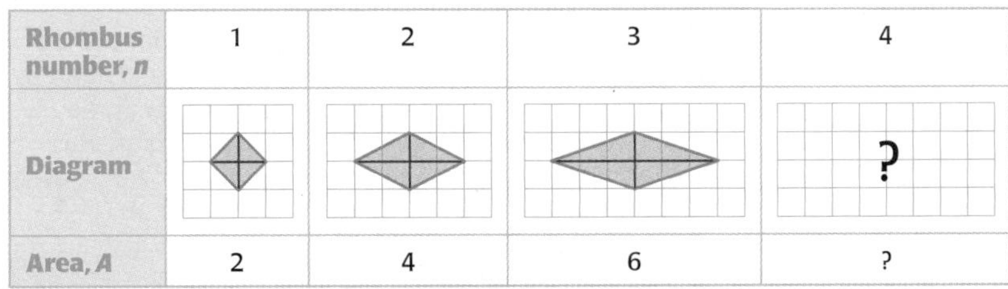

Rhombus number, n	1	2	3	4
Diagram				?
Area, A	2	4	6	?

b. **Use Algebra** *Describe* the relationship between the rhombus number n and the area of the rhombus. Then write an algebraic rule for finding the area of the nth rhombus. **The area of the rhombus is twice the value of n; $A_n = 2n$.**

c. **Compare** In each rhombus, the length of one diagonal (d_1) is 2. What is the length of the other diagonal (d_2) for the nth rhombus? Use the formula for the area of a rhombus to write a rule for finding the area of the nth rhombus. *Compare* this rule with the one you wrote in part (b). **$2n$; $A_n = \frac{1}{2}(2)(2n) = 2n$; the rules are the same.**

39. ★ SHORT RESPONSE Look back at the Activity on page 729. *Explain* how the results for kites in Explore 2 can be used to justify Theorem 11.5, the formula for the area of a rhombus.
If the kite in the activity were a rhombus, the results would be the same.

Reading Strategy

Exercise 40 When students analyze the problem statement, encourage them to look at the trapezoid as the sum of the colored triangles, and to use the formulas for the area of a triangle to find the area of the trapezoid. The area of the blue triangle is $\frac{1}{2}h(b_1)$ and the area of the orange triangle is $\frac{1}{2}h(b_2)$. Their sum simplifies to the familiar area formula for a trapezoid, $A = \frac{1}{2}h(b_1 + b_2)$.

Mathematical Reasoning

Exercise 41 Since the longer diagonal of a kite bisects the shorter diagonal, you can derive the area formula from the areas of two triangles, each with height $\frac{1}{2}d_1$ and base d_2.

Exercise 43 Additional information about James A. Garfield can be found at www.whitehouse.gov/history/presidents/jg20.html

35.

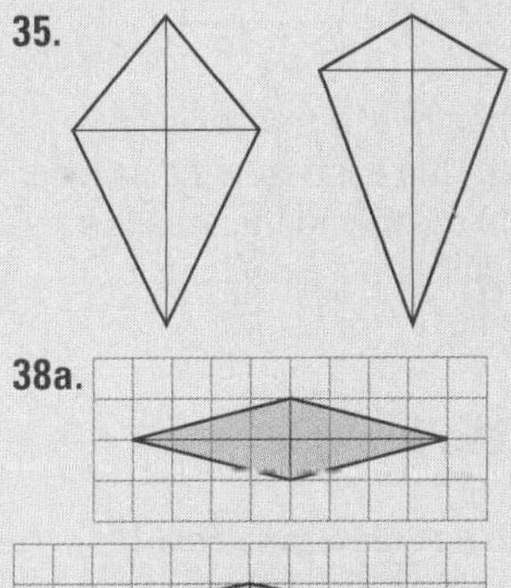

38a.

5 ASSESS AND RETEACH

Daily Homework Quiz

Transparency Available

Find the area of each figure.

1. 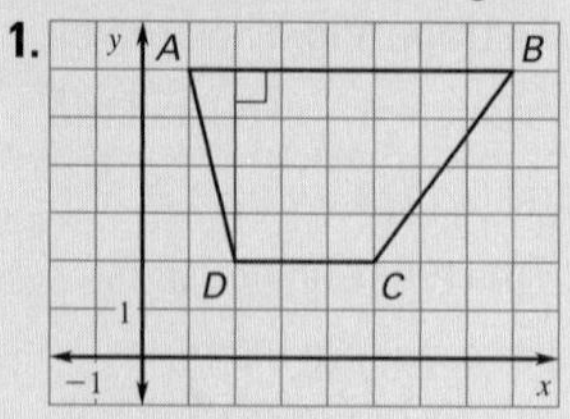

20 square units

2. 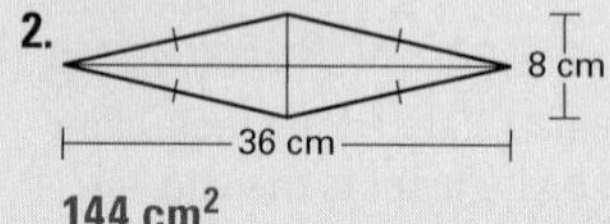

144 cm^2

3. 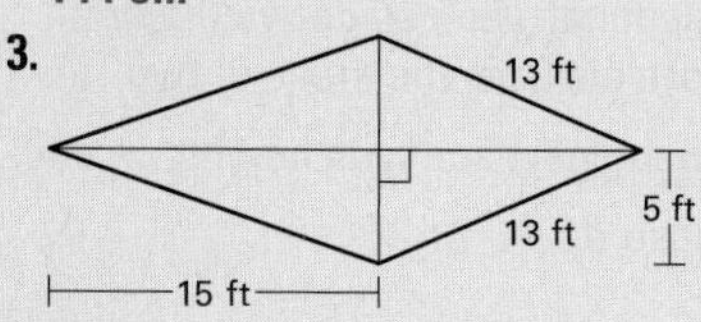

135 ft^2

4. 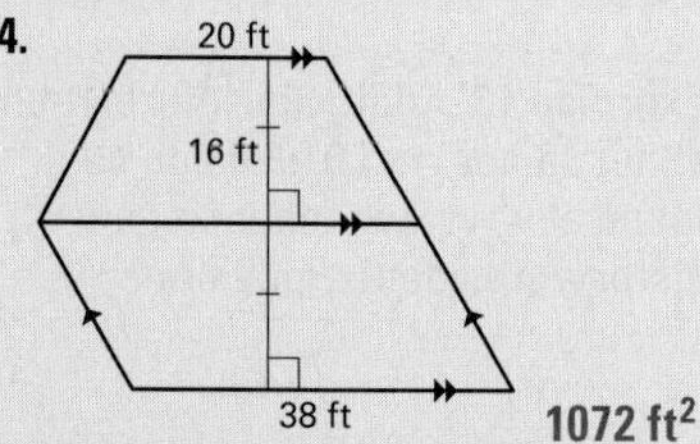

1072 ft^2

5. The height of a trapezoid is 8 feet. One base is twice as long as the other, and the area is 72 square feet. How long is each base? 6 ft; 12 ft

Online Quiz

Available at **classzone.com**

Diagnosis/Remediation

- Practice A, B, C in Chapter 11 Resource Book, pp. 20–25
- Study Guide in Chapter 11 Resource Book, pp. 26–27
- Practice Workbook, pp. 208–210
- @HomeTutor

Challenge

Additional challenge is available in the Chapter 11 Resource Book, p. 30.

40, 41, 42a, 43. See Additional Answers beginning on p. AA1.

PROVING THEOREMS 11.4 AND 11.6 Use the triangle area formula and the triangles in the diagram to write a plan for the proof. 40, 41. See margin.

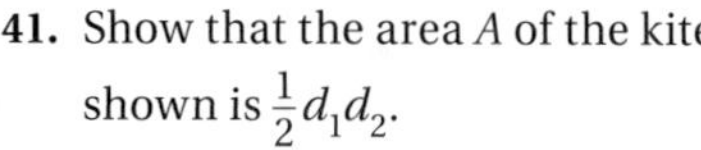

40. Show that the area A of the trapezoid shown is $\frac{1}{2}h(b_1 + b_2)$.

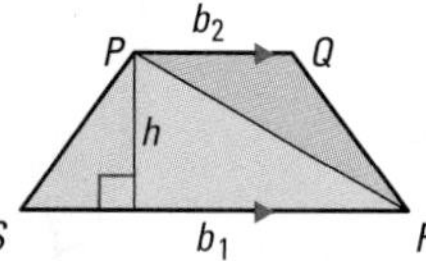

41. Show that the area A of the kite shown is $\frac{1}{2}d_1d_2$.

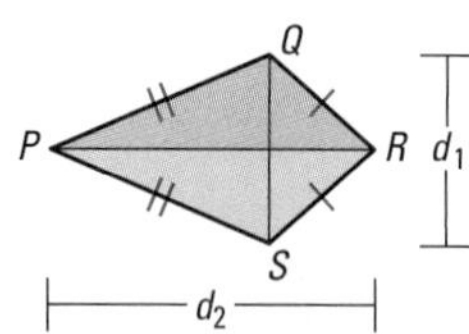

C **42. ★ EXTENDED RESPONSE** You will explore the effect of moving a diagonal.

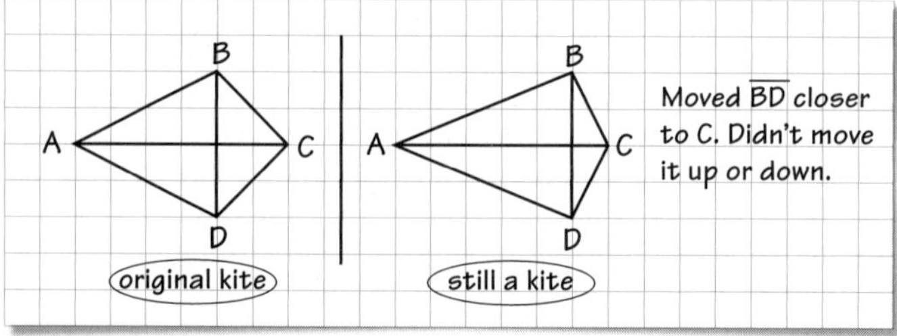

a. **Investigate** Draw a kite in which the longer diagonal is horizontal. Suppose this diagonal is fixed and you can slide the vertical diagonal left or right and up or down. You can keep sliding as long as the diagonals continue to intersect. Draw and identify each type of figure you can form. See margin.

b. **Justify** Is it possible to form any shapes that are not quadrilaterals? *Explain.* Yes; when you slide the vertical diagonal to one side or to the top or bottom, you get triangles.

c. **Compare** Compare the areas of the different shapes you found in part (b). What do you notice about the areas? *Explain.*

42c. The areas are all the same; the measures of the diagonals remain constant and become the base and height measures in the triangle.

43. CHALLENGE James A. Garfield, the twentieth president of the United States, discovered a proof of the Pythagorean Theorem in 1876. His proof involved the fact that a trapezoid can be formed from two congruent right triangles and an isosceles right triangle. Use the diagram to show that $a^2 + b^2 = c^2$. See margin.

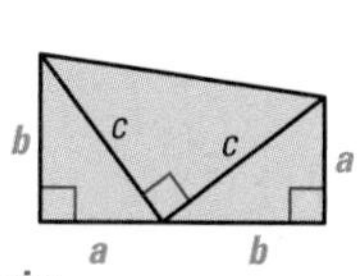

MIXED REVIEW

Solve for the indicated variable. Write a reason for each step. *(p. 105)* 44–46. See margin.

44. $d = rt$; solve for t

45. $A = \frac{1}{2}bh$; solve for h

46. $P = 2\ell + 2w$; solve for w

47. Find the angle measures of an isosceles triangle if the measure of a base angle is 4 times the measure of the vertex angle. *(p. 264)* 20°, 80°, 80°

PREVIEW
Prepare for Lesson 11.3 in Ex. 48.

48. In the diagram at the right, $\triangle PQR \sim \triangle STU$. The perimeter of $\triangle STU$ is 81 inches. Find the height h and the perimeter of $\triangle PQR$. *(p. 372)* 12 in., 54 in.

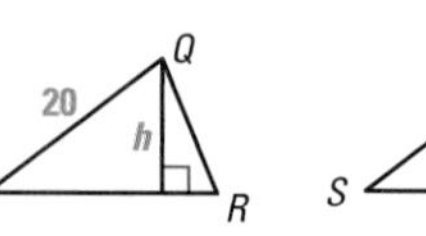

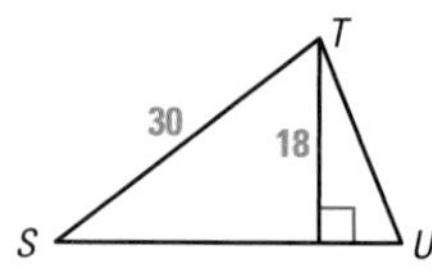

44. $t = \frac{d}{r}$; Division Property of Equality

45. $h = \frac{2A}{b}$; Multiplication Property of Equality

46. $P = 2(\ell + w)$; Distributive Property,
$\frac{1}{2}P = \ell + w$; Multiplication Property of Equality,
$w = \frac{1}{2}P - \ell$; Subtraction Property of Equality

11.3 Perimeter and Area of Similar Figures

Before You used ratios to find perimeters of similar figures.

Now You will use ratios to find areas of similar figures.

Why So you can apply similarity in cooking, as in Example 3.

Key Vocabulary
- **regular polygon,** *p. 43*
- **corresponding sides,** *p. 225*
- **similar polygons,** *p. 372*

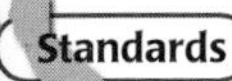

Standards

11.0 Students determine how changes in dimensions affect the perimeter, area, and volume **of common geometric figures** and solids.

8.0 Students know, derive, and solve problems involving the perimeter, circumference, **area,** volume, lateral area, and surface area **of common geometric figures.**

In Chapter 6 you learned that if two polygons are similar, then the ratio of their perimeters, or of any two corresponding lengths, is equal to the ratio of their corresponding side lengths. As shown below, the areas have a different ratio.

Ratio of perimeters

$$\frac{\text{Blue}}{\text{Red}} = \frac{10t}{10} = t$$

Ratio of areas

$$\frac{\text{Blue}}{\text{Red}} = \frac{6t^2}{6} = t^2$$

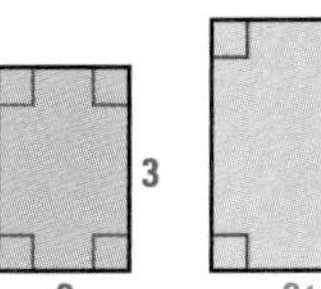

THEOREM *For Your Notebook*

THEOREM 11.7 Areas of Similar Polygons

If two polygons are similar with the lengths of corresponding sides in the ratio of $a:b$, then the ratio of their areas is $a^2:b^2$.

$$\frac{\text{Side length of Polygon I}}{\text{Side length of Polygon II}} = \frac{a}{b}$$

$$\frac{\text{Area of Polygon I}}{\text{Area of Polygon II}} = \frac{a^2}{b^2}$$

Justification: Ex. 30, p. 742

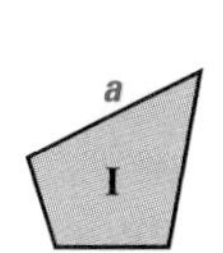

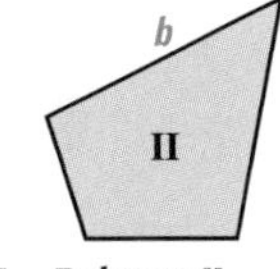

Polygon I ~ Polygon II

EXAMPLE 1 Find ratios of similar polygons

In the diagram, $\triangle ABC \sim \triangle DEF$. Find the indicated ratio.

a. Ratio (red to blue) of the perimeters

b. Ratio (red to blue) of the areas

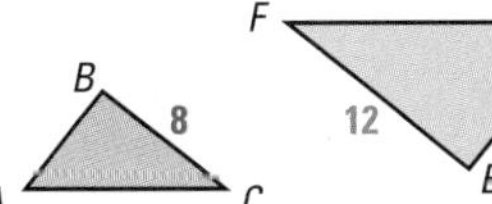

INTERPRET RATIOS
You can also compare the measures with fractions. The perimeter of $\triangle ABC$ is two thirds of the perimeter of $\triangle DEF$. The area of $\triangle ABC$ is four ninths of the area of $\triangle DEF$.

Solution

The ratio of the lengths of corresponding sides is $\frac{8}{12} = \frac{2}{3}$, or 2:3.

a. By Theorem 6.1 on page 374, the ratio of the perimeters is 2:3.

b. By Theorem 11.7 above, the ratio of the areas is $2^2:3^2$, or 4:9.

1 PLAN AND PREPARE

Warm-Up Exercises

Transparency Available

1. Two polygons are similar and the ratio of corresponding sides is 3:4. What is the ratio of the perimeters? **3:4**
2. Solve $\frac{12}{x} = \frac{18}{6}$. **4**
3. A rectangle has area 108 square feet and the length is three times the width. What are the dimensions of the rectangle? **18 ft by 6 ft**

Notetaking Guide

Transparency Available

Promotes interactive learning and notetaking skills, pp. 288–291.

Pacing

Basic: 1 day
Average: 1 day
Advanced: 1 day
Block: 0.5 block with 11.2
- See *Teaching Guide/Lesson Plan.*

2 FOCUS AND MOTIVATE

Essential Question

Big Idea 2, p. 719

How is the ratio of the areas of two similar polygons related to the ratio of corresponding sides? **Tell students they will learn how to answer this question by looking at the ratios of areas and sides of similar figures.**

Resource Planning Guide

Chapter Resource Book
- Teaching Guide/Lesson Plan (pp. 31–32)
- Activity Master (p. 33)
- Practice levels A, B, C (pp. 34–39)
- Study Guide (pp. 40–41)
- Catch-up for Absent Students (p. 42)
- Problem Solving Workshop (p. 43)
- Challenge (p. 45)

Workbooks
- Notetaking Guide (pp. 288–291)
- Practice Workbook (pp. 211–213)

Teaching Options
- **Power Presentations CD-ROM** provides dynamic electronic teaching resources for the classroom.
- **Activity Generator CD-ROM** provides editable activities for all ability levels.

Interactive Technology
- Easy Planner
- Power Presentations CD-ROM
- Activity Generator CD-ROM
- Animated Geometry
- Test Generator CD-ROM
- Online Quiz
- eWorkbook
- eEdition
- @HomeTutor

Resources for English Learners
- Quick Reference for English Learners
- Spanish Study Guide
- Multi-Language Visual Glossary
- Student Resources in Spanish

See also the *Geometry Toolkit* for more strategies for meeting individual needs.

Motivating the Lesson

Tell students that one TV screen is 32 in. by 20 in. and another is 48 in. by 30 in. Ask them to show that the screens are similar. Then ask them to calculate the area of each screen, the ratio of corresponding sides, and the ratio of areas. Tell students that this lesson explores how the ratios of corresponding sides of similar figures is related to the ratios of the perimeters and areas of the figures.

3 TEACH

Extra Example 1

In the diagram, Figure I ~ Figure II. Find the indicated ratio.

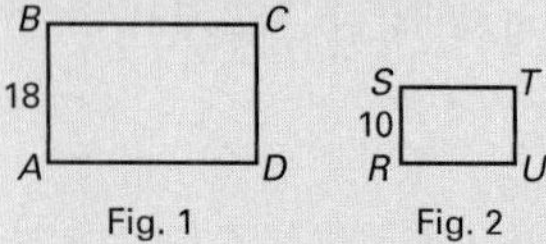

Fig. 1 Fig. 2

a. the ratio of the perimeters **9:5**

b. the ratio of the areas **81:25**

Key Question to Ask for Example 1

- Will each pair of corresponding sides have the same ratio as the perimeters? **yes**

Extra Example 2

You are painting a ceiling of the room in Example 2. You need 7 quarts of paint to paint the larger ceiling. How many quarts do you need to paint the smaller ceiling? **D**

Ⓐ $\frac{7}{25}$ quart Ⓑ $\frac{5}{7}$ quart

Ⓒ $\frac{7}{5}$ quarts Ⓓ $\frac{25}{7}$ quarts

EXAMPLE 2 Standardized Test Practice

You are installing the same carpet in a bedroom and den. The floors of the rooms are similar. The carpet for the bedroom costs \$225. Carpet is sold by the square foot. How much does it cost to carpet the den?

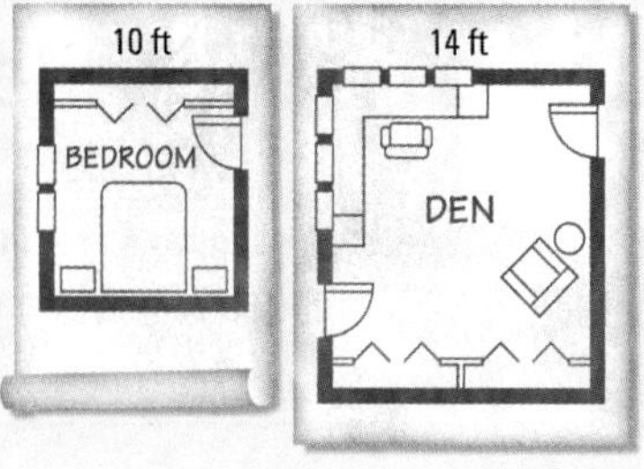

Ⓐ \$115 Ⓑ \$161

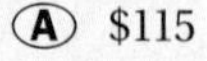

Ⓒ \$315 Ⓓ \$441

USE ESTIMATION
The cost for the den is $\frac{49}{25}$ times the cost for the bedroom. Because $\frac{49}{25}$ is a little less than 2, the cost for the den is a little less than twice \$225. The only possible choice is D.

Solution

The ratio of a side length of the den to the corresponding side length of the bedroom is 14 : 10, or 7 : 5. So, the ratio of the areas is $7^2 : 5^2$, or 49 : 25. This ratio is also the ratio of the carpeting costs. Let x be the cost for the den.

$\frac{49}{25} = \frac{x}{225}$ ← **cost of carpet for den** / ← **cost of carpet for bedroom**

$x = 441$ **Solve for *x*.**

▸ It costs \$441 to carpet the den. The correct answer is D. Ⓐ Ⓑ Ⓒ Ⓓ

GUIDED PRACTICE for Examples 1 and 2

1. The perimeter of $\triangle ABC$ is 16 feet, and its area is 64 square feet. The perimeter of $\triangle DEF$ is 12 feet. Given $\triangle ABC \sim \triangle DEF$, find the ratio of the area of $\triangle ABC$ to the area of $\triangle DEF$. Then find the area of $\triangle DEF$. **$\frac{16}{9}$; 36 ft^2**

EXAMPLE 3 Use a ratio of areas

COOKING A large rectangular baking pan is 15 inches long and 10 inches wide. A smaller pan is similar to the large pan. The area of the smaller pan is 96 square inches. Find the width of the smaller pan.

ANOTHER WAY
For an alternative method for solving the problem in Example 3, turn to page 744 for the **Problem Solving Workshop**.

Solution

First draw a diagram to represent the problem. Label dimensions and areas.

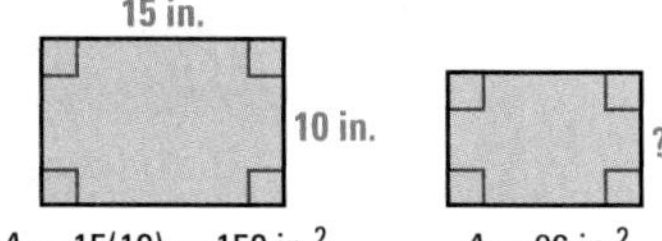

Then use Theorem 11.7. If the area ratio is $a^2 : b^2$, then the length ratio is $a : b$.

$\frac{\text{Area of smaller pan}}{\text{Area of large pan}} = \frac{96}{150} = \frac{16}{25}$ **Write ratio of known areas. Then simplify.**

$\frac{\text{Length in smaller pan}}{\text{Length in large pan}} = \frac{4}{5}$ **Find square root of area ratio.**

▸ Any length in the smaller pan is $\frac{4}{5}$, or 0.8, of the corresponding length in the large pan. So, the width of the smaller pan is 0.8(10 inches) = 8 inches.

REGULAR POLYGONS Consider two regular polygons with the same number of sides. All of the angles are congruent. The lengths of all pairs of corresponding sides are in the same ratio. So, any two such polygons are similar. Also, any two circles are similar.

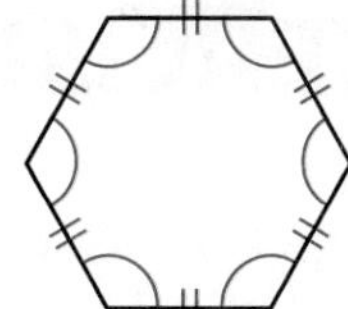

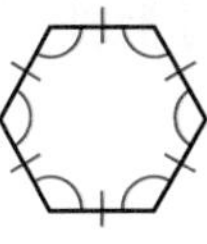

EXAMPLE 4 Solve a multi-step problem

GAZEBO The floor of the gazebo shown is a regular octagon. Each side of the floor is 8 feet, and the area is about 309 square feet. You build a small model gazebo in the shape of a regular octagon. The perimeter of the floor of the model gazebo is 24 inches. Find the area of the floor of the model gazebo to the nearest tenth of a square inch.

Solution

All regular octagons are similar, so the floor of the model is similar to the floor of the full-sized gazebo.

ANOTHER WAY
In Step 1, instead of finding the perimeter of the full-sized and comparing perimeters, you can find the side length of the model and compare side lengths. $24 \div 8 = 3$, so the ratio of side lengths is $\frac{8 \text{ ft.}}{3 \text{ in.}} = \frac{96 \text{ in.}}{3 \text{ in.}} = \frac{32}{1}$.

STEP 1 **Find** the ratio of the lengths of the two floors by finding the ratio of the perimeters. Use the same units for both lengths in the ratio.

$$\frac{\text{Perimeter of full-sized}}{\text{Perimeter of model}} = \frac{8(8 \text{ ft})}{24 \text{ in.}} = \frac{64 \text{ ft}}{24 \text{ in.}} = \frac{64 \text{ ft}}{2 \text{ ft}} = \frac{32}{1}$$

So, the ratio of corresponding lengths (full-sized to model) is 32 : 1.

STEP 2 **Calculate** the area of the model gazebo's floor. Let x be this area.

$$\frac{(\text{Length in full-sized})^2}{(\text{Length in model})^2} = \frac{\text{Area of full-sized}}{\text{Area of model}} \quad \textbf{Theorem 11.7}$$

$$\frac{32^2}{1^2} = \frac{309 \text{ ft}^2}{x \text{ ft}^2} \quad \textbf{Substitute.}$$

$$1024x = 309 \quad \textbf{Cross Products Property}$$

$$x \approx 0.302 \text{ ft}^2 \quad \textbf{Solve for } x.$$

STEP 3 **Convert** the area to square inches.

$$0.302 \text{ ft}^2 \cdot \frac{144 \text{ in.}^2}{1 \text{ ft}^2} \approx 43.5 \text{ in.}^2$$

▶ The area of the floor of the model gazebo is about 43.5 square inches.

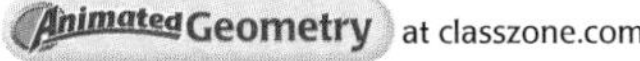
Animated Geometry at classzone.com

✓ GUIDED PRACTICE for Examples 3 and 4

2. The ratio of the areas of two regular decagons is 20 : 36. What is the ratio of their corresponding side lengths in simplest radical form? $\frac{\sqrt{5}}{3}$

3. Rectangles I and II are similar. The perimeter of Rectangle I is 66 inches. Rectangle II is 35 feet long and 20 feet wide. Show the steps you would use to find the ratio of the areas and then find the area of Rectangle I. $\frac{66}{1320} = \frac{1}{20}$ **is the ratio of sides, so the ratio of areas is** $\frac{1}{400}$, **252 in.**^{2}

Extra Example 3

A small flat screen TV is 24 inches wide and 18 inches long. A larger TV is similar to the smaller one. The area of the larger screen is 657 square inches. Find the width of the larger TV. **21.75 in.**

Extra Example 4

The Pentagon in Washington, D.C., is a regular pentagon. Each side of the base is about 900 ft and the area is about 1,400,000 ft^2. You have a scale model of the Pentagon for which the perimeter of the base is 30 yd. Find the area of the base of the model to the nearest square yard. **62 yd^2**

An **Animated Geometry** activity is available on-line for **Example 4**. This activity is also available on the **Power Presentations CD-ROM**.

Closing the Lesson

Have students summarize the major points of the lesson and answer the Essential Question: How is the ratio of the areas of two similar polygons related to the ratio of corresponding sides?

- **If the corresponding lengths of two similar figures are a_1 and a_2, then the ratio of their perimeters is $\frac{a_1}{a_2}$.**
- **If the corresponding lengths of two similar figures are a_1 and a_2, then the ratio of their areas is $\frac{(a_1)^2}{(a_2)^2}$.**

If two polygons are similar, then the ratio of the corresponding areas is the square of the ratio of their corresponding sides.

4 PRACTICE AND APPLY

Assignment Guide

Answer Transparencies available for all exercises

Basic:
Day 1: EP p. 906 Exs. 23–25
pp. 740–743
Exs. 1–20, 26–30, 35–41

Average:
Day 1: pp. 740–743
Exs. 1–4, 6–8, 10–22, 27–33, 35–41

Advanced:
Day 1: pp. 740–743
Exs. 1, 2, 6–14, 16–25*, 27–34*, 35–41 odd

Block:
pp. 740–743
Exs. 1–4, 6–8, 10–22, 27–33, 35–41 (with 11.2)

Differentiated Instruction

See *Geometry Best Practices Toolkit* for suggestions on addressing the needs of a diverse classroom.

Homework Check

For a quick check of student understanding of key concepts, go over the following exercises:

Basic: 4, 10, 16, 26, 27
Average: 6, 12, 16, 27, 28
Advanced: 8, 14, 17, 27, 29

Extra Practice

- Student Edition, p. 916
- Chapter 11 Resource Book: Practice levels A, B, C, pp. 34–39

Practice Worksheet

An easily-readable reduced practice page (with answers) for this lesson can be found on p. 718D.

11.3 EXERCISES

HOMEWORK KEY
○ = **WORKED-OUT SOLUTIONS** on p. WS14 for Exs. 7, 17, and 27
★ = **STANDARDIZED TEST PRACTICE** Exs. 2, 12, 18, 28, 32, and 33

SKILL PRACTICE

A

1. **VOCABULARY** Sketch two similar triangles. Use your sketch to explain what is meant by *corresponding side lengths.* **See margin.**

2. ★ **WRITING** Two regular n-gons are similar. The ratio of their side lengths is 3 : 4. Do you need to know the value of n to find the ratio of the perimeters or the ratio of the areas of the polygons? *Explain.* **See margin.**

EXAMPLES 1 and 2 on pp. 737–738 for Exs. 3–8

2. No; the ratio of perimeters is the same as the ratio of side lengths, and the ratio of areas is the square of the ratio of side lengths by Theorem 11.7.

FINDING RATIOS **Copy and complete the table of ratios for similar polygons.**

	Ratio of corresponding side lengths	Ratio of perimeters	Ratio of areas
3.	6 : 11	? **6:11**	? **36:121**
4.	? **5:9**	20 : 36 = ? **5:9**	? **25:81**

RATIOS AND AREAS **Corresponding lengths in similar figures are given. Find the ratios (red to blue) of the perimeters and areas. Find the unknown area.**

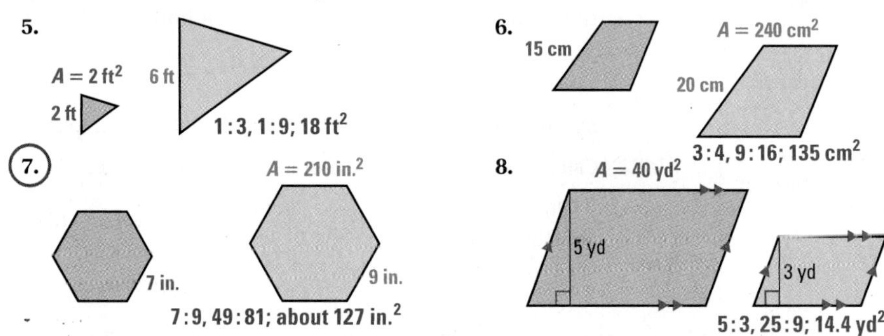

EXAMPLE 3 on p. 738 for Exs. 9–15

FINDING LENGTH RATIOS **The ratio of the areas of two similar figures is given. Write the ratio of the lengths of corresponding sides.**

9. Ratio of areas = 49 : 16 **7:4**
10. Ratio of areas = 16 : 121 **4:11**
11. Ratio of areas = 121 : 144 **11:12**

12. ★ **MULTIPLE CHOICE** The area of $\triangle LMN$ is 18 ft^2 and the area of $\triangle FGH$ is 24 ft^2. If $\triangle LMN \sim \triangle FGH$, what is the ratio of LM to FG? **C**

Ⓐ 3 : 4 Ⓑ 9 : 16 Ⓒ $\sqrt{3}$: 2 Ⓓ 4 : 3

FINDING SIDE LENGTHS **Use the given area to find XY.**

13. $\triangle DEF \sim \triangle XYZ$

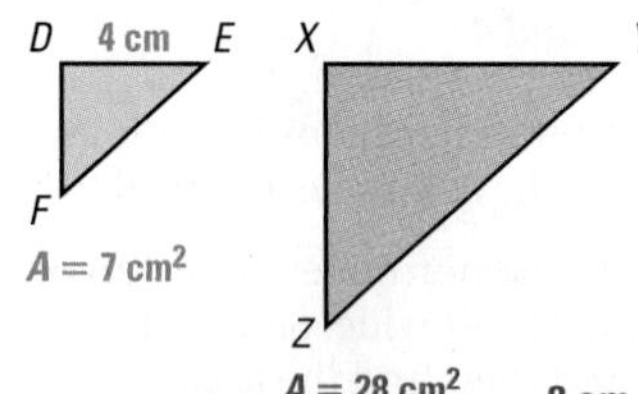

8 cm

14. $UVWXY \sim LMNPQ$

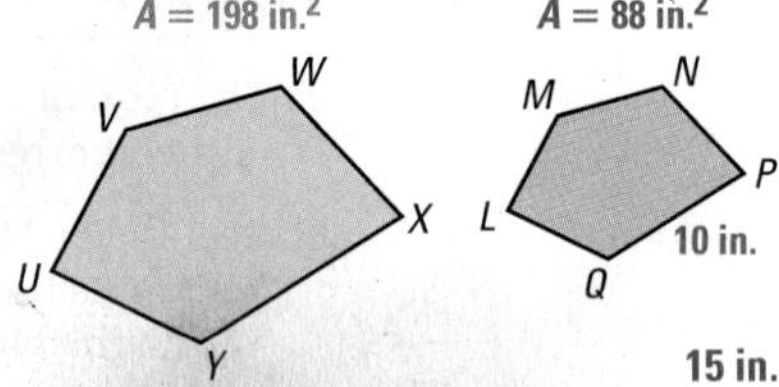

15 in.

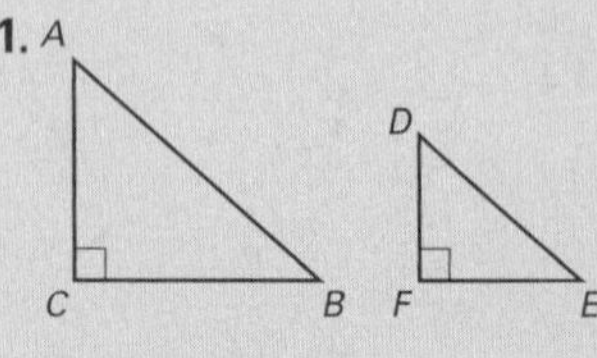

$\triangle ABC \sim \triangle DEF$ tells you that the sides in the same position are proportional. AB and DE are corresponding side lengths because the sides are both the hypotenuse of their respective triangle and are listed in the same order in the similarity statement.

15. **ERROR ANALYSIS** In the diagram, Rectangles $DEFG$ and $WXYZ$ are similar. The ratio of the area of $DEFG$ to the area of $WXYZ$ is 1 : 4. *Describe* and correct the error in finding ZY. **The ratio of areas is 1 : 4, so the ratio of side lengths is 1 : 2; $ZY = 2(12) = 24$.**

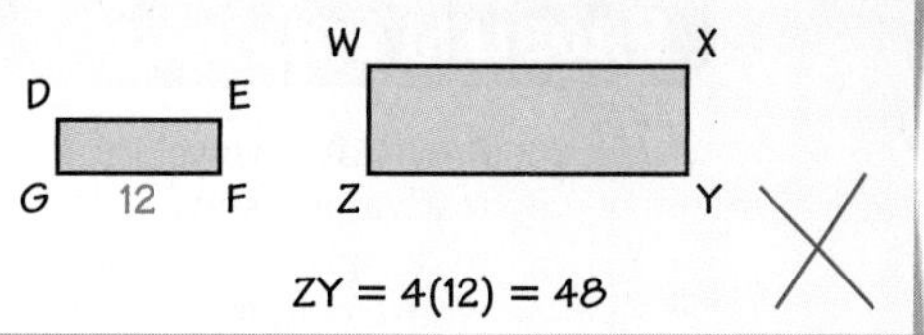

EXAMPLE 4 on p. 739 for Exs. 16–17

16. **REGULAR PENTAGONS** Regular pentagon $QRSTU$ has a side length of 12 centimeters and an area of about 248 square centimeters. Regular pentagon $VWXYZ$ has a perimeter of 140 centimeters. Find its area. **about 1350 cm^2**

17. **RHOMBUSES** Rhombuses $MNPQ$ and $RSTU$ are similar. The area of $RSTU$ is 28 square feet. The diagonals of $MNPQ$ are 25 feet long and 14 feet long. Find the area of $MNPQ$. Then use the ratio of the areas to find the lengths of the diagonals of $RSTU$. **175 ft^2; 10 ft, 5.6 ft**

8. Case 3, Case 1, Case 2; n Case 3 the enlargement s $\sqrt{5}$ which s about 2.24, which is ess than an enlargement of 3 n Case 1, which s less than an enlargement of 4 n Case 2.

18. **★ SHORT RESPONSE** You enlarge the same figure three different ways. In each case, the enlarged figure is similar to the original. List the enlargements in order from smallest to largest. *Explain.* **B**

Case 1 The side lengths of the original figure are multiplied by 3.
Case 2 The perimeter of the original figure is multiplied by 4.
Case 3 The area of the original figure is multiplied by 5.

REASONING In Exercises 19 and 20, copy and complete the statement using *always, sometimes,* or *never. Explain* your reasoning.

19. Doubling the side length of a square __?__ doubles the area.
Never; doubling the side length of a square always quadruples the area.

20. Two similar octagons __?__ have the same perimeter.
Sometimes; only when the octagons are also congruent will the perimeters be the same.

21. The triangles are similar since the ratio of the sides of $\triangle ABC$ to $\triangle DEF$ is 3 : 4. So, the ratio of the areas must be 9 : 16. Use this ratio with the area of $\triangle ABC$ to find the area of $\triangle DEF$.

21. **FINDING AREA** The sides of $\triangle ABC$ are 4.5 feet, 7.5 feet, and 9 feet long. The area is about 17 square feet. *Explain* how to use the area of $\triangle ABC$ to find the area of a $\triangle DEF$ with side lengths 6 feet, 10 feet, and 12 feet.

22. **RECTANGLES** Rectangles $ABCD$ and $DEFG$ are similar. The length of $ABCD$ is 24 feet and the perimeter is 84 feet. The width of $DEFG$ is 3 yards. Find the ratio of the area of $ABCD$ to the area of $DEFG$. **4 : 1**

C **SIMILAR TRIANGLES *Explain* why the red and blue triangles are similar. Find the ratio (red to blue) of the areas of the triangles. Show your steps.** **23, 24. See margin.**

23.

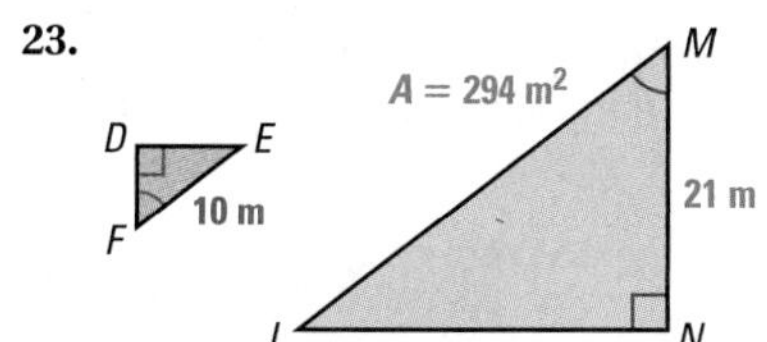

24.

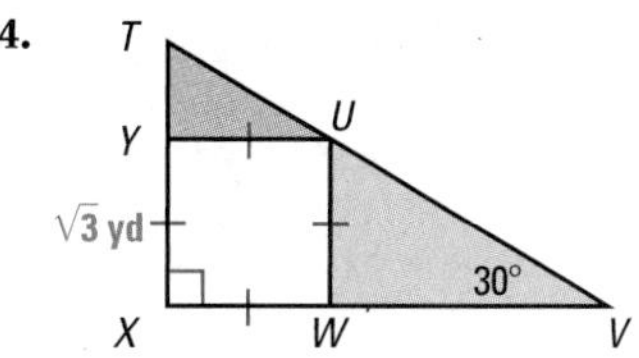

25. **CHALLENGE** In the diagram shown, $ABCD$ is a parallelogram. The ratio of the area of $\triangle AGB$ to the area of $\triangle CGE$ is 9 : 25, $CG = 10$, and $GE = 15$.

a. Find AG, GB, GF, and FE. Show your methods. **See margin.**

b. Give two area ratios other than 9 : 25 or 25 : 9 for pairs of similar triangles in the figure. *Explain.*
***Sample answer:* 1 : 1 , 72 : 72, for $\triangle ABC$ which is congruent to $\triangle CDA$**

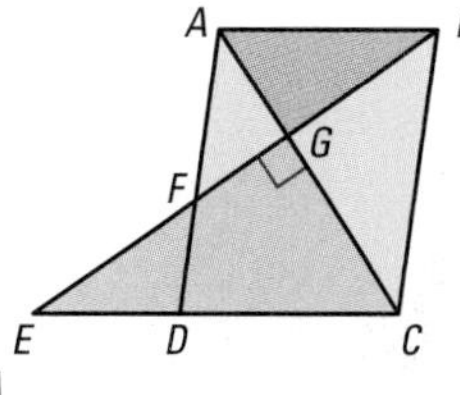

Teaching Strategy

Exercise 17 Remind students that they need to use the area formula for a rhombus, $A = \frac{1}{2}d_1d_2$, where d_1 and d_2 are the lengths of the diagonals, to find the area of rhombus $MNPQ$. Since the lengths of the diagonals in similar figures have the same ratio as the lengths of the sides, students should realize that they need to use the square root of the ratio of the areas to find the ratio of the lengths of the diagonals.

23. AA Similarity Postulate; $294 = \frac{1}{2} \cdot LN \cdot 21$, $LN = 28$ m, $LM = \sqrt{21^2 + 28^2} = 35$ m, $\frac{10}{35} = \frac{2}{7}$ is the ratio of side lengths, so the ratio of areas is 4 : 49.

24. $YUWX$ is a square, so $\overline{YX} \parallel \overline{UW}$; therefore $\angle YTU \cong \angle WUV$. $\overline{UW} \perp \overline{XV}$, so $\angle UWV$ is 90°; by the AA Similarity Postulate $\triangle YTU \sim \triangle WUV$. In $\triangle UVW$, the side opposite the 30° angle is given as $\sqrt{3}$. In $\triangle TUY$, $\overline{YU}$ is $\sqrt{3}$, so by the properties of 30°-60°-90° triangles, the side opposite the 30° angle is 1. So the ratio of side lengths is $1 : \sqrt{3}$, which makes the ratio of the areas 1 : 3.

25a. 6, 9, 5.4, 9.6; the ratio of areas is 9 : 25, so the ratio of side lengths is 3 : 5. Since we are given that $CG = 10$, then the side ratio tells us that $AG = 6$, and we are given that $GE = 15$, so $GB = 9$. We can also show that $\triangle AGF \sim \triangle CGB$ by the AA Similarity Postulate and has a side ratio of 6 : 10, so $GF = 5.4$. Since $\overline{GF}$ is on $\overline{GE}$, $15 - 5.4 = 9.6$ is the length of $\overline{FE}$.

Teaching Strategy

Exercise 31 Point out that students should look at the graphs of the mystery books and science fiction books as graphs of rectangles. Then the graphs are misleading because the rectangles have an area ratio of 4 : 1 while the data imply a ratio of 2 : 1.

31. There were twice as many mysteries read, but the area of the mystery bar is about 4 times the area of the science fiction bar, giving the impression that 4 times as many mysteries were read.

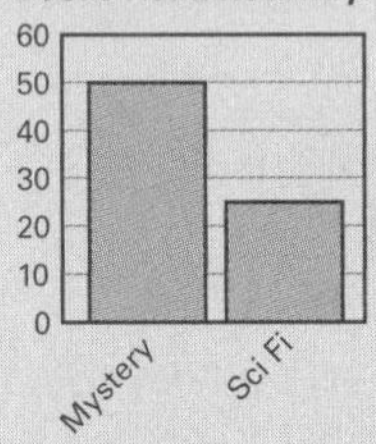

32.

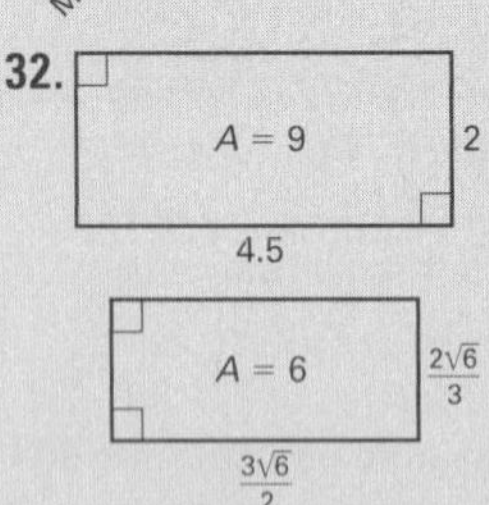

$3 : \sqrt{6} = \sqrt{6} : 2$

33c. $\frac{10}{9} = \frac{20}{10 + x}$

$180 = 100 + 10x$

$x = 8$

OR

$20(9) = (10 + x)(10)$

$180 = 100 + 10x$

$x = 8$

34a. ***M* and *N* are vertices of the cube, and therefore $\overline{MP} \cong \overline{NP}$ and forms a right angle by the definition of a cube. Also since $\overline{JL} \cong \overline{KL}$ and all angles with vertices at *L* measure 90°, you have SAS Similarity.**

PROBLEM SOLVING

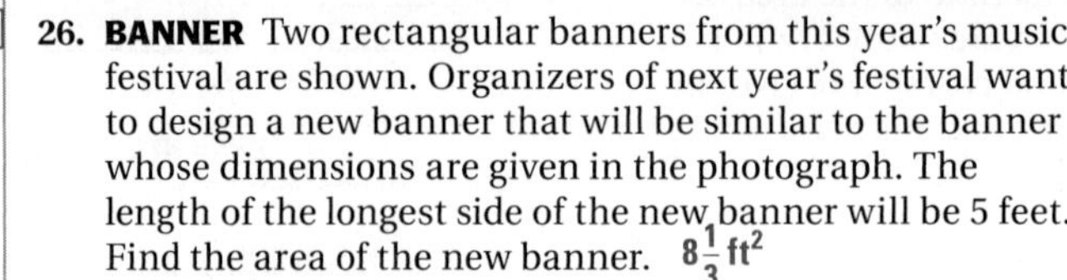

A

26. BANNER Two rectangular banners from this year's music festival are shown. Organizers of next year's festival want to design a new banner that will be similar to the banner whose dimensions are given in the photograph. The length of the longest side of the new banner will be 5 feet. Find the area of the new banner. **$8\frac{1}{3}$ ft²**

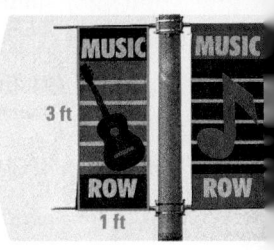

@HomeTutor for problem solving help at classzone.com

EXAMPLE 3 on p. 738 for Ex. 27

27. PATIO A new patio will be an irregular hexagon. The patio will have two long parallel sides and an area of 360 square feet. The area of a similar shaped patio is 250 square feet, and its long parallel sides are 12.5 feet apart. What will be the corresponding distance on the new patio? **15 ft**

@HomeTutor for problem solving help at classzone.com

28. ★ MULTIPLE CHOICE You need 20 pounds of grass seed to plant grass inside the baseball diamond shown. About how many pounds do you need to plant grass inside the softball diamond? **B**

Ⓐ 6 Ⓑ 9

Ⓒ 13 Ⓓ 20

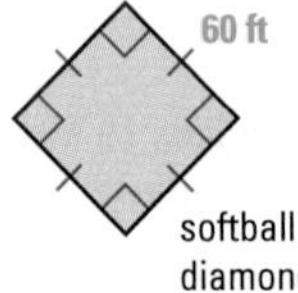

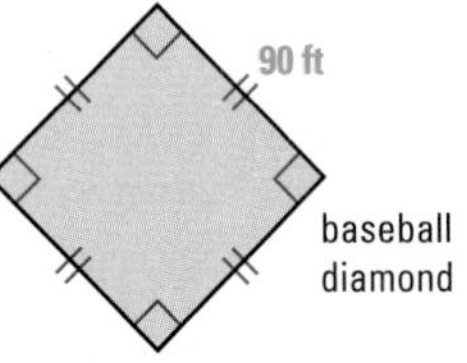

B

29. MULTI-STEP PROBLEM Use graph paper for parts (a) and (b). **a, b. Check students' work.**

a. Draw a triangle and label its vertices. Find the area of the triangle.

b. Mark and label the midpoint of each side of the triangle. Connect the midpoints to form a smaller triangle. Show that the larger and smaller triangles are similar. Then use the fact that the triangles are similar to find the area of the smaller triangle.
The area of the smaller triangle is one-fourth the area of the larger triangle.

30. JUSTIFYING THEOREM 11.7 Choose a type of polygon for which you know the area formula. Use algebra and the area formula to prove Theorem 11.7 for that polygon. (*Hint:* Use the ratio for the corresponding side lengths in two similar polygons to express each dimension in one polygon as $\frac{a}{b}$ times the corresponding dimension in the other polygon.)
Check students' work. The results should be side ratio $a : b$ and area ratio $a^2 : b^2$.

31. MISLEADING GRAPHS A student wants to show that the students in a science class prefer mysteries to science fiction books. Over a two month period, the students in the class read 50 mysteries, but only 25 science fiction books. The student makes a bar graph of these data. *Explain* why the graph is visually misleading. Show how the student could redraw the bar graph. **See margin.**

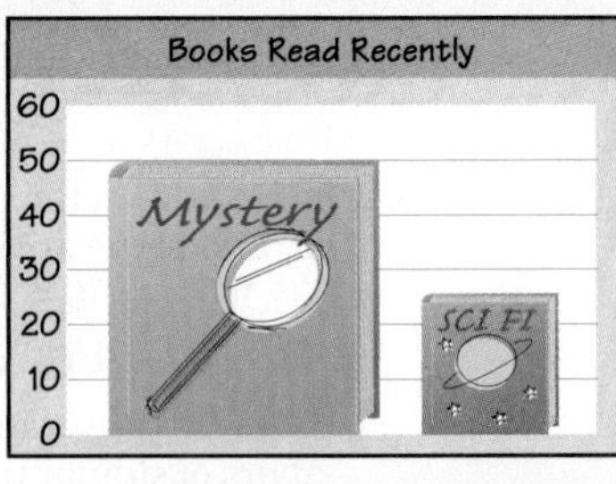

○ = WORKED-OUT SOLUTIONS on p. WS1

★ = STANDARDIZED TEST PRACTICE

32. ★ **OPEN-ENDED MATH** The ratio of the areas of two similar polygons is 9 : 6. Draw two polygons that fit this description. Find the ratio of their perimeters. Then write the ratio in simplest radical form. **See margin.**

33. ★ **EXTENDED RESPONSE** Use the diagram shown at the right.
   a. Name as many pairs of similar triangles as you can. *Explain* your reasoning.
   b. Find the ratio of the areas for one pair of similar triangles. ***Sample answer:* 100 : 81**
   c. Show two ways to find the length of $\overline{DE}$. **See margin.**

33a. $\triangle ACD \sim \triangle AEB$, $\triangle BCF \sim \triangle DEF$; **AA Similarity Postulate**

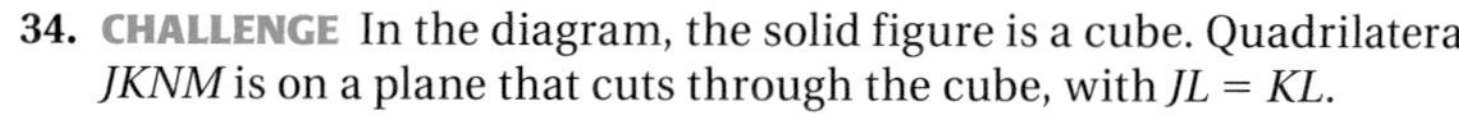

C 34. **CHALLENGE** In the diagram, the solid figure is a cube. Quadrilateral *JKNM* is on a plane that cuts through the cube, with $JL = KL$.
   a. *Explain* how you know that $\triangle JKL \sim \triangle MNP$. **See margin.**
   b. Suppose $\frac{JK}{MN} = \frac{1}{3}$. Find the ratio of the area of $\triangle JKL$ to the area of one face of the cube. **1 : 18**
   c. Find the ratio of the area of $\triangle JKL$ to the area of pentagon *JKQRS*. **1 : 17**

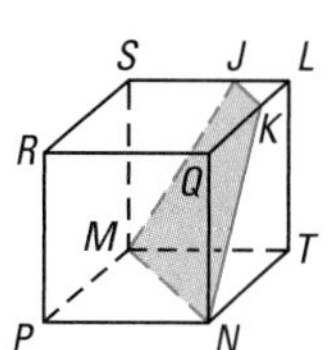

MIXED REVIEW

PREVIEW
Prepare for Lesson 11.4 in Exs. 35–38.

Find the circumference of the circle with the given radius *r* or diameter *d*. Use $\pi \approx 3.14$. Round your answers to the nearest hundredth. *(p. 49)*

35. $d = 4$ cm **12.56 cm** 36. $d = 10$ ft **31.40 ft** 37. $r = 2.5$ yd **15.70 yd** 38. $r = 3.1$ m **19.47 m**

Find the value of *x*.

39. *(p. 295)*

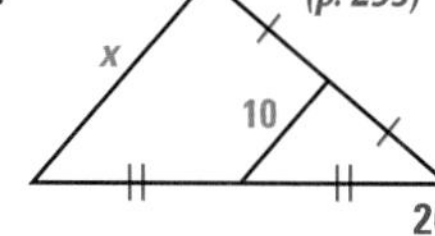

20

40. *(p. 672)*

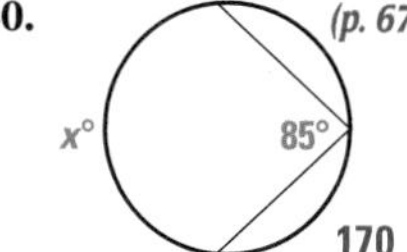

170

41. *(p. 680)*

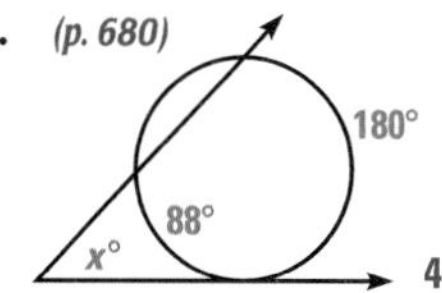

46

QUIZ *for Lessons 11.1–11.3*

1. The height of ▱*ABCD* is 3 times its base. Its area is 108 square feet. Find the base and the height. *(p. 720)* **6 ft, 18 ft**

Find the area of the figure.

2. *(p. 720)*

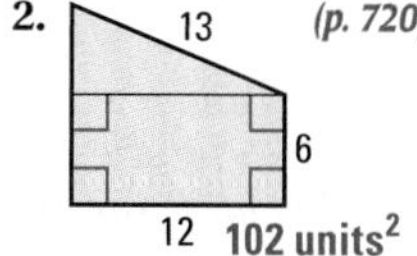

102 units^2

3. *(p. 730)*

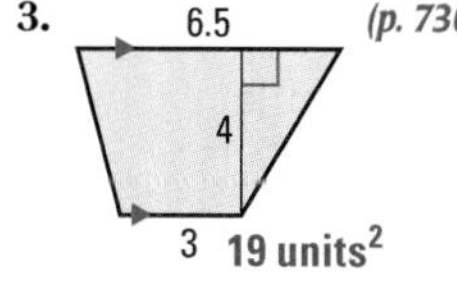

19 units^2

4. *(p. 730)*

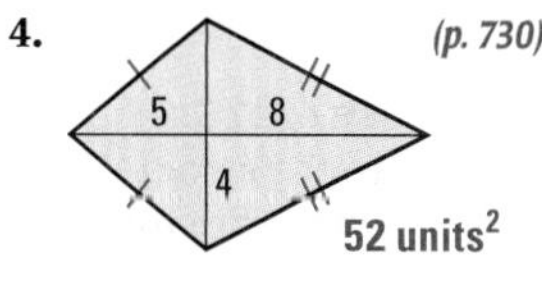

52 units^2

5. The ratio of the lengths of corresponding sides of two similar heptagons is 7 : 20. Find the ratio of their perimeters and their areas. *(p. 737)* **7 : 20, 49 : 400**

6. Triangles *PQR* and *XYZ* are similar. The area of $\triangle PQR$ is 1200 ft^2 and the area of $\triangle XYZ$ is 48 ft^2. Given $PQ = 50$ ft, find *XY*. *(p. 737)* **10 ft**

5 ASSESS AND RETEACH

Daily Homework Quiz

Transparency Available

Figure I ~ Figure II. Find the ratio of the perimeters and the ratio of the areas. Then find the unknown area.

1. I: 24 ft, $A = 60$ ft^2; II: 18 ft

ratio of perimeters: 4 : 3; ratio of areas: 16 : 9; 33.75 ft^2

2. I: 12 cm

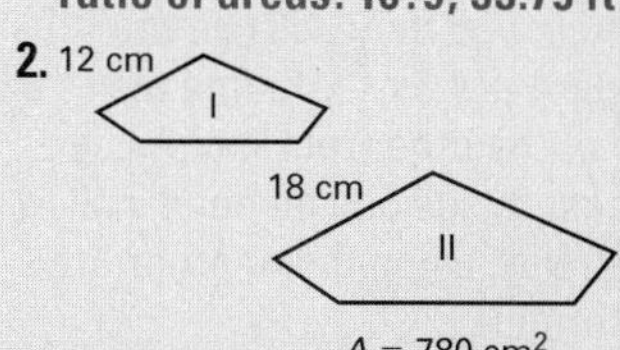

ratio of perimeters: 2 : 3; ratio of areas: 4 : 9; $346\frac{2}{3}$ cm^2

3. Rectangle I ~ Rectangle II. In Rectangle I, the length is 20 feet and the perimeter is 64 feet. In Rectangle II, the width is 8 yards. Find the ratio of the area of Rectangle I to the area of Rectangle II. **1 : 4**

Online Quiz

Available at **classzone.com**

Diagnosis/Remediation

- Practice A, B, C in Chapter 11 Resource Book, pp. 34–39
- Study Guide in Chapter 11 Resource Book, pp. 40–41
- Practice Workbook, pp. 211–213
- @HomeTutor

Challenge

Additional challenge is available in the Chapter 11 Resource Book, p. 45.

Quiz

An easily-readable reduced copy of the quiz (with answers) on Lessons 11.1–11.3 from the Assessment Book can be found on p. 718G.

Using ALTERNATIVE METHODS

Alternative Strategy

The formula A = length $\times$ width can be used to find the width of the smaller pan. This may be useful to students because they are familiar with the area formula for a rectangle.

Teaching Strategy

Point out that the alternative method also uses a ratio when it uses the fact that the length of the larger pan is 1.5 times its width.

Study Strategy

For Exercise 1, using the alternative method means students will first find the area of the second rectangle and they will use the formula $A = 1.5x \cdot x$ to find the width of the other rectangle. The other exercises can be done in a similar way, using the appropriate area formula.

Another Way to Solve Example 3, page 738

MULTIPLE REPRESENTATIONS In Example 3 on page 738, you used proportional reasoning to solve a problem about cooking. You can also solve the problem by using an area formula.

PROBLEM

COOKING A large rectangular baking pan is 15 inches long and 10 inches wide. A smaller pan is similar to the large pan. The area of the smaller pan is 96 square inches. Find the width of the smaller pan.

METHOD

Using a Formula You can use what you know about side lengths of similar figures to find the width of the pan.

Standards

8.0 Students know, derive, and **solve problems involving the** perimeter, circumference, **area**, volume, lateral area, and surface area **of common geometric figures.**

STEP 1 **Use** the given dimensions of the large pan to write expressions for the dimensions of the smaller pan. Let x represent the width of the smaller pan.

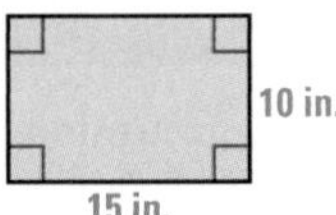

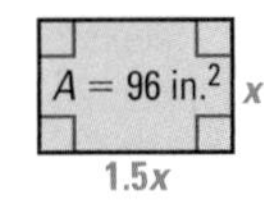

The length of the larger pan is 1.5 times its width. So, the length of the smaller pan is also 1.5 times its width, or $1.5x$.

STEP 2 **Use** the formula for the area of a rectangle to write an equation.

$A = \ell w$	Formula for area of a rectangle
$96 = 1.5x \cdot x$	Substitute $1.5x$ for ℓ and x for w.
$8 = x$	Solve for a positive value of x.

▶ The width of the smaller pan is 8 inches.

PRACTICE

1. **COOKING** A third pan is similar to the large pan shown above and has 1.44 times its area. Find the length of the third pan. **18 in.**

2. **TRAPEZOIDS** Trapezoid $PQRS$ is similar to trapezoid $WXYZ$. The area of $WXYZ$ is 28 square units. Find WZ. **8 units**

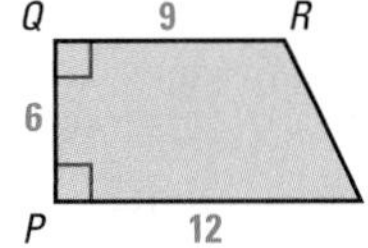

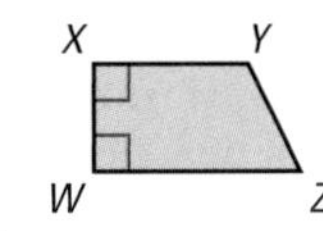

3. **SQUARES** One square has sides of length s. If another square has twice the area of the first square, what is its side length? $s\sqrt{2}$

4. **REASONING** $\triangle ABC \sim \triangle DEF$ and the area of $\triangle DEF$ is 11.25 square centimeters. Find DE and DF. *Explain* your reasoning.

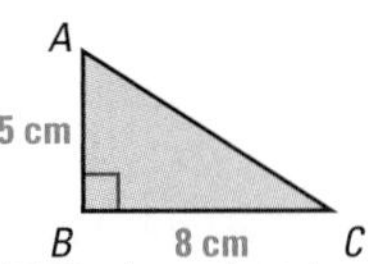

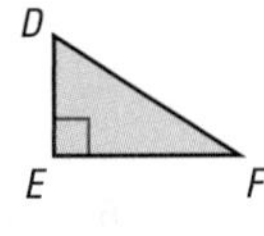

3.75, about 7.08; since the triangles are similar, the ratio of areas is equal to the ratio of side lengths squared. The ratio of the areas is 16 : 9, so the ratio of side lengths is 4 : 3.

Lessons 11.1–11.3

1. **MULTI-STEP PROBLEM** The diagram below represents a rectangular flower bed. In the diagram, $AG = 9.5$ feet and $GE = 15$ feet.

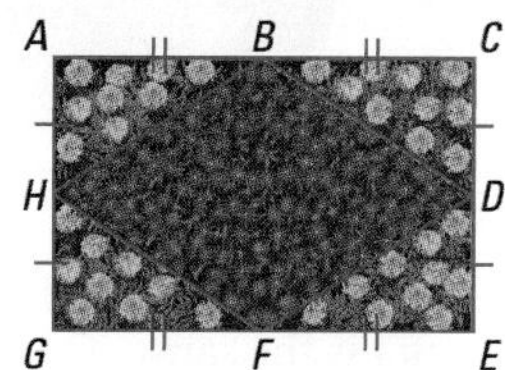

   a. *Explain* how you know that *BDFH* is a rhombus. **See margin.**

   b. Find the area of rectangle *ACEG* and the area of rhombus *BDFH*. **142.5 ft^2, 71.25 ft^2**

   c. You want to plant asters inside rhombus *BDFH* and marigolds in the other parts of the flower bed. It costs about \$.30 per square foot to plant marigolds and about \$.40 per square foot to plant asters. How much will you spend on flowers? **about \$49.88**

2. **OPEN-ENDED** A polygon has an area of 48 square meters and a height of 8 meters. Draw three different triangles that fit this description and three different parallelograms. *Explain* your thinking. **See margin.**

3. **EXTENDED RESPONSE** You are tiling a 12 foot by 21 foot rectangular floor. Prices are shown below for two sizes of square tiles.

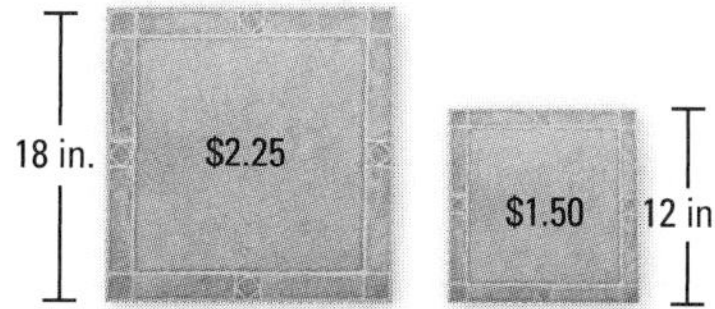

   a. How many small tiles would you need for the floor? How many large tiles? **252 small tiles, 112 large tiles**

   b. Find the cost of buying large tiles for the floor and the cost of buying small tiles for the floor. Which tile should you use if you want to spend as little as possible? **\$252, \$378; large tiles**

   c. *Compare* the side lengths, the areas, and the costs of the two tiles. Is the cost per tile based on side length or on area? *Explain.* **The ratio of side lengths is 2 : 3, the ratio of areas is 4 : 9, and the ratio of costs is 2 : 3; side length; the ratio of cost is 2:3 which is the ratio of the side lengths.**

4. **SHORT RESPONSE** What happens to the area of a rhombus if you double the length of each diagonal? if you triple the length of each diagonal? *Explain* what happens to the area of a rhombus if each diagonal is multiplied by the same number n. **See margin.**

5. **MULTI-STEP PROBLEM** The pool shown is a right triangle with legs of length 40 feet and 41 feet. The path around the pool is 40 inches wide.

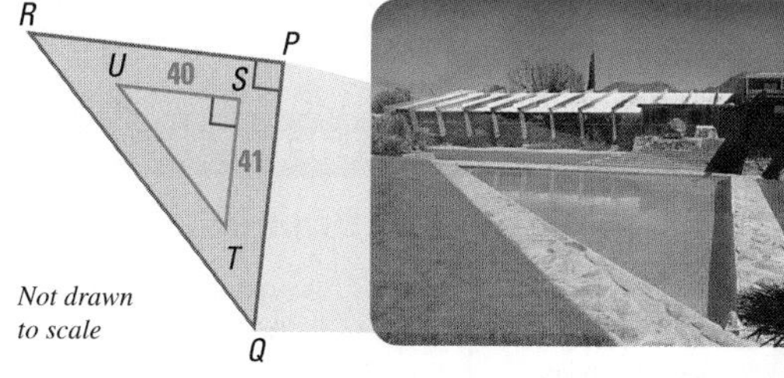

   a. Find the area of $\triangle STU$. **820 ft^2**

   b. In the diagram, $\triangle PQR \sim \triangle STU$, and the scale factor of the two triangles is 1.3 : 1. Find the perimeter of $\triangle PQR$. **about 180 ft**

   c. Find the area of $\triangle PQR$. Then find the area of the path around the pool. **about 1386 ft^2; about 566 ft**

6. **GRIDDED ANSWER** In trapezoid *ABCD*, $\overline{AB} \parallel \overline{CD}$, $m\angle D = 90°$, $AD = 5$ inches, and $CD = 3 \cdot AB$. The area of trapezoid *ABCD* is 1250 square inches. Find the length (in inches) of $\overline{CD}$. **375**

7. **EXTENDED RESPONSE** In the diagram below, $\triangle EFH$ is an isosceles right triangle, and $\triangle FGH$ is an equilateral triangle.

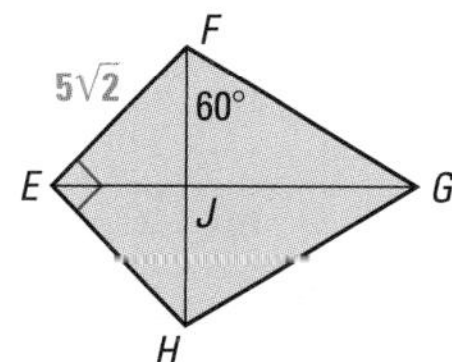

   a. Find *FH*. *Explain* your reasoning.

   b. Find *EG*. *Explain* your reasoning. **a, b. See margin.**

   c. Find the area of *EFGH*. **about 68.3 units^2**

1a. The four edges are corresponding parts of congruent triangles.

2. See Additional Answers beginning on p. AA1.

4. 4 times larger; 9 times larger; n^2 times larger; the formula for the area of a rhombus is $\frac{1}{2}d_1d_2$, if you multiply each diagonal by the same value n, you get $\frac{1}{2}(nd_1)(nd_2)$ which simplifies to $\frac{1}{2}n^2d_1d_2$.

7a. 10 units; since $\triangle EFH$ is a right isosceles triangle with side $EF = 5\sqrt{2}$, then $\overline{EH}$ must also measure $5\sqrt{2}$. Therefore the Pythagorean theorem gives $FH = 10$.

7b. $5 + 5\sqrt{3}$; in $\triangle FJG$, $FG = 10$ because it is an equilateral triangle. Using the properties of 30°-60°-90° triangles and 45°-45°-90° triangles, $EJ = 5$ and $JG = 5\sqrt{3}$.

1 PLAN AND PREPARE

Warm-Up Exercises

Transparency Available

Simplify the expression.

1. $\frac{45}{360}$ **$\frac{1}{8}$**
2. $\frac{120}{360} \cdot 9\pi$ **3π**
3. $\frac{15\pi}{3}$ **5π**
4. $\frac{60}{360}(15\pi)$ **$\frac{5\pi}{2}$**
5. A central angle of a circle measures 82°. Find the measure of the intercepted arc. **82°**
6. Solve $\frac{3.8}{x} = \frac{120}{360}$. **11.4**

Notetaking Guide

Transparency Available

Promotes interactive learning and notetaking skills, pp. 292–295.

Pacing

Basic: 2 days

Average: 2 days

Advanced: 2 days

Block: 1 block

- See *Teaching Guide/Lesson Plan.*

2 FOCUS AND MOTIVATE

Essential Question

Big Idea 3, p. 719

How do you find the length of an arc of a circle? **Tell students they will learn how to answer this question by using the ratio of the part of the circumference to the entire circle.**

11.4 Circumference and Arc Length

Before You found the circumference of a circle.

Now You will find arc lengths and other measures.

Why? So you can find a running distance, as in Example 5.

Key Vocabulary
- **circumference**
- **arc length**
- **radius,** *p. 651*
- **diameter,** *p. 651*
- **measure of an arc,** *p. 659*

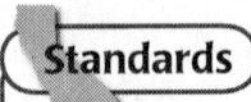

Standards

8.0 Students know, derive, and solve problems involving the perimeter, **circumference**, area, volume, lateral area, and surface area of common geometric figures.

The **circumference** of a circle is the distance around the circle. For all circles, the ratio of the circumference to the diameter is the same. This ratio is known as π, or *pi*. In Chapter 1, you used 3.14 to approximate the value of π. Throughout this chapter, you should use the π key on a calculator, then round to the hundredths place unless instructed otherwise.

THEOREM *For Your Notebook*

THEOREM 11.8 Circumference of a Circle

The circumference C of a circle is $C = \pi d$ or $C = 2\pi r$, where d is the diameter of the circle and r is the radius of the circle.

Justification: Ex. 2, p. 769

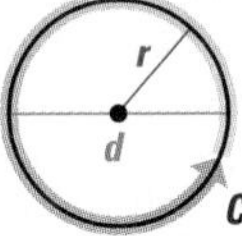

$C = \pi d = 2\pi r$

EXAMPLE 1 Use the formula for circumference

Find the indicated measure.

a. Circumference of a circle with radius 9 centimeters

b. Radius of a circle with circumference 26 meters

Solution

a. $C = 2\pi r$ Write circumference formula.

$= 2 \cdot \pi \cdot 9$ Substitute 9 for r.

$= 18\pi$ Simplify.

≈ 56.55 Use a calculator.

▶ The circumference is about 56.55 centimeters.

ANOTHER WAY
You can give an exact measure in terms of π. In Example 1, part (a), the exact circumference is 18π. The exact radius in Example 1, part (b) is $\frac{26}{2\pi}$, or $\frac{13}{\pi}$.

b. $C = 2\pi r$ Write circumference formula.

$26 = 2\pi r$ Substitute 26 for C.

$\frac{26}{2\pi} = r$ Divide each side by 2π.

$4.14 \approx r$ Use a calculator.

▶ The radius is about 4.14 meters.

Resource Planning Guide

Chapter Resource Book
- Teaching Guide/Lesson Plan (pp. 46–47)
- Activity Master (p. 48)
- Practice levels A, B, C (pp. 49–54)
- Study Guide (pp. 55–56)
- Catch-up for Absent Students (p. 57)
- Application (p. 58)
- Challenge (p. 59)

Workbooks
- Notetaking Guide (pp. 292–295)
- Practice Workbook (pp. 214–216)

Teaching Options
- **Power Presentations CD-ROM** provides dynamic electronic teaching resources for the classroom.
- **Activity Generator CD-ROM** provides editable activities for all ability levels.

Interactive Technology
- Easy Planner
- Power Presentations CD-ROM
- Activity Generator CD-ROM
- Animated Geometry
- Test Generator CD-ROM
- Online Quiz
- eWorkbook
- eEdition
- @HomeTutor

Resources for English Learners
- Quick Reference for English Learners
- Spanish Study Guide
- Multi-Language Visual Glossary
- Student Resources in Spanish

See also the *Geometry Toolkit* for more strategies for meeting individual needs.

EXAMPLE 2 Use circumference to find distance traveled

TIRE REVOLUTIONS The dimensions of a car tire are shown at the right. To the nearest foot, how far does the tire travel when it makes 15 revolutions?

5.5 in.
15 in.
5.5 in.

Solution

STEP 1 **Find** the diameter of the tire.

$d = 15 + 2(5.5) = 26$ in.

STEP 2 **Find** the circumference of the tire.

$C = \pi d = \pi(26) \approx 81.68$ in.

STEP 3 **Find** the distance the tire travels in 15 revolutions. In one revolution, the tire travels a distance equal to its circumference. In 15 revolutions, the tire travels a distance equal to 15 times its circumference.

$$\text{Distance traveled} = \text{Number of revolutions} \cdot \text{Circumference}$$

$$\approx 15 \cdot 81.68 \text{ in.}$$

$$= 1225.2 \text{ in.}$$

AVOID ERRORS
Always pay attention to units. In Example 2, you need to convert units to get a correct answer.

STEP 4 **Use** unit analysis. Change 1225.2 inches to feet.

$$1225.2 \text{ in.} \cdot \frac{1 \text{ ft}}{12 \text{ in.}} = 102.1 \text{ ft}$$

▶ The tire travels approximately 102 feet.

✓ GUIDED PRACTICE for Examples 1 and 2

1. Find the circumference of a circle with diameter 5 inches. Find the diameter of a circle with circumference 17 feet. **about 15.71 in.; about 5.41 ft**
2. A car tire has a diameter of 28 inches. How many revolutions does the tire make while traveling 500 feet? **about 68 revolutions**

ARC LENGTH An **arc length** is a portion of the circumference of a circle. You can use the measure of the arc (in degrees) to find its length (in linear units).

COROLLARY *For Your Notebook*

ARC LENGTH COROLLARY

In a circle, the ratio of the length of a given arc to the circumference is equal to the ratio of the measure of the arc to 360°.

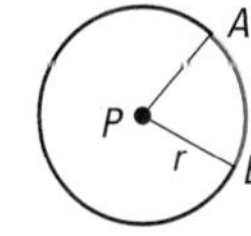

$$\frac{\text{Arc length of } \widehat{AB}}{2\pi r} = \frac{m\widehat{AB}}{360^\circ}, \text{ or Arc length of } \widehat{AB} = \frac{m\widehat{AB}}{360^\circ} \cdot 2\pi r$$

Motivating the Lesson

Ask students how they could find how far a bicycle travels when a wheel with diameter 26 inches makes one complete revolution (about 6.8 ft). Then ask how they could find how many times the wheel would revolve if the bicycle travels 1 mile (about 776 revolutions). Tell students that they will explore the circumference of a circle in this lesson.

3 TEACH

Extra Example 1

Find the indicated measure.

a. Circumference of a circle with radius 15 in. **about 94.25 in.**

b. Radius of a circle with circumference 36 ft **about 5.73 ft**

Key Questions to Ask for Example 1

- What formula can you use to find d if you know C? $d = \frac{C}{\pi}$
- What formula can you use to find r if you know C? $r = \frac{C}{2\pi}$

Extra Example 2

The diameter of a bicycle tire is 30 inches. To the nearest foot, how far does the tire travel when it makes 100 revolutions? **785 ft**

Key Question to Ask for Example 2

- What is the relationship between C, the circumference of the tire, and ℓ, the distance covered in one revolution of the tire? **They are equal.**

Differentiated Instruction

Below Level Have students cut a large circle from heavy paper and mark a point A on the rim. Then have them mark a starting point on the floor and line it up with point A with the circle upright. Then have them roll the circle for one revolution in a straight line along its rim and mark the new location of point A. Ask them to measure the distance between the two locations of point A. This is the length of one revolution, R. Ask them to find the circumference of the circle and compare it to R. (They should be approximately equal.)

See also the *Geometry Toolkit* for more strategies.

Extra Example 3

Find the length of each arc $\widehat{AB}$.

a. 7.07 in.

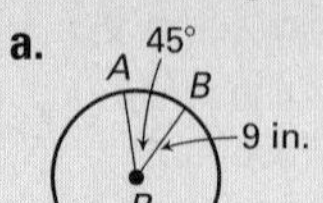

b. 11.78 in.

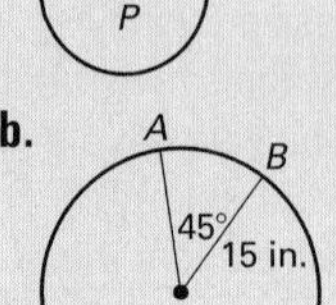

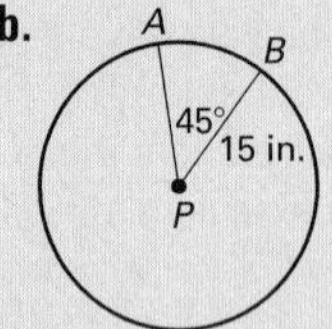

c. 23.56 in.

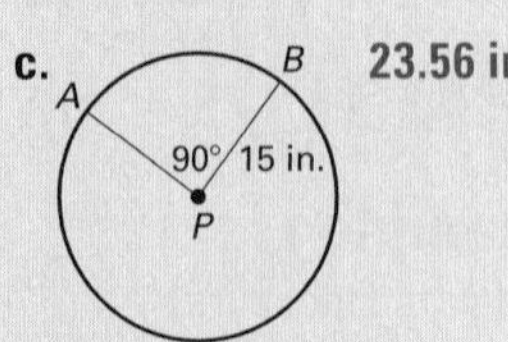

Extra Example 4

Find the indicated measure.

a. Circumference C 32.74 cm

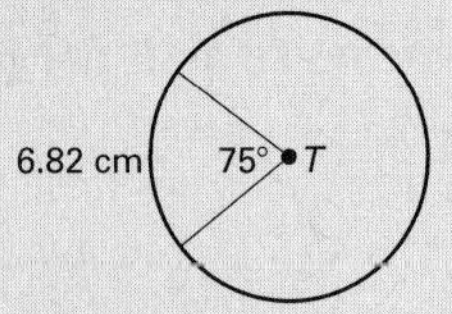

b. $m\widehat{AB}$ 150°

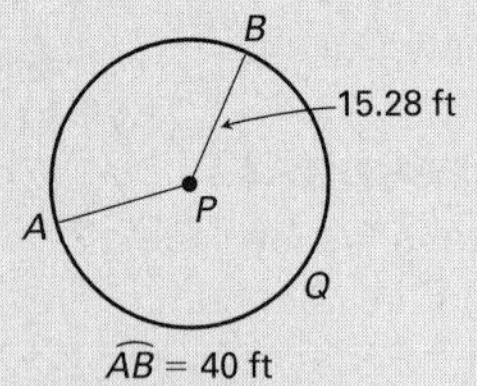

Key Questions to Ask for Example 4

- What fraction of the circumference is the arc length in part (a)? $\frac{40}{360} = \frac{1}{9}$
- What fraction of the circumference is the arc length in part (b)? about $\frac{165}{360} = \frac{11}{24}$

EXAMPLE 3 Find arc lengths

INTERPRET DIAGRAMS
In Example 3, $\widehat{AB}$ and $\widehat{EF}$ have the same measure. However, they have different lengths because they are in circles with different circumferences.

Find the length of each red arc.

a.

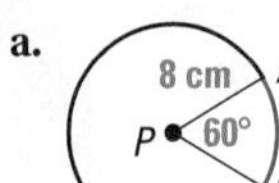

b.

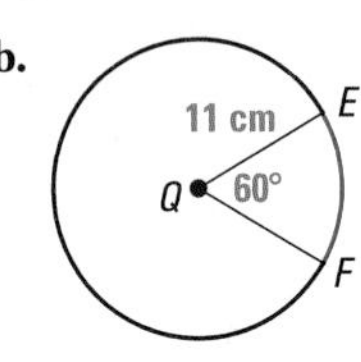

c.

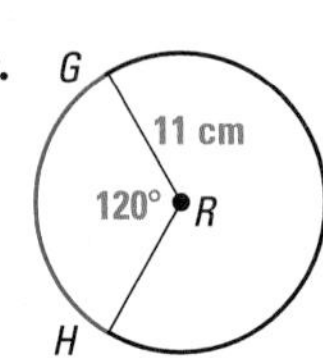

Solution

a. Arc length of $\widehat{AB} = \frac{60°}{360°} \cdot 2\pi(8) \approx 8.38$ centimeters

b. Arc length of $\widehat{EF} = \frac{60°}{360°} \cdot 2\pi(11) \approx 11.52$ centimeters

c. Arc length of $\widehat{GH} = \frac{120°}{360°} \cdot 2\pi(11) \approx 23.04$ centimeters

EXAMPLE 4 Use arc lengths to find measures

Find the indicated measure.

a. Circumference C of $\odot Z$

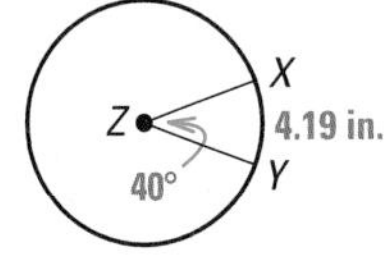

b. $m\widehat{RS}$

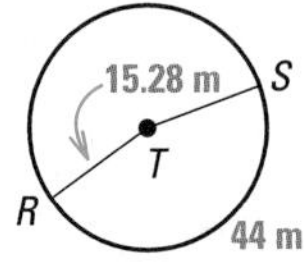

Solution

a.
$$\frac{\text{Arc length of } \widehat{XY}}{C} = \frac{m\widehat{XY}}{360°}$$
$$\frac{4.19}{C} = \frac{40°}{360°}$$
$$\frac{4.19}{C} = \frac{1}{9}$$
▸ $37.71 \text{ in.} = C$

b.
$$\frac{\text{Arc length of } \widehat{RS}}{2\pi r} = \frac{m\widehat{RS}}{360°}$$
$$\frac{44}{2\pi(15.28)} = \frac{m\widehat{RS}}{360°}$$
$$360° \cdot \frac{44}{2\pi(15.28)} = m\widehat{RS}$$
▸ $165° \approx m\widehat{RS}$

✓ GUIDED PRACTICE for Examples 3 and 4

Find the indicated measure.

3. Length of $\widehat{PQ}$

Q
9 yd
75°
R
S
P

about 5.89 yd

4. Circumference of $\odot N$

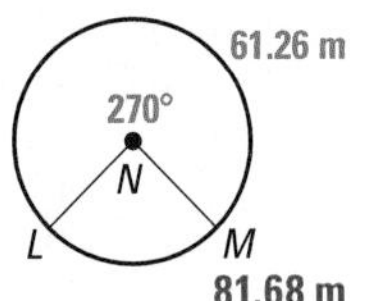

81.68 m

5. Radius of $\odot G$

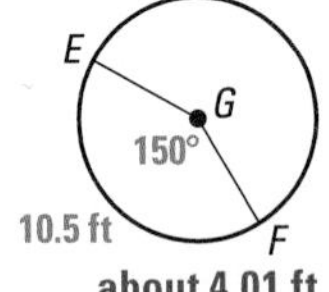

about 4.01 ft

Differentiated Instruction

Kinesthetic Learners To assist students in understanding how two arcs can have the same arc measure but can have different arc lengths, have them construct one circle with a diameter of 4 centimeters and another with a diameter of 6 centimeters. Instruct them to draw a 60° angle with vertex at the center of each circle. Ask them to identify the measure of each arc (60°). Then, have them use a piece of string to measure the length of each arc. Students will quickly notice that the arcs do not have the same length. See also the *Geometry Toolkit* for more strategies.

EXAMPLE 5 Use arc length to find distances

TRACK The curves at the ends of the track shown are 180° arcs of circles. The radius of the arc for a runner on the red path shown is 36.8 meters. About how far does this runner travel to go once around the track? Round to the nearest tenth of a meter.

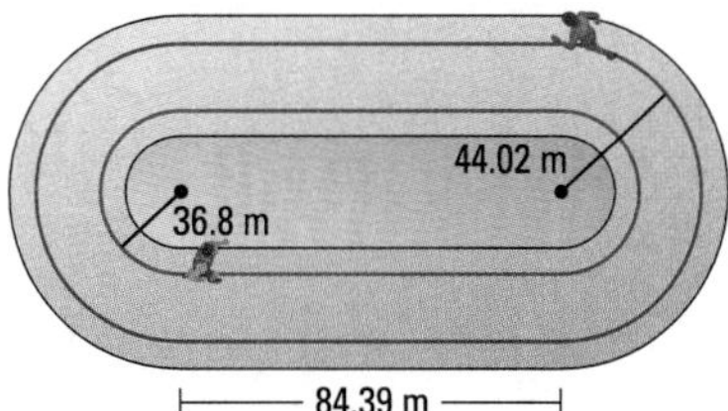

Solution

USE FORMULAS
The arc length of a semicircle is half the circumference of the circle with the same radius. So, the arc length of a semicircle is $\frac{1}{2} \cdot 2\pi r$, or πr.

The path of a runner is made of two straight sections and two semicircles. To find the total distance, find the sum of the lengths of each part.

$$\text{Distance} = 2 \cdot \text{Length of each straight section} + 2 \cdot \text{Length of each semicircle}$$

$$= 2(84.39) + 2 \cdot \left(\frac{1}{2} \cdot 2\pi \cdot 36.8\right)$$

$$\approx 400.0 \text{ meters}$$

▶ The runner on the red path travels about 400 meters.

Animated Geometry at classzone.com

✓ GUIDED PRACTICE for Example 5

6. In Example 5, the radius of the arc for a runner on the blue path is 44.02 meters, as shown in the diagram. About how far does this runner travel to go once around the track? Round to the nearest tenth of a meter. **about 445.4 m**

11.4 EXERCISES

HOMEWORK KEY
○ = **WORKED-OUT SOLUTIONS** on p. WS15 for Exs. 23, 25, and 35
★ = **STANDARDIZED TEST PRACTICE** Exs. 2, 31, 32, and 38

SKILL PRACTICE

A **In Exercises 1 and 2, refer to the diagram of ⊙P shown.**

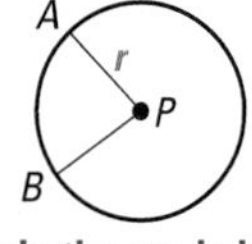

1. **VOCABULARY** Copy and complete the equation: $\frac{?}{2\pi r} = \frac{m\widehat{AB}}{?}$. **arc length of $\widehat{AB}$, 360°**

2. ★ **WRITING** *Describe* the difference between the *arc measure* and the *arc length* of $\widehat{AB}$. **Arc measure is the number of degrees of a circle the arc is bounded by, and the arc length is the part of the circumference of the circle that the arc occupies.**

EXAMPLE 1 on p. 746 for Exs. 3–7

USING CIRCUMFERENCE Use the diagram to find the indicated measure.

3. Find the circumference. **about 37.70 in.**

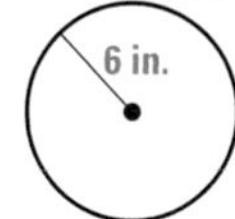

4. Find the circumference. **about 53.41 cm**

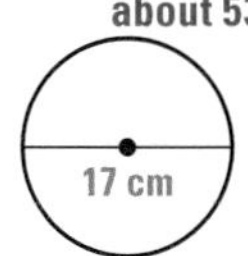

5. Find the radius. **about 10.03 ft**

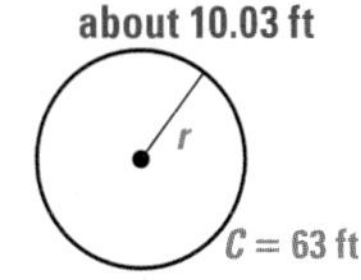

Extra Example 5

A track and football field is shown below. The track lane forms a 180° arc of a circle at each end of the track. The radius of the inner arc is 80 ft and the radius of the outer arc is 120 ft. Find the distance around the track, to the nearest foot, for a runner using the middle of the track. **about 1228 ft**

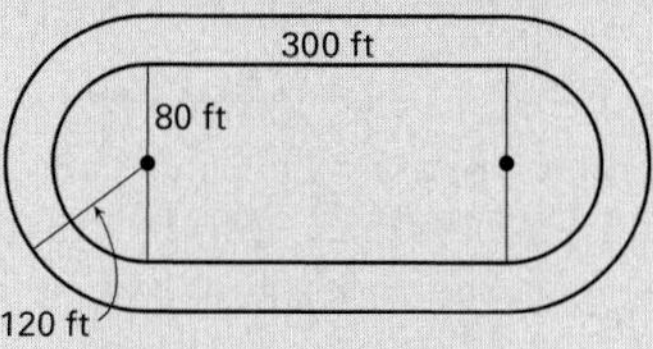

An **Animated Geometry** activity is available on-line for **Example 5**. This activity is also available on the **Power Presentations CD-ROM**.

Closing the Lesson

Have students summarize the major points of the lesson and answer the Essential Question: How do you find the length of an arc of a circle?

- **The circumference C of a circle is given by $C = 2\pi r$ or $C = \pi d$, where r is the radius and d is the diameter.**
- **In a circle, $\frac{\text{Arc length of } \widehat{AB}}{2\pi r} = \frac{m\widehat{AB}}{360°}$, or Arc length of $\widehat{AB} = \frac{m\widehat{AB}}{360°} \cdot 2\pi r$.**
- **To find the length of an arc of a circle you use the formula Arc length of $\widehat{AB} = \frac{m\widehat{AB}}{360°} \cdot 2\pi r$, where $\widehat{AB}$ is the arc whose length you are trying to find and r is the radius of the circle on which $\widehat{AB}$ lies.**

4 PRACTICE AND APPLY

Assignment Guide

Answer Transparencies available for all exercises

Basic:
Day 1: pp. 749–752
Exs. 1–10, 26–29, 37, 46–48
Day 2: pp. 749–752
Exs. 11–25, 35, 36, 38, 42–45

Average:
Day 1: pp. 749–752
Exs. 1–10, 26–29, 37, 38, 46–48
Day 2: pp. 749–752
Exs. 11–14, 18–25, 30–32, 35, 36, 39, 42–45

Advanced:
Day 1: pp. 749–752
Exs. 1–10, 26–29, 33*, 37, 38, 48
Day 2: pp. 749–752
Exs. 11–13, 19–25, 30–32, 34, 39–42*, 44

Block:
pp. 749–752
Exs. 1–14, 18–32, 35–39, 42–48

Differentiated Instruction

See *Geometry Best Practices Toolkit* for suggestions on addressing the needs of a diverse classroom.

Homework Check

For a quick check of student understanding of key concepts, go over the following exercises:
Basic: 4, 8, 12, 21, 37
Average: 6, 9, 19, 22, 37
Advanced: 7, 10, 20, 24, 37

Extra Practice

- Student Edition, p. 916
- Chapter 11 Resource Book: Practice levels A, B, C, pp. 49–54

Practice Worksheet

An easily-readable reduced practice page (with answers) for this lesson can be found on p. 718D.

FINDING EXACT MEASURES **Find the indicated measure.**

6. The exact circumference of a circle with diameter 5 inches **5π in.**

7. The exact radius of a circle with circumference 28π meters **14 m**

EXAMPLE 2 on p. 747 for Exs. 8–10

FINDING CIRCUMFERENCE **Find the circumference of the red circle.**

8. 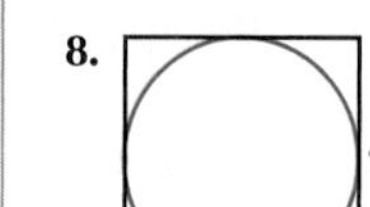

about 43.98 units

9. 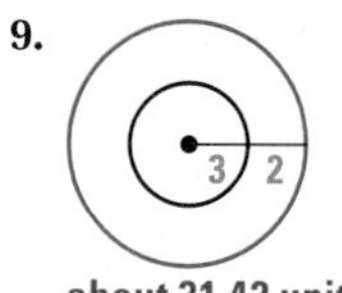

about 31.42 units

10. 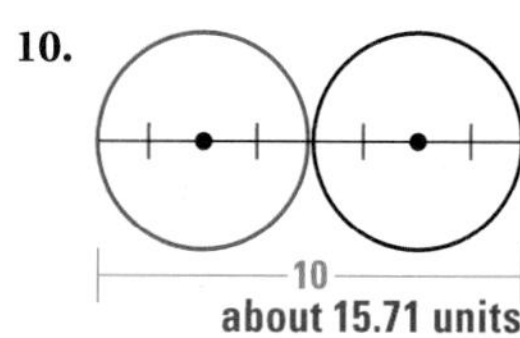

about 15.71 units

EXAMPLE 3 on p. 748 for Exs. 11–20

FINDING ARC LENGTHS **Find the length of $\overset{\frown}{AB}$.**

11. 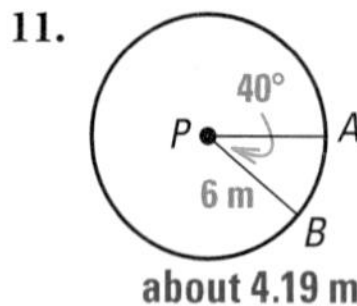

about 4.19 m

12. 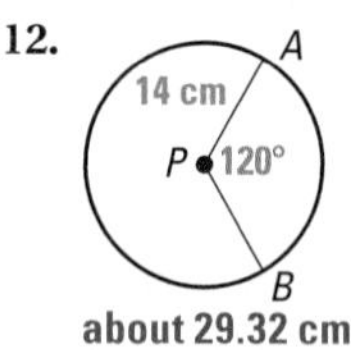

about 29.32 cm

13. 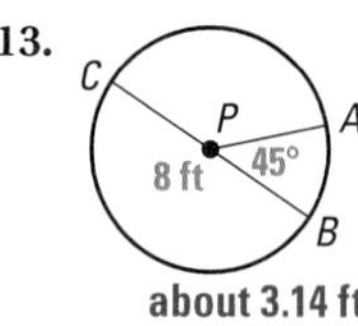

about 3.14 ft

14. **ERROR ANALYSIS** A student says that two arcs from different circles have the same arc length if their central angles have the same measure. *Explain* the error in the student's reasoning.
The arc measures are the same only if the circles have the same circumference.

FINDING MEASURES **In $\odot P$ shown at the right, $\angle QPR \cong \angle RPS$. Find the indicated measure.**

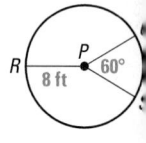

15. $m\overset{\frown}{QRS}$ **300°**

16. Length of $\overset{\frown}{QRS}$ **about 41.89 ft**

17. $m\overset{\frown}{QR}$ **150°**

18. $m\overset{\frown}{RSQ}$ **210°**

19. Length of $\overset{\frown}{QR}$ **about 20.94 ft**

20. Length of $\overset{\frown}{RSQ}$ **about 29.32 ft**

EXAMPLE 4 on p. 748 for Exs. 21–23

USING ARC LENGTH **Find the indicated measure.**

21. $m\overset{\frown}{AB}$

22. Circumference of $\odot Q$

23. Radius of $\odot Q$

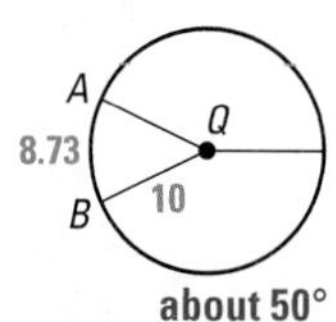

about 50°

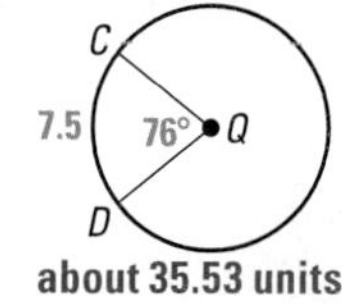

about 35.53 units

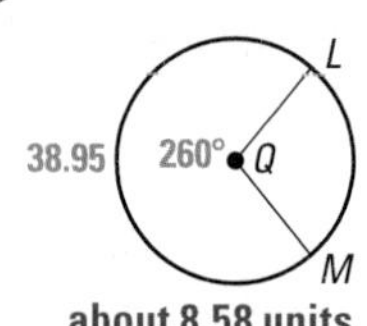

about 8.58 units

EXAMPLE 5 on p. 749 for Exs. 24–25

FINDING PERIMETERS **Find the perimeter of the shaded region.**

24. 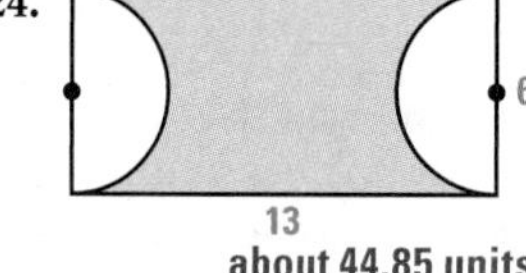

about 44.85 units

25. 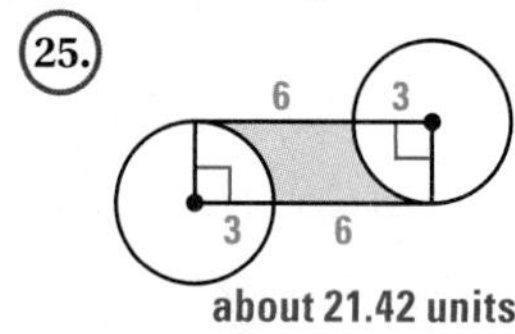

about 21.42 units

B **COORDINATE GEOMETRY** **The equation of a circle is given. Find the circumference of the circle. Write the circumference in terms of π.**

26. $x^2 + y^2 = 16$ **8π**

27. $(x + 2)^2 + (y - 3)^2 = 9$ **6π**

28. $x^2 + y^2 = 18$ **$6\sqrt{2}\pi$**

29. **ALGEBRA** Solve the formula $C = 2\pi r$ for r. Solve the formula $C = \pi d$ for d. Use the rewritten formulas to find r and d when $C = 26\pi$.
$r = \frac{C}{2\pi}$; $d = \frac{C}{\pi}$; 13, 26

○ = WORKED-OUT SOLUTIONS on p. WS1 ★ = STANDARDIZED TEST PRACTICE

30. **FINDING VALUES** In the table below, $\widehat{AB}$ refers to the arc of a circle. Copy and complete the table.

Radius	?	2	0.8	4.2	?	$4\sqrt{2}$	**5.09; 2.05**
$m\widehat{AB}$	45°	60°	?	183°	90°	?	**21.49°; 28.97°**
Length of $\widehat{AB}$	4	?	0.3	?	3.22	2.86	**2.09; 13.41**

31. ★ **SHORT RESPONSE** Suppose $\widehat{EF}$ is an arc on a circle with radius r. Let $x°$ be the measure of $\widehat{EF}$. *Describe* the effect on the length of $\widehat{EF}$ if you (a) double the radius of the circle, and (b) double the measure of $\widehat{EF}$. **a. twice as large b. twice as large**

32. ★ **MULTIPLE CHOICE** In the diagram, $\overline{WY}$ and $\overline{XZ}$ are diameters of $\odot T$, and $WY = XZ = 6$. If $m\widehat{XY} = 140°$, what is the length of $\widehat{YZ}$? **A**

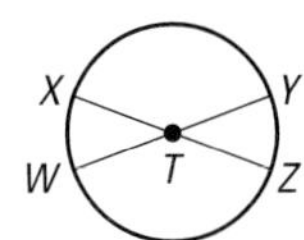

Ⓐ $\frac{2}{3}\pi$ Ⓑ $\frac{4}{3}\pi$ Ⓒ 6π Ⓓ 4π

C 33. **CHALLENGE** Find the circumference of a circle inscribed in a rhombus with diagonals that are 12 centimeters and 16 centimeters long. *Explain.*

3. About 3.16 cm; since the diagonals of a rhombus are perpendicular bisectors, the rhombus can be broken into 4 congruent right triangles, by finding the altitude from this center to the hypotenuse of any side, this becomes the radius of the circle (r = 4.8 cm).

34. **FINDING CIRCUMFERENCE** In the diagram, the measure of the shaded red angle is 30°. The arc length a is 2. *Explain* how to find the circumference of the blue circle without finding the radius of either the red or the blue circles. **See margin.**

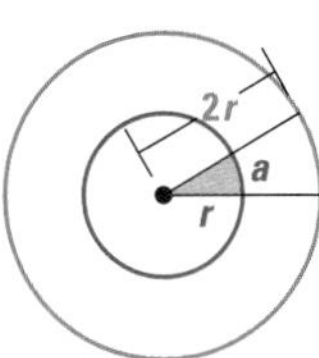

PROBLEM SOLVING

A (35.) **TREES** A group of students wants to find the diameter of the trunk of a young sequoia tree. The students wrap a rope around the tree trunk, then measure the length of rope needed to wrap one time around the trunk. This length is 21 feet 8 inches. *Explain* how they can use this length to estimate the diameter of the tree trunk to the nearest half foot.

5. 21 feet 8 inches represents the circumference of the tree, so if you divide by π, you will get the diameter, about 7 feet.

@HomeTutor for problem solving help at classzone.com

36. **INSCRIBED SQUARE** A square with side length 6 units is inscribed in a circle so that all four vertices are on the circle. Draw a sketch to represent this problem. Find the circumference of the circle. **See margin for art; about 26.66 units.**

@HomeTutor for problem solving help at classzone.com

EXAMPLE 2 on p. 747 for Ex. 37

37. **MEASURING WHEEL** As shown, a measuring wheel is used to calculate the length of a path. The diameter of the wheel is 8 inches. The wheel rotates 87 times along the length of the path. About how long is the path? **about 2187 in.**

Avoiding Common Errors

Exercises 24–25 Students may have difficulty organizing their steps in finding the perimeter of the shaded region. Encourage students to label the segments and arcs so they can write the total distance as a sum.

Teaching Strategy

Exercises 26–28 Point out that the circumference depends only the length of the radius, not on where the circle is graphed in the coordinate plane.

Mathematical Reasoning

Exercises 31, 34 Since circumference, radius, diameter, and arc length are linear dimensions, if you double one dimension, the effect is that the other quantities are also doubled. For example, if you double the radius of a circle, the diameter doubles, the circumference doubles, and each arc length doubles.

Exercise 39 Additional information about Eratosthenes can be found at www.pbs.org/wnet/hawking/cosmostar/html/cstars_eratho.html

34. Since the radius of the blue circle is twice the radius of the red circle, the arc of the blue circle that corresponds with a is $2a = 2(2) = 4$ units. Since the arc represents 30° or $\frac{1}{12}$ of the circle, then 4 is $\frac{1}{12}$ of the circumference and therefore the circumference of the blue circle is 48 units.

36.

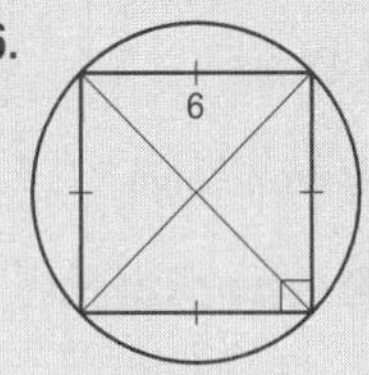

5 ASSESS AND RETEACH

Daily Homework Quiz

Transparency Available

Find the indicated measure.

1. Circumference **about 81.68 in.**

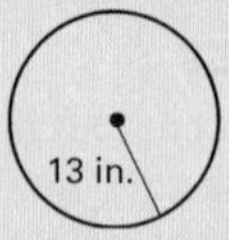

2. Radius **about 7.64 ft**

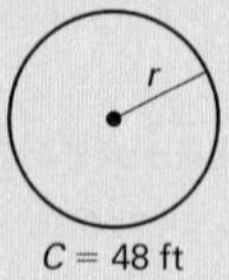

3. length of $\overset{\frown}{AB}$ **8.64 cm**

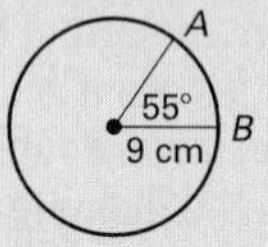

4. Find the total circumference of the circles. **100.53 cm**

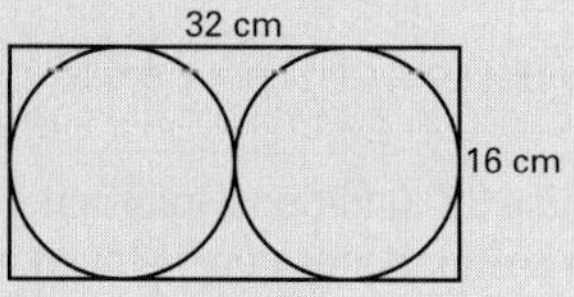

Find the indicated measure.

5. Radius **about 21.88 cm**

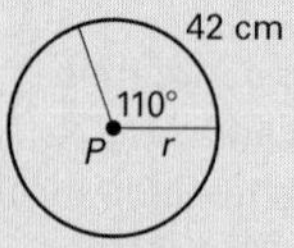

6. Circumference **about 222.72 in.**

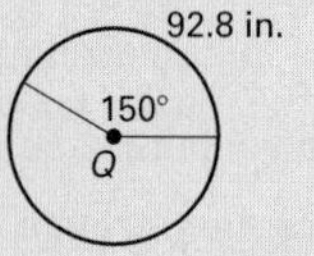

Online Quiz

Available at **classzone.com**

Diagnosis/Remediation

- Practice A, B, C in Chapter 11 Resource Book, pp. 49–54
- Study Guide in Chapter 11 Resource Book, pp. 55–56
- Practice Workbook, pp. 214–216
- @HomeTutor

Challenge

Additional challenge is available in the Chapter 11 Resource Book, p. 59.

38a. About 25 in.; since the chain only touches about half of each sprocket, determine half the circumference of each sprocket and add the sum of the long segments between the sprockets.

38b. About 46 teeth; since the chain only touches about half of each sprocket, determine half of the teeth of each sprocket.

B

38. ★ EXTENDED RESPONSE A motorized scooter has a chain drive. The chain goes around the front and rear sprockets.

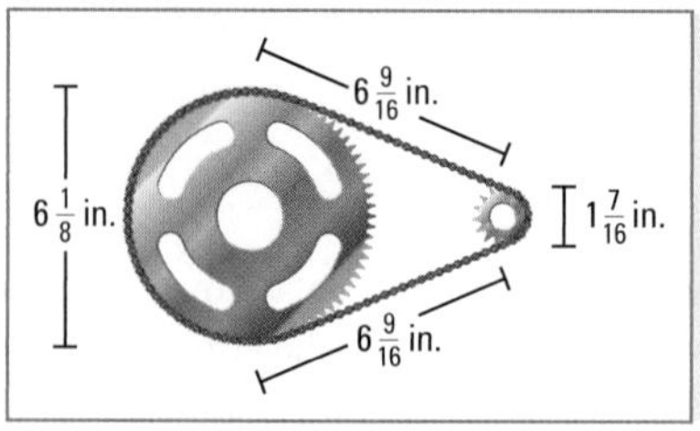

a. About how long is the chain? *Explain.*

b. Each sprocket has teeth that grip the chain. There are 76 teeth on the larger sprocket, and 15 teeth on the smaller sprocket. About how many teeth are gripping the chain at any given time? *Explain.*

39. SCIENCE Over 2000 years ago, the Greek scholar Eratosthenes estimated Earth's circumference by assuming that the Sun's rays are parallel. He chose a day when the Sun shone straight down into a well in the city of Syene. At noon, he measured the angle the Sun's rays made with a vertical stick in the city of Alexandria. Eratosthenes assumed that the distance from Syene to Alexandria was equal to about 575 miles.

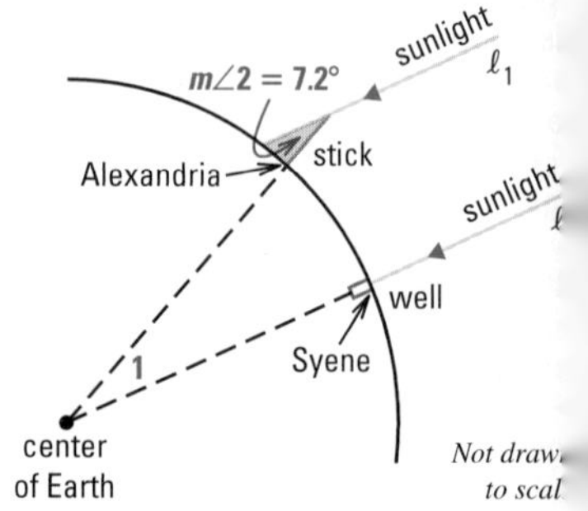

Find $m\angle 1$. Then estimate Earth's circumference. **7.2°; 28,750 mi**

C

CHALLENGE Suppose $\overline{AB}$ is divided into four congruent segments, and semicircles with radius *r* are drawn.

40. What is the sum of the four arc lengths if the radius of each arc is r? **$4\pi r$**

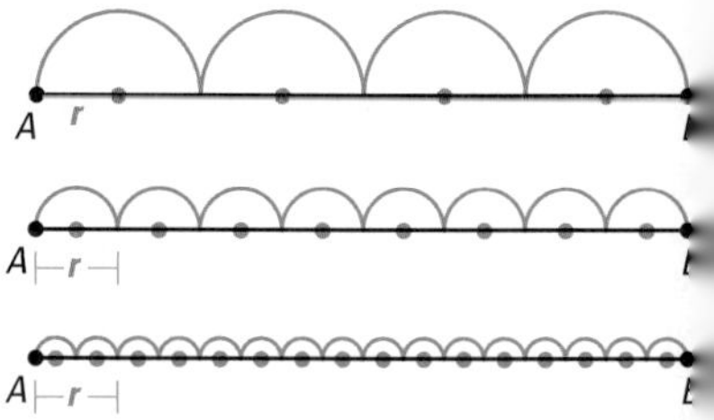

41. Suppose that $\overline{AB}$ is divided into n congruent segments and that semicircles are drawn, as shown. What will the sum of the arc lengths be for 8 segments? for 16 segments? for n segments? *Explain* your thinking.
$4\pi r$; $4\pi r$; $4\pi r$; the length is the same, just allocated differently.

MIXED REVIEW

PREVIEW
Prepare for Lesson 11.5 in Exs. 42–45.

Find the area of a circle with radius *r*. Round to the nearest hundredth. *(p. 49)*

42. $r = 6$ cm **113.10 cm²**

43. $r = 4.2$ in. **55.42 in.²**

44. $r = 8\frac{3}{4}$ mi **240.53 mi²**

45. $r = 1\frac{3}{8}$ in. **5.94 in.²**

Find the value of *x*. *(p. 689)*

46.

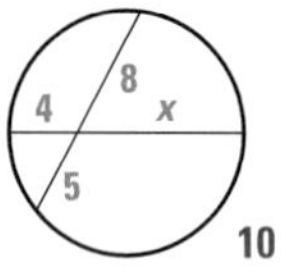

10

47.

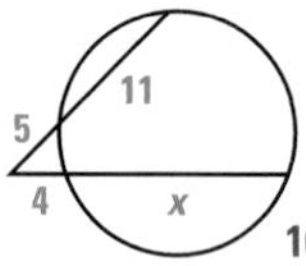

16

48.

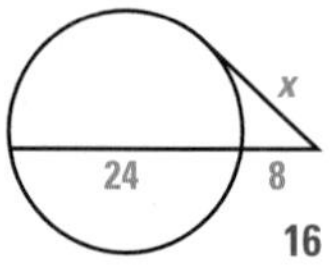

16

Extension

Use after Lesson 11.4

Geometry on a Sphere

GOAL Compare Euclidean and spherical geometries.

Key Vocabulary
- great circle

Standards
Enrichment Topic; not required by California Standards.

In Euclidean geometry, a plane is a flat surface that extends without end in all directions. A line in the plane is a set of points that extends without end in two opposite directions. Geometry on a sphere is different.

In *spherical geometry,* a plane is the surface of a sphere. A line is defined as a **great circle**, which is a circle on the sphere whose center is the center of the sphere.

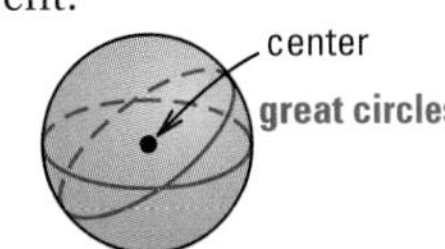

KEY CONCEPT — *For Your Notebook*

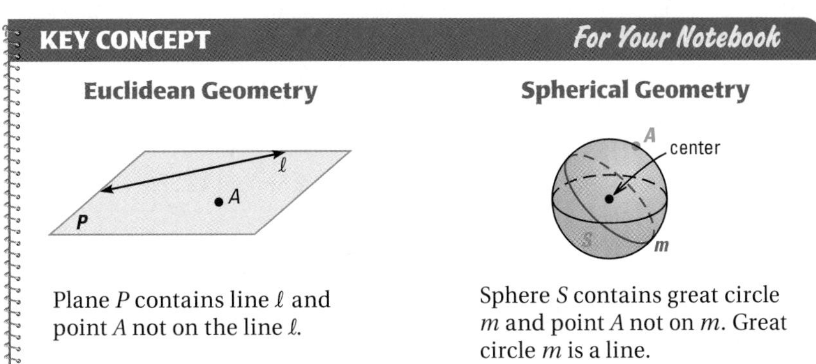

Euclidean Geometry	Spherical Geometry
Plane P contains line ℓ and point A not on the line ℓ.	Sphere S contains great circle m and point A not on m. Great circle m is a line.

HISTORY NOTE
Spherical geometry is sometimes called *Riemann geometry* after Bernhard Riemann, who wrote the first description of it in 1854.

Some properties and postulates in Euclidean geometry are true in spherical geometry. Others are not, or are true only under certain circumstances. For example, in Euclidean geometry, Postulate 5 states that through any two points there exists exactly one line. On a sphere, this postulate is true only for points that are not the endpoints of a diameter of the sphere.

EXAMPLE 1 Compare Euclidean and spherical geometry

Tell whether the following postulate in Euclidean geometry is also true in spherical geometry. Draw a diagram to support your answer.

Parallel Postulate: If there is a line ℓ and a point A not on the line, then there is exactly one line through the point A parallel to the given line ℓ.

Solution

Parallel lines do not intersect. The sphere shows a line ℓ (a great circle) and a point A not on ℓ. Several lines are drawn through A. Each great circle containing A intersects ℓ. So, there can be no line parallel to ℓ. The parallel postulate is not true in spherical geometry.

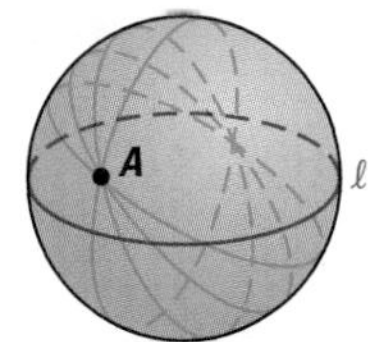

1 PLAN AND PREPARE

Warm-Up Exercises

1. Find the length of a 60° arc in a circle with radius 8 meters. **about 8.38 m**
2. Find the exact value of x if $\frac{12}{2\pi \cdot 8} = \frac{x}{360}$. $\frac{270}{\pi}$

Find the exact length of the arc.

3. $\overset{\frown}{ACB}$ 30π m

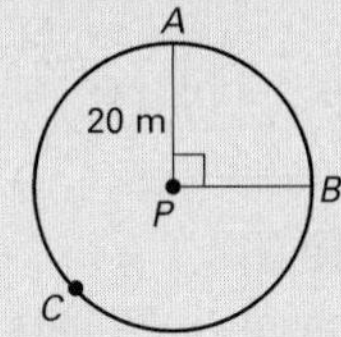

4. $\overset{\frown}{AB}$ $13\frac{1}{3}$ cm

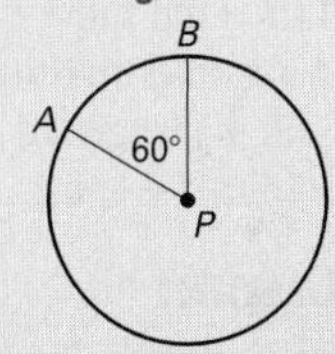

Circumference = 80 cm

2 FOCUS AND MOTIVATE

Essential Question

Big Idea 3, p. 719

On the surface of a sphere, how can you identify the shortest distance between two points? **Tell students they will learn how to answer this question by identifying a great circle on the sphere.**

3 TEACH

Extra Example 1

Tell whether the following postulate in Euclidean geometry is also true in spherical geometry. Draw a diagram to support your answer. Postulate 5: Through any two points there exists exactly one line.
False; if the two points are the endpoints of a diameter, many great circles contain the two points.

Extra Example 2

The diameter of a sphere is 24 units, and for two points A and B on the sphere, $m\overset{\frown}{AB} = 135°$. Find the distance between A and B on the minor arc and on the major arc of a great circle. **9π units; 15π units**

Closing the Lesson

Have students summarize the major points of the lesson and answer the Essential Question: On the surface of a sphere, how can you identify the shortest distance between two points?

- **A line on a sphere is a great circle.**
- **Some postulates from Euclidean geometry are not true for spherical geometry.**

Find the minor arc length on the great circle that contains the two points.

4 PRACTICE AND APPLY

Teaching Strategy

Exercise 3 Suggest that students draw sketches to support their conjecture for this exercise.

DISTANCES In Euclidean geometry, there is exactly one distance that can be measured between any two points. On a sphere, there are two distances that can be measured between two points. These distances are the lengths of the major and minor arcs of the great circle drawn through the points.

READ DIAGRAMS
The diagram below is a cross section of the sphere in Example 2. It shows $\overset{\frown}{AB}$ and $\overset{\frown}{ACB}$ on a great circle.

EXAMPLE 2 Find distances on a sphere

The diameter of the sphere shown is 15, and $m\overset{\frown}{AB} = 60°$. Find the distances between A and B.

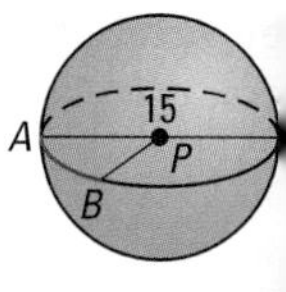

Solution

Find the lengths of the minor arc $\overset{\frown}{AB}$ and the major arc $\overset{\frown}{ACB}$ of the great circle shown. In each case, let x be the arc length.

$$\frac{\text{Arc length of } \overset{\frown}{AB}}{2\pi r} = \frac{m\overset{\frown}{AB}}{360°} \qquad \frac{\text{Arc length of } \overset{\frown}{ACB}}{2\pi r} = \frac{m\overset{\frown}{ACB}}{360°}$$

$$\frac{x}{15\pi} = \frac{60°}{360°} \qquad \frac{x}{15\pi} = \frac{360° - 60°}{360°}$$

$$x = 2.5\pi \qquad x = 12.5\pi$$

▶ The distances are 2.5π and 12.5π.

PRACTICE

1. **WRITING** Lines of latitude and longitude are used to identify positions on Earth. Which of the lines shown in the figure are great circles? Which are not? *Explain* your reasoning.
Equator and longitude lines; latitude lines; the equator and lines of longitude have the center of Earth as the center. Lines of latitude do not have the center of Earth as the center.

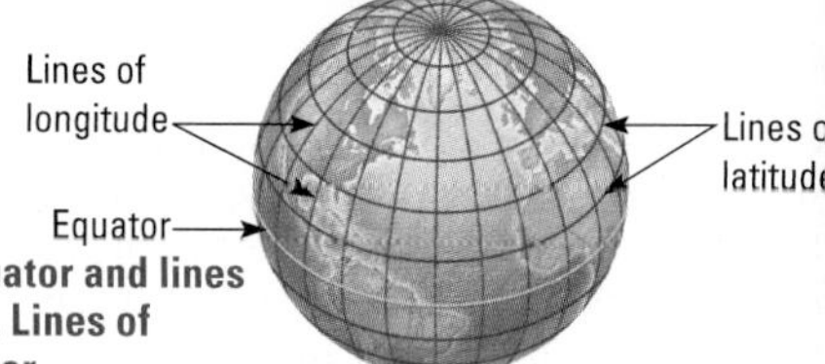

EXAMPLE 1
on p. 753
for Exs. 2–3

2. **COMPARING GEOMETRIES** Draw sketches to show that there is more than one line through the endpoints of a diameter of a sphere, but only one line through two points that are *not* endpoints of a diameter. **See margin.**

3. **COMPARING GEOMETRIES** The following statement is true in Euclidean geometry: If two lines intersect, then their intersection is exactly one point. Rewrite this statement to be true for lines on a sphere.
If two lines intersect then their intersection is exactly 2 points.

EXAMPLE 2
on p. 754
for Exs. 4–6

FINDING DISTANCES **Use the diagram and the given arc measure to find the distances between points A and B. Leave your answers in terms of π.**

4. $m\overset{\frown}{AB} = 120°$

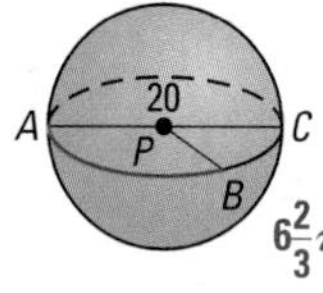

$6\frac{2}{3}\pi$

5. $m\overset{\frown}{AB} = 90°$

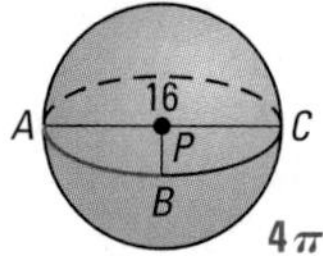

4π

6. $m\overset{\frown}{AB} = 140°$

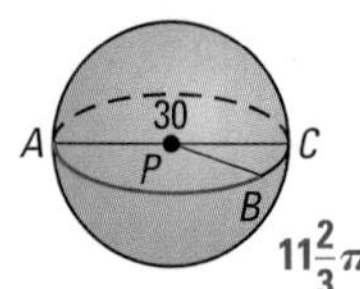

$11\frac{2}{3}\pi$

2.

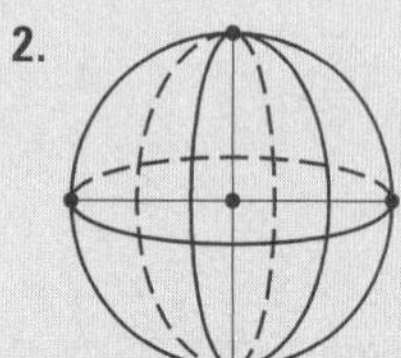

More than 1 line through endpoints of diameter on a sphere

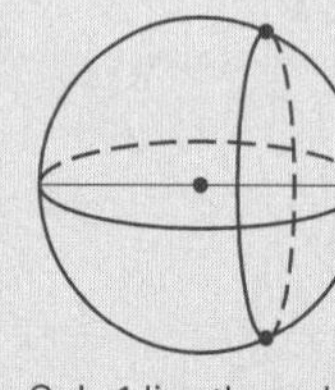

Only 1 line through 2 points not endpoints of diameter

11.5 Areas of Circles and Sectors

Before You found circumferences of circles.
Now You will find the areas of circles and sectors.
Why So you can estimate walking distances, as in Ex. 38.

Key Vocabulary
- sector of a circle

Standards
8.0 Students know, derive, and solve problems involving the perimeter, circumference, **area**, volume, lateral area, and surface area **of common geometric figures.**

In Chapter 1, you used the formula for the area of a circle. This formula is presented below as Theorem 11.9.

THEOREM *For Your Notebook*

THEOREM 11.9 Area of a Circle

The area of a circle is π times the square of the radius.

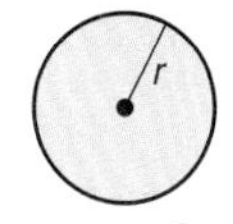

$A = \pi r^2$

Justification: Ex. 43, p. 761; Ex. 3, p. 769

EXAMPLE 1 Use the formula for area of a circle

Find the indicated measure.

a. Area

$r = 2.5$ cm

b. Diameter

$A = 113.1\text{ cm}^2$

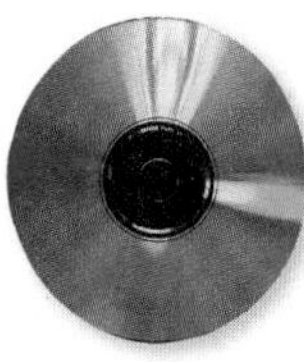

Solution

a. $A = \pi r^2$ — Write formula for the area of a circle.
$= \pi \cdot (2.5)^2$ — Substitute 2.5 for r.
$= 6.25\pi$ — Simplify.
≈ 19.63 — Use a calculator.

▶ The area of $\odot A$ is about 19.63 square centimeters.

b. $A = \pi r^2$ — Write formula for the area of a circle.
$113.1 = \pi r^2$ — Substitute 113.1 for A.
$\frac{113.1}{\pi} = r^2$ — Divide each side by π.
$6 \approx r$ — Find the positive square root of each side.

▶ The radius is about 6 cm, so the diameter is about 12 centimeters.

1 PLAN AND PREPARE

Warm-Up Exercises

Transparency Available

Find the area of a circle with the given measure.

1. Radius: 8 cm **about 201.06 cm²**
2. Radius: $1\frac{1}{3}$ mi **about 5.59 mi²**
3. Circumference: 4π ft **4π ft²**
4. Solve $x^2 = \frac{100}{\pi}$. **about ±5.64**

Notetaking Guide

Transparency Available

Promotes interactive learning and notetaking skills, pp. 296–299.

Pacing

Basic: 2 days
Average: 2 days
Advanced: 2 days
Block: 1 block
- See *Teaching Guide/Lesson Plan.*

2 FOCUS AND MOTIVATE

Essential Question

Big Idea 3, p. 719

How do you find the area of a sector of a circle? **Tell students they will learn how to answer this question by using the ratio of the measure of the intercepted arc to 360°.**

Resource Planning Guide

Chapter Resource Book
- Teaching Guide/Lesson Plan (pp. 60–61)
- Activity Master (p. 62)
- Practice levels A, B, C (pp. 64–69)
- Study Guide (pp. 70–71)
- Catch-up for Absent Students (p. 72)
- Application (p. 73)
- Challenge (p. 74)

Workbooks
- Notetaking Guide (pp. 296–299)
- Practice Workbook (pp. 217–219)

Teaching Options
- **Power Presentations CD-ROM** provides dynamic electronic teaching resources for the classroom.
- **Activity Generator CD-ROM** provides editable activities for all ability levels.

Interactive Technology
- Easy Planner
- Power Presentations CD-ROM
- Activity Generator CD-ROM
- Animated Geometry
- Test Generator CD-ROM
- Online Quiz
- eWorkbook
- eEdition
- @HomeTutor

Resources for English Learners
- Quick Reference for English Learners
- Spanish Study Guide
- Multi-Language Visual Glossary
- Student Resources in Spanish

See also the *Geometry Toolkit* for more strategies for meeting individual needs.

Motivating the Lesson

Draw two pizzas, with the same radius, one cut into 6 equal slices and the other cut into 10 equal slices. Ask students to identify the central angle formed by each slice (60°, 36°) and ask which slice is larger. Tell students that in the lesson they will investigate how to calculate the area of a slice based on the radius and either the central angle or arc length of the slice.

3 TEACH

Extra Example 1

Find the indicated measure.

a. Area **b.** Diameter

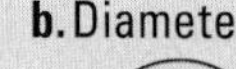

about 8.3 in.^{2} **about 6 cm**

Extra Example 2

Find the areas of the sectors formed by $\angle HJK$.

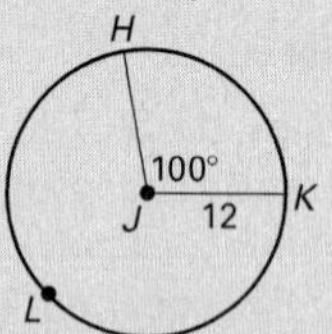

125.66 square units; 326.73 square units

Key Question to Ask for Example 2

- What ratios appear in the area of a sector formula? **The ratios are $\frac{\text{area of sector}}{\text{area of entire circle}}$ and $\frac{\text{measure of arc}}{360°}$.**

SECTORS A **sector of a circle** is the region bounded by two radii of the circle and their intercepted arc. In the diagram below, sector APB is bounded by $\overline{AP}$, $\overline{BP}$, and $\widehat{AB}$. Theorem 11.10 gives a method for finding the area of a sector.

THEOREM *For Your Notebook*

THEOREM 11.10 Area of a Sector

The ratio of the area of a sector of a circle to the area of the whole circle (πr^2) is equal to the ratio of the measure of the intercepted arc to 360°.

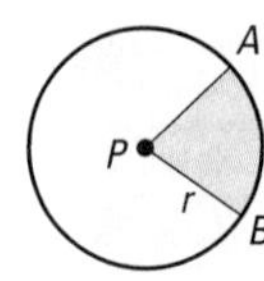

$$\frac{\text{Area of sector } APB}{\pi r^2} = \frac{m\widehat{AB}}{360°}, \text{ or Area of sector } APB = \frac{m\widehat{AB}}{360°} \cdot \pi r^2$$

EXAMPLE 2 Find areas of sectors

Find the areas of the sectors formed by $\angle UTV$.

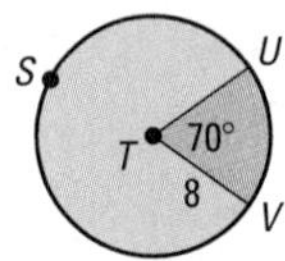

Solution

STEP 1 **Find** the measures of the minor and major arcs.

Because $m\angle UTV = 70°$, $m\widehat{UV} = 70°$ and $m\widehat{USV} = 360° - 70° = 290°$.

STEP 2 **Find** the areas of the small and large sectors.

Area of small sector	$= \frac{m\widehat{UV}}{360°} \cdot \pi r^2$	**Write formula for area of a sector.**
	$= \frac{70°}{360°} \cdot \pi \cdot 8^2$	**Substitute.**
	≈ 39.10	**Use a calculator.**
Area of large sector	$= \frac{m\widehat{USV}}{360°} \cdot \pi r^2$	**Write formula for area of a sector.**
	$= \frac{290°}{360°} \cdot \pi \cdot 8^2$	**Substitute.**
	≈ 161.97	**Use a calculator.**

▶ The areas of the small and large sectors are about 39.10 square units and 161.97 square units, respectively.

GUIDED PRACTICE for Examples 1 and 2

Use the diagram to find the indicated measure.

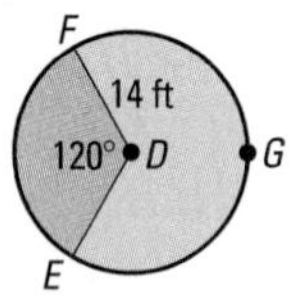

1. Area of $\odot D$ **about 615.75 ft^2**
2. Area of red sector **about 205.25 ft^2**
3. Area of blue sector **about 410.50 ft^2**

EXAMPLE 3 Use the Area of a Sector Theorem

Use the diagram to find the area of $\odot V$.

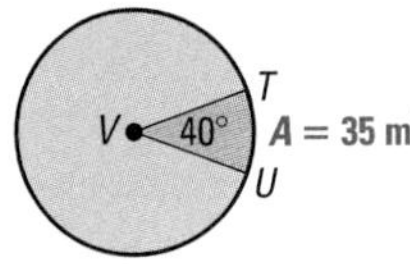

Solution

Area of sector $TVU = \frac{m\overset{\frown}{TU}}{360°} \cdot$ Area of $\odot V$	**Write formula for area of a sector.**
$35 = \frac{40°}{360°} \cdot$ Area of $\odot V$	**Substitute.**
$315 =$ Area of $\odot V$	**Solve for Area of $\odot V$.**

▶ The area of $\odot V$ is 315 square meters.

EXAMPLE 4 Standardized Test Practice

A rectangular wall has an entrance cut into it. You want to paint the wall. To the nearest square foot, what is the area of the region you need to paint?

Ⓐ 357 ft^2 Ⓑ 479 ft^2

Ⓒ 579 ft^2 Ⓓ 936 ft^2

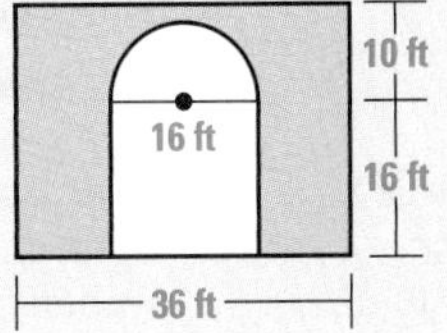

Solution

AVOID ERRORS
Use the radius (8 ft), not the diameter (16 ft) when you calculate the area of the semicircle.

The area you need to paint is the area of the rectangle minus the area of the entrance. The entrance can be divided into a **semicircle** and a **square**.

$$\text{Area of wall} = \text{Area of rectangle} - (\text{Area of semicircle} + \text{Area of square})$$

$$= 36(26) - \left[\frac{180°}{360°} \cdot (\pi \cdot 8^2) + 16^2\right]$$

$$= 936 - [32\pi + 256]$$

$$\approx 579.47$$

The area is about 579 square feet.

▶ The correct answer is C. Ⓐ Ⓑ Ⓒ Ⓓ

GUIDED PRACTICE for Examples 3 and 4

4. Find the area of $\odot H$.

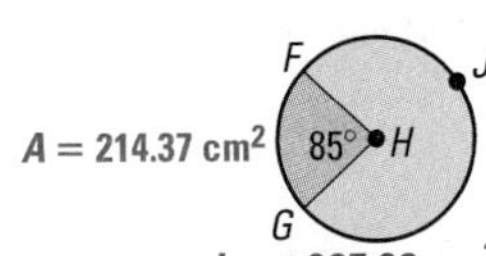

about 907.92 cm^2

5. Find the area of the figure.

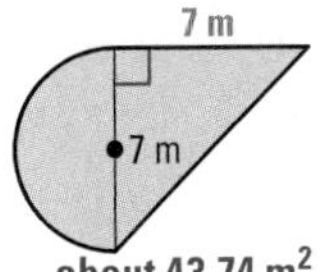

about 43.74 m^2

6. If you know the area and radius of a sector of a circle, can you find the measure of the intercepted arc? *Explain.*
Yes; the formula for the area of a sector is $A = \frac{m}{360}\pi r^2$ and if you solve this for m, you get $\frac{360A}{\pi r^2}$.

Mathematical Reasoning

In Example 2, point out that another way to find the area of the large sector is to calculate the area of the entire circle, and from it subtract the area of the small sector.

Extra Example 3

Use the diagram to find the area of $\odot S$.

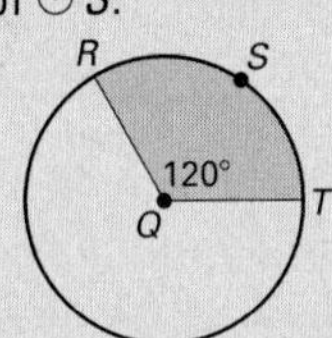

Area of $RSTQ = 48$ ft^2

144 ft^2

Extra Example 4

In this large circular painting, two white congruent circles just fit into a gray circle. What is the area that appears gray? **B**

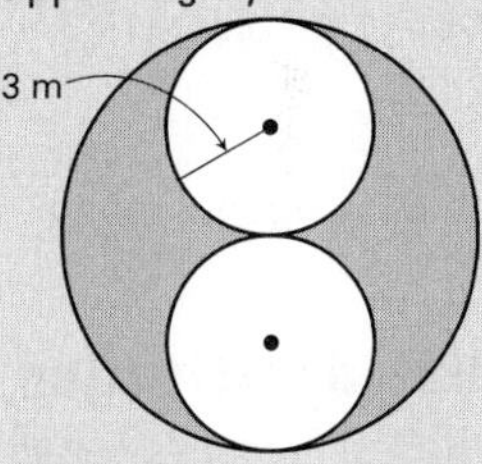

Ⓐ 18 m^2 Ⓑ 56.55 m^2

Ⓒ 75.40 m^2 Ⓓ 84.82 m^2

Closing the Lesson

Have students summarize the major points of the lesson and answer the Essential Question: How do you find the area of a sector of a circle?

- **For a circle of radius r, $A = \pi r^2$.**
- **A sector of a circle is a region bounded by two radii and their intercepted arc. Its area is given by $A = \frac{\text{measure of arc}}{360°} \cdot \pi r^2$.**

Use the given values of the arc measure (or central angle) and the area of the entire circle to find the area of the sector of the circle by using the formula Area of sector $= \frac{\text{measure of arc}}{360°} \cdot \pi r^2$.

Differentiated Instruction

Kinesthetic Learners To get more practice with finding areas in real-world situations, have students work in small groups to find a problem similar to that in **Example 4** to solve. Encourage them to find something they can easily measure using a tape measure. Instruct them to draw a diagram, find the necessary measurements, and calculate the area. Invite groups of students to share their work with the class.

See also the *Geometry Toolkit* for more strategies.

11.5 EXERCISES

HOMEWORK KEY

○ = WORKED-OUT SOLUTIONS on p. WS15 for Exs. 7, 17, and 39

★ = STANDARDIZED TEST PRACTICE Exs. 2, 19, 40, and 42

4 PRACTICE AND APPLY

Assignment Guide

Answer Transparencies available for all exercises

Basic:
Day 1: pp. 758–761
Exs. 1–13, 37, 38, 48–51
Day 2: pp. 758–761
Exs. 14–28, 39–41, 45–47

Average:
Day 1: pp. 758–761
Exs. 1, 2, 4–6, 8–13, 33, 34, 37, 38, 48–51
Day 2: pp. 758–761
Exs. 14–19, 23–32, 39–43, 46

Advanced:
Day 1: pp. 758–761
Exs. 1, 2, 4–6, 8, 9, 11–13, 33–38*, 48, 50
Day 2: pp. 758–761
Exs. 15–19, 24–32, 39–44*, 47

Block:
pp. 758–761
Exs. 1, 2, 4–6, 8–19, 23–34, 37–43, 46, 48–51

Differentiated Instruction

See *Geometry Best Practices Toolkit* for suggestions on addressing the needs of a diverse classroom.

Homework Check

For a quick check of student understanding of key concepts, go over the following exercises:

Basic: 4, 11, 14, 18, 37
Average: 6, 12, 15, 19, 38
Advanced: 8, 13, 16, 19, 40

Extra Practice

- Student Edition, p. 917
- Chapter 11 Resource Book: Practice levels A, B, C, pp. 64–69

Practice Worksheet

An easily-readable reduced practice page (with answers) for this lesson can be found on p. 718E.

SKILL PRACTICE

A

1. **VOCABULARY** Copy and complete: A __?__ of a circle is the region bounded by two radii of the circle and their intercepted arc. **sector**

2. ★ **WRITING** Suppose you double the arc measure of a sector in a given circle. Will the area of the sector also be doubled? *Explain.*
Yes; doubling the arc measure will make the sector twice as big, which would double the area.

EXAMPLE 1 on p. 755 for Exs. 3–9

FINDING AREA Find the exact area of a circle with the given radius *r* or diameter *d*. Then find the area to the nearest hundredth.

3. $r = 5$ in. **25π in.^{2}; 78.54 in.^{2}**
4. $d = 16$ ft **64π ft^2; 201.06 ft^2**
5. $d = 23$ cm
6. $r = 1.5$ km

5. **132.25π cm^2; 415.48 cm^2**
6. **2.25π km^2; 7.07 km^2**

USING AREA In Exercises 7–9, find the indicated measure.

7. The area of a circle is 154 square meters. Find the radius. **about 7 m**
8. The area of a circle is 380 square inches. Find the radius. **about 11 in.**
9. The area of a circle is 676π square centimeters. Find the diameter. **52 cm**

EXAMPLE 2 on p. 756 for Exs. 10–13

10. **ERROR ANALYSIS** In the diagram at the right, the area of $\odot Z$ is 48 square feet. A student writes a proportion to find the area of sector XZY. *Describe* and correct the error in writing the proportion. Then find the area of sector XZY.

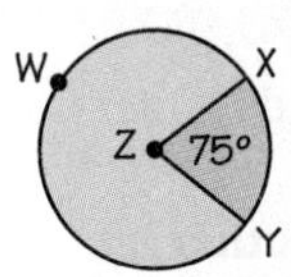

Let n be the area of sector XZY.
$$\frac{n}{360°} = \frac{48}{285°}$$

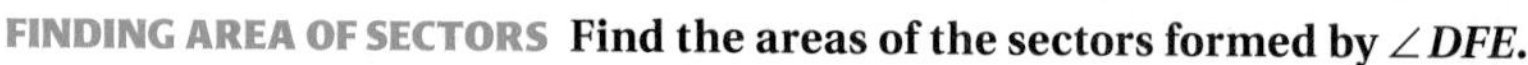

10. The area of the sector needs to be divided by the area of the circle, and the right side should be 75 divided by 360; $\frac{n}{48} = \frac{75}{360}$, $n = 10$ ft^2.

FINDING AREA OF SECTORS Find the areas of the sectors formed by $\angle DFE$.

11.

about 52.36 in.^{2}, about 261.80 in.^{2}

12.
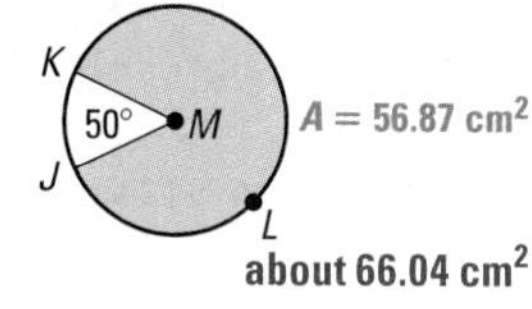

about 177.88 cm^2, about 437.87 cm^2

13.
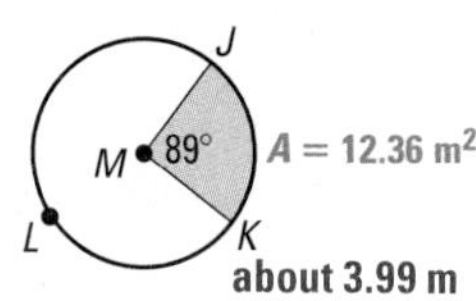

about 937.31 m^2, about 1525.70 cm^2

EXAMPLE 3 on p. 757 for Exs. 14–16

USING AREA OF A SECTOR Use the diagram to find the indicated measure.

14. Find the area of $\odot M$.

about 84.02 m^2

15. Find the area of $\odot M$.
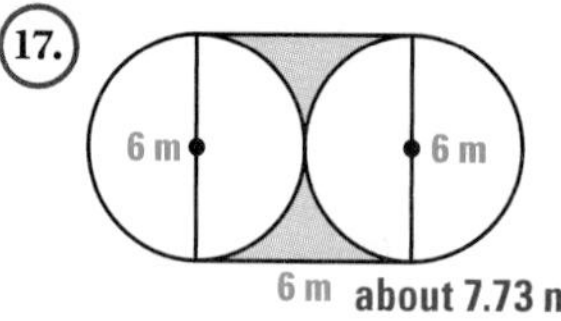

about 66.04 cm^2

16. Find the radius of $\odot M$.
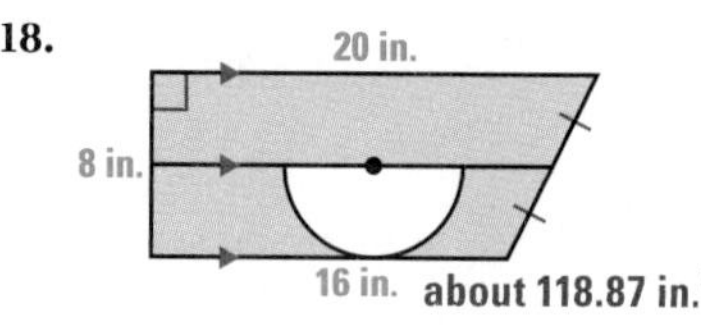

about 3.99 m

EXAMPLE 4 on p. 757 for Exs. 17–19

FINDING AREA Find the area of the shaded region.

17.

about 7.73 m^2

18.

about 118.87 in.^{2}

19. ★ **MULTIPLE CHOICE** The diagram shows the shape of a putting green at a miniature golf course. One part of the green is a sector of a circle. To the nearest square foot, what is the area of the putting green? **A**

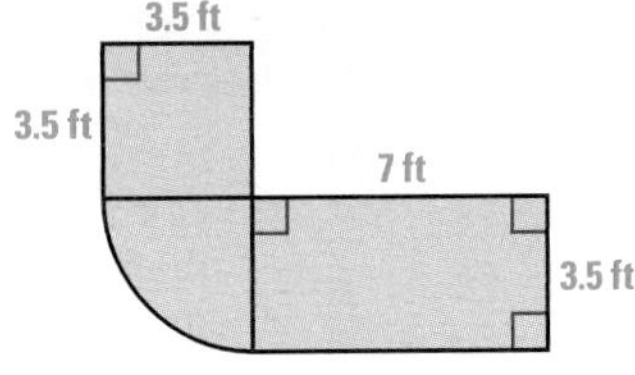

Ⓐ 46 ft^2 Ⓑ 49 ft^2

Ⓒ 56 ft^2 Ⓓ 75 ft^2

B **FINDING MEASURES** **The area of $\odot M$ is 260.67 square inches. The area of sector KML is 42 square inches. Find the indicated measure.**

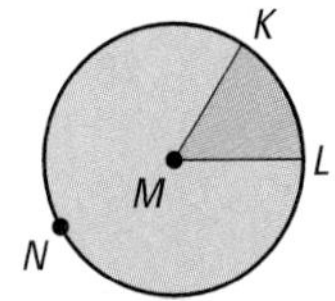

20. Radius of $\odot M$ **about 9.11 in.**

21. Circumference of $\odot M$ **about 57.23 in.**

22. $m\widehat{KL}$ **about 58°**

23. Perimeter of blue region **about 66.24 in.**

24. Length of $\widehat{KL}$ **about 9.22 in.**

25. Perimeter of red region **about 27.44 in.**

FINDING AREA **Find the area of the shaded region.**

26. 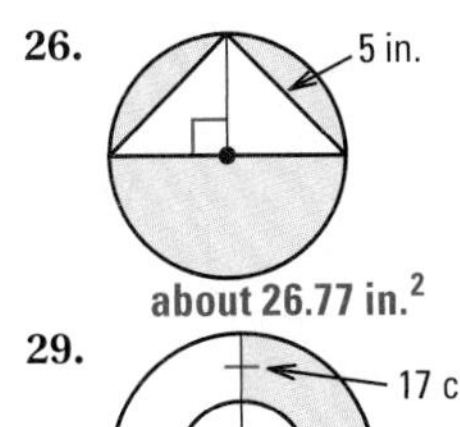

about 26.77 in.²

27. 109° 5.2 ft **about 33.51 ft²**

28. 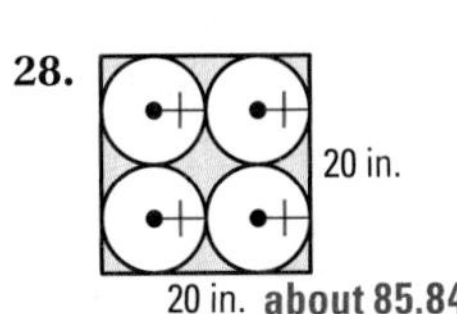

about 85.84 in.²

29. 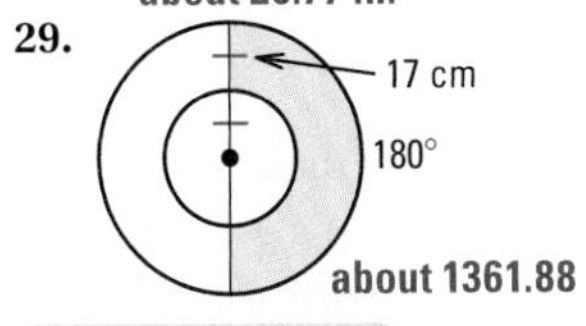

about 1361.88 cm²

30. 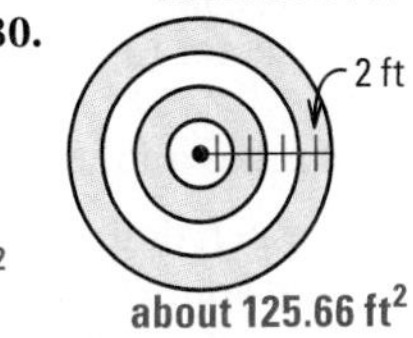

about 125.66 ft²

31. 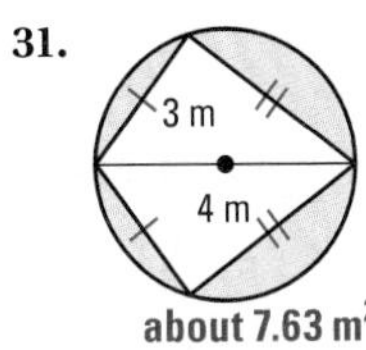

about 7.63 m²

Animated Geometry at classzone.com

32. **TANGENT CIRCLES** In the diagram at the right, $\odot Q$ and $\odot P$ are tangent, and P lies on $\odot Q$. The measure of $\widehat{RS}$ is 108°. Find the area of the red region, the area of the blue region, and the area of the yellow region. Leave your answers in terms of π.
red: 19.2π units², blue: 16π units², yellow: 28.8π units²

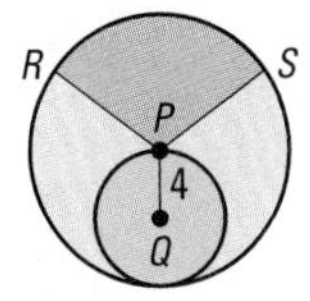

33. **SIMILARITY** Look back at the Perimeters of Similar Polygons Theorem on page 374 and the Areas of Similar Polygons Theorem on page 737. How would you rewrite these theorems to apply to circles? *Explain.*

34. **ERROR ANALYSIS** The ratio of the lengths of two arcs in a circle is 2 : 1. A student claims that the ratio of the areas of the sectors bounded by these arcs is 4 : 1, because $\left(\frac{2}{1}\right)^2 = \frac{4}{1}$. *Describe* and correct the error. **Theorem 11.7 applies to similar figures; these sectors are not similar. The correct ratio is 2 : 1.**

C 35. **DRAWING A DIAGRAM** A square is inscribed in a circle. The same square is also circumscribed about a smaller circle. Draw a diagram. Find the ratio of the area of the large circle to the area of the small circle. **See margin for art; 2 : 1.**

36. **CHALLENGE** In the diagram at the right, $\widehat{FG}$ and $\widehat{EH}$ are arcs of concentric circles, and $\overline{EF}$ and $\overline{GH}$ lie on radii of the larger circle. Find the area of the shaded region. **160 m²**

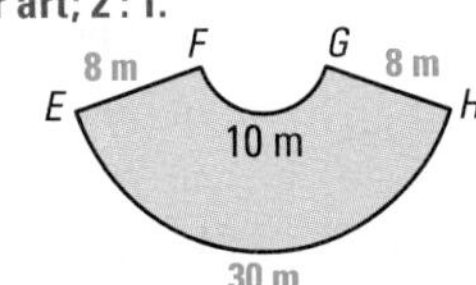

33. For any two circles, the ratio of their circumferences is equal to the ratio of their radii; for any two circles, if the length of their radii is in the ratio of $a : b$, then the ratio of their areas is $a^2 : b^2$; all circles are similar, so you do not need to include similarity in the hypothesis.

Teaching Strategy

Exercises 17–19, 26–31 Encourage students to use Example 4 as a model and write a written description of the parts of each shaded region. Then they can write and evaluate an area formula for each of the parts.

An **Animated Geometry** activity is available on-line for **Exercises 26–31.** This activity is also available on the **Power Presentations CD-ROM**.

35. ***Sample:***

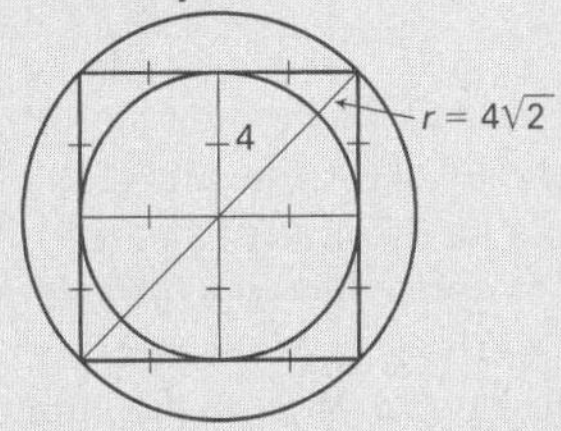

Mathematical Reasoning

Exercise 38 One way to answer this problem is solve for r in $138{,}656 = \pi r^2$ and then use that value to find the circumference. Ask students to compare that method with these steps: rewrite $A = \pi r^2$ as $r = \sqrt{\frac{A}{\pi}}$, rewrite $C = 2\pi r$ as $C = 2\pi\sqrt{\frac{A}{\pi}}$, and then substitute 138,656 for A.

39b.

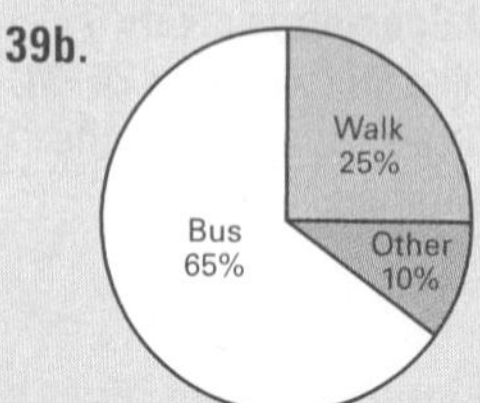

43b. You can use the formula for the circumference of a circle and then the formula for the area of a parallelogram to derive the area formula for a circle. The area of the circle is approximately the same as the area of the parallelogram.

44. Let the legs of the triangle be $2y$ and $2x$. The hypotenuse is then $\sqrt{4y^2 + 4x^2}$. The area of the triangle is then $2xy$. The area of the large semicircle is $\frac{\pi}{2}\left(\frac{\sqrt{4y^2 + 4x^2}}{2}\right)^2 = \frac{4\pi y^2 + 4\pi x^2}{8}$. The area of the other two semicircles is $\frac{\pi x^2}{2}$ and $\frac{\pi y^2}{2}$. To find the shaded area, add the area of the smaller semicircles, subtract the area of the large semicircle, and then add the area of the triangle: $\frac{\pi x^2}{2} + \frac{\pi y^2}{2} - \frac{4\pi y^2 + 4\pi x^2}{8} + 2xy = \frac{4\pi x^2 + 4\pi y^2}{8} - \frac{4\pi y^2 + 4\pi x^2}{8} + 2xy = 2xy$, which is the area of the triangle.

PROBLEM SOLVING

EXAMPLE 1 [A] on p. 755 for Ex. 37

37. METEOROLOGY The *eye of a hurricane* is a relatively calm circular region in the center of the storm. The diameter of the eye is typically about 20 miles. If the eye of a hurricane is 20 miles in diameter, what is the area of the land that is underneath the eye? **about 314.16 mi²**

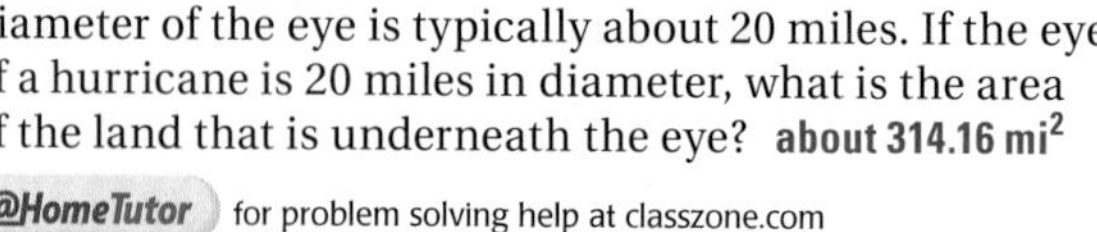

@HomeTutor for problem solving help at classzone.com

38. WALKING The area of a circular pond is about 138,656 square feet. You are going to walk around the entire edge of the pond. About how far will you walk? Give your answer to the nearest foot. **1320 ft**

@HomeTutor for problem solving help at classzone.com

39a. A circle graph is appropriate because the data values add up to 100%.

39b. Bus: 234°, walk: 90°, other: 36°; see margin for art.

41a. ***Sample answer:*** **Old: about 371 mm², new: 682 mm²; about 84%**

41b. ***Sample answer:*** **No; the increase in overall area of the "a" is about 30%, which is much less than the percent increase in the interior area.**

42a. 2 14-in. pizzas; the area is larger than needed, but the cost of 2 14-inch pizzas is less than buying any other combination of pizzas to feed the 8 people.

42b. One 14-in. pizza and 2 10-in. pizzas; there will be enough pizza to feed everyone and it is cheaper than any other combination.

(39.) CIRCLE GRAPH The table shows how students get to school.

Method	% of Students
Bus	65%
Walk	25%
Other	10%

a. *Explain* why a circle graph is appropriate for the data.

b. You will represent each method by a sector of a circle graph. Find the central angle to use for each sector. Then use a protractor and a compass to construct the graph. Use a radius of 2 inches.

c. Find the area of each sector in your graph. **bus: 8.2 in.², walk: bus: 3.1 in.², other: 1.3 in.²,**

40. ★ SHORT RESPONSE It takes about $\frac{1}{4}$ cup of dough to make a tortilla with a 6 inch diameter. How much dough does it take to make a tortilla with a 12 inch diameter? *Explain* your reasoning.**1 cup; the area of a 6-inch tortilla is 9π, the area of a 12-inch tortilla is 36π, since the 12-inch is four times larger, you need 4 times as much dough.**

[B] **41. HIGHWAY SIGNS** A new typeface has been designed to make highway signs more readable. One change was to redesign the form of the letters to increase the space inside letters.

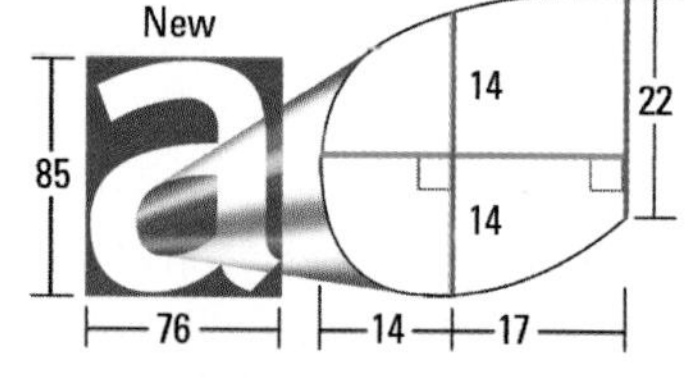

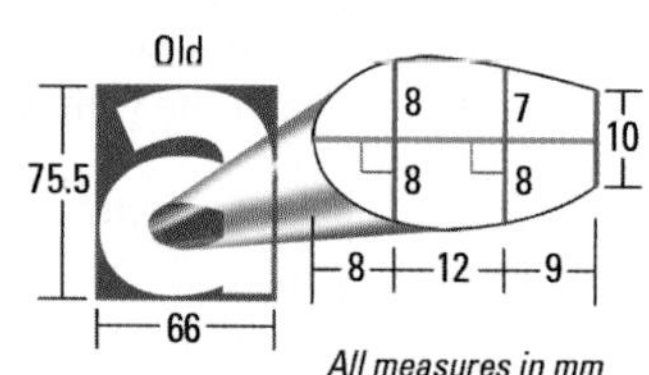

All measures in mm

a. Estimate the interior area for the old and the new "a." Then find the percent increase in interior area.

b. Do you think the change in interior area is just a result of a change in height and width of the letter *a*? *Explain.*

42. ★ EXTENDED RESPONSE A circular pizza with a 12 inch diameter is enough for you and 2 friends. You want to buy pizza for yourself and 7 friends. A 10 inch diameter pizza with one topping costs \$6.99 and a 14 inch diameter pizza with one topping costs \$12.99. How many 10 inch and 14 inch pizzas should you buy in each situation below? *Explain.*

a. You want to spend as little money as possible.

b. You want to have three pizzas, each with a different topping.

c. You want to have as much of the thick outer crust as possible. **4 10-in.; you have more circumference here and therefore more crust.**

○ = WORKED-OUT SOLUTIONS on p. WS1 ★ = STANDARDIZED TEST PRACTICE

43. **JUSTIFYING THEOREM 11.9** You can follow the steps below to justify the formula for the area of a circle with radius r.

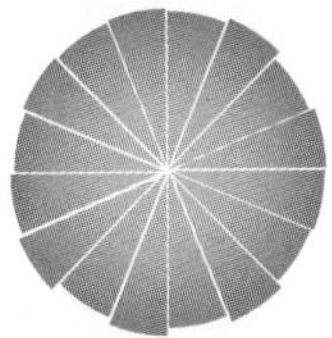

Divide a circle into 16 congruent sectors. Cut out the sectors.

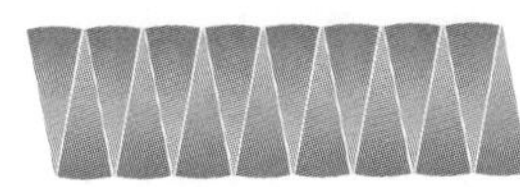

Rearrange the 16 sectors to form a shape resembling a parallelogram.

a. Write expressions in terms of r for the approximate height and base of the parallelogram. Then write an expression for its area.

b. *Explain* how your answers to part (a) justify Theorem 11.9. **See margin.**

43a. height: r, base: πr, area: πr^2

C 44. **CHALLENGE** Semicircles with diameters equal to the three sides of a right triangle are drawn, as shown. Prove that the sum of the areas of the two shaded crescents equals the area of the triangle. **See margin.**

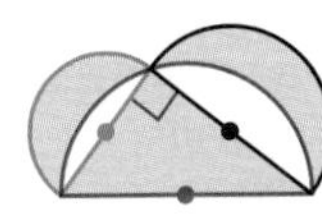

MIXED REVIEW

PREVIEW Prepare for Lesson 11.6 in Exs. 45–47.

Triangle DEG is isosceles with altitude $\overline{DF}$. Find the given measurement. *Explain* your reasoning. *(p. 319)*

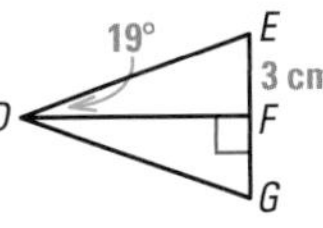

45. $m\angle DFG$ 46. $m\angle FDG$ 47. FG

45. 90°; definition of an altitude

46. 19°; since the altitude bisects the angle, $m\angle FDG = m\angle EDF$.

47. 3 cm; the altitude of an isosceles triangle bisects the base, so $FG = EF = 3$ cm.

Sketch the indicated figure. Draw all of its lines of symmetry. *(p. 619)* **48, 49. See margin.**

48. Isosceles trapezoid 49. Regular hexagon

Graph $\triangle ABC$. Then find its area. *(p. 720)* **50, 51. See margin for art.**

50. $A(2, 2), B(9, 2), C(4, 16)$ **49 units^2** 51. $A(-8, 3), B(-3, 3), C(-1, -10)$ **32.5 units^2**

QUIZ for Lessons 11.4–11.5

Find the indicated measure. *(p. 746)*

1. Length of $\widehat{AB}$

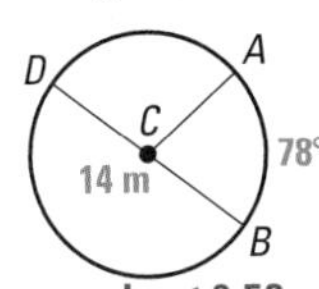

about 9.53 m

2. Circumference of $\odot F$

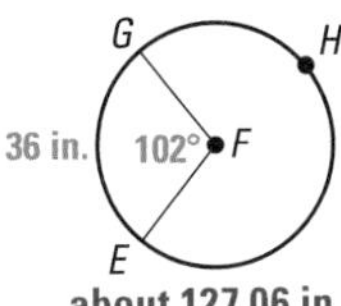

about 127.06 in.

3. Radius of $\odot L$

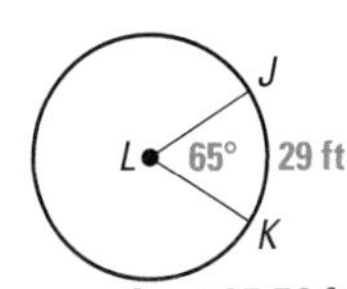

about 25.56 ft

Find the area of the shaded region. *(p. 755)*

4.

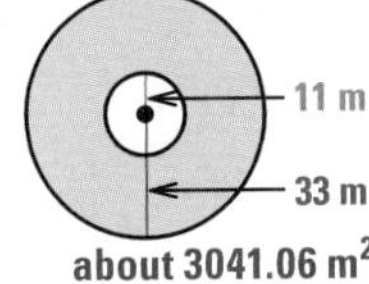

about 3041.06 m^2

5.

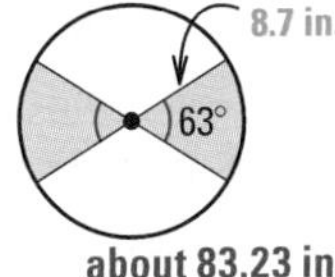

about 83.23 in.^{2}

6.

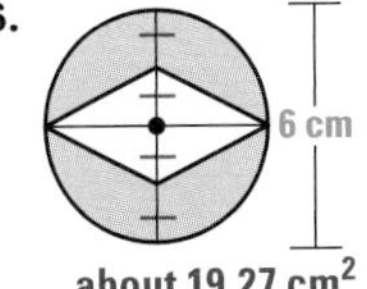

about 19.27 cm^2

48.

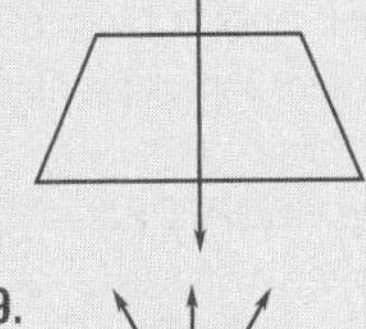

49.

50.

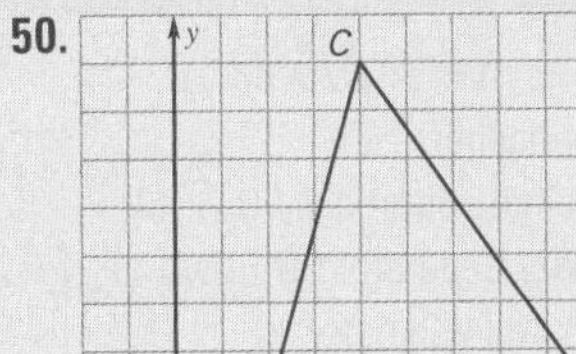

51.

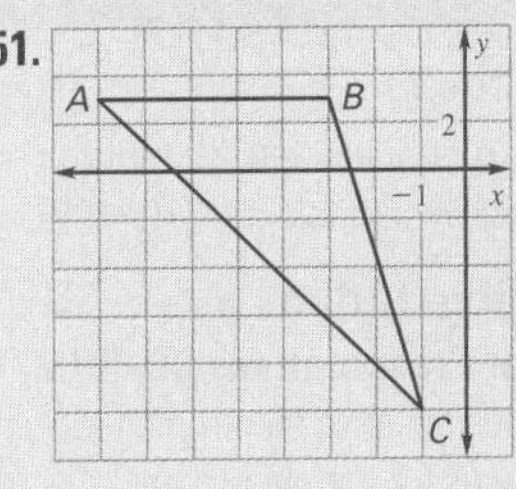

5 ASSESS AND RETEACH

Daily Homework Quiz

Transparency Available

1. Find the area of the sectors formed by $\angle DEF$. **106.03 in.^{2}, 141.31 in.^{2}**

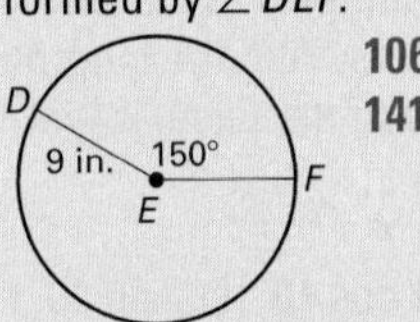

2. Use the area of the sector to find the area of $\odot R$. **211.09 cm^2**

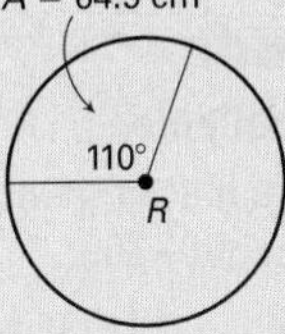

3. Find the area of the shaded region. **23.18 ft^2**

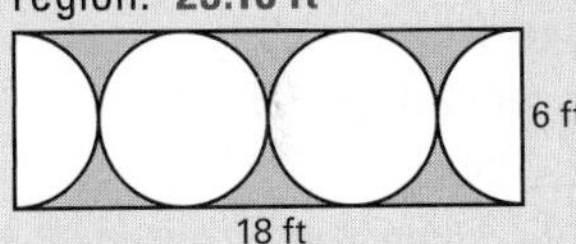

Available at **classzone.com**

Diagnosis/Remediation

- Practice A, B, C in Chapter 11 Resource Book, pp. 64–69
- Study Guide in Chapter 11 Resource Book, pp. 70–71
- Practice Workbook, pp. 217–219
- @HomeTutor

Challenge

Additional challenge is available in the Chapter 11 Resource Book, p. 74.

Quiz

An easily-readable reduced copy of the quiz (with answers) on Lessons 11.4–11.5 from the Assessment Book can be found on p. 718G.

1 PLAN AND PREPARE

Warm-Up Exercises

Transparency Available

1. An isosceles triangle has side lengths 20 meters, 26 meters, and 26 meters. Find the length of the altitude to the base. **24 m**
2. Solve $18 = \frac{1}{2} \cdot x$. **36**
3. Evaluate $(4 \cos 10°)(10 \sin 20°)$. **13.47**
4. Evaluate $\frac{10}{\tan 88°}$. **0.3492**

Notetaking Guide

Transparency Available

Promotes interactive learning and notetaking skills, pp. 300–303.

Pacing

Basic: 2 days
Average: 2 days
Advanced: 2 days
Block: 1 block
- See *Teaching Guide/Lesson Plan.*

2 FOCUS AND MOTIVATE

Essential Question

Big Idea 1, p. 719

How do you find the area of a regular polygon? **Tell students they will learn how to answer this question by dividing the polygon into *n* isosceles triangles.**

11.6 Areas of Regular Polygons

Before You found areas of circles.

Now You will find areas of regular polygons inscribed in circles.

Why? So you can understand the structure of a honeycomb, as in Ex. 44.

Key Vocabulary
- **center of a polygon**
- **radius of a polygon**
- **apothem of a polygon**
- **central angle of a regular polygon**

The diagram shows a regular polygon inscribed in a circle. The **center of the polygon** and the **radius of the polygon** are the center and the radius of its circumscribed circle.

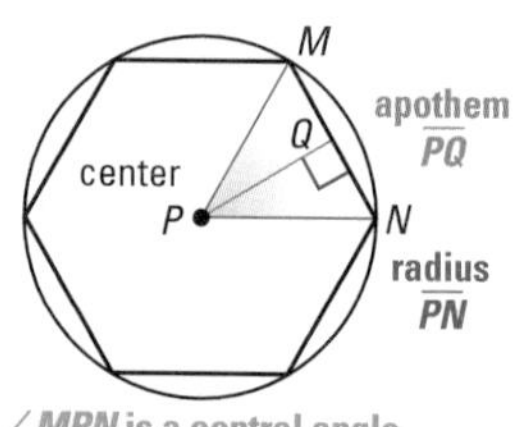

$\angle MPN$ is a central angle.

The distance from the center to any side of the polygon is called the **apothem of the polygon**. The apothem is the height to the base of an isosceles triangle that has two radii as legs.

A **central angle of a regular polygon** is an angle formed by two radii drawn to consecutive vertices of the polygon. To find the measure of each central angle, divide 360° by the number of sides.

EXAMPLE 1 Find angle measures in a regular polygon

In the diagram, *ABCDE* is a regular pentagon inscribed in $\odot F$. Find each angle measure.

a. $m\angle AFB$ **b.** $m\angle AFG$ **c.** $m\angle GAF$

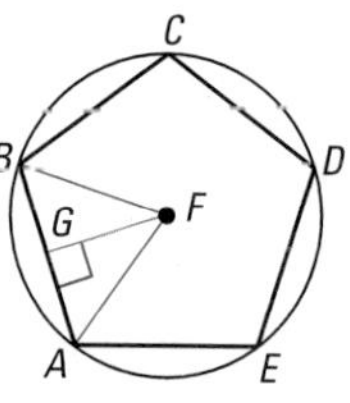

READ DIAGRAMS

A segment whose length is *the apothem* is sometimes called *an apothem*. The segment is an altitude of an isosceles triangle, so it is also a median and angle bisector of the isosceles triangle.

Solution

a. $\angle AFB$ is a central angle, so $m\angle AFB = \frac{360°}{5}$, or 72°.

b. $\overline{FG}$ is an apothem, which makes it an altitude of isosceles $\triangle AFB$. So, $\overline{FG}$ bisects $\angle AFB$ and $m\angle AFG = \frac{1}{2} m\angle AFB = 36°$.

c. The sum of the measures of right $\triangle GAF$ is 180°. So, $90° + 36° + m\angle GAF = 180°$, and $m\angle GAF = 54°$.

GUIDED PRACTICE for Example 1

In the diagram, *WXYZ* is a square inscribed in $\odot P$.

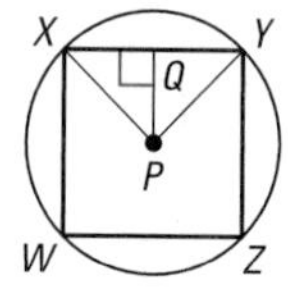

1. Identify the center, a radius, an apothem, and a central angle of the polygon. ***P*, $\overline{PY}$ or $\overline{XP}$, $\overline{PQ}$, $\angle XPY$**
2. Find $m\angle XPY$, $m\angle XPQ$, and $m\angle PXQ$. **90°, 45°, 45°**

Resource Planning Guide

Chapter Resource Book
- Teaching Guide/Lesson Plan (pp. 75–76)
- Practice levels A, B, C (pp. 78–83)
- Study Guide (pp. 84–85)
- Catch-up for Absent Students (p. 86)
- Application (p. 87)
- Challenge (p. 88)

Workbooks
- Notetaking Guide (pp. 300–303)
- Practice Workbook (pp. 220–222)

Teaching Options
- **Power Presentations CD-ROM** provides dynamic electronic teaching resources for the classroom.
- **Activity Generator CD-ROM** provides editable activities for all ability levels.

Interactive Technology
- Easy Planner
- Power Presentations CD-ROM
- Activity Generator CD-ROM
- Animated Geometry
- Test Generator CD-ROM
- Online Quiz
- eWorkbook
- eEdition
- @HomeTutor

Resources for English Learners
- Quick Reference for English Learners
- Spanish Study Guide
- Multi-Language Visual Glossary
- Student Resources in Spanish

See also the *Geometry Toolkit* for more strategies for meeting individual needs.

AREA OF AN n-GON You can find the area of any regular n-gon by dividing it into congruent triangles.

A = Area of one triangle • Number of triangles

$= \left(\frac{1}{2} \cdot s \cdot a\right) \cdot n$ — Base of triangle is s and height of triangle is a. Number of triangles is n.

$= \frac{1}{2} \cdot a \cdot (n \cdot s)$ — Commutative and Associative Properties of Equality

$= \frac{1}{2}a \cdot P$ — There are n congruent sides of length s, so perimeter P is $n \cdot s$.

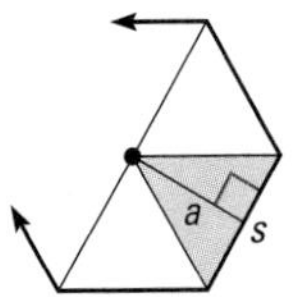

READ DIAGRAMS

In this book, a point shown inside a regular polygon marks the center of the circle that can be circumscribed about the polygon.

Standards

8.0 Students know, derive, and solve problems involving the perimeter, circumference, **area,** volume, lateral area, and surface area **of common geometric figures.**

10.0 Students compute areas of polygons, including rectangles, scalene triangles, **equilateral triangles,** rhombi, parallelograms, and trapezoids.

21.0 Students prove and solve problems regarding relationships among chords, secants, tangents, inscribed angles, and **inscribed** and circumscribed **polygons of circles.**

THEOREM *For Your Notebook*

THEOREM 11.11 Area of a Regular Polygon

The area of a regular n-gon with side length s is one half the product of the apothem a and the perimeter P, so $A = \frac{1}{2}aP$, or $A = \frac{1}{2}a \cdot ns$.

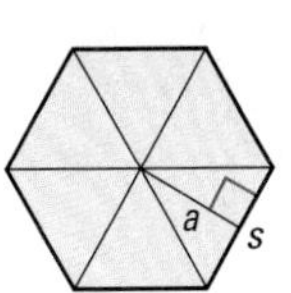

EXAMPLE 2 Find the area of a regular polygon

DECORATING You are decorating the top of a table by covering it with small ceramic tiles. The table top is a regular octagon with 15 inch sides and a radius of about 19.6 inches. What is the area you are covering?

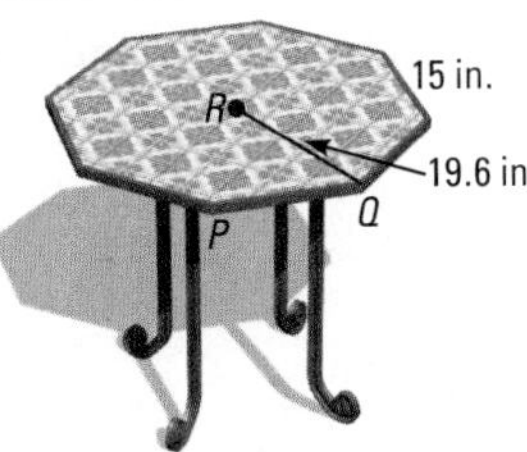

Solution

STEP 1 **Find** the perimeter P of the table top.
An octagon has 8 sides, so $P = 8(15) = 120$ inches.

STEP 2 **Find** the apothem a. The apothem is height RS of $\triangle PQR$. Because $\triangle PQR$ is isosceles, altitude $\overline{RS}$ bisects $\overline{QP}$.

So, $QS = \frac{1}{2}(QP) = \frac{1}{2}(15) = 7.5$ inches.

To find RS, use the Pythagorean Theorem for $\triangle RQS$.

$a = RS \approx \sqrt{19.6^2 - 7.5^2} = \sqrt{327.91} \approx 18.108$

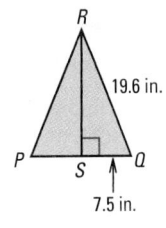

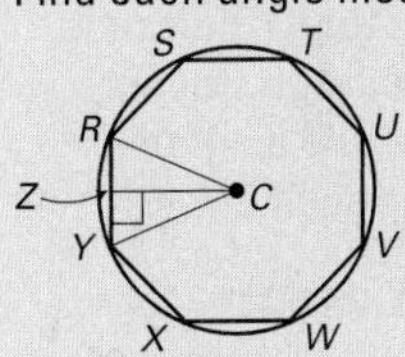

STEP 3 **Find** the area A of the table top.

$A = \frac{1}{2}aP$ — Formula for area of regular polygon

$\approx \frac{1}{2}(18.108)(120)$ — Substitute.

≈ 1086.5 — Simplify.

▶ So, the area you are covering with tiles is about 1086.5 square inches.

ROUNDING

In general, your answer will be more accurate if you avoid rounding until the last step. Round your final answers to the nearest tenth unless you are told otherwise.

Motivating the Lesson

Take students through the first steps of finding the area of a stop sign with side length 25 inches: Ask them to describe the shape of a stop sign (a regular octagon), and ask how many isosceles triangles can be formed by segments from the center to the vertices (8). Then ask the measure of the vertex angle for each triangle (45°). Tell them that in this lesson they will use trigonometry ratios to measure the height of each triangle, and they will develop a formula for the area of a regular polygon.

3 TEACH

Extra Example 1

In the diagram, $RSTUVWXY$ is a regular octagon inscribed in $\odot C$. Find each angle measure.

S T R U Z C Y V X W

a. $m\angle RCY$ **45°**

b $m\angle RCZ$ **22.5°**

c. $m\angle ZYC$ **67.5°**

Key Question to Ask for Example 1

• Why do you divide by 5 in part (a)? **There are 5 congruent central angles in a regular pentagon.**

Extra Example 2

You are tiling a floor with ceramic regular hexagons with side length 8 inches. What is the area that a tile will cover? **166.3 in.^{2}**

Reading Strategy

Make sure students read and understand the guidelines on rounding given on this page.

Extra Example 3

A regular decagon is inscribed in a circle with radius 8 units. Find the perimeter and area of the decagon.

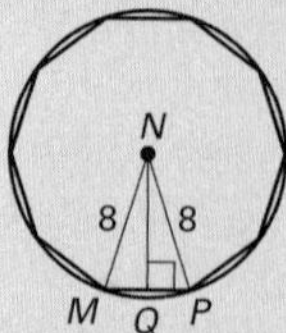

49.4 units; 188.1 units^2

Key Question to Ask for Example 3

- How is trigonometry used to find the side length and the apothem? **Half of the side length is found using the sine ratio for 20°, and the apothem is found using the cosine ratio for 20°.**

Avoiding Common Errors

A common error is to incorrectly calculate the perimeter as *n* times the radius rather than *n* times the side length. Encourage students to read problems and diagrams carefully to avoid such errors.

Closing the Lesson

Have students summarize the major points of the lesson and answer the Essential Question: How do you find the area of a regular polygon?

- **The center and radius of a regular polygon are the center and radius of its circumscribed circle.**
- **The distance from the center to a side of a regular polygon is the apothem.**
- **A central angle of a regular polygon is formed by two consecutive radii.**
- **The area of a regular polygon is $A = \frac{1}{2}aP$ where a is the apothem and P is the perimeter.**

Find the length a of the apothem and the perimeter P of the polygon. Substitute those values into the formula for the area of a regular polygon $A = \frac{1}{2}aP$.

EXAMPLE 3 Find the perimeter and area of a regular polygon

A regular nonagon is inscribed in a circle with radius 4 units. Find the perimeter and area of the nonagon.

Solution

The measure of central $\angle JLK$ is $\frac{360°}{9}$, or 40°. Apothem $\overline{LM}$ bisects the central angle, so $m\angle KLM$ is 20°. To find the lengths of the legs, use trigonometric ratios for right $\triangle KLM$.

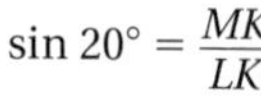

$$\sin 20° = \frac{MK}{LK} \qquad \cos 20° = \frac{LM}{LK}$$

$$\sin 20° = \frac{MK}{4} \qquad \cos 20° = \frac{LM}{4}$$

$$4 \cdot \sin 20° = MK \qquad 4 \cdot \cos 20° = LM$$

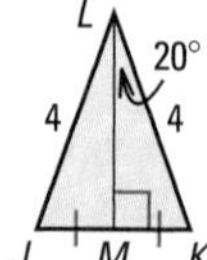

The regular nonagon has side length $s = 2MK = 2(4 \cdot \sin 20°) = 8 \cdot \sin 20°$ and apothem $a = LM = 4 \cdot \cos 20°$.

▶ So, the perimeter is $P = 9s = 9(8 \cdot \sin 20°) = 72 \cdot \sin 20° \approx 24.6$ units, and the area is $A = \frac{1}{2}aP = \frac{1}{2}(4 \cdot \cos 20°)(72 \cdot \sin 20°) \approx 46.3$ square units.

GUIDED PRACTICE for Examples 2 and 3

Find the perimeter and the area of the regular polygon.

3.

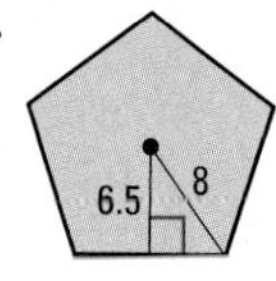

4. **5.**

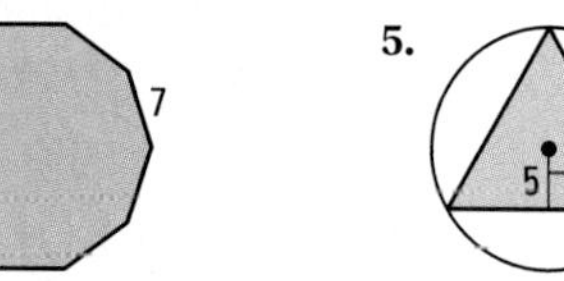

6. Which of Exercises 3–5 above can be solved using special right triangles? **Exercise 5**

3. about 46.6 units, about 151.5 units^2

4. 70 units, about 377.0 units^2

5. $30\sqrt{3} \approx 52.0$ units, about 129.9 units^2

CONCEPT SUMMARY *For Your Notebook*

Finding Lengths in a Regular *n*-gon

To find the area of a regular *n*-gon with radius *r*, you may need to first find the apothem *a* or the side length *s*.

You can use...	... when you know *n* and ...	... as in ...
Pythagorean Theorem: $\left(\frac{1}{2}s\right)^2 + a^2 = r^2$	Two measures: *r* and *a*, or *r* and *s*	Example 2 and Guided Practice Ex. 3.
Special Right Triangles	Any one measure: *r* or *a* or *s* **And** the value of *n* is 3, 4, or 6	Guided Practice Ex. 5.
Trigonometry	Any one measure: *r* or *a* or *s*	Example 3 and Guided Practice Exs. 4 and 5.

11.6 EXERCISES

HOMEWORK KEY
○ = **WORKED-OUT SOLUTIONS** on p. WS15 for Exs. 7, 21, and 37
★ = **STANDARDIZED TEST PRACTICE** Exs. 5, 18, 22, and 44

SKILL PRACTICE

A **VOCABULARY** In Exercises 1–4, use the diagram shown.

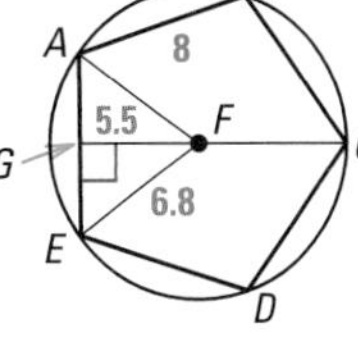

1. Identify the *center* of regular polygon *ABCDE*. **F**
2. Identify a *central angle* of the polygon. **∠AFE**
3. What is the *radius* of the polygon? **6.8 units**
4. What is the *apothem*? **5.5 units**

5. ★ **WRITING** *Explain* how to find the measure of a *central angle* of a regular polygon with n sides. **Divide 360° by the number of sides n of the polygon.**

EXAMPLE 1 on p. 762 for Exs. 6–13

MEASURES OF CENTRAL ANGLES Find the measure of a central angle of a regular polygon with the given number of sides. Round answers to the nearest tenth of a degree, if necessary.

6. 10 sides **36°**
7. 18 sides **20°**
8. 24 sides **15°**
9. 7 sides **51.4°**

FINDING ANGLE MEASURES Find the given angle measure for the regular octagon shown.

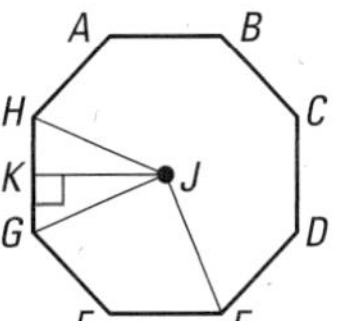

10. $m\angle GJH$ **45°**
11. $m\angle GJK$ **22.5°**
12. $m\angle KGJ$ **67.5°**
13. $m\angle EJH$ **135°**

EXAMPLE 2 on p. 763 for Exs. 14–17

FINDING AREA Find the area of the regular polygon.

14. 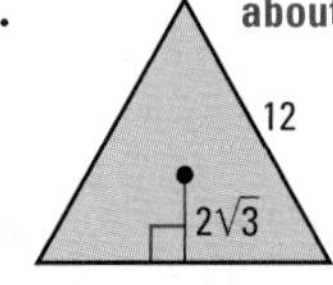

about 62.4 units²

15. 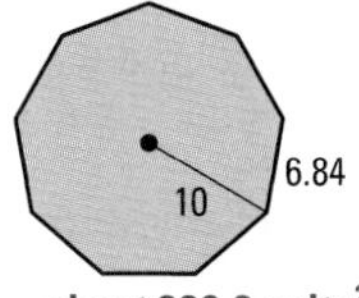

about 289.2 units²

16. 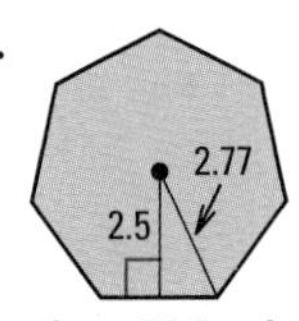

about 20.9 units²

Animated Geometry at classzone.com

17. **ERROR ANALYSIS** *Describe* and correct the error in finding the area of the regular hexagon.

$\sqrt{15^2 - 13^2} \approx 7.5$

$A = \frac{1}{2}a \cdot ns$

$A = \frac{1}{2}(13)(6)(7.5) = 292.5$

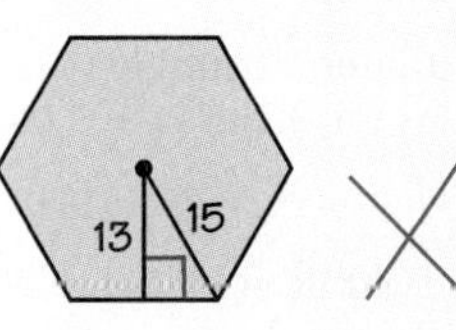

7.5 is not the measure of a side length, it is the measure of the base of the triangle, it needs to be doubled to become the measure of the side length;
$A \approx \frac{1}{2}(13)(6)(15) = 585$ **units²**.

EXAMPLE 3 on p. 764 for Exs. 18–25

18. ★ **MULTIPLE CHOICE** Which expression gives the apothem for a regular dodecagon with side length 8? **B**

Ⓐ $a = \frac{4}{\tan 30°}$ Ⓑ $a = \frac{4}{\tan 15°}$ Ⓒ $a = \frac{8}{\tan 15°}$ Ⓓ $a = 8 \cdot \cos 15°$

4 PRACTICE AND APPLY

Assignment Guide

Answer Transparencies available for all exercises

Basic:
Day 1: EP p. 909 Exs. 40–45
pp. 765–768
Exs. 1–13, 47–52
Day 2: pp. 765–768
Exs. 14–24, 26–30 even, 36–40

Average:
Day 1: pp. 765–768
Exs. 1–13, 47–52
Day 2: pp. 765–768
Exs. 15–18, 20–22, 24–26, 27–33 odd, 34, 36–44

Advanced:
Day 1: pp. 765–768
Exs. 1–13, 47–52
Day 2: pp. 765–768
Exs. 16–30 even, 31–36*, 38–46*

Block:
pp. 765–768
Exs. 1–13, 15–18, 20–22, 24–26, 27–33 odd, 34, 36–44, 47–52

Differentiated Instruction

See *Geometry Best Practices Toolkit* for suggestions on addressing the needs of a diverse classroom.

Homework Check

For a quick check of student understanding of key concepts, go over the following exercises:
Basic: 8, 14, 20, 36, 38
Average: 10, 15, 22, 36, 39
Advanced: 12, 16, 24, 36, 40

Extra Practice

- Student Edition, p. 917
- Chapter 11 Resource Book: Practice levels A, B, C, pp. 78–83

Practice Worksheet

An easily-readable reduced practice page (with answers) for this lesson can be found on p. 718E.

An **Animated Geometry** activity is available on-line for **Exercises 14–16**. This activity is also available on the **Power Presentations CD-ROM**.

Study Strategy

Exercises 23–25 Ask students to use these exercises to help them plan a general strategy to find the area of a regular polygon. Tell them to carefully identify and label the number of sides, the radius, and the apothem for each figure. Then have them write their purpose (for example, "Calculate the perimeter" or "Calculate the apothem") as a heading for each set of calculations.

22. Yes; about 24.7 in.^{2}; since a nonagon has 9 sides, $18 \div 9$ tells you that each side is 2 inches long, and $\frac{360}{9}$ tells you that the measure of the central angle is 40°. A right triangle can be constructed with a base of 1 inch and an angle of 20° opposite the base; $\tan 20° = \frac{1}{a}$ allows us to find the apothem and then the area is $\frac{1}{2}\left(\frac{1}{\tan 20°}\right)(18) \approx$ 24.7 square inches.

34. $A = \frac{1}{2}bh$

$= \frac{1}{2}s \cdot \frac{s\sqrt{3}}{2}$

$= \frac{\sqrt{3}s^2}{4}$

$A = \frac{1}{2}a \cdot ns$

$= \frac{1}{2}\left(\frac{s\sqrt{3}}{6}\right)(3s)$

$= \frac{3s^2\sqrt{3}}{12}$

$= \frac{\sqrt{3}s^2}{4}$

PERIMETER AND AREA **Find the perimeter and area of the regular polygon.**

19. **about 122.5 units, about 1131.4 units^2**

20. 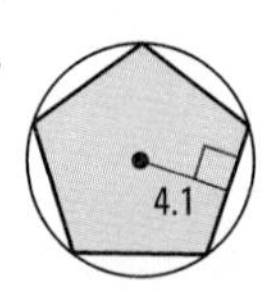

about 29.8 units, about 61.1 units^2

21. 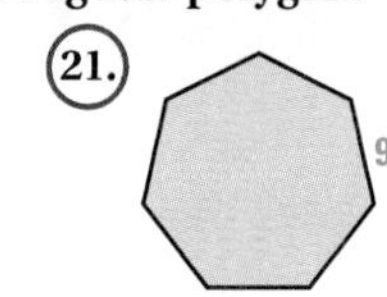

63 units, about 294.3 units^2

22. ★ **SHORT RESPONSE** The perimeter of a regular nonagon is 18 inches. Is that enough information to find the area? If so, find the area and *explain* your steps. If not, *explain* why not. **See margin.**

CHOOSE A METHOD **Identify any unknown length(s) you need to know to find the area of the regular polygon. Which methods in the table on page 764 can you use to find those lengths? Choose a method and find the area.**

23. 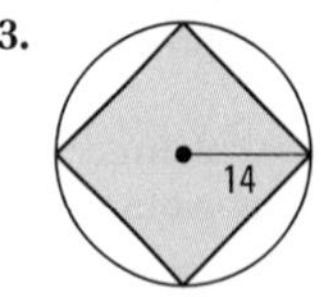

apothem, side length; special right triangles or trigonometry; 392 units^2

24. 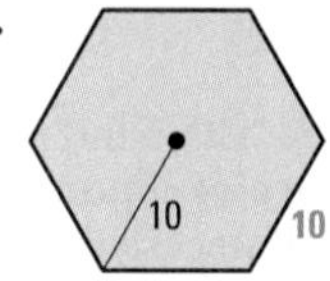

24. apothem; Pythagorean Theorem, special right triangles or trigonometry; about 259.8 units^2

25. **side length; Pythagorean Theorem or trigonometry; about 204.9 units^2**

B

26. **INSCRIBED SQUARE** Find the area of the *unshaded* region in Exercise 23. **about 223.8 units^2**

POLYGONS IN CIRCLES **Find the area of the shaded region.**

27. **about 79.6 units^2**

28. **about 117.9 units^2**

29. 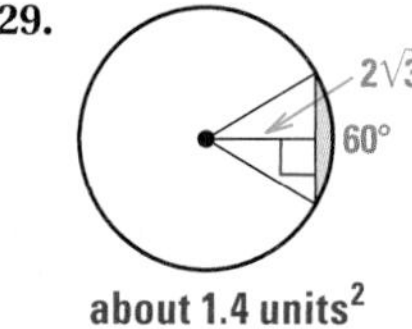

about 1.4 units^2

30. **COORDINATE GEOMETRY** Find the area of a regular pentagon inscribed in a circle whose equation is given by $(x - 4)^2 + (y + 2)^2 = 25$. **about 59.4 units^2**

REASONING **Decide whether the statement is *true* or *false*. *Explain.***

31. The area of a regular n-gon of fixed radius r increases as n increases.

31. True; since the radius is the same, the circle around the n-gons is the same but more and more of the circle is covered the larger n is.

32. The apothem of a regular polygon is always less than the radius.

32. True; the radius represents the hypotenuse of a right triangle with the apothem as a leg, therefore, the apothem must always be less than the radius.

33. The radius of a regular polygon is always less than the side length. **False; the radius can be equal to the side length as it is in a hexagon.**

34. **FORMULAS** In Exercise 44 on page 726, the formula $A = \frac{\sqrt{3}s^2}{4}$ for the area A of an equilateral triangle with side length s was developed. Show that the formulas for the area of a triangle and for the area of a regular polygon, $A = \frac{1}{2}bh$ and $A = \frac{1}{2}a \cdot ns$, also result in this formula when they are applied to an equilateral triangle with side length s. **See margin.**

C

35. **CHALLENGE** An equilateral triangle is shown inside a square inside a regular pentagon inside a regular hexagon. Write an expression for the exact area of the shaded regions in the figure. Then find the approximate area of the entire shaded region, rounded to the nearest whole unit. **shaded area = area of hexagon − area of pentagon + area of square − area of triangle; 92 units^2**

○ = WORKED-OUT SOLUTIONS on p. WS1 ★ = STANDARDIZED TEST PRACTICE

PROBLEM SOLVING

EXAMPLE 3 A on p. 764 for Ex. 36

A 36. **BASALTIC COLUMNS** Basaltic columns are geological formations that result from rapidly cooling lava. The Giant's Causeway in Ireland, pictured here, contains many hexagonal columns. Suppose that one of the columns is in the shape of a regular hexagon with radius 8 inches.

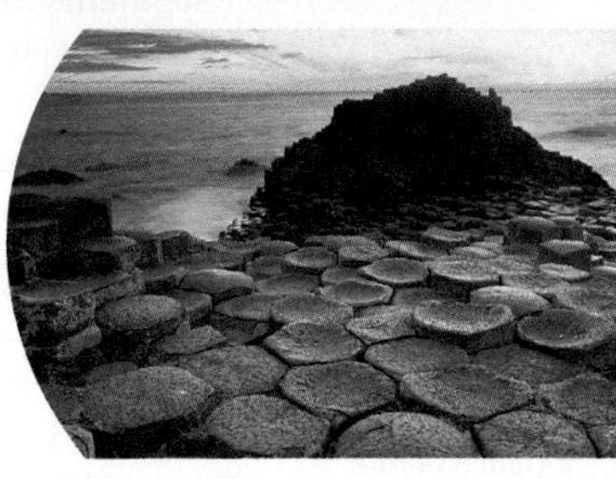

a. What is the apothem of the column? **$4\sqrt{3}$ in.**

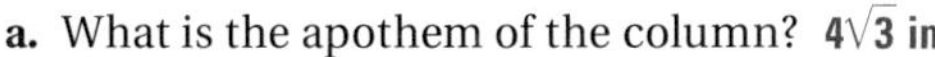

b. Find the perimeter and area of the column. Round the area to the nearest square inch.

36b. 48 in., 166 in.^{2}

@HomeTutor for problem solving help at classzone.com

37. **WATCH** A watch has a circular face on a background that is a regular octagon. Find the apothem and the area of the octagon. Then find the area of the silver border around the circular face.

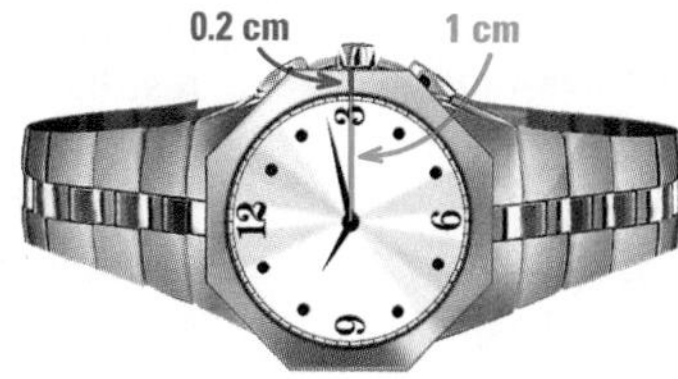

37. 1.2 cm, about 4.8 cm^2; about 1.6 cm^2

@HomeTutor for problem solving help at classzone.com

38. **COMPARING AREAS** *Predict* which figure has the greatest area and which has the smallest area. Check by finding the area of each figure. **Predictions may vary.**

a.

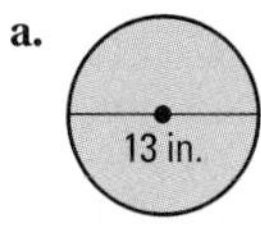

about 132.7 in.^{2}

b.

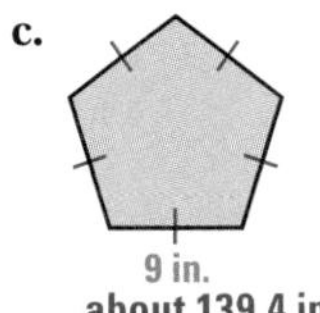

135 in.^{2}

c. 9 in.

about 139.4 in.^{2}

B 39. **CRAFTS** You want to make two wooden trivets, a large one and a small one. Both trivets will be shaped like regular pentagons. The perimeter of the small trivet is 15 inches, and the perimeter of the large trivet is 25 inches. Find the area of the small trivet. Then use the Areas of Similar Polygons Theorem to find the area of the large trivet. Round your answers to the nearest tenth. **15.5 in.^{2}; 43.0 in.^{2}**

40. **CONSTRUCTION** Use a ruler and compass.

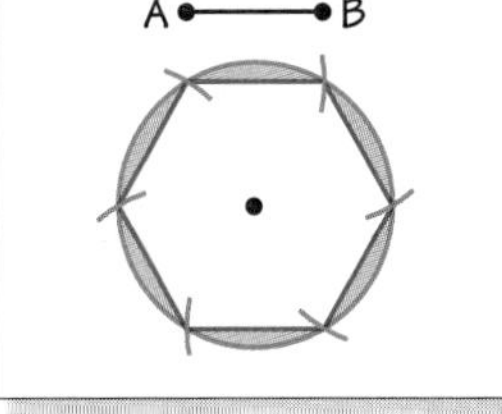

a. Draw $\overline{AB}$ with a length of 1 inch. Open the compass to 1 inch and draw a circle with that radius. Using the same compass setting, mark off equal parts along the circle. Then connect the six points where the compass marks and circle intersect to draw a regular hexagon as shown. **Check students' work.**

b. What is the area of the hexagon? of the shaded region?

c. *Explain* how to construct an equilateral triangle.

40b. about 2.6 in.^{2}, about 0.54 in.^{2}

40c. *Sample Answer:* Draw $\overline{AB}$ with length 1 in. Open compass to 1 inch and draw a circle with that radius, continue with this setting and mark off equal parts on the circle. Connect 2 consecutive points with the center of the circle.

41. **HEXAGONS AND TRIANGLES** Show that a regular hexagon can be divided into six equilateral triangles with the same side length. **See margin.**

42. **ALTERNATIVE METHODS** Find the area of a regular hexagon with side length 2 and apothem $\sqrt{3}$ in at least four different ways. **See margin.**

Internet Reference

Exercise 36 For more information about the Giant's Causeway, visit www.geographia.com/northern-ireland/ukiant01.htm

41. $\frac{360}{9} = 60$, so the central angle is 60°. All of the triangles are of the same side length r, and therefore all six triangles have a vertex at the center with central angle 60° and side lengths r.

42. Method 1: $A = \frac{1}{2}aP = \frac{1}{2}\sqrt{3}(12) = 6\sqrt{3}$;
Method 2: 6(Area of a central triangle) $= 6\left(\frac{1}{2}bh\right) = 6\left(\frac{1}{2} \cdot 2 \cdot \sqrt{3}\right) = 6\sqrt{3}$;
Method 3: $A = \frac{1}{2}a \cdot ns = \frac{1}{2}(\sqrt{3})(6)(2) = 6\sqrt{3}$;
Method 4: $A = 2$(Area of trapezoid) $= 2\left(\frac{1}{2}h(b_1 + b_2)\right) = 2\left(\frac{1}{2}\sqrt{3}(4+2)\right) = 6\sqrt{3}$.

5 ASSESS AND RETEACH

Daily Homework Quiz

Transparency Available

1. Find the measure of a central angle of a regular polygon with 24 sides. **15°**

Find the area of each regular polygon.

2. **110 cm^2**

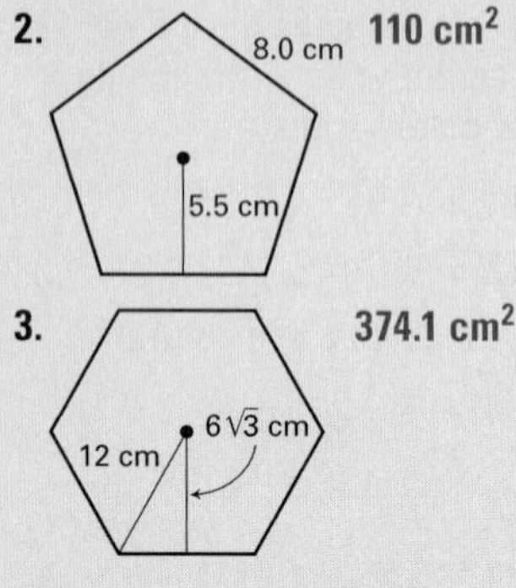

3. **374.1 cm^2**

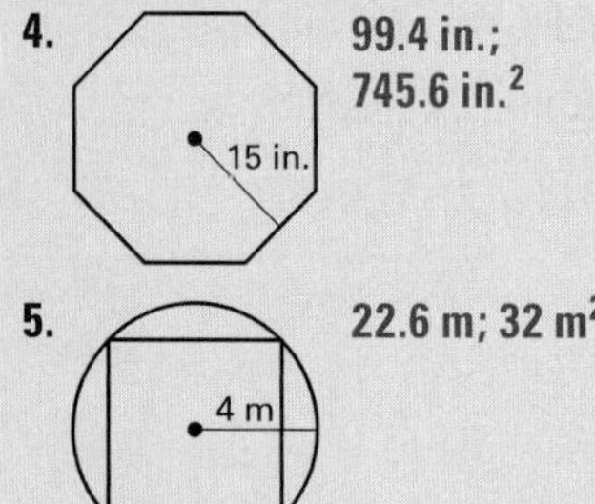

Find the perimeter and area of each regular polygon.

4. **99.4 in.; 745.6 in.^{2}** (15 in.)

5. **22.6 m; 32 m^2** (4 m)

Available at **classzone.com**

Diagnosis/Remediation

- Practice A, B, C in Chapter 11 Resource Book, pp. 78–83
- Study Guide in Chapter 11 Resource Book, pp. 84–85
- Practice Workbook, pp. 220–222
- @HomeTutor

Challenge

Additional challenge is available in the Chapter 11 Resource Book, p. 88.

43, 44d, 45a, 45c. See Additional Answers beginning on p. AA1.

44b. About 0.2 cm^2; $a = 0.26$ cm and when you construct a right triangle with a as the height and a 30° angle measure between a and the hypotenuse, you can use a tangent ratio to give you the base of the triangle to be 0.15, which means the side of a hexagon is 0.30. So the area of a cell is $\frac{1}{2}(0.26)(6 \cdot 0.3)$, or about 0.23 square centimeters.

44c. 23.4 cm^2; 0.23 dm^2

43. **APPLYING TRIANGLE PROPERTIES** In Chapter 5, you learned properties of special segments in triangles. Use what you know about special segments in triangles to show that radius CP in equilateral $\triangle ABC$ is twice the apothem DP. **See margin.**

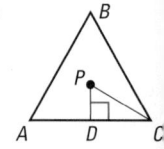

44. ★ **EXTENDED RESPONSE** Assume that each honeycomb cell is a regular hexagon. The distance is measured through the center of each cell.
    a. Find the average distance across a cell in centimeters. **0.52 cm**
    b. Find the area of a "typical" cell in square centimeters. Show your steps.
    c. What is the area of 100 cells in square centimeters? in square decimeters? (1 decimeter = 10 centimeters.)
    d. Scientists are often interested in the number of cells per square decimeter. *Explain* how to rewrite your results in this form. **See margin.**

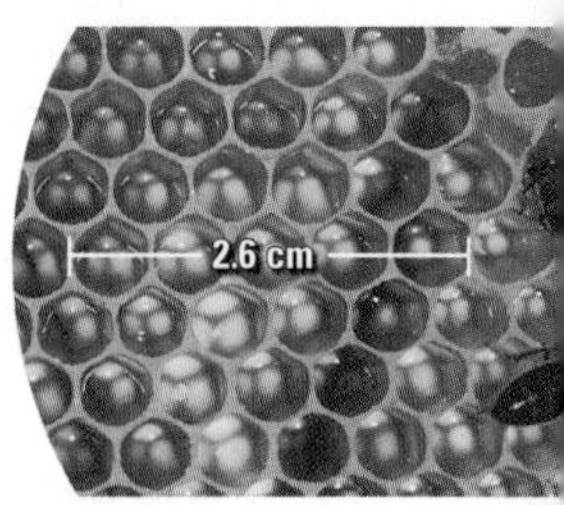

45. **CONSTANT PERIMETER** Use a piece of string that is 60 centimeters long.
    a. Arrange the string to form an equilateral triangle and find the area. Next form a square and find the area. Then do the same for a regular pentagon, a regular hexagon, and a regular decagon. What is happening to the area? **See margin.**
    b. Predict and then find the areas of a regular 60-gon and a regular 120-gon. **about 286.2 cm^2, about 286.4 cm^2**
    c. Graph the area A as a function of the number of sides n. The graph approaches a limiting value. What shape do you think will have the greatest area? What will that area be? **See margin for art; circle; about 286.5 cm^2.**

46. **CHALLENGE** Two regular polygons both have n sides. One of the polygons is inscribed in, and the other is circumscribed about, a circle of radius r. Find the area between the two polygons in terms of n and r.
$$A = r^2 n\left[\tan\left(\frac{180^\circ}{n}\right) - \cos\left(\frac{180^\circ}{n}\right)\sin\left(\frac{180^\circ}{n}\right)\right]$$

MIXED REVIEW

PREVIEW Prepare for Lesson 11.7 in Exs. 47–51.

A jar contains 10 red marbles, 6 blue marbles, and 2 white marbles. Find the probability of the event described. *(p. 893)*

47. You randomly choose one red marble from the jar, put it back in the jar, and then randomly choose a red marble. $\frac{25}{81}$

48. You randomly choose one blue marble from the jar, keep it, and then randomly choose one white marble. $\frac{2}{51}$

Find the ratio of the width to the length of the rectangle. Then simplify the ratio. *(p. 356)*

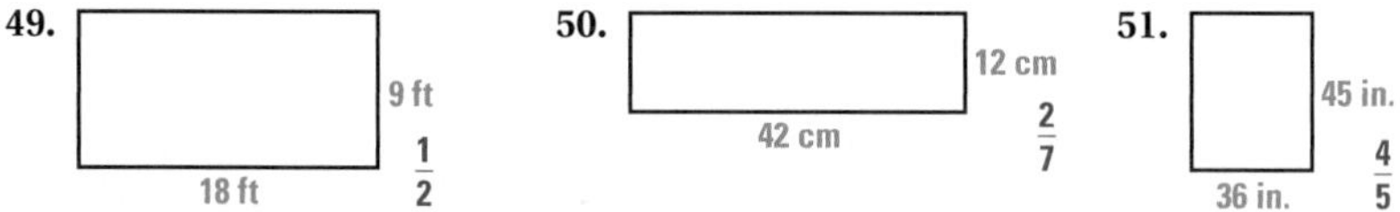

52. The vertices of quadrilateral $ABCD$ are $A(-3, 3)$, $B(1, 1)$, $C(1, -3)$, and $D(-3, -1)$. Draw $ABCD$ and determine whether it is a parallelogram. *(p. 522)* **See margin for art; parallelogram**

52.

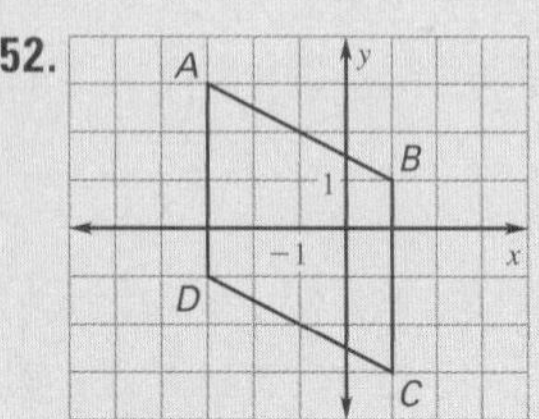

Spreadsheet **ACTIVITY** *Use after Lesson 11.6*

@HomeTutor classzone.com Keystrokes

11.6 Perimeter and Area of Polygons

MATERIALS • computer

QUESTION **How can you use a spreadsheet to find perimeters and areas of regular *n*-gons?**

First consider a regular octagon with radius 1.

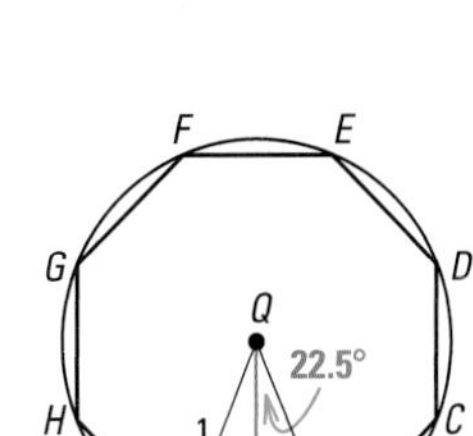

Because there are 8 central angles, $m\angle JQB$ is $\frac{1}{2}\left(\frac{360^\circ}{8}\right) = \frac{180^\circ}{8}$, or 22.5°.

You can express the side length and apothem using trigonometric functions.

$\sin 22.5^\circ = \frac{JB}{QB} = \frac{JB}{1} = JB$ $\qquad$ $\cos 22.5^\circ = \frac{QJ}{QB} = \frac{QJ}{1} = QJ$

So, **side length** $s = 2(JB) = 2 \cdot \sin 22.5^\circ$ $\qquad$ So, **apothem** a is $QJ = \cos 22.5^\circ$

Perimeter $P = 8s = 8(2 \cdot \sin 22.5^\circ) = 16 \cdot \sin 22.5^\circ$

Area $A = \frac{1}{2}aP = \frac{1}{2}(\cos 22.5^\circ)(16 \cdot \sin 22.5^\circ) = 8(\cos 22.5^\circ)(\sin 22.5^\circ)$

Using these steps for any regular n-gon inscribed in a circle of radius 1 gives

$$P = 2n \cdot \sin\left(\frac{180^\circ}{n}\right) \quad \text{and} \quad A = n \cdot \sin\left(\frac{180^\circ}{n}\right) \cdot \cos\left(\frac{180^\circ}{n}\right).$$

Standards

8.0 Students know, derive, and **solve problems involving the perimeter**, circumference, **area**, volume, lateral area, and surface area **of common geometric figures.**

21.0 Students prove and **solve problems regarding** relationships among chords, secants, tangents, inscribed angles, and **inscribed** and circumscribed **polygons of circles.**

EXAMPLE **Use a spreadsheet to find measures of regular *n*-gons**

STEP 1 ***Make a table*** Use a spreadsheet to make a table with three columns.

	A	B	C
1	Number of sides	Perimeter	Area
2	n	2*n*sin(180/n)	n*sin(180/n)*cos(180/n)
3	3	=2*A3*sin(180/A3)	=A3*sin(180/A3)*cos(180/A3)
4	=A3+1	=2*A4*sin(180/A4)	=A4*sin(180/A4)*cos(180/A4)

If your spreadsheet uses radian measure, use "pi()" instead of "180."

STEP 2 ***Enter formulas*** Enter the formulas shown in cells A4, B3, and C3. Then use the Fill Down feature to create more rows.

PRACTICE

1. What shape do the regular n-gons approach as the value of n gets very large? *Explain* your reasoning. **Circle; the more sides there are, the smaller the central angle is, making the shape more circular.**
2. What value do the perimeters approach as the value of n gets very large? *Explain* how this result justifies the formula for the circumference of a circle.
3. What value do the areas approach as the value of n gets very large? *Explain* how this result justifies the formula for the area of a circle.

2. 2π; $r = 1$ **and as** n **increases the value of** $n \cdot \sin\left(\frac{180}{n}\right)$ **approaches** π, **which suggests that if the number of sides were infinitely large, the circumference would be** $2\pi r$.

3. π; $r = 1$ **so** $r^2 = 1$, **and as** n **increases the value of** $n \cdot \sin\left(\frac{180}{n}\right) \cdot \sin\left(\frac{180}{n}\right)$ **approaches** π, **which suggests that if the number of sides were infinitely large, the area would be** πr^2.

1 PLAN AND PREPARE

Learn the Method

- Students will use a spreadsheet to find perimeters and areas of regular n-gons.
- Students can use a spreadsheet to check their answers to Exercises 14–16, 19–21, and 23–25 in Lesson 11.6.

2 TEACH

Tips for Success

Emphasize the need to enter the formulas carefully, using appropriate symbols for multiplication, division, and grouping.

Extra Example

Ask students to make a spreadsheet to find the measures of the interior angles of regular n-gons. **The spreadsheet should have two columns. Column A would be Number of sides, then n, 3, A3+1. Column B would be Measure of interior angle and then 180−360/n, 180−360/A3, 180−360/A4.**

3 ASSESS AND RETEACH

Find the perimeter and area of a regular 50-gon with radius 1 unit. **6.3 units; 3.1 units^2**

1 PLAN AND PREPARE

Explore the Concept

- Students will find geometric probabilities.
- This activity leads into the study of geometric probability in Lesson 11.7, Example 3.

Materials

Each student or group of students will need:

- graph paper
- small dried bean
- Activity Support Master (*Chapter 11 Resource Book*, p. 91)

Recommended Time

Work activity: 15 min

Discuss results: 5 min

Grouping

Students can work individually or in groups of two. If students work in groups, they can alternate tossing the bean and recording the data.

2 TEACH

Tips for Success

Emphasize the need to perform the experiment 50 or more times.

Key Question

- What will happen if you perform the experiment many, many times? **The experimental probability will approach the theoretical probability.**

Key Discovery

As the number of tosses increases, the experimental probability approaches the theoretical probability.

3 ASSESS AND RETEACH

For this exploration, what does a theoretical probability of 0.5 represent? **The sum of the areas of the polygons is half of the area of the target.**

11.7 Investigate Geometric Probability

Standards

8.0 Students know, derive, and **solve problems involving** the perimeter, circumference, **area**, volume, lateral area, and surface area **of common geometric figures.**

MATERIALS • graph paper • small dried bean

QUESTION How do theoretical and experimental probabilities compare?

EXPLORE Find geometric probabilities

STEP 1 ***Draw a target*** On a piece of graph paper, make a target by drawing some polygons. Choose polygons whose area you can calculate and make them as large as possible. Shade in the polygons. An example is shown.

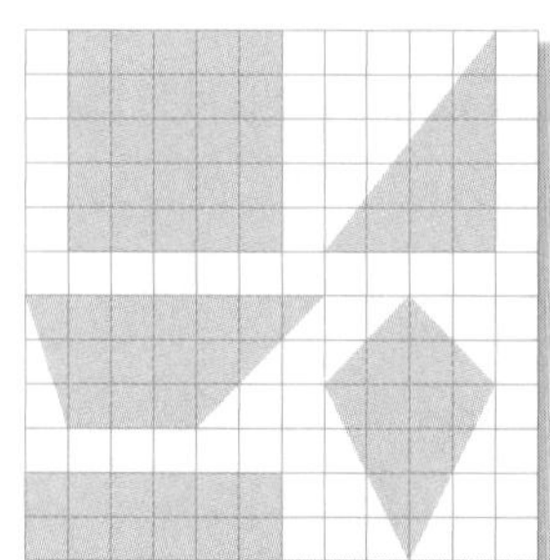

Sample target

STEP 2 ***Calculate theoretical probability*** Calculate the *theoretical* probability that a randomly tossed bean that lands on the target will land in a shaded region.

$$\text{Theoretical probability} = \frac{\text{Sum of areas of polygons}}{\text{Area of paper}}$$

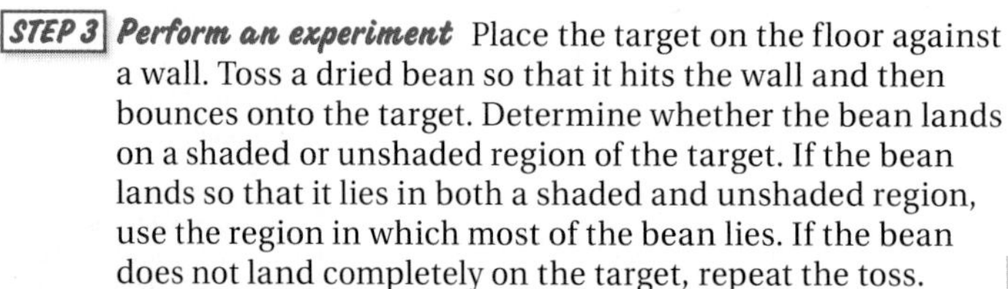

STEP 3 ***Perform an experiment*** Place the target on the floor against a wall. Toss a dried bean so that it hits the wall and then bounces onto the target. Determine whether the bean lands on a shaded or unshaded region of the target. If the bean lands so that it lies in both a shaded and unshaded region, use the region in which most of the bean lies. If the bean does not land completely on the target, repeat the toss.

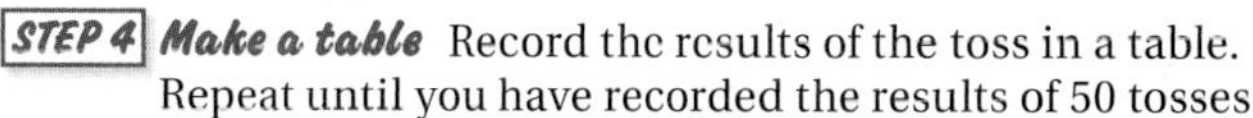

STEP 4 ***Make a table*** Record the results of the toss in a table. Repeat until you have recorded the results of 50 tosses.

Toss	Shaded area	Unshaded area
1	X	
2		X
...	...	...
50	X	

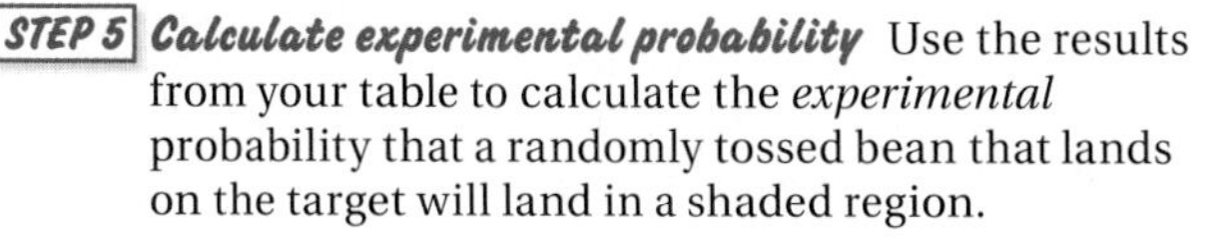

STEP 5 ***Calculate experimental probability*** Use the results from your table to calculate the *experimental* probability that a randomly tossed bean that lands on the target will land in a shaded region.

$$\text{Experimental probability} = \frac{\text{Number of times a bean landed on a shaded region}}{\text{Total number of tosses}}$$

DRAW CONCLUSIONS Use your observations to complete these exercises

1. *Compare* the theoretical probability from Step 2 with the experimental probability from Step 5. What do you notice? **Check students' work.**
2. Repeat Steps 3–5, this time using only 10 tosses. Calculate the experimental probability for those 10 tosses. *Compare* the experimental probability and the theoretical probability. **Check students' work.**
3. **REASONING** How does the number of tosses affect the relationship between the experimental and theoretical probabilities? *Explain.* **See margin.**

3. The more tosses you have, the closer the experimental probability should be to the theoretical probability. The theoretical probability is based on facts, where as the experimental probability is based on the number of trials. Therefore the theory is that, the more trials you do, the closer the experimental probability should get to the theoretical probability.

11.7 Use Geometric Probability

Before You found lengths and areas.

Now You will use lengths and areas to find geometric probabilities.

Why? So you can calculate real-world probabilities, as in Example 2.

Key Vocabulary
- probability
- geometric probability

Standards

8.0 Students know, derive, and **solve problems involving the** perimeter, circumference, **area,** volume, lateral area, and surface area **of common geometric figures.**

The **probability** of an event is a measure of the likelihood that the event will occur. It is a number between 0 and 1, inclusive, and can be expressed as a fraction, decimal, or percent. The probability of event A is written as $P(A)$.

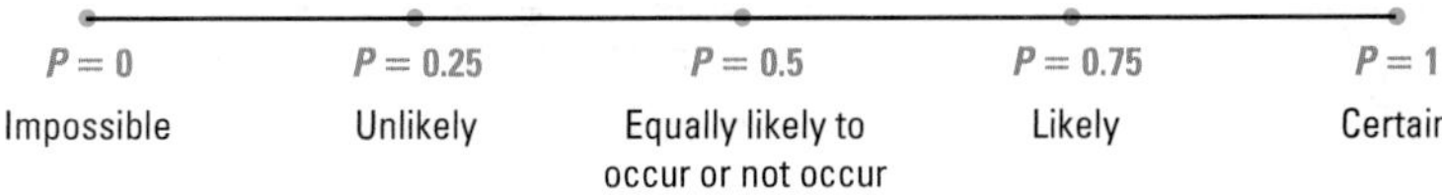

In a previous course, you may have found probability by calculating the ratio of the number of favorable outcomes to the total number of possible outcomes. In this lesson, you will find *geometric probabilities.*

A **geometric probability** is a ratio that involves a geometric measure such as length or area.

KEY CONCEPT — For Your Notebook

Probability and Length

Let $\overline{AB}$ be a segment that contains the segment $\overline{CD}$. If a point K on $\overline{AB}$ is chosen at random, then the probability that it is on $\overline{CD}$ is the ratio of the length of $\overline{CD}$ to the length of $\overline{AB}$.

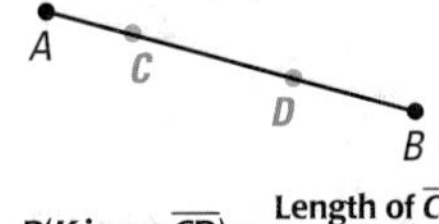

$$P(K \text{ is on } \overline{CD}) = \frac{\text{Length of } \overline{CD}}{\text{Length of } \overline{AB}}$$

Animated Geometry at classzone.com

EXAMPLE 1 Use lengths to find a geometric probability

USE A FORMULA
To apply the geometric probability formulas on this page and on page 772, you need to know that every point on the segment or in the region is *equally likely* to be chosen.

Find the probability that a point chosen at random on $\overline{PQ}$ is on $\overline{RS}$.

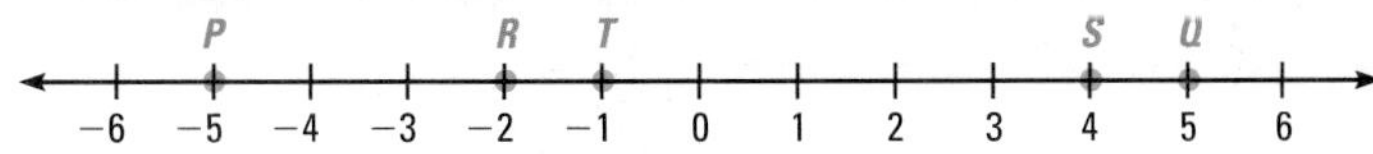

Solution

$$P(\text{Point is on } \overline{RS}) = \frac{\text{Length of } \overline{RS}}{\text{Length of } \overline{PQ}} = \frac{|4-(-2)|}{|5-(-5)|} = \frac{6}{10} = \frac{3}{5}, \text{ 0.6, or } 60\%.$$

1 PLAN AND PREPARE

Warm-Up Exercises

Transparency Available

1. Find the area of a circle with radius 5.2 cm. **84.9 cm^2**
2. Find the area of a right triangle with hypotenuse 18 in. and side length 8 in. **64.5 in.^{2}**
3. A rectangle with sides 4 inches and 5 inches is cut out of a square with sides 8 inches. Find the area that remains. **44 in.^{2}**

Notetaking Guide

Transparency Available

Promotes interactive learning and notetaking skills, pp. 304–307.

Pacing

Basic: 2 days
Average: 2 days
Advanced: 2 days
Block: 1 block
- See *Teaching Guide/Lesson Plan.*

2 FOCUS AND MOTIVATE

Essential Question

Big Idea 1, p. 719

How do you find the probability that a point randomly selected in a region is in a particular part of that region? **Tell students they will learn how to answer this question by comparing the measure of the part of the region to the measure of the entire region.**

Resource Planning Guide

Chapter Resource Book
- Teaching Guide/Lesson Plan (pp. 89–90)
- Practice levels A, B, C (pp. 92–97)
- Study Guide (pp. 98–99)
- Catch-up for Absent Students (p. 100)
- Problem Solving Workshop (p. 101)
- Challenge (p. 102)

Workbooks
- Notetaking Guide (pp. 304–307)
- Practice Workbook (pp. 223–225)

Teaching Options
- **Power Presentations CD-ROM** provides dynamic electronic teaching resources for the classroom.
- **Activity Generator CD-ROM** provides editable activities for all ability levels.

Interactive Technology
- Easy Planner
- Power Presentations CD-ROM
- Activity Generator CD-ROM
- Animated Geometry
- Test Generator CD-ROM
- Online Quiz
- eWorkbook
- eEdition
- @HomeTutor

Resources for English Learners
- Quick Reference for English Learners
- Spanish Study Guide
- Multi-Language Visual Glossary
- Student Resources in Spanish

See also the *Geometry Toolkit* for more strategies for meeting individual needs.

Motivating the Lesson

Draw two different-sized squares. Divide one in quarters using the diagonals and divide the other in quarters using horizontal segments. Shade one fourth of each square. Tell students that each square is a dartboard, and discuss with them whether one target is better than the other for hitting the shaded area. Tell students that this lesson explores and extends that question.

3 TEACH

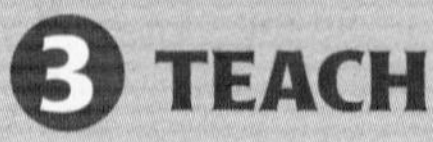

An **Animated Geometry** activity is available on-line for the **Key Concept**. This activity is also available on the **Power Presentations CD-ROM**.

Extra Example 1

Find the probability that a point chosen at random on $\overline{AE}$ is on $\overline{CD}$.

A B C D E

−4 −2 0 2 4 6

$\frac{3}{8}$ or 37.5%

Extra Example 2

A train leaves a station every 30 minutes. Your trip to the office takes 18 minutes. One morning you arrive at the station at 8:15. You need to be at work by 8:45. What is the probability that you will be there by 8:45? $\frac{2}{5}$ or 40%

Key Questions to Ask for Example 2

- What do the numbers 0–12 below the number line represent? **the number of minutes you may wait for a monorail**
- What do the numbers 8:46–8:58 represent? **what time it is as you wait**

EXAMPLE 2 Use a segment to model a real-world probability

MONORAIL A monorail runs every 12 minutes. The ride from the station near your home to the station near your work takes 9 minutes. One morning, you arrive at the station near your home at 8:46. You want to get to the station near your work by 8:58. What is the probability you will get there by 8:58?

Solution

STEP 1 **Find** the longest you can wait for the monorail and still get to the station near your work by 8:58. The ride takes 9 minutes, so you need to catch the monorail no later than 9 minutes before 8:58, or by 8:49. The longest you can wait is 3 minutes (8:49 − 8:46 = 3 min).

STEP 2 **Model** the situation. The monorail runs every 12 minutes, so it will arrive in 12 minutes or less. You need it to arrive within 3 minutes.

Time	8:46		8:48		8:50		8:52		8:54		8:56		8:58
Minutes waiting	0	1	2	3	4	5	6	7	8	9	10	11	12

The monorail needs to arrive within the first 3 minutes.

STEP 3 **Find** the probability.

$$P(\text{You get to the station by 8:58}) = \frac{\text{Favorable waiting time}}{\text{Maximum waiting time}} = \frac{3}{12} = \frac{1}{4}$$

▶ The probability that you will get to the station by 8:58 is $\frac{1}{4}$, or 25%.

✓ GUIDED PRACTICE for Examples 1 and 2

Find the probability that a point chosen at random on $\overline{PQ}$ is on the given segment. Express your answer as a fraction, a decimal, and a percent.

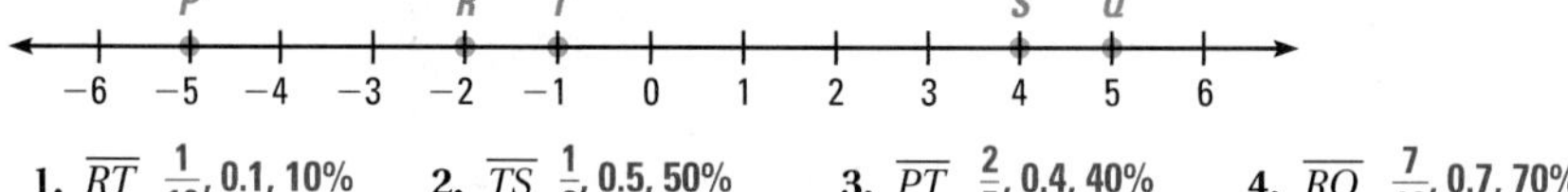

1. $\overline{RT}$ $\frac{1}{10}$, 0.1, 10%
2. $\overline{TS}$ $\frac{1}{2}$, 0.5, 50%
3. $\overline{PT}$ $\frac{2}{5}$, 0.4, 40%
4. $\overline{RQ}$ $\frac{7}{10}$, 0.7, 70%
5. **WHAT IF?** In Example 2, suppose you arrive at the station near your home at 8:43. What is the probability that you will get to the station near your work by 8:58? $\frac{1}{2}$ or 50%

PROBABILITY AND AREA Another formula for geometric probability involves the ratio of the areas of two regions.

KEY CONCEPT *For Your Notebook*

Probability and Area

Let J be a region that contains region M. If a point K in J is chosen at random, then the probability that it is in region M is the ratio of the area of M to the area of J.

$$P(K \text{ is in region } M) = \frac{\text{Area of } M}{\text{Area of } J}$$

EXAMPLE 3 Use areas to find a geometric probability

ARCHERY The diameter of the target shown at the right is 80 centimeters. The diameter of the red circle on the target is 16 centimeters. An arrow is shot and hits the target. If the arrow is equally likely to land on any point on the target, what is the probability that it lands in the red circle?

Solution

ANOTHER WAY All circles are similar and the Area of Similar Polygons Theorem also applies to circles. The ratio of radii is 8:40, or 1:5, so the ratio of areas is $1^2:5^2$, or 1:25.

Find the ratio of the area of the red circle to the area of the target.

$$P(\text{arrow lands in red region}) = \frac{\text{Area of red circle}}{\text{Area of target}} = \frac{\pi(8^2)}{\pi(40^2)} = \frac{64\pi}{1600\pi} = \frac{1}{25}$$

▶ The probability that the arrow lands in the red region is $\frac{1}{25}$, or 4%.

EXAMPLE 4 Estimate area on a grid to find a probability

SCALE DRAWING Your dog dropped a ball in a park. A scale drawing of the park is shown. If the ball is equally likely to be anywhere in the park, estimate the probability that it is in the field.

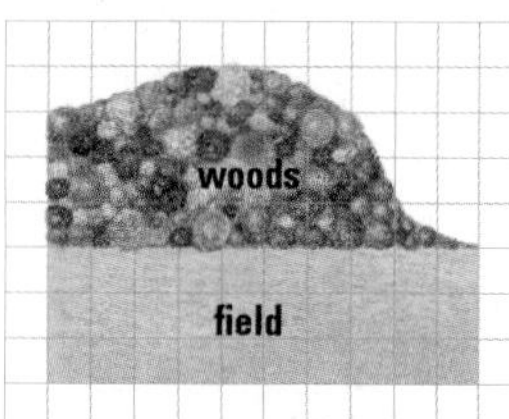

Solution

STEP 1 **Find** the area of the field. The shape is a rectangle, so the area is $bh = 10 \cdot 3 = 30$ square units.

STEP 2 **Find** the total area of the park.

Count the squares that are fully covered. There are 30 squares in the field and 22 in the woods. So, there are 52 full squares.

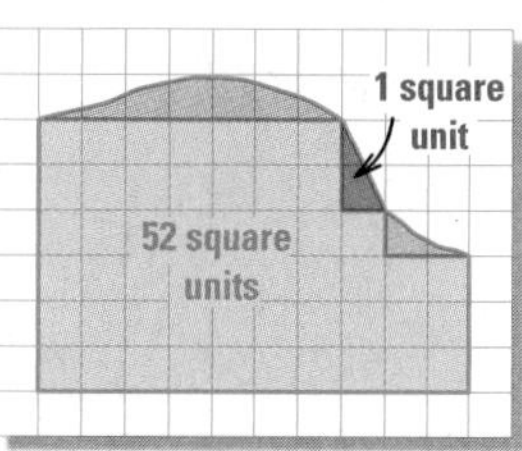

Make groups of partially covered squares so the combined area of each group is about 1 square unit. The total area of the partial squares is about 6 or 7 square units. So, use $52 + 6.5 = 58.5$ square units for the total area.

CHECK RESULTS The ball must be either in the field or in the woods, so check that the probabilities in Example 4 and Guided Practice Exercise 7 add up to 100%.

STEP 3 **Write** a ratio of the areas to find the probability.

$$P(\text{ball in field}) = \frac{\text{Area of field}}{\text{Total area of park}} \approx \frac{30}{58.5} = \frac{300}{585} = \frac{20}{39}$$

▶ The probability that the ball is in the field is about $\frac{20}{39}$, or 51.3%.

✓ **GUIDED PRACTICE** for Examples 3 and 4

6. In the target in Example 3, each ring is 8 centimeters wide. Find the probability that an arrow lands in a black region. **$\frac{14}{25}$ or 56%**
7. In Example 4, estimate the probability that the ball is in the woods. **$\frac{19}{39}$ or about 48.7%**

Extra Example 3

A dart game uses a target with concentric circles of radii 5, 8, and 12 inches. A dart is thrown toward the target. If the dart is equally likely to land on any point of the target, what is the probability that it will earn 20 points? **$\frac{25}{144}$ or 17.4%**

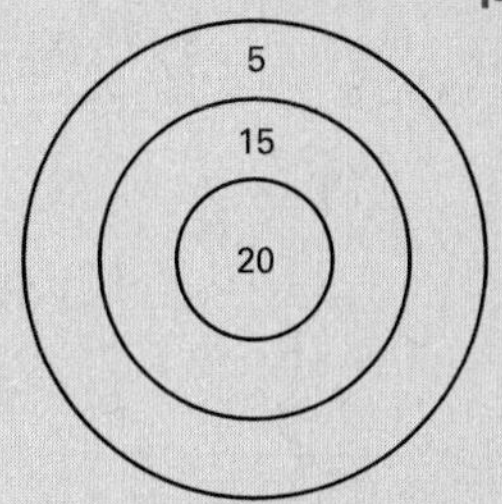

Extra Example 4

A community sets aside a sanctuary area for birds. If a bird is equally likely to be anywhere in the sanctuary, estimate the probability that it will be in the wooded area.

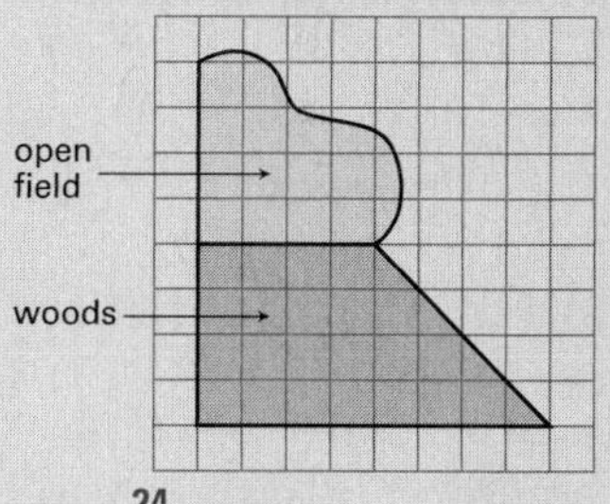

about $\frac{24}{38}$ or 63%

Key Question to Ask for Example 4

- Is the probability exact or an estimate? How do you know? **It is an estimate; the measures of the areas are estimates.**

Closing the Lesson

Have students summarize the major points of the lesson and answer the Essential Question: How do you find the probability that a point randomly selected in a region is in a particular part of that region?

- **The probability of an event is a measure of the likelihood that an event will occur. It is a number between 0 and 1, inclusive.**
- **Geometric probability is a ratio involving lengths or areas.**

Find the ratio of the measure of the specific part of the region to the measure of the entire region.

Differentiated Instruction

Inclusion Some students may need assistance with **Guided Practice Exercise 6**. Instruct them to draw a large diagram of the target. Ask students to think about how they can find the area of one of the black rings. Lead them to realize they must first find the area of the circle defined by the outer edge of the black ring and then subtract the area of the circle defined by the inner edge of that ring. They will do this twice—once for each black ring on the target.

See also the *Geometry Toolkit* for more strategies.

4 PRACTICE AND APPLY

Assignment Guide

Answer Transparencies available for all exercises

Basic:
Day 1: SRH p. 893 Exs. 1–5
pp. 774–777
Exs. 1–7, 16–19, 31–33, 42–44
Day 2: pp. 774–777
Exs. 8–15, 20–22, 30, 34, 35, 39–41

Average:
Day 1: pp. 774–777
Exs. 1–7, 16–19, 31–33, 36, 42–44
Day 2: pp. 774–777
Exs. 8–15, 21–26, 30, 34, 35–39 odd

Advanced:
Day 1: pp. 774–777
Exs. 1–7, 16–19, 29*, 31–33, 36, 42, 44
Day 2: pp. 774–777
Exs. 8–10, 13–15, 22–28, 30, 34, 35, 37, 38*, 41

Block:
pp. 774–777
Exs. 1–19, 21–26, 30–37, 39, 42–44

Differentiated Instruction

See *Geometry Best Practices Toolkit* for suggestions on addressing the needs of a diverse classroom.

Homework Check

For a quick check of student understanding of key concepts, go over the following exercises:
Basic: 4, 8, 12, 30, 31
Average: 6, 11, 13, 31, 32
Advanced: 7, 10, 14, 31, 34

Extra Practice

- Student Edition, p. 917
- Chapter 11 Resource Book: Practice levels A, B, C, pp. 92–97

Practice Worksheet

An easily-readable reduced practice page (with answers) for this lesson can be found on p. 718F.

11.7 EXERCISES

HOMEWORK KEY
○ = WORKED-OUT SOLUTIONS on p. WS16 for Exs. 3, 9, and 33
★ = STANDARDIZED TEST PRACTICE Exs. 2, 7, 23, 34, and 35

SKILL PRACTICE

A

1. **VOCABULARY** Copy and complete: If an event cannot occur, its probability is _?_. If an event is certain to occur, its probability is _?_. **0, 1**

2. ★ **WRITING** *Compare* a geometric probability and a probability found by dividing the number of favorable outcomes by the total number of possible outcomes. **See margin.**

EXAMPLE 1 on p. 771 for Exs. 3–7

PROBABILITY ON A SEGMENT **In Exercises 3–6, find the probability that a point K, selected randomly on $\overline{AE}$, is on the given segment. Express your answer as a fraction, decimal, and percent.**

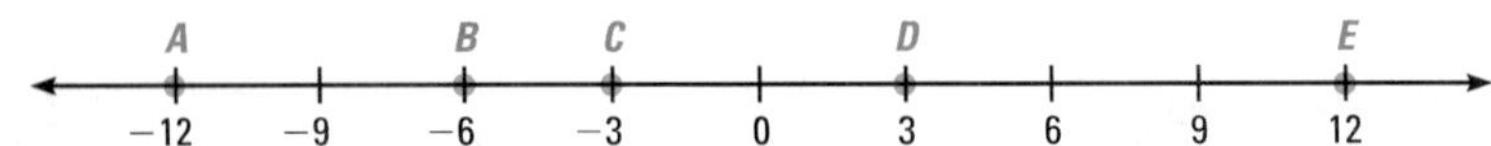

3. $\overline{AD}$ **$\frac{5}{8}$, 0.625, 62.5%**
4. $\overline{BC}$ **$\frac{1}{8}$, 0.125, 12.5%**
5. $\overline{DE}$ **$\frac{3}{8}$, 0.375, 37.5%**
6. $\overline{AE}$ **1, 1.0, 100%**

7. ★ **WRITING** Look at your answers to Exercises 3 and 5. *Describe* how the two probabilities are related. **$AD + DE = AE$, so $\frac{5}{8} + \frac{3}{8} = 1$**

EXAMPLE 3 on p. 773 for Exs. 8–11

FIND A GEOMETRIC PROBABILITY **Find the probability that a randomly chosen point in the figure lies in the shaded region.**

8. 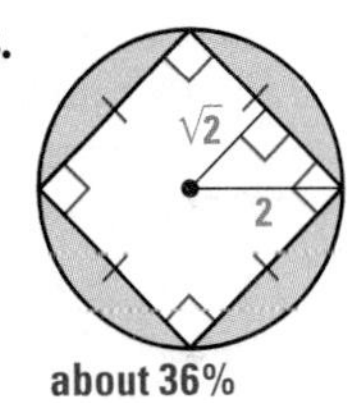

about 36%

9. 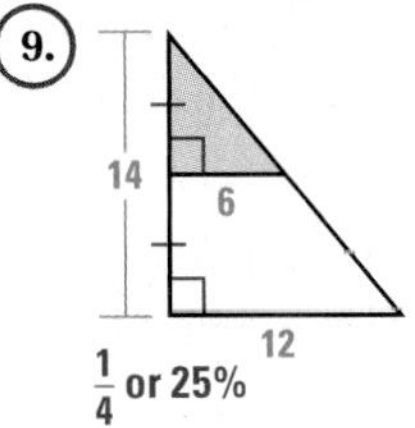

$\frac{1}{4}$ or 25%

10. 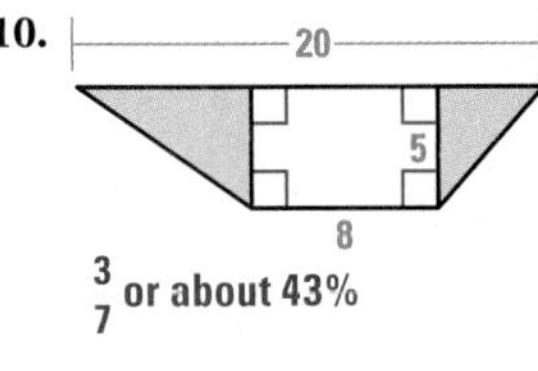

$\frac{3}{7}$ or about 43%

11. **ERROR ANALYSIS** Three sides of the rectangle are tangent to the semicircle. *Describe* and correct the error in finding the probability that a randomly chosen point in the figure lies in the shaded region. **See margin.**

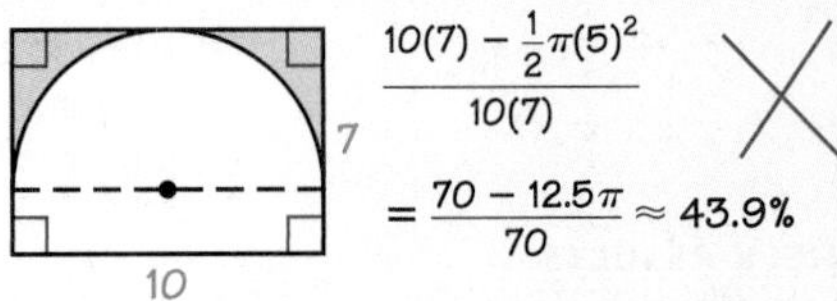

EXAMPLE 4 on p. 773 for Exs. 12–14

ESTIMATING AREA **Use the scale drawing.**

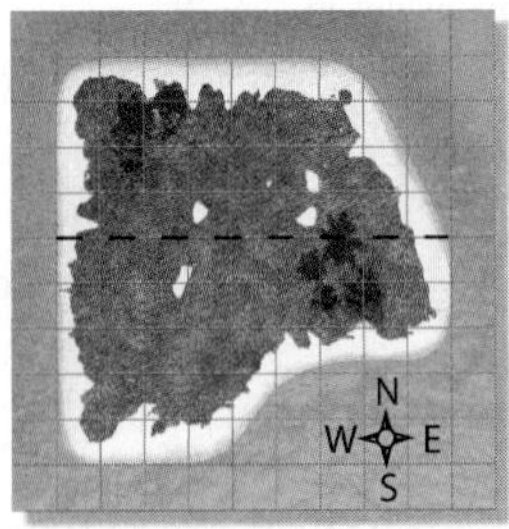

12. What is the approximate area of the north side of the island? the south side of the island? the whole island? ***Sample answers:* 31.5 units^2, 32.5 units^2, 64 units^2**

13. Find the probability that a randomly chosen location on the island lies on the north side.

13. $\frac{63}{128}$ or about 49.2%

14. Find the probability that a randomly chosen location on the island lies on the south side. **$\frac{65}{128}$ or about 50.8%**

2. Geometric probability is very similar to regular probability. Regular probability is found by taking the number of favorable outcomes divided by the total possible outcomes. Geometric probability is done by taking the probability of an event occurring in a specific region (on a line or in an area) and dividing it by the entire area possible.

11. There is more than a semicircle in the rectangle, so you need to take the area of the rectangle minus the sum of the area of the semicircle and the area of a small rectangle located under the semicircle that has dimensions of 10 × 2;

$$\frac{10(7) - \left(\frac{1}{2}\pi(5)^2 + 10(2)\right)}{7(10)} = \frac{70 - (12.5\pi + 20)}{70} \approx 0.153 \text{ or about } 15.3\%.$$

15. The two triangles are similar by the AA Similarity Postulate and the ratio of sides is the same; 7:14 or 1:2, so the ratio of the areas is 1:4.

B 15. **SIMILAR TRIANGLES** In Exercise 9, how do you know that the shaded triangle is similar to the whole triangle? *Explain* how you can use the Areas of Similar Polygons Theorem to find the desired probability.

ALGEBRA In Exercises 16–19, find the probability that a point chosen at random on the segment satisfies the inequality.

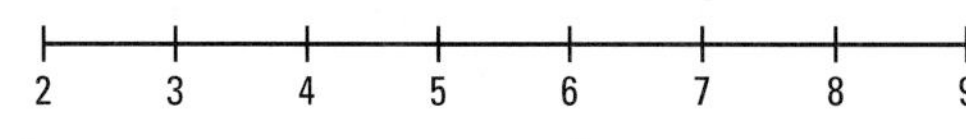

16. $x - 6 \le 1$ $\frac{5}{7}$ **17.** $1 \le 2x - 3 \le 5$ $\frac{2}{7}$ **18.** $\frac{x}{2} \ge 7$ **0** **19.** $3x \le 27$ **1**

FIND A GEOMETRIC PROBABILITY Find the probability that a randomly chosen point in the figure lies in the shaded region. *Explain* your steps. 20–22. See margin.

20.

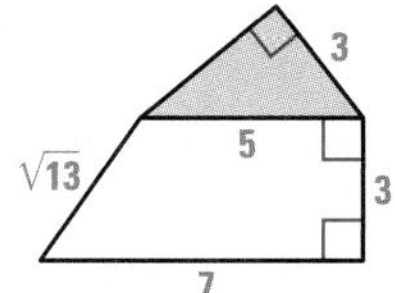

21.

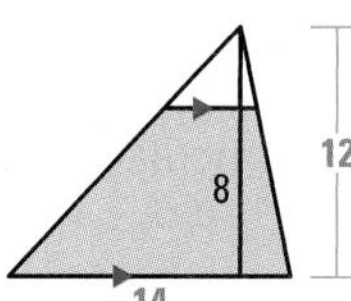

22.

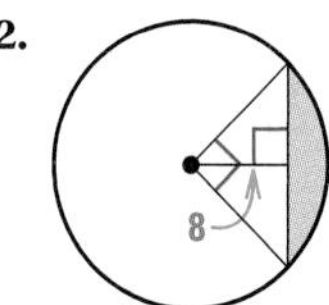

23. ★ **MULTIPLE CHOICE** A point X is chosen at random in region U, and U includes region A. What is the probability that X is not in A? **D**

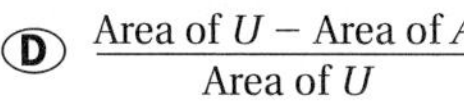

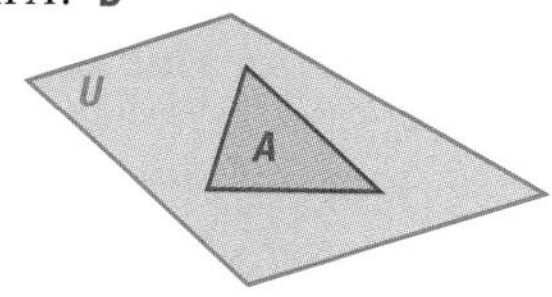

Ⓐ $\frac{\text{Area of } A}{\text{Area of } U}$ Ⓑ $\frac{\text{Area of } A}{\text{Area of } U - \text{Area of } A}$

Ⓒ $\frac{1}{\text{Area of } A}$ Ⓓ $\frac{\text{Area of } U - \text{Area of } A}{\text{Area of } U}$

24. **ARCS AND SECTORS** A sector of a circle intercepts an arc of 80°. Find the probability that a randomly chosen point on the circle lies on the arc. Find the probability that a randomly chosen point in the circle lies in the sector. *Explain* why the probabilities do not depend on the radius. $\frac{2}{9}, \frac{2}{9}$; the circumference and the area of a circle end up canceling with the values in the denominator.

INSCRIBED POLYGONS Find the probability that a randomly chosen point in the circle described lies in the inscribed polygon.

25. Regular hexagon inscribed in circle with circumference $C \approx 188.5$ **about 82.7%**

26. Regular octagon inscribed in circle with radius r **about 90%**

C 27. **INSCRIBED ANGLES** Points A and B are the endpoints of a diameter of ⊙D. Point C is chosen at random from the other points on the circle. What is the probability that $\triangle ABC$ is a right triangle? What is the probability that $m\angle CAB \le 45°$? **100%, 50%**

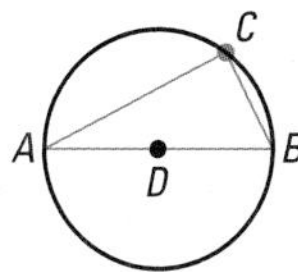

28. **COORDINATE GRAPHS** Graph the system of inequalities $0 \le x \le 2$, $0 \le y \le 3$, and $y \ge x$. If a point (x, y) is chosen at random in the solution region, what is the probability that $x^2 + y^2 \ge 4$? **See margin for art; about 60.7%.**

29. **CHALLENGE** You carry out a series of steps to paint a walking stick. In the first step, you paint half the length of the stick. For each following step, you paint half of the remaining unpainted portion of the stick. After n steps, you choose a point at random on the stick. Find a value of n so that the probability of choosing a point on the painted portion of the stick after the nth step is greater than 99.95%. $n \ge 11$ **steps**

Avoiding Common Errors

Exercises 16–19 If students have difficulty beginning these exercises, point out that they should find the length of the segment that contains the solution points for each inequality, then divide that length by the total length of the segment.

Exercises 20–22 Some students may incorrectly divide the area of the shaded region by the area of the non-shaded region. Remind students that the denominator must be the total area of both regions.

20. $\frac{1}{4}$ **or 25%; find the area of the trapezoid and add it to the area of the triangle to get the area of the whole figure; this becomes the denominator of the probability. The area of the triangle is the area of the shaded region and this is the numerator of the probability.**

21. $\frac{1}{9}$ **or 11.1%; find the area of the whole figure,** $\frac{1}{2}(14)(12) = 84$ **which is the denominator of the fraction. The top triangle is similar to the whole figure by the AA Similarity Postulate, so use proportions to find the base of the small triangle to be** $4\frac{2}{3}$**. Since the height of the small triangle is 4, the area is** $9\frac{1}{3}$**, which is the numerator of the fraction.**

22. About 9.1%; solve for the hypotenuse of the 45°-45°-90° triangle which is also the radius of the circle. Find the area of the circle to be $\pi(8\sqrt{2})^2 = 128\pi$**; this is the denominator of the fraction. Find the area of the sector to be** 32π**. Subtract the area of the triangle from the area of the sector,** $32\pi - 64 \approx 36.5$**; this is the area of the shaded region, which is the numerator of the fraction.**

28.

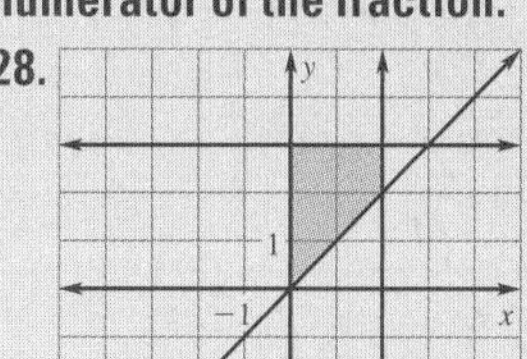

Teaching Strategy

Exercise 30 Point out that the area of the circle is not needed to calculate the probability that the dart hits the inner square, but that it is needed for hitting outside the square in the circle.

Internet Reference

Exercise 34 More information about the Beagle 2 can be found at www.esa.int/SPECIALS/Mars_Express/SEMPM75V9ED_0.html

35. The probability stays the same; the sector takes up the same percent of the area of the circle regardless of the length of the radius. *Sample answer:* Let the central angle be 90° and the radius be 2 units. The probability for that sector is $\frac{\frac{4\pi}{4}}{4\pi} = \frac{1}{4}$. Let the radius be doubled. The probability is $\frac{\frac{16\pi}{4}}{16\pi} = \frac{1}{4}$.

PROBLEM SOLVING

A

30. DARTBOARD A dart is thrown and hits the target shown. If the dart is equally likely to hit any point on the target, what is the probability that it hits inside the inner square? that it hits outside the inner square but inside the circle? **$\frac{1}{9}$ or about 11.1%; about 67.4%**

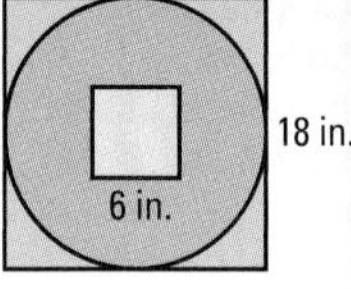

@HomeTutor for problem solving help at classzone.com

EXAMPLE 2 on p. 772 for Exs. 31–33

31. TRANSPORTATION A fair provides a shuttle bus from a parking lot to the fair entrance. Buses arrive at the parking lot every 10 minutes. They wait for 4 minutes while passengers get on and get off. Then the buses depart.

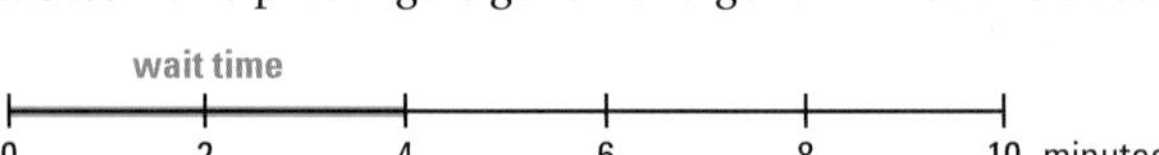

a. What is the probability that there is a bus waiting when a passenger arrives at a random time? **$\frac{2}{5}$ or 40%**

b. What is the probability that there is not a bus waiting when a passenger arrives at a random time? **$\frac{3}{5}$ or 60%**

@HomeTutor for problem solving help at classzone.com

32. FIRE ALARM Suppose that your school day is from 8:00 A.M. until 3:00 P.M. You eat lunch at 12:00 P.M. If there is a fire drill at a random time during the day, what is the probability that it begins before lunch? **$\frac{4}{7}$ or about 57.1%**

33. PHONE CALL You are expecting a call from a friend anytime between 7:00 P.M. and 8:00 P.M. You are practicing the drums and cannot hear the phone from 6:55 P.M. to 7:10 P.M. What is the probability that you missed your friend's call? **$\frac{1}{6}$ or about 16.7%**

B

34. ★ EXTENDED RESPONSE Scientists lost contact with the space probe Beagle 2 when it was landing on Mars in 2003. They have been unable to locate it since. Early in the search, some scientists thought that it was possible, though unlikely, that Beagle had landed in a circular crater inside the planned landing region. The diameter of the crater is 1 km.

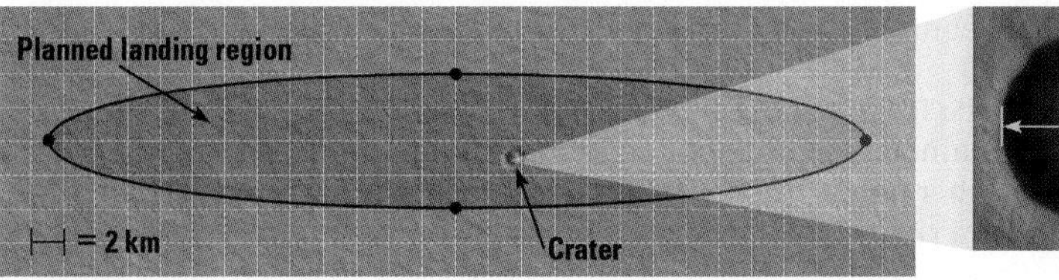

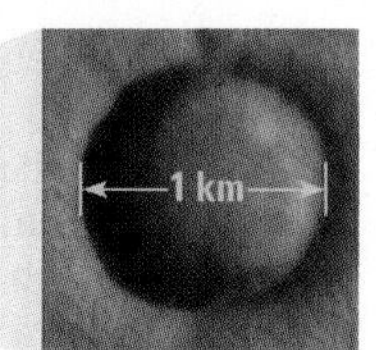

a. In the scale drawing, each square has side length 2 kilometers. Estimate the area of the planned landing region. *Explain* your steps.

34a. About 78 squares or 312 km²; begin by counting all of the whole grid pieces and then estimate the remaining pieces and since 1 grid has an area of 4 square kilometers multiply to get the area.

b. Estimate the probability of Beagle 2 landing in the crater if it was equally likely to land anywhere in the planned landing region. **about 0.25%**

35. ★ SHORT RESPONSE If the central angle of a sector of a circle stays the same and the radius of the circle doubles, what can you conclude about the probability of a randomly selected point being in the sector? *Explain.* Include an example with your explanation. **See margin.**

○ = WORKED-OUT SOLUTIONS on p. WS1 ★ = STANDARDIZED TEST PRACTICE

36. **PROBABILITY AND LENGTH** A 6 inch long rope is cut into two pieces at a random point. Find the probability both pieces are at least 1 inch long. **$\frac{2}{3}$ or about 66.7%**

37. **COMPOUND EVENTS** You throw two darts at the dartboard in Exercise 30 on page 776. Each dart hits the dartboard. The throws are independent of each other. Find the probability of the compound event described.

a. Both darts hit the yellow square. **$\frac{1}{81}$ or about 1.2%**

b. The first dart hits the yellow square and the second hits outside the circle. **about 2.4%**

c. Both darts hit inside the circle but outside the yellow square. **about 45.4%**

C 38. **CHALLENGE** A researcher used a 1 hour tape to record birdcalls. Eight minutes after the recorder was turned on, a 5 minute birdcall began. Later, the researcher accidentally erased 10 continuous minutes of the tape. What is the probability that part of the birdcall was erased? What is the probability that all of the birdcall was erased? **$\frac{23}{60}$ or about 38.3%; $\frac{1}{4}$ or 25%**

MIXED REVIEW

PREVIEW
Prepare for Lesson 12.1 in Exs. 39–41.

39. Draw a concave hexagon and a concave pentagon. *(p. 42)* **See margin.**

Think of each segment shown as part of a line.

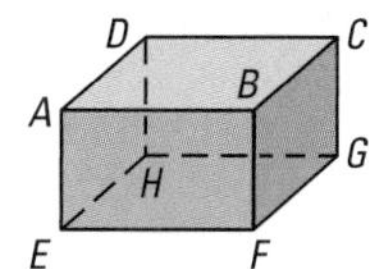

40. Name the intersection of plane *DCH* and plane *ADE*. *(p. 96)* **$\overleftrightarrow{DH}$**

41. Name a plane that appears to be parallel to plane *ADH*. *(p. 147)* ***Sample answer:* plane *BCF***

Find the area of the polygon.

42. *(p. 720)*

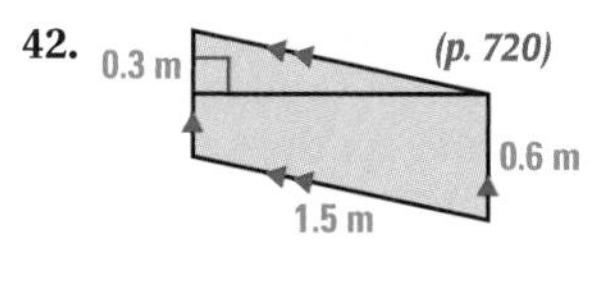

about 0.88 m^2

43. *(p. 730)*

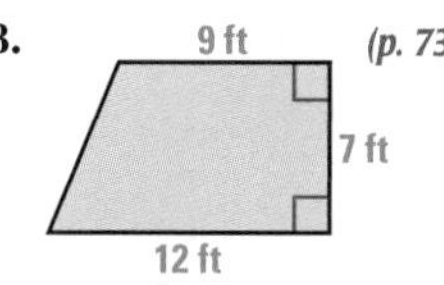

73.5 ft^2

44. *(p. 762)*

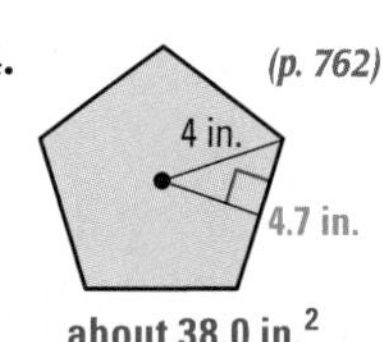

about 38.0 in.^{2}

QUIZ *for Lessons 11.6–11.7*

Find the area of the regular polygon. *(p. 762)*

1. **about 687.4 cm^2**

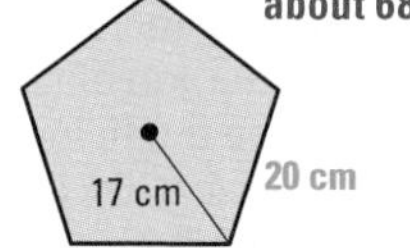

2. **about 1767.8 m^2**

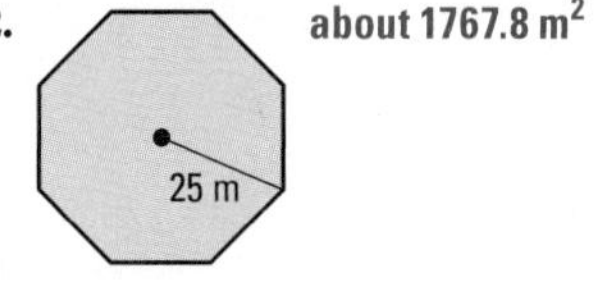

Find the probability that a randomly chosen point in the figure lies in the shaded region. *(p. 771)*

3. **$\frac{9}{100}$ or 9%**

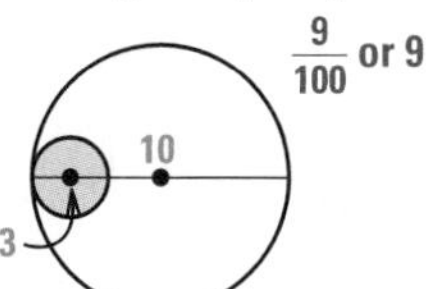

4. **$\frac{4}{5}$ or 80%**

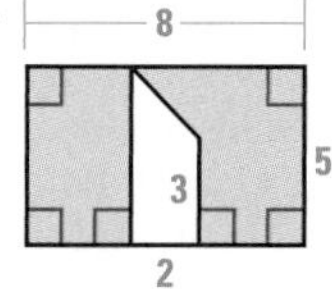

39.

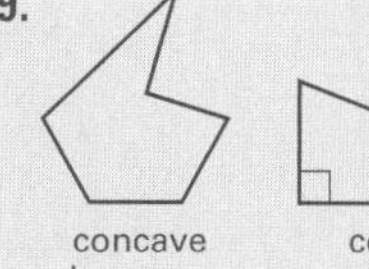

concave hexagon

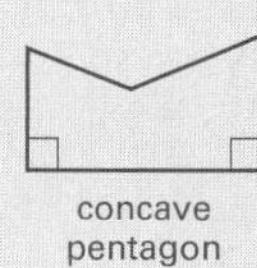

concave pentagon

5 ASSESS AND RETEACH

Daily Homework Quiz

Transparency Available

1. Find the probability that a point chosen at random on $\overline{JN}$ is on $\overline{KN}$.

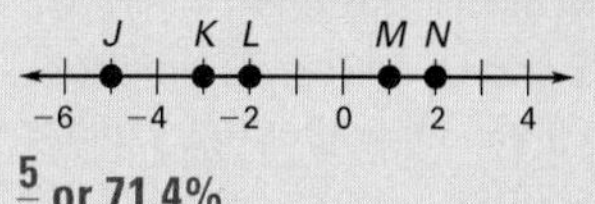

$\frac{5}{7}$ or 71.4%

2. Find the probability that a randomly chosen point in the figure will lie in the shaded region. **36.3%**

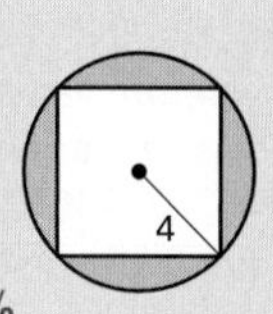

3. A bird is equally likely to be anywhere in the garden shown. What is the probability that the bird will be in the vegetables?

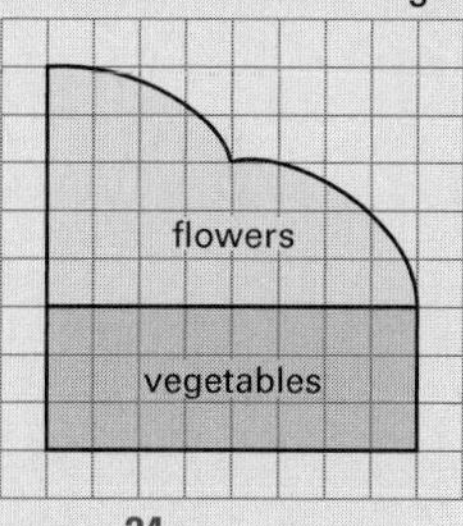

about $\frac{24}{51}$ or 47%

Available at **classzone.com**

Diagnosis/Remediation

- Practice A, B, C in Chapter 11 Resource Book, pp. 92–97
- Study Guide in Chapter 11 Resource Book, pp. 98–99
- Practice Workbook, pp. 223–225
- @HomeTutor

Challenge

Additional challenge is available in the Chapter 11 Resource Book, p. 102.

Quiz

An easily-readable reduced copy of the quiz (with answers) on Lessons 11.6–11.7 from the Assessment Book can be found on p. 718G.

3b. About 12.6 mi; the line the boat makes with the radii of the sector is an isosceles triangle such that the closest distance to the lighthouse is on a line from the lighthouse perpendicular to the line of the boat (the altitude). Use the Pythagorean Theorem to find the length of the altitude.

4b. 25 prizes; 400 times the probability gives the expected number of winners.

5. $4\pi + 2\sqrt{2}\pi$ units; 8π units^2. *Sample answer:* Since the triangle is an isosceles right triangle, the 45°-45°-90° special triangle property tells us that the hypotenuse must be $4\sqrt{2}$ and the legs measure 4. Two of the semicircles have $r = 2$ and the larger semicircle has $r = 2\sqrt{2}$. Use these lengths in the circumference and area formulas.

MIXED REVIEW of Problem Solving

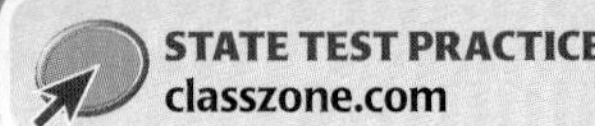

Lessons 11.4–11.7

1. **MULTI-STEP PROBLEM** The Hobby-Eberly optical telescope is located in Fort Davis, Texas. The telescope's primary mirror is made of 91 small mirrors that form a hexagon. Each small mirror is a regular hexagon with side length 0.5 meter.

a. Find the apothem of a small mirror. $\frac{\sqrt{3}}{4}$ m

b. Find the area of one of the small mirrors. about 0.65 m^2

c. Find the area of the primary mirror. about 58.5 m^2

2. **GRIDDED ANSWER** As shown, a circle is inscribed in a regular pentagon. The circle and the pentagon have the same center. Find the area of the shaded region. Round to the nearest tenth. **24.1**

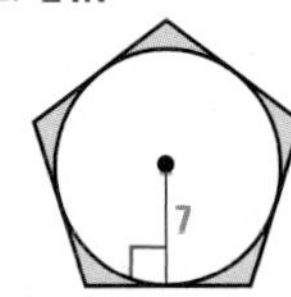

3. **EXTENDED RESPONSE** The diagram shows a projected beam of light from a lighthouse.

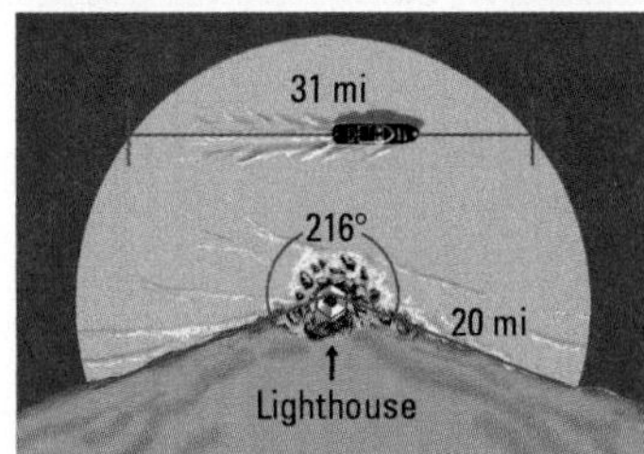

a. Find the area of the water's surface that is illuminated by the lighthouse. about 754.0 mi^2

b. A boat traveling along a straight line is illuminated by the lighthouse for about 31 miles. Find the closest distance between the lighthouse and the boat. *Explain* your steps. **See margin.**

4. **SHORT RESPONSE** At a school fundraiser, a glass jar with a circular base is filled with water. A circular red dish is placed at the bottom of the jar. A person donates a coin by dropping it into the jar. If the coin lands in the dish, the person wins a small prize.

a. Suppose a coin tossed into the jar has an equally likely chance of landing anywhere on the bottom of the jar, including in the dish. What is the probability that it will land in the dish? $\frac{1}{16}$ or 6.25%

b. Suppose 400 coins are dropped into the jar. About how many prizes would you expect people to win? *Explain.* **See margin.**

5. **SHORT RESPONSE** The figure is made of a right triangle and three semicircles. Write expressions for the perimeter and area of the figure in terms of π. *Explain* your reasoning. **See margin.**

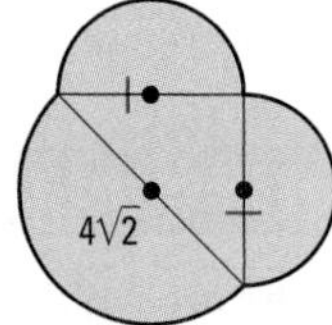

6. **OPEN-ENDED** In general, a fan with a greater area does a better job of moving air and cooling you. The fan below is a sector of a cardboard circle. Give an example of a cardboard fan with a smaller radius that will do a better job of cooling you. The intercepted arc should be less than 180°. *Sample answer:* $r = 8$ cm and an arc of 160°

CHAPTER SUMMARY

BIG IDEAS *For Your Notebook*

Big Idea 1

Using Area Formulas for Polygons

Polygon	Formula	
Triangle	$A = \frac{1}{2}bh$,	with base b and height h
Parallelogram	$A = bh$,	with base b and height h
Trapezoid	$A = \frac{1}{2}h(b_1 + b_2)$,	with bases b_1 and b_2 and height h
Rhombus	$A = \frac{1}{2}d_1d_2$,	with diagonals d_1 and d_2
Kite	$A = \frac{1}{2}d_1d_2$,	with diagonals d_1 and d_2
Regular polygon	$A = \frac{1}{2}a \cdot ns$,	with apothem a, n sides, and side length s

Sometimes you need to use the Pythagorean Theorem, special right triangles, or trigonometry to find a length in a polygon before you can find its area.

Big Idea 2

Relating Length, Perimeter, and Area Ratios in Similar Polygons

You can use ratios of corresponding measures to find other ratios of measures. You can solve proportions to find unknown lengths or areas.

If two figures are similar and ...	then ...
the ratio of side lengths is $a:b$	• the ratio of perimeters is also $a:b$. • the ratio of areas is $a^2:b^2$.
the ratio of perimeters is $c:d$	• the ratio of side lengths is also $c:d$. • the ratio of areas is $c^2:d^2$.
the ratio of areas is $e:f$	• the ratio of side lengths is $\sqrt{e}:\sqrt{f}$. • the ratio of perimeters is $\sqrt{e}:\sqrt{f}$.

Comparing Measures for Parts of Circles and the Whole Circle

Given $\odot P$ with radius r, you can use proportional reasoning to find measures of parts of the circle.

Arc length $\frac{\text{Arc length of } \overparen{AB}}{2\pi r} = \frac{m\overparen{AB}}{360^\circ}$ ← Part ← Whole

Area of sector $\frac{\text{Area of sector } APB}{\pi r^2} = \frac{m\overparen{AB}}{360^\circ}$ ← Part ← Whole

Additional Resources

The following resources are available to help review the materials in this chapter.

Chapter 11 Resource Book
- Chapter Review Games and Activities, p. 103
- Cumulative Practice, Chs. 1–11, pp. 106–107

Student Resources in Spanish

eWorkbook

@HomeTutor

Vocabulary Practice

Vocabulary practice is available at **classzone.com**

Extra Example 11.1

The area of $\triangle RST$ is 152 square units. Find its height h. **16 units**

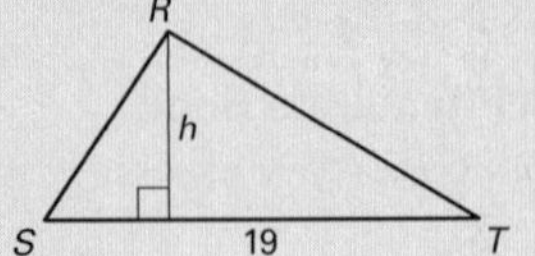

11 CHAPTER REVIEW

@HomeTutor
classzone.com
- Multi-Language Glossary
- Vocabulary practice

REVIEW KEY VOCABULARY

For a list of postulates and theorems, see pp. 926–931.

- bases of a parallelogram, *p. 720*
- height of a parallelogram, *p. 720*
- height of a trapezoid, *p. 730*
- circumference, *p. 746*
- arc length, *p. 747*
- sector of a circle, *p. 756*
- center of a polygon, *p. 762*
- radius of a polygon, *p. 762*
- apothem of a polygon, *p. 762*
- central angle of a regular polygon, *p. 762*
- probability, *p. 771*
- geometric probability, *p. 771*

VOCABULARY EXERCISES

1. Copy and complete: A *sector of a circle* is the region bounded by ___?___. **two radii of a circle and their intercepted arc**
2. **WRITING** *Explain* the relationship between the height of a parallelogram and the bases of a parallelogram. **Either pair of parallel sides can be used as the bases of a parallelogram and the height is the perpendicular distance between them.**

The diagram shows a square inscribed in a circle. Name an example of the given segment.

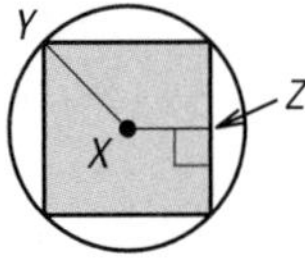

3. An apothem of the square $\overline{XZ}$
4. A radius of the square $\overline{XY}$

REVIEW EXAMPLES AND EXERCISES

Use the review examples and exercises below to check your understanding of the concepts you have learned in each lesson of Chapter 11.

11.1 Areas of Triangles and Parallelograms *pp. 720–726*

EXAMPLE

The area of $\square ABCD$ is 96 square units. Find its height h.

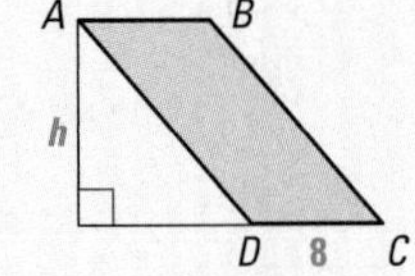

$A = bh$	**Formula for area of a parallelogram**
$96 = 8h$	**Substitute 96 for A and 8 for b.**
$h = 12$	**Solve.**

EXERCISES

EXAMPLES 1, 2, and 3 on pp. 721–722 for Exs. 5–8

Find the area of the polygon.

5. 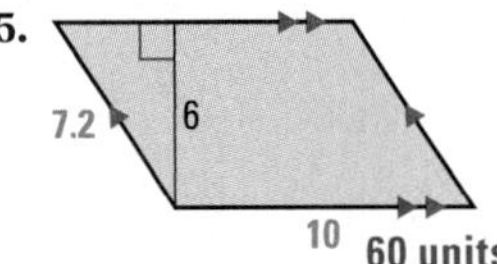

60 units²

6. 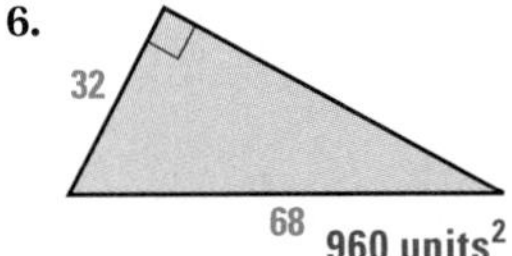

960 units²

7. 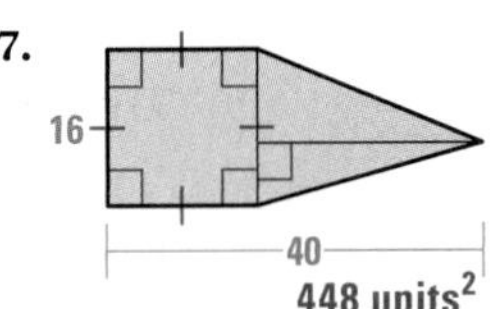

448 units²

8. The area of a triangle is 147 square inches and its height is 1.5 times its base. Find the base and the height of the triangle. **14 in., 21 in.**

11.2 Areas of Trapezoids, Rhombuses, and Kites *pp. 730–736*

EXAMPLE

Find the area of the kite.

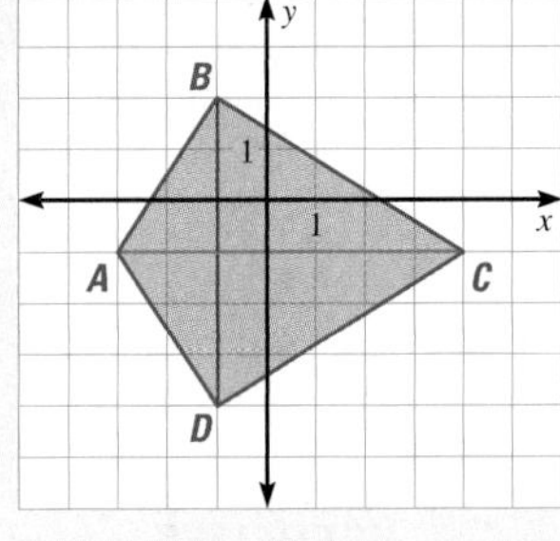

Find the lengths of the diagonals of the kite.

$d_1 = BD = |2 - (-4)| = 6$

$d_2 = AC = |4 - (-3)| = 7$

Find the area of $ABCD$.

$A = \frac{1}{2}d_1d_2$ **Formula for area of a kite**

$= \frac{1}{2}(6)(7) = 21$ **Substitute and simplify.**

▶ The area of the kite is 21 square units.

EXERCISES

EXAMPLE 4 on p. 732 for Exs. 9–11

Graph the polygon with the given vertices and find its area. **9–11. See margin for art.**

9. $L(2, 2), M(6, 2), N(8, 4), P(4, 4)$ **8 units²**

10. $Q(-3, 0), R(-2, 3), S(-1, 0), T(-2, -2)$ **5 units²**

11. $D(-1, 4), E(5, 4), F(3, -2), G(1, -2)$ **24 units²**

11.3 Perimeter and Area of Similar Figures *pp. 737–743*

EXAMPLE

Quadrilaterals *JKLM* and *WXYZ* are similar. Find the ratios (red to blue) of the perimeters and of the areas.

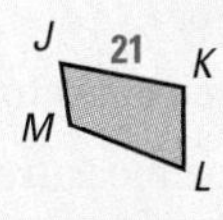

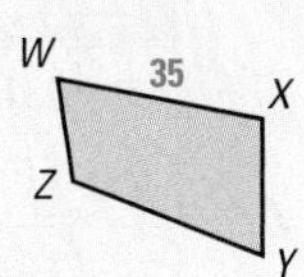

The ratio of the lengths of the corresponding sides is 21 : 35, or 3 : 5. Using Theorem 6.1, the ratio of the perimeters is 3 : 5. Using Theorem 11.7, the ratio of the areas is $3^2 : 5^2$, or 9 : 25.

EXERCISES

EXAMPLES 1, 2, and 3 on pp. 737–738 for Exs. 12–14

The polygons are similar. Find the ratio (red to blue) of the perimeters and of the areas. Then find the unknown area.

12. $\triangle ABC \sim \triangle DEF$ **3 : 4, 9 : 16; 8 ft²**

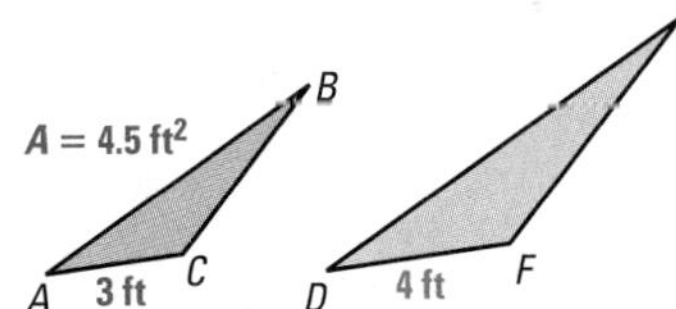

13. $WXYZ \sim ABCD$ **10 : 13, 100 : 169, 152.1 cm²**

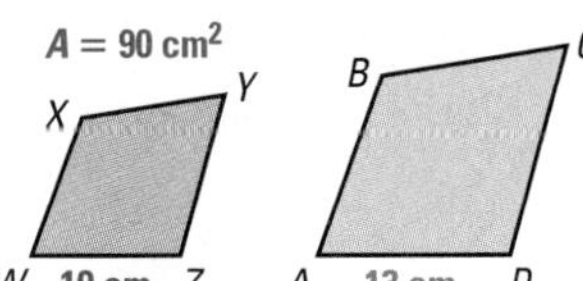

14. The ratio of the areas of two similar figures is 144 : 49. Write the ratio of the lengths of corresponding sides. **12 : 7**

Extra Example 11.2

Find the area of the trapezoid.

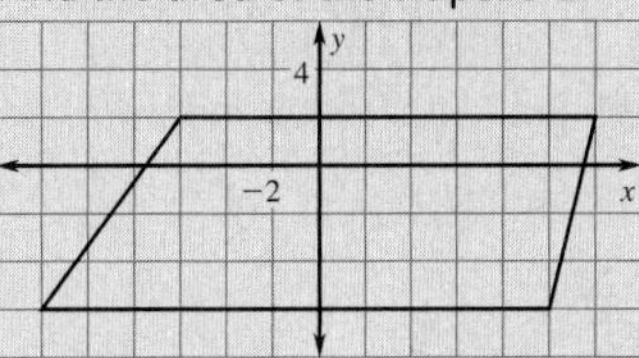

160 square units

Extra Example 11.3

$\triangle ABC$ and $\triangle SRT$ are similar. Find the ratios of the perimeters and areas of $\triangle ABC$ to $\triangle SRT$.

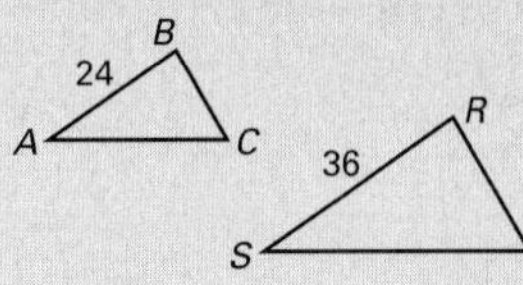

perimeters: 2 : 3; areas: 4 : 9

9.

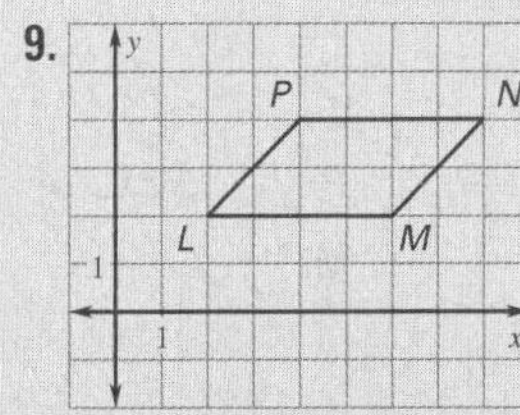

10.

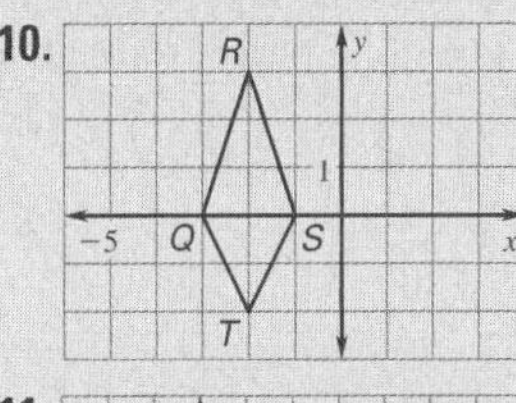

11.

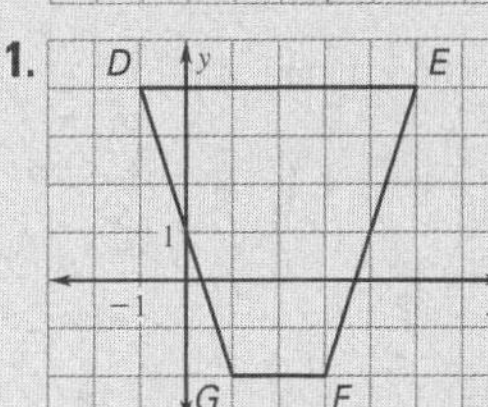

Extra Example 11.4

The arc length of $\overset{\frown}{AB}$ is 5.03 centimeters. Find the circumference of $\odot C$ to the nearest hundredth.

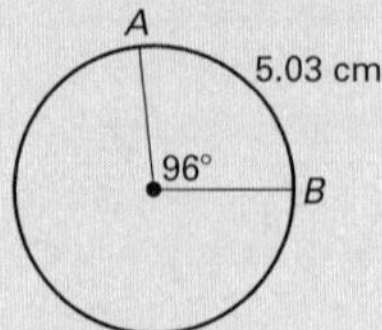

18.86 cm

Extra Example 11.5

Find the area of sector *ACB*.

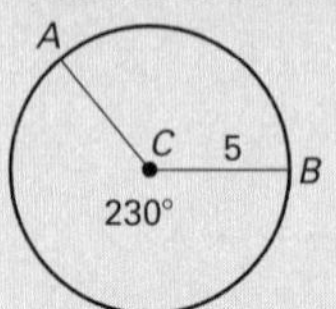

28.36 square units

11 CHAPTER REVIEW

11.4 Circumference and Arc Length

pp. 746–752

EXAMPLE

The arc length of $\overset{\frown}{QR}$ is 6.54 feet. Find the radius of $\odot P$.

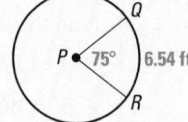

$$\frac{\text{Arc length of } \overset{\frown}{QR}}{2\pi r} = \frac{m\overset{\frown}{QR}}{360^\circ}$$ **Arc Length Corollary**

$$\frac{6.54}{2\pi r} = \frac{75^\circ}{360^\circ}$$ **Substitute.**

$$6.54(360^\circ) = 75^\circ(2\pi r)$$ **Cross Products Property**

$$r \approx 5.00 \text{ ft}$$ **Solve.**

EXERCISES

EXAMPLES 1, 3, and 4 on pp. 746, 748 for Exs. 15–17

Find the indicated measure.

15. Diameter of $\odot F$ **about 30 ft**

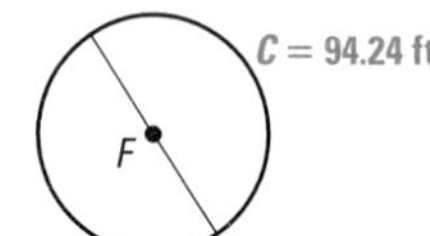

16. Circumference of $\odot F$ **about 56.57 cm**

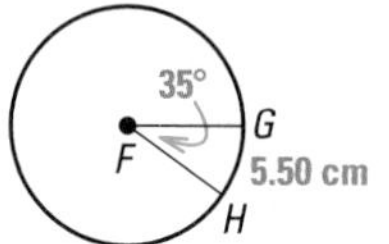

17. Length of $\overset{\frown}{GH}$ **about 26.09 in.**

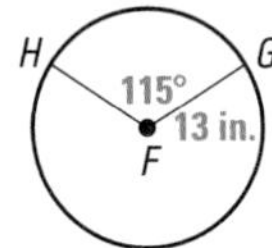

11.5 Areas of Circles and Sectors

pp. 755–761

EXAMPLE

Find the area of sector *ADB*.

First find the measure of the minor arc.

$m\angle ADB = 360^\circ - 280^\circ = 80^\circ$, so $m\overset{\frown}{AB} = 80^\circ$.

$$\text{Area of sector } ADB = \frac{m\overset{\frown}{AB}}{360^\circ} \cdot \pi r^2$$ **Formula for area of a sector**

$$= \frac{80^\circ}{360^\circ} \cdot \pi \cdot 10^2$$ **Substitute.**

$$\approx 69.81 \text{ units}^2$$ **Use a calculator.**

▶ The area of the small sector is about 69.81 square units.

EXERCISES

EXAMPLES 2, 3, and 4 on pp. 756–757 for Exs. 18–20

Find the area of the blue shaded region.

18.

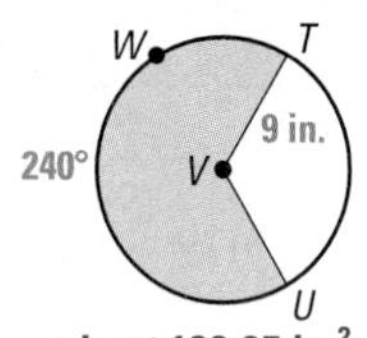

about 169.65 in.^{2}

19.

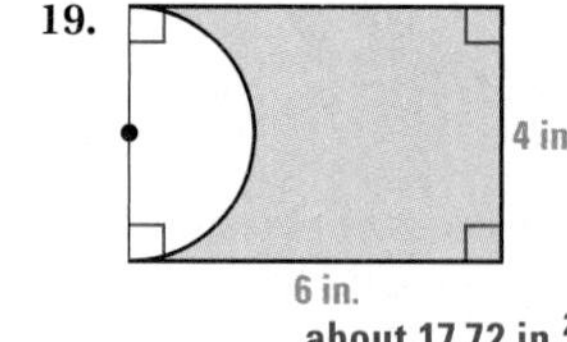

about 17.72 in.^{2}

20.

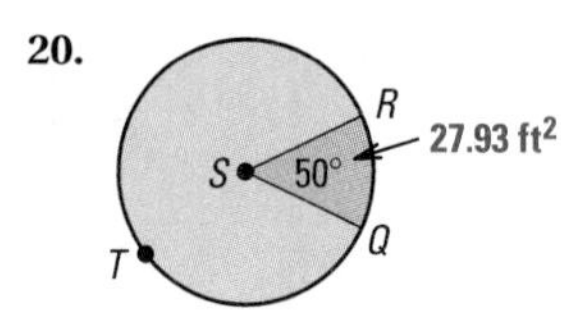

about 173.17 ft^2

@HomeTutor
classzone.com
Chapter Review Practice

11.6 Areas of Regular Polygons

pp. 762–768

EXAMPLE

A regular hexagon is inscribed in ⊙*H*. Find (a) $m\angle EHG$, and (b) the area of the hexagon.

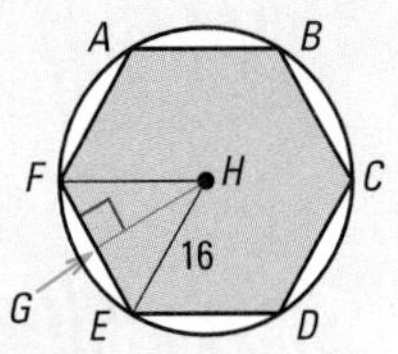

a. $\angle FHE$ is a central angle, so $m\angle FHE = \frac{360°}{6} = 60°$.
Apothem $\overline{GH}$ bisects $\angle FHE$. So, $m\angle EHG = 30°$.

b. Because $\triangle EHG$ is a 30°-60°-90° triangle, $GE = \frac{1}{2} \cdot HE = 8$ and $GH = \sqrt{3} \cdot GE = 8\sqrt{3}$. So, $s = 16$ and $a = 8\sqrt{3}$. Then use the area formula.

$$A = \frac{1}{2}a \cdot ns = \frac{1}{2}(8\sqrt{3})(6)(16) \approx 665.1 \text{ square units}$$

EXERCISES

EXAMPLES 2 and 3 on pp. 763–764 for Exs. 21–22

21. **PLATTER** A platter is in the shape of a regular octagon. Find the perimeter and area of the platter if its apothem is 6 inches. **about 39.8 in., about 119.3 in.^{2}**

22. **PUZZLE** A jigsaw puzzle is in the shape of a regular pentagon. Find its area if its radius is 17 centimeters and its side length is 20 centimeters. **about 687.4 cm^2**

11.7 Use Geometric Probability

pp. 771–777

EXAMPLE

A dart is thrown and hits the square dartboard shown. The dart is equally likely to land on any point on the board. Find the probability that the dart lands in the white region outside the concentric circles.

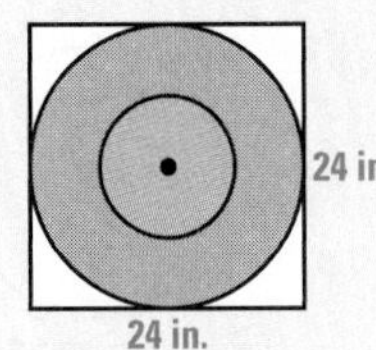

$$P(\text{dart lands in white region}) = \frac{\text{Area of white region}}{\text{Area of dart board}} = \frac{24^2 - \pi(12^2)}{24^2} \approx 0.215$$

▸ The probability that the dart lands in the white region is about 21.5%.

EXERCISES

EXAMPLES 1 and 3 on pp. 771, 773 for Exs. 23–26

23. A point K is selected randomly on $\overline{AC}$ at the right. What is the probability that K is on $\overline{AB}$? **$\frac{4}{7}$ or about 57.1%**

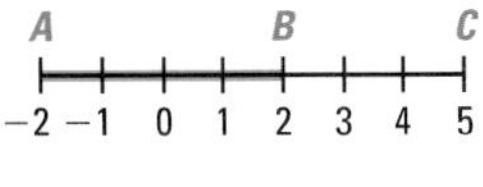

Find the probability that a randomly chosen point in the figure lies in the shaded region.

24.
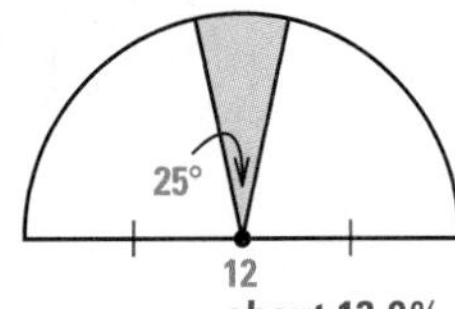

about 13.9%

25.
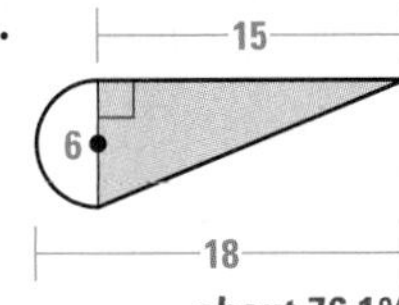

about 76.1%

26.
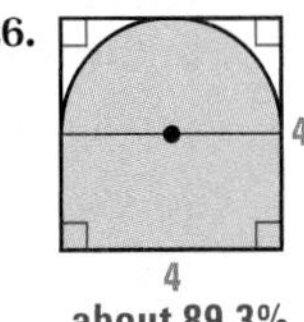

about 89.3%

Extra Example 11.6

A regular triangle is inscribed in ⊙*K*. Find (a) $m\angle PKQ$ and (b) the area of the triangle.

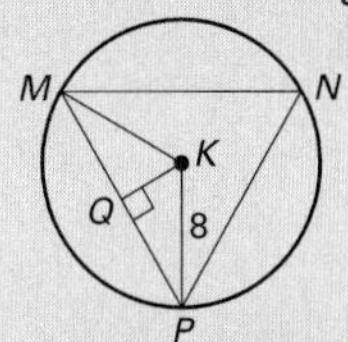

60°; 83.14 square units

Extra Example 11.7

An arrow shot toward a target is equally likely to land on any point of the target. The radii of the three circles are 9 in., 18 in., and 27 in. Find the probability that the arrow will land in the outer ring of the target. **55.6%**

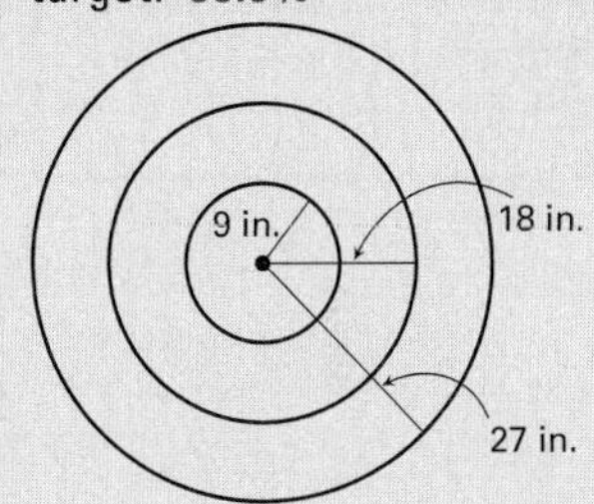

Additional Resources

Assessment Book

- Chapter Test, Levels A, B, C, pp. 158–163
- Standardized Chapter Test, pp. 164–165
- SAT/ACT Chapter Test, pp. 166–167
- Alternative Assessment, pp. 168–169

Test Generator CD-ROM

Chapter Test

Easily-readable reduced copies (with answers) of Chapter Test B, the Standardized Chapter Test, and the Alternative Assessment from the Assessment Book can be found on pp. 718G–718H.

11 CHAPTER TEST

In Exercises 1–6, find the area of the shaded polygon.

1.
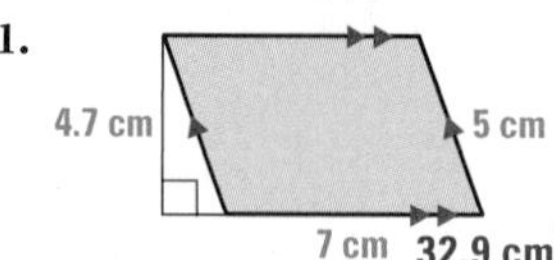

2.
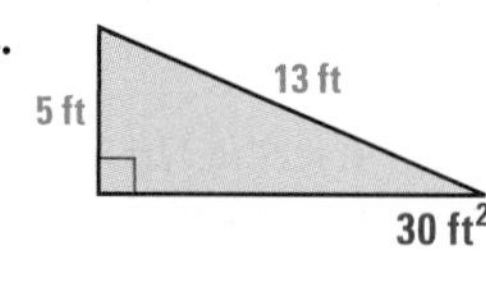

3.
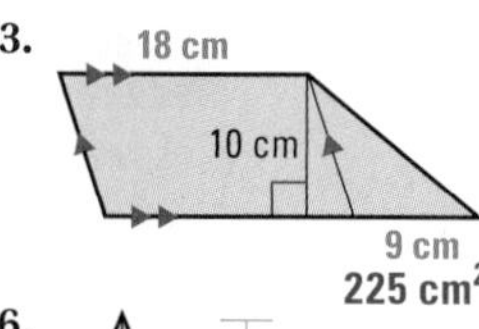

4.
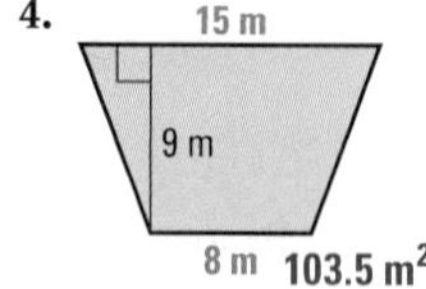

5.
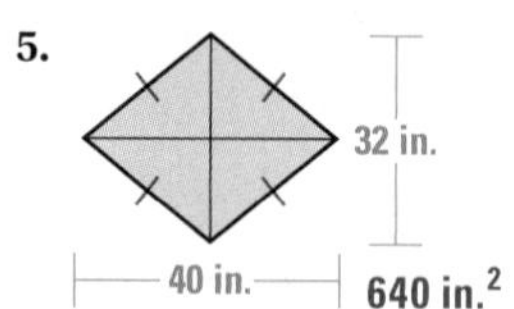

6.
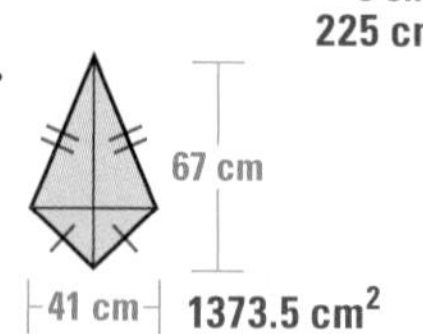

7. The base of a parallelogram is 3 times its height. The area of the parallelogram is 108 square inches. Find the base and the height. **18 in., 6 in.**

Quadrilaterals *ABCD* and *EFGH* are similar. The perimeter of *ABCD* is 40 inches and the perimeter of *EFGH* is 16 inches.

8. Find the ratio of the perimeters of *ABCD* to *EFGH*. **5 : 2**
9. Find the ratio of the corresponding side lengths of *ABCD* to *EFGH*. **5 : 2**
10. Find the ratio of the areas of *ABCD* to *EFGH*. **25 : 4**

Find the indicated measure for the circle shown.

11. Length of $\widehat{AB}$

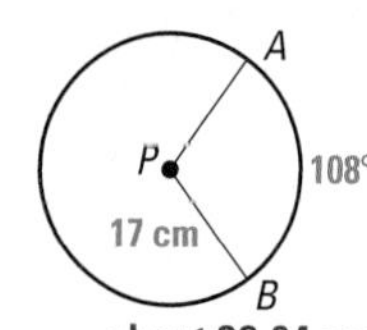

12. Circumference of $\odot F$

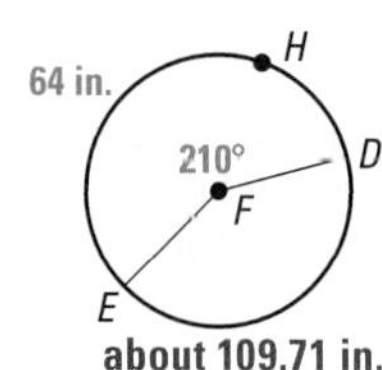

13. $m\widehat{GH}$

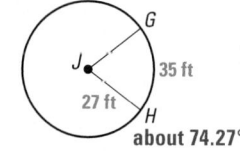

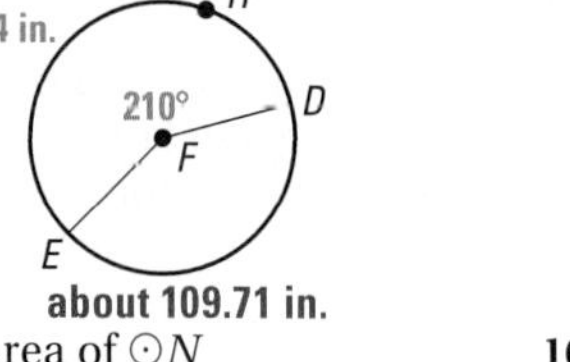

14. Area of shaded sector

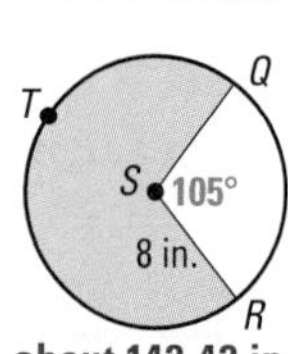

15. Area of $\odot N$

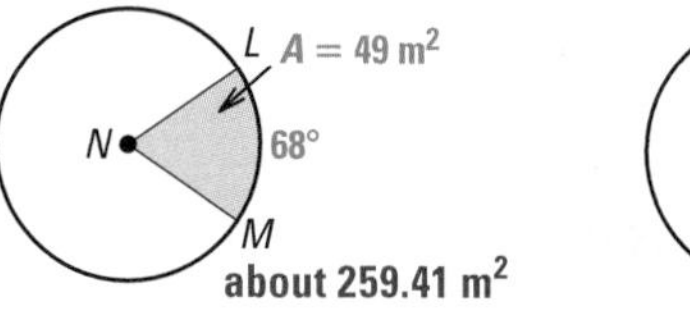

16. Radius of $\odot P$

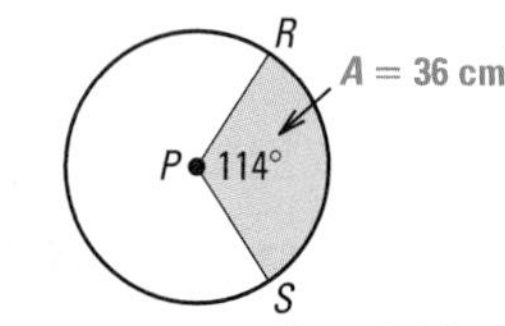

17. **TILING** A floor tile is in the shape of a regular hexagon and has a perimeter of 18 inches. Find the side length, apothem, and area of the tile. **3 in., about 2.60 in., about 23.4 in.²**

Find the probability that a randomly chosen point in the figure lies in the region described.

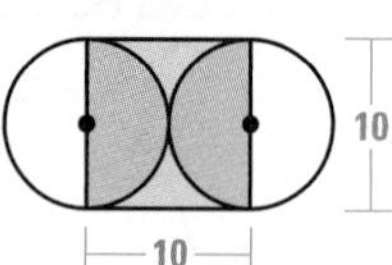

18. In the red region **about 44%**
19. In the blue region **about 12%**

ALGEBRA REVIEW

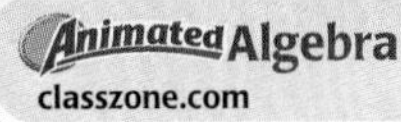

USE ALGEBRAIC MODELS TO SOLVE PROBLEMS

EXAMPLE 1 Write and solve an algebraic model for a problem

FUNDRAISER You are baking cakes to sell at a fundraiser. It costs \$3 to make each cake, and you plan to sell the cakes for \$8 each. You spent \$20 on pans and utensils. How many cakes do you need to sell to make a profit of \$50?

Solution

Let x represent the number of cakes sold.

Income − Expenses = Profit	**Write verbal model.**
$8x - (3x + 20) = 50$	**Substitute $8x$ for income, $3x + 20$ for expenses, and 50 for profit.**
$8x - 3x - 20 = 50$	**Distributive Property**
$5x - 20 = 50$	**Combine like terms.**
$x = 14$	**Solve for x.**

▶ You need to sell 14 cakes to make a profit of \$50.

EXERCISES

EXAMPLE 1
for Exs. 1–7

Write an algebraic model to represent the situation. Then solve the problem.

1. **BICYCLES** You ride your bike 14.25 miles in 90 minutes. At this rate, how far can you bike in 2 hours? $d = \left(\frac{14.25}{1.5}\right)(2)$; **19 mi**
2. **SHOPPING** Alma spent \$39 on a shirt and a jacket. The shirt cost \$12. Find the original cost of a jacket if Alma bought it on sale for 25% off. $12 + 0.75j = 39$; **\$36**
3. **CELL PHONES** Your cell phone provider charges \$29.50 per month for 200 minutes. You pay \$.25 per minute for each minute over 200 minutes. In May, your bill was \$32.75. How many additional minutes did you use? $29.50 + 0.25m = 32.75$; **13 min**
4. **EXERCISE** Jaime burns 12.1 calories per minute running and 7.6 calories per minute swimming. He wants to burn at least 400 calories and plans to swim for 20 minutes. How long does he need to run to meet his goal? $20(7.6) + 12.1r \geq 400$, $r \geq 20.5$ **min**
5. **CARS** You buy a car for \$18,000. The value of the car decreases 10% each year. What will the value of the car be after 5 years? $18{,}000(0.9)^5 = A$; **\$10,628.82**
6. **TICKETS** Student tickets for a show cost \$5 and adult tickets cost \$8. At one show, \$2065 was collected in ticket sales. If 62 more student tickets were sold than adult tickets, how many of each type of ticket was sold? $5s + 8a = 2065$ and $s = 62 + a$; **135 adult tickets and 197 student tickets**
7. **TENNIS** The height h in feet of a tennis ball is $h = -16t^2 + 47t + 6$, where t is the time in seconds after being hit. If the ball is not first hit by another player, how long does it take to reach the ground? $0 = -16t^2 + 47t + 6$; **about 3.06 sec**

Extra Example 1

A cell phone contract costs \$19.95 per month for the first 300 minutes, and \$.30 per minute for any minutes over 300. If your cell phone bill was \$56.55, how many minutes did you use your cell phone? **422 min**

Using Rubrics

The rubric given on the pupil page is a sample of a three-level rubric. Other rubrics may contain four, five, or six levels. For more information on rubrics, see the *Geometry Toolkit*.

Test-Taking Strategy

To plan the solution to the question, underline the phrases following key words like "find", "show", "which", or "explain". Then make sure each of these phrases are addressed in the solution by checking them off as they are done.

Teaching Strategy

Point out that the circles are different sizes for each different size cardboard square, and therefore the total area of the circles is different. However, the percent of the cardboard used is the same, so neither size gives more waste. The cost of the cardboard or the size of the circles may dictate which size cardboard to choose.

Scoring Rubric

Full Credit
- solution is complete and correct

Partial Credit
- solution is complete but has errors,

or
- solution is without error but incomplete

No Credit
- no solution is given,

or
- solution makes no sense

Standards

8.0 Students know, derive, and **solve problems involving the** perimeter, circumference, **area**, volume, lateral area, and surface area **of common geometric figures.**

EXTENDED RESPONSE QUESTIONS

PROBLEM

You are making circular signs for a pep rally at your school. You can cut 4 circles with diameter 10 inches from a cardboard square that is 20 inches long on each side, or 9 circles with diameter 12 inches from a cardboard square that is 36 inches long on each side.

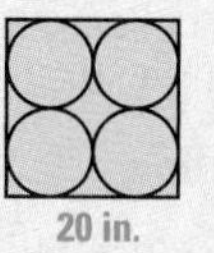

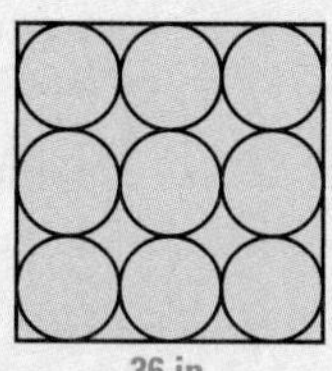

a. For each cardboard square, find the area of the cardboard that is used for the signs. Round to the nearest square inch. Show your work.

b. You want to waste as little of a cardboard square as possible. Does it matter which size of cardboard you use? If so, which size of cardboard should you choose if you want to use a greater percent of the cardboard's area for the signs? *Explain.*

Below are sample solutions to the problem. Read each solution and the comments in blue to see why the sample represents *full credit, partial credit,* or *no credit.*

SAMPLE 1: Full credit solution

In part (a), the student's work is shown and the calculations are correct.

a. For each cardboard square, multiply the number of circles by the area of one circle.

For the 20 inch square, the radius of each of the 4 circles is 5 inches.

$$\text{Area of 4 circles} = 4 \cdot \pi r^2 = 4 \cdot \pi(5)^2 \approx 314 \text{ in.}^2$$

For the 36 inch square, the radius of each of the 9 circles is 6 inches.

$$\text{Area of 9 circles} = 9 \cdot \pi r^2 = 9 \cdot \pi(6)^2 \approx 1018 \text{ in.}^2$$

The reasoning in part (b) is correct and the answer is correct.

b. For each cardboard square, find the percent of the cardboard square's area that is used for the circles.

$$\text{Percent for 20 inch square: } \frac{\text{Area of 4 circles}}{\text{Area of cardboard}} \approx \frac{314}{20^2} = 0.785 = 78.5\%$$

$$\text{Percent for 36 inch square: } \frac{\text{Area of 9 circles}}{\text{Area of cardboard}} \approx \frac{1018}{36^2} \approx 0.785 = 78.5\%$$

It doesn't matter which size of cardboard you use. In each case, you will use about 78.5% of the cardboard's area.

SAMPLE 2: Partial credit solution

In part (a), the answer is incomplete because the student does not find the area of all the circles.

a. Use the formula $A = \pi r^2$ to find the area of each circle. Divide each diameter in half to get the radius of the circle.

Area of 10 inch diameter circle $= \pi(5)^2 \approx 79$ in.^{2}
Area of 12 inch diameter circle $= \pi(6)^2 \approx 113$ in.^{2}

The reasoning in part (b) is correct, but the answer is wrong because the student did not consider the area of all the circles.

b. Find and compare the percents.

$$\frac{\text{Area of circles}}{\text{Area of 20 in. square}} \approx \frac{79}{20^2} = 0.1975 = 19.75\%$$

$$\frac{\text{Area of circles}}{\text{Area of 36 in. square}} \approx \frac{113}{36^2} \approx 0.0872 = 8.72\%$$

You use 19.75% of the 20 inch cardboard's area, but only 8.72% of the 36 inch cardboard's area. So, you should use the 20 inch cardboard.

SAMPLE 3: No credit solution

In part (a), the wrong formula is used.

a. Area $= \pi d = \pi(10) \approx 31$ in.^{2} Multiply by 4 to get 124 in.^{2}
Area $= \pi d = \pi(12) \approx 38$ in.^{2} Multiply by 9 to get 342 in.^{2}

In part (b), the reasoning and the answer are incorrect.

b. You use 342 in.^{2} of cardboard for 9 signs, and only 124 in.^{2} for 4 signs. You should use the 36 inch cardboard because you will use more of it.

PRACTICE Apply the Scoring Rubric

1. A student's solution to the problem on the previous page is given below. Score the solution as *full credit, partial credit,* or *no credit. Explain* your reasoning. If you choose *partial credit* or *no credit, explain* how you would change the solution so that it earns a score of full credit.

a. There are two sizes of circles you can make. Find the area of each.

Area of a circle made from the 20 inch square $= \pi(5)^2 \approx 78.5$ in.^{2}
Area of a circle made from the 36 inch square $= \pi(6)^2 \approx 113.1$ in.^{2}

Then multiply each area by the number of circles that have that area.

Area of circles in 20 inch square $\approx 4 \cdot 78.5 = 314$ in.^{2}
Area of circles in 36 inch square $\approx 9 \cdot 113.1 \approx 1018$ in.^{2}

Full credit; the solution is correct and the work is shown.

b. Find the percent of each square's area that is used for the signs.

$$\frac{\text{Area of 4 circles}}{\text{Area of 20 in. square}} = \frac{314}{20} = 15.7\%$$

$$\frac{\text{Area of 9 circles}}{\text{Area of 36 in. square}} = \frac{1018}{36} \approx 28.3\%$$

Because 28.3% > 15.7%, you use a greater percent of the cardboard's area when you use the 36 inch square. **Partial credit; the reasoning is correct, but the area of the square is incorrect.**

Teaching Strategy

For the Practice exercise, encourage students to check every statement in their solution. They should be able to answer the following questions about part (b) of the answer:

1. Is the area of the circle calculated correctly?
2. Is the area of the square calculated correctly?
3. Is the percent calculated correctly?

If they check off each question as they read and review the given situation, they will notice that questions 2 and 3 indicate places where the given solution is not correct.

1b. 6 ft; about 28.27 ft^2; since the leash is 18 feet and the shed is 12 feet, the dog has an additional 6 feet to move past the shed. The building and the leash are a straight angle, so the dog has an additional 90° where it can move around the corner.

2a.

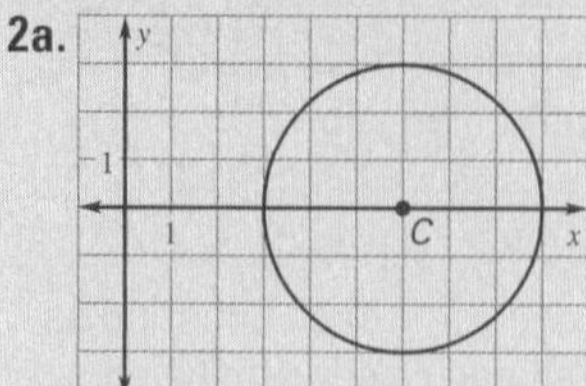

2b.

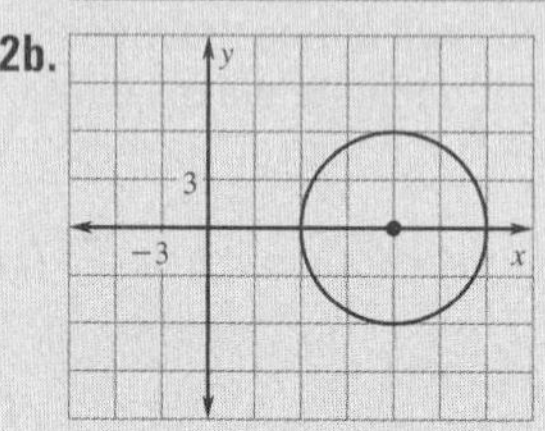

3a. 724.5 cm^2, 966 cm^2; the ratio of the small tray to the medium tray is 2:3, and the ratio of the small tray to the large tray is 2:4.

3b. About 98.0 cm, about 113 cm; since the ratio of areas is 2:3:4, the ratio of perimeters is the square root of that or $\sqrt{2}:\sqrt{3}:2$.

4a. 5; the diagonals of a rhombus bisect each other and are perpendicular, therefore the legs of the triangle formed are 3 and 4 which makes the hypotenuse 5.

EXTENDED RESPONSE

1. A dog is tied to the corner of a shed with a leash. The leash prevents the dog from moving more than 18 feet from the corner. In the diagram, the shaded sectors show the region over which the dog can roam.
   a. Find the area of the sector with radius 18 feet. **about 763.41 ft^2**
   b. What is the radius of the smaller sector? Find its area. *Explain.* **See margin.**
   c. Find the area over which the dog can move. *Explain.* **About 791.68 ft^2; add the areas of the sectors together.**

2. A circle passes through the points (3, 0), (9, 0), (6, 3), and (6, −3).
   a. Graph the circle in a coordinate plane. Give the coordinates of its center. **See margin for art; (6, 0).**
   b. Sketch the image of the circle after a dilation centered at the origin with a scale factor of 2. How are the coordinates of the center of the dilated circle related to the coordinates of the center of the original circle? *Explain.* **See margin for art; the center of the dilated circle is (12, 0), so the coordinates are twice the coordinates of the center of the original circle.**
   c. How are the circumferences of the circle and its image after the dilation related? How are the areas related? *Explain.* **Twice as large; four times as large; *r* grew by 2 so the circumference also doubled, but for the area, *r* increased by the square of 2 or 4.**

3. A caterer uses a set of three different-sized trays. Each tray is a regular octagon. The areas of the trays are in the ratio 2 : 3 : 4. **a, b. See margin.**

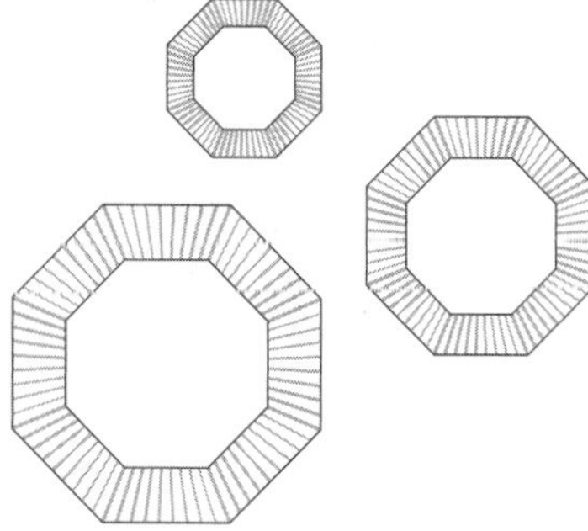

   a. The area of the smallest tray is about 483 square centimeters. Find the areas of the other trays to the nearest square centimeter. *Explain* your reasoning.
   b. The perimeter of the smallest tray is 80 centimeters. Find the approximate perimeters of the other trays. Round to the nearest tenth of a centimeter. *Explain* your reasoning.

4. In the diagram, the diagonals of rhombus *EFGH* intersect at point *J*, $EG = 6$, and $FH = 8$. A circle with center *J* is inscribed in *EFGH*, and $\overline{XY}$ is a diameter of $\odot J$.

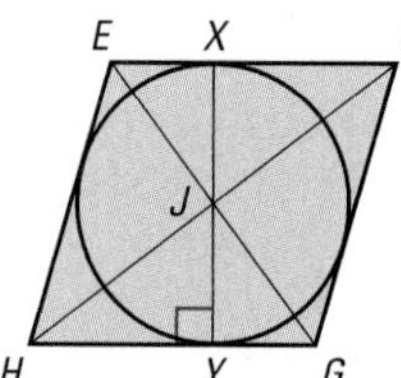

   a. Find *EF*. *Explain* your reasoning. **See margin.**
   b. Use the formula for the area of a rhombus to find the area of *EFGH*. **24 units^2**
   c. Use the formula for the area of a parallelogram to write an equation relating the area of *EFGH* from part (b) to *EF* and *XY*. **$24 = EF \cdot XY$**
   d. Find *XY*. Then find the area of the inscribed circle. *Explain* your reasoning. **4.8 units; $5.76\pi \approx 18.1$ units^2; *XY* is the diameter, so half of it is the radius.**

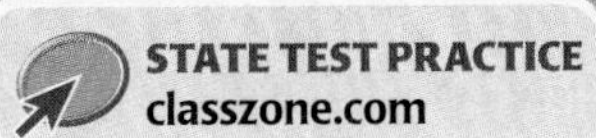

MULTIPLE CHOICE

5. In the diagram, J is the center of two circles, and K lies on $\overline{JL}$. Given $JL = 6$ and $KL = 2$, what is the ratio of the area of the smaller circle to the area of the larger circle? **D**

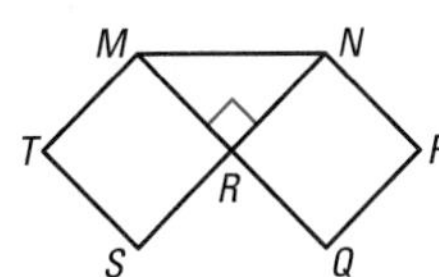

Ⓐ $\sqrt{2} : \sqrt{3}$

Ⓑ 1:3

Ⓒ 2:3

Ⓓ 4:9

6. In the diagram, $TMRS$ and $RNPQ$ are congruent squares, and $\triangle MNR$ is a right triangle. What is the probability that a randomly chosen point on the diagram lies inside $\triangle MNR$? **A**

Ⓐ 0.2 Ⓑ 0.25

Ⓒ 0.5 Ⓓ 0.75

GRIDDED ANSWER

7. You are buying fertilizer for a lawn that is shaped like a parallelogram. Two sides of the parallelogram are each 300 feet long, and the perpendicular distance between these sides is 150 feet. One bag of fertilizer covers 5000 square feet and costs $14. How much (in dollars) will you spend? **$126**

8. In square $ACDE$, $ED = 2$, $AB = BC$, and $AF = FE$. What is the area (in square units) of the shaded region? **1.5 units²**

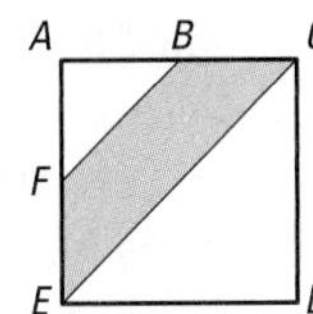

9. In the diagram, a rectangle's sides are tangent to two circles with centers at points P and Q. The circumference of each circle is 8π square units. What is the area (in square units) of the rectangle? **96 units²**

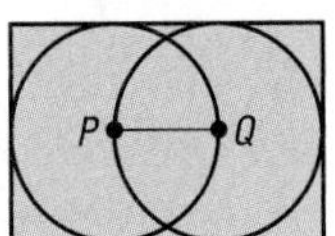

SHORT RESPONSE

10. You are designing a spinner for a board game. An arrow is attached to the center of a circle with diameter 7 inches. The arrow is spun until it stops. The arrow has an equally likely chance of stopping anywhere.

a. If $x° = 45°$, what is the probability that the arrow points to a red sector? *Explain.* **25%; there are 2 sectors of the circle that are 45°, so 90° of the circle is red which is one-fourth of the circle.**

b. You want to change the spinner so the probability that the arrow points to a blue sector is half the probability that it points to a red sector. What values should you use for x and y? *Explain.* **See margin.**

11. In quadrilateral $JKLM$, $JL = 3 \cdot KM$. The area of $JKLM$ is 54 square centimeters.

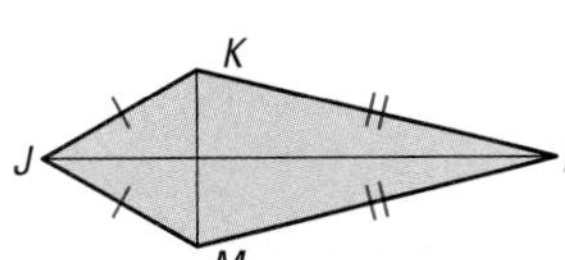

a. Find JL and KM. **18 cm, 6 cm**

b. Quadrilateral $NPQR$ is similar to $JKLM$, and its area is 486 square centimeters. Sketch $NPQR$ and its diagonals. Then find the length of $\overline{NQ}$. *Explain* your reasoning. **See margin.**

10b. $x = 120$, $y = 60$; the ratio of the probability of pointing at blue to the probability of pointing at red is 1:2, so the ratio of the two degree measures has to be 120:240. Since there are two x-values and two y-values, the value of x has to be 120 and the value of y has to be 60.

11b.

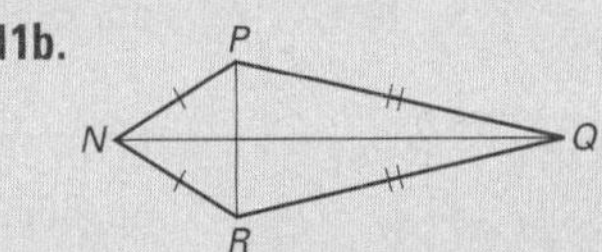

54 cm; the ratio of the areas is 1:9 so the ratio of the diagonals is 1:3. Since JL is proportional to NQ. So $NQ = 3 \cdot JL = 3 \cdot 18 = 54$ cm.

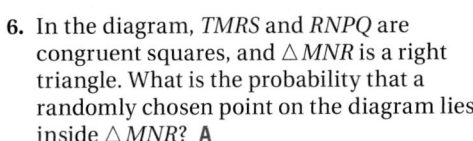

12 Pacing and Assignment Guide

REGULAR SCHEDULE

Pre-AP For pacing and assignments for a Pre-AP course, see the *Geometry Toolkit.*

Lesson	Les. Day	BASIC	AVERAGE	ADVANCED
12.1	Day 1	EP p. 897 Exs. 41–44; pp. 798–801 Exs. 1–20, 34, 35	pp. 798–801 Exs. 1–20, 32, 34, 35, 56, 59	pp. 798–801 Exs. 1–20, 32, 34, 35, 57, 60
	Day 2	pp. 798–801 Exs. 21–30, 36–42, 52–60	pp. 798–801 Exs. 21–27 odd, 28–31, 37–49, 53	pp. 798–801 Exs. 21, 24, 27–31, 33*, 38–51*, 54
12.2	Day 1	EP p. 917 Exs. 34, 35, 47, 48; pp. 806–809 Exs. 1–17, 22–26, 31–37	pp. 806–809 Exs. 1, 2–12 even, 13–20, 22–27, 31–37	pp. 806–809 Exs. 1, 2, 4–10 even, 13–22*, 24–30*, 32–36 even
12.3	Day 1	EP p. 908 Exs. 1–3; pp. 814–817 Exs. 1–9, 20, 21, 27–29, 35, 36	pp. 814–817 Exs. 1–9, 20, 21, 25, 27–29, 35, 36	pp. 814–817 Exs. 1–8, 20, 21, 25, 27–29, 35, 36
	Day 2	pp. 814–817 Exs. 10–19, 30, 31, 37–39	pp. 814–817 Exs. 10–19, 22–24, 30–33, 37–39	pp. 814–817 Exs. 11–15, 17–19, 22–24, 26*, 30–34*, 37–39
12.4	Day 1	EP p. 916 Exs. 9–12; pp. 822–825 Exs. 1–14	pp. 822–825 Exs. 1–14, 33	pp. 822–825 Exs. 1–12, 14, 33, 34*
	Day 2	pp. 822–825 Exs. 15–24, 28–32, 35–40	pp. 822–825 Exs. 15–26, 28–32, 35–39 odd	pp. 822–825 Exs. 16–32*, 36–40 even
12.5	Day 1	EP p. 909 Exs. 34–36; pp. 832–836 Exs. 1–14, 43–45	pp. 832–836 Exs. 1–14, 26, 43–45	pp. 832–836 Exs. 1–8, 11–14, 26–28*, 43–45
	Day 2	pp. 832–836 Exs. 15–22, 29–35, 46–52	pp. 832–836 Exs. 15–19, 21–25, 29–37, 46–52 even	pp. 832–836 Exs. 16–19, 23–25, 29, 33–42*, 48, 52
12.6	Day 1	pp. 842–845 Exs. 1–11, 31, 40–44	pp. 842–845 Exs. 1–11, 31, 40–44	pp. 842–845 Exs. 1–9, 11, 31, 40–44
	Day 2	pp. 842–845 Exs. 12–24, 30, 32–34	pp. 842–845 Exs. 13–15, 17–20, 22–28 even, 30, 32–36	pp. 842–845 Exs. 18–20, 21–27 odd, 28–30*, 33–39*
12.7	Day 1	pp. 850–854 Exs. 1–4, 7–9, 11–13, 16–20, 25–30, 36–48 even	pp. 850–854 Exs. 1, 2, 4, 5–9 odd, 10–16 even, 17, 18, 20, 21, 26–32, 37–47 odd	pp. 850–854 Exs. 1, 2, 5–7, 10, 14–18, 21–24*, 27–35*, 38, 42, 44, 48
Review	Day 1	pp. 857–860 Exs. 1–22	pp. 857–860 Exs. 1–22	pp. 857–860 Exs. 1–22
Assess	Day 1	Chapter 12 Test	Chapter 12 Test	Chapter 12 Test
Yearly Pacing		Chapter 12 Total – 14 days	Chapters 1–12 Total – 160 days	Remaining – 0 days

*Challenge Exercises EP = Extra Practice SRH = Skills Review Handbook

BLOCK SCHEDULE

DAY 1	DAY 2	DAY 3	DAY 4	DAY 5	DAY 6	DAY 7
12.1	12.2	12.3 (CONT.)	12.4 (CONT.)	12.5 (CONT.)	12.6 (CONT.)	REVIEW
pp. 798–801 Exs. 1–20, 21–27 odd, 28–32, 34, 35, 37–49, 53, 56, 59	pp. 806–809 Exs. 1, 2–12 even, 13–20, 22–27, 31–37	pp. 814–817 Exs. 10–19, 22–24, 30–33, 37–39	pp. 822–825 Exs. 15–26, 28–32, 35–39 odd	pp. 832–836 Exs. 15–19, 21–25, 29–37, 46–52 even	pp. 842–845 Exs. 13–15, 17–20, 22–28 even, 30, 32–36	pp. 857–860 Exs. 1–22
	12.3	12.4	12.5	12.6	12.7	ASSESS
	pp. 814–817 Exs. 1–9, 20, 21, 25, 27–29, 35, 36	pp. 822–825 Exs. 1–14, 33	pp. 832–836 Exs. 1–14, 26, 43–45	pp. 842–845 Exs. 1–11, 31, 40–44	pp. 850–854 Exs. 1, 2, 4, 5–9 odd, 10–16 even, 17, 18, 20, 21, 26–32, 37–47 odd	Chapter 12 Test

Yearly Pacing Chapter 12 Total – 7 days Chapters 1–12 Total – 80 days Remaining – 0 days

Chapter Resource Guide 12

RESOURCE MANAGER

Chapter Resource Book

CHAPTER SUPPORT							
Parents as Partners (Chapter Overview with home involvement exercises and activity)						p. 1	
LESSON SUPPORT	**12.1**	**12.2**	**12.3**	**12.4**	**12.5**	**12.6**	**12.7**
Teaching Guide/Lesson Plan	p. 3	p. 19	p. 33	p. 48	p. 62	p. 77	p. 90
Activity Masters			p. 35	p. 50			
Technology Activities & Keystrokes	p. 5				p. 64		
Activity Support Masters	p. 7	p. 21			p. 65		p. 92
Practice (3 levels)	p. 8	p. 22	p. 36	p. 51	p. 66	p. 79	p. 93
Study Guide	p. 14	p. 28	p. 42	p. 57	p. 72	p. 85	p. 99
Catch-Up for Absent Students	p. 16	p. 30	p. 44	p. 59	p. 74	p. 87	p. 101
Problem Solving/Application	p. 17	p. 31	p. 45	p. 60	p. 75	p. 88	p. 102
Challenge Practice	p. 18	p. 32	p. 47	p. 61	p. 76	p. 89	p. 103

REVIEW			
Chapter Review Games and Activities	p. 104	Cumulative Practice	p. 107
Project with Rubric	p. 105	Resource Book Answers	A1

Transparencies	*12.1*	*12.2*	*12.3*	*12.4*	*12.5*	*12.6*	*12.7*
Warm-Up/Daily Homework Quiz	✔	✔	✔	✔	✔	✔	✔
Notetaking Guide	✔	✔	✔	✔	✔	✔	✔
Teacher Support							
Answer Transparencies	✔	✔	✔	✔	✔	✔	✔

ASSESSMENT BOOK

Quizzes	p. 170	SAT/ACT Chapter Test	p. 181
Chapter Tests (3 levels)	p. 173	Alternative Assessment with Rubric	p. 183
Standardized Chapter Test	p. 179	Cumulative Test	p. 185

TECHNOLOGY

- Easy Planner
- Test and Practice Generator
- Power Presentations
- @HomeTutor
- Activity Generator
- Animated Geometry
- Classzone.com
- eEdition Plus Online
- eWorkbook Plus Online
- ML Assessment System

ADDITIONAL RESOURCES

- Worked-Out Solution Key
- Notetaking Guide
- Practice Wookbook
- Geometry Toolkit
- Benchmark Tests
- Remediation Book
- Spanish Study Guide
- Spanish Assessment Book
- Student Resources in Spanish
- Multi-Language Visual Glossary

LESSON 12.1 Practice B
For use with pages 792–801

Determine whether the solid is a polyhedron. If it is, name the polyhedron. *Explain* your reasoning.

1. 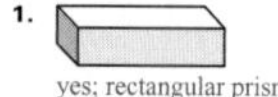 yes; rectangular prism
2. 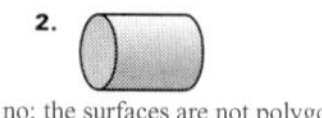 no; the surfaces are not polygons.
3. 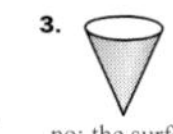 no; the surfaces are not polygons.

Use Euler's Theorem to find the value of n.

4. Faces: n 4
Vertices: 4
Edges: 6
5. Faces: 10
Vertices: n 16
Edges: 24
6. Faces: 14
Vertices: 24
Edges: n 36

Sketch the polyhedron.

7. Triangular pyramid 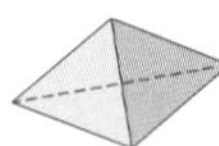
8. Pentagonal pyramid 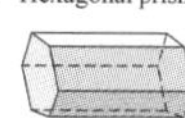
9. Hexagonal prism

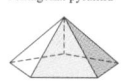

Find the number of faces, vertices, and edges of the polyhedron. Check your answer using Euler's Theorem.

10. 5, 5, 8 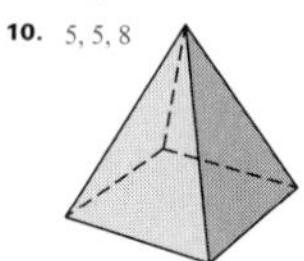
11.  6, 8, 12
12. 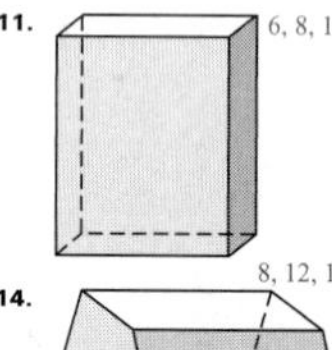 5, 6, 9
13. 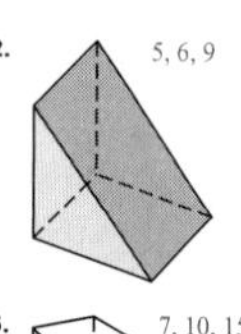 7, 7, 12
14. 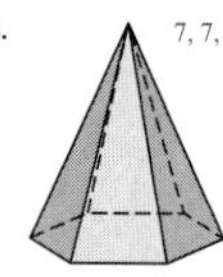 8, 12, 18
15. 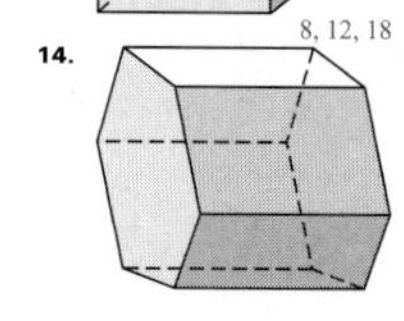 7, 10, 15

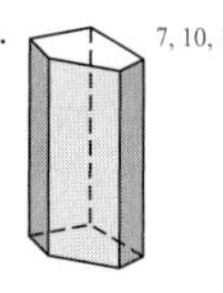

16. **Visual Thinking** An architect is designing a contemporary office building in the shape of a pyramid. The building will have eight sides. What is the shape of the base of the building? octagon

LESSON 12.1 Practice B *continued*
For use with pages 792–801

Determine whether the solid is *convex* or *concave*.

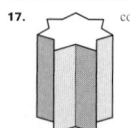

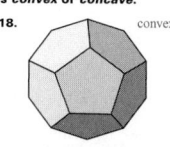

17. 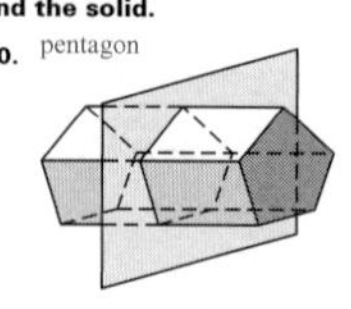 concave
18. 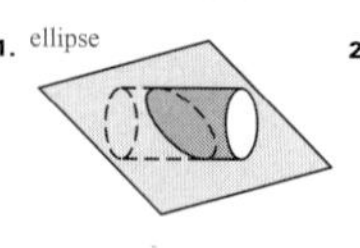 convex
19. 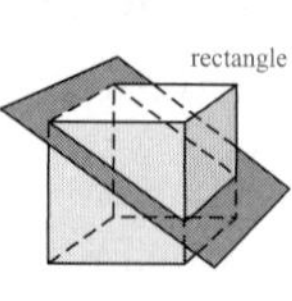 concave

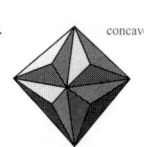

Describe the cross section formed by the intersection of the plane and the solid.

20. pentagon
21. ellipse
22. rectangle

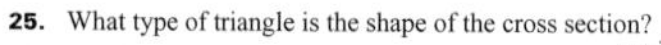

23. **Multiple Choice** Assume at least one face of a solid is congruent to at least one face of another solid. Which two solids can be adjoined by congruent faces to form a hexahedron? B
   A. A rectangular prism and a rectangular pyramid
   B. A triangular pyramid and a triangular pyramid
   C. A triangular prism and a triangular pyramid
   D. A cube and a triangular prism

24. **Reasoning** Of the four possible solid combinations in Exercise 23, which combination has the most faces? How many faces are there? rectangular prism and rectangular pyramid; 9 faces

In Exercises 25–27, use the following information.

Cross Section The figure at the right shows a cube that is intersected by a diagonal plane. The cross section passes through three vertices of the cube.

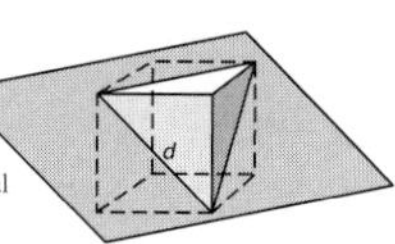

25. What type of triangle is the shape of the cross section? equilateral
26. If the edge length of the cube is 1, what is the length of the line segment d? $\sqrt{2}$
27. If the edge length of the cube is $4\sqrt{2}$, what is the perimeter of the cross section? 24

LESSON 12.2 Practice B
For use with pages 802–809

Find the surface area of the solid formed by the net. Round your answer to two decimal places.

1. 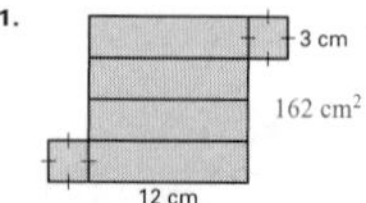

162 cm^2
2. 4656 in.^{2} 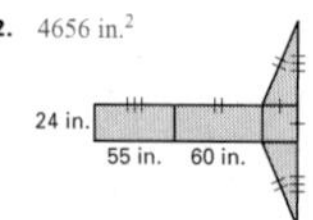

3. 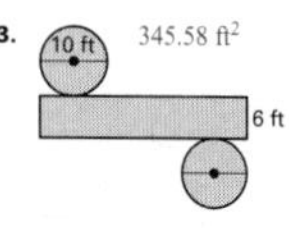

345.58 ft^2

Find the surface area of the right prism. Round your answer to two decimal places.

4. 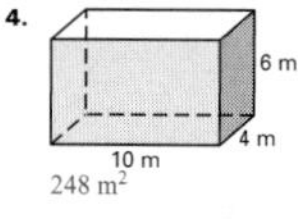

248 m^2
5. 309.21 ft^2 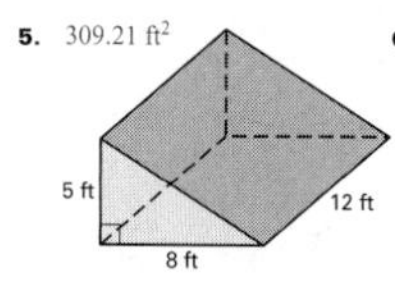

6. 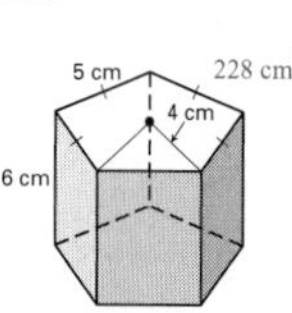

228 cm^2

Find the surface area of the right cylinder using the given radius r and height h. Round your answer to two decimal places.

7. $r = 5$ cm; $h = 15$ cm 628.32 cm^2

8. $r = 1.1$ ft; $h = 3.2$ ft 29.72 ft^2 
9. $r = 12$ in.; $h = 18$ in. 2261.95 in.^{2} 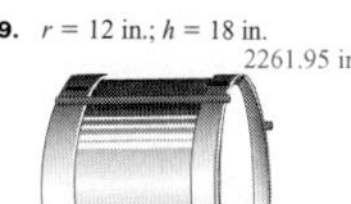

Solve for x given the surface area S of the right prism or right cylinder. Round your answer to two decimal places.

10. $S = 320$ m^2 8 m 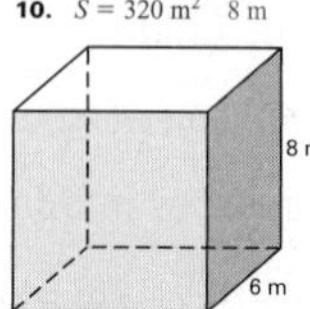

11. $S = 200$ ft^2 10.23 ft 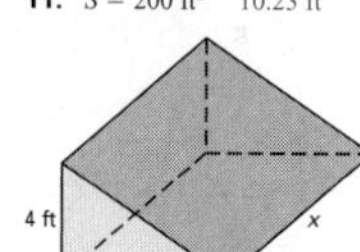

12. $S = 1000$ cm^2 11.89 cm 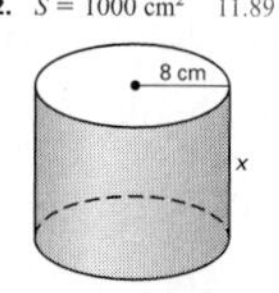

LESSON 12.2 Practice B *continued*
For use with pages 802–809

13. **Surface Area of a Prism** A rectangular prism has a base with a width of x units and a height of y units. The depth of the prism is z units. Write the surface area S in terms of x, y, and z. $S = 2xy + 2xz + 2yz$
14. **Surface Area of a Prism** A triangular prism with a right triangular base has one leg length that is 6 inches and the other leg length that is 8 inches. The height of the prism is 7 inches. What is the surface area of the prism? 216 in.^{2}
15. **Surface Area of a Prism** A triangular prism with a scalene triangular base has legs with lengths of 5 inches, 7 inches, and 8 inches. The height of the prism is 10 inches. What is the surface area of the prism? 234.64 in.^{2}
16. **Multiple Choice** The radius and height of a right cylinder are each multiplied by 2. What is the change in the surface area of the cylinder? B
   A. The surface area is 2 times the original surface area.
   B. The surface area is 4 times the original surface area.
   C. The surface area is 6 times the original surface area.
   D. The surface area is 8 times the original surface area.
17. **Surface Area of a Cylinder** The radius and height of a right cylinder are each divided by 2. What is the change in surface area of the cylinder? The new surface area is $\frac{1}{4}$ of the original surface area.
18. **Radius of a Cylinder** Find the radius of a right cylinder with a surface area of 48π square feet. The height of the cylinder is 5 feet. 3 ft
19. **Candy Box** As a birthday present for a friend, you buy a cylindrical box of candy. The diameter of the box is 6 inches and the height is 8 inches. What is the minimum amount of wrapping paper needed to wrap the gift? Round your answer to two decimal places. 207.35 in.^{2}

In Exercises 20–22, us the following information.

Water Drainage Pipe The figure at the right shows a drainage pipe that is needed for the construction of a new driveway. The pipe has a length of 15 feet and a diameter that is one tenth that of the length. Round your answers to two decimal places.

20. If the design is to have at least one foot of pavement over the drainage pipe, what is the minimum depth of the ditch? 2.5 ft
21. What is the surface area of the drainage pipe? 70.69 ft^2
22. What is the surface area of the drainage pipe, if the diameter of the pipe is one sixth of the length of the pipe? 117.81 ft^2

Practice B

For use with pages 810–817

Find the area of each lateral face of the regular pyramid. Round your answer to two decimal places.

1. 12 m²

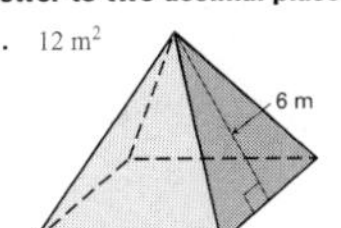

2. 48 ft²

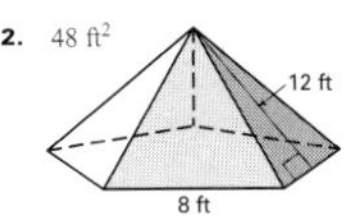

3. 232.05 cm²

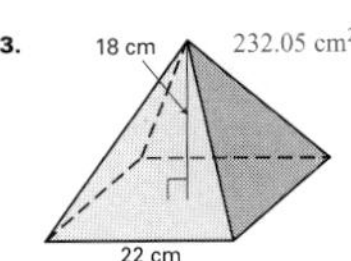

Find the surface area of the regular pyramid. Round your answer to two decimal places.

4. 189 m²

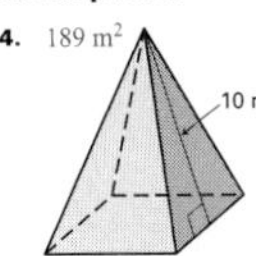

5. 588.44 ft²

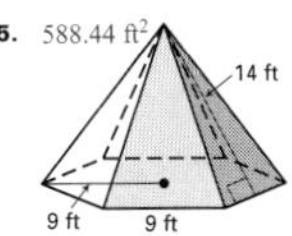

6. 287.68 cm²

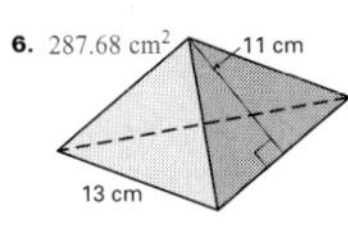

Find the lateral area of the right cone. Round your answer to two decimal places.

7. 157.08 m²

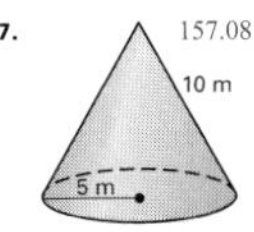

8. 188.5 ft²

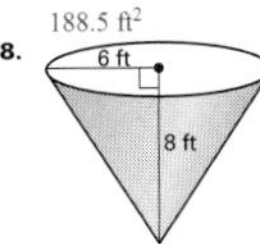

9. 304.52 cm²

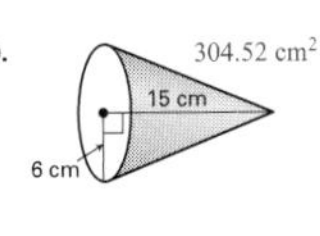

Find the surface area of the right cone. Round your answer to two decimal places.

10. 578.05 m²

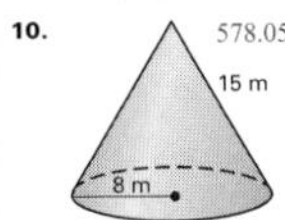

11. 440.67 ft²

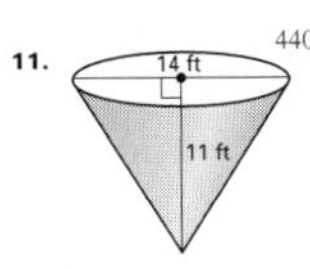

12. 1160.06 cm²

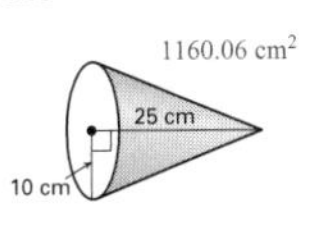

13. **Multiple Choice** The surface area of a regular pyramid with a square base is 1536 square meters. The base edge length is 24 meters and the slant height is 20 meters. What is the height of the pyramid? C

A. 8 **B.** 12 **C.** 16 **D.** 20

Practice B *continued*

LESSON 12.3 For use with pages 810–817

Sketch the described solid and find its surface area. Round your answer to two decimal places.

14. A regular pyramid has a slant height of 12 inches. Its base is a square with a base edge length of 18 inches. 756 in.²

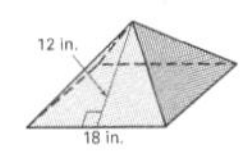

15. A regular pyramid has a height of 10 inches. Its base is an equilateral triangle with a base edge length of 12 inches. 252.85 in.²

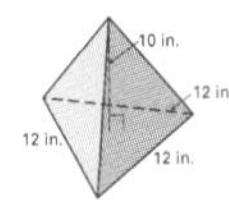

16. A right cone has a radius of 3 feet and a height of 9 feet. 117.72 ft²

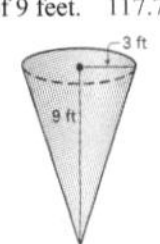

17. A right cone has a diameter of 12 meters and a slant height of 9 meters. 282.74 m²

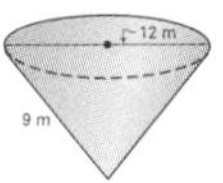

Find the surface area of the solid. The pyramids are regular and the cones are right. Round your answer to two decimal places.

18. 480 m²

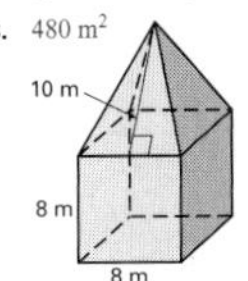

19. 119.38 in.²

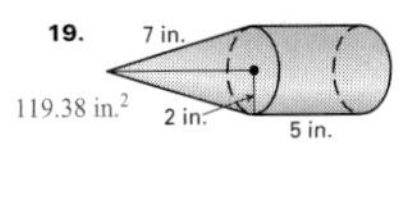

20. 124.71 cm²

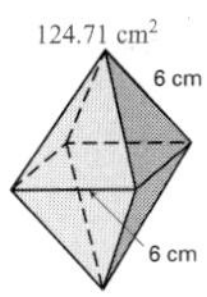

In Exercises 21–23, use the following information.

Great Pyramid of Khufu The Great Pyramid of Khufu is located in El Giza, Egypt. Pyramids were built to serve as tombs for the pharaohs of ancient Egypt. The Great Pyramid is 481 feet high and has a square base with a base edge length of 756 feet. Round your answers to two decimal places.

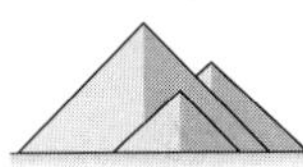

21. Approximate the slant height of the Great Pyramid. 611.76 ft

22. Approximate the area of each lateral face of the Great Pyramid. 231,243.64 ft²

23. Approximate the surface area of the Great Pyramid. 924,974.57 ft²

Practice B

LESSON 12.4 For use with pages 819–825

Find the volume of the solid by determining how many unit cubes are contained in the solid.

1. 120 cubic units

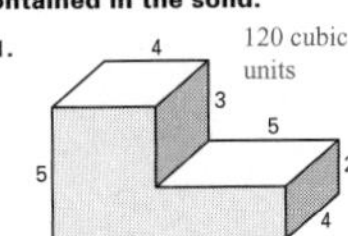

2. 120 cubic units

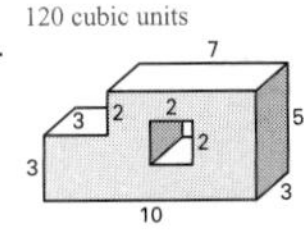

3. 136 cubic units

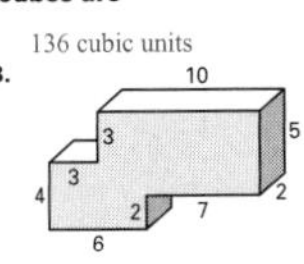

Find the volume of the right prism or right cylinder. Round your answer to two decimal places.

4. 96 m³

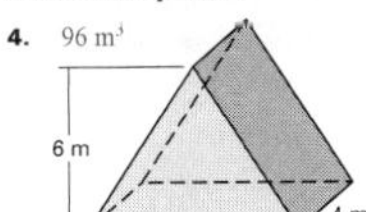

5. 189 in.³

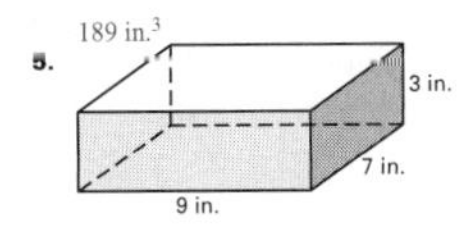

6. 831.38 cm³

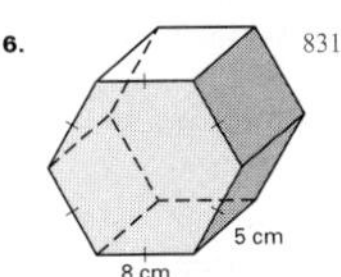

7. 113.1 ft³

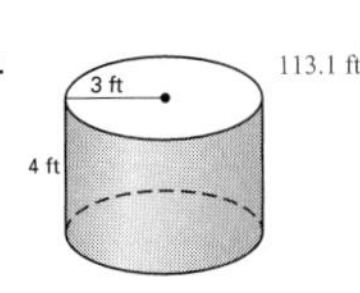

8. 942.48 in.³

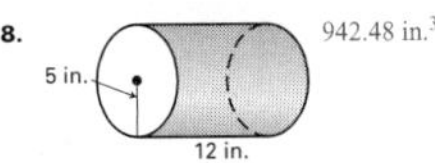

9. 276.46 cm³

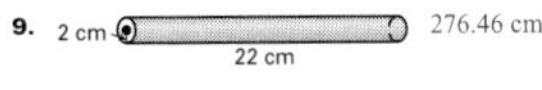

Find the length *x* using the given volume *V*.

10. $V = 1440\text{ m}^3$ 12 m

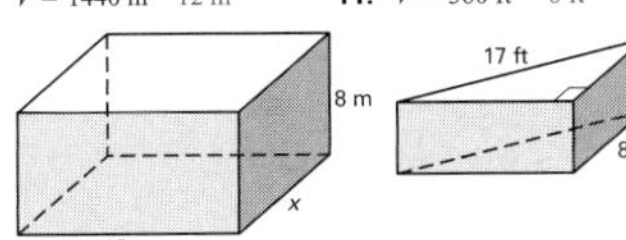

11. $V = 360\text{ ft}^3$ 6 ft

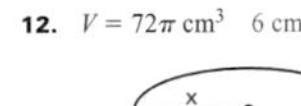

12. $V = 72\pi\text{ cm}^3$ 6 cm

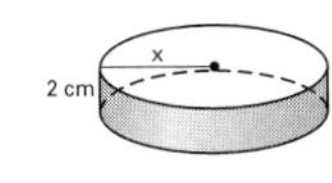

Practice B *continued*

LESSON 12.4 For use with pages 819–825

13. **Multiple Choice** How many 2 inch cubes can fit completely in a box that is 10 inches long, 8 inches wide, and 4 inches tall? C

A. 24 **B.** 32 **C.** 40 **D.** 320

Sketch the described solid and find its volume. Round your answer to two decimal places.

14. A rectangular prism with a height of 3 feet, width of 6 feet, and length of 9 feet. 162 ft³

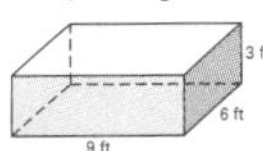

15. A right cylinder with a radius of 4 meters and a height of 8 meters. 402.12 m³

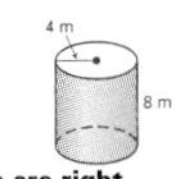

Find the volume of the solid. The prisms and cylinders are right. Round your answer to two decimal places.

16. 48 mm³

17. 502.65 in.³

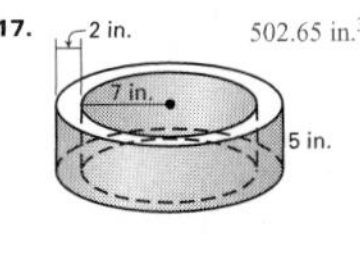

Use Cavalieri's Principle to find the volume of the oblique prism or cylinder. Round your answer to two decimal places.

18. 72 mm³

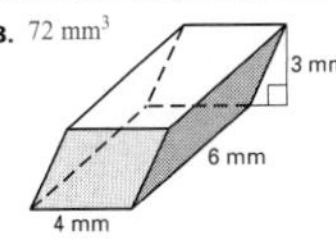

19. 62.83 in.³

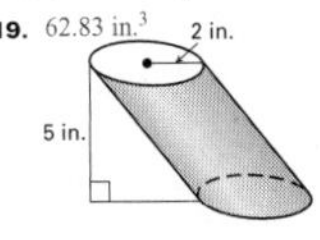

20. 301.59 cm³

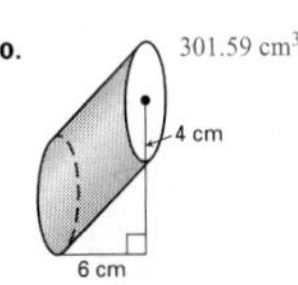

In Exercises 21–23, use the following information.

Pillars In order to model a home, you need to create four miniature pillars out of plaster of paris. The pillars will be shaped as regular hexagonal prisms with a face width of 2 inches and a height of 12 inches. Round your answers to two decimal places.

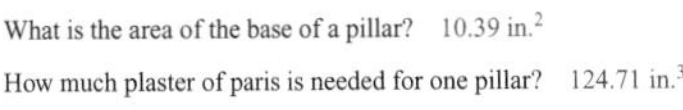

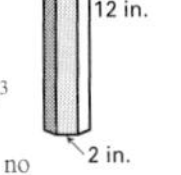

21. What is the area of the base of a pillar? 10.39 in.²

22. How much plaster of paris is needed for one pillar? 124.71 in.³

23. Is 480 cubic inches enough plaster of paris for all four pillars? no

12 Lesson Practice Level B

LESSON 12.5

Practice B

For use with pages 828–837

Find the volume of the solid. Round your answer to two decimal places.

1. 100.53 cm^3

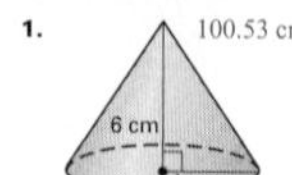

2. 20 $in.^3$

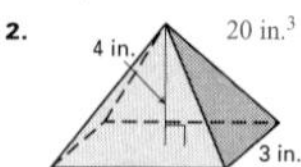

3. 10.67 cm^3

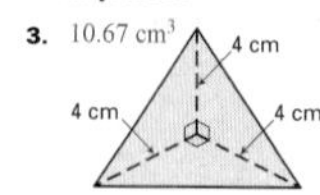

4. 414.69 m^3

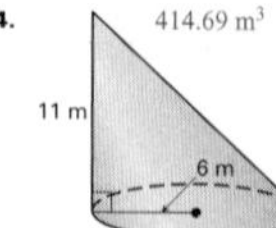

5. 126 $in.^3$

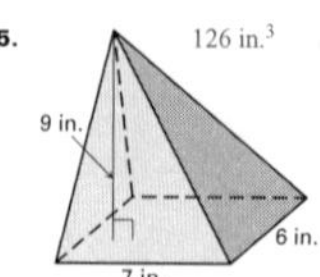

6. 163.49 cm^3

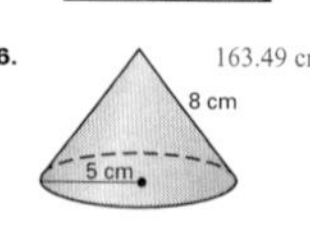

Find the value of *x*.

7. $V = 64\ in.^3$ 6 in.

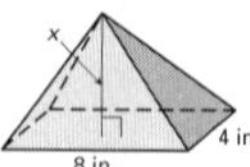

8. $V = 147\pi\ cm^3$ 7 cm

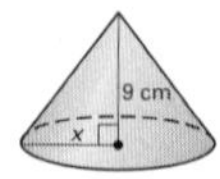

9. $V = 56\ m^3$ 7 m

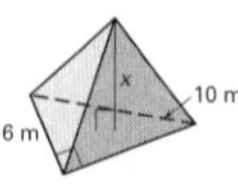

10. Multiple Choice A right cone has a height of 6 feet and a volume of 32π cubic feet. What is its radius? C

A. 2 ft **B.** 3 ft

C. 4 ft **D.** 5 ft

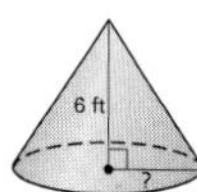

Find the volume of the right cone. Round your answer to two decimal places.

11. 2035.75 cm^3

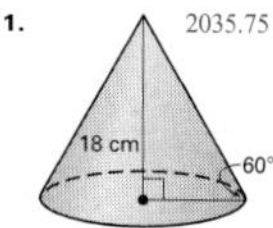

12. 3681.88 m^3

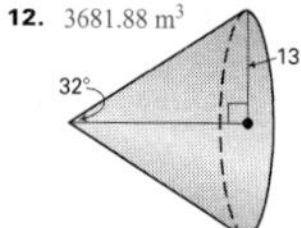

13. 2652.53 ft^3

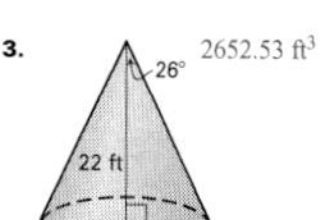

LESSON 12.5

LESSON 12.5

Practice B *continued*

For use with pages 828–837

Find the volume of the solid. The prisms, pyramids, and cones are right. Round your answer to two decimal places.

14. 448 m^3

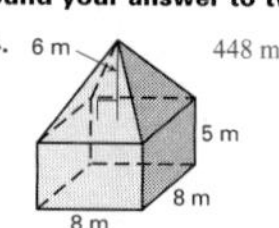

15. 90.93 $in.^3$

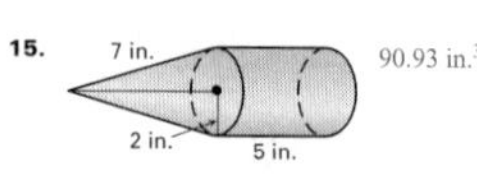

16. 144 cm^3

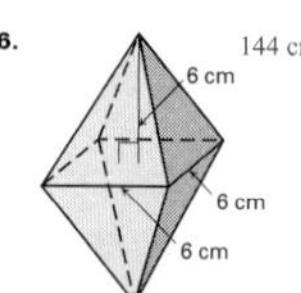

17. 190.87 mm^3

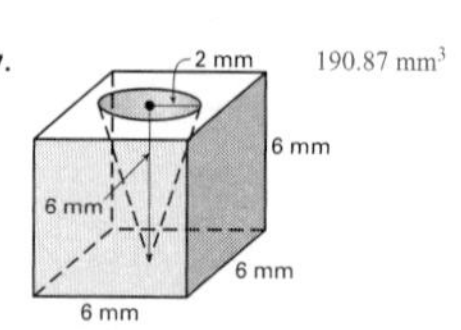

18. 103.72 $in.^3$

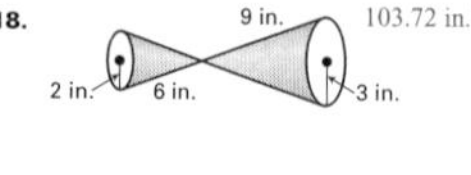

19. 122.67 m^3

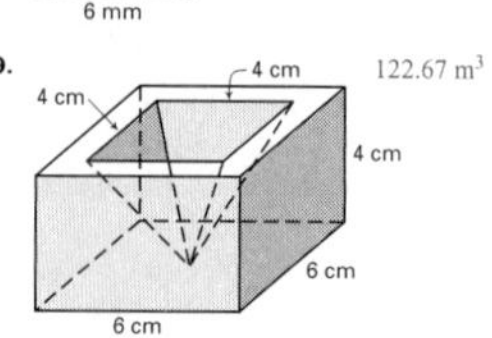

20. Height of a Pyramid A right pyramid with a square base has a volume of 16 cubic feet. The height is six times the base edge length. What is the height of the pyramid? 12 ft

In Exercises 21–23, use the following information.

Concrete To complete a construction job, a contractor needs 78 cubic yards of concrete. The contractor has a conical pile of concrete mix that measures 22 feet in diameter and 12 feet high.

21. How many cubic feet of concrete are available to the contractor? 1520.53 ft^3

22. How many cubic yards of concrete are available to the contractor? 56.32 yd^3

23. Does the contractor have enough concrete to finish the job? no

LESSON 12.6

Practice B

For use with pages 838–845

Find the surface area of the sphere. Round your answer to two decimal places.

1. 201.06 cm^2 (4 cm)

2. 28.27 $in.^2$

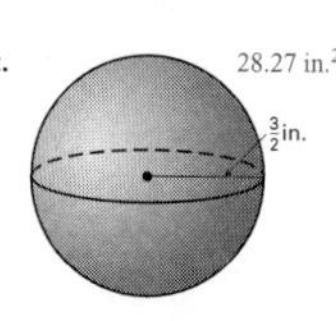

3. 615.75 m^2

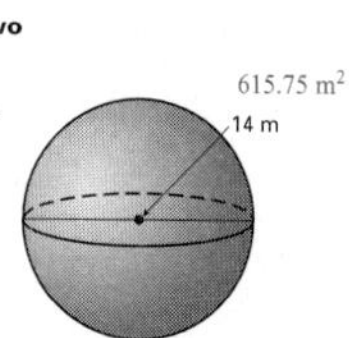

4. Multiple Choice What is the approximate radius of a sphere with a surface area of 40π square feet? B

A. 2 ft **B.** 3.16 ft **C.** 6.32 ft **D.** 10 ft

In Exercises 5–7, use the sphere below. The center of the sphere is *C* and its circumference is 7π centimeters.

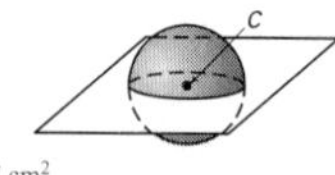

5. Find the radius of the sphere. $\frac{7}{2}$ cm

6. Find the diameter of the sphere. 7 cm

7. Find the surface area of one hemisphere. Round your answer to two decimal places. 76.97 cm^2

8. Great Circle The circumference of a great circle of a sphere is 24.6π meters. What is the surface area of the sphere? Round your answer to two decimal places. 1901.17 m^2

Find the volume of the sphere. Round your answer to two decimal places.

9. 1436.76 ft^3

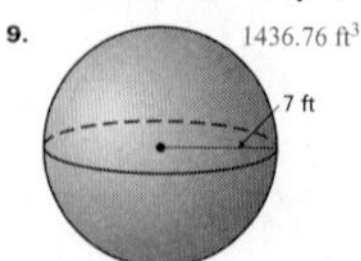

10. 381.7 yd^3

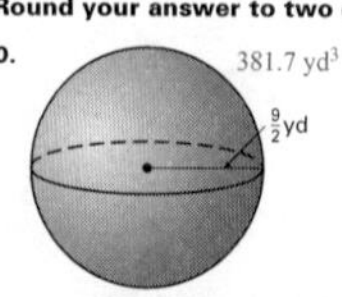

11. 2144.66 m^3

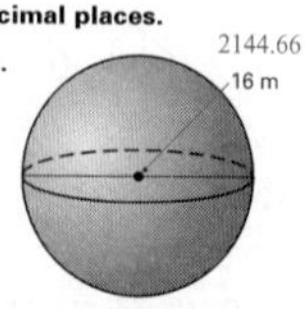

Find the radius of the sphere with the given volume *V*. Round your answer to two decimal places.

12. $V = 64\ in.^3$ 2.48 in. **13.** $V = 150\pi\ cm^3$ 4.83 cm **14.** $V = 152\ m^3$ 3.31 m

15. Multiple Choice What is the approximate radius of a sphere with a volume of 128π cubic centimeters? B

A. 2.5 cm **B.** 4.58 cm **C.** 6.62 cm **D.** 8 cm

LESSON 12.6

LESSON 12.6

Practice B *continued*

For use with pages 838–845

Find the surface area and the volume of the solid. The cylinders and cones are right. Round your answer to two decimal places.

16.

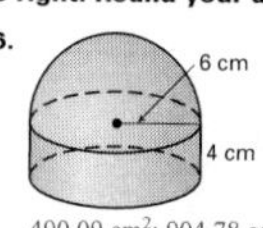

490.09 cm^2; 904.78 cm^3

17.

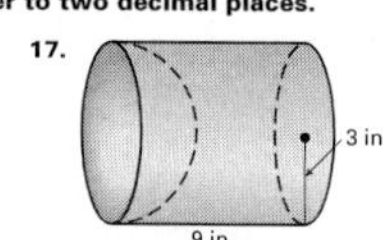

254.47 $in.^2$; 197.92 $in.^3$

18. 566.01 ft^2; 1093.27 ft^3

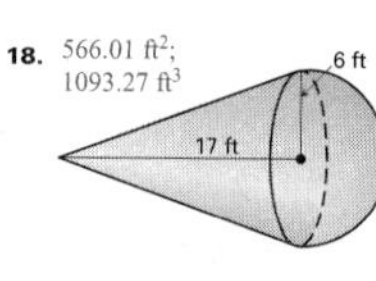

Complete the table below. Leave your answers in terms of π.

	Radius of sphere	Circumference of great circle	Surface area of sphere	Volume of sphere
19.	12 mm	24π mm	$576\pi\ mm^2$	$2304\pi\ mm^3$
20.	4 in.	8π in.	$64\pi\ in.^2$	$\frac{256}{3}\pi\ in.^3$
21.	$\frac{7}{2}$ ft	7π ft	$49\pi\ ft^2$	$\frac{343}{6}\pi\ ft^3$
22.	6 m	12π m	$144\pi\ m^2$	$288\pi\ m^3$

23. Finding a Diameter The volume of a sphere is 972π cubic centimeters. What is the diameter of the sphere? 18 cm

In Exercises 24–26, use the following information.

Golf Balls A standard golf ball has a diameter of 1.68 inches. Golf balls are often sold in a box of four. Assume that the balls are packed tightly so that they touch the lateral sides and the bases of the box.

24. What is the surface area of a golf ball? 8.87 $in.^2$

25. What is the volume of a golf ball? 2.48 $in.^3$

26. What is the amount of volume inside the box that is not taken up by the golf balls? 9.05 $in.^3$

LESSON 12.6

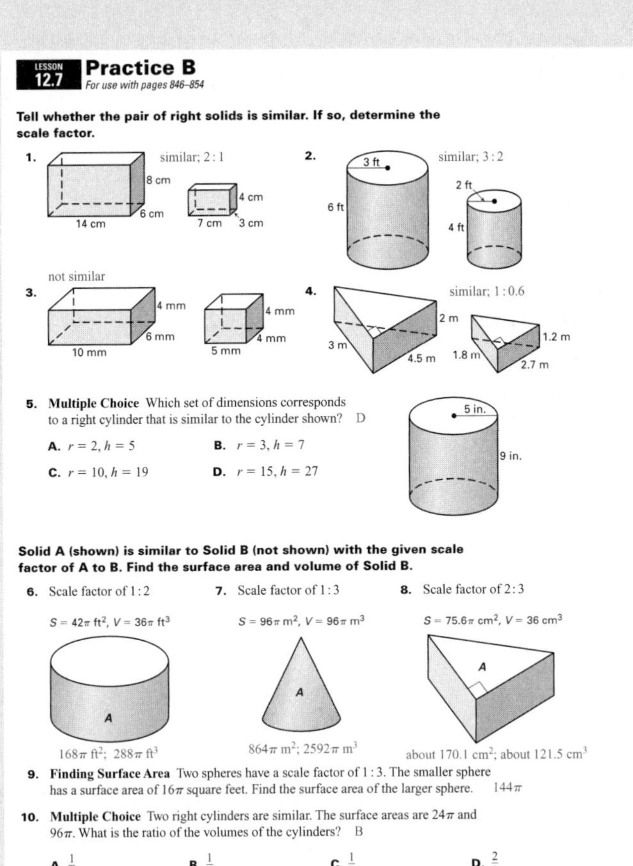

LESSON 12.7

Practice B

For use with pages 846–854

Tell whether the pair of right solids is similar. If so, determine the scale factor.

1. similar; 2 : 1

8 cm, 14 cm, 6 cm; 4 cm, 7 cm, 3 cm

2. similar; 3 : 2

3 ft, 6 ft; 2 ft, 4 ft

3. not similar

4 mm, 10 mm, 6 mm; 4 mm, 5 mm, 4 mm

4. similar; 1 : 0.6

2 m, 3 m, 4.5 m; 1.2 m, 1.8 m, 2.7 m

5. Multiple Choice Which set of dimensions corresponds to a right cylinder that is similar to the cylinder shown? D

5 in., 9 in.

A. $r = 2, h = 5$ **B.** $r = 3, h = 7$

C. $r = 10, h = 19$ **D.** $r = 15, h = 27$

Solid A (shown) is similar to Solid B (not shown) with the given scale factor of A to B. Find the surface area and volume of Solid B.

6. Scale factor of 1 : 2

$S = 42\pi$ ft², $V = 36\pi$ ft³

168π ft²; 288π ft³

7. Scale factor of 1 : 3

$S = 96\pi$ m², $V = 96\pi$ m³

864π m²; 2592π m³

8. Scale factor of 2 : 3

$S = 75.6\pi$ cm², $V = 36$ cm³

about 170.1 cm²; about 121.5 cm³

9. Finding Surface Area Two spheres have a scale factor of 1 : 3. The smaller sphere has a surface area of 16π square feet. Find the surface area of the larger sphere. 144π

10. Multiple Choice Two right cylinders are similar. The surface areas are 24π and 96π. What is the ratio of the volumes of the cylinders? B

A. $\frac{1}{4}$ **B.** $\frac{1}{8}$ **C.** $\frac{1}{2}$ **D.** $\frac{2}{3}$

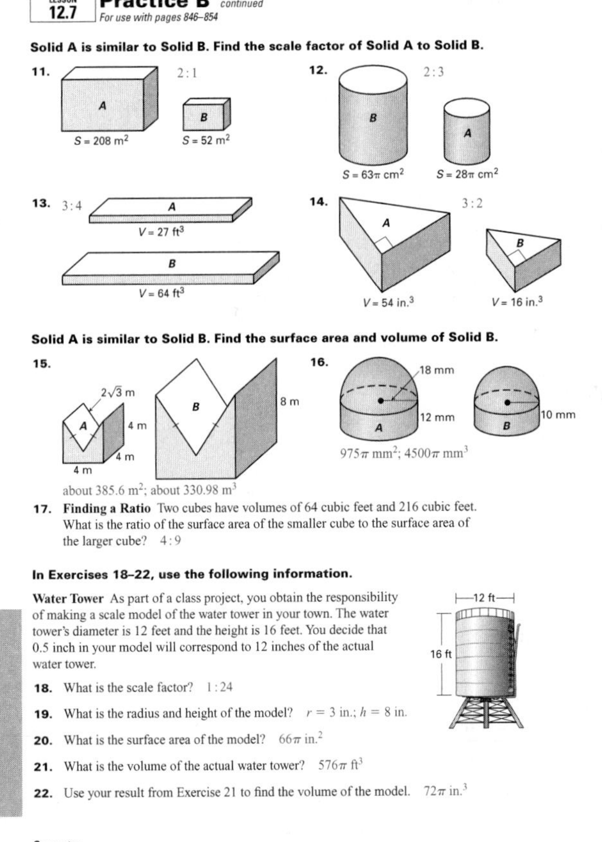

LESSON 12.7

Practice B *continued*

For use with pages 846–854

Solid A is similar to Solid B. Find the scale factor of Solid A to Solid B.

11. 2 : 1

$S = 208$ m²; $S = 52$ m²

12. 2 : 3

$S = 63\pi$ cm²; $S = 28\pi$ cm²

13. 3 : 4

$V = 27$ ft³; $V = 64$ ft³

14. 3 : 2

$V = 54$ in.³; $V = 16$ in.³

Solid A is similar to Solid B. Find the surface area and volume of Solid B.

15. $2\sqrt{3}$ m, 4 m, 4 m, 4 m; 8 m

about 385.6 m²; about 330.98 m³

16. 18 mm, 12 mm; 10 mm

975π mm²; 4500π mm³

17. Finding a Ratio Two cubes have volumes of 64 cubic feet and 216 cubic feet. What is the ratio of the surface area of the smaller cube to the surface area of the larger cube? 4 : 9

In Exercises 18–22, use the following information.

Water Tower As part of a class project, you obtain the responsibility of making a scale model of the water tower in your town. The water tower's diameter is 12 feet and the height is 16 feet. You decide that 0.5 inch in your model will correspond to 12 inches of the actual water tower.

12 ft, 16 ft

18. What is the scale factor? 1 : 24

19. What is the radius and height of the model? $r = 3$ in.; $h = 8$ in.

20. What is the surface area of the model? 66π in.²

21. What is the volume of the actual water tower? 576π ft³

22. Use your result from Exercise 21 to find the volume of the model. 72π in.³

LESSON 12.7

12 Assessment

CHAPTER 12 Quiz 1
For use after Lessons 12.1–12.3

1. A polyhedron has 6 vertices and 9 edges. How many faces does the polyhedron have?

Find the surface area of the right prism or right cylinder. Round your answer to two decimal places.

2.
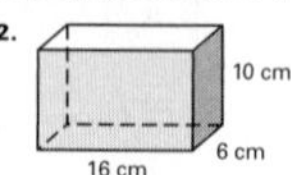

3.
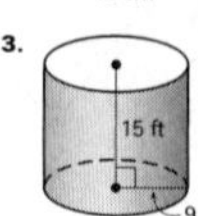

4.
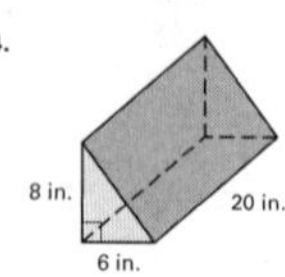

Find the surface area of the regular pyramid or right cone. Round your answer to two decimal places.

5.
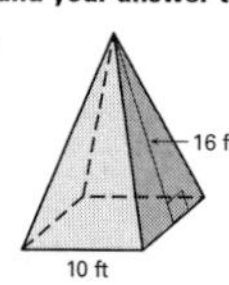

6.
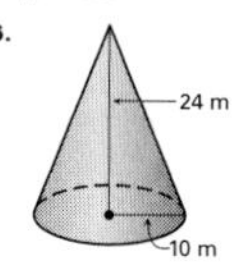

Answers

1. 5 faces
2. 632 cm^2
3. 1357.17 ft^2
4. 528 $in.^2$
5. 420 ft^2
6. 1130.97 m^2

CHAPTER 12 Quiz 2
For use after Lessons 12.4–12.5

Find the volume of the figure. Round your answer to two decimal places, if needed.

1.
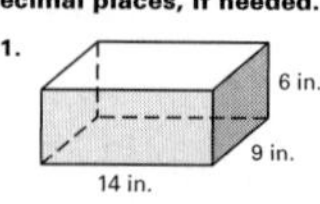

2.
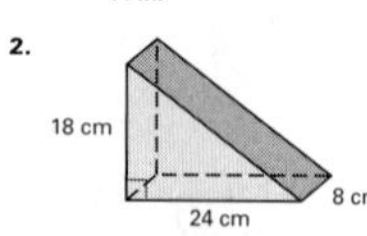

3.
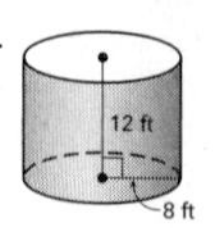

4.
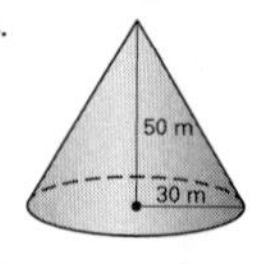

5.
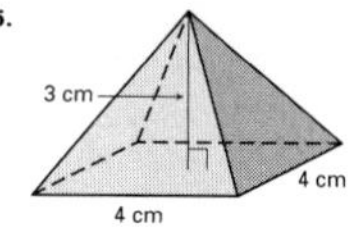

Answers

1. 756 $in.^3$
2. 1728 cm^3
3. 2412.74 ft^3
4. 47,123.89 m^3
5. 16 cm^3

CHAPTER 12 Quiz 3
For use after Lessons 12.6–12.7

Find the surface area and volume of the sphere. Round your answers to two decimal places.

1.
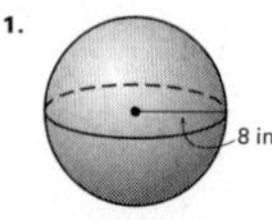

2.
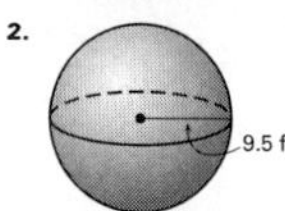

3.
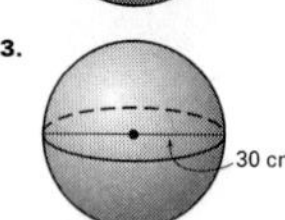

Solid A (shown) is similar to Solid B (not shown) with the given scale factor of A to B. Find the surface area *S* and volume *V* of Solid B.

4. Scale factor 1 : 2
$S = 120\text{ ft}^2$
$V = 60\text{ ft}^3$

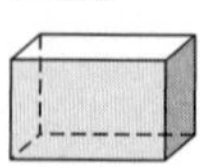

5. Scale factor 1 : 4
$S = 180\pi\text{ cm}^2$
$V = 400\pi\text{ cm}^3$

6. Two similar spheres have surface areas 784π square meters and 289π square feet. What is the scale factor of the larger sphere to the smaller sphere?

Answers

1. 804.25 $in.^2$; 2144.16 $in.^3$
2. 1134.11 ft^2; 3591.36 ft^3
3. 2827.43 cm^2; 14,137.17 cm^3
4. 480 ft^2, 480 ft^3
5. 9047.79 cm^2, 80,424.77 cm^3
6. 28 : 17

CHAPTER 12 Chapter Test B
For use after Chapter 12

Tell whether the solid is a polyhedron. If it is, find the number of faces, vertices, and edges.

1.
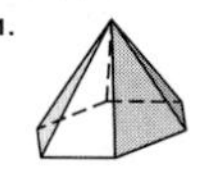

2.

3.

Use Euler's Theorem to find the value of *n*.

4. Faces: 8
Vertices: 12
Edges: *n*

5. Faces: 9
Vertices: *n*
Edges: 21

6. Faces: *n*
Vertices: 16
Edges: 24

Find the surface area of the solid. The pyramids are regular and the prisms, cones, and cylinders are right. Round your answers to two decimal places, if necessary.

7.
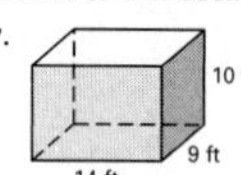

8.

9.
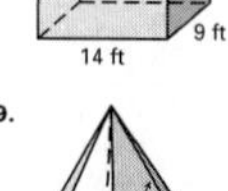
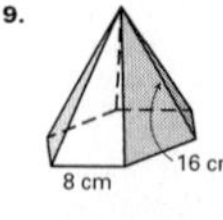

10.
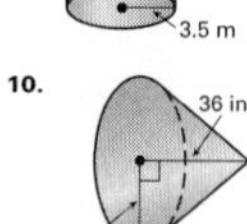

11.
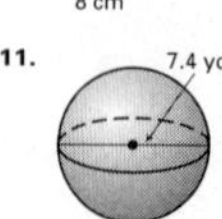

12.
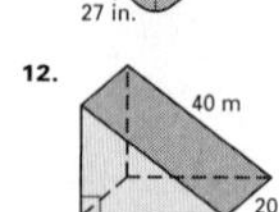

Solve for *x* given the surface area *S* of the right solid. Round your answer to the nearest meter.

13. $S = 6372\text{ m}^2$

14. $S = 325\text{ m}^2$
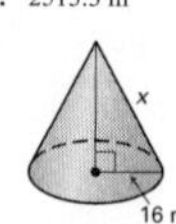
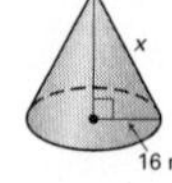

15. 2513.3 m^2

Answers

1. polyhedron; 7 faces, 7 vertices, 12 edges
2. not a polyhedron
3. polyhedron; 10 faces, 16 vertices, 24 edges
4. 18
5. 14
6. 10
7. 712 ft^2
8. 226.51 m^2
9. 538.04 cm^2
10. 6107.26 $in.^2$
11. 172.03 yd^2
12. 2048 m^2
13. 50 m
14. 7 m
15. 34 m

CHAPTER 12

Chapter Test B *continued*

For use after Chapter 12

Find the volume of the solid. The pyramids are regular and the prisms, cones, and cylinders are right. Round your answers to two decimal places, if necessary.

16.

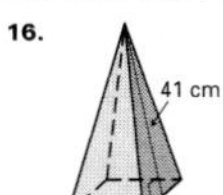

17.

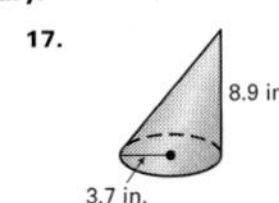

18. $3\frac{1}{2}$ km

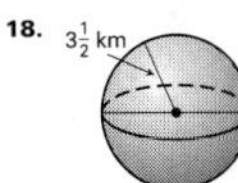

19. 8 m

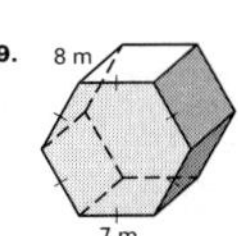

Find the surface area and volume of the solid. The pyramids are regular and the prisms, cones, and cylinders are right. Round your answer to two decimal places, if necessary.

20.

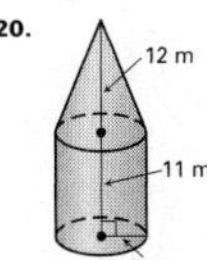

21. 5 cm

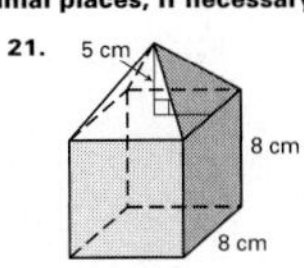

Find the volume of the solid. The cylinders and prisms are right. Round your answer to two decimal places, if necessary.

22.

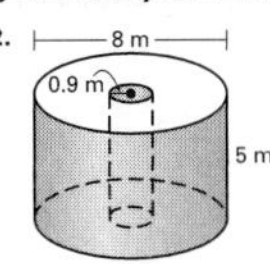

23.

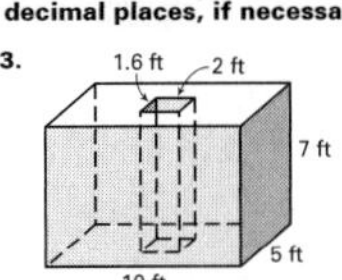

24. Two cones have a scale factor of 2 : 5. The smaller cone has a surface area of 96π square yards. Find the surface area of the larger cone. Write your answer in terms of π.

25. Two spheres have a scale factor of 3 : 8. The smaller sphere has a volume of about 54π cubic meters. Find the volume of the larger sphere. Write your answer in terms of π.

Answers

16. 4320 cm^3
17. 127.59 in.^{3}
18. 179.59 km^3
19. 1018.45 m^3
20. S = 628.32 m^2, V = 1178.1 m^3
21. S = 486.45 cm^2, V = 618.67 cm^3
22. 238.60 m^3
23. 327.6 ft^3
24. 600π yd^2
25. 1024π m^3

CHAPTER 12

Standardized Test

For use after Chapter 12

Multiple Choice

1. Which figure is *not* a polyhedron? C

Ⓐ 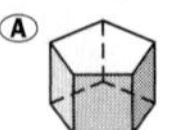

Ⓑ 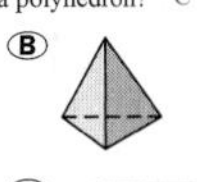

Ⓒ 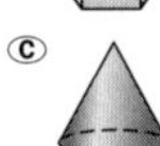

Ⓓ 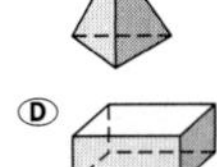

2. Which equation represents Euler's Theorem? A

Ⓐ $F + V = E + 2$ Ⓑ $F + E = V + 2$

Ⓒ $E + V = F + 2$ Ⓓ $F + V = E - 2$

3. The two-dimensional representation of the faces of a polyhedron is called _?_. D

Ⓐ lateral area Ⓑ surface area

Ⓒ lateral edge Ⓓ a net

4. Find the surface area of the right prism. B

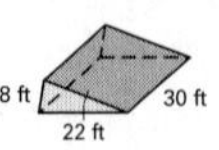

Ⓐ 855.07 ft^2 Ⓑ 1733.07 ft^2

Ⓒ 1342.47 ft^2 Ⓓ 2625.68 ft^2

5. Find the surface area of the right cylinder. A

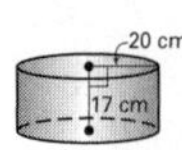

Ⓐ 4647.2 cm^2 Ⓑ 2960 cm^2

Ⓒ 2323.6 cm^2 Ⓓ 1480 cm^2

6. A polyhedron in which the base is a polygon and the lateral faces are triangles with a common vertex is a _?_. C

Ⓐ prism Ⓑ cone

Ⓒ pyramid Ⓓ dodecahedron

7. Find the surface area of the regular pyramid. B

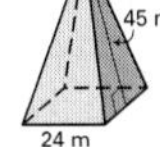

Ⓐ 1656 m^2 Ⓑ 2736 m^2

Ⓒ 4896 m^2 Ⓓ 2184 m^2

8. Find the surface area of the right cone. D

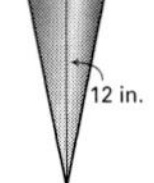

Ⓐ 141.3 in.^{2}

Ⓑ 266.9 in.^{2}

Ⓒ 90 in.^{2}

Ⓓ 282.6 in.^{2}

9. Find the volume of a 6-inch tall glass with a 3-inch diameter. A

Ⓐ 42.39 in.^{3} Ⓑ 169.56 in.^{3}

Ⓒ 54 in.^{3} Ⓓ 56.52 in.^{3}

10. Find the volume of the solid (in cubic meters). D

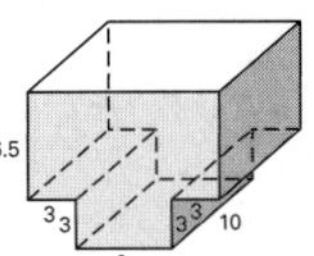

Ⓐ 780 m^3 Ⓑ 840 m^3

Ⓒ 570 m^3 Ⓓ 960 m^3

11. Find the volume of the pyramid. B

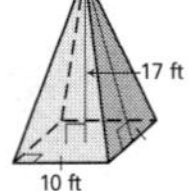

Ⓐ 1700 ft^3

Ⓑ 566.67 ft^3

Ⓒ 283.33 ft^3

Ⓓ 850 ft^3

CHAPTER 12

Standardized Test *continued*

For use For use after Chapter 12

12. Find the volume of the cone. B

10 in. 14 in. 4 in.

Ⓐ 234.45 in.^{3}

Ⓑ 167.47 in.^{3}

Ⓒ 502.4 in.^{3}

Ⓓ 334.94 in.^{3}

13. The set of all points in space equidistant from a given point is a _?_. A

Ⓐ sphere Ⓑ plane

Ⓒ circle Ⓓ great circle

14. Find the surface area of a globe with a 24-inch diameter. A

Ⓐ 1808.64 in.^{2} Ⓑ 7234.56 in.^{2}

Ⓒ 904.32 in.^{2} Ⓓ 3627.28 in.^{2}

15. If an intersecting plane contains the center of the sphere, then the intersection is a _?_ of the sphere. D

Ⓐ hemisphere Ⓑ great sphere

Ⓒ half circle Ⓓ great circle

16. Find the volume of the solid. C

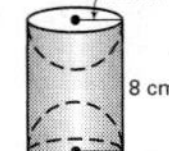

Ⓐ 226.08 cm^3 Ⓑ 188.4 cm^3

Ⓒ 113.04 cm^3 Ⓓ 141.3 cm^3

17. Which solid is similar to a solid with a length of 5 inches, width of 2 inches, and a height of $2\frac{1}{2}$ inches? D

Ⓐ $\ell = 4$ in., $w = 1$ in., $h = 1\frac{1}{2}$ in.

Ⓑ $\ell = 10$ in., $w = 7$ in., $h = 7\frac{1}{2}$ in.

Ⓒ $\ell = 10$ in., $w = 4$ in., $h = 4\frac{1}{2}$ in.

Ⓓ $\ell = 2$ in., $w = \frac{4}{5}$ in., $h = 1$ in.

Gridded Answer

18. Find the volume of the solid.

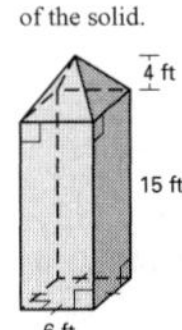

5 8 8

Short Response

19. A ball has a 10-inch radius.

a. Find the volume of the ball 4186.67 in.^{3}

b. Find the volume of a ball with half the radius. Is the volume half that of the larger ball? *Explain.* No; 523.33 in.^{3}

Extended Response

20. A stainless steel tank is 8 feet tall with a 12-foot diameter.

a. Find the surface area of the tank. 527.52 ft^2

b. Find the volume of the tank. 904.32 ft^3

c. How long will it take to drain $\frac{7}{8}$ of a tank at a rate of 3.5 cubic feet per minute? 226.08 min

d. If carbonated water and corn syrup are mixed at a 5 : 2 ratio, how much of each do you need to fill the tank? water: 645.94 ft^3; syrup; 258.38 ft^3

CHAPTER 12

Alternative Assessment and Math Journal

For use after Chapter 12

Journal **1.** Without using variables, explain how to find the volumes of right prisms, right cylinders, regular pyramids, right cones, and spheres.

Multi-Step Problem **2.** A ready-to-assemble home furnishings company packages its products in compact cardboard boxes.

a. A dining table is packaged in a box that is in the shape of a rectangular prism. The box is 5 feet long, 3 feet wide, and 1 foot deep. Find the volume and surface area of the box.

b. A trapezoidal desk is packaged in the box shown. Find the volume of the box.

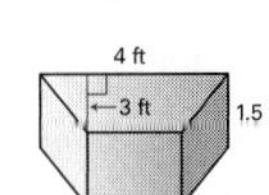

c. A cylindrical side table is packaged in the rectangular prism as shown. How much space is not taken up by the table inside the box?

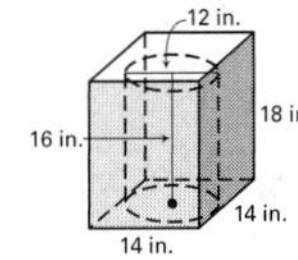

d. The company also sells hanging lights like the one shown. The right cones are similar with a scale factor of 3 : 5. The surface area of the smaller cone is approximately 61.2 square inches and the volume of the smaller cone is approximately 31.8 cubic inches. Find the volume and surface area of the larger cone.

e. The leg of a couch that the company sells is formed by cutting off the top one-third of a pyramid as shown. Explain how to find the volume of the couch leg.

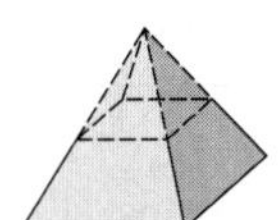

1. Find the volume of a right prism or right cylinder by multiplying the area of the base by the height. Find the volume of a regular pyramid or right cone by finding one third of the product of the area of the base and the height. Find the area of a sphere by finding four thirds of the product of pi and the cube of the radius.

2. a. 15 ft^3; 46 ft^2 **b.** 13.5 ft^2 **c.** about 1718.44 in.^{3} **d.** about 147.22 in.^{3}; 170 in.^{2}

e. Subtract the volume of the pyramid that is cut off from the main pyramid.

PLAN AND PREPARE

Main Ideas

In this chapter students identify and name solids, including Platonic solids, and use Euler's Theorem to relate the number of faces, vertices, and edges of solids. Students describe cross sections of solids, find the surface areas and lateral areas of prisms and cylinders, and use nets to find surface area. They find the surface area and volume of prisms, cylinders, cones, pyramids, spheres, and composite solids. Finally, they use scale factors in similar solids to compare the ratios of the surface areas and the ratios of the volumes of the solids.

Prerequisite Skills

- Reviewing area of a regular polygon and describing what it means for two polygons to be similar
- Using the Pythagorean Theorem to find the unknown side lengths of a right triangle
- Finding the circumference and area of a circle with given dimensions

Additional resources for reviewing prerequisite skills are:

- Skills Review Handbook, pp. 869–895
- @HomeTutor

1. $A = \frac{1}{2}a \cdot P$, **where** a **is the apothem and** P **is the perimeter, or** $A = \frac{1}{2}a \cdot ns$, **where** n **is the number of sides and** s **is the side length**

12 Surface Area and Volume of Solids

Before

In previous chapters, you learned the following skills, which you'll use in Chapter 12: properties of similar polygons, areas and perimeters of two-dimensional figures, and right triangle trigonometry.

Prerequisite Skills

VOCABULARY CHECK

1. Copy and complete: The area of a regular polygon is given by the formula $A = \underline{\ ?\ }$. **See margin.**
2. *Explain* what it means for two polygons to be similar. **Two polygons are similar if corresponding angles are congruent and corresponding side lengths are proportional.**

SKILLS AND ALGEBRA CHECK

Use trigonometry to find the value of x. *(Review pp. 466, 473 for 12.2–12.5.)*

3.
about 14.0

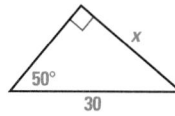

4.
about 14.6

5.
about 23.0

Find the circumference and area of the circle with the given dimension. *(Review pp. 746, 755 for 12.2–12.5.)*

6. $r = 2$ m
12.6 m, 12.6 m²
7. $d = 3$ in.
9.42 in., 7.07 in.²
8. $r = 2\sqrt{5}$ cm
28.1 cm, 62.8 cm²

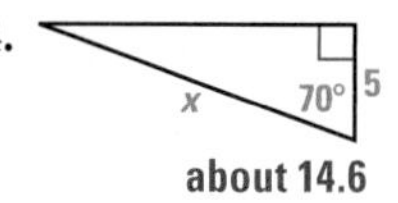

@HomeTutor Prerequisite skills practice at classzone.com

790

Chapter Planning Guide

Chapter 12 Resource Book
- Teaching Guide/Lesson Plan (pp. 3, 19, 33, 48, 62, 77, 90)
- Project with Rubric (p. 105)

Assessment and Intervention
- Assessment Book (pp. 170–184)
- Benchmark Tests
- Remediation Book

Interactive Technology
- Easy Planner
- Power Presentations CD-ROM
- Activity Generator CD-ROM
- Animated Geometry
- Test Generator CD-ROM
- Online Quizzes
- eWorkbook
- eEdition
- @HomeTutor

Resources for English Learners
- Quick Reference for English Learners
- Spanish Study Guide
- Multi-Language Visual Glossary
- Student Resources in Spanish

California Standards for Chapter 12

Geometry: 8.0, 9.0, 11.0

Now

In Chapter 12, you will apply the big ideas listed below and reviewed in the Chapter Summary on page 856. You will also use the key vocabulary listed below.

Big Ideas

1. **Exploring solids and their properties**
2. **Solving problems using surface area and volume**
3. **Connecting similarity to solids**

KEY VOCABULARY

- polyhedron, *p. 794* face, edge, vertex
- Platonic solids, *p. 796*
- cross section, *p. 797*
- prism, *p. 803*
- surface area, *p. 803*
- lateral area, *p. 803*
- net, *p. 803*
- right prism, *p. 804*
- oblique prism, *p. 804*
- cylinder, *p. 805*
- right cylinder, *p. 805*
- pyramid, *p. 810*
- regular pyramid, *p. 810*
- cone, *p. 812*
- right cone, *p. 812*
- volume, *p. 819*
- sphere, *p. 838*
- great circle, *p. 839*
- hemisphere, *p. 839*
- similar solids, *p. 847*

Why?

Knowing how to use surface area and volume formulas can help you solve problems in three dimensions. For example, you can use a formula to find the volume of a column in a building.

Animated Geometry

The animation illustrated below for Exercise 31 on page 825 helps you answer this question: What is the volume of the column?

You can use the height and circumference of a column to find its volume.

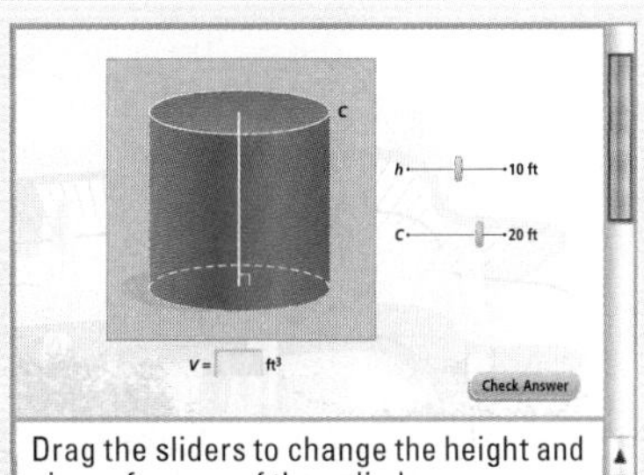

Drag the sliders to change the height and circumference of the cylinder.

Animated Geometry at classzone.com

Other animations for Chapter 12: pages 795, 805, 821, 833, 841, and 852

Geometry Toolkit

- Reading Strategies for Chapter 12, pp. 31–32
- Differentiated Instruction Notes, pp. 83–86
- English Learners Notes, pp. 113–114
- Inclusion Notes, pp. 143–144
- Teaching Strategies with Sample Worksheets, pp. 145–168
- Using Technology in the Classroom, pp. 169–174
- Tips for New Teachers, pp. 197–198
- Math Background Notes, pp. 238–240
- Pre-AP Strategies and Copymasters, pp. 305–306, 393–400
- Teacher Survival Activities, pp. 443–444, 467–468
- Bulletin Board Idea, p. 480
- Teacher Tool Transparencies, following p. 480

1 PLAN AND PREPARE

Explore the Concept

- Students will investigate solids using nets.
- This activity leads into the study of solids and Euler's Theorem in Lesson 12.1.

Materials

Each student will need:

- poster board
- scissors
- tape
- straightedge
- Activity Support Master (*Chapter 12 Resource Book*, p. 7)

Recommended Time

Work activity: 15 min
Discuss results: 5 min

Grouping

Students should work individually.

2 TEACH

Tips for Success

Make sure students are familiar with the terms *faces*, *vertices*, and *edges*.

Key Questions

- To make a net for a solid, can you use any regular polygon for all the faces? **no**
- Is there a relationship between the number of vertices, edges, and faces for each solid? **yes**

Alternative Strategy

Demonstrate a net for each exploration. Show students several nets for a cube.

Key Discovery

There is a relationship between F, V, and E given by $F + V = E + 2$.

12.1 Investigate Solids

MATERIALS • poster board • scissors • tape • straightedge

Standards

Prepare for 9.0 *Students compute the* volumes and *surface areas of prisms, pyramids,* cylinders, cones, and spheres; and students commit to memory the formulas for prisms, pyramids, and cylinders.

QUESTION **What solids can be made using congruent regular polygons?**

Platonic solids, named after the Greek philosopher Plato (427 B.C.–347 B.C.), are solids that have the same congruent regular polygon as each *face,* or side of the solid.

EXPLORE 1 **Make a solid using four equilateral triangles**

STEP 1

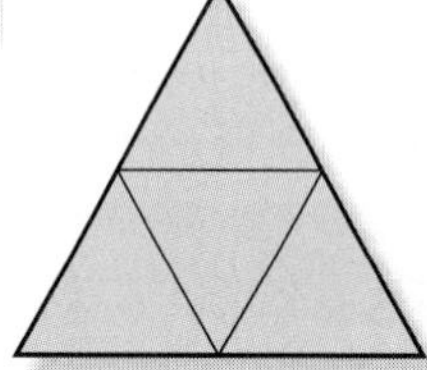

Make a net Copy the full-sized triangle from page 793 on poster board to make a template. Trace the triangle four times to make a *net* like the one shown.

STEP 2

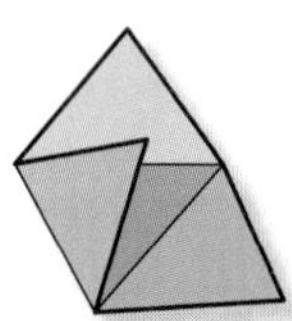

Make a solid Cut out your net. Fold along the lines. Tape the edges together to form a solid. How many faces meet at each *vertex*? **3**

EXPLORE 2 **Make a solid using eight equilateral triangles**

STEP 1

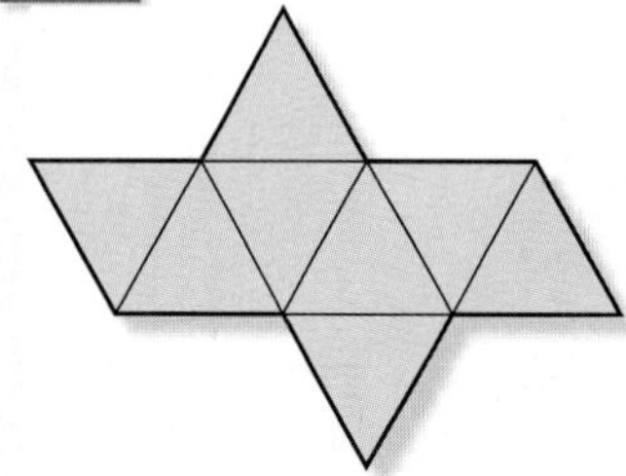

Make a net Trace your triangle template from Explore 1 eight times to make a net like the one shown.

STEP 2

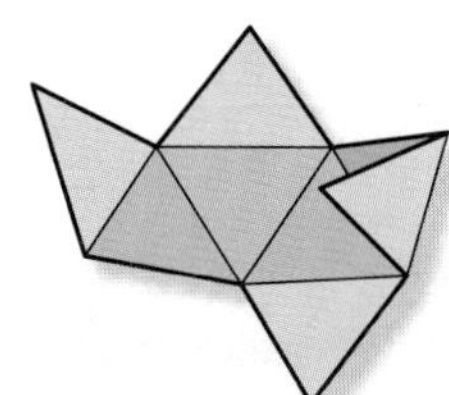

Make a solid Cut out your net. Fold along the lines. Tape the edges together to form a solid. How many faces meet at each vertex? **4**

EXPLORE 3 Make a solid using six squares

STEP 1

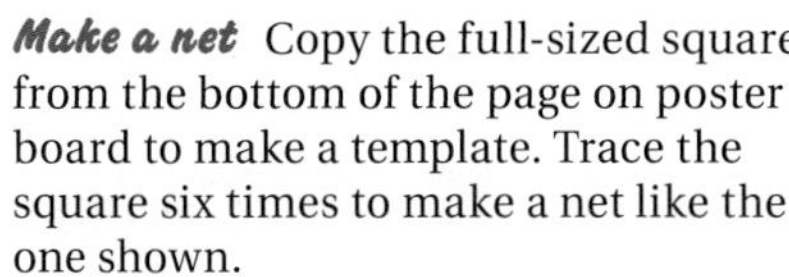

Make a net Copy the full-sized square from the bottom of the page on poster board to make a template. Trace the square six times to make a net like the one shown.

STEP 2

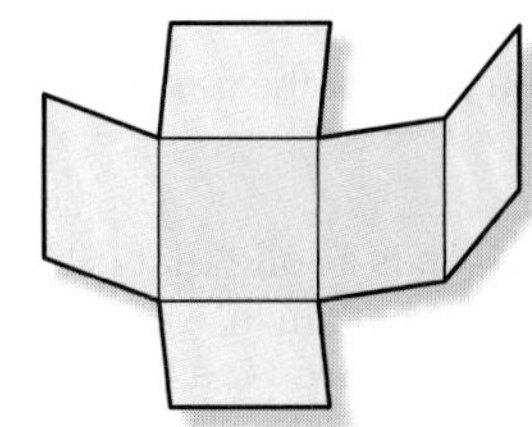

Make a solid Cut out your net. Fold along the lines. Tape the edges together to form a solid. How many faces meet at each vertex? **3**

DRAW CONCLUSIONS Use your observations to complete these exercises

1. The two other convex solids that you can make using congruent, regular faces are shown below. For each of these solids, how many faces meet at each vertex?

a. **3**

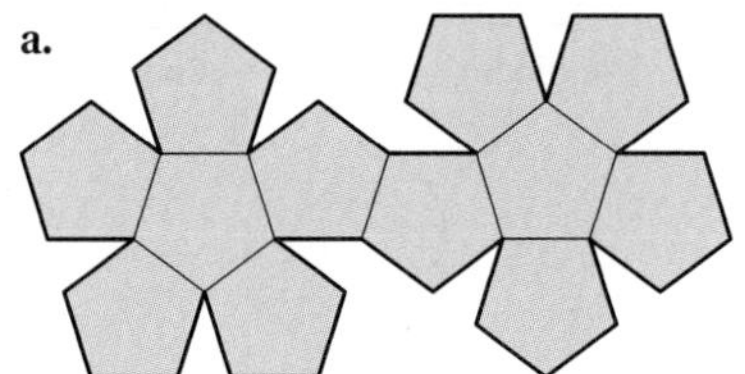

b. **5**

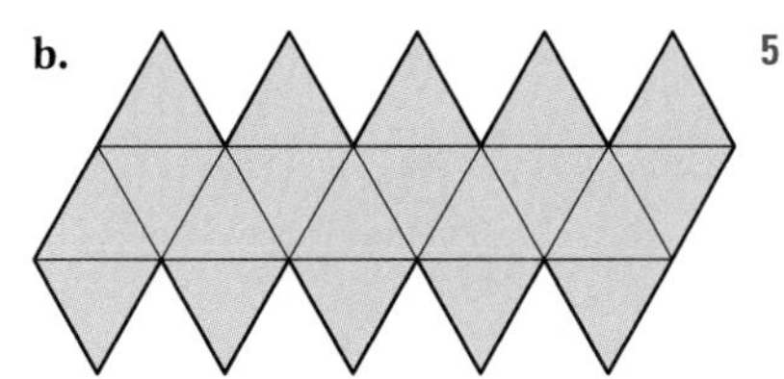

2. *Explain* why it is not possible to make a solid that has six congruent equilateral triangles meeting at each vertex. **See margin.**
3. *Explain* why it is not possible to make a solid that has three congruent regular hexagons meeting at each vertex. **See margin.**
4. Count the number of vertices V, edges E, and faces F for each solid you made. Make a conjecture about the relationship between the sum $F + V$ and the value of E. $\mathbf{F + V = E + 2}$

Templates:

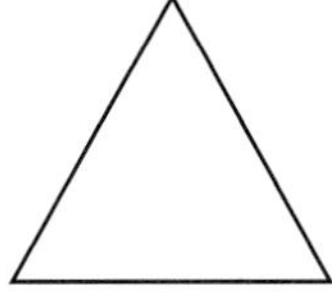

3 ASSESS AND RETEACH

1. How many faces are in the solids for this activity? **4 faces; 8 faces; 6 faces; 12 faces; 20 faces**

2. How many edges does the solid in Exploration 3 have? **12 edges**

2. The vertices of 6 congruent equilateral triangles meeting at a point would form a circle, since $6 \cdot 60° = 360°$. Since a circle is in a plane, the vertices would not form a solid, whose faces are non-coplanar. The sum of the angle measures at a vertex must be less than 360°.

3. Each angle measure of a regular hexagon is 120°. The vertices of 3 congruent regular hexagons meeting at a point would form a circle, since $3 \cdot 120° = 360°$. Since a circle is in a plane, the vertices would not form a solid, whose faces are non-coplanar. The sum of the angle measures at a vertex must be less than 360°.

1 PLAN AND PREPARE

Warm-Up Exercises

Transparency Available

Name the polygon by the number of sides.

1. 6 **hexagon**
2. 10 **decagon**
3. 5 **pentagon**
4. What is a regular polygon? **a polygon with all congruent sides and all congruent angles**
5. What is the length of a diagonal of a square with side length 6? **$6\sqrt{2}$**

Notetaking Guide

Transparency Available

Promotes interactive learning and notetaking skills, pp. 309–312.

Pacing

Basic: 2 days

Average: 2 days

Advanced: 2 days

Block: 1 block

- See *Teaching Guide/Lesson Plan.*

2 FOCUS AND MOTIVATE

Essential Question

Big Idea 1, p. 791

When is a solid a polyhedron?

Tell students they will learn how to answer this question by looking at the faces of the solid.

12.1 Explore Solids

Before You identified polygons.

Now You will identify solids.

Why So you can analyze the frame of a house, as in Example 2.

Key Vocabulary
- **polyhedron** face, edge, vertex
- **base**
- **regular polyhedron**
- **convex polyhedron**
- **Platonic solids**
- **cross section**

Standards

Prepare for 9.0 *Students compute the volumes and surface areas of prisms, pyramids, cylinders, cones, and spheres;* and students commit to memory the formulas for prisms, pyramids, and cylinders.

A **polyhedron** is a solid that is bounded by polygons, called **faces**, that enclose a single region of space. An **edge** of a polyhedron is a line segment formed by the intersection of two faces. A **vertex** of a polyhedron is a point where three or more edges meet. The plural of polyhedron is *polyhedra* or *polyhedrons.*

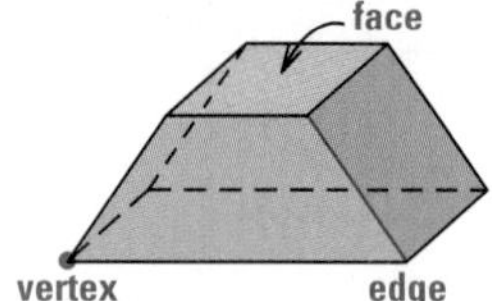

KEY CONCEPT *For Your Notebook*

Types of Solids

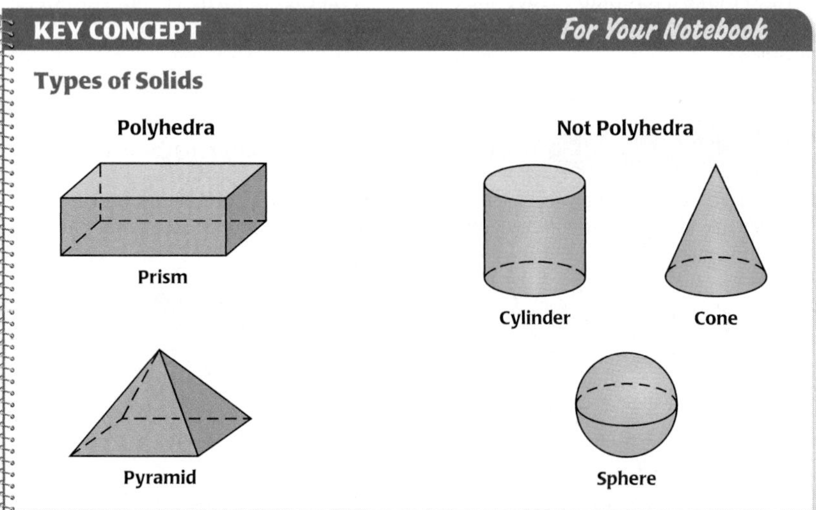

CLASSIFYING SOLIDS Of the five solids above, the prism and the pyramid are polyhedra. To name a prism or a pyramid, use the shape of the *base.*

Pentagonal prism

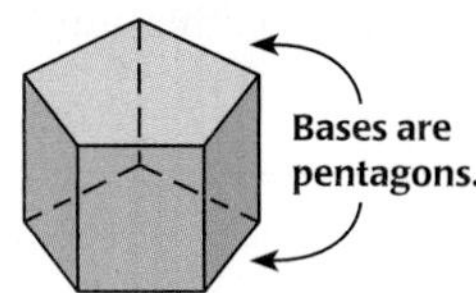

The two **bases** of a prism are congruent polygons in parallel planes.

Triangular pyramid

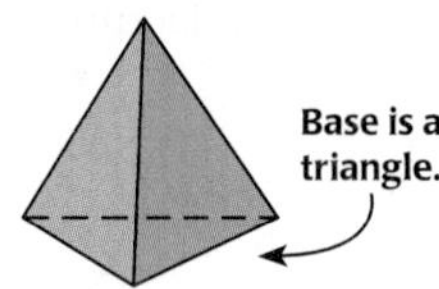

The **base** of a pyramid is a polygon.

Resource Planning Guide

Chapter Resource Book
- Teaching Guide/Lesson Plan (pp. 3–4)
- Activity Master (p. 5)
- Practice levels A, B, C (pp. 8–13)
- Study Guide (pp. 14–15)
- Catch-up for Absent Students (p. 16)
- Application (p. 17)
- Challenge (p. 18)

Workbooks
- Notetaking Guide (pp. 309–312)
- Practice Workbook (pp. 226–228)

Teaching Options
- **Power Presentations CD-ROM** provides dynamic electronic teaching resources for the classroom.
- **Activity Generator CD-ROM** provides editable activities for all ability levels.

Interactive Technology
- Easy Planner
- Power Presentations CD-ROM
- Activity Generator CD-ROM
- Animated Geometry
- Test Generator CD-ROM
- Online Quiz
- eWorkbook
- eEdition
- @HomeTutor

Resources for English Learners
- Quick Reference for English Learners
- Spanish Study Guide
- Multi-Language Visual Glossary
- Student Resources in Spanish

See also the *Geometry Toolkit* for more strategies for meeting individual needs.

EXAMPLE 1 Identify and name polyhedra

Tell whether the solid is a polyhedron. If it is, name the polyhedron and find the number of faces, vertices, and edges.

a. 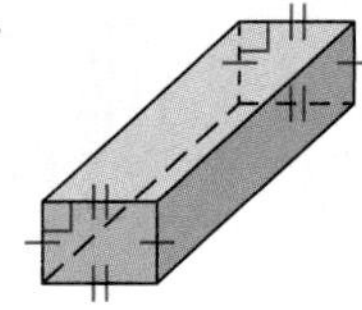

b. 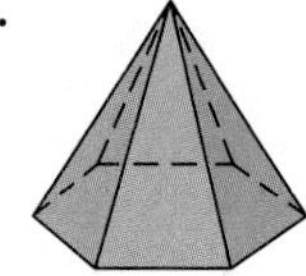

c. 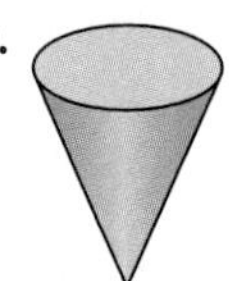

Solution

a. The solid is formed by polygons, so it is a polyhedron. The two bases are congruent rectangles, so it is a rectangular prism. It has 6 faces, 8 vertices, and 12 edges.

b. The solid is formed by polygons, so it is a polyhedron. The base is a hexagon, so it is a hexagonal pyramid. It has 7 faces, consisting of 1 base, 3 visible triangular faces, and 3 non-visible triangular faces. The polyhedron has 7 faces, 7 vertices, and 12 edges.

c. The cone has a curved surface, so it is not a polyhedron.

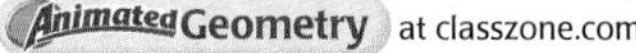

GUIDED PRACTICE for Example 1

Tell whether the solid is a polyhedron. If it is, name the polyhedron and find the number of faces, vertices, and edges.

1. 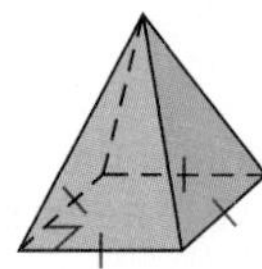

polyhedron; square pyramid, 5, 5, 8

2. 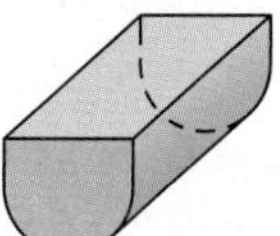

not a polyhedron

3. 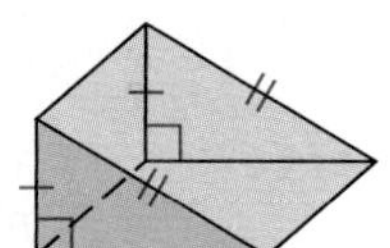

polyhedron; triangular prism, 5, 6, 9

EULER'S THEOREM Notice in Example 1 that the sum of the number of faces and vertices of the polyhedra is two more than the number of edges. This suggests the following theorem, proved by the Swiss mathematician Leonhard Euler (pronounced "oi′-ler"), who lived from 1707 to 1783.

THEOREM *For Your Notebook*

THEOREM 12.1 Euler's Theorem

The number of faces (F), vertices (V), and edges (E) of a polyhedron are related by the formula $F + V = E + 2$.

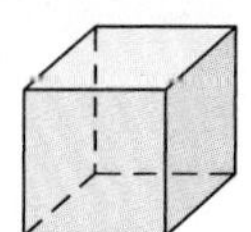

$F = 6, V = 8, E = 12$
$6 + 8 = 12 + 2$

Motivating the Lesson

Ask students to describe solids such as the shape of their classroom and the shape of a paper towel roll. For each solid, discuss whether or not all the faces are polygons. Tell students that this lesson investigates solids for which all the faces are polygons.

3 TEACH

Extra Example 1

Tell whether the solid is a polyhedron. If it is, name it and find the number of faces, vertices, and edges.

a. 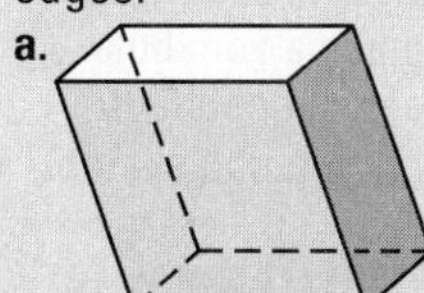

yes; prism; 6 faces, 8 vertices, 12 edges

b. 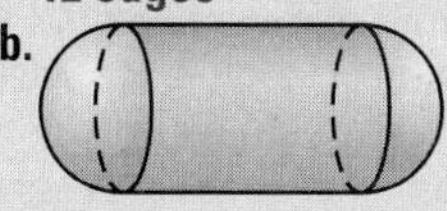

no

c. 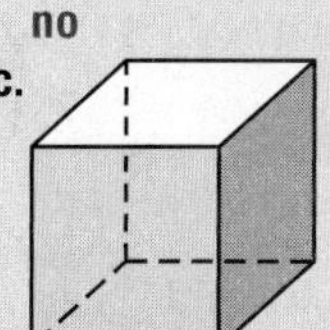

yes; square prism; 6 faces, 8 vertices, 12 edges

Animated Geometry classzone.com

An **Animated Geometry** activity is available on-line for **Example 1**. This activity is also available on the **Power Presentations CD-ROM**.

Differentiated Instruction

Below Level Provide students with many different solids. Ask them to list the solids in one column of a chart and to provide columns for the numbers of faces, vertices, and edges. Then ask them to tell whether each solid is a polyhedron. If it is, they should count the number of faces, vertices, and edges and record the results in the chart.

See also the *Geometry Toolkit* for more strategies.

Extra Example 2

Find the number of edges on the "wedge" of cheese. **9 edges**

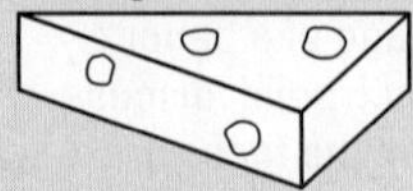

Key Question to Ask for Example 2

- How could you rewrite Euler's Theorem to find the number of edges directly? $E = F + V - 2$

Vocabulary

This lesson contains a great number of new vocabulary terms, including names of polyhedra and other solids. Students should be encouraged to make a vocabulary chart showing each vocabulary term and its definition and sketch.

Extra Example 3

Find the number of faces, vertices, and edges of the regular tetrahedron. Check your answer using Euler's Theorem.

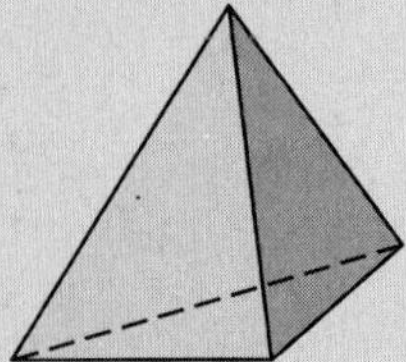

4 faces, 4 vertices, 6 edges; $4 + 4 = 6 + 2$, so $F + V = E + 2$.

Key Question to Ask for Example 3

- What is the shape of each face of the regular octahedron? **a regular triangle**

EXAMPLE 2 Use Euler's Theorem in a real-world situation

HOUSE CONSTRUCTION Find the number of edges on the frame of the house.

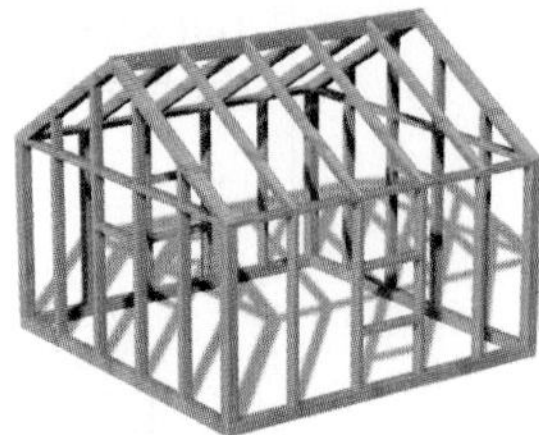

Solution

The frame has one face as its foundation, four that make up its walls, and two that make up its roof, for a total of 7 faces.

To find the number of vertices, notice that there are 5 vertices around each pentagonal wall, and there are no other vertices. So, the frame of the house has 10 vertices.

Use Euler's Theorem to find the number of edges.

$F + V = E + 2$	**Euler's Theorem**
$7 + 10 = E + 2$	**Substitute known values.**
$15 = E$	**Solve for *E*.**

▶ The frame of the house has 15 edges.

REGULAR POLYHEDRA A polyhedron is **regular** if all of its faces are congruent regular polygons. A polyhedron is **convex** if any two points on its surface can be connected by a segment that lies entirely inside or on the polyhedron. If this segment goes outside the polyhedron, then the polyhedron is nonconvex, or *concave*.

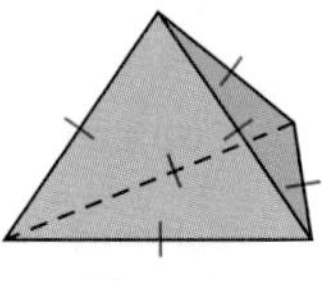

regular, convex

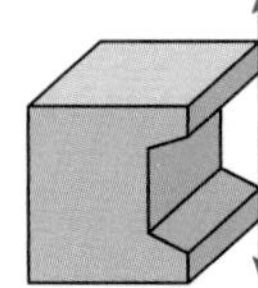

nonregular, concave

There are five regular polyhedra, called **Platonic solids** after the Greek philosopher Plato (c. 427 B.C.–347 B.C.). The five Platonic solids are shown.

READ VOCABULARY

Notice that the names of four of the Platonic solids end in "hedron." *Hedron* is Greek for "side" or "face." Sometimes a cube is called a regular *hexahedron*.

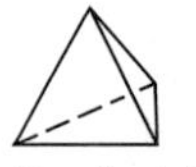

Regular tetrahedron
4 faces

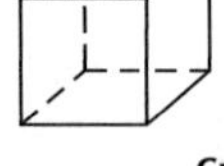

Cube
6 faces

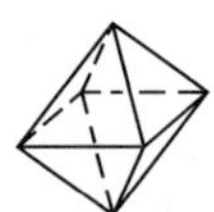

Regular octahedron
8 faces

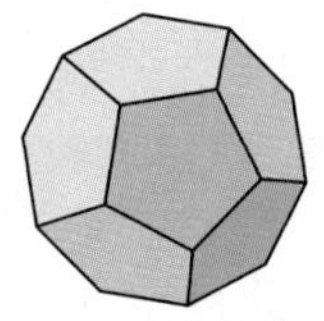

Regular dodecahedron
12 faces

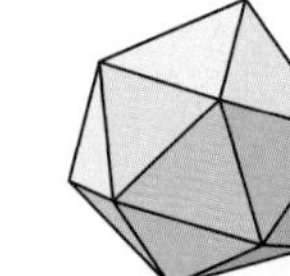

Regular icosahedron
20 faces

There are only five regular polyhedra because the sum of the measures of the angles that meet at a vertex of a convex polyhedron must be less than 360°. This means that the only possible combinations of regular polygons at a vertex that will form a polyhedron are 3, 4, or 5 triangles, 3 squares, and 3 pentagons.

Differentiated Instruction

English Learners Explain to students that plural words like *polyhedra* often come from a foreign language, such as Latin. In English, the words often keep their foreign plural and also take on an English plural, such as polyhedrons. Point out that the foreign plural is more often used in a technical sense.

See also the *Geometry Toolkit* for more strategies.

EXAMPLE 3 Use Euler's Theorem with Platonic solids

Find the number of faces, vertices, and edges of the regular octahedron. Check your answer using Euler's Theorem.

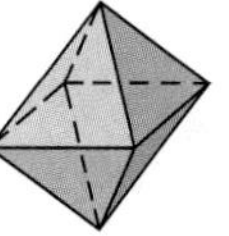

ANOTHER WAY

An octahedron has 8 faces, each of which has 3 vertices and 3 edges. Each vertex is shared by 4 faces; each edge is shared by 2 faces. They should only be counted once.

$V = \frac{8 \cdot 3}{4} = 6$

$E = \frac{8 \cdot 3}{2} = 12$

Solution

By counting on the diagram, the octahedron has 8 faces, 6 vertices, and 12 edges. Use Euler's Theorem to check.

$F + V = E + 2$ Euler's Theorem

$8 + 6 = 12 + 2$ Substitute.

$14 = 14$ ✓ This is a true statement. So, the solution checks.

CROSS SECTIONS Imagine a plane slicing through a solid. The intersection of the plane and the solid is called a **cross section**. For example, the diagram shows that an intersection of a plane and a triangular pyramid is a triangle.

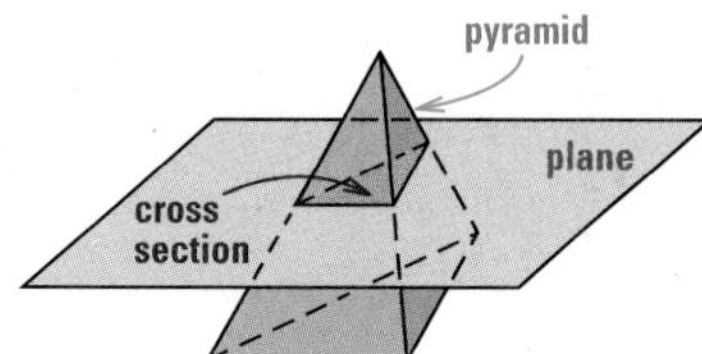

EXAMPLE 4 Describe cross sections

Describe the shape formed by the intersection of the plane and the cube.

a. 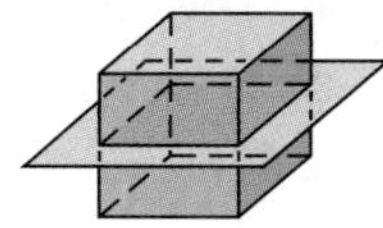

b. 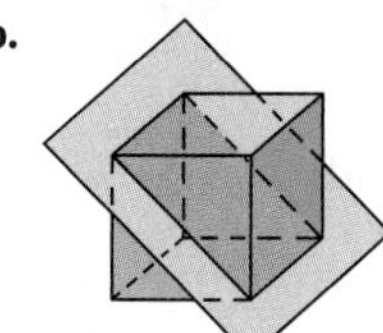

c. 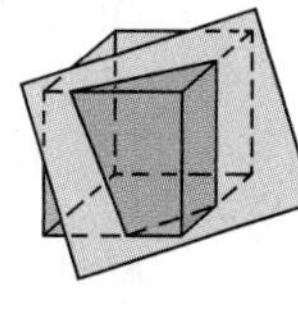

Solution

a. The cross section is a square.

b. The cross section is a rectangle.

c. The cross section is a trapezoid.

✓ **GUIDED PRACTICE** for Examples 2, 3, and 4

4. Find the number of faces, vertices, and edges of the regular dodecahedron on page 796. Check your answer using Euler's Theorem.
faces: 12, vertices: 20, edges: 30; $F + V = E + 2$, $12 + 20 = 30 + 2$, $32 = 32$ ✓

Describe **the shape formed by the intersection of the plane and the solid.**

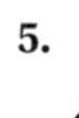

5. 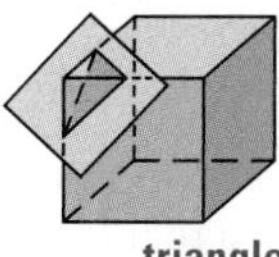
triangle

6. 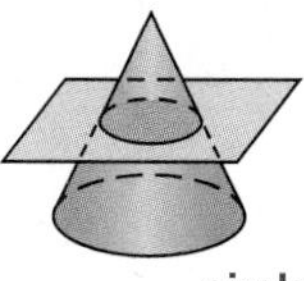
circle

7. 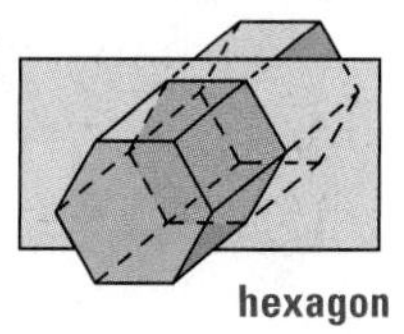
hexagon

Extra Example 4

Describe the shape formed by the intersection of the plane and the closed cylinder.

a. **circle**

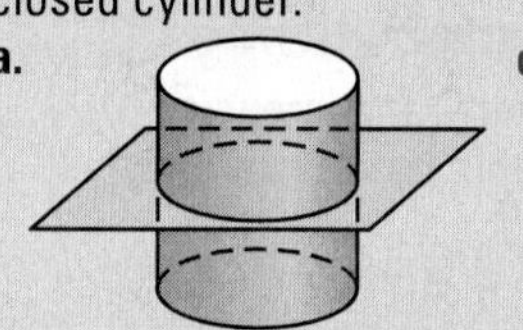

b. **rectangle**

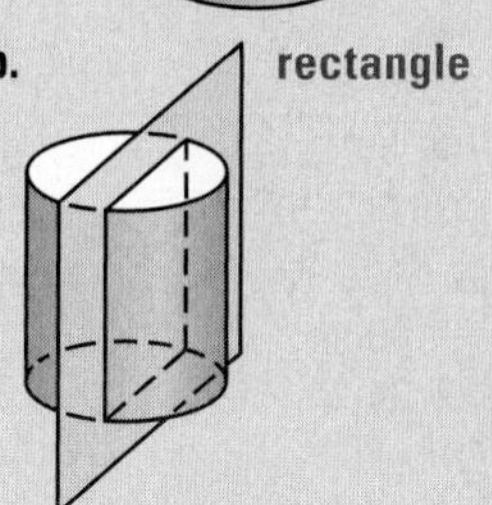

c. **ellipse**

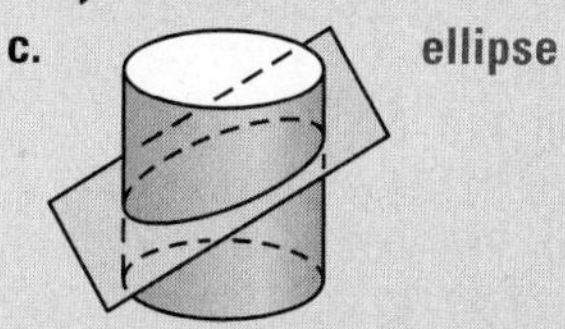

Key Questions to Ask for Example 4

- In part (c), why is the cross section a trapezoid? **It is a quadrilateral with one pair of opposite sides parallel.**
- In which cross section is the plane either parallel or perpendicular to each face of the solid? **part (a)**

Closing the Lesson

Have students summarize the major points of the lesson and answer the Essential Question: When is a solid a polyhedron?

- **A solid is a polyhedron if it is bounded by polygons. A polyhedron is regular if all of its faces are congruent regular polygons.**
- **For a polyhedron, $F + V = E + 2$.**
- **The intersection of a plane and a solid is a cross section.**

If all the faces of a solid are polygons, then the solid is a polyhedron.

4 PRACTICE AND APPLY

Assignment Guide

Answer Transparencies available for all exercises

Basic:
Day 1: EP p. 897 Exs. 41–44
pp. 798–801
Exs. 1–20, 34, 35
Day 2: pp. 798–801
Exs. 21–30, 36–42, 52–60

Average:
Day 1: pp. 798–801
Exs. 1–20, 32, 34, 35, 56, 59
Day 2: pp. 798–801
Exs. 21–27 odd, 28–31, 37–49, 53

Advanced:
Day 1: pp. 798–801
Exs. 1–20, 32, 34, 35, 57, 60
Day 2: pp. 798–801
Exs. 21, 24, 27–31, 33*, 38–51*, 54

Block:
pp. 798–801
Exs. 1–20, 21–27 odd, 28–32, 34, 35, 37–49, 53, 56, 59

Differentiated Instruction

See *Geometry Best Practices Toolkit* for suggestions on addressing the needs of a diverse classroom.

Homework Check

For a quick check of student understanding of key concepts, go over the following exercises:
Basic: 4, 16, 22, 26, 34
Average: 8, 18, 23, 27, 37
Advanced: 10, 20, 24, 28, 38

Extra Practice

- Student Edition, p. 918
- Chapter 12 Resource Book: Practice levels A, B, C, pp. 8–13

Practice Worksheet

An easily-readable reduced practice page (with answers) for this lesson can be found on p. 790C.

12.1 EXERCISES

HOMEWORK KEY
○ = **WORKED-OUT SOLUTIONS** on p. WS16 for Exs. 11, 25, and 35
★ = **STANDARDIZED TEST PRACTICE** Exs. 2, 21, 28, 30, 31, 39, and 41

SKILL PRACTICE

A

1. **VOCABULARY** Name the five Platonic solids and give the number of faces for each. **tetrahedron, 4 faces; hexahedron or cube, 6 faces; octahedron, 8 faces; dodecahedron, 12 faces; icosahedron, 20 faces**

2. ★ **WRITING** State Euler's Theorem in words. **The sum of the number of faces and vertices of a polyhedron is 2 more than the number of edges.**

EXAMPLE 1 on p. 795 for Exs. 3–10

IDENTIFYING POLYHEDRA **Determine whether the solid is a polyhedron. If it is, name the polyhedron. *Explain* your reasoning.**

3. 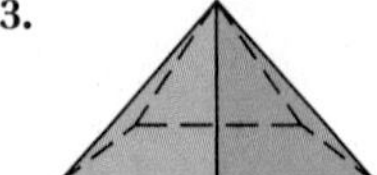

4. 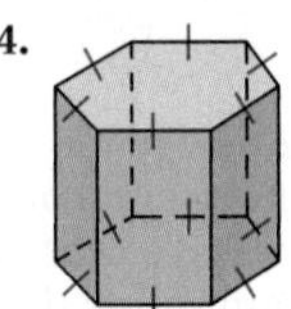

5. 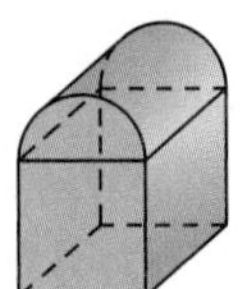

3. Polyhedron; pentagonal pyramid; the solid is formed by polygons and the base is a pentagon.
4. Polyhedron; hexagonal prism; the solid is formed by polygons and the two bases are congruent hexagons.
5. Not a polyhedron; the solid is not formed by polygons.

6. **ERROR ANALYSIS** *Describe* and correct the error in identifying the solid. **The bases are triangles; the solid is a triangular prism.**

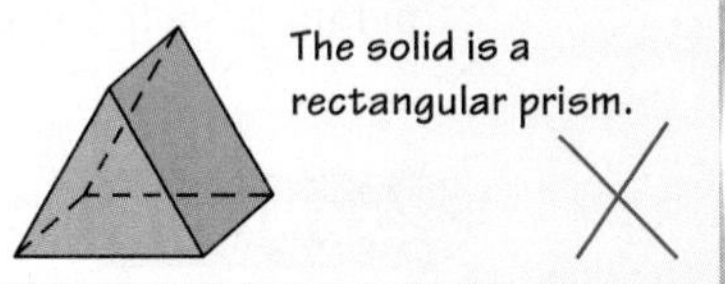

SKETCHING POLYHEDRA **Sketch the polyhedron.** **7–10. See margin.**

7. Rectangular prism
8. Triangular prism
9. Square pyramid
10. Pentagonal pyramid

EXAMPLES 2 and 3 on pp. 796–797 for Exs. 11–24

APPLYING EULER'S THEOREM **Use Euler's Theorem to find the value of *n*.**

11. Faces: n
Vertices: 12
Edges: 18 **8**

12. Faces: 5
Vertices: n
Edges: 8 **5**

13. Faces: 10
Vertices: 16
Edges: n **24**

14. Faces: n
Vertices: 12
Edges: 30 **20**

APPLYING EULER'S THEOREM **Find the number of faces, vertices, and edges of the polyhedron. Check your answer using Euler's Theorem.**

15. 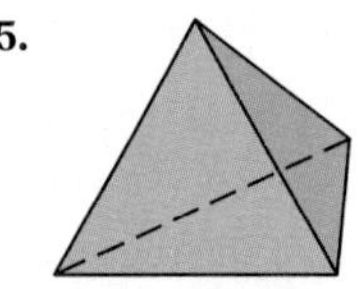 **4, 4, 6**

16. 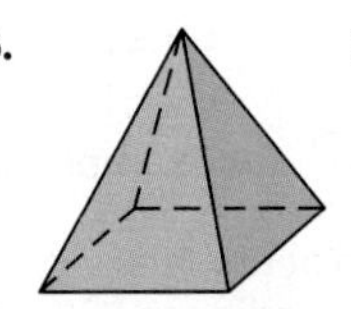 **5, 5, 8**

17. 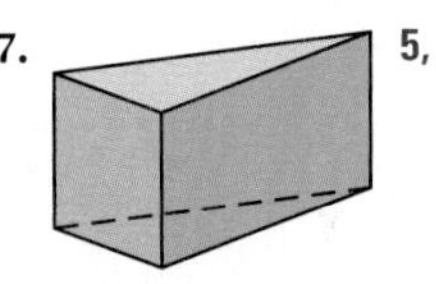 **5, 6, 9**

18. **5, 6, 9**

19. 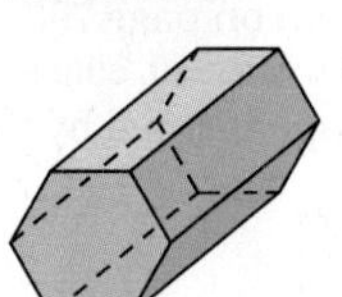 **8, 12, 18**

20. 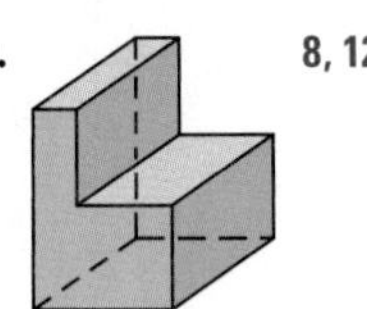 **8, 12, 18**

21. ★ **WRITING** *Explain* why a cube is also called a regular hexahedron. **A cube has six faces, and "hexa" means six.**

7. 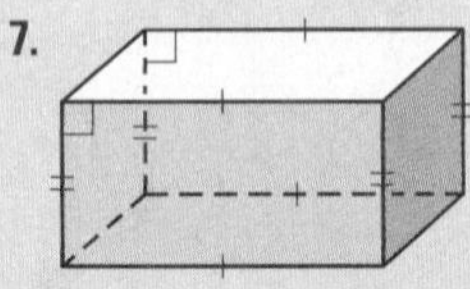

8. 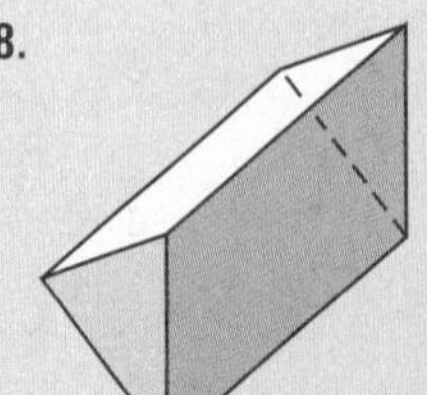

9. 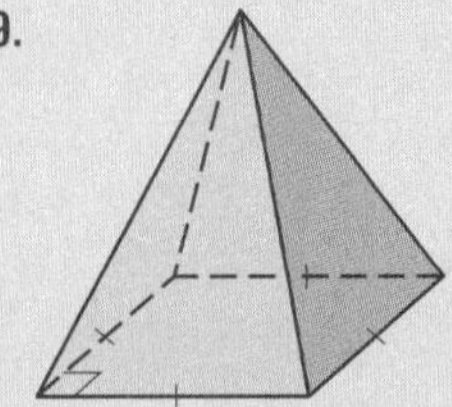

PUZZLES **Determine whether the solid puzzle is *convex* or *concave*.**

22\. 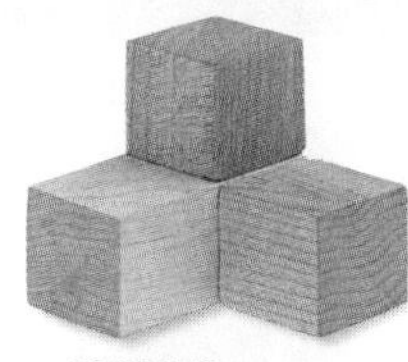
concave

23\. 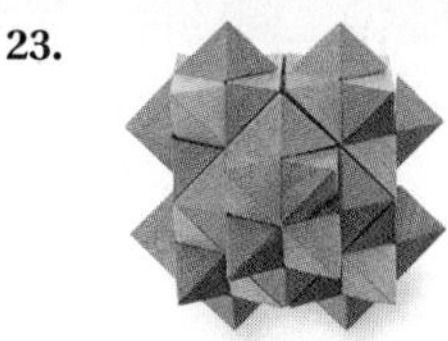
concave

24\. 
convex

EXAMPLE 4 on p. 797 for Exs. 25–28

CROSS SECTIONS **Draw and *describe* the cross section formed by the intersection of the plane and the solid.** 25–27. See margin for art.

25\. 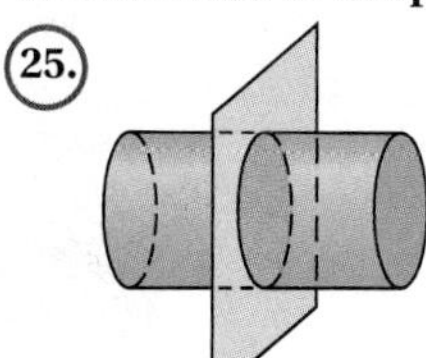
circle

26\. 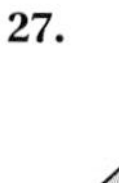 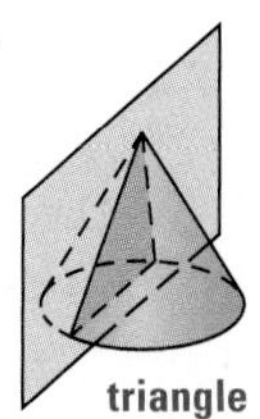
rectangle

27\. 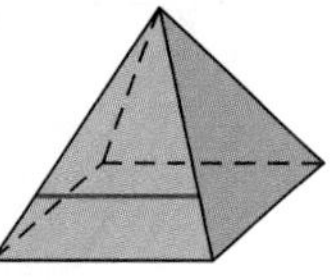
triangle

28\. ★ **MULTIPLE CHOICE** What is the shape of the cross section formed by the plane parallel to the base that intersects the red line drawn on the square pyramid? **A**

Ⓐ Square Ⓑ Triangle

Ⓒ Kite Ⓓ Trapezoid

B

29\. **ERROR ANALYSIS** *Describe* and correct the error in determining that a tetrahedron has 4 faces, 4 edges, and 6 vertices. **The concepts of edge and vertex are confused; the number of vertices is 4, and the number of edges is 6.**

30\. ★ **MULTIPLE CHOICE** Which two solids have the same number of faces? **C**

Ⓐ A triangular prism and a rectangular prism

Ⓑ A triangular pyramid and a rectangular prism

Ⓒ A triangular prism and a square pyramid

Ⓓ A triangular pyramid and a square pyramid

31\. ★ **MULTIPLE CHOICE** How many faces, vertices, and edges does an octagonal prism have? **D**

Ⓐ 8 faces, 6 vertices, and 12 edges

Ⓑ 8 faces, 12 vertices, and 18 edges

Ⓒ 10 faces, 12 vertices, and 20 edges

Ⓓ 10 faces, 16 vertices, and 24 edges

32\. **EULER'S THEOREM** The solid shown has 32 faces and 90 edges. How many vertices does the solid have? *Explain* your reasoning. **60 vertices; use Euler's Theorem, $32 + n = 90 + 2$ and solve for n.**

C

33\. **CHALLENGE** *Describe* how a plane can intersect a cube to form a hexagonal cross section. **If a plane intersects a cube at an angle so the plane touches each of the six faces, then the cross section will be hexagonal.**

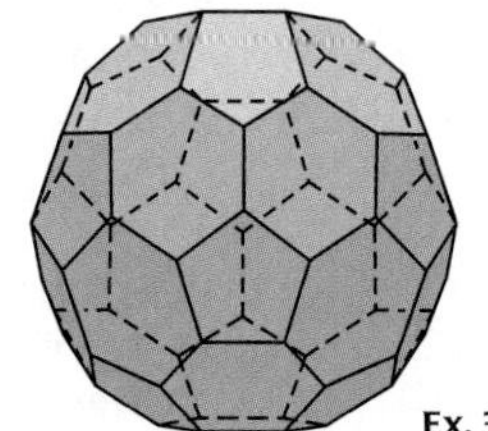
Ex. 32

Avoiding Common Errors

Exercises 15–20 If students have difficulty counting the number of faces, suggest they classify the polygonal base of the solid. Then they can count the faces by counting the top, the bottom, and the number of sides of the base.

Exercise 31 If students have trouble visualizing or sketching an octagonal prism, remind them that a prism has two congruent polygons as bases and parallelograms for the other sides. If it is an octagonal prism, then the bases are octagons.

25\. 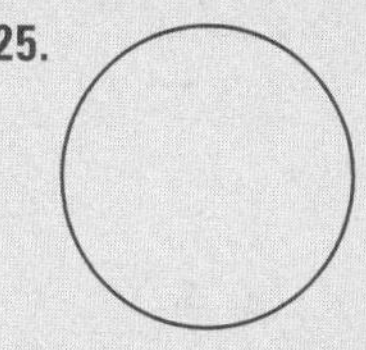

26\. 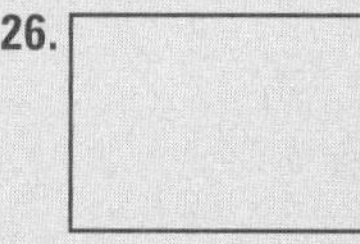

27\. 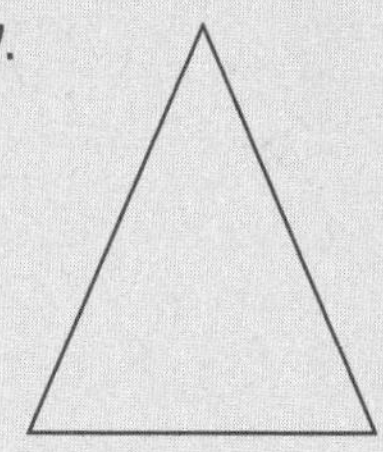

10\. 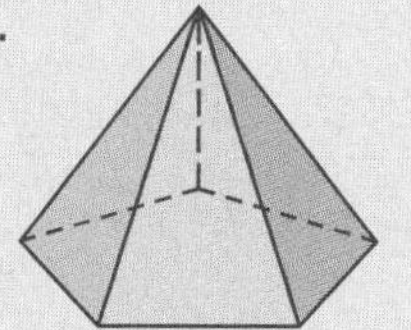

Teaching Strategy

Exercises 43–48 You may want to use modeling clay and a straightedge to demonstrate the various ways a plane can intersect a cube.

Vocabulary

Exercise 51 *Angle defect* may be new and unfamiliar. Help students understand that if the sum were 360°, then all the faces that meet at that vertex would lie in a plane.

41b. ***Sample:***

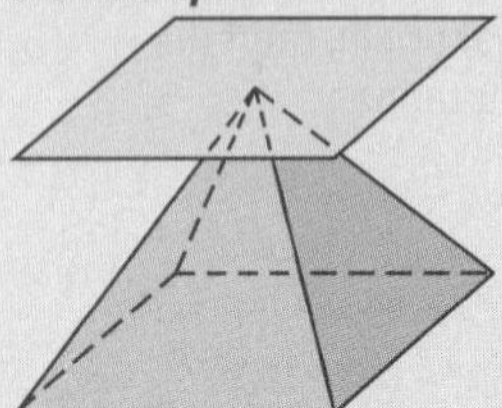

41d. ***Sample:***

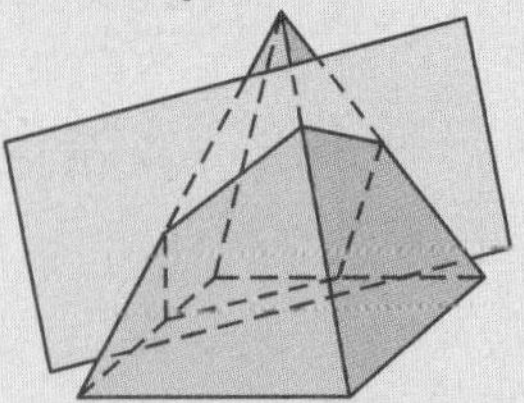

42. See below.

44. ***Sample:***

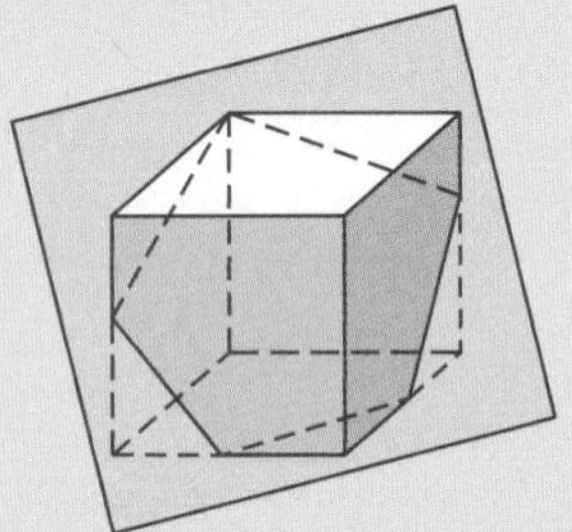

47. ***Sample:***

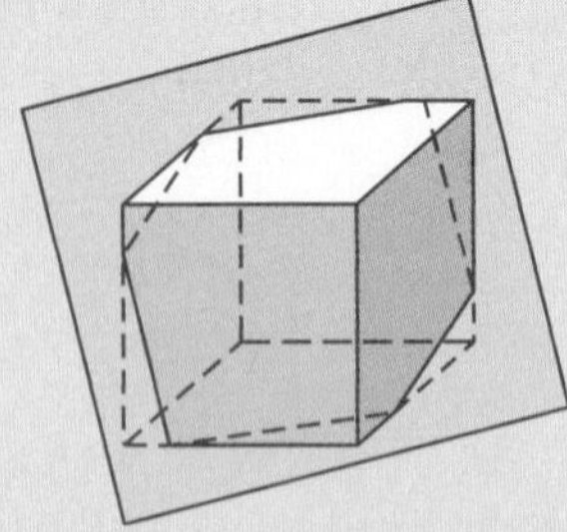

PROBLEM SOLVING

EXAMPLE 2 [A] on p. 796 for Exs. 34–35

34. MUSIC The speaker shown at the right has 7 faces. Two faces are pentagons and 5 faces are rectangles.

a. Find the number of vertices. **10 vertices**

b. Use Euler's Theorem to determine how many edges the speaker has. **15 edges**

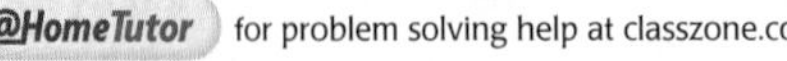
@HomeTutor for problem solving help at classzone.com

(35.) CRAFT BOXES The box shown at the right is a hexagonal prism. It has 8 faces. Two faces are hexagons and 6 faces are squares. Count the edges and vertices. Use Euler's Theorem to check your answer. **18 edges, 12 vertices**

@HomeTutor for problem solving help at classzone.com

FOOD *Describe* **the shape that is formed by the cut made in the food shown.**

36. Watermelon

circle

37. Bread

square

38. Cheese

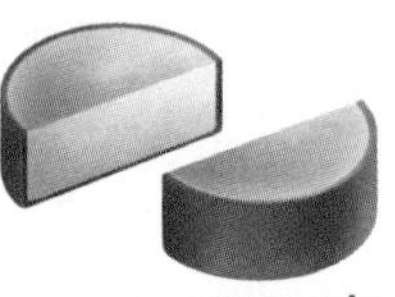

rectangle

[B] **39. ★ SHORT RESPONSE** Name a polyhedron that has 4 vertices and 6 edges. Can you draw a polyhedron that has 4 vertices, 6 edges, and a different number of faces? *Explain* your reasoning.
Tetrahedron; no; you cannot have a different number of faces because of Euler's Theorem.

40. MULTI-STEP PROBLEM The figure at the right shows a plane intersecting a cube through four of its vertices. An edge length of the cube is 6 inches.

a. *Describe* the shape formed by the cross section. **rectangle**

b. What is the perimeter of the cross section? **$(12 + 12\sqrt{2})$ in.**

c. What is the area of the cross section? **$36\sqrt{2}$ in.^{2}**

41. ★ EXTENDED RESPONSE Use the diagram of the square pyramid intersected by a plane.

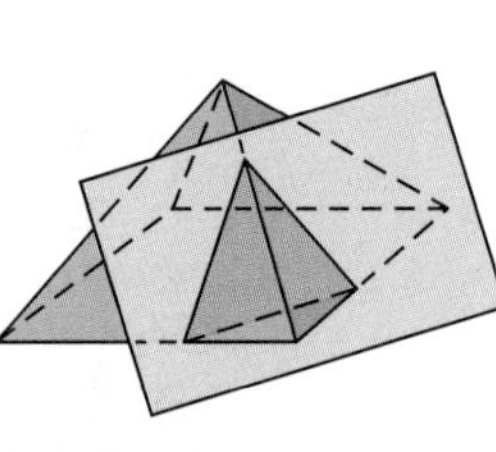

a. *Describe* the shape of the cross section shown. **trapezoid**

b. Can a plane intersect the pyramid at a point? If so, sketch the intersection. **Yes; see margin for art.**

c. *Describe* the shape of the cross section when the pyramid is sliced by a plane parallel to its base. **square**

d. Is it possible to have a pentagon as a cross section of this pyramid? If so, draw the cross section. **Yes; see margin for art.**

42. PLATONIC SOLIDS Make a table of the number of faces, vertices, and edges for the five Platonic solids. Use Euler's Theorem to check each answer. **See margin.**

○ = WORKED-OUT SOLUTIONS on p. WS1 ★ = STANDARDIZED TEST PRACTICE

42.

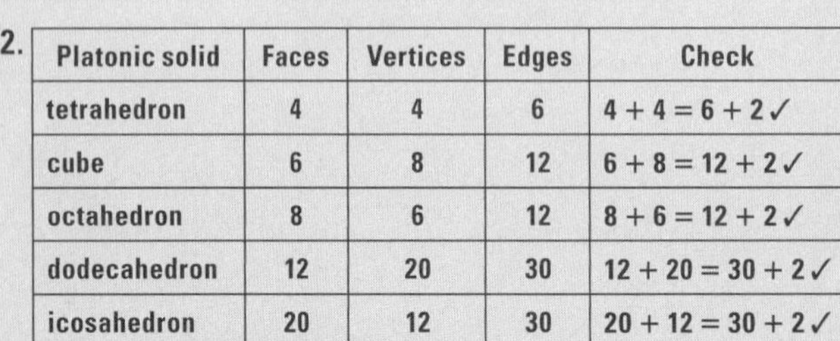

Platonic solid	Faces	Vertices	Edges	Check
tetrahedron	4	4	6	4 + 4 = 6 + 2✓
cube	6	8	12	6 + 8 = 12 + 2✓
octahedron	8	6	12	8 + 6 = 12 + 2✓
dodecahedron	12	20	30	12 + 20 = 30 + 2✓
icosahedron	20	12	30	20 + 12 = 30 + 2✓

REASONING Is it possible for a cross section of a cube to have the given shape? If yes, *describe* or sketch how the plane intersects the cube.

43. Circle **no**

44. Pentagon **Yes; see margin for art.**

45. Rhombus

46. Isosceles triangle

47. Regular hexagon **Yes; see margin for art.**

48. Scalene triangle

49. CUBE *Explain* how the numbers of faces, vertices, and edges of a cube change when you cut off each feature. **a–d. See margin.**

a. A corner **b.** An edge **c.** A face **d.** 3 corners

50. TETRAHEDRON *Explain* how the numbers of faces, vertices, and edges of a regular tetrahedron change when you cut off each feature. **a–d. See margin.**

a. A corner **b.** An edge **c.** A face **d.** 2 edges

51. CHALLENGE The *angle defect D* at a vertex of a polyhedron is defined as follows:

$D = 360° - $ (sum of all angle measures at the vertex)

Verify that for the figures with regular bases below, $DV = 720°$ where V is the number of vertices.

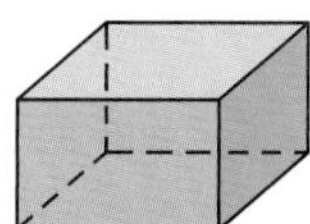
rectangular prism: $D = 360 - (90 \cdot 3) = 90°$, $DV = 90(8) = 720°$

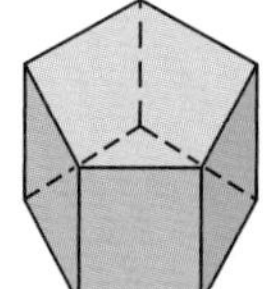
regular pentagonal prism: $D = 360 - (108 + 90 + 90) = 72°$, $DV = 72(10) = 720°$

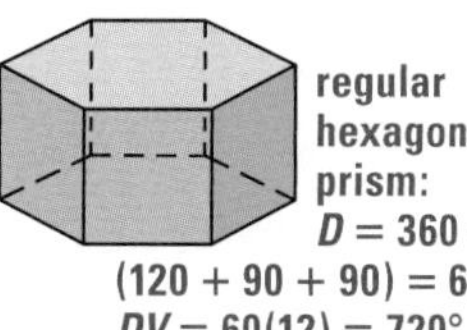
regular hexagonal prism: $D = 360 - (120 + 90 + 90) = 60°$, $DV = 60(12) = 720°$

MIXED REVIEW

Find the value of x. *(p. 680)*

52. **77**

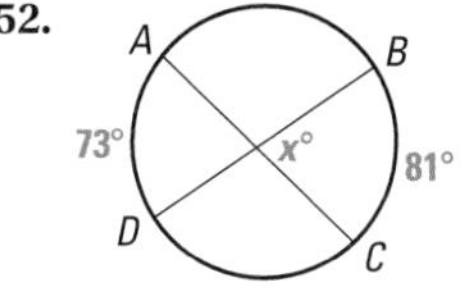

53. **159**

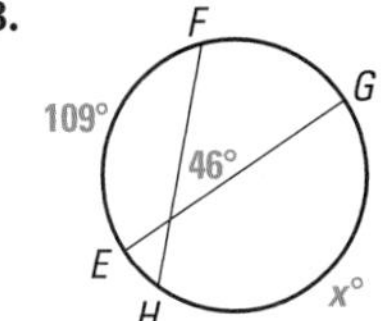

54. **52.5**

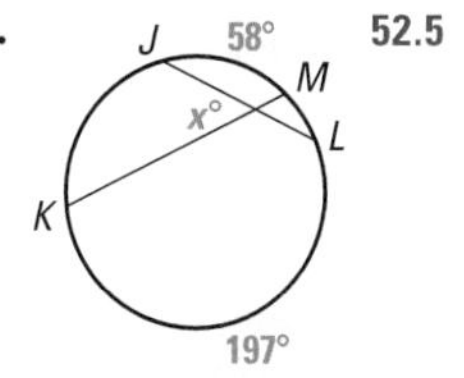

PREVIEW
Prepare for Lesson 12.2 in Exs. 55–60.

Use the given radius r or diameter d to find the circumference and area of the circle. Round your answers to two decimal places. *(p. 755)*

55. $r = 11$ cm **69.12 cm, 380.13 cm^2**

56. $d = 28$ in. **87.96 in., 615.75 $in.^2$**

57. $d = 15$ ft **47.12 ft, 176.71 ft^2**

Find the perimeter and area of the regular polygon. Round your answers to two decimal places. *(p. 762)*

58.

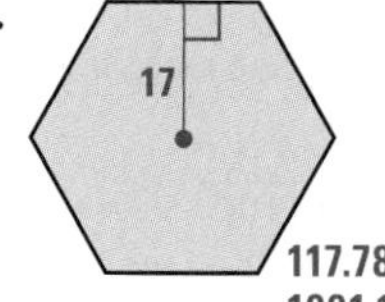

117.78 units, 1001.13 $units^2$

59.

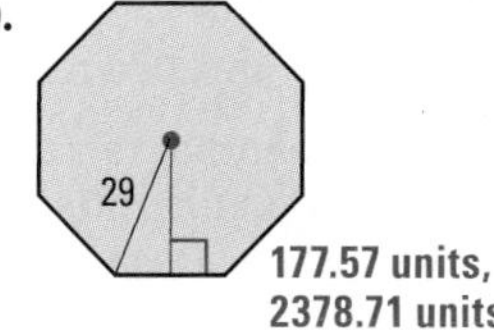

177.57 units, 2378.71 $units^2$

60.

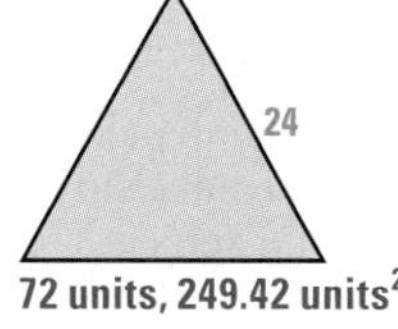

72 units, 249.42 $units^2$

45. Yes, if the rhombus is a square; *Sample answer:* The plane intersects the cube parallel to a base so it forms a square, which is a rhombus.

46. Yes. *Sample answer:* The plane intersects the 3 edges that make up a vertex so that it forms a triangle with two congruent sides along two faces.

48. Yes. *Sample answer:* The plane intersects the 3 edges that make up a vertex so that it forms a scalene triangle with 2 sides along two faces.

5 ASSESS AND RETEACH

Daily Homework Quiz

Transparency Available

Determine whether the solid is a polyhedron. If it is, name it.

1. 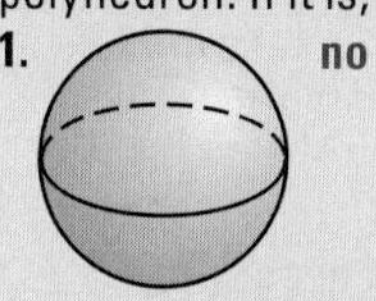 **no**
2. 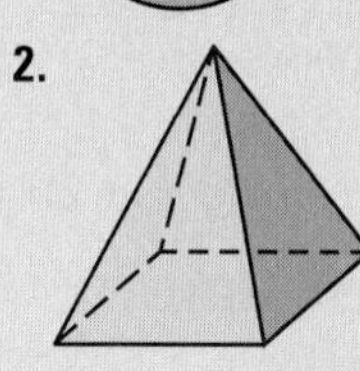 **yes; rectangular pyramid**
3. 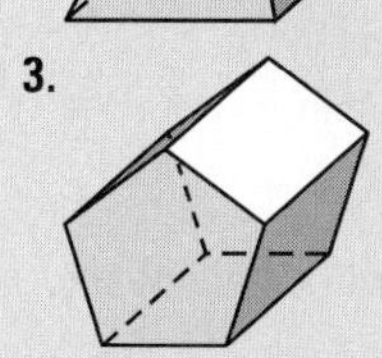 **yes; pentagonal prism**
4. Find the number of faces, vertices and edges of each polyhedron in Exercises 2 and 3. **pyramid: 5 faces, 5 vertices, 8 edges; prism: 7 faces, 10 vertices, 15 edges**
5. A plane intersects a cone, but does not intersect the base of the cone. Describe the possible cross sections. **a point, a circle, an ellipse**

Available at **classzone.com**

Diagnosis/Remediation

- Practice A, B, C in Chapter 12 Resource Book, pp. 8–13
- Study Guide in Chapter 12 Resource Book, pp. 14–15
- Practice Workbook, pp. 226–228
- @HomeTutor

Challenge

Additional challenge is available in the Chapter 12 Resource Book, p. 18.

49a–d, 50a–d. See Additional Answers beginning on p. AA1.

12.2 Investigate Surface Area

MATERIALS • graph paper • scissors • tape

QUESTION How can you find the surface area of a polyhedron?

A *net* is a pattern that can be folded to form a polyhedron. To find the *surface area* of a polyhedron, you can find the area of its net.

Standards

Prepare for
8.0 *Students* know, derive, and solve problems involving the perimeter, circumference, area, volume, lateral area, and *surface area of common geometric figures.*
9.0 Students compute the volumes and **surface areas of prisms**, pyramids, cylinders, cones, and spheres; and students commit to memory the formulas for prisms, pyramids, and cylinders.

EXPLORE Create a polyhedron using a net

STEP 1 ***Draw a net*** Copy the net below on graph paper. Be sure to label the sections of the net.

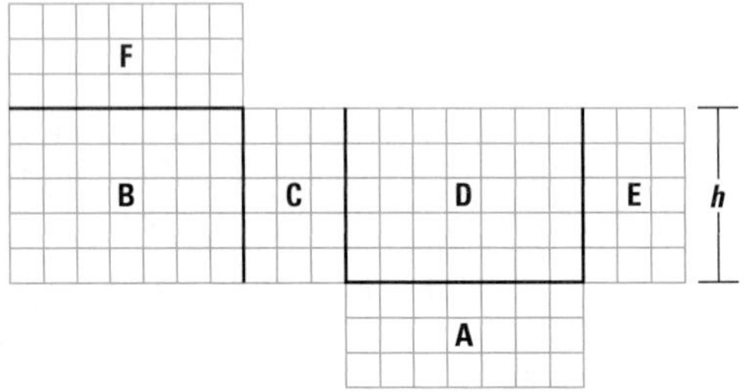

STEP 2 ***Create a polyhedron*** Cut out the net and fold it along the black lines to form a polyhedron. Tape the edges together. Describe the polyhedron. Is it regular? Is it convex? **rectangular prism; no; yes**

STEP 3 ***Find surface area*** The *surface area* of a polyhedron is the sum of the areas of its faces. Find the surface area of the polyhedron you just made. (Each square on the graph paper measures 1 unit by 1 unit.) **142 units^2**

DRAW CONCLUSIONS Use your observations to complete these exercises

1. Lay the net flat again and find the following measures.
   A: the area of Rectangle A **21 units^2**
   P: the perimeter of Rectangle A **20 units**
   h: the height of Rectangles B, C, D, and E **5 units**
2. Use the values from Exercise 1 to find $2A + Ph$. *Compare* this value to the surface area you found in Step 3 above. What do you notice? **142 units^2; the values are the same.**
3. Make a conjecture about the surface area of a rectangular prism. **See margin.**
4. Use graph paper to draw the net of another rectangular prism. Fold the net to make sure that it forms a rectangular prism. Use your conjecture from Exercise 3 to calculate the surface area of the prism. **See margin for art. *Sample answer*: 76 units^2**

1 PLAN AND PREPARE

Explore the Concept
- Students will investigate surface area.
- This activity leads into the study of surface area in Lesson 12.2, Example 1.

Materials
Each student will need:
- graph paper, scissors, tape
- Activity Support Master (*Chapter 12 Resource Book*, p. 21)

Recommended Time
Work activity: 10 min
Discuss results: 5 min

Grouping
Students should work individually.

2 TEACH

Tips for Success
After students have folded and taped the rectangular prism, ask them to draw the prism. Then have them label the area of each face and compare the total to the results of the activity.

Key Question
- What solid is formed by the net? **a rectangular prism**

Alternative Strategy
Instead of using graph paper, have students cut apart a cereal box as an alternate net for a rectangular prism. Students can measure the sides and use the net to find the surface area.

Key Discovery
The surface area of a prism is twice the area of the base, plus the perimeter of the base times the height.

3 ASSESS AND RETEACH

1. What is the surface area of a rectangular prism with length 8 cm, width 6 cm, and height 5 cm? **236 cm^2**

3. The surface area of a rectangular prism is twice the area of the base plus the perimeter of the base times the height.

4. *Sample:*

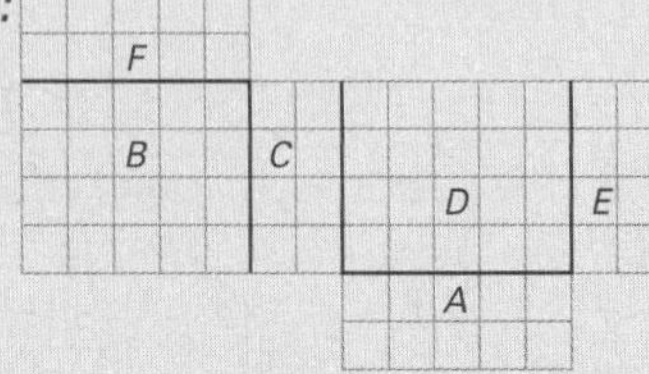

12.2 Surface Area of Prisms and Cylinders

Before You found areas of polygons.

Now You will find the surface areas of prisms and cylinders.

Why? So you can find the surface area of a drum, as in Ex. 22.

Key Vocabulary
- **prism**
- lateral faces, lateral edges
- **surface area**
- **lateral area**
- **net**
- **right prism**
- **oblique prism**
- **cylinder**
- **right cylinder**

Standards

9.0 Students compute the volumes and **surface areas of prisms,** pyramids, **cylinders,** cones, and spheres; and **students commit to memory the formulas for prisms,** pyramids, **and cylinders.**

8.0 Students know, derive, and solve problems involving the perimeter, circumference, area, volume, **lateral area, and surface area of common geometric figures.**

A **prism** is a polyhedron with two congruent faces, called *bases*, that lie in parallel planes. The other faces, called **lateral faces**, are parallelograms formed by connecting the corresponding vertices of the bases. The segments connecting these vertices are **lateral edges**. Prisms are classified by the shapes of their bases.

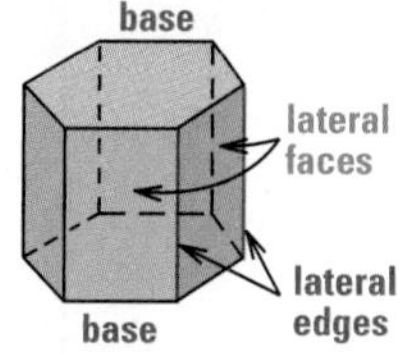

The **surface area** of a polyhedron is the sum of the areas of its faces. The **lateral area** of a polyhedron is the sum of the areas of its lateral faces.

Imagine that you cut some edges of a polyhedron and unfold it. The two-dimensional representation of the faces is called a **net**. As you saw in the Activity on page 802, the surface area of a prism is equal to the area of its net.

EXAMPLE 1 Use the net of a prism

Find the surface area of a rectangular prism with height 2 centimeters, length 5 centimeters, and width 6 centimeters.

Solution

STEP 1 **Sketch** the prism. Imagine unfolding it to make a net.

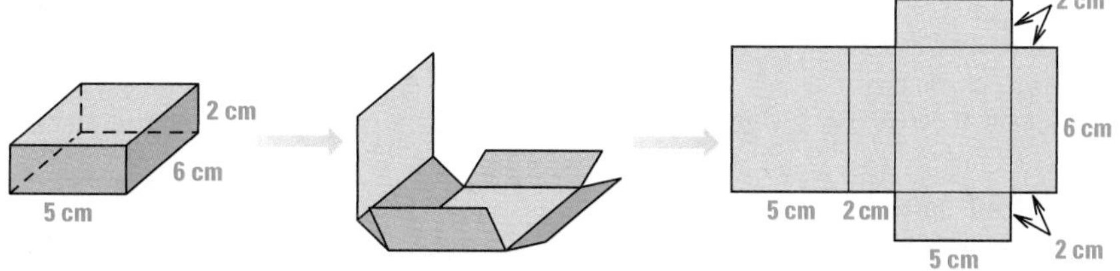

STEP 2 **Find** the areas of the rectangles that form the faces of the prism.

Congruent faces	Dimensions	Area of each face
Left and right faces	6 cm by 2 cm	$6 \cdot 2 = 12 \text{ cm}^2$
Front and back faces	5 cm by 2 cm	$5 \cdot 2 = 10 \text{ cm}^2$
Top and bottom faces	6 cm by 5 cm	$6 \cdot 5 = 30 \text{ cm}^2$

STEP 3 **Add** the areas of all the faces to find the surface area.

▶ The surface area of the prism is $S = 2(12) + 2(10) + 2(30) = 104 \text{ cm}^2$.

1 PLAN AND PREPARE

Warm-Up Exercises

Transparency Available

1. Evaluate $2xy + 2yz + 2xz$ for $x = 9$, $y = 6$, and $z = 4$. **228**
2. Evaluate $2\pi x^2 + 2\pi xy$ for $x = 4$ and $y = 7$. Use 3.14 for π. **276.32**
3. Find the area of a circle with radius 8 cm. Use 3.14 for π. **200.96 cm^2**
4. Find the area of a right triangle with hypotenuse 13 in. and a side length of 5 in. **30 in.^{2}**
5. Find the area of a regular pentagon with apothem 4.13 ft and side length 6 ft. **61.95 ft^2**

Notetaking Guide

Transparency Available

Promotes interactive learning and notetaking skills, pp. 313–316.

Pacing

Basic: 1 day
Average: 1 day
Advanced: 1 day
Block: 0.5 block with 12.3
- See *Teaching Guide/Lesson Plan.*

2 FOCUS AND MOTIVATE

Essential Question

Big Idea 2, p. 791

How do you find the surface area of a prism? **Tell students they will learn how to answer this question by developing and using a formula.**

Resource Planning Guide

Chapter Resource Book
- Teaching Guide/Lesson Plan (pp. 19–20)
- Practice levels A, B, C (pp. 22–27)
- Study Guide (pp. 28–29)
- Catch-up for Absent Students (p. 30)
- Problem Solving Workshop (p. 31)
- Challenge (p. 32)

Workbooks
- Notetaking Guide (pp. 313–316)
- Practice Workbook (pp. 229–231)

Teaching Options
- **Power Presentations CD-ROM** provides dynamic electronic teaching resources for the classroom.
- **Activity Generator CD-ROM** provides editable activities for all ability levels.

Interactive Technology
- Easy Planner
- Power Presentations CD-ROM
- Activity Generator CD-ROM
- Animated Geometry
- Test Generator CD-ROM
- Online Quiz
- eWorkbook
- eEdition
- @HomeTutor

Resources for English Learners
- Quick Reference for English Learners
- Spanish Study Guide
- Multi-Language Visual Glossary
- Student Resources in Spanish

See also the *Geometry Toolkit* for more strategies for meeting individual needs.

Motivating the Lesson

Ask students to describe the relationships between the dimensions of a rectangular solid and the areas of the six faces of the solid. Tell students that in this lesson they will use those relationships to develop a formula for the surface area of a rectangular solid and develop formulas for the surface areas of other solids.

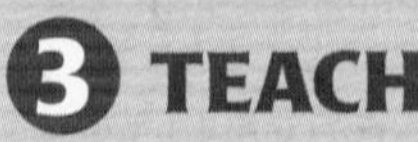

3 TEACH

Extra Example 1

Find the surface area of a rectangular prism with height 3 cm, length 6 cm, and width 8 cm. **180 cm^2**

Key Questions to Ask for Example 1

- Do the solid and the net contain the same number of rectangles? **yes**
- How is the chart in Step 2 helpful? **It organizes the calculations of the areas of all the faces.**

Extra Example 2

Find the surface area of the right hexagonal prism. **1696.14 ft^2**

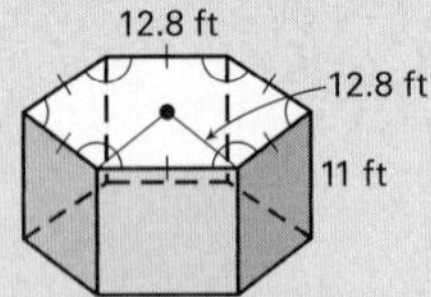

Key Question to Ask for Example 2

- What part of the calculation uses the apothem? **finding the area of the base of the prism**

RIGHT PRISMS The height of a prism is the perpendicular distance between its bases. In a **right prism**, each lateral edge is perpendicular to both bases. A prism with lateral edges that are not perpendicular to the bases is an **oblique prism**.

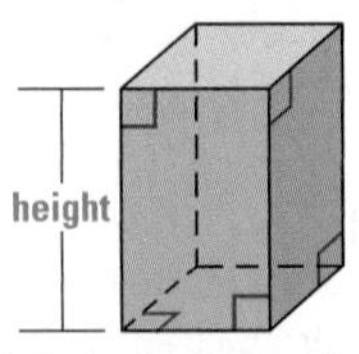

Right rectangular prism

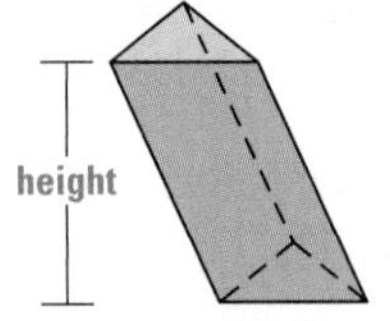

Oblique triangular prism

THEOREM *For Your Notebook*

THEOREM 12.2 Surface Area of a Right Prism

The surface area S of a right prism is

$$S = 2B + Ph = aP + Ph,$$

where a is the apothem of the base, B is the area of a base, P is the perimeter of a base, and h is the height.

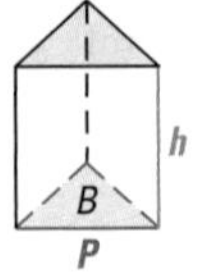

$S = 2B + Ph = aP + Ph$

EXAMPLE 2 Find the surface area of a right prism

Find the surface area of the right pentagonal prism.

7.05 ft, 6 ft, 9 ft

Solution

STEP 1 **Find** the perimeter and area of a base of the prism.

Each base is a regular pentagon.

Perimeter $P = 5(7.05) = 35.25$

Apothem $a = \sqrt{6^2 - 3.525^2} \approx 4.86$

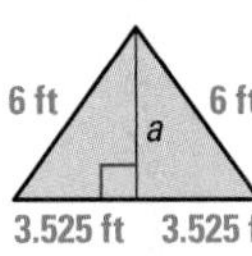

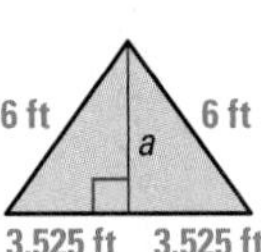

REVIEW APOTHEM
For help with finding the apothem, see p. 762.

STEP 2 **Use** the formula for the surface area that uses the apothem.

$S = aP + Ph$	**Surface area of a right prism**
$\approx (4.86)(35.25) + (35.25)(9)$	**Substitute known values.**
≈ 488.57	**Simplify.**

▶ The surface area of the right pentagonal prism is about 488.57 square feet.

GUIDED PRACTICE for Examples 1 and 2

1. Draw a net of a triangular prism. **See margin.**
2. Find the surface area of a right rectangular prism with height 7 inches, length 3 inches, and width 4 inches using (a) a net and (b) the formula for the surface area of a right prism.

2a. NET: Left and right faces: $7 \cdot 4 = 28$ in.^{2} Top and bottom faces: $3 \cdot 4 = 12$ in.^{2} Front and back faces: $3 \cdot 7 = 21$ in.^{2} $S = 2(28) + 2(12) + 2(21) = 122$ in.^{2}

2b. $S = 2B + Ph = 2(3 \cdot 4) + 14 \cdot 7 = 122$ in.^{2}

Differentiated Instruction

Kinesthetic Learners To help students understand how to draw the net of a triangular prism in **Guided Practice Exercise 1**, have them construct a triangular prism out of cardboard or posterboard. Then have them unfold it to make a net. Point out that there is more than one way to draw a net for a particular prism depending on which edges are cut and which are folded. Have students compare their nets with those of other students. See also the *Geometry Toolkit* for more strategies.

CYLINDERS A **cylinder** is a solid with congruent circular bases that lie in parallel planes. The height of a cylinder is the perpendicular distance between its bases. The radius of a base is the *radius* of the cylinder. In a **right cylinder**, the segment joining the centers of the bases is perpendicular to the bases.

base
radius r
height h
base

The lateral area of a cylinder is the area of its curved surface. It is equal to the product of the circumference and the height, or $2\pi rh$. The surface area of a cylinder is equal to the sum of the lateral area and the areas of the two bases.

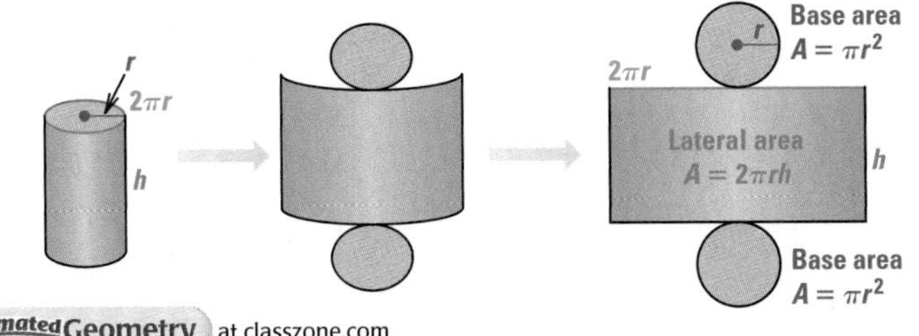

Animated Geometry at classzone.com

THEOREM *For Your Notebook*

THEOREM 12.3 Surface Area of a Right Cylinder

The surface area S of a right cylinder is

$S = 2B + Ch = 2\pi r^2 + 2\pi rh$,

where B is the area of a base, C is the circumference of a base, r is the radius of a base, and h is the height.

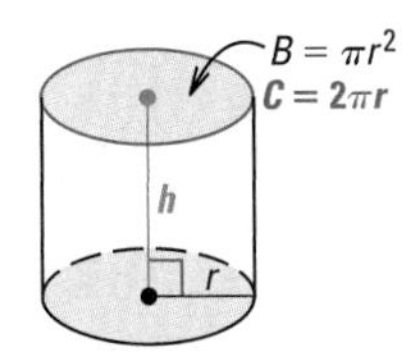

$S = 2B + Ch = 2\pi r^2 + 2\pi rh$

EXAMPLE 3 Find the surface area of a cylinder

COMPACT DISCS You are wrapping a stack of 20 compact discs using a shrink wrap. Each disc is cylindrical with height 1.2 millimeters and radius 60 millimeters. What is the minimum amount of shrink wrap needed to cover the stack of 20 discs?

Solution

The 20 discs are stacked, so the height of the stack will be $20(1.2) = 24$ mm. The radius is 60 millimeters. The minimum amount of shrink wrap needed will be equal to the surface area of the stack of discs.

$S = 2\pi r^2 + 2\pi rh$	**Surface area of a cylinder**
$= 2\pi(60)^2 + 2\pi(60)(24)$	**Substitute known values.**
$\approx 31{,}667$	**Use a calculator.**

▶ You will need at least 31,667 square millimeters, or about 317 square centimeters of shrink wrap.

An **Animated Geometry** activity is available on-line for the area formula of a right cylinder. This activity is also available on the **Power Presentations CD-ROM**.

Extra Example 3

You are wrapping a poster in a cardboard cylinder. The cylinder has a height of 36 in. and a radius of 4 in. What is the minimum amount of cardboard needed to cover the poster, including the two bases of the cylinder? **at least 1005.3 in.^{2}**

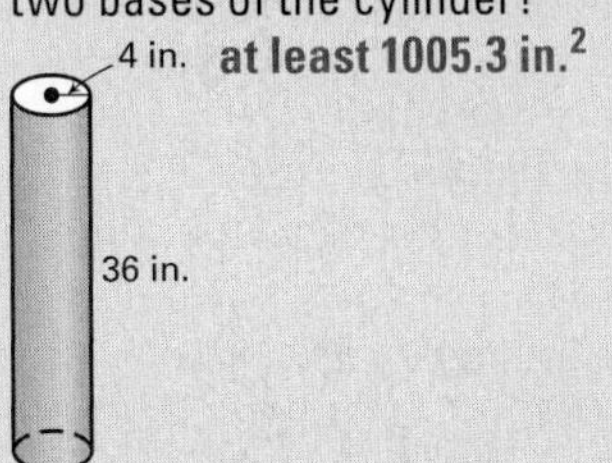

Key Question to Ask for Example 3

- What values do you use in the surface area formula? **π, the height, and the radius of the base**

Teaching Strategy

Point out that students are familiar with "right" cylinders because cans and other familiar cylinders are right cylinders. In the definition, emphasize that the axis (the segment joining the centers of the bases) is perpendicular to the bases. As a contrast you can show students examples of oblique cylinders.

1.

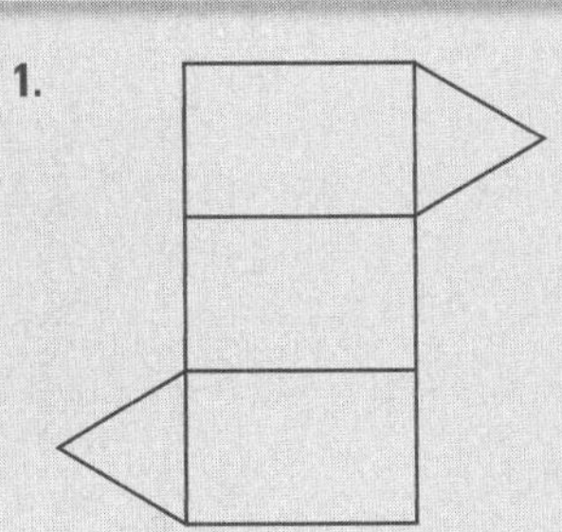

Extra Example 4

Find the height of the right cylinder, which has a surface area of 262.64 cm^2. **7.2 cm**

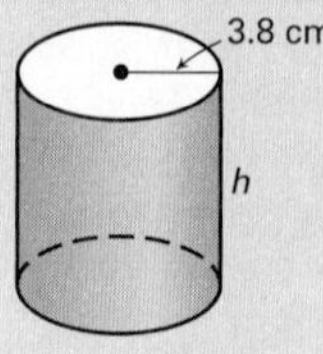

Closing the Lesson

Have students summarize the major points of the lesson and answer the Essential Question: How do you find the surface area of a prism?

- **The lateral area of a prism or a cylinder is the area of the lateral faces or curved surface, respectively. The surface area is the lateral area plus the area of the bases.**
- **For a prism, $S = 2B + Ph = aP + Ph$.**
- **For a cylinder, $S = 2B + Ch = 2\pi r^2 + 2\pi rh$.**

Use the formula $S = 2B + Ph$ where B is the area of a base, P is the perimeter of the base, and h is the height of the prism.

EXAMPLE 4 Find the height of a cylinder

Find the height of the right cylinder shown, which has a surface area of 157.08 square meters.

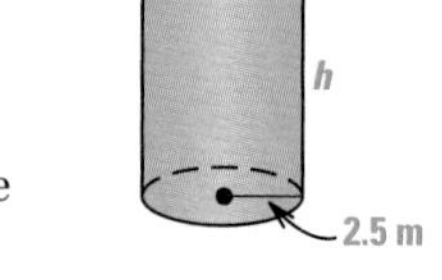

Solution

Substitute known values in the formula for the surface area of a right cylinder and solve for the height h.

$S = 2\pi r^2 + 2\pi rh$	Surface area of a cylinder
$157.08 = 2\pi(2.5)^2 + 2\pi(2.5)h$	Substitute known values.
$157.08 = 12.5\pi + 5\pi h$	Simplify.
$157.08 - 12.5\pi = 5\pi h$	Subtract 12.5π from each side.
$117.81 \approx 5\pi h$	Simplify. Use a calculator.
$7.5 \approx h$	Divide each side by 5π.

▸ The height of the cylinder is about 7.5 meters.

GUIDED PRACTICE for Examples 3 and 4

3. Find the surface area of a right cylinder with height 18 centimeters and radius 10 centimeters. Round your answer to two decimal places. **1759.29 cm^2**
4. Find the radius of a right cylinder with height 5 feet and surface area 208π square feet. **8 ft**

12.2 EXERCISES

HOMEWORK KEY
○ = **WORKED-OUT SOLUTIONS** on p. WS16 for Exs. 7, 9, and 23
★ = **STANDARDIZED TEST PRACTICE** Exs. 2, 17, 24, 25, and 26

SKILL PRACTICE

A

1. **VOCABULARY** Sketch a triangular prism. Identify its *bases*, *lateral faces*, and *lateral edges*. **See margin.**
2. ★ **WRITING** *Explain* how the formula $S = 2B + Ph$ applies to finding the surface area of both a right prism and a right cylinder. **See margin.**

EXAMPLE 1 on p. 803 for Exs. 3–5

USING NETS **Find the surface area of the solid formed by the net. Round your answer to two decimal places.**

3. 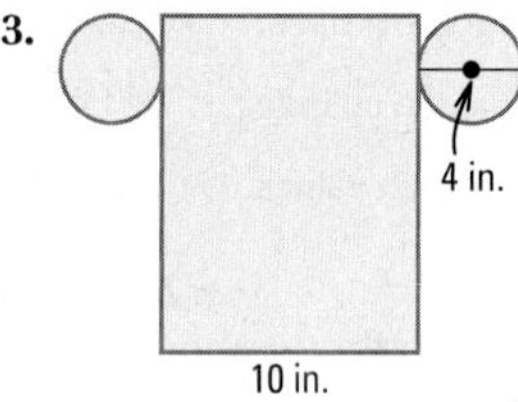

150.80 $in.^2$

4. 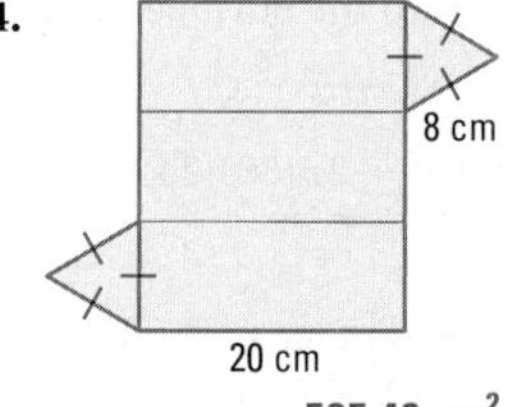

535.43 cm^2

5. 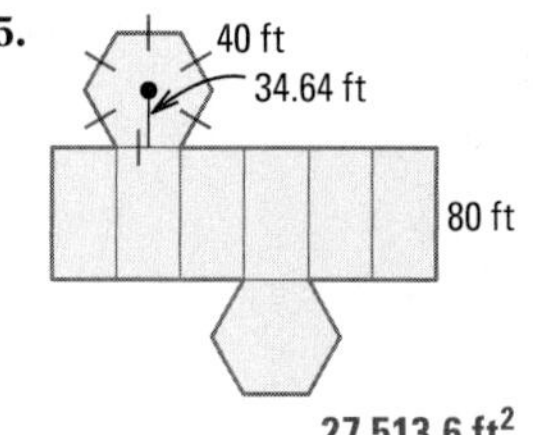

27,513.6 ft^2

1.

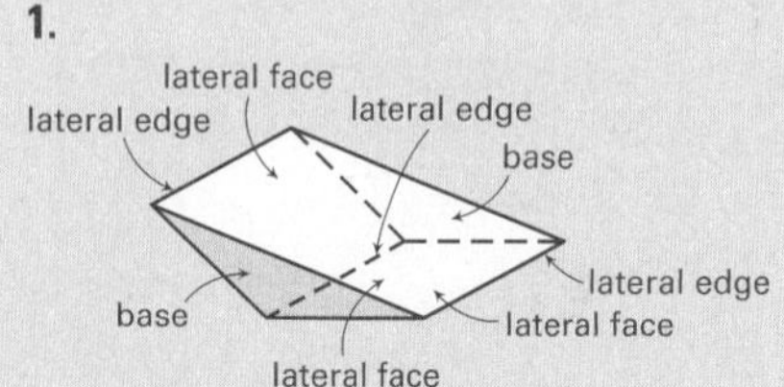

2. For a prism, use B = area of the base depending on shape and P = perimeter of the base depending on shape. For a cylinder, use $B = \pi r^2$ and P = the circumference $= 2\pi r$, where r = radius.

XAMPLE 2
n p. 804
or Exs. 6–8

SURFACE AREA OF A PRISM Find the surface area of the right prism. Round your answer to two decimal places.

6. 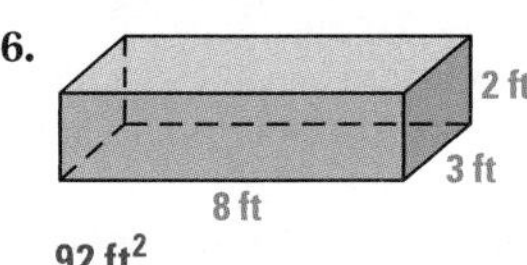

92 ft²

7. 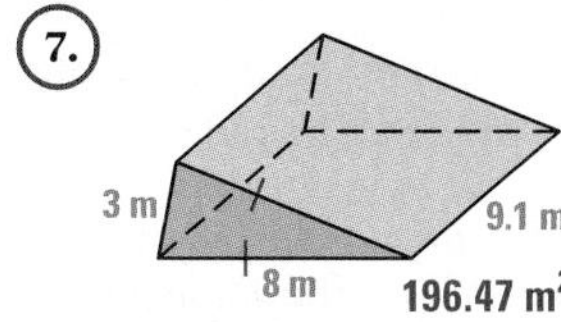

196.47 m²

8. 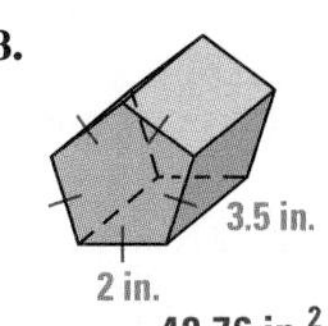

48.76 in.²

XAMPLE 3
n p. 805
or Exs. 9–12

SURFACE AREA OF A CYLINDER Find the surface area of the right cylinder using the given radius r and height h. Round your answer to two decimal places.

9. 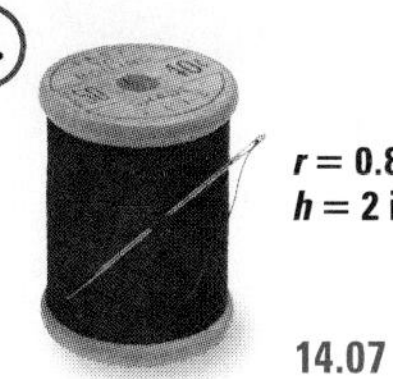
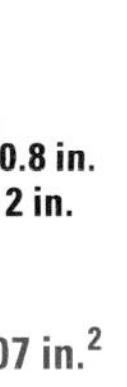
$r = 0.8$ in.
$h = 2$ in.
14.07 in.²

10. 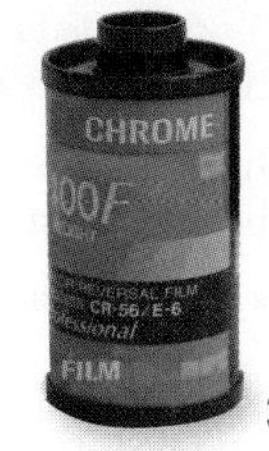

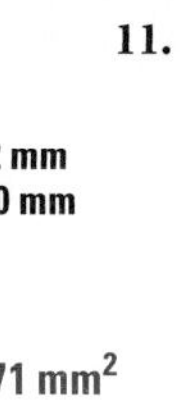
$r = 12$ mm
$h = 40$ mm
3920.71 mm²

11. 
$r = 8$ in.
$h = 8$ in.
804.25 in.²

12. **ERROR ANALYSIS** *Describe* and correct the error in finding the surface area of the right cylinder.
The diameter of the cylinder is used in the formula instead of the radius; $S = 2\pi(3^2) + 2\pi(3)(8) = 2\pi(9) + 2\pi(24) = 66\pi \approx 207.35$ cm².

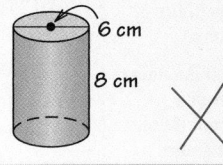

$S = 2\pi(6^2) + 2\pi(6)(8)$
$= 2\pi(36) + 2\pi(48)$
$= 168\pi$
≈ 528 cm²

6 cm
8 cm

XAMPLE 4 B
n p. 806
or Exs. 13–15

ALGEBRA Solve for x given the surface area S of the right prism or right cylinder. Round your answer to two decimal places.

13. $S = 606$ yd² **9 yd**

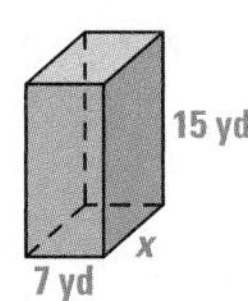

14. $S = 1097$ m² **13.09 m**

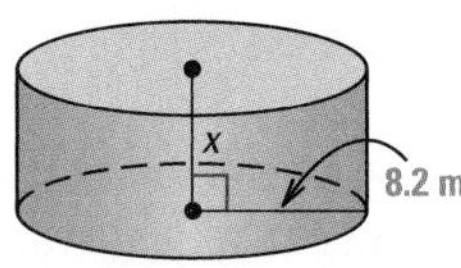

15. $S = 616$ in.² **10.96 in.**

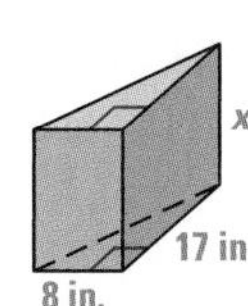

16. **SURFACE AREA OF A PRISM** A triangular prism with a right triangular base has leg length 9 units and hypotenuse length 15 units. The height of the prism is 8 units. Sketch the prism and find its surface area. **See margin for art; 396 units².**

17. ★ **MULTIPLE CHOICE** The length of each side of a cube is multiplied by 3. What is the change in the surface area of the cube? **C**

Ⓐ The surface area is 3 times the original surface area.

Ⓑ The surface area is 6 times the original surface area.

Ⓒ The surface area is 9 times the original surface area.

Ⓓ The surface area is 27 times the original surface area.

18. **SURFACE AREA OF A CYLINDER** The radius and height of a right cylinder are each divided by $\sqrt{5}$. What is the change in surface area of the cylinder? **$\frac{1}{5}$ as much**

4 PRACTICE AND APPLY

Assignment Guide

Answer Transparencies available for all exercises

Basic:
Day 1: EP p. 917 Exs. 34, 35, 47, 48
pp. 806–809
Exs. 1–17, 22–26, 31–37

Average:
Day 1: pp. 806–809
Exs. 1, 2–12 even, 13–20, 22–27, 31–37

Advanced:
Day 1: pp. 806–809
Exs. 1, 2, 4–10 even, 13–22*, 24–30*, 32–36 even

Block:
pp. 806–809
Exs. 1, 2–12 even, 13–20, 22–27, 31–37 (with 12.3)

Differentiated Instruction

See *Geometry Best Practices Toolkit* for suggestions on addressing the needs of a diverse classroom.

Homework Check

For a quick check of student understanding of key concepts, go over the following exercises:

Basic: 3, 6, 9, 13, 22
Average: 4, 6, 10, 14, 24
Advanced: 6, 8, 10, 15, 25

Extra Practice

- Student Edition, p. 918
- Chapter 12 Resource Book: Practice levels A, B, C, pp. 22–27

Practice Worksheet

An easily-readable reduced practice page (with answers) for this lesson can be found on p. 790C.

16. 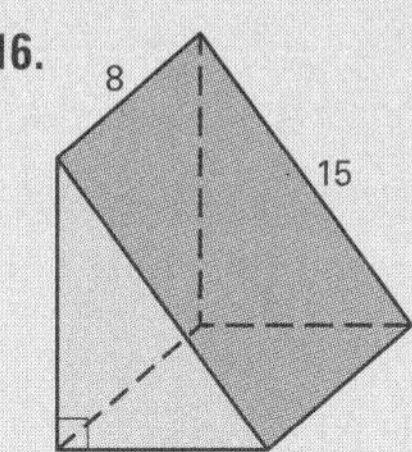

Avoiding Common Errors

Exercises 3–5 Encourage students to start with a verbal model of each set of areas to help organize their formulas and calculations.

Teaching Strategy

Exercises 8, 19 Remind students that they need to find the apothem in order to find the area of the regular polygonal bases.

Exercise 27 As students plan how to do this exercise, remind them to draw a diagram, if necessary, to help them visualize the new solid after cubes are removed. Drawing each of the six views may help students find the surface area of the solid with cubes missing. Point out that when cubes are removed, some faces will show that were not initially part of the surface area.

Internet Reference

Exercise 22 For more information about the bass drum, visit www.mathcs.duq.edu/~iben/bassdrum.htm

Mathematical Reasoning

Exercise 28 The cylindrical hole with radius r_2 will decrease the surface area by two circles with radius r_2, but it will increase the area by the side of the inner cylinder $(A = 2\pi r_2 \times h)$.

---

19. SURFACE AREA OF A PRISM Find the surface area of a right hexagonal prism with all edges measuring 10 inches. **about 1119.62 in.^{2}**

20. HEIGHT OF A CYLINDER Find the height of a cylinder with a surface area of 108π square meters. The radius of the cylinder is twice the height. **3 m**

C **21. CHALLENGE** The *diagonal* of a cube is a segment whose endpoints are vertices that are not on the same face. Find the surface area of a cube with diagonal length 8 units. **128 units^2**

PROBLEM SOLVING

EXAMPLE 3 A on p. 805 for Ex. 22

22. BASS DRUM A bass drum has a diameter of 20 inches and a depth of 8 inches. Find the surface area of the drum.

@HomeTutor for problem solving help at classzone.com

22. about 1130.97 in.^{2}

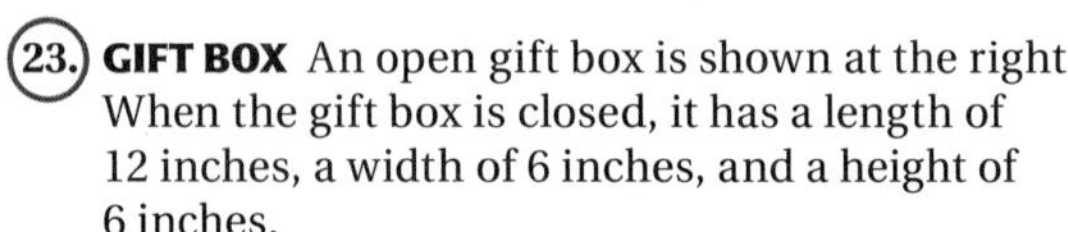

23. GIFT BOX An open gift box is shown at the right. When the gift box is closed, it has a length of 12 inches, a width of 6 inches, and a height of 6 inches.

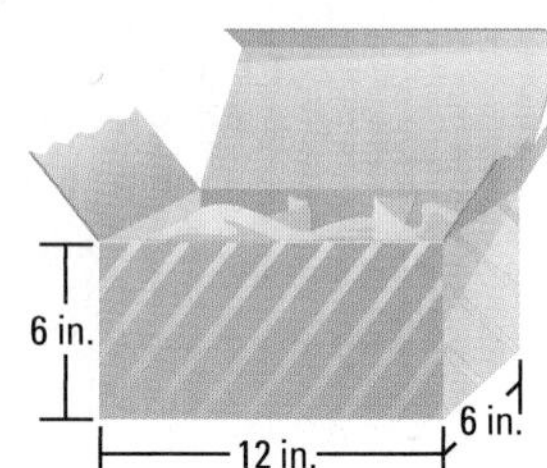

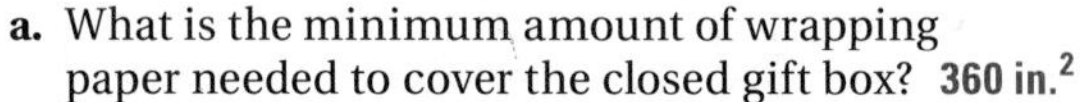

a. What is the minimum amount of wrapping paper needed to cover the closed gift box? **360 in.^{2}**

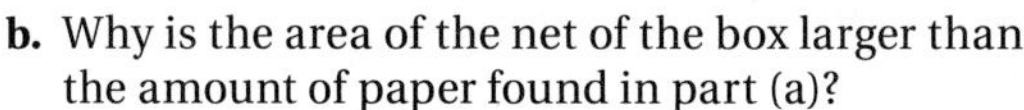

b. Why is the area of the net of the box larger than the amount of paper found in part (a)?

c. When wrapping the box, why would you want more paper than the amount found in part (a)?

@HomeTutor for problem solving help at classzone.com

23b. There is overlap in some of the sides of the box.

23c. It is easier to wrap a present if you have some overlap of wrapping paper.

24. ★ EXTENDED RESPONSE A right cylinder has a radius of 4 feet and height of 10 feet.

a. Find the surface area of the cylinder. **about 351.86 ft^2**

b. Suppose you can either *double the radius* or *double the height*. Which do you think will create a greater surface area? **doubling the radius**

c. Check your answer in part (b) by calculating the new surface areas. **If the radius is 8 and height is 10, then $S \approx 904.78$; if the radius is 4 and height is 20, then $S \approx 603.19$.**

25. ★ MULTIPLE CHOICE Which three-dimensional figure does the net represent? **A**

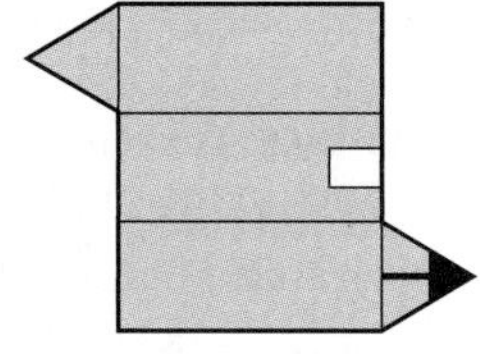

Ⓐ 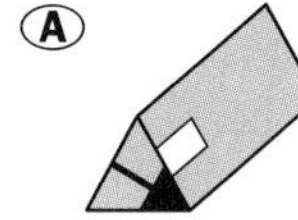

Ⓑ 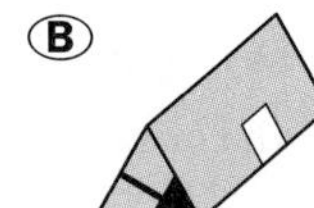

Ⓒ 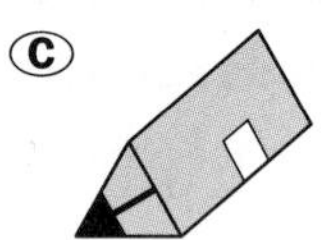

Ⓓ 

○ = WORKED-OUT SOLUTIONS on p. WS1

★ = STANDARDIZED TEST PRACTICE

29.

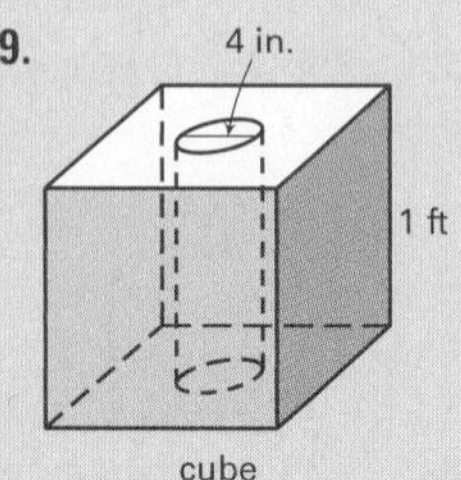

30a.

c. When the
d cubes are
moved, inner
ces of the
ubes remaining
place the
ea of the red
ubes that are
st. When the
ue cubes
e removed,
ere are still
faces of the
ue cubes
hose area is
ot replaced by
ner faces of
e remaining
ubes.
herefore, the
rea of the solid
fter removing
lue cubes is
square units
ss than the
olid after
emoving red
ubes.

B

26. ★ **SHORT RESPONSE** A company makes two types of recycling bins. One type is a right rectangular prism with length 14 inches, width 12 inches, and height 36 inches. The other type is a right cylinder with radius 6 inches and height 36 inches. Both types of bins are missing a base, so the bins have one open end. Which bin requires more material to make? *Explain.* **Right rectangular prism; the bin that is a right rectangular prism has an area of 2040 square inches, and the bin that is a cylinder has an area of about 1470.27 square inches.**

27. MULTI-STEP PROBLEM Consider a cube that is built using 27 unit cubes as shown at the right.

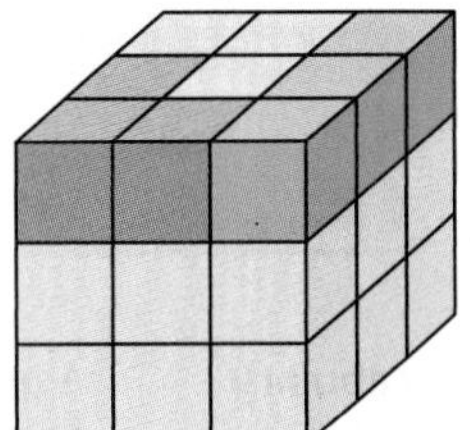

a. Find the surface area of the solid formed when the red unit cubes are removed from the solid shown. **54 units^2**

b. Find the surface area of the solid formed when the blue unit cubes are removed from the solid shown. **52 units^2**

c. Why are your answers different in parts (a) and (b)?

C

28. SURFACE AREA OF A RING The ring shown is a right cylinder of radius r_1 with a cylindrical hole of radius r_2. The ring has height h.

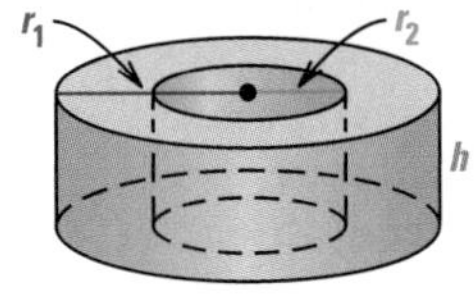

a. Find the surface area of the ring if r_1 is 12 meters, r_2 is 6 meters, and h is 8 meters. Round your answer to two decimal places. **1583.36 m^2**

b. Write a formula that can be used to find the surface area S of any cylindrical ring where $0 < r_2 < r_1$.

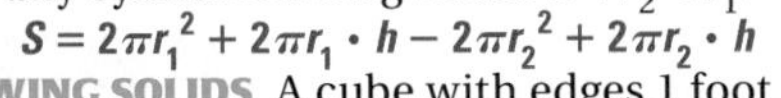

$S = 2\pi r_1^2 + 2\pi r_1 \cdot h - 2\pi r_2^2 + 2\pi r_2 \cdot h$

29. DRAWING SOLIDS A cube with edges 1 foot long has a cylindrical hole with diameter 4 inches drilled through one of its faces. The hole is drilled perpendicular to the face and goes completely through to the other side. Draw the figure and find its surface area. **See margin for art; about 989.66 in.^{2}**

30. CHALLENGE A cuboctahedron has 6 square faces and 8 equilateral triangle faces, as shown. A cuboctahedron can be made by slicing off the corners of a cube.

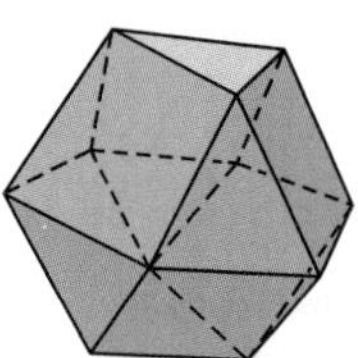

a. Sketch a net for the cuboctahedron. **See margin.**

b. Each edge of a cuboctahedron has a length of 5 millimeters. Find its surface area. **about 236.60 millimeters^2**

MIXED REVIEW

The sum of the measures of the interior angles of a convex polygon is given. Classify the polygon by the number of sides. *(p. 507)*

31. 1260° **nonagon** **32.** 1080° **octagon** **33.** 720° **hexagon** **34.** 1800° **dodecagon**

PREVIEW
Prepare for Lesson 12.3 in Exs. 35–37.

Find the area of the regular polygon. *(p. 762)*

35.

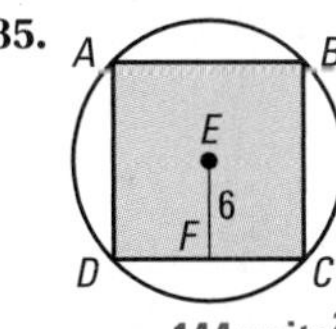

144 units^2

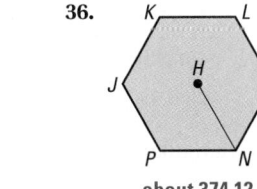

36. K L J H M 12 P N

about 374.12 units^2

37.

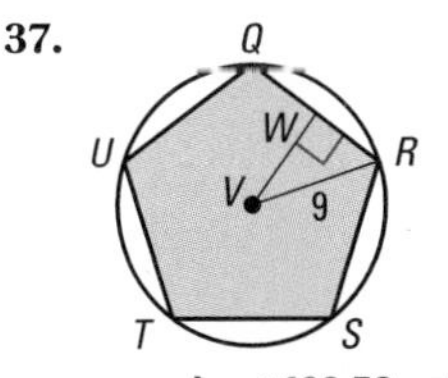

about 192.59 units^2

5 ASSESS AND RETEACH

Daily Homework Quiz

Transparency Available

1. Find the surface area of the solid formed by the net. **288 cm^2**

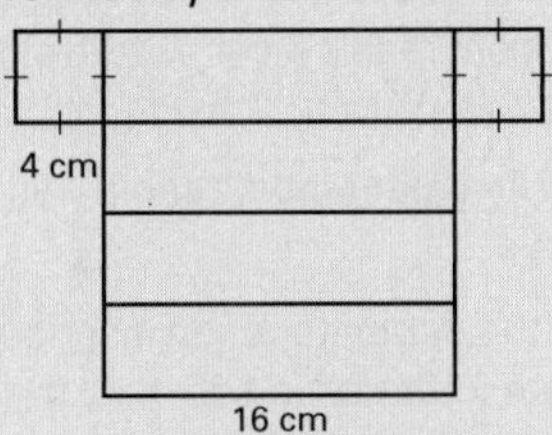

Find the surface area of the right prism or right cylinder.

2.

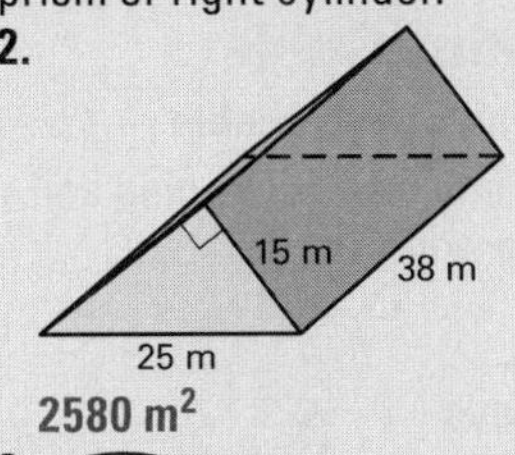

2580 m^2

3.

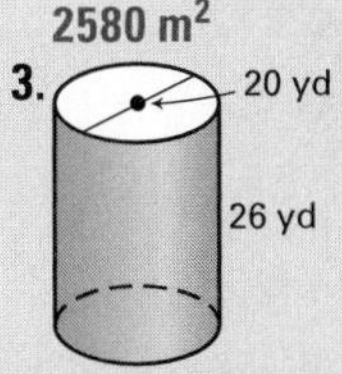

2261.95 yd^2

4. A rectangular prism has surface area 1848 ft^2. Solve for x. **18**

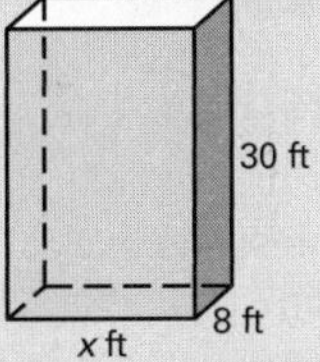

Available at **classzone.com**

Diagnosis/Remediation

- Practice A, B, C in Chapter 12 Resource Book, pp. 22–27
- Study Guide in Chapter 12 Resource Book, pp. 28–29
- Practice Workbook, pp. 229–231
- @HomeTutor

Challenge

Additional challenge is available in the Chapter 12 Resource Book, p. 32.

1 PLAN AND PREPARE

Warm-Up Exercises

Transparency Available

Find the area of each regular polygon or circle.

1. Hexagon, radius 8 cm **166.28 cm^2**
2. Circle, radius 4 in. **50.27 in.^{2}**
3. Inscribed pentagon, radius 1 yd **2.38 yd^2**
4. Find the perimeter of an inscribed square with radius 1 ft. **5.66 ft**
5. Find the circumference of a circle with diameter 12.8 in. **40.21 in.**

Notetaking Guide

Transparency Available

Promotes interactive learning and notetaking skills, pp. 317–320.

Pacing

Basic: 2 days
Average: 2 days
Advanced: 2 days
Block: 0.5 block with 12.2
0.5 block with 12.4

- See *Teaching Guide/Lesson Plan.*

2 FOCUS AND MOTIVATE

Essential Question

Big Idea 2, p. 791

How do you find the surface area of a regular pyramid? **Tell students they will learn how to answer this question by developing and using a formula.**

12.3 Surface Area of Pyramids and Cones

Before You found surface areas of prisms and cylinders.
Now You will find surface areas of pyramids and cones.
Why? So you can find the surface area of a volcano, as in Ex. 33.

Key Vocabulary
- pyramid
- vertex of a pyramid
- regular pyramid
- slant height
- cone
- vertex of a cone
- right cone
- lateral surface

A **pyramid** is a polyhedron in which the base is a polygon and the lateral faces are triangles with a common vertex, called the **vertex of the pyramid**. The intersection of two lateral faces is a *lateral edge*. The intersection of the base and a lateral face is a *base edge*. The height of the pyramid is the perpendicular distance between the base and the vertex.

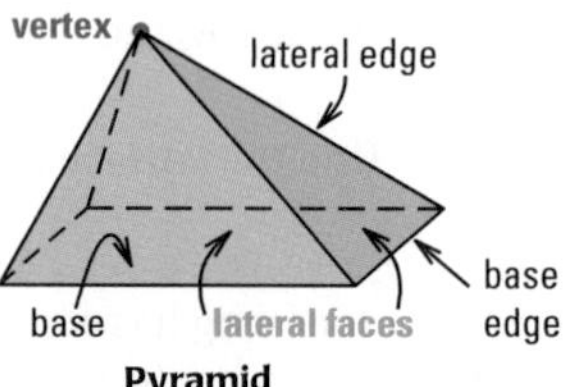

Pyramid

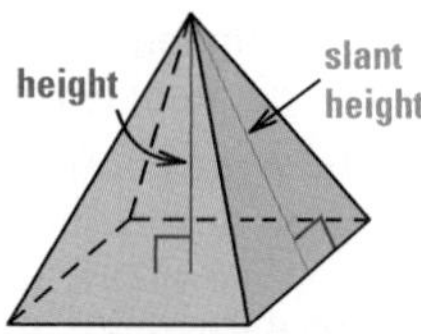

Regular pyramid

NAME PYRAMIDS
Pyramids are classified by the shapes of their bases.

A **regular pyramid** has a regular polygon for a base, and the segment joining the vertex and the center of the base is perpendicular to the base. The lateral faces of a regular pyramid are congruent isosceles triangles. The **slant height** of a regular pyramid is the height of a lateral face of the regular pyramid. A nonregular pyramid does not have a slant height.

Standards

9.0 Students compute the volumes and **surface areas of** prisms, **pyramids**, cylinders, **cones**, and spheres; and **students commit to memory the formulas for** prisms, **pyramids**, and cylinders.

8.0 Students know, derive, and solve problems involving the perimeter, circumference, area, volume, **lateral area, and surface area of common geometric figures.**

EXAMPLE 1 Find the area of a lateral face of a pyramid

A regular square pyramid has a height of 15 centimeters and a base edge length of 16 centimeters. Find the area of each lateral face of the pyramid.

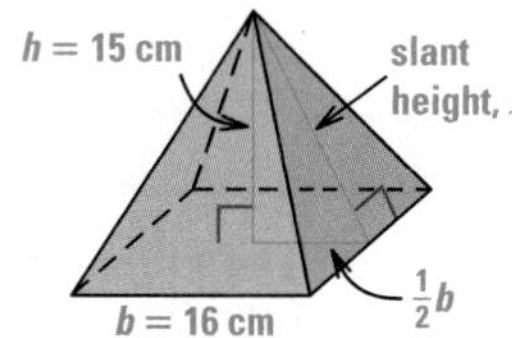

Solution

Use the Pythagorean Theorem to find the slant height ℓ.

$\ell^2 = h^2 + \left(\frac{1}{2}b\right)^2$	Write formula.
$\ell^2 = 15^2 + 8^2$	Substitute for h and $\frac{1}{2}b$.
$\ell^2 = 289$	Simplify.
$\ell = 17$	Find the positive square root.

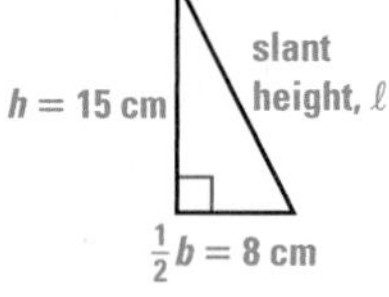

▶ The area of each triangular face is $A = \frac{1}{2}b\ell = \frac{1}{2}(16)(17) = 136$ square centimeters.

Resource Planning Guide

Chapter Resource Book
- Teaching Guide/Lesson Plan (pp. 33–34)
- Activity Master (p. 35)
- Practice levels A, B, C (pp. 36–41)
- Study Guide (pp. 42–43)
- Catch-up for Absent Students (p. 44)
- Problem Solving Workshop (p. 45)
- Challenge (p. 47)

Workbooks
- Notetaking Guide (pp. 317–320)
- Practice Workbook (pp. 232–234)

Teaching Options
- **Power Presentations CD-ROM** provides dynamic electronic teaching resources for the classroom.
- **Activity Generator CD-ROM** provides editable activities for all ability levels.

Interactive Technology
- Easy Planner
- Power Presentations CD-ROM
- Activity Generator CD-ROM
- Animated Geometry
- Test Generator CD-ROM
- Online Quiz
- eWorkbook
- eEdition
- @HomeTutor

Resources for English Learners
- Quick Reference for English Learners
- Spanish Study Guide
- Multi-Language Visual Glossary
- Student Resources in Spanish

See also the *Geometry Toolkit* for more strategies for meeting individual needs.

SURFACE AREA A regular hexagonal pyramid and its net are shown at the right. Let b represent the length of a base edge, and let ℓ represent the slant height of the pyramid.

The area of each lateral face is $\frac{1}{2}b\ell$ and the perimeter of the base is $P = 6b$. So, the surface area S is as follows.

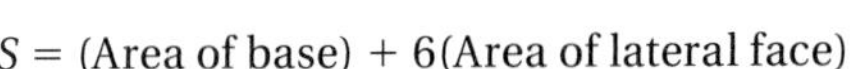

$S =$ (Area of base) + 6(Area of lateral face)

$S = B + 6\left(\frac{1}{2}b\ell\right)$ **Substitute.**

$S = B + \frac{1}{2}(6b)\ell$ **Rewrite $6\left(\frac{1}{2}b\ell\right)$ as $\frac{1}{2}(6b)\ell$.**

$S = B + \frac{1}{2}P\ell$ **Substitute P for $6b$.**

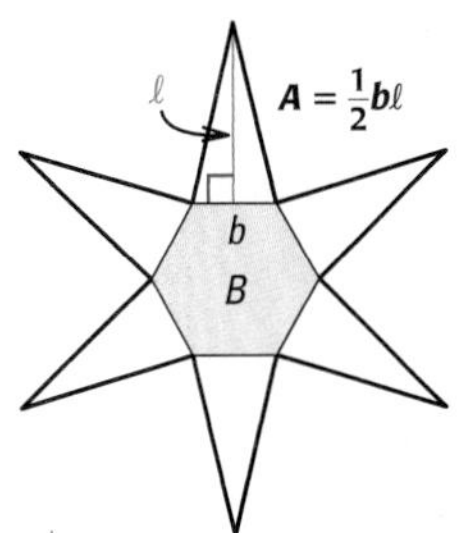

THEOREM *For Your Notebook*

THEOREM 12.4 Surface Area of a Regular Pyramid

The surface area S of a regular pyramid is

$$S = B + \frac{1}{2}P\ell,$$

where B is the area of the base, P is the perimeter of the base, and ℓ is the slant height.

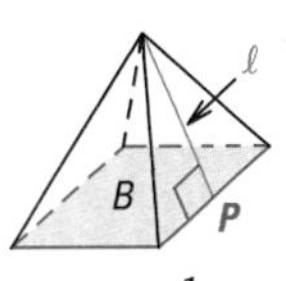

EXAMPLE 2 Find the surface area of a pyramid

Find the surface area of the regular hexagonal pyramid.

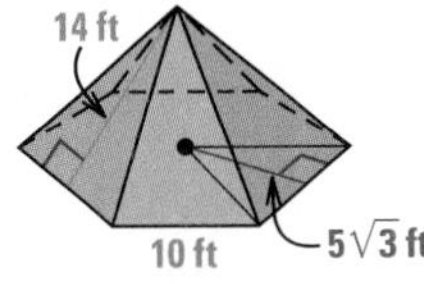

REVIEW AREA
For help with finding the area of regular polygons, see p. 762.

Solution

First, find the area of the base using the formula for the area of a regular polygon, $\frac{1}{2}aP$. The apothem a of the hexagon is $5\sqrt{3}$ feet and the perimeter P is $6 \cdot 10 = 60$ feet. So, the area of the base B is $\frac{1}{2}(5\sqrt{3})(60) = 150\sqrt{3}$ square feet. Then, find the surface area.

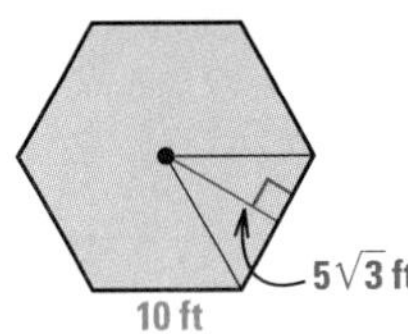

$S = B + \frac{1}{2}P\ell$ **Formula for surface area of regular pyramid**

$= 150\sqrt{3} + \frac{1}{2}(60)(14)$ **Substitute known values.**

$= 150\sqrt{3} + 420$ **Simplify.**

≈ 679.81 **Use a calculator.**

▶ The surface area of the regular hexagonal pyramid is about 679.81 ft^2.

Motivating the Lesson

Ask students to describe the faces of various kinds of pyramids. Discuss the shape of the sides (triangles) and the shapes of the bases (polygons). Tell students that this lesson develops a formula for the surface area of a pyramid, and formulas for other shapes.

3 TEACH

Extra Example 1

A regular square pyramid has a height of 12 ft and a base edge length of 10 ft. Find the area of each lateral face of the pyramid. **65 ft^2**

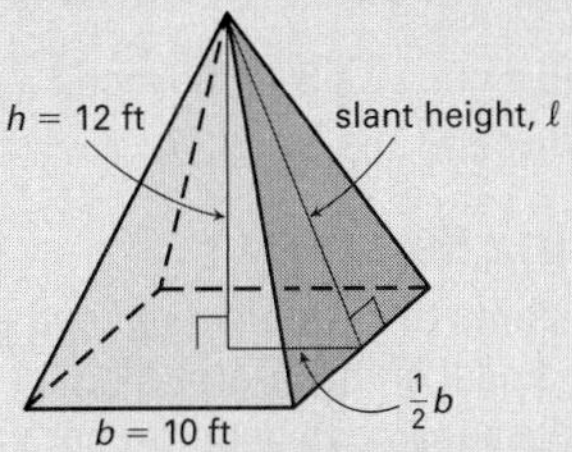

Vocabulary

The *vertex of a pyramid* is the point that is the common vertex of all the triangular sides. Make sure students don't confuse the *vertex of a pyramid* with a vertex of the base.

Extra Example 2

Find the surface area of a regular octagonal pyramid if the slant height is 18 ft, the apothem of the base is 15.7 ft, and the sides of the base are 13 ft. **1752.4 ft^2**

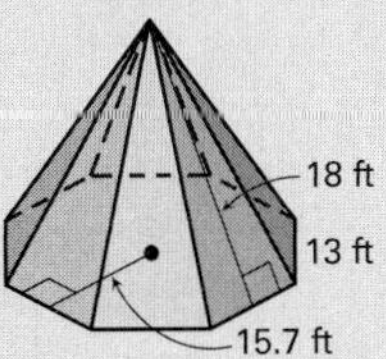

Differentiated Instruction

Below Level Ask students to draw a net for a square pyramid by drawing equilateral triangles on the sides of a square. Then ask them to measure and label the height and base of each triangle. Have them cut out the net, make the pyramid, and use the pyramid to approximate its height. Finally, have them compare the slant height and height of the pyramid.

See also the *Geometry Toolkit* for more strategies.

Key Question to Ask for Examples 1 and 2

- Which is longer, the slant height or the height? Why? **The slant height; in a right triangle with sides that are the height and half-the-base, the slant height is the hypotenuse.**

Extra Example 3

What is the surface area of the right cone? **B**

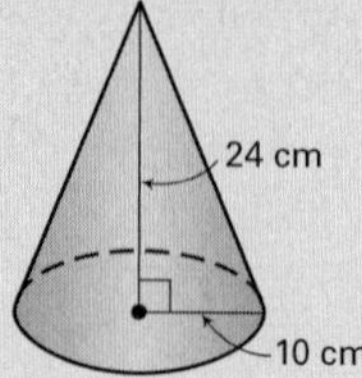

Ⓐ 340π cm² Ⓑ 360π cm²
Ⓒ 440π cm² Ⓓ 580π cm²

Reading Strategy

Ask students to carefully read and make a model of the information on page 812 so they can understand how the formulas for lateral area and surface area of a cone are developed. As the diagram shows, the lateral area can be thought of as a sector with arc length equal to the circumference of the base and radius equal to the slant height.

✓ GUIDED PRACTICE for Examples 1 and 2

1. Find the area of each lateral face of the regular pentagonal pyramid shown. **29.2 m²**
2. Find the surface area of the regular pentagonal pyramid shown. **256 m²**

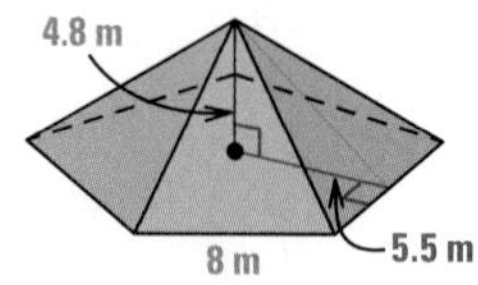

CONES A **cone** has a circular base and a **vertex** that is not in the same plane as the base. The radius of the base is the *radius* of the cone. The height is the perpendicular distance between the vertex and the base.

In a **right cone**, the segment joining the vertex and the center of the base is perpendicular to the base, and the slant height is the distance between the vertex and a point on the base edge.

The **lateral surface** of a cone consists of all segments that connect the vertex with points on the base edge.

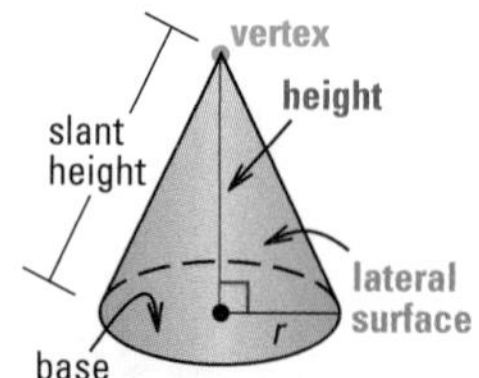

Right cone

SURFACE AREA When you cut along the slant height and base edge and lay a right cone flat, you get the net shown at the right.

The circular base has an area of πr^2 and the lateral surface is the sector of a circle. You can use a proportion to find the area of the sector, as shown below.

$$\frac{\text{Area of sector}}{\text{Area of circle}} = \frac{\text{Arc length}}{\text{Circumference of circle}}$$ **Set up proportion.**

$$\frac{\text{Area of sector}}{\pi \ell^2} = \frac{2\pi r}{2\pi \ell}$$ **Substitute.**

$$\text{Area of sector} = \pi \ell^2 \cdot \frac{2\pi r}{2\pi \ell}$$ **Multiply each side by $\pi \ell^2$.**

$$\text{Area of sector} = \pi r \ell$$ **Simplify.**

The surface area of a cone is the sum of the base area, πr^2, and the lateral area, $\pi r \ell$. Notice that the quantity $\pi r \ell$ can be written as $\frac{1}{2}(2\pi r)\ell$, or $\frac{1}{2}C\ell$.

THEOREM *For Your Notebook*

THEOREM 12.5 Surface Area of a Right Cone

The surface area S of a right cone is

$$S = B + \frac{1}{2}C\ell = \pi r^2 + \pi r \ell,$$

where B is the area of the base, C is the circumference of the base, r is the radius of the base, and ℓ is the slant height.

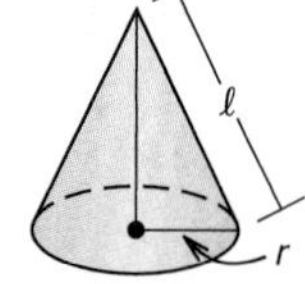

$S = B + \frac{1}{2}C\ell = \pi r^2 + \pi r \ell$

Differentiated Instruction

Advanced Ask students to find an expression for the angle formed by the two slant height segments in the cone net on page 812. They should conclude that the "missing" part of the circumference is $2\pi\ell - 2\pi r$, so the measure of the angle is $\frac{2\pi\ell - 2\pi r}{2\pi\ell} \times 360°$ or $\frac{\ell - r}{\ell} \times 360°$. Ask them to test their calculations by making and folding a net for a cone for given values of ℓ and r.

See also the *Geometry Toolkit* for more strategies.

EXAMPLE 3 Standardized Test Practice

What is the surface area of the right cone?

Ⓐ $72\pi\ m^2$ Ⓑ $96\pi\ m^2$

Ⓒ $132\pi\ m^2$ Ⓓ $136\pi\ m^2$

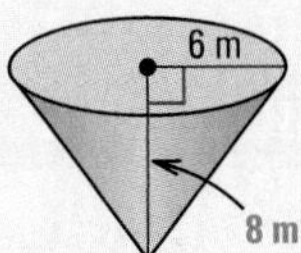

Solution

To find the slant height ℓ of the right cone, use the Pythagorean Theorem.

$\ell^2 = h^2 + r^2$ **Write formula.**

$\ell^2 = 8^2 + 6^2$ **Substitute.**

$\ell = 10$ **Find positive square root.**

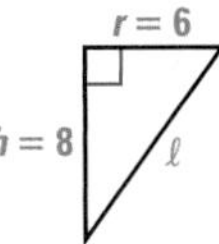

ANOTHER WAY

You can use a Pythagorean triple to find ℓ.
$6 = 2 \cdot 3$ and $8 = 2 \cdot 4$, so $\ell = 2 \cdot 5 = 10$.

Use the formula for the surface area of a right cone.

$S = \pi r^2 + \pi r\ell$ **Formula for surface area of a right cone**

$= \pi(6^2) + \pi(6)(10)$ **Substitute.**

$= 96\pi$ **Simplify.**

▶ The correct answer is B. Ⓐ Ⓑ Ⓒ Ⓓ

EXAMPLE 4 Find the lateral area of a cone

TRAFFIC CONE The traffic cone can be approximated by a right cone with radius 5.7 inches and height 18 inches. Find the approximate lateral area of the traffic cone.

Solution

To find the slant height ℓ, use the Pythagorean Theorem.

$\ell^2 = 18^2 + (5.7)^2$, so $\ell \approx 18.9$ inches.

Find the lateral area.

Lateral area $= \pi r\ell$ **Write formula.**

$\approx \pi(5.7)(18.9)$ **Substitute known values.**

$= 338.4$ **Simplify and use a calculator.**

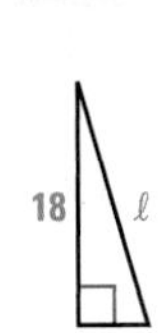

▶ The lateral area of the traffic cone is about 338.4 square inches.

✓ **GUIDED PRACTICE** for Examples 3 and 4

3. Find the lateral area of the right cone shown. **about 1178 yd^2**
4. Find the surface area of the right cone shown. **about 1885 yd^2**

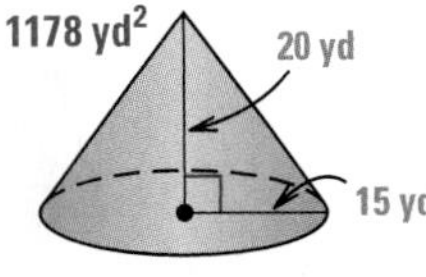

Extra Example 4

A carpenter uses a weight in the shape of a right cone to identify vertical lines. The cone has a radius of 6.5 mm and a height of 13 mm. Find the approximate lateral area of the weight. **297 mm^2**

Closing the Lesson

Have students summarize the major points of the lesson and answer the Essential Question: How do you find the surface area of a regular pyramid?

- **A pyramid is a polyhedron with a polygonal base and with triangular sides meeting in a common vertex.**
- **For a regular pyramid, $S = B + \frac{1}{2}P\ell$**
- **A cone has a circular base and a vertex not in the same plane as the base.**
- **For a cone, $S = B + \frac{1}{2}C\ell = \pi r^2 + \pi r\ell$**

Find the surface area using the formula $S = B + \frac{1}{2}P\ell$ or $S = \frac{1}{2}aP + \frac{1}{2}P\ell$

Differentiated Instruction

Inclusion Instruct students to read problems very carefully so they determine exactly what the question asks. In **Example 3**, the question asks for surface area, but in **Example 4**, the question asks for lateral area. As students complete the exercises in this lesson, have them first write down what it is they are asked to find.

See also the *Geometry Toolkit* for more strategies.

12.3 EXERCISES

HOMEWORK KEY
○ = **WORKED-OUT SOLUTIONS** on p. WS17 for Exs. 7, 11, and 29
★ = **STANDARDIZED TEST PRACTICE** Exs. 2, 17, and 31

SKILL PRACTICE

A

1. **VOCABULARY** Draw a regular square pyramid. Label its *height, slant height,* and *base.* **See margin.**

2. ★ **WRITING** *Compare* the height and slant height of a right cone. **See margin.**

EXAMPLE 1 on p. 810 for Exs. 3–5

AREA OF A LATERAL FACE **Find the area of each lateral face of the regular pyramid.**

3.
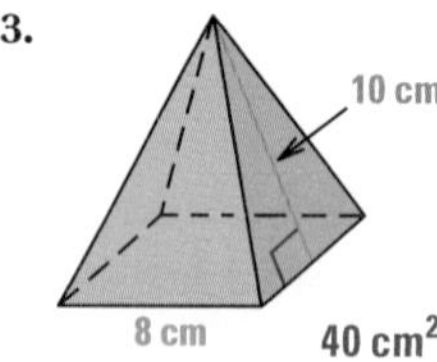

40 cm²

4.
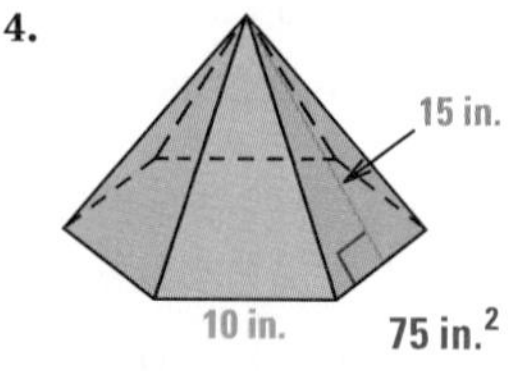

75 in.²

5.
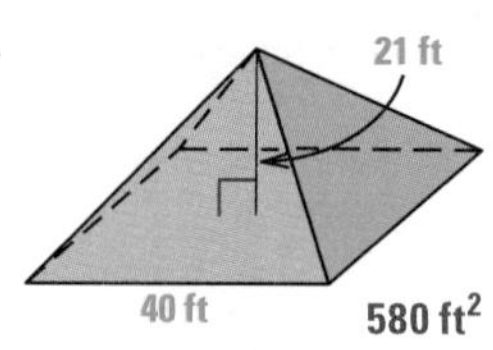

580 ft²

EXAMPLE 2 on p. 811 for Exs. 6–9

2. The slant height is the height of a lateral face, while the height is the distance from the vertex to the center of the base.

SURFACE AREA OF A PYRAMID **Find the surface area of the regular pyramid. Round your answer to two decimal places.**

6.
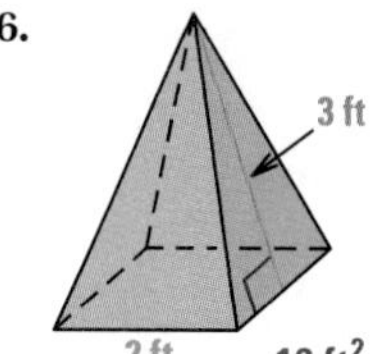

16 ft²

(7.)
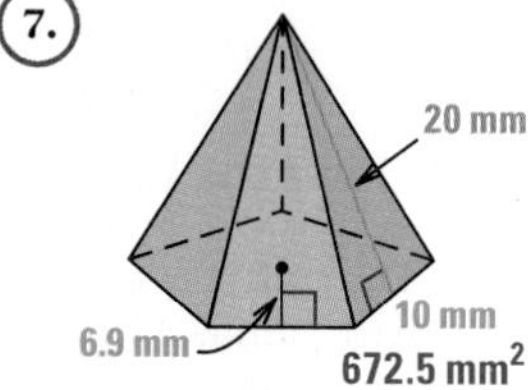

672.5 mm²

8.
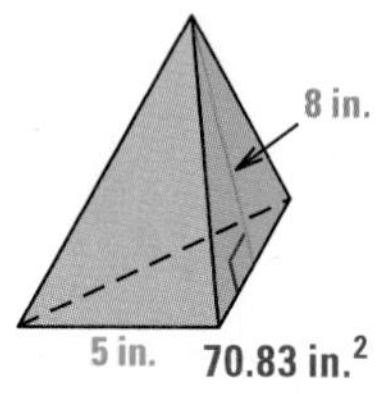

70.83 in.²

9. **ERROR ANALYSIS** *Describe* and correct the error in finding the surface area of the regular pyramid.

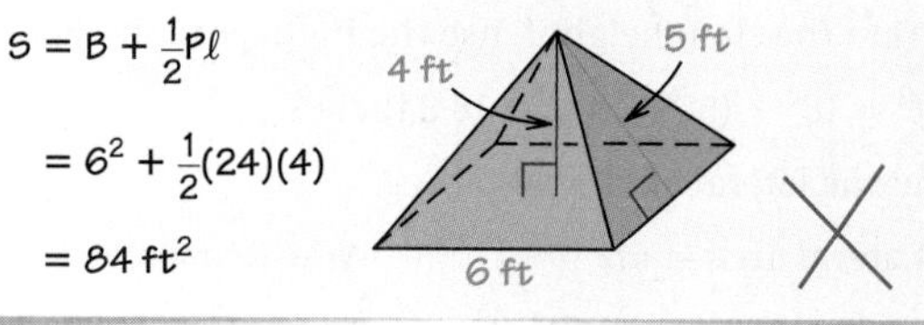

The height of the pyramid is used rather than the slant height; $S = 6^2 + \frac{1}{2}(24)(5) = 96\ ft^2$.

EXAMPLES 3 and 4 on p. 813 for Exs. 10–17

LATERAL AREA OF A CONE **Find the lateral area of the right cone. Round your answer to two decimal places.**

10.
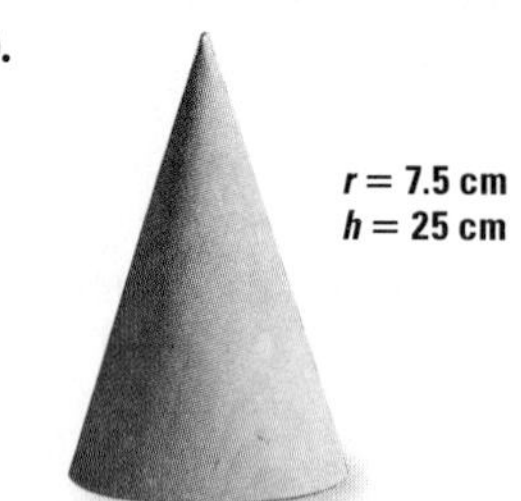
$r = 7.5$ cm
$h = 25$ cm
614.98 cm²

(11.)

$r = 1$ in.
$h = 4$ in.
12.95 in.²

12.

$d = 7$ in.
$h = 1$ ft
137.44 in.²

4 PRACTICE AND APPLY

Assignment Guide

Answer Transparencies available for all exercises

Basic:
Day 1: EP p. 908 Exs. 1–3
pp. 814–817
Exs. 1–9, 20, 21, 27–29, 35, 36
Day 2: pp. 814–817
Exs. 10–19, 30, 31, 37–39

Average:
Day 1: pp. 814–817
Exs. 1–9, 20, 21, 25, 27–29, 35, 36
Day 2: pp. 814–817
Exs. 10–19, 22–24, 30–33, 37–39

Advanced:
Day 1: pp. 814–817
Exs. 1–8, 20, 21, 25, 27–29, 35, 36
Day 2: pp. 814–817
Exs. 11–15, 17–19, 22–24, 26*, 30–34*, 37–39

Block:
pp. 814–817
Exs. 1–9, 20, 21, 25, 27–29, 35, 36 (with 12.2)
pp. 814–817
Exs. 10–19, 22–24, 30–33, 37–39 (with 12.4)

Differentiated Instruction

See *Geometry Best Practices Toolkit* for suggestions on addressing the needs of a diverse classroom.

Homework Check

For a quick check of student understanding of key concepts, go over the following exercises:
Basic: 3, 6, 10, 27, 28
Average: 4, 9, 12, 28, 30
Advanced: 5, 6, 14, 30, 31

Extra Practice

- Student Edition, p. 918
- Chapter 12 Resource Book: Practice levels A, B, C, pp. 36–41

Practice Worksheet

An easily-readable reduced practice page (with answers) for this lesson can be found on p. 790D.

1. height
slant height
base

SURFACE AREA OF A CONE **Find the surface area of the right cone. Round your answer to two decimal places.**

13.

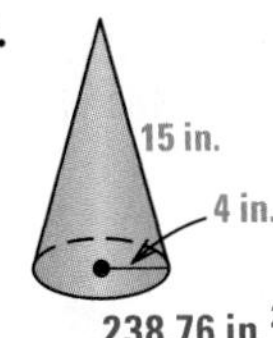

238.76 in.^{2}

14.

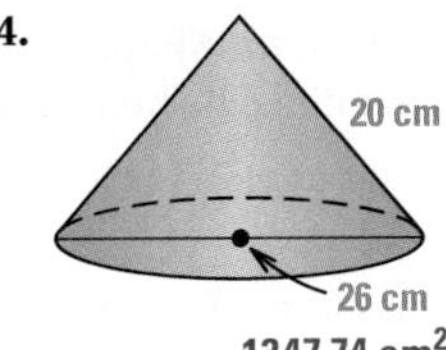

1347.74 cm^2

15.

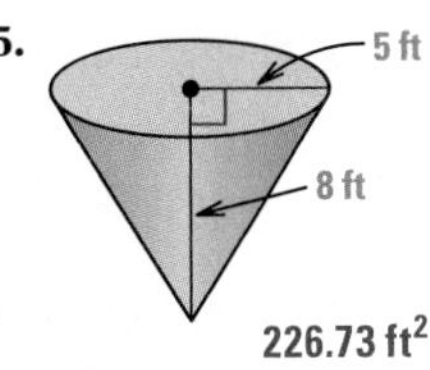

226.73 ft^2

16. **ERROR ANALYSIS** *Describe* and correct the error in finding the surface area of the right cone.

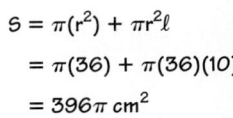

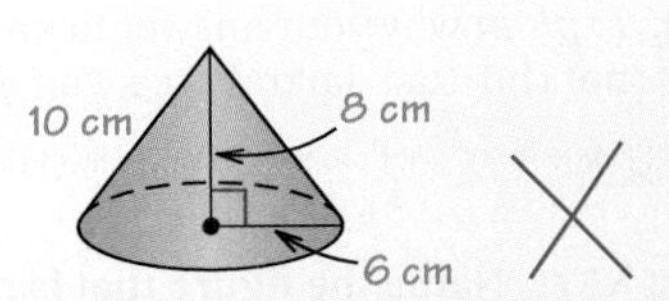

The second r should not be squared; $S = \pi r^2 + \pi r\ell = \pi(36) + \pi(6)(10) = 96\pi \text{ cm}^2$.

B **17.** ★ **MULTIPLE CHOICE** The surface area of the right cone is 200π square feet. What is the slant height of the cone? **B**

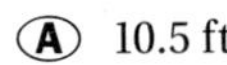

Ⓐ 10.5 ft Ⓑ 17 ft

Ⓒ 23 ft Ⓓ 24 ft

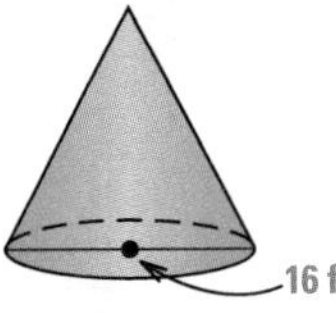

VISUAL REASONING **In Exercises 18–21, sketch the described solid and find its surface area. Round your answer to two decimal places.** 18–21. See margin for art.

18. A right cone has a radius of 15 feet and a slant height of 20 feet. **1649.34 ft^2**

19. A right cone has a diameter of 16 meters and a height of 30 meters. **981.39 m^2**

20. A regular pyramid has a slant height of 24 inches. Its base is an equilateral triangle with a base edge length of 10 inches. **403.30 in.^{2}**

21. A regular pyramid has a hexagonal base with a base edge length of 6 centimeters and a slant height of 9 centimeters. **255.53 cm^2**

COMPOSITE SOLIDS **Find the surface area of the solid. The pyramids are regular and the cones are right. Round your answers to two decimal places, if necessary.**

22.

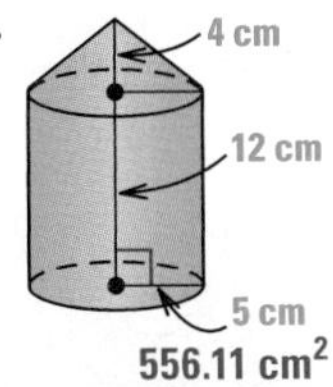

556.11 cm^2

23.

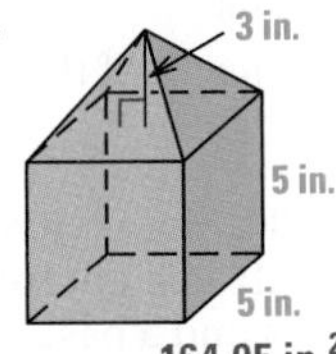

164.05 in.^{2}

24.

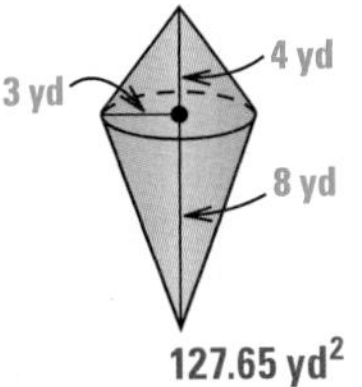

127.65 yd^2

25. **TETRAHEDRON** Find the surface area of a regular tetrahedron with edge length 4 centimeters. **about 27.71 cm^2**

C **26.** **CHALLENGE** A right cone with a base of radius 4 inches and a regular pyramid with a square base both have a slant height of 5 inches. Both solids have the same surface area. Find the length of a base edge of the pyramid. Round your answer to the nearest hundredth of an inch. **6.75 in.**

Avoiding Common Errors

Exercise 17 If students have difficulty with this exercise, remind them that the surface area includes the area of the circular base, so the equation to solve is $200\pi = \pi \cdot 8^2 + \pi(8)\ell$, where 8 is the radius and ℓ is the slant height.

18.

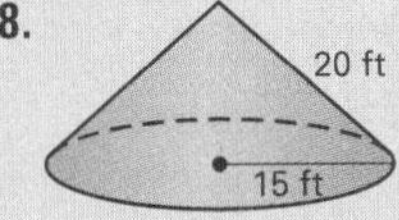

19.

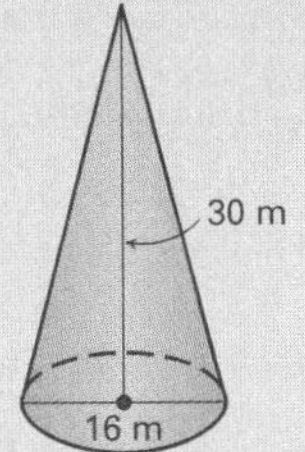

20.

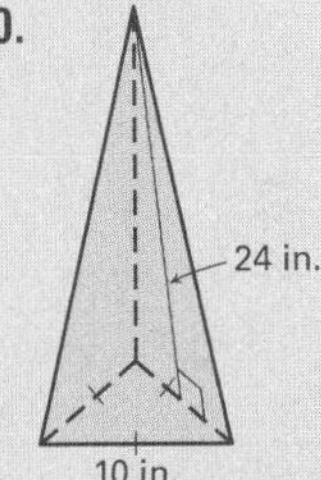

21.

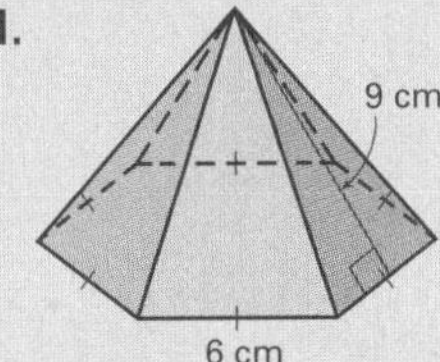

Internet Reference

Exercise 33 Additional information about Mount St. Helens can be found at www.fs.fed.us/gpnf/mshnvm

31a. Given: $\overline{AB} \perp \overline{AC}$, $\overline{DE} \perp \overline{DC}$
Prove: $\triangle ABC \sim \triangle DEC$

Statements (Reasons)

1. $\overline{AB} \perp \overline{AC}$, $\overline{DE} \perp \overline{DC}$ (Given)
2. $\angle BAC$ and $\angle EDC$ are right angles. (Definition of perpendicular)
3. $\angle BAC \cong \angle EDC$ (Right angles are congruent.)
4. $\angle ACB \cong \angle DCE$ (Reflexive Property)
5. $\triangle ABC \sim \triangle DEC$ (AA Similarity Postulate)

PROBLEM SOLVING

EXAMPLE 2 A on p. 811 for Ex. 27

27. CANDLES A candle is in the shape of a regular square pyramid with base edge length 6 inches. Its height is 4 inches. Find its surface area. **96 in.^{2}**

@HomeTutor for problem solving help at classzone.com

28. LAMPSHADE A glass lampshade is shaped like a regular square pyramid.

a. Approximate the lateral area of the lampshade shown. **224 in.^{2}**

b. *Explain* why your answer to part (a) is not the exact lateral area. **Part of the pyramid is cut off at the top.**

@HomeTutor for problem solving help at classzone.com

B **USING NETS** **Name the figure that is represented by the net. Then find its surface area. Round your answer to two decimal places.**

(29.)

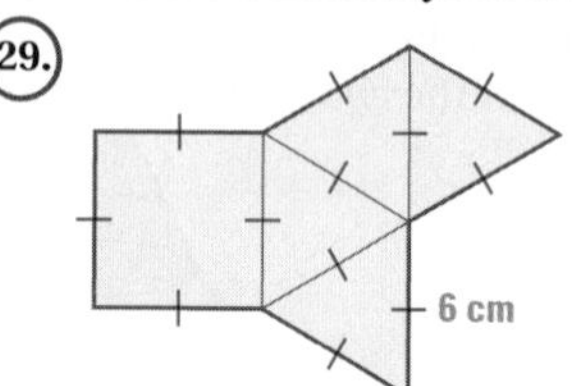

square pyramid; 98.35 cm^2

30. **cone; 113.10 in.^{2}**

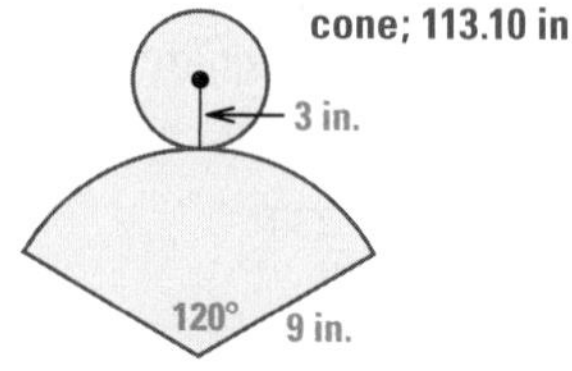

31c. Larger cone: 24π units^2, smaller cone: 6π units^2. *Sample answer*: The small cone has 25% of the surface area of the large cone.

31. ★ **SHORT RESPONSE** In the figure, $AC = 4$, $AB = 3$, and $DC = 2$.

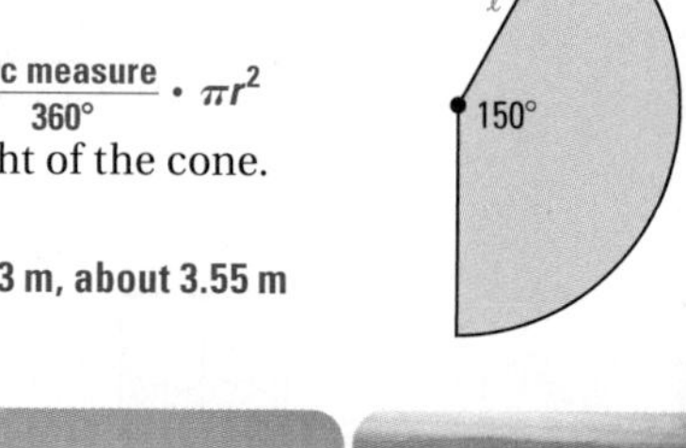

a. Prove $\triangle ABC \sim \triangle DEC$. **See margin.**

b. Find BC, DE, and EC. **$5, \frac{3}{2}, \frac{5}{2}$**

c. Find the surface areas of the larger cone and the smaller cone in terms of π. *Compare* the surface areas using a percent.

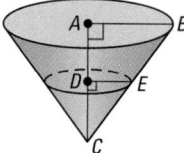

32b. about 3.91 m; solve $20 = \frac{150°}{360°} \cdot \pi\ell^2$ for ℓ to get $\ell \approx 3.91$ meters.

32. MULTI-STEP PROBLEM The sector shown can be rolled to form the lateral surface of a right cone. The lateral surface area of the cone is 20 square meters.

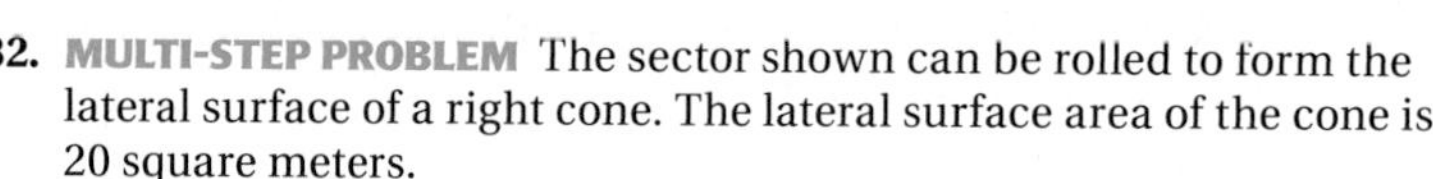

a. Write the formula for the area of a sector. **$A = \frac{\text{arc measure}}{360°} \cdot \pi r^2$**

b. Use the formula in part (a) to find the slant height of the cone. *Explain* your reasoning.

c. Find the radius and height of the cone. **about 1.63 m, about 3.55 m**

33. VOLCANOES Before 1980, Mount St. Helens was a conic volcano with a height from its base of about 1.08 miles and a base radius of about 3 miles. In 1980, the volcano erupted, reducing its height to about 0.83 mile.

Approximate the lateral area of the volcano after 1980. (*Hint:* The ratio of the radius of the destroyed cone-shaped top to its height is the same as the ratio of the radius of the original volcano to its height.) **about 28.44 mi^2**

Before

After

○ = WORKED-OUT SOLUTIONS on p. WS1 ★ = STANDARDIZED TEST PRACTICE

816

 **34. CHALLENGE** An *Elizabethan collar* is used to prevent an animal from irritating a wound. The angle between the opening with a 16 inch diameter and the side of the collar is 53°. Find the surface area of the collar shown. **about 287 in.^{2}**

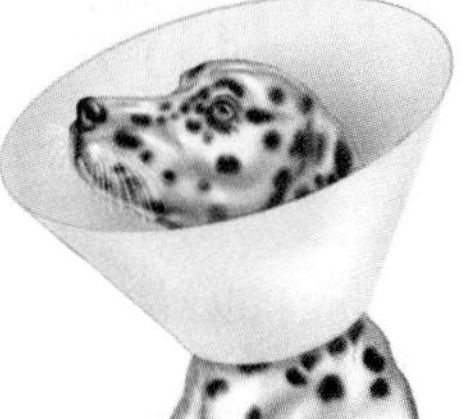

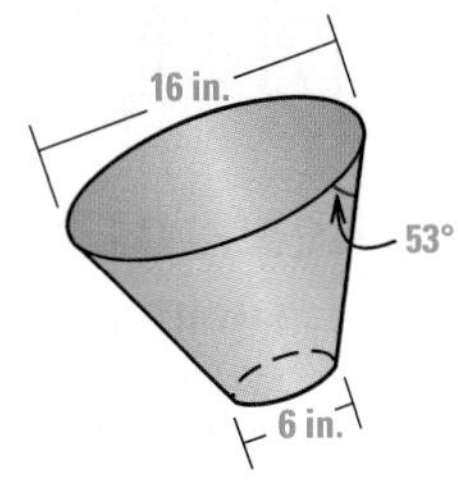

MIXED REVIEW

Find the value of x. *(p. 310)*

35. 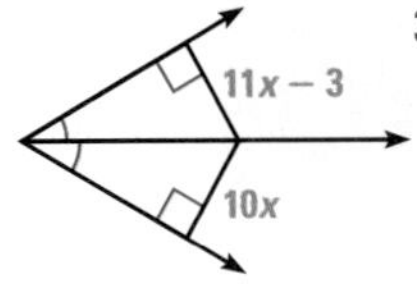

3

36. 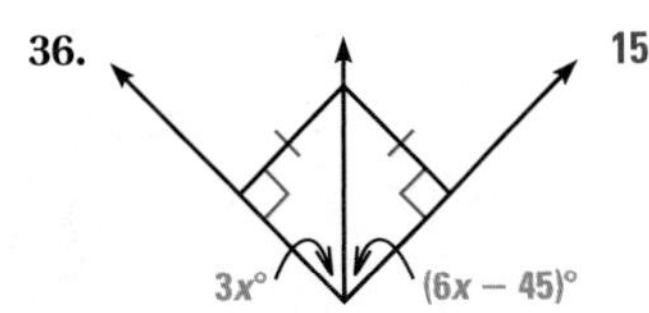

15

PREVIEW
Prepare for Lesson 12.4 in Exs. 37–39.

In Exercises 37–39, find the area of the polygon. *(pp. 720, 730)*

37. 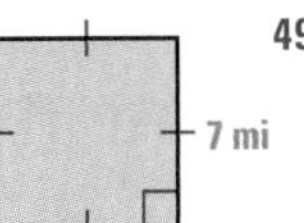

49 mi^2

38. 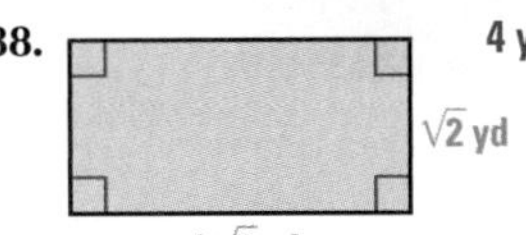

4 yd^2

39. 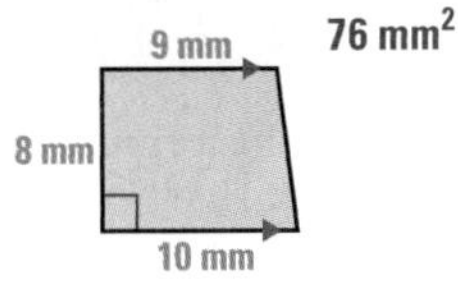

76 mm^2

QUIZ for Lessons 12.1–12.3

1. A polyhedron has 8 vertices and 12 edges. How many faces does the polyhedron have? *(p. 794)* **6 faces**

Solve for x given the surface area S of the right prism or right cylinder. Round your answer to two decimal places. *(p. 803)*

2. $S = 366$ ft^2 **5 ft**

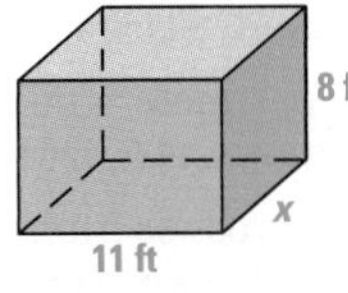

3. $S = 717$ in.^{2} **12.61 in.**

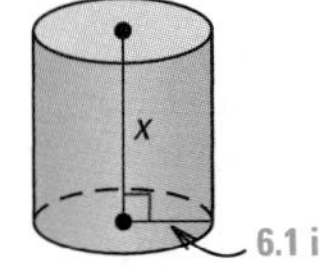

4. $S = 567$ m^2 **11.90 m**

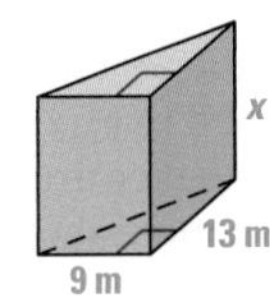

Find the surface area of the regular pyramid or right cone. Round your answer to two decimal places. *(p. 810)*

5. **360 cm^2**

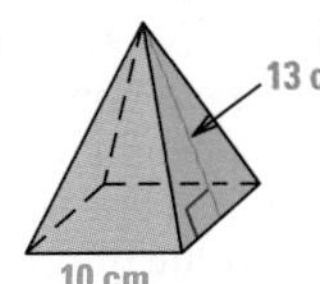

6. **163.36 ft^2**

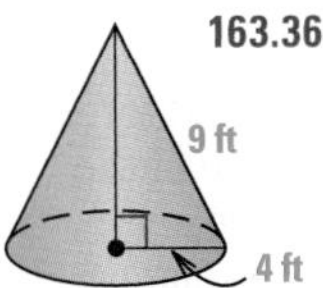

7. **906.91 m^2**

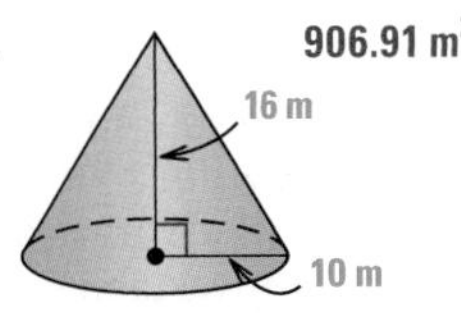

5 ASSESS AND RETEACH

Daily Homework Quiz

Transparency Available

1. Find the lateral area of the regular pyramid. **300 cm^2**

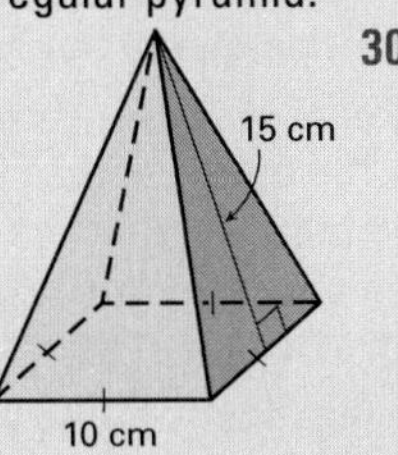

2. Find the surface area of the cone. Round to the nearest hundredth. **1882.97 in.^{2}**

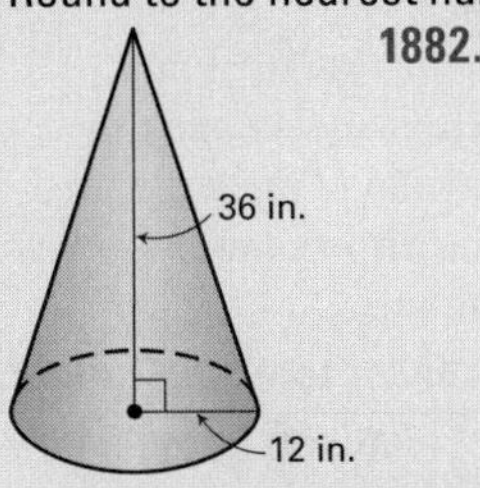

3. A right cone has radius 8 m and surface area 224π m^2. Find its slant height. **20 m**

Available at **classzone.com**

Diagnosis/Remediation

- Practice A, B, C in Chapter 12 Resource Book, pp. 36–41
- Study Guide in Chapter 12 Resource Book, pp. 42–43
- Practice Workbook, pp. 232–234
- @HomeTutor

Challenge

Additional challenge is available in the Chapter 12 Resource Book, p. 47.

Quiz

An easily-readable reduced copy of the quiz (with answers) on Lessons 12.1–12.3 from the Assessment Book can be found on p. 790G.

STATE TEST PRACTICE
classzone.com

1. A polyhedron with 6 vertices and 7 edges must have 3 faces, by Euler's Theorem: $F + V = E + 2$, so $3 + 6 = 7 + 2$. A polyhedron with only 3 faces is not possible.

2. Method 1: Find the area of each face and add them up. Method 2: Use the formula: Area = 2 • Area of the base + Perimeter of base • height.

3a. S is the surface area of the pencil. r is the radius of the circumscribed circle for the base and the length of a side of the hexagon. h is the height of the pencil.

3d. $D = \frac{3\sqrt{3}}{2}r^2 + 6r - \pi r\sqrt{r^2 + 1}$, where r is the radius of the circumscribed circle and the length of a side of the hexagon, and D is the difference in the two surface areas.

5. You can substitute one-half the diameter, $\frac{d}{2}$, into the formula for the surface area of a cone to get $S = \pi\left(\frac{d}{2}\right)^2 + \pi\left(\frac{d}{2}\right) \cdot \ell$.

Lessons 12.1–12.3

1. **SHORT RESPONSE** Using Euler's Theorem, *explain* why it is not possible for a polyhedron to have 6 vertices and 7 edges. **See margin.**

2. **SHORT RESPONSE** *Describe* two methods of finding the surface area of a rectangular solid. **See margin.**

3. **EXTENDED RESPONSE** Some pencils are made from slats of wood that are machined into right regular hexagonal prisms.

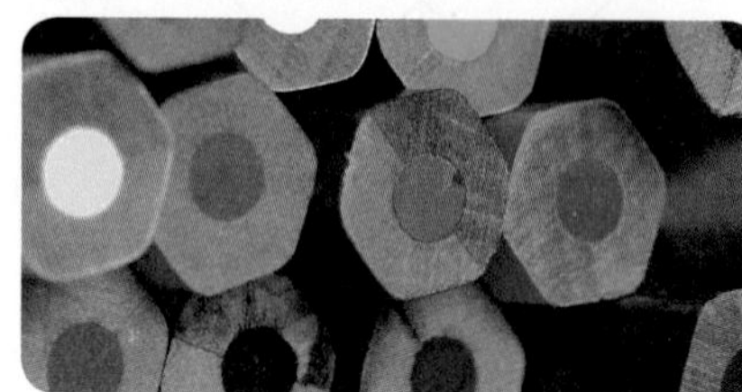

   a. The formula for the surface area of a new unsharpened pencil without an eraser is

   $$S = 3\sqrt{3}r^2 + 6rh.$$

   Tell what each variable in this formula represents. **See margin.**

   b. After a pencil is painted, a metal band that holds an eraser is wrapped around one end. Write a formula for the surface area of the visible portion of the pencil, shown below. $S = \frac{3\sqrt{3}}{2}r^2 + 6rx$

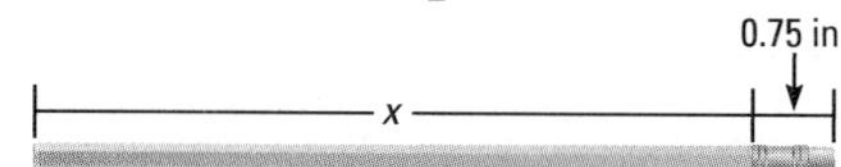

   c. After a pencil is sharpened, the end is shaped like a cone. Write a formula to find the surface area of the visible portion of the pencil, shown below. $S = 6rx - 6r + \pi r\sqrt{r^2 + 1}$

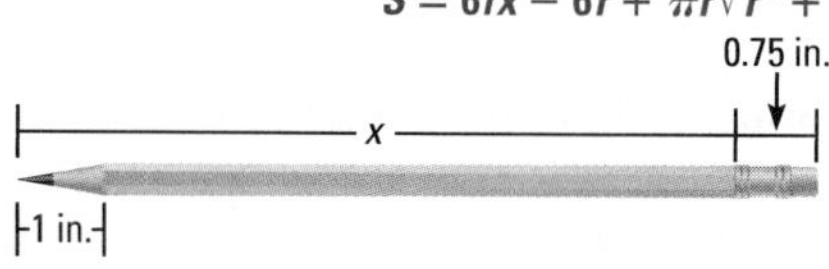

   d. Use your formulas from parts (b) and (c) to write a formula for the difference of the surface areas of the two pencils. Define any variables in your formula. **See margin.**

4. **GRIDDED ANSWER** The amount of paper needed for a soup can label is approximately equal to the lateral area of the can. Find the lateral area of the soup can in square inches. Round your answer to two decimal places. **35.19 in.^{2}**

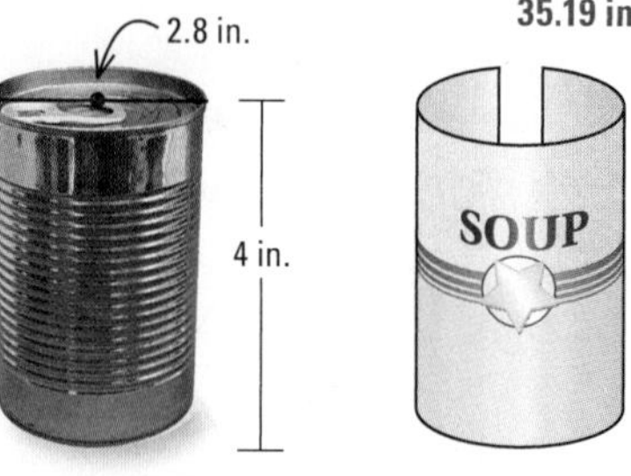

5. **SHORT RESPONSE** If you know the diameter d and slant height ℓ of a right cone, how can you find the surface area of the cone? **See margin.**

6. **OPEN-ENDED** Identify an object in your school or home that is a rectangular prism. Measure its length, width, and height to the nearest quarter inch. Then approximate the surface area of the object. **Check students' work.**

7. **MULTI-STEP PROBLEM** The figure shows a plane intersecting a cube parallel to its base. The cube has a side length of 10 feet.

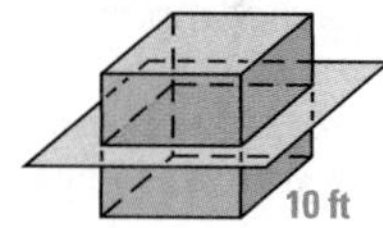

   a. Describe the shape formed by the cross section. **square**

   b. Find the perimeter and area of the cross section. **40 ft, 100 ft^2**

   c. When the cross section is cut along its diagonal, what kind of triangles are formed? **isosceles right triangles**

   d. Find the area of one of the triangles formed in part (c). **50 ft^2**

8. **SHORT RESPONSE** A cone has a base radius of $3x$ units and a height of $4x$ units. The surface area of the cone is 1944π square units. Find the value of x. *Explain* your steps. **See margin.**

8. 9 units; since the base is $3x$ units and the height is $4x$ units, the slant height is $5x$ units by the Pythagorean Theorem. Then substitute into the area formula and solve.

$S = \pi r^2 + \pi r\ell$

$1944\pi = \pi(3x)^2 + \pi(3x)(5x)$ Substitute $3x$ for r and $5x$ for ℓ.

$1944 = 24x^2$ Divide both sides by π.

$x = 9$ Solve for x.

12.4 Volume of Prisms and Cylinders

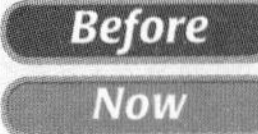

Before	You found surface areas of prisms and cylinders.
Now	You will find volumes of prisms and cylinders.
Why	So you can determine volume of water in an aquarium, as in Ex. 33.

Key Vocabulary
- volume

The **volume** of a solid is the number of cubic units contained in its interior. Volume is measured in cubic units, such as cubic centimeters (cm^3).

Standards

9.0 Students compute the volumes and **surface areas of prisms,** pyramids, **cylinders,** cones, and spheres; **and students commit to memory the formulas for prisms,** pyramids, **and cylinders.**

8.0 Students know, derive, **and solve problems involving** the perimeter, circumference, area, **volume,** lateral area, and surface area of common geometric figures.

POSTULATES *For Your Notebook*

POSTULATE 27 Volume of a Cube Postulate

The volume of a cube is the cube of the length of its side.

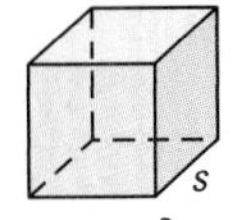

POSTULATE 28 Volume Congruence Postulate

If two polyhedra are congruent, then they have the same volume.

POSTULATE 29 Volume Addition Postulate

The volume of a solid is the sum of the volumes of all its nonoverlapping parts.

EXAMPLE 1 Find the number of unit cubes

3-D PUZZLE Find the volume of the puzzle piece in cubic units.

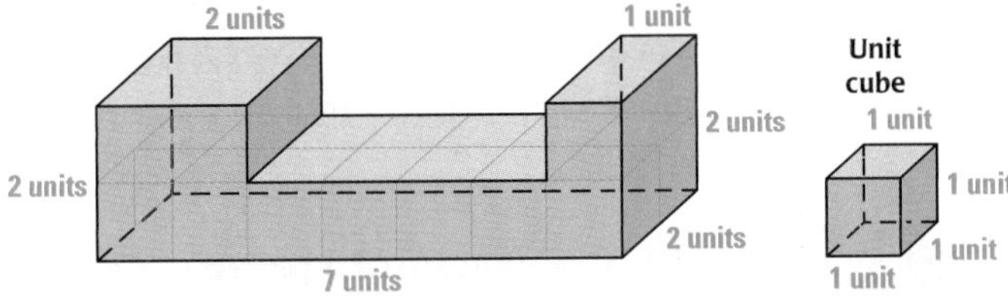

Solution

To find the volume, find the number of unit cubes it contains. Separate the piece into three rectangular boxes as follows:

The *base* is 7 units by 2 units. So, it contains 7 • 2, or 14 unit cubes.

The *upper left box* is 2 units by 2 units. So, it contains 2 • 2, or 4 unit cubes.

The *upper right box* is 1 unit by 2 units. So, it contains 1 • 2, or 2 unit cubes.

▶ By the Volume Addition Postulate, the total volume of the puzzle piece is $14 + 4 + 2 = 20$ cubic units.

1 PLAN AND PREPARE

Warm-Up Exercises

Transparency Available

Find the area of each polygon or circle.

1. Trapezoid, bases 12 ft and 18 ft, height 3 ft **45 ft²**
2. Circle, diameter 8.2 in. **52.8 in.²**
3. Regular hexagon, side length 14 cm **509.22 cm²**

Notetaking Guide

Transparency Available

Promotes interactive learning and notetaking skills, pp. 321–324.

Pacing

Basic: 2 days
Average: 2 days
Advanced: 2 days
Block: 0.5 block with 12.3
0.5 block with 12.5

- See *Teaching Guide/Lesson Plan.*

2 FOCUS AND MOTIVATE

Essential Question

Big Idea 2, p. 791

How do you find the volume of a right prism or right cylinder? **Tell students they will learn how to answer this question by developing and using formulas for volume.**

Resource Planning Guide

Chapter Resource Book
- Teaching Guide/Lesson Plan (pp. 48–49)
- Activity Master (p. 50)
- Practice levels A, B, C (pp. 51–56)
- Study Guide (pp. 57–58)
- Catch-up for Absent Students (p. 59)
- Application (p. 60)
- Challenge (p. 61)

Workbooks
- Notetaking Guide (pp. 321–324)
- Practice Workbook (pp. 235–237)

Teaching Options
- **Power Presentations CD-ROM** provides dynamic electronic teaching resources for the classroom.
- **Activity Generator CD-ROM** provides editable activities for all ability levels.

Interactive Technology
- Easy Planner
- Power Presentations CD-ROM
- Activity Generator CD-ROM
- Animated Geometry
- Test Generator CD-ROM
- Online Quiz
- eWorkbook
- eEdition
- @HomeTutor

Resources for English Learners
- Quick Reference for English Learners
- Spanish Study Guide
- Multi-Language Visual Glossary
- Student Resources in Spanish

See also the *Geometry Toolkit* for more strategies for meeting individual needs.

Motivating the Lesson

A large cylinder, resting on a base, contains 50 gallons of water and the water is 3 feet deep. Ask students how they could find how much water is in the cylinder if the water is 2 feet, 8 feet, or 12 feet deep. Tell students that this lesson uses the height and base of a cylinder (or prism) to develop volume formulas.

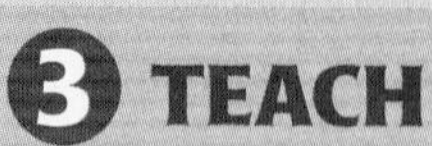

Extra Example 1

Find the volume of the puzzle piece.

37 units^3

Extra Example 2

Find the volume of the right hexagonal prism or right cylinder.

a.

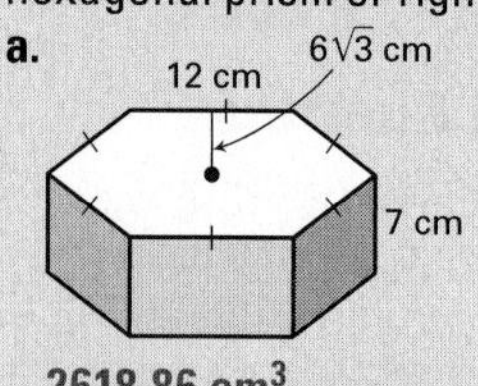

2618.86 cm^3

b. 40 ft, 10 ft

50,265.48 ft^3

VOLUME FORMULAS The volume of any right prism or right cylinder can be found by multiplying the area of its base by its height.

THEOREMS *For Your Notebook*

THEOREM 12.6 Volume of a Prism

The volume V of a prism is

$V = Bh$,

where B is the area of a base and h is the height.

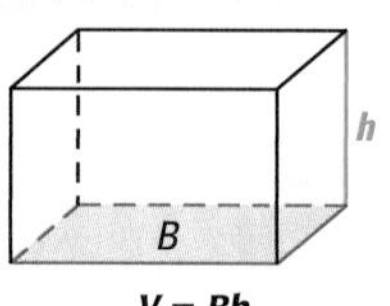

$V = Bh$

THEOREM 12.7 Volume of a Cylinder

The volume V of a cylinder is

$V = Bh = \pi r^2 h$,

where B is the area of a base, h is the height, and r is the radius of a base.

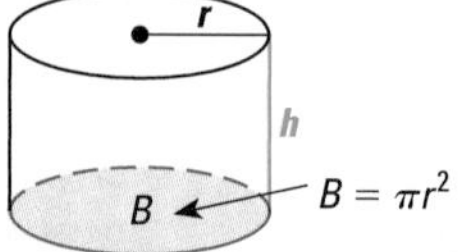

$V = Bh = \pi r^2 h$

EXAMPLE 2 Find volumes of prisms and cylinders

Find the volume of the solid.

a. Right trapezoidal prism

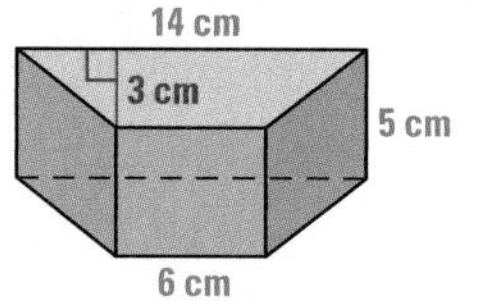

b. Right cylinder

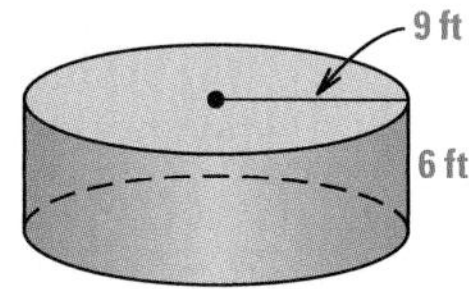

Solution

REVIEW AREA For help with finding the area of a trapezoid, see p. 730.

a. The area of a base is $\frac{1}{2}(3)(6 + 14) = 30\text{ cm}^2$ and $h = 5$ cm.

$V = Bh = 30(5) = 150\text{ cm}^3$

b. The area of the base is $\pi \cdot 9^2$, or $81\pi\text{ ft}^2$. Use $h = 6$ ft to find the volume.

$V = Bh = 81\pi(6) = 486\pi \approx 1526.81\text{ ft}^3$

EXAMPLE 3 Use volume of a prism

ALGEBRA The volume of the cube is 90 cubic inches. Find the value of x.

Solution

A side length of the cube is x inches.

$V = x^3$	Formula for volume of a cube
$90\text{ in.}^3 = x^3$	Substitute for V.
$4.48\text{ in.} \approx x$	Find the cube root.

GUIDED PRACTICE for Examples 1, 2, and 3

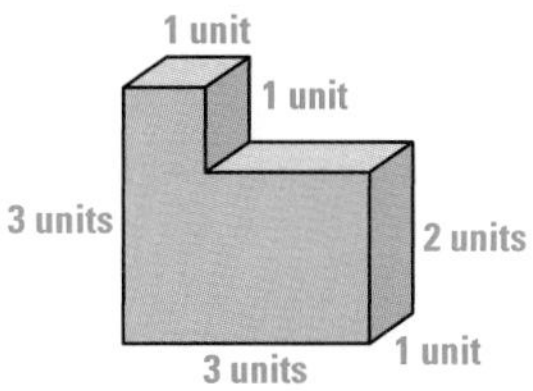

1. Find the volume of the puzzle piece shown in cubic units. **7 units^3**
2. Find the volume of a square prism that has a base edge length of 5 feet and a height of 12 feet. **300 ft^3**
3. The volume of a right cylinder is 684π cubic inches and the height is 18 inches. Find the radius. **$\sqrt{38}$ in.**

USING CAVALIERI'S PRINCIPLE Consider the solids below. All three have equal heights h and equal cross-sectional areas B. Mathematician Bonaventura Cavalieri (1598–1647) claimed that all three of the solids have the same volume. This principle is stated below.

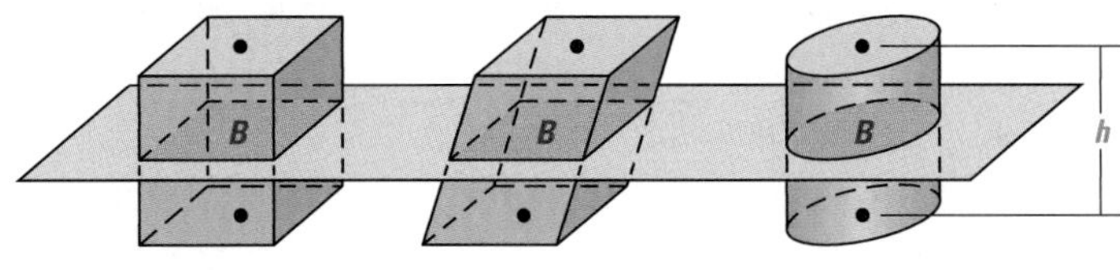

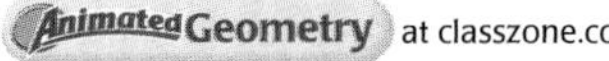 at classzone.com

THEOREM *For Your Notebook*

THEOREM 12.8 Cavalieri's Principle

If two solids have the same height and the same cross-sectional area at every level, then they have the same volume.

EXAMPLE 4 Find the volume of an oblique cylinder

Find the volume of the oblique cylinder.

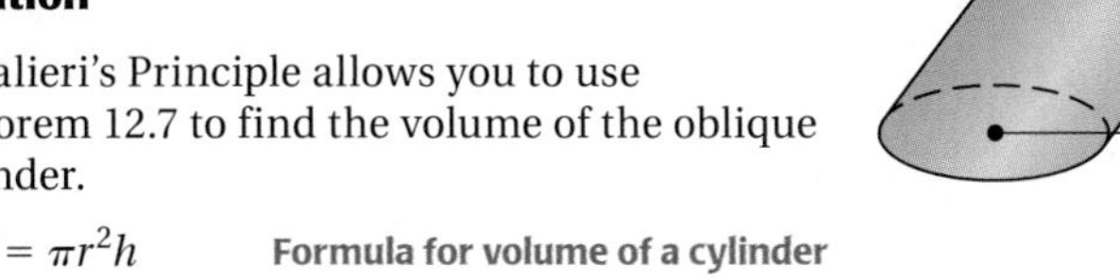

APPLY THEOREMS
Cavalieri's Principle tells you that the volume formulas on page 820 work for oblique prisms and cylinders.

Solution

Cavalieri's Principle allows you to use Theorem 12.7 to find the volume of the oblique cylinder.

$V = \pi r^2 h$ **Formula for volume of a cylinder**

$= \pi(4^2)(7)$ **Substitute known values.**

$= 112\pi$ **Simplify.**

≈ 351.86 **Use a calculator.**

▶ The volume of the oblique cylinder is about 351.86 cm^3.

Extra Example 3

The volume of the gift box cube is 108 in.^{3} Find the value of x.

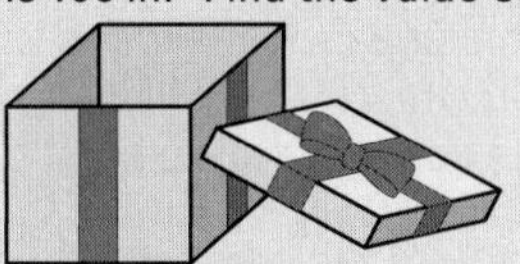

about 4.76 in.

Key Question to Ask for Example 3

- If the side length doubled, what would be the ratio of the new volume to the old? **8 : 1**

An **Animated Geometry** activity is available on-line for **Cavalieri's Principle**. This activity is also available on the **Power Presentations CD-ROM**.

Extra Example 4

Find the volume of the oblique cylinder. **3053.6 m^3**

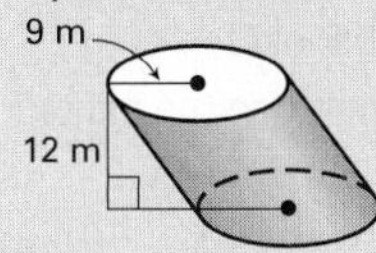

Key Questions to Ask for Example 4

- How do you measure the height of an oblique cylinder? **Measure the length of the segment perpendicular to and between the two bases.**
- What is the relationship between the volume formulas for a right cylinder and an oblique cylinder? **They are the same.**

Differentiated Instruction

Visual Learners Assist students in visualizing how the puzzle piece in **Guided Practice Exercise 1** can be broken down into smaller pieces. Ask the following questions: "Where could you draw a line to break the given piece into two smaller pieces? What are the dimensions of the two smaller pieces? How do you find the volume of each piece?"

See also the *Geometry Toolkit* for more strategies.

Extra Example 5

A cistern is a large tank used to collect rainwater. It is made of concrete that is 3 inches thick and is open at the top. Find the volume of concrete needed to make the sides and bottom of the cistern. **8340.93 in.^{3}**

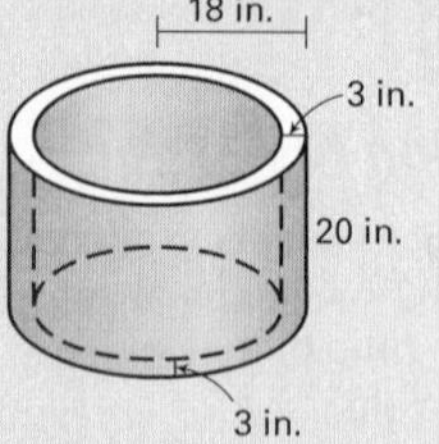

Key Questions to Ask for Example 5

- Could the volume have been calculated in a different way? **Yes; you could add the individual volumes of the rectangular prisms making up the sculpture.**
- What was the basic method used to solve this problem? **Find the area of the irregular base and multiply it by the height.**

Closing the Lesson

Have students summarize the major points of the lesson and answer the Essential Question: How do you find the volume of a right prism or right cylinder?

- **For a prism, $V = Bh$.**
- **For a cylinder, $V = Bh = \pi r^2 h$.**
- **Cavalieri's Principle says the volume formulas work for both right and oblique prisms and cylinders.**

The volume of a right prism or right cylinder is the product of the height and the area of the base.

EXAMPLE 5 Solve a real-world problem

ANOTHER WAY
For alternative methods for solving the problem in Example 5, turn to page 826 for the **Problem Solving Workshop**.

SCULPTURE The sculpture is made up of 13 beams. In centimeters, suppose the dimensions of each beam are 30 by 30 by 90. Find its volume.

Romartyr Hamburg, 1989 © Carl Andre/licensed by VAGA, NY

Solution

The area of the base B can be found by subtracting the area of the small rectangles from the area of the large rectangle.

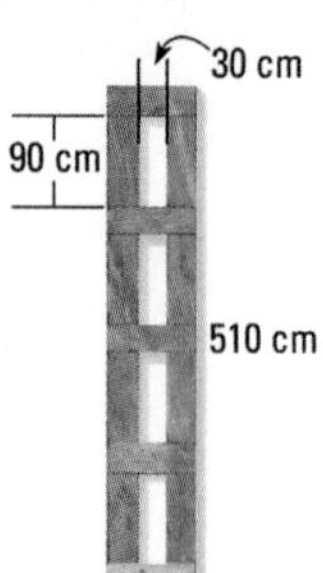

B = Area of large rectangle − 4 • Area of small rectangle

$= 90 \cdot 510 - 4(30 \cdot 90)$

$= 35{,}100 \text{ cm}^2$

Use the formula for the volume of a prism.

$V = Bh$ **Formula for volume of a prism**

$= 35{,}100(30)$ **Substitute.**

$= 1{,}053{,}000 \text{ cm}^3$ **Simplify.**

▶ The volume of the sculpture is $1{,}053{,}000 \text{ cm}^3$, or 1.053 m^3.

✓ GUIDED PRACTICE for Examples 4 and 5

4. Find the volume of the oblique prism shown below.

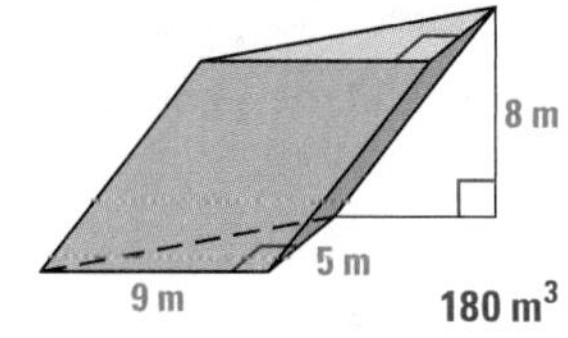

180 m^3

5. Find the volume of the solid shown below.

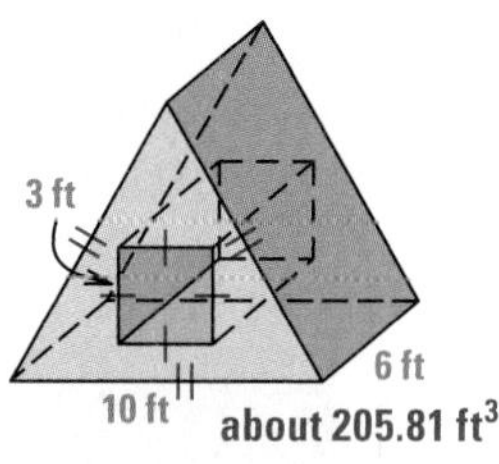

about 205.81 ft^3

12.4 EXERCISES

HOMEWORK KEY
○ = **WORKED-OUT SOLUTIONS** on p. WS17 for Exs. 7, 11, and 29
★ = **STANDARDIZED TEST PRACTICE** Exs. 2, 3, 21, and 33

SKILL PRACTICE

A

1. **VOCABULARY** In what type of units is the volume of a solid measured? **cubic units**

2. ★ **WRITING** Two solids have the same surface area. Do they have the same volume? *Explain* your reasoning. **Sometimes; volume does not depend on surface so if two surface areas are the same, their volumes can be different.**

EXAMPLE 1 on p. 819 for Exs. 3–6

3. ★ **MULTIPLE CHOICE** How many 3 inch cubes can fit completely in a box that is 15 inches long, 9 inches wide, and 3 inches tall? **A**

Ⓐ 15 Ⓑ 45 Ⓒ 135 Ⓓ 405

USING UNIT CUBES **Find the volume of the solid by determining how many unit cubes are contained in the solid.**

4. 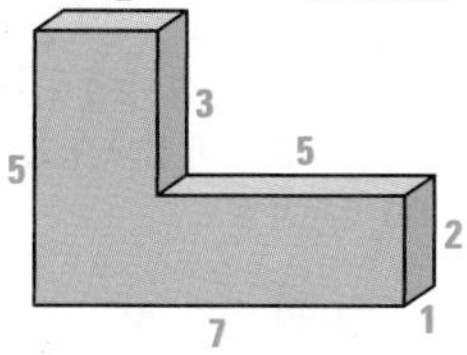

20 units^3

5. 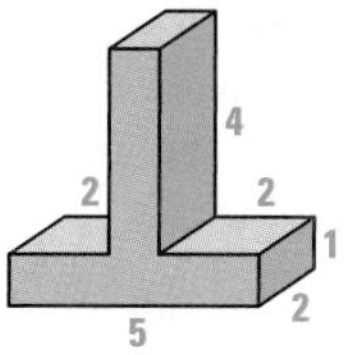

18 units^3

6. 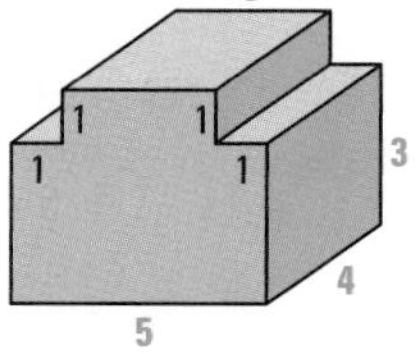

72 units^3

EXAMPLE 2 on p. 820 for Exs. 7–13

FINDING VOLUME **Find the volume of the right prism or right cylinder. Round your answer to two decimal places.**

(7.) 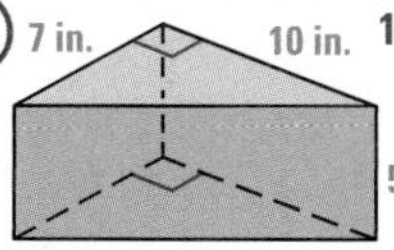

175 in.^{3}

8. 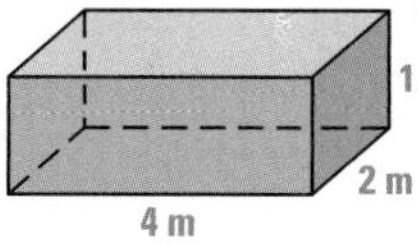

12 m^3

9. 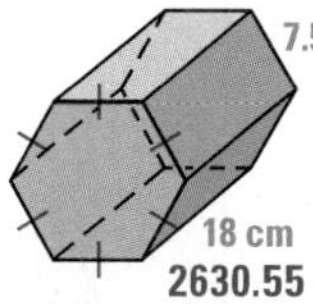

2630.55 cm^3

10. 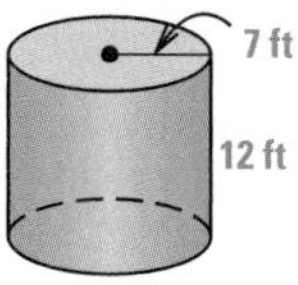

1847.26 ft^3

(11.) 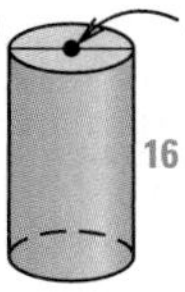

1256.64 in.^{3}

12. 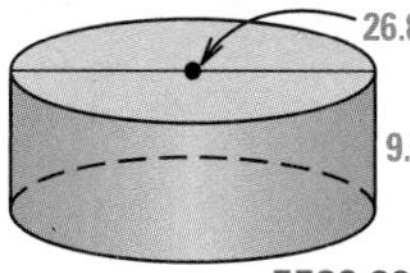

5528.22 cm^3

13. **ERROR ANALYSIS** *Describe* and correct the error in finding the volume of a right cylinder with radius 4 feet and height 3 feet.

$V = 2\pi rh$

$= 2\pi(4)(3)$

$= 24\pi \text{ ft}^3$

The area of a circle (the base) is πr^2, not $2\pi r$; $V = \pi r^2 h = \pi(4^2)(3) = 48\pi \text{ ft}^3$.

B

14. **FINDING VOLUME** Sketch a rectangular prism with height 3 feet, width 11 inches, and length 7 feet. Find its volume. **See margin for art; 19.25 ft^3.**

EXAMPLE 3 on p. 820 for Exs. 15–17

ALGEBRA **Find the length x using the given volume V.**

15. $V = 1000 \text{ in.}^3$ **10 in.**

16. $V = 45 \text{ cm}^3$ **about 2.08 cm**

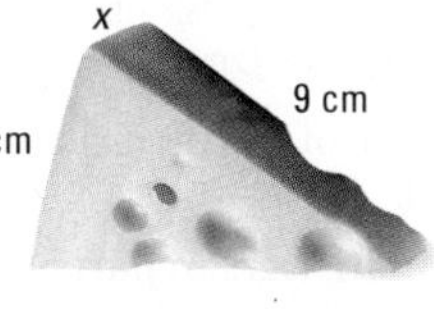

17. $V = 128\pi \text{ in.}^3$ **8 in.**

COMPOSITE SOLIDS **Find the volume of the solid. The prisms and cylinders are right. Round your answer to two decimal places, if necessary.**

18. 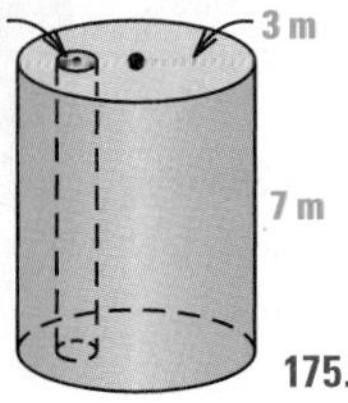

175.93 m^3

19. 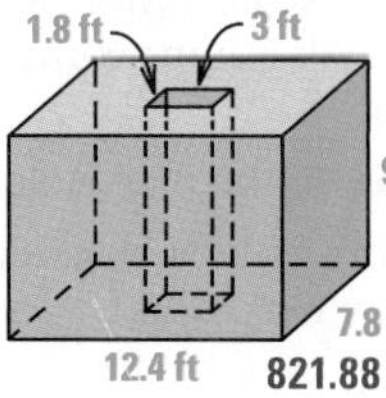

821.88 ft^3

20. 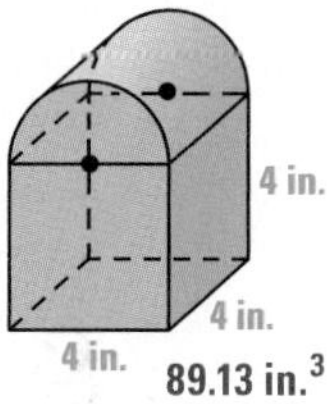

89.13 in.^{3}

4 PRACTICE AND APPLY

Assignment Guide

Answer Transparencies available for all exercises

Basic:
Day 1: EP p. 916 Exs. 9–12
pp. 822–825
Exs. 1–14
Day 2: pp. 822–825
Exs. 15–24, 28–32, 35–40

Average:
Day 1: pp. 822–825
Exs. 1–14, 33
Day 2: pp. 822–825
Exs. 15–26, 28–32, 35–39 odd

Advanced:
Day 1: pp. 822–825
Exs. 1–12, 14, 33, 34*
Day 2: pp. 822–825
Exs. 16–32*, 36–40 even

Block:
pp. 822–825
Exs. 1–14, 33 (with 12.3)
pp. 822–825
Exs. 15–26, 28–32, 35–39 odd
(with 12.5)

Differentiated Instruction

See *Geometry Best Practices Toolkit* for suggestions on addressing the needs of a diverse classroom.

Homework Check

For a quick check of student understanding of key concepts, go over the following exercises:

Basic: 4, 8, 15, 24, 28
Average: 5, 10, 16, 25, 30
Advanced: 6, 12, 17, 26, 30

Extra Practice

- Student Edition, p. 919
- Chapter 12 Resource Book: Practice levels A, B, C, pp. 51–56

Practice Worksheet

An easily-readable reduced practice page (with answers) for this lesson can be found on p. 790D.

14. 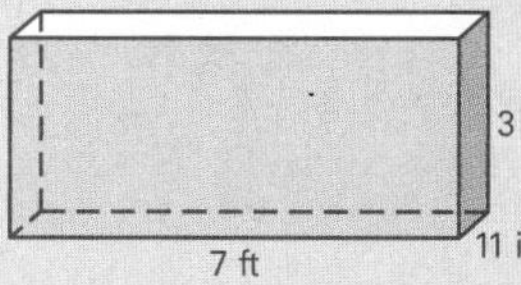

Teaching Strategy

Exercises 4–6 Tell students that they can also use the strategy from Example 5 to find each volume. That is, they can find the area of the front face and multiply by the depth or height of the solid.

Exercise 30 Additional information about the Blue Hole can be found at soundwaves.usgs.gov/2001/06

An **Animated Geometry** activity is available on-line for **Exercise 31**. This activity is also available on the **Power Presentations CD-ROM**.

Vocabulary

Exercise 32 In mathematics, a *solid of revolution* is a solid figure obtained by rotating a plane figure about a line (axis).

21. ★ **MULTIPLE CHOICE** What is the height of a cylinder with radius 4 feet and volume 64π cubic feet? **A**

   (A) 4 feet (B) 8 feet (C) 16 feet (D) 256 feet

22. **FINDING HEIGHT** The bases of a right prism are right triangles with side lengths of 3 inches, 4 inches, and 5 inches. The volume of the prism is 96 cubic inches. What is the height of the prism? **16 in.**

23. **FINDING DIAMETER** A cylinder has height 8 centimeters and volume 1005.5 cubic centimeters. What is the diameter of the cylinder? **about 12.65 cm**

EXAMPLE 4 on p. 821 for Exs. 24–26

VOLUME OF AN OBLIQUE SOLID Use Cavalieri's Principle to find the volume of the oblique prism or cylinder. Round your answer to two decimal places.

24.
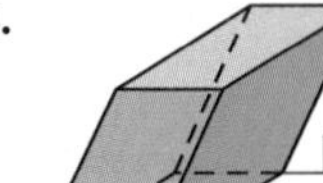

168 in.^{3}

25.
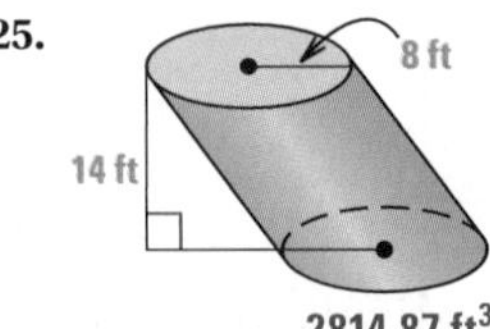

2814.87 ft^3

26.
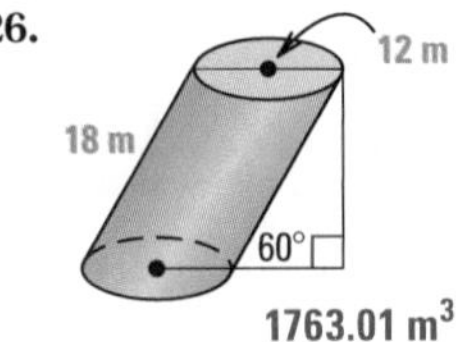

1763.01 m^3

C 27. **CHALLENGE** The bases of a right prism are rhombuses with diagonals 12 meters and 16 meters long. The height of the prism is 8 meters. Find the lateral area, surface area, and volume of the prism. **320 m^2, 512 m^2, 768 m^3**

PROBLEM SOLVING

EXAMPLE 5 on p. 822 for Exs. 28–30

A 28. **JEWELRY** The bead at the right is a rectangular prism of length 17 millimeters, width 9 millimeters, and height 5 millimeters. A 3 millimeter wide hole is drilled through the smallest face. Find the volume of the bead.

@HomeTutor for problem solving help at classzone.com

28. about 644.83 mm^3

(29.) **MULTI-STEP PROBLEM** In the concrete block shown, the holes are 8 inches deep.

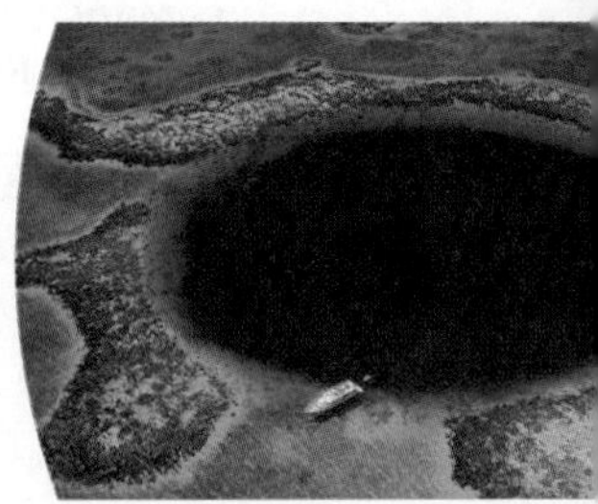

a. Find the volume of the block using the Volume Addition Postulate. **720 in.^{3}**

b. Find the volume of the block using the formula in Theorem 12.6. **720 in.^{3}**

c. *Compare* your answers in parts (a) and (b). **They are the same.**

@HomeTutor for problem solving help at classzone.com

30. **OCEANOGRAPHY** The Blue Hole is a cylindrical trench located on Lighthouse Reef Atoll, an island off the coast of Central America. It is approximately 1000 feet wide and 400 feet deep.

a. Find the volume of the Blue Hole. **about 314,159,265 ft^3**

b. About how many gallons of water does the Blue Hole contain? ($1\text{ ft}^3 = 7.48$ gallons) **about 2,349,911,302 gal**

○ = WORKED-OUT SOLUTIONS on p. WS1 ★ = STANDARDIZED TEST PRACTICE

B 31. **ARCHITECTURE** A cylindrical column in the building shown has circumference 10 feet and height 20 feet. Find its volume. Round your answer to two decimal places. **159.15 ft³**

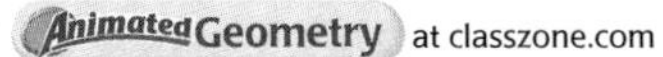

32. **ROTATIONS** A 3 inch by 5 inch index card is rotated around a horizontal line and a vertical line to produce two different solids, as shown. Which solid has a greater volume? *Explain* your reasoning. **The solid produced by rotating around the vertical line; it is 75π cubic inches, while the other volume is 45π cubic inches.**

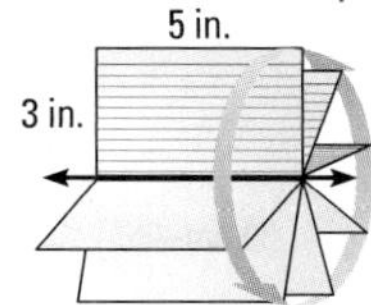

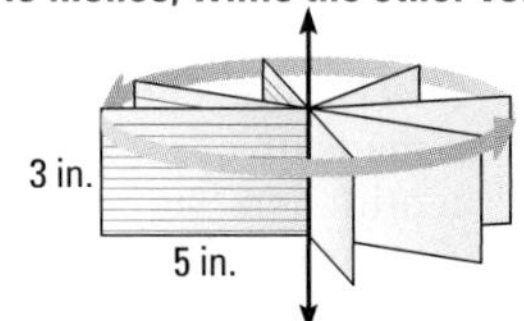

33. ★ **EXTENDED RESPONSE** An aquarium shaped like a rectangular prism has length 30 inches, width 10 inches, and height 20 inches.

a. **Calculate** You fill the aquarium $\frac{3}{4}$ full with water. What is the volume of the water? **4500 in.³**

b. **Interpret** When you submerge a rock in the aquarium, the water level rises 0.25 inch. Find the volume of the rock. **75 in.³**

c. **Interpret** How many rocks of the same size as the rock in part (b) can you place in the aquarium before water spills out? **20 rocks**

C 34. **CHALLENGE** A barn is in the shape of a pentagonal prism with the dimensions shown. The volume of the barn is 9072 cubic feet. Find the dimensions of each half of the roof. **15 ft by 36 ft**

MIXED REVIEW

PREVIEW
Prepare for Lesson 12.5 in Exs. 35–40.

Find the value of x. Round your answer to two decimal places. *(pp. 466, 473)*

35.
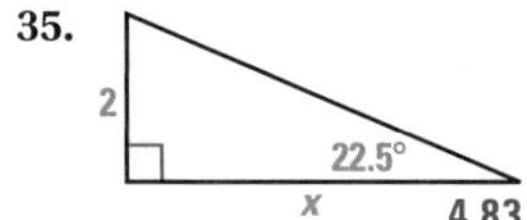

4.83

36.
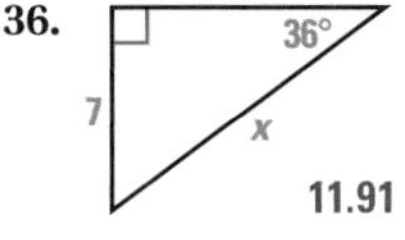

11.91

37.
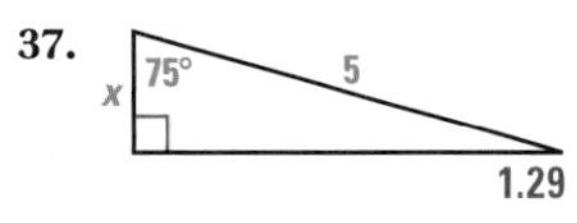

1.29

Find the area of the figure described. Round your answer to two decimal places. *(pp. 755, 762)*

38. A circle with radius 9.5 inches **283.53 in.²**

39. An equilateral triangle with perimeter 78 meters and apothem 7.5 meters **292.5 m²**

40. A regular pentagon with radius 10.6 inches **267.15 in.²**

5 ASSESS AND RETEACH

Daily Homework Quiz

Transparency Available

1. Find the volume of the solid with regular pentagonal bases. **5437.5 in.³**

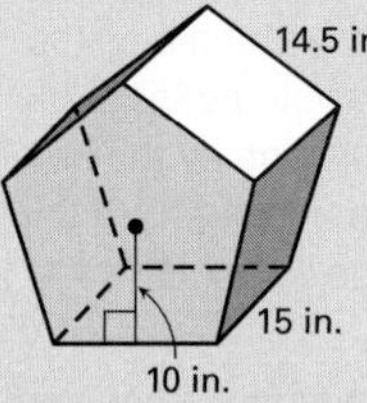

2. Find the volume of a right triangular prism with height 32 in., base height 12 in., and base length 18 in. **3456 in.³**
3. Find the volume of a right cylinder with height 30 ft and diameter 14 ft. **4618.14 ft³**
4. A cylindrical beaker with diameter 10 in. and height 12 in. is filled with water that is then poured into a rectangular pan that is 14 in. by 9 in. by 3 in. What is the volume of each solid? Would the water overflow the pan? If so, what is the height of the water in the beaker *after* the pan is filled? **cylinder: 942.48 in.³; pan: 378 in.³; Yes, it would overflow the pan. After the pan is filled, the height of the water in the beaker will be about 7.2 in.**

Available at **classzone.com**

Diagnosis/Remediation

- Practice A, B, C in Chapter 12 Resource Book, pp. 51–56
- Study Guide in Chapter 12 Resource Book, pp. 57–58
- Practice Workbook, pp. 235–237
- @HomeTutor

Challenge

Additional challenge is available in the Chapter 12 Resource Book, p. 61.

Using ALTERNATIVE METHODS

Alternative Strategy

Three methods are presented to find the volume of the sculpture:

A. Find the area of a base (4 small rectangles subtracted from a large rectangle) and multiply the base times the height (page 822).

B. Use the large rectangle as the base, find the volume for that base by multiplying by the height, and calculate and subtract the volumes of the 4 "holes" (Method 1).

C. Note that the sculpture is made of 13 congruent solids, so find the volume of one of them and multiply by 13 (Method 2).

All three methods are useful to know because each one may be the simplest method for a particular problem.

Another Way to Solve Example 5, page 822

MULTIPLE REPRESENTATIONS In Lesson 12.4, you used volume postulates and theorems to find volumes of prisms and cylinders. Now, you will learn two different ways to solve Example 5 on page 822.

PROBLEM

SCULPTURE The sculpture is made up of 13 beams. In centimeters, suppose the dimensions of each beam are 30 by 30 by 90. Find its volume.

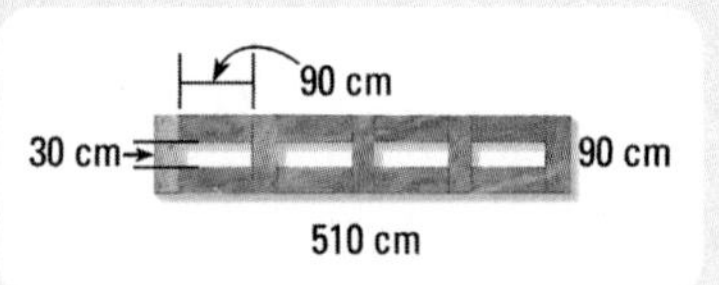

METHOD 1

Standards

8.0 Students know, derive, **and solve problems involving** the perimeter, circumference, area, **volume,** lateral area, and surface area of common geometric figures.

9.0 Students compute the volumes and **surface areas of prisms,** pyramids, **cylinders,** cones, and spheres; and students commit to memory the formulas for prisms, pyramids, and cylinders.

Finding Volume by Subtracting Empty Spaces One alternative approach is to compute the volume of the prism formed if the holes in the sculpture were filled. Then, to get the correct volume, you must subtract the volume of the four holes.

STEP 1 **Read** the problem. In centimeters, each beam measures 30 by 30 by 90.

The dimensions of the entire sculpture are 30 by 90 by $(4 \cdot 90 + 5 \cdot 30)$, or 30 by 90 by 510.

The dimensions of each hole are equal to the dimensions of one beam.

STEP 2 **Apply** the Volume Addition Postulate. The volume of the sculpture is equal to the volume of the larger prism minus 4 times the volume of a hole.

$$\begin{aligned}\text{Volume } V \text{ of sculpture} &= \text{Volume of larger prism} - \text{Volume of 4 holes}\\ &= 30 \cdot 90 \cdot 510 - 4(30 \cdot 30 \cdot 90)\\ &= 1{,}377{,}000 - 4 \cdot 81{,}000\\ &= 1{,}377{,}000 - 324{,}000\\ &= 1{,}053{,}000\end{aligned}$$

▶ The volume of the sculpture is 1,053,000 cubic centimeters, or 1.053 cubic meters.

STEP 3 **Check** page 822 to verify your new answer, and confirm that it is the same.

METHOD 2 **Finding Volume of Pieces** Another alternative approach is to use the dimensions of each beam.

STEP 1 **Look** at the sculpture. Notice that the sculpture consists of 13 beams, each with the same dimensions. Therefore, the volume of the sculpture will be 13 times the volume of one beam.

STEP 2 **Write** an expression for the volume of the sculpture and find the volume.

Volume of sculpture = 13(Volume of one beam)

$= 13(30 \cdot 30 \cdot 90)$

$= 13 \cdot 81{,}000$

$= 1{,}053{,}000$

▶ The volume of the sculpture is 1,053,000 cm^3, or 1.053 m^3.

PRACTICE

1. **PENCIL HOLDER** The pencil holder has the dimensions shown.

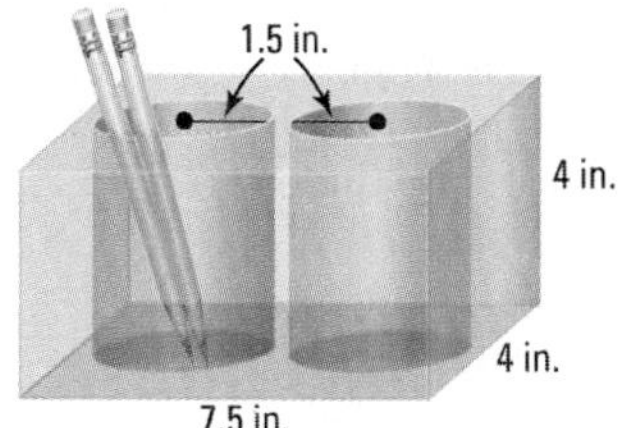

   a. Find its volume using the Volume Addition Postulate. **about 63.45 in.^{3}**

   b. Use its base area to find its volume. **about 63.45 in.^{3}**

2. **ERROR ANALYSIS** A student solving Exercise 1 claims that the surface area is found by subtracting four times the base area of the cylinders from the surface area of the rectangular prism. *Describe* and correct the student's error. **See margin.**

3. **REASONING** You drill a circular hole of radius r through the base of a cylinder of radius R. Assume the hole is drilled completely through to the other base. You want the volume of the hole to be half the volume of the cylinder. Express r as a function of R. $r = \frac{R\sqrt{2}}{2}$

4. **FINDING VOLUME** Find the volume of the solid shown below. Assume the hole has square cross sections. **35 ft^3**

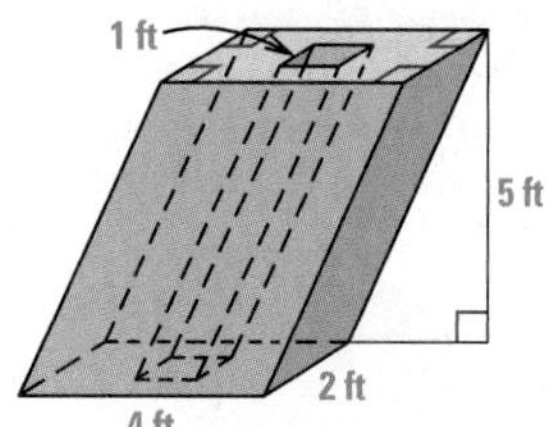

5. **FINDING VOLUME** Find the volume of the solid shown to the right. **about 7.33 in.^{3}**

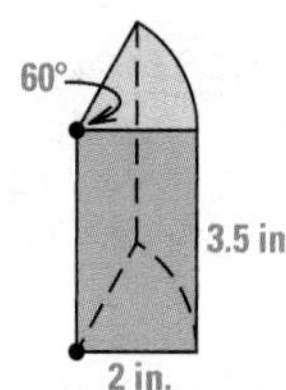

6. **SURFACE AREA** Refer to the diagram of the sculpture on page 826. **a, b. See margin.**

   a. *Describe* a method to find the surface area of the sculpture.

   b. *Explain* why adding the individual surface areas of the beams will give an incorrect result for the total surface area.

Teaching Strategy

For Exercise 1, point out that applying the Volume Addition Postulate means finding the volume of the larger prism and then subtracting the volume of the two cylinders. Find other solids around the classroom to demonstrate this method.

2. The error is subtracting 4 times the base area from the surface area of the prism; the surface area is found by subtracting 1 times the base area from the surface area of the prism, then the lateral area of the cylinders must also be added as "surfaces" that are exposed. Surface Area = Surface area of prism − Area of 2 circles + Lateral area of 2 cylinders = $2 \cdot 7.5 \cdot 4 + 2 \cdot 7.5 \cdot 4 + 2 \cdot 4 \cdot 4 - 2(\pi \cdot 1.5^2) + 2(2\pi \cdot 1.5 \cdot 4) \approx 152 - 2 \cdot 7.07 + 2 \cdot 37.7 = 213.26$ in.^{2}

The surface area is about 213.26 square inches.

6a. Find the perimeter of the sculpture, multiply it by the height, and add the areas of the two bases.

6b. It would not take into account the loss in surface area of the face when each pair of pieces is joined together.

1 PLAN AND PREPARE

Explore the Concept

- Students will compare the volume of a prism and a pyramid using nets.
- This activity leads into the study of volume of a solid in Lesson 12.5, Example 1.

Materials

Each student or group of students will need:

- ruler, poster board, scissors, tape
- uncooked rice
- Activity Support Master (*Chapter 12 Resource Book*, p. 65)

Recommended Time

Work activity: 15 min

Discuss results: 5 min

Grouping

Students can work individually or in groups of two. If students work in groups, they can each create a solid.

2 TEACH

Tips for Success

Find the height of the pyramid after it is constructed, either by measuring or by calculating it. It should be close to $1\frac{7}{16}$ inches, the height of the prism.

Alternative Strategy

Demonstrate the relationship between the solids with plastic models.

Key Discovery

The volume of a pyramid is $\frac{1}{3}$ the volume of a prism with the same base area and height.

3 ASSESS AND RETEACH

1. The side of a cube is 4 cm. What is the volume of a pyramid with the same base area and height as the cube? $21\frac{1}{3}$ cm^3

12.5 Investigate the Volume of a Pyramid

MATERIALS • ruler • poster board • scissors • tape • uncooked rice

Standards

Prepare for 8.0
Students know, **derive** and solve problems involving the perimeter, circumference, area, **volume**, lateral area, and surface area of common geometric figures.

QUESTION **How is the volume of a pyramid related to the volume of a prism with the same base and height?**

EXPLORE **Compare the volume of a prism and a pyramid using nets**

STEP 1 ***Draw nets*** Use a ruler to draw the two nets shown below on poster board. (Use $1\frac{7}{16}$ inches to approximate $\sqrt{2}$ inches.)

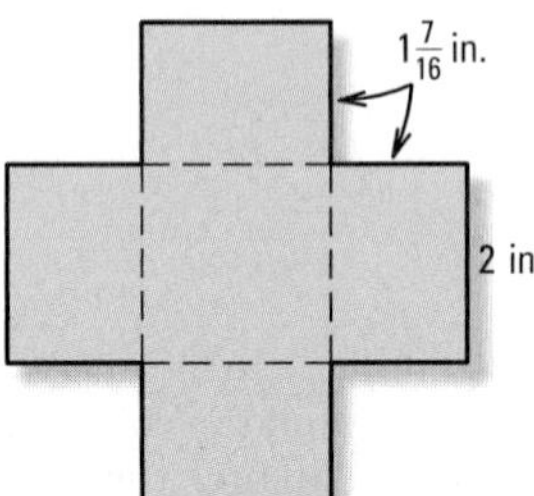

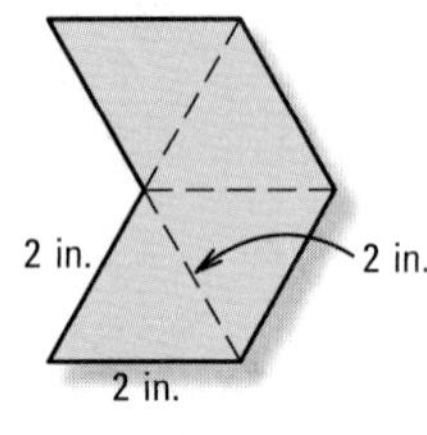

STEP 2 ***Create an open prism and an open pyramid*** Cut out the nets. Fold along the dotted lines to form an open prism and an open pyramid, as shown below. Tape each solid to hold it in place, making sure that the edges do not overlap.

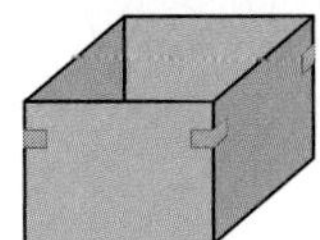

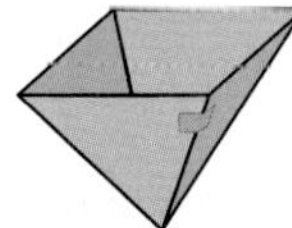

STEP 3 ***Compare volumes*** Fill the pyramid with uncooked rice and pour it into the prism. Repeat this as many times as needed to fill the prism. How many times did you fill the pyramid? What does this tell you about the volume of the solids? **3; the volume of the prism is 3 times the volume of the pyramid.**

DRAW CONCLUSIONS **Use your observations to complete these exercises**

1. *Compare* the area of the base of the pyramid to the area of the base of the prism. Placing the pyramid inside the prism will help. What do you notice? **The areas of the bases are equal.**
2. *Compare* the heights of the solids. What do you notice? **The heights of the solids are the same.**
3. Make a conjecture about the ratio of the volumes of the solids. **See margin.**
4. Use your conjecture to write a formula for the volume of a pyramid that uses the formula for the volume of a prism.
   Volume of pyramid = $\frac{1}{3}Bh$, where B is the area of the base and h is the height.

3. The ratio of the volume of the pyramid to the volume of the prism is 1 to 3.

12.5 Volume of Pyramids and Cones

Before You found surface areas of pyramids and cones.
Now You will find volumes of pyramids and cones.
Why? So you can find the edge length of a pyramid, as in Example 2.

Key Vocabulary
- **pyramid,** *p. 810*
- **cone,** *p. 812*
- **volume,** *p. 819*

Standards

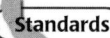

9.0 Students compute the volumes and surface areas **of** prisms, **pyramids**, cylinders, **cones**, and spheres; and students commit to memory the formulas for prisms, pyramids, and cylinders.

8.0 Students know, derive, and **solve problems involving** the perimeter, circumference, area, **volume**, lateral area, and surface area of common geometric figures.

Recall that the volume of a prism is Bh, where B is the area of a base and h is the height. In the figure at the right, you can see that the volume of a pyramid must be less than the volume of a prism with the same base area and height. As suggested by the Activity on page 828, the volume of a pyramid is one third the volume of a prism.

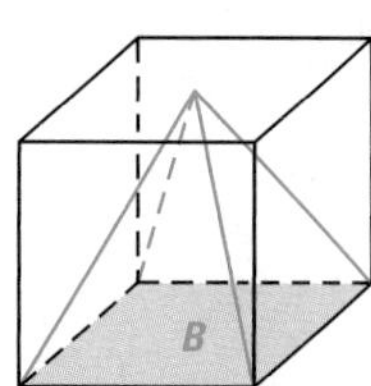

THEOREMS *For Your Notebook*

THEOREM 12.9 Volume of a Pyramid

The volume V of a pyramid is

$$V = \frac{1}{3}Bh,$$

where B is the area of the base and h is the height.

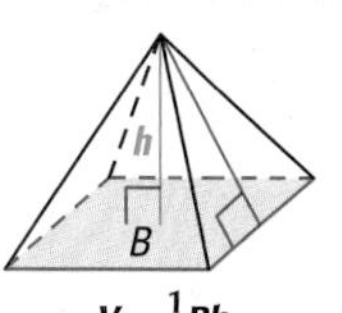

THEOREM 12.10 Volume of a Cone

The volume V of a cone is

$$V = \frac{1}{3}Bh = \frac{1}{3}\pi r^2 h,$$

where B is the area of the base, h is the height, and r is the radius of the base.

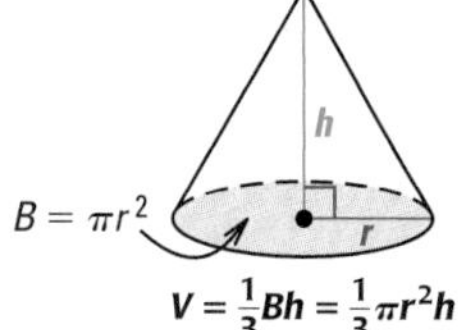

EXAMPLE 1 Find the volume of a solid

APPLY FORMULAS
The formulas given in Theorems 12.9 and 12.10 apply to right and oblique pyramids and cones. This follows from Cavalieri's Principle, stated on page 821.

Find the volume of the solid.

a.

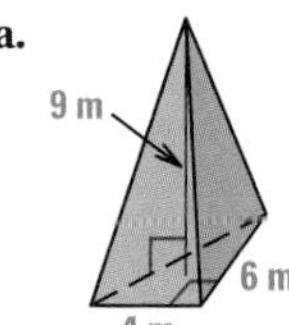

$V = \frac{1}{3}Bh$

$= \frac{1}{3}\left(\frac{1}{2} \cdot 4 \cdot 6\right)(9)$

$= 36 \text{ m}^3$

b.

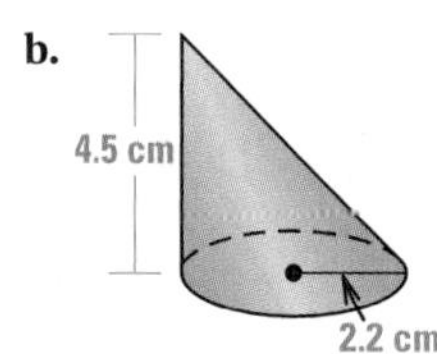

$V = \frac{1}{3}Bh$

$= \frac{1}{3}(\pi r^2)h$

$= \frac{1}{3}(\pi \cdot 2.2^2)(4.5)$

$= 7.26\pi$

$\approx 22.81 \text{ cm}^3$

1 PLAN AND PREPARE

Warm-Up Exercises

Transparency Available

Find the area of each polygon or circle.

1. Regular hexagon, side length 9 in. **210.44 in.²**
2. Circle, radius 15 m **706.86 m²**
3. Right triangle, hypotenuse 12 cm, side length 6 cm **31.18 cm²**
4. Solve $\frac{(2\sqrt{3})^2\sqrt{3}}{12} \cdot x = 15\sqrt{3}$. **15**

Notetaking Guide

Transparency Available

Promotes interactive learning and notetaking skills, pp. 325–328.

Pacing

Basic: 2 days
Average: 2 days
Advanced: 2 days
Block: 0.5 block with 12.4
0.5 block with 12.6
- See *Teaching Guide/Lesson Plan.*

2 FOCUS AND MOTIVATE

Essential Question

Big Idea 2, p. 791

How do you find the volume of a pyramid or cone? **Tell students they will learn how to answer this question by looking at the relationship between pyramids and prisms and the relationship between cones and cylinders.**

Resource Planning Guide

Chapter Resource Book
- Teaching Guide/Lesson Plan (pp. 62–63)
- Practice levels A, B, C (pp. 66–71)
- Study Guide (pp. 72–73)
- Catch-up for Absent Students (p. 74)
- Problem Solving Workshop (p. 75)
- Challenge (p. 76)

Workbooks
- Notetaking Guide (pp. 325–328)
- Practice Workbook (pp. 238–240)

Teaching Options
- **Power Presentations CD-ROM** provides dynamic electronic teaching resources for the classroom.
- **Activity Generator CD-ROM** provides editable activities for all ability levels.

Interactive Technology
- Easy Planner
- Power Presentations CD-ROM
- Activity Generator CD-ROM
- Animated Geometry
- Test Generator CD-ROM
- Online Quiz
- eWorkbook
- eEdition
- @HomeTutor

Resources for English Learners
- Quick Reference for English Learners
- Spanish Study Guide
- Multi-Language Visual Glossary
- Student Resources in Spanish

See also the *Geometry Toolkit* for more strategies for meeting individual needs.

Motivating the Lesson

Tell students to think about putting a pyramid into a box where the bases and heights match. Ask students to think about the volume of the box that is not filled by the pyramid, and ask them to compare the volume of the pyramid with the unfilled volume of the box. Tell students that this lesson will let them compare the volumes exactly. (Students will find that the unfilled volume is twice the volume of the pyramid.)

3 TEACH

Extra Example 1

Find the volume of each solid.

a. **653.33 m^3**

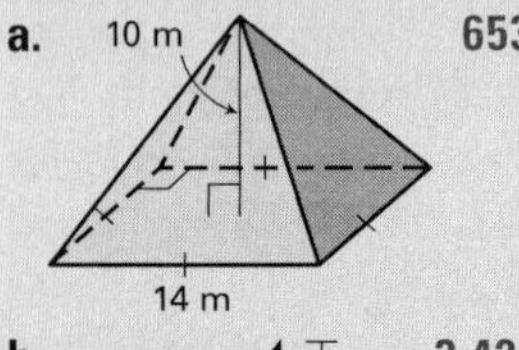

b. **3.42 cm^3**

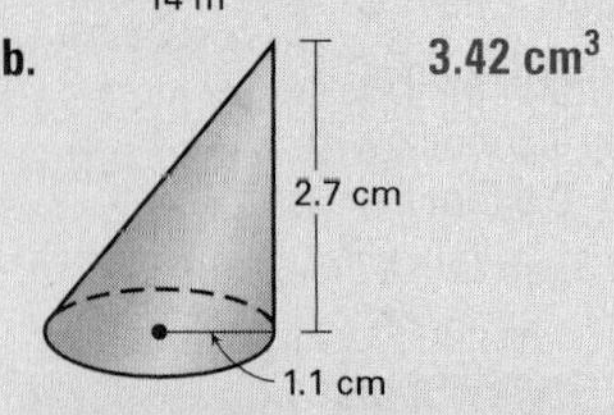

Extra Example 2

The Pyramid of the Sun in Teotihuacan, Mexico, is a regular square pyramid with height 63 m and volume 970,725 m^3. Find the side length of the base. **215 m**

Extra Example 3

Find the volume of the right cone. **2167.96 cm^3**

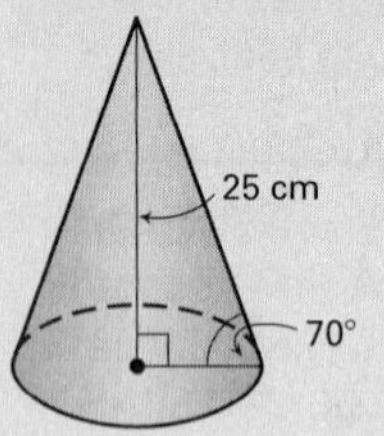

EXAMPLE 2 Use volume of a pyramid

ALGEBRA Originally, the pyramid had height 144 meters and volume 2,226,450 cubic meters. Find the side length of the square base.

Khafre's Pyramid, Egypt

Solution

$V = \frac{1}{3}Bh$	Write formula.
$2{,}226{,}450 = \frac{1}{3}(x^2)(144)$	Substitute.
$6{,}679{,}350 = 144x^2$	Multiply each side by 3.
$46{,}384 \approx x^2$	Divide each side by 144.
$215 \approx x$	Find the positive square root.

▶ Originally, the side length of the base was about 215 meters.

GUIDED PRACTICE for Examples 1 and 2

Find the volume of the solid. Round your answer to two decimal places, if necessary.

1. Hexagonal pyramid **152.42 yd^3**

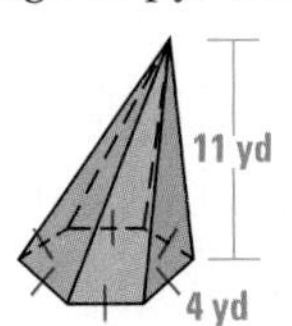

2. Right cone **163.49 m^3**

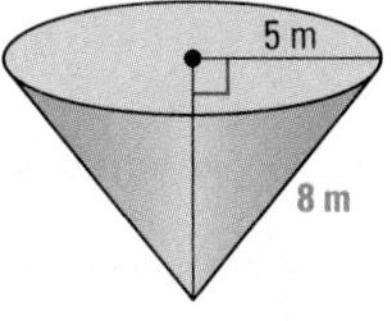

3. The volume of a right cone is 1350π cubic meters and the radius is 18 meters. Find the height of the cone. **12.5 m**

EXAMPLE 3 Use trigonometry to find the volume of a cone

Find the volume of the right cone.

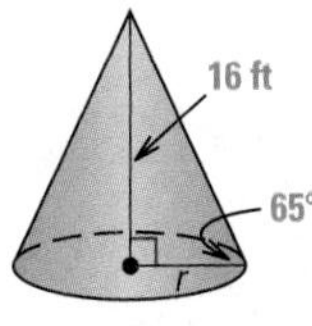

Solution

To find the radius r of the base, use trigonometry.

$\tan 65° = \frac{\text{opp.}}{\text{adj.}}$	Write ratio.
$\tan 65° = \frac{16}{r}$	Substitute.
$r = \frac{16}{\tan 65°} \approx 7.46$	Solve for r.

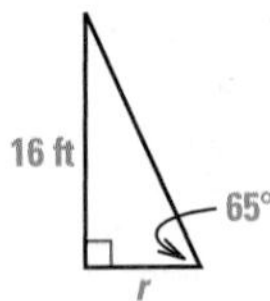

Use the formula for the volume of a cone.

$$V = \frac{1}{3}(\pi r^2)h \approx \frac{1}{3}\pi(7.46^2)(16) \approx 932.45 \text{ ft}^3$$

EXAMPLE 4 Find volume of a composite solid

Find the volume of the solid shown.

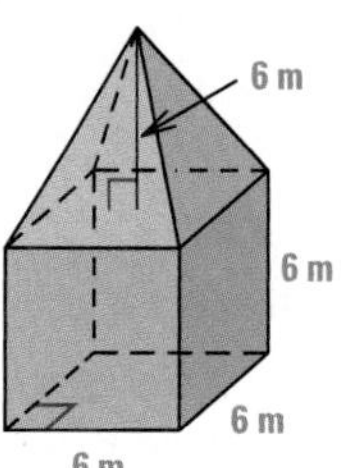

Solution

Volume of solid	=	Volume of cube	+	Volume of pyramid

$= s^3 + \frac{1}{3}Bh$ **Write formulas.**

$= 6^3 + \frac{1}{3}(6)^2 \cdot 6$ **Substitute.**

$= 216 + 72$ **Simplify.**

$= 288$ **Add.**

▶ The volume of the solid is 288 cubic meters.

EXAMPLE 5 Solve a multi-step problem

SCIENCE You are using the funnel shown to measure the coarseness of a particular type of sand. It takes 2.8 seconds for the sand to empty out of the funnel. Find the flow rate of the sand in milliliters per second. (1 mL = 1 cm^3)

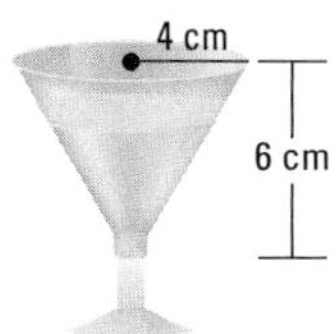

Solution

STEP 1 **Find** the volume of the funnel using the formula for the volume of a cone.

$$V = \frac{1}{3}(\pi r^2)h = \frac{1}{3}\pi(4^2)(6) \approx 101 \text{ cm}^3 = 101 \text{ mL}$$

STEP 2 **Divide** the volume of the funnel by the time it takes the sand to empty out of the funnel.

$$\frac{101 \text{ mL}}{2.8 \text{ s}} \approx 36.07 \text{ mL/s}$$

▶ The flow rate of the sand is about 36.07 milliliters per second.

GUIDED PRACTICE for Examples 3, 4, and 5

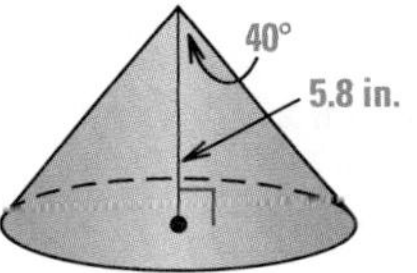

4. Find the volume of the cone at the right. Round your answer to two decimal places. **143.86 in.^{3}**

5. A right cylinder with radius 3 centimeters and height 10 centimeters has a right cone on top of it with the same base and height 5 centimeters. Find the volume of the solid. Round your answer to two decimal places. **329.87 cm^3**

6. **WHAT IF?** In Example 5, suppose a different type of sand is used that takes 3.2 seconds to empty out of the funnel. Find its flow rate. **about 31.56 mL/s**

Extra Example 4

Find the volume of the solid shown, which is formed by two cones.

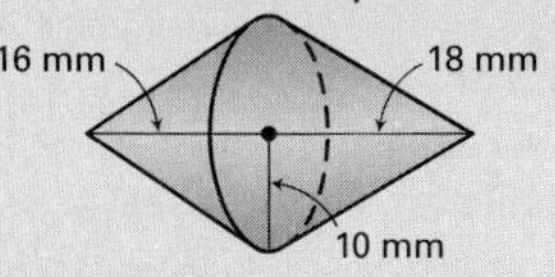

3560.47 mm^3

Key Questions to Ask for Example 4

- How do the bases of the pyramid and prism compare? How do the heights compare? **the same; the same**
- How do the volumes compare? **The volume of the pyramid is $\frac{1}{3}$ the volume of the prism.**

Extra Example 5

You are making coffee using a cone-shaped filter. It takes 14 minutes to brew coffee. Find the flow rate of the coffee in cubic inches per minute.

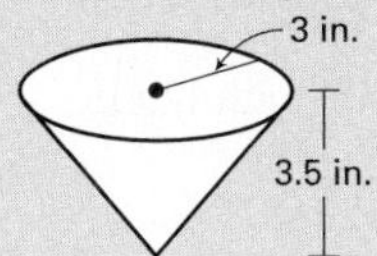

about 2.36 in.^{3}/min

Key Question to Ask for Example 5

- What does "flow rate" mean? **It refers to the volume of the substance that passes through the end of the funnel in one unit of time.**

Closing the Lesson

Have students summarize the major points of the lesson and answer the Essential Question: How do you find the volume of a pyramid or cone?

- **For a pyramid, $V = \frac{1}{3}Bh$.**
- **For a cone, $V = \frac{1}{3}Bh = \frac{1}{3}\pi r^2 h$.**

For a cone or pyramid, the volume is one third the area of the base times the height.

Differentiated Instruction

Visual Learners When discussing **Guided Practice Exercise 5,** direct students to draw a diagram of the cylinder with the right cone on top. Have them label the radius and height of the cylinder and the radius and height of the cone. Have them use their diagrams to help them find the volume of the solid.

See also the *Geometry Toolkit* for more strategies.

12.5 EXERCISES

HOMEWORK KEY
○ = **WORKED-OUT SOLUTIONS** on p. WS17 for Exs. 3, 17, and 33
★ = **STANDARDIZED TEST PRACTICE** Exs. 2, 11, 18, and 35
◆ = **MULTIPLE REPRESENTATIONS** Ex. 39

SKILL PRACTICE

A

1. **VOCABULARY** *Explain* the difference between a *triangular prism* and a *triangular pyramid*. Draw an example of each. **See margin.**

2. ★ **WRITING** *Compare* the volume of a square pyramid to the volume of a square prism with the same base and height as the pyramid.
The volume of the square pyramid is $\frac{1}{3}$ the volume of the square prism.

EXAMPLE 1 on p. 829 for Exs. 3–11

VOLUME OF A SOLID Find the volume of the solid. Round your answer to two decimal places.

3. 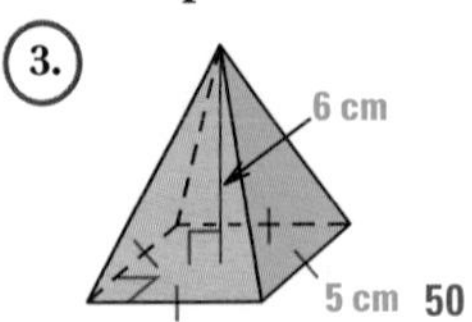

50 cm³

4. 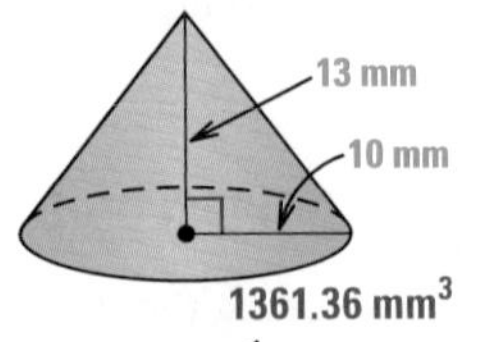

1361.36 mm³

5. 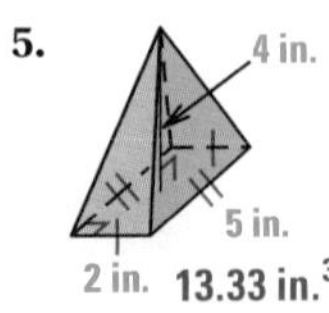

13.33 in.³

6. 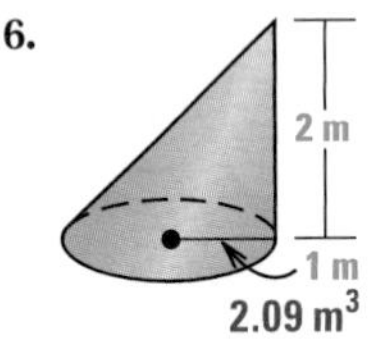

2.09 m³

7. 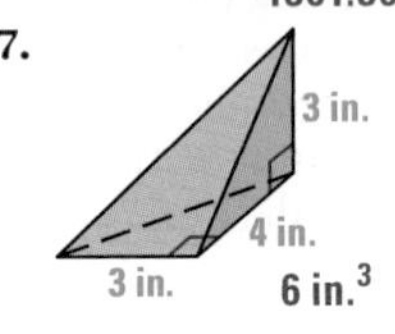

6 in.³

8. 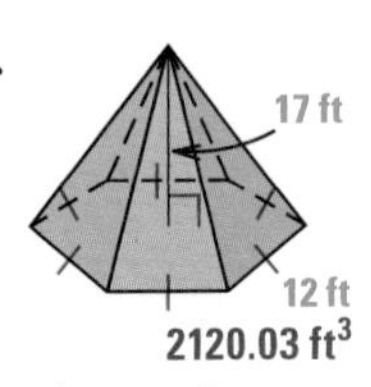

2120.03 ft³

ERROR ANALYSIS ***Describe*** **and correct the error in finding the volume of the right cone or pyramid.** **9, 10. See margin.**

9. 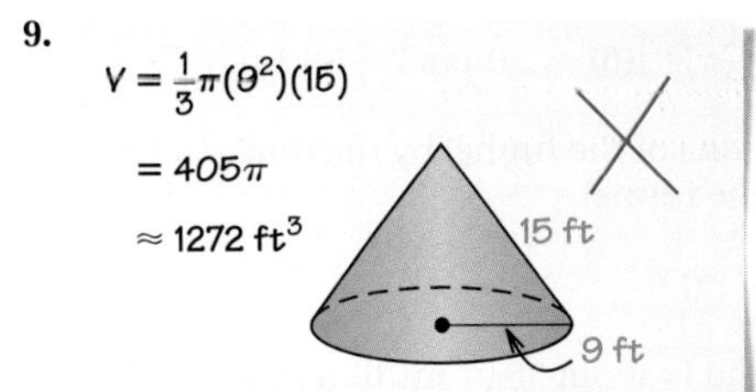

10. 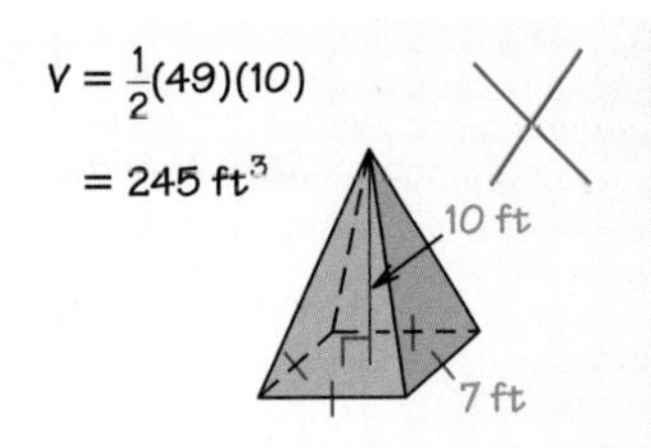

11. ★ **MULTIPLE CHOICE** The volume of a pyramid is 45 cubic feet and the height is 9 feet. What is the area of the base? **D**

Ⓐ 3.87 ft² Ⓑ 5 ft² Ⓒ 10 ft² Ⓓ 15 ft²

EXAMPLE 2 on p. 830 for Exs. 12–14

ALGEBRA Find the value of *x*.

12. Volume = 200 cm³ **6 cm**
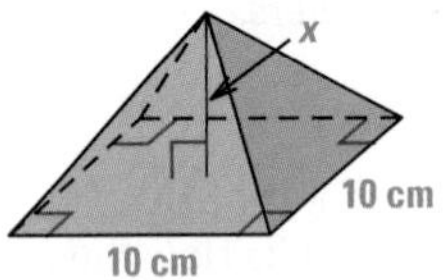

13. Volume = 216π in.³ **6 in.**
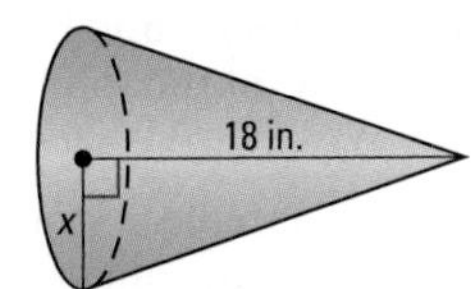

14. Volume = $7\sqrt{3}$ ft³ **7 ft**
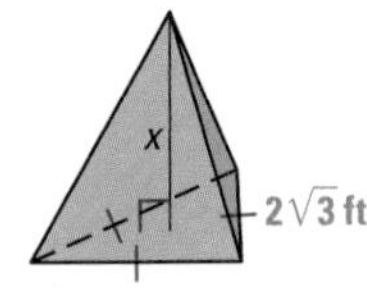

4 PRACTICE AND APPLY

Assignment Guide

Answer Transparencies available for all exercises

Basic:
Day 1: EP p. 909 Exs. 34–36
pp. 832–836
Exs. 1–14, 43–45
Day 2: pp. 832–836
Exs. 15–22, 29–35, 46–52

Average:
Day 1: pp. 832–836
Exs. 1–14, 26, 43–45
Day 2: pp. 832–836
Exs. 15–19, 21–25, 29–37, 46–52 even

Advanced:
Day 1: pp. 832–836
Exs. 1–8, 11–14, 26–28*, 43–45
Day 2: pp. 832–836
Exs. 16–19, 23–25, 29, 33–42*, 48, 52

Block:
pp. 832–836
Exs. 1–14, 26, 43–45 (with 12.4)
pp. 832–836
Exs. 15–19, 21–25, 29–37, 46–52 even (with 12.6)

Differentiated Instruction

See *Geometry Best Practices Toolkit* for suggestions on addressing the needs of a diverse classroom.

Homework Check

For a quick check of student understanding of key concepts, go over the following exercises:
Basic: 4, 12, 15, 20, 29
Average: 6, 13, 16, 22, 29
Advanced: 8, 14, 19, 24, 29

Extra Practice

- Student Edition, p. 919
- Chapter 12 Resource Book: Practice levels A, B, C, pp. 66–71

Practice Worksheet

An easily-readable reduced practice page (with answers) for this lesson can be found on p. 790E.

1. A triangular prism is a solid with two bases that are triangles and parallelograms for the lateral faces, while a triangular pyramid is a solid with a triangle for a base and triangles for lateral faces; see margin for art.

1.
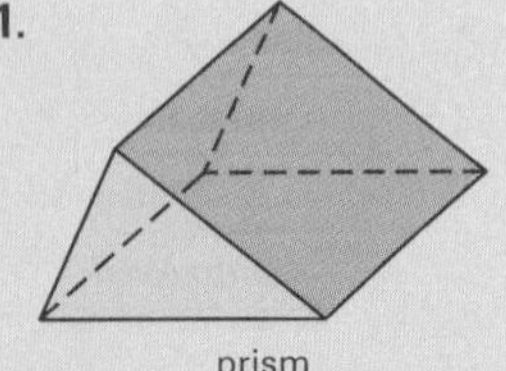
prism

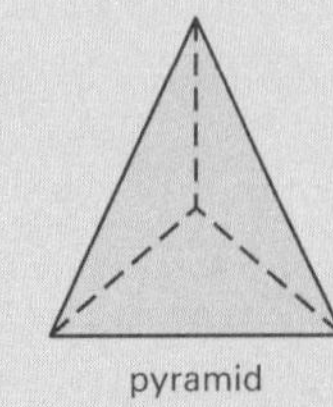
pyramid

9. The slant height is used in the volume formula instead of the height; $V = \frac{1}{3}\pi(9^2)(12) = 324\pi \approx 1018$ ft³.

10. The volume formula is wrong. The fraction should be $\frac{1}{3}$ instead of $\frac{1}{2}$; $V = \frac{1}{3}(49)(10) = 163\frac{1}{3}$ ft³.

EXAMPLE 3
on p. 830
for Exs. 15–19

VOLUME OF A CONE **Find the volume of the right cone. Round your answer to two decimal places.**

15.

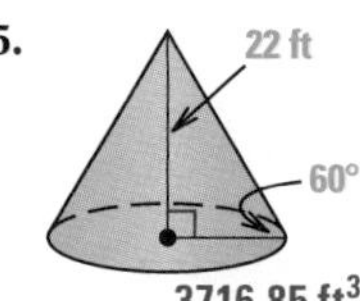

3716.85 ft^3

16. 14 yd, 32°

574.82 yd^3

(17.)

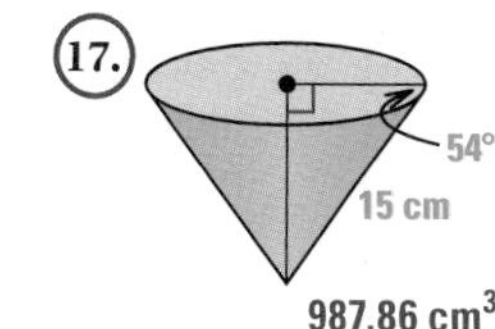

987.86 cm^3

18. ★ **MULTIPLE CHOICE** What is the approximate volume of the cone? **B**

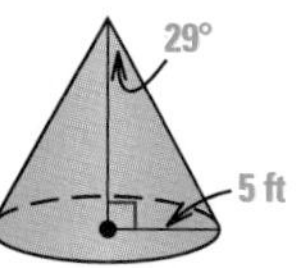

Ⓐ 47.23 ft^3 Ⓑ 236.15 ft^3

Ⓒ 269.92 ft^3 Ⓓ 354.21 ft^3

B **19.** **HEIGHT OF A CONE** A cone with a diameter of 8 centimeters has volume 143.6 cubic centimeters. Find the height of the cone. Round your answer to two decimal places. **8.57 cm**

EXAMPLE 4
on p. 831
for Exs. 20–25

COMPOSITE SOLIDS **Find the volume of the solid. The prisms, pyramids, and cones are right. Round your answer to two decimal places.**

20.

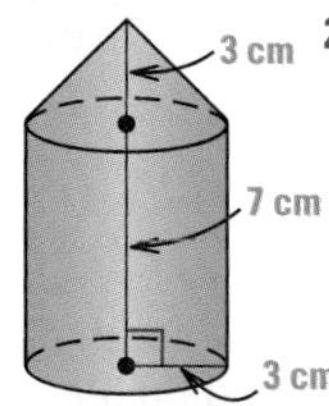

226.19 cm^3

21. 10 in., 10 in., 10 in.

833.33 $in.^3$

22.

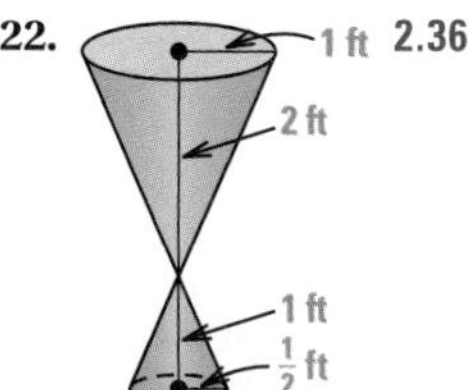

2.36 ft^3

23.

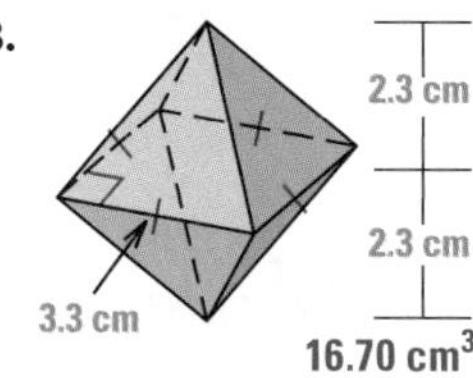

16.70 cm^3

24.

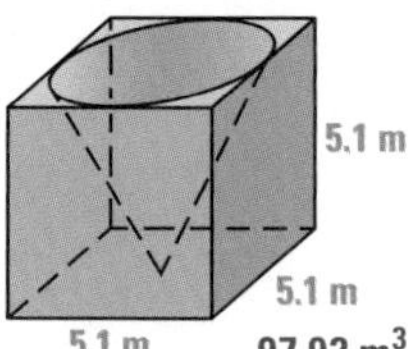

97.92 m^3

25.

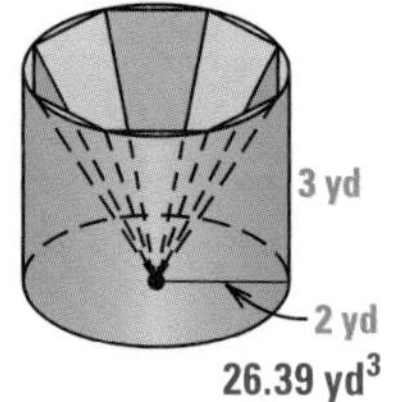

26.39 yd^3

Animated Geometry at classzone.com

26. **FINDING VOLUME** The figure at the right is a cone that has been warped but whose cross sections still have the same area as a right cone with equal base area and height. Find the volume of this solid. **about 12.57 cm^3**

C **27.** **FINDING VOLUME** Sketch a regular square pyramid with base edge length 5 meters inscribed in a cone with height 7 meters. Find the volume of the cone. *Explain* your reasoning. **See margin.**

28. **CHALLENGE** Find the volume of the regular hexagonal pyramid. Round your answer to the nearest hundredth of a cubic foot. In the diagram, $m\angle ABC = 35°$. **16.37 ft^3**

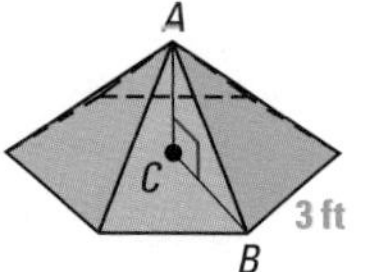

Avoiding Common Errors

Exercises 11–14 Remind students not to forget the factor $\frac{1}{3}$ in these exercises.

Teaching Strategy

Exercises 15–17, 28 Before doing these exercises, you may want to review the trigonometric functions for a right triangle.

An **Animated Geometry** activity is available on-line for **Exercises 20–25**. This activity is also available on the **Power Presentations CD-ROM**.

27.

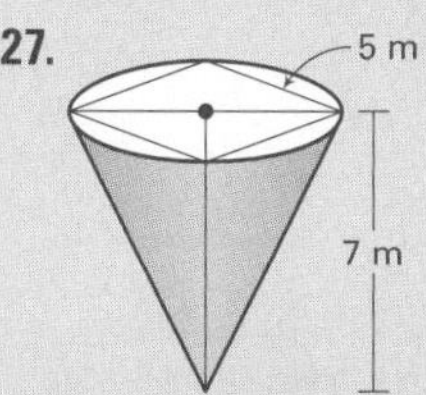

About 91.63 m^3; drawing a diagonal in the square creates two 45°-45°-90° triangles. The diagonal then has a length of $5\sqrt{2}$ meters, which is also the diameter of the base of the cone. Use $\frac{5\sqrt{2}}{2}$ as the length of the radius to find the volume of the cone.

Teaching Strategy

Exercise 35 Encourage students to sketch the pyramids described in this exercise. Accurate sketches will provide a visual aid to help answer the questions.

33.

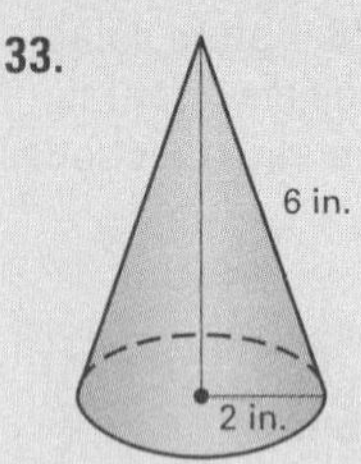

34.

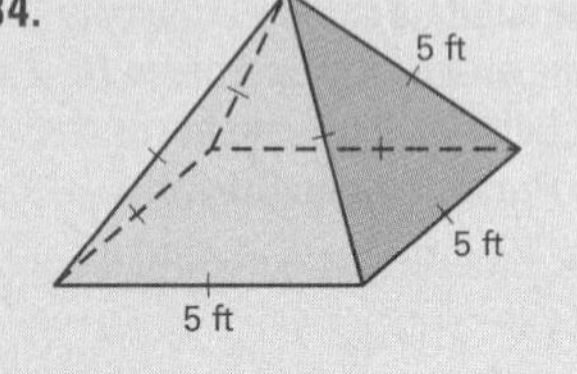

PROBLEM SOLVING

EXAMPLE 5 A on p. 831 for Ex. 30

29. CAKE DECORATION A pastry bag filled with frosting has height 12 inches and radius 4 inches. A cake decorator can make 15 flowers using one bag of frosting.

a. How much frosting is in the pastry bag? Round your answer to the nearest cubic inch. **201 in.^{3}**

b. How many cubic inches of frosting are used to make each flower? **13.4 in.^{3}**

@HomeTutor for problem solving help at classzone.com

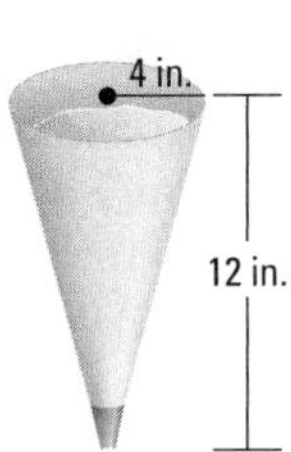

POPCORN A snack stand serves a small order of popcorn in a cone-shaped cup and a large order of popcorn in a cylindrical cup.

30. Find the volume of the small cup. **about 75.4 in.^{3}**

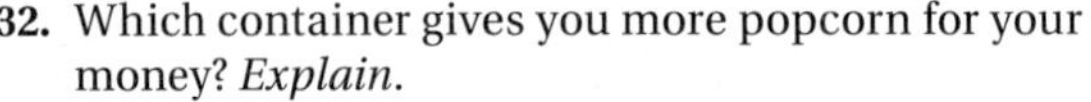

@HomeTutor for problem solving help at classzone.com

31. How many small cups of popcorn do you have to buy to equal the amount of popcorn in a large container? Do not perform any calculations. *Explain.*

32. Which container gives you more popcorn for your money? *Explain.*

31. 3; since the cone and cylinder have the same radius and height, the volume of the cone will be $\frac{1}{3}$ the volume of the cylinder.

32. The cylinder; three cones fit into the cylinder, and 3 cones would cost $3.75, which is more than the large container costing $2.50.

USING NETS In Exercises 33 and 34, use the net to sketch the solid. Then find the volume of the solid. Round your answer to two decimal places. **33, 34. See margin for art.**

33.

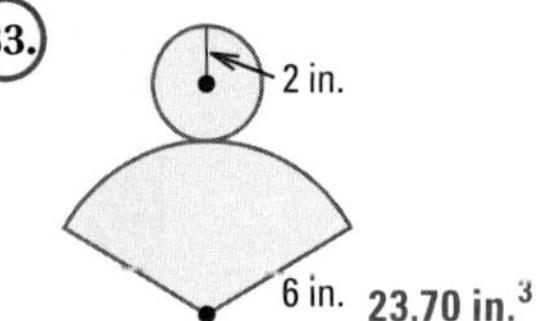

23.70 in.^{3}

34.

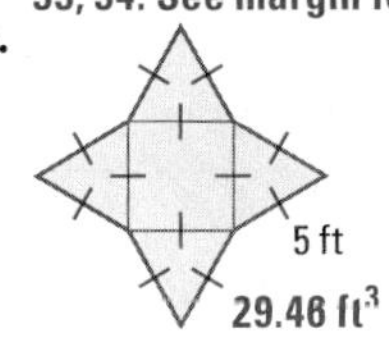

29.46 ft^3

B

35. ★ EXTENDED RESPONSE A pyramid has height 10 feet and a square base with side length 7 feet.

a. How does the volume of the pyramid change if the base stays the same and the height is doubled? **The volume doubles.**

b. How does the volume of the pyramid change if the height stays the same and the side length of the base is doubled? **The volume is multiplied by 4.**

c. *Explain* why your answers to parts (a) and (b) are true for any height and side length.

35c. If you replace the height h by $2h$ in the volume formula, it will multiply the volume by 2. If you replace the side length s by $2s$ in the volume formula, it will multiply the volume by 4 because $(2s)^2 = 4s^2$.

36. AUTOMATIC FEEDER Assume the automatic pet feeder is a right cylinder on top of a right cone of the same radius. (1 cup = 14.4 in.^{3})

a. Calculate the amount of food in cups that can be placed in the feeder. **about 12 c**

b. A cat eats one third of a cup of food, twice per day. How many days will the feeder have food without refilling it? **18 days**

○ = WORKED-OUT SOLUTIONS on p. WS1 ★ = STANDARDIZED TEST PRACTICE ◆ = MULTIPLE REPRESENTATIONS

37. **NAUTICAL PRISMS** The nautical deck prism shown is composed of the following three solids: a regular hexagonal prism with edge length 3.5 inches and height 1.5 inches, a regular hexagonal prism with edge length 3.25 inches and height 0.25 inch, and a regular hexagonal pyramid with edge length 3 inches and height 3 inches. Find the volume of the deck prism. **about 78 in.^{3}**

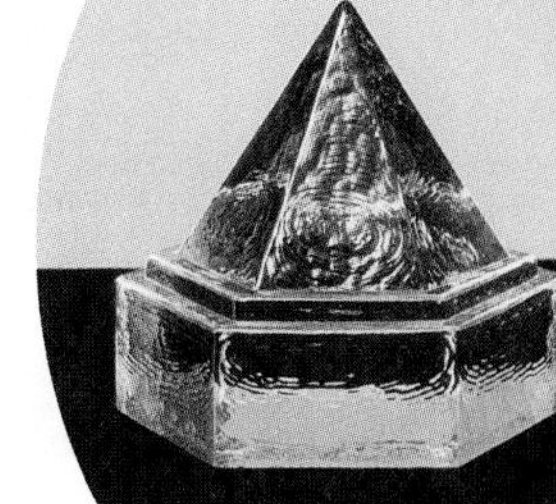

C 38. **MULTI-STEP PROBLEM** Calculus can be used to show that the average value of r^2 of a circular cross section of a cone is $\frac{r_b^2}{3}$, where r_b is the radius of the base.

a. Find the average area of a circular cross section of a cone whose base has radius R. **$\frac{\pi R^2}{3}$**

b. Show that the volume of the cone can be expressed as follows:

V_{cone} = (Average area of a circular cross section) • (Height of cone)

39. **MULTIPLE REPRESENTATIONS** Water flows into a reservoir shaped like a right cone at the rate of 1.8 cubic meters per minute. The height and diameter of the reservoir are equal.

a. **Using Algebra** As the water flows into the reservoir, the relationship $h = 2r$ is always true. Using this fact, show that $V = \frac{\pi h^3}{12}$.

b. **Making a Table** Make a table that gives the height h of the water after 1, 2, 3, 4, and 5 minutes. **See margin.**

c. **Drawing a Graph** Make a graph of height versus time. Is there a linear relationship between the height of the water and time? *Explain.* **See margin for art; no; the points of the graph do not lie in a straight line.**

FRUSTUM A frustum of a cone is the part of the cone that lies between the base and a plane parallel to the base, as shown. Use the information to complete Exercises 40 and 41.

One method for calculating the volume of a frustum is to add the areas of the two bases to their geometric mean, then multiply the result by $\frac{1}{3}$ the height.

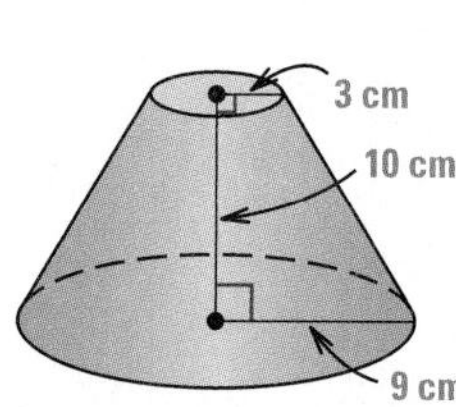

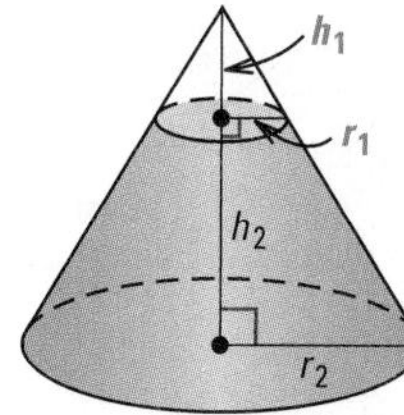

40. Use the measurements in the diagram at the left above to calculate the volume of the frustum. **390π cm^3**

41. Complete parts (a) and (b) below to write a formula for the volume of a frustum that has bases with radii r_1 and r_2 and a height h_2.

a. Use similar triangles to find the value of h_1 in terms of h_2, r_1, and r_2. **$h_1 = \frac{r_1h_2}{r_2 - r_1}$**

b. Write a formula in terms of h_2, r_1, and r_2 for $V_{frustum}$ = (Original volume) − (Removed volume). **b, c. See margin.**

c. Show that your formula in part (b) is equivalent to the formula involving geometric mean described above.

38b. $V_{cone} = \frac{1}{3}Bh = \frac{1}{3}\pi R^2 \cdot h = \frac{\pi R^2 h}{3} = \frac{\pi R^2}{3} \cdot h$, **where B is the area of the base of the cone, $\frac{\pi R^2}{3}$ is the average area of a circular cross section, and h is the height**

39a. $V_{cone} = \frac{1}{3}Bh = \frac{1}{3}\pi r^2 \cdot h = \frac{\pi\left(\frac{1}{2}h\right)^2 \cdot h}{3} = \frac{\pi h^3}{12}$, **where B is the area of the base of the cone, r is the radius, and h is the height**

41b. $V = \frac{\pi r_2^2(h_1 + h_2)}{3} - \frac{\pi r_1^2 h_1}{3} = \frac{\pi r_2^2\left(\frac{r_1h_2}{r_2 - r_1} + h_2\right)}{3} - \frac{\pi r_1^2\left(\frac{r_1h_2}{r_2 - r_1}\right)}{3}$

41c. $\frac{\pi r_2^2\left(\frac{r_1h_2}{r_2 - r_1} + h_2\right)}{3} - \frac{\pi r_1^2\left(\frac{r_1h_2}{r_2 - r_1}\right)}{3} = \frac{\pi r_2^2\left(\frac{r_1h_2 + h_2r_2 - h_2r_1}{r_2 - r_1}\right)}{3} - \frac{\pi\left(\frac{r_1^2 \cdot r_1h_2}{r_2 - r_1}\right)}{3} = \frac{\pi}{3} \cdot \left[\frac{r_2^2r_1h_2 + r_2^2h_2r_2 - r_2^2h_2r_1}{r_2 - r_1} - \frac{r_1^2 \cdot r_1h_2}{r_2 - r_1}\right] = \frac{\pi}{3} \cdot \left[\frac{r_2^2r_1h_2 + r_2^3h_2 - r_2^2h_2r_1}{r_2 - r_1} - \frac{r_1^3h_2}{r_2 - r_1}\right] = \frac{\pi}{3} \cdot \left[\frac{r_2^3h_2}{r_2 - r_1} - \frac{r_1^3h_2}{r_2 - r_1}\right] = \frac{\pi}{3} \cdot \frac{h_2(r_2^3 - r_1^3)}{r_2 - r_1} = \frac{\pi h_2}{3}(r_1^2 + r_1 \cdot r_2 + r_2^2) = \frac{h_2}{3}(\pi r_1^2 + \pi r_1r_2 + \pi r_2^2)$

This formula shows that you add areas of the two bases to their geometric mean, then multiply the result by $\frac{1}{3}$ the height.

39b.

Number of minutes	Height, h (m)
1	1.90
2	2.40
3	2.74
4	3.02
5	3.25

39c.

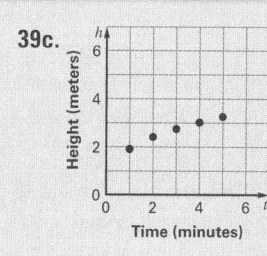

Height (meters) h: 0, 2, 4, 6
Time (minutes) t: 0, 2, 4, 6

5 ASSESS AND RETEACH

Daily Homework Quiz

Transparency Available

Find the volume of each solid.

1. **96 in.^{3}**

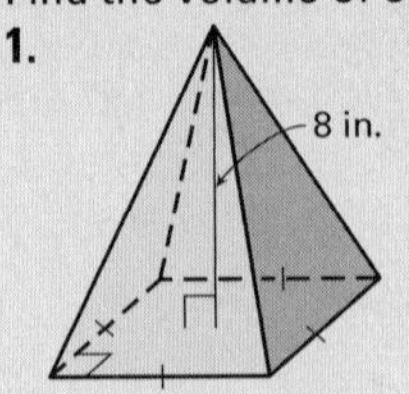

2. **3619.11 mm^3**

24 mm

12 mm

3. Find the volume of the cube after the cone is removed. **232.11 mm^3**

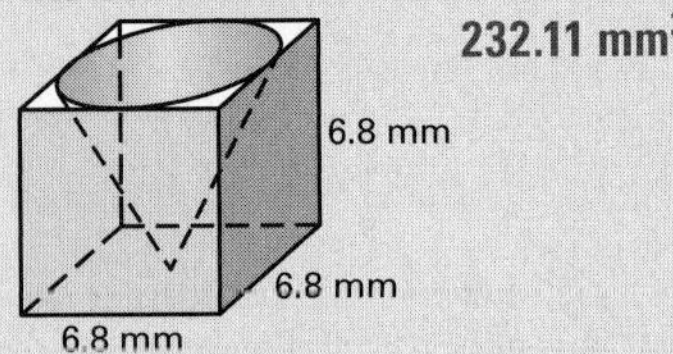

4. The volume of a right cone with height 32 in. and radius r in. is 2144.66 in.^{3}. Find r. **8.0 in.**

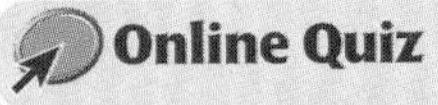

Available at **classzone.com**

Diagnosis/Remediation

- Practice A, B, C in Chapter 12 Resource Book, pp. 66–71
- Study Guide in Chapter 12 Resource Book, pp. 72–73
- Practice Workbook, pp. 238–240
- @HomeTutor

Challenge

Additional challenge is available in the Chapter 12 Resource Book, p. 76.

Quiz

An easily-readable reduced copy of the quiz (with answers) on Lessons 12.4–12.5 from the Assessment Book can be found on p. 790G.

42. **CHALLENGE** A square pyramid is inscribed in a right cylinder so that the base of the pyramid is on a base of the cylinder, and the vertex of the pyramid is on the other base of the cylinder. The cylinder has radius 6 feet and height 12 feet. Find the volume of the pyramid. Round your answer to two decimal places. **288 ft^3**

MIXED REVIEW

PREVIEW Prepare for Lesson 12.6 in Exs. 46–52.

In Exercises 43–45, find the value of x. *(p. 397)*

43. **7**

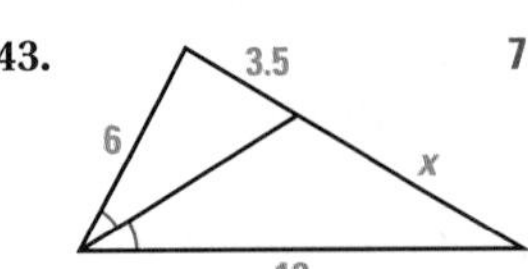

44. **6**

x, 8, 15, 20

45. **3**

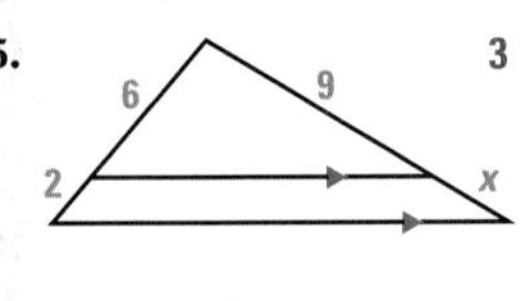

46. Copy the diagram at the right. Name a radius, diameter, and chord. *(p. 651)* ***Sample answer:*** $\overline{AF}$, $\overline{BE}$, $\overline{CD}$

47. Name a minor arc of $\odot F$. *(p. 659)* ***Sample answer:*** $\overset{\frown}{AB}$

48. Name a major arc of $\odot F$. *(p. 659)* ***Sample answer:*** $\overset{\frown}{AEC}$

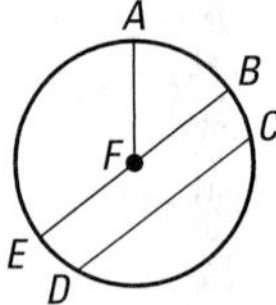

Find the area of the circle with the given radius r, diameter d, or circumference C. *(p. 755)*

49. $r = 3$ m **about 28.27 m^2**

50. $d = 7$ mi **about 38.48 mi^2**

51. $r = 0.4$ cm **about 0.50 cm^2**

52. $C = 8\pi$ in. **about 50.27 in.^{2}**

QUIZ for Lessons 12.4–12.5

Find the volume of the figure. Round your answer to two decimal places, if necessary. *(pp. 819, 829)*

1. 10 cm, 15 cm, 7 cm **525 cm^3**

2. 6 in., 10 in. **1130.97 in.^{3}**

3. 9 m, 16 m **1017.88 m^3**

4. **6 cm^3**

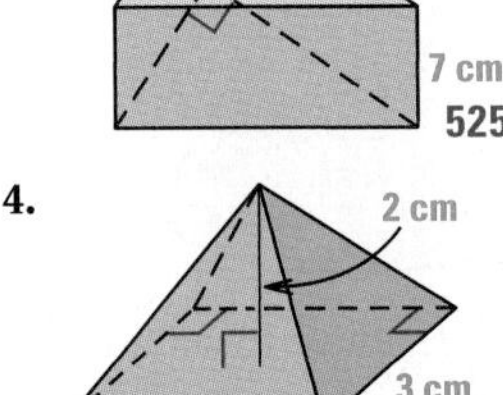

5. **37,699.11 ft^3**

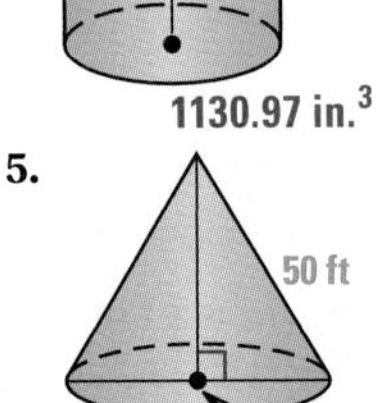

6. **1005.31 yd^3**

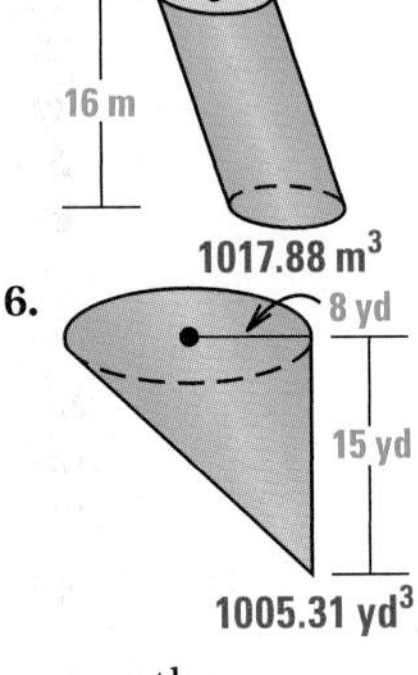

7. Suppose you fill up a cone-shaped cup with water. You then pour the water into a cylindrical cup with the same radius. Both cups have a height of 6 inches. Without doing any calculation, determine how high the water level will be in the cylindrical cup once all of the water is poured into it. *Explain* your reasoning. *(p. 829)*
2 in.; since a cone has $\frac{1}{3}$ the volume of a cylinder with the same height and radius, find $\frac{1}{3}(6) = 2$.

@HomeTutor
classzone.com
Keystrokes

12.5 Minimize Surface Area

MATERIALS • computer

QUESTION **How can you find the minimum surface area of a solid with a given volume?**

A manufacturer needs a cylindrical container with a volume of 72 cubic centimeters. You have been asked to find the dimensions of such a container so that it has a minimum surface area.

Standards

8.0 Students know, derive, and **solve problems involving** the perimeter, circumference, area, **volume,** lateral area, **and surface area** of common geometric figures.

EXAMPLE **Use a spreadsheet**

STEP 1 ***Make a table*** Make a table with the four column headings shown in Step 4. The first column is for the given volume *V*. In cell A2, enter 72. In cell A3, enter the formula "=A2".

STEP 2 ***Enter radius*** The second column is for the radius *r*. Cell B2 stores the starting value for *r*. So, enter 2 into cell B2. In cell B3, use the formula "=B2 + 0.05" to increase *r* in increments of 0.05 centimeter.

STEP 3 ***Enter formula for height*** The third column is for the height. In cell C2, enter the formula "=A2/(PI()*B2^2)". *Note:* Your spreadsheet might use a different expression for π.

STEP 4 ***Enter formula for surface area*** The fourth column is for the surface area. In cell D2, enter the formula "=2*PI()*B2^2+2*PI()*B2*C2".

	A	B	C	D
1	Volume V	Radius r	Height= $V/(\pi r^2)$	Surface area $S=2\pi r^2+2\pi rh$
2	72.00	2.00	=A2/(PI()*B2^2)	=2*PI()*B2^2+2*PI()*B2*C2
3	=A2	=B2+0.05		

STEP 5 ***Create more rows*** Use the *Fill Down* feature to create more rows. Rows 3 and 4 of your spreadsheet should resemble the one below.

	A	B	C	D
...				
3	72.00	2.05	5.45	96.65
4	72.00	2.10	5.20	96.28

PRACTICE

1. From the data in your spreadsheet, which dimensions yield a minimum surface area for the given volume? *Explain* how you know. **See margin.**
2. **WHAT IF?** Find the dimensions that give the minimum surface area if the volume of a cylinder is instead 200π cubic centimeters.
With these increments, $r = 4.65$, $h = 9.25$; precise answer, $r = 4.64$, $h = 9.29$

1 PLAN AND PREPARE

Learn the Method

- Students will use a spreadsheet to find the minimum surface area of a solid with a given volume.
- Students can use the spreadsheet to find the surface area for solids with given volumes in Lesson 12.5.

2 TEACH

Tips for Success

Remind students that "*" indicates "multiply." Unlike some graphing calculators, it must be entered when entering the product of a number and a variable.

Alternative Strategy

Demonstrate the spreadsheet on an overhead screen. Have students use calculators to find values if computers are not available.

Extra Example 1

A manufacturer needs a cylindrical container with a volume of 100 in.^{3}. Find the dimensions of such a container so that it has a minimum surface area. **radius 2.5 in.; height 5.09 in.**

3 ASSESS AND RETEACH

1. If the volume of the cylindrical container is doubled to 144 cm^3, what radius gives the minimum surface area? **2.8 cm**
2. If the volume of the cylindrical container is reduced by $\frac{1}{4}$, what dimensions give the minimum surface area? **radius 2.05 cm; height 4.09 cm**

1. $r = 2.25$ and $h = 4.527$; the value in column D decreases as you approach 95.81 and then it increases after that number.

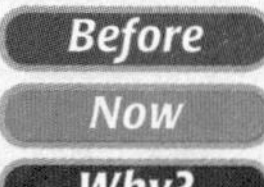

1 PLAN AND PREPARE

Warm-Up Exercises

Transparency Available

Find the area of each circle.

1. Radius 17 m **907.92 m²**
2. Diameter 7.8 in. **47.78 in.²**

Find the volume of each solid.

3. Cylinder, radius 6 ft, height 10 ft **1130.97 ft³**
4. Cone, radius 3.1 cm and height 11.8 cm **118.75 cm³**
5. Find the circumference of a circle with radius 48 m. **301.59 m**

Notetaking Guide

Transparency Available

Promotes interactive learning and notetaking skills, pp. 329–332.

Pacing

Basic: 2 days
Average: 2 days
Advanced: 2 days
Block: 0.5 block with 12.5
0.5 block with 12.7

- See *Teaching Guide/Lesson Plan.*

2 FOCUS AND MOTIVATE

Essential Question

Big Idea 2, p. 791

How do you find the volume of a sphere? **Tell students they will learn how to answer this question by using a formula for the volume of a sphere.**

12.6 Surface Area and Volume of Spheres

Before	You found surface areas and volumes of polyhedra.
Now	You will find surface areas and volumes of spheres.
Why?	So you can find the volume of a tennis ball, as in Ex. 33.

Key Vocabulary
- **sphere**
  center, radius, chord, diameter
- **great circle**
- **hemispheres**

Standards

9.0 Students compute the volumes and surface areas of prisms, pyramids, cylinders, cones, and **spheres;** and students commit to memory the formulas for prisms, pyramids, and cylinders.

8.0 Students know, derive, and solve problems involving the perimeter, circumference, area, **volume,** lateral area, **and surface area** of common geometric figures.

A **sphere** is the set of all points in space equidistant from a given point. This point is called the **center** of the sphere. A **radius** of a sphere is a segment from the center to a point on the sphere. A **chord** of a sphere is a segment whose endpoints are on the sphere. A **diameter** of a sphere is a chord that contains the center.

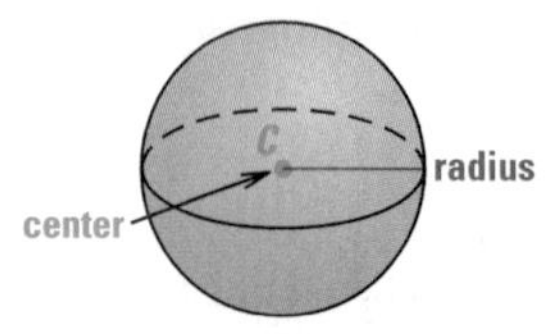

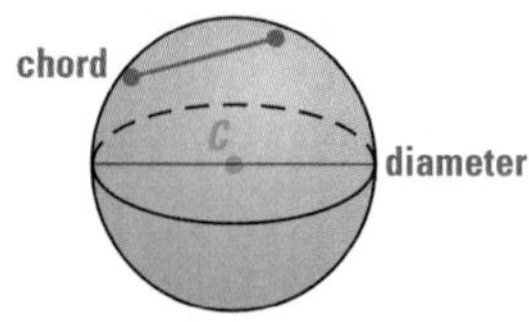

As with circles, the terms radius and diameter also represent distances, and the diameter is twice the radius.

THEOREM *For Your Notebook*

THEOREM 12.11 Surface Area of a Sphere

The surface area S of a sphere is

$S = 4\pi r^2$,

where r is the radius of the sphere.

$S = 4\pi r^2$

USE FORMULAS
If you understand how a formula is derived, then it will be easier for you to remember the formula.

SURFACE AREA FORMULA To understand how the formula for the surface area of a sphere is derived, think of a baseball. The surface area of a baseball is sewn from two congruent shapes, each of which resembles two joined circles, as shown.

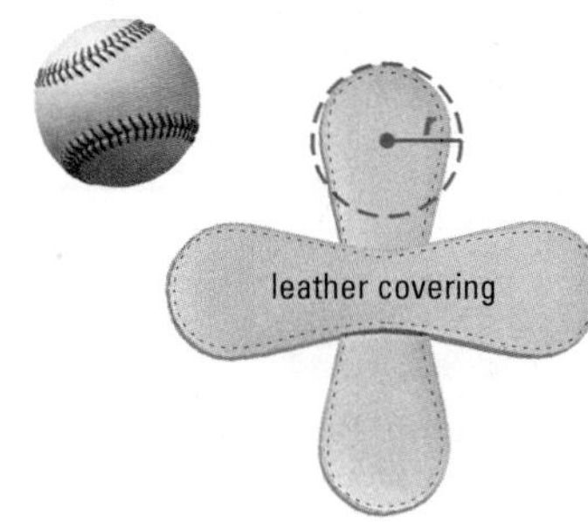

So, the entire covering of the baseball consists of four circles, each with radius r. The area A of a circle with radius r is $A = \pi r^2$. So, the area of the covering can be approximated by $4\pi r^2$. This is the formula for the surface area of a sphere.

Resource Planning Guide

Chapter Resource Book
- Teaching Guide/Lesson Plan (pp. 77–78)
- Practice levels A, B, C (pp. 79–84)
- Study Guide (pp. 85–86)
- Catch-up for Absent Students (p. 87)
- Application (p. 88)
- Challenge (p. 89)

Workbooks
- Notetaking Guide (pp. 329–332)
- Practice Workbook (pp. 241–243)

Teaching Options
- **Power Presentations CD-ROM** provides dynamic electronic teaching resources for the classroom.
- **Activity Generator CD-ROM** provides editable activities for all ability levels.

Interactive Technology
- Easy Planner
- Power Presentations CD-ROM
- Activity Generator CD-ROM
- Animated Geometry
- Test Generator CD-ROM
- Online Quiz
- eWorkbook
- eEdition
- @HomeTutor

Resources for English Learners
- Quick Reference for English Learners
- Spanish Study Guide
- Multi-Language Visual Glossary
- Student Resources in Spanish

See also the *Geometry Toolkit* for more strategies for meeting individual needs.

EXAMPLE 1 Find the surface area of a sphere

Find the surface area of the sphere.

Solution

$S = 4\pi r^2$	Formula for surface area of a sphere
$= 4\pi(8^2)$	Substitute 8 for r.
$= 256\pi$	Simplify.
≈ 804.25	Use a calculator.

▶ The surface area of the sphere is about 804.25 square inches.

EXAMPLE 2 Standardized Test Practice

The surface area of the sphere is 20.25π square centimeters. What is the diameter of the sphere?

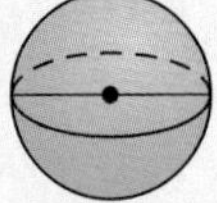

Ⓐ 2.25 cm Ⓑ 4.5 cm

Ⓒ 5.5 cm Ⓓ 20.25 cm

Solution

$S = 4\pi r^2$	Formula for surface area of a sphere
$20.25\pi = 4\pi r^2$	Substitute 20.25π for S.
$5.0625 = r^2$	Divide each side by 4π.
$2.25 = r$	Find the positive square root.

The diameter of the sphere is $2r = 2 \cdot 2.25 = 4.5$ centimeters.

▶ The correct answer is B. Ⓐ Ⓑ Ⓒ Ⓓ

AVOID ERRORS
Be sure to multiply the value of r by 2 to find the diameter.

GUIDED PRACTICE for Examples 1 and 2

1. The diameter of a sphere is 40 feet. Find the surface area of the sphere. **about 5026.55 ft²**
2. The surface area of a sphere is 30π square meters. Find the radius of the sphere. **about 2.74 m**

GREAT CIRCLES If a plane intersects a sphere, the intersection is either a single point or a circle. If the plane contains the center of the sphere, then the intersection is a **great circle** of the sphere. The circumference of a great circle is the circumference of the sphere. Every great circle of a sphere separates the sphere into two congruent halves called **hemispheres**.

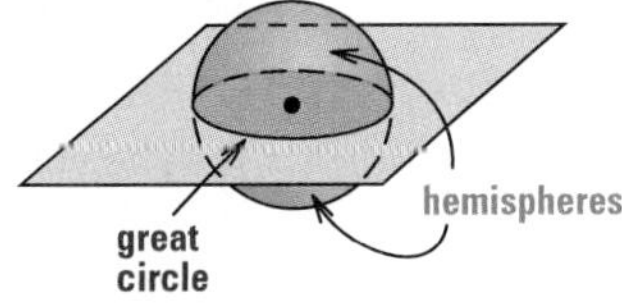

Motivating the Lesson

Have students describe the surface of a half sphere, and ask them how they might calculate its surface area. Discuss with them that the surface area consists of the flat, circular base, for which they can use the area formula $A = \pi r^2$, and half a ball-shaped surface. Tell them that in this lesson they will learn and apply formulas for the surface area and volume of a sphere.

3 TEACH

Extra Example 1

Find the surface area of the sphere.

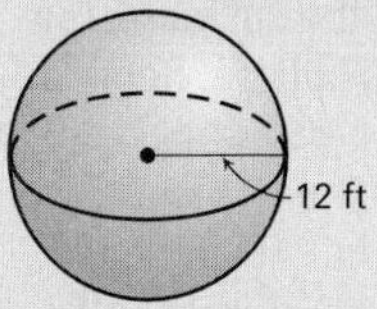

576π ft² or approx. 1809.56 ft²

Extra Example 2

The surface area of a sphere is 40.96π in.² What is the diameter of the sphere? **B**

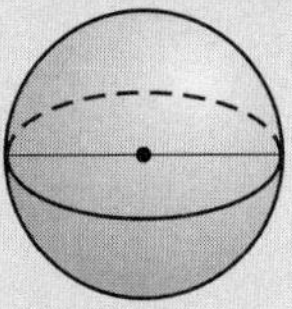

Ⓐ 3.2 in. Ⓑ 6.4 in.
Ⓒ 8.6 in. Ⓓ 40.96 in.

Differentiated Instruction

Below Level Ask students how they could calculate the radius of a hemisphere whose total surface area, including the flat base, is 363π in.² They should see that the area of a hemisphere with radius r is $A = \frac{1}{2}$(surface area of whole sphere) + (area of circular base) $= \frac{1}{2}(4\pi r^2) + \pi r^2 = 3\pi r^2$, so if $363\pi = 3\pi r^2$, then $r = 11$ in.

See also the *Geometry Toolkit* for more strategies.

Extra Example 3

A globe of Earth is a model of a sphere. The diameter of this globe is 18 in. Find the surface area of the globe. **about 1017.88 in.^{2}**

Avoiding Common Errors

Students may write the wrong formula or use the wrong exponent when calculating the surface area or the volume of a sphere. Remind them that area is measured in square units (exponent 2) and volume in cubic units (exponent 3).

EXAMPLE 3 Use the circumference of a sphere

EXTREME SPORTS In a sport called *sphereing*, a person rolls down a hill inside an inflatable ball surrounded by another ball. The diameter of the outer ball is 12 feet. Find the surface area of the outer ball.

Solution

The diameter of the outer sphere is 12 feet, so the radius is $\frac{12}{2} = 6$ feet.

Use the formula for the surface area of a sphere.

$S = 4\pi r^2 = 4\pi(6^2) = 144\pi$

▸ The surface area of the outer ball is 144π, or about 452.39 square feet.

✓ GUIDED PRACTICE for Example 3

3. In Example 3, the circumference of the inner ball is 6π feet. Find the surface area of the inner ball. Round your answer to two decimal places. **113.10 ft^2**

VOLUME FORMULA Imagine that the interior of a sphere with radius r is approximated by n pyramids, each with a base area of B and a height of r. The volume of each pyramid is $\frac{1}{3}Br$ and the sum of the base areas is nB. The surface area of the sphere is approximately equal to nB, or $4\pi r^2$. So, you can approximate the volume V of the sphere as follows.

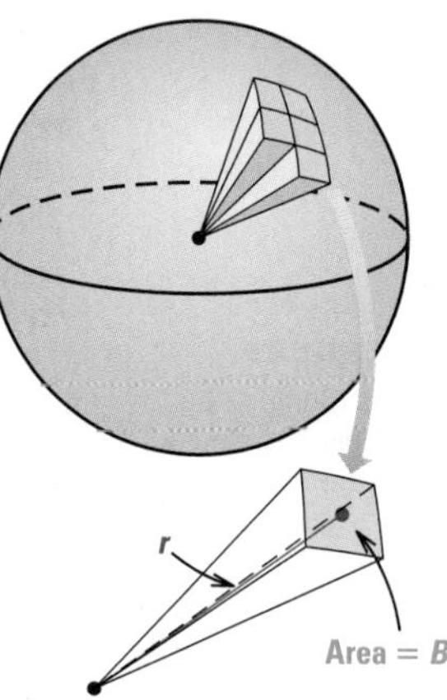

$V \approx n\left(\frac{1}{3}Br\right)$	**Each pyramid has a volume of $\frac{1}{3}Br$.**
$\approx \frac{1}{3}(nB)r$	**Regroup factors.**
$= \frac{1}{3}(4\pi r^2)r$	**Substitute $4\pi r^2$ for nB.**
$= \frac{4}{3}\pi r^3$	**Simplify.**

THEOREM *For Your Notebook*

THEOREM 12.12 Volume of a Sphere

The volume V of a sphere is

$V = \frac{4}{3}\pi r^3$,

where r is the radius of the sphere.

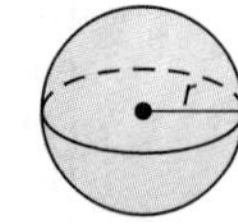

Differentiated Instruction

Auditory Learners Students may be better able to commit the formulas for volume to memory if they recite them out loud. Have students say each formula several times, first using the full names for the variables (for example, saying "volume" instead of "V"). Then have them repeat the formulas again using the variables.

See also the *Geometry Toolkit* for more strategies.

EXAMPLE 4 Find the volume of a sphere

The soccer ball has a diameter of 9 inches. Find its volume.

Solution

The diameter of the ball is 9 inches, so the radius is $\frac{9}{2} = 4.5$ inches.

$V = \frac{4}{3}\pi r^3$	Formula for volume of a sphere
$= \frac{4}{3}\pi(4.5)^3$	Substitute.
$= 121.5\pi$	Simplify.
≈ 381.70	Use a calculator.

▶ The volume of the soccer ball is 121.5π, or about 381.70 cubic inches.

EXAMPLE 5 Find the volume of a composite solid

Find the volume of the composite solid.

Solution

2 in.
2 in.

Volume of solid = Volume of cylinder − Volume of hemisphere

$= \pi r^2 h - \frac{1}{2}\left(\frac{4}{3}\pi r^3\right)$	Formulas for volume
$= \pi(2)^2(2) - \frac{2}{3}\pi(2)^3$	Substitute.
$= 8\pi - \frac{2}{3}(8\pi)$	Multiply.
$= \frac{24}{3}\pi - \frac{16}{3}\pi$	Rewrite fractions using least common denominator.
$= \frac{8}{3}\pi$	Simplify.

▶ The volume of the solid is $\frac{8}{3}\pi$, or about 8.38 cubic inches.

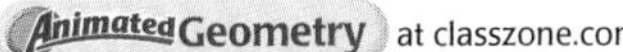 at classzone.com

GUIDED PRACTICE for Examples 4 and 5

4. The radius of a sphere is 5 yards. Find the volume of the sphere. Round your answer to two decimal places. **523.60 yd^3**

5. A solid consists of a hemisphere of radius 1 meter on top of a cone with the same radius and height 5 meters. Find the volume of the solid. Round your answer to two decimal places. **7.33 m^3**

Extra Example 4

This beach ball has a diameter of 15 inches. Find its volume.

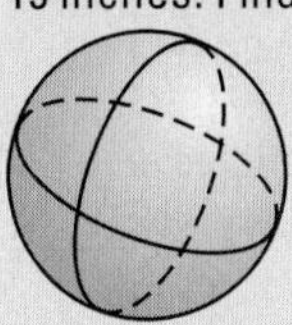

about 1767.15 in.^{3}

Extra Example 5

Find the volume of the composite solid.

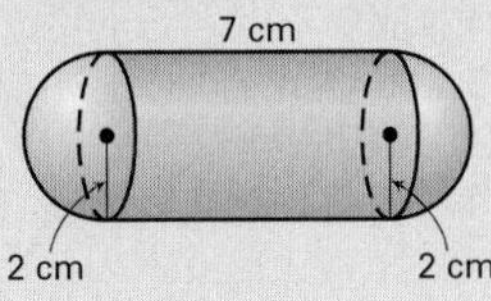

$\frac{116}{3}\pi$ or about 121.47 cm^3

An **Animated Geometry** activity is available on-line for **Example 5**. This activity is also available on the **Power Presentations CD-ROM**.

Closing the Lesson

Have students summarize the major points of the lesson and answer the Essential Question: How do you find the volume of a sphere?

- **For a sphere, $S = 4\pi r^2$.**
- **For a sphere, $V = \frac{4}{3}\pi r^3$.**

The formula for the volume V of a sphere is $V = \frac{4}{3}\pi r^3$. To find the volume, substitute the value for r.

Differentiated Instruction

Advanced Show students this diagram of a square with a diagonal and a quarter circle. Ask them to imagine the figure rotated in space around $\overleftrightarrow{AB}$. Ask them to describe the three solids formed (cylinder, hemisphere, cone), and ask them to calculate the extended ratio of the volumes of the solids. Students should see that the volumes are πs^3, $\frac{2}{3}\pi s^3$, and $\frac{1}{3}\pi s^3$, so the extended ratio is 3 : 2 : 1.

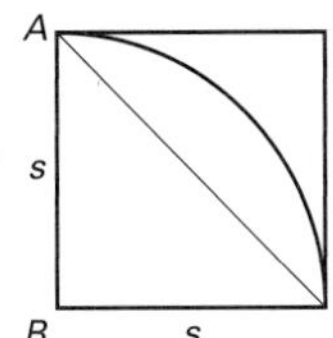

See also the *Geometry Toolkit* for more strategies.

12.6 EXERCISES

HOMEWORK KEY

◯ = **WORKED-OUT SOLUTIONS** on p. WS18 for Exs. 3, 13, and 31

★ = **STANDARDIZED TEST PRACTICE** Exs. 2, 6, 20, 28, 33, and 34

4 PRACTICE AND APPLY

Assignment Guide

Answer Transparencies available for all exercises

Basic:
Day 1: pp. 842–845
Exs. 1–11, 31, 40–44
Day 2: pp. 842–845
Exs. 12–24, 30, 32–34

Average:
Day 1: pp. 842–845
Exs. 1–11, 31, 40–44
Day 2: pp. 842–845
Exs. 13–15, 17–20, 22–28 even, 30, 32–36

Advanced:
Day 1: pp. 842–845
Exs. 1–9, 11, 31, 40–44
Day 2: pp. 842–845
Exs. 18–20, 21–27 odd, 28–30*, 33–39*

Block:
pp. 842–845
Exs. 1–11, 31, 40–44 (with 12.5)
pp. 842–845
Exs. 13–15, 17–20, 22–28 even, 30, 32–36 (with 12.7)

Differentiated Instruction

See *Geometry Best Practices Toolkit* for suggestions on addressing the needs of a diverse classroom.

Homework Check

For a quick check of student understanding of key concepts, go over the following exercises:

Basic: 4, 6, 7, 12, 30
Average: 4, 6, 8, 15, 30
Advanced: 5, 6, 9, 15, 30

Extra Practice

- Student Edition, p. 919
- Chapter 12 Resource Book: Practice levels A, B, C, pp. 79–84

Practice Worksheet

An easily-readable reduced practice page (with answers) for this lesson can be found on p. 790E.

SKILL PRACTICE

A

1. **VOCABULARY** What are the formulas for finding the surface area of a sphere and the volume of a sphere? **$S = 4\pi r^2$, $V = \frac{4}{3}\pi r^3$, where r is the radius of the sphere**

2. ★ **WRITING** When a plane intersects a sphere, what point in the sphere must the plane contain for the intersection to be a great circle? *Explain.* **See margin.**

2. The center point; if the plane contains the center, then the circumference of the circular intersection is the circumference of the sphere, and the intersection is a great circle.

EXAMPLE 1 on p. 839 for Exs. 3–5

FINDING SURFACE AREA **Find the surface area of the sphere. Round your answer to two decimal places.**

3.

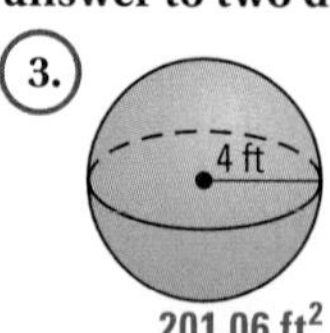

201.06 ft^2

4.

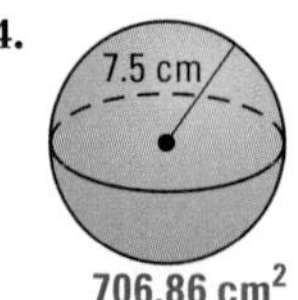

706.86 cm^2

5.

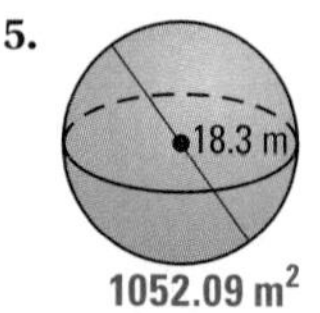

1052.09 m^2

EXAMPLE 2 on p. 839 for Ex. 6

6. ★ **MULTIPLE CHOICE** What is the approximate radius of a sphere with surface area 32π square meters? **B**

Ⓐ 2 meters　Ⓑ 2.83 meters　Ⓒ 4.90 meters　Ⓓ 8 meters

EXAMPLE 3 on p. 840 for Exs. 7–11

USING A GREAT CIRCLE **In Exercises 7–9, use the sphere below. The center of the sphere is C and its circumference is 9.6π inches.**

7. Find the radius of the sphere. **4.8 in.**

8. Find the diameter of the sphere. **9.6 in.**

9. Find the surface area of one hemisphere. **about 144.76 in.^{2}**

10. **ERROR ANALYSIS** *Describe* and correct the error in finding the surface area of a hemisphere with radius 5 feet.

$S = 4\pi r^2$
$= 4\pi(5)^2$
$= 100\pi$
≈ 314.16 ft^2

5 ft

The surface area of a hemisphere is one-half the surface area of a sphere; $S = 2\pi r^2 = 2\pi(5)^2 = 50\pi \approx 157.08$ ft^2.

11. **GREAT CIRCLE** The circumference of a great circle of a sphere is 48.4π centimeters. What is the surface area of the sphere? **about 7359.37 cm^2**

EXAMPLE 4 on p. 841 for Exs. 12–15

FINDING VOLUME **Find the volume of the sphere using the given radius r or diameter d. Round your answer to two decimal places.**

12. $r = 6$ in. **904.78 in.^{3}**　　13. $r = 40$ mm **268,082.57 mm^3**　　14. $d = 5$ cm **65.45 cm^3**

15. **ERROR ANALYSIS** *Describe* and correct the error in finding the volume of a sphere with diameter 16 feet. **The radius should be cubed; $V = \frac{4}{3}\pi r^3 = \frac{4}{3}\pi(8)^3 \approx 682.67\pi = 2144.66$ ft³.**

$$V = \frac{4}{3}\pi r^2$$
$$= \frac{4}{3}\pi(8)^2$$
$$= 85.33\pi \approx 268.08 \text{ ft}^2$$

B **USING VOLUME In Exercises 16–18, find the radius of a sphere with the given volume V. Round your answers to two decimal places.**

16. $V = 1436.76$ m³ **7.00 m**
17. $V = 91.95$ cm³ **2.80 cm**
18. $V = 20{,}814.37$ in.³ **17.06 in.**

19. **FINDING A DIAMETER** The volume of a sphere is 36π cubic feet. What is the diameter of the sphere? **6 ft**

20. ★ **MULTIPLE CHOICE** Let V be the volume of a sphere, S be the surface area of the sphere, and r be the radius of the sphere. Which equation represents the relationship between these three measures? **A**

Ⓐ $V = \frac{rS}{3}$ Ⓑ $V = \frac{r^2S}{3}$ Ⓒ $V = \frac{3}{2}rS$ Ⓓ $V = \frac{3}{2}r^2S$

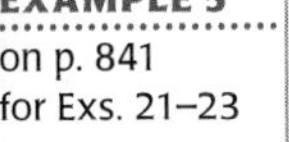
EXAMPLE 5
on p. 841
for Exs. 21–23

COMPOSITE SOLIDS Find the surface area and the volume of the solid. The cylinders and cones are right. Round your answers to two decimal places.

21.
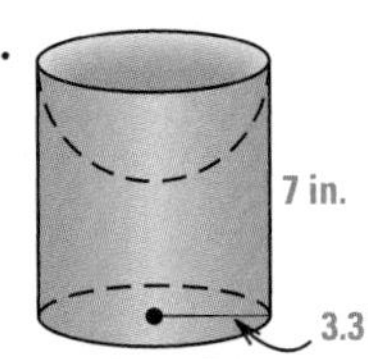

247.78 in.², 164.22 in.³

22.
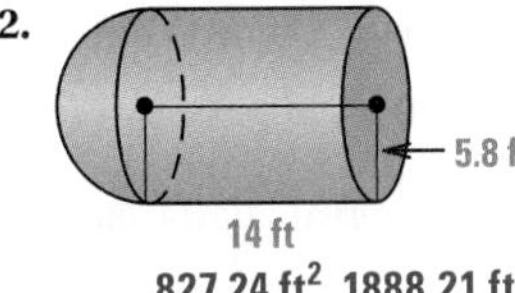

827.24 ft², 1888.21 ft³

23.
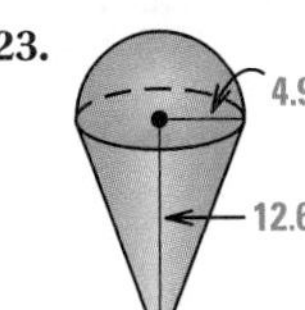

358.97 cm², 563.21 cm³

USING A TABLE Copy and complete the table below. Leave your answers in terms of π.

	Radius of sphere	Circumference of great circle	Surface area of sphere	Volume of sphere
24.	10 ft	?	?	?
25.	?	26π in.	?	?
26.	?	?	2500π cm²	?
27.	?	?	?	$12{,}348\pi$ m³

28. ★ **MULTIPLE CHOICE** A sphere is inscribed in a cube with volume 64 cubic centimeters. What is the surface area of the sphere? **C**

Ⓐ 4π cm² Ⓑ $\frac{32}{3}\pi$ cm² Ⓒ 16π cm² Ⓓ 64π cm²

C 29. **CHALLENGE** The volume of a right cylinder is the same as the volume of a sphere. The radius of the sphere is 1 inch.

a. Give three possibilities for the dimensions of the cylinder.

b. Show that the surface area of the cylinder is sometimes greater than the surface area of the sphere. **The surface area of the cylinder will be greater than the surface area of the sphere when $2\pi rh + 2\pi r^2 > 4\pi$. Solve to get $r(h + r) > 2$. The surface area of the cylinder will be greater than the surface area of the sphere when the product of the radius and the sum of the height and the radius of the cylinder is greater than 2.**

24. 20π ft; 400π ft²; $\frac{4000}{3}\pi$ ft³
25. 13 in.; 676π in.²; $\frac{8788}{3}\pi$ in.³
26. 25 cm; 50π cm; $\frac{62{,}500}{3}\pi$ cm³
27. 21 m; 42π m; 1764π m²
29a. *Sample answer:* $r = 1$ in., $h = \frac{4}{3}$ in.; $r = 2$ in., $h = \frac{1}{3}$ in.; $r = \frac{\sqrt{3}}{3}$ in., $h = 4$ in.

Avoiding Common Errors

Exercises 9, 10 A common error when finding the surface area of a hemisphere is to forget that it includes the flat, circular base. Caution students to add the area of a great circle to half of the surface area of a sphere.

Mathematical Reasoning

Exercise 20 Students can solve this equation directly by starting with the ratio $\frac{V}{S}$. Then they can write the proportion $\frac{V}{S} = \frac{\frac{4}{3}\pi r^3}{4\pi r^2}$ and solve for V.

PROBLEM SOLVING

EXAMPLE 5 A on p. 841 for Ex. 30

30. **GRAIN SILO** A grain silo has the dimensions shown. The top of the silo is a hemispherical shape. Find the volume of the grain silo. **about 20,944 ft^3**

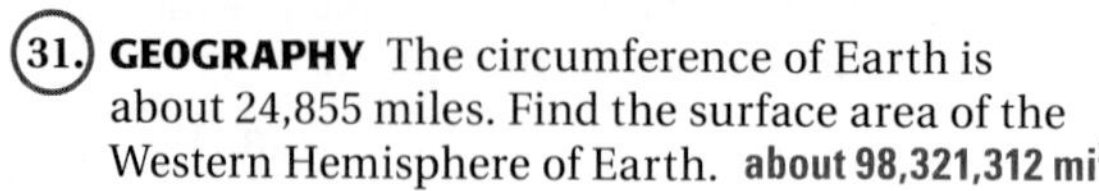

@HomeTutor for problem solving help at classzone.com

31. **GEOGRAPHY** The circumference of Earth is about 24,855 miles. Find the surface area of the Western Hemisphere of Earth. **about 98,321,312 mi^2**

@HomeTutor for problem solving help at classzone.com

32. **MULTI-STEP PROBLEM** A ball has volume 1427.54 cubic centimeters.
    a. Find the radius of the ball. Round your answer to two decimal places. **6.99 cm**
    b. Find the surface area of the ball. Round your answer to two decimal places. **613.99 cm^2**

B

33. ★ **SHORT RESPONSE** Tennis balls are stored in a cylindrical container with height 8.625 inches and radius 1.43 inches.
    a. The circumference of a tennis ball is 8 inches. Find the volume of a tennis ball. **about 8.65 $in.^3$**
    b. There are 3 tennis balls in the container. Find the amount of space within the cylinder not taken up by the tennis balls. **about 29.47 $in.^3$**

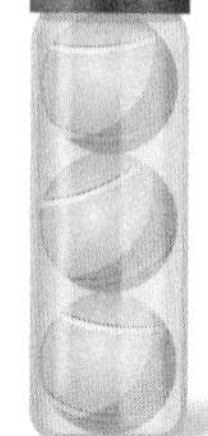

34. ★ **EXTENDED RESPONSE** A partially filled balloon has circumference 27π centimeters. Assume the balloon is a sphere.
    a. **Calculate** Find the volume of the balloon. **about 10,306 cm^3**
    b. **Predict** Suppose you double the radius by increasing the air in the balloon. *Explain* what you expect to happen to the volume.
    c. **Justify** Find the volume of the balloon with the radius doubled. Was your prediction from part (b) correct? What is the ratio of this volume to the original volume? **about 82,448; yes; 8:1**

34b. You would expect the volume to be 8 times as much because $(2r)^3 = 8r^3$.

35. **GEOGRAPHY** The Torrid Zone on Earth is the area between the Tropic of Cancer and the Tropic of Capricorn, as shown. The distance between these two tropics is about 3250 miles. You can think of this distance as the height of a cylindrical belt around Earth at the equator, as shown.
    a. Estimate the surface area of the Torrid Zone and the surface area of Earth. (Earth's radius is about 3963 miles at the equator.)
    b. A meteorite is equally likely to hit anywhere on Earth. Estimate the probability that a meteorite will land in the Torrid Zone. **about 41%**

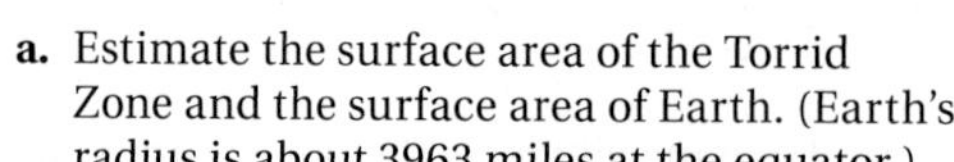

35a. about 80,925,856 mi^2, about 197,359,488 mi^2

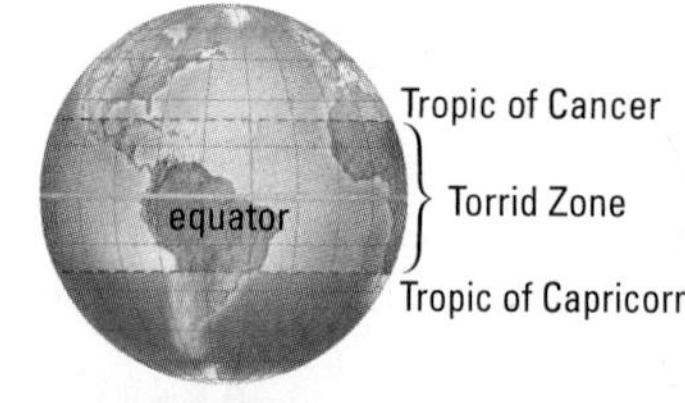

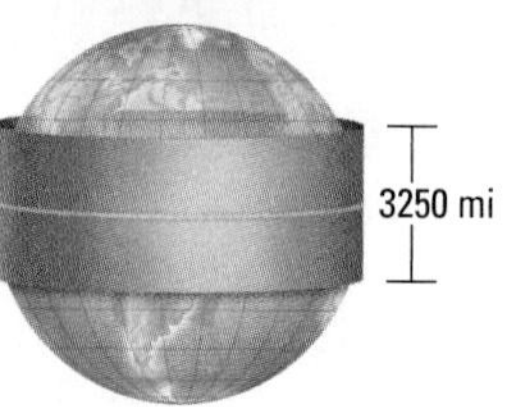

○ = WORKED-OUT SOLUTIONS on p. WS1 ★ = STANDARDIZED TEST PRACTICE

38a. Let r = radius of the cylinder. Then solve for r by using the Pythagorean Theorem for a right triangle with hypotenuse 8 meters and legs r meters and x meters. $r = \sqrt{8^2 - x^2} = \sqrt{64 - x^2}$. Substitute known values into the volume formula for a cylinder, $V = \pi \cdot \text{radius}^2 \cdot \text{height} = \pi \cdot (\sqrt{64 - x^2})^2 \cdot 2x = 2\pi x(64 - x^2)$.

38b.

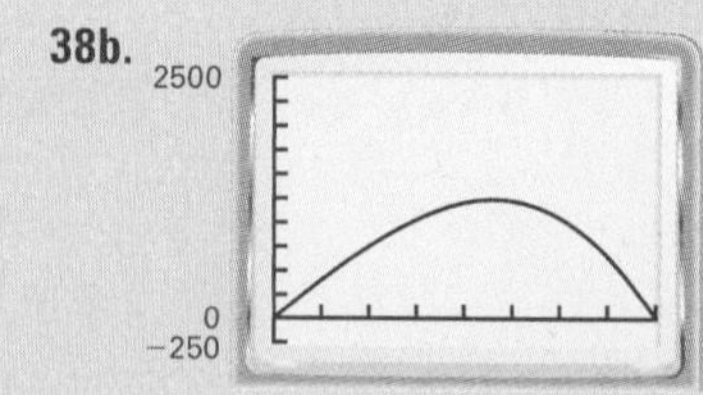

36. **REASONING** List the following three solids in order from least to greatest for (a) surface area and (b) volume. **a. Solid I, Solid III, Solid II b. Solid III, Solid I, Solid II**

Solid I **Solid II** **Solid III**

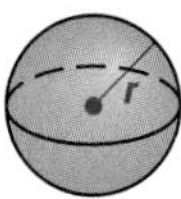

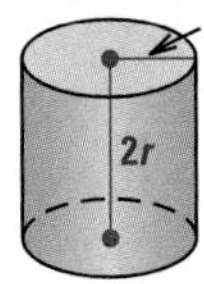

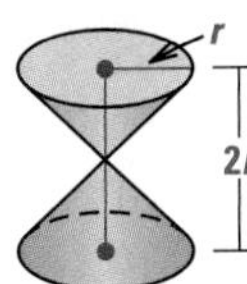

37. **ROTATION** A circle with diameter 18 inches is rotated about its diameter. Find the surface area and the volume of the solid formed. **324π in.^{2}, 972π in.^{3}**

C 38. **TECHNOLOGY** A cylinder with height $2x$ is inscribed in a sphere with radius 8 meters. The center of the sphere is the midpoint of the altitude that joins the centers of the bases of the cylinder.

a. Show that the volume V of the cylinder is $2\pi x(64 - x^2)$. **See margin.**

b. Use a graphing calculator to graph $V = 2\pi x(64 - x^2)$ for values of x between 0 and 8. Find the value of x that gives the maximum value of V. **See margin for art; about 4.62 m.**

c. Use the value for x from part (b) to find the maximum volume of the cylinder. **about 1238.22 m^3**

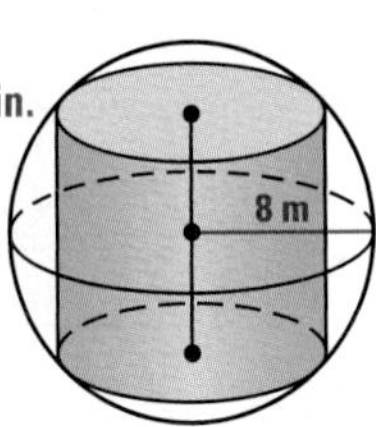

39. **CHALLENGE** A sphere with radius 2 centimeters is inscribed in a right cone with height 6 centimeters. Find the surface area and the volume of the cone. **about 91.5 cm^2, about 56.5 cm^3**

MIXED REVIEW

PREVIEW
Prepare for Lesson 12.7 in Exs. 40–41.

In Exercises 40 and 41, the polygons are similar. Find the ratio (red to blue) of their areas. Find the unknown area. Round your answer to two decimal places. *(p. 737)*

40. Area of $\triangle ABC = 42$ ft^2
Area of $\triangle DEF$ = ? **64:25; 16.41 ft^2**

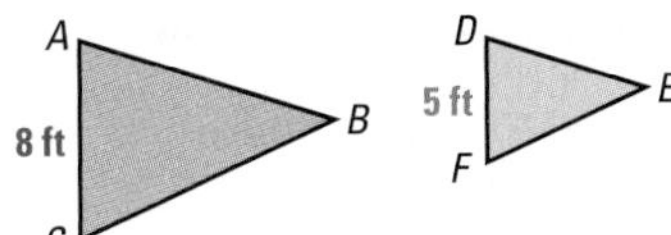

41. Area of $PQRS = 195$ cm^2
Area of $JKLM$ = ? **25:49; 99.49 cm^2**

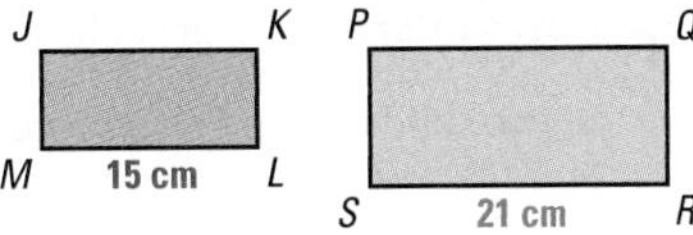

Find the probability that a randomly chosen point in the figure lies in the shaded region. *(p. 771)*

42. 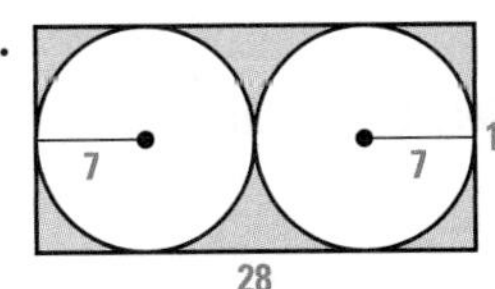

about 21.5%

43. 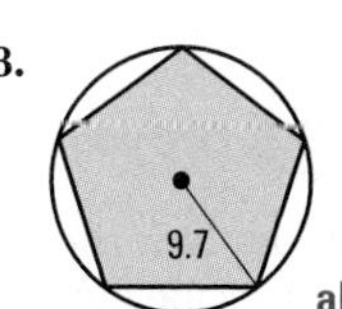

about 75.7%

44. A cone is inscribed in a right cylinder with volume 330 cubic units. Find the volume of the cone. *(pp. 819, 829)* **110 units^3**

5 ASSESS AND RETEACH

Daily Homework Quiz

Transparency Available

Find the surface area and volume of each sphere.

1. 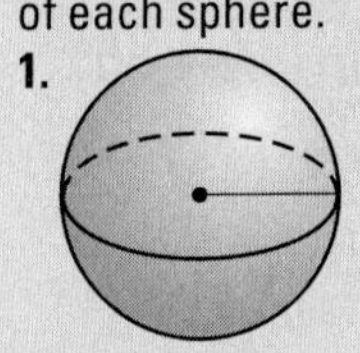

452.39 ft^2; 904.78 ft^3

2. 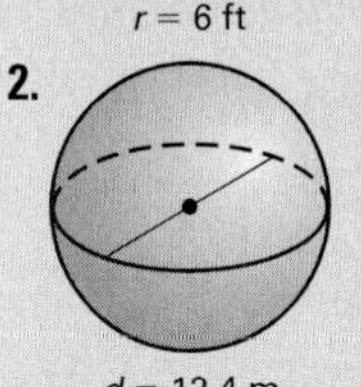

483.05 m^2; 998.31 m^3

3. A great circle of a sphere has circumference 16π in. Find the volume of the sphere. **2144.66 in.^{3}**
4. Find the radius of a sphere with volume 4445.18 ft^3. **10.2 ft**
5. Find the surface area and volume of the solid. **251.33 m^2; 335.10 m^3**

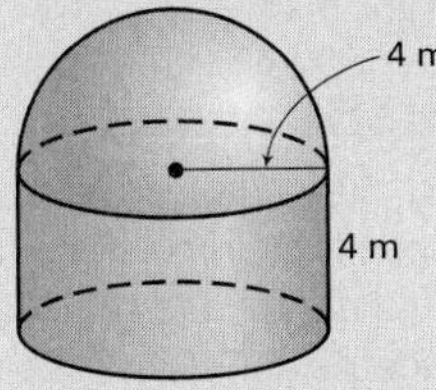

Available at **classzone.com**

Diagnosis/Remediation

- Practice A, B, C in Chapter 12 Resource Book, pp. 79–84
- Study Guide in Chapter 12 Resource Book, pp. 85–86
- Practice Workbook, pp. 241–243
- @HomeTutor

Challenge

Additional challenge is available in the Chapter 12 Resource Book, p. 89.

1 PLAN AND PREPARE

Explore the Concept

- Students will compare surface areas and volumes of similar solids.
- This activity leads into the study of similar solids in Lesson 12.7.

Materials

Each student will need:

- Activity Support Master (*Chapter 12 Resource Book*, p. 92)

Recommended Time

Work activity: 10 min
Discuss results: 5 min

Grouping

Students should work individually.

2 TEACH

Tips for Success

Caution students to write the ratios in a consistent order from one solid to the other.

Alternative Strategy

If models of similar solids are available, have students measure their dimensions and extend the table in Step 1. Students can use these measurements to verify the results from the Activity.

Key Discovery

If the scale factor of two similar solids is $a:b$, then the ratio of the surface areas is $a^2:b^2$ and the ratio of the volumes is $a^3:b^3$.

3 ASSESS AND RETEACH

1. The heights of 2 similar solids are in the ratio 2:3. What is the ratio of their surface areas? What is the ratio of their volumes? **4:9; 8:27**

12.7 Investigate Similar Solids

MATERIALS • paper • pencil

Standards
11.0 Students determine how changes in dimensions affect the perimeter, **area, and volume of common geometric** figures and **solids.**

QUESTION **How are the surface areas and volumes of similar solids related?**

EXPLORE **Compare the surface areas and volumes of similar solids**

The solids shown below are *similar.*

Pair 1

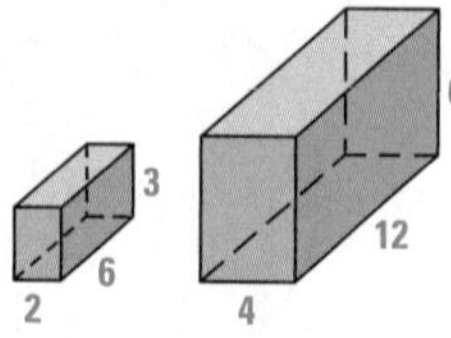

Pair 2

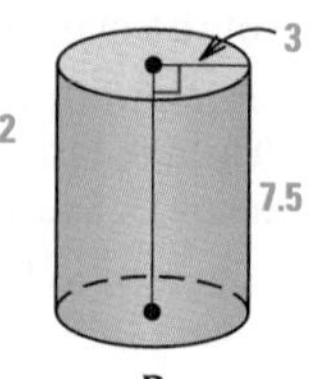

Pair 3

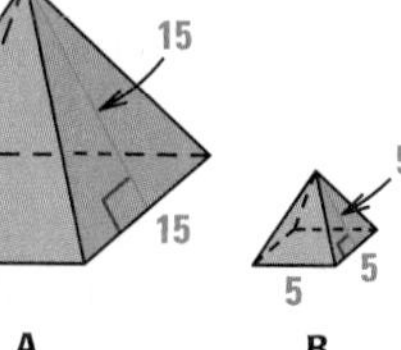

STEP 1 ***Make a table*** Copy and complete the table below. **Step 1–3. See margin.**

	Scale factor of Solid A to Solid B	Surface area of Solid A, S_A	Surface area of Solid B, S_B	$\frac{S_A}{S_B}$
Pair 1	$\frac{1}{2}$	?	?	?
Pair 2	?	?	63π	?
Pair 3	?	?	?	$\frac{9}{1}$

STEP 2 ***Insert columns*** Insert columns for V_A, V_B, and $\frac{V_A}{V_B}$. Use the dimensions of the solids to find V_A, the volume of Solid A, and V_B, the volume of Solid B. Then find the ratio of these volumes.

STEP 3 ***Compare ratios*** Compare the ratios $\frac{S_A}{S_B}$ and $\frac{V_A}{V_B}$ to the scale factor.

DRAW CONCLUSIONS **Use your observations to complete these exercises**

1. Make a conjecture about how the surface areas and volumes of similar solids are related to the scale factor. **The ratio of surface areas is the square of the scale factor, and the ratio of volumes is the cube of the scale factor.**
2. Use your conjecture to write a ratio of surface areas and volumes if the dimensions of two similar rectangular prisms are ℓ, w, h, and $k\ell$, kw, kh. $\frac{1}{k^2}, \frac{1}{k^3}$

Step 1: Pair 1: 72, 288, $\frac{1}{4}$; Pair 2: $\frac{2}{3}$, 28π, $\frac{4}{9}$; Pair 3: $\frac{3}{1}$, 675, 75

Step 2: Pair 1: 36, 288, $\frac{1}{8}$; Pair 2: 20π, 67.5π, $\frac{8}{27}$; Pair 3: 974.28, 36.08, $\frac{27}{1}$

Step 3: $\frac{S_A}{S_B}$ is the square of the scale factor, while $\frac{V_A}{V_B}$ is the cube of the scale factor.

12.7 Explore Similar Solids

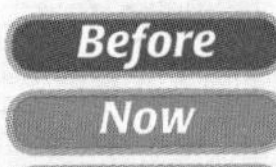

Before You used properties of similar polygons.

Now You will use properties of similar solids.

Why So you can determine a ratio of volumes, as in Ex. 26.

Key Vocabulary
similar solids

Standards

11.0 Students determine how changes in dimensions affect the perimeter, **area, and volume of common geometric** figures and **solids.**

8.0 Students know, derive, and **solve problems involving** the perimeter, circumference, area, **volume,** lateral area, **and surface area of common geometric figures.**

Two solids of the same type with equal ratios of corresponding linear measures, such as heights or radii, are called **similar solids**. The common ratio is called the *scale factor* of one solid to the other solid. Any two cubes are similar, as well as any two spheres.

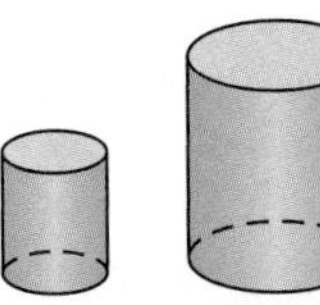

Similar cylinders

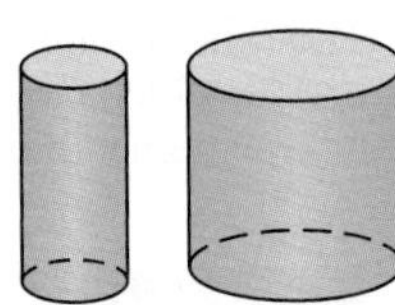

Nonsimilar cylinders

The green cylinders shown above are not similar. Their heights are equal, so they have a 1 : 1 ratio. The radii are different, however, so there is no common ratio.

EXAMPLE 1 Identify similar solids

Tell whether the given right rectangular prism is similar to the right rectangular prism shown at the right.

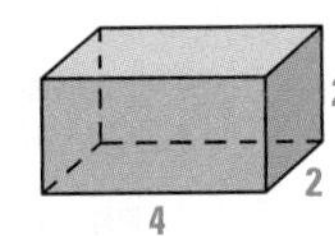

a.

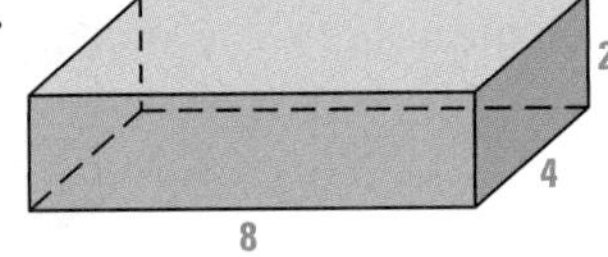

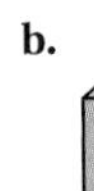

b.

Solution

a. Lengths $\frac{4}{8} = \frac{1}{2}$ Widths $\frac{2}{4} = \frac{1}{2}$ Heights $\frac{2}{2} = \frac{1}{1}$

▶ The prisms are not similar because the ratios of corresponding linear measures are not all equal.

b. Lengths $\frac{4}{6} = \frac{2}{3}$ Widths $\frac{2}{3}$ Heights $\frac{2}{3}$

▶ The prisms are similar because the ratios of corresponding linear measures are all equal. The scale factor is 2 : 3.

COMPARE RATIOS
To compare the ratios of corresponding side lengths, write the ratios as fractions in simplest form.

1 PLAN AND PREPARE

Warm-Up Exercises

Transparency Available

Find the surface area and volume of each solid.

1. Right rectangular prism, side lengths 8 in., 5 in., and 10 in. **340 in.^{2}; 400 in.^{3}**
2. Right cone, radius 3 m, height 4 m **75.40 m^2; 37.70 m^3**
3. Sphere, radius 7.3 ft **669.66 ft^2; 1629.51 ft^3**

Notetaking Guide

Transparency Available

Promotes interactive learning and notetaking skills, pp. 333–336.

Pacing

Basic: 1 day
Average: 1 day
Advanced: 1 day
Block: 0.5 block with 12.6
- See *Teaching Guide/Lesson Plan.*

2 FOCUS AND MOTIVATE

Essential Question

Big Idea 3, p. 791

If two solids are similar, what is the ratio of their surface areas and what is the ratio of their volumes? **Tell students they will learn how to answer this question by using the square and the cube of the scale factor.**

Resource Planning Guide

Chapter Resource Book
- Teaching Guide/Lesson Plan (pp. 90–91)
- Practice levels A, B, C (pp. 93–98)
- Study Guide (pp. 99–100)
- Catch-up for Absent Students (p. 101)
- Problem Solving Workshop (p. 102)
- Challenge (p. 103)

Workbooks
- Notetaking Guide (pp. 333–336)
- Practice Workbook (pp. 244–246)

Teaching Options
- **Power Presentations CD-ROM** provides dynamic electronic teaching resources for the classroom.
- **Activity Generator CD-ROM** provides editable activities for all ability levels.

Interactive Technology
- Easy Planner
- Power Presentations CD-ROM
- Activity Generator CD-ROM
- Animated Geometry
- Test Generator CD-ROM
- Online Quiz
- eWorkbook
- eEdition
- @HomeTutor

Resources for English Learners
- Quick Reference for English Learners
- Spanish Study Guide
- Multi-Language Visual Glossary
- Student Resources in Spanish

See also the *Geometry Toolkit* for more strategies for meeting individual needs.

Motivating the Lesson

Draw two cubes with sides 2 units and 3 units. Ask students if the cubes are similar solids (yes) and ask them for the ratio of the sides (2:3). Then ask students to calculate the area and volume of each cube and find the ratio of the areas and the ratio of the volumes. Tell students that this lesson explores the ratios of sides, areas, and volumes of similar solids.

3 TEACH

Extra Example 1

Tell whether right cylinder *P* is similar to each of right cylinders *A* and *B*.

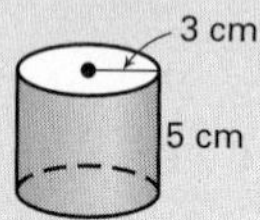

Cylinder *P*

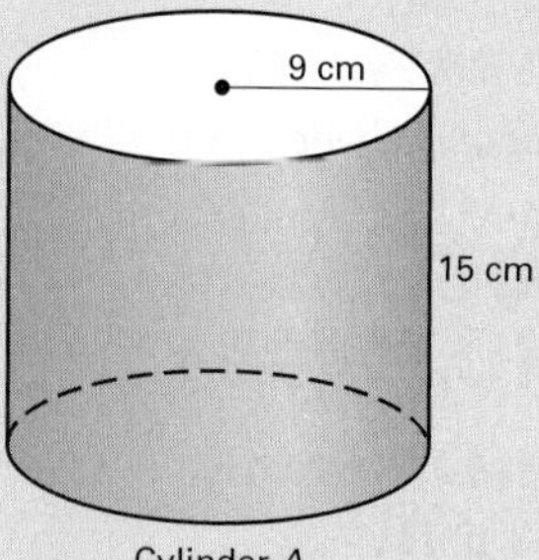

Cylinder *A*

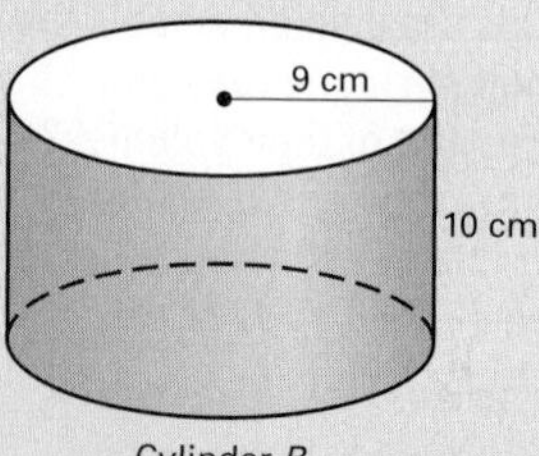

Cylinder *B*

yes for cylinder *A*; no for cylinder *B*

✓ GUIDED PRACTICE for Example 1

Tell whether the pair of right solids is similar. *Explain* your reasoning.

1.

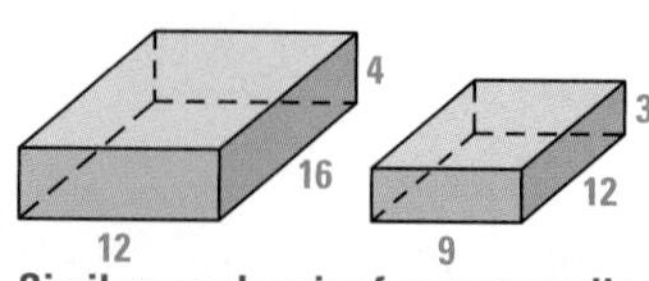

Similar; each pair of corresponding sides is in the ratio 4:3.

2.

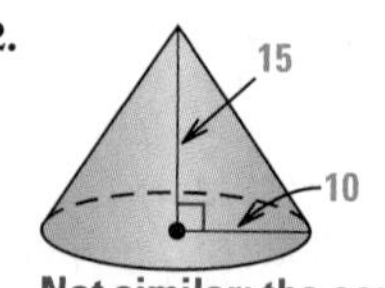

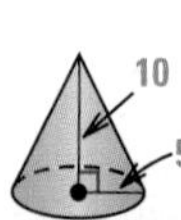

Not similar; the corresponding dimensions are not in the same ratio.

SIMILAR SOLIDS THEOREM The surface areas *S* and volumes *V* of the similar solids in Example 1, part (b), are as follows.

Prism	Dimensions	Surface area, $S = 2B + Ph$	Volume, $V = Bh$
Smaller	4 by 2 by 2	$S = 2(8) + 12(2) = 40$	$V = 8(2) = 16$
Larger	6 by 3 by 3	$S = 2(18) + 18(3) = 90$	$V = 18(3) = 54$

The ratio of side lengths is 2 : 3. Notice that the ratio of surface areas is 40 : 90, or 4 : 9, which can be written as $2^2 : 3^2$, and the ratio of volumes is 16 : 54, or 8 : 27, which can be written as $2^3 : 3^3$. This leads to the following theorem.

READ VOCABULARY

In Theorem 12.13, areas can refer to any pair of corresponding areas in the similar solids, such as lateral areas, base areas, and surface areas.

THEOREM *For Your Notebook*

THEOREM 12.13 Similar Solids Theorem

If two similar solids have a scale factor of $a : b$, then corresponding areas have a ratio of $a^2 : b^2$, and corresponding volumes have a ratio of $a^3 : b^3$.

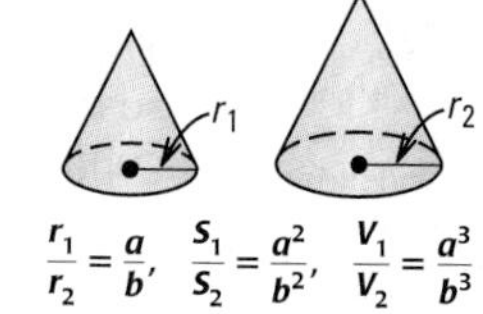

$\frac{r_1}{r_2} = \frac{a}{b}$, $\frac{S_1}{S_2} = \frac{a^2}{b^2}$, $\frac{V_1}{V_2} = \frac{a^3}{b^3}$

EXAMPLE 2 **Use the scale factor of similar solids**

PACKAGING The cans shown are similar with a scale factor of 87 : 100. Find the surface area and volume of the larger can.

$S = 51.84 \text{ in.}^2$
$V = 28.27 \text{ in.}^3$

Solution

Use Theorem 12.13 to write and solve two proportions.

$$\frac{\text{Surface area of I}}{\text{Surface area of II}} = \frac{a^2}{b^2} \qquad \frac{\text{Volume of I}}{\text{Volume of II}} = \frac{a^3}{b^3}$$

$$\frac{51.84}{\text{Surface area of II}} = \frac{87^2}{100^2} \qquad \frac{28.27}{\text{Volume of II}} = \frac{87^3}{100^3}$$

$$\text{Surface area of II} \approx 68.49 \qquad \text{Volume of II} \approx 42.93$$

▸ The surface area of the larger can is about 68.49 square inches, and the volume of the larger can is about 42.93 cubic inches.

EXAMPLE 3 Find the scale factor

The pyramids are similar. Pyramid P has a volume of 1000 cubic inches and Pyramid Q has a volume of 216 cubic inches. Find the scale factor of Pyramid P to Pyramid Q.

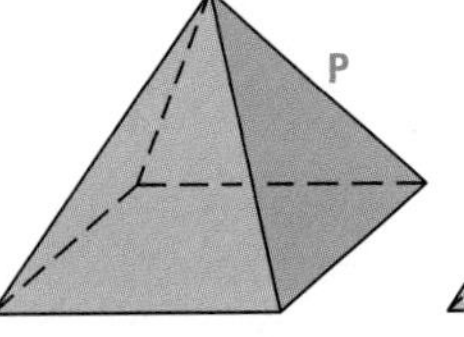

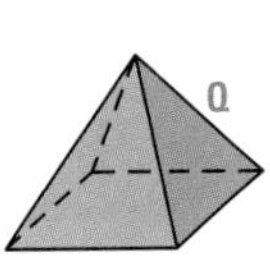

Solution

Use Theorem 12.13 to find the ratio of the two volumes.

$\frac{a^3}{b^3} = \frac{1000}{216}$ **Write ratio of volumes.**

$\frac{a}{b} = \frac{10}{6}$ **Find cube roots.**

$\frac{a}{b} = \frac{5}{3}$ **Simplify.**

▶ The scale factor of Pyramid P to Pyramid Q is 5 : 3.

EXAMPLE 4 Compare similar solids

CONSUMER ECONOMICS A store sells balls of yarn in two different sizes. The diameter of the larger ball is twice the diameter of the smaller ball. If the balls of yarn cost \$7.50 and \$1.50, respectively, which ball of yarn is the better buy?

Solution

STEP 1 **Compute** the ratio of volumes using the diameters.

$\frac{\text{Volume of large ball}}{\text{Volume of small ball}} = \frac{2^3}{1^3} = \frac{8}{1}$, or 8 : 1

STEP 2 **Find** the ratio of costs.

$\frac{\text{Price of large ball}}{\text{Price of small ball}} = \frac{\$7.50}{\$1.50} = \frac{5}{1}$, or 5 : 1

STEP 3 **Compare** the ratios in Steps 1 and 2.

If the ratios were the same, neither ball would be a better buy. Comparing the smaller ball to the larger one, the price increase is less than the volume increase. So, you get more yarn for your dollar if you buy the larger ball of yarn.

▶ The larger ball of yarn is the better buy.

GUIDED PRACTICE for Examples 2, 3, and 4

3. Cube C has a surface area of 54 square units and Cube D has a surface area of 150 square units. Find the scale factor of C to D. Find the edge length of C, and use the scale factor to find the volume of D. **3:5; 3 units, 125 units^3**
4. **WHAT IF?** In Example 4, calculate a new price for the larger ball of yarn so that neither ball would be a better buy than the other. **\$12.00**

Differentiated Instruction

Visual Learners When discussing **Guided Practice Exercise 3**, have students draw a diagram of Cube C and a diagram of Cube D. Have them label the edge lengths of Cube C. For an extra challenge, have them use the scale factor of C to D to find the edge length of D.

See also the *Geometry Toolkit* for more strategies.

Extra Example 2

The beach balls shown are similar with a scale factor of 7 : 6. Find the surface area and volume of the smaller ball.

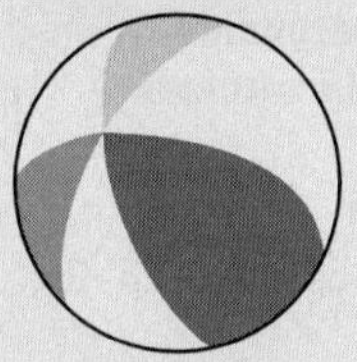
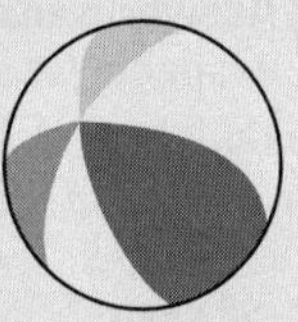

$S = 249.55$ in.^{2}
$V = 371.61$ in.^{3}

$S = 183.34$ in.^{2}; $V = 234.02$ in.^{3}

Extra Example 3

The cones are similar. Cone A has a volume of 125 m^3 and cone B has a volume of 512 m^3. Find the scale factor of cone A to cone B. **5 : 8**

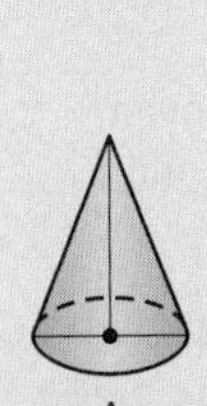

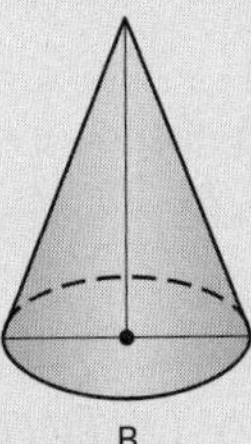

Extra Example 4

A garden store sells gravel in boxes that are cubes. The edge of the smaller cube, which sells for \$40, is three-fourths of the edge of the larger cube, which sells for \$99.50. Which box is the better buy? **the smaller box**

Closing the Lesson

Have students summarize the major points of the lesson and answer the Essential Question: If two solids are similar, what is the ratio of their surface areas and what is the ratio of their volumes?

- **Similar solids are of the same type with equal ratios of corresponding linear measures.**
- **If the scale factor of two similar solids is $a : b$, then the ratio of the areas is $a^2 : b^2$ and the ratio of the volumes is $a^3 : b^3$.**

For two similar solids with a scale factor $a : b$, the ratio of the areas of the solids is $a^2 : b^2$ and the ratio of their volumes is $a^3 : b^3$.

4 PRACTICE AND APPLY

Assignment Guide

Answer Transparencies available for all exercises

Basic:
Day 1: pp. 850–854
Exs. 1–4, 7–9, 11–13, 16–20, 25–30, 36–48 even

Average:
Day 1: pp. 850–854
Exs. 1, 2, 4, 5–9 odd, 10–16 even, 17, 18, 20, 21, 26–32, 37–47 odd

Advanced:
Day 1: pp. 850–854
Exs. 1, 2, 5–7, 10, 14–18, 21–24*, 27–35*, 38, 42, 44, 48

Block:
pp. 850–854
Exs. 1, 2, 4, 5–9 odd, 10–16 even, 17, 18, 20, 21, 26–32, 37–47 odd (with 12.6)

Differentiated Instruction

See *Geometry Best Practices Toolkit* for suggestions on addressing the needs of a diverse classroom.

Homework Check

For a quick check of student understanding of key concepts, go over the following exercises:

Basic: 4, 8, 12, 25, 28
Average: 5, 10, 14, 26, 29
Advanced: 6, 10, 18, 29, 30

Extra Practice

- Student Edition, p. 919
- Chapter 12 Resource Book: Practice levels A, B, C, pp. 93–98

Practice Worksheet

An easily-readable reduced practice page (with answers) for this lesson can be found on p. 790F.

12.7 EXERCISES

HOMEWORK KEY
○ = **WORKED-OUT SOLUTIONS** on p. WS18 for Exs. 3, 9, and 27
★ = **STANDARDIZED TEST PRACTICE** Exs. 2, 7, 16, 28, 31, and 33
◆ = **MULTIPLE REPRESENTATIONS** Ex. 34

SKILL PRACTICE

A

1. **VOCABULARY** What does it mean for two solids to be similar?
They are the same type of solid and corresponding linear measures have the same ratio.

2. ★ **WRITING** How are the volumes of similar solids related?
If the corresponding linear measures have ratio $a:b$, then the volumes are in the ratio $a^3:b^3$.

EXAMPLE 1 on p. 847 for Exs. 3–7

IDENTIFYING SIMILAR SOLIDS **Tell whether the pair of right solids is similar. *Explain* your reasoning.**

3. 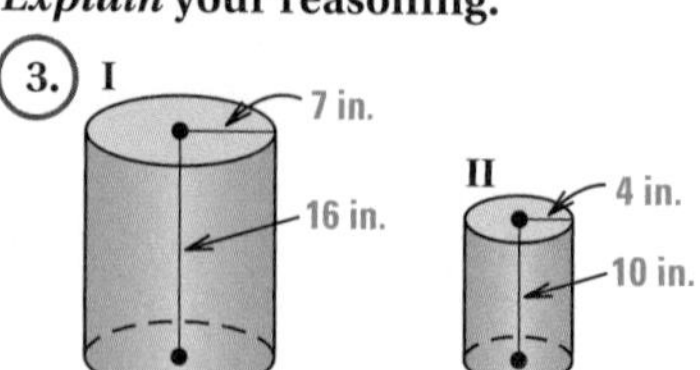

Not similar; the corresponding dimensions are not in the same ratio.

4. 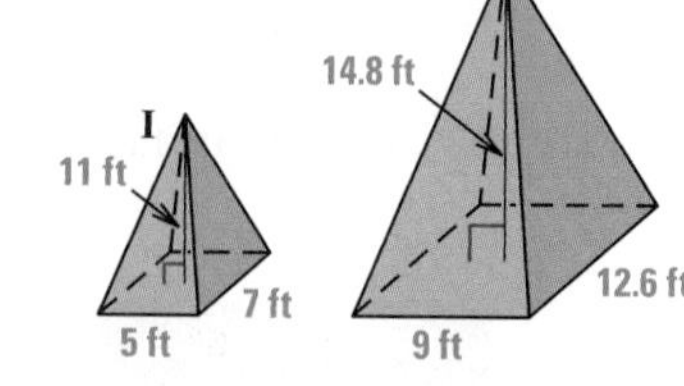

4. Not similar; the corresponding dimensions are not in the same ratio.

5. 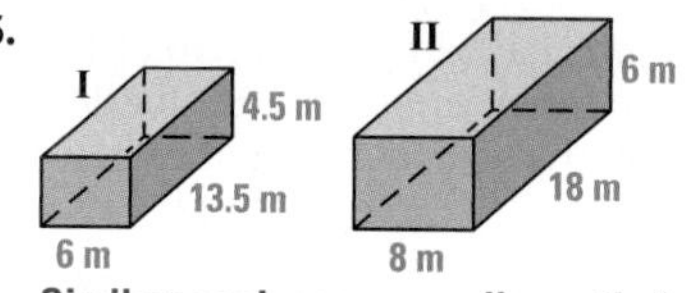

Similar; each corresponding ratio is 3:4.

6. 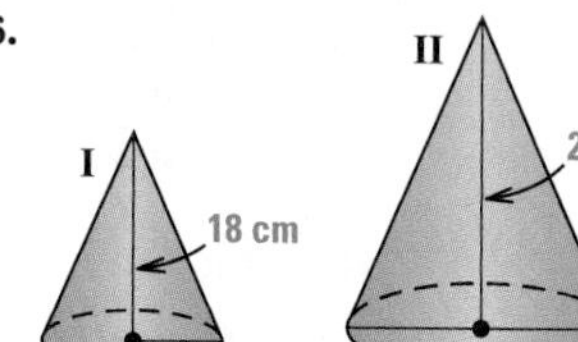

6. Similar; each corresponding ratio is 2:3.

7. ★ **MULTIPLE CHOICE** Which set of dimensions corresponds to a triangular prism that is similar to the prism shown? **D**
Ⓐ 2 feet by 1 foot by 5 feet Ⓑ 4 feet by 2 feet by 8 feet
Ⓒ 9 feet by 6 feet by 20 feet Ⓓ 15 feet by 10 feet by 25 feet

10 ft, 6 ft, 4 ft

EXAMPLE 2 on p. 848 for Exs. 8–11

USING SCALE FACTOR **Solid A (shown) is similar to Solid B (not shown) with the given scale factor of A to B. Find the surface area and volume of Solid B.**

8. Scale factor of 1 : 2
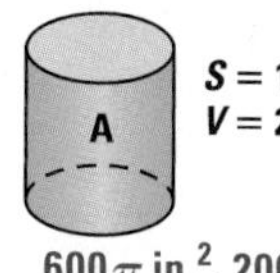

$S = 150\pi$ in.^{2}
$V = 250\pi$ in.^{3}
600π in.^{2}, 2000π in.^{3}

9. Scale factor of 3 : 1
A
$S = 1500$ m^2
$V = 3434.6$ m^3
about 166.67 m^2, about 127.21 m^3

10. Scale factor of 5 : 2
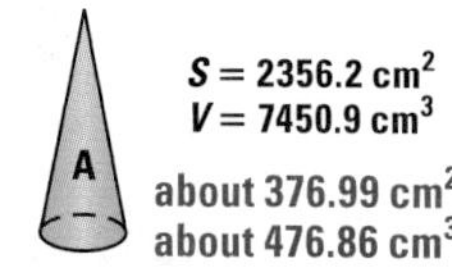

about 376.99 cm^2, about 476.86 cm^3

11. **ERROR ANALYSIS** The scale factor of two similar solids is 1 : 4. The volume of the smaller Solid A is 500π. *Describe* and correct the error in writing an equation to find the volume of the larger Solid B.
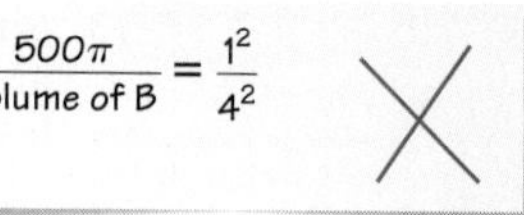

The volumes are related by the third power; $\frac{500\pi}{\text{Volume of B}} = \frac{1^3}{4^3}$.

EXAMPLE 3
on p. 849
for Exs. 12–18

FINDING SCALE FACTOR In Exercises 12–15, Solid I is similar to Solid II. Find the scale factor of Solid I to Solid II.

12. 2:5 **13.** 1:3

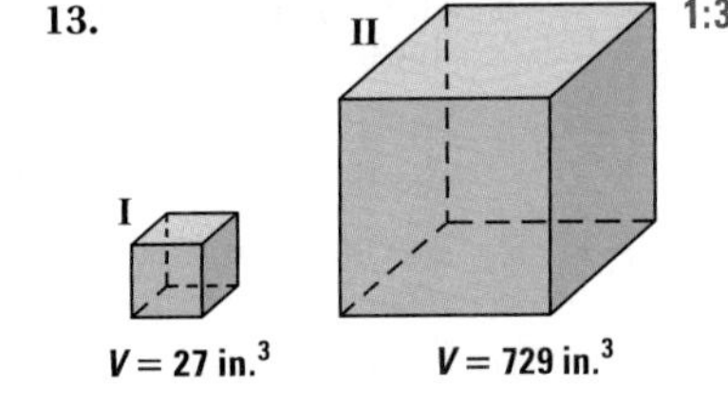

14. 3:2 **15.** 4:3

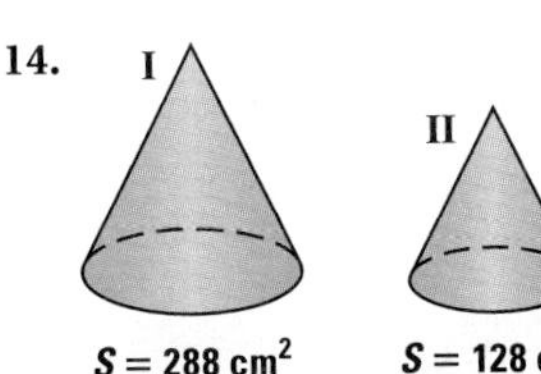
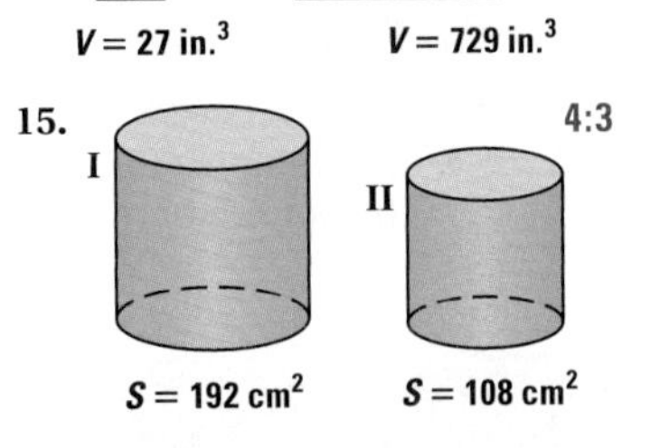

16. ★ **MULTIPLE CHOICE** The volumes of two similar cones are 8π and 27π. What is the ratio of the lateral areas of the cones? **C**

Ⓐ $\frac{8}{27}$ Ⓑ $\frac{1}{3}$ Ⓒ $\frac{4}{9}$ Ⓓ $\frac{2}{3}$

17. **FINDING A RATIO** Two spheres have volumes of 2π cubic feet and 16π cubic feet. What is the ratio of the surface area of the smaller sphere to the surface area of the larger sphere? **1:4**

18. **FINDING SURFACE AREA** Two similar cylinders have a scale factor of 2 : 3. The smaller cylinder has a surface area of 78π square meters. Find the surface area of the larger cylinder. **175.5π m^2**

B **COMPOSITE SOLIDS In Exercises 19–22, Solid I is similar to Solid II. Find the surface area and volume of Solid II.**

19. **20.**

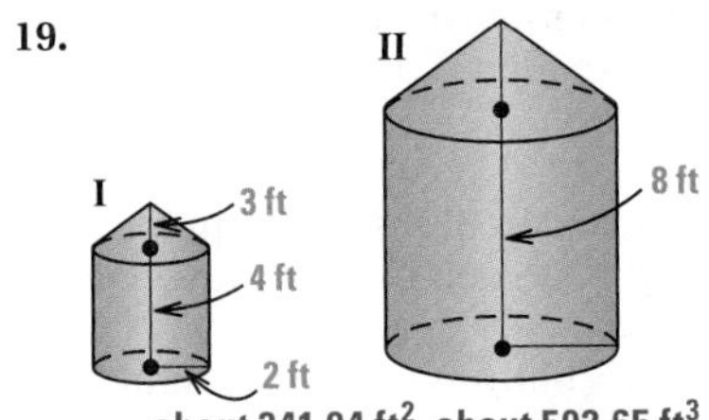

about 341.94 ft^2, about 502.65 ft^3

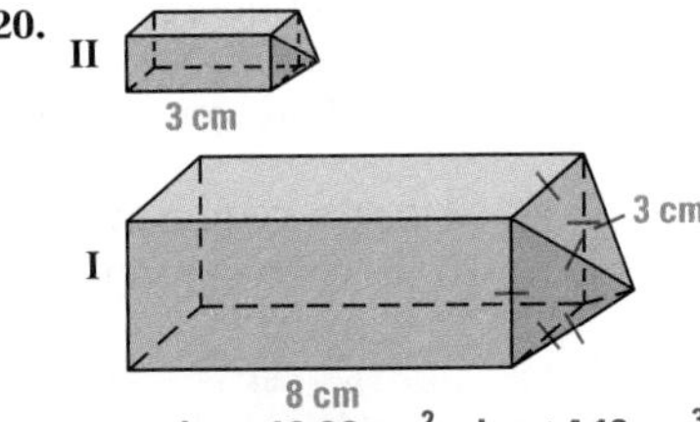

about 16.96 cm^2, about 4.13 cm^3

21. **22.**

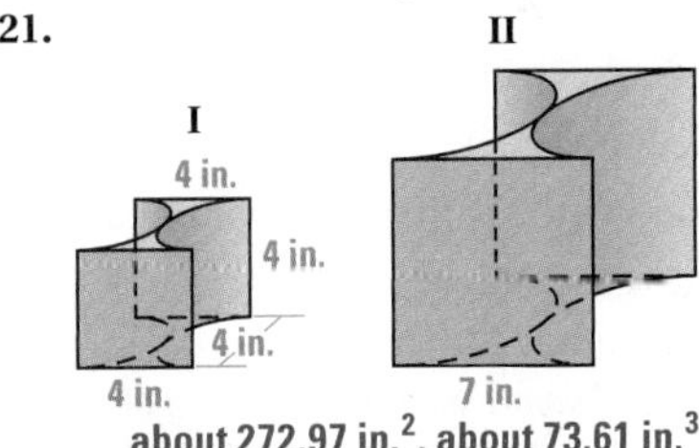

about 272.97 in.^{2}, about 73.61 in.^{3}

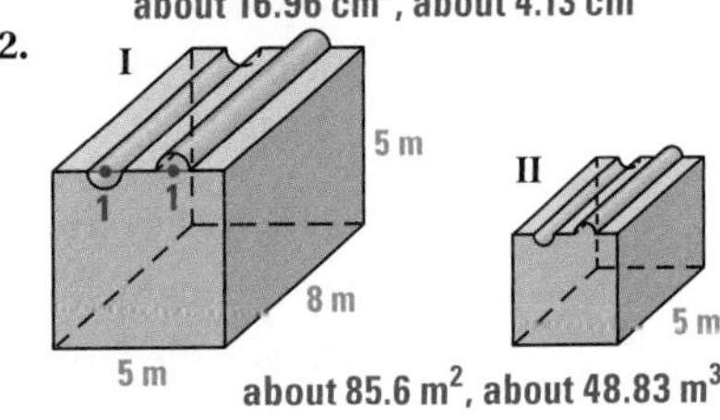

about 85.6 m^2, about 48.83 m^3

C **23.** **ALGEBRA** Two similar cylinders have surface areas of 54π square feet and 384π square feet. The height of each cylinder is equal to its diameter. Find the radius and height of both cylinders. **$r = 3$ ft, $h = 6$ ft; $r = 8$ ft, $h = 16$ ft**

Teaching Strategy

Exercises 3–6 Point out that the actual volumes and surface areas are not needed in order to determine if two solids are similar. The only necessary relationship is that all pairs of corresponding linear dimensions are in the same proportion.

Mathematical Reasoning

Exercises 19–22 Students will have to set up a proportion between the actual volume of the left figure and the cube of the scale factor between the figures to find the new volume. Also, they will have to set up a proportion between the actual surface area of the left figure and the square of the scale factor to find the new surface area.

Mathematical Reasoning

Exercise 24 Students should understand that the ratio of the slant heights will be the scale factor 10 : 8 or 5 : 4, while the areas will have the ratio 25 : 16 and the volumes will have the ratio 125 : 64.

An **Animated Geometry** activity is available on-line for **Exercise 29.** This activity is also available on the **Power Presentations CD-ROM**.

24. CHALLENGE A plane parallel to the base of a cone divides the cone into two pieces with the dimensions shown. Find each ratio described.

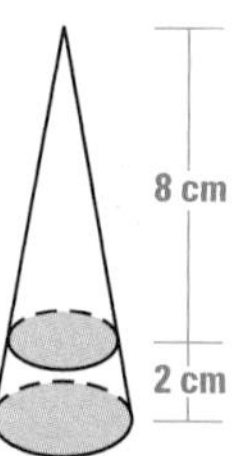

a. The area of the top shaded circle to the area of the bottom shaded circle **16 : 25**

b. The slant height of the top part of the cone to the slant height of the whole cone **4 : 5**

c. The lateral area of the top part of the cone to the lateral area of the whole cone **16 : 25**

d. The volume of the top part of the cone to the volume of the whole cone **64 : 125**

e. The volume of the top part of the cone to the volume of the bottom part **64 : 61**

PROBLEM SOLVING

EXAMPLE 4 on p. 849 for Exs. 25–27

A 25. **COFFEE MUGS** The heights of two similar coffee mugs are 3.5 inches and 4 inches. The larger mug holds 12 fluid ounces. What is the capacity of the smaller mug? **about 8.04 fl oz**

 for problem solving help at classzone.com

26. **ARCHITECTURE** You have a pair of binoculars that is similar in shape to the structure on page 847. Your binoculars are 6 inches high, and the height of the structure is 45 feet. Find the ratio of the volume of your binoculars to the volume of the structure. **1 : 729,000**

@HomeTutor for problem solving help at classzone.com

27. **PARTY PLANNING** Two similar punch bowls have a scale factor of 3 : 4. The amount of lemonade to be added is proportional to the volume. How much lemonade does the smaller bowl require if the larger bowl requires 64 fluid ounces? **27 fl oz**

28. ★ **OPEN-ENDED MATH** Using the scale factor 2 : 5, sketch a pair of solids in the correct proportions. Label the dimensions of the solids. **Check students' work.**

B 29. MULTI-STEP PROBLEM Two oranges are both spheres with diameters 3.2 inches and 4 inches. The skin on both oranges has an average thickness of $\frac{1}{8}$ inch.

a. Find the volume of each unpeeled orange.

b. *Compare* the ratio of the diameters to the ratio of the volumes.

c. Find the diameter of each orange after being peeled.

d. *Compare* the ratio of surface areas of the peeled oranges to the ratio of the volumes of the peeled oranges. ***Sample answer:*** **The ratio of surface area multiplied by the ratio of the corresponding diameters equals the ratio of the volumes.**

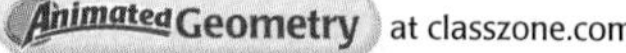

29a. large orange: about 33.51 in.^{3}, small orange: about 17.16 in.^{3}

29b. The ratio of the volumes is the cube of the ratio of diameters.

29c. large orange: 3.75 in., small orange: 2.95 in.

○ = WORKED-OUT SOLUTIONS on p. WS1 ★ = STANDARDIZED TEST PRACTICE

30b. $\frac{2}{3}\pi a^3$; $\frac{2}{3}\pi b^3$

33. About 11.5 kg; the ratio of the small snowball to the medium snowball is 5:7, so the ratio of their volumes is $5^3:7^3$. Solve $\frac{5^3}{7^3} = \frac{1.2}{x}$ to find the weight of the middle ball. Similarly, find the weight of the large ball.

34a. $P = \frac{k}{s^3}$, where k is the constant of variation and s is the side length.

30. **ALGEBRA** Use the two similar cones shown.

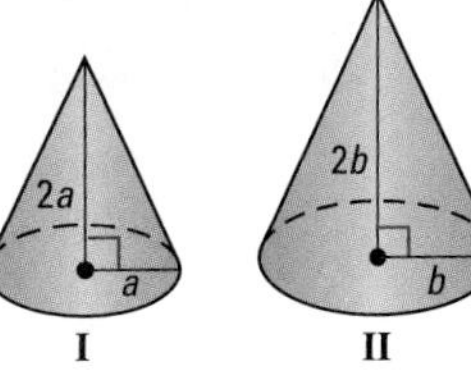

a. What is the scale factor of Cone I to Cone II? What should the ratio of the volume of Cone I to the volume of Cone II be? **a : b; $a^3 : b^3$**

b. Write an expression for the volume of each solid.

c. Write and simplify an expression for the ratio of the volume of Cone I to the volume of Cone II. Does your answer agree with your answer to part (a)? *Explain.* $\frac{\frac{2}{3}\pi a^3}{\frac{2}{3}\pi b^3} = \frac{a^3}{b^3}$**; yes; the ratios are the same.**

31. ★ **EXTENDED RESPONSE** The scale factor of the model car at the right to the actual car is 1 : 18.

a. The model has length 8 inches. What is the length of the actual car? **144 in.**

b. Each tire of the model has a surface area of 12.1 square inches. What is the surface area of each tire of the actual car? **3920.4 in.^{2}**

c. The actual car's engine has volume 8748 cubic inches. Find the volume of the model car's engine. **1.5 in.^{3}**

32. **USING VOLUMES** Two similar cylinders have volumes 16π and 432π. The larger cylinder has lateral area 72π. Find the lateral area of the smaller cylinder. **8π**

C 33. ★ **SHORT RESPONSE** A snow figure is made using three balls of snow with diameters 25 centimeters, 35 centimeters, and 45 centimeters. The smallest weighs about 1.2 kilograms. Find the total weight of the snow used to make the snow figure. *Explain* your reasoning.

34. **MULTIPLE REPRESENTATIONS** A gas is enclosed in a cubical container with side length s in centimeters. Its temperature remains constant while the side length varies. By the *Ideal Gas Law*, the pressure P in atmospheres (atm) of the gas varies inversely with its volume.

a. **Writing an Equation** Write an equation relating P and s. You will need to introduce a constant of variation k.

b. **Making a Table** Copy and complete the table below for various side lengths. Express the pressure P in terms of the constant k.

Side length s (cm)	$\frac{1}{4}$	$\frac{1}{2}$	1	2	4
Pressure P (atm)	? **64k**	8k	k	? **$\frac{k}{8}$**	? **$\frac{k}{64}$**

c. **Drawing a Graph** For this particular gas, $k = 1$. Use your table to sketch a graph of P versus s. Place P on the vertical axis and s on the horizontal axis. Does the graph show a linear relationship? *Explain.* **See margin for art; no; the points lie on a curve, not a straight line.**

35. **CHALLENGE** A plane parallel to the base of a pyramid separates the pyramid into two pieces with equal volumes. The height of the pyramid is 12 feet. Find the height of the top piece. **about 9.52 ft**

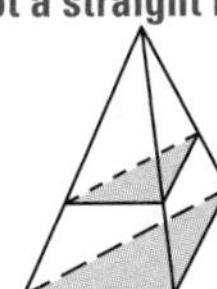

34c.

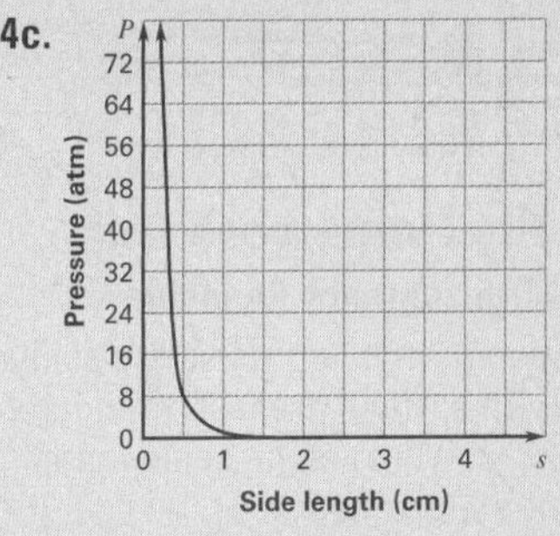

5 ASSESS AND RETEACH

Daily Homework Quiz

Transparency Available

1. Two triangular prisms are similar, with surface areas 9 ft^2 and 25 ft^2. What is the scale factor of the prisms? **3:5**
2. Two spheres have volumes 125π m^3 and 216π m^3. What is the scale factor of the spheres? What is the ratio of the surface areas? **5:6; 25:36**
3. The volumes of two similar square pyramids are 8 ft^3 and 27 ft^3. What is the ratio of the surface area of the smaller pyramid to the larger? **4:9**
4. The two solids are similar. Find the surface area and volume of Solid II.

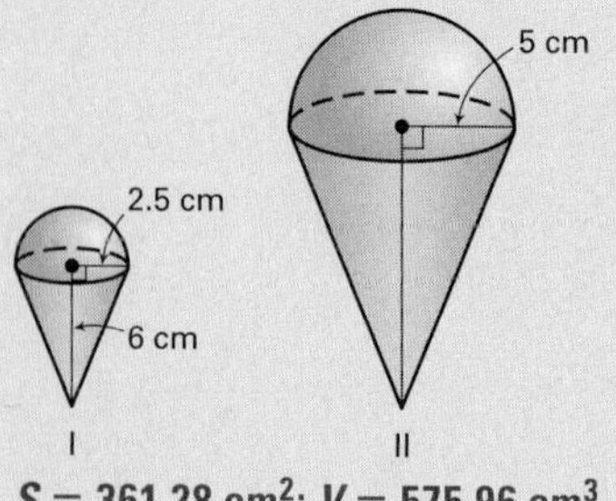

$S = 361.28$ cm^2; $V = 575.96$ cm^3

Available at **classzone.com**

Diagnosis/Remediation

- Practice A, B, C in Chapter 12 Resource Book, pp. 93–98
- Study Guide in Chapter 12 Resource Book, pp. 99–100
- Practice Workbook, pp. 244–246
- @HomeTutor

Challenge

Additional challenge is available in the Chapter 12 Resource Book, p. 103.

Quiz

An easily-readable reduced copy of the quiz (with answers) on Lessons 12.6–12.7 from the Assessment Book can be found on p. 790G.

MIXED REVIEW

Determine whether the triangles are similar. If they are, write a similarity statement. *(p. 381)*

36. 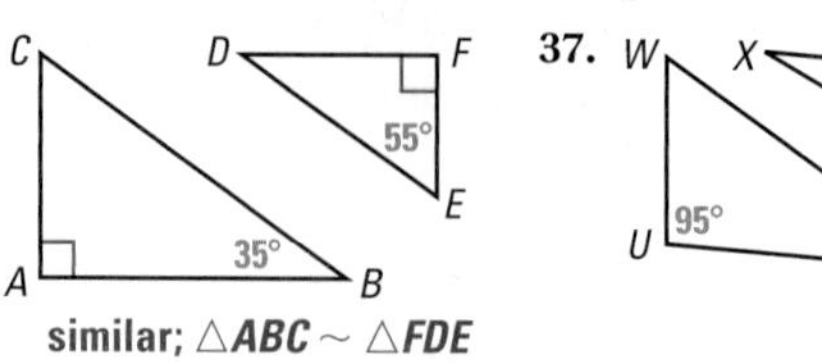

similar; $\triangle ABC \sim \triangle FDE$

37. not similar

38. 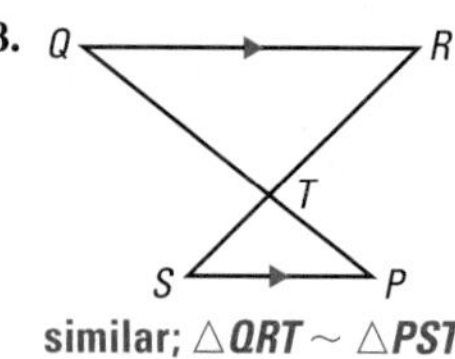

similar; $\triangle QRT \sim \triangle PST$

The sum of the measures of the interior angles of a convex polygon is given. Classify the polygon by the number of sides. *(p. 507)*

39. 900° **heptagon**
40. 180° **triangle**
41. 540° **pentagon**
42. 1080° **octagon**

Write a standard equation of the circle with the given center and radius. *(p. 699)*

43. Center (2, 5), radius 4 **$(x-2)^2 + (y-5)^2 = 16$**
44. Center (−3, 2), radius 6 **$(x+3)^2 + (y-2)^2 = 36$**

Sketch the described solid and find its surface area. Round your answer to two decimal places, if necessary. *(p. 803)* **45–48. See margin for art.**

45. Right rectangular prism with length 8 feet, width 6 feet, and height 3 feet **180 ft^2**
46. Right regular pentagonal prism with all edges measuring 12 millimeters **1215.50 mm^2**
47. Right cylinder with radius 4 inches and height 4 inches **201.06 in.^{2}**
48. Right cylinder with diameter 9 centimeters and height 7 centimeters **325.15 cm^2**

QUIZ for Lessons 12.6–12.7

Find the surface area and volume of the sphere. Round your answers to two decimal places. *(p. 838)*

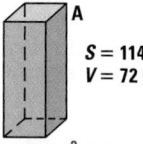

1. 7 cm — **615.75 cm^2, 1436.76 cm^3**
2. 11.5 m — **1661.90 m^2, 6370.63 m^3**
3. 21.4 ft — **1438.72 ft^2, 5131.45 ft^3**

Solid A (shown) is similar to Solid B (not shown) with the given scale factor of A to B. Find the surface area S and volume V of Solid B. *(p. 847)*

4. Scale factor of 1:3 — A: $S = 114$ in.^{2}, $V = 72$ in.^{3} — **1026 in.^{2}, 1944 in.^{3}**
5. Scale factor of 2:3 — A: $S = 170\pi$ m^2, $V = 300\pi$ m^3 — **382.5π m^2, 1012.5π m^3**
6. Scale factor of 5:4 — A: $S = 383$ cm^2, $V = 440$ cm^3 — **245.12 cm^2, 225.28 cm^3**
7. Two similar cones have volumes 729π cubic feet and 343π cubic feet. What is the scale factor of the larger cone to the smaller cone? *(p. 847)* **9:7**

EXTRA PRACTICE for Lesson 12.7, p. 919

45. 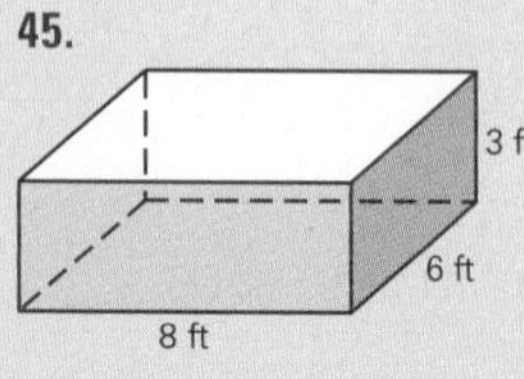

46. 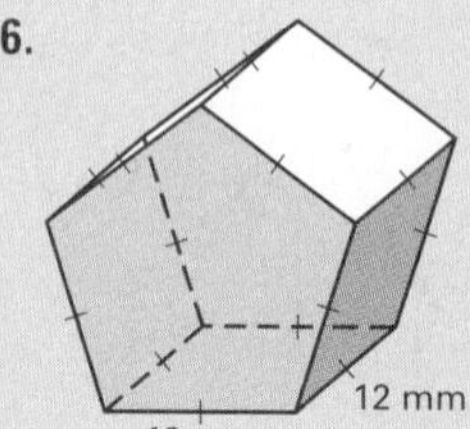

47. 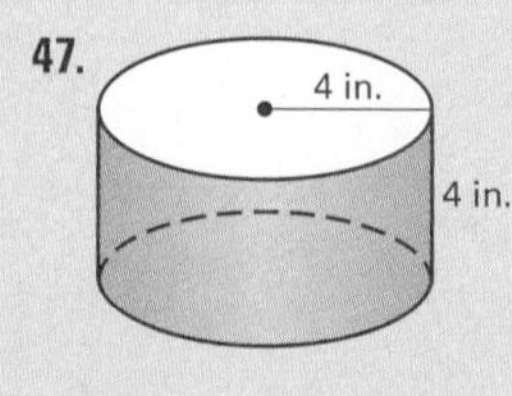

48. 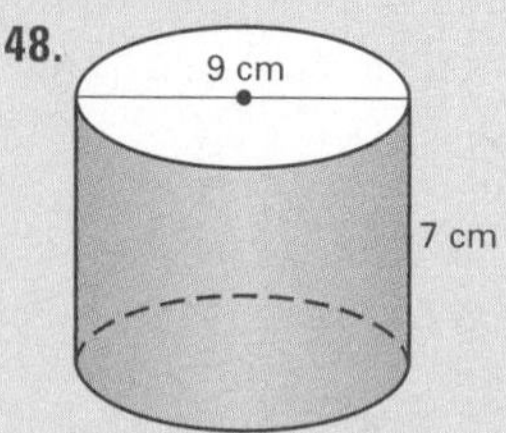

MIXED REVIEW *of Problem Solving*

Lessons 12.4–12.7

1. **MULTI-STEP PROBLEM** You have a container in the shape of a right rectangular prism with inside dimensions of length 24 inches, width 16 inches, and height 20 inches.
   a. Find the volume of the inside of the container. **7680 in.^{3}**
   b. You are going to fill the container with boxes of cookies that are congruent right rectangular prisms. Each box has length 8 inches, width 2 inches, and height 3 inches. Find the volume of one box of cookies. **48 in.^{3}**
   c. How many boxes of cookies will fit inside the cardboard container? **160 boxes of cookies**

2. **SHORT RESPONSE** You have a cup in the shape of a cylinder with inside dimensions of diameter 2.5 inches and height 7 inches.
   a. Find the volume of the inside of the cup. **about 34.36 in.^{3}**
   b. You have an 18 ounce bottle of orange juice that you want to pour into the cup. Will all of the juice fit? *Explain* your reasoning. (1 in.$^3 \approx$ 0.554 fluid ounces)

Yes; 34.36 • 0.554 ounces $\approx$ 19 ounces, so 18 ounces will fit.

3. **EXTENDED RESPONSE** You have a funnel with the dimensions shown.

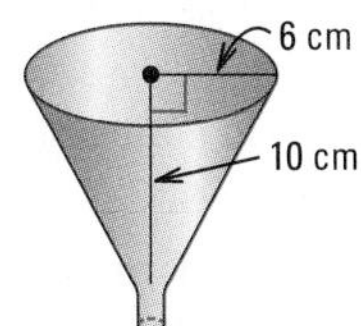

   a. Find the approximate volume of the funnel. **about 377 cm^3**
   b. You are going to use the funnel to put oil in a car. Oil flows out of the funnel at a rate of 45 milliliters per second. How long will it take to empty the funnel when it is full of oil? (1 mL = 1 cm^3) **about 8.38 sec**
   c. How long would it take to empty a funnel with radius 10 cm and height 6 cm? **about 14 sec**
   d. *Explain* why you can claim that the time calculated in part (c) is greater than the time calculated in part (b) without doing any calculations. **The volume in part (c) will be greater than the volume in part (a) because the unit that is squared (radius) is larger. Therefore the time will be greater, since the rate is the same for both funnels.**

4. **EXTENDED RESPONSE** An official men's basketball has circumference 29.5 inches. An official women's basketball has circumference 28.5 inches.
   a. Find the surface area and volume of the men's basketball. **about 277 in.^{2}, about 433.53 in.^{3}**
   b. Find the surface area and volume of the women's basketball using the formulas for surface area and volume of a sphere. **about 258.55 in.^{2}, about 390.92 in.^{3}**
   c. Use your answers in part (a) and the Similar Solids Theorem to find the surface area and volume of the women's basketball. Do your results match your answers in part (b)? **about 258.54 in.^{2}, about 390.92 in.^{3}; yes**

5. **GRIDDED ANSWER** To accurately measure the radius of a spherical rock, you place the rock into a cylindrical glass containing water. When you do so, the water level rises $\frac{9}{64}$ inch. The radius of the glass is 2 inches. What is the radius of the rock? **$\frac{3}{4}$ in.**

6. **SHORT RESPONSE** Sketch a rectangular prism and label its dimensions. Change the dimensions of the prism so that its surface area increases and its volume decreases. **See margin.**

7. **SHORT RESPONSE** A hemisphere and a right cone have the same radius and the height of the cone is equal to the radius. *Compare* the volumes of the solids. **The volume of the hemisphere is twice the volume of the cone.**

8. **SHORT RESPONSE** *Explain* why the height of a right cone is always less than its slant height. Include a diagram in your answer. **See margin.**

6. ***Sample answer:***

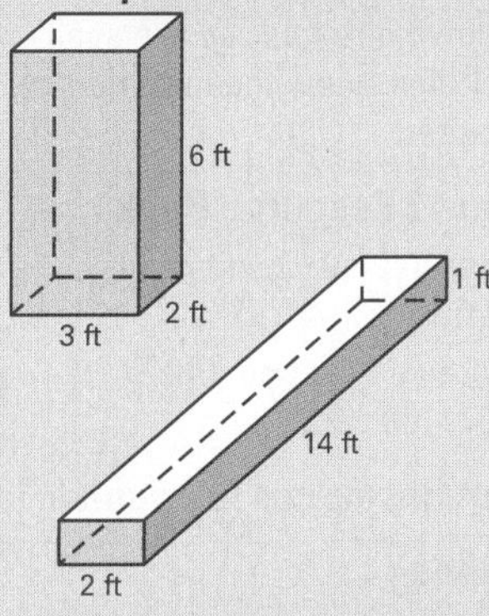

length: 3 ft, width: 2 ft, height: 6 ft; length: 2 ft, width: 14 ft, height: 1 ft

8. The height of a cone and the radius of a cone form two legs of a right triangle while the slant height forms the hypotenuse. Each leg of a right triangle is always less than the hypotenuse.

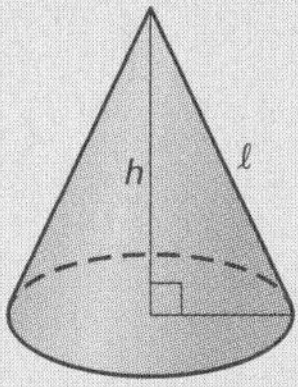

Additional Resources

The following resources are available to help review the materials in this chapter.

Chapter 12 Resource Book

- Chapter Review Games and Activities, p. 104
- Cumulative Practice, Chs. 1–12, pp. 107–108

Student Resources in Spanish

eWorkbook

@HomeTutor

Vocabulary Practice

Vocabulary practice is available at **classzone.com**

12 CHAPTER SUMMARY

BIG IDEAS *For Your Notebook*

Big Idea 1

Exploring Solids and Their Properties

Euler's Theorem is useful when finding the number of faces, edges, or vertices on a polyhedron, especially when one of those quantities is difficult to count by hand.

For example, suppose you want to find the number of edges on a regular icosahedron, which has 20 faces. You count 12 vertices on the solid. To calculate the number of edges, use Euler's Theorem:

$F + V = E + 2$	**Write Euler's Theorem.**
$20 + 12 = E + 2$	**Substitute known values.**
$30 = E$	**Solve for *E*.**

Big Idea 2

Solving Problems Using Surface Area and Volume

Figure	Surface Area	Volume
Right prism	$S = 2B + Ph$	$V = Bh$
Right cylinder	$S = 2B + Ch$	$V = Bh$
Regular pyramid	$S = B + \frac{1}{2}P\ell$	$V = \frac{1}{3}Bh$
Right cone	$S = B + \frac{1}{2}C\ell$	$V = \frac{1}{3}Bh$
Sphere	$S = 4\pi r^2$	$V = \frac{4}{3}\pi r^3$

The volume formulas for prisms, cylinders, pyramids, and cones can be used for oblique solids.

While many of the above formulas can be written in terms of more detailed variables, it is more important to remember the more general formulas for a greater understanding of why they are true.

Big Idea 3

Connecting Similarity to Solids

The similarity concepts learned in Chapter 6 can be extended to 3-dimensional figures as well.

Suppose you have a right cylindrical can whose surface area and volume are known. You are then given a new can whose linear dimensions are k times the dimensions of the original can. If the surface area of the original can is S and the volume of the original can is V, then the surface area and volume of the new can can be expressed as k^2S and k^3V, respectively.

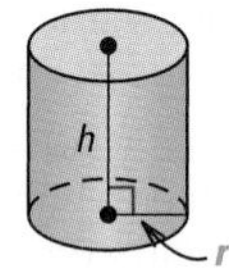

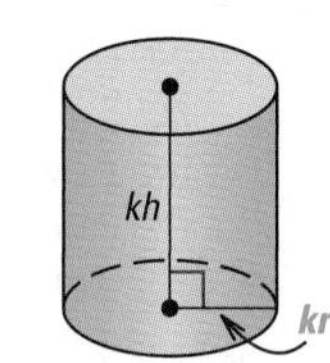

12 CHAPTER REVIEW

@HomeTutor
classzone.com
• Multi-Language Glossary
• Vocabulary practice

REVIEW KEY VOCABULARY

For a list of postulates and theorems, see pp. 926–931.

- polyhedron, *p. 794*
  face, edge, vertex, base
- regular polyhedron, *p. 796*
- convex polyhedron, *p. 796*
- Platonic solids, *p. 796*
- tetrahedron, *p. 796*
- cube, *p. 796*
- octahedron, *p. 796*
- dodecahedron, *p. 796*
- icosahedron, *p. 796*
- cross section, *p. 797*
- prism, *p. 803*
  lateral faces, lateral edges
- surface area, *p. 803*
- lateral area, *p. 803*
- net, *p. 803*
- right prism, *p. 804*
- oblique prism, *p. 804*
- cylinder, *p. 805*
- right cylinder, *p. 805*
- pyramid, *p. 810*
- vertex of a pyramid, *p. 810*
- regular pyramid, *p. 810*
- slant height, *p. 810*
- cone, *p. 812*
- vertex of a cone, *p. 812*
- right cone, *p. 812*
- lateral surface, *p. 812*
- volume, *p. 819*
- sphere, *p. 838*
  center, radius, chord, diameter
- great circle, *p. 839*
- hemisphere, *p. 839*
- similar solids, *p. 847*

VOCABULARY EXERCISES

1. Copy and complete: A __?__ is the set of all points in space equidistant from a given point. **sphere**

2. **WRITING** Sketch a right rectangular prism and an oblique rectangular prism. *Compare* the prisms. **See margin for art. *Sample answer:* The prisms have the same dimensions and the same volume.**

REVIEW EXAMPLES AND EXERCISES

Use the review examples and exercises below to check your understanding of the concepts you have learned in each lesson of Chapter 12.

12.1 Explore Solids *pp. 794–801*

EXAMPLE

A polyhedron has 16 vertices and 24 edges. How many faces does the polyhedron have?

$F + V = E + 2$ **Euler's Theorem**

$F + 16 = 24 + 2$ **Substitute known values.**

$F = 10$ **Solve for *F*.**

▶ The polyhedron has 10 faces.

EXERCISES

EXAMPLES 2 and 3 on pp. 796–797 for Exs. 3–5

Use Euler's Theorem to find the value of *n*.

3. Faces: 20
   Vertices: n
   Edges: 30 **12**

4. Faces: n
   Vertices: 6
   Edges: 12 **8**

5. Faces: 14
   Vertices: 24
   Edges: n **36**

Extra Example 12.1
A polyhedron has 12 vertices and 18 edges. How many faces does the polyhedron have? **8 faces**

2. *Sample:*

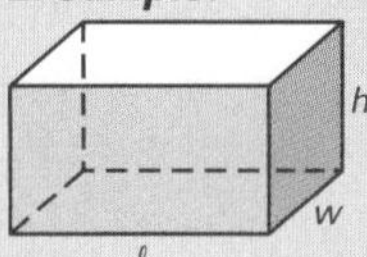

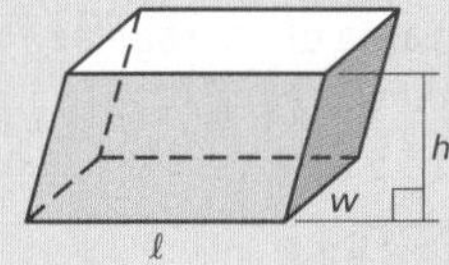

Extra Example 12.2

Find the surface area of the right prism. **700 cm²**

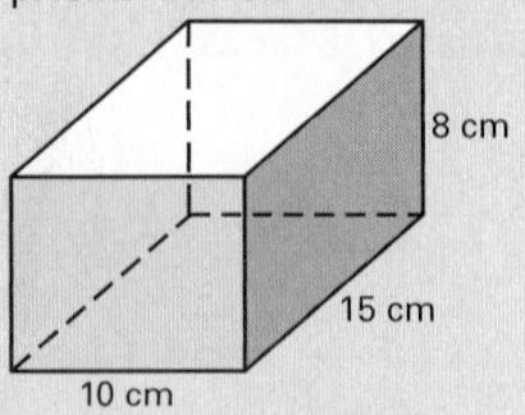

Extra Example 12.3

Find the lateral area of the regular square pyramid. **60 ft²**

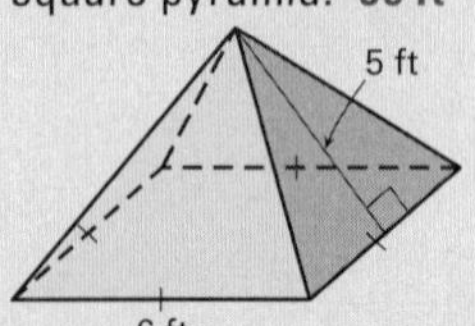

12 CHAPTER REVIEW

12.2 Surface Area of Prisms and Cylinders *pp. 803–809*

EXAMPLE

Find the surface area of the right cylinder.

25 in.
16 in.

$S = 2\pi r^2 + 2\pi rh$	**Write formula.**
$= 2\pi(16)^2 + 2\pi(16)(25)$	**Substitute for r and h.**
$= 1312\pi$	**Simplify.**
≈ 4121.77	**Use a calculator.**

▸ The surface area of the cylinder is about 4121.77 square inches.

EXERCISES

EXAMPLES 2, 3, and 4 on pp. 804–806 for Exs. 6–9

Find the surface area of the right prism or right cylinder. Round your answer to two decimal places, if necessary.

6.

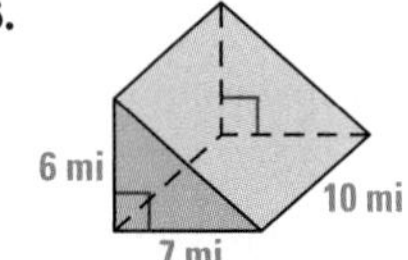

264.20 mi²

7.

12 ft
15 ft

2035.75 ft²

8.

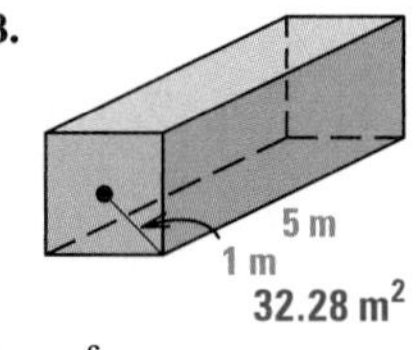

32.28 m²

9. A cylinder has a surface area of 44π square meters and a radius of 2 meters. Find the height of the cylinder. **9 m**

12.3 Surface Area of Pyramids and Cones *pp. 810–817*

EXAMPLE

Find the lateral area of the right cone.

Lateral area $= \pi r\ell$	**Write formula.**
$= \pi(6)(16)$	**Substitute for r and ℓ.**
$= 96\pi$	**Simplify.**
≈ 301.59	**Use a calculator.**

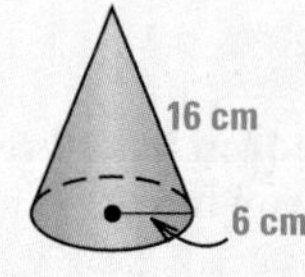

▸ The lateral area of the cone is about 301.59 square centimeters.

EXERCISES

EXAMPLES 1, 2, and 4 on pp. 810–813 for Exs. 10–12

10. Find the surface area of a right square pyramid with base edge length 2 feet and height 5 feet. **about 24.40 ft²**

11. The surface area of a cone with height 15 centimeters is 500π square centimeters. Find the radius of the base of the cone. Round your answer to two decimal places. **14.29 cm**

12. Find the surface area of a right octagonal pyramid with height 2.5 yards, and its base has apothem length 1.5 yards. **about 21.95 yd²**

@HomeTutor
classzone.com
Chapter Review Practice

12.4 Volume of Prisms and Cylinders

pp. 819–825

EXAMPLE

Find the volume of the right triangular prism.

The area of the base is $B = \frac{1}{2}(6)(8) = 24$ square inches. Use $h = 5$ to find the volume.

$V = Bh$	**Write formula.**
$= 24(5)$	**Substitute for *B* and *h*.**
$= 120$	**Simplify.**

▶ The volume of the prism is 120 cubic inches.

EXERCISES

EXAMPLES 2 and 4 on pp. 820–821 for Exs. 13–15

Find the volume of the right prism or oblique cylinder. Round your answer to two decimal places.

13. 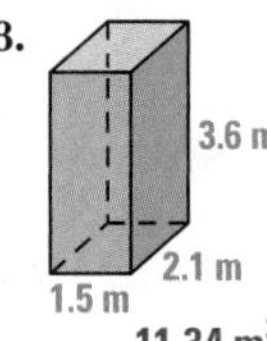

11.34 m³

14. 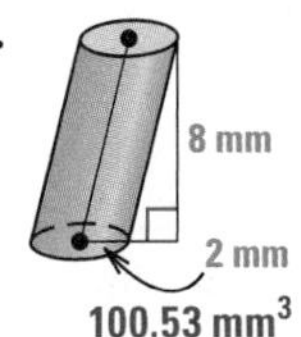

100.53 mm³

15. 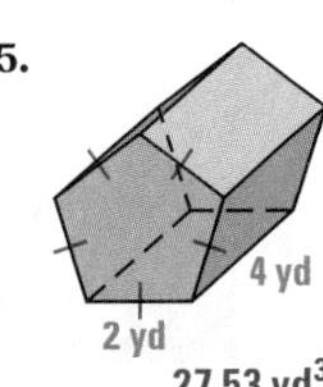

27.53 yd³

12.5 Volume of Pyramids and Cones

pp. 829–836

EXAMPLE

Find the volume of the right cone.

The area of the base is $B = \pi r^2 = \pi(11)^2 \approx 380.13 \text{ cm}^2$. Use $h = 20$ to find the volume.

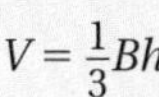

$V = \frac{1}{3}Bh$	**Write formula.**
$\approx \frac{1}{3}(380.13)(20)$	**Substitute for *B* and *h*.**
≈ 2534.2	**Simplify.**

▶ The volume of the cone is about 2534.2 cubic centimeters.

EXERCISES

EXAMPLES 1 and 2 on pp. 829–830 for Exs. 16–17

16. A cone with diameter 16 centimeters has height 15 centimeters. Find the volume of the cone. Round your answer to two decimal places. **1005.31 cm³**

17. The volume of a pyramid is 60 cubic inches and the height is 15 inches. Find the area of the base. **12 in.²**

Extra Example 12.4

Find the volume of the oblique cylinder. **197.92 m³**

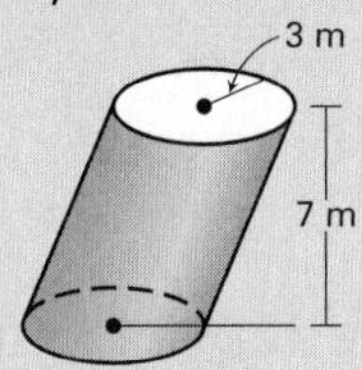

Extra Example 12.5

Find the volume of the square pyramid. **1242 ft³**

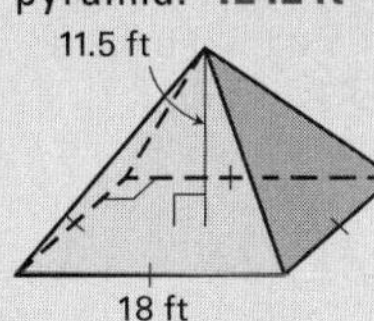

Extra Example 12.6

Find the volume of the sphere. **904.78 ft^3**

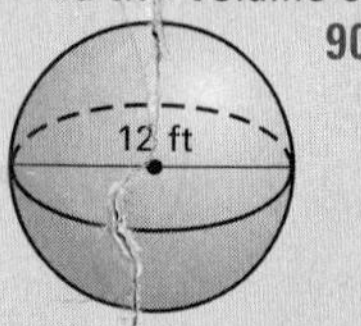

Extra Example 12.7

The surface area of Pyramid I is 144 cm^2 and its volume is 64 cm^3. Pyramid II is similar to Pyramid I, and the scale factor of Pyramid I to Pyramid II is 1 : 3. Find the surface area and volume of Pyramid II.

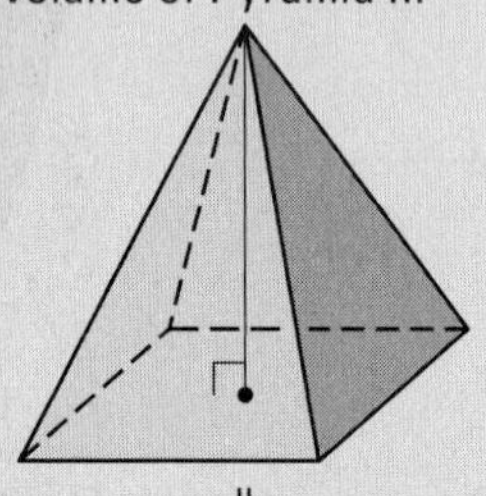

$S = 1296$ cm^2; $V = 1728$ cm^3

12 CHAPTER REVIEW

12.6 Surface Area and Volume of Spheres

pp. 838–845

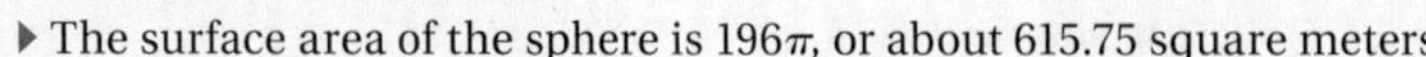

EXAMPLE

Find the surface area of the sphere.

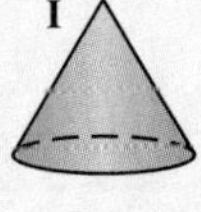

$S = 4\pi r^2$ **Write formula.**

$= 4\pi(7)^2$ **Substitute 7 for r.**

$= 196\pi$ **Simplify.**

▶ The surface area of the sphere is 196π, or about 615.75 square meters.

EXERCISES

EXAMPLES 1, 4, and 5 on pp. 839, 841 for Exs. 18–19

18. ASTRONOMY The shape of Pluto can be approximated as a sphere of diameter 2390 kilometers. Find the surface area and volume of Pluto. **17,945,091 km^2; 7,148,128,073 km^3**

19. A solid is composed of a cube with side length 6 meters and a hemisphere with diameter 6 meters. Find the volume of the solid. Round your answer to two decimal places. **272.55 m^3**

12.7 Explore Similar Solids

pp. 847–854

EXAMPLE

The cones are similar with a scale factor of 1 : 2. Find the surface area and volume of Cone II given that the surface area of Cone I is 384π square inches and the volume of Cone I is 768π cubic inches.

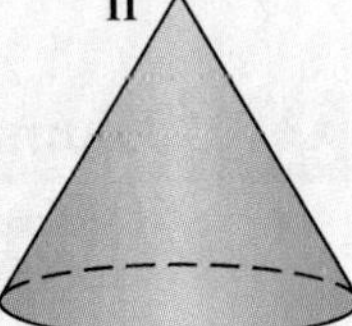

Use Theorem 12.13 to write and solve two proportions.

$$\frac{\text{Surface area of I}}{\text{Surface area of II}} = \frac{a^2}{b^2} \qquad \frac{\text{Volume of I}}{\text{Volume of II}} = \frac{a^3}{b^3}$$

$$\frac{384\pi}{\text{Surface area of II}} = \frac{1^2}{2^2} \qquad \frac{768\pi}{\text{Volume of II}} = \frac{1^3}{2^3}$$

$$\text{Surface area of II} = 1536\pi \text{ in.}^2 \qquad \text{Volume of II} = 6144\pi \text{ in.}^3$$

▶ The surface area of Cone II is 1536π, or about 4825.49 square inches, and the volume of Cone II is 6144π, or about 19,301.95 cubic inches.

EXERCISES

EXAMPLE 2 on p. 848 for Exs. 20–22

Solid A is similar to Solid B with the given scale factor of A to B. The surface area and volume of Solid A are given. Find the surface area and volume of Solid B.

20. Scale factor of 1 : 4
$S = 62$ cm^2
$V = 30$ cm^3
992 cm^2; 1920 cm^3

21. Scale factor of 1 : 3
$S = 112\pi$ m^2
$V = 160\pi$ m^3
1008π m^2; 4320π m^3

22. Scale factor of 2 : 5
$S = 144\pi$ yd^2
$V = 288\pi$ yd^3
900π yd^2; 4500π yd^3

12 CHAPTER TEST

Find the number of faces, vertices, and edges of the polyhedron. Check your answer using Euler's Theorem.

1. 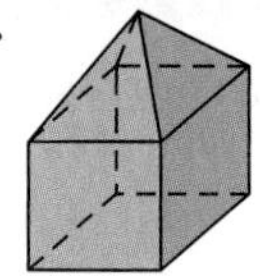 **9, 9, 16**

2. 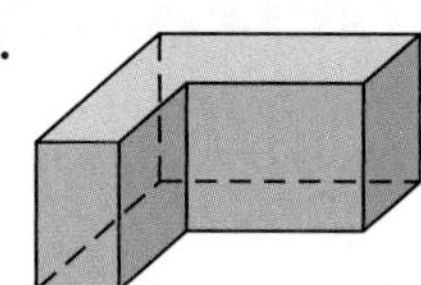 **8, 12, 18**

3. 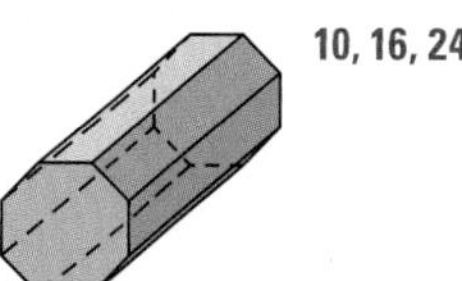 **10, 16, 24**

Find the surface area of the solid. The prisms, pyramids, cylinders, and cones are right. Round your answer to two decimal places, if necessary.

4. 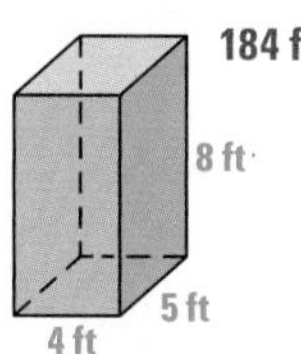

184 ft²

5. 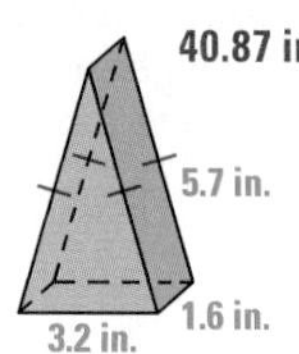

40.87 in.²

6. 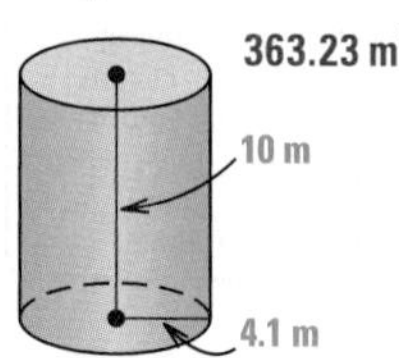

363.23 m²

7. 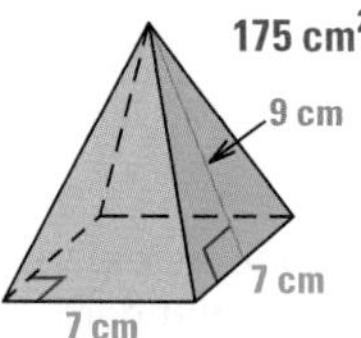

175 cm²

8. 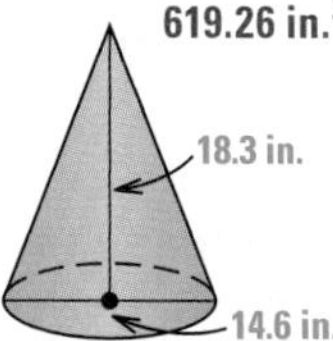

619.26 in.²

9. 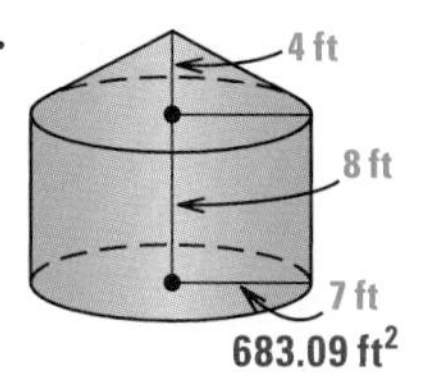

683.09 ft²

Find the volume of the right prism or right cylinder. Round your answer to two decimal places, if necessary.

10. 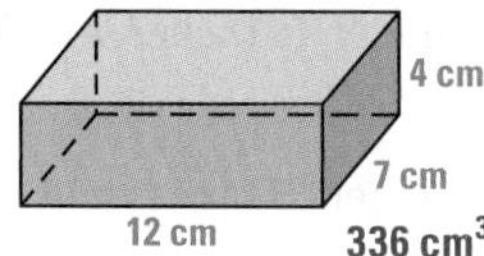

336 cm³

11. 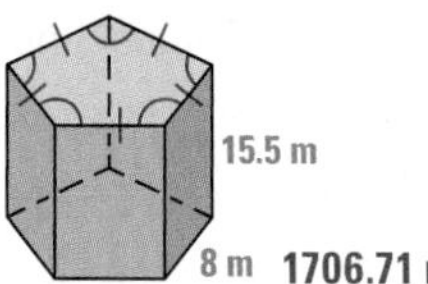

1706.71 m³

12. 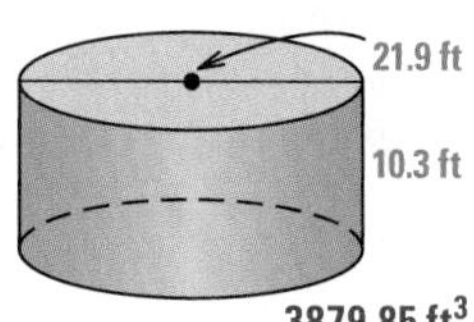

3879.85 ft³

In Exercises 13–15, solve for x.

13. Volume = 324 in.^{3} **12 in.**

14. Volume = $\frac{32\pi}{3}$ ft^3 **2 ft**

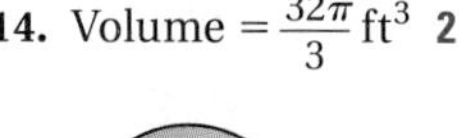

15. Volume = 180π cm^3 **6 cm**

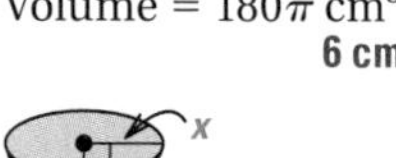

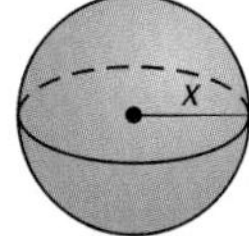

16. **MARBLES** The diameter of the marble shown is 35 millimeters. Find the surface area and volume of the marble. **about 3848.45 mm²; about 22,449.30 mm³**

17. **PACKAGING** Two similar cylindrical cans have a scale factor of 2 : 3. The smaller can has surface area 308π square inches and volume 735π cubic inches. Find the surface area and volume of the larger can. **693π in.²; about 2481π in.³**

Additional Resources

Assessment Book

- Chapter Test, Levels A, B, C, pp. 173–178
- Standardized Chapter Test, pp. 179–180
- SAT/ACT Chapter Test, pp. 181–182
- Alternative Assessment, pp. 183–184

Test Generator CD-ROM

Chapter Test

Easily-readable reduced copies (with answers) of Chapter Test B, the Standardized Chapter Test, and the Alternative Assessment from the Assessment Book can be found on pp. 790G–790H.

Test-Taking Strategy

Interpreting a diagram, graph, or table is a very useful test-taking strategy because it offers a visual connection for students, especially those who are good visual learners. To use this strategy well, students need to gather as much information as possible from the diagram and study how the diagram relates to the information given in words. Using this strategy means working from the diagram and written information to formulate a plan to solve the problem.

CONTEXT-BASED MULTIPLE CHOICE QUESTIONS

Some of the information you need to solve a context-based multiple choice question may appear in a table, a diagram, or a graph.

Standards

8.0 Students know, derive, and **solve problems involving** the perimeter, circumference, area, **volume**, lateral area, **and surface area of common geometric figures.**

PROBLEM 1

One cubic foot of concrete weighs about 150 pounds. What is the approximate weight of the cylindrical section of concrete pipe shown?

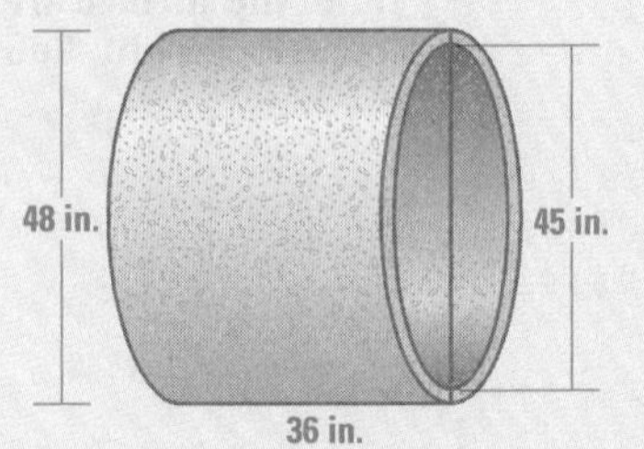

Ⓐ 145 lb Ⓑ 684 lb

Ⓒ 2738 lb Ⓓ 5653 lb

Plan

INTERPRET THE DIAGRAM The pipe is a cylinder with length 36 inches and diameter 48 inches. The hollow center is also a cylinder with length 36 inches and diameter 45 inches. Find the volume of concrete used (in cubic feet). Then multiply by 150 pounds per cubic foot to find the weight of the concrete.

Solution

STEP 1 Find the volume of concrete used in the pipe.

Find the volume of a cylinder with diameter 48 inches and height 36 inches.

$V = \pi r^2 h = \pi(24^2)(36) \approx 65{,}144 \text{ in.}^3$

Find the volume of a cylinder with diameter 45 inches and height 36 inches.

$V = \pi r^2 h = \pi(22.5^2)(36) \approx 57{,}256 \text{ in.}^3$

To find the volume of concrete used in the pipe, subtract the smaller volume from the larger volume.

Volume of concrete used in pipe $\approx 65{,}144 - 57{,}256 = 7888 \text{ in.}^3$

STEP 2 Convert the volume to cubic feet.

Use unit analysis to convert 7888 cubic inches to cubic feet. There are 12 inches in 1 foot, so there are $12^3 = 1728$ cubic inches in 1 cubic foot.

$7888 \cancel{\text{in.}^3} \cdot \frac{1 \text{ ft}^3}{1728 \cancel{\text{in.}^3}} \approx 4.56 \text{ ft}^3$

STEP 3 Find the weight of the pipe.

To find the weight of the pipe, multiply the volume of the concrete used in the pipe by the weight of one cubic foot of concrete.

Weight of pipe $\approx 4.56 \cancel{\text{ft}^3} \cdot \frac{150 \text{ lb}}{1 \cancel{\text{ft}^3}} = 684 \text{ lb}$

The weight of the pipe is about 684 pounds.

The correct answer is B. Ⓐ Ⓑ Ⓒ Ⓓ

PROBLEM 2

What is the ratio of the surface area of Cone I to the surface area of Cone II?

Ⓐ 1:2 Ⓑ 1:4

Ⓒ 3:5 Ⓓ 3:8

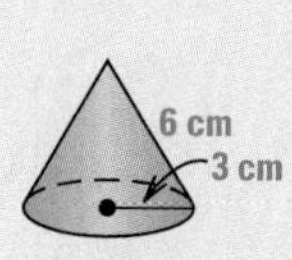

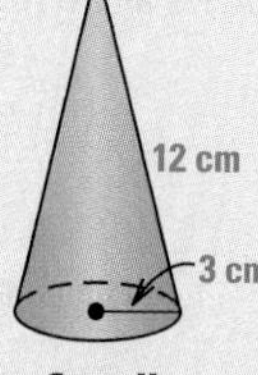

Plan

INTERPRET THE DIAGRAM The diagram shows that the cones have the same radius, but different slant heights. Find and compare the surface areas.

Solution

STEP 1 Find the surface area of each cone.

Use the formula for the surface area of a cone.

Surface area of Cone I $= \pi r^2 + \pi r\ell = \pi(3^2) + \pi(3)(6) = 9\pi + 18\pi = 27\pi$

Surface area of Cone II $= \pi r^2 + \pi r\ell = \pi(3^2) + \pi(3)(12) = 9\pi + 36\pi = 45\pi$

STEP 2 Compare the surface areas.

Write a ratio.

$\frac{\text{Surface area of Cone I}}{\text{Surface area of Cone II}} = \frac{27\pi}{45\pi} = \frac{3}{5}$, or 3:5

The correct answer is C. Ⓐ Ⓑ Ⓒ Ⓓ

PRACTICE

1. The amount a cannister can hold is proportional to its volume. The large cylindrical cannister in the table holds 2 kilograms of flour. About how many kilograms does the similar small cannister hold? **A**

Size	Diameter
Small	24 cm
Medium	30 cm
Large	37.5 cm

Ⓐ 0.5 kg Ⓑ 1 kg

Ⓒ 1.3 kg Ⓓ 1.6 kg

2. The solid shown is made of a rectangular prism and a square pyramid. The height of the pyramid is one third the height of the prism. What is the volume of the solid? **C**

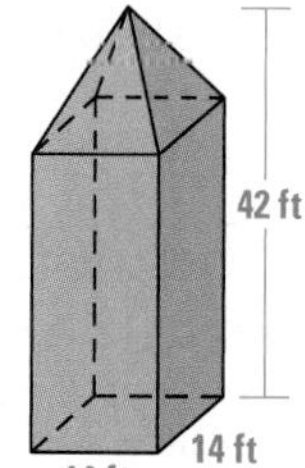

Ⓐ $457\frac{1}{3}$ ft^3 Ⓑ $6402\frac{2}{3}$ ft^3

Ⓒ 6860 ft^3 Ⓓ 10,976 ft^3

Avoiding Common Errors

Problem 2 Students may jump to the conclusion that the ratio of the surface areas is 1:1 because both bases have the same radius. Point out that these cones are not similar, so there is no scale factor ratio.

Teaching Strategy

Exercise 1 The exercise states that volume is proportional to how much a canister can hold, so the ratio of the weights is the same as the ratio of the volumes.

12 ★ Standardized TEST PRACTICE

MULTIPLE CHOICE

In Exercises 1 and 2, use the diagram, which shows a bin for storing wood.

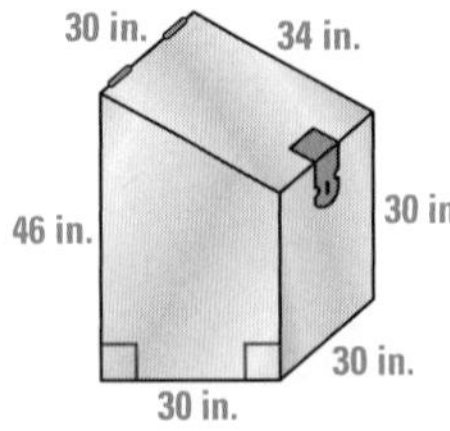

1. The bin is a prism. What is the shape of the base of the prism? **D**

Ⓐ Triangle Ⓑ Rectangle

Ⓒ Square Ⓓ Trapezoid

2. What is the surface area of the bin? **B**

Ⓐ 3060 in.^{2} Ⓑ 6480 in.^{2}

Ⓒ 6960 in.^{2} Ⓓ 8760 in.^{2}

3. In the paperweight shown, a sphere with diameter 5 centimeters is embedded in a glass cube. What percent of the volume of the paperweight is taken up by the sphere? **A**

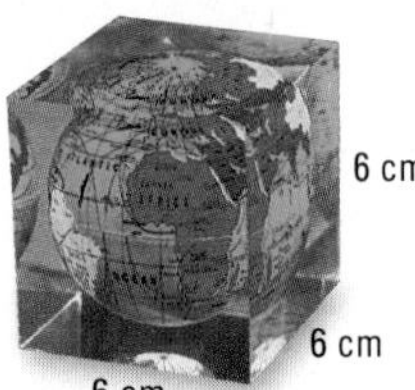

Ⓐ About 30% Ⓑ About 40%

Ⓒ About 50% Ⓓ About 60%

4. What is the volume of the solid formed when rectangle *JKLM* is rotated 360° about $\overline{KL}$? **D**

Ⓐ π Ⓑ 3π

Ⓒ 6π Ⓓ 9π

5. The skylight shown is made of four glass panes that are congruent isosceles triangles. One square foot of the glass used in the skylight weighs 3.25 pounds. What is the approximate total weight of the glass used in the four panes? **D**

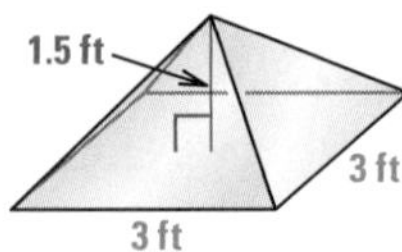

Ⓐ 10 lb Ⓑ 15 lb

Ⓒ 29 lb Ⓓ 41 lb

6. The volume of the right cone shown below is 16π cubic centimeters. What is the surface area of the cone? **C**

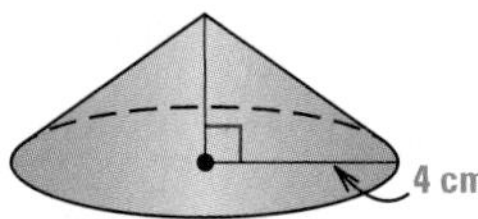

Ⓐ 12π cm^2 Ⓑ 18π cm^2

Ⓒ 36π cm^2 Ⓓ 72π cm^2

7. The shaded surface of the skateboard ramp shown is divided into a flat rectangular portion and a curved portion. The curved portion is one fourth of a cylinder with radius r feet and height h feet. Which equation can be used to find the area of the top surface of the ramp? **D**

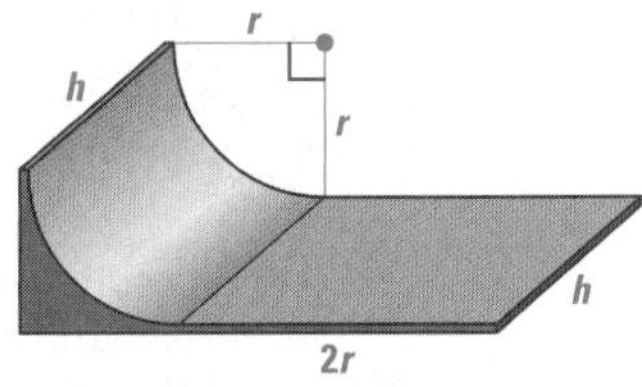

Ⓐ $2rh + 2\pi r^2$ Ⓑ $2rh + 2\pi rh$

Ⓒ $2rh + \frac{1}{4}\pi r^2$ Ⓓ $2rh + \frac{1}{2}\pi rh$

GRIDDED ANSWER

8. The scale factor of two similar triangular prisms is 3 : 5. The volume of the larger prism is 175 cubic inches. What is the volume (in cubic inches) of the smaller prism? **37.8**

9. Two identical octagonal pyramids are joined together at their bases. The resulting polyhedron has 16 congruent triangular faces and 10 vertices. How many edges does it have? **24**

10. The surface area of Sphere A is 27 square meters. The surface area of Sphere B is 48 square meters. What is the ratio of the diameter of Sphere A to the diameter of Sphere B, expressed as a decimal? **0.75**

11. The volume of a square pyramid is 54 cubic meters. The height of the pyramid is 2 times the length of a side of its base. What is the height (in meters) of the pyramid? Round your answer to the nearest hundredth. **8.65**

SHORT RESPONSE

12. Two cake layers are right cylinders, as shown. The top and sides of each layer will be frosted, including the portion of the top of the larger layer that is under the smaller layer. One can of frosting covers 100 square inches. How many cans do you need to frost the cake? **3 cans**

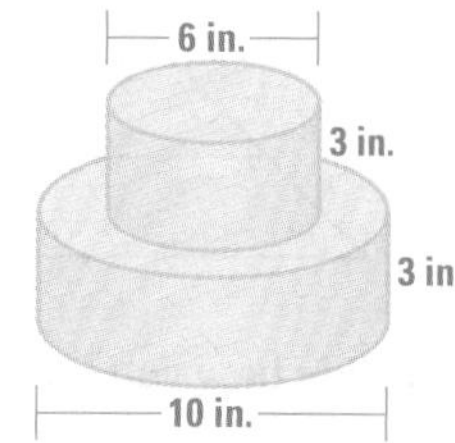

13. The height of Cylinder B is twice the height of Cylinder A. The diameter of Cylinder B is half the diameter of Cylinder A. Let r be the radius and let h be the height of Cylinder A. Write expressions for the radius and height of Cylinder B. Which cylinder has a greater volume? *Explain.*
$\frac{r}{2}$, $2h$; Cylinder A; its volume is $\pi r^2 h$ and the volume of cylinder B is $\pi\left(\frac{1}{2}r\right)^2 \cdot 2h = \frac{1}{2}\pi r^2 h$.

EXTENDED RESPONSE

14. A cylindrical oil tank for home use has the dimensions shown.

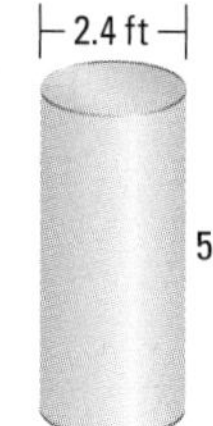

a. Find the volume of the tank to the nearest tenth of a cubic foot. **22.6 ft^3**

b. Use the fact that 1 cubic foot = 7.48 gallons to find how many gallons of oil are needed to fill the tank. **about 169 gal**

c. A homeowner uses about 1000 gallons of oil in a year. Assuming the tank is empty each time it is filled, how many times does the tank need to be filled during the year? **6 times**

15. A manufacturer is deciding whether to package a product in a container shaped like a prism or one shaped like a cylinder. The manufacturer wants to use the least amount of material possible. The prism is 4 inches tall and has a square base with side length 3 inches. The height of the cylinder is 5 inches, and its radius is 1.6 inches.

a. Find the surface area and volume of each container. If necessary, round to the nearest tenth. **prism surface area: 66 in.^{2}, volume: 36 in.^{3}; cylinder surface area: 66.4 in.^{2}, volume: 40.2 in.^{3}**

b. For each container, find the ratio of the volume to the surface area. *Explain* why the manufacturer should compare the ratios before making a decision. **Prism: 6 to 11, cylinder: about 20 to 33; since the surface areas are about the same, the manufacturer should compare the ratios to get the most volume for a given surface area.**

Additional Resources

The following resources are available to help review the materials in Chapters 1–12.

Chapter Resource Books

- Chapter 10 CRB, Cumulative Review, pp. 104–105
- Chapter 11 CRB, Cumulative Review, pp. 106–107
- Chapter 12 CRB, Cumulative Review, pp. 107–108

Assessment Book

- Cumulative Test, Chapters 7–12, pp. 185–188
- Cumulative Test, Chapters 1–12, pp. 189–192

Find the value of x that makes $m \parallel n$. *(p. 161)*

1. 75

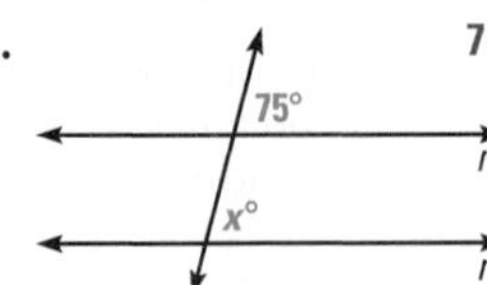

2. 10

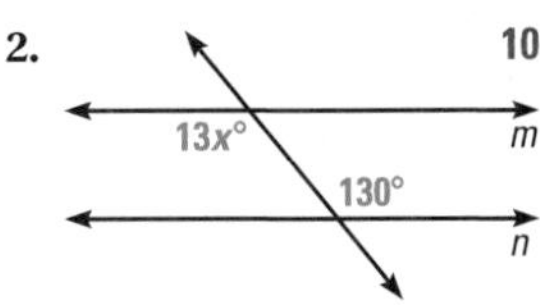

3. 16

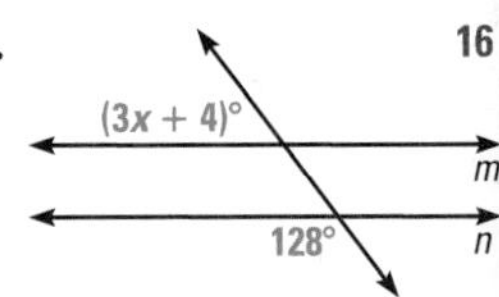

Find the value of the variable. *(p. 397)*

4. $\frac{24}{5}$

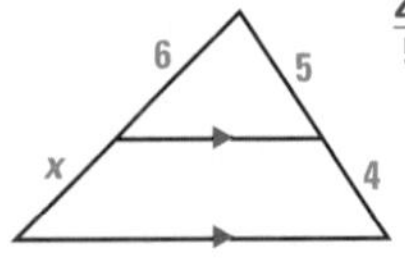

5. 4

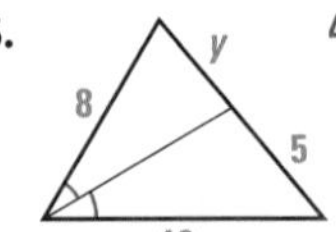

6. 12

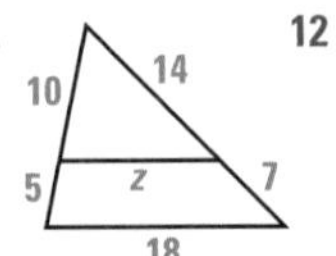

Explain **how you know that the quadrilateral is a parallelogram.** *(p. 522)*

7.

Both pairs of opposite angles are congruent.

8. 16, 16

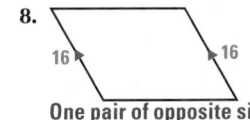

One pair of opposite sides are congruent and parallel.

9.

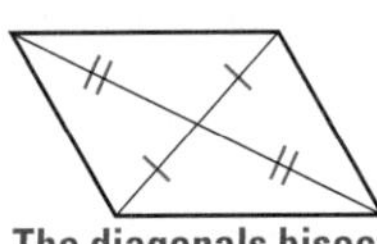

The diagonals bisect each other.

Find the value of the variable. *(pp. 651, 672, 689)*

10. 16

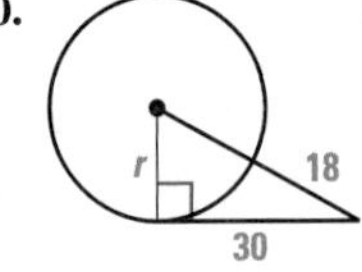

11. 45

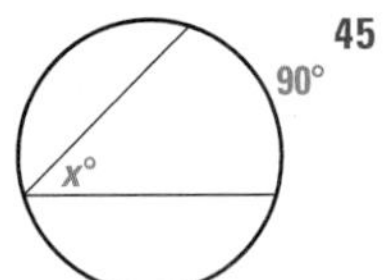

12. 10

y, 2, 3, 5

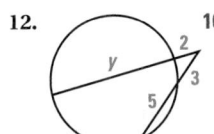

Find the area of the shaded region. *(p. 755)*

13.

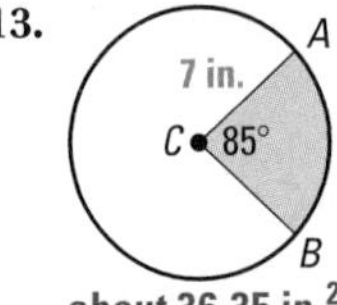

about 36.35 in.^{2}

14.

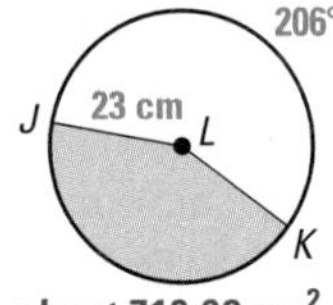

about 710.92 cm^2

15.

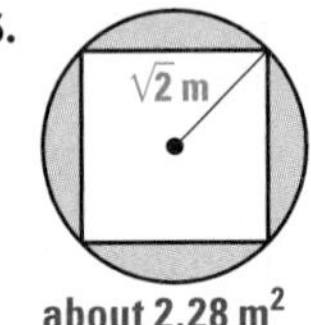

about 2.28 m^2

Find the surface area and volume of the right solid. Round your answer to two decimal places. *(pp. 803, 810, 819, 829)*

16.

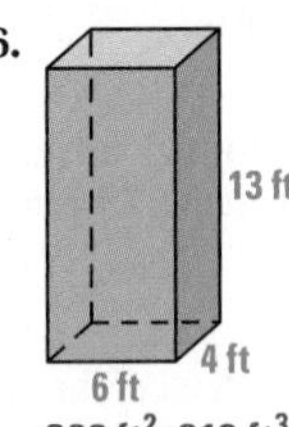

308 ft^2, 312 ft^3

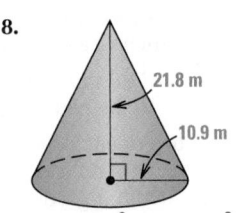

17.

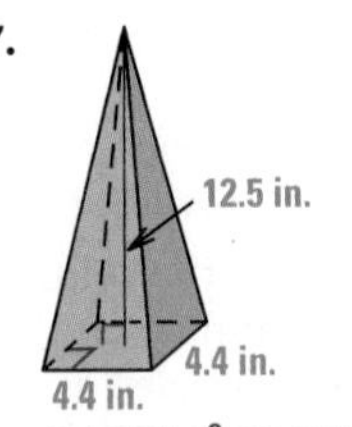

131.05 in.^{2}, 80.67 in.^{3}

18. 21.8 m, 10.9 m

1207.87 m^2, 2712.30 m^3

19. **PHYSICS** Find the coordinates of point P that will allow the triangular plate of uniform thickness to be balanced on a point. *(p. 319)* **(4, 2)**

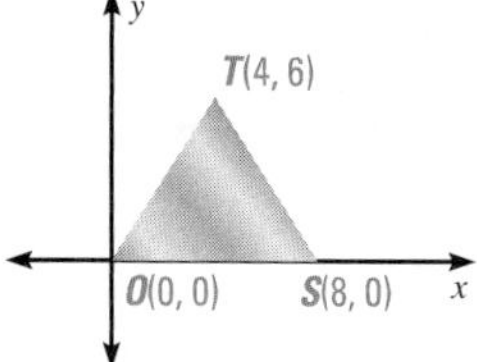

20. **SYMMETRY** Copy the figure on the right. Determine whether the figure has *line symmetry* and whether it has *rotational symmetry.* Identify all lines of symmetry and angles of rotation that map the figure onto itself. *(p. 619)* **Line symmetry: the 2 perpendicular lines that are vertical and horizontal and intersect at the center of the figure; rotational symmetry: 180° about the center of the figure.**

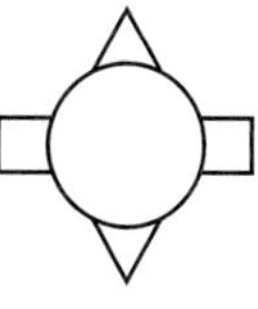

21. **TWO-WAY RADIOS** You and your friend want to test a pair of two-way radios. The radios are expected to transmit voices up to 6 miles. Your location is identified by the point $(-2, 4)$ on a coordinate plane where units are measured in miles. *(p. 699)*

    a. Write an inequality that represents the area expected to be covered by the radios. $\mathbf{(x + 2)^2 + (y - 4)^2 \leq 36}$

    b. Determine whether your friend should be able to hear your voice when your friend is located at $(2, 0)$, $(3, 9)$, $(-6, -1)$, $(-6, 8)$, and $(-7, 5)$. *Explain* your reasoning.

21b. (2, 0): yes; it is a solution of the inequality. (3, 9): no; it is not a solution of the inequality. (−6, −1): no; it is not a solution of the inequality. (−6, 8): yes; it is a solution of the inequality. (−7, 5): yes; it is a solution of the inequality.

22. **COVERED BRIDGE** A covered bridge has a roof with the dimensions shown. The top ridge of the roof is parallel to the base of the roof. The hidden back and left sides are the same as the front and right sides. Find the total area of the roof. *(pp. 720, 730)* **3591 ft²**

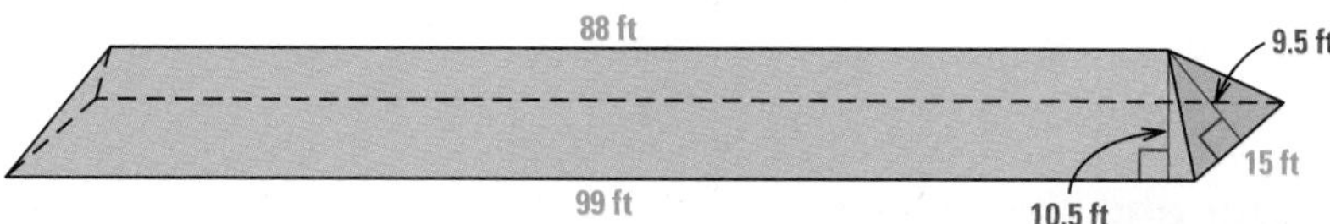

23. **CANDLES** The candle shown has diameter 2 inches and height 5.5 inches. *(pp. 803, 819)*

    a. Find the surface area and volume of the candle. Round your answers to two decimal places. **40.84 in.², 17.28 in.³**

    b. The candle has a burning time of about 30 hours. Find the approximate volume of the candle after it has burned for 18 hours. **about 6.91 in.³**

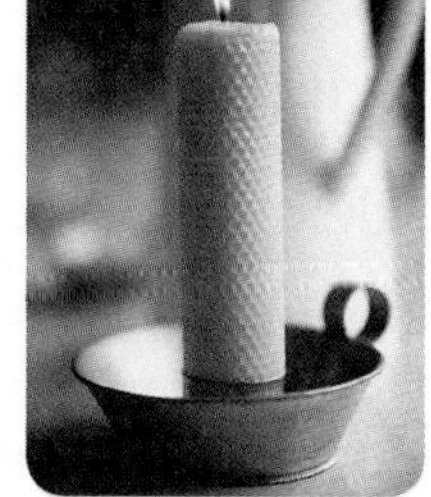

24. **GEOGRAPHY** The diameter of Earth is about 7920 miles. If approximately 70 percent of Earth's surface is covered by water, how many square miles of water are on Earth's surface? Round your answer to two decimal places. *(p. 838)* **137,942,558.20 mi²**

867

Contents of Student Resources

Operations with Rational Numbers

EXAMPLE **Add or subtract: a. $-\frac{3}{4}+\frac{5}{8}$ b. 8.5 − (−1.4)**

a. Write the fractions with the same denominator, then add.

$$-\frac{3}{4}+\frac{5}{8}=-\frac{6}{8}+\frac{5}{8}=\frac{-6+5}{8}=\frac{-1}{8}=-\frac{1}{8}$$

b. To subtract a rational number, add its opposite.

$8.5-(-1.4)=8.5+1.4=9.9$ **The opposite of −1.4 is 1.4, because (−1.4) + (1.4) = 0.**

The product or quotient of two numbers with the *same* sign is **positive**.

The product or quotient of two numbers with *different* signs is **negative**.

EXAMPLE **Multiply: a. 4(5) b. (−4)(−5) c. 4(−5)**

a. $4(5)=20$ **b.** $(-4)(-5)=20$ **c.** $4(-5)=-20$

EXAMPLE **Divide $-\frac{1}{4}\div\frac{2}{5}$.**

To divide by a fraction, multiply by its reciprocal.

$-\frac{1}{4}\div\frac{2}{5}=-\frac{1}{4}\times\frac{5}{2}=-\frac{1\times5}{4\times2}=-\frac{5}{8}$ **The reciprocal of $\frac{2}{5}$ is $\frac{5}{2}$, because $\frac{2}{5}\times\frac{5}{2}=1$.**

PRACTICE

Add, subtract, multiply, or divide.

1. $4-(-7)$ **11**
2. $-13+28$ **15**
3. $-5\cdot3$ **−15**
4. $32\div(-8)$ **−4**
5. $(-2)(-3)(-4)$ **−24**
6. $-8.1+4.5$ **−3.6**
7. $(-2.7)\div(-9)$ **0.3**
8. $0.85-0.9$ **−0.05**
9. $12.1+(-0.5)$ **11.6**
10. $(-2.6)\cdot(-8.1)$ **21.06**
11. $-1.5-3.4$ **−4.9**
12. $-3.6\div1.5$ **−2.4**
13. $-3.1\cdot4.2$ **−13.02**
14. $0.48\div4$ **0.12**
15. $-5.4+(-3.8)$ **−9.2**
16. $0.6-1.8$ **−1.2**
17. $-\frac{5}{6}-\frac{1}{4}$ $-1\frac{1}{12}$
18. $-\frac{3}{4}\cdot\frac{7}{12}$ $-\frac{7}{16}$
19. $\frac{4}{7}\div\frac{2}{3}$ $\frac{6}{7}$
20. $-\frac{11}{12}+\frac{7}{9}$ $-\frac{5}{36}$
21. $-\frac{2}{3}+\left(-\frac{1}{4}\right)$ $-\frac{11}{12}$
22. $\frac{5}{12}\div\frac{3}{8}$ $1\frac{1}{9}$
23. $\frac{7}{9}-\left(-\frac{1}{6}\right)$ $\frac{17}{18}$
24. $\frac{5}{8}\cdot\frac{2}{11}$ $\frac{5}{44}$

Simplifying and Evaluating Expressions

To evaluate expressions involving more than one operation, mathematicians have agreed on the following set of rules, called the **order of operations**.

1. **Evaluate** expressions inside grouping symbols.
2. **Evaluate** powers.
3. **Multiply** and **divide** from left to right.
4. **Add** and **subtract** from left to right.

EXAMPLE **Simplify: a. $10 + (1 - 5)^2 \div (-8)$ b. $3|-9 + 2| - 2 \cdot 6$**

a. $10 + (1 - 5)^2 \div (-8)$

$= 10 + (-4)^2 \div (-8)$ **Subtract.**

$= 10 + 16 \div (-8)$ **Evaluate powers.**

$= 10 + (-2)$ **Divide.**

$= 8$ **Add.**

b. $3|-9 + 2| - 2 \cdot 6$

$= 3|-7| - 2 \cdot 6$ **Add.**

$= 3(7) - 2 \cdot 6$ **Absolute value**

$= 21 - 12$ **Multiply.**

$= 9$ **Subtract.**

To evaluate an algebraic expression, substitute values for the variables. Evaluate the resulting numerical expression using the order of operations.

EXAMPLE **Evaluate the expression when $x = 4$ and $y = 9$.**

a. $\frac{x^2 - 1}{x + 2} = \frac{4^2 - 1}{4 + 2} = \frac{16 - 1}{4 + 2} = \frac{15}{6} = \frac{5}{2} = 2\frac{1}{2}$

b. $[(2x + y) - 3x] \div 2 = (-x + y) \div 2 = (-4 + 9) \div 2 = 5 \div 2 = 2.5$

c. $2|x - 3y| = 2|4 - 3(9)| = 2|4 - 27| = 2|-23| = 2(23) = 46$

PRACTICE

Simplify the expression.

1. $5^2 - (-2)^3$ **33**
2. $-8 \cdot 3 - 12 \div 2$ **−30**
3. $21|-7 + 4| - 4^3$ **−1**
4. $24 \div (8 - |5 - 1|)$ **6**
5. $4(2 - 5)^2$ **36**
6. $4 + 21 \div 7 - 6^2$ **−29**
7. $19.6 \div (2.8 \div 0.4)$ **2.8**
8. $20 - 4[2 + (10 - 3^2)]$ **8**
9. $\frac{6 + 3 \cdot 4}{2^2 - 7}$ **−6**
10. $\frac{18 + |-2|}{(4 - 6)^2}$ **5**
11. $3(6x) + 7x$ **25x**
12. $3|-5y + 4y|$ **3|−y|**

Evaluate the expression when $x = -3$ and $y = 5$.

13. $-4x^2$ **−36**
14. $(-4x)^2$ **144**
15. $x(x + 8)$ **−15**
16. $(11 - x) \div 2$ **7**
17. $3 \cdot |x - 2|$ **15**
18. $7x^2 - 2y$ **53**
19. $5 - |3x + y|$ **1**
20. $4x^3 + 3y$ **−93**
21. $\frac{y^2 - 1}{5 - y^2}$ $-\frac{6}{5}$
22. $|6y| - |x|$ **27**
23. $\frac{-6(2x + y)}{5 - x}$ $\frac{3}{4}$
24. $\frac{x - 7}{x + 7} + 1$ $-\frac{3}{2}$

Properties of Exponents

An **exponent** tells you how many times to multiply a **base**. The expression ^{5} is called a **power** with base 4 and exponent 5.

$4^5 = 4 \times 4 \times 4 \times 4 \times 4 = 1024$

Product of Powers	Power of a Product	Power of a Power	
$a^m \cdot a^n = a^{m+n}$ Add exponents.	$(a \cdot b)^m = a^m \cdot b^m$ Find the power of each factor.	$(a^m)^n = a^{mn}$ Multiply exponents.	
Quotient of Powers	**Power of a Quotient**	**Negative Exponent**	**Zero Exponent**
$\frac{a^m}{a^n} = a^{m-n}, a \neq 0$ Subtract exponents.	$\left(\frac{a}{b}\right)^m = \frac{a^m}{b^m}, b \neq 0$ Find the power of the numerator and the power of the denominator.	$a^{-n} = \frac{1}{a^n}, a \neq 0$	$a^0 = 1, a \neq 0$

EXAMPLE Simplify the expression. Use positive exponents.

a. $x^2 \cdot x^5 = x^{2+5} = x^7$

b. $(2xy)^3 = 2^3 \cdot x^3 \cdot y^3 = 8x^3y^3$

c. $(y^4)^5 = y^{4 \cdot 5} = y^{20}$

d. $(-35)^0 = 1$

e. $\frac{m^9}{m^6} = m^{9-6} = m^3$

f. $\left(\frac{z}{4}\right)^3 = \frac{z^3}{4^3} = \frac{z^3}{64}$

g. $12^{-4} = \frac{1}{12^4} = \frac{1}{20{,}736}$

h. $\frac{20x^2y^{-4}z^5}{4x^4yz^3} = \frac{20}{4}x^{(2-4)}y^{(-4-1)}z^{(5-3)} = 5x^{-2}y^{-5}z^2 = \frac{5z^2}{x^2y^5}$

PRACTICE

Evaluate the power.

1. 5^2 **25**
2. $\left(-\frac{1}{2}\right)^3$ $\mathbf{-\frac{1}{8}}$
3. 4^{-2} $\mathbf{\frac{1}{16}}$
4. 13^0 **1**
5. $5^3 \cdot 5^4$ **78,125**
6. $\left(\frac{3}{5}\right)^{-2}$ $\mathbf{\frac{25}{9}}$
7. $(7^8)^4$ $\mathbf{7^{32} \approx 1.1 \times 10^{27}}$
8. $\frac{4^6}{4^4}$ **16**

Simplify the expression. Write your answer using only positive exponents.

9. $a^5 \cdot a \cdot a^{-2}$ $\mathbf{a^4}$
10. $3x^8 \cdot (2x)^3$ $\mathbf{24x^{11}}$
11. $5a^5 \cdot b^{-4}$ $\mathbf{\frac{5a^5}{b^4}}$
12. $(m^{-2})^{-3}$ $\mathbf{m^6}$
13. $\left(\frac{3}{n}\right)^4$ $\mathbf{\frac{81}{n^4}}$
14. $\left(\frac{x^5}{x^2}\right)^3$ $\mathbf{x^9}$
15. $\frac{1}{m^{-2}}$ $\mathbf{m^2}$
16. $\left(\frac{a^3}{3b}\right)^{-2}$ $\mathbf{\frac{9b^2}{a^6}}$
17. $(4 \cdot x^3 \cdot y)^2$ $\mathbf{16x^6y^2}$
18. $(2n)^4 \cdot (3n)^2$ $\mathbf{144n^6}$
19. $(5a^3b^{-2}c)^{-1}$ $\mathbf{\frac{b^2}{5a^3c}}$
20. $(r^2st^3)^0$ **1**
21. $\frac{16x^2y}{2xy}$ $\mathbf{8x}$
22. $\frac{(3r^{-3}s)^2}{10s}$ $\mathbf{\frac{9s}{10r^6}}$
23. $\frac{3a^2b^0c}{21a^{-3}b^4c^2}$ $\mathbf{\frac{a^5}{7b^4c}}$
24. $\left(\frac{6kn}{9k^2}\right)^2$ $\mathbf{\frac{4n^2}{9k^2}}$
25. $6x^2 \cdot 5xy$ $\mathbf{30x^3y}$
26. $2(r^{-4}s^2t)^{-3}$ $\mathbf{\frac{2r^{12}}{s^6t^3}}$
27. $(5a^{-3}bc^4)^{-2} \cdot 15a^8$ $\mathbf{\frac{3a^{14}}{5b^2c^8}}$
28. $(3x^2y)^2 \cdot (-4xy^3)$ $\mathbf{-36x^5y^5}$

871

Using the Distributive Property

You can use the **Distributive Property** to simplify some expressions. Here are four forms of the Distributive Property.

$a(b + c) = ab + ac$	and	$(b + c)a = ba + ca$	**Addition**
$a(b - c) = ab - ac$	and	$(b - c)a = ba - ca$	**Subtraction**

EXAMPLE **Write the expression without parentheses.**

a. $x(x - 7) = x(x) - x(7)$
$= x^2 - 7x$

b. $(n + 5)(-3) = n(-3) + (5)(-3)$
$= -3n - 15$

Like terms are terms of an expression that have identical variable parts. You can use the Distributive Property to combine like terms and to simplify expressions that include adding, subtracting, factoring, and dividing polynomials.

EXAMPLE **Simplify the expression.**

a. $-2x^2 + 6x^2 = (-2 + 6)x^2 = 4x^2$

b. $9y - 4y + 8y = (9 - 4 + 8)y = 13y$

c. $5(x^2 - 3x) + (x + 2) = 5x^2 - 15x + x + 2 = 5x^2 + (-15 + 1)x + 2 = 5x^2 - 14x + 2$

d. $(3x^2 - 4x + 1) - (2x^2 - x - 7) = (3 - 2)x^2 + (-4 + 1)x + (1 + 7) = x^2 - 3x + 8$

e. $\frac{2x^2 - 4x}{2x} = \frac{2x(x - 2)}{2x} = \frac{\cancel{2x}(x - 2)}{\cancel{2x}} = x - 2$

PRACTICE

Use the Distributive Property to write an equivalent expression.

1. $3(x + 7)$ $\mathbf{3x + 21}$

2. $-2(9a - 5)$ $\mathbf{-18a + 10}$

3. $(5n - 2)8$ $\mathbf{40n - 16}$

4. $x(3x - 4)$ $\mathbf{3x^2 - 4x}$

5. $-(x + 6)$ $\mathbf{-x - 6}$

6. $(5b + c)(2a)$ $\mathbf{10ab + 2ac}$

7. $4(3x^2 - 2x + 4)$ $\mathbf{12x^2 - 8x + 16}$

8. $-5a(-a + 3b - 1)$ $\mathbf{5a^2 - 15ab + 5a}$

Simplify the expression.

9. $3x^2 - 9x^2 + x^2$ $\mathbf{-5x^2}$

10. $4x - 7x + 12x$ $\mathbf{9x}$

11. $3n + 5 - n$ $\mathbf{2n + 5}$

12. $-6r + 3s - 5r + 8$ $\mathbf{-11r + 3s + 8}$

13. $12h^2 + 5h^3 - 7h^2$ $\mathbf{5h^3 + 5h^2}$

14. $6.5a + 2.4 - 5a$ $\mathbf{1.5a + 2.4}$

15. $(x + 8) - (x - 2)$ $\mathbf{10}$

16. $4.5(2r - 6) - 3r$ $\mathbf{6r - 27}$

17. $\frac{1}{2}a + \frac{2}{5}a$ $\mathbf{\frac{9}{10}a}$

18. $\frac{1}{4}(x^2 - 4) + x$ $\mathbf{\frac{1}{4}x^2 + x - 1}$

19. $\frac{15n + 20}{5}$ $\mathbf{3n + 4}$

20. $\frac{16r^3 - 12r^2}{2r}$ $\mathbf{8r^2 - 6r}$

21. $(a^2 - 81) + (a^2 + 6a + 5)$ $\mathbf{2a^2 + 6a - 76}$

22. $(5a^2 + 3a - 2) - (2a^2 - a + 6)$ $\mathbf{3a^2 + 4a - 8}$

23. $2x + 3x(x - 4) + 5$ $\mathbf{3x^2 - 10x + 5}$

24. $3r(5r + 2) - 4(2r^2 - r + 3)$ $\mathbf{7r^2 + 10r - 12}$

25. $\frac{8a^3b + 4a^2b^2 - 2ab}{2ab}$ $\mathbf{4a^2 + 2ab - 1}$

26. $\frac{7h^2 - 14h - 35 + 21h}{7}$ $\mathbf{h^2 + h - 5}$

Binomial Products

To multiply two binomials, you can use the Distributive Property systematically. Multiply the *first* terms, the *outer* terms, the *inner* terms, and the *last* terms of the binomials. This method is called **FOIL** for the words **F**irst, **O**uter, **I**nner, and **L**ast.

For certain binomial products, you can also use a special product pattern.

$(a + b)^2 = a^2 + 2ab + b^2$ $\quad (a - b)^2 = a^2 - 2ab + b^2$ $\quad (a - b)(a + b) = a^2 - b^2$

EXAMPLE **Find the product.**

$(x + 2)(3x - 4) = x(3x) + x(-4) + 2(3x) + 2(-4)$

First, Outer, Inner, Last

$= 3x^2 - 4x + 6x - 8$

$= 3x^2 + 2x - 8$

a. $(x + 5)^2$
$= x^2 + 2(x)(5) + 5^2$
$= x^2 + 10x + 25$

b. $(y - 3)^2$
$= y^2 - 2(y)(3) + 3^2$
$= y^2 - 6y + 9$

c. $(z + 4)(z - 4)$
$= z^2 - 4^2$
$= z^2 - 16$

To simplify some expressions, multiply binomials first.

EXAMPLE **Simplify the expression.**

$2(x + 1)(x + 6) - 4(x^2 - 5x + 4) = 2(x^2 + 7x + 6) - 4(x^2 - 5x + 4)$ **Multiply binomials.**

$= 2x^2 + 14x + 12 - 4x^2 + 20x - 16$ **Distributive Property**

$= -2x^2 + 34x - 4$ **Combine like terms.**

PRACTICE

Find the product.

1. $(a - 2)(a - 9)$ $\mathbf{a^2 - 11a + 18}$
2. $(y - 4)^2$ $\mathbf{y^2 - 8y + 16}$
3. $(t - 5)(t + 8)$ $\mathbf{t^2 + 3t - 40}$
4. $(5n + 1)(n - 4)$ $\mathbf{5n^2 - 19n - 4}$
5. $(5a + 2)^2$ $\mathbf{25a^2 + 20a + 4}$
6. $(x - 10)(x + 10)$ $\mathbf{x^2 - 100}$
7. $(c + 4)(4c - 3)$ $\mathbf{4c^2 + 13c - 12}$
8. $(n + 7)^2$ $\mathbf{n^2 + 14n + 49}$
9. $(8 - z)^2$ $\mathbf{z^2 - 16z + 64}$
10. $(a + 1)(a - 1)$ $\mathbf{a^2 - 1}$
11. $(2x + 1)(x + 1)$ $\mathbf{2x^2 + 3x + 1}$
12. $(-7z + 6)(3z - 4)$ $\mathbf{21z^2 + 46z - 24}$
13. $(2x - 3)(2x + 3)$ $\mathbf{4x^2 - 9}$
14. $(5 + n)^2$ $\mathbf{n^2 + 10n + 25}$
15. $(2d - 1)(3d + 2)$ $\mathbf{6d^2 + d - 2}$
16. $(a + 3)(a + 3)$ $\mathbf{a^2 + 6a + 9}$
17. $(k - 1.2)^2$ $\mathbf{k^2 - 2.4k + 1.44}$
18. $(6x - 5)(2x - 3)$ $\mathbf{12x^2 - 28x + 15}$
19. $(6 - z)(6 + z)$ $\mathbf{-z^2 + 36}$
20. $(4 - 5g)(3g + 2)$ $\mathbf{-15g^2 + 2g + 8}$

Simplify the expression.

21. $3(y - 4)(y + 2) + (2y - 1)(y + 8)$ $\mathbf{5y^2 + 9y - 32}$
22. $4(t^2 + 3t - 4) + 2(t - 1)(t + 5)$ $\mathbf{6t^2 + 20t - 26}$
23. $2(x + 2)(x - 2) + (x - 3)(x + 3)$ $\mathbf{3x^2 - 17}$
24. $2(2c^2 + 3c - 1) + 7(c + 2)^2$ $\mathbf{11c^2 + 34c + 26}$

SKILLS REVIEW HANDBOOK

Radical Expressions

A **square root** of a number n is a number m such that $m^2 = n$. For example, $9^2 = 81$ and $(-9)^2 = 81$, so the square roots of 81 are 9 and -9.

Every positive number has two square roots, one positive and one negative. Negative numbers have no real square roots. The square root of zero is zero.

The radical symbol, $\sqrt{\ }$, represents a nonnegative square root: $\sqrt{81} = 9$. The opposite of a square root is negative: $-\sqrt{81} = -9$.

A **perfect square** is a number that is the square of an integer. So, 81 is a perfect square. A **radicand** is a number or expression inside a radical symbol.

Properties of Radicals	Simplest Form of a Radical Expression
For $a \geq 0$ and $b \geq 0$:	• No perfect square factors other than 1 in the radicand
$\sqrt{ab} = \sqrt{a} \cdot \sqrt{b}$	• No fractions in the radicand
$\sqrt{\frac{a}{b}} = \frac{\sqrt{a}}{\sqrt{b}} = \frac{\sqrt{ab}}{b}$	• No radical signs in the denominator of a fraction

EXAMPLE **Simplify the expression.**

a. $\sqrt{9 + 36} = \sqrt{45} = \sqrt{9 \cdot 5} = \sqrt{9} \cdot \sqrt{5} = 3\sqrt{5}$

b. $\sqrt{50} - \sqrt{32} = \sqrt{25 \cdot 2} - \sqrt{16 \cdot 2} = 5\sqrt{2} - 4\sqrt{2} = (5 - 4)\sqrt{2} = 1\sqrt{2} = \sqrt{2}$

c. $\sqrt{18} \cdot \sqrt{72} = \sqrt{18 \cdot 72} = \sqrt{1296} = 36$

d. $(8\sqrt{3})^2 = 8^2 \cdot (\sqrt{3})^2 = 64 \cdot 3 = 192$

e. $\frac{6}{\sqrt{2}} = \frac{6}{\sqrt{2}} \cdot \frac{\sqrt{2}}{\sqrt{2}} = \frac{6 \cdot \sqrt{2}}{(\sqrt{2})^2} = \frac{6 \cdot \sqrt{2}}{2} = 3\sqrt{2}$

f. $\frac{\sqrt{20}}{\sqrt{500}} = \sqrt{\frac{20}{500}} = \sqrt{\frac{1}{25}} = \frac{1}{5}$

PRACTICE

Find all square roots of the number or write *no square roots*.

1. 100 **±10** **2.** 64 **±8** **3.** $\frac{1}{4}$ **$\pm\frac{1}{2}$** **4.** $\frac{9}{25}$ **$\pm\frac{3}{5}$**

5. −16 **no square roots** **6.** 0 **0** **7.** 0.81 **±0.9** **8.** 0.0016 **±0.04**

Simplify the expression.

9. $\sqrt{121}$ **11** **10.** $-\sqrt{169}$ **−13** **11.** $-\sqrt{99}$ **$-3\sqrt{11}$** **12.** $\sqrt{48}$ **$4\sqrt{3}$**

13. $\sqrt{16 + 4}$ **$2\sqrt{5}$** **14.** $\sqrt{(-4)^2 + 6^2}$ **$2\sqrt{13}$** **15.** $\sqrt{175} - \sqrt{28}$ **$3\sqrt{7}$** **16.** $\sqrt{32} + \sqrt{162}$ **$13\sqrt{2}$**

17. $\sqrt{8} \cdot \sqrt{10}$ **$4\sqrt{5}$** **18.** $4\sqrt{6} \cdot 2\sqrt{15}$ **$24\sqrt{10}$** **19.** $\sqrt{210 \cdot 420}$ **$210\sqrt{2}$** **20.** $(9\sqrt{3})^2$ **243**

21. $\sqrt{137} \cdot \sqrt{137}$ **137** **22.** $\sqrt{12} \cdot \sqrt{48}$ **24** **23.** $5\sqrt{18} \cdot \sqrt{2}$ **30** **24.** $3\sqrt{7} \cdot 5\sqrt{11}$ **$15\sqrt{77}$**

25. $\frac{\sqrt{192}}{\sqrt{3}}$ **8** **26.** $\sqrt{\frac{2}{49}}$ **$\frac{\sqrt{2}}{7}$** **27.** $\frac{12}{\sqrt{6}}$ **$2\sqrt{6}$** **28.** $\frac{2}{\sqrt{5}}$ **$\frac{2\sqrt{5}}{5}$**

874

Solving Linear Equations

To solve a linear equation, you isolate the variable.

Add the same number to each side of the equation.

Subtract the same number from each side of the equation.

Multiply each side of the equation by the same nonzero number.

Divide each side of the equation by the same nonzero number.

EXAMPLE **Solve the equation: a. $3x - 5 = 13$ b. $2(y - 3) = y + 4$**

a. $3x - 5 = 13$

$3x - 5 + 5 = 13 + 5$	**Add 5.**
$3x = 18$	**Simplify.**
$\frac{3x}{3} = \frac{18}{3}$	**Divide by 3.**
$x = 6$	**Simplify.**

CHECK $3x - 5 = 13$

$3(6) - 5 \stackrel{?}{=} 13$

$13 = 13$ ✓

b. $2(y - 3) = y + 4$

$2y - 6 = y + 4$	**Distributive Property**
$2y - y - 6 = y - y + 4$	**Subtract *y*.**
$y - 6 = 4$	**Simplify.**
$y - 6 + 6 = 4 + 6$	**Add 6.**
$y = 10$	**Simplify.**

CHECK $2(y - 3) = y + 4$

$2(10 - 3) \stackrel{?}{=} 10 + 4$

$14 = 14$ ✓

PRACTICE

Solve the equation.

1. $x - 8 = 23$ **31**
2. $n + 12 = 0$ **−12**
3. $-18 = 3y$ **−6**
4. $\frac{a}{6} = 7$ **42**
5. $\frac{2}{3}r = 26$ **39**
6. $-\frac{4}{5}t = -8$ **10**
7. $-4.8 = 1.5z$ **−3.2**
8. $0 = -3x + 12$ **4**
9. $72 = 90 - x$ **18**
10. $7(y - 2) = 21$ **5**
11. $5 = 4k + 2 - k$ **1**
12. $4n + 1 = -2n + 8$ $\mathbf{\frac{7}{6}}$
13. $2c + 3 = 4(c - 1)$ $\mathbf{\frac{7}{2}}$
14. $9 - (3r - 1) = 12$ $\mathbf{-\frac{2}{3}}$
15. $12m + 3(2m + 6) = 0$ **−1**
16. $\frac{6}{5}y - 2 = 10$ **10**
17. $\frac{w - 8}{3} = 4$ **20**
18. $-\frac{1}{4}(12 + h) = 7$ **−40**
19. $2c - 8 = 24$ **16**
20. $2.8(5 - t) = 7$ **2.5**
21. $2 - c = -3(2c + 1)$ **−1**
22. $-4k + 8 = 12 - 5k$ **4**
23. $3(z - 2) + 8 = 23$ **7**
24. $12 = 5(-3r + 2) - (r - 1)$ $\mathbf{-\frac{1}{16}}$
25. $12(z + 12) = 15^2$ $\mathbf{\frac{27}{4}}$
26. $2 \cdot 3.14 \cdot r = 94.2$ **15**
27. $3.1(2f + 1.2) = 0.2(f - 6)$ **−0.82**
28. $5(3t - 2) = -3(7 - t)$ $\mathbf{-\frac{11}{12}}$
29. $20a - 12(a - 3) = 4$ **−4**
30. $5.5(h - 5.5) = 18.18$ **about 8.8**
31. $\frac{1}{2} \cdot b \cdot 8 = 10$ $\mathbf{\frac{5}{2}}$
32. $\frac{4x + 12}{2} = 3x - 5$ **11**
33. $\frac{10 + 7y}{4} = \frac{5 - y}{3}$ $\mathbf{-\frac{2}{5}}$
34. $\frac{9 - 2x}{7} = x$ **1**
35. $\frac{23 - 11c}{7} = 5c$ $\mathbf{\frac{1}{2}}$
36. $\frac{4n - 28}{3} = 2n$ **−14**

SKILLS REVIEW HANDBOOK

1. −4 −2 0 2 4 6 8
2. 11 −4 0 4 8 12 16 20
3. −4 −2 0 2 4 6 8
4. $-\frac{9}{2}$ −6 −4 −2 0 2 4 6
5. −8 −6 −4 −2 0 2 4
6. −6 −4 −2 0 2 4 6
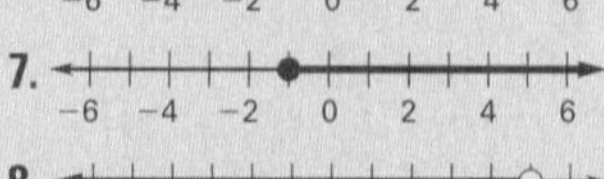
7. −6 −4 −2 0 2 4 6
8. −6 −4 −2 0 2 4 6
9. −4 −2 0 2 4 6 8
10. −6 −4 −2 0 2 4 6
11. −6 −4 −2 0 2 4 6
12. −10 −8 −6 −4 −2 0 2
13. −6 −4 −2 0 2 4 6
14. −6 −4 −2 0 2 4 6
15. −2 0 2 4 6 8 10
16. −10 −8 −6 −4 −2 0 2
17. 0 2 4 6 8 10 12
18. −8 −6 −4 −2 0 2 4

SKILLS REVIEW HANDBOOK

Solving and Graphing Linear Inequalities

You can graph solutions to equations and inequalities on a number line.

Symbol	Meaning	Equation or Inequality	Graph
=	equals	$x = 3$	1 2 3 4 5
<	is less than	$x < 3$	1 2 3 4 5
≤	is less than or equal to	$x \le 3$	1 2 3 4 5
>	is greater than	$x > 3$	1 2 3 4 5
≥	is greater than or equal to	$x \ge 3$	1 2 3 4 5

You can use properties of inequalities to solve linear inequalities.

Add the same number to each side of the inequality.

Subtract the same number from each side of the inequality.

Multiply each side of the inequality by the same positive number. If you multiply by a negative number, reverse the direction of the inequality symbol.

Divide each side of the inequality by the same positive number. If you divide by a negative number, reverse the direction of the inequality symbol.

EXAMPLE **Solve the inequality. Graph the solution.**

a. $2x + 1 \le 5$

$2x \le 4$ Subtract 1 from each side.

$x \le 2$ Divide each side by 2.

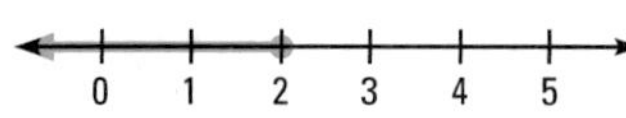

b. $-4y < 18$

$\frac{-4y}{-4} > \frac{18}{-4}$ Divide by −4 and change < to >.

$y > -4.5$ Simplify.

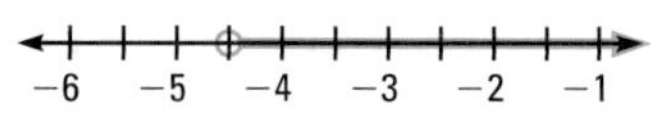

PRACTICE

Solve the inequality. Graph the solution. **1–18. See margin for art.**

1. $x - 2 < 5$ **$x < 7$**

2. $16 < x + 5$ **$x > 11$**

3. $10 - n \ge 6$ **$n \le 4$**

4. $2z \ge -9$ **$z \ge -\frac{9}{2}$**

5. $8c + 24 < 0$ **$c < -3$**

6. $6 \ge -3a$ **$a \ge -2$**

7. $5a - 3 \ge -8$ **$a \ge -1$**

8. $2n + 7 < 17$ **$n < 5$**

9. $5 > 0.5y + 3$ **$y < 4$**

10. $5 - 3x \le x + 13$ **$x \ge -2$**

11. $5r + 2r \le 6r - 1$ **$r \le -1$**

12. $y - 3 \le 2y + 5$ **$y \ge -8$**

13. $-2.4m \ge 3.6m - 12$ **$m \le 2$**

14. $-2(t - 6) > 7t - 6$ **$t < 2$**

15. $4(8 - z) + 2 > 3z - 8$ **$z < 6$**

16. $-\frac{3}{4}n > 3$ **$n < -4$**

17. $\frac{c}{5} - 8 \le -6$ **$c \le 10$**

18. $\frac{n - 5}{2} \ge \frac{2n - 6}{3}$ **$n \le -3$**

Solving Formulas

A **formula** is an equation that relates two or more real-world quantities. You can rewrite a formula so that any one of the variables is a function of the other variable(s). In each case you isolate a variable on one side of the equation.

EXAMPLE **Solve the formula for the indicated variable.**

a. Solve $C = 2\pi r$ for r.

$C = 2\pi r$

$\frac{C}{2\pi} = \frac{2\pi r}{2\pi}$ **Divide by 2π.**

$\frac{C}{2\pi} = r$ **Simplify.**

$r = \frac{C}{2\pi}$ **Rewrite.**

b. Solve $P = a + b + c$ for a.

$P = a + b + c$

$P - b - c = a + b - b + c - c$ **Subtract.**

$P - b - c = a$ **Simplify.**

$a = P - b - c$ **Rewrite.**

EXAMPLE **Rewrite the equation so that y is a function of x.**

a. $2x + y = 3$

$2x - 2x + y = 3 - 2x$ **Subtract $2x$.**

$y = 3 - 2x$ **Simplify.**

b. $\frac{1}{4}y = x$

$4 \cdot \frac{1}{4}y = 4 \cdot x$ **Multiply by 4.**

$y = 4x$ **Simplify.**

PRACTICE

Solve the formula for the indicated variable.

1. Solve $P = 4s$ for s. $s = \frac{P}{4}$
2. Solve $d = rt$ for r. $r = \frac{d}{t}$
3. Solve $V = \ell wh$ for ℓ. $\ell = \frac{V}{wh}$
4. Solve $V = \pi r^2 h$ for h. $h = \frac{V}{\pi r^2}$
5. Solve $A = \frac{1}{2}bh$ for b. $b = \frac{2A}{h}$
6. Solve $d = \frac{m}{v}$ for v. $v = \frac{m}{d}$
7. Solve $P = 2(\ell + w)$ for w. $w = \frac{P}{2} - \ell$
8. Solve $I = prt$ for r. $r = \frac{I}{pt}$
9. Solve $F = \frac{9}{5}C + 32$ for C. $C = \frac{5}{9}(F - 32)$
10. Solve $A = \frac{1}{2}h(b_1 + b_2)$ for h. $h = \frac{2A}{b_1 + b_2}$
11. Solve $S = 2\pi r^2 + 2\pi rh$ for h. $h = \frac{S - 2\pi r^2}{2\pi r}$
12. Solve $A = P(1 + r)^t$ for P. $P = \frac{A}{(1 + r)^t}$

Rewrite the equation so that y is a function of x.

13. $2x + y = 7$ $y = -2x + 7$
14. $5x + 3y = 0$ $y = -\frac{5}{3}x$
15. $3x - y = -2$ $y = 3x + 2$
16. $y + 1 = -2(x - 2)$ $y = -2x + 3$
17. $\frac{4}{5}y = x$ $y = \frac{5}{4}x$
18. $\frac{1}{4}x + 2y = 5$ $y = -\frac{1}{8}x + \frac{5}{2}$
19. $1.8x - 0.3y = 4.5$ $y = 6x - 15$
20. $y - 4 = \frac{1}{3}(x + 6)$ $y = \frac{1}{3}x + 6$

7–12.

13.

14.

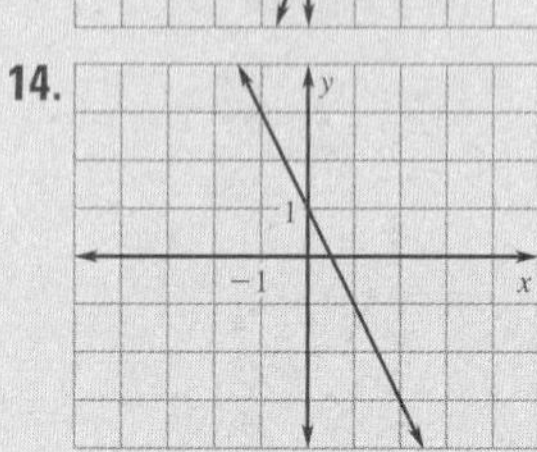

15.

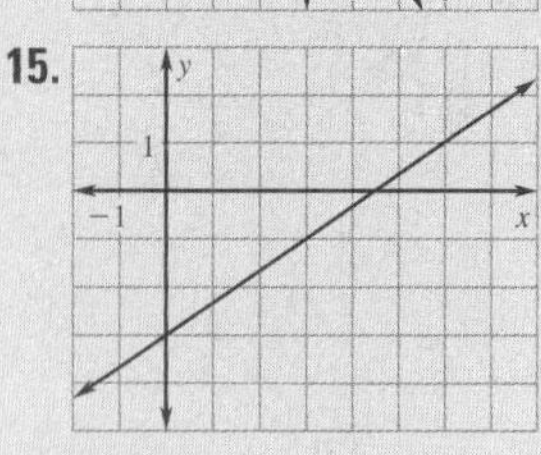

16.

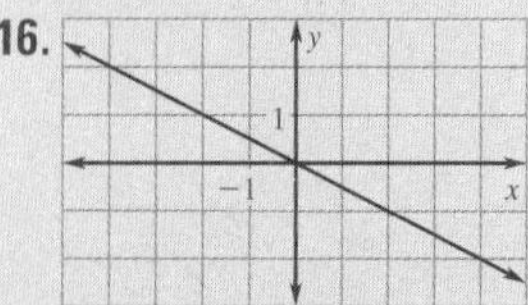

17.

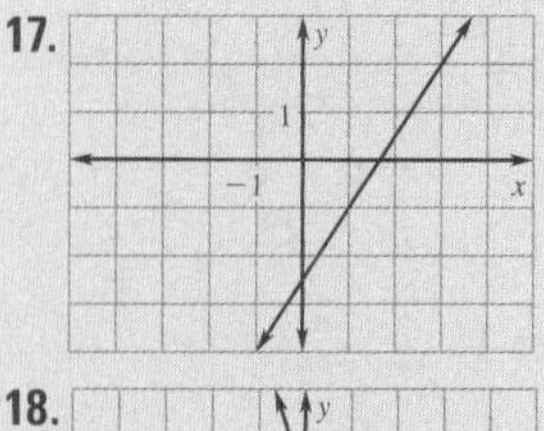

18.

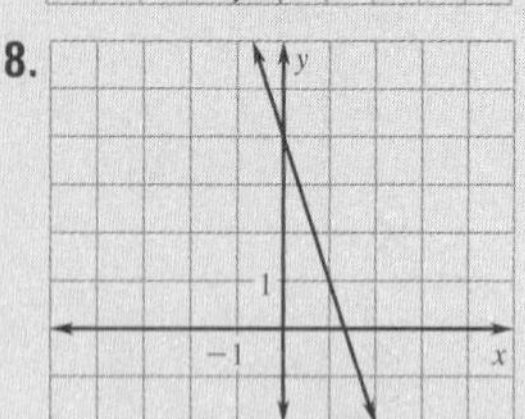

Graphing Points and Lines

A **coordinate plane** is formed by the intersection of a horizontal number line called the ***x*-axis** and a vertical number line called the ***y*-axis**. The axes meet at a point called the **origin** and divide the coordinate plane into four **quadrants**, labeled I, II, III, and IV.

Each point in a coordinate plane is represented by an **ordered pair**. The first number is the ***x*-coordinate**, and the second number is the ***y*-coordinate**.

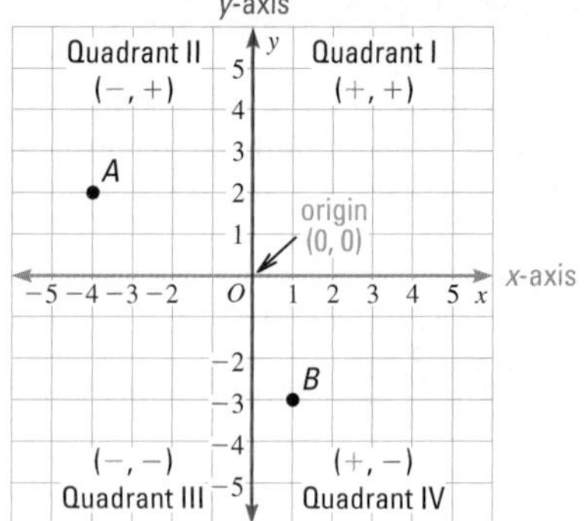

EXAMPLE Give the coordinates of points *A* and *B* in the graph above.

Start at the origin. Count 4 units left and 2 units up. Point *A* is at (−4, 2).
Start at the origin. Count 1 unit right and 3 units down. Point *B* is at (1, −3).

A **solution** of an equation in *x* and *y* is an ordered pair (*x*, *y*) that makes the equation true. The graph of such an equation is the set of points in a coordinate plane that represent all the solutions. A **linear equation** has a line as its graph.

EXAMPLE Graph the equation $y = 2x - 3$.

Make a table of values, graph each point, and draw the line.

x	$y = 2x - 3$	(x, y)	
0	$y = 2(0) - 3 = -3$	(0, −3)	→ 0 units right or left, 3 units down
1	$y = 2(1) - 3 = -1$	(1, −1)	→ 1 unit right, 1 unit down
2	$y = 2(2) - 3 = 1$	(2, 1)	→ 2 units right, 1 unit up

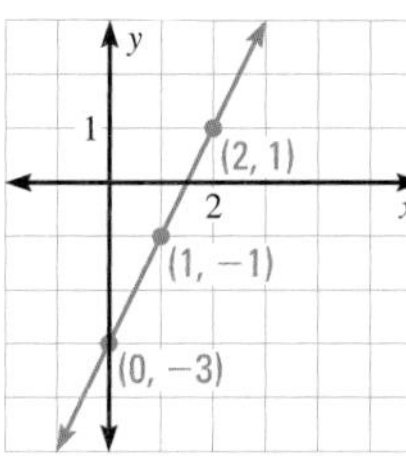

PRACTICE

Use the graph shown. Give the coordinates of the point.

1. *C* **(3, 1)**
2. *D* **(−1, −2)**
3. *E* **(0, 2)**
4. *F* **(−3, 0)**
5. *G* **(3, −3)**
6. *H* **(−2, 3)**

Plot the point in a coordinate plane. **7–12. See margin.**

7. $J(-3, 1)$
8. $K(2, -2)$
9. $L(0, -1)$
10. $M\left(\frac{3}{2}, 3\right)$
11. $N\left(-\frac{5}{2}, -\frac{1}{2}\right)$
12. $P(4.5, 0)$

Use a table of values to graph the equation. **13–20. See margin.**

13. $y = 3x - 2$
14. $y = -2x + 1$
15. $y = \frac{2}{3}x - 3$
16. $y = -\frac{1}{2}x$
17. $y = 1.5x - 2.5$
18. $y = 4 - 3x$
19. $4x + 2y = 0$
20. $2x - y = 3$

19.

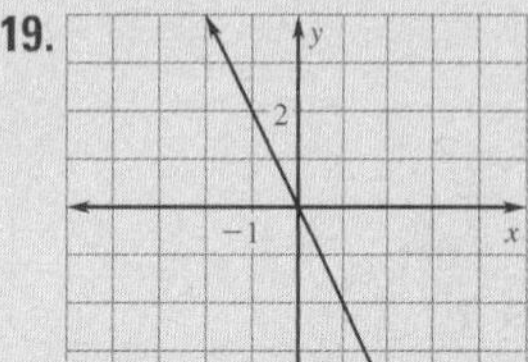

20.

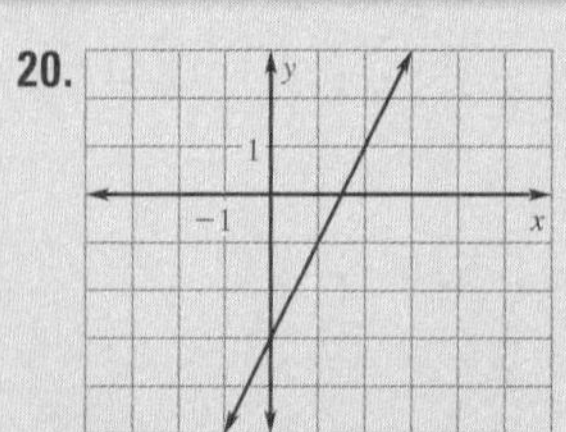

Slope and Intercepts of a Line

The **slope** of a nonvertical line is the ratio of the vertical change, called the **rise**, to the horizontal change, called the **run**. The table below shows some types of lines and slopes.

Rising Line	Falling Line	Horizontal Line	Vertical Line
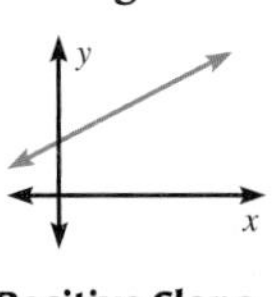	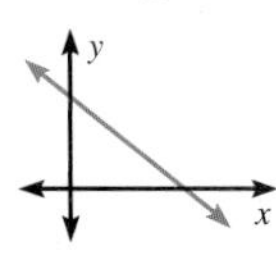	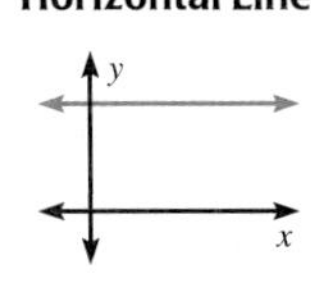	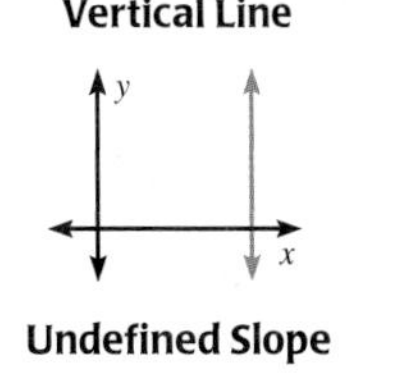
Positive Slope	Negative Slope	Zero Slope	Undefined Slope

EXAMPLE **Find the slope of the line.**

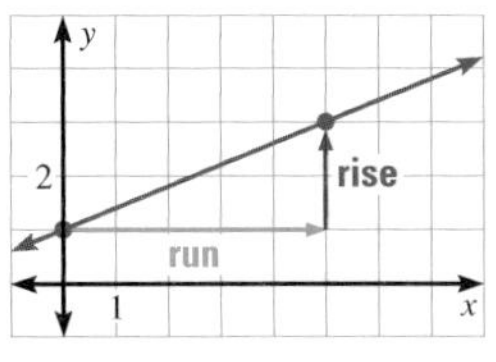

Use the graph of the line.

$$\text{Slope} = \frac{\text{rise}}{\text{run}} = \frac{2 \text{ units up}}{5 \text{ units right}} = \frac{2}{5}$$

An ***x*-intercept** is the x-coordinate of a point where a graph crosses the x-axis. A ***y*-intercept** is the y-coordinate of a point where a graph crosses the y-axis. The line graphed at the right has x-intercept 2 and y-intercept 3.

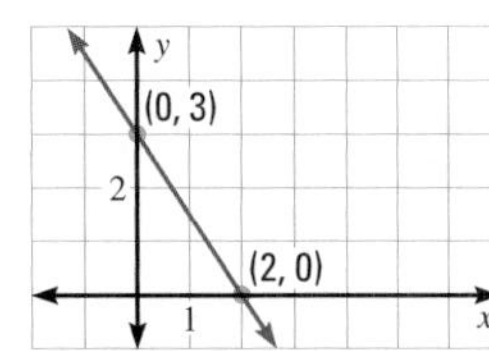

EXAMPLE **Find the *x*-intercept and the *y*-intercept of the graph of $x - 4y = 8$.**

To find the x-intercept, let $y = 0$.

$x - 4(0) = 8$

$x = 8$

The *x*-intercept is 8.

To find the y-intercept, let $x = 0$.

$0 - 4y = 8$

$y = -2$

The *y*-intercept is −2.

PRACTICE

Find the slope and intercept(s) of the line graphed. **1–4. See margin.**

1. 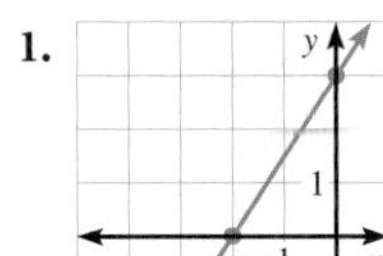 

2. 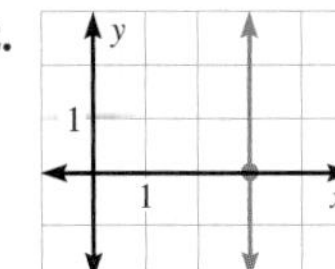

3. 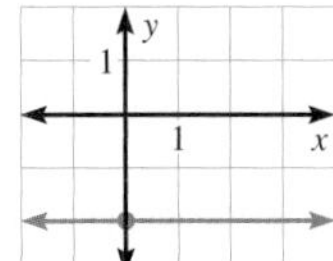

4. 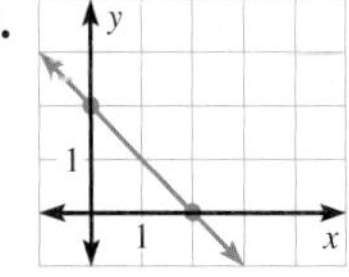

Find the intercepts of the line with the given equation. **5–12. See margin.**

5. $5x - y = 15$ **6.** $2x + 4y = 12$ **7.** $y = -x + 3$ **8.** $y = 3x - 2$

9. $-3x + y = -6$ **10.** $y = -2x - 7$ **11.** $y = 5x$ **12.** $9x - 3y = 15$

1. $\frac{3}{2}$, x-intercept: −2, y-intercept: 3
2. undefined, x-intercept: 3, y-intercept: none
3. 0, x-intercept: none, y-intercept: −2
4. −1, x-intercept: 2, y-intercept: 2
5. x-intercept: 3, y-intercept: −15
6. x-intercept: 6, y-intercept: 3
7. x-intercept: 3, y-intercept: 3
8. x-intercept: $\frac{2}{3}$, y-intercept: −2
9. x-intercept: 2, y-intercept: −6
10. x-intercept: $-\frac{7}{2}$, y-intercept: −7
11. x-intercept: 0, y-intercept: 0
12. x-intercept: $\frac{5}{3}$, y-intercept: −5

Systems of Linear Equations

A **system of linear equations** in two variables is shown at the right. A **solution** of such a system is an ordered pair (x, y) that satisfies both equations. A solution must lie on the graph of both equations.

$x + 2y = 5$	Equation 1
$x - y = -1$	Equation 2

EXAMPLE **Use substitution to solve the linear system above.**

Solve Equation 2 for x. $\quad x - y = -1$

$x = y - 1$ **Revised Equation 2**

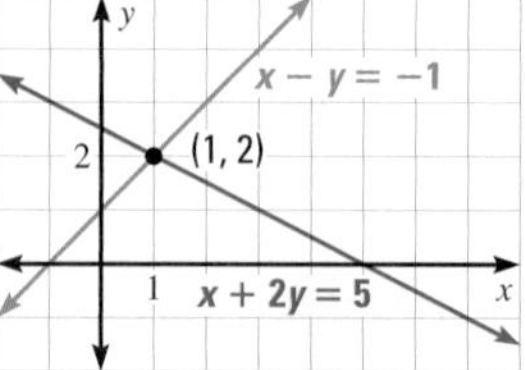

In Equation 1, substitute $y - 1$ for x. Solve for y.

$$x + 2y = 5$$
$$(y - 1) + 2y = 5$$
$$3y = 6$$
$$y = 2$$

In Revised Equation 2, substitute 2 for y. $\quad x = y - 1 = 2 - 1 = 1$

Because $x = 1$ and $y = 2$, the solution (x, y) is $(1, 2)$.

The graph verifies that $(1, 2)$ is the point of intersection of the lines.

EXAMPLE **Use elimination to solve the linear system above.**

Multiply Equation 2 by 2, then add equations.

$$x + 2y = 5 \longrightarrow x + 2y = 5$$
$$x - y = -1 \longrightarrow 2x - 2y = -2$$
$$3x = 3$$
$$x = 1$$

Substitute 1 for x in Equation 2 and solve for y. $\quad 1 - y = -1$

$$2 = y$$

Because $x = 1$ and $y = 2$, the solution (x, y) is $(1, 2)$.

Substitute 1 for x and 2 for y in each original equation to check.

PRACTICE

Use substitution to solve the linear system. Check your solution.

1. $3x - 5y = 1$; $y = 2x - 3$ **(2, 1)**
2. $7x + 4y = -13$; $x = -6y + 9$ **(−3, 2)**
3. $-4x + 3y = -19$; $2x + y = 7$ **(4, −1)**
4. $x + y = -7$; $2x - 5y = 21$ **(−2, −5)**
5. $4x + 9y = -3$; $x + 2y = 0$ **(6, −3)**
6. $0.5x + y = 5$; $1.5x - 2.5y = 4$ **(6, 2)**
7. $2x + 4y = -18$; $3x - y = 1$ **(−1, −4)**
8. $4x + 7y = 3$; $6x + y = 14$ **(2.5, −1)**

Use elimination to solve the linear system. Check your solution.

9. $3x - 6y = -3$; $12x + 6y = 48$ **(3, 2)**
10. $12x + 20y = 56$; $-12x - 7y = -4$ **(−2, 4)**
11. $4x - y = 1$; $2x + 3y = -17$ **(−1, −5)**
12. $10x + 15y = 90$; $5x - 4y = -1$ **(3, 4)**
13. $18x + 63y = -27$; $3x + 9y = -6$ **(−5, 1)**
14. $5x + 7y = 23$; $20x - 30y = 5$ **(2.5, 1.5)**
15. $8x - 5y = 14$; $10x - 2y = 9$ **(0.5, −2)**
16. $-5x + 8y = 4$; $6x - 5y = -14$ **(−4, −2)**

p. 881

1.

2.

3.

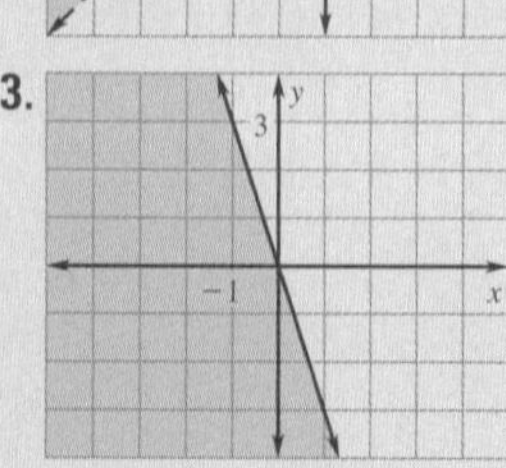

4.

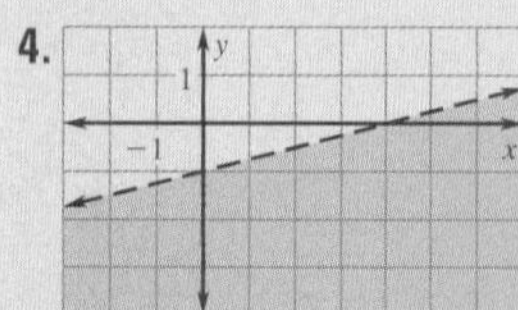

5.

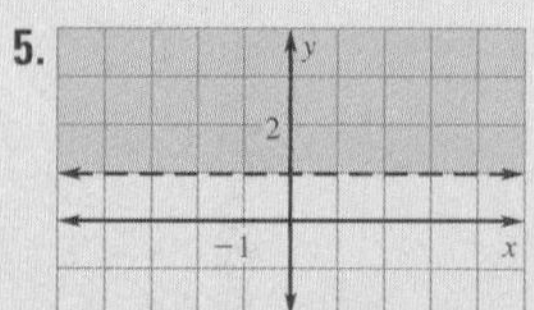

6.

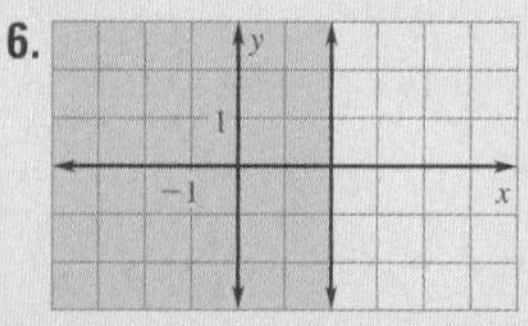

Linear Inequalities

A **linear inequality** in x and y can be written in one of the forms shown at the right. A **solution** of a linear inequality is an ordered pair (x, y) that satisfies the inequality. A **graph** of a linear inequality is the graph of all the solutions.

$ax + by < c$	$ax + by > c$
$ax + by \le c$	$ax + by \ge c$

EXAMPLE **Graph the linear inequality $x + y < 4$.**

Graph the corresponding equation $x + y = 4$. Use a dashed line to show that the points on the line are not solutions of the inequality.

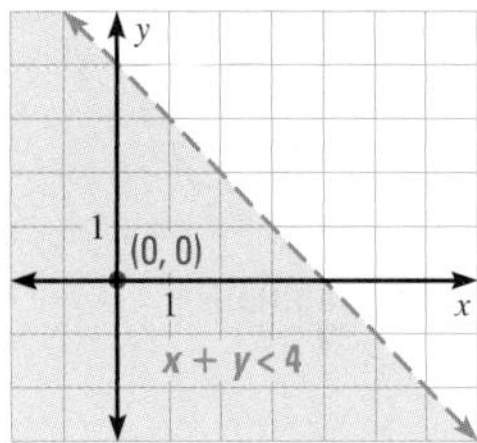

Test a point on either side of the line to see if it is a solution.

Test (3, 2) in $x + y < 4$:	Test (0, 0) in $x + y < 4$:
$3 + 2 < 4$ ✗	$0 + 0 < 4$ ✓
So (3, 2) is not a solution.	So (0, 0) is a solution.

Shade the *half-plane* that includes a test point that is a solution.

Two or more linear inequalities form a **system of linear inequalities**. A **solution** of such a system is an ordered pair (x, y) that satisfies all the inequalities in the system. A **graph** of the system shows all the solutions of the system.

EXAMPLE **Graph the system of linear inequalities $x \ge -2$ and $y \le 3$.**

Graph the linear inequality $x \ge -2$. Use a solid line for the graph of $x = 2$ to show that the points on the line are solutions of the inequality. Shade the half-plane to the right of the line.

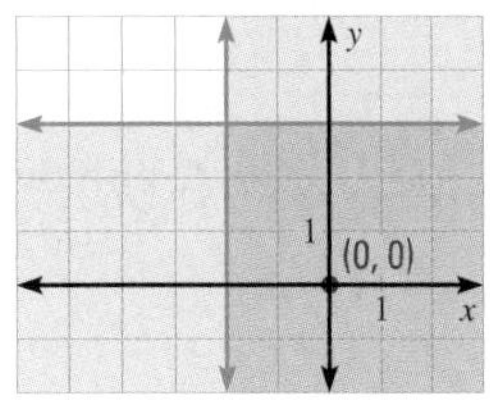

Graph the linear inequality $y \le 3$. Use a solid line for the graph of $y = 3$. Shade the half-plane below the line.

The intersection of the shaded half-planes is a graph of the system.

Check solution point (0, 0) in both inequalities $x \ge -2$ and $y \le 3$.

$0 \ge -2$ ✓ and $0 \le 3$ ✓

PRACTICE

Graph the linear inequality. 1–8. See margin.

1. $x + y \ge 3$
2. $x - y < -2$
3. $y \le -3x$
4. $x - 4y > 4$
5. $y > 1$
6. $x \le 2$
7. $5x - y > 5$
8. $2x + 5y < 10$

Graph the system of linear inequalities. 9–16. See margin.

9. $x > 1$; $y > -2$
10. $x \le 4$; $x \ge -2$
11. $x - y \le 1$; $x + y < 5$
12. $y < x$; $y \ge 3x$
13. $2x - y \le 1$; $2x - y \ge -3$
14. $x \ge 0$; $y \ge 0$; $4x + 3y < 12$
15. $y > -4$; $y < -2$; $x > -3$
16. $x + y \ge 0$; $4x - y \ge -5$; $7x + 2y \le 10$

10.

11.

12.

13.

14.

15.

16.

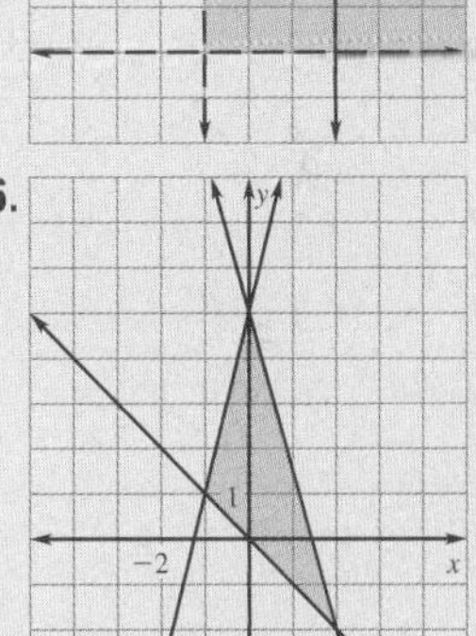

7.

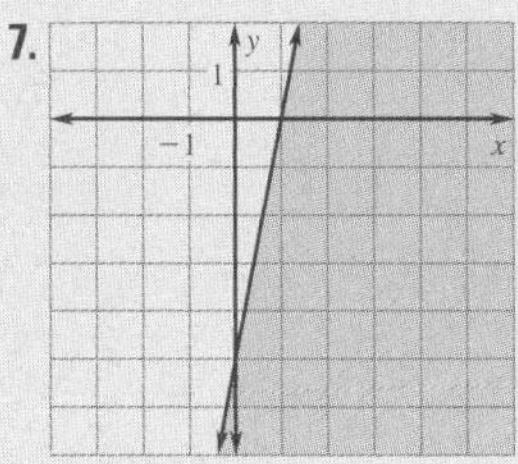

8.

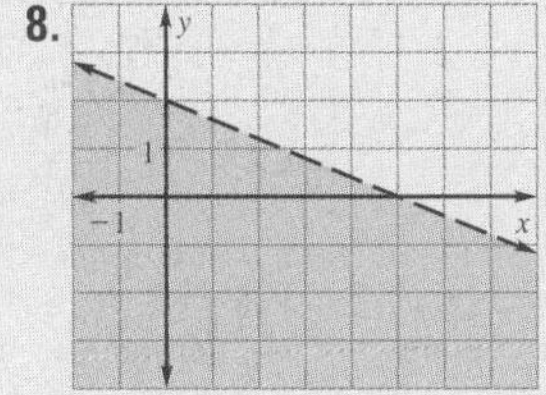

9.

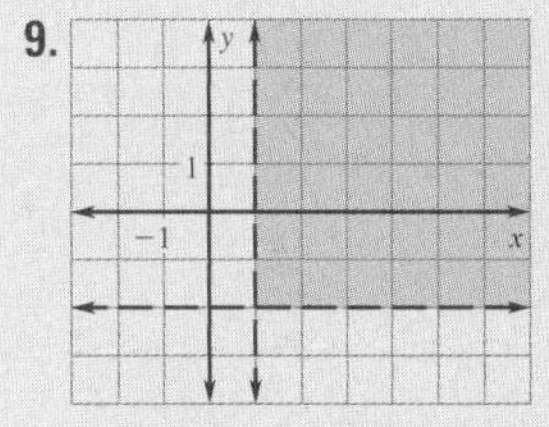

Quadratic Equations and Functions

A **quadratic equation** is an equation that can be written in the *standard form* $ax^2 + bx + c = 0$, where $a \neq 0$. A quadratic equation can have two solutions, one solution, or no real solutions. When $b = 0$, you can use square roots to solve the quadratic equation.

EXAMPLE **Solve the quadratic equation.**

a. $x^2 + 5 = 29$
$x^2 = 24$
$x = \pm\sqrt{24}$
$x = \pm 2\sqrt{6} \approx \pm 4.90$

Two solutions

b. $3x^2 - 4 = -4$
$3x^2 = 0$
$x^2 = 0$
$x = 0$

One solution

c. $-6x^2 + 3 = 21$
$-6x^2 = 18$
$x^2 = -3$

No real solution

A **quadratic function** is a function that can be written in the standard form $y = ax^2 + bx + c$, where $a \neq 0$.

The graph of a quadratic equation is a U-shaped curve called a **parabola**. The **vertex** is the lowest point of a parabola that opens upward ($a > 0$) or the highest point of a parabola that opens downward ($a < 0$). The vertical line passing through the vertex is the **axis of symmetry**.

To graph a quadratic function, you can make a table of values, plot the points, and draw the parabola. The x-intercepts of the graph (if any) are the real solutions of the corresponding quadratic equation.

EXAMPLE **Graph the quadratic function. Label the vertex.**

a. $y = x^2 - 4$

x	y
−2	0
−1	−3
0	−4
1	−3
2	0

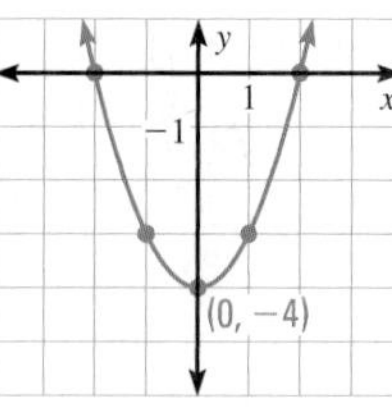

Two x-intercepts

b. $y = -x^2$

x	y
−2	−4
−1	−1
0	0
1	−1
2	−4

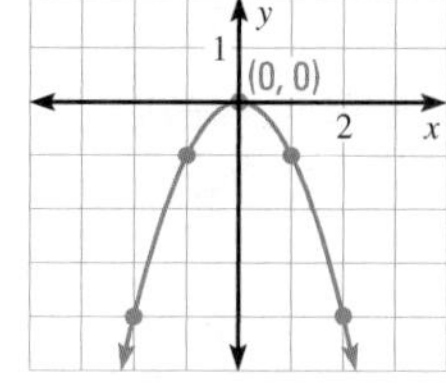

One x-intercept

c. $y = x^2 + 1$

x	y
−2	5
−1	2
0	1
1	2
2	5

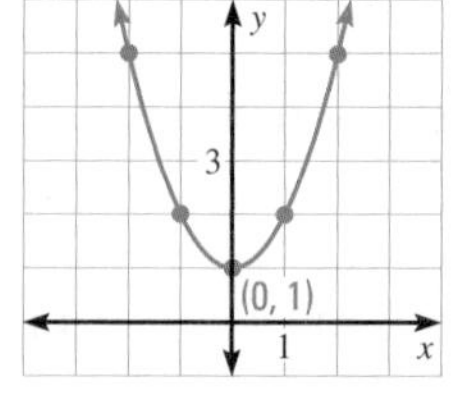

No x-intercepts

13.

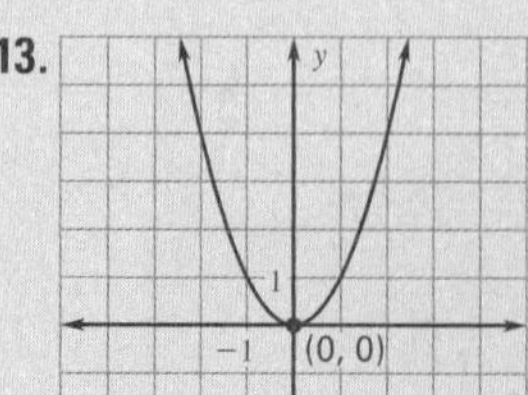

14.

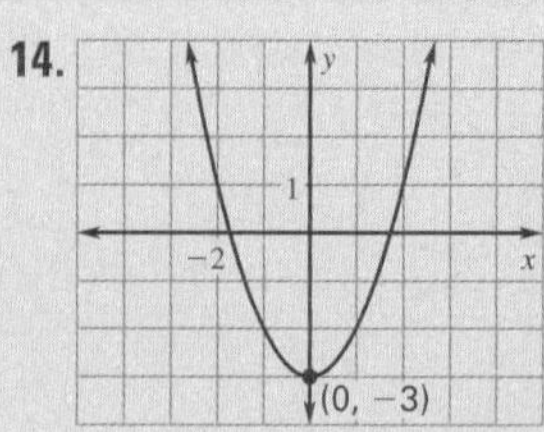

You can use the **quadratic formula** to solve any quadratic equation.

The solutions of the quadratic equation $ax^2 + bx + c = 0$ are

$$x = \frac{-b \pm \sqrt{b^2 - 4ac}}{2a} \text{ where } a \neq 0 \text{ and } b^2 - 4ac \geq 0.$$

EXAMPLE **Use the quadratic formula to solve the equation $8x^2 + 6x = 1$.**

Write the equation in standard form and identify a, b, and c.

The equation $8x^2 + 6x = 1$ is equivalent to $8x^2 + 6x - 1 = 0$. So, $a = 8$, $b = 6$, and $c = -1$.

Use the quadratic formula and simplify.

$$x = \frac{-b \pm \sqrt{b^2 - 4ac}}{2a} = \frac{-6 \pm \sqrt{6^2 - 4(8)(-1)}}{2(8)} = \frac{-6 \pm \sqrt{68}}{16} = \frac{-6 \pm 2\sqrt{17}}{16} = \frac{-3 \pm \sqrt{17}}{8}$$

▶ The solutions of the equation are $\frac{-3 + \sqrt{17}}{8} \approx 0.14$ and $\frac{-3 - \sqrt{17}}{8} \approx -0.89$.

Check the solutions in the original equation.

$8(0.14)^2 + 6(0.14) \stackrel{?}{=} 1$ $\qquad$ $8(-0.89)^2 + 6(-0.89) \stackrel{?}{=} 1$

$0.9968 \approx 1$ ✓ $\qquad$ $0.9968 \approx 1$ ✓

PRACTICE

Solve the quadratic equation.

1. $x^2 = 144$ **±12**
2. $x^2 + 7 = -5$ **no real solutions**
3. $x^2 - (x + 1)^2 = 5$ **−3**
4. $x^2 - 18 = 0$ **$\pm 3\sqrt{2}$**
5. $8x^2 + 3 = 3$ **0**
6. $5x^2 - 2 = -12$ **no real solutions**
7. $(2x + 3)^2 - 4 = 4x^2 - 7$ **−1**
8. $3x^2 + 2 = 14$ **±2**
9. $1 - 4x^2 = 13$ **no real solutions**
10. $12 - 5x^2 = 12$ **0**
11. $15 - 9x^2 = 10$ **$\pm\frac{\sqrt{5}}{3}$**
12. $(x + 2)^2 + 2 = (x - 2)^2 + 8$ **$\frac{3}{4}$**

Graph the quadratic function. Label the vertex. **13–24. See margin.**

13. $y = x^2$
14. $y = x^2 - 3$
15. $y = -x^2 + 4$
16. $y = -2x^2$
17. $y = x^2 + 2$
18. $y = -x^2 - 1$
19. $y = \frac{1}{2}x^2$
20. $y = -\frac{1}{4}x^2$
21. $y = \frac{3}{4}x^2 - 2$
22. $y = 3x^2 + 1$
23. $y = (x - 1)^2$
24. $y = -(x + 2)^2$

Use the quadratic formula to solve the quadratic equation.

25. $x^2 + 6x + 5 = 0$ **−5, −1**
26. $x^2 - 4x - 2 = 0$ **$2 \pm \sqrt{6}$**
27. $x^2 + 6x = -9$ **−3**
28. $2x = 8x^2 - 3$ **$-\frac{1}{2}, \frac{3}{4}$**
29. $x^2 + 7x + 5 = 1$ **$\frac{-7 \pm \sqrt{33}}{2}$**
30. $x^2 + 2x + 5 = 0$ **no real solutions**
31. $2x^2 + 8x - 3 = -11$ **−2**
32. $x^2 + 5x = 6$ **−6, 1**
33. $5x^2 - 6 = 2x$ **$\frac{1 \pm \sqrt{31}}{5}$**
34. $3x^2 + 7x - 4 = 0$ **$\frac{-7 \pm \sqrt{97}}{6}$**
35. $2x^2 - 3x = -4$ **no real solutions**
36. $4x + 4 = 3x^2$ **$-\frac{2}{3}, 2$**
37. $3x^2 - x = 5$ **$\frac{1 \pm \sqrt{61}}{6}$**
38. $(x + 4)(x - 4) = 8$ **$\pm 2\sqrt{6}$**
39. $(x + 2)(x - 2) = 1$ **$\pm\sqrt{5}$**

18.
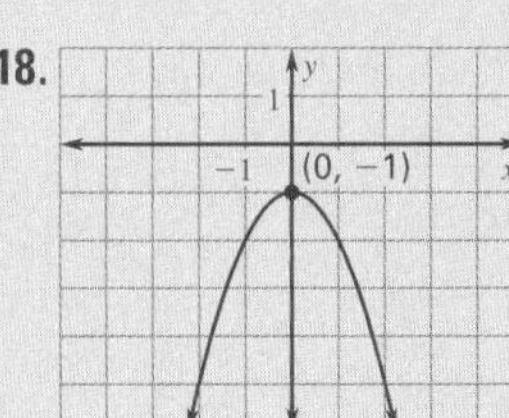

19.
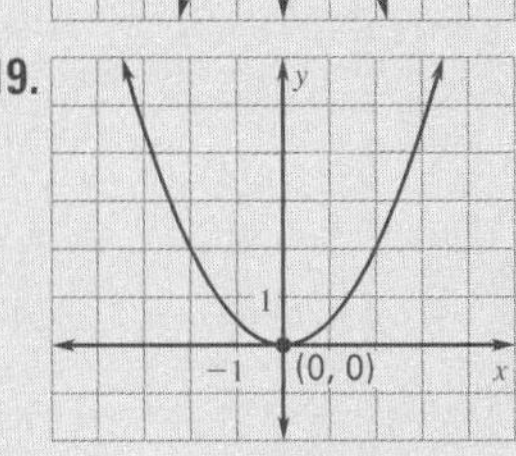

20.
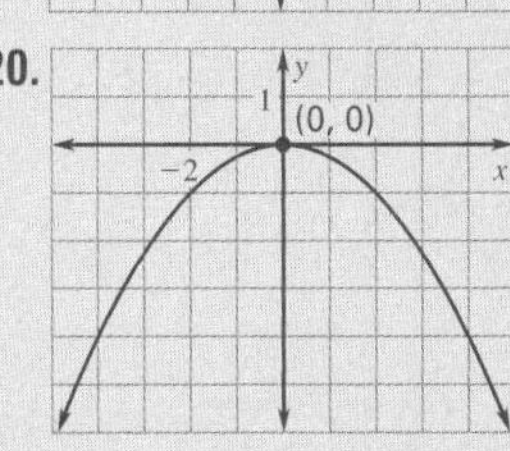

21.
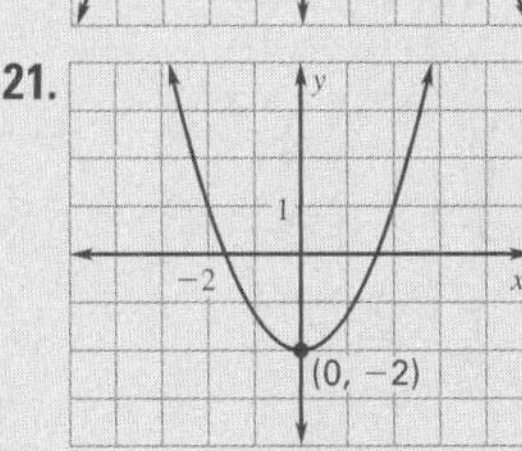

22.
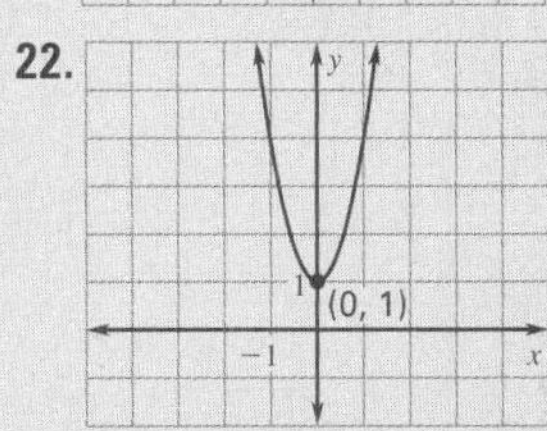

23.
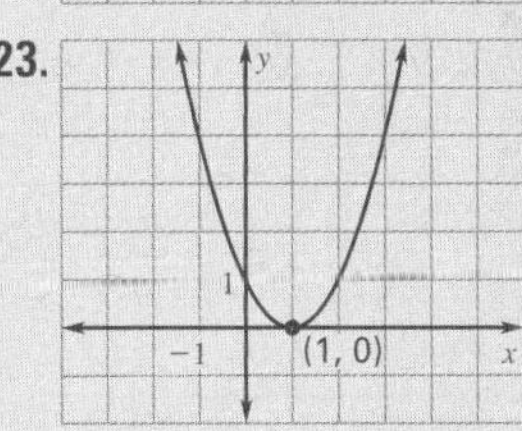

24.
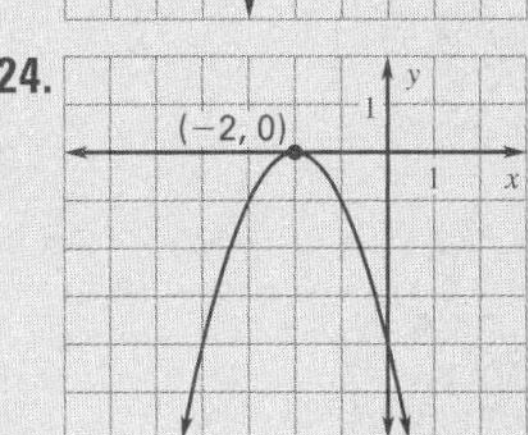

15.
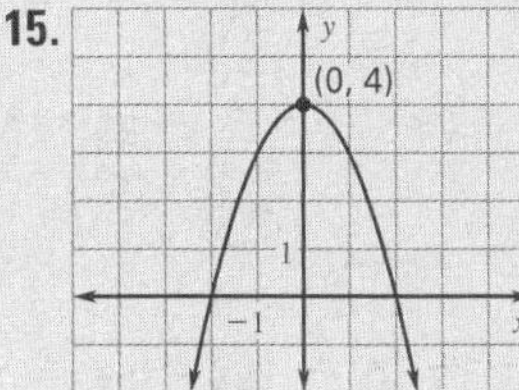

16.
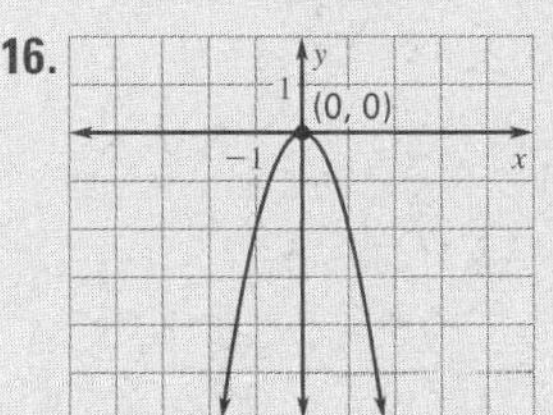

17.
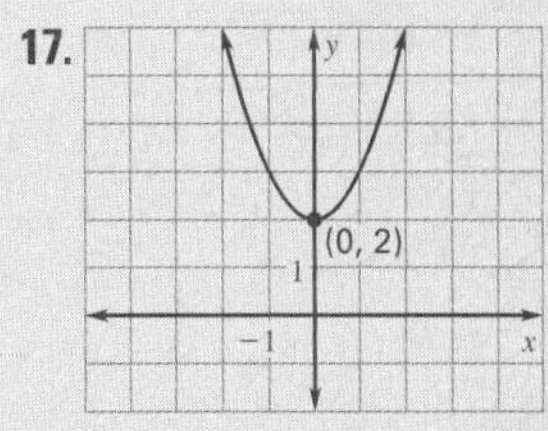

1–8. Check students' tables.

1.

2.

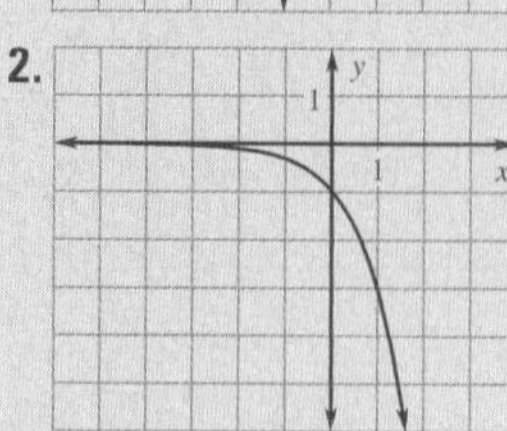

3.

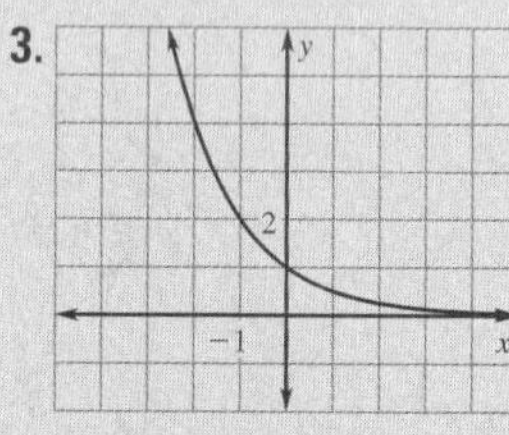

4.

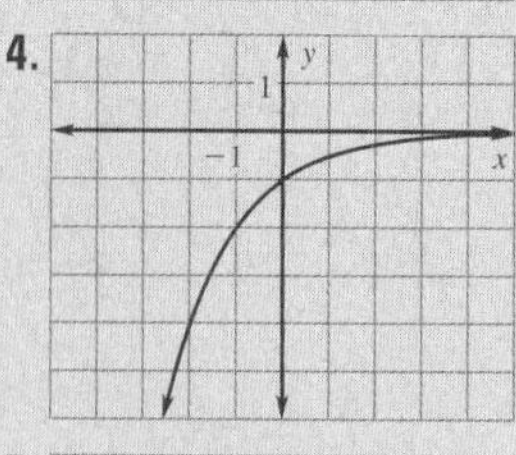

5.

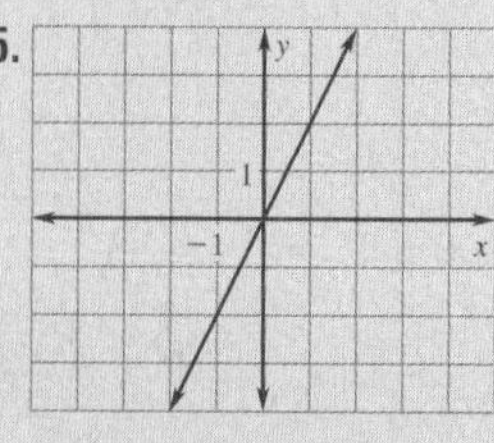

6.

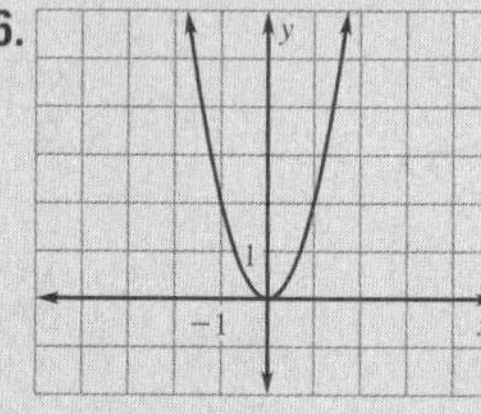

7.

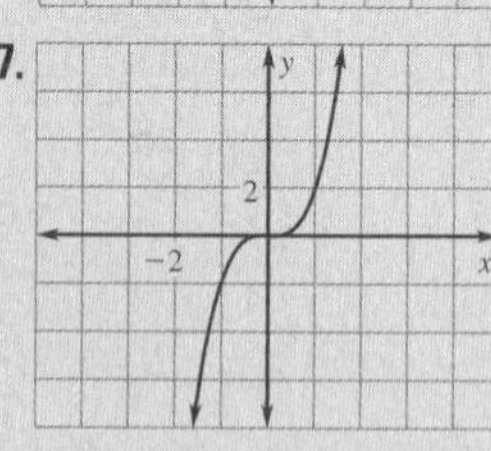

8.

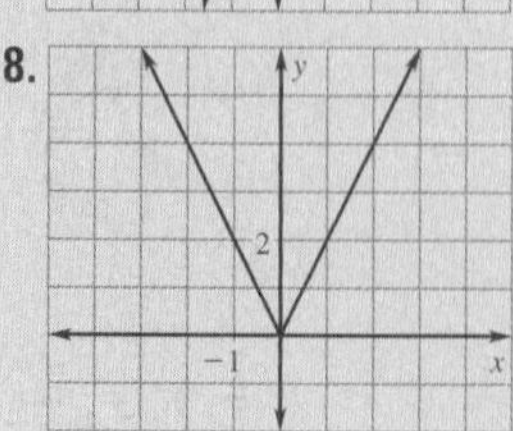

SKILLS REVIEW HANDBOOK

Functions

A function can be described by a table of values, a graph, an equation, or words.

EXAMPLE **Graph the exponential functions $y = 2^x$ and $y = -2^x$.**

For each function, make a table of values, plot the points, and draw a curve.

x	$y = 2^x$	(x, y)
−2	$2^{-2} = \frac{1}{4}$	$\left(-2, \frac{1}{4}\right)$
0	$2^0 = 1$	(0, 1)
1	$2^1 = 2$	(1, 2)
2	$2^2 = 4$	(2, 4)

x	$y = -2^x$	(x, y)
−2	$-2^{-2} = -\frac{1}{4}$	$\left(-2, -\frac{1}{4}\right)$
0	$-2^0 = -1$	(0, −1)
1	$-2^1 = -2$	(1, −2)
2	$-2^2 = -4$	(2, −4)

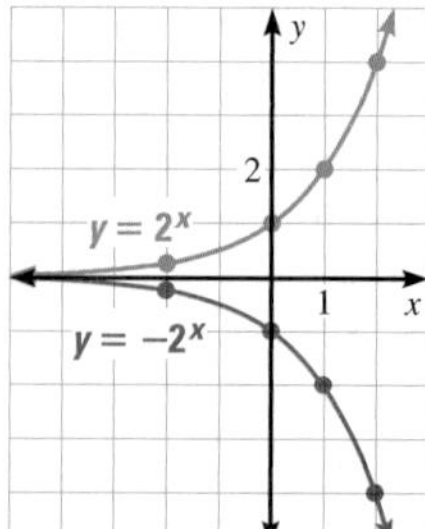

EXAMPLE **The table shows Luke's earnings. Write an equation using his hourly pay rate. How much does Luke earn in 25 hours?**

Hours worked	Earnings (dollars)
8	66
15	123.75
40	330

Use the values in the table to find Luke's hourly pay rate.

$66 \div 8 = 8.25$ $\quad 123.75 \div 15 = 8.25$ $\quad 330 \div 40 = 8.25$

Write an equation using words. Then use variables.

Earnings = Hourly pay rate • Hours worked

$e = 8.25h$ **Let e be earnings and h be hours worked.**

$= 8.25(25)$ **Substitute 25 for h.**

$= 206.25$ **Multiply.**

▶ Luke earns $206.25 in 25 hours.

PRACTICE

Make a table of values and graph the function. **1–8. See margin.**

1. $y = 3^x$
2. $y = -3^x$
3. $y = (0.5)^x$
4. $y = -(0.5)^x$
5. $y = 2x$
6. $y = 2x^2$
7. $y = 2x^3$
8. $y = |2x|$

Write an equation for the function described by the table.

9.

x	1	2	3	4
y	1	4	9	16

$y = x^2$

10.

x	−2	−1	0	1
y	2	1	0	−1

$y = -x$

11. Write an equation using Sue's hourly pay rate of $12. How much does Sue earn in 6 hours? How many hours must Sue work to earn $420? **$y = 12x$; $72; 35 h**

Problem Solving with Percents

You can use equations to solve problems with percents. Replace words with symbols as shown in the table. To estimate with percents, use compatible numbers.

Words	a is p percent of b.
Symbols	$a = p \cdot b$

EXAMPLE **Use the percent equation to answer the question.**

a. What is 45% of 60?

$a = 0.45 \times 60$

$a = 27$

b. What percent of 28 is 7?

$7 = p \times 28$

$7 \div 28 = p$

$0.25 = p$

$25\% = p$

c. 30% of what number is 12?

$12 = 0.3 \times b$

$12 \div 0.3 = b$

$40 = b$

EXAMPLE **Solve the problem.**

a. Estimate 77% of 80.

$77\% \text{ of } 80 \approx 75\% \times 80$

$= \frac{3}{4} \times 80 = 60$

b. Find the percent of change from \$25 to \$36.

$\frac{\text{new} - \text{old}}{\text{old}} = \frac{36 - 25}{25}$

$= \frac{11}{25}$

$= 0.44 = 44\% \text{ increase}$

PRACTICE

1. A history test has 30 questions. How many questions must you answer correctly to earn a grade of 80%? **24 questions**
2. A class of 27 students has 15 girls. What percent of the class is boys? **about 44%**
3. Jill's goal is to practice her clarinet daily at least 80% of the time. She practiced 25 days in October. Did Jill meet her goal in October? **yes**
4. The price of a CD player is \$98. About how much will the CD player cost with a 25% discount? **\$73.50**
5. A jacket is on sale for \$48. The original price was \$60. What is the percent of discount? **20%**
6. A choir had 38 singers, then 5 more joined. What is the percent of increase? **about 13%**
7. A newspaper conducts a survey and finds that 475 of the residents who were surveyed want a new city park. The newspaper reports that 95% of those surveyed want a new park. How many residents were surveyed? **500 residents**
8. Ron received a raise at work. Instead of earning \$8.75 per hour, he will earn \$9.25. What is the percent of increase in Ron's hourly wage? **about 5.7%**
9. A school has 515 students. About 260 students ride the school bus. Estimate the percent of the school's students who ride the school bus. **about 50%**

SKILLS REVIEW HANDBOOK

885

Converting Measurements and Rates

The Table of Measures on page 921 gives many statements of equivalent measures. For each statement, you can write two different conversion factors.

Statement of Equivalent Measures	Conversion Factors
100 cm = 1 m	$\frac{100 \text{ cm}}{1 \text{ m}} = 1$ and $\frac{1 \text{ m}}{100 \text{ cm}} = 1$

To convert from one unit of measurement to another, multiply by a conversion factor. Use a conversion factor that allows you to divide out the original unit and keep the desired unit. You can also convert from one rate to another.

EXAMPLE **Copy and complete: a. 5.4 m = _?_ cm b. 9 ft^2 = _?_ in.^{2}**

a. $5.4 \not{\text{m}} \times \frac{100 \text{ cm}}{1 \not{\text{m}}} = 540 \text{ cm}$

b. 1 ft = 12 in., so 1 ft^2 = 12 • 12 = 144 in.^{2}

Use the conversion factor $\frac{144 \text{ in.}^2}{1 \text{ ft}^2}$.

$9 \not{\text{ft}^2} \times \frac{144 \text{ in.}^2}{1 \not{\text{ft}^2}} = 1296 \text{ in.}^2$

EXAMPLE **Copy and complete: $425 \frac{\text{ft}}{\text{min}} = \underline{?} \frac{\text{mi}}{\text{h}}$.**

Use the conversion factors $\frac{60 \text{ min}}{1 \text{ h}}$ and $\frac{1 \text{ mi}}{5280 \text{ ft}}$.

$425 \frac{\not{\text{ft}}}{\not{\text{min}}} \times \frac{60 \not{\text{min}}}{1 \text{ h}} \times \frac{1 \text{ mi}}{5280 \not{\text{ft}}} \approx 4.8 \frac{\text{mi}}{\text{h}}$

PRACTICE

Copy and complete the statement.

1. 500 cm = _?_ m **5**
2. 7 days = _?_ hours **168**
3. 48 oz = _?_ lb **3**
4. 14.8 kg = _?_ g **14,800**
5. 3200 mL = _?_ L **3.2**
6. 1200 sec = _?_ min **20**
7. 10 gal = _?_ cups **160**
8. 1 km = _?_ mm **1,000,000**
9. 1 mi = _?_ in. **63,360**
10. 90 ft^2 = _?_ yd^2 **10**
11. 4 ft^2 = _?_ in.^{2} **576**
12. 12 cm^2 = _?_ mm^2 **1200**
13. 3 m^3 = _?_ cm^3 **3,000,000**
14. 2 yd^3 = _?_ in.^{3} **93,312**
15. 6500 mm^3 = _?_ cm^3 **6.5**
16. $12 \frac{\text{mi}}{\text{min}} = \underline{?} \frac{\text{mi}}{\text{h}}$ **720**
17. $17 \frac{\text{km}}{\text{sec}} = \underline{?} \frac{\text{km}}{\text{min}}$ **1020**
18. $0.9 \frac{\text{m}}{\text{min}} = \underline{?} \frac{\text{mm}}{\text{min}}$ **900**
19. $58 \frac{\text{mi}}{\text{min}} = \underline{?} \frac{\text{ft}}{\text{sec}}$ **5104**
20. $82 \frac{\text{cm}}{\text{min}} = \underline{?} \frac{\text{m}}{\text{h}}$ **49.2**
21. $60 \frac{\text{mi}}{\text{h}} = \underline{?} \frac{\text{ft}}{\text{min}}$ **5280**
22. $17 \frac{\text{km}}{\text{h}} = \underline{?} \frac{\text{m}}{\text{sec}}$ $\mathbf{\frac{85}{18}}$
23. $0.09 \frac{\text{m}^3}{\text{min}} = \underline{?} \frac{\text{mm}^3}{\text{min}}$ **90,000,000**
24. $0.6 \frac{\text{km}^2}{\text{year}} = \underline{?} \frac{\text{m}^2}{\text{month}}$ **50,000**

Mean, Median, and Mode

Three measures of *central tendency* are mean, median, and mode. One or more of these measures may be more representative of a given set of data than the others.

The **mean** of a data set is the sum of the values divided by the number of values. The mean is also called the *average*.	The **median** of a data set is the middle value when the values are written in numerical order. If a data set has an even number of values, the median is the mean of the two middle values.	The **mode** of a data set is the value that occurs most often. A data set can have no mode, one mode, or more than one mode.

SKILLS REVIEW HANDBOOK

EXAMPLE **The website hits for one week are listed. Which measure of central tendency best represents the data? *Explain.***

Website Hits for One Week	
Day	**Number of hits**
Monday	88
Tuesday	95
Wednesday	87
Thursday	84
Friday	92
Saturday	95
Sunday	11

Mean Add the values. Then divide by the number of values.

$88 + 95 + 87 + 84 + 92 + 95 + 11 = 552$

$\text{Mean} = 552 \div 7 \approx 79$

Median Write the values in order from least to greatest. Then find the middle value(s).

11, 84, 87, **88**, 92, 95, 95

Median = 88

Mode Find the value that occurs most often.
Mode = 95

An *outlier* is a value that is much greater or lower than the other values in a data set. In the data set above, the outlier 11 causes the mean to be lower than the other six data values. So, the **mean** does not represent the data well. The **mode**, 95, does not represent the data well because it is the highest value. The **median**, 88, best represents the data because all but one value lie close to it.

PRACTICE

Tell which measure of central tendency best represents the given data. *Explain.*

1. Daily high temperatures (°F) for a week: 75, 74, 74, 70, 69, 68, 67
   Mean or median; all of the values are close to these measures.
2. Movie ticket prices: \$6.75, \$7.50, \$7.25, \$6.75, \$7, \$7.50, \$7.25, \$6.75, \$7
   Mean or median; all of the values are close to these measures.
3. Number of eggs bought: 12, 12, 12, 6, 12, 18, 18, 12, 6, 12, 12, 12, 24, 18
   Median or mode; most of the values are equal to or close to these measures.
4. Number of children in a family: 0, 0, 0, 1, 1, 1, 2, 2, 2, 2, 2, 2, 2, 3, 3, 4, 4, 5
   Mean, median, or mode; most of the values are equal to or close to these measures.
5. Ages of employees: 36, 22, 30, 27, 41, 58, 33, 27, 62, 39, 21, 24, 22
   Median; the mean is too high and the mode is too low.
6. Shoe sizes in a shipment: 5, $5\frac{1}{2}$, 6, $6\frac{1}{2}$, 7, $7\frac{1}{2}$, $7\frac{1}{2}$, 8, 8, 8, $8\frac{1}{2}$, 9, $9\frac{1}{2}$, 10
   Median; the mean does not reflect the data and the mode is too high.
7. Test scores: 97%, 65%, 68%, 98%, 72%, 60%, 94%, 100%, 99%
   Mean; there is no mode and the median is too high.
8. Favorite of 3 colors: blue, yellow, red, yellow, red, red, blue, red, red, blue
   Mode; it is the only measure of central tendency that applies to this data.

Displaying Data

There are many ways to display data. An appropriate data display can help you analyze the data. The table summarizes how data are shown in some data displays.

Circle Graph	Bar Graph	Histogram	Line Graph	Stem-and-Leaf Plot	Box-and-Whisker Plot
Shows data as parts of a whole.	Compares data in distinct categories.	Compares data in intervals.	Shows how data change over time.	Shows data in numerical order.	Shows distribution of data in quartiles.

EXAMPLE **The table shows bike sales at a shop. Display the data in two appropriate ways. *Describe* what each display shows about the data.**

Season	Winter	Spring	Summer	Fall
Bikes sold	15	51	49	25

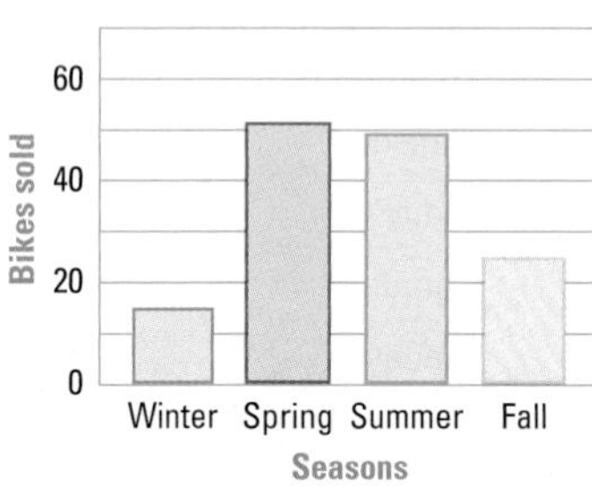

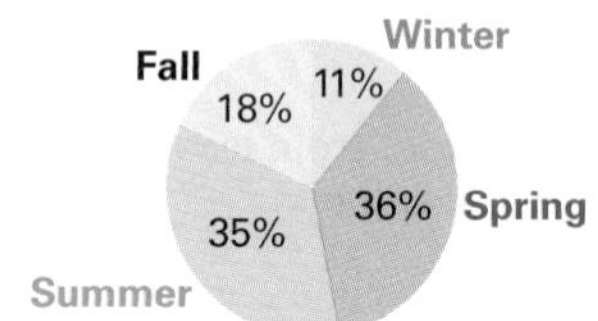

In the bar graph, the heights of the bars can be used to compare sales for the four seasons. Bikes sales were strongest in the spring and summer.

The circle graph shows the percent of annual sales for each season. Almost $\frac{3}{4}$ of the bikes were sold in the spring and summer.

EXAMPLE **The test scores for a class were 82, 99, 68, 76, 84, 100, 85, 79, 92, 100, 82, 81, 60, 95, 98, 74, 95, 84, 88. Display the distribution of the scores.**

Use a stem-and-leaf plot to organize the data. Identify the *lower* and *upper extremes*, the median, and the *lower* and *upper quartiles* (the medians of the lower and upper half of the ordered data set.)

Stem	Leaves
6	0 8
7	4 6 9
8	1 2 2 4 4 5 8
9	2 5 5 8 9
10	0 0

Key: 7 | 4 = 74

Lower and upper extremes: 60 and 100

Median: 84

Lower and upper quartiles: 79 and 95

Then make a box-and-whisker plot. Draw a number line. Below it, plot the lower extreme (60), the lower quartile (79), the median (84), the upper quartile (95), and the upper extreme (100). Draw boxes and "whiskers," as shown.

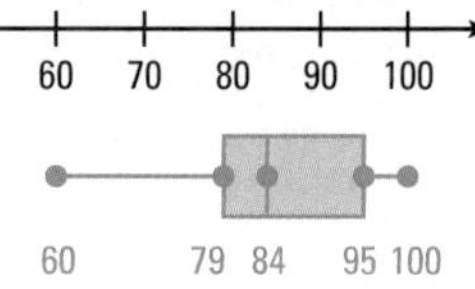

4.

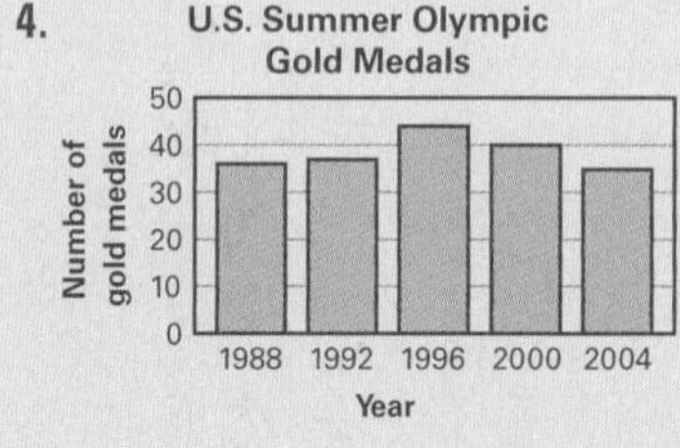

5.

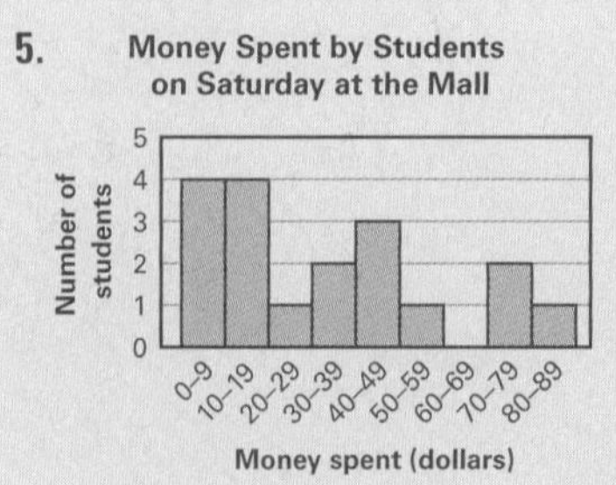

PRACTICE

Name a data display that would be appropriate for the situation. (There may be more than one choice.) *Explain* your reasoning.

1. A store owner keeps track of how many cell phones are sold each week. The owner wants to see how sales change over a six-month period.
   Line graph; this type of graph shows change over time and this is what the storeowner wants to evaluate.
2. You measure the daily high temperature for 31 days in July. You want to see the distribution of the temperatures.
   Bar graph or stem-and-leaf plot; both will show how the data is distributed.
3. The ages of people in a survey are grouped into these intervals: 20–29, 30–39, 40–49, 50–59, 60–69, 70–79. You want to compare the numbers of people in the various groups. **Histogram; this displays data in intervals.**

Make a data display that can be used to answer the question. *Explain* why you chose this display. Then answer the question. **4, 5. See margin for art.**

4. The table gives the number of gold medals won by U.S. athletes at five Summer Olympic games. *Question:* How has the number of medals won changed over time?

Year	1988	1992	1996	2000	2004
Number of gold medals	36	37	44	40	35

The data is broken into distinct categories; the number of gold medals increased until 1996 and is now decreasing.

5. Students were surveyed about the amounts they spent at a mall one Saturday. These are the amounts (in dollars): 5, 70, 10, 40, 42, 45, 50, 4, 3, 10, 12, 15, 20, 5, 30, 35, 70, 80. *Question*: If the dollar amounts are grouped into intervals such as 0–9, 10–19, and so on, in which intervals do the greatest number of students fall?
   The intervals 0–9 and 10–19 include more students than any others.

Display the data in two appropriate ways. *Describe* what each display shows about the data. **6–8. See margin for art.**

6. During a game, a high school soccer team plays 2 forwards, 4 midfielders, 4 defenders, and 1 goalkeeper. **The bar graph compares the number of players at each position. The circle graph shows how each position contributes to the size of the entire team.**
7. A high school has 131 students taking Geometry. The number of students in each class are: 18, 16, 17, 15, 16, 14, 17 and 18. **See margin.**
8. The table gives the number of calories in 8 different pieces of fresh fruit.

Fruit	Apple	Banana	Mango	Orange	Peach	Pear	Plum	Tangerine
Calories	117	100	85	65	35	60	40	35

The bar graph shows how the number of calories in each type of fruit compare to each other. The stem-and-leaf plot shows that the data are widely dispersed with just a few values in the middle of the range of values.

The ages of actors in a community theater play are 18, 25, 19, 32, 26, 15, 33, 12, 36, 16, 18, 30, 25, 24, 32, 30, 13, 15, 37, 35, 72, 35. Use these data for Exercises 9–11.
9–11. See margin for art.

9. Make a stem-and-leaf plot of the data. Identify the lower and upper extremes, the median, and the lower and upper quartiles of the data set. **12, 72; 25.5; 18, 33**
10. Make a box-and-whisker plot of the data. About what percent of the actors are over 18? How does the box-and-whisker plot help you answer this question?
    75%; 18 is the lower quartile and the graph displays the data in intervals of 25%.
11. Suppose the two oldest actors drop out of the play. Draw a new box-and-whisker plot without the data values for those actors. How does the distribution of the data change? *Explain.* **The data is more closely related to the mean and median in the new box-and-whisker plot than before dropping the 2 highest ages.**

SKILLS REVIEW HANDBOOK

6.

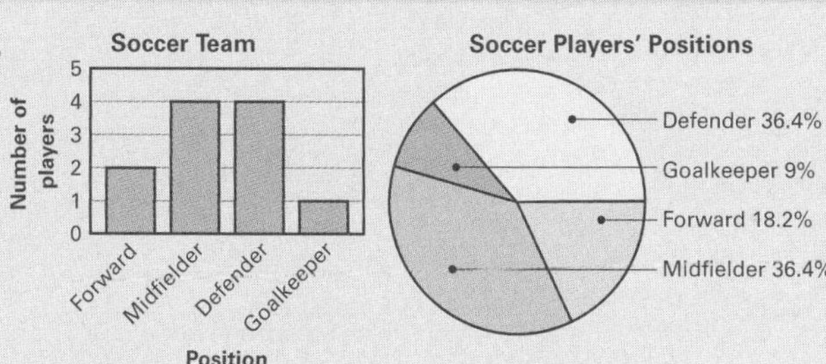

7.

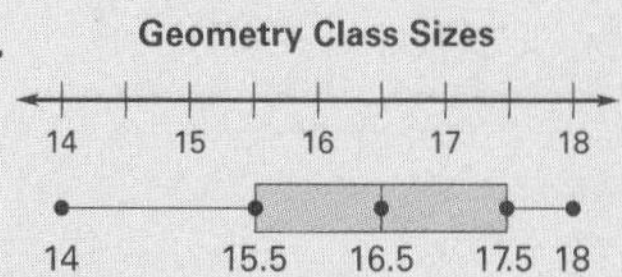

The box-and-whisker plot shows how the class sizes relate to each other.

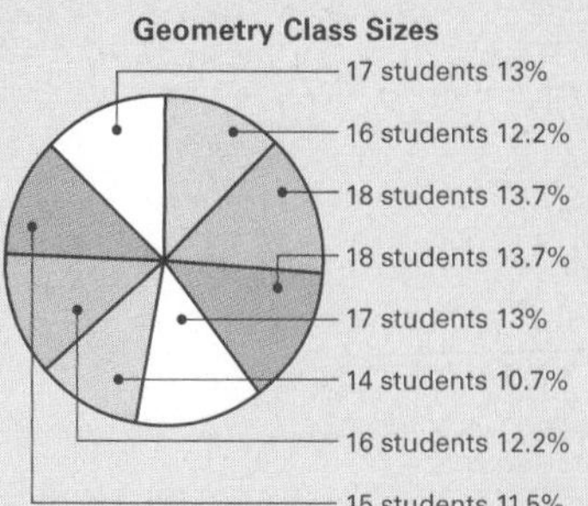

The circle graph shows how each class size contributes to the total number of students enrolled in Geometry.

8.

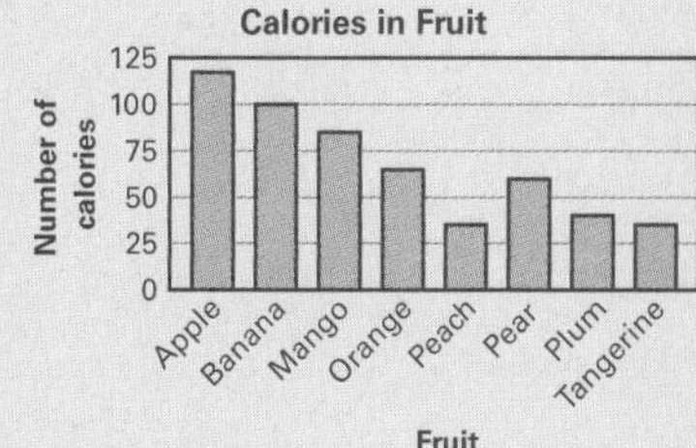

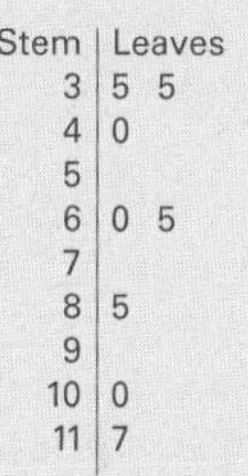

Stem	Leaves
3	5 5
4	0
5	
6	0 5
7	
8	5
9	
10	0
11	7

Key: 11 | 7 = 117

9.

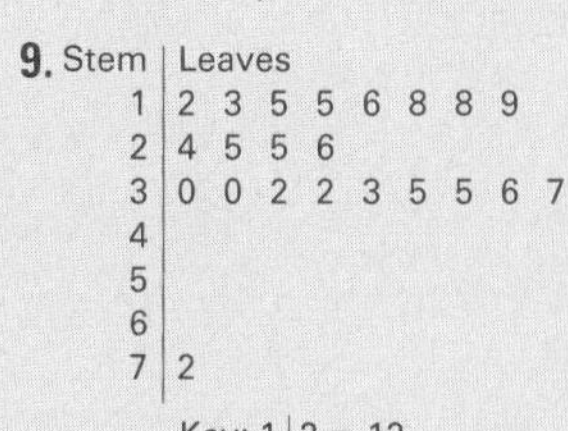

Stem	Leaves
1	2 3 5 5 6 8 8 9
2	4 5 5 6
3	0 0 2 2 3 5 5 6 7
4	
5	
6	
7	2

Key: 1 | 2 = 12

10.
11.

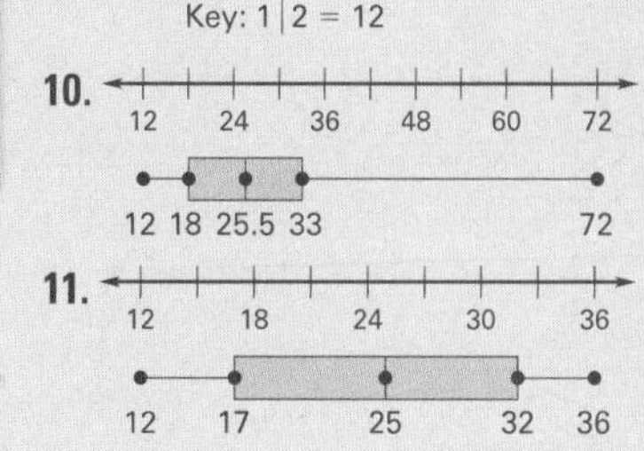

SKILLS REVIEW HANDBOOK

Sampling and Surveys

A *survey* is a study of one or more characteristics of a group. A **population** is the group you want information about. A **sample** is part of the population. In a **random sample**, every member of a population has an equal chance of being selected for a survey. A random sample is most likely to represent the population. A sample that is not representative is a *biased sample*.

Using a biased sample may affect the results of a survey. In addition, survey results may be influenced by the use of *biased questions*. A biased question encourages a particular response.

EXAMPLE **Read the description of the survey. Identify any biased samples or questions. *Explain*.**

a. A movie theater owner wants to know how often local residents go to the movies each month. The owner asks every tenth ticket buyer.

▸ The sample (every tenth ticket buyer) is unlikely to represent the population (local residents). It is biased because moviegoers are over-represented.

b. The mayor's office asks a random sample of the city's residents the following question: Do you support the necessary budget cuts proposed by the mayor?

▸ The sample is random, so it is not biased. The question is biased because the word *necessary* suggests that people should support the budget cuts.

PRACTICE

Read the description of the survey. Identify any biased samples or questions. *Explain*.

1. The coach of a high school soccer team wants to know whether students are more likely to come watch the team's games on Wednesdays or Thursdays. The team's first game is on a Friday. The coach asks all the students who come to watch which day they prefer. **Biased sample; the sample is unlikely to represent the entire population of students because only students at a soccer game are asked which day they prefer.**
2. A town's recreation department wants to know whether to build a new skateboard park. The head of the department visits a local park and asks people at the park whether they would like to have a skateboard park built. **Biased sample; the sample is unlikely to represent the entire population because only people at a park are asked their opinion.**
3. A television producer wants to know whether people in a city would like to watch a one-hour local news program or a half-hour local news program. A television advertisement is run several times during the day asking viewers to e-mail their preference. **Biased sample; the sample is biased because only people with e-mail can respond.**
4. The teachers at a music school want to know whether the students at the school practice regularly. Five of the ten teachers at the school ask their students the following question: How many hours do you spend practicing each day? **Biased question; the question is biased because it assumes that the students practice daily.**
5. A skating rink owner wants to know the ages of people who use the rink. Over a two-week period, the owner asks every tenth person who uses the rink his or her age. **The sample is random and the question is not biased.**
6. A cello teacher asks some of his students, "Do you practice every day?" **The sample is random and the question is not biased.**

Counting Methods

To count the number of possibilities in a situation, you can make an organized list, draw a tree diagram, make a table, or use the counting principle.

The Counting Principle
If one event can occur in m ways, and for each of these ways a second event can occur in n ways, then the number of ways that the two events can occur together is $m \times n$.

The counting principle can be extended to three or more events.

EXAMPLE **Use four different counting methods to find the number of possible salad specials.**

Salad Special $5.95

Choose 1 salad and 1 dressing

Salad: Lettuce or Spinach

Dressing: Ranch, Blue cheese, or Italian

Method 1 Make an Organized List

Pair each salad with each dressing and list each possible special.

Lettuce salad with ranch

Lettuce salad with blue cheese

Lettuce salad with Italian

Spinach salad with ranch

Spinach salad with blue cheese

Spinach salad with Italian

Count the number of specials listed. There are 6 possible salad specials.

Method 2 Draw a Tree Diagram

Arrange the salads and dressings in a tree diagram.

Salad **Dressing**

Lettuce — Ranch, Blue cheese, Italian

Spinach — Ranch, Blue cheese, Italian

Count the number of branches in the tree diagram. There are 6 possible salad specials.

Method 3 Make a Table

List the salads in the left column. List the dressings in the top row.

	Ranch	Blue cheese	Italian
Lettuce	Lettuce, Ranch	Lettuce, Blue cheese	Lettuce, Italian
Spinach	Spinach, Ranch	Spinach, Blue cheese	Spinach, Italian

Count the number of cells filled. There are 6 possible salad specials.

Method 4 Use the Counting Principle

There are 2 choices of salad, so $m = 2$. There are 3 choices of dressing, so $n = 3$. By the counting principle, the number of ways that the salad and dressing choices can be combined is $m \times n = 2 \times 3 = 6$.

There are 6 possible salad specials.

891

SKILLS REVIEW HANDBOOK

EXAMPLE **Tyler must choose a 4-digit password for his bank account. Find the number of possible 4-digit passwords using four different digits.**

Because there are many possible passwords, use the counting principle.

For one of the digits in the password, there are 10 choices: 0, 1, 2, 3, 4, 5, 6, 7, 8, and 9. Because one of these digits will be used for the first digit, there are only 9 choices for the next, 8 for the next after that, and so on.

10 choices for first digit	$\times$	9 choices for second digit	$\times$	8 choices for third digit	$\times$	7 choices for fourth digit

$10 \times 9 \times 8 \times 7 = 5040$

▸ There are 5040 possible 4-digit passwords using four different digits.

PRACTICE

Use one of the methods described in the Examples on pages 891 and 892 to solve each problem. ***Explain*** **your reasoning.** **1–10. Check students' work.**

1. Ann takes three pairs of shorts (red, blue, and green) and five T-shirts (black, white, yellow, orange, and brown) on a trip. Find the number of different shorts and T-shirt outfits Ann can wear while on the trip. **15 outfits**

2. Art students can choose any two pieces of colored paper for a project. There are six colors available and students must choose two different colors. Find the number of different color combinations that can be chosen. **15 combinations**

3. Steve must choose four characters for his computer password. Each character can be any letter from A through Z or any digit from 0 through 9. All letters and digits may be used more than once. Find the number of possible passwords. **1,679,616 passwords**

4. A restaurant offers a pizza special, as shown at the right. Assuming that two different toppings are ordered, find the number of two-topping combinations that can be ordered. **28 combinations**

5. Each of the locker combinations at a gym uses three numbers from 0 through 49. Find the number of different locker combinations that are possible. **125,000 combinations**

Large Pizza Special	
Any 2 toppings for $12.49	
Pepperoni	**Green Olive**
Sausage	**Green Pepper**
Ground Beef	**Red Onion**
Black Olive	**Mushroom**

6. A movie theater sells three sizes of popcorn and six different soft drinks. Each soft drink can be bought in one of three sizes. Find the number of different popcorn and soft drink pairs that can be ordered. **54 pairs**

7. A class has 28 students and elects two students to be class officers. One student will be president and one will be vice president. How many different pairs of class officers are possible? **756 pairs**

8. Some students are auditioning for parts in the play *Our Town*. Twenty girls try out for the parts listed at the right. In how many different ways can 5 of the 20 girls be assigned these roles? **1,860,480 ways**

9. Bill, Allison, James, and Caroline are friends. In how many different ways can they stand in a row for a photo? **24 ways**

10. A cafeteria serves 4 kinds of sandwiches: cheese, veggie, peanut butter, and bologna. Students can choose any two sandwiches for lunch. How many different sandwich combinations are possible? **6 combinations**

Parts in *Our Town*
Emily Webb
Mrs. Gibbs
Mrs. Webb
Mrs. Soames
Rebecca Gibbs

Probability

The **probability** of an event is a measure of the likelihood that the event will occur. An event that cannot occur has a probability of 0, and an event that is certain to occur has a probability of 1. Other probabilities lie between 0 and 1. You can write a probability as a decimal, a fraction, or a percent.

Probability of an Event
When all outcomes are equally likely, the probability of an event, P(event), is $\frac{\text{number of favorable outcomes}}{\text{number of possible outcomes}}$.

When you consider the probability of two events occurring, the events are called **compound events**. Compound events can be dependent or independent.

Two events are **independent events** if the occurrence of one event *does not* affect the occurrence of another.	Two events are **dependent events** if the occurrence of one event *does* affect the occurrence of another.
For two independent events A and B, $P(A \text{ and } B) = P(A) \cdot P(B)$.	For two dependent events A and B, $P(A \text{ and } B) = P(A) \cdot P(B \mid A)$, where $P(B \mid A)$ is the probability of B given that A has occurred.

EXAMPLE **A box holds 12 yellow marbles and 12 orange marbles. Without looking, you take a marble. Then you take another marble without replacing the first. Find the probability that both marbles are yellow.**

There are 24 marbles in the box when you take the first one, and only 23 when you take the second. So, the events are dependent.

$$P(A \text{ and } B) = P(A) \cdot P(B \mid A) = \frac{12}{24} \cdot \frac{11}{23} = \frac{11}{46} \approx 0.24, \text{ or } 24\%$$

PRACTICE

Identify the events as *independent* or *dependent*. Then answer the question.

1. There are 20 socks in your drawer, and 12 of them are white. You grab a sock without looking. Then you grab a second sock without putting the first one back. What is the probability that both socks are white? **dependent; $\frac{33}{95} \approx 0.347$ or about 34.7%**
2. You flip a coin two times. What is the probability that you get heads each time? **independent; $\frac{1}{4} = 0.25$ or 25%**
3. Your math, literature, Spanish, history, and science homework assignments are organized in five folders. You randomly choose one folder, finish your assignment, and then choose a new folder. What is the probability that you do your math homework first, and then history? **dependent; $\frac{1}{20} = 0.05$ or 5%**
4. You roll a red number cube and a blue number cube. What is the probability that you roll an even number on the red cube and a number greater than 2 on the blue cube? **independent; $\frac{1}{3} \approx 0.333$ or about 33.3%**
5. You flip a coin three times. What is the probability that you do not get heads on any of the flips? **dependent; $\frac{1}{8} = 0.125$ or 12.5%**

Problem Solving Plan and Strategies

Here is a 4-step **problem solving plan** that you can use to solve problems.

STEP 1	**Read and understand the problem.**	Read the problem carefully. Organize the given information and decide what you need to find. Check for unnecessary or missing information. Supply missing facts, if needed.
STEP 2	**Make a plan to solve the problem.**	Choose a problem solving strategy. Choose the correct operations to use. Decide if you will use a tool such as a calculator, graph, or spreadsheet.
STEP 3	**Carry out the plan to solve the problem.**	Use the problem solving strategy and any tools you have chosen. Estimate before you calculate, if possible. Do any calculations that are needed. Answer the question that the problem asks.
STEP 4	**Check to see if your answer is reasonable.**	Reread the problem. See if your answer agrees with the given information and with any estimate you have made.

Here are some **problem solving strategies** that you can use to solve problems.

Strategy	When to use	How to use
Guess, check, and revise	Guess, check, and revise when you need a place to start or you want to see how the problem works.	Make a reasonable guess. Check to see if your guess solves the problem. If it does not, revise your guess and check again.
Draw a diagram or a graph	Draw a diagram or a graph when a problem involves any relationships that you can represent visually.	Draw a diagram or a graph that shows given information. See what your diagram reveals that can help you solve the problem.
Make a table or an organized list	Make a table or list when a problem requires you to record, generate, or organize information.	Make a table with columns, rows, and any given information. Generate a systematic list that can help you solve the problem.
Use an equation or a formula	Use an equation or a formula when you know a relationship between quantities.	Write an equation or formula that shows the relationship between known quantities. Solve the equation to solve the problem.
Use a proportion	Use a proportion when you know that two ratios are equal.	Write a proportion using the two equal ratios. Solve the proportion to solve the problem.
Look for a pattern	Look for a pattern when a problem includes numbers or diagrams that you need to analyze.	Look for a pattern in any given information. Organize, extend, or generalize the pattern to help you solve the problem.
Break a problem into parts	Break a problem into parts when a problem cannot be solved in one step but can be solved in parts.	Break the problem into parts and solve each part. Put the answers together to help you solve the original problem.
Solve a simpler or related problem	Solve a simpler or related problem when a problem seems difficult and can be made easier by using simpler numbers or conditions.	Think of a way to make the problem easier. Solve the simpler or related problem. Use what you learned to help you solve the original problem.
Work backward	Work backward when a problem gives you an end result and you need to find beginning conditions.	Work backward from the given information until you solve the problem. Work forward through the problem to check your answer.

EXAMPLE **A marching band receives a $2800 donation to buy new drums and piccolos. Each drum costs $350 and each piccolo costs $400. How many of each type of instrument can the band buy?**

STEP 1 **Choose** two strategies, *Use an Equation* and *Draw a Graph.*

STEP 2 **Write** an inequality. Let d = the number of drums and p = the number of piccolos.

Cost of drums	·	Number of drums	+	Cost of piccolos	·	Number of piccolos	≤	$2800

$350d + 400p \le 2800$

STEP 3 **Graph** and shade the solution region of the inequality.

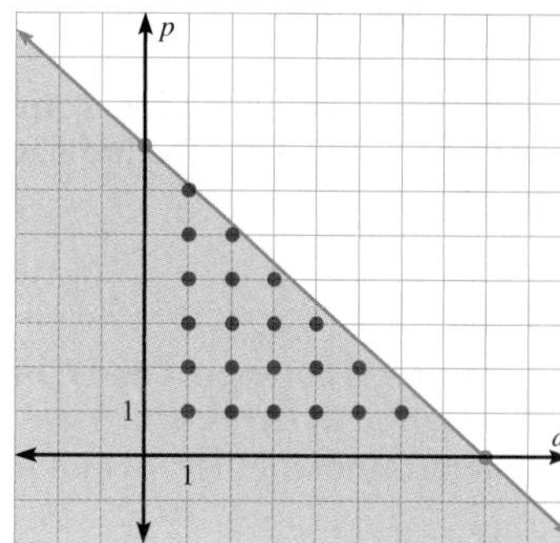

The band can buy only whole numbers of instruments. Also, you can assume that the band will buy at least one of each type of instrument. Mark each point in the solution region that has whole number coordinates greater than or equal to 1.

▸ The red points on the graph show 21 different ways that the band can buy drums and piccolos without spending more than $2800.

PRACTICE

1. A cell phone company offers a plan with an initial registration fee of $25 and a monthly fee of $15. How much will the plan cost for one year? **$205**
2. Rita wants to attend a swim camp that costs $220. She has $56 in a bank account. She also earns $25 each week walking dogs. Will Rita be able to make a full payment for the camp in 5 weeks? *Explain* your reasoning. **No; Rita will earn $125 walking dogs in 5 weeks, when you add this to the $56 she has already saved, she will only have $181 for camp.**
3. What is the 97th number in the pattern 4, 3, 2, 1, 4, 3, 2, 1, 4, 3, 2, 1, . . .? **4**
4. Sam makes a down payment of $120 on a $360 bike. He will pay $30 each month until the balance is paid. How many monthly payments will he make? **8 monthly payments**
5. Marie is buying tree seedlings for the school. She can spend no more than $310 on aspen and birch trees. She wants at least 20 trees in all and twice as many aspen trees as birch trees. Find three possible ways that Marie can buy the trees. **14 aspen and 7 birch, 16 aspen and 8 birch, or 18 aspen and 9 birch**

Tree Seedlings

Aspen	$10 each
Birch	$12 each

6. In how many different ways can you make 75¢ in change using quarters, dimes, and nickels? **18 different ways**
7. Charlie is cutting a rectangular cake that is 9 inches by 13 inches into equal-sized rectangular pieces. Each piece of cake should be at least 2 inches on each side. What is the greatest number of pieces Charlie can cut? **24 pieces**
8. Streamers cost $1.70 per roll and balloons cost $1.50 per bag. If the student council has $40 to spend for parent night and buys 10 rolls of streamers, how many bags of balloons can the student council buy? **15 bags of balloons**

12. $(x + 3) + (2x + 1) = 10$; $x = 2$; $AB = 5$, $BC = 5$; congruent

13. $(3x - 7) + (3x - 1) = 16$; $x = 4$; $AB = 5$, $BC = 11$; not congruent

14. $(11x - 16) + (8x - 1) = 78$; $x = 5$; $AB = 39$, $BC = 39$; congruent

15. $(4x - 5) + (2x - 7) = 54$; $x = 11$; $AB = 39$, $BC = 15$; not congruent

16. $(14x + 5) + (10x + 15) = 80$; $x = 2.5$; $AB = 40$, $BC = 40$; congruent

17. $(3x - 7) + (2x + 5) = 108$; $x = 22$; $AB = 59$, $BC = 49$; not congruent

EXTRA PRACTICE

Extra Practice

Chapter 1

1.1 In Exercises 1–5, use the diagram.

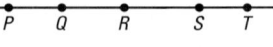

1. Name three points that are collinear. Then give a name for the line that contains the points. **Sample answer: A, F, B; $\overleftrightarrow{AB}$**

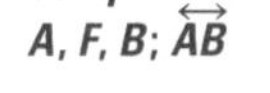

2. Name the intersection of plane *ABC* and $\overleftrightarrow{EG}$. **F**

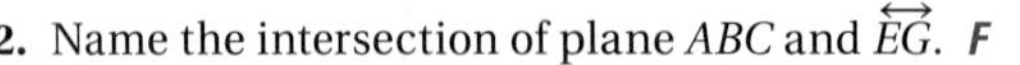

3. Name two pairs of opposite rays. **Sample answer: $\overrightarrow{FA}$, $\overrightarrow{FB}$**

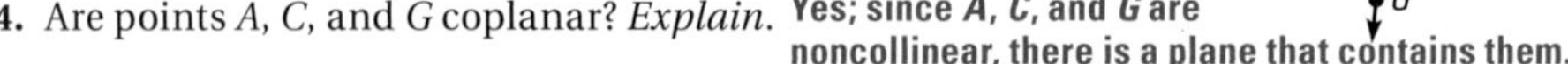

4. Are points *A*, *C*, and *G* coplanar? *Explain.* **Yes; since A, C, and G are noncollinear, there is a plane that contains them.**
5. Name a line that intersects plane *AFD* at more than one point. **Sample answer: $\overleftrightarrow{AB}$**

1.2 In the diagram, *P*, *Q*, *R*, *S*, and *T* are collinear, $PT = 54$, $QT = 42$, $QS = 31$, and $RS = 17$. Find the indicated length.

6. *PQ* **12**
7. *PS* **43**
8. *QR* **14**
9. *PR* **26**
10. *ST* **11**
11. *RT* **28**

1.2 Point *B* is between *A* and *C* on $\overline{AC}$. Use the given information to write an equation in terms of *x*. Solve the equation. Then find *AB* and *BC*, and determine whether $\overline{AB}$ and $\overline{BC}$ are congruent. **12–17. See margin.**

12. $AB = x + 3$, $BC = 2x + 1$, $AC = 10$
13. $AB = 3x - 7$, $BC = 3x - 1$, $AC = 16$
14. $AB = 11x - 16$, $BC = 8x - 1$, $AC = 78$
15. $AB = 4x - 5$, $BC = 2x - 7$, $AC = 54$
16. $AB = 14x + 5$, $BC = 10x + 15$, $AC = 80$
17. $AB = 3x - 7$, $BC = 2x + 5$, $AC = 108$

1.3 Find the coordinates of the midpoint of the segment with the given endpoints.

18. $A(2, -4)$, $B(7, 1)$ **$\left(\frac{9}{2}, -\frac{3}{2}\right)$**
19. $C(-3, -2)$, $D(-8, 4)$ **$\left(-\frac{11}{2}, 1\right)$**
20. $E(-2.3, -1.9)$, $F(3.1, -9.7)$ **(0.4, −5.8)**
21. $G(3, -7)$, $H(-1, 9)$ **(1, 1)**
22. $I(4, 3)$, $J(2, 2)$ **$\left(3, \frac{5}{2}\right)$**
23. $K(1.7, -7.9)$, $L(8.5, -8.2)$ **(5.1, −8.05)**

1.3 Find the length of the segment with given endpoint and midpoint *M*.

24. $Z(0, 1)$ and $M(7, 1)$ **14**
25. $Y(4, 3)$ and $M(1, 7)$ **10**
26. $X(0, -1)$ and $M(12, 4)$ **26**
27. $W(5, 3)$ and $M(-10, -5)$ **34**
28. $V(-3, -4)$ and $M(9, 5)$ **30**
29. $U(3, 2)$ and $M(11, -4)$ **20**

1.4 Use the given information to find the indicated angle measure.

30. $m\angle QPS =$? **121°**

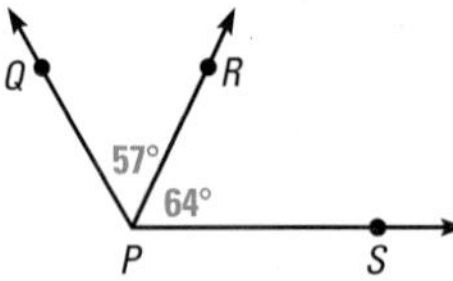

31. $m\angle LMN =$? **104°**

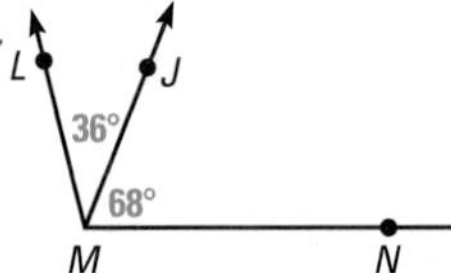

32. $m\angle XWZ =$? **86°**

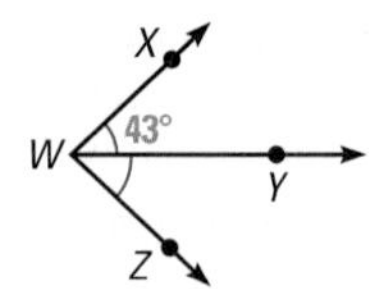

1.4 **33.** Given $m\angle ABC = 133°$, find $m\angle ABD$. **88°**

34. Given $m\angle GHK = 17°$, find $m\angle KHJ$. **17°**

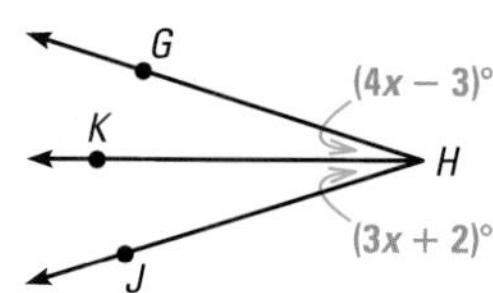

1.5 **Tell whether ∠1 and ∠2 are *vertical angles, adjacent angles,* a *linear pair, complementary,* or *supplementary.* There may be more than one answer.**

35.

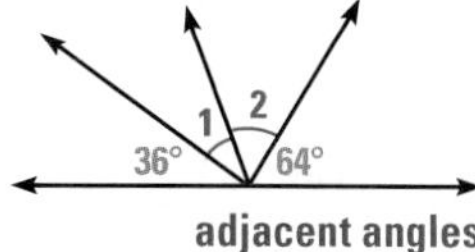

adjacent angles

36.

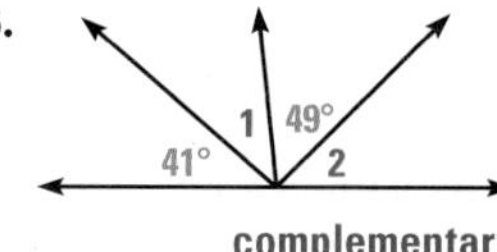

complementary

37.

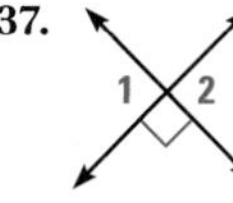

vertical angles, supplementary

1.5 **Use the diagram.**

38. Name two supplementary angles that are not a linear pair. ***Sample answer:* ∠*ACB*, ∠*DCE***

39. Name two vertical angles that are not complementary. ***Sample answer:* ∠*ACE*, ∠*BCF***

40. Name three pairs of complementary angles. Tell whether each pair contains vertical angles, adjacent angles, or neither.
∠*ECF*, ∠*BCD*, neither; ∠*ECF*, ∠*ACB*, vertical angles; ∠*ACB*, ∠*BCD*, adjacent angles

1.6 **Tell whether the figure is a polygon. If it is not, *explain* why. If it is, tell whether it is *convex* or *concave.***

41.

polygon; concave

42.

42, 43. See margin.

43.

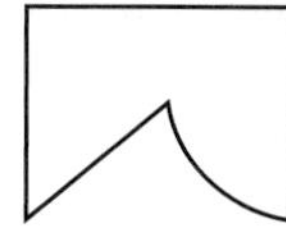

44.

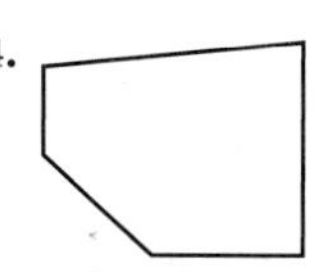

polygon; convex

1.6 **In Exercises 45 and 46, use the diagram.**

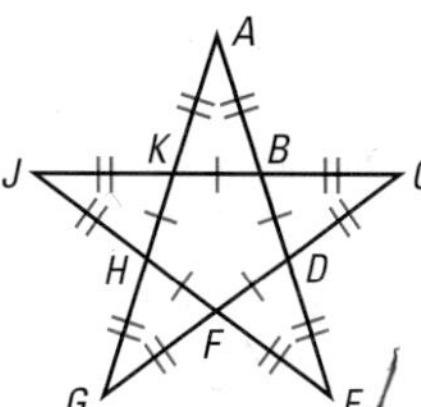

45. Identify two different equilateral polygons in the diagram. Classify each by the number of sides.
***DFHKB*, pentagon; *ABCDEFGHJK*, decagon**

46. Name one of each of the following figures as it appears in the five-pointed star diagram: triangle, quadrilateral, pentagon, hexagon, heptagon.
Sample answer:* triangle *ADG*; quadrilateral *ADFH*; pentagon *DFHKB*; hexagon *ADGHJK*; heptagon *ABCDEFG

1.7 **Use the information about the figure to find the indicated measure.**

47. Area = 91 cm²
Find the length ℓ.

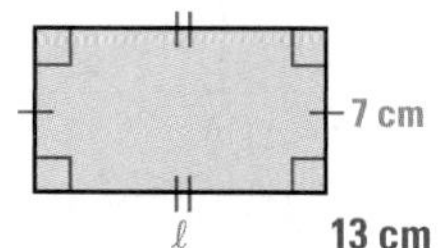

13 cm

48. Find the area of the triangle.

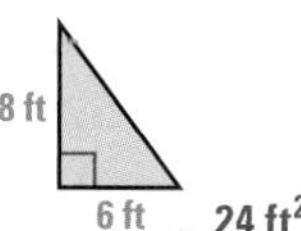

24 ft²

49. Area = 66 m²
Find the height h.

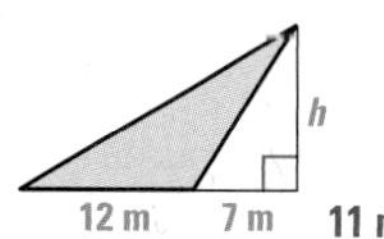

11 m

1.7 **Find the perimeter and area of the triangle with the given vertices. Round to the nearest tenth.**

50. $A(2, 1)$, $B(3, 6)$, $C(6, 1)$
about 14.9 units, 10 units²

51. $D(1, 1)$, $E(3, 1)$, $F(6, 5)$
about 13.4 units, 4 units²

42. Not a polygon; one segment intersects more than 2 segments.
43. Not a polygon; part of the figure is not a line segment.

EXTRA PRACTICE

1. Add 6 for the next number, then subtract 8 for the next number; 11.

2. Each number is $\frac{1}{2}$ the previous number; 0.03125.

3. prime numbers; 17

4. Each number is 0.5 more than the previous number; 9.0.

5. Each number is $\frac{1}{3}$ of the previous number; $\frac{1}{81}$.

6. Each number is the sum of the two previous numbers; 42.

10. If-then form: If two lines intersect, then they form two pairs of vertical angles. Converse: If two lines form two pairs of vertical angles, then the two lines intersect. Inverse: If two lines do not intersect, then they do not form two pairs of vertical angles. Contrapositive: If two lines do not form two pairs of vertical angles, then the two lines do not intersect.

11. If-then form: If a figure is a square, then it is a four-sided regular polygon. Converse: If a figure is a four-sided regular polygon, then it is a square. Inverse: If a figure is not a square, then it is not a four-sided regular polygon. Contrapositive: If a figure is not a four-sided regular polygon, then it is not a square.

12. *Sample:*

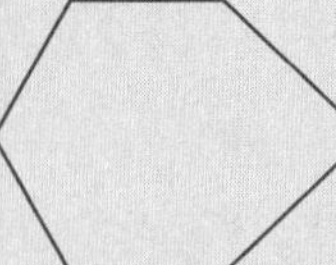

EXTRA PRACTICE

Chapter 2

2.1 ***Describe*** **the pattern in the numbers. Write the next number in the pattern.** 1–6. See margin.

1. 17, 23, 15, 21, 13, 19,... **2.** 1, 0.5, 0.25, 0.125, 0.0625,... **3.** 2, 3, 5, 7, 11, 13,...

4. 7.0, 7.5, 8.0, 8.5,... **5.** $1, \frac{1}{3}, \frac{1}{9}, \frac{1}{27}, \ldots$ **6.** 2, 2, 4, 6, 10, 16, 26,...

2.1 Show the conjecture is false by finding a counterexample. 7–9. Sample answers are given.

7. The difference of any two numbers is a value that lies between those two numbers. $-8 - (-5) = -3$

8. The value of $2x$ is always greater than the value of x. $x = 0$

9. If an angle A can be bisected, then angle A must be obtuse. $m\angle A = 90°$

2.2 For the given statement, write the if-then form, the converse, the inverse, and the contrapositive. 10, 11. See margin.

10. Two lines that intersect form two pairs of vertical angles.

11. All squares are four-sided regular polygons.

2.2 Decide whether the statement is *true* or *false*. If false, provide a counterexample.

12. If a figure is a hexagon, then it is a regular polygon. False; see margin for art.

13. If two angles are complementary, then the sum of their measures is 90°. true

2.3 Write the statement that follows from the pair of statements that are given.

14. If a triangle is equilateral, then it has congruent angles.
If a triangle has congruent angles, then it is regular. If a triangle is equilateral, then it is regular.

15. If two coplanar lines are not parallel, then they intersect.
If two lines intersect, then they form congruent vertical angles.
If two coplanar lines are not parallel, then they form congruent vertical angles.

2.3 Select the word(s) that make(s) the conclusion true.

16. John only does his math homework when he is in study hall. John is doing his math homework. So, John (*is, may be, is not*) in study hall. is

17. May sometimes buys pretzels when she goes to the supermarket. May is at the supermarket. So, she (*will, might, will not*) buy pretzels. might

2.4 Use the diagram to determine if the statement is *true* or *false*.

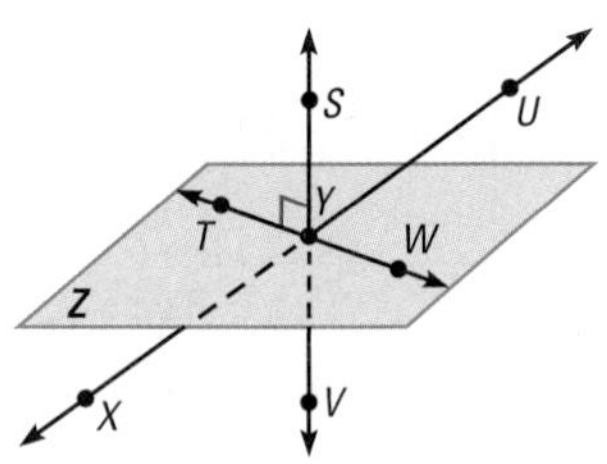

18. $\overleftrightarrow{SV} \perp$ plane Z true

19. $\overleftrightarrow{XU}$ intersects plane Z at point Y. true

20. $\overleftrightarrow{TW}$ lies in plane Z. true

21. $\angle SYT$ and $\angle WYS$ are vertical angles. false

22. $\angle SYT$ and $\angle TYV$ are complementary angles. false

23. $\angle TYU$ and $\angle UYW$ are a linear pair. true

24. $\angle UYV$ is acute. false

2.5 Solve the equation. Write a reason for each step. **25–30. See margin.**

25. $4x + 15 = 39$ **26.** $6x + 47 = 10x - 9$ **27.** $2(-7x + 3) = -50$

28. $54 + 9x = 3(7x + 6)$ **29.** $13(2x - 3) - 20x = 3$ **30.** $31 + 25x = 7x - 14 + 3x$

2.6 Copy and complete the statement. Name the property illustrated.

31. If $m\angle JKL = m\angle GHI$ and $m\angle GHI = m\angle ABC$, then $\underline{?} = \underline{?}$. **$m\angle JKL$, $m\angle ABC$; Transitive Property of Equality**

32. If $m\angle MNO = m\angle PQR$, then $m\angle PQR = \underline{?}$ **$m\angle MNO$; Symmetric Property of Equality**

33. $m\angle XYZ = \underline{?}$ **$m\angle XYZ$; Reflexive Property of Equality**

2.6 34. Copy and complete the proof. **See margin.**

GIVEN ▶ Point C is in the interior of $\angle ABD$. $\angle ABD$ is a right angle.

PROVE ▶ $\angle ABC$ and $\angle CBD$ are complementary.

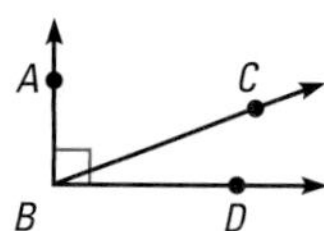

STATEMENTS	REASONS
1. $\angle ABD$ is a right angle.	1. Given
2. $m\angle ABD = 90°$	2. ?
3. ?	3. Given
4. $m\angle ABD = m\angle ABC + m\angle CBD$	4. ?
5. ? $= m\angle ABC + m\angle CBD$	5. Substitution Property of Equality
6. ?	6. Definition of complementary angles

2.6 35. Use the given information and the diagram to prove the statement. **See margin.**

GIVEN ▶ $\overline{XY} \cong \overline{YZ} \cong \overline{ZX}$

PROVE ▶ The perimeter of $\triangle XYZ$ is $3 \cdot XY$.

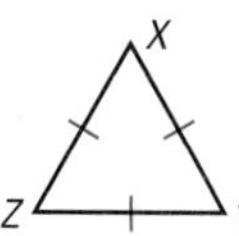

2.7 Copy and complete the statement. $\angle AGD$ is a right angle and $\overleftrightarrow{AB}$, $\overleftrightarrow{CD}$, and $\overleftrightarrow{EF}$ intersect at point G.

36. If $m\angle CGF = 158°$, then $m\angle EGD = \underline{?}$. **158°**

37. If $m\angle EGA = 67°$, then $m\angle FGD = \underline{?}$. **23°**

38. If $m\angle FGC = 149°$, then $m\angle EGA = \underline{?}$. **59°**

39. $m\angle DGB = \underline{?}$ **90°**

40. $m\angle FGH = \underline{?}$ **90°**

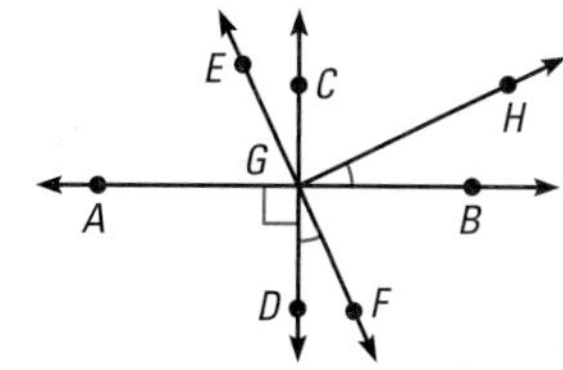

2.7 41. Write a two-column proof. **See margin.**

GIVEN ▶ $\angle UKV$ and $\angle VKW$ are complements.

PROVE ▶ $\angle YKZ$ and $\angle XKY$ are complements.

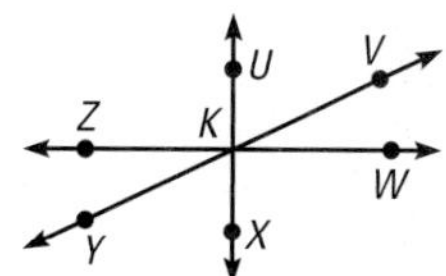

25. $4x + 15 = 39$ (Write original equation.)
$4x = 24$ (Subtraction Property of Equality)
$x = 6$ (Division Property of Equality)

26. $6x + 47 = 10x - 9$ (Write original equation.)
$47 = 4x - 9$ (Subtraction Property of Equality)
$56 = 4x$ (Addition Property of Equality)
$14 = x$ (Division Property of Equality)

27. $2(-7x + 3) = -50$ (Write original equation.)
$-14x + 6 = -50$ (Distributive Property)
$-14x = -56$ (Subtraction Property of Equality)
$x = 4$ (Division Property of Equality)

28. $54 + 9x = 3(7x + 6)$ (Write original equation.)
$54 + 9x = 21x + 18$ (Distributive Property)
$54 = 12x + 18$ (Subtraction Property of Equality)
$36 = 12x$ (Subtraction Property of Equality)
$3 = x$ (Division Property of Equality)

29. $13(2x - 3) - 20x = 3$ (Write original equation.)
$26x - 39 - 20x = 3$ (Distributive Property)
$6x - 39 = 3$ (Simplify.)
$6x = 42$ (Addition Property of Equality)
$x = 7$ (Division Property of Equality)

30. $31 + 25x = 7x - 14 + 3x$ (Write original equation.)
$31 + 25x = 10x - 14$ (Simplify.)
$31 + 15x = -14$ (Subtraction Property of Equality)
$15x = -45$ (Subtraction Property of Equality)
$x = -3$ (Division Property of Equality)

34. Reason 2: Definition of right angle; Statement 3: Point C is in the interior of $\angle ABD$. Reason 4: Angle Addition Postulate; Statement 5: 90°; Statement 6: $\angle ABC$ and $\angle CBD$ are complementary.

35. Statements (Reasons)
1. $\overline{XY} \cong \overline{YZ} \cong \overline{ZX}$ (Given)
2. $XY = YZ = ZX$ (Definition of congruent segments)
3. Perimeter of $\triangle XYZ = XY + YZ + ZX$ (Perimeter formula)
4. Perimeter of $\triangle XYZ = XY + XY + XY$ (Substitution)
5. Perimeter of $\triangle XYZ = 3 \cdot XY$ (Simplify.)

41. Statements (Reasons)
1. $\angle UKV$ and $\angle VKW$ are complements. (Given)
2. $m\angle UKV + m\angle VKW = 90°$ (Definition of complementary angles)
3. $\angle UKV \cong \angle XKY$, $\angle VKW \cong \angle YKZ$ (Vertical angles are congruent.)
4. $m\angle UKV = m\angle XKY$, $m\angle VKW = m\angle YKZ$ (Definition of congruent angles)
5. $m\angle YKZ + m\angle XKY = 90°$ (Substitution)
6. $\angle YKZ$ and $\angle XKY$ are complements. (Definition of complementary angles)

Chapter 3

3.1 Classify the angle pair as *corresponding, alternate interior, alternate exterior,* or *consecutive interior* angles.

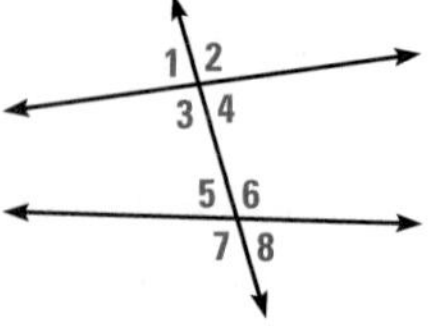

1. $\angle 6$ and $\angle 2$ corresponding
2. $\angle 7$ and $\angle 2$ alternate exterior
3. $\angle 5$ and $\angle 3$ consecutive interior
4. $\angle 4$ and $\angle 5$ alternate interior
5. $\angle 1$ and $\angle 5$ corresponding
6. $\angle 3$ and $\angle 6$ alternate interior

3.1 Copy and complete the statement. List all possible correct answers.

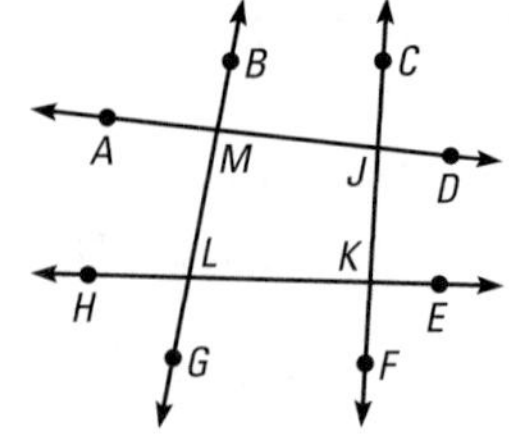

7. $\angle AMB$ and __?__ are corresponding angles. $\angle HLM$ and $\angle MJC$
8. $\angle AML$ and __?__ are alternate interior angles. $\angle MLK$
9. $\angle CJD$ and __?__ are alternate exterior angles. $\angle FKL$ and $\angle AML$
10. $\angle LMJ$ and __?__ are consecutive interior angles. $\angle MLK$ and $\angle MJK$
11. __?__ is a transversal of $\overleftrightarrow{AD}$ and $\overleftrightarrow{HE}$. $\overleftrightarrow{BG}$ and $\overleftrightarrow{CF}$

3.2 Find $m\angle 1$ and $m\angle 2$. *Explain* your reasoning. 12–14. See margin.

12.

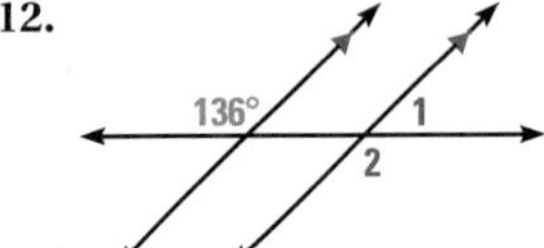

13.

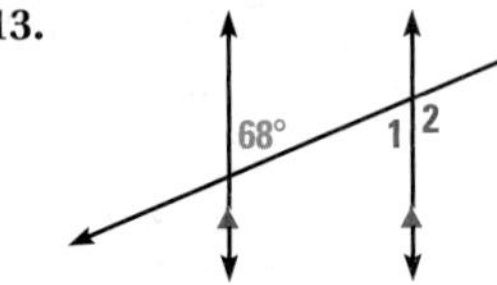

14.

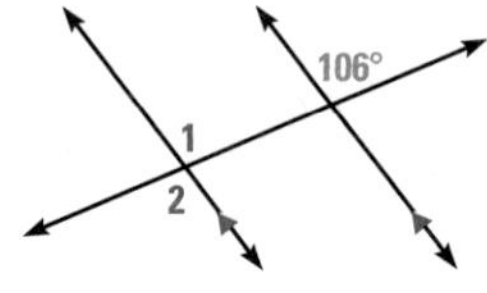

3.2 Find the values of x and y.

15.

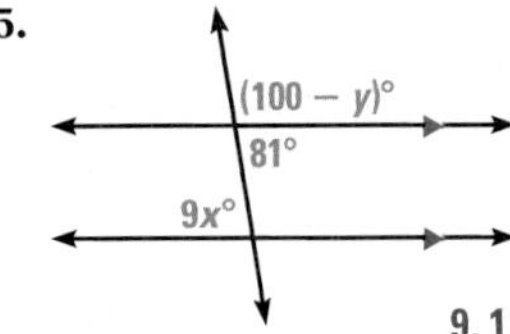

9, 1

16.

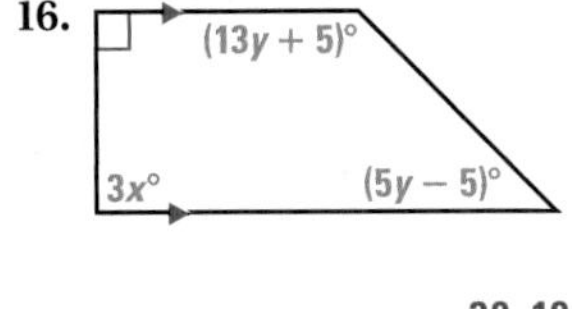

30, 10

17.

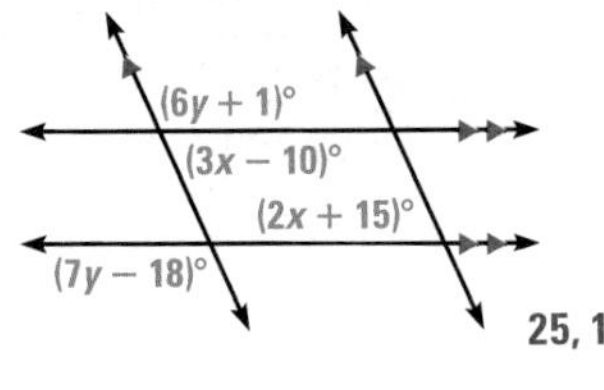

25, 19

3.3 Is there enough information to prove $m \parallel n$? If so, state the postulate or theorem you would use.

18.

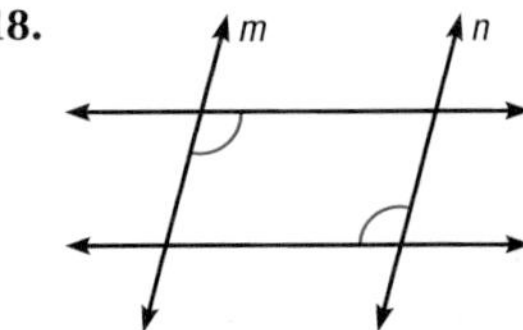

no

19.

19, 20. See margin

20.

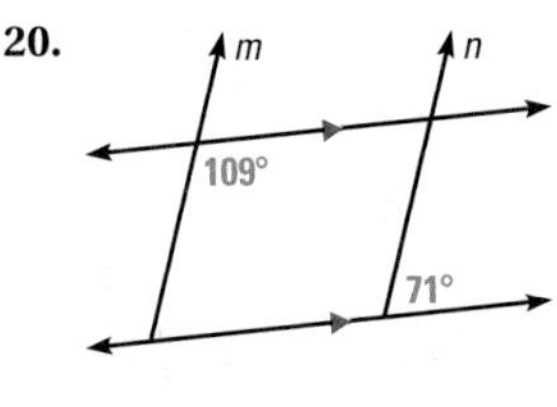

3.3 Can you prove that lines *a* and *b* are parallel? If so, *explain* how. 21–23. See margin.

21.

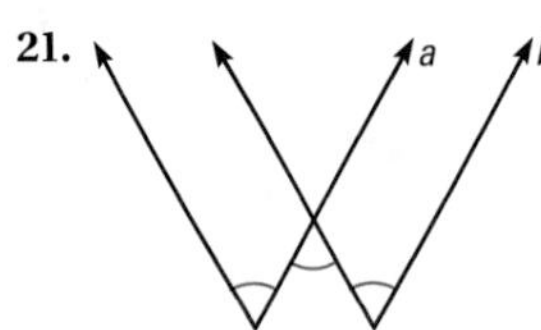

22.

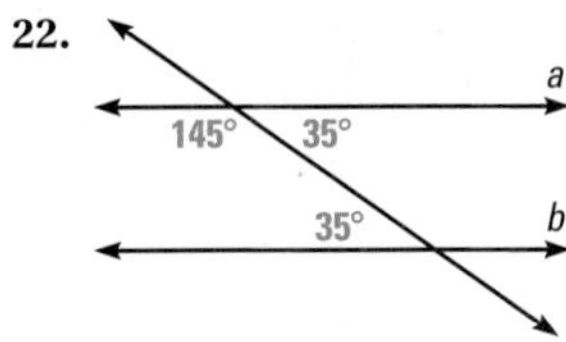

23.

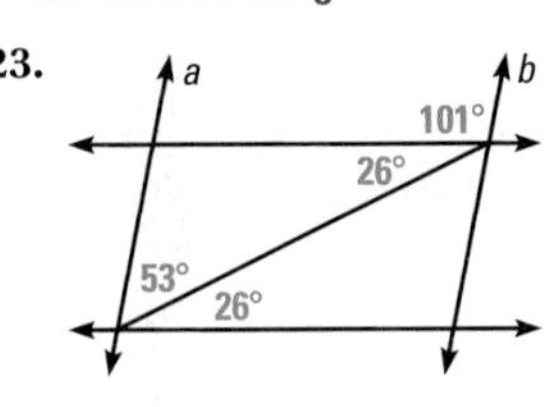

EXTRA PRACTICE

12. 44°, 136°; $m\angle 2 = 136°$ because if two parallel lines are cut by a transversal, then the alternate exterior angles are congruent; $m\angle 1 = 44°$ because it is a linear pair with $\angle 2$.
13. 68°, 112°; $m\angle 1 = 68°$ because if two parallel lines are cut by a transversal, then the alternate interior angles are congruent; $m\angle 2 = 112°$ because it is a linear pair with $\angle 1$.
14. 106°, 106°; $m\angle 1 = 106°$ because if two parallel lines are cut by a transversal, then the corresponding angles are congruent; $m\angle 2 = 106°$ because $\angle 1$ and $\angle 2$ are vertical angles.
19. Yes; if two lines are cut by a transversal so that a pair of consecutive interior angles are supplementary, then the lines are parallel.
20. Yes; if two lines are cut by a transversal so that a pair of consecutive interior angles are supplementary, then the lines are parallel.
21. Yes; if two lines are cut by a transversal so that alternate interior angles are congruent, then the lines are parallel.
22. Yes; if two lines are cut by a transversal so that a pair of consecutive interior angles are supplementary, then the lines are parallel. Or if two lines are cut by a transversal so that the alternate interior angles are congruent, then the lines are parallel.
23. Yes; if two lines are cut by a transversal so that a pair of consecutive interior angles are supplementary, then the lines are parallel.

3.4 **Tell whether the lines through the given points are *parallel, perpendicular,* or *neither. Justify* your answer.**

24. **Line 1:** (7, 4), (10, 5)
Line 2: (2, 3), (8, 5)
Parallel; the slopes are equal.

25. **Line 1:** (−3, 1), (−2, 5)
Line 2: (−1, −3), (5, −2)
25, 26. See margin.

26. **Line 1:** (−6, 0), (8, 7)
Line 2: (1, 4), (2, 2)

3.4 **Tell which line through the given points is steeper.**

27. **Line 1:** (0, −6), (−4, −9)
Line 2: (−2, 5), (1, 9)
Line 2

28. **Line 1:** (−1, −5), (−1, 3)
Line 2: (−3, 4), (−5, 4)
Line 1

29. **Line 1:** (1, 1), (2, 6)
Line 2: (1, 1), (3, 10)
Line 1

3.5 **Write an equation of the line that passes through the given point *P* and has the given slope *m*.**

30. $P(4, 7), m = 2$
$y = 2x - 1$

31. $P(-3, 0), m = \frac{2}{3}$
$y = \frac{2}{3}x + 2$

32. $P(9, 4), m = -\frac{1}{3}$
$y = -\frac{1}{3}x + 7$

3.5 **Write an equation of the line that passes through point *P* and is parallel to the line with the given equation.**

33. $P(1, -2), y = -2x - 6$
$y = -2x$

34. $P(6, 3), y = -\frac{1}{3}x + 12$
$y = -\frac{1}{3}x + 5$

35. $P(-7, 3), y = x + 3$
$y = x + 10$

36. $P(0, 3), y = 4x - 2$
$y = 4x + 3$

37. $P(-9, 4), y = \frac{2}{5}x + 1$
$y = \frac{2}{5}x + \frac{38}{5}$

38. $P(8, -3), y = x - 5$
$y = x - 11$

3.6 **Find $m\angle ADB$.**

39.

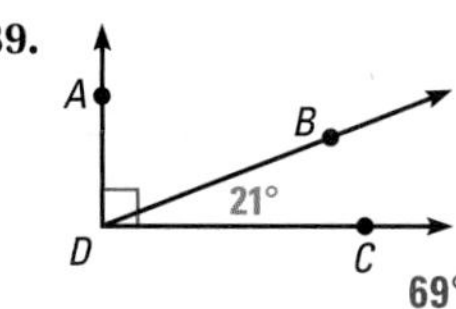

69°

40.

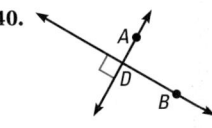

90°

41.

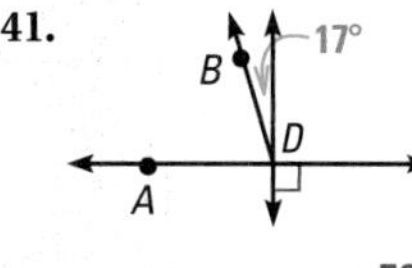

73°

42.

52°

43.

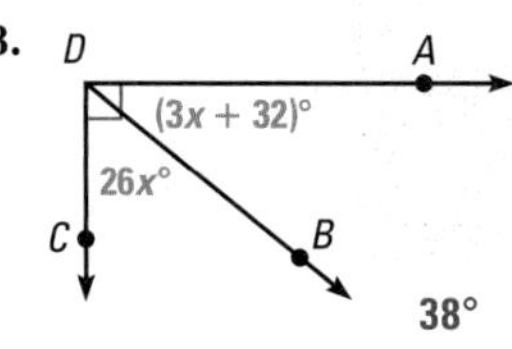

38°

44.

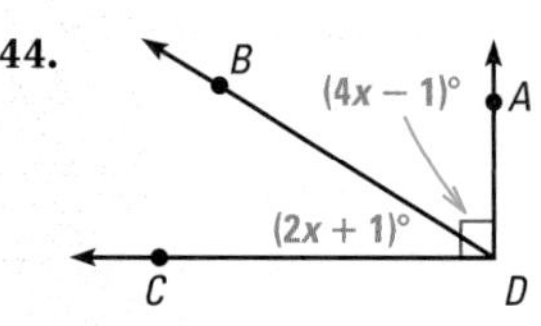

59°

3.6 **45.** Copy and complete the proof.

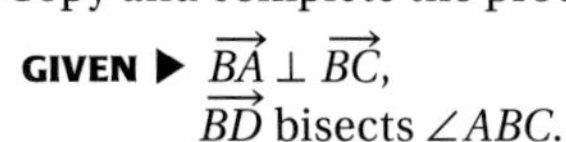

GIVEN ▶ $\overrightarrow{BA} \perp \overrightarrow{BC}$,
$\overrightarrow{BD}$ bisects $\angle ABC$.

PROVE ▶ $m\angle ABD = 45°$

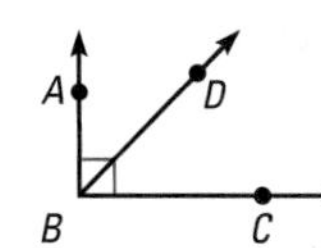

STATEMENTS	REASONS
1. $\overrightarrow{BA} \perp \overrightarrow{BC}$	1. ? Given
2. ? $\angle ABC$ is a right angle.	2. Definition of perpendicular lines
3. $m\angle ABC = 90°$	3. ? Definition of right angle
4. ? $\overrightarrow{BD}$ bisects $\angle ABC$.	4. Given
5. $m\angle ABD = m\angle DBC$	5. ? Definition of angle bisector
6. $m\angle ABC$ = ? + ? $m\angle ABD$, $m\angle DBC$	6. Angle Addition Postulate
7. $m\angle ABD + m\angle DBC = 90°$	7. ? Transitive Property of Equality
8. $m\angle ABD$ + ? = 90° $m\angle ABD$	8. Substitution Property of Equality
9. $2(m\angle ABD) = 90°$	9. ? Simplify.
10. $m\angle ABD = 45°$	10. ? Division Property of Equality

25. Neither; the slopes are not equal and they are not opposite reciprocals.

26. Perpendicular; the slopes are opposite reciprocals.

EXTRA PRACTICE

1.

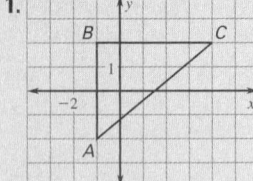

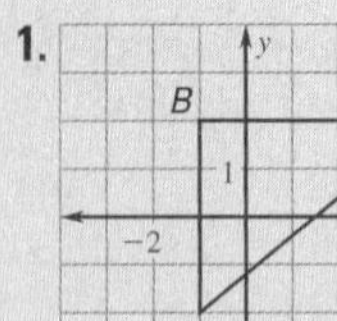

scalene; right triangle

2.

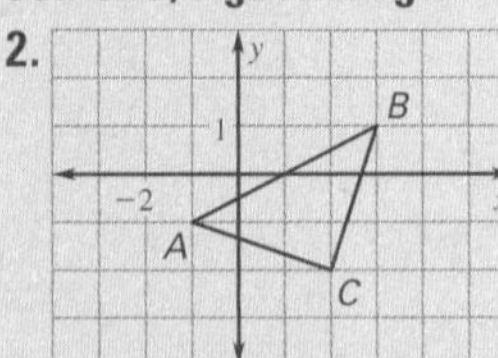

isosceles; right triangle

3.

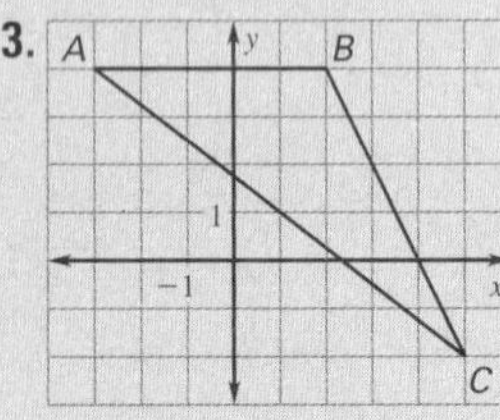

scalene; not a right triangle

7. $\triangle DFG \cong \triangle FDE$; SAS Congruence Postulate or ASA Congruence Postulate

8. $\triangle JNM \cong \triangle KML$; since $\overline{JN} \parallel \overline{KM}$, $\angle J \cong \angle KML \cong \angle N$. Use the SAS Congruence Postulate, the SSS Congruence Postulate, or the ASA Congruence Postulate.

9. $STWX \cong UTWV$; all pairs of corresponding angles and sides are congruent.

12. No; a true congruence statement would be $\triangle PQR \cong \triangle TVU$.

13. No; a true congruence statement would be $\triangle JKM \cong \triangle LKM$.

14. Yes; use the Segment Addition Postulate to get $\overline{AC} \cong \overline{BD}$. Also, $\overline{CD} \cong \overline{CD}$, so use the SSS Congruence Postulate.

18. $\triangle NRM \cong \triangle PRQ$; $\angle NRM \cong \angle PRQ$ since they are vertical angles, and with the information given in the diagram you can use the SAS Congruence Postulate.

19. $\triangle HJL \cong \triangle KLJ$; use alternate interior angles to get $\angle HJL \cong \angle JLK$. Since $\overline{JL} \cong \overline{JL}$, with the information given in the diagram you can use the SAS Congruence Postulate.

EXTRA PRACTICE

Chapter 4

4.1 A triangle has the given vertices. Graph the triangle and classify it by its sides. Then determine if it is a right triangle. 1–3. See margin.

1. $A(-1, -2), B(-1, 2), C(4, 2)$ 2. $A(-1, -1), B(3, 1), C(2, -2)$ 3. $A(-3, 4), B(2, 4), C(5, -2)$

4.1 Find the value of x. Then classify the triangle by its angles.

4.

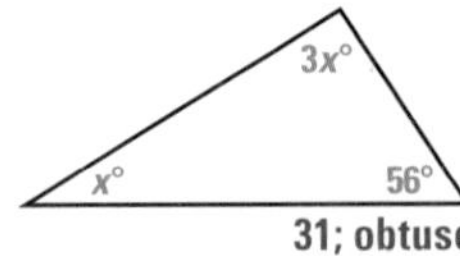

31; obtuse

5.

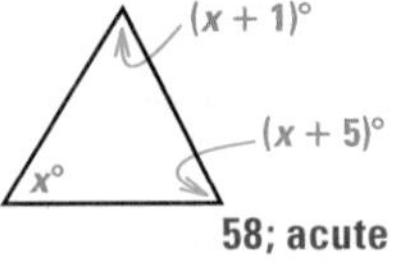

58; acute

6.

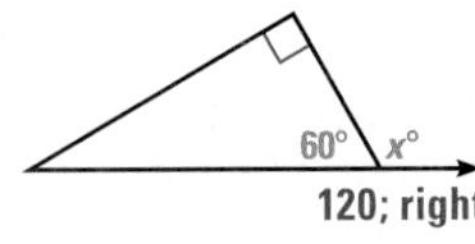

120; right

4.2 Write a congruence statement for any figures that can be proved congruent. *Explain* your reasoning. 7–9. See margin.

7.

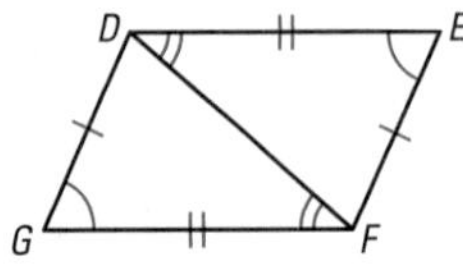

8.

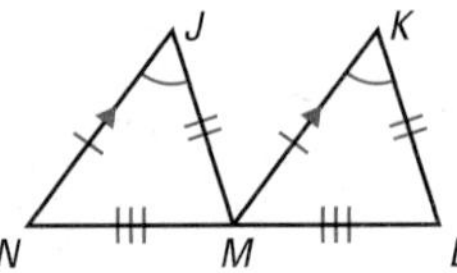

9.

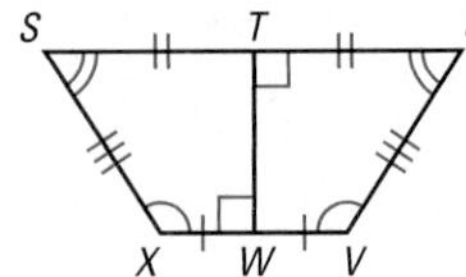

4.2 Find the value of x.

10.

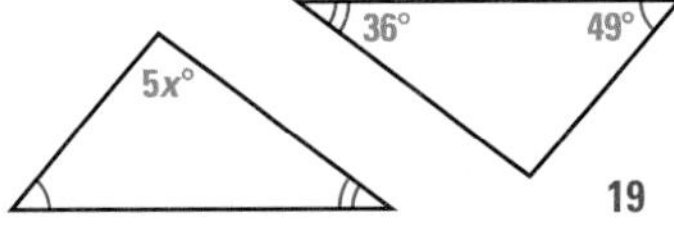

19

11.

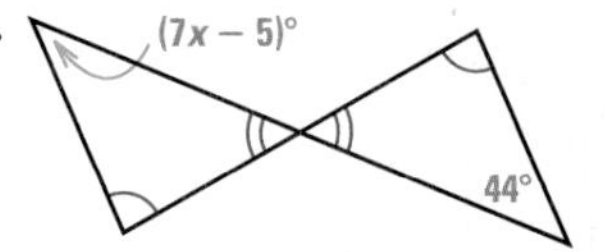

7

4.3 Decide whether the congruence statement is true. *Explain* your reasoning. 12–14. See margin.

12. $\triangle PQR \cong \triangle TUV$

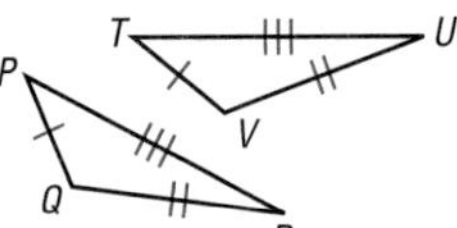

13. $\triangle JKM \cong \triangle LMK$

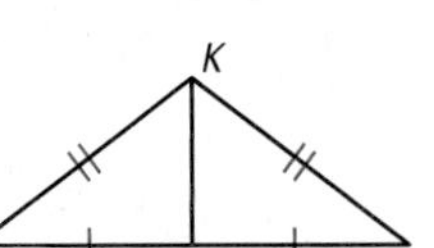

14. $\triangle ACD \cong \triangle BDC$

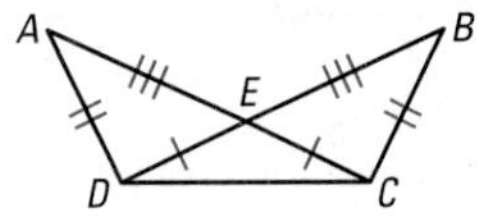

4.3 Use the given coordinates to determine if $\triangle ABC \cong \triangle PQR$.

15. $A(-2, 1), B(2, 6), C(6, 2), P(-1, -2), Q(3, 3), R(7, -1)$ congruent

16. $A(-4, 5), B(2, 6), C(-2, 3), P(2, 1), Q(8, 2), R(5, -1)$ not congruent

4.4 Name the congruent triangles in the diagram. *Explain*.

17.

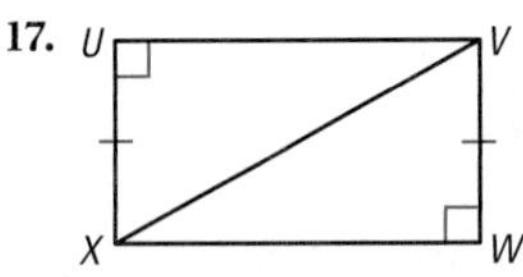

$\triangle XUV \cong \triangle VWX$; since $\overline{XV} \cong \overline{XV}$, with the givens you can use the HL Congruence Theorem.

18.

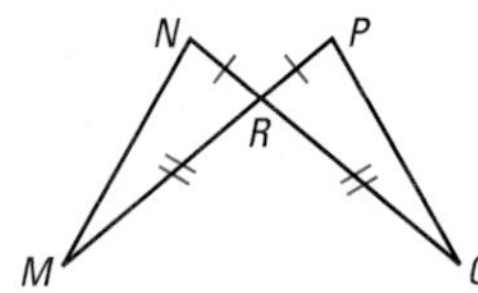

18, 19. See margin.

19.

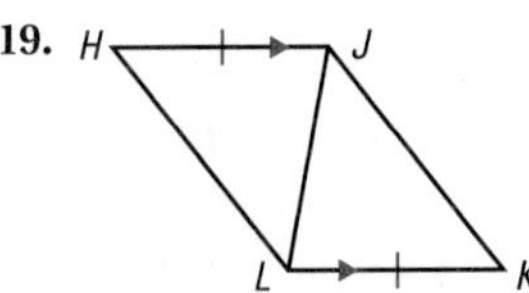

4.5 Is it possible to prove that the triangles are congruent? If so, state the postulate or theorem you would use.

20. $\triangle GHL$, $\triangle JKL$

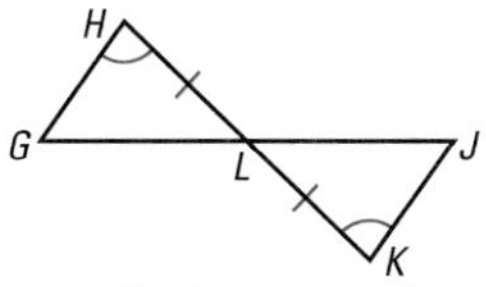

yes; ASA Congruence Postulate

21. $\triangle MNQ$, $\triangle PNQ$

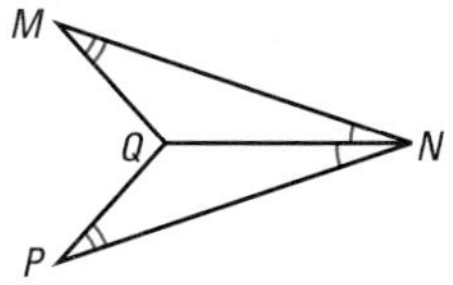

yes; AAS Congruence Theorem

22. $\triangle STW$, $\triangle UVW$

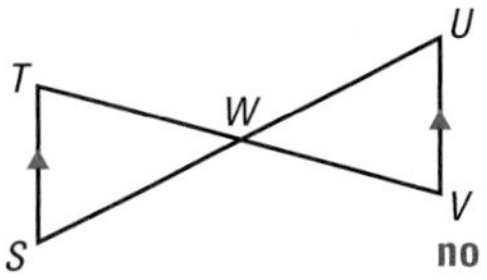

no

4.5 Tell whether you can use the given information to determine whether $\triangle ABC \cong \triangle DEF$. *Explain* your reasoning.

23. $\angle A \cong \angle D$, $\overline{AB} \cong \overline{DE}$, $\angle B \cong \angle E$
Yes; use the ASA Congruence Postulate.

24. $\overline{AB} \cong \overline{DE}$, $\overline{BC} \cong \overline{EF}$, $\angle A \cong \angle D$
No; there is no SSA Congruence Postulate.

4.6 Use the information in the diagram to write a plan for proving that $\angle 1 \cong \angle 2$. 25–27. See margin.

25.

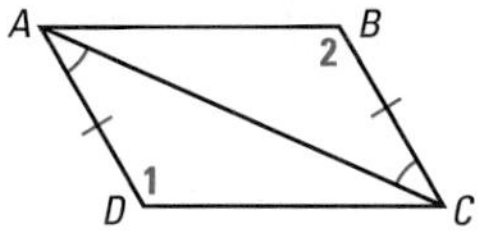

26.

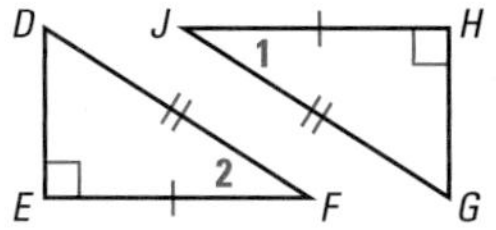

27.

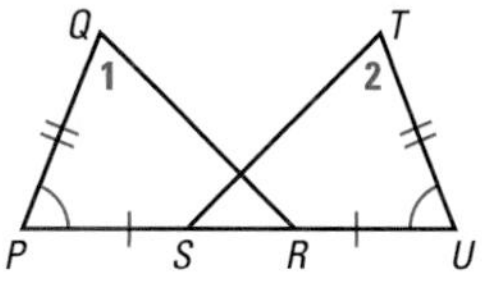

4.6 Use the vertices of $\triangle ABC$ and $\triangle DEF$ to show that $\angle A \cong \angle D$. *Explain.* 28, 29. See margin.

28. $A(0, 8)$, $B(6, 0)$, $C(0, 0)$, $D(3, 10)$, $E(9, 2)$, $F(3, 2)$

29. $A(-3, -2)$, $B(-2, 3)$, $C(2, 2)$, $D(5, 1)$, $E(6, 6)$, $F(10, 5)$

4.7 Find the value(s) of the variable(s).

30.

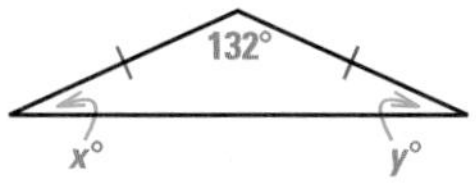

$x = 24, y = 24$

31.

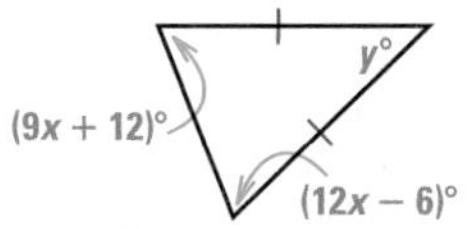

$x = 6, y = 48$

32.

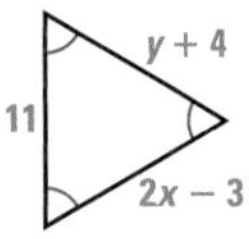

$x = 7, y = 7$

33.

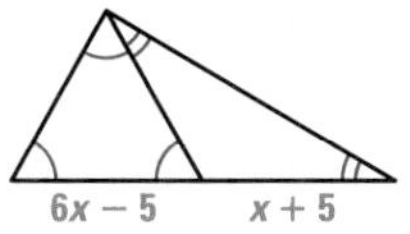

$x = 2$

34.

$x = 30, y = 56$

35.

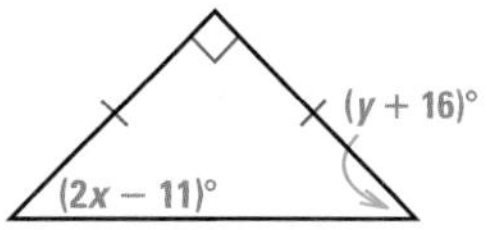

$x = 28, y = 29$

4.8 Copy the figure and draw its image after the transformation. 36–38. See margin.

36. Reflection: in the y-axis

37. Reflection: in the x-axis

38. Translation: $(x, y) \rightarrow (x - 3, y + 7)$

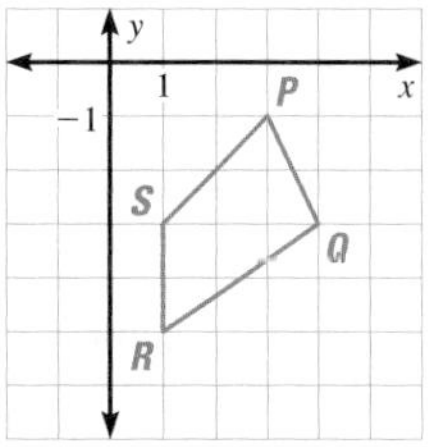

4.8 Use the coordinates to graph $\overline{AB}$ and $\overline{CD}$. Tell whether $\overline{CD}$ is a rotation of $\overline{AB}$ about the origin. If so, give the angle and direction of rotation. 39, 40. See margin for art.

39. $A(4, 2)$, $B(1, 1)$, $C(-4, -2)$, $D(-1, -1)$
yes; 180°

40. $A(-1, 3)$, $B(0, 2)$, $C(-1, 2)$, $D(-3, 1)$ no

27. State the given information from the diagram, and state that $\overline{SR} \cong \overline{SR}$ by the Reflexive Property of Congruence. Then use the Segment Addition Postulate to show that $\overline{PR} \cong \overline{US}$. Use the SAS Congruence Postulate to prove $\triangle QPR \cong \triangle TUS$, and state $\angle 1 \cong \angle 2$ because corresponding parts of congruent triangles are congruent.

28. $AB = DE = 10$; $AC = DF = 8$; $BC = EF = 6$; $\triangle ABC \cong \triangle DEF$ by the SSS Congruence Postulate, and $\angle A \cong \angle D$ because corresponding parts of congruent triangles are congruent.

29. $AB = DE = \sqrt{26}$; $AC = DF = \sqrt{41}$; $BC = EF = \sqrt{17}$; $\triangle ABC \cong \triangle DEF$ by the SSS Congruence Postulate, and $\angle A \cong \angle D$ because corresponding parts of congruent triangles are congruent.

36–38. See Additional Answers beginning on p. AA1.

39.

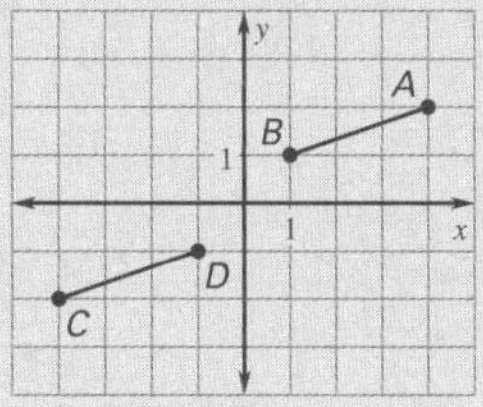

40.

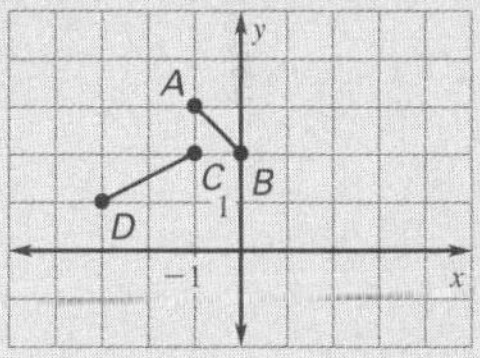

25. State the given information from the diagram, and state that $\overline{AC} \cong \overline{AC}$ by the Reflexive Property of Congruence. Then use the SAS Congruence Postulate to prove $\triangle ABC \cong \triangle CDA$, and state $\angle 1 \cong \angle 2$ because corresponding parts of congruent triangles are congruent.

26. State the given information from the diagram. Prove $\triangle DEF \cong \triangle GHJ$ by the HL Congruence Theorem, and state $\angle 1 \cong \angle 2$ because corresponding parts of congruent triangles are congruent.

Chapter 5

5.1 Copy and complete the statement.

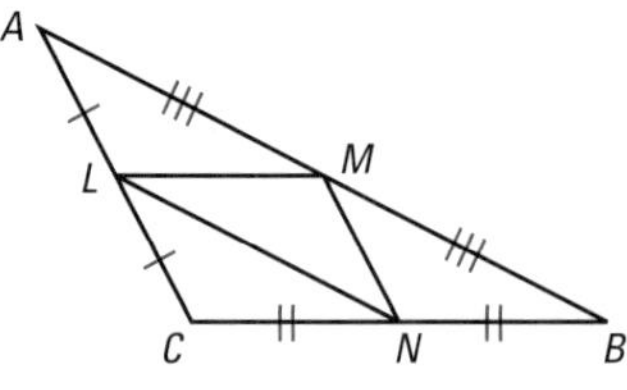

1. $\overline{LN} \parallel$ __?__ **$\overline{AB}$**
2. $\overline{CB} \parallel$ __?__ **$\overline{LM}$**
3. $\overline{MN} \parallel$ __?__ **$\overline{AC}$**
4. $AM =$ __?__ $=$ __?__ **MB, LN**
5. $MN =$ __?__ $=$ __?__ **LC, AL**

5.1 Place the figure in a coordinate plane in a convenient way. Assign coordinates to each vertex. **6–9. See margin for art.**

6. Isosceles right triangle: leg length is 4 units **A(0, 0), B(0, 4), C(4, 0)**
7. Scalene triangle: one side length is 6 units ***Sample answer:* A(1, 0), B(0, 4), C(7, 0)**
8. Square: side length is 5 units **A(0, 0), B(0, 5), C(5, 5), D(5, 0)**
9. Right triangle: leg lengths are s and t **A(0, 0), B(0, s), C(t, 0)**

5.2 Find the length of $\overline{AB}$.

10. 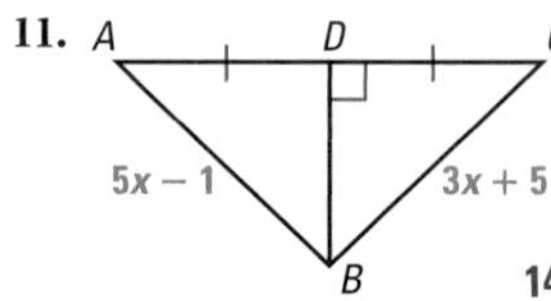

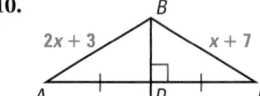

11

11. A, D, C; $5x - 1$; $3x + 5$; B **14**

12. 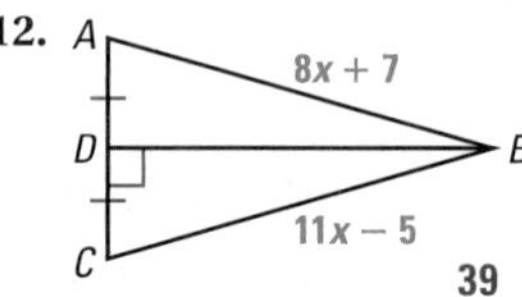

39

5.2 In Exercises 13–17, use the diagram. $\overrightarrow{LN}$ is the perpendicular bisector of $\overline{JK}$.

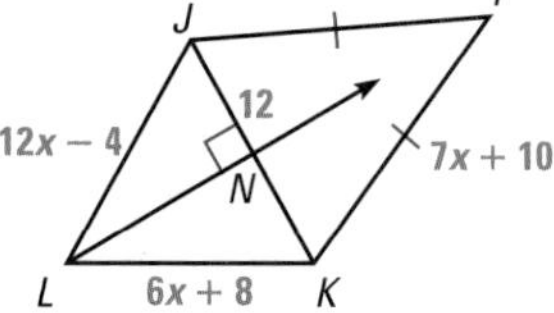

13. Find KN. **12**
14. Find LJ. **20**
15. Find KP. **24**
16. Find JP. **24**
17. Is P on $\overrightarrow{LN}$? **yes**

5.3 Use the information in the diagram to find the measure.

18. Find $m\angle ABC$. **32°**

19. Find EH. **15**

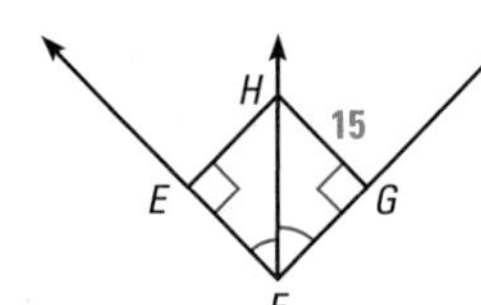

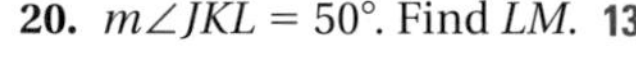

20. $m\angle JKL = 50°$. Find LM. **13**

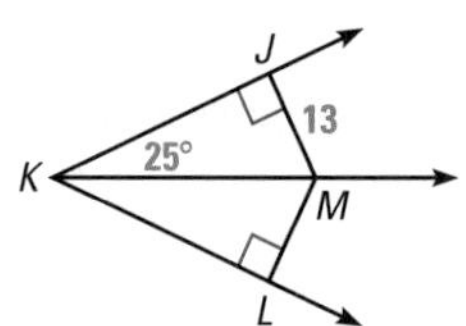

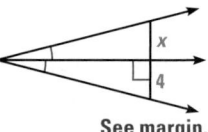

5.3 Can you find the value of x? *Explain.*

21. 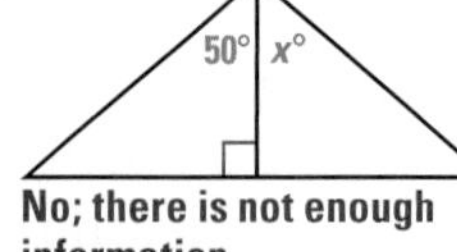

No; there is not enough information.

22. 

See margin.

23. 
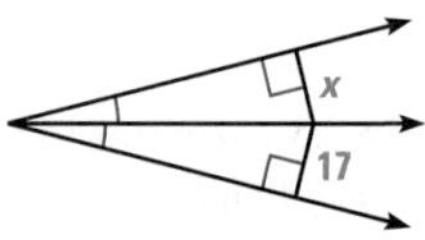

Yes; x = 17 by the Angle Bisector Theorem.

6.

7. *Sample:*

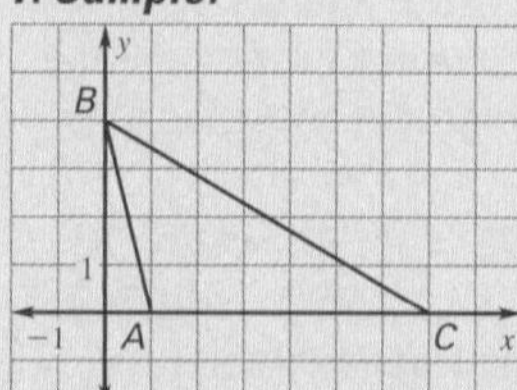

8.

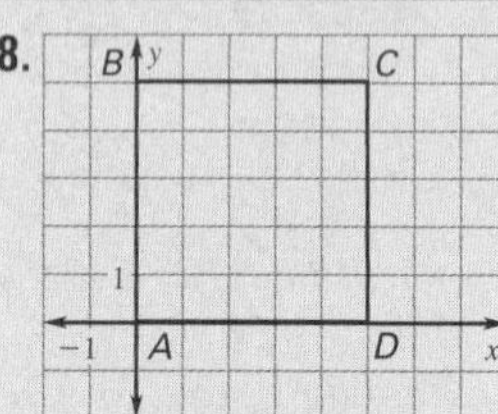

9.

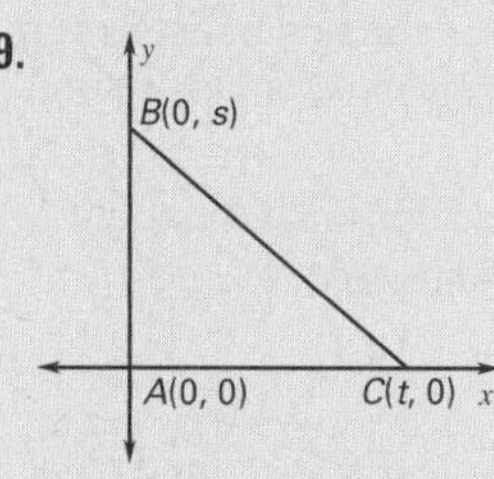

22. Yes; $x = 4$ because the triangles are congruent by the ASA Congruence Theorem.

5.4 ***P* is the centroid of $\triangle DEF$, $FP = 14$, $RE = 24$, and $PS = 8.5$. Find the length of the segment.**

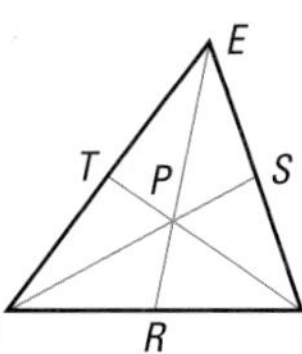

24. $\overline{TF}$ **21**
25. $\overline{DP}$ **17**
26. $\overline{DS}$ **25.5**
27. $\overline{PR}$ **8**

5.4 **Use the diagram shown and the given information to decide whether $\overline{BD}$ is a *perpendicular bisector*, an *angle bisector*, a *median*, or an *altitude* of $\triangle ABC$.**

28. $\overline{BD} \perp \overline{AC}$ **altitude**
29. $\angle ABD \cong \angle CBD$ **angle bisector**
30. $\overline{AD} \cong \overline{CD}$ **median**
31. $\overline{BD} \perp \overline{AC}$ and $\overline{AD} \cong \overline{CD}$ **perpendicular bisector**
32. $\triangle ABD \cong \triangle CBD$ **perpendicular bisector and angle bisector**
33. $\overline{BD} \perp \overline{AC}$ and $\overline{AB} \cong \overline{CB}$ **perpendicular bisector, angle bisector, median,and altitude**

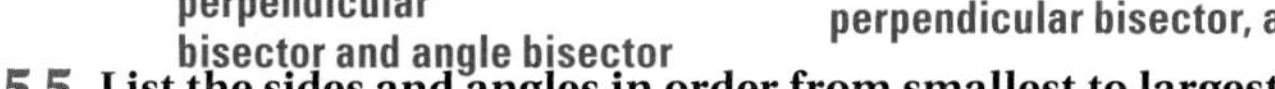

5.5 **List the sides and angles in order from smallest to largest.**

34.

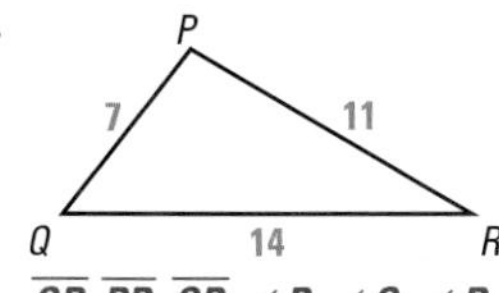

$\overline{QP}$, $\overline{PR}$, $\overline{QR}$, $\angle R$, $\angle Q$, $\angle P$

35.

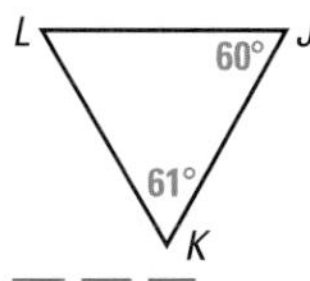

$\overline{JK}$, $\overline{LK}$, $\overline{JL}$, $\angle L$, $\angle J$, $\angle K$

36.

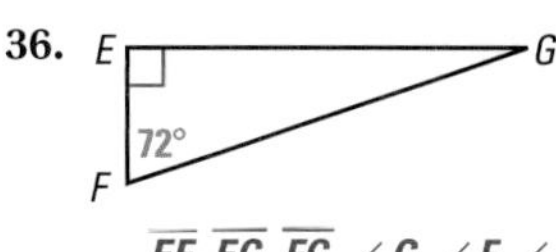

$\overline{EF}$, $\overline{EG}$, $\overline{FG}$, $\angle G$, $\angle F$, $\angle E$

5.5 ***Describe* the possible lengths of the third side of the triangle given the lengths of the other two sides.**

37. 9 inches, 8 inches **1 in. < ℓ < 17 in.**
38. 24 feet, 13 feet **11 ft < ℓ < 37 ft**
39. 3 inches, 9 inches **6 in. < ℓ < 12 in.**
40. 1 foot, 17 inches **5 in. < ℓ < 29 in.**
41. 4 feet, 2 yards **2 ft < ℓ < 10 ft**
42. 2 yards, 6 feet **0 ft < ℓ < 12 ft**

5.6 **Copy and complete with >, < or = . *Explain.*** **43–51. See margin.**

43. LN __?__ PR

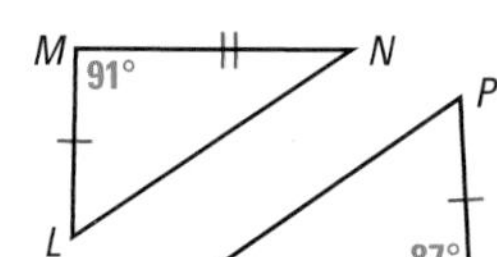

44. VU __?__ ST

45. $m\angle WYX$ __?__ $m\angle WYZ$

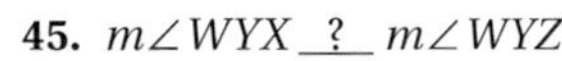

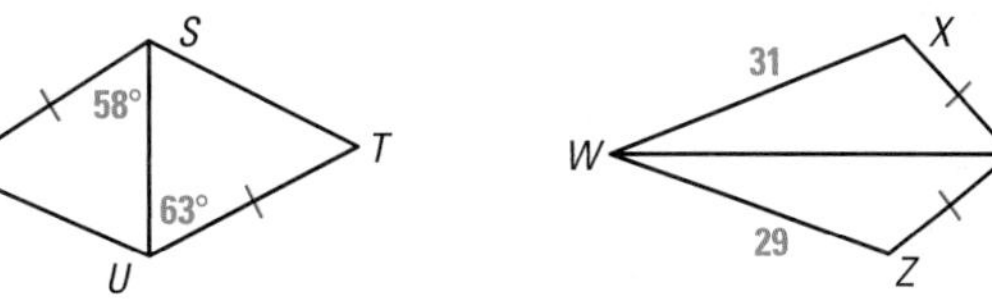

46. $m\angle 1$ __?__ $m\angle 2$

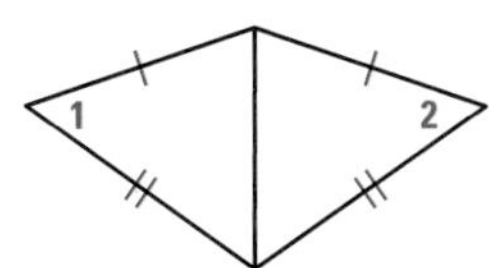

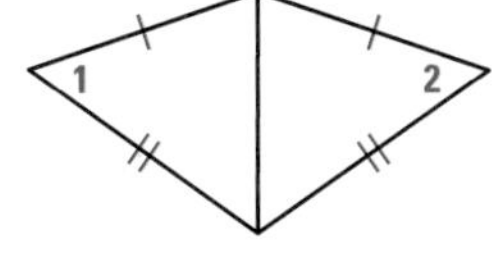

47. JK __?__ MN

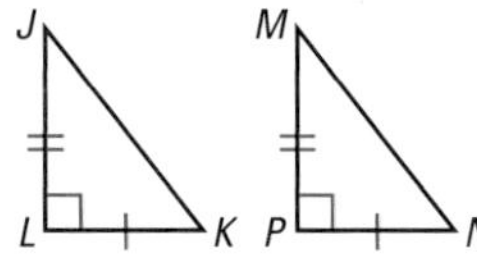

48. BC __?__ DE

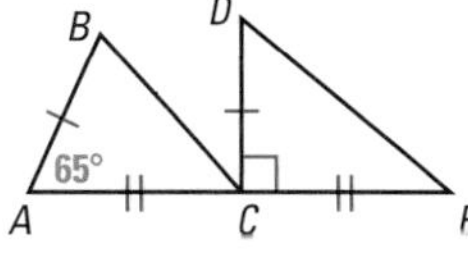

49. GH __?__ QR

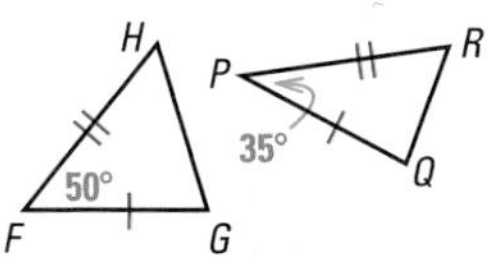

50. $m\angle 3$ __?__ $m\angle 4$

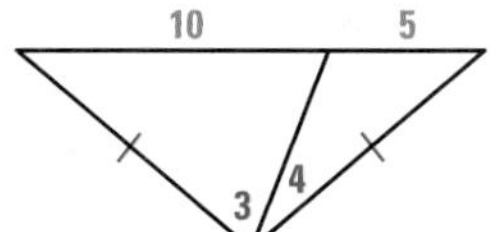

51. $m\angle 5$ __?__ $m\angle 6$

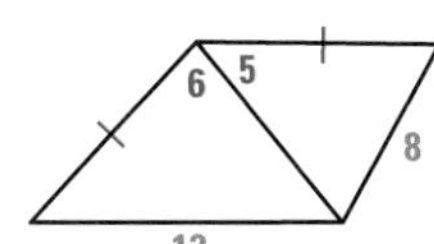

EXTRA PRACTICE

43. >; if two sides of one triangle are congruent to two sides of another triangle, and the included angle of the first is larger than the included angle of the second, then the third side of the first is longer than the third side of the second (Hinge Theorem).

44. <; if two sides of one triangle are congruent to two sides of another triangle, and the included angle of the first is larger than the included angle of the second, then the third side of the first is longer than the third side of the second (Hinge Theorem).

45. >; if two sides of one triangle are congruent to two sides of another triangle, and the third side of the first is longer than the third side of the second, then the included angle of the first is larger than the included angle of the second (Converse of the Hinge Theorem).

46. =; with the reflexive side, all three pairs of corresponding sides are congruent, so the triangles are congruent by the SSS Congruence Postulate, and corresponding parts of congruent triangles are congruent.

47. =; the triangles are congruent by the SAS Congruence Postulate, and corresponding parts of congruent triangles are congruent.

48. <; if two sides of one triangle are congruent to two sides of another triangle, and the included angle of the first is larger than the included angle of the second, then the third side of the first is longer than the third side of the second (Hinge Theorem).

49. >; if two sides of one triangle are congruent to two sides of another triangle, and the included angle of the first is larger than the included angle of the second, then the third side of the first is longer than the third side of the second (Hinge Theorem).

50. >; if two sides of one triangle are congruent to two sides of another triangle, and the third side of the first is longer than the third side of the second, then the included angle of the first is larger than the included angle of the second (Converse of the Hinge Theorem).

51. <; if two sides of one triangle are congruent to two sides of another triangle, and the third side of the first is longer than the third side of the second, then the included angle of the first is larger than the included angle of the second (Converse of the Hinge Theorem).

Chapter 6

6.1 The measures of the angles of a triangle are in the extended ratio given. Find the measures of the angles of the triangle.

1. 1:3:5 **20°, 60°, 100°**
2. 1:5:6 **15°, 75°, 90°**
3. 2:3:5 **36°, 54°, 90°**
4. 5:6:9 **45°, 54°, 81°**

6.1 Solve the proportion.

5. $\frac{x}{14} = \frac{6}{21}$ **4**
6. $\frac{15}{y} = \frac{20}{4}$ **3**
7. $\frac{3}{2z+1} = \frac{1}{7}$ **10**
8. $\frac{a-3}{2} = \frac{2a-1}{6}$ **8**
9. $\frac{6}{3} = \frac{x+8}{-1}$ **−10**
10. $\frac{x+6}{3} = \frac{x-5}{2}$ **27**
11. $\frac{x-2}{4} = \frac{x+10}{10}$ **10**
12. $\frac{12}{8} = \frac{5+t}{t-3}$ **19**

6.1 Find the geometric mean of the two numbers.

13. 4 and 9 **6**
14. 3 and 48 **12**
15. 9 and 16 **12**
16. 7 and 11 **$\sqrt{77}$**

6.2 Copy and complete the statement.

17. If $\frac{7}{x} = \frac{9}{y}$, then $\frac{x}{7} = \frac{?}{?}$. **$\frac{y}{9}$**

18. If $\frac{2}{8} = \frac{1}{x}$, then $\frac{8+2}{2} = \frac{?}{?}$. **$\frac{x+1}{1}$**

6.2 Use the diagram and the given information to find the unknown length.

19. Given $\frac{NJ}{NK} = \frac{NL}{NM}$, find NK. **4**

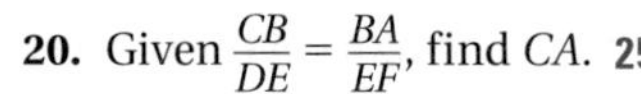

20. Given $\frac{CB}{DE} = \frac{BA}{EF}$, find CA. **25**

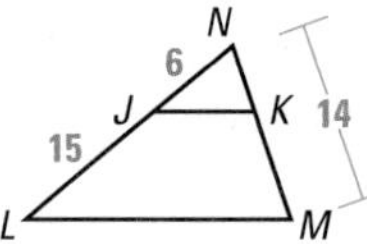

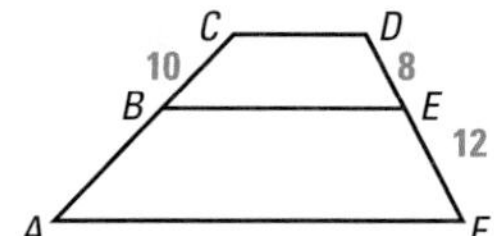

6.3 Determine whether the polygons are similar. If they are, write a similarity statement and find the scale factor.

21.

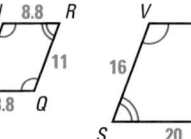

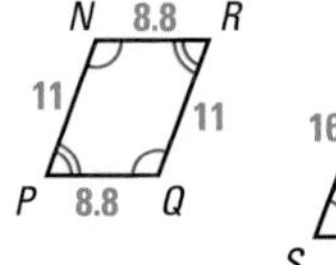

similar; $RQPN \sim STUV$, 11 : 20

22.

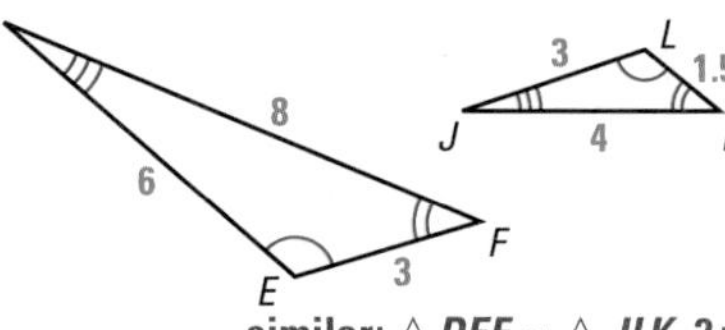

similar; $\triangle DEF \sim \triangle JLK$, 2 : 1

6.3 In the diagram, $\triangle PQR \sim \triangle LMN$.

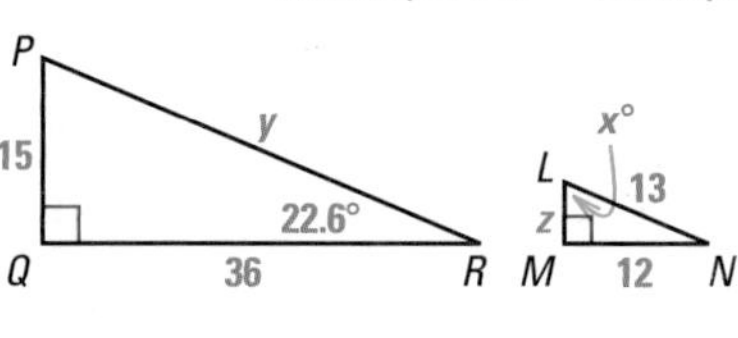

23. Find the scale factor of $\triangle PQR$ to $\triangle LMN$. **3 : 1**
24. Find the values of x, y, and z. **67.4, 39, 5**
25. Find the perimeter of each triangle. **$\triangle PQR$: 90, $\triangle LMN$: 30**

6.3 $\triangle ABC \sim \triangle DEF$. Identify the blue special segment and find the value of y.

26.

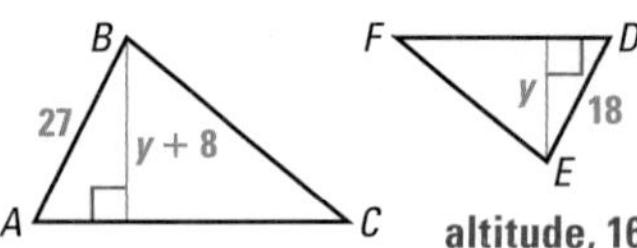

altitude, 16

27.

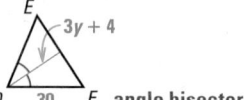

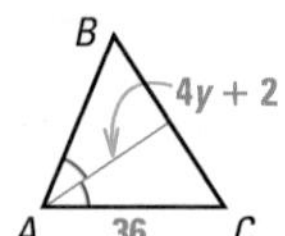

E, 3y + 4, D, 30, F **angle bisector, 7**

6.4 **In Exercises 28–31, determine whether the triangles are similar. If they are, write a similarity statement. *Explain* your reasoning.** 28–31. See margin.

28.

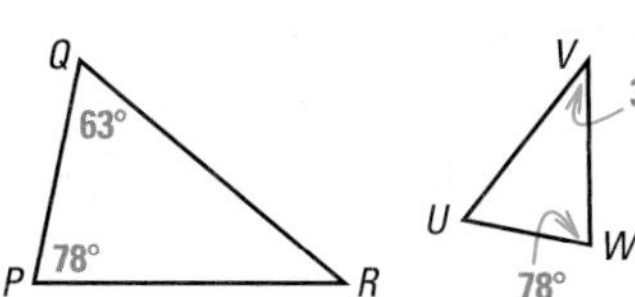

29.

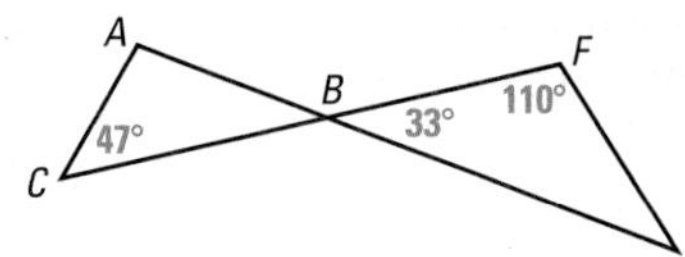

30.

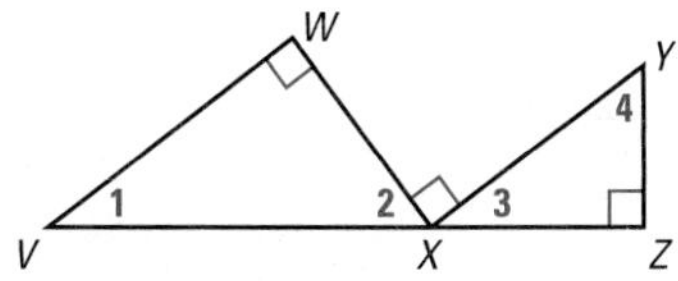

31.

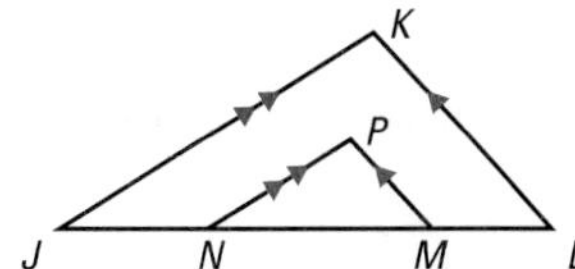

6.5 **Show that the triangles are similar and write a similarity statement. *Explain* your reasoning.** 32, 33. See margin.

32.

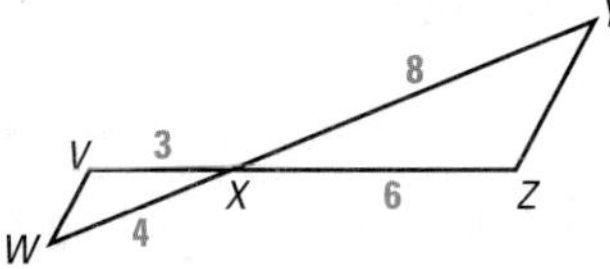

33.

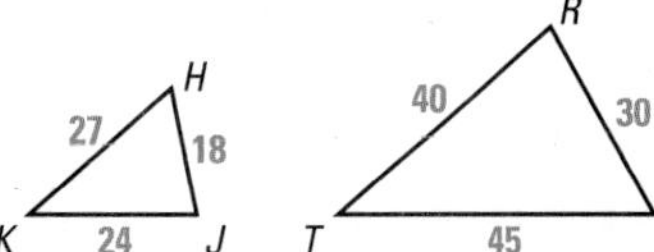

6.6 **Use the diagram to find the value of each variable.**

34.

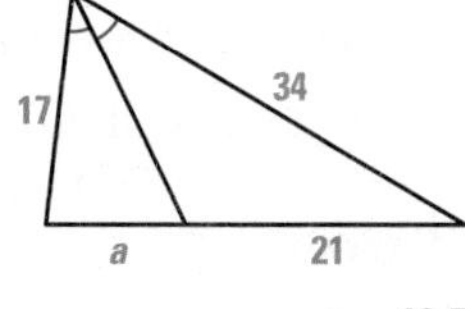

$a = 10.5$

35.

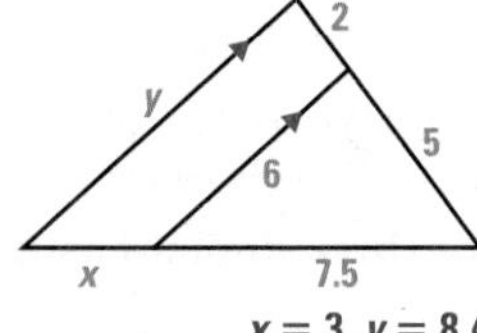

$x = 3, y = 8.4$

36.

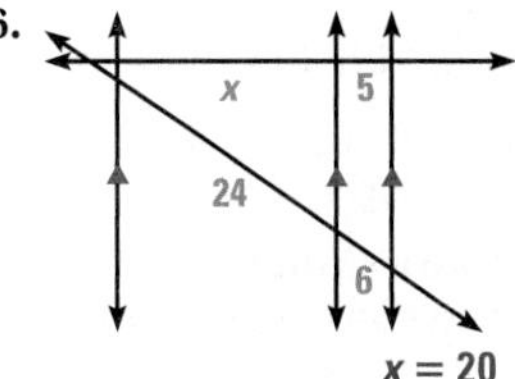

$x = 20$

6.7 **Draw a dilation of the polygon with the given vertices using the given scale factor of *k*.** 37–40. See margin.

37. $A(1, 1), B(4, 1), C(1, 2); k = 3$

38. $A(2, 2), B(-2, 2), C(-1, -1), D(2, -1); k = 5$

39. $A(2, 2), B(8, 2), C(2, 6); k = \frac{1}{2}$

40. $A(3, -6), B(6, -6), C(6, 9), D(-3, 9); k = \frac{1}{3}$

6.7 **Determine whether the dilation from Figure A to Figure B is a *reduction* or an *enlargement*. Then find its scale factor.**

41.

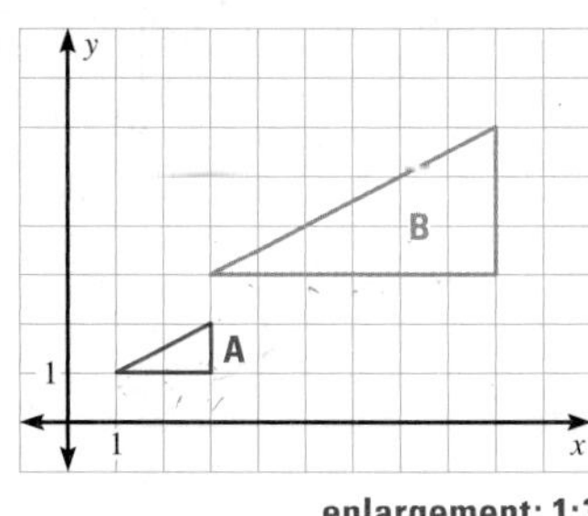

enlargement; 1:3

42.

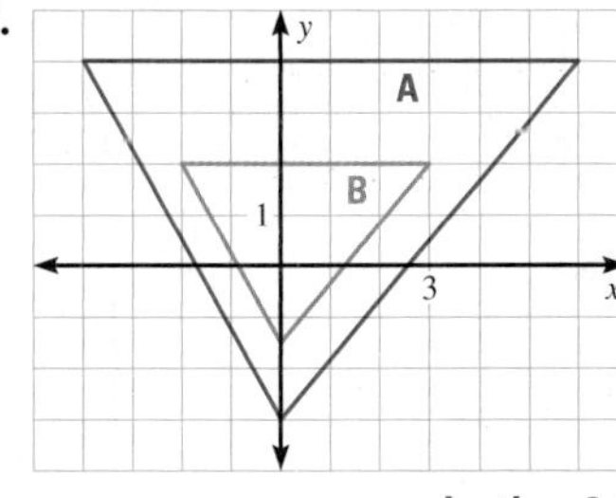

reduction; 2:1

EXTRA PRACTICE

28. Similar; $\triangle PQR \sim \triangle WUV$; use the Triangle Sum Theorem to get $m\angle U = 63°$; they are similar by the AA Similarity Postulate.

29. not similar

30. Similar; $\triangle VWX \sim \triangle XZY$; since $\angle W \cong \angle WXY$, $\overline{VW} \parallel \overline{XY}$ by the converse of the Alternate Interior Angles Theorem, and $\angle 1 \cong \angle 3$ by the Corresponding Angles Postulate. Then the triangles are similar by the AA Similarity Postulate.

31. Similar; $\triangle JKL \sim \triangle NPM$; since $\overline{JK} \parallel \overline{NP}$ and $\overline{KL} \parallel \overline{PM}$, $\angle J \cong \angle PNM$ and $\angle L \cong \angle PMN$ by the Corresponding Angles Postulate. Then the triangles are similar by the AA Similarity Postulate.

32. Since $\frac{VX}{ZX} = \frac{WX}{YX} = \frac{1}{2}$ and $\angle WXV \cong \angle YXZ$ because they are vertical angles, $\triangle WVX \sim \triangle YZX$ by the SAS Similarity Theorem.

33. Since $\frac{KH}{TS} = \frac{KJ}{TR} = \frac{HJ}{SR} = \frac{3}{5}$, $\triangle KHJ \sim \triangle TSR$ by the SSS Similarity Theorem.

37.

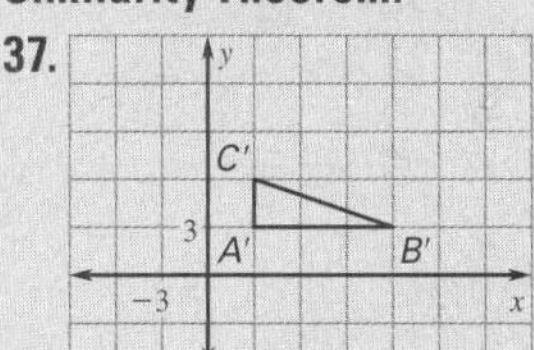

38.

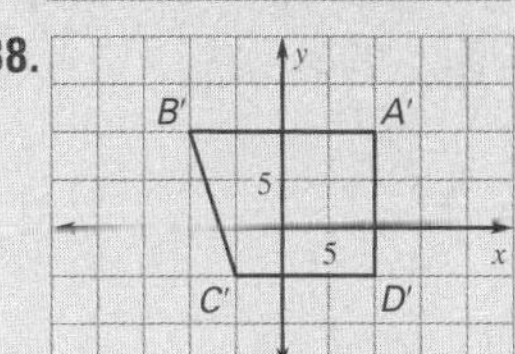

39.

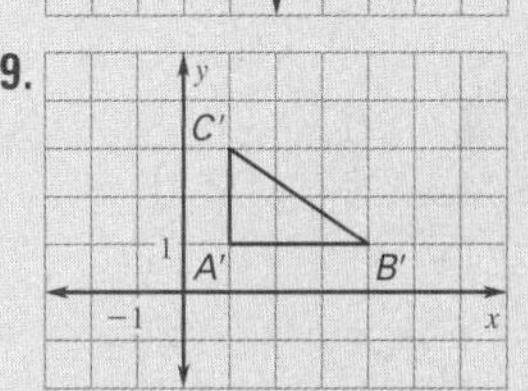

40.

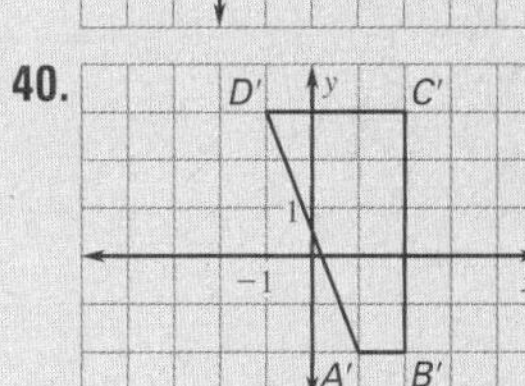

Chapter 7

7.1 Find the unknown side length of the right triangle using the Pythagorean Theorem or a Pythagorean triple.

1. 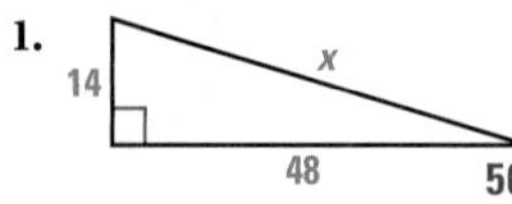

50

2. 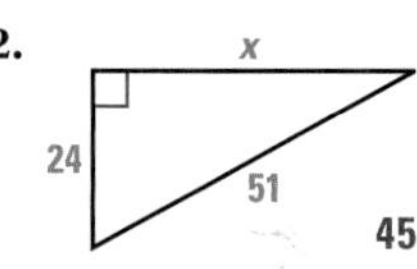

45

3. 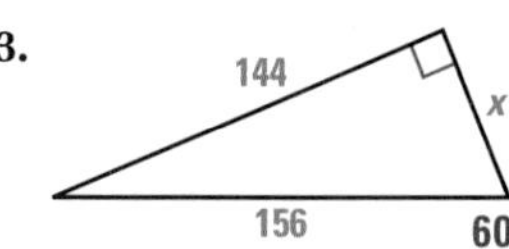

60

7.1 Find the area of the isosceles triangle.

4. 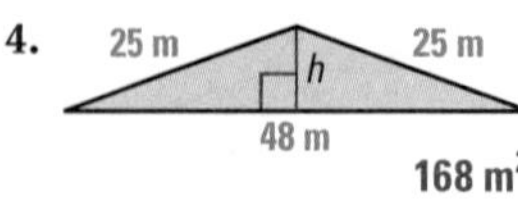

168 m^2

5. 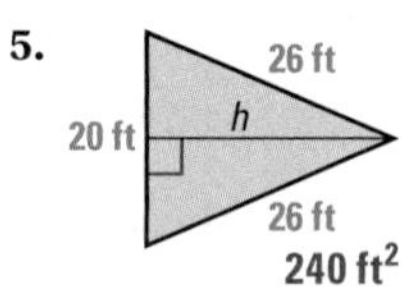

240 ft^2

6. 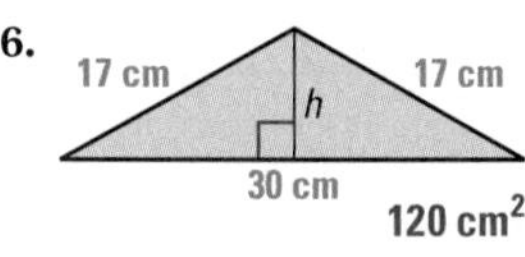

120 cm^2

7.2 Tell whether the given side lengths of a triangle can represent a right triangle.

7. 24, 32, and 40 **right triangle**
8. 21, 72, and 75 **right triangle**
9. 11, 25, and 27 **not a right triangle**
10. 7, 11, and 13 **not a right triangle**
11. 17, 19, and $5\sqrt{26}$ **right triangle**
12. 9, 10, and $\sqrt{181}$ **right triangle**

7.2 Decide if the segment lengths form a triangle. If so, would the triangle be *acute, right,* or *obtuse*?

13. 14, 21, and 25 **triangle; acute**
14. 32, 60, and 68 **triangle; right**
15. 11, 19, and 32 **not a triangle**
16. 3, 9, and $3\sqrt{11}$ **triangle; obtuse**
17. 12, 15, and $3\sqrt{40}$ **triangle; acute**
18. $4\sqrt{21}$, 25, and 31 **triangle; right**

7.3 Write a similarity statement for the three similar triangles in the diagram. Then complete the proportion.

19. $\frac{AB}{AD} = \frac{BC}{?}$

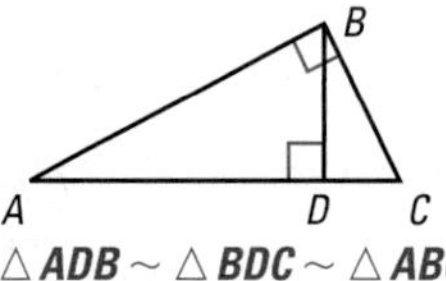

$\triangle ADB \sim \triangle BDC \sim \triangle ABC$; BD

20. $\frac{KJ}{HJ} = \frac{?}{JG}$

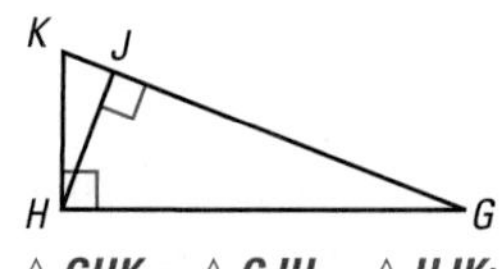

$\triangle GHK \sim \triangle GJH \sim \triangle HJK$; JH

21. $\frac{SR}{RQ} = \frac{RQ}{?}$

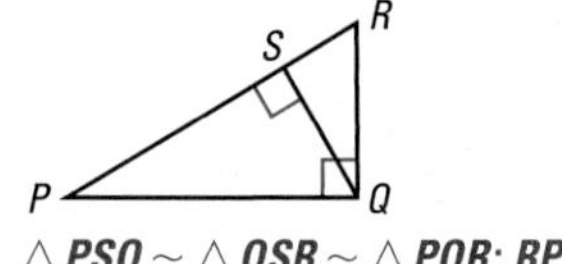

$\triangle PSQ \sim \triangle QSR \sim \triangle PQR$; RP

7.3 Find the value of the variable. Round decimal answers to the nearest tenth.

22. 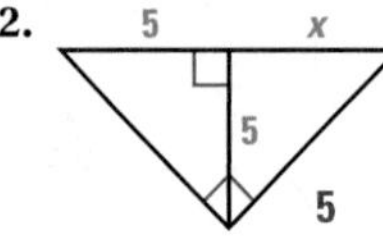

5

23. 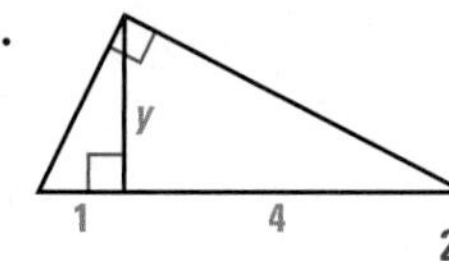

2

24. 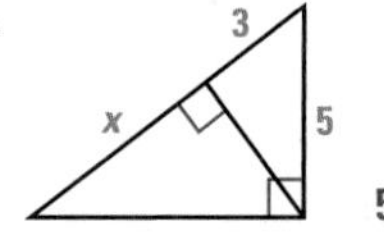

5.3

25. 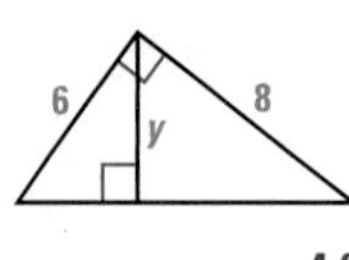

4.8

26. 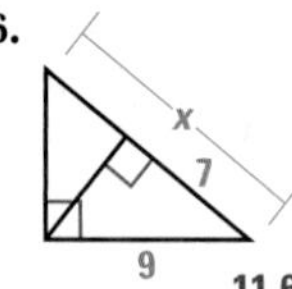

11.6

27. 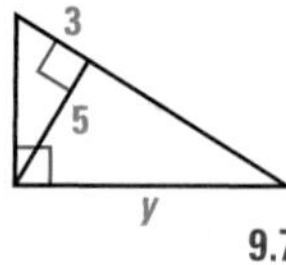

9.7

7.4 Find the value of each variable. Write your answers in simplest radical form.

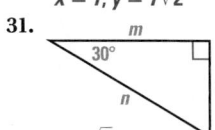

28. $x = 7$, $y = 7\sqrt{2}$

29.

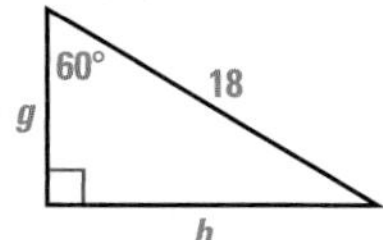

$g = 9$, $h = 9\sqrt{3}$

30.

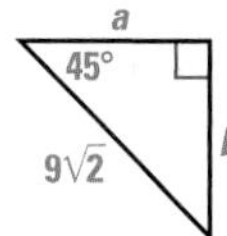

$a = 9$, $b = 9$

31. $m = 5\sqrt{3}$, $n = 10$

32.

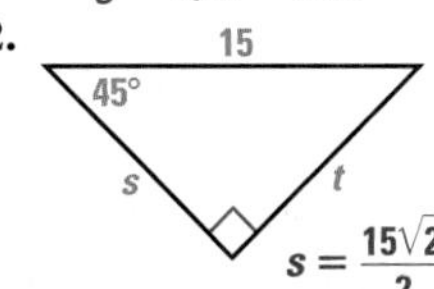

$s = \frac{15\sqrt{2}}{2}$, $t = \frac{15\sqrt{2}}{2}$

33.

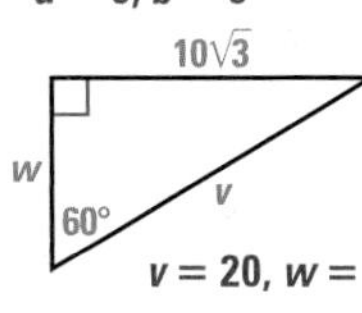

$v = 20$, $w = 10$

7.5 Find tan *A* and tan *B*. Write each answer as a fraction and as a decimal rounded to four places.

34.

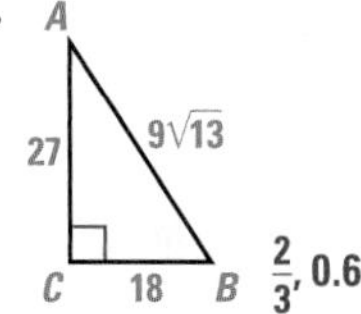

$\frac{2}{3}$, 0.6667; $\frac{3}{2}$, 1.5

35.

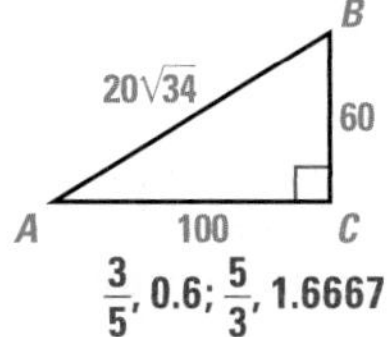

$\frac{3}{5}$, 0.6; $\frac{5}{3}$, 1.6667

36.

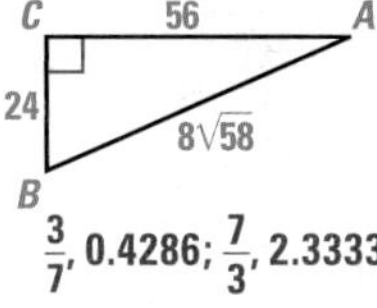

$\frac{3}{7}$, 0.4286; $\frac{7}{3}$, 2.3333

7.5 Use a tangent ratio to find the value of *x*. Round to the nearest tenth. Check your solution using the tangent of the other acute angle.

37.

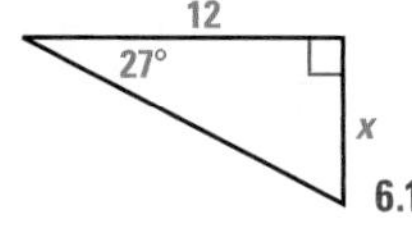

6.1

38.

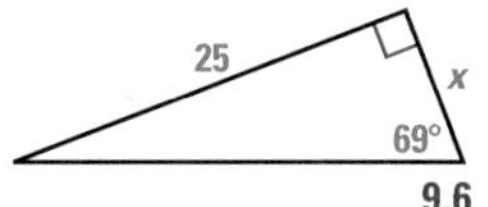

9.6

39.

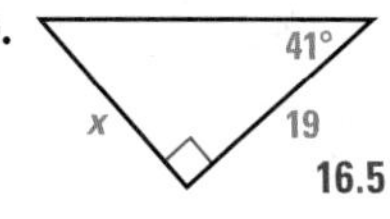

16.5

7.6 Use a sine or cosine ratio to find the value of each variable. Round decimals to the nearest tenth.

40.

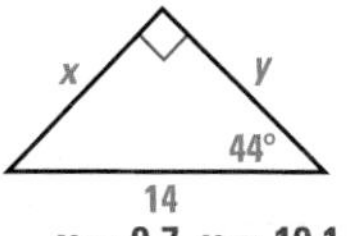

$x = 9.7$, $y = 10.1$

41.

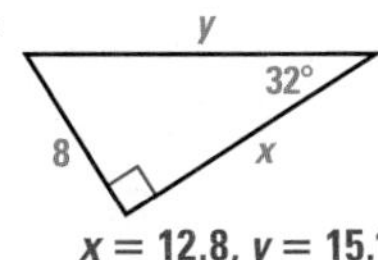

$x = 12.8$, $y = 15.1$

42.

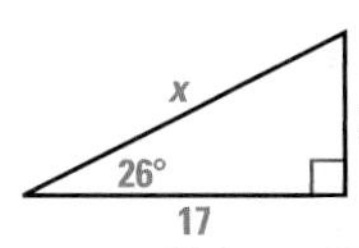

$x = 18.9$, $y = 8.3$

43.

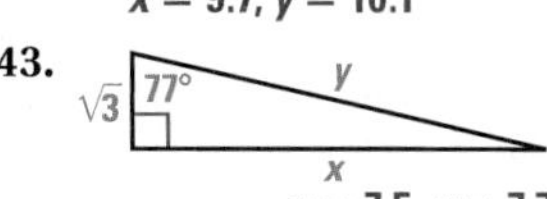

$x = 7.5$, $y = 7.7$

44.

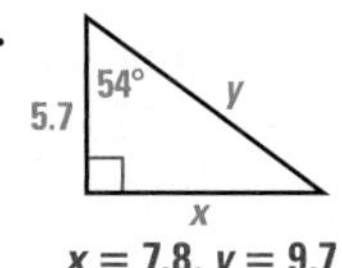

$x = 7.8$, $y = 9.7$

45.

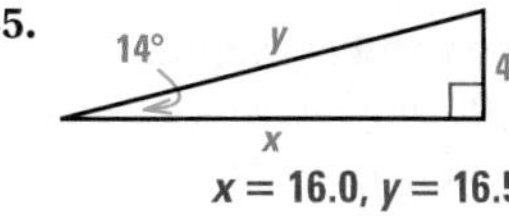

$x = 16.0$, $y = 16.5$

7.7 Solve the right triangle. Round decimal answers to the nearest tenth.

46.

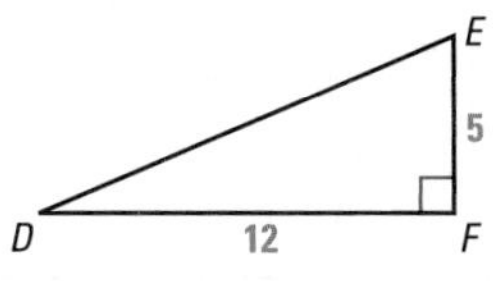

$DE = 13$, $m\angle D = 22.6°$, $m\angle E = 67.4°$

47.

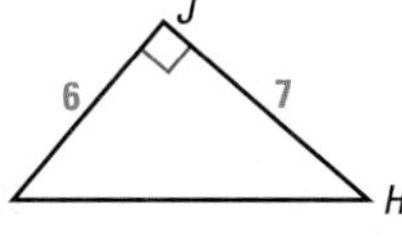

$GH = 9.2$, $m\angle G = 49.4°$, $m\angle H = 40.6°$

48.

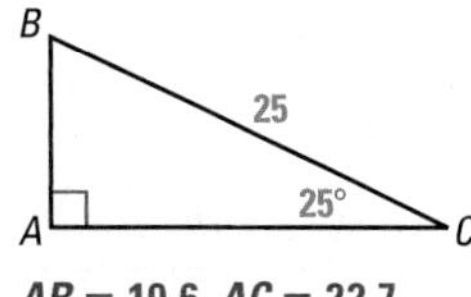

$AB = 10.6$, $AC = 22.7$, $m\angle B = 65°$

EXTRA PRACTICE

Chapter 8

8.1 Find the value of *x*.

1. 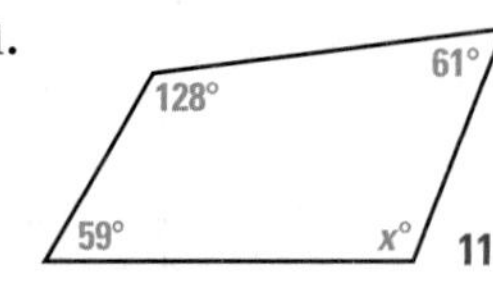
112

2. 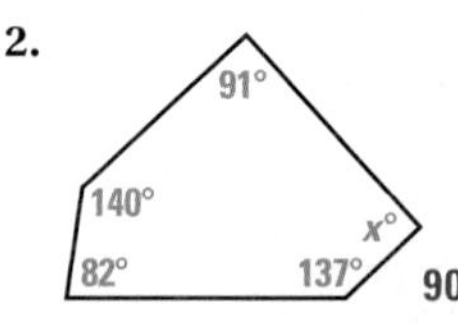
90

3. 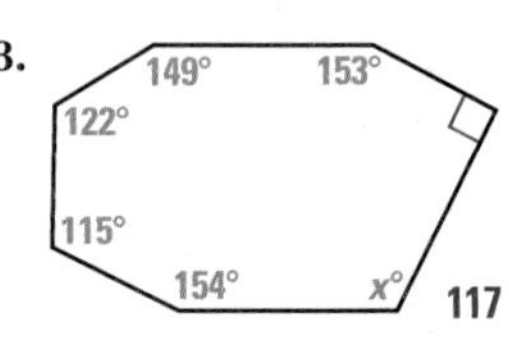
117

4. 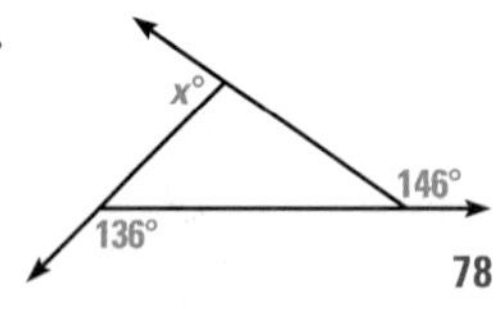
78

5. 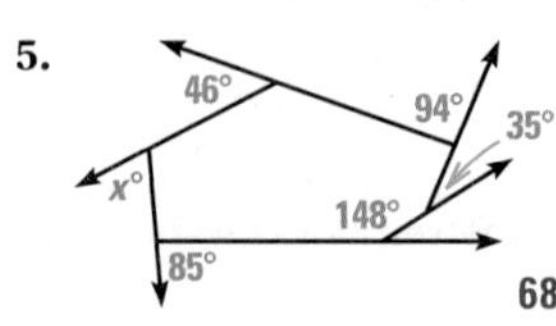
68

6. 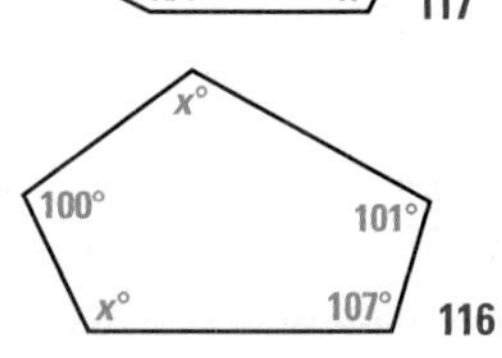
116

8.1 Find the measure of an interior angle and an exterior angle of the indicated regular polygon.

7. Regular hexagon
120°, 60°

8. Regular 9-gon
140°, 40°

9. Regular 17-gon
about 158.8°, about 21.2°

8.2 Find the value of each variable in the parallelogram.

10. 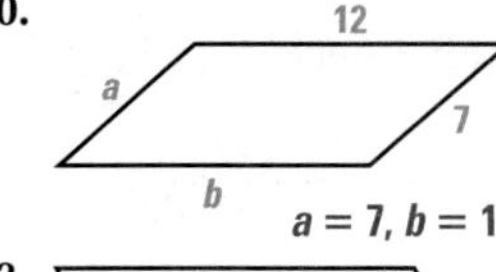
$a = 7, b = 12$

11. 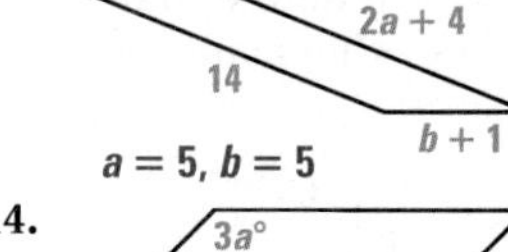
$a = 5, b = 5$

12. 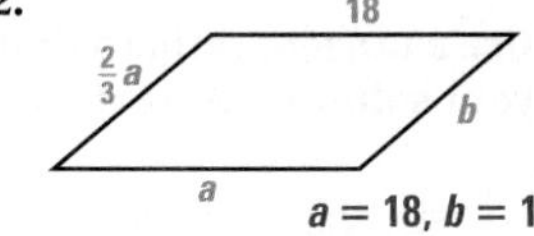
$a = 18, b = 12$

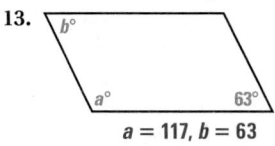

13.
$a = 117, b = 63$

14. 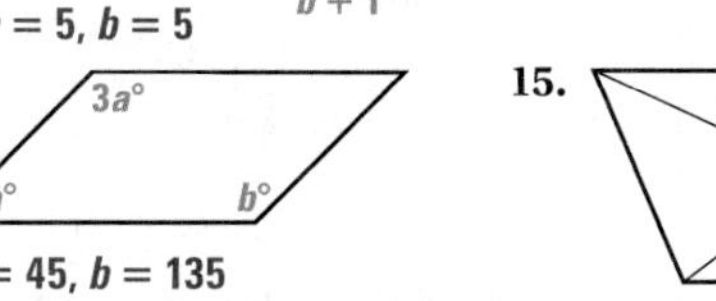
$a = 45, b = 135$

15. 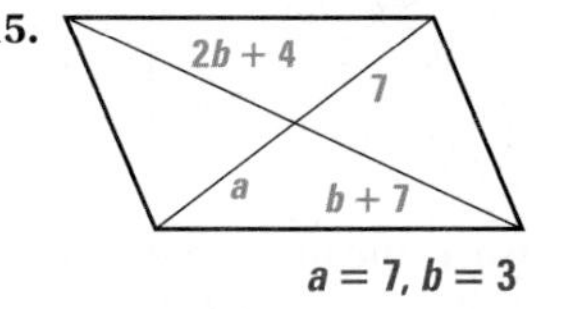
$a = 7, b = 3$

8.2 Use the diagram to copy and complete the statement.

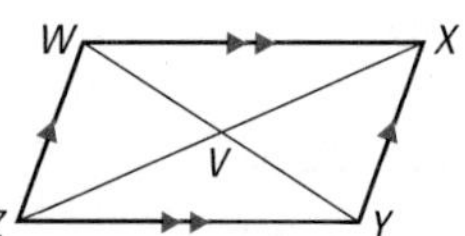

16. $\angle WXV \cong$ __?__ $\angle YZV$

17. $\angle ZWV \cong$ __?__ $\angle XYV$

18. $\angle WVX \cong$ __?__ $\angle YVZ$

19. $WV =$ __?__ YV

20. $WZ =$ __?__ YX

21. $2 \cdot ZV =$ __?__ ZX

8.3 The vertices of quadrilateral *ABCD* are given. Draw *ABCD* in a coordinate plane and show that it is a parallelogram. 22–25. See margin for art.

22. $A(5, 6), B(7, 3), C(5, -2), D(3, 1)$ $\overline{AB} \parallel \overline{DC}, \overline{AD} \parallel \overline{BC}$

23. $A(-8, 2), B(-6, 3), C(-1, 2), D(-3, 1)$ $\overline{AB} \parallel \overline{DC}, \overline{AD} \parallel \overline{BC}$

24. $A(-1, 11), B(2, 14), C(6, 11), D(3, 8)$ $\overline{AB} \parallel \overline{DC}, \overline{AD} \parallel \overline{BC}$

25. $A(-1, -5), B(4, -4), C(6, -9), D(1, -10)$ $\overline{AB} \parallel \overline{DC}, \overline{AD} \parallel \overline{BC}$

8.3 *Describe* how to prove that quadrilateral *PQRS* is a parallelogram. 26–28. See margin.

26. 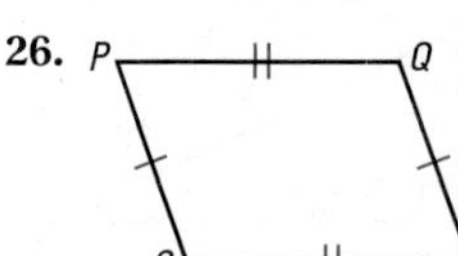

27. 

28. 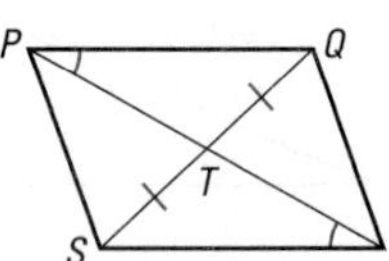

22.

23. 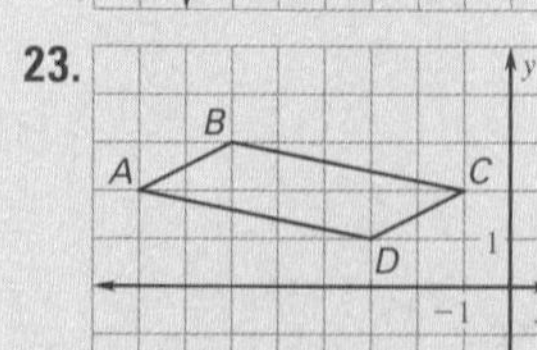

24. 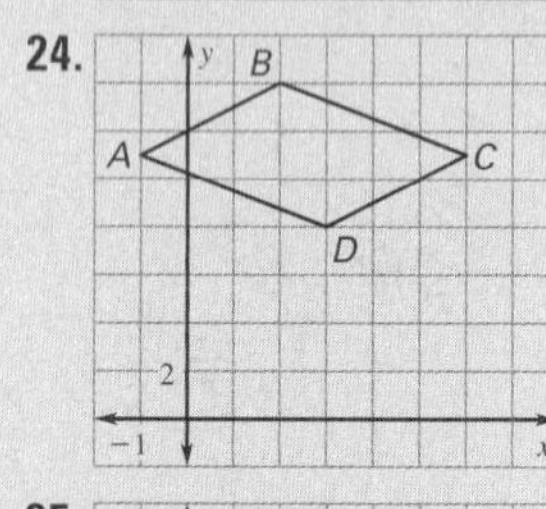

25. 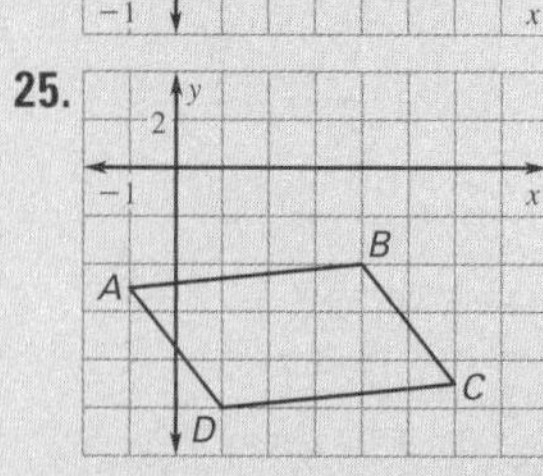

26. Since pairs of opposite sides are congruent, the quadrilateral is a parallelogram.

27. Show $\angle QPR \cong \angle SRP$, making $\angle SPQ \cong \angle QRS$. You now have pairs of opposite angles congruent, which makes the quadrilateral a parallelogram.

28. Show $\triangle STR \cong \triangle QTP$ using AAS, which makes $\overline{PT} \cong \overline{RT}$. Since the diagonals of the quadrilateral bisect one another, the quadrilateral is a parallelogram.

8.4 **Classify the special quadrilateral. *Explain* your reasoning.** 29–31. See margin.

29. 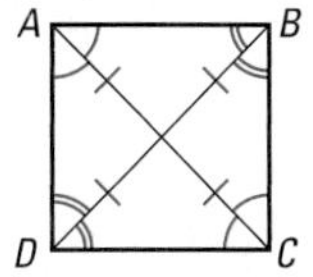

30. 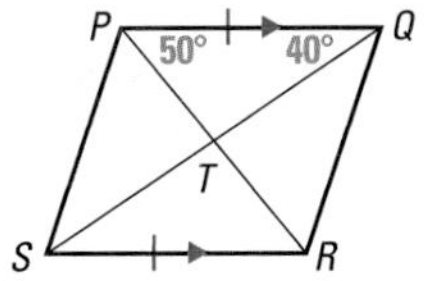

31. 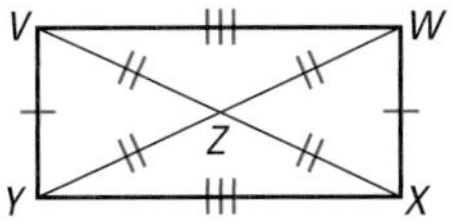

8.4 **The diagonals of rhombus *LMNP* intersect at *Q*. Given that *LM* = 5 and $m\angle QLM = 30°$, find the indicated measure.**

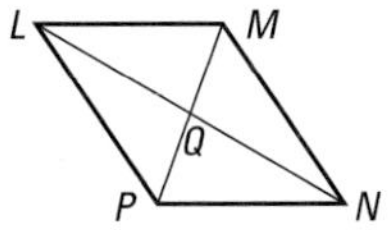

32. $m\angle LMQ$ 60°

33. $m\angle LQM$ 90°

34. *MN* 5

8.5 **Find the value of *x*.**

35. 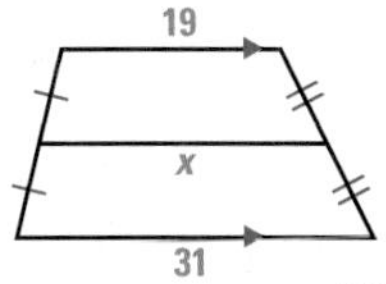

25

36. 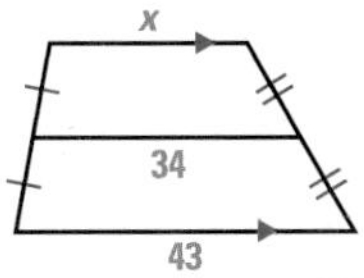

25

37. 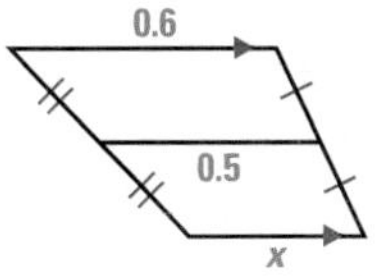

0.4

8.5 ***RSTV* is a kite. Find $m\angle V$.**

38. 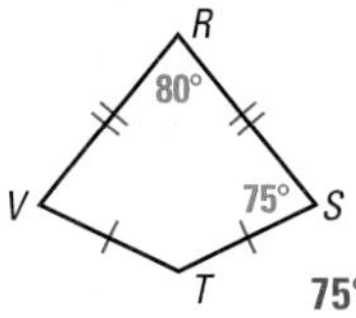

75°

39. 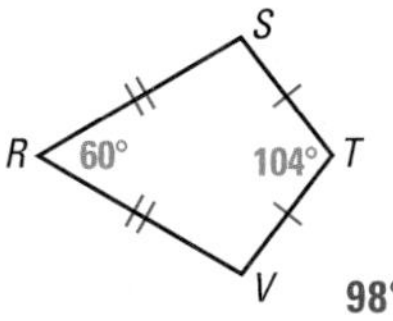

98°

40. 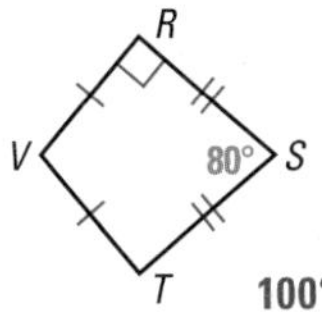

100°

8.6 **Give the most specific name for the quadrilateral. *Explain* your reasoning.** 41–46. See margin.

41. 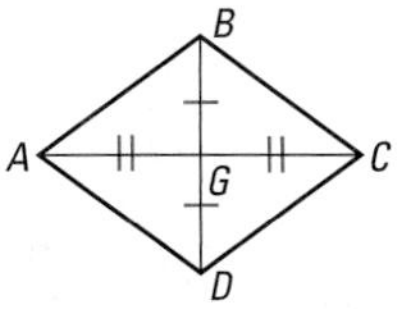

42. 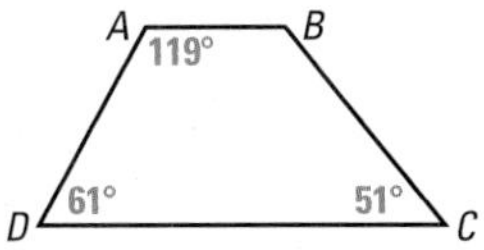

43. 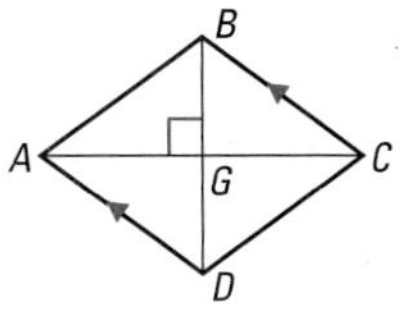

44. 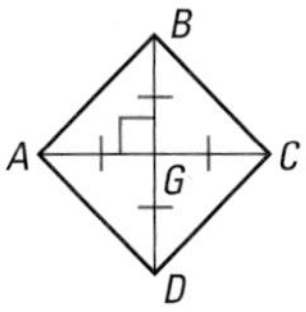

45. 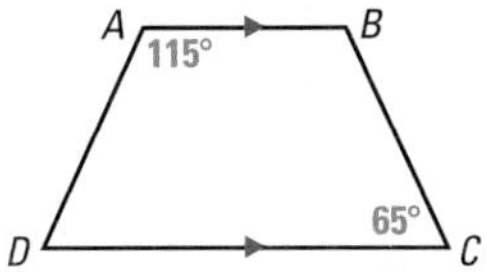

46. 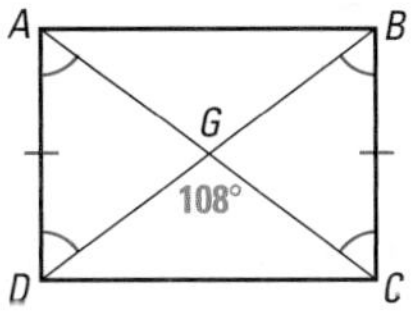

8.6 **The vertices of quadrilateral *DEFG* are given. Give the most specific name for *DEFG*. *Justify* your answer.** 47–50. See margin.

47. $D(6, 8), E(9, 12), F(12, 8), G(9, 6)$

48. $D(1, 2), E(4, 1), F(3, -2), G(0, -1)$

49. $D(10, 3), E(14, 4), F(20, 2), G(12, 0)$

50. $D(-2, 10), E(1, 13), F(5, 13), G(-2, 6)$

EXTRA PRACTICE

29. Square; since the quadrilateral is both a rectangle and rhombus, it is a square.

30. Rhombus; the diagonals are perpendicular so it is a rhombus.

31. Rectangle; since the quadrilateral is a parallelogram with congruent diagonals, it is a rectangle.

41. Parallelogram; the diagonals bisect one another.

42. Trapezoid; one pair of consecutive angles are supplementary, so it has one pair of parallel opposite sides.

43. Rhombus; it is a parallelogram with perpendicular diagonals.

44. Square; the diagonals are perpendicular and bisect each other, so it is a rhombus and a rectangle.

45. Isosceles trapezoid; it has one pair of parallel opposite sides and congruent base angles.

46. Rectangle; it is a quadrilateral with four right angles but not four congruent sides.

47. Kite; it has consecutive pairs of congruent sides and perpendicular diagonals.

48. Square; it has four congruent sides and four right angles.

49. Trapezoid; it has one pair of parallel sides.

50. Isosceles trapezoid; it has one pair of parallel sides and one pair of non-parallel congruent sides.

8. $\begin{bmatrix} 5 & -4 \\ -13 & 5 \end{bmatrix}$

10.

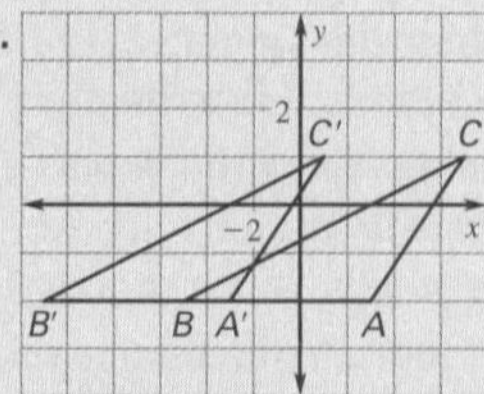

11.

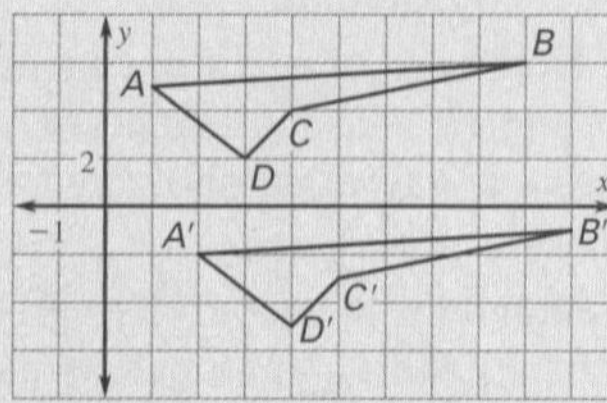

12.

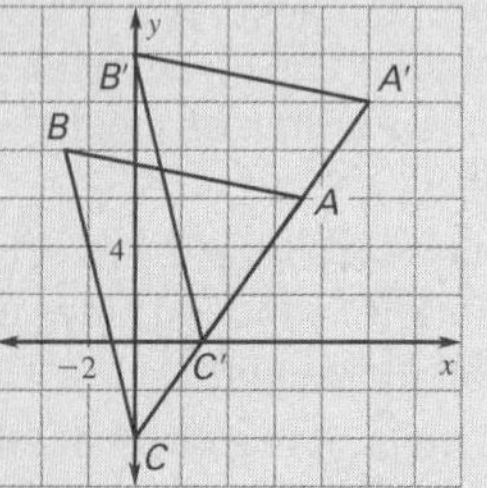

13.

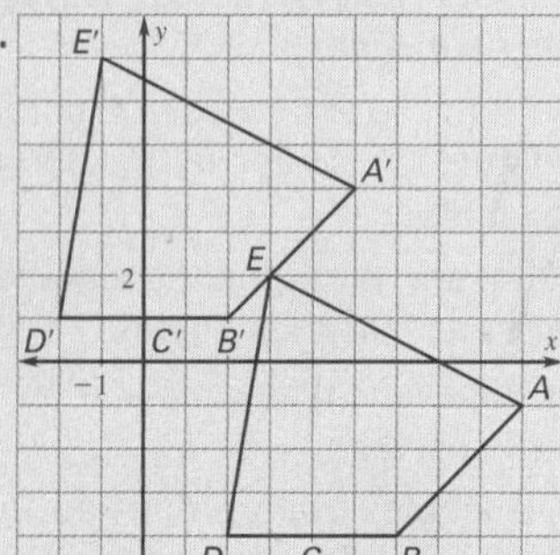

14.

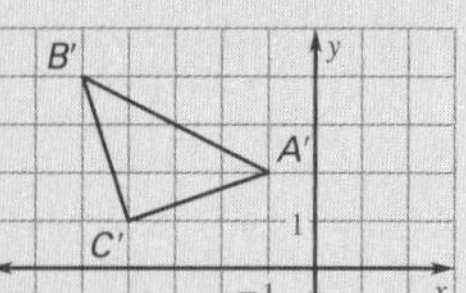

15.

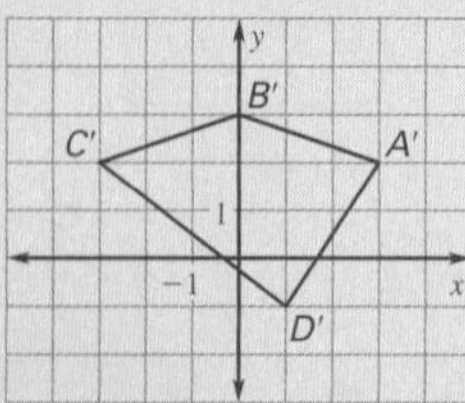

16.

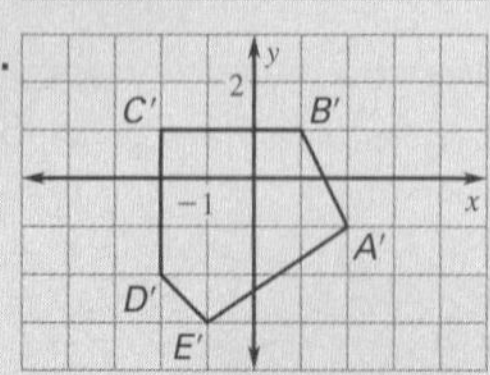

EXTRA PRACTICE

Chapter 9

9.1 **$\triangle A'B'C'$ is the image of $\triangle ABC$ after a translation. Write a rule for the translation. Then *verify* that the translation is an isometry.**

1.

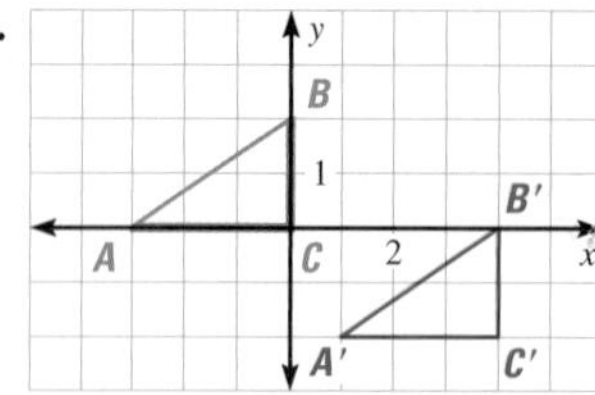

$(x, y) \to (x + 4, y - 2)$; $AB = A'B'$, $BC = B'C'$, $AC = A'C'$

2.

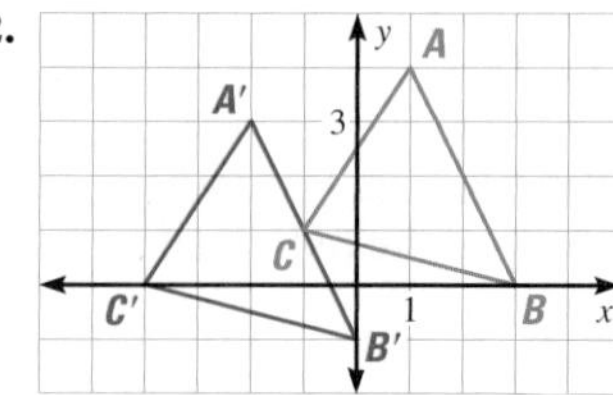

$(x, y) \to (x - 3, y - 1)$; $AB = A'B'$, $BC = B'C'$, $AC = A'C'$

9.1 **Use the point $P(7, -3)$. Find the component form of the vector that describes the translation to P'.**

3. $P'(-3, 4)$ **$\langle -10, 7\rangle$**
4. $P'(1, -1)$ **$\langle -6, 2\rangle$**
5. $P'(3, 2)$ **$\langle -4, 5\rangle$**
6. $P'(-8, -11)$ **$\langle -15, -8\rangle$**

9.2 **Add, subtract, or multiply.**

7. $\begin{bmatrix} 2 \\ 7 \end{bmatrix} + \begin{bmatrix} 3 \\ 4 \end{bmatrix}$ **$\begin{bmatrix} 5 \\ 11 \end{bmatrix}$**

8. $\begin{bmatrix} 5 & -3 \\ -9 & 4 \end{bmatrix} - \begin{bmatrix} 0 & 1 \\ 4 & -1 \end{bmatrix}$ **See margin.**

9. $\begin{bmatrix} 7 & -3 \\ 5 & 9 \end{bmatrix}\begin{bmatrix} 2 & -1 \\ 6 & 8 \end{bmatrix}$ **$\begin{bmatrix} -4 & -31 \\ 64 & 67 \end{bmatrix}$**

9.2 **Find the image matrix that represents the translation of the polygon. Then graph the polygon and its image.** **10–13. See margin for art.**

10. $\begin{bmatrix} 3 & -5 & 7 \\ -2 & -2 & 1 \end{bmatrix}$; 6 units left **$\begin{bmatrix} -3 & -11 & 1 \\ -2 & -2 & 1 \end{bmatrix}$**

11. $\begin{bmatrix} 1 & 9 & 4 & 3 \\ 5 & 6 & 4 & 2 \end{bmatrix}$; 1 unit right and 7 units down **$\begin{bmatrix} 2 & 10 & 5 & 4 \\ -2 & -1 & -3 & -5 \end{bmatrix}$**

12. $\begin{bmatrix} 7 & -3 & 0 \\ 6 & 8 & -4 \end{bmatrix}$; 3 units right and 4 units up **$\begin{bmatrix} 10 & 0 & 3 \\ 10 & 12 & 0 \end{bmatrix}$**

13. $\begin{bmatrix} 9 & 6 & 4 & 2 & 3 \\ -1 & -4 & -4 & -4 & 2 \end{bmatrix}$; 4 units left and 5 units up **$\begin{bmatrix} 5 & 2 & 0 & -2 & -1 \\ 4 & 1 & 1 & 1 & 7 \end{bmatrix}$**

9.3 **Graph the reflection of the polygon in the given line.**

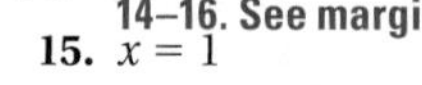

14–16. See margin.

14. y-axis
15. $x = 1$
16. $y = x$

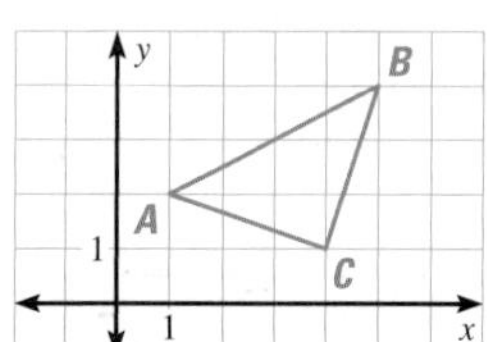

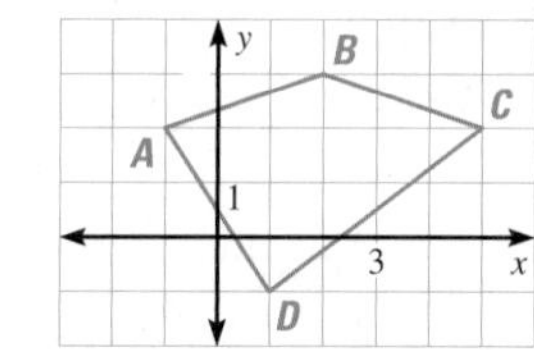

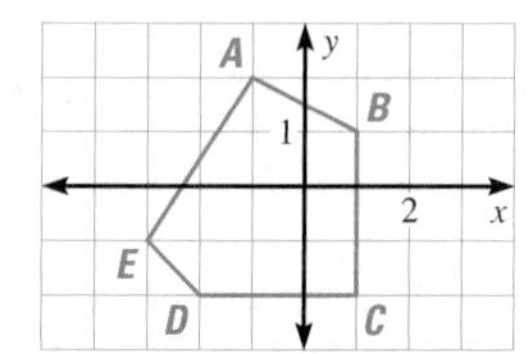

9.4 **Rotate the figure the given number of degrees about the origin. List the coordinates of the vertices of the image.**

17. 270° **$A'(1, 2)$, $B'(2, -4)$, $C'(0, -1)$**

18. 180° **$A'(3, -3)$, $B'(-1, -2)$, $C'(-1, 1)$, $D'(5, 0)$**

19. 90° **$A'(-1, 2)$, $B'(-1, 5)$, $C'(2, 6)$, $D'(3, 3)$, $E'(1, -1)$**

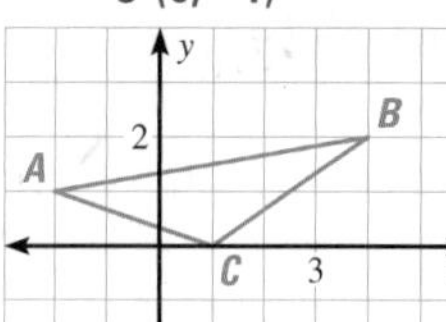

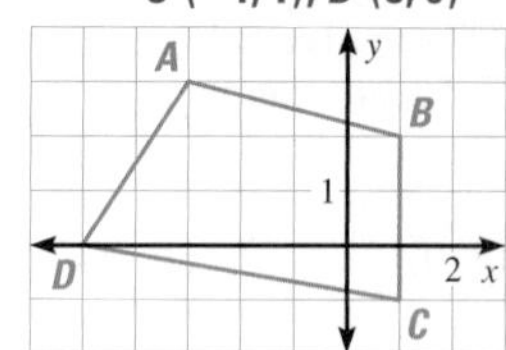

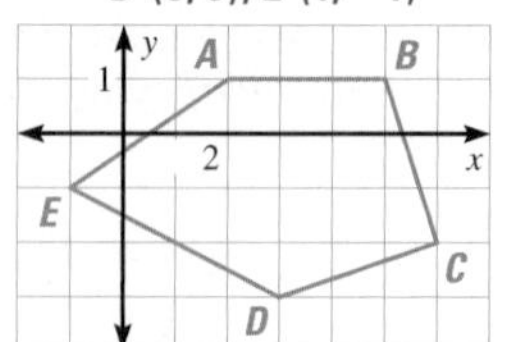

9.4 **Find the image matrix that represents the rotation of the polygon about the origin. Then graph the polygon and its image.** **20–22. See margin.**

20. $\begin{matrix} P & Q & R \end{matrix}$ $\begin{bmatrix} 1 & 2 & 4 \\ 4 & 1 & 3 \end{bmatrix}$; 180°

21. $\begin{matrix} S & T & V \end{matrix}$ $\begin{bmatrix} 4 & 2 & 1 \\ 2 & -3 & 0 \end{bmatrix}$; 90°

22. $\begin{matrix} A & B & C & D \end{matrix}$ $\begin{bmatrix} 4 & -1 & -2 & 1 \\ 0 & -1 & -2 & -3 \end{bmatrix}$; 270°

9.5 **The vertices of $\triangle ABC$ are $A(1, 1)$, $B(4, 1)$, and $C(2, 4)$. Graph the image of $\triangle ABC$ after a composition of the transformations in the order they are listed.** **23–26. See margin for art.**

23. **Translation:** $(x, y) \rightarrow (x - 2, y + 3)$
Rotation: 270° about the origin

24. **Reflection:** in the line $x = 2$
Translation: $(x, y) \rightarrow (x + 3, y)$

25. **Rotation:** 180° about the origin
Reflection: in the line $y = -2$

26. **Translation:** $(x, y) \rightarrow (x - 4, y - 4)$
Reflection: in the line $y = x$

9.5 **Find the angle of rotation that maps A onto A''.**

27.

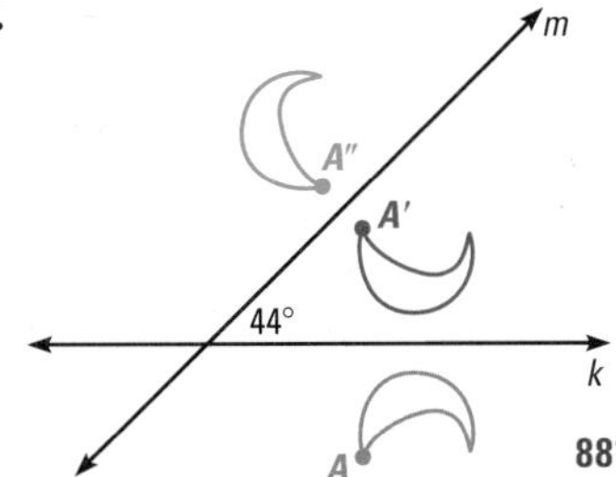

88°

28.

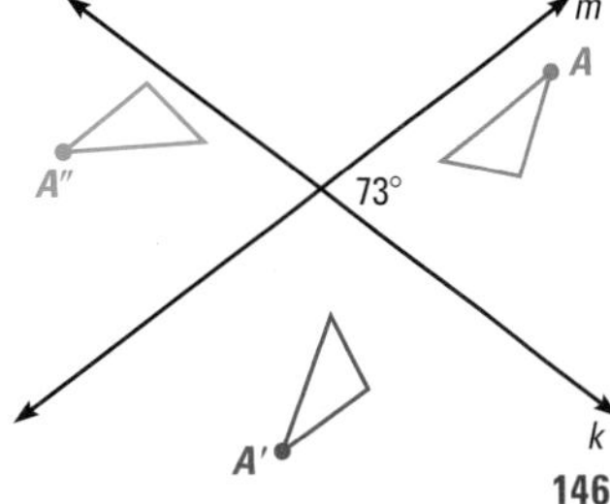

146°

9.6 **Determine whether the flag has *line symmetry* and whether it has *rotational symmetry*. Identify all lines of symmetry and angles of rotation that map the figure onto itself.** **29–31. See margin.**

29.

30.

31.

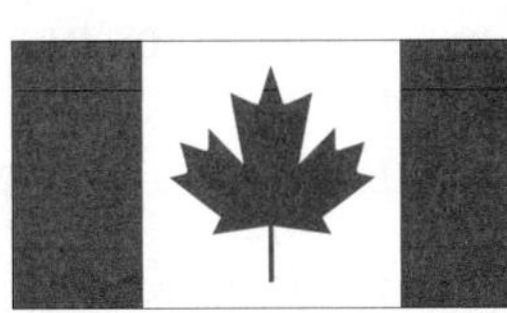

9.7 **Copy the diagram. Then draw the given dilation.** **32–37. See margin.**

32. Center B; $k = 2$

33. Center E; $k = 3$

34. Center D; $k = \frac{1}{2}$

35. Center A; $k = \frac{2}{3}$

36. Center C; $k = \frac{3}{2}$

37. Center E; $k = \frac{1}{3}$

9.7 **Find the image matrix that represents a dilation of a polygon centered at the origin with a given scale factor. Then graph the polygon and its image.** **38–40. See margin.**

38. $\begin{matrix} G & H & J \end{matrix}$ $\begin{bmatrix} 1 & 3 & 4 \\ 4 & 2 & 4 \end{bmatrix}$; $k = 3$

39. $\begin{matrix} K & L & M & N \end{matrix}$ $\begin{bmatrix} 2 & 4 & 5 & 6 \\ -2 & -2 & 4 & 0 \end{bmatrix}$; $k = \frac{1}{2}$

40. $\begin{matrix} P & Q & R \end{matrix}$ $\begin{bmatrix} -3 & -3 & -1 \\ -1 & -3 & -3 \end{bmatrix}$; $k = 4$

EXTRA PRACTICE

26.

29. Line symmetry, rotational symmetry; the flag has two lines of symmetry, one line passing horizontally through the center of the circle and the other passing vertically through the center of the circle; it has rotational symmetry of 180°.

30. Line symmetry, no rotational symmetry; the flag has one line of symmetry passing horizontally through its center; it does not have rotational symmetry.

31. Line symmetry, no rotational symmetry; the flag has one line of symmetry passing vertically through its center; it does not have rotational symmetry.

32.

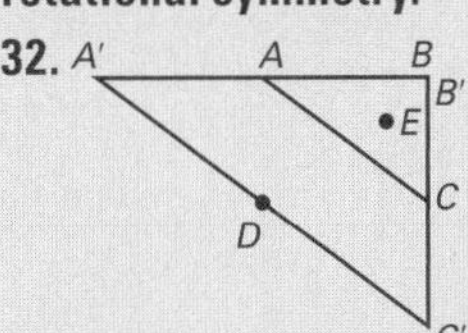

33.

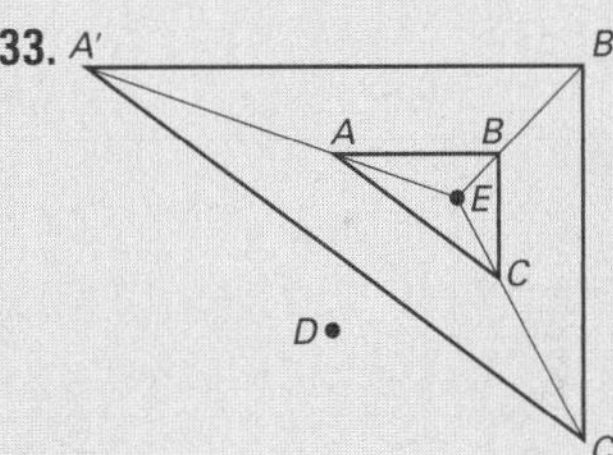

34.

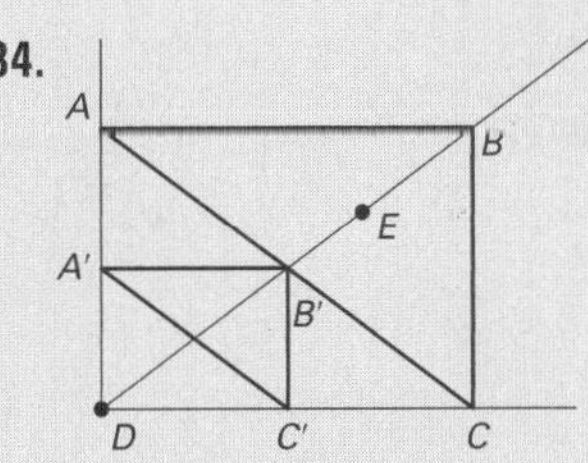

35–40. See Additional Answers beginning on p. AA1.

20–22. See Additional Answers beginning on p. AA1.

23.

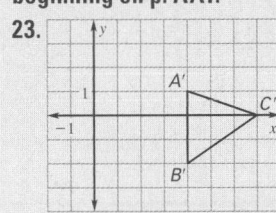

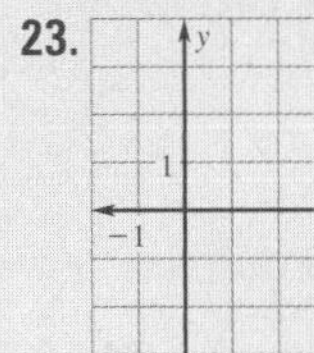

24.

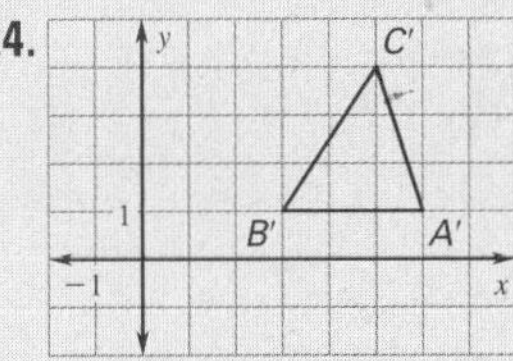

25.

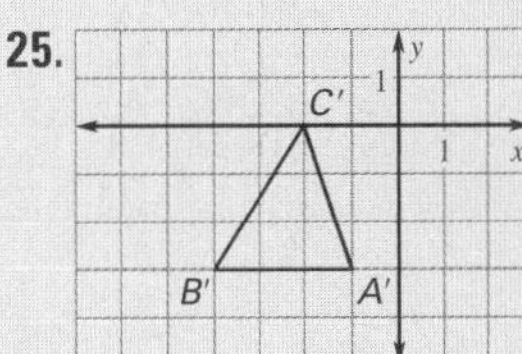

Chapter 10

10.1 Use the diagram to give an example of the term.

1. Radius *Sample answer:* $\overline{KF}$
2. Common tangent $\overleftrightarrow{AF}$
3. Tangent *Sample answer:* $\overleftrightarrow{CD}$
4. Secant $\overleftrightarrow{EH}$
5. Center *Sample answer:* K
6. Point of tangency *Sample answer:* A
7. Chord $\overline{GH}$
8. Diameter $\overline{JF}$

10.1 Find the value(s) of the variable. *P, Q,* and *R* are points of tangency.

9. 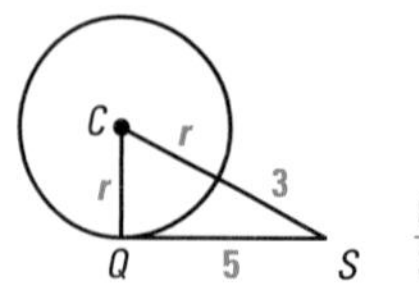

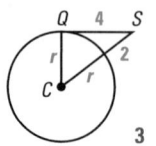

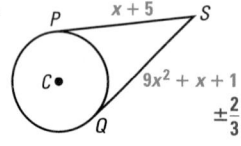

$\frac{8}{3}$

10. Q 4 S r 2 r C — **3**

11. 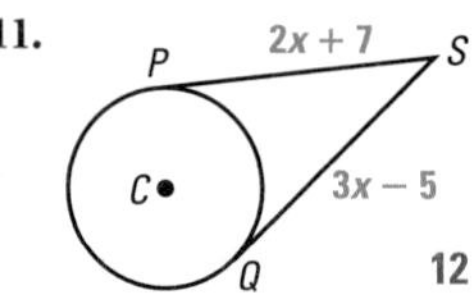

12

12. P $x + 5$ S C $9x^2 + x + 1$ Q — $\pm\frac{2}{3}$

13. 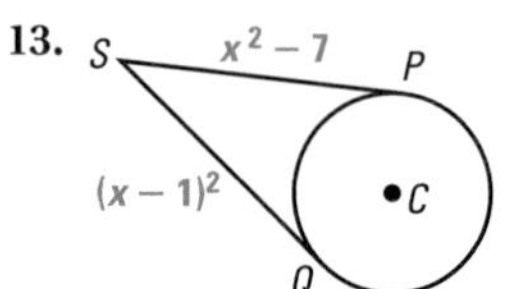

4

14. 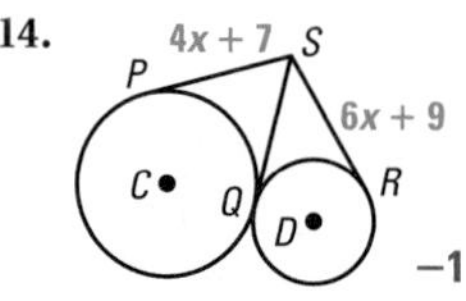

−1

10.2 $\overline{AC}$ and $\overline{BD}$ are diameters of $\odot G$. Determine whether the arc is a *minor arc*, a *major arc*, or a *semicircle* of $\odot G$. Then find the measure of the arc.

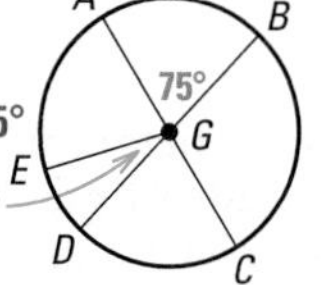

15. $\overset{\frown}{ED}$ **minor arc; 30°**
16. $\overset{\frown}{EB}$ **minor arc; 150°**
17. $\overset{\frown}{EC}$ **minor arc; 105°**
18. $\overset{\frown}{BEC}$ **major arc; 255°**
19. $\overset{\frown}{BC}$ **minor arc; 105°**
20. $\overset{\frown}{BCD}$ **semicircle; 180°**

10.2 In $\odot C$, $m\overset{\frown}{AD} = 50°$, *B* bisects $\overset{\frown}{AD}$, and $\overline{AE}$ is a diameter. Find the measure of the arc.

21. $\overset{\frown}{AED}$ **310°**
22. $\overset{\frown}{BD}$ **25°**
23. $\overset{\frown}{DE}$ **130°**
24. $\overset{\frown}{BAE}$ **205°**

10.3 Find the measure of $\overset{\frown}{AB}$.

25. 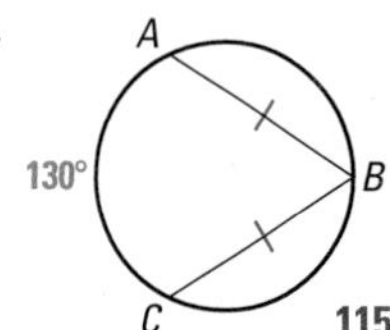

115°

26. 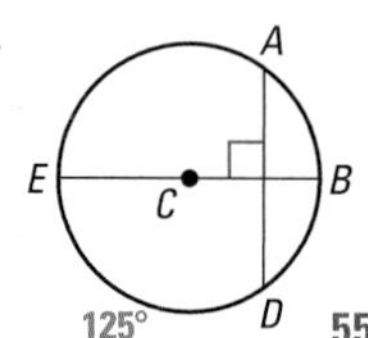

55°

27. 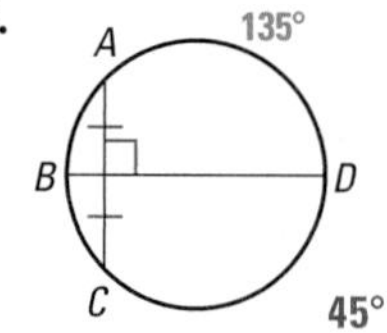

45°

10.3 In Exercises 28–30, what can you conclude about the diagram shown? State theorems to justify your answer.

28. 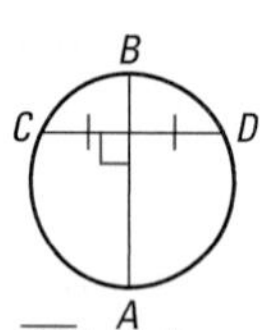

$\overline{AB}$ is a diameter using Theorem 10.4.

29. 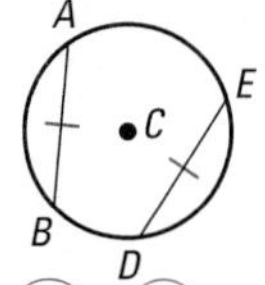

$\overset{\frown}{AB} \cong \overset{\frown}{DE}$ using Theorem 10.3.

30. 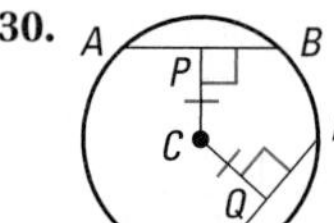

***Sample answer:* $\overline{AB} \cong \overline{DE}$ using Theorem 10.6.**

EXTRA PRACTICE

10.4 Find the values of the variables.

31.

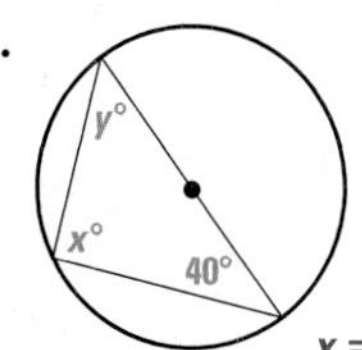

$x = 90, y = 50$

32.

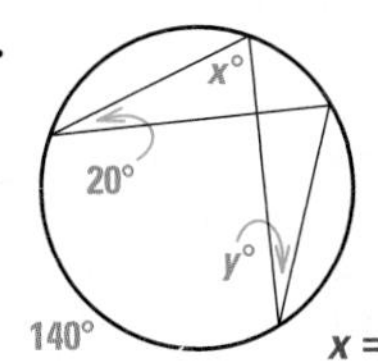

$x = 70, y = 20$

33.

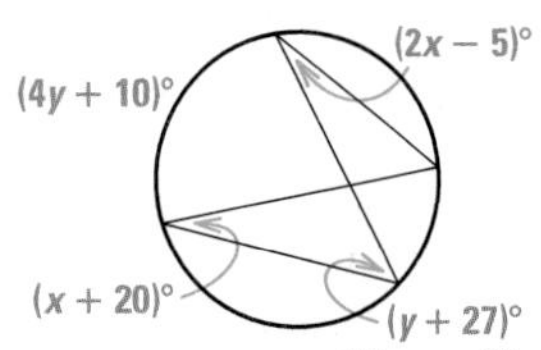

$x = 25, y = 22$

34.

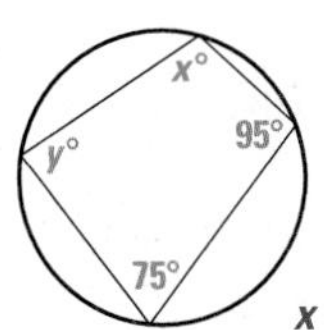

$x = 105, y = 85$

35.

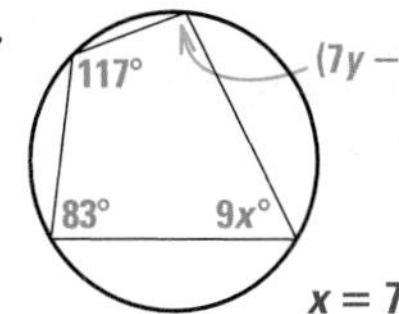

$x = 7, y = 14$

36.

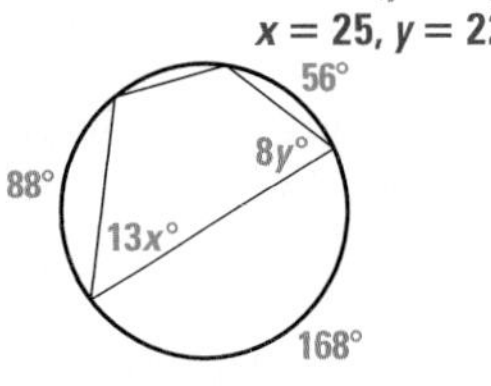

$x = 4, y = 8.5$

10.5 Find the value of *x*.

37.

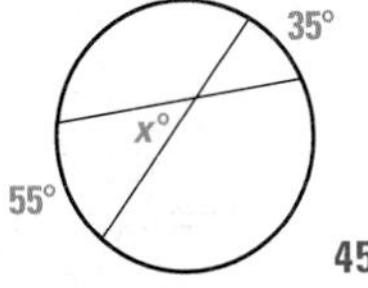

45

38.

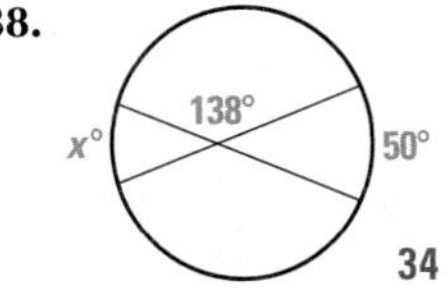

34

39.

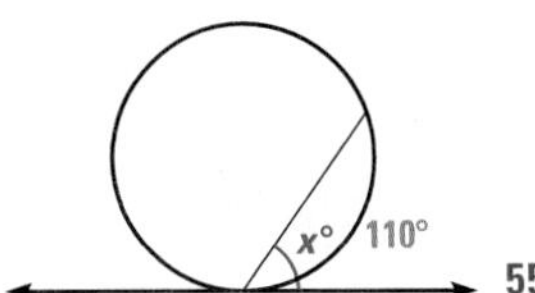

55

40.

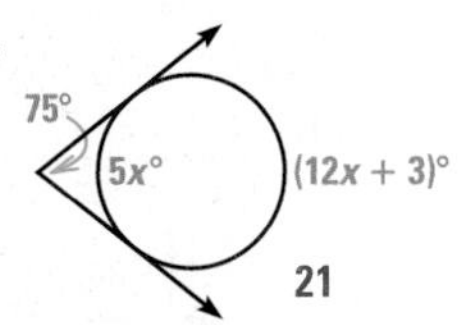

21

41.

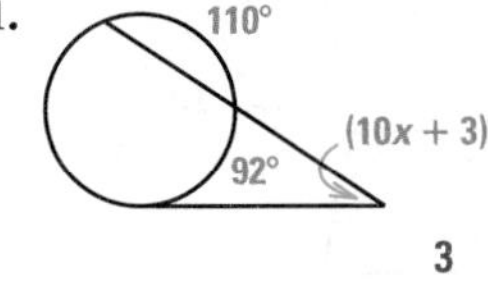

3

42.

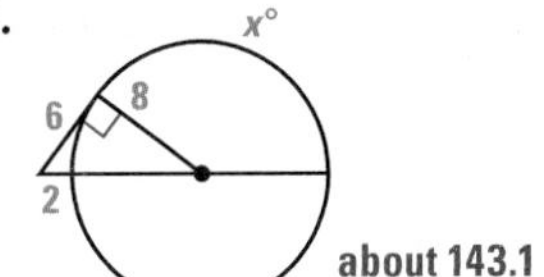

about 143.1

10.6 Find the value of *x*.

43.

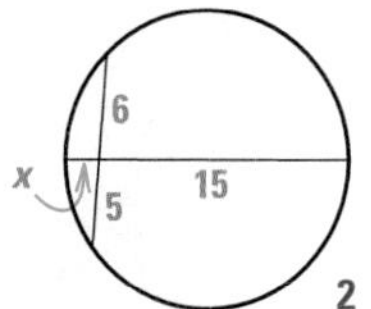

2

44.

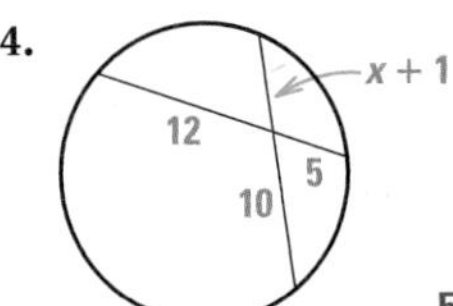

5

45.

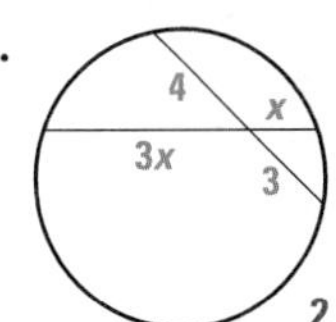

2

46.

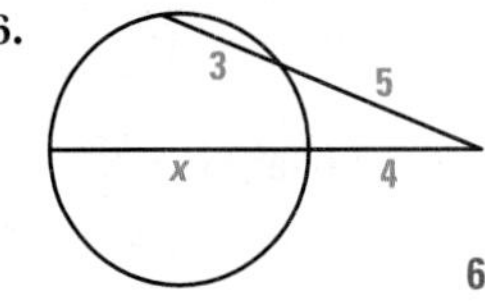

6

47.

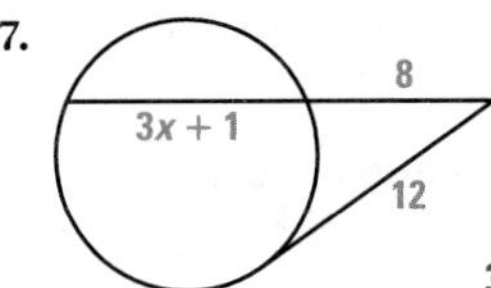

3

48.

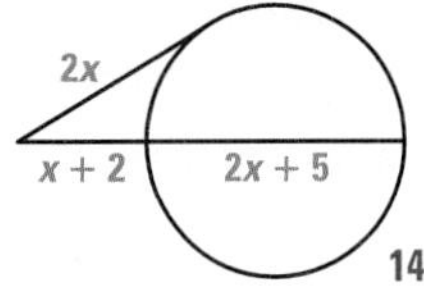

14

10.7 Use the given information to write the standard equation for the circle.

49. The center is (0, −2), and the radius is 4 units. $x^2 + (y + 2)^2 = 16$

50. The center is (2, −3), and a point on the circle is (7, −8). $(x - 2)^2 + (y + 3)^2 = 50$

51. The center is (m, n), and a point on the circle is $(m + h, n + k)$. $(x - m)^2 + (y - n)^2 = h^2 + k^2$

10.7 Graph the equation. 52–54. See margin.

52. $x^2 + y^2 = 25$ 53. $x^2 + (y - 5)^2 = 121$ 54. $(x + 4)^2 + (y - 1)^2 = 49$

EXTRA PRACTICE

52.

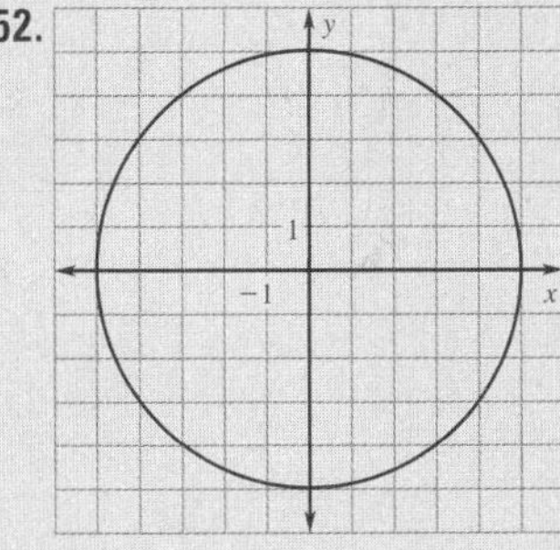

53.

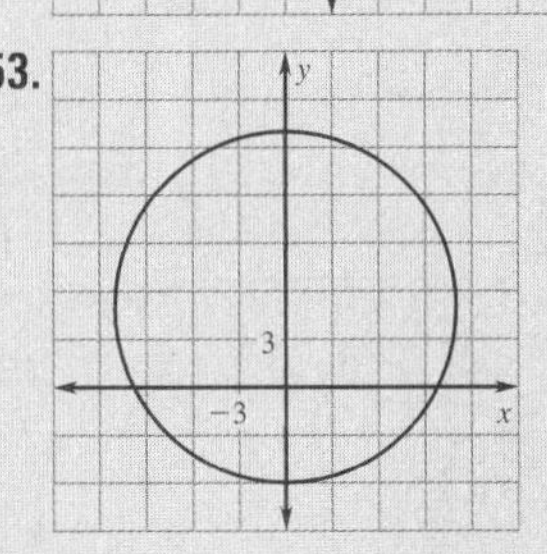

54.

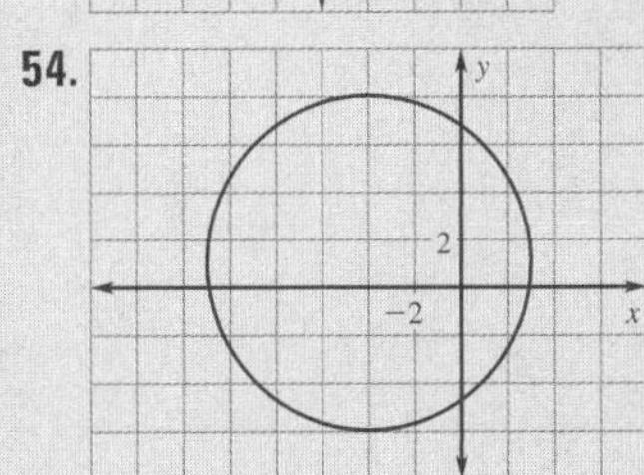

Chapter 11

11.1 Find the area of the polygon.

1. 13, 11 **143 units²**

2. 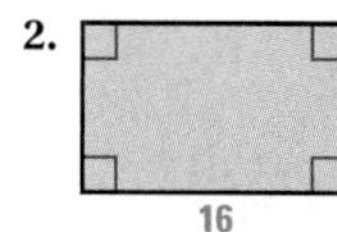

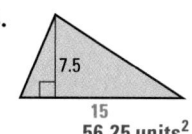

160 units²

3. 7.5, 15 **56.25 units²**

4. 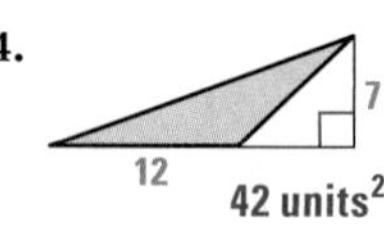

42 units²

11.1 The lengths of the hypotenuse and one leg of a right triangle are given. Find the perimeter and area of the triangle.

5. Hypotenuse: 25 cm; leg: 20 cm **60 cm, 150 cm²**

6. Hypotenuse: 51 ft; leg: 24 ft **120 ft, 540 ft²**

11.1 Find the value of *x*.

7. $A = 22\text{ ft}^2$ **5**

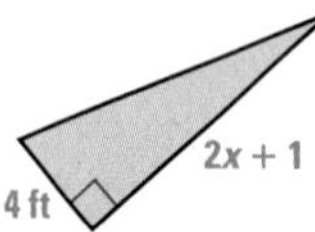

8. $A = 14.3\text{ in.}^2$ **13**

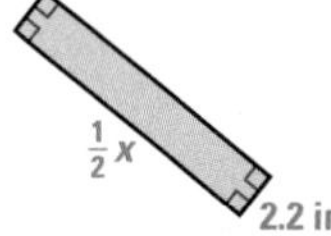

9. $A = 7.2\text{ m}^2$ **0.8**

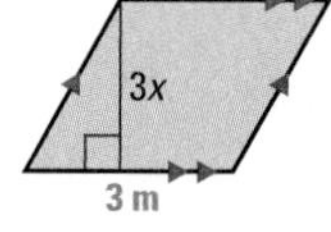

10. $A = 276\text{ cm}^2$ **4**

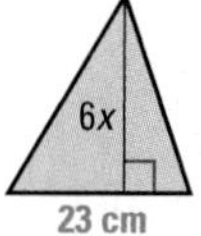

11.2 Find the area of the trapezoid.

11. 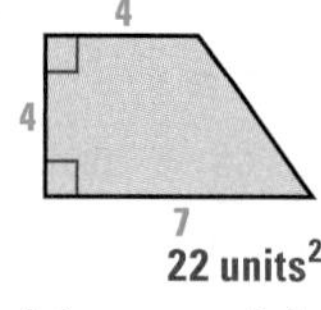

22 units²

12. 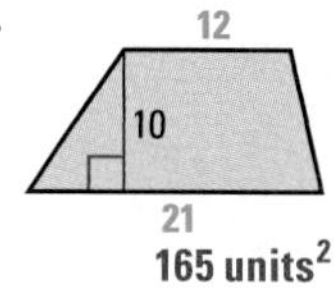

165 units²

13. 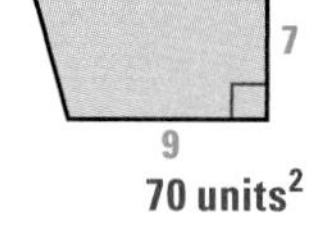

70 units²

14. 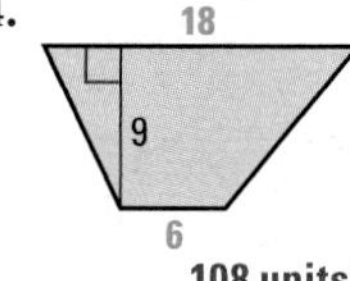

108 units²

11.2 Find the area of the rhombus or kite.

15. 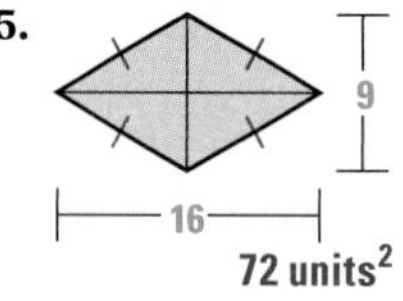

72 units²

16. 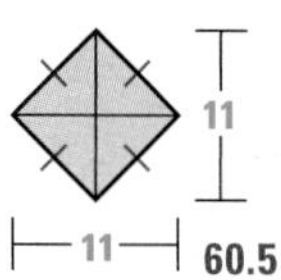

60.5 units²

17. 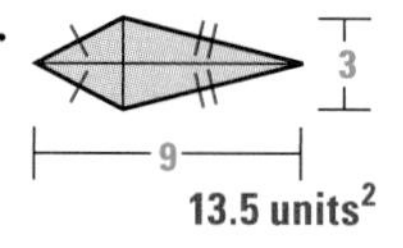

13.5 units²

18. 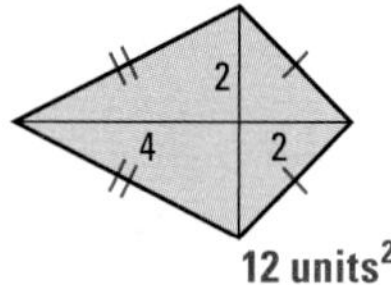

12 units²

11.3 The ratio of the areas of two similar figures is given. Write the ratio of the lengths of the corresponding sides.

19. Ratio of areas = 100 : 81 **10 : 9**

20. Ratio of areas = 25 : 100 **5 : 10**

21. Ratio of areas = 8 : 1 **$2\sqrt{2}$: 1**

11.3 Use the given area to find *ST*.

22. $\triangle ABC \sim \triangle RST$ **$\frac{5\sqrt{2}}{2}$ in.**

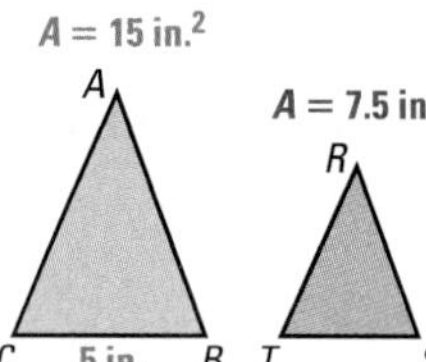

23. *DEFG* ~ *RSTU* **14 m**

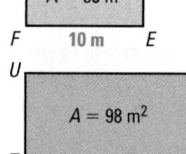

G, D, A = 50 m², F, 10 m, E, U, R, A = 98 m², T, S

24. *HJKL* ~ *RSTU* **15 in.**

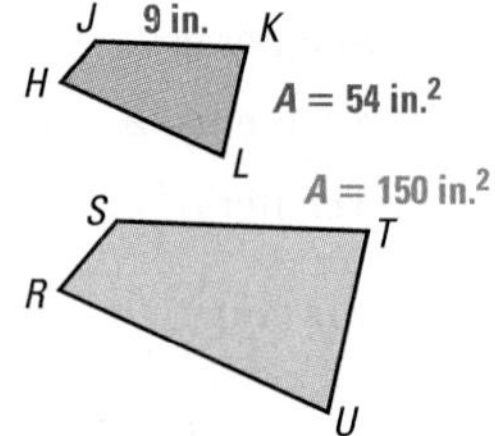

11.4 Find the circumference of the red circle.

25.

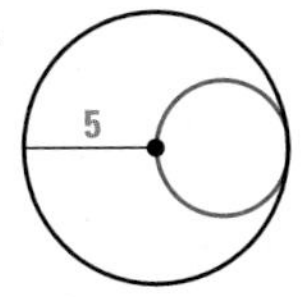

about 15.71 units

26.

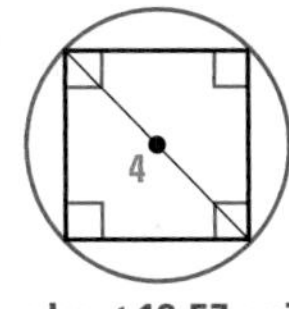

about 12.57 units

27.

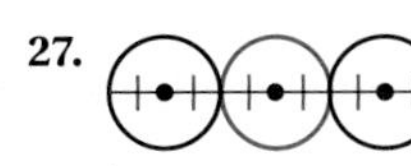

about 28.27 units

28.

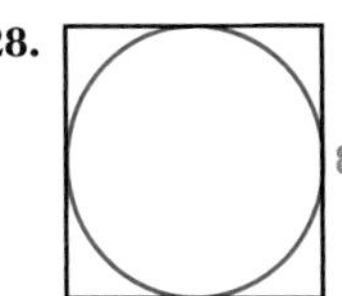

about 25.13 units

11.4 Find the length of $\widehat{AB}$.

29.

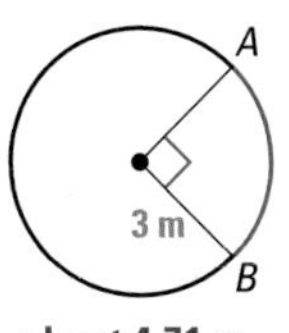

about 4.71 m

30.

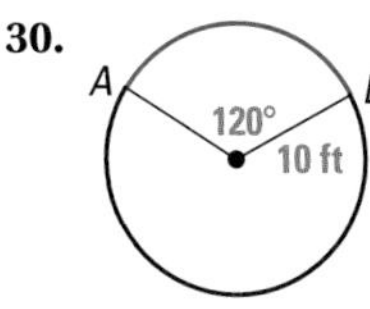

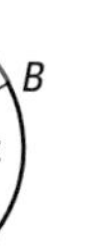

about 20.94 ft

31.

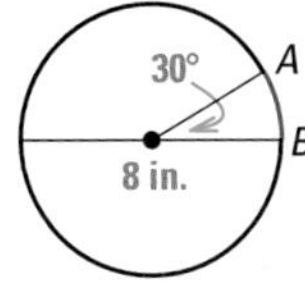

about 2.09 in.

32.

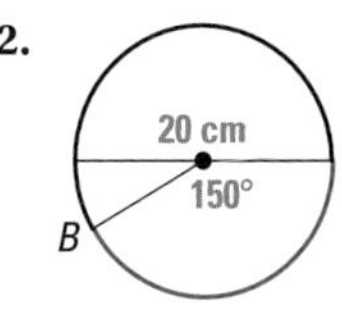

about 26.18 cm

11.5 Find the exact area of a circle with the given radius r or diameter d. Then find the area to the nearest hundredth.

33. $r = 3$ in. **9π in.^{2}; 28.27 in.^{2}**

34. $r = 2.5$ cm **6.25π cm^2; 19.63 cm^2**

35. $d = 20$ ft **100π ft^2; 314.16 ft^2**

36. $d = 13$ m **42.25π m^2; 132.73 m^2**

11.5 Find the areas of the sectors formed by $\angle DFE$.

37.

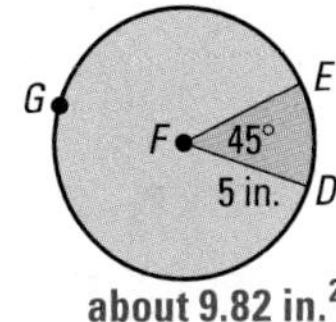

about 9.82 in.^{2}

38.

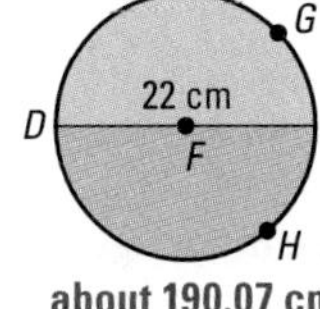

about 190.07 cm^2

39.

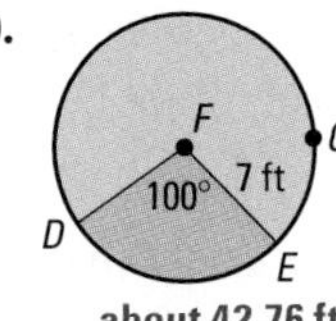

about 42.76 ft^2

40.

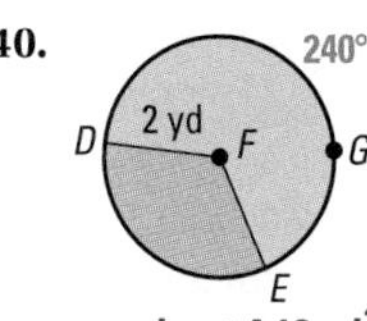

about 4.19 yd^2

11.6 Find the measure of a central angle of a regular polygon with the given number of sides.

41. 8 sides **45°**

42. 12 sides **30°**

43. 20 sides **18°**

44. 25 sides **14.4°**

11.6 Find the perimeter and area of the regular polygon.

45.

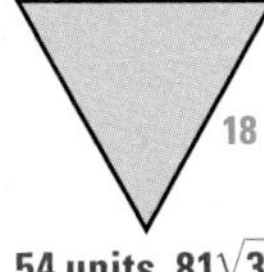

54 units, $81\sqrt{3}$ units^2

46.

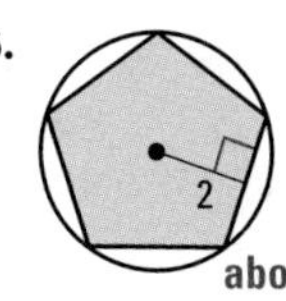

about 14.53 units, about 14.53 units^2

47.

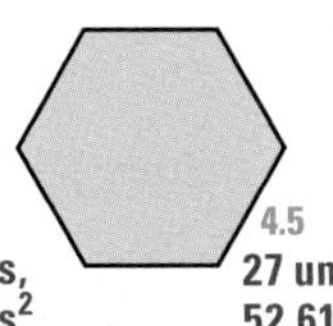

27 units, about 52.61 units^2

48.

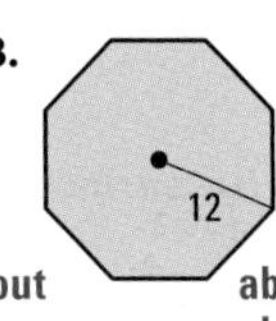

about 73.48 units, about 407.29 units^2

11.7 Find the probability that a randomly chosen point in the figure lies in the shaded region.

49.

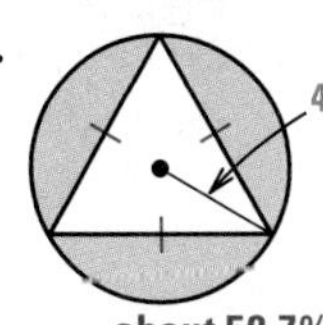

about 58.7%

50.

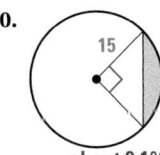

15

about 9.1%

51.

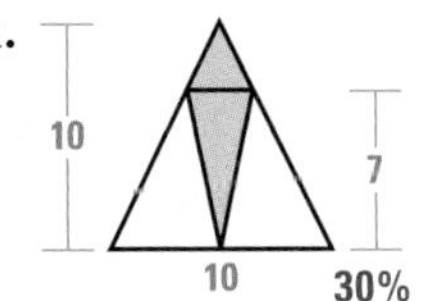

30%

52.

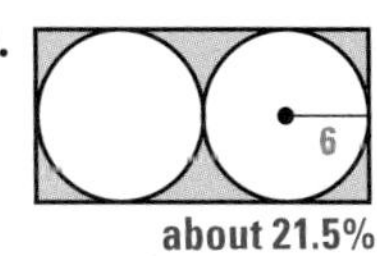

about 21.5%

11.7 **53.** A local radio station plays your favorite song once every two hours. Your favorite song is 4.5 minutes long. If you randomly turn on the radio, what is the probability that your favorite song will be playing? **3.75%**

EXTRA PRACTICE

1. Polyhedron; pentagonal prism; it is a solid bounded by polygons.

2. Not a polyhedron; it is not bounded by polygons.

3. Polyhedron; triangular pyramid; it is a solid bounded by polygons.

4. Not a polyhedron; the bases are not polygons.

EXTRA PRACTICE

Chapter 12

12.1 Determine whether the solid is a polyhedron. If it is, name the polyhedron. *Explain* your reasoning. 1–4. See margin.

1. 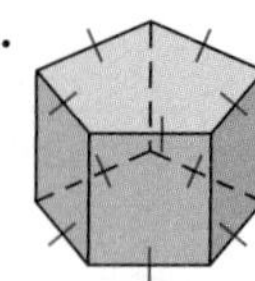

2. 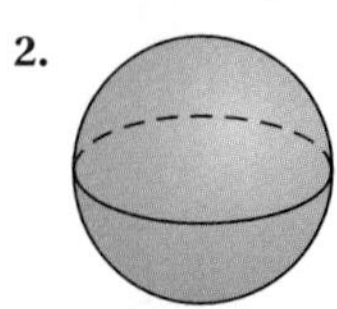

3. 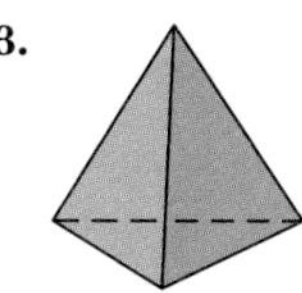

4. 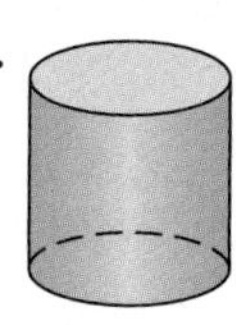

12.1 **5.** Determine the number of faces on a solid with six vertices and ten edges. **6 faces**

12.2 Find the surface area of the right prism. Round to two decimal places.

6. 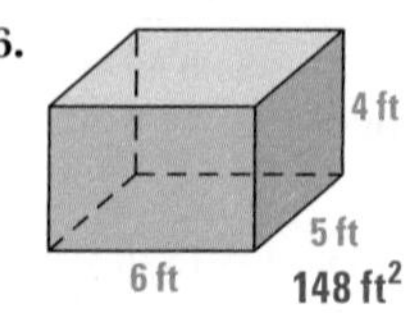

148 ft^2

7. 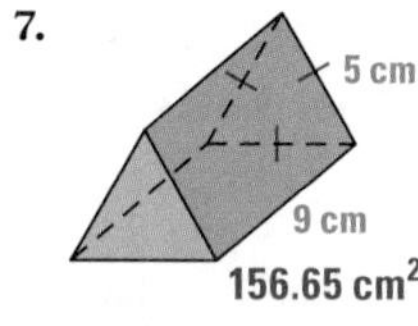

156.65 cm^2

8. 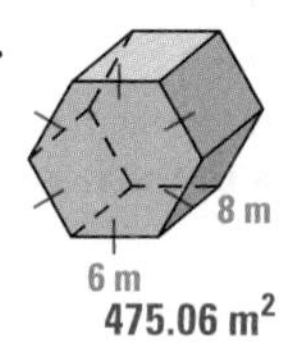

475.06 m^2

12.2 Find the surface area of the right cylinder with the given radius r and height h. Round to two decimal places.

9. $r = 2$ cm, $h = 11$ cm **163.36 cm^2**

10. $r = 1$ m, $h = 1$ m **12.57 m^2**

11. $r = 22$ in., $h = 9$ in. **4285.13 in.^{2}**

12. $r = 17$ mm, $h = 5$ mm **2349.91 mm^2**

12.2 Solve for x given the surface area S of the right prism or right cylinder. Round to two decimal places.

13. $S = 192$ in.^{2}

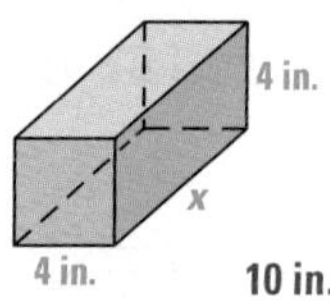

10 in.

14. $S = 33.7$ m^2

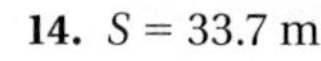

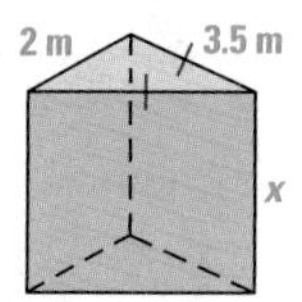

2.96 m

15. $S = 754$ ft^2

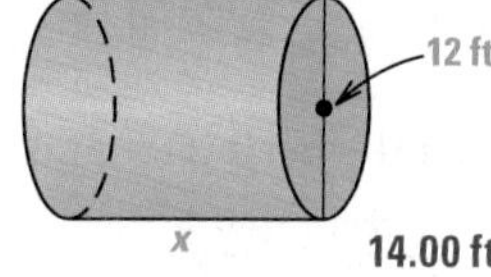

14.00 ft

12.3 Find the surface area of the regular pyramid. Round to two decimal places.

16. 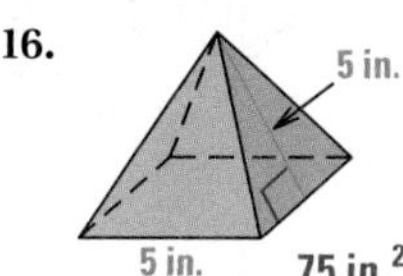

75 in.^{2}

17. 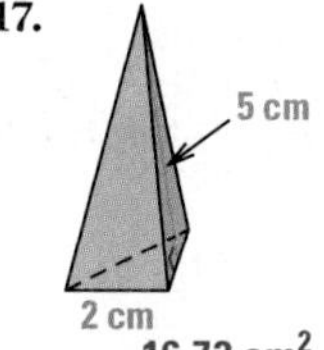

16.73 cm^2

18. 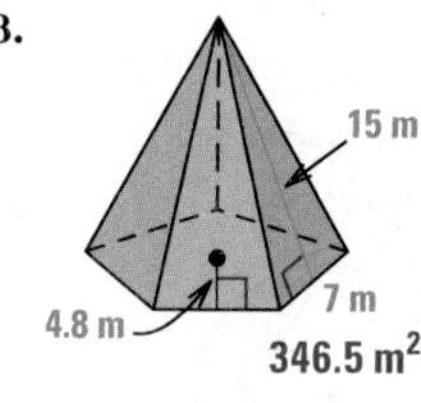

346.5 m^2

12.3 Find the surface area of the right cone. Round to two decimal places.

19. 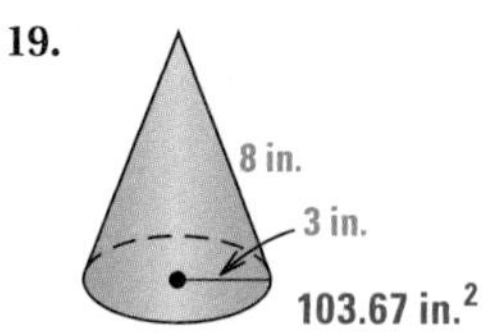

103.67 in.^{2}

20. 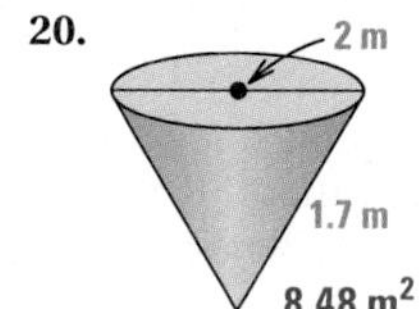

8.48 m^2

21. 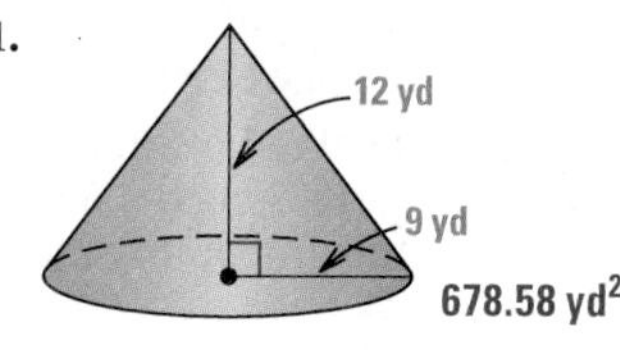

678.58 yd^2

12.4 Find the volume of the right prism or right cylinder. Round to two decimal places.

22.
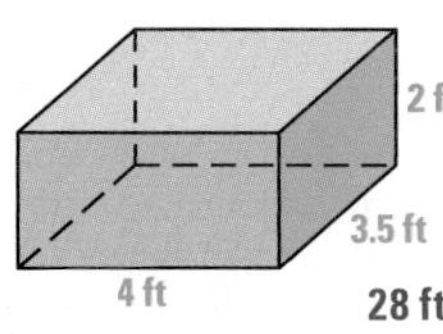

28 ft^3

23.
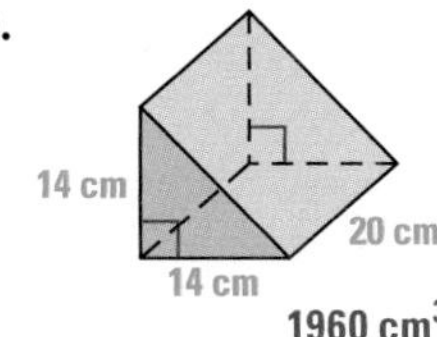

1960 cm^3

24.
2.3 mm
7.2 mm
29.91 mm^3

12.4 Find the value of x. Round to two decimal places, if necessary.

25. $V = 8\text{ cm}^3$
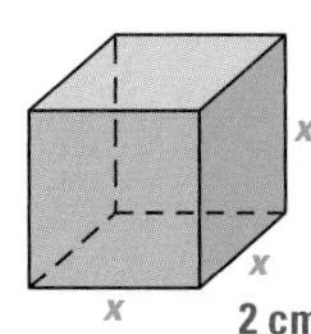

2 cm

26. $V = 72\text{ ft}^3$
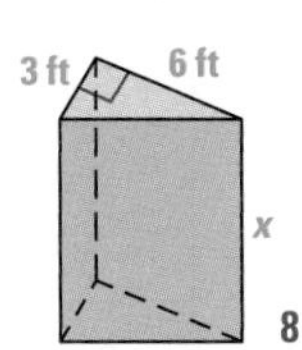

8 ft

27. $V = 628\text{ in.}^3$
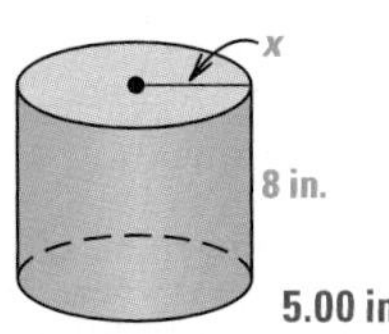

5.00 in.

12.5 Find the volume of the solid. Round to two decimal places.

28.
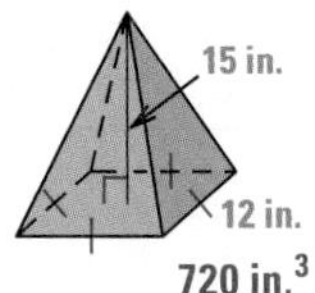

720 in.^{3}

29.
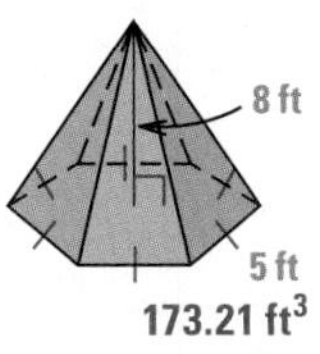

173.21 ft^3

30.
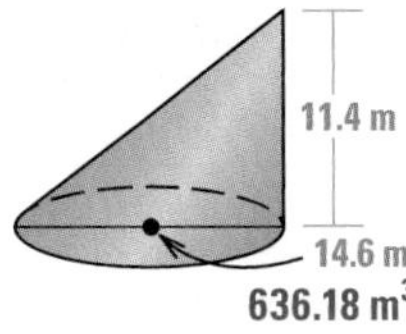

636.18 m^3

12.5 Find the volume of the right cone. Round to two decimal places.

31.
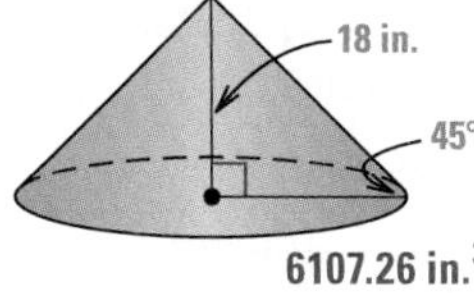

6107.26 in.^{3}

32.
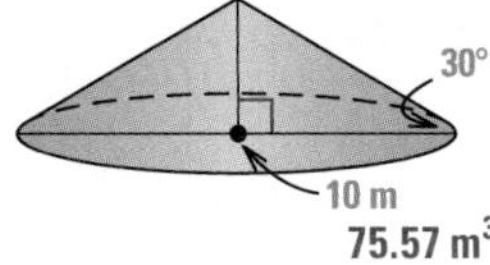

75.57 m^3

33.
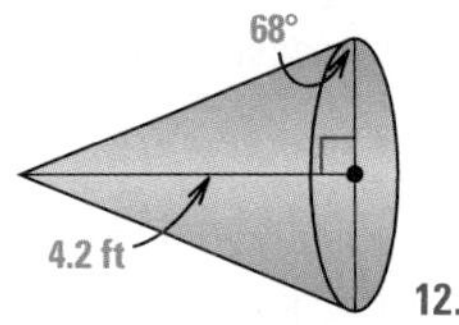

12.66 ft^3

12.6 Find the surface area and volume of a sphere with the given radius r or diameter d. Round to two decimal places.

34. $r = 13$ m
2123.72 m^2, 9202.77 m^3

35. $r = 1.8$ in.
40.72 in.^{2}, 24.43 in.^{3}

36. $d = 28$ yd
2463.01 yd^2, 11,494.04 yd^3

37. $d = 13.7$ cm
589.65 cm^2, 1346.36 cm^3

38. $r = 20$ in.
5026.55 in.^{2}, 33,510.32 in.^{3}

39. $r = 17.5$ mm
See margin.

40. $d = 15.2$ m
725.83 m^2, 1838.78 m^3

41. $d = 23$ ft
1661.90 ft^2, 6370.63 ft^3

12.7 Solid A (shown) is similar to Solid B (not shown) with the given scale factor of A to B. Find the surface area and volume of Solid B.

42. Scale factor of 3 : 2

A
$S = 324\pi\text{ in.}^2$
$V = 972\pi\text{ in.}^3$
$144\pi\text{ in.}^2$, $288\pi\text{ in.}^3$

43. Scale factor of 2 : 1
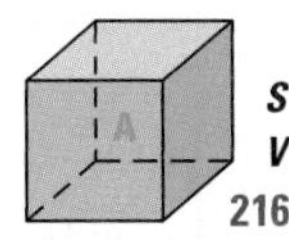

$S = 864\text{ ft}^2$
$V = 1728\text{ ft}^3$
216 ft^2, 216 ft^3

44. Scale factor of 4 : 7
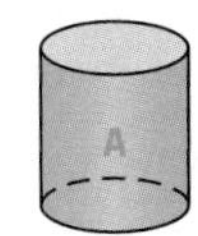

$S = 64\pi\text{ cm}^2$
$V = 64\pi\text{ cm}^3$
$196\pi\text{ cm}^2$, $343\pi\text{ cm}^3$

12.7 45. Two similar cylinders have volumes 12π cubic units and 324π cubic units. Find the scale factor of the smaller cylinder to the larger cylinder. **1:3**

39. 3848.45 mm^2, 22,449.30 mm^3

EXTRA PRACTICE

Tables

Symbols

Symbol	Meaning	Page
$-a$	opposite of a	**xxii**
$\overleftrightarrow{AB}$	line AB	**2**
$\overline{AB}$	segment AB	**3**
$\overrightarrow{AB}$	ray AB	**3**
$\cdot$	multiplication, times	**8**
AB	the length of $\overline{AB}$	**9**
$\lvert x \rvert$	absolute value of x	**9**
x_1	x sub one	**9**
(x, y)	ordered pair	**11**
$=$	is equal to	**11**
$\cong$	is congruent to	**11**
$\sqrt{a}$	square root of a	**14**
$\angle ABC$	angle ABC	**24**
$m\angle A$	measure of angle A	**24**
$^\circ$	degree(s)	**24**
$\urcorner$	right angle symbol	**25**
n-gon	polygon with n sides	**43**
π	pi; irrational number ≈ 3.14	**49**
$\approx$	is approximately equal to	**50**
$\ldots$	and so on	**72**
$\perp$	is perpendicular to	**81**
$\rightarrow$	implies	**94**
$\leftrightarrow$	if and only if	**94**
$\sim p$	negation of statement p	**94**
$\parallel$	is parallel to	**147**
m	slope	**171**
$\triangle ABC$	triangle ABC	**217**

Symbol	Meaning	Page
$\triangle$s	triangles	**227**
$\angle$s	angles	**250**
$\rightarrow$	maps to	**272**
$<$	is less than	**328**
$>$	is greater than	**328**
$\neq$	is not equal to	**337**
$\frac{a}{b}$, $a:b$	ratio of a to b	**356**
$\sim$	is similar to	**372**
$\stackrel{?}{=}$	is this statement true?	**389**
$\nparallel$	is not parallel to	**398**
tan	tangent	**466**
sin	sine	**473**
cos	cosine	**473**
$\sin^{-1}$	inverse sine	**483**
$\cos^{-1}$	inverse cosine	**483**
$\tan^{-1}$	inverse tangent	**483**
$\square ABCD$	parallelogram $ABCD$	**515**
$\ncong$	is not congruent to	**531**
A'	A prime	**572**
$\overrightarrow{AB}$	vector AB	**574**
$\langle a, b\rangle$	component form of a vector	**574**
A''	A double prime	**608**
$\odot P$	circle with center P	**651**
$m\widehat{AB}$	measure of minor arc AB	**659**
$m\widehat{ABC}$	measure of major arc ABC	**659**
$P(A)$	probability of event A	**771**

Measures

Time	
60 seconds (sec) = 1 minute (min) 60 minutes = 1 hour (h) 24 hours = 1 day 7 days = 1 week 4 weeks (approx.) = 1 month	365 days, 52 weeks (approx.), 12 months = 1 year 10 years = 1 decade 100 years = 1 century

Metric	United States Customary
Length 10 millimeters (mm) = 1 centimeter (cm) 100 cm, 1000 mm = 1 meter (m) 1000 m = 1 kilometer (km)	**Length** 12 inches (in.) = 1 foot (ft) 36 in., 3 ft = 1 yard (yd) 5280 ft, 1760 yd = 1 mile (mi)
Area 100 square millimeters (mm^2) = 1 square centimeter (cm^2) 10,000 cm^2 = 1 square meter (m^2) 10,000 m^2 = 1 hectare (ha)	**Area** 144 square inches ($in.^2$) = 1 square foot (ft^2) 9 ft^2 = 1 square yard (yd^2) 43,560 ft^2, 4840 yd^2 = 1 acre (A)
Volume 1000 cubic millimeters (mm^3) = 1 cubic centimeter (cm^3) 1,000,000 cm^3 = 1 cubic meter (m^3)	**Volume** 1728 cubic inches ($in.^3$) = 1 cubic foot (ft^3) 27 ft^3 = 1 cubic yard (yd^3)
Liquid Capacity 1000 milliliters (mL), 1000 cubic centimeters (cm^3) = 1 liter (L) 1000 L = 1 kiloliter (kL)	**Liquid Capacity** 8 fluid ounces (fl oz) = 1 cup (c) 2 c = 1 pint (pt) 2 pt = 1 quart (qt) 4 qt = 1 gallon (gal)
Mass 1000 milligrams (mg) = 1 gram (g) 1000 g = 1 kilogram (kg) 1000 kg = 1 metric ton (t)	**Weight** 16 ounces (oz) = 1 pound (lb) 2000 lb = 1 ton
Temperature **Degrees Celsius (°C)** 0°C = freezing point of water 37°C = normal body temperature 100°C = boiling point of water	**Temperature** **Degrees Fahrenheit (°F)** 32°F = freezing point of water 98.6°F = normal body temperature 212°F = boiling point of water

TABLES

921

Formulas

Angles

Sum of the measures of the interior angles of a triangle: 180° *(p. 218)*

Sum of the measures of the interior angles of a convex n-gon: $(n - 2) \cdot 180°$ *(p. 507)*

Exterior angle of a triangle:

$m\angle 1 = m\angle A + m\angle B$ *(p. 219)*

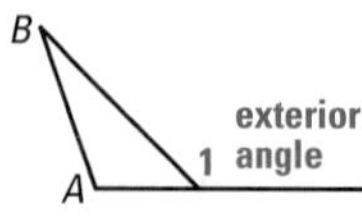

Sum of the measures of the exterior angles of a convex polygon: 360° *(p. 509)*

Right Triangles

Pythagorean Theorem:
$c^2 = a^2 + b^2$ *(p. 433)*

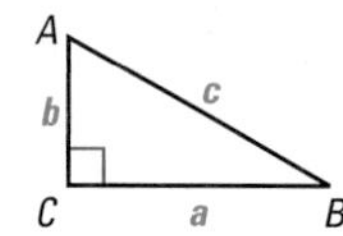

Trigonometric ratios:

$\sin A = \frac{BC}{AB}$ *(p. 473)* $\quad \sin^{-1}\frac{BC}{AB} = m\angle A$ *(p. 483)*

$\cos A = \frac{AC}{AB}$ *(p. 473)* $\quad \cos^{-1}\frac{AC}{AB} = m\angle A$ *(p. 483)*

$\tan A = \frac{BC}{AC}$ *(p. 466)* $\quad \tan^{-1}\frac{BC}{AC} = m\angle A$ *(p. 483)*

45°-45°-90° triangle *(p. 457)*

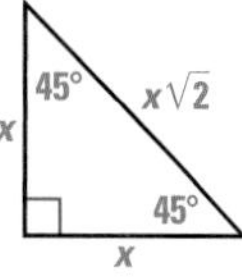

Ratio of sides: $1:1:\sqrt{2}$

30°-60°-90° triangle *(p. 459)*

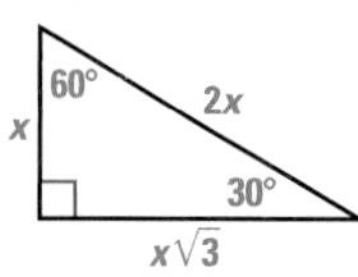

Ratio of sides: $1:\sqrt{3}:2$

$\triangle ABC \sim \triangle ACD \sim \triangle CBD$
(p. 449)

$\frac{BD}{CD} = \frac{CD}{AD}, \frac{AB}{CB} = \frac{CB}{DB}, \frac{AB}{AC} = \frac{AC}{AD}$
(p. 451)

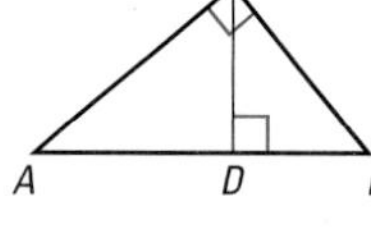

$\frac{BD}{CD} = \frac{CD}{AD}$, and $CD = \sqrt{AD \cdot DB}$ *(pp. 359, 452)*

Circles

Angle and segments formed by two chords:

$m\angle 1 = \frac{1}{2}(m\overset{\frown}{CD} + m\overset{\frown}{AB})$ *(p. 681)*

$EA \cdot EC = EB \cdot ED$ *(p. 689)*

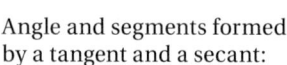

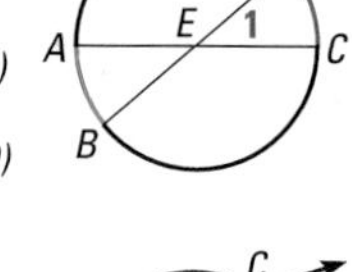

Angle and segments formed by a tangent and a secant:

$m\angle 2 = \frac{1}{2}(m\overset{\frown}{BC} - m\overset{\frown}{AB})$ *(p. 681)*

$EB^2 = EA \cdot EC$ *(p. 691)*

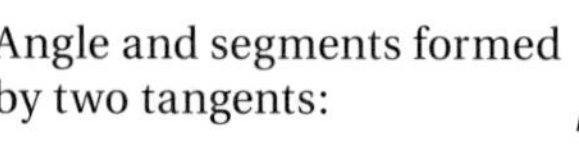

Angle and segments formed by two tangents:

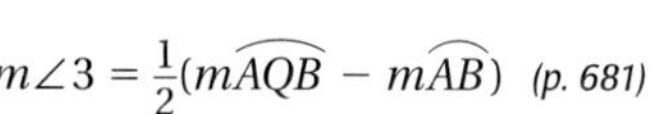

$m\angle 3 = \frac{1}{2}(m\overset{\frown}{AQB} - m\overset{\frown}{AB})$ *(p. 681)*

$EA = EB$ *(p. 654)*

Angle and segments formed by two secants:

$m\angle 4 = \frac{1}{2}(m\overset{\frown}{CD} - m\overset{\frown}{AB})$ *(p. 681)*

$EA \cdot EC = EB \cdot ED$ *(p. 690)*

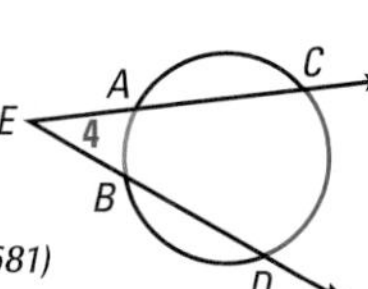

Coordinate Geometry

Given: points $A(x_1, y_1)$ and $B(x_2, y_2)$

Midpoint of $\overline{AB} = \left(\frac{x_1 + x_2}{2}, \frac{y_1 + y_2}{2}\right)$ *(p. 16)*

$AB = \sqrt{(x_2 - x_1)^2 + (y_2 - y_1)^2}$ *(p. 17)*

Slope of $\overleftrightarrow{AB} = \frac{\text{rise}}{\text{run}} = \frac{y_2 - y_1}{x_2 - x_1}$ *(p. 171)*

Slope-intercept form of a linear equation with slope m and y-intercept b: $y = mx + b$ *(p. 180)*

Standard equation of a circle with center (h, k) and radius r: $(x - h)^2 + (y - k)^2 = r^2$ *(p. 699)*

Taxicab distance $AB = |x_2 - x_1| + |y_2 - y_1|$ *(p. 198)*

TABLES

Perimeter

P = perimeter, C = circumference, s = side, ℓ = length, w = width, a, b, c = lengths of the sides of a triangle, d = diameter, r = radius

Polygon:	P = sum of side lengths	*(p. 49)*
Square:	$P = 4s$	*(p. 49)*
Rectangle:	$P = 2\ell + 2w$	*(p. 49)*
Triangle:	$P = a + b + c$	*(p. 49)*
Regular n-gon:	$P = ns$	*(pp. 49, 765)*
Circle:	$C = \pi d = 2\pi r$	*(p. 49)*
Arc length of $\widehat{AB}$	$= \frac{m\widehat{AB}}{360^\circ} \cdot 2\pi r$	*(p. 747)*

Area

A = area, s = side, b = base, h = height, ℓ = length, w = width, d = diagonal, a = apothem, P = perimeter, r = radius

Square:	$A = s^2$	*(pp. 49, 720)*
Rectangle:	$A = lw$	*(pp. 49, 720)*
Triangle:	$A = \frac{1}{2}bh$	*(pp. 49, 721)*
Parallelogram:	$A = bh$	*(p. 721)*
Trapezoid:	$A = \frac{1}{2}h(b_1 + b_2)$	*(p. 730)*
Rhombus:	$A = \frac{1}{2}d_1d_2$	*(p. 731)*
Kite:	$A = \frac{1}{2}d_1d_2$	*(p. 731)*
Equilateral triangle:	$A = \frac{1}{4}\sqrt{3}s^2$	*(pp. 726, 766)*
Regular polygon:	$A = \frac{1}{2}aP$	*(p. 763)*
Circle:	$A = \pi r^2$	*(pp. 49, 755)*
Area of a sector:	$A = \frac{m\widehat{AB}}{360^\circ} \cdot \pi r^2$	*(p. 756)*

Surface Area

B = area of a base, P = perimeter, C = circumference, h = height, r = radius, ℓ = slant height

Right prism:	$S = 2B + Ph$	*(p. 804)*
Right cylinder:	$S = 2B + Ch = 2\pi r^2 + 2\pi rh$	*(p. 805)*
Regular pyramid:	$S = B + \frac{1}{2}P\ell$	*(p. 811)*
Right cone:	$S = B + \frac{1}{2}C\ell = \pi r^2 + \pi r\ell$	*(p. 812)*
Sphere:	$S = 4\pi r^2$	*(p. 838)*

Volume

V = volume, B = area of a base, h = height, r = radius, s = side length

Cube:	$V = s^3$	*(p. 819)*
Prism:	$V = Bh$	*(p. 820)*
Cylinder:	$V = Bh = \pi r^2h$	*(p. 820)*
Pyramid:	$V = \frac{1}{3}Bh$	*(p. 829)*
Cone:	$V = \frac{1}{3}Bh = \frac{1}{3}\pi r^2h$	*(p. 829)*
Sphere:	$V = \frac{4}{3}\pi r^3$	*(p. 840)*

Miscellaneous

Geometric mean of a and b: $\sqrt{a \cdot b}$ *(p. 359)*

Euler's Theorem for Polyhedra, F = faces, V = vertices, E = edges: $F + V = E + 2$ *(p. 795)*

Given: similar polygons or similar solids with a scale factor of $a:b$

Ratio of perimeters $= a:b$ *(p. 374)*

Ratio of areas $= a^2:b^2$ *(p. 737)*

Ratio of volumes $= a^3:b^3$ *(p. 848)*

Given a quadratic equation $ax^2 + bx + c = 0$, the solutions are given by the formula:

$$x = \frac{-b \pm \sqrt{b^2 - 4ac}}{2a}$$ *(pp. 641, 883)*

TABLES

Squares and Square Roots

No.	Square	Sq. Root
1	1	1.000
2	4	1.414
3	9	1.732
4	16	2.000
5	25	2.236
6	36	2.449
7	49	2.646
8	64	2.828
9	81	3.000
10	100	3.162
11	121	3.317
12	144	3.464
13	169	3.606
14	196	3.742
15	225	3.873
16	256	4.000
17	289	4.123
18	324	4.243
19	361	4.359
20	400	4.472
21	441	4.583
22	484	4.690
23	529	4.796
24	576	4.899
25	625	5.000
26	676	5.099
27	729	5.196
28	784	5.292
29	841	5.385
30	900	5.477
31	961	5.568
32	1024	5.657
33	1089	5.745
34	1156	5.831
35	1225	5.916
36	1296	6.000
37	1369	6.083
38	1444	6.164
39	1521	6.245
40	1600	6.325
41	1681	6.403
42	1764	6.481
43	1849	6.557
44	1936	6.633
45	2025	6.708
46	2116	6.782
47	2209	6.856
48	2304	6.928
49	2401	7.000
50	2500	7.071

No.	Square	Sq. Root
51	2601	7.141
52	2704	7.211
53	2809	7.280
54	2916	7.348
55	3025	7.416
56	3136	7.483
57	3249	7.550
58	3364	7.616
59	3481	7.681
60	3600	7.746
61	3721	7.810
62	3844	7.874
63	3969	7.937
64	4096	8.000
65	4225	8.062
66	4356	8.124
67	4489	8.185
68	4624	8.246
69	4761	8.307
70	4900	8.367
71	5041	8.426
72	5184	8.485
73	5329	8.544
74	5476	8.602
75	5625	8.660
76	5776	8.718
77	5929	8.775
78	6084	8.832
79	6241	8.888
80	6400	8.944
81	6561	9.000
82	6724	9.055
83	6889	9.110
84	7056	9.165
85	7225	9.220
86	7396	9.274
87	7569	9.327
88	7744	9.381
89	7921	9.434
90	8100	9.487
91	8281	9.539
92	8464	9.592
93	8649	9.644
94	8836	9.695
95	9025	9.747
96	9216	9.798
97	9409	9.849
98	9604	9.899
99	9801	9.950
100	10,000	10.000

No.	Square	Sq. Root
101	10,201	10.050
102	10,404	10.100
103	10,609	10.149
104	10,816	10.198
105	11,025	10.247
106	11,236	10.296
107	11,449	10.344
108	11,664	10.392
109	11,881	10.440
110	12,100	10.488
111	12,321	10.536
112	12,544	10.583
113	12,769	10.630
114	12,996	10.677
115	13,225	10.724
116	13,456	10.770
117	13,689	10.817
118	13,924	10.863
119	14,161	10.909
120	14,400	10.954
121	14,641	11.000
122	14,884	11.045
123	15,129	11.091
124	15,376	11.136
125	15,625	11.180
126	15,876	11.225
127	16,129	11.269
128	16,384	11.314
129	16,641	11.358
130	16,900	11.402
131	17,161	11.446
132	17,424	11.489
133	17,689	11.533
134	17,956	11.576
135	18,225	11.619
136	18,496	11.662
137	18,769	11.705
138	19,044	11.747
139	19,321	11.790
140	19,600	11.832
141	19,881	11.874
142	20,164	11.916
143	20,449	11.958
144	20,736	12.000
145	21,025	12.042
146	21,316	12.083
147	21,609	12.124
148	21,904	12.166
149	22,201	12.207
150	22,500	12.247

Trigonometric Ratios

Angle	Sine	Cosine	Tangent
1°	.0175	.9998	.0175
2°	.0349	.9994	.0349
3°	.0523	.9986	.0524
4°	.0698	.9976	.0699
5°	.0872	.9962	.0875
6°	.1045	.9945	.1051
7°	.1219	.9925	.1228
8°	.1392	.9903	.1405
9°	.1564	.9877	.1584
10°	.1736	.9848	.1763
11°	.1908	.9816	.1944
12°	.2079	.9781	.2126
13°	.2250	.9744	.2309
14°	.2419	.9703	.2493
15°	.2588	.9659	.2679
16°	.2756	.6313	.2867
17°	.2924	.9563	.3057
18°	.3090	.9511	.3249
19°	.3256	.9455	.3443
20°	.3420	.9397	.3640
21°	.3584	.9336	.3839
22°	.3746	.9272	.4040
23°	.3907	.9205	.4245
24°	.4067	.9135	.4452
25°	.4226	.9063	.4663
26°	.4384	.8988	.4877
27°	.4540	.8910	.5095
28°	.4695	.8829	.5317
29°	.4848	.8746	.5543
30°	.5000	.8660	.5774
31°	.5150	.8572	.6009
32°	.5299	.8480	.6249
33°	.5446	.8387	.6494
34°	.5592	.8290	.6745
35°	.5736	.8192	.7002
36°	.5878	.8090	.7265
37°	.6018	.7986	.7536
38°	.6157	.7880	.7813
39°	.6293	.7771	.8098
40°	.6428	.7660	.8391
41°	.6561	.7547	.8693
42°	.6691	.7431	.9004
43°	.6820	.7314	.9325
44°	.6947	.7193	.9657
45°	.7071	.7071	1.0000

Angle	Sine	Cosine	Tangent
46°	.7193	.6947	1.0355
47°	.7314	.6820	1.0724
48°	.7431	.6991	1.1106
49°	.7547	.6561	1.1504
50°	.7660	.6428	1.1918
51°	.7771	.6293	1.2349
52°	.7880	.6157	1.2799
53°	.7986	.6018	1.3270
54°	.8090	.5878	1.3764
55°	.8192	.5736	1.4281
56°	.8290	.5592	1.4826
57°	.8387	.5446	1.5399
58°	.8480	.5299	1.6003
59°	.8572	.5150	1.6643
60°	.8660	.5000	1.7321
61°	.8746	.4848	1.8040
62°	.8829	.4695	1.8807
63°	.8910	.4540	1.9626
64°	.8988	.4384	2.0503
65°	.9063	.4226	2.1445
66°	.9135	.4067	2.2460
67°	.9205	.3907	2.3559
68°	.9272	.3746	2.4751
69°	.9336	.3584	2.6051
70°	.9397	.3420	2.7475
71°	.9455	.3256	2.9042
72°	.9511	.3090	0.0777
73°	.9563	.3746	3.2709
74°	.9613	.3584	3.4874
75°	.9659	.3420	3.7321
76°	.9703	.2419	4.0108
77°	.9744	.2250	4.3315
78°	.9781	.2079	4.7046
79°	.9816	.1908	5.1446
80°	.9848	.1736	5.6713
81°	.9877	.1564	6.3138
82°	.9903	.1392	7.1154
83°	.9925	.1219	8.1443
84°	.9945	.1045	9.5144
85°	.9962	.0872	11.4301
86°	.9976	.0698	14.3007
87°	.9986	.0523	19.0811
88°	.9994	.0349	28.6363
89°	.9998	.0175	52.2900

Postulates

1 Ruler Postulate The points on a line can be matched one to one with the real numbers. The real number that corresponds to a point is the coordinate of the point. The distance between points A and B, written as AB, is the absolute value of the difference between the coordinates of A and B. *(p. 9)*

2 Segment Addition Postulate If B is between A and C, then $AB + BC = AC$. If $AB + BC = AC$, then B is between A and C. *(p. 10)*

3 Protractor Postulate Consider $\overrightarrow{OB}$ and a point A on one side of $\overrightarrow{OB}$. The rays of the form $\overrightarrow{OA}$ can be matched one to one with the real numbers from 0 to 180. The measure of $\angle AOB$ is equal to the absolute value of the difference between the real numbers for $\overrightarrow{OA}$ and $\overrightarrow{OB}$. *(p. 24)*

4 Angle Addition Postulate If P is in the interior of $\angle RST$, then $m\angle RST = m\angle RSP + m\angle PST$. *(p. 25)*

5 Through any two points there exists exactly one line. *(p. 96)*

6 A line contains at least two points. *(p. 96)*

7 If two lines intersect, then their intersection is exactly one point. *(p. 96)*

8 Through any three noncollinear points there exists exactly one plane. *(p. 96)*

9 A plane contains at least three noncollinear points. *(p. 96)*

10 If two points lie in a plane, then the line containing them lies in the plane. *(p. 96)*

11 If two planes intersect, then their intersection is a line. *(p. 96)*

12 Linear Pair Postulate If two angles form a linear pair, then they are supplementary. *(p. 126)*

13 Parallel Postulate If there is a line and a point not on the line, then there is exactly one line through the point parallel to the given line. *(p. 148)*

14 Perpendicular Postulate If there is a line and a point not on the line, then there is exactly one line through the point perpendicular to the given line. *(p. 148)*

15 Corresponding Angles Postulate If two parallel lines are cut by a transversal, then the pairs of corresponding angles are congruent. *(p. 154)*

16 Corresponding Angles Converse If two lines are cut by a transversal so the corresponding angles are congruent, then the lines are parallel. *(p. 161)*

17 Slopes of Parallel Lines In a coordinate plane, two nonvertical lines are parallel if and only if they have the same slope. Any two vertical lines are parallel. *(p. 172)*

18 Slopes of Perpendicular Lines In a coordinate plane, two nonvertical lines are perpendicular if and only if the product of their slopes is -1. Horizontal lines are perpendicular to vertical lines. *(p. 172)*

19 Side-Side-Side (SSS) Congruence Postulate If three sides of one triangle are congruent to three sides of a second triangle, then the two triangles are congruent. *(p. 234)*

20 Side-Angle-Side (SAS) Congruence Postulate If two sides and the included angle of one triangle are congruent to two sides and the included angle of a second triangle, then the two triangles are congruent. *(p. 240)*

21 Angle-Side-Angle (ASA) Congruence Postulate If two angles and the included side of one triangle are congruent to two angles and the included side of a second triangle, then the two triangles are congruent. *(p. 249)*

22 Angle-Angle (AA) Similarity Postulate If two angles of one triangle are congruent to two angles of another triangle, then the two triangles are similar. *(p. 381)*

23 Arc Addition Postulate The measure of an arc formed by two adjacent arcs is the sum of the measures of the two arcs. *(p. 660)*

24 Area of a Square Postulate The area of a square is the square of the length of its side, or $A = s^2$. *(p. 720)*

25 Area Congruence Postulate If two polygons are congruent, then they have the same area. *(p. 720)*

26 Area Addition Postulate The area of a region is the sum of the areas of its nonoverlapping parts. *(p. 720)*

27 Volume of a Cube The volume of a cube is the cube of the length of its side, or $V = s^3$. *(p. 819)*

28 Volume Congruence Postulate If two polyhedra are congruent, then they have the same volume. *(p. 819)*

29 Volume Addition Postulate The volume of a solid is the sum of the volumes of all its nonoverlapping parts. *(p. 819)*

926

Theorems

2.1 Properties of Segment Congruence Segment congruence is reflexive, symmetric, and transitive.

Reflexive: For any segment AB, $\overline{AB} \cong \overline{AB}$.

Symmetric: If $\overline{AB} \cong \overline{CD}$, then $\overline{CD} \cong \overline{AB}$.

Transitive: If $\overline{AB} \cong \overline{CD}$ and $\overline{CD} \cong \overline{EF}$, then $\overline{AB} \cong \overline{EF}$. *(p. 113)*

2.2 Properties of Angles Congruence Angle congruence is reflexive, symmetric, and transitive.

Reflexive: For any angle A, $\angle A \cong \angle A$.

Symmetric: If $\angle A \cong \angle B$, then $\angle B \cong \angle A$.

Transitive: If $\angle A \cong \angle B$ and $\angle B \cong \angle C$, then $\angle A \cong \angle C$. *(p. 113)*

2.3 Right Angles Congruence Theorem All right angles are congruent. *(p. 124)*

2.4 Congruent Supplements Theorem If two angles are supplementary to the same angle (or to congruent angles), then the two angles are congruent. *(p. 125)*

2.5 Congruent Complements Theorem If two angles are complementary to the same angle (or to congruent angles), then the two angles are congruent. *(p. 125)*

2.6 Vertical Angles Congruence Theorem Vertical angles are congruent. *(p. 126)*

3.1 Alternate Interior Angles Theorem If two parallel lines are cut by a transversal, then the pairs of alternate interior angles are congruent. *(p. 155)*

3.2 Alternate Exterior Angles Theorem If two parallel lines are cut by a transversal, then the pairs of alternate exterior angles are congruent. *(p. 155)*

3.3 Consecutive Interior Angles Theorem If two parallel lines are cut by a transversal, then the pairs of consecutive interior angles are supplementary. *(p. 155)*

3.4 Alternate Interior Angles Converse If two lines are cut by a transversal so the alternate interior angles are congruent, then the lines are parallel. *(p. 162)*

3.5 Alternate Exterior Angles Converse If two lines are cut by a transversal so the alternate exterior angles are congruent, then the lines are parallel. *(p. 162)*

3.6 Consecutive Interior Angles Converse If two lines are cut by a transversal so the consecutive interior angles are supplementary, then the lines are parallel. *(p. 162)*

3.7 Transitive Property of Parallel Lines If two lines are parallel to the same line, then they are parallel to each other. *(p. 164)*

3.8 If two lines intersect to form a linear pair of congruent angles, then the lines are perpendicular. *(p. 190)*

3.9 If two lines are perpendicular, then they intersect to form four right angles. *(p. 190)*

3.10 If two sides of two adjacent acute angles are perpendicular, then the angles are complementary. *(p. 191)*

3.11 Perpendicular Transversal Theorem If a transversal is perpendicular to one of two parallel lines, then it is perpendicular to the other. *(p. 192)*

3.12 Lines Perpendicular to a Transversal Theorem In a plane, if two lines are perpendicular to the same line, then they are parallel to each other. *(p. 192)*

4.1 Triangle Sum Theorem The sum of the measures of the interior angles of a triangle is 180°. *(p. 218)*

Corollary The acute angles of a right triangle are complementary. *(p. 220)*

4.2 Exterior Angle Theorem The measure of an exterior angle of a triangle is equal to the sum of the measures of the two nonadjacent interior angles. *(p. 219)*

4.3 Third Angles Theorem If two angles of one triangle are congruent to two angles of another triangle, then the third angles are also congruent. *(p. 227)*

4.4 Properties of Triangle Congruence Triangle congruence is reflexive, symmetric, and transitive.

Reflexive: For any $\triangle ABC$, $\triangle ABC \cong \triangle ABC$.

Symmetric: If $\triangle ABC \cong \triangle DEF$, then $\triangle DEF \cong \triangle ABC$.

Transitive: If $\triangle ABC \cong \triangle DEF$ and $\triangle DEF \cong \triangle JKL$, then $\triangle ABC \cong \triangle JKL$. *(p. 228)*

927

4.5 Hypotenuse-Leg (HL) Congruence Theorem If the hypotenuse and a leg of a right triangle are congruent to the hypotenuse and a leg of a second right triangle, then the two triangles are congruent. *(p. 241)*

4.6 Angle-Angle-Side (AAS) Congruence Theorem If two angles and a non-included side of one triangle are congruent to two angles and the corresponding non-included side of a second triangle, then the two triangles are congruent. *(p. 249)*

4.7 Base Angles Theorem If two sides of a triangle are congruent, then the angles opposite them are congruent. *(p. 264)*

Corollary If a triangle is equilateral, then it is equiangular. *(p. 265)*

4.8 Converse of the Base Angles Theorem If two angles of a triangle are congruent, then the sides opposite them are congruent. *(p. 264)*

Corollary If a triangle is equiangular, then it is equilateral. *(p. 265)*

5.1 Midsegment Theorem The segment connecting the midpoints of two sides of a triangle is parallel to the third side and is half as long as that side. *(p. 295)*

5.2 Perpendicular Bisector Theorem If a point is on a perpendicular bisector of a segment, then it is equidistant from the endpoints of the segment. *(p. 303)*

5.3 Converse of the Perpendicular Bisector Theorem If a point is equidistant from the endpoints of a segment, then it is on the perpendicular bisector of the segment. *(p. 303)*

5.4 Concurrency of Perpendicular Bisectors Theorem The perpendicular bisectors of a triangle intersect at a point that is equidistant from the vertices of the triangle. *(p. 305)*

5.5 Angle Bisector Theorem If a point is on the bisector of an angle, then it is equidistant from the two sides of the angle. *(p. 310)*

5.6 Converse of the Angle Bisector Theorem If a point is in the interior of an angle and is equidistant from the sides of the angle, then it lies on the bisector of the angle. *(p. 310)*

5.7 Concurrency of Angle Bisectors of a Triangle The angle bisectors of a triangle intersect at a point that is equidistant from the sides of the triangle. *(p. 312)*

5.8 Concurrency of Medians of a Triangle The medians of a triangle intersect at a point that is two thirds of the distance from each vertex to the midpoint of the opposite side. *(p. 319)*

5.9 Concurrency of Altitudes of a Triangle The lines containing the altitudes of a triangle are concurrent. *(p. 320)*

5.10 If one side of a triangle is longer than another side, then the angle opposite the longer side is larger than the angle opposite the shorter side. *(p. 328)*

5.11 If one angle of a triangle is larger than another angle, then the side opposite the larger angle is longer than the side opposite the smaller angle. *(p. 328)*

5.12 Triangle Inequality Theorem The sum of the lengths of any two sides of a triangle is greater than the length of the third side. *(p. 330)*

5.13 Hinge Theorem If two sides of one triangle are congruent to two sides of another triangle, and the included angle of the first is larger than the included angle of the second, then the third side of the first is longer than the third side of the second. *(p. 335)*

5.14 Converse of the Hinge Theorem If two sides of one triangle are congruent to two sides of another triangle, and the third side of the first is longer than the third side of the second, then the included angle of the first is larger than the included angle of the second. *(p. 335)*

6.1 If two polygons are similar, then the ratio of their perimeters is equal to the ratios of their corresponding side lengths. *(p. 374)*

6.2 Side-Side-Side (SSS) Similarity Theorem If the corresponding side lengths of two triangles are proportional, then the triangles are similar. *(p. 388)*

6.3 Side-Angle-Side (SAS) Similarity Theorem If an angle of one triangle is congruent to an angle of a second triangle and the lengths of the sides including these angles are proportional, then the triangles are similar. *(p. 390)*

6.4 Triangle Proportionality Theorem If a line parallel to one side of a triangle intersects the other two sides, then it divides the two sides proportionally. *(p. 397)*

6.5 Converse of the Triangle Proportionality Theorem If a line divides two sides of a triangle proportionally, then it is parallel to the third side. *(p. 397)*

6.6 If three parallel lines intersect two transversals, then they divide the transversals proportionally. *(p. 398)*

6.7 If a ray bisects an angle of a triangle, then it divides the opposite side into segments whose lengths are proportional to the lengths of the other two sides. *(p. 398)*

7.1 **Pythagorean Theorem** In a right triangle, the square of the length of the hypotenuse is equal to the sum of the squares of the lengths of the legs. *(p. 433)*

7.2 **Converse of the Pythagorean Theorem** If the square of the length of the longest side of a triangle is equal to the sum of the squares of the lengths of the other two sides, then the triangle is a right triangle. *(p. 441)*

7.3 If the square of the length of the longest side of a triangle is less than the sum of the squares of the lengths of the other two sides, then the triangle is an acute triangle. *(p. 442)*

7.4 If the square of the length of the longest side of a triangle is greater than the sum of the squares of the lengths of the other two sides, then the triangle is an obtuse triangle. *(p. 442)*

7.5 If the altitude is drawn to the hypotenuse of a right triangle, then the two triangles formed are similar to the original triangle and to each other. *(p. 449)*

7.6 **Geometric Mean (Altitude) Theorem** In a right triangle, the altitude from the right angle to the hypotenuse divides the hypotenuse into two segments. The length of the altitude is the geometric mean of the lengths of the two segments. *(p. 452)*

7.7 **Geometric Mean (Leg) Theorem** In a right triangle, the altitude from the right angle to the hypotenuse divides the hypotenuse into two segments. The length of each leg of the right triangle is the geometric mean of the lengths of hypotenuse and the segment of the hypotenuse that is adjacent to the leg. *(p. 452)*

7.8 **45°-45°-90° Triangle Theorem** In a 45°-45°-90° triangle, the hypotenuse is $\sqrt{2}$ times as long as each leg. *(p. 457)*

7.9 **30°-60°-90° Triangle Theorem** In a 30°-60°-90° triangle, the hypotenuse is twice as long as the shorter leg, and the longer leg is $\sqrt{3}$ times as long as the shorter leg. *(p. 459)*

8.1 **Polygon Interior Angles Theorem** The sum of the measures of the interior angles of a convex n-gon is $(n - 2) \cdot 180°$. *(p. 507)*

Corollary The sum of the measures of the interior angles of a quadrilateral is 360°. *(p. 507)*

8.2 **Polygon Exterior Angles Theorem** The sum of the measures of the exterior angles of a convex polygon, one angle at each vertex, is 360°. *(p. 509)*

8.3 If a quadrilateral is a parallelogram, then its opposite sides are congruent. *(p. 515)*

8.4 If a quadrilateral is a parallelogram, then its opposite angles are congruent. *(p. 515)*

8.5 If a quadrilateral is a parallelogram, then its consecutive angles are supplementary. *(p. 516)*

8.6 If a quadrilateral is a parallelogram, then its diagonals bisect each other. *(p. 517)*

8.7 If both pairs of opposite sides of a quadrilateral are congruent, then the quadrilateral is a parallelogram. *(p. 522)*

8.8 If both pairs of opposite angles of a quadrilateral are congruent, then the quadrilateral is a parallelogram. *(p. 522)*

8.9 If one pair of opposite sides of a quadrilateral are congruent and parallel, then the quadrilateral is a parallelogram. *(p. 523)*

8.10 If the diagonals of a quadrilateral bisect each other, then the quadrilateral is a parallelogram. *(p. 523)*

Rhombus Corollary A quadrilateral is a rhombus if and only if it has four congruent sides. *(p. 533)*

Rectangle Corollary A quadrilateral is a rectangle if and only if it has four right angles. *(p. 533)*

Square Corollary A quadrilateral is a square if and only if it is a rhombus and a rectangle. *(p. 533)*

8.11 A parallelogram is a rhombus if and only if its diagonals are perpendicular. *(p. 535)*

8.12 A parallelogram is a rhombus if and only if each diagonal bisects a pair of opposite angles. *(p. 535)*

8.13 A parallelogram is a rectangle if and only if its diagonals are congruent. *(p. 535)*

8.14 If a trapezoid is isosceles, then both pairs of base angles are congruent. *(p. 543)*

8.15 If a trapezoid has a pair of congruent base angles, then it is an isosceles trapezoid. *(p. 543)*

8.16 A trapezoid is isosceles if and only if its diagonals are congruent. *(p. 543)*

8.17 **Midsegment Theorem for Trapezoids** The midsegment of a trapezoid is parallel to each base and its length is one half the sum of the lengths of the bases. *(p. 544)*

8.18 If a quadrilateral is a kite, then its diagonals are perpendicular. *(p. 545)*

8.19 If a quadrilateral is a kite, then exactly one pair of opposite angles are congruent. *(p. 545)*

9.1 **Translation Theorem** A translation is an isometry. *(p. 573)*

9.2 **Reflection Theorem** A reflection is an isometry. *(p. 591)*

9.3 **Rotation Theorem** A rotation is an isometry. *(p. 601)*

9.4 **Composition Theorem** The composition of two (or more) isometries is an isometry. *(p. 609)*

9.5 **Reflections in Parallel Lines** If lines k and m are parallel, then a reflection in line k followed by a reflection in line m is the same as a translation. If P'' is the image of P, then:

(1) $\overline{PP'}$ is perpendicular to k and m, and
(2) $PP'' = 2d$, where d is the distance between k and m. *(p. 609)*

9.6 **Reflections in Intersecting Lines** If lines k and m intersect at point P, then a reflection in k followed by a reflection in m is the same as a rotation about point P. The angle of rotation is $2x°$, where $x°$ is the measure of the acute or right angle formed by k and m. *(p. 610)*

10.1 In a plane, a line is tangent to a circle if and only if the line is perpendicular to a radius of the circle at its endpoint on the circle. *(p. 653)*

10.2 Tangent segments from a common external point are congruent. *(p. 654)*

10.3 In the same circle, or in congruent circles, two minor arcs are congruent if and only if their corresponding chords are congruent. *(p. 664)*

10.4 If one chord is a perpendicular bisector of another chord, then the first chord is a diameter. *(p. 665)*

10.5 If a diameter of a circle is perpendicular to a chord, then the diameter bisects the chord and its arc. *(p. 665)*

10.6 In the same circle, or in congruent circles, two chords are congruent if and only if they are equidistant from the center. *(p. 666)*

10.7 **Measure of an Inscribed Angle Theorem** The measure of an inscribed angle is one half the measure of its intercepted arc. *(p. 672)*

10.8 If two inscribed angles of a circle intercept the same arc, then the angles are congruent. *(p. 673)*

10.9 If a right triangle is inscribed in a circle, then the hypotenuse is a diameter of the circle. Conversely, if one side of an inscribed triangle is a diameter of the circle, then the triangle is a right triangle and the angle opposite the diameter is the right angle. *(p. 674)*

10.10 A quadrilateral can be inscribed in a circle if and only if its opposite angles are supplementary. *(p. 675)*

10.11 If a tangent and a chord intersect at a point on a circle, then the measure of each angle formed is one half the measure of its intercepted arc. *(p. 680)*

10.12 **Angles Inside the Circle** If two chords intersect inside a circle, then the measure of each angle is one half the sum of the measures of the arcs intercepted by the angle and its vertical angle. *(p. 681)*

10.13 **Angles Outside the Circle** If a tangent and a secant, two tangents, or two secants intersect outside a circle, then the measure of the angle formed is one half the difference of the measures of the intercepted arcs. *(p. 681)*

10.14 **Segments of Chords Theorem** If two chords intersect in the interior of a circle, then the product of the lengths of the segments of one chord is equal to the product of the lengths of the segments of the other chord. *(p. 689)*

10.15 **Segments of Secants Theorem** If two secant segments share the same endpoint outside a circle, then the product of the lengths of one secant segment and its external segment equals the product of the lengths of the other secant segment and its external segment. *(p. 690)*

10.16 **Segments of Secants and Tangents Theorem** If a secant segment and a tangent segment share an endpoint outside a circle, then the product of the lengths of the secant segment and its external segment equals the square of the length of the tangent segment. *(p. 691)*

11.1 **Area of a Rectangle** The area of a rectangle is the product of its base and height. $A = bh$ *(p. 720)*

11.2 Area of a Parallelogram The area of a parallelogram is the product of a base and its corresponding height. $A = bh$ *(p. 721)*

11.3 Area of a Triangle The area of a triangle is one half the product of a base and its corresponding height. $A = \frac{1}{2}bh$ *(p. 721)*

11.4 Area of a Trapezoid The area of a trapezoid is one half the product of the height and the sum of the lengths of the bases.
$A = \frac{1}{2}h(b_1 + b_2)$ *(p. 730)*

11.5 Area of a Rhombus The area of a rhombus is one half the product of the lengths of its diagonals. $A = \frac{1}{2}d_1d_2$ *(p. 731)*

11.6 Area of a Kite The area of a kite is one half the product of the lengths of its diagonals.
$A = \frac{1}{2}d_1d_2$ *(p. 731)*

11.7 Areas of Similar Polygons If two polygons are similar with the lengths of corresponding sides in the ratio of $a : b$, then the ratio of their areas is $a^2 : b^2$. *(p. 737)*

11.8 Circumference of a Circle The circumference C of a circle is $C = \pi d$ or $C = 2\pi r$, where d is the diameter of the circle and r is the radius of the circle. *(p. 746)*

Arc Length Corollary In a circle, the ratio of the length of a given arc to the circumference is equal to the ratio of the measure of the arc to 360°.

$$\frac{\text{Arc length of } \widehat{AB}}{2\pi r} = \frac{m\widehat{AB}}{360°}, \text{ or}$$

$$\text{Arc length of } \widehat{AB} = \frac{m\widehat{AB}}{360°} \cdot 2\pi r$$ *(p. 747)*

11.9 Area of a Circle The area of a circle is π times the square of the radius. $A = \pi r^2$ *(p. 755)*

11.10 Area of a Sector The ratio of the area A of a sector of a circle to the area of the whole circle (πr^2) is equal to the ratio of the measure of the intercepted arc to 360°.

$$\frac{A}{\pi r^2} = \frac{m\widehat{AB}}{360°}, \text{ or } A = \frac{m\widehat{AB}}{360°} \cdot \pi r^2$$ *(p. 756)*

11.11 Area of a Regular Polygon The area of a regular n-gon with side length s is half the product of the apothem a and the perimeter P, so $A = \frac{1}{2}aP$, or $A = \frac{1}{2}a \cdot ns$. *(p. 763)*

12.1 Euler's Theorem The number of faces (F), vertices (V), and edges (E) of a polyhedron are related by the formula $F + V = E + 2$. *(p. 795)*

12.2 Surface Area of a Right Prism The surface area S of a right prism is $S = 2B + Ph = aP + Ph$, where a is the apothem of the base, B is the area of a base, P is the perimeter of a base, and h is the height. *(p. 804)*

12.3 Surface Area of a Right Cylinder The surface area S of a right cylinder is $S = 2B + Ch = 2\pi r^2 + 2\pi rh$, where B is the area of a base, C is the circumference of a base, r is the radius of a base, and h is the height. *(p. 805)*

12.4 Surface Area of a Regular Pyramid The surface area S of a regular pyramid is $S = B + \frac{1}{2}P\ell$, where B is the area of the base, P is the perimeter of the base, and ℓ is the slant height. *(p. 811)*

12.5 Surface Area of a Right Cone The surface area S of a right cone is $S = B + \frac{1}{2}C\ell = \pi r^2 + \pi r\ell$, where B is the area of the base, C is the circumference of the base, r is the radius of the base, and ℓ is the slant height. *(p. 812)*

12.6 Volume of a Prism The volume V of a prism is $V = Bh$, where B is the area of a base and h is the height. *(p. 820)*

12.7 Volume of a Cylinder The volume V of a cylinder is $V = Bh = \pi r^2h$, where B is the area of a base, h is the height, and r is the radius of a base. *(p. 820)*

12.8 Cavalieri's Principle If two solids have the same height and the same cross-sectional area at every level, then they have the same volume. *(p. 821)*

12.9 Volume of a Pyramid The volume V of a pyramid is $V = \frac{1}{3}Bh$, where B is the area of the base and h is the height. *(p. 829)*

12.10 Volume of a Cone The volume V of a cone is $V = \frac{1}{3}Bh = \frac{1}{3}\pi r^2h$, where B is the area of the base, h is the height, and r is the radius of the base. *(p. 829)*

12.11 Surface Area of a Sphere The surface area S of a sphere with radius r is $S = 4\pi r^2$. *(p. 838)*

12.12 Volume of a Sphere The volume V of a sphere with radius r is $V = \frac{4}{3}\pi r^3$. *(p. 840)*

12.13 Similar Solids Theorem If two similar solids have a scale factor of $a : b$, then corresponding areas have a ratio of $a^2 : b^2$, and corresponding volumes have a ratio of $a^3 : b^3$. *(p. 848)*

POSTULATES AND THEOREMS

Additional Proofs

Proof of Theorem 4.5 Hypotenuse-Leg (HL) Congruence Theorem

THEOREM 4.5
PAGE 241

If the hypotenuse and a leg of a right triangle are congruent to the hypotenuse and a leg of a second right triangle, then the two triangles are congruent.

GIVEN ▶ In $\triangle ABC$, $\angle C$ is a right angle.
In $\triangle DEF$, $\angle F$ is a right angle.
$\overline{AB} \cong \overline{DE}$, $\overline{AC} \cong \overline{DF}$

PROVE ▶ $\triangle ABC \cong \triangle DEF$

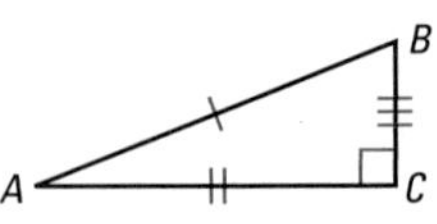

Plan for Proof Construct $\triangle DGF$ with $\overline{GF} \cong \overline{BC}$, as shown. Prove that $\triangle ABC \cong \triangle DGF$. Then use the fact that corresponding parts of congruent triangles are congruent to show that $\triangle DGF \cong \triangle DEF$. By the Transitive Property of Congruence, you can show that $\triangle ABC \cong \triangle DEF$.

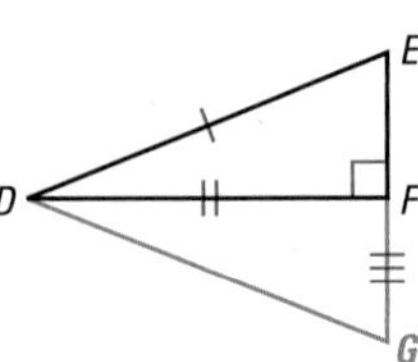

STATEMENTS	REASONS
1. $\angle C$ is a right angle. $\angle DFE$ is a right angle.	**1.** Given
2. $\overline{DF} \perp \overline{EG}$	**2.** Definition of perpendicular lines
3. $\angle DFG$ is a right angle.	**3.** If 2 lines are $\perp$, then they form 4 rt. $\angle$s.
4. $\angle C \cong \angle DFG$	**4.** Right Angles Congruence Theorem
5. $\overline{AC} \cong \overline{DF}$	**5.** Given
6. $\overline{BC} \cong \overline{GF}$	**6.** Given by construction
7. $\triangle ABC \cong \triangle DGF$	**7.** SAS Congruence Postulate
8. $\overline{DG} \cong \overline{AB}$	**8.** Corresp. parts of $\cong$ $\triangle$s are $\cong$.
9. $\overline{AB} \cong \overline{DE}$	**9.** Given
10. $\overline{DG} \cong \overline{DE}$	**10.** Transitive Property of Congruence
11. $\angle E \cong \angle G$	**11.** If 2 sides of a $\triangle$ are $\cong$, then the $\angle$s opposite them are $\cong$.
12. $\angle DFG \cong \angle DFE$	**12.** Right Angles Congruence Theorem
13. $\triangle DGF \cong \triangle DEF$	**13.** AAS Congruence Theorem
14. $\triangle ABC \cong \triangle DEF$	**14.** Transitive Property of $\cong$ $\triangle$s

ADDITIONAL PROOFS

Proof of Theorem 5.4
Concurrency of Perpendicular Bisectors of a Triangle

THEOREM 5.4
PAGE 305
The perpendicular bisectors of a triangle intersect at a point that is equidistant from the vertices of the triangle.

GIVEN ▶ $\triangle ABC$; the $\perp$ bisectors of $\overline{AB}$, $\overline{BC}$, and $\overline{AC}$

PROVE ▶ The $\perp$ bisectors intersect in a point; that point is equidistant from A, B, and C.

Plan for Proof Show that P, the point of intersection of the perpendicular bisectors of $\overline{AB}$ and $\overline{BC}$, also lies on the perpendicular bisector of $\overline{AC}$. Then show that P is equidistant from the vertices of the triangle, A, B, and C.

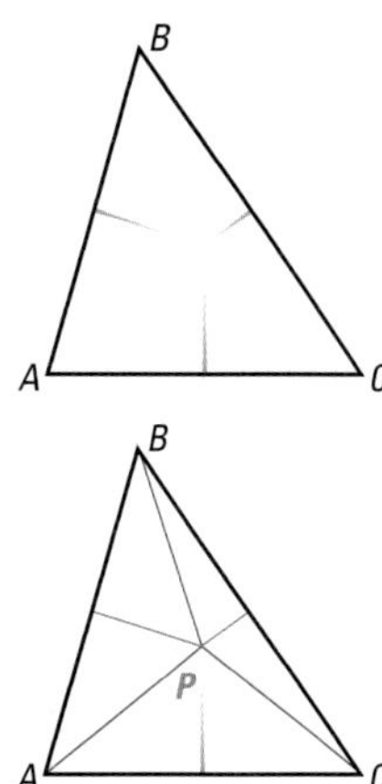

STATEMENTS	REASONS
1. $\triangle ABC$; the $\perp$ bisectors of $\overline{AB}$, $\overline{BC}$, and $\overline{AC}$	**1.** Given
2. The perpendicular bisectors of $\overline{AB}$ and $\overline{BC}$ intersect at some point P.	**2.** ABC is a triangle, so its sides $\overline{AB}$ and $\overline{BC}$ cannot be parallel; therefore, segments perpendicular to those sides cannot be parallel. So, the perpendicular bisectors must intersect in some point. Call it P.
3. Draw $\overline{PA}$, $\overline{PB}$, and $\overline{PC}$.	**3.** Through any two points there is exactly one line.
4. $PA = PB$, $PB = PC$	**4.** In a plane, if a point is on the perpendicular bisector of a segment, then it is equidistant from the endpoints of the segment. (Theorem 5.2)
5. $PA = PC$	**5.** Substitution Property of Equality
6. P is on the perpendicular bisector of $\overline{AC}$.	**6.** In a plane, if a point is equidistant from the endpoints of a segment, then it is on the perpendicular bisector of the segment. (Theorem 5.3)
7. $PA = PB = PC$, so P is equidistant from the vertices of the triangle.	**7.** From the results of Steps 4 and 5 and the definition of equidistant

Proof of Theorem 5.8 Concurrency of Medians of a Triangle

THEOREM 5.8
PAGE 319
The medians of a triangle intersect at a point that is two thirds of the distance from each vertex to the midpoint of the opposite side.

GIVEN ▶ $\triangle OBC$; medians $\overline{OM}$, $\overline{BN}$, and $\overline{CQ}$

PROVE ▶ The medians intersect in a point P; that point is two thirds of the distance from vertices O, B, and C to midpoints M, N, and Q.

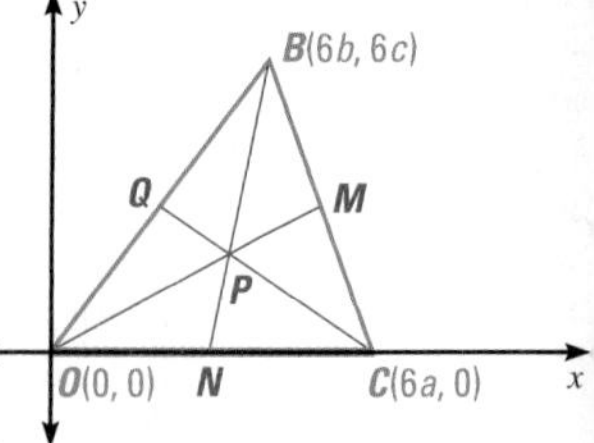

Plan for Proof The medians $\overline{OM}$ and $\overline{BN}$ intersect at some point P. Show that point P lies on $\overleftrightarrow{CQ}$. Then show that $OP = \frac{2}{3}OM$, $BP = \frac{2}{3}BN$, and $CP = \frac{2}{3}CQ$.

WRITE PROOFS
Because you want to prove something involving the fraction $\frac{2}{3}$, it is convenient to position the vertices at points whose coordinates are multiples of both 2 and 3.

STEP 1 **Find** the equations of the lines containing the medians $\overline{OM}$, $\overline{BN}$, and $\overline{CQ}$.

By the *Midpoint Formula*,

the coordinates of M are $\left(\frac{6b + 6a}{2}, \frac{6c + 0}{2}\right) = (3b + 3a, 3c)$;

the coordinates of N are $\left(\frac{0 + 6a}{2}, \frac{0 + 0}{2}\right) = (3a, 0)$;

the coordinates of Q are $\left(\frac{6b + 0}{2}, \frac{6c + 0}{2}\right) = (3b, 3c)$.

By the *slope formula*,

slope of $\overline{OM} = \frac{3c - 0}{(3b + 3a) - 0} = \frac{3c}{3b + 3a} = \frac{c}{b + a}$;

slope of $\overline{BN} = \frac{6c - 0}{6b - 3a} = \frac{6c}{6b - 3a} = \frac{2c}{2b - a}$;

slope of $\overline{CQ} = \frac{0 - 3c}{6a - 3b} = \frac{-3c}{6a - 3b} = \frac{-c}{2a - b} = \frac{c}{b - 2a}$.

Using the *point-slope form of an equation of a line*,

the equation of $\overleftrightarrow{OM}$ is $y - 0 = \frac{c}{b + a}(x - 0)$, or $y = \frac{c}{b + a}x$;

the equation of $\overleftrightarrow{BN}$ is $y - 0 = \frac{2c}{2b - a}(x - 3a)$, or $y = \frac{2c}{2b - a}(x - 3a)$;

the equation of $\overleftrightarrow{CQ}$ is $y - 0 = \frac{c}{b - 2a}(x - 6a)$, or $y = \frac{c}{b - 2a}(x - 6a)$.

STEP 2 **Find** the coordinates of the point P where two medians (say, $\overline{OM}$ and $\overline{BN}$) intersect. Using the substitution method, set the values of y in the equations of $\overleftrightarrow{OM}$ and $\overleftrightarrow{BN}$ equal to each other:

$$\frac{c}{b + a}x = \frac{2c}{2b - a}(x - 3a)$$

$$cx(2b - a) = 2c(x - 3a)(b + a)$$

$$2cxb - cxa = 2cxb + 2cxa - 6cab - 6ca^2$$

$$-3cxa = -6cab - 6ca^2$$

$$x = 2b + 2a$$

Substituting to find y, $y = \frac{c}{b + a}x = \frac{c}{b + a}(2b + 2a) = 2c$.

So, the coordinates of P are $(2b + 2a, 2c)$.

ADDITIONAL PROOFS

STEP 3 **Show** that P is on $\overleftrightarrow{CQ}$.

Substituting the x-coordinate for P into the equation of $\overleftrightarrow{CQ}$,
$y = \frac{c}{b-2a}([2b + 2a] - 6a) = \frac{c}{b-2a}(2b - 4a) = 2c.$

So, $P(2b + 2a, 2c)$ is on $\overleftrightarrow{CQ}$ and the three medians intersect at the same point.

STEP 4 **Find** the distances OM, OP, BN, BP, CQ, and CP.
Use the *Distance Formula.*

$$OM = \sqrt{((3b + 3a) - 0)^2 + (3c - 0)^2} = \sqrt{(3(b + a))^2 + (3c)^2} = \sqrt{9\left((b + a)^2 + c^2\right)} = 3\sqrt{(b + a)^2 + c^2}$$

$$OP = \sqrt{((2b + 2a) - 0)^2 + (2c - 0)^2} = \sqrt{(2(b + a))^2 + (2c)^2} = \sqrt{4\left((b + a)^2 + c^2\right)} = 2\sqrt{(b + a)^2 + c^2}$$

$$BN = \sqrt{(3a - 6b)^2 + (0 - 6c)^2} = \sqrt{(3a - 6b)^2 + (-6c)^2} = \sqrt{(3(a - 2b))^2 + (3(-2c))^2} = \sqrt{9(a - 2b)^2 + 9\left(4c^2\right)} = \sqrt{9\left((a - 2b)^2 + 4c^2\right)} = 3\sqrt{(a - 2b)^2 + 4c^2}$$

$$BP = \sqrt{((2b + 2a) - 6b)^2 + (2c - 6c)^2} = \sqrt{(2a - 4b)^2 + (-4c)^2} = \sqrt{(2(a - 2b))^2 + (2(-2c))^2} = \sqrt{4(a - 2b)^2 + 4\left(4c^2\right)} = \sqrt{4\left((a - 2b)^2 + 4c^2\right)} = 2\sqrt{(a - 2b)^2 + 4c^2}$$

$$CQ = \sqrt{(6a - 3b)^2 + (0 - 3c)^2} = \sqrt{(3(2a - b))^2 + (-3c)^2} = \sqrt{9\left((2a - b)^2 + c^2\right)} = 3\sqrt{(2a - b)^2 + c^2}$$

$$CP = \sqrt{(6a - (2b + 2a))^2 + (0 - 2c)^2} = \sqrt{(4a - 2b)^2 + (-2c)^2} = \sqrt{(2(2a - b))^2 + 4c^2} = \sqrt{4\left((2a - b)^2 + c^2\right)} = 2\sqrt{(2a - b)^2 + c^2}$$

STEP 5 **Multiply** OM, BN, and CQ by $\frac{2}{3}$.

$$\frac{2}{3}OM = \frac{2}{3}\left(3\sqrt{(b + a)^2 + c^2}\right) = 2\sqrt{(b + a)^2 + c^2}$$

$$\frac{2}{3}BN = \frac{2}{3}\left(3\sqrt{(a - 2b)^2 + 4c^2}\right) = 2\sqrt{(a - 2b)^2 + 4c^2}$$

$$\frac{2}{3}CQ = \frac{2}{3}\left(3\sqrt{(2a - b)^2 + c^2}\right) = 2\sqrt{(2a - b)^2 + c^2}$$

Thus, $OP = \frac{2}{3}OM$, $BP = \frac{2}{3}BN$, and $CP = \frac{2}{3}CQ$.

ADDITIONAL PROOFS

Proof of Theorem 5.9
Concurrency of Altitudes of a Triangle

THEOREM 5.9
PAGE 320
The lines containing the altitudes of a triangle are concurrent.

GIVEN ▶ $\triangle OGH$

PROVE ▶ The altitudes to the sides of $\triangle OGH$ all intersect at J.

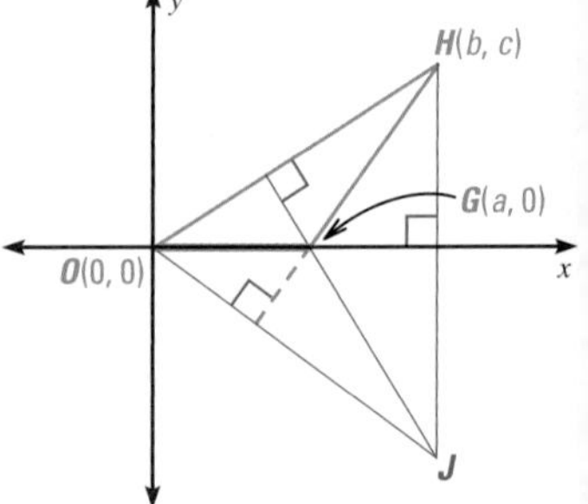

Plan for Proof Find the equations of the lines containing the altitudes of $\triangle OGH$. Find the intersection point of two of these lines. Show that the intersection point is also on the line containing the third altitude.

STEP 1 **Find** the slopes of the lines containing the sides $\overline{OH}$, $\overline{GH}$, and $\overline{OG}$.

Slope of $\overleftrightarrow{OH} = \frac{c}{b}$ Slope of $\overleftrightarrow{GH} = \frac{c}{b-a}$ Slope of $\overleftrightarrow{OG} = 0$

WRITE PROOFS
Choose a general triangle, with one vertex at the origin and one side along an axis. In the proof shown, the triangle is obtuse.

STEP 2 **Use** the *Slopes of Perpendicular Lines Postulate* to find the slopes of the lines containing the altitudes.

Slope of line containing altitude to $\overline{OH} = \frac{-b}{c}$

Slope of line containing altitude to $\overline{GH} = \frac{-(b-a)}{c} = \frac{a-b}{c}$

The line containing the altitude to $\overline{OG}$ has an undefined slope.

STEP 3 **Use** the *point-slope form of an equation of a line* to write equations for the lines containing the altitudes.

An equation of the line containing the altitude to $\overline{OH}$ is

$$y - 0 = \frac{-b}{c}(x - a), \text{ or } y = \frac{-b}{c}x + \frac{ab}{c}.$$

An equation of the line containing the altitude to $\overline{GH}$ is

$$y - 0 = \frac{a-b}{c}(x - 0), \text{ or } y = \frac{a-b}{c}x.$$

An equation of the vertical line containing the altitude to $\overline{OG}$ is $x = b$.

STEP 4 **Find** the coordinates of the point J where the lines containing two of the altitudes intersect. Using substitution, set the values of y in two of the above equations equal to each other, then solve for x:

$$\frac{-b}{c}x + \frac{ab}{c} = \frac{a-b}{c}x$$

$$\frac{ab}{c} = \frac{a-b}{c}x + \frac{b}{c}x$$

$$\frac{ab}{c} = \frac{a}{c}x$$

$$x = b$$

Next, substitute to find y: $y = \frac{-b}{c}x + \frac{ab}{c} = \frac{-b}{c}(b) + \frac{ab}{c} = \frac{ab - b^2}{c}$.

So, the coordinates of J are $\left(b, \frac{ab - b^2}{c}\right)$.

STEP 5 **Show** that J is on the line that contains the altitude to side $\overline{OG}$. J is on the vertical line with equation $x = b$ because its x-coordinate is b. Thus, the lines containing the altitudes of $\triangle OGH$ are concurrent.

ADDITIONAL PROOFS

Proof of Theorem 8.17
Midsegment Theorem for Trapezoids

THEOREM 8.17
PAGE 544
The midsegment of a trapezoid is parallel to each base and its length is one half the sum of the lengths of the bases.

GIVEN ▶ Trapezoid $ABCD$ with midsegment $\overline{MN}$

PROVE ▶ $\overline{MN} \parallel \overline{AB}$, $\overline{MN} \parallel \overline{DC}$,

$MN = \frac{1}{2}(AB + DC)$

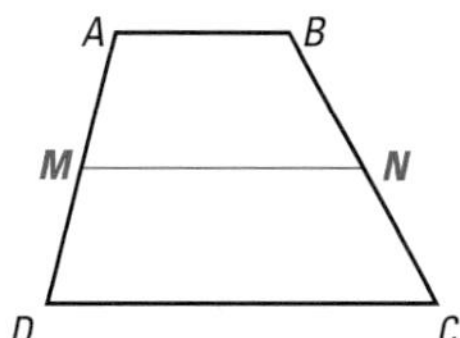

Plan for Proof Draw $\overline{AN}$, then extend $\overline{AN}$ and $\overline{DC}$ so that they intersect at point G. Then prove that $\triangle ANB \cong \triangle GNC$, and use the fact that $\overline{MN}$ is a midsegment of $\triangle ADG$ to prove that $MN = \frac{1}{2}(AB + DC)$.

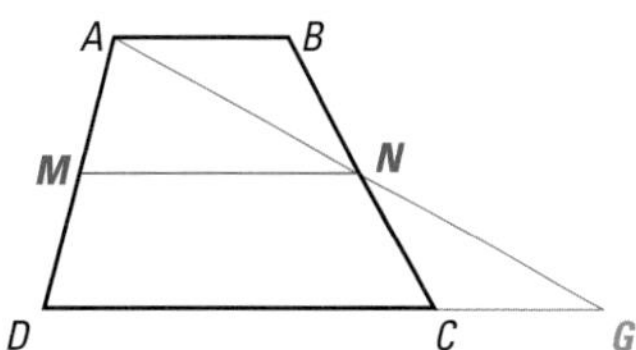

STATEMENTS	REASONS
1. $ABCD$ is a trapezoid with midsegment $\overline{MN}$.	**1.** Given
2. Draw $\overline{AN}$, then extend $\overline{AN}$ and $\overline{DC}$ so that they intersect at point G.	**2.** Through any two points there is exactly one line.
3. N is the midpoint of $\overline{BC}$.	**3.** Definition of midsegment of a trapezoid
4. $\overline{BN} \cong \overline{NC}$	**4.** Definition of midpoint
5. $\overline{AB} \parallel \overline{DC}$	**5.** Definition of trapezoid
6. $\angle ABN \cong \angle GCN$	**6.** Alternate Interior ∠s Theorem
7. $\angle ANB \cong \angle GNC$	**7.** Vertical angles are congruent.
8. $\triangle ANB \cong \triangle GNC$	**8.** ASA Congruence Postulate
9. $\overline{AN} \cong \overline{GN}$	**9.** Corresp. parts of ≅ △s are ≅.
10. N is the midpoint of $\overline{AG}$.	**10.** Definition of midpoint
11. $\overline{MN}$ is a midsegment of $\triangle AGD$.	**11.** Definition of midsegment of a △
12. $\overline{MN} \parallel \overline{DG}$ (so $\overline{MN} \parallel \overline{DC}$)	**12.** Midsegment of a △ Theorem
13. $\overline{MN} \parallel \overline{AB}$	**13.** Two lines ∥ to the same line are ∥.
14. $MN = \frac{1}{2}DG$	**14.** Midsegment of a △ Theorem
15. $DG = DC + CG$	**15.** Segment Addition Postulate
16. $\overline{CG} \cong \overline{AB}$	**16.** Corresp. parts of ≅ △s are ≅.
17. $CG = AB$	**17.** Definition of congruent segments
18. $DG = DC + AB$	**18.** Substitution Property of Equality
19. $MN = \frac{1}{2}(DC + AB)$	**19.** Substitution Property of Equality

ADDITIONAL PROOFS

Proof of Theorem 10.10
A Theorem about Inscribed Quadrilaterals

THEOREM 10.10 PAGE 675
A quadrilateral can be inscribed in a circle if and only if its opposite angles are supplementary.

STEP 1 **Prove** that if a quadrilateral is inscribed in a circle, then its opposite angles are supplementary.

GIVEN ▶ *DEFG* is inscribed in $\odot C$.

PROVE ▶ $\angle D$ and $\angle F$ are supplementary, $\angle E$ and $\angle G$ are supplementary.

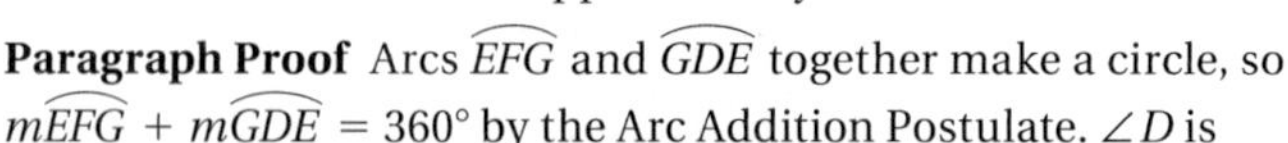

Paragraph Proof Arcs $\overset{\frown}{EFG}$ and $\overset{\frown}{GDE}$ together make a circle, so $m\overset{\frown}{EFG} + m\overset{\frown}{GDE} = 360°$ by the Arc Addition Postulate. $\angle D$ is inscribed in $\overset{\frown}{EFG}$ and $\angle F$ is inscribed in $\overset{\frown}{GDE}$, so the angle measures are half the arc measures. Using the Substitution and Distributive Properties, the sum of the measures of the opposite angles is

$$m\angle D + m\angle F = \frac{1}{2}m\overset{\frown}{EFG} + \frac{1}{2}m\overset{\frown}{GDE} = \frac{1}{2}(m\overset{\frown}{EFG} + m\overset{\frown}{GDE}) = \frac{1}{2}(360°) = 180°.$$

So, $\angle D$ and $\angle F$ are supplementary by definition. Similarly, $\angle E$ and $\angle G$ are inscribed in $\overset{\frown}{FGD}$ and $\overset{\frown}{DEF}$ and $m\angle E + m\angle G = 180°$. Then $\angle E$ and $\angle G$ are supplementary by definition.

STEP 2 **Prove** that if the opposite angles of a quadrilateral are supplementary, then the quadrilateral can be inscribed in a circle.

GIVEN ▶ $\angle E$ and $\angle G$ are supplementary (or $\angle D$ and $\angle F$ are supplementary).

PROVE ▶ *DEFG* is inscribed in $\odot C$.

Plan for Proof Draw the circle that passes through *D*, *E*, and *F*. Use an *indirect proof* to show that the circle also passes through *G*. Begin by assuming that *G* does not lie on $\odot C$.

Case 1 *G lies inside* $\odot C$. Let *H* be the intersection of $\overrightarrow{DG}$ and $\odot C$. Then *DEFH* is inscribed in $\odot C$ and $\angle E$ is supplementary to $\angle DHF$ (by proof above). Then $\angle DGF \cong \angle DHF$ by the given information and the Congruent Supplements Theorem. This implies that $\overline{FG} \parallel \overline{FH}$, which is a contradiction.

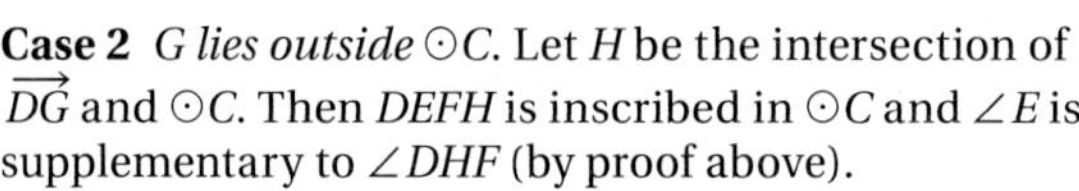

Case 2 *G lies outside* $\odot C$. Let *H* be the intersection of $\overrightarrow{DG}$ and $\odot C$. Then *DEFH* is inscribed in $\odot C$ and $\angle E$ is supplementary to $\angle DHF$ (by proof above). Then $\angle DGF \cong \angle DHF$ by the given information and the Congruent Supplements Theorem. This implies that $\overline{FG} \parallel \overline{FH}$, which is a contradiction.

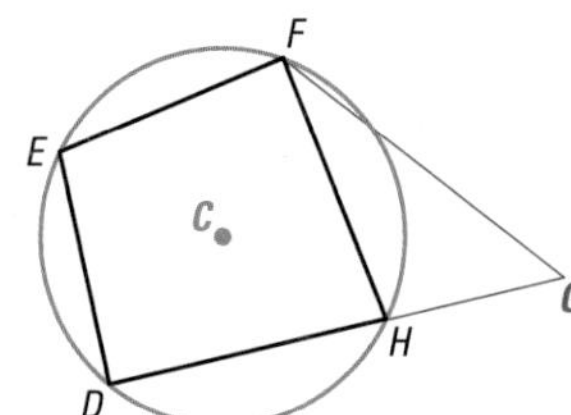

Because the original assumption leads to a contradiction in both cases, *G* lies on $\odot C$ and *DEFG* is inscribed in $\odot C$.

ADDITIONAL PROOFS

English–Spanish Glossary

A

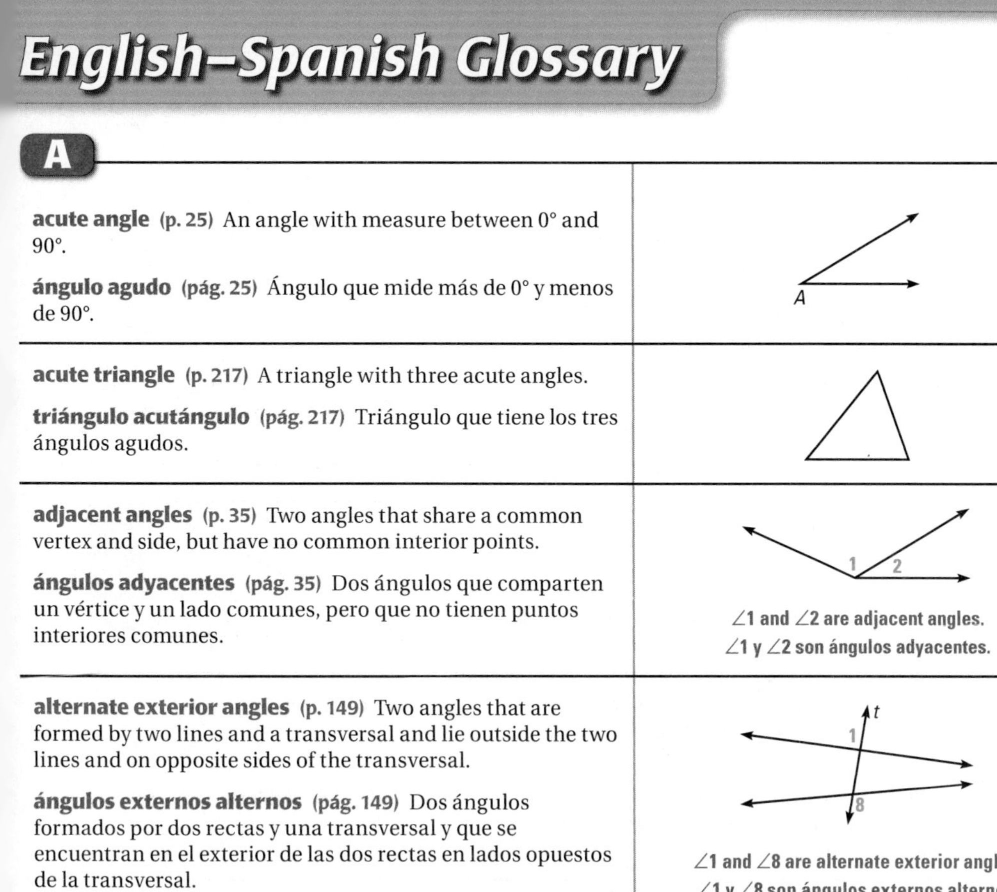

acute angle (p. 25) An angle with measure between 0° and 90°.

ángulo agudo (pág. 25) Ángulo que mide más de 0° y menos de 90°.

acute triangle (p. 217) A triangle with three acute angles.

triángulo acutángulo (pág. 217) Triángulo que tiene los tres ángulos agudos.

adjacent angles (p. 35) Two angles that share a common vertex and side, but have no common interior points.

ángulos adyacentes (pág. 35) Dos ángulos que comparten un vértice y un lado comunes, pero que no tienen puntos interiores comunes.

$\angle 1$ and $\angle 2$ are adjacent angles.
$\angle 1$ y $\angle 2$ son ángulos adyacentes.

alternate exterior angles (p. 149) Two angles that are formed by two lines and a transversal and lie outside the two lines and on opposite sides of the transversal.

ángulos externos alternos (pág. 149) Dos ángulos formados por dos rectas y una transversal y que se encuentran en el exterior de las dos rectas en lados opuestos de la transversal.

$\angle 1$ and $\angle 8$ are alternate exterior angles.
$\angle 1$ y $\angle 8$ son ángulos externos alternos.

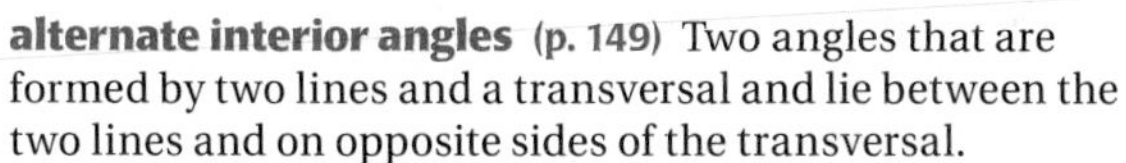

alternate interior angles (p. 149) Two angles that are formed by two lines and a transversal and lie between the two lines and on opposite sides of the transversal.

ángulos internos alternos (pág. 149) Dos ángulos formados por dos rectas y una transversal y que se encuentran entre las dos rectas en lados opuestos de la transversal.

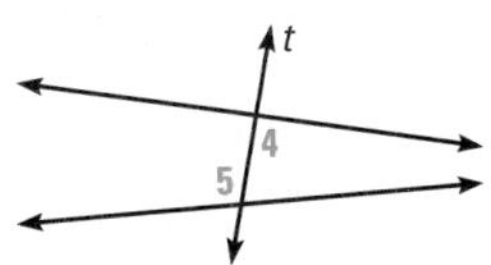

$\angle 4$ and $\angle 5$ are alternate interior angles.
$\angle 4$ y $\angle 5$ son ángulos internos alternos.

altitude of a triangle (p. 320) The perpendicular segment from one vertex of the triangle to the opposite side or to the line that contains the opposite side.

altura de un triángulo (pág. 320) El segmento perpendicular que va desde uno de los vértices del triángulo hasta el lado opuesto o hasta la recta que contiene el lado opuesto.

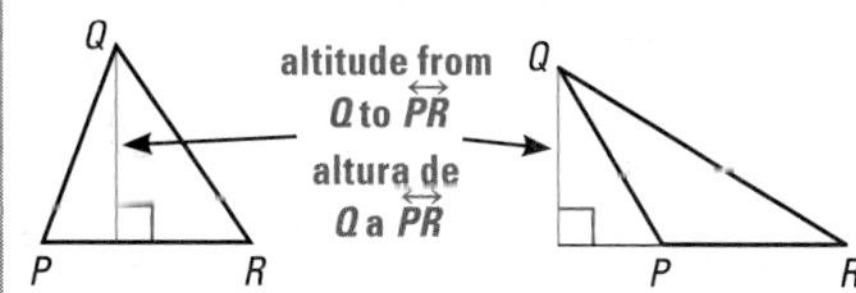

ENGLISH-SPANISH GLOSSARY

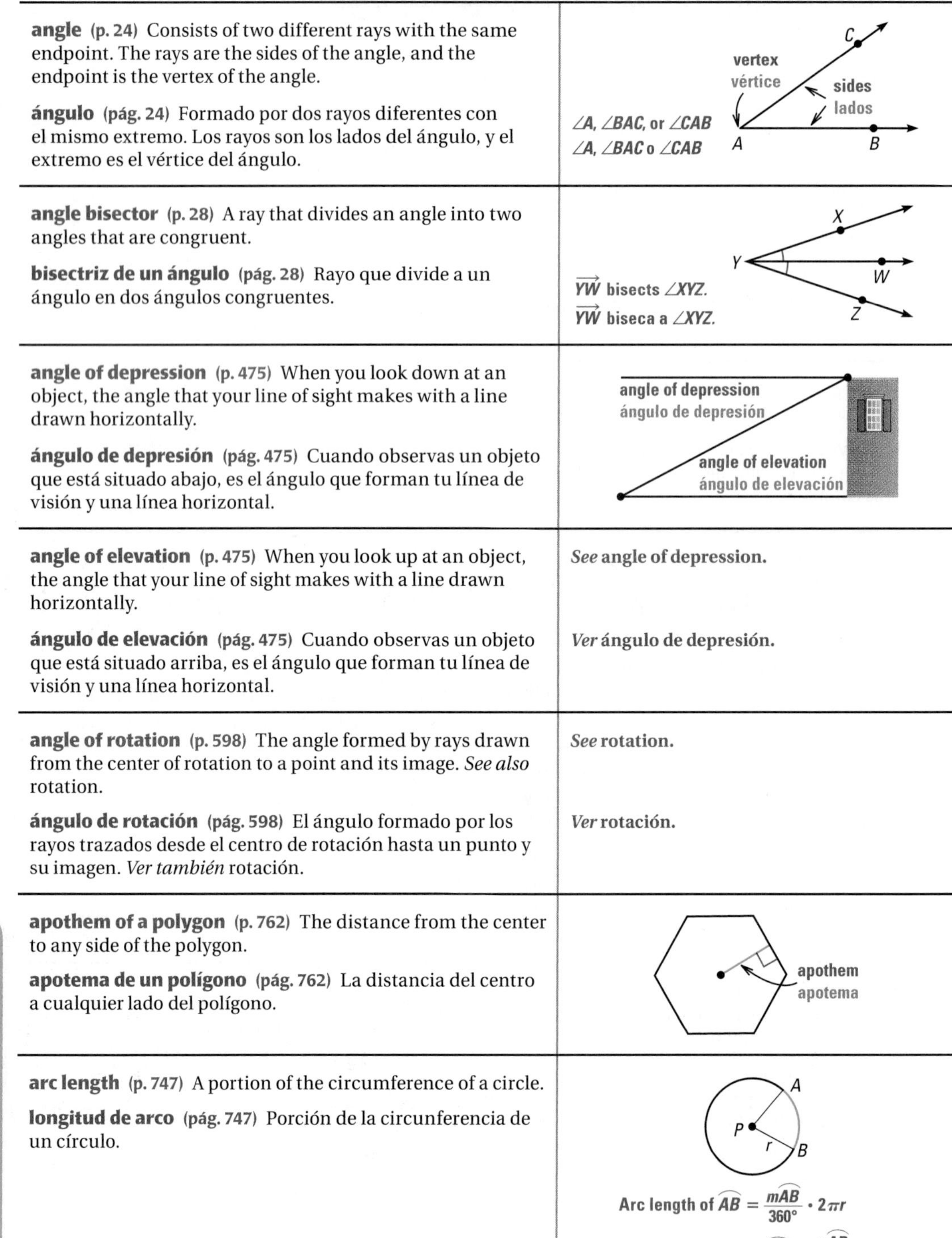

angle (p. 24) Consists of two different rays with the same endpoint. The rays are the sides of the angle, and the endpoint is the vertex of the angle.

ángulo (pág. 24) Formado por dos rayos diferentes con el mismo extremo. Los rayos son los lados del ángulo, y el extremo es el vértice del ángulo.

angle bisector (p. 28) A ray that divides an angle into two angles that are congruent.

bisectriz de un ángulo (pág. 28) Rayo que divide a un ángulo en dos ángulos congruentes.

angle of depression (p. 475) When you look down at an object, the angle that your line of sight makes with a line drawn horizontally.

ángulo de depresión (pág. 475) Cuando observas un objeto que está situado abajo, es el ángulo que forman tu línea de visión y una línea horizontal.

angle of elevation (p. 475) When you look up at an object, the angle that your line of sight makes with a line drawn horizontally.

See **angle of depression.**

ángulo de elevación (pág. 475) Cuando observas un objeto que está situado arriba, es el ángulo que forman tu línea de visión y una línea horizontal.

Ver **ángulo de depresión.**

angle of rotation (p. 598) The angle formed by rays drawn from the center of rotation to a point and its image. *See also* rotation.

See **rotation.**

ángulo de rotación (pág. 598) El ángulo formado por los rayos trazados desde el centro de rotación hasta un punto y su imagen. *Ver también* rotación.

Ver **rotación.**

apothem of a polygon (p. 762) The distance from the center to any side of the polygon.

apotema de un polígono (pág. 762) La distancia del centro a cualquier lado del polígono.

arc length (p. 747) A portion of the circumference of a circle.

longitud de arco (pág. 747) Porción de la circunferencia de un círculo.

ENGLISH-SPANISH GLOSSARY

axiom (p. 9) *See* postulate. **axioma** (pág. 9) *Ver* postulado.	*See* postulate. *Ver* postulado.

B

base angles of a trapezoid (p. 542) Either pair of angles whose common side is a base of a trapezoid. **ángulos básicos de un trapecio** (pág. 542) Cualquier par de ángulos cuyo lado común es una base del trapecio.	B C A D $\angle A$ and $\angle D$ are a pair of base angles. $\angle B$ and $\angle C$ are another pair. $\angle A$ y $\angle D$ son un par de ángulos básicos. $\angle B$ y $\angle C$ son otro par.
base angles of an isosceles triangle (p. 264) The two angles that are adjacent to the base of an isosceles triangle. **ángulos básicos de un triángulo isósceles** (pág. 264) Los dos ángulos adyacentes a la base de un triángulo isósceles.	*See* vertex angle of an isosceles triangle. *Ver* ángulo del vértice de un triángulo isósceles.
base of a parallelogram (p. 720) Either pair of parallel sides of a parallelogram. **base de un paralelogramo** (pág. 720) Uno de los pares de lados paralelos de un paralelogramo.	base base base base
base of a prism (p. 794) *See* prism. **base de un prisma** (pág. 794) *Ver* prisma.	*See* prism. *Ver* prisma.
base of a pyramid (p. 794) *See* pyramid. **base de una pirámide** (pág. 794) *Ver* pirámide.	*See* pyramid. *Ver* pirámide.
base of an isosceles triangle (p. 264) The noncongruent side of an isosceles triangle that has only two congruent sides. **base de un triángulo isósceles** (pág. 264) El lado no congruente de un triángulo isósceles que tiene sólo dos lados congruentes.	*See* isosceles triangle. *Ver* triángulo isósceles.
bases of a trapezoid (p. 542) The parallel sides of a trapezoid. **bases de un trapecio** (pág. 542) Los lados paralelos de un trapecio.	*See* trapezoid. *Ver* trapecio.

ENGLISH-SPANISH GLOSSARY

941

between (p. 10) When three points lie on a line, you can say that one point is *between* the other two. **entre** (pág. 10) Cuando tres puntos están en una recta, se puede decir que un punto está *entre* los otros dos.	A B C **Point *B* is between points *A* and *C*.** **El punto *B* está entre los puntos *A* y *C*.**
biconditional statement (p. 82) A statement that contains the phrase "if and only if." **enunciado bicondicional** (pág. 82) Enunciado que contiene la frase "si y sólo si".	**Two lines are perpendicular if and only if they intersect to form a right angle.** **Dos rectas son perpendiculares si y sólo si se cortan para formar un ángulo recto.**

C

center of a circle (p. 651) *See* circle. **centro de un círculo** (pág. 651) *Ver* círculo.	***See* circle.** ***Ver* círculo.**
center of a polygon (p. 762) The center of a polygon's circumscribed circle. **centro de un polígono** (pág. 762) El centro del círculo circunscrito de un polígono.	P center centro N
center of a sphere (p. 838) *See* sphere. **centro de una esfera** (pág. 838) *Ver* esfera.	***See* sphere.** ***Ver* esfera.**
center of dilation (p. 409) In a dilation, the fixed point about which the figure is enlarged or reduced. **centro de dilatación** (pág. 409) En una dilatación, el punto fijo en torno al cual la figura se amplía o se reduce.	***See* dilation.** ***Ver* dilatación.**
center of rotation (p. 598) *See* rotation. **centro de rotación** (pág. 598) *Ver* rotación.	***See* rotation.** ***Ver* rotación.**
center of symmetry (p. 620) *See* rotational symmetry. **centro de simetría** (pág. 620) *Ver* simetría rotacional.	***See* rotational symmetry.** ***Ver* simetría rotacional.**
central angle of a circle (p. 659) An angle whose vertex is the center of the circle. **ángulo central de un círculo** (pág. 659) Ángulo cuyo vértice es el centro del círculo.	P C Q **$\angle PCQ$ is a central angle of $\odot C$.** **$\angle PCQ$ es un ángulo central de $\odot C$.**

central angle of a regular polygon (p. 762) An angle formed by two radii drawn to consecutive vertices of the polygon.

ángulo central de un polígono regular (pág. 762) Ángulo formado por dos radios trazados hasta los vértices consecutivos del polígono.

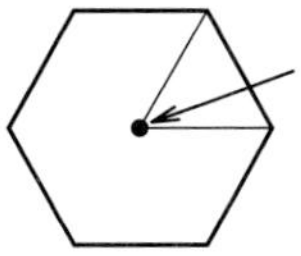

central angle
ángulo central

centroid of a triangle (p. 319) The point of concurrency of the three medians of the triangle.

baricentro de un triángulo (pág. 319) El punto de concurrencia de las tres medianas del triángulo.

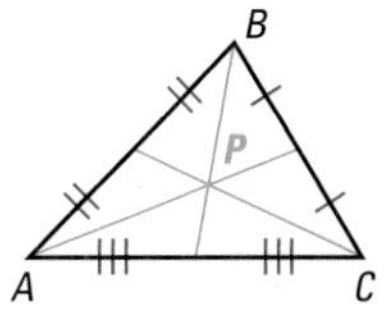

P is the centroid of $\triangle ABC$.
P es el baricentro de $\triangle ABC$.

chord of a circle (p. 651) A segment whose endpoints are on a circle.

cuerda de un círculo (pág. 651) Segmento cuyos extremos están en un círculo.

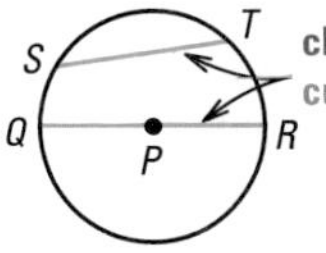

chords
cuerdas

chord of a sphere (p. 838) A segment whose endpoints are on a sphere.

cuerda de una esfera (pág. 838) Segmento cuyos extremos están en una esfera.

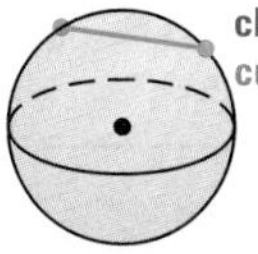

chord
cuerda

circle (p. 651) The set of all points in a plane that are equidistant from a given point called the center of the circle.

círculo (pág. 651) El conjunto de todos los puntos de un plano que son equidistantes de un punto dado, llamado centro del círculo.

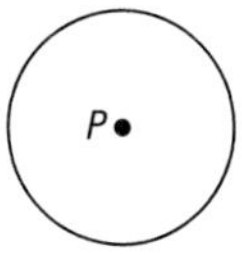

Circle with center *P*, or $\odot P$
Círculo con centro *P*, o $\odot P$

circumcenter of a triangle (p. 306) The point of concurrency of the three perpendicular bisectors of the triangle.

circuncentro de un triángulo (pág. 306) El punto de concurrencia de las tres mediatrices del triángulo.

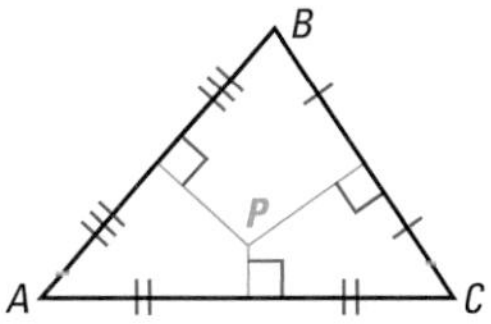

P is the circumcenter of $\triangle ABC$.
P es el circuncentro de $\triangle ABC$.

943

circumference (p. 746) The distance around a circle. **circunferencia** (pág. 746) La distancia por el contorno de un círculo.	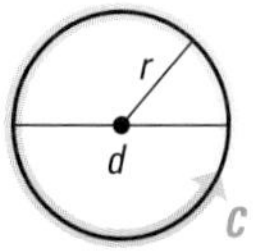 r d C
circumscribed circle (p. 674) The circle that contains the vertices of an inscribed polygon. **círculo circunscrito** (pág. 674) El círculo que contiene los vértices de un polígono inscrito.	circumscribed circles círculos circunscritos
collinear points (p. 2) Points that lie on the same line. **puntos colineales** (pág. 2) Puntos situados sobre la misma recta.	 A B C *A*, *B*, and *C* are collinear. *A*, *B* y *C* son colineales.
complementary angles (p. 35) Two angles whose measures have the sum 90°. The sum of the measures of an angle and its *complement* is 90°. **ángulos complementarios** (pág. 35) Dos ángulos cuyas medidas suman 90°. La suma de las medidas de un ángulo y de su *complemento* es 90°.	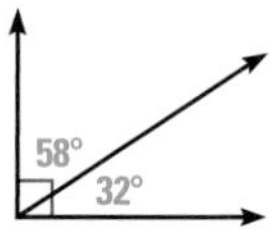 58° 32°
component form of a vector (p. 574) The form of a vector that combines the horizontal and vertical components of the vector. **forma de componentes de un vector** (pág. 574) La forma de un vector que combina los componentes horizontal y vertical del vector.	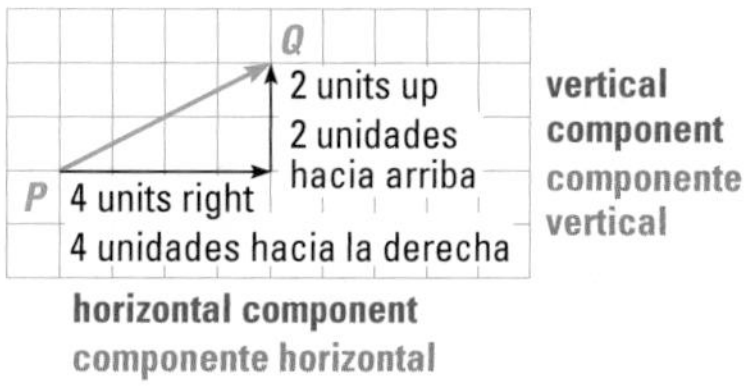 Q 2 units up 2 unidades hacia arriba vertical component componente vertical P 4 units right 4 unidades hacia la derecha horizontal component componente horizontal The component form of $\overrightarrow{PQ}$ is $\langle 4, 2\rangle$. La forma de componentes de $\overrightarrow{PQ}$ es $\langle 4, 2\rangle$.
composition of transformations (p. 609) The result when two or more transformations are combined to produce a single transformation. **composición de transformaciones** (pág. 609) El resultado de combinar dos o más transformaciones para producir una sola transformación.	A glide reflection is an example of a composition of transformations. La reflexión con desplazamiento y traslación es un ejemplo de composición de transformaciones.
concave polygon (p. 42) A polygon that is not convex. *See also* convex polygon. **polígono cóncavo** (pág. 42) Polígono que no es convexo. *Ver también* polígono convexo.	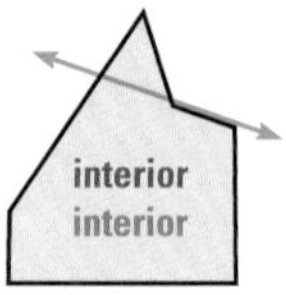 interior interior

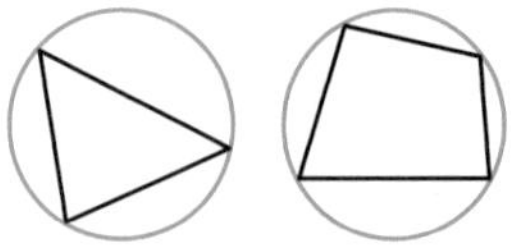

ENGLISH-SPANISH GLOSSARY

conclusion (p. 79) The "then" part of a conditional statement. **conclusión** (pág. 79) La parte de "entonces" de un enunciado condicional.	*See* conditional statement. *Ver* enunciado condicional.
concurrent (p. 305) Three or more lines, rays, or segments that intersect in the same point. **concurrentes** (pág. 305) Tres o más rectas, rayos o segmentos que se cortan en el mismo punto.	*See* point of concurrency. *Ver* punto de concurrencia.
conditional statement (p. 79) A type of logical statement that has two parts, a hypothesis and a conclusion. **enunciado condicional** (pág. 79) Tipo de enunciado lógico que tiene dos partes, una hipótesis y una conclusión.	conditional statement If $m\angle A = 90°$, then $\angle A$ is a right angle. Hypothesis — Conclusion enunciado condicional Si $m\angle A = 90°$, entonces $\angle A$ es un ángulo recto. Hipótesis — Conclusión
cone (p. 812) A solid that has one circular base and a vertex that is not in the same plane as the base. **cono** (pág. 812) Sólido que tiene una base circular y cuyo vértice no está en el mismo plano que la base.	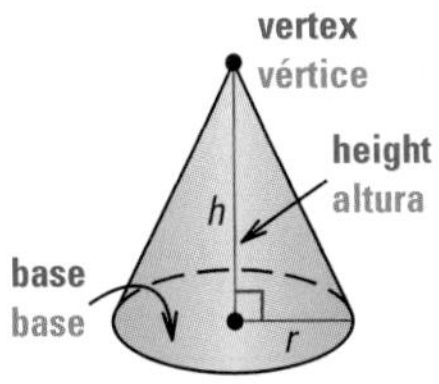 vertex / vértice height / altura base / base h, r
congruence transformation (p. 272) A transformation that preserves length and angle measure. Also called *isometry.* **transformación de congruencia** (pág. 272) Transformación que conserva la longitud y la medida de los ángulos. También se llama *isometría.*	Translations, reflections, and rotations are three types of congruence transformations. Las traslaciones, las reflexiones y las rotaciones son tres tipos de transformaciones de congruencia.
congruent angles (p. 26) Angles that have the same measure. **ángulos congruentes** (pág. 26) Ángulos que tienen la misma medida.	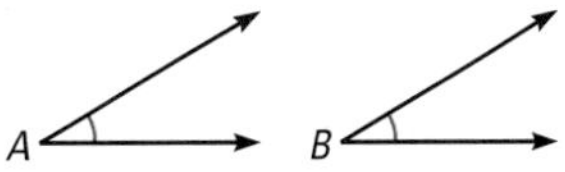 A, B $\angle A \cong \angle B$
congruent arcs (p. 660) Two arcs that have the same measure and are arcs of the same circle or of congruent circles. **arcos congruentes** (pág. 660) Dos arcos que tienen la misma medida y son arcos del mismo círculo o de círculos congruentes.	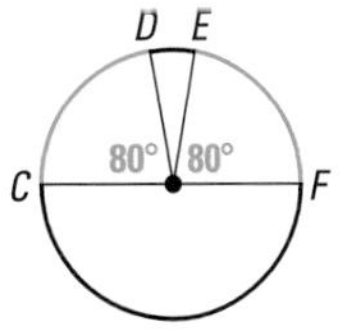 D, E, C, F, 80°, 80° $\overset{\frown}{CD} \cong \overset{\frown}{EF}$

ENGLISH-SPANISH GLOSSARY

congruent circles (p. 660) Two circles that have the same radius. **círculos congruentes** (pág. 660) Dos círculos que tienen el mismo radio.	P 4 m, Q 4 m $\odot P \cong \odot Q$
congruent figures (p. 225) Two geometric figures that have exactly the same size and shape. When two figures are congruent, all pairs of corresponding sides and corresponding angles are congruent. **figuras congruentes** (pág. 225) Dos figuras geométricas de igual tamaño y forma. Cuando dos figuras son congruentes, todos los pares de lados correspondientes y de ángulos correspondientes son congruentes.	$\triangle ABC \cong \triangle FED$ $\angle A \cong \angle F$, $\angle B \cong \angle E$, $\angle C \cong \angle D$ $\overline{AB} \cong \overline{FE}$, $\overline{BC} \cong \overline{ED}$, $\overline{AC} \cong \overline{FD}$
congruent segments (p. 11) Line segments that have the same length. **segmentos congruentes** (pág. 11) Segmentos de recta que tienen la misma longitud.	A B C D $\overline{AB} \cong \overline{CD}$
conjecture (p. 73) An unproven statement that is based on observations. **conjetura** (pág. 73) Enunciado sin demostrar que se basa en observaciones.	Conjecture: All prime numbers are odd. Conjetura: Todos los números primos son impares.
consecutive interior angles (p. 149) Two angles that are formed by two lines and a transversal and lie between the two lines and on the same side of the transversal. Also called *same-side interior angles.* **ángulos internos consecutivos** (pág. 149 Dos ángulos formados por dos rectas y una transversal y que se encuentran entre las dos rectas en el mismo lado de la transversal. También se llaman *ángulos internos colaterales.*	t 3 5 $\angle 3$ and $\angle 5$ are consecutive interior angles. $\angle 3$ y $\angle 5$ son ángulos internos consecutivos.
construction (p. 33) A geometric drawing that uses a limited set of tools, usually a compass and straightedge. **construcción** (pág. 33) Dibujo geométrico que requiere una serie limitada de instrumentos, que por lo general son un compás y una regla.	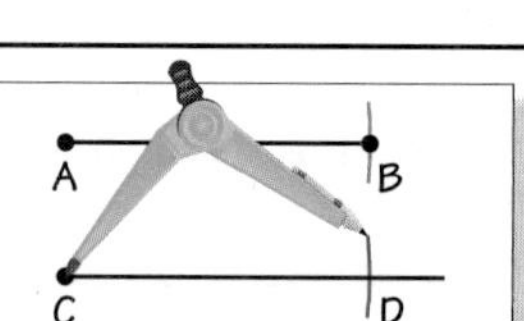

ENGLISH-SPANISH GLOSSARY

contrapositive (p. 80) The equivalent statement formed by negating the hypothesis and conclusion of the converse of a conditional statement.

contrapositivo (pág. 80) El enunciado equivalente formado al negar la hipótesis y la conclusión del recíproco de un enunciado condicional.

Statement: If $m\angle A = 90°$, then $\angle A$ is right.
Contrapositive: If $\angle A$ is not right, then $m\angle A \neq 90°$.

Enunciado: Si $m\angle A = 90°$, entonces $\angle A$ es recto.
Contrapositivo: Si $\angle A$ no es recto, entonces $m\angle A \neq 90°$.

---

converse (p. 80) The statement formed by exchanging the hypothesis and conclusion of a conditional statement.

recíproco (pág. 80) El enunciado formado al intercambiar la hipótesis y la conclusión de un enunciado condicional.

Statement: If $m\angle A = 90°$, then $\angle A$ is right.
Converse: If $\angle A$ is right, then $m\angle A = 90°$.

Enunciado: Si $m\angle A = 90°$, entonces $\angle A$ es recto.
Recíproco: Si $\angle A$ es recto, entonces $m\angle A = 90°$.

---

convex polygon (p. 42) A polygon such that no line containing a side of the polygon contains a point in the interior of the polygon. A polygon that is not convex is nonconvex or concave.

polígono convexo (pág. 42) Polígono tal que ninguna recta que contiene un lado del polígono contiene un punto del interior del polígono. Un polígono que no es convexo se conoce como no convexo o cóncavo.

interior
interior

---

convex polyhedron (p. 796) A polyhedron is convex if any two points on its surface can be connected by a segment that lies entirely inside or on the polyhedron. If this segment goes outside the polyhedron, then the polyhedron is nonconvex or concave.

poliedro convexo (pág. 796) Un poliedro es convexo si dos puntos cualesquiera de su superficie pueden unirse mediante un segmento situado totalmente sobre el poliedro o en su interior. Si el segmento se extiende al exterior del poliedro, entonces es un poliedro cóncavo o no convexo.

convex
convexo

concave
cóncavo

---

coordinate (p. 9) The real number that corresponds to a point on a line.

coordenada (pág. 9) El número real que corresponde a un punto de una recta.

A B
x_1 x_2
coordinates of points
coordenadas de puntos

---

coordinate proof (p. 296) A type of proof that involves placing geometric figures in a coordinate plane.

prueba de coordenadas (pág. 296) Tipo de prueba en la que se colocan figuras geométricas en un plano de coordenadas.

***See* Example 5 on page 297.**

***Ver* el ejemplo 5 de la página 297.**

ENGLISH-SPANISH GLOSSARY

947

coplanar points (p. 2) Points that lie in the same plane.

puntos coplanarios (pág. 2) Puntos situados sobre el mismo plano.

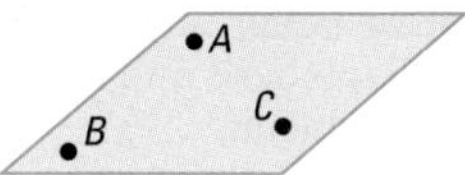

***A, B,* and *C* are coplanar.**
***A, B* y *C* son coplanarios.**

---

corollary to a theorem (p. 220) A statement that can be proved easily using the theorem.

corolario de un teorema (pág. 220) Enunciado que puede demostrarse fácilmente usando el teorema.

The Corollary to the Triangle Sum Theorem states that the acute angles of a right triangle are complementary.

El corolario del teorema de la suma de los ángulos del triángulo establece que los ángulos agudos de un triángulo rectángulo son complementarios.

---

corresponding angles (p. 149) Two angles that are formed by two lines and a transversal and occupy corresponding positions.

ángulos correspondientes (pág. 149) Dos ángulos formados por dos rectas y una transversal y que ocupan posiciones correspondientes.

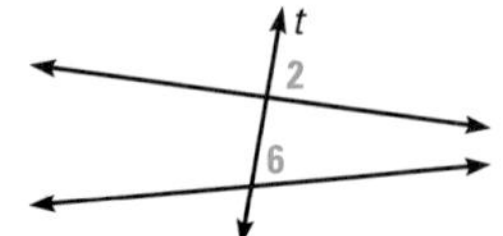

$\angle 2$ and $\angle 6$ are corresponding angles.
$\angle 2$ y $\angle 6$ son ángulos correspondientes.

---

corresponding parts (p. 225) A pair of sides or angles that have the same relative position in two congruent or similar figures.

partes correspondientes (pág. 225) Un par de lados o ángulos que tienen la misma posición relativa en dos figuras congruentes o semejantes.

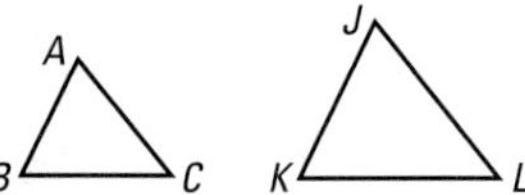

$\angle A$ and $\angle J$ are corresponding angles.
$\overline{AB}$ and $\overline{JK}$ are corresponding sides.

$\angle A$ y $\angle J$ son ángulos correspondientes.
$\overline{AB}$ y $\overline{JK}$ son lados correspondientes.

---

cosine (p. 473) A trigonometric ratio, abbreviated as *cos*. For a right triangle *ABC*, the cosine of the acute angle *A* is $\cos A = \frac{\text{length of leg adjacent to } \angle A}{\text{length of hypotenuse}} = \frac{AC}{AB}$.

coseno (pág. 473) Razón trigonométrica, abreviada *cos*. Para un triángulo rectángulo *ABC*, el coseno del ángulo agudo *A* es $\cos A = \frac{\text{longitud del cateto adyacente a } \angle A}{\text{longitud de la hipotenusa}} = \frac{AC}{AB}$.

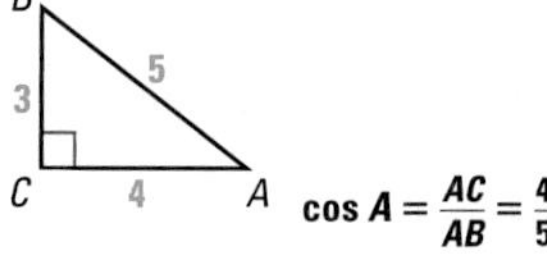

$\cos A = \frac{AC}{AB} = \frac{4}{5}$

948

counterexample (p. 74) A specific case that shows a conjecture is false.

contraejemplo (pág. 74) Caso específico que muestra la falsedad de una conjetura.

Conjecture: All prime numbers are odd.
Counterexample: 2, a prime number that is not odd

Conjetura: Todos los números primos son impares.
Contraejemplo: 2, un número primo que no es impar

cross section (p. 797) The intersection of a plane and a solid.

sección transversal (pág. 797) La intersección de un plano y un sólido.

cube (p. 796) A polyhedron with six congruent square faces.

cubo (pág. 796) Poliedro con seis caras cuadradas congruentes.

cylinder (p. 805) A solid with congruent circular bases that lie in parallel planes.

cilindro (pág. 805) Sólido con bases circulares congruentes que se encuentran en planos paralelos.

D

decagon (p. 43) A polygon with ten sides.

decágono (pág. 43) Polígono con diez lados.

deductive reasoning (p. 87) A process that uses facts, definitions, accepted properties, and the laws of logic to form a logical argument.

razonamiento deductivo (pág. 87) Proceso que usa datos, definiciones, propiedades aceptadas y las leyes de la lógica para formar un argumento lógico.

You use deductive reasoning in writing geometric proofs.

Puedes usar el razonamiento deductivo para escribir pruebas geométricas.

defined terms (p. 3) Terms that can be described using known words.

términos definidos (pág. 3) Términos que pueden describirse con palabras conocidas.

Line segment and *ray* are two defined terms.

Segmento de recta y *rayo* son dos términos definidos.

diagonal of a polygon (p. 507) A segment that joins two nonconsecutive vertices of a polygon. **diagonal de un polígono** (pág. 507) Segmento que une dos vértices no consecutivos de un polígono.	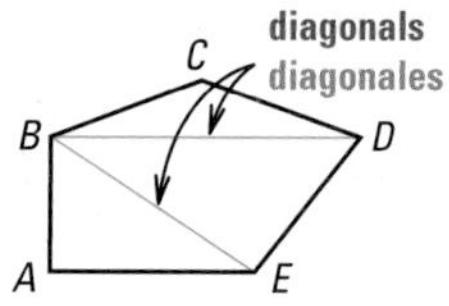
diameter of a circle (p. 651) A chord that passes through the center of a circle. The distance across a circle through its center. **diámetro de un círculo** (pág. 651) Cuerda que pasa por el centro de un círculo. La distancia de un punto a otro de un círculo pasando por el centro.	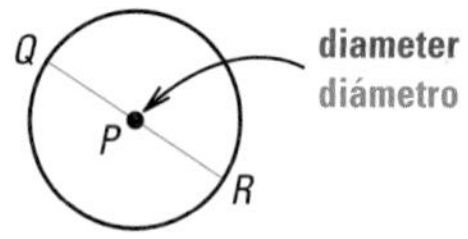
diameter of a sphere (p. 838) A chord that contains the center of a sphere. The distance across a sphere through its center. **diámetro de una esfera** (pág. 838) Cuerda que contiene el centro de una esfera. La distancia de un punto a otro de una esfera pasando por el centro.	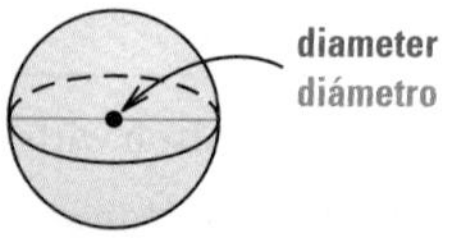
dilation (pp. 409, 626) A transformation that stretches or shrinks a figure to create a similar figure. **dilatación** (págs. 409, 626) Transformación que expande o contrae una figura para crear una figura semejante.	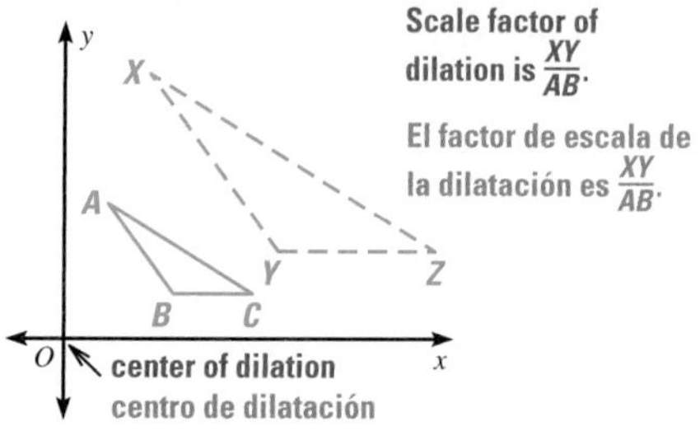
dimensions of a matrix (p. 580) The numbers of rows and columns in the matrix. If a matrix has m rows and n columns, the dimensions of the matrix are $m \times n$. **dimensiones de una matriz** (pág. 580) El número de filas y columnas que hay en una matriz. Si la matriz tiene m filas y n columnas, sus dimensiones son $m \times n$.	The dimensions of a matrix with 3 rows and 4 columns is 3×4 ("3 by 4"). Las dimensiones de una matriz con 3 filas y 4 columnas son 3×4 ("3 por 4").
distance between two points on a line (p. 9) The absolute value of the difference of the coordinates of the points. The distance between points A and B, written as AB, is also called the length of $\overline{AB}$. **distancia entre dos puntos de una recta** (pág. 9) El valor absoluto de la diferencia entre las coordenadas de los puntos. La distancia entre los puntos A y B, escrita AB, también se llama longitud de $\overline{AB}$.	

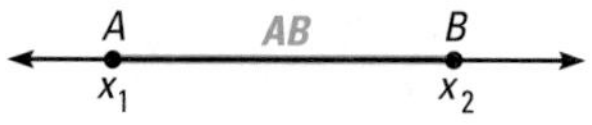

ENGLISH-SPANISH GLOSSARY

distance from a point to a line (p. 192) The length of the perpendicular segment from the point to the line.

distancia de un punto a una recta (pág. 192) La longitud del segmento perpendicular del punto a la recta.

Q
P m

The distance from Q to m is QP.
La distancia de Q a m es QP.

dodecagon (p. 43) A polygon with twelve sides.

dodecágono (pág. 43) Polígono con doce lados.

dodecahedron (p. 796) A polyhedron with twelve faces.

dodecaedro (pág. 796) Poliedro con doce caras.

E

edge of a polyhedron (p. 794) A line segment formed by the intersection of two faces of a polyhedron.

arista de un poliedro (pág. 794) Segmento de recta formado por la intersección de dos caras de un poliedro.

edge
arista

element of a matrix (p. 580) A number in a matrix. Also called *entry*.

elemento de una matriz (pág. 580) Número de una matriz. También se llama *entrada*.

See matrix.

Ver matriz.

endpoints (p. 3) *See* line segment.

extremos (pág. 3) *Ver* segmento de recta.

See line segment.

Ver segmento de recta.

enlargement (p. 409) A dilation with a scale factor greater than 1.

ampliación (pág. 409) Dilatación con un factor de escala mayor que 1.

A dilation with a scale factor of 2 is an enlargement.

Una dilatación con un factor de escala de 2 es una ampliación.

equiangular polygon (p. 43) A polygon with all of its interior angles congruent.

polígono equiángulo (pág. 43) Polígono que tiene todos los ángulos interiores congruentes.

equiangular triangle (p. 217) A triangle with three congruent angles. **triángulo equiángulo** (pág. 217) Triángulo que tiene los tres ángulos congruentes.	
equidistant (p. 303) The same distance from one figure as from another figure. **equidistante** (pág. 303) Situado a igual distancia de dos figuras.	X Y Z *X* is equidistant from *Y* and *Z*. *X* es equidistante de *Y* y *Z*.
equilateral polygon (p. 43) A polygon with all of its sides congruent. **polígono equilátero** (pág. 43) Polígono que tiene todos los lados congruentes.	
equilateral triangle (p. 217) A triangle with three congruent sides. **triángulo equilátero** (pág. 217) Triángulo que tiene los tres lados congruentes.	
equivalent statements (p. 80) Two statements that are both true or both false. **enunciados equivalentes** (pág. 80) Dos enunciados que son ambos verdaderos o ambos falsos.	A conditional statement and its contrapositive are equivalent statements. Un enunciado condicional y su contrapositivo son enunciados equivalentes.
exterior angles of a triangle (p. 218) When the sides of a triangle are extended, the angles that are adjacent to the interior angles. **ángulos exteriores de un triángulo** (pág. 218) Los ángulos adyacentes a los ángulos interiores al prolongar los lados del triángulo.	
external segment (p. 690) The part of a secant segment that is outside the circle. **segmento externo** (pág. 690) La parte de un segmento secante que está en el exterior del círculo.	external segment segmento externo
extremes of a proportion (p. 358) The first and last terms of a proportion. *See also* proportion. **extremos de una proporción** (pág. 358) Los términos primero y último de una proporción. *Ver también* proporción.	The extremes of $\frac{a}{b} = \frac{c}{d}$ are a and d. Los extremos de $\frac{a}{b} = \frac{c}{d}$ son a y d.

F

face of a polyhedron (p. 794) *See* polyhedron. **cara de un poliedro** (pág. 794) *Ver* poliedro.	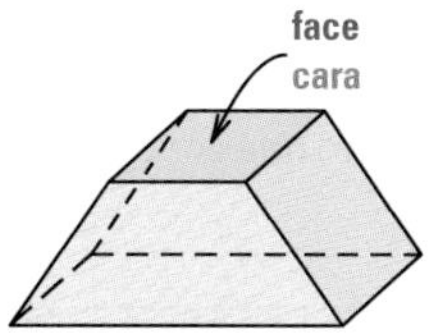 face cara
flow proof (p. 250) A type of proof that uses arrows to show the flow of a logical argument. **prueba de flujo** (pág. 250) Tipo de prueba que usa flechas para indicar el flujo de un argumento lógico.	*See* Example 2 on page 250. *Ver* el ejemplo 2 de la página 250.
fractal (p. 406) An object that is self-similar. *See* self-similar. **fractal** (pág. 406) Objeto autosemejante. *Ver* autosemejante.	

G

geometric mean (p. 359) For two positive numbers a and b, the positive number x that satisfies $\frac{a}{x} = \frac{x}{b}$. So, $x^2 = ab$ and $x = \sqrt{ab}$. **media geométrica** (pág. 359) Para dos números positivos a y b, el número positivo x que satisface $\frac{a}{x} = \frac{x}{b}$. Así pues, $x^2 = ab$ y $x = \sqrt{ab}$.	The geometric mean of 4 and 16 is $\sqrt{4 \cdot 16}$, or 8. La media geométrica de 4 y 16 es $\sqrt{4 \cdot 16}$, ó 8.
geometric probability (p. 771) A probability that involves a geometric measure such as length or area. **probabilidad geométrica** (pág. 771) Probabilidad relacionada con una medida geométrica, como la longitud o el área.	 A C D B $P(K \text{ is on } \overline{CD}) = \frac{\text{Length of } \overline{CD}}{\text{Length of } \overline{AB}}$ $P(K \text{ está en } \overline{CD}) = \frac{\text{Longitud de } \overline{CD}}{\text{Longitud de } \overline{AB}}$
glide reflection (p. 608) A transformation in which every point P is mapped to a point P'' by the following steps. (1) A translation maps P to P'. (2) A reflection in a line k parallel to the direction of the translation maps P' to P''. **reflexión con desplazamiento y traslación** (pág. 608) Transformación en la que cada punto P se hace corresponder con un punto P'' siguiendo estos pasos. (1) Al realizar una traslación, se hace corresponder P con P'. (2) Al realizar una reflexión sobre una recta k paralela a la dirección de la traslación, se hace corresponder P' con P''.	P' Q' Q'' P'' P Q k

ENGLISH-SPANISH GLOSSARY

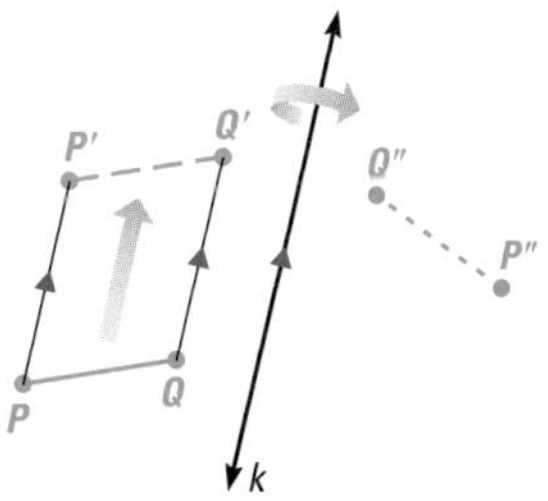

great circle (pp. 753, 839) The intersection of a sphere and a plane that contains the center of the sphere. **círculo máximo** (págs. 753, 839) La intersección de una esfera y un plano que contiene el centro de la esfera.	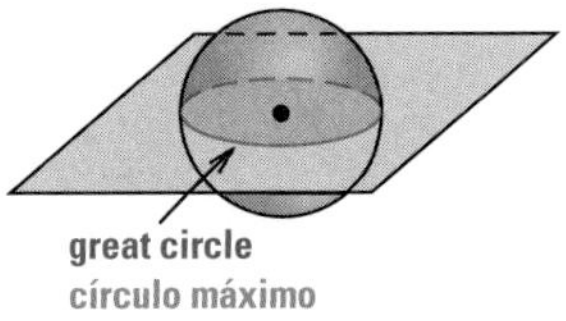
greatest possible error (p. 727) The maximum amount that a measured length can differ from an actual length. **máximo error posible** (pág. 727) La cantidad máxima que una longitud medida puede diferir de una longitud real.	If the unit of measure is $\frac{1}{8}$ inch, the greatest possible error is $\frac{1}{16}$ inch. Si la unidad de medida es $\frac{1}{8}$ pulgada, el máximo error posible es $\frac{1}{16}$ pulgada.

H

height of a parallelogram (p. 720) The perpendicular distance between the bases of a parallelogram. **altura de un paralelogramo** (pág. 720) La distancia perpendicular entre las bases de un paralelogramo.	
height of a trapezoid (p. 730) The perpendicular distance between the bases of a trapezoid. **altura de un trapecio** (pág. 730) La distancia perpendicular entre las bases de un trapecio.	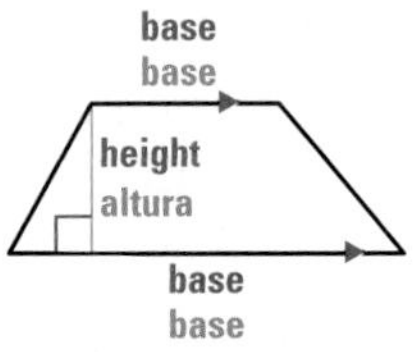
hemisphere (p. 839) Half of a sphere, formed when a great circle separates a sphere into two congruent halves. **hemisferio** (pág. 839) Media esfera, formada cuando un círculo máximo divide a una esfera en dos mitades congruentes.	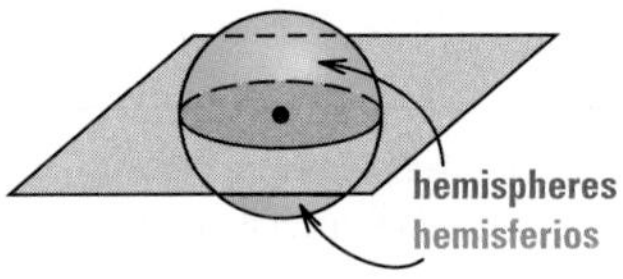
heptagon (p. 43) Polygon with seven sides. **heptágono** (pág. 43) Polígono con siete lados.	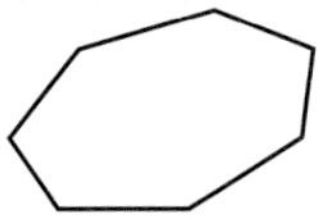
hexagon (p. 43) Polygon with six sides. **hexágono** (pág. 43) Polígono con seis lados.	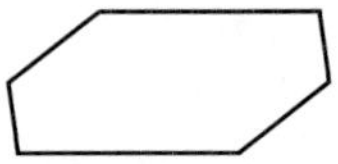
horizontal component of a vector (p. 574) The horizontal change from the initial point to the terminal point of a vector. **componente horizontal de un vector** (pág. 574) El cambio horizontal desde el punto inicial al punto final del vector.	*See* component form of a vector. *Ver* forma de componentes de un vector.

hypotenuse (p. 241) In a right triangle, the side opposite the right angle.

hipotenusa (pág. 241) En un triángulo rectángulo, el lado opuesto al ángulo recto.

hypotenuse
hipotenusa

hypothesis (p. 79) The "if" part of a conditional statement.

hipótesis (pág. 79) La parte de "si" de un enunciado condicional.

See **conditional statement.**

Ver **enunciado condicional.**

I

icosahedron (p. 796) A polyhedron with twenty faces.

icosaedro (pág. 796) Poliedro con veinte caras.

if-then form (p. 79) The form of a conditional statement that uses the words "if" and "then." The "if" part contains the hypothesis and the "then" part contains the conclusion.

forma de "si…, entonces…" (pág. 79) La forma de un enunciado condicional que usa las palabras "si" y "entonces". La parte de "si" contiene la hipótesis, y la parte de "entonces" contiene la conclusión.

See **conditional statement.**

Ver **enunciado condicional.**

image (pp. 272, 572) The new figure that is produced in a transformation. *See also* preimage.

imagen (págs. 272, 572) La nueva figura que resulta tras una transformación. *Ver también* preimagen.

Q R P Q′ R′ P′

$\triangle P'Q'R'$ is the image of $\triangle PQR$ after a translation.

$\triangle P'Q'R'$ es la imagen de $\triangle PQR$ tras una traslación.

incenter of a triangle (p. 312) The point of concurrency of the three angle bisectors of the triangle.

incentro de un triángulo (pág. 312) El punto de concurrencia de las tres bisectrices de los ángulos del triángulo.

B P A C

P is the incenter of $\triangle ABC$.

P es el incentro de $\triangle ABC$.

ENGLISH-SPANISH GLOSSARY

indirect proof (p. 337) A proof in which you prove that a statement is true by first assuming that its opposite is true. If this assumption leads to an impossibility, then you have proved that the original statement is true. **prueba indirecta** (pág. 337) Prueba en la que, para demostrar que un enunciado es verdadero, primero se supone que su opuesto es verdadero. Si esta suposición lleva a una imposibilidad, entonces se habrá demostrado que el enunciado original es verdadero.	*See* Example 4 on page 338. *Ver* el ejemplo 4 de la página 338.
inductive reasoning (p. 73) A process that includes looking for patterns and making conjectures. **razonamiento inductivo** (pág. 73) Proceso en el que se buscan patrones y se hacen conjeturas.	Given the number pattern 1, 5, 9, 13, ..., you can use inductive reasoning to determine that the next number in the pattern is 17. Dado el patrón numérico 1, 5, 9, 13, ..., puedes utilizar el razonamiento inductivo para determinar que el número siguiente del patrón es 17.
initial point of a vector (p. 574) The starting point of a vector. **punto inicial de un vector** (pág. 574) El punto de partida del vector.	*See* vector. *Ver* vector.
inscribed angle (p. 672) An angle whose vertex is on a circle and whose sides contain chords of the circle. **ángulo inscrito** (pág. 672) Ángulo cuyo vértice está en un círculo y cuyos lados contienen cuerdas del círculo.	
inscribed polygon (p. 674) A polygon whose vertices all lie on a circle. **polígono inscrito** (pág. 674) Polígono que tiene todos los vértices en un círculo.	
intercepted arc (p. 672) The arc that lies in the interior of an inscribed angle and has endpoints on the angle. **arco interceptado** (pág. 672) El arco situado en el interior de un ángulo inscrito y que tiene los extremos en el ángulo.	*See* inscribed angle. *Ver* ángulo inscrito.

ENGLISH-SPANISH GLOSSARY

interior angles of a triangle (p. 218) When the sides of a triangle are extended, the three original angles of the triangle.

ángulos interiores de un triángulo (pág. 218) Los tres ángulos originales de un triangulo al prolongar los lados del triángulo.

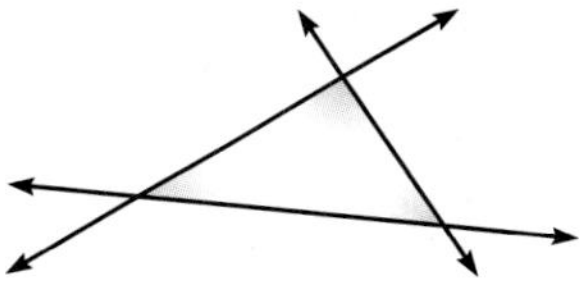

intersection (p. 4) The set of points that two or more geometric figures have in common.

intersección (pág. 4) El conjunto de puntos que dos o más figuras geométricas tienen en común.

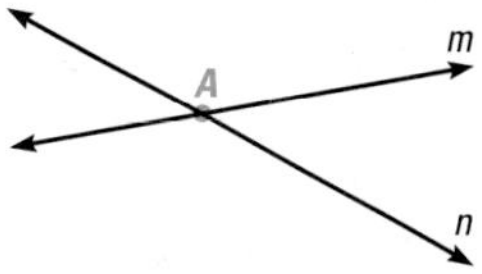

The intersection of lines *m* and *n* is point *A*.
La intersección de las rectas *m* y *n* es el punto *A*.

inverse (p. 80) The statement formed by negating the hypothesis and conclusion of a conditional statement.

inverso (pág. 80) El enunciado formado al negar la hipótesis y la conclusión de un enunciado condicional.

Statement: If $m\angle A = 90°$, then $\angle A$ is right.
Inverse: If $m\angle A \neq 90°$, then $\angle A$ is not right.

Enunciado: Si $m\angle A = 90°$, entonces $\angle A$ es recto.
Inverso: Si $m\angle A \neq 90°$, entonces $\angle A$ no es recto.

inverse cosine (p. 483) An inverse trigonometric ratio, abbreviated as cos^{-1}. For acute angle A, if $\cos A = z$, then $\cos^{-1} z = m\angle A$.

coseno inverso (pág. 483) Razón trigonométrica inversa, abreviada cos^{-1}. Para el ángulo agudo A, si $\cos A = z$, entonces $\cos^{-1} z = m\angle A$.

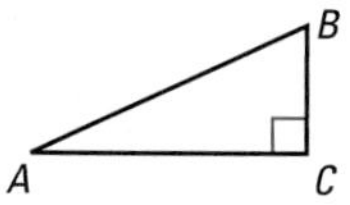

$\cos^{-1} \frac{AC}{AB} = m\angle A$

inverse sine (p. 483) An inverse trigonometric ratio, abbreviated as sin^{-1}. For acute angle A, if $\sin A = y$, then $\sin^{-1} y = m\angle A$.

seno inverso (pág. 483) Razón trigonométrica inversa, abreviada sen^{-1}. Para el ángulo agudo A, si $\text{sen}\, A = y$, entonces $\text{sen}^{-1} y = m\angle A$.

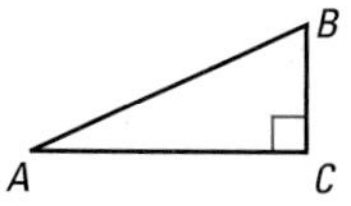

$\sin^{-1} \frac{BC}{AB} = m\angle A$

$\text{sen}^{-1} \frac{BC}{AB} = m\angle A$

inverse tangent (p. 483) An inverse trigonometric ratio, abbreviated as tan^{-1}. For acute angle A, if $\tan A = x$, then $\tan^{-1} x = m\angle A$.

tangente inversa (pág. 483) Razón trigonométrica inversa, abreviada tan^{-1}. Para el ángulo agudo A, si $\tan A = x$, entonces $\tan^{-1} x = m\angle A$.

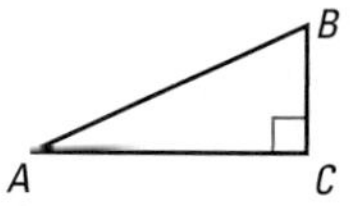

$\tan^{-1} \frac{BC}{AC} = m\angle A$

957

isometric drawing (p. 550) A technical drawing that looks three-dimensional and can be created on a grid of dots using three axes that intersect to form 120° angles. **dibujo isométrico** (pág. 550) Dibujo técnico de aspecto tridimensional; puede crearse en una cuadrícula de puntos usando tres ejes que al cortarse forman ángulos de 120°.	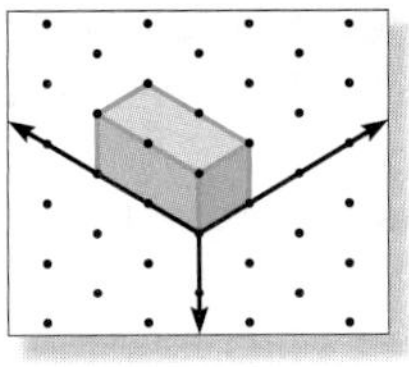
isometry (p. 573) A transformation that preserves length and angle measure. Also called *congruence transformation.* **isometría** (pág. 573) Transformación que conserva la longitud y la medida de los ángulos. También se llama *transformación de congruencia.*	Translations, reflections, and rotations are three types of isometries. Las traslaciones, las reflexiones y las rotaciones son tres tipos de isometrías.
isosceles trapezoid (p. 543) A trapezoid with congruent legs. **trapecio isósceles** (pág. 543) Trapecio que tiene los catetos congruentes.	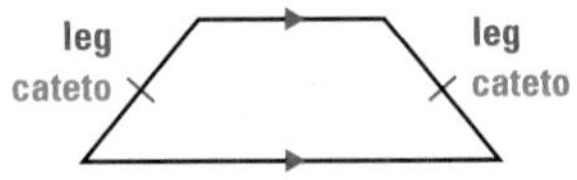 leg / cateto; leg / cateto
isosceles triangle (p. 217) A triangle with at least two congruent sides. **triángulo isósceles** (pág. 217) Triángulo que tiene al menos dos lados congruentes.	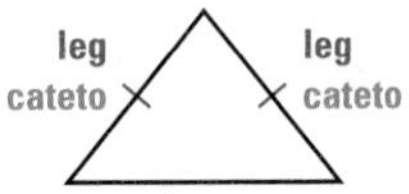 leg / cateto; leg / cateto; base / base
iteration (p. 406) A repetition of a sequence of steps. **iteración** (pág. 406) Repetición de una secuencia de pasos.	Fractals are created using iterations. Los fractales se crean usando iteraciones.

K

kite (p. 545) A quadrilateral that has two pairs of consecutive congruent sides, but in which opposite sides are not congruent. **cometa** (pág. 545) Cuadrilátero que tiene dos pares de lados congruentes consecutivos pero cuyos lados opuestos no son congruentes.	

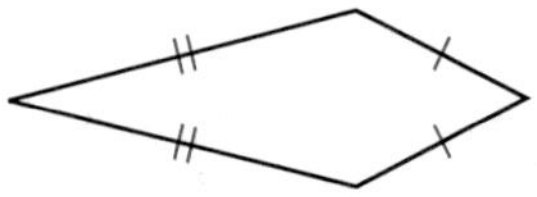

L

lateral area (p. 803) The sum of the areas of the lateral faces of a polyhedron or other solid with one or two bases. **área lateral** (pág. 803) La suma de las áreas de las caras laterales de un poliedro o de otro sólido con una o dos bases.	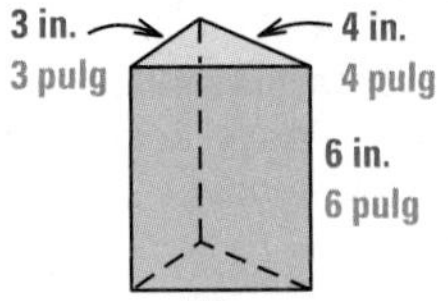 3 in. / 3 pulg; 4 in. / 4 pulg; 6 in. / 6 pulg; 5 in. / 5 pulg Lateral area $= 5(6) + 4(6) + 3(6) = 72$ in.^{2} Área lateral $= 5(6) + 4(6) + 3(6) = 72$ pulg^2

ENGLISH-SPANISH GLOSSARY

lateral edges of a prism (p. 803) The segments connecting the corresponding vertices of the bases of a prism. **aristas laterales de un prisma** (pág. 803) Los segmentos que unen los vértices correspondientes de las bases de un prisma.	base / base; lateral faces / caras laterales; lateral edges / aristas laterales; base / base
lateral faces of a prism (p. 803) The faces of a prism that are parallelograms formed by connecting the corresponding vertices of the bases of the prism. **caras laterales de un prisma** (pág. 803) Las caras de un prisma que son paralelogramos formados al unir los vértices correspondientes de las bases del prisma.	*See* lateral edges of a prism. *Ver* aristas laterales de un prisma.
lateral surface of a cone (p. 812) Consists of all segments that connect the vertex with points on the edge of the base. **superficie lateral de un cono** (pág. 812) Todos los segmentos que unen el vértice con los puntos de la arista de la base.	lateral surface / superficie lateral; base / base
legs of a right triangle (p. 241) In a right triangle, the sides adjacent to the right angle. **catetos de un triángulo rectángulo** (pág. 241) En un triángulo rectángulo, los lados adyacentes al ángulo recto.	leg / cateto; leg / cateto
legs of a trapezoid (p. 542) The nonparallel sides of a trapezoid. **catetos de un trapecio** (pág. 542) Los lados no paralelos de un trapecio.	*See* trapezoid. *Ver* trapecio.
legs of an isosceles triangle (p. 264) The two congruent sides of an isosceles triangle that has only two congruent sides. **catetos de un triángulo isósceles** (pág. 264) Los dos lados congruentes de un triángulo isósceles que tiene sólo dos lados congruentes.	*See* isosceles triangle. *Ver* triángulo isósceles.

ENGLISH-SPANISH GLOSSARY

line (p. 2) A line has one dimension. It is usually represented by a straight line with two arrowheads to indicate that the line extends without end in two directions. In this book, lines are always straight lines. *See also* undefined term. **recta** (pág. 2) Una recta tiene una dimensión. Normalmente se representa por una línea recta con dos puntas de flecha para así indicar que la recta se prolonga sin fin en dos direcciones. En este texto las líneas son siempre líneas rectas. *Ver también* término indefinido.	ℓ A B line ℓ, $\overleftrightarrow{AB}$, or $\overleftrightarrow{BA}$ recta ℓ, $\overleftrightarrow{AB}$ o $\overleftrightarrow{BA}$
line of reflection (p. 589) *See* reflection. **eje de reflexión** (pág. 589) *Ver* reflexión.	*See* reflection. *Ver* reflexión.
line of symmetry (p. 619) *See* line symmetry. **eje de simetría** (pág. 619) *Ver* simetría lineal.	*See* line symmetry. *Ver* simetría lineal.
line perpendicular to a plane (p. 98) A line that intersects the plane in a point and is perpendicular to every line in the plane that intersects it at that point. **recta perpendicular a un plano** (pág. 98) Recta que corta al plano en un punto y es perpendicular a cada recta del plano que la corta en ese punto.	n P a b Line *n* is perpendicular to plane *P*. La recta *n* es perpendicular al plano *P*.
line segment (p. 3) Part of a line that consists of two points, called endpoints, and all points on the line that are between the endpoints. Also called *segment*. **segmento de recta** (pág. 3) Parte de una recta que consta de dos puntos, llamados extremos, y de todos los puntos de la recta situados entre los extremos. También se llama *segmento*.	A B $\overline{AB}$ with endpoints *A* and *B* $\overline{AB}$ con extremos *A* y *B*
line symmetry (p. 619) A figure in the plane has line symmetry if the figure can be mapped onto itself by a reflection in a line. This line of reflection is a line of symmetry. **simetría lineal** (pág. 619) Una figura del plano tiene simetría lineal si se corresponde a sí misma al realizar una reflexión sobre una recta. Este eje de reflexión es un eje de simetría.	Two lines of symmetry Dos ejes de simetría

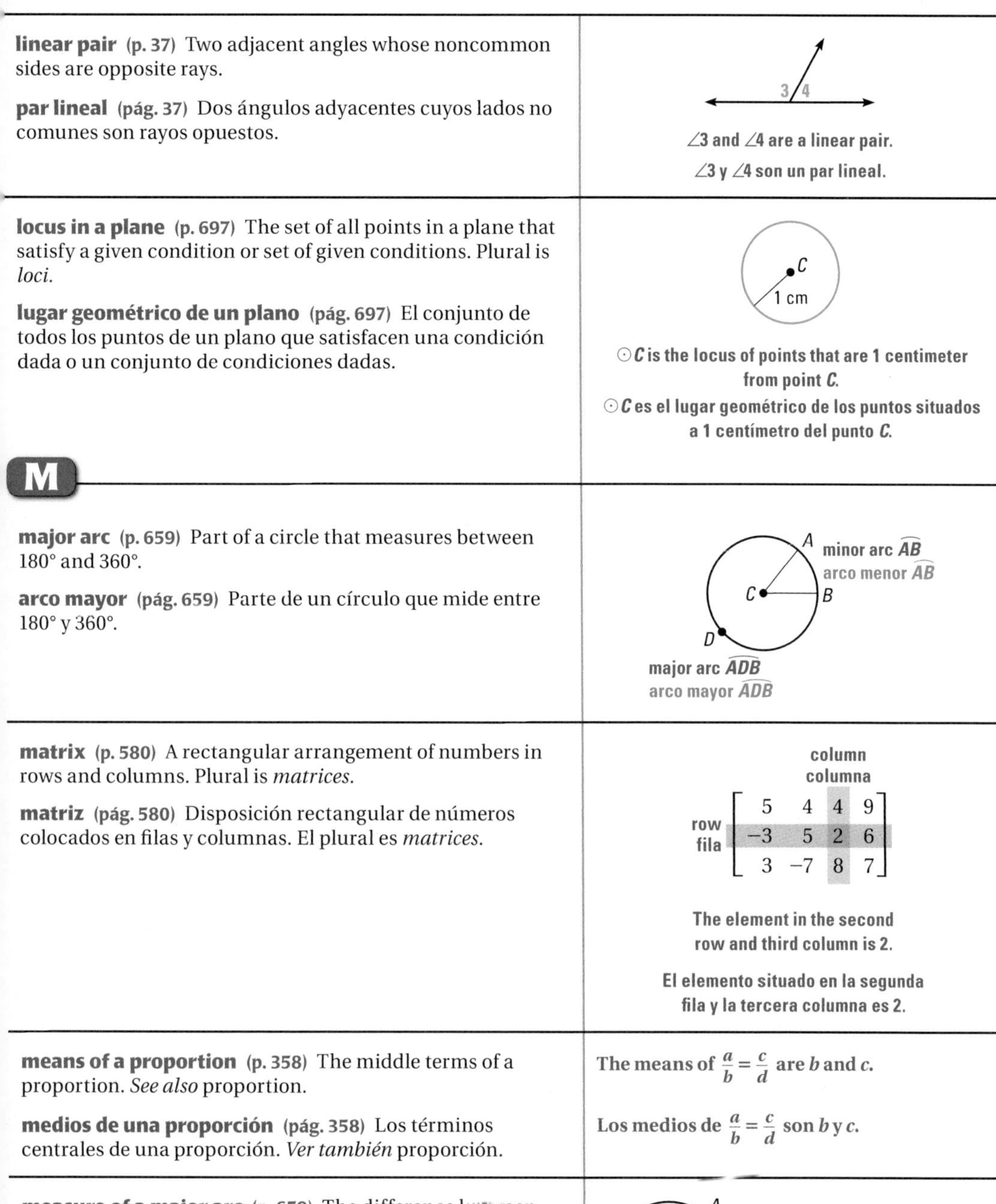

linear pair (p. 37) Two adjacent angles whose noncommon sides are opposite rays.

par lineal (pág. 37) Dos ángulos adyacentes cuyos lados no comunes son rayos opuestos.

$\angle 3$ and $\angle 4$ are a linear pair.

$\angle 3$ y $\angle 4$ son un par lineal.

locus in a plane (p. 697) The set of all points in a plane that satisfy a given condition or set of given conditions. Plural is *loci*.

lugar geométrico de un plano (pág. 697) El conjunto de todos los puntos de un plano que satisfacen una condición dada o un conjunto de condiciones dadas.

$\odot C$ is the locus of points that are 1 centimeter from point C.

$\odot C$ es el lugar geométrico de los puntos situados a 1 centímetro del punto C.

M

major arc (p. 659) Part of a circle that measures between 180° and 360°.

arco mayor (pág. 659) Parte de un círculo que mide entre 180° y 360°.

matrix (p. 580) A rectangular arrangement of numbers in rows and columns. Plural is *matrices*.

matriz (pág. 580) Disposición rectangular de números colocados en filas y columnas. El plural es *matrices*.

column
columna

row
fila

$$\begin{bmatrix} 5 & 4 & 4 & 9 \\ -3 & 5 & 2 & 6 \\ 3 & -7 & 8 & 7 \end{bmatrix}$$

The element in the second row and third column is 2.

El elemento situado en la segunda fila y la tercera columna es 2.

means of a proportion (p. 358) The middle terms of a proportion. *See also* proportion.

medios de una proporción (pág. 358) Los términos centrales de una proporción. *Ver también* proporción.

The means of $\frac{a}{b} = \frac{c}{d}$ are b and c.

Los medios de $\frac{a}{b} = \frac{c}{d}$ son b y c.

measure of a major arc (p. 659) The difference between 360° and the measure of the related minor arc.

medida de un arco mayor (pág. 659) La diferencia entre 360° y la medida del arco menor relacionado.

$$m\overparen{ADB} = 360° - m\overparen{AB} = 360° - 50° = 310°$$

ENGLISH-SPANISH GLOSSARY

measure of a minor arc (p. 659) The measure of the arc's central angle.

medida de un arco menor (pág. 659) La medida del ángulo central del arco.

See measure of a major arc.

Ver medida de un arco mayor.

measure of an angle (p. 24) Consider $\overleftrightarrow{OB}$ and a point A on one side of $\overleftrightarrow{OB}$. The rays of the form $\overrightarrow{OA}$ can be matched one to one with the real numbers from 0 to 180. The measure of $\angle AOB$ is equal to the absolute value of the difference between the real numbers for $\overrightarrow{OA}$ and $\overrightarrow{OB}$.

medida de un ángulo (pág. 24) Considera $\overleftrightarrow{OB}$ y un punto A situado sobre un lado de $\overleftrightarrow{OB}$. Los rayos de la forma $\overrightarrow{OA}$ pueden hacerse corresponder de uno en uno con los números reales de 0 a 180. La medida de $\angle AOB$ es igual al valor absoluto de la diferencia entre los números reales correspondientes a $\overrightarrow{OA}$ y a $\overrightarrow{OB}$.

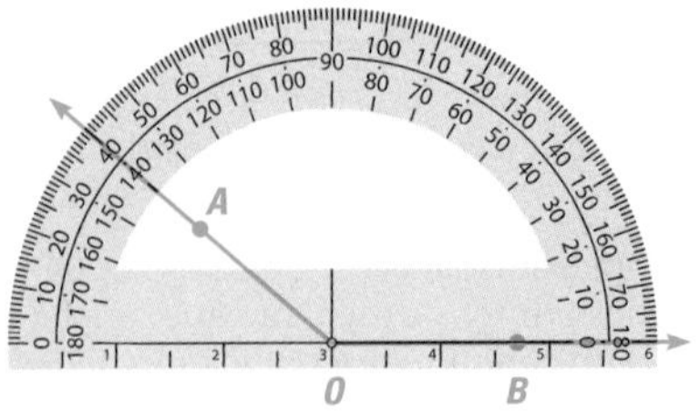

$m\angle AOB = 140°$

median of a triangle (p. 319) A segment from one vertex of the triangle to the midpoint of the opposite side.

mediana de un triángulo (pág. 319) Segmento que va desde uno de los vértices del triángulo hasta el punto medio del lado opuesto.

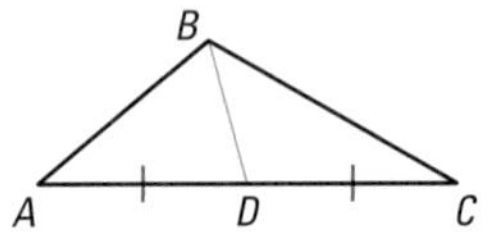

$\overline{BD}$ is a median of $\triangle ABC$.

$\overline{BD}$ es una mediana de $\triangle ABC$.

midpoint (p. 15) A point that divides, or bisects, a segment into two congruent segments.

punto medio (pág. 15) Punto que divide, o biseca, a un segmento separándolo en dos segmentos congruentes.

M is the midpoint of $\overline{AB}$.

M es el punto medio de $\overline{AB}$.

midsegment of a trapezoid (p. 544) A segment that connects the midpoints of the legs of a trapezoid.

paralela media de un trapecio (pág. 544) Segmento que une los puntos medios de los catetos del trapecio.

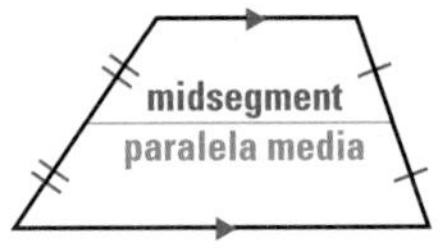

midsegment

paralela media

midsegment of a triangle (p. 295) A segment that connects the midpoints of two sides of the triangle.

paralela media de un triángulo (pág. 295) Segmento que une los puntos medios de dos lados del triángulo.

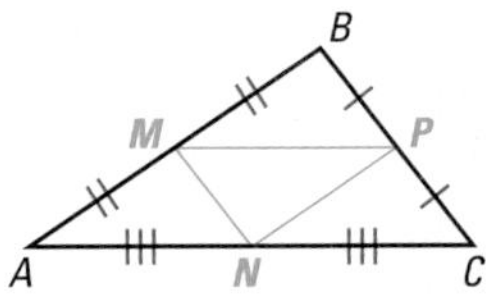

The midsegments of $\triangle ABC$ are $\overline{MP}$, $\overline{MN}$, and $\overline{NP}$.

Las paralelas medias de $\triangle ABC$ son $\overline{MP}$, $\overline{MN}$ y $\overline{NP}$.

minor arc (p. 659) Part of a circle that measures less than 180°.

arco menor (pág. 659) Parte de un círculo que mide menos de 180°.

See major arc.

Ver arco mayor.

N

negation (p. 79) The opposite of a statement. The symbol for negation is ~.

negación (pág. 79) El opuesto de un enunciado. El símbolo de la negación es ~.

Statement: The ball is red.
Negation: The ball is not red.

Enunciado: La pelota es roja.
Negación: La pelota no es roja.

net (p. 803) The two-dimensional representation of the faces of a polyhedron.

patrón (pág. 803) La representación bidimensional de las caras de un poliedro.

2 cm
6 cm
5 cm 2 cm
5 cm
2 cm

***n*-gon** (p. 43) A polygon with *n* sides.

***n*-gono** (pág. 43) Polígono con *n* lados.

A polygon with 14 sides is a 14-gon.

Un polígono con 14 lados es un 14-gono.

nonagon (p. 43) A polygon with nine sides.

nonágono (pág. 43) Polígono con nueve lados.

O

oblique prism (p. 804) A prism with lateral edges that are not perpendicular to the bases.

prisma oblicuo (pág. 804) Prisma con aristas laterales que no son perpendiculares a las bases.

height
altura

obtuse angle (p. 25) An angle with measure between 90° and 180°.

ángulo obtuso (pág. 25) Ángulo que mide más de 90° y menos de 180°.

A

obtuse triangle (p. 217) A triangle with one obtuse angle.

triángulo obtusángulo (pág. 217) Triángulo que tiene un ángulo obtuso.

octagon (p. 43) A polygon with eight sides.

octágono (pág. 43) Polígono con ocho lados.

963

octahedron (p. 796) A polyhedron with eight faces. **octaedro** (pág. 796) Poliedro con ocho caras.	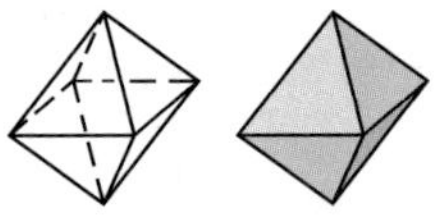
opposite rays (p. 3) If point C lies on $\overleftrightarrow{AB}$ between A and B, then $\overrightarrow{CA}$ and $\overrightarrow{CB}$ are opposite rays. **rayos opuestos** (pag. 3) Si el punto C se encuentra sobre $\overleftrightarrow{AB}$ entre A y B, entonces $\overrightarrow{CA}$ y $\overrightarrow{CB}$ son rayos opuestos.	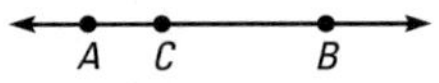 A C B $\overrightarrow{CA}$ and $\overrightarrow{CB}$ are opposite rays. $\overrightarrow{CA}$ y $\overrightarrow{CB}$ son rayos opuestos.
orthocenter of a triangle (p. 321) The point at which the lines containing the three altitudes of the triangle intersect. **ortocentro de un triángulo** (pág. 321) El punto donde se cortan las rectas que contienen las tres alturas del triángulo.	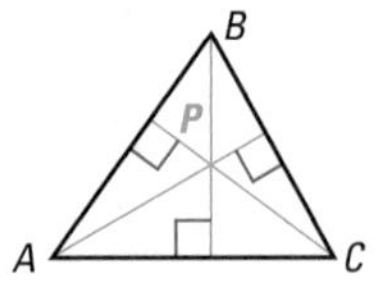 B P A C P is the orthocenter of $\triangle ABC$. P es el ortocentro de $\triangle ABC$.
orthographic projection (p. 551) A technical drawing that is a two-dimensional drawing of the front, top, and side views of an object. **proyección ortográfica** (pág. 551) Dibujo técnico bidimensional de las vistas delantera, superior y lateral de un objeto.	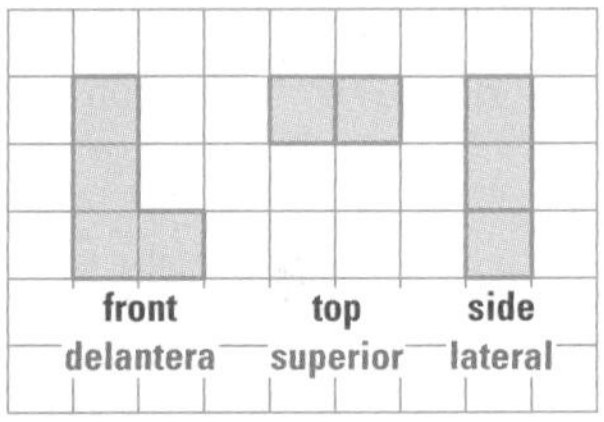 front top side delantera superior lateral

P

paragraph proof (p. 163) A type of proof written in paragraph form. **prueba en forma de párrafo** (pág. 163) Tipo de prueba escrita en forma de párrafo.	*See* Example 4 on page 163. *Ver* el ejemplo 4 de la página 163.
parallel lines (p. 147) Two lines that do not intersect and are coplanar. **rectas paralelas** (pág. 147) Dos rectas que no se cortan y que son coplanarias.	ℓ m $\ell \parallel m$
parallel planes (p. 147) Two planes that do not intersect. **planos paralelos** (pág. 147) Dos planos que no se cortan.	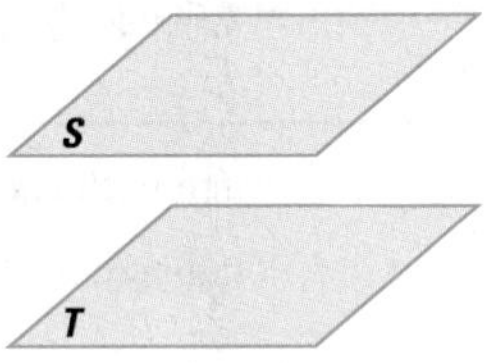 S T $S \parallel T$

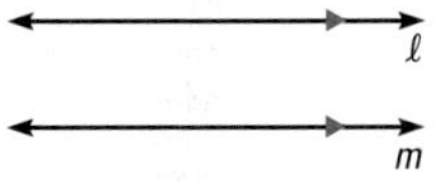

parallelogram (p. 515) A quadrilateral with both pairs of opposite sides parallel. **paralelogramo** (pág. 515) Cuadrilátero que tiene ambos pares de lados opuestos paralelos.	Q R P S ▱PQRS
pentagon (p. 43) A polygon with five sides. **pentágono** (pág. 43) Polígono con cinco lados.	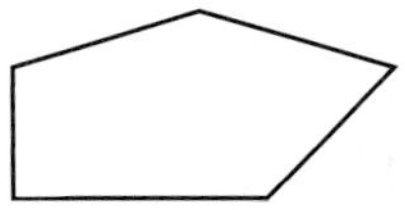
perpendicular bisector (p. 303) A segment, ray, line, or plane that is perpendicular to a segment at its midpoint. **mediatriz** (pág. 303) Segmento, rayo, recta o plano que es perpendicular a un segmento en su punto medio.	C A P B
perpendicular lines (p. 81) Two lines that intersect to form a right angle. **rectas perpendiculares** (pág. 81) Dos rectas que se cortan para formar un ángulo recto.	ℓ m
plane (p. 2) A plane has two dimensions. It is usually represented by a shape that looks like a floor or a wall. You must imagine that the plane extends without end, even though the drawing of a plane appears to have edges. *See also* undefined term. **plano** (pág. 2) Un plano tiene dos dimensiones. Normalmente se representa por una figura que parece un suelo o una pared. Hay que imaginar que el plano se prolonga sin fin, aunque dibujado parezca tener bordes. *Ver también* término indefinido.	A M C B plane ***M*** or plane ***ABC*** plano ***M*** o plano ***ABC***
Platonic solids (p. 796) Five regular polyhedra, named after the Greek mathematician and philosopher Plato. **sólidos platónicos** (pág. 796) Cinco poliedros regulares, que llevan el nombre del matemático y filósofo griego Platón.	The Platonic solids include a regular tetrahedron, a cube, a regular octahedron, a regular dodecahedron, and a regular icosahedron. Los sólidos platónicos son el tetraedro regular, el cubo, el octaedro regular, el dodecaedro regular y el icosaedro regular.
point (p. 2) A point has no dimension. It is usually represented by a dot. *See also* undefined term. **punto** (pág. 2) Un punto no tiene dimensiones. Normalmente se representa por un pequeño punto. *Ver también* término indefinido.	A point ***A*** punto ***A***

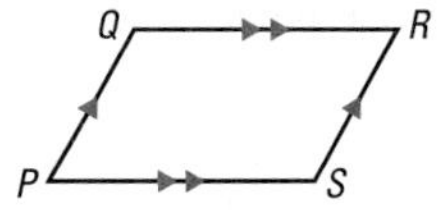

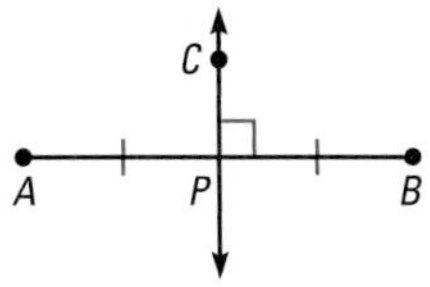

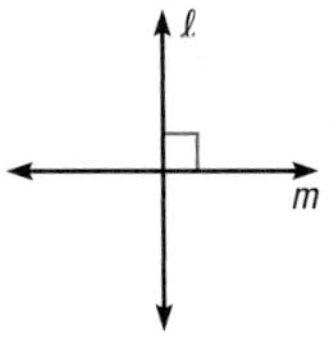

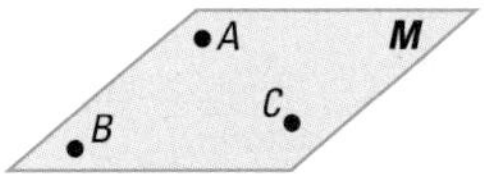

point of concurrency (p. 305) The point of intersection of concurrent lines, rays, or segments. **punto de concurrencia** (pág. 305) El punto de intersección de rectas, rayos o segmentos concurrentes.	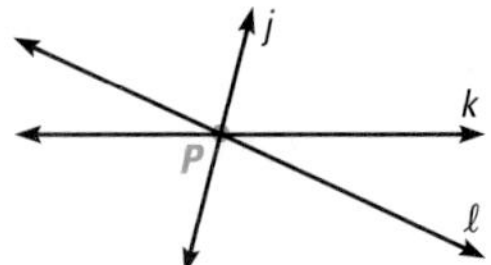 **P is the point of concurrency for lines j, k, and ℓ.** **P es el punto de concurrencia de las rectas j, k y ℓ.**
polygon (p. 42) A closed plane figure with the following properties. (1) It is formed by three or more line segments called sides. (2) Each side intersects exactly two sides, one at each endpoint, so that no two sides with a common endpoint are collinear. **polígono** (pág. 42) Figura plana cerrada que tiene las siguientes propiedades. (1) Está formada por tres o más segmentos de recta, llamados lados. (2) Cada lado corta a sólo dos lados, uno en cada extremo, de modo que en ningún caso son colineales dos lados que tienen un extremo común.	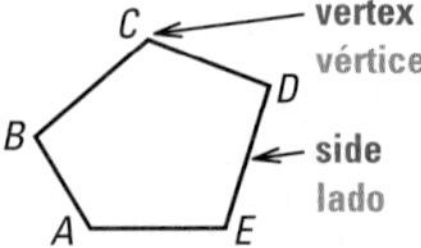 **Polygon *ABCDE*** **Polígono *ABCDE***
polyhedron (p. 794) A solid that is bounded by polygons, called faces, that enclose a single region of space. Plural is *polyhedra* or *polyhedrons*. **poliedro** (pág. 794) Sólido limitado por polígonos, llamados caras, que rodean una sola región del espacio.	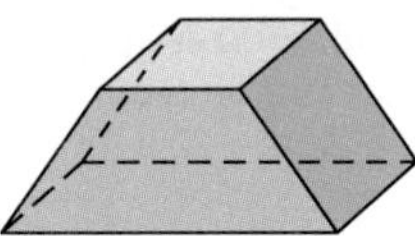
postulate (p. 9) A rule that is accepted without proof. Also called *axiom*. **postulado** (pág. 9) Regla aceptada sin necesidad de pruebas. También se llama *axioma*.	**The Segment Addition Postulate states that if B is between A and C, then $AB + BC = AC$.** **El postulado de la suma de segmentos establece que si B está entre A y C, entonces $AB + BC = AC$.**
preimage (p. 572) The original figure in a transformation. *See also* image. **preimagen** (pág. 572) La figura original en una transformación. *Ver también* imagen.	***See* image.** ***Ver* imagen.**
prism (p. 803) A polyhedron with two congruent faces, called bases, that lie in parallel planes. **prisma** (pág. 803) Poliedro con dos caras congruentes, llamadas bases, que se encuentran en planos paralelos.	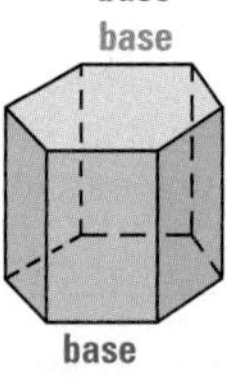

ENGLISH-SPANISH GLOSSARY

probability (p. 771) A number from 0 to 1 that measures the likelihood that an event will occur. It can be expressed as a fraction, decimal, or percent. **probabilidad** (pág. 771) Número comprendido entre 0 y 1 que mide la posibilidad de que ocurra un suceso. Este número puede expresarse en forma de fracción, decimal o porcentaje.	*See* **geometric probability.** *Ver* **probabilidad geométrica.**
proof (p. 112) A logical argument that shows a statement is true. **prueba** (pág. 112) Argumento lógico que muestra que un enunciado es verdadero.	*See* **two-column proof, paragraph proof,** *and* **flow proof.** *Ver* **prueba de dos columnas, prueba en forma de párrafo** *y* **prueba de flujo.**
proportion (p. 358) An equation that states that two ratios are equal. **proporción** (pág. 358) Ecuación que establece la igualdad entre dos razones.	$\frac{2}{3} = \frac{4}{6}$ **and** $\frac{5}{7} = \frac{15}{x}$ **are proportions.** $\frac{2}{3} = \frac{4}{6}$ **y** $\frac{5}{7} = \frac{15}{x}$ **son proporciones.**
pyramid (p. 810) A polyhedron in which the base is a polygon and the lateral faces are triangles with a common vertex, called the vertex of the pyramid. **pirámide** (pág. 810) Poliedro que tiene por base un polígono y cuyas caras laterales son triángulos que tienen un vértice común, llamado vértice de la pirámide.	
Pythagorean triple (p. 435) A set of three positive integers a, b, and c that satisfy the equation $c^2 = a^2 + b^2$. **terna pitagórica** (pág. 435) Conjunto de tres números enteros positivos a, b y c que satisfacen la ecuación $c^2 = a^2 + b^2$.	**Common Pythagorean triples:** **3, 4, 5** **5, 12, 13** **8, 15, 17** **7, 24, 25** **Algunas ternas pitagóricas comunes son:** **3, 4, 5** **5, 12, 13** **8, 15, 17** **7, 24, 25**

Q

quadrilateral (p. 43) A polygon with four sides. **cuadrilátero** (pág. 43) Polígono con cuatro lados.	

ENGLISH-SPANISH GLOSSARY

R

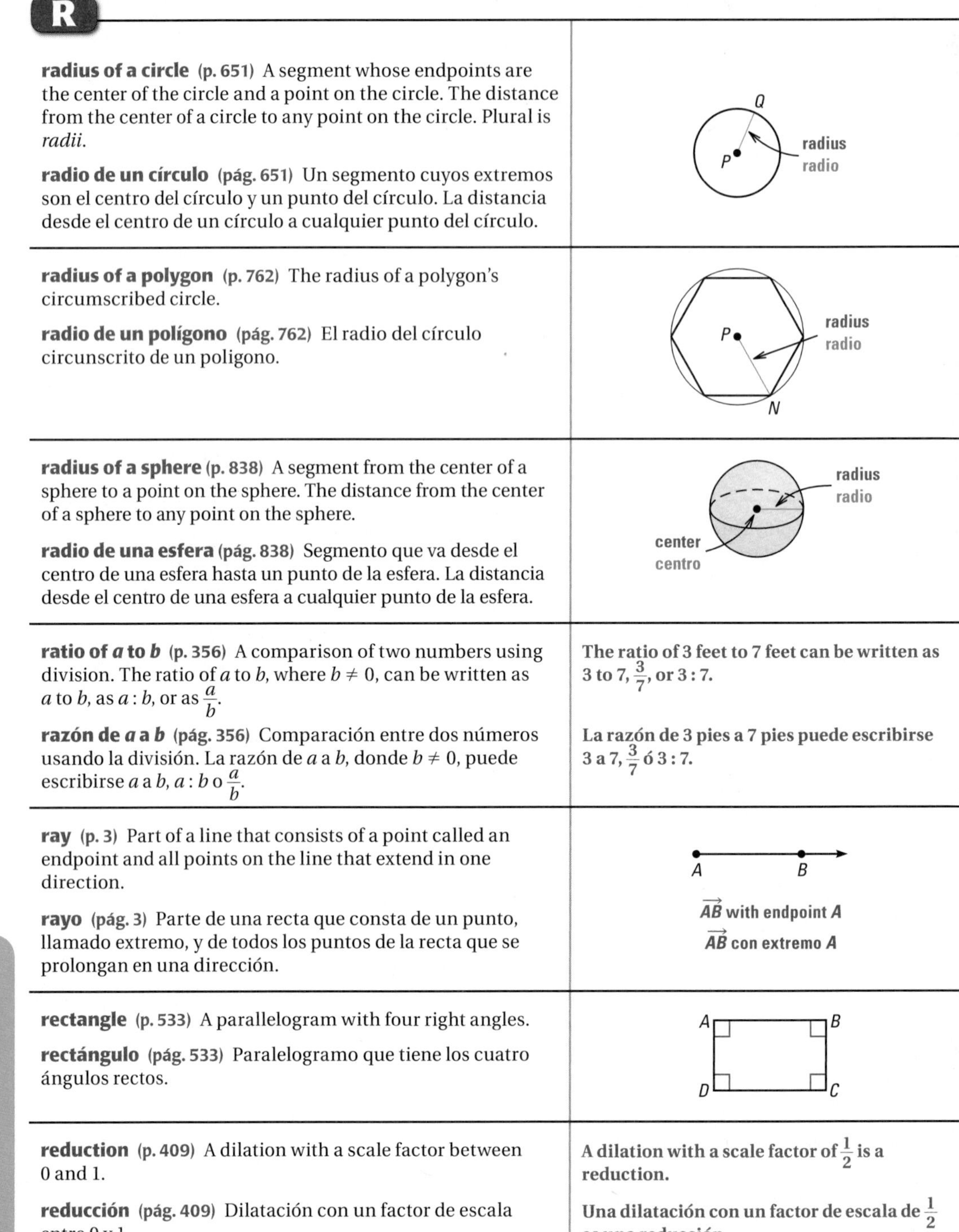

radius of a circle (p. 651) A segment whose endpoints are the center of the circle and a point on the circle. The distance from the center of a circle to any point on the circle. Plural is *radii.*

radio de un círculo (pág. 651) Un segmento cuyos extremos son el centro del círculo y un punto del círculo. La distancia desde el centro de un círculo a cualquier punto del círculo.

radius of a polygon (p. 762) The radius of a polygon's circumscribed circle.

radio de un polígono (pág. 762) El radio del círculo circunscrito de un poligono.

radius of a sphere (p. 838) A segment from the center of a sphere to a point on the sphere. The distance from the center of a sphere to any point on the sphere.

radio de una esfera (pág. 838) Segmento que va desde el centro de una esfera hasta un punto de la esfera. La distancia desde el centro de una esfera a cualquier punto de la esfera.

ratio of *a* to *b* (p. 356) A comparison of two numbers using division. The ratio of a to b, where $b \neq 0$, can be written as a to b, as $a : b$, or as $\frac{a}{b}$.

razón de *a* a *b* (pág. 356) Comparación entre dos números usando la división. La razón de a a b, donde $b \neq 0$, puede escribirse a a b, $a : b$ o $\frac{a}{b}$.

The ratio of 3 feet to 7 feet can be written as 3 to 7, $\frac{3}{7}$, or 3 : 7.

La razón de 3 pies a 7 pies puede escribirse 3 a 7, $\frac{3}{7}$ ó 3 : 7.

ray (p. 3) Part of a line that consists of a point called an endpoint and all points on the line that extend in one direction.

rayo (pág. 3) Parte de una recta que consta de un punto, llamado extremo, y de todos los puntos de la recta que se prolongan en una dirección.

rectangle (p. 533) A parallelogram with four right angles.

rectángulo (pág. 533) Paralelogramo que tiene los cuatro ángulos rectos.

reduction (p. 409) A dilation with a scale factor between 0 and 1.

reducción (pág. 409) Dilatación con un factor de escala entre 0 y 1.

A dilation with a scale factor of $\frac{1}{2}$ is a reduction.

Una dilatación con un factor de escala de $\frac{1}{2}$ es una reducción.

968

reflection (pp. 272, 589) A transformation that uses a line of reflection to create a mirror image of the original figure. **reflexión** (págs. 272, 589) Transformación que usa un eje de reflexión para crear una imagen especular de la figura original.	
regular polygon (p. 43) A polygon that has all sides and all angles congruent. **polígono regular** (pág. 43) Polígono que tiene todos los lados y todos los ángulos congruentes.	
regular polyhedron (p. 796) A convex polyhedron in which all of the faces are congruent regular polygons. **poliedro regular** (pág. 796) Poliedro convexo en el que todas las caras son polígonos regulares congruentes.	
regular pyramid (p. 810) A pyramid that has a regular polygon for a base and in which the segment joining the vertex and the center of the base is perpendicular to the base. **pirámide regular** (pág. 810) Pirámide que tiene por base un polígono regular y en la que el segmento que une el vértice y el centro de la base es perpendicular a la base.	
relative error (p. 727) The ratio of the greatest possible error to the measured length. **error relativo** (pág. 727) La razón entre el máximo error posible y la longitud medida.	**If the greatest possible error of a measure is 0.5 inch and the measured length of an object is 8 inches, then the relative error is $\frac{0.5}{8} = 0.0625 = 6.25\%$.** **Si el máximo error posible de una medida es 0.5 pulgada y la longitud medida de un objeto es de 8 pulgadas, entonces el error relativo es $\frac{0.5}{8} = 0.0625 = 6.25\%$.**
rhombus (p. 533) A parallelogram with four congruent sides. **rombo** (pág. 533) Paralelogramo que tiene los cuatro lados congruentes.	
right angle (p. 25) An angle with measure equal to 90°. **ángulo recto** (pág. 25) Ángulo que mide 90°.	

right cone (p. 812) A cone in which the segment joining the vertex and the center of the base is perpendicular to the base. The slant height is the distance between the vertex and a point on the base edge.

cono recto (pág. 812) Cono en el que el segmento que une el vértice y el centro de la base es perpendicular a la base. El apotema lateral es la distancia entre el vértice y un punto de la arista de la base.

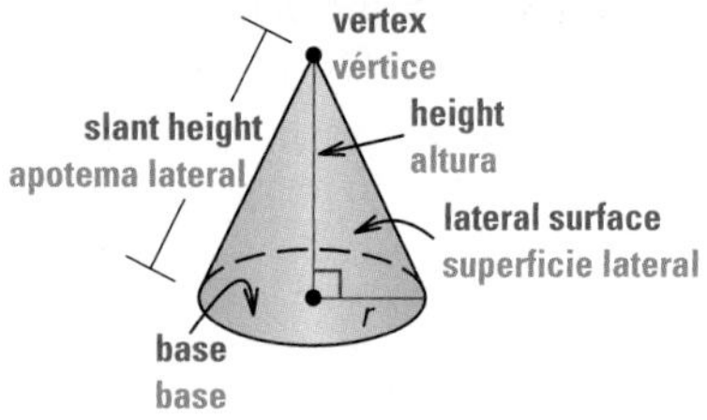

vertex
vértice
slant height
apotema lateral
height
altura
lateral surface
superficie lateral
r
base
base

right cylinder (p. 805) A cylinder in which the segment joining the centers of the bases is perpendicular to the bases.

cilindro recto (pág. 805) Cilindro en el que el segmento que une los centros de las bases es perpendicular a las bases.

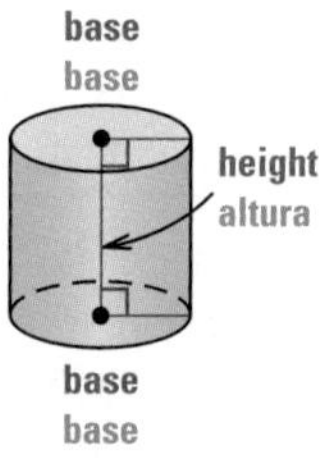

base
base
height
altura
base
base

right prism (p. 804) A prism in which each lateral edge is perpendicular to both bases.

prisma recto (pág. 804) Prisma en el que cada arista lateral es perpendicular a ambas bases.

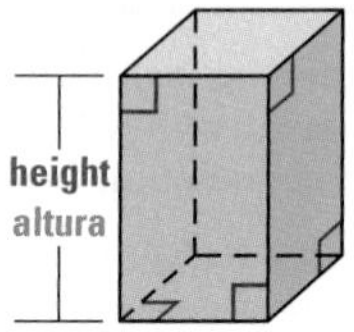

height
altura

right triangle (pp. 217, 241) A triangle with one right angle.

triángulo rectángulo (págs. 217, 241) Triángulo que tiene un ángulo recto.

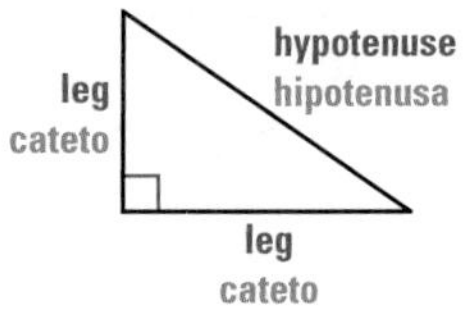

hypotenuse
hipotenusa
leg
cateto
leg
cateto

rotation (pp. 272, 598) A transformation in which a figure is turned about a fixed point called the center of rotation.

rotación (págs. 272, 598) Transformación en la que una figura gira en torno a un punto fijo, llamado centro de rotación.

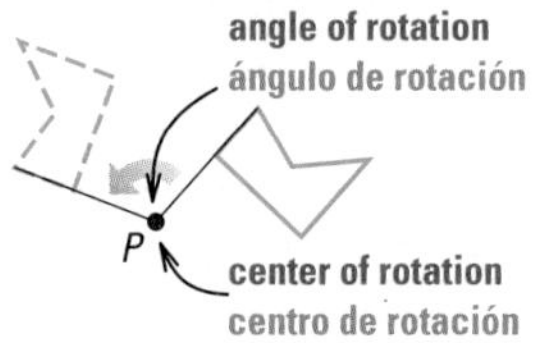

angle of rotation
ángulo de rotación
P
center of rotation
centro de rotación

rotational symmetry (p. 620) A figure in the plane has rotational symmetry if the figure can be mapped onto itself by a rotation of 180° or less about the center of the figure. This point is the center of symmetry.

simetría rotacional (pág. 620) Una figura del plano tiene simetría rotacional si se corresponde a sí misma al realizar una rotación de 180° ó menos en torno al centro de la figura. Este punto es el centro de simetría.

center of symmetry
centro de simetría

Rotations of 90° and 180° map the figure onto itself.
Al realizar rotaciones de 90° y 180°, la figura se corresponde.

S

scalar multiplication (p. 627) The process of multiplying each element of a matrix by a real number, or scalar.

multiplicación escalar (pág. 627) El proceso de multiplicar cada elemento de una matriz por un número real, o escalar.

$$3\begin{bmatrix} 5 & -2 & 1 \\ 0 & 2 & -3 \end{bmatrix} = \begin{bmatrix} 15 & -6 & 3 \\ 0 & 6 & -9 \end{bmatrix}$$

scale (p. 365) A ratio that describes how the dimensions in a scale drawing are related to the actual dimensions of the object.

escala (pág. 365) Razón que describe qué relación hay entre las dimensiones de un dibujo a escala y las dimensiones reales del objeto.

The scale 1 in. : 12 ft on a floor plan means that 1 inch in the floor plan represents an actual distance of 12 feet.

La escala 1 pulg : 12 pies de un plano significa que 1 pulgada del plano representa una distancia real de 12 pies.

scale drawing (p. 365) A drawing that is the same shape as the object it represents.

dibujo a escala (pág. 365) Dibujo que tiene la misma forma que el objeto que representa.

A floor plan of a house is a scale drawing.

El plano de una casa es un dibujo a escala.

scale factor of a dilation (p. 409) In a dilation, the ratio of a side length of the image to the corresponding side length of the original figure.

factor de escala de una dilatación (pág. 409) En una dilatación, la razón entre una longitud de lado de la imagen y la longitud de lado correspondiente de la figura original.

See dilation.

Ver dilatación.

scale factor of two similar polygons (p. 373) The ratio of the lengths of two corresponding sides of two similar polygons.

factor de escala entre dos polígonos semejantes (pág. 373) La razón entre las longitudes de dos lados correspondientes de dos polígonos semejantes.

F 16 J 20 12 H G 24 Z 20 W 25 15 X Y 30

The scale factor of $ZYXW$ to $FGHJ$ is $\frac{5}{4}$.
El factor de escala entre $ZYXW$ y $FGHJ$ es $\frac{5}{4}$.

ENGLISH-SPANISH GLOSSARY

scalene triangle (p. 217) A triangle with no congruent sides. **triángulo escaleno** (pág. 217) Triángulo que no tiene lados congruentes.	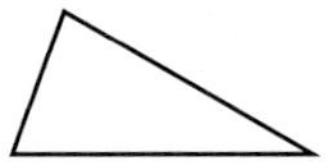
secant line (p. 651) A line that intersects a circle in two points. **recta secante** (pág. 651) Recta que corta a un círculo en dos puntos.	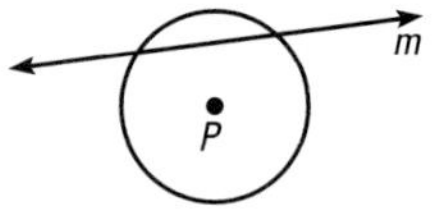 m, P Line m is a secant. La recta m es una secante.
secant segment (p. 690) A segment that contains a chord of a circle and has exactly one endpoint outside the circle. **segmento secante** (pág. 690) Segmento que contiene una cuerda de un círculo y tiene sólo un extremo en el exterior del círculo.	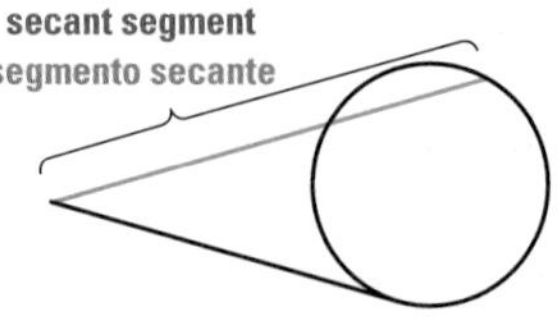 secant segment segmento secante
sector of a circle (p. 756) The region bounded by two radii of the circle and their intercepted arc. **sector de un círculo** (pág. 756) La región limitada por dos radios del círculo y su arco interceptado.	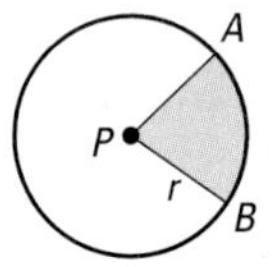 A, P, r, B sector APB
segment (p. 3) *See* line segment. **segmento** (pág. 3) *Ver* segmento de recta.	*See* line segment. *Ver* segmento de recta.
segment bisector (p. 15) A point, ray, line, segment, or plane that intersects a segment at its midpoint. **bisectriz de un segmento** (pág. 15) Punto, rayo, recta, segmento o plano que corta a un segmento en su punto medio.	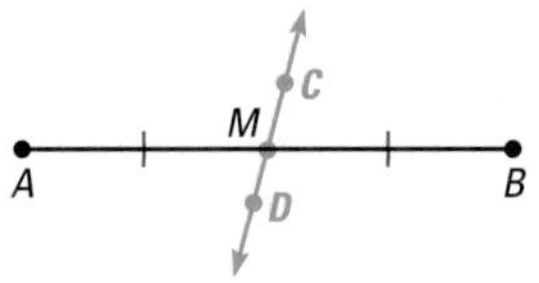 C, M, A, B, D $\overleftrightarrow{CD}$ is a segment bisector of $\overline{AB}$. $\overleftrightarrow{CD}$ es una bisectriz del segmento $\overline{AB}$.
segments of a chord (p. 689) When two chords intersect in the interior of a circle, each chord is divided into two segments called segments of the chord. **segmentos de una cuerda** (pág. 689) Cuando dos cuerdas se cortan en el interior de un círculo, cada cuerda se divide en dos segmentos, llamados segmentos de la cuerda.	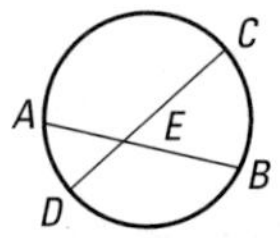 C, A, E, B, D $\overline{EA}$ and $\overline{EB}$ are segments of chord $\overline{AB}$. $\overline{DE}$ and $\overline{EC}$ are segments of chord $\overline{DC}$. $\overline{EA}$ y $\overline{EB}$ son segmentos de la cuerda $\overline{AB}$. $\overline{DE}$ y $\overline{EC}$ son segmentos de la cuerda $\overline{DC}$.

ENGLISH-SPANISH GLOSSARY

self-similar (p. 406) An object such that one part of the object can be enlarged to look like the whole object. **autosemejante** (pág. 406) Objeto tal que una parte de él puede ampliarse de modo que parece el objeto entero.	*See* fractal. *Ver* fractal.
semicircle (p. 659) An arc with endpoints that are the endpoints of a diameter of a circle. The measure of a semicircle is 180°. **semicírculo** (pág. 659) Arco cuyos extremos son los extremos de un diámetro de un círculo. Un semicírculo mide 180°.	Q P R S $\overset{\frown}{QSR}$ is a semicircle. $\overset{\frown}{QSR}$ es un semicírculo.
side of a polygon (p. 42) Each line segment that forms a polygon. *See also* polygon. **lado de un polígono** (pág. 42) Cada segmento de recta que forma un polígono. *Ver también* polígono.	*See* polygon. *Ver* polígono.
sides of an angle (p. 24) *See* angle. **lados de un ángulo** (pág. 24) *Ver* ángulo.	*See* angle. *Ver* ángulo.
similar polygons (p. 372) Two polygons such that their corresponding angles are congruent and the lengths of corresponding sides are proportional. **polígonos semejantes** (pág. 372) Dos polígonos tales que los ángulos correspondientes son congruentes y las longitudes de los lados correspondientes son proporcionales.	B C A D F G E H $ABCD \sim EFGH$
similar solids (p. 847) Two solids of the same type with equal ratios of corresponding linear measures, such as heights or radii. **sólidos semejantes** (pág. 847) Dos sólidos del mismo tipo y con razones iguales de medidas lineales correspondientes, como las alturas o los radios.	
sine (p. 473) A trigonometric ratio, abbreviated as *sin*. For a right triangle *ABC*, the sine of the acute angle *A* is $\sin A = \frac{\text{length of leg opposite } \angle A}{\text{length of hypotenuse}} = \frac{BC}{AB}$. **seno** (pág. 473) Razón trigonométrica, abreviada *sen*. Para un triángulo rectángulo *ABC*, el seno del ángulo agudo *A* es $\text{sen } A = \frac{\text{longitud del cateto opuesto a } \angle A}{\text{longitud de la hipotenusa}} = \frac{BC}{AB}$.	B 3 5 C 4 A $\sin A = \frac{BC}{AB} = \frac{3}{5}$ $\text{sen } A = \frac{BC}{AB} = \frac{3}{5}$

ENGLISH-SPANISH GLOSSARY

973

skew lines (p. 147) Lines that do not intersect and are not coplanar.

rectas alabeadas (pág. 147) Rectas que no se cortan y que no son coplanarias.

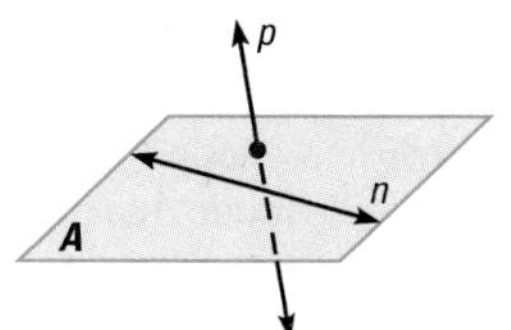

Lines *n* and *p* are skew lines.

Las rectas *n* y *p* son rectas alabeadas.

slant height of a regular pyramid (p. 810) The height of a lateral face of the regular pyramid.

apotema lateral de una pirámide regular (pág. 810) La altura de una cara lateral de la pirámide regular.

See **regular pyramid.**

Ver **pirámide regular.**

slope of a line (p. 171) The slope m of a nonvertical line is the ratio of the vertical change (the *rise*) to horizontal change (the *run*) between any two points on the line: $m = \frac{y_2 - y_1}{x_2 - x_1}$.

pendiente de una recta (pág. 171) La pendiente m de una recta no vertical es la razón entre el cambio vertical (la *distancia vertical*) y el cambio horizontal (la *distancia horizontal*) entre dos puntos cualesquiera de la recta: $m = \frac{y_2 - y_1}{x_2 - x_1}$.

slope-intercept form (p. 180) A linear equation written in the form $y = mx + b$ where m is the slope and b is the y-intercept of the equation's graph.

forma pendiente-intercepto (pág. 180) Ecuación lineal escrita en la forma $y = mx + b$, donde m es la pendiente y b es el intercepto en y de la gráfica de la ecuación.

The equation $y = 3x + 4$ is in slope-intercept form. The slope of the line is 3, and the y-intercept is 4.

La ecuación $y = 3x + 4$ está en la forma pendiente-intercepto. La pendiente de la recta es 3, y el intercepto en y es 4.

solve a right triangle (p. 483) To find the measures of all of the sides and angles of a right triangle.

resolver un triángulo rectángulo (pág. 483) Hallar las medidas de todos los lados y todos los ángulos de un triángulo rectángulo.

You can solve a right triangle if you know either of the following:

- **Two side lengths**
- **One side length and the measure of one acute angle**

Puedes resolver un triángulo rectángulo conociendo uno de estos grupos:

- **Las longitudes de dos lados**
- **La longitud de un lado y la medida de un ángulo agudo**

sphere (p. 838) The set of all points in space equidistant from a given point called the center of the sphere. **esfera** (pág. 838) El conjunto de todos los puntos del espacio que son equidistantes de un punto dado, llamado centro de la esfera.	
square (p. 533) A parallelogram with four congruent sides and four right angles. **cuadrado** (pág. 533) Paralelogramo que tiene los cuatro lados congruentes y los cuatro ángulos rectos.	
standard equation of a circle (p. 699) The standard equation of a circle with center (h, k) and radius r is $(x - h)^2 + (y - k)^2 = r^2$. **ecuación general de un círculo** (pág. 699) La ecuación general de un círculo con centro (h, k) y radio r es $(x - h)^2 + (y - k)^2 = r^2$.	The standard equation of a circle with center (2, 3) and radius 4 is $(x - 2)^2 + (y - 3)^2 = 16$. La ecuación general de un círculo con centro (2, 3) y radio 4 es $(x - 2)^2 + (y - 3)^2 = 16$.
standard form of a linear equation (p. 182) A linear equation written in the form $Ax + By = C$, where A, B, and C are real numbers and A and B are not both zero. **forma general de una ecuación lineal** (pág. 182) Ecuación lineal escrita en la forma $Ax + By = C$, donde A, B y C son números reales y A y B no son ambos cero.	The equation $2x + 3y = 12$ is in standard form. La ecuación $2x + 3y = 12$ está en la forma general.
straight angle (p. 25) An angle with measure equal to 180°. **ángulo llano** (pág. 25) Ángulo que mide 180°.	
supplementary angles (p. 35) Two angles whose measures have the sum 180°. The sum of the measures of an angle and its *supplement* is 180°. **ángulos suplementarios** (pág. 35) Dos ángulos cuyas medidas suman 180°. La suma de las medidas de un ángulo y de su *suplemento* es 180°.	
surface area (p. 803) The sum of the areas of the faces of a polyhedron or other solid. **área superficial** (pág. 803) La suma de las áreas de las caras de un poliedro o de otro sólido.	 $S = 2(3)(4) + 2(4)(6) + 2(3)(6) = 108 \text{ ft}^2$ $S = 2(3)(4) + 2(4)(6) + 2(3)(6) = 108 \text{ pies}^2$

T

tangent (p. 466) A trigonometric ratio, abbreviated as *tan*. For a right triangle ABC, the tangent of the acute angle A is $\tan A = \frac{\text{length of leg opposite } \angle A}{\text{length of leg adjacent to } \angle A} = \frac{BC}{AC}$.

tangente (pág. 466) Razón trigonométrica, abreviada *tan*. Para un triángulo rectángulo ABC, la tangente del ángulo agudo A es $\tan A = \frac{\text{longitud del cateto opuesto a } \angle A}{\text{longitud del cateto adyacente a } \angle A} = \frac{BC}{AC}$.

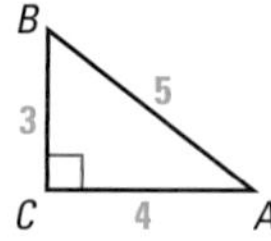

$\tan A = \frac{BC}{AC} = \frac{3}{4}$

tangent line (p. 651) A line in the plane of a circle that intersects the circle in exactly one point, the point of tangency.

recta tangente (pág. 651) Recta del plano de un círculo que corta al círculo en sólo un punto, el punto de tangencia.

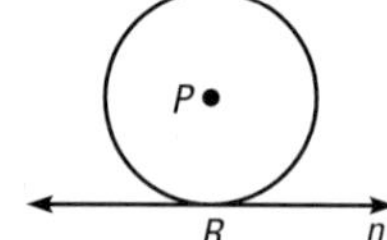

Line *n* is a tangent. *R* is the point of tangency.

La recta *n* es una tangente. *R* es el punto de tangencia.

taxicab geometry (p. 198) A non-Euclidean geometry in which all lines are horizontal or vertical.

geometría de taxis (pág. 198) Geometría no euclidiana en la que todas las rectas son horizontales o verticales.

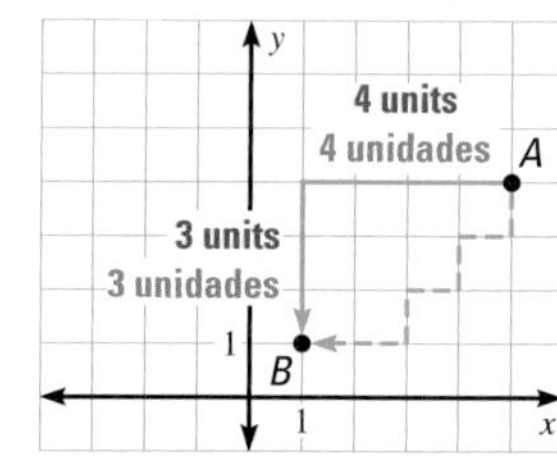

In taxicab geometry, the distance between *A* and *B* is 7 units.

En la geometría de taxis, la distancia entre *A* y *B* es de 7 unidades.

terminal point of a vector (p. 574) The ending point of a vector.

See vector.

punto final de un vector (pág. 574) El punto donde termina el vector.

Ver vector.

tessellation (p. 616) A collection of figures that cover a plane with no gaps or overlaps.

teselación (pág. 616) Colección de figuras que recubren un plano sin sobreponerse y sin huecos.

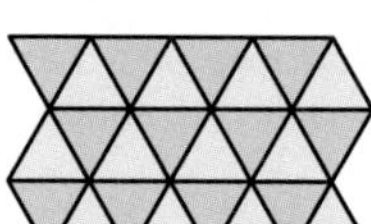

tetrahedron (p. 796) A polyhedron with four faces.

tetraedro (pág. 796) Poliedro con cuatro caras.

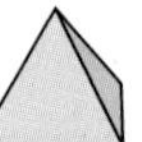

976

theorem (p. 113) A true statement that follows as a result of other true statements. **teorema** (pág. 113) Enunciado verdadero que surge como resultado de otros enunciados verdaderos.	**Vertical angles are congruent.** **Los ángulos opuestos por el vértice son congruentes.**
transformation (p. 272) An operation that moves or changes a geometric figure in some way to produce a new figure. **transformación** (pág. 272) Operación que desplaza o cambia de alguna manera una figura geométrica para crear una nueva figura.	**Four basic transformations are translations, reflections, rotations, and dilations.** **Cuatro transformaciones básicas son las traslaciones, las reflexiones, las rotaciones y las dilataciones.**
translation (pp. 272, 572) A transformation that moves every point of a figure the same distance in the same direction. **traslación** (págs. 272, 572) Transformación que desplaza cada punto de una figura la misma distancia en la misma dirección.	
transversal (p. 149) A line that intersects two or more coplanar lines at different points. **transversal** (pág. 149) Recta que corta a dos o más rectas coplanarias en distintos puntos.	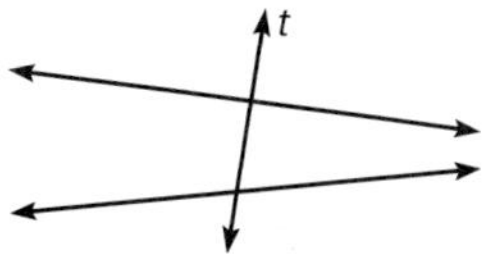 t transversal *t*
trapezoid (p. 542) A quadrilateral with exactly one pair of parallel sides, called bases. The nonparallel sides are legs. **trapecio** (pág. 542) Cuadrilátero que tiene sólo un par de lados paralelos, llamados bases. Los lados no paralelos son catetos.	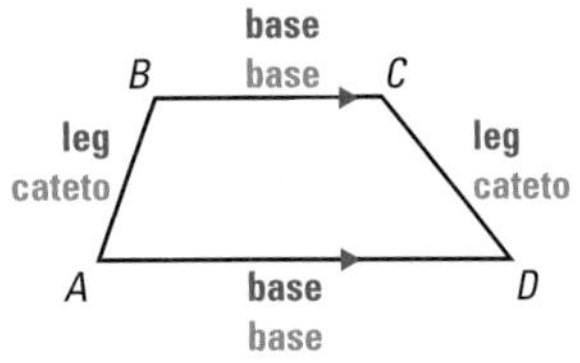 base / base, B, C, leg / cateto, leg / cateto, A, D, base / base
triangle (pp. 43, 217) A polygon with three sides. **triángulo** (págs. 43, 217) Polígono con tres lados.	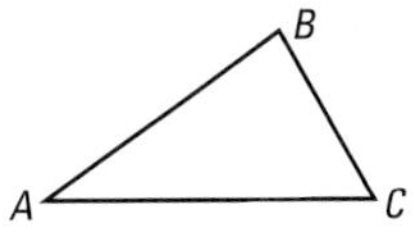 A, B, C $\triangle ABC$

ENGLISH-SPANISH GLOSSARY

trigonometric ratio (p. 466) A ratio of the lengths of two sides in a right triangle. *See also* sine, cosine, *and* tangent. **razón trigonométrica** (pág. 466) Razón entre las longitudes de dos lados de un triángulo rectángulo. *Ver también* seno, coseno *y* tangente.	**Three common trigonometric ratios are sine, cosine, and tangent.** **Tres razones trigonométricas comunes son el seno, el coseno y la tangente.** 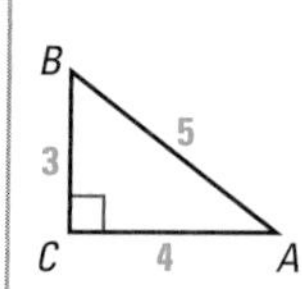 $\tan A = \frac{BC}{AC} = \frac{3}{4}$ $\sin A = \frac{BC}{AB} = \frac{3}{5}$ $\cos A = \frac{AC}{AB} = \frac{4}{5}$ $\tan A = \frac{BC}{AC} = \frac{3}{4}$ $\text{sen } A = \frac{BC}{AB} = \frac{3}{5}$ $\cos A = \frac{AC}{AB} = \frac{4}{5}$
truth table (p. 95) A table that shows the truth values for a hypothesis, a conclusion, and a conditional statement using the hypothesis and conclusion. **tabla de verdad** (pág. 95) Tabla que muestra los valores de verdad de una hipótesis, de una conclusión y de un enunciado condicional usando la hipótesis y la conclusión.	**Truth Table**: p / q / $p \rightarrow q$: T T T; T F F; F T T; F F T **Tabla de verdad**: p / q / $p \rightarrow q$: V V V; V F F; F V V; F F V
truth value of a statement (p. 95) The truth or falsity of the statement. **valor de verdad de un enunciado** (pág. 95) La verdad o falsedad de un enunciado.	*See* **truth table.** *Ver* **tabla de verdad.**
two-column proof (p. 112) A type of proof written as numbered statements and corresponding reasons that show an argument in a logical order. **prueba de dos columnas** (pág. 112) Tipo de prueba en la que se escriben enunciados numerados y razones correspondientes que muestran un argumento siguiendo un orden lógico.	*See* **Example 1 on page 112.** *Ver* **el ejemplo 1 de la página 112.**

U

undefined term (p. 2) A word that does not have a formal definition, but there is agreement about what the word means. **término indefinido** (pág. 2) Palabra que no tiene una definición establecida, pero cuyo significado se acepta comúnmente.	***Point, line,* and *plane* are undefined terms.** ***Punto, recta* y *plano* son términos indefinidos.**

Truth Table

p	q	$p \rightarrow q$
T	T	T
T	F	F
F	T	T
F	F	T

Tabla de verdad

p	q	$p \rightarrow q$
V	V	V
V	F	F
F	V	V
F	F	V

ENGLISH-SPANISH GLOSSARY

unit of measure (p. 727) The quantity or increment to which something is measured.

unidad de medida (pág. 727) La cantidad o el incremento con que algo se mide.

If a segment is measured using a ruler marked in eighths of an inch, the unit of measure is $\frac{1}{8}$ inch.

Si un segmento se mide con una regla que lleva señalados los octavos de pulgada, la unidad de medida es $\frac{1}{8}$ pulgada.

V

vector (p. 574) A quantity that has both direction and magnitude, and is represented in the coordinate plane by an arrow drawn from one point to another.

vector (pág. 574) Cantidad que tiene tanto dirección como magnitud y es representada en el plano de coordenadas por una flecha dibujada de un punto a otro.

G
F

$\overrightarrow{FG}$ with initial point F and terminal point G.

$\overrightarrow{FG}$ con punto inicial F y punto final G.

vertex angle of an isosceles triangle (p. 264) The angle formed by the legs of an isosceles triangle.

ángulo del vértice de un triángulo isósceles (pág. 264) El ángulo formado por los catetos de un triángulo isósceles.

vertex angle
ángulo del vértice
base angles
ángulos básicos

vertex of a cone (p. 812) *See* cone.

vértice de un cono (pág. 812) *Ver* cono.

See cone.

Ver cono.

vertex of a polygon (p. 42) Each endpoint of a side of a polygon. Plural is *vertices*. *See also* polygon.

vértice de un polígono (pág. 42) Cada extremo de un lado de un polígono. *Ver también* polígono.

See polygon.

Ver polígono.

vertex of a polyhedron (p. 794) A point where three or more edges of a polyhedron meet.

vértice de un poliedro (pág. 794) Punto donde confluyen tres o más aristas de un poliedro.

vertex
vértice

vertex of a pyramid (p. 810) *See* pyramid.

vértice de una pirámide (pág. 810) *Ver* pirámide.

See pyramid.

Ver pirámide.

vertex of an angle (p. 24) *See* angle.

vértice de un ángulo (pág. 24) *Ver* ángulo.

See angle.

Ver ángulo.

vertical angles (p. 37) Two angles whose sides form two pairs of opposite rays. **ángulos opuestos por el vértice** (pág. 37) Dos ángulos cuyos lados forman dos pares de rayos opuestos.	$\angle 1$ and $\angle 4$ are vertical angles. $\angle 2$ and $\angle 3$ are vertical angles. $\angle 1$ y $\angle 4$ son ángulos opuestos por el vértice. $\angle 2$ y $\angle 3$ son ángulos opuestos por el vértice.
vertical component of a vector (p. 574) The vertical change from the initial point to the terminal point of a vector. **componente vertical de un vector** (pág. 574) El cambio vertical entre el punto inicial y el punto final del vector.	*See* **component form of a vector.** *Ver* **forma de componentes de un vector.**
volume of a solid (p. 819) The number of cubic units contained in the interior of a solid. **volumen de un sólido** (pág. 819) El número de unidades cúbicas contenidas en el interior de un sólido.	3 ft / 3 pies, 4 ft / 4 pies, 6 ft / 6 pies Volume $= 3(4)(6) = 72 \text{ ft}^3$ Volumen $= 3(4)(6) = 72 \text{ pies}^3$

ENGLISH-SPANISH GLOSSARY

Credits

Photographs

Cover Jerry Dodrill/Outdoor Collection/Aurora Photos; **iv** *top* Meridian Creative Group; *top center* Robert C. Jenks, Jenks Studio; *bottom center* McDougal Littell; *bottom* Jerry Head Jr.; **viii** Greg Epperson/Index Stock Imagery; **ix** Chris Mellor/Getty Index Stock Imagery; **xii** Johannes Kroemer/Photonica/Getty Images; **xiii** Photowood/Corbis; **xiv** Steve Dunwell/Getty Images; **xv** Philip Gould/Corbis; **xvi** Veer; **xvii** Grant Faint/Getty Images; **xviii** Patrick Schneider/The Charlotte Observer/AP/Wide World Photos; **xix** Wes Thompson/Corbis; **1–2** Brian Bailey/Getty Images; **2** William Sallaz/Duomo/Corbis; **7** *center left* Robert Landau/Corbis; *center right* Daisuke Morita/Getty Images; *bottom* Davis Barber/PhotoEdit; *center* LUCKYLOOK/DanitaDelimont.com; **9** Ronan Coyne; **13** Buddy Mays/Corbis; **14** Doug Pensinger/Getty Images; **15** Brett Froomer/Getty Images; **21** *top* John Greim/Index Stock Imagery; *center* William R. Curtsinger/National Geographic Society; **24** Southern Stock/Getty Images; **27** Timothy Fadek/Polaris Images; **30** Collier Campbell Lifeworks/Corbis; **31** *top* "Bird in Flight" by Starr Kempf/Starr Enterprises. Photo by: Llewellyn Falco; *bottom* Robert Llewellyn/Corbis; **35** Jeff Greenberg/The Image Works; **40** Mark Duncan/AP/Wide World Photos; **42** Nancy Crane; **44** Ryan McVay/Getty Images; **46** *center left* S Meltzer/PhotoLink/Getty Images; *center right, left* PhotoDisc/Getty Images; *right* Thinkstock/PunchStock; **49** Hubble Heritage Team/AP/Wide World Photos; **51** Dennis MacDonald/AGE Fotostock; **53** *center left* Samba Photo/Photonica/Getty Images; *left* foodfolio/Alamy; *center right* School Division/Houghton Mifflin; *right* Burke/Triolo/Brand X Pictures/PictureQuest; *bee* Photospin Power Photos/Bugs & Buttterflies, Volume 8; **54** Will & Deni McIntyre/Stone/Getty Images; **55** *center right* Scott Ols/Getty Images; *bottom* NASA/AP/Wide World Photos; **70–71** Philip Rostron/Masterfile; **72** *top* Allsport Concepts/Mike Powell/Getty Images; **74** *both* Royalty-Free/Corbis; **78** PhotoDisc/Getty Images; **79** Martha Granger/Edge Productions/McDougal Littell; **80** Gerard Lacz/Animals Animals - Earth Scenes; **84** Jim Sugar/Corbis; **87** George H. H. Huey/Corbis; **89** Thomas Schmitt/Getty Images; **90** *left* Katrina Wittkamp/Getty Images; *right* William Whitehurst/Corbis; **91** Royalty-Free/Corbis; **92** *center right* Custom Medical Stock Photo; *center left* Kaj R. Svensson/Science Photo Library; *right* Michael Barnett/Science Photo Library; *left* Kaj R. Svensson/Science Photo Library; **96** Bernd Obermann/Corbis; **101** *top center* Caron Philippe/Sygma/Corbis; *top right* Jay Penni Photography/McDougal Littell; *top left* Bob Daemmrich/The Image Works; **105** Bob Thomas/Getty Images; **112** John Sohm/Alamy; **117** Charles D. Winters/Photo Researchers, Inc.; **119** Sculpture: "Adam" by Alexander Liberman. Photo Credit: Omni Photo Communications Inc./Index Stock Imagery; **124** Image du Sud/eStock Photo; **128** Image Farm/PictureQuest; **130** *bottom* Barbara Van Zanten/Lonely Planet Images; *top* Jay Penni Photography/McDougal Littell; **144–145** John Angerson/Alamy; **147** Gary Rhijnsburger/Masterfile; **148** Corbis/PictureQuest; **150** Michael Newman/PhotoEdit; **151** Mike Powell/Getty Images; **152** Paul Rocheleau Photography; **154** Gareth McCormack/Lonely Planet Images; **157** Paul Eekhoff/Masterfile; **159** *both* Copyright 2005 Parallax, Inc. Toddler is a registered trademark of Parallax, Inc. All rights reserved.; **161** Digital Vision/Getty Images; **164** Ryan McVay/Getty Images; **167** *bottom* Peter Sterling/Getty Images; *top* Erin Hogan/Getty Images; **168** C-Squared Studios/Getty Images; **170** *center left* Bruno Morandi/Getty Images; *bottom right* Paul A. Souders/Corbis; **171** SHOGORO/Photonica/Getty Images; **174** Courtesy of Cedar Point Amusement Park/Resort; **177** Bruce Leighty/Index Stock Imagery; **180** Lori Adamski Peek/Getty Images; **183** Bill Aron/PhotoEdit; **186** David R. Frazier PhotoLibrary, Inc/Alamy; **190** *First Aid Folly with waterwheel.* Parc de la Vilette, Paris, 1986, by Bernard Tschumi. Photo credit: Art on File/Corbis; **190**; **193** Sculpture: Lucas Samaras,"Chair Transformation #20B", 1996. Patinated bronze. 11'9"x7'2"x2'2-3/4" National Gallery of Art, Washington D.C. © Lucas Samaras, courtesy PaceWildenstein, New York. Photo credit: Ventura/FOLIO, Inc.; **195** *center* Jeffrey Becorn/Lonely Planet Images; *left* Ned Friary/Lonely Planet Images; *right* Image Source/ImageState; **196** Stephen Wilkes/Getty Images; **200** Dennis MacDonald/Alamy; **213** *right* plainpicture/Alamy; *left* Royalty-Free/Corbis; *center* Tom Benoit/SuperStock; **214–215** Bill Ross/Corbis; **217** *top* Nancy Sheehan/PhotoEdit; *bottom* Royalty-Free/Corbis; **220** Nicolas Sapieha/Corbis; **223** MedioImages/SuperStock; **225** Image Source/Alamy; **230** *top* Collier Campbell Lifeworks/Corbis; *center right* Tony Freeman/PhotoEdit; **234** Mark Downey/Getty Images; **240** Ron Watts/Corbis; **242** Terry W. Eggers/Corbis; **245** *right* Jeremy Woodhouse/Masterfile; *left* Photowood Inc./Corbis; **248** *top left* Comstock; *top right* William Harrigan/Lonely Planet Images; **249** ShotFile/Alamy; **250** *right* Richard Cummins/Lonely Planet Images; *center* SuperStock; *left* Doug Houghton/Alamy; **254** *bottom* Michael Melford/Getty Images; **256** *top* Douglas C Pizac, Staff/AP/Wide World Photos; *center* Max Earey/Alamy; **257** Richard Hamilton Smith/Corbis; **261** Buddy Mays/Corbis; **262** *top center* Scott Gilchrist/Masterfile; *top right* Ron Watts/Corbis; *top left* Royalty-Free/Corbis; **264** Morton Beebe/Corbis; **266** Jeff Baker/Getty Images; **268** *left* Bob Elsdale/Getty Images; *center* Royalty-Free/Corbis; *right* Radlund & Associates/PictureQuest; **269** *top right* JupiterImages/Comstock; *center right* Digital Vision/Getty Images; **272** *top* Michael Newman/PhotoEdit; *bottom* Digital Vision/Getty Images; **280** *center right* Jay Penni Photography/McDougal Littell; *bottom right* Michael Matisse/Getty Images; **286** Peter Christopher/Masterfile; **292–293** Johannes Kroemer/Photonica/Getty Images; **295** Bob Elsdale/Getty Images; **296** Alfred Pasieka/Science Photo Library; **300** *bottom* Graham Henderson/Elizabeth Whiting and Associates/Corbis; **303** Alex Wong/Getty Images; **306** *left* Dennis Hallinan/Alamy; *center* Royalty Free/PictureQuest; *right* Fernando Bueno/Getty Images; **310** Tracy Frankel/Getty Images; **317** Martin Llado/Lonely Planet Images; **318** *all* Jay Penni Photography/McDougal Littell; **319** Sculpture: Big Crinkley, Estate of Alexander Calder/Artists Rights Society (ARS), New York. Photo Credit: Owaki-Kulla/Corbis; **322** *left* Phil Jason/Getty Images; *center* Adrienne Cleveland, www.naturalsights.com; *right* Chris Daniels/Corbis; **324** Lawrence Lawry/Getty Images; **328** James Randklev/Corbis; **333** Jay Penni Photography/McDougal Littell; **335** Marc Romanelli/Getty Images; **340** Robert Brenner/PhotoEdit; **342** *top* DK Limited/Corbis; *bottom* Dorling Kindersley/Getty Images; **352** oote boe/Alamy; **354–355** age fotostock/SuperStock; **356** Karl Maslowski/Photo Researchers, Inc.; **357** Jeff Greenberg/The Image Works; **359** Mike Powell/Getty Images; **362** Stockdisc/Getty Images; **364** The Longaberger Company Home Office, Newark, Ohio; **366** Joseph Sohm/ChromoSohm, Inc./Corbis; **368** The Longaberger Company Home Office, Newark, Ohio; **369** *bottom* Erick Fowke/PhotoEdit; **369** *top* SciMat/Photo Researchers, Inc.; **371** *both* Barry Winiker/Index Stock Imagery; **372** Detlev Van Ravenswaay/Science Photo Library; **380** Royalty-Free/Corbis; **381** Steve Fitchett/Getty Images; **386** Hubert Stadler/Corbis; **388** Matthias Kulka/Corbis; **397** Premium Stock/Corbis; **406** Stephen Johnson/Corbis; **409** Tom Stewart/Corbis; **410** *both* Sean Justice/Getty Images; **414** Bonnie Kamin/PhotoEdit; **416** Main Street America/PhotoDisc/Veer;

CREDITS

430–431 Randy Lincks/Masterfile; **433** Paul Jaris/Stock Image/Alamy; **437** *center* Alan Schein Photography/Corbis; *right* Nick Dolding/Getty Images; *left* BananaStock/SuperStock; **441** Dick Blume/Syracuse Newspapers/The Image Works; **443** Annebicque Bernard/Sygma/Corbis; **445** Jay Penni Photography/McDougal Littell; **446** Jeff Greenberg/PhotoEdit; **449** Royalty-Free/Corbis; **453** *center* Marko Hagerty/Getty Images; *right* Ken Davies/Masterfile; *left* John Elk III/Lonely Planet Images; **455** Philippe McClelland/Getty Images; **456** Royalty-Free/Corbis; **457** Adrienne Cleveland, www.naturalsights.com; **459** Thinkstock/PictureQuest; **460** Wendy Rock; **463** Andrea McDonough; **465** Mike Smith; **466** SuperStock/Alamy; **468** Owaiki-Kulla/Corbis; **471** Walter Bibikow/Getty Images; **472** Digital Vision/Getty Images; **473** Ross Barnett/Lonely Planet Images; **476** Paul A. Souders/Corbis; **479** Profimedia.CZ s.r.o./Alamy; **481** Paul A. Souders/Corbis; **483** Royalty-Free/Corbis; **484** Adrienne Cleveland, www.naturalsights.com; **487** Mike Powell/Getty Images; **492** *top* Stockbyte Gold/Alamy; *bottom* Massimo Listri/Corbis; **498** Macduff Everton/Corbis; **504–505** Richard Hamilton Smith/Corbis; **507** Paul J.Sutton/Duomo/Corbis; **508** Jay Penni Photography/McDougal Littell; **512** Decagon Greenhouse picture courtesy of Lowfield Limited (FAWT Greenhouses); **515** Mark Langford; **517** Jim Seiner/McDougal Littell; **519** Dynamic Graphics Group/Creatas/Alamy; **522** IT Stock Free/PictureQuest; **524** © Stephen Bax; **528** *all* Jay Penni Photography/McDougal Littell; **532** *right* from *Sky & Telescope*. Copyright ©1993 by Sky Publishing Corp. Reprinted by permission.; **533** Ariel Skelley/Corbis; **537** *left* Royalty-Free/Corbis; *center* Sandro Vannini/Corbis; *right* Roman Soumar/Corbis; **542** Nikreates/Alamy; **545** Spencer Grant/PhotoEdit; **548** *center (all)* Topham/The Image Works; *top right* Royalty-Free/Stockbyte; **552** John Elk III/Lonely Planet Images; **556** *top left* David White/Index Stock Imagery; *top right* Christie's Images/Corbis; *top center* Arthur Thevenart/Corbis; *center right* Macduff Everton/Corbis; **558** *bottom left* David Sanger Photography/Alamy; *top left* Art on File/Corbis; **570–571** Araldo de Luca/Corbis; **572** Royalty-Free/Corbis; **577** *left* FK Photo/Corbis; *right* Steve Allen/PictureQuest; **579** Volker Steger/Christian Bardele/Science Photo Library; **580** David Young-Wolff/Getty Images; **586** Rick Gomez/Masterfile; **589** Andy Rouse/Getty Images; **595** *right* Mark & Audrey Gibson/Lonely Planet Images; *center* Gerald Hinde/Getty Images; *left* Royalty-Free/Corbis; **597** Phillip Spears/Getty Images; **598** Charles E. Pefley/Mira; **602** *center* Ron Kimball/Ron Kimball Stock; *left* Royalty-Free/Corbis; *right* Brannhage/Premium/Panoramic Images; **604** *top left* Danny Lehman/Corbis; *top center* Tim Wright/Corbis; *right* Neil Rabinowitz/Corbis; *center right* Image Source/PictureQuest; **608** Joel W. Rogers/Corbis; **613** Stock Connection Blue/Alamy; **619** *top* Saulius T. Kondrotas/Alamy; *bottom center* Robert Llewellyn/Corbis; *bottom right* Arco/C.Huetteer/Alamy; *bottom left* Rod Planck/Photo Researchers, Inc.; *center right* Leroy Simon/Getty Images; **622** *right* Artville; *left* Jay Penni Photography/McDougal Littell; *center* Danny Lehman/Corbis; **623** *all* Charles Krebs/Picture Arts; **624** Jim Wark/Lonely Planet Images; **626** *top* Raeanne Rubenstein/Index Stock Imagery; **626** *bottom left, bottom right* Royalty-Free/Corbis; **631** *left* Peter Chadwick/Science Photo Library/Photo Researchers, Inc.; *center* John T. Fowler/The Image Finders; *right* Rod Planck/Photo Researchers, Inc.; **634** *top* Sarah Buss/McDougal Littell; *bottom* Scott Berner/Index Stock Imagery; **644** Winchester Mystery House; **647** Don Stevenson/Mira; **648–649** DesignPics Inc./Index Stock Imagery; **651** Noel Hendrickson/Masterfile; **656** *dime, quarter* Artville; *button* Seide Preis/Getty Images; **659** Wolfgang Kaehler/Corbis; **663** Royalty-Free/Corbis; **664** BananaStock/Alamy; **672** David Young-Wolff/PhotoEdit; **677** Jay Penni Photography/McDougal Littell; **679** Original image courtesy of NASA/Corbis; **680** Jan Butchofsky-Houser/Corbis; **687** Joseph Sohm/ChromoSohm Inc./Corbis; **689** NASA/Photo Researchers, Inc.; **694** Barry Cronin/Zuma/Corbis; **697** PhotoDisc/Getty Images; **699** Jeff Greenberg/PhotoEdit; **701** Wally Santana/AP/Wide World Photos; **704** Lester Lefkowitz/Getty Images; **705** Ryan McVay/Getty Images; **706** Ashley Cooper/Alamy; **718–719** Mike Dobel/Alamy; **720** Dave G. Houser/Corbis; *bottom (all)* Jay Penni Photography/McDougal Littell; **722** Bruce Burkhardt/Corbis; **725** *bottom left* Jay Penni Photography/McDougal Littell; *top* B.A.E. Inc./Alamy; **728** Jay Penni Photography/McDougal Littell; **730** Ker Robertson/Getty Images; **731** *both* Stockbyte Royalty-Free; **735** Martyn Goddard/Getty Images; **737** Davis Barber/PhotoEdit; **739** Rudi Von Briel/PhotoEdit; **742** Jeff Greenberg/PhotoEdit; **745** *bottom left* School Division/Houghton Mifflin; *center right* Gerald French/Corbis; **746** Roy Ooms/Masterfile; **747** Ryan McVay/Getty Images; **751** Kim Karpeles/Alamy; **755** *top* Royalty-Free/Corbis; *center left* Howard Sokol/Index Stock Imagery; *center right* Tim O'Hara/Index Stock Imagery; **760** *top* NOAA/NASA; *center (both)* Meeker & Associates, Inc.; **762** CuboImages srl/Alamy; **767** Gareth McCormack/Lonely Planet Images; **768** Stephen Dalton/Photo Researcher, Inc.; **771** Bill Bachman; **773** Terry Husebye/Getty Images; **778** *left* Bob Daemmrich Photography; **790–791** Richard Cummins/Lonely Planet Images; **794** Arthur S Aubury/PhotoDisc Royalty-Free/Getty Images; **799** *all* School Division/Houghton Mifflin; **800** *top right* JupiterImages/Comstock; **803** Matthias Tunger/Digital Vision/Getty Images; **805** McDougal Littell; **807** *left* PhotoDisc/Getty Images; *center* Michael Booth/Alamy; *right* Brand X Pictures; **808** Royalty-Free/Corbis; **810** Jack Smith, staff/AP/Wide World Photos; **813** Siede Preis/PhotoDisc/Getty Images; **814** *center* C-Squared Studios/PhotoDisc/Getty Images; *left* Rhoda Peacher/R Photographs; *right* Steve Cole/PhotoDisc/Getty Images; **816** *left* Kirkendall-Spring Photographers; *right* Harvey Lloyd/Getty Images; **818** *right* David R. Frazier Photolibrary, Inc/Alamy; **818** *left* Andrew Paterson/Alamy; **819** Mark E. Gibson/Gibson Stock Photography; **820** PhotoObjects; **822** Romartyr Hamburg, 1998, aluminum and acrylic glass, © Carl Andre/Licensed by VAGA, New York, NY. Photo Credit: Bridgeman Art Library; **823** *bottom left* C-Squared Studios/Getty Images; *bottom center* Eising Food Photography/Stockfood America; *bottom right* PhotoObjects; **824** *center right* Jay Penni Photography/McDougal Littell; *bottom right* Schafer & Hill/Getty Images; **825** Claire Rydell/Index Stock Imagery; **829** Amr Nabil/AP/Wide World Photos; **830** Sylvain Grandadam/Getty Images; **834** Thinkstock/PictureQuest; **835** Mystic Seaport Museum - Mystic, CT; **838** *bottom* Royalty-Free/Corbis; *top* Bob Daemmrich/PhotoEdit; **840** Jump Photography Archive; **841** Corbis; **842** *bottom left* Royalty-Free/Getty Images; *bottom center* Michel Tcherevkoff/Getty Images; *bottom right* Bonnie Jacobs/Alamy; **844** Richard Price/Getty Images; **847** © Claes Oldenburg, Coosje van Bruggen, *Binoculars*,1991 Steel frame. Exterior: concrete and cement plaster painted with elastomeric paint. Interior: gypsum plaster 45 x 44 x 18 ft. (13.7 x 13.4 x 5.5 m) Central component of a building designed by Frank O. Gehry and Associates, 340 Main St., Venice, California. Photo Credit: Nik Wheeler/Corbis; **852** PhotoObjects/PictureQuest; **855** *top right* Royalty-Free/Corbis; **861** Royalty-Free/Corbis; **864** Eric Kamp/Index Stock Imagery; **867** James Morrell/Getty Images.

Illustrations and Maps

Argosy **1, 71, 145, 199, 215, 290** *top right,* **290** *top left,* **293, 355, 386** *top center,* **426, 431, 463** *top left,* **503** *bottom right,* **503** *center right,* **505, 523, 532** *center left,* **566, 567, 571, 578** *center,* **579, 613, 620, 624** *top right,* **640, 644, 647** *bottom,* **649, 682, 685** *center right,* **694** *center right,* **716, 717, 719, 730, 732, 735, 742, 761, 788** *center right,* **791, 800** *center,* **808, 816, 818** *left,* **831, 834** *top,* **838, 844** *center right,* **855** *right*; Kenneth Batelman **226, 300, 315** *bottom right,* **386** *center right,* **394** *center right,* **417, 424, 475** *center,* **685** *top right,* **706** *right,* **749**; Steve Cowden **6, 21, 36, 39, 41, 58** *bottom,* **77, 101, 115, 156**; Stephen Durke **187, 223, 308** *top center,* **308** *bottom right,* **317** *top right,* **319, 320, 335, 335, 340, 342** *center right,* **383, 390, 416** *left,* **439, 450, 479** *bottom right,* **479** *center right,* **485, 488** *top,* **575, 578** *center right,* **596** *center,* **657** *center,* **674, 687** *top left,* **774, 834** *center right*; John Francis **336, 393, 475** *top,* **520** *center,* **539, 614, 623, 624** *center right,* **631, 760, 778** *bottom left,* **778** *top right,* **822, 826**; Patrick Gnan/Deborah Wolfe, Ltd. **10** *bottom right,* **31, 110, 119, 167, 238** *bottom right,* **248** *bottom right,* **254, 254, 305, 334, 339, 352** *center right,* **403** *both,* **422, 445, 471, 474, 488** *center,* **536, 663** *center right,* **665, 670, 686, 698, 745** *left,* **751, 763, 776, 796, 825**; Chris Lyons **238** *top,* **333** *center,* **512** *center,* **526, 543, 591, 595, 597**; Steve McEntee **159** *top,* **196, 261, 262, 311, 317, 452, 482, 596** *center right,* **752, 752** *top right*; Sarah Buss/McDougal Littell **578** *top right*; Karen Minot **91, 168, 333** *center right,* **369, 703, 738, 754, 844** *bottom right*; Paul Mirocha **298, 834** *bottom right*; Laurie O'Keefe **363, 694** *top right,* **773, 778** *bottom right,* **817**; Jun Park **848**; David Puckett **329, 329**; Tony Randazzo/American Artists **706** *left,* **726, 767**; Mark Schroeder **365, 520** *top,* **528, 548, 663** *top right,* **669** *center,* **669** *bottom,* **692, 827, 853**; Dan Stuckenschneider **151, 162, 170** *top left,* **170** *center right,* **176, 177, 278** *center,* **315** *center right,* **316, 324** *top right,* **438, 455, 463** *top right*; Robert Ulrich **510**; Carol Zuber-Mallison **32** *top,* **159** *bottom,* **213, 695**. All other illustrations © McDougal Littell/Houghton Mifflin Company.

CREDITS

Worked-Out Solutions

This section of the book provides step-by-step solutions to exercises with circled exercise numbers. These solutions provide models that can help guide your work with the homework exercises.

The separate **Selected Answers** section follows this section. It provides numerous answers that you can use to check your own answers.

Chapter 1

Lesson 1.1 (pp. 5–8)

15.

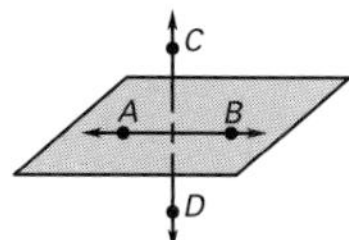

19. Plane PQS and plane HGS intersect at $\overleftrightarrow{RS}$.

43. A 4-legged table may rock from side to side because four points are not necessarily coplanar. A 3-legged table would not rock because three points determine a unique plane.

Lesson 1.2 (pp. 12–14)

13.

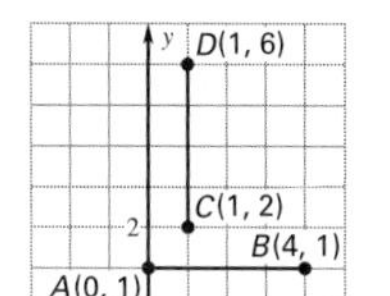

$AB = |4 - 0| = 4$

$CD = |6 - 2| = 4$

So, $\overline{AB} \cong \overline{CD}$.

17. $JL = |1 - (-6)| = |1 + 6| = 7$

33. a. $AC = AB + BC = 1282 + 601 = 1883$ mi

b. $d = rt \rightarrow 2000 = r(40) \rightarrow r \approx 50$ mi/h

Lesson 1.3 (pp. 19–22)

15. $SM = MU$

$x + 15 = 4x - 45 \rightarrow x = 20$

$SU = SM + MU = x + 15 + 4x - 45 = 70$

35. Length: $|3 - (-4)| = 7$ units

Coordinate of midpoint: $\dfrac{x_1 + x_2}{2} = \dfrac{-4 + 3}{2}$

$= -\dfrac{1}{2}$

49.

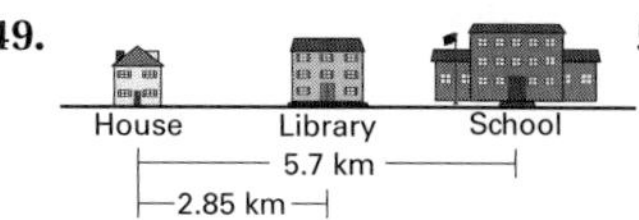

$5.7 \div 2 = 2.85$ km

Lesson 1.4 (pp. 28–32)

15. Another name for $\angle ACB$ is $\angle BCA$. The angle is a right angle because it is labeled with a red square.

23. $m\angle ADC = m\angle ADB + m\angle CDB$

$= 21° + 44° = 65°$

53. a. $m\angle DEF = m\angle ABC = 112°$

b. $m\angle ABG = \frac{1}{2} \cdot m\angle ABC = \frac{1}{2}(112°) = 56°$

c. $m\angle CBG = \frac{1}{2} \cdot m\angle ABC = \frac{1}{2}(112°) = 56°$

d. $m\angle DEG = \frac{1}{2} \cdot m\angle DEF = \frac{1}{2}(112°) = 56°$

Lesson 1.5 (pp. 38–41)

9. $m\angle 1 + m\angle 2 = 90° \rightarrow 21° + m\angle 2 = 90° \rightarrow m\angle 2 = 69°$

21. $\angle 1$ and $\angle 2$ are a linear pair.

47. Neither, because the sum of their measures is greater than 180°.

Lesson 1.6 (pp. 44–47)

13. The polygon is a quadrilateral because it has 4 sides. It is equiangular but not equilateral, so it is not regular.

19. A decagon is sometimes regular, because all of its sides and all of its angles can be congruent, but they don't have to be.

33. The polygon has 3 sides, so it is a triangle. It appears to be regular.

Lesson 1.7 (pp. 52–56)

7. $P = a + b + c = 30 + 72 + 78 = 180$ yd

$A = \frac{1}{2}bh = \frac{1}{2}(72)(30) = 1080 \text{ yd}^2$

21. $13 \cancel{\text{ft}^2} \cdot \frac{1 \text{ yd}^2}{9 \cancel{\text{ft}^2}} \approx 1.44 \text{ yd}^2$

41. $A = \ell w = 45(30) = 1350$

$P = 2\ell + 2w = 2(45) + 2(30) = 150$

You need to cover 1350 square yards with grass seed, and you need

$150 \cancel{\text{yd}} \cdot \frac{3 \text{ ft}}{1 \cancel{\text{yd}}} = 450$ feet of fencing.

Chapter 2

Lesson 2.1 (pp. 75–78)

7. 3, 12, 48, 192, . . .
×4 ×4 ×4 ×4

Each number in the pattern is four times the previous number. The next number is 768.

15. Counterexample:

$(2 + 5)^2 = 7^2 = 49 \neq 2^2 + 5^2 = 4 + 25 = 29$

33. *Sample answer:* Conjecture: In 2004, more than 7 trillion e-mail messages will be sent. The number of e-mail messages has increased each year for 7 years prior to 2004. If this pattern continues, the total will exceed 7 trillion in 2004.

Lesson 2.2 (pp. 82–85)

11. False; a polygon could have 5 sides without being a regular pentagon.

Counterexample: 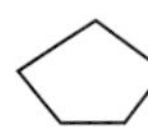

17. False; it is not marked that $\overleftrightarrow{PQ}$ and $\overleftrightarrow{ST}$ intersect at a right angle, so you do not know that they are perpendicular.

33. You can show that the statement is false by finding a counterexample: swimming is a sport, but the participants do not wear helmets.

Lesson 2.3 (pp. 90–93)

7. If a rectangle has four equal side lengths, then it is a regular polygon.

17. If the bakery's revenue is greater than its costs, you will get a raise.

21. Deductive reasoning; the conclusion is reached by using laws of logic and the facts about school rules and what you did that day.

Lesson 2.4 (pp. 99–102)

7. Line p intersects line q at point H.

13. False. *Sample answer:* Consider any pair of opposite sides of a prism, which do not intersect.

31. Postulate 7: If two lines intersect, then their intersection is exactly one point.

Lesson 2.5 (pp. 108–111)

9.

$3(2x + 11) = 9$	Given
$6x + 33 = 9$	Distributive Property
$6x = -24$	Subtraction Property of Equality
$x = -4$	Division Property of Equality

21. If $AB = 20$, then $AB + CD = 20 + CD$.

31.

$P = 2\ell + 2w$	Given
$P - 2w = 2\ell$	Subtraction Property of Equality
$\frac{P}{2} - w = \ell$	Division Property of Equality

When $P = 55$ and $w = 11$:

$\ell = \frac{55}{2} - 11 = 16.5$ meters

Lesson 2.6 (pp. 116–119)

7. If $\angle F \cong \angle J$ and $\angle J \cong \angle L$, then $\angle F \cong \angle L$.

15. Cottage — Snack shop — Bike rentals — Arcade — Kite shop

21.

Statements	Reasons
1. $\overrightarrow{TV}$ bisects $\angle UTW$.	1. Given
2. $\angle 1 \cong \angle 2$	2. Definition of angle bisector
3. $\angle 2 \cong \angle 3$	3. Given
4. $\angle 1 \cong \angle 3$	4. Transitive Property of Angle Congruence

Lesson 2.7 (pp. 127–131)

5. $\angle FGH \cong \angle WXZ$; $\angle WXZ$ is a right angle because $58° + 32° = 90°$, so they are congruent by the Right Angles Congruence Theorem.

13. Using the Vertical Angles Congruence Theorem:

$4x = 6x - 26 \rightarrow x = 13$

$6y + 8 = 7y - 12 \rightarrow y = 20$

39.

Statements	Reasons
1. $\overline{JK} \perp \overline{JM}$, $\overline{KL} \perp \overline{ML}$, $\angle J \cong \angle M$, $\angle K \cong \angle L$	1. Given
2. $\angle J$ is a right angle; $\angle L$ is a right angle.	2. Definition of perpendicular lines
3. $\angle M$ is a right angle; $\angle K$ is a right angle.	3. Right Angles Congruence Theorem
4. $\overline{JM} \perp \overline{ML}$, $\overline{JK} \perp \overline{KL}$	4. Definition of perpendicular lines

Chapter 3

Lesson 3.1 (pp. 150–152)

11. The pairs of corresponding angles are $\angle 1$ and $\angle 5$, $\angle 2$ and $\angle 6$, $\angle 3$ and $\angle 7$, and $\angle 4$ and $\angle 8$.

25. If two lines are not coplanar, then they never intersect.

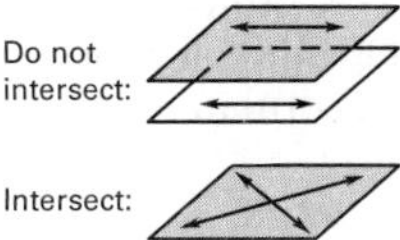

35. The arm is skew to a telephone pole.

Lesson 3.2 (pp. 157–160)

5. If $m\angle 7 = 110°$, then $m\angle 2 = 110°$, by the Alternate Exterior Angles Theorem.

9. Corresponding Angles Postulate

39. a. yes; $\angle 1$ and $\angle 5$, $\angle 2$ and $\angle 6$; yes; $\angle 1$ and $\angle 2$, $\angle 1$ and $\angle 6$, $\angle 2$ and $\angle 5$, $\angle 5$ and $\angle 6$

b. Because the bars are parallel, corresponding angles between the bars and the foot are congruent. Because the body and the foot are parallel, the bars act as transversals, and so the alternate interior angles are congruent. (See diagram.) This forces the foot to stay parallel with the floor.

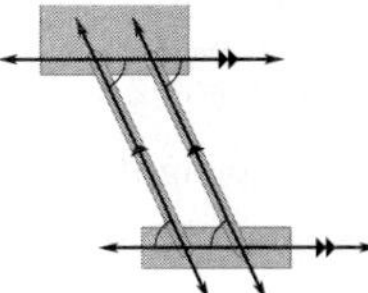

Lesson 3.3 (pp. 165–169)

11. Yes; Alternate Exterior Angles Converse

29. Because the alternate interior angles are congruent, you know that the top of the picnic table is parallel to the ground.

37. It is given that $\angle 3$ and $\angle 5$ are supplementary. $\angle 3$ is supplementary to $\angle 4$ because they form a straight angle. $\angle 4 \cong \angle 5$ by the Congruent Supplements Theorem. Therefore, $m \parallel n$ by the Alternate Interior Angles Converse.

Lesson 3.4 (pp. 175–178)

7. $m = \dfrac{y_2 - y_1}{x_2 - x_1} = \dfrac{6 - 5}{5 - 3} = \dfrac{1}{2}$

13. Line 1: $m_1 = \dfrac{y_2 - y_1}{x_2 - x_1} = \dfrac{4 - 0}{7 - 1} = \dfrac{2}{3}$

Line 2: $m_2 = \dfrac{y_2 - y_1}{x_2 - x_1} = \dfrac{6 - 0}{3 - 7} = -\dfrac{3}{2}$

Because $m_1 \cdot m_2 = \frac{2}{3} \cdot \left(-\frac{3}{2}\right) = -1$, the lines are perpendicular.

35.

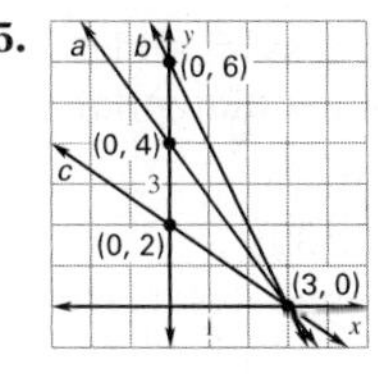

Line b is the most steep because the absolute value of its slope is the greatest. Line c is the least steep because the absolute value of its slope is the least.

WORKED-OUT SOLUTIONS

Lesson 3.5 (pp. 184–187)

17. $P(5, 4)$, $m = 4$

$y = mx + b \rightarrow 4 = 4(5) + b \rightarrow b = -16$

An equation of the line is $y = 4x - 16$.

23. The slope of a line parallel to $y = -2x + 3$ is $m = -2$.

$y = mx + b \rightarrow -1 = -2(0) + b \rightarrow b = -1$

An equation of the line is $y = -2x - 1$.

61. x = days since age 14; y = weight (in kg)

$y = 2.1x + 2000$

The slope, 2.1, represents the rate of weight gain, in kilograms per day. The y-intercept, 2000, represents the weight, in kilograms, at age 14.

Lesson 3.6 (pp. 194–197)

19. Line f is parallel to line g because they are both perpendicular to line d.

23. Slope of parallel lines: $m = \frac{4 - 0}{1 - 0} = 4$

A perpendicular segment joining the two lines has endpoints (0, 0) and (4, −1), since its slope is $-\frac{1}{4}$.

Distance from (4, −1) to (0, 0):

$d = \sqrt{(4 - 0)^2 + (-1 - 0)^2} \approx 4.1$

29. Jump to point C, because the shortest distance is the length of the perpendicular segment.

Chapter 4

Lesson 4.1 (pp. 221–224)

9. The triangle has 3 congruent sides and 3 congruent angles, so it is an equiangular equilateral triangle.

15. $x° + 3x° + 60° = 180° \rightarrow x = 30$

$3x° = 3(30)° = 90°$

Because the triangle has a right angle, it is a right triangle.

41. [diagram: rectangle divided into x, x, x; 6 in.]

$3x = 6 \rightarrow x = 2$

Each side of the triangle is 2 inches.

The measure of each angle is $180° \div 3 = 60°$.

Lesson 4.2 (pp. 228–231)

9. $\triangle LNM \cong \triangle ZYX$

15. By the Triangle Sum Theorem, $m\angle M = 180° - 90° - 70° = 20°$. By the Third Angles Theorem, $x° = m\angle M = 20°$, so $x = 20$.

25. The length, height, and depth have to be the same.

Lesson 4.3 (pp. 236–239)

7. True; $\overline{DE} \cong \overline{DG}$, $\overline{EF} \cong \overline{GF}$, and $\overline{FD} \cong \overline{FD}$ by the Reflexive Property.

So, $\triangle DEF \cong \triangle DGF$ by the SSS Congruence Postulate.

9. $AB = 6$, $BC = 8$,

$CA = \sqrt{(-2 - 4)^2 + (-2 - 6)^2} = 10$

$DE = 6$, $EF = 8$,

$FD = \sqrt{(5 - 13)^2 + (7 - 1)^2} = 10$

By the SSS Congruence Postulate, $\triangle ABC \cong \triangle DEF$.

25. Because $\overline{WY} \cong \overline{VY}$ and $\overline{YZ} \cong \overline{YX}$, then $\overline{WZ} \cong \overline{VX}$. By the Reflexive Property, $\overline{WV} \cong \overline{VW}$. It is given that $\overline{WX} \cong \overline{VZ}$. So, by the SSS Congruence Postulate, $\triangle VWX \cong \triangle WVZ$.

Lesson 4.4 (pp. 243–246)

13. There is enough information given, since $\overline{GH} \cong \overline{EF}$, $\angle GHF \cong \angle EFH$, and $\overline{HF} \cong \overline{FH}$.

WS4

19. Because $\overline{FH} \cong \overline{HA} \cong \overline{BD} \cong \overline{DE}$, then $\overline{FA} \cong \overline{BE}$. Because $\overline{CB} \cong \overline{BA} \cong \overline{GF} \cong \overline{FE}$, then $\overline{CA} \cong \overline{GE}$. Also, $\triangle ACF$ and $\triangle EGB$ are right triangles. So, $\triangle ACF \cong \triangle EGB$ by the Hypotenuse-Leg Congruence Theorem.

31. SAS Congruence Postulate

Lesson 4.5 (pp. 252–255)

5. Yes; ASA Congruence Postulate

9. $\angle F \cong \angle L$

27. AAS Congruence Theorem

Lesson 4.6 (pp. 259–263)

19. Let J represent the midpoint of $\overline{KM}$. Use the SSS Congruence Postulate to prove $\triangle JKN \cong \triangle JMN$. Then use the SAS Congruence Postulate to prove $\triangle JKL \cong \triangle JML$. Because $\triangle JKL \cong \triangle JML$, $\angle 1 \cong \angle 2$.

23.

Statements	Reasons
1. $\angle X \cong \angle Z$, $\angle U \cong \angle T$, $\overline{ZY} \cong \overline{XY}$	1. Given
2. $\triangle TYZ \cong \triangle UYX$	2. AAS Congruence Postulate
3. $\angle VYX \cong \angle Z + \angle T$, $\angle WYZ \cong \angle X + \angle U$	3. Exterior Angle Theorem
4. $\angle VYX \cong \angle Z + \angle T$, $\angle WYZ \cong \angle Z + \angle T$	4. Substitution
5. $\angle VYX \cong \angle WYZ$	5. Transitive Property of Congruence

31. A; Once you show that $\angle XWZ \cong \angle YZW$ by the Alternate Interior Angles Theorem, $\overline{WZ} \cong \overline{ZW}$ by the Reflexive Property, and $\angle Y \cong \angle X$ by the Right Angles Congruence Theorem, you can show that $\triangle WYZ \cong \triangle ZXW$ by the AAS Congruence Theorem. This means that $\overline{WY} \cong \overline{ZX}$.

Lesson 4.7 (pp. 267–270)

5. If $\angle D \cong \angle CED$, then $\overline{CE} \cong \overline{CD}$ by the Converse of Base Angles Theorem.

17. $9y° = x°$ by the Base Angles Theorem and $9y° + x° = 90°$ by the Corollary to the Triangle Sum Theorem. So, $9y° + x° = 90° \rightarrow 9y° + 9y° = 90 \rightarrow 18y° = 90 \rightarrow y = 5$ and $x° = 9y° \rightarrow x = 9(5) = 45$.

41. a.

Statements	Reasons
1. $\angle BAC \cong \angle BCA \cong \angle DCE \cong \angle DEC$	1. Given
2. $\overline{BA} \cong \overline{BC} \cong \overline{DC} \cong \overline{DE}$	2. Converse of Base Angles Theorem
3. $\angle CBD \cong \angle CDB$	3. Base Angles Theorem
4. $\angle BCA \cong \angle CBD$	4. Alternate Interior Angles Theorem
5. $\angle CDB \cong \angle BAC$	5. Substitution
6. $\triangle ABC \cong \triangle BCD$	6. AAS Congruence Postulate

b. $\triangle ABC$, $\triangle CDE$, $\triangle EFG$, $\triangle BCD$, $\triangle DEF$

c. $\angle CDE$, $\angle EFG$, $\angle BCD$, $\angle DEF$

Lesson 4.8 (pp. 276–279)

11. $(x, y) \rightarrow (x + 4, y + 1)$

$A(-3, 1) \rightarrow (1, 2)$

$B(2, 3) \rightarrow (6, 4)$

$C(3, 0) \rightarrow (7, 1)$

$D(-1, -1) \rightarrow (3, 0)$

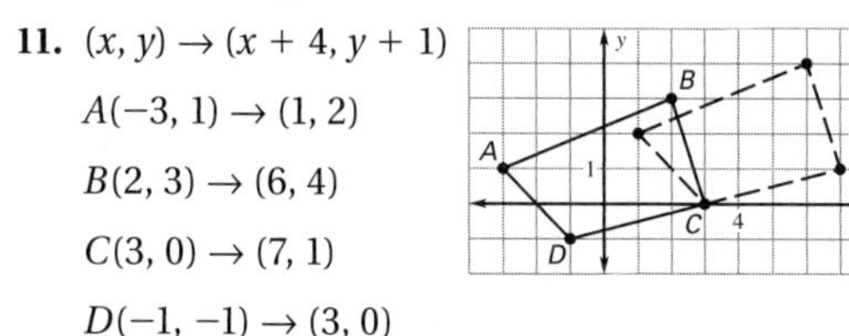

23.

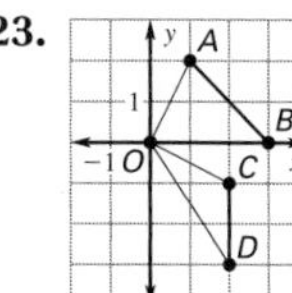

$m\angle AOC > m\angle BOD$

This is not a rotation.

39. From A to B, use a 90° clockwise rotation. From A to C, use a 90° counterclockwise rotation.

WORKED-OUT SOLUTIONS

WS5

Chapter 5

Lesson 5.1 (pp. 298–301)

9. $\overline{YJ} \cong \overline{JX} \cong \overline{LK}$

21.

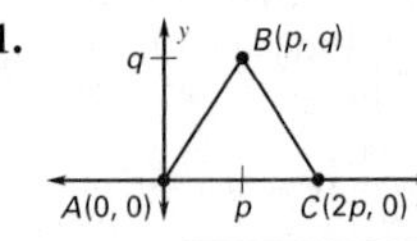

$AB = \sqrt{(p-0)^2 + (q-0)^2} = \sqrt{p^2 + q^2}$

$BC = \sqrt{(2p-p)^2 + (0-q)^2} = \sqrt{p^2 + q^2}$

$AC = 2p$

$m_{AB} = \dfrac{q-0}{p-0} = \dfrac{q}{p}$

$m_{BC} = \dfrac{0-q}{2p-p} = -\dfrac{q}{p}$

$m_{AC} = \dfrac{0-0}{2p-0} = 0$

$M_{AB}\left(\dfrac{0+p}{2}, \dfrac{0+q}{2}\right) = \left(\dfrac{p}{2}, \dfrac{q}{2}\right)$

$M_{BC}\left(\dfrac{p+2p}{2}, \dfrac{q+0}{2}\right) = \left(\dfrac{3p}{2}, \dfrac{q}{2}\right)$

$M_{AC}\left(\dfrac{0+2p}{2}, \dfrac{0+0}{2}\right) = (p, 0)$

$\triangle ABC$ is not a right triangle because the angle measurements depend on the values of p and q. $\triangle ABC$ is isoceles because $AB = BC$.

37. $W\left(\dfrac{0+6}{2}, \dfrac{0+6}{2}\right) = W(3, 3)$

$V\left(\dfrac{6+8}{2}, \dfrac{6+0}{2}\right) = V(7, 3)$

$m_{WV} = \dfrac{3-3}{7-3} = 0 = m_{OH} = \dfrac{0-0}{8-0} = 0 \rightarrow$

$\overline{WV} \parallel \overline{OH}$

$WV = |7-3| = 4,\ OH = |8-0| = 8 \rightarrow$

$WV = \frac{1}{2}OH$

Lesson 5.2 (pp. 306–309)

15. Because $LK = LM$, L lies on the perpendicular bisector of $\overline{KM}$ by the Converse of the Perpendicular Bisector Theorem.

17. By Theorem 5.4, $GA = GB = GC = 11$.

25. Connect the three houses with line segments. Fold your house to Mike's house, Mike's house to Ken's house, and Ken's house to your house. The folded lines are the perpendicular bisectors. You should meet where they intersect.

Lesson 5.3 (pp. 313–316)

7. Not enough information is given.

15. No, because you do not know that the blue line segments are perpendicular to the sides of the angle.

29. Build the fountain where the angle bisectors meet at the incenter, which is equidistant from the 3 sides.

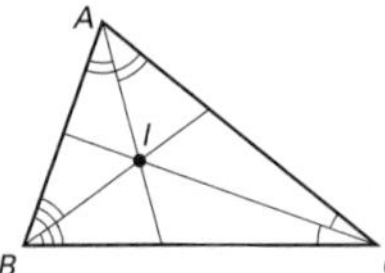

Lesson 5.4 (pp. 322–325)

5. $AG = \frac{2}{3}AE \rightarrow AG = \frac{2}{3}(15) \rightarrow AG = 10$

21. Because $\triangle XYW \cong \triangle ZYW$, $\overline{YW}$ is a perpendicular bisector, an angle bisector, a median, and an altitude.

39. Base of red triangle $= \frac{1}{2}(9) = 4.5$

Height of red triangle $= 3$

Area of red triangle $= \frac{1}{2}(4.5)(3) = 6.75 \text{ in.}^2$

The altitude was used.

Lesson 5.5 (pp. 331–334)

9. $\overline{KL}, \overline{JL}, \overline{JK}$, and $\angle J, \angle K, \angle L$ by Theorem 5.10.

17. No, because $3 + 6 \not> 9$.

39. a. Using the Triangle Inequality Theorem:

$x + 489 > 565 \qquad x < 565 + 489$

$x > 76 \qquad x < 1054$

A value of $x = 1080$ does not satisfy $x > 1054$.

b. No, $x = 40$ does not satisfy $x > 76$.

c. $x > 76$; $x < 1054$

d. Because $m\angle 2 < m\angle 1$, $x < 489$. Because $m\angle 2 < m\angle 3$, $x < 565$. Since $x < 489$ and $x < 565$, the distance is less than 489 kilometers

Lesson 5.6 (pp. 338–341)

5. $TR < UR$ by the Hinge Theorem, because $\angle TQR < \angle USR$.

7. $m\angle 1 = m\angle 2$ because both triangles are congruent using the SSS Congruence Postulate.

23. E, A, D, B, C

Chapter 6

Lesson 6.1 (pp. 360–363)

5. $\frac{6 \text{ L}}{10 \text{ mL}} = \frac{6 \cancel{\text{L}}}{10 \cancel{\text{mL}}} \cdot \frac{1000 \cancel{\text{mL}}}{1 \cancel{\text{L}}} = \frac{6000}{10} = \frac{600}{1}$

27. $\frac{1}{c+5} = \frac{3}{24} \rightarrow 24 = 3(c+5) \rightarrow c = 3$

59. Total amount of trail mix $= 36\left(\frac{1}{2}\right) = 18$ cups.

$5x + 1x + 4x = 18 \rightarrow x = \frac{9}{5}$ cups

Peanuts: $5\left(\frac{9}{5}\right) = 9$ cups

Chocolate chips: $1\left(\frac{9}{5}\right) = \frac{9}{5} = 1\frac{4}{5}$ cups

Raisins: $4\left(\frac{9}{5}\right) = \frac{36}{5} = 7\frac{1}{5}$ cups

Lesson 6.2 (pp. 367–370)

11. $\frac{CB}{BA} = \frac{DE}{EF} \rightarrow \frac{6}{x} = \frac{4}{7} \rightarrow 6(7) = 4x \rightarrow 10.5 = x$

So, $BA = 10.5$.

13. $\frac{1 \text{ inch}}{50 \text{ yards}} = \frac{2 \text{ inches}}{x \text{ yards}} \rightarrow x = 2(50) = 100$ yards

25. $\frac{1 \text{ inch}}{3.2 \text{ miles}} \approx \frac{2.5 \text{ inches}}{x \text{ miles}} \rightarrow x \approx 3.2(2.5) = 8$ miles

Lesson 6.3 (pp. 376–379)

3. $\angle A \cong \angle L$, $\angle B \cong \angle M$, and $\angle C \cong \angle N$

$\frac{AB}{LM} = \frac{BC}{MN} = \frac{CA}{NL}$

7. $\frac{RS}{WX} = \frac{64}{32} = 2 \qquad \frac{ST}{XY} = \frac{48}{24} = 2$

$\frac{TU}{YZ} = \frac{64}{32} = 2 \qquad \frac{UR}{ZW} = \frac{48}{24} = 2$

The ratios are equal, so the corresponding side lengths are proportional, and the polygons are similar. So, $RSTU \sim WXYZ$, and the scale factor is 2.

31. $\frac{9 \text{ ft long}}{78 \text{ ft long}} = \frac{3}{26} \qquad \frac{5 \text{ ft wide}}{36 \text{ ft wide}} = \frac{5}{36}$

The ratios are not equal, so the corresponding side lengths are not proportional, and the surfaces are not similar.

Lesson 6.4 (pp. 384–387)

9. Yes; $\angle H \cong \angle J$, and $m\angle F = 42°$ by the Triangle Sum Theorem, so $\angle F \cong \angle K$. So, $\triangle GFH \sim \triangle LKJ$ by the AA Similarity Postulate.

13. By the Triangular Sum Theorem, $m\angle YZX = 50°$ and $m\angle U = 45°$. So, $\triangle XYZ \sim \triangle UYW$ by the AA Similarity Postulate.

33. All angles of any two equilateral triangles are congruent, so the triangles are similar by the AA Similarity Postulate

Lesson 6.5 (pp. 391–395)

3. $\frac{AB}{DE} = \frac{15}{10} = \frac{3}{2} \qquad \frac{BC}{EF} = \frac{18}{12} = \frac{3}{2} \qquad \frac{AC}{DF} = \frac{12}{8} = \frac{3}{2}$

Because $\frac{AB}{DE} = \frac{BC}{EF} = \frac{AC}{DF}$, $\triangle ABC \sim \triangle DEF$.

The scale factor of $\triangle ABC$ to $\triangle DEF$ is $\frac{3}{2}$.

7. Yes, because $\frac{DE}{WY} = \frac{9}{6} = \frac{3}{2} = \frac{FD}{XW} = \frac{15}{10} = \frac{3}{2}$, and $\angle D \cong \angle W$. $\triangle DEF \sim \triangle WYX$, and the scale factor of $\triangle WYX$ to $\triangle DEF$ is $\frac{2}{3}$.

31. To use the SAS Similarity Theorem, you need $\angle CBD \cong \angle CAE$.

WORKED-OUT SOLUTIONS

WS7

Lesson 6.6 (pp. 400–403)

5. Yes, by Theorem 6.5 because

$$\frac{LK}{KJ} = \frac{8}{5} = \frac{LM}{MN} = \frac{12}{7.5} = \frac{8}{5}.$$

9. $\frac{15}{x} = \frac{21}{14} \rightarrow 21x = 210 \rightarrow x = 10$

21. Let x = the distance along University Avenue from 12th Street to Washington Street.

$$\frac{200}{400} = \frac{x}{700} \rightarrow 400x = 140{,}000 \rightarrow x = 350 \text{ yards}$$

Lesson 6.7 (pp. 412–415)

5. $(x, y) \rightarrow (1.5x, 1.5y)$

$A(1, 1) \rightarrow L(1.5, 1.5)$

$B(6, 1) \rightarrow M(9, 1.5)$

$C(6, 3) \rightarrow N(9, 4.5)$

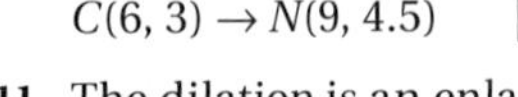

11. The dilation is an enlargement.

A: (2, 0), (1, 2), and (3, 2)

B: (6, 0), (3, 6), and (9, 6)

For each vertex (x, y) of Figure A, the corresponding vertex of Figure B is $(3x, 3y)$. The scale factor is 3.

27. The scale factor is $\frac{15 \text{ ft}}{6 \text{ ft}} = \frac{5}{2}$, or 2.5.

Chapter 7

Lesson 7.1 (pp. 436–439)

9. $13.4^2 = 9.8^2 + x^2$

$179.56 = 96.04 + x^2$

$83.52 = x^2 \rightarrow 9.139 \approx x$

x is about 9.1 inches.

11. $8^2 + h^2 = 17^2$

$h^2 = 225$

$h = 15$

Area $= \frac{1}{2}bh = \frac{1}{2}(16)(15) = 120 \text{ m}^2$

33. *Sample answer:* The longest side of the triangle is opposite the largest angle, which in a right triangle is the right angle.

Lesson 7.2 (pp. 444–447)

7. $(\sqrt{26})^2 \stackrel{?}{=} 5^2 + 1^2 \rightarrow 26 \stackrel{?}{=} 25 + 1 \rightarrow 26 = 26$ ✓

The triangle is a right triangle.

17. $24 + 30 = 54$ $\quad$ $30 + 6\sqrt{43} \approx 69.3$

$54 > 6\sqrt{43}$ $\quad$ $69.3 > 24$

$6\sqrt{43} + 24 \approx 63.3$

$63.3 > 30$

The segment lengths form a triangle.

Because $(6\sqrt{43})^2 > 24^2 + 30^2$, the segment lengths form an obtuse triangle.

37. a. Let $x = BC$.

$12^2 + x^2 = 13^2 \rightarrow x^2 = 25 \rightarrow x = 5 = BC$

b. Because $5^2 = 3^2 + 4^2$, $\triangle ABC$ is a right triangle.

c. *Sample answer:*

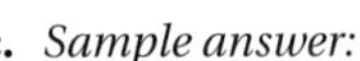

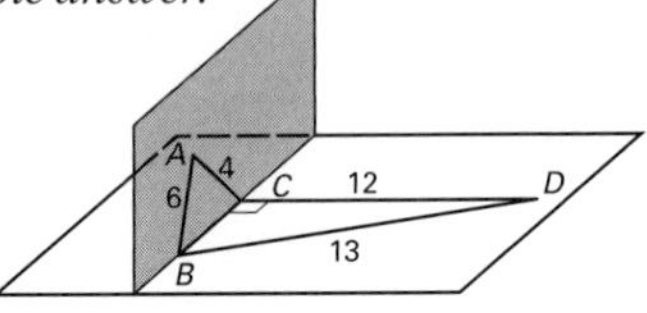

Lesson 7.3 (pp. 453–456)

5. $\frac{107.5}{76} = \frac{76}{h} \rightarrow 107.5h = 5776 \rightarrow h \approx 53.7 \text{ ft}$

15. $\frac{z}{27} = \frac{27}{16} \rightarrow 16z = 729 \rightarrow z \approx 45.6$

29. Let c represent the hypotenuse of the large triangle.

$1.5^2 + 1.5^2 = c^2 \rightarrow 4.5 = c^2 \rightarrow \sqrt{4.5} = c$

$\frac{x}{1.5} = \frac{1.5}{\sqrt{4.5}} \rightarrow \sqrt{4.5}x = 2.25 \rightarrow x \approx 1.1 \text{ ft}$

Lesson 7.4 (pp. 461–464)

5. hypotenuse = leg $\cdot \sqrt{2} \rightarrow 3\sqrt{2} = x \cdot \sqrt{2} \rightarrow 3 = x$

9. $3\sqrt{3} = x\sqrt{3} \rightarrow x = 3$

$y = 2x = 2(3) = 6$

27. $11 = 2 \cdot h \rightarrow h = 5.5$ feet

Lesson 7.5 (pp. 469–472)

5. $\tan A = \frac{\text{opp. } \angle A}{\text{adj. to } \angle A} = \frac{48}{20} = \frac{12}{5} = 2.4000$

$\tan B = \frac{\text{opp. } \angle B}{\text{adj. to } \angle B} = \frac{20}{48} = \frac{5}{12} \approx 0.4167$

7. $\tan 27° = \frac{\text{opp.}}{\text{adj.}} = \frac{x}{15} \rightarrow x \approx 7.6$

31. 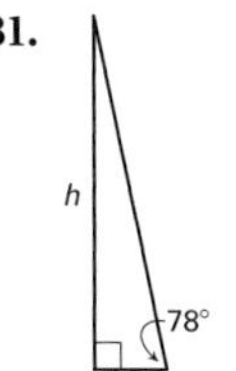

$\tan 78° = \frac{h}{118}$

$118(4.7046) \approx h$

$h \approx 555$ feet

Lesson 7.6 (pp. 477–480)

5. $\sin D = \frac{\text{opp. } \angle D}{\text{hyp.}} = \frac{28}{53} \approx 0.5283$

$\sin E = \frac{\text{opp. } \angle E}{\text{hyp.}} = \frac{45}{53} \approx 0.8491$

9. $\cos X = \frac{\text{adj. to } \angle X}{\text{hyp.}} = \frac{13}{26} = \frac{1}{2} = 0.5$

$\cos Y = \frac{\text{adj. to } \angle Y}{\text{hyp.}} = \frac{13\sqrt{3}}{26} = \frac{\sqrt{3}}{2} \approx 0.8660$

33. 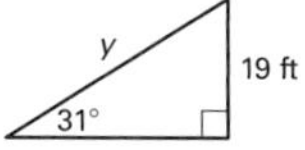

$\sin 31° = \frac{19}{y} \rightarrow y = \frac{19}{\sin 31°} \rightarrow y \approx 36.9$ ft

Lesson 7.7 (pp. 485–489)

5. $\tan A = \frac{14}{4} = \frac{7}{2} = 3.5$

$m\angle A = \tan^{-1} 3.5 \approx 74.1°$

13. $9^2 + 12^2 = (AC)^2 \rightarrow 225 = (AC)^2 \rightarrow 15 = AC$

$\tan A = \frac{9}{12} = 0.75$

$m\angle A = \tan^{-1} 0.75 \approx 36.9°$

$180° \approx 90° + 36.9° + m\angle C \rightarrow m\angle C \approx 53.1°$

The side lengths are 9 units, 12 units, and 15 units. The angle measures are 90°, about 36.9°, and about 53.1°.

35. The angle of depression is 90° minus the measure of the angle you can find:

$90 - \tan^{-1}\left(\frac{7}{12}\right) \approx 90 - \tan^{-1} 0.5833 \approx$

$90 - 30.3° = 59.7°$.

Chapter 8

Lesson 8.1 (pp. 510–513)

9. $(n - 2) \cdot 180° = 1980° \rightarrow n - 2 = 11 \rightarrow n = 13$

The polygon is a 13-gon.

11. Pentagon; $(5 - 2) \cdot 180° = 540°$

$x° + 86° + 140° + 138° + 59° = 540° \rightarrow x = 117$

29. Hexagon; $(6 - 2) \cdot 180° = 720°$

Lesson 8.2 (pp. 518–521)

9. $m\angle A + m\angle B = 180°$

$51° + m\angle B = 180°$

$m\angle B = 129°$

13. $b - 1 = 9 \rightarrow b = 10$ and $5a = 15 \rightarrow a = 3$

39. a. $PQRS$ is a parallelogram, so $\overline{PQ} \cong \overline{RS}$.

$RS = PQ = 3$ inches

b. $PQRS$ is a parallelogram, so $\angle Q \cong \angle S$.

$m\angle S = m\angle Q = 70°$

c. The sum of the measures of the interior angles always is 360°. As $m\angle Q$ increases so does $m\angle S$, therefore $m\angle P$ must decrease to maintain the sum of 360°. As $m\angle Q$ decreases $m\angle P$ increases, moving Q farther away from S.

Lesson 8.3 (pp. 526–529)

5. Theorem 8.7, because both pairs of opposite sides are congruent.

11. $BC = 12 - 4 = 8$;

$AD = 8 - 0 = 8$

So, $\overline{BC} \cong \overline{AD}$.

Slope of $\overline{BC} = \frac{4 - 4}{12 - 4} = 0$

Slope of $\overline{AD} = \frac{1 - 1}{8 - 0} = 0$

Slopes are equal, so $\overline{BC} \parallel \overline{AD}$.

$\overline{BC} \cong \overline{AD}$ and $\overline{BC} \parallel \overline{AD}$, so $ABCD$ is a parallelogram.

31. a. *Quadrilateral EFJK*:

Because $\overline{EG} \cong \overline{KH}$, and F and J are midpoints of $\overline{EG}$ and $\overline{KH}$, then $\overline{EF} \cong \overline{FG} \cong \overline{KJ} \cong \overline{JH}$. Because $\overline{EF} \cong \overline{KJ}$ and $\overline{EK} \cong \overline{FJ}$, $EFJK$ is a parallelogram.

Quadrilateral FGHJ:

Because $\overline{FG} \cong \overline{JH}$ and $\overline{FJ} \cong \overline{GH}$, $FGHJ$ is a parallelogram.

Quadrilateral EGHK:

Because $\overline{EG} \cong \overline{KH}$ and $\overline{EK} \cong \overline{GH}$, $EGHK$ is a parallelogram.

b. Although the angles may change, $\overline{EG}$ is always congruent to $\overline{KH}$ and $\overline{EK}$ is always congruent to $\overline{GH}$. So, $EGHK$ is always a parallelogram. Therefore $\overline{EG}$ is always parallel to $\overline{KH}$.

Lesson 8.4 (pp. 537–540)

7. 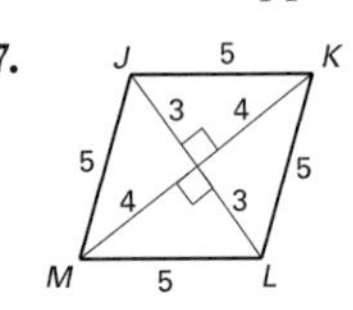

The diagonals are congruent if the rhombus is a square. Or, you can sketch a rhombus that has the diagonals shown. So, the statement is sometimes true.

15. The quadrilateral is a square because it is a parallelogram with four congruent sides and four right angles.

55. Use the tape measure to measure the diagonals. If they are congruent, the region is a square.

Lesson 8.5 (pp. 546–549)

11. Because $\angle E$ and $\angle H$ are right angles, $\overline{EF} \parallel \overline{HG}$. $\overline{EH}$ is not parallel to $\overline{FG}$, so $EFGH$ is a trapezoid.

19. By Theorem 8.19, because $\overline{EF} \cong \overline{EH}$, then $\angle F \cong \angle H$.

$$m\angle G + m\angle E + m\angle F + m\angle H = 360^\circ$$

$$m\angle G + 60^\circ + 110^\circ + 110^\circ = 360^\circ$$

$$m\angle G = 80^\circ$$

35. 120° 120° 30°

Lesson 8.6 (pp. 554–557)

3.

Property	▱	Rectangle	Rhombus	Square	Kite	Trapezoid
All sides are ≅.			X	X		

15. Trapezoid; it has exactly one pair of parallel sides ($\overline{PS}$ and $\overline{QR}$).

33. A trapezoid is outlined. The figure has only one pair of parallel sides. Since the non-parallel sides are not congruent, the figure is not an isosceles trapezoid.

Chapter 9

Lesson 9.1 (pp. 576–579)

7. $(x, y) \to (x + 4, y + 6)$

$P(-2, 3) \to P'(2, 9)$

$Q(1, 2) \to Q'(5, 8)$

$R(3, -1) \to R'(7, 5)$

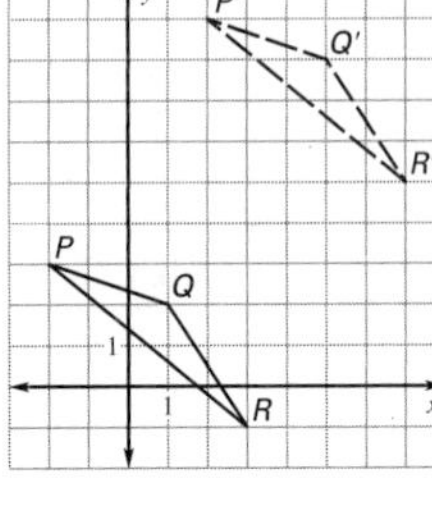

11. A rule is $(x, y) \to (x - 5, y + 2)$.

$AC = A'C' = 4$

$AB = \sqrt{(4 - 1)^2 + (1 + 1)^2} = \sqrt{13}$

$A'B' = \sqrt{(-1 + 4)^2 + (3 - 1)^2} = \sqrt{13}$

$BC = \sqrt{(5 - 4)^2 + (-1 - 1)^2} = \sqrt{5}$

$B'C' = \sqrt{(0 + 1)^2 + (1 - 3)^2} = \sqrt{5}$

By the SSS Congruence Postulate, $\triangle ABC \cong \triangle A'B'C'$, so the translation is an isometry.

35. From cabin to ski lodge:

$\langle 1 - 0, 2 - 0 \rangle = \langle 1, 2 \rangle$

Lesson 9.2 (pp. 584–587)

13. $$\begin{bmatrix} 0 & 0 & 0 \\ 4 & 4 & 4 \end{bmatrix} + \overset{\begin{matrix} A & B & C \end{matrix}}{\begin{bmatrix} -2 & 2 & 1 \\ 4 & 1 & -3 \end{bmatrix}} = \overset{\begin{matrix} A' & B' & C' \end{matrix}}{\begin{bmatrix} -2 & 2 & 1 \\ 8 & 5 & 1 \end{bmatrix}}$$

Translation matrix — Polygon matrix — Image matrix

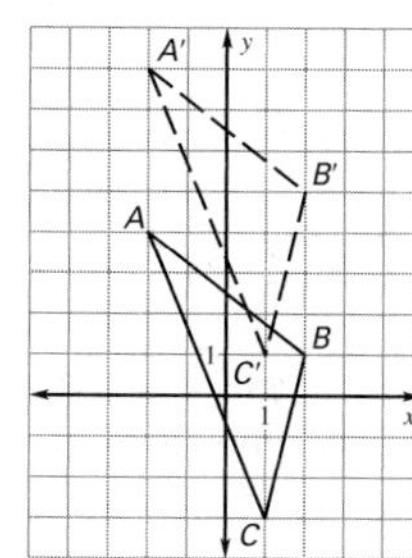

19. $$\begin{bmatrix} 1.2 & 3 \end{bmatrix} \begin{bmatrix} -2 \\ -1.5 \end{bmatrix} = \begin{bmatrix} 1.2(-2) + 3(-1.5) \end{bmatrix} = \begin{bmatrix} -6.9 \end{bmatrix}$$

31. Equipment matrix:

	Mice	CDs	Keyboards
Lab 1	25	10	18
Lab 2	15	20	12

Cost matrix:

	Dollars
Mice	10
CDs	32
Keyboards	15

Total cost:

$$\begin{bmatrix} 25 & 10 & 18 \\ 15 & 20 & 12 \end{bmatrix} \begin{bmatrix} 10 \\ 32 \\ 15 \end{bmatrix} = \begin{bmatrix} 840 \\ 970 \end{bmatrix}$$

Lab 1: \$840; Lab 2: \$970

Lesson 9.3 (pp. 593–596)

5.

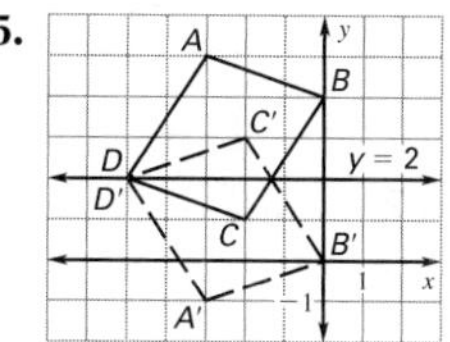

13. $$\begin{bmatrix} 1 & 0 \\ 0 & -1 \end{bmatrix} \overset{\begin{matrix} A & B & C \end{matrix}}{\begin{bmatrix} -2 & 3 & 4 \\ 5 & -3 & 6 \end{bmatrix}} = \overset{\begin{matrix} A' & B' & C' \end{matrix}}{\begin{bmatrix} -2 & 3 & 4 \\ -5 & 3 & -6 \end{bmatrix}}$$

Reflection matrix — Polygon matrix — Image matrix

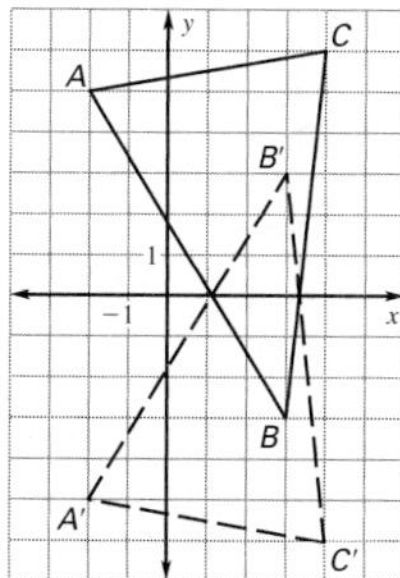

33. Case 1

Lesson 9.4 (pp. 602–605)

13. $(a, b) \rightarrow (-a, -b)$

$J(1, 4) \rightarrow J'(-1, -4)$

$K(5, 5) \rightarrow K'(-5, -5)$

$L(7, 2) \rightarrow L'(-7, -2)$

$M(2, 2) \rightarrow M'(-2, -2)$

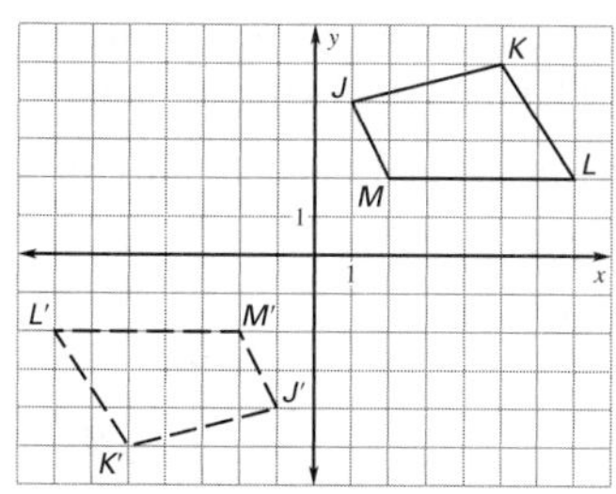

15.

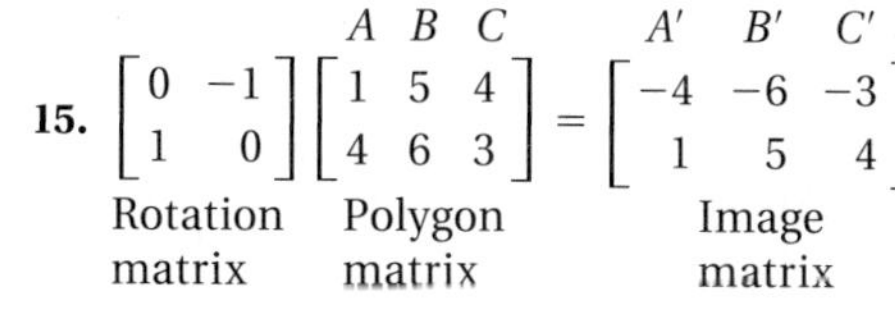

$$\begin{bmatrix} 0 & -1 \\ 1 & 0 \end{bmatrix} \overset{\begin{matrix} A & B & C \end{matrix}}{\begin{bmatrix} 1 & 5 & 4 \\ 4 & 6 & 3 \end{bmatrix}} = \overset{\begin{matrix} A' & B' & C' \end{matrix}}{\begin{bmatrix} -4 & -6 & -3 \\ 1 & 5 & 4 \end{bmatrix}}$$

Rotation matrix — Polygon matrix — Image matrix

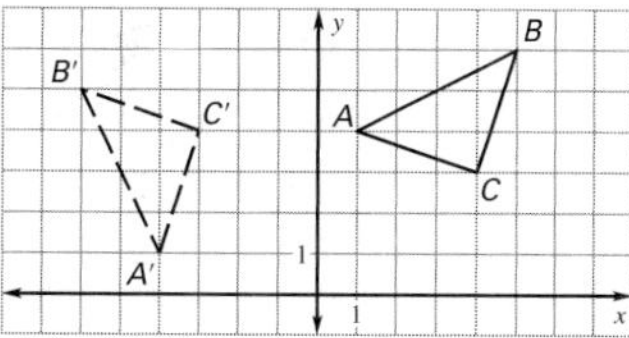

WORKED-OUT SOLUTIONS

WS11

29. Rotation of 270°, because it would take three of the four 90° rotations for the blade to reach its original starting point.

Lesson 9.5 (pp. 611–615)

7.

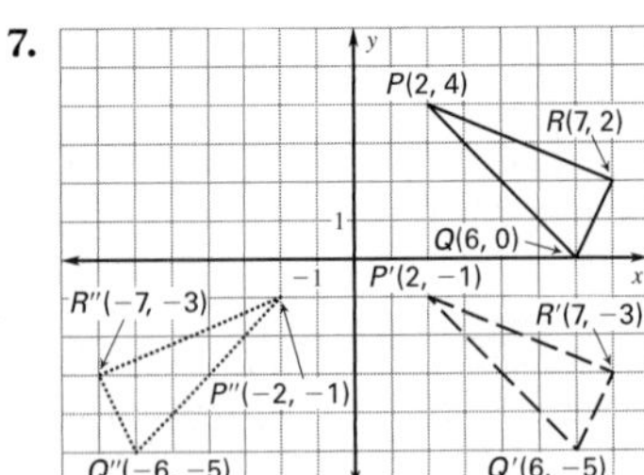

17. *Sample answer*: $\overline{CC'} \parallel \overleftrightarrow{BB''}$ and $\overline{AA'} \parallel \overleftrightarrow{BB''}$

27. 9 in. 9 in. 9 in.

Translate 9 inches to the right, reflect in the x-axis.

Lesson 9.6 (pp. 621–624)

7. Yes; a rotation of 72° or 144° about the center maps the figure onto itself.

13. C; there are no lines of symmetry, but a rotation of 90° maps the figure onto itself.

31. There are 8 lines of symmetry, so $n = 8$.

$n(m\angle 1) = 180°$

$8(m\angle 1) = 180°$

$m\angle 1 = 22.5°$

The angle between the mirrors is 22.5°.

Lesson 9.7 (pp. 629–632)

7.

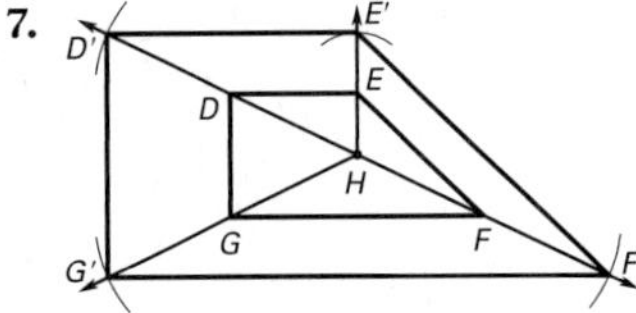

19. $\frac{1}{2}\begin{bmatrix} -2 & 0 & 6 \\ -4 & 2 & -2 \end{bmatrix} = \begin{bmatrix} -1 & 0 & 3 \\ -2 & 1 & -1 \end{bmatrix}$ (columns G, H, J and G', H', J')

Scale factor; Polygon matrix; Image matrix

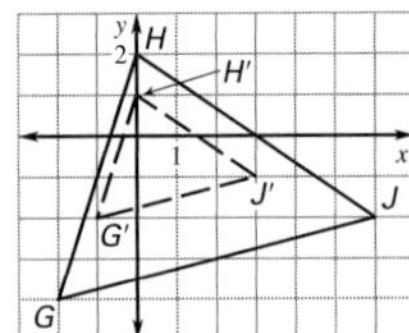

35. $k = 20$; $20 = \frac{x}{47} \rightarrow x = 940$

The length of the dragonfly seen through the magnifying glass is 940 mm, or 94 cm.

Chapter 10

Lesson 10.1 (pp. 655–658)

7. $\overleftrightarrow{AE}$ is a tangent line because it intersects the circle in exactly one point.

19. No; because $9^2 + 15^2 \neq 18^2$, $\triangle ABC$ is not a right triangle and $\overline{AB}$ is not perpendicular to $\overline{BC}$.

37.

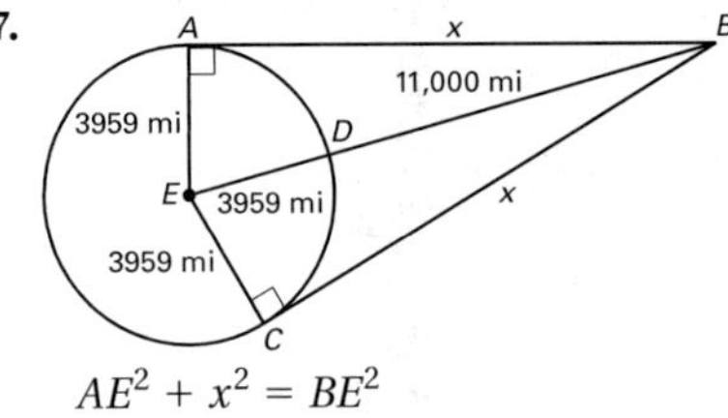

$AE^2 + x^2 = BE^2$

$3959^2 + x^2 = (3959 + 11{,}000)^2$

$x^2 = 208{,}098{,}000$

$x \approx 14{,}426$

The length of $\overline{BA}$ and of $\overline{BC}$ is about 14,426 miles.

Lesson 10.2 (pp. 661–663)

5. $\overset{\frown}{DB}$ is a minor arc.

$m\overset{\frown}{DB} = 180° - m\overset{\frown}{DE} = 180° - 45° = 135°$

13. No; $\overset{\frown}{LP}$ and $\overset{\frown}{MN}$ have the same measure, but are arcs of circles that are not congruent.

23. The measure of each arc is $360° \div 20 = 18°$.

Lesson 10.3 (pp. 667–670)

7. Because $\overline{LN}$ is a diameter and $\overline{LN} \perp \overline{PM}$, $\overline{LN}$ bisects $\overline{PM}$.

So, $2x + 9 = 5x - 6 \rightarrow x = 5$.

9. Because $\overline{AB}$ and $\overline{CD}$ are equidistant from the center, $\overline{AB} \cong \overline{CD}$.

So, $18 = 5x - 7 \rightarrow x = 5$.

25. $\overline{AB}$ and $\overline{BC}$ must be congruent in order for $\widehat{AB}$ and $\widehat{BC}$ to be congruent.

Lesson 10.4 (pp. 676–679)

11. $\angle JMK$ and $\angle JLK$ intercept the same arc, so $\angle JMK \cong \angle JLK$. Also, $\angle MKL$ and $\angle MJL$ intercept the same arc, so $\angle MKL \cong \angle MJL$.

13. $x° + 80° = 180° \rightarrow x = 100$

$y° + 95° = 180° \rightarrow y = 85$

29. If a right triangle is inscribed in a circle, its hypotenuse is a diameter of the circle, so the length of the hypotenuse is twice the radius.

Lesson 10.5 (pp. 683–686)

3. $m\widehat{AB} = 2(65°) = 130°$

9. $180° - x° = \frac{1}{2}(30° + (2x - 30)°)$

$180° - x° = \frac{1}{2}(2x°)$

$180° = 2x°$

$90 = x$

23. Let D and E represent the points shown in the diagram. Because $\overline{CE}$ is a diameter, $m\widehat{CDE} = 180°$.

$x° = \frac{1}{2}m\widehat{CD}$

$x° = \frac{1}{2}(m\widehat{CDE} - m\widehat{DE})$

$x° = \frac{1}{2}(180° - 80°)$

$x = 50$

Lesson 10.6 (pp. 692–695)

3. $12x = 10(6)$

$x = 5$

9. $x^2 = 9(9 + 7)$

$x^2 = 144$

$x = 12$

21. Given: Chords $\overline{AB}$ and $\overline{CD}$ intersect in the interior of the circle.

Prove: $EA \cdot EB = EC \cdot ED$

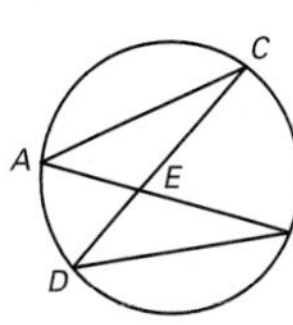

Statements	Reasons
1. $m\angle AEC \cong m\angle DEB$	1. Vertical Angles Theorem
2. $m\angle CAB \cong m\angle CDB$	2. Theorem 10.8
3. $\triangle AEC \sim \triangle DEB$	3. AA Similarity Postulate
4. $\frac{EA}{ED} = \frac{EC}{EB}$	4. Definition of similarity
5. $EA \cdot EB = ED \cdot EC$	5. Cross Products Property

Lesson 10.7 (pp. 702–705)

7. Center (50, 50); radius 10

$(x - h)^2 + (y - k)^2 = r^2$

$(x - 50)^2 + (y - 50)^2 = 10^2$

$(x - 50)^2 + (y - 50)^2 = 100$

17. $r = \sqrt{(0 - 0)^2 + (6 - 0)^2} = 6$

$(h, k) = (0, 0)$

$(x - h)^2 + (y - k)^2 = r^2$

$(x - 0)^2 + (y - 0)^2 = 6^2$

$x^2 + y^2 = 36$

37. Outside edge: $(h, k) = (0, 0)$; $r = 2.4$

$(x - 0)^2 + (y - 0)^2 = 2.4^2$

$x^2 + y^2 = 5.76$

Edge of hole: $(h, k) = (0, 0)$; $r = 0.3$

$(x - 0)^2 + (y - 0)^2 = 0.3^2$

$x^2 + y^2 = 0.09$

WS13

Chapter 11

Lesson 11.1 (pp. 723–726)

7. $30^2 = b^2 + 18^2 \rightarrow b^2 = 576 \rightarrow b = 24$

$A = \frac{1}{2}bh = \frac{1}{2}(24)(18) = 216$ square units

23. Area = Area of Parallelogram

+ Area of left triangle

+ Area of right triangle

$= (18)(13) + \frac{1}{2}(9)(13) + \frac{1}{2}(11)(13)$

$= 234 + 58.5 + 71.5$

$= 364 \text{ cm}^2$

37. Triangular plot: $A = \frac{1}{2}bh = \frac{1}{2}(24)(25) = 300 \text{ yd}^2$

$300 \cancel{\text{yd}^2} \cdot \frac{1 \text{ min}}{10 \cancel{\text{yd}^2}} = 30 \text{ min}$

It takes you 30 minutes to mow the triangular plot.

Rectangular plot: $A = bh = 24(36) = 864 \text{ yd}^2$

$864 \cancel{\text{yd}^2} \cdot \frac{1 \text{ min}}{10 \cancel{\text{yd}^2}} = 86.4 \text{ min}$

It takes you 86.4 minutes to mow the rectangular plot.

Lesson 11.2 (pp. 733–736)

9. $A = \frac{1}{2}d_1 d_2 = \frac{1}{2}(18)(21) = 189$ square units

17. $A = \frac{1}{2}h(b_1 + b_2)$

$300 = \frac{1}{2}(20)[x + 10]$

$300 = 10x + 100$

$200 = 10x$

$20 = x$

$x = 20 \text{ m}$

35. $A = \frac{1}{2}d_1 d_2 = \frac{1}{2}(5)(8) = 20$ square millimeters

Sample answer:

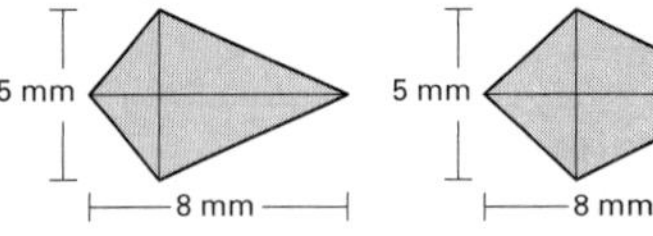

Lesson 11.3 (pp. 740–743)

7. The ratio of the lengths of corresponding sides is $\frac{7}{9}$, or 7 : 9.

The ratio of perimeters is 7 : 9.

The ratio of areas is $\frac{7^2}{9^2} = \frac{49}{81}$, or 49 : 81.

$\frac{\text{Red area}}{\text{Blue area}} = \frac{49}{81}$

$\frac{\text{Red area}}{210} = \frac{49}{81}$

Red area $= \frac{10{,}290}{81} \approx 127$ square inches

17.

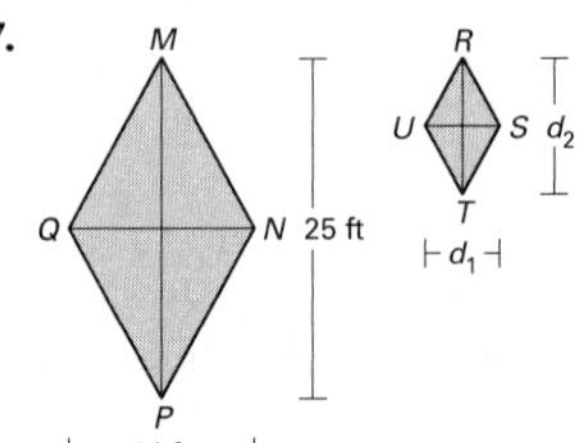

Area of $MNPQ = \frac{1}{2}(14)(25) = 175 \text{ ft}^2$

Area of $RSTU = 28 \text{ ft}^2$

Ratio of areas $= \frac{175 \text{ ft}^2}{28 \text{ ft}^2} = \frac{25}{4} = \frac{5^2}{2^2}$

Ratio of corresponding lengths $= \frac{5}{2}$

$\frac{14}{d_1} = \frac{5}{2} \rightarrow d_1 = 5.6 \text{ ft}$; $\frac{25}{d_2} = \frac{5}{2} \rightarrow d_2 = 10 \text{ ft}$

The lengths of the diagonals of $RSTU$ are 5.6 feet and 10 feet.

27. New patio: x, $A = 360 \text{ ft}^2$

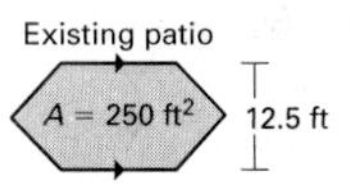

Ratio of areas $= \frac{360 \text{ ft}^2}{250 \text{ ft}^2} = \frac{36}{25} = \frac{6^2}{5^2}$

Ratio of corresponding lengths $= \frac{6}{5}$

Let x represent the distance between the long parallel sides of the new patio.

$\frac{x}{12.5} = \frac{6}{5} \rightarrow x = 15$ feet

Lesson 11.4 (pp. 749–752)

23. $\dfrac{\text{Arc length of } \widehat{LM}}{2\pi r} = \dfrac{m\widehat{LM}}{360°}$

$\dfrac{38.95}{2\pi r} = \dfrac{260°}{360°}$

$r = \dfrac{38.95(360°)}{2\pi(260°)}$

$r = \dfrac{7011}{260\pi} \approx 8.58$

25. $\boxed{\text{Perimeter}} = 2 \cdot \boxed{\text{Length of each straight section}} + 2 \cdot \boxed{\text{Length of each quarter circle}}$

$= 2(6) + 2 \cdot \left(\dfrac{90°}{360°} \cdot 2\pi(3)\right)$

$= 12 + 3\pi$

≈ 21.42 units

35. The length 21 feet 8 inches represents the circumference of the trunk. They can substitute $21\frac{8}{12} = \frac{65}{3}$ for C in the equation $C = \pi d$ and solve for d.

$\dfrac{65}{3} = \pi d \rightarrow d \approx 7$ feet

Lesson 11.5 (pp. 758–761)

7. $A = \pi r^2$

$154 = \pi r^2$

$\dfrac{154}{\pi} = r^2$

$7 \approx r$

The radius is about 7 meters.

17. $\boxed{\text{Shaded area}} = \boxed{\text{Area of rectangle}} - 2 \cdot \boxed{\text{Area of semicircle}}$

$= 6(6) - 2 \cdot \left(\dfrac{180°}{360°}\right)(\pi \cdot 3^2)$

$= 36 - 9\pi$

≈ 7.7

The shaded area is about 7.73 square meters.

39. a. A circle graph is appropriate because the data values add up to 100%.

b. Bus: central angle $= 0.65(360°) = 234°$

Walk: central angle $= 0.25(360°) = 90°$

Other: central angle $= 0.10(360°) = 36°$

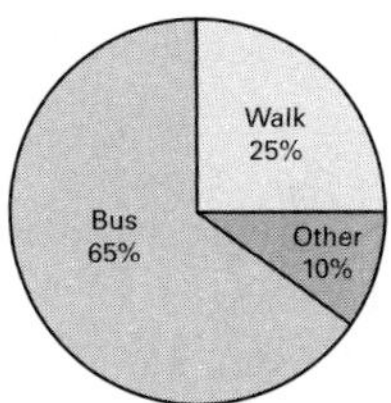

c. *Sample answer:* Use $r \approx 2$ in.

Area of "bus" sector $= \dfrac{234°}{360°} \cdot (\pi \cdot 2^2)$

≈ 8.2 in.^{2}

Area of "walk" sector $= \dfrac{90°}{360°} \cdot (\pi \cdot 2^2)$

≈ 3.1 in.^{2}

Area of "other" sector $= \dfrac{36°}{360°} \cdot (\pi \cdot 2^2)$

≈ 1.3 in.^{2}

Lesson 11.6 (pp. 765–768)

7. $\dfrac{360°}{18} = 20°$

21. $P = 7s = 7(9) = 63$ units

$m\angle DEF = \dfrac{360°}{7}$

$m\angle DEG = \dfrac{1}{2}\left(\dfrac{360}{7}\right)^\circ = \left(\dfrac{180}{7}\right)^\circ$

$\tan\left(\dfrac{180}{7}\right)^\circ = \dfrac{4.5}{a}$

$a = \dfrac{4.5}{\tan\left(\frac{180}{7}\right)^\circ}$

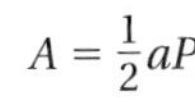

$A = \dfrac{1}{2}aP$

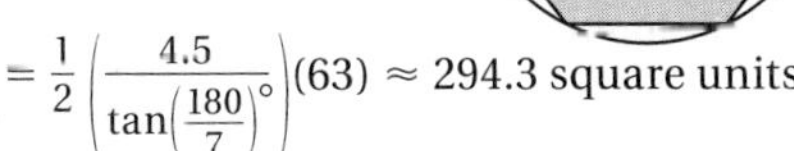

$= \dfrac{1}{2}\left(\dfrac{4.5}{\tan\left(\frac{180}{7}\right)^\circ}\right)(63) \approx 294.3$ square units.

37. Apothem $= a = 0.2 + 1 = 1.2$ centimeters

$\theta = \frac{1}{2}\left(\frac{360^\circ}{8}\right) = 22.5^\circ$

$\frac{x}{a} = \tan\theta$

$\frac{x}{1.2} = \tan 22.5^\circ$

$x = 1.2 \tan 22.5^\circ$

$s = 2x = 2.4 \tan 22.5^\circ$

Area of octagon $= \frac{1}{2}a \cdot ns$

$= \frac{1}{2}(1.2)(8)(2.4 \tan 22.5^\circ)$

≈ 4.8 square centimeters

Area of silver border

$=$ Area of octagon $-$ Area of circle

$= \frac{1}{2}a \cdot ns - \pi r^2$

$\approx 4.77 - \pi(1^2)$

≈ 1.6 square centimeters

Lesson 11.7 (pp. 774–777)

3. $P(K \text{ is on } \overline{AD}) = \frac{AD}{AE} = \frac{|3 - (-12)|}{|12 - (-12)|} = \frac{5}{8}$, 0.625, or 62.5%

9. $P(\text{Point lies in shading}) = \frac{\text{Area of shaded region}}{\text{Area of large triangle}}$

$= \frac{\frac{1}{2}(6)(7)}{\frac{1}{2}(12)(14)} = \frac{1}{4}$,

0.25, or 25%

33. $P(\text{You miss call}) = \frac{\text{Time from 7:00–7:10}}{\text{Time from 7:00–8:00}}$

$= \frac{10 \text{ min}}{60 \text{ min}} = \frac{1}{6} \approx 0.167$

The probability that you missed your friend's call is about 16.7%.

Chapter 12

Lesson 12.1 (pp. 798–801)

11. $F + V = E + 2$

$n + 12 = 18 + 2$

$n = 8$

25. The cross section is a circle.

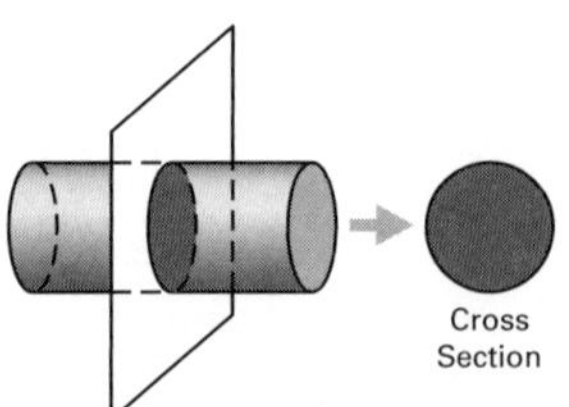

35. There are 6 vertices around each hexagonal face, and there are no other vertices. Each hexagonal face has 6 edges, and there are 6 additional edges between the square faces. So, there are $2(6) = 12$ vertices and $2(6) + 6 = 18$ edges.

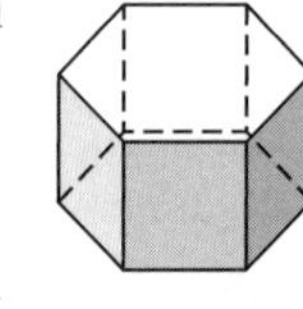

Check:

$F + V = E + 2$

$8 + 12 \stackrel{?}{=} 18 + 2$

$20 = 20$ ✓

Lesson 12.2 (pp. 806–809)

7. Base of prism:

$x^2 + 1.5^2 = 8^2$

$x = \sqrt{61.75}$ meters

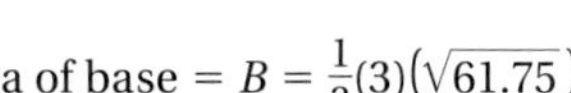

Area of base $= B = \frac{1}{2}(3)(\sqrt{61.75})$

$S = 2B + Ph$

$\approx 2\left(\frac{1}{2} \cdot 3\sqrt{61.75}\right) + (8 + 8 + 3)(9.1)$

≈ 196.47 square meters

9. $S = 2\pi r^2 + 2\pi rh$

$= 2\pi(0.8)^2 + 2\pi(0.8)(2)$

≈ 14.07 square inches

23. a. $S = 2(6 \cdot 6) + 2(6 \cdot 12) + 2(6 \cdot 12) = 360$

The minimum amount of wrapping paper needed is 360 square inches.

b. The area of the net of the box is larger because there are flaps that fold over and overlap.

c. You would want more than 360 square inches of wrapping paper so that you could wrap the paper around the box and fold it down to fit; this causes sections of paper to overlap.

Lesson 12.3 (pp. 814–817)

7. Area of base $= \frac{1}{2}aP$

$= \frac{1}{2}(6.9)(5 \cdot 10)$

$= 172.5$

$S = B + \frac{1}{2}P\ell$

$= 172.5 + \frac{1}{2}(50)(20)$

$= 672.5$ square millimeters

11. $\ell^2 = 4^2 + 1^2 \rightarrow \ell = \sqrt{17}$ inches

Lateral area $= \pi r\ell$

$= \pi(1)(\sqrt{17})$

≈ 12.95 square inches

1 in.
4 in.
ℓ

29. The net represents a regular square pyramid.

Area of one triangle $= \frac{1}{2}bh = \frac{1}{2}(6)(3\sqrt{3})$

$= 9\sqrt{3}$

Surface area = area of square + 4(area of triangle)

$= 6^2 + 4 \cdot 9\sqrt{3}$

$= 36 + 36\sqrt{3} \approx 98.35 \text{ cm}^2$

Lesson 12.4 (pp. 822–825)

7. Area of base $= \frac{1}{2}(7)(10) = 35 \text{ in.}^2$

Volume $= Bh = 35(5) = 175 \text{ in.}^3$

11. Volume $= \pi r^2 h$

$= \pi(5^2)(16) \approx 1256.64 \text{ in.}^3$

29. a. Visualize the concrete block broken into five parts:

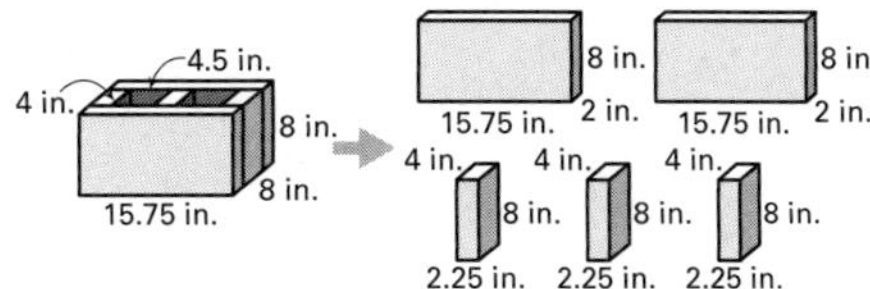

Total volume $= 2(15.75 \cdot 2 \cdot 8)$

$+ 3(2.25 \cdot 4 \cdot 8) = 720 \text{ in.}^3$

b. Volume of block = Volume of large prism − Volume of holes

$= (15.75 \cdot 8)(8) - 2(4 \cdot 4.5)(8) = 720 \text{ in.}^3$

c. The volumes found in parts (a) and (b) are equal.

Lesson 12.5 (pp. 832–836)

3. Area of base $= 5^2 = 25 \text{ cm}^2$

$V = \frac{1}{3}Bh$

$= \frac{1}{3}(25)(6)$

$= 50 \text{ cm}^3$

17. r
54°
h
15 cm

$\sin 54° = \frac{h}{15}$

$h = 15 \sin 54°$

$\cos 54° = \frac{r}{15}$

$r = 15 \cos 54°$

$V = \frac{1}{3}\pi r^2 h$

$= \frac{1}{3}\pi(15 \cos 54°)^2 (15 \sin 54°)$

$\approx 987.86 \text{ cm}^3$

33.

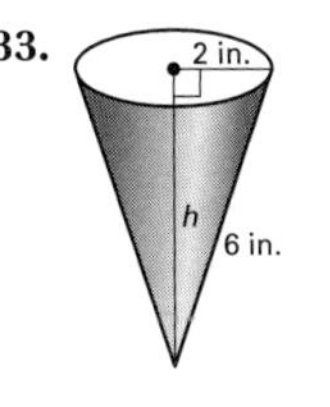

$h^2 + 2^2 = 6^2$

$h = 4\sqrt{2}$ in.

$V = \frac{1}{3}\pi r^2 h$

$= \frac{1}{3}\pi(2^2)(4\sqrt{2})$

$\approx 23.70 \text{ in.}^3$

WORKED-OUT SOLUTIONS

Lesson 12.6 (pp. 842–845)

3. $S = 4\pi r^2 = 4\pi(4^2) \approx 201.06 \text{ ft}^2$

13. $V = \frac{4}{3}\pi r^3 = \frac{4}{3}\pi(40^3) \approx 268{,}082.57 \text{ mm}^3$

31. $C = 2\pi r$

$24{,}855 = 2\pi r$

$r = \frac{24{,}855}{2\pi}$

Surface area of Western Hemisphere

$= \frac{1}{2}(4\pi r^2) = \frac{1}{2}(4\pi)\left(\frac{24{,}855}{2\pi}\right)^2 \approx 98{,}321{,}312 \text{ mi}^2$

Lesson 12.7 (pp. 850–854)

3. Radii: $\frac{7}{4}$ Heights: $\frac{16}{10} = \frac{8}{5}$

The cylinders are not similar because the ratios of corresponding linear measures are not equal.

9. $\frac{\text{Surface area of } A}{\text{Surface area of } B} = \frac{3^2}{1^2}$

$\frac{1500}{\text{Surface area of } B} = \frac{9}{1}$

Surface area of $B \approx 166.67 \text{ m}^2$

$\frac{\text{Volume of } A}{\text{Volume of } B} = \frac{3^3}{1^3}$

$\frac{3434.6}{\text{Volume of } B} = \frac{27}{1}$

Volume of $B \approx 127.21 \text{ m}^3$

27. Let x represent the amount to be added to the smaller bowl and y represent the amount to be added to the larger bowl.

$\frac{x}{y} = \frac{3^3}{4^3}$

$\frac{x}{64} = \frac{27}{64}$

$x = 27$

The smaller bowl needs 27 fluid ounces to be added.

WORKED-OUT SOLUTIONS

Chapter 1

1.1 Skill Practice (pp. 5–7) **1. a.** point Q **b.** line segment MN **c.** ray ST **d.** line FG **3.** $\overleftrightarrow{QW}$, line g **5.** *Sample answer:* points R, Q, S; point T **7.** Yes; through any three points not on the same line, there is exactly one plane. **9.** $\overrightarrow{VY}$, $\overrightarrow{VX}$, $\overrightarrow{VZ}$, $\overrightarrow{VW}$ **11.** $\overrightarrow{WX}$

15. *Sample:*

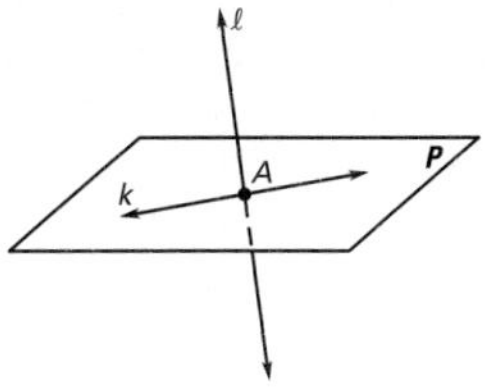

17. point R **19.** $\overleftrightarrow{RS}$ **21.** yes; yes

23. *Sample:*

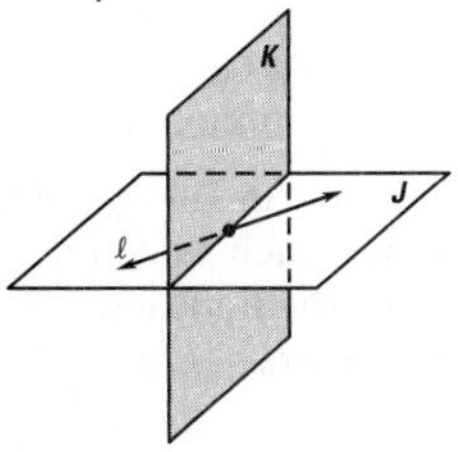

25. *Sample:*

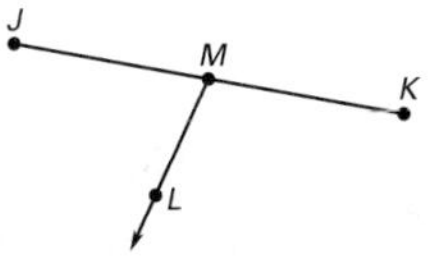

27. on the line **29.** not on the line **31.** on the line

33. 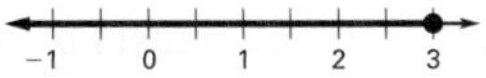

ray

35. 

segment

1.1 Problem Solving (pp. 7–8) **41.** intersection of a line and a plane **43.** Four points are not necessarily coplanar; no; three points determine a unique plane.

45. a–c.

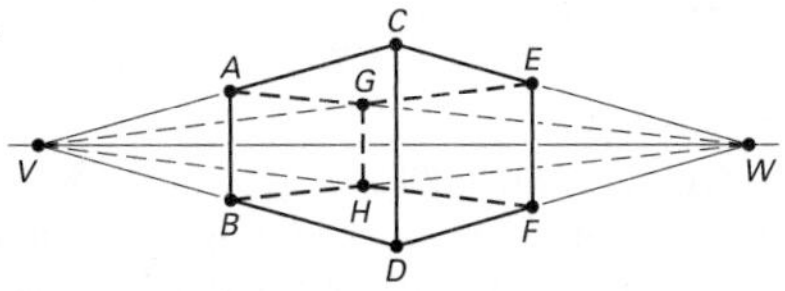

1.2 Skill Practice (pp. 12–13) **1.** $\overline{MN}$ means segment MN while MN is the length of $\overline{MN}$. **3.** 2.1 cm **5.** 3.5 cm **7.** 44 **9.** 23 **11.** 13 **13.** congruent **15.** not congruent **17.** 7 **19.** 9 **21.** 10 **23.** 20 **25.** 30 **29.** $(3x - 16) + (4x - 8) = 60$; 12; 20, 40

1.2 Problem Solving (pp. 13–14) **33. a.** 1883 mi **b.** about 50 mi/h **35. a.** *Sample:*

b. 21 ft

1.3 Skill Practice (pp. 19–20) **1.** Distance Formula **3.** $10\frac{1}{4}$ in. **5.** 26 cm **7.** $4\frac{3}{4}$ in. **9.** $2\frac{3}{8}$ in. **11.** 10 **13.** 1 **15.** 70 **17.** (5, 5) **19.** (1, 4) **21.** $\left(1\frac{1}{2}, -1\right)$ **23.** $\left(\frac{m}{2}, \frac{n}{2}\right)$; when x_2 and y_2 are replaced by zero in the Midpoint Formula and x_1 and y_1 are replaced by m and n the result is $\left(\frac{m}{2}, \frac{n}{2}\right)$. **25.** (−3, 10) **27.** (4, 8) **29.** (−18, 22) **31.** 4.5 **33.** 5.7 **35.** 7; $-\frac{1}{2}$ **37.** 40; 5 **39.** 9; $-3\frac{1}{2}$ **43.** $AB = 3\sqrt{5}$, $CD = 2\sqrt{10}$; not congruent **45.** $JK = 8\sqrt{2}$, $LM = \sqrt{130}$; not congruent

1.3 Problem Solving (pp. 21–22)

49. 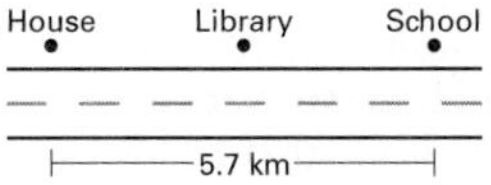

2.85 km

51. objects B and D; objects A and C **53. a.** 191 yd **b.** 40 yd **c.** About 1.5 min; find the total distance, about 230 yards, and divide by 150 yards per minute.

1.4 Skill Practice (pp. 28–31)

1. *Sample:*

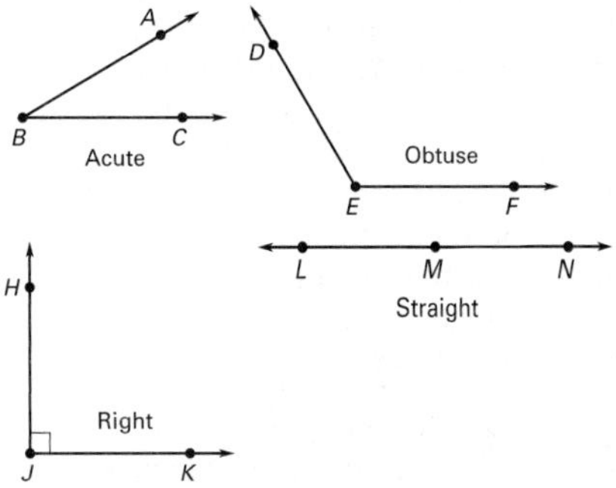

3. $\angle ABC$, $\angle B$, $\angle CBA$; B, $\overrightarrow{BA}$, $\overrightarrow{BC}$ **5.** $\angle MTP$, $\angle T$, $\angle PTM$; T, $\overrightarrow{TM}$, $\overrightarrow{TP}$ **7.** straight **9.** right **11.** 90°; right **13.** 135°; obtuse **15–19.** Sample answers are given. **15.** $\angle BCA$; right **17.** $\angle DFB$; straight **19.** $\angle CDB$; acute **23.** 65° **25.** 55° **29.** $m\angle XWY = 104°$, $m\angle ZWY = 52°$

SA1

31. $m\angle XWZ = 35.5°$, $m\angle YWZ = 35.5°$ **33.** 38° **35.** 142° **37.** 53°

39. If a ray bisects $\angle AGC$, then its endpoint must be point *G*. *Sample:*

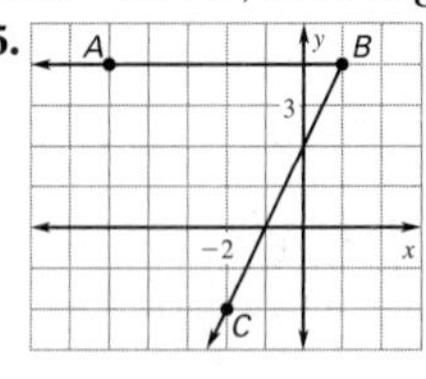

41. 80° **43.** 75°; both angle measures are 5° less.

45. Acute. *Sample answer:* (−2, 0)

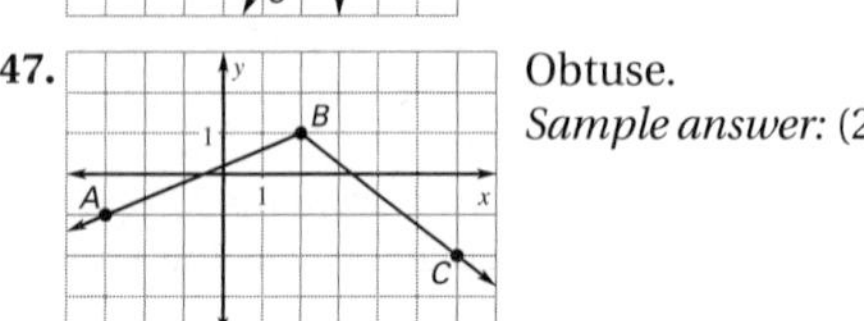

47. Obtuse. *Sample answer:* (2, 0)

1.4 Problem Solving (pp. 31–32) **51.** 32° **53. a.** 112° **b.** 56° **c.** 56° **d.** 56° **55.** *Sample answer:* acute: $\angle ABG$, obtuse: $\angle ABC$, right: $\angle DGE$, straight: $\angle DGF$ **57.** about 140° **59.** about 62° **61.** about 107°

1.5 Skill Practice (pp. 38–40)

1. No. *Sample answer:* Any two angles whose angle measures add up to 90° are complementary, but they do not have to have a common vertex and side.

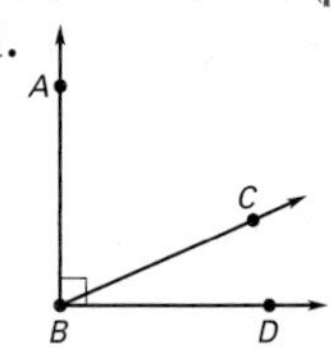

3. adjacent **5.** adjacent **7.** $\angle GLH$ and $\angle HLJ$, $\angle GLJ$ and $\angle JLK$ **9.** 69° **11.** 85° **13.** 25° **15.** 153° **17.** 135°, 45° **19.** 54°, 36° **21.** linear pair **23.** vertical angles **25.** linear pair **27.** neither **29.** The angles are complementary so they should be equal to 90°; $x + 3x = 90°$, $4x = 90$, $x = 22.5$. **31.** 10, 35 **33.** 55, 30 **35.** Never; a straight angle is 180°, and it is not possible to have a complement of an angle that is 180°. **37.** Always; the sum of complementary angles is 90°, so each angle must be less than 90°, making them acute. **39.** 71°, 19° **41.** 68°, 22° **43.** 58°, 122°

1.5 Problem Solving (pp. 40–41) **47.** neither **49–51.** Sample answers are given. **49.** $\angle FGB$, $\angle BGC$ **51.** $\angle AGE$, $\angle EGD$ **53.** *Sample answer:* Subtract 90° from $m\angle FGB$. **55. a.** $y_1 = 90 - x$, $0 < x < 90$; $y_2 = 180 - x$, $0 < x < 180$; the measure of the complement must be less than 90° and the measure of its supplement must be less than 180°.

55. b.

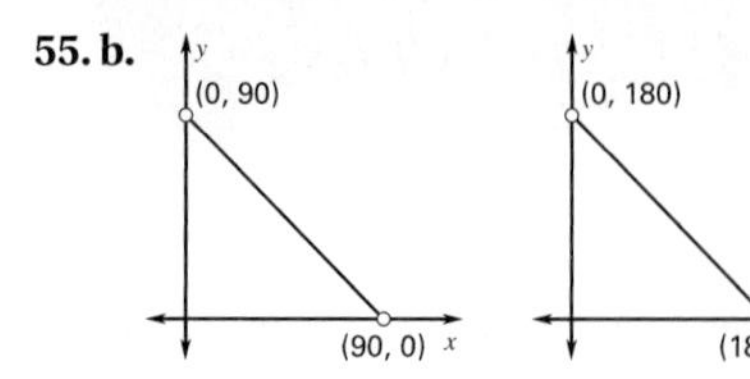

$0 < y_1 < 90$ $\quad 0 < y_2 < 180$

1.6 Skill Practice (pp. 44–46) **1.** An *n*-gon is a polygon with *n* sides. **3.** polygon; concave **5.** polygon; convex **9.** Pentagon; regular; it has 5 congruent sides and angles. **11.** Triangle; none of these; the sides and/or the angles are not all congruent. **13.** Quadrilateral; equiangular; it has 4 congruent angles. **15.** 8 in. **17.** 3 ft **19.** sometimes **21.** never **23.** never **25.** *Sample:* **27.** *Sample:*

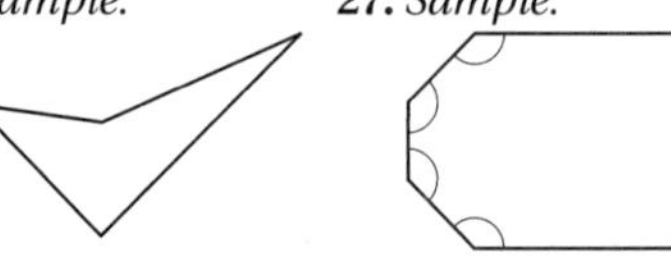

29. 1

1.6 Problem Solving (pp. 46–47) **33.** triangle; regular **35.** octagon; regular **39.** 105 mm; each side of the button is 15 millimeters long, so the perimeter of the button is 15(7) = 105 millimeters. **41. a.** 3 **b.** 5 **c.** 6 **d.** 8

1.7 Skill Practice (pp. 52–54) **1.** *Sample answer:* The diameter is twice the radius. **3.** (52)(9) must be divided by 2; $\frac{52(9)}{2} = 234 \text{ ft}^2$. **5.** 22.4 m, 29.4 m^2 **7.** 180 yd, 1080 yd^2 **9.** 36 cm, 36 cm^2 **11.** 84.8 cm, 572.3 cm^2 **13.** 76.0 cm, 459.7 cm^2

15. 59.3 cm, 280.4 cm^2

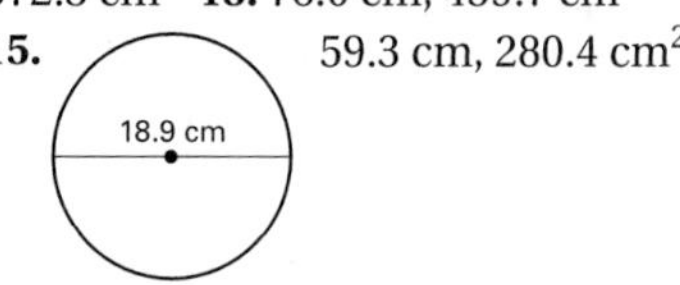

17. 12.4 **21.** 1.44 **23.** 8,000,000 **25.** 3,456 **27.** 14.5 m **29.** 4.5 in. **31.** 6 in., 3 in. **33.** Octagon; dodecagon; the square has 4 sides, so a polygon with the same side length and twice the perimeter would have to have 2(4) = 8 sides, an octagon; a polygon with the same side length and three times the perimeter would have to have 4(3) = 12 sides, a dodecagon. **35.** $\sqrt{346}$ in. **37.** $5\sqrt{42}$ km

1.7 Problem Solving (pp. 54–56) **41.** 1350 yd^2; 450 ft **43. a.** 15 in. **b.** 6 in.; the spoke is 21 inches long from the center to the tip, and it is 15 inches from the center to the outer edge, so 21 − 15 = 6 inches is the length of the handle.

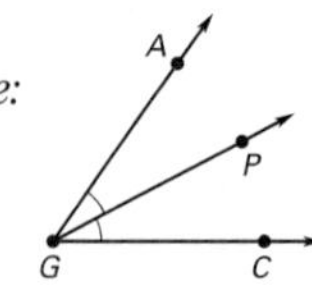

SELECTED ANSWERS

45. a. 106.4 m^2 **b.** 380 rows, 175 columns. *Sample answer:* The panel is 1520 centimeters high and each module is 4 centimeters so there are $1520 \div 4 = 380$ rows; the panel is 700 centimeters wide and each module is 4 centimeters therefore there are $700 \div 4 = 175$ columns.

1.7 Problem Solving Workshop (p. 57)
1. 2.4 h **3.** $26,730

Chapter Review (pp. 60–63) **1.** endpoints **3.** midpoint **5.** *Sample answer:* points *P*, *Y*, *Z* **7.** $\overrightarrow{YZ}$, $\overrightarrow{YX}$ **9.** 1.2 **11.** 7 **13.** 16 **15.** 8.6; (3.5, 3.5) **17.** 16.4; (5, −0.5) **19.** 5 **21.** 162°; obtuse **23.** 7° **25.** 88° **27.** 124° **29.** 168° **31.** 92°, 88°; obtuse **33.** Quadrilateral; equiangular; it has four congruent angles but its four sides are not all congruent. **35.** 21 **37.** 14 in., 11.3 in.^{2} **39.** 5 m

Algebra Review (p. 65) **1.** 6 **3.** −2 **5.** $1\frac{1}{2}$ **7.** 4 **9.** −11 **11.** 17 people

Chapter 2

2.1 Skill Practice (pp. 75–76) **1.** *Sample answer:* A guess based on observation

3.

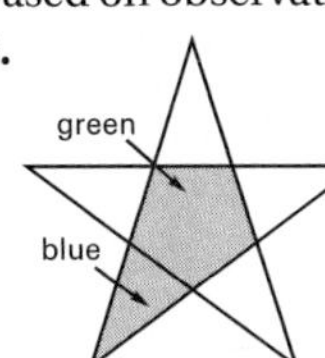

7. The numbers are 4 times the previous number; 768. **9.** The rate of decrease is increasing by 1; −6. **11.** The numbers are increasing by successive multiples of 3; 25. **13.** even **15.** *Sample answer:* $(3 + 4)^2 = 7^2 = 49 \neq 3^2 + 4^2 = 9 + 16 = 25$ **17.** *Sample answer:* $3 \cdot 6 = 18$ **19.** To be true, a conjecture must be true for all cases. **21.** $y = 2x$ **23.** Previous numerator becomes the next denominator while the numerator is one more than the denominator; $\frac{6}{5}$.

25. 0.25 is being added to each number; 1.45.

27. Multiply the first number by 10 to get the second number, take half of the second number to get the third number, and repeat the pattern; 500.

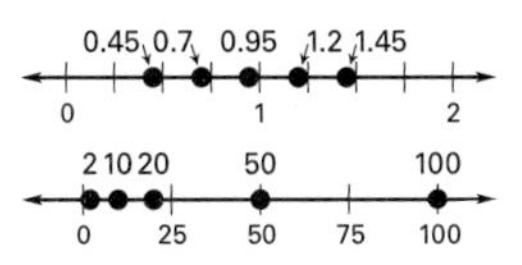

29. $r > 1$; $0 < r < 1$; raising numbers greater than one by successive natural numbers increases the result while raising a number between 0 and 1 by successive natural numbers decreases the result.

2.1 Problem Solving (pp. 77–78) **33.** *Sample answer:* The number of e-mail messages will increase in 2004; the number of e-mail messages has increased for the past 7 years.

35. a.

x	*y*
−3	−5
0	1
5	11
7	15
12	25
15	31

b.

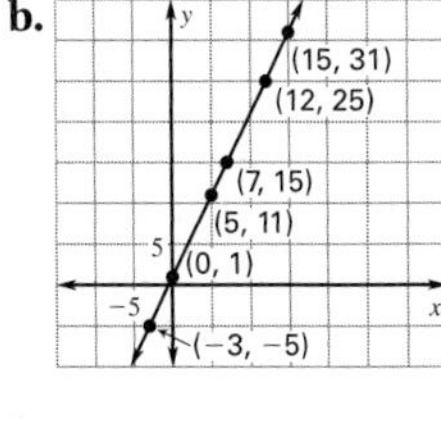

c. Double the value of *x* and add 1 to the result, $y = 2x + 1$. **37. a.** sum, two **b.** 144, 233, 377 **c.** *Sample answer:* spiral patterns on the head of a sunflower

2.2 Skill Practice (pp. 82–84) **1.** converse **3.** If $x = 6$, then $x^2 = 36$. **5.** If a person is registered to vote, then they are allowed to vote. **7.** If two angles are complementary, then they add to 90°; if two angles add to 90°, then they are complementary; if two angles are not complementary, then they do not add to 90°; if two angles do not add to 90°, then they are not complementary. **9.** If $x = 2$, then $3x + 10 = 16$; if $3x + 10 = 16$, then $x = 2$; if $x \neq 2$, then $3x + 10 \neq 16$; if $3x + 10 \neq 16$, then $x \neq 2$.

11. False. *Sample:*

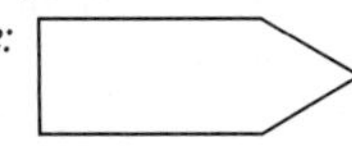

13. False. *Sample answer:* $m\angle ABC = 60°$, $m\angle GEF = 120°$ **15.** False. *Sample answer:* 2 **17.** False; there is no indication of a right angle in the diagram. **19.** An angle is obtuse if and only if its measure is between 90° and 180°. **21.** Points are coplanar if and only if they lie in the same plane. **23.** good definition **27.** If $-x > -6$, then $x < 6$; true. **29.** *Sample answer:* If the dog sits, she gets a treat.

2.2 Problem Solving (pp. 84–85) **31.** true **33.** Find a counterexample. *Sample answer:* Tennis is a sport, but the participants do not wear helmets. **35.** *Sample answer:* If a student is a member of the jazz band, then the student is a member of the band but not the chorus. **37.** no

2.3 Skill Practice (pp. 90–91) **1.** Detachment **3.** *Sample answer:* The door to this room is closed. **5.** $-15 < -12$ **7.** If a rectangle has four equal side lengths, then it is a regular polygon. **9.** If you play the clarinet, then you are a musician. **11.** The sum is even; the sum of two even integers is even; $2n$ and $2m$ are even, $2n + 2m = 2(n + m)$, $2(n + m)$ is even.

SA3

13. Linear pairs are not the only pairs of angles that are supplementary; angles *C* and *D* are supplementary, the sum of their measures is 180°.

2.3 Problem Solving (pp. 91–93) **17.** You will get a raise if the revenue is greater than its costs. **19.** is **21.** Deductive; laws of logic were used to reach the conclusion. **23.** $2n + (2n + 1) = (2n + 2n) + 1 = 4n + 1$, which is odd because $4n$ is even. **25.** True; since the game is not sold out, Arlo goes and buys a hot dog. **27.** False; Mia will buy popcorn.

Extension (p. 95) **1.** $\sim q \rightarrow \sim p$ **3.** Polygon *ABCDE* is not equiangular and equilateral. **5.** Polygon *ABCDE* is equiangular and equilateral if and only if it is a regular polygon. **7.** No; it is false when the hypothesis is true while the conclusion is false.

2.4 Skill Practice (pp. 99–100) **1.** line perpendicular to a plane **3.** Postulate 5 **5. a.** If three points are not collinear, then there exists exactly one plane that contains all three points. **b.** If there exists exactly one plane that contains three points, then the three points are noncollinear; if three points are collinear, then there does not exist exactly one plane that contains all three; if there is not exactly one plane containing three points, then the three points are collinear. **c.** contrapositive **7.** *Sample answer:* Lines *p* and *q* intersecting in point *H*

9. *Sample:*

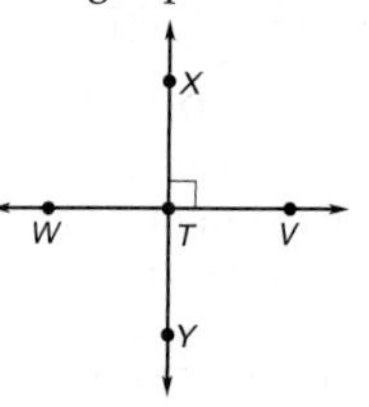

no; $\overline{XY}$ does not necessarily bisect $\overline{WV}$.

11. False. *Sample answer:* Consider a highway with two houses on the right side and one house on the left. **13.** False. *Sample answer:* Consider any pair of opposite sides of a rectangular prism. **15.** false **17.** false **19.** true **21.** true **23.** false

25. *Sample:* Postulate 5

Highway
m
City B
City A

Sample: Postulate 7

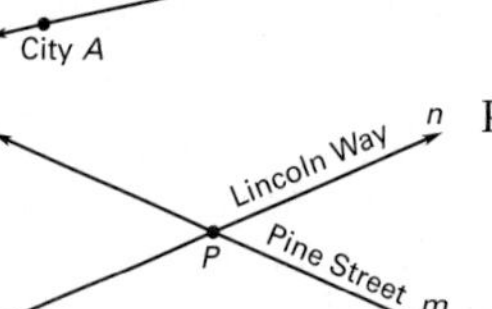

Sample: Postulate 8

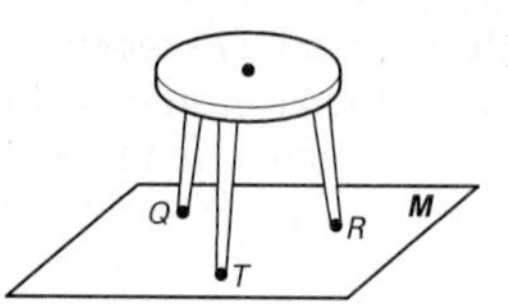

27. *Sample answer:* Postulate 9 guarantees three noncollinear points in a plane while Postulate 5 guarantees that through any two there exists exactly one line, therefore there exists at least one line in the plane.

2.4 Problem Solving (pp. 101–102) **31.** Postulate 7 **33.** *Sample answer:* A stoplight with a red, yellow, and green light. **35.** *Sample answer:* Through point *Z* and point *U* there exists $\overleftrightarrow{ZU}$. **37.** *Sample answer:* The floor is a plane containing points *W*, *X*, and *Y*.

39. a. *Sample:*

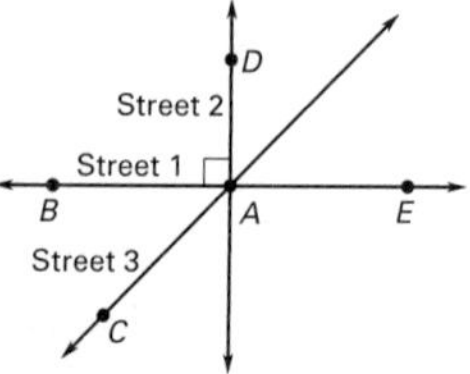

b. Building A **c.** right angle **d.** No; since $\angle CAE$ is obtuse, Building E must be on the east side of Building A. **e.** Street 1

41. They must be collinear. *Sample:*

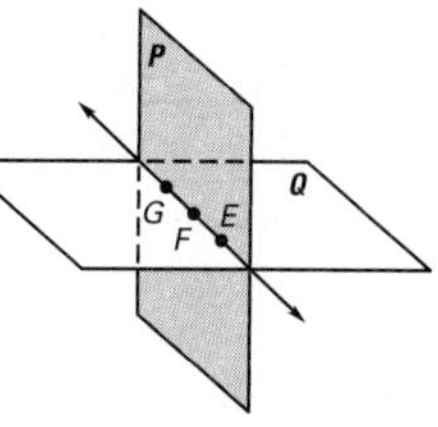

They must be noncollinear. *Sample:*

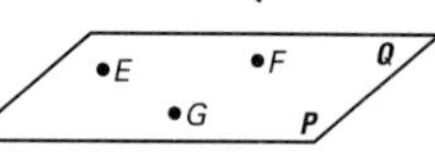

43. *Sample:*

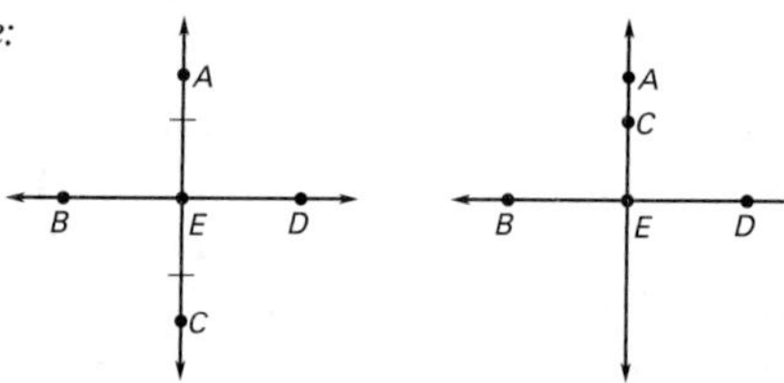

2.5 Skill Practice (pp. 108–109) **1.** Reflexive Property of Equality for Angle Measure **3.** Subtraction Property of Equality, Addition Property of Equality, Division Property of Equality

7. $4x + 9 = 16 - 3x$ Given
$7x + 9 = 16$ Addition Property of Equality
$7x = 7$ Subtraction Property of Equality
$x = 1$ Division Property of Equality

9. $3(2x + 11) = 9$ Given
$6x + 33 = 9$ Distributive Property
$6x = -24$ Subtraction Property of Equality
$x = -4$ Division Property of Equality

11. $44 - 2(3x + 4) = -18x$ Given
$44 - 6x - 8 = -18x$ Distributive Property
$36 - 6x = -18x$ Simplify.
$36 = -12x$ Addition Property of Equality
$-3 = x$ Division Property of Equality

13. $2x - 15 - x = 21 + 10x$ Given
$x - 15 = 21 + 10x$ Simplify.
$-15 = 21 + 9x$ Subtraction Property of Equality
$-36 = 9x$ Subtraction Property of Equality
$-4 = x$ Division Property of Equality

15. $5x + y = 18$ Given
$y = 18 - 5x$ Subtraction Property of Equality

17. $12 - 3y = 30x$ Given
$-3y = 30x - 12$ Subtraction Property of Equality
$y = \frac{30x - 12}{-3}$ Division Property of Equality
$y = -10x + 4$ Simplify.

19. $2y + 0.5x = 16$ Given
$2y = -0.5x + 16$ Subtraction Property of Equality
$y = \frac{-0.5x + 16}{2}$ Division Property of Equality
$y = -0.25x + 8$ Simplify.

21. $20 + CD$ **23.** AB, CD **25.** $m\angle 1 = m\angle 3$ **27.** *Sample answer:* Look in the mirror and see your reflection; 12 in. = 1 ft, so 1 ft = 12 in.; 10 pennies = 1 dime and 1 dime = 2 nickels, so 10 pennies = 2 nickels.

29. $AD = CB$ Given
$DC = BA$ Given
$AC = AC$ Reflexive Property of Equality
$AD + DC = CB + DC$ Addition Property of Equality
$AD + DC = CB + BA$ Substitution
$AD + DC + AC = CB + BA + AC$ Addition Property of Equality

2.5 Problem Solving (pp. 110–111)

31. $P = 2\ell + 2w$ Given
$P - 2w = 2\ell$ Subtraction Property of Equality
$\frac{P - 2w}{2} = \ell$ Division Property of Equality
length: 16.5 m

33. Row 1: Marked in diagram; Row 2: Substitute $m\angle GHF$ for 90°; Row 3: Angle Addition Postulate; Row 4: Substitution Property of Equality; Row 5: $m\angle 1 + m\angle 2 = m\angle 3 + m\angle 1$; Substitution Property of Equality; Row 6: Subtract $m\angle 1$ from both sides. **35.** 116°

2.6 Skill Practice (pp. 116–117) **1.** A theorem is a statement that can be proven; a postulate is a rule that is accepted without proof. **3.** 3. Substitution; 4. $AC = 11$ **5.** $\overline{SE}$ **7.** $\angle J, \angle L$ **9.** Reflexive Property of Congruence **11.** Reflexive Property of Equality **13.** The reason is the Transitive Property of Congruence, not the Reflexive Property of Congruence.

15. Cottage — Snack Shop — Bike Rentals — Arcade — Kite Shop

17. Because $\overline{QR}$ and $\overline{RS}$ are both congruent to $\overline{PQ}$, $\overline{QR} \cong \overline{RS}$ by the Transitive Property. Using the given segment lengths, $2x + 5 = 10 - 3x$. Using properties of algebra, this is equivalent to $5x + 5 = 10$, $5x = 5$, and $x = 1$. **19.** A proof is deductive reasoning because it uses facts, definitions, accepted properties, and laws of logic.

2.6 Problem Solving (pp. 118–119) **21.** 2. Definition of angle bisector; 4. Transitive Property of Congruence

23.

Statements	Reasons
1. $2AB = AC$	1. Given
2. $AC = AB + BC$	2. Segment Addition Postulate
3. $2AB = AB + BC$	3. Transitive Property of Segment Equality
4. $AB = BC$	4. Subtraction Property of Equality

25.

Statements	Reasons
1. A is an angle.	1. Given
2. $m\angle A = m\angle A$	2. Reflexive Property of Equality
3. $\angle A \cong \angle A$	3. Definition of congruent angles

27. Equiangular; the Transitive Property of Congruent Angles implies $\angle 1 \cong \angle 3$, so all angle measures are the same.

29. a. R, S, M, C, F, D — Restaurant, Shoe store, Movie theater, Cafe, Florist, Dry cleaners

b. Given: $\overline{RS} \cong \overline{CF}$, $\overline{SM} \cong \overline{MC} \cong \overline{FD}$, Prove: $\overline{RM} \cong \overline{CD}$

c.

Statements	Reasons
1. $\overline{RS} \cong \overline{CF}$, $\overline{SM} \cong \overline{MC} \cong \overline{FD}$	1. Given
2. $RS + SM = RM$	2. Segment Addition Postulate
3. $CF + FD = CD$	3. Segment Addition Postulate
4. $CF + FD = RM$	4. Substitution Property of Equality
5. $RM = CD$	5. Transitive Property of Equality
6. $\overline{RM} \cong \overline{CD}$	6. Definition of congruent segments

2.6 Problem Solving Workshop (p. 121) **1. a.** *Sample answer:* The logic used is similar; one uses segment length and the other uses segment congruence. **b.** *Sample answer:* Both the same; the logic is similar.

3. F, M, S, B, T

M is midpoint of $\overline{FS}$ → $FM = MS$; S is midpoint of $\overline{MB}$ → $MS = SB$; B is midpoint of $\overline{ST}$ → $SB = BT$

$FM = MS$ and $MS = SB$ → $FM = SB$; $FM = SB$ and $SB = BT$ → $FM = BT$

Statements	Reasons
1. M is halfway between F and S; S is halfway between M and B; B is halfway between S and T.	1. Given
2. M is the midpoint of $\overline{FS}$; S is the midpoint of $\overline{MB}$; B is the midpoint of $\overline{ST}$.	2. Definition of midpoint
3. $FM = MS$, $MS = SB$, $SB = BT$	3. Definition of midpoint
4. $FM = SB$	4. Transitive Property of Equality
5. $FM = BT$	5. Transitive Property of Equality

5. a. *Sample answer:* The proof on page 114 is angle congruence, while this one is segment congruence. **b.** *Sample answer:* If $\overline{FG} \cong \overline{DE}$ is the second statement, the reason would have to be Symmetric Property of Segment Congruence and that is what is being proven and you cannot use a property that you are proving as a reason in the proof.

2.7 Skill Practice (pp. 127–129) **1.** vertical **3.** $\angle MSN$ and $\angle PSQ$, $\angle NSP$ and $\angle QSR$, $\angle MSP$ and $\angle PSR$; indicated in diagram, Congruent Complements Theorem, Right Angles Congruence Theorem **5.** $\angle FGH$ and $\angle WXZ$; Right Angles Congruence Theorem **7.** Yes; perpendicular lines form right angles, and all right angles are congruent. **9.** 168°, 12°, 12° **11.** 118°, 118°, 62° **13.** $x = 13$, $y = 20$ **15.** *Sample answer:* It was assumed that $\angle 1$ and $\angle 3$, and $\angle 2$ and $\angle 4$ are linear pairs, but they are not; $\angle 1$ and $\angle 4$, and $\angle 2$ and $\angle 3$ are not vertical angles and are not congruent. **17.** 30° **19.** 27° **21.** 58° **23.** true **25.** false **27.** true **29.** 140°, 40°, 140°, 40° **31.** $\angle FGH$ and $\angle EGH$; Definition of angle bisector **33.** *Sample answer:* $\angle CEB$ and $\angle DEB$; Right Angles Congruence Theorem

2.7 Problem Solving (pp. 129–131)
37. 1. Given; 2. Definition of complementary angles; 3. $m\angle 1 + m\angle 2 = m\angle 1 + m\angle 3$; 4. $m\angle 2 = m\angle 3$; 5. Definition of congruent angles

39.

Statements	Reasons
1. $\overline{JK} \perp \overline{JM}$, $\overline{KL} \perp \overline{ML}$, $\angle J \cong \angle M$, $\angle K \cong \angle L$	1. Given
2. $\angle J$ and $\angle L$ are right angles.	2. Definition of perpendicular lines
3. $\angle M$ and $\angle K$ are right angles.	3. Right Angles Congruence Theorem
4. $\overline{JM} \perp \overline{ML}$ and $\overline{JK} \perp \overline{KL}$	4. Definition of perpendicular lines

41.

Statements	Reasons
1. $\angle 1$ and $\angle 2$ are complementary; $\angle 3$ and $\angle 4$ are complementary; $\angle 1 \cong \angle 4$.	1. Given
2. $m\angle 1 + m\angle 2 = 90°$, $m\angle 3 + m\angle 4 = 90°$	2. Definition of complementary angles
3. $m\angle 1 = m\angle 4$	3. Definition of congruent angles
4. $m\angle 1 + m\angle 2 = m\angle 3 + m\angle 4$	4. Transitive Property of Equality
5. $m\angle 1 + m\angle 2 = m\angle 3 + m\angle 1$	5. Substitution
6. $m\angle 2 = m\angle 3$	6. Subtraction Property of Equality
7. $\angle 2 \cong \angle 3$	7. Definition of congruent angles

SELECTED ANSWERS

43.

Statements	Reasons
1. $\angle QRS$ and $\angle PSR$ are supplementary.	1. Given
2. $\angle QRS$ and $\angle QRL$ are a linear pair.	2. Definition of linear pair
3. $\angle QRS$ and $\angle QRL$ are supplementary.	3. Linear pair Postulate
4. $\angle QRL$ and $\angle PSR$ are supplementary.	4. Congruent Supplements Theorem

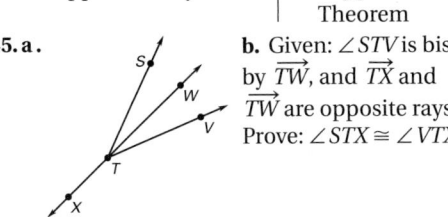

45. a.

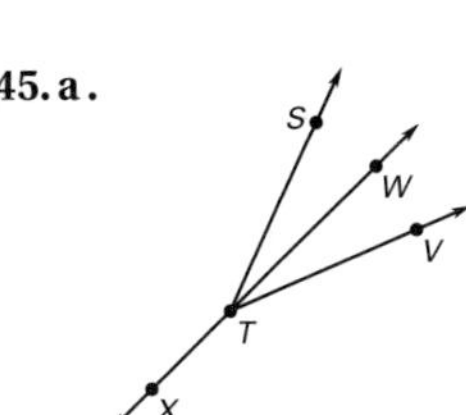

b. Given: $\angle STV$ is bisected by $\overrightarrow{TW}$, and $\overrightarrow{TX}$ and $\overrightarrow{TW}$ are opposite rays
Prove: $\angle STX \cong \angle VTX$

c.

Statements	Reasons
1. $\angle STV$ is bisected by $\overrightarrow{TW}$; $\overrightarrow{TX}$ and $\overrightarrow{TW}$ are opposite rays.	1. Given
2. $\angle STW \cong \angle VTW$	2. Definition of angle bisector
3. $\angle VTW$ and $\angle VTX$ are a linear pair; $\angle STW$ and $\angle STX$ are a linear pair.	3. Definition of linear pair
4. $\angle VTW$ and $\angle VTX$ are supplementary; $\angle STW$ and $\angle STX$ are supplementary.	4. Linear pair Postulate
5. $\angle STX \cong \angle VTX$	5. Congruent Supplements Theorem

Chapter Review (pp. 134–137) **1.** theorem
3. $m\angle A = m\angle C$ **5.** *Sample answer:* $\frac{-10}{-2} = 5$
7. Yes. *Sample answer:* This is the definition for complementary angles. **9.** $\angle B$ measures 90°.
11. The sum of two odd integers is even. *Sample answer:* $7 + 1 = 8$; $2n + 1$ and $2m + 1$ are odd, but their sum $(2n + 1) + (2m + 1) = 2m + 2n + 2 = 2(m + n + 1)$ is even.

15.

$15x + 22 = 7x + 62$	Given
$8x + 22 = 62$	Subtraction Property of Equality
$8x = 40$	Subtraction Property of Equality
$x = 5$	Division Property of Equality

17.

$5x + 2(2x - 23) = -154$	Given
$5x + 4x - 46 = -154$	Distributive Property
$9x - 46 = -154$	Simplify.
$9x = -108$	Addition Property of Equality
$x = -12$	Division Property of Equality

19. Reflexive Property of Congruence

21.

Statements	Reasons
1. $\angle A \cong \angle B$, $\angle B \cong \angle C$	1. Given
2. $m\angle A = m\angle B$, $m\angle B = m\angle C$	2. Definition of congruent angles
3. $m\angle A = m\angle C$	3. Transitive Property of Equality
4. $\angle A \cong \angle C$	4. Definition of congruent angles

23. 123°, 57°, 123°

Algebra Review (p. 139) **1.** $\frac{x^2}{4}$ **3.** $m + 7$ **5.** $\frac{k + 3}{-2k + 3}$
7. 2 **9.** $\frac{x - 2}{2x - 1}$ **11.** $-6\sqrt{5}$ **13.** $-2\sqrt{2} + 2\sqrt{6}$ **15.** $20\sqrt{2}$
17. $100\sqrt{2}$ **19.** 25 **21.** a **23.** $\sqrt{13}$

Chapter 3

3.1 Skill Practice (pp. 150–151) **1.** transversal **3.** $\overleftrightarrow{AB}$
5. $\overleftrightarrow{BF}$ **7.** $\overleftrightarrow{MK}$, $\overleftrightarrow{LS}$ **9.** No. *Sample answer:* The lines intersect. **11.** $\angle 1$ and $\angle 5$, $\angle 3$ and $\angle 7$, $\angle 2$ and $\angle 6$, $\angle 4$ and $\angle 8$ **13.** $\angle 1$ and $\angle 8$, $\angle 2$ and $\angle 7$ **15.** $\angle 1$ and $\angle 8$ are not in corresponding positions. $\angle 1$ and $\angle 8$ are alternate exterior angles.

17. 1 line

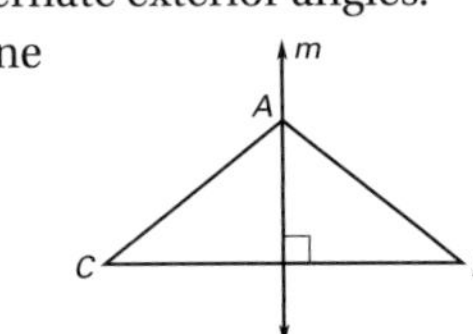

19. consecutive interior **21.** alternate exterior **23.** corresponding

25. never

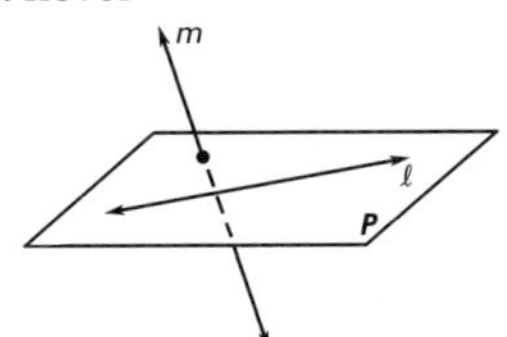

27. sometimes

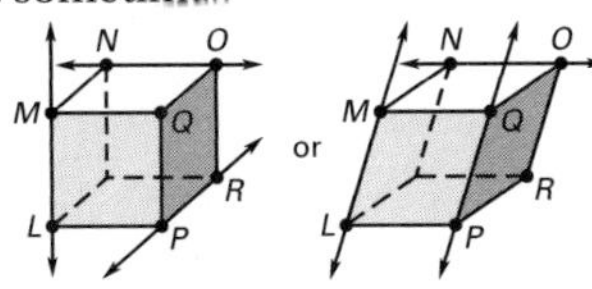

29. $\angle CFJ$, $\angle HJG$ **31.** $\angle DFC$, $\angle CJH$

3.1 Problem Solving (pp. 151–152) **35.** skew **39.** The adjacent interior angles are supplementary thus the measure of the other two angles must be 90°. **41.** false

3.2 Skill Practice (pp. 157–158)

1. *Sample:*

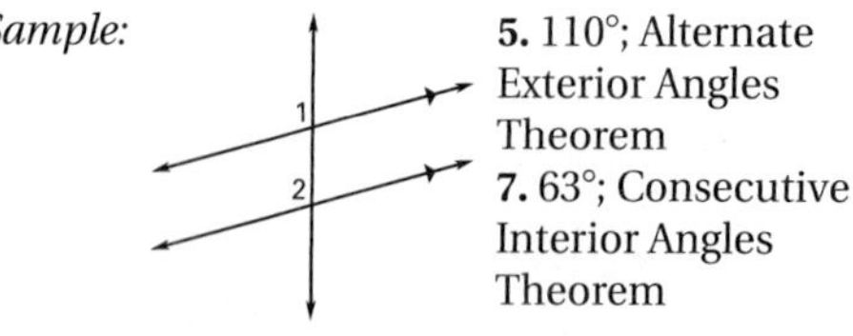

5. 110°; Alternate Exterior Angles Theorem **7.** 63°; Consecutive Interior Angles Theorem

9. Corresponding Angles Postulate **11.** Alternate Interior Angles Theorem **13.** Alternate Exterior Angles Theorem **15.** Alternate Exterior Angles Theorem **17.** $m\angle 1 = 150°$, Corresponding Angles Postulate; $m\angle 2 = 150°$, Vertical Angles Congruence Theorem **19.** $m\angle 1 = 122°$, $m\angle 2 = 58°$; Alternate Interior Angles Theorem, Consecutive Interior Angles Theorem **21.** *Sample answer:* $\angle 1 \cong \angle 4$ by the Alternate Exterior Angles Theorem; $\angle 1 \cong \angle 2 \cong \angle 3 \cong \angle 4$ by Vertical Angles Congruence Theorem, Alternate Interior Angles Theorem, and the Transitive Property of Angle Congruence. **23.** $m\angle 1 = 90°$, supplementary to the right angle by the Consecutive Interior Angles Theorem; $m\angle 3 = 65°$, it forms a linear pair with the angle measuring 115°; $m\angle 2 = 115°$, supplementary to $\angle 3$ by the Consecutive Interior Angles Theorem **25.** *Sample answer:* $\angle BAC$ and $\angle DCA$, $\angle ABD$ and $\angle CDB$ **27.** 45, 85 **29.** 65, 60 **31.** 13, 12

3.2 Problem Solving (pp. 159–160)

37.

Statements	Reasons
1. $p \parallel q$	1. Given
2. $\angle 1 \cong \angle 3$	2. Corresponding Angles Postulate
3. $\angle 3 \cong \angle 2$	3. Vertical Angles Congruence Theorem
4. $\angle 1 \cong \angle 2$	4. Transitive Property of Angle Congruence

39. a. yes; $\angle 1$ and $\angle 5$, $\angle 2$ and $\angle 6$; yes; $\angle 1$ and $\angle 2$, $\angle 1$ and $\angle 6$, $\angle 2$ and $\angle 5$, $\angle 5$ and $\angle 6$. **b.** *Sample answer:* The transversal stays parallel to the floor.

41.

Statements	Reasons
1. $n \parallel p$	1. Given
2. $\angle 1 \cong \angle 3$	2. Alternate Interior Angles Postulate
3. $m\angle 1 = m\angle 3$	3. Definition of congruent angles
4. $m\angle 2 + m\angle 3 = 180°$	4. Definition of supplementary angles
5. $m\angle 2 + m\angle 1 = 180°$	5. Substitution
6. $\angle 1$ and $\angle 2$ are supplementary.	6. Definition of supplementary angles.

3.3 Skill Practice (pp. 165–167)

1. *Sample:* $\angle 1$ and $\angle 8$, $\angle 2$ and $\angle 7$

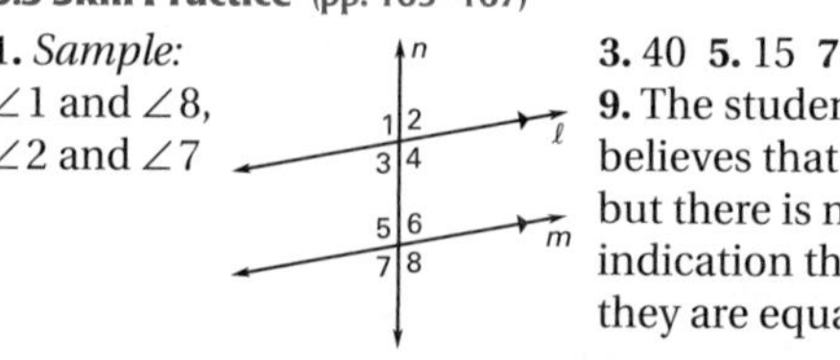

3. 40 **5.** 15 **7.** 60 **9.** The student believes that $x = y$ but there is no indication that they are equal.

11. yes; Alternate Exterior Angles Converse **13.** yes; Corresponding Angles Converse **15.** yes; Alternate Exterior Angles Converse **17. a.** $m\angle DCG = 115°$, $m\angle CGH = 65°$ **b.** They are consecutive interior angles and they are supplementary. **c.** yes; Consecutive Interior Angles Converse **19.** yes; Consecutive Interior Angles Converse **21.** no **25.** *Sample answer:* $\angle 1 \cong \angle 4$ therefore $\angle 4$ and $\angle 7$ are supplementary. Lines j and k are parallel by the Consecutive Interior Angles Converse. **27. a.** 1 line **b.** an infinite number of lines **c.** 1 plane

3.3 Problem Solving (pp. 167–169) **29.** Alternate Interior Angles Converse **31.** Substitution, Definition of supplementary angles, Consecutive Interior Angles Converse **33.** Yes. *Sample answer:* E 20th is parallel to E 19th by the Corresponding Angles Converse. E 19th is parallel to E 18th by the Alternate Exterior Angles Converse. E 18th is parallel to E 17th by the Alternate Interior Angles Converse. They are all parallel by the Transitive Property of Parallel Lines.

35.

Statements	Reasons
1. $a \parallel b$, $\angle 2 \cong \angle 3$	1. Given
2. $\angle 2$ and $\angle 4$ are supplementary.	2. Consecutive Interior Angles Theorem
3. $\angle 3$ and $\angle 4$ are supplementary.	3. Substitution
4. $c \parallel d$	4. Consecutive Interior Angles Converse

37. You are given that $\angle 3$ and $\angle 5$ are supplementary. By the Linear Pair Postulate, $\angle 5$ and $\angle 6$ are also supplementary. So $\angle 3 \cong \angle 6$ by the Congruent Supplements Theorem. By the converse of the Alternate Interior Angles Theorem, $m \parallel n$.

39. a. *Sample answer:* Corresponding Angles Converse **b.** Slide the triangle along a fixed horizontal line and use the edge that forms the 90° angle to draw vertical lines. **40–44.** Sample answers are given. **41.** Corresponding Angles Converse **43.** Vertical Angles Congruence Theorem followed by the Corresponding Angles Converse

3.4 Skill Practice (pp. 175–176) **1.** The slope of a nonvertical line is the ratio of vertical change (rise) to horizontal change (run) between any two points on the line. **7.** $\frac{1}{2}$ **9.** 0 **11.** Slope was computed using $\frac{\text{run}}{\text{rise}}$, it should be $\frac{\text{rise}}{\text{run}}$; $m = \frac{3}{4}$. **13.** Perpendicular; the product of their slopes is -1. **15.** Perpendicular; the product of their slopes is -1.

17.

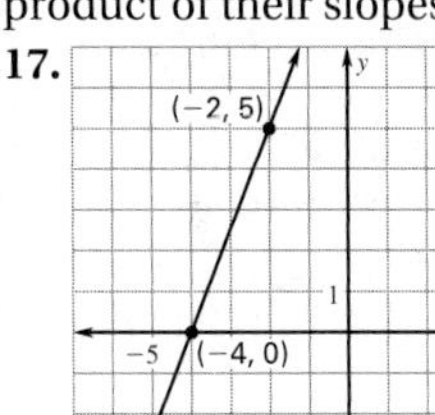

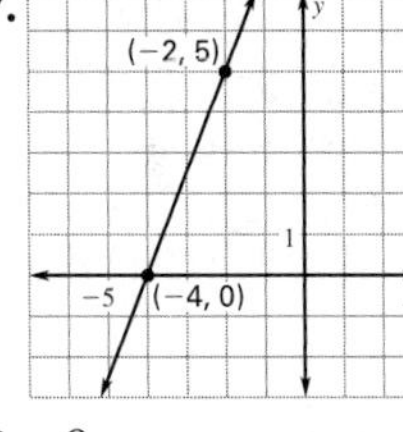

19. line 2 **21.** line 1

23. -2

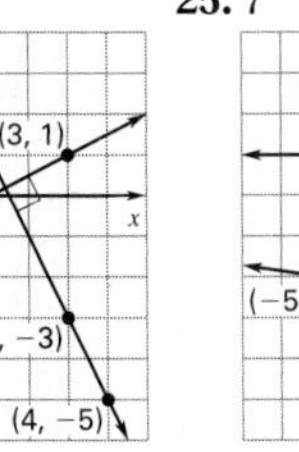

25. 7

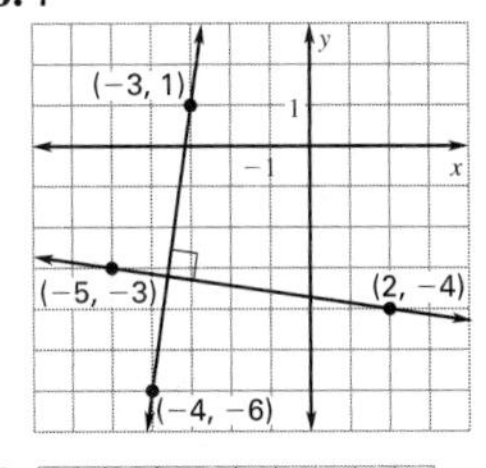

27.

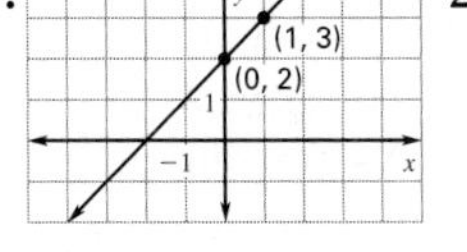

29.

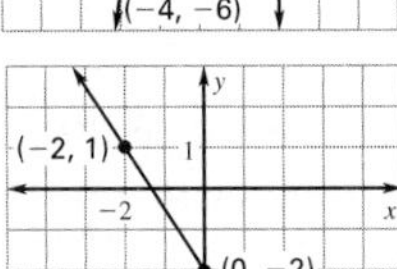

3.4 Problem Solving (pp. 176–178) **33.** $\frac{2}{3}$

35. line *b*; line *c*. *Sample:*

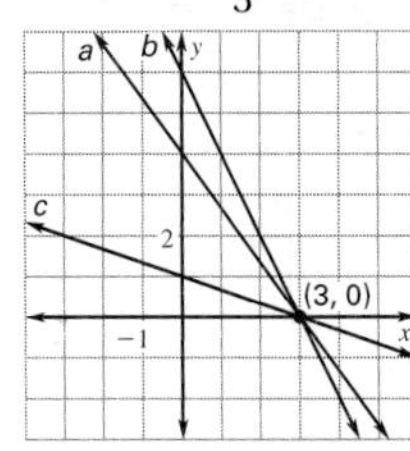

37. a.

Horizontal Distance (ft)	50	100	150	200	250	300	350
Height (ft)	29	58	87	116	145	174	203

Horizontal Distance (ft)	400	450	500	550	600	650	700
Height (ft)	232	261	290	319	348	377	406

406 ft

b. $\frac{29}{50}$

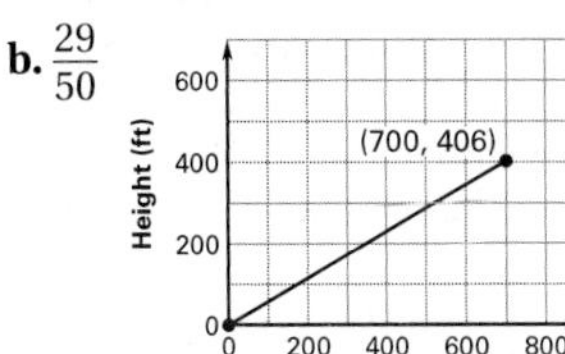

c. $\frac{144}{271}$; Duquesne

39. \$1150 per year **41. a.** 1985 to 1990. *Sample answer:* about 2 million people per year **b.** 1995 to 2000. *Sample answer:* about 3 million people per year **c.** *Sample answer:* There was moderate but steady increase in attendance for the NFL over the time period of 1985–2000.

3.5 Skill Practice (pp. 184–186) **1.** The point of intersection on the *y*-axis when graphing a line. **3.** $y = \frac{4}{3}x - 4$ **5.** $y = -\frac{3}{2}x - \frac{1}{2}$ **7.** $y = \frac{3}{2}x - \frac{3}{2}$ **11.** $y = 3x + 2$ **13.** $y = -\frac{5}{2}x$ **15.** $y = -\frac{11}{5}x - 12$ **17.** $y = 4x - 16$ **19.** $y = -\frac{2}{3}x - \frac{22}{3}$ **21.** $y = 7$ **23.** $y = -2x - 1$ **25.** $y = \frac{1}{5}x + \frac{37}{5}$ **27.** $y = -\frac{5}{2}x - 4$ **31.** $y = -\frac{3}{7}x + \frac{4}{7}$ **33.** $y = \frac{1}{2}x + 2$ **35.** $y = -\frac{5}{3}x - \frac{40}{3}$

37.

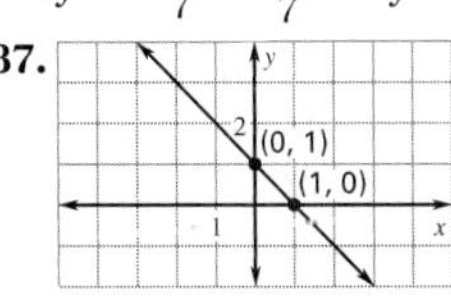

39.

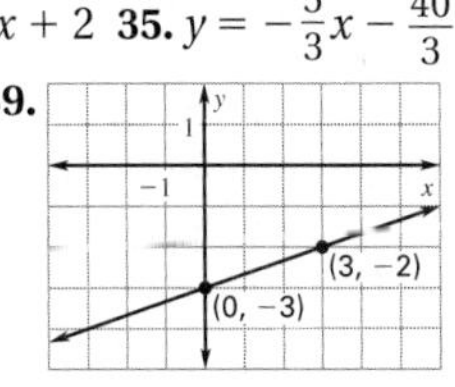

45. To find the *x*-intercept, let $y = 0$, $5x - 3(0) = -15$, $x = -3$, $(-3, 0)$. To find the *y*-intercept, let $x = 0$, $5(0) - 3y = -15$, $y = 5$, $(0, 5)$. **47.** $y = 0.5x + 7$ and $-x + 2y = -5$ **49.** 4, 4; $y = -x + 4$ **51.** -20, 10; $y = \frac{1}{2}x + 10$

SELECTED ANSWERS

53. 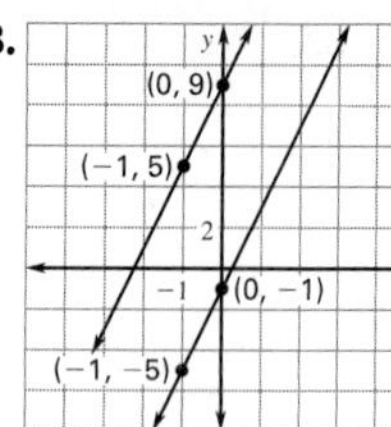

none

55. 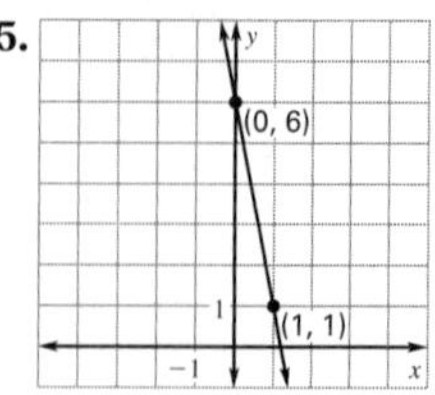

infinitely many

57. 4

3.5 Problem Solving (pp. 186–187) **61.** $y = 2.1x + 2000$; slope: gain in weight per day, y-intercept: starting weight before the growth spurt **63.** $2x + 3y = 24$; A: cost of a small slice, B: cost of a large slice, C: amount of money you can spend **65. a.** $2b + c = 13$, $5b + 2c = 27.50$

b. 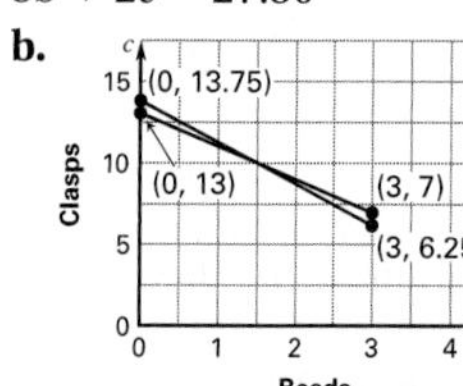

c. *Sample answer:* It's where the number of packages of beads and the number of packages of clasps would be the same for both girls.

3.5 Problem Solving Workshop (p. 189) **1.** 27 h **3.** 115 buttons **5.** *Sample answer:* In each case an equation modeling the situation was solved.

3.6 Skill Practice (pp. 194–195) **1.** $\overline{AB}$; it's $\perp$ to the parallel lines. **3.** If two sides of two adjacent acute angles are perpendicular, then the angles are complementary. **5.** 25° **7.** 52° **9.** Since the two angles labeled $x°$ form a linear pair of congruent angles, $t \perp n$; since the two lines are perpendicular to the same line, they are parallel to each other. **11.** *Sample answer:* Draw a line. Construct a second line perpendicular to the first line. Construct a third line perpendicular to the second line. **13.** There is no information to indicate that $y \parallel z$ or $y \perp x$. **15.** 13 **17.** 33 **19.** Lines f and g; they are perpendicular to line d. **23.** 4.1 **27.** 2.5

3.6 Problem Solving (pp. 196–197) **29.** Point C; the shortest distance is the length of the perpendicular segment. **31.** Linear Pair Postulate; $m\angle 1 + m\angle 2 = 180°$; Definition of congruent angles; Division Property of Equality; $\angle 1$ is a right angle.; Definition of perpendicular lines

33. 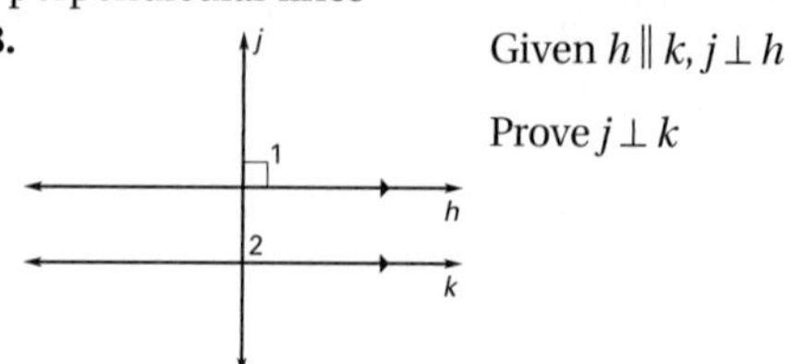

Given $h \parallel k$, $j \perp h$

Prove $j \perp k$

Statements	Reasons
1. $h \parallel k$, $j \perp h$	1. Given
2. $\angle 1 \cong \angle 2$	2. Corresponding Angles Postulate
3. $\angle 1$ is a right angle.	3. $\perp$ lines intersect to form 4 right angles
4. $m\angle 1 = 90°$	4. Definition of right angle
5. $m\angle 1 = m\angle 2$	5. Definition of congruent angles
6. $m\angle 2 = 90°$	6. Substitution
7. $\angle 2$ is a right angle.	7. Definition of right angle
8. $j \perp k$	8. Definition of perpendicular lines

Extension (p. 199) **1.** 6 **3.** 16 **5.** 2

7. 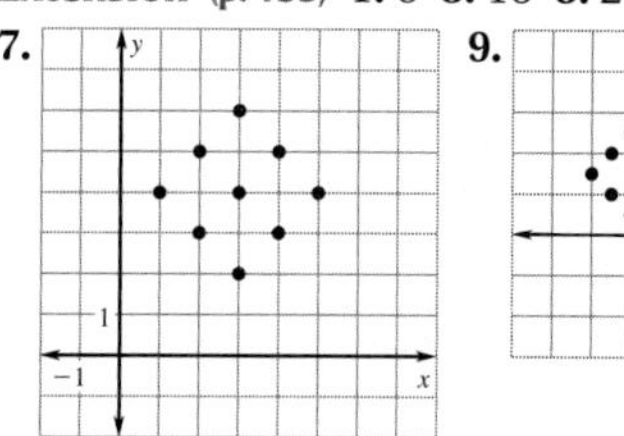

9.

11. (1, 0) **13.** (10, 4)

Chapter Review (pp. 202–205) **1.** skew lines **3.** $\angle 5$ **5.** $\angle 6$ **7.** standard form **9.** $\overleftrightarrow{NR}$ **11.** $\overleftrightarrow{JN}$ **13.** $m\angle 1 = 54°$, vertical angles; $m\angle 2 = 54°$, corresponding angles **15.** $m\angle 1 = 135°$, corresponding angles; $m\angle 2 = 45°$, supplementary angles **17.** 13, 132 **19.** 35°. *Sample answer:* $\angle 2$ and $\angle 3$ are complementary, so $m\angle 2 = 90° - 55° = 35°$. $m\angle 1 = m\angle 2$ because $\angle 1$ and $\angle 2$ are corresponding angles for two parallel lines cut by a transversal. **21.** 133 **23.** perpendicular **25. a.** $y = 6x - 19$ **b.** $y = -\frac{1}{6}x - \frac{1}{2}$ **27.** 3.2

SA10

Algebra Review (p. 207)

1.

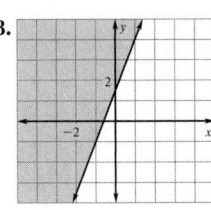

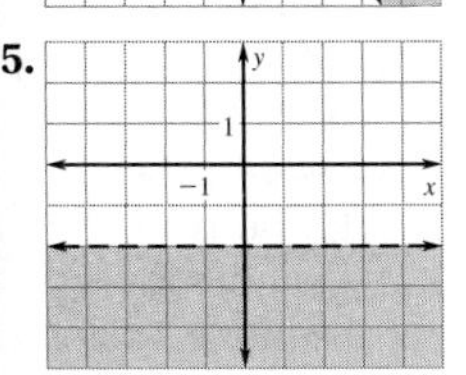

3.

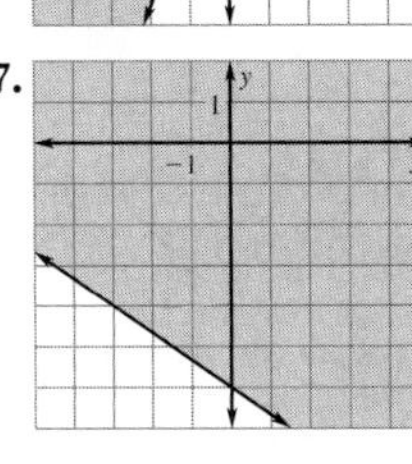

5.

7.

9. 6 mo **11.** after 100 min

Cumulative Review (pp. 212–213) **1.** 28, 56 **3.** acute **5.** acute **7.** 40 in., 84 in.^{2} **9.** 15.2 yd, 14.44 yd^2 **11.** Each number is being multiplied by $\frac{1}{4}$; $\frac{1}{2}$. **13.** $x < 7$ **15.** The musician is playing a stringed instrument.

17.

Equation	**Reason**
$-4(x + 3) = -28$	Given
$x + 3 = 7$	Division Property of Equality
$x = 4$	Subtraction Property of Equality

19. 29 **21.** $x = 9, y = 31$ **23.** $x = 101, y = 79$ **25.** 0 **27.** 2 **29. a.** $y = -x + 10$ **b.** $y = x + 14$ **31.** Yes; if two lines intersect to form a linear pair of congruent angles, then the lines are perpendicular. **33.** *Sample answer:* parallel and perpendicular lines **35.** 89 mi **37.** you want the lowest television prices, then come see Matt's TV Warehouse; you want the lowest television prices; come see Matt's TV Warehouse. **39.** Yes. *Sample answer:* Transitive Property of Congruence of Segments

Chapter 4

4.1 Skill Practice (pp. 221–222) **1.** C **3.** F **5.** B **7.** No; in a right triangle, the other two angles are complementary so they are both less than 90°. **9.** equilateral, equiangular

11.

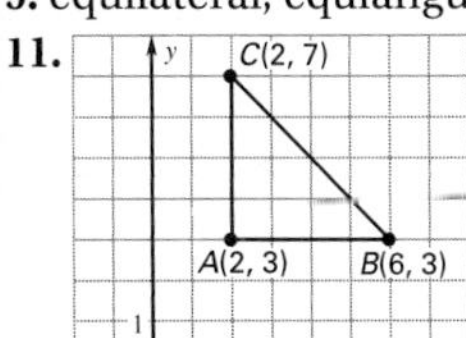

isosceles; right triangle

13.

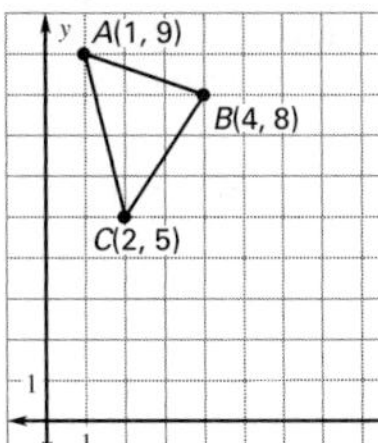

scalene; not a right triangle

15. 30; right **17.** 92° **19.** 158° **21.** 50° **23.** 50° **25.** 40° **27.** $m\angle P = 45°$, $m\angle Q = 90°$, $m\angle R = 45°$ **29.** Isosceles does not guarantee the third side is congruent to the two congruent sides; so if $\triangle ABC$ is equilateral, then it is isosceles as well. **33.** 118, 96 **35.** 26, 64 **37.** 35, 37

4.1 Problem Solving (pp. 223–224) **41.** 2 in.; 60°; in an equilateral triangle all sides have the same length $\left(\frac{6}{3}\right)$. In an equiangular triangle the angles always measure 60°. **45.** 115° **47.** 65° **49. a.** $2\sqrt{2x} + 5\sqrt{2x} + 2\sqrt{2x} = 180$ **b.** 40°, 100°, 40° **c.** obtuse **51.** *Sample answer:* They both reasoned correctly but their initial plan was incorrect. The measure of the exterior angle should be 150°.

4.2 Skill Practice (pp. 228–229)

1.

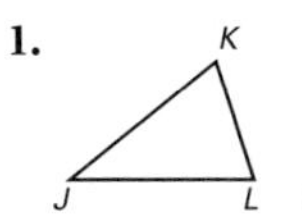

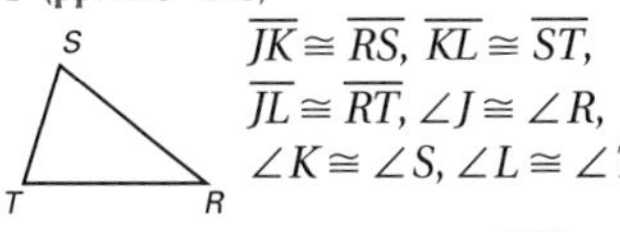

$\overline{JK} \cong \overline{RS}$, $\overline{KL} \cong \overline{ST}$, $\overline{JL} \cong \overline{RT}$, $\angle J \cong \angle R$, $\angle K \cong \angle S$, $\angle L \cong \angle T$

3. $\angle A$ and $\angle D$, $\angle C$ and $\angle F$, $\angle B$ and $\angle E$, $\overline{AB}$ and $\overline{DE}$, $\overline{AC}$ and $\overline{DF}$, $\overline{BC}$ and $\overline{EF}$. *Sample answer:* $\triangle CAB \cong \triangle FDE$. **5.** 124° **7.** 8 **9.** $\triangle ZYX$ **11.** $\triangle XYZ \cong \triangle ZWX$; all corresponding sides and angles are congruent. **13.** $\triangle BAG \cong \triangle CDF$; all corresponding sides and angles are congruent. **15.** 20 **17.** Student still needs to show that corresponding sides are congruent. **19.** 3, 1

4.2 Problem Solving (pp. 230–231) **23.** Transitive Property of Congruent Triangles **25.** length, width, and depth

27.

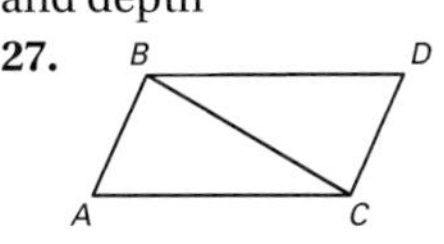

Yes; alternate interior angles are congruent.

29. no

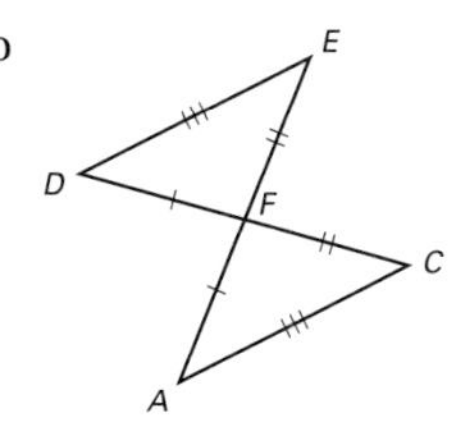

SELECTED ANSWERS

31. a. Corresponding parts of congruent figures are congruent. **b.** They are supplementary to two congruent angles and therefore are congruent. **c.** *Sample answer:* All right angles are congruent. **d.** Yes; all corresponding parts of both triangles are congruent.

4.2 Problem Solving Workshop (p. 232)

1. a.

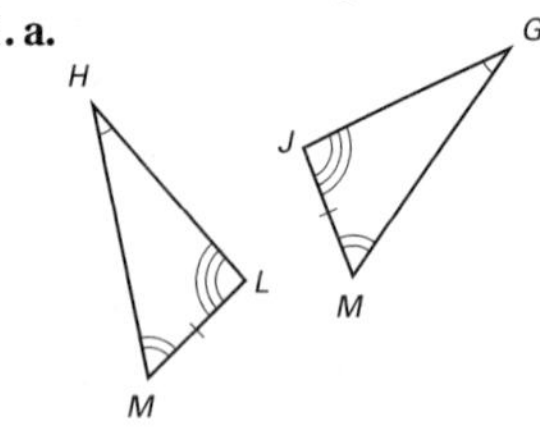

b.

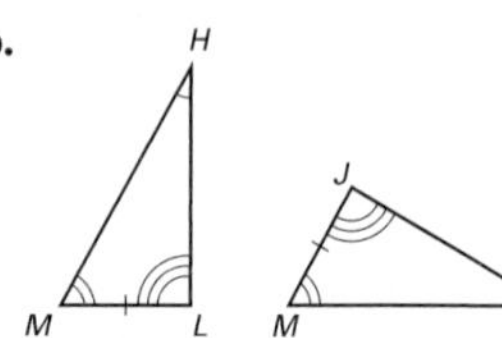

4.3 Skill Practice (pp. 236–237) **1.** corresponding angles **3.** corresponding sides **5.** not true; $\triangle RST \cong \triangle PQT$ **7.** true; SSS **9.** congruent **11.** congruent **13.** Stable; the figure has diagonal support with fixed side lengths. **15.** Stable; the figure has diagonal support with fixed side lengths. **19.** Not congruent; the congruence statement should read $\triangle ABC \cong \triangle FED$.

4.3 Problem Solving (pp. 238–239) **23.** Gate 1. *Sample answer:* Gate 1 has a diagonal support that forms two triangles with fixed side lengths, and these triangles cannot change shape. Gate 2 is not stable because that gate is a quadrilateral which can take many different shapes.

25.

Statements	Reasons
1. $\overline{WX} \cong \overline{VZ}$, $\overline{WY} \cong \overline{VY}$, $\overline{YZ} \cong \overline{YX}$	1. Given
2. $\overline{WV} \cong \overline{VW}$	2. Reflexive Property of Congruence
3. $WY = VY$, $YZ = YX$	3. Definition of congruent segments
4. $WY + YZ = VY + YZ$	4. Addition Property of Equality
5. $WY + YZ = VY + YX$	5. Substitution Property of Equality
6. $WZ = VX$	6. Segment Addition Postulate
7. $\overline{WZ} \cong \overline{VX}$	7. Definition of congruent segments
8. $\triangle VWX \cong \triangle WVZ$	8. SSS

27.

Statements	Reasons
1. $\overline{FM} \cong \overline{FN}$, $\overline{DM} \cong \overline{HN}$, $\overline{EF} \cong \overline{GF}$, $\overline{DE} \cong \overline{HG}$	1. Given
2. $MN = NM$	2. Reflexive Property of Equality
3. $FM = FN$, $DM = HN$, $EF = GF$	3. Definition of congruent segments
4. $EF + FN = GF + FN$, $DM + MN = HN + MN$	4. Addition Property of Equality
5. $EF + FN = GF + FM$, $DM + MN = HN + NM$	5. Substitution Property of Equality
6. $EN = GM$, $DN = HM$	6. Segment Addition Postulate
7. $\overline{EN} \cong \overline{GM}$, $\overline{DN} \cong \overline{HM}$	7. Definition of congruent segments
8. $\triangle DEN \cong \triangle HGM$	8. SSS

29. Only one triangle can be created from three fixed sides.

4.4 Skill Practice (pp. 243–244) **1.** included **3.** $\angle XYW$ **5.** $\angle ZWY$ **7.** $\angle XYZ$ **9.** not enough **11.** not enough **13.** enough **17.** *Sample answer:* $\triangle STU$, $\triangle RVU$; they are congruent by SAS.

19.

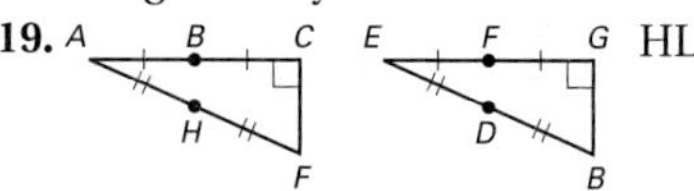

HL

21. SAS **23.** Yes; they are congruent by the SAS Congruence Postulate. **25.** $\overline{AC} \cong \overline{DF}$ **27.** $\overline{BC} \cong \overline{EF}$ **29.** Because $\overline{RM} \perp \overline{PQ}$, $\angle RMQ$ and $\angle RMP$ are right angles and thus are congruent. $\overline{QM} \cong \overline{MP}$ and $\overline{MR} \cong \overline{MR}$. It follows that $\triangle RMP \cong \triangle RMQ$ by SAS.

4.4 Problem Solving (pp. 245–246) **31.** SAS **33.** Two sides and the included angle of one sail need to be congruent to two sides and the included angle of the second sail; the two sails need to be right triangles with congruent hypotenuses and one pair of congruent legs.

35.

Statements	Reasons
1. $\overline{PQ}$ bisects $\angle SPT$, $\overline{SP} \cong \overline{TP}$	1. Given
2. $\angle SPQ \cong \angle TPQ$	2. Definition of angle bisector
3. $\overline{PQ} \cong \overline{PQ}$	3. Reflexive Property of Congruence
4. $\triangle SPQ \cong \triangle TPQ$	4. SAS

37.

Statements	Reasons
1. $\overline{JM} \cong \overline{LM}$	1. Given
2. $\angle KJM$ and $\angle KLM$ are right angles.	2. Given
3. $\triangle JKM$ and $\triangle LKM$ are right triangles.	3. Definition of right triangle
4. $\overline{KM} \cong \overline{KM}$	4. Reflexive Property of Congruence
5. $\triangle JKM \cong \triangle LKM$	5. HL

4.5 Skill Practice (pp. 252–253) **1.** *Sample answer:* A flow proof shows the flow of a logical argument. **3.** yes; AAS **5.** yes; ASA **9.** $\angle F, \angle L$ **11.** $\angle AFE \cong \angle DFB$ by the Vertical Angles Congruence Theorem. **13.** $\angle EDA \cong \angle DCB$ by the Corresponding Angles Postulate. **15.** No; there is no AAA postulate or theorem. **17.** No; the segments that are congruent are not corresponding sides.
19. yes; the SAS Congruence Postulate **21. a.** $\overline{BC}$ and $\overline{AD}$ are parallel with $\overline{AC}$ being a transversal. The Alternate Interior Angles Theorem applies. **b.** $\overline{AB}$ and $\overline{CD}$ are parallel with $\overline{AC}$ being a transversal. The Alternate Interior Angles Theorem applies. **c.** Using parts 21a, 21b, and the fact that $\overline{AC} \cong \overline{CA}$, they are congruent by ASA.

4.5 Problem Solving (pp. 254–255) **23.** Two pairs of angles and an included pair of sides are congruent. The triangles are congruent by ASA.

25.

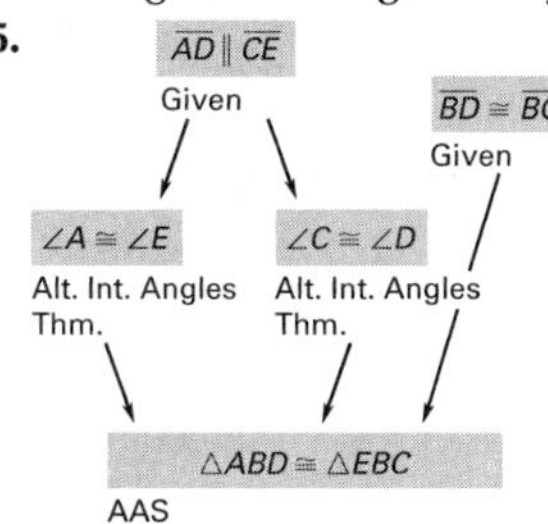

27. AAS **29.** Since all right angles are congruent the two triangles are congruent by either AAS, if the side is not included, or ASA if it is the included side.

31.

Statements	Reasons
1. $\overline{AK} \cong \overline{CJ}, \angle BJK \cong \angle BKJ, \angle A \cong \angle C$	1. Given
2. $\triangle ABK \cong \triangle CBJ$	2. ASA

33.

$\angle NKM \cong \angle LMK$, $\angle L \cong \angle N$ — Given → $\triangle NMK \cong \triangle LKM$ — AAS

$\overline{KM} \cong \overline{MK}$ — Reflexive Prop. of Congruence

4.6 Skill Practice (pp. 259–260) **1.** congruent **3.** $\triangle CBA$, $\triangle CBD$; SSS **5.** $\triangle JKM$, $\triangle LKM$; HL **7.** $\triangle JNH$, $\triangle KLG$; AAS **9.** The angle is not the included angle; the triangles cannot be said to be congruent. **11.** Show $\triangle NML \cong \triangle PQL$ by AAS since $\angle NLM \cong \angle PLQ$ by the Vertical Angles Congruence Theorem. Then $\overline{LM} \cong \overline{LQ}$ because corresponding parts of congruent triangles are congruent. **13.** 20, 120, ± 6 **15.** Show $\triangle KFG \cong \triangle HGF$ by AAS, which gives you $\overline{HG} \cong \overline{KF}$. This along with $\angle FJK \cong \angle GJH$ by vertical angles gives you $\triangle FJK \cong \triangle GJH$, therefore $\angle 1 \cong \angle 2$.
17. Show $\triangle STR \cong \triangle QTP$ by ASA using the givens and vertical angles STR and QTP. Since $\overline{PT} \cong \overline{RT}$ and using vertical angles PTS and RTQ, by SAS, $\triangle PTS \cong \triangle RTQ$ which gives you $\angle 1 \cong \angle 2$. **19.** Show $\triangle KNP \cong \triangle MNP$ by SSS. Now $\angle KPL \cong \angle MPL$ and $\overline{PL} \cong \overline{PL}$ leads to $\triangle LKP \cong \triangle LMP$ by SAS, which gives you $\angle 1 \cong \angle 2$. **21.** The triangles are congruent by SSS.

23.

Statements	Reasons
1. $\angle T \cong \angle U, \angle Z \cong \angle X, \overline{YZ} \cong \overline{YX}$	1. Given
2. $\triangle TYZ \cong \triangle UYX$	2. AAS
3. $\angle TYZ \cong \angle UYX$	3. Corr. parts of $\cong$ ⚠ are $\cong$.
4. $m\angle TYZ = m\angle UYX$	4. Definition of congruent angles
5. $m\angle TYW + m\angle WYZ = m\angle TYZ$, $m\angle TYW + m\angle VYX = m\angle UYX$	5. Angle Addition Postulate
6. $m\angle TYW + m\angle WYZ = m\angle TYW + m\angle VYX$	6. Transitive Property of Equality
7. $m\angle WYZ = m\angle VYX$	7. Subtraction Property of Equality
8. $\angle WYZ \cong \angle VYX$	8. Definition of congruent angles

4.6 Problem Solving (pp. 261–263)

29.

Statements	Reasons
1. $\overline{PQ} \parallel \overline{VS}, \overline{QU} \parallel \overline{ST}, \overline{PQ} \cong \overline{VS}$	1. Given
2. $\angle QPU \cong \angle SVT$, $\angle QUP \cong \angle STV$	2. Corresponding Angles Postulate
3. $\triangle PQU \cong \triangle VST$	3. AAS
4. $\angle Q \cong \angle S$	4. Corr. parts of $\cong$ ⚠ are $\cong$.

33. No; the given angle is not an included angle.
35. Yes; $\angle BDA \cong \angle BDC$, $\overline{AD} \cong \overline{CD}$ and $\overline{BD} \cong \overline{BD}$. By SAS, $\triangle ABD \cong \triangle CBD$. Corr. parts of $\cong$ ⚠ are $\cong$, so $\overline{AB} \cong \overline{BC}$.

SELECTED ANSWERS

SA13

37.

Statements	Reasons
1. $\overline{MN} \cong \overline{KN}$, $\angle PMN \cong \angle NKL$	1. Given
2. $\angle MNP \cong \angle KNL$	2. Vertical Angles Congruence Theorem
3. $\triangle PMN \cong \triangle LKN$	3. ASA
4. $\overline{MP} \cong \overline{KL}$, $\angle MPJ \cong \angle KLQ$	4. Corr. parts of $\cong$ $\triangle$s are $\cong$.
5. $\overline{MJ} \perp \overline{PN}$, $\overline{KQ} \perp \overline{LN}$	5. Given in diagram
6. $\angle KQL$ and $\angle MJP$ are right angles.	6. Theorem 3.9
7. $\angle KQL \cong \angle MJP$	7. Right Angles Congruence Theorem
8. $\triangle MJP \cong \triangle KQL$	8. AAS
9. $\angle 1 \cong \angle 2$	9. Corr. parts of $\cong$ $\triangle$s are $\cong$.

4.7 Skill Practice (pp. 267–268) **1.** The angle formed by the legs is the vertex angle. **3.** *A*, *D*; Base Angles Theorem **5.** $\overline{CD}$, $\overline{CE}$; Converse of Base Angles Theorem **7.** 12 **9.** 60° **11.** 20 **13.** 8 **15.** 39, 39 **17.** 45, 5 **21.** There is not enough information to find *x* or *y*. We need to know the measure of one of the vertex angles. **23.** 16 ft **25.** 39 in. **27.** possible **29.** possible **31.** $\triangle ABD \cong \triangle CBD$ by SAS making $\overline{BA} \cong \overline{BC}$ because corresponding parts of congruent triangles are congruent. **33.** 60, 120; solve the system $x + y = 180$ and $180 + 2x - y = 180$. **35.** 50°, 50°, 80°; 65°, 65°, 50°; there are two distinct exterior angles. If the angle is supplementary to the base angle, the base angle measures 50°. If the angle is supplementary to the vertex angle, then the base angles measure 65°.

4.7 Problem Solving (pp. 269–270)

39. 60°; 5 cm; 5 cm; 60°; 60°; 5 cm

41. a. $\angle A$, $\angle ACB$, $\angle CBD$, and $\angle CDB$ are congruent and $\overline{BC} \cong \overline{CB}$ making $\triangle ABC \cong \triangle BCD$ by AAS. **b.** $\triangle ABC$, $\triangle BCD$, $\triangle CDE$, $\triangle DEF$, $\triangle EFG$ **c.** $\angle BCD$, $\angle CDE$, $\angle DEF$, $\angle EFG$

43. 90°, 45°, 45°

47. No; $m\angle 1 = 50°$, so $m\angle 2 = 50°$ and it corresponds to the angle measuring 45°; therefore, *p* is not parallel to *q*. **49.** *Sample answer:* Choose point $P(x, y) \neq (2, 2)$ and set $PT = PU$. Solve the equation $\sqrt{x^2 + (y - 4)^2} = \sqrt{(x - 4)^2 + y^2}$ and get $y = x$. The point (2, 2) is excluded because it is a point on $\overleftrightarrow{TU}$.

4.8 Skill Practice (pp. 276–277) **1.** Subtract one from each *x*-coordinate and add 4 to each *y*-coordinate. **3.** translation **5.** reflection **7.** no

9.

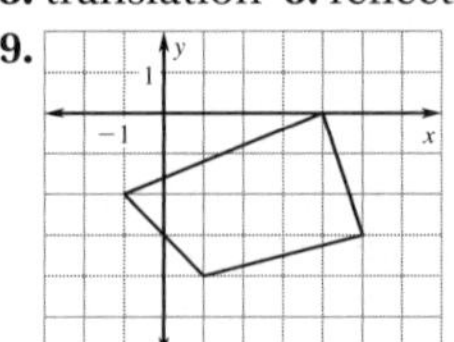

11.

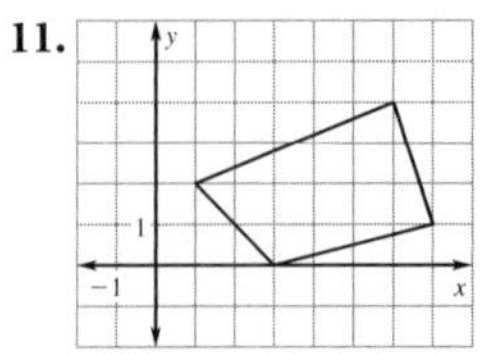

13. $(x, y) \rightarrow (x - 4, y - 2)$ **15.** $(x, y) \rightarrow (x + 2, y - 1)$

17.

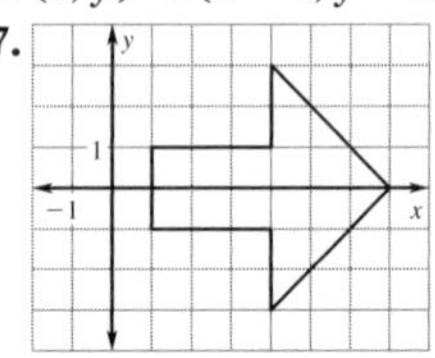

19.

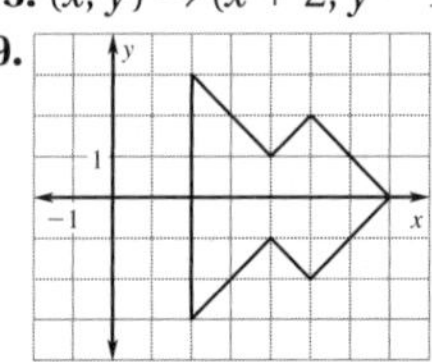

21.

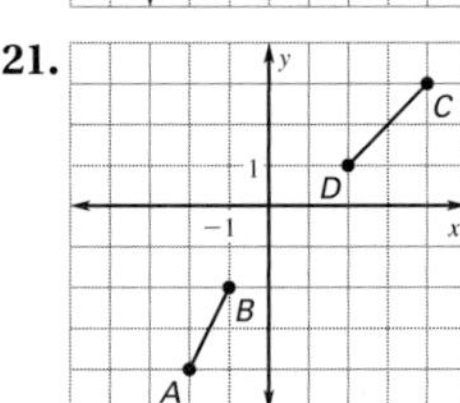

not a rotation

23.

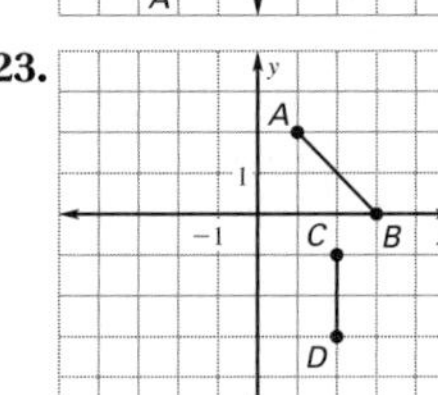

not a rotation

25. Yes; take any point or any line segment and rotate 360°.

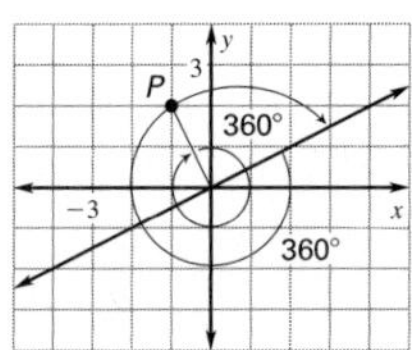

27. (3, 4) **29.** (2, 3) **31.** (13, −5) **33.** $\overline{UV}$ **35.** $\triangle DST$

SELECTED ANSWERS

4.8 Problem Solving (pp. 278–279) **39.** 90° clockwise, 90° counterclockwise **41. a.** $(x, y) \to (x - 1, y + 2)$ **b.** $(x, y) \to (x + 2, y - 1)$ **c.** No; the translation needed does not match a knight's move.

Chapter Review (pp. 282–285) **1.** equiangular **3.** An isosceles triangle has at least two congruent sides, while a scalene triangle has no congruent sides. **5.** $\angle P$ and $\angle L$, $\angle Q$ and $\angle M$, $\angle R$ and $\angle N$; $\overline{PQ}$ and $\overline{LM}$, $\overline{QR}$ and $\overline{MN}$, $\overline{RP}$ and $\overline{NL}$ **7.** 120° **9.** 60° **11.** 60° **13.** 18 **15.** true; SSS **17.** true; SAS **19.** $\angle F$, $\angle J$ **21.** Show $\triangle ACD$ and $\triangle BED$ are congruent by AAS, which makes $\overline{AD}$ congruent to $\overline{BD}$. $\triangle ABD$ is then an isosceles triangle, which makes $\angle 1$ and $\angle 2$ congruent. **23.** Show $\triangle QVS$ congruent to $\triangle QVT$ by SSS, which gives us $\angle QSV$ congruent to $\angle QTV$. Using vertical angles and the Transitive Property you get $\angle 1$ congruent to $\angle 2$. **25.** 20

27.

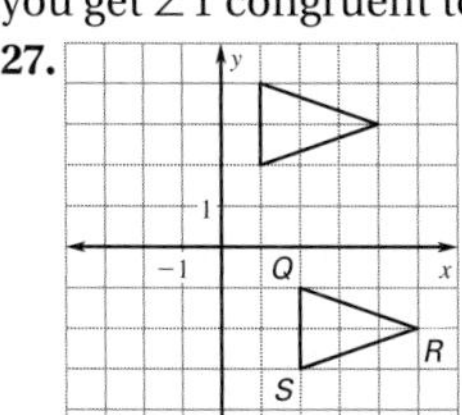

29.

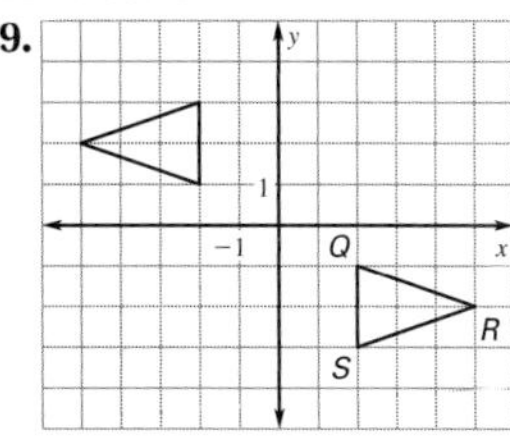

Algebra Review (p. 287)

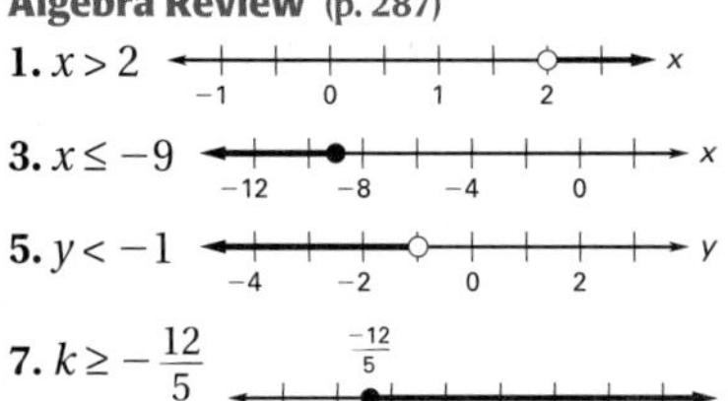

1. $x > 2$

3. $x \le -9$

5. $y < -1$

7. $k \ge -\frac{12}{5}$

9. $x < -\frac{5}{2}$

11. $n \ge -3$

13. 2, 8 **15.** 0, 8 **17.** $-\frac{7}{3}$, 3 **19.** −0.8, 3.4 **21.** $-\frac{1}{3}$, 1 **23.** −5, 14 **25.** $-\frac{6}{5}$, 2 **27.** $\frac{7}{3}$, 5

Chapter 5

5.1 Skill Practice (pp. 298–299) **1.** midsegment **3.** 13 **5.** 6 **7.** $\overline{XZ}$ **9.** $\overline{JX}$, $\overline{KL}$ **11.** $\overline{YL}$, $\overline{LZ}$ **13.** (0, 0), (7, 0), (0, 7) **15.** *Sample answer:* (0, 0), (2m, 0), (a, b) **17.** (0, 0), (s, 0), (s, s), (0, s) **19.** *Sample answer:* (0, 0), (r, 0), (0, s)

21.

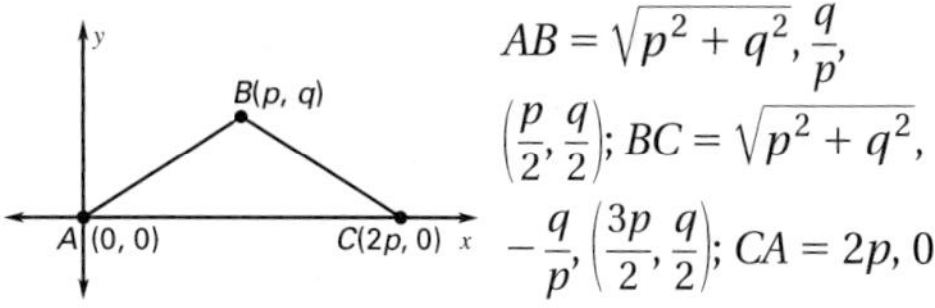

$AB = \sqrt{p^2 + q^2}$, $\frac{q}{p}$, $\left(\frac{p}{2}, \frac{q}{2}\right)$; $BC = \sqrt{p^2 + q^2}$, $-\frac{q}{p}$, $\left(\frac{3p}{2}, \frac{q}{2}\right)$; $CA = 2p$, 0, $(p, 0)$; no; yes; it's not a right triangle because none of the slopes are negative reciprocals, and it is isosceles because two of the sides have the same length.

23. $AB = m$, 0, $\left(\frac{m}{2}, n\right)$, $BC = n$, undefined, $\left(m, \frac{n}{2}\right)$, $CA = \sqrt{m^2 + n^2}$, $-\frac{n}{m}$, $\left(\frac{m}{2}, \frac{n}{2}\right)$; yes; no; one side is vertical and one side is horizontal thus the triangle is a right triangle. It is not isosceles since none of the sides have the same length.

25. 13 **27.** You don't know that $\overline{DE}$ and $\overline{BC}$ are parallel. **29.** (0, k). *Sample answer:* Since $\triangle OPQ$ and $\triangle RSQ$ are right triangles with $\overline{OP} \cong \overline{RS}$ and $\overline{PQ} \cong \overline{SQ}$, the triangles are congruent by SAS. **33.** $GE = \frac{1}{2}DB$, $EF = \frac{1}{2}BC$, area of $\triangle EFG = \frac{1}{2}\left[\frac{1}{2}DB\left(\frac{1}{2}BC\right)\right] = \frac{1}{8}(DB)(BC)$, area of $\triangle BCD = \frac{1}{2}(DB)(BC)$.

5.1 Problem Solving (pp. 300–301) **35.** 10 ft **37.** The coordinates of W are (3, 3) and the coordinates of V are (7, 3). The slope of $\overline{WV}$ is 0 and the slope of $\overline{OH}$ is 0 making $\overline{WV} \parallel \overline{OH}$. $WV = 4$ and $OH = 8$ thus $WV = \frac{1}{2}OH$. **39.** 16. *Sample answer:* DE is half the length of $\overline{FG}$ which makes $FG = 8$. FG is half the length of $\overline{AC}$ which makes $AC = 16$. **41.** *Sample answer:* You already know the coordinates of D are (q, r) and can show the coordinates of F are $(p, 0)$ since $\left(\frac{2p + 0}{2}, \frac{0 + 0}{2}\right) = (p, 0)$. The slope of $\overline{DF}$ is $\frac{r - 0}{q - p} = \frac{r}{q - p}$ and the slope of $\overline{BC}$ is $\frac{2r - 0}{2q - 2p} = \frac{r}{q - p}$ making them parallel. $DF = \sqrt{(q - p)^2 + r^2}$ and $BC = \sqrt{(2q - 2p)^2 + (2r)^2} = 2\sqrt{(q - p)^2 + r^2}$ making $DF = \frac{1}{2}BC$. **43. a.** $\frac{1}{2}$ **b.** $\frac{5}{4}$ **c.** $\frac{19}{8}$ **45.** *Sample answer:* $\triangle ABD$ and $\triangle CBD$ are congruent right isosceles triangles with $A(0, p)$, $B(0, 0)$, $C(p, 0)$ and $D\left(\frac{p}{2}, \frac{p}{2}\right)$. $AB = p$, $BC = p$, and $\overline{AB}$ is a vertical line and $\overline{BC}$ is a horizontal line, so $\overline{AB} \perp \overline{BC}$. By definition, $\triangle ABC$ is a right isosceles triangle.

SA15

5.1 Problem Solving Workshop (p. 302) **1.** The slopes of $\overline{AC}$ and $\overline{BC}$ are negative reciprocals of each other, so $\overline{AC} \perp \overline{BC}$ making $\angle C$ a right angle; $AC = h\sqrt{2}$ and $BC = h\sqrt{2}$ making $\triangle ABC$ isosceles.

3. a. $JL = LK = h$ and $\overline{JL}$ is a horizontal line and $\overline{LK}$ is a vertical line, so $\overline{JL} \perp \overline{LK}$; $h\sqrt{2}$, $\left(\frac{h}{2}, \frac{h}{2}\right)$.

K(h, h)
J (0, 0)
L(h, 0)

b. $JL = LK = 2h\sqrt{2}$ and the slope of $\overline{JL} = 1$ and the slope of $\overline{LK} = -1$, so $\overline{JL} \perp \overline{LK}$; $4h$, $(0, 0)$.

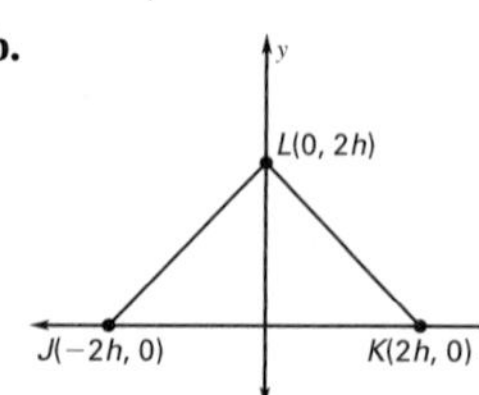

5. *Sample answer:* $PQRS$ with $P(0, 0)$, $Q(0, m)$, $R(n, m)$, and $S(n, 0)$. $PR = QS = \sqrt{m^2 + n^2}$ making $\overline{PR} \cong \overline{QS}$.

5.2 Skill Practice (pp. 306–307) **1.** circumcenter **3.** 15 **5.** 55 **7.** yes **11.** 35 **13.** 50 **15.** Yes; the Converse of the Perpendicular Bisector Theorem guarantees L is on $\overleftrightarrow{JP}$. **17.** 11

19. *Sample:*

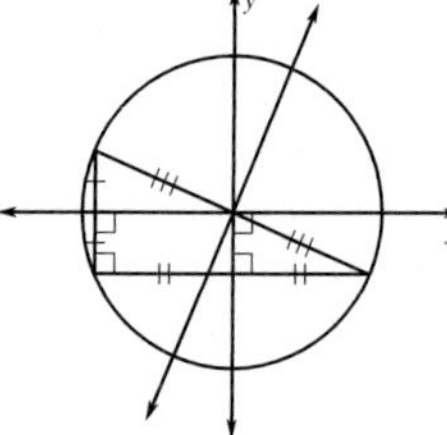

21. Always; congruent sides are created.

5.2 Problem Solving (pp. 308–309) **25.** Theorem 5.4 shows you that you can find a point equidistant from three points by using the perpendicular bisectors of the sides of the triangle formed by the three points.

27.

Statements	Reasons
1. $CA = CB$	1. Given
2. Draw $\overleftrightarrow{PC} \perp \overline{AB}$ through point C.	2. Perpendicular Postulate
3. $\overline{CA} \cong \overline{CB}$	3. Definition of congruent segments
4. $\overline{CP} \cong \overline{CP}$	4. Reflexive Property of Segment Congruence
5. $\angle CPA$ and $\angle CPB$ are right angles.	5. Definition of $\perp$ lines
6. $\triangle CPA$ and $\triangle CPB$ are right triangles.	6. Definition of right triangle
7. $\triangle CPA \cong \triangle CPB$	7. HL
8. $\overline{PA} \cong \overline{PB}$	8. Corr. parts of $\cong$ ▲ are $\cong$.
9. P is the midpoint of $\overline{AB}$.	9. Definition of midpoint
10. C is on the perpendicular bisector of $\overline{AB}$.	10. Definition of perpendicular bisector

5.3 Skill Practice (pp. 313–314) **1.** bisector **3.** 20° **5.** 9 **7.** No; you don't know that $\angle BAD \cong \angle CAD$. **9.** No; you don't know that $\overline{HG} \cong \overline{HF}$, $\overline{HF} \perp \overrightarrow{EF}$, or $\overline{HG} \perp \overrightarrow{EG}$. **11.** No; you don't know that $\overline{HF} \perp \overrightarrow{EF}$, or $\overline{HG} \perp \overrightarrow{EG}$. **13.** 4 **15.** No; the segments with length x and 3 are not perpendicular to their respective rays. **17.** Yes; $x = 7$ using the Angle Bisector Theorem. **19.** 9

21. GD is not the perpendicular distance from G to $\overline{CE}$. The same is true about GF; the distance from G to each side of the triangle is the same. **25.** 0.5

5.3 Problem Solving (pp. 315–316)

29. at the incenter of the pond

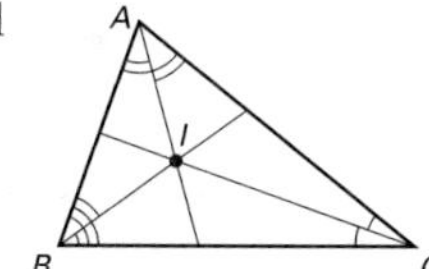

31. a. Equilateral; 3; the angle bisector would also be the perpendicular bisector. **b.** Scalene; 6; each angle bisector would be different than the corresponding perpendicular bisector. **33.** perpendicular bisectors; (10, 10); 100 yd; about 628 yd

SELECTED ANSWERS

35.

Statements	Reasons
1. $\angle BAC$ with D interior, $\overline{DB} \perp \overrightarrow{AB}$, $\overline{DC} \perp \overrightarrow{AC}$, $DB = DC$	1. Given
2. $\angle ABD$ and $\angle ACD$ are right angles.	2. Definition of perpendicular
3. $\triangle ABD$ and $\triangle ACD$ are right triangles.	3. Definition of right triangle
4. $\overline{DB} \cong \overline{DC}$	4. Definition of congruent segments
5. $\overline{AD} \cong \overline{AD}$	5. Reflexive Property of Segment Congruence
6. $\triangle ABD \cong \triangle ACD$	6. HL
7. $\angle BAD \cong \angle CAD$	7. Corr. parts of $\cong$ $\triangle$s are $\cong$.
8. $\overrightarrow{AD}$ bisects $\angle BAC$.	8. Definition of angle bisector

37. a. Use the Concurrency of Angle Bisectors of a Triangle Theorem; if you move the circle to any other spot it will extend into the walkway.

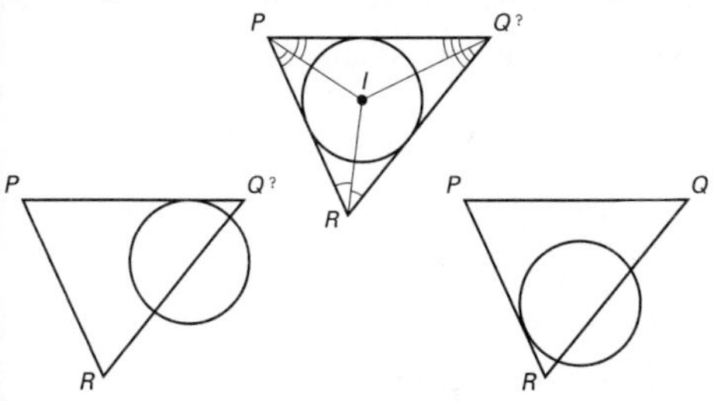

b. Yes; the incenter will allow the largest tent possible.

5.4 Skill Practice (pp. 322–323) **1.** circumcenter: when it is an acute triangle, when it is a right triangle, when it is an obtuse triangle; incenter: always, never, never; centroid: always, never, never; orthocenter: when it is an acute triangle, when it is a right triangle, when it is an obtuse triangle **3.** 12 **5.** 10 **9.** (3, 2)

11.

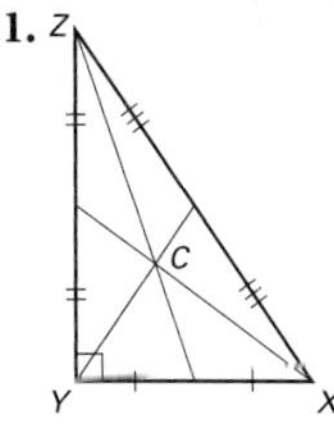

13. no; no; yes **15.** no; yes; no **17.** altitude **19.** median **21.** perpendicular bisector, angle bisector, median, altitude **23.** 6, 22°; $\triangle ABD \cong \triangle CBD$ by HL, use Corr. parts of $\cong$ $\triangle$s are $\cong$. **25.** 3 **27.** $\frac{3}{2}$

29. **31.**

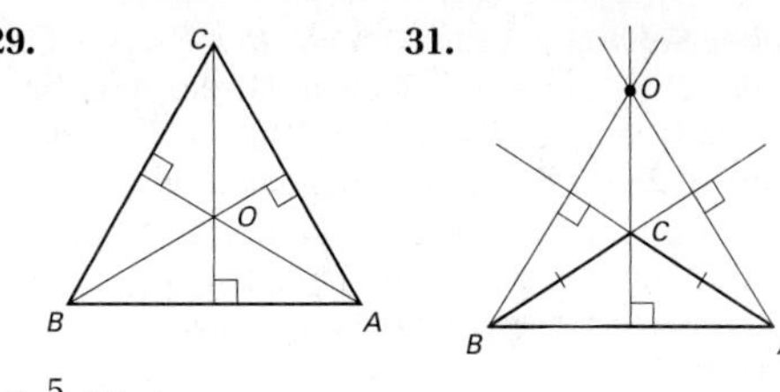

33. $\frac{5}{2}$ **35.** 4

5.4 Problem Solving (pp. 324–325) **37.** *B*; it is the centroid of the triangle. **39.** about 12.3 in.^{2}; median

41. (0, 2)

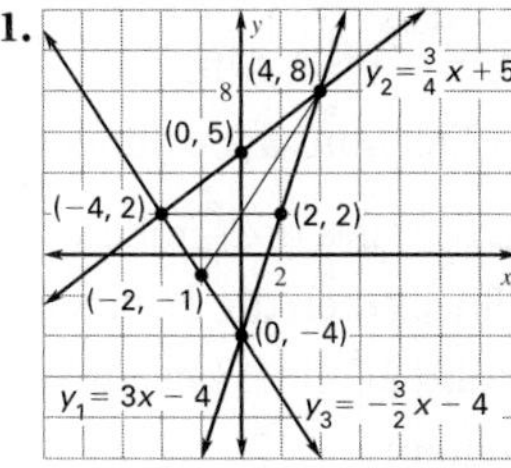

43. b. Their areas are the same. **c.** They weigh the same; it means the weight of $\triangle ABC$ is evenly distributed around its centroid.

5.5 Skill Practice (pp. 331–332) **1.** $\angle A$, $\overline{BC}$; $\angle B$, $\overline{CA}$; $\angle C$, $\overline{AB}$ **3.** *Sample answer:* The longest side is opposite the largest angle. The shortest side is opposite the smallest angle. **5.** *Sample answer:* The longest side is opposite the obtuse angle and the two angles with the same measure are opposite the sides with the same length. **7.** $\overline{XY}$, $\overline{YZ}$, $\overline{ZX}$; $\angle Z$, $\angle X$, $\angle Y$ **9.** $\overline{KL}$, $\overline{JL}$, $\overline{JK}$; $\angle J$, $\angle K$, $\angle L$ **11.** $\overline{DF}$, $\overline{FG}$, $\overline{GD}$; $\angle G$, $\angle D$, $\angle F$

13. **15.**

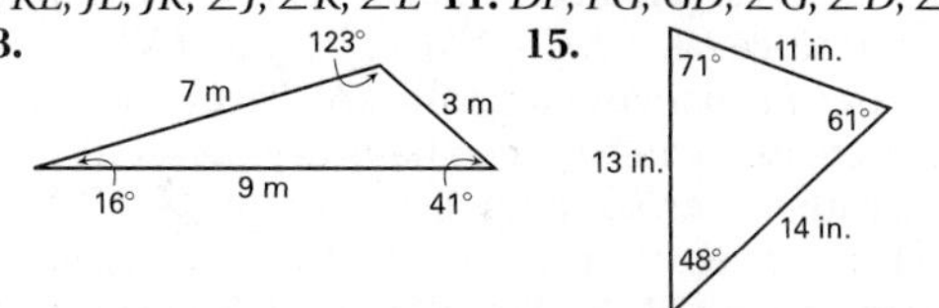

17. No; 3 + 6 is not greater than 9. **19.** yes **21.** 7 in. $< x <$ 17 in. **23.** 6 ft $< x <$ 30 ft **25.** 16 in. $< x <$ 64 in. **27.** $\angle A$ and $\angle B$ are the nonadjacent interior angles to $\angle 1$ thus by the Exterior Angle Theorem $m\angle 1 = m\angle A + m\angle B$, which guarantees $m\angle 1 > m\angle A$ and $m\angle 1 > m\angle B$. **29.** The longest side is not opposite the largest angle. **31.** yes; $\angle Q$, $\angle P$, $\angle R$ **33.** $2 < x < 15$ **35.** $\angle WXY$, $\angle Z$, $\angle ZXY$, $\angle WYX$ and $\angle ZYX$, $\angle W$; $\angle ZYX$ is the largest angle in $\triangle ZYX$ and $\angle WYX$ is the middle sized angle in $\triangle WXY$ making $\angle W$ the largest angle. $m\angle WXY + m\angle W = m\angle Z + m\angle ZXY$ making $\angle WXY$ the smallest.

SELECTED ANSWERS

SA17

5.5 Problem Solving (pp. 333–334) **37.** $m\angle P < m\angle Q$, $m\angle P < m\angle R$; $m\angle Q = m\angle R$ **39. a.** The sum of the other two side lengths is less than 1080. **b.** No; the sum of the distance from Granite Peak to Fort Peck Lake and Granite Peak to Glacier National Park must be more than 565. **c.** $d > 76$ km, $d < 1054$ km **d.** The distance is less than 489 kilometers.
41. *Sample:*

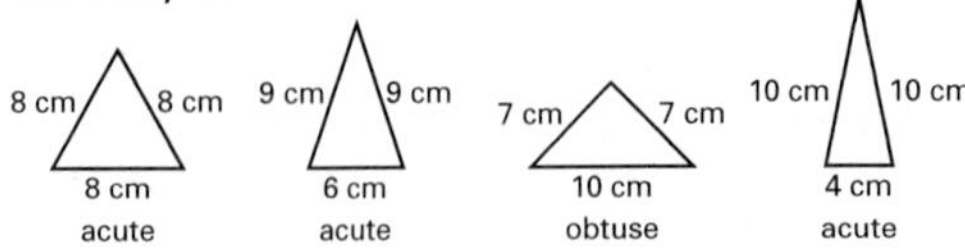

43. *Sample answer:* 3, 4, 17; 2, 5, 17; 4, 4, 16
45. $1\frac{1}{4}$ mi $\le d \le 2\frac{3}{4}$ mi; if the locations are collinear then the distance could be $1\frac{1}{4}$ miles or $2\frac{3}{4}$ miles. If the locations are not collinear then the distance must be between $1\frac{1}{4}$ miles and $2\frac{3}{4}$ miles because of the Triangle Inequality Theorem.

5.6 Skill Practice (pp. 338–339) **1.** You temporarily assume that the desired conclusion is false and this leads to a logical contradiction. **3.** > **5.** < **7.** = **11.** Suppose *xy* is even. **13.** $\angle A$ could be a right angle or a straight angle. **15.** The Hinge Theorem is about triangles not quadrilaterals. **17.** $x > \frac{1}{2}$ **19.** Using the Converse of the Hinge Theorem, $\angle NRQ > \angle NRP$. Since $\angle NRQ$ and $\angle NRP$ are a linear pair, $\angle NRQ$ must be obtuse and $\angle NRP$ must be acute.
5.6 Problem Solving (pp. 340–341) **23.** E, A, D, B, C **25. a.** It gets larger; it gets smaller. **b.** *KM* **c.** *Sample answer:* Since $NL = NK = NM$ and as $m\angle LNK$ increases *KL* increases and $m\angle KNM$ decreases as *KM* decreases, you have two pairs of congruent sides with $m\angle LNK$ eventually larger than $m\angle KNM$. The Hinge Theorem guarantees *KL* will eventually be larger than *KM*. **27.** Prove: If *x* is divisible by 4, then *x* is even. Proof: Since *x* is divisible by 4, $x = 4a$. When you factor out a 2, you get $x = 2(2a)$ which is in the form $2n$, which implies *x* is an even number; your temporary assumption in the indirect proof is the same as the hypothesis in the direct proof.

Chapter Review (pp. 344–347) **1.** midpoint **3.** B **5.** C **7.** 45 **9.** *BA* and *BC*, *DA* and *DC* **11.** 25 **13.** 15 **15.** $(-2, 4)$ **17.** 3.5 **19.** 4 in. $< \ell <$ 12 in. **21.** 8 ft $< \ell <$ 32 ft **23.** $\overline{LM}, \overline{MN}, \overline{LN}$; $\angle N, \angle L, \angle M$ **25.** > **27.** C, B, A, D

Algebra Review (p. 349) **1. a.** $\frac{3}{1}$ **b.** $\frac{1}{4}$ **3.** $\frac{5}{4}$ **5.** 9% decrease **7.** 12.5% increase **9.** 0.25% decrease **11.** 84%; 37.8 h **13.** 107.5%; 86 people

Chapter 6

6.1 Skill Practice (pp. 360–361) **1.** means: *n* and *p*, extremes: *m* and *q* **3.** 4 : 1 **5.** 600 : 1 **7.** $\frac{7}{1}$ **9.** $\frac{24}{5}$ **11.** $\frac{5 \text{ in.}}{15 \text{ in.}}$; $\frac{1}{3}$ **13.** $\frac{320 \text{ cm}}{1000 \text{ cm}}$; $\frac{8}{25}$ **15.** $\frac{5}{2}$ **17.** $\frac{4}{3}$ **19.** 8, 28 **21.** 20°, 70°, 90° **23.** 4 **25.** 42 **27.** 3 **29.** 3 **31.** 6 **33.** 16 **35.** $5\sqrt{2}$ **37.** The unit conversion should be $\frac{1 \text{ ft}}{12 \text{ in.}}$; $\frac{8 \text{ in.}}{3 \text{ ft}} \cdot \frac{1 \text{ ft}}{12 \text{ in.}} = \frac{8}{36} = \frac{2}{9}$. **39.** $\frac{12}{5}$ **41.** $\frac{4}{3}$ **43.** $\frac{7}{11}$ **45.** ± 6 **47.** Obtuse; since the angles are supplementary, $x + 4x = 180$. Find $x = 36$, so the measure of the interior angle is 144°. **49.** 9 **51.** 5 **53.** 72 in., 60 in. **55.** 45, 30

6.1 Problem Solving (pp. 362–363) **57.** 18 ft, 15 ft, 270 ft^2; 270 tiles; $534.60 **59.** 9 cups, 1.8 cups, 7.2 cups **61.** about 189 hits **63.** All three ratios reduce to 4 : 3. **65.** 600 Canadian dollars **67.** $\frac{a}{b} = \frac{c}{d}$, $b \ne 0$, $d \ne 0$; $\frac{a}{b} \cdot bd = \frac{c}{d} \cdot bd$; $ad = cb$; $ad = bc$

6.2 Skill Practice (pp. 367–368) **1.** scale drawing **3.** $\frac{x}{y}$ **5.** $\frac{y + 15}{15}$ **7.** true **9.** true **11.** 10.5 **13.** about 100 yd **15.** 4 should have been added to numerator of the the second fraction instead of 3; $\frac{a + 3}{3} = \frac{c + 4}{4}$. **17.** $\frac{49}{3}$

6.2 Problem Solving (pp. 368–370) **23.** 1 in. : $\frac{1}{3}$ mi **25.** about 8 mi **27.** about 0.022 mm **29.** 48 ft

31.
$$\frac{a}{b} = \frac{c}{d}$$
$$\frac{a}{b} \cdot bd = \frac{c}{d} \cdot bd$$
$$ad = cb$$
$$ad \cdot \frac{1}{ac} = cb \cdot \frac{1}{ac}$$
$$\frac{d}{c} = \frac{b}{a}$$

33.
$$\frac{a}{b} = \frac{c}{d}$$
$$\frac{a}{b} + 1 = \frac{c}{d} + 1$$
$$\frac{a}{b} + \frac{b}{b} = \frac{c}{d} + \frac{d}{d}$$
$$\frac{a + b}{b} = \frac{c + d}{d}$$

35.
$$\frac{a + c}{b + d} = \frac{a - c}{b - d}$$
$$(a + c)(b - d) = (a - c)(b + d)$$
$$ab - ad + bc - cd = ab + ad - bc - cd$$
$$-ad + bc = ad - bc$$
$$-2ad = -2bc$$
$$ad = bc$$
$$\frac{a}{b} = \frac{c}{d}$$

SELECTED ANSWERS

6.3 Skill Practice (pp. 376–377) **1.** congruent, proportional **3.** $\angle A \cong \angle L$, $\angle B \cong \angle M$, $\angle C \cong \angle N$; $\frac{AB}{LM} = \frac{BC}{MN} = \frac{CA}{NL}$ **5.** $\angle H \cong \angle W$, $\angle J \cong \angle X$, $\angle K \cong \angle Y$, $\angle L \cong \angle Z$; $\frac{HJ}{WX} = \frac{JK}{XY} = \frac{KL}{YZ} = \frac{LH}{ZW}$ **7.** similar; $RSTU \sim WXYZ$, $\frac{2}{1}$ **9.** $\frac{5}{2}$ **11.** 85, 34 **13.** The larger triangle's perimeter was doubled but should have been halved; perimeter of B = 14. **15.** always **17.** never **19.** altitude, 24 **21.** $10\frac{2}{3}$ in., $13\frac{1}{3}$ in. **23.** $\frac{11}{5}$ **25.** $17\frac{3}{5}$ **27.** No; in similar triangles corresponding angles are congruent.

6.3 Problem Solving (pp. 378–379) **31.** No; the lengths are not proportional. **33. a.** 2.8, 4.2, 5.6, 2.1 **b.**

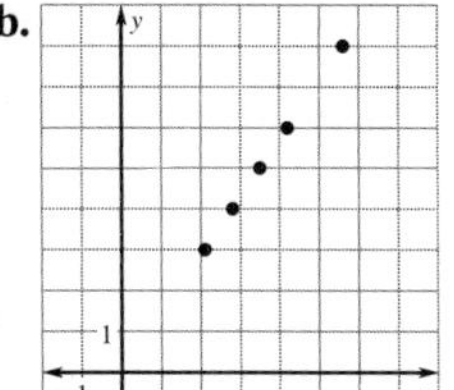

yes **c.** $y = \frac{10}{7}x$; $\frac{10}{7}$; they are the same.

35. Yes; if $\ell = w$ then the larger and smaller image would be similar. *Sample answer:* Let $\ell = 8$, $w = 8$, and $a = 4$; $\frac{w}{w + a} = \frac{8}{12} = \frac{2}{3}$, $\frac{\ell}{\ell + a} = \frac{8}{12} = \frac{2}{3}$. **37. a.** They have the same slope. **b.** $\angle BOA \cong \angle DOC$ by the Vertical Angles Theorem. $\angle OBA \cong \angle ODC$ by the Alternate Interior Angles Theorem. $\angle BAO \cong \angle DCO$ by the Alternate Interior Angles Theorem. **c.** $(-3, 0)$, $(0, 4)$, $(6, 0)$, $(0, -8)$; $AO = 3$, $OB = 4$, $BA = 5$, $CO = 6$, $OD = 8$, $DC = 10$ **d.** Since corresponding angles are congruent and the ratios of corresponding sides are all the same the triangles are similar.

6.4 Skill Practice (pp. 384–385) **1.** similar **3.** $\triangle FED$ **5.** 15, y **7.** 20 **9.** similar; $\triangle FGH \sim \triangle KLJ$ **11.** not similar **13.** similar; $\triangle YZX \sim \triangle YWU$ **15.** The AA Similarity Postulate is for triangles, not quadrilaterals. **17.** 5 should be replaced by 9, which is the length of the corresponding side of the larger triangle. *Sample answer:* $\frac{4}{9} = \frac{6}{x}$.

19. *Sample:*

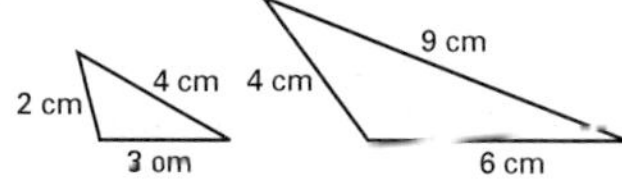

21. (10, 0) **23.** (24, 0)

25. a. A 8 B, 6, E, 10, 15, D, C **b.** *Sample answer:* $\angle ABE$ and $\angle CDE$, $\angle BAE$ and $\angle DCE$ **c.** $\triangle ABE$ and $\triangle CDE$, $\triangle ABE \sim \triangle CDE$ **d.** 4, 20

27. Yes; either $m\angle X$ or $m\angle Y$ could be 90°, and the other angles could be the same. **29.** No; since $m\angle J + m\angle K = 85°$ then $m\angle L = 95°$. Since $m\angle Y + m\angle Z = 80°$ then $m\angle X = 100°$ and thus neither $\angle Y$ nor $\angle Z$ can measure 95°.

6.4 Problem Solving (pp. 386–387) **31.** about 30.8 in. **33.** The measure of all angles in an equilateral triangle is 60°. *Sample:*

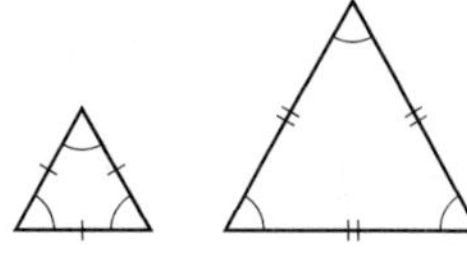

35.

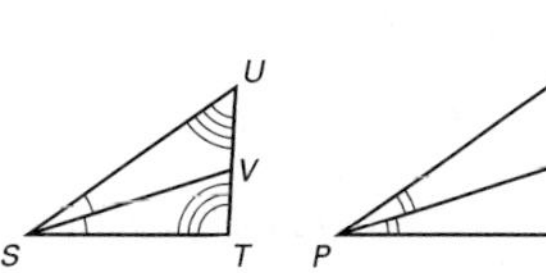

Since $\triangle STU \sim \triangle PQR$ you know that $\angle T \cong \angle Q$ and $\angle UST \cong \angle RPQ$. Since $\overline{SV}$ bisects $\angle TSU$ and $\overline{PN}$ bisects $\angle QPR$ you know that $\angle USV \cong \angle VST$ and $\angle RPN \cong \angle NPQ$ by definition of angle bisector. You know that $m\angle USV + m\angle VST = m\angle UST$ and $m\angle RPN + m\angle NPQ = m\angle RPQ$, therefore, $2m\angle VST = 2m\angle NPQ$ using the Substitution Property of Equality. You now have $\angle VST \cong \angle NPQ$, which makes $\triangle VST \sim \triangle NPQ$ using the AA Similarity Postulate. From this you know that $\frac{SV}{PN} = \frac{ST}{PQ}$.

37. a. *Sample:*

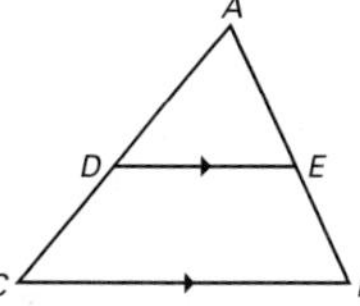

b. $m\angle ADE = m\angle ACB$ and $m\angle AED = m\angle ABC$ **c.** $\triangle ADE \sim \triangle ACB$ **d.** *Sample answer:* $\frac{AD}{AC} = \frac{AE}{AB} = \frac{DE}{CB} = \frac{1}{2}$ **e.** The measures of the angles change, but the equalities remain the same. The lengths of the sides change, but they remain proportional; yes; the triangles remain similar by the AA Similarity Postulate.

SELECTED ANSWERS

SA19

6.5 Skill Practice (pp. 391–393) **1.** $\frac{AC}{PX} = \frac{CB}{XQ} = \frac{AB}{PQ}$

3. $\frac{18}{12} = \frac{15}{10} = \frac{12}{8}; \frac{3}{2}$ **5.** $\triangle RST$ **7.** similar; $\triangle FDE \sim \triangle XWY$; 2 : 3

9. 3

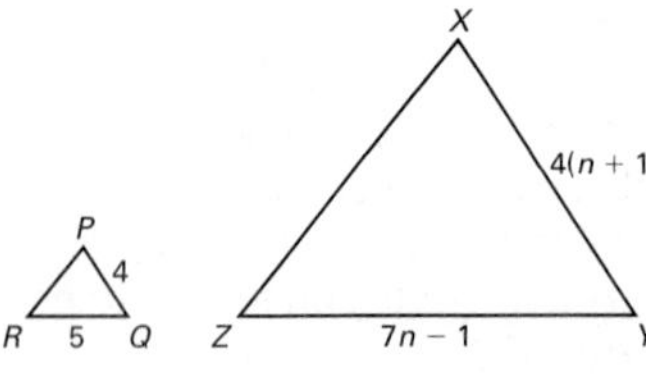

11. $\triangle ABC \sim \triangle DEC$; $\angle ACB \cong \angle DCE$ by the Vertical Angles Congruence Theorem and $\frac{AC}{DC} = \frac{BC}{EC} = \frac{3}{2}$. The triangles are similar using the SAS Similarity Theorem. **13.** *Sample answer:* The triangle correspondence is not listed in the correct order; $\triangle ABC \sim \triangle RQP$.

15.

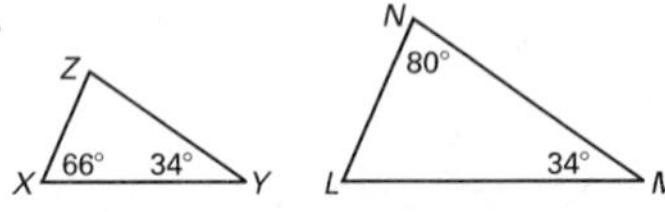

They are similar by the AA Similarity Postulate.

17.

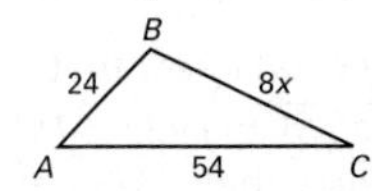

They are not similar since the ratio of corresponding sides is not constant.

19. 45° **21.** 24 **23.** $16\sqrt{2}$

6.5 Problem Solving (pp. 393–395) **29.** The triangle whose sides measure 4 inches, 4 inches, and 7 inches is similar to the triangle whose sides measure 3 inches, 3 inches, and 5.25 inches. **31.** $\angle CBD \cong \angle CAE$ **33. a.** AA Similarity Postulate **b.** 75 ft **c.** 66 ft **35.** *Sample answer:* Given that D and E are midpoints of $\overline{AB}$ and $\overline{BC}$ respectively the Midsegment Theorem guarantees that $\overline{AC} \parallel \overline{DE}$. By the Corresponding Angles Postulate $\angle A \cong \angle BDE$ and so $\angle BDE$ is a right angle. Reasoning similarly $\overline{AB} \parallel \overline{EF}$. By the Alternate Interior Angles Congruence Theorem $\angle BDE \cong \angle DEF$. This makes $\angle DEF$ a right angle that measures 90°.

6.6 Skill Practice (pp. 400–401)

1. If a line parallel to one side of a triangle intersects the other two sides then it divides the two sides proportionally.

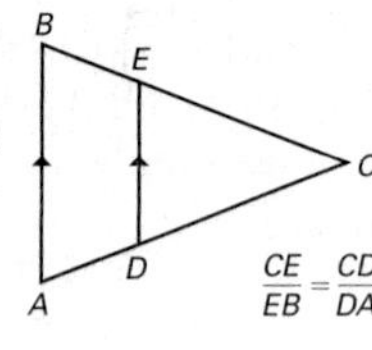

3. 9 **5.** Parallel; $\frac{8}{5} = \frac{12}{7.5}$ so the Converse of the Triangle Proportionality Theorem applies. **7.** Parallel; $\frac{20}{18} = \frac{25}{22.5}$ so the Converse of the Triangle Proportionality Theorem applies. **9.** 10 **11.** 1 **15.** 9 **17.** $a = 9$, $b = 4$, $c = 3$, $d = 2$

19. a–b. See figure in part (c).

c.

Theorem 6.6 guarantees that parallel lines divide transversals proportionally. Since $\frac{AD}{DE} = \frac{DE}{EF} = \frac{EF}{FG} = 1$ implies $\frac{AJ}{JK} = \frac{JK}{KL} = \frac{KL}{LB} = 1$ which means $AJ = JK = KL = LB$.

6.6 Problem Solving (pp. 402–403) **21.** 350 yd **23.** Since $k_1 \parallel k_2 \parallel k_3$, $\angle FDA \cong \angle CAD$ and $\angle CDA \cong \angle FAD$ by the Alternate Interior Angles Congruence Theorem. $\triangle ACD \sim \triangle DFA$ by the AA Similarity Postulate. Let point G be at the intersection of $\overline{AD}$ and $\overline{BE}$. Using the Triangle Proportionality Theorem $\frac{CB}{BA} = \frac{DG}{GA}$ and $\frac{DE}{EF} = \frac{DG}{GA}$. Using the Transitive Property of Equality $\frac{CB}{BA} = \frac{DE}{EF}$.

25. In an isosceles triangle, the legs are congruent, so the ratio of their lengths is 1 : 1. By Theorem 6.7, this ratio is equal to the ratio of the lengths of the segments created by the ray, so it is also 1 : 1.

27. Since $\overline{XW} \parallel \overline{AZ}$, $\angle XZA \cong \angle WXZ$ using the Alternate Interior Angles Congruence Theorem. This makes $\triangle AXZ$ isosceles because it is shown that $\angle A \cong \angle WXZ$ and by the Converse of the Base Angles Theorem, $AX = XZ$. Since $\overline{XW} \parallel \overline{AZ}$ using the Triangle Proportionality Theorem you get $\frac{YW}{WZ} = \frac{XY}{AX}$. Substituting you get $\frac{YW}{WX} = \frac{XY}{XZ}$.

6.6 Problem Solving Workshop (p. 405)
1. a. 270 yd **b.** 67.5 yd **3.** 4.5 mi/h **5.** 5.25, 7.5

Extension (p. 407) **1.** 3 : 1. *Sample answer:* It's one unit longer; each of the three edges went from measuring one unit to four edges each measuring $\frac{1}{3}$ of a unit.

SELECTED ANSWERS

3. a.

1 unit

1 unit

b. *Sample answer:* The upper left square is simply a smaller version of the whole square.

c.

Stage	Number of colored squares	Area of 1 colored square	Total Area
0	0	0	0
1	1	$\frac{1}{9}$	$\frac{1}{9}$
2	8	$\frac{1}{81}$	$\frac{17}{81}$
3	64	$\frac{1}{729}$	$\frac{217}{729}$

6.7 Skill Practice (pp. 412–413) **1.** similar

3.

5.

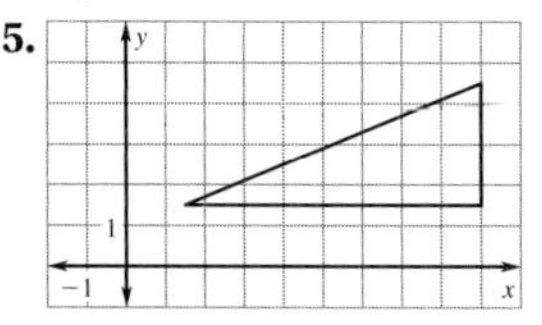

9. reduction; $\frac{1}{2}$ **11.** enlargement; 3 **15.** The figures are not similar. **17.** reflection **19.** 2; $m = 4$, $n = 5$

6.7 Problem Solving (pp. 414–415)

25. 24 ft by 12 ft **27.** $\frac{5}{2}$

29. a.

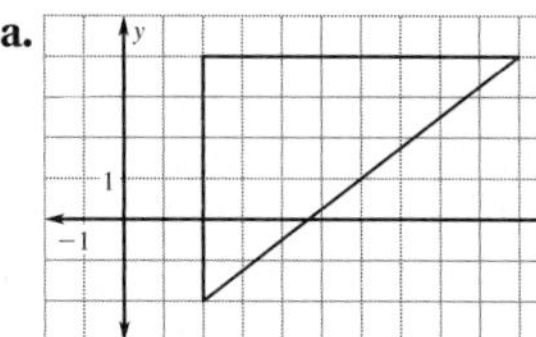

b. $\frac{2}{3}$; they are the same. **c.** $\frac{4}{9}$; it's the square of the scale factor.

31. Perspective drawings use converging lines to give the illusion that an object is three dimensional. Since the back of the drawing is similar to the front, a dilation can be used to create this illusion with the vanishing point as the center of dilation.

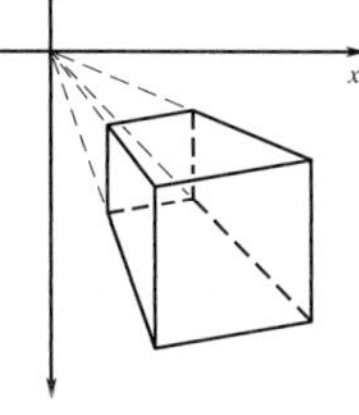

33. The slope of $\overline{PQ}$ is $\frac{d-b}{c-a}$ and the slope of $\overline{XY}$ is $\frac{kd-kb}{kc-ka} = \frac{k(d-b)}{k(c-a)} = \frac{d-b}{c-a}$. Since the slopes are the same, the lines are parallel.

Chapter Review (pp. 418–421) **1.** dilation **3.** In a ratio two numbers are compared. In a proportion two ratios are set equal to one another. *Sample answer:* $\frac{2}{4}, \frac{6}{10} = \frac{3}{5}$ **5.** 45°, 45°, 90° **7.** $\frac{20}{3}$ **9.** similar; $ABCD \sim EFGH$, $\frac{4}{3}$ **11.** 68 in. **13.** By the Triangle Sum Theorem $m\angle D = 60°$ so $\angle A \cong \angle D$. $\angle C \cong \angle F$ by the Right Angles Congruence Theorem. So, $\triangle ABC \sim \triangle DEF$ by the AA Similarity Postulate.

15. Since $\frac{4}{8} = \frac{3.5}{7}$ and the included angle, $\angle C$, is congruent to itself, $\triangle BCD \sim \triangle ACE$ by the SAS Similarity Theorem. **17.** not parallel

19.

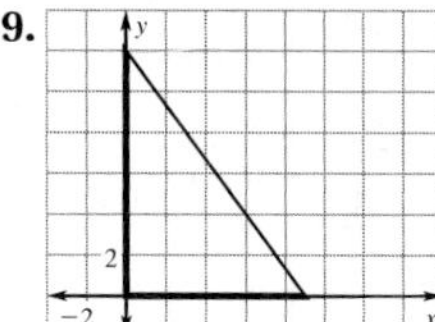

21.

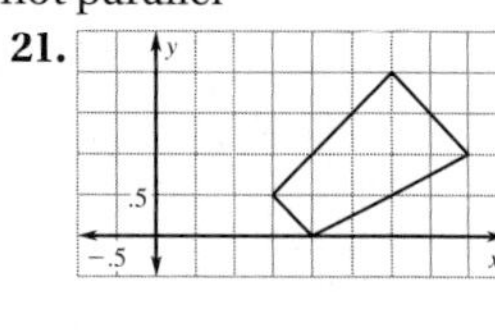

Algebra Review (p. 423) **1.** ± 10 **3.** $\pm\sqrt{17}$ **5.** $\pm\sqrt{10}$ **7.** $\pm 2\sqrt{5}$ **9.** $\pm 3\sqrt{2}$ **11.** $\frac{\sqrt{15}}{5}$ **13.** $\frac{\sqrt{21}}{2}$ **15.** $\frac{1}{10}$ **17.** $\frac{\sqrt{2}}{2}$

Cumulative Review (pp. 428–429) **1. a.** 33° **b.** 123° **3. a.** 2° **b.** 92°

5.

$3x - 19 = 47$	Given
$3x = 66$	Addition Property of Equality
$x = 22$	Division Property of Equality

7.

$-5(x + 2) = 25$	Given
$x + 2 = -5$	Division Property of Equality
$x = -7$	Subtraction Property of Equality

9. Alternate Interior Angles Theorem **11.** Corresponding Angles Postulate **13.** Linear Pair Postulate **15.** 78°, 78°, 24°; acute **17.** congruent; $\triangle ABC \cong \triangle CDA$, SSS Congruence Theorem **19.** not congruent **21.** 8 **23.** similar; $\triangle FCD \sim \triangle FHG$, SAS Similarity Theorem **25.** not similar **27. a.** $y = 59x + 250$ **b.** The slope is the monthly membership and the y-intercept is the initial cost to join the club. **c.** \$958 **29.** *Sample answer:* Since $\overline{BC} \parallel \overline{AD}$, you know that $\angle CBD \cong \angle ADB$ by the Alternate Interior Angles Theorem. $\overline{BD} \cong \overline{BD}$ by the Reflexive Property of Segment Congruence and with $\overline{BC} \cong \overline{AD}$ given, then $\triangle BCD \cong \triangle DAB$ by the SAS Congruence Theorem. **31.** 43 mi $< d <$ 397 mi

Chapter 7

7.1 Skill Practice (pp. 436–438) **1.** Pythagorean triple **3.** 130 **5.** 58 **7.** In Step 2, the Distributive Property was used incorrectly; $x^2 = 49 + 576$, $x^2 = 625$, $x = 25$.

SELECTED ANSWERS

9. about 9.1 in. **11.** 120 m^2 **13.** 48 cm^2 **15.** 40 **19.** 15, leg **21.** 52, hypotenuse **23.** 21, leg **25.** $11\sqrt{2}$

7.1 Problem Solving (pp. 438–439) **31.** about 127.3 ft **33.** *Sample answer:* The longest side of the triangle is opposite the largest angle, which in a right triangle is the right angle.

35. a–b.

BC	AC	CE	AC + CE
10	60.8	114.0	174.8
20	63.2	104.4	167.6
30	67.1	94.9	162
40	72.1	85.4	157.6
50	78.1	76.2	154.3
60	84.9	67.1	152
70	92.2	58.3	150.5
80	100	50	150
90	108.2	42.4	150.6
100	116.6	36.1	152.7
110	125.3	31.6	156.9
120	134.2	30	164.2

150 ft

c.

7.2 Skill Practice (pp. 444–445) **1.** hypotenuse **3.** right triangle **5.** not a right triangle **7.** right triangle **9.** right triangle **11.** right triangle **13.** right triangle **15.** yes; acute **17.** yes; obtuse **19.** yes; right **21.** no **23.** yes; obtuse

27.

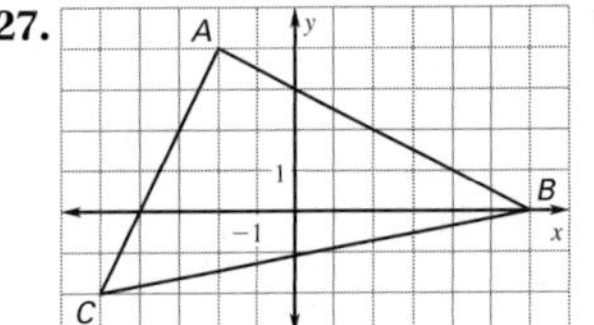

right

29. right **31.** < **33.** $8 < x < 12$

7.2 Problem Solving (pp. 445–447) **35.** Measure diagonally across the painting and it should be about 12.8 inches. **37. a.** 5 **b.** $3^2 + 4^2 = 5^2$ therefore $\triangle ABC$ is a right triangle.

c. *Sample:*

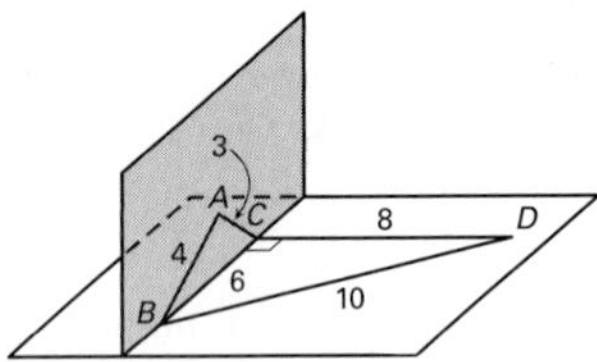

39. a. yes; $12^2 + 16^2 = 20^2$ **b.** no; $9^2 + 12^2 \neq 18^2$ **c.** No; if the car was not in an accident, the angles should form a right triangle.

41. Given: In $\triangle ABC$, $c^2 > a^2 + b^2$, where c is the length of the longest side.
Prove: $\triangle ABC$ is obtuse.

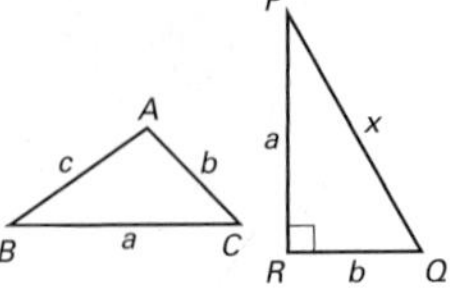

Statements	Reasons
1. In $\triangle ABC$, $c^2 > a^2 + b^2$ where c is the length of the longest side. In $\triangle PQR$, $\angle R$ is a right angle.	1. Given
2. $a^2 + b^2 = x^2$	2. Pythagorean Theorem
3. $c^2 > x^2$	3. Substitution
4. $c > x$	4. A property of square roots
5. $m\angle R = 90°$	5. Definition of a right angle
6. $m\angle C > m\angle R$	6. Converse of the Hinge Theorem
7. $m\angle C > 90°$	7. Substitution Property
8. $\angle C$ is an obtuse angle.	8. Definition of an obtuse angle
9. $\triangle ABC$ is an obtuse triangle.	9. Definition of an obtuse triangle

43. $\triangle ABC \sim \triangle DEC$, $\angle BAC$ is 90°, so $\angle EDC$ must also be 90°.

7.3 Skill Practice (pp. 453–454) **1.** similar **3.** $\triangle FHG \sim \triangle HEG \sim \triangle FEH$ **5.** about 53.7 ft **7.** about 6.7 ft **9.** $\triangle QSR \sim \triangle STR \sim \triangle QTS$; RQ **11.** *Sample answer:* The proportion must compare corresponding parts, $\frac{v}{z} = \frac{z}{w + v}$ **13.** about 6.7 **15.** about 45.6 **17.** about 6.3 **21.** 3 **23.** $x = 9$, $y = 15$, $z = 20$ **25.** right triangle; about 6.7 **27.** 25, 12

7.3 Problem Solving (pp. 455–456) **29.** about 1.1 ft **31.** 15 ft; no; the values are slightly off because the measurements are not exact. **33. a.** $\overline{FH}$, $\overline{GF}$, $\overline{EF}$; each segment has a vertex as an endpoint and is perpendicular to the opposite side. **b.** $\sqrt{35}$ **c.** about 35.5

37.

Statements	Reasons
1. $\triangle ABC$ is a right triangle; $\overline{CD}$ is the altitude to $\overline{AB}$.	1. Given
2. $\triangle ABC \sim \triangle CBD$	2. Theorem 7.5
3. $\frac{AB}{CB} = \frac{CB}{DB}$	3. Definition of similar figures
4. $\triangle ABC \sim \triangle ACD$	4. Theorem 7.5
5. $\frac{AB}{AC} = \frac{AC}{AD}$	5. Definition of similar figures

7.4 Skill Practice (pp. 461–462) **1.** an isosceles right triangle **3.** $7\sqrt{2}$ **5.** 3 **7.** 2; 4 in. **9.** $x = 3, y = 6$

11.

a	7	11	$5\sqrt{2}$	6	$\sqrt{5}$
b	7	11	$5\sqrt{2}$	6	$\sqrt{5}$
c	$7\sqrt{2}$	$11\sqrt{2}$	10	$6\sqrt{2}$	$\sqrt{10}$

13. $x = \frac{15}{2}\sqrt{3}, y = \frac{15}{2}$ **15.** $p = 12, q = 12\sqrt{3}$ **17.** $t = 4\sqrt{2}, u = 7$ **21.** The hypotenuse of a 45°-45°-90° triangle should be $x\sqrt{2}$; if $x = \sqrt{5}$, then the hypotenuse is $\sqrt{10}$. **23.** $f = \frac{20\sqrt{3}}{3}, g = \frac{10\sqrt{3}}{3}$ **25.** $x = 4, y = \frac{4\sqrt{3}}{3}$

7.4 Problem Solving (pp. 463–464) **27.** 5.5 ft **29.** *Sample answer:* Method 1. Use the Angle-Angle Similarity postulate, because by definition of an isosceles triangle, the base angles must be the same and in a right isosceles triangle, the angles are 45°. Method 2. Use the Side-Angle-Side Similarity Theorem, because the right angle is always congruent to another right angle and the ratio of sides of an isosceles triangle will always be the same. **31.** $10\sqrt{3}$ in. **33. a.** 45°-45°-90° for all triangles **b.** $\frac{3\sqrt{2}}{2}$ in. $\times$ $\frac{3\sqrt{2}}{2}$ in. **c.** 1.5 in. $\times$ 1.5 in.

7.5 Skill Practice (pp. 469–470) **1.** the opposite leg, the adjacent leg **3.** $\frac{24}{7}$ or 3.4286, $\frac{7}{24}$ or 0.2917 **5.** $\frac{12}{5}$ or 2.400, $\frac{5}{12}$ or 0.4167 **7.** 7.6 **9.** 6; 6; they are the same. **11.** 6.9282; $4\sqrt{3}$; they are the same. **13.** Tangent is the ratio of the opposite and the adjacent side, not adjacent to hypotenuse; $\frac{80}{18}$. **15.** You need to know: that the triangle is a right triangle, which angle you will be applying the ratio to, and the lengths of the opposite side and the adjacent side to the angle. **19.** 15.5 **21.** 77.4 **23.** 60.6 **25.** 27.6 **27.** 60; 54.0 **29.** 82; 154.2

7.5 Problem Solving (pp. 471–472) **31.** 555 ft **33.** about 33.4 ft **35.** $\tan A = \frac{a}{b}$, $\tan B = \frac{b}{a}$; the tangent of one acute angle is the reciprocal of the other acute angle; complementary. **37. a.** 29 ft **b.** 3 ramps and 2 landings;

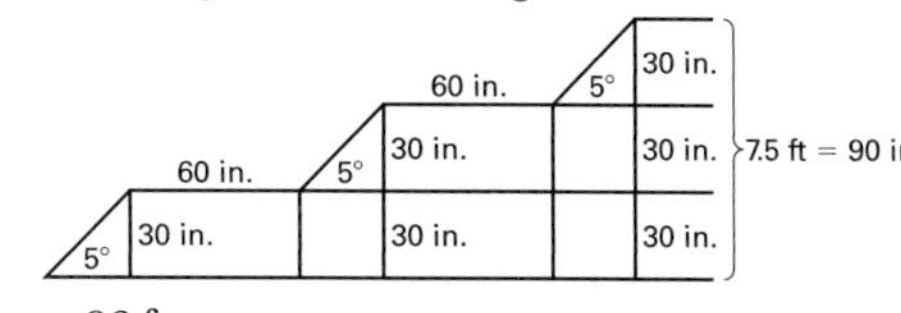

c. 96 ft

7.6 Skill Practice (pp. 477–478) **1.** the opposite leg, the hypotenuse **3.** $\frac{4}{5}$ or 0.8, $\frac{3}{5}$ or 0.6 **5.** $\frac{28}{53}$ or 0.5283, $\frac{45}{53}$ or 0.8491 **7.** $\frac{3}{5}$ or 0.6, $\frac{4}{5}$ or 0.8 **9.** $\frac{1}{2}$ or 0.5, $\frac{\sqrt{3}}{2}$ or 0.8660 **11.** $a = 14.9, b = 11.1$ **13.** $s = 17.7, r = 19.0$ **15.** $m = 6.7, n = 10.4$ **17.** The triangle must be a right triangle, and you need either an acute angle measure and the length of one side or the lengths of two sides of the triangle. **19.** 3.0 **21.** 20.2 **23.** 12; $\frac{2\sqrt{2}}{2}$ or 0.9428, $\frac{1}{3}$ or 0.3333 **25.** 3; $\frac{\sqrt{5}}{5}$ or 0.4472, $\frac{2\sqrt{5}}{5}$ or 0.8944 **27.** 33; $\frac{56}{65}$ or 0.8615, $\frac{33}{65}$ or 0.5077 **31.** about 18 cm

7.6 Problem Solving (pp. 479–480) **33.** about 36.9 ft

35. a.

20 ft
41°
5 ft

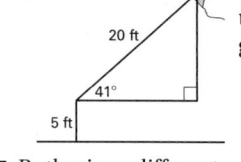

b. About 18.1 ft; the height that the spool is off the ground has to be added.

37. Both; since different angles are used in each ratio, both the sine and cosine relationships can be used to correctly answer the question.

39. a.

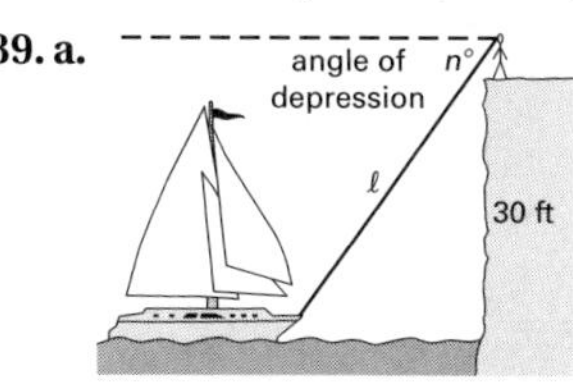

b.

n°	40°	50°	60°	70°	80°
ℓ (ft)	46.7	39.2	34.6	31.9	30.5

c. 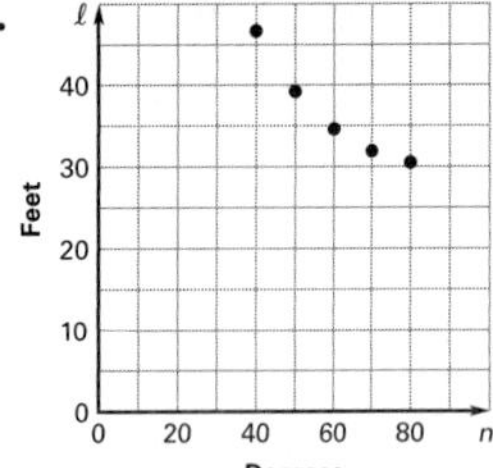

d. *Sample answer:* 60 ft

7.6 Problem Solving Workshop (p. 482) **1.** about 8.8 ft, about 18 ft **3.** $\cos 34° = \frac{x}{17}$, $\tan 34° = \frac{9.5}{x}$, $x^2 + 9.5^2 = 17^2$ **5.** The cosine ratio is the adjacent side over the hypotenuse, not opposite over adjacent; $\cos A = \frac{7}{25}$.

7.7 Skill Practice (pp. 485–487) **1.** angles, sides **3.** 33.7°; $\tan^{-1} 12/7 \approx 59.7°$ **5.** 74.1° **7.** 53.1° **11.** $N = 25°$, $NP \approx 21.4$, $NQ \approx 23.7$ **13.** $A \approx 36.9°$, $B \approx 53.1°$, $AC = 15$ **15.** $G \approx 29°$, $J \approx 61°$, $HJ = 7.7$ **17.** $D \approx 29.7°$, $E \approx 60.3°$, $ED \approx 5.4$ **19.** Since an angle was given, the $\sin^{-1}$ should not have been used; $\sin 36° = \frac{7}{WX}$.
21. 30° **23.** 70.7° **25.** 45° **27.** 11° **31.** 45°; 60°

7.7 Problem Solving (pp. 487–489) **35.** about 59.7°; $\tan^{-1}\frac{12}{7} \approx 59.7°$ **37.** $\tan^{-1}\frac{BC}{AC}$. *Sample answer:* The information needed to determine the measure of *A* is given. If you use the tangent ratio, this will make the answer more accurate since no rounding has occurred.

39. a.

x (in.)	20	21	22	23
y (°)	28.8°	27.6°	26.6°	25.6°

x (in.)	24	25	26	27
y (°)	24.6°	23.7°	22.9°	22.2°

b. 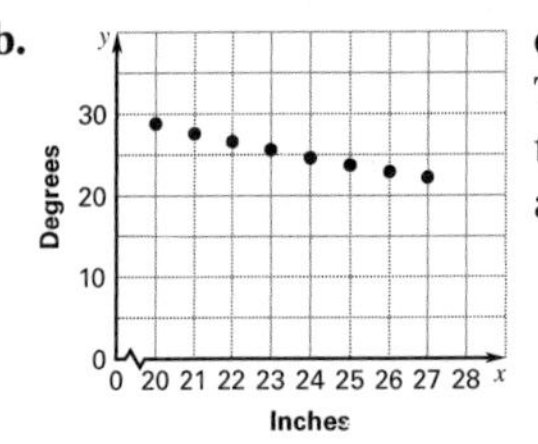

c. *Sample answer:* The longer the rack, the closer to 20° the angle gets.

41. a. 38.4 ft **b.** about 71.2 ft **c.** about 48.7 ft **d.** About 57.4°, about 38.0°; neither; the sides are not the same, so the triangles are not congruent, and the angles are not the same, so the triangles are not similar. **e.** I used tangent because the height and the distance along the ground form a tangent relationship for the angle of elevation.

Extension (p. 491) **1.** $C = 66°$, $a \approx 4.4$, $c \approx 8.3$ **3.** $B \approx 81.8°$, $C \approx 47.2°$, $b \approx 22.9$ **5.** $A \approx 58.1°$, $B \approx 85.6°$, $C \approx 36.2°$ **7.** about 10 blocks

Chapter Review (pp. 494–497) **1.** $a^2 + b^2 = c^2$ **3.** *Sample answer:* The difference is your perspective on the situation. The angle of depression is the measure from your line of sight down, and the angle of elevation is the measure from your line of sight up, but if you construct the parallel lines in any situation, the angles are alternate interior angles and are congruent by Theorem 3.1. **5.** $2\sqrt{34}$ **7.** acute **9.** right **11.** right **13.** 13.5 **15.** $2\sqrt{10}$ **17.** 9 **19.** $6\sqrt{2}$ **21.** $16\sqrt{3}$ **23.** about 5.7 ft **25.** 9.3 **27.** $\frac{3}{5} = 0.6$, $\frac{4}{5} = 0.8$ **29.** $\frac{55}{73} \approx 0.7534$, $\frac{48}{73} \approx 0.6575$ **31.** $L = 53°$, $ML \approx 4.5$, $NL \approx 7.5$ **33.** 50°, 40°, 50°; about 6.4, about 13.1, about 8.4

Algebra Review (p. 499)

1. 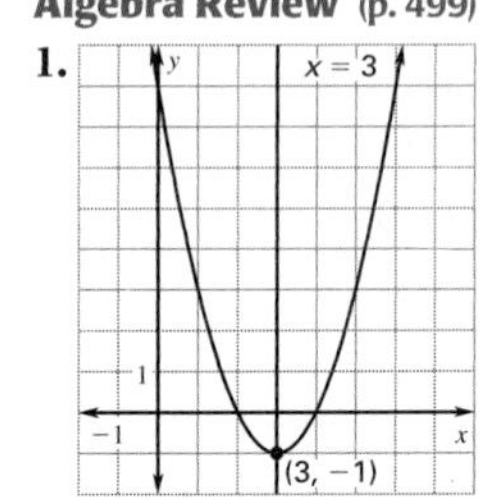

3. 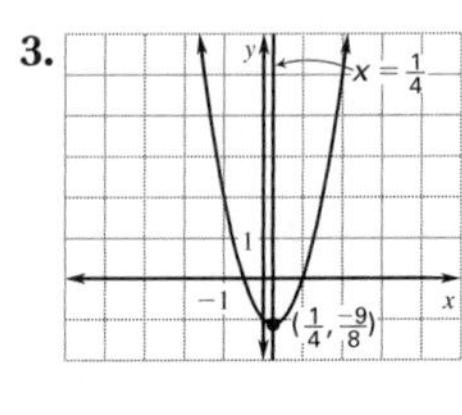

5. 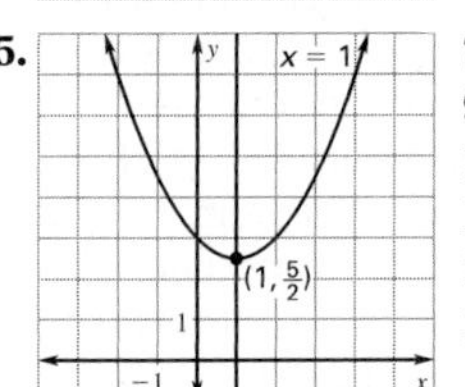

7. −2, 3
9. no solution
11. no solution
13. 0, 8
15. 2, 4
17. −5

Chapter 8

8.1 Skill Practice (pp. 510–511)

1. *Sample:* 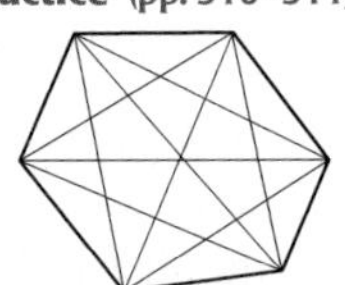

3. 1260° **5.** 2520° **7.** quadrilateral **9.** 13-gon **11.** 117 **13.** $28\frac{1}{3}$ **15.** 66

17. The student thinks that because an octagon has 8 exterior angles while a hexagon has only 6 exterior angles, the sum of the measures of the 8 angles must be greater than the sum of the measures of the 6 angles. The sum of the measures of the exterior angles of any convex *n*-gon is always 360°. **19.** 108°, 72° **21.** 176°, 4° **23.** The interior angle measures are the same in both pentagons and the ratios of corresponding sides would be the same. **25.** 40

SA24

8.1 Problem Solving (pp. 512–513) **29.** 720° **31.** 144°; 36° **33.** In a pentagon, draw all the diagonals from one vertex. Observe that the polygon is divided up into three triangles. Since the sum of the measures of the interior angles of each triangle is 180°, the sum of the measures of the interior angles of the pentagon is $(5 - 2) \cdot 180° = 3 \cdot 180° = 540°$.
35. *Sample answer:* In a convex n-gon, the sum of the measures of the n interior angles is $(n - 2) \cdot 180°$ by the Polygon Interior Angles Theorem. Since each of the n interior angles forms a linear pair with its corresponding exterior angle, you know that the sum of the measures of the interior and exterior angles is $180°n$. Subtracting the sum of the interior angle measures from the sum of the measures of the linear pairs $(180°n - (n - 2) \cdot 180°)$, you get 360°.
37. a.

Polygon	Number of sides	Number of triangles	Sum of measures of interior angles
Quadrilateral	4	2	$2 \cdot 180° = 360°$
Pentagon	5	3	$3 \cdot 180° = 540°$
Hexagon	6	4	$4 \cdot 180° = 720°$
Heptagon	7	5	$5 \cdot 180° = 900°$

b. $s(n) = (n - 2) \cdot 180°$; the table shows that the number of triangles is two less than the number of sides.

8.2 Skill Practice (pp. 518–519) **1.** A parallelogram is a quadrilateral with both pairs of opposite sides parallel; opposite sides are congruent, opposite angles are congruent, consecutive angles are supplementary, and the diagonals bisect each other. **3.** $x = 9, y = 15$ **5.** $a = 55$ **7.** $d = 126, z = 28$ **9.** 129° **11.** 61° **13.** $a = 3, b = 10$ **15.** $x = 4, y = 4$ **17.** $\overline{BC}$; opposite sides of a parallelogram are congruent. **19.** $\angle DAC$; alternate interior angles are congruent. **21.** 47°; consecutive angles of a parallelogram are supplementary and alternate interior angles are congruent. **23.** 120°; $\angle EJF$ and $\angle FJG$ are a linear pair. **25.** 35°; Triangle Sum Theorem **27.** 130°; sum of the measures of $\angle HGE$ and $\angle EGF$. **31.** 26°, 154° **33.** 20, 60°; $UV = TS = QR$ using the fact that opposite sides are congruent and the Transitive Property of Equality. $\angle TUS \cong \angle VSU$ by the Alternate Interior Angles Congruence Theorem and $m\angle TSU = 60°$ by the Triangle Sum Theorem. **35.** *Sample answer:* In a parallelogram, opposite angles are congruent. $\angle A$ and $\angle C$ are opposite angles but not congruent.

8.2 Problem Solving (pp. 520–521) **39. a.** 3 in. **b.** 70° **c.** It decreases; it gets longer; the sum of the measures of the interior angles always is 360°. As $m\angle Q$ increases so does $m\angle S$ therefore $m\angle P$ must decrease to maintain the sum of 360°. As $m\angle Q$ decreases $m\angle P$ increases moving Q farther away from S.
41. *Sample:*

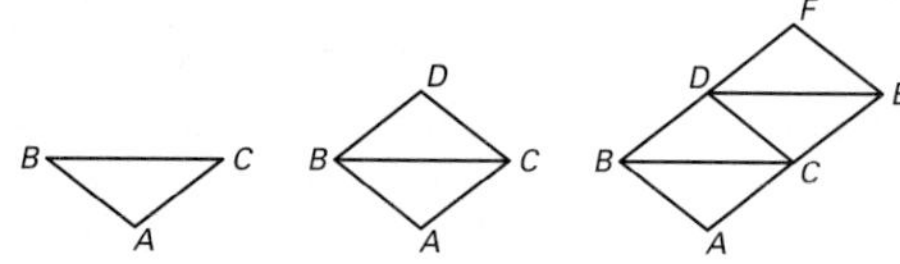

Since $\triangle ABC \cong \triangle DCB$ you know $\angle ACB \cong \angle DBC$ and $\angle ABC \cong \angle DCB$. By the Alternate Interior Angles Converse, $\overline{BD} \parallel \overline{AC}$ and $\overline{AB} \parallel \overline{CD}$ thus making $ABDC$ a parallelogram; if two more triangles are positioned the same as the first, you can line up the pair of congruent sides and form a larger parallelogram since corresponding angles are congruent and the ratios of the lengths of corresponding sides are equal, $\square ABCD \sim \square ABFE$ by definition. **43.** *Sample answer:* Given that $PQRS$ is a parallelogram you know that $\overline{QR} \parallel \overline{PS}$ with $\overline{QP}$ a transversal. By definition and the fact that $\angle Q$ and $\angle P$ are consecutive interior angles, they are supplementary by the Consecutive Interior Angles Theorem. $x° + y° = 180°$ by definition of supplementary angles.

8.3 Skill Practice (pp. 526–527) **1.** The definition of a parallelogram is that it is a quadrilateral with opposite pairs of parallel sides. Since $\overline{AB}, \overline{CD}$ and $\overline{AD}, \overline{BC}$ are opposite pairs of parallel sides the quadrilateral $ABCD$ is a parallelogram. **3.** The congruent sides must be opposite one another. **5.** Theorem 8.7 **7.** Since both pairs of opposite sides of $JKLM$ always remain congruent, $JKLM$ is always a parallelogram and $\overline{JK}$ remains parallel to $\overline{ML}$. **9.** 8

11.

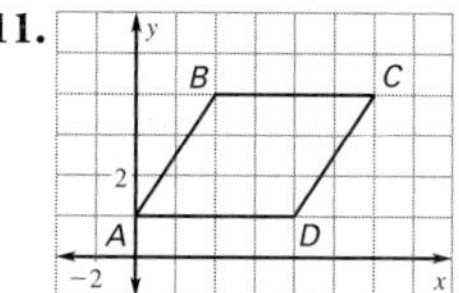

Sample answer: $AB = CD = 5$ and $BC = DA = 8$

13.

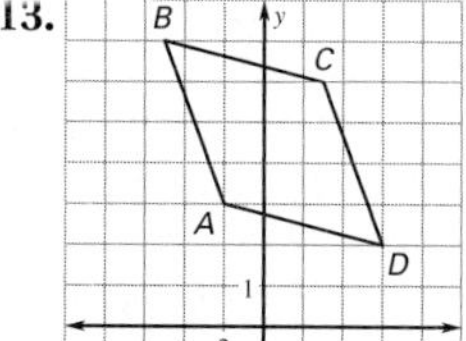

Sample answer: $AB = CD = 5$ and $BC = DA = \sqrt{65}$

SELECTED ANSWERS

15. *Sample answer:* Show $\triangle ADB \cong \triangle CBD$ by the SAS Congruence Postulate. This makes $\overline{AD} \cong \overline{CB}$ and $\overline{BA} \cong \overline{CD}$ because corresponding parts of congruent triangles are congruent. **17.** *Sample answer:* Show $\overline{AB} \parallel \overline{DC}$ by the Alternate Interior Angles Converse, and show $\overline{AD} \parallel \overline{BC}$ by the Corresponding Angles Converse. **19.** 114 **21.** 50
23. *PQRS* is a parallelogram if and only if $\angle P \cong \angle R$ and $\angle Q \cong \angle S$. **25.** $(-3, 2)$; since $\overline{DA}$ must be parallel and congruent to $\overline{BC}$, use the slope and length of $\overline{BC}$ to find point *D* by starting at point *A*. **27.** $(-5, -3)$; since $\overline{DA}$ must be parallel and congruent to $\overline{BC}$, use the slope and length of $\overline{BC}$ to find point *D* by starting at point *A*.
29. *Sample answer:* Draw a line passing through points *A* and *B*. At points *A* and *B* construct $\overrightarrow{AP}$ and $\overrightarrow{BQ}$ such that the angle each ray makes with the line is the same. Mark off congruent segments starting at *A* and *B* along $\overrightarrow{AP}$ and $\overrightarrow{BQ}$ respectively. Draw the line segment joining these two endpoints.

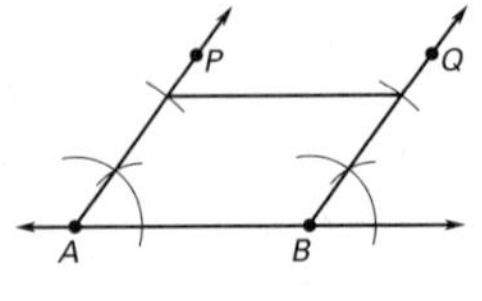

8.3 Problem Solving (pp. 528–529) **31. a.** *EFJK, FGHJ, EGHK*; in each case opposite pairs of sides are congruent. **b.** Since *EGHK* is a parallelogram, opposite sides are parallel. **33.** Alternate Interior Angles Congruence Theorem, Reflexive Property of Segment Congruence, Given, SAS, Corr. Parts of $\cong \triangle$ are $\cong$, Theorem 8.7

35.

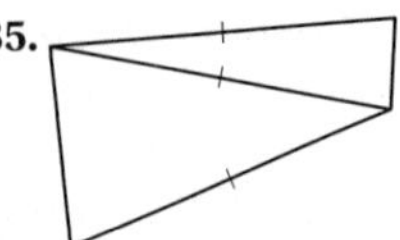

The opposite sides that are not marked in the given diagram are not necessarily the same length.

37. In a quadrilateral, if consecutive angles are supplementary, then the quadrilateral is a parallelogram; in *ABCD* you are given $\angle A$ and $\angle B$, $\angle C$ and $\angle B$ are supplementary which gives you $m\angle A = m\angle C$. Also $\angle B$ and $\angle C$, $\angle C$ and $\angle D$ are supplementary, which gives you $m\angle B = m\angle D$. So *ABCD* is a parallelogram by Theorem 8.8.

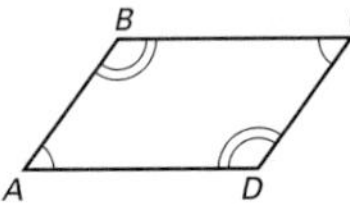

39. It is given that $\overline{KP} \cong \overline{MP}$ and $\overline{JP} \cong \overline{LP}$ by definition of segment bisector. $\angle KPL \cong \angle MPJ$ and $\angle KPJ \cong \angle MPL$ since they are vertical angles. $\triangle KPL \cong \triangle MPJ$ and $\triangle KPJ \cong \triangle MPL$ by the SAS Congruence Postulate. Because corresponding parts of congruent triangles are congruent, $\overline{KJ} \cong \overline{ML}$ and $\overline{JM} \cong \overline{LK}$. By Theorem 8.7, *JKLM* is a parallelogram.
41. *Sample answer:* Consider the diagram.

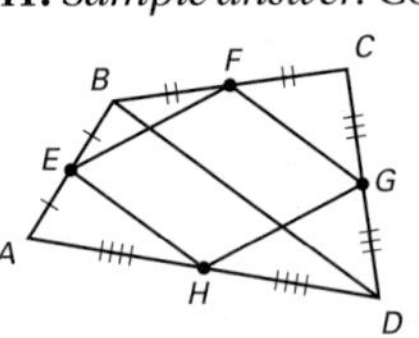

$\overline{FG}$ is the midsegment of $\triangle CBD$ and therefore is parallel to $\overline{BD}$ and half of its length. $\overline{EH}$ is the midsegment of $\triangle ABD$ and therefore is parallel to $\overline{BD}$ and half of its length. This makes $\overline{EH}$ and $\overline{FG}$ both parallel and congruent. By Theorem 8.9, *EFGH* is a parallelogram.

8.3 Problem Solving Workshop (p. 531) **1.** The slope of $\overline{AB}$ and $\overline{CD}$ is $\frac{2}{5}$ and the slope of $\overline{BC}$ and $\overline{DA}$ is -1. *ABCD* is a parallelogram by definition. **3.** No; the slope of the line segment joining Newton to Packard is $\frac{1}{3}$ while the slope of the line segment joining Riverdale to Quarry is $\frac{2}{7}$. **5.** $\overline{PQ}$ and $\overline{QR}$ are not opposite sides. $\overline{PQ}$ and $\overline{RS}$ are opposite sides, so they should be parallel and congruent. The slope of $\overline{PQ} = \frac{4-2}{3-2} = 2$. The slope of $\overline{RS} = \frac{5-4}{6-3} = \frac{1}{3}$. They are not parallel, so *PQRS* is not a parallelogram.

8.4 Skill Practice (pp. 537–539) **1.** square
3. Sometimes; *JKLM* would need to be a square.
5. Always; in a rhombus all four sides are congruent.
7. Sometimes; diagonals are congruent if the rhombus is a square. **9.** Always; in a rectangle all interior angles measure 90°. **11.** Sometimes; adjacent sides are congruent if the rectangle is a square. **13.** Sometimes; diagonals are perpendicular if the rectangle is a square. **15.** Square; the quadrilateral has four congruent sides and angles. **17.** Rhombus. *Sample answer:* The fourth angle measure is 40°, meaning that both pairs of opposite sides are parallel. So the figure is a parallelogram with two consecutive sides congruent. But this is only possible if the remaining two sides are also congruent, so the quadrilateral is a rhombus.
19. rectangle, square **21.** rhombus, square
23. parallelogram, rectangle, rhombus, square
25. $7x - 4$ is not necessarily equal to $3x + 14$;

$(7x - 4) + (3x + 4) = 90, x = 9$. **27.** Rectangle; *JKLM* is a quadrilateral with four right angles; $x = 10, y = 15$. **29.** Parallelogram; *EFGH* is a quadrilateral with opposite pairs of sides congruent; $x = 13, y = 2$. **33.** 90° **35.** 16 **37.** about 12 **39.** 112° **41.** 5 **43.** about 5.6 **45.** 45° **47.** 1 **49.** $\sqrt{2}$

51.

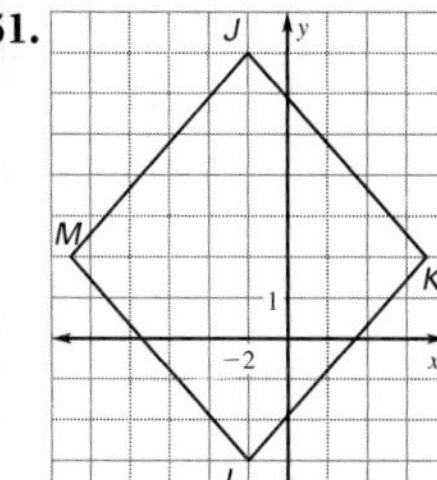

Rhombus; four congruent sides and opposite sides are parallel; $4\sqrt{106}$.

8.4 Problem Solving (pp. 539–540) **55.** Measure the diagonals. If they are the same it is a square. **57.** If a quadrilateral is a rhombus, then it has four congruent sides; if a quadrilateral has four congruent sides, then it is a rhombus; the conditional statement is true since a rhombus is a parallelogram with four congruent sides; the converse is true since a quadrilateral with four congruent sides is also a parallelogram with four congruent sides making it a rhombus. **59.** If a quadrilateral is a square, then it is a rhombus and a rectangle; if a quadrilateral is a rhombus and a rectangle, then it is a square; the conditional statement is true since a square is a parallelogram with four right angles and four congruent sides; the converse is true since a rhombus has four congruent sides and a rectangle has four right angles and is therefore a square. **61.** Since *WXYZ* is a rhombus $\overline{WX} \cong \overline{XY} \cong \overline{YZ} \cong \overline{ZW}$. By Theorem 8.6 $\overline{WV} \cong \overline{YV}$ and $\overline{ZV} \cong \overline{XV}$. By the SSS Congruence Postulate, $\triangle WVX \cong \triangle WVZ \cong \triangle YVX \cong \triangle YVZ$. Since corresponding parts of congruent triangles are congruent, $\angle WVZ \cong \angle WVX$ and $\angle YVZ \cong \angle YVX$, which means $\overline{WY}$ bisects $\angle ZWX$ and $\angle XYZ$. Similarly $\angle VZW \cong \angle VZY$ and $\angle VXW \cong \angle VXY$. This means $\overline{ZX}$ bisects $\angle WZY$ and $\angle YXW$. **63.** *Sample answer:* Let rectangle *ABCD* have vertices (0, 0), (*a*, 0), (*a*, *b*), and (0, *b*) respectively. The diagonal $\overline{AC}$ has a length of $\sqrt{a^2 + b^2}$ and diagonal $\overline{BD}$ has a length of $\sqrt{a^2 + b^2}$, $AC = BD = \sqrt{a^2 + b^2}$.

8.5 Skill Practice (pp. 546–547)

1.

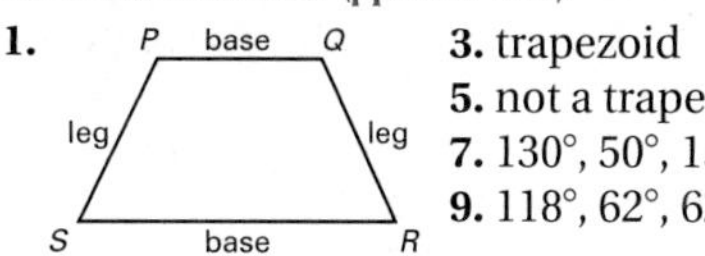

3. trapezoid **5.** not a trapezoid **7.** 130°, 50°, 150° **9.** 118°, 62°, 62°

11. Trapezoid; $\overline{EF} \parallel \overline{HG}$ since they are both perpendicular to $\overline{EH}$. **13.** 14 **15.** 66.5 **17.** Only one pair of opposite angles in a kite is congruent. In this case $m\angle B = m\angle D = 120°$; $m\angle A + m\angle B + m\angle C + m\angle D = 360°$, $m\angle A + 120° + 50° + 120° = 360°$, so $m\angle A = 70°$. **19.** 80° **21.** $WX = XY = 3\sqrt{2}$, $YZ = ZW = \sqrt{34}$ **23.** $XY = YZ = 5\sqrt{5}$, $WX = WZ = \sqrt{461}$ **25.** 2 **27.** 2.3

29.

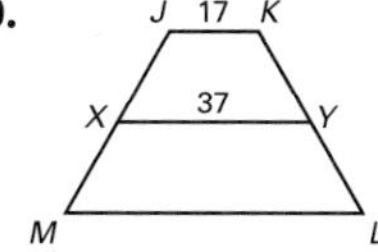

57

33. A kite or a quadrilateral that is not a parallelogram or a trapezoid would have no pair of opposite sides parallel. So, no consecutive angles would be supplementary. So, the measure of an interior angle could be greater than 180°.

8.5 Problem Solving (pp. 548–549)

35. *Sample:*

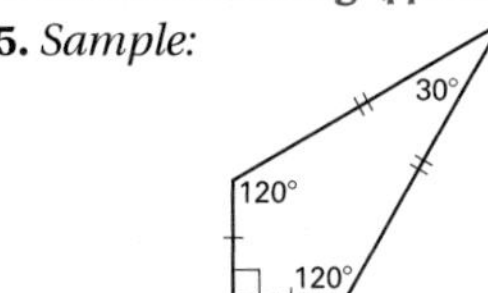

37. Since $\overline{BC} \parallel \overline{AE}$ and $\overline{AB} \parallel \overline{EC}$, *ABCE* is a parallelogram which makes $\overline{AB} \cong \overline{EC}$. By the Transitive Property of Segment Congruence, $\overline{CE} \cong \overline{CD}$ making $\triangle ECD$ isosceles. Since $\triangle ECD$ is isosceles $\angle D \cong \angle CED$. $\angle A \cong \angle CED$ by the Corresponding Angles Congruence Postulate, therefore $\angle A \cong \angle D$ by the Transitive Property of Angle Congruence. $\angle CED$ and $\angle CEA$ form a linear pair and therefore are supplementary. $\angle A$ and $\angle ABC$, $\angle CEA$ and $\angle ECB$ are supplementary since they are consecutive pairs of angles in a parallelogram. By the Congruent Supplements Theorem $\angle B \cong \angle BCD$. **39.** Given *JKLM* is an isosceles trapezoid with $\overline{KL} \parallel \overline{JM}$ and $\overline{JK} \cong \overline{LM}$. Since pairs of base angles are congruent in an isosceles trapezoid, $\angle JKL \cong \angle MLK$. By the Reflexive Property of Segment Congruence $\overline{KL} \cong \overline{KL}$. $\triangle JKL \cong \triangle MLK$ by the SAS Congruence Postulate. Because corresponding parts of congruent triangles are congruent, $\overline{JL} \cong \overline{KM}$.

SA27

41. Given $ABCD$ is a kite with $\overline{AB} \cong \overline{CB}$ and $\overline{AD} \cong \overline{CD}$. By the Reflexive Property of Segment Congruence, $\overline{BD} \cong \overline{BD}$ and $\overline{ED} \cong \overline{ED}$. By the SSS Congruence Postulate, $\triangle BAD \cong \triangle BCD$. Since corresponding parts of congruent triangles are congruent, $\angle CDE \cong \angle ADE$. By the SAS Congruence Postulate, $\triangle CDE \cong \triangle ADE$. Since corresponding parts of congruent triangles are congruent, $\angle CED \cong \angle AED$. Since $\angle CED$ and $\angle AED$ are congruent and form a linear pair, they are right angles. This makes $\overline{AC} \perp \overline{BD}$.

Extension (p. 551)

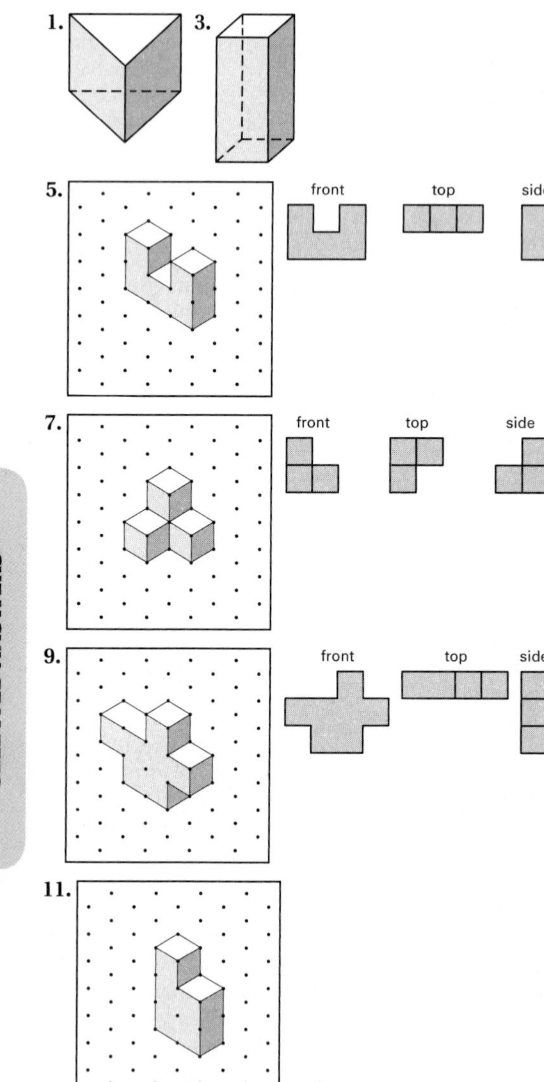

8.6 Skill Practice (pp. 554–555) **1.** isosceles trapezoid

	Property	Parallelogram	Rectangle	Rhombus	Square	Kite	Trapezoid
3.	All sides are ≅.			✗	✗		
5.	Both pair of opp. sides are ∥.	✗	✗	✗	✗		
7.	All ∠s are ≅.		✗		✗		
9.	Diagonals are ⊥.			✗	✗	✗	
11.	Diagonals bisect each other.	✗	✗	✗	✗		

15. Trapezoid; there is one pair of parallel sides.
17.

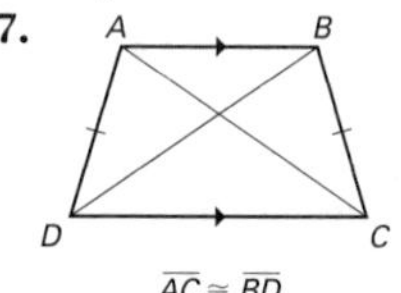

isosceles trapezoid

19. No; $m\angle F = 109°$ which is not equal to $m\angle E$. **21.** Kite; it has two pair of consecutive congruent sides. **23.** Rectangle; opposite sides are parallel with four right angles. **25. a.** rhombus, square, kite **b.** Parallelogram, rectangle, trapezoid; two consecutive pairs of sides are always congruent and one pair of opposite angles remain congruent. **27.** *Sample answer:* $m\angle B = 60°$ or $m\angle C = 120°$; then $\overline{AB} \parallel \overline{DC}$ and the base angles would be congruent. **29.** No; if $m\angle JKL = m\angle KJM = 90°$, $JKLM$ would be a rectangle. **31.** Yes; $JKLM$ has one pair of non-congruent parallel sides with congruent diagonals.

8.6 Problem Solving (pp. 556–557) **33.** trapezoid **35.** parallelogram **37.** Consecutive interior angles are supplementary making each interior angle 90°. **39. a.** Using the definition of a regular hexagon, $\overline{UV} \cong \overline{VQ} \cong \overline{RS} \cong \overline{ST}$ and $\angle V \cong \angle S$. So, $\triangle QVU$ and $\triangle RST$ are isosceles. Using the SAS Congruence Postulate, $\triangle QVU \cong \triangle RST$. **b.** By the definition of a regular hexagon, $\overline{QR} \cong \overline{UT}$. Since corresponding parts of congruent triangles are congruent, $\overline{QU} \cong \overline{RT}$. **c.** Since $\angle Q \cong \angle R \cong \angle T \cong \angle U$ and $\angle VUQ \cong \angle VQU \cong \angle STR \cong \angle SRT$, you know that $\angle UQR \cong \angle QRT \cong \angle RTU \cong \angle TUQ$ by the Angle Addition Postulate; 90°. **d.** Rectangle; there are 4 right angles and opposite sides are congruent.

Chapter Review (pp. 560–563) **1.** midsegment **3.** Prove the trapezoid has a pair of congruent base angles or the diagonals are congruent. **5.** A **7.** 24-gon; 165° **9.** 82

SA28

11. 40°; the sum of the measures of the exterior angles is always 360°, and there are nine congruent external angles in a nonagon. **13.** $c = 6$, $d = 10$

15.

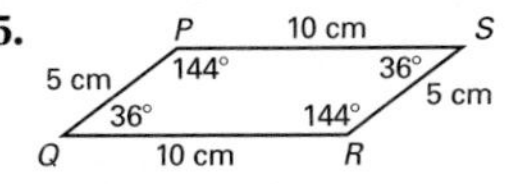

17. 100°, 80°; solve $5x + 4x = 180$ for x. **19.** 3 **21.** rectangle; 9, 5 **23.** 79°, 101°, 101° **25.** Rhombus; since all four sides are congruent, it is a rhombus. There are no known right angles. **27.** Parallelogram; since opposite pairs of sides are congruent, it is a parallelogram. There are no known right angles.

Algebra Review (p. 565)

1.

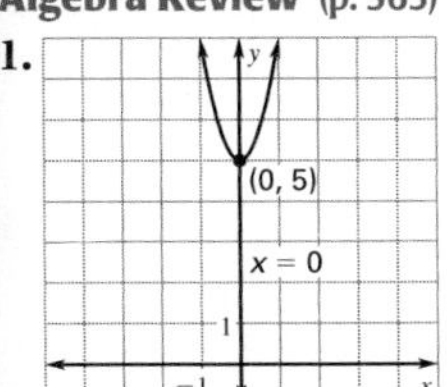

3.

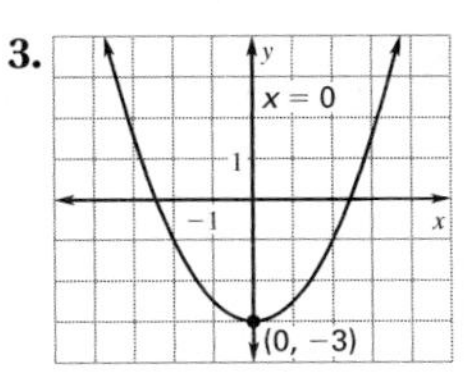

5.

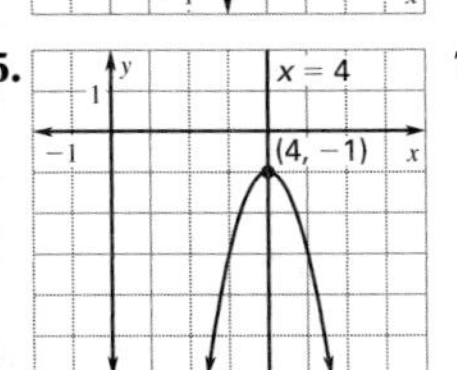

7.

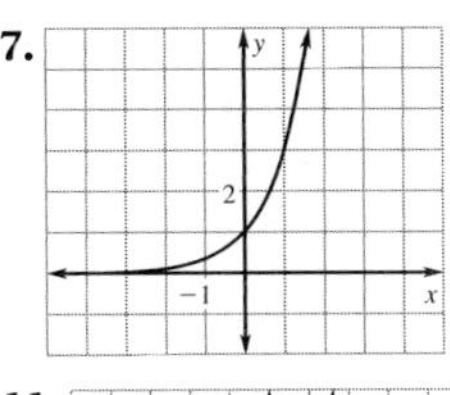

9.

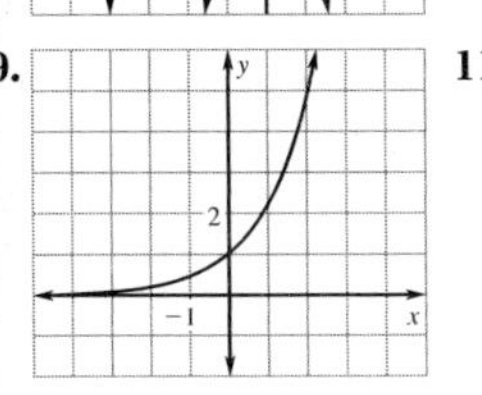

11.

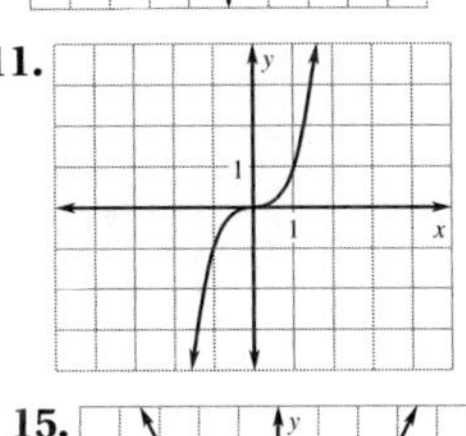

13.

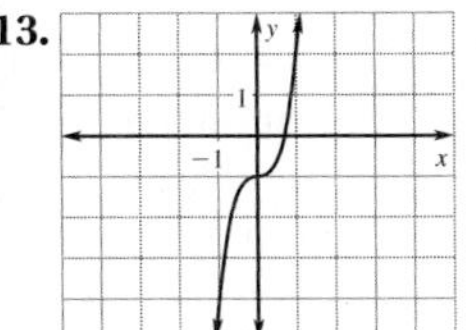

15.

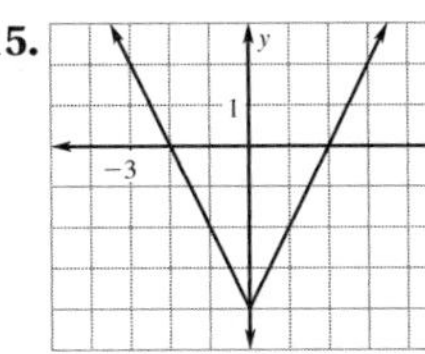

Chapter 9

9.1 Skill Practice (pp. 576–577) **1.** vector, direction **3.** $A'(-6, 10)$ **5.** $C(5, -14)$

7.

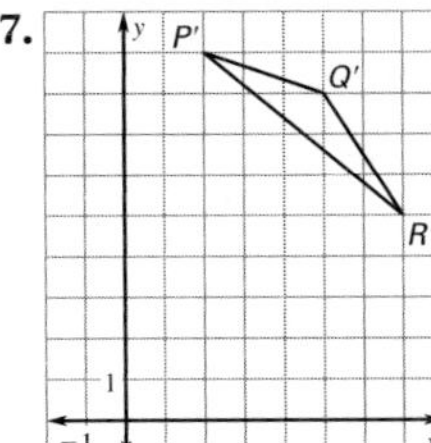

9.

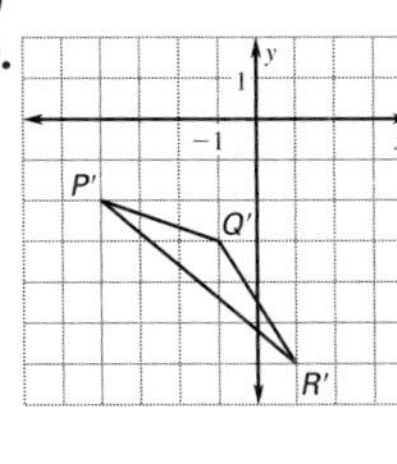

11. $(x, y) \to (x - 5, y + 2)$; $AB = A'B' = \sqrt{13}$, $AC = A'C' = 4$, and $BC = B'C' = \sqrt{5}$. $\triangle ABC \cong \triangle A'B'C'$ using the SSS Congruence Postulate.

13. The image should be 1 unit to the left instead of right and 2 units down instead of up.

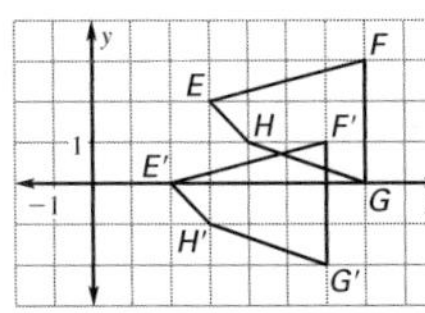

15. $\overrightarrow{CD}$, $\langle 7, -3\rangle$ **17.** $\overrightarrow{JP}$, $\langle 0, 4\rangle$ **19.** $\langle -1, 2\rangle$ **21.** $\langle 0, -11\rangle$ **23.** The vertical component is the distance from the ground up to the plane entrance.

25. $D'(7, 4)$, $E'(11, 2)$, $F'(9, -1)$

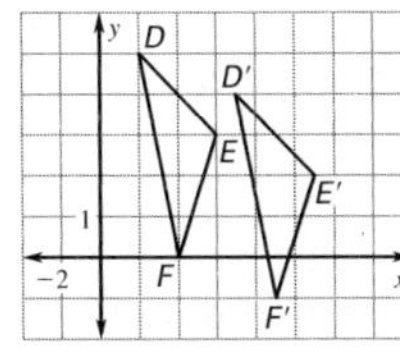

27. $D'(0, 1)$, $E'(4, -1)$, $F'(2, -4)$

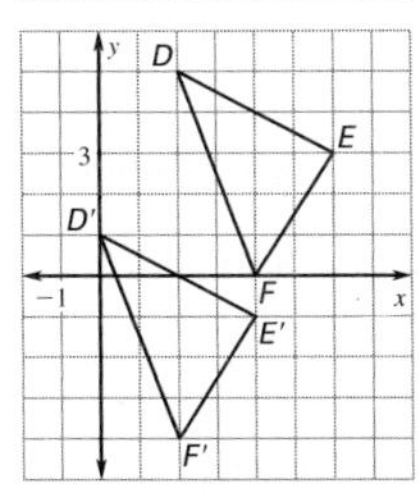

29. $a = 35$, $b = 14$, $c = 5$ **31. a.** $Q'(-1, -5)$, $R'(-1, 2)$, $S'(2, 2)$, $T'(2, -5)$; 21, 21 **b.** The areas are the same; the area of an image and its preimage under a translation are the same.

9.1 Problem Solving (pp. 578–579) **33.** $(x, y) \to (x + 6, y)$, $(x, y) \to (x, y - 4)$, $(x, y) \to (x + 3, y - 4)$, $(x, y) \to (x + 6, y - 4)$ **35.** $\langle 1, 2\rangle$ **37.** $\langle -4, -2\rangle$ **39.** $\langle 3, 1\rangle$ **41.** $\langle 22, 5\rangle$; about 22.6 km **43. a.** 5 squares to the right followed by 4 squares down. **b.** $2\sqrt{41}$ mm **c.** about 0.523 mm/sec **45. a.** The graph is 4 units lower. **b.** The graph is 4 units to the right.

9.2 Skill Practice (pp. 584–585) **1.** elements

3. $\begin{bmatrix} -1 & 2 & 6 \\ -2 & 2 & 1 \end{bmatrix}$ **5.** $\begin{matrix} B & C & D & E \end{matrix}$ $\begin{bmatrix} 2 & 6 & 5 & -1 \\ 2 & 1 & -1 & -2 \end{bmatrix}$ **7.** $\begin{bmatrix} 12 & 7 \end{bmatrix}$

9. $\begin{bmatrix} 16 & 9 \\ 0 & 0 \\ -5 & -3 \end{bmatrix}$ **11.** $\begin{bmatrix} -13 & -4 \\ -12 & 16 \end{bmatrix}$

13. $\begin{matrix} A' & B' & C' \end{matrix}$ $\begin{bmatrix} -2 & 2 & 1 \\ 8 & 5 & 1 \end{bmatrix}$

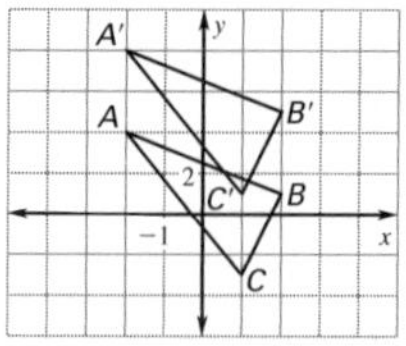

15. $\begin{matrix} L' & M' & N' & P' \end{matrix}$ $\begin{bmatrix} 6 & 4 & 6 & 7 \\ 1 & 5 & 5 & 1 \end{bmatrix}$

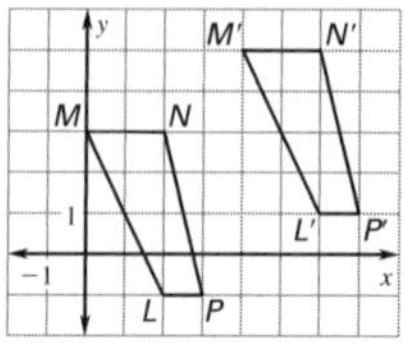

19. $\begin{bmatrix} -6.9 \end{bmatrix}$ **21.** $\begin{bmatrix} -4 & 15.2 \\ -32.3 & -43.4 \end{bmatrix}$ **23.** $\begin{bmatrix} 38 \\ 36 \end{bmatrix}$

25. *Sample answer:* $\begin{bmatrix} -2 & 1 \\ 0 & 4 \end{bmatrix}$, $\begin{bmatrix} 1 & 1 \\ 2 & 1 \end{bmatrix}$; $\begin{bmatrix} 0 & -1 \\ 8 & 4 \end{bmatrix}$

27. $\begin{matrix} A & B & C & D \end{matrix}$ $\begin{bmatrix} -7 & 0 & 0 & -7 \\ 3 & 3 & -1 & -1 \end{bmatrix}$ **29.** $a = 8$, $b = -20$, $c = 20$, $m = 21$, $n = -1$, $v = -7$, $w = 12$; the sum of the corresponding elements on the left equals the corresponding elements on the right; (21, −1), (20, −9), (−8, 13).

9.2 Problem Solving (pp. 586–587) **31.** Lab 1: \$840, Lab 2: \$970 **33. a.** $AB = BA$ **b.** $\begin{bmatrix} -3 & 15 \\ -14 & 30 \end{bmatrix}$, $\begin{bmatrix} 25 & -7 \\ 10 & 2 \end{bmatrix}$, $AB \neq BA$ **c.** Matrix multiplication is not commutative.

35. $\begin{bmatrix} 2 & 36 \\ 16 & 68 \end{bmatrix}$, $\begin{bmatrix} 2 & 36 \\ 16 & 68 \end{bmatrix}$; the Distributive Property holds for matrices.

9.3 Skill Practice (pp. 593–594) **1.** a line which acts like a mirror to reflect an image across the line

3.

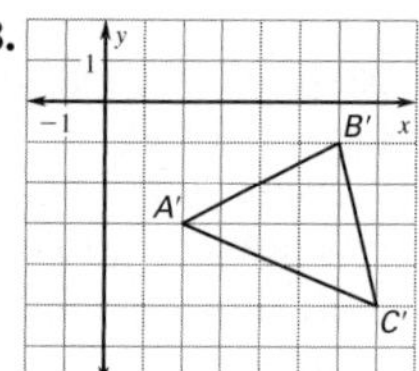

5.

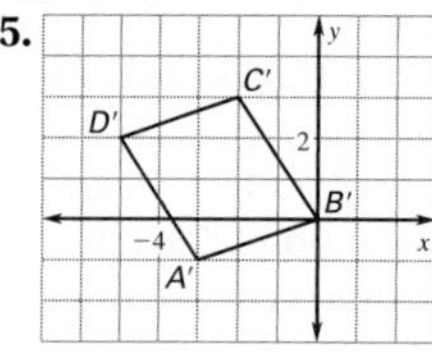

13.

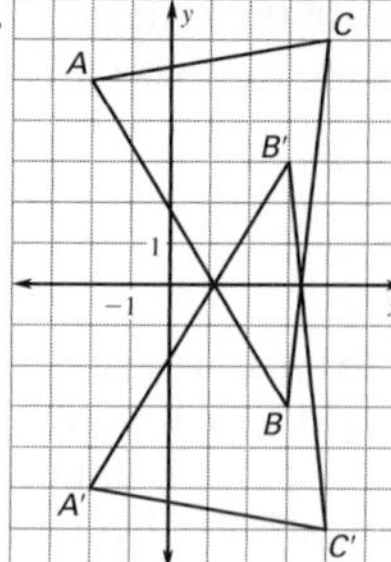

15. $\begin{matrix} A & B & C \end{matrix}$ $\begin{bmatrix} 1 & 4 & 3 \\ 2 & 2 & -2 \end{bmatrix}$; $\begin{matrix} A' & B' & C' \end{matrix}$ $\begin{bmatrix} -1 & -4 & -3 \\ 2 & 2 & -2 \end{bmatrix}$

17. $\begin{matrix} A & B & C \end{matrix}$ $\begin{bmatrix} -4 & 3 & 2 \\ -2 & 1 & -3 \end{bmatrix}$; $\begin{matrix} A' & B' & C' \end{matrix}$ $\begin{bmatrix} 4 & -3 & -2 \\ -2 & 1 & -3 \end{bmatrix}$

19. (5, 0) **21.** (−4, 0)

23.

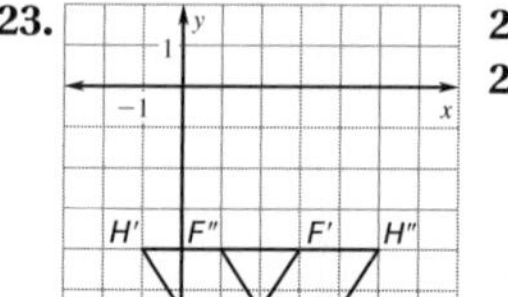

25. The order is reversed. **27.** $y = -3x - 4$

29.

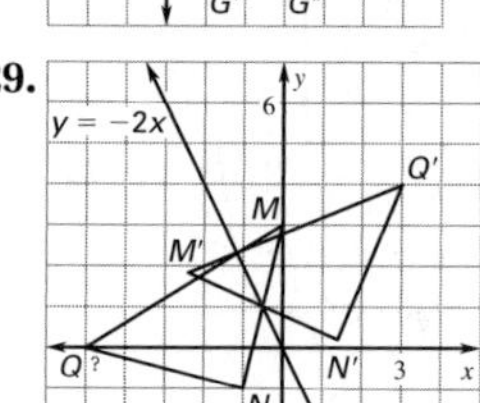

9.3 Problem Solving (pp. 595–596) **31.** Case 4 **33.** Case 1

35. a. Given: a reflection in m maps P to P' and Q to Q'. Using the definition of a line of reflection $\overline{QS} \cong \overline{Q'S}$ and $\angle QSR \cong \angle Q'SR$. By the Reflexive Property of Segment Congruence, $\overline{RS} \cong \overline{RS}$. By the SAS Congruence Postulate, $\triangle RSQ \cong \triangle RSQ'$.

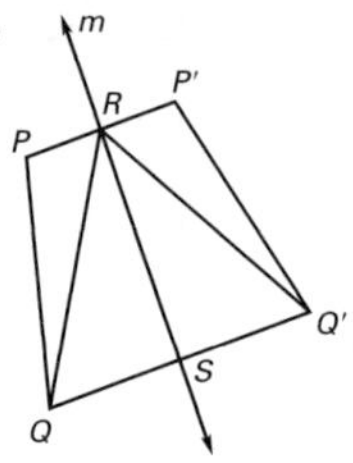

SA30

b. Because corresponding parts of congruent triangles are congruent, $\overline{RQ} \cong \overline{RQ'}$. By the definition of a line of reflection $\overline{PR} \cong \overline{P'R}$. Since $\overline{PP'}$ and $\overline{QQ'}$ are both perpendicular to m, they are parallel. By the Alternate Interior Angles Theorem, $\angle SQ'R \cong \angle P'RQ'$ and $\angle SQR \cong \angle PRQ$. Because corresponding parts of congruent triangles are congruent, $\angle SQ'R \cong \angle SQR$. By the Transitive Property of Angle Congruence, $\angle P'RQ' \cong \angle PRQ$. $\triangle PRQ \cong \triangle P'RQ'$ by the SAS Congruence Postulate. Because corresponding parts of congruent triangles are congruent, $\overline{PQ} \cong \overline{P'Q'}$ which implies $PQ = P'Q'$. **37.** Given: a reflection in m maps P to P' and Q to Q'. Also, P lies on m, and $\overline{PQ}$ is not perpendicular to m. Draw $\overline{Q'Q}$ intersecting m at point R. Using the definition of a line of reflection, m is the perpendicular bisector of $\overline{Q'Q}$, which implies $\overline{Q'R} \cong \overline{QR}$, $\angle Q'RP' \cong \angle QRP$, and P and P' are the same point. By the Reflexive Property of Segment Congruence, $\overline{RP} \cong \overline{RP}$. By the SAS Congruence Postulate, $\triangle Q'RP' \cong \triangle QRP$. Because corresponding parts of congruent triangles are congruent, $\overline{Q'P'} \cong \overline{QP}$ which implies $Q'P' = QP$. **39. a.** (3, 5) **b.** (0, 6); (−1, 4) **c.** In each case point C bisects each line segment.

9.4 Skill Practice (pp. 602–603) **1.** a point which a figure is turned about during a rotation transformation **3.** Reflection; the horses are reflected across the edge of the stream which acts like a line of symmetry. **5.** Translation; the train moves horizontally from right to left. **7.** A

9.

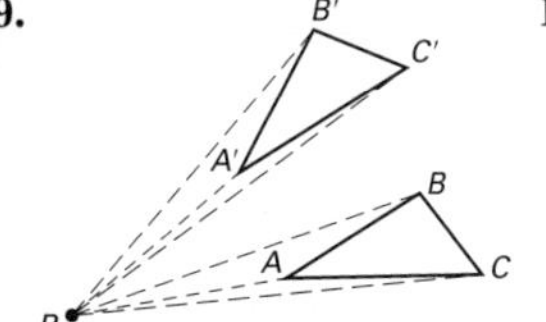

11.

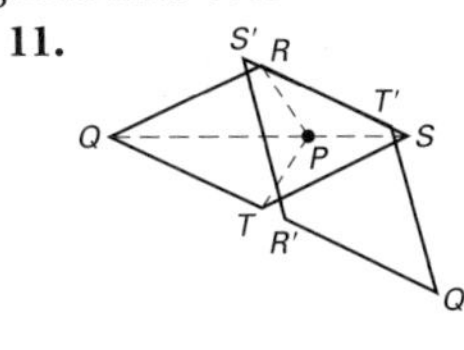

13. $J'(-1, -4)$, $K'(-5, -5)$, $L'(-7, -2)$, $M'(-2, -2)$

15. $\begin{matrix} A' & B' & C' \end{matrix}$ $\begin{bmatrix} -4 & -6 & -3 \\ 1 & 5 & 4 \end{bmatrix}$

17. $\begin{matrix} P' & Q' & R' & S' \end{matrix}$ $\begin{bmatrix} -4 & -2 & -5 & -7 \\ 4 & -2 & -2 & 4 \end{bmatrix}$

19. The rotation matrix should be first; $\begin{bmatrix} 0 & 1 \\ -1 & 0 \end{bmatrix}\begin{bmatrix} -1 & 2 \\ 1 & 3 \end{bmatrix}$. **25.** (−3, 2, 0)

9.4 Problem Solving (pp. 604–605) **29.** 270°; the line segment joining A' to the center of rotation is perpendicular to the line segment joining A to the center of rotation. **31.** 120°; the line segment joining A' to the center of rotation is rotated $\frac{1}{3}$ of a circle from the line segment joining A to the center of rotation. **33.** a rotation about a point, Angle Addition Postulate, Transitive, Subtraction, $\triangle RPQ \cong \triangle R'PQ'$, Corr. Parts of ≅ ▲ are ≅, definition of segment congruence **35.** Given: a rotation about P maps Q to Q' and R to R'. P and R are the same point. Using the definition of rotation about a point P, $PQ = PQ'$ and P, R, and R' are the same point. Substituting R for P on the left and R' for P on the right side, you get $RQ = R'Q'$.

37. a.

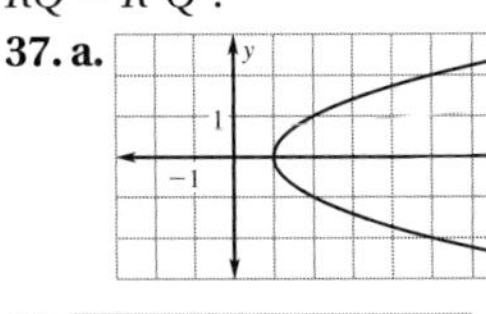

b. 270° **c.** No; the image does not pass the vertical line test.

39.

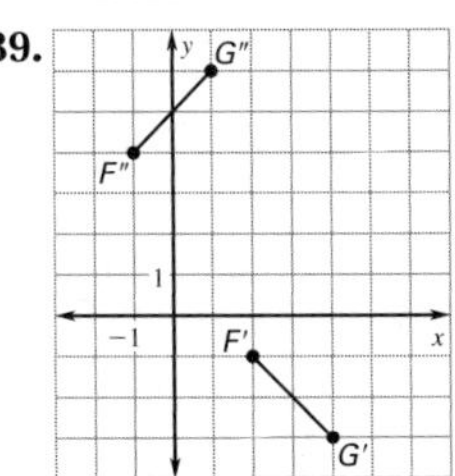

9.4 Problem Solving Workshop (p. 606)

1.

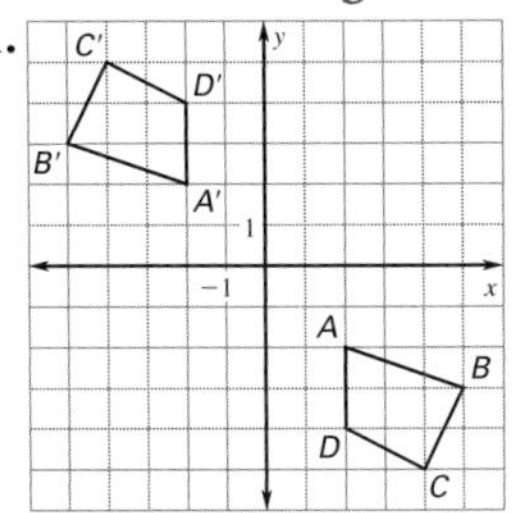

3. Since they are rotating in opposite directions they will each place you at 90° below your reference line. **5.** The x-coordinate is now −4; the y-coordinate is now 3.

9.5 Skill Practice (pp. 611–613) **1.** parallel

3.

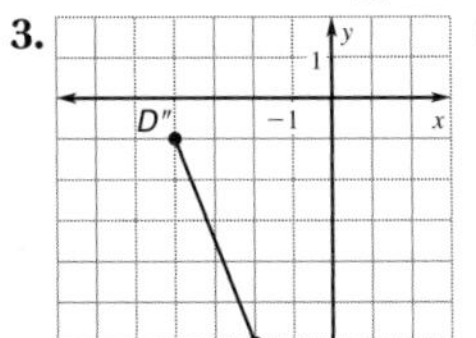

5.

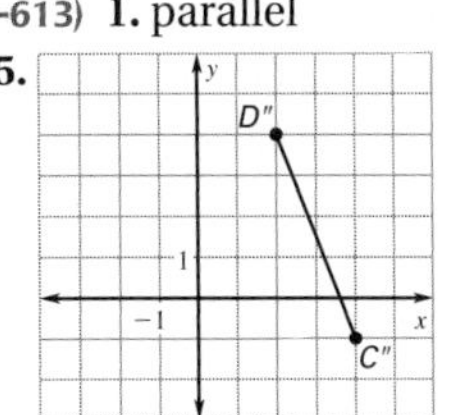

SELECTED ANSWERS

7.

9.

11. yes

13. $(x, y) \rightarrow (x + 5, y + 1)$ followed by a rotation of 180° about the origin.
15. $\triangle A''B''C''$
17. *Sample answer:* $\overline{AA'}$, $\overline{AA''}$

19. yes; definition of reflection of a point over a line
21. 30°
23. $\begin{bmatrix} -1 & -3 & -7 \\ 9 & 3 & 6 \end{bmatrix}$ (columns P', Q', R')

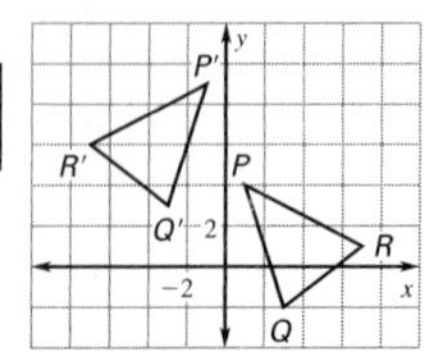

9.5 Problem Solving (pp. 613–615) **27.** *Sample answer:* $(x, y) \rightarrow (x + 9, y)$, reflected over a horizontal line that separates the left and right prints **31.** reflection **33.** translation **35.** Use the Rotation Theorem followed by the Reflection Theorem. **37.** Given a reflection in ℓ maps $\overline{JK}$ to $\overline{J'K'}$, a reflection in m maps $\overline{J'K'}$ to $\overline{J''K''}$, $\ell \parallel m$ and the distance between ℓ and m is d. Using the definition of reflection ℓ is the perpendicular bisector of $\overline{KK'}$ and m is perpendicular bisector of $\overline{K'K''}$. Using the Segment Addition Postulate, $KK' + K'K'' = KK''$. It follows that $\overline{KK'}$ is perpendicular to ℓ and m. Using the definition of reflection the distance from K to ℓ is the same as the distance from ℓ to K' and the distance from K' to m is the same as the distance from m to K''. Since the distance from ℓ to K' plus the distance from K' to m is d, it follows that $K'K'' = 2d$. **39. a.** translation and a rotation **b.** One transformation is not followed by the second. They are done simultaneously.

Extension (pp. 617–618) **1.** yes; regular **3.** yes; not regular **5. a.** 360°; the sum of the angle measures at any vertex is 360°. **b.** The sum of the measures of the interior angles is 360°.

7. *Sample:*

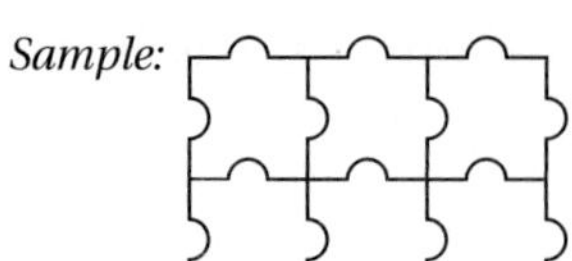

9. a. **b.** **c.**

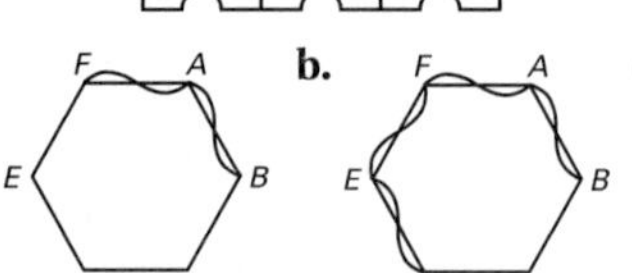

d.

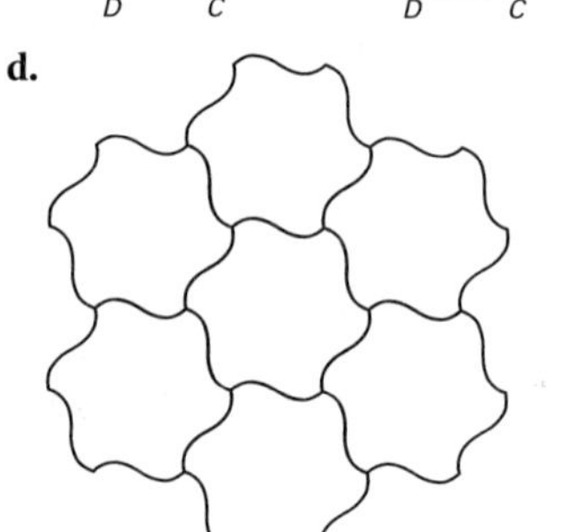

11. *Sample:*

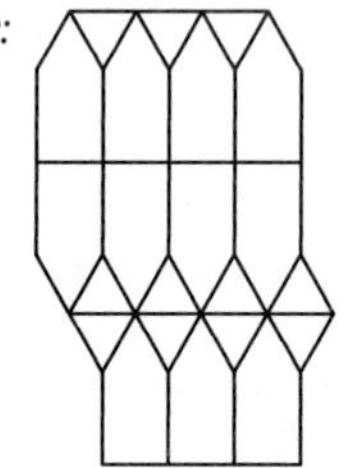

13. *Sample:*

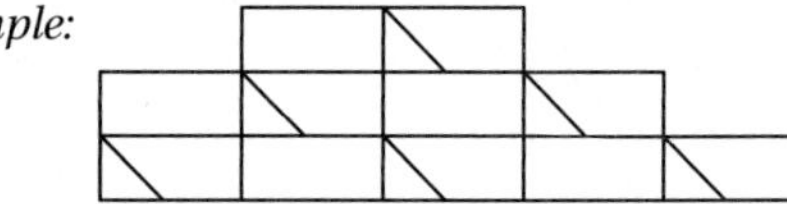

15. translation **17.** rotations

9.6 Skill Practice (pp. 621–623) **1.** If a figure has rotational symmetry it is the point about which the figure is rotated. **3.** 1 **5.** 1 **7.** yes; 72° or 144° about the center **9.** no **11.** Line symmetry, rotational symmetry; there are four lines of symmetry, two passing through the outer opposite pairs of leaves and two passing through the inner opposite pairs of leaves; 90° or 180° about the center. **15.** There is no rotational symmetry; the figure has 1 line of symmetry but no rotational symmetry.

17. *Sample:*

19. *Sample:*

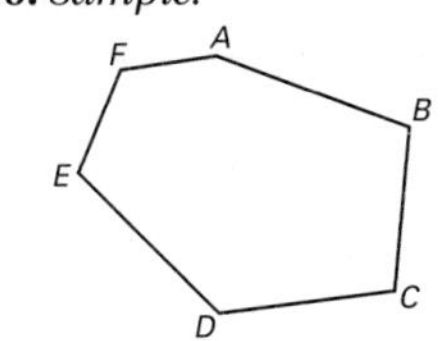

21. *Sample:*

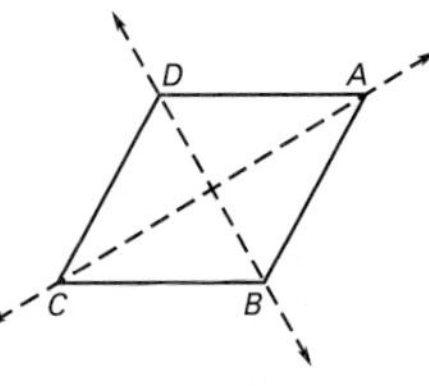

23. No; what's on the left and right of the first line would have to be the same as what's on the left and right of the second line which is not possible. **25.** 5

9.6 Problem Solving (pp. 623–624) **27.** no line symmetry, rotational symmetry of 180° about the center of the letter *O*. **29.** It has a line of symmetry passing horizontally through the center of each *O*, no rotational symmetry. **31.** 22.5° **33.** 15° **35. a.** line symmetry and rotational symmetry **b.** planes, *z*-axis

9.7 Skill Practice (pp. 629–630) **1.** a real number **3.** $\frac{7}{3}$; enlargement; 8 **5.** $\frac{3}{2}$; enlargement; 10

7.

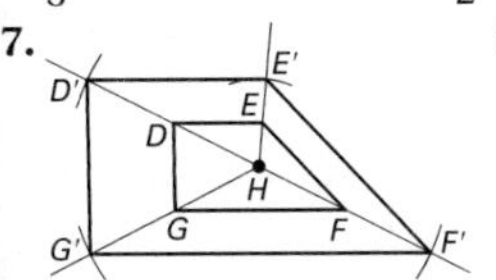

9.

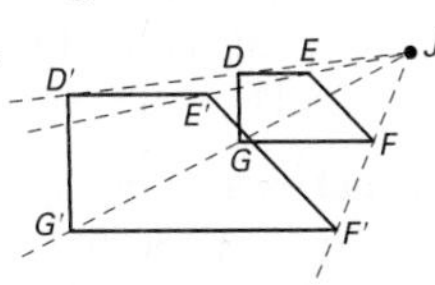

15. $\begin{bmatrix} 12 & 28 & 16 \\ 0 & 36 & -4 \end{bmatrix}$ **17.** $\begin{bmatrix} 0 & 27 & 18 \\ -9 & 63 & 0 \end{bmatrix}$

19.

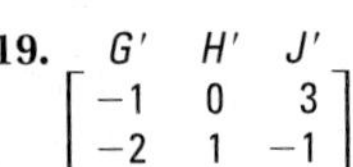

$\begin{matrix} G' & H' & J' \end{matrix}$
$\begin{bmatrix} -1 & 0 & 3 \\ -2 & 1 & -1 \end{bmatrix}$

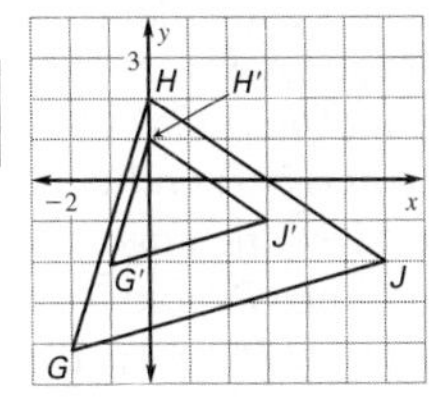

21.

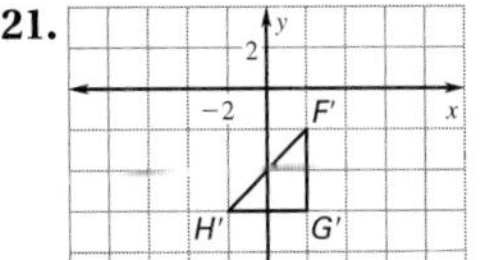

23.

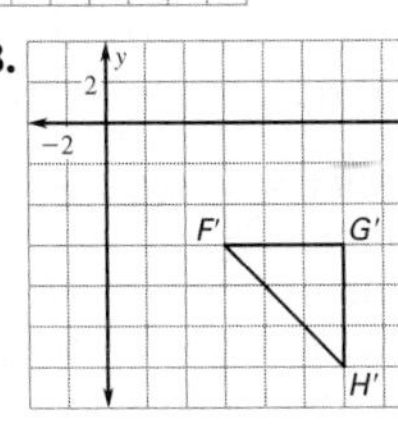

27. *Sample:*

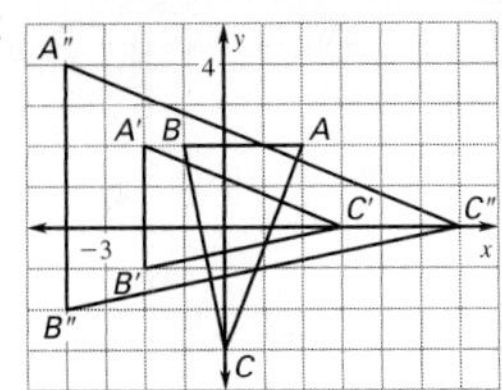

No; the result is the same.

31. No; the ratio of the lengths of corresponding sides is not the same.

9.7 Problem Solving (pp. 631–632) **33.** 300 mm **35.** 940 mm **37. a.** $\frac{6}{1}$ **b.** 8.75 in.

39. a. $\begin{matrix} F & G & H \end{matrix}$ $\begin{bmatrix} 0 & 4 & -2 \\ 2 & 2 & -2 \end{bmatrix}$; $\begin{matrix} F' & G' & H' \end{matrix}$ $\begin{bmatrix} 0 & -8 & 4 \\ -4 & -4 & 4 \end{bmatrix}$

b.

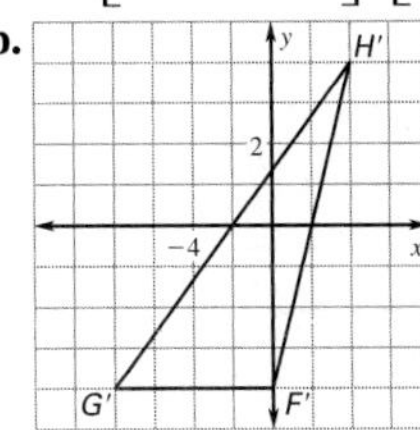

c. $\begin{matrix} F'' & G'' & H'' \end{matrix}$ $\begin{bmatrix} 0 & -2 & 1 \\ -1 & -1 & 1 \end{bmatrix}$

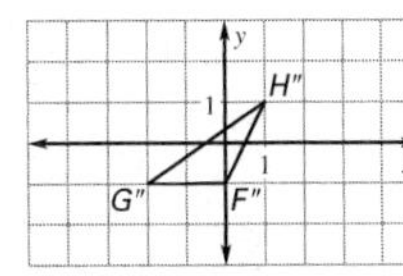

d. A reflection in both the *x*-axis and *y*-axis occurs as well as dilation. **41.** It's the center point of the dilation.

Chapter Review (pp. 636–639) **1.** isometry **3.** Count the number of rows, *n*, and the number of columns, *m*. The dimensions are $n \times m$.

Sample answer: 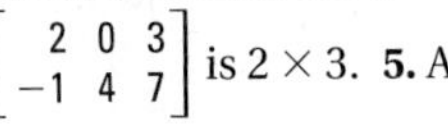 $\begin{bmatrix} 2 & 0 & 3 \\ -1 & 4 & 7 \end{bmatrix}$ is 2×3. **5.** A

7.

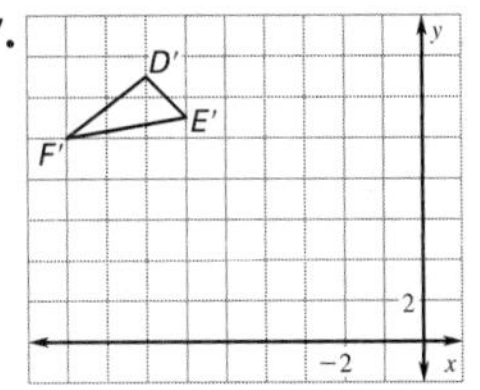

SELECTED ANSWERS

9. 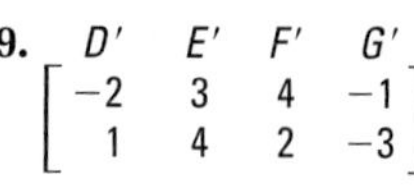

$$\begin{array}{cccc} D' & E' & F' & G' \end{array}$$
$$\begin{bmatrix} -2 & 3 & 4 & -1 \\ 1 & 4 & 2 & -3 \end{bmatrix}$$

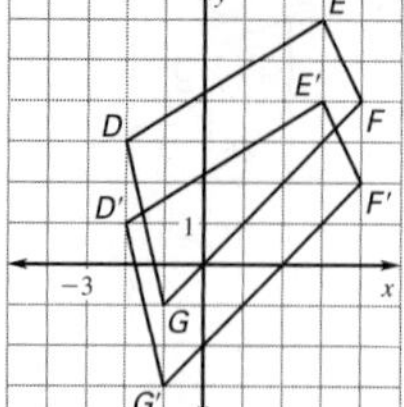

11. 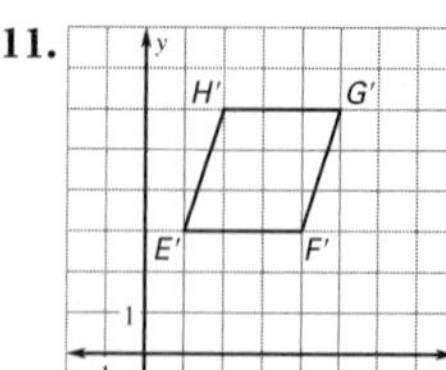

13. $\begin{array}{ccc} Q' & R' & S' \end{array}$
$$\begin{bmatrix} -3 & -4 & -1 \\ 0 & -5 & 2 \end{bmatrix}$$

15. 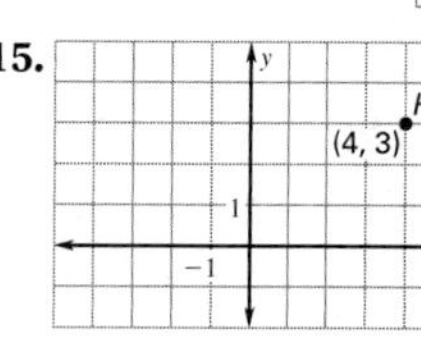

17. line symmetry, no rotational symmetry; one **19.** line symmetry, rotational symmetry; two, 180° about the center

21. 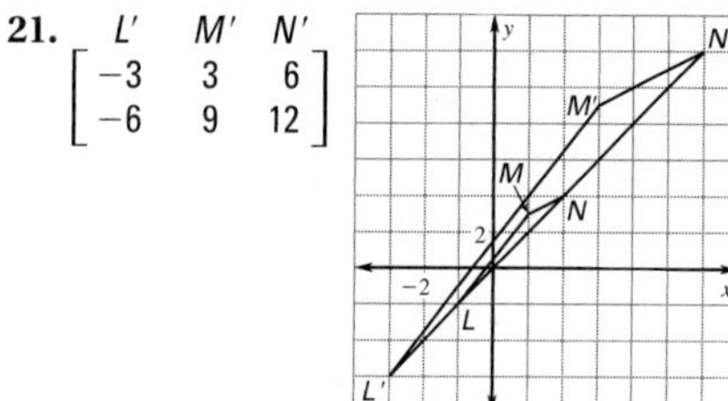

Algebra Review (p. 641) **1.** $x^2 + x - 6$ **3.** $x^2 - 16$ **5.** $49x^2 + 84x + 36$ **7.** $4x^2 - 1$ **9.** $2x^2 + 3xy + y^2$ **11.** 3, 4 **13.** $-2, -\frac{1}{4}$ **15.** $\frac{-1 \pm \sqrt{29}}{2}$ **17.** $\frac{-11 \pm \sqrt{105}}{2}$

Cumulative Review (pp. 646–647) **1.** neither **3.** $x = 4$ **5.** $y = \frac{1}{2}x - 2$ **7.** $\overline{QP} \cong \overline{SR}$ **9.** altitude **11.** median **13.** triangle; right **15.** not a triangle **17.** triangle; right **19.** Rectangle; the diagonals are congruent and they bisect each other; 5, 3.

21. 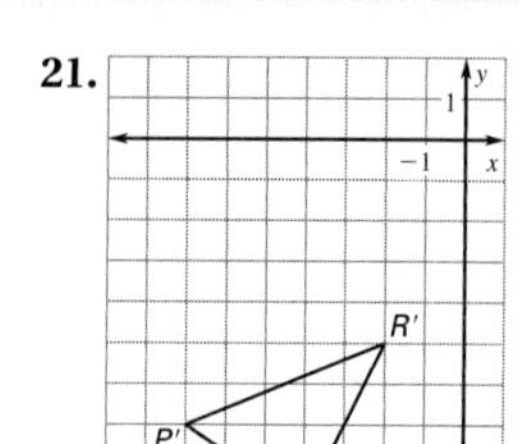

23. $\angle 4, \angle 5, \angle 8$ **25.** 132° **27.** about 135 mi **29.** about \$7.69 **31.** translation and rotation

Chapter 10

10.1 Skill Practice (pp. 655–657) **1.** diameter **3.** G **5.** C **7.** F **9.** B **11.** $\overline{AB}$ is not a secant it is a chord; the length of chord $\overline{AB}$ is 6. **13.** 6, 12 **15.** 4 **17.** 1

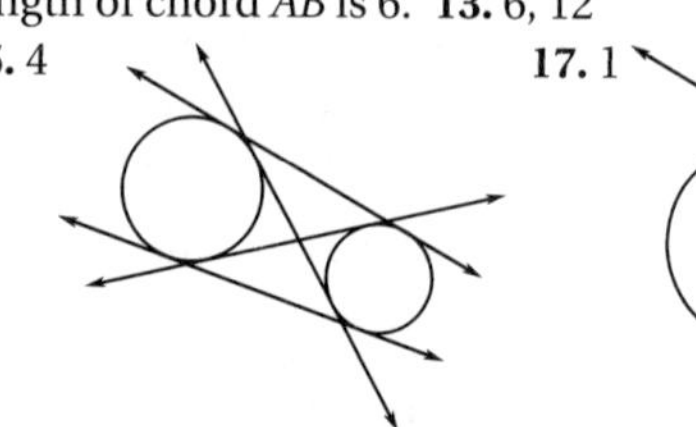

19. not tangent; $9^2 + 15^2 \neq 18^2$ **21.** 10 **23.** 10.5 **25.** ± 2 **27.** external **31.** They will be parallel if they are tangent to opposite endpoints of the same diameter; lines perpendicular to the same line are parallel. **33.** No; no; no matter what the distance the external point is from the circle there will always be two tangents.

10.1 Problem Solving (pp. 657–658) **35.** radial spokes **37.** 14,426 mi **39. a.** Since R is exterior to $\odot Q$, $QR > QP$. **b.** Since $\overline{QR}$ is perpendicular to line m it must be the shortest distance from Q to line m, thus $QR < QP$. **c.** It was assumed $\overline{QP}$ was not perpendicular to line m but $\overline{QR}$ was perpendicular to line m. Since R is outside of $\odot Q$ you know that $QR > QP$, but Exercise 39b tells you that $QR < QP$ which is a contradiction. Therefore, line m is perpendicular to $\overline{QP}$. **41.** Given $\overline{SR}$ and $\overline{ST}$ are tangent to $\odot P$. Construct $\overline{PR}$, $\overline{PT}$, and $\overline{PS}$. Since $\overline{PR}$ and $\overline{PT}$ are radii of $\odot P$, $\overline{PR} \cong \overline{PT}$. With $\overline{PS} \cong \overline{PS}$, using the HL Congruence Theorem $\triangle RSP \cong \triangle TSP$. Using corresponding parts of congruent triangles are congruent, $\overline{SR} \cong \overline{ST}$.

10.2 Skill Practice (pp. 661–662) **1.** congruent **3.** minor arc; 70° **5.** minor arc; 135° **7.** minor arc; 115° **9.** major arc; 245° **13.** Not congruent; they are arcs of circles that are not congruent. **15.** You can tell that the circles are congruent since they have the same radius $\overline{CD}$. **19.** *Sample answer:* 15°, 175°

10.2 Problem Solving (p. 663) **23.** 18°

10.3 Skill Practice (pp. 667–668) **1.** *Sample answer:* Point Y bisects $\overset{\frown}{XZ}$ if $\overset{\frown}{XY} \cong \overset{\frown}{YZ}$. **3.** 75° **5.** 8 **7.** 5; use Theorem 10.5 and solve $5x - 6 = 2x + 9$. **9.** 5; use Theorem 10.6 and solve $18 = 5x - 7$. **11.** $\frac{7}{3}$; use Theorem 10.6 and solve $4x + 1 = x + 8$. **13.** $\overline{JH}$ bisects $\overline{FG}$ and $\overset{\frown}{FG}$; Theorem 10.5. **17.** You don't know that $\overline{AC} \perp \overline{DB}$ therefore you can't show $\overset{\frown}{BC} \cong \overset{\frown}{CD}$.
19. Diameter; the two triangles are congruent by the SAS Congruence Postulate which makes $\overline{AB}$ the perpendicular bisector of $\overline{CD}$. Use Theorem 10.4.
21. Using the facts that $\triangle APB$ is equilateral which makes it equiangular and that $m\overset{\frown}{AC} = 30°$, you can conclude that $m\angle APD = m\angle BPD = 30°$. You now know that $m\overset{\frown}{BC} = 30°$ which makes $\overline{AC} \cong \overline{BC}$. $\triangle APD \cong \triangle BPD$ by the SAS Congruence Postulate since $\overline{BP} \cong \overline{AP}$ and $\overline{PD} \cong \overline{PD}$. Because corresponding parts of congruent triangles are congruent, $\overline{AD} \cong \overline{BD}$. Along with $\overline{DC} \cong \overline{DC}$ you have $\triangle ADC \cong \triangle BDC$ by the SSS Congruence Postulate. **23.** From the diagram, $m\overset{\frown}{AC} = m\overset{\frown}{CB}$ and $m\overset{\frown}{AB} = x°$, so you know that $m\overset{\frown}{AC} + m\overset{\frown}{CB} + x° = 360°$. Replacing $m\overset{\frown}{CB}$ by $m\overset{\frown}{AC}$ and solving for $m\overset{\frown}{AC}$ you get $m\overset{\frown}{AC} = \frac{360° - x°}{2}$. This along with the fact that all arcs have integral measure implies that x is even.

10.3 Problem Solving (pp. 669–670) **25.** $\overline{AB}$ should be congruent to $\overline{BC}$. **27.** Given $\overline{AB} \cong \overline{CD}$. Since $\overline{PA}$, $\overline{PB}$, $\overline{PC}$, and $\overline{PD}$ are radii of $\odot P$, they are congruent. By the SSS Congruence Postulate, $\triangle PCD \cong \triangle PAB$. Because corresponding parts of congruent triangles are congruent, $\angle CPD \cong \angle APB$. With $m\angle CPD = m\angle APB$ and the fact they are both central angles, you now have $m\overset{\frown}{CD} = m\overset{\frown}{AB}$ which leads to $\overset{\frown}{CD} \cong \overset{\frown}{AB}$.
29. a. longer chord
b. The length of a chord in a circle increases as the distance from the center of the circle to the chord decreases.
c. Given radius r and real numbers a and b such that $r > a > b > 0$. Let a be the distance from one chord to the center of the circle and b be the distance from a second chord to the center of the circle. By the Pythagorean Theorem, the length of the chord a units away from the center is $2\sqrt{r^2 - a^2}$ and the length of the chord b units away from the center is $2\sqrt{r^2 - b^2}$. Using properties of real numbers, $\sqrt{r^2 - b^2} > \sqrt{r^2 - a^2}$. **31.** Given: $\overline{QS}$ is perpendicular bisector of $\overline{RT}$ in $\odot L$. Suppose center L is not on $\overline{QS}$. Since $\overline{LT}$ and $\overline{LR}$ are radii of the circle they are congruent. With $\overline{PL} \cong \overline{PL}$, $\triangle RLP \cong \triangle TLP$ by the SSS Congruence Postulate. $\angle RPL$ and $\angle TPL$ are congruent and they form a linear pair. This makes them right angles and leads to $\overline{PL}$ being perpendicular to $\overline{RT}$. By the Perpendicular Postulate, L must be on $\overline{QS}$ and thus $\overline{QS}$ must be a diameter.

10.4 Skill Practice (pp. 676–677) **1.** inscribed **3.** 42° **5.** 10° **7.** 120° **9.** The measure of the arcs add up to 370°; change the measure of $\angle Q$ to 40° or change the measure of $\overset{\frown}{QS}$ to 90°. **11.** $\angle JMK$, $\angle JLK$ and $\angle LKM$, $\angle LJM$ **13.** $x = 100$, $y = 85$ **15.** $a = 20$, $b = 22$ **17. a.** 36°; 180° **b.** about 25.7°; 180° **c.** 20°; 180° **19.** 90° **21.** Yes; opposite angles are 90° and thus are supplementary. **23.** No; opposite angles are not supplementary. **25.** Yes; opposite angles are supplementary.

10.4 Problem Solving (pp. 677–679)
27. 220,000 km

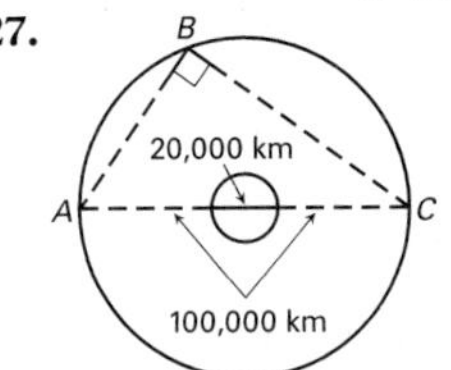

29. Double the length of the radius. **31.** Given $\angle B$ inscribed in $\odot Q$. Let $m\angle B = x°$. Point Q lies on $\overline{BC}$. Since all radii of a circle are congruent, $\overline{AQ} \cong \overline{BQ}$. Using the Base Angles Theorem, $\angle B \cong \angle A$ which implies $m\angle A = x°$. Using the Exterior Angles Theorem, $m\angle AQC = 2x°$ which implies $m\overset{\frown}{AC} = 2x°$. Solving for x, you get $\frac{1}{2}m\overset{\frown}{AC} = x°$. Substituting you get $\frac{1}{2}m\overset{\frown}{AC} = m\angle B$. **33.** Given: $\angle ABC$ is inscribed in $\odot Q$. Point Q is in the exterior of $\angle ABC$; Prove: $m\angle ABC = \frac{1}{2}m\overset{\frown}{AC}$; construct the diameter $\overline{BD}$ of $\odot Q$ and show $m\angle ABD = \frac{1}{2}m\overset{\frown}{AD}$ and $m\angle CBD = \frac{1}{2}m\overset{\frown}{CD}$. Use the Arc Addition Postulate and the Angle Addition Postulate to show $m\angle ABD - m\angle CBD = m\angle ABC$. Then use substitution to show $2m\angle ABC = m\overset{\frown}{AC}$.

35. Case 1: Given: $\odot D$ with inscribed $\triangle ABC$ where $\overline{AC}$ is a diameter of $\odot D$; Prove: $\triangle ABC$ is a right triangle; let E be a point on $\widehat{AC}$. Show that $m\widehat{AEC} = 180°$ and then that $m\angle B = 90°$. Case 2: Given: $\odot D$ with inscribed $\triangle ABC$ with $\angle B$ a right angle; Prove: $\overline{AC}$ is a diameter of $\odot D$; using the Measure of an Inscribed Angle Theorem, show that $m\widehat{AC} = 180°$. **39.** yes

10.5 Skill Practice (pp. 683–684) **1.** outside **3.** 130° **5.** 130° **7.** 115 **9.** 90 **11.** 56 **15.** $m\angle LPJ \le 90°$; if $\overrightarrow{PL}$ is perpendicular to $\overline{KJ}$ at K, then $m\angle LPJ = 90°$, otherwise it would measure less than 90°.
17. 120°, 100°, 140°
19. a.

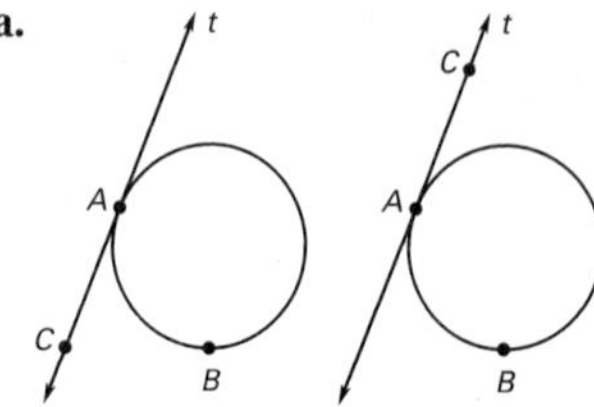

b. $m\widehat{AB} = 2m\angle BAC$, $m\widehat{AB} = 2(180 - m\angle BAC)$
c. when $\overline{AB}$ is perpendicular to line t at point A

10.5 Problem Solving (pp. 685–686) **23.** 50° **25.** about 2.8° **27.** Given $\overleftrightarrow{CA}$ tangent to $\odot Q$ at A and diameter $\overline{AB}$. Using Theorem 10.1, $\overline{AB}$ is perpendicular to $\overleftrightarrow{CA}$. It follows that $m\angle CAB = 90°$. This is half of 180°, which is $m\widehat{AB}$; Case 1: the center of the circle is interior to $\angle CAB$, Case 2: the center of the circle is exterior to $\angle CAB$.

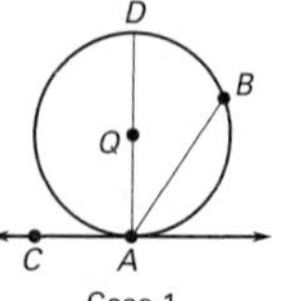

Case 1

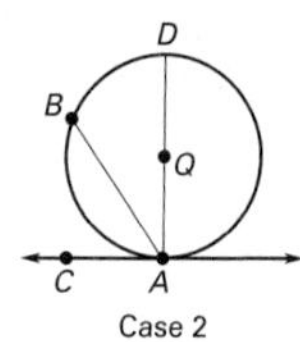

Case 2

Construct diameter $\overline{AD}$. Case 1: Let B be a point on the right semicircle. Use Theorem 10.1 to show $m\angle CAB = 90°$. Use the Angle Addition Postulate and the Arc Addition Postulate to show that $m\angle CAD = \frac{1}{2}m\widehat{AB}$. Case 2: Let B be a point on the left semicircle. Prove similarly to Case 1.

10.6 Skill Practice (pp. 692–693) **1.** external segment **3.** 5 **5.** 4 **7.** 6 **9.** 12 **11.** 4 **13.** 5 **15.** 1 **17.** 18

10.6 Problem Solving (pp. 694–695)

21.

Statements	Reasons
1. Two intersecting chords in the same circle.	1. Given
2. Draw $\overline{AC}$ and $\overline{BD}$.	2. Two points determine a line.
3. $\angle ACD \cong \angle ABD$, $\angle CAB \cong \angle CDB$	3. Theorem 10.8
4. $\triangle AEC \sim \triangle DEB$	4. AA Similarity Postulate
5. $\frac{EA}{ED} = \frac{EC}{EB}$	5. If two triangles are similar, then the ratios of corresponding sides are equal.
6. $EA \cdot EB = EC \cdot ED$	6. Cross Products Property

23. Given: EA is a tangent segment to circle P, ED is a secant segment of circle P, and ED is a diameter of circle P. Prove: $EA^2 = EC \cdot ED$

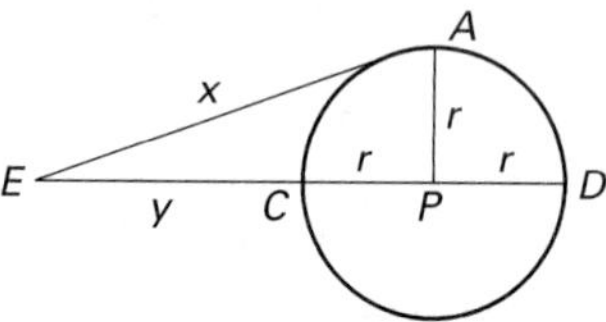

By Theorem 10.1, $EA \perp AP$, so $\triangle EAP$ is a right triangle. By the Pythagorean Theorem, $(y + r)^2 = x^2 + r^2$. So, $y^2 + 2yr + r^2 = x^2 + r^2$. By the Subtraction Property of Equality, $y^2 + 2yr = x^2$. Factoring, this is $y(y + 2r) = x^2$, or $EC \cdot ED = EA^2$.

25. Given $\overline{EB}$ and $\overline{ED}$ are secant segments. Draw $\overline{AD}$ and $\overline{BC}$. Using the Measure of an Inscribed Angle Theorem, $m\angle B = \frac{1}{2}m\widehat{AC}$ and $m\angle D = \frac{1}{2}m\widehat{AC}$ which implies $\angle B \cong \angle D$. Using the Reflexive Property of Angle Congruence, $\angle E \cong \angle E$. Using the AA Similarity Postulate, $\triangle BCE \sim \triangle DAE$. Using corresponding sides of similar triangles are proportional, $\frac{EA}{EC} = \frac{ED}{EB}$. Cross multiplying you get $EA \cdot EB = EC \cdot ED$. **27. a.** 60° **b.** Using the Vertical Angles Theorem, $\angle ACB \cong \angle FCE$. Since $m\angle CAB = 60°$ and $m\angle EFD = 60°$, then $\angle CAB \cong \angle EFD$. Using the AA Similarity Postulate, $\triangle ABC \sim \triangle FEC$. **c.** $\frac{y}{3} = \frac{x + 10}{6}$; $y = \frac{x + 10}{2}$ **d.** $y^2 = x(x + 16)$ **e.** 2, 6 **f.** Since $\frac{CE}{CB} = \frac{2}{1}$, let $CE = 2x$ and $CB = x$. Using Theorem 10.14, $2x^2 = 60$ which implies $x = \sqrt{30}$ which implies $CE = 2\sqrt{30}$.

SELECTED ANSWERS

10.6 Problem Solving Workshop (p. 696) **1.** $2\sqrt{13}$ **3.** $\frac{24}{5}$

Extension (p. 698)

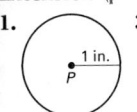

1. **3.**

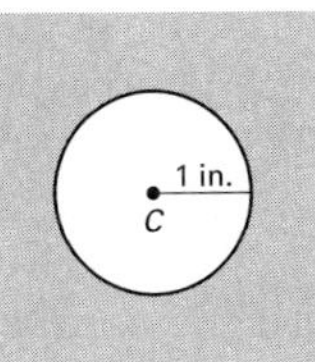

5. The locus of points consists of two points on line ℓ each 3 centimeters away from P.

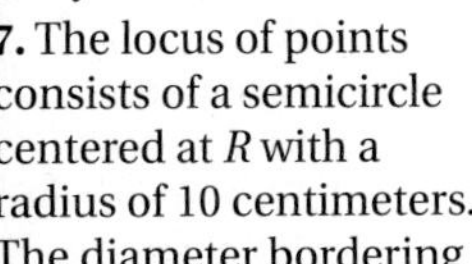

7. The locus of points consists of a semicircle centered at R with a radius of 10 centimeters. The diameter bordering the semicircle is 10 centimeters from line k and parallel to line k.

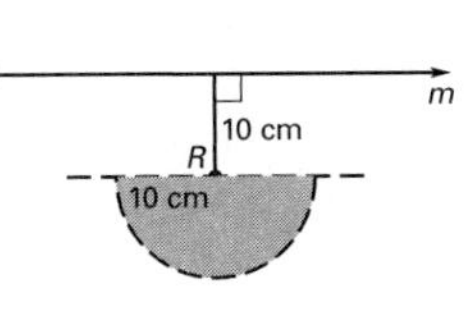

9.

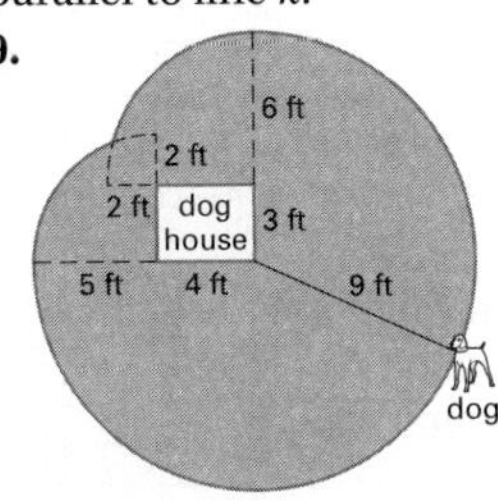

10.7 Skill Practice (pp. 702–703) **1.** center, radius **3.** $x^2 + y^2 = 4$ **5.** $x^2 + y^2 = 400$ **7.** $(x - 50)^2 + (y - 50)^2 = 100$ **9.** $x^2 + y^2 = 49$ **11.** $(x - 7)^2 + (y + 6)^2 = 64$ **13.** $(x - 3)^2 + (y + 5)^2 = 49$ **15.** If (h, k) is the center of a circle with a radius r, the equation of the circle should be $(x - h)^2 + (y - k)^2 = r^2$; $(x + 3)^2 + (y + 5)^2 = 9$. **17.** $x^2 + y^2 = 36$ **19.** $(x + 3)^2 + (y - 5)^2 = 25$

21.

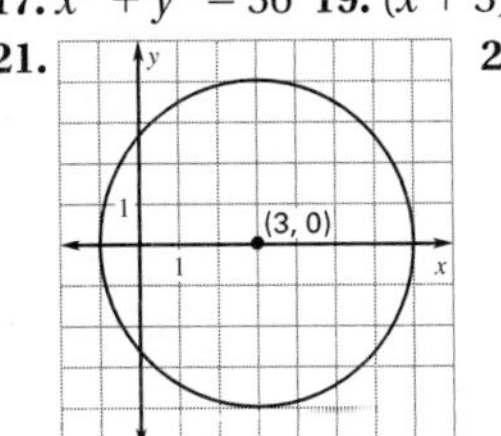

23.

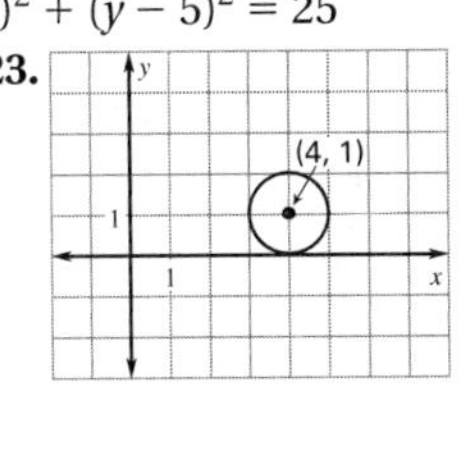

27. circle; $x^2 + (y - 3)^2 = 4$ **29.** circle; $x^2 + (y + 2)^2 = 17$ **31.** secant **33.** secant

10.7 Problem Solving (pp. 703–705) **37.** $x^2 + y^2 = 5.76$, $x^2 + y^2 = 0.09$ **39.** $(x - 3)^2 + y^2 = 49$ **41.** The height (or width) always remains the same as the figure is rolled on its edge. **43. a.** (1, 9), 5 **b.** $(x - 1)^2 + (y - 9)^2 = 169$

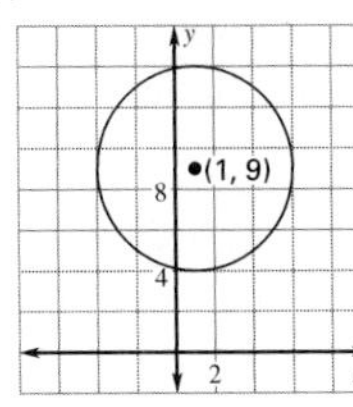

Chapter Review (pp. 708–711) **1.** diameter **3.** The measure of the central angle and the corresponding minor arc are the same. The measure of the major arc is 360° minus the measure of the minor arc. **5.** C **7.** 2 **9.** 12 **11.** 60° **13.** 80° **15.** 65° **17.** $c = 28$ **19.** $q = 100$, $r = 20$ **21.** 16 **23.** $10\frac{2}{3}$ ft **25.** $(x - 8)^2 + (y - 6)^2 = 36$ **27.** $x^2 + y^2 = 81$ **29.** $(x - 6)^2 + (y - 21)^2 = 16$ **31.** $(x - 10)^2 + (y - 7)^2 = 12.25$

Algebra Review (p. 713) **1.** $6x^2(3x^2 + 1)$ **3.** $3r(3r - 5s)$ **5.** $2t(4t^3 + 3t - 5)$ **7.** $y^3(5y^3 - 4y^2 + 2)$ **9.** $3x^2y(2x + 5y^2)$ **11.** $(y - 3)(y + 2)$ **13.** $(z - 4)^2$ **15.** $(5b - 1)(b - 3)$ **17.** $(5r - 9)(5r + 9)$ **19.** $(x + 3)(x + 7)$ **21.** $(y + 3)(y - 2)$ **23.** $(x - 7)(x + 7)$

Chapter 11

11.1 Skill Practice (pp. 723–724) **1.** bases, height **3.** 28 units^2 **5.** 225 units^2 **7.** 216 units^2 **9.** $A = 10(16) = 160$ units^2 or $A = 8(20) = 160$ units^2; the results are the same. **11.** 7 is not the base of the parallelogram; $A = bh = 3(4) = 12$ units^2. **13.** 80 ft, 240 ft^2 **15.** 70 cm, 210 cm^2 **17.** 23 ft **19.** 4 ft, 2 ft

21.

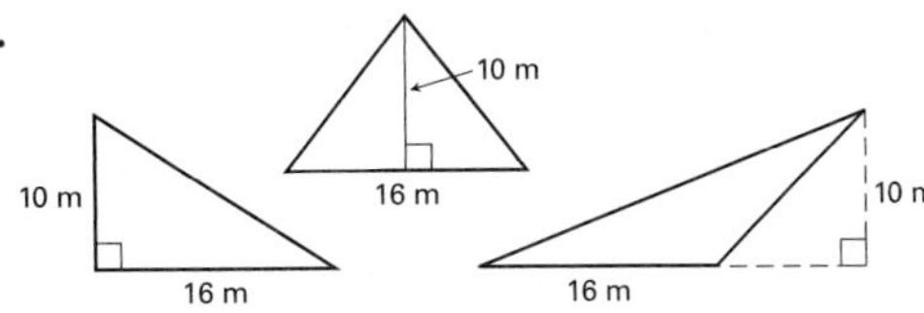

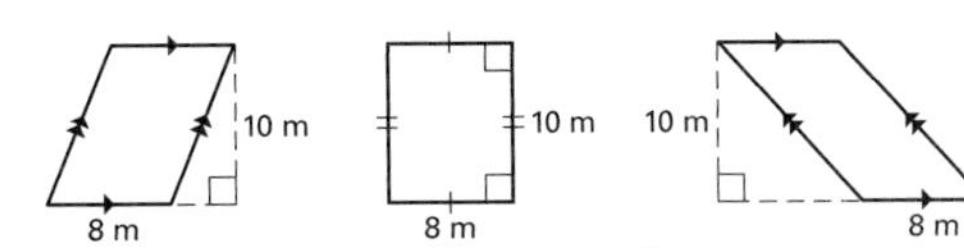

23. 364 cm^2 **25.** 625 in.^{2} **27.** 52 in.^{2}

29. 7.5 units^2

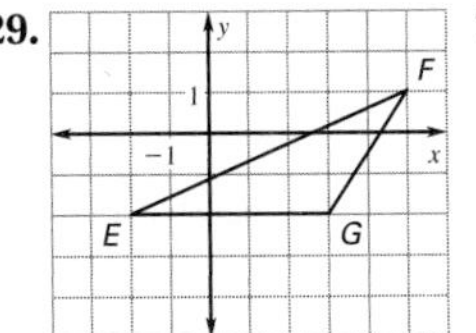

SELECTED ANSWERS

11.1 Problem Solving (pp. 725–726) **37.** 30 min; 86.4 min **39.** No; 2 inch square; the area of a square is side length squared, so $2^2 = 4$. **41.** 23 cm × 34 cm; 611 cm²; 171 cm² **43.** Opposite pairs of sides are congruent making *XYZW* a parallelogram. The area of the parallelogram is *bh*, and since the parallelogram is made of two congruent triangles, the area of one triangle, $\triangle XYW$, is $\frac{1}{2}bh$. **45.** The base and the height are not necessarily side lengths of the parallelogram; yes; no; if the base and height represent a rectangle, then the perimeter is 20 ft, the greatest possible perimeter cannot be determined from the given data.
Extension (p. 728) **1.** Precision depends on the greatest possible error while accuracy depends on the relative error. *Sample answer:* Consider a target, if you are consistently hitting the same area, that is precision, if you hit the bull's eye, that is accuracy. **3.** 1 m; 0.5 m **5.** $\frac{1}{16}$ yd; $\frac{1}{32}$ yd **7.** about 1.8% **9.** about 0.04% **11.** This measurement is more accurate if you are measuring large items, if you are measuring small items, this would not be very accurate. **13.** 18.65 ft is more precise; 18.65 ft is more accurate. **15.** 35 in. is more precise; they are about the same level of accuracy.

11.2 Skill Practice (pp. 733–734) **1.** height **3.** 95 units² **5.** 31 units² **7.** 1500 units² **9.** 189 units² **11.** 360 units² **13.** 13 is not the height of the trapezoid; $A = \frac{1}{2}(12)(14 + 19)$, $A = 198$ cm². **17.** 20 m **19.** 10.5 units² **21.** 10 units² **23.** 5 cm and 13 cm **25.** 168 units² **27.** 67 units² **29.** 42 units²
31. 38 units, 66 units²

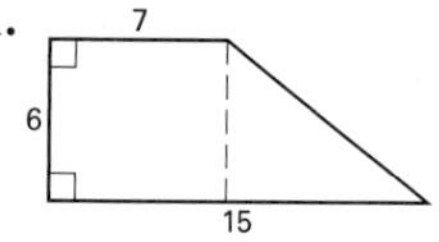

11.2 Problem Solving (pp. 735–736)
35. 20 mm²;

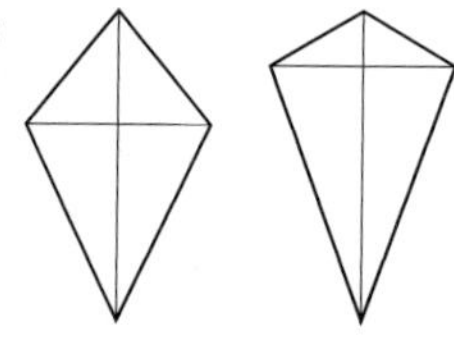

37. a. right triangle and trapezoid **b.** 103,968 ft²; 11,552 yd² **39.** If the kite in the activity were a rhombus, the results would be the same.
41. $A_{\triangle PSR} = \frac{1}{2}\left(\frac{1}{2}d_1\right)d_2$ and $A_{\triangle PQR} = \frac{1}{2}\left(\frac{1}{2}d_1\right)d_2$, so $A_{\triangle PSR} = \frac{1}{4}d_1d_2$ and $A_{\triangle PQR} = \frac{1}{4}d_1d_2$; $A_{PQRS} = A_{\triangle PQR} + A_{\triangle PSR}$
$A_{PQRS} = \frac{1}{4}d_1d_2 + \frac{1}{4}d_1d_2 = \frac{1}{2}d_1d_2$

11.3 Skill Practice (pp. 740–741)
1.

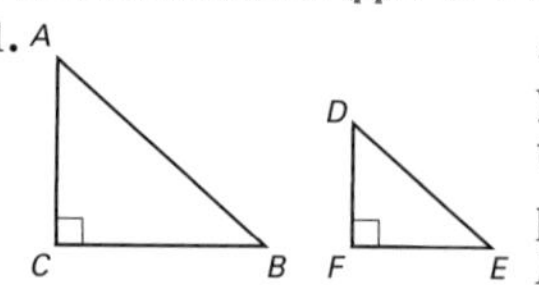

$\triangle ABC \sim \triangle DEF$ tells you that the sides in the same position are proportional. *AB* and *DE* are corresponding side lengths because the sides are both the hypotenuse of their respective triangle and are listed in the same order in the similarity statement. **3.** 6 : 11, 36 : 121 **5.** 1 : 3, 1 : 9; 18 ft² **7.** 7 : 9, 49 : 81; about 127 in.² **9.** 7 : 4 **11.** 11 : 12 **13.** 8 cm **15.** The ratio of areas is 1 : 4, so the ratio of side lengths is 1 : 2; $ZY = 2(12) = 24$. **17.** 175 ft²; 10 ft, 5.6 ft **19.** Never; doubling the side length of a square always quadruples the area. **21.** The triangles are similar since the ratio of sides is 3 : 4. So, the ratio of areas must be 9 : 16. Use this ratio with the area of $\triangle ABC$ to find the area of $\triangle DEF$. **23.** AA Similarity Postulate; $\frac{10}{35} = \frac{2}{7}$ is the ratio of side lengths, so the ratio of areas is 4 : 49.

11.3 Problem Solving (pp. 742–743) **27.** 15 ft
31. There were twice as many mysteries read, but the area of the mystery bar is 4 times the area of the science fiction bar, giving the impression that 4 times as many mysteries were read.

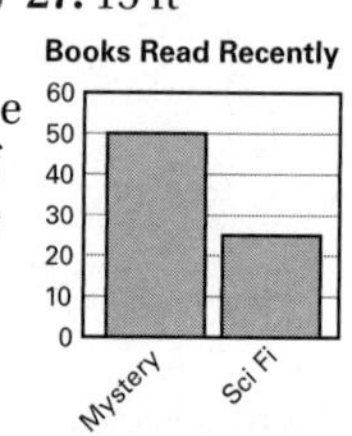

33. a. $\triangle ACD \sim \triangle AEB$, $\triangle BCF \sim \triangle DEF$; AA Similarity Postulate **b.** *Sample answer:* 100 : 81 **c.** $\frac{10}{9} = \frac{20}{10 + x}$, $180 = 100 + 10x$, $x = 8$ OR $20(9) = (10 + x)(10)$, $180 = 100 + 10x$, $x = 8$

11.3 Problem Solving Workshop (p. 744) **1.** 18 in. **3.** $s\sqrt{2}$

11.4 Skill Practice (pp. 749–751) **1.** arc length of $\widehat{AB}$, 360° **3.** about 37.70 in. **5.** about 10.03 ft **7.** 14 m **9.** about 31.42 units **11.** about 4.19 m **13.** about 3.14 ft **15.** 300° **17.** 150° **19.** about 20.94 ft **21.** about 50° **23.** about 8.58 units **25.** about 21.42 units **27.** 6π **29.** $r = \frac{C}{2\pi}$; $d = \frac{C}{\pi}$; $r = 13$, $d = 26$ **31. a.** twice as large **b.** twice as large

11.4 Problem Solving (pp. 751–752) **35.** 21 feet 8 inches represents the circumference of the tree, so if you divide by π, you will get the diameter; about 7 ft. **37.** about 2187 in. **39.** 7.2°; 28,750 mi

Extension (p. 754) **1.** Equator and longitude lines; latitude lines; the equator and lines of longitude

SELECTED ANSWERS

have the center of Earth as the center. Lines of latitude do not have the center of Earth as the center. **3.** If two lines intersect then their intersection is exactly 2 points. **5.** 4π

11.5 Skill Practice (pp. 758–759) **1.** sector **3.** 25π in.^{2}; 78.54 in.^{2} **5.** 132.25π cm^2; 415.48 cm^2 **7.** about 7 m **9.** 52 cm **11.** about 52.36 in.^{2}, about 261.80 in.^{2} **13.** about 937.31 m^2, about 1525.70 cm^2 **15.** about 66.04 cm^2 **17.** about 7.73 m^2 **21.** about 57.23 in. **23.** about 66.24 in. **25.** about 27.44 in. **27.** about 33.51 ft^2 **29.** about 1361.88 cm^2 **31.** about 7.63 m^2 **33.** For any two circles the ratio of their circumferences is equal to the ratio of their radii; for any two circles, if the length of their radii is in the ratio of $a:b$, then the ratio of their areas is $a^2:b^2$; all circles are similar, so you do not need to include similarity in the hypothesis.

35. *Sample:* 2:1

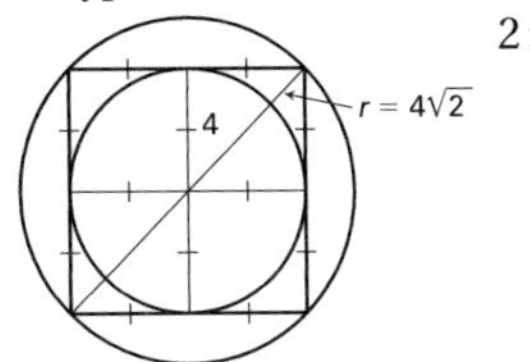

11.5 Problem Solving (pp. 760–761)
37. about 314.16 mi^2 **39. a.** The data is in percentages.
b. bus: 234°, walk: 90°, other: 36°

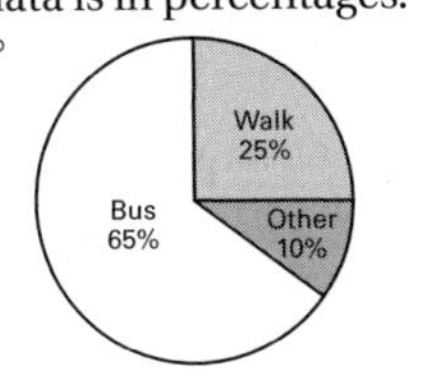

c. bus: $\frac{13}{20}\pi r^2$, walk: $\frac{1}{4}\pi r^2$, other: $\frac{1}{10}\pi r^2$ **41. a.** old: about 371 mm^2, new: 682 mm^2; about 84%
b. *Sample answer:* No, the increase in overall area of the "a" is about 30%, which is much less than the percent increase in the interior area.

11.6 Skill Practice (pp. 765–766) **1.** F **3.** 6.8 **5.** Divide 360° by the number of sides n of the polygon. **7.** 20° **9.** 51.4° **11.** 22.5° **13.** 135° **15.** about 289.2 units^2 **17.** 7.5 is not the measure of a side length, it is the measure of the base of the triangle, it needs to be doubled to become the measure of the side length; $A = \frac{1}{2}a \cdot ns$, $A \approx \frac{1}{2}(13)(6)(15) = 585$ units^2. **19.** about 122.5 units, about 1131.8 units^2 **21.** 63 units, about 294.3 units^2 **23.** apothem, side length; special right triangles or trigonometry; about 392 units^2 **25.** side length; Pythagorean Theorem or trigonometry; about 204.9 units^2 **27.** about 79.6 units^2 **29.** about 1.4 units^2 **31.** True; since the radius is the same, the circle around the n-gons is the same but more and more of the circle is covered as the value of n increases. **33.** False; the radius can be equal to the side length as it is in a hexagon.

11.6 Problem Solving (pp. 767–768) **37.** 1.2 cm, about 4.8 cm^2; about 1.6 cm^2 **39.** 15.5 in.^{2}; 43.0 in.^{2} **41.** $\frac{360}{6} = 60$, so the central angle is 60°. All of the triangles are of the same side length, r, and therefore all six triangles have a vertex on the center with central angle 60° and side lengths r.
43. Because P is both the incenter and circumcenter of $\triangle ABC$ and letting E be the midpoint of $\overline{AB}$, you can show that $\overline{BD}$ and $\overline{CE}$ are both medians of $\triangle ABC$ and they intersect at P. By the Concurrency of Medians of a Triangle Theorem, $BP = \frac{2}{3}BD$ and $CP = \frac{2}{3}CE$. Using algebra, show that $2DP = CP$.
45. a. About 141.4 cm^2; square: about 225 cm^2, pentagon: about 247.7 cm^2, hexagon: about 259.9 cm^2, decagon: about 277 cm^2; the area is getting larger with each larger polygon. **b.** about 286.2 cm^2, about 286.4 cm^2
c.

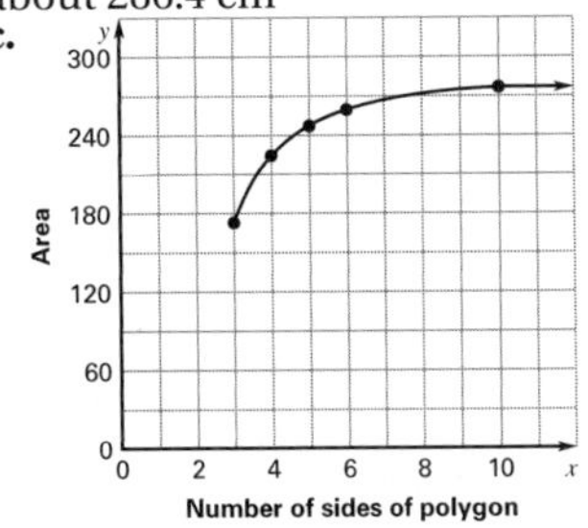

circle; about 286.5 cm^2

11.7 Skill Practice (pp. 774–775) **1.** 0, 1 **3.** $\frac{5}{8}$, 0.625, 62.5% **5.** $\frac{3}{8}$, 0.375, 37.5% **7.** $AD + DE = AE$, so $\frac{5}{8} + \frac{3}{8} = 1$ **9.** $\frac{1}{4}$ or 25% **11.** There is more than a semicircle in the rectangle, so you need to take the area of the rectangle minus the sum of the area of the semicircle and the area of a small rectangle located under the semicircle that has dimensions of 10×2;

$$\frac{10(7) - \left(\frac{1}{2}\pi(5)^2 + 10(2)\right)}{7(10)} = \frac{70 - (12.5\pi + 20)}{70} \approx 0.153 \text{ or}$$

about 15.3%. **13.** $\frac{63}{128}$ or about 49.2% **15.** The two triangles are similar by the AA Similarity Postulate and the ratio of sides is the same; 7:14 or 1:2, so the ratio of the areas is 1:4. **17.** $\frac{2}{7}$ **19.** 1 **21.** $\frac{1}{9}$ or 11.1%; find the area of the whole figure, $\frac{1}{2}(14)(12) = 84$

which is the denominator of the fraction. The top triangle is similar to the whole figure by the AA Similarity Postulate, so use proportions to find the base of the small triangle to be $4\frac{2}{3}$. Since the height of the small triangle is 4, the area is $9\frac{1}{3}$, which is the numerator of the fraction. **25.** about 82.7% **27.** 100%, 50%

11.7 Problem Solving (pp. 776–777) **31. a.** $\frac{2}{5}$ or 40% **b.** $\frac{3}{5}$ or 60% **33.** $\frac{1}{6}$ or about 16.7%

35. The probability stays the same; the sector takes up the same percent of the area of the circle regardless of the length of the radius. *Sample answer:* Let the central angle be 90° and the radius be 2 units. The probability for that sector is $\frac{\frac{4\pi}{4}}{4\pi} = \frac{1}{4}$. Let the radius be doubled. The probability is $\frac{\frac{16\pi}{4}}{16\pi} = \frac{1}{4}$. **37. a.** $\frac{1}{81}$ or about 1.2% **b.** about 2.4% **c.** about 45.4%

Chapter Review (pp. 780–783) **1.** two radii of a circle and their intercepted arc **3.** $\overline{XZ}$ **5.** 60 units^2 **7.** 448 units^2

9. 8 units^2

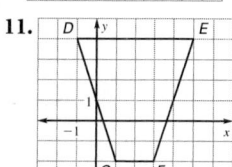

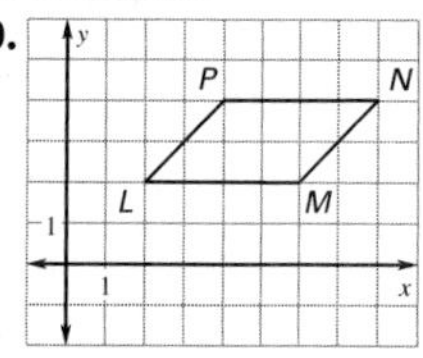

11. 24 units^2

13. 10 : 13, 100 : 169, 152.1 cm^2 **15.** about 30 ft **17.** about 26.09 in. **19.** about 17.72 in.^{2} **21.** about 39.8 in., about 119.3 in.^{2} **23.** $\frac{4}{7}$ or about 57.1% **25.** about 76.1%

Algebra Review (p. 785) **1.** $d = \left(\frac{14.25}{1.5}\right)(2)$; 19 mi **3.** $29.50 + 0.25m = 32.75$; 13 min **5.** $18{,}000(1 - 0.1)^5 = A$; \$10,628.82 **7.** $0 = -16t^2 + 47t + 6$; about 3.06 sec

Chapter 12

12.1 Skill Practice (pp. 798–799) **1.** tetrahedron, 4 faces; hexahedron or cube, 6 faces; octahedron, 8 faces; dodecahedron, 12 faces; icosahedron, 20 faces **3.** Polyhedron; pentagonal pyramid; the solid is formed by polygons and the base is a pentagon. **5.** Not a polyhedron; the solid is not formed by polygons.

7.

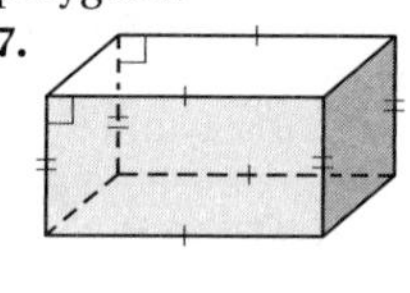

9.

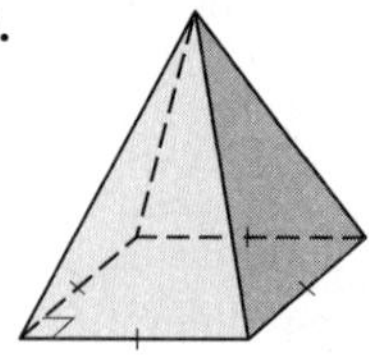

11. 8 **13.** 24 **15.** 4, 4, 6 **17.** 5, 6, 9 **19.** 8, 12, 18 **21.** A cube has six faces, and "hexa" means six. **23.** concave

25. circle

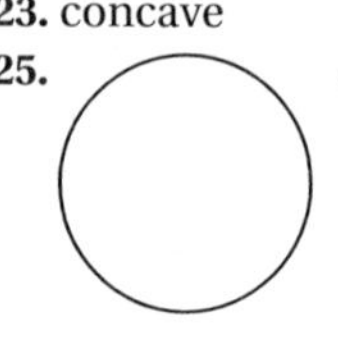

27. triangle

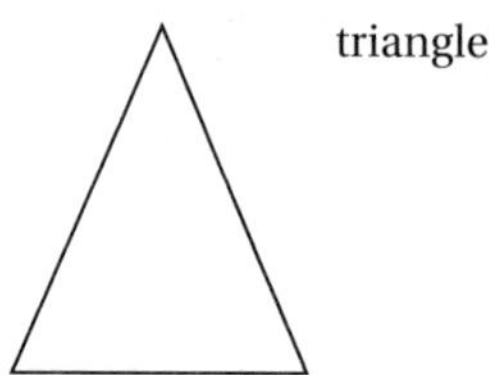

29. The concepts of edge and vertex are confused; the number of vertices is 4, and the number of edges is 6.

12.1 Problem Solving (pp. 800–801) **35.** 18, 12 **37.** square **39.** Tetrahedron; no; you cannot have a different number of faces because of Euler's Theorem. **41. a.** trapezoid

b. Yes. *Sample:*

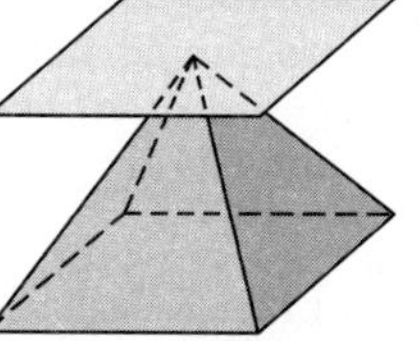

c. square

d. Yes. *Sample:*

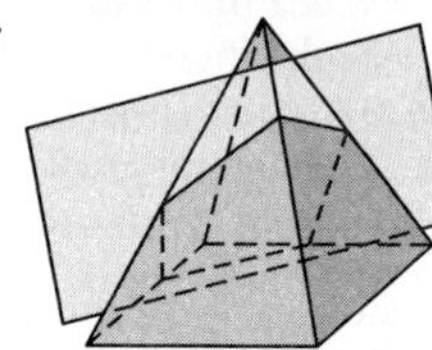

43. no **45.** Yes, but only if the rhombus is a square; *Sample answer:* The plane intersects the cube parallel to a base so it forms a square, which is a rhombus.

47. Yes. *Sample:*

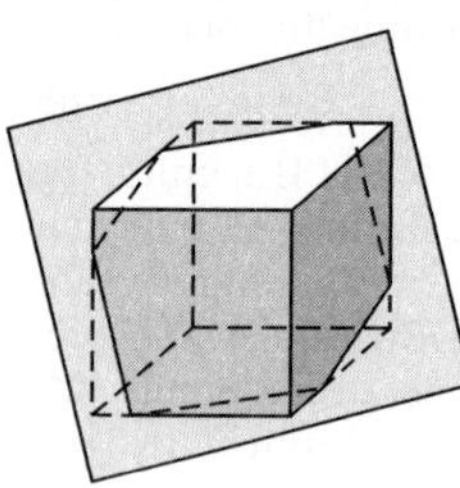

SELECTED ANSWERS

49. a. It will increase the number of faces by 1, the number of vertices by 2, and the number of edges by 3. **b.** It will increase the number of faces by 1, the number of vertices by 2, and the number of edges by 3. **c.** It will not change the number of faces, vertices, or edges. **d.** It will increase the number of faces by 3, the number of vertices by 6, and the number of edges by 9.

12.2 Skill Practice (pp. 806–808)

1.

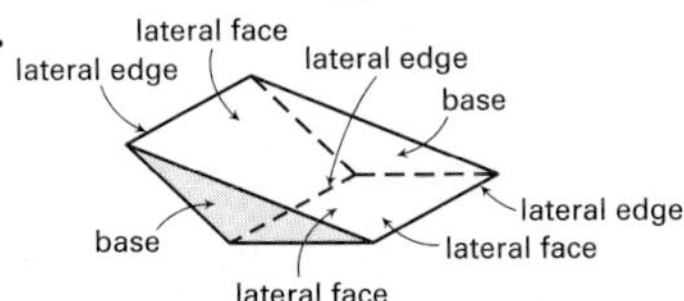

3. 150.80 in.^{2} **5.** 27,513.6 ft^2 **7.** 196.47 m^2 **9.** 14.07 in.^{2} **11.** 804.25 in.^{2} **13.** 9 yd **15.** 10.96 in. **19.** 1119.62 in.^{2}

12.2 Problem Solving (pp. 808–809) **23. a.** 360 in.^{2} **b.** There is overlap in some of the sides of the box. **c.** *Sample answer:* It is easier to wrap a present if you have some overlap of wrapping paper. **27. a.** 54 units^2 **b.** 52 units^2 **c.** When the red cubes are removed, inner faces of the cubes remaining replace the area of the red cubes that are lost. When the blue cubes are removed, there are still 2 faces of the blue cubes whose area is not replaced by inner faces of the remaining cubes. Therefore, the area of the solid after removing blue cubes is 2 units^2 less than the solid after removing red cubes.

29. 989.66 in.^{2}

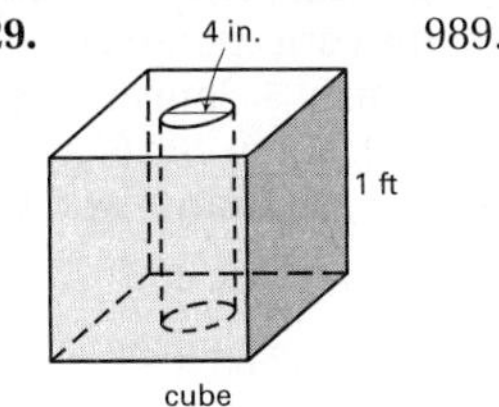

12.3 Skill Practice (pp. 814–815)

1.

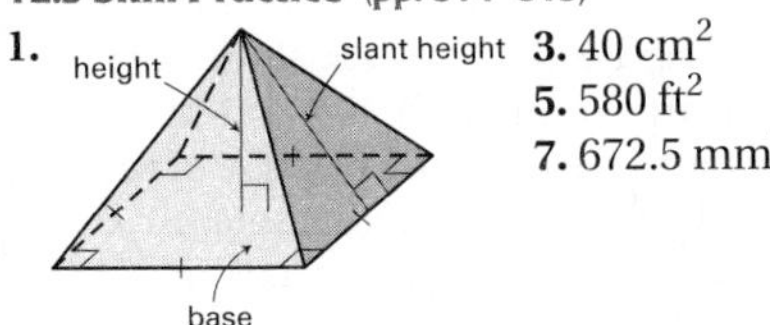

3. 40 cm^2 **5.** 580 ft^2 **7.** 672.5 mm^2

9. The height of the pyramid is used rather than the slant height; $S = 6^2 + \frac{1}{2}(24)(5) = 96$ ft^2. **11.** 12.95 in.^{2} **13.** 238.76 in.^{2} **15.** 226.73 ft^2

19. 981.39 m^2

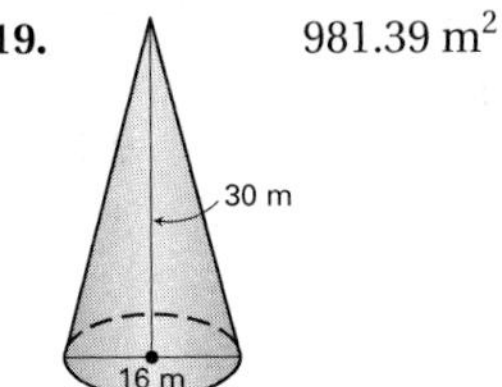

21. 255.53 cm^2

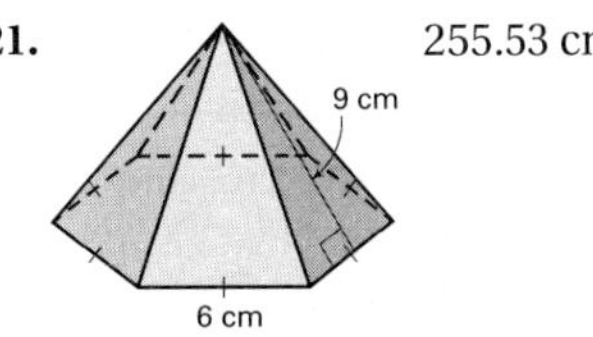

23. 164.05 in.^{2}
25. 27.71 cm^2

12.3 Problem Solving (pp. 816–817) **27.** 96 in.^{2} **29.** square pyramid; 98.35 cm^2
31. a. Given: $\overline{AB} \perp \overline{AC}$; $\overline{DE} \perp \overline{DC}$
Prove: $\triangle ABC \sim \triangle DEC$

Statements	Reasons
1. $\overline{AB} \perp \overline{AC}$; $\overline{DE} \perp \overline{DC}$	1. Given
2. $\angle BAC$ and $\angle EDC$ are right angles.	2. Definition of perpendicular
3. $\angle BAC \cong \angle EDC$	3. Right angles are congruent.
4. $\angle ACB \cong \angle DCE$	4. Reflexive Property
5. $\triangle ABC \sim \triangle DEC$	5. AA Similarity Postulate

b. 5, $\frac{3}{2}$, $\frac{5}{2}$ **c.** larger cone: 24π units^2, smaller cone: 6π units^2; the small cone has 25% of the surface area of the large cone. **33.** about 28.44 mi^2

12.4 Skill Practice (pp. 822–824) **1.** cubic units **5.** 18 units^3 **7.** 175 in.^{3} **9.** 2630.55 cm^3 **11.** 1256.64 in.^{3} **13.** The area of a circle (the base) is πr^2, not $2\pi r$; $V = \pi r^2 h = \pi(4^2)(3) = 48\pi$ ft^3. **15.** 10 in. **17.** 8 in. **19.** 821.88 ft^3 **23.** 12.65 cm **25.** 2814.87 ft^3

12.4 Problem Solving (pp. 824–825) **29. a.** 720 in.^{3} **b.** 720 in.^{3} **c.** They are the same. **31.** 159.15 ft^3 **33. a.** 4500 in.^{3} **b.** 75 in.^{3} **c.** 20 rocks

12.4 Problem Solving Workshop (p. 827) **1. a.** about 63.45 in.^{3} **b.** about 63.45 in.^{3} **3.** $r = \frac{R\sqrt{2}}{2}$ **5.** about 7.33 in.^{3}

12.5 Skill Practice (pp. 832–833) **1.** A triangular prism is a solid with two bases that are triangles and parallelograms for the lateral faces, while a triangular pyramid is a solid with a triangle for a base and triangles for lateral faces.

SA41

prism pyramid

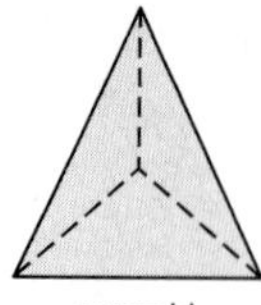

3. 50 cm^3 **5.** 13.33 in.^{3} **7.** 6 in.^{3} **9.** The slant height is used in the volume formula instead of the height; $V = \frac{1}{3}\pi(9^2)(12) = 324\pi \approx 1018$ ft^3. **13.** 6 in. **15.** 3716.85 ft^3 **17.** 987.86 cm^3 **19.** 8.57 cm **21.** 833.33 in.^{3} **23.** 16.70 cm^3 **25.** 26.39 yd^3

27. about 91.63 m^3

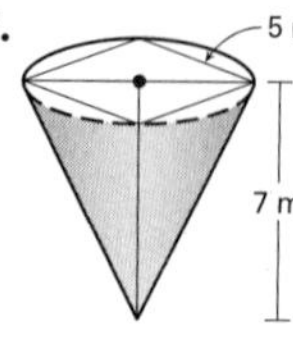

12.5 Problem Solving (pp. 834–836) **29. a.** 201 in.^{3} **b.** 13.4 in.^{3} **31.** 3; since the cone and cylinder have the same radius and height, the volume of the cone will be $\frac{1}{3}$ the volume of the cylinder.

33. 23.70 in.^{3}

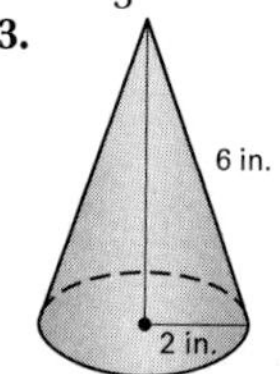

35. a. The volume doubles. **b.** The volume is multiplied by 4. **c.** If you replace the height h by $2h$ in the volume formula, it will multiply the volume by 2. If you replace the side length s by $2s$ in the volume formula, it will multiply the volume by 4 because $(2s)^2 = 4s^2$. **37.** about 78 in.^{3}

39. a. $V_{\text{cone}} = \frac{1}{3}Bh = \frac{1}{3}\pi r^2 \cdot h = \frac{\pi\left(\frac{1}{2}h\right)^2 \cdot h}{3} = \frac{\pi h^3}{12}$, where B is the area of the base of the cone, r is the radius, and h is the height

b.

Time (min)	Height h (m)
1	1.90
2	2.40
3	2.74
4	3.02
5	3.25

c.

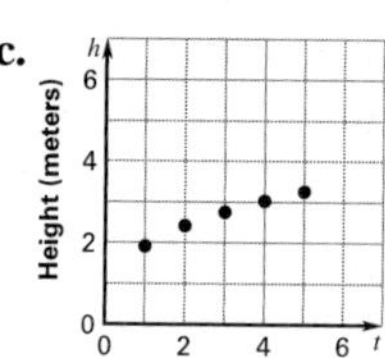

No; the points of the graph do not lie in a straight line.

41. a. $h_1 = \frac{r_1 h_2}{r_2 - r_1}$ **b.** $V = \frac{\pi r_2^2(h_1 + h_2)}{3} - \frac{\pi r_1^2 h_1}{3} = \frac{\pi r_2^2(\frac{r_1 h_2}{r_2 - r_1} + h_2)}{3} - \frac{\pi r_1^2(\frac{r_1 h_2}{r_2 - r_1})}{3}$

12.6 Skill Practice (pp. 842–843) **1.** $S = 4\pi r^2$, $V = \frac{4}{3}\pi r^3$, where r is the radius of the sphere **3.** 201.06 ft^2 **5.** 1052.09 m^2 **7.** 4.8 in. **9.** about 144.76 in.^{2} **11.** about 7359.37 cm^2 **13.** 268,082.57 mm^3 **15.** The radius should be cubed; $V = \frac{4}{3}\pi r^3 = \frac{4}{3}\pi(8)^3 \approx 682.67\pi \approx 2144.66$ ft^3. **17.** 2.80 cm **19.** 6 ft **21.** 247.78 in.^{2}, 164.22 in.^{3} **23.** 358.97 cm^2, 563.21 cm^3 **25.** 13 in.; 676π in.^{2}; $\frac{8788}{3}\pi$ in.^{3} **27.** 21 m; 42π m; 1764π m^2

12.6 Problem Solving (pp. 844–845) **31.** about 98,321,312 mi^2 **33. a.** 8.65 in.^{3} **b.** 29.47 in.^{3} **35. a.** about 80,925,856 mi^2, about 197,359,488 mi^2 **b.** about 41% **37.** 324π in.^{2}, 972π in.^{3}

12.7 Skill Practice (pp. 850–852) **1.** They are the same type of solid and corresponding linear measures have the same ratio. **3.** Not similar; the corresponding dimensions are not in the same ratio. **5.** Similar; each corresponding ratio is 3 : 4. **9.** about 166.67 m^2, about 127.21 m^3 **11.** The volumes are related by the third power; $\frac{500\pi}{\text{Volume of B}} = \frac{1^3}{4^3}$. **13.** 1 : 3 **15.** 4 : 3 **17.** 1 : 4 **19.** about 341.94 ft^2, about 502.65 ft^3 **21.** about 272.97 in.^{2}, about 73.61 in.^{3} **23.** $r = 3$ ft, $h = 6$ ft; $r = 8$ ft, $h = 16$ ft

12.7 Problem Solving (pp. 852–853) **25.** about 8.04 fl oz **27.** 27 fl oz **29. a.** large orange: about 33.51 in.^{3}, small orange: about 17.16 in.^{3} **b.** The ratio of the volumes is the cube of the ratio of diameters. **c.** large orange: 3.75 in., small orange: 2.95 in. **d.** The ratio of surface area multiplied by the ratio of the corresponding diameters equals the ratio of the volumes. **31. a.** 144 in. **b.** 3920.4 in.^{2} **c.** 1.5 in.^{3} **33.** About 11.5 kg; the ratio of the small snowball to the medium snowball is 5 : 7, so the ratio of their volumes is $5^3 : 7^3$. Solve $\frac{5^3}{7^3} = \frac{1.2}{x}$ to find the weight of the middle ball. Similarly, find the weight of the large ball.

Chapter Review (pp. 857–860) **1.** sphere **3.** 12 **5.** 36 **7.** 2035.75 ft^2 **9.** 9 m **11.** 14.29 cm **13.** 11.34 m^3 **15.** 27.53 yd^3 **17.** 12 $in.^2$ **19.** 272.55 m^3 **21.** $1008\pi\ m^2$; $4320\pi\ m^3$

Cumulative Review (pp. 866–867) **1.** 75 **3.** 16 **5.** 4 **7.** Both pairs of opposite angles are congruent. **9.** The diagonals bisect each other. **11.** 45 **13.** about 36.35 $in.^2$ **15.** about 2.28 m^2 **17.** 131.05 $in.^2$, 80.67 $in.^3$ **19.** (4, 2) **21. a.** $(x + 2)^2 + (y - 4)^2 \le 36$ **b.** (2, 0): yes, because it is a solution of the inequality; (3, 9): no, because it is not a solution of the inequality; (−6, −1): no, because it is not a solution of the inequality; (−6, 8): yes, because it is a solution of the inequality; (−7, 5): yes, because it is a solution of the inequality. **23. a.** 40.84 $in.^2$, 17.28 $in.^3$ **b.** about 6.91 $in.^3$

Skills Review Handbook

Operations with Rational Numbers (p. 869) **1.** 11 **3.** −15 **5.** −24 **7.** 0.3 **9.** 11.6 **11.** −4.9 **13.** −13.02 **15.** 29.2 **17.** $-\frac{13}{12}$ **19.** $\frac{6}{7}$ **21.** $-\frac{11}{12}$ **23.** $\frac{17}{18}$

Simplifying and Evaluating Expressions (p. 870) **1.** 33 **3.** −1 **5.** 36 **7.** 2.8 **9.** −6 **11.** $25x$ **13.** −36 **15.** −15 **17.** 15 **19.** 1 **21.** $-\frac{6}{5}$ **23.** $\frac{3}{4}$

Properties of Exponents (p. 871) **1.** 25 **3.** $\frac{1}{16}$ **5.** 78,125 **7.** 7^{32} **9.** a^4 **11.** $\frac{5a^5}{b^4}$ **13.** $\frac{81}{n^4}$ **15.** m^2 **17.** $16x^6y^2$ **19.** $\frac{b^2}{5a^3c}$ **21.** $8x$ **23.** $\frac{a^5}{7b^4c}$ **25.** $30x^3y$ **27.** $\frac{3a^{14}}{5b^2c^8}$

Using the Distributive Property (p. 872) **1.** $3x + 21$ **3.** $40n - 16$ **5.** $-x - 6$ **7.** $12x^2 - 8x + 16$ **9.** $-5x^2$ **11.** $2n + 5$ **13.** $5h^3 + 5h^2$ **15.** 10 **17.** $\frac{9}{10}a$ **19.** $3n + 4$ **21.** $2a^2 + 6a - 76$ **23.** $3x^2 - 10x + 5$ **25.** $4a^2 + 2ab - 1$

Binomial Products (p. 873) **1.** $a^2 - 11a + 18$ **3.** $t^2 + 3t - 40$ **5.** $25a^2 + 20a + 4$ **7.** $4c^2 + 13c - 12$ **9.** $z^2 - 16z + 64$ **11.** $2x^2 + 3x + 1$ **13.** $4x^2 - 9$ **15.** $6d^2 + d - 2$ **17.** $k^2 - 2.4k + 1.44$ **19.** $-z^2 + 36$ **21.** $5y^2 + 9y - 32$ **23.** $3x^2 - 17$

Radical Expressions (p. 874) **1.** ± 10 **3.** $\pm\frac{1}{2}$ **5.** no square roots **7.** ± 0.9 **9.** 11 **11.** $-3\sqrt{11}$ **13.** $2\sqrt{5}$ **15.** $3\sqrt{7}$ **17.** $4\sqrt{5}$ **19.** $210\sqrt{2}$ **21.** 137 **23.** 30 **25.** 8 **27.** $2\sqrt{6}$

Solving Linear Equations (p. 875) **1.** 31 **3.** −6 **5.** 39 **7.** 23.2 **9.** 18 **11.** 1 **13.** $\frac{7}{2}$ **15.** −1 **17.** 20 **19.** 16 **21.** −1 **23.** 7 **25.** 6.75 **27.** −0.82 **29.** −4 **31.** $\frac{5}{2}$ **33.** $-\frac{2}{5}$ **35.** $\frac{1}{2}$

Solving and Graphing Linear Inequalities (p. 876)

1. $x < 7$ 

3. $n \le 4$ 

Solving Formulas (p. 877) **1.** $s = \frac{P}{4}$ **3.** $\ell = \frac{V}{wh}$ **5.** $b = \frac{2A}{h}$ **7.** $w = \frac{P}{2} - \ell$ **9.** $C = \frac{5}{9}(F - 32)$ **11.** $h = \frac{S - 2\pi r^2}{2\pi r}$ **13.** $y = -2x + 7$ **15.** $y = 3x + 2$ **17.** $y = \frac{5}{4}x$ **19.** $y = 62 - 15$

Graphing Points and Lines (p. 878) **1.** (3, 1) **3.** (0, 2) **5.** (3, −3)

7–12. 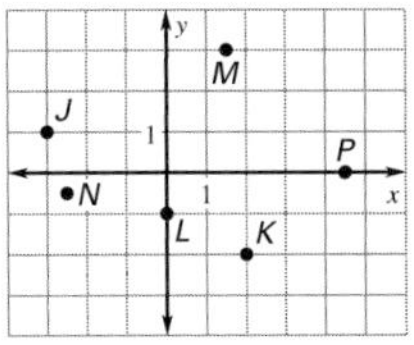

13. 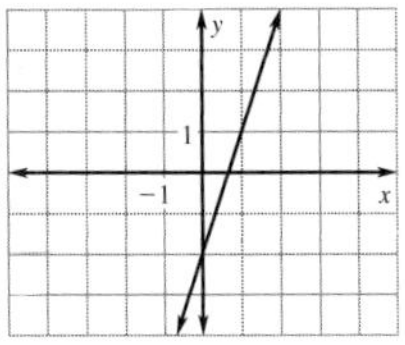

15. 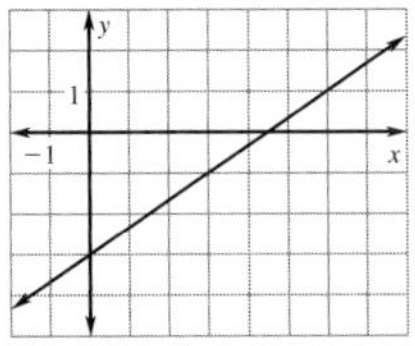

Slope and Intercepts of a Line (p. 879) **1.** $\frac{3}{2}$, x-intercept −2, y-intercept 3 **3.** 0, no x-intercept, y-intercept −2 **5.** x-intercept 3, y-intercept −15 **7.** x-intercept 3, y-intercept 3 **9.** x-intercept 2, y-intercept −6 **11.** x-intercept 0, y-intercept 0

Systems of Linear Equations (p. 880) **1.** (2, 1) **3.** (4, −1) **5.** (6, −3) **7.** (−1, −4) **9.** (3, 2) **11.** (−1, −5) **13.** (−5, 1) **15.** (0.5, −2)

Linear Inequalities (p. 881)

1. 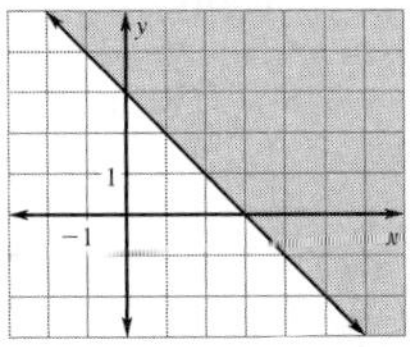

3. 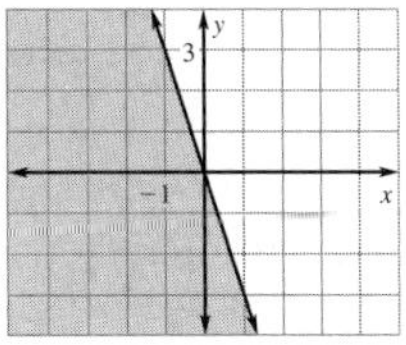

SA43

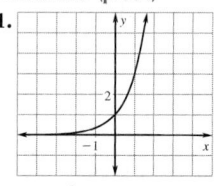

9. 11.

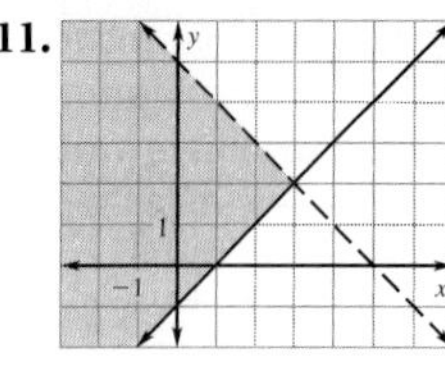

Quadratic Equations and Functions (p. 883)

1. ± 12 **3.** -3 **5.** 0 **7.** -1 **9.** no real solutions **11.** $\pm \frac{\sqrt{5}}{3}$

13. 15.

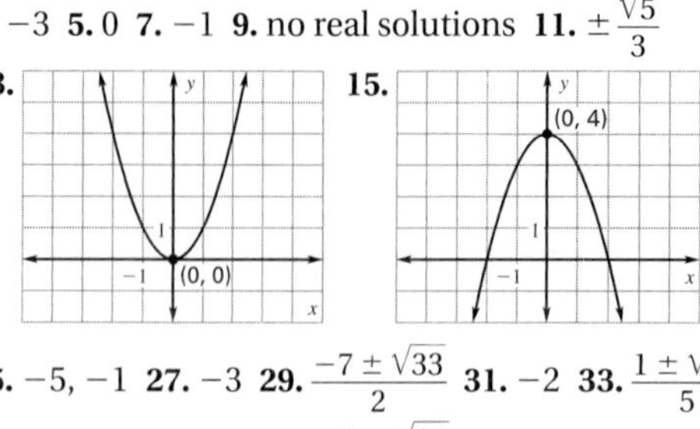

25. $-5, -1$ **27.** -3 **29.** $\frac{-7 \pm \sqrt{33}}{2}$ **31.** -2 **33.** $\frac{1 \pm \sqrt{31}}{5}$ **35.** no real solutions **37.** $\frac{1 \pm \sqrt{61}}{6}$ **39.** $\pm\sqrt{5}$

Functions (p. 884)

1. 3.

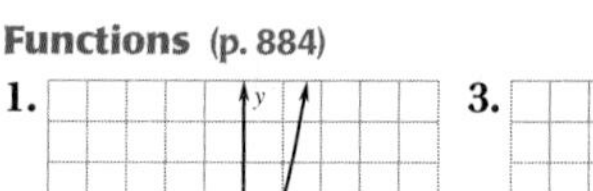

9. $y = x^2$ **11.** $y = 12x$; \$72; 35 h

Problem Solving with Percents (p. 885)

1. 24 questions **3.** yes **5.** 20% **7.** 500 residents **9.** about 50%

Converting Measurements and Rates (p. 886)

1. 5 **3.** 3 **5.** 3.2 **7.** 160 **9.** 63,360 **11.** 576 **13.** 3,000,000 **15.** 6.5 **17.** 1020 **19.** 5104 **21.** 5280 **23.** 90,000,000

Mean, Median, and Mode (p. 887)

1. The mean or the median best represent the given data because all of the values are close to these measures. **3.** The median or the mode best represent the data because all of the values are close to these measures.
5. Median; the mean is too high and the mode is too low. **7.** Mean; there is no mode and the median is too high.

Displaying Data (p. 889)

1. Line graph; this type of graph shows change over time and this is what the storeowner wants to evaluate. **3.** Histogram; this displays data in intervals.

5.

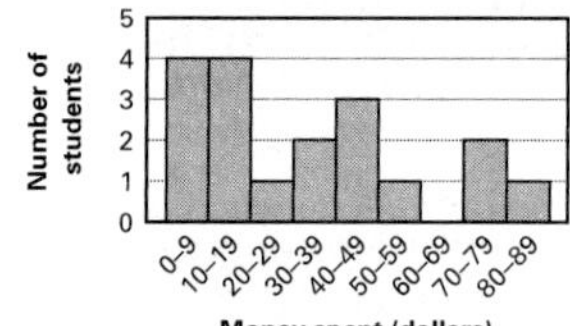

The data is put into intervals; \$0–\$19 and 10–19.

7.

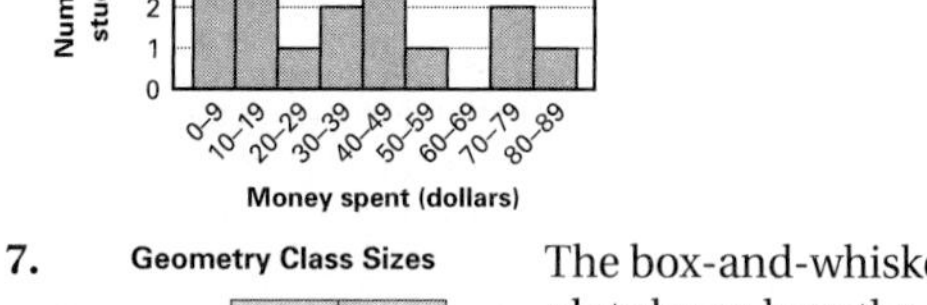

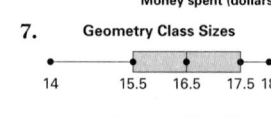

The box-and-whisker plot shows how the class sizes relate to each other.

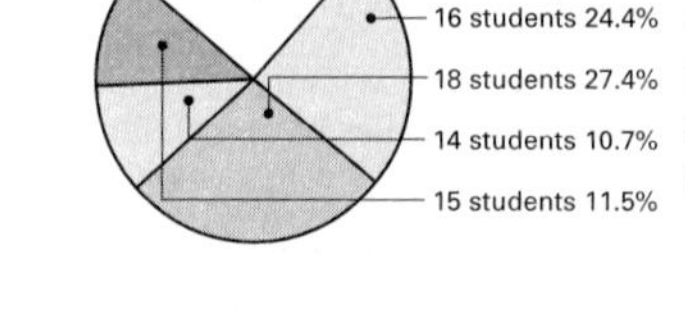

The circle graph shows how each class size contributes to the total number of students enrolled in Geometry.

9.

Stem	Leaves
1	2 3 5 5 6 8 8 9
2	4 5 5 6
3	0 0 2 2 3 5 5 6 7
4	
5	
6	
7	2

Key: 1|2 = 12

12, 72, 25.5, 18, 33

11.

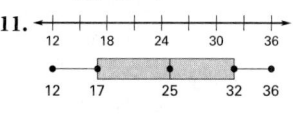

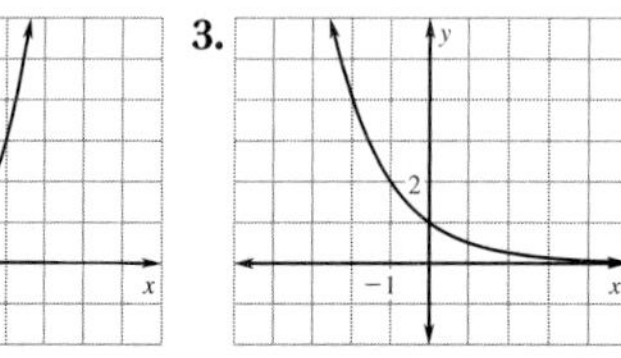

The data is more closely related to the mean and median in the new box-and-whisker plot than before dropping the two highest ages.

Sampling and Surveys (p. 890)

1. Biased sample; the sample is unlikely to represent the entire population of students because only students at a soccer game are asked which day they prefer. **3.** Biased sample; the sample is biased because only people with e-mail can respond. **5.** The sample and the question are random.

Counting Methods (p. 892)

1. 15 outfits **3.** 1,679,616 passwords **5.** 125,000 combinations **7.** 756 pairs **9.** 24 ways

Probability (p. 893)

1. dependent; $\frac{33}{95} \approx 0.347$ or about 34.7% **3.** dependent; $\frac{1}{20} = 0.05$ or 5% **5.** dependent; $\frac{1}{8} = 0.125$ or 12.5%

SELECTED ANSWERS

Extra Practice

Chapter 1 (pp. 896–897) **1.** *Sample answer: A, F, B;* $\overleftrightarrow{AB}$ **3.** *Sample answer:* $\overrightarrow{FA}$, $\overrightarrow{FB}$ **5.** *Sample answer:* $\overleftrightarrow{AB}$ **7.** 43 **9.** 26 **11.** 28 **13.** $(3x - 7) + (3x - 1) = 16$; $x = 4$; $AB = 5$, $BC = 11$; not congruent **15.** $(4x - 5) + (2x - 7) = 54$; $x = 11$; $AB = 39$, $BC = 15$; not congruent **17.** $(3x - 7) + (2x + 5) = 108$; $x = 22$; $AB = 59$, $BC = 49$; not congruent **19.** $\left(-4\frac{1}{2}, 1\right)$ **21.** (1, 1) **23.** (5.1, −8.05) **25.** 10 **27.** 34 **29.** 20 **31.** 104° **33.** 88° **35.** adjacent angles **37.** vertical angles, supplementary **39.** *Sample answer:* $\angle ACE$, $\angle BCF$ **41.** polygon; concave **43.** Not a polygon; part of the figure is not a line segment. **45.** *DFHKB*, pentagon; *ABCDEFGHJK*, decagon **47.** 13 cm **49.** 11 m **51.** about 13.4 units, 4 units^2

Chapter 2 (pp. 898–899) **1.** Add 6 for the next number, then subtract 8 for the next number; 11. **3.** no pattern **5.** Each number is $\frac{1}{3}$ of the previous number; $\frac{1}{81}$. **7.** *Sample answer:* $-8 - (-5) = -3$ **9.** *Sample answer:* $m\angle A = 90°$ **11.** If-then form: if a figure is a square, then it is a four-sided regular polygon; Converse: if a figure is a four-sided regular polygon, then it is a square; Inverse: if a figure is not a square, then it is not a four-sided regular polygon; Contrapositive: if a figure is not a four-sided regular polygon, then it is not a square. **13.** true **15.** If two coplanar lines are not parallel, then they form congruent vertical angles. **17.** might **19.** true **21.** false **23.** true

25.

$4x + 15 = 39$	Write original equation.
$4x = 24$	Subtraction Property of Equality
$x = 6$	Division Property of Equality

27.

$2(-7x + 3) = -50$	Write original equation.
$-14x + 6 = -50$	Distributive Property
$-14x = -56$	Subtraction Property of Equality
$x = 4$	Division Property of Equality

29.

$13(2x - 3) - 20x = 3$	Write original equation.
$26x - 39 - 20x = 3$	Distributive Property
$6x - 39 = 3$	Simplify.
$6x = 42$	Addition Property of Equality
$x = 7$	Division Property of Equality

31. $m\angle JKL$, $m\angle ABC$; Transitive Property of Equality **33.** $m\angle XYZ$; Reflexive Property of Equality

21.

Statements	Reasons
1. $\overline{XY} \cong \overline{YZ} \cong \overline{ZX}$	1. Given
2. $XY = YZ = ZX$	2. Definition of congruence for segments
3. Perimeter of $\triangle XYZ = XY + YZ + ZX$	3. Perimeter formula
4. Perimeter of $\triangle XYZ = XY + XY + XY$	4. Substitution
5. Perimeter of $\triangle XYZ = 3 \cdot XY$	5. Simplify.

37. 23° **39.** 90°

41.

Statements	Reasons
1. $\angle UKV$ and $\angle VKW$ are complements.	1. Given
2. $m\angle UKV + m\angle VKW = 90°$	2. Definition of complementary angles
3. $\angle UKV \cong \angle XKY$, $\angle VKW \cong \angle YKZ$	3. Vertical angles are congruent.
4. $m\angle UKV = m\angle XKY$, $m\angle VKW = m\angle YKZ$	4. Definition of angle congruence
5. $m\angle YKZ + m\angle XKY = 90°$	5. Substitution
6. $\angle YKZ$ and $\angle XKY$ are complements.	6. Definition of complementary angles

Chapter 3 (pp. 900–901) **1.** corresponding **3.** consecutive interior **5.** corresponding **7.** $\angle HLM$ and $\angle MJC$ **9.** $\angle FKL$ and $\angle AML$ **11.** $\overleftrightarrow{BG}$ and $\overleftrightarrow{CF}$ **13.** 68°, 112°; $m\angle 1 = 68°$ because if two parallel lines are cut by a transversal, then the alternate interior angles are congruent, $m\angle 2 = 112°$ because it is a linear pair with $\angle 1$. **15.** 9, 1 **17.** 25, 19 **19.** Yes; if two lines are cut by a transversal so that a pair of consecutive interior angles are supplementary, then the lines are parallel. **21.** Yes; if two lines are cut by a transversal so that alternate interior angles are congruent, then the lines are parallel. **23.** Yes; if two lines are cut by a transversal so that a pair of consecutive interior angles are supplementary, then the lines are parallel. **25.** Neither; the slopes are not equal and they are not opposite reciprocals. **27.** Line 2 **29.** Line 1 **31.** $y = \frac{2}{3}x + 2$ **33.** $y = -2x$ **35.** $y = x + 10$ **37.** $y = \frac{2}{5}x + \frac{38}{5}$ **39.** 69° **41.** 73° **43.** 38° **45.** 1. Given; 2. $\angle ABC$ is a right angle.; 3. Definition of right angle; 4. $\overrightarrow{BD}$ bisects $\angle ABC$.; 5. Definition of angle bisector; 6. $m\angle ABD$, $m\angle DBC$; 7. Substitution Property of Equality; 8. $m\angle ABD$; 9. Simplify; 10. Division Property of Equality

Chapter 4 (pp. 902–903)

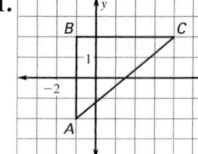

1. 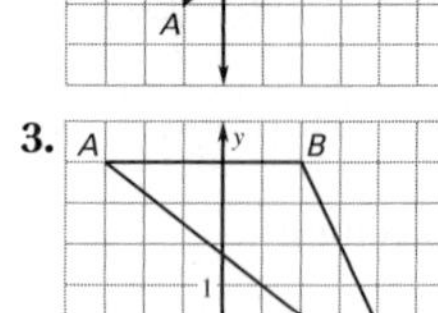 scalene; right triangle

3. 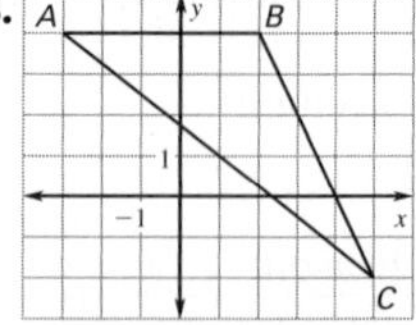 scalene; not a right triangle

5. 58; acute **7.** $\triangle DFG \cong \triangle FDE$; SAS Congruence Postulate or ASA Congruence Postulate
9. $STWX \cong UTWV$; all pairs of corresponding angles and sides are congruent. **11.** 7 **13.** No; a true congruence statement would be $\triangle JKM \cong \triangle LKM$.
15. congruent **17.** $\triangle XUV \cong \triangle VWX$; since $\overline{XV} \cong \overline{XV}$, with the givens you can use the HL Congruence Theorem. **19.** $\triangle HJL \cong \triangle KLJ$; use alternate interior angles to get $\angle HJL \cong \angle JLK$. Since $\overline{JL} \cong \overline{JL}$, with the given you can use the SAS Congruence Postulate.
21. yes; AAS Congruence Theorem **23.** Yes; use the ASA Congruence Postulate. **25.** State the givens from the diagram, and state that $\overline{AC} \cong \overline{AC}$ by the Reflexive Property of Congruence. Then use the SAS Congruence Postulate to prove $\triangle ABC \cong \triangle CDA$, and state $\angle 1 \cong \angle 2$ because corresponding parts of congruent triangles are congruent.
27. State the givens from the diagram and state that $\overline{SR} \cong \overline{SR}$ by the Reflexive Property of Congruence. Then use the Segment Addition Postulate to show that $\overline{PR} \cong \overline{US}$. Use the SAS Congruence Postulate to prove $\triangle QPR \cong \triangle TUS$, and state $\angle 1 \cong \angle 2$ because corresponding parts of congruent triangles are congruent. **29.** $AB = DE = \sqrt{26}$; $AC = DF = \sqrt{41}$; $BC = EF = \sqrt{17}$; $\triangle ABC \cong \triangle DEF$ by the SSS Congruence Postulate, and $\angle A \cong \angle D$ because corresponding parts of congruent triangles are congruent. **31.** $x = 6, y = 48$ **33.** $x = 2$
35. $x = 28, y = 29$

37. 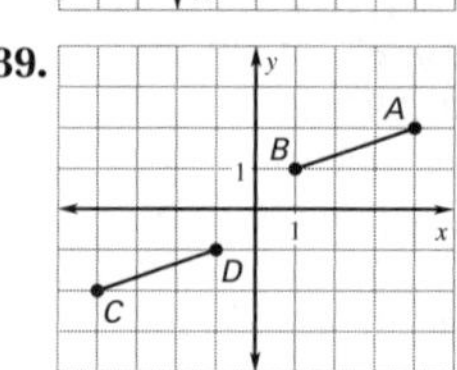

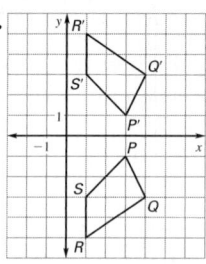

39. yes; 180°

Chapter 5 (pp. 904–905) **1.** $\overline{AB}$ **3.** $\overline{AC}$ **5.** LC, AL
7. *Sample answer:* 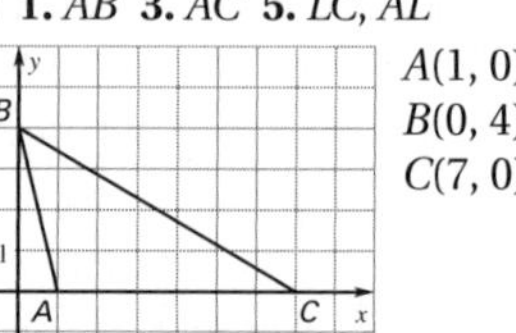 $A(1, 0)$, $B(0, 4)$, $C(7, 0)$

9. 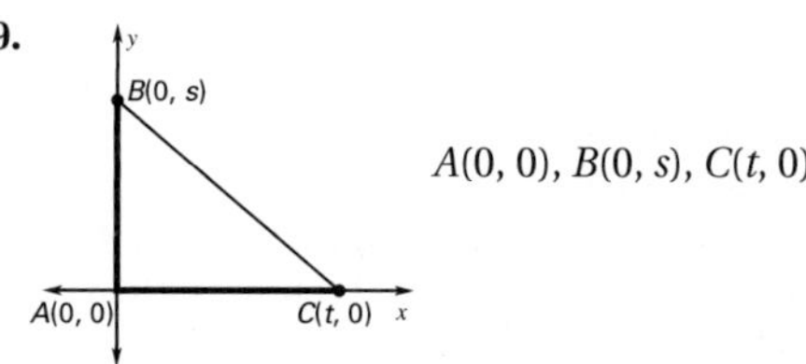 $A(0, 0)$, $B(0, s)$, $C(t, 0)$

11. 14 **13.** 12 **15.** 24 **17.** yes **19.** 15 **21.** No; there is not enough information. **23.** Yes; $x = 17$ by the Angle Bisector Theorem. **25.** 17 **27.** 8 **29.** angle bisector
31. perpendicular bisector **33.** perpendicular bisector and angle bisector **35.** $\overline{JK}, \overline{LK}, \overline{JL}, \angle L, \angle J, \angle K$
37. 1 in. $< \ell <$ 17 in. **39.** 6 in. $< \ell <$ 12 in.
41. 2 ft $< \ell <$ 10 ft **43.** $>$ **45.** $>$ **47.** $=$ **49.** $>$ **51.** $<$

Chapter 6 (pp. 906–907) **1.** 20°, 60°, 100° **3.** 36°, 54°, 90°
5. 4 **7.** 10 **9.** −10 **11.** 10 **13.** 6 **15.** 12 **17.** $\frac{y}{9}$ **19.** 4
21. similar; $RQPN \sim STUV$, 11 : 20 **23.** 3 : 1
25. $\triangle PQR$: 90, $\triangle LMN$: 30 **27.** angle bisector, 7
29. not similar **31.** Similar; $\triangle JKL \sim \triangle NPM$; since $\overline{JK} \parallel \overline{NP}$ and $\overline{KL} \parallel \overline{PM}$, $\angle J \cong \angle PNM$ and $\angle L \cong \angle PMN$ by the Corresponding Angles Postulate. Then the triangles are similar by the AA Similarity Postulate.
33. Since $\frac{KH}{TS} = \frac{KJ}{TR} = \frac{HJ}{SR} = \frac{3}{5}$, $\triangle KHJ \sim \triangle TSR$ by the SSS Similarity Theorem. **35.** $x = 3, y = 8.4$

37. 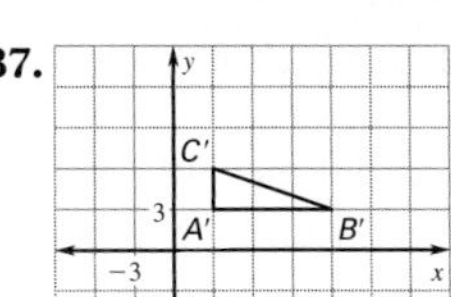

39. 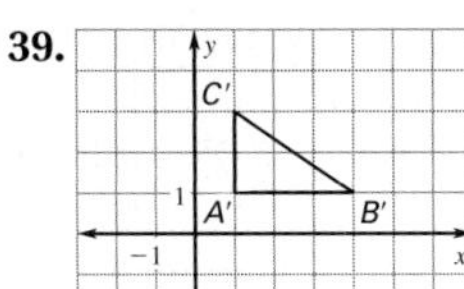

41. enlargement; 1 : 3

Chapter 7 (pp. 908–909) **1.** 50 **3.** 60 **5.** 240 ft^2 **7.** right triangle **9.** not a right triangle **11.** right triangle **13.** triangle; acute **15.** not a triangle **17.** triangle; acute **19.** $\triangle ADB \sim \triangle BDC \sim \triangle ABC$; DB **21.** $\triangle PSQ \sim \triangle QSR \sim \triangle PQR$; RP **23.** 2 **25.** 4.8 **27.** 9.7 **29.** $g = 9$, $h = 9\sqrt{3}$ **31.** $m = 5\sqrt{3}$, $n = 10$ **33.** $v = 20$, $w = 10$ **35.** $\frac{3}{5}$, 0.6; $\frac{5}{3}$, 1.6667 **37.** 6.1 **39.** 16.5 **41.** $x = 12.8$, $y = 15.1$ **43.** $x = 7.5$, $y = 7.7$ **45.** $x = 16.0$, $y = 16.5$ **47.** $GH = 9.2$, $m\angle G = 49.4°$, $m\angle H = 40.6°$

Chapter 8 (pp. 910–911) **1.** 112 **3.** 117 **5.** 68 **7.** 120°, 60° **9.** about 158.8°, about 21.2° **11.** $a = 5$, $b = 5$ **13.** $a = 117°$, $b = 63°$ **15.** $a = 7$, $b = 3$ **17.** $\angle XYV$ **19.** YV **21.** ZX

23. 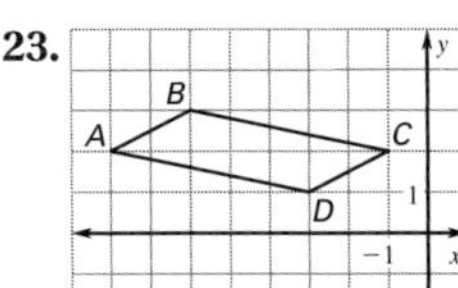

$\overline{AB} \parallel \overline{DC}$, $\overline{AD} \parallel \overline{BC}$

25. 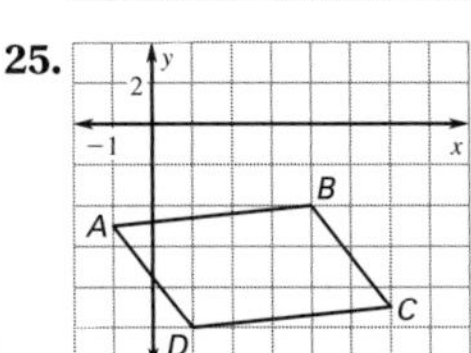

$\overline{AB} \parallel \overline{DC}$, $\overline{AD} \parallel \overline{BC}$

27. Show $\angle QPR \cong \angle SRP$ making $\angle SPQ \cong \angle QRS$. You now have opposite pairs of angles congruent which makes the quadrilateral a parallelogram. **29.** Square; since the quadrilateral is both a rectangle and rhombus it is a square. **31.** Rectangle; since the quadrilateral is a parallelogram with congruent diagonals it is a rectangle. **33.** 90° **35.** 25 **37.** 0.4 **39.** 98° **41.** Parallelogram; the diagonals bisect one another. **43.** Rhombus; it is a parallelogram with perpendicular diagonals. **45.** Isosceles trapezoid; it has one pair of parallel opposite sides and congruent base angles. **47.** Kite; it has consecutive pairs of congruent sides and perpendicular diagonals. **49.** Trapezoid; it has one pair of parallel sides.

Chapter 9 (pp. 912–913) **1.** $(x, y) \rightarrow (x + 4, y - 2)$; $AB = A'B'$, $BC = B'C'$, $AC = A'C'$ **3.** $\langle -10, 7 \rangle$ **5.** $\langle -4, 5 \rangle$ **7.** $\begin{bmatrix} 5 \\ 11 \end{bmatrix}$ **9.** $\begin{bmatrix} -4 & -31 \\ 64 & 67 \end{bmatrix}$

11. $\begin{bmatrix} 2 & 10 & 5 & 4 \\ -2 & -1 & -3 & -5 \end{bmatrix}$

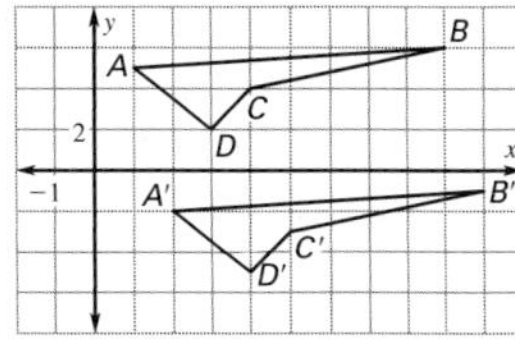

13. $\begin{bmatrix} 5 & 2 & 0 & -2 & -1 \\ 4 & 1 & 1 & 1 & 7 \end{bmatrix}$

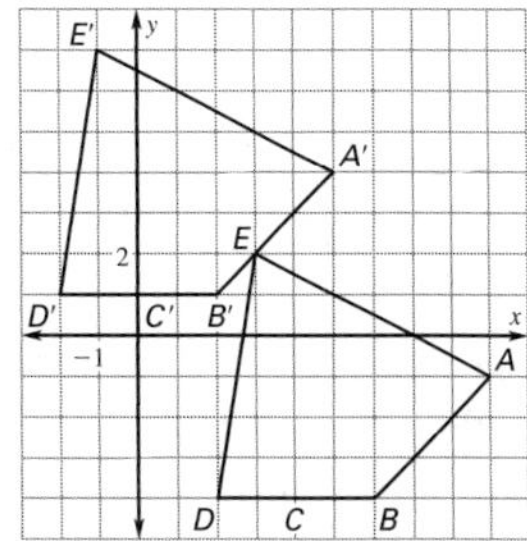

15. 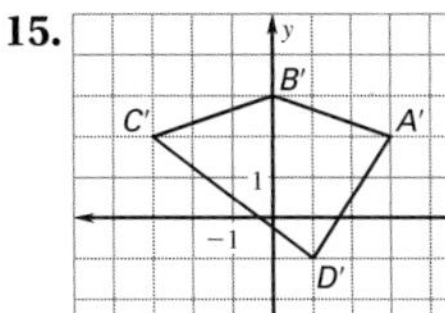

17. $A'(1, 2)$, $B'(2, -4)$, $C'(0, -1)$ **19.** $A'(-1, 2)$, $B'(-1, 5)$, $C'(2, 6)$, $D'(3, 3)$, $E'(1, -1)$

21. $\begin{array}{ccc} S' & T' & V' \end{array}$ $\begin{bmatrix} -2 & 3 & 0 \\ 4 & 2 & 1 \end{bmatrix}$

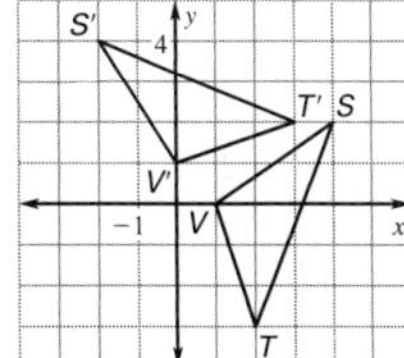

23. 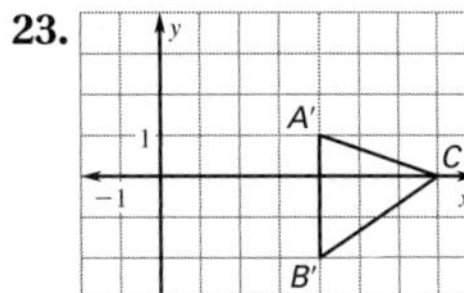

25. 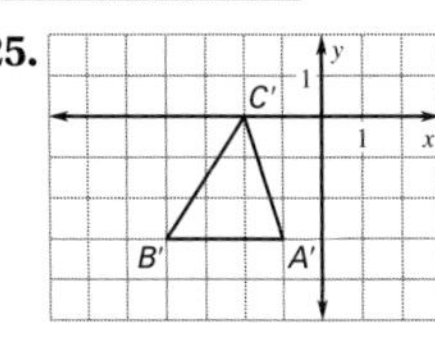

27. 88° **29.** Line symmetry, rotational symmetry; the flag has two lines of symmetry, one line passing horizontally through the center of the circle and the other passing vertically through the center of the circle; it has rotational symmetry of 180°. **31.** Line symmetry, no rotational symmetry; the flag has one line of symmetry passing vertically through the center of the rectangle; it does not have rotational symmetry.

SELECTED ANSWERS

33. A′ B′ A B E C D C′ **35.** A′ A B′ B E C′ D C

39.

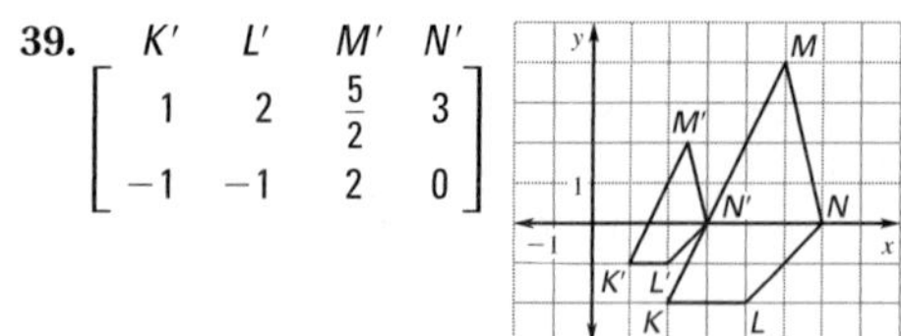

Chapter 10 (pp. 914–915) **1.** *Sample answer:* $\overline{KF}$ **3.** *Sample answer:* $\overleftrightarrow{CD}$ **5.** *Sample answer: K* **7.** $\overline{GH}$ **9.** $\frac{8}{3}$ **11.** 12 **13.** 4 **15.** minor arc; 30° **17.** minor arc; 105° **19.** minor arc; 105° **21.** 310° **23.** 130° **25.** 115° **27.** 45° **29.** $\widehat{AB} \cong \widehat{DE}$ using Theorem 10.3. **31.** $x = 90°$, $y = 50°$ **33.** $x = 25, y = 22$ **35.** $x = 7, y = 14$ **37.** 45 **39.** 55 **41.** 3 **43.** 2 **45.** 2 **47.** 3 **49.** $x^2 + (y + 2)^2 = 16$ **51.** $(x - m)^2 + (y - n)^2 = h^2 + k^2$

53.

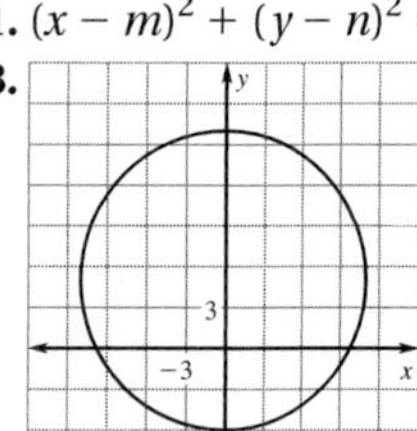

Chapter 11 (pp. 916–917) **1.** 143 units² **3.** 56.25 units² **5.** 60 cm, 150 cm² **7.** 5 **9.** 0.8 **11.** 22 units² **13.** 70 units² **15.** 72 units² **17.** 13.5 units² **19.** 10 : 9 **21.** $2\sqrt{2}:1$ **23.** 14 m **25.** about 15.71 units **27.** about 28.27 units **29.** about 4.71 m **31.** about 2.09 in. **33.** 9π in.²; 28.27 in.² **35.** 100π ft²; 314.16 ft² **37.** about 9.82 in.² **39.** about 42.76 ft² **41.** 45° **43.** 18° **45.** 54 units, $81\sqrt{3}$ units² **47.** 27 units, about 52.61 units² **49.** about 58.7% **51.** 30% **53.** 3.75%

Chapter 12 (pp. 918–919) **1.** Polyhedron; pentagonal prism; it is a solid bounded by polygons. **3.** Polyhedron; triangular pyramid; it is a solid bounded by polygons. **5.** 6 faces **7.** 156.65 cm² **9.** 163.36 cm² **11.** 4285.13 in.² **13.** 10 in. **15.** 14 ft **17.** 16.73 cm² **19.** 103.67 in.² **21.** 678.58 yd² **23.** 1960 cm³ **25.** 2 cm **27.** 5.00 in. **29.** 173.21 ft³ **31.** 6107.26 in.³ **33.** 12.66 ft³ **35.** 40.72 in.², 24.43 in.³ **37.** 589.65 cm², 1346.36 cm³ **39.** 3848.45 mm², 22,449.30 mm³ **41.** 1661.90 ft², 6370.63 ft³ **43.** 216 ft², 216 ft³ **45.** 1 : 3

SELECTED ANSWERS

SA48

Teacher's Edition Index

Pupil's Edition in black
Teacher's Edition in blue

A

INDEX

INDEX

INDEX

INDEX

N

O

INDEX

R

INDEX

INDEX

INDEX

T

U

V

INDEX

Additional Answers

Chapter 1

1.1 Problem Solving (pp. 7–8)

45. a–c.

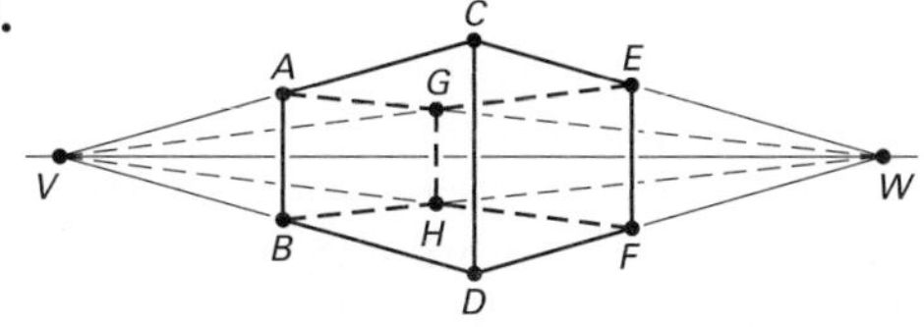

1.2 Problem Solving (pp. 13–14)

36.

	City A	City B	City C	City D
City A		12.5 mi	15 mi	25 mi
City B	12.5 mi		2.5 mi	12.5 mi
City C	15 mi	2.5 mi		10 mi
City D	25 mi	12.5 mi	10 mi	

1.5 Mixed Review (p. 41)

57.

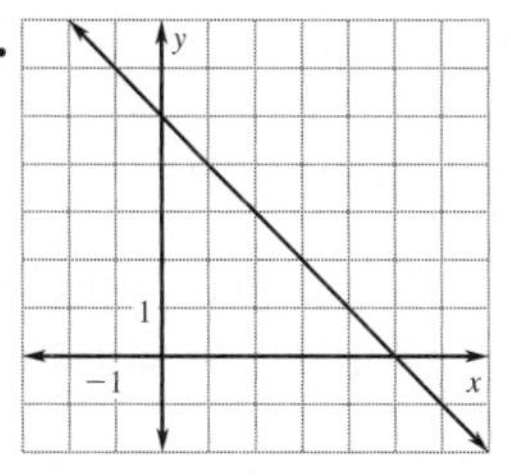

58.

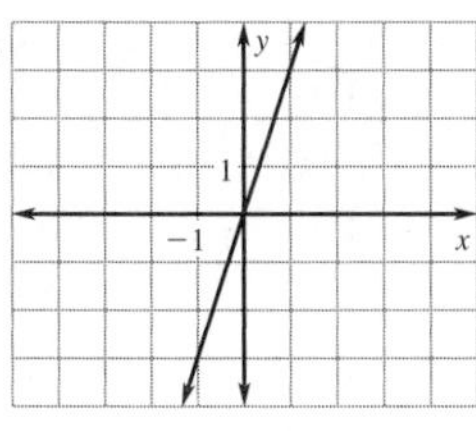

59.

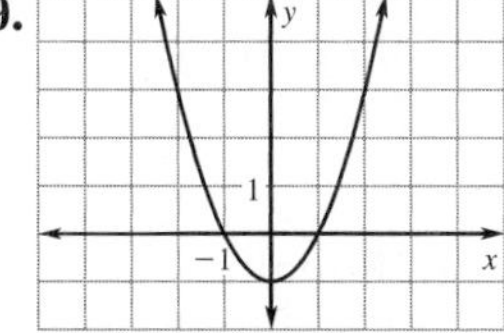

60.

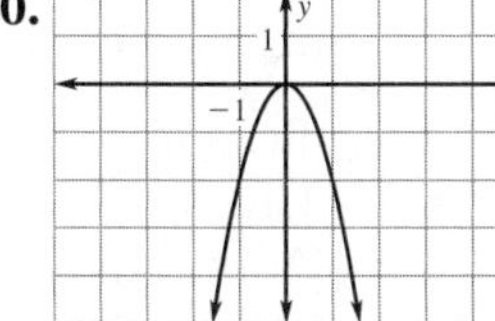

1.6 Guided Practice (pp. 43–44)

1. *Sample:*

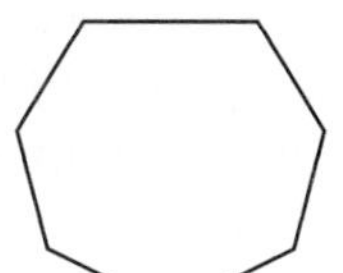

Sample:

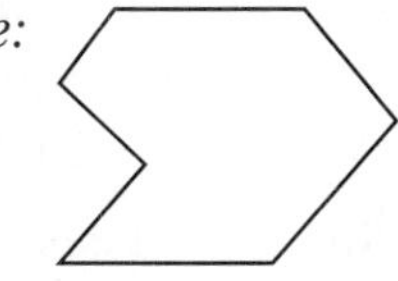

1.6 Problem Solving (pp. 46–47)

42.

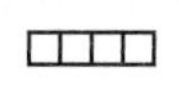

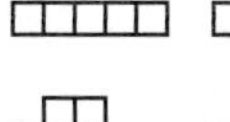

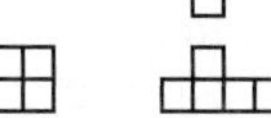

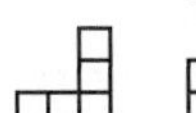

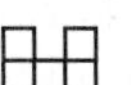

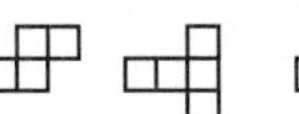

Chapter 2

2.1 Guided Practice (pp. 72–74)

1.

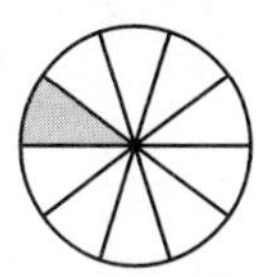

2.1 Problem Solving (pp. 77–78)

36. a.

Raffle tickets sold	0	1	2	3	4	5	10	20
Income (dollars)	0	0.25	0.50	0.75	1.00	1.25	2.50	5.00

b.

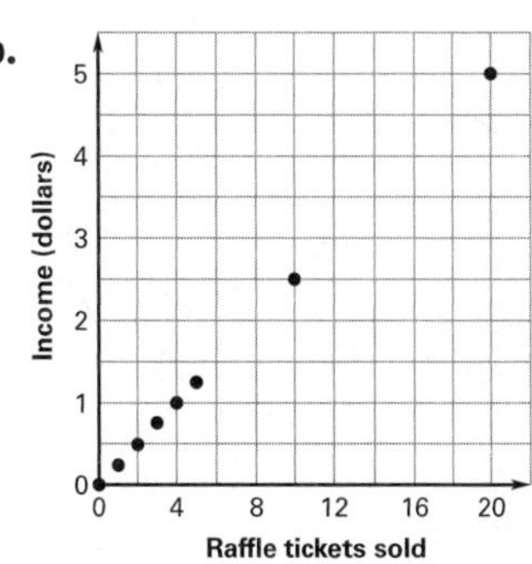

The graph is linear and increasing.

2.4 Problem Solving (pp. 101–102)

40. a–e. *Sample:*

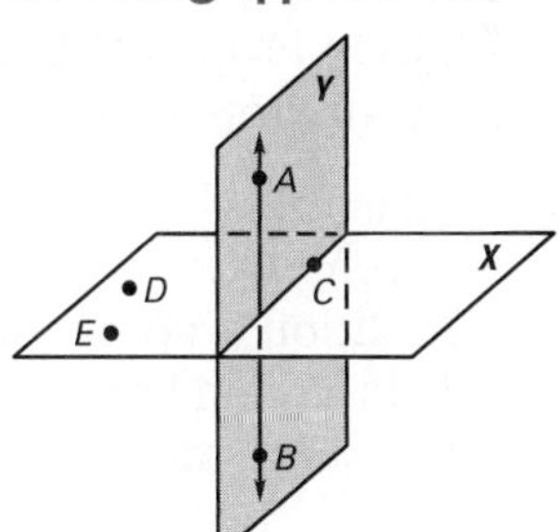

41. *Sample:*

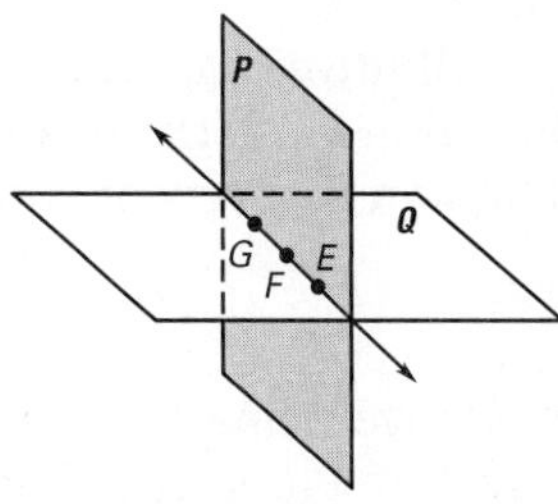

Sample:

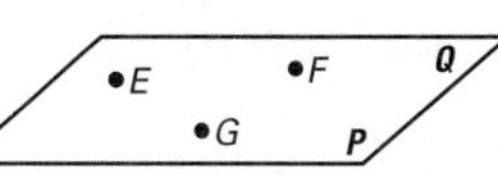

ADDITIONAL ANSWERS

42–44. Sample answers are given.

42.

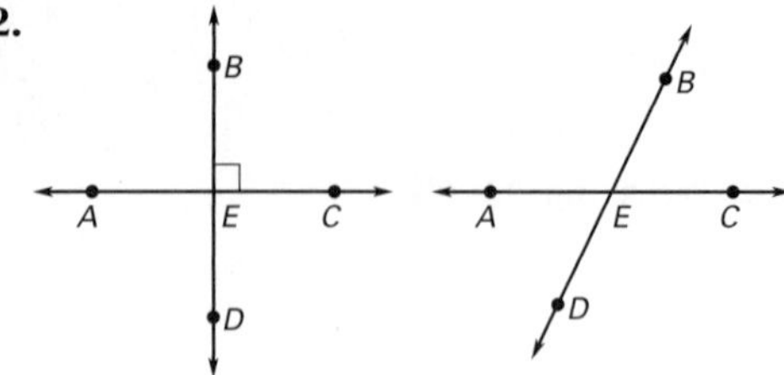

43.

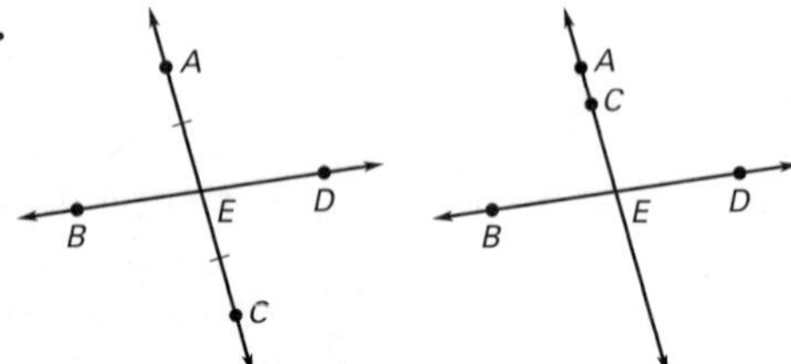

44.

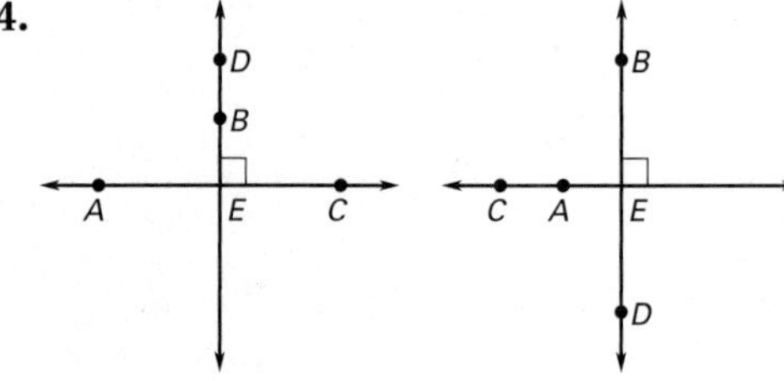

2.5 Skill Practice (pp. 108–109)

6.

Equation	Reason
$5x - 10 = -40$	Given
$5x = -30$	Addition Property of Equality
$x = -6$	Division Property of Equality

7.

Equation	Reason
$4x + 9 = 16 - 3x$	Given
$7x + 9 = 16$	Addition Property of Equality
$7x = 7$	Subtraction Property of Equality
$x = 1$	Division Property of Equality

8.

Equation	Reason
$5(3x - 20) = -10$	Given
$15x - 100 = -10$	Distributive Property
$15x = 90$	Addition Property of Equality
$x = 6$	Division Property of Equality

9.

Equation	Reason
$3(2x + 11) = 9$	Given
$6x + 33 = 9$	Distributive Property
$6x = -24$	Subtraction Property of Equality
$x = -4$	Division Property of Equality

10.

Equation	Reason
$2(-x - 5) = 12$	Given
$-2x - 10 = 12$	Distributive Property
$-2x = 22$	Addition Property of Equality
$x = -11$	Division Property of Equality

11.

Equation	Reason
$44 - 2(3x + 4) = -18x$	Given
$44 - 6x - 8 = -18x$	Distributive Property
$36 - 6x = -18x$	Simplify.
$36 = -12x$	Addition Property of Equality
$-3 = x$	Division Property of Equality

12.

Equation	Reason
$4(5x - 9) = -2(x + 7)$	Given
$20x - 36 = -2x - 14$	Distributive Property
$22x - 36 = -14$	Addition Property of Equality
$22x = 22$	Addition Property of Equality
$x = 1$	Division Property of Equality

13.

Equation	Reason
$2x - 15 - x = 21 + 10x$	Given
$x - 15 = 21 + 10x$	Simplify.
$-15 = 21 + 9x$	Subtraction Property of Equality
$-36 = 9x$	Subtraction Property of Equality
$-4 = x$	Division Property of Equality

14.

Equation	Reason
$3(7x - 9) - 19x = -15$	Given
$21x - 27 - 19x = -15$	Distributive Property
$2x - 27 = -15$	Simplify.
$2x = 12$	Addition Property of Equality
$x = 6$	Division Property of Equality

15.

Equation	Reason
$5x + y = 18$	Given
$y = 18 - 5x$	Subtraction Property of Equality

16.

Equation	Reason
$-4x + 2y = 8$	Given
$2y = 4x + 8$	Addition Property of Equality
$y = 2x + 4$	Division Property of Equality

17.

Equation	Reason
$12 - 3y = 30x$	Given
$-3y = 30x - 12$	Subtraction Property of Equality
$y = -10x + 4$	Division Property of Equality

18.

Equation	Reason
$3x + 9y = -7$	Given
$9y = -3x - 7$	Subtraction Property of Equality
$y = -\frac{1}{3}x - \frac{7}{9}$	Division Property of Equality

19.

Equation	Reason
$2y + 0.5x = 16$	Given
$2y = -0.5x + 16$	Subtraction Property of Equality
$y = -0.25x + 8$	Division Property of Equality

20. Equation | Reason

Equation	Reason
$\frac{1}{2}x - \frac{3}{4}y = -2$	Given
$-\frac{3}{4}y = -\frac{1}{2}x - 2$	Subtraction Property of Equality
$y = \frac{2}{3}x + \frac{8}{3}$	Multiplication Property of Equality

2.5 Problem Solving (pp. 110–111)

36. a.

Equation	Reason
$C = \frac{5}{9}(F - 32)$	Given
$\frac{9}{5}C = F - 32$	Multiplication Property of Equality
$\frac{9}{5}C + 32 = F$	Addition Property of Equality

b.

°C	°F
0	32
20	68
32	89.6
41	105.8

c.

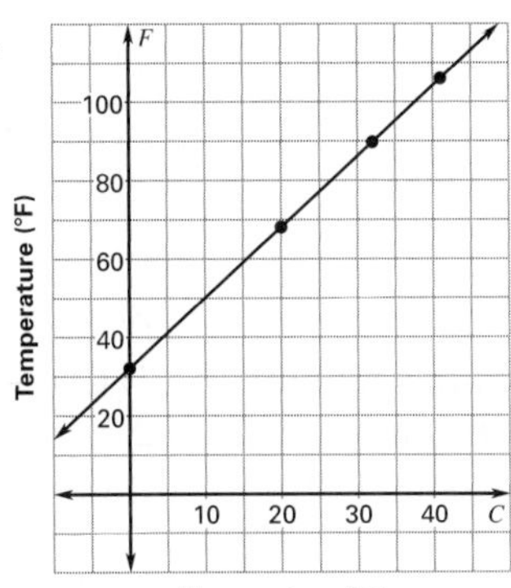

yes

Quiz for Lessons 2.4–2.5 (p. 111)

4.

Equation	Reason
$x + 20 = 35$	Given
$x = 15$	Subtraction Property of Equality

5.

Equation	Reason
$5x - 14 = 16 + 3x$	Given
$2x - 14 = 16$	Subtraction Property of Equality
$2x = 30$	Addition Property of Equality
$x = 15$	Division Property of Equality

2.6 Problem Solving (pp. 118–119)

30. a. *Sample:*

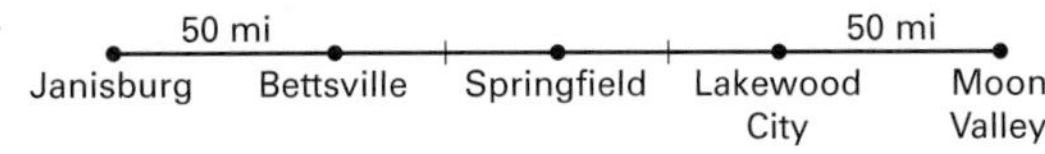

b. *Sample:*

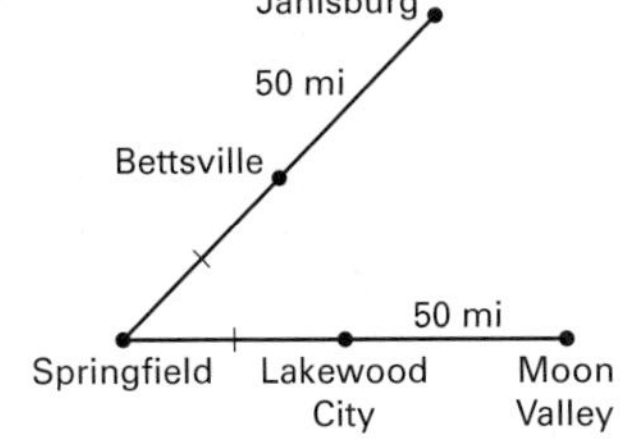

2.6 Problem Solving Workshop (p. 121)

3.

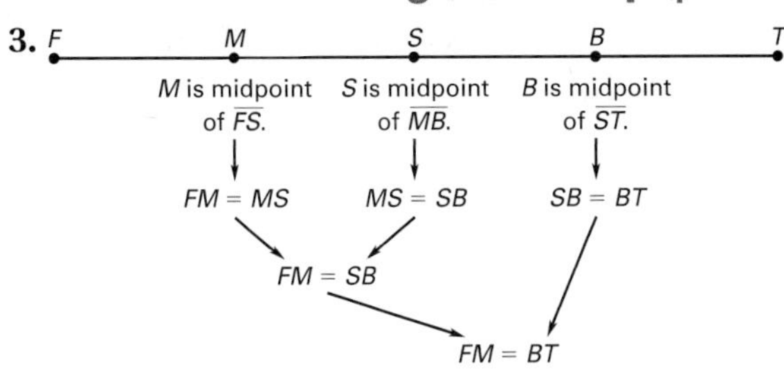

Statements	Reasons
1. M is halfway between F and S; S is halfway between M and B; B is halfway between S and T.	1. Given
2. M is the midpoint of $\overline{FS}$; S is the midpoint of $\overline{MB}$; B is the midpoint of $\overline{ST}$.	2. Definition of midpoint
3. $FM = MS$, $MS = SB$, $SB = BT$	3. Definition of midpoint
4. $FM = SB$	4. Transitive Property of Equality
5. $FM = BT$	5. Transitive Property of Equality

4.

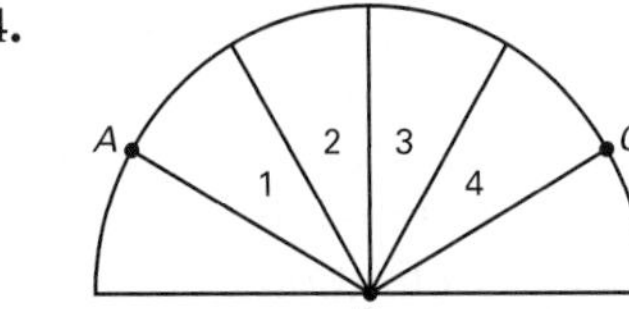

$m\angle 1 = m\angle 2 = m\angle 3 = m\angle 4$

$m\angle 1 + m\angle 2 + m\angle 3 + m\angle 4 = m\angle ABC$

$2(m\angle 2 + m\angle 3) = m\angle ABC$

$m\angle 2 + m\angle 3 = \frac{1}{2}m\angle ABC$

Statements	Reasons
1. $\angle 1 \cong \angle 2 \cong \angle 3 \cong \angle 4$	1. Given
2. $m\angle 1 = m\angle 2 = m\angle 3 = m\angle 4$	2. Definition of congruent angles
3. $m\angle 1 + m\angle 2 + m\angle 3 + m\angle 4 = m\angle ABC$	3. Angle Addition Postulate
4. $m\angle 2 + m\angle 2 + m\angle 3 + m\angle 3 = m\angle ABC$	4. Substitution
5. $2m\angle 2 + 2m\angle 3 = m\angle ABC$	5. Simplify.
6. $2(m\angle 2 + m\angle 3) = m\angle ABC$	6. Distributive Property
7. $m\angle 2 + m\angle 3 = \frac{1}{2}m\angle ABC$	7. Division Property of Equality

2.7 Guided Practice (pp. 125–127)

2.

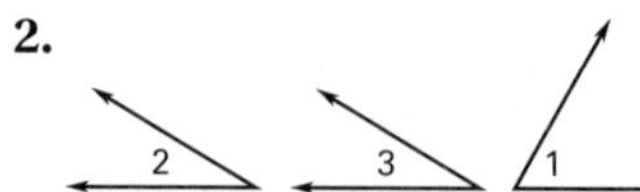

If ∠2 and ∠3 are complementary to ∠1, then ∠2 ≅ ∠3.

Given: ∠2 and ∠3 are complementary to ∠1.
Prove: ∠2 ≅ ∠3

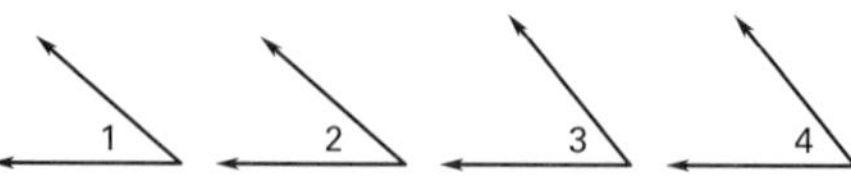

If ∠1 ≅ ∠2, ∠3 is complementary to ∠1, and ∠4 is complementary to ∠2, then ∠3 ≅ ∠4.

Given: ∠1 ≅ ∠2, ∠3 is complementary to ∠1, and ∠4 is complementary to ∠2.
Prove: ∠3 ≅ ∠4

2.7 Problem Solving (pp. 129–131)

44.

Statements	Reasons
1. ∠1 and ∠3 are complementary; ∠2 and ∠4 are complementary.	1. Given
2. $m\angle 1 + m\angle 3 = 90°$; $m\angle 2 + m\angle 4 = 90°$	2. Definition of complementary
3. ∠2 ≅ ∠3	3. Vertical Angles Congruence Theorem
4. $m\angle 1 + m\angle 2 = 90°$	4. Substitution
5. $m\angle 1 + m\angle 2 = m\angle 2 + m\angle 4$	5. Transitive Property of Equality
6. $m\angle 1 = m\angle 4$	6. Subtraction Property of Equality
7. ∠1 ≅ ∠4	7. Definition of congruent angles

45. a.

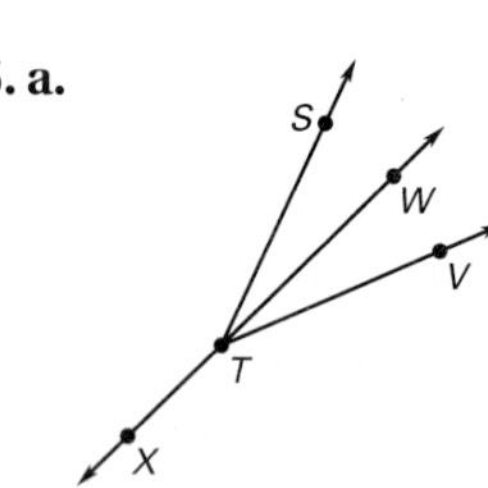

b. Given: ∠*STV* is bisected by $\overrightarrow{TW}$, and $\overrightarrow{TX}$ and $\overrightarrow{TW}$ are opposite rays.
Prove: ∠*STX* ≅ ∠*VTX*

c.

Statements	Reasons
1. ∠*STV* is bisected by $\overrightarrow{TW}$; $\overrightarrow{TX}$ and $\overrightarrow{TW}$ are opposite rays.	1. Given
2. ∠*STW* ≅ ∠*VTW*	2. Definition of angle bisector
3. ∠*VTW* and ∠*VTX* are a linear pair; ∠*STW* and ∠*STX* are a linear pair.	3. Definition of linear pair
4. ∠*VTW* and ∠*VTX* are supplementary; ∠*STW* and ∠*STX* are supplementary.	4. Linear Pair Postulate
5. ∠*STX* ≅ ∠*VTX*	5. Congruent Supplements Theorem

47.

Statements	Reasons
1. $m\angle WYZ = m\angle TWZ = 45°$	1. Given
2. ∠*TWZ* and ∠*SWZ* are a linear pair; ∠*WYZ* and ∠*XYW* are a linear pair.	2. Definition of linear pair
3. ∠*TWZ* and ∠*SWZ* are supplementary; ∠*WYZ* and ∠*XYW* are supplementary.	3. Linear Pair Postulate
4. $m\angle TWZ + m\angle SWZ = 180°$; $m\angle WYZ + m\angle XYW = 180°$	4. Definition of supplementary angles
5. $m\angle TWZ + m\angle SWZ = m\angle WYZ + m\angle XYW$	5. Transitive Property of Equality
6. $45° + m\angle SWZ = 45° + m\angle XYW$	6. Substitution
7. $m\angle SWZ = m\angle XYW$	7. Subtraction Property of Equality
8. ∠*SWZ* ≅ ∠*XYW*	8. Definition of congruent angles

48.

Statements	Reasons
1. The hexagon is regular.	1. Given
2. ∠1 is congruent to an interior angle of the hexagon.	2. Vertical Angles Congruence Theorem
3. ∠2 is supplementary to an interior angle of the hexagon.	3. Linear Pair Postulate
4. ∠2 is supplementary to ∠1.	4. Substitution
5. $m\angle 1 + m\angle 2 = 180°$	5. Definition of supplementary angles

2.7 Mixed Review (p. 131)

49–52. Sample answers are given.

49.

50.

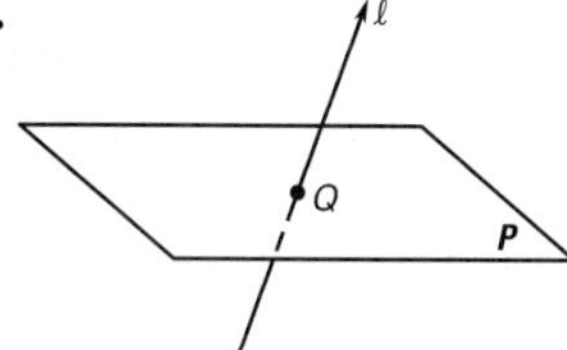

51.

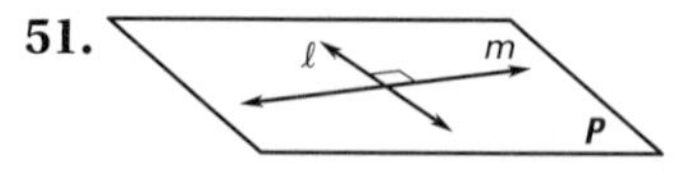

52.

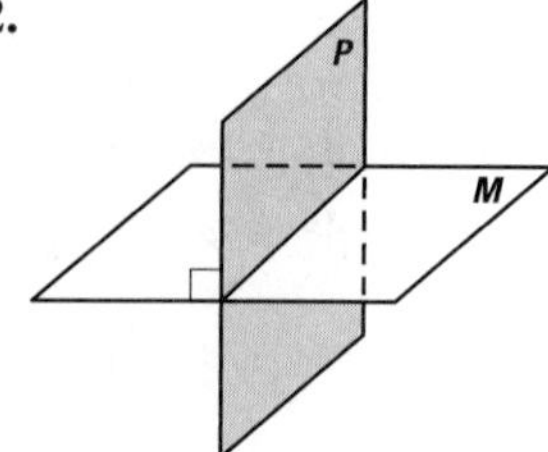

ADDITIONAL ANSWERS

Quiz for Lessons 2.6–2.7 (p. 131)

4.

Statements	Reasons
1. $\angle XWY$ and $\angle ZWV$ are straight angles.	1. Given
2. $\angle XWV$ and $\angle ZWY$ are vertical angles.	2. Definition of vertical angles
3. $\angle XWV \cong \angle ZWY$	3. Vertical Angles Congruence Theorem

Chapter 3

3.2 Problem Solving (pp. 159–160)

42.

Statements	Reasons
1. $t \perp r$; $r \parallel s$	1. Given
2. $\angle 1$ is a right angle.	2. Definition of perpendicular lines
3. $m\angle 1 = 90°$	3. Definition of right angle
4. $\angle 1 \cong \angle 2$	4. Corresponding Angles Postulate
5. $m\angle 1 = m\angle 2$	5. Definition of congruent angles
6. $m\angle 2 = 90°$	6. Substitution
7. $\angle 2$ is a right angle.	7. Definition of right angle
8. $t \perp s$	8. Definition of perpendicular lines

3.3 Skill Practice (pp. 165–167)

16. *Sample answer:*

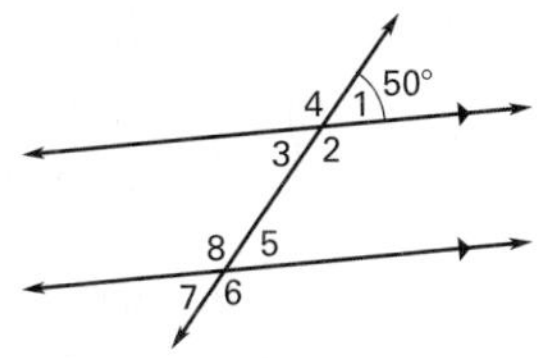

$m\angle 3 = 50°$, Vertical Angles Congruence Theorem; $m\angle 4 = 130°$, Linear Pair Postulate; $m\angle 2 = 130°$, Vertical Angles Congruence Theorem; $m\angle 8 = 130°$, Alternate Interior Angles Theorem; $m\angle 6 = 130°$, Vertical Angles Congruence Theorem; $m\angle 5 = 50°$, Linear Pair Postulate; $m\angle 7 = 50°$, Vertical Angles Congruence Theorem

3.3 Problem Solving (pp. 167–169)

40–44. Sample answers are given. **40.** Consecutive Interior Angles Converse **41.** Corresponding Angles Converse **42.** Corresponding Angles Converse **43.** Vertical Angles Congruence Theorem followed by the Corresponding Angles Converse **44.** Consecutive Interior Angles Converse

45. a.

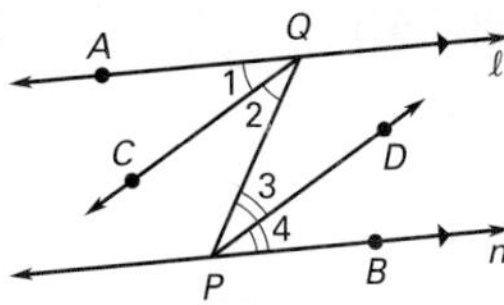

b. Yes; if two parallel lines are cut by a transversal, the angle bisectors of alternate interior angle pairs are parallel.

Statements	Reasons
1. $\ell \parallel n$	1. Given
2. $\angle AQP \cong \angle BPQ$	2. Alternate Interior Angles Theorem
3. $m\angle 1 + m\angle 2 = m\angle AQP$, $m\angle 4 + m\angle 3 = m\angle BPQ$	3. Angle Addition Postulate
4. $m\angle 1 = m\angle 2$, $m\angle 3 = m\angle 4$	4. Definition of angle bisector
5. $m\angle 2 + m\angle 2 = m\angle AQP$, $m\angle 3 + m\angle 3 = m\angle BPQ$	5. Substitution
6. $2m\angle 2 = 2m\angle 3$	6. Transitive Property of Equality
7. $m\angle 2 = m\angle 3$	7. Division Property of Equality
8. $\angle 2 \cong \angle 3$	8. Definition of congruent angles
9. $\overrightarrow{QC} \parallel \overrightarrow{PD}$	9. Alternate Interior Angles Converse

3.4 Mixed Review (p. 178)

47.

Equation	Reason
$6x + 4y = 40$	Given
$4y = 40 - 6x$	Subtraction Property of Equality
$y = \frac{40 - 6x}{4}$	Division Property of Equality
$y = 10 - \frac{3}{2}x$	Simplify.

48.

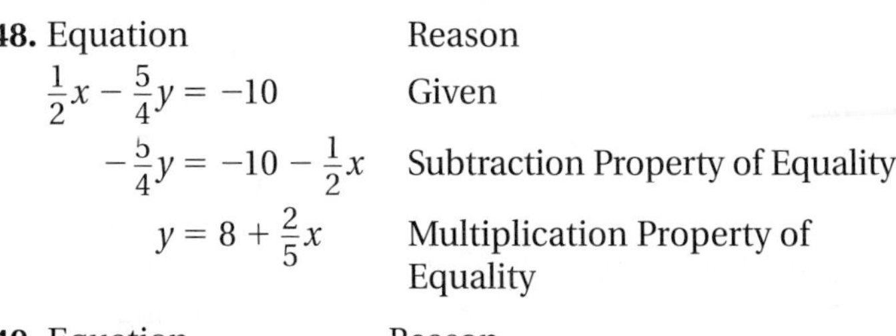

Equation	Reason
$\frac{1}{2}x - \frac{5}{4}y = -10$	Given
$-\frac{5}{4}y = -10 - \frac{1}{2}x$	Subtraction Property of Equality
$y = 8 + \frac{2}{5}x$	Multiplication Property of Equality

49.

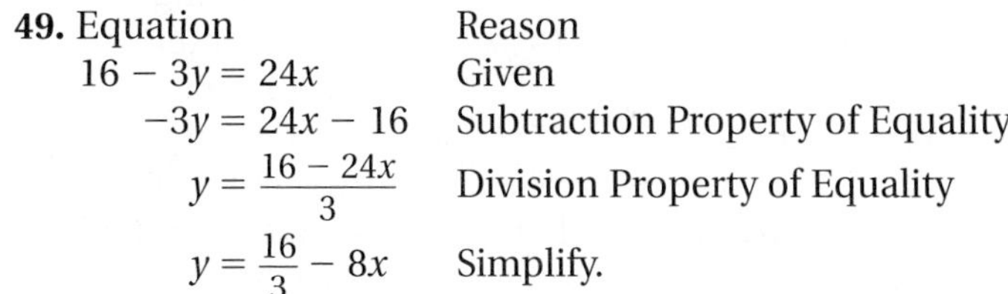

Equation	Reason
$16 - 3y = 24x$	Given
$-3y = 24x - 16$	Subtraction Property of Equality
$y = \frac{16 - 24x}{3}$	Division Property of Equality
$y = \frac{16}{3} - 8x$	Simplify.

3.5 Guided Practice (pp. 181–183)

3.

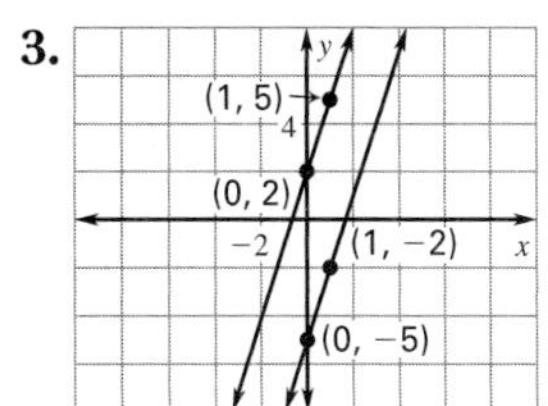

3.6 Problem Solving (pp. 196–197)

33. Given: $h \parallel k$, $j \perp h$
Prove: $j \perp k$

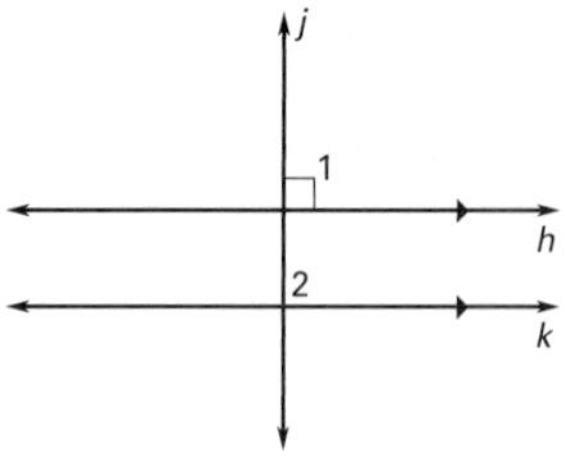

Statements	Reasons
1. $h \parallel k$, $j \perp h$	1. Given
2. $\angle 1 \cong \angle 2$	2. Corresponding Angles Postulate
3. $m\angle 1 = m\angle 2$	3. Definition of congruent angles
4. $\angle 1$ is a right angle.	4. Perpendicular lines intersect to form four right angles.
5. $m\angle 1 = 90°$	5. Definition of right angle
6. $m\angle 2 = 90°$	6. Substitution
7. $\angle 2$ is a right angle.	7. Definition of right angle
8. $j \perp k$	8. Definition of perpendicular lines

Chapter 4

4.1 Problem Solving (pp. 223–224)

53.

Statements	Reasons
1. $\triangle ABC$, $\overline{AB} \parallel \overline{CD}$	1. Given
2. $m\angle ACE = 180°$	2. Definition of straight angle
3. $m\angle 3 + m\angle 4 + m\angle 5 = m\angle ACE$	3. Angle Addition Postulate
4. $m\angle 3 + m\angle 4 + m\angle 5 = 180°$	4. Substitution
5. $\angle 1 \cong \angle 5$	5. Corresponding Angles Postulate
6. $m\angle 1 = m\angle 5$	6. Definition of congruent angles
7. $\angle 2 \cong \angle 4$	7. Alternate Interior Angles Theorem
8. $m\angle 2 = m\angle 4$	8. Definition of congruent angles
9. $m\angle 3 + m\angle 2 + m\angle 1 = 180°$	9. Substitution Property of Equality

4.2 Problem Solving (pp. 230–231)

28.

Statements	Reasons
1. $\angle A \cong \angle D$, $\angle B \cong \angle E$	1. Given
2. $m\angle A + m\angle B + m\angle C = 180°$, $m\angle D + m\angle E + m\angle F = 180°$	2. Triangle Sum Theorem
3. $m\angle A + m\angle B + m\angle C = m\angle D + m\angle E + m\angle F$	3. Transitive Property of Equality
4. $m\angle A = m\angle D$, $m\angle B = m\angle E$	4. Definition of congruent angles
5. $m\angle D + m\angle E + m\angle C = m\angle D + m\angle E + m\angle F$	5. Substitution Property of Equality
6. $m\angle C = m\angle F$	6. Subtraction Property of Equality
7. $\angle C \cong \angle F$	7. Definition of congruent angles

32.

Statements	Reasons
1. $\overline{WX} \perp \overrightarrow{VZ}$ at Y, Y is the midpoint of $\overline{WX}$, $\overline{VW} \cong \overline{VX}$, $\overrightarrow{VZ}$ bisects $\angle WVX$.	1. Given
2. $\angle WYV$ and $\angle XYV$ are right angles.	2. Definition of perpendicular lines
3. $\angle WYV \cong \angle XYV$	3. Right Angle Congruence Theorem
4. $\angle WVY \cong \angle XVY$	4. Definition of angle bisector
5. $\angle YXV \cong \angle YWV$	5. Third Angles Theorem
6. $\overline{WY} \cong \overline{XY}$	6. Definition of midpoint
7. $\overline{VY} \cong \overline{VY}$	7. Reflexive Property of Equality
8. $\triangle VWY \cong \triangle VXY$	8. Definition of congruent figures

4.3 Problem Solving (pp. 238–239)

30.

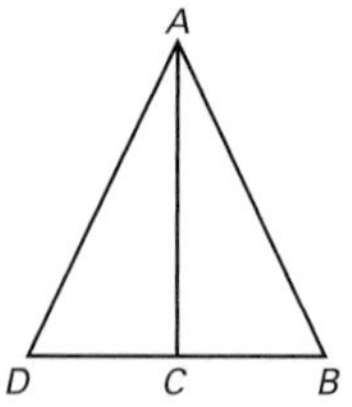

Statements	Reasons
1. $\triangle ABD$ is isosceles, C is the midpoint of $\overline{BD}$.	1. Given
2. $\overline{AB} \cong \overline{AD}$	2. Definition of isosceles triangle
3. $\overline{CA} \cong \overline{CA}$	3. Reflexive Property of Congruence
4. $\overline{DC} \cong \overline{BC}$	4. Definition of midpoint
5. $\triangle ACD \cong \triangle ACB$	5. SSS

Quiz for Lessons 4.1–4.3 (p. 239)

1.

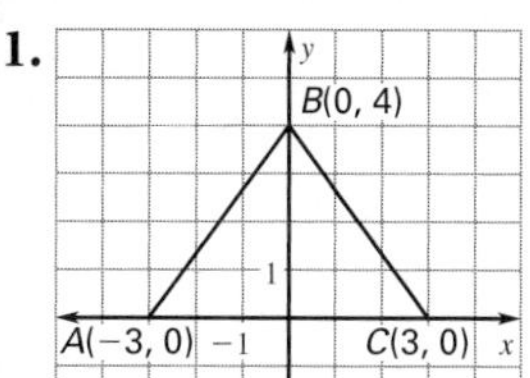

2.

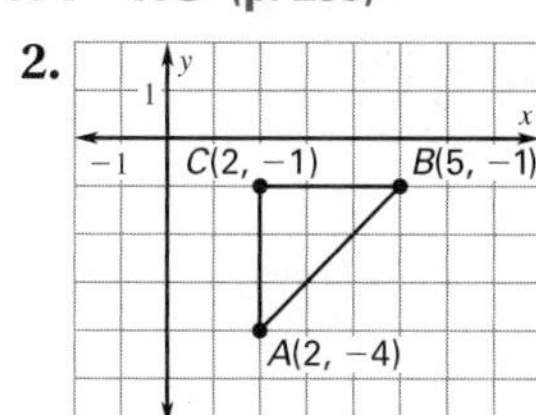

3.

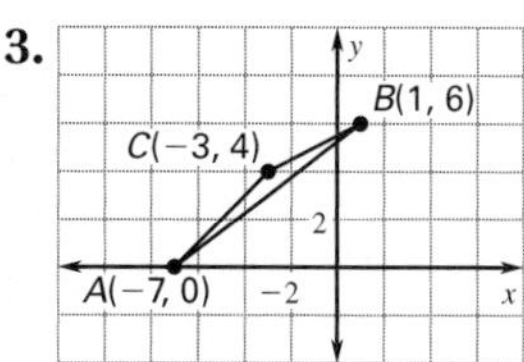

6.

Statements	Reasons
1. $\overline{AB} \cong \overline{AC}$, $\overline{AD}$ bisects $\overline{BC}$.	1. Given
2. $\overline{AD} \cong \overline{AD}$	2. Reflexive Property of Congruence
3. $\overline{DB} \cong \overline{DC}$	3. Definition of segment bisector
4. $\triangle ABD \cong \triangle ACD$	4. SSS

4.4 Guided Practice (pp. 241–242)

1.

Statements	Reasons
1. $\overline{RT} \perp \overline{SU}$; $\overline{SV} \cong \overline{VU}$.	1. Given
2. $\angle SVR$ and $\angle UVR$ are right angles.	2. Definition of perpendicular lines
3. $\angle SVR \cong \angle UVR$	3. Right Angles Congruence Theorem
4. $\overline{VR} \cong \overline{VR}$	4. Reflexive Property of Congruence
5. $\triangle SVR \cong \triangle UVR$	5. SAS

2.

Statements	Reasons
1. $ABCD$ is a square; R, S, T, and U are midpoints of the sides of $ABCD$; $\angle B$ and $\angle D$ are right angles.	1. Given
2. $BC = DA$, $BA = DC$	2. Definition of segment congruence
3. $BS = SC$, $DU = UA$, $BR = RA$, $DT = TC$	3. Definition of midpoint
4. $BS + SC = BC$, $DU + UA = DA$, $BR + RA = BA$, $DT + TC = DC$	4. Segment Addition Postulate
5. $2BS = BC$, $2DU = DA$, $2BR = BA$, $2DT = DC$	5. Substitution Property of Equality
6. $2BS = 2DU$, $2BR = 2DT$	6. Substitution Property of Equality
7. $BS = DU$, $BR = DT$	7. Division Property of Equality
8. $\overline{BS} \cong \overline{DU}$, $\overline{BR} \cong \overline{DT}$	8. Definition of congruent segments
9. $\angle B \cong \angle D$	9. Right Angles Congruence Theorem
10. $\triangle BSR \cong \triangle DUT$	10. SAS

3.

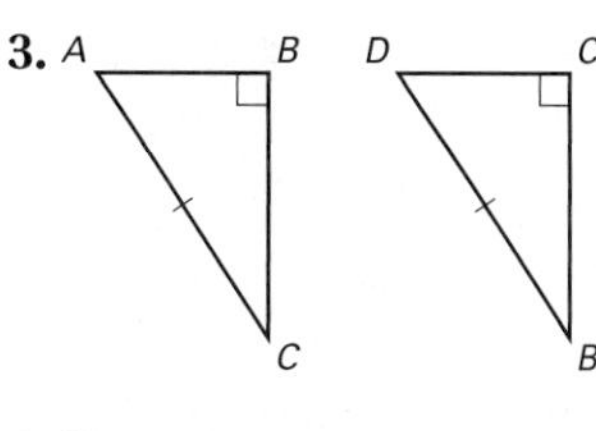

4.

Statements	Reasons
1. $\angle ABC$ and $\angle DCB$ are right angles, $\overline{AC} \cong \overline{DB}$.	1. Given
2. $\triangle ACB$ and $\triangle DBC$ are right triangles.	2. Definition of right triangle
3. $\overline{BC} \cong \overline{CB}$	3. Reflexive Property of Congruence
4. $\triangle ACB \cong \triangle DBC$	4. HL

4.4 Problem Solving (pp. 245–246)

37.

Statements	Reasons
1. $\overline{JM} \cong \overline{LM}$	1. Given
2. $\angle KJM$ and $\angle KLM$ are right angles.	2. Given in diagram
3. $\triangle JKM$ and $\triangle LKM$ are right triangles.	3. Definition of right triangle
4. $\overline{KM} \cong \overline{KM}$	4. Reflexive Property of Congruence
5. $\triangle JKM \cong \triangle LKM$	5. HL

38.

Statements	Reasons
1. D is the midpoint of $\overline{AC}$.	1. Given
2. $\overline{BD} \perp \overline{AC}$	2. Given in diagram
3. $\angle BDA$ and $\angle BDC$ are right angles.	3. Definition of perpendicular lines
4. $\angle BDA \cong \angle BDC$	4. Right Angles Congruence Theorem
5. $\overline{DA} \cong \overline{DC}$	5. Definition of midpoint
6. $\overline{BD} \cong \overline{BD}$	6. Reflexive Property of Congruence
7. $\triangle ABD \cong \triangle CBD$	7. SAS

40.

Statements	Reasons
1. $\overline{CR} \cong \overline{CS}$, $\overline{QC} \perp \overline{CR}$, $\overline{QC} \perp \overline{CS}$	1. Given
2. $\angle SCQ$ and $\angle RCQ$ are right angles.	2. Definition of perpendicular lines
3. $\angle SCQ \cong \angle RCQ$	3. Right Angles Congruence Theorem
4. $\overline{QC} \cong \overline{QC}$	4. Reflexive Property of Congruence
5. $\triangle QCR \cong \triangle QCS$	5. SAS

41. Find the length of each side of the two triangles and show that pairs of corresponding sides have the same length and therefore are congruent.

Statements	Reasons
1. $MO = 4\sqrt{2}$, $MN = 4\sqrt{2}$	1. Distance formula
2. $\overline{MO} \cong \overline{MN}$	2. Definition of congruent segments
3. $\overline{MP} \cong \overline{MP}$	3. Reflexive Property of Congruence
4. slope of $\overline{MP} = -1$, slope of $\overline{NO} = 1$	4. Slope formula
5. $\overline{MP} \perp \overline{NO}$	5. Slopes of Perpendicular Lines Postulate
6. $\angle OMP$ and $\angle NMP$ are right angles.	6. Definition of perpendicular lines
7. $\angle OMP \cong \angle NMP$	7. Right Angles Congruence Theorem
8. $\triangle PMO \cong \triangle PMN$	8. SAS

Sample answer: Both methods involve the use of the distance formula, with the first method involving calculating the lengths of all the sides of the two triangles. The second method also requires finding the slopes of two of the sides in order to show they are perpendicular and that right triangles are formed.

4.5 Guided Practice (pp. 250–251)

2.

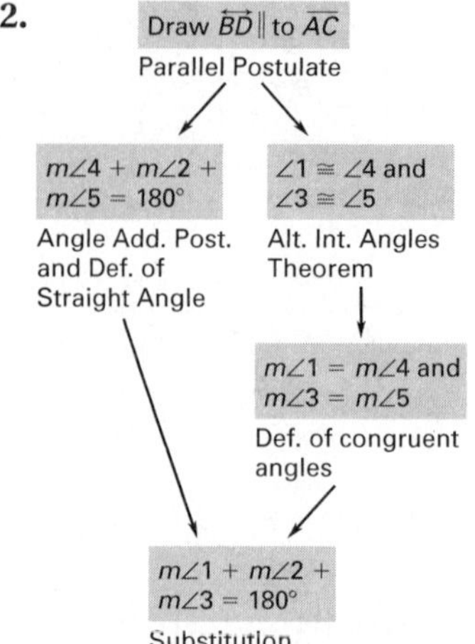

4.5 Problem Solving (pp. 254–255)

34.

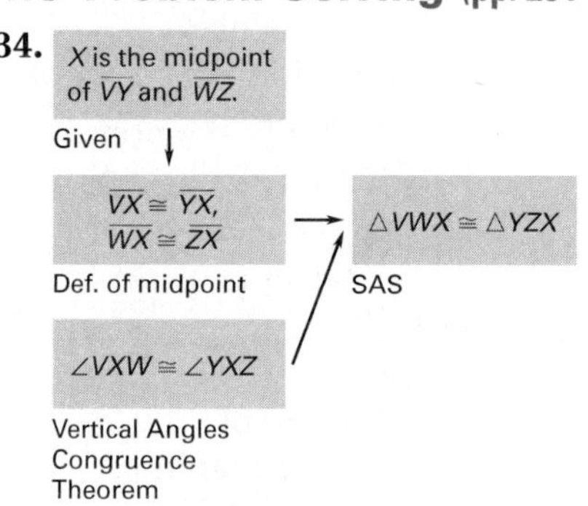

ADDITIONAL ANSWERS

35.

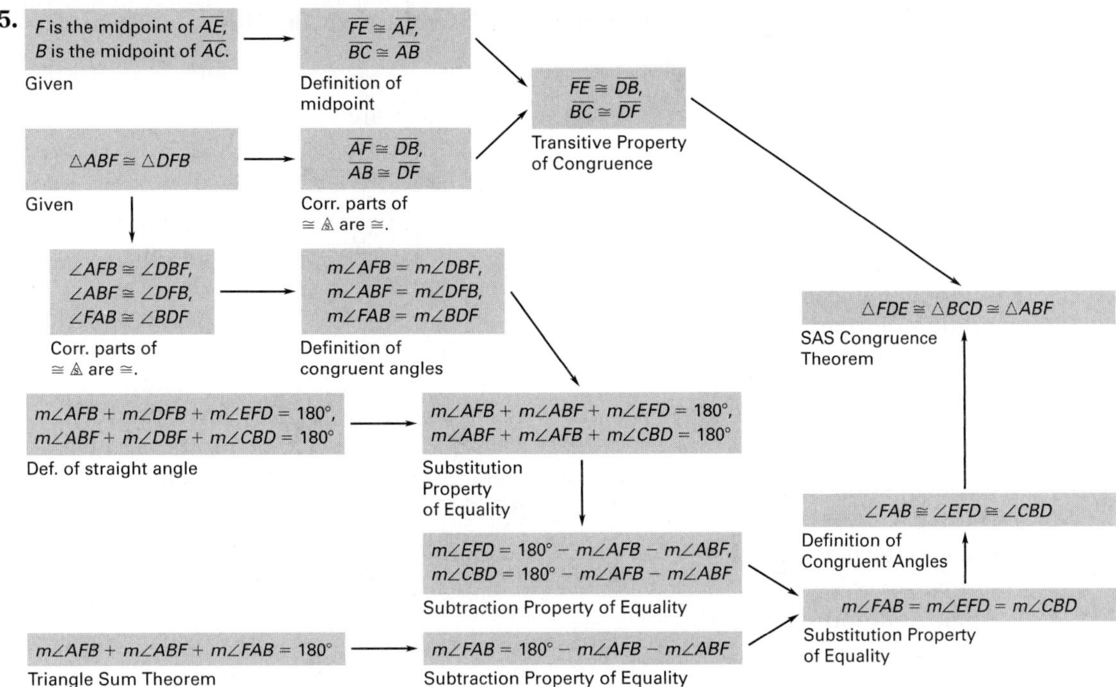

4.6 Skill Practice (pp. 259–260)

23.

Statements	Reasons
1. $\angle T \cong \angle U$, $\angle Z \cong \angle X$, $\overline{YZ} \cong \overline{YX}$	1. Given
2. $\triangle TYZ \cong \triangle UYX$	2. AAS
3. $\angle TYZ \cong \angle UYX$	3. Corr. parts of ≅ △s are ≅.
4. $m\angle TYZ = m\angle UYX$	4. Definition of congruent angles
5. $m\angle TYW + m\angle WYZ = m\angle TYZ$, $m\angle TYW + m\angle VYX = m\angle UYX$	5. Angle Addition Postulate
6. $m\angle TYW + m\angle WYZ = m\angle TYW + m\angle VYX$	6. Substitution
7. $m\angle WYZ = m\angle VYX$	7. Subtraction Property of Equality
8. $\angle WYZ \cong \angle VYX$	8. Definition of congruent angles

24.

Statements	Reasons
1. $\overline{FG} \cong \overline{HG} \cong \overline{JG} \cong \overline{KG}$, $\overline{JM} \cong \overline{KM} \cong \overline{LM} \cong \overline{NM}$	1. Given
2. $\angle FGJ \cong \angle HGK$, $\angle JML \cong \angle KMN$	2. Vertical Angles Congruence Theorem
3. $\triangle FGJ \cong \triangle HGK$, $\triangle JML \cong \triangle KMN$	3. SAS
4. $\overline{FJ} \cong \overline{HK}$, $\overline{JL} \cong \overline{KN}$	4. Corr. parts of ≅ △s are ≅.
5. $FJ = HK$, $JL = KN$	5. Definition of congruent segments
6. $FJ + JL = HK + KN$	6. Addition Property of Equality
7. $FL = HN$	7. Segment Addition Postulate
8. $\overline{FL} \cong \overline{HN}$	8. Definition of congruent segments

25.

Statements	Reasons
1. $\angle PRU \cong \angle QVS$, $\overline{RS} \cong \overline{UV}$, $\angle TSU \cong \angle USW \cong \angle TUS \cong \angle SUW$	1. Given
2. $\overline{SU} \cong \overline{SU}$	2. Reflexive Property of Congruence
3. $SU = SU$, $RS = UV$	3. Definition of segment congruence
4. $RS + SU = SU + UV$	4. Addition Property of Equality
5. $RU = SV$	5. Segment Addition Postulate
6. $\overline{RU} \cong \overline{SV}$	6. Definition of segment congruence
7. $\triangle QSV \cong \triangle PUR$	7. ASA
8. $\overline{PU} \cong \overline{QS}$, $\angle RPU \cong \angle VQS$	8. Corr. parts of $\cong$ $\triangle$s are $\cong$.
9. $m\angle TSU + m\angle USW = m\angle TSW$, $m\angle TUS + m\angle SUW = m\angle TUW$	9. Angle Addition Postulate
10. $m\angle TSU = m\angle USW = m\angle TUS = m\angle SUW$	10. Definition of angle congruence
11. $m\angle TSU + m\angle TSU = m\angle TSW$, $m\angle TSU + m\angle TSU = m\angle TUW$	11. Substitution
12. $m\angle TSW = m\angle TUW$	12. Transitive Property of Equality
13. $\angle TSW \cong \angle TUW$	13. Definition of angle congruence
14. $\triangle PUX \cong \triangle QSY$	14. ASA

26.

Statements	Reasons
1. $\overline{AD} \cong \overline{GD} \cong \overline{FD} \cong \overline{BD}$	1. Given
2. $\angle ADC \cong \angle GDE$, $\angle FDC \cong \angle BDE$	2. Vertical Angles Congruence Theorem
3. $m\angle ADC = m\angle GDE$, $m\angle FDC = m\angle BDE$	3. Definition of angle congruence
4. $m\angle ADC + m\angle FDC = m\angle ADF$, $m\angle BDE + m\angle GDE = m\angle GDB$	4. Angle Addition Postulate
5. $m\angle ADC + m\angle FDC = m\angle GDB$	5. Substitution Property of Equality
6. $m\angle ADF = m\angle GDB$	6. Transitive Property of Equality
7. $\angle ADF \cong \angle GDB$	7. Definition of angle congruence
8. $\triangle ADF \cong \triangle GDB$	8. SAS
9. $\angle FAD \cong \angle BGD$	9. Corr. parts of $\cong$ $\triangle$s are $\cong$.
10. $\triangle ADC \cong \triangle GDE$	10. ASA
11. $\overline{AC} \cong \overline{GE}$	11. Corr. parts of $\cong$ $\triangle$s are $\cong$.

4.6 Problem Solving (pp. 261–263)

39.

Statements	Reasons
1. $\overline{BA} \cong \overline{BC}$, D and E are midpoints, $\angle A \cong \angle C$, $\overline{DF} \cong \overline{EF}$.	1. Given
2. $\overline{BD} \cong \overline{DA}$, $\overline{BE} \cong \overline{EC}$	2. Definition of midpoint
3. $BD = DA$, $BE = EC$	3. Definition of segment congruence
4. $BD + DA = BE + EC$	4. Segment Addition Postulate
5. $BD + BD = BE + BE$, $DA + DA = EC + EC$	5. Substitution Property of Equality
6. $2BD = 2BE$, $2DA = 2EC$	6. Simplify.
7. $BD = BE$, $DA = EC$	7. Division Property of Equality
8. $\overline{BD} \cong \overline{BE}$, $\overline{DA} \cong \overline{EC}$	8. Definition of segment congruence
9. $\overline{BJ}$ containing point F	9. Construction
10. $\overline{BF} \cong \overline{BF}$	10. Reflexive Property of Congruence
11. $\triangle BFD \cong \triangle BFE$	11. SSS
12. $\angle BFE \cong \angle BFD$, $\angle BEF \cong \angle BDF$	12. Corr. parts of $\cong$ $\triangle$s are $\cong$.
13. $\angle BFE \cong \angle GFJ$, $\angle BFD \cong \angle HFJ$	13. Vertical Angles Congruence Theorem
14. $\angle GFJ \cong \angle HFJ$	14. Substitution
15. $\overline{FJ} \cong \overline{FJ}$	15. Reflexive Property of Segment Congruence
16. $\angle BEF$ and $\angle CEG$ are supplementary, $\angle BDF$ and $\angle ADH$ are supplementary.	16. Definition of supplementary angles
17. $\angle CEG \cong \angle ADH$	17. Congruent Supplements Theorem
18. $\triangle CEG \cong \triangle ADH$	18. ASA
19. $\angle EGJ \cong \angle DHJ$	19. Corr. parts of $\cong$ $\triangle$s are $\cong$.
20. $\triangle GFJ \cong \triangle HFJ$	20. AAS
21. $\overline{FG} \cong \overline{FH}$	21. Corr. parts of $\cong$ $\triangle$s are $\cong$.

40.

Statements	Reasons
1. $\overline{AB} \parallel \overline{EC}$, $\overline{AC} \parallel \overline{ED}$, $\overline{AB} \cong \overline{ED}$, $\overline{AC} \cong \overline{EC}$	1. Given
2. $\angle DEC \cong \angle ECA$, $\angle ECA \cong \angle BAC$	2. Alternate Interior Angles Theorem
3. $\angle DEC \cong \angle BAC$	3. Transitive Property of Angle Congruence
4. $\triangle DEC \cong \triangle BAC$	4. SAS
5. $\overline{BC} \cong \overline{CD}$, $\angle BCA \cong \angle DCE$	5. Corr. parts of $\cong$ $\triangle$s are $\cong$.
6. $m\angle BCA = m\angle DCE$	6. Definition of congruent angles
7. $m\angle BCA + m\angle ACE = m\angle DCE + m\angle ACE$	7. Addition Property of Equality
8. $m\angle BCE = m\angle DCA$	8. Angle Addition Postulate
9. $\angle BCE \cong \angle DCA$	9. Definition of congruent angles
10. $\triangle BCE \cong \triangle DCA$	10. SAS
11. $\overline{AD} \cong \overline{EB}$	11. Corr. parts of $\cong$ $\triangle$s are $\cong$.

Quiz for Lessons 4.4–4.6 (p. 263)

4.

Statements	Reasons
1. $\angle BAC \cong \angle DCA$, $\overline{AB} \cong \overline{CD}$	1. Given
2. $\overline{AC} \cong \overline{CA}$	2. Reflexive Property of Congruence
3. $\triangle ABC \cong \triangle CDA$	3. SAS

5.

Statements	Reasons
1. $\angle W \cong \angle Z$, $\overline{VW} \cong \overline{YZ}$	1. Given
2. $\angle WXV \cong \angle ZXY$	2. Vertical Angles Congruence Theorem
3. $\triangle VWX \cong \triangle YZX$	3. AAS

6. Show that $\triangle QPL \cong \triangle NML$ by Vertical Angles Congruence Theorem and AAS. Use corresponding parts of congruent triangles are congruent to show that $\overline{QL} \cong \overline{NL}$.

4.7 Problem Solving (pp. 269–270)

49.

Statements	Reasons
1. $\triangle ABC$ is equilateral, $\angle CAD \cong \angle ABE \cong \angle BCF$.	1. Given
2. $m\angle CAD = m\angle ABE = m\angle BCF$	2. Definition of angle congruence
3. $m\angle CAD + m\angle DAB = m\angle CAB$, $m\angle ABE + m\angle EBC = m\angle ABC$, $m\angle BCF + m\angle FCA = m\angle BCA$	3. Angle Addition Postulate
4. $m\angle CAB = m\angle ABC = m\angle BCA$	4. Corollary to the Base Angles Theorem
5. $m\angle CAD + m\angle DAB = m\angle ABE + m\angle EBC = m\angle BCF + m\angle FCA$	5. Substitution
6. $m\angle CAD + m\angle DAB = m\angle CAD + m\angle EBC = m\angle CAD + m\angle FCA$	6. Substitution Property of Equality
7. $m\angle DAB = m\angle EBC = m\angle FCA$	7. Subtraction Property of Equality
8. $\angle DAB \cong \angle EBC \cong \angle FCA$	8. Definition of angle congruence
9. $\triangle ACF \cong \triangle CBE \cong \triangle BAD$	9. ASA
10. $\angle BEC \cong \angle ADB \cong \angle CFA$	10. Corr. parts of $\cong$ $\triangle$s are $\cong$.
11. $\angle BEC$ and $\angle DEF$, $\angle ADB$ and $\angle EDF$, $\angle CFA$ and $\angle DFE$ are linear pairs and are supplementary.	11. Definition of linear pair
12. $\angle DEF \cong \angle EDF \cong \angle DFE$	12. Congruent Supplements Theorem
13. $\triangle DEF$ is equiangular.	13. Definition of equiangular triangle
14. $\triangle DEF$ is equilateral.	14. Corollary to the Converse of Base Angles Theorem

50. *Sample answer:* Choose point $p(x, y) \neq (2, 2)$ and set $PT = PU$. Solve the equation $\sqrt{x^2 + (y-4)^2} = \sqrt{(x-4)^2 + y^2}$ and get $y = x$. The point (2, 2) is excluded because it is a point on $\overrightarrow{TU}$.

Chapter 5

5.1 Investigating Geometry Activity (p. 294)

Step 3.

	Case 1	Case 2
D	(0, 4)	(0, 5.5)
E	(3, 0)	(2.5, 0)
slope of $\overline{AB}$	$-\frac{4}{3}$	$-\frac{11}{5}$
slope of $\overline{DE}$	$-\frac{4}{3}$	$-\frac{11}{5}$
length of $\overline{AB}$	10	$\sqrt{146}$
length of $\overline{DE}$	5	$\sqrt{36.5}$

1. *Sample:*

	Case 3	Case 4
O	(0, 0)	(0, 0)
A	(0, 6)	(0, 3)
B	(4, 0)	(8, 0)
D	(0, 3)	(0, 1.5)
E	(2, 0)	(4, 0)
slope of $\overline{AB}$	$-\frac{3}{2}$	$-\frac{3}{8}$
slope of $\overline{DE}$	$-\frac{3}{2}$	$-\frac{3}{8}$
length of $\overline{AB}$	$2\sqrt{13}$	$\sqrt{73}$
length of $\overline{DE}$	$\sqrt{13}$	$\frac{1}{2}\sqrt{73}$

2–3.

	Case 5	Case 6
O	(0, 0)	(0, 0)
A	(0, *n*)	(0, 2*n*)
B	(*k*, 0)	(2*k*, 0)
D	$\left(0, \frac{n}{2}\right)$	(0, *n*)
E	$\left(\frac{k}{2}, 0\right)$	(*k*, 0)
slope of $\overline{AB}$	$-\frac{n}{k}$	$-\frac{n}{k}$
slope of $\overline{DE}$	$-\frac{n}{k}$	$-\frac{n}{k}$
length of $\overline{AB}$	$\sqrt{n^2 + k^2}$	$2\sqrt{n^2 + k^2}$
length of $\overline{DE}$	$\frac{1}{2}\sqrt{n^2 + k^2}$	$\sqrt{n^2 + k^2}$

5.1 Guided Practice (pp. 295–297) **7.** $(p, 0)$; slope of $\overline{EF} = \frac{r - 0}{(q + p) - p} = \frac{r}{q}$, slope of $\overline{OB} = \frac{2r - 0}{2q - 0} = \frac{r}{q}$, the slopes of $\overline{EF}$ and $\overline{OB}$ are both $\frac{r}{q}$ making $\overline{EF} \parallel \overline{OB}$.

8. *Sample:*

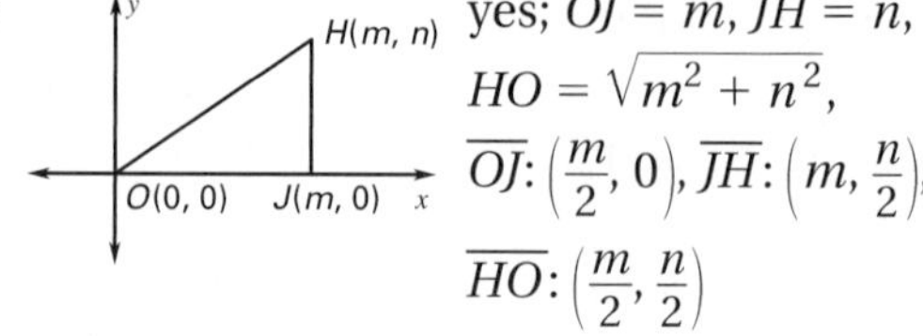

yes; $OJ = m$, $JH = n$, $HO = \sqrt{m^2 + n^2}$, $\overline{OJ}$: $\left(\frac{m}{2}, 0\right)$, $\overline{JH}$: $\left(m, \frac{n}{2}\right)$, $\overline{HO}$: $\left(\frac{m}{2}, \frac{n}{2}\right)$

5.1 Problem Solving (pp. 300–301) **44.** *Sample answer:* Isosceles right triangle ABC with $A(0, p)$, $B(0, 0)$, $C(p, 0)$, and right angle B. $D\left(\frac{p}{2}, \frac{p}{2}\right)$ is the midpoint of $\overline{AC}$. $AB = p$, $BD = \frac{p\sqrt{2}}{2}$, $DA = \frac{p\sqrt{2}}{2}$, $CB = p$, $DC = \frac{p\sqrt{2}}{2}$ which makes the triangles congruent by SSS. In each triangle, pairs of sides are congruent making each triangle isosceles. Since $\angle CDB$ and $\angle ADB$ are a linear pair and are congruent, they are right angles, which makes the triangles congruent isosceles right triangles. **45.** *Sample answer:* $\triangle ABD$ and $\triangle CBD$ are congruent right isosceles triangles with $A(0, p)$, $B(0, 0)$, $C(p, 0)$, and $D\left(\frac{p}{2}, \frac{p}{2}\right)$. $AB = p$, $BC = p$, and $\overline{AB}$ is a vertical line and $\overline{BC}$ is a horizontal line, so $\overline{AB} \perp \overline{BC}$. By definition, $\triangle ABC$ is an isosceles right triangle. **46.** *Sample answer:* A segment joining the midpoints of $\overline{DL}$ and $\overline{EN}$; the length of the the quarter-segment will be $\frac{3}{4}$ the length of $\overline{LN}$ and the length of the eighth-segment will be $\frac{7}{8}$ the length of $\overline{LN}$; $\triangle LMN$, midsegment $\overline{XY}$, quarter-segment $\overline{DE}$, and eighth-segment $\overline{FG}$. $L(0, 0)$, $M(a, b)$, and $N(c, 0)$ leading to $X\left(\frac{a}{2}, \frac{b}{2}\right)$, $Y\left(\frac{a + c}{2}, \frac{b}{2}\right)$, $D\left(\frac{a}{4}, \frac{b}{4}\right)$, $E\left(\frac{a + 3c}{4}, \frac{b}{4}\right)$, $F\left(\frac{a}{8}, \frac{b}{8}\right)$, and $G\left(\frac{a + 7c}{8}, \frac{b}{8}\right)$. $LN = c$, $XY = \frac{c}{2}$, $DE = \frac{3}{4}c$, and $FG = \frac{7}{8}c$.

ADDITIONAL ANSWERS

5.2 Problem Solving (pp. 308–309)

31. Case 1: Given: D, E, and B are collinear.
Prove: $\overline{AB} \cong \overline{BC}$

Statements	Reasons
1. D, E, and B are collinear; $\overline{AD} \cong \overline{CD}$, $\overline{AE} \cong \overline{CE}$.	1. Given
2. Draw $\overleftrightarrow{DB}$ containing point E.	2. Two points determine a line.
3. $\overline{DE} \cong \overline{DE}$	3. Reflexive Property of Segment Congruence
4. $\triangle DAE \cong \triangle DCE$	4. SSS
5. $\angle AED \cong \angle CED$	5. Corr. parts of $\cong$ ⚠ are $\cong$.
6. $\angle AED$ and $\angle AEB$, $\angle CED$ and $\angle CEB$ are linear pairs.	6. Definition of linear pair
7. $\angle AED$ and $\angle AEB$ are supplementary, $\angle CED$ and $\angle CEB$ are supplementary.	7. Linear Pair Postulate
8. $\angle AEB \cong \angle CEB$	8. Congruent Supplements Theorem
9. $\overline{EB} \cong \overline{EB}$	9. Reflexive Property of Segment Congruence
10. $\triangle AEB \cong \triangle CEB$	10. SAS
11. $\overline{AB} \cong \overline{BC}$	11. Corr. parts of $\cong$ ⚠ are $\cong$.

Case 2: Given: $\overline{AB} \cong \overline{BC}$
Prove: D, E, and B are collinear.

Statements	Reasons
1. Draw $\overline{DE}$, $\overline{EB}$, and $\overline{AC}$.	1. Two points determine a line.
2. $\overline{AB} \cong \overline{BC}$, $\overline{AD} \cong \overline{CD}$, $\overline{AE} \cong \overline{CE}$	2. Given
3. $AB = CB$, $AD = CD$, $AE = CE$	3. Definition of congruent segments
4. B is on the perpendicular bisector of $\overline{AC}$, D is on the perpendicular bisector of $\overline{AC}$, E is on the perpendicular bisector of $\overline{AC}$.	4. Converse of the Perpendicular Bisector Theorem
5. There exists only one line that is the perpendicular bisector of $\overline{AC}$, so B, D, and E are all on that same line.	5. Through a point not on a line, there exists only one line through the point perpendicular to the given line.
6. D, E, and B are collinear.	6. Definition of collinear

32.

Statements	Reasons
1. $PQRST$ is a regular polygon, $\overline{SV} \cong \overline{RV}$.	1. Given
2. $\overline{TP} \cong \overline{QP}$, $\overline{TS} \cong \overline{QR}$, $\angle S \cong \angle R$	2. Definition of regular polygon
3. Draw $\overline{TV}$ and $\overline{QV}$.	3. Through any two points there exists exactly one line.
4. $\triangle TSV \cong \triangle QRV$	4. SAS
5. $\overline{VT} \cong \overline{VQ}$	5. Corr. parts of $\cong$ ⚠ are $\cong$.
6. $VT = VQ$, $PT = PQ$	6. Definition of congruent segments
7. V lies on the perpendicular bisector of $\overline{TQ}$; P lies on the perpendicular bisector of $\overline{TQ}$.	7. Converse of the Perpendicular Bisector Theorem
8. $\overline{PV}$ is the perpendicular bisector of $\overline{TQ}$.	8. Perpendicular Postulate

33.

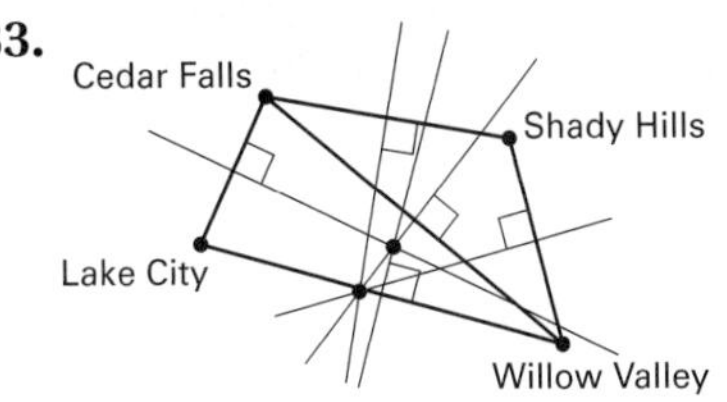

Quiz for Lessons 5.1–5.2 (p. 309)

4.

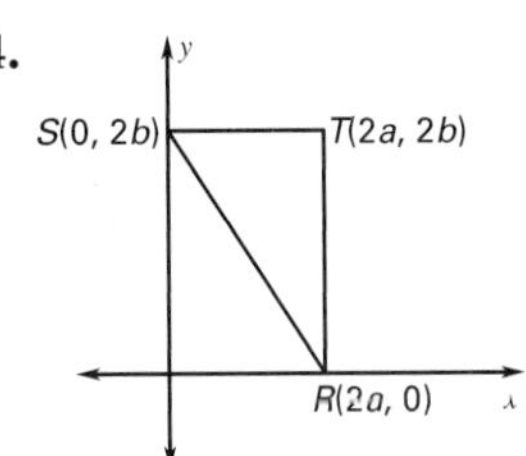

ADDITIONAL ANSWERS

5.3 Problem Solving (pp. 315–316)

36.

Statements	Reasons
1. $\triangle ABC$, $\overline{AD}$ bisects $\angle CAB$, $\overline{BD}$ bisects $\angle CBA$, $\overline{DE} \perp \overline{AB}$, $\overline{DF} \perp \overline{BC}$, $\overline{DG} \perp \overline{CA}$.	1. Given
2. $\angle DGC$, $\angle DFC$, $\angle DFB$, and $\angle DEB$ are right angles.	2. Definition of perpendicular lines
3. $\triangle CGD$, $\triangle CFD$, $\triangle BED$, and $\triangle BFD$ are right triangles.	3. Definition of right triangle
4. $\overline{BD} \cong \overline{BD}$, $\overline{CD} \cong \overline{CD}$	4. Reflexive Property of Segment Congruence
5. $\angle EBD \cong \angle FBD$	5. Definition of angle bisector
6. The angle bisector of $\angle ACB$ passes through point D, the incenter of $\triangle ABC$.	6. Definition of incenter
7. $\angle GCD \cong \angle FCD$	7. Definition of angle bisector
8. $\triangle CGD \cong \triangle CFD$, $\triangle DEB \cong \triangle DFB$	8. AAS
9. $\overline{DG} \cong \overline{DF}$, $\overline{DE} \cong \overline{DF}$	9. Corr. parts of $\cong$ ▲ are $\cong$.
10. $\overline{DG} \cong \overline{DE} \cong \overline{DF}$	10. Transitive Property of Segment Congruence

37. a.

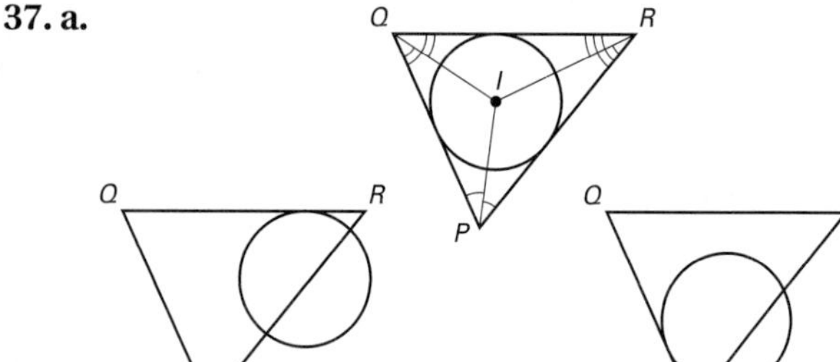

5.4 Problem Solving (pp. 324–325)

45. a.

Statements	Reasons
1. $\overline{LP}$ and $\overline{MQ}$ are medians of scalene $\triangle LMN$, R is on $\overrightarrow{LP}$ such that $\overline{LP} \cong \overline{PR}$, S is on $\overrightarrow{MQ}$ such that $\overline{MQ} \cong \overline{QS}$.	1. Given
2. $\overline{MP} \cong \overline{NP}$, $\overline{QL} \cong \overline{QN}$	2. Definition of median
3. $\angle MPL \cong \angle NPR$, $\angle MQL \cong \angle SQN$	3. Vertical Angles Congruence Theorem
4. $\triangle MPL \cong \triangle NPR$, $\triangle MQL \cong \triangle SQN$	4. SAS
5. $\overline{ML} \cong \overline{NR}$, $\overline{ML} \cong \overline{NS}$	5. Corr. parts of $\cong$ ▲ are $\cong$.
6. $\overline{NR} \cong \overline{NS}$	6. Transitive Property of Segment Congruence

b.

Statements	Reasons
1. $\triangle MPL \cong \triangle NPR$, $\triangle MQL \cong \triangle SQN$	1. Exercise 45a
2. $\angle MLP \cong \angle NRP$, $\angle MLQ \cong \angle SNQ$	2. Corr. parts of $\cong$ ▲ are $\cong$.
3. $\overline{LM} \parallel \overline{RN}$, $\overline{LM} \parallel \overline{SN}$	3. Converse of Alternate Interior Angles Theorem

c.

Statements	Reasons
1. $\overline{LM} \parallel \overline{RN}$, $\overline{LM} \parallel \overline{SN}$	1. Exercise 45b
2. There is exactly one line through N parallel to $\overline{LM}$, so $\overleftrightarrow{RN}$ and $\overleftrightarrow{SN}$ are the same line.	2. Parallel Postulate
3. S, N, and R are collinear.	3. Definition of collinear points

ADDITIONAL ANSWERS

5.5 Problem Solving (pp. 333–334)

47.

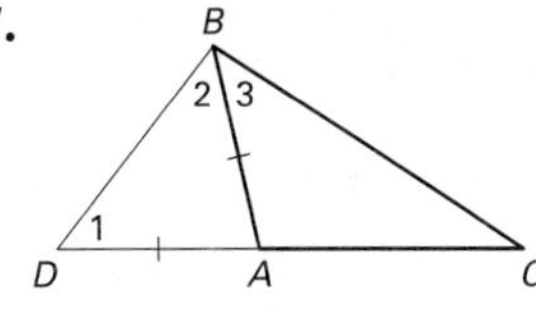

One side, say $\overline{BC}$, is longer than or at least as long as each of the other sides. Then (1) and (2) are true. The proof for (3) follows.

Statements	Reasons
1. $\triangle ABC$	1. Given
2. Extend $\overline{AC}$ to D so that $\overline{AB} \cong \overline{AD}$.	2. Ruler Postulate
3. $AB = AD$	3. Definition of segment congruence
4. $AD + AC = DC$	4. Segment Addition Postulate
5. $\angle 1 \cong \angle 2$	5. Base Angles Theorem
6. $m\angle 1 = m\angle 2$	6. Definition of segment congruence
7. $m\angle DBC > m\angle 2$	7. Protractor Postulate
8. $m\angle DBC > m\angle 1$	8. Substitution Property
9. $DC > BC$	9. If one angle of a triangle is larger than another angle, then the side opposite the larger angle is longer than the side opposite the smaller angle.
10. $AD + AC > BC$	10. Substitution Property
11. $AB + AC > BC$	11. Substitution Property

48. a.

Statements	Reasons
1. $\triangle ABC$ and median $\overline{AM}$	1. Given
2. Extend $\overline{AM}$ to point D such that $\overline{AM} \cong \overline{DM}$, draw $\triangle CDB$.	2. Construction
3. $\overline{MB} \cong \overline{MC}$	3. Definition of median
4. $\angle AMB \cong \angle DMC$	4. Vertical Angles Congruence Theorem
5. $\triangle AMB \cong \triangle DMC$	5. SAS
6. $\overline{AB} \cong \overline{DC}$	6. Corr. parts of $\cong$ $\triangle$s are $\cong$.
7. $AB = DC$, $AM = DM$	7. Definition of segment congruence
8. $AM + MD = AD$	8. Segment Addition Postulate
9. $AM + AM = AD$	9. Substitution Property of Equality
10. $2AM = AD$	10. Simplify.
11. $AD < AC + CD$	11. Triangle Inequality Theorem
12. $AD < AC + AB$	12. Substitution Property
13. $2AM < AC + AB$	13. Substitution
14. $AM < \frac{1}{2}(AC + AB)$	14. Multiplication Property of Equality
15. $\frac{1}{2}(AB + AC) < \frac{1}{2}(AB + AC + BC)$	15. Property of Real Numbers
16. $AM < \frac{1}{2}(AB + AC + BC)$	16. Transitive Property

b. In $\triangle ABC$, let $\overline{AX}$, $\overline{BY}$, and $\overline{CZ}$ be medians. By the Concurrence of Medians of Triangle Theorem and the Triangle Inequality Theorem, $\frac{2}{3}AX + \frac{2}{3}BY > AB$, $\frac{2}{3}AX + \frac{2}{3}CZ > AC$, and $\frac{2}{3}BY + \frac{2}{3}CZ > BC$. Adding the left sides and right sides of the three inequalities you get $\frac{4}{3}(AX + BY + CZ) > AB + AC + BC$. Multiplying both sides by $\frac{3}{4}$ you get $AX + BY + CZ > \frac{3}{4}(AB + AC + BC)$. Therefore $AX + BY + CZ > \frac{1}{2}(AB + AC + BC)$.

5.5 Mixed Review (p. 334)

52.
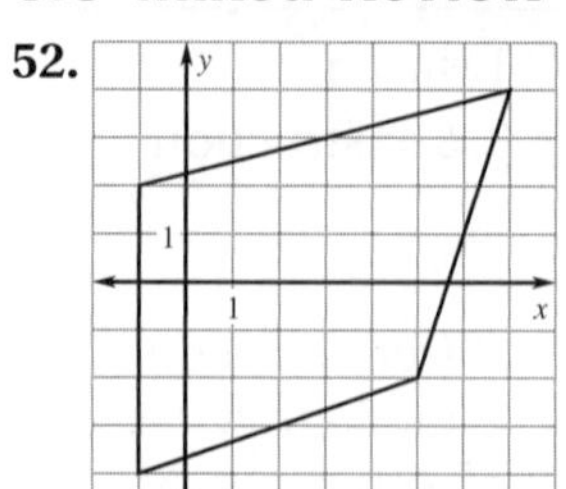

53.
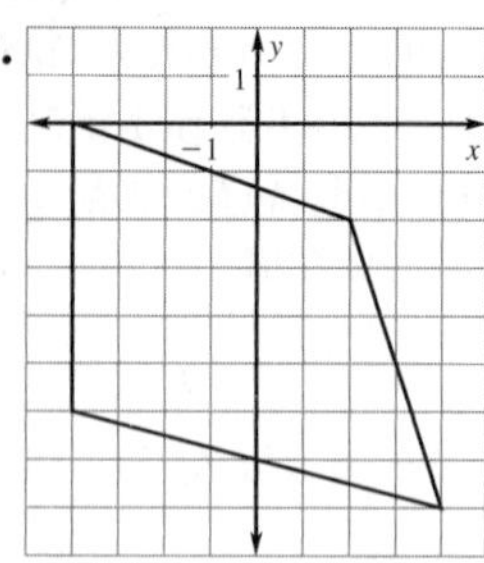

54.
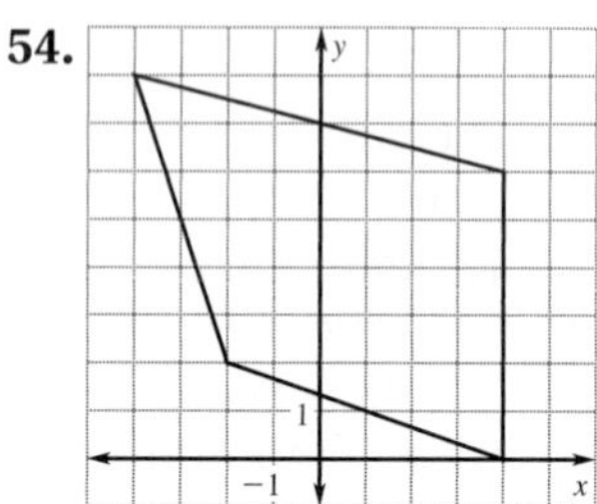

5.6 Problem Solving (pp. 340–341)

28. *Sample answer:* Step 1: Since $\overline{BC} \cong \overline{EF}$, $\angle CBP \cong \angle FED$ by construction, and $\overline{BP} \cong \overline{ED}$ by construction, you have $\triangle PBC \cong \triangle DEF$ by SAS. Step 2: Since $\overrightarrow{BH}$ bisects $\angle PBA$ by construction, you have $\angle PBH \cong \angle ABH$. Using the Transitive Property of Segment Congruence, you know that $\overline{AB} \cong \overline{PB}$. Using the Reflexive Property of Segment Congruence, you have $\overline{BH} \cong \overline{BH}$. Therefore $\triangle ABH \cong \triangle PBH$ by SAS. Step 3: $AC = AH + HC$ by the Segment Addition Postulate. $AH + HC = PH + HC$ by corr. parts of $\cong$ ▲ are $\cong$. $PH + HC > PC$ by the Triangle Inequality Theorem. $PC = DF$ by corr. parts of $\cong$ ▲ are $\cong$. So, $AC > DF$.

Chapter 6

6.2 Problem Solving (pp. 368–370)

34.
$$\frac{a-b}{a+b} = \frac{c-d}{c+d}$$
$$(a-b)(c+d) = (a+b)(c-d)$$
$$ac + ad - bc - bd = ac - ad + bc - bd$$
$$2ad = 2bc$$
$$ad = bc$$
$$\frac{a}{b} = \frac{c}{d}$$

35.
$$\frac{a+c}{b+d} = \frac{a-c}{b-d}$$
$$(a+c)(b-d) = (a-c)(b+d)$$
$$ab - ad + bc - cd = ab + ad - bc - cd$$
$$-2ad = -2bc$$
$$ad = bc$$
$$\frac{a}{b} = \frac{c}{d}$$

36. $\frac{a}{b} = r$, $a = br$, $c = dr$, $e = fr$;
$$\frac{a+c+e}{b+d+f} = \frac{br+dr+fr}{b+d+f} = \frac{r(b+d+f)}{b+d+f} = r = \frac{a}{b}$$

6.6 Problem Solving (pp. 402–403)

29. Draw $\overline{AN}$ and $\overline{CM}$ so they are both parallel to $\overline{BY}$. $\triangle APN \sim \triangle MPC$, $\triangle CXM \sim \triangle BXP$, and $\triangle BZP \sim \triangle AZN$ using the AA Similarity Postulate. From $\triangle APN \sim \triangle MPC$ you get $\frac{AP}{MP} = \frac{AN}{MC}$ using the definition of similarity. Similarly from $\triangle CXM \sim \triangle BXP$ and $\triangle BZP \sim \triangle AZN$ you get $\frac{CX}{BX} = \frac{MC}{PB}$ and $\frac{BZ}{AZ} = \frac{BP}{AN}$, respectively. Using Theorem 6.4 and $\triangle ACM$, you get $\frac{AY}{YC} = \frac{AP}{PM}$. Now $\frac{AY}{YC} \cdot \frac{CX}{BX} \cdot \frac{BZ}{AZ} = \frac{AN}{MC} \cdot \frac{MC}{PB} \cdot \frac{BP}{AN} = 1$.

Extension (p. 407)

2. a.

1 unit

Stage 0, 1, 2, 3, 4, 5

b.

Stage	Number of segments	Segment length	Total length
0	1	1	1
1	2	$\frac{1}{3}$	$\frac{5}{3}$
2	4	$\frac{1}{9}$	$\frac{19}{9}$
3	8	$\frac{1}{27}$	$\frac{65}{27}$
4	16	$\frac{1}{81}$	$\frac{211}{81}$
5	32	$\frac{1}{243}$	$\frac{665}{243}$

3. a.
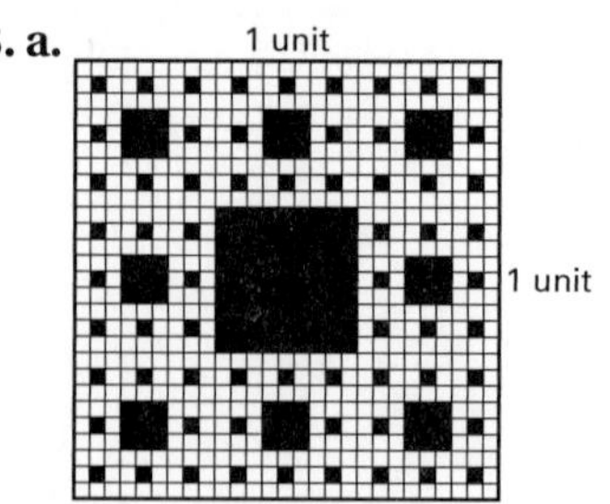

c.

Stage	Number of colored squares	Area of 1 colored square	Total area
0	0	0	0
1	1	$\frac{1}{9}$	$\frac{1}{9}$
2	8	$\frac{1}{81}$	$\frac{17}{81}$
3	64	$\frac{1}{729}$	$\frac{217}{729}$

6.7 Investigating Geometry Activity (p. 408)

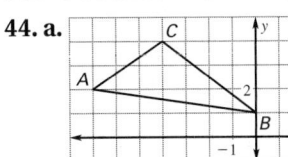

2.

Chapter 7

7.2 Problem Solving (pp. 445–447)

44. a.

c. $\triangle ABC$ is not a right triangle; $\overline{AB}$ is the longest side, so when you find the lengths of the sides and plug them into the Pythagorean Theorem, you get $(\sqrt{13})^2 + 5^2 \stackrel{?}{=} (5\sqrt{2})^2$ and since this statement is false, the triangle is not a right triangle.

7.3 Problem Solving (pp. 455–456)

35.

Statements	Reasons
1. $\triangle ABC$ is a right triangle; altitude $\overline{CD}$ is drawn to hypotenuse $\overline{AB}$.	1. Given
2. $\angle CDB$ is a right angle.	2. Definition of altitude
3. $\angle B \cong \angle B$	3. Reflexive Property of Congruence
4. $\angle CDB \cong \angle ACB$	4. Right Angle Congruence Theorem
5. $\triangle CBD \sim \triangle ABC$	5. AA Similarity Postulate
6. $\angle CDA$ is a right angle.	6. Definition of altitude
7. $\angle A \cong \angle A$	7. Reflexive Property of Congruence
8. $\angle CDA \cong \angle BCA$	8. Right Angle Congruence Theorem
9. $\triangle ACD \sim \triangle ABC$	9. AA Similarity Postulate
10. $\angle ACD \cong \angle B$	10. Congruent Complements Theorem
11. $\angle ADC \cong \angle CDB$	11. Right Angle Congruence Theorem
12. $\triangle ADC \sim \triangle CDB$	12. AA Similarity Postulate

36.

Statements	Reasons
1. $\triangle ABC$ is a right triangle; altitude $\overline{CD}$ is drawn to hypotenuse $\overline{AB}$.	1. Given
2. $\triangle ADC \sim \triangle CBD$	2. If an altitude is drawn to the hypotenuse of a right triangle, then the two triangles formed are similar to the original triangle and to each other.
3. $\frac{CD}{AD} = \frac{BD}{CD}$	3. Definition of similar figures

37.

Statements	Reasons
1. $\triangle ABC$ is a right triangle; altitude $\overline{CD}$ is drawn to hypotenuse $\overline{AB}$.	1. Given
2. $\triangle ABC \sim \triangle CBD$	2. If an altitude is drawn to the hypotenuse of a right triangle, then the two triangles formed are similar to the original triangle and to each other.
3. $\frac{AB}{CB} = \frac{CB}{DB}$	3. Definition of similar figures
4. $\triangle ABC \sim \triangle ACD$	4. If an altitude is drawn to the hypotenuse of a right triangle, then the two triangles formed are similar to the original triangle and to each other.
5. $\frac{AB}{AC} = \frac{AC}{AD}$	5. Definition of similar figures

7.4 Problem Solving (pp. 463–464)

34. a. $r = \sqrt{2}$, $s = \sqrt{3}$, $t = 2$, $u = \sqrt{5}$, $v = \sqrt{6}$, $w = \sqrt{7}$; r is the hypotenuse of an isosceles right triangle, so it must be $\sqrt{2}$, this then becomes a leg of another right triangle. With the Pythagorean Theorem and the given fact that the other leg is 1, I determined the value of the hypotenuse, and continued the procedure.

35. a.

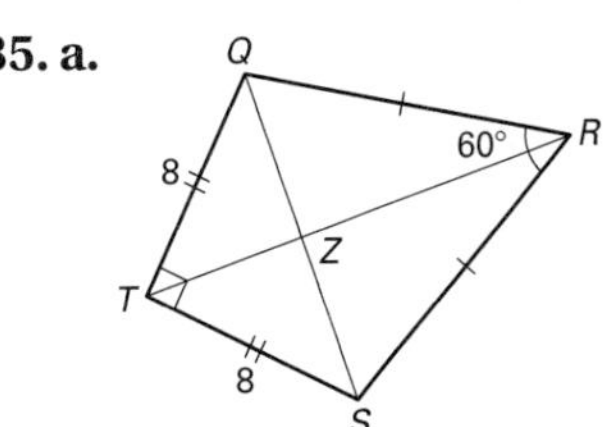

7.5 Problem Solving (pp. 471–472)

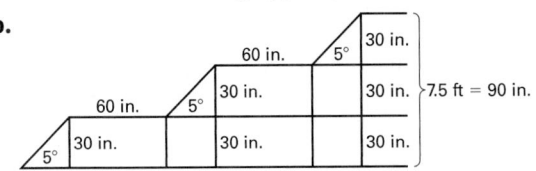

37. b.

7.6 Problem Solving (pp. 479–480)

39. a.

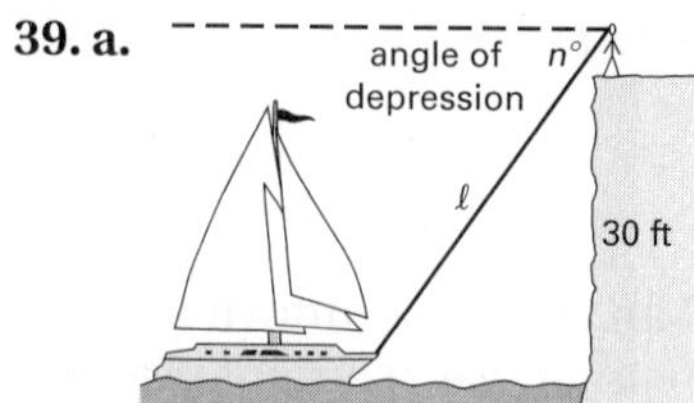

b.

n (degrees)	40	50	60	70	80
ℓ (feet)	46.7	39.2	34.6	31.9	30.5

c.

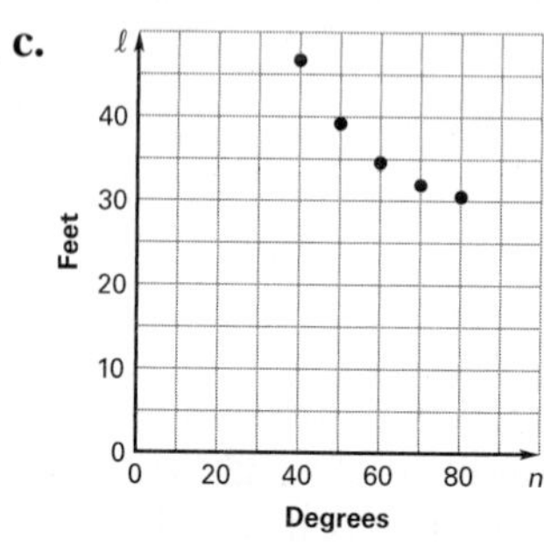

40. The Pythagorean Theorem tells us that $GT = \sqrt{3}$, so $\cos G = \frac{\sqrt{3}}{2}$. Since $\triangle EQU$ is equilateral, all angles must be 60°. To determine the height, drop an altitude from one angle down. This bisects the angle and you have a 30°-60°-90° triangle with $\sin E = \frac{\sqrt{3}}{2}$. Therefore $\sin E = \cos G$.

41. a.

θ	$\sin\theta$	$\cos\theta$
17°	0.2924	0.9563
30°	0.5	0.8660
34°	0.5592	0.8290
45°	0.7071	0.7071
56°	0.8290	0.5592
60°	0.8660	0.5
73°	0.9563	0.2924
90°	1	0

7.7 Mixed Review (p. 489)

43.

Number of sides	Type of polygon
5	Pentagon
12	Dodecagon
8	Octagon
3	Triangle
7	Heptagon
n	n-gon
4	Quadrilateral
10	Decagon
9	Nonagon
6	Hexagon

Chapter 8

8.1 Problem Solving (pp. 512–513)

37. a.

Polygon	Number of sides	Number of triangles	Sum of measures of interior angles
Quadrilateral	4	2	$2 \cdot 180° = 360°$
Pentagon	5	3	$3 \cdot 180° = 540°$
Hexagon	6	4	$4 \cdot 180° = 720°$
Heptagon	7	5	$5 \cdot 180° = 900°$

8.2 Skill Practice (pp. 518–519)

37.

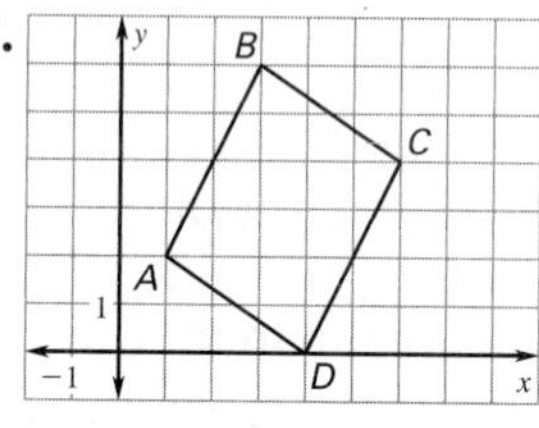

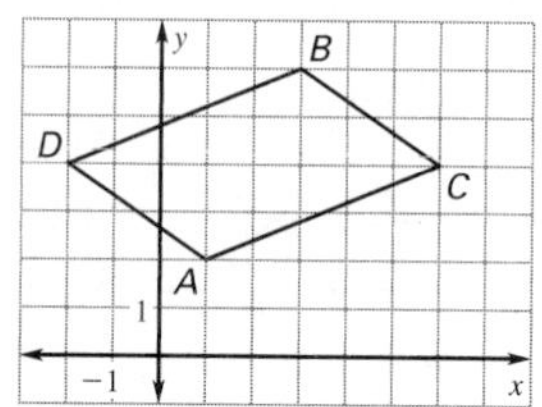

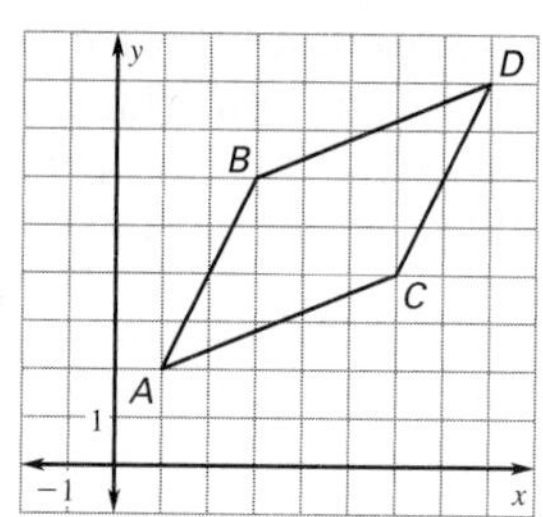

8.2 Problem Solving (pp. 520–521)

44.

Statements	Reasons
1. $PQRS$ is a parallelogram.	1. Given
2. $\overline{PQ} \cong \overline{RS}$, $\overline{QR} \cong \overline{SP}$	2. If a quadrilateral is a parallelogram, then its opposite sides are congruent.
3. $\angle QPR \cong \angle SRP$, $\angle PQS \cong \angle RSQ$; $\angle RPS \cong \angle QRP$, $\angle PSQ \cong \angle RQS$	3. Alternate Interior Angles Congruence Theorem
4. $\triangle PMQ \cong \triangle RMS$, $\triangle QMR \cong \triangle SMP$	4. ASA
5. $\overline{QM} \cong \overline{SM}$, $\overline{PM} \cong \overline{RM}$	5. Corr. parts of $\cong$ △s are $\cong$.
6. M bisects $\overline{QS}$ and $\overline{PR}$.	6. Definition of segment bisector

45. *Sample answer:* $\triangle DCG \sim \triangle ACF$ and $\triangle DAE \sim \triangle ACF$ using the AA Similarity Postulate. $\frac{DG}{AF} = \frac{DC}{AC}$ and $\frac{DE}{AF} = \frac{DA}{AC}$ since the ratios of corresponding sides of similar triangles are equal. Adding you get $\frac{DE}{AF} + \frac{DG}{AF} = \frac{DA}{AC} + \frac{DC}{AC}$, which implies $\frac{DE + DG}{AF} = \frac{DA + DC}{AC}$, which implies $\frac{DE + DG}{AF} = \frac{AC}{AC}$, which implies $\frac{DE + DG}{AF} = 1$, which implies $DE + DG = AF$.

ADDITIONAL ANSWERS

8.3 Skill Practice (pp. 526–527)

11. 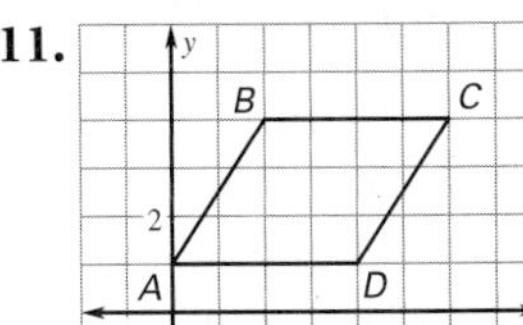

Sample answer: $AB = CD = 5$ and $BC = DA = 8$

12. 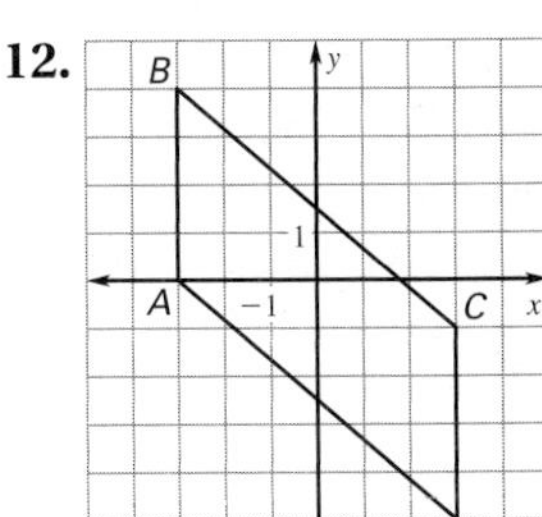

Sample answer: $AB = CD = 4$ and $BC = DA = \sqrt{61}$

13. 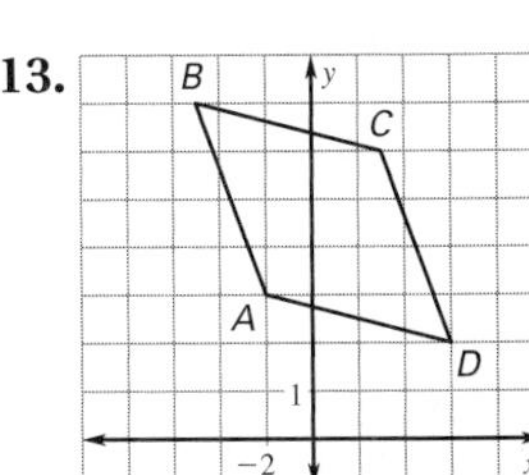

Sample answer: $AB = CD = 5$ and $BC = DA = \sqrt{65}$

14. 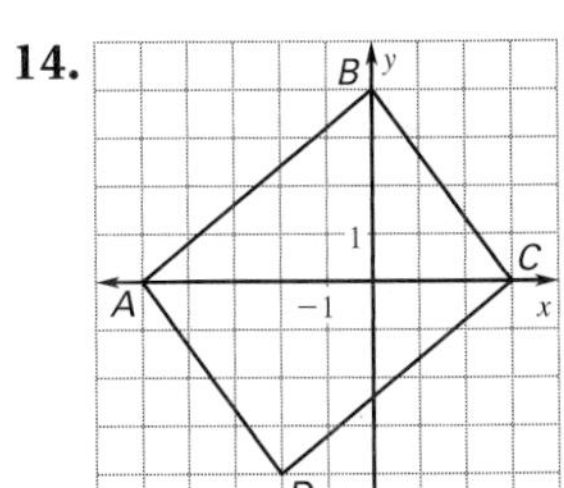

Sample answer: $AB = CD = \sqrt{41}$ and $BC = DA = 5$

29. *Sample answer:* Draw a line passing through points A and B. At points A and B, construct $\overrightarrow{AP}$ and $\overrightarrow{BQ}$ such that the angle each ray makes with the line is the same. Mark off congruent segments starting at points A and B along $\overrightarrow{AP}$ and $\overrightarrow{BQ}$, respectively. Draw the line segment joining these two endpoints.

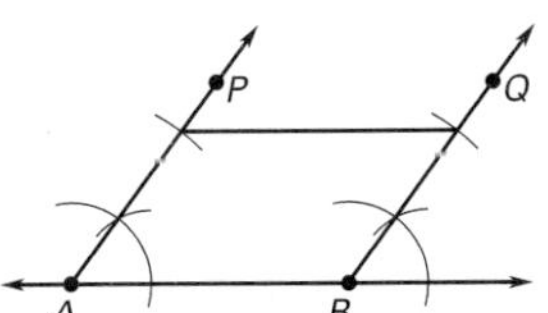

8.3 Problem Solving (pp. 528–529)

40. It is given that $DEBF$ is a parallelogram and $AE = CF$. Since $DEBF$ is a parallelogram, you know that $FD = EB$, $\angle BFD \cong \angle DEB$, and $ED = FB$. $AE + EB = CF + FD$ which implies that $AB = CD$, which implies that $\overline{AB} \cong \overline{CD}$. $\angle BFC$ and $\angle BFD$, and $\angle DEB$ and $\angle DEA$ form linear pairs, thus making them supplementary. Using the Congruent Supplements Theorem, $\angle BFC \cong \angle DEA$ making $\triangle AED \cong \triangle CFB$ using SAS. Using corresponding parts of congruent triangles are congruent, $\overline{AD} \cong \overline{CB}$. Theorem 8.7 tells you that $ABCD$ is a parallelogram.

41. *Sample answer:* Consider the diagram. $\overline{FG}$ is the midsegment of $\triangle CBD$ and therefore is parallel to $\overline{BD}$ and half of its length. $\overline{EH}$ is the midsegment of $\triangle ABD$ and therefore is parallel to $\overline{BD}$ and half of its length. This makes $\overline{EH}$ and $\overline{FG}$ both parallel and congruent. Using Theorem 8.9, $EFGH$ is a parallelogram.

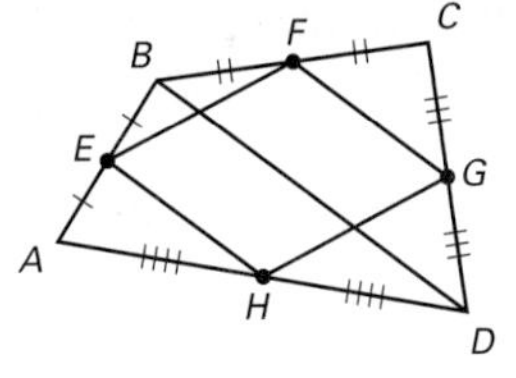

42. $\overline{FJ}$ is the midsegment of $\triangle AED$ and therefore is parallel to $\overline{AD}$ and half of its length. $\overline{GH}$ is the midsegment of $\triangle BEC$ and therefore is parallel to $\overline{BC}$ and half of its length. Together this gives you $\overline{FJ} \cong \overline{GH}$ and $\overline{FJ} \parallel \overline{GH}$. Using Theorem 8.9, $FGHJ$ is a parallelogram.

8.4 Skill Practice (pp. 537–539)

9–14. Check students' diagrams. **9.** Always; in a rectangle all interior angles measure 90°. **10.** Always; in a rectangle opposite pairs of sides are congruent. **11.** Sometimes; adjacent sides are congruent if the rectangle is a square. **12.** Always; diagonals of a rectangle are congruent. **13.** Sometimes; diagonals are perpendicular if the rectangle is a square. **14.** Sometimes; interior angles are bisected if the rectangle is a square. **15.** Square; the quadrilateral has four congruent sides and angles. **16.** Rectangle; both pairs of opposite sides are congruent and all of the angles are right angles. **17.** Rhombus. *Sample answer:* The fourth angle measure is 40°, meaning that both pairs of opposite sides are parallel. So the figure is a parallelogram with two consecutive sides congruent. But this is only possible if the remaining two sides are also congruent, so the quadrilateral is a rhombus.

18.

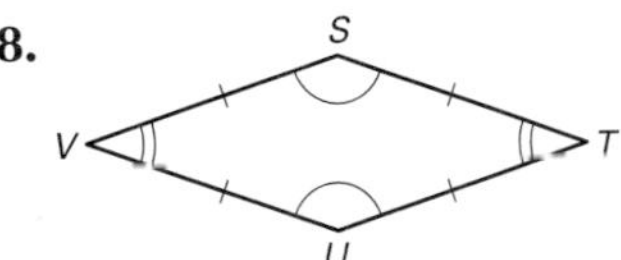

8.4 Problem Solving (pp. 539–540)

62. a. $\angle ABD \cong \angle CDB$ using the Alternate Interior Angles Theorem; $\angle ADB \cong \angle ABD$; $\overline{AB} \cong \overline{AD}$; $\angle ADB \cong \angle ABD$ using the Transitive Property of Congruence and $\overline{AB} \cong \overline{AD}$ using the Converse of Base Angles Theorem. **b.** Rhombus; if $\overline{AD} \parallel \overline{BC}$, then the quadrilateral is a parallelogram by definition. Using the fact that opposite sides of a parallelogram are congruent along with the fact that $\overline{AB} \cong \overline{AD}$, as shown in part (a), means all four sides of the parallelogram are congruent. Therefore, $ABCD$ is a rhombus by definition. **63.** *Sample answer:* Let rectangle $ABCD$ have vertices (0, 0), $(a, 0)$, (a, b), and $(0, b)$ respectively. The diagonal $\overline{AC}$ has a length of $\sqrt{a^2 + b^2}$ and diagonal $\overline{BD}$ has a length of $\sqrt{a^2 + b^2}$. So, $AC = BD = \sqrt{a^2 + b^2}$.

64. *Sample answer:* Let parallelogram *DFGH* have vertices $D(a, \sqrt{b^2 - a^2})$, $F(b, 0)$, $G(-a, -\sqrt{b^2 - a^2})$, and $H(-b, 0)$, respectively. The slope of $\overline{HG}$ and $\overline{DF}$ is $\frac{\sqrt{b^2 - a^2}}{a - b}$ and the slope of $\overline{HD}$ and $\overline{GF}$ is $\frac{\sqrt{b^2 - a^2}}{a + b}$. The product of the slopes of $\overline{HG}$ and $\overline{GF}$, $\overline{GF}$ and $\overline{DF}$, $\overline{DF}$ and $\overline{HD}$, and $\overline{HD}$ and $\overline{HG}$ is -1, making each pair of consecutive segments perpendicular and each angle a right angle. Therefore, parallelogram *DFGH* is a rectangle.

8.5 Problem Solving (pp. 548–549) **38.** Since $\overline{FG} \parallel \overline{EJ}$ and $\overline{EF} \parallel \overline{JG}$, *EFGJ* is a parallelogram. Using the Corresponding Angles Theorem, $\angle E \cong \angle GJH$. It was given that $\angle E \cong \angle H$, therefore $\angle GJH \cong \angle H$ using the Transitive Property of Congruence. By the Converse of the Base Angles Theorem, $\triangle GHJ$ is isosceles with $\overline{JG} \cong \overline{HG}$. Since *EFGH* is a parallelogram, $\overline{JG} \cong \overline{EF}$. Using the Transitive Property of Congruence, $\overline{EF} \cong \overline{HG}$. This makes *EFGJ* an isosceles trapezoid. **39.** Given: *JKLM* is an isosceles trapezoid with $\overline{KL} \parallel \overline{JM}$ and $\overline{JK} \cong \overline{LM}$. Since pairs of base angles are congruent in an isosceles trapezoid, $\angle JKL \cong \angle MLK$. Using the Reflexive Property of Congruence, $\overline{KL} \cong \overline{KL}$. $\triangle JKL \cong \triangle MLK$ using the SAS Congruence Postulate. Using corresponding parts of congruent triangles are congruent, $\overline{JL} \cong \overline{KM}$. **40.** In a triangle the midsegment's length is half the length of the third side, therefore $BG = \frac{1}{2}CD$ and $GE = \frac{1}{2}AF$. This implies that $BG + GE = \frac{1}{2}CD + \frac{1}{2}AF$, which implies $BE = \frac{CD + AF}{2}$. **41.** Given: *ABCD* is a kite with $\overline{AB} \cong \overline{CB}$ and $\overline{AD} \cong \overline{CD}$. Using the Reflexive Property of Congruence, $\overline{BD} \cong \overline{BD}$ and $\overline{ED} \cong \overline{ED}$. Using the SSS Congruence Postulate, $\triangle BAD \cong \triangle BCD$. Using corresponding parts of congruent triangles are congruent, $\angle CDE \cong \angle ADE$. Using the SAS Congruence Postulate, $\triangle CDE \cong \triangle ADE$. Using corresponding parts of congruent triangles are congruent, $\angle CED \cong \angle AED$. Since $\angle CED$ and $\angle AED$ are congruent and form a linear pair, they are right angles. This makes $\overline{AC} \perp \overline{BD}$. **42.** Given: *EFGH* is a kite with $\overline{EF} \cong \overline{GF}$ and $\overline{EH} \cong \overline{GH}$. Construct $\overline{FH}$. Using the Reflexive Property of Congruence, $\overline{FH} \cong \overline{FH}$. Using the SSS Congruence Postulate, $\triangle FGH \cong \triangle FEH$. Using corresponding parts of congruent triangles are congruent, $\angle G \cong \angle E$. Now suppose $\angle F \cong \angle H$. This would make *EFGH* a parallelogram and *EFGH* would not be a kite. This contradicts the given, thus $\angle F$ is not congruent to $\angle H$.

43. If the diagonals of a trapezoid are congruent, then the trapezoid is isosceles. Given: trapezoid *JKLM* with $\overline{KM} \cong \overline{JL}$. Draw $\overline{KP}$ perpendicular to $\overline{JM}$ at point *P* and draw $\overline{LQ}$ perpendicular to $\overline{JM}$ at point *Q*. *KLQP* is a rectangle with $\overline{KP} \cong \overline{LQ}$. Since $\triangle LQJ$ and $\triangle KPM$ are right triangles, they are congruent by the HL Congruence Theorem. Using corresponding parts of congruent triangles are congruent, $\angle LJM \cong \angle KMJ$. Using the Reflexive Property of Congruence, $\overline{JM} \cong \overline{JM}$. $\triangle LJM \cong \triangle KMJ$ by the SAS Congruence Postulate. Using corresponding parts of congruent triangles are congruent, $\overline{KJ} \cong \overline{LM}$. Trapezoid *JKLM* is isosceles.

Extension (p. 551)

4. front top side

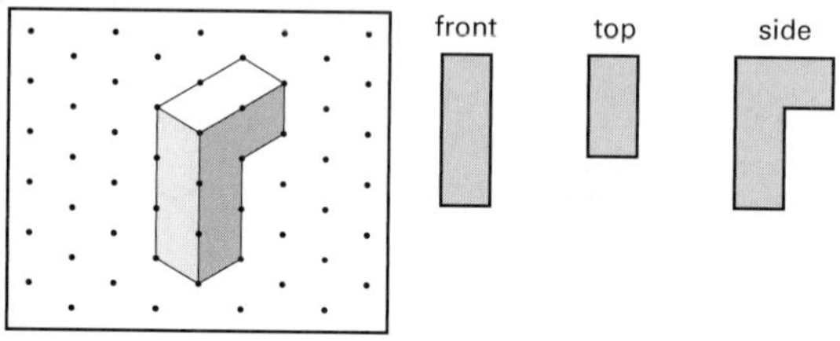

5. front top side

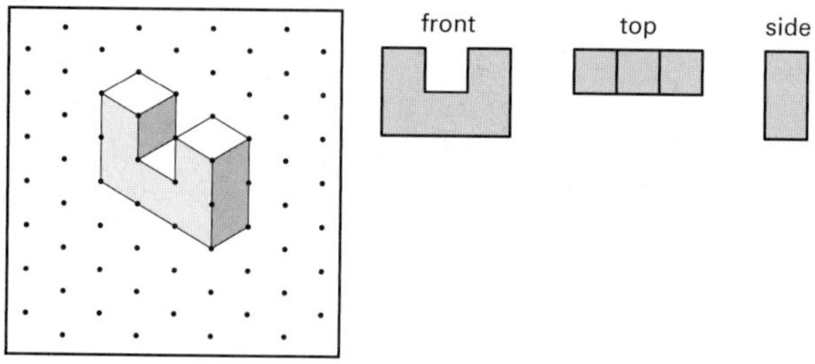

6. front top side

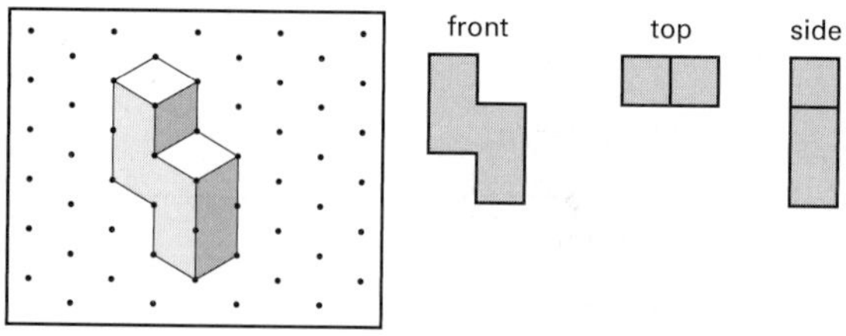

7. front top side

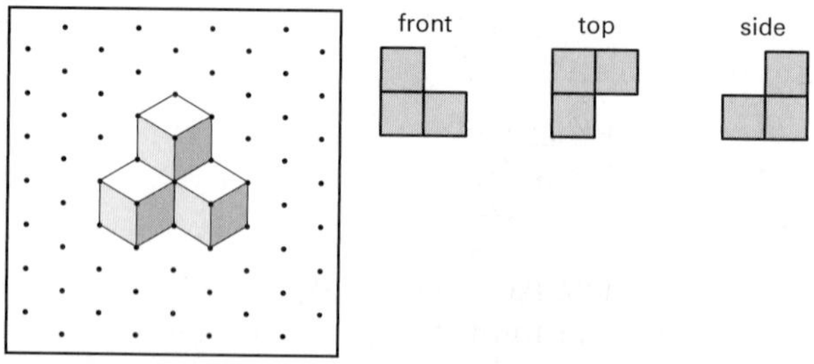

8. front top side

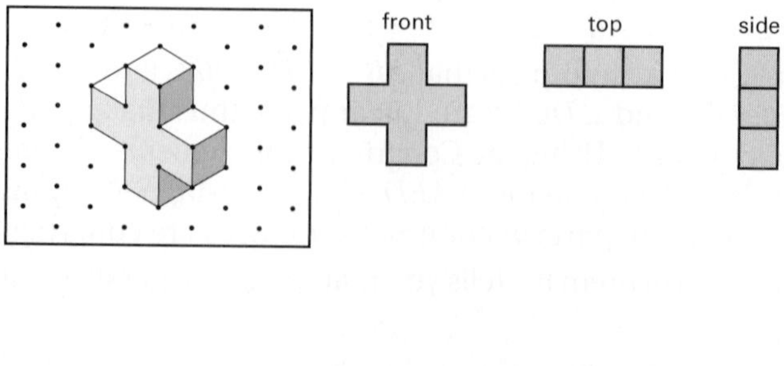

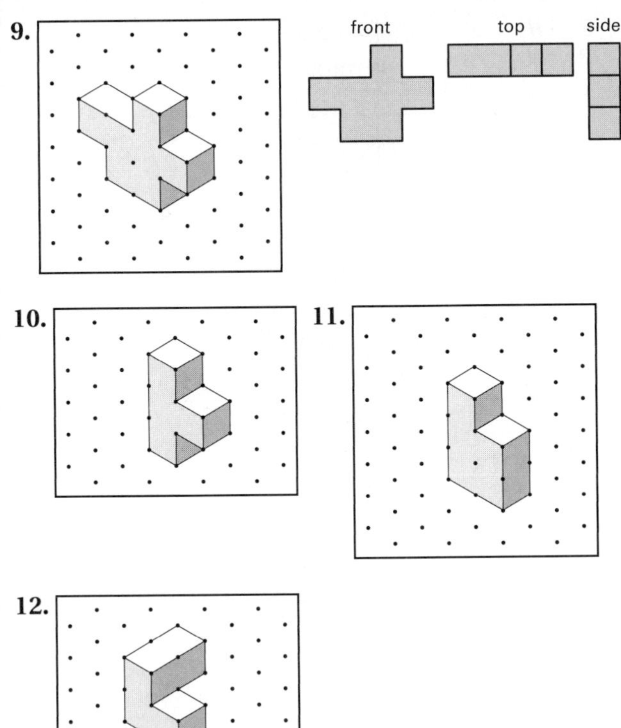

8.6 Mixed Review (p. 557)

45. 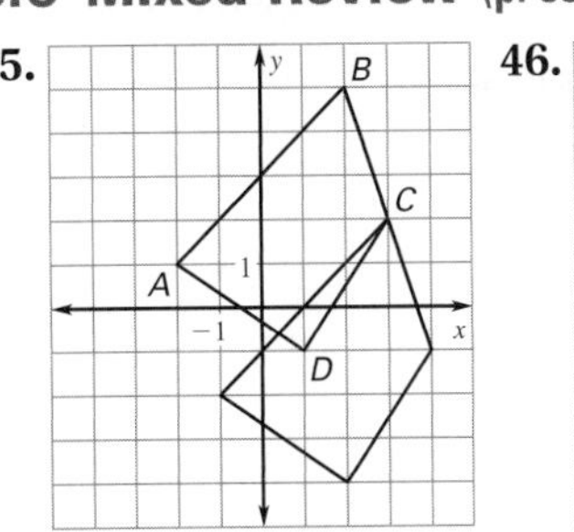

46. 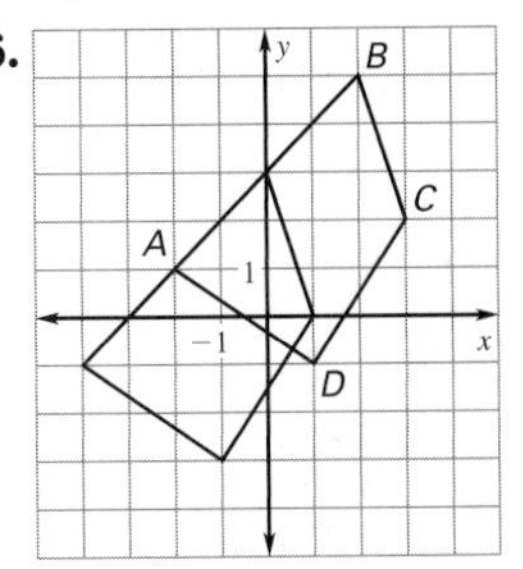

Algebra Review (p. 565)

7. 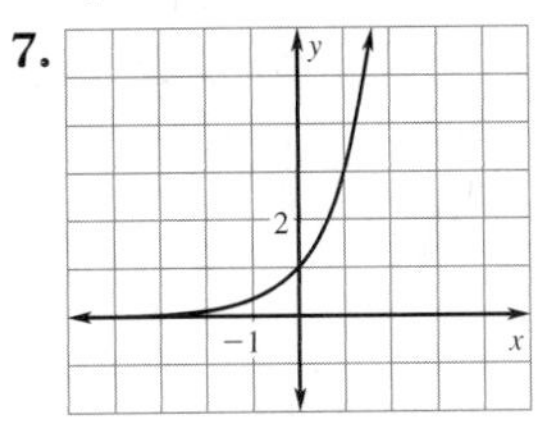

8. 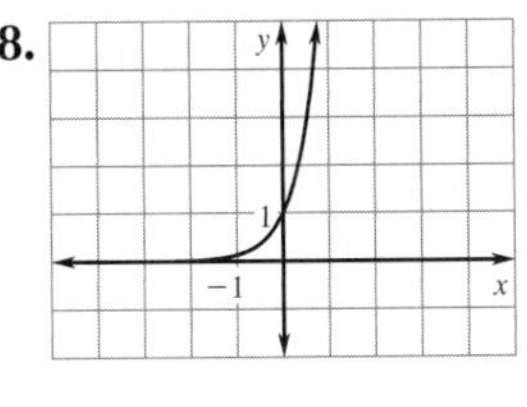

9. 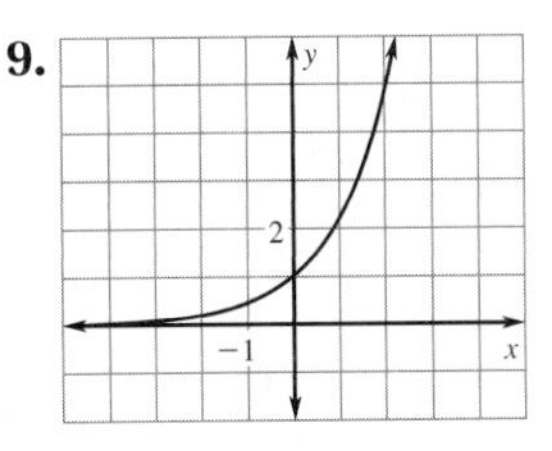

10. 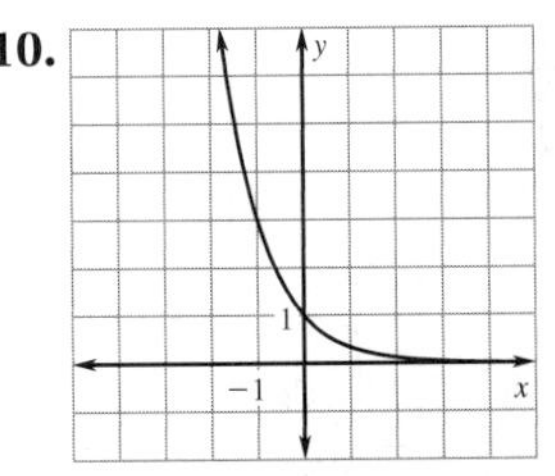

11. 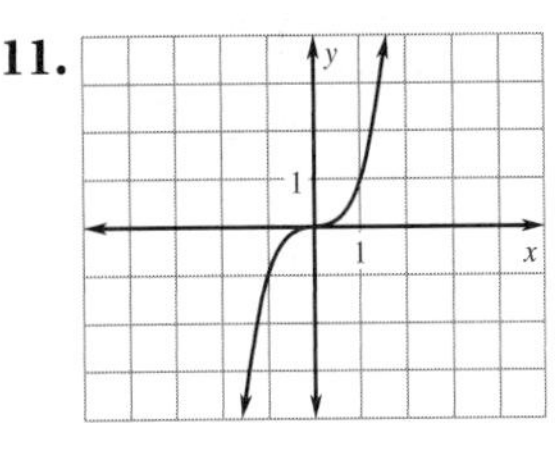

12. 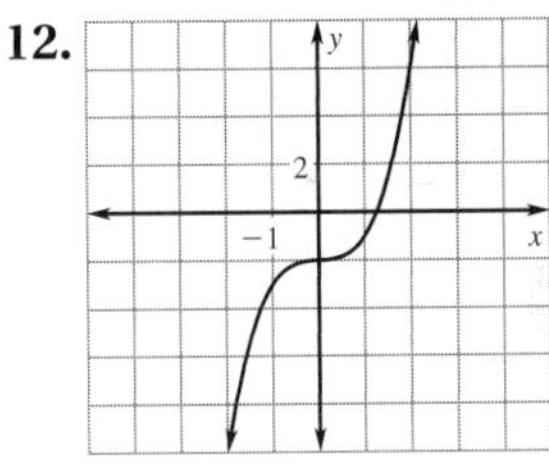

13. 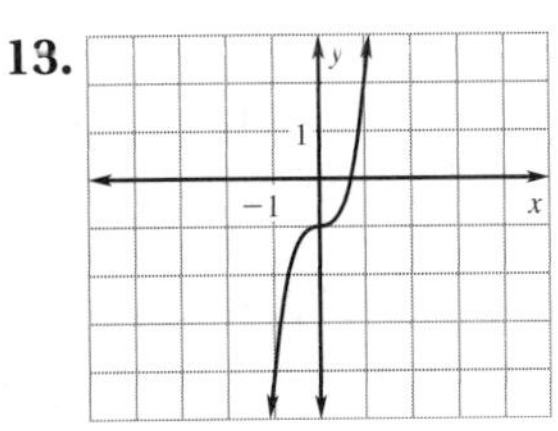

14. 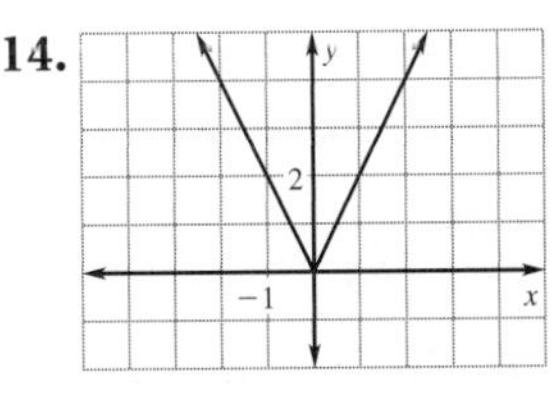

15. 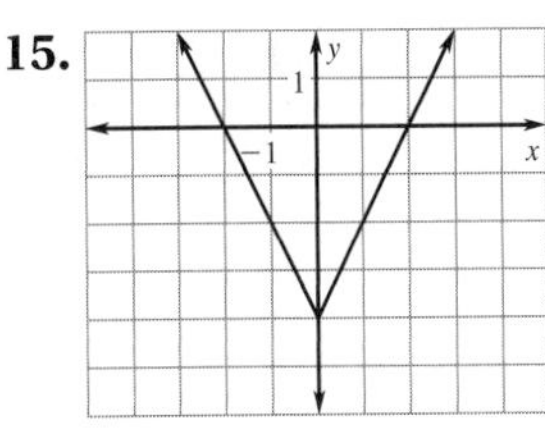

16. 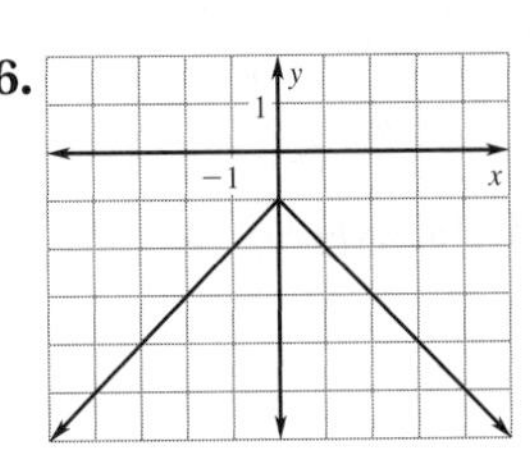

8.6 Problem Solving (pp. 556–557) **41.** Square; Given: *PQRS* is a square with *E, F, G,* and *H* midpoints of the square. Using the definition of a square and the definition of midpoint, $\overline{FQ} \cong \overline{QG} \cong \overline{GR} \cong \overline{RH} \cong \overline{HS} \cong \overline{SE} \cong \overline{PE} \cong \overline{PF}$. Using the definition of a square, $\angle P \cong \angle Q \cong \angle R \cong \angle S$. Using the SAS Congruence Theorem, $\triangle EPF \cong \triangle FQG \cong \triangle GRH \cong \triangle HSE$. Using corresponding parts of congruent triangles are congruent, $\overline{EF} \cong \overline{FG} \cong \overline{GH} \cong \overline{HE}$. Since the base angles of all four triangles measure 45°, $m\angle EFG = m\angle FGH = m\angle GHE = m\angle HEF$. By definition, *PQRS* is a square. **42.** Rhombus; Given: Three-dimensional figure and $\overline{JK} \cong \overline{LM}$; *E, F, G,* and *H* are the midpoints of $\overline{JL}$, $\overline{KL}$, $\overline{KM}$, and $\overline{JM}$, respectively. Using the definition of midsegment, $\overline{FG}$ and $\overline{EH}$ are parallel to $\overline{LM}$ and each measures half of its length. This makes $\overline{FG} \parallel \overline{EH}$ and $\overline{FG} \cong \overline{EH}$. Using the definition of midsegment, $\overline{GH}$ and $\overline{FE}$ are parallel to $\overline{JK}$ and each measures half of its length. This makes $\overline{GH} \parallel \overline{FE}$ and $\overline{GH} \cong \overline{FE}$. Since $\overline{JK} \cong \overline{LM}$, you know that $\overline{FG} \cong \overline{EH} \cong \overline{GH} \cong \overline{FE}$ by the Transitive Property of Congruence. By definition, *EFGH* is a rhombus.

ADDITIONAL ANSWERS

Chapter 9

9.1 Guided Practice (pp. 572–575)

1. 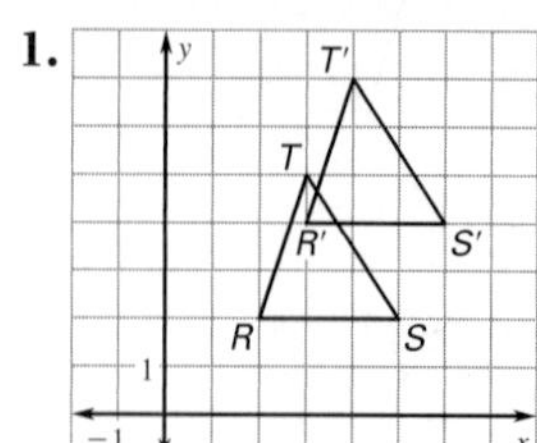

9.1 Skill Practice (pp. 576–577)

7. 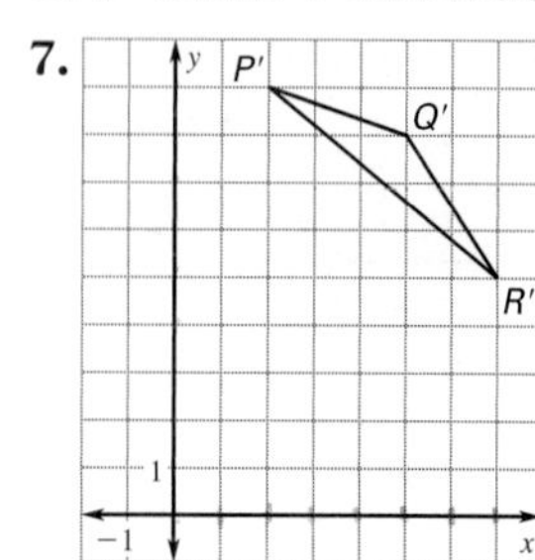

8. 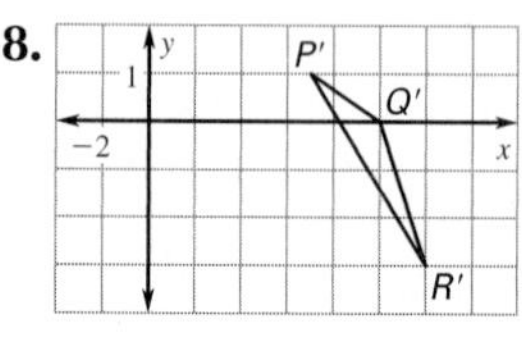

9. 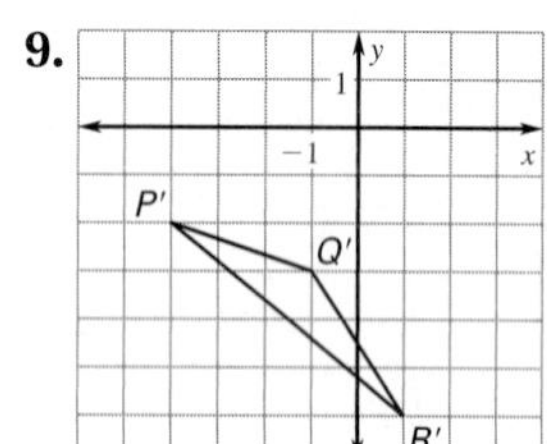

10. 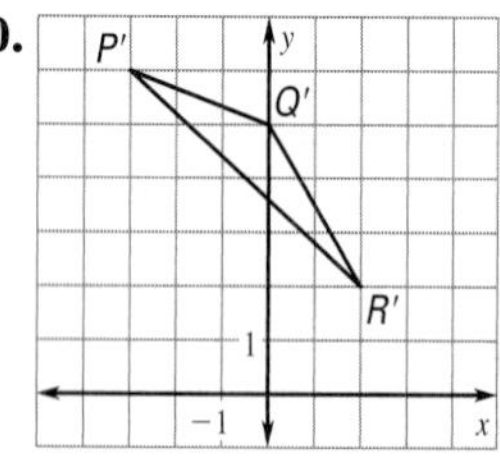

13. 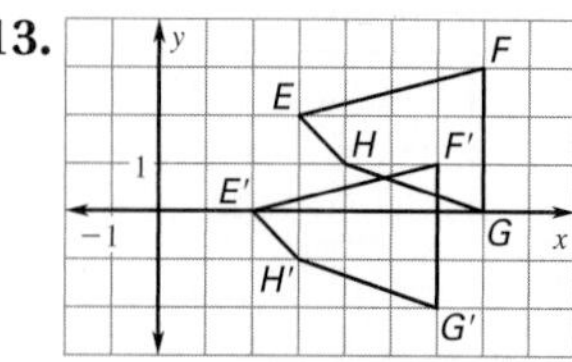

9.2 Guided Practice (pp. 580–583)

5. 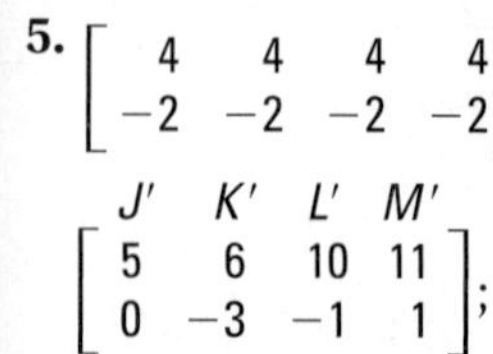

$\begin{bmatrix} 4 & 4 & 4 & 4 \\ -2 & -2 & -2 & -2 \end{bmatrix}$,

J' K' L' M'

$\begin{bmatrix} 5 & 6 & 10 & 11 \\ 0 & -3 & -1 & 1 \end{bmatrix}$;

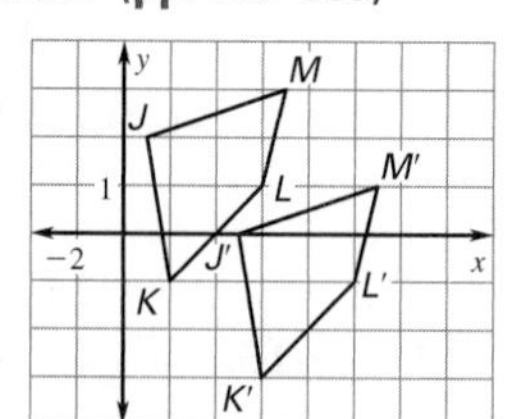

9.2 Skill Practice (pp. 584–585)

13. A' B' C'

$\begin{bmatrix} -2 & 2 & 1 \\ 8 & 5 & 1 \end{bmatrix}$

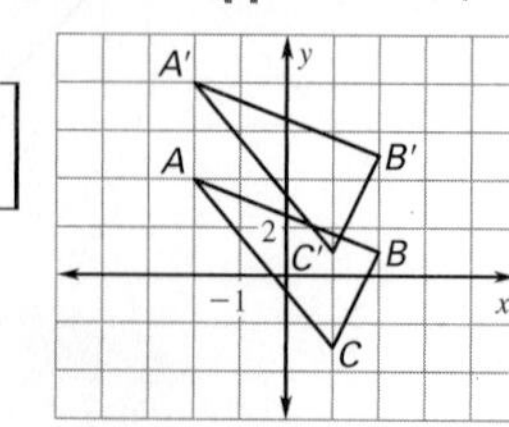

14. F' G' H' J'

$\begin{bmatrix} 0 & 3 & 6 & 3 \\ -1 & 0 & -2 & -4 \end{bmatrix}$

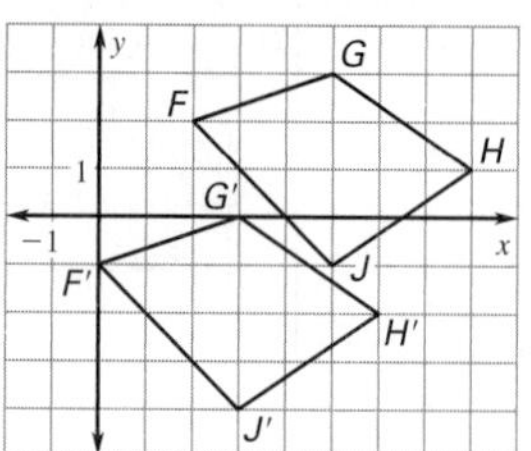

15. 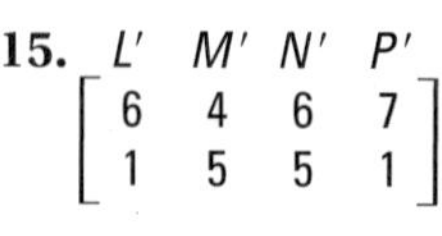

L' M' N' P'

$\begin{bmatrix} 6 & 4 & 6 & 7 \\ 1 & 5 & 5 & 1 \end{bmatrix}$

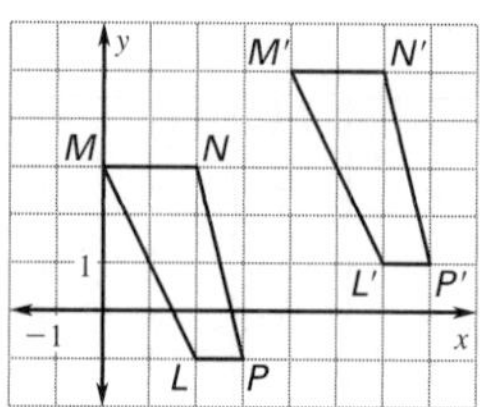

16. 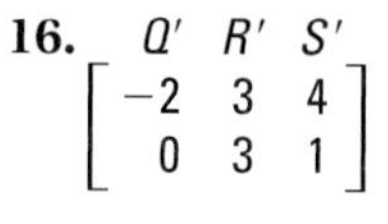

Q' R' S'

$\begin{bmatrix} -2 & 3 & 4 \\ 0 & 3 & 1 \end{bmatrix}$

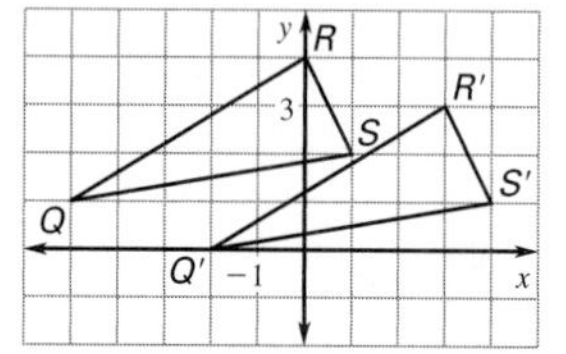

9.3 Guided Practice (pp. 589–592)

1. 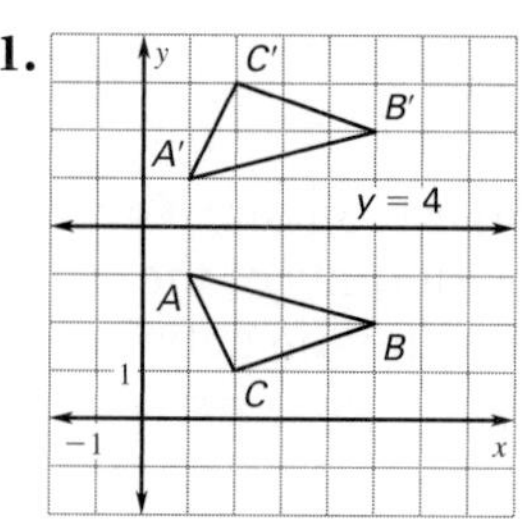

2. 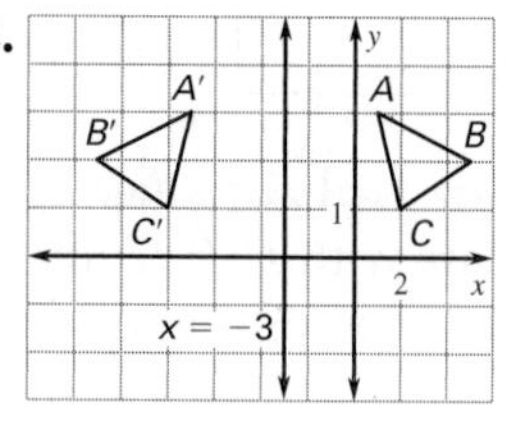

3. 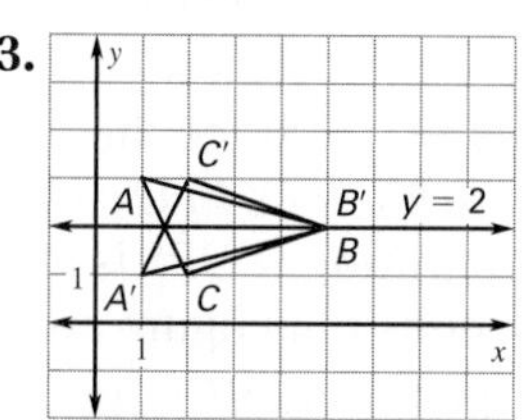

9.3 Skill Practice (pp. 593–594)

3. 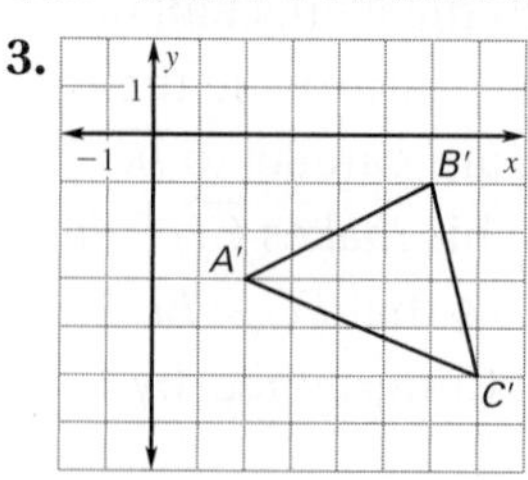

4. 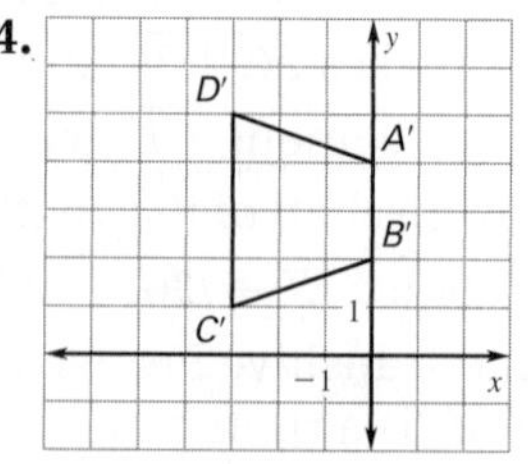

5. 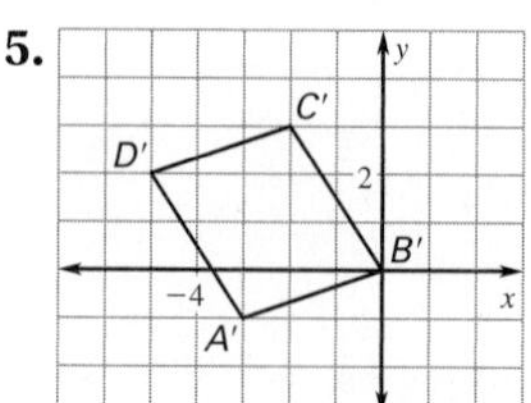

6. 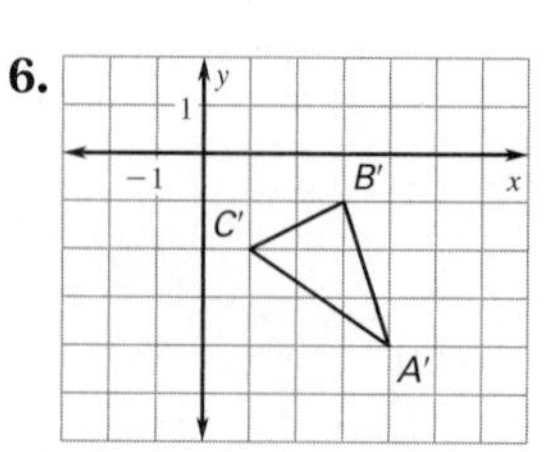

7.

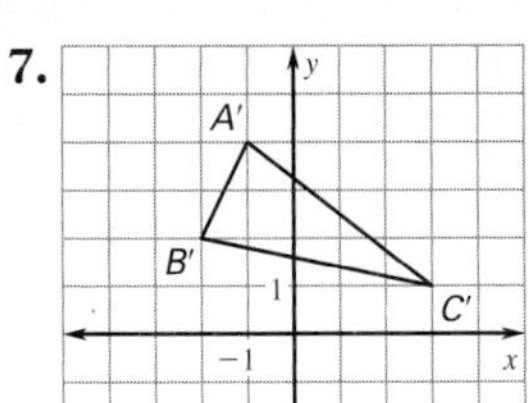

8.

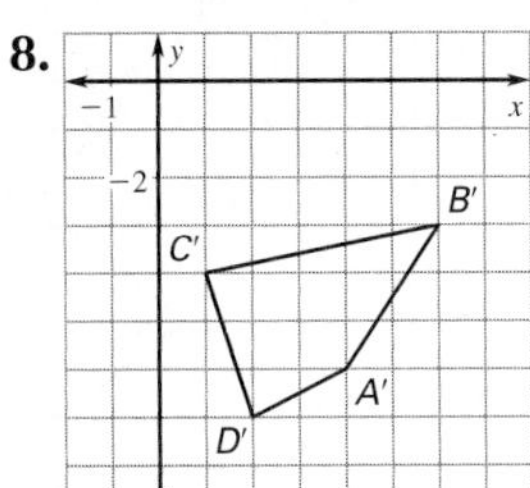

9.

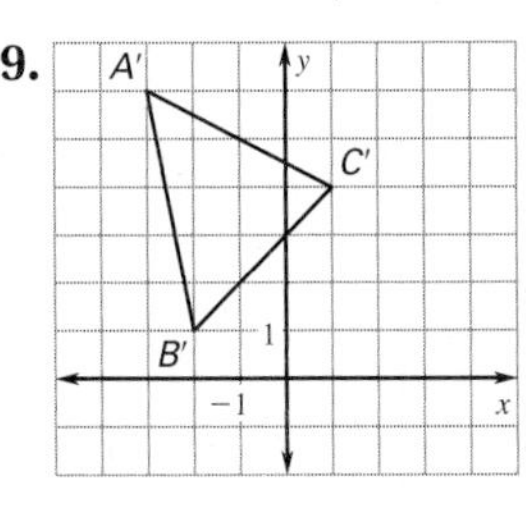

10.

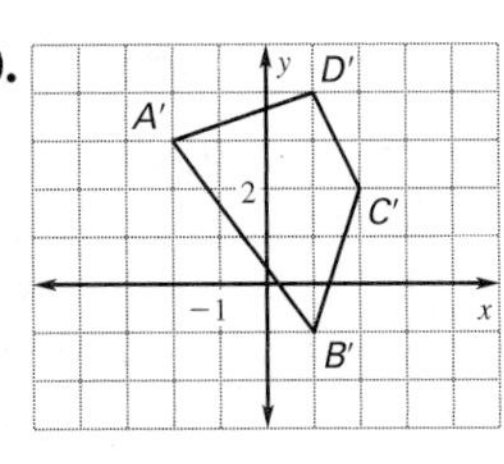

11.

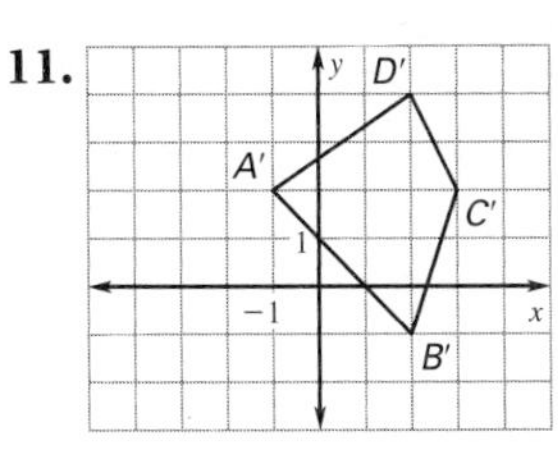

13.

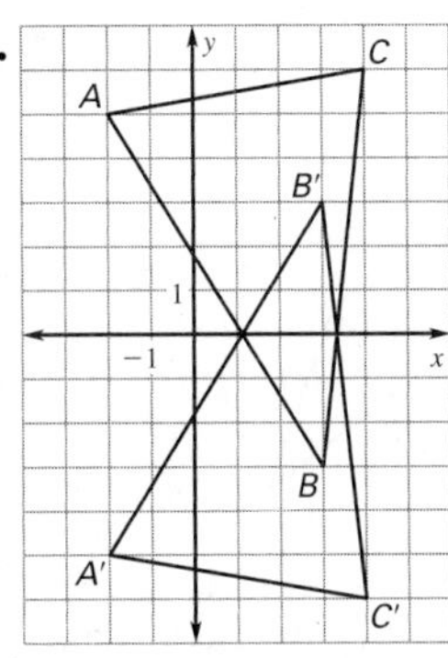

14.

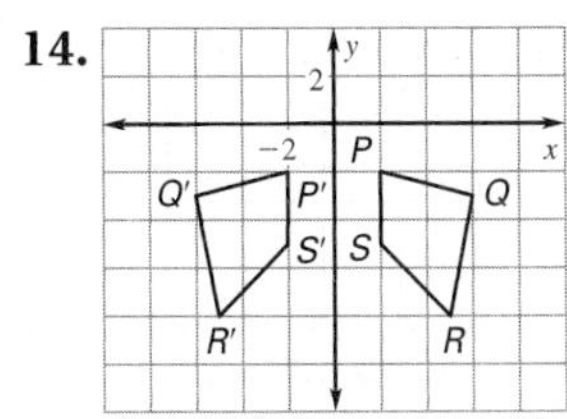

22.

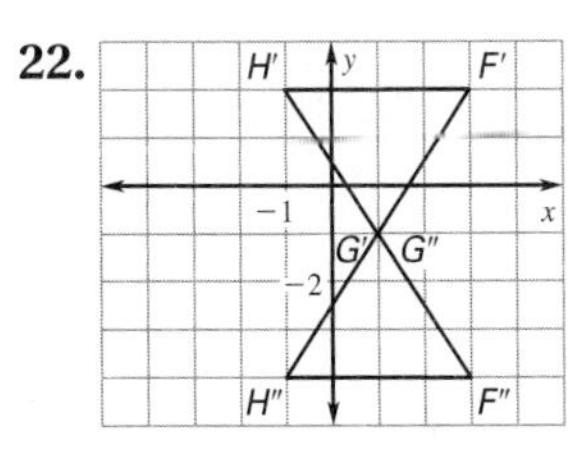

23.

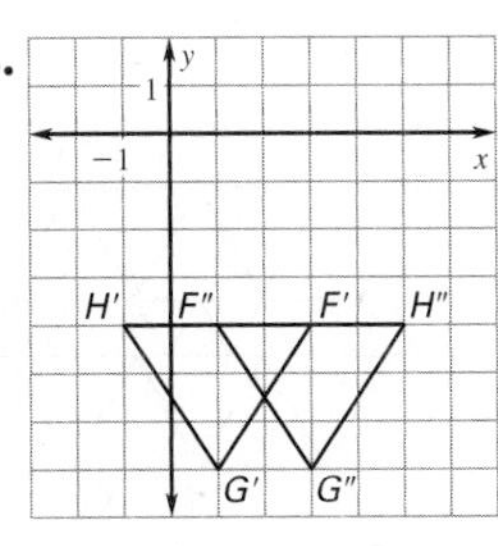

24.

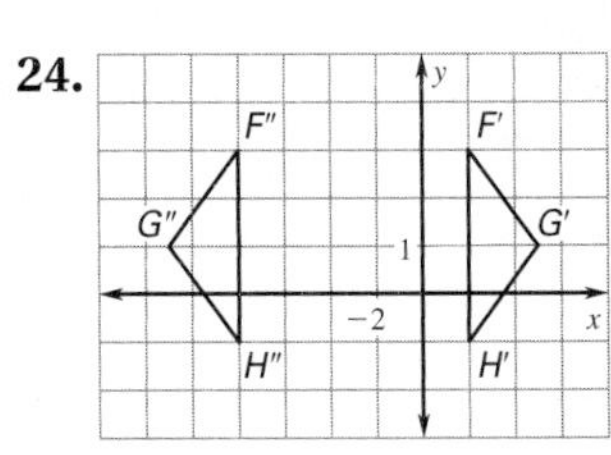

26. Steps 1–3:

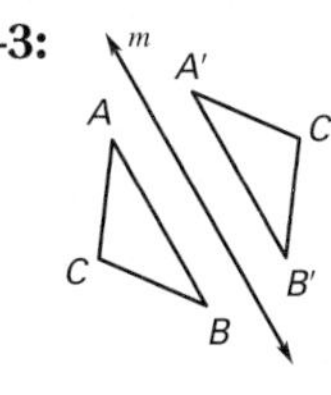

9.3 Problem Solving (pp. 595–596)

36. Given: A reflection in m maps P to P' and Q to Q'. $\overline{PQ}$ intersects m at point R. Using the definition of a line of reflection, m is the perpendicular bisector of $\overline{PP'}$ at point S and of $\overline{QQ'}$ at point T. From this you know that $\overline{P'S} \cong \overline{PS}$, $\overline{Q'T} \cong \overline{QT}$, $\angle P'SR \cong \angle PSR$, and $\angle QTR \cong \angle Q'TR$. The Reflexive Property of Congruence says $\overline{RS} \cong \overline{RS}$ and $\overline{RT} \cong \overline{RT}$. Using the SAS Congruence Postulate, $\triangle P'RS \cong \triangle PRS$ and $\triangle QRT \cong \triangle Q'RT$. Using corresponding parts of congruent triangles are congruent, $\overline{P'R} \cong \overline{PR}$ and $\overline{RQ} \cong \overline{RQ'}$. From this it follows the $P'R + RQ' = PR + RQ$, which implies $P'Q' = PQ$. **37.** Given: A reflection in m maps P to P' and Q to Q'. Also, P lies on m, and $\overline{PQ}$ is not perpendicular to m. Draw $\overline{Q'Q}$ intersecting m at point R. Using the definition of a line of reflection, m is the perpendicular bisector of $\overline{Q'Q}$, which implies $\overline{Q'R} \cong \overline{QR}$, $\angle Q'RP' \cong \angle QRP$, and P and P' are the same point. Using the Reflexive Property of Congruence, $\overline{RP} \cong \overline{RP}$. Using the SAS Congruence Postulate, $\triangle Q'RP' \cong \triangle QRP$. Using corresponding parts of congruent triangles are congruent, $\overline{Q'P'} \cong \overline{QP}$ which implies $Q'P' = QP$. **38.** Given: A reflection in m maps P to P' and Q to Q'. Also, Q lies on m, and $\overline{PQ}$ is perpendicular to m. Using the definition of a line of reflection, point Q remains in the same location and is also known as Q'. Furthermore, m is the perpendicular bisector of $\overline{PP'}$ at point Q which makes $PQ = P'Q'$.

9.4 Guided Practice (pp. 599–601)

1.

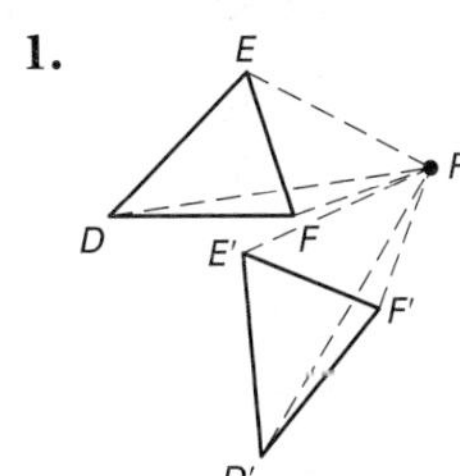

2.

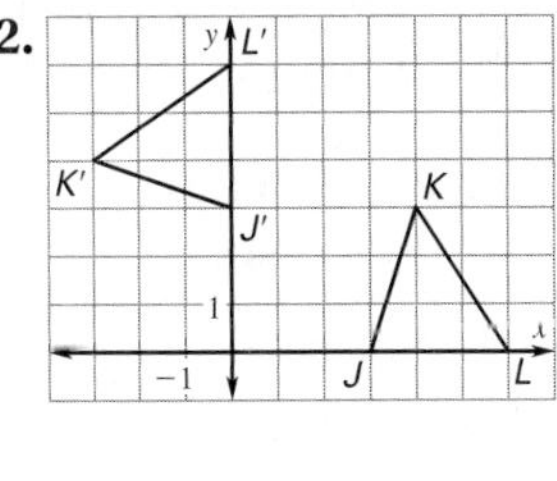

9.4 Skill Practice (pp. 602–603)

12.

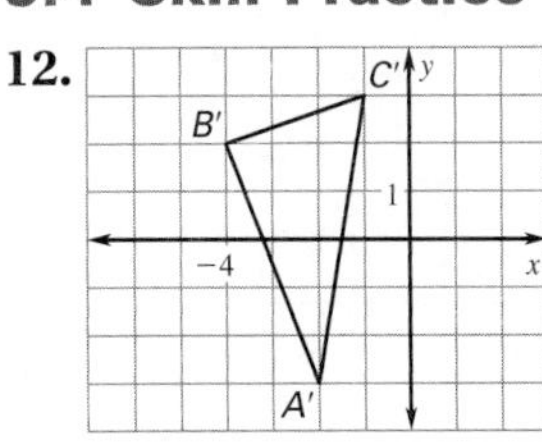

13.

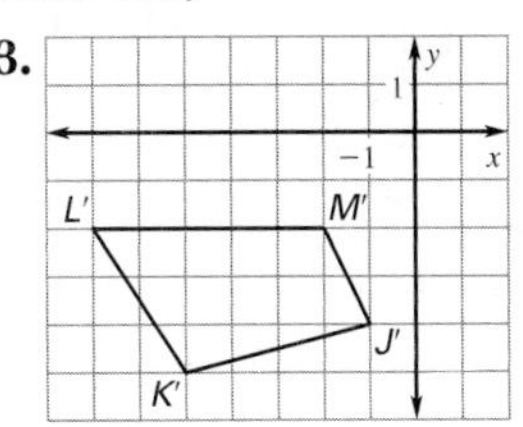

14.

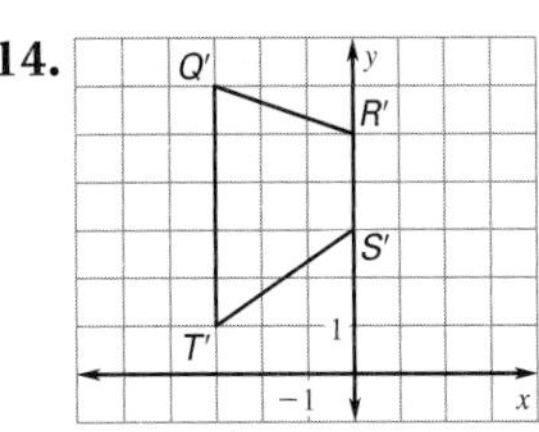

22.

	90°	180°	270°	360°
A(2, 0)	(0, 2)	(−2, 0)	(0, −2)	(2, 0)
B(3, 4)	(−4, 3)	(−3, −4)	(4, −3)	(3, 4)
C(5, 2)	(−2, 5)	(−5, −2)	(2, −5)	(5, 2)

	450°	540°	630°	720°
A(2, 0)	(0, 2)	(−2, 0)	(0, −2)	(2, 0)
B(3, 4)	(−4, 3)	(−3, −4)	(4, −3)	(3, 4)
C(5, 2)	(−2, 5)	(−5, −2)	(2, −5)	(5, 2)

9.5 Problem Solving (pp. 613–615)

38a–b. Given: k and m intersect at point P. Q is any point not on k or m. Reflect Q over k to Q' followed by Q' reflected over m to Q''. Using the definition of reflection, k is the perpendicular bisector of $\overline{QQ'}$ at A and m is the perpendicular bisector of $\overline{Q'Q''}$ at B. It follows that $\overline{QA} \cong \overline{Q'A}$, $\overline{Q'B} \cong \overline{Q''B}$, and $\triangle QAP$, $\triangle Q'AP$, $\triangle Q'BP$, and $\triangle Q''BP$ are right triangles. Using the Reflexive Property of Congruence, $\overline{AP} \cong \overline{AP}$ and $\overline{BP} \cong \overline{BP}$. Using the SAS Congruence Postulate, $\triangle QAP \cong \triangle Q'AP$ and $\triangle Q'BP \cong \triangle Q''BP$. Using corresponding parts of congruent triangles are congruent, $\overline{QP} \cong \overline{Q'P}$ and $\overline{Q'P} \cong \overline{Q''P}$. Using the Transitive Property of Congruence, $\overline{QP} \cong \overline{Q''P}$. Using corresponding parts of congruent triangles are congruent, $\angle QPA \cong \angle Q'PA$ and $\angle Q'PB \cong \angle Q''PB$. Using the Angle Addition Postulate, $m\angle QPA + m\angle Q'PA + m\angle Q'PB + m\angle Q''PB = m\angle QPQ''$ and $m\angle Q'PA + m\angle Q'PB = m\angle APB$. Using the definition of angle congruence and substitution, you get $m\angle Q'PA + m\angle Q'PA + m\angle Q'PB + m\angle Q'PB = m\angle QPQ''$ or $2(m\angle Q'PA + m\angle Q'PB) = m\angle QPQ''$. Using substitution, it follows that $m\angle QPQ'' = 2m\angle APB$.

9.5 Mixed Review (p. 615)

45.
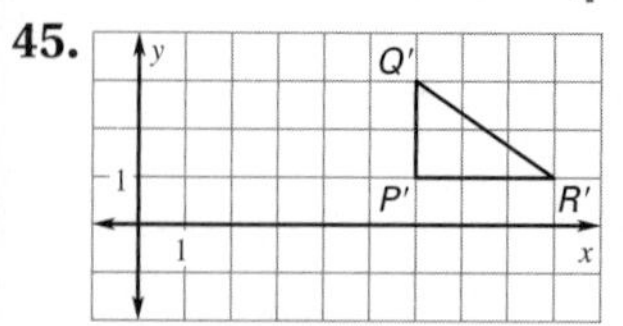

46.
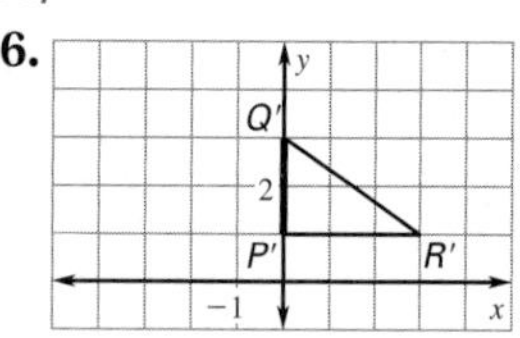

47.
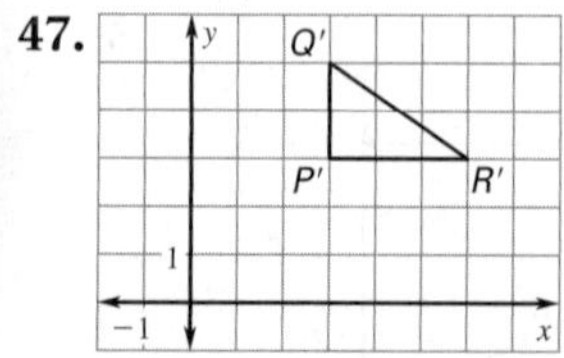

48.
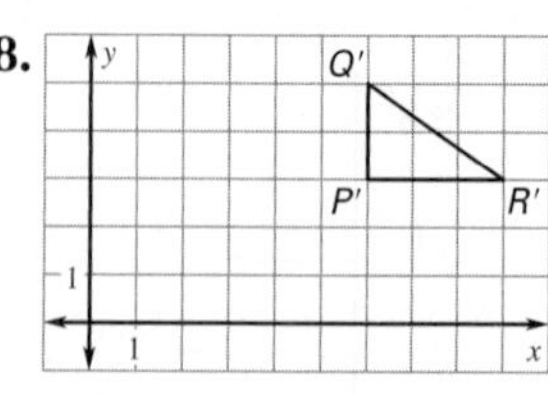

Quiz for Lessons 9.3–9.5 (p. 615)

1.
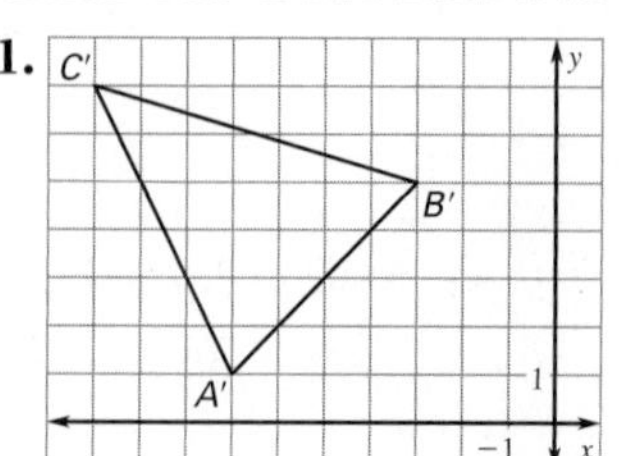

2.
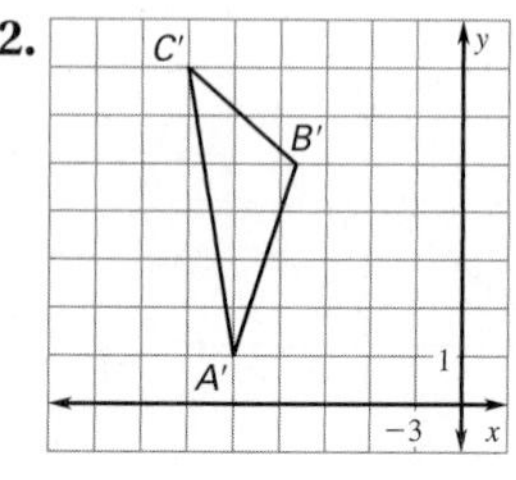

3.
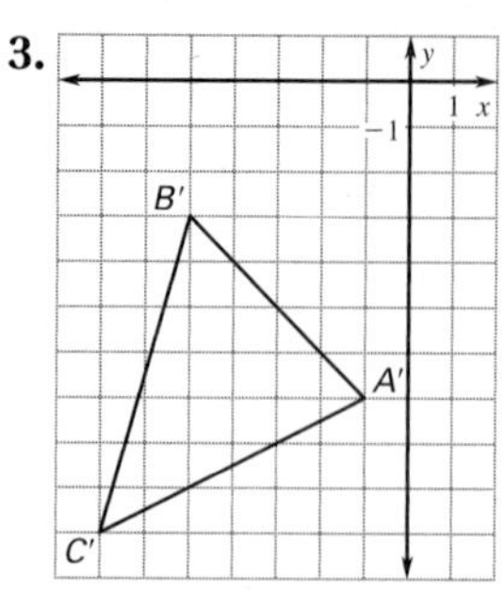

7.
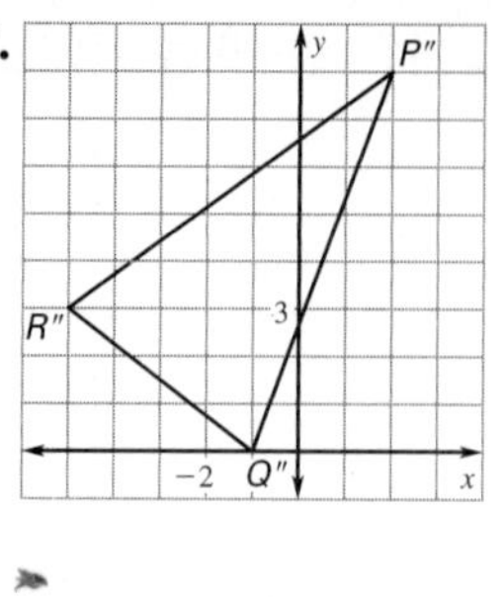

8.
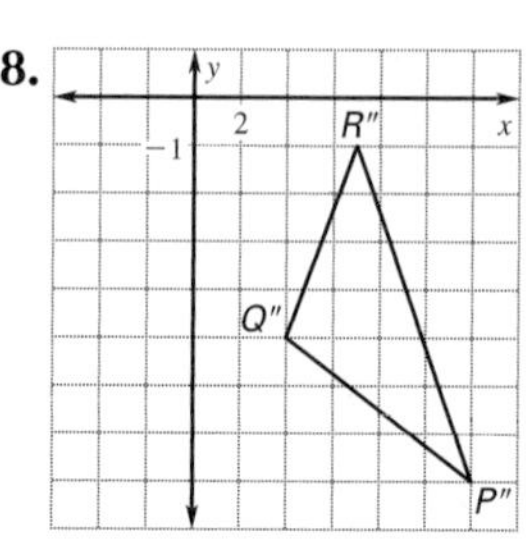

9.
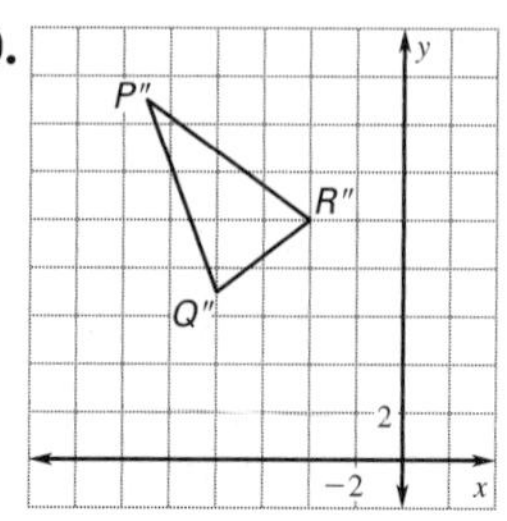

10.
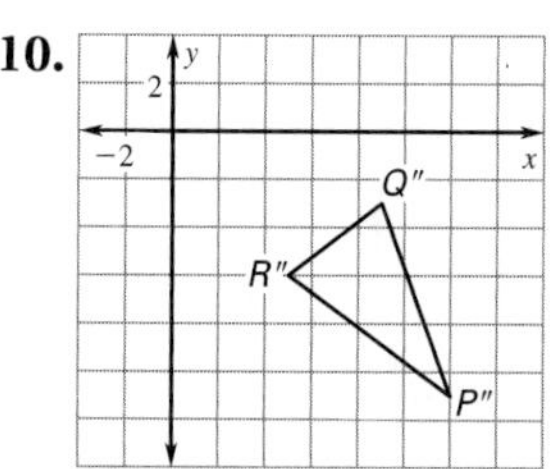

Extension (pp. 617–618)

10.
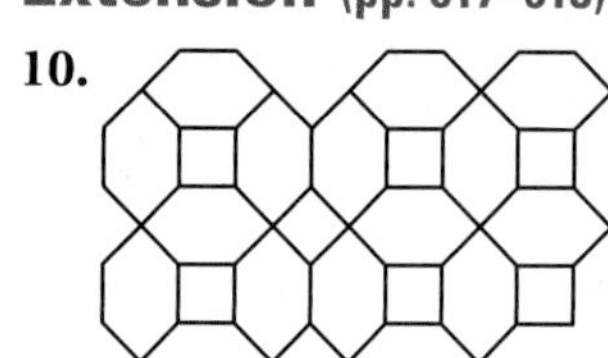

11. *Sample:*
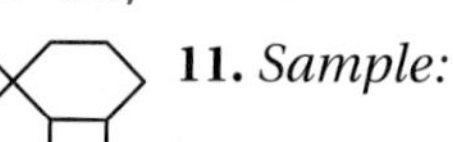
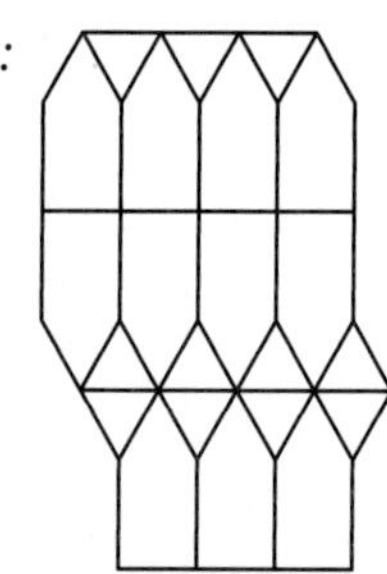

12. *Sample:*
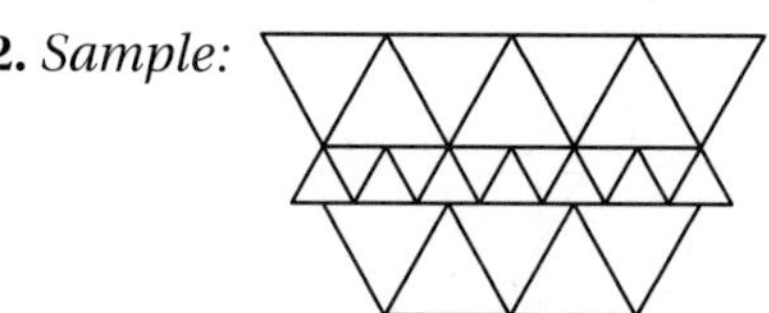

9.6 Guided Practice (pp. 619–621)

4.
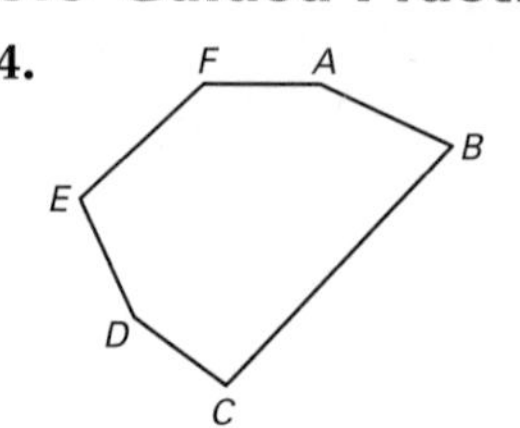

ADDITIONAL ANSWERS

9.7 Investigating Geometry Activity (p. 625)

2. *Sample:* **4.** *Sample:*

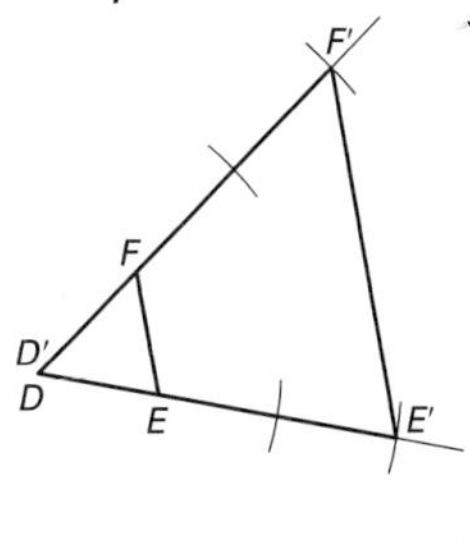

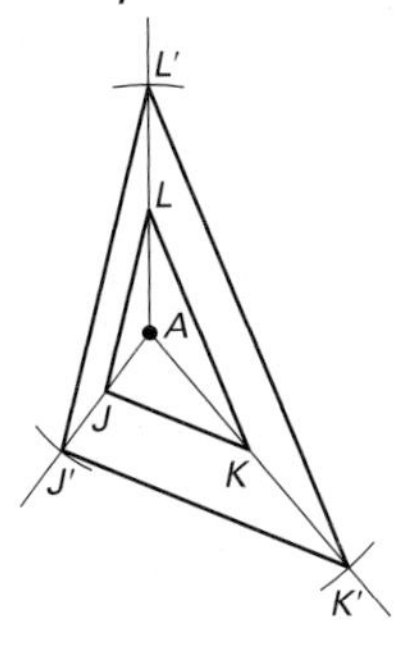

9.7 Skill Practice (pp. 629–630)

7. **8.**

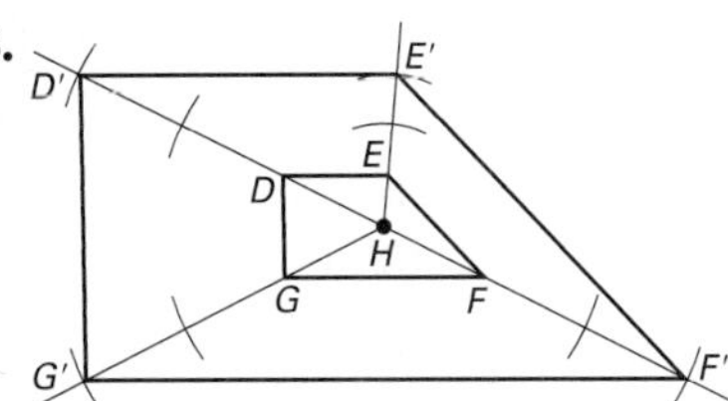

9. **10.**

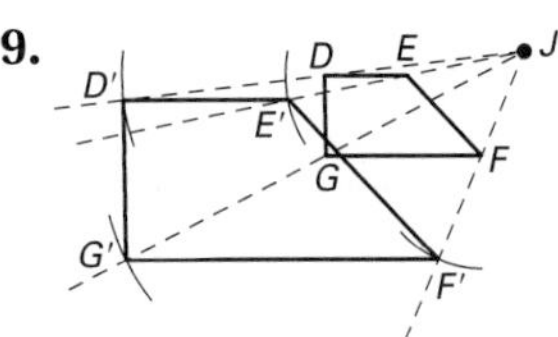

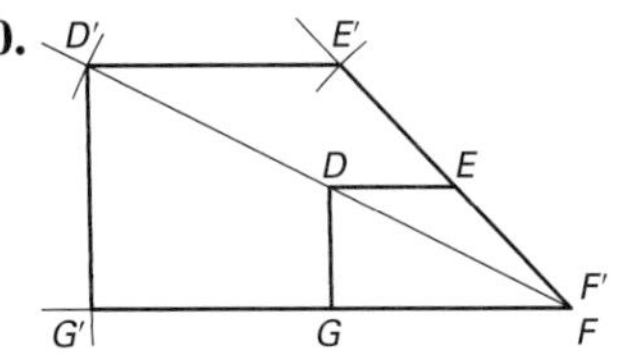

11. **12.**

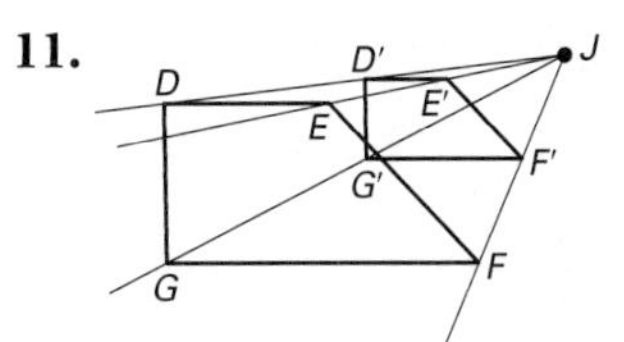

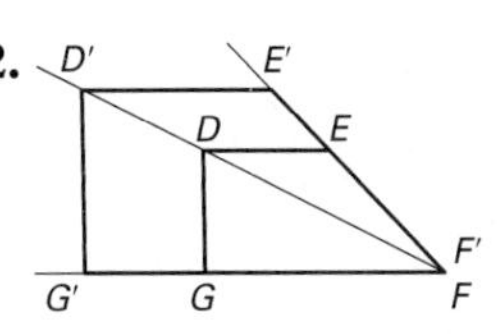

13. **14.**

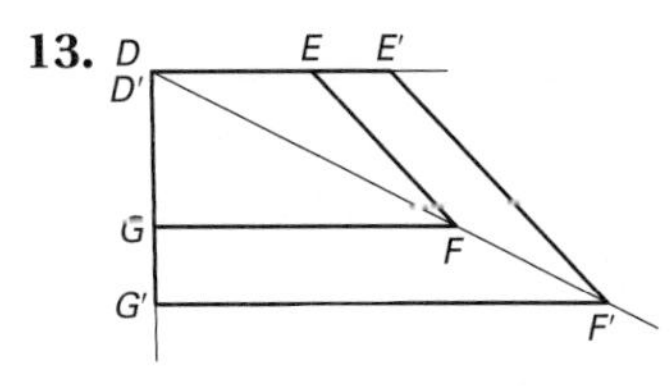

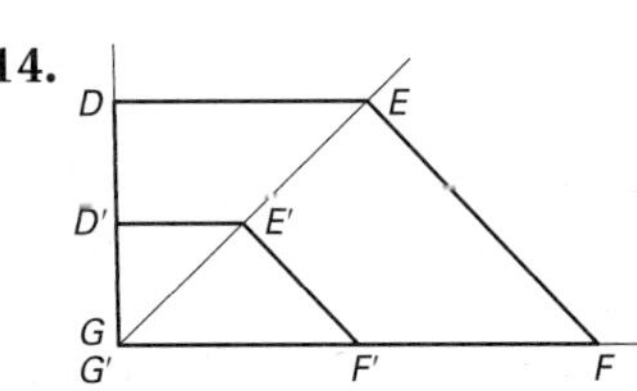

18.

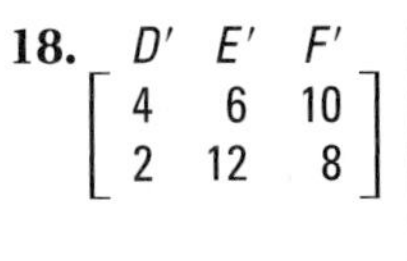

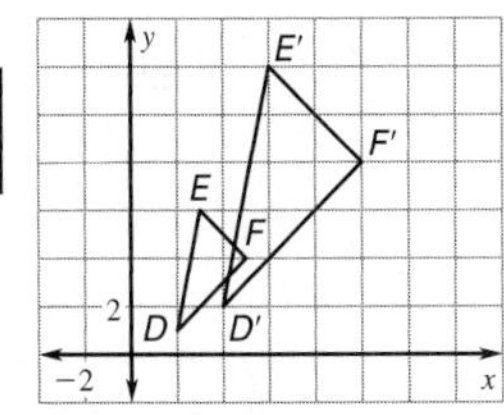

19. $\begin{bmatrix} -1 & 0 & 3 \\ -2 & 1 & -1 \end{bmatrix}$ (columns G', H', J')

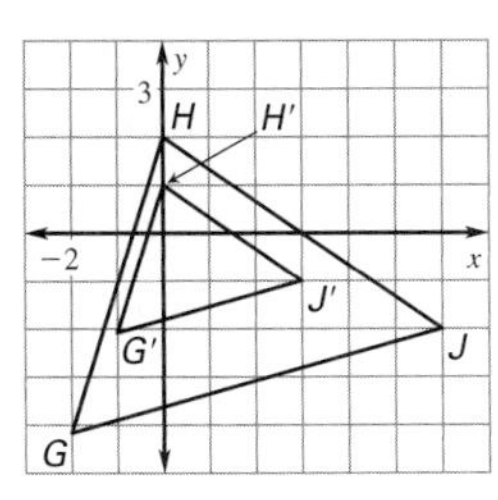

20.

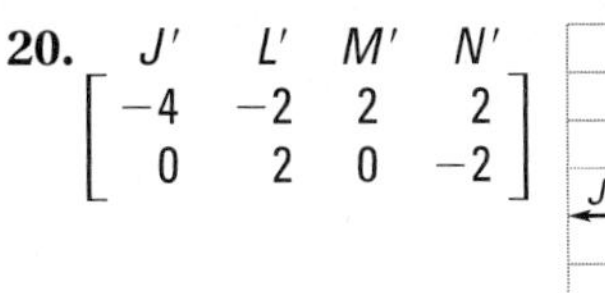

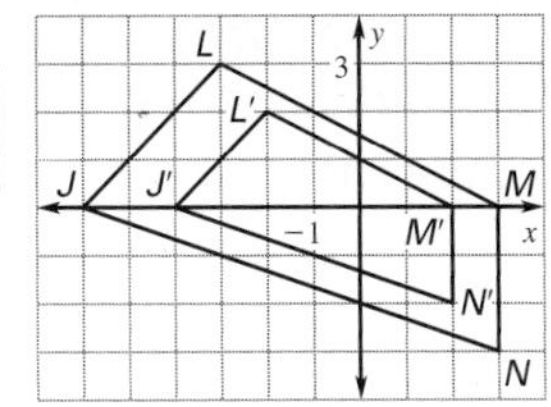

9.7 Problem Solving (pp. 631–632)

42.

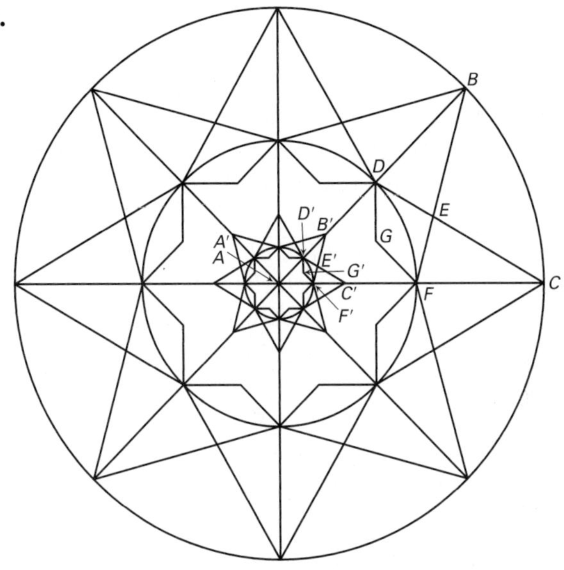

Chapter 10

10.1 Problem Solving (pp. 657–658) **40.** Assume that m is not tangent to $\odot Q$ at P. This implies there is a second point Y that is on both m and $\odot Q$. Since Y is on $\odot Q$, you must now have $QP = QY$. Since $\overline{QP}$ is perpendicular to m, then QP is the shortest distance making $QY > QP$. This is a contradiction because QY cannot be both equal to and greater than QP. This means that point Y meeting the assumed conditions cannot exist. Thus m is tangent to $\odot Q$ at P. **41.** Given: $\overline{SR}$ and $\overline{ST}$ are tangent to $\odot P$. Construct $\overline{PR}$, $\overline{PT}$, and $\overline{PS}$. Since $\overline{PR}$ and $\overline{PT}$ are radii of $\odot P$, $\overline{PR} \cong \overline{PT}$. With $\overline{PS} \cong \overline{PS}$, using the HL Congruence Theorem gives $\triangle RSP \cong \triangle TSP$. Using corresponding parts of congruent triangles are congruent, $\overline{SR} \cong \overline{ST}$.

10.3 Problem Solving (pp. 669–670) **32.** Given: $\overline{EG}$ is a diameter of $\odot L$ and $\overline{EG} \perp \overline{DF}$. Since all radii are congruent, $\overline{LD} \cong \overline{LF}$. Since $\overline{EG} \perp \overline{DF}$, $\triangle DLC$ and $\triangle FLC$ are right triangles. Since $\overline{LC} \cong \overline{LC}$, $\triangle DLC \cong \triangle FLC$ by the HL Congruence Theorem. Using corresponding parts of congruent triangles are congruent, $\overline{CD} \cong \overline{CF}$ and $\angle DLC \cong \angle FLC$. With $m\angle DLC = m\angle FLC$, we now have $m\angle DLC = m\overset{\frown}{DG}$ and $m\angle FLC = m\overset{\frown}{FG}$. This leads to $\overset{\frown}{DG} \cong \overset{\frown}{FG}$.

33. Case 1: In the same circle or in congruent circles, if two chords are equidistant from the center of the circle, the chords are congruent. Given: $EF = EG$, $\overline{EF} \perp \overline{AB}$, and $\overline{EG} \perp \overline{CD}$, then $\overline{EF} \cong \overline{EG}$. Draw radii $\overline{EA}$, $\overline{EB}$, $\overline{EC}$, and $\overline{ED}$. Since all radii are congruent and $\triangle EAF$, $\triangle EBF$, $\triangle ECG$, and $\triangle EDG$ are right triangles, then $\triangle EAF \cong \triangle EBF \cong \triangle ECG \cong \triangle EDG$ by the HL Congruence Theorem. Using corresponding parts of congruent triangles are congruent, $\overline{AF} \cong \overline{FB} \cong \overline{CG} \cong \overline{GD}$. This implies that all four segments have the same length. Using the Segment Addition Postulate, $AF + FB = AB$ and $CG + GD = CD$. From this you can use substitution to conclude that $AB = CD$, which implies $\overline{AB} \cong \overline{CD}$. Case 2: In the same circle or in congruent circles, if two chords are congruent, the distance from the center to each chord is the same. Given: Congruent chords $\overline{CD}$ and $\overline{AB}$ in $\odot E$. Draw radii $\overline{EA}$, $\overline{EB}$, $\overline{EC}$, and $\overline{ED}$. Since all radii are congruent, $\triangle ECD \cong \triangle EAB$ by the SSS Congruence Postulate. Using corresponding parts of congruent triangles are congruent, $\angle D \cong \angle A$. $\overline{EF} \perp \overline{EB}$ and $\overline{EG} \perp \overline{CD}$, so $\angle EFA$ and $\angle EGD$ are right angles and are congruent. Then $\triangle EAF \cong \triangle EDG$ using the AAS Congruence Theorem. Using corresponding parts of congruent triangles are congruent, $\overline{EF} \cong \overline{EG}$. This implies that $EF = EG$. **34.** Given: $\widehat{AB}$ with the bottom panel of the car parallel to the ground. Let C be the point where the tire touches the ground. A line on the ground parallel to the panel passing through C is tangent to the wheel. Create a line segment perpendicular to the line at C passing through the center of the wheel and intersecting the opposite side of the wheel, creating a diameter. The diameter is perpendicular to the bottom panel. Since the bottom of the panel is also a chord of the wheel, Theorem 10.5 can be used to show the diameter bisects the intercepted arc of the chord. Thus C bisects $\widehat{AB}$.

10.4 Mixed Review (p. 679)

46. **47.**

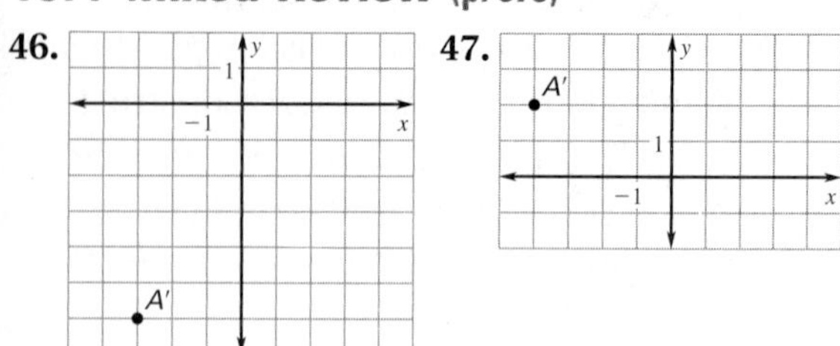

10.5 Problem Solving (pp. 685–686)

30. Given: Q and R are points on $\odot C$ with P a point outside of $\odot C$. $\overline{PQ}$ and $\overline{PR}$ are tangent to $\odot C$. Suppose that $\overline{QR}$ is a diameter of $\odot C$. Using Theorem 10.1, $\overline{QC} \perp \overline{PQ}$ and $\overline{RC} \perp \overline{PR}$. This makes $m\angle PQC = 90°$ and $m\angle PRC = 90°$. Using the Polygon Interior Angles Theorem, the sum of the measures of the interior angles of a triangle is 180°. Since the sum of the measures of the interior angles of $\triangle PQR$ would be greater than 180°, $\overline{QR}$ cannot be a diameter.

10.6 Problem Solving (pp. 694–695)

25. Given: $\overline{EB}$ and $\overline{ED}$ are secant segments. Draw $\overline{AD}$ and $\overline{BC}$. Using the Measure of an Inscribed Angle Theorem, $m\angle B = \frac{1}{2}m\widehat{AC}$ and $m\angle D = \frac{1}{2}m\widehat{AC}$, which implies $\angle B \cong \angle D$. Using the Reflexive Property of Angle Congruence, $\angle E \cong \angle E$. Using the AA Similarity Postulate, $\triangle BCE \sim \triangle DAE$. Using corresponding sides of similar triangles are proportional, $\frac{EA}{EC} = \frac{ED}{EB}$. Cross multiplying gives $EA \cdot EB = EC \cdot ED$. **26.** Given: A secant segment and a tangent segment sharing an endpoint outside of a circle. Draw $\overline{AC}$ and $\overline{AD}$. $\angle ADC$ is inscribed, therefore $m\angle ADC = \frac{1}{2}m\widehat{AC}$. $\angle CAE$ is formed by a secant and a tangent, therefore $m\angle CAE = \frac{1}{2}m\widehat{AC}$. This implies $\angle ADC \cong \angle CAE$. $\angle E \cong \angle E$ by the Reflexive Property of Angle Congruence, therefore $\triangle AEC \sim \triangle DEA$ using the AA Similarity Postulate. Using corresponding sides of similar triangles are proportional, $\frac{EA}{EC} = \frac{ED}{EA}$. Cross multiplying gives $EA^2 = EC \cdot ED$.

Extension (p. 698)

5. The locus of points consists of two points on ℓ each 3 centimeters away from P.

6. The locus of points consists of four points on a circle with center at Q and a radius of 5 centimeters. The four points are the intersections of the circle and two lines parallel to and 3 centimeters away from m.

7. The locus of points consists of a semicircle centered at R with a radius of 10 centimeters. The diameter bordering the semicircle is 10 centimeters from k and parallel to k.

8. *Sample answer:* The portions of lines ℓ and m that are no more than 8 centimeters from point P and the portion of the circle with center P and radius 8 centimeters that is between lines ℓ and m, plus all of the points in the interior of the region bounded by the portions of the circle and lines described.

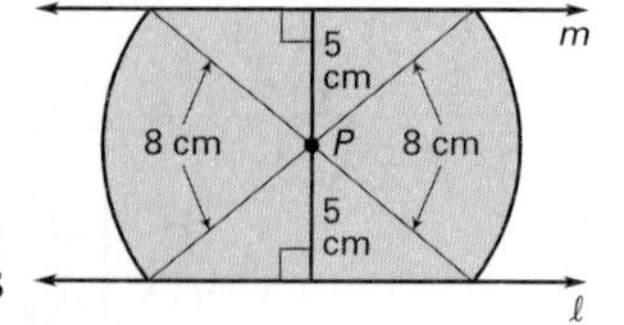

9.

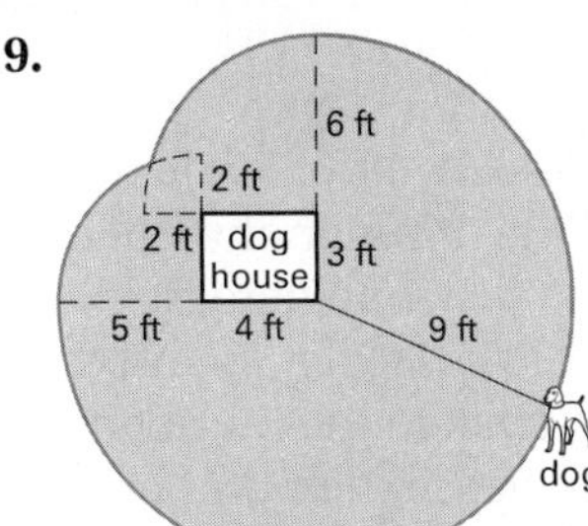

Quiz for Lessons 10.6–10.7 (p. 705)

6.

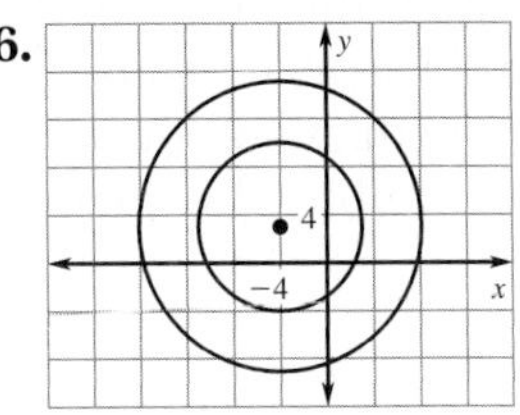

Chapter 11

11.1 Skill Practice (pp. 723–724)

21.

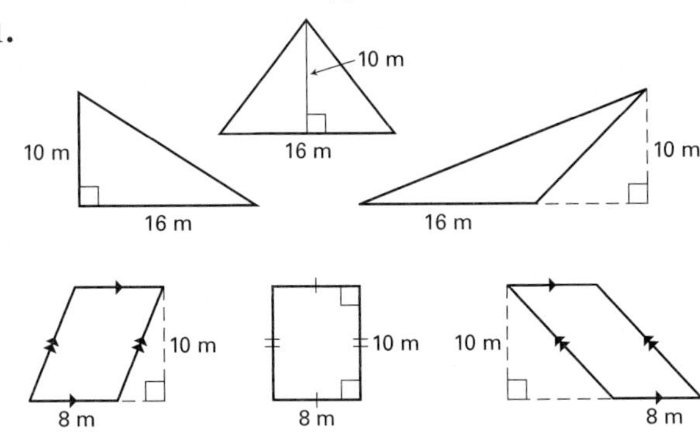

11.1 Problem Solving (pp. 725–726) **46. a.** Since $\angle UVS$ is a straight angle and $\angle RVU$ is a right angle, $\angle RVS$ is a right angle. Similarly, $\angle NRV$ is a right angle. The length of the sides of $RNSV$ are all h, so by definition, $RNSV$ is a square. Similarly $UVTQ$ is a square. $MNPQ$ is a square when you use the Segment Addition Postulate; $RNSV$: h^2, $UVTQ$: b^2, $MNPQ$: $(b + h)^2$.

b.

$$(b + h)^2 = A + b^2 + h^2 + A$$
$$\frac{(b + h)^2 - b^2 - h^2}{2} = A$$
$$\frac{b^2 + 2bh + h^2 - b^2 - h^2}{2} = A$$
$$\frac{2bh}{2} = A$$
$$bh = A$$

47. $y = -x + 8$ and $y = -x$; yes, two other lines are possible: $x = 2 + 2\sqrt{2}$ and $x = 2 - 2\sqrt{2}$. *Sample answer:* In each case, the triangle formed is an isosceles right triangle with legs of length $2\sqrt{2}$ units. The coordinates of point A are (2, 2) in all four cases. When the equation of $\overleftrightarrow{BC}$ is $y = -x + 8$, the coordinates of point B are (4, 4) and the coordinates of point C are (6, 2); when the equation is $y = -x$, the points are $B(0, 0)$ and $C(-2, 2)$; when the equation is $x = 2 + 2\sqrt{2}$, the coordinates are $B(2 + 2\sqrt{2}, 2 + 2\sqrt{2})$ and $C(2 + 2\sqrt{2}, 2)$; and when the equation is $x = 2 - 2\sqrt{2}$, the coordinates are $B(2 - 2\sqrt{2}, 2 - 2\sqrt{2})$ and $C(2 - 2\sqrt{2}, 2)$.

11.2 Problem Solving (pp. 735–736)

40. $A_{\triangle PSR} = \frac{1}{2}b_1h$ and $A_{\triangle PQR} = \frac{1}{2}b_2h$

$$A_{\triangle PSR} + A_{\triangle PQR} = A_{\text{trapezoid}}$$
$$\frac{1}{2}b_1h + \frac{1}{2}b_2h = A_{\text{trapezoid}}$$
$$\frac{1}{2}h(b_1 + b_2) = A_{\text{trapezoid}}$$

41. $A_{\triangle PSR} = \frac{1}{2}\left(\frac{1}{2}d_1\right)d_2$ and $A_{\triangle PQR} = \frac{1}{2}\left(\frac{1}{2}d_1\right)d_2$, so

$A_{\triangle PSR} = \frac{1}{4}d_1d_2$ and $A_{\triangle PQR} = \frac{1}{4}d_1d_2$.

$$A_{PQRS} = A_{\triangle PQR} + A_{\triangle PSR}$$
$$A_{PQRS} = \frac{1}{4}d_1d_2 + \frac{1}{4}d_1d_2$$
$$A_{PQRS} = \frac{1}{2}d_1d_2$$

42. a. Check students' work. In addition to a variety of kites, an isosceles triangle and a right triangle are possible.

43. $\frac{1}{2}(a + b)(a + b) = \frac{ab}{2} + \frac{ab}{2} + \frac{c^2}{2}$

$$\frac{a^2 + 2ab + b^2}{2} \stackrel{?}{=} \frac{2ab + c^2}{2}$$
$$a^2 + 2ab + b^2 = 2ab + c^2$$
$$a^2 + b^2 = c^2$$

11.3 Mixed Review of Problem Solving (p. 745)

2.

The formula for the area of a triangle is $A = \frac{1}{2}bh$. As long as $h = 8$ and the area is 48, the base of the triangle can be 12 meters and shaped in various ways to create different triangles. For the parallelograms, a rectangle that is 8 meters by 6 meters has an area of 48 square meters; show two differently shaped parallelograms with base 6 meters and height 8 meters.

11.6 Problem Solving (pp. 767–768)

43. Because P is both the incenter and circumcenter of $\triangle ABC$ and letting E be the midpoint of $\overline{AB}$, you can show that $\overline{BD}$ and $\overline{CE}$ are both medians of $\triangle ABC$ and they intersect at P. By the Concurrency of Medians of a Triangle Theorem, $BP = \frac{2}{3}BD$ and $CP = \frac{2}{3}CE$. Using algebra, show that $2PD = CP$.

44. d. Since the area of 100 cells is about 0.23 square decimeters, divide 100 by 0.23 to get about 435 cells per square decimeter (427 cells per square decimeter without intermediate rounding. **45. a.** About 173.2 cm^2; square: 225 cm^2, pentagon: about 247.7 cm^2, hexagon: about 259.8 cm^2, decagon: about 277 cm^2; the area is increasing with each larger polygon.

c.

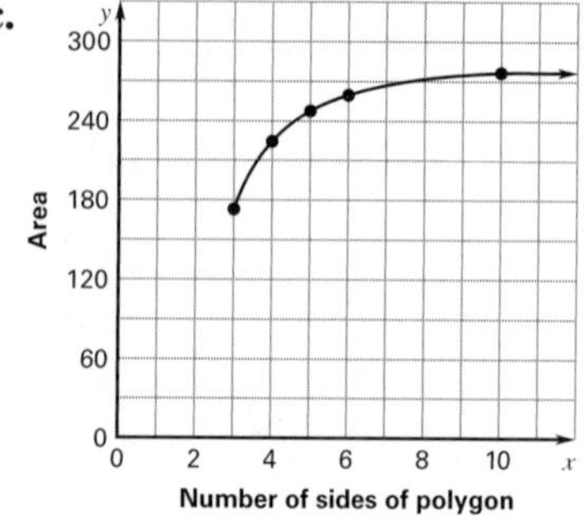

Chapter 12

12.1 Problem Solving (pp. 800–801)

49. a. It will increase the number of faces by 1, the number of vertices by 2, and the number of edges by 3. **b.** It will increase the number of faces by 1, the number of vertices by 2, and the number of edges by 3. **c.** It will not change the number of faces, vertices, or edges. **d.** It will increase the number of faces by 3, the number of vertices by 6, and the number of edges by 9. **50. a.** It will increase the number of faces by 1, the number of vertices by 2, and the number of edges by 3. **b.** It will increase the number of faces by 1, the number of vertices by 2, and the number of edges by 3. **c.** It will not change the number of faces, vertices, or edges. **d.** It will increase the number of faces by 2, the number of vertices by 3, and the number of edges by 5.

Extra Practice

Chapter 4 (pp. 902–903)

36.

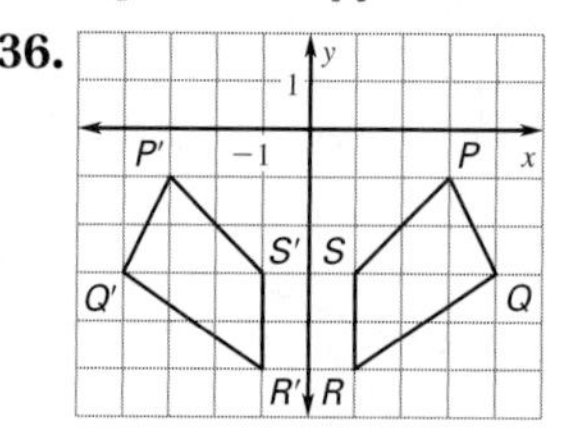

37.

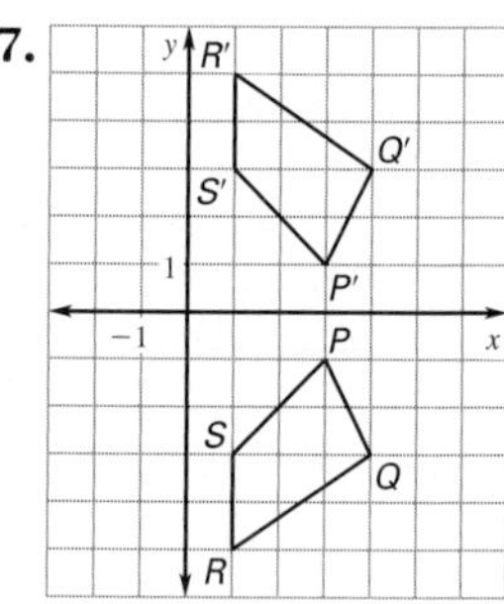

38.

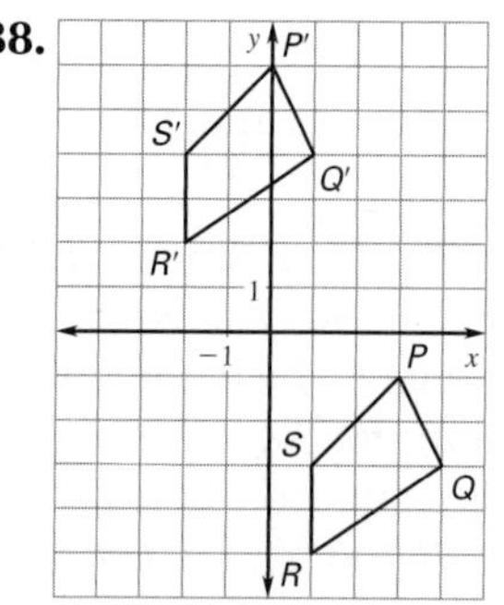

Chapter 9 (pp. 912–913)

20.
$$\begin{array}{ccc} P' & Q' & R' \end{array}$$
$$\begin{bmatrix} -1 & -2 & -4 \\ -4 & -1 & -3 \end{bmatrix}$$

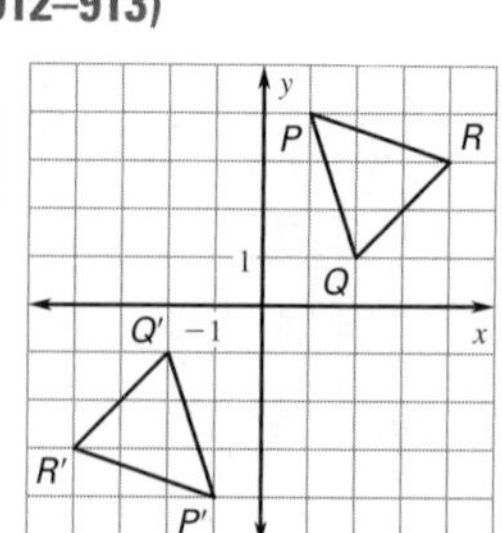

21.

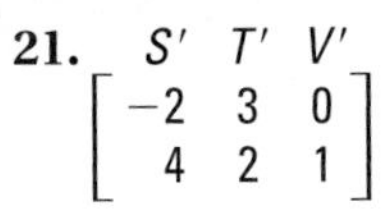

$$\begin{matrix} S' & T' & V' \end{matrix}$$
$$\begin{bmatrix} -2 & 3 & 0 \\ 4 & 2 & 1 \end{bmatrix}$$

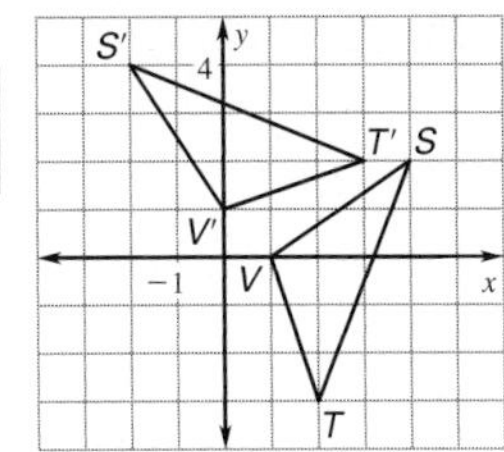

22.

$$\begin{matrix} A' & B' & C' & D' \end{matrix}$$
$$\begin{bmatrix} 0 & -1 & -2 & -3 \\ -4 & 1 & 2 & -1 \end{bmatrix}$$

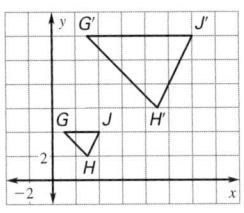

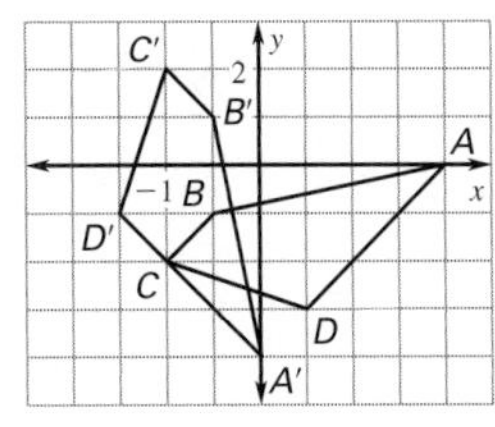

35.

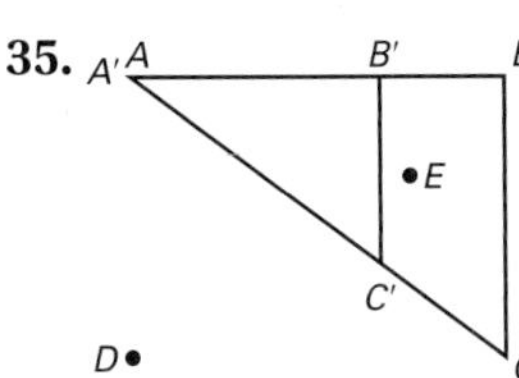

36.

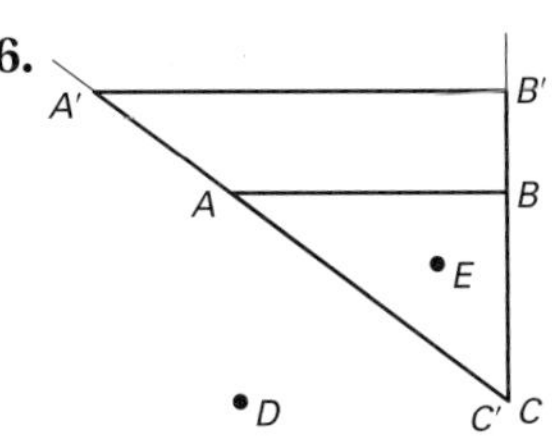

37.

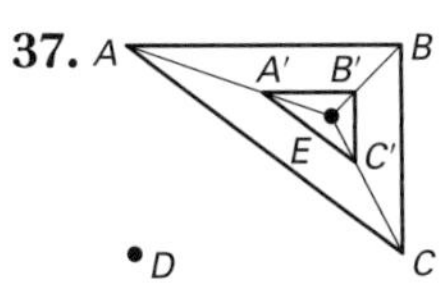

38.

$$\begin{matrix} G' & H' & J' \end{matrix}$$
$$\begin{bmatrix} 3 & 9 & 12 \\ 12 & 6 & 12 \end{bmatrix}$$

39.

$$\begin{matrix} K' & L' & M' & N' \end{matrix}$$
$$\begin{bmatrix} 1 & 2 & \frac{5}{2} & 3 \\ -1 & -1 & 2 & 0 \end{bmatrix}$$

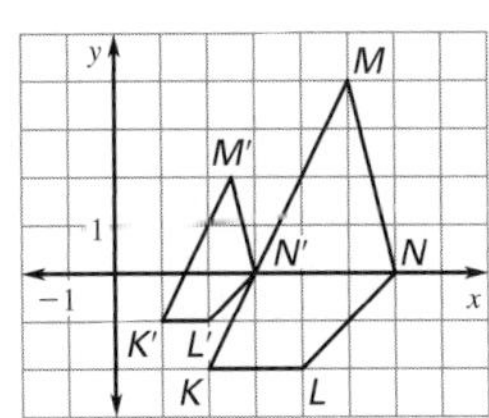

40.

$$\begin{matrix} P' & Q' & R' \end{matrix}$$
$$\begin{bmatrix} -12 & -12 & -4 \\ -4 & -12 & -12 \end{bmatrix}$$

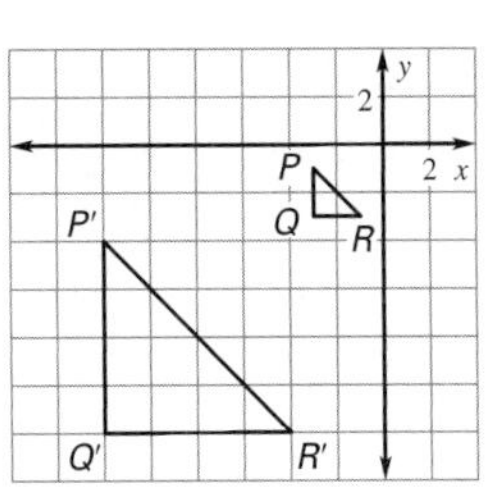

ADDITIONAL ANSWERS